Stanley Gibbons
SIMPLIFIED
CATALOGUE

Stamps of the World

2005 Edition

IN COLOUR

An illustrated and priced four-volume guide to the postage stamps of the whole world, excluding changes of paper, perforation, shade and watermark

VOLUME 1

COUNTRIES A–D

STANLEY GIBBONS LTD
London and Ringwood

**By Appointment to
Her Majesty the Queen
Stanley Gibbons Limited
London
Philatelists**

70th Edition

**Published in Great Britain by
Stanley Gibbons Ltd
Publications Editorial, Sales Offices and Distribution Centre
Parkside, Christchurch Road,
Ringwood, Hampshire BH24 3SH
Telephone 01425 472363**

ISBN: 085259-568-9

**Published as Stanley Gibbons Simplified Stamp
Catalogue from 1934 to 1970, renamed Stamps of the
World in 1971, and produced in two (1982-88), three
(1989-2001) or four (from 2002) volumes as Stanley Gibbons
Simplified Catalogue of Stamps of the World.
This volume published October 2004**

S.G. Item No. 2881 (05)

Printed in Great Britain by CPI Bath Press, Somerset

Stanley Gibbons
SIMPLIFIED CATALOGUE

Stamps of the World

This popular catalogue is a straightforward listing of the stamps that have been issued everywhere in the world since the very first–Great Britain's famous Penny Black in 1840.

This edition, in which both the text and the illustrations have been captured electronically, is arranged completely alphabetically in a four-volume format. Volume 1 (Countries A–D), Volume 2 (Countries E–J), Volume 3 (Countries K–R) and Volume 4 (Countries S–Z).

Readers are reminded that the Catalogue Supplements, published in each issue of **Gibbons Stamp Monthly**, can be used to update the listings in **Stamps of the World** as well as our 22-part standard catalogue. To make the supplement even more useful the Type numbers given to the illustrations are the same in the Stamps of the World as in the standard catalogues. The first Catalogue Supplement to this Volume appeared in the September 2004 issue of **Gibbons Stamp Monthly**.

Gibbons Stamp Monthly can be obtained through newsagents or on postal subscription from Stanley Gibbons Publications, Parkside, Christchurch Road, Ringwood, Hants BH24 3SH.

The catalogue has many important features:

- The vast majority of illustrations are now in full colour to aid stamp identification.
- All Commonwealth and all Western Europe miniature sheets are now included.
- As an indication of current values virtually every stamp is priced. Thousands of alterations have been made since the last edition.
- By being set out on a simplified basis that excludes changes of paper, perforation, shade, watermark, gum or printer's and date imprints it is particularly easy to use. (For its exact scope see "Information for users" pages following.)
- The thousands of colour illustrations and helpful descriptions of stamp designs make it of maximum appeal to collectors with thematic interests.
- Its catalogue numbers are the world-recognised Stanley Gibbons numbers throughout.
- Helpful introductory notes for the collector are included, backed by much historical, geographical and currency information.
- A very detailed index gives instant location of countries in this volume, and a cross-reference to those included in the other volumes.

Over 3,475 stamps and miniature sheets and 1,040 new illustrations have been added to the listings in this volume. This year's four-volumes now contain over 417,545 stamps and 100,767 illustrations.

The listings in this edition are based on the standard catalogues: Part 1, Commonwealth & British Empire Stamps 1840–1952, Part 2 (Austria & Hungary) (6th edition), Part 3 (Balkans) (4th edition), Part 4 (Benelux) (5th edition), Part 5 (Czechoslovakia & Poland) (6th edition), Part 6 (France) (5th edition), Part 7 (Germany) (6th edition), Part 8 (Italy & Switzerland) (6th edition), Part 9 (Portugal & Spain) (4th edition), Part 10 (Russia) (5th edition), Part 11 (Scandinavia) (5th edition), Part 12 (Africa since Independence A-E) (2nd edition), Part 13 (Africa since Independence F-M) (1st edition), Part 14 (Africa since Independence N-Z) (1st edition), Part 15 (Central America) (2nd edition), Part 16 (Central Asia) (3rd edition), Part 17 (China) (6th edition), Part 18 (Japan & Korea) (4th edition), Part 19 (Middle East) (5th edition), Part 20 (South America) (3rd edition), Part 21 (South-East Asia) (4th edition) and Part 22 (United States) (5th edition).

This edition includes major repricing for some Western Europe countries in addition to the changes for South-East Asia Part 21.

Acknowledgements

A wide-ranging revision of prices for Western European countries has been undertaken for this edition with the intention that the catalogue should be more accurate to reflect the market for foreign issues.

Many dealers in both Great Britain and overseas have participated in this scheme by supplying copies of their retail price lists on which the research has been based.

We would like to acknowledge the assistance of the following for this edition:

ALMAZ CO
of Brooklyn, U.S.A.

AMATEUR COLLECTOR LTD, THE
of London, England

E. ANGELOPOULOS
of Thessaloniki, Greece

AVION THEMATICS
of Nottingham, England

J BAREFOOT LTD
of York, England

BELGIAN PHILATELIC SPECIALISTS INC
of Larchmont, U.S.A.

Sir CHARLES BLOMEFIELD
of Chipping Camden, England

T. BRAY
of Shipley, West Yorks, England

CENTRAL PHILATELIQUE
of Brussels, Belgium

JEAN-PIERRE DELMONTE
of Paris, France

EUROPEAN & FOREIGN STAMPS
of Pontypridd, Wales

FILATELIA LLACH SL
of Barcelona, Spain

FILATELIA RIVA RENO
of Bologna, Italy

FILATELIA TORI
of Barcelona, Spain

FORMOSA STAMP COMPANY, THE
of Koahsiung, Taiwan

FORSTAMPS
of Battle, England

ANTHONY GRAINGER
of Leeds, England

HOLMGREN STAMPS
of Bollnas, Sweden

INDIGO
of Orewa, New Zealand

ALEC JACQUES
of Selby, England

M. JANKOWSKI
of Warsaw, Poland

D.J.M. KERR
of Earlston, England

H. M. NIELSEN
of Vejle, Denmark

LEO BARESCH LTD
of Hassocks, England

LORIEN STAMPS
of Chesterfield, England

MANDARIN TRADING CO
of Alhambra, U.S.A.

MICHAEL ROGERS INC
of Winter Park, U.S.A.

PHILATELIC SUPPLIES
of Letchworth, England

PHIL-INDEX
of Eastbourne, England

PHILTRADE A/S
of Copenhagen, Denmark

PITTERI SA
of Chiasso, Switzerland

KEVIN RIGLER
of Shifnal, England

ROLF GUMMESSON AB
of Stockholm, Sweden

R. D. TOLSON
of Undercliffe, England

JAY SMITH
of Snow Camp, U.S.A.

R. SCHNEIDER
of Belleville, U.S.A.

ROBSTINE STAMPS
of Hampshire, England

SOUTHERN MAIL
of Eastbourne, England

STAMP CENTER
of Reykjavik, Iceland

REX WHITE
of Winchester, England

Some Western European countries have been repriced this year in Stamps of the World and where there is no up-to-date specialised foreign volume in a country these will be the new Stanley Gibbons prices.

It is hoped that this improved pricing scheme will be extended to other foreign countries and thematic issues as information is consolidated.

Information for users

Aim

The aim of this catalogue is to provide a straightforward illustrated and priced guide to the postage stamps of the whole world to help you to enjoy the greatest hobby of the present day.

Arrangement

The catalogue lists countries in alphabetical order and there is a complete index at the end of each volume. For ease of reference country names are also printed at the head of each page.

Within each country, postage stamps are listed first. They are followed by separate sections for such other categories as postage due stamps, parcel post stamps, express stamps, official stamps, etc.

All catalogue lists are set out according to dates of issue of the stamps, starting from the earliest and working through to the most recent.

Scope of the Catalogue

The *Simplified Catalogue of Stamps of the World* contains listings of postage stamps only. Apart from the ordinary definitive, commemorative and air-mail stamps of each country – which appear first in each list – there are sections for the following where appropriate:

- postage due stamps
- parcel post stamps
- official stamps
- express and special delivery stamps
- charity and compulsory tax stamps
- newspaper and journal stamps
- printed matter stamps
- registration stamps
- acknowledgement of receipt stamps
- late fee and too late stamps
- military post stamps
- recorded message stamps
- personal delivery stamps

We receive numerous enquiries from collectors about other items which do not fall within the categories set out above and which consequently do not appear in the catalogue lists. It may be helpful, therefore, to summarise the other kinds of stamp that exist but which we deliberately exclude from this postage stamp catalogue.

We do *not* list the following:

Fiscal or revenue stamps: stamps used solely in collecting taxes or fees for non-postal purposes. Examples would be stamps which pay a tax on a receipt, represent the stamp duty on a contract or frank a customs document. Common inscriptions found include: Documentary, Proprietary, Inter. Revenue, Contract Note.

Local stamps: postage stamps whose validity and use are limited in area, say to a single town or city, though in some cases they provided, with official sanction, services in parts of countries not covered by the respective government.

Local carriage labels and Private local issues: many labels exist ostensibly to cover the cost of ferrying mail from one of Great Britain's offshore islands to the nearest mainland post office. They are not recognised as valid for national or international mail. Examples: Calf of Man, Davaar, Herm, Lundy, Pabay, Stroma. Items from some other places have only the status of tourist souvenir labels.

Telegraph stamps: stamps intended solely for the prepayment of telegraphic communication.

Bogus or "phantom" stamps: labels from mythical places or non-existent administrations. Examples in the classical period were Sedang, Counani, Clipperton Island and in modern times Thomond and Monte Bello Islands. Numerous labels have also appeared since the War from dissident groups as propaganda for their claims and without authority from the home governments. Common examples are labels for "Free Albania", "Free Rumania" and "Free Croatia" and numerous issues for Nagaland, Indonesia and the South Moluccas ("Republik Maluku Selatan").

Railway letter fee stamps: special stamps issued by railway companies for the conveyance of letters by rail. Example: Talyllyn Railway. Similar services are now offered by some bus companies and the labels they issue likewise do not qualify for inclusion in the catalogue.

Perfins ("perforated initials"): numerous postage stamps may be found with initial letters or designs punctured through them by tiny holes. These are applied by private and public concerns as a precaution against theft and do not qualify for separate mention.

Information for users

Labels: innumerable items exist resembling stamps but – as they do not prepay postage – they are classified as labels. The commonest categories are:

- propaganda and publicity labels: designed to further a cause or campaign;
- exhibition labels: particularly souvenirs from philatelic events;
- testing labels: stamp-size labels used in testing stamp-vending machines;
- Post Office training school stamps: British stamps overprinted with two thick vertical bars or SCHOOL SPECIMEN are produced by the Post Office for training purposes;
- seals and stickers: numerous charities produce stamp-like labels, particularly at Christmas and Easter, as a means of raising funds and these have no postal validity.

Cut-outs: items of postal stationery, such as envelopes, cards and wrappers, often have stamps impressed or imprinted on them. They may usually be cut out and affixed to envelopes, etc., for postal use if desired, but such items are not listed in this catalogue.

Collectors wanting further information about exact definitions are referred to *Philatelic Terms Illustrated*, published by Stanley Gibbons and containing many illustrations in colour.

There is also a priced listing of the postal fiscals of Great Britain in our *Commonwealth & British Empire Stamps 1840–1952* Catalogue and in Volume 1 of the *Great Britain Specialised* Catalogue (5th and later editions).

Catalogue Numbers

Stanley Gibbons catalogue numbers are recognised universally and any individual stamp can be identified by quoting the catalogue number (the one at the left of the column) prefixed by the name of the country and the letters "S.G.". Do not confuse the catalogue number with the type numbers which refer to illustrations.

Prices

Prices in the left-hand column are for unused stamps and those in the right-hand column for used. Prices are given in pence and pounds:

100 pence (p) 1 pound (£1).

Prices are shown as follows:

10 means 10p (10 pence);
1.50 means £1.50 (1 pound and 50 pence);
For £100 and above, prices are in whole pounds.

Our prices are for stamps in fine condition, and in issues where condition varies we may ask more for the superb and less for the sub-standard.

The minimum catalogue price quoted is 10p. For individual stamps prices between 10p and 45p are provided as a guide for catalogue users. The lowest price charged for individual stamps purchased from Stanley Gibbons is 50p.

The prices quoted are generally for the cheapest variety of stamps but it is worth noting that differences of watermark, perforation, or other details, outside the scope of this catalogue, may often increase the value of the stamp.

Prices quoted for mint issues are for single examples. Those in se-tenant pairs, strips, blocks or sheets may be worth more.

Where prices are not given in either column it is either because the stamps are not known to exist in that particular condition, or, more usually, because there is no reliable information as to value.

All prices are subject to change without prior notice and we give no guarantee to supply all stamps priced. Prices quoted for albums, publications, etc. advertised in this catalogue are also subject to change without prior notice.

Due to different production methods it is sometimes possible for new editions of Parts 2 to 22 to appear showing revised prices which are not included in that year's *Stamps of the World.*

Unused Stamps

In the case of stamps from *Great Britain* and the *Commonwealth,* prices for unused stamps of Queen Victoria to King George V are for lightly hinged examples; unused prices of King Edward VIII to Queen Elizabeth II issues are for unmounted mint. The prices of unused Foreign stamps are for lightly hinged examples for those issued before 1946, thereafter for examples unmounted mint.

Used Stamps

Prices for used stamps generally refer to fine postally used examples, though for certain issues they are for cancelled-to-order.

Information for users

Guarantee

All stamps supplied by us are guaranteed originals in the following terms:

If not as described, and returned by the purchaser, we undertake to refund the price paid to us in the original transaction. If any stamp is certified as genuine by the Expert Committee of the Royal Philatelic Society, London, or by B.P.A. Expertising Ltd., the purchaser shall not be entitled to make any claim against us for any error, omission or mistake in such certificate.

Consumers' statutory rights are not affected by the above guarantee.

Currency

At the beginning of each country brief details give the currencies in which the values of the stamps are expressed. The dates, where given, are those of the earliest stamp issues in the particular currency. Where the currency is obvious, e.g. where the colony has the same currency as the mother country, no details are given.

Illustrations

Illustrations of any surcharges and overprints which are shown and not described are actual size; stamp illustrations are reduced to $\frac{3}{4}$ linear, *unless otherwise stated.*

"Key-Types"

A number of standard designs occur so frequently in the stamps of the French, German, Portuguese and Spanish colonies that it would be a waste of space to repeat them. Instead these are all illustrated on page xiv together with the descriptive names and letters by which they are referred to in the lists.

Type Numbers

These are the bold figures found below each illustration. References to "Type **6**", for example, in the lists of a country should therefore be understood to refer to the illustration below which the number **"6"** appears. These type numbers are also given in the second column of figures alongside each list of stamps, thus indicating clearly the design of each stamp. In the case of Key-Types – see above – letters take the place of the type numbers.

Where an issue comprises stamps of similar design, represented in this catalogue by one illustration, the corresponding type numbers should be taken as indicating this general design.

Where there are blanks in the type number column it means that the type of the corresponding stamps is that shown by the last number above in the type column of the same issue.

A dash (–) in the type column means that no illustration of the stamp is shown.

Where type numbers refer to stamps of another country, e.g. where stamps of one country are overprinted for use in another, this is always made clear in the text.

Stamp Designs

Brief descriptions of the subjects of the stamp designs are given either below or beside the illustrations, at the foot of the list of the issue concerned, or in the actual lists. Where a particular subject, e.g. the portrait of a well-known monarch, recurs frequently the description is not repeated, nor are obvious designs described.

Generally, the unillustrated designs are in the same shape and size as the one illustrated, except where otherwise indicated.

Surcharges and Overprints

Surcharges and overprints are usually described in the headings to the issues concerned. Where the actual wording of a surcharge or overprint is given it is shown in bold type.

Some stamps are described as being "Surcharged in words", e.g. **TWO CENTS**, and others "Surcharged in figures and words", e.g. **20 CENTS**, although of course many surcharges are in foreign languages and combinations of words and figures are numerous. There are often bars, etc., obliterating old values or inscriptions but in general these are only mentioned where it is necessary to avoid confusion.

No attention is paid in this catalogue to colours of overprints and surcharges so that stamps with the same overprints in different colours are not listed separately.

Numbers in brackets after the descriptions of overprinted or surcharged stamps are the catalogue numbers of the unoverprinted stamps.

Note – the words "inscribed" or "inscription" always refer to wording incorporated in the design of a stamp and not surcharges or overprints.

Coloured Papers

Where stamps are printed on coloured paper the description is given as e.g. "4 c. black on blue" – a stamp printed in black on blue paper. No attention is paid in this catalogue to difference in the texture of paper, e.g. laid, wove.

Information for users

Watermarks

Stamps having different watermarks, but otherwise the same, are not listed separately. No reference is therefore made to watermarks in this volume.

Stamp Colours

Colour names are only required for the identification of stamps, therefore they have been made as simple as possible. Thus "scarlet", "vermilion", "carmine" are all usually called red. Qualifying colour names have been introduced only where necessary for the sake of clearness.

Where stamps are printed in two or more colours the central portion of the design is in the first colour given, unless otherwise stated.

Perforations

All stamps are perforated unless otherwise stated. No distinction is made between the various gauges of perforation but early stamp issues which exist both imperforate and perforated are usually listed separately.

Where a heading states "Imperf. or perf". or "Perf. or rouletted" this does not necessarily mean that all values of the issue are found in both conditions.

Dates of Issue

The date given at the head of each issue is that of the appearance of the earliest stamp in the series. As stamps of the same design or issue are usually grouped together a list of King George VI stamps, for example, headed "1938" may include stamps issued from 1938 to the end of the reign.

Se-tenant Pairs

Many modern issues are printed in sheets containing different designs or face values. Such pairs, blocks, strips or sheets are described as being "se-tenant" and they are outside the scope of this catalogue, although reference to them may occur in instances where they form a composite design.

Miniature Sheets

As an increasing number of stamps are now only found in miniature sheets, Stamps of the World will, in future, list these items. This edition lists all Commonwealth countries' miniature sheets, plus those of all non-Commonwealth countries which have appeared in the catalogue supplement during the past year. Earlier miniature sheets of non-Commonwealth countries will be listed in future editions.

"Appendix" Countries

We regret that, since 1968, it has been necessary to establish an Appendix (at the end of each country as appropriate) to which numerous stamps have had to be consigned. Several countries imagine that by issuing huge quantities of unnecessary stamps they will have a ready source of income from stamp collectors – and particularly from the less-experienced ones. Stanley Gibbons refuse to encourage this exploitation of the hobby and we do not stock the stamps concerned.

Two kinds of stamp are therefore given the briefest of mentions in the Appendix, purely for the sake of record. Administrations issuing stamps greatly in excess of true postal needs have the offending issues placed there. Likewise it contains stamps which have not fulfilled all the normal conditions for full catalogue listing.

These conditions are that the stamps must be issued by a legitimate postal authority, recognised by the government concerned, and are adhesives, valid for proper postal use in the class of service for which they are inscribed. Stamps, with the exception of such categories as postage dues and officials, must be available to the general public at face value with no artificial restrictions being imposed on their distribution.

The publishers of this catalogue have observed, with concern, the proliferation of 'artificial' stamp-issuing territories. On several occasions this has resulted in separately inscribed issues for various component parts of otherwise united states or territories.

Stanley Gibbons Publications have decided that where such circumstances occur, they will not, in the future, list these items in the SG catalogue without first satisfying themselves that the stamps represent a genuine political, historical or postal division within the country concerned. Any such issues which do not fulfil this stipulation will be recorded in the Catalogue Appendix only.

Stamps in the Appendix are kept under review in the light of any newly acquired information about them. If we are satisfied that a stamp qualifies for proper listing in the body of the catalogue it is moved there.

Information for users

"Undesirable Issues"

The rules governing many competitive exhibitions are set by the Federation Internationale de Philatelie and stipulate a downgrading of marks for stamps classed as "undesirable issues".

This catalogue can be taken as a guide to status. All stamps in the main listings and Addenda are acceptable. Stamps in the Appendix should not be entered for competition as these are the "undesirable issues".

Particular care is advised with Aden Protectorate States, Ajman, Bhutan, Chad, Fujeira, Khor Fakkan, Manama, Ras al Khaima, Sharjah, Umm al Qiwain and Yemen. Totally bogus stamps exist (as explained in Appendix notes) and these are to be avoided also for competition. As distinct from "undesirable stamps" certain categories are not covered in this catalogue purely by reason of its scope (see page viii). Consult the particular competition rules to see if such are admissable even though not listed by us.

Where to Look for More Detailed Listings

The present work deliberately omits details of paper, perforation, shade and watermark. But as you become more absorbed in stamp collecting and wish to get greater enjoyment from the hobby you may well want to study these matters.

All the information you require about any particular postage stamp will be found in the main Stanley Gibbons Catalogues.

Commonwealth countries before 1952 are covered by the Commonwealth & British Empire Stamps 1840–1952 published annually.

For foreign countries you can easily find which catalogue to consult by looking at the country headings in the present book.

To the right of each country name are code letters specifying which volume of our main catalogues contains that country's listing.

The code letters are as follows:

Pt. 2 Part 2
Pt. 3 Part 3 etc.

(See page xiii for complete list of Parts.)

So, for example, if you want to know more about Chinese stamps than is contained in the *Simplified Catalogue of Stamps of the World* the reference to

CHINA Pt. 17

guides you to the Gibbons Part 17 *(China)* Catalogue listing for the details you require.

New editions of Parts 2 to 22 appear at irregular intervals.

Correspondence

Whilst we welcome information and suggestions we must ask correspondents to include the cost of postage for the return of any stamps submitted plus registration where appropriate. Letters should be addressed to The Catalogue Editor at Ringwood.

Where information is solicited purely for the benefit of the enquirer we regret we cannot undertake to reply.

Identification of Stamps

We regret we do not give opinions as to the genuineness of stamps, nor do we identify stamps or number them by our Catalogue.

Users of this catalogue are referred to our companion booklet entitled *Stamp Collecting – How to Identify Stamps.* It explains how to look up stamps in this catalogue, contains a full checklist of stamp inscriptions and gives help in dealing with unfamiliar scripts.

Stanley Gibbons would like to complement your collection

At Stanley Gibbons we offer a range of services which are designed to complement your collection.

Our modern stamp shop, the largest in Europe, together with our rare stamp department has one of the most comprehensive stocks of Great Britain in the world, so whether you are a beginner or an experienced philatelist you are certain to find something to suit your special requirements.

Alternatively, through our Mail Order services you can control the growth of your collection from the comfort of your own home. Our Postal Sales Department regularly sends out mailings of Special Offers. We can also help with your wants list—so why not ask us for those elusive items?

Why not take advantage of the many services we have to offer? Visit our premises in the Strand or, for more information, write to the appropriate address on page x.

The Stanley Gibbons Group Addresses

Stanley Gibbons Limited,
Stanley Gibbons Auctions

339 Strand, London WC2R 0LX
Telephone 020 7836 8444, Fax 020 7836 7342,
E-mail: enquiries@stanleygibbons.co.uk
Internet: www.stanleygibbons.com for all departments.

Auction Room and Specialist Stamp Departments.
Open Monday–Friday 9.30 a.m. to 5 p.m.

Shop. Open Monday–Friday 9 a.m. to 5.30 p.m. and Saturday 9.30 a.m. to 5.30 p.m.

Stanley Gibbons Publications

Parkside, Christchurch Road, Ringwood, Hants BH24 3SH.
Telephone 01425 472363 (24 hour answer phone service), Fax 01425 470247,
E-mail: info@stanleygibbons.co.uk

Publications Mail Order. FREEPHONE 0800 611622
Monday–Friday 8.30 a.m. to 5 p.m.

Fraser's
(a division of Stanley Gibbons Ltd)

399 Strand, London WC2R 0LX
Autographs, photographs, letters and documents

Telephone 020 7836 8444, Fax 020 7836 7342,
E-mail: info@frasersautographs.co.uk
Internet: www.frasersautographs.com

Monday–Friday 9 a.m. to 5.30 p.m. and Saturday 10 a.m. to 4 p.m.

Stanley Gibbons Publications Overseas Representation

Stanley Gibbons Publications are represented overseas by the following sole distributors (*), distributors (**) or licensees (***).

Australia
Lighthouse Philatelic (Aust.) Pty. Ltd.*
Locked Bag 5900 Botany DC, New South Wales, 2019 Australia.

Stanley Gibbons (Australia) Pty. Ltd.***
Level 6, 36 Clarence Street, Sydney, New South Wales 2000, Australia.

Belgium and Luxembourg**
Davo c/o Philac, Rue du Midi 48, Bruxelles, 1000 Belgium.

Canada*
Lighthouse Publications (Canada) Ltd., 255 Duke Street, Montreal Quebec, Canada H3C 2M2.

Denmark**
Samlerforum/Davo, Ostergade 3, DK 7470 Karup, Denmark.

Finland**
Davo c/o Kapylan Merkkiky Pohjolankatu 1 00610 Helsinki, Finland.

France*
Davo France (Casteilla), 10, Rue Leon Foucault, 78184 St. Quentin Yvelines Cesex, France.

Hong Kong**
Po-on Stamp Service, GPO Box 2498, Hong Kong.

Israel**
Capital Stamps, P.O. Box 3769, Jerusalem 91036, Israel.

Italy*
Ernesto Marini Srl, Via Struppa 300, I-16165, Genova GE, Italy.

Japan**
Japan Philatelic Co. Ltd., P.O. Box 2, Suginami-Minami, Tokyo, Japan.

Netherlands*
Davo Publications, P.O. Box 411, 7400 AK Deventer, Netherlands.

New Zealand***
Mowbray Collectables.
P.O. Box 80, Wellington, New Zealand.

Norway**
Davo Norge A/S, P.O. Box 738 Sentrum, N-0105, Oslo, Norway.

Singapore**
Stamp Inc Collectibles Pte Ltd., 10 Ubi Cresent, #01-43 Ubi Tech Park, Singapore 408564.

Sweden*
Chr Winther Soerensen AB, Box 43, S-310 Knaered, Sweden.

Switzerland**
Phila Service, Burgstrasse 160, CH 4125, Riehen, Switzerland.

Abbreviations

Anniv.	denotes	Anniversary
Assn.	,,	Association
Bis.	,,	Bistre
Bl.	,,	Blue
Bldg.	,,	Building
Blk.	,,	Black
Br.	,,	British or Bridge
Brn.	,,	Brown
B.W.I.	,,	British West Indies
C.A.R.I.F.T.A.	,,	Caribbean Free Trade Area
Cent.	,,	Centenary
Chest.	,,	Chestnut
Choc.	,,	Chocolate
Clar.	,,	Claret
Coll.	,,	College
Commem.	,,	Commemoration
Conf.	,,	Conference
Diag.	,,	Diagonally
E.C.A.F.E.	,,	Economic Commission for Asia and Far East
Emer.	,,	Emerald
E.P.T. Conference	,,	European Postal and Telecommunications Conference
Exn.		Exhibition
F.A.O.	,,	Food and Agriculture Organization
Fig.	,,	Figure
G.A.T.T.	,,	General Agreement on Tariffs and Trade
G.B.	,,	Great Britain
Gen.	,,	General
Govt.	,,	Government
Grn.	,,	Green
Horiz.	,,	Horizontal
H.Q.	,,	Headquarters
Imperf.	,,	Imperforate
Inaug.	,,	Inauguration
Ind.	,,	Indigo
Inscr.	,,	Inscribed or inscription
Int.	,,	International
I.A.T.A.	,,	International Air Transport Association
I.C.A.O.	,,	International Civil Aviation Organization
I.C.Y.	,,	International Co-operation Year
I.G.Y.	,,	International Geophysical Year
I.L.O.	,,	International Labour Office (or later, Organization)
I.M.C.O.	,,	Inter-Governmental Maritime Consultative Organization
I.T.U.	,,	International Telecommunication Union
Is.	,,	Islands
Lav.	,,	Lavender
Mar.	,,	Maroon
mm.	,,	Millimetres
Mult.	,,	Multicoloured

Mve.	denotes	Mauve
Nat.	,,	National
N.A.T.O.	,,	North Atlantic Treaty Organization
O.D.E.C.A.	,,	Organization of Central American States
Ol.	,,	Olive
Optd.	,,	Overprinted
Orge. or oran.	,,	Orange
P.A.T.A.	,,	Pacific Area Travel Association
Perf.	,,	Perforated
Post.	,,	Postage
Pres.	,,	President
P.U.	,,	Postal Union
Pur.	,,	Purple
R.	,,	River
R.S.A.	,,	Republic of South Africa
Roul.	,,	Rouletted
Sep.	,,	Sepia
S.E.A.T.O.	,,	South East Asia Treaty Organization
Surch.	,,	Surcharged
T.	,,	Type
T.U.C.	,,	Trades Union Congress
Turq.	,,	Turquoise
Ultram.	,,	Ultramarine
U.N.E.S.C.O.	,,	United Nations Educational, Scientific Cultural Organization
U.N.I.C.E.F.	,,	United Nations Children's Fund
U.N.O.	,,	United Nations Organization
U.N.R.W.A.	,,	United Nations Relief and Works Agency for Palestine Refugees in the Near East
U.N.T.E.A.	,,	United Nations Temporary Executive Authority
U.N.R.R.A.	,,	United Nations Relief and Rehabilitation Administration
U.P.U.	,,	Universal Postal Union
Verm.	,,	Vermilion
Vert.	,,	Vertical
Vio.	,,	Violet
W.F.T.U.	,,	World Federation of Trade Unions
W.H.O.	,,	World Health Organization
Yell.	,,	Yellow

Arabic Numerals

As in the case of European figures, the details of the Arabic numerals vary in different stamp designs, but they should be readily recognised with the aid of this illustration:

٠	١	٢	٣	٤
0	1	2	3	4
٥	٦	٧	٨	٩
5	6	7	8	9

Stanley Gibbons Stamp Catalogue
Complete List of Parts

1 Commonwealth & British Empire Stamps 1840–1952 (Annual)

Foreign Countries

2 Austria & Hungary (6th edition, 2002)
Austria · U.N. (Vienna) · Hungary

3 Balkans (4th edition, 1998)
Albania · Bosnia & Herzegovina · Bulgaria · Croatia · Greece & Islands · Macedonia · Rumania · Slovenia · Yugoslavia

4 Benelux (5th edition, 2003)
Belgium & Colonies · Luxembourg · Netherlands & Colonies

5 Czechoslovakia & Poland (6th edition, 2002)
Czechoslovakia · Czech Republic · Slovakia · Poland

6 France (5th edition, 2001)
France · Colonies · Post Offices · Andorra · Monaco

7 Germany (6th edition, 2002)
Germany · States · Colonies · Post Offices

8 Italy & Switzerland (6th edition, 2003)
Italy & Colonies · Liechtenstein · San Marino · Switzerland · U.N. (Geneva) · Vatican City

9 Portugal & Spain (4th edition, 1996)
Andorra · Portugal & Colonies · Spain & Colonies

10 Russia (5th edition, 1999)
Russia · Armenia · Azerbaijan · Belarus · Estonia · Georgia · Kazakhstan · Kyrgyzstan · Latvia · Lithuania · Moldova · Tajikistan · Turkmenistan · Ukraine · Uzbekistan · Mongolia

11 Scandinavia (5th edition, 2001)
Aland Islands · Denmark · Faroe Islands · Finland · Greenland · Iceland · Norway · Sweden

12 Africa since Independence A-E (2nd edition, 1983)
Algeria · Angola · Benin · Burundi · Cameroun · Cape Verdi · Central African Republic · Chad · Comoro Islands · Congo · Djibouti · Equatorial Guinea · Ethiopia

13 Africa since Independence F-M (1st edition, 1981)
Gabon · Guinea · Guinea-Bissau · Ivory Coast · Liberia · Libya · Malagasy Republic · Mali · Mauritania · Morocco · Mozambique

14 Africa since Independence N-Z (1st edition, 1981)
Niger Republic · Rwanda · St. Thomas & Prince · Senegal · Somalia · Sudan · Togo · Tunisia · Upper Volta · Zaire

15 Central America (2nd edition, 1984)
Costa Rica · Cuba · Dominican Republic · El Salvador · Guatemala · Haiti · Honduras · Mexico · Nicaragua · Panama

16 Central Asia (3rd edition, 1992)
Afghanistan · Iran · Turkey

17 China (6th edition,1998)
China · Taiwan · Tibet · Foreign P.O.s · Hong Kong · Macao

18 Japan & Korea (4th edition, 1997)
Japan · Korean Empire · South Korea · North Korea

19 Middle East (5th edition, 1996)
Bahrain · Egypt · Iraq · Israel · Jordan · Kuwait · Lebanon · Oman · Qatar · Saudi Arabia · Syria · U.A.E. · Yemen

20 South America (3rd edition, 1989)
Argentina · Bolivia · Brazil · Chile · Colombia · Ecuador · Paraguay · Peru · Surinam · Uruguay · Venezuela

21 South-East Asia (4th edition, 2004)
Bhutan · Burma · Indonesia · Kampuchea · Laos · Nepal · Philippines · Thailand · Vietnam

22 United States (5th edition, 2000)
U.S. & Possessions · Marshall Islands · Micronesia · Palau · U.N. (New York, Geneva, Vienna)

Thematic Catalogues

Stanley Gibbons Catalogues for use with **Stamps of the World.**
Collect Aircraft on Stamps (out of print)
Collect Birds on Stamps (5th edition, 2003)
Collect Chess on Stamps (2nd edition, 1999)
Collect Fish on Stamps (1st edition, 1999)
Collect Fungi on Stamps (2nd edition, 1997)
Collect Motor Vehicles on Stamps (1st edition, 2004)
Collect Railways on Stamps (3rd edition, 1999)
Collect Shells on Stamps (1st edition, 1995)
Collect Ships on Stamps (3rd edition, 2001)

Key-Types

(see note on page vii)

French Group

A. "Blanc."

B. "Mouchon."

C "Merson."

D. "Tablet."

"International Colonial Exhibition."

E. F. G. H.

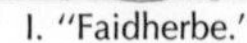

I. "Faidherbe."

J. "Palms."

K. "Balay."

L. "Natives."

M. "Figure."

German Group

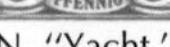

N. "Yacht."

O. "Yacht."

Spanish Group

X. "Alfonso XII."

Y. "Baby."

Z. "Curly Head"

Portuguese Group

P. "Crown."

Q. "Embossed."

R. "Figures."

S. "Carlos."

T. "Manoel."

U. "Ceres."

V. "Newspaper."

W. "Due."

STANLEY GIBBONS SIMPLIFIED CATALOGUE OF STAMPS OF THE WORLD—VOLUME 1 COUNTRIES A–D

ABU DHABI Pt. 1, Pt. 19

The largest of the Trucial States in the Persian Gulf. Treaty relations with Great Britain expired on 31 December 1966, when Abu Dhabi took over the postal services. On 18 July 1971, seven of the Gulf sheikhdoms, including Abu Dhabi, agreed to form the State of the United Arab Emirates. The federation came into being on 1 August 1972.

1964. 100 naye paise = 1 rupee.
1966. 1,000 fils = 1 dinar.

1 Shaikh Shakhbut bin Sultan

3 Ruler's Palace

1964.

No.	Type	Description		
1	**1**	5n.p. green	1·75	2·50
2		15n.p. brown	2·00	1·75
3		20n.p. blue	2·50	1·75
4		30n.p. orange	3·25	1·50
5	–	40n.p. violet	3·25	1·00
6	–	50n.p. bistre	4·25	2·75
7	–	75n.p. black	4·25	4·00
8	**3**	1r. green	4·00	1·25
9		2r. black	7·50	3·25
10	–	5r. red	17·00	10·00
11	–	10r. blue	23·00	14·00

DESIGNS: As Type **1**: 40 to 75n.p. Mountain gazelle; As Type **3**: 5, 10r. Oil rig and camels.

5 Saker Falcon

1965. Falconry.

No.	Type	Description		
12	**5**	20n.p. brown and blue	11·00	2·00
13	–	40n.p. brown and blue	14·00	3·00
14	–	2r. sepia and turquoise	24·00	14·00

DESIGNS: 40n.p., 2r. Other types of Saker falcon on gloved hand.

1966. Nos. 1/11 surch in new currency ("Fils" only on Nos. 5/7) and ruler's portrait obliterated with bars.

No.	Type	Description		
15	**1**	5f. on 5n.p. green	9·00	5·50
16		15f. on 15n.p. brown	9·00	7·00
17		20f. on 20n.p. blue	11·00	8·00
18		30f. on 30n.p. orange	10·00	15·00
19	–	40f. on 40n.p. violet	14·00	1·00
20	–	50f. on 50n.p. bistre	25·00	27·00
21	–	75f. on 75n.p. black	25·00	27·00
22	**3**	100f. on 1r. green	16·00	3·50
23		200f. on 2r. black	18·00	13·00
24	–	500f. on 5r. red	30·00	38·00
25	–	1d. on 10r. blue	42·00	65·00

9 Shaikh Zaid bin Sultan al Nahayyan

10

1967.

No.	Type	Description		
26	–	5f. red and green	40	15
27	–	15f. red and brown	50	10
28	–	20f. red and blue	70	15
29	–	35f. red and violet	85	20
30	**9**	40f. green	80	20
38	**10**	40f. green	1·10	85
31	**9**	50f. brown	1·00	25
39	**10**	50f. brown	1·40	60
32	**9**	60f. blue	1·10	30
40	**10**	60f. blue	2·40	85
33	**9**	100f. red	1·75	40
41	**10**	100f. red	6·50	1·60
34	–	125f. brown and green	3·50	1·40
35	–	200f. brown and blue	15·00	3·00
36	–	500f. violet and orange	11·00	5·50
37	–	1d. blue and green	20·00	10·00

DESIGNS—As Types **9/10**—VERT: 5f. to 35f. National flag. HORIZ: (47 × 27 mm); 125f. Mountain gazelle; 200f. Lanner falcon; 500f., 1d. Palace. Each with portrait of Ruler.

11 Human Rights Emblem and Shaikh Zaid

1968. Human Rights Year.

No.	Type	Description		
42	**11**	35f. multicoloured	1·25	50
43		60f. multicoloured	2·00	60
44		150f. multicoloured	3·75	1·40

12 Arms and Shaikh Zaid

1968. Anniv of Shaikh Zaid's Accession.

No.	Type	Description		
45	**12**	5f. multicoloured	1·25	20
46		10f. multicoloured	1·25	20
47		100f. multicoloured	3·50	1·25
48		125f. multicoloured	5·00	1·90

13 New Construction

1968. 2nd Anniv of Shaikh's Accession. "Progress in Abu Dhabi". Multicoloured.

49	5f. Type **13**	55	20
50	10f. Airport buildings (46½ × 34 mm)	1·25	50
51	35f. Shaikh Zaid, bridge and Northern goshawk (59 × 34 mm)	9·50	2·75

14 Petroleum Installations

1969. 3rd Anniv of Shaikh's Accession. Petroleum Industry. Multicoloured.

52	35f. Type **14**	75	30
53	60f. Marine drilling platform	3·25	95
54	125f. Separator platform, Zakum field	4·50	1·50
55	200f. Tank farm	5·00	2·25

15 Shaikh Zaid

1970.

No.	Type	Description		
56	–	5f. multicoloured	30	15
57	**15**	10f. multicoloured	40	15
58	–	25f. multicoloured	75	15
59	**15**	35f. multicoloured	1·00	15
60		50f. multicoloured	1·50	25
61	–	60f. multicoloured	1·60	30
62	**15**	70f. multicoloured	2·50	45
63	–	90f. multicoloured	3·25	75
64	–	125f. multicoloured	4·50	1·25
65	–	150f. multicoloured	5·50	1·50
66	–	500f. multicoloured	20·00	8·00
67	–	1d. multicoloured	35·00	13·00

DESIGNS: Nos. 56, 58, 61 and 63 as Type **15**, but frames changed, and smaller country name; 125f. Arab stallion; 150f. Mountain gazelle; 500f. Fort Jahili; 1d. Great Mosque.

No. 67 has face value in Arabic only.

17 Shaikh Zaid and "Mt. Fuji" (T. Hayashi)

1970. "Expo 70" World Fair, Osaka, Japan.

No.	Type	Description		
68	**17**	25f. multicoloured	1·50	45
69		35f. multicoloured	1·75	45
70		60f. multicoloured	2·75	1·75

18 Abu Dhabi Airport

19 Pres. G. A. Nasser

1970. 40th Anniv of Shaikh's Accession. Completion of Abu Dhabi Airport. Mult.

71	25f. Type **18**	1·75	40
72	60f. Airport entrance	3·00	95
73	150f. Aerial view of Abu Dhabi (vert)	7·00	3·25

1971. Gamal Nasser (President of Egypt) Commemoration.

No.	Type	Description		
74	**19**	25f. black on pink	3·75	1·00
75		35f. black on lilac	3·75	1·10

20 Motorized Patrol

1971. 5th Anniv of Shaikh's Accession. Defence Force. Multicoloured.

76	35f. Type **20**	2·50	80
77	60f. Patrol-boat "Baniyas"	3·75	1·25
78	125f. Armoured car	7·00	1·75
79	150f. Hawker Hunter FGA.76 jet fighters	9·00	2·75

1971. No. 60 surch.

No.	Type	Description		
80	**15**	5f. on 50f. multicoloured	48·00	40·00

22 Dome of the Rock

1972. Dome of the Rock, Jerusalem. Multicoloured.

81	35f. Type **22**	6·25	2·25
82	60f. Mosque entrance	9·50	3·00
83	125f. Mosque dome	17·00	6·75

1972. Provisional Issue. Nos. 56/67 optd **UAE** and arabic inscr.

No.	Type	Description		
84	–	5f. multicoloured	1·75	1·75
85	**15**	10f. multicoloured	1·75	70
86	–	25f. multicoloured	2·25	1·75
87	**15**	35f. multicoloured	3·25	1·75
88		50f. multicoloured	4·50	4·50
89	–	60f. multicoloured	5·00	5·00
90	**15**	70f. multicoloured	6·00	6·00
91	–	90f. multicoloured	8·00	8·00
92	–	125f. multicoloured	22·00	22·00
93	–	150f. multicoloured	30·00	30·00
94	–	500f. multicoloured	70·00	70·00
95	–	1d. multicoloured	£130	£130

For later issues see **UNITED ARAB EMIRATES**.

ADEN Pt. 1

Peninsula on southern coast of Arabia. Formerly part of the Indian Empire. A Crown Colony from 1 April 1937 to 18 January 1963, when Aden joined the South Arabian Federation, whose stamps it then used.

1937. 16 annas = 1 rupee.
1951. 100 cents = 1 shilling.

1 Dhow

1937.

No.	Type	Description		
1	**1**	½a. green	3·75	2·00
2		9p. green	3·75	2·50
3		1a. brown	3·75	80
4		2a. red	3·75	2·25
5		2½a. blue	4·00	1·00
6		3a. red	10·00	7·00
7		3½a. blue	7·50	3·00
8		8a. purple	24·00	6·50
9		1r. brown	38·00	7·50
10		2r. yellow	55·00	19·00
11		5r. purple	£100	70·00
12		10r. olive	£325	£350

2 King George VI and Queen Elizabeth

1937. Coronation.

No.	Type	Description		
13	**2**	1a. brown	65	1·25
14		2½a. blue	75	1·40
15		3½a. blue	1·00	2·75

3 Aidrus Mosque, Crater

1939.

No.	Type	Description		
16	**3**	½a. green	50	60
17	–	¾a. brown	1·50	1·25
18	–	1a. blue	20	40
19	–	1½a. red	55	60
20	**3**	2a. brown	20	25
21	–	2½a. blue	40	30
22	–	3a. brown and red	60	25
23	–	8a. orange	55	40
23a	–	14a. brown and blue	2·50	1·00
24	–	1r. green	2·25	2·00
25	–	2r. blue and mauve	4·75	2·25
26	–	5r. brown and olive	13·00	8·00
27	–	10r. brown and violet	50·00	11·00

DESIGNS: ¾a., 5r. Adenese Camel Corps; 1a., 2r. Harbour; 1½a., 1r. Adenese dhow; 2½, 8a. Mukalla; 3, 14a., 10r. "Capture of Aden, 1839" (Capt. Rundle).

9 Houses of Parliament, London

1946. Victory.

No.	Type	Description		
28	**9**	1½a. red	15	1·25
29		2½a. blue	15	·50

10

11 King George VI and Queen Elizabeth

1949. Royal Silver Wedding.
30 **10** 1½a. red . . . . 40 1·25
31 **11** 10r. purple . . . . 27·00 32·00

1949. 75th Anniv of U.P.U. As T **20/23** of Antigua surch with new values.
32 2½a. on 20c. blue . . . . 50 1·50
33 3a. on 30c. red . . . . 1·75 1·50
34 8a. on 50c. orange . . . . . . 1·10 1·50
35 1r. on 1s. blue . . . . 1·60 2·75

1951. Stamps of 1939 surch in cents or shillings.
36 5c. on 1a. blue 15 40
37 10c. on 2a. brown 15 45
38 15c. on 2½a. blue . . . . 20 1·25
39 20c. on 3a. brown and red . . 30 40
40 30c. on 8a. orange 30 65
41 50c. on 8a. orange 30 35
42 70c. on 14a. brown and blue 2·00 1·50
43 1s. on 1r. green 35 30
44 2s. on 2r. blue and mauve . . 9·00 2·75
45 5s. on 5r. brown and olive . . 16·00 9·50
46 10s. on 10r. brown and violet 25·00 11·00

13 Queen Elizabeth II

14 Minaret

15 Camel Transport

1953. Coronation.
47 **13** 15c. black and green . . . . 70 1·25

1953.
48 **14** 5c. green 20 10
49a 5c. turquoise . . . . 10 1·00
50 **15** 10c. orange 40 10
51 10c. red 10 30
52 – 15c. turquoise . . . . 1·25 60
79 – 15c. grey . . . . 50 3·50
80 – 25c. red 50 40
56 – 35c. blue . . . . 2·50 2·00
58 – 50c. blue 20 10
60 – 70c. grey 20 10
61a – 70c. black . . . . 1·00 20
62 – 1s. brown and violet . . . 30 10
63 – 1s. black and violet . . . . 1·50 10
64 – 1s.25 blue and black . . . 2·25 60
65 – 2s. brown and red . . . . 1·25 50
66 – 2s. black and red . . . . . 8·50 50
67 – 5s. brown and blue . . . . 1·50 1·00
68 – 5s. black and blue . . . . 6·00 1·25
69 – 10s. brown and green . . . 1·75 8·00
70 – 10s. black and bronze . . . 13·00 1·75
71 – 20s. brown and lilac . . . 6·50 10·00
72 – 20s. black and lilac . . . . 45·00 14·00
DESIGNS—HORIZ: 15c. Crater; 25c. Mosque; 1s. Dhow building; 20s. (38 × 27 mm); Aden in 1572. VERT: 35c. Dhow; 50c. Map; 70c. Salt works; 1s.25, Colony's badge; 2s. Aden Protectorate Levy; 5s. Crater Pass; 10s. Tribesmen.

1954. Royal Visit. As No. 62 but inscr "ROYAL VISIT 1954".
73 1s. sepia and violet 50 55

1959. Revised Constitution. Optd **REVISED CONSTITUTION 1959** (in Arabic on No. 74).
74 15c. green (No. 53) . . . . . 30 2·00
75 1s.25 blue and black (No. 64) 1·00 1·00

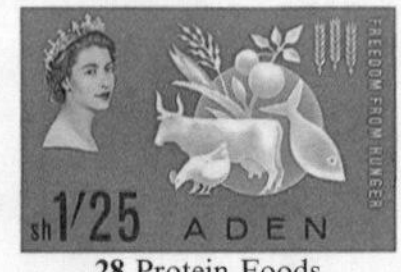

28 Protein Foods

1963. Freedom from Hunger.
76 **28** 1s.25 green . . . . 1·25 1·75

For later issues see **SOUTH ARABIAN FEDERATION**.

AFGHANISTAN Pt. 16

An independent country in Asia, to N.W. of Pakistan. Now a republic, the country was formerly ruled by monarchs from 1747 to 1973.

1871. 60 paisa = 12 shahi = 6 sanar = 3 abasi = 2 kran = 1 rupee.
1920. 60 paisa = 2 kran = 1 rupee.
1926. 100 poul (pul) = 1 afghani (rupee).

The issues from 1860 to 1892 (Types **1** to **16**) are difficult to classify because the values of each set are expressed in native script and are generally all printed in the same colour. As it is not possible to list these in an intelligible simplified form we would refer users to the detailed list in the Stanley Gibbons Part 16 (Central Asia) Catalogue.

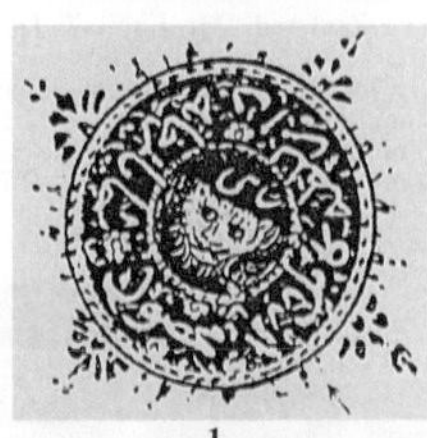
1

4

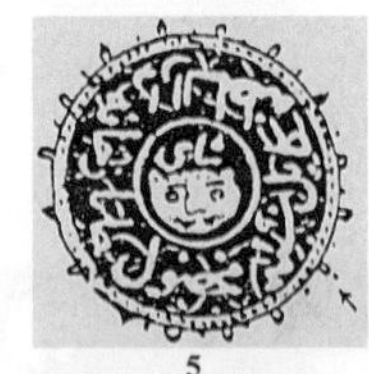
5

6

8

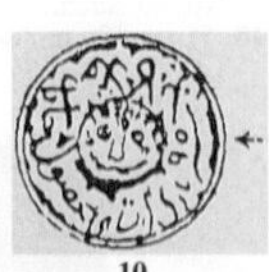
10

12

16

17 National Coat of Arms

1893. Dated "1310".
147 **17** 1a. black on green . . . . 2·75 2·75
148 1a. black on red . . . . 3·00 2·75
149a 1a. black on purple . . . 3·25 3·00
150 1a. black on yellow . . . 3·00 2·75
151 1a. black on orange . . . 3·75 2·50
152 1a. black on blue . . . . 5·00 4·25

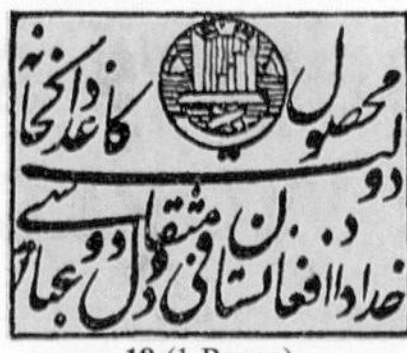
18 (1 Rupee)

1894. Undated.
153 **18** 2a. black on green . . . . 10·00 6·00
154 1r. black on green . . . . 12·00 7·50

20 1 Abasi

23

24 National Coat of Arms

1907. Imperf, roul or perf.
156a **20** 1a. green . . . . 10·00 8·50
157 – 2a. blue . . . . 5·50 5·50
158 – 1r. green . . . . 7·50 9·00
The 2a. and 1r. are in similar designs.

1909. Perf.
165 **23** 2 paisa brown . . . . . 2·50 3·50
166 **24** 1a. blue . . . . 4·50 1·50
168 1a. red 90 80
169 – 2a. green . . . . 2·25 2·00
170a – 2a. bistre . . . . 1·50 2·25
171 – 1r. brown . . . . 4·00 4·25
172 – 1r. olive . . . . 5·50 5·50
The frames of the 2a. and 1r. differ from Type **24**.

27 Royal Star of Order of Independence

29 Crest of King Amanullah

(28)

1920. 1st Anniv of End of War of Independence. Size 39 × 47 mm.
173 **27** 10p. red . . . . 22·00 22·00
174 20p. purple . . . . 40·00 42·00
175 30p. green . . . . 80·00 85·00

1921. Size 23 × 29 mm.
177 **27** 10p. red 75 75
178 20p. purple . . . . . . 1·50 1·50
180b 30p. green . . . . 2·50 2·25

1923. 5th Independence Day. Optd with T **28**.
181 **27** 10p. red . . . . 35·00 35·00
181a 20p. brown . . . . 40·00 40·00
182 30p. green . . . . 45·00 45·00

1924. 6th Independence Day.
183 **29** 10p. brown (24 × 32 mm) 30·00 30·00

29a

30 Crest of King Amanullah

1924.
183b **29a** 5k. blue . . . . 30·00 35·00
183c 5r. mauve . . . . 14·00 20·00

1925. 7th Independence Day.
184 **29** 10p. brown (29 × 37 mm) 30·00 28·00

1926. 7th Anniv of Independence.
185 **29** 10p. blue (26 × 33 mm) . . 5·50 7·50

1927. 8th Anniv of Independence.
186 **30** 10p. mauve . . . . 10·00 9·00

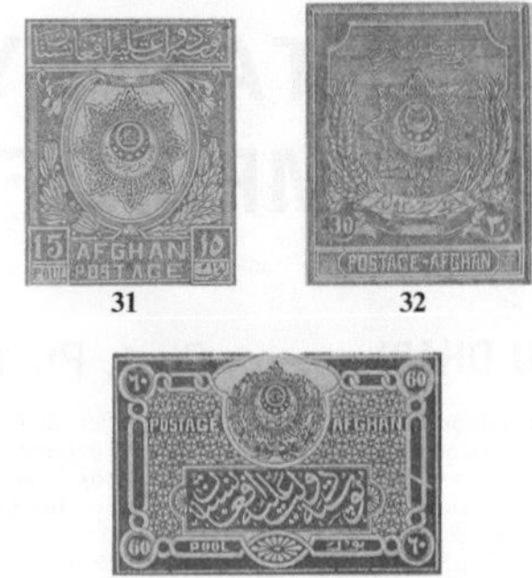
31 **32** **33**

Types **31/3**, **36/37** and **41**, National Seal.

1927. Perf or imperf.
188 **31** 15p. red 85 75
189 **32** 30p. green . . . . 1·40 85
190 **33** 60p. blue . . . . 2·25 2·00
See also Nos. 207/13.

34 Crest of King Amanullah

1928. 9th Anniv of Independence.
191 **34** 15p. red . . . . 3·50 3·25

36

37

1928.
193 **36** 10p. green 85 65
194 **37** 25p. red . . . . 1·00 75
195 – 40p. blue . . . . 1·25 95
196 – 50p. red . . . . 1·75 95
The frames of the 40 and 50p. differ from Type **37**.
See also Nos. 207/13.

41

42 Independence Memorial

1929.
207 **36** 10p. brown . . . . 1·75 1·25
208 **31** 15p. blue . . . . 1·75 1·10
209 **37** 25p. blue . . . . 1·75 1·10
210 **41** 30p. green . . . . 2·25 1·25
211 – 40p. red . . . . 2·50 1·50
212 – 50p. blue . . . . 2·50 2·00
213 **33** 60p. black . . . . 2·75 2·00

1931. 13th Independence Day.
214 **42** 20p. red . . . . 3·25 2·25

46 National Assembly Building

50 Mosque at Balkh

1932. Inauguration of National Council.
215 – 40p. brown (31 × 24 mm) 65 65
216 – 60p. violet (29 × 26 mm) . . 95 85
217 **46** 80p. red . . . . 1·25 1·00
218 – 1a. black (24 × 27 mm) . . 10·00 9·00
219 – 2a. blue (36 × 25 mm) . . . 4·50 4·25
220 – 3a. green (36 × 24 mm) . . 5·00 4·00
DESIGNS: Nos. 215/16, 218/19, Council Chamber; 3a. National Assembly Building (different).

1932.
221 **50** 10p. brown 50 30
222 – 15p. brown 40 35
223 – 20p. red 60 25
224 – 25p. green 75 25
225 – 30p. red 75 25
226 – 40p. orange 90 45
227 – 50p. blue . . . . 1·40 1·40
228 – 60p. blue . . . . 1·25 1·00
229 – 80p. violet . . . . 2·25 2·00
230 – 1a. blue . . . . 4·25 80

231 – 2a. purple 4·50 2·50
232 – 3a. red 5·50 3·25
DESIGNS—32 × 23 mm: 15p. Kabul Fortress; 20, 25p. Parliament House, Darul Funun, Kabul; 40p. Memorial Pillar of Knowledge and Ignorance, Kabul; 1a. Ruins at Balkh; 2a. Minarets at Herat. 32 × 16 mm: 30p. Arch of Paghman. 23 × 32 mm: 60p. Minaret at Herat. 23 × 25 mm: 30p. Arch at Qalai Bust, near Kandahar; 50p. Independence Memorial, Kabul. 16 × 32 mm: 3a. Great Buddha at Bamian.
See also Nos. 237/51.

62 Independence Memorial
63 National Liberation Monument, Kabul

1932. 14th Independence Day.
233 **62** 1a. red 5·50 3·75

1932. Commemorative Issue.
234 **63** 80p. red 2·75 2·00

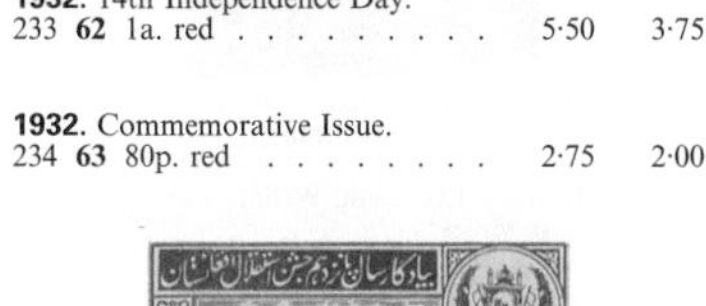

64 Arch of Paghman

1933. 15th Independence Day.
235 **64** 50p. blue 2·75 2·00

65 Independence Memorial

1934. 16th Independence Day.
236 **65** 50p. green 3·25 2·75

1934. As Nos. 219/20 and 221/30, but colours changed and new values.
237 **50** 10p. violet 25 15
238 – 15p. green 40 15
239 – 20p. mauve 45 15
240 – 25p. red 50 25
241 – 30p. orange 60 30
242 – 40p. black 65 35
243 – 45p. blue 2·00 1·50
244 – 45p. red 45 25
245 – 50p. red 75 25
246 – 60p. violet 80 45
247 – 75p. red 3·00 2·25
248 – 75p. blue 1·00 80
248b – 80p. brown 1·50 85
249 – 1a. mauve 2·25 2·00
250 – 2a. grey 4·25 3·00
251 – 3a. blue 4·50 3·50
DESIGNS (new values)—34 × 23 mm: 45p. Royal Palace, Kabul. 20 × 34 mm: 75p. Hunters Canyon Pass, Hindu Kush.

68 Independence Memorial
69 Firework Display

1935. 17th Independence Day.
252 **68** 50p. blue 3·25 2·75

1936. 18th Independence Day.
253 **69** 50p. mauve 3·50 2·75

70 Independence Memorial and Mohamed Nadir Shah
71 Mohamed Nadir Shah

1937. 19th Independence Day. Perf or imperf.
254 **70** 50p. brown and violet 2·50 2·25

1938. 20th Independence Day. Perf or imperf.
255 **71** 50p. brown and blue 2·25 2·25

72 Aliabad Hospital
74 Mohamed Nadir Shah

1938. Obligatory Tax. Int Anti-cancer Fund.
256 **72** 10p. green 3·25 5·00
257 – 15p. blue 3·25 5·00
DESIGN—44 × 28 mm: 15p. Pierre and Marie Curie.

1939. 21st Independence Day.
258 **74** 50p. red 2·25 1·50

76 Darul Funun Parliament House, Kabul
79 Independence Memorial

82 Mohamed Zahir Shah

83 Sugar Mill, Baghlan

1939.
259 **76** 10p. purple (36½ × 24 mm) 25 20
260 15p. green (34 × 21 mm) 35 20
261 20p. purple (34 × 22½ mm) 40 25
262 – 25p. red 45 30
263 – 25p. green 30 25
264 – 30p. orange 40 25
265 – 35p. orange 1·00 65
266 – 40p. grey 80 45
267 **79** 45p. red 80 40
268 50p. orange 60 25
269 60p. violet 75 25
270 – 70p. violet 1·50 65
271 – 70p. purple 1·50 65
272 – 75p. blue 2·25 75
273 – 75p. purple 1·75 1·90
274 – 75p. red 2·50 2·50
275 – 80p. brown 1·50 80
276 **82** 1a. purple 1·50 75
277 – 1a. purple 1·50 80
278d **83** 1a.25 blue 1·60 70
279a – 2a. red 2·25 1·00
280 – 3a. blue 3·50 1·60
DESIGNS—31 × 19 mm: 25, 30p. Royal Palace, Kabul. 30 × 18 mm: 40p. Royal Palace, Kabul. 30 × 21 mm: 70p. Ruins at Qalai Bust, near Kandahar. 35½ × 21½ mm: 75p. Independence Memorial and Mohamed Nadir Shah. 34½ × 21 mm: 80p. As 75p. 35 × 20 mm: 1a. (No. 277), 2a. Mohamed Zahir Shah; 3a. As Type **82** but head turned more to left. 19 × 31 mm: 35p. Minarets at Herat.

85 Potez 25A2 over Kabul

1939. Air.
280a **85** 5a. orange 3·50 4·50
280b 10a. blue 3·75 4·50
280c 20a. green 6·50 7·50
See also Nos. 300/2.

86 Mohamed Nadir Shah
87 Arch of Paghman

1940. 22nd Independence Day.
281 **86** 50p. green 2·25 1·50

1941. 23rd Independence Day.
282 – 15p. green 6·00 3·75
283 **87** 50p. brown 1·75 1·50
DESIGN: (19 × 29½ mm): 15p. Independence Memorial.

87b Mohamed Nadir Shah and Arch of Paghman
88 Independence Memorial and Mohamed Nadir Shah

1942. 24th Independence Day.
284 – 35p. green 4·25 3·75
285 **87b** 125p. blue 2·75 2·25
DESIGN—VERT: 35p. Independence Memorial in medallion.

1943. 25th Independence Day.
286 – 35p. red 12·00 9·50
287 **88** 1a.25 blue 2·50 2·25
DESIGN—HORIZ: 35p. Independence Memorial seen through archway and Mohamed Nadir Shah in oval frame.

89 Arch of Paghman
90 Independence Memorial and Mohamed Nadir Shah

1944. 26th Independence Day.
288 **89** 35p. red 1·25 75
289 **90** 1a.25 blue 2·25 2·00

91 Mohamed Nadir Shah and Independence Memorial
92 Arch of Paghman and Mohamed Nadir Shah

1945. 27th Independence Day.
290 **91** 35p. red 2·25 75
291 **92** 1a.25 blue 3·75 2·00

93 Independence Memorial
94 Mohamed Nadir Shah and Independence Memorial

1946. 28th Independence Day. Dated "1946".
292 – 15p. green 1·25 75
293 **93** 20p. mauve 2·00 85
294 – 125p. blue 3·25 2·00
DESIGNS—HORIZ: 15p. Mohamed Zahir Shah. VERT: 125p. Mohamed Nadir Shah.

1947. 29th Independence Day. Dated "1947".
295 – 15p. green 1·00 60
296 – 35p. mauve 1·25 75
297 **94** 125p. blue 3·25 2·00
DESIGNS—HORIZ: 15p. Mohamed Zahir Shah and ruins of Kandahar Fort; 35p. Mohamed Zahir Shah and Arch of Paghman.

95 Hungry Boy
96 Independence Memorial

1948. Child Welfare Fund.
298 **95** 35p. green 5·00 4·25
299 – 125p. blue 5·00 4·25
DESIGN—26 × 33½ mm: 125p. Hungry boy in vert frame.
See also No. 307.

1948. Air. As T **85** but colours changed.
300 **85** 5a. green 25·00 25·00
301 10a. orange 25·00 25·00
302 20a. blue 25·00 25·00

1948. 30th Independence Day. Dated "1948".
303 – 15p. green 75 35
304 **96** 20p. mauve 1·00 40
305 – 125p. blue 2·00 1·00
DESIGNS—VERT: 15p. Arch of Paghman. HORIZ: 125p. Mohamed Nadir Shah.

97 U.N. Symbol

1948. 3rd Anniv of U.N.O.
306 **97** 1a.25 blue 11·00 9·00

98 Hungry Boy
99 Victory Monument

1949. Obligatory Tax. Child Welfare Fund.
307 – 35p. orange 3·25 1·75
308 **98** 125p. blue 3·25 1·75
DESIGN—HORIZ: 35p. As Type **98** but 29 × 22½ mm.

1949. 31st Independence Day. Dated "1949" (Nos. 310/11).
309 **99** 25p. green 80 40
310 – 35p. mauve 1·00 45
311 – 1a.25 blue 2·25 1·25
DESIGNS—HORIZ: 35p. Mohamed Zahir Shah and ruins of Kandahar Fort; 1a.25, Independence Memorial and Mohamed Nadir Shah.

100 Arch of Paghman

1949. Obligatory Tax. 4th Anniv of U.N.O.
312 **100** 125p. green 16·00 10·00

101 King Mohamed Zahir Shah and Map of Afghanistan

1950. Obligatory Tax. Return of King Mohamed Zahir Shah from Visit to Europe.
313 **101** 125p. green 3·75 1·50

102 Hungry Boy
103 Mohamed Nadir Shah

1950. Obligatory Tax. Child Welfare Fund.
314 **102** 125p. green 4·50 2·50

1950. 32nd Independence Day.
315 **103** 35p. brown 70 45
316 125p. blue 2·25 75

104

1950. Obligatory Tax. 5th Anniv of U.N.O.
317 **104** 1a.25 blue . . . . 7·50 4·50

106

1950. 19th Anniv of Faculty of Medicine, Kabul.
318 **106** 35p. green (postage) . . . 1·25 75
319 – 1a.25 blue . . . . 4·25 2·25

320 **106** 35p. red (obligatory tax) 1·25 60
321 – 1a.25 black . . . . 8·50 2·75
DESIGN: Nos. 319 and 321, Sanatorium. Nos. 318 and 320 measure 38½ × 25½ mm and Nos. 319 and 321, 45 × 30 mm.

107 Minaret at Herat **109** Mohamed Zahir Shah

110 Mosque at Balkh **118**

1951.
322 **107** 10p. brown and yellow . . 25 20
323 15p. brown and blue . . . 40 20
324 – 20p. black . . . . 8·00 4·25
325 **109** 25p. green 40 15
326 **110** 30p. red 45 20
327 **109** 35p. violet 50 20
328 – 40p. brown 55 20
329 – 45p. blue 55 20
330 – 50p. black . . . . 1·50 25
331 – 60p. black . . . . 1·25 25
332 – 70p. black, red and green 60 25
333 – 75p. red . . . . 1·00 40
334 – 80p. black and red . . . 1·75 75
335 – 1a. violet and green . . . 1·25 60
336 **118** 125p. black and purple . . 1·40 75
337 2a. blue . . . . 2·25 70
338 3a. blue and black . . . . 4·25 1·00
DESIGNS—19 × 29 mm: 20p. Buddha of Bamian; 45p. Maiwand Victory Monument; 60p. Victory Towers, Ghazni. 22 × 28 mm: 75, 80p., 1a. Mohamed Zahir Shah. 28 × 19 mm: 40p. Ruins at Qalai Bust; 70p. Flag. 30 × 19 mm: 50p. View of Kandahar.
See also Nos. 425/425k.

119 Douglas DC-3 over Kabul

1951. Air.
339 **119** 5a. red . . . . 3·50 75
339a 5a. green . . . . 1·60 55
340 10a. grey . . . . 8·00 1·60
341 20a. blue . . . . 12·00 2·75
See also Nos. 415a/b.

120 Shepherdess **121** Arch of Paghman

(122) (123)

1951. Obligatory Tax. Child Welfare Fund.
342 **120** 35p. green . . . . 1·50 95
343 – 125p. blue . . . . 1·50 95
DESIGN—34½ × 44 mm: 125p. Young shepherd.

1951. 33rd Independence Day. Optd with T **122**.
344 **121** 35p. black and green . . 1·10 60
345 – 125p. blue . . . . 2·75 1·25
DESIGN (34 × 18½ mm): 125p. Mohamed Nadir Shah and Independence Memorial.
See also Nos. 360/1b and 418/19.

IMPERF STAMPS. From 1951 many issues were made available imperf from limited printings.

124 Flag of Pashtunistan

1951. Obligatory Tax. Pashtunistan Day.
346 **124** 35p. brown . . . . 1·75 1·00
347 – 125p. blue . . . . 3·25 2·25
DESIGN—42½ × 21½ mm: 125p. Afridi tribesman.

125 Dove and Globe **126** Avicenna (physician)

1951. Obligatory Tax. United Nations Day.
348 **125** 35p. mauve . . . . 1·00 50
349 – 125p. blue . . . . 2·50 2·00
DESIGN—VERT: 125p. Dove and globe.

1951. Obligatory Tax. 20th Anniv of Faculty of Medicine.
350 **126** 35p. mauve . . . . 3·00 1·25
351 125p. blue . . . . 1·00 3·25

127 Amir Sher Ali and First Stamp **128** Children and Postman

1951. Obligatory Tax. 76th Anniv of U.P.U.
352 **127** 35p. brown 75 50
353 – 35p. mauve 75 50
354 **127** 125p. blue . . . . 1·25 75
355 – 125p. blue . . . . 1·25 75
DESIGN: Nos. 353 and 355, Mohamed Zahir Shah and first stamp.

1952. Obligatory Tax. Child Welfare Fund.
356 **128** 35p. brown 75 60
357 – 125p. violet . . . . . . 1·50 85
DESIGN—HORIZ: 125p. Girl dancing (33 × 23 mm).

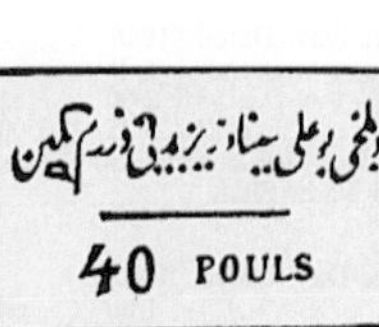

(129) **131** Soldier and Flag of Pashtunistan

1952. Obligatory Tax. Birth Millenary of Avicenna (physician and philosopher). (a) Surch with T **129**.
358 **110** 40p. on 30p. red . . . . 3·50 2·50

(b) Surch **MILLIEME ANNIVERSAIRE DE BOALI SINAI BALKI 125 POULS** in frame.
359 **110** 125p. on 30p. red . . . . 4·50 2·75

1952. 34th Independence Day. As Nos. 344/5.
(a) Optd with T **123**.
360 35p. black and green . . . . 3·25 2·25
361 125p. blue . . . . 3·25 2·25

(b) Without opt.
361a 35p. black and green . . . 1·50 65
361b 125p. blue . . . . 3·25 1·25

1952. Obligatory Tax. Pashtunistan Day.
362 **131** 35p. red 65 55
363 125p. blue . . . . 1·10 1·10

132 Orderly and Wounded Soldier **134** Staff of Aesculapius

133

1952. Obligatory Tax. Red Crescent Day.
364 **132** 10p. green 50 40

1952. Obligatory Tax. United Nations Day.
365 **133** 35p. red 75 50
366 125p. turquoise . . . . . 1·75 1·25

1952. Obligatory Tax. 21st Anniv of Faculty of Medicine.
367 **134** 35p. brown 80 50
368 125p. blue . . . . 2·25 1·50

135 Stretcher Bearers and Wounded

1953. Obligatory Tax. Red Crescent Day.
369 **135** 10p. green and brown . . 70 70
370 – 10p. brown and orange 70 70
DESIGN: No. 370, Wounded soldier, orderly and eagle.

136 Prince Mohamed Nadir **138** Flags of Afghanistan and Pashtunistan

137 Mohamed Nadir Shah and Flag-bearer

1953. Obligatory Tax. Children's Day.
371 **136** 35p. orange 40 25
372 125p. blue 85 60

1953. 35th Year of Independence. Inscr "1953".
373 **137** 35p. green 40 35
374 – 125p. violet . . . . . . 1·10 65
DESIGN—VERT: 125p. Independence Memorial and Mohamed Nadir Shah.

1953. Obligatory Tax. Pashtunistan Day. Inscr "1953".
375 **138** 35p. red 40 20
376 – 125p. blue 85 55
DESIGN—HORIZ: 125p. Badge of Pashtunistan (26 × 20 mm).

139 U.N. Emblem **140** Mohamed Nadir Shah

1953. Obligatory Tax. United Nations Day.
377 **139** 35p. mauve 85 75
378 125p. blue . . . . 2·00 1·25

1953. Obligatory Tax. 22nd Anniv of Faculty of Medicine.
379 **140** 35p. orange . . . . . . 1·25 1·25
380 – 125p. blue . . . . 2·50 2·75
DESIGN: 125p. As Type **140** but inscribed "1953" and with French inscription.
No. 379 was wrongly inscribed "23rd" in Arabic (the extreme right-hand figure in the second row of the inscription) and No. 380 was wrongly inscr "XXIII" and had the words "ANNIVERSAIRE" and "MEDECINE" wrongly spelt "ANNIVERAIRE" and "MADECINE". These mistakes were subsequently corrected but the corrected stamps are much rarer than the original issue.

141 Children's Band and Map of Afghanistan

1954. Obligatory Tax. Child Welfare Fund.
381 **141** 35p. violet 50 25
382 125p. blue . . . . 1·50 1·00

142 Mohamed Nadir Shah and Cannon

1954. 36th Independence Day.
383 **142** 35p. red 75 50
384 125p. blue . . . . 2·25 1·00

143 Hoisting the Flag **144**

1954. Obligatory Tax. Pashtunistan Day.
385 **143** 35p. orange 75 50
386 125p. blue . . . . 2·00 1·10

1954. Red Crescent Day.
387 **144** 20p. red and blue 75 30

145 U.N. Flag and Map **146** Globe and Clasped Hands

1954. United Nations Day and 9th Anniv of U.N.O.
388 **145** 35p. red . . . . 1·25 1·25
389 125p. blue . . . . 3·25 3·25

1955. 10th Anniv of Signing of U.N. Charter.
390 **146** 35p. green 75 50
391 – 125p. blue . . . . 1·75 1·00
DESIGN—28½ × 36 mm. 125p. U.N. emblem and flags.
See also Nos. 403/4.

147 Amir Sher Ali and Mohamed Zahir Shah

1955. 85th Anniv of Postal Service.
392 **147** 35p.+15p. red . . . . . 1·25 55
393 125p.+25p. grey . . . . 2·00 1·00

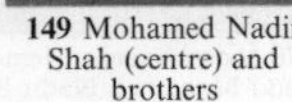

148 Children on Swing **149** Mohamed Nadir Shah (centre) and brothers

1955. Child Welfare Fund.
394 **148** 35p.+15p. green . . . . . 1·00 60
395 125p.+25p. violet . . . . 2·00 1·10

1955. 37th Year of Independence.
396 **149** 35p. blue 70 45
397 35p. mauve 70 45
398 – 125p. violet . . . . . . 1·50 1·00
399 – 125p. purple . . . . . . 1·50 1·00
DESIGN: 125p. Mohamed Zahir Shah and battle scene.

150 **151** Red Crescent

1955. Obligatory Tax. Pashtunistan Day.
400 **150** 35p. brown 60 30
401 125p. green . . . . 1·75 50

1955. Obligatory Tax. Red Crescent Day.
402 **151** 20p. red and grey 40 40

152 U.N. Flag **153** Child on Slide

1955. Obligatory Tax. 10th Anniv of United Nations.
403 **152** 35p. brown 90 60
404 125p. blue . . . . 1·75 1·10

1956. Children's Day.
405 **153** 35p.+15p. blue 60 40
406 140p.+15p. brown . . . . 1·90 85

154 Independence Memorial and Mohamed Nadir Shah **155** Exhibition Building

1956. 38th Year of Independence.
407 **154** 35p. green 60 35
408 140p. blue . . . . 2·40 95

1956. International Exhibition, Kabul.
409 **155** 50p. brown 75 35
410 50p. blue 75 35

156 Pashtun Square, Kabul **157** Mohamed Zahir Shah and Crescent

1956. Pashtunistan Day.
411 **156** 35p.+15p. violet 40 25
412 140p.+15p. brown . . . . 1·00 70

1956. Obligatory Tax. Red Crescent Day.
413 **157** 20p. green and red . . . 55 25

158 Globe and Sun **159** Children on See-saw

1956. U.N. Day and 10th Anniv of Admission of Afghanistan into U.N.O.
414 **158** 35p.+15p. blue . . . . . 1·00 95
415 140p.+15p. brown . . . . 2·00 1·75

1957. Air. As Nos. 339/40, but colours changed.
415a **119** 5a. blue . . . . 2·50 60
415b 10a. violet . . . . . . 3·50 1·25

1957. Child Welfare Fund.
416 **159** 35p.+15p. red 75 55
417 140p.+15p. blue . . . . . 1·40 1·25

1957. 39th Independence Day. As Nos. 344/5 but 35p. has longer Arabic opt (19 mm) and 125p. optd **39 em Anv.**
418 **121** 35p. black and green . . 85 45
419 125p. blue . . . . 1·10 85

162 Pashtu Flag **163** Red Crescent Headquarters, Kabul

1957. Pashtunistan Day.
420 **162** 50p. red . . . . 1·00 60
421 155p. violet . . . . . . 1·50 1·10
No. 421 is inscr "JOURNEE DU PASHTUNISTAN" beneath flag instead of Pushtu characters.

1957. Obligatory Tax. Red Crescent Day.
422 **163** 20p. blue and red 50 25

164 U.N. Headquarters, New York **166** Children Bathing

165 Buzkashi Game

1957. U.N. Day.
423 **164** 35p.+15p. brown 50 40
424 140p.+15p. blue . . . . . 1·00 1·00

1957. As stamps of 1951, but colours changed and new value.
425 **110** 30p. brown 40 20
425a – 40p. red 55 20
425b – 50p. yellow 75 15
425c – 60p. blue 85 15
425d – 75p. violet 95 15
425e – 80p. brown and violet . . 1·10 15
425f – 1a. blue and red 75 20
425g **165** 140p. purple and green . 2·25 60
425k **118** 2a. blue . . . . 5·75 50
425h 3a. black and orange . . 2·75 1·10

1958. Child Welfare Fund.
426 **166** 35p.+15p. red 65 40
427 140p.+15p. brown 75 65

167 Mohamed Nadir Shah and Old Soldier

1958. 40th Independence Day.
428 **167** 35p. green 45 25
429 140p. brown . . . . . . 1·10 85

168 Exhibition Buildings

1958. International Exhibition, Kabul.
430 **168** 35p. green 40 25
431 140p. red . . . . 1·10 65

169 **170** President Bayar

1958. Pashtunistan Day.
432 **169** 35p.+15p. turquoise . . . 40 25
433 140p.+15p. brown . . . . 1·10 65

1958. Visit of Turkish President.
434 **170** 50p. blue 45 25
435 100p. brown 75 35

171 Red Crescent and Map of Afghanistan

1958. Obligatory Tax. Red Crescent Day.
436 **171** 25p. red and green . . . 35 15

172

1958. "Atoms for Peace".
437 **172** 50p. blue 50 40
438 100p. purple 85 65

173 Flags of U.N. and Afghanistan **174** U.N.E.S.C.O. Headquarters, Paris

1958. U.N. Day.
439 **173** 50p. multicoloured . . . 75 75
440 100p. multicoloured . . . 1·50 1·25

1958. Inauguration of U.N.E.S.C.O. Headquarters Building, Paris.
441 **174** 50p. green 75 65
442 100p. brown 75 75

175 Globe and Torch

1958. 10th Anniv of Declaration of Human Rights.
443 **175** 50p. mauve 40 40
444 100p. purple 60 70

176 Tug-of-War

1959. Child Welfare Fund.
445 **176** 35p.+15p. purple 45 40
446 165p.+15p. mauve . . . . 1·25 60

177 Mohamed Nadir Shah and Flags

1959. 41st Independence Day.
447 **177** 35p. red 50 40
448 165p. violet . . . . . . 1·25 60

178 Tribal Dance

1959. Pashtunistan Day.
449 **178** 35p.+15p. green 40 25
450 165p.+15p. orange . . . 1·00 65

179 Badge-sellers **180** Horseman

1959. Obligatory Tax. Red Crescent Day.
451 **179** 25p. red and violet . . . 35 15

1959. United Nations Day.
452 **180** 35p.+15p. orange 30 25
453 165p.+15p. green 65 45

181 "Uprooted Tree" **182** Buzkashi Game

183 Buzkashi Game

1960. World Refugee Year.
454 **181** 50p. orange 15 10
455 165p. blue 35 25

1960.
456 **182** 25p. pink 50 20
457 25p. violet 50 20
458 25p. olive 60 15
459 50p. turquoise . . . . . 1·25 50
460 50p. blue . . . . 1·25 15
460a 50p. orange 40 15
461 **183** 100p. olive 65 25
462 150p. orange 55 25
463 175p. brown . . . . . . 2·50 50
464 2a. green . . . . 1·25 85

184 Children receiving Ball

1960. Child Welfare Fund.
465 **184** 75p.+25p. blue 50 30
466 175p.+25p. green 80 40

185 Douglas DC-6 over Mountains

1960. Air.
467 **185** 75p. violet 65 25
468 125p. blue 75 35
469 5a. olive . . . . 1·75 60

186 Independence Monument, Kabul **188** Insecticide Sprayer

187

1960. 42nd Independence Day.
470 **186** 50p. blue 40 25
471 175p. mauve . . . . . . 1·10 35

1960. Pashtunistan Day.
472 **187** 50p.+50p. red 50 25
473 175p.+50p. blue . . . . . 1·25 95

1960. Anti-Malaria Campaign Day.
474 **188** 50p.+50p. orange . . . . 1·25 1·25
475 175p.+50p. brown . . . . 2·75 1·60

189 Mohamed Zahir Shah

1960. King's 46th Birthday.
476 **189** 50p. brown 60 50
477 150p. red . . . . 1·60 45

190 Ambulance

1960. Red Crescent Day.
478 **190** 50p.+50p. violet & red . . 75 55
479 175p.+50p. blue & red . . 1·90 1·10

191 Teacher with Globe and Children

1960. Literacy Campaign.
480 **191** 50p. mauve 45 35
481 100p. green . . . . 1·10 45

192 Globe and Flags

195 Mir Wais Nika (patriot)

1960. U.N. Day.
482 **192** 50p. purple 30 30
483 175p. blue . . . . 1·00 65

1960. Olympic Games, Rome. Optd **1960** in figures and in Arabic and Olympic Rings.
484 **183** 175p. brown . . . . . . 1·50 1·75

1960. World Refugee Year. Nos. 454/5 surch **+25 Ps.**
485 **181** 50p.+25p. orange . . . . 1·25 1·75
486 165p.+25p. blue . . . . . 1·25 1·75

1960. Mir Wais Nika Commemoration.
487 **195** 50p. mauve 65 40
488 175p. blue . . . . 1·10 55

The very numerous issues of Afghanistan which we do not list appeared between 21 April 1961 and 15 March 1964 (both dates inclusive), and were made available to the philatelic trade by an agency acting under the authority of a contract granted by the Afghanistan Government.

It later became evident that token supplies were only placed on sale in Kabul for a few hours and some of these sets contained stamps of very low denominations for which there was no possible postal use.

When the contract for the production of these stamps expired in 1963 it was not renewed and the Afghanistan Government set up a Philatelic Advisory Board to formulate stamp policy. The issues from No. 489 onwards were made in usable denominations and placed on sale without restriction in Afghanistan and distributed to the trade by the Philatelic Department of the G.P.O. in Kabul.

Issues not listed here will be found recorded in the Appendix at the end of this country. It is believed that some of the higher values from the agency sets were utilised for postage in late 1979.

196 Band Amir Lake

1961.
489 **196** 3a. blue 45 25
490 10a. purple . . . . 1·25 1·00

197 Independence Memorial

1963. 45th Independence Day.
491 **197** 25p. green 25 20
492 50p. orange 25 20
493 150p. mauve 45 25

198 Tribesmen

1963. Pashtunistan Day.
494 **198** 25p. violet 20 20
495 50p. blue 25 20
496 150p. brown 55 35

199 Assembly Building

1963. National Assembly.
497 **199** 25p. brown 15 15
498 50p. red 20 20
499 75p. brown 25 20
500 100p. olive 25 15
501 125p. lilac 30 20

200 Balkh Gate

201 Kemal Ataturk

1963.
502 **200** 3a. brown 95 25

1963. 25th Death Anniv of Kemal Ataturk.
503 **201** 1a. blue 15 20
504 3a. violet 60 40

202 Mohamed Zahir Shah

203 Afghan Stamp of 1878

1963. King's 49th Birthday.
505 **202** 25p. green 20 20
506 50p. grey 25 20
507 75p. red 25 25
508 100p. brown 35 20

1964. "Philately". Stamp Day.
509 **203** 1a.25 black, green & gold 25 20
510 5a. black, red and gold 45 35

204 Kabul International Airport

1964. Air. Inauguration of Kabul Int Airport.
511 **204** 10a. green and purple . . 75 25
512 20a. purple and green . . 1·10 40
513 50a. turquoise and blue 2·50 1·00

205 Kandahar International Airport

1964. Air. Inauguration of Kandahar Int Airport.
514 **205** 7a.75 brown 65 40
515 9a.25 blue 85 75
516 10a.50 green . . . . . . 1·10 90
517 13a.75 red . . . . 1·25 90

206 Unisphere and Flags

207 "Flame of Freedom"

1964. New York World's Fair.
518 **206** 6a. black, red and green 25 20

1964. 1st U.N. Human Rights Seminar, Kabul.
519 **207** 3a.75 multicoloured . . . 25 15

208 Snow Leopard

1964. Afghan Wildlife.
520 **208** 25p. blue and yellow . . . 55 15
521 – 50p. green and red . . . 60 15
522 – 75p. purple and blue . . . 60 15
523 – 5a. brown and green . . . 75 20
ANIMALS—VERT: 50p. Ibex. HORIZ: 75p. Argali; 5a. Yak.

209 Herat

210 Hurdling

1964. Tourist Publicity. Inscr "1964".
524 **209** 25p. brown and blue . . . 20 15
525 – 75p. blue and ochre . . . 25 15
526 – 3a. black, red and green 40 25
DESIGNS—VERT: 75p. Tomb of Gowhar Shad, Herat. HORIZ: 3a. Map and flag.

1964. Olympic Games, Tokyo.
527 **210** 25p. sepia, red and bistre 15 10
528 – 1a. sepia, red and blue . . 15 10
529 – 3a.75 sepia, red and green 40 25
530 – 5a. sepia, red and brown 50 25
DESIGNS—VERT: 1a. Diving. HORIZ: 3a.75, Wrestling; 5a. Football.

211 Afghan Flag

212 Pashtu Flag

1964. 46th Independence Day.
531 **211** 25p. multicoloured . . . 20 15
532 75p. multicoloured . . . 25 15
On the above the Pushtu inscription "33rd Anniversary" is blocked out in gold.

1964. Pashtunistan Day.
533 **212** 100p. multicoloured . . . 20 15

213 Mohamed Zahir Shah

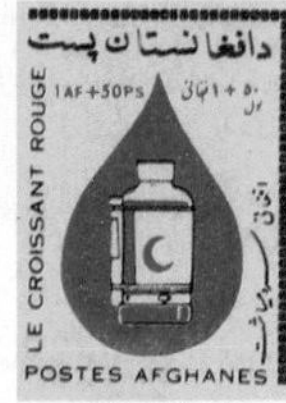

214 "Blood Transfusion"

1964. King's 50th Birthday.
534 **213** 1a.25 green and gold . . 25 20
535 3a.75 red and gold . . . 40 35
536 50a. black and gold . . . 2·75 2·00

1964. Red Crescent Day.
537 **214** 1a.+50p. red and black 20 15

215 Badges of Afghanistan and U.N.

1964. U.N. Day.
538 **215** 5a. blue, black and gold 20 15

216 Doves with Necklace

217 M. Jami

1964. Women's Day.
539 **216** 25p. blue, green and pink 15 15
540 75p. blue, green & lt blue 15 15
541 1a. blue, green and silver 25 10

1964. 550th Birth Anniv of Mowlana Jami (poet).
542 **217** 1a.50 cream, green & blk 1·00 85

218 Scaly-bellied Green Woodpecker

220 "The Red City"

219 I.T.U. Emblem and Symbols

1965. Birds. Multicoloured.
543 1a.25 Type **218** . . . . . . 2·25 50
544 3a.75 Lanceolated jay (vert) 4·50 1·25
545 5a. Himalayan monal pheasant (vert) . . . . . . 5·25 2·40

1965. Centenary of I.T.U.
546 **219** 5a. black, red and blue . . 50 25

1965. Tourist Publicity. Inscr "1965". Mult.
547 1a. Type **220** 25 10
548 3a.75 Bami Yan (valley and mountains) 35 20
549 5a. Band-E-Amir (lake and mountains) 55 25

221 I.C.Y. Emblem

1965. International Co-operation Year.
550 **221** 5a. multicoloured 40 35

222 Douglas DC-3 and Emblem

1965. 10th Anniv of Afghan Airlines (ARIANA).
551 **222** 1a.25 multicoloured . . . 30 10
552 – 5a. black, blue & purple 85 20
553 – 10a. multicoloured . . . 1·50 50
DESIGNS: 5a. Convair CV 240; 10a. Douglas DC-6A.

223 Mohamed Nadir Shah **224** Pashtu Flag

1965. 47th Independence Day.
554 **223** 1a. brown, black & green 40 10

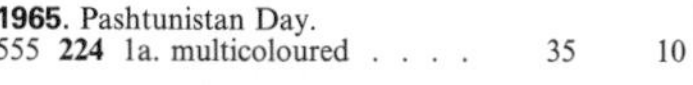

1965. Pashtunistan Day.
555 **224** 1a. multicoloured 35 10

225 Promulgation of New Constitution

1965. New Constitution.
556 **225** 1a.50 black and green . . 30 15

226 Mohamed Zahir Shah **227** First Aid Post

1965. King's 51st Birthday.
557 **226** 1a.25 brown, blue & pink 25 10
558 6a. indigo, purple & blue 35 30
See also Nos. 579/80, 606/7 and 637/8.

1965. Red Crescent Day.
559 **227** 1a.50+50 brn, grn & red 20 15

228 U.N. and Afghan Flags

1965. U.N. Day.
560 **228** 5a. multicoloured 20 20

229 Fat-tailed Gecko

1966. Reptiles. Multicoloured.
561 3a. Type **229** 40 20
562 4a. "Agama caucasica" (lizard) 55 20
563 8a. "Testudo horsfieldi" (tortoise) 70 35

230 Cotton **231** Footballer

1966. Agriculture Day. Multicoloured.
564 1a. Type **230** 20 10
565 5a. Silkworm moth (caterpillar) 40 20
566 7a. Oxen 45 30

1966. World Cup Football Championship, England.
567 **231** 2a. black and red 25 15
568 6a. black and blue 50 25
569 12a. black and brown . . 1·00 50

232 Independence Memorial

1966. Independence Day.
570 **232** 1a. multicoloured 15 10
571 3a. multicoloured 30 15

233 Pashtu Flag

1966. Pashtunistan Day.
572 **233** 1a. blue 25 10

234 Founding Members

1966. Red Crescent Day.
573 **234** 2a.+1a. green and red . . 25 10
574 5a.+1a. brown & mve . . 45 15

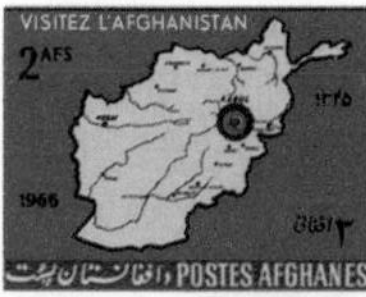

235 Map of Afghanistan

1966. Tourist Publicity. Multicoloured.
575 2a. Type **235** 20 10
576 4a. Bagh-i-Bala, former Palace of Abdur Rahman 40 20
577 8a. Tomb of Abdur Rahman, Kabul 55 40

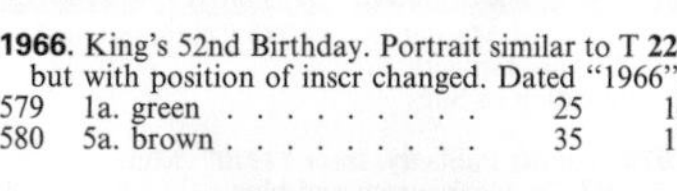

1966. King's 52nd Birthday. Portrait similar to T **226** but with position of inscr changed. Dated "1966".
579 1a. green 25 10
580 5a. brown 35 15

236 Mohamed Zahir Shah and U.N. Emblem

1966. U.N. Day. Inscr "20TH ANNIVERSAIRE DES REFUGIES".
581 **236** 5a. green, brown & emer 35 15
582 10a. red, green & yellow 70 25

237 Children Dancing

1966. Child Welfare Day.
583 **237** 1a.+1a. red and green . . 20 10
584 3a.+2a. brown & yell . . 40 20
585 7a.+3a. green & purple 65 40

238 Construction of Power Station **239** U.N.E.S.C.O. Emblem

1967. Afghan Industrial Development. Mult.
586 2a. Type **238** 20 10
587 5a. Handwoven carpet (vert) 25 15
588 8a. Cement works 35 25

1967. 20th Anniv (1966) of U.N.E.S.C.O.
589 **239** 2a. multicoloured 25 15
590 6a. multicoloured 40 15
591 12a. multicoloured . . . 85 20

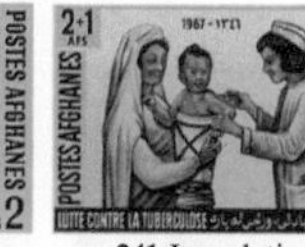

240 I.T.Y. Emblem **241** Inoculation

1967. International Tourist Year.
592 **240** 2a. black, blue and yellow 10 10
593 – 6a. black, blue and brown 35 20
DESIGN: 6a. I.T.Y. emblem on map of Afghanistan.

1967. Anti-tuberculosis Campaign.
595 **241** 2a.+1a. black & yellow 15 10
596 5a.+2a. brown & pink . . 35 25

242 Hydroelectric Power Station, Dorunta **243** Rhesus Macaque

1967. Development of Electricity for Agriculture.
597 **242** 1a. lilac and green 10 10
598 – 6a. turquoise and brown 30 20
599 – 8a. blue and purple . . . 35 25
DESIGNS—VERT: 6a. Dam. HORIZ: 8a. Reservoir, Jalalabad.

1967. Wildlife.
600 **243** 2a. blue and buff 30 10
601 – 6a. sepia and green . . . 55 25
602 – 12a. brown and blue . . . 85 50
ANIMALS—HORIZ: 6a. Striped hyena; 12a. Goitred gazelles.

244 "Saving the Guns at Maiwand" (after R. Caton Woodville)

1967. Independence Day.
603 **244** 1a. brown and red . . . 20 10
604 2a. brown and mauve . . 30 15

245 Pashtu Dancers

1967. Pashtunistan Day.
605 **245** 2a. violet and purple . . . 25 10

1967. King's 53rd Birthday. Portrait similar to T **226** but with position of inscr changed. Dated "1967".
606 2a. brown 15 10
607 8a. blue 50 25

246 Red Crescent **247** U.N. Emblem and Fireworks

1967. Red Crescent Day.
608 **246** 3a.+1a. red, blk & ol . . 15 10
609 5a.+1a. red, blk & blue 25 15

1967. U.N. Day.
610 **247** 10a. multicoloured . . . 45 25

248 Wrestling **249** Said Jamal-ud-Din Afghan

1967. Olympic Games, Mexico City.
611 **248** 4a. purple and green . . . 25 10
612 – 6a. brown and red . . . 40 15
DESIGN: 6a. Wrestling throw.

1967. 70th Death Anniv of Said Afghan.
614 **249** 1a. purple 10 10
615 5a. brown 35 15

250 Bronze Vase **251** W.H.O. Emblem

1967. Archaeological Treasures (11th–12th century Ghasnavide era).
616 **250** 3a. brown and green . . . 25 10
617 – 7a. green and yellow . . . 45 20
DESIGN: 7a. Bronze jar.

1968. 20th Anniv of W.H.O.
619 **251** 2a. blue and bistre . . . 15 10
620 7a. blue and red 25 15

252 Karakul Sheep

1968. Agricultural Day.
621 **252** 1a. black and yellow . . . 10 10
622 6a. brown, black and blue 40 15
623 12a. brown, sepia & blue 55 25

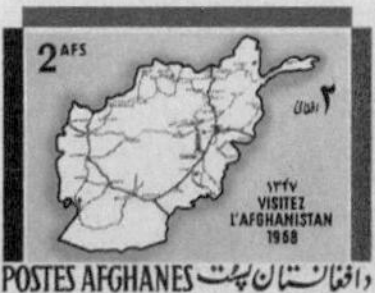

253 Road Map of Afghanistan

1968. Tourist Publicity. Multicoloured.
624 2a. Type **253** 20 10
625 3a. Victory Tower, Ghazni (21 × 31 mm) 25 10
626 16a. Mausoleum, Ghazni (21 × 31 mm) 65 35

254 Queen Humaira **255** Cinereous Vulture

1968. Mothers' Day.
627 **254** 2a.+2a. brown 15 15
628 7a.+2a. green 50 35

1968. Wild Birds. Multicoloured.
629 1a. Type **255** . . . . 1·00 40
630 6a. Eagle owl . . . . 2·25 1·25
631 7a. Greater flamingos . . . . 3·25 1·40

256 "Pig-sticking"

1968. Olympic Games, Mexico. Multicoloured.
632 2a. Olympic flame and rings (21 × 31 mm) 15 10
633 8a. Type **256** 35 20
634 12a. Buzkashi game 50 30

257 Flowers on Army Truck

1968. Independence Day.
635 **257** 6a. multicoloured 25 15

258 Pashtu Flag **259** Red Crescent

1968. Pashtunistan Day.
636 **258** 3a. multicoloured 20 10

1968. King's 54th Birthday. Portrait similar to T **226** but differently arranged and in smaller size (21 × 31 mm).
637 2a. blue 20 10
638 8a. brown 30 25

1968. Red Crescent Day.
639 **259** 4a.+1a. multicoloured . . 30 20

260 Human Rights Emblem **261** Maolala Djalalodine Balkhi

1968. U.N. Day and Human Rights Year.
640 **260** 1a. brown, bistre & green 10 10
641 2a. black, bistre & violet 15 10
642 6a. violet, bistre & purple 35 15

1968. 695th Death Anniv of Maolala Djalalodine Balkhi (historian).
644 **261** 4a. mauve and green . . . 20 10

262 Temple Painting **263** I.L.O. Emblem

1969. Archaeological Treasures (Bagram era).
645 **262** 1a. red, yellow and green 25 10
646 – 3a. purple and violet . . . 45 20
DESIGN: 3a. Carved vessel.

1969. 50th Anniv of I.L.O.
648 **263** 5a. black and yellow . . . 25 15
649 8a. black and blue 45 20

264 Red Cross Emblems **266** Mother and Child

1969. 50th Anniv of League of Red Cross Societies.
650 **264** 3a.+1a. multicoloured . . 45 20
651 5a.+1a. multicoloured . . 65 20

On Nos. 650/1 the commemorative inscr in English and Pushtu for the 50th anniv of the League of Red Cross Societies has been obliterated by gold bars.

1969. Mothers' Day.
654 **266** 1a.+1a. brown & yell . . 20 20
655 4a.+1a. violet & mve . . 40 40

267 Road Map of Afghanistan **268** Bust (Hadda era)

1969. Tourist Publicity. Badakshan and Pamir Region. Multicoloured.
657 2a. Type **267** 25 10
658 4a. Pamir landscape 25 15
659 7a. Mountain mule transport 45 25

1969. Archaeological Discoveries. Multicoloured.
661 1a. Type **268** 10 10
662 5a. Vase and jug (Bagram period) 40 15
663 10a. Statuette (Bagram period) 65 20

269 Mohamed Zahir Shah and Queen Humaira **270** Map and Rising Sun

1969. Independence Day.
664 **269** 5a. red, blue and gold . . 40 15
665 10a. green, purple & gold 55 25

1969. Pashtunistan Day.
666 **270** 2a. red and blue 25 10

271 Mohamed Zahir Shah **272** Red Crescent

1969. King's 55th Birthday.
667 **271** 2a. multicoloured 20 10
668 6a. multicoloured 45 15

1969. Red Crescent Day.
669 **272** 6a.+1a. multicoloured . . 60 20

273 U.N. Emblem, Afghan Arms and Flag

1969. United Nations Day.
670 **273** 5a. multicoloured 25 15

274 I.T.U. Emblem **275** Indian Crested Porcupine

1969. World Telecommunications Day.
671 **274** 6a. multicoloured 20 15
672 12a. multicoloured . . . 40 25

1969. Wild Animals. Multicoloured.
673 1a. Type **275** 20 10
674 3a. Wild boar 45 10
675 8a. Bactrian red deer 65 15

276 Footprint on the Moon **277** "Cancer the Crab"

1969. 1st Man on the Moon.
676 **276** 1a. multicoloured 10 10
677 3a. multicoloured 15 10
678 6a. multicoloured 20 15
679 10a. multicoloured . . . 35 30

1970. W.H.O. "Fight Cancer" Day.
680 **277** 2a. red, dp green & green 15 10
681 6a. red, deep blue & blue 25 20

278 Mirza Bedel **279** I.E.Y. Emblem

1970. 250th Death Anniv of Mirza Abdul Quader Bedel (poet).
682 **278** 5a. multicoloured 30 10

1970. International Education Year.
683 **279** 1a. black 10 10
684 6a. red 25 10
685 12a. green 50 25

280 Mother and Child **281** U.N. Emblem, Scales and Satellite

1970. Mothers' Day.
686 **280** 6a. multicoloured 25 20

1970. 25th Anniv of United Nations.
687 **281** 4a. blue, dp blue & yellow 15 15
688 6a. blue, deep blue & red 25 15

282 Road Map of Afghanistan with Location of Sites **283** Common Quail

1970. Tourist Publicity. Inscr "1970". Mult.
689 **282** 2a. black, green and blue 20 10
690 – 3a. multicoloured 25 10
691 – 7a. multicoloured 55 15
DESIGNS (36 × 26 mm): 3a. Lakeside mosque, Kabul; 7a. Arch of Paghman.

1970. Wild Birds. Multicoloured.
692 2a. Type **283** . . . . 1·40 50
693 4a. Golden eagle . . . . . . 2·75 80
694 6a. Common pheasant . . . 3·25 1·25

284 Shah Reviewing Troops

1970. Independence Day.
695 **284** 8a. multicoloured 35 35

285 Group of Pashtus

1970. Pashtunistan Day.
696 **285** 2a. blue and red 35 10

286 Mohamed Zahir Shah **287** Red Crescent Emblems

1970. King's 56th Birthday.
697 **286** 3a. violet and green . . . 15 10
698 7a. purple and blue . . . 55 15

1970. Red Crescent Day.
699 **287** 2a. black, red and gold 15 10

288 U.N. Emblem and Plaque

1970. United Nations Day.
700 **288** 1a. multicoloured 10 10
701 5a. multicoloured 15 25

289 Afghan Stamps of 1871

1970. Centenary of First Afghan Stamps.
702 **289** 1a. black, blue & orange 20 10
703 4a. black, yellow & blue 25 15
704 12a. black, blue and lilac 45 25

290 Global Emblem

1971. World Telecommunications Day.
705 **290** 12a. multicoloured . . . 50 25

291 "Callimorpha principalis" **292** Lower half of old Kushan Statue

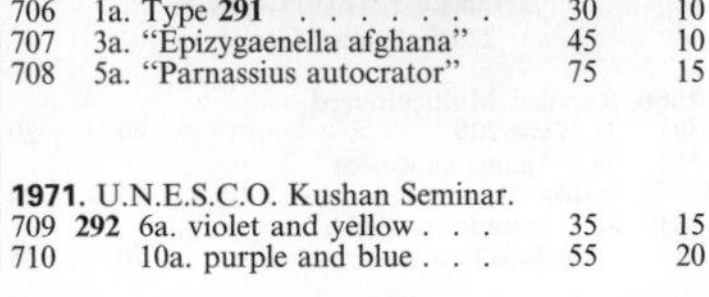

1971. Butterflies and Moths. Multicoloured.
706 1a. Type **291** 30 10
707 3a. "Epizygaenella afghana" 45 10
708 5a. "Parnassius autocrator" 75 15

1971. U.N.E.S.C.O. Kushan Seminar.
709 **292** 6a. violet and yellow . . . 35 15
710 10a. purple and blue . . . 55 20

293 Independence Memorial

1971. Independence Day.
711 **293** 7a. multicoloured 40 15
712 9a. multicoloured 55 20

294 Pashtunistan Square, Kabul

1971. Pashtunistan Day.
713 **294** 5a. purple 35 15

295 Mohamed Zahir Shah and Kabul Airport

1971. Air. Multicoloured.
714 50a. Type **295** . . . . 3·25 3·00
715 100a. King, airline emblem and Boeing 727 airplane 3·50 2·50

296 Mohamed Zahir Shah
297 Map, Nurse and Patients

1971. King's 57th Birthday.
716 **296** 9a. multicoloured 40 25
717 17a. multicoloured . . . 75 35

1971. Red Crescent Day.
718 **297** 8a. multicoloured 40 15

298 Emblem of Racial Equality Year
299 Human Heart

1971. United Nations Day.
719 **298** 24a. blue . . . . 1·25 50

1972. World Health Day and World Heart Month.
720 **299** 9a. multicoloured 35 20
721 12a. multicoloured . . . 45 25

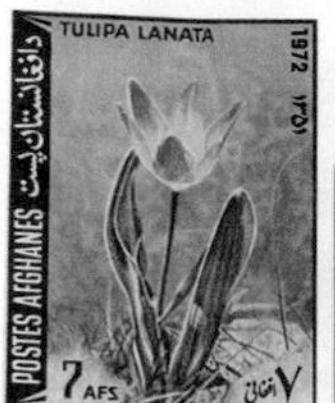

300 "Tulipa lanata"
301 Buddha of Hadda

1972. Afghan Flora and Fauna. Multicoloured.
722 7a. Type **300** 60 60
723 10a. Chukar partridge (horiz) 3·75 1·40
724 12a. Lynx (horiz) . . . . . 1·25 1·00
725 18a. "Allium stipitatum" . . 1·25 1·10

1972. Tourist Publicity.
726 **301** 3a. blue and brown . . . 25 15
727 – 7a. green and red 40 20
728 – 9a. purple and green . . . 50 25
DESIGNS: 7a. Greco-Bactrian seal, 250 B.C.; 9a. Greek temple, Ai-Khanum, 3rd–2nd century B.C.

302 King with Queen Humaira at Independence Parade

1972. Independence Day.
729 **302** 25a. multicoloured . . . 1·50 1·25

303 Wrestling

1972. Olympic Games, Munich. Various Wrestling Holds as T **303**.
730 4a. multicoloured 25 10
731 8a. multicoloured 40 20
732 10a. multicoloured 55 25
733 19a. multicoloured 75 30
734 21a. multicoloured 95 30

304 Pathan and Mountain View
305 Mohamed Zahir Shah

1972. Pashtunistan Day.
736 **304** 5a. multicoloured 40 10

1972. King's 58th Birthday.
737 **305** 7a. blue, black and gold 50 15
738 14a. brown, black & gold 90 35

306 Ruined Town and Refugees

1972. Red Crescent Day.
739 **306** 7a. black, red and blue . . 50 15

307 E.C.A.F.E. Emblem

1972. U.N. Day. 25th Anniv of U.N. Economic Commission for Asia and the Far East.
740 **307** 12a. black and blue . . . 45 25

308 Ceramics

1973. Afghan Handicrafts. Multicoloured.
741 7a. Type **308** 40 25
742 9a. Embroidered coat (vert) 55 25
743 12a. Coffee set (vert) 65 35
744 16a. Decorated boxes 90 35

309 W.M.O. and Afghan Emblems

1973. Cent of World Meteorological Organization.
746 **309** 7a. green and mauve . . . 50 15
747 14a. red and blue . . . . 1·00 30

310 Emblems and Harvester

1973. 10th Anniv of World Food Programme.
748 **310** 14a.+7a. purple & blue 1·00 1·00

311 Al-Biruni
312 Association Emblem

1973. Birth Millenary of Abu-al Rayhan al-Biruni (mathematician and philosopher).
749 **311** 10a. multicoloured . . . 60 30

1973. Family Planning Week.
750 **312** 9a. purple and orange . . 60 20

313 Himalayan Monal Pheasant

1973. Birds. Multicoloured.
751 8a. Type **313** . . . . 2·25 2·00
752 9a. Great crested grebe . . . 2·75 2·25
753 12a. Himalayan snowcock . . 3·25 3·00

314 Buzkashi Game

1973. Tourism.
754 **314** 8a. black 40 15

315 Firework Display

1973. Independence Day.
755 **315** 12a. multicoloured . . . 55 25

316 Landscape and Flag

1973. Pashtunistan Day.
756 **316** 9a. multicoloured 60 20

317 Red Crescent

1973. Red Crescent.
757 **317** 10a. multicoloured . . . 85 25

318 Kemal Ataturk

1973. 50th Anniv of Turkish Republic.
758 **318** 1a. blue 25 10
759 7a. brown 80 15

319 Human Rights Flame

1973. 25th Anniv of Declaration of Human Rights.
760 **319** 12a. blue, black and silver 40 25

320 Asiatic Black Bears

1974. Wild Animals. Multicoloured.
761 5a. Type **320** 35 10
762 7a. Afghan hound 55 20
763 10a. Goitred gazelle 70 25
764 12a. Leopard 90 30

321 "Workers"

1974. Labour Day.
766 **321** 9a. multicoloured 35 15

322 Arch of Paghman and Independence Memorial

1974. Independence Day.
767 **322** 4a. multicoloured 40 10
768 11a. multicoloured . . . 50 20

323 Arms of Afghanistan and Hands clasping Seedling

1974. 1st Anniv of Republic. Multicoloured.
769 4a. Type **323** 40 10
770 5a. Republican flag (36 × 26 mm) 50 15
771 7a. Gen. Mohammed Daoud (26 × 36 mm) 65 15
772 15a. Soldiers and arms . . . 1·00 25

324 Lesser Spotted Eagle

1974. Afghan Birds. Multicoloured.
774 1a. Type **324** . . . . 1·25 40
775 6a. White-fronted goose, ruddy shelduck and greylag goose . . . . 2·75 70
776 11a. Black crane and common coots . . . . . . 4·25 1·10

325 Flags of Pashtunistan and Afghanistan

1974. Pashtunistan Day.
777 **325** 5a. multicoloured 20 15

326 Republic's Coat of Arms

1974.
778 **326** 100p. green 65 25

327 Pres. Daoud

328 Arms and Centenary Years

1974.
779 **327** 10a. multicoloured . . . 35 20
780 16a. multicoloured . . . 1·00 40
781 19a. multicoloured . . . 65 40
782 21a. multicoloured . . . 75 35
783 22a. multicoloured . . . 1·25 50
784 30a. multicoloured . . . 1·50 50

1974. Centenary of U.P.U.
785 **328** 7a. green, black and gold 20 10

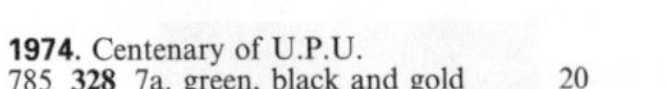

329 "UN" and U.N. Emblem

330 Pres. Daoud

1974. United Nations Day.
786 **329** 5a. blue and ultramarine 35 10

1975.
787 **330** 50a. multicoloured . . . 1·50 85
788 100a. multicoloured . . . 3·00 1·60

331 Minaret, Jam

1975. South Asia Tourist Year. Multicoloured.
789 7a. Type **331** 30 15
790 14a. "Griffon and Lady" (2nd century) 55 30
791 15a. Head of Buddha (4th–5th century) 65 30

332 Afghan Flag

1975. Independence Day.
793 **332** 16a. multicoloured . . . 70 25

333 Rejoicing Crowd

1975. 2nd Anniv of Revolution.
794 **333** 9a. multicoloured 45 15
795 12a. multicoloured . . . 65 20

334 I.W.Y. Emblem

335 Rising Sun and Flag

1975. International Women's Year.
796 **334** 9a. black, blue and purple 50 15

1975. Pashtunistan Day.
797 **335** 10a. multicoloured . . . 40 15

336 Wazir M. Akbar Khan

1976. 130th Death Anniv of Akbar Khan (resistance leader).
798 **336** 15a. multicoloured . . . 50 25

337 Independence Monument and Arms

1976. Independence Day.
799 **337** 22a. multicoloured . . . 60 30

338 Pres. Daoud raising Flag

339 Mountain

1976. 3rd Anniv of Republic.
800 **338** 30a. multicoloured . . . 85 50

1976. Pashtunistan Day.
801 **339** 16a. multicoloured . . . 50 30

340 Arms

1976.
802 – 25p. salmon 40 25
803 **340** 50p. green 50 15
804 1a. blue 50 10
DESIGN: 25p. As Type **340** but with Arms on left and inscription differently arranged.

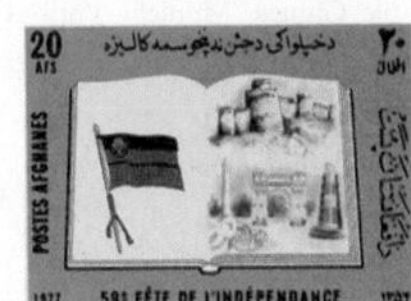
341 Flag and Monuments on Open Book

1977. Independence Day.
805 **341** 20a. multicoloured . . . 45 30

342 Presidential Address

1977. Election of First President and New Constitution. Multicoloured.
806 7a. President Daoud and Election (45 × 27 mm) . . . 40 10
807 8a. Type **342** 45 10
808 10a. Inaugural ceremony . . 65 15
809 18a. Promulgation of new constitution (45 × 27 mm) 85 30

343 Medal

344 Crowd with Afghan Flag

1977. 80th Death Anniv of Sayed Jamaluddin (Afghan reformer).
811 **343** 12a. black, blue & gold 40 20

1977. Republic Day.
812 **344** 22a. multicoloured . . . 65 35

345 Dancers around Fountain

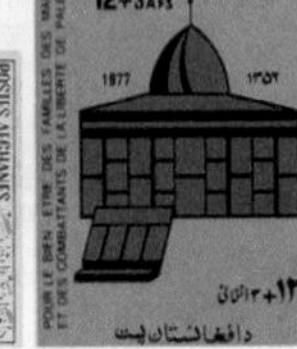
346 Dome of the Rock

1977. Pashtunistan Day.
813 **345** 30a. multicoloured . . . 90 50

1977. Palestinian Welfare.
814 **346** 12a.+3a. black, gold and pink . . . . 2·00 60

347 Arms and Carrier Pigeon

1977.
815 **347** 1a. blue and black 50 15

348 President Daoud acknowledging Crowd

1978. 1st Anniv of Presidential Election.
816 **348** 20a. multicoloured . . . 75 40

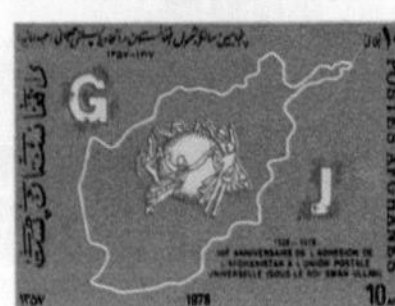
349 U.P.U. Emblem on Map of Afghanistan

1978. 50th Anniv of Admission to U.P.U.
817 **349** 10a. gold, green & black 40 15

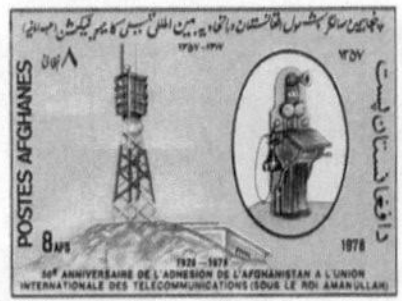
350 Transmitting Aerial and Early Telephone

1978. 50th Anniv of Admission to I.T.U.
818 **350** 8a. multicoloured 35 10

351 Red Crescent, Red Cross and Red Lion Emblems

1978. Red Crescent.
819 **351** 3a. black 40 15

352 Arms

1978.
820 **352** 1a. red and gold 45 15
821 4a. red and gold 75 10

353 Ruin, Qalai Bust

1978. Independence Day. Multicoloured.
822 16a. Buddha, Bamian 75 25
823 22a. Type **353** 85 40
824 30a. Women in national costume . . . . 1·50 75

354 Afghans with Flag

355 Crest and Symbols of the Five Senses

1978. Pashtunistan Day.
825 **354** 7a. red and blue 50 15

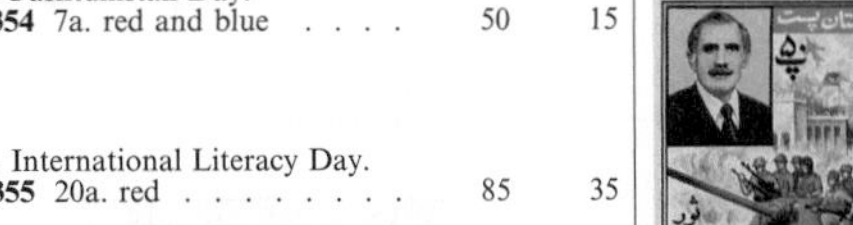

1978. International Literacy Day.
826 **355** 20a. red 85 35

356 Flag

1978. "The Mail is in the Service of the People".
827 **356** 8a. red, gold and brown 60 15
828 9a. red, gold and brown 90 15

357 Martyr

358 President Mohammed Taraki

1978. "The People's Democratic Party Honours its Martyrs".
829 **357** 18a. green 95 30

1978. 14th Anniv of People's Democratic Party.
830 **358** 12a. multicoloured . . . 85 10

359 Emancipated Woman

1979. Women's Day.
831 **359** 14a. blue and red 85 40

360 Farmers planting Tree

1979. Farmers' Day.
832 **360** 1a. multicoloured 45 15

361 Map and Census Taking

1979. 1st Complete Population Census.
833 **361** 3a. black, blue and red . . 50 15

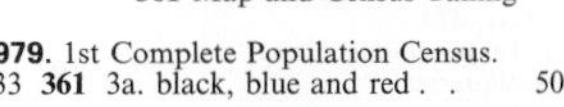

362 Pres. Taraki reading "Khalq"

1979. 1st Publication of "Khalq" (party newspaper).
834 **362** 2a. multicoloured 55 15

363 Pres. Taraki and Tank

364 Pres. Taraki

1979. 1st Anniv of Sawr Revolution (1st issue).
835 **363** 50p. multicoloured . . . 60 15

1979. 1st Anniv of Sawr Revolution (2nd issue). Multicoloured.
836 4a. Type **364** 40 10
837 5a. Revolutionary H.Q. and Tank Monument, Kabul (47 × 32 mm) 55 10
838 6a. Command room, Revolutionary H.Q. (vert) 65 15
839 12a. House where first Khalq Party Congress was held (vert) 90 25

365 Carpenter and Blacksmith

1979. Workers' Solidarity.
840 **365** 10a. multicoloured . . . 85 15

366 Children on Map of Afghanistan

1979. International Year of the Child.
841 **366** 16a. multicoloured . . . 1·50 65

367 Revolutionaries and Kabul Monuments

368 Afghans and Flag

1979. Independence Day.
842 **367** 30a. multicoloured . . . 1·25 65

1979. Pashtunistan Day.
843 **368** 9a. multicoloured 75 15

369 U.P.U. Emblem and Arms on Map

1979. Stamp Day.
844 **369** 15a. multicoloured . . . 60 20

370 Headstone and Tomb

1979. Martyrs' Day.
845 **370** 22a. multicoloured . . . 1·60 45

371 Doves around Globe

1979.
845a **371** 2a. blue and red 85 15

372 Woman with Baby, Dove and Rifle

374 Healthy Non-smoker and Prematurely Aged Smoker

373 Farmers receiving Land Grants

1980. International Women's Day.
846 **372** 8a. multicoloured . . . . 1·10 25

1980. Farmers' Day.
847 **373** 2a. multicoloured . . . . 1·75 65

1980. World Health Day. Anti-smoking Campaign.
848 **374** 5a. multicoloured . . . . 1·50 60

375 "Lenin speaking from Tribune"

1980. 110th Birth Anniv of Lenin.
849 **375** 12a. multicoloured . . . 2·50 75

376 Crowd and Clenched Fist

1980. 2nd Anniv of Sawr Revolution.
850 **376** 1a. multicoloured 65 15

377 Quarry Worker and Blacksmith

1980. Workers' Solidarity.
851 **377** 9a. multicoloured 45 15

378 Football

1980. Olympic Games, Moscow. Mult.
852 3a. Type **378** 60 15
853 6a. Wrestling 65 15
854 9a. Pigsticking 75 15
855 10a. Buzkashi 85 20

379 Soldiers attacking Fortress

1980. Independence Day.
856 **379** 3a. multicoloured 60 15

380 Pashtus with Flag

1980. Pashtunistan Day.
857 **380** 25a. multicoloured . . . 1·00 35

381 Post Office

1980. World U.P.U. Day.
858 **381** 20a. multicoloured . . . 85 35

382 Buzkashi

1980.
859 **382** 50a. multicoloured . . . 1·60 1·10
860 100a. multicoloured . . . 3·00 1·25

383 Arabic "H", Medina Mosque and Kaaba

1981. 1400th Anniv of Hegira.
861 **383** 13a.+2a. multicoloured . . 1·50 25

384 Mother and Child with Dove and Globe

1981. International Women's Day.
862 **384** 15a. multicoloured . . . 95 25

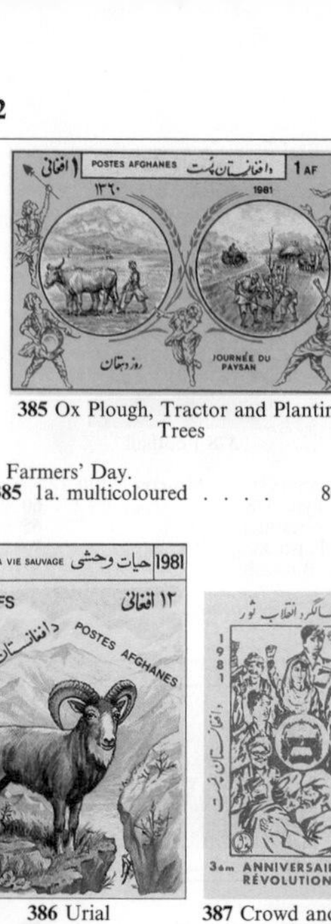

385 Ox Plough, Tractor and Planting Trees

1981. Farmers' Day.
863 **385** 1a. multicoloured 80 20

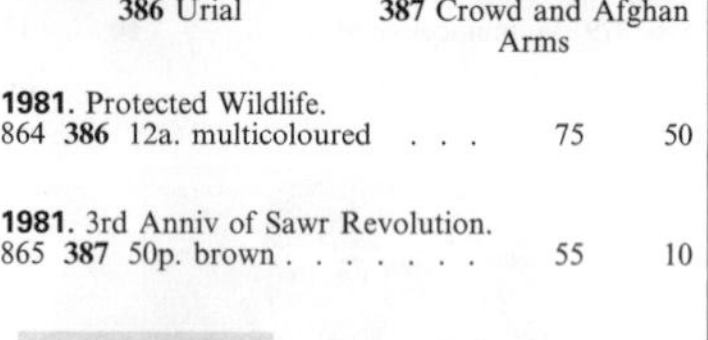

386 Urial

387 Crowd and Afghan Arms

1981. Protected Wildlife.
864 **386** 12a. multicoloured . . . 75 50

1981. 3rd Anniv of Sawr Revolution.
865 **387** 50p. brown 55 10

388 Road Workers in Ravine

389 Red Crescent enclosing Scenes of Disaster and Medical Aid

1981. Workers' Day.
866 **388** 10a. multicoloured . . . 65 20

1981. Red Crescent Day.
867 **389** 1a.+4a. multicoloured . . 50 60

390 Satellite Receiving Station

391 Map enclosing playing Children

1981. World Telecommunications Day.
868 **390** 9a. multicoloured 50 15

1981. International Children's Day.
869 **391** 15a. multicoloured . . . 65 30

392 Afghans and Monument

1981. Independence Day.
870 **392** 4a. multicoloured 65 15

393 Pashtus around Flag

394 Terracotta Horseman

1981. Pashtunistan Day.
871 **393** 2a. multicoloured 55 15

1981. World Tourism Day.
872 **394** 5a. multicoloured 50 10

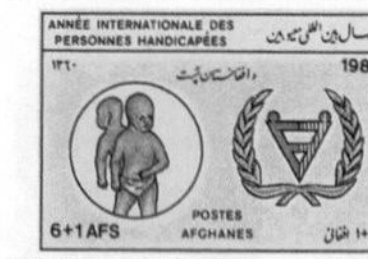

395 Siamese Twins and I.Y.D.P. Emblem

1981. International Year of Disabled Persons.
873 **395** 6a.+1a. multicoloured . . 65 40

396 Harvesting

1981. World Food Day.
874 **396** 7a. multicoloured 60 15

397 Peace, Solidarity and Friendship Organization Emblem

398 Heads and Clenched Fist on Globe and Emblem

1981. Afro-Asian Peoples' Solidarity Meeting.
875 **397** 8a. blue 65 15

1981. International Anti-apartheid Year.
876 **398** 4a. multicoloured 40 10

399 Lion (bas-relief at Stara Zagora)

1981. 1300th Anniv of Bulgarian State.
877 **399** 20a. stone, purple and red 1·10 40

400 Mother rocking Cradle

1982. Women's Day.
878 **400** 6a. multicoloured 45 10

401 Farmers

402 Judas Tree

1982. Farmers' Day.
879 **401** 4a. multicoloured 50 10

1982. Plants. Multicoloured.
880 3a. Type **402** 25 10
881 4a. Hollyhock 50 10
882 16a. Rhubarb 95 30

403 Hands holding Flags and Tulip

404 Dimitrov

1982. 4th Anniv of Sawr Revolution.
883 **403** 1a. multicoloured 85 15

1982. Birth Centenary of Georgi Dimitrov (Bulgarian statesman).
884 **404** 30a. multicoloured . . . 1·50 60

405 Blacksmith, Factory Workers, Weaver and Labourer

1982. Workers' Day.
885 **405** 10a. multicoloured . . . 60 20

406 White Storks

407 Brandt's Hedgehog

1982. Birds. Multicoloured.
886 6a. Type **406** . . . . . . 2·00 65
887 11a. Eurasian goldfinches . . 2·75 85

1982. Animals. Multicoloured.
888 3a. Type **407** 35 15
889 14a. Cobra 45 25

408 National Monuments

409 Pashtus and Flag

1982. Independence Day.
890 **408** 20a. multicoloured . . . 85 40

1982. Pashtunistan Day.
891 **409** 32a. multicoloured . . . 1·60 55

410 Tourists

1982. World Tourism Day.
892 **410** 9a. multicoloured 55 20

411 Postman delivering Letter, Post Office and U.P.U. Emblem

1982. World U.P.U. Day.
893 **411** 4a. multicoloured 60 20

412 Family eating Meal

413 U.N. Emblem illuminating Globe

1982. World Food Day.
894 **412** 9a. multicoloured 85 20

1982. 37th Anniv of United Nations.
895 **413** 15a. multicoloured . . . 80 30

414 Earth Satellite Station

1982. I.T.U. Delegates' Conference, Nairobi.
896 **414** 8a. multicoloured 55 15

415 Dr. Robert Koch

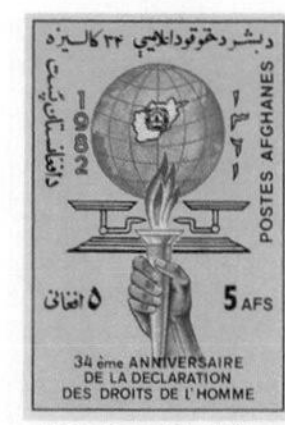

416 Hand holding Torch, Globe and Scales

1982. Centenary of Discovery of Tubercle Bacillus.
897 **415** 7a. black, brown & pink 40 25

1982. 34th Anniv of Declaration of Human Rights.
898 **416** 5a. multicoloured 30 15

417 Lions

1982. Wild Animals. Multicoloured.
899 2a. Type **417** 20 10
900 7a. Asiatic wild asses 40 25
901 12a. Sable (vert) 85 35

418 Woman releasing Dove

419 Mir Alicher-e-Nawai (poet)

1983. International Women's Day.
902 **418** 3a. multicoloured 20 10

1983. "Mir Alicher-e-Nawai and his Times" Study Decade.
903 **419** 22a. multicoloured . . . 65 25

420 Distributing Land Ownership Documents

1983. Farmers' Day.
904 **420** 10a. multicoloured . . . 50 20

421 Revolution Monument

1983. 5th Anniv of Sawr Revolution.
905 **421** 15a. multicoloured . . . 45 20

422 World Map and Hands holding Cogwheel

1983. Labour Day.
906 **422** 20a. multicoloured . . . 55 20

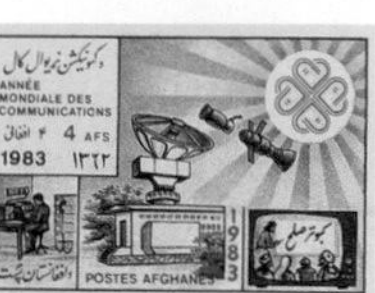

423 Broadcasting Studio, Dish Aerial, Satellites and Television

1983. World Communications Year. Multicoloured.
907 4a. Type **423** 25 10
908 11a. Telecommunications headquarters 45 15

424 Hands holding Child

425 Arms and Map of Afghanistan

1983. International Children's Day.
909 **424** 25a. multicoloured . . . 60 25

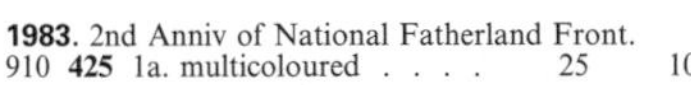

1983. 2nd Anniv of National Fatherland Front.
910 **425** 1a. multicoloured 25 10

426 Apollo

427 Racial Segregation

1983. Butterflies. Multicoloured.
911 9a. Type **426** 35 25
912 13a. Swallowtail 85 45
913 21a. Small tortoiseshell (horiz) . . . . 1·00 55

1983. Anti-apartheid Campaign.
914 **427** 10a. multicoloured . . . 35 15

428 National Monuments

429 Pashtus with Flag

1983. Independence Day.
915 **428** 6a. multicoloured 30 10

1983. Pashtunistan Day.
916 **429** 3a. multicoloured 30 10

430 Afghan riding Camel

1983. World Tourism Day.
917 **430** 5a. multicoloured 25 10
918 – 7a. brown and black . . . 35 15
919 – 12a. multicoloured . . . 45 15
920 – 16a. multicoloured . . . 65 15
DESIGNS—VERT: 7a. Stone carving. 16a. Carved stele. HORIZ: 12a. Three statuettes.

431 Winter Landscape

1983. Multicoloured.
921 50a. Type **431** . . . . 1·40 25
922 100a. Woman with camel . . 2·75 30

432 "Communications"

1983. World Communications Year. Mult.
923 14a. Type **432** 55 15
924 15a. Ministry of Communications, Kabul 55 15

433 Fish Breeding

1983. World Food Day.
925 **433** 14a. multicoloured . . . 80 15

434 Football

1983. Sports. Multicoloured.
926 1a. Type **434** 10 10
927 18a. Boxing 50 15
928 21a. Wrestling 65 15

435 Jewellery

1983. Handicrafts. Multicoloured.
929 2a. Type **435** 15 10
930 8a. Polished stoneware . . . 25 10
931 19a. Furniture 45 10
932 30a. Leather goods 95 15

436 Map, Sun, Scales and Torch

1983. 35th Anniv of Declaration of Human Rights.
933 **436** 20a. multicoloured . . . 65 15

437 Polytechnic Buildings and Emblem

1983. 20th Anniv of Kabul Polytechnic.
934 **437** 30a. multicoloured . . . 95 20

438 Ice Skating

439 Dove, Woman and Globe

1984. Winter Olympic Games, Sarajevo. Mult.
935 5a. Type **438** 20 10
936 9a. Skiing 25 10
937 11a. Speed skating 35 10
938 15a. Ice hockey 45 10
939 18a. Biathlon 50 10
940 20a. Ski jumping 55 10
941 22a. Bobsleigh 65 15

1984. International Women's Day.
942 **439** 4a. multicoloured 10 10

440 Ploughing with Tractor

1984. Farmers' Day. Multicoloured.
943 2a. Type **440** 10 10
944 4a. Digging irrigation channel 15 10
945 7a. Saddling donkey by water-mill 15 10
946 9a. Harvesting wheat 20 10
947 15a. Building haystack . . . 30 10
948 18a. Showing cattle 40 10
949 20a. Ploughing with oxen and sowing seed 45 10

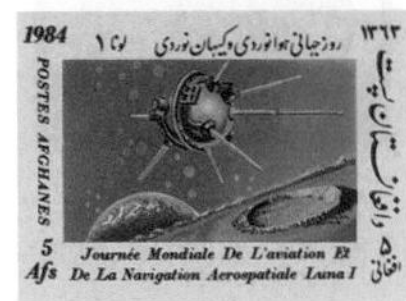
441 "Luna I"

1984. World Aviation and Space Navigation Day. Multicoloured.
950 5a. Type **441** 15 10
951 8a. "Luna II" 25 10
952 11a. "Luna III" 35 10
953 17a. "Apollo XI" 40 10
954 22a. "Soyuz VI" 55 15
955 28a. "Soyuz VII" 55 15
956 34a. "Soyuz VI", "VII" and "VIII" 75 15

442 Flags, Soldier and Workers

443 Hunting Dog

1984. 6th Anniv of Sawr Revolution.
958 **442** 3a. multicoloured 30 10

1984. Animals. Multicoloured.
959 1a. Type **443** 10 10
960 2a. Argali 20 10
961 6a. Przewalski's horse (horiz) 45 10
962 8a. Wild boar 60 10
963 17a. Snow leopard (horiz) . . 1·25 15
964 19a. Tiger (horiz) . . . . . 1·75 20
965 22a. Indian elephant . . . . 2·25 25

444 Postal Messenger

1984. 19th U.P.U. Congress, Hamburg. Mult.
966 25a. Type **444** 75 15
967 35a. Post rider . . . . 1·10 20
968 40a. Bird with letter . . . . 1·40 20

445 Antonov AN-2

1984. 40th Anniv of Ariana Airline. Mult.
970 1a. Type **445** 10 10
971 4a. Ilyushin Il-12 . . . . . 15 10
972 9a. Tupolev Tu-104A 45 10
973 10a. Ilyushin Il-18 . . . . . 70 10
974 13a. Yakovlev Yak-42 . . . 85 10
975 17a. Tupolev Tu-154 . . . . 1·10 15
976 21a. Ilyushin Il-86 . . . . . 1·25 15

446 Ettore Bugatti (motor manufacturer) and Bugatti Type 43 Sports car, 1927

1984. Motor Cars. Multicolored.
977 2a. Type **446** 10 10
978 5a. Henry Ford and Ford Model A two-seater, 1903 15 10
979 8a. Rene Panhard (engineer) and Panhard Limosine, 1899 . . . . 25 10
980 11a. Gottlieb Daimler (engineer) and Daimler DB 18 saloon, 1935 . . . . . 30 10
981 12a. Karl Benz and Benz Viktoria two-seater (inscr "Victoris"), 1893 . . . . . 40 10
982 15a. Armand Peugeot (motor manufacturer) and Peugeot vis-a-vis, 1892 . . . . . . 45 10
983 22a. Louis Chevrolet (car designer) and Chevrolet Superior sedan, 1925 . . . 55 10

447 Open Book showing Monuments and Fortress

1984. Independence Day.
984 **447** 6a. multicoloured 30 10

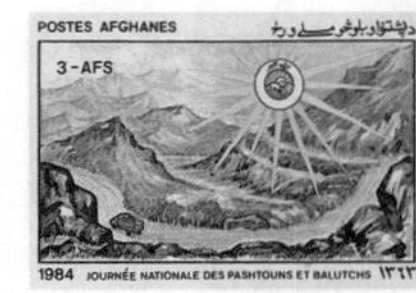
448 Truck on Mountain Road and Pashtunistan Badge

1984. Pashtunistan Day.
985 **448** 3a. multicoloured 25 10

449 Arch at Qalai Bust

450 Pine Cone

1984. World Tourism Day. Multicoloured.
986 1a. Type **449** 10 10
987 2a. Ornamented belt 15 10
988 5a. Kabul monuments . . . 15 10
989 9a. Statuette (vert) 25 10
990 15a. Buffalo riders in snow 45 10
991 19a. Camel in ornate caparison 60 10
992 21a. Buzkashi players 65 10

1984. World Food Day. Multicoloured.
993 2a. Type **450** 10 10
994 4a. Walnuts 20 10
995 6a. Pomegranate 25 10
996 9a. Apples 35 10
997 13a. Cherries 45 10
998 15a. Grapes 55 10
999 26a. Pears 85 10

451 Globe and Emblem

1985. 20th Anniv (1984) of Peoples' Democratic Party.
1000 **451** 25a. multicoloured . . . 85 10

452 Cattle

453 Map and Geologist

1985. Farmers' Day. Multicoloured.
1001 1a. Type **452** 10 10
1002 3a. Mare and foal 15 10
1003 7a. Galloping horse 25 10
1004 8a. Grey horse (vert) . . . 30 10
1005 15a. Karakul sheep and sheepskins 45 10
1006 16a. Herder watching over cattle and sheep 65 10
1007 25a. Family with pack camels 85 10

1985. Geologists' Day.
1008 **453** 4a. multicoloured . . . 25 10

454 Satellite

1985. 20th Anniv of "Intelsat" Communications Satellite. Multicoloured.

1009 6a. Type **454** 45 10
1010 9a. "Intelsat III" 55 10
1011 10a. Rocket launch (vert) . . 75 10

455 "Visitors for Lenin" (V. Serov)
456 Revolutionaries with Flags

1985. 115th Birth Anniv of Lenin. Multicoloured.

1012 10a. Type **455** 50 10
1013 15a. "With Lenin" (detail, V. Serov) 65 10
1014 25a. Lenin and Red Army fighters 85 10

1985. 7th Anniv of Sawr Revolution.

1016 **456** 21a. multicoloured . . . 85 10

457 Olympic Stadium and Moscow Skyline

1985. 12th World Youth and Students' Festival, Moscow. Multicoloured.

1017 7a. Type **457** 20 10
1018 12a. Festival emblem . . . 40 10
1019 13a. Moscow Kremlin . . . 45 10
1020 18a. Doll 60 10

458 Soviet Memorial, Berlin-Treptow, and Tank before Reichstag

1985. 40th Anniv of End of World War II. Multicoloured.

1021 6a. Type **458** 45 10
1022 9a. "Mother Homeland" war memorial, Volgograd, and fireworks over Moscow Kremlin 60 10
1023 10a. Cecilienhof Castle, Potsdam, and flags of United Kingdom, U.S.S.R. and U.S.A. . . . 75 10

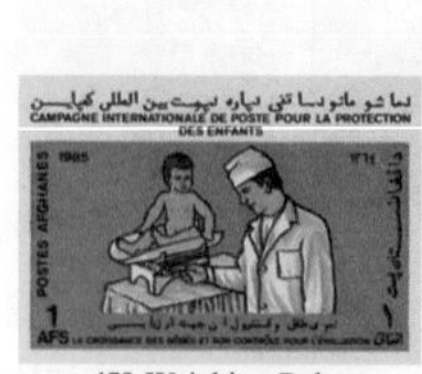

459 Weighing Baby
460 Purple Blewit

1985. U.N.I.C.E.F. Child Survival Campaign. Mult.

1024 1a. Type **459** 10 10
1025 2a. Vaccinating child . . . 15 10
1026 4a. Breast-feeding baby . . 25 10
1027 5a. Mother and child . . . 25 10

1985. Fungi. Multicoloured.

1028 3a. Type **460** 15 10
1029 4a. Flaky-stemmed witches' mushroom 25 15
1030 7a. The blusher 35 20
1031 11a. Brown birch bolete . . 50 35
1032 12a. Common ink cap . . . 60 35
1033 18a. "Hypholoma sp." . . . 85 40
1034 20a. "Boletus aurantiacus" 90 40

461 Emblems

1985. United Nations Decade for Women.

1035 **461** 10a. multicoloured . . . 50 10

462 Evening Primrose

1985. "Argentina "85" International Stamp Exhibition, Buenos Aires. Flowers. Multicoloured.

1036 2a. Type **462** 10 10
1037 4a. Cockspur coral tree . . 15 10
1038 8a. "Tillandsia aeranthos" 25 10
1039 13a. Periwinkle 40 10
1040 18a. Marvel-of-Peru 60 10
1041 25a. "Cypella herbertii" . . 85 10
1042 30a. "Clytostoma callistegioides" . . . . . 1·00 10

463 Building

1985. Independence Day.

1044 **463** 33a. multicoloured . . . 1·40 15

464 Dancers in Pashtunistan Square, Kabul

1985. Pashtunistan Day.

1045 **464** 25a. multicoloured . . . 1·10 10

465 Guldara Stupa

1985. 10th Anniv of World Tourism Organization. Multicoloured.

1046 1a. Type **465** 10 10
1047 2a. Mirwais tomb (vert) . . 10 10
1048 10a. Buddha of Bamian (vert) 35 10
1049 13a. No Gumbad mosque (vert) 50 10
1050 14a. Pule Kheshti mosque 55 10
1051 15a. Arch at Qalai Bust . . 60 10
1052 20a. Ghazni minaret (vert) 85 10

466 Boxing

1985. Sport. Multicoloured.

1053 1a. Type **466** 10 10
1054 2a. Volleyball 15 10
1055 3a. Football (vert) 40 10
1056 12a. Buzkashi 45 10
1057 14a. Weightlifting 55 10
1058 18a. Wrestling 55 10
1059 25a. Pigsticking 75 10

467 Fruit Stall

1985. World Food Day.

1060 **467** 25a. multicoloured . . . 75 10

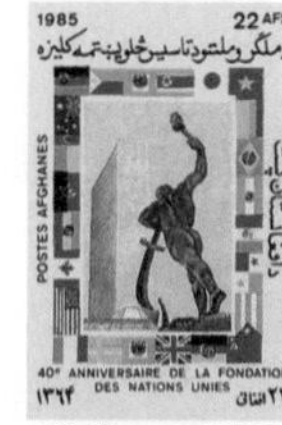

468 Flags and U.N. Building, New York
469 Black-billed Magpie

1985. 40th Anniv of United Nations Organization.

1061 **468** 22a. multicoloured . . . 75 10

1985. Birds. Multicoloured.

1062 2a. Type **469** 15 10
1063 4a. Green woodpecker . . . 75 35
1064 8a. Common pheasants . . 80 35
1065 13a. Bluethroat, Eurasian goldfinch and hoopoe . . 1·25 65
1066 18a. Peregrine falcons . . . 1·50 75
1067 25a. Red-legged partridge 2·10 1·10
1068 30a. Eastern white pelicans (horiz) . . . . 2·75 1·25

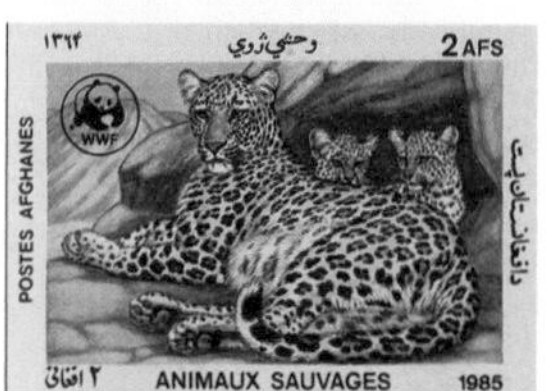

470 Leopard and Cubs

1985. World Wildlife Fund. The Leopard. Mult.

1070 2a. Type **470** 10 10
1071 9a. Head of leopard 35 10
1072 11a. Leopard 55 10
1073 15a. Leopard cub 85 10

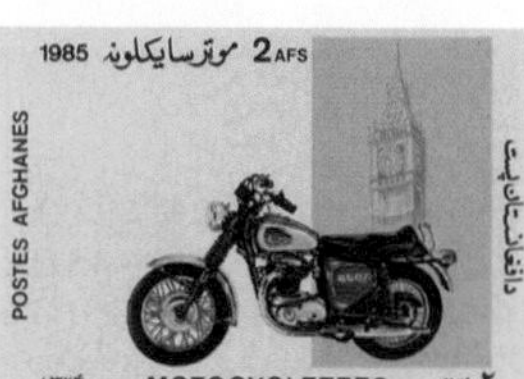

471 Triumph 650 and Big Ben Tower

1985. Motorcycles. Multicoloured.

1074 2a. Type **471** 10 10
1075 4a. Motobecane and Eiffel Tower, Paris 15 10
1076 8a. Bultaco motorcycles and Don Quixote monument, Madrid 25 10
1077 13a. Honda and Mt. Fuji, Japan 40 10
1078 18a. Jawa and Old Town Hall clock, Prague . . . 50 10
1079 25a. MZ motorcycle and T.V. Tower, Berlin . . . 70 10
1080 30a. Motorcycle and Colosseum, Rome 85 10

472 Crowd with Flags

1986. 21st Anniv of Peoples' Democratic Party.

1082 **472** 2a. multicoloured . . . 25 10

473 Lenin writing

1986. 27th Soviet Communist Party Congress, Moscow.

1083 **473** 25a. multicoloured . . . 70 10

474 "Vostok 1"

1986. 25th Anniv of First Manned Space Flight. Multicoloured.

1084 3a. Type **474** 10 10
1085 7a. Russian Cosmonaut Medal (vert) 25 10
1086 9a. Launch of "Vostok 1" (vert) 30 10
1087 11a. Yuri Gagarin (first man in space) (vert) 45 10
1088 13a. Cosmonauts reading newspaper 45 10
1089 15a. Yuri Gagarin and Sergei Pavlovich Korolev (rocket designer) 55 10
1090 17a. Valentina Tereshkova (first woman in space) (vert) 65 10

475 Footballers
476 Lenin

1986. World Cup Football Championship, Mexico.

1091 **475** 3a. multicoloured . . . 10 10
1092 – 4a. multicoloured (horiz) 15 10
1093 – 7a. multicoloured (horiz) 25 10
1094 – 11a. multicoloured . . . 45 10
1095 – 12a. mult (horiz) 45 10
1096 – 18a. multicoloured . . . 65 10
1097 – 20a. multicoloured . . . 75 10

DESIGNS: 4a. to 20a. Various footballing scenes.

1986. 116th Birth Anniv of Lenin.

1099 **476** 16a. multicoloured . . . 60 10

477 Delegates voting

1986. 1st Anniv of Supreme Council Meeting of Tribal Leaders.

1100 **477** 3a. brown, red and blue 25 10

478 Flags and Crowd
479 Worker with Cogwheel and Globe

1986. 8th Anniv of Sawr Revolution.

1101 **478** 8a. multicoloured . . . 30 10

1986. Labour Day.

1102 **479** 5a. multicoloured . . . 25 10

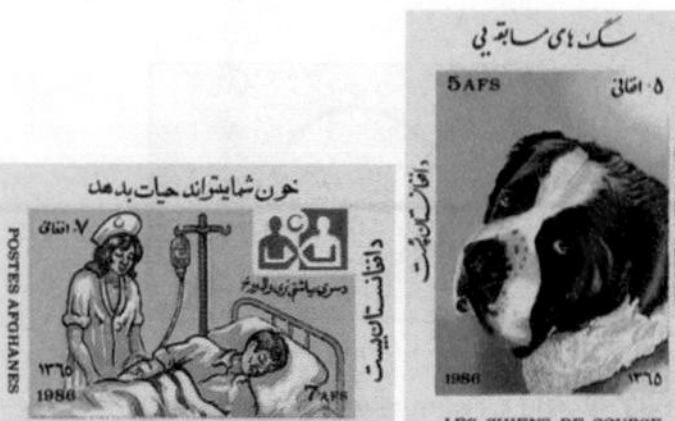

480 Patient receiving Blood Transfusion
481 St. Bernard

1986. International Red Cross/Crescent Day.
1103 **480** 7a. multicoloured 45 10

1986. Pedigree Dogs. Multicoloured.
1104 5a. Type **481** 20 10
1105 7a. Rough collie 25 10
1106 8a. Spaniel 35 10
1107 9a. Long-haired dachshund 35 10
1108 11a. German shepherd 45 10
1109 15a. Bulldog 60 10
1110 20a. Afghan hound 85 10

482 Tiger Barb

483 Mother and Children

1986. Fishes. Multicoloured.
1111 5a. Type **482** 25 15
1112 7a. Mbuna 45 15
1113 8a. Clown loach 55 15
1114 9a. Lisa 65 15
1115 11a. Figure-eight pufferfish 80 15
1116 15a. Six-barred distichodus 1·10 15
1117 20a. Sail-finned molly 1·40 15

1986. World Children's Day. Multicoloured.
1118 1a. Type **483** 10 10
1119 3a. Woman holding boy and emblem 15 10
1120 9a. Circle of children on map (horiz) 30 10

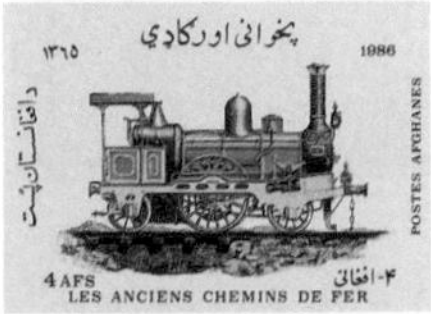

484 Italian Birkenhead Locomotive

1986. 19th-century Railway Locomotives. Mult.
1121 4a. Type **484** 40 10
1122 5a. Norris locomotive 60 10
1123 6a. Stephenson "Patentee" type locomotive 70 10
1124 7a. Bridges Adams locomotive 90 10
1125 8a. Ansoldo locomotive 1·10 10
1126 9a. Locomotive "St. David" 1·50 10
1127 11a. Jones & Potts locomotive 2·00 15

485 Cobra

1986. Animals. Multicoloured.
1128 3a. Type **485** 10 10
1129 4a. Lizards (vert) 10 10
1130 5a. Praying mantis 15 10
1131 8a. Beetle (vert) 20 15
1132 9a. Spider 25 20
1133 10a. Snake 25 20
1134 11a. Scorpions 25 20

Nos. 1130/2 and 1134 are wrongly inscr "Les Reptiles".

486 Profiles on Globe

1986. World Youth Day.
1135 **486** 15a. multicoloured 90 65

487 National Monuments

1986. Independence Day.
1136 **487** 10a. multicoloured 40 10

488 11th-century Ship

1986. "Stockholmia 86" International Stamp Exhibition. Sailing Ships. Multicoloured.
1137 4a. Type **488** 40 25
1138 5a. Roman galley 55 25
1139 6a. English royal kogge 85 25
1140 7a. Early dhow 90 25
1141 8a. Nao 1·00 25
1142 9a. Ancient Egyptian ship 1·10 25
1143 11a. Medieval galeasse 1·10 25

489 Tribesmen

490 State Arms

1986. Pashtunistan Day.
1145 **489** 4a. multicoloured 25 10

1986. Supreme Council Meeting of Tribal Leaders.
1146 **490** 3a. gold, blue and black 25 10

491 Labourer reading

492 Dove and U.N. Emblem

1986. World Literacy Day.
1147 **491** 2a. multicoloured 20 10

1986. International Peace Year.
1148 **492** 12a. black and blue 40 10

493 Tulips, Flame and Man with Rifle

494 Crowd and Flags

1986. Afghanistan Youth Day.
1149 **493** 3a. red and black 25 10

1987. 9th Anniv of Sawr Revolution.
1150 **494** 3a. multicoloured 25 10

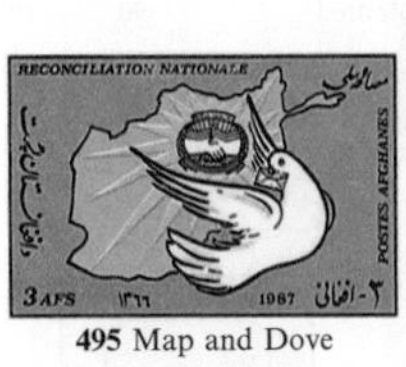

495 Map and Dove

496 Oral Rehydration

1987. National Reconciliation.
1151 **495** 3a. multicoloured 25 10

1987. International Children's Day. Multicoloured.
1152 1a. Type **496** 10 10
1153 5a. Weighing babies 15 10
1154 9a. Vaccinating babies 25 10

497 Conference Delegates

498 "Pieris sp."

1987. 1st Anniv of Tribal Conference.
1155 **497** 5a. multicoloured 25 10

1987. Butterflies and Moths. Multicoloured.
1156 7a. Type **498** 30 20
1157 9a. Brimstone and unidentified butterfly 35 20
1158 10a. Garden tiger moth (horiz) 40 25
1159 12a. "Parnassius sp." 45 25
1160 15a. Butterfly (unidentified) (horiz) 60 40
1161 22a. Butterfly (unidentified) (horiz) 65 40
1162 25a. Butterfly (unidentified) 75 45

499 People on Hand

1987. 1st Local Government Elections.
1163 **499** 1a. multicoloured 20 10

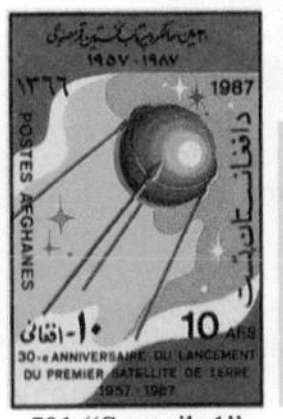

501 "Sputnik 1"

502 Old and Modern Post Offices

1987. 30th Anniv of Launch of "Sputnik 1" (first artificial satellite). Multicoloured.
1165 10a. Type **501** 35 10
1166 15a. Rocket launch 45 10
1167 25a. "Soyuz"–"Salyut" space complex 65 10

1987. World U.P.U. Day.
1168 **502** 22a. multicoloured 75 10

503 Monument and Arch of Paghman

1987. Independence Day.
1169 **503** 3a. multicoloured 20 10

504 "Communications"

1987. United Nations Day.
1170 **504** 42a. multicoloured 3·75 75

505 Lenin

506 Castor Oil Plant

1987. 70th Anniv of Russian Revolution.
1171 **505** 25a. multicoloured 95 10

1987. Plants. Multicoloured.
1172 3a. Type **506** 15 10
1173 6a. Liquorice 30 10
1174 9a. Camomile 40 10
1175 14a. Thorn apple 60 10
1176 18a. Chicory 80 10

507 Field Mice

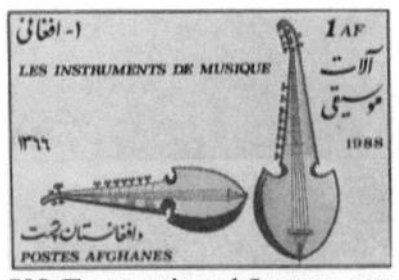

508 Four-stringed Instrument

1987. Mice. Multicoloured.
1177 2a. Type **507** 15 10
1178 4a. Brown and white mice (horiz) 20 10
1179 8a. Ginger mice (horiz) 25 10
1180 16a. Black mice (horiz) 45 10
1181 20a. Spotted and ginger mice (horiz) 55 10

1988. Musical Instruments. Multicoloured.
1182 1a. Type **508** 10 10
1183 3a. Drums 15 10
1184 5a. Two-stringed instruments with two pegs 20 10
1185 15a. Two-stringed instrument with ten pegs 45 10
1186 18a. Two-stringed instruments with fourteen or ten pegs 60 10
1187 25a. Four-stringed bowed instruments 85 10
1188 33a. Two-stringed bowed instruments 1·25 10

509 Mixed Arrangement

510 Emblems and Means of Communication

1988. Flowers. Multicoloured.
1189 3a. Type **509** 15 10
1190 5a. Tulips (horiz) 20 10
1191 7a. Mallows 25 10
1192 9a. Small mauve flowers 35 10
1193 12a. Marguerites 50 10
1194 15a. White flowers 65 10
1195 24a. Red and blue flowers (horiz) 1·00 10

1988. 60th Anniv of Membership of U.P.U. and I.T.U.
1196 **510** 20a. multicoloured 65 10

511 Tank Monument, Kabul, and Flags

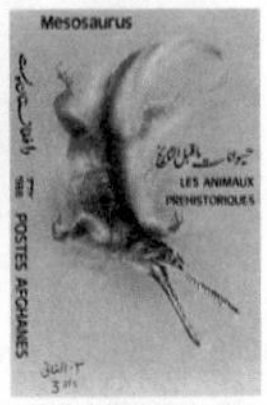

512 Mesosaurus

1988. 10th Anniv of Sawr Revolution.
1197 **511** 10a. multicoloured 40 10

1988. Prehistoric Animals. Multicoloured.
1198 3a. Type **512** 15 10
1199 5a. Styracosaurus (horiz) 25 10
1200 10a. Uintatherium (horiz) 45 10
1201 15a. Protoceratops (horiz) 65 10
1202 20a. Stegosaurus (horiz) 85 10
1203 25a. Ceratosaurus 1·10 10
1204 30a. Moa ("Dinornis maximus") 2·00 1·25

513 Baskets and Bowl of Fruit

1988. Fruit. Multicoloured
1205 2a. Type **513** 10 10
1206 4a. Baskets of fruit 15 10
1207 7a. Large basket of fruit . . 25 10
1208 8a. Bunch of grapes on branch (vert) 25 10
1209 16a. Buying fruit from market stall 45 10
1210 22a. Arranging fruit on market stall 65 10
1211 25a. Stallholder weighing fruit (vert) 80 10

514 Memorial Pillar of Knowledge and Ignorance, Kabul

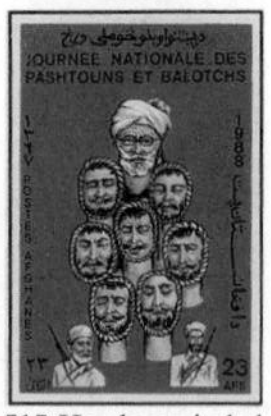

515 Heads encircled with Rope

1988. Independence Day.
1212 **514** 24a. multicoloured . . . 90 10

1988. Pashtunistan Day.
1213 **515** 23a. multicoloured . . . 80 10

516 Flags and Globe

517 Anniversary Emblem

1988. Afghan–Soviet Space Flight.
1214 **516** 32a. multicoloured . . . 90 10

1988. 125th Anniv of International Red Cross.
1215 **517** 10a. multicoloured . . . 50 10

518 Rocket and V. Tereshkova

1988. 25th Anniv of First Woman Cosmonaut Valentina Tereshkova's Space Flight. Mult.
1216 10a. Type **518** 80 20
1217 15a. Bird, globe and rocket (vert) 65 10
1218 25a. "Vostok 6" and globe 90 10

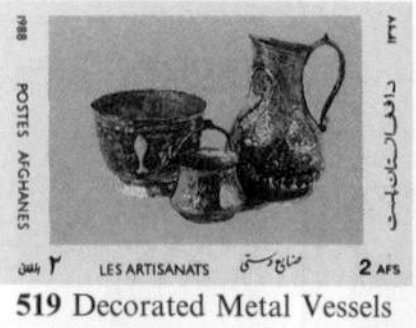

519 Decorated Metal Vessels

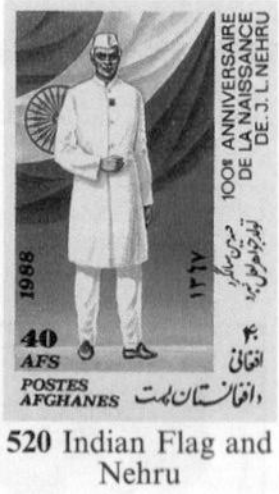

520 Indian Flag and Nehru

1988. Traditional Crafts. Multicoloured.
1219 2a. Type **519** 10 10
1220 4a. Pottery 15 10
1221 5a. Clothing (vert) 20 10
1222 9a. Carpets 25 10
1223 15a. Bags 45 10
1224 23a. Jewellery 65 10
1225 50a. Furniture . . . . . . 1·25 10

1988. Birth Centenary of Jawaharlal Nehru (Indian statesman).
1226 **520** 40a. multicoloured . . . 1·50 25

521 Emeralds

522 Ice Skating

1988. Gemstones. Multicoloured.
1227 13a. Type **521** 60 15
1228 37a. Lapis lazuli . . . . . 1·40 25
1229 40a. Rubies . . . . 1·75 25

1988. Winter Olympic Games, Calgary. Mult.
1230 2a. Type **522** 10 10
1231 5a. Slalom 20 10
1232 9a. Two-man bobsleigh . . 35 10
1233 22a. Biathlon 65 10
1234 37a. Speed skating . . . . 1·40 20

523 Old City

1988. International Campaign for Preservation of Old Sana'a, Yemen.
1236 **523** 32a. multicoloured . . . 90 10

524 Emblem

1989. 2nd Anniv of Move for Nat Reconciliation.
1237 **524** 4a. multicoloured . . . 20 10

525 Bishop and Game from "The Three Ages of Man" (attr. Estienne Porchier)

1989. Chess. Multicoloured.
1238 2a. Type **525** 10 10
1239 3a. Faience queen and 14th century drawing of Margrave Otto IV of Brandenburg and his wife playing chess 20 10
1240 4a. French king and game 25 10
1241 7a. King and game 35 10
1242 16a. Knight and game . . . 55 10
1243 24a. Arabian knight and "Great Chess" 85 10
1244 45a. Bishop and teaching of game . . . . 1·40 15

Nos. 1240/4 show illustrations from King Alfonso X's "Book of Chess, Dice and Tablings".

526 "The Old Jew"

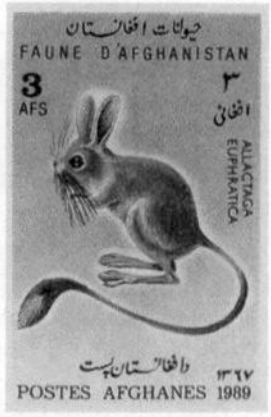

527 Euphrates Jerboa

1989. Picasso Paintings. Multicoloured.
1245 4a. Type **526** 25 10
1246 6a. "The Two Harlequins" 25 10
1247 8a. "Portrait of Ambrouse Vollar" 25 10
1248 22a. "Majorcan Woman" 65 10
1249 35a. "Acrobat on Ball" . . 1·25 15

1989. Animals. Multicoloured.
1251 3a. Type **527** 20 10
1252 4a. Asiatic wild ass 25 10
1253 14a. Lynx 60 10
1254 35a. Lammergeier . . . . . 2·40 1·40
1255 44a. Markhor . . . . . . 1·50 20

528 Bomb breaking, Dove and Woman holding Wheat

529 Cattle

1989. International Women's Day (1988).
1257 **528** 8a. multicoloured . . . 25 10

1989. Farmers' Day. Multicoloured.
1258 1a. Type **529** 10 10
1259 2a. Ploughing with oxen and tractors 10 10
1260 3a. Picking cotton 10 10

530 Dish Aerial

1989. World Meteorology Day. Multicoloured.
1261 27a. Type **530** . . . . . . 1·00 15
1262 32a. World Meteorological Organization emblem and state arms . . . . 1·25 15
1263 40a. Data-collecting equipment (vert) . . . . 1·50 15

531 Rejoicing Crowd

1989. 11th Anniv of Sawr Revolution.
1264 **531** 20a. multicoloured . . . 75 10

532 Outdoor Class

533 Eiffel Tower and Arc de Triomphe

1989. Teachers' Day.
1265 **532** 42a. multicoloured . . . 1·50 15

1989. Bicentenary of French Revolution.
1266 **533** 25a. multicoloured . . . 90 15

534 Transmission Mast

1989. 10th Anniv of Asia-Pacific Telecommunity.
1267 3a. Type **534** 10 10
1268 27a. Dish aerial . . . . . . 1·00 15

535 National Monuments

536 Pashtu

1989. Independence Day.
1269 **535** 25a. multicoloured . . . 90 15

1989. Pashtunistan Day.
1270 **536** 3a. multicoloured . . . 10 10

537 White Spoonbill

539 Mosque

538 Duchs Tourer, 1910

1989. Birds, Multicoloured.
1271 3a. Type **537** 15 15
1272 5a. Purple swamphen . . . 35 15
1273 10a. Eurasian bittern (horiz) 60 25
1274 15a. Eastern white pelican 80 35
1275 20a. Red-crested pochard . . 1·10 40
1276 25a. Mute swan . . . . . . 1·40 50
1277 30a. Great cormorant (horiz) . . . . 1·60 60

1989. Vintage Cars. Multicoloured.
1278 5a. Type **538** 20 10
1279 10a. Ford Model T touring car, 1911 . . . . 35 10
1280 20a. Renault Type AX two-seater, 1911 . . . . . . 75 10
1281 25a. Russo-Balte tourer, 1911 . . . . 90 15
1282 30a. Fiat 509 tourer, 1926 1·00 15

1989. Multicoloured.
1283 1a. Type **539** . . . .
1284 2a. Minaret, Jam . . . . .
1285 3a. Buzkashi (horiz) . . . .
1286 4a. Airplane over Hindu Kush (horiz) . . . . . .

NEWSPAPER STAMPS

N 35

1928.
N192 N **35** 2p. blue . . . . 3·50 4·50

1929.
N205 N **35** 2p. red 25 45

N 43

1932.
N215 N **43** 2p. red 40 60
N216 2p. black 25 65
N217 2p. green 25 75
N219 2p. red 45 75

N 75 Coat-of-Arms

1939.
N259 N **75** 2p. green 15 55
N260 2p. mauve (no gum) 15 75

1969. As Type N **75**, but larger and with different Pushtu inscr.
N652 100p. green 15 20
N653 150p. brown 15 20

OFFICIAL STAMPS

O 27

O 86

1909.
O173 O **27** (–) red . . . . 1·10 1·10

1939. Design $22\frac{1}{2} \times 28$ mm.
O281 O **86** 15p. green 85 75
O282 30p. brown . . . . . 1·25 1·25

O283		45p. red	1·00	1·00
O284		1a. mauve	1·60	1·50

1954. Design 24½ × 31 mm.

O285b	O **86**	50p. red	1·00	60

1965. Design 24 × 30½ mm.

O287	O **86**	50p. pink	1·25	60

PARCEL POST STAMPS

P 27

1909.

P173	P **27**	3s. brown	1·00	1·50
P174		3s. green	1·50	2·50
P175		1k. green	1·50	2·50
P176		1k. red	1·50	2·25
P177		1r. orange	2·75	2·75
P178		1r. grey	20·00	
P179		1r. brown	1·50	1·50
P180		2r. red	2·75	2·75
P181		2r. blue	5·00	5·50

P 28 Old Habibia College, Kabul

1921.

P182	P **28**	10p. brown	3·50	4·50
P183		15p. brown	4·50	5·50
P184		30p. purple	8·50	5·50
P185		1r. blue	10·00	10·00

1923. 5th Independence Day. Optd with T **28**.

P186	P **28**	10p. brown	60·00	
P187		15p. brown	65·00	
P188		30p. purple	£110	

P 35 P 36

1928.

P192	P **35**	2a. orange	5·50	4·25
P193	P **36**	3a. green	10·00	10·00

1930.

P214	P **35**	2a. green	6·50	6·50
P215	P **36**	3a. brown	8·50	10·00

REGISTRATION STAMP

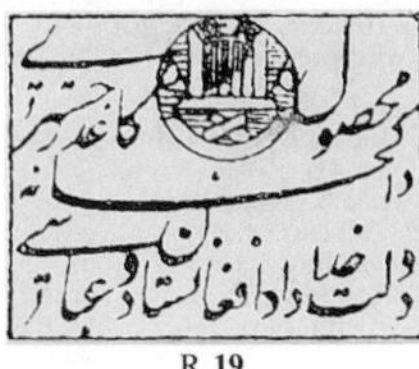

R 19

1894. Undated.

R155	R **19**	2a. black on green	8·00	7·00

APPENDIX

The following stamps have either been issued in excess of postal needs or have not been available to the public in reasonable quantities at face value. Such stamps may later be given full listing if there is evidence of regular postal use.

1961.

Agriculture Day. Fauna and Flora. 2, 2, 5, 10, 15, 25, 50, 100, 150, 175p.

Child Welfare. Sports and Games. 2, 2, 5, 10, 15, 25, 50, 100, 150, 175p.

U.N.I.C.E.F. Surch on 1961 Child Welfare issue. 2+25, 2+25, 5+25, 10+25, 15p.+25p.

Women's Day. 50, 175p.

Independence Day. Mohamed Nadir Shah. 50, 175p.

International Exhibition, Kabul. 50, 175p.

Pashtunistan Day. 50, 175p.

National Assembly. 50, 175p.

Anti-malaria Campaign. 50, 175p.

King's 47th Birthday. 50, 175p.

Red Crescent Day. Fruits. 2, 2, 5, 10, 15, 25, 50, 100, 150, 175p.

Afghan Red Crescent Fund. 1961 Red Crescent Day issue surch 2+25, 2+25, 5+25, 10+25, 15p.+25p.

United Nations Day. 1, 2, 3, 4, 50, 75, 175p.

Teachers' Day. Flowers and Educational Scenes. 2, 2, 5, 10, 15, 25, 50, 100, 150, 175p.

U.N.E.S.C.O. 1961 Teachers' Day issue surch 2+25, 2+25, 5+25, 10+25, 15p.+25p.

1962.

15th Anniv (1961) of U.N.E.S.C.O. 2, 2, 5, 10, 15, 25, 50, 75, 100p.

Ahmed Shah Baba. 50, 75, 100p.

Agriculture Day. Animals and Products. 2, 2, 5, 10, 15, 25, 50, 75, 100, 125p.

Independence Day. Marching Athletes. 25, 50, 150p.

Women's Day. Postage 25, 50p.; Air 100, 175p.

Pashtunistan Day. 25, 50, 150p.

Malaria Eradication. 2, 2, 5, 10, 15, 25, 50, 75, 100, 150, 175p.

National Assembly. 25, 50, 75, 100, 125p.

4th Asian Games, Djakarta, Indonesia. Postage 1, 2, 3, 4, 5p.; Air 25, 50, 75, 100, 150, 175p.

Children's Day. Sports and Produce. Postage 1, 2, 3, 4, 5p.; Air 75, 150, 200p.

King's 48th Birthday. 25, 50, 75, 100p.

Red Crescent Day. Fruits and Flowers. Postage 1, 2, 3, 4, 5p.; Air 25, 50, 100p.

Boy Scouts' Day. Postage 1, 2, 3, 4p.; Air 25, 50, 75, 100p.

1st Anniv of Hammarskjold's Death. Surch on 1961 U.N.E.S.C.O. issue. 2+20, 2+20, 5+20, 10+20, 15+20, 25+20, 50+20, 75+20, 100p.+20p.

United Nations Day. Postage 1, 2, 3, 4, 5p.; Air 75, 100, 125p.

Teachers' Day. Sport and Flowers. Postage 1, 2, 3, 4, 5p.; Air 100, 150p.

World Meteorological Day. 50, 100p.

1963.

Famous Afghans Pantheon, Kabul. 50, 75, 100p.

Agriculture Day. Sheep and Silkworms. Postage 1, 2, 3, 4, 5p.; Air 100, 150, 200p.

Freedom from Hunger. Postage 2, 3, 300p.; Air 500p.

Malaria Eradication Fund. 1962 Malaria Eradication issue surch 2+15, 2+15, 5+15, 10+15, 15+15, 25+15, 50+15, 75+15, 100+15, 150+15, 175p.+15p.

World Meteorological Day. Postage 1, 2, 3, 4, 5p.; Air 200, 300, 400, 500p.

"GANEFO" Athletic Games, Djakarta, Indonesia. Postage 2, 3, 4, 5, 10p., 9a.; Air 300, 500p.

Red Cross Centenary Postage 2, 3, 4, 5, 10p.; Air 100, 200p., 4, 6a.

Nubian Monuments Preservation. Postage 100, 200, 500p.; Air 5a., 7a.50.

1964.

Women's Day (1963). 2, 3, 4, 5, 10p.

Afghan Boy Scouts and Girl Guides. Postage 2, 3, 4, 5, 10p.; Air 2, 2, 2a.50, 3, 4, 5, 12a.

Child Welfare Day (1963). Sports and Games. Postage 2, 3, 4, 5, 10p.; Air 200, 300p.

Afghan Red Crescent Society. Postage 100, 200p.; Air 5a., 7a.50.

Teachers' Day (1963). Flowers. Postage 2, 3, 4, 5, 10p.; Air 3a., 3a.50.

United Nations Day (1963). Postage 2, 3, 4, 5, 10p.; Air 100p., 2, 3a.

15th Anniv of Human Rights Declaration. Surch on 1964 United Nations Day issue. Postage 2+50, 3+50, 4+50, 5+50, 10p.+50p.; Air 100p.+50p., 2a.+50p., 3a.+50p.

U.N.I.C.E.F. (dated 1963). Postage 100, 200p.; Air 5a. 7a.50.

Malaria Eradication (dated 1963). Postage 2, 3, 4, 5p., 10p. on 4p.; Air 2, 10a.

AITUTAKI Pt. 1

Island in the South Pacific.

1903. 12 pence = 1 shilling;
20 shillings = 1 pound.
1967. 100 cents = 1 dollar.

A. NEW ZEALAND DEPENDENCY.

The British Government, who had exercised a protectorate over the Cook Islands group since the 1880s, handed the islands, including Aitutaki, to New Zealand administration in 1901. Cook Islands stamps were used from 1932 to 1972.

1903. Pictorial stamps of New Zealand surch **AITUTAKI.** and value in native language.

1	**23**	½d. green	4·50	6·50
2	**42**	1d. red	4·75	5·50
4	**26**	2½d. blue	11·00	12·00
5	**28**	3d. brown	18·00	15·00
6	**31**	6d. red	30·00	25·00
7	**34**	1s. red	50·00	85·00

1911. King Edward VII stamps of New Zealand surch **AITUTAKI.** and value in native language.

9	**51**	½d. green	1·00	3·50
10	**53**	1d. red	3·00	10·00
11	**51**	6d. red	45·00	£100
12		1s. red	50·00	£140

1916. King George V stamps of New Zealand surch **AITUTAKI.** and value in native language.

13a	**62**	6d. red	7·50	27·00
14		1s. red	17·00	90·00

1917. King George V stamps of New Zealand optd **AITUTAKI.**

19	**62**	½d. green	1·00	6·00
20	**53**	1d. red	4·00	28·00
21	**62**	1½d. grey	3·75	30·00
22		1½d. brown	80	7·00
15a		2½d. blue	1·75	15·00
16a		3d. brown	1·50	24·00
17a		6d. red	4·75	21·00
18a		1s. red	12·00	32·00

1920. As 1920 pictorial stamps of Cook Islands but inscr "AITUTAKI".

30		½d. black and green	2·00	13·00
31		1d. black and red	6·00	7·00
26		1½d. black and brown	6·00	12·00
32		2½d. black and blue	7·50	55·00
27		3d. black and blue	2·50	14·00
28		6d. brown and grey	5·50	14·00
29		1s. black and purple	9·50	16·00

B. PART OF COOK ISLANDS

On 9 August 1972 Aitutaki became a Port of Entry into the Cook Islands. Whilst remaining part of the Cook Islands, Aitutaki has a separate postal service.

1972. Nos. 227/8, 230, 233/4, 238, 240/1, 243 and 244 of Cook Islands optd **Aitutaki**.

33	**79**	½c. multicoloured	30	80
34	–	1c. multicoloured	70	1·40
35	–	2½c. multicoloured	2·25	7·00
36	–	4c. multicoloured	70	85
37	–	5c. multicoloured	2·50	7·50
38	–	10c. multicoloured	2·50	5·50
39	–	20c. multicoloured	3·75	1·00
40	–	25c. multicoloured	70	1·00
41	–	50c. multicoloured	2·75	2·75
42	–	$1 multicoloured	4·00	5·50

1972. Christmas. Nos. 406/8 of Cook Islands optd **Aitutaki**.

43	**130**	1c. multicoloured	10	10
44	–	5c. multicoloured	15	15
45	–	10c. multicoloured	15	25

1972. Royal Silver Wedding. As Nos. 413 and 415 of Cook Islands, but inscr "COOK ISLANDS Aitutaki".

46	**131**	5c. black and silver	3·50	2·75
47	–	15c. black and silver	1·50	1·50

1972. No. 245 of Cook Islands optd **AITUTAKI.**

48		$2 multicoloured	50	75

1972. Nos. 227/8, 230, 233, 234, 238, 240, 241, 243 and 244 of Cook Islands optd **AITUTAKI** within ornamental oval.

49	**79**	½c. multicoloured	15	10
50	–	1c. multicoloured	15	10
51	–	2½c. multicoloured	20	10
52	–	4c. multicoloured	25	15
53	–	5c. multicoloured	25	15
54	–	10c. multicoloured	35	25
55	–	20c. multicoloured	1·25	50
56	–	25c. multicoloured	50	55
57	–	50c. multicoloured	75	90
58	–	$1 multicoloured	1·25	1·75

13 "Christ Mocked" (Grunewald)

16 Red Hibiscus and Princess Anne

1973. Easter. Multicoloured.

59	1c. Type **13**	15	10
60	1c. "St. Veronica" (Van der Weyden)	15	10
61	1c. "The Crucified Christ with Virgin Mary, Saints and Angels" (Raphael)	15	10
62	1c. "Resurrection" (Piero della Francesca)	15	10
63	5c. "The Last Supper" (Master of Amiens)	20	15
64	5c. "Condemnation" (Holbein)	20	15
65	5c. "Christ on the Cross" (Rubens)	20	15
66	5c. "Resurrection" (El Greco)	20	15
67	10c. "Disrobing of Christ" (El Greco)	25	15
68	10c. "St. Veronica" (Van Oostsanen)	25	15
69	10c. "Christ on the Cross" (Rubens)	25	15
70	10c. "Resurrection" (Bouts)	25	15

1973. Silver Wedding Coinage. Nos. 417/23 of Cook Islands optd **AITUTAKI.**

71	**132**	1c. black, red and gold	10	10
72	–	2c. black, blue and gold	10	10
73	–	5c. black, green and silver	15	10
74	–	10c. black, blue and silver	20	10
75	–	20c. black, green and silver	30	15
76	–	50c. black, red and silver	50	30
77	–	$1 black, blue and silver	70	45

1973. 10th Anniv of Treaty Banning Nuclear Testing. Nos. 236, 238, 240 and 243 of Cook Islands optd **AITUTAKI** within ornamental oval and **TENTH ANNIVERSARY CESSATION OF NUCLEAR TESTING TREATY.**

78	8c. multicoloured	15	15
79	10c. multicoloured	15	15
80	20c. multicoloured	30	20
81	50c. multicoloured	70	50

1973. Royal Wedding. Multicoloured.

82	25c. Type **16**	25	10
83	30c. Capt. Mark Phillips and blue hibiscus	25	10
MS84	114 × 65 mm. Nos. 82/3	50	40

17 "Virgin and Child" (Montagna)

1973. Christmas. "Virgin and Child" paintings by artists listed below. Multicoloured.

85	1c. Type **17**	10	10
86	1c. Crivelli	10	10
87	1c. Van Dyck	10	10
88	1c. Perugino	10	10
89	5c. Veronese (child at shoulder)	25	10
90	5c. Veronese (child on lap)	25	10
91	5c. Cima	25	10
92	5c. Memling	25	10
93	10c. Memling	25	10
94	10c. Del Colle	25	10
95	10c. Raphael	25	10
96	10c. Lotto	25	10

18 Rose-branch Murex

1974. Sea Shells. Multicoloured.

97	½c. Type **18**	90	1·00
98	1c. New Caledonia nautilus	90	1·00
99	2c. Common or major harp	90	1·00
100	3c. Striped bonnet	90	1·00
101	4c. Mole cowrie	90	1·00
102	5c. Pontifical mitre	90	1·00
103	8c. Trumpet triton	90	1·00
104	10c. Venus comb murex	90	80
105	20c. Red-mouth olive	1·25	80
106	25c. Ruddy frog shell	1·25	80

107 60c. Widest pacific conch . . 4·00 1·25
108 $1 Maple-leaf triton or winged frog shell . . . . . 2·50 1·40
109 $2 Queen Elizabeth II and Marlin-spike auger . . . . 6·00 9·00
110 $5 Queen Elizabeth II and Tiger cowrie . . . . 29·00 10·00
The $2 and $5 are larger, 53 × 25 mm.

19 Bligh and H.M.S. "Bounty"

1974. William Bligh's Discovery of Aitutaki. Multicoloured
114 1c. Type **19** 55 55
115 1c. H.M.S. "Bounty" 55 55
116 5c. Bligh, and H.M.S. "Bounty" at Aitutaki . . . 90 90
117 5c. Aitutaki chart of 1856 . . 90 90
118 8c. Captain Cook and H.M.S. "Resolution" . . . 1·25 1·25
119 8c. Map of Aitutaki and inset location map . . . . . . 1·25 1·25
See also Nos. 123/8.

20 Aitutaki Stamps of 1903, Sand Map

1974. Centenary of U.P.U. Multicoloured.
120 25c. Type **20** 75 50
121 50c. Stamps of 1903 and 1920, and map . . . . . . 1·00 75
MS122 66 × 75 mm. Nos. 120/1 1·25 2·75

1974. Air. As Nos. 114/119 in larger size (46 × 26 mm), additionally inscr "AIR MAIL".
123 10c. Type **19** 60 65
124 10c. H.M.S. "Bounty" . . . 60 65
125 25c. Bligh, and H.M.S. "Bounty" at Aitutaki . . . 70 75
126 25c. Aitutaki chart of 1856 70 75
127 30c. Captain Cook and H.M.S. "Resolution" . . . 80 85
128 30c. Map of Aitutaki and inset location map 80 85

21 "Virgin and Child" (Hugo van der Goes)

22 Churchill as Schoolboy

1974. Christmas. "Virgin and Child" paintings by artists named. Multicoloured.
129 1c. Type **21** 10 15
130 5c. Bellini 10 20
131 8c. Gerard David 10 20
132 10c. Antonello da Messina 10 15
133 25c. Joos van Cleve 20 30
134 30c. Master of the Life of St. Catherine 20 30
MS135 127 × 134 mm. Nos. 129/34 1·40 1·75

1974. Birth Centenary of Sir Winston Churchill. Multicoloured.
136 10c. Type **22** 20 25
137 25c. Churchill as young man 25 40
138 30c. Churchill with troops . . 25 45
139 50c. Churchill painting . . . 30 60
140 $1 Giving "V" sign 40 75
MS141 115 × 108 mm. Nos. 136/40 1·25 1·50

1974. Children's Christmas Fund. Nos. 129/34 surch.
142 **21** 1c.+1c. multicoloured . . . 10 10
143 – 5c.+1c. multicoloured . . . 10 10
144 – 8c.+1c. multicoloured . . . 10 10
145 – 10c.+1c. multicoloured . . 10 10
146 – 25c.+1c. multicoloured . . 20 20
147 – 30c.+1c. multicoloured . . 20 20

24 Soviet and U.S. Flags

1975. "Apollo–Soyuz" Space Project. Mult.
148 25c. Type **24** 30 20
149 50c. Daedalus with space capsule 40 30
MS150 123 × 61 mm. Nos. 148/9 1·25 1·10

25 St. Francis

26 "The Descent" (detail, 15th-century Flemish School)

1975. Christmas. Multicoloured.
151 6c. Type **25** 10 10
152 6c. Madonna and Child . . . 10 10
153 6c. St. John 10 10
154 7c. King and donkey 10 10
155 7c. Madonna, Child and King 10 10
156 7c. Kings with gifts 10 10
157 15c. Madonna and Child . . 15 15
158 15c. St. Onufrius 15 15
159 15c. John the Baptist 15 15
160 20c. Shepherd and cattle . . 20 15
161 20c. Madonna and Child . . 20 15
162 20c. Shepherds 20 15
MS163 104 × 201 mm. Nos. 151/62 2·25 2·50
Stamps of the same value were printed together, se-tenant, each strip forming a composite design of a complete painting as follows: Nos. 151/3, "Madonna and Child with Saints Francis and John" (Lorenzetti); 154/6, "Adoration of the Kings" (Van der Weyden); 157/9, "Madonna and Child Enthroneth with Saints Onufrius and John the Baptist" (Montagna); 160/2, "Adoration of the Shepherds" (Reni).

1975. Children's Christmas Fund. Nos. 151/62 surch.
164 **25** 6c.+1c. multicoloured . . . 10 10
165 – 6c.+1c. multicoloured . . . 10 10
166 – 6c.+1c. multicoloured . . . 10 10
167 – 7c.+1c. multicoloured . . . 10 10
168 – 7c.+1c. multicoloured . . . 10 10
169 – 7c.+1c. multicoloured . . . 10 10
170 – 15c.+1c. multicoloured . . 15 15
171 – 15c.+1c. multicoloured . . 15 15
172 – 15c.+1c. multicoloured . . 15 15
173 – 20c.+1c. multicoloured . . 20 20
174 – 20c.+1c. multicoloured . . 20 20
175 – 20c.+1c. multicoloured . . 20 20

1976. Easter. Multicoloured.
176 15c. Type **26** 15 10
177 30c. "The Descent" (detail) 20 15
178 35c. "The Descent" (detail) 25 20
MS179 87 × 67 mm. Nos. 176/8 forming a complete picture of "The Descent" . . . . 1·00 1·25

27 Left Detail

30 "The Visitation"

28 Cycling

1976. Bicentenary of American Revolution. Paintings by John Turnbull.
180 **27** 30c. multicoloured 25 10
181 – 30c. multicoloured 25 10
182 – 30c. multicoloured 25 10
183 – 35c. multicoloured 25 15
184 – 35c. multicoloured 25 15
185 – 35c. multicoloured 25 15
186 – 50c. multicoloured 25 15
187 – 50c. multicoloured 25 15
188 – 50c. multicoloured 25 15
MS189 132 × 120 mm. Nos. 180/8 1·75 1·10
PAINTINGS: Nos. 180/2, "The Declaration of Independence"; 183/5, "The Surrender of Lord Cornwallis at Yorktown"; 186/8, "The Resignation of General Washington".
Stamps of the same value were printed together, se-tenant, each strip forming a composite design of the whole painting.

1976. Olympic Games, Montreal. Multicoloured.
190 15c. Type **28** 80 15
191 35c. Sailing 45 20
192 60c. Hockey . . . . 1·00 25
193 70c. Sprinting 70 30
MS194 107 × 97 mm. Nos. 190/3 2·50 1·25

1976. Royal Visit to the U.S.A. Nos. 190/3 optd **ROYAL VISIT JULY 1976.**
195 **28** 15c. multicoloured 50 15
196 – 35c. multicoloured 45 25
197 – 60c. multicoloured 80 40
198 – 70c. multicoloured 70 45
MS199 107 × 97 mm. Nos. 195/8 2·00 1·25

1976. Christmas.
200 **30** 6c. gold and green 10 10
201 – 6c. gold and green 10 10
202 – 7c. gold and purple 10 10
203 – 7c. gold and purple 10 10
204 – 15c. gold and blue 10 10
205 – 15c. gold and blue 10 10
206 – 20c. gold and violet . . . 15 15
207 – 20c. gold and violet . . . 15 15
MS208 128 × 96 mm. As Nos. 200/7 but with borders on three sides 1·00 1·40
DESIGNS: No. 201, Angel; 202, Angel; 203, Shepherds; 204, Joseph; 205, Mary and the Child; 206, Wise Man; 207, Two Wise Men.
Stamps of the same value were printed together, se-tenant, each pair forming a composite design.

1976. Children's Christmas Fund. Nos. 200/7 surch.
209 **30** 6c.+1c. gold and green . . 10 10
210 – 6c.+1c. gold and green . . 10 10
211 – 7c.+1c. gold and purple . . 10 10
212 – 7c.+1c. gold and purple . . 10 10
213 – 15c.+1c. gold and blue . . 15 15
214 – 15c.+1c. gold and blue . . 15 15
215 – 20c.+1c. gold and violet . . 15 15
216 – 20c.+1c. gold and violet . . 15 15
MS217 128 × 96 mm. As Nos. 209/16 but with a premium of "+2c." and borders on three sides . . . . 80 1·40

32 Alexander Graham Bell and First Telephone

1977. Centenary (1976) of Telephone.
218 **32** 25c. black, gold and red . . 20 15
219 – 70c. black, gold and lilac 40 40
MS220 116 × 59 mm. As Nos. 218/19 but with different colours . . . 70 1·00
DESIGN: 70c. Satellite and Earth station.

33 "Christ on the Cross" (detail)

1977. Easter. 400th Birth Anniv of Rubens. Mult.
221 15c. Type **33** 45 15
222 20c. "Lamentation for Christ" 60 20
223 35c. "Christ with Straw" . . 75 25

34 Captain Bligh, George III and H.M.S. "Bounty"

1977. Silver Jubilee. Multicoloured.
225 25c. Type **34** 35 35
226 35c. Rev. Williams, George IV and Aitutaki Church . . 40 40
227 50c. Union Jack, Queen Victoria and island map . . 45 45
228 $1 Balcony scene, 1953 . . . 50 50
MS229 130 × 87 mm. As Nos. 225/8 but with gold borders . . . . 1·25 1·25

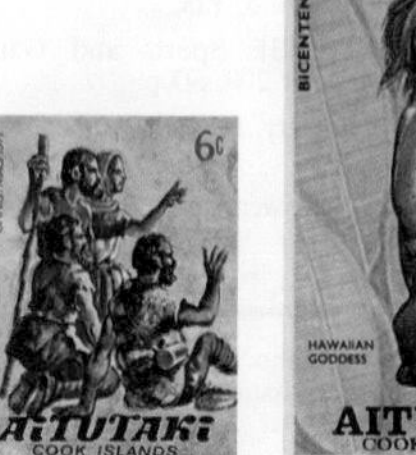

35 The Shepherds

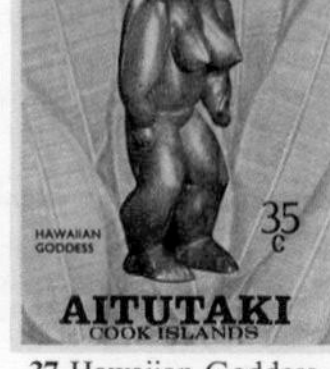

37 Hawaiian Goddess

1977. Christmas. Multicoloured
230 6c. Type **35** 10 10
231 6c. Angel 10 10
232 7c. Mary, Jesus and ox . . . 10 10
233 7c. Joseph and donkey . . . 10 10
234 15c. Three Kings 10 10
235 15c. Virgin and Child 10 10
236 20c. Joseph 10 10
237 20c. Mary and Jesus on donkey 10 10
MS238 130 × 95 mm. Nos. 230/7 70 1·25
Stamps of the same value were printed together, se-tenant, forming composite designs.

1977. Children's Christmas Fund. Nos. 230/7 surch **+1c.**
239 6c.+1c. Type **35** 10 10
240 6c.+1c. Angel 10 10
241 7c.+1c. Mary, Jesus and ox 10 10
242 7c.+1c. Joseph and donkey 10 10
243 15c.+1c. Three Kings 15 10
244 15c.+1c. Virgin and Child . . 15 10
245 20c.+1c. Joseph 15 10
246 20c.+1c. Mary and Jesus on donkey 15 10
MS247 130 × 95 mm. Nos. 239/46 but each with premium of "+2c." 70 85

1978. Bicentenary of Discovery of Hawaii. Mult.
248 35c. Type **37** 35 25
249 50c. Figurehead of H.M.S. "Resolution" (horiz) . . . 60 40
250 $1 Hawaiian temple figure . . 70 70
MS251 168 × 75 mm. Nos. 248/50 1·50 1·75

38 "Christ on the Way to Calvary" (Martini)

39 The Yale of Beaufort

1978. Easter. Paintings from the Louvre, Paris. Mult.
252 15c. Type **38** 15 10
253 20c. "Pieta of Avignon" (E. Quarton) 20 10
254 35c. "The Pilgrims at Emmaus" (Rembrandt) . . 25 10
MS255 108 × 83 mm. Nos. 252/4 75 75

1978. Easter. Children's Charity. Designs as Nos. 252/4, but smaller (34 × 26 mm) and without margins, in separate miniature sheets 75 × 58 mm, each with a face value of 50c. + 5c.
MS256 As Nos. 252/4 Set of 3 sheets 1·00 1·00

1978. 25th Anniv of Coronation. Multicoloured.
257 $1 Type **39** 30 50
258 $1 Queen Elizabeth II . . . 30 50
259 $1 Aitutaki ancestral statue 30 50
MS260 98 × 127 mm. Nos 257/9 × 2 75 75
Stamps from No. **MS**260 have coloured borders, the upper row in lavender and the lower in green.

40 "Adoration of the Infant Jesus"

41 "Captain Cook" (Nathaniel Dance)

1978. Christmas. 450th Death Anniv of Durer. Multicoloured.
261 15c. Type **40** 35 15
262 17c. "The Madonna with Child" 40 15
263 30c. "The Madonna with the Iris" 55 20
264 35c. "The Madonna of the Siskin" 60 25
MS265 101 × 109 mm. As Nos. 261/4 but each with premium of "+2c." 1·10 1·00

1979. Death Bicent of Captain Cook. Mult.
266 50c. Type **41** . . . . 1·00 80
267 75c. "H.M.S. 'Resolution' and 'Adventure' at Matavai Bay," Tahiti (W. Hodges) . . . . . . 1·75 95
MS268 94 × 58 mm. Nos. 266/7 2·00 2·25

42 Girl with Flowers

43 "Man writing a Letter" (painting by Gabriel Metsu)

1979. International Year of the Child. Multicoloured.
269 30c. Type **42** 15 15
270 35c. Boy playing guitar 20 20
271 65c. Children in canoe 30 30
MS272 104 × 80 mm. As Nos. 269/71, but each with a premium of "+3c." 70 1·00

1979. Death Centenary of Sir Rowland Hill. Multicoloured.
273 50c. Type **43** 45 45
274 50c. Sir Rowland Hill with Penny Black, 1903 ½d. and 1911 1d. stamps 45 45
275 50c. "Girl in Blue reading a Letter" (Jan Vermeer) 45 45
276 65c. "Woman writing a Letter" (Gerard Terborch) 50 50
277 65c. Sir Rowland Hill, with Penny Black, 1903 3d. and 1920 ½d. stamps 50 50
278 65c. "Lady reading a Letter" (Jan Vermeer) 50 50
MS279 151 × 85 mm. 30c. × 6. As Nos. 273/8 1·75 1·75

44 "The Burial of Christ" (left detail) (Quentin Metsys)

45 Einstein as a Young Man

1980. Easter. Multicoloured.
280 20c. Type **44** 40 25
281 30c. "The Burial of Christ" (centre detail) 50 35
282 35c. "The Burial of Christ" (right detail) 65 45
MS283 93 × 71 mm. As Nos. 280/2, but each with premium of "+2c." 75 75

1980. 25th Death Anniv of Albert Einstein (physicist). Multicoloured.
284 12c. Type **45** 60 60
285 12c. Atom and "E = mc²" equation 60 60
286 15c. Einstein in middle-age 65 65
287 15c. Cross over nuclear explosion (Test Ban Treaty, 1963) 65 65
288 20c. Einstein as an old man 75 75
289 20c. Hand preventing atomic explosion 75 75
MS290 113 × 118 mm. Nos 284/9 3·00 3·00

46 Ancestor Figure, Aitutaki

47 "Virgin and Child" (13th century)

1980. 3rd South Pacific Festival of Arts. Mult.
291 6c. Type **46** 10 10
292 6c. Staff god image, Rarotonga 10 10
293 6c. Trade adze, Mangaia 10 10
294 6c. Carved image of Tangaroa, Rarotonga 10 10
295 12c. Wooden image Aitutaki 10 10
296 12c. Hand club, Rarotonga 10 10
297 12c. Carved mace "god", Mangaia 10 10
298 12c. Fisherman's god, Rarotonga 10 10
299 15c. Ti'i image, Aitutaki 15 15
300 15c. Fisherman's god, Rarotonga (different) 15 15
301 15c. Carved mace "god", Cook Islands 15 15
302 15c. Carved image of Tangaroa, Rarotonga (different) 15 15
303 20c. Chief's headdress, Aitutaki 15 15
304 20c. Carved mace "god", Cook Islands (different) 15 15
305 20c. Staff god image, Rarotonga (different) 15 15
306 20c. Carved image of Tangaroa, Rarotonga (different) 15 15
MS307 134 × 194 mm. Nos. 291/306 1·60 1·75

1980. Christmas. Sculptures of "The Virgin and Child". Multicoloured.
308 15c. Type **47** 20 15
309 20c. 14th century 20 15
310 25c. 15th century 20 15
311 35c. 15th century (different) 30 20
MS312 82 × 120 mm. As Nos. 306/11 but each with premium of 2c. 70 80

48 "Mourning Virgin"

49 Gouldian Finch

1981. Easter. Details of Sculpture "Burial of Christ" by Pedro Roldan.
313 **48** 30c. gold and green 25 25
314 – 40c. gold and lilac 30 30
315 – 50c. gold and blue 30 30
MS316 107 × 60 mm. As Nos. 313/15 but each with premium of 2c. 75 85
DESIGNS: 40c. "Christ"; 50c. "Saint John".

1981. Birds (1st series). Multicoloured.
317 1c. Type **49** 45 30
318 1c. Common starling 45 30
319 2c. Golden whistler 50 30
320 2c. Scarlet robin 50 30
321 3c. Rufous fantail 60 30
322 3c. Peregrine falcon 60 30
323 4c. Java sparrow 70 30
324 4c. Barn owl 70 30
325 5c. Tahitian lory 70 30
326 5c. White-breasted wood swallow 70 30
327 6c. Purple swamphen 70 30
328 6c. Feral rock pigeon 70 30
329 10c. Chestnut-breasted mannikin 90 30
330 10c. Zebra dove 90 30
331 12c. Reef heron 1·00 40
332 12c. Common mynah 1·00 40
333 15c. Whimbrel (horiz) 1·25 40
334 15c. Black-browed albatross (horiz) 1·25 40
335 20c. Pacific golden plover (horiz) 1·50 55
336 20c. White tern (horiz) 1·50 55
337 25c. Pacific black duck (horiz) 1·75 70
338 25c. Brown booby (horiz) 1·75 70
339 30c. Great frigate bird (horiz) 2·00 85
340 30c. Pintail (horiz) 2·00 85
341 35c. Long-billed reed warbler 2·25 1·00
342 35c. Pomarine skua 2·25 1·00
343 40c. Buff-banded rail 2·75 1·25
344 40c. Spotted triller 2·75 1·25
345 50c. Royal albatross 3·00 1·50
346 50c. Stephen's lory 3·00 1·50
347 70c. Red-headed parrot-finch 5·50 3·00
348 70c. Orange dove 5·50 3·00
349 $1 Blue-headed flycatcher 5·50 3·75
350 $2 Red-bellied flycatcher 6·50 8·00
351 $4 Red munia 11·00 14·00
352 $5 Flat-billed kingfisher 12·00 16·00
See also Nos. 475/94.

50 Prince Charles

52 Footballers

1981. Royal Wedding. Multicoloured.
391 60c. Type **50** 30 40
392 80c. Lady Diana Spencer 40 55
393 $1.40 Prince Charles and Lady Diana (87 × 70 mm) 60 80

1981. International Year for Disabled Persons. Nos. 391/3 surch **+5c.**
394 60c.+5c. Type **50** 60 90
395 80c.+5c. Lady Diana Spencer 70 1·10
396 $1.40+5c. Prince Charles and Lady Diana 90 1·60

1981. World Cup Football Championship, Spain (1982). Football Scenes. Multicoloured.
397 12c. Ball to left of stamp 50 35
398 12c. Ball to right 50 35
399 15c. Ball to right 55 40
400 15c. Ball to left 55 40
401 20c. Ball to left 55 50
402 20c. Ball to right 55 50
403 25c. Type **52** 60 55
404 25c. "ESPANA 82" inscription 60 55
MS405 100 × 137 mm. 12c.+2c., 15c.+2c., 20c.+2c., 25c.+2c., each × 2. As Nos. 397/404 3·50 3·00

53 "The Holy Family"

54 Princess of Wales

1981. Christmas. Etchings by Rembrandt. Each brown and gold.
406 15c. Type **53** 45 45
407 30c. "Virgin with Child" 70 70
408 40c. "Adoration of the Shepherds" (horiz) 95 95
409 50c. "The Holy Family" (horiz) 1·25 1·25
MS410 Designs as Nos. 406/9 in separate miniature sheets, 65 × 82 mm or 82 × 65 mm, each with a face value of 80c.+5c. Set of 4 sheets 4·00 3·00

1982. 21st Birthday of Princess of Wales. Mult.
411 70c. Type **54** 2·00 60
412 $1 Prince and Princess of Wales 2·00 75
413 $2 Princess Diana (different) 3·25 1·50
MS414 82 × 91 mm. Nos. 411/13 6·00 2·75

1982. Birth of Prince William of Wales (1st issue). Nos. 391/3 optd.
415 60c. Type **50** 90 70
416 60c. Type **50** 90 70
417 80c. Lady Diana Spencer 1·10 80
418 80c. Lady Diana Spencer 1·10 80
419 $1.40 Prince Charles and Lady Diana 1·25 1·00
420 $1.40 Prince Charles and Lady Diana 1·25 1·00
OPTS: Nos. 415, 417 and 419, **21 JUNE 1982. PRINCE WILLIAM OF WALES**. Nos. 416, 418 and 420, **COMMEMORATING THE ROYAL BIRTH**.

1982. Birth of Prince William of Wales (2nd issue). As Nos. 411/13 but inscr "ROYAL BIRTH 21 JUNE 1982 PRINCE WILLIAM OF WALES".
421 70c. Type **54** 70 60
422 $1 Prince and Princess of Wales 80 75
423 $2 Princess Diana (different) 1·60 1·50
MS424 81 × 91 mm. Nos. 421/3 5·50 3·00

56 "Virgin and Child" (12th-century sculpture)

57 Aitutaki Bananas

1982. Christmas. Religious Sculptures. Multicoloured.
425 18c. Type **56** 70 70
426 36c. "Virgin and Child" (12th-century) 85 85
427 48c. "Virgin and Child" (13th-century) 1·00 1·00
428 60c. "Virgin and Child" (15th-century) 1·40 1·40
MS429 99 × 115 mm. As Nos. 425/8 but each with 2c. charity premium 2·50 2·75

1983. Commonwealth Day. Multicoloured.
430 48c. Type **57** 1·00 50
431 48c. Ancient Ti'i image 1·00 50
432 48c. Tourist canoeing 1·00 50
433 48c. Captain William Bligh and chart 1·00 50

58 Scouts around Campfire

1983. 75th Anniv of Boy Scout Movement. Mult.
434 36c. Type **58** 65 65
435 48c. Scout saluting 75 75
436 60c. Scouts hiking 80 80
MS437 78 × 107 mm. As Nos. 434/6 but each with premium of 3c. 1·50 1·75

1983. 15th World Scout Jamboree, Alberta, Canada. Nos. 434/6 optd **15TH WORLD SCOUT JAMBOREE**.
438 36c. Type **58** 80 45
439 48c. Scout saluting 1·00 55
440 60c. Scouts hiking 1·25 75
MS441 78 × 107 mm. As Nos. 438/40 but each with a premium of 3c. 1·50 2·00

60 Modern Sport Balloon

63 International Mail

1983. Bicentenary of Manned Flight.
442 **60** 18c. multicoloured 55 30
443 – 36c. multicoloured 75 50
444 – 48c. multicoloured 90 60
445 – 60c. multicoloured 1·00 80
MS446 – 64 × 80 mm. $2.50, mult (48½ × 28½ mm) 1·50 2·00
DESIGNS: 36c. to $2.50, showing different modern sports balloons.

1983. Various stamps surch (a) Nos. 335/48 and 352.
447 18c. on 20c. Pacific golden plover 2·75 1·25
448 18c. on 20c. White tern 2·75 1·25
449 36c. on 25c. Pacific black duck 3·75 1·50
450 36c. on 25c. Brown booby 3·75 1·50
451 36c. on 30c. Great frigate bird 3·75 1·50
452 36c. on 30c. Pintail 3·75 1·50
453 36c. on 35c. Long-billed reed warbler 3·75 1·50
454 36c. on 35c. Pomarine skua 3·75 1·50
455 48c. on 40c. Buff-banded rail 4·25 1·50
456 48c. on 40c. Spotted triller 4·25 1·50
457 48c. on 50c. Royal albatross 4·25 1·50
458 48c. on 50c. Stephen's lory 4·25 1·50
459 72c. on 70c. Red-headed parrot finch 7·50 3·00
460 72c. on 70c. Orange dove 7·50 3·00
461 $5.60 on $5 Flat-billed kingfisher (vert) 21·00 10·00

(b) Nos. 392/3 and 412/3.
462 96c. on 80c. Lady Diana Spencer 3·00 2·50
463 96c. on $1 Prince and Princess of Wales 2·75 2·00
464 $1.20 on $1.40 Prince Charles and Lady Diana 3·00 2·50
465 $1.20 on $2 Princess Diana 2·75 2·00

1983. World Communications Year. Multicoloured.
466 48c. Type **63** 65 50
467 60c. Telecommunications 95 70
468 96c. Space satellite 1·40 1·00
MS469 126 × 53 mm. Nos. 466/8 2·50 2·50

64 "Madonna of the Chair"

1983. Christmas. 500th Birth Anniv of Raphael. Multicoloured.
470 36c. Type **64** 75 40
471 48c. "The Alba Madonna" 90 50
472 60c. "Constable Madonna" 1·25 70
MS473 95 × 116 mm. Nos. 470/2, but each with a premium of 3c. 2·75 1·40

1983. Christmas. 500th Brith Anniv of Raphael. Children's Charity. Designs as Nos. 470/2 in separate miniature sheets 46 × 47 mm, but with different frames and a face value of 85c.+5c. Imperf.
MS474 As Nos. 470/2 Set of 3 sheets 3·75 2·75

65 Gouldian Finch

66 Javelin throwing

1984. Birds (2nd series). Multicoloured.
475 2c. Type **65** 1·75 1·00
476 3c. Common starling 1·75 1·00
477 5c. Scarlet robin 1·75 1·10
478 10c. Golden whistler 2·25 1·10
479 12c. Rufous fantail 2·25 1·10
480 18c. Peregrine falcon 2·25 1·50
481 24c. Barn owl 2·25 1·50
482 30c. Java sparrow 2·25 1·50
483 36c. White-breasted wood swallow 2·25 1·50
484 48c. Tahitian lory 2·25 1·50

485 50c. Feral rock pigeon . . . 2·50 2·25
486 60c. Purple swamphen . . . 2·50 2·25
487 72c. Zebra dove . . . . . . 3·00 2·25
488 96c. Chestnut-breasted mannikin . . . . 3·00 2·25
489 $1.20 Common mynah . . . 3·00 3·25
490 $2.10 Reef heron . . . . . . 4·00 3·75
491 $3 Blue-headed flycatcher . . 6·50 6·00
492 $4.20 Red-bellied flycatcher 3·75 9·00
493 $5.60 Red munia . . . . . . 4·50 9·50
494 $9.60 Flat-billed kingfisher 7·50 12·00

1984. Olympic Games. Los Angeles. Multicoloured.
495 36c. Type **66** 35 35
496 48c. Shot-putting 40 45
497 60c. Hurdling 45 55
498 $2 Basketball . . . . 1·75 1·50
MS499 88 × 117 mm. As Nos. 495/8, but each with a charity premium of 5c. . . . . 3·50 3·50
DESIGNS: 48c. to $2, show Memorial Coliseum and various events.

1984. Olympic Gold Medal Winners. Nos. 495/8 optd.
500 36c. Type **66** (optd **Javelin Throw Tessa Sanderson Great Britain**) 35 35
501 48c. Shot-putting (optd **Shot Put Claudia Losch Germany**) 40 45
502 60c. Hurdling (optd **Heptathlon Glynis Nunn Australia**) 45 55
503 $2 Basketball (optd **Team Basketball United States**) 1·10 1·50

67 Captain William Bligh and Chart

1984. "Ausipex" International Stamp Exhibition, Melbourne. Multicoloured.
504 60c. Type **67** . . . . 3·75 3·50
505 96c. H.M.S. "Bounty" and map . . . . 3·75 3·75
506 $1.40 Aitutaki stamps of 1974, 1979 and 1981 with map . . . . 3·75 4·00
MS507 85 × 113 mm. As Nos. 504/6, but each with a premium of 5c. 7·50 4·00

1984. Birth of Prince Henry (1st issue). No. 391 optd **15-9-84 Birth Prince Henry** and surch also.
508 $3 on 60c. Type **50** . . . . 2·25 3·25

69 The Annunciation

70 Princess Diana with Prince Henry

1984. Christmas. Details from Altarpiece, St Paul's Church, Palencia, Spain. Multicoloured.
509 36c. Type **69** 30 35
510 48c. The Nativity 40 45
511 60c. The Epiphany 45 50
512 96c. The Flight into Egypt 75 80
MS513 Designs as Nos. 509/12 in separate miniature sheets, each 45 × 53 mm and with a face value of 90c.+7c. Imperf. Set of 4 sheets 2·50 3·25

1984. Birth of Prince Henry (2nd issue). Mult.
514 48c. Type **70** . . . . 2·75 2·25
515 60c. Prince William with Prince Henry . . . . . . 2·75 2·25
516 $2.10 Prince and Princess of Wales with children . . . 3·50 4·00
MS517 113 × 65 mm. As Nos. 514/16, but each with a face value of 96c.+7c. . . . . . . 7·00 4·50

71 Grey Kingbird ("Gray Kingbird")

1985. Birth Bicentenary of John J. Audubon (ornithologist). Designs showing original paintings. Multicoloured.
518 55c. Type **71** . . . . 1·10 1·10
519 65c. Bohemian waxwing . . . 1·25 1·25
520 75c. Summer tanager . . . . 1·40 1·40
521 95c. Common cardinal ("Cardinal") . . . . 1·50 1·50
522 $1.15 White-winged crossbill 1·90 1·90

72 The Queen Mother, aged Seven

1985. Life and Times of Queen Elizabeth the Queen Mother. Multicoloured.
523 55c. Type **72** 45 50
524 65c. Engagement photograph, 1922 . . . . 50 55
525 75c. With young Princess Elizabeth 60 65
526 $1.30 With baby Prince Charles . . . . 1·00 1·10
MS527 75 × 49 mm. $3 Queen Mother on her 63rd birthday 2·25 2·40

73 "The Calmady Children" (T. Lawrence)

1985. International Youth Year. Multicoloured.
528 75c. Type **73** . . . . 3·00 2·75
529 90c. "Madame Charpentier's Children" (Renoir) . . . . 3·00 3·00
530 $1.40 "Young Girls at Piano" (Renoir) . . . . 3·75 4·00
MS531 103 × 104 mm. As Nos. 528/30, but each with a premium of 10c. . . . . 4·75 3·75

74 "Adoration of the Magi" (Giotto) and "Giotto" Spacecraft

1985. Christmas. Appearance of Halley's Comet (1st issue). Multicoloured.
532 95c. Type **74** . . . . 1·75 1·75
533 95c. As Type **74** but showing "Planet A" spacecraft . . . 1·75 1·75
534 $1.15 Type **74** . . . . 1·75 1·75
535 $1.15 As No. 533 . . . . . . 1·75 1·75
MS536 52 × 55 mm. $6.40. As Type **74** but without spacecraft (30 × 31 mm). Imperf . . . . . 14·00 8·50

75 Halley's Comet A.D. 684 (from "Nuremberg Chronicle")

1986. Appearance of Halley's Comet (2nd issue). Multicoloured.
537 90c. Type **75** 90 90
538 $1.25 Halley's Comet, 1066 (from Bayeux Tapestry) . . 1·10 1·10
539 $1.75 Halley's Comet, 1456 (from "Lucerne Chronicles") . . . . 1·50 1·50
MS540 107 × 82 mm. As Nos. 537/9, but each with a face value of 95c. 5·50 2·50
MS541 65 × 80 mm. $4.20, "Melencolia I" (Albrecht Dürer woodcut) (61 × 76 mm). Imperf 6·00 3·50

76 Queen Elizabeth II on Coronation Day (from photo by Cecil Beaton)

78 Prince Andrew and Miss Sarah Ferguson

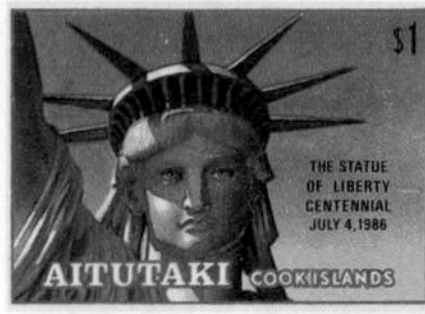

77 Head of Statue of Liberty

1986. 60th Birthday of Queen Elizabeth II.
542 **76** 95c. multicoloured . . . . 1·75 2·00
MS543 58 × 68 mm. $4.20, As T **76**, but showing more of the portrait without oval frame . . . . . 5·50 5·50

1986. Centenary of Statue of Liberty. Mult.
544 $1 Type **77** . . . . 1·25 1·25
545 $2.75 Statue of Liberty at sunset . . . . 2·75 2·75
MS546 91 × 79 mm. As Nos. 544/5, but each with a face value of $1.25 3·25 2·50

1986. Royal Wedding.
547 **78** $2 multicoloured . . . . . 2·00 2·00
MS548 85 × 70 mm. Type **78** multicoloured . . . . 6·50 8·00

1986. "Stampex '86" Stamp Exhibition, Adelaide. No. **MS**507 with "Ausipex" emblems obliterated in gold.
MS549 As Nos. 504/6, but each with a premium of 5c. . . . . . . 11·00 12·00
The "Stampex '86" exhibition emblem is overprinted on the sheet margin.

1986. 86th Brithday of Queen Elizabeth the Queen Mother. Nos. 523/6 in miniature sheet, 132 × 82 mm.
MS550 Nos. 523/6 . . . . 11·00 10·00

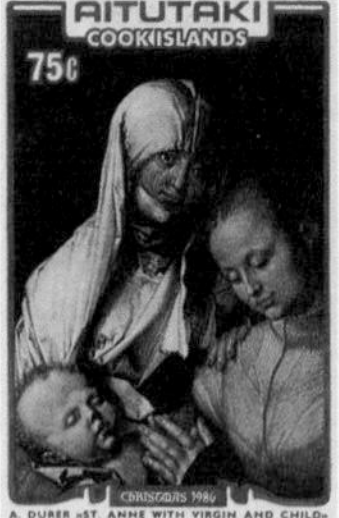

79 "St. Anne with Virgin and Child"

83 Angels

1986. Christmas. Paintings by Durer. Multicoloured.
551 75c. Type **79** . . . . 1·25 1·25
552 $1.35 "Virgin and Child" . . 1·75 1·75
553 $1.95 "The Adoration of the Magi" . . . . 2·25 2·25
554 $2.75 "Madonna of the Rosary" . . . . 3·00 3·00
MS555 88 × 125 mm. As Nos. 551/4, but each with a face value of $1.65 13·00 14·00

1986. Visit of Pope John Paul II to South Pacific. Nos. 551/4 optd **NOVEMBER 21-24 1986 FIRST VISIT TO SOUTH PACIFIC** and surch also.
556 75c.+10c. Type **79** . . . . . 2·75 2·50
557 $1.35+10c. "Virgin and Child" . . . . 3·25 3·00
558 $1.95+10c. "The Adoration of the Magi" . . . . . . 4·00 3·50
559 $2.75+10c. "Madonna of the Rosary" . . . . 5·00 5·00
MS560 88 × 125 mm. As No. 556/9, but each with a face value of $1.65+10c. . . . . 16·00 15·00

1987. Hurricane Relief Fund. Nos. 544/5, 547, 551/4 and 556/9 surch **HURRICANE RELIEF +50c**.
561 75c.+50c. Type **79** . . . . 3·25 2·75
562 75c.+10c.+50c. Type **79** . . 4·00 3·50
563 $1+50c. Type **77** . . . . . 3·50 3·00
564 $1.35+50c. "Virgin and Child" (Durer) . . . . . . 3·75 3·25
565 $1.35+10c.+50c. "Virgin and Child" (Durer) . . . . . 4·50 4·00
566 $1.95+50c. "The Adoration of the Magi" (Durer) . . . 4·50 4·00
567 $1.95+10c.+50c. "The Adoration of the Magi" (Durer) . . . . 5·00 4·50
568 $2+50c. Type **78** . . . . . 4·50 4·00
569 $2.75+50c. Statue of Liberty at sunset . . . . 5·00 4·50
570 $2.75+50c. "Madonna of the Rosary" (Durer) . . . . . 5·00 4·50
571 $2.75+10c.+50c. "Madonna of the Rosary" (Durer) . . 6·50 5·50

1987. Royal Ruby Wedding. Nos. 391/3 surch **2.50 Royal Wedding 40th Anniv.**
572 $2.50 on 60c. Type **50** . . . 2·00 2·50
573 $2.50 on 80c. Lady Diana Spencer . . . . 2·00 2·50
574 $2.50 on $1.40 Prince Charles and Lady Diana (87 × 70 mm) . . . . . . 2·00 2·50

1987. Christmas. Details of angels from "Virgin with Garland" by Rubens.
575 **83** 70c. multicoloured . . . . 2·00 2·00
576 – 85c. multicoloured . . . . 2·00 2·00
577 – $1.50 multicoloured . . . 2·25 2·25
578 – $1.85 multicoloured . . . 3·25 3·25
MS579 92 × 120 mm. As Nos. 575/8, but each with a face value of 95c. 11·00 12·00
MS580 96 × 85 mm. $6 "Virgin with Garland" (diamond, 56 × 56 mm) 10·00 12·00

84 Chariot Racing and Athletics

1988. Olympic Games, Seoul. Ancient and modern Olympic sports. Multicoloured.
581 70c. Type **84** . . . . 2·25 2·00
582 85c. Greek runners and football . . . . 2·50 2·25
583 95c. Greek wrestling and handball . . . . 2·50 2·25
584 $1.40 Greek hoplites and tennis . . . . 3·25 3·00
MS585 103 × 101 mm. As Nos. 581 and 584, but each with face value of $2 . . . . 8·00 8·50

1988. Olympic Medal Winners, Los Angeles. Nos. 581/4 optd.
586 70c. Type **84** (optd **FLORENCE GRIFFITH JOYNER UNITED STATES 100 M AND 200 M**) . . . . 2·00 2·00
587 85c. Greek runners and football (optd **GELINDO BORDIN ITALY MARATHON**) . . . . . 2·00 2·00
588 95c. Greek wrestling and handball (optd **HITOSHI SAITO JAPAN JUDO**) . . 2·00 2·00
589 $1.40 Greek hoplites and tennis (optd **STEFFI GRAF WEST GERMANY WOMEN'S TENNIS**) . . 4·50 4·00

85 "Adoration of the Shepherds" (detail)

1988. Christmas. Paintings by Rembrandt. Mult.
590 55c. Type **85** . . . . 2·00 1·75
591 70c. "The Holy Family" . . 2·25 2·00
592 85c. "Presentation in the Temple" . . . . 2·50 2·25
593 95c. "The Holy Family" (different) . . . . 2·50 2·25
594 $1.15 "Presentation in the Temple" (different) . . . . 2·75 2·50
MS595 85 × 101 mm. $4.50, As Type **85** but 52 × 34 mm. . . . 5·50 6·50

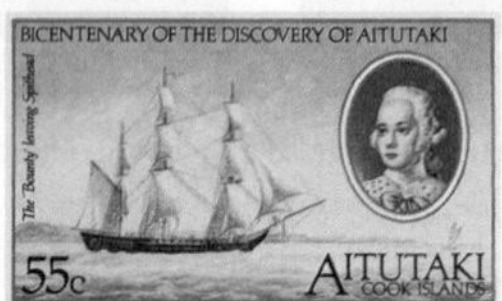

86 H.M.S. "Bounty" leaving Spithead and King George III

1989. Bicentenary of Discovery of Aitutaki by Captain Bligh. Multicoloured.
596 55c. Type **86** . . . . 1·75 1·75
597 65c. Breadfruit plants . . . . 2·00 2·00
598 75c. Old chart showing Aitutaki and Captain Bligh 2·25 2·25
599 95c. Native outrigger and H.M.S. "Bounty" off Aitutaki . . . . 2·50 2·50
600 $1.65 Fletcher Christian confronting Bligh . . . . 3·00 3·00
MS601 94 × 72 mm. $4.20, "Mutineers casting Bligh adrift" (Robert Dodd) (60 × 45 mm) 8·00 9·50

87 "Apollo 11" Astronaut on Moon

1989. 20th Anniv of First Manned Landing on Moon. Multicoloured.
602 75c. Type **87** . . . . 2·75 2·00
603 $1.15 Conducting experiment on Moon . . . . 3·25 2·50
604 $1.80 Astronaut on Moon carrying equipment . . . . 4·00 3·50
MS605 105 × 86 mm. $6.40, Astronaut on Moon with U.S. flag (40 × 27 mm) . . . . 8·00 9·50

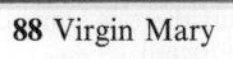

88 Virgin Mary **91** "Madonna of the Basket" (Correggio)

89 Human Comet striking Earth

1989. Christmas. Details from "Virgin in the Glory" by Titian. Multicoloured.
606 70c. Type **88** . . . . 2·50 2·00
607 85c. Christ Child . . . . . . 3·00 2·50
608 95c. Angel . . . . 3·25 2·75
609 $1.25 Cherubs . . . . 3·75 3·25
MS610 80 × 100 mm. $6 "Virgin in the Glory" (45 × 60 mm) . . . 8·00 9·50

1990. Protection of the Environment. Mult.
611 $1.75 Type **89** . . . . 2·25 2·25
612 $1.75 Comet's tail . . . . . 2·25 2·25
MS613 108 × 43 mm. Nos. 611/12 3·50 4·50
Nos. 611/12 were printed together, se-tenant, forming a composite design.

1990. 90th Birthday of Queen Elizabeth the Queen Mother. No. **MS**550 optd **Ninetieth Birthday**.
MS614 132 × 82 mm. Nos. 523/6 13·00 12·00

1990. Christmas. Religious Paintings. Mult.
615 70c. Type **91** . . . . 1·50 1·50
616 85c. "Virgin and Child" (Morando) . . . . 1·60 1·60
617 95c. "Adoration of the Child" (Tiepolo) . . . . . 1·75 1·75
618 $1.75 "Mystic Marriage of St. Catherine" (Memling) 2·50 2·75
MS619 165 × 93 mm. $6 "Donne Triptych" (Memling) (horiz) . . 12·00 13·00

1990. "Birdpex '90" Stamp Exhibition, Christchurch, New Zealand. Nos. 349/50 optd **Birdpex '90** and bird's head.
620 $1 Blue-headed flycatcher . . 4·50 4·50
621 $2 Red-bellied flycatcher . . 6·00 6·00

1991. 65th Birthday of Queen Elizabeth II. No. 352 optd **COMMEMORATING 65th BIRTHDAY OF H.M. QUEEN ELIZABETH II**.
622 $5 Flat-billed kingfisher . . . 12·00 12·00

93 "The Holy Family" (A. Mengs)

1991. Christmas. Religious Paintings. Mult.
623 80c. Type **93** . . . . 1·50 1·50
624 90c. "Virgin and the Child" (Lippi) . . . . 1·60 1·60
625 $1.05 "Virgin and Child" (A. Durer) . . . . 1·75 1·75
626 $1.75 "Adoration of the Shepherds" (G. de la Tour) 2·50 3·00
MS627 79 × 103 mm. "The Holy Family" (Michelangelo) . . . 11·00 12·00

94 Hurdling

1992. Olympic Games, Barcelona. Mult.
628 95c. Type **94** . . . . 1·75 1·50
629 $1.25 Weightlifting . . . . . 2·00 1·75
630 $1.50 Judo . . . . 2·50 2·25
631 $1.95 Football . . . . 2·75 2·75

95 Vaka Motu Canoe

1992. 6th Festival of Pacific Arts, Rarotonga. Sailing Canoes. Multicoloured.
632 30c. Type **95** 65 65
633 50c. Hamatafua 80 80
634 95c. Alia Kalia Ndrua . . . 1·50 1·50
635 $1.75 Hokule'a Hawaiian . . 2·25 2·75
636 $1.95 Tuamotu Pahi . . . . 2·50 3·00

1992. Royal Visit by Prince Edward. Nos. 632/6 optd **ROYAL VISIT**.
637 30c. Type **95** 95 95
638 50c. Hamatafua . . . . . . 1·40 1·40
639 95c. Alia Kalia Ndrua . . . 2·25 2·25
640 $1.75 Hokule'a Hawaiian . . 3·00 3·25
641 $1.95 Tuamotu Pahi . . . . 3·00 3·25

96 "Virgin's Nativity" (detail) (Reni)

1992. Christmas. Different details from "Virgin's Nativity" by Guido Reni.
642 **96** 80c. multicoloured . . . . 1·40 1·40
643 – 90c. multicoloured . . . . 1·60 1·60
644 – $1.05 multicoloured . . . 1·75 1·75
645 – $1.75 multicoloured . . . 2·50 3·00
MS646 – 101 × 86 mm. $6 multicoloured (as $1.05, but larger (36 × 46 mm)) . . . . 6·50 8·00

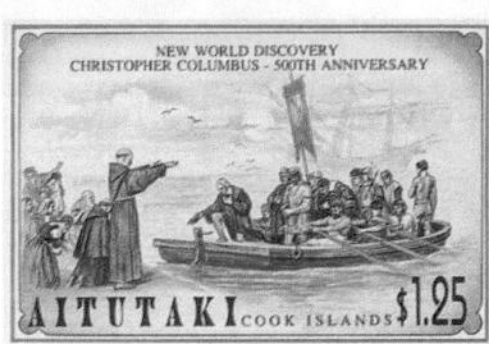

97 The Departure from Palos

1992. 500th Anniv of Discovery of America by Columbus. Multicoloured.
647 $1.25 Type **97** . . . . 2·25 2·50
648 $1.75 Map of voyages . . . 2·75 3·00
649 $1.95 Columbus and crew in New World . . . . 3·25 3·50

98 Queen Victoria and King Edward VII

1993. 40th Anniv of Coronation. Mult.
650 $1.75 Type **98** . . . . 3·25 2·75
651 $1.75 King George V and King George VI . . . . . 3·25 2·75
652 $1.75 Queen Elizabeth II in 1953 and 1986 . . . . . . 3·25 2·75

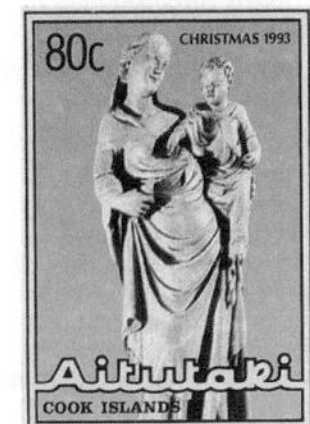

99 "Madonna and Child" (Nino Pisano)

1993. Christmas. Religious Sculptures. Mult.
653 80c. Type **99** 90 90
654 90c. "Virgin on Rosebush" (Luca della Robbia) . . . 1·00 1·00
655 $1.15 "Virgin with Child and St. John" (Juan Francisco Rustici) . . . . 1·40 1·40
656 $1.95 "Virgin with Child" (Miguel Angel) . . . . . 2·25 2·25
657 $3 "Madonna and Child" (Jacopo della Quercia) (32 × 47 mm) . . . . . . 3·25 4·00

100 Ice Hockey

1994. Winter Olympic Games, Lillehammer. Multicoloured.
658 $1.15 Type **100** . . . . . . 3·50 3·00
659 $1.15 Ski-jumping . . . . . 3·50 3·00
660 $1.15 Cross-country skiing 3·50 3·00

101 "Ipomoea pes-caprae" **103** "The Madonna of the Basket" (Correggio)

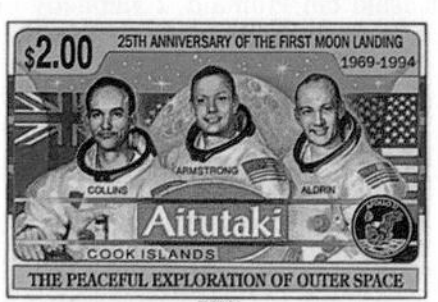

102 Cook Islands and U.S.A. Flags with Astronauts Collins, Armstrong and Aldrin

1994. Flowers. Multicoloured.
661 5c. Type **101** 10 10
662 10c. "Plumeria alba" 10 10
663 15c. "Hibiscus rosa-sinensis" 10 15
664 20c. "Allamanda cathartica" 15 20
665 25c. "Delonix regia" 15 20
666 30c. "Gardenia taitensis" . . 20 25
667 50c. "Plumeria rubra" . . . 30 35
668 80c. "Ipomoea littoralis" . . 50 55
669 85c. "Hibiscus tiliaceus" . . 55 60
670 90c. "Erythrina variegata" . . 60 65
671 $1 "Solandra nitida" 65 70
672 $2 "Cordia subcordata" . . . 1·25 1·40
673 $3 "Hibiscus rosa-sinensis" (different) (34 × 47mm) . . 1·90 2·00
674 $5 As $3 (34 × 47mm) . . . 3·25 3·50
675 $8 As $3 (34 × 47mm) . . . . 5·00 5·25
Nos. 671/5 include a portrait of Queen Elizabeth II at top right.

1994. 25th Anniv of First Manned Moon Landing. Multicoloured.
676 $2 Type **102** . . . . 7·50 7·50
677 $2 "Apollo 11" re-entering atmosphere and landing in sea . . . . 7·50 7·50

1994. Christmas. Religious Paintings. Mult.
678 85c. Type **103** . . . . 1·00 1·10
679 85c. "The Virgin and Child with Saints" (Memling) . . 1·00 1·10
680 85c. "The Virgin and Child with Flowers" (Dolci) . . . 1·00 1·10
681 85c. "The Virgin and Child with Angels" (Bergognone) 1·00 1·10
682 90c. "Adoration of the Kings" (Dosso) . . . . . 1·00 1·10
683 90c. "The Virgin and Child" (Bellini) . . . . 1·00 1·10
684 90c. "The Virgin and Child" (Schiavone) . . . . 1·00 1·10
685 90c. "Adoration of the Kings" (Dolci) . . . . . . 1·00 1·10
No. 678 is inscribed "Corregio" in error.

104 Battle of Britain

1995. 50th Anniv of End of Second World War. Multicoloured.
686 $4 Type **104** . . . . 9·00 8·50
687 $4 Battle of Midway . . . . 9·00 8·50

105 Queen Elizabeth the Queen Mother

1995. 95th Birthday of Queen Elizabeth the Queen Mother.
688 **105** $4 multicoloured . . . . 7·50 8·00

106 Globe, Doves, United Nations Emblem and Headquarters

1995. 50th Anniv of United Nations.
689 **106** $4.25 multicoloured . . . 5·50 7·00

107 Green Turtle

1995. Year of the Sea Turtle. Multicoloured.
690 95c. Type **107** . . . . 1·75 1·75
691 $1.15 Leatherback turtle . . 2·00 2·00
692 $1.50 Olive Ridley turtle . . 2·25 2·25
693 $1.75 Loggerhead turtle . . . 2·50 2·50

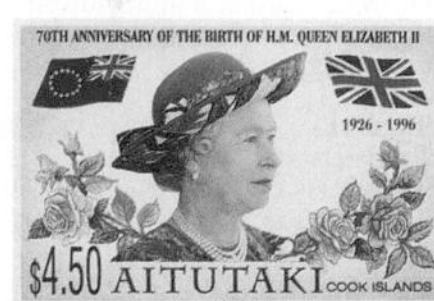

108 Queen Elizabeth II

1996. 70th Birthday of Queen Elizabeth II.
694 **108** $4.50 multicoloured . . . 8·50 8·00

109 Baron Pierre de Coubertin, Torch and Opening of 1896 Olympic Games

1996. Centenary of Modern Olympic Games. Multicoloured.
695 $2 Type **109** . . . . 5·00 5·00
696 $2 Athletes and American flag, 1996 . . . . 5·00 5·00

110 Princess Elizabeth and Lieut. Philip Mountbatten with King George VI and Queen Elizabeth, 1947

1997. Golden Wedding of Queen Elizabeth and Prince Philip.
697 **110** $2.50 multicoloured . . . 4·00 3·50
MS698 78 × 102 mm. **110** $6 multicoloured . . . . 8·00 8·50

111 Diana, Princess of Wales

1998. Diana, Princess of Wales Commemoration.
699 **111** $1 multicoloured . . . . 1·25 1·00
MS700 70 × 100 mm. $4 Diana, Princess of Wales . . . . . . 3·25 3·75

1998. Children's Charities. No. **MS**1427 surch +$1 CHILDREN'S CHARITIES.
MS701 70 × 100 mm. $4 + $1 Diana, Princess of Wales . . . . . . 3·75 4·50

1999. New Millennium. Nos. 632/6 optd **KIA ORANA THIRD MILLENNIUM.**
702 30c. Type **95** 50 50
703 50c. Hamatafua 60 60
704 95c. Alia Kalia Ndrua . . . 85 85
705 $1.75 Hokule'a Hawaiian . . 1·40 1·60
706 $1.95 Tuamotu Pahi . . . . 1·60 1·75

2000. Queen Elizabeth the Queen Mother's 100th Birthday. As T **277** of Cook Islands.
707 $3 blue and brown . . . . . 3·00 3·00
708 $3 multicoloured . . . . . . 3·00 3·00
709 $3 multicoloured . . . . . . 3·00 3·00
710 $3 green and brown . . . . 3·00 3·00
MS711 73 × 100 mm. $7.50, multicoloured . . . . 5·50 7·00
DESIGNS: No. 707, Queen Mother in evening dress and tiara; 708, Queen Mother in evening dress standing by table; 709, Queen Mother in Garter robes; 710, King George VI and Queen Elizabeth; **MS**711 Queen Mother holding lilies.

2000. Olympic Games, Sydney. As T **278** of Cook Islands. Multicoloured.
712 $2 Ancient Greek wrestlers 2·00 2·25
713 $2 Modern wrestlers . . . . 2·00 2·25
714 $2 Ancient Greek boxer . . . 2·00 2·25
715 $2 Modern boxers . . . . . 2·00 2·25
MS716 99 × 90 mm. $2.75, Olympic torch and Cook Island canoes 2·25 2·50

113 Blue Lorikeets and Flowers

2002. Endangered Species. Blue Lorikeet. Multicoloured.
717 80c. Type **113** 75 80
718 90c. Lorikeets and bananas 85 90
719 $1.15 Lorikeets on palm leaf 1·10 1·25
720 $1.95 Lorikeets in tree trunk 1·50 1·75

2003. "United We Stand". Support for Victims of 11 September 2001 Terrorist Attacks. Design as T **282** of Cook Islands. Multicoloured.
MS721 75 × 109 mm. $1.15 × 4 Twin Towers and flags of U.S.A. and Cook Islands 85 90

OFFICIAL STAMPS

1978. Nos. 98/105, 107/10 and 227/8 optd **O.H.M.S.** or surch also.
O 1 1c. multicoloured 90 10
O 2 2c. multicoloured . . . . . 1·00 10
O 3 3c. multicoloured . . . . . 1·00 10
O 4 4c. multicoloured . . . . . 1·00 10
O 5 5c. multicoloured . . . . . 1·00 10
O 6 8c. multicoloured . . . . . 1·25 10
O 7 10c. multicoloured . . . . . 1·50 15
O 8 15c. on 60c. multicoloured 2·75 20
O 9 18c. on 60c. multicoloured 2·75 20
O10 20c. multicoloured . . . . . 2·75 20
O11 50c. multicoloured . . . . . 1·00 55
O12 60c. multicoloured . . . . . 10·00 70
O13 $1 multicoloured (No. 108) 10·00 80
O14 $2 multicoloured . . . . . 9·00 75
O15 $4 on $1 mult (No. 228) . . 1·75 75
O16 $5 multicoloured . . . . . 11·00 1·25

1985. Nos. 351/2, 430/3, 475 and 477/94 optd **O.H.M.S.** or surch also.
O17 2c. Type **65** . . . . 1·00 1·25
O18 5c. Scarlet robin . . . . . 1·25 1·25
O19 10c. Golden whistler . . . . 1·50 1·50
O20 12c. Rufous fantail . . . . 1·60 1·75
O21 18c. Peregrine falcon . . . . 2·75 2·00
O22 20c. on 24 c Barn owl . . . 2·75 2·00
O23 30c. Java sparrow . . . . . 2·00 1·50
O24 40c. on 36c. White-breasted wood swallow . . . . . . 2·00 1·50
O25 50c. Feral rock pigeon . . . 2·00 1·50
O26 55c. on 48c. Tahitian lory . . 2·00 1·50
O27 60c. Purple swamphen . . . 2·25 1·75
O28 65c. on 72c. Zebra dove . . 2·25 1·75
O38 75c. on 48c. Type **57** . . . 1·00 1·25
O39 75c. on 48c. Ancient Ti'i image . . . . 1·00 1·25
O40 75c. on 48c. Tourist canoeing . . . . 1·00 1·25
O41 75c. on 48c. Captain William Bligh and chart . . . . . 1·00 1·25
O29 80c. on 96c. Chestnut-breasted mannikin . . . . 2·25 1·50
O30 $1.20 Common mynah . . . 3·00 2·25
O31 $2.10 Reef heron . . . . . 4·00 3·50
O32 $3 Blue-headed flycatcher . . 6·00 6·00
O33 $4.20 Red-bellied flycatcher 7·00 7·00
O34 $5.60 Red munia . . . . . 8·00 8·00
O35 $9.60 Flat-billed kingfisher 13·00 13·00
O36 $14 on $4 Red munia (35 × 48 mm) . . . . . . 15·00 15·00
O37 $18 on $5 Flat-billed kingfisher (35 × 48 mm) . . 17·00 17·00

AJMAN Pt. 19

One of the Trucial States in the Persian Gulf. On 18 July 1971, seven Gulf sheikhdoms, including Ajman, formed the State of the United Arab Emirates. The federation became effective on 1 August 1972.

1964. 100 naye paise = 1 rupee.
1967. 100 dirhams = 1 riyal.

1 Shaikh Rashid bin Humaid al Naimi and Arab Stallion **2** Kennedy in Football Kit

1964. Multicoloured. (a) Size 34½ × 23 mm.
1 1n.p. Type **1** 15 15
2 2n.p. Regal angelfish 15 15
3 3n.p. Dromedary 15 15
4 4n.p. Yellow-banded angelfish 15 15
5 5n.p. Tortoise 15 15
6 10n.p. Jewel cichlid 25 15
7 15n.p. White stork 40 15
8 20n.p. Black-headed gulls . . . 40 15
9 30n.p. Lanner falcon 40 15

(b) Size 42½ × 27 mm.
10 40n.p. Type **1** 20 20
11 50n.p. Regal angelfish 25 20
12 70n.p. Dromedary 25 25
13 1r. Yellow-banded angelfish 50 30
14 1r.50 Tortoise 50 50
15 2r. Jewel cichlid . . . . . . 1·25 75

(c) Size 53 × 34 mm.
16 3r. White stork . . . . 1·25 25
17 5r. Black-headed gulls . . . . 1·60 1·50
18 10r. Lanner falcon . . . . . 3·50 1·75

1964. Pres. Kennedy Commem. Perf or imperf.
19 **2** 10n.p. purple and green . . . 15 15
20 – 15n.p. violet and turquoise 15 15
21 – 50n.p. blue and brown . . . 20 20
22 – 1r. turquoise and sepia . . . 35 35
23 – 2r. olive and purple 75 65
24 – 3r. brown and green . . . . 1·25 95
25 – 5r. brown and violet . . . . 2·25 2·10
26 – 10r. brown and blue . . . . 5·00 3·75
DESIGNS—Various pictures of Kennedy: 15n.p. Diving; 50n.p. As naval officer; 1r. Sailing with Mrs. Kennedy; 2r. With Mrs. Eleanor Roosevelt; 3r. With wife and child; 5r. With colleagues; 10r. Full-face portrait.

3 Start of Race

1965. Olympic Games, Tokyo. Perf or imperf.
27 **3** 5n.p. slate, brown & mauve 15 15
28 – 10n.p. red, bronze and blue 15 15
29 **3** 15n.p. brown, violet & green 15 15
30 – 25n.p. black, blue and red . . 15 15
31 – 50n.p. slate, purple and blue 20 20
32 – 1r. blue, green and purple . . 70 35
33 – 1r.50 purple, violet and green 75 50
34 – 2r. blue, purple and ochre . . 1·25 90
35 – 3r. violet, brown and blue . . 2·25 1·40
36 – 5r. purple, green and yellow 2·50 2·10
DESIGNS: 10n.p., 1r.50, Boxing; 25n.p., 2r. Judo; 50n.p., 5r. Gymnastics; 1, 3r. Sailing.

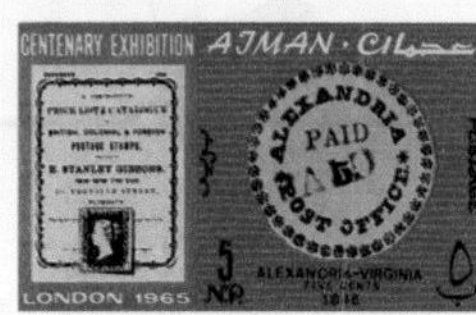

4 First Gibbons Catalogue and Alexandria (U.S.) 5c. Postmaster's Stamp

1965. Stanley Gibbons Catalogue Centenary Exhibition, London. Multicoloured.
37 5n.p. Type **4** 15 15
38 10n.p. Austria (6k.) scarlet "Mercury" newspaper stamp 15 15
39 15n.p. British Guiana "One Cent", 1856 . . . . 15 15
40 25n.p. Canada "Twelvepence Black", 1851 . . . . 15 15
41 50n.p. Hawaii "Missionary" 2c., 1851 . . . . 25 25
42 1r. Mauritius "Post Office" 2d. blue, 1847 . . . . 40 40
43 3r. Switzerland "Double Geneva" 5c.+5c., 1843 . . . 1·40 1·25
44 5r. Tuscany 3 lire, 1860 . . . 2·75 2·10
The 5, 15 and 50n.p. and 3r. also include the First Gibbons Catalogue and the others, the Gibbons "Elizabethan" Catalogue.

1965. Pan Arab Games, Cairo. Perf or imperf. Nos. 29, 31 and 33/5 optd. (a) Optd **PAN ARAB GAMES CAIRO 1965.**
45 **3** 15n.p. brown, violet & green 15 15
46 – 50n.p. slate, purple and blue 25 25
47 – 1r.50 purple, violet & green 90 90
48 – 2r. blue, red and ochre . . . 1·25 1·25
49 – 3r. violet, brown and blue . . 2·00 2·00

(b) Optd as Nos. 45/9 but equivalent in Arabic.
50 **3** 15n.p. brown, violet & green 15 15
51 – 50n.p. slate, purple and blue 25 25
52 – 1r.50 purple, violet and green 90 90
53 – 2r. blue, red and ochre . . . 1·25 1·25
54 – 3r. violet, brown and blue . . 2·00 2·00

1965. Air. Designs similar to Nos. 1/9, but inscr "AIR MAIL". Mult. (a) Size 42½ × 25½ mm.
55 15n.p. Type **1** 15 15
56 25n.p. Regal angelfish 15 15
57 35n.p. Dromedary 20 15
58 50n.p. Yellow-banded angelfish 25 15
59 75n.p. Tortoise 40 20
60 1r. Jewel cichlid 75 25

(b) Size 53 × 34 mm.
61 2r. White stork . . . . 1·10 30
62 3r. Black-headed gull . . . . 1·60 30
63 5r. Lanner falcon . . . . . . 3·25 50

1966. Stamp Cent Exn, Cairo. Nos. 38/9 and 41/3 optd **STAMP CENTENARY EXHIBITION CAIRO, JANUARY 1966** and pyramid motif.
73 10n.p. multicoloured 15 15
74 15n.p. multicoloured 15 15
75 50n.p. multicoloured 25 25
76 1r. multicoloured 65 65
77 3r. multicoloured . . . . . . 1·75 1·75

8 Sir Winston Churchill and Tower Bridge

1966. Churchill Commemoration. Each design includes portrait of Churchill. Multicoloured.
79 25n.p. Type **8** 15 15
80 50n.p. Buckingham Palace . . 25 15
81 75n.p. Blenheim Palace . . . 40 20
82 1r. British Museum 50 25
83 2r. St. Paul's Cathedral in wartime . . . . 1·00 40
84 3r. National Gallery and St. Martin in the Fields Church . . . . 1·50 60
85 5r. Westminster Abbey . . . . 2·50 90
86 7r.50 Houses of Parliament at night . . . . 3·75 1·60

9 Rocket

1966. Space Achievements. Multicoloured. (a) Postage. Size as T **9**.
88 1n.p. Type **9** 15 15
89 3n.p. Capsule 15 15
90 5n.p. Astronaut entering capsule in space 15 15
91 10n.p. Astronaut outside capsule in space 15 15
92 15n.p. Astronauts and globe 15 15
93 25n.p. Astronaut in space . . 25 15

(b) Air. Size 38 × 38 mm.
95 50n.p. As Type **9** 25 15
96 1r. Astronauts and globe . . . 40 20
97 3r. Astronaut outside capsule in space . . . . 1·25 40
98 5r. Capsule . . . . 3·25 90

1967. Various issues with currency names changed by overprinting in **Dh.** or **Riyals.** (a) Postage. Nos. 1/18 (1964 Definitives).
99 1d. on 1n.p. 15 15
100 2d. on 2n.p. 15 15
101 3d. on 3n.p. 15 15
102 4d. on 4n.p. 15 15
103 5d. on 5n.p. 15 15
104 10d. on 10n.p. 15 15
105 15d. on 15n.p. . . . . . . 1·25 15
106 20d. on 20n.p. . . . . . . 1·25 15
107 30d. on 30n.p. . . . . . . 1·25 15
108 40d. on 40n.p. 20 15
109 50d. on 50n.p. 30 15
110 70d. on 70n.p. 40 25
111 1r. on 1r. 65 25
112 1r.50 on 1r.50 . . . . 65 30
113 2r. on 2r. . . . . 1·50 65
114 3r. on 3r. . . . . 1·50 70
115 5r. on 5r. . . . . 2·50 1·25
116 10r. on 10r. . . . . 7·50 2·75

(b) Air. Nos. 55/63 (Airmails).
117 15d. on 15n.p. 15 15
118 25d. on 25n.p. 20 15
119 35d. on 35n.p. 25 15
120 50d. on 50n.p. 30 15
121 75d. on 75n.p. 45 25
122 1r. on 1r. 65 50
123 2r. on 2r. . . . . 1·25 70
124 3r. on 3r. . . . . 2·50 1·25
125 5r. on 5r. . . . . 3·50 2·40

NEW CURRENCY SURCHARGES. Nos. 19/44 and 79/98 are known surch in new currency (dirhams and riyals), in limited quantities, but there is some doubt as to whether they were in use locally.

11 Fiat 1500 Saloon, 1962

1967. Transport.
135 **11** 1d. brown & blk (postage) 15 15
136 – 2d. blue and brown 15 15
137 – 3d. mauve and black . . . 15 15
138 – 4d. blue and brown 15 15
139 – 5d. green and black . . . 30 15
140 – 15d. blue and brown . . . 50 15
141 – 30d. brown and black . . . 25 15
142 – 50d. black and brown . . . 50 15
143 – 70d. violet and black . . . 65 15

144 **11** 1r. green and brown (air) 40 15
145 – 2r. mauve and black . . . 1·00 25
146 – 3r. black and brown . . . 1·60 40
147 – 5r. brown and black . . . 2·25 1·00
148 – 10r. blue and brown . . . 6·75 1·50
DESIGNS: 2d., 2r. Motor coach; 3d., 3r. Motor cyclist; 4d., 5r. Boeing 707 airliner; 5d., 10r. "Brasil" (liner); 15d. "Yankee" (sail training and cruise ship); 30d. Cameleer; 50d. Arab horse; 70d. Sikorsky S-58 helicopter.

OFFICIAL STAMPS

1965. Designs similar to Nos. 1/9, additionally inscr "ON STATE'S SERVICE". Multicoloured. (i) Postage. Size 43 × 26 mm.
O64 25n.p. Type **1** 15 15
O65 40n.p. Regal angelfish . . . 20 15
O66 50n.p. Dromedary 20 15
O67 75n.p. Yellow-banded angelfish 55 25
O68 1r. Tortoise 85 40

(ii) Air. (a) Size 43 × 26 mm.
O69 75n.p. Jewel cichlid 50 15

(b) Size 53 × 34 mm.
O70 2r. White stork . . . . . . 1·25 35
O71 3r. Black-headed gulls . . . 1·75 50
O72 5r. Lanner falcon . . . . . 5·50 1·25

1967. Nos. O64/72 with currency names changed by overprinting in **Dh.** or **Riyals.**
O126 25d. on 25n.p. 15 15
O127 40d. on 40n.p. 20 15
O128 50d. on 50n.p. 20 15
O129 75d. on 75n.p. (No. O67) 55 45
O130 75d. on 75n.p. (No. O69) 55 45
O131 1r. on 1r. 60 60
O132 2r. on 2r. . . . . 6·00 3·00
O133 3r. on 3r. . . . . 11·00 4·50
O134 5r. on 5r. . . . . 17·00 8·50
For later issues see **UNITED ARAB EMIRATES.**

APPENDIX

From June 1967 very many stamp issues were made by a succession of agencies which had been awarded contracts by the Ruler, sometimes two agencies operating at the same time. Several contradictory statements were made as to the validity of some of these issues which appeared 1967–72 and for this reason they are only listed in abbreviated form.

1967.

50th Birth Anniv of President J. F. Kennedy. Air 10, 20, 40, 70d., 1r.50, 2, 3, 5r.

Paintings. Postage. Arab Paintings 1, 2, 3, 4, 5, 30, 70d.; Air. Asian Paintings 1, 2, 3, 5r.; Indian Painting 10r.

Tales from "The Arabian Nights". Postage 1, 2, 3, 10, 30, 50, 70d.; Air 90d., 1, 2, 3r.

World Scout Jamboree, Idaho. Postage 30, 70d., 1r.; Air 2, 3, 4r.

Olympic Games, Mexico (1968). Postage 35, 65, 75d., 1r.; Air 1r.25, 2, 3, 4r.

Winter Olympic Games, Grenoble (1968). Postage 5, 35, 60, 75d.; Air 1, 1r.25, 2, 3r.

Pres. J. F. Kennedy Memorial. Die-stamped on gold foil. Air 10r.

Paintings by Renoir and Terbrugghen. Air 35, 65d., 1, 2r. × 3.

1968.

Paintings by Velasquez. Air 1r. × 2, 2r. × 2.

Winter Olympic Games, Grenoble. Die-stamped on gold foil. Air 7r.

Paintings from Famous Galleries. Air 1r. × 4, 2r. × 6.

Costumes. Air 30d. × 2, 70d. × 2, 1r. × 2, 2r. × 2.

Olympic Games, Mexico. Postage 1r. × 4; Air 2r. × 4.

Satellites and Spacecraft. Air 30d. × 2, 70d. × 2, 1r. × 2, 2r. × 2, 3r. × 2.

Paintings. Hunting Dogs. Air 2r. × 6.

Paintings. Adam and Eve. Air 2r. × 4.

Human Rights Year. Kennedy Brothers and Martin Luther King. Air 1r. × 3, 2r. × 3.

Kennedy Brothers Memorial. Postage 2r.; Air 5r.

Sports Champions. Inter-Milano Football Club. Postage 5, 10, 15, 20, 25d.; Air 10r.

Sports Champions. Famous Footballers. Postage 15, 20, 50, 75d., 1r.; Air 10r.

Cats. Postage 1, 2, 3d.; Air 2, 3r.

Olympic Games, Mexico. Die-stamped on gold foil. 5r.

5th Death Anniv of Pres. J. F. Kennedy. On gold foil. Air 10r.

Paintings of the Madonna. Air 30, 70d., 1, 2, 3r.

Space Exploration. Postage 5, 10, 15, 20, 25d.; Air 15r.

Olympic Games, Mexico. Gold Medals. Postage 2r. × 4; Air 5r. × 4.

Christmas. Air 5r.

1969.

Sports Champions. Cyclists. Postage 1, 2, 5, 10, 15, 20d.; Air 12r.

Sports Champions. German Footballers. Postage 5, 10, 15, 20, 25d.; Air 10r.

Sports Champions. Motor-racing Drivers. Postage 1, 5, 10, 15, 25d.; Air 10r.

Motor-racing Cars. Postage 1, 5, 10, 15, 25d.; Air 10r.

Sports Champions. Boxers. Postage 5, 10, 15, 20d.; Air 10r.

Sports Champions. Baseball Players. Postage 1, 2, 5, 10, 15d.; Air 10r.

Birds. Air 1r. × 11.

Roses. 1r. × 6.

Wild Animals. Air 1r. × 6.

Paintings. Italian Old Masters. 5, 10, 15, 20d., 10r.

Paintings. Famous Composers. Air 5, 10, 25d., 10r.

Paintings. French Artists. 1r. × 4.

Paintings. Nudes. Air 2r. × 4.

Three Kings Mosaic. Air 1r. × 2, 3r. × 2.

Kennedy Brothers. Air 2, 3, 10r.

Olympic Games, Mexico. Gold Medal Winners. Postage 1, 2d., 10r.; Air 10d., 5, 10r.

Paintings of the Madonna. Postage 10d.; Air 10r.

Space Flight of "Apollo 9". Optd on 1968 Space Exploration issue. Air 15r.

Space Flight of "Apollo 10". Optd on 1968 Space Exploration issue. Air 15r.

1st Death Anniv of Gagarin. Optd on 1968 Space Exploration issue. 5d.

2nd Death Anniv of Edward White. Optd on 1968 Space Exploration issue. 10d.

1st Death Anniv of Robert Kennedy. Optd on 1969 Kennedy Brothers issue. Air 2r.

European Football Championship. Optd on 1968 Famous Footballers issue. Air 10r.

Olympic Games, Munich (1972). Optd on 1969 Mexico Gold Medal Winners issue. Air 10d., 5, 10r.

Moon Landing of "Apollo 11". Air 1, 2, 5r.

Moon Landing of "Apollo 11". Circular designs on gold or silver foil. Air 3r. × 3, 5r. × 3, 10r. × 14.

Paintings. Christmas. Postage 1, 2, 3, 4, 5, 15d.; Air 2, 3r.

1970.

"Apollo" Space Flights. Postage 1, 2, 4, 5, 10d.; Air 3, 5r.

Birth Bicentenary of Napoleon Bonaparte. Die-stamped on gold foil. Air 20r.

Paintings. Easter. Postage 5, 10, 12, 30, 50, 70d.; Air 1, 2r.

Moon Landing. Die-stamped on gold foil. Air 20r.

Paintings by Michelangelo. Postage 1, 2, 4, 5, 8, 10d.; Air 3, 5r.

World Cup Football Championship, Mexico. Air 25, 50, 75d., 1, 2, 3r.

"Expo 70" World Fair, Osaka, Japan. Japanese Paintings. Postage 1, 2, 3, 4, 5, 10, 15d.; Air 1, 5r.

Birth Bicent Napoleon Bonaparte. Postage 1, 2, 4, 5, 10d.; Air 3, 5r.

Paintings. Old Masters. Postage 1, 2, 5, 6, 10d.; Air 1, 2, 3r.

Space Flight of "Apollo 13". Air 50, 75, 80d., 1, 2, 3r.

World Cup Football Championship, Mexico. Die-stamped on gold foil. Air 20r.

Olympic Games, 1960–1972. Postage 15, 30, 50, 70d.; Air 2, 5r.

"Expo 70" World Fair, Osaka, Japan. Pavilions. Postage 1, 2, 3, 4, 10, 15d.; Air 1, 3r.

Brazil's Victory in World Cup Football Championship. Optd on 1970 World Football Cup issue. Air 25, 50, 75d., 1, 2, 3r.

"Gemini" and "Apollo" Space Flights. Postage 1, 2, 3, 4, 5, 6, 8, 10, 12, 15, 20, 25, 30, 35, 40, 50d.; Air 1, 1r.50, 2, 3r.

Vintage and Veteran Cars. Postage 1, 2, 4, 5, 8, 10d.; Air 2, 3r.

Pres. D. Eisenhower Commem. Postage 30, 50, 70d.; Air 1, 2, 3r.

Paintings by Ingres. Air 25, 30, 35, 50, 70, 85d., 1, 2r.

500th Birth Anniv (1971) of Albrecht Durer. Air 25, 30, 35, 50, 70, 85d., 1, 2r.

Christmas Paintings. Air 25, 30, 35, 50, 70, 85d., 1, 2r.

Winter Olympic Games, Sapporo, Japan (1972). Die-stamped on gold foil. Air 20r.

Meeting of Eisenhower and De Gaulle, 1942. Die-stamped on gold foil. Air 20r.

General De Gaulle Commem. Air 25, 50, 75d., 1, 2, 3r.

Winter Olympic Games, Sapporo, Japan (1972). Sports. Postage 1, 2, 5, 10d.; Air 3, 5r.

J. Rindt, World Formula 1 Motor-racing Champion. Die-stamped on gold foil. Air 20r.

1971.

"Philatokyo" Stamp Exhibition, Tokyo. Japanese Paintings. Air 25, 30, 35, 50, 70, 85d., 1, 2r.

Mars Space Project. Air 50, 75, 80d., 1, 2, 3r.

Napoleonic Military Uniforms. Postage 5, 10, 15, 20, 25, 30d.; Air 2, 3r.

Olympic Games, Munich (1972). Sports. Postage 10, 15, 25, 30, 40d.; Air 1, 2, 3r.

Paintings by Modern Artists. Air 25, 30, 35, 50, 70, 85d.; 1, 2r.

Paintings by Famous Artists. Air 25, 30, 35, 50, 70, 85d., 1, 2r.

25th Anniv of United Nations. Optd on 1971 Modern Artists issue. Air 25, 30, 35, 50, 70, 85d., 1, 2r.

Olympic Games, Munich (1972). Sports. Postage 1, 2, 3, 4, 5, 6, 8, 10, 12, 15, 20, 25, 30, 35, 40, 50d.; Air 1, 1r.50, 2, 3r.

Butterflies. Air 25, 30, 35, 50, 70, 85d., 1, 2r.

Space Flight of "Apollo 14". Postage 15, 25, 50, 60, 70d.; Air 5r.

Winter Olympic Games, 1924–1968. Postage 30, 40, 50, 75d., 1r.; Air 2r.

Signs of the Zodiac. 1, 2, 5, 10, 12, 15, 25, 30, 35, 45, 50, 60d.

Famous Men. Air 65, 70, 75, 80, 85, 90d., 1, 1r.25, 1r.50, 2, 2r.50, 3r.

Death Bicent of Beethoven. 20, 30, 40, 60d., 1r.50, 2r.

Dr. Albert Schweitzer Commem. 20, 30, 40, 60d., 1r.50, 2r.

Tropical Birds. Postage 1, 2, 3, 4, 5, 10d.; Air 2, 3r.

Paintings by French Artists. Postage 1, 2, 3, 4, 5, 10d.; Air 2, 3r.

Paintings by Modern Artists. Postage 1, 2, 3, 4, 5, 10d.; Air 2, 3r.

Paintings by Degas. Postage 1, 2, 3, 4, 5, 10d.; Air 2, 3r.

Paintings by Titian. Postage 1, 2, 3, 4, 5, 10d.; Air 2, 3r.

Paintings by Renoir. Postage 1, 2, 3, 4, 5, 10d.; Air 2, 3r.

Space Flight of "Apollo 15". Postage 25, 40, 50, 60d., 1r.; Air 6r.

"Philatokyo" Stamp Exhibition, Tokyo. Stamps. Postage 10, 15, 20, 30, 35, 50, 60, 80d.; Air 1, 2r.

Tropical Birds. Postage 1, 2, 3, 5, 7, 10, 12, 15, 20, 25, 30, 40d.; Air 50, 80d., 1, 3r.

Paintings depicting Venus. Postage 1, 2, 3, 4, 5, 10d.; Air 2, 3r.

13th World Scout Jamboree, Asagiri, Japan. Scouts. Postage 1, 2, 3, 5, 7, 10, 12, 15, 20, 25, 30, 35, 40, 50, 65, 80d.; Air 1, 1r.25, 1r.50, 2r.

Lions International Clubs. Optd on 1971 Famous Paintings issue. Air 25, 30, 35, 50, 70, 85d., 1, 2r.

13th World Scout Jamboree, Asagiri, Japan. Japanese Paintings. Postage 20, 30, 40, 60, 75d.; Air 3r.

25th Anniv of U.N.I.C.E.F. Optd on 1971 Scout Jamboree (paintings) issue. Postage 20, 30, 40, 60, 75d.; Air 3r.

Christmas 1971. (1st series. Plain frames). Portraits of Popes. Postage 1, 2, 3, 4, 5, 10d.; Air 2, 3r.

Modern Cars. Postage 10, 15, 25, 40, 50d.; Air 3r.

Olympic Games, Munich (1972). Show-jumping. Embossed on gold foil. Air 20r.

Exploration of Outer Space. Postage 15, 25, 50, 60, 70d.; Air 5r.

Royal Visit of Queen Elizabeth II to Japan. Postage 1, 2, 3, 4, 5, 10d.; Air 2, 3r.

Meeting of Pres. Nixon and Emperor Hirohito of Japan in Alaska. Design as 3r. value of 1970 Eisenhower issue but value changed and optd with commemorative inscr. Air 5r. (silver opt), 5r. (gold opt).

"Apollo" Astronants. Postage 5, 20, 35, 40, 50d.; Air 1, 2, 3r.

Discoverers of the Universe. Astronomers and Space Scientists. Postage 5, 10, 15, 20, 25, 30d.; Air 2, 5r.

"ANPHILEX 71" Stamp Exn, New York. Air 2r.50.

Christmas 1971. Portraits of Popes (2nd series. Ornamental frames). Postage 1, 2, 3, 4, 5, 10d.; Air 2, 3r.

Royal Silver Wedding of Queen Elizabeth II and Prince Philip (1972). Air 1, 2, 3r.

Space Flight of "Apollo 16". Postage 20, 30, 40, 50, 60d.; Air 3, 4r.

Fairy Tales. "Baron Munchhausen" Stories. Postage 1, 2, 4, 5, 10d.; Air 3r.

World Fair, Philadelphia (1976). Paintings. Postage 25, 50, 75d.; Air 5r.

Fairy Tales. Stories of the Brothers Grimm. Postage 1, 2, 4, 5, 10d.; Air 3r.

European Tour of Emperor Hirohito of Japan. Postage 1, 2, 4, 5, 10d.; Air 6r.

13th World Scout Jamboree, Asagiri, Japan. Postage 5, 10, 15, 20, 25d.; Air 5r.

Winter Olympic Games, Sapporo, Japan (1972). Postage 5, 10, 15, 20, 25d.; Air 5r.

Olympic Games, Munich (1972). Postage 5, 10, 15, 20, 25d.; Air 5r.

"Japanese Life". Postage 10d. × 4, 20d. × 4, 30d. × 4, 40d. × 4, 50d. × 4; Air 3r. × 4.

Space Flight of "Apollo 15". Postage 5, 10, 15, 20, 25, 50d.; Air 1, 2, 3, 5r.

"Soyuz 11" Disaster. Air 50d., 1r., 1r.50.

"The Future in Space". Postage 5, 10, 15, 20, 25, 50d.

2500th Anniv of Persian Empire. Postage 10, 20, 30, 40, 50d., Air 3r.

Cats. Postage 10, 15, 20, 25d.; Air 50d., 1r.

50th Anniv of Tutankhamun Tomb Discovery. Postage 1, 2, 3, 4, 5, 6, 7, 8, 9, 10, 11, 12, 13, 14, 15, 16d.; Air 1r. × 4.

400th Birth Anniv of Johannes Kepler (astronomer). Postage 50d.; Air 5r.

Famous Men. Air. 1r. × 5.

1972.

150th Death Anniv of Napoleon Bonaparte (1971). Postage 10, 20, 30, 40d.; Air 1, 2, 3, 4r.

1st Death Anniv of General de Gaulle. Postage 10, 20, 30, 40d.; Air 1, 2, 3, 4r.

Wild Animals (1st series). Postage 5, 10, 15, 20, 25, 30, 35, 40d.

Tropical Fishes. Postage 5, 10, 15, 20, 25d.; Air 50, 75d., 1r.

Famous Musicians. Postage 5d. × 3, 10d. × 3, 15d. × 3, 20d. × 3, 25d. × 3, 30d. × 3, 35d. × 3, 40d. × 3.

Easter. Postage 5, 10, 15, 20, 25d.; Air 5r.

Wild Animals (2nd series). Postage 5, 10, 15, 20, 25d.; Air 5r.

"Tour de France" Cycle Race. Postage 5, 10, 15, 20, 25, 30, 35, 40, 45, 50, 55d.; Air 60, 65, 70, 75, 80, 85, 90, 95d., 1r.

Many other issues were released between 1 September 1971 and 1 August 1972, but their authenticity has been denied by the Ajman Postmaster-General. Certain issues of 1967–69 exist overprinted to commemorate other events but the Postmaster General states that these are unofficial.

Ajman joined the United Arab Emirates on 1 August 1972 and the Ministry of Communications assumed responsibility for the postal services. Further stamps inscribed "Ajman" issued after that date were released without authority and had no validity.

ALAND ISLANDS Pt. 11

Aland is an autonomous province of Finland. From 1984 separate stamps were issued for the area although stamps of Finland could also still be used there. On 1 January 1993 Aland assumed control of its own postal service and Finnish stamps ceased to be valid there.

1984. 100 pennia = 1 markka.
2002. 100 cents = 1 euro.

1 Fishing Boat

2 "Pommern" (barque) and Car Ferries, Mariehamn West Harbour

1984.

1	1	10p. mauve	15	20
2		20p. green	20	20
3		50p. green	20	20
4	–	1m. green	35	35
5	1	1m.10 blue	35	40
6		1m.20 black	35	40
7		1m.30 green	40	50
8	–	1m.40 multicoloured	95	75
9a	–	1m.50 multicoloured	45	55
10	–	1m.90 multicoloured	55	70
12	–	3m. blue, green and black	75	85
14	–	10m. black, chestnut & brn	3·50	2·75
15	–	13m. multicoloured	3·25	3·75

DESIGNS—20 × 29 mm: 1m.50, Midsummer pole, Storby village. 21 × 31 mm: 13m. Rug, 1793. 26 × 32 mm: 3m. Map of Aland Islands. 30 × 20 mm: 1m. Farjsund Bridge. 31 × 21 mm: 1m.40, Aland flag; 1m.90, Mariehamn Town Hall. 32 × 26 mm: 10m. Seal of Aland showing St. Olaf (patron saint).

1984. 50th Anniv of Society of Shipowners.

16	2	2m. multicoloured	95	1·50

3 Grove of Ashes and Hazels

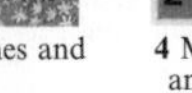
4 Map, Compass and Measuring Instrument

1985. Aland Scenes. Multicoloured.

17	2m. Type **3**	85	70
18	5m. Kokar Church and shore (horiz)	1·40	1·40
19	8m. Windmill and farm (horiz)	2·00	2·00

1986. Nordic Orienteering Championships, Aland.

20	4	1m.60 multicoloured	1·80	1·50

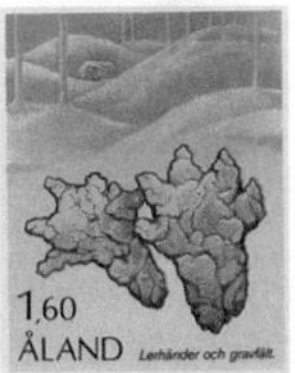

5 Clay Hands and Burial Mounds, Skamkulla

6 "Onnigeby" (drawing, Victor Westerholm)

1986. Archaeology. Multicoloured.

21	1m.60 Type **5**	95	75
22	2m.20 Bronze staff from Finby and Apostles	80	70
23	20m. Monument at ancient court site, Saltvik, and court in session (horiz)	4·25	5·50

1986. Centenary of Onnigeby Artists' Colony.

24	6	3m.70 multicoloured	1·60	1·60

7 Eiders

8 Firemen in Horse-drawn Cart

1987. Birds. Multicoloured.

25	1m.70 Type **7**	4·75	5·00
26	2m.30 Tufted ducks	2·40	2·20
27	12m. Velvet scoters	2·75	4·25

1987. Centenary of Mariehamn Fire Brigade.

28	8	7m. multicoloured	3·50	5·00

9 Meeting and Item 3 of Report

10 Loading Mail Barrels at Eckero

1987. 70th Anniv of Aland Municipalities Meeting, Finstrom.

29	9	1m.70 multicoloured	70	90

1988. 350th Anniv of Postal Service in Aland.

30	10	1m.80 multicoloured	1·20	1·50

11 Ploughing with Horses

12 Baltic Galleass "Albanus"

1988. Centenary of Agricultural Education in Aland.
31 **11** 2m.20 multicoloured . . . . 1·00 1·40

1988. Sailing Ships. Multicoloured.
32 1m.80 Type **12** . . . . 1·10 1·30
33 2m.40 Schooner "Ingrid" (horiz) . . . . 2·20 2·40
34 11m. Barque "Pamir" (horiz) 4·25 5·00

13 St. Olaf's Church, Jomala

14 Elder-flowered Orchid

1988.
35 **13** 1m.40 multicoloured . . . . 95 1·10

1989. Orchids. Multicoloured.
36 1m.50 Type **14** . . . . 1·40 1·40
37 2m.50 Narrow-leaved helleborine . . . . 1·40 1·60
38 14m. Lady's slipper . . . . . 6·50 7·00

15 Teacher and Pupils

16 St. Michael's Church, Finstrom

1989. 350th Anniv of First Aland School, Saltvik.
39 **15** 1m.90 multicoloured 70 90

1989.
40 **16** 1m.50 multicoloured 75 95

17 Baltic Herring

18 St. Andrew's Church, Lumparland

1990. Fishes. Multicoloured.
41 1m.50 Type **17** 60 75
42 2m. Northern pike 65 75
43 2m.70 European flounder . . 85 1·00

1990.
44 **18** 1m.70 multicoloured 65 70

19 "St. Catherine" (fresco, St. Anna's Church, Kumlinge)

20 West European Hedgehog

1990.
45 **19** 2m. multicoloured 70 75

1991. Mammals. Multicoloured.
46 1m.60 Type **20** 65 75
47 2m.10 Eurasian red squirrel . . 75 80
48 2m.90 Roe deer . . . . 85 1·10

21 Volleyball

MS49 2m.10; Type **21**; 2m.10; Shooting; 2m.10; Football; 2m.10, Running . . . . 3·50 3·00

22 Canoeing

23 "League of Nations Meeting, Geneva, 1921" (print by F. Rackwitz)

1991. Nordic Countries' Postal Co-operation. Tourism. Multicoloured.
50 2m.10 Type **22** 65 75
51 2m.90 Cycling . . . . 80 1·00

1991. 70th Anniv of Aland Autonomy.
52 **23** 16m. multicoloured . . . . 4·50 5·00

24 St. Mathias's Church, Vardo

25 Von Knorring (after Karl Jansson)

1991.
53 **24** 1m.80 multicoloured 60 75

1992. Birth Bicentenary of Rev. Frans Peter von Knorring (social reformer).
54 **25** 2 klass (1m.60) mult 85 80

26 Barque "Herzogen Cecilie" and Wheat Transport Route Map

27 Ranno Lighthouse

1992. 48th International Association of Cape Horners Congress, Mariehamn.
55 **26** 1 klass (2m.10) mult . . . . 95 1·10

1992. Lighthouses. Multicoloured.
56 2m.10 Type **27** . . . . 2·75 1·90
57 2m.10 Salskar . . . . 2·75 1·90
58 2m.10 Lagskar . . . . 2·75 1·90
59 2m.10 Market . . . . 2·75 1·90

28 "Lemland Landscape"

1992. Birth Cent of Joel Pettersson (painter). Mult.
60 2m.90 Type **28** 80 90
61 16m. "Self-portrait" . . . . . 4·25 5·00

29 Delegates processing to Church Service

30 St. Catherine's Church, Hammarland

1992. 70th Anniv of First Aland Provincial Parliament.
62 **29** 3m.40 multicoloured . . . . 1·00 1·20

1992.
63 **30** 1m.80 multicoloured 65 75

31 Arms

32 Fiddler

1993. Postal Autonomy. Multicoloured.
64 1m.60 Type **31** 50 60
MS65 129 × 80 mm. 1m.90 Cover with Kastelholm single-line postmark (26 × 35 mm); 1m.90 Mareinhamm Post Office; 1m.90 Post van leaving *Alfågeln* (ferry); 1m.90 Postal emblem (26 × 31 mm) . . . . 2·40 2·30

1993. Nordic Countries' Postal Co-operation. Tourism. Exhibits from Jan Karlsgarden Open-air Museum.
66 **32** 2m. red, pink and black . . 70 70
67 – 2m.30 blue, black and azure 75 80
DESIGN—HORIZ: 2m.30, Boat-house.

33 Saltvik Woman

34 Boulder Field, Dano Gamlan

1993. Costumes. Multicoloured.
68 1m.90 Type **33** 75 70
69 3m.50 Eckero and Brando women and Mariehamn couple . . . . 1·10 1·30
70 17m. Finstrom couple . . . . 5·00 5·25

1993. Aland Geology. Multicoloured.
71 10p. Type **34** 25 20
72 1m.60 Drumlin (hillock), Markusbole 55 60
73 2m. Diabase dyke, Sottunga 70 55
74 2m.30 Pitcher of Kallskar . . 75 65
75 2m.70 Pillow lava, Kumlinge 75 80
76 2m.90 Red Cow (islet), Lumpurn . . . . 90 1·00
77 3m.40 Erratic boulder, Torsskar, Kokar Osterbygge (horiz) . . . . 95 1·10
78 6m. Folded gneiss . . . . . 1·70 1·80
79 7m. Pothole, Bano Foglo (horiz) . . . . 2·30 2·30

35 Mary Magdalene Church, Sottunga

37 Glanville's Fritillary ("Melitaea cinxia")

1993.
80 **35** 1m.80 multicoloured 70 85

1994. Butterflies. Multicoloured.
81 2m.30 Type **37** 85 90
82 2m.30 "Quercusia querqus" . . 85 90
83 2m.30 Clouded apollo ("Parnassius mnemosyne") 85 90
84 2m.30 "Hesperia comma" . . 85 90

38 Genetic Diagram

39 Comb Ceramic and Pitted Ware Pottery

1994. Europa. Medical Discoveries. Multicoloured.
85 2m.30 Type **38** (discovery of Von Willebrand's disease (hereditary blood disorder)) 1·30 1·50
86 2m.90 Molecular diagram (purification of heparin by Erik Jorpes) . . . . 1·40 1·50

1994. The Stone Age.
87 **39** 2m.40 brown 80 90
88 – 2m.80 blue . . . . 90 1·10
89 – 18m. green . . . . 5·75 6·00
DESIGNS—VERT: 2m.80, Stone tools. HORIZ: 18m. Canoe and tent by river (reconstruction of Stone-age village, Langbergsoda).

40 St. John the Baptist's Church, Sund

42 "Skuta" (Cargo Sailing Boat)

1994.
90 **40** 2m. multicoloured . . . . . 1·00 1·00

1995. Cargo Sailing Ships. Multicoloured.
91 2m.30 Type **42** . . . . 95 1·10
92 2m.30 "Sump" (well-boat) . . 80 1·00
93 2m.30 "Storbat" (farm boat) 80 1·00
94 2m.30 "Jakt" . . . . 85 1·10

43 National Colours and E.U. Emblem

44 Doves and Cliffs

1995. Admission of Aland Islands to European Union.
95 **43** 2m.90 multicoloured . . . . 95 1·20

1995. Europa. Peace and Freedom. Multicoloured.
96 2m.80 Type **44** . . . . 95 1·20
97 2m.90 Dove, night sky and island . . . . 1·10 1·20

45 Golf

46 Racing Dinghies

1995. Nordic Countries' Postal Co-operation. Tourism. With service indicator. Multicoloured.
98 2 klass (2m.) Type **45** . . . . 90 1·00
99 1 klass (2m.30) Sport fishing 1·10 1·10

1995. Optimist World Dinghy Championships, Mariehamn.
100 **46** 3m.40 multicoloured . . . 1·20 1·30

47 St. George's Church, Geta

48 "St. Olaf" (Wooden Carving from Sund Church)

1995.
101 **47** 2m. multicoloured 80 85

1995. Birth Millenary of St. Olaf.
102 **48** 4m.30 multicoloured . . . 1·30 1·70

49 Fish holding Flag in Mouth ("Greetings from Aland")

50 Landing on Branch

1996. Greetings Stamps. With service indicator. Multicoloured.
103 1 klass Type **49** . . . . . . 1·00 95
104 1 klass Bird holding flower in beak ("Congratulations") 95 90

1996. Endangered Species. The Eagle Owl. Multicoloured.
105 2m.40 Type **50** 85 95
106 2m.40 Perched on branch . . 85 1·00
107 2m.40 Adult owl 85 95
108 2m.40 Juvenile owl . . . . . 85 1·00
Nos. 105/6 form a composite design.

51 Sally Salminen (novelist)

1996. Europa. Famous Women. Multicoloured.
109 2m.80 Type **51** . . . . . . 1·00 1·00
110 2m.90 Fanny Sundstrom (politician) . . . . 1·00 1·10

52 Choir **53** "Haircut"

1996. "Aland 96" Song and Music Festival, Mariehamn.
111 **52** 2m.40 multicoloured . . . 85 95

1996. 150th Birth Anniv of Karl Jansson (painter).
112 **53** 18m. multicoloured . . . . 5·75 6·25

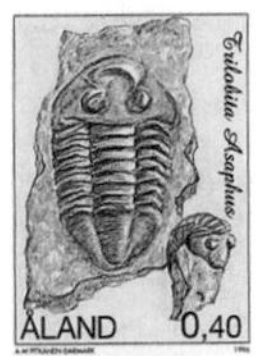

54 "Trilobita asaphus" **55** Brando Church

1996. Fossils. Multicoloured.
113 40p. Type **54** 25 25
114 9m. "Gastropoda euomophalus" . . . . . . 2·75 2·75

1996.
115 **55** 2m. multicoloured 85 85

56 Giant Isopod ("Saduria entomon") and Opossum Shrimp ("Mysis relicta") **57** Coltsfoot ("Tussilago farfara")

1997. Marine Survivors from the Ice Age. Multicoloured.
116 30p. Type **56** 25 25
117 2m.40 Four-horned sculpin ("Myotocephalus quadricornis") 75 80
118 4m.30 Ringed seal ("Phoca hispida botrica") . . . . . 1·40 1·50

1997. Spring Flowers. Multicoloured.
119 2m.40 Type **57** . . . . . . 90 1·00
120 2m.40 Blue anemone ("Hepatica nobilis") . . . 90 1·00
121 2m.40 Wood anemone ("Anemone nemorosa") . . 90 1·00
122 2m.40 Yellow anemone ("Anemone ranunculoides") . . . . . 90 1·00

58 Floorball **59** The Devil's Dance

1997. 1st Women's Floorball World Championship, Mariehamn and Godby.
123 **58** 3m.40 multicoloured . . . 1·00 1·10

1997. Europa. Tales and Legends.
124 **59** 2m.90 multicoloured . . . 1·00 1·10

60 Kastelholm Castle and Arms

1997. 600th Anniv of Kalmar Union between Sweden, Denmark and Norway.
125 **60** 2m.40 multicoloured . . . 95 1·10

61 Hologram of Schooner "Linden" and "75 Years"

MS126 **61** 20m. multicoloured . . 6·00 6·25

62 "Thornbury" (freighter) **63** St George's Church, Mariehamn

1997. Steam Freighters. Multicoloured.
127 2m.80 Type **62** . . . . . . 1·00 1·00
128 3m.50 "Osmo" (freighter) . . 1·30 1·30

1997. 70th Anniv of Mariehamn Church.
129 **63** 1m.90 multicoloured . . . 80 90

64 Man harvesting Apples

1998. Horticulture. Multicoloured.
130 2m. Type **64** 80 85
131 2m.40 Woman harvesting cucumbers 75 75

65 Boy on Moped **66** Midsummer Celebrations

1998. Youth Activities. Multicoloured.
132 2m.40 Type **65** 85 95
133 2m.40 Laptop computer . . . 85 1·00
134 2m.40 CD disk and headphones . . . . 85 1·00
135 2m.40 Step aerobics . . . . 85 1·00

1998. Europa. National Festivals.
136 **66** 4m.20 multicoloured . . . 1·30 1·50

67 "Isabella" (car ferry)

1998. Nordic Countries' Postal Co-operation. Shipping.
137 **67** 2m.40 multicoloured . . . 90 95

68 Waves breaking

1998. International Year of the Ocean.
138 **68** 6m.30 multicoloured . . . 1·70 2·00

69 Players

1998. Association of Tennis Professionals Senior Tour, Mariehamn. Self-adhesive.
139 **69** 2m.40 multicoloured . . . 85 90

70 Schooner, Compass Rose and Knots

1998. Ninth International Sea Scout Camp, Bomarsund Fortress, Aland.
140 **70** 2m.80 multicoloured . . . 1·00 1·10

71 Seffers Homestead, Onningeby **72** Eckero Church

1998. Traditional Porches. Multicoloured.
141 1m.60 Type **71** 70 70
142 2m. Labbas homestead, Storby 75 80
143 2m.90 Abras homestead, Bjorko . . . . 90 1·00

1998.
144 **72** 1m.90 multicoloured . . . 75 80

73 Sword and Dagger

1999. Bronze Age Relics. Multicoloured.
145 2m. Type **73** 70 75
146 2m.20 "Ship" tumulus (vert) 70 85

74 Wardrobe

1999. Folk Art. Decorated Furniture. Mult.
147 2m.40 Type **74** . . . . . . 1·10 1·00
148 2m.40 Distaff . . . . 1·00 90
149 2m.40 Chest . . . . 1·00 90
150 2m.40 Spinning wheel . . . . 1·00 90

75 "'Pamir' and 'Passat' (barques) off Port Victoria" (R. Castor) **76** Cowslip

1999. 50th Anniv of Rounding of Cape Horn by "Pamir" on Last Wheat-carrying Voyage.
151 **75** 3m.40 multicoloured . . . 1·20 1·10

1999. Provincial Plant of Aland. Self-adhesive.
152 **76** 2m.40 multicoloured . . . 80 80

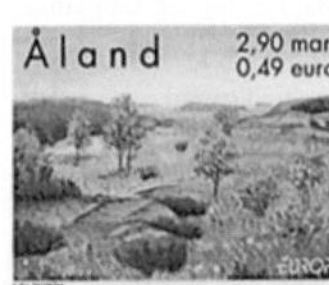

77 Ido Island, Kokar

1999. Europa. Parks and Gardens.
153 **77** 2m.90 multicoloured . . . 95 1·00
No. 153 is denominated both in markkas and in euros.

78 Racing Yachts **79** Puffed Shield Lichen ("Hypogymnia physodes")

1999. Sailing
154 **78** 2m.70 multicoloured . . . 85 1·00

1999. Lichens. With service indicator. Mult.
155 2 klass (2m.) Type **79** . . . 85 90
156 1 klass (2m.40) Common orange lichen ("Xanthoria parietina") . . . . 90 1·00

80 Loading Mail Plane **81** St. Bridget's Church, Lemland

1999. 125th Anniv of Universal Postal Union
157 **80** 2m.90 multicoloured . . . 80 95

1999.
158 **81** 1m.90 multicoloured . . . 70 75

82 Runners **83** Arctic Tern (*Sterna paradisaea*)

1999. Finnish Cross-country Championships, Mariehamn.
159 **82** 3m.50 multicoloured . . . 1·10 1·10

DENOMINATION. From No. 162 Aland Islands stamps are denominated both in markkas and in euros. As no cash for the latter is in circulation, the catalogue continues to use the markka value.

2000. Sea Birds. Multicoloured.
162 1m.80 Type **83** 60 60
164 2m.20 Mew gull (*Larus canus*) (vert) 80 75
166 2m.60 Great black-backed gull (*Larus marinus*) . . . 85 85

84 International Peace Symbol and State Flag

MS171 **84** 3m.40, yellow; 3m.40, red; 3m.40, blue; 3m.40, white . . . 3·50 3·50

85 Elk **86** "Building Europe"

2000. The Elk (*Alces alces*). Multicoloured.
172 2m.60 Type **85** 95 85
173 2m.60 With young 90 85
174 2m.60 Beside lake 95 85
175 2m.60 In snow 90 85

2000. Europa.
176 **86** 3m. multicoloured 95 95

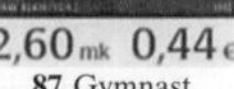

87 Gymnast **88** Crew and *Linden* (schooner)

2000. Finno-Swedish Gymnastics Association Exhibition, Mariehamn. Self-adhesive.
177 **87** 2m.60 multicoloured . . . 80 80

2000. Visit by *Cutty Sark* Tall Ships' Race Competitors to Mariehamn.
178 **88** 3m.40 multicoloured . . . 1·00 1·00

89 Lange on prow of Longship

2000. Death Millenary of Hlodver Lange the Viking.
179 **89** 4m.50 multicoloured . . . 1·50 1·50

90 Wooden Ornamented Swiss-style House, Mariehamn

2000. 48th Death Anniv of Hilda Hongell (architect). Multicoloured.
180 3m.80 Type **90** . . . . . . 1·00 1·10
181 10m. House with central front entrance, Mariehamn 2·75 2·75

91 The Nativity

2000. 2000 Years of Christianity.
182 **91** 3m. multicoloured 80 85

92 Kokar Church **93** Steller's Eider in Flight

2000.
183 **92** 2m. multicoloured 65 70

2001. Endangered Species. The Steller's Eider (*Polysticta stelleri*). Multicoloured.
184 2m.70 Type **93** 80 90
185 2m.70 Duck and drake . . . 80 90
186 2m.70 Duck and drake swimming 80 90
187 2m.70 Drake swimming . . . 50 50

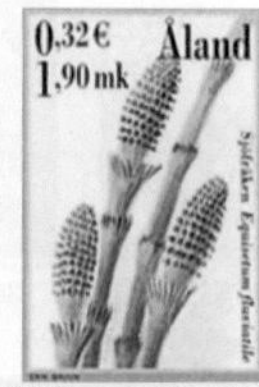

94 Swamp Horsetail (*Equisetum fluviatile*)

2001. Plants. Multicoloured.
188 1m.90 Type **94** 65 65
189 2m.80 Stiff clubmoss (*Lycopodium annotinum*) . . 65 70
190 3m.50 Polypody (*Polybodium vulgare*) . . . . 1·00 1·00

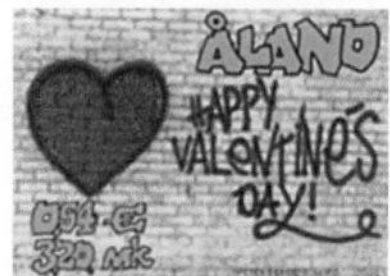

95 Heart and Graffiti on Brick Wall

2001. St. Valentine's Day.
200 **95** 3m.20 multicoloured . . . 80 85

96 Fisherman and Fish

2001. Europa. Water Resources.
201 **96** 3m.20 multicoloured . . . 85 90

97 Archipelago Windmill **98** Golden Retriever

2001. Windmills. Multicoloured.
202 3m. Type **97** 80 85
203 7m. Timbered windmill (horiz) . . . . 1·80 1·90
204 20m. Nest windmill (horiz) 5·00 5·75

2001. Puppies. Multicoloured.
205 2 klass (2m.30) Type **98** . . 75 75
206 1 klass (2m.70) Wire-haired dachshund 90 85

99 Foglo Church **100** Smooth Snake (*Coronella Austriaca*)

2001.
207 **99** 2m. multicoloured 60 55

New Currency: 100 cents = 1 euro

2002. Endangered Animals. Multicoloured.
208 5c. Type **100** 15 15
209 70c. Great crested newt (*Triturus cristatus*) . . . . 1·00 1·10

101 Woman pushing Shopping Trolley

2002. Euro Currency.
210 **101** 60c. multicoloured 90 95

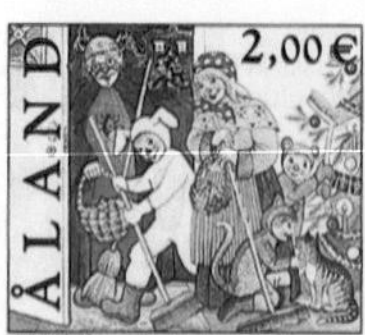

102 Tidying up Christmas

2002. St. Canute's Day.
211 **102** €2 multicoloured . . . . 3·00 3·25

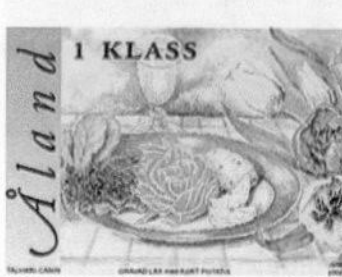

103 Spiced Salmon and New Potatoes

2002. Traditional Dishes. Multicoloured.
212 1 klass (55c.) Type **103** . . . 90 90
213 1 klass (55c.) Fried herring, mashed potatoes and beetroot 90 90
212 1 klass (55c.) Black bread and butter . . . . 90 1·20
212 1 klass (55c.) Aland pancake with stewed prune sauce and whipped cream 90 90

104 Building

2002. Inauguration of New Post Terminal, Sviby.
216 **104** €1 multicoloured . . . . 1·50 1·30

105 Circus Elephant and Rider

2002. Europa. Circus.
217 **105** 40c. multicoloured 65 80

106 "Radar II" (sculpture, Stefan Lindfors)

2002. Nordic Countries' Postal Co-operation. Modern Art.
218 **106** €3 multicoloured . . . . 4·25 3·75

107 Kayaking **108** 8th-century Buckle, Persby, Sud

2002.
219 **107** 90c. multicoloured . . . . 1·20 2·50

2002. Iron Age Jewellery found on Aland. Multicoloured.
220 2 klass. (45c.) Type **108** . . . 65 1·00
221 1 klass. (55c.) 8th-century pin, Sylloda, Saltvik . . . 90 90

109 Saltvik Church **110** Holmen

2002.
222 **109** 35c. multicoloured 65 60

2002. Janne Holmen (Olympic gold medallist, men's marathon).
223 **110** 1 klass. (55c.) multicoloured 95 90

111 *Cantharellus cibarius* **112** Tovis (kitten)

2003. Fungi. Multicoloured.
224 10c. Type **111** 15 15
225 50c. *Boletus edulis* 70 70
226 €2.50 *Macrolepiota procera* 3·50 3·50

2003. Cat Photograph Competition Winners. Multicoloured.
227 2 klass (45c.) Type **112** . . . 60 60
228 1 klass (55c.) Randi (cat) (horiz) 75 75

113 "Landscape in Summer" (detail) (Elin Danielson-Gambogi) **114** "Freedom of Speech and Press" (Kurt Simons)

2003. Designs showing details of the painting. Multicoloured.
229 1 klass (55c.) Type **113** . . . 75 75
230 1 klass (55c.) Trees and flowers 75 75
231 1 klass (55c.) Sunset over sea 75 75
232 1 klass (55c.) Shoreline and boats 75 75

2003. Europa. Poster Art.
233 **114** 45c. multicoloured 60 60

115 "Pommern" (Arthur Victor Gregory)

2003. Centenary of *Pommern* (four mast steel barque, now museum). Self-adhesive.
234 **115** 55c. multicoloured 75 75

116 Two Boys

2003. "My Aland". Mark Levengood.
235 **116** 55c. multicoloured 75 75

117 Fiddle Player **118** Kumlinge Church

2003. 50th Anniv of Aland Folk Music Association.
236 **117** €1.10 multicoloured . . 1·50 1·50

2003.
237 **118** 40c. multicoloured 55 55

119 Children dressed as St. Lucia and her Attendants

2003. St. Lucia Celebrations.
238 **119** 60c. multicoloured 80 80

120 Ermine (*Mustela erminea*) 121 Fenja and Menja (giantesses)

2004. Predators. Multicoloured.
239 20c. Type **120** 25 25
240 60c. Fox (*Vulpes vulpes*) 80 80
241 €3 Pine martin (*Martes martes*) 4·00 4·00

2004. Nordic Mythology. Sheet 105 × 70 mm.
MS250 **121** 55c. multicoloured 75 75
Stamps of a similar theme were issued by Denmark, Faroe Islands, Finland, Greenland, Iceland, Norway and Sweden.

122 Flag

2004. 50th Anniv of Aland Flag. Self-adhesive.
251 **122** 1klass (60c.) multicoloured 75 75

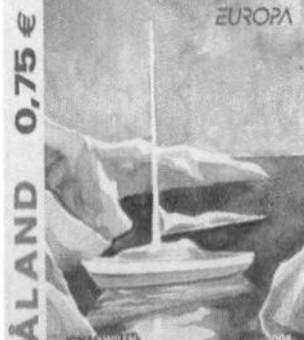

123 *Cajsa* (longboat) and Passengers, 1986 124 Yacht moored in Inlet

2004. "My Aland". Mauno Koivisto (Finnish president 1982–94).
252 **123** 90c. multicoloured 1·20 1·20

2004. Europa. Holidays
253 **124** 75c. multicoloured 1·00 1·00

ALAOUITES Pt. 19

A coastal district of Syria, placed under French mandate in 1920. Became the Republic of Latakia in 1930. Incorporated with Syria in 1937.

100 centimes = 1 piastre.

1925. Stamps of France surch **ALAOUITES** and value in French and Arabic.
1 **11** 0p.10 on 2c. purple 1·75 4·25
2 **18** 0p.25 on 5c. orange 2·25 3·50
3 **15** 0p.75 on 15c. green 3·00 4·50
4 **18** 1p. on 20c. brown 2·25 3·50
5 1p.25 on 25c. blue 2·25 2·50
6 1p.50 on 30c. red 9·00 11·00
7 2p. on 35c. violet 80 4·00
8 **13** 2p. on 40c. red and blue 3·50 5·25
9 2p. on 45c. green and blue 8·00 12·00
10 3p. on 60c. violet and blue 2·50 6·75
11 **15** 3p. on 60c. violet 10·50 11·00
12 4p. on 85c. red 1·60 3·25
13 **13** 5p. on 1f. red and yellow 4·00 8·75
14 10p. on 2f. orange & grn 4·50 10·00
15 25p. on 5f. blue and buff 8·50 8·00

1925. "Pasteur" issue of France surch **ALAOUITES** and value in French and Arabic.
16 **30** 0p.50 on 10c. green 1·75 3·50
17 0p.75 on 15c. green 1·50 3·50
18 1p.50 on 30c. red 1·25 4·00
19 2p. on 45c. red 2·25 4·25
20 2p.50 on 50c. blue 3·00 4·50
21 4p. on 75c. blue 2·25 5·50

1925. Air. Stamps of France optd **ALAOUITES Avion** and value in French and Arabic.
22 **13** 2p. on 40c. red and blue 6·25 11·00
23 3p. on 60c. violet and blue 7·25 18·00
24 5p. on 1f. red and yellow 6·25 10·50
25 10p. on 2f. orange & green 6·00 10·00

1925. Pictorial stamps of Syria (1925) optd **ALAOUITES** in French and Arabic.
26 0p.10 violet 45 3·00
27 0p.25 black 70 3·00
28 0p.50 green 75 1·75
29 0p.75 red 95 3·00
30 1p. purple 95 2·25
31 1p.25 green 1·75 2·25
32 1p.50 pink 95 2·25
33 2p. brown 1·75 3·75
34 2p.50 blue 1·75 3·75
35 3p. brown 95 2·50
36 5p. violet 1·75 2·75
37 10p. purple 1·90 3·00
38 25p. blue 2·50 6·75

1925. Air. Nos. 33 and 35/37 optd **AVION** in French and Arabic.
40 2p. brown 1·10 4·00
41 3p. brown 1·00 3·75
42 5p. violet 1·10 4·00
43 10p. purple 1·10 4·00

1926. Air. Air stamps of Syria with airplane overprint optd **ALAOUITES** in French and Arabic.
44 2p. brown 2·00 5·25
45 3p. brown 2·00 5·25
46 5p. violet 2·00 5·25
47 10p. purple 2·00 5·25
See also Nos. 59/60 and 63.

1926. Pictorial stamps of 1925 surcharged.
53 05 on 0p.10 violet 25 3·00
54 2p. on 1p.25 green 8·00 7·00
48 3p.50 on 0p.75 red 1·00 2·25
49 4p. on 0p.25 black 85 2·25
56 4p.50 on 0p.75 red 2·50 3·75
50 6p. on 2p.50 blue 1·25 2·25
57 7p.50 on 2p.50 blue 2·50 1·90
51 12p. on 1p.25 green 2·75 3·25
58 15p. on 25p. blue 7·25 6·25
52 20p. on 1p.25 green 2·75 4·25

1929. Air. (a) Pictorial stamps of Syria optd with airplane and **ALAOUITES** in French and Arabic.
59 0p.50 green 2·00 4·25
60 1p. purple 4·50 9·00
61 25p. blue 22·00 30·00

(b) Nos. 54 and 58 of Alaouites optd with airplane.
62 2p. on 1p.25 green 2·75 5·00
63 15p. on 25p. blue 19·00 25·00

POSTAGE DUE STAMPS

1925. Postage Due stamps of France surch **ALAOUITES** and value in French and Arabic.
D26 D **11** 0p.50 on 10c. brown 2·10 4·75
D27 1p. on 20c. green 2·10 5·00
D28 2p. on 30c. red 2·10 5·00
D29 3p. on 50c. purple 2·10 5·25
D30 5p. on 1f. pur on yell 2·10 5·00

1925. Postage Due stamps of Syria (Nos. D192/6) optd **ALAOUITES** in French and Arabic.
D44 0p.50 brown on yellow 75 3·25
D45 1p. red on red 75 3·50
D46 2p. black on blue 1·25 4·00
D47 3p. brown on red 1·25 4·75
D48 5p. black on green 2·40 5·00

For later issues see **LATAKIA**.

ALBANIA Pt. 3

Albania, formerly part of the Turkish Empire, was declared independent on 28 November 1912, and this was recognized by Turkey in the treaty of 30 May 1913. After chaotic conditions during and after the First World War a republic was established in 1925. Three years later the country became a kingdom. From 7 April 1939 until December 1944, Albania was occupied, firstly by the Italians and then by the Germans. Following liberation a republic was set up in 1946.

1913. 40 paras = 1 piastre or grosch.
1913. 100 qint = 1 franc.
1947. 100 qint = 1 lek.

1913. Various types of Turkey optd with double-headed eagle and **SHQIPENIA**.
3 **28** 2pa. green (No. 271) £225 £200
4 5pa. brown (No. 261) £225 £200
2 **25** 10pa. green (No. 252) £350 £300
5 **28** 10pa. green (No. 262) £190 £130
12 10pa. green (No. 289) £375 £375
11 10pa. on 20pa. red £600 £600
6 20pa. red (No. 263) £180 £110
13 20pa. red (No. 290) £400 £350
7 1pi. blue (No. 264) £130 £120
14a 1pi. blue (No. 291) £900 £900
15 1pi. blk on red (No. D288) £1500 £1500
8 2pi. black (No. 265) £250 £200
14b 2pi. black (No. 292)
1 **25** 2½pi. brown (No. 239) £450 £350
9 **28** 5pi. purple (No. 267) £700 £600
10 10pi. red (No. 268) £2500 £2500

2

1913.
16 **2** 10pa. violet 8·00 6·00
17 20pa. red and grey 10·00 8·00
18 1g. grey 10·00 10·00
19 2g. blue and violet 12·00 9·50
20 5g. violet and blue 15·00 12·00
21 10g. blue and violet 15·00 12·00

3 4 Skanderbeg (after Heinz Kautsch)

1913. Independence Anniv.
22 **3** 10pa. black and green 2·75 1·75
23 20pa. black and red 3·00 2·75
24 30pa. black and violet 3·50 2·75
25 1g. black and blue 5·00 3·50
26 2g. black 8·00 6·00

1913.
27 **4** 2q. brown and yellow 1·00 1·00
28 5q. green and yellow 1·00 1·00
29 10q. red 1·10 1·10
30 25q. blue 1·25 1·25
31 50q. mauve and red 5·00 4·00
32 1f. brown 8·00 8·00

1914. Arrival of Prince William of Wied. Optd **7 Mars 1461 RROFTE MBRETI 1914**.
33 **4** 2q. brown and yellow 22·00 18·00
34 5q. green and yellow 22·00 18·00
35 10q. red and rose 22·00 18·00
36 25q. blue 22·00 18·00
37 50q. mauve and rose 22·00 18·00
38 1f. brown 22·00 18·00

1914. Surch.
40 **4** 5pa. on 2q. brown & yellow 1·75 1·75
41 10pa. on 5q. green & yellow 1·75 1·75
42 20pa. on 10q. red 2·25 1·75
43 1g. on 25q. blue 2·75 2·50
44 2g. on 50q. mauve and red 3·50 3·50
45 5g. on 1f. brown 15·00 10·00

1914. Valona Provisional Issue. Optd **POSTE D'ALBANIE** and Turkish inscr in circle with star in centre.
45a **4** 2q. brown and yellow £150 £150
45b 5q. green and yellow
45c 10q. red and rose 8·50 8·50
45d 25q. blue 8·50 8·50
45e 50q. mauve and red 8·50 8·50
45f 1f. brown £475
45g 5pa. on 2q. brown & yellow 25·00 25·00
45h 10pa. on 5q. green & yellow 50·00 50·00
45i 20pa. on 10q. red and rose 13·00 13·00
45j 1gr. on 25q. blue 7·50 7·50
45k 2gr. on 50q. mauve and red 13·00 13·00
45l 5gr. on 1f. brown 18·00 18·00

11 12

1917. Inscribed "SHQIPERIE KORCE VETQEVERITARE" or "REPUBLIKA KORCE SHQIPETARE" or "QARKU-POSTES-I-KORCES".
75 **11** 1c. brown and green 2·00 4·00
76 2c. brown and green 2·00 4·00
77 3c. grey and green 2·00 4·00
78 5c. green and black 2·75 2·50
79 10c. red and black 2·75 2·50
72 25c. blue and black 9·00 6·25
80 50c. purple and black 5·00 4·50
81 1f. brown and black 16·00 15·00

1918. No. 78 surch **QARKUI KORCES 25 CTS**.
81a 25c. on 5c. green and black 60·00 48·00

1919. Fiscal stamps used by the Austrians in Albania. Handstamped with control.
83 **12** (2)q. on 2h. brown 5·50 5·50
84 05q. on 16h. green 5·50 5·50
85 10q. on 8h. red 5·50 5·50
86 25q. on 64h. blue 5·50 5·50
87a 50q. on 32h. violet 5·50 5·50
88 1f. on 1.28k. brown on blue 8·00 8·00
Three sets may be made of this issue according to whether the handstamped control is a date, a curved comet or a comet with straight tail.

1919. No. 43 optd **SHKODER 1919**.
103 **4** 1g. on 25q. blue 8·00 8·00

1919. Fiscal stamps surch **POSTAT SHQIPTARE** and new value.
104 **12** 10q. on 2h. brown 4·50 4·50
111 10q. on 8h. red 4·50 4·50
112 15q. on 8h. red 4·50 4·50
113 20q. on 16h. green 4·50 4·50
113b 25q. on 32h. violet 4·50 4·50
107 25q. on 64h. blue 4·50 4·50
108 50q. on 32h. violet 4·50 4·50
113c 50q. on 64h. blue 10·00 10·00
113d 1f. on 96h. orange 6·00 6·00
113e 2f. on 160h. violet 8·50 8·50

17 Prince William I 19 Skanderbeg

1920. Optd with double-headed eagle and **SHKORDA** or surch also.
114 **17** 1q. grey 21·00 40·00
115 2q. on 10q. red 3·50 6·25
116 5q. on 10q. red 3·50 6·25
117 10q. red 3·25 6·25
118 20q. brown 12·00 22·00
119 25q. blue £140 £275
120 25q. on 10q. red 3·50 7·00
121 50q. violet 17·00 32·00
122 50q. on 10q. red 3·50 7·00

1920. Optd with posthorn.
123 **19** 2q. orange 5·00 6·25
124 5q. green 6·75 11·00
125 10q. red 13·50 22·00
126 25q. blue 26·00 22·00
127 50q. green 5·00 7·50
128 1f. mauve 5·00 7·50
Stamps as Type **19** also exist optd **BESA** meaning "Loyalty".

1922. No. 123 surch with value in frame.
143 **19** 1q. on 2q. orange 3·50 2·00

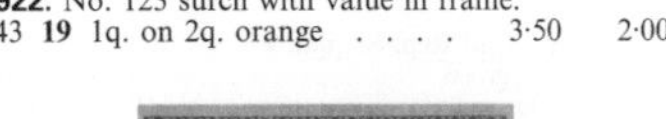

24

1922. Views.
144 **24** 2q. orange (Gjinokaster) 80 1·75
145 5q. green (Kanina) 50 75
146 10q. red (Berat) 50 75
147 25q. blue (Veziri Bridge) 50 75
148 50q. green (Rozafat Fortress, Shkoder) 60 75
149 1f. lilac (Korce) 1·10 1·25
150 2f. green (Durres) 2·75 4·00

1924. Opening of National Assembly. Optd **TIRANE KALLNUER 1924** in frame with **Mbledhje Kushtetuese** above.
151 **24** 2q. orange 4·75 8·00
152 5q. green 4·75 8·00
153 10q. red 4·75 8·00
154 25q. blue 4·75 8·00
155 50q. green 4·75 8·00

1924. No. 144 surch with value and bars.
156 **24** 1 on 2q. orange 2·50 3·75

1924. Red Cross. (a) Surch with small red cross and premium.
157 **24** 5q.+5q. green 7·50 7·50
158 10q.+5q. red 7·50 7·50
159 25q.+5q. blue 7·50 7·50
160 50q.+5q. green 7·50 7·50

(b) Nos. 157/60 with further surch of large red cross and premium.
161 **24** 5q.+5q.+5q. green 7·50 7·50
162 10q.+5q.+5q. red 7·50 7·50
163 25q.+5q.+5q. blue 7·50 7·50
164 50q.+5q.+5q. green 7·50 7·50

1925. Return of Government to Capital in 1924. Optd **Triumf' i legalitetit 24 Dhetuer 1924**.
164a **24** 1 on 2q. orange (No. 156) 2·50 3·25
165 2q. orange 2·50 3·25
166 5q. green 2·50 3·25
167 10q. red 2·50 3·25
168 25q. blue 2·50 3·25
169 50q. green 2·50 3·25
170 1f. lilac 2·50 3·25

1925. Proclamation of Republic. Optd **Republika Shqiptare 21 Kallnduer 1925**.
171 **24** 1 on 2q. orange (No. 156) 2·50 3·25
172 2q. orange 2·50 3·25
173 5q. green 2·50 3·25
174 10q. red 2·50 3·25
175 25q. blue 2·50 3·25
176 50q. green 2·50 3·25
177 1f. lilac 2·50 3·25

1925. Optd **Republika Shqiptare**.
178 **24** 1 on 2q. orange (No. 156) 65 85
179 2q. orange 65 85
180 5q. green 65 85
181 10q. red 65 85
182 25q. blue 65 85
183 50q. green 65 85
184 1f. lilac 2·75 3·75
185 2f. green 2·75 3·75

32

1925. Air.
186 32 5q. green . . . . 3·25 3·25
187 10q. red . . . . 3·50 3·50
188 25q. blue . . . . 3·50 3·50
189 50q. green . . . . 5·00 5·00
190 1f. black and violet . . . . 8·25 8·25
191 2f. violet and olive . . . . 11·00 11·00
192 3f. green and brown . . . 19·00 19·00

33 Pres. Ahmed Zogu, later King Zog I
34

1925.
193 33 1q. yellow 15 10
194 2q. brown 15 10
195 5q. green 15 10
196 10q. red 15 10
197 15q. brown 75 75
198 25q. blue 15 10
199 50q. green 75 75
200 34 1f. blue and red . . . . . 1·25 1·25
201 2f. orange and green . . . 1·75 1·25
202 3f. violet . . . . 3·50 3·00
203 5f. black and violet . . . . 4·25 4·75

1927. Air. Optd **Rep. Shqiptare**.
204 32 5q. green . . . . 10·00 10·00
205 10q. red . . . . 10·00 10·00
206 25q. blue . . . . 8·50 8·50
207 50q. green . . . . 8·00 8·00
208 1f. black and violet . . . . 8·00 8·00
209 2f. violet and olive . . . . 9·75 9·75
210 3f. green and brown . . . 17·00 17·00

1927. Optd **A.Z.** and wreath.
211 33 1q. yellow 50 65
212 2q. brown 20 25
213 5q. green . . . . 1·10 35
214 10q. red 20 20
215 15q. brown . . . . 6·00 7·00
216 25q. blue 50 25
217 50q. green 50 25
218 34 1f. blue and red 50 25
219 2f. orange and green . . . 75 50
220 3f. violet and brown . . . 1·10 1·00
221 5f. black and violet . . . . 1·75 2·00

1928. Inauguration of Vlore (Valona)-Brindisi Air Service. Optd **REP. SHQYPTARE Fluturim' i I-ar Vlone-Brindisi 21.IV.1928.**
222 32 5q. green . . . . 9·25 11·50
223 10q. red . . . . 9·25 11·50
224 25q. blue . . . . 9·25 9·50
225 50q. green . . . . 10·50 14·50
226 1f. black and violet . . . . 95·00 £110
227 2f. violet and olive £100 £110
228 3f. green and brown . . . £100 £120

1928. Surch in figures and bars.
229 33 1 on 10q. red (No. 214) . . 50 40
230 5 on 25q. blue (No. 216) 50 40

39 Pres. Ahmed Zogu, later King Zog I
40

1928. National Assembly. Optd **Kujtim i Mbledhjes Kushtetuese 25.8.28.**
231 39 1q. brown . . . . 3·50 4·25
232 2q. grey . . . . 3·50 4·25
233 5q. green . . . . 3·50 4·25
234 10q. red . . . . 3·50 4·25
235 15q. brown . . . . 9·00 14·00
236 25q. blue . . . . 4·25 3·75
237 50q. lilac . . . . 6·75 5·00
238 40 1f. black and blue . . . . 4·25 3·75

1928. Accession of King Zog I. Optd **Mbretnia-Shqiptare Zog I 1.IX.1928.**
239 39 1q. brown . . . . 8·50 13·00
240 2q. grey . . . . 8·50 13·00
241 5q. green . . . . 6·50 11·00
242 10q. red . . . . 6·00 6·25
243 15q. brown . . . . 6·00 7·50
244 25q. blue . . . . 6·00 7·50
245 50q. lilac . . . . 6·75 8·75
246 40 1f. black and blue . . . . 8·25 11·00
247 2f. black and green . . . . 8·25 11·00

1928. Optd **Mbretnia-Shqiptare** only.
248 39 1q. brown 50 50
249 2q. grey 45 35
250 5q. green . . . . 2·50 50
251 10q. red 50 35
252 15q. brown . . . . 10·00 12·00
253 25q. blue 50 35
254 50q. lilac 75 35
255 40 1f. black and blue . . . . 1·50 1·90
256 2f. black and green . . . . 1·50 2·10
257 3f. olive and red . . . . . 4·00 2·75
258 5f. black and violet . . . . 5·25 7·50

1929. Surch **Mbr. Shqiptare** and new value.
259 33 1 on 50q. green 25 40
260 5 on 25q. blue 30 40
261 15 on 10q. red 50 70

1929. King Zog's 35th Birthday. Optd **RROFT-MBRETI 8.X.1929.**
262 33 1q. yellow . . . . 4·50 6·75
263 2q. brown . . . . 4·50 6·75
264 5q. green . . . . 4·50 6·75
265 10q. red . . . . 4·50 6·75
266 25q. blue . . . . 4·50 6·75
267 50q. green . . . . 5·00 8·00
268 34 1f. blue and red . . . . . 8·00 12·00
269 2f. orange and green . . . 8·50 12·50

1929. Air. Optd **Mbr. Shqiptare**.
270 32 5q. green . . . . 8·00 12·00
271 10q. red . . . . 8·00 12·00
272 25q. blue . . . . 15·00 12·50
273 50q. green . . . . 45·00 60·00
274 1f. black and violet £250 £325
275 2f. violet and olive £275 £350
276 3f. green and brown . . . £500 £550

49 Lake Butrinto
50 King Zog I

1930. 2nd Anniv of Accession of King Zog I.
277 49 1q. grey 15 20
278 2q. red 15 20
279 50 5q. green 15 15
280 10q. red 25 30
281 15q. brown 25 30
282 25q. blue 20 30
283 49 50q. green 40 45
284 – 1f. violet 85 60
285 – 2f. blue . . . . 1·00 60
286 – 3f. green . . . . 2·50 95
287 – 5f. brown . . . . 3·25 2·50
DESIGNS—VERT: 1, 2f. Ahmed Zog Bridge, River Mati. HORIZ: 3, 5f. Ruins of Zogu Castle.

53 Junkers F-13 (over Tirana)

1930. Air. T **53** and similar view.
288 53 5q. green . . . . 2·10 2·10
289 15q. red . . . . 2·10 2·10
290 20q. blue . . . . 2·10 2·10
291 50q. olive . . . . 3·75 3·75
292 – 1f. blue . . . . 6·25 6·25
293 – 2f. brown . . . . 21·00 21·00
294 – 3f. violet . . . . 24·00 24·00

1931. Air. Optd **TIRANE-ROME 6 KORRIK 1931.**
295 53 5q. green . . . . 9·00 9·00
296 15q. red . . . . 9·00 9·00
297 20q. blue . . . . 9·00 9·00
298 50q. olive . . . . 9·00 9·00
299 – 1f. blue . . . . 50·00 50·00
300 – 2f. brown . . . . 50·00 50·00
301 – 3f. violet . . . . 50·00 50·00

1934. 10th Anniv of Revolution. Optd **1924-24 Dhetuer-1934.**
302 49 1q. grey . . . . 2·00 3·50
303 2q. orange . . . . 2·00 3·50
304 50 5q. green . . . . 2·00 3·50
305 10q. red . . . . 2·00 3·50
306 15q. brown . . . . 2·00 3·50
307 25q. blue . . . . 3·00 3·75
308 49 50q. turquoise . . . . . . 3·00 3·75
309 – 1f. violet (No. 284) . . . . 4·00 7·50
310 – 2f. blue (No. 285) . . . . 8·00 13·00
311 – 3f. green (No. 286) . . . 14·00 18·00

56 Horse and Flag of Skanderbeg
57 Albania in Chains

1937. 25th Anniv of Independence.
312 56 1q. violet 15 15
313 57 2q. brown 25 20
314 – 5q. green 40 20
315 56 10q. olive 45 50
316 57 15q. red 60 45
317 – 25q. blue . . . . 1·25 1·50
318 56 50q. green . . . . 1·75 2·00
319 57 1f. violet . . . . 5·00 5·25
320 – 2f. brown . . . . 8·00 8·50
MS320a 140 × 140 mm. 20q. purple (T 56) . . . . 12·00 18·00
DESIGN: 5, 25q., 2f. As Type 57, but eagle with opened wings (Liberated Albania).

58 Countess Geraldine Apponyi and King Zog

1938. Royal Wedding.
321 58 1q. purple 20 20
322 2q. brown 20 20
323 5q. green 20 25
324 10q. olive 50 50
325 15q. red 50 50
326 25q. blue 65 85
327 50q. green . . . . 3·50 2·75
328 1f. violet . . . . 4·75 3·75
MS328a 110 × 140 mm. 2 each 20q. purple, 30q. brown . . . . . 20·00 27·00

59 National Emblems
60 King Zog

1938. 10th Anniv of Accession.
329 – 1q. purple 15 35
330 59 2q. red 25 35
331 – 5q. green 35 40
332 60 10q. brown . . . . 65 1·00
333 – 15q. red . . . . 65 1·00
334 60 25q. blue . . . . 85 1·10
335 59 50q. black . . . . 5·00 3·75
336 60 1f. green . . . . 7·50 5·50
MS336a 110 × 65 mm. 15q. red (333), 20q. green (59), 30q. violet (60) . . . . 16·00 25·00
DESIGN: 1, 5, 15q. As Type 60, but Queen Geraldine's portrait.

ITALIAN OCCUPATION

1939. Optd **Mbledhja Kushtetuese 12-IV-1939 XVII.**
(a) Postage.
337 49 1q. grey 35 35
338 2q. red 35 35
339 50 5q. green 30 30
340 10q. red 30 30
341 15q. brown 70 75
342 25q. blue 80 95
343 49 50q. turquoise . . . . . . 1·00 1·25
344 – 1f. violet (No. 284) . . . . 2·00 2·75
345 – 2f. blue (No. 285) . . . . 2·25 3·00
346 – 3f. green . . . . 5·00 7·50
347 – 5f. brown . . . . 6·75 8·50
(b) Air. Optd as Nos. 337/47 or surch also.
348 53 5q. green . . . . 4·25 3·75
349 15q. red . . . . 3·00 3·75
350 20q. on 50q. olive . . . . 7·25 7·25

62 Gheg

64 Broken Columns, Botrint

63 King Victor Emmanuel
65 King and Fiat G18V on Tirana–Rome Service

1939.
351 62 1q. blue (postage) 40 25
352 – 2q. brown 30 10
353 – 3q. brown 30 10
354 – 5q. green 40 10
355 63 10q. brown 40 15
356 15q. red 50 15
357 25q. blue 50 25
358 30q. violet 80 60
359 – 50q. violet . . . . 1·10 60
360 – 65q. red . . . . 2·25 2·50
361 – 1f. green . . . . 2·50 1·50
362 – 2f. red . . . . 6·50 8·00
363 64 3f. black . . . . 10·00 14·50
364 – 5f. purple . . . . 12·00 18·00
365 65 20q. brown (air) . . . . 45·00 10·50
DESIGNS—SMALL: 2q. Tosk man; 3q. Gheg woman; 5, 65q. Profile of King Victor Emmanuel; 50q. Tosk woman. LARGE: 1f. Kruje Fortress; 2f. Bridge over River Kiri at Mes; 5f. Amphitheatre ruins, Berat.

66 Sheep Farming

67 King Victor Emmanuel

1940. Air.
366 66 5q. green . . . . 1·25 1·25
367 – 15q. red . . . . 1·75 1·60
368 – 20q. blue . . . . 4·00 2·40
369 – 50q. brown . . . . 4·50 4·75
370 – 1f. green . . . . 6·00 6·00
371 – 2f. black . . . . 13·50 14·00
372 – 3f. purple . . . . 55·00 24·00
DESIGNS: Savoia Marchetti S.M.75 airplane and—HORIZ: 20q. King of Italy and Durres harbour; 1f. Bridge over River Kiri at Mes. VERT: 15q. Aerial map; 50q. Girl and valley; 2f. Archway and wall, Durres; 3f. Women in North Eprius.

1942. 3rd Anniv of Italian Occupation.
373 67 5q. green 60 75
374 10q. brown 60 75
375 15q. red . . . . 75 1·25
376 25q. blue . . . . 75 1·25
377 65q. brown . . . . 1·75 2·00
378 1f. green . . . . 1·75 2·00
379 2f. purple . . . . 1·75 2·50

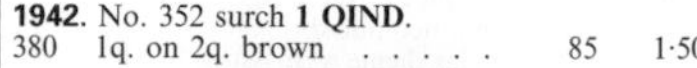
1942. No. 352 surch **1 QIND**.
380 1q. on 2q. brown . . . . . 85 1·50

69

1943. Anti-tuberculosis Fund.
381 69 5q.+5q. green 50 85
382 10q.+10q. brown 50 85
383 15q.+10q. red 50 85
384 25q.+15q. blue . . . . . . 1·00 1·60
385 30q.+20q. violet . . . . . 1·00 1·60
386 50q.+25q. orange . . . . 1·00 1·60
387 65q.+30q. grey . . . . . . 1·25 2·10
388 1f.+40q. brown . . . . . 1·75 3·00

GERMAN OCCUPATION

1943. Postage stamps of 1939 optd **14 Shtator 1943** or surch also.
389 – 1q. on 3q. brn (No. 353) 1·00 3·00
390 – 2q. brown (No. 352) . . . 1·00 3·00
391 – 3q. brown (No. 353) . . . 1·00 3·00
392 – 5q. green (No. 354) . . . . 1·00 3·00
393 63 10q. brown . . . . 1·00 3·00
394 – 15q. red (No. 356) . . . . 1·00 3·00
395 – 25q. blue (No. 357) . . . . 1·00 3·00
396 – 30q. violet (No. 358) . . . 1·00 3·00
397 – 50q. on 65q. brn (No. 360) 1·25 6·00
398 – 65q. red (No. 360) . . . . 1·25 6·00
399 – 1f. green (No. 361) . . . . 6·00 18·00
400 – 2f. red (No. 362) . . . . 10·00 70·00
401 64 3f. black . . . . 50·00 £225

71 War Refugees

(73)

1944. War Refugees' Relief Fund.
402 71 5q.+5q. green . . . . . . 2·50 12·00
403 10q.+5q. brown . . . . . 2·50 12·00
404 15q.+5q. red . . . . . . 2·50 12·00
405 25q.+10q. blue . . . . . . 2·50 12·00
406 1f.+50q. green . . . . . . 2·50 12·00
407 2f.+1f. violet . . . . . . 2·50 12·00
408 3f.+1f.50 orange . . . . . 2·50 12·00

INDEPENDENT STATE

1945. Nos. 353/8 and 360/2 surch **QEVERIJA DEMOKRAT. E SHQIPERISE 22-X-1944** and value.
409 30q. on 3q. brown . . . . 4·25 5·00
410 40q. on 5q. green . . . . 4·25 5·00
411 50q. on 10q. brown . . . . 4·25 5·00
412 60q. on 15q. red . . . . . 4·25 5·00
413 80q. on 25q. blue . . . . . 4·25 5·00
414 1f. on 30q. violet . . . . . 4·25 5·00
415 2f. on 65q. brown . . . . . 4·25 5·00
416 3f. on 1f. green . . . . . . 4·25 5·00
417 5f. on 2f. red . . . . 4·25 5·00

1945. 2nd Anniv of Formation of People's Army. Surch as T **73**.
418 49 30q. on 1q. grey . . . . . 2·50 3·75
419 60q. on 1q. grey . . . . . 2·50 3·75
420 80q. on 1q. grey . . . . . 2·75 3·75
421 1f. on 1q. grey . . . . . . 6·00 7·50
422 2f. on 2q. red . . . . 7·50 8·75
423 3f. on 50q. green . . . . . 13·50 16·00
424 – 5f. on 2f. blue (No. 285) 20·00 25·00

1945. Red Cross Fund. Surch with Red Cross, **JAVA E K.K. SHQIPTAR 4-11 MAJ 1945** and value.
425 69 30q.+15q. on 5q.+5q. green 5·00 6·50
426 50q.+25q. on 10q.+10q. brown . . . . 5·00 6·50
427 1f.+50q. on 15q.+10q. red 14·00 16·00
428 2f.+1f. on 25q.+15q. blue 20·00 22·00

75 Labinot **77** Globe, Dove and Olive Branch

1945.
429 **75** 20q. green 50 85
430 30q. orange 75 1·25
431 – 40q. brown 75 1·25
432 – 60q. red 1·00 1·75
433 – 1f. red 2·00 3·75
434 – 3f. blue 12·00 15·00
DESIGNS: 40, 60q. Bridge at Berat; 1f., 3f. Permet landscape.

1946. Constitutional Assembly. Optd **ASAMBLEJA KUSHTETUESE 10 KALLNUER 1946.**
435 **75** 20q. green 1·25 1·25
436 30q. orange 1·75 1·75
437 – 40q. brown (No. 431) 2·00 2·00
438 – 60q. red (No. 432) 3·50 3·50
439 – 1f. red (No. 433) 12·00 12·00
440 – 3f. blue (No. 434) 20·00 20·00

PEOPLE'S REPUBLIC

1946. Int Women's Congress. Perf or imperf.
441 **77** 20q. mauve and red 85 85
442 40q. lilac and red 1·25 1·25
443 50q. violet and red 1·75 1·75
444 1f. blue and red 4·25 4·25
445 2f. blue and red 6·25 6·25

1946. Proclamation of Albanian People's Republic. Optd **REPUBLIKA POPULLORE E SHQIPERISE.**
446 **75** 20q. green 1·40 1·40
447 30q. orange 1·60 1·60
448 – 40q. brown (No. 431) 2·75 2·75
449 – 60q. red (No. 432) 5·50 5·50
450 – 1f. red (No. 433) 12·00 12·00
451 – 3f. blue (No. 434) 22·00 22·00

1946. Albanian Red Cross Congress. Surch **KONGRESI K.K.SH. 24-25-11-46** and premium.
452 **75** 20q.+10q. green 20·00 20·00
453 30q.+15q. orange 20·00 20·00
454 – 40q.+20q. brown 20·00 20·00
455 – 60q.+30q. red 20·00 20·00
456 – 1f.+50q. red 20·00 20·00
457 – 3f.+1f.50 blue 20·00 20·00

79 Athletes **80** Qemal Stafa

1946. Balkan Games.
458 **79** 1q. black 14·00 11·50
459 2q. green 14·00 11·50
460 5q. brown 14·00 11·50
461 10q. red 14·00 11·50
462 20q. blue 14·00 11·50
463 40q. lilac 16·00 11·50
464 1f. orange 32·00 30·00

1947. 5th Death Anniv of Qemal Stafa (Communist activist).
465 **80** 20q. dp brown & brown 9·00 9·00
466 28q. deep blue and blue 9·00 9·00
467 40q. dp brown & brown 9·00 9·00

81 Railway Construction

1947. Construction of Durres–Elbasan Railway.
468 **81** 1q. black and drab 5·00 1·25
469 4q. deep green and green 5·00 1·25
470 10q. dp brown & brown 5·25 1·60
471 15q. red and rose 5·25 1·60
472 20q. black and blue 12·00 1·75
473 28q. deep blue and blue 17·00 2·25
474 40q. red and purple 32·00 2·50
475 68q. dp brown & brown 40·00 22·00

82 Partisans **83** Enver Hoxha and Vasil Shanto

1947. 4th Anniv of Formation of People's Army. Inscr "1943–1947".
476 **82** 16q. brown 4·50 4·50
477 **83** 20q. brown 4·50 4·50
478 – 28q. blue 4·50 4·50
479 – 40q. brown and mauve 4·50 4·50
DESIGNS—HORIZ: 28q. Infantry column. VERT: 40q. Portrait of Vojo Kushi.

84 Ruined Conference Building

1947. 5th Anniv of Peza Conference.
480 **84** 2l. purple and mauve 6·00 4·00
481 2l.50 deep blue and blue 6·00 4·00

85 War Invalids **86** Peasants

1947. 1st Congress of War Invalids.
482 **85** 1l. red 10·00 10·00

1947. Agrarian Reform. Inscr "REFORMA AGRARE".
483 **86** 1l.50 purple 7·50 6·50
484 – 2l. brown 7·50 6·50
485 – 2l.50 blue 7·50 6·50
486 – 3l. red 7·50 6·50
DESIGNS—HORIZ: 2l. Banquet; 2l.50, Peasants rejoicing. VERT: 3l. Soldier being chaired.

87 Burning Village

1947. 3rd Anniv of Liberation. Inscr "29-XI-1944–1947".
487 **87** 1l.50 red 3·75 3·75
488 – 2l.50 purple 3·75 3·75
489 – 5l. blue 8·00 6·00
490 – 8l. mauve 12·00 8·00
491 – 12l. brown 20·00 14·00
DESIGNS: 2l.50, Riflemen; 5l. Machine-gunners; 8l. Mounted soldier; 12l. Infantry column.

1948. Nos. 429/34 surch **Lek** and value.
492 **75** 0l.50 on 30q. orange 35 35
493 1l. on 20q. green 90 90
494 – 2l.50 on 60q. red 2·50 2·25
495 – 3l. on 1f. red 3·00 3·00
496 – 5l. on 3f. blue 6·00 5·50
497 – 12l. on 40q. brown 15·00 12·50

88 Railway Construction

1948. Construction of Durres–Tirana Railway.
498 **88** 0l.50 red 2·50 1·00
499 1l. green 2·75 1·10
500 1l.50 red 4·25 1·10
501 2l.50 brown 5·25 2·00
502 5l. blue 10·00 2·75
503 8l. orange 16·00 4·75
504 12l. purple 20·00 8·00
505 20l. black 40·00 18·00

89 Parade of Infantrymen **90** Labourer, Globe and Flag

1948. 5th Anniv of People's Army.
506 **89** 2l.50 brown 3·00 2·50
507 5l. blue 5·00 4·50
508 – 8l. slate (Troops in action) 8·00 6·00

1949. Labour Day.
509 **90** 2l.50 brown 1·00 1·00
510 5l. blue 2·25 2·25
511 8l. purple 4·00 4·00

91 Soldier and Map **92** Albanian and Kremlin Tower

1949. 6th Anniv of People's Army.
512 **91** 2l.50 brown 1·10 1·10
513 5l. blue 2·25 2·25
514 8l. orange 4·00 4·00

1949. Albanian–Soviet Amity.
515 **92** 2l.50 brown 1·25 1·50
516 5l. blue 3·00 3·25

93 Gen. Enver Hoxha **94** Soldier and Flag

1949.
517 **93** 0l.50 purple 25 10
518 1l. green 30 10
519 1l.50 red 40 10
520 2l.50 brown 65 10
521 5l. blue 1·60 25
522 8l. purple 3·00 1·75
523 12l. purple 10·50 3·00
524 20l. slate 12·50 4·00

1949. 5th Anniv of Liberation.
525 **94** 2l.50 brown 70 70
526 – 3l. red 1·75 1·90
527 **94** 5l. violet 2·50 2·75
528 – 8l. black 5·25 5·50
DESIGN—HORIZ: 3, 8l. Street fighting.

96 Joseph Stalin

1949. Stalin's 70th Birthday.
529 **96** 2l.50 brown 1·00 1·25
530 5l. blue 1·90 2·50
531 8l. lake 4·25 5·50

97 **98** Sami Frasheri

1950. 75th Anniv of U.P.U.
532 **97** 5l. blue 2·75 4·00
533 8l. purple 5·00 5·75
534 12l. black 9·00 10·00

1950. Literary Jubilee. Inscr "1950-JUBILEU I SHKRIMTAREVE TE RILINDJES".
535 **98** 2l. green 1·10 85
536 – 2l.50 brown 1·50 1·40
537 – 3l. red 1·75 2·00
538 – 5l. blue 3·00 3·00
PORTRAITS: 2l.50, A. Zako (Cajupi); 3l. Naim Frasheri; 5l. K. Kristoforidhi.

99 Vuno-Himare **100** Stafa and Shanto

1950. Air.
539 **99** 0l.50 black 90 90
540 – 1l. purple 90 90
541 – 2l. blue 1·60 1·60
542 **99** 5l. green 5·50 5·50
543 – 10l. blue 12·00 12·00
544 – 20l. violet 20·00 20·00
DESIGNS: Douglas DC-3 airplane over—1, 10l. Rozafat Shkodor; 2, 20l. Keshtjelle-Butrinto.

1950. Albanian Patriots.
545 – 2l. green 1·25 1·25
546 – 2l.50 violet 1·50 1·50
547 – 3l. red 2·50 2·25
548 – 5l. blue 3·00 2·50
549 **100** 8l. brown 8·00 7·25
PORTRAITS: 2l. Ahmet Haxhia, Hydajet Lezha, Naim Gjylbegu, Ndoc Mazi and Ndoc Deda; 2l.50, Asim Zeneli, Ali Demi, Kajo Karafili, Dervish Hakali and Asim Vokshi; 3l. Ataz Shehu, Baba Faja, Zoja Cure, Mustafa Matohiti and Gjok Doci; 5l. Perlat Rexhepi, Bako, Vojo Kushi, Reshit Collaku and Misto Mame.

101 Arms and Flags **102** Skanderbeg

1951. 5th Anniv of Republic.
550 **101** 2l.50 red 1·50 1·60
551 5l. blue 3·75 3·75
552 8l. black 5·50 5·75

1951. 483rd Death Anniv of Skanderbeg (patriot).
553 **102** 2l.50 brown 1·50 1·40
554 5l. violet 3·00 3·25
555 8l. bistre 4·75 4·75

103 Gen. Enver Hoxha and Assembly **104** Child and Globe

1951. 7th Anniv of Permet Congress.
556 **103** 2l.50 brown 90 90
557 3l. red 1·10 1·10
558 5l. blue 2·00 2·00
559 8l. mauve 3·75 3·75

1951. International Children's Day.
560 **104** 2l. green 1·50 1·10
561 – 2l.50 brown 1·75 1·50
562 – 3l. red 2·50 1·75
563 **104** 5l. blue 3·50 2·40
DESIGN—HORIZ: 2l.50, 3l. Nurse weighing baby.

105 Enver Hoxha and Meeting-house

1951. 10th Anniv of Albanian Communists.
564 **105** 2l.50 brown 55 55
565 3l. red 65 65
566 5l. blue 1·00 1·00
567 8l. black 2·25 2·25

106 Young Partisans

1951. 10th Anniv of Albanian Young Communists' Union. Inscr "1941–1951".
568 **106** 2l.50 brown 75 90
569 – 5l. blue 4·75 2·75
570 – 8l. red 3·50 3·50

DESIGNS: Schoolgirl, railway, tractor and factories; 8l. Miniature portraits of Stafa, Spiru, Mame and Kondi.

1952. Air. Surch in figures.
571 – 0.50l. on 2l. blue (No. 541) £160 £130
572 **99** 0.50l. on 5l. green . . . . 35·00 25·00
573 2l.50 on 5l. green £250 £140
574 – 2l.50 on 10l. blue (No. 543) 35·00 25·00

108 Factory

1953.
575 **108** 0l.50 brown 75 10
576 – 1l. green 75 10
577 – 2l.50 sepia . . . . . . 1·60 20
578 – 3l. red . . . . 2·00 35
579 – 5l. blue . . . . 3·75 90
580 – 8l. olive . . . . 4·00 1·10
581 – 12l. purple . . . . . . 5·50 1·40
582 – 20l. blue . . . . 12·50 3·25
DESIGNS—HORIZ: 1l. Canal; 2l.50, Girl and cotton mill; 3l. Girl and sugar factory; 5l. Film studio; 8l. Girl and textile machinery; 20l. Dam. VERT: 12l. Pylon and hydroelectric station.

109 Soldiers and Flags

1954. 10th Anniv of Liberation.
583 **109** 0l.50 lilac 15 15
584 1l. green 65 15
585 2l.50 brown . . . . . . 1·10 70
586 3l. red . . . . 2·00 85
587 5l. blue . . . . 2·75 1·25
588 8l. purple . . . . . . 5·25 3·50

110 First Albanian School **111**

1956. 70th Anniv of Albanian Schools.
589 **110** 2l. purple 30 20
590 – 2l.50 green 85 30
591 – 5l. blue . . . . 1·60 1·25
592 **110** 10l. turquoise . . . . . 4·25 3·50
DESIGN: 2l.50, 5l. Portraits of P. Sotiri, P. N. Luarasi and N. Naci.

1957. 15th Anniv of Albanian Workers' Party.
593 **111** 2l.50 brown 75 20
594 – 5l. blue . . . . 1·50 65
595 – 8l. purple . . . . . . 3·25 2·25
DESIGNS: 5l. Party headquarters, Tirana; 8l. Marx and Lenin.

112 Congress Emblem

1957. 4th World Trade Unions Congress, Leipzig.
596 **112** 2l.50 purple 50 20
597 3l. red 75 50
598 5l. blue . . . . 1·25 85
599 8l. green . . . . 3·50 2·25

113 Lenin and Cruiser "Aurora" **114** Raising the Flag

1957. 40th Anniv of Russian Revolution.
600 **113** 2l.50 brown . . . . . . 1·25 55
601 5l. blue . . . . 2·10 1·60
602 8l. black . . . . 3·60 2·25

1957. 45th Anniv of Proclamation of Independence.
603 **114** 1l.50 purple 75 30
604 2l.50 brown . . . . . . 1·10 75
605 5l. blue . . . . 3·00 1·40
606 8l. green . . . . 4·25 2·75

115 N. Veqilharxhi **116** L. Gurakuqi

1958. 160th Birth Anniv of Veqilharxhi (patriot).
607 **115** 2l.50 brown 80 30
608 5l. blue . . . . 1·50 60
609 8l. purple . . . . . . 3·25 1·50

1958. Removal of Ashes of Gurakuqi (patriot).
610 **116** 1l.50 green 20 20
611 2l.50 brown 75 60
612 5l. blue . . . . 1·10 75
613 8l. sepia . . . . 3·00 1·10

117 Freedom Fighters **118** Soldiers in Action

1958. 50th Anniv of Battle of Mashkullore.
614 **117** 2l.50 ochre 60 20
615 – 3l. green 80 20
616 **117** 5l. blue . . . . 1·25 75
617 – 8l. brown . . . . 2·50 1·50
DESIGN: 3, 8l. Tree and buildings.

1958. 15th Anniv of Albanian People's Army.
618 **118** 1l.50 green 20 15
619 – 2l.50 brown 60 25
620 **118** 8l. red . . . . 1·60 1·40
621 – 11l. blue . . . . 2·40 2·25
DESIGN: 2l.50, 11l. Tank-driver, sailor, infantryman and tanks.

119 Bust of Apollo and Butrinto Amphitheatre **120** F. Joliot-Curie and Council Emblem

1959. Cultural Monuments Week.
622 **119** 2l.50 brown 75 25
623 6l.50 green . . . . . . 3·00 1·40
624 11l. blue . . . . 4·25 2·50

1959. 10th Anniv of World Peace Council.
625 **120** 1l.50 red . . . . 2·25 80
626 2l.50 violet . . . . . . 5·00 2·00
627 11l. blue . . . . 10·50 6·00

121 Basketball **122** Soldier

1959. 1st National Spartacist Games.
628 **121** 1l.50 violet 75 35
629 – 2l.50 green . . . . . . 1·10 35
630 – 5l. red . . . . 1·75 1·40
631 – 11l. blue . . . . 6·25 3·75
DESIGNS: 2l.50, Football; 5l. Running; 11l. Runners with torches.

1959. 15th Anniv of Liberation.
632 **122** 1l.50 red 50 25
633 – 2l.50 brown . . . . . . 1·40 40
634 – 3l. green . . . . 1·60 50
635 – 6l.50 red . . . . 3·25 4·50
MS635a 141 × 96 mm. Nos. 632/5 but in red. Imperf . . . . . 10·00 10·00
DESIGNS: 2l.50, Security guard. 3l. Harvester; 6l.50, Laboratory workers.

123 Mother and Child **124**

1959. 10th Anniv of Declaration of Human Rights.
636 **123** 5l. blue . . . . 7·25 2·00
MS636a 72 × 65 mm. No. 636. Imperf . . . . 9·00 9·00

1960. 50th Anniv of International Women's Day.
637 **124** 2l.50 brown . . . . . . 1·00 55
638 11l. red . . . . 4·00 1·40

125 Congress Building **126** A. Moisiu **127** Lenin

1960. 40th Anniv of Lushnje Congress.
639 **125** 2l.50 brown 55 25
640 7l.50 blue . . . . 1·50 80

1960. 80th Birth Anniv of Alexandre Moisiu (actor).
641 **126** 3l. brown 65 45
642 11l. green . . . . 2·25 80

1960. 90th Birth Anniv of Lenin.
643 **127** 4l. turquoise . . . . . . 1·75 35
644 11l. red . . . . 5·50 1·25

128 Vaso Pasha **129** Frontier Guard **130** Family with Policeman

1960. 80th Anniv of Albanian Alphabet Study Association.
645 **128** 1l. olive 30 20
646 – 1l.50 brown 85 25
647 – 6l.50 blue . . . . 1·75 85
648 – 11l. red . . . . 4·25 1·60
DESIGNS: 1l.50, Jani Vreto; 6l.50, Sami Frasheri; 11l. Association statutes.

1960. 15th Anniv of Frontier Force.
649 **129** 1l.50 red 50 30
650 11l. blue . . . . 3·00 1·40

1960. 15th Anniv of People's Police.
651 **130** 1l.50 green 55 25
652 8l.50 brown . . . . 3·00 1·25

131 Normal School, Elbasan **132** Soldier and Cannon

1960. 50th Anniv of Normal School, Elbasan.
653 **131** 5l. green . . . . 2·50 1·40
654 6l.50 purple . . . . . . 2·50 1·40

1960. 40th Anniv of Battle of Vlore.
655 **132** 1l.50 brown 75 25
656 2l.50 purple . . . . . . 1·10 40
657 5l. blue . . . . 2·50 90

133 Tirana Clock Tower, Kremlin and Tupolev Tu-104A Jetliner **134** Federation Emblem

1960. 2nd Anniv of Tirana–Moscow Jet Air Service.
658 **133** 1l. brown . . . . 1·00 75
659 7l.50 blue . . . . 3·75 1·50
660 11l.50 grey . . . . 6·00 3·00

1960. 15th Anniv of World Democratic Youth Federation.
661 **134** 1l.50 blue 25 15
662 8l.50 red . . . . 1·40 55

135 Ali Kelmendi **136** Flags of Albania and Russia, and Clasped Hands **137** Marx and Lenin

1960. 60th Birth Anniv of Kelmendi (Communist).
663 **135** 1l.50 olive 55 20
664 11l. purple . . . . 1·40 85

1961. 15th Anniv of Albanian-Soviet Friendship Society.
665 **136** 2l. violet 55 20
666 8l. purple . . . . 1·75 75

1961. 4th Albanian Workers' Party Congress.
667 **137** 2l. red 55 20
668 8l. blue . . . . 1·60 80

138 Malsi e Madhe (Shkoder) Costume **139** European Otter

1961. Provincial Costumes.
669 **138** 1l. black 75 20
670 – 1l.50 purple . . . . . . 1·10 25
671 – 6l.50 blue . . . . 3·75 1·10
672 – 11l. red . . . . 7·25 2·40
COSTUMES: 1l.50, Malsi e Madhe (Shkoder) (female); 6l.50, Lume; 11l. Mirdite.

1961. Albanian Fauna.
673 **139** 2l.50 blue . . . . 4·00 1·00
674 – 6l.50 green (Eurasian badger) . . . . 8·00 2·50
675 – 11l. brown (Brown bear) 13·50 5·00

140 Dalmatian Pelicans **141** Cyclamen

1961. Albanian Birds.
676 **140** 1l.50 red on pink . . . . 3·50 60
677 – 7l.50 violet on blue . . . 5·75 1·60
678 – 11l. brown on pink . . . 8·75 2·00
BIRDS: 7l.50, Grey heron; 11l. Little egret.

1961. Albanian Flowers.
679 **141** 1l.50 purple and blue . . 2·50 50
680 – 8l. orange and purple . . 5·00 2·00
681 – 11l. red and green . . . . 8·00 2·50
FLOWERS: 8l. Forsythia; 11l. Lily.

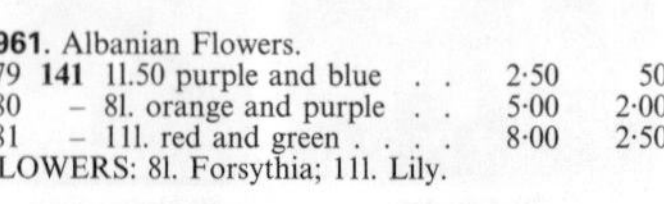

142 M. G. Nikolla **143** Lenin and Marx on Flag

1961. 50th Birth Anniv of Nikolla (poet).
682 **142** 0l.50 brown 40 30
683 8l.50 green . . . . 2·00 1·40

1961. 20th Anniv of Albanian Workers' Party.
684 **143** 2l.50 red 90 25
685 7l.50 purple . . . . . . 2·00 90

144 **145** Yuri Gagarin and "Vostok 1"

1961. 20th Anniv of Albanian Young Communists' Union.
686 **144** 2l.50 blue 90 25
687 7l.50 mauve . . . . . . 1·60 1·00

1962. World's First Manned Space Flight. (a) Postage.
688 **145** 0l.50 blue 90 15
689 4l. purple . . . . 3·75 90
690 11l. green . . . . 9·00 3·00

(b) Air. Optd **POSTA AJRORE**.
691 **145** 0l.50 blue on cream . . . 35·00 35·00
692 4l. purple on cream . . . 35·00 35·00
693 11l. green on cream . . . 35·00 35·00

147 P. N. Luarasi

148 Campaign Emblem

1962. 50th Death Anniv of Petro N. Luarasi (patriot).
694 **147** 0l.50 blue 75 15
695 8l.50 brown . . . . . . 3·00 75

IMPERF STAMPS. Many Albanian stamps from No. 696 onwards exist imperf and/or in different colours from limited printings.

1962. Malaria Eradication.
696 **148** 1l.50 green 15 10
697 2l.50 red 20 10
698 10l. purple . . . . 1·10 65
699 11l. blue . . . . 1·60 90
MS699a 90 × 106 mm. Nos. 696/9 40·00 40·00

149 Camomile

150 Throwing the Javelin

1962. Medicinal Plants.
700 **149** 0l.50 yellow, green & blue 35 20
701 – 8l. green, yellow and grey 1·60 1·00
702 – 11l.50 violet, grn & ochre 2·75 1·25
PLANTS: 8l. Silver linden; 11l.50, Sage.

1962. Olympic Games, Tokyo, 1964 (1st issue). Inscr as in T **102**.
703 – 0l.50 black and blue . . . 20 15
704 – 2l.50 sepia and brown . . 70 15
705 – 3l. black and blue 90 20
706 **150** 9l. purple and red . . . . 2·50 75
707 – 10l. black and olive . . . 2·75 1·00
MS707a 81 × 63 mm. 15l. (as 3l.) 50·00 50·00
DESIGNS—VERT: 0l.50, Diving; 2l.50, Pole-vaulting; 10l. Putting the shot. HORIZ: 3l. Olympic flame.
See also Nos. 754/**MS**758a, 818/**MS**821a and 842/**MS**851a.

151 "Sputnik 1" in Orbit

152 Footballer and Ball in Net

1962. Cosmic Flights.
708 **151** 0l.50 yellow and violet . . 60 20
709 – 1l. sepia and green . . . 85 25
710 – 11l.50 yellow and red . . . 1·40 35
711 – 20l. blue and purple . . . 9·00 3·00
MS711a 101 × 76 mm. 14l. (+ 6l.) brown and blue (rocket) . . . 50·00 50·00
DESIGNS: 1l. Dog "Laika" and "Sputnik 2"; 11l.50, Artificial satellite and Sun; 20l. "Lunik 3" photographing Moon.

1962. World Cup Football Championship, Chile.
712 **152** 1l. violet and orange . . . 20 15
713 – 2l.50 blue and green . . . 1·00 20
714 **152** 6l.50 purple and brown 2·00 25
715 – 15l. purple and green . . 2·75 70
MS715a 82 × 66 mm. 20l. brown and green (as 713 but larger) . . . 50·00 50·00
DESIGN: 2l.50, 15l. As Type **152** but globe in place of ball in net.

153 "Europa" and Albanian Maps

154 Dardhe Woman

1962. Tourist Publicity.
716 **153** 0l.50 red, yellow & green 30 30
717 – 1l. red, purple and blue 1·40 1·40
718 – 2l.50 red, purple and blue 8·00 8·00
719 **153** 11l. red, yellow and grey 16·00 16·00
MS719a 82 × 63 mm. 7l. red, yellow and grey (**153**), 8l. red and grey (as 717) . . . . 50·00 50·00
DESIGN: 1, 2l.50, Statue and map.

1962. Costumes of Albania's Southern Region.
720 **154** 0l.50 red, purple and blue 25 10
721 – 1l. brown and buff . . . 30 15
722 – 2l.50 black, violet & grn 1·40 40
723 – 14l. red, brown and green 4·25 1·60
COSTUMES: 1l. Devoll man; 2l.50, Lunxheri woman; 14l. Gjirokaster man.

155 Chamois

156 Golden Eagle

1962. Albanian Animals.
724 **155** 0l.50 purple and green . . 50 15
725 – 1l. black and yellow . . 1·40 30
726 – 1l.50 black and brown . . 2·00 35
727 – 15l. brown and green . . 20·00 3·75
MS727a 72 × 89 mm. 20l. brown and green (as 727 but larger) . . . £120 £120
ANIMALS—HORIZ. 1l. Lynx; 1l.50, Wild boar. VERT: 15l. Roe deer.

1962. 50th Anniv of Independence.
728 **156** 1l. brown and red 40 35
729 – 3l. black and brown . . . 1·75 75
730 – 16l. black and mauve . . 4·75 1·90
DESIGNS: 3l. I. Qemali; 16l. "RPSH" and golden eagle.

157 Revolutionaries

158 Henri Dunant and Globe

1963. 45th Anniv of October Revolution.
731 **157** 5l. violet and yellow . . . 1·10 55
732 – 10l. black and red . . . . 2·25 1·25
DESIGN: 10l. Statue of Lenin.

1963. Red Cross Centenary. Cross in red.
733 **158** 1l.50 black and red . . . 65 20
734 2l.50 black, red and blue 85 40
735 6l. black, red and green 1·60 90
736 10l. black, red and yellow 3·50 1·75

159 Stalin and Battle

160 Nikolaev and "Vostok 3"

1963. 20th Anniv of Battle of Stalingrad.
737 **159** 8l. black & grn (postage) 9·00 2·50
738 – 7l. red and green (air) . . 9·00 2·00
DESIGN: 7l. "Lenin" flag, map, tanks, etc.

1963. 1st "Team" Manned Space Flights.
739 **160** 2l.50 brown and blue . . 75 30
740 – 7l.50 black and blue . . . 1·75 1·00
741 – 20l. brown and violet . . 6·00 2·75
MS741a 88 × 73 mm. 25l. blue and brown (Popovich and Nikolaev) 35·00 35·00
DESIGNS—HORIZ: 7l.50, Globe, "Vostok 3" and "Vostok 4". VERT: 20l. P. Popovic and "Vostok 4".

161 Crawling Cockchafer

162 Policeman and Allegorical Figure

1963. Insects.
742 **161** 0l.50 brown and green . . 75 30
743 – 1l. brown and blue . . . 1·50 75
744 – 8l. purple and red . . . . 6·50 1·75
745 – 10l. black and yellow . . 8·00 3·25
INSECTS: 1l.50, Stagbeetle; 8l. "Procerus gigas" (ground beetle); 10l. "Cicindela albanica" (tiger beetle).

1963. 20th Anniv of Albanian Security Police.
746 **162** 2l.50 black, purple & red 90 50
747 7l.50 black, lake and red 3·25 80

163 Great Crested Grebe

164 Official Insignia and Postmark of 1913

1963. Birds. Multicoloured.
748 0l.50 Type **163** 80 25
749 3l. Golden eagle . . . . . . 2·00 30
750 6l.50 Grey partridge . . . . 3·25 1·10
751 11l. Western capercaillie . . . 6·75 1·75

1963. 50th Anniv of First Albanian Stamps.
752 **164** 5l. multicoloured . . . . . 1·90 90
753 – 10l. green, black and red 3·50 1·60
DESIGN: 10l. Albanian stamps of 1913, 1937 and 1962.

165 Boxing

166 Gen. Enver Hoxha and Labinoti Council Building

1963. Olympic Games, Tokyo (1964) (2nd issue).
754 **165** 2l. green, red and yellow 65 65
755 – 3l. brown, blue & orange 85 25
756 – 5l. purple, brown and blue . . . . 1·25 35
757 – 6l. black, grey and green 1·75 90
758 – 9l. blue and brown . . . 3·50 1·40
MS758a 61 × 82 mm. 15l. multicoloured (Torch, rings and map) . . . . 25·00 25·00
SPORTS: 3l. Basketball; 5l. Volleyball; 6l. Cycling; 9l. Gymnastics.

1963. 20th Anniv of Albanian People's Army.
759 **166** 1l.50 yellow, black & red 40 20
760 – 2l.50 bistre, brown & blue 1·00 30
761 – 5l. black, drab & turq . . 1·90 90
762 – 6l. blue, buff and brown 2·75 1·40
DESIGNS: 2l.50, Soldier with weapons; 5l. Soldier attacking; 6l. Peacetime soldier.

167 Gagarin

1963. Soviet Cosmonauts. Portraits in yellow and brown.
763 **167** 3l. violet . . . . 1·00 20
764 – 5l. blue . . . . 1·40 40
765 – 7l. violet and grey . . . . 2·25 65
766 – 11l. blue and purple . . . 3·75 1·00
767 – 14l. blue and turquoise . . 4·75 1·40
768 – 20l. blue . . . . 7·25 3·50
COSMONAUTS: 5l. Titov; 7l. Nikolaev; 11l. Popovich; 14l. Bykovsky; 20l. Valentina Tereshkova.

168 Volleyball (Rumania)

1963. European Sports Events, 1963.
769 **168** 2l. red, black and olive . . 85 20
770 – 3l. bistre, black and red 85 30
771 – 5l. orange, black & green 1·25 65
772 – 7l. green, black and pink 1·90 85
773 – 8l. red, black and blue . . 3·50 1·10
SPORTS: 3l. Weightlifting (Sweden); 5l. Football (European Cup); 7l. Boxing (Russia); 8l. Ladies' Rowing (Russia).

169 Celadon Swallowtail

1963. Butterflies and Moths.
774 **169** 1l. black, yellow and red 75 25
775 – 2l. black, red and blue . . 90 30
776 – 4l. black, yellow & purple 2·00 85
777 – 5l. multicoloured . . . . 2·75 75
778 – 8l. black, red and brown 4·75 1·60
779 – 10l. orange, brown & blue 6·25 2·25
DESIGNS: 2l. Jersey tiger moth; 4l. Brimstone; 5l. Death's-head hawk moth; 8l. Orange tip; 10l. Peacock.

170 Lunik 1

1963. Air. Cosmic Flights.
780 **170** 2l. olive, yellow & orange 40 25
781 – 3l. multicoloured . . . . 1·00 25
782 – 5l. olive, yellow & purple 1·60 65
783 – 8l. red, yellow and violet 2·50 1·10
784 – 12l. red, orange and blue 4·50 3·50
DESIGNS: 3l. Lunik 2; 5l. Lunik 3; 8l. Venus 1; 12l. Mars 1.

171 Food Processing Works

172 Shield and Banner

1963. Industrial Buildings.
785 **171** 2l.50 red on pink 90 20
786 – 20l. green on green . . . 4·75 1·25
787 – 30l. purple on blue . . . 7·50 1·90
788 – 50l. bistre on cream . . . 9·50 3·50
DESIGNS—VERT: 20l. Naphtha refinery; 30l. Fruit-bottling plant. HORIZ: 50l. Copper-processing works.

1963. 1st Army and Defence Aid Assn Congress.
789 **172** 2l. multicoloured 70 25
790 8l. multicoloured . . . . 2·00 1·40

173 Young Men of Three Races

1963. 15th Anniv of Declaration of Human Rights.
791 **173** 3l. black and ochre . . . 65 55
792 5l. blue and ochre . . . . 1·40 85
793 7l. violet and ochre . . . 2·25 1·40

174 Bobsleighing

175 Lenin

1963. Winter Olympic Games, Innsbruck. Inscr "1964".
794 **174** 0l.50 black and blue . . . 20 20
795 – 2l.50 black, red and grey 90 25
796 – 6l.50 black, yellow & grey 1·75 35
797 – 12l.50 red, black & green 3·50 1·60
MS797a 56 × 75 mm. 12l.50 black, green and blue (Ski jumper) (49 × 31 mm) . . . . 30·00 30·00
DESIGNS—VERT: 2l.50, Skiing; 12l.50, Figure-skating. HORIZ: 6l.50, Ice-hockey.

1964. 40th Death Anniv of Lenin.
798 **175** 5l. olive and bistre . . . 1·10 35
799 10l. olive and bistre . . . 1·50 85

176 Hurdling **177** Common Sturgeon

1964. "GANEFO" Games, Djakarta (1963).
800 **176** 2l.50 blue and lilac 85 25
801 – 3l. brown and green 1·25 30
802 – 6l.50 red and blue 1·60 40
803 – 8l. ochre and blue 2·50 90
SPORTS—HORIZ. 3l. Running; 6l.50, Rifle-shooting. VERT: 8l. Basketball.

1964. Fishes. Multicoloured.
804 0l.50 Type **177** 30 10
805 1l. Gilthead seabream 75 20
806 1l.50 Flat-headed grey mullet 1·00 30
807 2l.50 Common carp 1·50 50
808 6l.50 Atlantic mackerel 3·00 1·25
809 10l. Lake Ochrid salmon 5·00 2·00

178 Eurasian Red Squirrel

1964. Forest Animals. Multicoloured.
810 1l. Type **178** 30 20
811 1l.50 Beech marten 50 25
812 2l. Red fox 70 30
813 2l.50 East European hedgehog 80 30
814 3l. Brown hare 1·00 70
815 5l. Golden jackal 1·75 70
816 7l. Wild cat 3·00 90
817 8l. Wolf 4·50 1·10

179 Lighting Olympic Torch

1964. Olympic Games, Tokyo (3rd issue). Inscr "DREJT TOKIOS".
818 **179** 3l. yellow, buff and green 30 15
819 – 5l. blue, violet and red 65 25
820 – 7l. lt blue, blue & yellow 90 30
821 – 10l. multicoloured 1·25 85
MS821a 81 × 91 mm. 15l. buff, blue and violet (as 820) (49 × 62 mm) 25·00 25·00
DESIGNS: 5l. Torch and globes; 7l. Olympic flag and Mt. Fuji; 10l. Olympic Stadium, Tokyo.

180 Soldiers, Hand clutching Rifle, and Inscription

1964. 20th Anniv of Permet Congress.
822 **180** 2l. sepia, red and orange 75 50
823 – 5l. multicoloured 2·00 1·50
824 – 8l. sepia, red and brown 3·50 3·00
DESIGNS (each with different inscription at right): 5l. Albanian Arms; 8l. Gen. Enver Hoxha.

181 Revolutionaries with Flag **183** Full Moon

1964. 40th Anniv of Revolution.
825 **181** 2l.50 black and red 25 20
826 7l.50 black and mauve 1·00 45

1964. "Verso Tokyo" Stamp Exhibition, Rimini (Italy). Optd **Rimini 25-VI-64**.
827 10l. blue, violet, orange and black (No. 821) 7·25 7·25

1964. Moon's Phases.
828 **183** 1l. yellow and violet 30 15
829 – 5l. yellow and blue 1·10 65
830 – 8l. yellow and blue 1·75 85
831 – 11l. yellow and green 4·25 1·25
MS831a 67 × 78 mm. 15l. yellow and blue (New Moon) (34 × 39 mm). Imperf 25·00 25·00
PHASES: 5l. Waxing Moon; 8l. Half-Moon; 11l. Waning Moon.

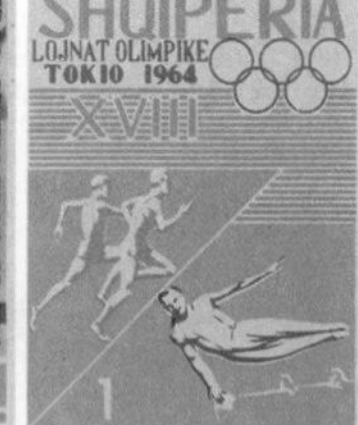

184 Winter Wren **186** Running and Gymnastics

1964. Albanian Birds. Multicoloured.
832 0l.50 Type **184** 35 25
833 1l. Penduline tit 60 30
834 2l.50 Green woodpecker 85 40
835 3l. Common treecreeper 1·25 40
836 4l. Eurasian nuthatch 1·40 60
837 5l. Great tit 1·75 60
838 6l. Eurasian goldfinch 2·00 60
839 18l. Golden oriole 4·75 2·10

1964. Air. Riccione "Space" Exhibition. Optd **Riccione 23-8-1964**.
840 **170** 2l. olive, yellow & orange 10·50 10·50
841 – 8l. red, yellow and violet (No.783) 25·00 25·00

1964. Olympic Games, Tokyo.
842 **186** 1l. red, blue and green 20 15
843 – 2l. brown, blue and violet 25 20
844 – 3l. brown, violet and olive 35 20
845 – 4l. olive, turquoise & blue 50 25
846 – 5l. turquoise, purple & red 85 65
847 – 6l. ultram, lt blue & orge 1·00 75
848 – 7l. green, orange and blue 1·40 90
849 – 8l. grey, green and yellow 1·40 1·10
850 – 9l. lt blue, yellow & purple 1·40 1·25
851 – 10l. brown, green & turq 1·90 1·60
MS851a 70 × 96 mm. 20l. violet and bistre (Winners on Dais) (40 × 67 mm) 35·00 35·00
SPORTS: 2l. Weightlifting and judo; 3l. Horse-jumping and cycling; 4l. Football and water-polo; 5l. Wrestling and boxing; 6l. Various sports and hockey; 7l. Swimming and yachting; 8l. Basketball and volleyball; 9l. Rowing and canoeing; 10l. Fencing and pistol-shooting.

187 Chinese Republican Emblem **188** Karl Marx

1964. 15th Anniv of Chinese People's Republic. Inscr "I TETOR 1949 1964.".
852 **187** 7l. red, black and yellow 1·60 85
853 – 8l. black, red and yellow 2·75 1·25
DESIGN—HORIZ: 8l. Mao Tse-tung.

1964. Centenary of "First International".
854 **188** 2l. black, red and lavender 90 20
855 – 5l. slate 2·40 75
856 – 8l. black, red and buff 4·00 1·25
DESIGNS: 5l. St. Martin's Hall, London; 8l. F. Engels.

189 J. de Rada **190** Arms and Flag

1964. 150th Birth Anniv of Jeronim de Rada (poet).
857 **189** 7l. green 1·60 65
858 8l. violet 2·50 1·10

1964. 20th Anniv of Liberation.
859 **190** 1l. multicoloured 20 20
860 – 2l. blue, red and yellow 65 20
861 – 3l. brown, red and yellow 1·00 65
862 – 4l. green, red and yellow 1·40 85
863 – 10l. black, red and blue 3·50 1·60
DESIGNS—HORIZ: 2l. Industrial scene; 3l. Agricultural scene. 4l. Laboratory worker. VERT: 10l. Hands holding Constitution, hammer and sickle.

191 Mercury **192** Chestnut

1964. Solar System Planets. Multicoloured.
864 1l. Type **191** 25 20
865 2l. Venus 45 25
866 3l. Earth 70 30
867 4l. Mars 85 35
868 5l. Jupiter 1·10 40
869 6l. Saturn 1·60 50
870 7l. Uranus 1·90 65
871 8l. Neptune 2·00 1·25
872 9l. Pluto 2·10 1·60
MS872a 88 × 72 mm. 15l. Solar system and rocket (61 × 51 mm). Imperf 35·00 35·00

1965. Winter Fruits. Multicoloured.
873 1l. Type **192** 25 15
874 2l. Medlars 35 20
875 3l. Persimmon 75 25
876 4l. Pomegranate 95 35
877 5l. Quince 1·60 40
878 10l. Orange 2·75 1·10

193 "Industry" **194** Buffalo Grazing

1965. 20th Anniv of Albanian Trade Unions. Inscr "B.P.S.H. 1945–1965".
879 **193** 2l. red, pink and black 3·50 3·00
880 – 5l. black, grey and ochre 7·00 6·00
881 – 8l. blue, lt blue & black 8·50 6·50
DESIGNS: 5l. Set square, book and dividers ("Technocracy"); 8l. Hotel, trees and sunshade ("Tourism").

1965. Water Buffaloes.
882 **194** 1l. multicoloured 50 15
883 – 2l. multicoloured 1·10 20
884 – 3l. multicoloured 1·90 30
885 – 7l. multicoloured 4·50 1·10
886 – 12l. multicoloured 8·00 2·50
DESIGNS: 2l. to 12l. As Type **194**, showing different views of buffalo.

195 Coastal View

1965. Albanian Scenery. Multicoloured.
887 1l.50 Type **195** 1·60 80
888 2l.50 Mountain forest 2·75 1·10
889 3l. Lugina Peak (vert) 3·50 1·40
890 4l. White River, Thethi (vert) 4·25 1·90
891 5l. Dry Mountain 5·25 2·50
892 9l. Lake of Flowers, Lure 12·00 4·50

196 Frontier Guard **197** Rifleman

1965. 20th Anniv of Frontier Force.
893 **196** 2l.50 multicoloured 1·40 85
894 12l.50 multicoloured 8·00 3·50

1965. European Shooting Championships, Bucharest.
895 **197** 1l. purple, red and violet 20 15
896 – 2l. purple, ultram & blue 65 20
897 – 3l. red and pink 85 30
898 – 4l. multicoloured 1·25 30
899 – 15l. multicoloured 5·00 95
DESIGNS: 2, 15l. Rifle-shooting (different); 3l. "Target" map; 4l. Pistol-shooting.

198 I.T.U. Emblem and Symbols **199** Belyaev

1965. Centenary of I.T.U.
900 **198** 2l.50 mauve, black & grn 1·60 20
901 12l.50 blue, black & violet 6·00 1·40

1965. Space Flight of "Voskhod 2".
902 **199** 1l.50 brown and blue 20 10
903 – 2l. blue, ultram & lilac 30 15
904 – 6l.50 brown and mauve 1·25 35
905 – 20l. yellow, black & blue 4·50 1·25
MS906 71 × 86 mm. 20l. yellow, black and blue (as 905 but larger, 59 × 51 mm). Imperf 20·00 20·00
DESIGNS: 2l. "Voskhod 2"; 6l.50, Leonov; 20l. Leonov in space.

200 Marx and Lenin **201** Mother and Child

1965. Postal Ministers' Congress, Peking.
907 **200** 2l.50 sepia, red & yellow 75 30
908 7l.50 green, red & yellow 3·25 1·25

1965. International Children's Day. Multicoloured.
909 1l. Type **201** 25 15
910 2l. Children planting tree 45 20
911 3l. Children and construction toy (horiz) 75 20
912 4l. Child on beach 90 30
913 15l. Child reading book 4·25 1·75

202 Wine Vessel **203** Fuchsia

1965. Albanian Antiquities. Multicoloured.
914 1l. Type **202** 20 10
915 2l. Helmet and shield 40 15
916 3l. Mosaic of animal (horiz) 85 25
917 4l. Statuette of man 1·60 30
918 15l. Statuette of headless and limbless man 4·25 1·60

1965. Albanian Flowers. Multicoloured.
919 1l. Type **203** 25 15
920 2l. Cyclamen 75 20
921 3l. Lilies 1·10 25
922 3l.50 Iris 1·40 25
923 4l. Dahlia 1·60 35
924 4l.50 Hydrangea 1·75 35
925 5l. Rose 2·00 70
926 7l. Tulips 2·75 90

(currency revaluation 10 (old) leks = 1 (new) lek.)

1965. Surch.
927 5q. on 30l. (No. 787) 20 20
928 15q. on 30l. (No. 787) 45 20
929 25q. on 50l. (No. 788) 65 25
930 80q. on 50l. (No. 788) 2·10 90
931 1l.10 on 20l. (No. 786) 3·25 1·10
932 2l. on 20l. (No. 786) 6·25 2·10

205 White Stork

206 "War Veterans" (after painting by B. Sejdini)

1965. Migratory Birds. Multicoloured.

No.	Description	Unused	Used
933	10q. Type **205**	35	35
934	20q. European cuckoo	65	35
935	30q. Hoopoe	1·10	50
936	40q. European bee-eater	1·75	60
937	50q. European nightjar	2·00	70
938	1l.50 Common quail	6·00	2·00

1965. War Veterans Conference.

No.	Description	Unused	Used
939	**206** 25q. brown and black	3·25	85
940	65q. blue and black	7·25	1·75
941	1l.10 black	10·00	2·50

207 Hunter stalking Western Capercaillie

208 "Nerium oleander"

1965. Hunting.

No.	Description	Unused	Used
942	**207** 10q. multicoloured	85	25
943	– 20q. brown, sepia & grn	85	25
944	– 30q. multicoloured	1·90	80
945	– 40q. purple and green	2·25	90
946	– 50q. brown, blue & black	2·00	55
947	– 1l. brown, bistre & green	4·25	1·00

DESIGNS: 20q. Shooting roe deer; 30q. Common pheasant; 40q. Shooting mallard; 50q. Dogs chasing wild boar; 1l. Hunter and brown hare.

1965. Mountain Flowers. Multicoloured.

No.	Description	Unused	Used
948	10q. Type **208**	30	20
949	20q. "Myosotis alpestris"	40	20
950	30q. "Dianthus glacialis"	65	30
951	40q. "Nymphaea alba"	1·25	40
952	50q. "Lotus corniculatus"	1·60	50
953	1l. "Papaver rhoeas"	3·75	1·60

209 Tourist Hotel, Fier

210 Freighter "Teuta"

1965. Public Buildings.

No.	Description	Unused	Used
954	**209** 5q. black and blue	10	10
955	– 10q. black and buff	15	10
956	– 15q. black and green	20	10
957	– 25q. black and violet	75	15
958	– 65q. black and brown	1·25	35
959	– 80q. black and green	1·50	45
960	– 1l.10 black and purple	2·25	50
961	– 1l.60 black and blue	3·00	1·25
962	– 2l. black and pink	4·25	1·40
963	– 3l. black and grey	8·00	2·40

BUILDINGS: 10q. Peshkopi Hotel; 15q. Sanatorium, Tirana; 25q. "House of Rest", Pogradec; 65q. Partisans Sports Palace, Tirana; 80q. "House of Rest", Dajti Mountain; 1l.10. Palace of Culture, Tirana; 1l.60, Adriatic Hotel, Durres; 2l. Migjeni Theatre, Shkoder; 3l. "A. Moisiu" Cultural Palace, Durres.

1965. Evolution of Albanian Ships.

No.	Description	Unused	Used
964	**210** 10q. green and light green	40	20
965	– 20q. bistre and green	55	20
966	– 30q. ultramarine and blue	75	35
967	– 40q. violet and light violet	1·00	45
968	– 50q. red and rose	2·10	55
969	– 1l. brown and ochre	4·25	1·00

DESIGNS: 20q. Punt; 30q. 19th-century sailing ship; 40q. 18th-century brig; 50q. Freighter "Vlora"; 1l. Illyrian galliots.

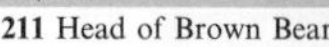

211 Head of Brown Bear

212 Championships Emblem

1965. Brown Bears. Different Bear designs as T **211**.

No.	Description	Unused	Used
970	– 10q. brown and buff	30	15
971	– 20q. brown and buff	75	20
972	– 30q. brown, red and buff	1·00	35
973	– 35q. brown and buff	1·25	40
974	– 40q. brown and buff	1·60	45
975	**211** 50q. brown and buff	2·50	50
976	– 55q. brown and buff	3·50	85
977	– 60q. brown, red and buff	5·00	2·75

The 10q. to 40q. are vert.

1965. 7th Balkan Basketball Championships, Tirana. Multicoloured.

No.	Description	Unused	Used
978	10q. Type **212**	20	10
979	20q. Competing players	40	15
980	30q. Clearing ball	85	20
981	50q. Attempted goal	2·10	25
982	1l.40 Medal and ribbon	4·25	1·00

213 Arms on Book

214 Cow

1966. 20th Anniv of Albanian People's Republic.

No.	Description	Unused	Used
983	**213** 10q. gold, red and brown	15	10
984	– 20q. gold, blue & ultram	20	15
985	– 30q. gold, yellow and brown	75	20
986	– 60q. gold, lt grn & green	1·40	65
987	– 80q. gold, red and brown	2·25	75

DESIGNS (Arms and): 20q. Chimney stacks; 30q. Ear of corn; 60q. Hammer, sickle and open book; 80q. Industrial plant.

1966. Domestic Animals. Animals in natural colours; inscr in black: frame colours given.

No.	Description	Unused	Used
988	**214** 10q. turquoise	30	20
989	– 20q. green	85	25
990	– 30q. blue	1·25	30
991	– 35q. lavender	1·40	35
992	– 40q. pink	1·75	35
993	– 50q. yellow	2·00	40
994	– 55q. blue	2·25	70
995	– 60q. yellow	4·50	95

ANIMALS—HORIZ. 20q. Pig; 30q. Sheep; 35q. Goat; 40q. Dog. VERT: 50q. Cat; 55q. Horse; 60q. Ass.

215 Football

216 A. Z. Cajupi

1966. World Cup Football Championships (1st series).

No.	Description	Unused	Used
996	**215** 5q. orange grey & buff	15	10
997	– 10q. multicoloured	20	10
998	– 15q. blue, yellow & buff	25	15
999	– 20q. multicoloured	35	20
1000	– 25q. sepia, red and buff	45	20
1001	– 30q. brown, green & buff	50	30
1002	– 35q. green, blue and buff	85	30
1003	– 40q. brown red and buff	90	35
1004	– 50q. multicoloured	1·00	65
1005	– 70q. multicoloured	1·40	90

DESIGNS—Footballer and map showing: 10q. Montevideo (1930); 15q. Rome (1934); 20q. Paris (1938); 25q. Rio de Janeiro (1950); 30q. Berne (1954); 35q. Stockholm (1958); 40q. Santiago (1962); 50q. London (1966); 70q. World Cup and football.
See also Nos. 1035/42.

1966. Birth Centenary of Andon Cajupi (poet).

No.	Description	Unused	Used
1006	**216** 40q. indigo and blue	1·10	55
1007	1l.10 bronze and green	2·50	1·10

217 Painted Lady

218 W.H.O. Building

1966. Butterflies and Dragonflies. Multicoloured.

No.	Description	Unused	Used
1008	10q. Type **217**	35	20
1009	20q. "Calopteryx virgo"	50	20
1010	30q. Pale clouded yellow	70	20
1011	35q. Banded agrion	85	25
1012	40q. Banded agrion (different)	1·10	30
1013	50q. Swallowtail	1·50	40
1014	55q. Danube clouded yellow	2·00	50
1015	60q. Hungarian glider	5·00	1·25

The 20, 35 and 40q. are dragonflies, remainder are butterflies.

1966. Inaug of W.H.O. Headquarters, Geneva.

No.	Description	Unused	Used
1016	**218** 25q. black and blue	45	15
1017	– 35q. blue and orange	1·25	20
1018	– 60q. red, blue and green	1·60	35
1019	– 80q. blue, yellow & brn	2·75	65

DESIGNS—VERT: 35q. Ambulance and patient; 60q. Nurse and mother weighing baby. HORIZ: 80q. Medical equipment.

219 Leaf Star

220 "Luna 10"

1966. "Starfish". Multicoloured.

No.	Description	Unused	Used
1020	15q. Type **219**	30	15
1021	25q. Spiny Star	50	20
1022	35q. Brittle Star	1·10	25
1023	45q. Sea Star	1·60	30
1024	50q. Blood Star	1·75	40
1025	60q. Sea Cucumber	2·25	40
1026	70q. Sea Urchin	4·00	1·75

1966. "Luna 10". Launching.

No.	Description	Unused	Used
1027	**220** 20q. multicoloured	70	20
1028	– 30q. multicoloured	90	25
1029	**220** 70q. multicoloured	1·75	35
1030	– 80q. multicoloured	3·50	1·00

DESIGN: 30, 80q. Earth, Moon and trajectory of "Luna 10".

221 Water-level Map of Albania

222 Footballers (Uruguay, 1930)

1966. International Hydrological Decade.

No.	Description	Unused	Used
1031	**221** 20q. black, orge & red	50	20
1032	– 30q. multicoloured	1·00	25
1033	– 70q. black and violet	2·10	40
1034	– 80q. multicoloured	2·75	1·25

DESIGNS: 30q. Water scale and fields; 70q. Turbine and electricity pylon; 80q. Hydrological decade emblem.

1966. World Cup Football Championship (2nd series). Inscriptions and values in black.

No.	Description	Unused	Used
1035	**222** 10q. purple and ochre	20	10
1036	– 20q. olive and blue	30	15
1037	– 30q. slate and red	75	15
1038	– 35q. red and blue	85	20
1039	– 40q. brown and green	1·00	20
1040	– 50q. green and brown	1·25	50
1041	– 55q. green and mauve	1·25	95
1042	– 60q. ochre and red	2·50	1·40

DESIGNS—Various footballers representing World Cup winners: 20q. Italy, 1934; 30q. Italy, 1938; 35q. Uruguay, 1950; 40q. West Germany, 1954; 50q. Brazil, 1958; 55q. Brazil, 1962; 60q. Football and names of 16 finalists in 1966 Championship.

223 Tortoise

1966. Reptiles. Multicoloured.

No.	Description	Unused	Used
1043	10q. Type **223**	20	15
1044	15q. Grass snake	30	20
1045	25q. Swamp tortoise	45	25
1046	30q. Lizard	55	30
1047	35q. Salamander	70	35
1048	45q. Green lizard	1·25	40
1049	50q. Slow-worm	1·25	75
1050	90q. Sand viper	3·25	1·40

224 Siamese Cat

225 P. Budi (writer)

1966. Cats. Multicoloured.

No.	Description	Unused	Used
1051	10q. Type **224**	25	15
1052	15q. Tabby	30	20
1053	25q. Kitten	90	30
1054	45q. Persian	1·75	40
1055	60q. Persian	2·25	90
1056	65q. Persian	2·50	1·00
1057	80q. Persian	3·25	1·25

Nos. 1053/7 are horiz.

1966. 400th Birth Anniv of P. Budi.

No.	Description	Unused	Used
1058	**225** 25q. bronze and flesh	40	25
1059	1l.75 purple and green	3·25	1·90

226 U.N.E.S.C.O. Emblem

1966. 20th Anniv of U.N.E.S.C.O. Multicoloured.

No.	Description	Unused	Used
1060	5q. Type **226**	20	15
1061	15q. Tulip and open book	35	20
1062	25q. Albanian dancers	95	25
1063	1l.55 Jug and base of column	4·75	1·60

227 Borzoi

1966. Dogs. Multicoloured.

No.	Description	Unused	Used
1064	10q. Type **227**	40	15
1065	15q. Kuvasz	50	20
1066	25q. Setter	1·25	25
1067	45q. Cocker spaniel	1·90	85
1068	60q. Bulldog	2·00	1·00
1069	65q. St. Bernard	2·75	1·10
1070	80q. Dachshund	3·50	1·60

228 Hand holding Book

229 Ndre Mjeda (poet)

1966. 5th Workers Party Congress, Tirana. Multicoloured.

No.	Description	Unused	Used
1071	15q. Type **228**	40	15
1072	25q. Emblems of agriculture and industry	85	15
1073	65q. Hammer and sickle, wheat and industrial skyline	1·90	35
1074	95q. Hands holding banner on bayonet and implements	3·25	65

1966. Birth Centenary of Ndre Mjeda.

No.	Description	Unused	Used
1075	**229** 25q. brown and blue	65	20
1076	1l.75 brown and green	3·75	1·40

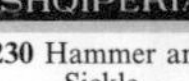

230 Hammer and Sickle

231 Young Communists and Banner

1966. 25th Anniv of Albanian Young Communists' Union. Multicoloured.

No.	Description	Unused	Used
1077	15q. Type **230**	35	10
1078	25q. Soldier leading attack	75	10
1079	65q. Industrial worker	1·60	30
1080	95q. Agricultural and industrial vista	2·75	55

1966. 25th Anniv of Young Communists' Union. Multicoloured.

No.	Description	Unused	Used
1081	5q. Manifesto (vert)	10	10
1082	10q. Type **231**	20	10
1083	1l.85 Partisans and banner (vert)	3·25	1·10

232 Golden Eagle

233 European Hake

1966. Birds of Prey. Multicoloured,

1084	10q. Type **232**	75	25
1085	15q. White-tailed sea eagle	1·10	40
1086	25q. Griffon vulture	1·90	90
1087	40q. Northern sparrow hawk	2·75	1·10
1088	50q. Osprey	3·50	1·40
1089	70q. Egyptian vulture	4·75	2·00
1090	90q. Common kestrel	5·25	2·75

1967. Fishes. Multicoloured.

1091	10q. Type **233**	30	15
1092	15q. Striped red mullet	45	15
1093	25q. Opali	1·00	20
1094	40q. Atlantic wolffish	1·25	30
1095	65q. Lumpsucker	1·60	70
1096	80q. Swordfish	2·50	80
1097	1l.15 Short-spined sea-scorpion	2·75	1·40

234 Dalmatian Pelicans

1967. Dalmatian Pelicans. Multicoloured.

1098	10q. Type **234**	35	25
1099	15q. Three pelicans	75	35
1100	25q. Pelican and chicks at nest	2·00	55
1101	50q. Pelicans "taking off" and airborne	4·25	70
1102	2l. Pelican "yawning"	11·00	3·50

235 "Camellia williamsi"

236 Congress Emblem

1967. Flowers. Multicoloured.

1103	5q. Type **235**	20	10
1104	10q. "Chrysanthemum indicum"	25	15
1105	15q. "Althaea rosea"	30	15
1106	25q. "Abutilon striatum"	90	20
1107	35q. "Paeonia chinensis"	1·25	20
1108	65q. "Gladiolus gandavensis"	2·00	40
1109	80q. "Freesia hybrida"	2·50	65
1110	1l.15 "Dianthus caryophyllus"	2·75	1·75

1967. 6th Trade Unions Congress, Tirana.

1111	**236** 25q. red, sepia and lilac	90	15
1112	1l.75 red, green and grey	4·00	1·60

237 Rose

1967. Roses.

1113	**237** 5q. multicoloured	25	10
1114	– 10q. multicoloured	55	10
1115	– 15q. multicoloured	70	15
1116	– 25q. multicoloured	85	15
1117	– 35q. multicoloured	1·00	25
1118	– 65q. multicoloured	1·50	40
1119	– 80q. multicoloured	1·90	50
1120	– 1l.65 multicoloured	4·50	1·25

DESIGNS: 10q. to 1l.65 Various roses as Type **237**.

238 Borsh Coast

1967. Albanian Riviera. Multicoloured.

1121	15q. Butrinti (vert)	40	20
1122	20q. Type **238**	50	20
1123	25q. Piqeras village	90	30
1124	45q. Coastal view	1·40	30
1125	50q. Himara coast	1·60	40
1126	65q. Fishing boat, Saranda	2·25	55
1127	80q. Dhermi	2·50	1·00
1128	1l. Sunset at sea (vert)	4·25	1·60

239 Fawn

1967. Roe Deer. Multicoloured.

1129	15q. Type **239**	50	15
1130	20q. Head of buck (vert)	50	20
1131	25q. Head of doe (vert)	95	20
1132	30q. Doe and fawn	95	25
1133	35q. Doe and new-born fawn	1·40	30
1134	40q. Young buck (vert)	1·40	35
1135	65q. Buck and doe (vert)	2·75	1·00
1136	70q. Running deer	3·50	1·40

240 Costumes of Malesia e Madhe Region

241 Battle Scene and Newspaper

1967. National Costumes. Multicoloured.

1137	15q. Type **240**	35	15
1138	20q. Zadrima	45	20
1139	25q. Kukesi	55	20
1140	45q. Dardhe	70	35
1141	50q. Myzeqe	75	70
1142	65q. Tirana	1·40	85
1143	80q. Dropulli	1·75	1·00
1144	1l. Laberise	2·25	1·25

1967. 25 Years of the Albanian Popular Press. Mult.

1145	25q. Type **241**	70	20
1146	75q. Newspapers and printery	1·90	50
1147	2l. Workers with newspaper	4·25	1·60

242 University, Torch and Open Book

243 Soldiers and Flag

1967. 10th Anniv of Tirana University.

1148	**242** 25q. multicoloured	45	30
1149	1l.75 multicoloured	2·75	1·10

1967. 25th Anniv of Albanian Democratic Front. Multicoloured.

1150	15q. Type **243**	25	15
1151	65q. Pick, rifle and flag	1·00	25
1152	1l.20 Torch and open book	1·90	75

244 Grey Rabbits

1967. Rabbit-breeding. Multicoloured.

1153	15q. Type **244**	20	10
1154	20q. Black and white rabbit (vert)	30	15
1155	25q. Brown hare	75	15
1156	35q. Brown rabbits	1·10	20
1157	40q. Common rabbits	1·40	20
1158	50q. Grey rabbit (vert)	1·75	65
1159	65q. Head of white rabbit (vert)	2·50	85
1160	1l. White rabbit	3·50	1·25

245 "Shkoder Wedding" (detail, Kole Idromeno)

1967. Albanian Paintings.

1161	**245** 15q. multicoloured	55	10
1162	– 20q. multicoloured	80	10
1163	– 25q. multicoloured	1·10	10
1164	– 45q. multicoloured	2·25	10
1165	– 50q. multicoloured	2·40	15
1166	– 65q. multicoloured	3·25	55
1167	– 80q. multicoloured	4·25	80
1168	– 1l. multicoloured	7·25	1·10

DESIGNS—VERT: 20q. "Head of the Prophet David" (detail, 16th-century fresco); 45q. Ancient mosaic head (from Durres); 50q. Detail, 16th-century icon (30 × 51 mm); 1l. "Our Sister" (K. Idromeno). HORIZ (51 × 30 mm): 25q. "Commandos of the Hakmarrja Battalion" (S. Shijaku); 65q. "Co-operative" (farm women, Z. Shoshi); 80q. "Street in Korce" (V. Mio).

246 Lenin and Stalin

1967. 50th Anniv of October Revolution. Mult.

1169	15q. Type **246**	20	15
1170	25q. Lenin with soldiers (vert)	65	15
1171	50q. Lenin addressing meeting (vert)	1·10	25
1172	1l.10 Revolutionaries	2·75	70

247 Common Turkey

248 First Aid

1967. Domestic Fowl. Multicoloured.

1173	15q. Type **247**	20	10
1174	20q. Goose	50	10
1175	25q. Hen	75	15
1176	45q. Cockerel	1·25	20
1177	50q. Helmeted guineafowl	1·40	50
1178	65q. Greylag goose (horiz)	1·90	65
1179	80q. Mallard (horiz)	2·50	85
1180	1l. Chicks (horiz)	3·50	1·25

1967. 6th Red Cross Congress, Tirana. Mult.

1181	15q.+5q. Type **248**	1·00	65
1182	25q.+5q. Stretcher case	1·90	1·00
1183	65q.+25q. Heart patient	5·00	3·50
1184	80q.+40q. Nurse holding child	8·75	5·25

249 Arms of Skanderbeg

1967. 500th Death Anniv of Castriota Skanderbeg (patriot) (1st issue). Multicoloured.

1185	10q. Type **249**	20	10
1186	15q. Skanderbeg	20	15
1187	25q. Helmet and sword	50	15
1188	30q. Kruja Castle	65	20
1189	35q. Petrela Castle	75	25
1190	65q. Berati Castle	1·40	30
1191	80q. Meeting of chiefs	1·75	65
1192	90q. Battle of Albulena	1·90	2·25

See also Nos. 1200/7.

250 Winter Olympic Emblem

1967. Winter Olympic Games, Grenoble. Mult.

1193	15q. Type **250**	15	10
1194	25q. Ice hockey	20	15
1195	30q. Figure skating	25	15
1196	50q. Skiing (slalom)	40	20
1197	80q. Skiing (downhill)	70	30
1198	1l. Ski jumping	1·60	40
MS1199	58 × 67 mm. 2l. As Type **250** but larger. Imperf	9·00	9·00

251 Skanderbeg Memorial, Tirana

1968. 500th Death Anniv of Castriota Skanderbeg (2nd issue). Multicoloured.

1200	10q. Type **251**	25	10
1201	15q. Skanderbeg portrait	30	15
1202	25q. Skanderbeg portrait (different)	90	15
1203	30q. Equestrian statue, Kruja (vert)	1·10	20
1204	35q. Skanderbeg and mountains	1·40	20
1205	65q. Bust of Skanderbeg	2·50	20
1206	80q. Title page of biography	2·75	85
1207	90q. "Skanderbeg battling with the Turks" (painting) (vert)	3·50	1·25

252 Alpine Dianthus

1968. Flowers. Multicoloured.

1208	15q. Type **252**	20	10
1209	20q. Chinese dianthus	25	15
1210	25q. Pink carnation	30	15
1211	50q. Red carnation and bud	85	20
1212	80q. Two red carnations	1·40	50
1213	1l.10 Yellow carnations	1·90	85

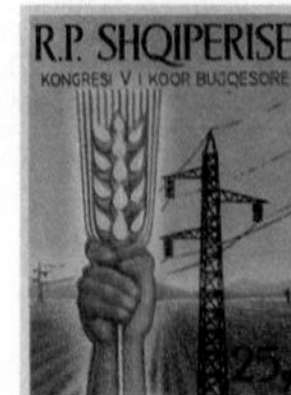
253 Ear of Wheat and Electricity Pylon

1968. 5th Agricultural Co-operative Congress. Mult.

1214	25q. Type **253**	40	15
1215	65q. Tractor (horiz)	1·25	45
1216	1l.10 Cow	1·90	40

254 Long-horned Goat

1968. Goats. Multicoloured.

1217	15q. Zane female	20	10
1218	20q. Kid	20	10
1219	25q. Long-haired capore	30	15
1220	30q. Black goat at rest	35	15

1221 40q. Kids dancing 75 20
1222 50q. Red and piebald goats 90 20
1223 80q. Long-haired ankara 1·60 30
1224 1l.40 Type **254** 2·75 85
The 15q., 20q. and 25q. are vert.

255 Zef Jubani **256** Doctor using Stethoscope

1968. 150th Birth Anniv of Zef Jubani (patriot).
1225 **255** 25q. brown and yellow 20 15
1226 1l.75 blue, black & vio 2·75 65

1968. 20th Anniv of W.H.O.
1227 **256** 25q. red and green 35 10
1228 – 65q. black, blue & yellow 75 20
1229 – 1l.10 brown and black 1·25 35
DESIGNS—HORIZ: 65q. Hospital and microscope. VERT: 1l.10, Mother feeding child.

257 Servicewoman

1968. 25th Anniv of Albanian Women's Union.
1230 **257** 15q. red and orange 25 15
1231 – 25q. turquoise and green 35 20
1232 – 60q. brown and ochre 1·00 30
1233 – 1l. violet and light violet 1·75 55
DESIGNS: 25q. Teacher; 60q. Farm-girl; 1l. Factory-worker.

258 Karl Marx

1968. 150th Birth Anniv of Karl Marx. Mult.
1234 15q. Type **258** 40 20
1235 25q. Marx addressing students 85 20
1236 65q. "Das Kapital", "Communist Manifesto" and marchers 1·60 65
1237 95q. Karl Marx 3·50 85

259 Heliopsis

1968. Flowers. Multicoloured.
1238 15q. Type **259** 10 10
1239 20q. Red flax 15 10
1240 25q. Orchid 20 10
1241 30q. Gloxinia 30 15
1242 40q. Orange lily 50 15
1243 80q. Hippeastrum 1·40 25
1244 1l.40 Purple magnolia 2·75 90

260 A. Frasheri and Torch

1968. 90th Anniv of Prizren Defence League.
1245 **260** 25q. black and green 40 15
1246 – 40q. multicoloured 95 20
1247 – 85q. multicoloured 1·60 40
DESIGNS: 40q. League headquarters; 85q. Frasheri's manifesto and partisans.

261 "Shepherd" (A. Kushi)

1968. Paintings in Tirana Gallery. Multicoloured.
1248 15q. Type **261** 15 10
1249 20q. "Tirana" (V. Mio) (horiz) 20 10
1250 25q. "Highlander" (G. Madhi) 25 15
1251 40q. "Refugees" (A. Buza) 75 15
1252 80q. "Partisans at Shahin Matrakut" (S. Xega) 1·40 50
1253 1l.50 "Old Man" (S. Papadhimitri) 2·75 1·00
1254 1l.70 "Shkoder Gate" (S. Rrota) 3·50 1·25
MS1255 90×114 mm. 2l.50 "Shkoder Costume" (Z. Colombi) (51×71 mm) 4·00 2·50

262 Soldiers and Armoured Vehicles

1968. 25th Anniv of People's Army. Multicoloured.
1256 15q. Type **262** 35 15
1257 25q. Sailor and naval craft 1·25 30
1258 65q. Pilot and Ilyushin Il-28 and Mikoyan Gurevich MiG-17 aircraft (vert) 2·50 85
1259 95q. Soldier and patriots 3·75 1·25

263 Common Squid

1968. Marine Fauna. Multicoloured.
1260 15q. Type **263** 25 10
1261 20q. Common lobster 20 10
1262 25q. Common northern whelk 65 15
1263 50q. Edible crab 1·00 40
1264 70q. Spiny lobster 1·40 65
1265 80q. Common green crab 1·75 85
1266 90q. Norwegian lobster 1·90 1·40

264 Relay-racing

1968. Olympic Games, Mexico. Multicoloured.
1267 15q. Type **264** 15 10
1268 20q. Running 20 10
1269 25q. Throwing the discus 25 10
1270 30q. Horse-jumping 30 15
1271 40q. High-jumping 35 15
1272 50q. Hurdling 40 20
1273 80q. Football 80 30
1274 1l.40 High diving 1·75 85
MS1275 90×81 mm. 2l. Olympic Stadium (64×54 mm.) 4·00 2·50

265 Enver Hoxha (Party Secretary) **266** Alphabet Book

1968. Enver Hoxha's 60th Birthday.
1276 **265** 25q. blue 35 25
1277 35q. purple 85 30
1278 80q. violet 1·75 90
1279 1l.10 brown 1·90 1·40
MS1280 80½×91 mm. **265** 1l.50 violet, red and gold. Imperf £120 £120

1968. 60th Anniv of Monastir Language Congress.
1281 **266** 15q. lake and green 65 15
1282 85q. brown and green 3·25 55

267 Bohemian Waxwing

1968. Birds. Multicoloured.
1283 15q. Type **267** 55 20
1284 20q. Rose-coloured starling 75 20
1285 25q. River kingfishers 1·10 30
1286 50q. Long-tailed tit 1·60 75
1287 80q. Wallcreeper 3·25 90
1288 1l.10 Bearded reedling 4·00 1·40

268 Mao Tse-tung

1968. Mao Tse-tung's 75th Birthday.
1289 **268** 25q. black, red and gold 85 30
1290 1l.75 black, red and gold 4·25 1·75

269 Adem Reka (dock foreman)

1969. Contemporary Heroes. Multicoloured.
1291 5q. Type **269** 10 10
1292 10q. Pjeter Lleshi (telegraph linesman) 15 10
1293 15q. M. Shehu and M. Kepi (fire victims) 20 15
1294 25q. Shkurte Vata (railway worker) 2·25 35
1295 65q. Agron Elezi (earthquake victim) 95 25
1296 80q. Ismet Bruca (schoolteacher) 1·25 40
1297 1l.30 Fuat Cela (blind Co-op leader) 1·90 50

270 Meteorological Equipment

1969. 20th Anniv of Albanian Hydro-meteorology. Multicoloured.
1298 15q. Type **270** 65 20
1299 25q. "Arrow" indicator 1·00 25
1300 1l.60 Meteorological balloon and isobar map 4·75 1·50

271 "Student Revolutionaries" (P. Mele)

1969. Albanian Paintings since 1944. Mult.
1301 5q. Type **271** 15 10
1302 25q. "Partisans 1914" (F. Haxhiu) (horiz) 20 10
1303 65q. "Steel Mill" (C. Ceka) (horiz) 75 15
1304 80q. "Reconstruction" (V. Kilica) (horiz) 85 30
1305 1l.10 "Harvest" (N. Jonuzi) (horiz) 1·40 35
1306 1l.15 "Seaside Terraces" (S. Kaceli) (horiz) 1·75 1·00
MS1307 111×91 mm. 2l. "Partisans' Meeting" (N. Zajmi). Imperf 2·50 2·00
SIZES: The 25q., 80q., 1l.10 and 1l.15 are 50×30 mm.

272 "Self-portrait" **273** Congress Building

1969. 450th Death Anniv of Leonardo da Vinci.
1308 **272** 25q. agate, brown & gold 30 15
1309 – 35q. agate, brown & gold 65 20
1310 – 40q. agate, brown & gold 85 20
1311 – 1l. multicoloured 1·90 85
1312 – 2l. agate, brown & gold 3·75 1·75
MS1313 65×95 mm. 2l. multicoloured. Imperf 7·00 4·50
DESIGNS—VERT: 35q. "Lilies"; 1l. "Portrait of Beatrice"; 2l. "Portrait of a Lady". HORIZ: 40q. Design for "Helicopter".

1969. 25th Anniv of Permet Congress. Mult.
1314 25q. Type **273** 35 25
1315 2l.25 Two partisans 4·25 2·75
MS1316 95×101 mm. 1l. Albanian arms. Imperf 45·00 40·00

274 "Viola albanica" **275** Plum

1969. Flowers. Viola Family. Multicoloured.
1317 5q. Type **274** 10 10
1318 10q. "Viola hortensis" 15 10
1319 15q. "Viola heterophylla" 20 15
1320 20q. "Viola hortensis" (different) 25 20
1321 25q. "Viola odorata" 35 20
1322 80q. "Viola hortensis" (different) 1·25 85
1323 1l.95 "Viola hortensis" (different) 2·25 1·75

1969. Fruit Trees. Blossom and Fruit. Mult.
1324 10q. Type **275** 15 20
1325 15q. Lemon 15 15
1326 25q. Pomegranate 50 15
1327 50q. Cherry 1·00 20
1328 80q. Apricot 1·75 85
1329 1l.20 Apple 2·75 1·40

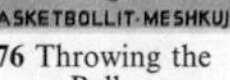

276 Throwing the Ball **277** Gymnastics

1969. 16th European Basketball Championships, Naples. Multicoloured.
1330 10q. Type **276** 20 10
1331 15q. Trying for goal 20 10
1332 25q. Ball and net (horiz) 35 15
1333 80q. Scoring a goal 1·10 25
1334 2l.20 Intercepting a pass 2·75 1·00

1969. National Spartakiad. Multicoloured.
1335 5q. Pickaxe, rifle, flag and stadium 15 10
1336 10q. Type **277** 15 10

1337 15q. Running 20 10
1338 20q. Pistol-shooting 25 15
1339 25q. Swimmer on starting block 30 15
1340 80q. Cycling 1·00 25
1341 95q. Football 1·25 45

278 Mao Tse-tung
279 Enver Hoxha

1969. 20th Anniv of Chinese People's Republic. Multicoloured
1342 25q. Type **278** 1·25 50
1343 85q. Steel ladle and control room (horiz) 4·00 1·25
1344 1l.40 Rejoicing crowd 6·00 2·25

1969. 25th Anniv of 2nd National Liberation Council Meeting, Berat. Multicoloured.
1345 25q. Type **279** 25 15
1346 80q. Star and Constitution 85 20
1347 1l.45 Freedom-fighters 1·60 40

280 Entry of Provisional Government, Tirana

1969. 25th Anniv of Liberation. Multicoloured.
1348 25q. Type **280** 20 10
1349 30q. Oil refinery 35 10
1350 35q. Combine harvester 75 15
1351 45q. Hydroelectric power station 1·10 15
1352 55q. Soldier and partisans 1·60 65
1353 1l.10 People rejoicing 2·75 1·25

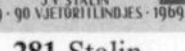
281 Stalin
282 Head of Woman

1969. 90th Birth Anniv of Joseph Stalin.
1354 **281** 15q. lilac 15 10
1355 25q. blue 20 15
1356 1l. brown 1·10 30
1357 1l.10 blue 1·25 35

1969. Mosaics. (1st series). Multicoloured.
1358 15q. Type **282** 15 10
1359 25q. Floor pattern 20 10
1360 80q. Bird and tree 85 20
1361 1l.10 Diamond floor pattern 1·10 30
1362 1l.20 Corn in oval pattern 1·60 35
Nos. 1359/61 are horiz.
See also Nos. 1391/6, 1564/70 and 1657/62.

283 Manifesto and Congress Building

285 "Lilium cernum"

284 "25" and Workers

1970. 50th Anniv of Lushnje Congress.
1363 **283** 25q. black, red and grey 30 20
1364 – 1l.25 black, yell & grn 1·90 85
DESIGN: 1l.25, Lushnje postmark of 1920.

1970. 25th Anniv of Albanian Trade Unions.
1365 **284** 25q. multicoloured 30 15
1366 1l.75 multicoloured 1·90 90

1970. Lilies. Multicoloured.
1367 5q. Type **285** 25 10
1368 15q. "Lilium candidum" 40 10
1369 25q. "Lilium regale" 70 20
1370 80q. "Lilium martagon" 1·75 30
1371 1l.10 "Lilium tigrinum" 2·25 75
1372 1l.15 "Lilium albanicum" 2·50 90
Nos. 1370/2 are horiz.

286 Lenin

1970. Birth Cent of Lenin. Each blk, silver & red.
1373 5q. Type **286** 10 10
1374 15q. Lenin making speech 15 15
1375 25q. As worker 20 15
1376 95q. As revolutionary 95 35
1377 1l.10 Saluting 1·40 40
Nos. 1374/6 are horiz.

287 Frontier Guard

1970. 25th Anniv of Frontier Force.
1378 **287** 25q. multicoloured 50 10
1379 1l.25 multicoloured 2·00 75

288 Jules Rimet Cup

1970. World Cup Football Championship, Mexico. Multicoloured.
1380 5q. Type **288** 10 10
1381 10q. Aztec Stadium 15 10
1382 15q. Three footballers 20 10
1383 25q. Heading goal 25 15
1384 65q. Two footballers 40 20
1385 80q. Two footballers 1·00 25
1386 2l. Two footballers 2·50 45
MS1387 81 × 74 mm. 2l. Mexican horseman and Mt. Popocatepetl 4·00 3·00
The design of **MS**1387 is larger, 56 × 45 mm.

289 New U.P.U. Headquarters Building

1970. New U.P.U. Headquarters Building, Berne.
1388 **289** 25q. blue, black and light blue 20 15
1389 1l.10 pink, black & orge 1·25 35
1390 1l.15 turq, blk & grn 1·40 45

290 Birds and Grapes

1970. Mosaics (2nd series). Multicoloured.
1391 5q. Type **290** 15 10
1392 10q. Waterfowl 20 10
1393 20q. Pheasant and tree stump 20 10
1394 25q. Bird and leaves 30 15
1395 65q. Fish 90 25
1396 2l.25 Peacock (vert) 2·25 85

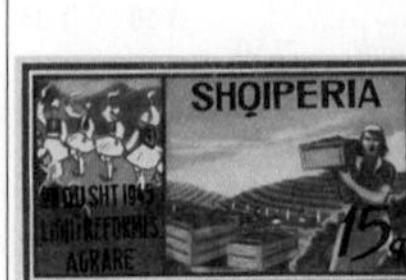
291 Harvesters and Dancers
292 Partisans going into Battle

1970. 25th Anniv of Agrarian Reform.
1397 **291** 15q. lilac and black 20 10
1398 – 25q. blue and black 25 10
1399 – 80q. brown and black 85 20
1400 – 1l.30 brown and black 1·25 35
DESIGNS: 25q. Ploughed fields and open-air conference; 80q. Cattle and newspapers; 1l.30, Combine-harvester and official visit.

1970. 50th Anniv of Battle of Vlore.
1401 **292** 15q. brown, orge & black 20 10
1402 – 25q. brown, yell & black 30 15
1403 – 1l.60 myrtle, grn & blk 1·40 85
DESIGNS: 25q. Victory parade; 1l.60, Partisans.

293 "The Harvesters" (I. Sulovari)

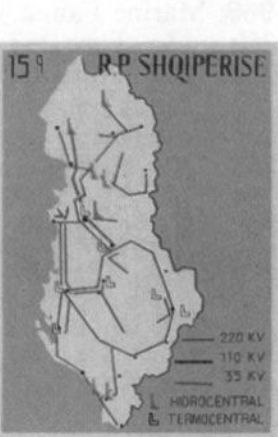
294 Electrification Map

1970. 25th Anniv of Liberation. Prize-winning Paintings. Multicoloured.
1404 5q. Type **293** 10 10
1405 15q. "Return of the Partisan" (D. Trebicka) (horiz) 15 10
1406 25q. "The Miners" (N. Zajmi) (horiz) 20 10
1407 65q. "Instructing the Partisans" (H. Nallbani) (horiz) 35 20
1408 95q. "Making Plans" (V. Kilica) (horiz) 85 50
1409 2l. "The Machinist" (Z. Shoshi) 2·50 90
MS1410 67 × 96 mm. 2l. "The Guerrilla" (S. Shijaku). (54 × 75 mm). Imperf 3·50 2·50

1970. Rural Electrification Completion. Mult.
1411 15q. Type **294** 20 10
1412 25q. Lamp and graph 25 15
1413 80q. Erecting power lines 85 20
1414 1l.10 Uses of electricity 1·40 50

295 Engels

296 Beethoven's Birthplace

295a Tractor Factory, Tirana

1970. 150th Birth Anniv of Friedrich Engels.
1415 **295** 25q. blue and bistre 25 15
1416 – 1l.10 purple and bistre 1·25 55
1417 – 1l.15 olive and bistre 1·25 70
DESIGNS: 1l.10, Engels as a young man; 1l.15, Engels making speech.

1971. Industry. Multicoloured.
1417a 10q. Type **295a** £130 75·00
1417b 15q. Fertiliser factory, Fier £130 75·00
1417c 20q. Superphosphate factory, Lac (vert) £130 75·00
1417d 25q. Cement factory, Elbasan £130 75·00

1970. Birth Bicentenary of Beethoven.
1418 **296** 5q. violet and gold 20 10
1419 – 15q. purple and silver 20 20
1420 – 25q. green and gold 50 20
1421 – 65q. purple and silver 1·00 50
1422 – 1l.10 blue and gold 1·50 50
1423 – 1l.80 black and silver 3·00 1·00
DESIGNS—VERT: Beethoven: 15q. In silhouette; 25q. As young man; 65q. Full-face; 1l.10, Profile. HORIZ: 1l.80, Stage performance of "Fidelio".

297 Republican Emblem

1971. 25th Anniv of Republic.
1424 **297** 15q. multicoloured 10 10
1425 – 25q. multicoloured 15 10
1426 – 80q. black, gold & green 90 15
1427 – 1l.30 black, gold & brn 1·25 65
DESIGNS: 25q. Proclamation; 80q. Enver Hoxha; 1l.30, Patriots.

298 "Storming the Barricades"

1971. Centenary of Paris Commune.
1428 – 25q. blue and deep blue 40 10
1429 – 50q. green and grey 50 20
1430 **298** 65q. chestnut and brown 80 20
1431 – 1l.10 lilac and violet 1·50 80
DESIGNS—VERT: 25q. "La Marseillaise"; 50q. Women Communards. HORIZ: 1l.10, Firing squad.

299 "Conflict of Race"
300 Tulip

1971. Racial Equality Year.
1432 **299** 25q. black and brown 20 15
1433 – 1l.10 black and red 85 25
1434 – 1l.15 black and red 95 30
DESIGNS—VERT: 1l.10, Heads of three races; 1l.15, Freedom fighters.

1971. Hybrid Tulips.
1435 **300** 5q. multicoloured 15 10
1436 – 10q. multicoloured 15 10
1437 – 15q. multicoloured 20 10
1438 – 20q. multicoloured 20 10
1439 – 25q. multicoloured 55 15
1440 – 80q. multicoloured 1·40 20
1441 – 1l. multicoloured 1·90 65
1442 – 1l.45 multicoloured 3·50 1·40
DESIGNS: 10q. to 1l.45, Different varieties of tulips.

301 "Postrider" **302** Globe and Satellite (1970)

1971. 500th Birth Anniv of Albrecht Durer (painter and engraver).

1443 **301** 10q. black and green . . 15 10
1444 – 15q. black and blue . . 30 10
1445 – 25q. black and blue . . 50 15
1446 – 45q. black and purple . . 85 15
1447 – 65q. multicoloured . . . 1·25 25
1448 – 2l.40 multicoloured . . . 3·25 1·00
MS1449 93 × 90 mm. 2l.50 multicoloured. Imperf . . . . 5·00 3·50

DESIGNS—VERT: 15q. "Three Peasants"; 25q. "Peasant Dancers"; 45q. "The Bagpiper". HORIZ: 65q. "View of Kalchreut"; 2l.40, "View of Trient". LARGER: 2l.50, Self-portrait.

1971. Chinese Space Achievements. Multicoloured.

1450 60q. Type **302** 75 20
1451 1l.20 Public Building, Tirana 1·25 30
1452 2l.20 Globe and satellite (1971) . . . . 2·50 60
MS1453 65 × 112 mm. 2l.50 Globe and arrow. Imperf . . . . . . 5·00 3·50

The date on No. 1451 refers to the passage of Chinese satellite over Tirana.

303 Mao Tse-tung

1971. 50th Anniv of Chinese Communist Party. Multicoloured.

1454 25q. Type **303** 70 20
1455 1l.05 Party Birthplace (horiz) . . . . 1·75 70
1456 1l.20 Chinese celebrations (horiz) . . . . 2·50 1·00

304 Crested Tit

1971. Birds. Multicoloured.

1457 5q. Type **304** 25 20
1458 10q. European serin 30 20
1459 15q. Linnet 40 20
1460 25q. Firecrest 60 20
1461 45q. Rock thrush 90 25
1462 60q. Blue tit . . . . 1·40 60
1463 2l.40 Chaffinch . . . . . . 5·25 4·00

305 Running

1971. Olympic Games (1972). (1st issue). Mult.

1464 5q. Type **305** 10 10
1465 10q. Hurdling 15 10
1466 15q. Canoeing 15 10
1467 25q. Gymnastics 25 15
1468 80q. Fencing 55 25
1469 1l.05 Football . . . . . . 1·10 25
1470 3l.60 Diving . . . . 4·00 1·10
MS1471 70 × 83 mm. 2l. Runner breasting tape (47 × 54 mm). Imperf . . . . 4·00 3·00

See also Nos. 1522/**MS**1530.

306 Workers with Banner **307** "XXX" and Red Flag

1971. 6th Workers' Party Congress. Multicoloured.

1472 25q. Type **306** 25 15
1473 1l.05 Congress hall . . . . 1·40 95
1474 1l.20 "VI", flag, star and rifle (vert) . . . . 1·75 1·25

1971. 30th Anniv of Albanian Workers' Party. Multicoloured.

1475 15q. Workers and industry (horiz) . . . . 2·50 15
1476 80q. Type **307** . . . . . . 1·00 75
1477 1l.55 Enver Hoxha and flags (horiz) . . . . 2·00 1·75

308 "Young Man" (R. Kuci)

1971. Albanian Paintings. Multicoloured.

1478 5q. Type **308** 10 10
1479 15q. "Building Construction" (M. Fushekati) 15 10
1480 25q. "Partisan" (D. Jukniu) 20 10
1481 80q. "Fighter Pilots" (S. Kristo) (horiz) . . . . 1·00 20
1482 1l.20 "Girl Messenger" (A. Sadikaj) (horiz) . . . 1·40 65
1483 1l.55 "Medieval Warriors" (S. Kamberi) (horiz) . . . 2·00 1·25
MS1484 89 × 70 mm. 2l. "Partisans in the Mountains" (I. Lulani). Imperf . . . . 4·00 3·00

309 Emblems and Flags

1971. 30th Anniv of Albanian Young Communists' Union.

1485 **309** 15q. multicoloured . . . 15 10
1486 1l.35 multicoloured . . . 1·60 80

310 Village Girls

1971. Albanian Ballet "Halili and Hajria". Mult.

1487 5q. Type **310** 15 10
1488 10q. Parting of Halili and Hajria 20 10
1489 15q. Hajria before Sultan Suleiman 20 10
1490 50q. Hajria's marriage . . . 85 20
1491 80q. Execution of Halili . . 1·25 65
1492 1l.40 Hajria killing her husband . . . . 2·25 1·25

311 Rifle-shooting (Biathlon)

1972. Winter Olympic Games, Sapporo, Japan. Multicoloured.

1493 5q. Type **311** 10 10
1494 10q. Tobogganing 15 10
1495 15q. Ice-hockey 15 10
1496 20q. Bobsleighing 20 10
1497 50q. Speed skating 30 20
1498 1l. Slalom skiing . . . . . 1·10 30
1499 2l. Ski jumping . . . . . . 2·00 95
MS1500 71 × 91 mm. 2l.50 Figure skating. Imperf . . . . 4·00 3·00

312 Wild Strawberries

1972. Wild Fruits, Multicoloured.

1501 5q. Type **312** 15 10
1502 10q. Blackberries 15 10
1503 15q. Hazelnuts 20 10
1504 20q. Walnuts 25 15
1505 25q. Strawberry-tree fruit . . 30 15
1506 30q. Dogwood berries . . . 45 20
1507 2l.40 Rowanberries . . . . 2·50 1·10

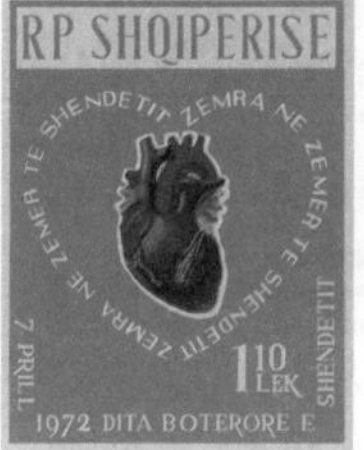

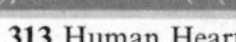

313 Human Heart **314** Congress Delegates

1972. World Health Day. Multicoloured.

1508 1l.10 Type **313** . . . . . . 1·10 30
1509 1l.20 Treatment of cardiac patient . . . . 1·25 75

1972. 7th Albanian Trade Unions Congress. Mult.

1510 25q. Type **314** 30 20
1511 2l.05 Congress Hall . . . . 1·90 1·00

315 Memorial Flame

1972. 30th Anniv of Martyrs' Day, and Death of Qemal Stafa.

1512 **315** 15q. multicoloured . . . 20 10
1513 – 25q. black, orge & grey 25 15
1514 – 1l.90 black and ochre . . 1·90 35

DESIGNS—VERT: 25q. "Spirit of Defiance" (statue). HORIZ: 1l.90, Qemal Stafa.

316 "Camellia japonica Kamelie"

1972. Camellias.

1515 **316** 5q. multicoloured . . . 15 10
1516 – 10q. multicoloured . . . 20 10
1517 – 15q. multicoloured . . . 20 10
1518 – 25q. multicoloured . . . 25 10
1519 – 45q. multicoloured . . . 40 15
1520 – 50q. multicoloured . . . 50 20
1521 – 2l.50 multicoloured . . . 3·50 2·25

DESIGNS: Nos. 1516/21, Various camellias as Type **316**.

317 High Jumping

1972. Olympic Games, Munich (2nd issue). Mult.

1522 5q. Type **317** 10 10
1523 10q. Running 10 10
1524 15q. Putting the shot . . . 15 10
1525 20q. Cycling 15 10
1526 25q. Pole-vaulting 20 10
1527 50q. Hurdling 35 15
1528 75q. Hockey 65 25
1529 2l. Swimming 90 75
MS1530 59 × 76 mm. 2l.50 High-diving (vert). Imperf . . . . . 4·00 3·00

318 Articulated bus

1972. Modern Transport. Multicoloured.

1531 15q. Type **318** 15 10
1532 25q. Czechoslovakian Class T699 diesel locomotive . . 2·00 15
1533 80q. Freighter "Tirana" . . 1·40 30
1534 1l.05 Motor-car 80 25
1535 1l.20 Container truck . . . 1·25 50

319 "Trial of Strength"

1972. 1st Nat Festival of Traditional Games. Mult.

1536 5q. Type **319** 10 10
1537 10q. Pick-a-back ball game 15 10
1538 15q. Leaping game 15 10
1539 25q. Rope game 20 10
1540 90q. Leap-frog 65 20
1541 2l. Women's throwing game 1·60 75

320 Newspaper "Mastheads"

1972. 30th Anniv of Press Day.

1542 **320** 15q. black and blue . . 20 10
1543 – 25q. green, red & black 25 15
1544 – 1l.90 black and mauve 1·90 95

DESIGNS: 25q. Printing-press and partisan; 1l.90, Workers with newspaper.

321 Location Map and Commemorative Plaque

1972. 30th Anniv of Peza Conference. Mult.

1545 15q. Type **321** 30 20
1546 25q. Partisans with flag . . 45 30
1547 1l.90 Conference Memorial 2·00 1·25

322 "Partisans Conference" (S. Capo)

1972. Albanian Paintings. Multicoloured.

1548 5q. Type **322** 10 10
1549 10q. "Head of Woman" (I. Lulani) (vert) 15 10
1550 15q. "Communists" (L. Shkreli) (vert) 15 10
1551 20q. "Nendorit, 1941" (S. Shijaku) (vert) 20 10
1552 50q. "Farm Woman" (Z. Shoshi) (vert) 65 20
1553 1l. "Landscape" (D. Trebicka) . . . . . . 1·25 50
1554 2l. "Girls with Bicycles" (V. Kilica) . . . . 2·50 1·25
MS1555 55 × 83 mm. 2l.30 "Folk Dance" (A. Buza) (vert, 40 × 67 mm). Imperf . . . . . 4·00 3·00

323 Congress Emblem **324** Lenin

1972. 6th Congress of Young Communists' Union.
1556 **323** 25q. gold, red and silver 30 15
1557 – 2l.05 multicoloured . . . 2·00 1·00
DESIGN: 2l.05, Young worker and banner.

1972. 55th Anniv of Russian October Revolution. Multicoloured.
1558 – 1l.10 multicoloured . . . 1·25 65
1559 **324** 1l.20 red, blk & pink . . 1·25 75
DESIGN: 1l.10, Hammer and Sickle.

325 Albanian Soldiers

1972. 60th Anniv of Independence.
1560 **325** 15q. blue, red and black 15 15
1561 – 25q. black, red & yellow 25 20
1562 – 65q. multicoloured . . . 45 20
1563 – 1l.25 black and red . . . 1·00 75
DESIGNS—VERT: 25q. Ismail Qemali; 1l.25, Albanian double-eagle emblem. HORIZ: 65q. Proclamation of Independence, 1912.

326 Cockerel (mosaic)

1972. Ancient Mosaics from Apolloni and Butrint (3rd series). Multicoloured.
1564 5q. Type **326** 10 10
1565 10q. Bird (vert) 15 10
1566 15q. Partridges (vert) . . . 20 10
1567 25q. Warrior's leg 25 15
1568 45q. Nude on dolphin (vert) 35 20
1569 50q. Fish (vert) 40 20
1570 2l.50 Warrior's head . . . . 3·25 1·75

327 Nicolas Copernicus

1973. 500th Birth Anniv of Copernicus. Mult.
1571 5q. Type **327** 10 10
1572 10q. Copernicus and signatures 15 10
1573 25q. Engraved portrait . . . 20 15
1574 80q. Copernicus at desk . . 1·00 25
1575 1l.20 Copernicus and planets 1·60 65
1576 1l.60 Planetary diagram . . 1·90 85

328 Policeman and Industrial Scene

1973. 30th Anniv of State Security Police.
1577 **328** 25q. black, blue & lt blue 30 20
1578 – 1l.80 multicoloured . . . 1·90 1·40
DESIGN: 1l.80, Prisoner under escort.

329/30 Cactus Flowers

1973. Cacti. As T **329/30**.
1579 **329** 10q. multicoloured . . . 10 10
1580 **330** 15q. multicoloured . . . 15 10
1581 – 20q. multicoloured . . . 20 10
1582 – 25q. multicoloured . . . 20 10
1583 – 30q. multicoloured . . . 4·50 1·75
1584 – 65q. multicoloured . . . 85 20
1585 – 80q. multicoloured . . . 1·00 25
1586 – 2l. multicoloured . . . . 1·90 85
Nos. 1579/86 were issued together se-tenant within the sheet and in alternate formats as Types **329/30**.

331 Common Tern

1973. Sea Birds. Multicoloured.
1587 5q. Type **331** 25 20
1588 15q. White-winged black tern 35 25
1589 25q. Black-headed gull . . . 40 25
1590 45q. Great black-headed gull 75 45
1591 80q. Slender-billed gull . . . 1·40 80
1592 2l.40 Sandwich tern . . . . 3·50 2·10

332 Postmark of 1913, and Letters

1973. 60th Anniv of First Albanian Stamps. Mult.
1593 25q. Type **332** . . . . . . 1·00 35
1594 1l.80 Postman and postmarks . . . . 4·00 1·50

333 Albanian Woman

1973. 7th Albanian Women's Congress.
1595 **333** 25q. red and pink . . . 25 15
1596 – 1l.80 black, orge & yell 1·75 1·40
DESIGN: 1l.80, Albanian female workers.

334 "Creation of the General Staff" (G. Madhi)

1973. 30th Anniv of Albanian People's Army. Mult.
1597 25q. Type **334** . . . . . . 12·00 5·00
1598 40q. "August 1949" (sculpture by Sh. Haderi) (vert) . . . . 12·00 5·00
1599 60q. "Generation after Generation" (Statue by H. Dule) (vert) . . . . . 12·00 5·00
1600 80q. "Defend Revolutionary Victories" (M. Fushekati) 12·00 5·00

335 "Electrification" (S. Hysa)

1973. Albanian Paintings. Multicoloured.
1601 5q. Type **335** 10 10
1602 10q. "Textile Worker" (E. Nallbani) (vert) . . . 15 10
1603 15q. "Gymnastics Class" (M. Fushekati) 15 10
1604 50q. "Aviator" (F. Stamo) (vert) 65 15
1605 80q. "Downfall of Fascism" (A. Lakuriqi) 90 20
1606 1l.20 "Koci Bako" (demonstrators (P. Mele)) (vert) . . . . 1·40 25
1607 1l.30 "Peasant Girl" (Z. Shoshi) (vert) . . . . 1·75 30
MS1608 100 × 69 mm. 2l.05 "Battle of Tendes se Qypit" (F. Haxhiu) (88 × 47 mm). Imperf . . . . . 4·00 3·00

336 "Mary Magdalene" **338** Weightlifting

337 Goalkeeper with Ball

1973. 400th Birth Anniv of Caravaggio. Paintings. Multicoloured.
1609 5q. Type **336** 10 10
1610 10q. "The Guitar Player" (horiz) 15 10
1611 15q. Self-portrait 20 10
1612 50q. "Boy carrying Fruit" 65 20
1613 80q. "Basket of Fruit" (horiz) 90 25
1614 1l.20 "Narcissus" . . . . . 1·40 65
1615 1l.30 "Boy peeling Apple" 2·25 90
MS1616 80 × 102 mm. 2l.05 "Man in Feathered Hat". Imperf . . . 5·00 3·50

1973. World Cup Football Championship, Munich (1974) (1st issue). Multicoloured.
1617 **337** 5q. multicoloured . . . 10 10
1618 – 10q. multicoloured . . . 15 10
1619 – 15q. multicoloured . . . 15 10
1620 – 20q. multicoloured . . . 20 10
1621 – 25q. multicoloured . . . 25 15
1622 – 90q. multicoloured . . . 1·40 20
1623 – 1l.20 multicoloured . . . 1·90 30
1624 – 1l.25 multicoloured . . . 1·90 85
MS1625 80 × 50 mm. 2l.05 multicoloured (Ball in net, and list of Championships). Imperf . . 5·00 3·50
DESIGNS: Nos. 1618/24 are similar to Type **337**, showing goalkeepers saving goals.
See also Nos. 1663/70.

1973. World Weightlifting Championships, Havana, Cuba.
1626 **338** 5q. multicoloured . . . 10 10
1627 – 10q. multicoloured . . . 15 10
1628 – 25q. multicoloured . . . 20 10
1629 – 90q. multicoloured . . . 90 25
1630 – 1l.20 mult (horiz) . . . 1·10 35
1631 – 1l.60 mult (horiz) . . . 1·60 40
DESIGNS: Nos. 1627/31 are similar to Type **338**, showing various lifts.

339 Ballet Scene **340** Mao Tse-tung

1973. "Albanian Life and Work". Multicoloured.
1632 5q. Cement Works, Kavaje 10 10
1633 10q. Ali Kelmendi truck factory and trucks (horiz) 15 10
1634 15q. Type **339** 20 10
1635 20q. Combine-harvester (horiz) 25 15
1636 25q. "Telecommunications" 25 15
1637 35q. Skier and hotel, Dajt (horiz) 35 15
1638 60q. Llogora holiday village (horiz) 50 20
1639 80q. Lake scene 65 25
1640 1l. Textile mill (horiz) . . . 50 20
1641 1l.20 Furnacemen (horiz) . . 80 25
1642 2l.40 Welder and pipeline (horiz) . . . . 2·00 50
1643 3l. Skanderbeg Statue, Tirana . . . . 2·75 65
1644 5l. Roman arches, Durres 4·25 1·75

1973. 80th Birth Anniv of Mao Tse-tung. Mult.
1645 85q. Type **340** . . . . . . 1·00 20
1646 1l.20 Mao Tse-tung at parade . . . . 1·75 85

341 "Horse's Head" (Gericault)

1974. 150th Death Anniv of Jean-Louis Gericault (French painter).
1647 **341** 10q. multicoloured . . . 15 10
1648 – 15q. multicoloured . . . 15 10
1649 – 20q. black and gold . . . 20 10
1650 – 25q. black, lilac and gold 25 15
1651 – 1l.20 multicoloured . . . 1·60 30
1652 – 2l.20 multicoloured . . . 3·50 1·25
MS1653 90 × 68 mm. 2l.05 multicoloured. Imperf . . . . . 4·00 3·00
DESIGNS—VERT: 15q. "Male Model" (Gericault); 20q. "Man and Dog"; 25q. "Head of a Negro"; 1l.20, Self-portrait. HORIZ: 2l.20, "Battle of the Giants".

342 "Lenin with Crew of the 'Aurora'" (D. Trebicka)

1974. 50th Death Anniv of Lenin. Multicoloured.
1654 25q. Type **342** 25 15
1655 60q. "Lenin" (P. Mele) (vert) . . . . 1·00 20
1656 1l.20 "Lenin" (seated) (V. Kilica) (vert) . . . . 2·00 1·25

343 Duck

1974. Ancient Mosaics from Butrint, Pogradec and Apolloni (4th series). Multicoloured.
1657 5q. Duck (different) 10 10
1658 10q. Bird and flower 15 10
1659 15q. Ornamental basket and grapes 15 10
1660 25q. Type **343** 20 10
1661 40q. Donkey and cockerel 35 20
1662 2l.50 Dragon . . . . 2·75 1·10

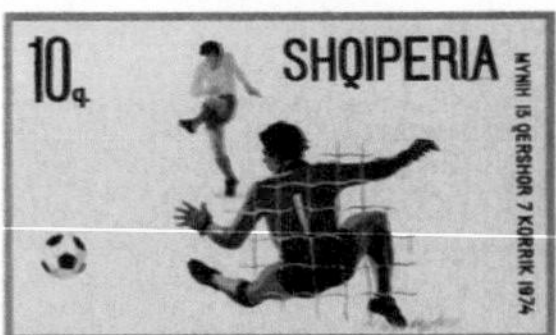

344 Shooting at Goal

1974. World Cup Football Championships, Munich (2nd issue).
1663 **344** 10q. multicoloured . . . 15 10
1664 – 15q. multicoloured . . . 15 10
1665 – 20q. multicoloured . . . 20 10
1666 – 25q. multicoloured . . . 25 10
1667 – 40q. multicoloured . . . 35 15
1668 – 80q. multicoloured . . . 1·00 25
1669 – 1l. multicoloured . . . . 1·25 25
1670 – 1l.20 multicoloured . . . 1·60 45
MS1671 72 × 75 mm. 2l.05 multicoloured (Trophy and names of competing countries). Imperf 4·00 3·00
DESIGNS: Nos. 1664/70, Players in action similar to Type **344**.

345 Memorial and Arms **346** "Solanum dulcamara"

1974. 30th Anniv of Permet Congress. Mult.
1672 25q. Type **345** 20 15
1673 1l.80 Enver Hoxha and text 1·40 40

1974. Useful Plants. Multicoloured.
1674 10q. Type **346** 15 10
1675 15q. "Arbutus uva-ursi" (vert) 15 10
1676 20q. "Convallaria majalis" (vert) 15 10
1677 25q. "Colchicum autumnale" (vert) 20 10
1678 40q. "Borago officinalis" . . 75 20
1679 80q. "Saponaria officinalis" 1·40 25
1680 2l.20 "Gentiana lutea" . . . 3·50 1·40

347 Revolutionaries

1974. 50th Anniv of 1924 Revolution.
1681 **347** 25q. mauve, black & red 20 15
1682 – 1l.80 multicoloured . . . 1·25 40
DESIGN—VERT: 1l.80, Prominent revolutionaries.

348 Redwing

1974. Song Birds. Multicoloured.
1683 10q. Type **348** 20 20
1684 15q. European robin 20 20
1685 20q. Western greenfinch . . 20 20
1686 25q. Northern bullfinch (vert) 45 20
1687 40q. Hawfinch (vert) 55 20
1688 80q. Blackcap (vert) . . . . 1·25 60
1689 2l.20 Nightingale (vert) . . . 3·00 1·90

349 Globe and Post Office Emblem

1974. Centenary of Universal Postal Union. Multicoloured.
1690 **349** 85q. multicoloured . . . 1·00 50
1691 – 1l.20 green, lilac & violet 1·50 75
MS1692 78 × 78 mm. 2l.05 multicoloured. Imperf . . . . 22·00 22·00
DESIGNS—Vert: 1l.20, U.P.U. emblem. Square: (70 × 70 mm.) 2l.50, Text on globe.

350 "Widows" (Sali Shijaku)

1974. Albanian Paintings. Multicoloured.
1693 10q. Type **350** 10 10
1694 15q. "Road Construction" (Danish Jukniu) (vert) . . 20 10
1695 20q. "Fulfilling the Plans" (Clirim Ceka) 25 10
1696 25q. "The Call to Action" (Spiro Kristo) (vert) . . . 30 20
1697 40q. "The Winter Battle" (Sabaudin Xhaferi) . . . 40 20

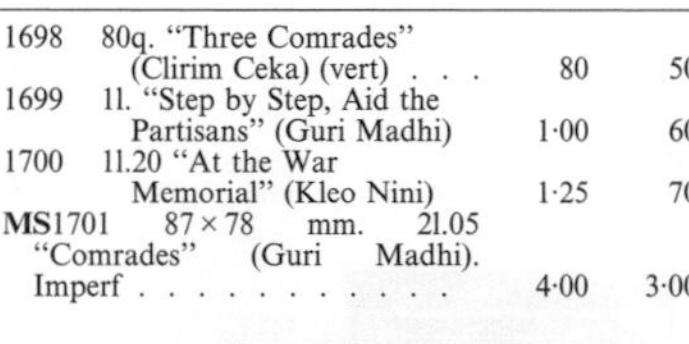

1698 80q. "Three Comrades" (Clirim Ceka) (vert) . . . 80 50
1699 1l. "Step by Step, Aid the Partisans" (Guri Madhi) 1·00 60
1700 1l.20 "At the War Memorial" (Kleo Nini) 1·25 70
MS1701 87 × 78 mm. 2l.05 "Comrades" (Guri Madhi). Imperf . . . . 4·00 3·00

351 Chinese Festivities

1974. 25th Anniv of Chinese People's Republic. Multicoloured.
1702 **351** 85q. multicoloured . . . 85 25
1703 – 1l.20 black, red and gold 1·25 30
DESIGN—VERT: 1l.20, Mao Tse-tung.

352 Volleyball **353** Berat

1974. National Spartakiad. Multicoloured.
1704 10q. Type **352** 10 10
1705 15q. Hurdling 10 10
1706 20q. Hoop exercises 15 10
1707 25q. Stadium parade 15 10
1708 40q. Weightlifting 20 10
1709 80q. Wrestling 40 20
1710 1l. Rifle shooting 75 25
1711 1l.20 Football 85 25

1974. 30th Anniv of 2nd Berat Liberal Council Meeting.
1712 **353** 25q. red and black . . . 20 15
1713 – 80q. yellow, brown and black 75 20
1714 – 1l. purple and black . . 1·10 50
DESIGNS—HORIZ: 80q. "Liberation" frieze. VERT: 1l. Council members walking to meeting.

354 Security Guards patrolling Industrial Plant

1974. 30th Anniv of Liberation. Multicoloured.
1715 25q. Type **354** 15 10
1716 35q. Chemical industry . . . 20 10
1717 50q. Agricultural produce 30 15
1718 80q. Cultural activities . . . 40 20
1719 1l. Scientific technology . . 80 25
1720 1l.20 Railway construction 2·50 50
MS1721 81 × 70 mm. 2l.05 Albanians with book (60 × 40 mm). Imperf . . . . . 4·00 3·00

355 Head of Artemis **356** Clasped hands

1974. Archaeological Discoveries. Multicoloured.
1722 **355** 10q. black, mauve & sil 10 10
1723 – 15q. black, green and silver 15 10
1724 – 20q. black, buff & silver 15 10
1725 – 25q. black, mauve & sil 20 10
1726 – 40q. multicoloured . . . 20 10
1727 – 80q. black, blue & silver 70 20
1728 – 1l. black, green & silver 90 20
1729 – 1l.20 black, sepia & sil 1·75 75
MS1730 96 × 96 mm. 2l.05 multicoloured. Imperf . . . . 4·00 3·00

DESIGNS: 15q. Statue of Zeus; 20q. Statue of Poseidon; 25q. Illyrian helmet; 40q. Greek amphora; 80q. Bust of Agrippa; 1l. Bust of Demosthenes; 1l.20, Bust of Bilia. Square: (84 × 84 mm.) 2l.50, Head of Artemis and Greek vase.

1975. 30th Anniv of Albanian Trade Unions. Mult.
1731 25q. Type **356** 20 15
1732 1l.80 Workers with arms raised (horiz) . . . . . . 1·25 50

357 "Cichorium intybus"

1975. Albanian Flowers. Multicoloured.
1733 5q. Type **357** 10 10
1734 10q. "Sempervivum montanum" 10 10
1735 15q. "Aquilegia alpina" . . 10 10
1736 20q. "Anemone hortensis" 15 10
1737 25q. "Hibiscus trionum" . . 15 10
1738 30q. "Gentiana kochiana" 20 10
1739 35q. "Lavatera arborea" . . 20 10
1740 2l.70 "Iris graminea" . . . 1·90 70

358 Head of Jesus (detail, Doni Tondo)

1975. 500th Birth Anniv of Michelangelo. Mult.
1741 **358** 5q. multicoloured . . . 10 10
1742 – 10q. brown, grey & gold 10 10
1743 – 15q. brown, grey & gold 15 10
1744 – 20q. sepia, grey and gold 20 10
1745 – 25q. multicoloured . . . 20 10
1746 – 30q. brown, grey & gold 20 10
1747 – 1l.20 brn, grey & gold 85 30
1748 – 3l.90 multicoloured . . . 2·50 1·00
MS1749 77 × 86 mm. 2l.05 multicoloured. Imperf . . . . 4·50 3·00
DESIGNS: 10q. "The Heroic Captive"; 15q. "Head of Dawn"; 20q. "Awakening Giant" (detail); 25q. "Cumaenian Sybil" (detail, Sistine chapel); 30q. "Lorenzo di Medici"; 1l.20, Head and shoulders of "David"; 3l.90, "Delphic Sybil" (detail, Sistine chapel). 70 × 77 mm. 2l.05, Head of Michelangelo.

359 Horseman

1975. "Albanian Transport of the Past". Mult.
1750 5q. Type **359** 10 10
1751 10q. Horse and cart 15 10
1752 15q. Ferry 40 15
1753 20q. Barque 40 15
1754 25q. Horse-drawn cab . . . 30 15
1755 3l.35 Early car . . . . . . 2·75 85

360 Frontier Guard

1975. 30th Anniv of Frontier Force. Mult.
1756 25q. Type **360** 20 15
1757 1l.80 Guards patrolling industrial plant . . . . . 1·75 90

361 Patriot affixing Anti-fascist Placard

1975. 30th Anniv of "Victory over Fascism". Mult.
1758 25q. Type **361** 15 10
1759 60q. Partisans in battle . . . 30 10
1760 1l.20 Patriot defeating Nazi soldier . . . . 1·25 55

362 European Wigeon

1975. Albanian Wildfowl. Multicoloured.
1761 5q. Type **362** 20 20
1762 10q. Red-crested pochard 20 20
1763 15q. White-fronted goose . . 20 20
1764 20q. Pintail 20 20
1765 25q. Red-breasted merganser 20 20
1766 30q. Eider 35 20
1767 35q. Whooper swans . . . 45 20
1768 2l.70 Common shoveler . . 2·75 1·40

363 "Shyqyri Kanapari" (Musa Qarri)

1975. Albanian Paintings. People's Art Exhibition, Tirana. Multicoloured.
1769 5q. Type **363** 10 10
1770 10q. "Sea Rescue" (Agim Faja) 10 10
1771 15q. "28 November 1912" (Petri Ceno) (horiz) . . . 10 10
1772 20q. "Workers' Meeting" (Sali Shijaka) 15 10
1773 25q. "Shota Galica" (Ismail Lulani) 15 10
1774 30q. "Victorious Fighters" (Nestor Jonuzi) 20 15
1775 80q. "Partisan Comrades" (Vilson Halimi) 65 20
1776 2l.25 "Republic Day Celebration" (Fatmir Haxhiu) (horiz) . . . . . 1·60 1·25
MS1777 68 × 98 mm. 2l.05 "Folk dance" (Abdurahim Buza). Imperf 3·00 2·00

364 Farmer with Declaration of Reform

1975. 30th Anniv of Agrarian Reform. Mult.
1778 15q. Type **364** 15 15
1779 2l. Agricultural scene . . . 1·40 75

365 Dead Man's Fingers **366** Cycling

1975. Marine Corals. Multicoloured.
1780 5q. Type **365** 10 10
1781 10q. "Paramuricea chamaeleon" 15 10
1782 20q. Red Coral 15 10
1783 25q. Tube Coral or Sea Fan 30 15
1784 3l.70 "Cladocora cespitosa" 4·25 1·75

1975. Olympic Games, Montreal (1976). Mult.
1785 5q. Type **366** 10 10
1786 10q. Canoeing 10 10
1787 15q. Handball 15 10
1788 20q. Basketball 15 10
1789 25q. Water-polo 20 10
1790 30q. Hockey 20 10
1791 1l.20 Pole vaulting 85 25
1792 2l.05 Fencing . . . . 1·40 35
MS1793 73 × 77 mm. 2l.15 Games emblem and sportsmen. Imperf 6·00 6·00

367 Power Lines leading to Village

1975. 5th Anniv of Electrification of Albanian Countryside. Multicoloured.
1794 **367** 15q. multicoloured . . . 15 15
1795 – 25q. violet, red and lilac 20 15
1796 – 80q. black, turq & green 85 20
1797 – 85q. buff, brn & ochre 1·25 85
DESIGNS: 25q. High power insulators; 80q. Dam and power station; 85q. T.V. pylons and emblems of agriculture and industry.

368 Berat

1975. Air. Tourist Resorts. Multicoloured.
1798 20q. Type **368** 25 15
1799 40q. Gjirokaster 40 20
1800 60q. Sarande 70 30
1801 90q. Durres 90 40
1802 1l.20 Krujae . . . . . . 1·25 50
1803 2l.40 Boga . . . . 2·40 1·00
1804 4l.05 Tirana . . . . . . 3·50 1·75

369 Child, Rabbit and Bear planting Saplings

1975. Children's Tales. Multicoloured.
1805 5q. Type **369** 10 10
1806 10q. Mrs. Fox and cub . . 10 10
1807 15q. Ducks in school . . . 15 10
1808 20q. Bears building 15 10
1809 25q. Animals watching television 20 10
1810 30q. Animals with log and electric light bulbs 20 10
1811 35q. Ants with spade and guitar 35 15
1812 2l.70 Boy and girl with sheep and dog . . . . . 1·90 85

370 Arms and Rejoicing Crowd

1976. 30th Anniv of Albanian People's Republic. Multicoloured.
1813 25q. Type **370** 20 15
1814 1l.90 Folk-dancers . . . . . 1·40 40

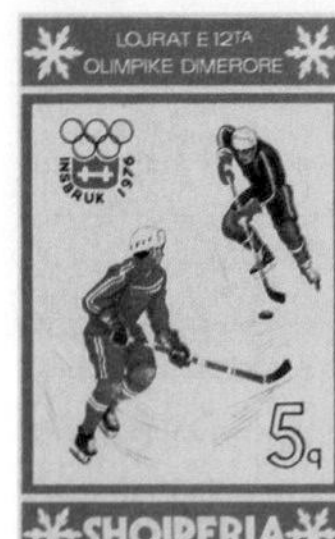

371 Ice Hockey

1976. Winter Olympic Games, Innsbruck. Mult.
1815 5q. Type **371** 10 10
1816 10q. Speed skating 15 10
1817 15q. Rifle shooting (biathlon) 20 10
1818 50q. Ski jumping 30 15
1819 1l.20 Skiing (slalom) 90 25
1820 2l.30 Bobsleighing . . . . . 1·90 45
MS1821 66 × 80 mm. 2l.15 Figure skating (pairs) . . . . 3·00 2·00

372 "Colchicum autumnale"

1976. Medicinal Plants. Multicoloured.
1822 5q. Type **372** 10 10
1823 10q. "Atropa belladonna" 15 10
1824 15q. "Gentiana lutea" . . . 15 10
1825 20q. "Aesculus hippocastanum" 15 10
1826 70q. "Polystichum filix" . . 35 20
1827 80q. "Althaea officinalis" 55 20
1828 2l.30 "Datura stamonium" 2·25 1·00

373 Wooden Bowl and Spoon

1976. Ethnographical Studies Conference, Tirana. Albanian Artifacts. Multicoloured.
1829 10q. Type **373** 10 10
1830 15q. Flask (vert) 15 10
1831 20q. Ornamental handles (vert) 20 10
1832 25q. Pistol and dagger . . . 25 10
1833 80q. Hand-woven rug (vert) 70 20
1834 1l.20 Filigree buckle and earrings . . . . 1·00 25
1835 1l.40 Jugs with handles (vert) . . . . 1·25 85

374 "Founding the Co-operatives" (Zef Shoshi)

1976. Albanian Paintings. Multicoloured.
1836 5q. Type **374** 10 10
1837 10q. "Going to Work" (Agim Zajmi) (vert) . . . 10 10
1838 25q. "Listening to Broadcast" (Vilson Kilica) 15 10
1839 40q. "Female Welder" (Sabaudin Xhaferi) (vert) 25 10
1840 50q. "Steel Workers" (Isuf Sulovari) (vert) 35 15
1841 1l.20 "1942 Revolt" (Lec Shkreli) (vert) 90 25
1842 1l.60 "Returning from Work" (Agron Dine) . . 1·25 35
MS1843 93 × 79 mm. 2l.05 "The Young Pioneer" (Andon Lakuriqi) 3·00 1·75

375 Demonstrators attacking Police **376** Party Flag, Industry and Agriculture

1976. 35th Anniv of Hoxha's Anti-fascist Demonstration. Multicoloured.
1844 25q. Type **375** 20 15
1845 1l.90 Crowd with flag . . . 1·40 55

1976. 7th Workers' Party Congress. Multicoloured.
1846 25q. Type **376** . . . . . . 1·75 45
1847 1l.20 Hand holding Party symbols, and flag 85 30

377 Communist Advance

1976. 35th Anniv of Workers' Party. Mult.
1848 15q. Type **377** 20 10
1849 25q. Hands holding emblems and revolutionary army . . . 20 10
1850 80q. "Reconstruction" . . . 40 20
1851 1l.20 "Heavy Industry and Agriculture" 95 30
1852 1l.70 "The Arts" (ballet) . . 1·40 40

378 Young Communist

1976. 35th Anniv of Young Communists' Union. Multicoloured.
1853 80q. Type **378** . . . . . . 1·90 45
1854 1l.25 Young Communists in action 90 40

379 Ballet Dancers

1976. Albanian Ballet "Cuca e Malexe".
1855 **379** 10q. multicoloured . . . 10 10
1856 – 15q. multicoloured . . . 15 10
1857 – 20q. multicoloured . . . 20 10
1858 – 25q. multicoloured . . . 25 10
1859 – 80q. multicoloured . . . 45 20
1860 – 1l.20 multicoloured . . . 70 25
1861 – 1l.40 multicoloured . . . 85 30
MS1862 77 × 67 mm. 2l.05 multicoloured. Imperf . . . . 4·00 3·00
DESIGNS: 15q. to 2l.50, Various ballet scenes.

380 Bashtoves Castle **381** Skanderbeg's Shield and Spear

1976. Albanian Castles.
1863 **380** 10q. black and blue . . . 10 10
1864 – 15q. black and green . . 10 10
1865 – 20q. black and grey . . . 20 15
1866 – 25q. black and ochre . . 30 20
1867 – 80q. black, pink and red 90 50
1868 – 1l.20 black and blue . . 1·25 80
1869 – 1l.40 black, red & pink 1·75 90
DESIGNS: 15q. Gjirokaster; 20q. All Pash Tepelenes; 25q. Petreles; 80q. Berat; 1l.20, Durres; 1l.40, Krujes.

1977. Crest and Arms of Skanderbeg's Army. Mult.
1870 15q. Type **381** . . . . . . 1·25 70
1871 80q. Helmet, sword and scabbard . . . . 4·00 2·50
1872 1l. Halberd, spear, bow and arrows . . . . 6·00 3·00

382 Ilya Oiqi **383** Polyvinyl-chloride Plant, Vlore

1977. Albanian Heroes. Multicoloured.
1873 5q. Type **382** 10 10
1874 10q. Ilia Dashi 20 10
1875 25q. Fran Ndue Ivanaj . . . 75 30
1876 80q. Zeliha Allmetaj . . . . 1·25 35
1877 1l. Ylli Zaimi . . . . 1·50 50
1878 1l.90 Isuf Plloci . . . . . . 2·50 80

1977. 6th Five-year Plan. Multicoloured.
1879 15q. Type **383** 25 20
1880 25q. Naphtha plant, Ballsh 40 25
1881 65q. Hydroelectric station, Fjerzes 80 50
1882 1l. Metallurgical combinate, Elbasan . . . . 1·60 80

384 Shote Galica **385** Crowd and Martyrs' Monument, Tirana

1977. 50th Death Anniv of Shote Galica (Communist partisan).
1883 **384** 80q. red and pink . . . 80 40
1884 – 1l.25 grey and blue . . 1·50 75
DESIGN: 1l.25, Shote Galica and father.

1977. 35th Anniv of Martyrs' Day. Multicoloured.
1885 25q. Type **385** 40 25
1886 80q. Clenched fist and Albanian flag . . . . . . 1·00 40
1887 1l.20 Bust of Qemal Stafa 1·75 70

386 Doctor calling at Village House **387** Workers outside Factory

1977. "Socialist Transformation of the Villages". Multicoloured.
1888 5q. Type **386** 10 10
1889 10q. Cowherd with cattle . . 15 10
1890 20q. Harvesting 20 20
1891 80q. Modern village . . . . 1·00 40
1892 2l.95 Tractor and greenhouse . . . . 3·50 70

1977. 8th Trade Unions Congress. Multicoloured.
1893 25q. Type **387** 25 20
1894 1l.80 Three workers with flags . . . . 1·50 80

388 Advancing Soldiers **389** Two Girls with Handkerchiefs

1977. "All the People are Soldiers". Multicoloured.
1895 15q. Type **388** 20 10
1896 25q. Enver Hoxha and marching soldiers 25 10
1897 80q. Soldiers and workers 75 25

1898 1l. The Armed Forces . . . 1·00 35
1899 1l.90 Marching soldiers and workers . . . . 2·00 40

1977. National Costume Dances (1st series). Mult.
1900 5q. Type **389** 15 10
1901 10q. Two male dancers . . 15 10
1902 15q. Man and woman in kerchief dance 15 15
1903 25q. Two male dancers (different) 20 15
1904 80q. Two women dancers with kerchiefs 55 25
1905 1l.20 "Elbow dance" 85 30
1906 1l.55 Two women with kerchiefs (different) . . . 1·10 50
MS1907 56 × 74 mm. 2l.05 Sabre dance . . . . 4·00 3·00
See also Nos. 1932/6 and 1991/5.

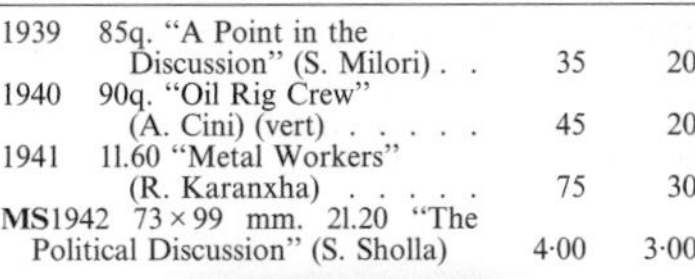

390 Armed Worker with Book **391** "Beni Ecen Vet"

1977. New Constitution.
1908 **390** 25q. gold, red and black 25 15
1909 – 1l.20 gold, red and black 1·10 35
DESIGN: 1l.20, Industrial and agricultural symbols and hand with book.

1977. Albanian Films.
1910 **391** 10q. green and grey . . 20 10
1911 – 15q. multicoloured . . . 30 10
1912 – 25q. green, black & grey 40 20
1913 – 80q. multicoloured . . . 1·00 50
1914 – 1l.20 brown and grey . . 1·50 60
1915 – 1l.60 multicoloured . . . 2·50 90
DESIGNS: 15q. "Rruge te Bardha"; 25q. "Rrugicat qe Kerkonin Diell"; 80q. "Ne Fillim te Veres"; 1l.20, "Lulekuqet Mbi Mure"; 1l.60, "Zonja nga Qyteti".

392 Rejoicing Crowd and Independence Memorial, Tirana **393** "Farm Workers"

1977. 65th Anniv of Independence. Multicoloured.
1916 15q. Type **392** 15 15
1917 25q. Independence leaders marching in Tirana . . . 25 15
1918 1l.65 Albanians dancing under national flag . . . 1·25 45

1977. Paintings by V. Mio. Multicoloured.
1919 5q. Type **393** 10 10
1920 10q. "Landscape in the Snow" 10 10
1921 15q. "Sheep under a Walnut Tree, Springtime" 15 10
1922 25q. "Street in Korce" . . . 25 10
1923 80q. "Riders in the Mountains" 65 20
1924 1l. "Boats by the Seashore" 85 25
1925 1l.75 "Tractors Ploughing" 1·10 30
MS1926 67 × 102 mm. 2l.05 "Self-portrait" . . . . 4·00 2·50

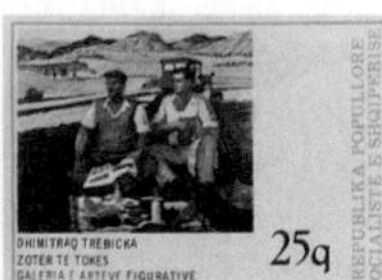

394 Pan Flute **395** "Tractor Drivers" (D. Trebicka)

1978. Folk Music Instruments.
1927 **394** 15q. red, black and green 30 15
1928 – 25q. yellow, black & vio 60 25
1929 – 80q. red, black and blue 1·50 40
1930 – 1l.20 yellow, blk & blue 3·00 60
1931 – 1l.70 lilac, black & grn 5·00 1·25
DESIGNS: 25q. Single-string goat's head fiddle; 80q. Trumpet; 1l.20, Drum; 1l.70, Bagpipes.

1978. National Costume Dances (2nd series). As T **389**. Multicoloured.
1932 5q. Girl dancers with scarves 10 10
1933 25q. Male dancers 20 15
1934 80q. Kneeling dancers . . . 40 20
1935 1l. Female dancers 70 25
1936 2l.30 Male dancers with linked arms . . . . . . 1·75 50

1978. Paintings of the Working Class. Mult.
1937 25q. Type **395** 15 10
1938 80q. "Steeplejack" (S. Kristo) 30 20
1939 85q. "A Point in the Discussion" (S. Milori) . . 35 20
1940 90q. "Oil Rig Crew" (A. Cini) (vert) 45 20
1941 1l.60 "Metal Workers" (R. Karanxha) 75 30
MS1942 73 × 99 mm. 2l.20 "The Political Discussion" (S. Sholla) 4·00 3·00

396 Boy and Girl

1978. International Children's Day. Multicoloured.
1943 5q. Type **396** 10 10
1944 10q. Boy and girl with pickaxe and rifle 15 10
1945 25q. Children dancing . . . 25 20
1946 1l.80 Classroom scene . . . 2·00 45

397 Woman with Pickaxe and Rifle

1978. 8th Women's Union Congress.
1947 **397** 25q. red and gold . . . 30 10
1948 – 1l.95 red and gold . . . 2·50 75
DESIGN: 1l.95, Peasant, Militia Guard and industrial installation.

398 Battle of Mostar Bridge **399** Guerillas and Flag

1978. Centenary of the League of Prizren.
1949 **398** 10q. multicoloured . . . 15 10
1950 – 25q. multicoloured . . . 20 15
1951 – 80q. multicoloured . . . 45 20
1952 – 1l.20 blue, black & vio 75 30
1953 – 1l.65 multicoloured . . . 1·00 40
1954 – 2l.60 lt grn, blk & grn 1·60 60
MS1955 75 × 69 mm. 2l.20 multicoloured . . . . 4·00 2·50
DESIGNS: 25q. Spirit of Skanderbeg; 80q. Albanians marching under national flag; 1l.20, Riflemen; 1l.65, Abdyl Frasheri (founder); 2l.20, League building, crossed rifles, pens and paper; 2l.60, League Headquarters, Prizren.

1978. 35th Anniv of People's Army.
1956 5q. Type **399** 35 15
1957 25q. Men of armed forces (horiz) 75 30
1958 1l.90 Men of armed forces, civil guards and Young Pioneers . . . . 4·00 1·50

1978. International Fair, Riccione. No. 1832 surch **3.30L. RICCIONE 78 26.8.78.**
1959 3l.30 on 25q. multicoloured 10·00 3·25

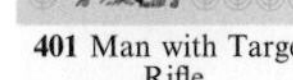

401 Man with Target Rifle **402** Kerchief Dance

1978. 32nd National Shooting Championships.
1960 **401** 25q. black and yellow . . 20 15
1961 – 80q. black and orange 40 20
1962 – 95q. black and red . . . 50 25
1963 – 2l.40 black and red . . . 1·75 50
DESIGNS—VERT: 80q. Woman with machine carbine; 2l.40, Pistol shooting. HORIZ: 95q. Shooting from prone position.

1978. National Folklore Festival, Gjirokaster. Mult.
1964 10q. Type **402** 10 10
1965 15q. Musicians 15 10
1966 25q. Fiddle player 20 15
1967 80q. Singers 45 20
1968 1l.20 Sabre dance 80 25
1969 1l.90 Girl dancers . . . . . 1·40 35

403 Enver Hoxha (after V. Kilica) **404** Woman with Wheatsheaf

1978. Enver Hoxha's 70th Birthday.
1970 **403** 80q. multicoloured . . . 65 20
1971 1l.20 multicoloured . . . 90 25
1972 2l.40 multicoloured . . . 1·40 65
MS1973 68 × 88 mm. **403** 2l.20 multicoloured . . . . 4·00 3·00

1978. Agriculture and Stock Raising. Multicoloured.
1974 15q. Type **404** 30 20
1975 25q. Woman with boxes of fruit 40 30
1976 80q. Shepherd and flock . . 1·25 60
1977 2l.60 Dairymaid and cattle 4·00 2·00

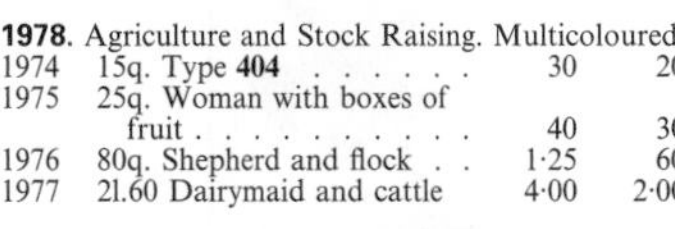

405 Pupils entering School **406** Dora D'Istria

1978.
1978 **405** 5q. brown, lt brn & gold 15 10
1979 – 10q. blue, lt bl & gold 20 10
1980 – 15q. violet, lilac and gold 30 15
1981 – 20q. brown, drab & gold 45 20
1982 – 25q. red, pink and gold 55 25
1983 – 60q. green, lt grn & gold 1·75 45
1984 – 80q. blue, lt blue & gold 2·50 55
1985 – 1l.20 magenta, mauve and gold . . . . . . 3·50 90
1986 – 1l.60 blue, lt blue & gold 12·00 1·40
1987 – 2l.40 grn, lt grn & gold 6·00 2·10
1988 – 3l. blue, lt blue & gold 7·50 3·75
DESIGNS: 10q. Telephone, letters, telegraph wires and switchboard operators; 15q. Pouring molten iron; 20q. Dancers, musical instruments, book and artist's materials; 25q. Newspapers, radio, television and broadcasting tower; 60q. Assistant in clothes shop; 80q. Militiamen and women, tanks, ships, aircraft and radar equipment; 1l.20, Industrial complex and symbols of industry; 1l.60, Train and truck; 2l.40, Workers hoeing fields, cattle and girl holding wheat sheaf; 3l. Microscope and nurse holding up baby.

1979. 150th Birth Anniv of Dora D'Istria (pioneer of women's rights).
1989 **406** 80q. green and black . . 85 20
1990 – 1l.10 grey and black . . 1·25 1·00
DESIGN: 1l.10, Full-face portrait.

1979. National Costume Dances (3rd series). As T **389**. Multicoloured.
1991 15q. Girl dancers with scarves 15 10
1992 25q. Male dancers 20 10
1993 80q. Girl dancers with scarves (different) 50 25
1994 1l.20 Male dancers with pistols 80 40
1995 1l.40 Female dancers with linked arms . . . . . . 1·25 45

407 Stone-built Galleried House **408** Aleksander Moissi

1979. Traditional Albanian Houses (1st series). Multicoloured.
1996 15q. Type **407** 15 10
1997 25q. Tower house (vert) . . 20 10
1998 80q. House with wooden galleries 85 25
1999 1l.20 Galleried tower house (vert) . . . . 1·25 40
2000 1l.40 Three-storied fortified house (vert) . . . . . . 1·75 65
MS2001 62 × 75 mm. 1l.90 Fortified tower house . . . . 4·00 3·00
See also Nos. 2116/19.

1979. Birth Centenary of Aleksander Moissi (actor).
2002 **408** 80q. green, black & gold 65 20
2003 – 1l.10 brown, blk & gold 1·00 25
DESIGN: 1l.10, Aleksander Moissi (different).

409 Vasil Shanto

1979. Anti-fascist Heroes (1st series). Multicoloured.
2004 15q. Type **409** 25 10
2005 25q. Qemal Stafa 30 15
2006 60q. Type **409** 80 20
2007 90q. As 25q. . . . . 1·25 60
See also Nos. 2052/5, 2090/3, 2126/9, 2167/70, 2221/4, 2274/7 and 2313/5.

410 Soldier, Crowd and Coat of Arms

1979. 35th Anniv of Permet Congress. Mult.
2008 25q. Soldier, factories and wheat 40 20
2009 1l.65 Type **410** . . . . . . 2·00 1·00

411 Albanian Flag

1979. 5th Albanian Democratic Front Congress.
2010 **411** 25q. multicoloured . . . 40 20
2011 1l.65 multicoloured . . . 2·00 1·00

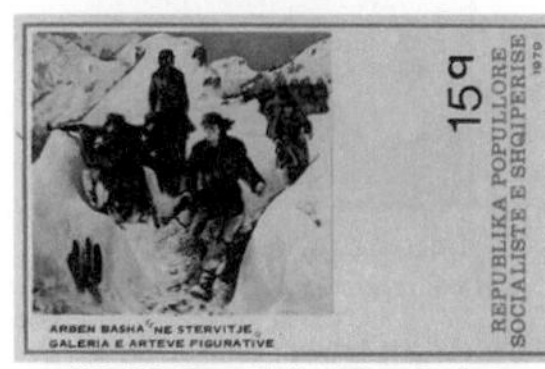

412 "Ne Stervitje" (Arben Basha)

1979. Paintings. Multicoloured.
2012 15q. Type **412** 10 10
2013 25q. "Shtigje Lufte" (Ismail Lulani) 20 10
2014 80q. "Agim me Fitore" (Myrteza Fushekati) . . . 75 25
2015 1l.20 "Gjithe Populli ushtare" (Muhamet Deliu) 1·10 35
2016 1l.40 "Zjarret Ndezur Mbajme" (Jorgji Gjikopulli) . . . . 1·40 85
MS2017 78 × 103 mm. 1l.90 "Cajime Rrethime" (Fatmir Haxhiu) . . 4·00 3·00

413 Athletes round Party Flag **414** Founder-president

1979. 35th Anniv of Liberation Spartakiad. Mult.
2018 15q. Type **413** 10 10
2019 25q. Shooting 20 10
2020 80q. Girl gymnast 65 25
2021 1l.10 Football 90 35
2022 1l.40 High jump . . . . . 1·10 35

1979. Centenary of Albanian Literary Society.
2023 – 25q. black, brown and gold 20 15
2024 **414** 80q. black, brown and gold 45 20
2025 – 1l.20 black, blue & gold 70 30
2026 – 1l.55 black, vio & gold 95 40
MS2027 78 × 66 mm. 1l.90 black, buff and gold . . . . 3·00 2·50
DESIGNS: 25q. Foundation document and seal of 1880; 1l.20, Headquarters building, 1979; 1l.55, Headquarters building, 1879; 1l.90, Four founder members, book and quill.

415 Congress Building

1979. 35th Anniv of Berat Congress. Multicoloured.

2028	25q. Arms and congress document	80	50
2029	1l.65 Type **415**	3·00	2·00

416 Workers and Industrial Complex **417** Joseph Stalin

1979. 35th Anniv of Liberation. Multicoloured.

2030	25q. Type **416**	20	10
2031	80q. Wheat and hand grasping hammer and pickaxe	45	25
2032	1l.20 Open book, star and musical instrument	60	30
2033	1l.55 Open book, compasses and gear wheel	1·00	45

1979. Birth Centenary of Joseph Stalin.

2034	**417**	80q. blue and red	40	25
2035	–	1l.10 blue and red	85	40

DESIGN: 1l.10, Stalin and Enver Hoxha.

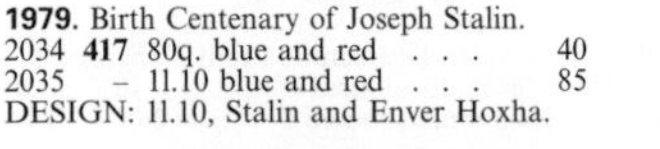

418 Fireplace and Pottery, Korce

1980. Interiors (1st series). Multicoloured.

2036	25q. Type **418**	20	20
2037	80q. Carved bed alcove and weapons, Shkoder	50	40
2038	1l.20 Cooking hearth and carved chair, Mirdite	1·10	85
2039	1l.35 Turkish-style chimney, dagger and embroidered jacket, Gjirokaster	1·40	90

See also Nos. 2075/8.

419 Lacework **420** Aleksander Xhuvani

1980. Handicrafts. Multicoloured.

2040	25q. Pipe and flask	20	20
2041	80q. Leather handbags	55	35
2042	1l.20 Carved eagle and embroidered rug	75	60
2043	1l.35 Type **419**	95	65

1980. Birth Centenary of Dr. Aleksander Xhuvani.

2044	**420**	80q. blue, grey and black	1·00	50
2045	–	1l. brown, grey and black	1·50	1·00

421 Insurrectionists

1980. 70th Anniv of Kosovo Insurrection.

2046	**421**	80q. black and red	1·00	50
2047	–	1l. black and red	1·50	1·00

DESIGN: 1l. Battle scene.

422 "Soldiers and Workers helping Stricken Population" (D. Jukniu and L. Lulani)

1980. 1979 Earthquake Relief.

2048	**422**	80q. multicoloured	1·00	50
2049		1l. multicoloured	1·50	1·00

423 Lenin

1980. 110th Birth Anniv of Lenin.

2050	**423**	80q. grey, red and pink	1·00	50
2051		1l. multicoloured	1·50	1·00

424 Misto Mame and Ali Demi

1980. Anti-fascist Heroes (2nd series). Mult.

2052	25q. Type **424**	25	10
2053	80q. Sadik Staveleci, Vojo Kushi and Xhoxhi Martini	60	30
2054	1l.20 Bule Naipi and Persefoni Kokedhima	90	60
2055	1l.35 Ndoc Deda, Hydajet Lezha, Naim Gjylbegu, Ndoc Mazi and Ahmet Haxhia	1·00	70

425 "Mirela"

1980. Children's Tales. Multicoloured.

2056	15q. Type **425**	10	10
2057	25q. "Shkarravina"	20	15
2058	80q. "Ariu Artist"	45	40
2059	2l.40 "Pika e Ujit"	2·25	1·40

426 "The Enver Hoxha Tractor Combine" (S. Shijaku and M. Fushekati)

1980. Paintings from Gallery of Figurative Arts, Tirana. Multicoloured.

2060	25q. Type **426**	20	15
2061	80q. "The Welder" (Harilla Dhima)	50	35
2062	1l.20 "Steel Erector (Petro Kokushta)	70	65
2063	1l.35 "Harvest Festival" (Pandeli Lena)	80	75
MS2064	65 × 82 mm. 1l.80 "Communists" (Vilson Kilica) (48 × 71 mm)	4·00	4·00

427 Decorated Door (Pergamen miniature)

1980. Art of the Middle Ages. Each black and gold.

2065	25q. Type **427**	15	10
2066	80q. Bird (relief)	45	25
2067	1l.20 Crowned lion (relief)	75	65
2068	1l.35 Pheasant (relief)	80	75

428 Divjaka

1980. National Parks. Multicoloured.

2069	80q. Type **428**	45	30
2070	1l.20 Lura	1·00	75
2071	1l.60 Thethi	1·75	1·00
MS2072	89 × 90 mm. 1l.80 Llogara (77 × 80 mm)	4·00	4·00

429 Flag, Arms and rejoicing Albanians

1981. 35th Anniv of Albanian People's Republic. Multicoloured.

2073	80q. Type **429**	75	30
2074	1l. Crowd and flags outside People's Party headquarters	75	45

1981. Interiors (2nd series). Multicoloured.

2075	25q. As T **418**	20	15
2076	80q. Sleeping mats and spirit keg, Labara	45	30
2077	1l.20 Fireplace and covered dish mat	1·00	50
2078	1l.35 Interior and embroidered jacket, Dibres	1·25	65

430 Wooden Cot

1981. Folk Art. Multicoloured.

2079	25q. Type **430**	20	15
2080	80q. Bucket and flask	60	30
2081	1l.20 Embroidered slippers	70	40
2082	1l.35 Jugs	80	85

431 Footballers

1981. World Cup Football Championship Eliminating Rounds. Multicoloured.

2083	25q. Type **431**	1·25	60
2084	80q. Tackle	3·75	1·75
2085	1l.20 Player kicking ball	5·25	2·25
2086	1l.35 Goalkeeper saving goal	6·25	2·75

432 Rifleman **433** Acrobats

1981. Cent of Battle of Shtimje. Each purple & red.

2087	80q. Type **432**	65	35
2088	1l. Albanian with sabre	80	50
MS2089	84 × 68 mm. 1l.80 Albanian with pistol	2·50	2·50

1981. Anti-fascist Heroes (3rd series). As T **424**. Multicoloured.

2090	25q. Perlat Rexhepi and Branko Kadia	20	15
2091	80q. Xheladin Beqiri and Hajdah Dushi	50	35
2092	1l.20 Koci Bako, Vasil Laci and Mujo Ulqinaku	85	55
2093	1l.35 Mine Peza and Zoja Cure	95	70

1981. Children's Circus.

2094	–	15q. black, green & stone	15	10
2095	–	25q. black, blue and grey	20	15
2096	**433**	80q. black, mve & pink	45	35
2097	–	2l.40 black, orge & yell	1·60	1·40

DESIGNS: 15q. Monocyclists. 25q. Human pyramid; 2l.40, Acrobats spinning from marquee pole.

434 "Rallying to the Flag, December 1911" (A. Zajmi)

1981. Paintings. Multicoloured.

2098	25q. "Allies" (Sh. Hysa) (horiz)	20	15
2099	80q. "Azem Galica breaking the Ring of Turks" (A. Buza) (horiz)	50	30
2100	1l.20 Type **434**	70	45
2101	1l.35 "My Flag is my Heart" (L. Cefa)	1·10	90
MS2102	81 × 109 mm. 1l.80 "Unite under the Flag" (N. Vasia) (55 × 79 mm)	3·00	3·00

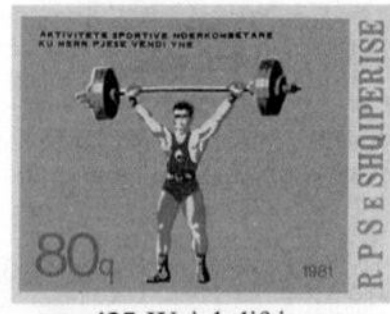

435 Weightlifting

1981. Albanian Participation in Inter Sports. Mult.

2103	25q. Rifle shooting	15	10
2104	80q. Type **435**	45	30
2105	1l.20 Volleyball	65	45
2106	1l.35 Football	1·00	70

436 Flag and Hands holding Pickaxe and Rifle **437** Industrial and Agricultural Symbols

1981. 8th Workers' Party Congress.

2107	**436**	80q. red, brown & black	55	35
2108	–	1l. red and black	70	50

DESIGN: 1l. Party flag, hammer and sickle.

1981. 40th Anniv of Workers' Party. Mult.

2109	80q. Type **437**	2·00	45
2110	2l.80 Albanian flag and hand holding pickaxe and rifle	2·00	1·25
MS2111	79 × 98 mm. 1l.80 Enver Hoxha and book (50 × 68 mm)	3·50	2·50

438 Pickaxe, Rifle and Young Communists Flag **439** F. S. Noli

1981. 40th Anniv of Young Communists' Union. Multicoloured.

2112	80q. Type **438**	1·25	40
2113	1l. Workers' Party flag and Young Communists emblem	2·00	85

1981. Birth Centenary of F. S. Noli (author).

2114	**439**	80q. green and gold	75	35
2115		1l.10 brown and gold	90	45

1982. Traditional Albanian Houses (2nd series). As T **407**, but vert. Multicoloured.

2116	25q. House in Bulqize	25	15
2117	80q. House in Kosovo	80	50

2118 1l.20 House in Bicaj . . . . 1·10 75
2119 1l.55 House in Mat . . . . 1·50 1·00

440 Map, Globe and Bacillus

1982. Centenary of Discovery of Tubercle Bacillus.
2120 **440** 80q. multicoloured . . . 1·75 80
2121 – 1l.10 brown & dp brown 3·00 1·50
DESIGN: 1l.10, Robert Koch (discoverer), microscope and bacillus.

441 "Prizren Castle" (G. Madhi)

1982. Paintings of Kosovo. Multicoloured.
2122 25q. Type **441** 25 20
2123 80q. "House of the Albanian League, Prizren" (K. Buza) (horiz) 75 60
2124 1l.20 "Mountain Gorge, Rogove" (K. Buza) . . . 1·25 75
2125 1l.55 "Street of the Hadhji, Zekes" (G. Madhi) . . . 1·75 1·00

1982. Anti-fascist Heroes (4th series). As T **424**. Multicoloured.
2126 25q. Hibe Palikuqi and Liri Gero 20 15
2127 80q. Mihal Duri and Kojo Karafili 60 40
2128 1l.20 Fato Dudumi, Margarita Tutulani and Shejnaze Juka 80 50
2129 1l.55 Memo Meto and Gjok Doci . . . . 1·10 75

442 Factories and Workers

1982. 9th Trade Unions Congress. Multicoloured.
2130 80q. Type **442** . . . . . . 1·50 75
2131 1l.10 Congress emblem . . . 2·00 1·00

443 Ship in Harbour

1982. Children's Paintings. Multicoloured.
2132 15q. Type **443** 25 15
2133 80q. Forest camp 75 45
2134 1l.20 House 90 70
2135 1l.65 House and garden . . 1·50 80

444 "Village Festival" (Danish Jukniu)

1982. Paintings from Gallery of Figurative Arts, Tirana. Multicoloured.
2136 25q. Type **444** 25 15
2137 80q. "The Hydroelectric Station Builders" (Ali Miruku) 60 40
2138 1l.20 "Steel Workers" (Clirim Ceka) . . . . . . 1·00 60
2139 1l.55 "Oil Drillers" (Pandeli Lena) . . . . 1·25 85
MS2140 75 × 90 mm. 1l.90 "First Tapping of the Furnace" (Jorgji Gjikopulli) . . . . 3·50 2·50

445 "Voice of the People" (party newspaper)
446 Heroes of Peza Monument

1982. 40th Anniv of Popular Press. Multicoloured.
2141 80q. Type **445** . . . . . . 65·00 65·00
2142 1l.10 Hand duplicator producing first edition of "Voice of the People" . . 65·00 65·00

1982. 40th Anniv of Democratic Front. Mult.
2143 80q. Type **446** . . . . . . 2·50 1·50
2144 1l.10 Peza Conference building and marchers with flag . . . . 3·75 2·00

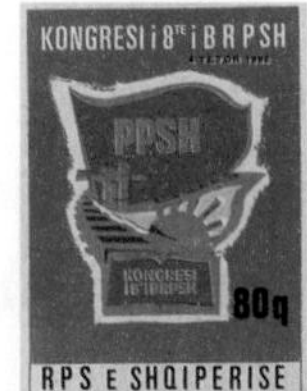

447 Congress Emblem

1982. 8th Young Communists' Union Congress.
2145 **447** 80q. multicoloured . . . 3·00 1·50
2146 1l.10 multicoloured . . . 4·50 2·25

448 Tapestry

1982. Handicrafts. Multicoloured.
2147 25q. Type **448** 25 15
2148 80q. Bags (vert) 60 40
2149 1l.20 Butter churns 85 55
2150 1l.55 Jug (vert) . . . . . . 1·25 1·10

449 Freedom Fighters

1982. 70th Anniv of Independence.
2151 **449** 20q. deep red, red & blk 20 15
2152 – 1l.20 black, grn & red 85 60
2153 – 2l.40 brown, buff and red . . . . 1·90 1·50
MS2154 90 × 89 mm. 1l.90 multicoloured . . . . 4·00 3·00
DESIGNS: 20q. Ismail Qemali (patriot) and crowd around building; 2l.40, Six freedom fighters. (58 × 55 mm) 1l.90, Independence Monument, Tirana.

450 Dhermi

1982. Coastal Views. Multicoloured.
2155 25q. Type **450** 20 15
2156 80q. Sarande 55 35
2157 1l.20 Ksamil 85 55
2158 1l.55 Lukove . . . . 1·10 1·00

451 Male Dancers
452 Karl Marx

1983. Folk Dance Assemblies Abroad. Mult.
2159 25q. Type **451** 15 10
2160 80q. Male dancers and drummer 50 30
2161 1l.20 Musicians 70 40
2162 1l.55 Group of female dancers . . . . 1·00 90

1983. Death Centenary of Karl Marx.
2163 **452** 80q. multicoloured . . . 1·00 50
2164 1l.10 multicoloured . . . 1·25 60

453 Electricity Generation

1983. Energy Development.
2165 **453** 80q. blue and orange . . 55 35
2166 – 1l.10 mauve and green 90 55
DESIGN: 1l.10, Gas and oil production.

1983. Anti-fascist Heroes (5th series). As T **424**. Multicoloured.
2167 25q. Asim Zeneli and Nazmi Rushiti 20 15
2168 80q. Shyqyri Ishmi, Shyqyri Alimerko and Myzafer Asqeriu 55 35
2169 1l.20 Qybra Sokoli, Qeriba Derri and Ylbere Bilibashi 90 55
2170 1l.55 Themo Vasi and Abaz Shehu . . . . 1·25 75

454 Congress Emblem
456 Soldier and Militia

455 Cycling

1983. 9th Women's Union Congress.
2171 **454** 80q. multicoloured . . . 60 50
2172 1l.10 multicoloured . . . 70 60

1983. Sport and Leisure. Multicoloured.
2173 25q. Type **455** 25 15
2174 80q. Chess . . . . 1·00 50
2175 1l.20 Gymnastics . . . . . 1·25 70
2176 1l.55 Wrestling . . . . . . 1·40 80

1983. 40th Anniv of People's Army.
2177 **456** 20q. gold and red . . . 20 15
2178 – 1l.20 gold and red . . . 85 50
2179 – 2l.40 gold and brown . . 1·75 1·40
DESIGNS: 1l.20, Soldier; 2l.40 Factory guard.

457 "Sunny Day" (Myrteza Fushekati)

1983. Paintings from Gallery of Figurative Arts, Tirana. Multicoloured.
2180 25q. Type **457** 20 15
2181 80q. "Morning Gossip" (Niko Progri) 55 40
2182 1l.20 "29th November, 1944" (Harilla Dhimo) . . 85 50
2183 1l.55 "Demolition" (Pandi Mele) . . . . 1·10 70
MS2184 111 × 74 mm. 1l.90 "Partisan Assault" (Sali Shijaku and Myrteza Fushekati) (99 × 59 mm) . . . . 7·00 6·00

1983. National Folklore Festival, Gjirokaster. As T **402**. Multicoloured.
2185 25q. Sword dance 25 15
2186 80q. Kerchief dance 75 45
2187 1l.20 Musicians . . . . . . 1·10 70
2188 1l.55 Women dancers with garlands . . . . 1·25 85

458 Enver Hoxha

1983. 75th Birthday of Enver Hoxha.
2189 **458** 80q. multicoloured . . . 45 35
2190 1l.20 multicoloured . . . 75 50
2191 1l.80 multicoloured . . . 1·40 85
MS2192 77 × 98 mm. 1l.90 multicoloured (as T **458** but with inscriptions differently arranged) 3·00 2·50

459 W.C.Y. Emblem and Globe

1983. World Communications Year.
2193 **459** 60q. multicoloured . . . 40 25
2194 1l.20 blue, orange & blk 65 45

460 "Combine to Triumph" (J. Keraj)

1983. Skanderbeg Epoch in Art. Multicoloured.
2195 25q. Type **460** 20 15
2196 80q. "The Heroic Resistance at Krujes" (N. Bakalli) . . 60 35
2197 1l.20 "United we are Unconquerable by our Enemies" (N. Progri) . . 90 55
2198 1l.55 "Assembly at Lezhe" (B. Ahmeti) . . . . . . 1·25 70
MS2199 77 × 90 mm. 1l.90 "Victory over the Turks" (G. Madhi) . . 4·00 3·00

461 Amphitheatre, Butrint (Buthrotum)

1983. Graeco-Roman Remains in Illyria. Mult.
2200 80q. Type **461** . . . . . . 1·00 75
2201 1l.20 Colonnade, Apoloni Cesma (Apollonium) . . . 1·50 90
2202 1l.80 Vaulted gallery of amphitheatre, Dyrrah (Epidamnus) . . . . . . 1·90 1·25

462 Man's Head from Apoloni
463 Clock Tower, Gjirokaster

1984. Archaeological Discoveries (1st series). Mult.
2203 15q. Type **462** 20 15
2204 25q. Tombstone from Korce 25 15
2205 80q. Woman's head from Apoloni 55 35
2206 1l.10 Child's head from Tren 85 65
2207 1l.20 Man's head from Dyrrah 90 70
2208 2l.20 Bronze statuette of Eros from Dyrrah . . . . 1·75 1·25
See also Nos. 2258/61.

1984. Clock Towers.
2209 **463** 15q. purple 20 15
2210 – 25q. brown 25 15
2211 – 80q. violet 55 35
2212 – 1l.10 red 85 65

2213 – 1l.20 green 90 70
2214 – 2l.20 brown . . . . . . 1·75 1·25
DESIGNS: 25q. Kavaje; 80q. Elbasan; 1l.10, Tirana; 1l.20, Peqin; 2l.20, Kruje.

464 Student with Microscope **465** Enver Hoxha

1984. 40th Anniv of Liberation (1st issue). Mult.
2215 15q. Type **464** 20 15
2216 25q. Soldier with flag . . . 25 15
2217 80q. Schoolchildren 65 35
2218 1l.10 Soldier, ships, airplanes and weapons . . 95 65
2219 1l.20 Workers with flag . . 1·10 75
2220 2l.20 Armed guards on patrol . . . . 4·00 1·75
See also Nos. 2255/6.

1984. Anti-fascist Heroes (6th series). As T **424**. Multicoloured.
2221 15q. Manush Alimani, Mustafa Matohiti and Kastriot Muco 15 10
2222 25q. Zaho Koka, Reshit Collaku and Maliq Muco 20 15
2223 1l.20 Lefter Talo, Tom Kola and Fuat Babani 85 55
2224 2l.20 Myslysm Shyri, Dervish Hekali and Skender Caci . . . . . . 1·75 1·25

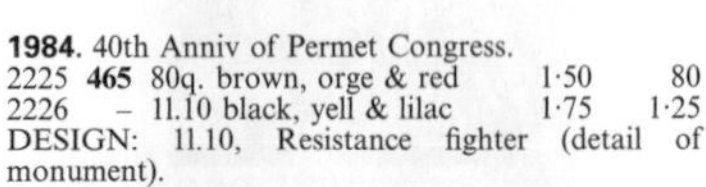

1984. 40th Anniv of Permet Congress.
2225 **465** 80q. brown, orge & red 1·50 80
2226 – 1l.10 black, yell & lilac 1·75 1·25
DESIGN: 1l.10, Resistance fighter (detail of monument).

466 Children reading Comic **467** Football in Goal

1984. Children. Multicoloured.
2227 15q. Type **466** 20 15
2228 25q. Children with toys . . 25 20
2229 60q. Children gardening and rainbow 55 35
2230 2l.80 Children flying kite bearing Albanian arms . . 2·25 1·75

1984. European Football Championship Finals. Multicoloured.
2231 15q. Type **467** 40 20
2232 25q. Referee and football . . 60 30
2233 1l.20 Football and map of Europe . . . . 1·25 60
2234 2l.20 Football and pitch . . 3·50 1·75

468 "Freedom is Here" (Myrteza Fushekati)

1984. Paintings from Gallery of Figurative Arts, Tirana. Multicoloured.
2235 15q. Type **468** 20 15
2236 25q. "Morning" (Zamir Mati) (vert) 25 15
2237 80q. "My Darling" (Agim Zajmi) (vert) 70 40
2238 2l.60 "For the Partisans" (Arben Basha) . . . . . 2·00 1·75
MS2239 80 × 93 mm. 1l.90 "Albania" (Zamir Mati) . . . 7·00 5·00

469 Mulberry **471** Truck driving through Forest

470 Sabre Dance

1984. Flowers. Multicoloured.
2240 15q. Type **469** 25 15
2241 25q. Plantain 65 15
2242 1l.20 Hypericum . . . . . 3·25 1·10
2243 2l.20 Edelweiss . . . . . . 6·25 2·50

1984. "Ausipex 84" International Stamp Exhibition, Melbourne. Sheet 72 × 88 mm.
MS2244 **470** 1l.90 multicoloured 3·00 3·00

1984. Forestry. Multicoloured.
2245 15q. Type **471** 40 25
2246 25q. Transporting logs on overhead cable 75 40
2247 1l.20 Sawmill in forest . . . 2·25 75
2248 2l.20 Lumberjack sawing down trees . . . . . . 3·00 1·60

472 Gjirokaster **473** Football

1984. "Eurphila '84" Int Stamp Exn, Rome.
2249 **472** 1l.20 multicoloured . . . 1·10 90

1984. 5th National Spartakiad. Multicoloured.
2250 15q. Type **473** 20 15
2251 25q. Running 25 15
2252 80q. Weightlifting 65 35
2253 2l.20 Pistol shooting . . . . 1·75 1·40
MS2254 70 × 90 mm. 1l.90 Opening ceremony . . . . 3·00 2·50

474 Agriculture and Industry

1984. 40th Anniv of Liberation (2nd issue). Mult.
2255 80q. Type **474** 80 40
2256 1l.10 Soldiers and flag . . . 1·25 60
MS2257 68 × 89 mm. 1l.90 Enver Hoxha making liberation speech 4·00 3·00

1985. Archaeological Discoveries (2nd series). As T **462**, showing Illyrian finds. Multicoloured.
2258 15q. Pot 25 15
2259 80q. Terracotta head of woman 65 35
2260 1l.20 Terracotta bust of Aphrodite . . . . 1·00 65
2261 1l.70 Bronze statuette of Nike . . . . 1·75 1·25

476 Kapo (bust) **477** Running

1985. 70th Birthday of Hysni Kapo (politician).
2262 **476** 90q. black and red . . . 90 60
2263 1l.10 black and blue . . 1·25 75

1985. "Olymphilex '85" Olympic Stamps Exhibition, Lausanne. Multicoloured.
2264 25q. Type **477** 25 15
2265 60q. Weightlifting 50 25

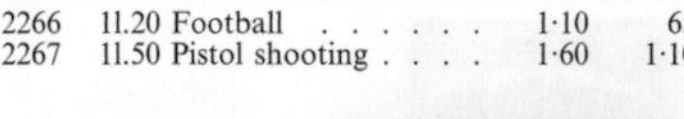

2266 1l.20 Football . . . . . . 1·10 65
2267 1l.50 Pistol shooting . . . . 1·60 1·10

478 Bach **479** Hoxha

1985. 300th Birth Anniv of Johann Sebastian Bach (composer).
2268 **478** 80q. orange, brn & blk 6·50 4·50
2269 – 1l.20 blue, dp blue & blk 7·50 5·50
DESIGN—1l.20, Bach's birthplace, Eisenach.

1985. Enver Hoxha Commemoration.
2270 **479** 80q. multicoloured . . . 1·00 80
MS2271 67 × 90 mm. **479** 1l.90 multicoloured . . . . 1·50 1·50

480 Frontier Guards **481** Scarf on Rifle Barrel

1985. 40th Anniv of Frontier Force. Multicoloured.
2272 25q. Type **480** 75 50
2273 80q. Frontier guard . . . . 1·75 1·00

1985. Anti-fascist Heroes (7th series). As T **424**. Multicoloured.
2274 25q. Mitro Xhani, Nimete Progonati and Kozma Nushi 40 25
2275 40q. Ajet Xhindoli, Mustafa Kacaci and Estref Caka 60 40
2276 60q. Celo Sinani, Llambro Andoni and Meleo Gosnishti 80 50
2277 1l.20 Thodhori Mastora, Fejzi Micoli and Hysen Cino . . . . 1·50 1·00

1985. 40th Anniv of V.E. (Victory in Europe) Day. Multicoloured.
2278 25q. Type **481** 75 50
2279 80q. Crumpled swastika and hand holding rifle butt . . 1·75 1·00

482 "Primary School" (Thoma Malo)

1985. Paintings from Gallery of Figurative Arts, Tirana. Multicoloured.
2280 25q. Type **482** 25 15
2281 80q. "Heroes and Mother" (Hysen Devolli) (vert) . . 90 35
2282 90q. "Mother writing" (Angjelin Dodmasej) (vert) 1·00 70
2283 1l.20 "Women off to Work" (Ksenofen Dilo) . . . . 1·40 70
MS2284 74 × 88 mm. 1l.90 "Foundry Workers" (Mikel Gurashi) . . 4·00 3·00

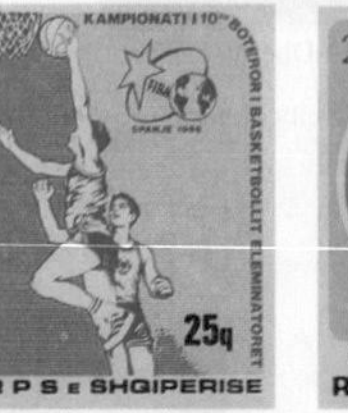

483 Scoring a Goal **484** Oranges

1985. 10th World Basketball Championship, Spain.
2285 **483** 25q. blue and black . . 25 15
2286 – 80q. green and black . . 65 35
2287 – 1l.20 violet and black . . 1·00 70
2288 – 1l.60 red and black . . . 1·60 1·10
DESIGNS: 80q. Player running with ball; 1l.20, Defending goal; 1l.60, Defender capturing ball.

1985. Fruit Trees. Multicoloured.
2289 25q. Type **484** . . . . . . 1·50 55
2290 80q. Plums . . . . 2·25 80
2291 1l.20 Apples . . . . 3·25 1·50
2292 1l.60 Cherries . . . . 6·50 2·75

485 Kruja **486** War Horse Dance

1985. Architecture.
2293 **485** 25q. black and red . . . 25 15
2294 – 80q. black, grey and brown . . . . 1·25 35
2295 – 1l.20 black, brown & bl 1·75 65
2296 – 1l.60 black, brown & red 2·50 1·10
DESIGNS: 80q. Gjirokastra; 1l.20, Berat; 1l.60, Shkoder.

1985. National Folklore Festival. Dances.
2297 **486** 25q. brown, red & black 25 15
2298 – 80q. brown, red & black 65 35
2299 – 1l.20 brown, red & blk 1·00 65
2300 – 1l.60 brown, red & blk 1·60 1·10
MS2301 56 × 82 mm. 1l.90 multicoloured. Imperf . . . . 3·00 2·00
DESIGNS: 80q. Pillow dance; 1l.20, Ladies' kerchief dance; 1l.60, Men's one-legged pair dance; 1l.90, Fortress dance.

487 State Arms **488** Dam across River Drin

1986. 40th Anniv of Albanian People's Republic.
2302 **487** 25q. gold, red and black 60 40
2303 – 80q. multicoloured . . . 1·50 80
DESIGN: 80q. "Comrade Hoxha announcing the News to the People" (Vilson Kilica) and arms.

1986. Enver Hoxha Hydroelectric Power Station. Multicoloured.
2304 25q. Type **488** . . . . . . 2·50 1·00
2305 80q. Control building . . . 5·50 3·00

489 "Gymnospermium shqipetarum" **490** Maksim Gorki (writer)

1986. Flowers. Multicoloured.
2306 25q. Type **489** 60 40
2307 1l.20 "Leucojum valentinum" . . . . . . 3·00 1·50

1986. Anniversaries.
2308 **490** 25q. brown 25 15
2309 – 80q. violet . . . . . . 1·25 65
2310 – 1l.20 green . . . . . . 2·50 2·00
2311 – 2l.40 purple . . . . . . 4·25 2·75
MS2312 88 × 72 mm. 1l.90 violet, blue and yellow . . . . . . 4·75 3·00
DESIGNS: 25q. Type **490** (50th death anniv); 80q. Andre Ampere (physicist and mathematician, 150th death anniv); 1l.20, James Watt (inventor, 250th birth); 2l.40, Franz Liszt (composer, death cent). 88 × 72 mm. 1l.90, Heads of Gorki, Ampere, Watt and Liszt.

1986. Anti-fascist Heroes (8th series). As T **424**. Multicoloured.
2313 25q. Ramiz Aranitasi, Inajete Dumi and Laze Nuro Ferraj 80 60
2314 80q. Dine Kalenja, Kozma Naska, Met Hasa and Fahri Raalbani . . . . . 2·00 1·00
2315 1l.20 Hiqmet Buzi, Bajram Tusha, Mumin Selami and Hajredin Bylyshi . . . . 3·00 2·00

491 Trophy on Globe

1986. World Cup Football Championship, Mexico. Multicoloured.
2316 25q. Type **491** 30 20
2317 1l.20 Goalkeeper's hands and ball . . . . 1·25 1·00
MS2318 97 × 63 mm. 1l.90 Globe-football (40 × 32 mm) . . . . 3·00 2·50

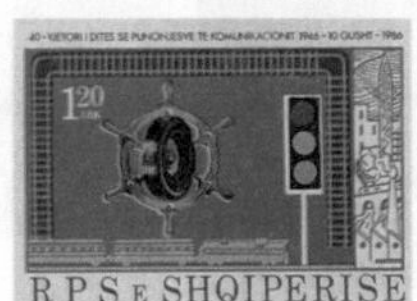
492 Car Tyre within Ship's Wheel, Diesel Train and Traffic Lights

1986. 40th Anniv of Transport Workers' Day.
2319 **492** 1l.20 multicoloured . . . 4·25 1·25

493 Naim Frasheri (poet)

1986. Anniversaries. Multicoloured.
2320 30q. Type **493** (140th birth anniv) 50 15
2321 60q. Ndre Mjeda (poet, 120th birth anniv) . . . . 1·00 65
2322 90q. Petro Nini Luarasi (jounalist, 75th death anniv) . . . . 1·50 1·00
2323 1l. Andon Zaka Cajupi (poet, 120th birth anniv) 1·60 1·10
2324 1l.20 Millosh Gjergj Nikolla (Migjeni) (revolutionary writer, 75th birth anniv) 2·00 1·40
2325 2l.60 Urani Rumbo (women's education pioneer, 50th death anniv) 4·25 2·75

494 Congress Emblem **495** Party Stamp and Enver Hoxha's Signature

1986. 9th Workers' Party Congress, Tirana.
2326 **494** 30q. multicoloured . . . 5·75 4·25

1986. 45th Anniv of Workers' Party.
2327 **495** 30q. red, grey and gold 1·10 55
2328 – 1l.20 red, orange & gold 4·75 2·40
DESIGNS: 1l.20, Profiles of Marx, Engels, Lenin and Stalin and Tirana house where Party was founded.

496 "Mother Albania" **497** Marble Head of Aesculapius

1986.
2329 **496** 10q. blue 10 10
2330 20q. red 10 10
2331 30q. red 10 10
2332 50q. brown 20 15
2333 60q. green 25 15
2334 80q. red 30 20
2335 90q. blue 35 25
2336 1l.20 green 45 30
2337 1l.60 purple 60 40
2338 2l.20 green 85 55
2339 3l. brown . . . . 1·10 75
2340 6l. yellow . . . . 2·25 1·50

1987. Archaeological Discoveries. Multicoloured.
2341 30q. Type **497** 45 30
2342 80q. Terracotta figure of Aphrodite . . . . 1·10 75
2343 1l. Bronze figure of Pan . . 1·40 95
2344 1l.20 Limestone head of Jupiter . . . . 1·75 1·10

498 Monument and Centenary Emblem **499** Victor Hugo (writer, 185th birth anniv)

1987. Centenary of First Albanian School.
2345 **498** 30q. brown, lt brn & yell 30 20
2346 – 80q. multicoloured . . . 80 55
2347 – 1l.20 multicoloured . . . 1·25 85
DESIGNS: 80q. First school building; 1l.20, Woman soldier running, girl reading book and boy doing woodwork.

1987. Anniversaries.
2348 **499** 30q. vio, lavender & blk 30 20
2349 – 80q. brown, lt brn & blk 80 60
2350 – 90q. dp blue, blue & blk 90 65
2351 – 1l.30 dp grn, grn & brn 1·25 90
DESIGNS: 80q. Galileo Galilei (astronomer, 345th death); 90q. Charles Darwin (naturalist, 105th death); 1l.30. Miguel de Cervantes Saavedra (writer, 440th birth).

500 "Forsythia europaea" **501** Congress Emblem

1987. Flowers. Multicoloured.
2352 30q. Type **500** 30 20
2353 90q. "Moltkia doerfleri" . . 90 60
2354 2l.10 "Wulfenia baldacii" . . 2·10 1·40

1987. 10th Trade Unions Congress, Tirana.
2355 **501** 1l.20 dp red, red & gold 3·00 2·00

502 "The Bread of Industry" (Myrteza Fushekati)

1987. Paintings from Gallery of Figurative Arts, Tirana. Multicoloured.
2356 30q. Type **502** 25 20
2357 80q. "Partisan Gift" (Skender Kokobobo) . . 65 50
2358 1l. "Sowers" (Bujar Asllani) (horiz) 80 60
2359 1l.20 "At the Foundry" (Clirim Ceka) (horiz) . . 90 75

503 Throwing the Hammer

1987. World Light Athletics Championships, Rome. Multicoloured.
2360 30q. Type **503** 25 20
2361 90q. Running 75 55
2362 1l.10 Putting the shot . . . 95 70
MS2363 85 × 59 mm. 1l.90 Runner, winners' podium and banner (64 × 24 mm) . . . . 1·50 1·50

504 Themistokli Germenji (revolutionary, 70th death)

1987. Anniversaries.
2364 **504** 30q. brown, red & black 35 25
2365 – 80q. red, scarlet & black 1·00 65
2366 – 90q. violet, red and black . . . . 1·10 75
2367 – 1l.30 green, red & black 1·60 1·10
DESIGNS: 80q. Bajram Curri (organizer of Albanian League, 125th birth); 90q. Aleks Stavre Drenova (poet, 40th death); 1l.30, Gjerasim Qiriazi (educational pioneer, 126th birth).

505 Emblem **506** National Flag

1987. 9th Young Communists' Union Congress, Tirana.
2368 **505** 1l.20 multicoloured . . . 4·00 2·75

1987. 75th Anniv of Independence.
2369 **506** 1l.20 multicoloured . . . 4·00 2·75

507 Post Office Emblem **508** Lord Byron (writer, bicentenary)

1987. 75th Anniv of Albanian Postal Administration. Multicoloured.
2370 90q. Type **507** . . . . . . 6·00 4·00
2371 1l.20 National emblem on bronze medallion . . . . 8·50 5·75

1988. Birth Anniversaries.
2372 **508** 30q. black and orange 2·75 2·25
2373 – 1l.20 black and mauve 10·50 8·50
DESIGN: 1l.20, Eugene Delacroix (painter, 190th anniv).

509 Oil Derrick, Tap, Houses and Wheat Ears **510** "Sideritis raeseri"

1988. 40th Anniv of W.H.O.
2374 **509** 90q. multicoloured . . . 17·00 14·00
2375 1l.20 multicoloured . . . 23·00 19·00

1988. Flowers. Multicoloured.
2376 30q. Type **510** . . . . . . 2·25 1·75
2377 90q. "Lunaria telekiana" . . 6·75 5·50
2378 2l.10 "Sanguisorba albanica" . . . . 16·00 13·00

511 Flag and Woman with Book

1988. 10th Women's Union Congress, Tirana.
2379 **511** 90q. black, red & orange 7·00 6·00

512 Footballers **513** Clasped Hands

1988. 8th European Football Championship, West Germany. Multicoloured.
2380 30q. Type **512** 65 50
2381 80q. Players jumping for ball . . . . 1·75 1·25
2382 1l.20 Tackling . . . . . . 2·50 1·90
MS2383 78 × 67 mm. 1l.90 Goalkeeper saving ball. Imperf 6·75 6·75

1988. 110th Anniv of League of Prizren. Mult.
2384 30q. Type **513** . . . . . . 6·50 6·50
2385 1l.20 League Headquarters, Prizren . . . . 27·00 27·00

514 Flag, Woman with Rifle and Soldier **515** Mihal Grameno (writer)

1988. 45th Anniv of People's Army. Multicoloured.
2386 60q. Type **514** . . . . . . 15·00 15·00
2387 90q. Army monument, partisans and Labinot house . . . . 23·00 23·00

1988. Multicoloured.
2388 30q. Type **515** . . . . . . 5·50 5·50
2389 90q. Bajo Topulli (revolutionary) . . . . . 16·00 16·00
2390 1l. Murat Toptani (sculptor and poet) . . . . 18·00 18·00
2391 1l.20 Jul Variboba (poet) . . 22·00 22·00

516 Migjeni

1988. 50th Death Anniv of Millosh Gjergj Nikolla (Migjeni) (writer).
2392 **516** 90q. silver and brown . . 6·75 6·00

517 "Dede Skurra" **518** Bride wearing Fezzes, Mirdita

1988. Ballads. Each black and grey.
2393 30q. Type **517** . . . . . . 5·00 5·00
2394 90q. "Young Omer" . . . . 15·00 15·00
2395 1l.20 "Gjergj Elez Alia" . . 19·00 19·00

1988. National Folklore Festival, Gjirokaster. Wedding Customs. Multicoloured.
2396 30q. Type **518** . . . . . . 9·00 9·00
2397 1l.20 Pan Dance, Gjirokaster . . . . 35·00 35·00

519 Hoxha

1988. 80th Birth Anniv of Enver Hoxha. Mult.
2398 90q. Type **519** . . . . . . 3·00 3·00
2399 1l.20 Enver Hoxha Museum (horiz) . . . . 4·00 4·00

520 Detail of Congress Document

1988. 80th Anniv of Monastir Language Congress. Multicoloured.
2400 60q. Type **520** . . . . . 12·50 12·50
2401 90q. Alphabet book and Congress building . . . . 16·00 16·00

521 Steam Locomotive and Map showing 1947 Railway line

1989. Railway Locomotives. Multicoloured.

2402 30q. Type **521** 40 10
2403 90q. Polish steam locomotive and map of 1949 network . . . . . . 1·25 35
2404 1l.20 Diesel locomotive and 1978 network . . . . . . 1·60 45
2405 1l.80 Diesel locomotive and 1985 network . . . . . . 2·40 70
2406 2l.40 Czechoslovakian diesel-electric locomotive and 1988 network . . . . 3·25 90

522 Entrance to Two-storey Tomb

1989. Archaeological Discoveries in Illyria.

2407 **522** 30q. black, brown & grey 15 10
2408 – 90q. black and green . . 50 35
2409 – 2l.10 multicoloured . . . 1·10 75

DESIGNS: 90q. Buckle showing battle scene; 2l.10, Earring depicting head.

523 Mother mourning Son

524 "Aster albanicus"

1989. "Kostandini and Doruntina" (folk tale). Mult.

2410 30q. Type **523** 15 10
2411 80q. Mother weeping over tomb and son rising from dead 45 30
2412 1l. Son and his sister on horseback 55 35
2413 1l.20 Mother and daughter reunited 65 45

1989. Flowers. Multicoloured.

2414 30q. Type **524** 15 10
2415 90q. "Orchis paparisti" . . 50 35
2416 2l.10 "Orchis albanica" . . 1·10 75

525 Johann Strauss (composer, 90th death anniv)

526 State Arms, Workers' Party Flag and Crowd

1989. Anniversaries. Each brown and gold.

2417 30q. Type **525** 15 10
2418 80q. Marie Curie (physicist, 55th death anniv) 45 30
2419 1l. Federico Garcia Lorca (writer, 53rd death anniv) 55 35
2420 1l.20 Albert Einstein (physicist, 110th birth anniv) 65 45

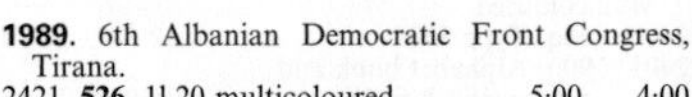

1989. 6th Albanian Democratic Front Congress, Tirana.

2421 **526** 1l.20 multicoloured . . . 5·00 4·00

527 Storming of the Bastille

1989. Bicentenary of French Revolution. Mult.

2422 90q. Type **527** 40 30
2423 1l.20 Monument 55 40

528 Galley

529 Pjeter Bogdani (writer, 300th anniv)

1989. Ships.

2424 **528** 30q. green and black . . 30 15
2425 – 80q. blue and black . . 75 35
2426 – 90q. blue and black . . 95 45
2427 – 1l.30 lilac and black . . 1·25 60

DESIGNS: 80q. Kogge; 90q. Schooner; 1l.30, "Tirana" (freighter).

1989. Death Anniversaries. Multicoloured.

2428 30q. Type **529** 20 15
2429 80q. Gavril Dara (writer, centenary) 50 35
2430 90q. Thimi Mitko (writer, centenary (1990)) 60 40
2431 1l.30 Kole Idromeno (painter, 50th anniv) . . . 85 55

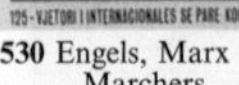

530 Engels, Marx and Marchers

531 Gymnastics

1989. 125th Anniv of "First International". Mult.

2432 90q. Type **530** 40 30
2433 1l.20 Factories, marchers and worker with pickaxe and rifle 55 40

1989. 6th National Spartakiad.

2434 **531** 30q. black, orange & red 15 10
2435 – 80q. black, lt grn & grn 40 25
2436 – 1l. black, blue & dp blue 50 35
2437 – 1l.20 black, pur & red 55 35

DESIGNS: 80q. Football; 1l. Cycling; 1l.20, Running.

532 Soldier

533 Chamois

1989. 45th Anniv of Liberation. Multicoloured.

2438 30q. Type **532** 15 10
2439 80q. Date 35 25
2440 1l. State arms 45 30
2441 1l.20 Young couple 50 35

1990. Endangered Animals. The Chamois. Mult.

2442 10q. Type **533** 10 10
2443 30q. Mother and young . . 25 20
2444 80q. Chamois keeping lookout 65 50
2445 90q. Head of chamois . . . 70 55

534 Eagle Mask

1990. Masks. Multicoloured.

2446 30q. Type **534** 10 10
2447 90q. Sheep 35 25
2448 1l.20 Goat 50 35
2449 1l.80 Stork 70 45

535 Caesar's Mushroom

1990. Fungi. Multicoloured.

2450 30q. Type **535** 30 15
2451 90q. Parasol mushroom . . 85 40
2452 1l.20 Cep . . . . 1·10 50
2453 1l.80 "Clathrus cancelatus" 1·60 80

536 Engraving Die

1990. 150th Anniv of the Penny Black. Mult.

2454 90q. Type **536** 50 40
2455 1l.20 Mounted postal messenger 65 55
2456 1l.80 Mail coach passengers reading letters 95 80

537 Mascot and Flags

1990. World Cup Football Championship, Italy. Multicoloured.

2457 30q. Type **537** 15 10
2458 90q. Mascot running . . . 40 25
2459 1l.20 Mascot preparing to kick ball 55 35
MS2460 80 × 62 mm. 3l.30 Mascot as goalkeeper. Imperf . . . . 1·50 1·50

538 Young Van Gogh and Paintings

1990. Death Centenary of Vincent van Gogh (painter). Multicoloured.

2461 30q. Type **538** 15 10
2462 90q. Van Gogh and woman in field 40 25
2463 2l.10 Van Gogh in asylum 90 60
MS2464 88 × 73 mm. 2l.40 Van Gogh and "Wheatfield with Crows". Imperf . . . . 1·00 1·00

539 Gjergj Elez Alia lying wounded

1990. Gjergj Elez Alia (folk hero). Multicoloured.

2465 30q. Type **539** 15 10
2466 90q. Alia being helped onto horse 40 25

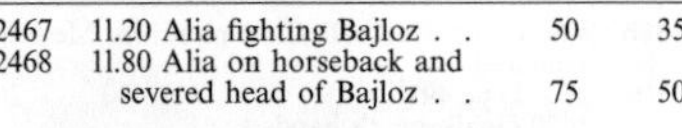

2467 1l.20 Alia fighting Bajloz . . 50 35
2468 1l.80 Alia on horseback and severed head of Bajloz . . 75 50

540 Mosque

541 Pirroja

1990. 2400th Anniv of Berat. Multicoloured.

2469 30q. Type **540** 10 10
2470 90q. Triadha's Church . . . 30 20
2471 1l.20 River 40 25
2472 1l.80 Onufri (artist) 60 40
2473 2l.40 Nikolla 80 55

1990. Illyrian Heroes. Each black.

2474 30q. Type **541** 10 10
2475 90q. Teuta 30 20
2476 1l.20 Bato 40 25
2477 1l.80 Bardhyli 65 45

542 School and "Globe" of Books

543 "Albanian Horsemen" (Eugene Delacroix)

1990. International Literacy Year.

2478 **542** 90q. multicoloured . . . 30 20
2479 1l.20 multicoloured . . . 40 25

1990. Albanians in Art. Multicoloured.

2480 30q. Type **543** 15 10
2481 1l.20 "Albanian Woman" (Camille Corot) 50 40
2482 1l.80 "Skanderbeg" (anon) 75 55

544 Boletini

545 Armorial Eagle

1991. 75th Death Anniv of Isa Boletini (revolutionary). Multicoloured.

2483 90q. Type **544** 20 15
2484 1l.20 Boletini and flag . . . 30 25

1991. 800th Anniv (1990) of Founding of Arberi State.

2485 **545** 90q. multicoloured . . . 20 15
2486 1l.20 multicoloured . . . 30 25

546 "Woman reading"

547 "Cistus albanicus"

1991. 150th Birth Anniv of Pierre Auguste Renoir (artist). Multicoloured.

2487 30q. Type **546** 15 10
2488 90q. "The Swing" 50 40
2489 1l.20 "The Boat Club" (horiz) 85 50
2490 1l.80 Still life (detail) (horiz) 95 70
MS2491 94 × 75 mm. 3l. "Portrait of Artist with Beard". Imperf . . 2·00 2·00

1991. Flowers. Multicoloured.

2492 30q. Type **547** 15 10
2493 90q. "Trifolium pilczii" . . 35 25
2494 1l.80 "Lilium albanicum" 75 55

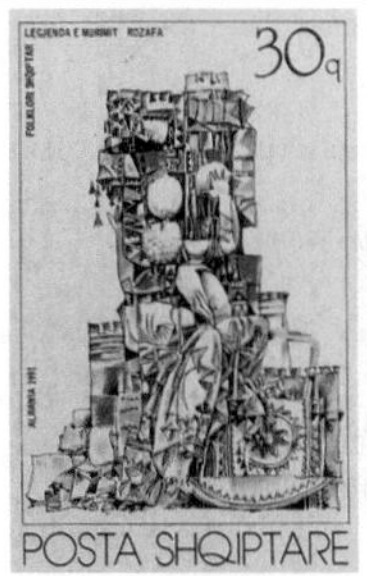

548 Rozafa breastfeeding Child

549 Mozart conducting

1991. Imprisonment of Rozafa (folk tale). Mult.
2495 30q. Type **548** 10 10
2496 90q. The three brothers talking to old man . . . 30 25
2497 1l.20 Building of walls around Rozafa 40 30
2498 1l.80 Figures symbolizing water flowing between stones 60 45

1991. Death Bicentenary of Wolfgang Amadeus Mozart (composer). Multicoloured.
2499 90q. Type **549** 30 25
2500 1l.20 Mozart and score . . 45 35
2501 1l.80 Mozart composing . . 65 50
MS2502 88 × 69 mm. 3l. Mozart medallion and score. Imperf . . 1·10 1·10

550 Vitus Bering

1992. Explorers. Multicoloured.
2503 30q. Type **550** 10 10
2504 90q. Christopher Columbus and his flagship "Santa Maria" 50 25
2505 1l.80 Ferdinand Magellan and his flagship "Vitoria" 90 50

551 Otto Lilienthal's Biplane Glider, 1896

1992. Aircraft.
2506 **551** 30q. black, red and blue 10 10
2507 – 80q. multicoloured . . . 25 20
2508 – 90q. multicoloured . . . 30 25
2509 – 1l.20 multicoloured . . . 40 30
2510 – 1l.80 multicoloured . . . 55 40
2511 – 2l.40 black, grey & mve 75 55
DESIGNS: 80q. Clement Ader's "Avion III", 1897; 90q. Wright Brothers' Type A, 1903; 1l.20, Concorde supersonic jetliner; 1l.80, Tupolev Tu-144 jetliner (wrongly inscr "114"); 2l.40, Dornier Do-31E (wrongly inscr "Dernier").

552 Ski Jumping

1992. Winter Olympic Games, Albertville. Mult.
2512 30q. Type **552** 10 10
2513 90q. Skiing 30 25
2514 1l.20 Ice skating (pairs) . . 40 30
2515 1l.80 Luge 60 45

553 "Europe" and Doves

1992. Admission of Albania to European Security and Co-operation Conference at Foreign Ministers' Meeting, Berlin. Multicoloured.
2516 90q. Type **553** 30 25
2517 1l.20 Members' flags and map of Europe 45 35

554 Envelopes and Emblem

1992. Admission of Albania to E.P.T. Conference. Multicoloured.
2518 90q. Type **554** 30 25
2519 1l.20 Emblem and tape reels 45 35

555 Everlasting Flame

1992. National Martyrs' Day. Multicoloured.
2520 90q. Type **555** 25 20
2521 4l.10 Poppies (horiz) . . . . 1·10 85

556 Pictograms

1992. European Football Championship, Sweden.
2522 **556** 30q. light green & green 10 10
2523 – 90q. red and blue . . . 35 25
2524 – 10l.80 ochre and brown 4·00 3·00
MS2525 90 × 69 mm. 5l. pink, ochre and green. Imperf . . . . . . 2·10 2·10
DESIGNS: 90q. to 5l., Different pictograms.

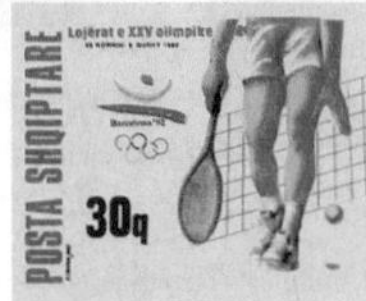

557 Lawn Tennis

1992. Olympic Games, Barcelona. Multicoloured.
2526 30q. Type **557** 10 10
2527 90q. Baseball 35 25
2528 1l.80 Table tennis 75 55
MS2529 89 × 69 mm. 5l. Torch bearer and running tracks. Imperf 2·10 2·10

558 Map and Doves

1992. European Unity.
2530 **558** 1l.20 multicoloured . . . 35 25

559 Native Pony

1992. Horses. Multicoloured.
2531 30q. Type **559** 10 10
2532 90q. Hungarian nonius . . . 25 20
2533 1l.20 Arab (vert) 35 25
2534 10l.60 Haflinger (vert) . . . 3·25 2·40

560 Map of Americas, Columbus and Ships

1992. Europa. 500th Anniv of Discovery of America by Columbus. Multicoloured.
2535 60q. Type **560** 60 20
2536 3l.20 Map of Americas and Columbus meeting Amerindians . . . . . . 1·10 1·85
MS2537 90 × 70 mm. 5l. Map of America and Columbus. Imperf 23·00 23·00

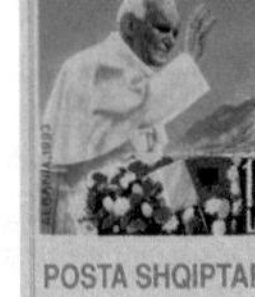

561 Mother Teresa and Child

562 Pope John Paul II

1992. Mother Teresa (Agnes Gonxhe Bojaxhi) (founder of Missionaries of Charity).
2538 **561** 40q. red 10 10
2539 60q. brown 10 10
2540 1l. violet 10 10
2541 1l.80 grey 10 10
2542 2l. red 15 10
2543 2l.40 green 15 10
2544 3l.20 blue 20 15
2545 5l. violet 25 20
2546 5l.60 purple 35 25
2547 7l.20 green 45 35
2548 10l. orange 55 40
2549 18l. orange 85 65
2550 20l. purple 30 25
2551 25l. green . . . . 1·00 75
2552 60l. green 85 65

1993. Papal Visit.
2555 **562** 16l. multicoloured . . . 95 70

1993. Nos. 2329/32 and 2335 surch **POSTA SHQIPTARE** and new value.
2556 **496** 3l. on 10q. blue 25 20
2557 6l.50 on 20q. red 50 35
2558 13l. on 30q. red . . . . 1·00 1·75
2559 20l. on 90q. blue . . . . 1·50 1·10
2560 30l. on 50q. brown . . . 2·25 1·75

564 Lef Nosi (first Postal Minister)

565 "Life Weighs Heavily on Man" (A. Zajmi)

1993. 80th Anniv of First Albanian Stamps.
2561 **564** 6l.50 brown and green 35 25

1993. Europa. Contemporary Art. Multicoloured.
2562 3l. Type **565** 30 25
2563 7l. "The Green Star" (E. Hila) (horiz) 70 55
MS2564 116 × 121 mm. 20l. "Gjirokaster" (B. Ahmeti). Imperf 1·60 1·60

566 Running

1993. Mediterranean Games, Agde and Roussillon (Languedoc), France. Multicoloured.
2565 3l. Type **566** 20 15
2566 16l. Canoeing . . . . 1·10 85
2567 21l. Cycling . . . . 1·40 1·10
MS2568 117 × 84 mm. 20l. Map of Mediterranean. Imperf . . . . 1·10 1·10

567 Bardhi

568 Mascot and Flags around Stadium

1993. 350th Death Anniv of Frang Bardhi (scholar).
2569 **567** 6l.50 brown and stone 45 35
MS2570 94 × 107 mm. 20l. brown and gold. Imperf . . . . . . 1·40 1·40
DESIGN: 20l. Bardhi writing at desk.

1994. World Cup Football Championship, U.S.A. Multicoloured.
2571 42l. Type **568** 50 40
2572 68l. Mascot kicking ball . . 80 60

569 Gjovalin Gjadri (construction engineer)

571 Richard Wagner

570 Emblem and Benz

1994. Europa. Discoveries and Inventions.
2573 **569** 50l. dp brn, ches & brn 70 55
2574 – 100l. dp brn, ches & brn 1·75 1·25
MS2575 60 × 80 mm. 150l. drab and brown. Imperf . . . . 2·00 2·00
DESIGN: 100l. Karl Ritter von Ghega (railway engineer); 150l. Sketch of traffic project.

1995. 150th Birth Anniv (1994) of Karl Benz (motor manufacturer). Multicoloured.
2576 5l. Type **570** 10 10
2577 10l. Mercedes-Benz C-class saloon, 1995 Daimler motor carriage, 1886 . . . 20 15
2578 60l. First four-wheel Benz motor-car, 1886 . . . . . 1·00 75
2579 125l. Mercedes-Benz 540 K cabriolet, 1936 . . . . . 2·10 1·60

1995. Composers. Each brown and gold.
2580 3l. Type **571** 10 10
2581 6l.50 Edvard Grieg 10 10
2582 11l. Charles Gounod . . . 20 15
2583 20l. Pyotr Tchaikovsky . . 35 25

572 Intersections

1995. 50th Anniv (1994) of Liberation.
2584 **572** 50l. black and red . . . 75 55

573 Ali Pasha

1995. 250th Birth Anniv (1994) of Ali Pasha of Tepelene (Pasha of Janina, 1788–1820).
2585 **573** 60l. black, yellow & brn 95 70
MS2586 80 × 60 mm. 100l. brown and orange (Administration building, Tepelene). Imperf . . 1·40 1·40

574 Veskopoja, 1744 (left half)

1995. 250th Anniv (1994) of Veskopoja Academy. Multicoloured.
2587 42l. Type **574** 60 45
2588 68l. Veskopoja, 1744 (right half) . . . . 1·00 75
Nos. 2587/8 were issued together, se-tenant, forming a composite design.

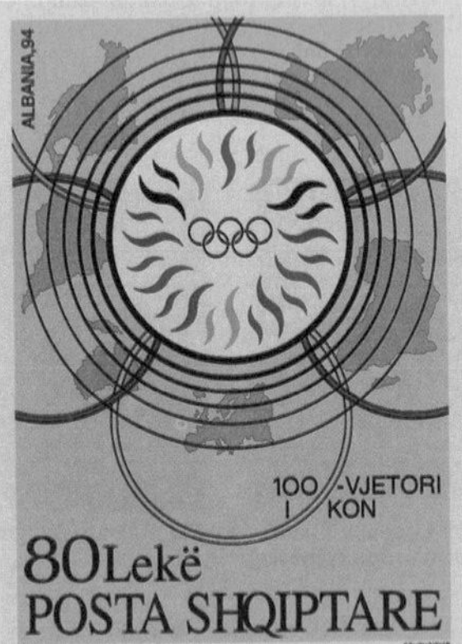

575 Olympic Rings and Map

1995. Centenary of International Olympic Committee. Sheet 60 × 80 mm. Imperf.
MS2589 **575** 80l. multicoloured 1·25 1·25

576 Palace of Europe, Strasbourg

1995. Admission of Albania to Council of Europe. Multicoloured.
2590 25l. Type **576** 30 25
2591 85l. State arms and map of Europe . . . . 1·40 1·10

577 Hands holding Olive Branch **579** Bee on Flower

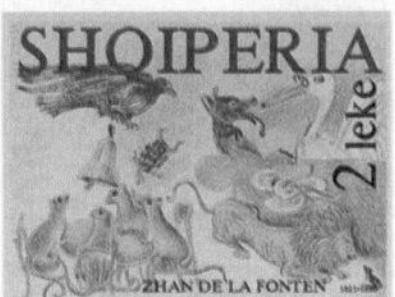

578 Mice sitting around Table and Stork with Fox

1995. Europa. Peace and Freedom. Multicoloured.
2592 50l. Type **577** 80 60
2593 100l. Dove flying over hands 1·60 1·25
MS2594 80 × 60 mm. 150l. Figure stretching out hands. Imperf 2·50 2·50

1995. 300th Death Anniv of Jean de La Fontaine (writer). Multicoloured.
2595 2l. Type **578** 10 10
2596 3l. Stork with foxes around table 10 10
2597 25l. Frogs under tree . . . 45 35
MS2598 80 × 60 mm. 60l. La Fontaine and animals. Imperf 1·00 75

1995. The Honey Bee. Multicoloured.
2599 5l. Type **579** 10 10
2600 10l. Bee and honeycomb . . 20 15
2601 25l. Bee on comb 45 35

580 Fridtjof Nansen **582** Male Chorus

581 Flags outside U.N. Building, New York

1995. Polar Explorers. Multicoloured.
2602 25l. Type **580** 55 45
2603 25l. James Cook 55 45
2604 25l. Roald Amundsen . . . 55 45
2605 25l. Robert Scott 55 45
Nos. 2602/5 were issued together, se-tenant, forming a composite design.

1995. 50th Anniv of U.N.O. Multicoloured.
2606 2l. Type **581** 10 10
2607 100l. Flags flying to right outside U.N. building, New York . . . . 1·60 1·25

1995. National Folklore Festival, Berat. Mult.
2608 5l. Type **582** 10 10
2609 50l. Female participant . . . 85 65

583 "Poet" **584** Church and Preacher, Berat Kruje

1995. Jan Kukuzeli (11th-century poet, musician and teacher). Abstract representations of Kukuzeli. Multicoloured.
2610 18l. Type **583** 30 25
2611 20l. "Musician" 35 25
MS2612 80 × 80 mm. 100l. "Teacher". Imperf . . . . . . 1·60 1·60

1995. 20th Anniv of World Tourism Organization. Multicoloured.
2613 18l. Type **584** 30 25
2614 20l. Street, Shkoder 35 25
2615 42l. Buildings, Gjirokaster 70 35

585 Paul Eluard **586** Louis, Film Reel and Projector

1995. Poets' Birth Centenaries. Multicoloured.
2616 25l. Type **585** 35 25
2617 50l. Sergei Yessenin 75 55

1995. Centenary of Motion Pictures. Lumiere Brothers (developers of cine camera). Mult.
2618 10l. Type **586** 25 20
2619 85l. Auguste, film reel and cinema audience . . . . 1·50 40

587 Presley

1995. 60th Birth Anniv of Elvis Presley (entertainer). Multicoloured.
2620 3l. Type **587** 10 10
2621 60l. Presley (different) . . . 1·00 75

588 Banknotes of 1925 **589** "5", Crumbling Star, Open Book and Peace Dove

1995. 70th Anniv of Albanian National Bank. Mult.
2622 10l. Type **588** 20 15
2623 25l. Modern banknotes . . 45 35

1995. 5th Anniv of Democratic Movement. Mult.
2624 5l. Type **589** 10 10
2625 50l. Woman planting tree 85 65

590 Mother Teresa **591** Football, Union Flag, Map of Europe and Stadium

1996. Europa. Famous Women. Mother Teresa (founder of Missionaries of Charity).
2626 **590** 25l. multicoloured . . . 45 35
2627 100l. multicoloured . . . 1·75 1·25
MS2628 60 × 80 mm. 150l. Mother Teresa (different). Imperf . . . 2·50 2·50

1996. European Football Championship, England, Multicoloured.
2629 25l. Type **591** 65 35
2630 100l. Map of Europe, ball and player . . . . 1·75 1·25

592 Satellite and Radio Mast **593** Running

1996. Inaug of Cellular Telephone Network. Mult.
2631 10l. Type **592** 20 10
2632 60l. User, truck, container ship and mobile telephone (vert) . . . . 1·75 75

1996. Olympic Games, Atlanta, U.S.A. Mult.
2633 5l. Type **593** 10 10
2634 25l. Throwing the hammer 45 35
2635 60l. Long jumping . . . . . 1·00 75
MS2636 60 × 80 mm. 100l. Games emblem. Imperf . . . . 1·75 1·75

594 Linked Hands **596** "The Naked Maja"

595 Gottfried Wilhelm Leibniz (350th)

1996. 75th Anniv of Albanian Red Cross.
2637 **594** 50l.+10l. mult . . . . . 1·00 1·00

1996. Philosopher-mathematicians' Birth Annivs. Multicoloured.
2638 10l. Type **595** 20 10
2639 85l. Rene Descartes (400th) 1·50 1·10

1996. 250th Birth Anniv of Francisco de Goya (artist). Multicoloured.
2640 10l. Type **596** 20 10
2641 60l. "Dona Isabel Cobos de Porcel" . . . . 1·00 75
MS2642 80 × 60 mm. 100l. "Self-portrait" (24 × 29 mm) . . . . 1·75 1·75

597 Book Binding **598** Princess

1996. Christian Art Exhibition. Multicoloured.
2643 5l. Type **597** 10 10
2644 25l. Book clasp showing crucifixion 45 35
2645 85l. Book binding (different) 1·50 1·10

1996. 50th Anniv of U.N.I.C.E.F. Children's Paintings. Multicoloured.
2646 5l. Type **598** 10 10
2647 10l. Woman 20 15
2648 25l. Sea life 45 35
2649 50l. Harbour 85 65

599 State Arms, Book and Fishta **600** Omar Khayyam and Writing Materials

1996. 125th Birth Anniv of Gjergj Fishta (writer and politician). Multicoloured.
2650 10l. Type **599** 20 15
2651 60l. Battle scene and Fishta 1·00 75

1997. 950th Birth Anniv of Omar Khayyam (astronomer and poet). Multicoloured.
2652 20l. Type **600** 35 25
2653 50l. Omar Khayyam and symbols of astronomy . . 85 65
Nos. 2652/3 are inscribed "850" in error.

601 Gutenberg **602** Pelicans

1997. 600th Birth Anniv of Johannes Gutenberg (printer). Multicoloured.
2654 20l. Type **601** 40 25
2655 60l. Printing press . . . . . 1·00 75
Nos. 2654/5 were issued together, se-tenant, forming a composite design.

1997. The Dalmatian Pelican. Multicoloured.
2656 10l. Type **602** 20 15
2657 80l. Pelicans on shore and in flight . . . . 1·40 45
Nos. 2656/7 were issued together, se-tenant, forming a composite design.

603 Dragon **604** Konica

1997. Europa. Tales and Legends. "The Blue Pool". Multicoloured.
2658 30l. Type **603** 50 40
2659 100l. Dragon drinking from pool . . . . 1·75 1·25

1997. 55th Death Anniv of Faik Konica (writer and politician).
2660 **604** 10l. brown and black . . 20 15
2661 25l. blue and black . . . 45 35
MS2662 60 × 80 mm. **604** 80l. brown 1·40 1·40

605 Male Athlete **606** Skanderbeg

1997. Mediterranean Games, Bari. Multicoloured.
2663 20l. Type **605** 35 25
2664 30l. Female athlete and rowers 50 40
MS2665 60 × 80 mm. 100l. Discus-thrower, javelin-thrower and runner. Imperf . . . . 1·75 1·75

1997.
2666 **606** 5l. red and brown . . . 10 10
2667 10l. green and olive . . . 10 10
2668 20l. green and deep green 20 15
2669 25l. mauve and purple 25 20
2670 30l. violet and lilac . . . 30 25
2671 50l. grey and black . . . 50 40
2672 60l. lt brown & brown 60 45
2673 80l. lt brown & brown 80 60
2674 100l. red and lake . . . 1·00 75
2675 110l. blue and deep blue 1·10 85

1997. Mother Teresa (founder of Missionaries of Charity) Commemoration. No. 2627 optd **HOMAZH 1910–1997.**
2676 **590** 100l. multicoloured . . . 1·00 75

608 Codex Aureus (11th century) **609** Twin-headed Eagle (postal emblem)

1997. Codices (1st series). Multicoloured.
2677 10l. Type **608** 10 10
2678 25l. Codex Purpureus Beratinus (7th century) showing mountain and scribe 25 20
2679 60l. Codex Purpureus Beratinus showing church and scribe 60 45
See also Nos. 2712/14.

1997. 85th Anniv of Albanian Postal Service.
2680 **609** 10l. multicoloured . . . 10 10
2681 30l. multicoloured . . . 30 25
The 30l. differs from Type **609** in minor parts of the design.

610 Nikete of Ramesiana

611 Man sitting at Table

1998. Nikete Dardani, Bishop of Ramesiana (philosopher and composer).
2682 **610** 30l. multicoloured . . . 25 20
2683 100l. multicoloured . . . 85 65
There are minor differences of design between the two values.

1998. Legend of Pogradeci Lake. Multicoloured.
2684 30l. Type **611** 25 20
2685 50l. The Three Graces . . . 40 30
2686 60l. Women drawing water 50 40
2687 80l. Man of ice 70 55

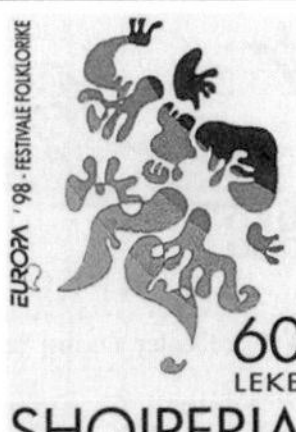

612 Stylized Dancers

1998. Europa. National Festivals. Multicoloured.
2688 60l. Type **612** 50 40
2689 100l. Female dancer 85 65
MS2690 60 × 80 mm. 150l. Two dancers. Imperf . . . . 1·30 1·30

613 Abdyl Frasheri (founder)

614 Player with Ball

1998. 120th Anniv of League of Prizren. Mult.
2691 30l. Type **613** 25 15
2692 50l. Sulejman Vokshi and partisan 40 30
2693 60l. Iljaz Pashe Dibra and crossed rifles 50 35
2694 80l. Ymer Prizreni and partisans 70 50

1998. World Cup Football Championship, France. Multicoloured.
2695 60l. Type **614** 50 35
2696 100l. Player with ball (different) 85 65
MS2697 60 × 80 mm. 120l. Championship mascot. Imperf 1·10 1·10

615 Wrestlers in National Costume

616 Cacej

1998. European Junior Wrestling Championship. Multicoloured.
2698 30l. Type **615** 25 15
2699 60l. Ancient Greek wrestlers 25 15

1998. 90th Birth Anniv of Eqerem Cabej (linguist).
2700 **616** 60l. black and yellow . . 25 15
2701 80l. yellow, black & red 70 50

617 Diana, Princess of Wales

1998. Diana, Princess of Wales Commemoration. Multicoloured.
2702 60l. Type **617** 55 30
2703 100l. With Mother Teresa 90 45

618 Mother Teresa holding Child

1998. Mother Teresa (founder of Missionaries of Charity) Commemoration. Multicoloured.
2704 60l. Type **618** 55 30
2705 100l. Mother Teresa (vert) 90 45

619 Detail of Painting

1998. 150th Birth Anniv of Paul Gauguin (artist). Multicoloured.
2706 60l. Type **619** 55 30
2707 80l. "Women of Tahiti" . . 70 35
MS2708 60 × 80 mm. 120l. Face. Imperf . . . . 1·10 1·10

620 Epitaph

1998. 625th Anniv of Epitaph of Gllavenica (embroidery of dead Christ). Multicoloured.
2709 30l. Type **620** 25 10
2710 80l. Close-up of upper body 70 35
MS2711 80 × 60 mm. 100l. Detail of epitaph (24 × 29 mm) 90 90

621 Page of Codex

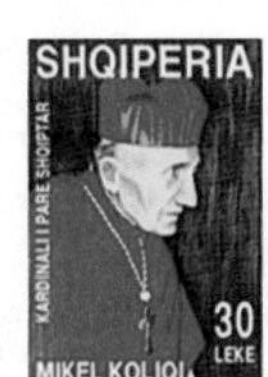

623 Koliqi

1998. Codices (2nd series). 11th-century Manuscripts. Multicoloured.
2712 30l. Type **621** 25 10
2713 50l. Front cover of manuscript 45 20
2714 80l. Page showing mosque 70 35

1998. "Italia '98" International Stamp Exhibition. No. MS2628 optd **Italia 98.**
MS2715 60 × 80 mm. 150l. mult 2·75 2·75

1998. 1st Death Anniv of Cardinal Mikel Koliqi (first Albanian Cardinal). Multicoloured.
2716 30l. Type **623** 25 15
2717 100l. Koliqi (different) . . . 90 45

624 George Washington (first President, 1789–97)

1999. American Anniversaries. Multicoloured.
2718 150l. Type **624** (death bicentenary) . . . . . . 1·40 70
2719 150l. Abraham Lincoln (President 1861–65, 190th birth anniv) . . . . . . 1·40 70
2720 150l. Martin Luther King Jr. (civil rights campaigner, 70th birth anniv) . . . . 1·40 70

625 Monk Seals

1999. The Monk Seal. Multicoloured.
2721 110l. Type **625** . . . . . . 1·00 50
2722 110l. Two seals (both facing left) . . . . 1·00 50
2723 150l. As No. 2722 but both facing right . . . . 1·40 70
2724 150l. As Type **625** but seal at back facing left and seal at front facing right 1·40 70
Nos. 2721/4 were issued together, se-tenant, forming a composite design.

1999. 50th Anniv of Council of Europe. No. 2590 surch **150 LEKE** and emblem.
2725 **576** 150l. on 25l. mult . . . 1·40 70

1999. "iBRA '99" International Stamp Exhibition, Nuremberg, Germany. No. 2496 surch **150 LEKE** in black (new value) and multicoloured (emblem).
2726 150l. on 90q. multicoloured 1·40 70

628 Dove, Airplane and NATO Emblem

629 Mickey Mouse

1999. 50th Anniv of North Atlantic Treaty Organization.
2727 **628** 10l. multicoloured . . . 10 10
2728 100l. multicoloured . . . 90 45
MS2729 69 × 85 mm. 250l. multicoloured . . . . 2·00 2·00

1999. Mickey Mouse (cartoon film character). Multicoloured.
2730 60l. Type **629** 55 30
2731 80l. Mickey writing letter . . 70 35
2732 110l. Mickey thinking . . . 1·00 50
2733 150l. Wearing black and red jumper . . . . 1·40 70

630 Thethi National Park, Shkoder

1999. Europa. Parks and Gardens. Multicoloured.
2734 90l. Type **630** 80 40
2735 310l. Lura National Park, Dibra . . . . 2·75 1·40
MS2736 80 × 60 mm. 350l. Divjaka National Park, Lushnje. Imperf 3·25 3·25

631 Coin

1999. Illyrian Coins. Multicoloured.
2737 10l. Type **631** 10 10
2738 20l. Coins from Labeateve, Bylisi and Scutari 20 10
2739 200l. Coins of King Monuni 1·75 90
MS2740 80 × 60 mm. 310l. Coin of King Gent (29 × 49 mm) . . . 2·75 2·75

1999. "Philexfrance 99" International Stamp Exhibition, Paris. No. 2512 surch with new value and Exhibition logo.
2741 **552** 150l. on 30q. mult . . . 1·40 70

633 Chaplin

634 Neil Armstrong on Moon

1999. 110th Birth Anniv of Charlie Chaplin (film actor and director). Multicoloured.
2742 30l. Type **633** 25 10
2743 50l. Raising hat 45 25
2744 250l. Dancing . . . . 2·25 1·10

1999. 30th Anniv of First Manned Moon Landing. Multicoloured.
2745 30l. Type **634** 25 10
2746 150l. Lunar module . . . . 1·40 70
2747 300l. Astronaut and American flag . . . . . 2·75 1·40
MS2748 60 × 80 mm. 280l. Launch of "Apollo 1" (25 × 29 mm) . . 2·50 2·50
Nos. 2745/7 were issued together, se-tenant, forming a composite design.

635 Prisoner behind Bars

636 Emblem

1999. The Nazi Holocaust.
2749 **635** 30l. multicoloured . . . 25 10
2750 150l. black and yellow 1·40 70

1999. 125th Anniv of Universal Postal Union.
2751 **636** 20l. multicoloured . . . 20 10
2752 60l. multicoloured . . . 55 30

1999. "China 1999" International Stamp Exhibition, Peking. No. 2497 surch **150 LEKE**.
2753 150l. on 11.20 multicoloured 1·40 70

638 Javelin **639** Madonna and Child

1999. 70th Anniv of National Athletic Championships. Multicoloured.
2754 10l. Type **638** 10 10
2755 20l. Discus 20 10
2756 200l. Running . . . . . . 1·90 85

1999. Icons by Onufri Shek (artist). Multicoloured.
2757 30l. Type **639** 25 10
2758 300l. The Resurrection . . . 2·75 1·40

640 Bilal Golemi (veterinary surgeon)

1999. Birth Anniversaries. Multicoloured.
2759 10l. Type **640** (centenary) . . 10 10
2760 20l. Azem Galica (revolutionary) (centenary) 20 10
2761 50l. Viktor Eftimiu (writer) (centenary) 45 20
2762 300l. Lasgush Poradeci (poet) (centenary (2000)) 2·75 1·40

641 Carnival Mask

1999. Carnivals. Multicoloured.
2763 30l. Type **641** 25 10
2764 300l. Turkey mask . . . . 2·75 1·40

642 Bell and Flowers **643** Woman's Costume, Librazhdi

2000. New Millennium. The Peace Bell. Mult.
2765 40l. Type **642** 35 15
2766 90l. Bell and flowers (different) 80 40

2000. Regional Costumes (1st series). Mult.
2767 5l. Type **643** 10 10
2768 10l. Woman's costume, Malesia E Madhe 10 10
2769 15l. Man's costume, Malesia E Madhe 15 10
2770 20l. Man's costume, Tropoje 20 10
2771 30l. Man's costume, Dumrea 30 15
2772 35l. Man's costume, Tirana 30 15
2773 40l. Woman's costume, Tirana 35 15
2774 45l. Woman's costume, Arbereshe 40 20
2775 50l. Man's costume, Gjirokastra 45 25
2776 55l. Woman's costume, Lunxheri 50 25
2777 70l. Woman's costume, Cameria 65 30
2778 90l. Man's costume, Laberia 80 40
See also Nos. 2832/43, 2892/2903 and 2943/54.

644 Majer **645** Donald Duck

2000. 150th Birth Anniv of Gustav Majer (etymologist).
2779 **644** 50l. green 45 25
2780 130l. red . . . . 1·25 65

2000. Donald and Daisy Duck (cartoon film characters). Multicoloured.
2781 10l. Type **645** 10 10
2782 30l. Donald Duck 30 15
2783 90l. Daisy Duck 80 40
2784 250l. Donald Duck . . . . 2·25 1·10

646 Early Racing Car

2000. Motor Racing. Multicoloured.
2785 30l. Type **646** 30 15
2786 30l. Two-man racing car . . 30 15
2787 30l. Racing car with wire nose 30 15
2788 30l. Racing car with solid wheels 30 15
2789 30l. Car No. 1 . . . . . . 30 15
2790 30l. Car No. 2 . . . . . . 30 15
2791 30l. White Formula 1 racing car (facing left) 30 15
2792 30l. Blue Formula 1 racing car 30 15
2793 30l. Red Formula 1 racing car 30 15
2794 30l. White Formula 1 racing car (front view) 30 15

647 Ristoz of Mborja Church, Korca

2000. Birth Bimillenary of Jesus Christ. Mult.
2795 15l. Type **647** 15 10
2796 40l. St. Kolli Church, Voskopoja 35 15
2797 90l. Church of Flori and Lauri, Kosovo 80 40
MS2798 80 × 60 mm. 250l. Fountain of Shengjin (mosaic), Tirana (37 × 37 mm) . . . . 2·75 2·75

648 "Building Europe" **650** Gustav Mahler (composer) (40th death anniv)

649 Wolf

2000. Europa. Multicoloured.
2799 130l. Type **648** . . . . 1·25 60
MS2800 60 × 80 mm. 300l. Detail of design showing boy holding star (24 × 29 mm) . . . . 3·40 3·40

2000. Animals. Multicoloured.
2801 10l. Type **649** 10 10
2802 40l. Brown bear 35 15
2803 90l. Wild boar 80 40
2804 220l. Red fox . . . . 2·00 1·00

2000. "WIPA 2000" International Stamp Exhibition, Vienna.
2805 **650** 130l. multicoloured . . . 1·25 1·00

651 Footballer saving Ball

2000. European Football Championship, Belgium and The Netherlands. Multicoloured.
2806 10l. Type **651** 10 10
2807 120l. Footballer heading ball 1·10 55
MS2808 80 × 60 mm. 260l. Footballer kicking ball. Imperf 3·00 3·00

652 Musicans

2000. Paintings by Picasso. Multicoloured.
2809 30l. Type **652** 30 15
2810 40l. Abstract face 35 15
2811 250l. Two women running along beach . . . . 2·25 1·10
MS2812 60 × 80 mm. 400l. Painting of man (24 × 29 mm) . . . . . 5·00 5·00

653 Basketball **655** "Self-portrait" (Picasso)

654 *LZ-1* (first Zeppelin airship) over Lake Constance, Friedrichshafen (first flight)

2000. Olympic Games, Sydney. Multicoloured.
2813 10l. Type **653** 10 10
2814 40l. Football 40 20
2815 90l. Athletics 85 45
2816 250l. Cycling . . . . 2·40 1·25

2000. Centenary of First Zeppelin Flight. Airship Development. Multicoloured.
2817 15l. Type **654** 15 10
2818 30l. Santos-Dumont airship *Ballon No. 5* and Eiffel Tower C attempted round trip from St. Cloud via Eiffel Tower, 1901) . . . 30 15
2819 300l. Beardmore airship *R-34* over New York (first double crossing of Atlantic) . . . . 2·75 1·25
MS2820 80 × 60 mm. 300l. Ferdinand von Zeppelin and airship (24 × 28 mm) . . . . . 3·40 3·40

2000. "Espana 2000" World Stamp Exhibition, Madrid.
2821 **655** 130l. multicoloured . . . 1·25 65

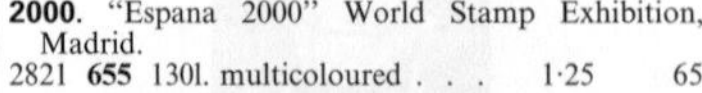

656 Yellow Gentian (*Gentiana lutea*) **658** Mother holding Child

657 Naim Frasheri (poet) and Landscape

2000. Medicinal Plants. Multicoloured.
2822 50l. Type **656** 50 25
2823 70l. Cross-leaved gentian (*Gentiana cruciata*) . . . 65 35

2000. Personalities. Multicoloured.
2824 30l. Type **657** 20 15
2825 50l. Bajram Curri (revolutionary) and landscape 50 25
Nos. 2824/5 were issued together, se-tenant, forming a composite design.

2000. 50th Anniv of United Nations High Commission for Refugees. Multicoloured.
2826 50l. Type **658** 50 25
2827 90l. Mother breastfeeding child 85 40

659 Dede Ahmed Myftar Ahmataj **661** Southern Magnolia (*Magnolia gandiflora*)

2001. Religious Leaders. Multicoloured.
2828 90l. Type **65** 85 45
2829 90l. Dede Sali Njazi 85 45

2001. "For Kosovo". Nos. 2592/3 surch **PER KOSOVEN** and new value.
2830 80l.+10l. on 50l. multicoloured 85 45
2831 130l.+20l. on 100l. multicoloured . . . . . . 1·40 70

2001. Regional Costumes (2nd series). As T **643**. Multicoloured.
2832 20l. Man's costume, Tropoje 20 10
2833 20l. Woman's costume, Lume 20 10
2834 20l. Woman's costume, Mirdite 20 10
2835 20l. Man's costume, Lume 20 10
2836 20l. Woman's costume, Zadrime 20 10
2837 20l. Woman's costume, Shpati 20 10
2838 20l. Man's costume, Kruje 20 10
2839 20l. Woman's costume, Macukulli 20 10
2840 20l. Woman's costume, Dardhe 20 10
2841 20l. Man's costume, Lushnje 20 10
2842 20l. Woman's costume, Dropulli 20 10
2843 20l. Woman's costume, Shmili 20 10

2001. Scented Flowers. Multicoloured.
2844 10l. Type **661** 10 10
2845 20l. Virginia rose (*Rosa virginiana*) 20 10
2846 90l. *Dianthus barbatus* . . . 85 45
2847 140l. Lilac (*Syringa vulgaris*) 1·25 65

662 Goofy in Shorts

2001. Goofy (cartoon film character). Multicoloured.
2848 20l. Type **662** 20 10
2849 50l. Goofy in blue hat . . . 50 25
2850 90l. Goofy in red trousers 85 45
2851 140l. Goofy in purple waistcoat . . . . 1·25 65

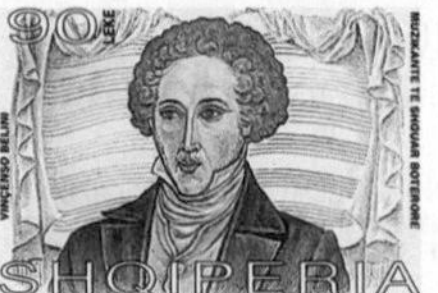

663 Vincenzo Bellini

2001. Composers' Anniversaries. Multicoloured.
2852 90l. Type **663** (birth centenary) 85 45
2853 90l. Guiseppe Verdi (death centenary) 85 45
MS2854 90 × 90 mm. 300l. Bellini and Verdi (75 × 38 mm) . . . 3·75 3·75

664 Cliffs and Stream

2001. Europa. Water Resources. Multicoloured.
2855 40l. Type **664** 40 20
2856 110l. Waterfall . . . . . . 1·10 55
2857 200l. Lake . . . . 1·90 95
MS2858 60 × 80 mm. 350l. Ripples (24 × 78 mm) . . . . 4·50 4·50

665 Horse

2001. Domestic Animals. Multicoloured.
2859 10l. Type **665** 10 10
2860 15l. Donkey 15 10
2861 80l. Siamese cat 75 40
2862 90l. Dog 85 45
MS2863 80 × 60 mm. 300l. Head of Siamese cat (49 × 29 mm) . . . 3·75 3·75

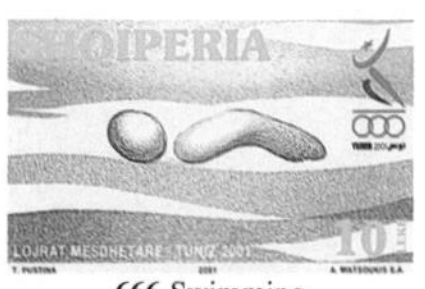

666 Swimming

2001. Mediterranean Games, Tunis. Multicoloured.
2864 10l. Type **666** 10 10
2865 90l. Athletics 85 45
2866 140l. Cycling . . . . 1·40 70
MS2867 60 × 80 mm. 260l. Discus (29 × 24 mm) . . . . 3·40 3·40

667 *Eole* (first powered take-off by Clement Ader, 1890)

2001. Aviation History. Multicoloured.
2868 40l. Type **667** 40 20
2869 40l. *Bleriot XI* (first powered crossing of English channel by Louis Bleriot, 1909) 40 20
2870 40l. *Spirit of St. Louis* (first solo non-stop crossing of North Atlantic from Paris to New York by Charles Lindbergh, 1927) 40 20
2871 40l. First flight to Tirana, 1925 . . . . 40 20
2872 40l. Antonov AH-10 (first flight, 1956) 40 20
2873 40l. Concorde (first flight, 1969) 40 20
2874 40l. Concorde (first commercial flight, 1970) 40 20
2875 40l. Space shuttle *Colombia* (first flight, 1981) 40 20

668 Tabakeve

669 Dimitri of Arber

2001. Old Bridges.
2876 **668** 10l. multicoloured . . . 10 10
2877 – 20l. multicoloured . . . 20 10
2878 – 40l. multicoloured . . . 40 20
2879 – 90l. black 85 45
MS2880 80 × 60 mm. 21.50 multicoloured . . . . 3·40 3·40
DESIGNS: 20l. Kamares; 40l. Golikut; 90l. Mesit. 49 × 22 mm—21.50, Tabakeve.

2001. Arms (1st series).
2881 20l. Type **669** 20 10
2882 45l. Balsha pricipality . . . 45 25
2883 50l. Muzaka family 50 25
2884 90l. George Castriot (Skanderbeg) 85 45
See also Nos. 2921/4 and 2965/8.

670 Children encircling Globe

2001. United Nations Year of Dialogue among Civilizations. Multicoloured, background colours given.
2885 **670** 45l. red, yellow and black 40 20
2886 50l. orange and green . . 45 20
2887 120l. black and red . . . 1·10 55
There are minor differences in Nos. 2886/7, with each colour forming a solid block above and below the central motif.

671 Award Ceremony (Medicins sans Frontieres, 1999 Peace Prize) and Medal

2001. Centenary of Nobel Prizes. Showing winners and Nobel medal. Multicoloured.
2888 10l. Type **671** 10 10
2889 20l. Wilhelm Konrad Rontgen (1901 Physics prize) 20 10
2890 90l. Ferid Murad (1998 Medicine Prize) 45 25
2891 200l. Mother Teresa (1979 Peace Prize) . . . . . . 2·00 1·00

2002. Regional Costumes (3rd series). As T **643**. Multicoloured.
2892 30l. Woman's costume, Gjakova 30 15
2893 30l. Woman's costume, Prizreni 30 15
2894 30l. Man's costume, Shkodra 30 15
2895 30l. Woman's costume, Shkodra 30 15
2896 30l. Man's costume, Berati 30 15
2897 30l. Woman's costume, Berati 30 15
2898 30l. Woman's costume, Elbasani 30 15
2899 30l. Man's costume, Elbasani 30 15
2900 30l. Woman's costume, Vlora 30 15
2901 30l. Man's costume, Vlora 30 15
2902 30l. Woman's costume, Gjirokastra 30 15
2903 30l. Woman's costume, Delvina 30 15

672 Bambi and Thumper

673 Fireplace

2002. Bambi (cartoon film character). Multicoloured.
2904 20l. Type **672** 20 40
2905 50l. Bambi alone amongst flowers 50 25
2906 90l. Bambi and Thumper looking right 90 45
2907 140l. Bambi with open mouth . . . . 1·40 70

2002. Traditional Fireplaces. T **673** and similar vert designs showing fireplaces. Multicoloured.
MS2908 30l. Type **673**: 40l. With columns at each side; 50l. With foliage arch; 90l. With three medallions in arch . . . . . . 4·25 4·25

674 Acrobatic Jugglers

2002. Europa. Circus. Multicoloured.
2909 40l. Type **674** 40 20
2910 90l. Female acrobat 90 45
2911 220l. Tightrope performers 2·25 1·10
MS2912 60 × 80 mm. 350l. Equestrienne performer (38 × 38 mm) . . . . 3·50 3·50

675 Heading the Ball

2002. Football World Championship, Japan and South Korea. Multicoloured.
2913 20l. Type **675** 20 10
2914 30l. Catching the ball . . . 30 15
2915 90l. Kicking the ball from horizontal position . . . 90 45
2916 120l. Player and ball . . . . 1·25 65
MS2917 80 × 60 mm. 360l. Emblem (50 × 30) . . . . 3·50 3·50

2002. Arms (2nd series). As T **669**. Multicoloured.
2918 20l. Gropa family 20 10
2919 45l. Skurra family 45 25
2920 50l. Bua family 50 25
2921 90l. Topia family 90 45

676 *Opuntia catingiola*

2002. Cacti. T **676** and similar triangular designs. Multicoloured.
MS2922 50l. Type **676**; 50l. *Neoporteria pseudoreicheana*; 50l. *Lobivia shaferi* 50l. *Hylocereus undatus*; 50l. *Borzicactus madisoniorum* . . . . 2·50 2·50

677 Blood Group Symbols with Wings

2002. 50th Anniv of Blood Bank Service. Multicoloured.
2923 90l. Type **677** 95 45
2924 90l. Blood group symbols containing figures 95 45

678 Naim Kryeziu (footballer)

2002. Sports Personalities. Multicoloured.
2925 50l. Type **678** 50 25
2926 50l. Riza Lushta (footballer) 50 25
2927 50l. Ymer Pampuri (weight lifter) 50 25
MS2928 61 × 81 mm. 300l. Loro BoriÇi (footballer) (vert). Imperf 3·00 3·00

679 Stamp, Torso and Emblem

2002. 50th Anniv International Federation of Stamp Dealers'Associations (IFSDA). Multicoloured.
2929 50l. Type **679** 50 25
2930 100l. Part of stamp enlarged and emblem . . . . . . 1·00 50

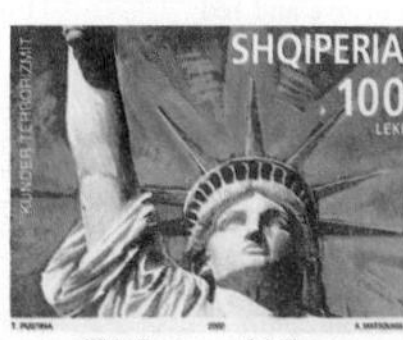

680 Statue of Liberty

2002. 1st Anniv of Attacks on World Trade Centre, New York. Multicoloured.
2931 100l. Type **680** . . . . . . 1·00 50
2932 150l. Burning towers and skyline . . . . 1·50 75
MS2933 61 × 81 mm. 350l. Statue of Liberty and World Trade Centre tower (vert) . . . . 3·50 3·50

681 Loggerhead Turtle (*Caretta caretta*)

2002. Fauna of Mediterranean Sea. Sheet 100 × 107 mm containing T **681** and similar horiz designs. Multicoloured.
MS2934 50l. Type **681**; 50l. Common dolphin (*Delphinus delphis*); 50l. Blue shark (*Prionace glaucai*); 50l. Fin whale (*Balenoptera physalus*); 50l. Ray (*Torpedo torpedo*); 50l. Octopus (*Octopus vulgaris*) . . . . . . 3·00 3·00

682 Tefta Tashko KoÇo

2002. Personalities. The Stage. Multicoloured.
2935 50l. Type **682** (singer) . . . 50 25
2936 50l. Naim Frasheri (actor) 50 25
2937 50l. Kristaq Antoniu (singer) 50 25
2938 50l. Panajot KanaÇi (choreographer) 50 25

683 Flags

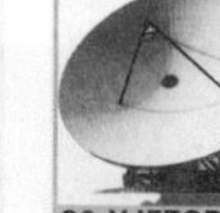

684 Satellite Dish and Outline of Stamp

2002. 90th Anniv of Independence. Multicoloured.
2939 20l. Type **683** 20 10
2940 90l. People and Albanian flag 95 45

2002. 90th Anniv of Albanian Post and Telecommunications. Multicoloured.
2941 20l. Type **684** 20 10
2942 90l. Airmail envelope and telegraph machine 95 45

2003. Regional Costumes (4th series). As T **643**. Multicoloured.
2943 30l. Woman's costume, Kelmendi 30 15
2944 30l. Man's costume, Zadrime 30 15
2945 30l. Woman's costume, Zerqani 30 15
2946 30l. Man's costume, Peshkopi 30 15
2947 30l. Man's costume, Malesia Tiranes 30 15
2948 30l. Woman's costume, Malesia Tiranes 30 15
2949 30l. Woman's costume, Fushe Kruje 30 15
2950 30l. Man's costume, Shpati 30 15
2951 30l. Woman's costume, Myzeqe 30 15
2952 30l. Woman's costume, Labinoti 30 15
2953 30l. Man's costume, Korce 30 15
2954 30l. Woman's costume, Laberi 30 15

685 Popeye and Bluto

687 Bearded Man

686 Port Palemo Castle

2003. Popeye (cartoon film character). Multicoloured.
2955 40l. Type **685** 40 20
2956 50l. Popeye running 50 25
2957 80l. Popeye and Olive Oyl 80 40
2958 150l. Popeye . . . . 1·50 70

2003. Castles. Sheet 118 × 98 mm. T **686** and similar horiz designs.
MS2959 grey and black; 20l. green and black; 50l. grey and black; 20l. mauve and black . . . . . 1·00 1·00
DESIGNS: 10l. Type **686**; 20l. Petrela; 50l. Kruja; 120l. Preza.

2003. Europa. Poster Art. Multicoloured.
2960 150l. Type **687** . . . . . . 1·50 75
2961 200l. Eye, apple and piano 2·00 1·00
MS2962 80 × 61 mm. 350l. Detail of No. 2960 . . . . 3·75 3·75

688 Envelopes

2003. 90th Anniv of Albanian Post and Telecommunications (2nd series). Multicoloured.
2963 50l. Type **688** 50 25
2964 1000l. Outline of stamps . . 10·00 5·00

2003. Arms (3rd series). As T **669**. Multicoloured.
2965 10l. Ariantet family 20 10
2966 20l. Jonimajt family 40 20
2967 70l. Dukagjini family . . . 1·40 70
2968 120l. Kopili family . . . . 1·20 60

689 Pomegranate (*Punica granatum*)

2003. Fruit. Multicoloured. Self-adhesive.
MS2969 50l. Type **689**; 60l. Citron (*Citrus medica*); 70l. Cantaloupe (*Cucumis melo*); 80l. Fig (*Ficus*) (inscr "Fieus") . . . . 2·50 2·50

690 Diocletian

2003. Roman Emperors. Multicoloured.
2970 70l. Type **690** . . . . 1·40 70
2971 70l. Justinian . . . . 1·40 70
2972 70l. Claudius II . . . . . . 1·40 70
2973 70l. Constantine . . . . . 1·40 70

691 White Stork (*Cicona cicona*)

2003. Birds. Sheet 100 × 119 mm containing T **691** and similar vert designs. Multicoloured.
MS2974 70l. Type **691**; 70l. Golden eagle (*Aquila chrysaetos*); 70l. Eagle owl (*Bubo bubo*); 70l. Capercaillie (*Tetrao urogallus*) 2·75 2·75

692 Players

693 "The Luncheon" (detail)

2003. 90th Anniv of Albanian Football. Each grey, black and red.
2975 80l. Type **692** . . . .
2976 80l. Group of players . . .
Nos. 2975/6 were issued together, se-tenant, forming a composite design.

2003. 120th Death Anniv of Edouard Manet (artist). Multicoloured.
2977 40l. Type **693** 80 40
2978 100l. "The Fifer" . . . . . 1·00 50
MS2979 80 × 60 mm. 250l. Edouard Manet (horiz) . . . . 2·60 2·50

694 Odhise Paskall

2003. Albanian Sculptors. Multicoloured.
2980 50l. Type **694** . . . . 1·00 50
2981 50l. Llazar Nikolla . . . . 1·00 50
2982 50l. Janaq Paco . . . . . . 1·00 50
2983 50l. Murat Toptani . . . . 1·00 50

695 Lake, Pelicans and Pine Trees (Divjaka forest)

2003. Natural Heritage. Multicoloured.
2984 20l. Type **695** 40 20
2985 30l. House and fir trees (Hotova forest) 60 30
2986 200l. Snow-covered fir trees (Drenova forest) . . . . 4·00 2·00

696 Stylized Cyclist and Map of France

2003. Centenary of Tour de France Cycle Race.
2987 **696** 50l. blue, red and black 1·00 50
2988 – 100l. multicoloured . . . 2·00 1·00
DESIGN: 100l. Two cyclists.

EXPRESS LETTER STAMPS
ITALIAN OCCUPATION

E **67** King Victor Emmanuel

1940.
E373 E **67** 25q. violet . . . . . . 2·00 2·50
E374 50q. red . . . . 4·00 6·25
No. E374 is inscr "POSTAT EXPRES".

1943. Optd **14 Shtator 1943**.
E402 E **67** 25q. violet . . . . . . 16·00 25·00

POSTAGE DUE STAMPS

1914. Optd **TAKSE** through large letter **T**.
D33 **4** 2q. brown and yellow . . . 6·00 2·00
D34 5q. green and yellow . . . 6·00 3·75
D35 10q. red and pink . . . . 8·00 2·25
D36 25q. blue . . . . 10·00 2·50
D37 50q. mauve and red . . . . 11·00 4·50

1914. Nos. 40/4 optd **TAKSE**.
D46 **4** 10pa. on 5q. green & yell 2·75 2·50
D47 20pa. on 10q. red and pink 2·75 2·50
D48 1g. on 25q. blue . . . . . 2·75 2·50
D49 2g. on 50q. mauve and red 2·75 2·50

1919. Fiscal stamps optd **TAXE**.
D89 **12** 4q. on 4h. pink . . . . . 6·75 6·75
D90 10q. on 10k. red on grn 6·75 6·75
D91 20q. on 2k. orge on lilac 6·75 6·75
D92 50q. on 5k. brown on yell 6·75 6·75

D **20** Fortress of Shkoder D **22** D **35**

1920. Optd with posthorn.
D129 D **20** 4q. olive 75 75
D130 10q. red . . . . . . 1·50 4·75
D131 20q. brown . . . . . 1·50 2·00
D132 50q. black . . . . . . 1·50 4·75

1922.
D141 D **22** 4q. black on red . . . 85 1·75
D142 10q. black on red . . 85 1·75
D143 20q. black on red . . 85 1·75
D144 50q. black on red . . 85 1·75

1922. Optd **Republika Shiqiptare**.
D186 D **22** 4q. black on red . . . 1·25 1·90
D187 10q. black on red . . 1·25 1·90
D188 20q. black on red . . 1·25 1·90
D189 50q. black on red . . 1·25 1·90

1925.
D204 D **35** 10q. blue 45 75
D205 20q. green 50 75
D206 30q. brown . . . . . 75 2·00
D207 50q. dark brown . . . 1·25 2·75

D **53** Arms of Albania D **67**

1930.
D288 D **53** 10q. blue . . . . . . 5·00 6·50
D289 20q. red . . . . 1·50 2·00
D290 30q. violet . . . . . . 1·50 2·00
D291 50q. green . . . . . . 1·50 2·00

1936. Optd **Takse**.
D312 **50** 10q. red . . . . 8·50 11·50

1940.
D373 D **67** 4q. red . . . . 20·00 25·00
D374 10q. violet . . . . . 20·00 25·00
D375 20q. brown . . . . . 20·00 25·00
D376 30q. blue . . . . . . 20·00 25·00
D377 50q. red . . . . . . 20·00 25·00

ALEXANDRETTA Pt. 6

The territory of Alexandretta. Autonomous under French control from 1923 to September 1938.

1938. 100 centiemes = 1 piastre.

1938. Stamps of Syria of 1930/1 optd **Sandjak d'Alexandrette** (Nos. 1, 4, 7 and 11) or **SANDJAK D'ALEXANDRETTE** (others), Nos. 7 and 11 surch also.
1 0p.10 purple . . . . 1·60 2·50
2 0p.20 red . . . . 1·50 2·75
3 0p.50 violet . . . . 1·60 2·75
4 0p.75 red . . . . 2·00 2·75
5 1p. brown . . . . 1·50 2·50
6 2p. violet . . . . 1·60 5·25
7 2p.50 on 4p. orange . . . . . 2·00 2·50
8 3p. green . . . . 2·00 3·50
9 4p. orange . . . . 2·75 2·75
10 6p. black . . . . 3·00 3·25
11 12p.50 on 15p. red (No. 267) 4·50 5·75
12 25p. purple . . . . 8·00 14·00

1938. Air. Stamps of Syria of 1937 (Nos. 322 etc) optd **SANDJAK D'ALEXANDRETTE**.
13 ½p. violet . . . . 1·50 2·50
14 1p. black . . . . 1·50 2·50
15 2p. green . . . . 2·25 3·50
16 3p. blue . . . . 3·25 4·50
17 5p. mauve . . . . 6·25 10·50
18 10p. brown . . . . 7·00 11·00
19 15p. brown . . . . 7·50 13·00
20 25p. blue . . . . 10·00 16·00

1938. Death of Kemal Ataturk. Nos. 4, 5, 7, 9 and 11 optd **10-11-1938** in frame.
27 0p.75 red . . . . 24·00 48·00
28 1p. brown . . . . 16·00 40·00
29 2p.50 on 4p. orange . . . . . 12·50 10·00
30 4p. orange . . . . 8·75 9·25
31 12p.50 on 15p. red . . . . . 45·00 50·00

POSTAGE DUE STAMPS

1938. Postage Due stamps of Syria of 1925 optd **SANDJAK D'ALEXANDRETTE**.
D21 D **20** 0p.50 brown on yellow 2·25 3·25
D22 1p. purple on pink . . 1·50 3·50
D23 2p. black on blue . . . 2·75 3·50
D24 3p. black on red . . . 3·25 5·75
D25 5p. black on green . . 4·50 5·25
D26 8p. black on blue . . . 7·50 5·25

ALEXANDRIA Pt. 6

Issues of the French P.O. in this Egyptian port. The French Post Offices in Egypt closed on 31 March 1931.

1899. 100 centimes = 1 franc.
1921. 10 milliemes = 1 piastre.

1899. Stamps of France optd **ALEXANDRIE**.
1 **10** 1c. black on blue . . . . . 1·25 1·10
2 2c. brown on yellow . . . . 1·75 2·50
3 3c. grey . . . . 1·40 2·25
4 4c. brown on grey . . . . . 1·10 2·50
5 5c. green . . . . 2·25 2·25
7 10c. black on lilac . . . . . 5·50 7·25
9 15c. blue . . . . 6·25 4·25
10 20c. red on green . . . . . 7·50 7·00
11 25c. black on red . . . . . 5·50 55
12 30c. brown . . . . 5·75 7·00
13 40c. red on yellow . . . . . 9·75 10·00
15 50c. red . . . . 19·00 12·50
16 1f. olive . . . . 12·00 14·00
17 2f. brown on blue . . . . . 70·00 75·00
18 5f. mauve on lilac . . . . . 95·00 85·00

1902. "Blanc", "Mouchon" and "Merson" key-types, inscr "ALEXANDRIE".
19 A 1c. grey . . . . 1·40 1·00
20 2c. purple . . . . 45 1·50
21 3c. red . . . . 55 1·00
22 4c. brown . . . . 35 1·00
24 5c. green . . . . 1·25 70
25 B 10c. red . . . . 2·75 75
26 15c. red . . . . 3·00 1·75
27 15c. orange . . . . 85 2·00
28 20c. brown . . . . 3·25 1·25
29 25c. blue . . . . 2·00 10
30 30c. mauve . . . . 4·25 3·25
31 C 40c. red and blue . . . . . 2·75 2·25
32 50c. brown and lilac . . . . 5·50 55
33 1f. red and green . . . . . 9·25 1·25
34 2f. lilac and buff . . . . . . 13·00 4·50
35 5f. blue and buff . . . . . 17·00 10·50

1915. Red Cross. Surch **5c** and Red Cross.
36 B 10c. + 5c. red . . . . 20 2·75

1921. Surch thus, **15 Mill.**, in one line (without bars).
37 A 2m. on 5c. green . . . . . . 3·00 6·00
38 3m. on 3c. red . . . . . . 6·00 7·50
39 B 4m. on 10c. red . . . . . . 4·00 5·00
40 A 5m. on 1c. grey . . . . . . 7·25 7·50
41 5m. on 4c. brown . . . . . 6·75 7·75
42 B 6m. on 15c. orange . . . . 2·50 4·50
43 8m. on 20c. brown . . . . . 4·00 5·25
44 10m. on 25c. blue . . . . . 1·75 3·75
45 12m. on 30c. mauve . . . . 11·50 12·50
46 A 15m. on 2c. purple . . . . . 6·00 3·25
47 C 15m. on 40c. red and blue 12·00 12·50
48 15m. on 50c. brown & lilac 6·00 10·00
49 30m. on 1f. red and green £120 £100
50 60m. on 2f. lilac and buff . . £140 £140
51 150m. on 5f. blue and buff £225 £225

1921. Surch thus, **15 MILLIEMES**, in two lines (without bars).
53 A 1m. on 1c. grey . . . . . . 2·50 3·50
54 2m. on 5c. green . . . . . . 1·75 3·25
55 B 4m. on 10c. red . . . . . . 3·00 4·25
65 4m. on 10c. green . . . . . 2·25 3·25
56 A 5m. on 3c. orange . . . . . 4·25 6·50
57 B 6m. on 15c. orange . . . . 2·25 3·50
58 8m. on 20c. brown . . . . . 1·75 3·00
59 10m. on 25c. blue . . . . . 1·90 2·25
60 10m. on 30c. mauve . . . . 4·25 4·25
61 C 15m. on 50c. brown & lilac 3·75 4·50
66 B 15m. on 50c. blue . . . . . 2·50 2·50
62 C 30m. on 1f. red and green 3·25 3·00
63 60m. on 2f. lilac and buff . . £1400 £1500
67 60m. on 2f. red and green 9·75 9·75
64 150m. on 5f. blue and buff 11·00 10·00

1925. Surch in milliemes with bars over old value.
68 A 1m. on 1c. grey . . . . . . 15 3·00
69 2m. on 5c. orange . . . . . 20 2·75
70 2m. on 5c. green . . . . . . 2·50 3·50
71 B 4m. on 10c. green . . . . . 20 3·25
72 A 5m. on 3c. red . . . . . . 80 2·50
73 B 6m. on 15c. orange . . . . 55 3·25
74 8m. on 20c. brown . . . . . 20 3·25
75 10m. on 25c. blue . . . . . 35 1·90
76 15m. on 50c. blue . . . . . 1·75 1·75
77 C 30m. on 1f. red and green 1·10 55
78 60m. on 2f. red and green 2·75 4·75
79 150m. on 5f. blue and buff 3·75 5·50

1927. Altered key-types, inscr "Mm" below value.
80 A 3m. orange . . . . 2·00 3·25
81 B 15m. blue . . . . 2·25 1·40
82 20m. mauve . . . . 4·00 5·00
83 C 50m. red and green . . . . 9·25 7·50
84 100m. blue and yellow . . . 11·50 10·50
85 250m. green and red . . . . 17·00 17·00

1927. Sinking Fund. As No. 81, colour changed, surch **+ 5 Mm Caisse d'Amortissement**.
86 B 15m.+5m. orange . . . . . 3·25 5·00
87 15m.+5m. red . . . . 4·50 5·00
88 15m.+5m. brown . . . . . . 7·50 10·00
89 15m.+5m. lilac . . . . . . 12·00 16·00

POSTAGE DUE STAMPS

1922. Postage Due Stamps of France surch in milliemes.
D65 D 11 2m. on 5c. blue . . . . 1·10 4·25
D66 4m. on 10c. brown . . 2·25 4·25
D67 10m. on 30c. red . . . 2·00 4·50
D68 15m. on 50c. purple . . 1·50 4·75
D69 30m. on 1f. pur on yell 1·25 6·25

D 10

1928.
D90 D 10 1m. grey . . . . 1·40 3·50
D91 2m. blue . . . . 2·75 3·50
D92 4m. pink . . . . 2·75 3·75
D93 5m. olive . . . . 2·75 3·25
D94 10m. red . . . . 3·00 3·75
D95 20m. purple . . . . . 3·00 3·50
D96 30m. green . . . . . . 5·75 6·25
D97 40m. lilac . . . . . . 5·00 6·25
This set was issued for use in both Alexandria and Port Said.

ALGERIA Pt. 6; Pt. 12

French territory in N. Africa. Stamps of France were used in Algeria from July 1958 until 3 July 1962, when the country achieved independence following a referendum.

1924. 100 centimes = 1 franc.
1964. 100 centimes = 1 dinar.

1924. Stamps of France optd **ALGERIE**.
1 11 ½c. on 1c. grey . . . . . . 35 1·75
2 1c. grey . . . . 65 2·25
3 2c. red . . . . 10 2·50
4 3c. red . . . . 40 2·25
5 4c. brown . . . . 65 2·50
6 18 5c. orange 95 75
7 11 5c. green 10 10
8 30 10c. green . . . . 1·40 1·25
9 18 10c. green 10 75
10 15 15c. green . . . . 1·50 1·40
11 30 15c. green . . . . 85 2·00
12 18 15c. brown . . . . 1·50 1·10
13 20c. brown . . . . 1·50 65
14 25c. blue 10 10
15 30 30c. red 75 70
16 18 30c. blue 10 10
17 30c. red* 30 90
18 35c. violet . . . . 1·25 1·50
19 13 40c. red and blue . . . . 1·60 1·75
20 18 40c. olive . . . . 1·25 1·90
21 13 45c. green and blue . . . . 1·25 2·25
22 30 45c. red 40 85
23 50c. blue . . . . 1·50 85
24 15 60c. violet . . . . 1·10 65
25 65c. red 25 60
26 30 75c. blue 25 45
27 15 80c. red 70 70
28 85c. red 35 50
29 13 1f. red and green . . . . 1·75 55
30 18 1f.05 red . . . . 55 1·75
31 13 2f. red and green . . . . 2·00 3·25
32 3f. violet and blue . . . . 2·00 3·00
33 5f. blue and yellow . . . . 8·00 8·50
*No. 17 was only issued pre-cancelled and the price in the unused column is for stamps with full gum.

3 Street in the Casbah

4 Mosque of Sidi Abderahman

5 Grand Mosque

6 Bay of Algiers

1926.
34 3 1c. green . . . . 40 1·25
35 2c. purple . . . . 30 1·50
36 3c. orange . . . . 10 1·40
37 5c. green 25 10
38 10c. mauve 35 10
39 4 15c. brown 10 10
40 20c. green 10 10
41 20c. red . . . . 1·40 10
43 25c. green 95 75
45 25c. blue 45 30
46 30c. blue . . . . 80 1·40
47 30c. green . . . . 1·25 40
48 35c. violet . . . . 1·25 3·25
49 40c. green 10 10
50 5 45c. purple 15 10
51 50c. blue . . . . 2·25 15
53 50c. red . . . . 1·10 10
54 60c. green 20 90
55 65c. brown . . . . 1·50 1·60
56 3 65c. blue . . . . 1·10 10
57 5 75c. red 10 20
58 75c. blue . . . . 2·50 10
59 80c. orange . . . . 35 2·10
60 90c. red . . . . 1·75 2·50
61 6 1f. purple and green 80 10
62 5 1f.05 brown . . . . 35 1·90
63 1f.10 mauve . . . . 3·50 6·00
64 6 1f.25 ultramarine and blue 1·00 3·50
65 1f.50 ultramarine and blue 70 10
66 2f. brown and green . . . . 1·40 35
67 3f. red and mauve . . . . . 3·25 1·50
68 5f. mauve and red . . . . . 3·75 3·00
69 10f. red and brown . . . . . 48·00 32·00
70 20f. green and violet . . . . 8·00 9·00

1926. Surch ½ **centime**.
71 3 ½c. on 1c. olive . . . . . . 10 1·75

1927. Wounded Soldiers of Moroccan War Charity Issue. Surch with star and crescent and premium.
72 3 5c.+5c. green . . . . 95 3·25
73 10c.+10c. mauve . . . . . . 90 3·25
74 4 15c.+15c. brown . . . . . . 90 3·25
75 20c.+20c. red . . . . 90 3·25
76 25c.+25c. green . . . . . . 80 3·25
77 30c.+30c. blue . . . . 1·10 3·25
78 35c.+35c. violet . . . . . . 55 3·25
79 40c.+40c. olive . . . . 80 3·25
80 5 50c.+50c. blue . . . . 85 3·75
81 80c.+80c. orange . . . . . . 85 3·75
82 6 1f.+1f. purple and green . . 1·25 3·75
83 2f.+2f. brown and green . . 22·00 40·00
84 5f.+5f. mauve and red . . . 35·00 55·00

1927. Surch in figures.
85 4 10 on 35c. violet 10 90
86 25 on 30c. blue 65 10
87 30 on 25c. green 15 10
88 5 65 on 60c. green . . . . . . 60 1·25
89 90 on 80c. orange 20 20
90 1f.10 on 1f.05 brown 10 15
91 6 1f.50 on 1f.25 ultramarine and blue . . . . 1·25 90

1927. Surch **5c.**
92 11 5c. on 4c. brown (No. 5) . . 45 1·75

11 Railway Terminus, Oran

1930. Centenary of French Occupation.
93 11 5c.+5c. orange . . . . . . 9·00 14·50
94 – 10c.+10c. olive . . . . . . 8·00 14·00
95 – 15c.+15c. brown . . . . . 6·25 13·50
96 – 25c.+25c. grey . . . . . . 6·00 13·50
97 – 30c.+30c. red . . . . . . 5·75 14·00
98 – 40c.+40c. green . . . . . 5·25 14·00
99 – 50c.+50c. blue . . . . . . 5·25 14·00
100 – 75c.+75c. purple . . . . . 5·00 13·50
101 – 1f.+1f. orange . . . . . . 5·50 13·50
102 – 1f.50+1f.50 blue . . . . . 5·75 13·50
103 – 2f.+2f. red . . . . 5·25 13·50
104 – 3f.+3f. green . . . . . . 5·75 13·50
105 – 5f.+5f. red and green . . . 10·50 35·00
DESIGNS—HORIZ: 10c. Constantine; 15c. Admiralty, Algiers; 25c. Algiers; 30c. Ruins of Timgad; 40c. Ruins of Djemila. VERT: 50c. Ruins of Djemila; 75c. Tlemcen; 1f. Ghardaia; 1f.50, Tolga; 2f. Tuaregs; 3f. Native quarter, Algiers; 5f. Mosque, Algiers.

12 Bay of Algiers, after painting by Verecque

1930. N. African International Philatelic Exn.
106 12 10f.+10f. brown . . . . . 24·00 30·00

15 Admiralty and Penon Lighthouse, Algiers

1936.
107 A 1c. blue . . . . 35 1·10
108 F 2c. purple 10 90
109 B 3c. green . . . . 65 1·50
110 C 5c. mauve 10 10
111 15 10c. green 70 65
112 D 15c. red 15 10
113 G 20c. green 20 10
114 E 25c. purple . . . . 2·00 20
115 C 30c. green 35 10
116 D 40c. purple 50 20
117 G 45c. blue . . . . 1·25 3·25
118 15 50c. red . . . . 2·25 10
119 A 65c. brown . . . . 6·25 8·25
120 65c. red . . . . 2·25 35
121 70c. brown 80 85
122 F 75c. slate 50 15
124 B 90c. red . . . . 85 1·50
125 E 1f. brown 30 10
126 15 1f.25 violet . . . . 1·90 60
127 1f.25 red . . . . 40 1·40
128 F 1f.50 blue . . . . 2·25 85
129 1f.50 red . . . . 3·50 3·50
130 C 1f.75 orange 95 70
131 B 2f. purple 40 10
132 A 2f.25 green . . . . 16·00 24·00
133 E 2f.25 blue . . . . 1·50 1·60
134 C 2f.50 blue . . . . 1·75 2·25
135 G 3f. mauve 55 25
136 E 3f.50 blue . . . . 2·25 2·75
137 15 5f. slate . . . . 1·25 1·50
138 F 10f. orange . . . . 75 2·00
139 D 20f. blue . . . . 1·90 3·00
DESIGNS—HORIZ: A, In the Sahara; B, Arc de Triomphe, Lambese; C, Ghardaia, Mzab; D, Marabouts, Touggourt; E, El Kebir Mosque, Algiers. VERT: F, Colomb Bechar-Oued; G, Cemetery, Tlemcen.

17 Exhibition Pavilion

18 Constantine in 1837

1937. Paris International Exhibition.
140 17 40c. green 40 30
141 50c. red 40 50
142 1f.50 blue . . . . 60 1·00
143 1f.75 black . . . . 95 1·25

1937. Centenary of Capture of Constantine.
144 18 65c. red 80 20
145 1f. brown . . . . 2·75 65
146 1f.75 blue 35 95
147 2f.15 purple 25 40

19 Ruins of Roman Villa

1938. Centenary of Philippeville.
148 19 30c. green . . . . 1·75 2·00
149 65c. blue 75 55
150 75c. purple . . . . 1·60 3·25
151 3f. red . . . . 3·75 2·50
152 5f. brown . . . . 4·25 5·00

1938. 20th Anniv of Armistice Day. No. 132 surch **1918 - 11 Nov. - 1938 0.65 + 0.35**.
153 65c.+35c. on 2f.25 green . . 1·00 3·75

1938. Surch **0,25**.
154 15 25c. on 50c. red 25 10

22 Caillie, Lavigerie and Duveyrier

1939. Sahara Pioneers' Monument Fund.
155 22 30c.+20c. green . . . . . 2·50 3·75
156 90c.+60c. red . . . . . . 1·10 3·25
157 2f.25+75c. blue . . . . . 8·50 2·00
158 5f.+5f. black . . . . . . 14·50 45·00

23 "Extavia" (freighter) in Algiers Harbour

1939. New York World's Fair.
159 23 20c. green . . . . 1·60 3·50
160 40c. purple . . . . 1·75 3·50
161 90c. brown . . . . 2·25 75
162 1f.25 red . . . . 6·00 6·50
163 2f.25 blue . . . . 2·25 2·40

1939. Surch with new values and bars or cross.
173 3 50c. on 65c. blue 30 10
173c B 90c.+60c. red (No. 124) . . 20 10
164 3 1f. on 90c. red 40 10

25 Algerian Soldiers

26 Algiers

1940. Soldiers' Dependants' Relief Fund. Surch + and premium.
166 25 1f.+1f. blue . . . . 2·25 3·00
167 1f.+2f. red . . . . 1·90 3·50
168 1f.+4f. green . . . . . . 2·00 3·75
169 1f.+9f. brown . . . . . . 2·25 4·25

1941.
170 26 30c. blue . . . . 75 1·25
171 70c. brown 15 10
172 1f. red 15 10

28 Marshal Petain

1941.
174 28 1f. blue . . . . 40 1·10

1941. National Relief Fund. As No. 174, but surch **+4 f** and colour changed.
175 1f.+4f. black . . . . 1·25 2·50

1942. National Relief Fund. Surch **SECOURS NATIONAL +4f.**
176 1f.+4f. blue (No. 174) . . . . 70 3·00

1942. Various altered types. (a) As T **26**, but without "RF".
177 26 30c. blue . . . . 20 2·75

(b) As T **5**, but without "REPUBLIQUE FRANCAISE".
178 5 40c. grey . . . . 25 3·00
179 50c. red . . . . 35 1·40

(c) As No. 129 but without "RF".
180 F 1f.50 red . . . . 1·10 65

32 Arms of Oran

34 Marshal Petain

1942. Coats-of-Arms.
190 A 10c. lilac . . . . 1·00 2·25
191 32 30c. green . . . . 1·00 3·00
181 B 40c. violet . . . . 45 2·75
192 40c. lilac . . . . 1·75 2·25
182 32 60c. red . . . . 1·40 1·60
194 B 70c. blue . . . . 1·25 2·25
195 A 80c. green . . . . 75 1·90
183 B 1f.20 green . . . . 1·10 2·00
184 A 1f.50 red 15 30
198 32 2f. blue 20 95
186 B 2f.40 red . . . . 1·25 1·00
187 A 3f. blue 20 45
188 B 4f. blue . . . . 1·00 1·10
201 32 4f.50 purple 80 10
189 5f. green . . . . 1·00 1·40
ARMS: A, Algiers; B, Constantine.

1943.
202 34 1f.50 red . . . . 15 2·50

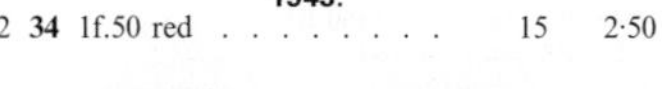

35 "La Marseillaise"

36 Allegory of Victory

1943.
203 35 1f.50 red . . . . 80 2·25
204 36 1f.50 blue 20 60

1943. Surch **2f.**
205 32 2f. on 5f. orange 15 90

38 Summer Palace, Algiers

39 Mother and Children

1943.
206 38 15f. grey . . . . 1·10 1·90
207 20f. green . . . . 1·50 1·90
208 50f. red . . . . 90 1·50
209 100f. blue . . . . 3·00 2·75
210 200f. brown . . . . 3·50 2·75

1943. Prisoners-of-war Relief Fund.
211 39 50c.+4f.50 pink . . . . . 60 3·50
212 1f.50+8f.50 green . . . . 30 3·50
213 3f.+12f. blue . . . . . . 30 3·50
214 5f.+15f. brown . . . . . . 55 3·50

40 "Marianne" 41 Gallic Cock

1944.
215 40 10c. grey 15 75
216 30c. lilac 15 65
217 50c. red 10 15
218 80c. green 25 1·00
219 1f.20 lilac 40 1·75
220 1f.50 blue 10 10
221 2f.40 red 10 35
222 3f. violet 15 15
223 4f.50 black 25 10

1944.
224 41 40c. red 30 2·75
225 1f. green 15 20
226 2f. red 15 15
227 2f. brown 40 90
228 4f. blue 1·60 10
229 10f. black 1·10 2·25

1944. Surch **0f.30**.
230 4 0f.30 on 15c. brown 25 60
No. 230 was only issued pre-cancelled and the price in the unused column is for stamps with full gum.

1945. Types of France optd **ALGERIE**.
247 239 10c. black and blue 10 2·75
231 217 40c. mauve 20 75
232 50c. blue 15 10
248 – 50c. brown, yellow and red (No. 973) 65 60
233 218 60c. blue 50 70
236 136 80c. green 1·00 1·25
237 1f. blue 80 10
234 218 1f. red 70 25
238 136 1f.20 violet 55 2·50
235 218 1f.50 lilac 70 1·50
239 136 2f. brown 20 10
242 219 2f. green 85 10
240 136 2f.40 red 70 1·75
241 3f. orange 55 95
243 219 3f. red 35 10
244 4f.50 blue 1·75 40
245 5f. green 10 25
246 10f. blue 1·75 1·25

1945. Airmen and Dependants Fund. As No. 742 of France (bombers) optd **RF ALGERIE**.
249 169 1f.50+3f.50 blue 1·50 3·00

1945. Postal Employees War Victims' Fund. As No. 949 of France overprinted **ALGERIE**.
250 223 4f.+6f. brown 55 3·00

1945. Stamp Day. As No. 955 of France (Louis XI) optd **ALGERIE**.
251 228 2f.+3f. purple 1·25 2·50

1946. No. 184 surch **0f50 RF**.
252 50c. on 1f.50 red 15 30

1946. Type of France optd **ALGERIE** and surch **2F**.
253 136 2f. on 1f.50 brown 15 10

46 Potez 56 over Algiers

1946. Air.
254 46 5f. red 35 50
255 10f. blue 20 10
256 15f. green 65 35
257a 20f. brown 70 10
258 25f. violet 70 20
259 40f. black 1·25 1·40

1946. Stamp Day. As No. 975 of France (De la Varane), optd **ALGERIE**.
260 241 3f.+2f. red 90 3·75

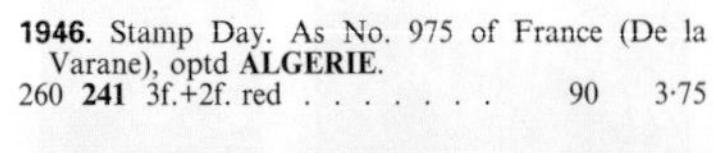

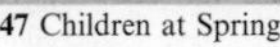

47 Children at Spring 49 Arms of Constantine

1946. Charity. Inscr as in T **47**.
261 47 3f.+17f. green 1·75 4·00
262 4f.+21f. red 1·25 3·75
263 8f.+27f. purple 3·00 9·50
264 10f.+35f. blue 1·75 4·00

DESIGNS—VERT: 4f. Boy gazing skywards; 8f. Laurel-crowned head. HORIZ: 10f. Soldier looking at Algerian coast.

1947. Air. Surch **-10%**.
265 46 "-10%" on 5f. red 20 55

1947. Stamp Day. As No. 1008 of France (Louvois), optd **ALGERIE**.
266 253 4f.50+5f.50 blue 35 3·25

1947. Various Arms.
267 49 10c. green and red 10 1·75
268 A 50c. black and orange 10 10
269 B 1f. blue and yellow 10 10
270 49 1f.30 black and blue 75 3·00
271 A 1f.50 violet and yellow 10 10
272 B 2f. black and green 10 10
273 49 2f.50 black and red 90 70
274 A 3f. red and green 10 65
275 B 3f.50 green and purple 45 10
276 49 4f. brown and green 10 10
277 A 4f.50 blue and red 10 10
278 5f. black and blue 10 10
279 B 6f. brown and red 20 10
280 8f. brown and blue 15 10
281 49 10f. pink and brown 25 10
282 A 15f. black and red 1·75 10
ARMS: A, Algiers; B, Oran. See also Nos. 364/8 and 381/3.

1947. Air. 7th Anniv of Gen. de Gaulle's Call to Arms. Surch with Lorraine Cross and **18 Juin 1940 + 10 Fr.**
283 46 10f.+10f. blue 2·50 3·50

1947. Resistance Movement. Type of France surch **ALGERIE+10f**.
284 261 5f.+10f. grey 1·25 3·25

1948. Stamp Day. Type of France (Arago) optd **ALGERIE**.
285 267 6f.+4f. green 1·25 3·75

1948. Air. 8th Anniv of Gen. de Gaulle's Call to Arms. Surch with Lorraine Cross and **18 JUIN 1940 + 10 Fr.**
286 46 5f.+10f. red 2·50 3·50

1948. General Leclerc Memorial. Type of France surch **ALGERIE + 4f**.
287 270 6f.+4f. red 1·40 3·50

57 Battleship "Richelieu" 58 White Storks over Minaret

1949. Naval Welfare Fund.
288 57 10f.+15f. blue 5·25 12·50
289 – 18f.+22f. red 8·75 12·50
DESIGN: 18f. Aircraft-carrier "Arromanches".

1949. Air.
290 58 50f. green 4·00 1·10
291 – 100f. brown 2·25 40
292 58 200f. red 11·00 3·75
293 – 500f. blue 29·00 28·00
DESIGN—HORIZ: 100, 500f. Dewoitine D-338 trimotor airplane over valley dwellings.

1949. Stamp Day. As No. 1054 of France (Choiseul) optd **ALGERIE**.
294 278 15f.+5f. mauve 45 4·50

60 French Colonials 61 Statue of Duke of Orleans

1949. 75th Anniv of U.P.U.
295 60 5f. green 1·60 3·75
296 15f. red 1·00 3·75
297 25f. blue 3·25 9·25

1949. Air. 25th Anniv of First Algerian Postage Stamp.
298 61 15f.+20f. brown 5·75 10·00

62 Grapes 63 Foreign Legionary

1950.
299 62 20f. purple, green & dp pur 85 65
300 – 25f. brown, green & black 1·75 55
301 – 40f. orange, green & brown 2·75 2·50
DESIGNS: 25f. Dates; 40f. Oranges and lemons.

1950. Stamp Day. As No. 1091 of France (Postman), optd **ALGERIE**.
302 292 12f.+3f. brown 1·60 4·50

1950. Foreign Legion Welfare Fund.
303 63 15f.+5f. green 85 4·50

64 R. P. de Foucauld and Gen. Laperrine

1950. 50th Anniv of French in the Sahara (25f.) and Unveiling of Monument to Abd-el-Kader (40f.).
304 64 25f.+5f. black and green 5·00 9·25
305 – 40f.+10f. dp brown & brn 4·75 9·25
DESIGN: 40f. Emir Abd-el-Kader and Marshal Bugeaud.

65 Col. C. d'Ornano

1951. Col. d'Ornano Monument Fund.
306 65 15f.+5f. purple, brn blk 1·25 3·75

1951. Stamp Day. As No. 1107 of France (Travelling Post Office sorting van), optd **ALGERIE**.
307 300 12f.+3f. brown 3·00 4·25

66 Apollo of Cherchel 67 Algerian War Memorial

1952.
308 66 10f. sepia 20 25
309 – 12f. brown 35 10
310 – 15f. blue 20 10
311 – 18f. red 40 30
312 – 20f. green 45 15
313 66 30f. blue 50 30
STATUES: 12, 18f. Isis of Cherchel; 15, 20f. Boy and eagle.

1952. Stamp Day. As No. 1140 of France (Mail Coach), optd **ALGERIE**.
314 319 12f.+3f. blue 2·25 4·75

1952. African Army Commemoration.
315 67 12f. green 85 2·25

68 Medaille Militaire 69 Fossil ("Berbericeras sekikensis")

1952. Military Medal Centenary.
316 68 15f.+5f. brown, yell & grn 2·50 4·75

1952. 19th Int Geological Convention, Algiers.
317 69 15f. red 2·50 5·00
318 – 30f. blue 1·50 3·25
DESIGN: 30f. Phonolite Dyke, Hoggar.

1952. 10th Anniv of Battle of Bir-Hakeim. As No. 1146 of France surch **ALGERIE+5 F.**
319 325 30f.+5f. blue 3·00 4·75

72 Bou-Nara 73 Members of Corps and Camel

1952. Red Cross Fund.
320 – 8f.+2f. red and blue 1·75 4·50
321 72 12f.+3f. red 2·75 6·75
DESIGN: 8f. El-Oued and map of Algeria.

1952. 50th Anniv of Sahara Corps.
322 73 12f. brown 2·00 3·00

1953. Stamp Day. As No. 1161 of France (Count D'Argenson), optd **ALGERIE**.
323 334 12f.+3f. violet 1·25 4·25

74 "Victory" of Cirta 75 E. Millon

1954. Army Welfare Fund.
324 74 15f.+5f. brown and sepia 70 3·25

1954. Military Health Service.
325 75 25f. sepia and green 95 30
326 – 40f. red and brown 90 25
327 – 50f. indigo and blue 1·25 25
DOCTORS—VERT: 40f. F. Maillot. HORIZ: 50f. A. Laveran.

1954. Stamp Day. As No. 1202 of France (Lavalette), optd **ALGERIE**.
328 346 12f.+3f. red 90 3·75

76 French and Algerian Soldiers 77 Foreign Legionary

1954. Old Soldiers' Welfare Fund.
329 76 15f.+5f. sepia 1·60 3·00

1954. Foreign Legion Welfare Fund.
330 77 15f.+5f. green 2·75 4·75

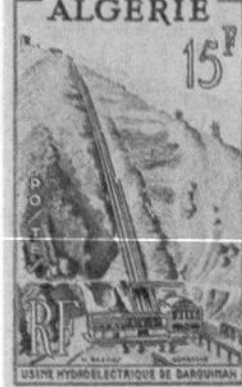

78 79 Darguinah Hydroelectric Station

1954. 3rd International Congress of Mediterranean Citrus Fruit Culture.
331 78 15f. blue and indigo 1·25 3·75

1954. 10th Anniv of Liberation. As No. 1204 of France ("D-Day") optd **ALGERIE**.
332 348 15f. red 75 2·25

1954. Inauguration of River Agrioun Hydroelectric Installations.
333 79 15f. purple 1·60 3·75

80 Courtyard of Bardo Museum

1954.
334 **80** 10f. brown & light brown . . . 15 10
335 12f. orange and brown (I) . . . 85 10
336 12f. orange and brown (II) . . . 25 60
337 15f. blue and light blue . . . 55 20
338 18f. carmine and red . . . 30 45
339 20f. green and light green . . . 25 1·10
340 25f. lilac and mauve . . . 30 10
12f. "POSTES" and "ALGERIE" in orange (I) or in white (II).

1954. 150th Anniv of Presentation of First Legion of Honour. As No. 1223 of France, optd **ALGERIE**.
341 **356** 12f. green . . . . 50 3·00

81 Red Cross Nurses **82** St. Augustine

1954. Red Cross Fund. Cross in red.
342 **81** 12f.+3f. blue . . . . . . 3·75 6·25
343 – 15f.+5f. violet . . . . . . 5·50 7·75
DESIGN: 15f. J.H. Dunant and Djemila ruins.

1954. 1600th Birth Anniv of St. Augustine.
344 **82** 15f. brown . . . . 1·50 3·00

83 Earthquake Victims and Ruins **84** Statue of Aesculapius and El Kettar Hospital

1954. Orleansville Earthquake Relief Fund. Inscr as in T **83**.
345 **83** 12f.+4f. brown . . . . . . 1·90 4·75
346 15f.+5f. blue . . . . . . 2·00 4·75
347 – 18f.+6f. mauve . . . . . . 2·25 4·75
348 – 20f.+7f. violet . . . . . . 2·50 4·75
349 – 25f.+8f. lake . . . . 2·75 5·25
350 – 30f.+10f. turquoise . . . . 2·50 5·75
DESIGNS—HORIZ: 18, 20f. Red Cross workers. 25, 30f. Stretcher-bearers.

1955. Stamp Day. As No. 1245 of France (Balloon Post), optd **ALGERIE**.
351 **364** 12f.+3f. blue . . . . . . 1·10 4·00

1955. 30th French Medical Congress.
352 **84** 15f. red . . . . 45 1·00

85 Ruins of Tipasa **86** Widows and Children

1955. Bimillenary of Tipasa.
353 **85** 50f. brown 50 20

1955. 50th Anniv of Rotary International. As No. 1235 of France optd **ALGERIE**.
354 **361** 30f. blue . . . . 90 2·00

1955. As Nos. 1238 and 1238b of France ("France") inscr "ALGERIE".
355 **362** 15f. red 15 10
356 20f. blue . . . . 90 1·50

1955. War Victims' Welfare Fund.
357 **86** 15f.+5f. indigo and blue . . 1·90 2·75

87 Grand Kabylie **88**

1955.
358 **87** 100f. indigo and blue . . . 2·25 30

1956. Anti-cancer Fund.
359 **88** 15f.+5f. brown . . . . . . 1·90 3·25

1956. Stamp Day. As No. 1279 of France ("Francis of Taxis"), optd **ALGERIE**.
360 **383** 12f.+3f. red . . . . . . 1·10 3·50

89 Foreign Legion Retirement Home, Sidi Bel Abbes

1956. Foreign Legion Welfare Fund.
361 **89** 15f.+5f. green . . . . . . 1·90 4·25

90 Marshal Franchet d'Esperey (after J. Ebstein)

1956. Birth Cent of Marshal Franchet d'Esperey.
362 **90** 15f. indigo and blue . . . 2·50 3·50

91 Marshal Leclerc and Memorial

1956. Marshal Leclerc Commemoration
363 **91** 15f. brown and sepia . . . 40 3·25

1956. Various arms as T **49**.
364 1f. green and red 25 70
365 3f. blue and green . . . . . 50 2·10
366 5f. blue and yellow 20 60
367 6f. green and red . . . . . . 50 2·50
368 12f. blue and red . . . . . . 90 3·25
DESIGNS: 1f. Bone; 3f. Mostaganem; 5f. Tlemcen; 6f. Algiers; 12f. Orleansville.

92 Oran

1956.
369 **92** 30f. purple . . . . 1·40 10
370 35f. red . . . . 2·00 3·50

1957. Stamp Day. As No. 1322 of France ("Felucca") optd **ALGERIE**.
371 **403** 12f.+3f. purple . . . . . 2·50 3·75

93 Electric Train Crossing Viaduct

1957. Electrification of Bone-Tebessa Railway Line.
372 **93** 40f. turquoise and green . . 1·75 20

94 Fennec Fox

1957. Red Cross Fund. Cross in red.
373 **94** 12f.+3f. brown . . . . . . 4·50 12·50
374 – 15f.+5f. sepia (White storks) . . . . 6·00 12·00

1957. 17th Anniv of Gen. de Gaulle's Call to Arms. Surch **18 JUIN 1940 + 5F**.
375 **91** 15f.+5f. red and carmine . . 1·10 4·00

96 Beni Bahdel Barrage, Tlemcen **97** "Horseman Crossing Ford" (after Delacroix)

1957. Air.
376 **96** 200f. red . . . . 6·00 8·00

1957. Army Welfare Fund. Inscr "OEUVRES SOCIALES DE L'ARMEE".
377 **97** 15f.+5f. red . . . . 6·00 12·50
378 – 20f.+5f. green . . . . . . 5·25 12·50
379 – 35f.+10f. blue . . . . . . 5·50 12·50
DESIGNS—HORIZ: 20f. "Lakeside View" (after Fromentin). VERT: 35f. "Arab Dancer" (after Chasseriau).

1958. Stamp Day. As No. 1375 of France (Rural Postal Service), optd **ALGERIE**.
380 **421** 15f.+5f. brown . . . . . 1·75 3·75

1958. Arms. As T **49** but inscr "REPUBLIQUE FRANCAISE" instead of "RF" at foot.
381 2f. red and blue . . . . . . 75 3·25
382 6f. green and red . . . . . . 32·00 42·00
383 10f. purple and green . . . . 85 3·00
ARMS: 2f. Tizi-Ouzou; 6f. Algiers; 10f. Setif.

99 "Strelitzia Reginae" **100**

1958. Algerian Child Welfare Fund.
384 **99** 20f.+5f. orge, vio & grn . . 4·00 5·25

1958. Marshal de Lattre Foundation.
385 **100** 20f.+5f. red, grn & bl . . 3·75 4·25

INDEPENDENT STATE

1962. Stamps of France optd **EA** and with bars obliterating "REPUBLIQUE FRANCAISE".
386 **344** 10c. green 70 35
387 **463** 25c. grey and red 45 20
393 – 45c. violet, purple and sepia (No. 1463) . . . 5·00 4·00
394 – 50c. pur & grn (No. 1464) 5·00 4·00
395 – 1f. brown, blue and myrtle (No. 1549) . . . 2·25 1·10

104 Flag, Rifle and Olive Branch

1963. "Return of Peace". Flag in green and red. Inscription and background colours given.
401 **104** 5c. bistre 15 10
402 10c. blue 20 10
403 25c. red . . . . 1·90 10
404 95c. violet . . . . 1·40 65
405 – 1f. green . . . . 1·25 30
406 – 2f. brown . . . . 3·00 65
407 – 5f. purple . . . . 5·50 2·50
408 – 10f. black . . . . 20·00 12·00
DESIGN: 1f. to 10f. As Type **104** but with dove and broken chain added.

105 Campaign Emblem and Globe

1963. Freedom from Hunger.
409 **105** 25c. yellow, green and red . . 40 20

106 Clasped Hands **107** Map and Emblems

1963. National Solidarity Fund.
410 **106** 50c.+20c. red, grn & blk . . 1·10 55

1963. 1st Anniv of Independence.
411 **107** 25c. multicoloured 50 20

108 "Arab Physicians" (13th-century MS.) **109** Branch of Orange Tree

1963. 2nd Arab Physicians Union Congress.
412 **108** 25c. brown, green & bistre . 1·60 45

1963.
413 **109** 8c. orange and bronze* . . 10 10
414 20c. orange and green* . . 15 10
415 40c. orange & turq* . . . 45 20
416 55c. orange and green* . . 80 45
*These stamps were only issued pre-cancelled, the unused prices being for stamps with full gum.

110 "Constitution" **111** "Freedom Fighters"

1963. Promulgation of Constitution.
417 **110** 25c. red, green and sepia . . 55 25

1963. 9th Anniv of Revolution.
418 **111** 25c. red, green and brown . . 55 20

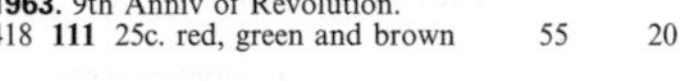

112 Centenary Emblem **113** Globe and Scales of Justice

103a Maps of Africa and Algeria

1962. War Orphans' Fund.
395a **103a** 1f.+9f. green, black and red £325

1962. As pictorial types of France but inscr "REPUBLIQUE ALGERIENNE".
396 – 5c. turquoise, grn & brn . . 15 10
397 **438** 10c. blue and sepia . . . 20 10
398 – 25c. red, slate & brown . . 45 10
399 – 95c. blue, buff and sepia . 2·75 80
400 – 1f. sepia and green . . . 1·90 1·40
DESIGNS—VERT: 5c. Kerrata Gorges; 25c. Tlemcen Mosque; 95c. Oil derrick and pipeline at Hassi-Massaoud, Sahara. HORIZ: 1f. Medea.

1963. Red Cross Centenary.
419 **112** 25c. blue, red and yellow 80 55

1963. 15th Anniv of Declaration of Human Rights.
420 **113** 25c. black and blue . . . 60 20

114 Labourers **115** Map of Africa and Flags

1964. Labour Day.
421 **114** 50c. multicoloured . . . . 1·10 35

1964. 1st Anniv of Africa Day, and African Unity Charter.
422 **115** 45c. red, orange and blue 80 30

116 Tractors **117** Rameses II in War Chariot, Abu Simbel

1964.
423 **116** 5c. purple 10 10
424 – 10c. brown 10 10
425 – 12c. green 45 15
426 – 15c. blue 35 15
427 – 20c. yellow 35 10
428 **116** 25c. red 45 10
429 – 30c. violet 40 10
430 – 45c. lake 55 20
431 – 50c. blue 55 10
432 – 65c. orange 65 15
433 **116** 85c. green . . . . 1·10 20
434 – 95c. red . . . . 1·40 20
DESIGNS: 10, 30, 65c. Apprentices; 12, 15, 45c. Research scientist; 20, 50, 95c. Draughtsman and bricklayer.

1964. Nubian Monuments Preservation.
435 **117** 20c. purple, red and blue 80 35
436 – 30c. ochre, turq & red . . 90 45
DESIGN: 30c. Heads of Rameses II.

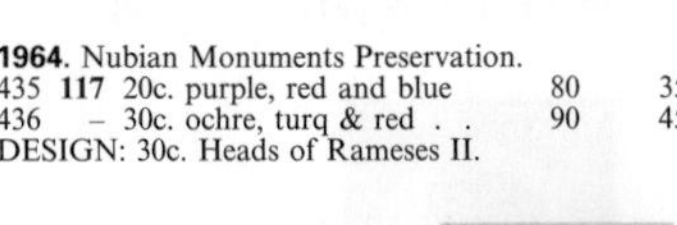

118 Hertzian-wave Radio Transmitting Pylon **119** Fair Emblems

1964. Inauguration of Algiers–Annaba Radio-Telephone Service.
437 **118** 85c. black, blue & brown 1·60 55

1964. Algiers Fair.
438 **119** 30c. blue, yellow and red 40 15

120 Gas Plant **121** Planting Trees

1964. Inaug of Natural Gas Plant at Arzew.
439 **120** 25c. blue, yellow & violet 65 45

1964. Reafforestation Campaign.
440 **121** 25c. green, red and yellow 40 20

122 Children **123** Mehariste Saddle

1964. Children's Charter.
441 **122** 15c. blue, green and red 40 20

1965. Saharan Handicrafts.
442 **123** 20c. multicoloured 45 20

124 Books Aflame **125** I.C.Y. Emblem

1965. Reconstitution of Algiers University Library.
443 **124** 20c.+5c. red, blk & grn 45 30

1965. International Co-operation Year.
444 **125** 30c. black, green and red 80 35
445 60c. black, green and blue 1·10 40

126 I.T.U. Emblem and Symbols

1965. Centenary of I.T.U.
446 **126** 60c. violet, ochre & green 80 40
447 95c. brown, ochre & lake 1·10 45

127 Musicians playing Rebbah and Lute

1965. Mohamed Racim's Miniatures (1st series). Multicoloured.
448 30c. Type **127** . . . . 1·40 55
449 60c. Musicians playing derbouka and tarr . . . . 1·90 85
450 5d. Algerian princess and sand gazelle . . . . 11·00 6·75
See also Nos. 471/3.

128 Cattle

1966. Rock-paintings of Tassili-N-Ajjer (1st series).
451 **128** 1d. brown, ochre & purple . . . . 4·00 2·25
452 – 1d. multicoloured . . . . . 4·00 2·25
453 – 2d. dp brown, buff & brn 8·25 4·00
454 – 3d. multicoloured . . . . 9·00 5·00
DESIGNS—VERT: No. 452, Peuhl shepherd; 454, Peuhl girls. HORIZ: No. 453, Ostriches.
See also Nos. 474/7.

129 Pottery **130** Meteorological Instruments

1966. Grand Kahylie Handicrafts.
455 **129** 40c. brown, sepia and blue 40 20
456 – 50c. orange, green & bl 55 30
457 – 70c. black, red and blue 1·10 45
DESIGNS—HORIZ: 50c. Weaving. VERT: 70c. Jewellery.

1966. World Meteorological Day.
458 **130** 1d. purple, green and blue 1·10 40

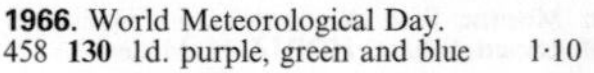

131 Open Book, Cogwheel and Ear of Corn **132** W.H.O. Building

1966. Literacy Campaign.
459 **131** 30c. black and ochre . . . 35 20
460 – 60c. red, black and grey 55 30
DESIGN: 60c. Open primer, cogwheel and ear of corn.

1966. Inaug of W.H.O. Headquarters, Geneva.
461 **132** 30c. turq, grn & brn . . . 40 30
462 60c. slate, blue and brown 70 35

133 Mohammedan Scout Emblem and Banner **134** Soldiers and Battle Casualty

1966. 30th Anniv of Algerian Mohammedan Scouts, and 7th Arab Scout Jamboree, Jedaid (Tripoli). Multicoloured.
463 30c. Type **133** 45 30
464 1d. Jamboree emblem . . . . 1·40 55

1966. Freedom Fighters' Day.
465 **134** 30c.+10c. mult 80 55
466 95c.+10c. mult . . . . . 1·40 1·10

135 Massacre Victims **136** Emir Abd-el-Kader

1966. Deir Yassin Massacre (1948).
467 **135** 30c. black and red 45 20

1966. Return of Emir Abd-el-Kader's Remains.
468 **136** 30c. multicoloured 20 10
469 95c. multicoloured 90 35
See also Nos. 498/502.

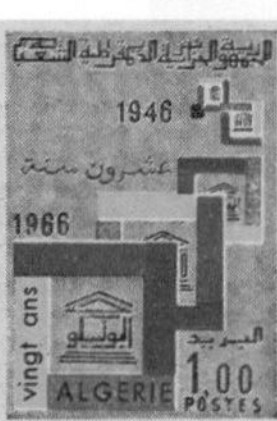

137 U.N.E.S.C.O. Emblems **138** Bardo Museum

1966. 20th Anniv of U.N.E.S.C.O.
470 **137** 1d. multicoloured 90 35

1966. Mohamed Racim's Miniatures (2nd series). As T **127**. Multicoloured.
471 1d. Horseman . . . . 3·25 1·10
472 1d.50 Algerian bride . . . . 5·00 1·60
473 2d. Barbarossa . . . . 7·75 2·75

1967. Rock-paintings of Tassili-N-Ajjer (2nd series). As T **128**.
474 1d. violet, buff and purple . . 3·25 1·60
475 2d. brown, buff and purple 5·50 3·25
476 2d. brown, purple and buff 5·00 2·75
477 3d. brown, buff and black . . 8·25 4·50
DESIGNS: No. 474, Cow; No. 475, Antelope; No. 476, Archers; No. 477, Warrior.

1967. "Musulman Art". Multicoloured.
478 35c. Type **138** 35 15
479 95c. La Kalaa minaret (vert) 80 40
480 1d.30 Sedrata ruins . . . . . 1·40 55

139 Ghardaia

1967. Air.
481 **139** 1d. brown, green & purple 1·10 45
482 – 2d. brown, green and blue 2·50 1·25
483 – 5d. brown, green and blue 6·75 2·75
DESIGNS: 2d. Sud Aviation SE210 Caravelle over El Oued (Souf); 5d. Tipasa.

140 View of Moretti

1967. International Tourist Year. Multicoloured.
484 40c. Type **140** 55 35
485 70c. Tuareg, Tassili (vert) . . 1·10 45

141 Boy and Girl, and Red Crescent **142** Ostrich

1967. Algerian Red Crescent Organization.
486 **141** 30c.+10c. brn, red & grn 65 40

1967. Saharan Fauna. Multicoloured.
487 5c. Shiny-tailed Lizard (horiz) 35 30
488 20c. Type **142** . . . . 2·25 75
489 40c. Sand gazelle 90 45
490 70c. Fennec foxes (horiz) . . 1·40 80

143 Dancers with Tambourines **144** "Athletics"

1967. National Youth Festival.
491 **143** 50c. black, yellow & blue 80 35

1967. 5th Mediterranean Games, Tunis.
492 **144** 30c. black, blue and red 50 30

145 Skiing **146** Scouts supporting Jamboree Emblem

1967. Winter Olympic Games, Grenoble (1968).
493 **145** 30c. blue, green & ultram 80 35
494 – 95c. green, violet & brown 1·40 65
DESIGN—HORIZ (36 × 26 mm): 95c. Olympic rings and competitors.

1967.
498 **136** 5c. purple 15 10
499 10c. green 10 10
500 25c. orange 20 10
501 30c. black 30 10
502 30c. violet 35 10
496 50c. red 50 15
497 70c. blue 50 20
The 10c. value exists in two versions, differing in the figures of value and inscription at bottom right.

1967. World Scout Jamboree, Idaho.
503 **146** 1d. multicoloured . . . . 1·60 65

1967. No. 428 surch.
504 **116** 30c. on 25c. red 50 15

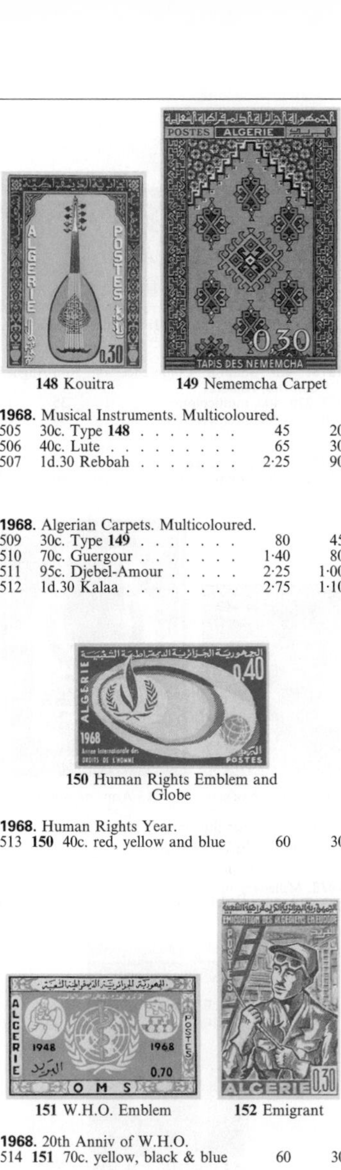

148 Kouitra **149** Nememcha Carpet

1968. Musical Instruments. Multicoloured.
505 30c. Type **148** 45 20
506 40c. Lute 65 30
507 1d.30 Rebbah . . . . 2·25 90

1968. Algerian Carpets. Multicoloured.
509 30c. Type **149** 80 45
510 70c. Guergour . . . . 1·40 80
511 95c. Djebel-Amour . . . . . 2·25 1·00
512 1d.30 Kalaa . . . . 2·75 1·10

150 Human Rights Emblem and Globe

1968. Human Rights Year.
513 **150** 40c. red, yellow and blue 60 30

151 W.H.O. Emblem **152** Emigrant

1968. 20th Anniv of W.H.O.
514 **151** 70c. yellow, black & blue 60 30

1968. Emigration of Algerians to Europe.
515 **152** 30c. brown, slate & blue 45 15

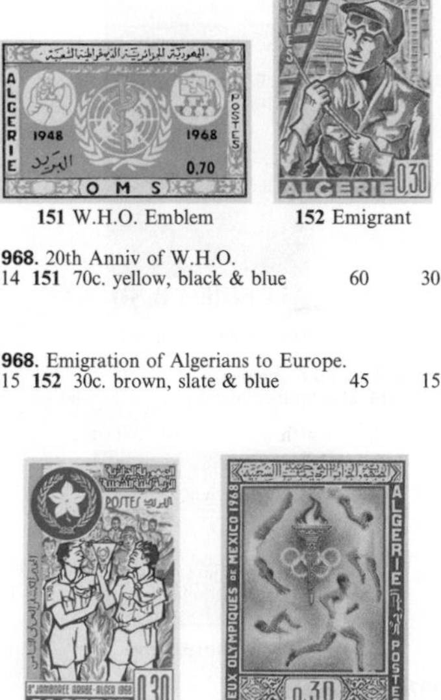

153 Scouts holding Jamboree Emblem **154** Torch and Athletes

1968. 8th Arab Scouts Jamboree, Algiers.
516 **153** 30c. multicoloured 55 20

1968. Olympic Games, Mexico. Multicoloured.
517 30c. Type **154** 50 35
518 50c. Football 85 40
519 1d. Allegory of Games (horiz) 1·40 80

155 Barbary Sheep **156** "Neptune's Chariot", Timgad

1968. Protected Animals. Multicoloured.
520 40c. Type **155** 65 30
521 1d. Red deer . . . . 1·60 55

1968. Roman Mosaics. Multicoloured.
522 40c. "Hunting Scene" (Djemila) (vert) 50 20
523 95c. Type **156** . . . . 1·10 45

157 Miner **158** Opuntia

1968. "Industry, Energy and Mines".
524 **157** 30c. multicoloured 40 15
525 – 30c. silver and red 40 15
526 – 95c. red, black and silver 1·10 35
DESIGNS: No. 525, Coiled spring ("Industry"); No. 526, Symbol of radiation ("Energy").

1969. Algerian Flowers. Multicoloured.
527 25c. Type **158** 55 45
528 40c. Dianthus 85 55
529 70c. Rose . . . . 1·40 65
530 95c. Strelitzia . . . . 2·25 1·10
See also Nos. 621/4.

159 Djorf Torba Dam, Oued Guir

1969. Saharan Public Works. Multicoloured.
531 30c. Type **159** 45 20
532 1d.50 Route Nationale No. 51 . . . . 1·60 65

160 Desert Mail-coach of 1870 **161** The Capitol, Timgad

1969. Stamp Day.
533 **160** 1d. sepia, brown and blue 1·40 55

1969. Roman Ruins in Algeria. Multicoloured.
534 30c. Type **161** 45 15
535 1d. Septimius Temple, Djemila (horiz) . . . . . 1·10 40

162 I.L.O. Emblem **164** Carved Bookcase

1969. 50th Anniv of I.L.O.
536 **162** 95c. red, yellow and black 1·00 40

1969. No. 425 surch.
537 20c. on 12c. green 35 10

1969. Handicrafts. Multicoloured.
538 30c. Type **164** 40 20
539 60c. Copper tray 60 30
540 1d. Arab saddle . . . . . . 1·25 50

165 "Africa" Head **166** Astronauts on Moon

1969. 1st Pan-African Cultural Festival, Algiers.
541 **165** 30c. multicoloured 35 20

1969. 1st Man on the Moon.
542 **166** 50c. multicoloured 85 35

167 Bank Emblem **168** Flood Victims

1969. 5th Anniv of African Development Bank.
543 **167** 30c. black, yellow blue . . 45 20

1969. Aid for 1969 Flood Victims.
544 **168** 30c.+10c. black, flesh and blue 60 40
545 – 95c.+25c. brown, blue and purple . . . . 1·25 70
DESIGN: 95c. Helping hand for flood victims.

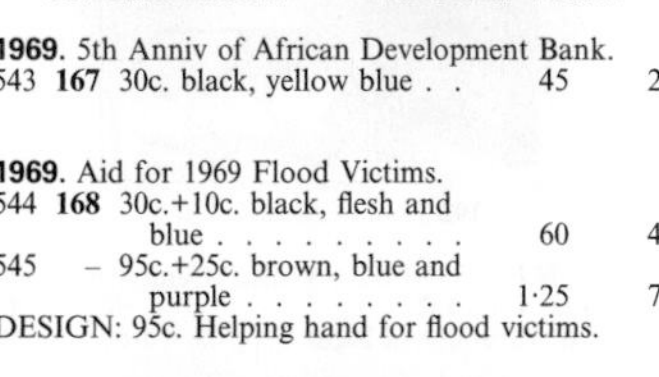

169 "Algerian Women" (Dinet)

1969. Dinet's Paintings. Multicoloured.
546 1d. Type **169** . . . . 1·60 65
547 1d.50 "The Look-outs" (Dinet) . . . . 2·25 1·00

170 "Mother and Child"

1969. "Protection of Mother and Child".
548 **170** 30c. multicoloured 50 30

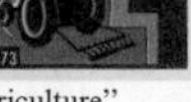

171 "Agriculture" **172** Postal Deliveries by Donkey and Renault R4 Mail Van

1970. Four Year Plan.
549 **171** 25c. multicoloured 20 15
550 – 30c. multicoloured . . . . 1·75 15
551 – 50c. black and purple . . 45 20
DESIGNS: (LARGER, 49 × 23 mm): 30c. "Industry and Transport"; 50c. "Industry" (abstract).

1970. Stamp Day.
552 **172** 30c. multicoloured 45 20

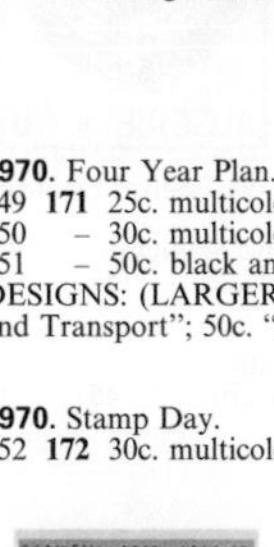

173 Royal Prawn **174** Oranges

1970. Marine Life. Multicoloured.
553 30c. Type **173** 45 20
554 40c. Noble pen (mollusc) . . 75 35
555 75c. Neptune's basket . . . . 1·10 45
556 1d. Red coral . . . . 1·60 65

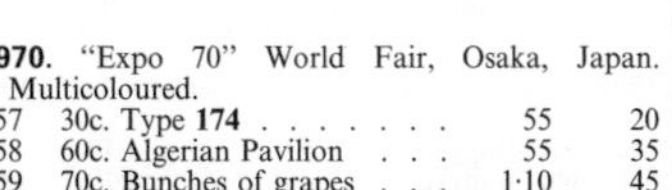

1970. "Expo 70" World Fair, Osaka, Japan. Multicoloured.
557 30c. Type **174** 55 20
558 60c. Algerian Pavilion . . . 55 35
559 70c. Bunches of grapes . . . 1·10 45

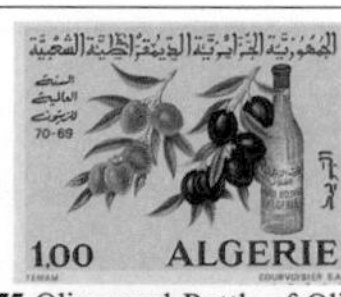

175 Olives and Bottle of Olive-oil

1970. World Olive-oil Year.
560 **175** 1d. multicoloured . . . . 1·40 65

176 New U.P.U. H.Q. Building

1970. Inaug of New U.P.U. Headquarters Building.
561 **176** 75c. multicoloured 60 30

177 Crossed Muskets

1970. Algerian 18th-century Weapons. Mult.
562 40c. Type **177** 85 45
563 75c. Sabre (vert) . . . . . . 1·10 65
564 1d. Pistol . . . . 1·60 90

178 Arab League Flag, Arms and Map **179** Lenin

1970. 25th Anniv of Arab League.
565 **178** 30c. multicoloured 45 15

1970. Birth Centenary of Lenin.
566 **179** 30c. bistre and ochre . . 1·10 30

180 Exhibition Palace

1970. 7th International Algiers Fair.
567 **180** 60c. green 55 35

181 I.E.Y. and Education Emblems

1970. International Education Year. Mult.
568 30c. Type **181** 35 15
569 3d. Illuminated Koran (30 × 41 mm) . . . . . . 2·40 1·40

182 Great Mosque, Tlemcen

1970. Mosques.
570 **182** 30c. multicoloured 30 15
571 – 40c. brown and bistre . . 45 15
572 – 1d. multicoloured 85 30
DESIGNS—VERT: 40c. Ketchaoua Mosque, Algiers; 1d. Sidi-Okba Mosque.

183 "Fine Arts"

1970. Algerian Fine Arts.
573 **183** 1d. orange, grn & lt grn . . . 90 35

184 G.P.O., Algiers 186 "Racial Equality"

185 Hurdling

1971. Stamp Day.
574 **184** 30c. multicoloured 65 30

1971. 6th Mediterranean Games, Izmir (Turkey).
575 **185** 20c. grey and blue 35 15
576 – 40c. grey and green . . . 50 30
577 – 75c. grey and brown . . . 85 40
DESIGNS—VERT: 40c. Gymnastics; 75c. Basket-ball.

1971. Racial Equality Year.
578 **186** 60c. multicoloured 60 30

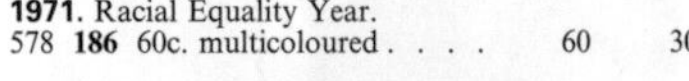

187 Symbols of Learning, and Students

1971. Inaug of Technological Institutes.
579 **187** 70c. multicoloured 65 20

188 Red Crescent Banner

1971. Red Crescent Day.
580 **188** 30c.+10c. red and green 55 35

189 Casbah, Algiers

1971. Air.
581 **189** 2d. multicoloured . . . . 1·90 85
582 – 3d. violet and black . . . 2·75 1·40
583 – 4d. multicoloured . . . . 3·25 1·60
DESIGNS: 3d. Port of Oran; 4d. Rhumel Gorges.

190 Aures Costume 191 U.N.I.C.E.F. Emblem, Tree and Animals

1971. Regional Costumes (1st series). Multicoloured.
584 50c. Type **190** 90 45
585 70c. Oran . . . . 1·00 65
586 80c. Algiers . . . . 1·25 80
587 90c. Djebel-Amour . . . . . 1·60 90
See also Nos. 610/13 and 659/62.

1971. 25th Anniv of U.N.I.C.E.F.
588 **191** 60c. multicoloured 60 35

192 Lion of St. Mark's

1971. U.N.E.S.C.O. "Save Venice" Campaign. Mult.
589 80c. Type **192** 90 45
590 1 d. 15 Bridge of Sighs . . . 1·60 80

193 Cycling 194 Book and Bookmark

1972. Olympic Games, Munich. Multicoloured.
591 25c. Type **193** 35 15
592 40c. Throwing the javelin (vert) 40 20
593 60c. Wrestling (vert) 65 40
594 1d. Gymnastics (vert) . . . . 1·10 45

1972. International Book Year.
595 **194** 1d.15 red, black and brown 70 40

195 Algerian Postmen 196 Jasmine

1972. Stamp Day.
596 **195** 40c. multicoloured 45 15

1972. Flowers. Multicoloured.
597 50c. Type **196** 50 30
598 60c. Violets 55 35
599 1d.15 Tuberose . . . . . . 1·40 50

197 Olympic Stadium 198 Festival Emblem

1972. Inaug of Cheraga Olympic Stadium.
600 **197** 50c. green, brown & violet 55 30

1972. 1st Festival of Arab Youth.
601 **198** 40c. brown, yellow & grn 45 15

199 Rejoicing Algerians 201 Child posting Letter

1972. 10th Anniv of Independence.
602 **199** 1d. multicoloured 95 50

1972. Regional Costumes (2nd series). As T **190**. Multicoloured.
610 50c. Hoggar . . . . 1·10 55
611 60c. Kabylie . . . . 1·10 55
612 70c. Mzab . . . . 1·40 80
613 90c. Tlemcen . . . . 1·60 90

1973. Stamp Day.
614 **201** 40c. multicoloured 35 15

202 Ho-Chi-Minh and Map 203 Annaba Embroidery

1973. "Homage to the Vietnamese People".
615 **202** 40c. multicoloured 60 30

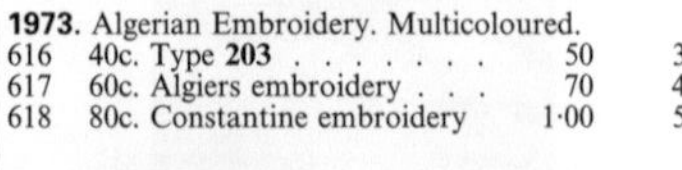

1973. Algerian Embroidery. Multicoloured.
616 40c. Type **203** 50 30
617 60c. Algiers embroidery . . . 70 40
618 80c. Constantine embroidery 1·00 50

204 "Food Cultivation" 206 O.A.U. Emblem

205 Serviceman and Flag

1973. 10th Anniv of World Food Programme.
619 **204** 1d.15 multicoloured . . . 65 30

1973. National Service.
620 **205** 40c. multicoloured 45 15

1973. Algerian Flowers. As T **158**. Multicoloured.
621 30c. Type **158** 45 20
622 40c. As No. 529 . . . . . . 55 35
623 1d. As No. 528 . . . . . . 1·25 55
624 1d.15 As No. 530 . . . . . 1·60 65

1973. 10th Anniv of Organization of African Unity.
625 **206** 40c. multicoloured 45 20

207 Peasant Family

1973. Agrarian Revolution.
626 **207** 40c. multicoloured 50 20

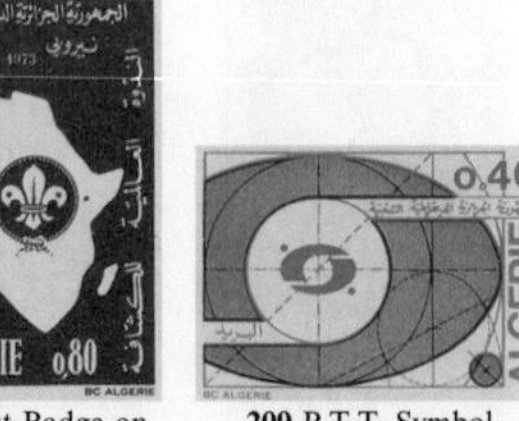
208 Scout Badge on Map 209 P.T.T. Symbol

1973. 24th World Scouting Congress, Nairobi, Kenya.
627 **208** 80c. mauve 60 30

1973. Inauguration of New P.T.T. Symbol.
628 **209** 40c. orange and blue . . 45 15

210 Conference Emblem 211 "Skikda Harbour"

1973. 4th Summit Conference of Non-Aligned Countries, Algiers.
629 **210** 40c. multicoloured 35 15
630 80c. multicoloured 60 20

1973. Opening of Skikda Port.
631 **211** 80c. multicoloured 60 30

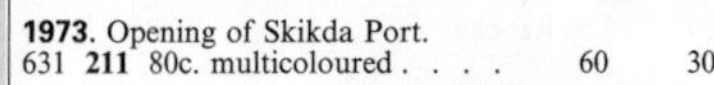

212 Young Workers 213 Arms of Algiers

1973. Volontariat Students' Volunteer Service.
632 **212** 40c. multicoloured 45 20

1973. Millenary of Algiers.
633 **213** 2d. multicoloured . . . . 2·25 1·10

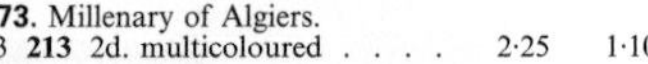

214 "Protected Infant"

1974. Anti-TB Campaign.
634 **214** 80c. multicoloured 60 30

215 Industrial Scene

1974. Four Year Plan.
635 **215** 80c. multicoloured 65 35

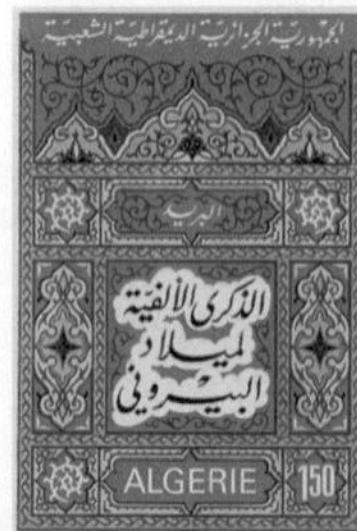
216 Arabesque Motif

1974. Birth Millenary of Abu-al Rayhan al-Biruni (mathematician and philosopher).
636 **216** 1d.50 multicoloured . . . 1·60 1·10

217 Map and Arrows 218 Upraised Weapon and Fist

1974. Meeting of Maghreb Committee for Co-ordination of Posts and Telecommunications, Tunis.
637 **217** 40c. multicoloured 45 20

1974. Solidarity with South African People's Campaign.
638 **218** 80c. black and red 55 20

219 Algerian Family

1974. Homage to Algerian Mothers.
639 **219** 85c. multicoloured 55 20

220 Urban Scene

1974. Children's Drawings. Multicoloured.
640 70c. Type **220** 60 15
641 80c. Agricultural scene . . . 70 30
642 90c. Tractor and sunrise . . 90 45
Nos. 641/2 are size 49 × 33 mm.

1974. "Floralies 1974" Flower Show, Algiers. Nos. 623/4 optd **FLORALIES 1974**.
643 1d. multicoloured . . . . . 1·25 65
644 1d.15 multicoloured . . . . 1·60 1·00

222 Automatic Stamp-vending Machine

223 U.P.U. Emblem on Globe

1974. Stamp Day.
645 **222** 80c. multicoloured 55 20

1974. Centenary of U.P.U.
646 **223** 80c. multicoloured 60 30

224 Revolutionaries

1974. 20th Anniv of Revolution. Multicoloured.
647 40c. Type **224** 35 15
648 70c. Armed soldiers (vert) . . 45 20
649 95c. Raising the flag (vert) . . 70 20
650 1d. Algerians looking to Independence 95 30

225 "Towards the Horizon"

226 Ewer

1974. "Horizon 1980".
651 **225** 95c. red, brown & black 60 30

1974. Algerian 17th-century Brassware. Mult.
652 50c. Type **226** 40 20
653 60c. Coffee pot 45 30
654 95c. Sugar basin 65 40
655 1d. Bath vessel 95 50

1975. No. 622 surch.
656 50c. on 40c. multicoloured . . 1·10 45

228 Games Emblem

1975. 7th Mediterranean Games (1st issue).
657 **228** 50c. violet, green & yellow 40 15
658 1d. orange, violet & blue 70 20
See also Nos. 671/5.

1975. Regional Costumes (3rd series). As T **190**. Multicoloured.
659 1d. Algiers . . . . 1·10 60
660 1d. The Hogger . . . . . . 1·10 60
661 1d. Oran . . . . 1·10 60
662 1d. Tlemcen . . . . 1·10 60

229 Labour Emblems

1975. 10th Anniv of Arab Labour Organization.
663 **229** 50c. brown 45 10

230 Transfusion

1975. Blood Collection and Transfusion Service.
664 **230** 50c. multicoloured 55 30

231 El Kantara Post Office

232 Policeman and Oil Rig on Map of Algeria

1975. Stamp Day.
665 **231** 50c. multicoloured 45 15

1975. Police Day.
666 **232** 50c. multicoloured 45 20

233 Ground Receiving Aerial

1975. Satellite Telecommunications. Mult.
667 50c. Type **233** 40 15
668 1d. Map of receiving sites . . 65 20
669 1d.20 Main and subsidiary ground stations 85 30

234 Revolutionary with Flag

235 Swimming

1975. 20th Anniv of "Skikda" Revolution.
670 **234** 1d. multicoloured 60 30

1975. 7th Mediterranean Games, Algiers (2nd issue). Multicoloured.
671 25c. Type **235** 15 10
672 50c. Wrestling 30 15
673 70c. Football (vert) 50 20
674 1d. Athletics (vert) 65 30
675 1d.20 Handball (vert) 85 45

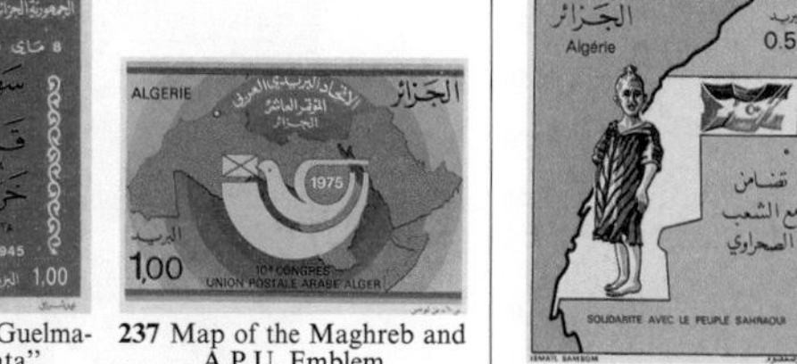
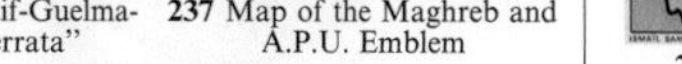

236 "Setif-Guelma-Kherrata"

237 Map of the Maghreb and A.P.U. Emblem

1975. 30th Anniv of Setif, Guelma and Kherrata Massacres (1st issue).
677 **236** 5c. black and orange . . 10 10
678 10c. black and green . . . 10 10
679 25c. black and blue . . . 15 10
680 30c. black and brown . . 20 10
681 50c. black and green . . . 30 10
682 70c. black and red 40 15
683 1d. black and red 60 30
See also No. 698.

1975. 10th Arab Postal Union Congress, Algiers.
684 **237** 1d. multicoloured 60 30

238 Mosaic, Palace of the Bey, Constantine

1975. Historic Buildings.
685 **238** 1d. multicoloured 85 35
686 – 2d. multicoloured . . . . 1·60 80
687 – 2d.50 black and brown . . 2·25 1·10
DESIGNS—VERT: 2d. Medersa Sidi-Boumedienne Oratory, Tlemcen. HORIZ: 2d.50, Palace of the Dey, Algiers.

239 University Building

240 Red-billed Fire Finch

1975. Millenary of Al-Azhar University, Cairo.
688 **239** 2d. multicoloured . . . . 1·60 65

1976. Algerian Birds (1st series). Multicoloured.
689 50c. Type **240** . . . . 1·25 60
690 1d.40 Black-headed bush shrike (horiz) . . . . . . 2·00 1·00
691 2d. Blue-tit . . . . 2·40 1·10
692 2d.50 Black-bellied sand-grouse (horiz) . . . . . . 2·75 1·50
See also Nos. 722/5.

241 Early and Modern Telephones

242 Map and Angolan Flag

1976. Telephone Centenary.
693 **241** 1d.40 multicoloured . . . 85 40

1976. "Solidarity with Republic of Angola".
694 **242** 50c. multicoloured 45 15

243 Child on Map

244 Postman

1976. Solidarity with People of Western Sahara.
695 **243** 50c. multicoloured 45 20

1976. Stamp Day.
696 **244** 1d.40 multicoloured . . . 85 35

245 People, Microscope and Slide

246 "Setif-Guelma-Kherrata"

1976. Campaign Against Tuberculosis.
697 **245** 50c. multicoloured 45 15

1976. 30th Anniv of Setif, Guelma and Kherrata Massacres (2nd issue).
698 **246** 50c. yellow and blue . . . 45 10

247 Ram's Head and Landscape

248 Algerians holding Torch

1976. Sheep Raising.
699 **247** 50c. multicoloured 45 20

1976. National Charter.
700 **248** 50c. multicoloured 50 15

249 Flag and Map

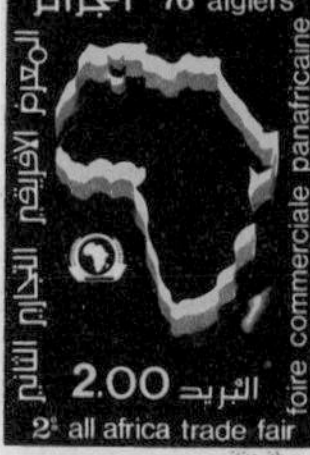

250 Map of Africa

1976. Solidarity with the Palestinian People.
701 **249** 50c. multicoloured 50 15

1976. 2nd Pan-African Commercial Fair, Algiers.
702 **250** 2d. multicoloured . . . . 1·40 50

251 Blind Man making Brushes

253 Soldiers planting Seedlings

252 Open Book

1976. Rehabilitation of the Blind. Multicoloured.
703 1d.20 Type **251** 80 35
704 1d.40 "The Blind Man" (E. Dinet) (horiz) . . . . . 1·10 50

1976. The Constitution.
705 **252** 2d. multicoloured . . . . 1·40 55

1976. Protection against Saharan Encroachment.
706 **253** 1d.40 multicoloured . . . 1·10 45

254 Arabic Inscription

1976. Election of President Boumedienne.
707 **254** 2d. multicoloured . . . . 1·40 55

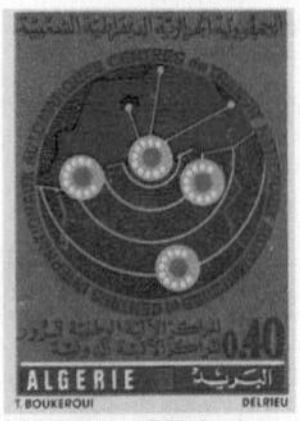

255 Map of Telephone Centres

256 "Pyramid" of Heads

1977. Inauguration of Automatic Telephone Dialling System.
708 **255** 40c. multicoloured 35 15

1977. 2nd General Population and Housing Census.
709 **256** 60c. on 50c. mult 45 15

257 Museum Building

258 El Kantara Gorges

1977. Sahara Museum, Ouargla.
710 **257** 60c. multicoloured 55 35

1977.
711 **258** 20c. green and cream . . 1·10 45
712 60c. mauve and cream . . 1·60 45
713 1d. brown and cream . . 6·00 50

259 Assembly in Session

1977. National Assembly.
714 **259** 2d. multicoloured . . . . 1·10 45

260 Soldiers with Flag

261 Soldier with Flag

1977. Solidarity with People of Zimbabwe.
715 **260** 2d. multicoloured . . . . 1·10 45

1977. Solidarity with People of Namibia.
716 **261** 3d. multicoloured . . . . 1·75 65

262 "Winter"

1977. Roman Mosaics. "The Seasons". Mult.
717 1d.20 Type **262** . . . . . . 1·25 65
718 1d.40 "Autumn" . . . . . . 1·35 65
719 2d. "Summer" . . . . 1·75 1·10
720 3d. "Spring" . . . . 2·40 1·40

1977. Algerian Birds (2nd series). As T **240**. Multicoloured.
722 60c. Tristram's warbler . . . 1·10 60
723 1d.40 Moussier's redstart (horiz) . . . . 1·50 75
724 2d. Temminck's horned lark (horiz) . . . . 2·25 1·10
725 3d. Hoopoe . . . . 3·50 1·60

263 Horseman

264 Ribbon and Games Emblem

1977. "The Cavaliers" (performing horsemen). Multicoloured.
726 2d. Type **263** . . . . 1·60 65
727 5d. Three horsemen (horiz) 3·75 1·60

1977. 3rd African Games, Algiers (1978) (1st issue). Multicoloured.
728 60c. Type **264** 45 20
729 1d.40 Symbolic design and emblem . . . . 1·10 45
See also Nos. 740/4.

265 Tessala el Merdja

1977. Socialist Agricultural Villages.
730 **265** 1d.40 multicoloured . . . 85 35

266 12th-century Almohad Dirham

1977. Ancient Coins. Multicolored.
731 60c. Type **266** 45 30
732 1d.40 12th-century Alomhad dinar . . . . 1·00 40
733 2d. 11th-century Almorarid dinar . . . . 1·40 70

267 Cherry ("Cerasus avium")

269 Children with Traffic Signs opposing Car

1978. Fruit Tree Blossom. Multicoloured.
734 60c. Type **267** 45 20
735 1d.20 "Persica vulgaris" (peach) 80 55
736 1d.30 "Amygdalus communis" (almond) . . . 80 55
737 1d.40 "Malus communis" (crab apple) . . . . 1·10 65

1978. Surch.
738 **236** 60c. on 50c. black & grn 55 15

1978. Road Safety for Children.
739 **269** 60c. multicoloured 50 20

270 Boxing and Map of Africa

1978. 3rd African Games, Algiers (2nd issue). Multicoloured.
740 40c. Sports emblems and volleyball (horiz) 20 10
741 60c. Olympic rings and table tennis symbol 35 15
742 1d.20 Basketball symbol (horiz) 70 30
743 1d.30 Hammerthrowing symbol 70 40
744 1d.40 Type **270** 90 40

271 Patient returning to Family

1978. Anti-tuberculosis Campaign.
745 **271** 60c. multicoloured 50 20

272 Ka'aba, Mecca

1978. Pilgrimage to Mecca.
746 **272** 60c. multicoloured 50 10

273 Road-building

274 Triangular Brooch

1978. African Unity Road.
747 **273** 60c. multicoloured 50 15

1978. Jewellery (1st series). Multicoloured.
748 1d.20 Type **274** 90 45
749 1d.35 Circular brooch . . . 1·10 55
750 1d.40 Anklet . . . . 1·40 65
See also Nos. 780/2 and 833/5.

275 President Houari Boumedienne

276 Books and Hands holding Torch

1979. President Boumedienne Commem (1st issue).
751 **275** 60c. brown, red & turq 45 20
See also No. 753.

1979. National Liberation Front Party Congress.
752 **276** 60c. multicoloured 40 15

277 President Houari Boumedienne

1979. President Boumedienne Commem (2nd issue).
753 **277** 1d.40 multicoloured . . . 95 40

278 Arabic Inscription

279 White Storks

1979. Election of President Chadli Bendjedid.
754 **278** 2d. multicoloured . . . . 1·25 35

1979. Air.
755 **279** 10d. blue, black and red 6·00 2·00

280 Ben Badis

281 Globe within Telephone Dial

1979. 90th Birth Anniv of Sheikh Abdelhamid Ben Badis (journalist and education pioneer).
756 **280** 60c. multicoloured 40 15

1979. "Telecom 79" Exhibition. Multicoloured.
757 1d.20 Type **281** 70 20
758 1d.40 Sound waves 90 35

282 Children dancing on Globe

1979. International Year of the Child. Mult.
759 60c. Picking Dates 40 10
760 1d.40 Type **282** (vert) 85 35

283 Kabylie Nuthatch

284 Fighting for the Revolution and Construction work

1979.
761 **283** 1d.40 multicoloured . . . 3·00 1·25

1979. 25th Anniv of Revolution. Multicoloured.
762 1d.40 Type **284** 80 20
763 3d. Algerians with flag . . . 1·75 65

285 Arabic Inscription

1979. 1400th Anniv of Hegira.
764 **285** 3d. gold, turquoise & blue . . . 1·60 65

286 Return of Dionysus (right detail) **287** Books

1980. Dionysus Mosaic, Setif. Multicoloured.
765 1d.20 Type **286** 80 35
766 1d.35 Centre detail 90 45
767 1d.40 Left detail . . . . . . 1·00 65
Nos. 765/7 were issued together, se-tenant, forming a composite design.

1980. Day of Knowledge.
768 **287** 60c. brown, yellow & grn . . 40 10

288 Five Year Plan **289** Olympic Flame

1980. Extraordinary Congress of National Liberation Front Party.
769 **288** 60c. multicoloured 40 15

1980. Olympic Games, Moscow. Multicoloured.
770 50c. Type **289** 35 10
771 1d.40 Olympic sports (horiz) . . 80 30

290 Figures supporting O.P.E.C. Emblem

1980. 20th Anniv of Organization of Petroleum Exporting Countries.
772 **290** 60c. green, blue and red . . 40 10
773 – 1d.40 green and blue . . 95 35
DESIGN: 1d.40, O.P.E.C. emblem on world map.

291 Aures

1980. World Tourism Conference, Manila. Mult.
774 50c. Type **291** 35 15
775 1d. El Oued 65 20
776 1d.40 Tassili 90 35
777 2d. Algiers . . . . 1·40 50

292 Ibn Sina

1980. Birth Millenary of Ibn Sina (Avicenna) (philosopher).
778 **292** 3d. multicoloured . . . . 1·60 65

293 Earthquake Devastation

1980. El Asnam Earthquake Relief.
779 **293** 3d. multicoloured . . . . 1·60 45

1980. Jewellery (2nd series). As T **274**. Mult.
780 60c. Necklace 45 20
781 1d.40 Earrings and bracelet . . 80 45
782 2d. Diadem (horiz) . . . . . 1·25 55

294 Emblem

1981. Five Year Plan.
783 **294** 60c. multicoloured 35 10

295 Basket-worker

1981. Traditional Arts. Multicoloured.
784 40c. Type **295** 20 10
785 60c. Spinning 35 15
786 1d. Copper-smith 55 20
787 1d.40 Jeweller 80 35

296 Cedar "Cedrus atlantica"

1981. World Tree Day. Multicoloured.
788 60c. Type **296** 35 10
789 1d.40 Cypress "Cupressus dupreziana" 80 35

297 Mohamed Bachir el Ibrahimi

298 Children and Blackboard (Basic Schooling)

1981. Day of Knowledge.
790 **297** 60c. multicoloured 35 10
791 **298** 60c. multicoloured 35 10

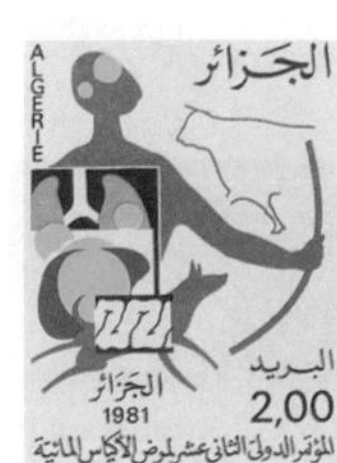

299 Archer, Dog and Internal Organs

1981. 12th Int Hydatidological Congress, Algiers.
792 **299** 2d. multicoloured . . . . 1·40 45

300 Dish Aerial and Caduceus **301** "Disabled"

1981. World Telecommunications Day.
793 **300** 1d.40 multicoloured . . . 80 20

1981. International Year of Disabled People.
794 **301** 1d.20 blue, red & orange 65 15
795 – 1d.40 multicoloured . . . 80 15
DESIGN: 1d.40, Disabled people and hand holding flower.

302 "Papilio machaon"

1981. Butterflies. Multicoloured.
796 60c. Type **302** 45 15
797 1d.20 "Rhodocera rhamni gonepteryx rhamni" . . . 80 35
798 1d.40 "Charaxes jasius" . . . 1·00 50
799 2d. "Papilio podalirius" . . . 1·40 65

303 Mediterranean Monk Seal **304** Man holding Ear of Wheat

1981. Nature Protection. Multicoloured.
800 60c. Type **303** 55 35
801 1d.40 Barbary ape . . . . . 1·10 80

1981. World Food Day.
802 **304** 2d. multicoloured . . . . 1·00 40

305 Cattle, Jabbaren

1981. Cave Paintings. Multicoloured.
803 60c. Mouflon, Tan Zoumaitek 35 15
804 1d. Type **305** 55 20
805 1d.60 Cattle, Iherir (horiz) . . 80 35
806 2d. One-horned bull, Jabbaren (horiz) . . . . . 1·10 40

306 Galley

1981. Algerian Ships of 17th and 18th Centuries. Multicoloured.
807 60c. Type **306** 60 25
808 1d.60 Xebec . . . . 1·50 45

307 Footballers with Cup **308** Microscope

1982. World Cup Football Championship, Spain. Multicoloured.
809 80c. Type **307** 45 15
810 2d.80 Footballers and ball (horiz) . . . . 1·40 50

1982. Centenary of Discovery of Tubercle Bacillus.
811 **308** 80c. blue, lt blue & orge 45 15

309 Mirror

1982. Popular Traditional Arts. Multicoloured.
812 80c. Type **309** 45 15
813 2d. Whatnot . . . . 1·00 40
814 2d.40 Chest (48 × 32 mm) . . 1·40 55

310 New Mosque, Algiers **311** "Callitris articulata"

1982. Views of Algeria before 1830 (1st series). Size 32 × 22 mm.
815 **310** 80c. brown 35 15
816 – 2d.40 violet 90 45
817 – 3d. green . . . . 1·25 55
DESIGNS: 2d.40, Sidi Boumedienne Mosque, Tlemcen; 3d. Garden of Dey, Algiers.
See also Nos. 859/62, 873/5, 880/2, 999/1001, 1054/6 and 1075/86.

1982. Medicinal Plants. Multicoloured.
818 50c. Type **311** 30 10
819 80c. "Artemisia herba-alba" 40 15
820 1d. "Ricinus communis" . . 55 20
821 2d.40 "Thymus fontanesii" 1·25 50

312 Independence Fighter **313** Congress House

1982. 20th Anniv of Independence. Mult.
822 50c. Type **312** 30 10
823 80c. Modern soldiers 40 15
824 2d. Algerians and symbols of prosperity . . . . 1·00 45

1982. Soumman Congress.
826 **313** 80c. multicoloured 45 10

314 Scout and Guide releasing Dove
315 Child

1982. 75th Anniv of Boy Scout Movement.
827 **314** 2d.80 multicoloured . . . 1·40 45

1982. Palestinian Children.
828 **315** 1d.60 multicoloured . . . 80 20

316 Waldrapp

1982. Nature Protection. Multicoloured.
829 50c. Type **316** 60 50
830 80c. Houbara bustard (vert) 75 75
831 2d. Tawny eagle . . . . . . 2·10 1·40
832 2d.40 Lammergeier (vert) . . 2·75 1·50

317 Mirror
318 "Abies numidica"

1983. Silver Work.
833 **317** 50c. silver, black and red 20 10
834 – 1d. multicoloured 45 30
835 – 2d. silver, black, & purple 90 45
DESIGNS—VERT. 1d. Perfume flasks. HORIZ: 2d. Belt buckle.

1983. World Tree Day. Multicoloured.
836 80c. Type **318** 40 15
837 2d.80 "Acacia raddiana" . . 1·50 55

319 Mineral
320 Customs Officer

1983. Mineral Resources.
838 **319** 70c. multicoloured 55 20
839 80c. multicoloured 55 30
840 1d.20 mult (horiz) 85 55
841 2d.40 mult (horiz) . . . . 1·60 90

1983. 30th Anniv of Customs Co-operation Council.
842 **320** 80c. multicoloured 55 20

321 Emir Abdelkader

1983. Death Centenary of Emir Abdelkader.
843 **321** 4d. multicoloured . . . . 1·75 70

322 Fly Agaric
323 Ibn Khaldoun

1983. Mushrooms. Multicoloured.
844 50c. Type **322** 65 25
845 80c. Death cap 95 50
846 1d.40 "Pleurotus eryngii" . . 2·10 75
847 2d.80 "Terfezia leonis" . . . 3·50 1·50

1983. Ibn Khaldoun Commemoration.
848 **323** 80c. multicoloured 55 20

324 W.C.Y. Emblem and Post Office

1983. World Communications Year. Mult.
849 80c. Type **324** 45 15
850 2d.40 W.C.Y. emblem and telephone switch box . . . 1·10 40

325 Goat and Tassili Mountains

1983. Tassili World Patrimony. Multicoloured.
851 50c. Type **325** 30 10
852 80c. Touaregs 40 15
853 2d.40 Rock paintings . . . . 1·10 40
854 2d.80 Rock formation . . . 1·40 55

326 Sloughi

1983. Sloughi. Multicoloured.
855 80c. Type **326** 55 20
856 2d.40 Sloughi . . . . 1·40 65

327 Symbols of Economic Progress

1983. 5th National Liberation Front Party Congress.
857 **327** 80c. multicoloured 55 30

1984. Views of Algeria before 1830 (2nd series). As T **310**.
859 10c. blue 10 10
860 1d. purple 40 15
861 2d. blue 80 35
862 4d. red . . . . 1·60 55
DESIGNS: 10c. Oran; 1d. Sidi Abderahmane Mosque, Et Taalibi; 2d. Bejaia; 4d. Constantine.

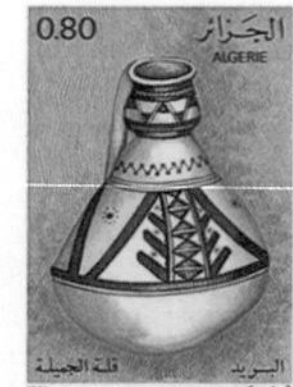

328 Jug
329 Fountain

1984. Pottery. Multicoloured.
863 80c. Type **328** 40 20
864 1d. Dish (horiz) 50 20
865 2d. Lamp . . . . 1·00 45
866 2d.40 Jug (horiz) . . . . . . 1·25 55

1984. Fountains of Old Algiers.
867 **329** 50c. multicoloured 20 15
868 – 80c. multicoloured 40 20
869 – 2d.40 multicoloured . . . 1·00 55
DESIGNS: 80c., 2d.40, Different fountains.

330 Dove, Flames and Olympic Rings
331 Stallion

1984. Olympic Games, Los Angeles.
870 **330** 1d. multicoloured 60 30

1984. Horses. Multicoloured.
871 80c. Type **331** 45 35
872 2d.40 Mare . . . . 1·40 80

1984. Views of Algeria before 1830 (3rd series). As T **310**.
873 5c. purple 10 10
874 20c. blue 10 10
875 70c. violet 30 15
DESIGNS: 5c. Mustapha Pacha; 20c. Bab Azzoun; 70c. Mostaganem.

332 Lute

1984. Musical Instruments. Multicoloured.
876 80c. Type **332** 45 20
877 1d. Drum 55 20
878 2d.40 One-stringed instrument 1·25 55
879 2d.80 Bagpipes . . . . . . 1·40 65

1984. Views of Algeria before 1830 (4th series). As T **310**.
880 30c. red and black 15 10
881 40c. black 20 10
882 50c. brown 30 10
DESIGNS: 30c. Algiers from Admiralty; 40c. Kolea; 50c. Algiers from aqueduct.

333 Partisans in Mountains and Flag

1984. 30th Anniv of Revolution.
883 **333** 80c. multicoloured 55 20

334 Map of M'Zab Valley

1984. M'Zab Valley. Multicoloured.
885 80c. Type **334** 45 10
886 2d.40 M'Zab town . . . . . 1·25 45

335 Coffee Pot
336 Blue-finned Tuna

1985. Ornamental Tableware.
887 **335** 80c. black, silver & yellow 35 20
888 – 2d. black, silver and green 90 45
889 – 2d.40 black, silver & pink 1·25 55
DESIGNS—HORIZ: 2d. Bowl. VERT: 2d.40, Lidded jar.

1985. Fishes. Multicoloured.
890 50c. Type **336** 45 20
891 80c. Gilthead seabream . . . 70 25
892 2d.40 Dusky grouper . . . . 2·00 90
893 2d.80 Smooth hound . . . . 2·40 1·10

337 Birds in Flight and Emblem

1985. National Games.
894 **337** 80c. multicoloured 50 15

338 Stylized Trees
339 Algiers Casbah

1985. Environmental Protection. Multicoloured.
895 80c. Type **338** 40 15
896 1d.40 Stylized waves 70 20

1985.
897 **339** 20c. blue and cream . . . 10 10
898 80c. green and cream . . 45 10
899 2d.40 brown and cream 1·25 10

340 Dove within "40"
341 Figures linking arms and Emblem

1985. 40th Anniv of U.N.O.
900 **340** 1d. multicoloured 60 20

1985. 1st National Youth Festival.
901 **341** 80c. multicoloured 50 15

342 Figures linking arms on Globe and Dove
343 O.P.E.C. Emblem

1985. International Youth Year. Multicoloured.
902 80c. Type **342** 45 15
903 1d.40 Doves making globe with laurels 65 20

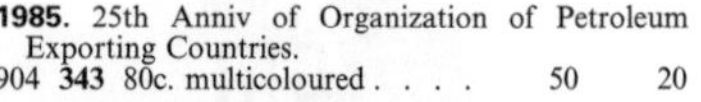

1985. 25th Anniv of Organization of Petroleum Exporting Countries.
904 **343** 80c. multicoloured 50 20

344 Mother and Children
345 Chetaibi Bay

1985. Family Planning. Multicoloured.
905 80c. Type **344** 40 15
906 1d.40 Doctor weighing baby 65 20
907 1d.70 Mother breast-feeding baby 85 30

1985. Tourist Sites.
908 **345** 80c. blue, green & brown 35 15
909 – 2d. brown, green & blue 1·00 30
910 – 2d.40 brown, green & bl 1·10 40
DESIGNS—VERT: 2d. El Meniaa. HORIZ: 2d.40, Bou Noura.

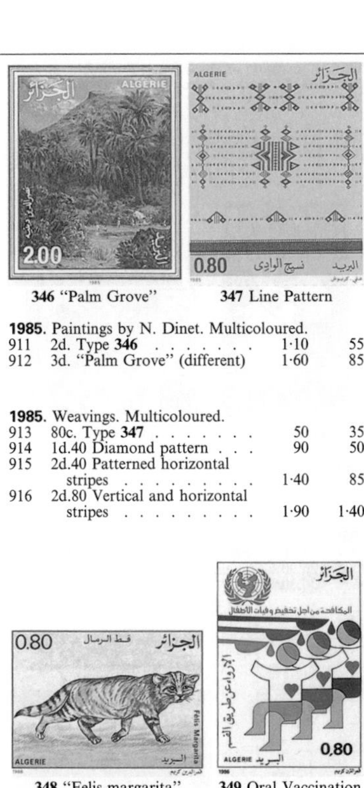

346 "Palm Grove" **347** Line Pattern

1985. Paintings by N. Dinet. Multicoloured.
911 2d. Type **346** . . . . 1·10 55
912 3d. "Palm Grove" (different) 1·60 85

1985. Weavings. Multicoloured.
913 80c. Type **347** 50 35
914 1d.40 Diamond pattern . . . 90 50
915 2d.40 Patterned horizontal stripes . . . . 1·40 85
916 2d.80 Vertical and horizontal stripes . . . . 1·90 1·40

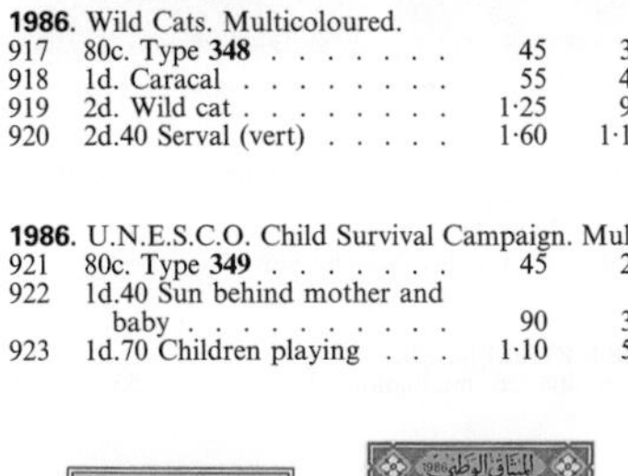

348 "Felis margarita" **349** Oral Vaccination

1986. Wild Cats. Multicoloured.
917 80c. Type **348** 45 35
918 1d. Caracal 55 45
919 2d. Wild cat . . . . 1·25 90
920 2d.40 Serval (vert) . . . . . 1·60 1·10

1986. U.N.E.S.C.O. Child Survival Campaign. Mult.
921 80c. Type **349** 45 20
922 1d.40 Sun behind mother and baby 90 35
923 1d.70 Children playing . . . 1·10 55

350 Industrial Skyline, Clasped Hands and Emblem **351** Books and Crowd

1986. 30th Anniv of Algerian General Workers' Union.
924 **350** 2d. multicoloured . . . . 1·10 45

1986. National Charter.
925 **351** 4d. multicoloured . . . . 2·25 1·00

352 Emblem on Book and Drawing Instruments **353** Children playing

1986. Disabled Persons' Day.
926 **352** 80c. multicoloured 50 20

1986. Anti-tuberculosis Campaign.
927 **353** 80c. multicoloured 55 30

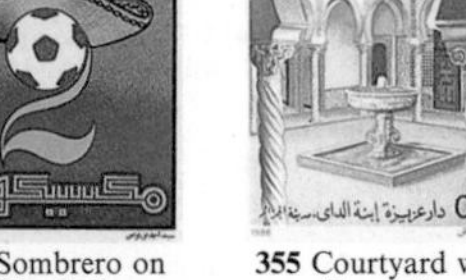

354 Sombrero on Football **355** Courtyard with Fountain

1986. World Cup Football Championship, Mexico. Multicoloured.
928 2d. Type **354** . . . . 1·00 40
929 2d.40 Players and ball . . . 1·25 45

1986. Traditional Dwellings. Multicoloured.
930 80c. Type **355** 45 20
931 2d.40 Courtyard with two beds of shrubs . . . . . . 1·40 70
932 3d. Courtyard with plants in tall pot . . . . 1·75 1·00

356 Heart forming Drop over Patient **357** Transmission Mast as Palm Tree

1986. Blood Donors.
933 **356** 80c. multicoloured 90 30

1986. Opening of Hertzian Wave Communications (Southern District).
934 **357** 60c. multicoloured 35 15

358 Studded Gate

1986. Mosque Gateways. Multicoloured.
935 2d. Type **358** . . . . 1·00 45
936 2d.40 Ornate gateway . . . . 1·25 65

359 Dove

1986. International Peace Year.
937 **359** 2d.40 multicoloured . . . 1·25 45

360 Girl dancing **361** "Narcissus tazetta"

1986. Folk Dances. Multicoloured.
938 80c. Type **360** 45 20
939 2d.40 Woman with purple dress dancing . . . . . . 1·25 55
940 2d.80 Veiled sword dancer . . 1·25 55

1986. Flowers. Multicoloured.
941 80c. Type **361** 45 20
942 1d.40 "Iris unguicularis" . . 80 45
943 2d.40 "Capparis spinosa" . . 1·10 65
944 2d.80 "Gladiolus segetum" 1·40 90

362 "Algerian Family" **363** Earrings

1987. Paintings by Mohammed Issiakhem in National Museum. Multicoloured.
945 2d. Type **362** . . . . 1·10 55
946 5d. "Man and Books" . . . 2·50 1·60

1987. Jewellery from Aures. Multicoloured.
947 1d. Type **363** 45 30
948 1d.80 Bangles 80 45
949 2d.90 Brooches . . . . . . 1·25 85
950 3d.30 Necklace (horiz) . . . 1·40 95

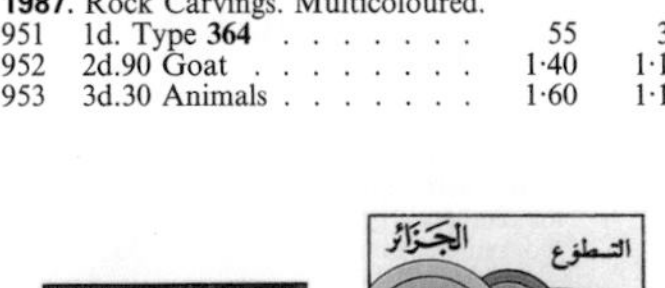

364 Boy and Girl

1987. Rock Carvings. Multicoloured.
951 1d. Type **364** 55 35
952 2d.90 Goat . . . . 1·40 1·10
953 3d.30 Animals . . . . 1·60 1·10

365 Baby holding Syringe "Umbrella" **366** Workers and Circles

1987. African Vaccination Year.
954 **365** 1d. multicoloured 45 20

1987. Voluntary Service.
955 **366** 1d. multicoloured 45 20

367 People and Buildings

1987. 3rd General Population Census.
956 **367** 1d. multicoloured 45 20

368 1962 War Orphans Fund Stamps and Magnifying Glass

1987. 25th Anniv of Independent Algeria Stamps.
957 **368** 1d.80 multicoloured . . . 80 50

369 Hand holding Torch **370** Actors in Spotlight

1987. 25th Anniv of Independence. Multicoloured.
958 **369** 1d. multicoloured 45 20

1987. Amateur Theatre Festival, Mostaganem. Multicoloured.
960 1d. Type **370** 40 15
961 1d.80 Theatre 70 40

371 Discus Thrower **372** Greater Flamingo

1987. Mediterranean Games, Lattaquie. Mult.
962 1d. Type **371** 40 15
963 2d.90 Tennis player (vert) . . 1·10 50
964 3d.30 Footballer . . . . . . 1·40 65

1987. Birds. Multicoloured.
965 1d. Type **372** 45 35
966 1d.80 Purple swamphen . . . 90 75
967 2d.50 Black-shouldered kite 1·75 95
968 2d.90 Red kite . . . . 1·90 1·25

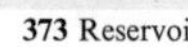

373 Reservoir **374** Map, Transmitter and Radio Waves

1987. Agriculture. Multicoloured.
969 1d. Type **373** 45 15
970 1d. Forestry (36 × 28 mm) . . 45 15
971 1d. Foodstuffs (25 × 37 mm) 45 15
972 1d. Erecting hedge against desert (25 × 37 mm) 45 15

1987. African Telecommunications Day.
973 **374** 1d. multicoloured 45 20

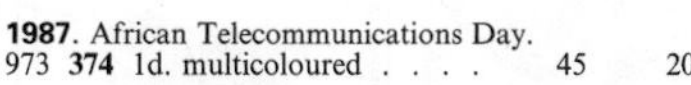

375 Motorway

1987. Transport. Multicoloured.
974 2d.90 Type **375** . . . . . . 1·10 45
975 3d.30 Diesel locomotive and passenger train . . . . . . 2·75 1·10

376 Houari Boumedienne University, Algiers

1987. Universities. Multicoloured.
976 1d. Type **376** 40 15
977 2d.50 Oran University . . . 90 35
978 2d.90 Constantine University 1·10 45
979 3d.30 Emir Abdelkader University, Constantine (vert) . . . . 1·40 55

377 Wheat, Sun and Farmer ploughing with Oxen **378** Emblem as Sun above Factories

1988. 10th Anniv of International Agricultural Development Fund.
980 **377** 1d. multicoloured 40 20

1988. Autonomy of State-owned Utilities.
981 **378** 1d. multicoloured 40 20

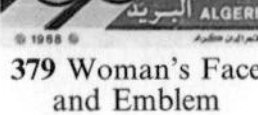

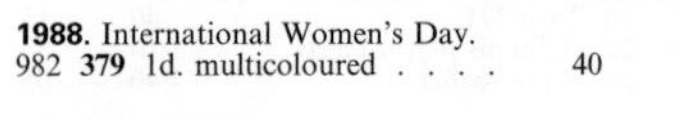

379 Woman's Face and Emblem　**380** Globe, Flag, Wood Pigeon and Scout Salute

1988. International Women's Day.
982 **379** 1d. multicoloured 40 20

1988. 75th Anniv of Arab Scouting.
983 **380** 2d. multicoloured 80 35

381 Bau-Hanifia　**382** Running

1988. Spas. Multicoloured.
984 1d. Type **381** 40 15
985 2d.90 Chellala . . . . 1·10 45
986 3d.30 Righa-Ain Tolba . . . 1·25 50

1988. Olympic Games, Seoul.
987 **382** 2d.90 multicoloured . . . 1·00 45

383 Pencil and Globe　**384** Barbary Ape

1988. International Literacy Day.
988 **383** 2d.90 multicoloured . . . 1·00 45

1988. Endangered Animals. Barbary Ape. Mult.
989 50c. Type **384** 20 10
990 90c. Ape family 35 15
991 1d. Ape's head and shoulders (vert) 40 20
992 1d.80 Ape in tree (vert) . . . 70 35

385 Family Group　**386** Different Races raising Fists

1988. 40th Anniv of W.H.O.
993 **385** 2d.90 multicoloured . . . 1·00 45

1988. Anti-apartheid Campaign.
994 **386** 2d.50 multicoloured . . . 85 35

387 Emblem　**388** Man irrigating Fields

1988. 6th National Liberation Front Party Congress.
995 **387** 1d. multicoloured 40 15

1988. Agriculture. Multicoloured.
996 1d. Type **388** 40 15
997 1d. Fields, cattle and man picking fruit 40 15

389 Constantine　**390** Courtyard

1989.
998 **389** 1d. deep green and green 30 10

1989. Views of Algeria before 1830 (5th series). As T **310**.
999 2d.50 green 70 35
1000 2d.90 green 80 15
1001 5d. brown and black . . . . 2·00 70
DESIGNS: 2d.50, Bay; 2d.90, Harbour; 5d. View of harbour through archway.

1989. National Achievements. Multicoloured.
1002 1d. Type **390** 35 20
1003 1d. Flats (housing) 35 20
1004 1d. Gateway, Timimoun (tourism) 35 20
1005 1d. Dish aerial and telephones (communications) 35 20

391 Oran Es Senia Airport

1989. Airports. Multicoloured.
1006 2d.90 Type **391** 85 35
1007 3d.30 Tebessa airport . . . 95 45
1008 5d. Tamanrasset airport (vert) . . . . 1·60 90

392 Irrigation　**393** Soldiers at Various Tasks

1989. Development of South. Multicoloured.
1009 1d. Type **392** 30 15
1010 1d.80 Ouargla secondary school 50 30
1011 2d.50 Gas complex, Hassi R'mel (vert) 70 35

1989. 20th Anniv of National Service.
1012 **393** 2d. multicoloured . . . 1·50 75

394 Locusts and Crop Spraying

1989. Anti-locusts Campaign.
1013 **394** 1d. multicoloured . . . 30 15

395 Mother and Baby

1989. International Children's Day.
1014 **395** 1d.+30c. mult 40 30

396 Moon

1989. 20th Anniv of First Manned Landing on Moon. Multicoloured.
1015 2d.90 Type **396** 85 35
1016 4d. Astronaut on moon . . 1·10 55

397 Globe and Emblem

1989. Centenary of Interparliamentary Union.
1017 **397** 2d.90 mauve, brn & gold 85 30

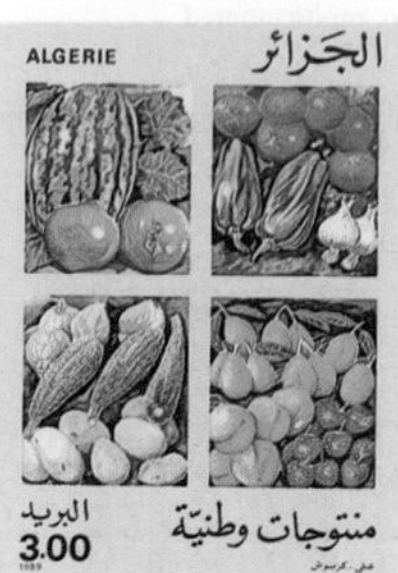

398 Fruits and Vegetables

1989. National Production.
1018 **398** 2d. multicoloured . . . 55 35
1019 – 3d. multicoloured . . . 85 50
1020 – 5d. multicoloured . . . 1·40 85
DESIGNS: 3, 5d. Various fruits and vegetables.

399 Atlantic Bonito　**400** "35" and Soldier with Rifle

1989. Fishes. Multicoloured.
1021 1d. Type **399** 45 15
1022 1d.80 John dory 95 30
1023 2d.90 Red seabream . . . . 1·40 45
1024 3d.30 Swordfish . . . . . . 1·60 55

1989. 35th Anniv of Revolution.
1025 **400** 1d. multicoloured . . . 30 10

401 Bank Emblem, Cogwheel, Factory and Wheat　**402** Satan's Mushroom

1989. 25th Anniv of African Development Bank.
1026 **401** 1d. multicoloured . . . 30 15

1989. Fungi. Multicoloured.
1027 1d. Type **402** 60 20
1028 1d.80 Yellow stainer . . . . 1·10 40
1029 2d.90 Parasol mushroom . . 1·75 60
1030 3d.30 Saffron milk cap . . . 1·90 70

403 Emblem　**404** Sun, Arm and Face

1990. 10th Anniv of Pan-African Postal Union.
1031 **403** 1d. multicoloured . . . 30 15

1990. Rational Use of Energy.
1032 **404** 1d. multicoloured . . . 30 15

405 Emblem　**406** Ceramics

1990. African Nations Cup Football Championship.
1033 **405** 3d. multicoloured . . . 85 40

1990. Industries. Multicoloured.
1034 2d. Type **406** 55 30
1035 2d.90 Car maintenance . . . 85 35
1036 3d.30 Fishing . . . . 1·75 45

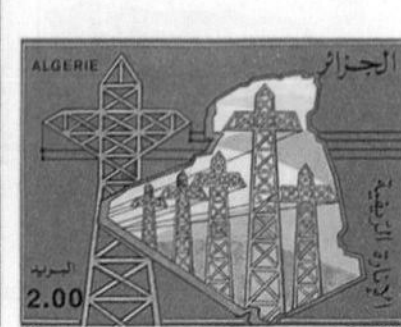

407 Pictogram and Olympic Rings　**408** Pylons on Map

1990. World Cup Football Championship, Italy. Multicoloured.
1037 2d.90 Type **407** 85 35
1038 5d. Trophy, ball and flag . . 1·40 65

1990. Rural Electrification.
1039 **408** 2d. multicoloured . . . 55 20

409 Young Workers　**410** Members' Flags

1990. Youth. Multicoloured.
1040 2d. Type **409** 55 20
1041 3d. Youth in crowd (vert) 85 30

1990. Arab Maghreb Union Summit Conference.
1042 **410** 1d. multicoloured . . . 30 15

411 Anniversary Emblem

1990. 30th Anniv of O.P.E.C.
1043 **411** 2d. multicoloured . . . 50 20

412 House and Hand holding Coin　**413** Flag, Rifle and Hands with Broken Manacles

1990. Savings Day.
1044 **412** 1d. multicoloured . . . 20 10

1990. Namibian Independence.
1045 **413** 3d. multicoloured . . . 60 15

414 Duck — **415** Dome of the Rock and Palestinians

1990. Domestic Animals. Multicoloured.
1046 1d. Type **414** 20 10
1047 2d. Hare (horiz) 45 20
1048 2d.90 Common turkey . . . 65 35
1049 3d.30 Red junglefowl (horiz) 90 55

1990. Palestinian "Intifada" Movement.
1050 **415** 1d.+30c. mult 35 20

416 Crowd with Banners — **417** Families in Countryside

1990. 30th Anniv of 11 December 1960 Demonstration.
1051 **416** 1d. multicoloured . . . 20 10

1990. Campaign against Respiratory Diseases.
1052 **417** 1d. multicoloured . . . 20 10

418 Sunburst, Torch and Open Book — **419** Bejaia

1991. 2nd Anniv of Constitution.
1053 **418** 1d. multicoloured . . . 20 10

1991. Views of Algeria before 1830 (6th series). As T **310**.
1054 1d.50 red 35 10
1055 4d.20 green 90 35
DESIGNS: 1d.50, Kolea; 4d.20, Constantine.

1991. Air. Multicoloured.
1056 10d. Type **419** . . . . . . 1·90 85
1057 20d. Annaba . . . . 4·00 1·90

420 "Jasminum fruticans" — **421** "Trip to the Country" (Mehdi Medrar)

1991. Flowers. Multicoloured.
1058 2d. Type **420** 45 20
1059 4d. "Dianthus crinitus" . . 90 35
1060 5d. "Cyclamen africanum" 1·10 55

1991. Children's Drawings. Multicoloured.
1061 3d. Type **421** . . . . 3·50 1·75
1062 4d. "Children playing" (Ouidad Bounab) 90 35

422 Emblem

1991. 3rd Anniv of Arab Maghreb Union Summit Conference, Zeralda.
1063 **422** 1d. multicoloured . . . 20 10

423 Figures and Emblem

1991. 40th Anniv of Geneva Convention on Status of Refugees.
1064 **423** 3d. multicoloured . . . 65 20

424 Coded Letter and Target

1991. World Post Day (1065) and "Telecom 91" International Telecommunications Exhibition, Geneva (1066). Multicoloured.
1065 1d.50 Type **424** 35 15
1066 4d.20 Exhibition and I.T.U. emblems (vert) 95 35

425 Spanish Festoon

1991. Butterflies. Multicoloured.
1067 2d. Type **425** 20 15
1068 4d. "Melitaea didyma" . . . 45 30
1069 6d. Red admiral 65 45
1070 7d. Large tortoiseshell . . . 90 65

426 Chest Ornament — **427** Woman

1991. Silver Jewellery from South Algeria. Mult.
1071 3d. Necklaces 35 20
1072 4d. Type **426** 45 30
1073 5d. Enamelled ornament . . 55 45
1074 7d. Bangles (horiz) 90 70

1992. Views of Algeria before 1830. As previous issues and new values. Size 30½ × 21 mm.
1075 5c. purple 10 10
1076 10c. blue 10 10
1077 20c. blue 10 10
1078 30c. red and black 20 10
1079 50c. brown 10 10
1080 70c. lilac 10 10
1081 80c. brown 10 10
1082 1d. brown 10 10
1083 2d. blue 10 10
1084 3d. green 20 10
1085 4d. red 25 10
1086 6d.20 blue 70 20
1087 7d.50 red 85 20
DESIGNS: 5c., 6d.20, As No. 873; 10c., 7d.50, As No. 859; 20c. As No. 1000; 30c. As No. 1001; 50c. As No. 882; 70c. As No. 875; 80c. Type **310**; 1d. As No. 860; 2d. As No. 861; 3d. As No. 817; 4d. As No. 1055.

1992. International Women's Day.
1095 **427** 1d.50 multicoloured . . 20 10

428 Dorcas Gazelle — **429** Algiers

1992. Gazelles. Multicoloured.
1096 1d.50 Type **428** 15 10
1097 6d.20 Edmi gazelle 70 45
1098 8d.60 Addra gazelle 95 55

1992.
1099 **429** 1d.50 brown & lt brown 15 10
1132 2d. blue 10 10
1147 3d. blue 10 10

430 Runners — **431** Doves and Flags

1992. Olympic Games, Barcelona.
1100 **430** 6d.20 multicoloured . . 70 30

1992. 30th Anniv of Independence.
1101 **431** 5d. green, red and black 55 20

432 "Ajuga iva" — **433** Computerized Post Office Equipment

1992. Medicinal Plants. Multicoloured.
1102 1d.50 Type **432** 15 10
1103 5d.10 Buckthorn 55 30
1104 6d.20 Milk thistle 70 35
1105 8d.60 French lavender . . . 1·00 50

1992. World Post Day. Modernization of Postal Service.
1106 **433** 1d.50 multicoloured . . 15 10

434 Boudiaf

1992. Mohammed Boudiaf (chairman of Committee of State) Commemoration.
1107 **434** 2d. multicoloured . . . 20 15
1108 8d.60 multicoloured . . 95 55

435 2nd-century B.C. Numidian Coin

1992. Coinage. Multicoloured.
1109 1d.50 Type **435** 15 10
1110 2d. 14th-century Zianide dinar 20 15
1111 5d.10 11th-century Almoravid dinar 55 20
1112 6d.20 19th-century Emir Abd-el-Kader coin . . . 70 35

436 Short-snouted Seahorse — **437** Algiers Door Knocker

1992. Marine Animals. Multicoloured.
1113 1d.50 Type **436** 20 10
1114 2d.70 Loggerhead turtle . . 35 15
1115 6d.20 Mediterranean moray 90 35
1116 7d.50 Lobster 85 50

1993. Door Knockers. Multicoloured.
1117 2d. Type **437** 10 10
1118 5d.60 Constantine 30 15
1119 8d.60 Tlemcen 50 25

438 Medlar Blossom

1993. Fruit-tree Blossom. Multicoloured.
1120 4d.50 Type **438** 25 10
1121 8d.60 Quince (vert) 50 25
1122 11d. Apricot (vert) 60 30

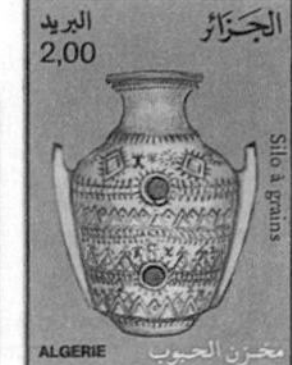

439 Patrol Boat, Emblem and Flag — **440** Grain Storage Jar

1993. 20th Anniv of Coastguard Service.
1123 **439** 2d. multicoloured . . . 20 10

1993. Traditional Utensils. Multicoloured.
1124 2d. Type **440** 10 10
1125 5d.60 Grindstone 30 15
1126 8d.60 Oil-press 50 25

441 Mauretanian Royal Mausoleum, Tipaza — **442** Jijelienne Coast

1993. Mausoleums. Multicoloured.
1127 8d.60 Type **441** 50 25
1128 12d. Royal Mausoleum, El Khroub 65 30

1993. Air.
1129 **442** 50d. green, brown & blue . . . . 2·75 1·25

443 Annaba — **444** Chameleon

1993. Ports. Multicoloured.
1130 2d. Type **443** 15 10
1131 8d.60 Arzew 95 25

1993. Reptiles. Multicoloured.
1133 2d. Type **444** 10 10
1134 8d.60 Desert monitor (horiz) 50 25

445 Tipaza — **446** Map, Processing Plant and Uses of Hydrocarbons

1993. Tourism. Multicoloured.
1135 2d. Type **445** 10 10
1136 8d.60 Kerzaz 25 10

1993. 30th Anniv of Sonatrach (National Society for Transformation and Commercialization of Hydrocarbons).
1137 **446** 2d. multicoloured . . . 10 10

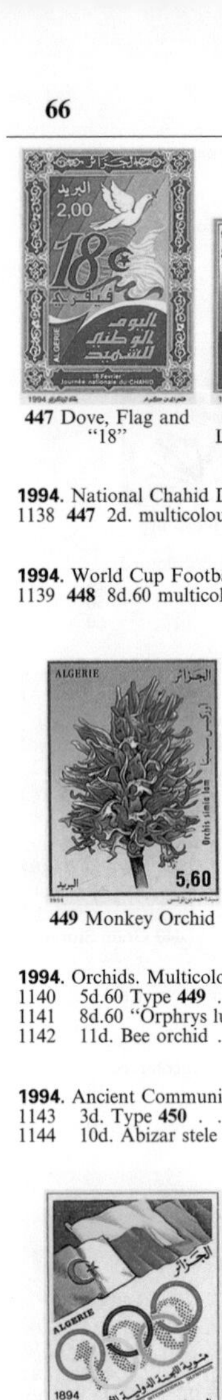

447 Dove, Flag and "18"

448 Crown of Statue of Liberty, Football, U.S. Flag and Trophy

1994. National Chahid Day.
1138 **447** 2d. multicoloured . . . 10 10

1994. World Cup Football Championship, U.S.A.
1139 **448** 8d.60 multicoloured . . 25 10

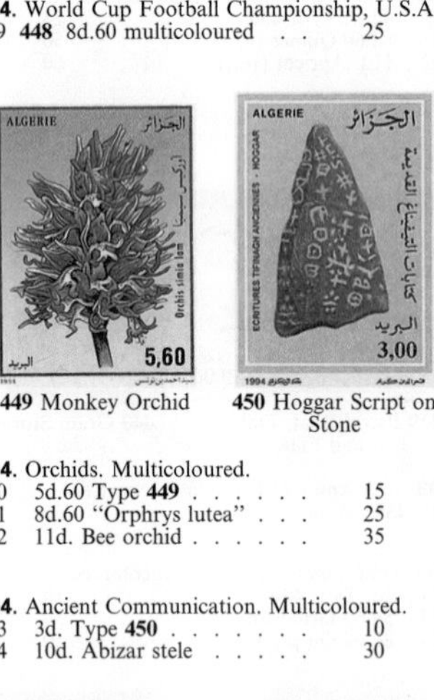

449 Monkey Orchid

450 Hoggar Script on Stone

1994. Orchids. Multicoloured.
1140 5d.60 Type **449** 15 10
1141 8d.60 "Orphrys lutea" . . . 25 10
1142 11d. Bee orchid 35 15

1994. Ancient Communication. Multicoloured.
1143 3d. Type **450** 10 10
1144 10d. Abizar stele 30 15

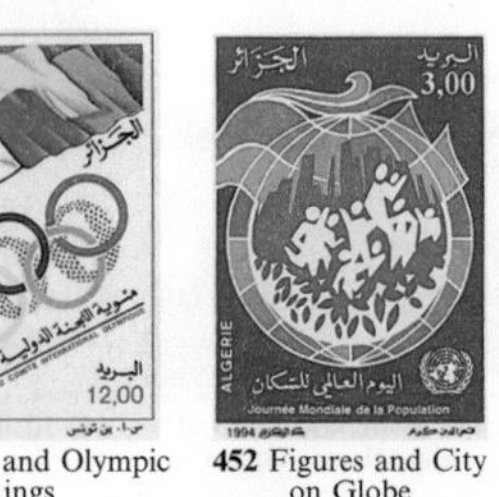

451 Flags and Olympic Rings

452 Figures and City on Globe

1994. Cent of International Olympic Committee.
1145 **451** 12d. multicoloured . . . 35 15

1994. World Population Day.
1146 **452** 3d. multicoloured . . . 10 10

453 Sandstone

454 Brooches

1994. Minerals. Multicoloured.
1148 3d. Type **453** 10 10
1149 5d. Cipolin 15 10
1150 10d. Turitella shells in chalk 25 15

1994. Saharan Silver Jewellery. Multicoloured.
1151 3d. Type **454** 10 10
1152 5d. Belt (horiz) 15 10
1153 12d. Bracelets (horiz) . . . 30 15

455 Soldiers

456 Ladybirds on Leaves

1994. 40th Anniv of Revolution.
1154 **455** 3d. multicoloured . . . 10 10

1994. Insects. Multicoloured.
1155 3d. Type **456** 10 10
1156 12d. Beetle ("Buprestidae") on plant 30 15

457 Virus and Family

1994. World Anti-AIDS Campaign Day.
1157 **457** 3d. black, blue & mauve 10 10

458 Algiers

459 Southern Algeria

1994. Regional Dances. Multicoloured.
1158 3d. Type **458** 10 10
1159 10d. Constantine 25 15
1160 12d. Alaoui 30 15

1995. 20th Anniv of World Tourism Organization.
1161 **459** 3d. multicoloured . . . 10 10

460 Honey Bee on Comb

461 Dahlia

1995. Bee-keeping. Multicoloured.
1162 3d. Type **460** 10 10
1163 13d. Bee on flower (horiz) 35 20

1995. Flowers. Multicoloured.
1164 3d. Type **461** 10 10
1165 10d. Zinnias 25 15
1166 13d. Lilac 35 20

462 Circular Design

463 Doves, Graves, Victims and Soldiers

1995. Stucco Work from Sedrata (4th century after Hegira).
1167 **462** 3d. brown 10 10
1168 – 4d. green 10 10
1169 – 5d. brown 15 10
DESIGNS—4d. Circular design within square; 5d. Stylized flowers.

1995. 50th Anniv of End of Second World War. Multicoloured.
1170 **463** 3d. multicoloured . . . 10 10

464 Water Pollution

465 Players and Anniversary Emblem

1995. Environmental Protection. Multicoloured.
1172 3d. Type **464** 10 10
1173 13d. Air pollution 35 20

1995. Centenary of Volleyball.
1174 **465** 3d. multicoloured . . . 10 10

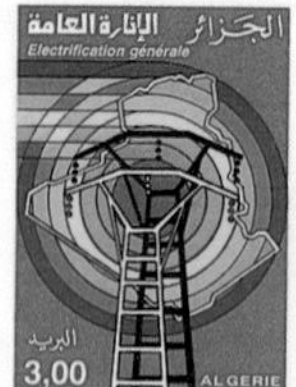

466 Map and Pylon

467 Children and Schoolbag Contents

1995. Electrification.
1175 **466** 3d. multicoloured . . . 10 10

1995. National Solidarity.
1176 **467** 3d.+50c. mult 10 10

468 Doves and Anniversary Emblem

469 Pitcher from Lakhdaria

1995. 50th Anniv of U.N.O.
1177 **468** 13d. multicoloured . . . 30 15

1995. Traditional Pottery.
1178 **469** 10d. brown 20 10
1179 – 20d. brown 45 25
1180 – 21d. brown 45 25
1181 – 30d. brown 65 35
DESIGNS: 20d. Water jug (Aokas); 21d. Jar (Larbaa nath Iraten); 30d. Jar (Ouadhia).

470 Common Shelduck

1995. Water Birds. Multicoloured.
1182 3d. Type **470** 10 10
1183 5d. Common snipe 10 10

471 Doves flying over Javelin Thrower and Olympic Rings

1996. Centenary of Modern Olympic Games and Olympic Games, Atlanta.
1184 **471** 20d. multicoloured . . . 45 25

472 Fringed Bag

473 Pasteur Institute

1996. Handicrafts. Leather Bags. Multicoloured.
1185 5d. Type **472** 10 10
1186 16d. Shoulder bag with handle (vert) 35 20

1996. Centenary (1994) of Algerian Pasteur Institute.
1187 **473** 5d. multicoloured . . . 10 10

474 Arabic Script and Computer

1996. Scientific and Technical Education Day. Multicoloured.
1188 5d. Type **474** 10 10
1189 16d. Dove, fountain pen and symbols (vert) 35 20
1190 23d. Pencil, pen, dividers and satellite over Earth on pages of open book (vert) 50 25

475 Iron Ore, Djebel Quenza

1996. Minerals. Multicoloured.
1191 10d. Type **475** 20 10
1192 20d. Gold, Tirek-Amesmessa 45 25

476 "Pandoriana pandora"

1996. Butterflies. Multicoloured.
1193 5d. Type **476** 10 10
1194 10d. "Coenonympha pamphilus" 20 10
1195 20d. Painted lady 45 25
1196 23d. Marbled white 50 25

477 Globe, Drug Addict and Drugs

1996. World Anti-drugs Day.
1197 **477** 5d. multicoloured . . . 10 10

478 "Woman with Pigeons"

1996. Paintings by Ismail Samsom. Multicoloured.
1198 20d. Type **478** 40 20
1199 30d. "Interrogation" 60 30

479 Ambulance and Paramedic holding Child (Medical Aid)

480 Children, Syringe and Pens

1996. Civil Defence. Multicoloured.
1200 5d. Type **479** 10 10
1201 23d. Globe resting in cupped hands (natural disaster prevention) (vert) 45 25

1996. 50th Anniv of U.N.I.C.E.F. Multicoloured.
1202 5d. Type **480** 10 10
1203 10d. Family holding pencil, key, syringe and flower 20 10

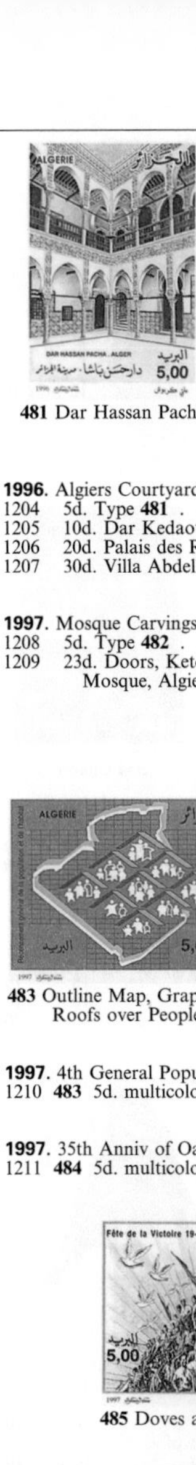

481 Dar Hassan Pacha

482 Minbar Inscription, Nedroma Mosque

1996. Algiers Courtyards. Multicoloured.

1204	5d. Type **481**	10	10
1205	10d. Dar Kedaoudj el Amia	20	10
1206	20d. Palais des Rais	40	20
1207	30d. Villa Abdellatif	60	30

1997. Mosque Carvings. Multicoloured.

1208	5d. Type **482**	10	10
1209	23d. Doors, Ketchaoua Mosque, Algiers	45	25

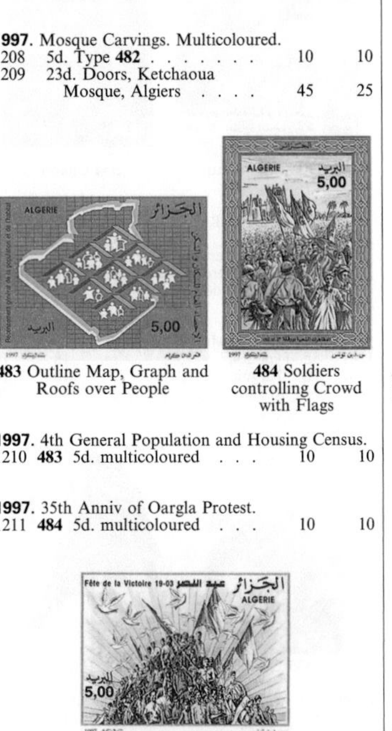

483 Outline Map, Graph and Roofs over People

484 Soldiers controlling Crowd with Flags

1997. 4th General Population and Housing Census.
1210 **483** 5d. multicoloured . . . 10 10

1997. 35th Anniv of Oargla Protest.
1211 **484** 5d. multicoloured . . . 10 10

485 Doves above Crowd with Flags

1997. 35th Anniv of Victory Day.
1212 **485** 5d. multicoloured . . . 10 10

486 "Ficaria verna"

1997. Flowers. Multicoloured.

1213	5d. Type **486**	10	10
1214	16d. Honeysuckle	35	20
1215	23d. Common poppy	45	25

487 "No Smoking" Sign on Map

488 Crowd and Map

1997. World No Smoking Day.
1216 **487** 5d. multicoloured . . . 10 10

1997. Legislative Elections.
1217 **488** 5d. multicoloured . . . 10 10

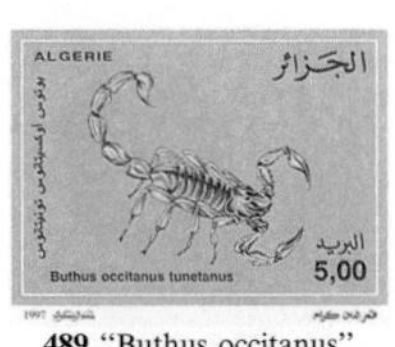

489 "Buthus occitanus"

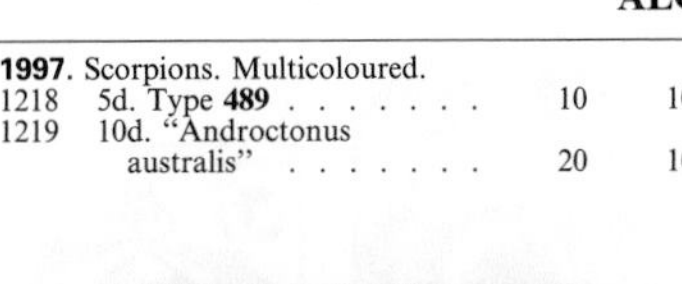

1997. Scorpions. Multicoloured.

1218	5d. Type **489**	10	10
1219	10d. "Androctonus australis"	20	10

490 Crowd with Flags

1997. 35th Anniv of Independence.
1220 **490** 5d. multicoloured . . . 10 10

491 Zakaria

1997. 20th Death Anniv of Moufdi Zakaria (poet).
1222 **491** 5d. multicoloured . . . 10 10

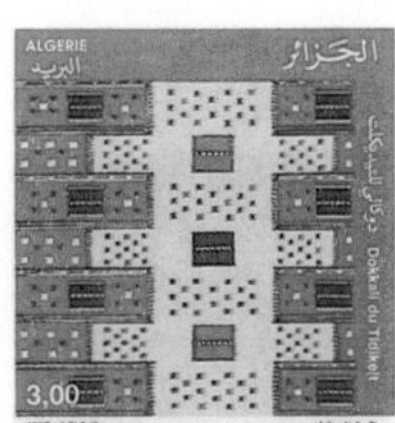

492 Dokkali Design, Tidikelt

1997. Textiles. Multicoloured.

1223	3d. Type **492**	10	10
1224	5d. Tellis design, Aures	10	10
1225	10d. Bou Taleb design, M'Sila	20	10
1226	20d. Ddil design, Ait-Hichem	40	20

493 Map, Emblem and Rainbow

1997. 25th Anniv of Pan-Arab Security Forces Organization.
1227 **493** 5d. multicoloured . . . 10 10

494 Packages and Express Mail Service Emblem

1997. World Post Day.
1228 **494** 5d. multicoloured . . . 10 10

495 Rising Sun on Map

1997. Local Elections.
1229 **495** 5d. multicoloured . . . 10 10

496 Tenes Lighthouse

1997. Lighthouses. Multicoloured.

1230	5d. Type **496**	10	10
1231	10d. Cap Caxine, Algiers (vert)	20	10

497 Mail Plane and Mail Van

1997. 1st Anniv of Aeropostale.
1232 **497** 5d. multicoloured . . . 10 10

498 Variable Scallop

1997. Sea Shells. Multicoloured.

1233	5d. Type **498**	10	10
1234	10d. "Bolinus brandaris"	20	10
1235	20d. "Hinia reticulata" (vert)	40	20

499 National Flag and Columned Facade

500 Flag, Ballot Box, Constitution and People

1997. Inauguration of Council of the Nation (upper parliamentary chamber).
1236 **499** 5d. multicoloured . . . 10 10

1997. Completion of Government Reform. Mult.

1237	5d. Type **500** (presidential election)	10	10
1238	5d. Constitution and torch (constitution referendum)	10	10
1239	5d. Ballot box and voting papers (elections to National Assembly (lower chamber of Parliament))	10	10
1240	5d. Flag, sun and rose (local elections)	10	10
1241	5d. Flag and Parliament (elections to National Council (upper chamber))	10	10

Nos. 1237/41 were issued together, se-tenant, forming a composite design.

501 Exhibition Emblem

1998. "Expo '98" World's Fair, Lisbon.
1242 **501** 5d. multicoloured . . . 10 10

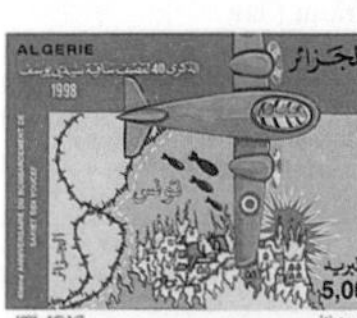

502 Aerial Bombardment

1998. 40th Anniv of Bombing of Sakiet Sidi Youcef.
1244 **502** 5d. multicoloured . . . 10 10

503 Archives Building

1998. National Archives.
1245 **503** 5d. multicoloured . . . 10 10

504 Lalla Fadhma N'Soumeur

1998. International Women's Day.
1246 **504** 5d. multicoloured . . . 10 10

505 Players and Eiffel Tower

506 View from Land

1998. World Cup Football Championship, France.
1247 **505** 24d. multicoloured . . . 50 25

1998. Algiers Kasbah. Multicoloured.

1248	5d. Type **506**	10	10
1249	10d. Street	20	10
1250	24d. View from sea (horiz)	50	25

507 Crescent and Flag

1998. Red Crescent.
1251 **507** 5d.+1d. red, green and black . . . 10 10

508 Battle Scene

1998. 150th Anniv of Insurrection of the Zaatcha.
1252 **508** 5d. multicoloured . . . 10 10

509 Parent and Child and Hand holding Rose

510 "Tourism and the Environment"

1998. International Children's Day. National Solidarity. Multicoloured.

1253	5d.+1d. Type **509**	10	10
1254	5d.+1d. Children encircling emblem (horiz)	10	10

1998. Tourism. Multicoloured.

1255	5d. Type **510**	10	10
1256	10d. Young tourists and methods of transportation (horiz)	10	10
1257	24d. Taghit (horiz)	50	25

511 Map of North Africa and Arabia

1998. Arab Post Day.
1258 **511** 5d. multicoloured . . . 10 10

512 Interpol and Algerian Police Force Emblems

1998. 75th Anniv of Interpol.
1259 **512** 5d. multicoloured . . . 10 10

513 Provisional Government and State Flag

1998. 40th Anniv of Creation of Provisional Government of Algerian Republic.
1260 **513** 5d. multicoloured . . . 10 10

514 Arrows leading from Algeria around the World

1998. National Diplomacy Day.
1261 **514** 5d. multicoloured . . . 10 10

515 Dove and Olympic Rings

1998. 35th Anniv of Algerian Olympic Committee.
1262 **515** 5d. multicoloured . . . 10 10

516 Osprey

1998. Birds. Multicoloured.
1263 5d. Type **516** 10 10
1264 10d. Audouin's gull 20 10
1265 24d. Shag (vert) 45 25
1266 30d. Common cormorant (vert) 55 30

517 Anniversary Emblem and Profiles

518 Comb

1998. 50th Anniv of Universal Declaration of Human Rights. Multicoloured.
1267 5d. Type **517** 10 10
1268 24d. Anniversary emblem, dove and people 45 25

1999. Spinning and Weaving Implements. Mult.
1269 5d. Type **518** 10 10
1270 10d. Carding (horiz) 20 10
1271 20d. Spindle 35 20
1272 24d. Loom 45 25

519 Dove, Torch, Flag and Soldiers

1999. National Chahid Day.
1273 **519** 5d. multicoloured . . . 10 10

520 Pear

1999. Fruit Trees. Multicoloured.
1274 5d. Type **520** 10 10
1275 10d. Plum 20 10
1276 24d. Orange (vert) 45 25

521 Calligraphy

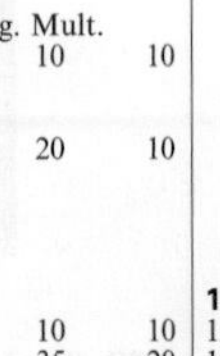

522 14th-century Ceramic Mosaic, Tlemcen

1999. Presidential Election.
1277 **521** 5d. multicoloured . . . 10 10

1999. Crafts. Multicoloured.
1278 5d. Type **522** 10 10
1279 10d. 11th-century ceramic mosaic, Kalaa des Beni Hammad 20 10
1280 20d. Cradle (horiz) 35 20
1281 24d. Table with raised rim (horiz) 45 25

523 Pictograms on Map of Africa and South African Flag

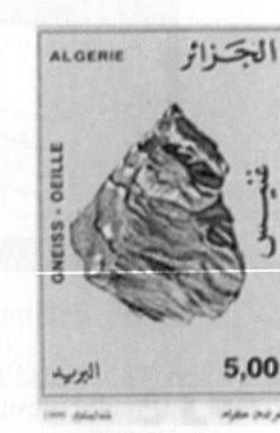

524 Gneiss

1999. 7th African Games, Johannesburg. Mult.
1282 5d. Type **523** 10 10
1283 10d. Pictograms of athletes and South African flag (horiz) 20 10

1999. Minerals. Multicoloured.
1284 5d. Type **524** 10 10
1285 20d. Granite 35 20
1286 24d. Sericite schist 45 25

525 Emblem

526 Family and Map of Africa

1999. Organization of African Unity Summit, Algiers.
1287 **525** 5d. multicoloured . . . 10 10

1999. 40th Anniv of Organization of African Unity Convention on Refugees.
1288 **526** 5d. multicoloured . . . 10 10

527 Emblem and Police Officers

1999. Police Day.
1289 **527** 5d. multicoloured . . . 10 10

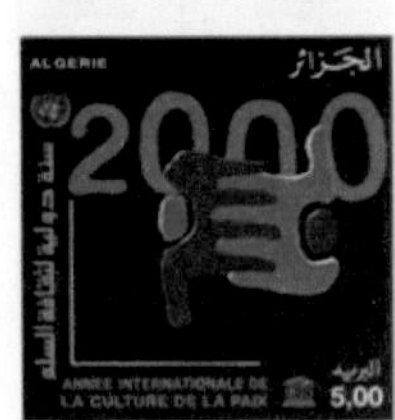

528 Linked Hands and "2000"

1999. International Year of Culture and Peace.
1290 **528** 5d. multicoloured . . . 10 10

529 Dentex Seabream

1999. Fishes. Multicoloured.
1291 5d. Type **529** 10 10
1292 10d. Striped red mullet . . . 15 10
1293 20d. Pink dentex 35 20
1294 24d. White seabream . . . 40 20

530 Rainbow

1999. Referendum.
1295 **530** 5d. multicoloured . . . 10 10

531 Emblem and Rainbow

1999. 125th Anniv of Universal Postal Union. Mult.
1296 5d. Type **531** 10 10
1297 5d. Globe, satellite and stamps 10 10

532 Woman's Face

1999. Rural Women's Day.
1298 **532** 5d. multicoloured . . . 10 10

533 Partisans and Helicopters

534 Chaoui

1999. 45th Anniv of Revolution. Multicoloured.
1299 5d. Type **533** 10 10
1300 5d. Partisans and fires . . . 10 10
Nos. 1299/300 were issued together, se-tenant, forming a composite design.

1999. Folk Dances. Multicoloured.
1301 5d. Type **534** 10 10
1302 10d. Targuie 15 10
1303 24d. M'zab 40 20

535 Doves

536 Chaffinches

2000. New Millennium. Mult. Self-adhesive.
1304 5d. Type **535** (peace) . . . 10 10
1305 5d. Plants and tree (environment) 10 10
1306 5d. Umbrella over ears of grain (food security) . . . 10 10
1307 5d. Wind farm (new energy sources) 10 10
1308 5d. Globe and ballot box (democracy) 10 10
1309 5d. Microscope (health) . . 10 10
1310 5d. Cargo ship at quayside (commerce) 10 10
1311 5d. Space satellite, dish aerial, jet plane and train (communications) 10 10
1312 5d. Astronaut and lunar buggy on Moon (space) 10 10
1313 5d. Film cave paintings, mandolin and music notes (culture) 10 10
1314 5d. Outline of dove (peace) 10 10
1315 5d. Hand above flora and fauna (environment) . . . 10 10
1316 5d. Space satellites, computer and printed circuits forming maps of Europe and Africa (communications) 10 10
1317 5d. Sun, clouds, flame and water (new energy sources) 10 10
1318 5d. Hand holding seedling (food security) 10 10
1319 5d. Staff of Aesculapius and heart (health) 10 10
1320 5d. Arrows around globe (communication) 10 10
1321 5d. Cave paintings, book, painting and violin (culture) 10 10
1322 5d. Parthenon and envelopes (democracy) 10 10
1323 5d. Space satellite, solar system, space shuttle and astronaut (space) 10 10

2000. Birds. Multicoloured.
1324 5d. Type **536** 10 10
1325 5d. Northern serin (horiz) 10 10
1326 10d. Northern bullfinch (horiz) 15 10
1327 24d. Eurasian goldfinch . . 40 20

537 Emblem

2000. "EXPO 2000" World's Fair, Hanover.
1328 **537** 5d. multicoloured . . . 10 10

538 Sydney Opera House and Sports Pictograms

2000. Olympic Games, Sydney.
1329 **538** 24d. multicoloured . . . 40 20

539 Emblem

540 Crowd, Linked Hands and White Doves

2000. Telethon 2000 (fundraising event).
1330 **539** 5d. multicoloured . . . 10 10

2000. "Concorde Civile". Multicoloured.
1331 5d. Type **540** 10 10
1332 10d. Hands releasing doves (horiz) 15 10
1333 20d. Flag, doves and hands forming heart (horiz) . . 35 20
1334 24d. Doves and clasped hands above flowers . . . 40 20

541 Building

2000. National Library.
1335 **541** 5d. multicoloured . . . 10 10

542 Hand holding Blood Droplet

2000. Blood Donation Campaign.
1336 **542** 5d. multicoloured . . . 10 10

543 Lock

2000. Touareg Cultural Heritage. Multicoloured.
1337 5d. Type **543** 10 10
1338 10d. Lock (vert) 20 10

544 Mohamed Racim (artist)

2000. Personalities. Multicoloured.
1339 10d. Type **544** 20 10
1340 10d. Mohammed Dib (writer) 20 10
1341 10d. Mustapha Kateb (theatre director) 20 10
1342 10d. Ali Maachi (musician) 20 10

545 Cock-chafer

546 Jug

2000. Insects. Multicoloured.
1343 5d. Type **545** 10 10
1344 5d. Carpet beetle 10 10
1345 10d. Drugstore beetle . . . 20 10
1346 24d. Carabus 45 25

2000. Roman Artefacts, Tipasa. Multicoloured.
1347 5d. Type **546** 10 10
1348 10d. Vase 20 10
1349 24d. Jug 45 25

547 *Limodorum abortivum*

2000. Orchids. Multicoloured.
1350 5d. Type **547** 10 10
1351 10d. *Orchis papilionacea* . . 20 10
1352 24d. *Orchis provincialis* . . . 45 25

548 Greylag Goose (*Anser anser*)

2001. Waterfowl. Multicoloured.
1353 5d. Type **548** 10 10
1354 5d. Avocet (*Recurvirostra avosetta*) (vert) 10 10
1355 10d. Eurasian bittern (*Botaurus stellaris*) (vert) 20 10
1356 24d. Western curlew (*Numenius arquata*) . . . 45 25

549 Painted Table

550 Forest, Belezma National Park, Batna

2001. Traditional Crafts. Multicoloured.
1357 5d. Type **549** 10 10
1358 10d. Decorated shelf (horiz) 20 10
1359 24d. Ornate mirror 45 25

2001. National Parks. Multicoloured.
1360 5d. Type **550** 10 10
1361 10d. Headland, Gouraya National Park, Bejaia (horiz) 20 10
1362 20d. Forest and mountains, Theneit el Had National Park, Tissemsilt (horiz) 35 20
1363 24d. El Tarf National Park 45 25

551 St. Augustine as Child (statue)

2001. St. Augustine of Hippo Conference, Algiers and Annaba. Multicoloured.
1364 5d. Type **551** 10 10
1365 24d. 4th-century Christian mosaic (43 × 31 mm) . . . 45 25

552 Obverse and Reverse of Ryal Boudjou, 1830

2001. Coins. Multicoloured.
1366 5d. Type **552** 10 10
1367 10d. Obverse and reverse of Double Boudjou, 1826 . . 20 10
1368 24d. Obverse and reverse of Ryal Drahem, 1771 . . . 45 25

553 Emblem and Scouts

2001. National Scouts' Day.
1369 **553** 5d. multicoloured . . . 10 10

554 Child throwing Stones

555 Asthma Sufferer

2001. Intifida.
1370 **554** 5d. multicoloured . . . 10 10

2001. National Asthma Day.
1371 **556** 5d. multicoloured . . . 10 10

556 Hopscotch

2001. Children's Games. Multicoloured.
1372 5d. Type **556** 10 10
1373 5d. Jacks 10 10
1374 5d. Spinning top 10 10
1375 5d. Marbles 10 10

557 Runners

2001. 50th Anniv of Mediterranean Games. Multicoloured.
1376 5d. Type **557** 10 10
1377 5d. Race winners and tile decoration 10 10

558 Emblem

559 Burning Lorry

2001. 15th World Festival of Youth and Students, Algiers.
1378 **558** 5d. multicoloured . . . 10 10

2001. Freedom Fighters' Day.
1379 **559** 5d. multicoloured . . . 10 10

560 Tree of Pencils

561 Children encircling Globe

2001. Teacher's Day.
1380 **560** 5d. multicoloured . . . 10 10

2001. United Nations Year of Dialogue among Civilisations.
1381 **561** 5d. multicoloured . . . 10 10

562 Dove and Explosion

2001. National Immigration Day. 40th Anniv of Demonstrations in Paris.
1382 **562** 5d. multicoloured . . . 10 10

563 El Mokrani

564 Bab el Oued (flood damaged town)

2001. Resistance Fighters. Multicoloured.
1383 5d. Type **563** 10 10
1384 5d. Cheikh Bouamama . . . 10 10

2001. Flood Victims Relief Fund.
1385 **564** 5d.+5d. multicoloured 15 10

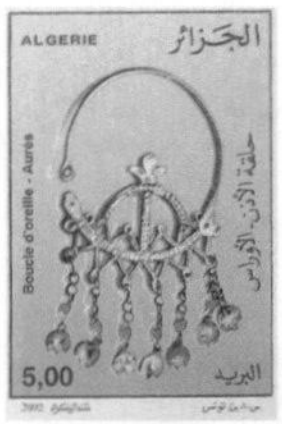

565 Earring

567 Flag, Doves and Soldiers

566 Ball, Net and Goalkeeper

2002. Silver Jewellery from Aures Region. Multicoloured.
1386 5d. Type **565** 10 10
1387 5d. Fibula 10 10
1388 24d. Pendant 35 20

2002. World Cup Football Championship, Japan and South Korea. Multicoloured.
1389 5d. Type **566** 10 10
1390 24d. Monk holding football (vert) 35 20

2002. 40th Anniv of Victory Day.
1391 **567** 5d. multicoloured . . . 10 10

568 Ksar Sidi Ouali Tamentit, Touat

2002. Fortified Castles. Multicoloured.
1392 5d. Type **568** 10 10
1393 5d. Ksar Ighzar, Gourara 10 10

569 Basket, Ball and Players

571 Book Illustration

570 Child and Table

2002. World Basketball Championship, Indianapolis, U.S.A.
1394 **569** 5d. multicoloured . . . 10 10

2002. Children's Day. Multicoloured.
1395 5d. Type **570** 10 10
1396 5d. Two girls 10 10

2002. 14th Death Anniv of Mohamed Temmam (artist and musician). Multicoloured.
1397 10d. Type **571** 10 10
1398 10d. Self-portrait 10 10

572 Anniversary Emblem

573 Calcite

2002. 40th Anniv of Independence. Multicoloured.
1399 5d. Type **572** 10 10
1400 24d. Flags and crowd . . . 35 20

2002. Minerals. Multicoloured.
1401 5d. Type **573** 10 10
1402 5d. Feldspar 10 10
1403 5d. Galena (horiz) 10 10
1404 5d. Conglomerate (pudding stone) (horiz) 10 10

574 Cherchell

2002. Lighthouses. Multicoloured.
1405 5d. Type **574** 10 10
1406 10d. Cap de Fer 10 10
1407 24d. Rachgoun island . . . 35 20

575 Postal Emblem

2002. Re-organization of Algerian Posts.
1408 **575** 5d. multicoloured . . . 10 10

576 Small Jug

2002. Pots. Multicoloured.
1409 5d. Type **576** 10 10
1410 5d. Pot for cooking cous-cous 10 10
1411 5d. Two-handled jar 10 10
1412 5d. Oil lamp 10 10

577 Dove and Rainbow

2002. International Day of Tolerance.
1413 **577** 24d. multicoloured . . . 35 20

578 *Venus verrucosa*

2002. Shells. Multicoloured.
1414 5d. Type **578** 10 10
1415 5d. *Acanthocardia aculeate* 10 10
1416 5d. *Xenophora crispa* 10 10
1417 5d. *Epitonium commune* . . 10 10

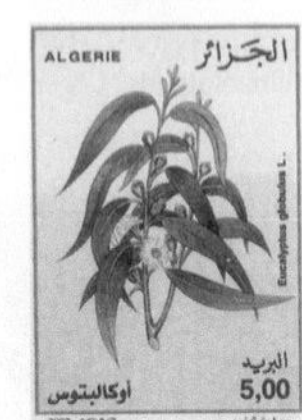
579 *Eucalyptus globules*

2002. Medicinal Plants. Multicoloured.
1418 5d. Type **579** 10 10
1419 10d. Mallow (*Malva sylvestris*) 10 10
1420 24d. Laurel (*Laurus nobilis* 35 20

POSTAGE DUE STAMPS

1926. As Postage Due stamps of France, but inscr "ALGERIE".
D 34 **D 11** 5c. blue . . . . 10 2·75
D 35 10c. brown 10 95
D 36 20c. olive . . . . . . 85 2·75
D 37 25c. red . . . . 95 3·25
D 38 30c. red 10 20
D 39 45c. green . . . . . . 2·00 3·25
D 40 50c. purple 10 20
D 41 60c. green . . . . . . 2·00 4·50
D 42 1f. red on yellow . . . 40 90
D249 1f.50 lilac . . . . . . 1·75 3·00
D 43 2f. mauve . . . . . . 35 1·10
D250 2f. blue . . . . 2·50 3·00
D 44 3f. blue . . . . 50 1·25
D251 5f. red . . . . 1·75 3·00
D252 5f. green . . . . . . 3·00 3·00

1926. As Postage Due stamps of France, but inscr "ALGERIE".
D45 **D 19** 1c. olive . . . . 20 2·75
D46 10c. violet . . . . . . 85 1·25
D47 30c. bistre 70 30
D48 60c. red . . . . 1·10 25
D49 1f. violet . . . . 7·75 2·10
D50 2f. blue . . . . 10·50 2·50

1927. Nos. D36, D39 and D37 surch.
D92 **D 11** 60 on 20c. olive . . . . 1·25 45
D93 2f. on 45c. green . . . 1·90 4·25
D94 3f. on 25c. red . . . . 1·10 3·50

1927. Nos. D45/8 surch.
D95 **D 19** 10c. on 30c. bistre . . . 3·25 6·50
D96 1f. on 1c. olive . . . . 1·50 2·50
D97 1f. on 60c. red . . . . 18·00 15
D98 2f. on 10c. violet . . . 7·25 23·00

1942. As 1926 issue, but without "RF".
D181 **D 11** 30c. red . . . . 1·90 2·75
D182 2f. mauve . . . . . . 2·25 2·75

1944. No. 208 surch **TAXE P. C. V. DOUANE 20Fr.**
D230 **38** 20f. on 50f. red . . . . 2·00 3·00

1944. Surch **T 0.50**.
D231 **4** 50c. on 20c. green . . . . 1·10 2·75

1947. Postage Due Stamps of France optd **ALGERIE**.
D283 10c. brown (No. D985) . . 10 3·00
D284 30c. purple (No. D986) . . 10 2·50

D 53

1947.
D285 **D 53** 20c. red . . . . 20 3·00
D286 60c. blue . . . . . . 45 2·75
D287 1f. brown . . . . . . 10 2·75
D288 1f.50 olive . . . . . . 1·00 3·50
D289 2f. red . . . . 20 2·25
D290 3f. violet . . . . . . 40 2·50
D291 5f. blue . . . . 35 1·00
D292 6f. black . . . . . . 40 1·75
D293 10f. purple . . . . . 1·10 80
D294 15f. myrtle . . . . . 2·00 3·25
D295 20f. green . . . . . . 1·40 95
D296 30f. red . . . . 3·00 3·25
D297 50f. black . . . . . . 3·75 4·00
D298 100f. blue . . . . . . 14·50 10·50

INDEPENDENT STATE

1962. Postage Due stamps of France optd **EA** and with bar obliterating "REPUBLIQUE FRANCAISE".
D391 **D 457** 5c. mauve . . . . . 11·00 11·00
D392 10c. red . . . . . . 11·00 11·00
D393 20c. brown . . . . . 11·00 11·00
D394 50c. green . . . . . 22·00 22·00
D395 1f. green . . . . . . 45·00 45·00

The above also exist with larger overprint applied with handstamps.

D 107 Scales of Justice

D 200 Ears of Corn

1963.
D411 **D 107** 5c. red and olive . . 10 10
D412 10c. olive and red . . 10 10
D413 20c. blue and black 35 20
D414 50c. brown and green 80 55
D415 1f. violet and orange 1·40 1·25

1968. No. D415 surch.
D508 **D 107** 60c. on 1f. violet and orange 55 40

1972.
D603 **D 200** 10c. brown 10 10
D604 20c. brown 10 10
D605 40c. orange 20 10
D606 50c. blue 20 10
D607 80c. brown 45 20
D608 1d. green 55 35
D609 2d. blue . . . . . . 1·10 65
D610 3d. violet 15 10
D611 4d. purple 20 10

ALLENSTEIN Pt. 7

A district of E. Prussia retained by Germany as the result of a plebiscite in 1920. Stamps issued during the plebiscite period.

100 pfennig = 1 mark.

1920. Stamps of Germany inscr "DEUTSCHES REICH" optd **PLEBISCITE OLSZTYN ALLENSTEIN**.
1 **17** 5pf. green 15 15
2 10pf. red 15 15
3 **24** 15pf. violet 15 15
4 15pf. purple . . . . 7·00 7·75
5 **17** 20pf. blue 15 15
6 30pf. black & orge on buff 30 35
7 40pf. black and red . . . 20 20
8 50pf. black & pur on buff 20 20
9 75pf. black and green . . . 65 60
10 **18** 1m. red . . . . 90 1·10
11 1m.25 green . . . . 95 1·00
12 1m.50 brown . . . . . . 1·25 3·00
13b **20** 2m.50 red . . . . 3·25 3·75
14 **21** 3m. black . . . . 2·00 2·40

1920. Stamps of Germany inscr "DEUTSCHES REICH" optd **TRAITE DE VERSAILLES** etc. in oval.
15 **17** 5pf. green 35 20
16 10pf. red 35 30
17 **24** 15pf. violet 20 35
18 15pf. purple . . . . 28·00 23·00
19 **17** 20pf. blue 35 35
20 30pf. black & orge on buff 40 20
21 40pf. black and red . . . 40 20
22 50pf. black & pur on buff 25 25
23 75pf. black and green . . . 25 25
24 **18** 1m. red . . . . 1·10 35
25 1m.25 green . . . . 1·10 50
26 1m.50 brown . . . . . . 1·10 50
27 **20** 2m.50 red . . . . 1·40 1·90
28 **21** 3m. black . . . . 1·40 2·50

ALSACE AND LORRAINE Pt. 7

Stamps used in parts of France occupied by the German army in the war of 1870–71, and afterwards temporarily in the annexed provinces of Alsace and Lorraine.

100 pfennig = 1 mark.

1

1870.
1 **1** 1c. green . . . . 42·00 85·00
3 2c. brown . . . . 65·00 £100
5 4c. grey . . . . 65·00 65·00
8 5c. green . . . . 40·00 6·75
10 10c. brown . . . . 45·00 10·00
14 20c. blue . . . . 55·00 8·00
16 25c. brown . . . . 90·00 65·00

For 1940 issues see separate lists for Alsace and Lorraine under German Occupations.

ALWAR Pt. 1

A state of Rajputana, N. India. Now uses Indian stamps.

12 pies = 1 anna; 16 annas = 1 rupee

1 Native Dagger

1877. Roul or perf.
1c **1** ¼a. blue . . . . 3·50 1·00
5 ¼a. green . . . . 3·75 2·50
2c 1a. brown . . . . 2·25 1·25

ANDORRA Pt. 6; Pt. 9

An independent state in the Pyrenees under the joint suzerainty of France and Spain.

FRENCH POST OFFICES

1931. 100 centimes = 1 franc.
2002. 100 cents = 1 euro.

1931. Stamps of France optd **ANDORRE**.
F 1 **11** ½c. on 1c. grey . . . . . 30 2·40
F 2 1c. grey 35 90
F 3 2c. red . . . . 40 2·75
F 4 3c. orange . . . . 45 3·00
F 5 5c. green . . . . 1·50 3·25
F 6 10c. lilac . . . . 2·75 4·50
F 7 **18** 15c. brown . . . . 5·50 6·50
F 8 20c. mauve . . . . 9·00 10·00
F 9 25c. brown . . . . 8·50 11·00
F10 30c. green . . . . 8·00 11·00
F11 40c. blue . . . . 9·50 13·50
F12 **15** 45c. violet . . . . 15·00 20·00
F13 50c. red . . . . 11·00 12·00
F14 65c. green . . . . 23·00 35·00
F15 75c. mauve . . . . 22·00 35·00
F16 **18** 90c. red . . . . 26·00 40·00
F17 **15** 1f. blue . . . . 30·00 38·00
F18 **18** 1f.50 blue . . . . 34·00 44·00
F19 **13** 2f. red and green . . . . 26·00 38·00
F20 3f. mauve and red . . . . 70·00 £110
F21 5f. blue and buff £100 £150
F22 10f. green and red . . . £200 £300
F23 20f. mauve and green . . . £250 £350

F 3 Our Lady's Chapel, Meritxell

F 5 St. Michael's Church, Engolasters

1932.
F24 **F 3** 1c. slate . . . . 20 2·00
F25 2c. violet . . . . 65 1·80
F26 3c. brown . . . . 60 1·90
F27 5c. green . . . . 40 2·20
F28 **A** 10c. lilac . . . . 1·20 2·50
F29 **F 3** 15c. red . . . . 1·90 2·50
F30 **A** 20c. mauve . . . . 15·00 13·00
F31 **F 5** 25c. brown . . . . 4·50 6·50
F32 **A** 25c. brown . . . . 13·50 23·00
F33 30c. green . . . . 2·75 3·75
F34 40c. blue . . . . 7·75 11·00
F35 40c. brown . . . . 1·30 3·00
F36 45c. red . . . . 11·00 14·00
F37 45c. green . . . . 5·75 9·25

F38 F 5 50c. mauve 8·75 12·50
F39 A 50c. violet 3·00 9·00
F40 50c. green 1·90 4·50
F41 55c. violet 22·00 28·00
F42 60c. brown 1·40 3·00
F43 F 5 65c. green 38·00 60·00
F44 A 65c. blue 18·00 18·00
F45 70c. red 1·60 4·00
F46 F 5 75c. violet 8·00 10·00
F47 A 75c. blue 3·00 9·50
F48 80c. green 18·00 43·00
F49 B 80c. green 1·20 3·75
F50 90c. red 7·25 6·75
F51 90c. green 6·75 7·50
F52 1f. green 21·00 18·00
F53 1f. red 19·00 28·00
F54 1f. blue 90 2·20
F55 1f. 20 violet 1·10 2·20
F56 F 3 1f. 25 mauve 46·00 50·00
F57 1f.25 red 5·25 7·00
F58 B 1f.30 brown 1·30 2·30
F59 C 1f.50 blue 20·00 20·00
F60 B 1f.50 red 1·00 2·30
F61 1f.75 violet 90·00 £120
F62 1f.75 blue 41·00 55·00
F63 2f. mauve 8·50 12·00
F64 F 3 2f. red 1·40 3·75
F65 2f. green 1·00 2·20
F66 2f.15 violet 55·00 70·00
F67 2f.25 blue 10·50 18·00
F68 2f.40 red 1·30 2·20
F69 2f.50 black 13·00 22·00
F70 2f.50 blue 2·00 6·00
F71 B 3f. brown 12·00 16·00
F72 F 3 3f. brown 1·50 2·30
F73 4f. blue 1·30 2·10
F74 4f.50 violet 1·30 3·50
F75 C 5f. brown 1·40 2·20
F76 10f. violet 1·60 2·50
F78 15f. blue 1·80 3·00
F79 20f. red 1·60 2·50
F81 A 50f. blue 2·75 4·25
DESIGNS—HORIZ: A, St. Anthony's Bridge; C, Andorra la Vella. VERT: B, Valley of Sant Julia.

1935. No. F38 surch **20c.**
F82 F 5 20c. on 50c. purple 11·00 22·00

F 9 | F 13 Andorra la Vella

F 10 | F 14 Councillor Jaume Bonell

1936.
F83 F 9 1c. black 25 1·50
F84 2c. blue 25 1·40
F85 3c. brown 35 1·50
F86 5c. red 15 1·40
F87 10c. blue 15 1·50
F88 15c. mauve 2·20 3·00
F89 20c. green 25 1·50
F90 30c. red 35 2·20
F91 30c. black 1·20 2·20
F92 35c. green 43·00 70·00
F93 40c. brown 85 2·20
F94 50c. green 95 2·20
F95 60c. blue 1·50 2·20
F96 70c. violet 1·30 2·20

1944.
F 97 F 10 10c. violet 10 1·60
F 98 30c. red 20 1·50
F 99 40c. blue 40 1·60
F100 50c. red 15 1·80
F101 60c. black 30 1·60
F102 70c. mauve 20 1·80
F103 80c. green 10 1·80
F104 1f. blue 60 2·20
F105 D 1f. purple 30 2·00
F106 1f.20 blue 15 3·75
F107 1f.50 red 55 1·80
F108 2f. green 55 1·40
F109 E 2f.40 red 20 1·60
F110 2f.50 red 2·75 3·75
F111 3f. brown 50 1·80
F112 D 3f. red 2·75 4·25
F113 E 4f. blue 30 2·00
F114 4f. green 55 2·50
F115 D 4f. brown 1·40 4·50
F116 E 4f.50 brown 55 3·25
F117 F 13 4f.50 blue 3·75 7·75
F118 5f. blue 40 3·75
F119 5f. green 1·00 2·30
F120 E 5f. green 1·90 4·75
F121 5f. violet 3·75 5·50
F122 F 13 6f. red 35 1·50
F123 6f. purple 30 1·90
F124 E 6f. green 2·30 5·00
F125 F 13 8f. blue 1·20 3·25
F126 E 8f. brown 60 2·30
F127 F 13 10f. green 40 1·80
F128 10f. blue 90 1·20
F129 12f. red 65 4·75
F130 12f. green 85 2·75
F131 F 14 15f. purple 35 2·20
F132 F 13 15f. red 50 2·20
F133 15f. brown 4·25 2·50
F134 F 14 18f. blue 1·80 4·25
F135 F 13 18f. red 8·75 19·00
F136 F 14 20f. blue 90 2·20
F137 20f. violet 2·40 4·00
F138 25f. red 2·10 4·25
F139 25f. blue 1·20 3·50
F140 30f. blue 14·00 18·00
F141 40f. green 1·80 4·00
F142 50f. brown 95 2·30
DESIGNS—HORIZ: D, Church of St. John of Caselles; E, House of the Valleys.

F 15 Chamois and Pyrenees | F 16 Les Escaldes

1950. Air.
F143 F 15 100f. blue 50·00 60·00

1955.
F144 F 16 1f. blue (postage) 15 1·30
F145 2f. green 40 1·30
F146 3f. red 50 1·10
F147 5f. brown 50 1·10
F148 – 6f. green 1·50 1·40
F149 – 8f. red 1·60 1·80
F150 – 10f. violet 2·75 1·80
F151 – 12f. blue 1·90 1·30
F152 – 15f. red 2·00 1·50
F153 – 18f. blue 1·60 2·40
F154 – 20f. violet 2·20 1·60
F155 – 25f. brown 2·75 2·75
F156 – 30f. blue 20·00 26·00
F157 – 35f. blue 9·50 10·50
F158 – 40f. green 25·00 44·00
F159 – 50f. red 3·50 3·00
F160 – 65f. violet 5·50 14·50
F161 – 70f. brown 4·50 12·00
F162 – 75f. blue 34·00 48·00
F163 – 100f. green (air) 8·50 8·50
F164 – 200f. red 15·00 14·50
F165 – 500f. blue 85·00 75·00
DESIGNS—VERT: 15f. to 25f. Gothic cross, Andorra la Vella; 100f. to 500f. East Valira River. HORIZ: 6f. to 12f. Santa Coloma Church; 30f. to 75f. Les Bons village.

New currency. 100 (old) francs = 1 (new) franc.

F 21 | F 22 Gothic Cross, Meritxell

1961.
F166 F 21 1c. grey, blue and slate (postage) 10 85
F167 2c. lt orge, blk & orge 50 85
F168 5c. lt grn, blk & grn 35 85
F169 10c. pink, blk & red 40 30
F170a 12c. yell, pur & grn 3·00 1·10
F171 15c. lt bl, blk & bl 60 85
F172 18c. pink, blk & mve 1·20 1·70
F173 20c. lt yell, brn & yell 70 20
F174 F 22 25c. blue, vio & grn 85 65
F175 30c. pur, red & grn 70 55
F175a 40c. green and brown 1·10 1·10
F176 45c. blue, ind & grn 15·00 24·00
F176a 45c. brown, bl & vio 1·10 1·80
F177 50c. multicoloured 1·70 1·50
F177a 60c. brown & chestnut 1·30 1·30
F178 65c. olive, bl & brn 18·00 34·00
F179 85c. multicoloured 18·00 25·00
F179a 90c. green, bl & brn 1·10 1·80
F180 1f. blue, brn & turq 1·80 1·60
F181 – 2f. green, red and purple (air) 1·80 1·40
F182 – 3f. purple, bl & grn 2·00 1·70
F183 – 5f. orange, pur & red 2·75 2·00
F184 – 10f. green and blue 5·50 3·75
DESIGNS—As Type F 22: 60c. to 1f. Engolasters Lake; 2f. to 10f. Incles Valley.

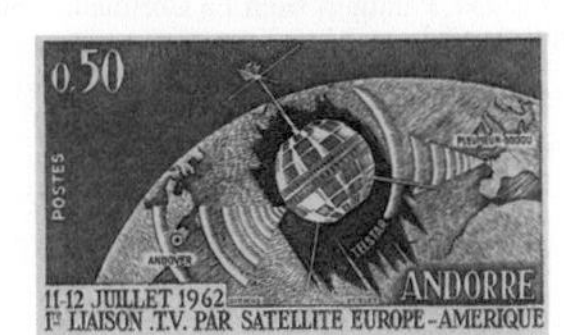

F 23 "Telstar" Satellite and part of Globe

1962. 1st Trans-Atlantic TV Satellite Link.
F185 F 23 50c. violet and blue 90 2·00

F 24 "La Sardane" (dance)

1963. Andorran History (1st issue).
F186 F 24 20c. purple, mve & grn 3·75 4·75
F187 – 50c. red and green 5·50 8·50
F188 – 1f. green, blue & brn 8·25 13·50
DESIGNS—LARGER (48½ × 27 mm): 50c. Charlemagne crossing Andorra. (48 × 27 mm): 1f. Foundation of Andorra by Louis le Debonnaire.
See also Nos. F190/1.

F 25 Santa Coloma Church and Grand Palais, Paris

1964. "PHILATEC 1964" International Stamp Exhibition, Paris.
F189 F 25 25c. green, pur & brn 95 2·20

1964. Andorran History (2nd issue). As Nos. F187/8, inscribed "1964".
F190 60c. green, chestnut and brown 9·50 23·00
F191 1f. blue, sepia and brown 11·00 23·00
DESIGNS (48½ × 27 mm): 60c. "Napoleon re-establishes the Andorran Statute, 1806"; 1f. "Confirmation of the Co-government, 1288".

F 26 Virgin of Santa Coloma | F 27 "Syncom", Morse Key and Pleumeur-Bodou centre

1964. Red Cross Fund.
F192 F 26 25c. + 10c. red, green and blue 12·50 24·00

1965. Centenary of I.T.U.
F193 F 27 60c. violet, blue and red 3·75 7·00

F 28 Andorra House, Paris | F 29 Chair-lift

1965. Opening of Andorra House, Paris.
F194 F 28 25c. brown, olive & bl 90 2·00

1966. Winter Sports.
F195 F 29 25c. green, purple & bl 90 1·80
F196 – 40c. brown, blue & red 1·30 2·75
DESIGN—HORIZ: 40c. Ski-lift.

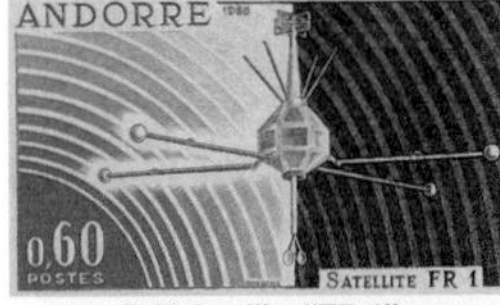

F 30 Satellite "FR 1"

1966. Launching of Satellite "FR 1".
F197 F 30 60c. blue, emer & grn 1·20 3·25

F 31 Europa "Ship" | F 32 Cogwheels

1966. Europa.
F198 F 31 60c. brown 3·25 5·50

1967. Europa.
F199 F 32 30c. indigo and blue 3·75 3·75
F200 60c. red and purple 6·75 6·00

F 33 "Folk Dancers" (statue) | F 34 Telephone and Dial

1967. Centenary (1966) of New Reform.
F201 F 33 30c. green, olive & slate 1·00 2·30

1967. Inaug of Automatic Telephone Service.
F202 F 34 60c. black, violet & red 1·30 2·75

F 35 Andorran Family

1967. Institution of Social Security.
F203 F 35 2f.30 brown & purple 5·50 13·00

F 36 "The Temptation" | F 37 Downhill Skiing

1967. 16th-century Frescoes in House of the Valleys (1st series).
F204 F 36 25c. red and black 75 1·70
F205 – 30c. purple and violet 65 1·90
F206 – 60c. blue and indigo 90 2·75
FRESCOES: 30c. "The Kiss of Judas"; 60c. "The Descent from the Cross".
See also Nos. F210/12.

1968. Winter Olympic Games, Grenoble.
F207 F 37 40c. purple, orge & red 80 2·40

F 38 Europa "Key"

1968. Europa.
F208 F 38 30c. blue and slate 7·75 6·25
F209 60c. violet & brown 12·00 10·00

1968. 16th-century Frescoes in House of the Valleys (2nd series). Designs as Type F **36**.
F210 25c. deep green and green 60 1·90
F211 30c. purple and brown 80 2·10
F212 60c. brown and red 1·50 3·25
FRESCOES: 25c. "The Beating of Christ"; 30c. "Christ Helped by the Cyrenians"; 60c. "The Death of Christ".

F 39 High Jumping

1968. Olympic Games, Mexico.
F213 F 39 40c. brown and blue 1·50 2·75

F 40 Colonnade | F 41 Canoeing

1969. Europa.
F214 F **40** 40c. grey, blue and red 8·25 6·25
F215 70c. red, green and blue . . . . 13·00 13·00

1969. World Kayak-Canoeing Championships, Bourg-St. Maurice.
F216 F **41** 70c. dp blue, bl & grn 1·70 4·00

F **41a** "Diamond Crystal" in Rain Drop

F **42** "The Apocalypse"

1969. European Water Charter.
F217 F **41a** 70c. black, blue and ultramarine . . . . 3·75 7·25

1969. Altar-screen, Church of St. John of Caselles (1st series). "The Revelation of St. John".
F218 F **42** 30c. red, violet & brn 85 1·80
F219 – 40c. bistre, brn & grey 1·10 2·20
F220 – 70c. purple, lake & red 1·40 2·75
DESIGNS: 40c. Angel "clothed with cloud with face as the sun, and feet as pillars of fire" (Rev. 10); 70c. Christ with sword and stars, and seven candlesticks.
See also Nos. F225/7, F233/5 and F240/2.

F **43** Handball Player

F **44** "Flaming Sun"

1970. 7th World Handball Championships, France.
F221 F **43** 80c. blue, brn & dp bl 1·90 3·75

1970. Europa.
F222 F **44** 40c. orange . . . . . 7·50 4·25
F223 80c. violet . . . . . . 12·50 10·00

F **45** Putting the Shot

F **46** Ice Skaters

1970. 1st European Junior Athletic Championships, Paris.
F224 F **45** 80c. purple and blue 2·20 4·00

1970. Altar-screen, Church of St. John of Caselles (2nd series). Designs as Type F **42**.
F225 30c. violet, brown and red 1·20 2·00
F226 40c. green and violet . . . 80 2·20
F227 80c. red, blue and green . . 2·10 3·00
DESIGNS: 30c. Angel with keys and padlock; 40c. Angel with pillar; 80c. St. John being boiled in cauldron of oil.

1971. World Ice Skating Championships, Lyon.
F228 F **46** 80c. violet, pur & red 2·40 4·00

F **47** Western Capercaillie

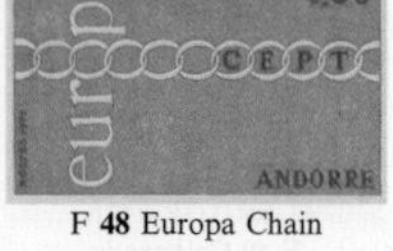

F **48** Europa Chain

1971. Nature Protection.
F229 F **47** 80c. multicoloured . . 3·50 4·00
F230 – 80c. brown, green & bl 3·00 3·75
DESIGN: No. F230, Brown bear.

1971. Europa.
F231 F **48** 50c. red . . . . 10·00 7·25
F232 80c. green . . . . . . 11·00 11·00

1971. Altar-screen, Church of St. John of Caselles (3rd series). As Type F **42**.
F233 30c. green, brown and myrtle . . . . 1·20 2·20
F234 50c. brown, orange and lake 1·50 2·50
F235 90c. blue, purple and brown 2·10 3·75
DESIGNS: 30c. St. John in temple at Ephesus; 50c. St. John with cup of poison; 90c. St. John disputing with pagan philosophers.

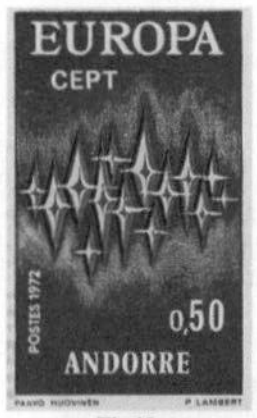

F **49** "Communications"

F **50** Golden Eagle

1972. Europa.
F236 F **49** 50c. multicoloured . . 9·75 6·50
F237 90c. multicoloured . . 15·00 11·50

1972. Nature Protection.
F238 F **50** 60c. olive, green & pur 3·75 4·75

F **51** Rifle-shooting

F **52** General De Gaulle

1972. Olympic Games, Munich.
F239 F **51** 1f. purple . . . . . . 2·75 2·75

1972. Altar-screen, Church of St. John of Caselles (4th series). As Type F **42**.
F240 30c. purple, grey and green 95 2·20
F241 50c. grey and blue . . . . 1·20 2·75
F242 90c. green and blue . . . . 1·70 3·25
DESIGNS: 30c. St. John in discussion with bishop; 50c. St. John healing a cripple; 90c. Angel with spear.

1972. 5th Anniv of Gen. De Gaulle's Visit to Andorra.
F243 F **52** 50c. blue . . . . . . 2·00 8·50
F244 – 90c. red . . . . 2·20 4·75
DESIGN: 90c. Gen. De Gaulle in Andorra la Vella, 1967.
See also Nos. F434/5.

F **53** Europa "Posthorn"

1973. Europa.
F245 F **53** 50c. multicoloured . . 9·00 7·50
F246 90c. multicoloured . . 15·00 12·50

F **54** "Virgin of Canolich" (wood carving)

F **55** Lily

1973. Andorran Art.
F247 F **54** 1f. lilac, blue and drab 2·50 3·75

1973. Pyrenean Flowers (1st series). Multicoloured.
F248 30c. Type F **55** . . . . . . 85 1·40
F249 50c. Columbine . . . . . . 1·40 2·50
F250 90c. Wild pinks . . . . . . 1·00 2·75
See also Nos. F253/5 and F264/6.

F **56** Blue Tit ("Mesange Bleue")

F **57** "The Virgin of Pal"

1973. Nature Protection. Birds. Multicoloured.
F251 90c. Type F **56** . . . . . . 2·50 3·25
F252 1f. Lesser spotted woodpecker ("Pic Epeichette") . . . . . . 2·50 2·20
See also Nos. F259/60.

1974. Pyrenean Wild Flowers (2nd series). As Type F **55**. Multicoloured.
F253 45c. Iris . . . . 45 1·50
F254 65c. Tobacco Plant . . . . 50 1·90
F255 90c. Narcissus . . . . . . 1·00 4·75

1974. Europa. Church Sculptures. Mult.
F256 50c. Type F **57** . . . . . . 11·00 9·00
F257 90c. "The Virgin of Santa Coloma" . . . . 17·00 8·00

F **58** Arms of Andorra

F **59** Letters crossing Globe

1974. Meeting of Co-Princes, Cahors.
F258 F **58** 1f. blue, violet & orge 1·00 2·40

1974. Nature Protection. Birds. As Type F **56**. Multicoloured.
F259 60c. Citril finch ("Venturon Montagnard") . . . . . 3·00 5·25
F260 80c. Northern bullfinch ("Boureuil") . . . . . . 2·75 3·75

1974. Centenary of U.P.U.
F261 F **59** 1f.20 red, grey & brn 1·70 3·25

F **60** "Calvary"

1975. Europa. Paintings from La Cortinada Church. Multicoloured.
F262 80c. Type F **60** . . . . . . 6·25 9·75
F263 1f.20 "Coronation of St. Martin" (horiz) . . . 9·50 14·00

1975. Pyrenean Flowers (3rd series). As Type F **55**.
F264 60c. multicoloured . . . . 50 1·40
F265 80c. multicoloured . . . . 1·40 3·25
F266 1f.20 yellow, red and green 70 2·10
DESIGNS: 60c. Gentian; 80c. Anemone; 1f.20, Colchicum.

F **61** "Arphila" Motif

1975. "Arphila 75" International Stamp Exhibition, Paris.
F267 F **61** 2f. red, green and blue 1·80 3·50

F **62** Pres. Pompidou (Co-prince of Andorra)

F **63** "La Pubilla" and Emblem

1976. President Pompidou of France Commem.
F268 F **62** 80c. black and violet 90 2·20

1976. International Women's Year.
F269 F **63** 1f.20 black, pur & bl 1·80 2·75

F **64** Skier

F **65** Telephone and Satellite

1976. Winter Olympic Games, Innsbruck.
F270 F **64** 1f.20 black, green & bl 1·10 2·50

1976. Telephone Centenary.
F271 F **65** 1f. green, black and red 1·40 2·50

F **66** Catalan Forge

1976. Europa.
F272 F **66** 80c. brown, blue & grn 2·40 2·75
F273 – 1f.20 red, green & blk 3·00 4·00
DESIGN: 1f.20, Andorran folk-weaving.

F **67** Thomas Jefferson

F **68** Ball-trap (clay pigeon) Shooting

1976. Bicentenary of American Revolution.
F274 F **67** 1f.20 dp grn, brn & grn 1·00 2·75

1976. Olympic Games, Montreal.
F275 F **68** 2f. brown, violet & grn 1·50 3·25

F **69** New Chapel

1976. New Chapel of Our Lady, Meritxell.
F276 F **69** 1f. green, purple & brn 90 2·30

F **70** Apollo

F **71** Stoat

1976. Nature Protection. Butterflies. Mult.
F277 80c. Type F **70** . . . . . . 2·50 4·75
F278 1f.40 Camberwell beauty . . 2·20 4·25

1977. Nature Protection.
F279 F **71** 1f. grey, black & blue 1·50 2·50

F 72 Church of St. John of Caselles
F 73 Book and Flowers

1977. Europa.
F280 F **72** 1f. purple, green & bl 5·75 2·75
F281 – 1f.40 indigo, grn & bl 9·00 3·50
DESIGN: 1f.40, St. Vicens Chateau.

1977. 1st Anniv of Institute of Andorran Studies.
F282 F **73** 80c. brown, green & bl 75 2·10

F **74** St. Roma

1977. Reredos, St. Roma's Chapel, Les Bons.
F283 F **74** 2f. multicoloured . . . 2·10 2·50

F **75** General Council Assembly Hall
F **76** Eurasian Red Squirrel

1977. Andorran Institutions.
F284 F **75** 1f.10 red, blue & brn 1·60 2·40
F285 – 2f. brown and red . . 1·60 2·40
DESIGN—VERT. 2f. Don Guillem d'Areny Plandolit.

1978. Nature Protection.
F286 F **76** 1f. brown, grn & olive 1·10 1·90

F **77** Escalls Bridge
F **78** Church at Pal

1978. 700th Anniv of Parity Treaties (1st issue).
F287 F **77** 80c. green, brown & bl 65 1·80
See also No. F292.

1978. Europa.
F288 F **78** 1f. brown, green & red 5·50 2·75
F289 – 1f.40 brown, bl & red 8·75 3·50
DESIGN: 1f.40, Charlemagne's House.

F **79** "Virgin of Sispony"

1978. Andorran Art.
F290 F **79** 2f. multicoloured . . . 1·60 2·30

F **80** Tribunal Meeting

1978. Tribunal of Visura.
F291 F **80** 1f.20 multicoloured . . 1·40 1·90

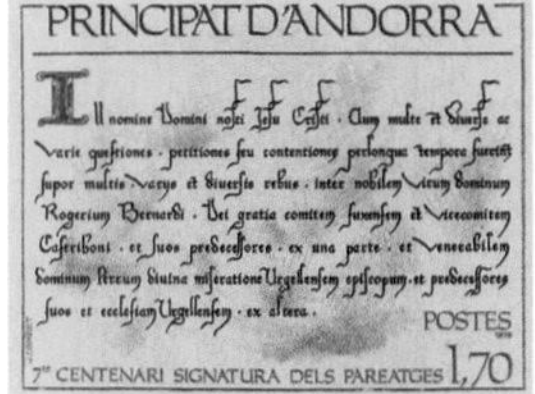
F **81** Treaty Text

1978. 700th Anniv of Parity Treaties (2nd issue).
F292 F **81** 1f.50 brown, grn & red 95 2·20

F **82** Chamois
F **83** Rock Ptarmigans ("Perdiu Blanca")

1978. Nature Protection.
F293 F **82** 1f. brown, lt brn & bl 70 1·50

1979. Nature Protection.
F294 F **83** 1f.20 multicoloured . . 1·20 3·00

F **84** Early 20th Century Postman and Church of St. John of Caselles
F **85** Wall painting, Church of St. Cerni, Nagol

1979. Europa.
F295 F **84** 1f.20 black, brn & grn 1·20 2·40
F296 – 1f.70 brown, grn & mve . . . . 1·60 3·00
DESIGN: 1f.70, Old French Post Office, Andorra.

1979. Pre-Romanesque Art.
F297 F **85** 2f. green, pink and brown . . . . 1·40 2·40
See also No. F309.

F **86** Boy with Sheep
F **87** Co-princes Monument (Luigiteruggi)

1979. International Year of the Child.
F298 F **86** 1f.70 multicoloured . . 80 1·80

1979. Co-princes Monument.
F299 F **87** 2f. dp green, grn & red 1·40 2·20

F **88** Judo
F **89** Cal Pal, La Cortinada

1979. World Judo Championships, Paris.
F300 F **88** 1f.30 black, dp bl & bl 90 1·90

1980.
F301 F **89** 1f.10 brown, bl & grn 55 1·80

F **90** Cross-country Skiing
F **91** Charlemagne

1980. Winter Olympics, Lake Placid.
F302 F **90** 1f.80 ultram, bl & red 1·20 2·50

1980. Europa.
F303 F **91** 1f.30 brn, chest & red 50 1·80
F304 – 1f.80 green and brown 75 2·00
DESIGN: 1f.80, Napoleon I.

F **93** Dog's-tooth Violet
F **94** Cyclists

1980. Nature Protection. Multicoloured.
F306 1f.10 Type F **93** . . . . . 40 1·70
F305 1f.30 Pyrenean lily . . . . 45 1·70

1980. World Cycling Championships.
F307 F **94** 1f.20 violet, mve & brn 65 1·70

F **95** House of the Valleys

1980. 400th Anniv of Restoration of House of the Valleys (meeting place of Andorran General Council).
F308 F **95** 1f.40 brown, vio & grn 75 1·80

1980. Pre-Romanesque Art. As Type F **85**. Mult.
F309 2f. Angel (wall painting, Church of St. Cerni, Nagol) (horiz) . . . . . 80 2·30

F **97** Shepherds' Huts, Mereig

1981. Architecture.
F310 F **97** 1f.40 brown and blue 85 1·40

F **98** Bear Dance (Emcamp Carnival)
F **99** Bonelli's Warbler

1981. Europa.
F311 F **98** 1f.40 black, green & bl 70 1·40
F312 – 2f. black, blue and red 70 1·90
DESIGN: 2f. El Contrapas (dance).

1981. Nature Protection. Birds. Multicoloured.
F313 1f.20 Type F **99** . . . . . 65 1·80
F314 1f.40 Wallcreeper . . . . . 65 1·80

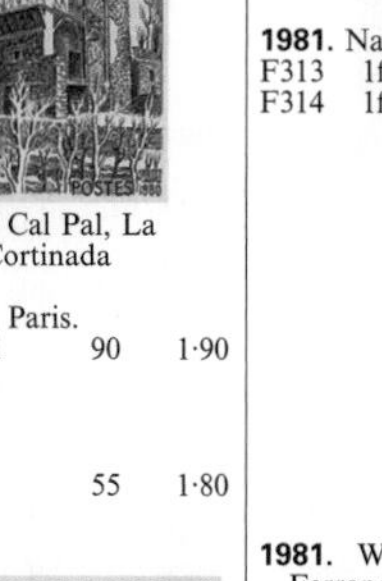

F **100** Fencing

1981. World Fencing Championships, Clermont-Ferrand.
F315 F **100** 2f. blue and black . . 65 1·90

F **101** Chasuble of St. Martin (miniature)

1981. Art.
F316 F **101** 3f. multicoloured . . 1·10 2·30

F **102** Fountain, Sant Julia de Loria
F **103** Symbolic Disabled

1981. International Decade of Drinking Water.
F317 F **102** 1f.60 blue and brown 50 1·80

1981. International Year of Disabled Persons.
F318 F **103** 2f.30 blue, red & grn 60 1·90

F **104** Scroll and Badge (creation of Andorran Executive Council, 1981)
F **105** Footballer running to right

1982. Europa.
F319 F **104** 1f.60 blue, brn & orge 70 1·40
F320 – 2f.30 blue, blk & orge 85 1·70
DESIGN: 2f.30, Hat and cloak (creation of Land Council, 1419).

1982. World Cup Football Championship, Spain.
F321 F **105** 1f.60 brown and red 90 3·25
F322 – 2f.60 brown and red 95 2·20
DESIGN: 2f.60, Footballer running to left.

F **106** 1f.25 Stamp, 1933

1982. 1st Official Exhibition of Andorran Postage Stamps.
MSF323 F **106** 5f. black and red 1·80 2·50

F **107** Wall Painting, La Cortinada Church

1982. Romanesque Art.
F324 F **107** 3f. multicoloured . . 90 2·30

F **108** Wild Cat F **109** Dr. Robert Koch

1982. Nature Protection.
F325 F **108** 1f.80 blk, grn & grey 1·00 2·10
F326 – 2f.60 brown & green 1·00 2·10
DESIGN: 2f.60, Scots Pine.

1982. Centenary of Discovery of Tubercle Bacillus.
F327 F **109** 2f.10 lilac . . . . . . 1·20 1·90

F **110** St. Thomas Aquinas F **111** Montgolfier and Charles Balloons over Tuileries, Paris

1982. St. Thomas Aquinas Commemoration.
F328 F **110** 2f. deep brown, brown and grey . . . . . 95 1·90

1983. Bicentenary of Manned Flight.
F329 F **111** 2f. green, red and brown . . . . . . 70 1·90

F **112** Silver Birch

1983. Nature Protection.
F330 F **112** 1f. red, brown and green . . . . 1·10 2·75
F331 – 1f.50 green, bl & brn 75 1·80
DESIGN: 1f.50, Brown trout.

F **113** Mountain Cheesery

1983. Europa.
F332 F **113** 1f. purple and violet 2·20 2·10
F333 – 2f.60 red, mve & pur 2·20 2·75
DESIGN: 2f.60, Catalan forge.

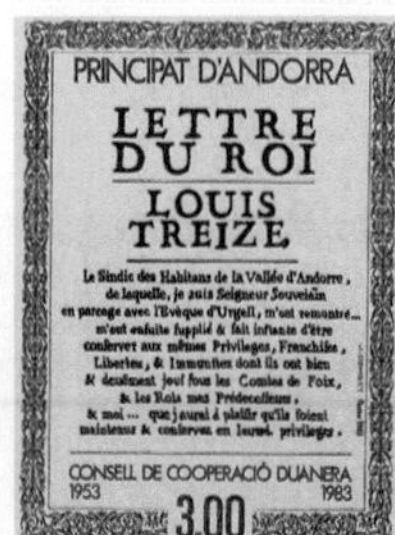

F **114** Royal Edict of Louis XIII

1983. 30th Anniv of Customs Co-operation Council.
F334 F **114** 3f. black and slate . . 1·20 2·75

F **115** Early Coat of Arms

1983. Inscr "POSTES".
F335 F **115** 5c. green and red . . 90 2·40
F336 10c. dp green & green 90 1·00
F337 20c. violet and mauve 90 55
F338 30c. purple and violet 55 1·10
F339 40c. blue & ultram . . 90 1·10
F340 50c. black and red . . 90 1·00
F341 1f. lake and red . . . 95 1·00
F342 1f.90 green . . . . . 1·60 3·25
F343 2f. red and brown . . 1·20 80
F344 2f.10 green . . . . . 1·20 1·20
F345 2f.20 red . . . . . . 40 1·70
F346 2f.30 red . . . . . . 1·20 2·00
F347 3f. green and mauve 1·30 2·00
F348 4f. orange and brown 1·90 2·75
F349 5f. brown and red . . 1·70 2·30
F350 10f. red and brown 3·00 3·00
F351 15f. green & dp green 3·75 5·50
F352 20f. blue and brown 4·00 5·00

For design as Type F **115** but inscribed "LA POSTE" see Nos. F446/9.

F **116** Wall Painting, La Cortinada Church F **117** Plandolit House

1983. Romanesque Art.
F354 F **116** 4f. multicoloured . . 1·40 3·00

1983.
F355 F **117** 1f.60 brown & green 45 1·50

F **118** Snowflakes and Olympic Torch

1984. Winter Olympic Games, Sarajevo.
F356 F **118** 2f.80 red, blue & grn 95 2·00

F **119** Pyrenees and Council of Europe Emblem

1984. Work Community of Pyrenees Region.
F357 F **119** 3f. blue and brown . . 85 2·40

F **120** Bridge

1984. Europa.
F358 F **120** 2f. green . . . . . . 3·50 2·00
F359 2f.80 red . . . . . . 4·25 2·30

F **121** Sweet Chestnut

1984. Nature Protection.
F360 F **121** 1f.70 grn, brn & pur 70 1·80
F361 – 2f.10 green & brown 60 2·00
DESIGN: 2f.10, Walnut.

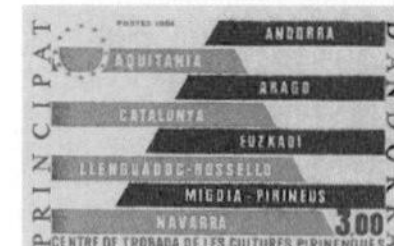

F **122** Centre Members

1984. Pyrenean Cultures Centre, Andorra.
F362 F **122** 3f. blue, orange & red 80 2·20

F **123** "St. George" (detail of fresco, Church of St. Cerni, Nagol)

1984. Pre-Romanesque Art.
F363 F **123** 5f. multicoloured . . 1·60 3·00

F **124** Sant Julia Valley F **125** Title Page of "Le Val d'Andorre" (comic opera)

1985.
F364 F **124** 2f. green, olive & brn 70 1·90

1985. Europa.
F365 F **125** 2f.10 green . . . . . 3·75 2·00
F366 – 3f. brown & dp brown 5·00 2·75
DESIGN: 3f. Musical instruments within frame.

F **126** Teenagers holding up ball F **127** Mallard

1985. International Youth Year.
F367 F **126** 3f. red and brown . . 70 2·20

1985. Nature Protection. Multicoloured.
F368 1f.80 Type F **127** . . . . . 1·00 2·00
F369 2f.20 Eurasian goldfinch . . 90 3·25

F **128** St. Cerni and Angel (fresco, Church of St. Cerni, Nagol)

1985. Pre-Romanesque Art.
F370 F **128** 5f. multicoloured . . 1·40 3·00

F **130** 1979 Europa Stamp

1986. Inauguration of Postal Museum.
F381 F **130** 2f.20 brown & green 65 1·90

F **131** Ansalonga F **132** Players

1986. Europa.
F382 F **131** 2f.20 black and blue 1·80 2·20
F383 – 3f.20 black and green 3·00 3·75
DESIGN: 3f.20, Pyrenean chamois.

1986. World Cup Football Championship, Mexico.
F384 F **132** 3f. grn, blk & dp grn 1·20 2·75

F **133** Angonella Lakes

1986.
F385 F **133** 2f.20 multicoloured 65 1·90

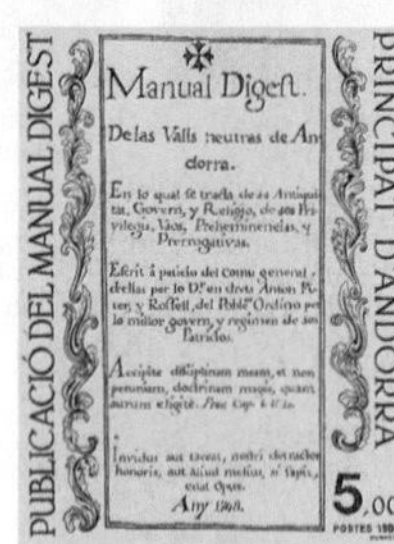

F **134** Title Page of "Manual Digest", 1748

1986. "Manual Digest".
F386 F **134** 5f. black, grn & brn 1·10 3·25

F **135** Dove with Twig F **136** St. Vincent's Chapel, Enclar

1986. International Peace Year.
F387 F **135** 1f.90 blue and indigo 85 2·10

1986.
F388 F **136** 1f.90 brn, blk & grn 70 2·10

F **137** Arms F **138** Meritxell Chapel

1987. Visit of French Co-prince (French president).
F389 F **137** 2f.20 multicoloured 1·30 3·25

1987. Europa.
F390 F **138** 2f.20 purple and red 5·50 2·40
F391 – 3f.40 violet and blue 7·75 3·00
DESIGN: 3f.40, Ordino.

F 139 Ransol F 140 Horse

1987.
F392 F **139** 1f.90 multicoloured 80 2·20

1987. Nature Protection. Multicoloured.
F393 1f.90 Type F **140** . . . . . 1·20 2·10
F394 2f.20 Isabel (moth) . . . . 1·30 2·50

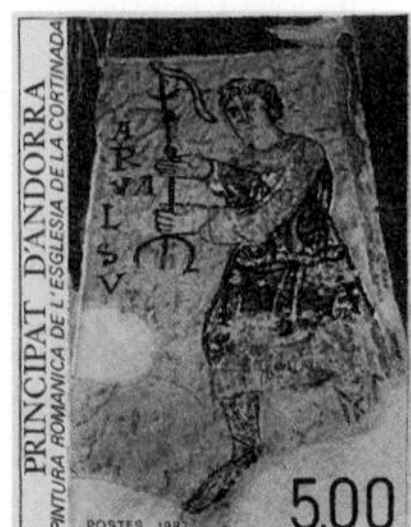

F **141** Arualsu (fresco, La Cortinada Church)

1987. Romanesque Art.
F395 F **141** 5f. multicoloured . . 1·50 3·25

F **142** Walker with Map by Signpost

1987. Walking.
F396 F **142** 2f. pur, grn & dp grn 65 2·00

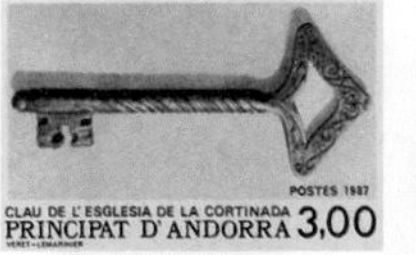

F **143** Key F **144** Arms

1987. La Cortinada Church Key.
F397 F **143** 3f. multicoloured . . 1·20 2·50

1988.
F398 F **144** 2f.20 red . . . . . . 70 2·10
F399 2f.30 red . . . . . . 1·20 2·10
F400 2f.50 red . . . . . . 3·00 2·10
F401 2f.80 red . . . . . . 60 2·10
Nos. F400/1 are inscribed "LA POSTE".

F **145** Bronze Boot and Mountains F **146** Players

1988. Archaeology.
F407 F **145** 3f. multicoloured . . 90 4·25

1988. Rugby.
F408 F **146** 2f.20 blk, yell & grn 80 2·20

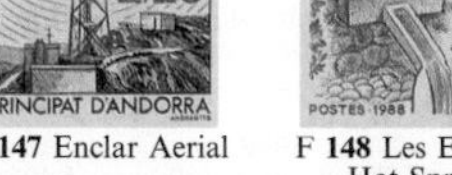
F **147** Enclar Aerial F **148** Les Escaldes Hot Spring

1988. Europa. Transport and Communications. Each green, brown and blue.
F409 2f.20 Type F **147** . . . . . 3·00 3·25
F410 3f.60 Hand pointing to map on screen (tourist information) . . . . . . 4·25 1·90

1988.
F411 F **148** 2f.20 blue, brn & grn 70 2·50

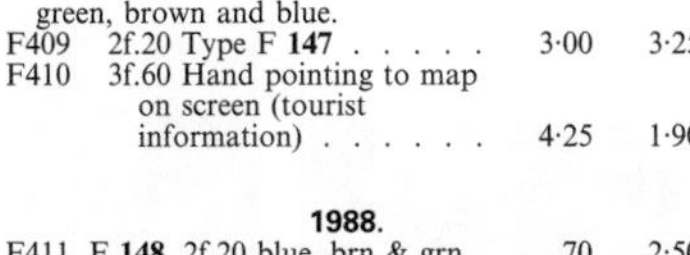

F **149** Ansalonga Pass F **150** Pyrenean Shepherd Dog

1988.
F412 F **149** 2f. blue, green & olive 55 2·20

1988. Nature Protection. Multicoloured.
F413 2f. Type F **150** . . . . . . 1·30 2·10
F414 2f.20 Hare . . . . 1·40 2·20

F **151** Fresco, Andorra La Vella Church

1988. Romanesque Art.
F415 F **151** 5f. multicoloured . . 1·70 2·75

F **152** Birds F **153** Pal

1989. Bicentenary of French Revolution.
F416 F **152** 2f.20 violet, blk & red 1·10 2·40

1989.
F417 F **153** 2f.20 violet and blue 75 2·00

F **154** The Strong Horse

1989. Europa. Children's Games. Each brown and cream.
F418 2f.20 Type F **154** . . . . . 2·50 2·10
F419 3f.60 The Handkerchief . . 3·25 2·75

F **155** Wounded Soldiers F **156** Archaeological Find and St. Vincent's Chapel, Enclar

1989. 125th Anniv of International Red Cross.
F420 F **155** 3f.60 brn, blk & red 1·10 2·75

1989. Archaeology.
F421 F **156** 3f. multicoloured . . 1·00 2·30

F **157** Wild Boar

1989. Nature Protection.
F422 F **157** 2f.20 blk, grn & brn 1·70 2·10
F423 – 3f.60 black, green and deep green . . . . 1·30 2·75
DESIGN: 3f.60, Palmate newt.

F **158** Retable of St. Michael de la Mosquera, Encamp

1989.
F424 F **158** 5f. multicoloured . . 1·80 3·25

F **159** La Margineda Bridge

1990.
F425 F **159** 2f.30 blue, brn & turq 75 2·00

F **160** Llorts Iron Ore Mines

1990.
F426 F **160** 3f.20 multicoloured 1·00 2·20

F **161** Exterior of Old Post Office, Andorra La Vella

1990. Europa. Post Office Buildings.
F427 F **161** 2f.30 red and black 3·00 2·10
F428 – 3f.20 violet and red 4·50 2·50
DESIGN: 3f.20, Interior of modern post office.

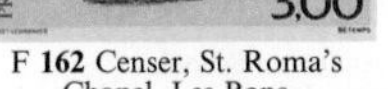
F **162** Censer, St. Roma's Chapel, Les Bons F **163** Wild Roses

1990.
F429 F **162** 3f. multicoloured . . 90 1·70

1990. Nature Protection. Multicoloured.
F430 2f.30 Type F **163** . . . . . 1·00 2·00
F431 3f.20 Otter (horiz) . . . . 1·10 2·40

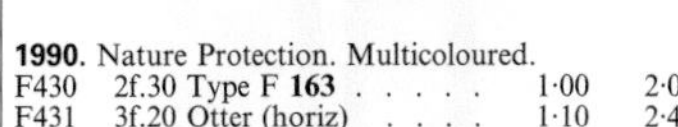

F **164** Tobacco-drying Sheds, Les Bons

1990.
F432 F **164** 2f.30 yell, blk & red 70 2·00

F **165** Part of Mural from Santa Coloma Church

1990.
F433 F **165** 5f. multicoloured . . 1·40 3·25

1990. Birth Centenary of Charles de Gaulle (French statesman). As Nos. F243/4 but values and inscriptions changed.
F434 F **52** 2f.30 blue . . . . . . 1·10 2·20
F435 3f.20 red . . . . 1·10 2·20

F **166** Coin from St. Eulalia's Church, Encamp

1990.
F436 F **166** 3f.20 multicoloured 1·30 2·30

F **167** Chapel of Sant Roma Dels Vilars F **168** Emblem and Track

1991.
F437 F **167** 2f.50 blue, blk & grn 75 1·90

1991. 4th European Small States Games.
F438 F **168** 2f.50 multicoloured 60 2·00

F **169** Television Satellite F **170** Bottles

1991. Europa. Europe in Space. Multicoloured.
F439 2f.50 Type F **169** . . . . . 5·25 2·10
F440 3f.50 Globe, telescope and eye (horiz) . . . . 8·00 2·40

1991. Artefacts from Tomb of St. Vincent of Enclar.
F441 F **170** 3f.20 multicoloured 1·10 2·20

F **171** Sheep

1991. Nature Protection.
F442 F **171** 2f.50 brown, bl & blk 1·30 3·00
F443 – 3f.50 brn, mve & blk 1·40 2·20
DESIGN: 3f.50, Pyrenean cow.

F **172** Players

1991. World Petanque Championship, Engordany.
F444 F **172** 2f.50 blk, bistre & red 95 2·10

F **173** Mozart, Quartet and Organ Pipes

1991. Death Bicentenary of Wolfgang Amadeus Mozart (composer).
F445 F **173** 3f.40 blue, blk & turq 1·60 2·40

1991. As Type F **115** but inscr "LA POSTE".
F446 F **115** 2f.20 green . . . . . 1·80 1·80
F447 2f.40 green . . . . . 1·80 1·90
F448 2f.50 red . . . . . . 1·40 1·90
F449 2f.70 green . . . . . 1·40 1·80
F450 2f.80 red . . . . . . 2·40 2·00
F451 3f. red . . . . 2·20 1·80

F **174** "Virgin of the Remedy of Sant Julia and Sant Germa"

F **175** Slalom

1991.
F455 F **174** 5f. multicoloured . . 1·50 3·00

1992. Winter Olympic Games, Albertville. Mult.
F456 2f.50 Type F **175** . . . . . 1·30 1·60
F457 3f.40 Figure skating . . . . 1·50 2·40

F **176** St. Andrew's Church, Arinsal

1992.
F458 F **176** 2f.50 black and buff 90 1·80

F **177** Navigation Instrument and Columbus's Fleet

F **178** Canoeing

1992. Europa. 500th Anniv of Discovery of America by Columbus. Multicoloured.
F459 2f.50 Type F **177** . . . . . 4·25 1·80
F460 3f.40 Fleet, Columbus and Amerindians . . . . . . 6·25 1·90

1992. Olympic Games, Barcelona. Multicoloured.
F461 2f.50 Type F **178** . . . . . 1·20 2·00
F462 3f.40 Shooting . . . . . . 1·50 1·80

F **179** Globe Flowers

F **180** "Martyrdom of St. Eulalia" (altarpiece, St. Eulalia's Church, Encamp)

1992. Nature Protection. Multicoloured.
F463 2f.50 Type F **179** . . . . . 90 1·90
F464 3f.40 Griffon vulture ("El Voltor") (horiz) . . . . . 1·40 1·90

1992.
F465 F **180** 4f. multicoloured . . 1·10 2·40

F **181** "Ordino Arcalis 91" (Mauro Staccioli)

1992. Modern Sculpture. Multicoloured.
F466 5f. Type F **181** . . . . . . 1·50 2·50
F467 5f. "Storm in a Teacup" (Dennis Oppenheim) (horiz) . . . . 1·80 2·50

F **182** Grau Roig

F **183** "Estructures Autogeneradores" (Jorge du Bon)

1993. Ski Resorts. Multicoloured.
F468 2f.50 Type F **182** . . . . . 1·40 1·60
F469 2f.50 Ordino . . . . 1·40 1·60
F470 2f.50 Soldeu el Tarter . . . 1·10 1·40
F471 3f.40 Pal . . . . 1·30 1·50
F472 3f.40 Arinsal . . . . 1·30 1·50

1993. Europa. Contemporary Art.
F473 F **183** 2f.50 dp bl, bl & vio 1·50 1·60
F474 – 3f.40 multicoloured 2·10 1·90
DESIGN—HORIZ: 3f.40, "Fisicromia per Andorra" (Carlos Cruz-Diez).

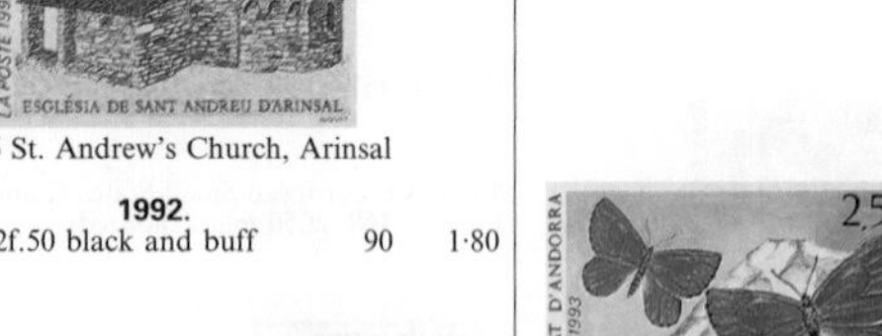

F **184** Common Blue

F **185** Cyclist

1993. Nature Protection. Butterflies. Multicoloured.
F475 2f.50 Type F **184** . . . . . 1·30 1·90
F476 4f.20 "Nymphalidae" . . . 1·70 2·40

1993. Tour de France Cycling Road Race.
F477 F **185** 2f.50 multicoloured 1·10 1·60

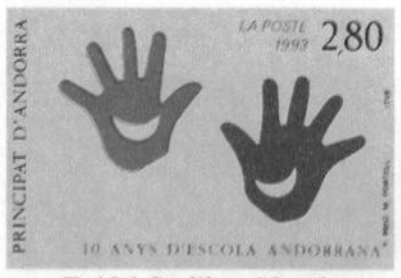

F **186** Smiling Hands

1993. 10th Anniv of Andorran School.
F478 F **186** 2f.80 multicoloured 1·20 1·80

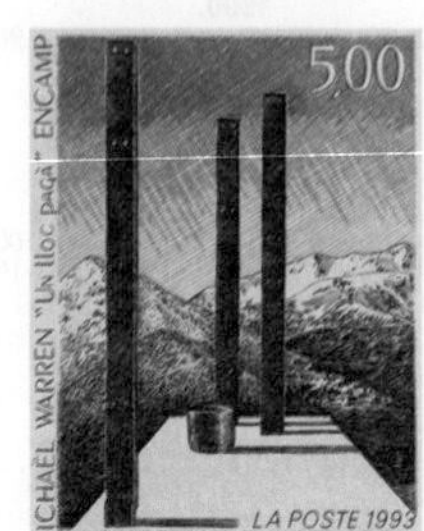

F **187** "A Pagan Place" (Michael Warren)

1993. Modern Sculpture.
F479 F **187** 5f. black and blue . . 1·90 2·50
F480 – 5f. multicoloured . . 10·50 2·50
DESIGN: No. F480, "Pep, Lu, Canolic, Ton, Meritxell, Anna, Pau, Carles, Eugenia,...and Others" (Erik Dietman).

F **188** Cross-country Skiing

F **189** Constitution Monument

1994. Winter Olympic Games, Lillehammer, Norway.
F481 F **188** 3f.70 multicoloured 1·20 1·80

1994. 1st Anniv of New Constitution.
F482 F **189** 2f.80 multicoloured 1·10 1·40
F483 – 3f.70 blk, yell & mve 1·40 1·70
DESIGN: 3f.70, Stone tablet.

F **190** AIDS Virus

1994. Europa. Discoveries and Inventions. Mult.
F484 2f.80 Type F **190** . . . . . 1·30 1·00
F485 3f.70 Radio mast . . . . . 1·70 1·80

F **191** Competitors' Flags and Football

F **192** Horse Riding

1994. World Cup Football Championship, U.S.A.
F486 F **191** 3f.70 multicoloured 1·20 1·80

1994. Tourist Activities. Multicoloured.
F487 2f.80 Type F **192** . . . . . 1·10 1·40
F488 2f.80 Mountain biking . . . 1·10 1·40
F489 2f.80 Climbing . . . . . . 1·10 1·40
F490 2f.80 Fishing . . . . 1·10 1·40

F **193** Scarce Swallowtail

F **194** "26 10 93"

1994. Nature Protection. Butterflies. Multicoloured.
F491 2f.80 Type F **193** . . . . . 1·30 1·60
F492 4f.40 Small tortoiseshell . . 1·80 2·20

1994. Meeting of Co-princes.
F493 F **194** 2f.80 multicoloured 1·00 1·30

F **195** Emblem

F **196** Globe, Goal and Player

1995. European Nature Conservation Year.
F494 F **195** 2f.80 multicoloured 1·00 1·40

1995. 3rd World Cup Rugby Championship, South Africa.
F495 F **196** 2f.80 multicoloured 1·00 1·30

F **197** Dove and Olive Twig ("Peace")

1995. Europa. Peace and Freedom. Multicoloured.
F496 2f.80 Type F **197** . . . . . 1·60 1·80
F497 3f.70 Flock of doves ("Freedom") . . . . . . 1·80 1·90

F **198** Emblem

1995. 15th Anniv of Caritas Andorrana (welfare organization).
F498 F **198** 2f.80 multicoloured 1·10 1·40

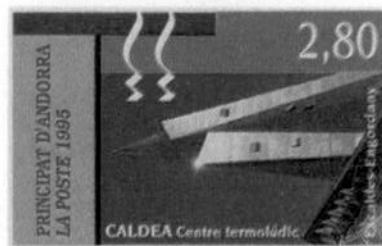

F **199** Caldea Thermal Baths, Les Escaldes-Engordany

1995.
F499 F **199** 2f.80 multicoloured 1·20 1·40

F **200** National Auditorium, Ordino

1995.
F500 F **200** 3f.70 black and buff 1·40 1·80

F **201** "Virgin of Meritxell"

1995.
F501 F **201** 4f.40 multicoloured 1·40 1·90

F **202** Brimstone

F **203** National Flag over U.N. Emblem

1995. Nature Protection. Butterflies. Multicoloured.
F502 2f.80 Type F **202** . . . . . 1·20 1·60
F503 3f.70 Marbled white (horiz) 1·70 2·10

1995. 50th Anniv of U.N.O. Multicoloured.
F504 2f.80 Type F **203** . . . . . 1·20 1·60
F505 3f.70 Anniversary emblem over flag . . . . 1·40 1·90

F **204** National Flag and Palace of Europe, Strasbourg

1995. Admission of Andorra to Council of Europe.
F506 F **204** 2f.80 multicoloured 1·20 1·40

F **205** Emblem

F **206** Basketball

1996. 4th Borrufa Trophy Skiing Competition.
F507 F **205** 2f.80 multicoloured 1·20 1·40

1996.
F508 F **206** 3f.70 red, blk & yell 1·40 1·80

F **207** Children

1996. 25th Anniv of Our Lady of Meritxell Special School.
F509 F **207** 2f.80 multicoloured 1·20 1·40

F **208** European Robin

1996. Nature Protection. Multicoloured.
F510 3f. Type F **208** . . . . . . 1·30 1·40
F511 3f.80 Great tit . . . . . . 1·50 1·90

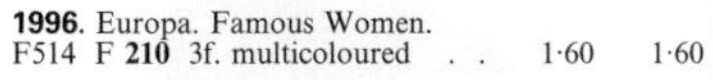
F **209** Cross, St. James's Church, Engordany — F **210** Ermessenda de Castellbo

1996. Religious Objects. Multicoloured.
F512 3f. Type F **209** . . . . . . 1·30 1·60
F513 3f.80 Censer, St. Eulalia's Church, Encamp (horiz) 1·50 1·80

1996. Europa. Famous Women.
F514 F **210** 3f. multicoloured . . 1·60 1·60

F **211** Chessmen — F **212** Canillo

1996. Chess.
F515 F **211** 4f.50 red, black & bl 7·25 1·80

1996. No value expressed. Self-adhesive.
F516 F **212** (3f.) multicoloured . . 1·50 1·80

F **213** Cycling, Running and Throwing the Javelin

1996. Olympic Games, Atlanta.
F517 F **213** 3f. multicoloured . . 1·20 1·40

F **214** Singers

1996. 5th Anniv of National Youth Choir.
F518 F **214** 3f. multicoloured . . 1·20 1·50

F **215** Man and Boy with Animals

1996. Livestock Fair.
F519 F **215** 3f. yellow, red and black . . . . 1·20 1·50

F **216** St. Roma's Chapel, Les Bons — F **217** Mitterrand

1996. Churches. Multicoloured.
F520 6f.70 Type F **216** . . . . . 2·20 2·75
F521 6f.70 Santa Coloma . . . . 2·20 2·75

1997. Francois Mitterrand (President of France and Co-prince of Andorra, 1981–95) Commemoration.
F522 F **217** 3f. multicoloured . . 1·20 1·60

F **218** Parish Emblem — F **219** Volleyball

1997. Parish of Encamp. No value expressed. Self-adhesive.
F523 F **218** (3f.) blue . . . . . . 1·40 1·80

1997.
F524 F **219** 3f. multicoloured . . 1·20 1·40

F **220** The White Lady — F **221** House Martin approaching Nest

1997. Europa. Tales and Legends.
F525 F **220** 3f. multicoloured . . 2·00 1·40

1997. Nature Protection.
F526 F **221** 3f.80 multicoloured 1·40 1·60

F **222** Mill and Saw-mill, Cal Pal — F **223** Monstrance, St. Iscle and St. Victoria's Church

1997. Tourism. Paintings by Francesc Galobardes. Multicoloured.
F527 3f. Type F **222** . . . . . . 1·20 1·40
F528 4f.50 Mill and farmhouse, Sole (horiz) . . . . . . 1·60 2·00

1997. Religious Silver Work. Multicoloured.
F529 3f. Type F **223** . . . . . . 1·40 1·40
F530 15f.50 Pax, St. Peter's Church, Aixirivall . . . . 5·00 5·00

F **224** The Legend of Meritxell — F **226** Harlequin juggling Candles

F **225** St. Michael's Chapel, Engolasters

1997. Legends. Multicoloured.
F531 3f. Type F **224** . . . . . . 1·20 1·20
F532 3f. The Seven-armed Cross 1·20 1·20
F533 3f.80 Wrestlers (The Fountain of Esmelicat) 1·50 1·50

1997. International Stamp Exn, Monaco.
F534 F **225** 3f. multicoloured . . 1·20 1·10

1998. Birthday Greetings Stamp.
F535 F **226** 3f. multicoloured . . 1·20 1·10

F **227** Super Giant Slalom — F **228** Arms of Ordino

1997. Winter Olympic Games, Nagano, Japan.
F536 F **227** 4f.40 multicoloured 1·40 1·60

1998. No value expressed. Self-adhesive.
F537 F **228** (3f.) multicoloured . . 1·40 1·20

F **229** Altarpiece and Vila Church

1998.
F538 F **229** 4f.50 multicoloured 1·50 1·70

F **230** Emblem and Cogwheels

1998. 20th Anniv of Rotary Int in Andorra.
F539 F **230** 3f. multicoloured . . 1·20 1·10

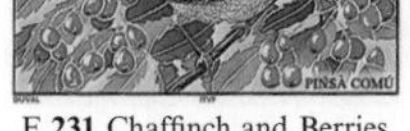
F **231** Chaffinch and Berries — F **232** Players

1998. Nature Protection.
F540 F **231** 3f.80 multicoloured 1·30 1·30

1998. World Cup Football Championship, France.
F541 F **232** 3f. multicoloured . . 1·00 1·10

F **233** Treble Score and Stylized Orchestra

1998. Europa. National Festivals. Music Festival.
F542 F **233** 3f. multicoloured . . 1·80 1·50

F **234** River

1998. "Expo '98" World's Fair, Lisbon, Portugal.
F543 F **234** 5f. multicoloured . . 1·70 1·80

F **235** Chalice — F **237** Andorra, 1717

1998. Chalice from the House of the Valleys.
F544 F **235** 4f.50 multicoloured 1·40 1·50

1998. French Victory in World Cup Football Championship. No. F541 optd **FINAL FRANCA/ BRASIL 3-0**.
F545 F **232** 3f. multicoloured . . 1·40 1·30

1998. Relief Maps. Multicoloured.
F546 3f. Type F **237** . . . . . . 1·20 1·10
F547 15f.50 Andorra, 1777 (horiz) . . . . 3·75 3·75

F **238** Museum

1998. Inauguration of Postal Museum.
F548 F **238** 3f. multicoloured . . 1·20 1·10

F **239** Front Page of First Edition — F **240** Arms of La Massana

1998. 250th Anniv of "Manual Digest".
F549 F **239** 3f.80 multicoloured 1·30 1·30

1999. No value expressed. Self-adhesive.
F550 F **240** (3f.) multicoloured . . 1·20 1·10

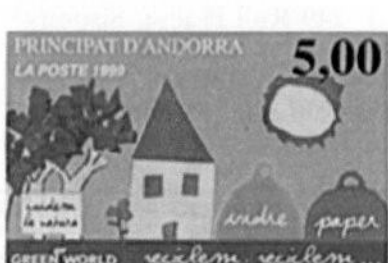

F **241** House and Recycling Bins

1999. "Green World". Recycling of Waste.
F551 F **241** 5f. multicoloured . . 1·50 1·60

F **242** Vall de Sorteny (½-size illustration)

1999. Europa. Parks and Gardens.
F552 F **242** 3f. multicoloured . . 1·60 1·40

F **243** Council Emblem and Seat, Strasbourg

1999. 50th Anniv of Council of Europe.
F553 F **243** 3f.80 multicoloured 1·20 1·20

F **244** "The First Mail Coach" — F **245** Footballer and Flags

1999.
F554 F **244** 2f.70 multicoloured 1·00 1·00

1999. Andorra–France Qualifying Match for European Nations Football Championship.
F555 F **245** 4f.50 multicoloured 1·40 1·50

F **246** St. Michael's Church, Engolasters, and Emblem

1999. "Philexfrance 99" International Stamp Exhibition, Paris, France.
F556 F **246** 3f. multicoloured . . 1·00 1·10

F **247** Winter Scene

1999. Paintings of Pal by Francesc Galobardes. Multicoloured.
F557 3f. Type F **247** . . . . . . 1·00 1·10
F558 3f. Summer scene (horiz) . . 1·00 1·10

F **248** Emblem and "50"

1999. 50th Anniv of International Photographic Art Federation.
F559 F **248** 4f.40 multicoloured 1·30 1·50

F **249** Rull House, Sispony

1999.
F560 F **249** 15f.50 multicoloured 3·75 4·50

F **250** Chest with Six Locks

1999.
F561 F **250** 6f.70 multicoloured 1·60 2·00

F **251** Angels

1999. Christmas.
F562 F **251** 3f. multicoloured . . 1·00 1·10

F **252** Revellers

F **253** Arms of La Vella

2000. New Millennium.
F563 F **252** 3f. multicoloured . . 1·00 1·00

2000. No value expressed. Self-adhesive.
F564 F **253** (3f.) multicoloured . . 1·10 1·00

F **254** Snow Boarder

F **255** Emblem

2000.
F565 F **254** 4f.50 blue, brown and black . . . . 1·40 1·40

2000. Montserrat Caballe International Opera Competition, Saint Julia de Loria.
F566 F **255** 3f.80 yellow and blue 1·10 1·20

F **256** *Campanula cochlearifolia*

F **257** "Building Europe"

2000.
F567 F **256** 2f.70 multicoloured 90 95

2000. Europa.
F568 F **257** 3f. multicoloured . . 1·70 1·40

F **258** Church (Canolich Festival)

F **259** Sparrow

2000. Festivals. Multicoloured.
F569 3f. Type F **258** . . . . . . 1·00 1·00
F570 3f. People at Our Lady's Chapel, Meritxell (Meritxell Festival) . . . 1·00 1·00

2000.
F571 F **259** 4f.40 multicoloured 1·30 1·40

F **260** Hurdling

F **261** Goat, Skier and Walker

2000. Olympic Games, Sydney.
F572 F **260** 5f. multicoloured . . 1·40 1·60

2000. Tourism Day.
F573 F **261** 3f. multicoloured . . 1·00 1·00

F **262** Flower, Text, Circuit Board and Emblems

2000. "EXPO 2000" World's Fair, Hanover.
F574 F **262** 3f. multicoloured . . 1·00 1·00

F **263** Stone Arch and Flag

2000. European Community.
F575 F **263** 3f.80 multicoloured 1·10 1·10

F **264** Pottery

2000. Prehistoric Pottery.
F576 F **264** 6f.70 multicoloured 1·80 2·00

F **265** Drawing

F **266** Arms of Saint Julia de Loria

2000. 25th Anniv of National Archives.
F577 F **265** 15f.50 multicoloured 3·50 4·25

2001. No value expressed. Self-adhesive.
F578 F **266** (3f.) multicoloured . . 1·50 1·20

F **267** Ski Lift

2001. Canillo Aliga Club.
F579 F **267** 4f.50 multicoloured 1·40 1·50

F **268** Decorative Metalwork

2001. Casa Cristo Museum.
F580 F **268** 6f.70 multicoloured 1·80 2·00

F **269** Legend of Lake Engolasters

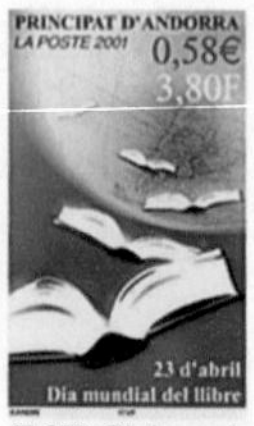

F **270** Globe and Books

2001. Legends. Multicoloured.
F581 3f. Type F **269** . . . . . . 1·00 1·00
F582 3f. Lords before King (foundation of Andorra) 1·00 1·00

2001. World Book Day.
F583 F **270** 3f.80 multicoloured 1·10 1·20

F **271** Water Splash

F **272** Raspberry

2001. Europa. Water Resources.
F584 F **271** 3f. multicoloured . . 1·30 1·30

2001. Multicoloured.
F585 3f. Type F **272** . . . . . . 1·00 1·00
F586 4f.40 Jay (horiz) . . . . . 1·40 1·50

F **273** Profiles talking

2001. European Year of Languages.
F587 F **273** 3f.80 multicoloured 1·10 1·20

F **274** Trumpeter

2001. Jazz Festival, Escaldes-Engordany.
F588 F **274** 3f. multicoloured . . 65 90

F **275** Kitchen

2001.
F589 F **275** 5f. multicoloured . . 1·00 1·50

F **276** Chapel

2001. 25th Anniv of Chapel of Our Lady, Meritxell.
F590 F **276** 3f. multicoloured . . 65 90

F **277** Hotel Pla

2001.
F591 F **277** 15f.50 black, violet and green . . . . . 3·25 4·50

F **278** Cross

F **279** State Arms

2001. Grossa Cross (boundary cross at the crossroads between Avinguda Meritxell and Carrer Bisbe Iglesias).
F592 F **278** 2f.70 multicoloured 70 90

New Currency
100 cents = 1 euro

2002. (a) With Face Value.
F593 F **279** 1c. multicoloured . . 10 15
F594 2c. multicoloured . . 10 15
F595 5c. multicoloured . . 10 15

(b) No value expressed.
F599 F **279** (46c.) multicoloured 65 1·10
No. F599 was sold at the rate for inland letters up to 20 grammes.

F **280** The Legend of Meritxell

F **281** Pedestrians on Crossing

2002. Legends. Desings as Nos. F525, F531/3 and F581/2 but with values in new currency as Type F **280**. Multicoloured.
F600 10c. Type F **280** 15 30
F601 20c. Wrestlers (The Fountain of Esmelicat) 30 50
F602 41c. The Piper (La joyeur de cornemuse) . . . . . 60 1·10
F603 50c. The Seven-armed Cross 70 1·10
F604 €1 Lords before King (foundation of Andorra) 1·40 2·40
F605 €2 Legend of Lake Engolasters . . . . . . 3·00 4·75
F606 €5 The White Lady . . . 7·25 11·00

2002. Schools' Road Safety Campaign.
F615 F **281** 69c. multicoloured . . 1·00 1·60

F **282** Skier

2002. Winter Olympic Games, Salt Lake City, U.S.A.
F616 F **282** 58c. multicoloured . . 85 1·40

F **283** Hotel Rosaleda

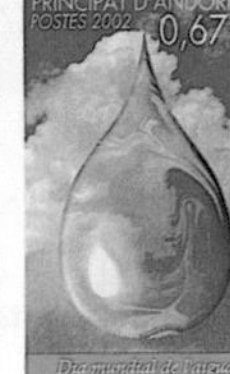

F **284** Water Droplet and Clouds

2002.
F617 F **283** 46c. multicoloured . . 65 1·10

2002. World Water Day.
F618 F **284** 67c. multicoloured . . 1·00 1·60

F **285** Clown

2002. Europa. Circus.
F619 F **285** 46c. multicoloured . . 95 1·30

F **286** Myrtle

F **287** Seated Nude (Josep Viladomat)

2002.
F620 F **286** 46c. multicoloured . . 65 1·10

2002.
F621 F **287** €2.26 multicoloured 3·25 5·50

F **288** Mountains from Tunnel Entrance

2002. Completion of the Envalira Road Tunnel between Andorra and France.
F622 F **288** 46c. multicoloured . . 65 1·10

F **289** Mural (detail) (Santa Coloma Church, Andorra la Vella)

2002.
F623 F **289** €1.02 multicoloured 1·50 2·50

F **290** Arms of Escaldes – Engordany

F **291** State Arms

2003. Arms. No value expressed. Self-adhesive.
F624 F **290** (46c.) multicoloured 65 65
No. F624 was sold at the rate for inland letters up to 20 grammes.

2003. Legends. "Legende du pin de la Margineda". Vert design as Type F **280**.
F625 69c. multicoloured 95 95

2003. 10th Anniv of Constitution.
F626 F **291** €2.36 multicoloured 3·25 3·25

F **292** Les Bons

F **293** Hotel Mirador

2003. Architecture.
F627 F **292** 67c. multicoloured . . 90 90

2003.
F628 F **293** €1.02 multicoloured 1·40 1·40

F **294** Man, Dog and Sheep

F **296** Cyclist and Map

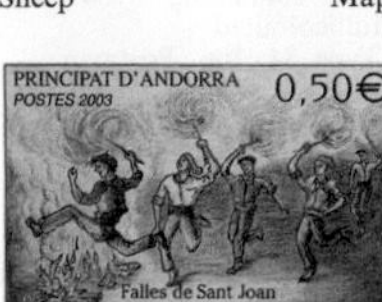

F **295** Dancers and Fire

2003. Europa. Poster Art.
F629 F **294** 46c. multicoloured . . 65 65

2003. Fires of St. John the Baptist Festival.
F630 F **295** 50c. multicoloured . . 70 70

2003. Centenary of Tour de France (cycle race).
F631 F **296** 50c. multicoloured . . 70 70

F **297** Pole Vault

F **298** *Greixa sparassis crispa*

2003. World Athletics Championship, Paris.
F632 F **297** 90c. multicoloured . . 1·20 1·20

2003.
F633 F **298** 45c. multicoloured . . 60 60

F **299** Red Currant

2003.
F634 F **299** 75c. multicoloured . . 1·00 1·00

F **300** Telephone, Satellite and Globe

2003. Centenary of First Telephone in Andorra.
F635 F **300** 50c. multicoloured . . 70 70

POSTAGE DUE STAMPS

1931. Postage Due stamps of France optd **ANDORRE**.
FD24 D **11** 5c. blue . . . . . . 90 3·25
FD25 10c. brown . . . . . 85 2·75
FD26 30c. red . . . . . . 50 1·50
FD27 50c. purple . . . . . 90 3·25
FD28 60c. green . . . . . 13·00 24·00
FD29 1f. brown on yellow 85 2·10
FD30 2f. mauve . . . . . . 7·50 18·00
FD31 3f. mauve . . . . . . 1·20 3·50

1931. Postage Due stamps of France optd **ANDORRE**.
FD32 D **43** 1c. green . . . . . . 65 2·75
FD33 10c. red . . . . . . 5·00 6·50
FD34 60c. red . . . . . . 18·00 28·00
FD35 1f. green . . . . . . 55·00 95·00
FD36 1f.20 on 2f. blue . . . 48·00 90·00
FD37 2f. brown £120 £150
FD38 5f. on 1f. purple . . . 55·00 £120

FD **7**

FD **10**

FD **11** Wheat Sheaves

1935.
FD82 FD **7** 1c. green . . . . . . 1·40 4·25

1937.
FD 97 FD **10** 5c. blue . . . . . 4·50 11·00
FD 98 10c. brown . . . . 2·40 18·00
FD 99 2f. mauve . . . . 5·25 14·00
FD100 5f. orange . . . . 18·00 24·00

1943.
FD101a FD **11** 10c. brown . . . 30 40
FD102 30c. mauve . . . 1·60 1·40
FD103 50c. green . . . 1·00 2·30
FD104 1f. blue . . . . 1·70 3·75
FD105 1f.50 red . . . 4·75 3·25
FD106 2f. blue . . . . 1·80 10·50
FD107 3f. red . . . . 2·20 3·75
FD108 4f. violet . . . 4·75 5·50
FD109 5f. mauve . . . 3·75 8·75
FD110 10f. orange . . . 5·00 8·50
FD111 20f. brown . . . 2·50 8·75

1946. As Type FD **11**, but inscr "TIMBRE-TAXE".
FD143 10c. brown . . . . 85 12·00
FD144 1f. blue . . . . 1·60 3·00
FD145 2f. blue . . . . 75 3·25
FD146 3f. brown . . . . 1·80 4·00
FD147 4f. violet . . . . 2·40 5·00
FD148 5f. red . . . . 1·30 3·75
FD149 10f. orange . . . . . . 2·40 5·50
FD150 20f. brown . . . . . . 6·50 11·00
FD151 50f. green . . . . . . 25·00 34·00
FD152 100f. green . . . . . . 55·00 £120

1961. As Nos. FD143/52 but new values and colours.
FD185 5c. red . . . . 2·75 7·25
FD186 10c. orange . . . . . . 5·25 14·50

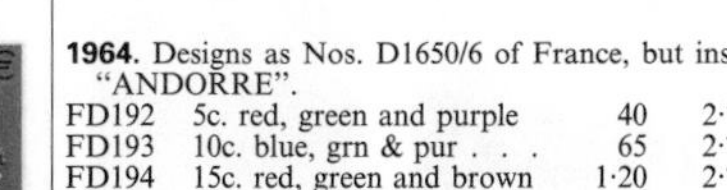
FD187 20c. brown . . . . 12·00 22·00
FD188 50c. green . . . . 20·00 37·00

1964. Designs as Nos. D1650/6 of France, but inscr "ANDORRE".
FD192 5c. red, green and purple 40 2·75
FD193 10c. blue, grn & pur . . . 65 2·75
FD194 15c. red, green and brown 1·20 2·75
FD195 20c. purple, green & turq 80 3·00
FD196 30c. blue, grn & brn . . . 70 1·20
FD197 40c. yellow, red and green 1·80 1·60
FD198 50c. red, green and blue 1·20 65

FD **129** Holly Berries

1985. Fruits.
FD371 FD **129** 10c. red and green 1·30 1·40
FD372 – 20c. brown & blue 1·30 1·40
FD373 – 30c. green and red 1·30 1·40
FD374 – 40c. brown & blk 1·30 1·40
FD375 – 50c. olive & violet 1·40 1·50
FD376 – 1f. green and blue 1·40 1·60
FD377 – 2f. red and brown 1·80 1·90
FD378 – 3f. purple & green 1·90 2·30
FD379 – 4f. olive and blue 2·20 3·00
FD380 – 5f. olive and red 2·75 3·50
DESIGNS: 20c. Wild plum; 30c. Raspberry; 40c. Dogberry; 50c. Blackberry; 1f. Juniper; 2f. Rose hip; 3f. Elder; 4f. Bilberry; 5f. Strawberry.

SPANISH POST OFFICES

1928. 100 centimos = 1 peseta.
2002. 100 cents = 1 euro.

1928. Stamps of Spain optd **CORREOS ANDORRA**.
1 **68** 2c. green 30 30
2 5c. red 40 40
3 10c. green 40 40
5 15c. blue . . . . 1·70 1·80
6 20c. violet . . . . 1·70 1·80
7 25c. red . . . . 1·70 10·50
8 30c. brown . . . . 9·50 8·25
9 40c. blue . . . . 9·50 7·50
10 50c. orange . . . . 10·00 7·50
11 **69** 1p. grey . . . . 12·00 12·50
12 4p. red . . . . 75·00 £140
13 10p. brown £150 £180

2 House of the Valleys

3 General Council of Andorra

1929.
14 **2** 2c. green . . . . 70 1·30
26 2c. brown 50 85
15 – 5c. purple . . . . 1·10 2·00
27 – 5c. brown . . . . 70 1·10
16 – 10c. green . . . . 1·10 2·00
17 – 15c. blue . . . . 1·80 2·75
30 – 15c. green . . . . 2·10 2·20
18 – 20c. violet . . . . 1·80 2·30
33 – 25c. red . . . . 1·10 2·10
20 **2** 30c. brown . . . . 49·00 65·00
34 30c. red . . . . 1·10 2·30
21 – 40c. blue . . . . 3·50 3·50
36 **2** 45c. red . . . . 70 1·20
22 – 50c. orange . . . . 3·50 3·50
38 **2** 60c. blue . . . . 1·80 2·10
23 **3** 1p. slate . . . . 9·00 15·00
39 4p. purple . . . . 18·00 28·00
40 10p. brown . . . . 39·00 35·00
DESIGNS: 5, 40c. Church of St. John of Caselles; 10, 20, 50c. Sant Julia de Loria; 15, 25c. Santa Coloma Church.

7 Councillor Manuel Areny Bons

11 Map

1948.
41 F 2c. olive 35 25
42 5c. orange 35 25
43 10c. blue 35 25
44 **7** 20c. purple . . . . 3·25 2·50
45 25c. orange . . . . 3·25 1·40
46 G 30c. green . . . . 8·50 4·50
47 H 50c. green . . . . 18·00 6·75
48 I 75c. blue . . . . 15·00 6·75
49 H 90c. purple . . . . 1·40 4·00
50 I 1p. red . . . . 15·00 6·75
51 G 1p.35 violet . . . . 6·25 7·25
52 **11** 4p. blue . . . . 11·00 11·50
53 10p. brown . . . . 20·00 14·00
DESIGNS—VERT: F. Edelweiss; G. Arms; H. Market Place, Ordino; I. Shrine near Meritxell Chapel.

12 Andorra La Vella   13 St. Anthony's Bridge

1951. Air.
54 **12** 1p. brown . . . . 18·00 11·50

1963.
55 **13** 25c. brown and black . . . 15 20
56 – 70c. black and green 20 30
57 – 1p. lilac and grey 25 50
58 – 2p. violet and lilac 40 80
59 – 2p.50 deep red and purple 25 70
60 – 3p. slate and black . . . . 55 1·00
61 – 5p. purple and brown . . . 1·60 1·80
62 – 6p. red and brown . . . . 2·10 2·10
DESIGNS—VERT: 70c. Anyos meadows (wrongly inscr "AYNOS"); 1p. Canillo; 2p. Santa Coloma Church; 2p.50, Arms; 6p. Virgin of Meritxell. HORIZ: 3p. Andorra la Vella; 5p. Ordino.

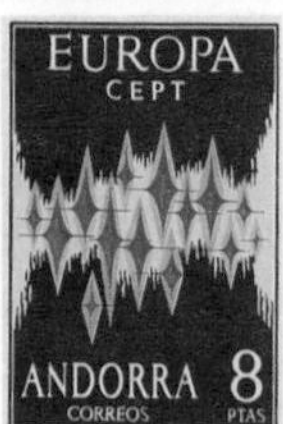

14 Daffodils   15 "Communications"

1966. Pyrenean Flowers.
63 **14** 50c. blue and slate 10 40
64 – 1p. purple and brown . . . 65 50
65 – 5p. blue and green . . . . 1·10 1·90
66 – 10p. slate and violet . . . . 55 1·50
DESIGNS: 1p. Carnation; 5p. Narcissus; 10p. Anemone (wrongly inscr "HELEBORUS CONI").

1972. Europa.
67 **15** 8p. multicoloured . . . . . 85·00 55·00

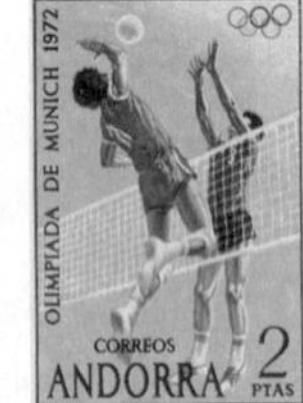

16 Encamp Valley   17 Volleyball

1972. Tourist Views. Multicoloured.
68 1p. Type **16** 40 55
69 1p.50 La Massana 50 55
70 2p. Skis and snowscape, Pas de la Casa . . . . 1·10 1·10
71 5p. Lake Pessons (horiz) . . . 1·30 1·10

1972. Olympic Games, Munich. Multicoloured.
72 2p. Type **17** 25 30
73 5p. Swimming (horiz) 30 55

18 St. Anthony's Auction

1972. Andorran Customs. Multicoloured.
74 1p. Type **18** 15 20
75 1p.50 "Les Caramelles" (choir) 15 20
76 2p. Nativity play (Christmas) 15 30
77 5p. Giant cigar (vert) 40 50
78 8p. Carved shrine, Meritxell (vert) 55 65
79 15p. "La Marratxa" (dance) 1·00 1·30

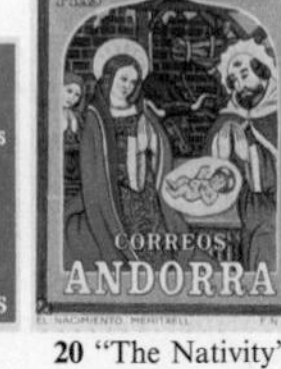

19 "Peoples of Europe"   20 "The Nativity"

1973. Europa.
80 **19** 2p. black, red and blue . . 25 35
81 – 8p. red, brown and black . . 70 85
DESIGN: 8p. Europa "Posthorn".

1973. Christmas. Frescoes from Meritxell Chapel. Multicoloured.
82 2p. Type **20** 20 30
83 5p. "Adoration of the Kings" 55 90

21 "Virgin of Ordino"   22 Oak Cupboard and Shelves

1974. Europa. Sculptures. Multicoloured.
84 2p. Type **21** . . . . 65 1·40
85 8p. Cross . . . . 1·50 2·40

1974. Arts and Crafts. Multicoloured.
86 10p. Type **22** . . . . 1·70 1·80
87 25p. Crown of the Virgin of the Roses . . . . 2·50 3·00

23 U.P.U. Monument, Berne

1974. Centenary of Universal Postal Union.
88 **23** 15p. multicoloured . . . . 1·10 1·60

24 "The Nativity"

1974. Christmas. Carvings from Meritxell Chapel. Multicoloured.
89 2p. Type **24** 55 75
90 5p. "Adoration of the Kings" 1·30 1·10

25 19th-century Postman and Church of St. John of Caselles   26 "Peasant with Knife"

1975. "Espana 75" Int Stamp Exhibition, Madrid.
91 **25** 3p. multicoloured 20 40

1975. Europa. 12th-century Romanesque Paintings from La Cortinada Church. Multicoloured.
92 3p. Type **26** . . . . 90 1·40
93 12p. "Christ" . . . . 1·50 2·75

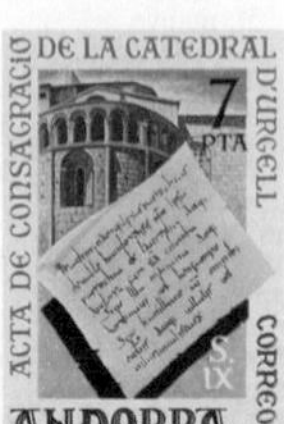

27 Cathedral and Consecration Text

1975. 1100th Anniv of Consecration of Urgel Cathedral.
94 **27** 7p. multicoloured . . . . . 1·00 1·90

28 "The Nativity"

1975. Christmas. Paintings from La Cortinada Church. Multicoloured.
95 3p. Type **28** 20 20
96 7p. "Adoration of The Kings" 35 65

29 Copper Cauldron   30 Slalom Skiing

1976. Europa. Multicoloured.
97 3p. Type **29** 20 50
98 12p. Wooden marriage chest (horiz) 60 70

1976. Olympic Games, Montreal. Multicoloured.
99 7p. Type **30** 20 40
100 15p. Canoeing (horiz) 45 75

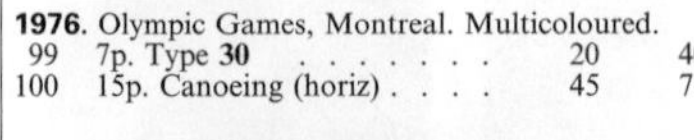

31 "The Nativity"

1976. Christmas. Carvings from La Massana Church. Multicoloured.
101 3p. Type **31** 15 20
102 25p. "Adoration of the Kings" . . . . 90 1·10

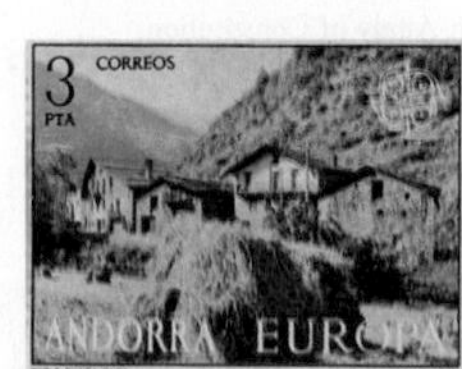

32 Ansalonga

1977. Europa. Multicoloured.
103 3p. Type **32** 15 30
104 12p. Xuclar 45 70

33 Boundary Cross   34 Map of Andorran Post Offices

1977. Christmas. Multicoloured.
105 5p. Type **33** 20 30
106 12p. St. Michael's Church, Engolasters 45 95

1978. 50th Anniv of Spanish Post Offices. Sheet 105 × 149 mm containing T **34** and similar vert designs. Multicoloured.
MS107 5p. Type **34**; 10p. Postman delivering letter, 1923; 20p. Spanish Post Office, Andorra la Vella, 1928; 25p. Andorran arms 70 2·75

35 House of the Valleys

1978. Europa. Multicoloured.
108 5p. Type **35** 15 30
109 12p. Church of St. John of Caselles 35 70

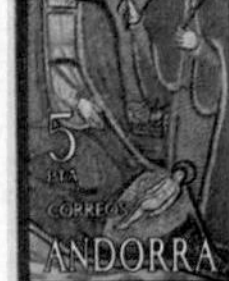

36 Crown, Mitre and Crook   37 "Holy Family"

1978. 700th Anniv of Parity Treaties.
110 **36** 5p. multicoloured 30 50

1978. Christmas. Frescoes in St. Mary's Church, Encamp. Multicoloured.
111 5p. Type **37** 15 20
112 25p. "Adoration of the Kings" 40 55

38 Young Woman's Costume   39 Old Mail Bus

1979. Local Costumes. Multicoloured.
113 3p. Type **38** 10 10
114 5p. Young man's costume . . 10 20
115 12p. Newly-weds 20 30

1979. Europa.
116 **39** 5p. green & blue on yellow 15 20
117 – 12p. lilac and red on yellow 30 60
DESIGN: 12p. Pre-stamp letters.

40 Drawing of Boy and Girl   41 Agnus Dei, Santa Coloma Church

1979. International Year of the Child.
118 **40** 19p. blue, red and black 30 50

1979. Christmas. Multicoloured.
119 **41** 8p. Santa Coloma Church 15 20
120 25p. Type **41** 30 50

42 Pere d'Urg   43 Antoni Fiter i Rosell

1979. Bishops of Urgel, Co-princes of Andorra (1st series).
121 **42** 1p. blue and brown 10 10
122 – 5p. red and violet 10 20
123 – 13p. brown and green . . . 15 30
DESIGNS: 5p. Joseph Caixal; 13p. Joan Benlloch.
See also Nos. 137/8, 171, 182 and 189.

1980. Europa.
124 **43** 8p. brown, ochre and green 15 20
125 – 19p. black, green & dp grn 35 55
DESIGN: 19p. Francesc Cairat i Freixes.

44 Skiing

1980. Olympic Games, Moscow.
126 **44** 5p. turquoise, red and blk 10 20
127 – 8p. multicoloured 10 20
128 – 50p. multicoloured 40 65
DESIGNS: 8p. Boxing; 50p. Shooting.

45 Nativity

46 Santa Anna Dance

1980. Christmas. Multicoloured.
129 10p. Type **45** 10 20
130 22p. Epiphany 20 45

1981. Europa. Multicoloured.
131 12p. Type **46** 15 15
132 30p. Festival of the Virgin of Canolich 35 55

47 Militia Members

1981. 50th Anniv of People's Militia.
133 **47** 30p. green, grey and black 30 65

48 Handicapped Child learning to Write

1981. International Year of Disabled Persons.
134 **48** 50p. multicoloured 50 90

49 "The Nativity"

50 Arms of Andorra

1981. Christmas. Carvings from Encamp Church. Multicoloured.
135 12p. Type **49** 15 30
136 30p. "The Adoration" . . . 25 45

1981. Bishops of Urgel, Co-princes of Andorra (2nd series). As T **42**.
137 7p. purple and blue 15 20
138 20p. brown and green 20 50
DESIGNS: 7p. Salvador Casanas; 20p. Josep de Boltas.

1982. With "PTA" under figure of value.
139 **50** 1p. mauve 10 10
140 3p. brown 10 10
141 7p. red 10 10
142 12p. red 10 20
143 15p. blue 20 20
144 20p. green 20 20
145 30p. red 20 35
146 50p. green (25 × 31 mm) . . 65 55
147 100p. blue (25 × 31 mm) . . 1·50 95
See also Nos. 203/6.

51 The New Reforms, 1866

1982. Europa. Multicoloured.
154 14p. Type **51** 30 20
155 33p. Reform of the Institutions, 1981 . . . . . 40 75

52 Footballers

1982. World Cup Football Championship, Spain. Multicoloured.
156 14p. Type **52** 45 55
157 33p. Tackle . . . . 85 1·10

53 Arms and 1929 1p. stamp

1982. National Stamp Exhibition.
158 **53** 14p. black and green . . . 30 50

54 Spanish and French Permanent Delegations Buildings

55 "Virgin and Child" (statue from Andorra la Vella Parish Church)

1982. Anniversaries.
159 **54** 9p. brown and blue 15 20
160 – 23p. blue and brown . . . 20 40
161 – 33p. black and green . . . 30 50
DESIGNS—VERT: 9p. Type **54** (centenary of Permanent Delegations); 23p. "St. Francis feeding the Birds" (after Ciambue) (800th birth anniv of St. Francis of Assisi); 33p. Title page of "Relacio sobre la Vall de Andorra" (birth centenary of Tomas Junoy (writer)).

1982. Christmas. Multicoloured.
162 14p. Type **55** 15 20
163 33p. Children beating log with sticks 30 50

56 Building Romanesque Church

57 "Lactarius sanguifluus"

1983. Europa.
164 **56** 16p. green, purple & black 20 20
165 – 38p. brown, blue and black 40 85
DESIGN: 38p. 16th-century water mill.

1983. Nature Protection.
166 **57** 16p. multicoloured 40 65

58 Ballot Box on Map and Government Building

1983. 50th Anniv of Universal Suffrage in Andorra.
167 **58** 10p. multicoloured 15 30

59 Mgr. Cinto Verdaguer

60 Jaume Sansa Nequi

1983. Centenary of Mgr. Cinto Verdaguer's Visit.
168 **59** 50p. multicoloured 50 80

1983. Air. Jaume Sansa Nequi (Verger-Episcopal) Commemoration.
169 **60** 20p. deep brown & brown 20 40

61 Wall Painting, Church of San Cerni, Nagol

1983. Christmas.
170 **61** 16p. multicoloured 20 30

1983. Bishops of Urgel, Co-princes of Andorra (3rd series). As T **42**.
171 26p. brown and red 30 40
DESIGN: 26p. Joan Laguarda.

62 Ski Jumping

1984. Winter Olympic Games, Sarajevo.
172 **62** 16p. multicoloured 20 40

63 Exhibition and F.I.P. Emblems

1984. "Espana 84" Int Stamp Exhibition, Madrid.
173 **63** 26p. multicoloured 30 40

64 Bridge

1984. Europa.
174 **64** 16p. brown 25 25
175 38p. blue 40 40

65 Hurdling

1984. Olympic Games, Los Angeles.
176 **65** 40p. multicoloured 40 70

66 Common Morel

1984. Nature Protection.
177 **66** 11p. multicoloured . . . . 2·00 4·50

67 Pencil, Brush and Pen

68 The Holy Family (wood carvings)

1984. Pyrenean Cultures Centre, Andorra.
178 **67** 20p. multicoloured 20 30

1984. Christmas.
179 **68** 17p. multicoloured 20 30

69 Mossen Enric Marfany and Score

1985. Europa.
180 **69** 18p. green, purple & brown 25 35
181 – 45p. brown and green . . . 55 70
DESIGN: 45p. Musician with viola (fresco detail, La Cortinada Church).

1985. Air. Bishops of Urgel, Co-princes of Andorra (4th series). As T **42**.
182 20p. brown and ochre . . . 20 30
DESIGN: 20p. Ramon Iglesias.

70 Beefsteak Morel

71 Pal

1985. Nature Protection.
183 **70** 30p. multicoloured 40 65

1985.
184 **71** 17p. deep blue and blue . . 20 30

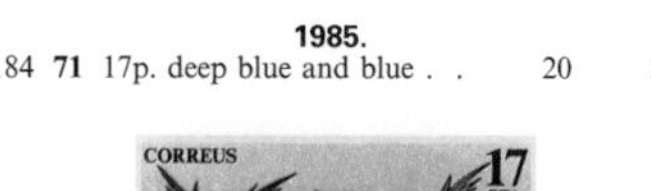

72 Angels (St. Bartholomew's Chapel)

1985. Christmas.
185 **72** 17p. multicoloured 20 30

73 Scotch Bonnet

74 Sun, Rainbow, Lighthouse and Fish

1986. Nature Protection.
186 **73** 30p. multicoloured 35 55

1986. Europa. Each blue, red and green.
187 17p. Type **74** 25 20
188 45p. Sun and trees on rocks 50 80

1986. Bishops of Urgel, Co-princes of Andorra (5th series). As T **42**.
189 35p. blue and brown 30 50
DESIGN: 35p. Justi Guitart.

75 Bell of St. Roma's Chapel, Les Bons

76 Arms

1986. Christmas.
190 **75** 19p. multicoloured 20 30

1987. Meeting of Co-princes.
191 **76** 48p. multicoloured 55 70

77 Interior of Chapel

79 Cep

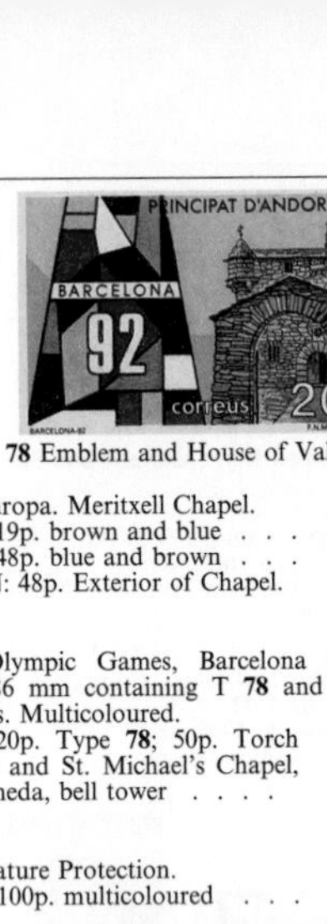

78 Emblem and House of Valleys

1987. Europa. Meritxell Chapel.
192 **77** 19p. brown and blue . . . 25 45
193 – 48p. blue and brown . . . 65 1·10
DESIGN: 48p. Exterior of Chapel.

1987. Olympic Games, Barcelona (1992). Sheet 122 × 86 mm containing T **78** and similar horiz designs. Multicoloured.
MS194 20p. Type **78**; 50p. Torch carrier and St. Michael's Chapel, Fontaneda, bell tower . . . . 4·00 4·00

1987. Nature Protection.
195 **79** 100p. multicoloured . . . 1·20 1·50

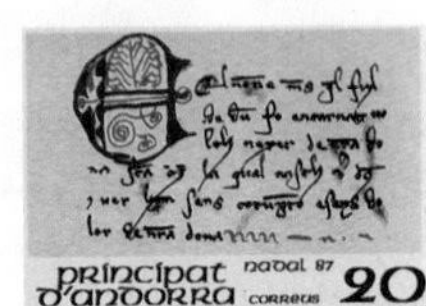

80 Extract from "Doctrina Pueril" by Ramon Llull

1987. Christmas.
196 **80** 20p. multicoloured 20 30

81 Copper Lance Heads

1988. Archaeology.
197 **81** 50p. multicoloured 50 75

82 Early 20th-century Trader and Pack Mules

83 Pyrenean Mountain Dog

1988. Europa. Communications. Each blue and red.
198 20p. Ancient road, Les Bons 35 40
199 45p. Type **82** 70 85

1988. Nature Protection.
200 **83** 20p. multicoloured 40 55

84 Commemorative Coin

86 Leap-frog

85 Church of St. John of Caselles

1988. 700th Anniv of Second Parity Treaty.
201 **84** 20p. black, grey and brown 20 30

1988. Christmas.
202 **85** 20p. multicoloured 20 30

1988. As T **50** but without "PTA" under figure of value.
203 20p. green 20 25
204 50p. green (25 × 31 mm) . . . 55 45
205 100p. blue (25 × 31 mm) . . . 1·30 90
206 500p. brown (25 × 31 mm) . . 6·00 6·75

1989. Europa. Children's Games. Multicoloured.
210 20p. Type **86** 35 70
211 45p. Girl trying to pull child from grip of other children (horiz) . . . . 70 1·30

87 St. Roma's Chapel, Les Bons

1989.
212 **87** 50p. black, green and blue 50 65

88 Anniversary Emblem

89 "Virgin Mary" (detail of altarpiece, Les Escaldes Church)

1989. 125th Anniv of International Red Cross.
213 **88** 20p. multicoloured 30 50

1989. Christmas.
214 **89** 20p. multicoloured 25 40

90 Old French and Spanish Post Offices, Andorra La Vella

1990. Europa. Post Office Buildings. Multicoloured.
215 20p. Type **90** 50 60
216 50p. Modern Spanish post office, Andorra La Vella (vert) . . . . 1·10 1·00

91 "Gomphidius rutilus"

1990. Nature Protection.
217 **91** 45p. multicoloured 55 55

92 Plandolit House

93 Angel, La Massana Church

1990.
218 **92** 20p. brown and yellow . . 20 20

1990. Christmas.
219 **93** 25p. brown, stone and red 25 40

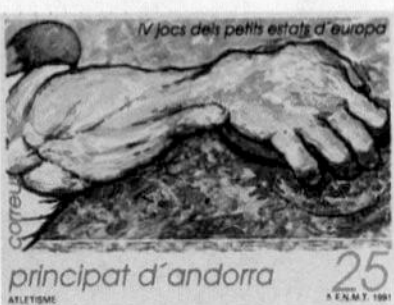

94 Throwing the Discus

1991. European Small States' Games. Multicoloured.
220 25p. Type **94** 55 70
221 45p. High jumping and running 85 85

95 "Olympus 1" Satellite

96 Parasol Mushroom

1991. Europa. Europe in Space. Multicoloured.
222 25p. Type **95** 35 75
223 55p. Close-up of "Olympus 1" telecommunications satellite (horiz) . . . . 70 1·20

1991. Nature Protection.
224 **96** 45p. multicoloured 55 70

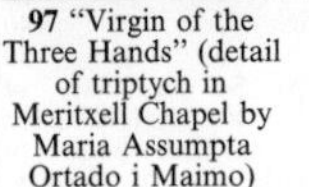

97 "Virgin of the Three Hands" (detail of triptych in Meritxell Chapel by Maria Assumpta Ortado i Maimo)

98 Woman fetching Water from Public Tap

1991. Christmas.
225 **97** 25p. multicoloured 25 40

1992.
226 **98** 25p. multicoloured 25 40

99 "Santa Maria"

100 White-water Canoeing

1992. Europa. 500th Anniv of Discovery of America by Columbus.
227 **99** 27p. multicoloured 70 70
228 – 45p. brown, red and orange . . . . 1·10 1·10
DESIGN—HORIZ: 45p. Engraving of King Ferdinand from map sent by Columbus to Ferdinand and Queen Isabella the Catholic.

1992. Olympic Games, Barcelona.
229 **100** 27p. multicoloured . . . 30 40

101 Benz Velo, 1894 and Sedanca de ville, 1920s

1992. National Motor Car Museum, Encamp.
230 **101** 27p. multicoloured . . . 30 40

102 "Nativity" (Fra Angelico)

1992. Christmas.
231 **102** 27p. multicoloured . . . 30 40

103 Chanterelle

1993. Nature Protection.
232 **103** 28p. multicoloured . . . 30 40

104 "Upstream" (J. A. Morrison)

1993. Europa. Contemporary Art. Multicoloured.
233 28p. Type **104** 45 50
234 45p. "Ritme" (Angel Calvente) (vert) 60 65

105 Society Emblem on National Colours

106 Illuminated "P" (Galceran de Vilanova Missal)

1993. 25th Anniv of Andorran Arts and Letters Circle.
235 **105** 28p. multicoloured . . . 30 40

1993. Christmas.
236 **106** 28p. multicoloured . . . 30 40

107 National Colours

1994. 1st Anniv of New Constitution. Sheet 105 × 78 mm.
MS237 **107** 29p. multicoloured 50 50

108 Sir Alexander Fleming and Penicillin

1994. Europa. Discoveries.
238 **108** 29p. multicoloured . . . 40 50
239 – 55p. blue and black . . . 65 85
DESIGN: 55p. Test tube and AIDS virus.

109 "Hygrophorus gliocyclus"

110 "Madonna and Child" (anon)

1994. Nature Protection.
240 **109** 29p. multicoloured . . . 30 45

1994. Christmas.
241 **110** 29p. multicoloured . . . 30 45

111 Madriu Valley (south)

1995. European Nature Conservation Year. Mult.
242 30p. Type **111** 30 40
243 60p. Madriu Valley (north) 50 75

112 Sun, Dove and Barbed Wire

113 "Flight into Egypt" (altarpiece, St. Mark and St. Mary Church, Encamp)

1995. Europa. Peace and Freedom.
244 **112** 60p. green, orange & blk 1·10 1·10

1995. Christmas.
245 **113** 30p. multicoloured . . . 30 40

114 Palace of Europe, Strasbourg

1995. Admission of Andorra to Council of Europe.
246 **114** 30p. multicoloured . . . 30 40

115 "Ramaria aurea"

1996. Nature Protection. Multicoloured.
247 30p. Type **115** 30 40
248 60p. Black truffles 40 85

116 Isabelle Sandy (writer)

1996. Europa. Famous Women.
249 **116** 60p. multicoloured . . . 1·40 1·30

117 Old Iron

1996. International Museums Day.
250 **117** 60p. multicoloured . . . 55 85

118 "The Annunciation" (altarpiece, St. Eulalia's Church, Encamp)

1996. Christmas.
251 **118** 30p. multicoloured . . . 30 40

119 Drais Velocipede, 1818

1997. Bicycle Museum (1st series). Multicoloured.
252 32p. Type **119** 25 45
253 65p. Michaux velocipede, 1861 . . . . 60 70
See also Nos. 258/9 and 264/5.

120 The Bear and The Smugglers

121 Dove and Cultural Symbols

1997. Europa. Tales and Legends.
254 **120** 65p. multicoloured . . . 1·40 1·40

1997. National U.N.E.S.C.O. Commission.
255 **121** 32p. multicoloured . . . 30 40

122 Catalan Crib Figure

1997. Christmas.
256 **122** 32p. multicoloured . . . 30 40

123 Giant Slalom

1998. Winter Olympic Games, Nagano, Japan.
257 **123** 35p. multicoloured . . . 30 45

1998. Bicycle Museum (2nd series). As T **119**. Multicoloured
258 35p. Kangaroo bicycle, Great Britain, 1878 . . . . . . 30 45
259 70p. The Swallow, France, 1889 . . . . 55 85

124 Harlequins of Canillo

1998. Europa. National Festivals.
260 **124** 70p. multicoloured . . . 1·10 1·10

125 Front Page of First Edition and Landscape

1998. 250th Anniv of "Manual Digest".
261 **125** 35p. multicoloured . . . 30 40

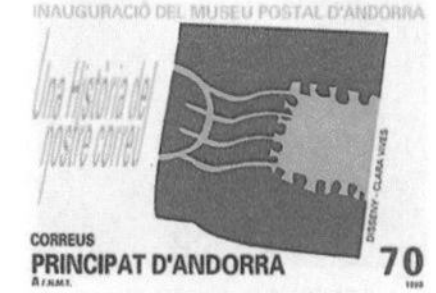

126 Emblem

1998. Inauguration of Postal Museum.
262 **126** 70p. violet and yellow . . 55 85

127 St. Lucia Fair

1998. Christmas.
263 **127** 35p. multicoloured . . . 30 40

1999. Bicycle Museum (3rd series). As T **119**. Multicoloured.
264 35p. Salvo tricycle, 1878 (vert) 25 40
265 70p. Rudge tricycle, Coventry, England 55 80

128 Mules

1999. Postal History.
266 **128** 35p. black and brown . . 30 40

129 Palace of Human Rights, Strasbourg

1999. 50th Anniv of Council of Europe.
267 **129** 35p. multicoloured . . . 30 30

130 Vall d'Incles National Park, Canillo

1999. Europa. Parks and Gardens.
268 **130** 70p. multicoloured . . . 1·10 1·10

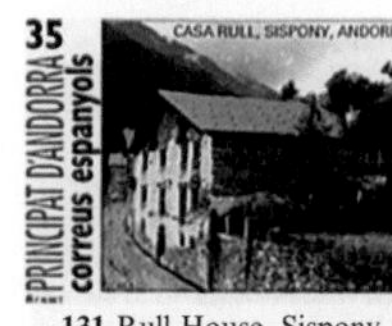

131 Rull House, Sispony

1999.
269 **131** 35p. multicoloured . . . 30 30

132 Angel (detail of altarpiece, St. Serni's Church, Canillo)

133 Santa Coloma Church

1999. Christmas.
270 **132** 35p. brown and light brown 30 40

1999. European Heritage.
271 **133** 35p. multicoloured . . . 30 40

134 "Building Europe"

2000. Europa.
272 **134** 70p. multicoloured . . . 1·10 1·10

135 Angonella Lakes, Ordino

2000.
273 **135** 35p. multicoloured . . . 30 40

136 Casa Lacruz

2000. 131st Birth Anniv of Josep Cadafalch (architect).
274 **136** 35p. multicoloured . . . 55 55

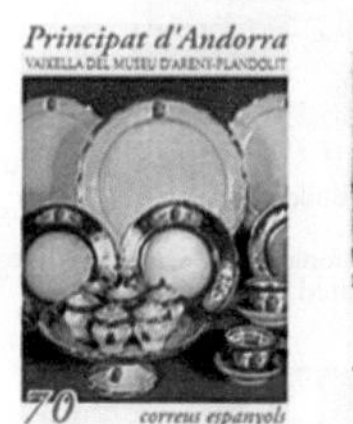

137 Dinner Service

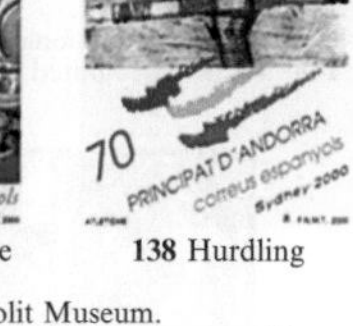

138 Hurdling

2000. D'Areny-Plandolit Museum.
275 **137** 70p. multicoloured . . . 55 75

2000. Olympic Games, Sydney.
276 **138** 70p. multicoloured . . . 55 75

139 United Nations Headquarters, Strasbourg

2000. 50th Anniv of United Nations Declaration of Human Rights.
277 **139** 70p. multicoloured . . . 55 75

140 Gradual, St. Roma, Les Bons

141 "Quadre de les Animes" (Joan Casanovas)

2000. 25th Anniv of the National Archives.
278 **140** 35p. multicoloured . . . 30 40

2000. Christmas.
279 **141** 35p. multicoloured . . . 30 40

142 Rec del Sola

2001. Natural Heritage.

280	**142**	40p. multicoloured	30	45

143 Roc del Metge (thermal spring), Escaldes-Engordany

2001. Europa. Water Resources.

281	**143**	75p. muticoloured	75	95

144 Casa Palau, Sant Julia de Loria

145 Part of Sanctuary, Meritxell

2001.

282	**144**	75p. multicoloured	55	85

2001. 25th Anniv of Chapel of Our Lady, Meritxell.

283	**145**	40p. multicoloured	30	45

146 Building

2001. 10th Anniv of National Auditorium, Ordino.

284	**146**	75p. multicoloured	30	70

147 Angel (detail of altarpiece, Church of St. John of Caselles)

2001. Christmas.

285	**147**	40p. multicoloured	30	55

New Currency
100 cents = 1 euro

148 State Arms

2002.

286	**148**	25c. orange	30	55
287		50c. red	65	1·10

149 Alpine Accentor (*Prunella collaris*)

2002. Native Birds. Multicoloured.

300		25c. Type **149**	30	55
301		50c. Snow finch (*Montifringilla nivalis*)	65	1·10

150 Emblem

2002. International Year of the Mountain.

302	**150**	50c. multicoloured	65	1·10

151 Tightrope Walker

2002. Europa. Circus.

303	**151**	50c. multicoloured	14·00	7·75

152 Casa Fusile, Escaldes-Engordany

153 Pinette Minim

2002. Architectural Heritage. Multicoloured.

304		€1.80 Type **152**	2·30	3·50
305		€2.10 Farga Rossell Iron Museum, La Massana	2·75	4·25

2002. History of the Motor Car (1st series). Multicoloured.

306		25c. Type **153**	30	55
307		50c. Rolls Royce Silver Wraith	65	1·10

See also Nos. 317/18.

154 Placa Benlloch, Areny-Plandolit

2002. Christmas.

308	**154**	25c. multicoloured	30	70

155 Painted Medallion

156 Sassanat Bridge

2002. Cultural Heritage. Romanesque Murals from Santa Coloma Church, Andorra la Vella.

309		25c. Type **155**	30	30
310		50c. Part of damaged fresco showing seated figure	65	65
311		75c. Frieze	95	95

2003.

312	**156**	26c. multicoloured	35	35

157 State Arms

2003. 10th Anniv of Constitution.

313	**157**	76c. multicoloured	1·00	1·00

158 Man drinking, Donkey and Market Stalls

159 Northern Wheatear (*Oenanthe oenanthe*)

2003. Europa. Poster Art.

314	**158**	76c. multicoloured	1·10	1·00

2003. Native Birds.

315	**159**	50c. multicoloured	70	70

160 Multicoloured Stripes

2003. 10th Anniv of Andorras' Membership of United Nations.

316	**160**	76c. multicoloured	1·00	1·00

161 Carter (1908)

2003. History of the Motor Car (2nd series). Multicoloured.

317		51c. Type **161**	70	70
318		76c. Peugeot (1928) (horiz)	1·00	1·00

162 Roadside Cross, Andorra la Vella

2003. Christmas.

319	**162**	26c. multicoloured	35	35

EXPRESS LETTER STAMPS

1928. Express Letter stamp of Spain optd **CORREOS ANDORRA**.

E15	E **53**	20c. red	30·00	55·00

E **4** Lammergeier over Pyrenees

E **12** Eurasian Red Squirrel (after Durer) and Arms

1929.

E41	E **4**	20c. red	3·50	5·50

1949.

E54	E **12**	25c. red	2·75	3·75

ANGOLA Pt. 9; Pt. 12

Republic of Southern Africa. Independent of Portugal since 11 November 1975.

1870. 1000 reis = 1 milreis.
1913. 100 centavos = 1 escudo.
1932. 100 centavos = 1 angolar.
1954. 100 centavos = 1 escudo.
1977. 100 lweis = 1 kwanza.

1870. "Crown" key-type inscr "ANGOLA".

7	P	5r. black	1·60	1·10
17		10r. yellow	16·00	9·25
31		10r. green	6·00	3·25
9		20r. bistre	1·70	1·50
26		20r. red	14·00	10·50
10		25r. red	8·25	6·00
27		25r. purple	9·00	3·75
19b		40r. blue	19·00	17·00
33		40r. yellow	8·25	3·75
12		50r. green	40·00	11·00
30		50r. blue	36·00	8·00
21a		100r. lilac	4·25	2·75
22		200r. orange	3·00	1·50
23a		300r. brown	4·25	2·75

1886. "Embossed" key-type inscr "PROVINCIA DE ANGOLA".

35	Q	5r. black	9·75	4·50
36		10r. green	9·75	4·50
37		20r. red	13·00	9·25
39		25r. mauve	9·75	3·00
40		40r. brown	12·00	5·50
41		50r. blue	15·00	3·00
42		100r. brown	21·00	7·75
43		200r. violet	28·00	9·50
44		300r. orange	29·00	10·50

1894. "Figures" key-type inscr "ANGOLA".

49	R	5r. orange	2·30	1·00
62		10r. mauve	3·25	2·00
63		15r. brown	4·00	1·80
54		20r. lavender	4·00	1·80
74		25r. green	4·00	1·80
66		50r. blue	5·00	2·40
67		75r. red	8·50	7·25
68		80r. green	9·75	5·25
69		100r. brown on buff	9·75	5·25
70		150r. red on rose	16·00	10·50
77		200r. blue on blue	16·00	10·50
78		300r. blue on brown	16·00	10·50

1894. No. N51 with circular surch **CORREIOS DE ANGOLA 25 REIS**.

79b	V	25r. on 2½r. brown	46·00	46·00

1898. "King Carlos" key-type inscr "ANGOLA".

80	S	2½r. grey	40	35
81		5r. orange	40	35
82		10r. green	40	35
83		15r. brown	2·30	1·20
142		15r. green	1·20	1·10
84		20r. lilac	50	40
85		25r. green	1·20	50
143		25r. red	60	35
86		50r. blue	2·10	70
144		50r. brown	5·75	1·90
145		65r. blue	6·00	4·25
87		75r. red	7·25	4·50
146		75r. purple	2·30	1·50
88		80r. mauve	7·25	2·30
89		100r. blue on blue	1·40	1·00
147		115r. brown on pink	8·00	5·50
148		130r. brown on yellow	8·00	5·50
90		150r. brown on buff	7·50	4·50
91		200r. purple on pink	4·25	1·30
92		300r. blue on pink	4·75	3·75
149		400r. blue on yellow	4·25	2·75
93		500r. black on blue	4·75	3·75
94		700r. mauve on yellow	23·00	11·50

1902. "Embossed", "Figures" and "Newspaper" key-types of Angola surch.

98	R	65r. on 5r. orange	6·50	4·50
100		65r. on 10r. mauve	8·00	4·50
102		65r. on 20r. violet	6·50	4·50
104		65r. on 25r. green	9·75	6·00
95	Q	65r. on 40r. brown	8·00	4·50
96		65r. on 300r. orange	8·00	4·50
106		115r. on 10r. green	6·50	3·75
109	R	115r. on 80r. green	24·00	6·00
111		115r. on 100r. brn on buff	9·75	5·25
113		115r. on 150r. red on rose	8·00	7·25
108	Q	115r. on 200r. violet	6·50	3·75
120	R	130r. on 15r. brown	4·50	3·75
116	Q	130r. on 50r. blue	9·25	3·75
124	R	130r. on 75r. red	4·75	3·25
118	Q	130r. on 100r. brown	6·00	3·75
126	R	130r. on 300r. blue on brn	13·00	11·00
136	V	400r. on 2½r. brown	1·20	1·10
127	Q	400r. on 5r. black	9·50	7·25
128		400r. on 20r. red	47·00	30·00
130		400r. on 25r. mauve	16·00	8·50
131	R	400r. on 50r. pale blue	6·50	4·00
133		400r. on 200r. blue on blue	6·50	5·50

1902. "King Carlos" key-type of Angola optd **PROVISORIO**.

138	S	15r. brown	1·60	1·10
139		25r. green	1·30	60
140		50r. blue	2·00	1·00
141		75r. red	3·25	3·00

1905. No. 145 surch **50 REIS** and bar.

150	S	50r. on 65r. blue	3·00	1·60

1911. "King Carlos" key-type optd **REPUBLICA**.

151	S	2½r. grey	40	30
152		5r. orange	40	30
153		10r. green	40	30
154		15r. green	35	35
155		20r. lilac	40	30
156		25r. red	40	30
157		50r. brown	1·10	85

232 50r. blue (No. 140) 1·10 95
224 75r. purple 1·10 75
234 75r. red (No. 141) 1·40 1·10
225 100r. blue on blue 1·60 1·60
160 115r. brown on pink 1·60 95
161 130r. brown on yellow 1·60 95
226 200r. purple on pink 1·50 1·00
163 400r. blue on yellow 2·20 95
164 500r. black on blue 2·20 1·10
165 700r. mauve on yellow 2·20 1·40

1912. "King Manoel" key-type inscr "ANGOLA" optd **REPUBLICA**.
166 T 2½r. lilac 40 30
167 5r. black 40 30
168 10r. green 40 30
169 20r. red 40 30
170 25r. brown 40 30
171 50r. blue 1·10 85
172 75r. brown 1·20 1·10
173 100r. brown on green 1·60 1·20
174 200r. green on pink 1·60 1·20
175 300r. black on blue 1·60 1·20

1912. "King Carlos" key-type of Angola optd **REPUBLICA** and surch.
176 S 2½ on 15r. green 2·50 1·60
177 5 on 15r. green 3·00 1·60
178 10 on 15r. green 1·90 1·60
179 25 on 75r. red (No. 141) 36·00 28·00
180 25 on 75r. purple 3·00 3·00

1913. Surch **REPUBLICA ANGOLA** and value in figures on "Vasco da Gama" issues of
(a) Portuguese Colonies.
181 ¼c. on 2½r. green 75 45
182 ½c. on 5r. red 75 45
183 1c. on 10r. purple 75 45
184 2½c. on 25r. green 75 45
185 5c. on 50r. blue 75 45
186 7½c. on 75r. brown 3·00 2·50
187 10c. on 100r. brown 1·60 1·10
188 15c. on 150r. bistre 95 80

(b) Macao.
189 ¼c. on ½a. green 1·10 95
190 ½c. on 1a. red 1·10 95
191 1c. on 2a. purple 95 70
192 2½c. on 4a. green 80 60
193 5c. on 8a. blue 80 65
194 7½c. on 12a. brown 3·50 1·60
195 10c. on 16a. brown 1·40 95
196 15c. on 24a. bistre 1·25 95

(c) Timor.
197 ¼c. on ½a. green 1·10 95
198 ½c. on 1a. red 1·10 95
199 1c. on 2a. purple 90 70
200 2½c. on 4a. green 1·90 60
201 5c. on 8a. blue 1·10 75
202 7½c. on 12a. brown 3·50 1·60
203 10c. on 16a. brown 1·40 95
204 15c. on 24a. bistre 1·30 95

1914. "Ceres" key-type inscr "ANGOLA".
296 U ¼c. olive 20 15
297 ½c. black 20 15
298 1c. green 20 15
299 1½c. brown 25 20
300 2c. red 25 20
301 2c. grey 35 30
281 2½c. violet 20 15
303 3c. orange 15 15
304 4c. red 15 15
305 4½c. grey 15 15
284a 5c. blue 95 80
307 6c. mauve 15 15
308 7c. blue 15 15
309 7½c. brown 25 20
288 8c. grey 20 20
311 10c. brown 20 15
312 12c. brown 35 30
313 12c. green 35 30
291 15c. purple 20 15
314 15c. pink 20 15
315 20c. green 85 70
316 24c. blue 70 60
317 25c. brown 90 70
217 30c. brown on green 1·20 1·10
318 30c. green 35 30
218 40c. brown on pink 1·20 1·10
319 40c. blue 70 35
219 50c. orange on pink 4·75 3·50
320 50c. purple 70 35
321 60c. blue 90 55
322 60c. red 43·00 26·00
322a 80c. pink 85 45
220 1e. green on blue 3·25 2·20
323 1e. red 85 45
325 1e. blue 1·40 85
326 2e. purple 1·20 60
327 5e. brown 7·25 5·75
328 10e. pink 16·00 13·00
329 20e. green 55·00 36·00

1914. Provisional stamps of 1902 optd **REPUBLICA**.
233 S 50r. on 65r. blue 3·00 2·10
256 Q 115r. on 10r. green 1·50 1·20
258 R 115r. on 80r. green 1·00 90
261 115r. on 100r. brn on buff 1·20 1·10
263 115r. on 150r. red on rose 90 90
266 Q 115r. on 200r. violet 1·30 1·10
267 R 130r. on 15r. brown 1·00 90
246 Q 130r. on 50r. blue 9·50 9·50
269 R 130r. on 75r. red 1·80 1·10
273 Q 130r. on 100r. brown 80 70
274 R 130r. on 300r. blue on brn 80 70
254 V 400r. on 2½r. brown 55 45

1919. Stamps of 1911, 1912 or 1914 surch.
332 S ½c. on 75r. purple 1·10 95
331 T ½c. on 75r. brown 90 75
336 1c. on 50r. blue 95 85
335 S 2½c. on 100r. blue on buff 1·10 80
334 2½c. on 100r. brown on grn 1·40 1·10
337 4c. on 130r. brown on yell 1·10 80
339 U $04 on 15c. purple 1·10 80
340 $04 on 15c. pink 9·00

341 T $00.5 on 75r. brown 1·10 90
342 U $00.5 on 7½c. brown 80 70

1925. Nos. 136 and 133 surch **Republica 40 C.**
345 V 40c. on 400r. on 2½r. brn 55 55
343 R 40c. on 400r. on 200r. blue on blue 60 45

1931. "Ceres" key-type of Angola surch.
347 U 50c. on 60c. red 1·10 95
348 70c. on 80c. pink 2·20 1·40
349 70c. on 1e. blue 1·80 1·40
350 1e.40 on 2e. purple 1·30 80

17 Ceres

1932.
351 17 1c. brown 15 15
352 5c. sepia 20 20
353 10c. mauve 20 20
354 15c. black 20 20
355 20c. grey 20 20
356 30c. green 20 20
357 35c. green 4·75 2·50
358 40c. red 30 15
359 45c. blue 85 70
360 50c. brown 20 15
361 60c. olive 65 20
362 70c. brown 65 20
363 80c. green 40 15
364 85c. red 2·50 1·20
365 1a. red 60 20
366 1a.40 blue 5·75 2·20
367 1a.75 blue 8·00 3·00
368 2a. mauve 2·50 30
369 5a. green 5·75 95
370 10a. brown 11·00 3·00
371 20a. orange 26·00 3·00

1934. Surch.
380 17 5c. on 80c. green (A) 65 30
419 5c. on 80c. green (B) 60 40
413 10c. on 45c. blue 1·10 70
381 10c. on 80c. green 85 45
414 15c. on 45c. blue 1·10 70
382 15c. on 80c. green 1·20 45
415 20c. on 85c. red 1·10 70
374 30c. on 1a.40 blue 1·90 1·40
416 35c. on 85c. red 1·10 70
417 50c. on 1a.40 blue 1·10 70
418 60c. on 1a. red 4·75 4·75
375 70c. on 2a. mauve 2·30 1·40
376 80c. on 5a. green 3·50 1·40
(A) surch **0,05 Cent.** in one line; (B) surch **5 CENTAVOS** in two lines.

1935. "Due" key-type surch **CORREIOS** and new value.
377 W 5c. on 6c. brown 1·20 85
378 30c. on 50c. grey 1·20 85
379 40c. on 50c. grey 1·20 85

22 Vasco da Gama
27 Airplane over Globe

1938. Name and value in black.
383 22 1c. olive (postage) 15 15
384 5c. brown 20 20
385 10c. red 20 20
386 15c. purple 20 20
387 20c. grey 20 20
388 – 30c. purple 30 30
389 – 35c. green 60 45
390 – 40c. brown 20 15
391 – 50c. mauve 30 15
392 – 60c. black 60 20
393 – 70c. violet 60 20
394 – 80c. orange 60 20
395 – 1a. red 50 20
396 – 1a.75 blue 1·20 60
397 – 2a. red 1·70 65
398 – 5a. olive 7·25 65
399 – 10a. blue 14·50 70
400 – 20a. brown 22·00 1·70
401 27 10c. red (air) 30 30
402 20c. violet 30 20
403 50c. orange 30 20
404 1a. blue 30 20
405 2a. red 60 20
406 3a. green 55 35
407 5a. brown 5·25 80
408 9a. red 4·25 8·50
409 10a. mauve 5·75 1·10
DESIGNS: 30c. to 50c. Mousinho de Albuquerque; 60c. to 1a. "Fomento" (symbolizing Progress); 1a.75, 2, 5a. Prince Henry the Navigator; 10, 20a. Afonso de Albuquerque.

28 Portuguese Colonial Column
31 Arms of Angola

1938. President's Colonial Tour.
410 28 80c. green 1·70 1·20
411 1a.75 blue 11·50 3·50
412 20a. brown 32·00 17·00

1945. Nos. 394/6 surch.
420 5c. on 80c. orange 50 35
421 50c. on 1a. red 50 35
422 50c. on 1a.75 blue 50 35

1947. Air.
423a 31 1a. brown 70 45
423b 2a. green 6·25 3·00
423c 3a. orange 6·25 3·00
423d 3a.50 orange 12·50 3·00
423e 5a. green 40·00 14·50
423f 6a. pink 40·00 9·50
423g 9a. red £140 £140
423h 10a. green 95·00 60·00
423i 20a. blue £130 60·00
423j 50a. black £200 £140
423k 100a. yellow £250 £225

32 Sao Miguel Fortress, Luanda
33 Our Lady of Fatima

1948. Tercentenary of Restoration of Angola. Inscr "Tricentenario da Restauracao de Angola 1648–1948".
424 32 5c. violet 15 10
425 – 10c. brown 45 15
426 – 30c. green 15 10
427 – 50c. purple 15 10
428 – 1a. red 45 10
429 – 1a.75 blue 70 10
430 – 2a. green 70 10
431 – 5a. black 2·30 35
432 – 10a. mauve 5·50 45
433 – 20a. blue 11·50 2·50
DESIGNS—HORIZ: 10c. Our Lady of Nazareth Hermitage, Luanda; 1a. Surrender of Luanda; 5a. Inscribed Rocks of Yelala; 20a. Massangano Fortress. VERT (portraits): 30c. Don John IV; 50c. Salvador Correia de Sa Benevides; 1a.75, Dioga Cao; 7a. Manuel Cerveira Pereira; 10a. Paulo Dias de Novais.

1948. Honouring Our Lady of Fatima.
434 33 50c. red 1·80 1·10
435 3a. blue 7·00 2·20
436 6a. orange 22·00 5·50
437 9a. red 60·00 7·00

35 River Chiumbe
36 Pedras Negras

1949.
438 35 20c. blue 30 15
439 36 40c. brown 30 10
440 – 50c. red 30 10
441 – 2a.50 blue 1·80 30
442 – 3a.50 grey 1·80 1·40
443 – 15a. green 14·50 1·40
444 – 50a. green 80·00 5·00
DESIGNS—As T 35: 50c. Luanda; 2a.50, Bandeira; 3a.50, Mocamedes; 50a. Braganza Falls. 31 × 26 mm: 15a. River Cubal.

37 Aircraft and Globe
38 "Tentativa Feliz"

1949. Air.
445 37 1a. orange 50 10
446 2a. brown 1·10 10
447 3a. mauve 1·40 15
448 6a. green 2·50 50
449 9a. purple 3·50 1·20

1949. Centenary of Founding of Mocamedes.
450 38 1a. purple 5·75 65
451 4a. green 14·50 1·80

39 Letter and Globe
40 Reproduction of "Crown" key-type

1949. 75th Anniv of U.P.U.
452 39 4a. green 7·25 1·60

1950. Philatelic Exhibition and 80th Anniv of First Angolan Stamp.
453 40 50a. green 1·00 30
454 1a. red 1·00 50
455 4a. black 3·25 1·30
MS455a 120 × 79 mm. Nos. 453/5 (sold at 6a.50) 15·00 11·00

41 Bells and Dove
42 Angels holding Candelabra

1950. Holy Year.
456 41 1a. violet 70 15
457 42 4a. black 3·25 60

43 Dark Chanting Goshawk
44 Our Lady of Fatima

1951. Birds. Multicoloured.
458 5c. Type 43 30 15
459 10c. Racquet-tailed roller 30 15
460 15c. Bateleur 45 15
461 20c. European bee eater 45 30
462 50c. Giant kingfisher 45 15
463 1a. Anchieta's barbet 45 15
464 1a.50 African open-bill stork 65 15
465 2a. Southern ground hornbill 65 15
466 2a.50 African skimmer 95 15
467 3a. Shikra 65 15
468 3a.50 Senham's bustard 95 15
469 4a. African golden oriole 1·00 15
470 4a.50 Magpie shrike 1·00 15
471 5a. Red-shouldered glossy starling 3·50 35
472 6a. Sharp-tailed glossy starling 5·00 95
473 7a. Fan-tailed whydah 5·75 1·20
474 10a. Half-collared kingfisher 23·00 1·60
475 12a.50 White-crowned shrike 6·25 2·00
476 15a. White-winged starling 5·75 2·00
477 20a. Southern yellow-billed hornbill 55·00 5·00
478 25a. Violet starling 20·00 4·25
479 30a. Sulphur-breasted bush shrike 20·00 5·00
480 40a. Secretary bird 29·00 7·00
481 50a. Peach-faced lovebird 70·00 14·50
The 10, 15 and 20c., 2a.50, 3a., 4a.50, 12a.50 and 30a. are horiz, the remainder vert.

1951. Termination of Holy Year.
482 44 4a. orange 2·30 1·10

45 Laboratory
46 The Sacred Face

1952. 1st Tropical Medicine Congress, Lisbon.
483 45 1a. grey and blue 80 30

1952. Missionary Art Exhibition.
484 46 10c. blue and flesh 15 15
485 50c. green and stone 65 15
486 2a. purple and flesh 2·30 45

47 Leopard

48 Stamp of 1853 and Colonial Arms

1953. Angolan Fauna. Multicoloured.

487		5c. Type **47**	15	15
488		10c. Sable antelope (vert)	15	15
489		20c. African elephant (vert)	15	15
490		30c. Eland (vert)	15	15
491		40c. Crocodile	15	15
492		50c. Impala (vert)	15	15
493		1a. Mountain zebra (vert)	20	15
494		1a.50 Sitatunga (vert)	20	15
495		2a. Black rhinoceros	20	15
496		2a.30 Gemsbok (vert)	20	15
497		2a.50 Lion (vert)	30	15
498		3a. African buffalo	35	15
499		3a.50 Springbok (vert)	35	15
500		4a. Blue wildebeest (vert)	12·50	15
501		5a. Hartebeest (vert)	60	15
502		7a. Warthog (vert)	85	15
503		10a. Waterbuck (vert)	1·80	15
504		12a.50 Hippopotamus (vert)	4·75	95
505		15a. Greater kudu (vert)	5·75	95
506		20a. Giraffe (vert)	7·25	60

1953. Portuguese Stamp Centenary.

507	**48**	50c. multicoloured	45	35

49 Father M. da Nobrega and Sao Paulo

50 Route of President's Tour

1954. 4th Centenary of Sao Paulo.

508	**49**	1e. black and buff	30	15

1954. Presidential Visit.

509	**50**	35c. multicoloured	10	10
510		4e.50 multicoloured	70	35

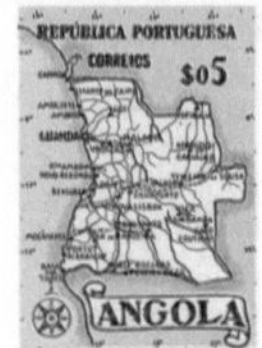

51 Map of Angola

52 Col. A. de Paiva

1955. Map mult. Angola territory in colour given.

511	**51**	5c. white	15	15
512		20c. salmon	15	15
513		50c. blue	15	15
514		1e. orange	15	15
515		2e.30 yellow	80	30
516		4e. blue	1·60	15
517		10e. green	1·40	15
518		20e. white	2·75	1·20

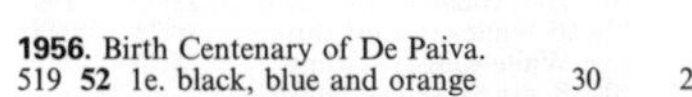

1956. Birth Centenary of De Paiva.

519	**52**	1e. black, blue and orange	30	20

53 Quela Chief

54 Father J. M. Antunes

1957. Natives. Multicoloured.

520		5c. Type **53**	15	15
521		10c. Andulo flute player	15	15
522		15c. Dembos man and woman	15	15
523		20c. Quissama dancer (male)	15	15
524		30c. Quibala family	15	15
525		40c. Bocolo dancer (female)	15	15
526		50c. Quissama woman	15	15
527		80c. Cuanhama woman	20	15
528		1e.50 Luanda widow	1·70	15
529		2e.50 Bocolo dancer (male)	1·70	15
530		4e. Muquixe man	85	15
531		10e. Cabinda chief	1·60	30

1957. Birth Centenary of Father Antunes.

532	**54**	1e. multicoloured	60	30

55 Exhibition Emblem, Globe and Arms

1958. Brussels International Exhibition.

533	**55**	1e.50 multicoloured	50	45

56 "Securidaca longipedunculata"

57 Native Doctor and Patient

1958. 6th Int Tropical Medicine Congress.

534	**56**	2e.50 multicoloured	1·90	65

1958. 75th Anniv of Maria Pia Hospital, Luanda.

535	**57**	1e. brown, black and blue	35	20
536	–	1e.50 multicoloured	85	45
537	–	2e.50 multicoloured	1·60	80

DESIGNS: 1e.50, 17th-century doctor and patient; 2e.50, Present-day doctor, orderly and patients.

58 Welwitschia (plant)

59 Old Map of West Africa

1959. Centenary of Discovery of Welwitschia.

538	**58**	1e.50 multicoloured	70	35
539	–	2e.50 multicoloured	1·10	45
540	–	5e. multicoloured	1·80	45
541	–	10e. multicoloured	5·50	1·40

DESIGNS: 2e.50, 5, 10e. Various types of Welwitschia ("Welwitschia mirabilis").

1960. 500th Death Anniv of Prince Henry the Navigator.

542	**59**	2e.50 multicoloured	45	20

60 "Agriculture" (distribution of seeds)

61

1960. 10th Anniv of African Technical Co-operation Commission.

543	**60**	2e.50 multicoloured	50	20

1961. Angolan Women. As T **61**. Portraits multicoloured; background colours given.

544		10c. green	10	10
545		15c. blue	10	10
546		30c. yellow	10	10
547		40c. grey	10	10
548		60c. brown	10	10
549		1e.50 turquoise	15	10
550		2e. lilac	80	10
551		2e.50 lemon	80	10
552		3e. pink	3·00	20
553		4e. olive	1·40	20
554		5e. blue	95	20
555		7e.50 yellow	1·30	65
556		10e. buff	95	50
557		15c. brown	1·40	65
558		25e. red	2·00	95
559		50e. grey	4·25	2·00

62 Weightlifting

1962. Sports. Multicoloured.

560		50e. Flying	15	15
561		1e. Rowing	85	15
562		1e.50 Water polo	60	20
563		2e.50 Throwing the hammer	70	20
564		4e.50 High jumping	60	45
565		15e. Type **62**	1·40	1·10

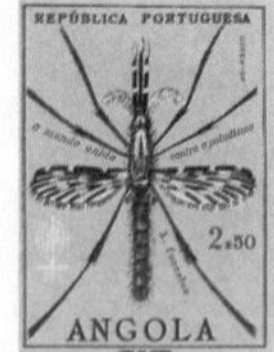

63 "Anopheles funestus" (mosquito)

64 Gen. Norton de Matos (statue)

1962. Malaria Eradication.

566	**63**	2e.50 multicoloured	1·30	60

1962. 50th Anniv of Nova Lisboa.

567	**64**	2e.50 multicoloured	45	20

65 Red Locusts

1963. 15th Anniv of Int Locust Eradication Service.

568	**65**	2e.50 multicoloured	1·30	35

66 Arms of St. Paul of the Assumption, Luanda

67 Rear-Admiral A. Tomas

1963. Angolan Civic Arms (1st series). Mult.

569		5c. Type **66**	15	15
570		10c. Massangano	15	15
571		30c. Muxima	15	15
572		50c. Carmona	15	15
573		1e. Salazar	50	15
574		1e.50 Malanje	95	15
575		2e. Henry of Carvalho	50	15
576		2e.50 Mocamedes	3·00	45
577		3e. Novo Redondo	70	15
578		3e.50 St. Salvador (Congo)	80	15
579		5e. Luso	70	20
580		7e.50 St. Philip (Benguela)	95	80
581		10e. Lobito	1·20	70
582		12e.50 Gabela	1·30	1·20
583		15e. Sa da Bandeira	1·30	1·20
584		17e.50 Silva Porto	2·20	1·90
585		20e. Nova Lisboa	2·20	1·60
586		22e.50 Cabinda	2·20	1·90
587		30e. Serpa Pinto	2·50	2·50

See also Nos. 589/610.

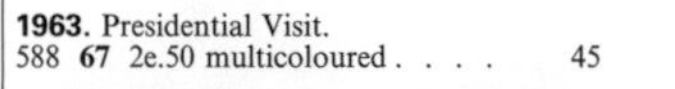

1963. Presidential Visit.

588	**67**	2e.50 multicoloured	45	15

68 Arms of Sanza-Pombo

69 Map of Africa, Boeing 707 and Lockheed Super Constellation Airliners

1963. Angolan Civic Arms (2nd series). Mult.

589		15c. Type **68**	15	15
590		20c. St. Antonio do Zaire	15	15
591		25c. Ambriz	15	15
592		40c. Ambrizete	15	15
593		50c. Catete	15	15
594		70c. Quibaxe	15	15
595		1e. Maquela do Zombo	15	15
596		1e.20 Bembe	15	15
597		1e.50 Caxito	50	15
598		1e.80 Dondo	50	45
599		2e.50 Damba	1·90	15
600		4e. Cuimba	45	15
601		6e.50 Negage	45	30
602		7e. Quitexe	65	45
603		8e. Mucaba	65	50
604		9e. 31 de Janeiro	95	80
605		11e. Novo Caipemba	1·10	95
606		14e. Songo	1·20	1·10
607		17e. Quimbele	1·30	1·20
608		25e. Noqui	1·60	1·20
609		35e. Santa Cruz	2·30	1·90
610		50e. General Freire	3·00	1·60

1963. 10th Anniv of T.A.P. Airline.

611	**69**	1e. multicoloured	85	30

70 Bandeira Cathedral

71 Dr. A. T. de Sousa

1963. Angolan Churches. Multicoloured.

612		10c. Type **70**	10	10
613		20c. Landana	10	10
614		30c. Luanda (Cathedral)	10	10
615		40c. Gabela	10	10
616		50c. St. Martin, Bay of Tigers (Chapel)	10	10
617		1e. Melange (Cathedral) (horiz)	15	15
618		1e.50 St. Peter, Chibia	15	15
619		2e. Benguela (horiz)	20	15
620		2e.50 Jesus, Luanda	20	15
621		3e. Camabatela (horiz)	30	15
622		3e.50 Cabinda Mission	45	15
623		4e. Vila Folgares (horiz)	45	20
624		4e.50 Arrabida, Lobito (horiz)	60	20
625		5e. Cabinda	60	30
626		7e.50 Cacuso, Malange (horiz)	95	50
627		10e. Lubanga Mission	1·20	50
628		12e.50 Huila Mission (horiz)	1·40	80
629		15e. Island Cape, Luanda (horiz)	1·60	85

1964. Centenary of National Overseas Bank.

630	**71**	2e.50 multicoloured	60	30

72 Arms and Palace of Commerce, Luanda

73 I.T.U. Emblem and St. Gabriel

1964. Cent of Luanda Commercial Association.

631	**72**	1e. multicoloured	20	15

1965. Centenary of I.T.U.

632	**73**	2e.50 multicoloured	85	45

74 Boeing 707 over Petroleum Refinery

75 Fokker F.27 Friendship over Luanda Airport

1965. Air. Multicoloured.

633		1e.50 Type **74**	80	10
634		2e.50 Cambabe Dam	85	10
635		3e. Salazar Dam	1·20	10
636		4e. Captain Trofilo Duarte Dam	1·20	15
637		4e.50 Creveiro Lopes Dam	85	15
638		5e. Cuango Dam	85	20
639		6e. Quanza Bridge	1·40	30
640		7e. Captain Trofilo Duarte Railway Bridge	2·00	30
641		8e.50 Dr. Oliveira Salazar Bridge	2·50	80
642		12e.50 Captain Silva Carvalho Railway Bridge	2·50	1·10

Nos. 634/42 are horiz and each design includes a Boeing 707 airliner overhead.

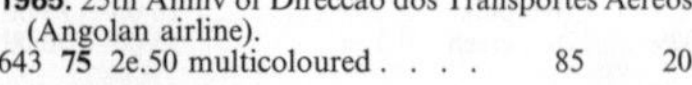

1965. 25th Anniv of Direccao dos Transportes Aereos (Angolan airline).

643	**75**	2e.50 multicoloured	85	20

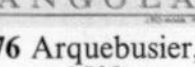

76 Arquebusier, 1539

77 St. Paul's Hospital, Luanda, and Sarmento Rodrigues Commercial and Industrial School

1966. Portuguese Military Uniforms. Multicoloured.

644		50c. Type **76**	10	10
645		1e. Arquebusier, 1640	10	10
646		1e.50 Infantry officer, 1777	15	10
647		2e. Infantry standard-bearer, 1777	25	10

648 2e.50 Infantryman, 1777 . . 25 10
649 3e. Cavalry officer, 1783 . . 35 10
650 4e. Trooper, 1783 . . . . . 40 15
651 4e.50 Infantry officer, 1807 50 25
652 5e. Infantryman, 1807 . . . 60 25
653 6e. Cavalry officer, 1807 . . 85 25
654 8e. Trooper, 1807 . . . . . 1·20 40
655 9e. Infantryman, 1873 . . . 1·20 60

1966. 40th Anniv of National Revolution.
656 **77** 1e. multicoloured 35 15

78 Emblem of Brotherhood

79 Mendes Barata and Cruiser "Don Carlos I"

1966. Centenary of Brotherhood of the Holy Spirit.
657 **78** 1e. multicoloured 25 15

1967. Centenary of Military Naval Assn. Mult.
658 1e. Type **79** 65 35
659 2e.50 Augusto de Castilho and sail/steam corvette "Mindelo" 85 35

80 Basilica of Fatima

81 17th-century Map and M. C. Pereira (founder)

1967. 50th Anniv of Fatima Apparitions.
660 **80** 50c. multicoloured 25 15

1967. 350th Anniv of Benguela.
661 **81** 50c. multicoloured 25 15

82 Town Hall, Uige-Carmona

83 "The Three Orders"

1967. 50th Anniv of Uige-Carmona.
662 **82** 1e. multicoloured 15 15

1967. Portuguese Civil and Military Orders. Mult.
663 50c. Type **83** 15 15
664 1e. "Tower and Sword" . . . 15 15
665 1e.50 "Avis" 15 15
666 2e. "Christ" 15 15
667 2e.50 "St. James of the Sword" 15 15
668 3e. "Empire" 25 15
669 4e. "Prince Henry" 35 35
670 5e. "Benemerencia" 40 35
671 10e. "Public Instruction" . . 75 85
672 20e. "Agricultural and Industrial Merit" . . . . . 1·60 95

84 Belmonte Castle

85 Francisco Inocencio de Souza Countinho

1968. 500th Birth Anniv of Pedro Cabral (explorer). Multicoloured.
673 50c. Our Lady of Hope (vert) 15 15
674 1e. Type **84** 25 15
675 1e.50 St. Jeronimo's hermitage (vert) 35 15
676 2e.50 Cabral's fleet (vert) . . 90 15

1969. Bicent of Novo Redondo (Angolan city).
677 **85** 2e. multicoloured 20 10

86 Gunboat "Loge" and Admiral Coutinho

87 Compass

1969. Birth Centenary of Admiral Gago Coutinho.
678 **86** 2e.50 multicoloured 75 25

1969. 500th Birth Anniv of Vasco da Gama (explorer).
679 **87** 1e. multicoloured 25 15

88 L. A. Rebello de Silva

89 Gate of Jeronimos

1969. Cent of Overseas Administrative Reforms.
680 **88** 1e.50 multicoloured 15 15

1969. 500th Birth Anniv of King Manoel I.
681 **89** 3e. multicoloured 25 15

90 "Angolasaurus bocagei"

91 Marshal Carmona

1970. Fossils and Minerals. Multicoloured.
682 50c. Type **90** 40 15
683 1e. Ferro-meteorite 40 15
684 1e.50 Dioptase 65 40
685 2e. "Gondwanidium validium" 65 40
686 2e.50 Diamonds 65 40
687 3e. Estromatolitos 65 40
688 3e.50 Giant-toothed shark ("Procarcharodon megalodon") . . . . . . 1·10 65
689 4e. Dwarf lungfish ("Microceratodus angolensis") . . 1·10 65
690 4e.50 Muscovite (mica) . . . 1·10 65
691 5e. Barytes . . . . 1·10 65
692 6e. "Nostoceras helicinum" 2·10 90
693 10e. "Rotula orbiculus angolensis" . . . . 2·20 1·30

1970. Birth Centenary of Marshal Carmona.
694 **91** 2e.50 multicoloured 35 15

92 Cotton-picking

1970. Centenary of Malanje Municipality.
695 **92** 2e.50 multicoloured 40 25

93 Mail Steamers "Infante Dom Henrique" and "Principe Perfeito" and 1870 5r. Stamp

94 Map and Emblems

1970. Stamp Centenary. Multicoloured.
696 1e.50 Type **93** (postage) . . . 40 25
697 4e.50 Beyer-Garratt steam locomotive and 25r. stamp of 1870 . . . . 2·20 2·20
698 2e.50 Fokker F.27 Friendship and Boeing 707 mail planes and 10r. stamp of 1870 (air) . . . . 1·50 65
MS699 150 × 105 mm. Nos. 696/8 (sold at 15e.) . . . . 9·50 9·50

1971. 5th Regional Soil and Foundation Engineering Conference, Luanda.
700 **94** 2e.50 multicoloured 25 15

96 16th-century Galleon at Mouth of Congo

97 Sailing Yachts

1972. 400th Anniv of Camoens' "The Lusiads" (epic poem).
704 **96** 1e. multicoloured 50 15

1972. Olympic Games, Munich.
705 **97** 50c. multicoloured 50 15

98 Fairey IIID Seaplane "Santa Cruz" near Fernando de Noronha

1972. 50th Anniv of 1st Flight Lisbon–Rio de Janeiro.
706 **98** 1e. multicoloured 25 15

99 W.M.O. Emblem

1974. Centenary of W.M.O.
707 **99** 1e. multicoloured 35 15

100 Dish Aerials

1974. Inauguration of Satellite Communications Station Network.
708 **100** 2e. multicoloured 35 25

101 Doris Harp

1974. Sea Shells. Multicoloured.
709 25c. Type **101** 10 10
710 30c. West African murex . . 10 10
711 50c. Scaly-ridged venus . . . 10 10
712 70c. Filose latirus 15 10
713 1e. "Cymbium cisium" . . . 15 10
714 1e.50 West African helmet . . 15 10
715 2e. Rat cowrie 15 10
716 2e.50 Butterfly cone 25 10
717 3e. Bubonian conch 35 15
718 3e.50 "Tympanotonus fuscatus" 40 15
719 4e. Great ribbed cockle . . . 40 15
720 5e. Lightning moon 50 15
721 6e. Lion's-paw scallop . . . 60 25
722 7e. Giant tun 75 25
723 10e. Rugose donax . . . . . 1·00 40
724 25e. Smith's distorsio . . . . 3·00 1·10
725 30e. "Olivancilaria acuminata" . . . . 3·00 1·30
726 35e. Giant hairy melongena 3·25 1·70
727 40e. Wavy-leaved turrid . . . 4·50 1·80
728 50e. American sundial . . . 5·75 2·20

1974. Youth Philately. No. 511 optd **1974 FILATELIA JUVENIL**.
729 **51** 5c. multicoloured 15 60

103 Arm with Rifle and Star

104 Diquiche-ua-Puheue Mask

1975. Independence.
730 **103** 1e.50 multicoloured . . . 10 10

1975. Angolan Masks. Multicoloured.
731 50c. Type **104** 10 10
732 3e. Bui ou Congolo mask . . 15 10

105 Workers

107 Pres. Agostinho Neto

1976. Workers' Day.
733 **105** 1e. multicoloured 10 10

1976. Stamp Day. Optd **DIA DO SELO 15 Junho 1976 REP. POPULAR DE.**
734 **51** 10e. multicoloured . . . . 1·50 1·25

1976. 1st Anniv of Independence.
735 **107** 50c. black and grey . . . 10 10
736 2e. purple and grey . . . 10 10
737 3e. blue and grey 10 10
738 5e. brown and buff . . . 15 10
739 10e. brown and drab . . 25 10

1976. St. Silvestre Games. Optd **S Silvestre Rep. Popular de.**
741 **62** 15e. multicoloured 55 35

1977. Nos. 518, 724/5 and 728 optd **REPUBLICA POPULAR DE.**
742 20e. Type **51** . . . . 3·50 3·50
743 25e. "Cymatium trigonum" 60 15
744 30e. "Olivancilaria acuminata" 75 25
745 50e. "Solarium granulatum" 1·25 40

111 Child receiving Vaccine

112 Map of Africa and Flag

1977. Polio Vaccination Campaign.
746 **111** 2k.50 blue and black . . 10 10

1977. MPLA Congress.
747 **112** 6k. multicoloured 20 15

113 Human Rights Flame

114 Emblem

1979. 30th Anniv of Declaration of Human Rights.
748 **113** 2k.50 yellow, red & black 15 10

1979. International Anti-apartheid Year.
749 **114** 1k. multicoloured 10 10

115 Child raising Arms to Light

117 Pres. Agostinho Neto

1980. International Year of the Child (1979).
750 **115** 3k.50 multicoloured . . . 15 10

1980. Nos. 697/8 optd **REPUBLICA POPULAR DE.**
751 4e.50 multicoloured (postage) 2·75 1·75
752 2e.50 multicoloured (air) . . 15 10

1980. National Heroes Day. Multicoloured.
753 4k.50 Type **117** 15 10
754 50k. Pres. Neto with machine-gun . . . . 1·25 70

118 Arms and Workers
119 "The Liberated Angolan" (A. Vaz de Carvalho)

1980. "Popular Power".
755 **118** 40k. blue and black . . . 1·00 55

1980. 5th Anniv of Independence.
756 **119** 5k.50 multicoloured . . . 15 10

120 Running
121 Millet

1980. Olympic Games, Moscow.
757 **120** 9k. pink and red 20 10
758 – 12k. light blue and blue 30 10
DESIGN: 12k. Swimming.

1980. Angolan Produce. Multicoloured.
759 50l. Type **121** 10 10
760 5k. Coffee 15 10
761 7k.50 Sunflower 20 10
762 13k.50 Cotton 30 15
763 14k. Petroleum 30 15
764 16k. Diamonds 35 20

1981. Nos. 708, 713/16 and 718/27 with "REPUBLICA PORTUGUESA" inscr obliterated.
(a) Dish aerials.
765 **100** 2e. multicoloured 10 10

(b) Sea Shells. Multicoloured.
766 1e. "Cymbium cisium" . . . 10 10
767 1e.50 West African helmet . . 15 10
768 2e. Rat cowrie 20 10
769 2e.50 Butterfly cone 25 10
770 3e.50 "Tympanotonus fuscatus" 30 10
771 4e. Great ribbed cockle . . . 35 15
772 5e. Lightning moon 40 15
773 6e. Lion's-paw scallop . . . 45 20
774 7e. Giant tun 50 20
775 10e. Rugose donax 70 25
776 25e. Smith's distorsio . . . . 1·75 30
777 30e. "Olivancilaria acuminata" . . . . 1·90 65
778 35e. Giant hairy melongena 2·40 90
779 40e. Wavy-leaved turrid . . . 3·00 1·00

122 Prisoner and Protesting Crowd

1981. 5th Anniv of Soweto Riots in South Africa.
780 **122** 4k.50 black, red & silver 20 15

123 Basketball and Volleyball

1981. 2nd Central African Games. Multicoloured.
781 50l. Cycling and Tennis . . . 10 10
782 5k. Judo and Boxing 20 15
783 6k. Type **123** 25 15
784 10k. Handball and football 40 20

124 Statuette
125 "Charaxes kahldeni f. homeyri"

1981. "Turipex 81".
785 **124** 9k. multicoloured 40 20

1982. Butterflies. Multicoloured.
787 50l. Type **125** 10 10
788 1k. "Abantis gambesiaca" . . 10 10
789 5k. "Catacroptera cloanthe" 25 30
790 9k. "Myrina ficedula" (vert) 60 25
791 10k. "Colotis danae" 60 25
792 15k. "Acraea acrita bella" . . 80 30
793 100k. "Precis hierta cebrese" 5·25 2·40

126 "Silence of Night"
127 Worker and Building

1982. 5th Anniv of Admission to United Nations. Multicoloured.
794 5k.50 Type **126** 25 15
795 7k.50 "Cotton Fields" . . . 35 15

1982. 20th Anniv of Angola Laboratory of Engineering. Multicoloured.
797 9k. Laboratory building (horiz) 40 20
798 13k. Type **127** (Research in construction materials) . . 45 25
799 100k. Geotechnical equipment 4·00 2·25

128 "Albizzia versicolor"

1983. Flowers (1st series). Multicoloured.
800 5k. "Dichrostachys glomerata" 25 10
801 12k. "Amblygonocarpus obtusangulus" 45 20
802 50k. Type **128** . . . . . . 2·00 1·10

129 Angolan Woman and Emblem

1983. 1st Angolan Women's Organization Congress.
803 **129** 20k. multicoloured . . . 80 25

130 M'pungi (horn)

1983. World Communications Year. Multicoloured.
804 6k.50 Type **130** 25 20
805 12k. Mondu (drum) 50 45

131 Spear breaking Chain around South Africa

1983. 30th Anniv of Organization of African Unity.
806 **131** 6k.50 multicoloured . . . 30 25

132 "Antestiopsis lineaticollis intricata"

1983. "Brasiliana 83" International Stamp Exn, Rio de Janeiro. Harmful Insects. Multicoloured.
807 4k.50 Type **132** 25 15
808 6k.50 "Stephanoderes hampei" 35 25
809 10k. "Zonocerus variegatus" 60 45

133 Map of Africa and E.C.A. Emblem

1983. 25th Anniv of Economic Commission for Africa.
810 **133** 10k. multicoloured . . . 45 40

134 Collecting Mail
136 Dove

135 "Parasa karschi"

1983. 185th Anniv of Postal Service. Multicoloured.
811 50l. Type **134** 10 10
812 3k.50 Unloading mail from aircraft (horiz) 20 15
813 5k. Sorting mail (horiz) . . . 35 25
814 15k. Posting letter 85 80
815 30k. Collecting mail from private box (horiz) . . . . 1·75 1·50

1984. Moths. Multicoloured.
817 50l. Type **135** 10 10
818 1k. "Diaphone angolensis" 10 10
819 3k.50 "Choeropais jucunda" 30 15
820 6k.50 "Hespagarista rendalli" 50 35
821 15k. "Euchromia guineensis" 95 80
822 17k.50 "Mazuca roseistriga" 1·10 95
823 20k. "Utetheisa callima" . . 1·40 1·25

1984. 1st National Union of Angolan Workers Congress.
824 **136** 30k. multicoloured . . . 1·75 1·50

137 Flag and Agostinho Neto

1984. 5th National Heroes Day. Multicoloured.
825 10k.50 Type **137** 50 45
826 36k.50 Flag and Agostinho Neto (different) . . . . 1·60 1·50

138 Southern Ground Hornbill

1984. Birds. Multicoloured.
827 10k.50 Type **138** 90 90
828 14k. Palm-nut vulture . . . . 1·25 1·25
829 16k. Goliath heron . . . . . 1·50 1·50
830 19k.50 Eastern white pelican 1·75 1·75
831 22k. African spoonbill . . . 2·00 2·00
832 26k. South African crowned crane . . . . 2·40 2·40

139 Greater Kudu

1984. Mammals. Multicoloured.
833 1k. Type **139** 10 10
834 4k. Springbok 25 15
835 5k. Chimpanzee 30 25
836 10k. African buffalo 55 50
837 15k. Sable antelope 80 65
838 20k. Aardvark . . . . 1·25 1·10
839 25k. Spotted hyena . . . . . 1·50 1·25

140 Sao Pedro da Barra Fortress

1985. Monuments. Multicoloured.
840 5k. Type **140** 25 20
841 12k.50 Nova Oerias ruins . . 60 55
842 18k. Antiga cathedral ruins, M'Banza Kongo 80 75
843 26k. Massangano fortress . . 1·25 1·10
844 39k. Escravatura museum . . 1·75 1·60

141 Flags on World Map

142 Flags and "XXV"

1985. 5th Anniv of Southern Africa Development Co-ordination Conference. Multicoloured.
845 1k. Type **141** 10 10
846 11k. Offshore drilling . . . . 1·25 50
847 57k. Conference session . . . 2·50 2·40

1985. 25th Anniv of National Union of Angolan Workers.
848 **142** 77k. multicoloured . . . 3·50 3·25

143 "Lonchocarpas sericeus"

1985. Medicinal Plants. Multicoloured.
849 1k. Type **143** 10 10
850 4k. "Gossypium sp." 20 15
851 11k. Senna 50 45
852 25k.50 "Gloriosa superba" 1·10 1·00
853 55k. "Cochlospermum angolensis" . . . . 2·50 2·40

144 Map of Angola as Dove and Conference Emblem

1984. Ministerial Conference of Non-aligned Countries, Luanda.
854 **144** 35k. multicoloured . . . 1·60 1·50

145 Dove and U.N. Emblem

1985. 40th Anniv of U.N.O.
855 **145** 12k.50 multicoloured . . 60 55

146 Cement Works

1985. 10th Anniv of Independence. Multicoloured.
856 50l. Type **146** 10 10
857 5k. Timber yard 20 15
858 7k. Quartz 30 25
859 10k. Iron works 50 45

147 Emblem, Open Book, Soldier, Farmer and Factory

1985. 2nd MPLA Congress.
861 **147** 20k. multicoloured . . . 90 85

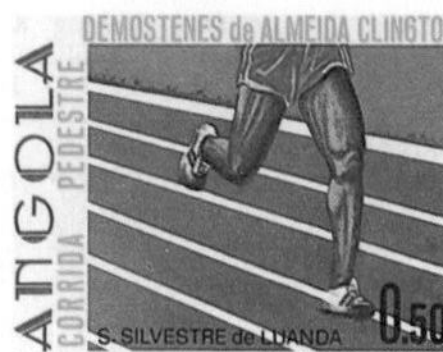

148 Runner on Track

1985. 30th Anniv of Demostenes de Almeida Clington Races. Multicoloured.
862 50l. Type **148** 10 10
863 5k. Two runners on road . . 20 15
864 6k.50 Three runners on road 30 25
865 10k. Two runners on track 50 45

149 Map, Stadium and Players

150 Crowd

1986. World Cup Football Championship, Mexico.
866 **149** 50l. multicoloured 10 10
867 – 3k.50 multicoloured . . . 15 15
868 – 5k. multicoloured 30 25
869 – 7k. multicoloured 35 30
870 – 10k. multicoloured . . . 50 45
871 – 18k. multicoloured . . . 85 70
DESIGNS: 3k.50 to 18k. Different footballers.

1986. 25th Anniv of Armed Independence Movement.
872 **150** 15k. multicoloured . . . 75 70

151 Soviet Space Project

1985. 25th Anniv of First Man in Space. Mult.
873 50l. Type **151** 10 10
874 1k. "Voskhod 1" 10 10
875 5k. Cosmonaut on space walk 20 15
876 10k. Moon vehicle 50 45
877 13k. "Soyuz"–"Apollo" link-up 60 55

152 National Flag and U.N. Emblem
153 People at Work

1986. 10th Anniv of Angolan Membership of U.N.O.
878 **152** 22k. multicoloured . . . 1·00 90

1986. 30th Anniv of Popular Movement for the Liberation of Angola. Multicoloured.
879 5k. Type **153** 20 15
880 5k. Emblem and people (29 × 36 mm) 20 15
881 5k. Soldiers fighting 20 15
Nos. 879/81 were printed together, se-tenant, forming a composite design.

154 Lecturer and Students (Faculty of Engineering)
155 Ouioca

1986. 10th Anniv of Agostinho Neto University. Multicoloured.
882 50l. Type **154** 10 10
883 7k. Students and Judges (Faculty of Law) 30 25
884 10k. Students using microscopes and surgeons operating (Faculty of Medicine) 50 45

1987. Traditional Hairstyles. Multicoloured.
885 1k. Type **155** 10 10
886 1k.50 Luanda 10 10
887 5k. Humbe 20 15
888 7k. Muila 35 25
889 20k. Muila (different) 80 70
890 30k. Lunda, Dilolo . . . . . 1·25 1·00

156 "Lenin in the Smolny Institute" (detail, Serov)
157 Pambala Beach

1987. 70th Anniv of Russian Revolution.
891 **156** 15k. multicoloured . . . 60 25

1987. Scenic Spots. Multicoloured.
892 50l. Type **157** 10 10
893 1k.50 Quedas do Dala (waterfalls) 10 10
894 3k.50 Black Feet Rocks, Pungo Adongo (vert) . . . 15 10
895 5k. Cuango River valley . . 20 15
896 10k. Luanda shore (vert) . . 40 35
897 20k. Serra da Leba road . . 80 75

158 Emblem
159 Dancers

1988. 2nd Angolan Women's Organization Congress. Multicoloured.
898 2k. Type **158** 10 10
899 10k. Women engaged in various pursuits 40 35

1988. 10th Anniv of Vitoria Carnival. Mult.
900 5k. Type **159** 15 10
901 10k. Revellers 40 35

160 Augusto N'Gangula (child revolutionary)

1989. Pioneers. Multicoloured.
902 12k. Type **160** (20th death anniv) 50 45
903 15k. Pioneers (25th anniv (1988) of Agostinho Neto Pioneers Organization) . . 60 55

161 Luanda 1st August Sports Club (1979–81)

1989. 10th National Football League Championship. Championship Winners. Multicoloured.
904 5k. Type **161** 15 15
905 5k. Luanda Petro Atletico (1982, 1984, 1986–88) . . . 15 15
906 5k. Benguela 1st May Sports Club (1983, 1985) 15 15

162 Watering Cabbages

1990. 10th Anniv (1987) of International Fund for Agricultural Development.
907 **162** 10k. multicoloured . . . 35 30

163 19th-century Middle-class Houses, Luanda

1990. Historical Buildings. Multicoloured.
908 1k. Type **163** 10 10
909 2k. Cidade Alta railway station, Luanda . . . . . 1·75 30
910 5k. National Anthropology Museum 20 15
911 15k. Palace of Ana Joaquina dos Santos 55 50
912 23k. Iron Palace 80 75
913 36k. Meteorological observatory (vert) . . . . 1·25 1·10
914 50k. Governor's palace . . . 1·75 1·60

164 "General Machado" and Route Map

1990. Benguela (915) and Luanda Railways. Mult.
915 5k. Type **164** 45 30
916 12k. Beyer-Garratt steam locomotive (facing left) . . 80 75
917 12k. Beyer-Garratt steam locomotive (facing right) 80 75
918 14k. Mikado steam locomotive . . . . 1·25 95

165 Hydroelectric Production

1990. 10th Anniv of Southern Africa Development Co-ordinating Conference. Multicoloured.
920 5k. Type **165** 20 15
921 9k. Oil industry 90 30

166 Map in Envelope

1990. 10th Anniv of Pan-African Postal Union. Multicoloured.
922 4k. Type **166** 15 10
923 10k. Map consisting of stamps and envelopes . . . 35 30

167 "Muxima"

1990. "Stamp World London 90" International Stamp Exn. Paintings by Raul Indipwo. Multicoloured.
924 6k. "Three Graces" (horiz) 20 15
925 9k. Type **167** 30 25

168 Antelope

1990. Protected Animals. Sable Antelope. Mult.
926 5k. Type **168** . . . . 2·40 1·90
927 5k. Male and female . . . . 2·40 1·90
928 5k. Female . . . . 2·40 1·90
929 5k. Female and young . . . 2·40 1·90

169 Porcelain Rose
170 Zebra Drinking

1990. "Belgica 90" International Stamp Exhibition, Brussels. Flowers. Multicoloured.
930 5k. Type **169** 20 15
931 8k. Indian carnation 30 25
932 10k. Allamanda 35 30

1990. International Literacy Year. Multicoloured.
934 5k. Type **170** 20 15
935 5k. Butterfly 20 15
936 5k. Horse's head 20 15

171 Flag and People

1990. 10th Anniv of People's Assembly.
938 **171** 10k. multicoloured . . . 35 30

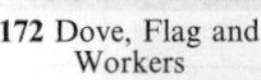

172 Dove, Flag and Workers — **174** Marimba

173 Uniform, 1961

1990. 3rd Popular Movement for the Liberation of Angola-Labour Party Congress.
939 **172** 14k. multicoloured . . . 50 45

1991. 30th Anniv of Armed Independence Movement. Freedom Fighters' Uniforms. Mult.
940 6k. Type **173** 20 15
941 6k. Pau N'Dulo, 1962–63 . . 20 15
942 6k. Military uniform, 1968 20 15
943 6k. Military uniform from 1972 . . . . 20 15

1991. Musical Instruments. Multicoloured.
944 6k. Type **174** 10 10
945 6k. Ngoma ya Mucupela (double-ended drum) . . . 10 10
946 6k. Ngoma la Txina (floor-standing drum) 10 10
947 6k. Kissange 10 10

175 Iona National Park

1991. African Tourism Year. Multicoloured.
948 3k. Type **175** 10 10
949 7k. Kalandula Falls 10 10
950 35k. Lobito Bay 70 30
951 60k. "Welwitschia mirabilis" 65 55

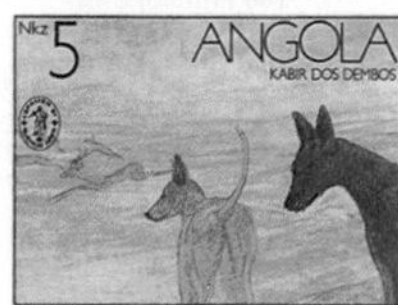

176 Kabir of the Dembos

1991. "Espamer '91" Spain–Latin America Stamp Exhibition, Buenos Aires. Dogs. Multicoloured.
953 5k. Type **176** 10 10
954 7k. Ombua 20 10
955 11k. Kabir massongo 15 10
956 12k. Kawa tchowe 15 10

177 Judo — **178** Mother and Child

1991. Olympic Games, Barcelona (1992) (1st issue). Multicoloured.
957 4k. Type **177** 10 10
958 6k. Yachting 10 10
959 10k. Marathon 15 10
960 100k. Swimming . . . . . . 1·10 95

1991. 13th Anniv of Angolan Red Cross. Mult.
961 20k.+5k. Type **178** 30 20
962 40k.+5k. Zebra and foal . . 50 40

179 Quadrant and Galleon

1991. "Iberex '91" Stamp Exhibition. Navigational Instruments. Multicoloured.
963 5k. Type **179** 15 10
964 15k. Astrolabe and caravel 30 10
965 20k. Cross-staff and caravel 50 20
966 50k. Navigation chart by Fran-cisco Rodrigues and galleon . . . . 1·50 60

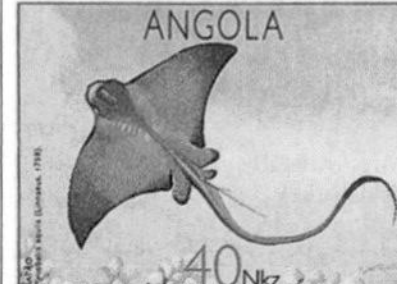

180 Common Eagle Ray — **181** Mukixi wa Mbwesu Mask

1992. Rays. Multicoloured.
967 40k. Type **180** 35 25
968 50k. Spotted eagle ray . . . 40 35
969 66k. Manta ray 55 40
970 80k. Brown ray 65 50

1992. Quioca Painted Masks (1st series).
972 – 60k. orange and brown 15 10
973 – 100k. black, verm & red 25 20
974 **181** 150k. pink and orange . . 35 30
975 – 250k. red and brown . . 60 50
DESIGNS: 60k. Kalelwa mask; 100k. Mikixe wa Kino mask; 250k. Cikunza mask.
See also Nos. 1006/7 and 1021/4.

182 "Ptaeroxylon obliquum" — **183** King and Missionaries

1992. "Lubrapex 92" Brazilian–Portuguese Stamp Exhibition, Lisbon. Medicinal Plants. Each brown, stone and deep brown.
976 200k. Type **182** 45 35
977 300k. "Spondias mombin" 70 55
978 500k. "Parinari curatellifolia" 1·25 1·00
979 600k. "Cochlospermum angolense" . . . . 1·40 1·10

1992. 500th Anniv (1991) of Baptism of First Angolans. Multicoloured.
980 150k. Type **183** 35 30
981 420k. Ruins of M'Banza Congo Church . . . . . . 1·00 80
982 470k. Muxima Church . . . 1·10 90
983 500k. Cross superimposed on children's faces . . . . . . 1·25 1·00

184 Dimba House — **185** Lovebirds

1992. "Expo '92" World's Fair, Seville. Traditional Houses. Multicoloured.
984 150k. Type **184** 35 30
985 330k. Cokwe house 80 65
986 360k. Mbali house 85 70
987 420k. Ambwela house . . . 1·00 80
988 500k. House of the Upper Zambezi . . . . 1·25 1·00

1992. Nature Protection. Peach-faced Lovebirds. Multicoloured.
989 150k. Type **185** 35 30
990 200k. Birds feeding 45 35
991 250k. Bird in hand 60 50
992 300k. Bird on perch 70 55

187 Hurdling — **188** Women with Nets

1992. Olympic Games, Barcelona (2nd issue). Mult.
994 120k. Type **187** 30 25
995 180k. Cycling 45 35
996 240k. Roller hockey 55 45
997 360k. Basketball 85 70

1992. Fishing. Multicoloured.
998 65k. Type **188** 20 10
999 90k. Fishermen pulling in nets 30 15
1000 100k. Fishermen checking traps 35 20
1001 120k. Fishing canoes . . . 30 25

190 Crowd with Ballot Papers around Ballot Box — **191** Mail Van

1992. 1st Free Elections. Multicoloured.
1003 120k. Type **190** 30 25
1004 150k. Doves, map, people and ballot box 35 30
1005 200k. Dove, crowd and ballot box 45 35

1992. Quioca Painted Masks (2nd series). As T **181**.
1006 72k. brown, black and yellow 15 10
1007 80k. red, black and brown 20 15
1008 120k. pink, black and red 30 25
1009 210k. black and yellow . . . 50 40
DESIGNS: 72k. Cihongo mask; 80k. Mbwasu mask; 120k. Cinhanga mask; 210k. Kalewa mask.

1992. Introduction of Express Mail Service in Angola. Multicoloured.
1010 450k. Type **191** 55 45
1011 550k. Boeing 707 airplane 65 50

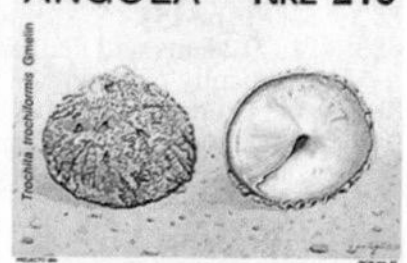

192 Weather Balloon — **193** Rayed Hat

1993. World Meteorology Day. Meteorological Instruments. Multicoloured.
1012 250k. Type **192** 10 10
1013 470k. Actinometer 10 10
1014 500k. Rain-gauge 10 10

1993. Molluscs. Multicoloured.
1015 210k. Type **193** 10 10
1016 330k. Bubonian conch . . . 15 10
1017 400k. African pelican's foot 15 10
1018 500k. White spindle 20 15

1993. Quioca Art (1st series). As T **181**.
1021 72k. grey, red and brown 10 10
1022 210k. pink and brown . . . 10 10
1023 420k. black, brown & orge 10 10
1024 600k. black, red and brown 10 10
DESIGNS: 72k. Men with vehicles; 210k. Rider on antelope; 420k. Bird-plane; 600k. Carrying "soba".
See also Nos. 1038/41 and 1050/3.

195 "Sansevieria cylindrica" — **196** Atlantic Hawksbill Turtle laying Eggs and Green Turtle

1993. Cacti and Succulents. Multicoloured.
1025 360k. Type **195** 10 10
1026 400k. Milk-bush 10 10
1027 500k. Indian fig 10 10
1028 600k. "Dracaena aubryana" 10 10

1993. Sea Turtles. Multicoloured.
1029 180k. Type **196** 10 10
1030 450k. Head of Atlantic hawksbill turtle and newly hatched turtles 10 10
1031 550k. Leather-back turtle . . 10 10
1032 630k. Loggerhead turtles . . 15 10
Nos. 1029/32 were issued together, se-tenant, forming a composite design.

198 Vimbundi Pipe — **199** St. George's Mushroom

1993. Tobacco Pipes. Multicoloured.
1034 72k. Type **198** 10 10
1035 200k. Vimbundi pipe (different) 10 10
1036 420k. Mutopa calabash water pipe 10 10
1037 600k. Pexi carved-head pipe 10 10

1993. Quioca Art (2nd series). As T **181**.
1038 300k. brown and orange . . 10 10
1039 600k. red and brown . . . 10 10
1040 800k. black, orange and deep orange 15 10
1041 1000k. orange and brown 20 15
DESIGNS: 300k. Leopard and dog; 600k. Rabbits; 800k. Birds; 1000k. Birds and cockerel.

1993. Fungi. Multicoloured.
1042 300k. Type **199** 55 15
1043 500k. Death cap 90 30
1044 600k. "Amanita vaginata" 1·10 35
1045 1000k. Parasol mushroom 1·90 60

200 "Cinganji" (figurine of dancer, Bie province) — **201** Orgy

1994. National Culture Day. "Hong Kong '94" International Stamp Exhibition. Multicoloured.
1046 500k. Type **200** 10 10
1047 1000k. Chief's staff with carved woman's head (Bie province) 20 15
1048 1200k. Statuette of traveller riding ox (Huambo province) 25 20
1049 2200k. Corn pestle (Ovimbundu) 45 35

1994. Quioca Art (3rd series). As T **181**.
1050 500k. multicoloured 10 10
1051 2000k. red and brown . . . 40 30
1052 2500k. red and brown . . . 50 40
1053 3000k. carmine and red . . 60 50
DESIGNS: 500k. Bird on plant; 2000k. Plant with roots; 2500k. Plant; 3000k. Fern.

1994. AIDS Awareness Campaign. Multicoloured.
1054 500k. Type **201** 10 10
1055 1000k. Masked figure using infected syringe passing box of condoms to young couple 10 10
1056 3000k. Victims 20 15

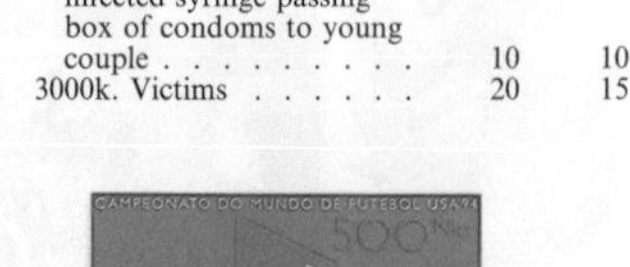

202 Flag, Arrows and Small Ball

1994. World Cup Football Championship, U.S.A. Multicoloured.
1057 500k. Type **202** 10 10
1058 700k. Flag, four arrows and large ball 10 10
1059 2200k. Flag, goal net and ball 10 10
1060 2500k. Flag, ball and boot 10 10

203 Brachiosaurus

1994. "Philakorea 1994" International and "Singpex '94" Stamp Exhibitions. Dinosaurs. Multicoloured.
1061 1000k. Type **203** 10 10
1062 3000k. Spinosaurus 10 10
1063 5000k. Ouranosaurus . . . 10 10
1064 10000k. Lesothosaurus . . . 15 10

204 Brown Snake Eagle, Ostrich, Yellow-billed Stork and Pink-backed Pelican

1994. Tourism. Multicoloured.
1066 2000k. Type **204** 10 10
1067 4000k. Animals 10 10
1068 8000k. Women 10 10
1069 10000k. Men 10 10

205 Dual-service Wall-mounted Post Box

1994. Post Boxes. Multicoloured.
1070 5000k. Type **205** 10 10
1071 7500k. Wall-mounted philatelic post box 10 10
1072 10000k. Free-standing post box 10 10
1073 21000k. Multiple service wall-mounted post box . . 25 15

206 "Heliothis armigera" (moth)

1994. Insects. Multicoloured.
1074 5000k. Type **206** 10 10
1075 6000k. "Bemisia tabasi" . . 10 10
1076 10000k. "Dysdercus sp." (bug) 10 10
1077 27000k. "Spodoptera exigua" (moth) 25 15

207 "100"

1994. Cent of International Olympic Committee.
1078 **207** 27000k. red, yell & blk 25 20

208 Pot

1995. Traditional Ceramics. With service indicator. Multicoloured. (a) INLAND POSTAGE. Inscr "PORTE NACIONAL".
1079 (1°) Type **208** 10 10
1080 (2°) Pot with figure of woman on lid 10 10

(b) INTERNATIONAL POSTAGE. Inscr "PORTE INTERNACIONAL".
1081 (1°) Pot with man's head on lid 20 15
1082 (2°) Duck-shaped pot . . . 25 20

209 Making Fire

1995. The !Kung (Khoisan tribe). Multicoloured.
1083 10000k. Type **209** 10 10
1084 15000k. Tipping darts with poison 15 10
1085 20000k. Smoking 20 15
1086 25000k. Hunting 20 15
1087 28000k. Women and children 25 20
1088 30000k. Painting animals on walls 25 20

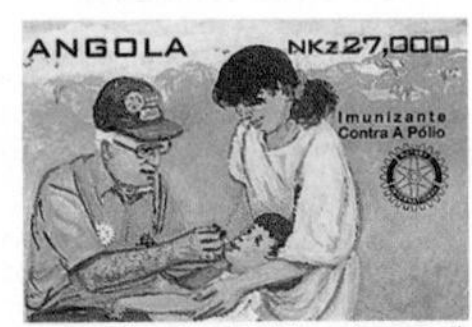

210 Vaccinating Child against Polio

1995. 90th Anniv of Rotary International. Multicoloured. (a) Inscr in Portuguese.
1089 27000k. Type **210** 15 10
1090 27000k. Examining baby . . 15 10
1091 27000k. Giving child vaccination 15 10

(b) Inscr in English.
1092 27000k. Type **210** 15 10
1093 27000k. As No. 1090 . . . 15 10
1094 27000k. As No. 1091 . . . 15 10

Nos. 1089/91 and 1092/4 respectively were issued together, se-tenant, forming composite designs.

211 "Sputnik 1" (satellite)

1995. World Telecommunications Day. Mult.
1096 27000k. Type **211** 15 10
1097 27000k. "Intelsat" satellite and space shuttle 15 10

212 Doves above Baby on Daisy-covered Map

1995. 20th Anniv of Independence.
1099 **212** 2900k. multicoloured . . 65 50

213 Child, Containers and Fork-lift Truck

1996. Goods Transportation. Multicoloured.
1100 200k. Type **213** 10 10
1101 1265k. Sailing boats and "Mount Cameroon" (ferry) 25 25
1102 2583k. Fork-lift trucks loading and unloading "Mount Cameroon" (ferry) 90 50
1103 2583k. Truck 60 50

214 Women in Agriculture

1996. 4th World Conference on Women, Peking (1995). Multicoloured.
1105 375k. Type **214** 10 10
1106 1106k. Women in education 25 20
1107 1265k. Women in business 30 25
1108 2900k. Dimba servant girl (vert) 65 50

215 Verdant Hawk Moth

1996. Flora and Fauna. Multicoloured.
1110 1500k. Type **215** 10 10
1111 1500k. Western honey buzzard 10 10
1112 1500k. Bateleur 10 10
1113 1500k. Common kestrel . . 10 10
1114 4400k. Water lily 20 15
1115 4400k. Red-crested turaco 20 15
1116 4400k. Giraffe 20 15
1117 4400k. African elephant . . 20 15
1118 5100k. Panther toad 20 15
1119 5100k. Hippopotamus . . . 20 15
1120 5100k. Cattle egret 20 15
1121 5100k. Lion 20 15
1122 6000k. African hunting ("wild") dog 25 20
1123 6000k. Helmeted turtle . . . 25 20
1124 6000k. African pygmy goose 25 20
1125 6000k. Egyptian plover . . 25 20

Nos. 1111/13, 1115/17, 1119/21 and 1123/5 respectively were issued together, se-tenant, forming composite designs.

216 California Quail

1997. Birds. Multicoloured.
1127 5500k. Type **216** 20 15
1128 5500k. Prairie chicken ("Greater Prairie Chicken") 20 15
1129 5500k. Indian blue quail ("Painted Quail") 20 15
1130 5500k. Golden pheasant . . 20 15
1131 5500k. Crested wood partridge ("Roulroul Partridge") 20 15
1132 5500k. Ceylon spurfowl ("Ceylon Sourfowl") . . . 20 15
1133 5500k. Himalayan snowcock 20 15
1134 5500k. Temminck's tragopan ("Temmincks Tragopan") 20 15
1135 5500k. Lady Amherst's pheasant 20 15
1136 5500k. Great curassow . . . 20 15
1137 5500k. Red-legged partridge 20 15
1138 5500k. Himalayan monal pheasant ("Impeyan Pheasant") 20 15
1139 5500k. Anna's hummingbird 20 15
1140 5500k. Blue-throated hummingbird 20 15
1141 5500k. Broad-tailed hummingbird 20 15
1142 5500k. Costa's hummingbird 20 15
1143 5500k. White-eared hummingbird 20 15
1144 5500k. Calliope hummingbird 20 15
1145 5500k. Violet-crowned hummingbird 20 15
1146 5500k. Rufous hummingbird 20 15
1147 5500k. Crimson topaz ("Crimson Topaz Hummingbird") 20 15
1148 5500k. Broad-billed hummingbird 20 15
1149 5500k. Frilled coquette ("Frilled Coquette Hummingbird") 20 15
1150 5500k. Ruby-throated hummingbird 20 15

217 Lions attacking Zebra

1996. African Wildlife. Multicoloured.
1152 180k. Type **217** 10 10
1153 180k. Lions watching zebras 10 10
1154 180k. African hunting dogs attacking gnu 10 10
1155 180k. Pack of hunting dogs chasing herd of gnu . . . 10 10
1156 450k. Lions stalking isolated zebra 10 10
1157 450k. Male lion 10 10
1158 450k. Hunting dogs surrounding gnu 10 10
1159 450k. Close-up of African hunting dog 10 10
1160 550k. Cheetah 10 10
1161 550k. Cheetah chasing springbok 10 10
1162 550k. Leopard 10 10
1163 550k. Leopard stalking oryx 10 10
1164 630k. Cheetah running beside herd of springbok 10 10
1165 630k. Cheetah overpowering springbok 10 10
1166 630k. Leopard approaching oryx 10 10
1167 630k. Leopard leaping at oryx 10 10

Nos. 1152/67 were issued together, se-tenant, in sheetlets with each horizontal strip forming a composite design of lions, cheetah, hunting dogs or leopard attacking prey.

218 Couple with Elderly Woman

1996. 50th Anniv of U.N.O. Multicoloured.
1168 3500k. Type **218** 15 10
1169 3500k. Children at water pump 15 10

219 "Styrbjorn" (Swedish sail warship), 1789

1996. Ships. Multicoloured.
1171 6000k. Type **219** 35 20
1172 6000k. U.S.S. "Constellation" (United States frigate), 1797 . . . 35 20
1173 6000k. "Taureau" (French torpedo-boat), 1865 . . . 35 20
1174 6000k. French bomb ketch 35 20
1175 6000k. "Sardegna" (Italian battleship), 1881 . . . . 35 20
1176 6000k. H.M.S. "Glasgow" (frigate), 1867 . . . . . 35 20
1177 6000k. U.S.S. "Essex" (frigate), 1812 . . . . . 35 20
1178 6000k. H.M.S. "Inflexible" (battleship), 1881 . . . . 35 20
1179 6000k. H.M.S. "Minotaur" (ironclad), 1863 . . . . . 35 20
1180 6000k. "Napoleon" (French steam ship of the line), 1854 . . . . 35 20
1181 6000k. "Sophia Amalia" (Danish galleon), 1650 . . 35 20
1182 6000k. "Massena" (French battleship), 1887 . . . . 35 20

220 Mask and Drilling Platform

1996. 20th Anniv of Sonangol. Multicoloured.
1184 1000k. Type **220** 30 10
1185 1000k. Storage tanks and mask of woman's face . . 10 10
1186 2500k. Mask with beard and gas bottles 10 10
1187 5000k. Refuelling airplane and mask of monkey's face 20 15

221 Slaves in Ship's Hold

1996. "Brapex 96" National Stamp Exhibition, Recife, Brazil. Multicoloured.
1188 20000k. Type **221** 10 10
1189 20000k. Ship capsizing . . . 20 10
1190 30000k. Boats punting out to ship 30 15
1191 30000k. Inspection of slaves 20 15

222 Mission Church, Huila **223** Handball

1996. Churches. Multicoloured.
1193 5000k. Type **222** 10 10
1194 10000k. Church of Our Lady, PoPulo 10 10
1195 10000k. Church of Our Lady, Nazare 10 10
1196 25000k. St. Adriao's Church 10 10

1996. Olympic Games, Atlanta, U.S.A. Mult.
1197 5000k. Type **223** 10 10
1198 10000k. Swimming (horiz) 10 10
1199 25000k. Athletics 10 10
1200 35000k. Shooting (horiz) 15 10

224 Dolphins, and Angola on Map of Africa

1996. 40th Anniv of Popular Movement for the Liberation of Angola (MPLA).
1202 **224** 30000k. multicoloured 15 10
The face value of No. 1202 is wrongly inscr as "300.00.00".

225 AVE, Spain

1997. Trains. Multicoloured.
1203 100000k. Type **225** 60 50
1204 100000k. "Hikari", Japan 60 50
1205 100000k. "Warbonnet" diesel locomotives, U.S.A. 60 50
1206 100000k. "Deltic" diesel locomotive, Great Britain 60 50
1207 100000k. "Eurostar", France and Great Britain 60 50
1208 100000k. ETR 450, Italy 60 50
1209 140000k. Class E1300 diesel locomotive, Morocco 85 70
1210 140000k. ICE, Germany 85 70
1211 140000k. Class X2000, Sweden 85 70
1212 140000k. TGV, France 85 70
1213 250000k. Steam locomotive 1·10 90
1214 250000k. Garratt steam locomotive 1·10 90
1215 250000k. General Electric electric locomotive 1·10 90
Nos. 1203/8 were issued together, se-tenant, forming a composite design.

226 Thoroughbred

1997. Horses. Multicoloured.
1217 100000k. Type **226** 45 35
1218 100000k. Palomino and Appaloosa 45 35
1219 100000k. Grey and white Arabs 45 35
1220 100000k. Arab colt 45 35
1221 100000k. Thoroughbred colt 45 35
1222 100000k. Mustang (with hind quarters of another mustang) 45 35
1223 100000k. Head of mustang and hind quarters of Furioso 45 35
1224 100000k. Head and shoulders of Furioso 45 35
1225 120000k. Thoroughbred 55 45
1226 120000k. Arab and palomino 55 45
1227 120000k. Arab and Chincoteague 55 45
1228 120000k. Pintos 55 45
1229 120000k. Przewalski's Horse 55 45
1230 120000k. Thoroughbred colt 55 45
1231 120000k. Arabs 55 45
1232 120000k. New Forest pony 55 45
1233 140000k. Selle Francais 65 50
1234 140000k. Fjord 65 50
1235 140000k. Percheron 65 50
1236 140000k. Italian heavy draught horse 65 50
1237 140000k. Shagya Arab 65 50
1238 140000k. Avelignese 65 50
1239 140000k. Czechoslovakian warmblood 65 50
1240 140000k. New Forest pony 65 50
Stamps of the same value were issued together, se-tenant, Nos. 1217/24 and 1225/32 respectively forming composite designs.

227 Jules Rimet Trophy (Uruguay, 1930)

1997. World Cup Football Championship, France.
1241 **227** 100000k. black 45 35
1242 – 100000k. black 45 35
1243 – 100000k. multicoloured 45 35
1244 – 100000k. multicoloured 45 35
1245 – 100000k. black 45 35
1246 – 100000k. multicoloured 45 35
1247 – 100000k. black 45 35
1248 – 100000k. black 45 35
1249 – 100000k. multicoloured 45 35
1250 – 100000k. multicoloured 45 35
1251 – 100000k. black 45 35
DESIGNS—Victory celebrations: No. 1240, Germany (1954); 1241, Brazil (1970); 1242, Maradona holding trophy (Argentina, 1986); 1243, Brazil (1994). Official team photographs: 1244, Germany (1954); 1245, Uruguay (1958); 1246, Italy (1938); 1247, Brazil (1962); 1248, Brazil (1970); 1249, Uruguay (1930).

228 House Insurance **230** Royal Assyrian ("Terinos terpander")

229 Coral

1998. 20th Anniv of ENSA Insurance. Mult.
1254 240000k. Type **228** 1·10 90
1255 240000k. Forklift truck carrying egg (industrial risks) 1·10 90
1256 240000k. Egg on cross (personal accidents) 1·10 90
1257 240000k. Egg on waves (pleasure boating) 1·10 90

1998. "Expo '98" World's Fair, Lisbon, Portugal. Multicoloured.
1259 100000k. Type **229** 45 35
1260 100000k. Sea urchin 45 35
1261 100000k. Seahorses 45 35
1262 100000k. Sea anemone 45 35
1263 240000k. Sea slug 1·10 90
1264 240000k. Finger coral 1·10 90

1998. Butterflies. Multicoloured.
1265 120000k. Type **230** 55 45
1266 120000k. Wanderer ("Bematistes aganice") 55 45
1267 120000k. Great orange-tip ("Hebomoia glaucippe") 55 45
1268 120000k. Alfalfa butterfly ("Colias eurytheme") 55 45
1269 120000k. Red-banded perelite ("Pereute leucodrosime") 55 45
1270 120000k. Large copper ("Lycaena dispar") 55 45
1271 120000k. Malachite ("Metamorpha stelenes") 55 45
1272 120000k. Tiger swallowtail ("Papilio glaucus") 55 45
1273 120000k. Monarch ("Danaus plexippus") 55 45
1274 120000k. Grecian shoemaker ("Catonephele numili") 55 45
1275 120000k. Silver-studded blue ("Plebejus argus") 55 45
1276 120000k. Common eggfly ("Hypolimnas bolina") 55 45
1277 120000k. Brazilian dynastor ("Dynastor napolean") (horiz) 55 45
1278 120000k. Saturn butterfly ("Zeuxidia amethystus") (horiz) 55 45
1279 120000k. Pipevine swallowtail ("Battus philenor") (horiz) 55 45
1280 120000k. Orange-barred sulphur ("Phoebis philea") (horiz) 55 45
1281 120000k. African monarch ("Danaus chrysippus") (horiz) 55 45
1282 120000k. Green-underside blue ("Glaucopsyche alexis") (horiz) 55 45
Nos. 1265/70, 1271/6 and 1277/82 respectively were issued together, se-tenant, forming composite designs.

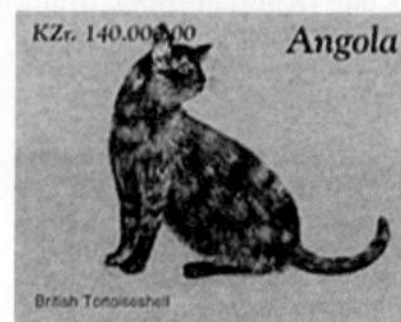

231 British Tortoiseshell

1998. Cats and Dogs. Multicoloured.
1284 140000k. Type **231** 65 55
1285 140000k. Chinchilla 65 55
1286 140000k. Russian blue 65 55
1287 140000k. Black persian (longhair) (wrongly inscribed "Longhiar") 65 55
1288 140000k. British red tabby 65 55
1289 140000k. Birman 65 55
1290 140000k. West Highland white terrier 65 55
1291 140000k. Red setter 65 55
1292 140000k. Dachshund 65 55
1293 140000k. St. John water-dog 65 55
1294 140000k. Shetland sheep-dog 65 55
1295 140000k. Dalmatian 65 55

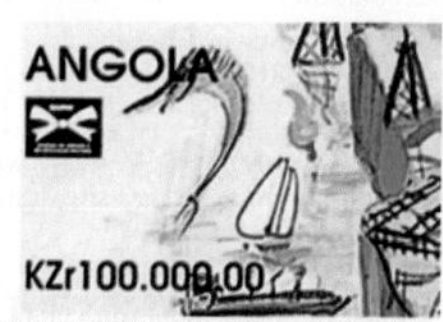

232 Dolphin, Yacht and Container Ship

1998. 1st Anniv of Government of Unity and National Reconciliation. Multicoloured.
1297 100000k. Type **232** 45 35
1298 100000k. Yacht, dolphin and container ship (different) 45 35
1299 100000k. Yacht, container ship and railway line 45 35
1300 100000k. Coastline and electricity pylons 45 35
1301 200000k. Grapes, goat and railway 95 75
1302 200000k. Village 95 75
1303 200000k. Tractor, grapes and railway 95 75
1304 200000k. Coal train 95 75
1305 200000k. Railway line with branch and pylons 95 75
1306 200000k. Elephant and tip of tree 95 75
1307 200000k. Edge of coastline with pylon 95 75
1308 200000k. Tree trunk and coastline 95 75
Nos. 1297/1308 were issued together, se-tenant, forming a composite design.

234 Lion

1998. Animals of the Grande Porte. Multicoloured.
1310 100000k. Type **234** 45 35
1311 100000k. Hippopotamus ("Hippopotamus amphibius") 45 35
1312 100000k. African elephant ("Loxodonta africana") 45 35
1313 100000k. Giraffe ("Giraffa campelopardalis") 45 35
1314 220000k. African buffalo ("Synceros caffer") 1·00 80
1315 220000k. Gorilla ("Gorilla gorilla") 1·00 80
1316 220000k. White rhinoceros ("Ceratotherium simum") 1·00 80
1317 220000k. Gemsbok ("Oryx gazella") 1·00 80
There are errors in the Latin inscriptions.

236 Diana, Princess of Wales **237** "Pagurites sp."

1998. Diana, Princess of Wales Commemoration. Multicoloured.
1319 100000k. Type **236** 45 35
1320 100000k. Wearing white balldress 45 35
1321 100000k. Holding handbag 45 35
1322 100000k. Wearing black evening dress 45 35
1323 100000k. Holding bouquet (white jacket) 45 35
1324 100000k. Wearing pearl necklace (looking down) 45 35
1325 100000k. Wearing pearl necklace (head raised) 45 35
1326 100000k. Speaking, wearing green velvet jacket 45 35
1327 100000k. Wearing sunglasses 45 35
1328 100000k. Wearing black jacket and white blouse 45 35
1329 100000k. Wearing green blouse 45 35
1330 100000k. Holding flowers (black jacket) 45 35
1331 150000k. With young girl amputee 70 55
1332 150000k. With two amputees 70 55
1333 150000k. Walking through minefield 70 55

1998. International Year of the Ocean. Mult.
1335 100000k. Type **237** 45 35
1336 100000k. "Callinectes marginatus" (crab) 45 35
1337 100000k. "Thais forbesi" 45 35
1338 100000k. "Ostrea tulipa" 45 35
1339 100000k. "Balanus amphitrite" 45 35
1340 100000k. "Uca tangeri" 45 35
1341 170000k. "Littorina angulifera" 80 65
1342 170000k. Great hairy melongena ("Semifusus morio") 80 65
1343 170000k. "Thais coronata" 80 65
1344 170000k. "Cerithium atratum" on red branch 80 65
1345 170000k. "Ostrea tulipa" (different) 80 65
1346 170000k. "Cerithium atratum" on green branch 80 65

238 Mangos

1998. "Portugal 98" International Stamp Exhibition, Lisbon. Fruit and Vegetables. Multicoloured.
1348 100000k. Type **238** 45 35
1349 100000k. Guava 45 35
1350 120000k. Chillies 55 45
1351 120000k. Sweet corn 55 45
1352 140000k. Sliced bananas 65 55
1353 140000k. Avocadoes 65 55

239 Bimba Canoe

1998. Canoes. Multicoloured.
1354 250000k. Type **239** 1·10 90
1355 250000k. Sailing canoe, Ndongo 1·10 90
1356 250000k. Building canoes in Ndongo 1·10 90

241 Ultralight Plane

1998. Aircraft. Multicoloured.
1358 150000k. Type **241** 70 55
1359 150000k. Gyroplane 70 55
1360 150000k. Business jet 70 55
1361 150000k. Convertible plane 70 55
1362 150000k. Chuterplane 70 55
1363 150000k. Twin-rotor craft 70 55
1364 150000k. Skycrane 70 55
1365 150000k. British Aerospace/Aerospatiale Concorde Supersonic airliner 70 55
1366 150000k. Flying boat 70 55
1367 200000k. Boeing 737-100 70 55
1368 200000k. Ilyushin Il-62M 70 55
1369 250000k. Pedal-powered plane 70 55
1370 250000k. Sail plane 70 55
1371 250000k. Aerobatic plane 70 55
1372 250000k. Hang-gliding 70 55
1373 250000k. Balloon 70 55
1374 250000k. Glidercraft 70 55
1375 250000k. Model airplane 70 55
1376 250000k. Air racing 70 55
1377 250000k. Solar-celled plane 70 55
Nos. 1358/66 and 1369/77 respectively were issued together, se-tenant, forming composite designs.

242 Parasaurolophus **243** Head

1998. Prehistoric Animals. Multicoloured.
1379 120000k. Type **242** 55 45
1380 120000k. Elaphosaurus . . . 55 45
1381 120000k. Iguanodon 55 45
1382 120000k. Maiasaura 55 45
1383 120000k. Brontosaurus . . . 55 45
1384 120000k. Plateosaurus . . . 55 45
1385 120000k. Brachiosaurus . . 55 45
1386 120000k. Anatosaurus . . . 55 45
1387 120000k. Tyrannosaurus rex 55 45
1388 120000k. Carnotaurus . . . 55 45
1389 120000k. Corythosaurus . . 55 45
1390 120000k. Stegosaurus . . . 55 45
1391 120000k. Iguanodon (different) 55 45
1392 120000k. Hadrosaurus (horiz) 55 45
1393 120000k. Ouranosaurus (horiz) 55 45
1394 120000k. Hypsilophodon (horiz) 55 45
1395 120000k. Brachiosaurus (horiz) 55 45
1396 120000k. Shunosaurus (horiz) 55 45
1397 120000k. Amargasaurus (horiz) 55 45
1398 120000k. Tuojiangosaurus (horiz) 55 45
1399 120000k. Monoclonius . . . 55 45
1400 120000k. Struthiosaurus (horiz) 55 45

1999. Endangered Species. The Lesser Flamingo (*Phoenicopterus minor*). Multicoloured.
1402 300000k. Type **243** . . . . 1·40 1·10
1403 300000k. Flamingo with wings outstretched . . . . 1·40 1·10
1404 300000k. Flamingo facing left . . . . 1·40 1·10
1405 300000k. Front view of flamingo . . . . 1·40 1·10

244 Hyacinth Macaw (*Anodorhynchus hyacinthinus*)

1999. Animals and Birds. Multicoloured.
1406 300000k. Type **244** . . . . 1·40 1·10
1407 300000k. Penguin (*Sphenisciformes*) (vert) . . 1·40 1·10
1408 300000k. Przewalski's horse (*Equus caballus przewalski*) (wrongly inscr "Equis") . . . . 1·40 1·10
1409 300000k. American bald eagle (*Haliaetus leucocephalus*) (vert) . . . 1·40 1·10
1410 300000k. Spectacled bear (*Tremarctos ornatus*) . . . 1·40 1·10
1411 300000k. Jay (*Aphelocoma*) 1·40 1·10
1412 300000k. Bare-legged scops owl (*Otus insularis*) . . . 1·40 1·10
1413 300000k. Whale-headed stork (*Balaeniceps rex*) . . 1·40 1·10
1414 300000k. Atlantic ridley turtle (*Lepidochelys kempii*) . . . . 1·40 1·10
1415 300000k. Canadian river otter (*Lutra canadensis*) 1·40 1·10
1416 300000k. Swift fox (*Vulpes velox hebes*) . . . . . . 1·40 1·10
1417 300000k. Deer (*Odocoileus*) 1·40 1·10
1418 300000k. Orang-utan (*Pongo pygmaeus*) . . . . 1·40 1·10
1419 300000k. Golden lion tamarin (*Leontopithecus rosalia rosalia*) (inscr "Leontopitecus") . . . . 1·40 1·10
1420 300000k. Tiger (*Panthera tigris altaica*) . . . . . . 1·40 1·10
1421 300000k. Polecat (wrongly inscr "Tragelaphus eurycerus") . . . . 1·40 1·10
MS1422 Two sheets, each 110 × 85 mm. (a) 1000000k. Brown bear (*Ursus arctos horribilis*): (b) 1000000k. Giant panda (*Ailuropoda melanoleuca*) . . . 9·50 9·50

245 Satellite circling Earth

1999. International Telecommunications Day.
1423 **245** 500000k. multicoloured 90 70

246 Waterfall, Andulo, Bie

1999. Waterfalls. Multicoloured.
1424 500000k. Type **246** 90 70
1425 500000k. Chiumbo, Lunda 90 70
1426 500000k. Ruacana, Cunene 90 70
1427 500000k. Coemba, Moxico 90 70

247 Emblem

1999. "Afrobasket '99" (Men's African Basketball Championship). Multicoloured.
1428 15000000k. Type **247** . . . 70 55
1429 15000000k. Ball teetering on the edge of net, and players' hands 70 55
1430 15000000k. Hand scooping ball from edge of net . . 70 55
1431 15000000k. Flower holding ball 70 55
MS1432 95 × 83 mm. 25000000k. Enlarged detail from No. 1441 (39 × 29 mm) . . . . 1·25 1·25

248 African Continent

1999. South African Development Community (S.A.D.C.).
1433 **248** 1000000k. multicoloured 50 40

249 Duke and Duchess of York, 1923 **250** Ekuikui II

1999. 100th Birthday of Queen Elizabeth, the Queen Mother. Multicoloured.
1434 **249** 200000k. black and gold 10 10
1435 – 200000k. mult 10 10
1436 – 200000k. mult 10 10
1437 – 200000k. mult 10 10
MS1438 154 × 157 mm. 500000k. Queen Mother in academic robes (37 × 50 mm) 25 25
DESIGNS: No. 1447, Portrait of Queen Mother wearing Star of the Garter; 1448, Queen Mother wearing fur stole; 1449, Queen Mother wearing blue hat.

1999. Rulers. Multicoloured.
1439 500000k. Type **250** 25 20
1440 500000k. Mvemba Nzinga 25 20
1441 500000k. Mwata Yamvu Nawej II 25 20
1442 500000k. Njinga Mbande . . 25 20
MS1443 104 × 76 mm. 1000000k. Mandume Ndemufayo 50 50

251 13th-century B.C. Pharaonic Barque

1999. Ships. Multicoloured.
1444 950000k. Type **251** 50 40
1445 950000k. Flemish carrack, 1480 . . . . 50 40
1446 950000k. H.M.S. *Beagle* (Darwin), 1830 . . . . . 50 40
1447 950000k. *North Star* (paddle-steamer), 1852 . . 50 40
1448 950000k. *Fram* (schooner, Amundsen and Nansen), 1892 . . . . 50 40
1449 950000k. *Unyo Maru* (sail/steam freighter), 1909 (inscr "Unyon") 50 40
1450 950000k. *Juan Sebastian de Elcano* (cadet schooner), 1927 . . . . 50 40
1451 950000k. *Tovarishch*, (three-masted cadet barque), 1933 . . . . 50 40
1452 950000k. *Bucentaur* (Venetian state galley), 1728 . . . . 50 40
1453 950000k. *Clermont* (first commercial paddle-steamer), 1807 . . . . . 50 40
1454 950000k. *Savannah* (paddle-steamer), 1819 . . . . . 50 40
1455 950000k. *Dromedary* (steam tug), 1844 . . . . . . 50 40
1456 950000k. *Iberia* (steam freighter), 1881 . . . . . 50 40
1457 950000k. *Gluckauf* (tanker), 1886 . . . . 50 40
1458 950000k. *Cidade de Paris* (ocean steamer), 1888 . . 50 40
1459 950000k. *Mauretania* (liner), 1906 . . . . 50 40
1460 950000k. *La Gloire* (first armoured-hull ship), 1859 50 40
1461 950000k. *L'Ocean*, (French battery ship), 1868 . . . 50 40
1462 950000k. *Dandolo* (Italian cruiser), 1876 (inscr "Dandalo") and stern of H.M.S. *Dreadnought* . . . 50 40
1463 950000k. H.M.S. *Dreadnought* (battleship), 1906 . . . . 50 40
1464 950000k. *Bismarck* (battleship), 1939 and stern of U.S.S. *Cleveland* 50 40
1465 950000k. U.S.S. *Cleveland* (cruiser), 1946 . . . . . 50 40
1466 950000k. U.S.S. *Boston* (first guided-missile cruiser), 1942 and stern of U.S.S. *Long Beach* 50 40
1467 950000k. U.S.S. *Long Beach* (first nuclear-powered cruiser), 1959 . . . . . . 50 40
MS1468 Four sheets, each 75 × 70 mm. (a) 5000000k. 18th-century junk; (b) 5000000k. *Madre de Dios* (carrack) (wrongly inscr "Deus"), 1609; (c) 5000000k. Catamaran, 1861; (d) 5000000k. *Natchez* (Mississippi paddle-steamer), 1870 . . . . 9·50 9·50
Nos. 1474/5, 1476/7 and 1478/9 respectively were issued together, se-tenant, forming a composite design.

252 Fly Agaric (*Amanita muscaria*)

1999. Fungi. Multicoloured.
1469 1000000k. Type **252** (wrongly inscr "Aminita") 50 40
1470 1000000k. Bronze boletus (*Boletus*) 50 40
1471 1000000k. Lawyer's wig (*Coprinus comatus*) . . . 50 40
1472 1000000k. The blusher (*Amanita rubescens*) (inscr "Aminita") 50 40
1473 1000000k. Slimy-branded cort (*Cortinarius collinitus*) 50 40
1474 1000000k. Devil's boletus (*Boletus satanas*) 50 40
1475 1000000k. Parasol mushroom (*Lepiota procera*) 50 40
1476 1000000k. Trumpet agaric (*Clitocybe geotropa*) . . . 50 40
1477 1000000k. *Morchella crassipes* 50 40
1478 1000000k. *Boletus rufescens* 50 40
1479 1000000k. Death cap (*Amanita phalloides*) . . . 50 40
1480 1000000k. *Collybia iocephala* 50 40
1481 1000000k. *Tricholoma aurantium* 50 40
1482 1000000k. *Cortinarius violaceus* 50 40
1483 1000000k. *Mycena polygramma* 50 40
1484 1000000k. *Psalliota augusta* 50 40
1485 1000000k. *Russula nigricans* 50 40
1486 1000000k. Granulated boletus (*Boletus granulatus*) 50 40
1487 1000000k. *Mycena strobilinoides* 50 40
1488 1000000k. Caesar's mushroom (*Amanita caesarea*) 50 40
1489 1000000k. Fly agaric (*Amanita muscaria*) (different) 50 40
1490 1000000k. *Boletus crocipodius* 50 40
1491 1000000k. Cracked green russula (*Russula virescens*) 50 40
1492 1000000k. Saffron milk cap (*Lactarius deliciosus*) . . . 50 40
1493 1250000k. Caesar's mushroom (*Amanita caesarea*) (different) . . . 60 50
1495 1250000k. Red cracked boletus (*Boletus chrysenteron*) (wrongly inscr "chyrsenteron") . . 60 50
1496 1250000k. Butter mushroom (*Boletus luteus*) 60 50
1497 1250000k. Lawyer's wig (*Coprinus comatus*) (different) 60 50
1498 1250000k. Witch's hat (*Hygrocybe conica*) . . . 60 50
1499 1250000k. *Psalliota xanthoderma* 60 50
MS1500 Two sheets, each 75 × 105 mm. (a) 5000000k. *Mycena lilacifolia*; (b) 5000000k. *Psalliota haemorrhoidaria* . . 5·00 5·00

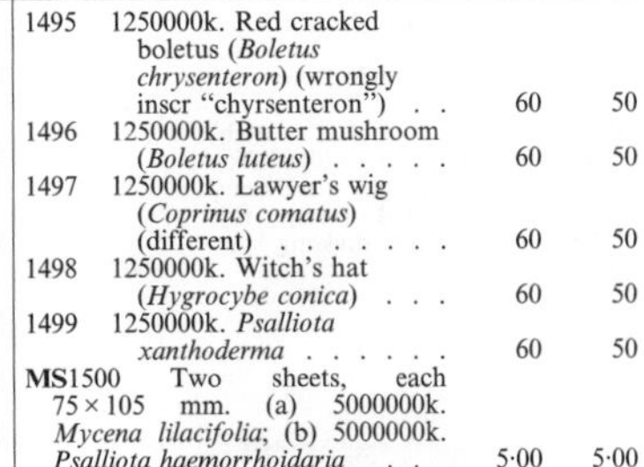

253 Mercury and Venus

1999. 30th Anniv of First Manned Moon Landing. Multicoloured.
1501 3500000k. Type **253** 70 55
1502 3500000k. Jupiter 70 55
1503 3500000k. Neptune and Pluto 70 55
1504 3500000k. Earth and Mars 70 55
1505 3500000k. Saturn 70 55
1506 3500000k. Uranus 70 55
1507 3500000k. Explorer 17 satellite, 1963 . . . . . . 70 55
1508 3500000k. Intelsat 4A satellite, 1975 . . . . . . 70 55
1509 3500000k. GOES-D (Geostationary Operational Environmental Satellite), 1980 . . . . 70 55
1510 3500000k. Intelsat 2 satellite, 1966 . . . . 70 55
1511 3500000k. Navstar 2 (Navigation System with Timing And Ranging), 1978 . . . . 70 55
1512 3500000k. S.M.S. (Solar Maximum Mission) satellite, 1980 . . . . . . 70 55
1513 3500000k. Earth and astronaut walking in space 70 55
1514 3500000k. Mariner 8 spacecraft 70 55
1515 3500000k. Viking 10 spacecraft 70 55
1516 3500000k. Ginga satellite . . 70 55
1517 3500000k. Soyuz 19 spacecraft (inscr "satelite") 70 55
1518 3500000k. Voyager spacecraft 70 55
1519 3500000k. Hubble space telescope (vert) 70 55
1520 3500000k. Launch of space shuttle *Atlantis* (vert) . . 70 55
1521 3500000k. Uhuru satellite (vert) 70 55
1522 3500000k. Mir space station (vert) 70 55
1523 3500000k. Gemini 7 spacecraft (vert) 70 55
1524 3500000k. Venera 7 spacecraft (vert) 70 55
MS1525 Five sheets (a) 95 × 85 mm. 6000000k. Astronaut from Apollo 17 walking on moon (vert); (b) 95 × 85 mm. 6000000k. Astronaut driving moon buggy (vert); (c) 85 × 110 mm. 12000000k. Launch of commercial satellite SBS 4 (vert); (d) 85 × 110 mm. Neil Armstrong (astronaut) (vert); (e) 110 × 85 mm. 12000000k. Earth and *Columbia* spacecraft . . . . 10·00 10·00
No. 1523 is inscribed "GEMNI" in error.

254 "Night Attack by 47 Ronins"

1999. 150th Death Anniv of Katushika Hokusai (artist). Multicoloured.
1526 3500000k. Type **254** 70 55
1527 3500000k. "Usigafuchi no Kudan" 70 55
1528 3500000k. Sketch of seated man 70 55
1529 3500000k. Sketch of animals and birds 70 55
1530 3500000k. "Autumn Pheasant" 70 55
1531 3500000k. Rural landscape 70 55
1532 3500000k. "Survey of the region" 70 55
1533 3500000k. Kabuki theatre 70 55
1534 3500000k. Sketch of hen . . 70 55
1535 3500000k. Sketch of wheelwright 70 55

1536 3500000k. "Excursion to Enoshima" 70 55
1537 3500000k. Sumida River landscape 70 55
MS1538 Two sheets, each 100 × 70 mm. (a) 12000000k. Japanese calligraphy between woman and child (vert); (b) 12000000k. Woman dressing hair (vert) . . . . 5·00 5·00

255 4-8-4 French Linder Local Express

2000. "PHILEX FRANCE 99" International Stamp Exhibition, Paris. Locomotives. Two sheets, each 111 × 80 mm containing T **255** and similar horiz design. Multicoloured.
MS1539 (a) 12k. Type **255** (b) 12k. French suburban linear-engine hovertrain . . . . 3·50 3·50

256 Zebra

2000. Fauna. Multicoloured.
1540 1k.50 Type **256** 45 35
1541 2k. Short-tailed fruit bat . . 65 50
1542 3k. California condor . . . 95 75
1543 5k.50 Lion . . . . 1·70 1·40
MS1544 Eight sheets:—140 × 179 mm. (a) 3k.50 × 6, Florida white-tailed deer; Turkey; Beaver; Bullfrog; Manatee; Greenback cutthroat trout; (b) 3k.50 × 6, White-faced sapajou; Toucan; Eyelash viper; Tree frog; Golden lion tamarin; Harpy eagle:—140 × 179 mm. (vert) (c) 3k.50 × 6, Mountain gorilla; Black rhino; Cape buffalo; Jackson chameleon; Cape cobra; Meerkats; (d) 3k.50 × 6, Kangaroo; Koala; Rainbow bee-eater; Red-eyed tree frog; Townsville blue-eye; Snake-necked tortoise:—107 × 77 mm. (vert) (e) 12k. Three-toed sloth; (f) 12k. Cheetah; (g) 12k. Orang-utan:—70 × 100 mm. (vert) 12k. Ring-tailed lemur . . . . 23·00 23·00

257 Harpy Eagle

2000. Birds. Multicoloured.
1545 1k.50 Type **257** 70 55
1546 2k. Andean condor 65 50
1547 3k. Lappet-faced vulture (vert) 95 75
MS1548 Eight sheets 128 × 127 mm. (a) 3k.50 × 6, American kestrel (*Falco sparverius*) (inscr "sperterius"); Spectacled owl (*Pulsatrix perspicillata*); White-tailed kite (*Eleanus leucurus*) (inscr "Elemus"); Boobook owl (*Ninox novaeseelandiae*) (inscr "novaseseelandiar"); *Polemaetus bellicosus* (inscr "Polmactus"); Caracara (*Polyborus plancus*); (b) 3k.50 × 6, Northern goshawk (*Accipiter gentiles*) (inscr "Acolpiler genttlis"); Hawk owl (*Surnia ulula*) (wrongly inscr "Surnis"); Peregrine falcon (*Falco prregrinus*); Eastern screech owl (*Otus asio*); African fish eagle (*Haliaeetus vocifer*) (inscr "Haliaectus"); Laughing falcon (*Herpetotheres cachinnans*) (inscr "Herpetothers"):—85 × 127 mm. (c) 6k.50 × 3, Verreaux's eagle; Bonelli's eagle; African fish eagle:—127 × 85 mm. (d) 6k.50 × 3, Bald eagle (vert); Tawny eagle (vert); Eagle (vert); (e) 85 × 110 mm. 12k. Lanner falcon (vert); (f) 110 × 85 mm. 12k. King vultures; (g) 85 × 111 mm. 15k. Secretary bird (*Sagittarius serpentarius*); (h) 15k. Golden eagle (*Aquila chrysaetos*) (inscr "chrysectos") 14·50 14·50

258 Zebra (*Equs zebra*)

2000. Animals and Birds. Multicoloured.
1549 1k.50 Type **258** 55 45
1550 1k.50 Golden palm weaver (*Ploceus xanthops*) 55 45
1551 1k.50 Hunting dog (*Lycaon pictus*) 55 45
1552 1k.50 Cheetah (*Acinonyx jubatus*) 55 45
1553 1k.50 Gemsbok (*Oryx gazelle*) 55 45
1554 1k.50 Cape fox (*Vulpes chama*) (inscr "Otocyon megalotis") 55 45
1555 1k.50 Giraffe (*Giraffa camelopardalis*) 55 45
1556 1k.50 Golden jackal (*Canis aureus*) (inscr "adustus") 55 45
1557 1k.50 Potto (*Perodicticus potto*) 55 45
1558 1k.50 Lion (*Panthera leo*) 55 45
1559 1k.50 Lilac-breasted roller (*Coracias caudate*) (inscr "Coracus") 55 45
1560 1k.50 Bat-eared fox (*Otocyon megalotis*) . . . 55 45
1561 2k. Ostrich (*Struthio camelus*) . . . . 1·30 1·00
1562 2k. African wild cat (*Felis lybica*) . . . . 1·30 1·00
1563 2k. Impala (*Aepyceros melampus*) . . . . 1·30 1·00
1564 2k. Savanna monkey (*Cercopithecus aethiops*) 1·30 1·00
1565 2k. Black rhino (*Diceros bicornis*) . . . . 1·30 1·00
1566 2k. Baboon (*Papio*) . . . . 1·30 1·00
1567 2k. Caracal (*Felis caracal*) 1·30 1·00
1568 2k. Secretary bird (*Sagittarius serpentarius*) 1·30 1·00
1569 2k. Warthog (*Phacochoerus aethiopicus*) . . . . 1·30 1·00
1570 2k. Afro-Australian fur seal (*Arctocephalus pusillus*) . . 1·30 1·00
1571 2k. Malachite kingfisher (*Alcedo cristata*) . . . . . 1·30 1·00
1572 2k. Hippopotamus (*Hippopotamus amphibious*) . . . . . . 1·30 1·00
MS1573 Two sheets. (a) 85 × 110 mm.12k. Savanna monkey (vert); (b) 110 × 85 mm. 12k. Elephant (*Loxodonta Africana*) (vert) . . . . 13·00 13·00

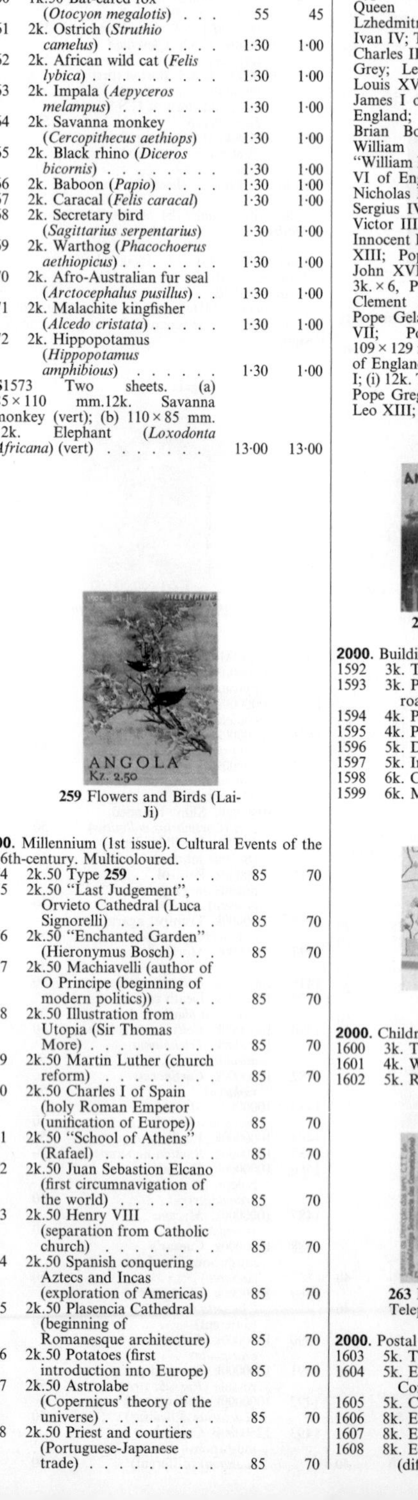

259 Flowers and Birds (Lai-Ji)

2000. Millennium (1st issue). Cultural Events of the 16th-century. Multicoloured.
1574 2k.50 Type **259** 85 70
1575 2k.50 "Last Judgement", Orvieto Cathedral (Luca Signorelli) 85 70
1576 2k.50 "Enchanted Garden" (Hieronymus Bosch) . . . 85 70
1577 2k.50 Machiavelli (author of O Principe (beginning of modern politics)) 85 70
1578 2k.50 Illustration from Utopia (Sir Thomas More) 85 70
1579 2k.50 Martin Luther (church reform) 85 70
1580 2k.50 Charles I of Spain (holy Roman Emperor (unification of Europe)) 85 70
1581 2k.50 "School of Athens" (Rafael) 85 70
1582 2k.50 Juan Sebastion Elcano (first circumnavigation of the world) 85 70
1583 2k.50 Henry VIII (separation from Catholic church) 85 70
1584 2k.50 Spanish conquering Aztecs and Incas (exploration of Americas) 85 70
1585 2k.50 Plasencia Cathedral (beginning of Romanesque architecture) 85 70
1586 2k.50 Potatoes (first introduction into Europe) 85 70
1587 2k.50 Astrolabe (Copernicus' theory of the universe) 85 70
1588 2k.50 Priest and courtiers (Portuguese-Japanese trade) 85 70
1589 2k.50 "Self Portrait" (Albrecht Durer (death, 1528)) (60 × 40 mm) . . . 85 70
1590 2k.50 Woman, hourglass, inkwell and cross (declaration of rights of indigenous Americans by Queen Isabel of Castille) 85 70

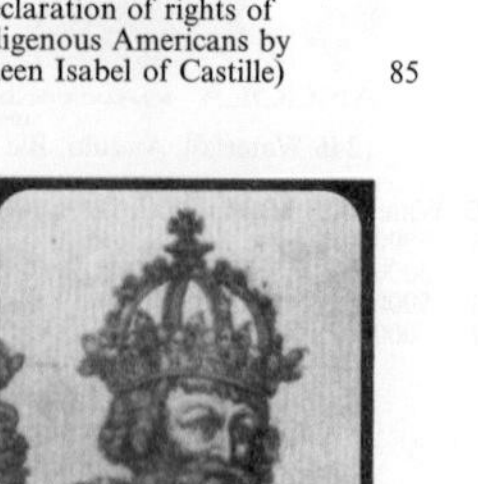

260 Henry II of Germany

2000. Millennium (2nd issue). Monarchs and Popes. Multicoloured.
MS1591 Twelve sheets:—165 × 198 mm. (a) 3k. × 4, Type **260**; Marina Mniszech, Queen Consort of Tsar Lzhedmitry (false Dmitri); Tsar Ivan IV; Tsar Ivan III; (b) 3k. × 4, Charles II of England; Lady Jane Grey; Leopold III of Belgium; Louis XV of France; (c) 3k. × 6, James I of England; James II of England; James VI of Scotland; Brian Boru, King of Ireland; William I of Prussia (inscr "William I of Germany"); Edward VI of England; (d) 3k. × 6, Pope Nicholas II; Pope Pascal II; Pope Sergius IV; Pope Victor II; Pope Victor III; Pope Urban III; Pope Innocent II; (e) 3k. × 6, Pope John XIII; Pope Agapetus II; Pope John XVIII; Pope Lucius II; (f) 3k. × 6, Pope Celestine II; Pope Clement II; Pope Clement III; Pope Gelasius II; Pope Benedict VII; Pope Gregory V:—109 × 129 mm. (g) 12k. William IV of England; (h) 12k. Tsar Fyodor I; (i) 12k. Tsar Lzhedmitry; (j) 12k. Pope Gregory VII; (k) 12k. Pope Leo XIII; (l) 12k. Pope Leo IX 16·00 16·00

261 Damaged Building, Kuito

2000. Buildings and People. Multicoloured.
1592 3k. Type **261** 75 60
1593 3k. People and Kunje–Kuito road 75 60
1594 4k. Post Office building . . 1·00 80
1595 4k. Police headquarters . . 1·00 80
1596 5k. Damaged apartments . . 1·10 85
1597 5k. Independence Plaza . . 1·10 85
1598 6k. Children . . . . 1·20 95
1599 6k. Man carrying sack . . . 1·20 95

262 Trees

2000. Children's Paintings. Multicoloured.
1600 3k. Type **262** 75 60
1601 4k. Wall . . . . 1·00 80
1602 5k. Rural scene . . . . . . 1·30 1·10

263 Directorate of Communications, Telephones and Telegraphs, Luanda

2000. Postal Buildings. Multicoloured.
1603 5k. Type **263** 85 65
1604 5k. ETP building, Mbanza Congo 85 65
1605 5k. CTT building, Namibe 85 65
1606 8k. ECP building, Luanda 1·30 1·00
1607 8k. ETP building, Lobito . . 1·30 1·00
1608 8k. ECP building, Luanda (different) . . . . 1·30 1·00

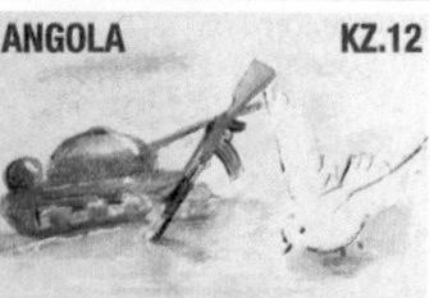

264 Tank, Rifle and Dove

2001. 25th Anniv of Independence. Sheet 140 × 47 mm containing T **264** and similar horiz design. Multicoloured.
MS1609 12k. Type **264**; 12k. Dove, mattock and tractor . . . . . 3·25 3·25

265 Radio Studio

2001. 25th Anniv of Public Radio (MS1613a, MS1613c) and Television (others). Four sheets containing T **265** and similar multicoloured designs.
MS1610 (a) 154 × 80 mm. 9k.50, Type **265**; 9k.50, Reporter in war zone; 9k.50 Carrying stretcher from burning aeroplane. (b) 154 × 80 mm. 9k.50, Television studio; 9k.50, Cameraman filming tank; 9k.50, Women and children crossing water. (c) 99 × 60 mm. 12k. Reporter in war zone (detail) (42 × 28 mm). (d) 99 × 60 mm. 12k. Cameraman filming tank (detail) (28 × 42 mm) (vert) . . . . . 10·50 10·50

266 Hands holding Book

2001. Africa Day. Multicoloured.
1611 10k. Type **266** . . . . . . 1·30 1·00
1612 10k. Hands and xylophone 1·30 1·00
MS1613 130 × 90 mm. 30k. Map of Africa . . . . 4·00 4·00

267 *Nicolaia speciosa*

2001. Flowers. Belgica 2001 International Stamp Exhibition. Multicoloured.
1614 8k. Type **267** . . . . 1·00 85
1615 9k. *Allamanda cathartica* (inscr "cathartca") . . . 1·10 85
1616 10k. *Welwitschia mirabilis* 1·30 1·00
1617 10k. *Tagetes patula* . . . . 1·30 1·00
MS1618 130 × 90 mm. 30k. No. 1618 4·00 4·00

268 Man wearing Dark Glasses

2001. Total Eclipse of the Sun, 21 June 2001. Sheet 130 × 90 mm.
MS1619 multicoloured . . . . . 4·00 4·00

APPENDIX

1995.

90th Anniv of Rotary International (on gold foil). 81000k.

CHARITY TAX STAMPS

Used on certain days of the year as an additional tax on internal letters. If one was not used in addition to normal postage, postage due stamps were used to collect the deficiency and the fine.

1925. Marquis de Pombal Commemorative stamps of Portugal but inscr "ANGOLA".
C343 C **73** 15c. violet 90 85
C344 – 15c. violet . . . . . . 4·50 3·25
C345 C **75** 15c. violet 90 85

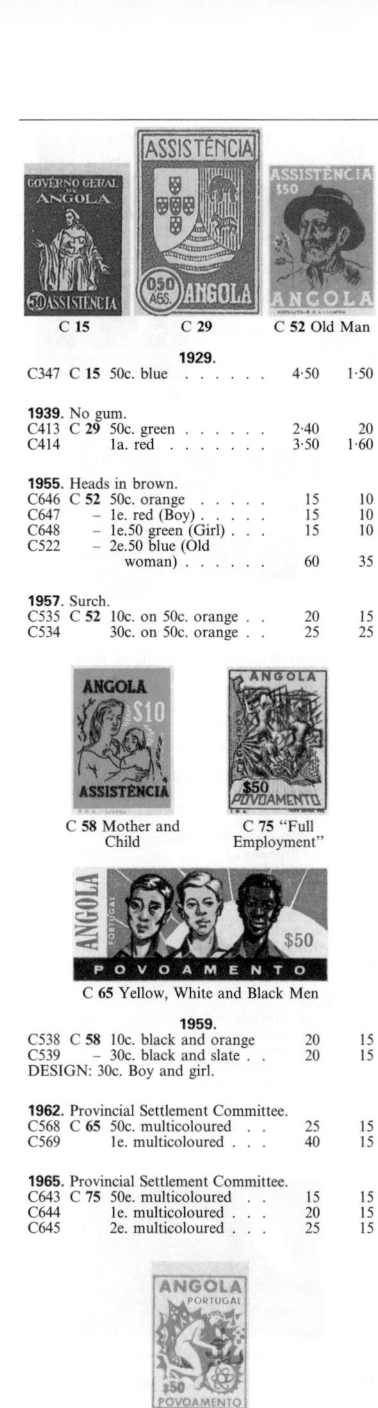

C 15 C 29 C 52 Old Man

1929.
C347 C **15** 50c. blue 4·50 1·50

1939. No gum.
C413 C **29** 50c. green 2·40 20
C414 1a. red 3·50 1·60

1955. Heads in brown.
C646 C **52** 50c. orange 15 10
C647 – 1e. red (Boy) 15 10
C648 – 1e.50 green (Girl) 15 10
C522 – 2e.50 blue (Old woman) 60 35

1957. Surch.
C535 C **52** 10c. on 50c. orange 20 15
C534 30c. on 50c. orange 25 25

C **58** Mother and Child C **75** "Full Employment"

C **65** Yellow, White and Black Men

1959.
C538 C **58** 10c. black and orange 20 15
C539 – 30c. black and slate 20 15
DESIGN: 30c. Boy and girl.

1962. Provincial Settlement Committee.
C568 C **65** 50c. multicoloured 25 15
C569 1e. multicoloured 40 15

1965. Provincial Settlement Committee.
C643 C **75** 50e. multicoloured 15 15
C644 1e. multicoloured 20 15
C645 2e. multicoloured 25 15

C **95** Planting Tree

1972. Provincial Settlement Committee.
C701 C **95** 50c. red and brown 15 15
C702 – 1e. black and green 15 15
C703 – 2e. black and brown 15 15
DESIGNS: 1e. Agricultural workers; 2e. Corncobs and flowers.

NEWSPAPER STAMP

1893. "Newspaper" key-type inscr "ANGOLA".
N51 V 2½r. brown 2·30 1·10

POSTAGE DUE STAMPS

1904. "Due" key-type inscr "ANGOLA".
D150 W 5r. green 30 30
D151 10r. grey 30 30
D152 20r. brown 65 35
D153 30r. orange 65 35
D154 50r. brown 85 55
D155 60r. brown 7·50 4·00
D156 100r. mauve 3·25 2·10
D157 130r. blue 3·25 2·10
D158 200r. red 4·50 2·40
D159 500r. lilac 4·50 2·50
See also Nos. D343/52.

1911. Nos. D150/9 optd **REPUBLICA**.
D166 W 5r. green 25 20
D167 10r. grey 25 20
D168 20r. brown 25 20
D169 30r. orange 40 20
D170 50r. brown 40 20
D171 60r. brown 1·10 70
D172 100r. mauve 1·10 70
D173 130r. blue 1·30 85
D174 200r. red 1·50 85
D175 500r. lilac 1·70 1·50

1921. Values in new currency.
D343 W ½c. green 25 20
D344 1c. grey 25 20
D345 2c. brown 25 20
D346 3c. orange 65 65
D347 5c. brown 25 20
D348 6c. brown 25 20
D349 10c. mauve 35 30
D350 13c. blue 70 65
D351 20c. red 70 65
D352 50c. grey 70 65

1925. Marquis de Pombal stamps of Angola, as Nos. C343/5, optd **MULTA**.
D353 C **73** 30c. violet 90 85
D354 – 30c. violet 90 85
D355 C **75** 30c. violet 90 85

1949. Surch **PORTEADO** and value.
D438 **17** 10c. on 20c. grey 25 20
D439 20c. on 30c. green 45 40
D440 30c. on 50c. brown 70 60
D441 40c. on 1a. red 1·00 95
D442 50c. on 2a. mauve 1·50 1·40
D443 1a. on 5a. green 1·70 1·60

D **45**

1952. Numerals in red, name in black.
D483 D **45** 10c. brown and olive 20 15
D484 30c. green and blue 20 15
D485 50c. brown & lt brn 20 15
D486 1a. blue, green & orge 40 40
D487 2a. brown and red 55 50
D488 5a. brown and blue 55 50

ANGRA Pt. 9

A district of the Azores, which used the stamps of the Azores except from 1892 to 1905.

1000 reis = 1 milreis.

1892. As T **4** of Funchal, inscr "ANGRA".
16 5r. yellow 2·25 1·40
5 10r. mauve 2·50 1·40
6 15r. brown 2·75 2·10
7 20r. violet 2·75 2·10
8 25r. green 3·50 55
9 50r. blue 5·75 3·25
10 75r. red 6·75 4·00
11 80r. green 8·00 7·75
24 100r. brown on yellow 29·00 11·00
13 150r. red on rose 40·00 32·00
14 200r. blue on blue 40·00 32·00
15 300r. blue on brown 40·00 32·00

1897. "King Carlos" key-type inscr "ANGRA".
28 S 2½r. grey 55 40
29 5r. red 55 40
30 10r. green 55 40
31 15r. brown 6·75 3·75
43 15r. green 60 45
32 20r. lilac 1·40 1·00
33 25r. green 2·10 1·00
44 25r. red 45 45
34 50r. blue 3·75 1·25
46 65r. blue 1·00 45
35 75r. red 2·50 1·25
47 75r. brown on yellow 9·75 8·50
36 80r. mauve 1·10 95
37 100r. blue on blue 2·00 1·25
48 115r. red on pink 2·00 1·60
49 130r. brown on cream 2·00 1·60
38 150r. brown on yellow 2·00 1·25
50 180r. grey on pink 2·25 2·10
39 200r. purple on pink 4·00 2·75
40 300r. blue on pink 5·75 4·50
41 500r. black on blue 13·00 10·50

ANGUILLA Pt. 1

St. Christopher, Nevis and Anguilla were granted Associated Statehood on 27 February 1967, but following a referendum Anguilla declared her independence and the St. Christopher authorities withdrew. On 7 July 1969, the Anguilla post office was officially recognised by the Government of St. Christopher, Nevis and Anguilla and normal postal communications via St. Christopher were resumed.

By the Anguilla Act of 27 July 1971, the island was restored to direct British control.

100 cents = 1 West Indian dollar.

1967. Nos. 129/44 of St. Kitts-Nevis optd **Independent Anguilla** and bar.
1 – ½c. sepia and blue 35·00 25·00
2 **33** 1c. multicoloured 38·00 8·00
3 – 2c. multicoloured 38·00 1·50
4 – 3c. multicoloured 38·00 4·50
5 – 4c. multicoloured 38·00 5·50
6 – 5c. multicoloured £130 24·00
7 – 6c. multicoloured 60·00 11·00
8 – 10c. multicoloured 38·00 7·50
9 – 15c. multicoloured 70·00 13·00
10 – 20c. multicoloured £110 15·00
11 – 25c. multicoloured £100 25·00
12 – 50c. multicoloured £2250 £450
13 – 60c. multicoloured £2750 £900
14 – $1 yellow and blue £1800 £400
15 – $2.50 multicoloured £1600 £300
16 – $5 multicoloured £1600 £300

Owing to the limited stocks available for overprinting, the sale of the stamps were personally controlled by the Postmaster and no orders from the trade were accepted.

2 Mahogany Tree, The Quarter

1967.
17 **2** 1c. green, brown and orange 10 85
18 – 2c. turquoise and black 10 1·25
19 – 3c. black and green 10 10
20 – 4c. blue and black 10 10
21 – 5c. multicoloured 10 10
22 – 6c. red and black 10 10
23 – 10c. multicoloured 15 10
24 – 15c. multicoloured 1·60 20
25 – 20c. multicoloured 1·25 2·00
26 – 25c. multicoloured 60 20
27 – 40c. green, blue and black 1·00 25
28 – 60c. multicoloured 4·00 4·25
29 – $1 multicoloured 1·75 3·25
30 – $2.50 multicoloured 2·00 4·25
31 – $5 multicoloured 3·00 4·25
DESIGNS: 2c. Sombrero Lighthouse; 3c. St. Mary's Church; 4c. Valley Police Station; 5c. Old Plantation House, Mt. Fortune; 6c. Valley Post Office; 10c. Methodist Church, West End; 15c. Wall Blake Airport; 20c. Beech A90 King Air aircraft over Sandy Ground; 25c. Island harbour; 40c. Map of Anguilla; 60c. Hermit crab and starfish; $1, Hibiscus; $2.50, Local scene; $5, Spiny lobster.

17 Yachts in Lagoon

1968. Anguillan Ships. Multicoloured.
32 10c. Type **17** 20 10
33 15c. Boat on beach 25 10
34 25c. Schooner "Warspite" 35 15
35 40c. Schooner "Atlantic Star" 40 20

18 Purple-throated Carib

1968. Anguillan Birds. Multicoloured.
36 10c. Type **18** 85 15
37 15c. Bananaquit 1·10 20
38 25c. Black-necked stilt (horiz) 1·40 20
39 40c. Royal tern (horiz) 1·60 30

19 Guides' Badge and Anniversary Years

1968. 35th Anniv of Anguillan Girl Guides. Mult.
40 10c. Type **19** 10 10
41 15c. Badge and silhouettes of guides (vert) 15 10
42 25c. Guides' badge and Headquarters 20 15
43 40c. Association and proficiency badges (vert) 25 15

20 The Three Kings

1968. Christmas.
44 **20** 1c. black and red 10 10
45 – 10c. black and blue 10 10
46 – 15c. black and brown 15 10
47 – 40c. black and blue 15 10
48 – 50c. black and green 20 15
DESIGNS—VERT: 10c. The Wise Men; 15c. Holy Family and manger. HORIZ: 40c. The Shepherds; 50c. Holy Family and donkey.

21 Bagging Salt

1969. Anguillan Salt Industry. Multicoloured.
49 10c. Type **21** 25 10
50 15c. Packing salt 30 10
51 40c. Salt pond 35 10
52 50c. Loading salt 35 10

1969. Expiration of Interim Agreement on Status of Anguilla. Nos. 17/22, 23, 24 and 26/7 optd **INDEPENDENCE JANUARY 1969**.
52a 1c. green, brown and orange 10 40
52b 2c. green and black 10 40
52c 3c. black and green 10 20
52d 4c. blue and black 10 20
52e 5c. multicoloured 10 20
52f 6c. red and black 10 20
52g 10c. multicoloured 10 30
52h 15c. multicoloured 90 30
52i 25c. multicoloured 80 30
52j 40c. green, blue and black 1·00 40
The remaining values of the 1967 series.
Nos. 17/31 also come with this overprint but these are outside the scope of this catalogue.

22 "The Crucifixion" (Studio of Massys)

1969. Easter Commemoration. Multicoloured.
53 25c. Type **22** 25 15
54 40c. "The Last Supper" (ascribed to Roberti) 35 15

23 Amaryllis

1969. Flowers of the Caribbean. Multicoloured.
55 10c. Type **23** 20 20
56 15c. Bougainvillea 25 25
57 40c. Hibiscus 50 50
58 50c. "Cattleya" orchid 1·50 1·60

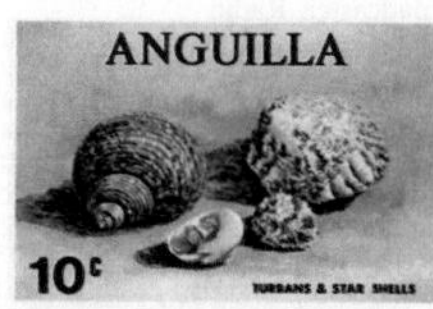

24 Superb Gaza, Channelled Turban, Chestnut Turban and Carved Star Shell

1969. Sea Shells. Multicoloured.
59 10c. Type **24** 20 20
60 15c. American thorny oysters 20 20
61 40c. Scotch, royal and smooth scotch bonnets 30 30
62 50c. Atlantic trumpet triton 40 30

1969. Christmas. Nos. 17 and 25/8 optd with different seasonal emblems.
63 1c. green, brown and orange 10 10
64 20c. multicoloured 20 10
65 25c. multicoloured 20 10
66 40c. green, blue and black 25 15
67 60c. multicoloured 40 20

30 Spotted Goatfish

1969. Fishes. Multicoloured.
68 10c. Type **30** 30 15
69 15c. Blue-striped grunt 45 15
70 40c. Nassau grouper 55 20
71 50c. Banded butterflyfish 65 20

31 "Morning Glory"

32 "The Crucifixion" (Masaccio)

1970. Flowers. Multicoloured.
72 10c. Type **31** 30 10
73 15c. Blue petrea 45 10
74 40c. Hibiscus 70 20
75 50c. "Flame Tree" 80 25

1970. Easter. Multicoloured.
76 10c. "The Ascent to Calvary" (Tiepolo) (horiz) 15 10
77 20c. Type **32** 20 10
78 40c. "Deposition" (Rosso Fiorentino) 25 15
79 60c. "The Ascent to Calvary" (Murillo) (horiz) 25 15

33 Scout Badge and Map

1970. 40th Anniv of Scouting in Anguilla. Multicoloured.
80 10c. Type **33** 15 15
81 15c. Scout camp, and cubs practising first aid 20 20
82 40c. Monkey bridge 25 30
83 50c. Scout H.Q. building and Lord Baden-Powell 35 30

34 Boatbuilding

1970. Multicoloured.
84 1c. Type **34** 30 40
85 2c. Road construction 30 40
86 3c. Quay, Blowing Point . . . 30 20
87 4c. Broadcaster, Radio Anguilla 30 50
88 5c. Cottage Hospital extension 40 50
89 6c. Valley Secondary School 30 50
90 10c. Hotel extension 30 30
91 15c. Sandy Ground 30 30
92 20c. Supermarket and cinema 55 30
93 25c. Bananas and mangoes . . 35 1·00
94 40c. Wall Blake Airport . . . 2·75 3·00
95 60c. Sandy Ground jetty . . . 65 3·25
96 $1 Administration buildings 1·25 1·40
97 $2.50 Livestock . . . . 1·50 3·75
98 $5 Sandy Hill Bay . . . . . . 2·75 3·75

35 "The Adoration of the Shepherds" (Reni)

1970. Christmas. Multicoloured.
99 1c. Type **35** 10 10
100 20c. "The Virgin and Child" (Gozzoli) 30 20
101 25c. "Mystic Nativity" (detail, Botticelli) 30 20
102 40c. "The Santa Margherita Madonna" (detail, Mazzola) 40 25
103 50c. "The Adoration of the Magi" (detail, Tiepolo) . . 40 25

36 "Ecce Homo" (detail, Correggio)

1971. Easter. Paintings. Multicoloured.
104 10c. Type **36** 25 10
105 15c. "Christ appearing to St Peter" (detail, Carracci) . . 25 10
106 40c. "Angels weeping over the Dead Christ" (detail, Guercino) (horiz) 30 10
107 50c. "The Supper at Emmaus" (detail, Caravaggio) (horiz) 30 15

37 "Hypolimnas misipus"

1971. Butterflies. Multicoloured.
108 10c. Type **37** . . . . 1·60 70
109 15c. "Junonia evarete" . . . 1·60 80
110 40c. "Agraulis vanillae" . . . 2·00 1·25
111 50c. "Danaus plexippus" . . . 2·00 1·50

38 "Magnanime" and "Aimable" in Battle

39 "The Ansidei Madonna" (detail, Raphael)

1971. Sea-battles of the West Indies. Multicoloured.
112 10c. Type **38** . . . . 1·10 1·40
113 15c. H.M.S. "Duke", "Glorieux" and H.M.S. "Agamemnon" . . . . . 1·25 1·60
114 25c. H.M.S. "Formidable" and H.M.S. "Namur" against "Ville de Paris" . . 1·50 1·75
115 40c. H.M.S. "Canada" . . . 1·60 1·90
116 50c. H.M.S. "St. Albans" and wreck of "Hector" . . 1·75 2·00

Nos. 112/116 were issued together, se-tenant, forming a composite design.

1971. Christmas. Multicoloured.
117 20c. Type **39** 25 30
118 25c. "Mystic Nativity" (detail, Botticelli) 25 30
119 40c. "Adoration of the Shepherds" (detail, ascr to Murillo) 30 40
120 50c. "The Madonna of the Iris" (detail, ascr to Durer) 35 70

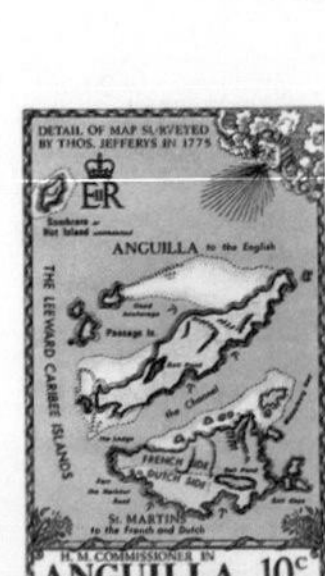

40 Map of Anguilla and St. Martin by Thomas Jefferys, 1775

41 "Jesus Buffeted"

1972. Caribbean Maps depicting Anguilla. Multicoloured.
121 10c. Type **40** 25 10
122 15c. Samuel Fahlberg's Map, 1814 . . . . 35 15
123 40c. Thomas Jefferys' Map, 1775 (horiz) 50 25
124 50c. Captain E. Barnett's Map, 1847 (horiz) 60 25

1972. Easter. Multicoloured.
125 10c. Type **41** 25 25
126 15c. "The Way of Sorrows" 30 30
127 25c. "The Crucifixion" . . . 30 30
128 40c. "Descent from the Cross" 35 35
129 50c. "The Burial" 40 40

42 Loblolly Tree

44 Flight into Egypt

1972. Multicoloured.
130 1c. Spear fishing 10 40
131 2c. Type **42** 10 40
132 3c. Sandy Ground 10 40
133 4c. Ferry at Blowing Point 1·75 20
134 5c. Agriculture . . . . . . 15 1·00
135 6c. St. Mary's Church . . . 25 20
136 10c. St. Gerard's Church . . 25 40
137 15c. Cottage hospital extension 25 30
138 20c. Public library 30 35
139 25c. Sunset at Blowing Point 40 2·00
140 40c. Boat building . . . . . 5·00 1·50
141 60c. Hibiscus . . . . 4·00 4·00
142 $1 Magnificent frigate bird ("Man-o'-War") . . . . 10·00 8·00
143 $2.50 Frangipani . . . . . 5·00 10·00
144 $5 Brown pelican . . . . . 16·00 17·00
144a $10 Green-back turtle . . . 15·00 18·00

1972. Royal Silver Wedding. As T **52** of Ascension, but with Schooner and Common dolphin in background.
145 25c. green 50 75
146 40c. brown 50 75

1972. Christmas. Multicoloured.
147 1c. Type **44** 10 10
148 20c. Star of Bethlehem . . . 20 20
149 25c. Holy Family 20 20
150 40c. Arrival of the Magi . . 20 25
151 50c. Adoration of the Magi 25 25

45 "The Betrayal of Christ"

1973. Easter. Multicoloured.
152 1c. Type **45** 10 10
153 10c. "The Man of Sorrows" 10 10
154 20c. "Christ bearing the Cross" 10 15
155 25c. "The Crucifixion" . . . 15 15
156 40c. "The Descent from the Cross" 15 15
157 50c. "The Resurrection" . . 15 20

46 "Santa Maria"

1973. Columbus Discovers the West Indies. Multicoloured.
159 1c. Type **46** 10 10
160 20c. Early map . . . . . . 1·50 1·25
161 40c. Map of voyages . . . . 1·60 1·40
162 70c. Sighting land . . . . . 1·90 1·75
163 $1.20 Landing of Columbus 2·50 2·25
MS164 193 × 93 mm. Nos. 159/63 6·00 7·00

47 Princess Anne and Captain Mark Phillips

49 "The Crucifixion" (Raphael)

48 "The Adoration of the Shepherds" (Reni)

1973. Royal Wedding. Multicoloured. Background colours given.
165 **47** 60c. green 20 15
166 $1.20 mauve 30 15

1973. Christmas. Multicoloured.
167 1c. Type **48** 10 10
168 10c. "The Madonna and Child with Saints Jerome and Dominic" (Filippino Lippi) 10 10
169 20c. "The Nativity" (Master of Brunswick) 15 15
170 25c. "Madonna of the Meadow" (Bellini) 15 15
171 40c. "Virgin and Child" (Cima) 20 20
172 50c. "Adoration of the Kings" (Geertgen) 20 20
MS173 148 × 149 mm. Nos. 167/72 80 1·60

1974. Easter.
174 **49** 1c. multicoloured 10 10
175 – 15c. multicoloured 10 10
176 – 20c. multicoloured 15 15
177 – 25c. multicoloured 15 15
178 – 40c. multicoloured 15 15
179 – $1 multicoloured 20 25
MS180 123 × 141 mm. Nos. 174/9 1·00 1·25

DESIGNS: 15c. to $1, Details of Raphael's "Crucifixion".

50 Churchill Making "Victory" Sign

1974. Birth Centenary of Sir Winston Churchill. Multicoloured.
181 1c. Type **50** 10 10
182 20c. Churchill with Roosevelt 20 20
183 25c. Wartime broadcast . . . 20 20
184 40c. Birthplace, Blenheim Palace 30 30
185 60c. Churchill's statue . . . 30 35
186 $1.20 Country residence, Chartwell 45 55
MS187 195 × 96 mm. Nos. 181/6 1·40 2·50

51 U.P.U. Emblem

1974. Centenary of U.P.U.
188 **51** 1c. black and blue 10 10
189 20c. black and orange . . 15 15
190 25c. black and yellow . . . 15 15
191 40c. black and mauve . . . 20 25
192 60c. black and green . . . 30 40
193 $1.20 black and blue . . . 50 60
MS194 195 × 96 mm. Nos. 188/93 1·25 2·25

52 Anguillan pointing to Star

1974. Christmas. Multicoloured.
195 1c. Type **52** 10 10
196 20c. Child in Manger 10 20

197 25c. King's offering 10 20
198 40c. Star over map of Anguilla 15 20
199 60c. Family looking at star 15 20
200 $1.20 Angels of Peace 20 30
MS201 177 × 85 mm. Nos. 195/200 1·00 2·00

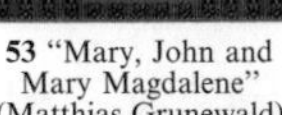

53 "Mary, John and Mary Magdalene" (Matthias Grunewald)

55 "Madonna, Child and the Infant John the Baptist" (Raphael)

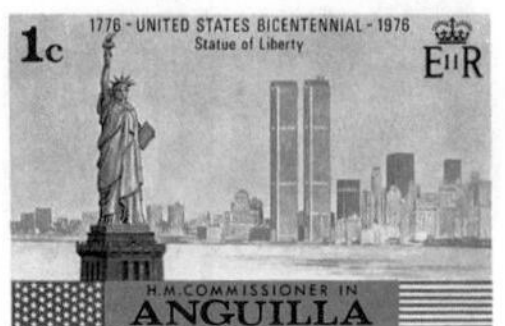

54 Statue of Liberty

1975. Easter. Details from Isenheim Altarpiece, Colmar Museum. Multicoloured.
202 1c. Type **53** 10 10
203 10c. "The Crucifixion" 15 15
204 15c. "St. John the Baptist" 15 15
205 20c. "St. Sebastian and Angels" 15 20
206 $1 "The Entombment" (horiz) 20 35
207 $1.50 "St. Anthony the Hermit" 25 45
MS208 134 × 127 mm. Nos. 202/7 (imperf) 1·00 2·00

1975. Bicentenary of American Revolution. Mult.
209 1c. Type **54** 10 10
210 10c. The Capitol 20 10
211 15c. "Congress voting for Independence" (Pine and Savage) 30 15
212 20c. Washington and map 30 15
213 $1 Boston Tea Party 45 40
214 $1.50 Bicentenary logo 50 60
MS215 198 × 97 mm. Nos. 209/14 1·25 2·50

1975. Christmas. "Madonna and Child" paintings by artists named. Multicoloured.
216 1c. Type **55** 10 10
217 10c. Cima 15 15
218 15c. Dolci 20 15
219 20c. Durer 20 20
220 $1 Bellini 35 25
221 $1.50 Botticelli 45 35
MS222 130 × 145 mm. Nos. 216/21 2·00 2·25

1976. New Constitution. Nos. 130 etc optd **NEW CONSTITUTION 1976** or surch also.
223 1c. Spear fishing 30 40
224 2c. on 1c. Spear fishing 30 40
225 2c. Type **42** 7·00 1·75
226 3c. on 40c. Boat building 75 70
227 4c. Ferry at Blowing Point 1·00 1·00
228 5c. on 40c. Boat building 30 50
229 6c. St. Mary's Church 30 50
230 10c. on 20c. Public library 30 50
231 10c. St. Gerard's Church 7·00 4·75
232 15c. Cottage Hospital extension 30 1·25
233 20c. Public library 30 50
234 25c. Sunset at Blowing Point 30 50
235 40c. Boat building 1·00 70
236 60c. Hibiscus 70 70
237 $1 Magnificent frigate bird 6·50 2·25
238 $2.50 Frangipani 2·25 2·25
239 $5 Brown pelican 8·00 8·00
240 $10 Green-back turtle 3·00 6·00

57 Almond

1976. Flowering Trees. Multicoloured.
241 1c. Type **57** 10 10
242 10c. Autograph 20 20
243 15c. Calabash 20 20
244 20c. Cordia 20 20
245 $1 Papaya 30 45
246 $1.50 Flamboyant 35 55
MS247 194 × 99 mm. Nos. 241/6 1·50 2·00

58 The Three Marys

1976. Easter. Showing portions of the Altar Frontal Tapestry, Rheinau. Multicoloured.
248 1c. Type **58** 10 10
249 10c. The Crucifixion 10 10
250 15c. Two Soldiers 15 15
251 20c. The Annunciation 15 15
252 $1 The complete tapestry (horiz) 65 65
253 $1.50 The Risen Christ 80 80
MS254 138 × 130 mm. Nos. 248/53 (imperf) 1·75 2·10

59 French Ships approaching Anguilla

1976. Bicentenary of Battle of Anguilla. Mult.
255 1c. Type **59** 10 10
256 3c. "Margaret" (sloop) leaving Anguilla 1·25 35
257 15c. Capture of "Le Desius" 1·50 55
258 25c. "La Vaillante" forced aground 1·50 80
259 $1 H.M.S. "Lapwing" 2·00 1·25
260 $1.50 "Le Desius" burning 2·25 1·75
MS261 205 × 103 mm. Nos. 255/60 7·50 6·00

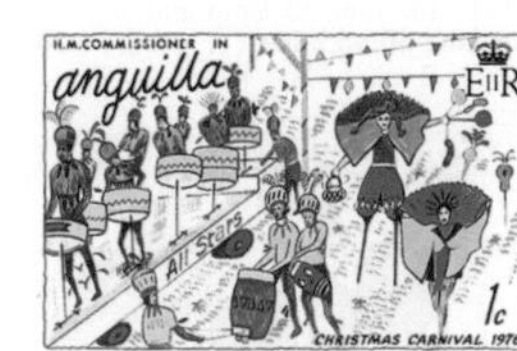

60 "Christmas Carnival" (A. Richardson)

1976. Christmas. Children's Paintings. Mult.
262 1c. Type **60** 10 10
263 3c. "Dreams of Christmas Gifts" (J. Connor) 10 10
264 15c. "Carolling" (P. Richardson) 15 15
265 25c. "Candle-light Procession" (A. Mussington) 20 20
266 $1 "Going to Church" (B. Franklin) 30 30
267 $1.50 "Coming Home for Christmas" (E. Gumbs) 40 40
MS268 232 × 147 mm. Nos. 262/7 1·50 1·75

61 Prince Charles and H.M.S. "Minerva" (frigate)

1977. Silver Jubilee. Multicoloured.
269 25c. Type **61** 15 10
270 40c. Prince Philip landing by launch at Road Bay, 1964 15 10
271 $1.20 Coronation scene 20 20
272 $2.50 Coronation regalia and map of Anguilla 25 30
MS273 145 × 96 mm. Nos. 269/72 65 90

62 Yellow-crowned Night Heron

1977. Multicoloured.
274 1c. Type **62** 30 1·25
275 2c. Great barracuda 30 2·00
276 3c. Queen or pink conch 2·00 3·00
277 4c. Spanish bayonet (flower) 40 70
278 5c. Honeycomb trunkfish 1·50 30
279 6c. Cable and Wireless building 30 30
280 10c. American kestrel ("American Sparrow Hawk") 5·00 2·75
281 15c. Ground orchid 2·75 1·75
282 20c. Stop-light parrotfish 3·25 75
283 22c. Lobster fishing boat 50 60
284 35c. Boat race 1·40 70
285 50c. Sea bean 90 50
286 $1 Sandy Island 60 50
287 $2.50 Manchineel 1·00 1·00
288 $5 Ground lizard 2·00 1·75
289 $10 Red-billed tropic bird 9·00 4·25

63 "The Crucifixion" (Massys)

1977. Easter. Paintings by Castagno ($1.50) or Ugolino (others). Multicoloured.
291 1c. Type **63** 10 10
292 3c. "The Betrayal" 10 10
293 22c. "The Way to Calvary" 20 20
294 30c. "The Deposition" 25 25
295 $1 "The Resurrection" 50 50
296 $1.50 "The Crucifixion" 65 65
MS297 192 × 126 mm. Nos. 291/6 1·60 1·75

1977. Royal Visit. Nos. 269/72 optd **ROYAL VISIT TO WEST INDIES**.
298 25c. Type **61** 10 10
299 40c. Prince Philip landing at Road Bay, 1964 10 15
300 $1.20 Coronation scene 20 25
301 $1.50 Coronation regalia and map of Anguilla 25 35
MS302 145 × 96 mm. Nos. 298/301 80 60

65 "Le Chapeau de Paille"

1977. 400th Birth Anniv of Rubens. Multicoloured.
303 25c. Type **65** 15 15
304 40c. "Helene Fourment and her Two Children" 20 25
305 $1.20 "Rubens and his Wife" 60 65
306 $2.50 "Marchesa Brigida Spinola-Doria" 75 95
MS307 90 × 145 mm. Nos. 303/6 2·00 2·10

1977. Christmas. Nos. 262/7 with old date blocked out and additionally inscr "1977", some also surch.
308 1c. Type **60** 10 10
309 5c. on 3c. "Dreams of Christmas Gifts" 10 10
310 12c. on 15c. "Carolling" 15 15
311 18c. on 25c. "Candle-light Procession" 20 20
312 $1 "Going to Church" 45 45
313 $2.50 on $1.50 "Coming Home for Christmas" 90 90
MS314 232 × 147 mm. Nos. 308/13 2·50 2·50

1978. Easter. Nos. 303/6 optd **EASTER 1978**.
315 25c. Type **65** 15 20
316 40c. "Helene Fourment with her Two Children" 15 20
317 $1.20 "Rubens and his Wife" 35 40
318 $2.50 "Marchesa Brigida Spinola-Doria" 45 60
MS319 93 × 145 mm. Nos. 315/18 1·25 1·50

68 Coronation Coach at Admiralty Arch

1978. 25th Anniv of Coronation. Multicoloured.
320 22c. Buckingham Palace 10 10
321 50c. Type **68** 10 10
322 $1.50 Balcony scene 15 15
323 $2.50 Royal coat of arms 25 25
MS324 138 × 92 mm. Nos. 320/3 60 60

1978. Anniversaries. Nos. 283/4 and 287 optd **VALLEY SECONDARY SCHOOL 1953–1978** and Nos. 285/6 and 288 optd **ROAD METHODIST CHURCH 1878–1978**, or surch also.
325 22c. Lobster fishing boat 20 15
326 35c. Boat race 30 20
327 50c. Sea bean 30 30
328 $1 Sandy Island 35 40
329 $1.20 on $5 Ground lizard 40 45
330 $1.50 on $2.50 Manchineel 45 55

71 Mother and Child

1978. Christmas. Children's Paintings. Mult.
331 5c. Type **71** 10 10
332 12c. Christmas masquerade 15 10
333 18c. Christmas dinner 15 10
334 22c. Serenading 15 10
335 $1 Child in manger 45 20
336 $2.50 Family going to church 90 40
MS337 191 × 101 mm. Nos. 331/6 1·60 1·75

1979. International Year of the Child. As Nos. 331/6, but additionally inscr "1979 INTERNATIONAL YEAR OF THE CHILD" and emblem. Borders in different colours.
338 5c. Type **71** 10 10
339 12c. Christmas masquerade 10 10
340 18c. Christmas dinner 10 10
341 22c. Serenading 10 10
342 $1 Child in manger 30 30
343 $2.50 Family going to church 50 50
MS344 205 × 112 mm. Nos. 338/43 2·25 2·50

1979. Nos. 274/7 and 279/80 surch.
345 12c. on 2c. Great barracuda 50 50
346 14c. on 4c. Spanish bayonet 40 50
347 18c. on 3c. Queen conch 80 55
348 25c. on 6c. Cable and Wireless building 55 50
349 38c. on 10c. American kestrel 2·50 70
350 40c. on 1c. Type **62** 2·50 70

73 Valley Methodist Church

1979. Easter. Church Interiors. Multicoloured.
351 5c. Type **73** 10 10
352 12c. St. Mary's Anglican Church, The Valley 10 10
353 18c. St. Gerard's Roman Catholic Church, The Valley 15 15
354 22c. Road Methodist Church 15 15
355 $1.50 St. Augustine's Anglican Church, East End 60 60
356 $2.50 West End Methodist Church 75 75
MS357 190 × 105 mm. Nos. 351/6 1·75 2·25

74 Cape of Good Hope 1d. "Woodblock" of 1881

1979. Death Centenary of Sir Rowland Hill. Multicoloured.
358 1c. Type **74** 10 10
359 1c. U.S.A. "inverted Jenny" of 1918 10 10
360 22c. Penny Black ("V.R." Official) 15 15
361 35c. Germany 2m, "Graf Zeppelin" of 1928 20 20
362 $1.50 U.S.A. $5 "Columbus" of 1893 40 60
363 $2.50 Great Britain £5 orange of 1882 60 95
MS364 187 × 123 mm. Nos. 358/63 1·25 2·40

75 Wright "Flyer I" (1st powered Flight, 1903)

1979. History of Powered Flight. Multicoloured.
365 5c. Type **75** 15 10
366 12c. Louis Bleriot at Dover after Channel crossing, 1909 20 10
367 18c. Vickers FB-27 Vimy (1st non-stop crossing of Atlantic, 1919) 25 15
368 22c. Ryan NYP Special "Spirit of St Louis" (1st solo Atlantic flight by Charles Lindbergh, 1927) 25 20
369 $1.50 Airship LZ 127 "Graf Zeppelin", 1928 60 60
370 $2.50 Concorde, 1979 2·75 90
MS371 200 × 113 mm. Nos. 365/70 3·50 3·00

76 Sombrero Island

1979. Outer Islands. Multicoloured.
372 5c. Type **76** 10 10
373 12c. Anguillita Island 10 10
374 18c. Sandy Island 15 15
375 25c. Prickly Pear Cays 15 15
376 $1 Dog Island 30 40
377 $2.50 Scrub Island 50 70
MS378 180 × 91 mm. Nos. 372/7 2·50 2·25

77 Red Poinsettia

1979. Christmas. Multicoloured.
379 22c. Type **77** 15 20
380 35c. Kalanchoe 20 30
381 $1.50 Cream poinsettia 40 50
382 $2.50 White poinsettia 60 70
MS383 146 × 164 mm. Nos. 379/82 1·75 2·25

78 Exhibition Scene

1979. "London 1980" International Stamp Exhibition (1st issue). Multicoloured.
384 35c. Type **78** 15 20
385 50c. Earls Court Exhibition Centre 15 25
386 $1.50 Penny Black and Two-penny Blue stamps 25 60
387 $2.50 Exhibition Logo 45 95
MS388 150 × 94 mm. Nos. 384/7 1·40 2·00
See also Nos. 407/9.

79 Games Site

1980. Winter Olympic Games, Lake Placid, U.S.A. Multicoloured.
389 5c. Type **79** 10 10
390 18c. Ice hockey 20 10
391 35c. Ice skating 20 20
392 50c. Bobsleighing 20 20
393 $1 Skiing 20 35
394 $2.50 Luge-tobogganing 40 80
MS395 136 × 128 mm. Nos. 389/94 1·00 2·00

80 Salt ready for "Reaping"

1980. Salt Industry. Multicoloured.
396 5c. Type **80** 10 10
397 12c. Tallying salt 10 10
398 18c. Unloading salt flats 15 15
399 22c. Salt storage heap 15 15
400 $1 Salt for bagging and grinding 30 40
401 $2.50 Loading salt for export 50 70
MS402 180 × 92 mm. Nos. 396/401 1·10 1·75

1980. Anniversaries. Nos. 280, 282 and 287/8 optd **50th Anniversary Scouting 1980** (10c., $2.50) or **75th Anniversary Rotary 1980** (others).
403 10c. American kestrel 1·75 15
404 20c. Stop-light parrotfish 1·00 20
405 $2.50 Manchineel 1·75 1·25
406 $5 Ground lizard 2·50 1·90

83 Palace of Westminster and Great Britain 1970 9d. "Philympia" Commemoration

1980. "London 1980" International Stamp Exhibition (2nd issue). Multicoloured.
407 50c. Type **83** 55 75
408 $1.50 City Hall, Toronto and "Capex 1978" stamp of Canada 85 1·25
409 $2.50 Statue of Liberty and 1976 "Interphil" stamp of U.S.A. 1·10 1·40
MS410 157 × 130 mm. Nos. 407/9 2·25 3·00

84 Queen Elizabeth the Queen Mother

85 Brown Pelicans ("Pelican")

1980. 80th Birthday of The Queen Mother.
411 **84** 35c. multicoloured 70 40
412 50c. multicoloured 85 50
413 $1.50 multicoloured 1·50 1·50
414 $3 multicoloured 2·25 2·50
MS415 160 × 110 mm. Nos. 411/14 5·50 4·50

1980. Christmas. Birds. Multicoloured.
416 5c. Type **85** 30 10
417 22c. Great blue heron ("Great Grey Heron") 75 20
418 $1.50 Barn swallow ("Swallow") 1·75 60
419 $3 Ruby-throated hummingbird ("Hummingbird") 2·25 1·40
MS420 126 × 160 mm. Nos. 416/19 9·50 7·50

1980. Separation from St. Kitts. Nos. 274, 277, 280/9, 334 and 418/19 optd **SEPARATION 1980** or surch also.
421 1c. Type **62** 20 80
422b 2c. on 4c. Spanish bayonet 20 80
423 5c. on 15c. Ground orchid 1·50 80
424 5c. on $1.50 Barn swallow 1·50 80
425 5c. on $3 Ruby-throated hummingbird 1·50 80
426 10c. American kestrel 1·75 80
427 12c. on $1 Sandy Island 20 80
428 14c. on $2.50 Manchineel 20 80
429 15c. Ground orchid 1·50 80
430 18c. on $5 Ground lizard 25 80
431 20c. Stop-light parrotfish 25 80
432 22c. Lobster fishing boat 25 80
433 25c. on 15c. Ground orchid 1·50 85
434 35c. Boat race 30 85
435 38c. on 22c. Serenading 30 85
436 40c. on 1c. Type **62** 30 85
437 50c. Sea bean 35 95
438 $1 Sandy Island 50 1·25
439 $2.50 Manchineel 1·25 3·00
440 $5 Ground lizard 2·25 4·00
441 $10 Red-billed tropic bird 5·00 6·00
442 $10 on 6c. Cable and Wireless Building 5·00 6·00

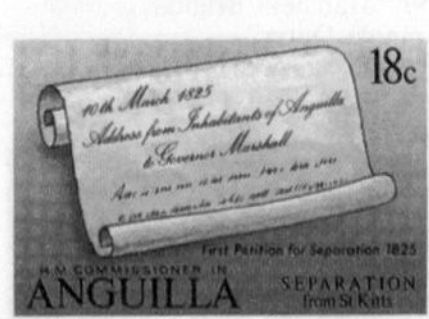

87 First Petition for Separation, 1825

1980. Separation from St. Kitts. Multicoloured.
443 18c. Type **87** 10 10
444 22c. Referendum ballot paper, 1967 15 10
445 35c. Airport blockade, 1967 15 15
446 50c. Anguillan flag 20 20
447 $1 Separation celebration, 1980 30 35
MS448 178 × 92 mm. Nos. 443/7 80 1·25

88 "Nelson's Dockyard" (R. Granger Barrett)

1981. 175th Death Anniv of Lord Nelson. Mult.
449 22c. Type **88** 1·50 40
450 35c. "Ships in which Nelson Served" (Nicholas Pocock) 1·75 60
451 50c. "H.M.S. Victory" (Monamy Swaine) 2·25 85
452 $3 "Battle of Trafalgar" (Clarkson Stanfield) 2·75 4·00
MS453 82 × 63 mm. $5 "Horatio Nelson" (L. F. Abbott) and coat of arms 3·00 3·25

89 Minnie Mouse being chased by Bees

1981. Easter. Walt Disney Cartoon Characters. Multicoloured.
454 1c. Type **89** 10 10
455 2c. Pluto laughing at Mickey Mouse 10 10
456 3c. Minnie Mouse tying ribbon round Pluto's neck 10 10
457 5c. Minnie Mouse confronted by love-struck bird who fancies her bonnet 10 10
458 7c. Dewey and Huey admiring themselves in mirror 10 10
459 9c. Horace Horsecollar and Clarabelle Cow out for a stroll 10 10
460 10c. Daisy Duck with hat full of Easter eggs 10 10
461 $2 Goofy unwrapping Easter hat 1·40 1·40
462 $3 Donald Duck in his Easter finery 1·60 1·60
MS463 134 × 108 mm. $5 Chip and Dale making off with hat 3·50 3·50

90 Prince Charles, Lady Diana Spencer and St. Paul's Cathedral

1981. Royal Wedding. Multicoloured.
464 50c. Type **90** 15 20
465 $2.50 Althorp 30 50
466 $3 Windsor Castle 35 60
MS467 90 × 72 mm. Buckingham Palace 1·25 1·50

91 Children playing in Tree

1981. 35th Anniv of U.N.I.C.E.F. Multicoloured.
470 5c. Type **91** 20 30
471 10c. Children playing by pool 20 30
472 15c. Children playing musical instruments 20 30
473 $3 Children playing with pets 2·50 3·00
MS474 78 × 106 mm. Children playing football (vert) 3·50 5·00

1981. Christmas. Designs as T **89** showing scenes from Walt Disney's cartoon film "The Night before Christmas".
475 1c. multicoloured 10 10
476 2c. multicoloured 10 10
477 3c. multicoloured 10 10
478 5c. multicoloured 15 10
479 7c. multicoloured 15 10
480 10c. multicoloured 15 10
481 12c. multicoloured 15 10
482 $2 multicoloured 3·75 1·25
483 $3 multicoloured 3·75 1·60
MS484 130 × 105 mm. $5 multicoloured 5·50 3·50

92 Red Grouper

1982. Multicoloured.
485 1c. Type **92** 15 1·00
486 5c. Ferry service, Blowing Point 30 1·00
487 10c. Island dinghies 20 60
488 15c. Majorettes 20 60
489 20c. Launching boat, Sandy Hill 40 60
490 25c. Corals 1·50 60
491 30c. Little Bay cliffs 30 75
492 35c. Fountain Cave interior 1·50 80
493 40c. Sunset over Sandy Island 30 75
494 45c. Landing at Sombrero 50 80
495 60c. Seine fishing 3·25 3·25
496 75c. Boat race at sunset, Sandy Ground 1·00 2·00
497 $1 Bagging lobster at Island Harbour 2·25 2·00
498 $5 Brown pelicans 16·00 13·00
499 $7.50 Hibiscus 11·00 15·00
500 $10 Queen triggerfish 16·00 15·00

1982. No. 494 surch **50c.**
501 50c. on 45c. Landing at Sombrero 50 35

94 Anthurium and "Heliconius charithonia"

95 Lady Diana Spencer in 1961

1982. Easter. Flowers and Butterflies. Multicoloured.
502 10c. Type **94** 95 10
503 35c. Bird of paradise and "Junonia evarete" 1·75 40
504 75c. Allamanda and "Danaus plexippus" 1·90 70
505 $3 Orchid tree and "Biblis hyperia" 3·25 2·25
MS506 65 × 79 mm. $5 Amaryllis and "Dryas julia" 2·75 3·50

1982. 21st Birthday of Princess of Wales. Mult.
507 10c. Type **95** 50 20
508 30c. Lady Diana Spencer in 1968 1·50 25
509 40c. Lady Diana in 1970 50 30
510 60c. Lady Diana in 1974 55 35
511 $2 Lady Diana in 1981 80 1·10
512 $3 Lady Diana in 1981 (different) 5·00 1·40
MS513 72 × 90 mm. $5 Princess of Wales 7·50 3·00
MS514 125 × 125 mm. As Nos. 507/12, but with buff borders 8·50 6·50

96 Pitching Tent

1982. 75th Anniv of Boy Scout Movement. Multicoloured.
515 10c. Type **96** 45 20
516 35c. Scout band 85 50
517 75c. Yachting 1·25 90
518 $3 On parade 3·00 2·75
MS519 90 × 72 mm. $5 Cooking 4·50 4·00

1982. World Cup Football Championship, Spain. Horiz designs as T **89** showing scenes from Walt Disney's cartoon film "Bedknobs and Broomsticks".
520 1c. multicoloured 10 10
521 3c. multicoloured 10 10
522 4c. multicoloured 10 10
523 5c. multicoloured 10 10
524 7c. multicoloured 10 10
525 9c. multicoloured 10 10
526 10c. multicoloured 10 10
527 $2.50 multicoloured 2·25 1·75
528 $3 multicoloured 2·25 2·00
MS529 126 × 101 mm. $5 multicoloured 7·50 7·50

1982. Commonwealth Games, Brisbane. Nos. 487, 495/6 and 498 optd **COMMONWEALTH GAMES 1982**.
530 10c. Island dinghies 15 25
531 60c. Seine fishing 45 60
532 75c. Boat race at sunset, Sandy Ground 60 80
533 $5 Brown pelicans 3·25 3·75

1982. Birth Cent of A. A. Milne (author). As T **89**.
534 1c. multicoloured 20 15
535 2c. multicoloured 20 15
536 3c. multicoloured 20 15
537 5c. multicoloured 30 15
538 7c, multicoloured 30 25
539 10c. multicoloured 40 15
540 12c. multicoloured 50 20
541 20c. multicoloured 80 25
542 $5 multicoloured 8·00 8·50
MS543 120 × 93 mm. $5 multicoloured 7·50 8·50

DESIGNS—HORIZ: 1c. to $5 Scenes from various "Winnie the Pooh" stories.

98 Culture

1983. Commonwealth Day. Multicoloured.
544 10c. Type **98** 10 15
545 35c. Anguilla and British flags 30 30
546 75c. Economic co-operation 60 1·00
547 $2.50 Salt industry (salt pond) . . . . 3·75 4·50
MS548 76 × 61 mm. World map showing positions of Commonwealth countries . . . 2·50 2·50

99 "I am the Lord Thy God"

101 Montgolfier Hot Air Balloon, 1783

100 Leatherback Turtle

1983. Easter. The Ten Commandments. Mult.
549 1c. Type **99** 10 10
550 2c. "Thou shalt not make any graven image" 10 10
551 3c. "Thou shalt not take My Name in vain" 10 10
552 10c. "Remember the Sabbath Day" 25 10
553 35c. "Honour thy father and mother" 65 20
554 60c. "Thou shalt not kill" . . 1·00 40
555 75c. "Thou shalt not commit adultery" . . . . 1·25 50
556 $2 "Thou shalt not steal" . . 2·75 1·50
557 $2.50 "Thou shalt not bear false witness" . . . . . . 3·00 1·50
558 $5 "Thou shalt not covet" . . 4·25 2·75
MS559 126 × 102 mm. $5 "Moses receiving the Tablets" (16th-century woodcut) . . . . 2·75 3·00

1983. Endangered Species. Turtles. Multicoloured.
560 10c. Type **100** . . . . 3·25 80
561 35c. Hawksbill turtle . . . . 6·00 1·25
562 75c. Green turtle . . . . . . 7·00 3·50
563 $1 Loggerhead turtle . . . . 8·00 7·50
MS564 93 × 72 mm. $5 Leatherback turtle (different) . . . . 14·00 3·50

1983. Bicentenary of Manned Flight. Multicoloured.
565 10c. Type **101** 50 50
566 60c. Blanchard and Jefferies crossing English Channel by balloon, 1785 . . . . . 1·25 85
567 $1 Henri Giffard's steam-powered dirigible airship, 1852 . . . . 1·75 1·25
568 $2.50 Otto Lillienthal and biplane glider, 1890–96 . . 2·50 2·50
MS569 72 × 90 mm. $5 Wilbur Wright flying round Statue of Liberty, 1909 . . . . 2·75 3·50

102 Boys' Brigade Band and Flag

1983. Centenary of Boys' Brigade. Multicoloured.
570 10c. Type **102** 50 15
571 $5 Brigade members marching . . . . 3·50 2·75
MS572 96 × 115 mm. Nos. 570/1 3·25 4·50

1983. 150th Anniv of Abolition of Slavery (1st issue). Nos. 487, 493 and 497/8 optd **150TH ANNIVERSARY ABOLITION OF SLAVERY ACT.**
573 10c. Island dinghies 20 10
574 40c. Sunset over Sandy Island 30 25
575 $1 Bagging lobster at Island Harbour 70 50
576 $5 Brown pelicans . . . . . 7·00 2·75
See also Nos. 616/23.

104 Jiminy on Clock ("Cricket on the Hearth")

1983. Christmas. Walt Disney Cartoon Characters. Multicoloured.
577 1c. Type **104** 10 10
578 2c. Jiminy with fiddle ("Cricket on the Hearth") 10 10
579 3c. Jiminy among toys ("Cricket on the Hearth") 10 10
580 4c. Mickey as Bob Cratchit ("A Christmas Carol") . . 10 10
581 5c. Donald Duck as Scrooge ("A Christmas Carol") . . 10 10
582 6c. Mini and Goofy in "The Chimes" 10 10
583 10c. Goofy sees an imp appearing from bells ("The Chimes") 10 10
584 $2 Donald Duck as Mr. Pickwick ("The Pickwick Papers") . . . . 3·25 2·75
585 $3 Disney characters as Pickwickians ("The Pickwick Papers") . . . . 3·75 2·25
MS586 130 × 104 mm. Donald Duck as Mr. Pickwick with gifts ("The Pickwick Papers") . . . . . . 8·50 9·50

105 100 Metres Race

1984. Olympic Games, Los Angeles. Multicoloured. (A) Inscr "1984 Los Angeles".
587A 1c. Type **105** 10 10
588A 2c. Long jumping 10 10
589A 3c. Shot-putting 10 10
590A 4c. High jumping 10 10
591A 5c. 400 metres race 10 10
592A 6c. Hurdling 10 10
593A 10c. Discus-throwing . . . 10 10
594A $1 Pole-vaulting . . . . . 3·25 1·25
595A $4 Javelin-throwing . . . . 6·00 3·50
MS596A 117 × 93 mm. $5 1500 metres race . . . . 7·50 4·50

(B) Inscr "1984 Olympics Los Angeles" and Olympic emblem.
587B 1c. Type **105** 10 10
588B 2c. Long jumping 10 10
589B 3c. Shot-putting 10 10
590B 4c. High jumping 10 10
591B 5c. 400 metres race 10 10
592B 6c. Hurdling 10 10
593B 10c. Discus-throwing . . . 10 10
594B $1 Pole-vaulting . . . . . 3·75 3·00
595B $4 Javelin-throwing . . . . 7·50 8·50
MS596B 117 × 93 mm. $5 1500 metres race . . . . 7·50 4·50

106 "Justice"

1984. Easter. Multicoloured.
597 10c. Type **106** 15 10
598 25c. "Poetry" 20 20
599 35c. "Philosophy" 30 30
600 40c. "Theology" 30 30
601 $1 "Abraham and Paul" . . . 85 95
602 $2 "Moses and Matthew" . . 1·60 2·25
603 $3 "John and David" . . . . 2·25 3·00
604 $4 "Peter and Adam" . . . . 2·50 3·00
MS605 83 × 110 mm. $5 "Astronomy" . . . . 3·50 3·00

Nos. 597/605 show details from "La Stanza della Segnatura" by Raphael.

1984. Nos. 485, 491, 498/500 surch.
606 25c. on $7.50 Hibiscus . . . 65 35
607 35c. on 30c. Little Bay cliffs 50 40
608 60c. on 1c. Type **92** 55 45
609 $2.50 on $5 Brown pelicans 3·00 1·50
610 $2.50 on $10 Queen triggerfish . . . . 1·75 1·50

108 1913 1d. Kangaroo Stamp

1984. "Ausipex 84" International Stamp Exhibition. Multicoloured.
611 10c. Type **108** 40 30
612 75c. 1914 6d. Laughing Kookaburra . . . . 1·25 1·25
613 $1 1932 2d. Sydney Harbour Bridge . . . . 1·75 1·75
614 $2.50 1938 10s. King George VI . . . . 2·25 3·25
MS615 95 × 86 mm. $5 £1 Bass and £2 Admiral King . . . . . . 4·50 6·50

109 Thomas Fowell Buxton

1984. 150th Anniv of Abolition of Slavery (2nd issue). Multicoloured.
616 10c. Type **109** 10 10
617 25c. Abraham Lincoln . . . 25 25
618 35c. Henri Christophe . . . 35 35
619 60c. Thomas Clarkson . . . 50 50
620 75c. William Wilberforce . . 60 60
621 $1 Olaudah Equiano 70 70
622 $2.50 General Charles Gordon . . . . 1·60 1·60
623 $5 Granville Sharp . . . . . 3·00 3·00
MS624 150 × 121 mm. Nos. 616/23 7·00 9·00

1984. Universal Postal Union Congress, Hamburg. Nos. 486/7 and 498 optd **U.P.U. CONGRESS HAMBURG 1984** or surch also (No 626).
625 5c. Ferry service, Blowing Point 30 10
626 20c. on 10c. Island dinghies 30 15
627 $5 Brown pelicans . . . . . 5·50 3·50

1984. Birth of Prince Henry. Nos. 507/12 optd **PRINCE HENRY BIRTH 15.9.84.**
628 10c. Type **95** 20 10
629 30c. Lady Diana Spencer in 1968 . . . . 40 25
630 40c. Lady Diana in 1970 . . 20 30
631 60c. Lady Diana in 1974 . . 30 45
632 $2 Lady Diana in 1981 . . . 75 1·25
633 $3 Lady Diana in 1981 (different) . . . . 1·25 1·75
MS634 72 × 90 mm. $5 Princess of Wales . . . . 2·00 3·00
MS635 125 × 125 mm. As Nos. 628/33, but with buff borders 2·50 4·00

112 Christmas in Sweden

1984. Christmas. Walt Disney Cartoon Characters. National Scenes. Multicoloured.
636 1c. Type **112** 10 10
637 2c. Italy 10 10
638 3c. Holland 10 10
639 4c. Mexico 10 10
640 5c. Spain 10 10
641 10c. Disneyland, U.S.A. . . . 10 10
642 $1 Japan . . . . 3·00 2·00
643 $2 Anguilla . . . . 4·00 4·75
644 $4 Germany . . . . 6·50 8·00
MS645 126 × 102 mm. $5 England 7·00 5·00

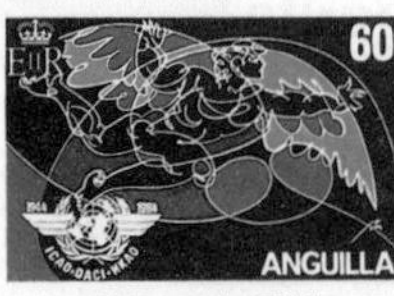

113 Icarus in Flight

1984. 40th Anniv of International Civil Aviation Authority. Multicoloured.
646 60c. Type **113** 60 75
647 75c. "Solar Princess" (abstract) 80 90
648 $2.50 I.C.A.O. emblem (vert) 2·25 3·00
MS649 65 × 49 mm. $5 Map of air routes serving Anguilla . . . . 3·00 4·50

114 Barn Swallow

115 The Queen Mother visiting King's College Hospital, London

1985. Birth Bicentenary of John J. Audubon (ornithologist). Multicoloured.
650 10c. Type **114** 80 65
651 60c. American wood stork ("Woodstork") . . . . . 1·50 1·25
652 75c. Roseate tern . . . . . . 1·50 1·25
653 $5 Osprey . . . . 4·50 6·00
MS654 Two sheets, each 73 × 103 mm. $4 Western tanager (horiz); (b) $4 Solitary vireo (horiz) Set of 2 sheets . . . . 8·00 5·00

1985. Life and Times of Queen Elizabeth the Queen Mother. Multicoloured.
655 10c. Type **115** 10 10
656 $2 The Queen Mother inspecting Royal Marine Volunteer Cadets, Deal . . 80 1·25
657 $3 The Queen Mother outside Clarence House . . . . . 1·10 1·50
MS658 56 × 85 mm. $5 At Ascot, 1979 . . . . 1·75 2·50

116 White-tailed Tropic Bird

1985. Birds. Multicoloured.
659 5c. Brown pelican . . . . . 1·75 1·75
660 10c. Mourning dove ("Turtle Dove") . . . . . 1·75 1·75
661 15c. Magnificent frigate bird (inscr "Man-o-War") . . 1·75 1·75
662 20c. Antillean crested hummingbird . . . . . . 1·75 1·75
663 25c. Type **116** . . . . . . 1·75 1·75
664 30c. Caribbean elaenia . . . 1·75 1·75
665 35c. Black-whiskered vireo 7·50 5·00
665a 35c. Lesser Antillean bullfinch . . . . 3·00 1·75
666 40c. Yellow-crowned night heron . . . . 1·75 1·75
667 45c. Pearly-eyed thrasher . . 1·75 1·75
668 50c. Laughing gull . . . . 1·75 1·75
669 65c. Brown booby . . . . . 1·75 1·75
670 80c. Grey kingbird . . . . 2·25 3·00
671 $1 Audubon's shearwater 2·25 3·00
672 $1.35 Roseate tern . . . . 1·75 3·00
673 $2.50 Bananaquit . . . . . 5·50 8·00
674 $5 Belted kingfisher . . . . 4·25 8·00
675 $10 Green-backed heron ("Green Heron") . . . . 7·00 10·00

1985. 75th Anniv of Girl Guide Movement. Nos. 486, 491, 496 and 498 optd **GIRL GUIDES 75TH ANNIVERSARY 1910–1985** and anniversary emblem.
676 5c. Ferry service, Blowing Point 30 30
677 30c. Little Bay cliffs 40 35
678 75c. Boat race at sunset, Sandy Ground 60 85
679 $5 Brown pelicans . . . . . 8·00 8·50

118 Goofy as Huckleberry Finn Fishing

1985. 150th Birth Anniv of Mark Twain (author). Walt Disney cartoon characters in scenes from "Huckleberry Finn". Multicoloured.
680 10c. Type **118** 65 20
681 60c. Pete as Pap surprising Huck . . . . 2·00 85
682 $1 "Multiplication tables" . . 2·50 1·25
683 $3 The Duke reciting Shakespeare . . . . 3·75 4·00
MS684 127 × 102 mm. $5 "In school but out" . . . . 8·50 8·00

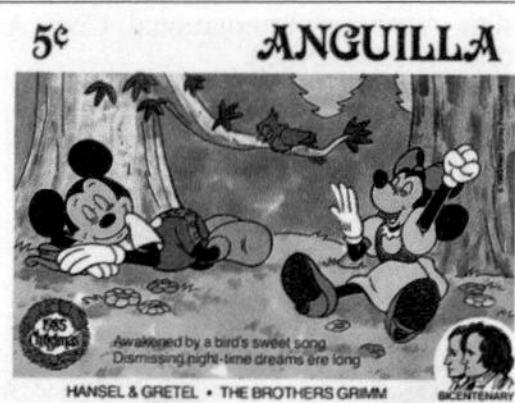

119 Hansel and Gretel (Mickey and Minnie Mouse) awakening in Forest

1985. Birth Bicentenaries of Grimm Brothers (folklorists). Designs showing Walt Disney cartoon characters in scenes from "Hansel and Gretel". Multicoloured.
685 5c. Type **119** 40 40
686 50c. Hansel and Gretel find the gingerbread house . . 1·25 45
687 90c. Hansel and Gretel meeting the Witch . . . . 1·75 1·00
688 $4 Hansel and Gretel captured by the Witch . . 3·25 4·75
MS689 128 × 101 mm. $5 Hansel and Gretel riding on swan . . . . 7·50 8·00

120 Statue of Liberty and "Danmark" (Denmark)

1985. Centenary of the Statue of Liberty (1986). The Statue of Liberty and Cadet ships.
690 10c. Type **120** 80 65
691 20c. "Eagle" (U.S.A.) . . . . 1·00 85
692 60c. "Amerigo Vespucci" (Italy) . . . . 1·25 1·50
693 75c. "Sir Winston Churchill" (Great Britain) . . . . . . 1·25 1·50
694 $2 "Nippon Maru" (Japan) 1·50 3·00
695 $2.50 "Gorch Fock" (West Germany) . . . . 1·50 3·00
MS696 96 × 69 mm. $5 Statue of Liberty (vert) . . . . 7·00 4·50

1985. 80th Anniv of Rotary (10, 35c.) and International Youth Year (others). Nos. 487, 491 and 497 optd or surch **80TH ANNIVERSARY ROTARY 1985** and emblem (10, 35c.) or **INTERNATIONAL YOUTH YEAR** and emblem ($1, $5).
697 10c. Island dinghies 25 15
698 35c. on 30c. Little Bay cliffs 55 30
699 $1 Bagging lobster at Island Harbour . . . . 1·25 80
700 $5 on 30c. Little Bay cliffs . . 4·00 4·50

123 Johannes Hevelius (astronomer) and Mayan Temple Observatory

1986. Appearance of Halley's Comet. Multicoloured.
701 5c. Type **123** 45 45
702 10c. "Viking Lander" space vehicle on Mars, 1976 . . 45 45
703 60c. Comet in 1664 (from "Theatri Cosmicum", 1668) 1·25 85
704 $4 Comet over Mississippi riverboat, 1835 (150th birth anniv of Mark Twain) . . 4·00 4·00
MS705 101 × 70 mm. $5 Halley's Comet over Anguilla . . . . . 4·50 6·00

124 "The Crucifixion" **125** Princess Elizabeth inspecting Guards, 1946

1986. Easter.
706 **124** 10c. multicoloured 20 20
707 – 25c. multicoloured 35 35
708 – 45c. multicoloured 65 65
709 – $4 multicoloured . . . . 3·25 3·75
MS710 – 93 × 75 mm. $5 multicoloured (horiz) . . . . . 5·50 7·50
DESIGNS: 25c. to $5 Different stained glass windows from Chartres Cathedral.

1986. 60th Birthday of Queen Elizabeth II.
711 **125** 20c. black and yellow . . 40 20
712 – $2 multicoloured . . . . 1·75 1·50
713 – $3 multicoloured . . . . 1·75 1·75
MS714 – 120 × 85 mm. $5 black and brown . . . . 2·75 3·75
DESIGNS: $2 Queen at Garter Ceremony; $3 At Trooping the Colour; $5 Duke and Duchess of York with baby Princess Elizabeth, 1926.

1986. "Ameripex" International Stamp Exhibition, Chicago. Nos. 659, 667, 671, 673 and 675 optd **AMERIPEX 1986.**
715 5c. Brown pelican 60 75
716 45c. Pearly-eyed thrasher . . 1·25 45
717 $1 Audubon's shearwater . . 2·00 1·10
718 $2.50 Bananaquit . . . . . 2·75 3·00
719 $10 Green-backed heron . . 6·50 8·50

127 Prince Andrew and Miss Sarah Ferguson **130** Christopher Columbus with Astrolabe

129 Trading Sloop

1986. Royal Wedding. Multicoloured.
720 10c. Type **127** 40 15
721 35c. Prince Andrew 70 35
722 $2 Miss Sarah Ferguson . . 2·00 1·50
723 $3 Prince Andrew and Miss Sarah Ferguson (diffferent) . . 2·25 2·00
MS724 119 × 90 mm. $6 Westminster Abbey . . . . 5·50 7·00

1986. International Peace Year. Nos. 616/23 optd **INTERNATIONAL YEAR OF PEACE.**
725 10c. Type **109** 60 30
726 25c. Abraham Lincoln . . . 85 45
727 35c. Henri Christophe . . . 1·00 55
728 60c. Thomas Clarkson . . . 1·50 80
729 75c. William Wilberforce . . 1·50 90
730 $1 Olaudah Equiano . . . . 1·50 1·00
731 $2.50 General Gordon . . . 2·75 4·00
732 $5 Granville Sharp . . . . 3·75 5·00
MS733 150 × 121 mm. Nos. 725/32 13·00 15·00

1986. Christmas. Ships. Multicoloured.
734 10c. Type **129** . . . . 1·50 60
735 45c. "Lady Rodney" (cargo liner) . . . . 2·50 1·10
736 80c. "West Derby" (19th-century sailing ship) 3·50 2·50
737 $3 "Warspite" (local sloop) 6·00 7·50
MS738 130 × 100 mm. $4 Boat-race day (vert) . . . . 16·00 17·00

1986. 500th Anniv (1992) of Discovery of America by Columbus (1st issue). Multicoloured.
739 5c. Type **130** 60 60
740 10c. Columbus on board ship 1·00 60
741 35c. "Santa Maria" . . . . 2·00 1·10
742 80c. King Ferdinand and Queen Isabella of Spain (horiz) . . . . 1·50 1·75
743 $4 Caribbean Indians smoking tobacco (horiz) . . 3·25 5·00
MS744 Two sheets, each 96 × 66 mm. (a) $5 Caribbean manatee (horiz). (b) $5 Dragon tree Set of 2 sheets . . . . . . 13·00 15·00
See also Nos. 902/6.

131 "Danaus plexippus"

1987. Easter. Butterflies. Multicoloured.
745 10c. Type **131** . . . . . . 1·50 60
746 80c. "Anartia jatrophae" . . 3·50 2·50
747 $1 "Heliconius charithonia" 3·75 2·50
748 $2 "Junonia evarete" . . . . 6·00 7·00
MS749 90 × 69 mm. $6 "Dryas julia" 11·00 13·00

132 Old Goose Iron and Modern Electric Iron

1987. 20th Anniv of Separation from St. Kitts-Nevis. Multicoloured.
750 10c. Type **132** 50 40
751 35c. Old East End School and Albena Lake-Hodge Comprehensive College . . 55 45
752 45c. Past and present markets 65 50
753 80c. Previous sailing ferry and new motor ferry, Blowing Point . . . . . . 1·75 1·00
754 $1 Original mobile post office and new telephone exchange . . . . 1·50 1·10
755 $2 Open-air meeting, Burrowes Park and House of Assembly in session . . 1·75 2·75
MS756 159 × 127 mm. Nos. 750/5 9·00 11·00

1987. "Capex '87" International Stamp Exhibition, Toronto. Nos. 665a, 667, 670 and 675 optd **CAPEX'87.**
757 35c. Lesser Antillean bullfinch . . . . 1·75 80
758 45c. Pearly-eyed thrasher . . 1·75 80
759 80c. Grey kingbird . . . . . 2·75 1·25
760 $10 Green-backed heron . . 9·00 11·00

1987. 20th Anniv of Independence. Nos. 659, 661/4 and 665a/75 optd **20 YEARS OF PROGRESS 1967–1987**, No. 762 surch also.
761 5c. Brown pelican . . . . . 2·25 2·25
762 10c. on 15c. Magnificent frigate bird . . . . 2·25 2·25
763 15c. Magnificent frigate bird 2·50 2·50
764 20c. Antillean crested hummingbird . . . . . . 2·50 2·50
765 25c. Type **116** . . . . 2·50 2·50
766 30c. Caribbean elaenia . . . 2·50 2·50
767 35c. Lesser Antillean bullfinch . . . . 2·50 2·50
768 40c. Yellow-crowned night heron . . . . 2·50 2·50
769 45c. Pearly-eyed thrasher . . 2·50 2·50
770 50c. Laughing gull . . . . . 2·50 2·50
771 65c. Brown booby . . . . . 2·75 2·75
772 80c. Grey kingbird . . . . . 2·75 2·75
773 $1 Audubon's shearwater . . 2·75 2·75
774 $1.35 Roseate tern . . . . . 3·25 3·50
775 $2.50 Bananaquit . . . . . 3·75 5·00
776 $5 Belted kingfisher . . . . 5·00 7·50
777 $10 Green-backed heron . . 7·00 10·00

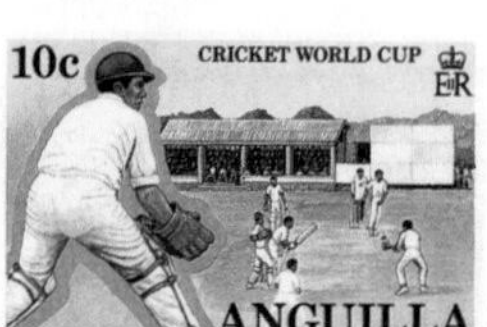

135 Wicket Keeper and Game in Progress

1987. Cricket World Cup. Multicoloured.
778 10c. Type **135** . . . . 1·50 70
779 35c. Batsman and local Anguilla team . . . . . . 2·00 70
780 45c. Batsman and game in progress . . . . 2·00 75
781 $2.50 Bowler and game in progress . . . . 4·00 6·00
MS782 100 × 75 mm. $6 Batsman and game in progress (different) 12·00 13·00

136 West Indian Top Shell

1987. Christmas. Sea Shells and Crabs. Mult.
783 10c. Type **136** . . . . 1·50 55
784 35c. Ghost crab . . . . . . 2·00 60
785 50c. Spiny Caribbean vase . . 2·75 1·40
786 $2 Great land crab . . . . . 4·25 6·50
MS787 101 × 75 mm. $6 Queen or pink conch . . . . 10·00 12·00

1987. Royal Ruby Wedding. Nos. 665a, 671/2 and 675 optd **40TH WEDDING ANNIVERSARY H.M. QUEEN ELIZABETH II H.R.H. THE DUKE OF EDINBURGH.**
788 35c. Lesser Antillean bullfinch . . . . 1·00 40
789 $1 Audubon's shearwater . . 1·60 80
790 $1.35 Roseate tern . . . . . 1·75 90
791 $10 Green-backed heron . . 6·50 8·50

138 "Crinum erubescens" **139** Relay Racing

1988. Easter. Lilies. Multicoloured.
792 30c. Type **138** 50 25
793 45c. Spider lily 60 25
794 $1 "Crinum macowanii" . . 1·50 85
795 $2.50 Day lily . . . . 1·75 3·00
MS796 100 × 75 mm. $6 Easter lily 2·75 4·50

1988. Olympic Games, Seoul. Multicoloured.
797 35c. Type **139** 45 30
798 45c. Windsurfing 55 45
799 50c. Tennis . . . . 1·50 1·10
800 80c. Basketball . . . . 4·50 2·75
MS801 104 × 78 mm. $6 Athletics 3·00 4·50

140 Common Sea Fan

1988. Christmas. Marine Life. Multicoloured.
802 35c. Type **140** 85 30
803 80c. Coral crab . . . . . . 1·40 70
804 $1 Grooved brain coral . . . 1·75 1·00
805 $1.60 Queen triggerfish . . . 2·25 3·25
MS806 103 × 78 mm. $6 West Indian spiny lobster . . . . 3·00 4·50

1988. Visit of Princess Alexandra. Nos. 665a, 670/1 and 673 optd **H.R.H. PRINCESS ALEXANDRA'S VISIT NOVEMBER 1988.**
807 35c. Lesser Antillean bullfinch . . . . 1·75 70
808 80c. Grey kingbird . . . . . 2·50 1·40
809 $1 Audubon's shearwater . . 2·50 1·60
810 $2.50 Bananaquit . . . . . 4·00 4·75

142 Wood Slave

1989. Lizards. Multicoloured.
811 45c. Type **142** . . . . 1·00 50
812 80c. Slippery back . . . . . 1·60 85
813 $2.50 "Iguana delicatissima" 3·50 4·25
MS814 101 × 75 mm. $6 Tree lizard 3·00 4·50

143 "Christ Crowned with Thorns" (detail) (Bosch) **144** University Arms

1989. Easter. Religious Paintings. Multicoloured.
815 35c. Type **143** 55 20
816 80c. "Christ bearing the Cross" (detail) (Gerard David) 85 55
817 $1 "The Deposition" (detail) (Gerard David) 90 60
818 $1.60 "Pieta" (detail) (Rogier van der Weyden) . . . . . 1·40 2·25
MS819 103 × 77 mm. $6 "Crucified Christ with the Virgin Mary and Saints" (detail) (Raphael) . . . 2·75 4·25

1989. 40th Anniv of University of the West Indies.
820 **144** $5 multicoloured . . . . 3·25 3·75

1989. 20th Anniv of First Manned Landing on Moon. Nos. 670/2 and 674 optd **20TH ANNIVERSARY MOON LANDING.**
821 80c. Grey kingbird . . . . . 2·00 90
822 $1 Audubon's shearwater . . 2·00 1·00
823 $1.35 Roseate tern . . . . . 2·25 1·75
824 $5 Belted kingfisher . . . . 6·00 8·00

146 Lone Star (house), 1930

1989. Christmas. Historic Houses. Multicoloured.
825 5c. Type **146** 35 60
826 35c. Whitehouse, 1906 . . . 75 45

827 45c. Hodges House 85 50
828 80c. Warden's Place . . . . 1·40 1·40
MS829 102 × 77 mm. $6 Wallblake House, 1787 . . . . 3·25 5·50

147 Bigeye ("Blear Eye")

1990. Fishes. Multicoloured.
830B 5c. Type **147** 60 75
831B 10c. Long-spined squirrelfish ("Redman") 60 75
832A 15c. Stop-light parrotfish ("Speckletail") 60 60
833A 25c. Blue-striped grunt . . 70 80
834A 30c. Yellow jack 70 80
835B 35c. Red hind 75 75
836A 40c. Spotted goatfish . . . 90 80
837A 45c. Queen triggerfish ("Old wife") 90 60
838A 50c. Coney ("Butter fish") 90 80
839A 65c. Smooth trunkfish ("Shell fish") . . . . . . 1·50 80
840A 80c. Yellow-tailed snapper 1·25 90
841A $1 Banded butterflyfish ("Katy") . . . . 1·25 1·00
842A $1.35 Nassau grouper . . . 1·50 1·50
843A $2.50 Blue tang ("Doctor fish") . . . . 2·25 3·00
844A $5 Queen angelfish . . . . 3·00 4·50
845A $10 Great barracuda . . . 4·75 7·00

148 The Last Supper

149 G.B. 1840 Penny Black

1990. Easter. Multicoloured.
846 35c. Type **148** 85 30
847 45c. The Trial 85 30
848 $1.35 The Crucifixion . . . . 2·25 2·25
849 $2.50 The Empty Tomb . . . 2·75 4·00
MS850 114 × 84 mm. $6 The Resurrection . . . . 7·50 9·50

1990. "Stamp World London 90" International Stamp Exhibition. Multicoloured.
851 25c. Type **149** 80 35
852 50c. G.B. 1840 Twopenny Blue . . . . 1·25 50
853 $1.50 Cape of Good Hope 1861 1d. "woodblock" (horiz) . . . . 2·25 2·50
854 $2.50 G.B. 1882 £5 (horiz) . . 2·75 3·50
MS855 86 × 71 mm. $6 Penny Black and Twopence Blue (horiz) . . 9·50 11·00

1990. Anniversaries and Events. Nos. 841/4 optd.
856 $1 Banded butterflyfish (optd **EXPO '90**) . . . . 1·50 1·00
857 $1.35 Nassau grouper (optd **1990 INTERNATIONAL LITERACY YEAR**) . . . 1·60 1·25
858 $2.50 Blue tang (optd **WORLD CUP FOOTBALL CHAMPIONSHIPS 1990**) 4·00 4·25
859 $5 Queen angelfish (optd **90TH BIRTHDAY H.M. THE QUEEN MOTHER**) 7·00 7·50

151 Mermaid Flag

1990. Island Flags. Multicoloured.
860 50c. Type **151** . . . . 1·00 50
861 80c. New Anguilla official flag . . . . 1·50 1·00
862 $1 Three Dolphins flag . . . 1·60 1·10
863 $5 Governor's official flag . . 4·25 6·50

152 Laughing Gulls

1990. Christmas. Sea Birds. Multicoloured.
864 10c. Type **152** 60 50
865 35c. Brown booby . . . . . 1·00 50
866 $1.50 Bridled tern . . . . . 2·00 2·00
867 $3.50 Brown pelican . . . . 3·25 4·75
MS868 101 × 76 mm. $6 Least tern 8·50 11·00

1991. Easter. Nos. 846/9 optd **1991**.
869 35c. Type **148** . . . . 1·00 60
870 45c. The Trial . . . . 1·10 60
871 $1.35 The Crucifixion . . . . 2·25 2·00
872 $2.50 The Empty Tomb . . . 3·50 5·50
MS873 114 × 84 mm. $6 The Resurrection . . . . 9·00 10·00

154 Angel

155 Angels with Palm Branches outside St. Gerard's Church

1991. Christmas.
874 **154** 5c. violet, brown & black 70 70
875 – 35c. multicoloured . . . . 1·75 55
876 – 80c. multicoloured . . . . 2·75 2·00
877 – $1 multicoloured . . . . 2·75 2·00
MS878 – 131 × 97 mm. $5 multicoloured . . . . 8·00 9·00
DESIGNS—VERT: 35c. Father Christmas. HORIZ: 80c. Church and house; $1 Palm trees at night; $5 Anguilla village.

1992. Easter. Multicoloured.
879 30c. Type **155** 95 45
880 45c. Angels singing outside Methodist Church . . . . 1·10 45
881 80c. Village (horiz) . . . . . 2·00 90
882 $1 Congregation going to St. Mary's Church . . . . 2·00 1·00
883 $5 Dinghy regatta (horiz) . . 5·50 8·00

1992. No. 834 surch **$1.60**.
884 $1.60 on 30c. Yellow jack . . 2·25 2·00

157 Anguillan Flags

1992. 25th Anniv of Separation from St. Kitts-Nevis. Multicoloured.
885 80c. Type **157** . . . . 2·00 1·50
886 $1 Present official seal . . . 2·00 1·50
887 $1.60 Anguillan flags at airport . . . . 3·25 3·25
888 $2 Royal Commissioner's official seal . . . . 3·25 3·75
MS889 116 × 117 mm. $10 "Independent Anguilla" overprinted stamps of 1967 (85 × 85 mm) . . . . 10·00 11·00

158 Dinghy Race

1992. Sailing Dinghy Racing.
890 **158** 20c. multicoloured . . . . 1·25 65
891 – 35c. multicoloured . . . . 1·50 60
892 – 45c. multicoloured . . . . 1·75 60
893 – 80c. multicoloured . . . . 2·50 3·50
894 – 80c. black and blue . . . 2·50 3·50
895 – $1 multicoloured . . . . 2·50 2·50
MS896 – 129 × 30 mm. $6 multicoloured . . . . 7·50 8·50
DESIGNS—VERT: 35c. Stylized poster; 80c. (No. 893) "Blue Bird" in race; 80c. (No. 894) Construction drawings of "Blue Bird" by Douglas Pyle; $1 Stylized poster (different). HORIZ: 45c. Dinghies on beach. (97 × 32 mm)—$6 Composite designs as 20 and 45c. values.

159 Mucka Jumbie on Stilts

1992. Christmas. Local Traditions. Mult.
897 20c. Type **159** 65 40
898 70c. Masqueraders . . . . . 1·50 60
899 $1.05 Baking in old style oven . . . . 1·75 1·25
900 $2.40 Collecting presents from Christmas tree . . . 2·75 3·75
MS901 128 × 101 mm. $5 As No. 900 3·50 5·50

160 Columbus landing in New World

1992. 500th Anniv of Discovery of America by Columbus (2nd issue).
902 **160** 80c. multicoloured . . . . 2·25 1·25
903 – $1 black and brown . . . 2·25 1·25
904 – $2 multicoloured . . . . 3·25 3·75
905 – $3 multicoloured . . . . 3·75 4·75
MS906 – 78 × 54 mm. $6 multicoloured . . . . 6·50 8·00
DESIGNS—VERT: $1 Christopher Columbus; $6 Columbus and map of West Indies. HORIZ: $2 Fleet of Columbus; $3 "Pinta".

161 "Kite Flying" (Kyle Brooks)

163 Lord Great Chamberlain presenting Spurs of Charity to Queen

162 Salt Picking

1993. Easter. Children's Paintings. Mult.
907 20c. Type **161** . . . . 1·25 60
908 45c. "Clifftop Village Service" (Kara Connor) . . 1·75 60
909 80c. "Morning Devotion on Sombrero" (Junior Carty) 2·50 1·40
910 $1.50 "Hill Top Church Service" (Leana Harris) . . 3·25 4·50
MS911 90 × 110 mm. $5 "Good Friday Kites" (Marvin Hazel and Kyle Brooks) (39 × 53 mm) . . 4·75 6·50

1993. Traditional Industries. Mult.
912 20c. Type **162** . . . . 2·25 90
913 80c. Tobacco growing . . . 2·25 1·25
914 $1 Cotton picking . . . . . 2·25 1·25
915 $2 Harvesting sugar cane . . 3·25 4·75
MS916 111 × 85 mm. $6 Fishing 10·00 12·00

1993. 40th Anniv of Coronation. Mult.
917 80c. Type **163** . . . . 1·50 80
918 $1 The Benediction . . . . . 1·75 90
919 $2 Queen Elizabeth II in Coronation robes . . . . 2·50 2·75
920 $3 St. Edward's Crown . . . 3·00 3·75
MS921 114 × 95 mm. $6 The Queen and Prince Philip in Coronation coach . . . . 10·00 12·00

164 Carnival Pan Player

1993. Anguilla Carnival. Multicoloured.
922 20c. Type **164** 70 40
923 45c. Revellers dressed as pirates 95 40
924 80c. Revellers dressed as stars 1·50 75
925 $1 Mas dancing . . . . . . 1·50 80
926 $2 Masked couple . . . . . 2·75 3·75
927 $3 Revellers dressed as commandos . . . . 3·25 4·25
MS928 123 × 94 mm. $5 Revellers in fantasy costumes . . . . . . 10·00 11·00

165 Mucka Jumbies Carnival Characters

167 Princess Alexandra, 1988

166 Travelling Branch Post Van at Sandy Ground

1993. Christmas. Multicoloured.
929 20c. Type **165** 75 60
930 35c. Local carol singers . . . 1·00 60
931 45c. Christmas home baking 1·10 60
932 $3 Decorating Christmas tree 4·00 5·50
MS933 123 × 118 mm. $4 Mucka Jumbies and carol singers (58½ × 47 mm) . . . . 3·25 4·75

1994. Delivering the Mail. Multicoloured.
934 20c. Type **166** . . . . 1·50 70
935 45c. "Betsy R" (mail schooner) at The Forest (vert) . . . . 2·00 70
936 80c. Mail van at old Post Office . . . . 2·50 1·40
937 $1 Jeep on beach, Island Harbour (vert) . . . . . 2·50 1·40
938 $4 New Post Office . . . . . 4·00 6·50

1994. Royal Visitors. Multicoloured.
939 45c. Type **167** . . . . 1·25 60
940 50c. Princess Alice, 1960 . . 1·25 60
941 80c. Prince Philip, 1993 . . . 2·00 1·25
942 $1 Prince Charles, 1973 . . . 2·25 1·25
943 $2 Queen Elizabeth II, 1994 2·75 4·00
MS944 162 × 90 mm. Nos. 939/43 8·50 9·50

168 "The Crucifixion"

170 "The Nativity" (Gustave Dore)

169 Cameroun Player and Pontiac Silverdome, Detroit

1994. Easter. Stained-glass Windows. Multicoloured.
945 20c. Type **168** 50 40
946 45c. "The Empty Tomb" . . . 65 45
947 80c. "The Resurrection" . . 1·25 90
948 $3 "Risen Christ with Disciples" . . . . 3·00 5·00

1994. World Cup Football Championship, U.S.A. Multicoloured.
949 20c. Type **169** 45 30
950 70c. Argentine player and Foxboro Stadium, Boston 85 65
951 $1.80 Italian player and RFK Memorial Stadium, Washington . . . . 1·75 2·50
952 $2.40 German player and Soldier Field, Chicago . . 2·00 3·25
MS953 112 × 85 mm. $6 American and Colombian players . . . . 9·00 10·00

1994. Christmas. Religious Paintings. Mult.
954 20c. Type **170** 65 60
955 30c. "The Wise Men guided by the Star" (Dore) . . . 80 60
956 35c. "The Annunciation" (Dore) 85 60

957 45c. "Adoration of the Shepherds" (detail) (Poussin) 95 60
958 $2.40 "The Flight into Egypt" (Dore) . . . . . . 2·75 4·00

171 Pair of Zenaida Doves

1995. Easter. Zenaida Doves. Multicoloured.
959 20c. Type **171** 50 40
960 45c. Dove on branch 75 50
961 50c. Guarding nest 80 55
962 $5 With chicks . . . . 5·50 7·00

172 Trygve Lie (first Secretary-General) and General Assembly

1995. 50th Anniv of United Nations. Multicoloured.
963 20c. Type **172** 30 30
964 80c. Flag and building showing "50" 60 65
965 $1 Dag Hammarskjold and U Thant (former Secretary-Generals) and U.N. Charter 70 75
966 $5 U.N. Building (vert) . . . 4·00 6·50

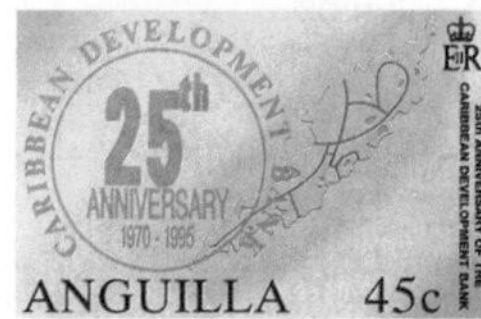

173 Anniversary Emblem and Map of Anguilla

1995. 25th Anniv of Caribbean Development Bank. Multicoloured.
967 45c. Type **173** . . . . 1·50 1·75
968 $5 Bank building and launches . . . . 3·00 4·25

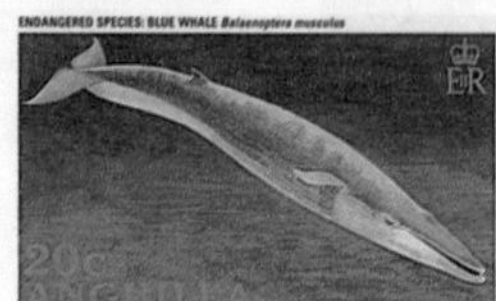

174 Blue Whale

1995. Endangered Species. Whales. Multicoloured.
969 20c. Type **174** . . . . 2·00 70
970 45c. Right whale (vert) . . . 2·25 60
971 $1 Sperm whale . . . . 2·75 1·50
972 $5 Humpback whale . . . . 7·50 8·50

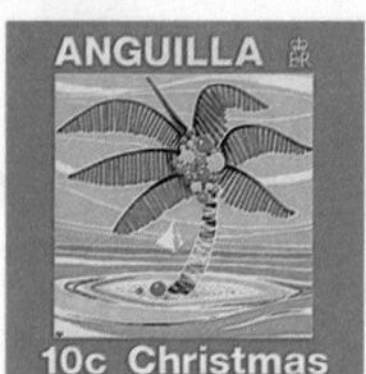

175 Palm Tree

1995. Christmas. Multicoloured.
973 10c. Type **175** 70 70
974 25c. Balloons and fishes . . . 90 60
975 45c. Shells . . . . 1·25 60
976 $5 Fishes in shape of Christmas tree . . . . . . 8·00 9·50

176 Deep Water Gorgonia

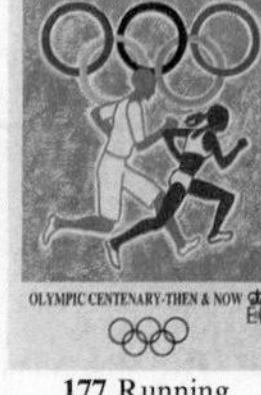

177 Running

1996. Corals. Multicoloured.
977 20c. Type **176** . . . . 1·50 70
978 80c. Common sea fan . . . . 2·50 1·00
979 $5 Venus sea fern . . . . . 7·50 9·00

1996. Olympic Games, Atlanta. Multicoloured.
980 20c. Type **177** 70 50
981 80c. Javelin throwing and wheelchair basketball . . . 2·00 1·00
982 $1 High jumping and hurdles 1·40 1·00
983 $3.50 Olympic rings and torch with Greek and American flags . . . . . . 4·00 4·75

178 Siege of Sandy Hill Fort

1996. Bicentenary of the Battle for Anguilla. Multicoloured.
984 60c. Type **178** . . . . 1·00 1·00
985 75c. French troops destroying church (horiz) . . . . . . 1·00 1·00
986 $1.50 Naval battle (horiz) . . 2·25 2·25
987 $4 French troops landing at Rendezvous Bay . . . . . 3·50 4·75

179 Gooseberry

1997. Fruit. Multicoloured.
988 10c. Type **179** 35 40
989 20c. West Indian cherry . . 40 30
990 40c. Tamarind 50 30
991 50c. Pomme-surette 60 40
992 60c. Sea almond 70 55
993 75c. Sea grape 80 65
994 80c. Banana 90 65
995 $1 Genip . . . . 1·00 1·00
996 $1.10 Coco plum . . . . . 1·25 1·40
997 $1.25 Pope . . . . 1·50 1·75
998 $1.50 Pawpaw . . . . . . 1·50 1·75
999 $2 Sugar apple . . . . . . 2·00 2·50
1000 $3 Soursop . . . . 2·50 3·25
1001 $4 Pomegranate . . . . . . 3·00 3·75
1002 $5 Cashew . . . . 3·50 4·25
1003 $10 Mango . . . . 6·00 7·00

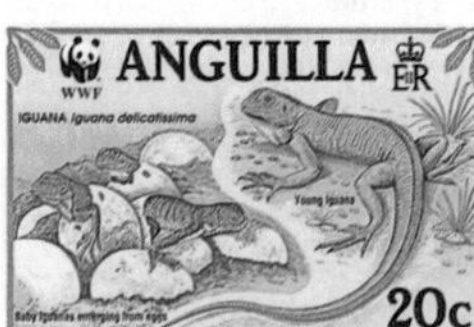

180 West Indian Iguanas hatching

1997. Endangered Species. West Indian Iguanas. Multicoloured.
1004 20c. Type **180** . . . . . . 1·50 1·25
1005 50c. On rock . . . . 1·75 1·40
1006 75c. On branch . . . . . . 1·90 1·60
1007 $3 Head of West Indian iguana . . . . 2·75 3·50

181 "Juluca, Rainbow Deity"

1997. Ancient Stone Carvings from Fountain Cavern. Multicoloured.
1008 30c. Type **181** 45 35
1009 $1.25 "Lizard with front legs extended" . . . . 90 1·00
1010 $2.25 "Chief" . . . . 1·60 2·50
1011 $2.75 "Jocahu, the Creator" 2·00 3·00

182 Diana, Princess of Wales

1998. Diana, Princess of Wales Commemoration. Multicoloured.
1012 15c. Type **182** . . . . . . 1·50 1·25
1013 $1 Wearing yellow blouse . 2·25 1·60
1014 $1.90 Wearing tiara . . . . 2·50 2·50
1015 $2.25 Wearing blue short-sleeved Red Cross blouse 2·75 2·75

183 "Treasure Island" (Valarie Alix)

1998. International Arts Festival. Multicoloured.
1016 15c. Type **183** 50 50
1017 30c. "Posing in the Light" (Melsadis Fleming) (vert) 50 40
1018 $1 "Pescadores de Anguilla" (Juan Garcia) (vert) . . . 80 80
1019 $1.50 "Fresh Catch" (Verna Hart) . . . . 1·00 1·60
1020 $1.90 "The Bell Tower of St. Mary's" (Ricky Racardo Edwards) (vert) 1·25 2·00

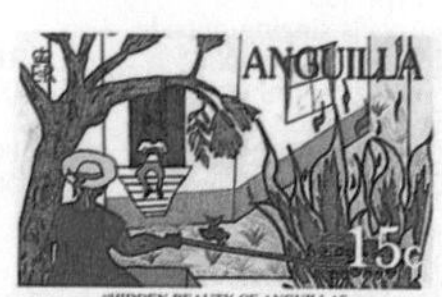

184 Roasting Corn-cobs on Fire

1998. Christmas. "Hidden Beauty of Anguilla". Children's Paintings. Multicoloured.
1021 15c. Type **184** 35 30
1022 $1 Fresh fruit and market stallholder 80 50
1023 $1.50 Underwater scene . . 1·00 1·25
1024 $3 Cacti and view of sea . . 1·60 2·50

185 University of West Indies Centre, Anguilla

1998. 50th Anniv of University of West Indies. Multicoloured.
1025 $1.50 Type **185** 80 90
1026 $1.90 Man with torch and University arms . . . . . 1·10 1·50

186 Sopwith Camel and Bristol F2B Fighters

1998. 80th Anniv of Royal Air Force. Multicoloured.
1027 30c. Type **186** 75 50
1028 $1 Supermarine Spitfire Mk II and Hawker Hurricane Mk I . . . . 1·40 80
1029 $1.50 Avro Lancaster . . . . 1·75 1·60
1030 $1.90 Panavia Tornado F3 and Harrier GR7 . . . . 1·90 2·25

187 Saturn 5 Rocket and "Apollo 11" Command Module

1999. 30th Anniv of First Manned Landing on Moon. Multicoloured.
1031 30c. Type **187** 55 33
1032 $1 Astronaut Edwin Aldrin, Lunar Module "Eagle" and first footprint on Moon . . . . 1·00 70
1033 $1.50 Lunar Module leaving Moon's surface . . . . . 1·00 1·00
1034 $1.90 Recovery of Command Module . . . 1·40 2·00

188 Albena Lake Hodge

189 Library and Resource Centre

1999. Anguillan Heroes and Heroines (1st series). Each black, green and cream.
1035 30c. Type **188** 40 30
1036 $1 Collins O. Hodge 80 65
1037 $1.50 Edwin Wallace Rey . 1·00 1·25
1038 $1.90 Walter G. Hodge . . 1·25 2·00

1999. Modern Architecture. Multicoloured.
1039 30c. Type **189** 35 30
1040 65c. Parliamentary building and Court House 55 50
1041 $1 Caribbean Commercial Bank 80 70
1042 $1.50 Police Headquarters 1·75 1·75
1043 $1.90 Post Office . . . . . 1·50 2·00

190 Beach Barbeque and Fireworks

1999. Christmas and New Millennium. Mult.
1044 30c. Type **190** 40 30
1045 $1 Musicians around globe 1·00 55
1046 $1.50 Family at Christmas dinner . . . . 1·50 1·50
1047 $1.90 Celebrations around decorated shrub . . . . . 1·75 2·25

191 Shoal Bay (East)

2000. Beaches. Multicoloured.
1048 15c. Type **191** 30 40
1049 30c. Maundys Bay 35 30
1050 $1 Rendezvous Bay 75 50
1051 $1.50 Meads Bay . . . . . 1·00 1·25
1052 $1.90 Little Bay . . . . . 1·25 1·75
1053 $2 Sandy Ground . . . . . 1·25 1·75
MS1054 144 × 144 mm. Nos. 1048/53 3·50 4·00

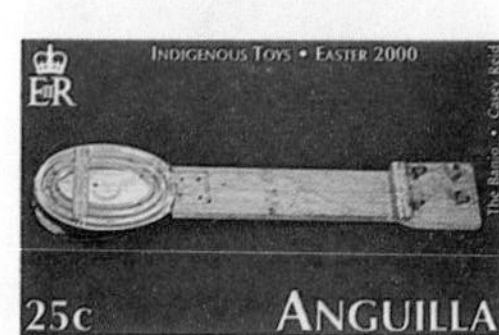

192 Toy Banjo (Casey Reid)

2000. Easter. Indigenous Toys. Multicoloured.
1055 25c. Type **192** 40 30
1056 30c. Spinning top (Johniela Harrigan) 40 30
1057 $1.50 Catapult (Akeem Rogers) . . . . 1·10 1·10
1058 $1.90 Roller (Melisa Mussington) . . . . . . 1·40 1·75
1059 $2.50 Killy Ban (trap) (Casey Reid) . . . . . . 1·75 2·25
MS1060 145 × 185 mm. 75c. Rag Doll (Jahia Esposito) (vert); $1 Kite (Javed Maynard) (vert); $1.25, Cricket ball (Jevon Lake) (vert); $4 Pond boat (Corvel Flemming) (vert) . . . . . . 4·25 5·00

193 Lanville Harrigan

2000. West Indies Cricket Tour and 100th Test Match at Lord's. Multicoloured.

1061	$2 Type **193**	1·75	1·75
1062	$4 Cardigan Connor	2·75	3·50
MS1063	119 × 102 mm. $6 Lord's Cricket Ground (horiz)	5·50	5·50

2000. "The Stamp Show 2000" International Stamp Exhibition, London. Beaches. As No. **MS**1054, but with exhibition logo on bottom margin. Mult.

MS1064	144 × 144 mm. Nos. 1048/53	3·75	5·00

194 Prince William and Royal Family after Trooping the Colour

2000. 18th Birthday of Prince William. Mult.

1065	30c. Type **194**	1·00	50
1066	$1 Prince and Princess of Wales with sons	1·75	85
1067	$1.90 With Prince Charles and Prince Harry	2·25	2·25
1068	$2.25 Skiing with father and brother	2·75	2·75
MS1069	125 × 95 mm. $8 Prince William as pupil at Eton	6·00	7·00

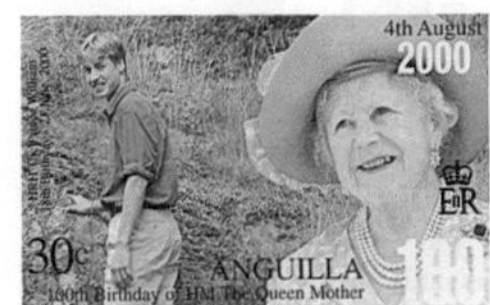

195 Queen Elizabeth the Queen Mother and Prince William

2000. 100th Birthday of Queen Elizabeth the Queen Mother. Showing different portraits. Multicoloured.

1070	30c. Type **195**	65	40
1071	$1.50 Island scene	1·50	1·00
1072	$1.90 Clarence House	1·75	1·60
1073	$5 Castle of Mey	3·25	4·00

196 "Anguilla Montage" (Weme Caster)

2000. International Arts Festival. Multicoloured.

1074	15c. Type **196**	30	40
1075	30c. "Serenity" (Damien Carty)	35	30
1076	65c. "Inter Island Cargo" (Paula Walden)	55	45
1077	$1.50 "Rainbow City where Spirits find Form" (Fiona Percy)	1·25	1·50
1078	$1.90 "Sailing Silver Seas" (Valerie Carpenter)	1·40	2·00
MS1079	75 × 100 mm. $7 "Historic Anguilla" (Melsadis Fleming) (42 × 28 mm)	4·25	5·50

197 Dried Flower Arrangement

2000. Christmas. Flower and Garden Show.

1080	**197**	15c. multicoloured	25	25
1081	–	25c. multicoloured	30	25
1082	–	30c. multicoloured	30	25
1083	–	$1 multicoloured	75	60
1084	–	$1.50 multicoloured	1·25	1·50
1085	–	$1.90 multicoloured	1·50	2·00

DESIGNS: 25c. to $1.90, Different floral arrangements.

198 Winning Primary School Football Team (Bank Sponsorship)

2000. 15th Anniv of National Bank of Anguilla. Multicoloured.

1086	30c. Type **198**	30	25
1087	$1 *De-Chan* (yacht) (Bank sponsorship) (vert)	70	60
1088	$1.50 Bank crest (vert)	1·25	1·50
1089	$1.90 New Bank Headquarters	1·50	2·00

199 Ebenezer Methodist Church in 19th Century

2000. 170th Anniv of Ebenezer Methodist Church.

1090	**199**	30c. brown and black	30	20
1091	–	$1.90 multicoloured	1·50	2·00

DESIGN: $1.90, Church in 2000.

200 Soroptomist Day Care Centre

2001. United Nations Women's Human Rights Campaign. Multicoloured.

1092	25c. Type **200**	30	30
1093	30c. Britannia Idalia Gumbs (Anguillan politician) (vert)	30	30
1094	$2.25 "Caribbean Woman II" (Leisel Renee Jobity) (vert)	1·60	2·25

201 John Paul Jones and U.S.S. *Ranger* (frigate)

2001. 225th Anniv of American War of Independence. Multicoloured.

1095	30c. Type **201**	70	45
1096	$1 George Washington and Battle of Yorktown	1·00	80
1097	$1.50 Thomas Jefferson and submission of Declaration of Independence to Congress	1·50	1·75
1098	$1.90 John Adams and the signing of the Treaty of Paris	1·75	2·00

202 Bahama Pintail

2001. Anguillian Birds. Multicoloured.

1099	30c. Type **202**	75	50
1100	$1 Black-faced grassquit (vert)	1·00	80
1101	$1.50 Common noddy	1·60	1·60
1102	$2 Black-necked stilt (vert)	2·00	2·25
1103	$3 Kentish plover ("Snowy Plover")	2·50	2·75
MS1104	124 × 88 mm. 25c. Snowy egret; 65c. Red-billed tropic bird; $1.35, Greater yellowlegs; $2.25, Sooty tern	4·50	4·50

203 "Children encircling Globe" (Urska Golob)

2001. U.N. Year of Dialogue among Civilisations.

1105	**203**	$1.90 multicoloured	1·40	2·00

204 Triangle

2001. Christmas. Indigenous Musical Instruments. Multicoloured.

1106	15c. Type **204**	25	30
1107	25c. Maracas	35	35
1108	30c. Guiro (vert)	35	35
1109	$1.50 Marimba	1·25	1·25
1110	$1.90 Tambu (hand drum) (vert)	1·50	1·75
1111	$2.50 Bass pan	2·00	2·50
MS1112	110 × 176 mm. 75c. Banjo (vert); $1 Quatro (vert); $1.25, Ukelele (vert); $3 Cello (vert)	4·00	5·00

205 Sombrero Lighthouse, 1962

206 Artist, Entertainer and Sportsmen

2002. Commissioning of New Sombrero Lighthouse. Multicoloured.

1113	30c. Type **205**	60	40
1114	$1.50 Old and new lighthouses (horiz)	1·50	1·50
1115	$1.90 New, fully-automated lighthouse, 2001	1·60	1·75

2002. 20th Anniv of Social Security Board. Multicoloured (except 30c.).

1116	30c. Type **206** (ultramarine and blue)	40	30
1117	75c. Anguillans of all ages	70	65
1118	$2.50 Anguillan workers (horiz)	2·25	2·50

207 H.M.S. *Antrim* (destroyer), 1967

2002. Ships of the Royal Navy. Multicoloured.

1119	30c. Type **207**	45	35
1120	50c. H.M.S. *Formidable* (aircraft carrier), 1939	65	50
1121	$1.50 H.M.S. *Dreadnought* (battleship), 1906	1·00	1·25
1122	$2 H.M.S. *Warrior* (ironclad), 1860	1·50	1·75
MS1123	102 × 77 mm. H.M.S. *Ark Royal* (aircraft carrier), 1981 (vert)	5·75	6·50

208 Princess Elizabeth with Prince Charles

2002. Golden Jubilee. Multicoloured.

1124	30c. Type **208**	40	30
1125	$1.50 Queen Elizabeth wearing white coat	1·10	1·10

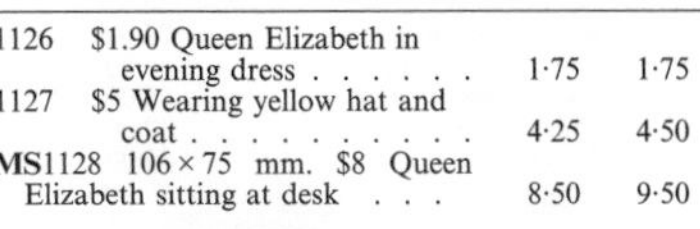

1126	$1.90 Queen Elizabeth in evening dress	1·75	1·75
1127	$5 Wearing yellow hat and coat	4·25	4·50
MS1128	106 × 75 mm. $8 Queen Elizabeth sitting at desk	8·50	9·50

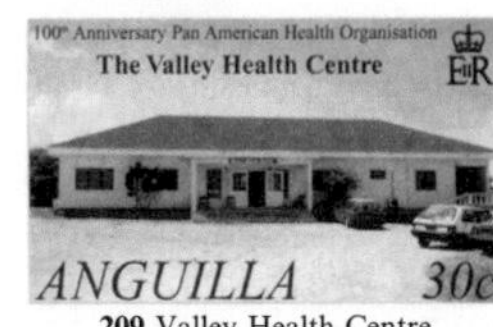

209 Valley Health Centre

2002. Centenary of Pan American Health Organization. Multicoloured.

1129	30c. Type **209**	30	25
1130	$1.50 Centenary of PAHO logo	95	1·25

210 *Finance* (sloop)

2003. Past Sailing Vessels of Anguilla. Multicoloured.

1131	15c. Type **210**	10	10
1132	30c. *Tiny Gull*	10	15
1133	65c. *Lady Laurel* (schooner)	25	30
1134	75c. *Spitfire* (gaff rigged sloop)	30	35
1135	$1 *Liberator* (schooner)	40	45
1136	$1.35 *Excelsior* (schooner)	60	65
1137	$1.50 *Rose Millicent*	60	65
1138	$1.90 *Betsy R.* (sloop)	75	80
1139	$2 *Sunbeam R.* (sloop)	80	85
1140	$2.25 *New London*	1·00	1·20
1141	$3 *Ismay* (schooner)	1·20	1·40
1142	$10 *Warspite* (schooner)	4·00	4·25

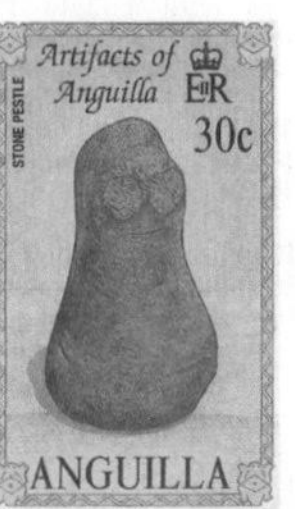

211 Stone Pestle

2003. Artifacts of Anguilla. Multicoloured.

1143	30c. Type **211**	10	15
1144	$1 Frog worked shell ornament	40	45
1145	$1.50 Pottery	60	65
1146	$1.90 Mask worked shell ornament	75	80

212 Frangipani Beach Club

2003. Hotels of Anguilla. Multicoloured

1147	75c. Type **212**	30	35
1148	$1 Pimms, Cap Juluca	40	45
1149	$1.35 Cocoloba Beach Resort	60	65
1150	$1.50 Malliouhana Hotel	60	65
1151	$1.90 Carmiar Beach Club	75	80
1152	$3 Covecastles	1·20	1·30

ANJOUAN Pt. 6

One of the Comoro Is. between Madagascar and the East coast of Africa. Used stamps of Madagascar from 1914 and became part of the Comoro Islands in 1950.

100 centimes = 1 franc.

1892. "Tablet" key-type inscr "SULTANAT D'ANJOUAN".

1	D	1c. black on blue	1·00	1·75
2		2c. brown on buff	2·00	2·00
3		4c. brown on grey	2·25	2·25
4		5c. green on green	4·00	3·75
5		10c. black on lilac	4·00	4·00
14		10c. red	11·50	13·50
6		15c. blue	4·25	5·00
15		15c. grey	7·25	9·00
7		20c. red on green	5·00	6·25
8		25c. black on pink	6·00	6·25
16		25c. blue	9·00	11·00
9		30c. brown on grey	14·50	12·50
17		35c. black on yellow	5·50	5·50
10		40c. red on yellow	19·00	18·00

18 45c. black on green . . . . 75·00 65·00
11 50c. red on pink . . . . . 21·00 22·00
19 50c. brown on blue . . . . 15·00 17·00
12 75c. brown on orange . . . 29·00 24·00
13 1f. green . . . . 65·00 60·00

1912. Surch in figures.
20 D 05 on 2c. brown on buff . . 2·50 3·00
21 05 on 4c. brown on grey . . 1·25 2·50
22 05 on 15c. blue . . . . . . 1·25 2·50
23 05 on 20c. red on green . . 1·50 3·00
24 05 on 25c. black on pink . . 1·10 2·50
25 05 on 30c. brown on grey . . 2·25 2·75
26 10 on 40c. red on yellow . . 1·25 2·25
27 10 on 45c. black on green . . 95 1·75
28 10 on 50c. red on pink . . . 2·25 4·75
29 10 on 75c. brown on orange . . 2·25 3·50
30 10 on 1f. green . . . . . . 3·25 3·75

ANNAM AND TONGKING Pt. 6

Later part of Indo-China and now included in Vietnam.

100 centimes = 1 franc.

1888. Stamps of French Colonies, "Commerce" type, surch **A & T** and value in figures.
1 J 1 on 2c. brown on yellow . . 38·00 32·00
2 1 on 4c. lilac on grey . . . 32·00 25·00
3 5 on 10c. black on lilac . . . 38·00 28·00

ANTIGUA Pt. 1

One of the Leeward Islands, Br. W. Indies. Used general issues for Leeward Islands, concurrently with Antiguan stamps until 1 July 1956. Ministerial Government introduced on 1 January 1960. Achieved Associated Statehood on 3 March 1967 and Independence within the Commonwealth on 1 November 1981.

Nos. 718/21 and 733 onwards are inscribed "Antigua and Barbuda".

1862. 12 pence = 1 shilling;
20 shillings = 1 pound.
1951. 100 cents = 1 West Indian dollar.

1

3

1862.
5 1 1d. mauve . . . . £130 50·00
25 1d. red . . . . 1·75 3·25
29 6d. green . . . . 60·00 £120

1879.
21 3 ½d. green . . . . 2·50 3·25
22 2½d. brown . . . . £170 55·00
27 2½d. blue . . . . 6·50 12·00
23 4d. blue . . . . £275 15·00
28 4d. brown . . . . 2·25 3·00
30 1s. mauve £160 £120

4

5

8

1903.
31 4 ½d. black and green . . . . 3·75 6·50
41 ½d. green . . . . 2·75 4·50
32 1d. black and red . . . . . 6·50 1·25
43 1d. red . . . . 6·00 2·25
45 2d. purple and brown . . . . 4·75 29·00
34 2½d. black and blue . . . . 9·00 15·00
46 2½d. blue . . . . 12·00 16·00
47 3d. green and brown . . . . 6·50 19·00
48 6d. purple and black . . . . 7·50 48·00
49 1s. blue and purple . . . . 15·00 70·00
50 2s. green and violet . . . . 80·00 85·00
39 2s.6d. black and purple . . . 18·00 55·00
40 5 5s. green and violet . . . . . 70·00 £100

1913. Head of King George V.
51 5 5s. green and violet . . . . . 70·00 £110

1916. Optd **WAR STAMP**.
52 4 ½d. green . . . . 2·00 2·50
54 1½d. orange . . . . 1·00 1·25

1921.
62 8 ½d. green . . . . 2·50 50
63 1d. red . . . . 2·75 50
64 1d. violet . . . . 4·50 1·50
67 1½d. orange . . . . 3·50 7·00
68 1½d. red . . . . 5·00 1·75
69 1½d. brown . . . . 3·00 60
70 2d. grey . . . . 3·00 75
72 2½d. yellow . . . . 2·50 17·00
73 2½d. blue . . . . 5·50 5·50
74 3d. purple on yellow . . . . 5·00 8·50
56 4d. black and red on yellow . . 2·25 5·50
75 6d. purple . . . . 4·00 6·50
57 1s. black on green . . . . . 4·25 9·00
58 2s. purple and blue on blue . . 13·00 19·00
78 2s.6d. black and red on blue . . 26·00 28·00
79 3s. green and violet . . . . . 30·00 90·00
80 4s. black and red . . . . . . 48·00 65·00
60 5s. green and red on yellow . . 8·50 50·00
61 £1 purple and black on red . . £190 £300

9 Old Dockyard, English Harbour

10 Government House, St. John's

1932. Tercentenary. Designs with medallion portrait of King George V.
81 9 ½d. green . . . . 2·75 7·50
82 – 1d. red . . . . 3·25 7·50
83 – 1½d. brown . . . . 3·25 4·75
84 10 2d. grey . . . . 4·25 18·00
85 2½d. blue . . . . 4·25 8·50
86 3d. orange . . . . 4·25 12·00
87 – 6d. violet . . . . 15·00 12·00
88 – 1s. olive . . . . 19·00 27·00
89 – 2s.6d. purple . . . . 40·00 65·00
90 – 5s. black and brown . . . . 95·00 £120
DESIGNS—HORIZ: 6d. to 2s.6d. Nelson's "Victory"; 5s. Sir Thomas Warner's "Conception".

13 Windsor Castle

1935. Silver Jubilee.
91 13 1d. blue and red . . . . . 2·00 3·00
92 1½d. blue and grey . . . . 2·75 55
93 2½d. brown and blue . . . . 6·50 1·25
94 1s. grey and purple . . . . 8·50 15·00

1937. Coronation. As T 2 of Aden.
95 1d. red . . . . 60 1·25
96 1½d. brown . . . . 60 1·50
97 2½d. blue . . . . 1·50 1·75

15 English Harbour

16 Nelson's Dockyard

1938.
98 15 ½d. green . . . . 40 1·25
99 16 1d. red . . . . 3·00 2·00
100a 1½d. brown . . . . 2·25 1·75
101 15 2d. grey 75 50
102 16 2½d. blue . . . . 1·00 80
103 – 3d. orange . . . . 1·00 1·00
104 – 6d. violet . . . . 3·00 1·25
105 – 1s. black and brown . . . 4·75 1·50
106a – 2s.6d. purple . . . . . . 24·00 12·00
107 – 5s. olive . . . . 14·00 7·50
108 16 10s. mauve . . . . 16·00 27·00
109 – £1 green . . . . 25·00 38·00
DESIGNS—HORIZ: 3d., 2s.6d., £1, Fort James. VERT: 6d., 1s., 5s. St. John's Harbour.

1946. Victory. As T 9 of Aden.
110 1½d. brown 20 10
111 3d. orange 20 50

1949. Silver Wedding. As T 10/11 of Aden.
112 2½d. blue . . . . 40 2·00
113 5s. green . . . . 8·50 8·50

20 Hermes, Globe and Forms of Transport

21 Hemispheres, Jet-powered Vickers Viking Airliner and Steamer

22 Hermes and Globe

23 U.P.U. Monument

1949. 75th Anniv of U.P.U.
114 20 2½d. blue 40 50
115 21 3d. orange . . . . 1·75 2·25
116 22 6d. purple . . . . 45 1·75
117 23 1s. brown . . . . 45 1·25

24 Arms of University

25 Princess Alice

1951. Inauguration of B.W.I. University College.
118 24 3c. black and brown . . . 45 1·00
119 25 12c. black and violet . . . 80 1·25

1953. Coronation. As T 13 of Aden.
120 2c. black and green 30 75

27 Martello Tower

1953. Designs as 1938 issues but with portrait of Queen Elizabeth II as in T 27.
120a – ½c. brown 30 30
121 15 1c. grey 30 70
122 16 2c. green 30 10
123 3c. black and yellow . . . 40 20
153 15 4c. red 30 75
154 16 5c. black and lilac 20 10
155 – 6c. yellow 60 30
156 27 8c. blue 30 20
157 – 12c. violet 40 20
129 – 24c. black and brown . . 2·50 15
130 27 48c. purple and blue . . . 7·00 2·75
131 – 60c. purple . . . . 7·50 80
132 – $1.20 olive . . . . 2·25 70
133 16 $2.40 purple . . . . . . 11·00 12·00
134 – $4.80 slate . . . . 15·00 24·00
DESIGNS—HORIZ: ½, 6, 60c., $4.80, Fort James. VERT: 12, 24c., $1.20, St John's Harbour.

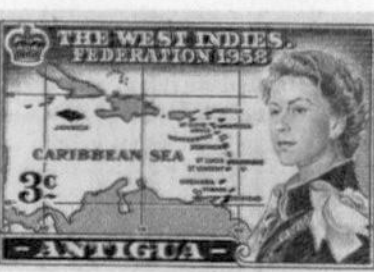

28 Federation Map

1958. Inaug of British Caribbean Federation.
135 28 3c. green . . . . 1·00 30
136 6c. blue . . . . 1·40 2·75
137 12c. red . . . . 1·60 75

1960. New Constitution. Nos. 123 and 157 optd **COMMEMORATION ANTIGUA CONSTITUTION**.
138 16 3c. black and yellow . . . 15 15
139 – 12c. violet 15 15

30 Nelson's Dockyard and Admiral Nelson

1961. Restoration of Nelson's Dockyard.
140 30 20c. purple and brown . . 90 1·40
141 30c. green and blue . . . . 1·10 1·60

31 Stamp of 1862 and R.M.S.P. "Solent I" at English Harbour

1962. Stamp Centenary.
142 31 3c. purple and green . . . 60 10
143 10c. blue and green 70 10
144 12c. sepia and green 80 10
145 50c. brown and green . . . 1·50 1·75

1963. Freedom from Hunger. As T 28 of Aden.
146 12c. green 15 15

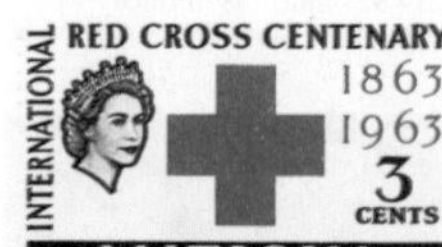

33 Red Cross Emblem

1963. Centenary of Red Cross.
147 33 3c. red and black 30 75
148 12c. red and blue . . . . . 45 1·25

34 Shakespeare and Memorial Theatre, Stratford-upon-Avon

1964. 400th Birth Anniv of Shakespeare.
164 34 12c. brown 30 10

1965. No. 157 surch **15c.**
165 15c. on 12c. violet 10 10

36 I.T.U. Emblem

1965. Centenary of I.T.U.
166 36 2c. blue and red 25 15
167 50c. yellow and blue 75 80

37 I.C.Y. Emblem

1965. International Co-operation Year.
168 37 4c. purple and turquoise . . 20 10
169 15c. green and lavender . . 30 20

38 Sir Winston Churchill, and St. Paul's Cathedral in Wartime

1966. Churchill Commemoration. Designs in black, red and gold with background in colours given.
170 **38** ½c. blue . . . . 10 1·75
171 4c. green 40 10
172 25c. brown . . . . 1·10 45
173 35c. violet . . . . 1·10 55

39 Queen Elizabeth II and Duke of Edinburgh

1966. Royal Visit.
174 **39** 6c. black and blue . . . . 1·25 1·10
175 15c. black and mauve . . . 1·25 1·40

40 Footballer's Legs, Ball and Jules Rimet Cup

1966. World Cup Football Championship.
176 **40** 6c. multicoloured 20 50
177 35c. multicoloured 60 25

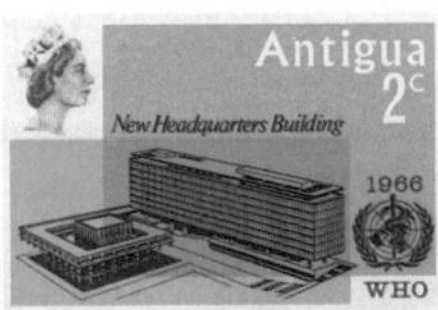

41 W.H.O. Building

1966. Inaug of W.H.O. Headquarters, Geneva.
178 **41** 2c. black, green and blue 20 25
179 15c. black, purple & brn 80 25

42 Nelson's Dockyard

1966.
180 **42** ½c. green and blue 10 40
181 – 1c. purple and mauve . . 10 30
182 – 2c. blue and orange . . . 10 20
183a – 3c. red and black 15 15
184a – 4c. violet and brown . . . 15 15
185 – 5c. blue and green 10 10
186 – 6c. orange and purple . . 30 10
187 – 10c. green and red . . . 15 10
188a – 15c. brown and blue . . . 55 10
189 – 25c. blue and brown . . . 35 20
190a – 35c. mauve and brown . . 60 1·00
191a – 50c. green and black . . . 70 2·25
192 – 75c. blue and ultramarine 1·50 2·50
193b – $1 mauve and green . . . 1·25 5·00
194 – $2.50 black and mauve 3·50 7·00
195 – $5 green and violet . . . 6·00 6·50
DESIGNS: 1c. Old Post Office, St John's; 2c. Health Centre; 3c. Teachers' Training College; 4c. Martello Tower, Barbuda; 5c. Ruins of Officers' Quarters, Shirley Heights; 6c. Government House, Barbuda; 10c. Princess Margaret School; 15c. Air terminal building; 25c. General Post Office; 35c. Clarence House; 50c. Government House, St. John's; 75c. Administration building; $1 Court-house, St. John's; $2.50, Magistrates' Court; $5 St. John's Cathedral.

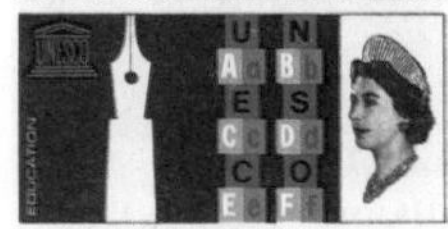

54 "Education"

55 "Science"

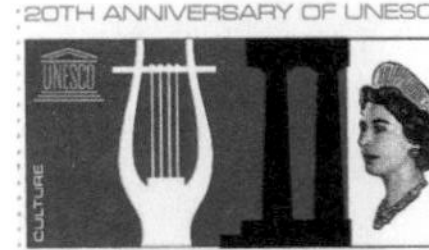

56 "Culture"

1966. 20th Anniv of U.N.E.S.C.O.
196 **54** 4c. violet, yellow & orange 15 10
197 **55** 25c. yellow, violet and olive 35 10
198 **56** $1 black, purple and orange . . . . 80 2·25

57 State Flag and Maps

1967. Statehood. Multicoloured.
199 4c. Type **57** 10 10
200 15c. State Flag 10 20
201 25c. Premier's Office and State Flag 10 25
202 35c. As 15c. 15 25

60 Gilbert Memorial Church

1967. Attainment of Autonomy by the Methodist Church.
203 **60** 4c. black and red 10 10
204 – 25c. black and green . . . 15 15
205 – 35c. black and blue 15 15
DESIGNS: 25c. Nathaniel Gilbert's House; 35c. Caribbean and Central American map.

63 Coat of Arms **66** Tracking Station

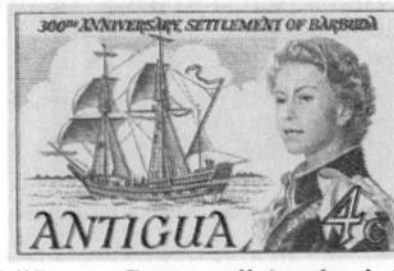

64 "Susan Constant" (settlers' ship)

1967. 300th Anniv of Treaty of Breda and Grant of New Arms.
206 **63** 15c. multicoloured 15 10
207 35c. multicoloured 15 10

1967. 300th Anniv of Barbuda Settlement.
208 **64** 4c. blue 30 10
209 – 6c. purple . . . . 30 1·25
210 **64** 25c. green 40 20
211 – 35c. black 40 25
DESIGN: 6, 35c. Blaeu's Map of 1665.

1968. N.A.S.A. Apollo Project. Inauguration of Dow Hill Tracking Station.
212 **66** 4c. blue, yellow and black 10 10
213 – 15c. blue, yellow and black 20 10
214 – 25c. blue, yellow and black 20 10
215 – 50c. blue, yellow and black 30 40
DESIGNS: 15c. Antenna and spacecraft taking off; 25c. Spacecraft approaching Moon; 50c. Re-entry of space capsule.

70 Limbo-dancing

1968. Tourism. Multicoloured.
216 ½c. Type **70** 10 20
217 15c. Water-skier and bathers 30 10
218 25c. Yachts and beach . . . 30 10
219 35c. Underwater swimming 30 10
220 50c. Type **70** . . . . 35 1·10

74 Old Harbour in 1768

1968. Opening of St. John's Deep Water Harbour.
221 **74** 2c. blue and red 10 40
222 – 15c. green and sepia . . . 35 10
223 – 25c. yellow and blue . . . 40 10
224 – 35c. salmon and emerald 50 10
225 **74** $1 black . . . . 90 2·00
DESIGNS: 15c. Old harbour in 1829; 25c. Freighter and chart of new harbour; 35c. New harbour.

78 Parliament Buildings

1969. Tercentenary of Parliament. Multicoloured.
226 4c. Type **78** 10 10
227 15c. Antigua Mace and bearer 20 10
228 25c. House of Representative's Room . . 20 10
229 50c. Coat of arms and Seal of Antigua . . . . 30 1·60

82 Freight Transport

1969. 1st Anniv of Caribbean Free Trade Area.
230 **82** 4c. black and purple . . . 10 10
231 15c. black and blue 20 30
232 – 25c. brown, black & ochre 25 30
233 – 35c. chocolate, blk & brn 25 30
DESIGN—VERT: 25, 35c. Crate of cargo.

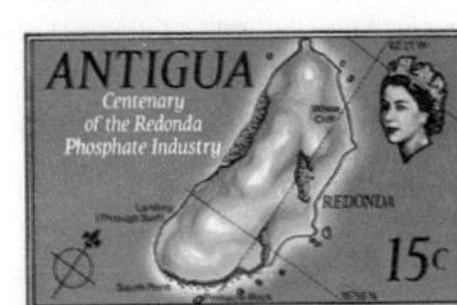

84 Island of Redonda (Chart)

1969. Centenary of Redonda Phosphate Industry. Multicoloured.
249 15c. Type **84** 20 10
250 25c. View of Redonda from the sea 20 10
251 50c. Type **84** 45 75

86 "The Adoration of the Magi" (Marcillat)

1969. Christmas. Stained Glass Windows. Mult.
252 6c. Type **86** 10 10
253 10c. "The Nativity" (unknown German artist, 15th century) 10 10
254 35c. Type **86** 25 10
255 50c. As 10c. 50 40

1970. Surch **20c** and bars.
256 20c. on 25c. (No. 189) . . . 10 10

89 Coat of Arms

90 Sikorsky S-38 Flying Boat

1970. Coil Stamps.
257A **89** 5c. blue 10 10
258A 10c. green 10 15
259A 25c. red 20 25

1970. 40th Anniv of Antiguan Air Services. Multicoloured.
260 5c. Type **90** 50 10
261 20c. Dornier Do-X flying boat . . . . 1·00 10
262 35c. Hawker Siddeley H.S.748 . . . . 1·25 10
263 50c. Douglas C-124C Globemaster II . . . . . 1·25 1·50
264 75c. Vickers Super VC-10 . . 1·50 2·00

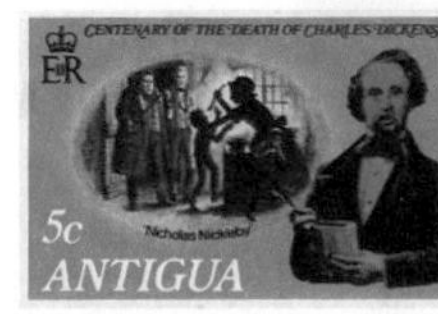

91 Dickens and Scene from "Nicholas Nickleby"

1970. Death Centenary of Charles Dickens.
265 **91** 5c. bistre, sepia and black 10 10
266 – 20c. turq, sepia & blk . . . 20 10
267 – 35c. blue, sepia and black 30 10
268 – $1 red, sepia and black . . 75 70
DESIGNS: All stamps show Dickens and scene from: 20c. "Pickwick Papers"; 35c. "Oliver Twist"; $1 "David Copperfield".

92 Carib Indian and War Canoe

1970. Multicoloured.
323 ½c. Type **92** 20 50
270 1c. Columbus and "Nina" . . 30 1·50
271 2c. Sir Thomas Warner's emblem and "Concepcion" 40 2·50
325 3c. Viscount Hood and H.M.S. "Barfleur" . . . . 35 1·25
273 4c. Sir George Rodney and H.M.S. "Formidable" . . 40 2·50
274 5c. Nelson and H.M.S. "Boreas" 50 40
275 6c. William IV and H.M.S. "Pegasus" . . . . 1·50 3·00
276 10c. "Blackbeard" and pirate ketch 80 20
277 15c. Collingwood and H.M.S. "Pelican" . . . . 5·00 1·00
278 20c. Nelson and H.M.S. "Victory" . . . . 1·25 40
279 25c. "Solent I" (paddle-steamer) . . . . 1·25 40
280 35c. George V (when Prince George) and H.M.S. "Canada" (screw corvette) 1·75 80
281 50c. H.M.S. "Renown" (battle cruiser) . . . . . . 4·00 4·75
331 75c. "Federal Maple" (freighter) . . . . 7·50 3·00
332 $1 "Sol Quest" (yacht) and class emblem . . . . . . 3·00 1·75
333 $2.50 H.M.S. "London" (destroyer) . . . . 2·75 6·50
285 $5 "Pathfinder" (tug) . . . . 3·00 6·00

93 "The Small Passion" (detail) (Durer)

94 4th King's Own Regiment, 1759

1970. Christmas.
286 **93** 3c. black and blue 10 10
287 – 10c. purple and pink . . . 10 10
288 **93** 35c. black and red 30 10
289 – 50c. black and lilac 45 50

DESIGN: 10, 50c. "Adoration of the Magi" (detail)(Durer).

1970. Military Uniforms (1st series). Mult.
290 ½c. Type **94** 10 10
291 10c. 4th West India Regiment, 1804 . . . . . 50 10
292 20c. 60th Regiment, The Royal American, 1809 . . 75 10
293 35c. 93rd Regiment, Sutherland Highlanders, 1826–34 . . . . 1·00 10
294 75c. 3rd West India Regiment, 1851 . . . . . 1·75 2·00
MS295 128 × 164 mm. Nos. 290/4 5·50 11·00
See also Nos. 303/8, 313/18, 353/8 and 380/5.

95 Market Woman casting Vote **96** "The Last Supper"

1971. 20th Anniv of Adult Suffrage.
296 **95** 5c. brown 10 10
297 – 20c. olive 10 10
298 – 35c. purple 10 10
299 – 50c. blue 15 30
DESIGNS: People voting: 20c. Executive; 35c. Housewife; 50c. Artisan.

1971. Easter. Works by Durer.
300 **96** 5c. black grey and red . . 10 10
301 – 35c. black, grey and violet 10 10
302 – 75c. black, grey and gold 20 30
DESIGNS: 35c. "The Crucifixion"; 75c. "The Resurrection".

1971. Military Uniforms (2nd series). As T **94**. Multicoloured.
303 ½c. Private, 12th Regiment, The Suffolk (1704) 10 10
304 10c. Grenadier, 38th Regiment, South Staffordshire (1751) . . . 35 10
305 20c. Light Company, 5th Regiment, Royal Northumberland Fusiliers (1778) 50 10
306 35c. Private, 48th Regiment, The Northamptonshire (1793) 60 10
307 75c. Private, 15th Regiment, East Yorks (1805) . . . . 1·00 3·00
MS308 127 × 144 mm. Nos. 303/7 4·50 6·50

97 "Madonna and Child" (detail, Veronese)

1971. Christmas. Multicoloured.
309 3c. Type **97** 10 10
310 5c. "Adoration of the Shepherds" (detail, Veronese) 10 10
311 35c. Type **97** 25 10
312 50c. As 5c. 40 30

1972. Military Uniforms (3rd series). As T **94**. Multicoloured.
313 ½c. Battalion Company Officer, 25th Foot, 1815 . . 10 10
314 10c. Sergeant, 14th Foot, 1837 . . . . 85 10
315 20c. Private, 67th Foot, 1853 1·60 15
316 35c. Officer, Royal Artillery, 1854 . . . . 1·90 20
317 75c. Private, 29th Foot, 1870 2·25 4·00
MS318 125 × 141 mm. Nos. 313/17 7·00 8·50

98 Reticulated Cowrie Helmet

1972. Shells. Multicoloured.
319 3c. Type **98** 50 10
320 5c. Measled cowrie 50 10
321 35c. West Indian fighting conch . . . . 1·40 15
322 50c. Hawk-wing conch . . . 1·60 3·00

99 St. John's Cathedral, Side View

1972. Christmas and 125th Anniv of St. John's Cathedral. Multicoloured.
335 35c. Type **99** 20 10
336 50c. Cathedral interior . . . 25 25
337 75c. St. John's Cathedral . . 30 60
MS338 165 × 102 mm. Nos. 335/7 65 1·00

1972. Royal Silver Wedding. As T **52** of Ascension, but with floral background.
339 20c. blue 15 15
340 35c. blue 15 15

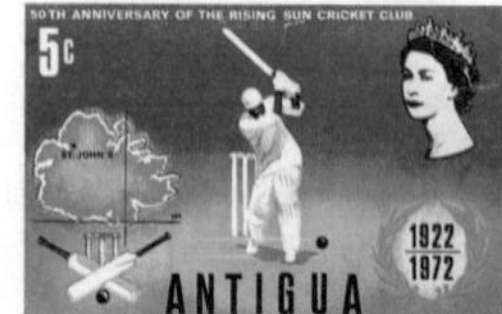

101 Batsman and Map

1972. 50th Anniv of Rising Sun Cricket Club. Multicoloured.
341 5c. Type **101** 55 15
342 35c. Batsman and wicket-keeper 65 10
343 $1 Club badge . . . . 1·00 2·25
MS344 88 × 130 mm. Nos. 341/3 3·25 7·50

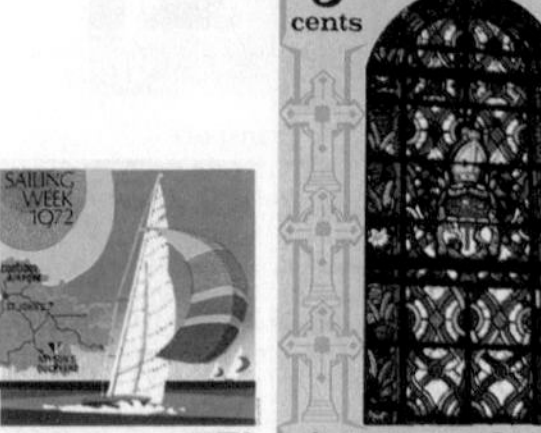

102 Yacht and Map **103** "Episcopal Coat of Arms"

1972. Inauguration of Antigua and Barbuda Tourist Office in New York. Multicoloured.
345 35c. Type **102** 15 10
346 50c. Yachts 20 15
347 75c. St. John's G.P.O. . . . 25 25
348 $1 Statue of Liberty 25 25
MS349 100 × 94 mm. Nos. 346, 348 75 1·25

1973. Easter. Multicoloured.
350 **103** 5c. Type **103** 10 10
351 – 35c. "The Crucifixion" . . 15 10
352 – 75c. "Arms of 1st Bishop of Antigua" 25 30
Nos. 350/2 show different stained-glass windows from St. John's Cathedral.

1973. Military Uniforms (4th series). As T **94**. Multicoloured.
353 ½c. Private, Zachariah Tiffin's Regiment of Foot, 1701 . . 10 10
354 10c. Private, 63rd Regiment of Foot, 1759 . . . . . . 40 10
355 20c. Light Company Officer, 35th Regiment of Foot, 1828 . . . . 50 15
356 35c. Private, 2nd West India Regiment, 1853 . . . . . 65 15
357 75c. Sergeant, 49th Regiment, 1858 . . . . 1·00 1·25
MS358 127 × 145 mm. Nos. 353/7 3·75 3·25

104 Butterfly Costumes

1973. Carnival. Multicoloured.
359 5c. Type **104** 10 10
360 20c. Carnival street scene . . 15 10
361 35c. Carnival troupe 20 10
362 75c. Carnival Queen 30 30
MS363 134 × 95 mm. Nos. 359/62 65 1·00

105 "Virgin of the Milk Porridge" (Gerard David)

1973. Christmas. Multicoloured.
364 3c. Type **105** 10 10
365 5c. "Adoration of the Magi" (Stomer) 10 10
366 20c. "The Granducal Madonna" (Raphael) . . . 15 10
367 35c. "Nativity with God the Father and Holy Ghost" (Battista) 20 10
368 $1 "Madonna and Child" (Murillo) 40 60
MS369 130 × 128 mm. Nos. 364/8 1·10 1·75

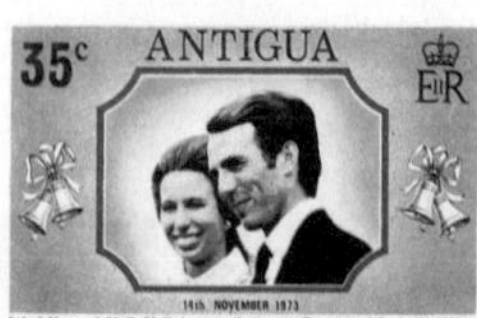

106 Princess Anne and Captain Mark Phillips

1973. Royal Wedding.
370 **106** 35c. multicoloured 10 10
371 – $2 multicoloured 25 25
MS372 78 × 100 mm. Nos. 370/1 50 40
The $2 is as Type **106** but has a different border.

1973. Nos. 370/1 optd **HONEYMOON VISIT DECEMBER 16TH 1973**.
373 **106** 35c. multicoloured 15 10
374 – $2 multicoloured 30 30
MS375 78 × 100 mm. Nos. 373/4 55 55

108 Coat of Arms of Antigua and University

1974. 25th Anniv of University of West Indies. Multicoloured.
376 5c. Type **108** 15 10
377 20c. Extra-mural art 20 10
378 35c. Antigua campus 20 10
379 75c. Antigua chancellor . . . 25 35

1974. Military Uniforms (5th series). As T **94**. Multicoloured.
380 ½c. Officer, 59th Foot, 1797 10 10
381 10c. Gunner, Royal Artillery, 1800 . . . . 35 10
382 20c. Private, 1st West India Regiment, 1830 . . . . . 50 10
383 35c. Officer, 92nd Foot, 1843 60 10
384 75c. Private, 23rd Foot, 1846 75 2·25
MS385 125 × 145 mm. Nos. 380/4 2·25 2·50

109 English Postman, Mailcoach and Westland Dragonfly Helicopter

1974. Centenary of U.P.U. Multicoloured.
386 ½c. Type **109** 10 10
387 1c. Bellman, mail steamer "Orinoco" and satellite . . 10 10
388 2c. Train guard, post-bus and hydrofoil 10 10
389 5c. Swiss messenger, Wells Fargo coach and Concorde 60 30
390 20c. Postilion, Japanese postmen and carrier pigeon 35 10
391 35c. Antiguan postman, Sikorsky S-88 flying boat and tracking station . . . 45 15
392 $1 Medieval courier, American express train and Boeing 747-100 . . . . . 1·75 2·00
MS393 141 × 161 mm. Nos. 386/92 3·50 2·50
On the ½c. English is spelt "Enlish" and on the 2c. Postal is spelt "Fostal".

110 Traditional Player **111** Footballers

1974. Antiguan Steel Bands.
394 **110** 5c. dp red, red and black 10 10
395 – 20c. brown, lt brn & blk 10 10
396 – 35c. lt green, green & blk 10 10
397 – 75c. blue, dp blue & blk 20 1·10
MS398 115 × 108 mm. Nos. 394/7 35 1·25
DESIGNS—HORIZ: 20c. Traditional band; 35c. Modern band. VERT: 75c. Modern player.

1974. World Cup Football Championships.
399 **111** 5c. multicoloured 10 10
400 – 35c. multicoloured 15 10
401 – 75c. multicoloured 30 30
402 – $1 multicoloured 35 40
MS403 135 × 130 mm. Nos. 399/402 85 90
Nos. 400/2 show various footballing designs similar to Type **111**.

1974. Earthquake Relief Fund. Nos. 400/2 and 397 optd or surch **EARTHQUAKE RELIEF**.
404 35c. multicoloured 20 10
405 75c. multicoloured 30 25
406 $1 multicoloured 40 30
407 $5 on 75c. deep blue, blue and black . . . . 1·25 2·00

113 Churchill as Schoolboy and School College Building, Harrow **114** "Madonna of the Trees" (Bellini)

1974. Birth Centenary of Sir Winston Churchill. Multicoloured.
408 5c. Type **113** 15 10
409 35c. Churchill and St. Paul's Cathedral 20 10
410 75c. Coat of arms and catafalque 30 65
411 $1 Churchill, "reward" notice and South African escape route . . . . 45 1·00
MS412 107 × 82 mm. Nos. 408/11 1·00 1·50

1974. Christmas. "Madonna and Child" paintings by named artists. Multicoloured.
413 ½c. Type **114** 10 10
414 1c. Raphael 10 10
415 2c. Van der Weyden 10 10
416 3c. Giorgione 10 10
417 5c. Mantegna 10 10
418 20c. Vivarini 20 10
419 35c. Montagna 30 10
420 75c. Lorenzo Costa . . . . . 55 1·10
MS421 139 × 126 mm. Nos. 413/20 95 1·40

1975. Nos. 390/2 and 331 surch.
422 50c. on 20c. multicoloured . . 1·25 2·00
423 $2.50 on 35c. multicoloured 2·00 5·50
424 $5 on $1 multicoloured . . . 6·50 7·00
425 $10 on 75c. multicoloured . . 2·50 7·50

116 Carib War Canoe, English Harbour, 1300

1975. Nelson's Dockyard. Multicoloured.
427 5c. Type **116** 20 10
428 15c. Ship of the line, English Harbour, 1770 . . . . . . 80 15
429 35c. H.M.S "Boreas" at anchor, and Lord Nelson, 1787 . . . . 1·25 15
430 50c. Yachts during "Sailing Week", 1974 . . . . . 1·25 1·50
431 $1 Yacht Anchorage, Old Dockyard, 1970 . . . . . 1·50 2·25
MS432 130 × 134 mm. As Nos. 427/31, but in larger format, 43 × 28 mm . . . . 3·25 2·00

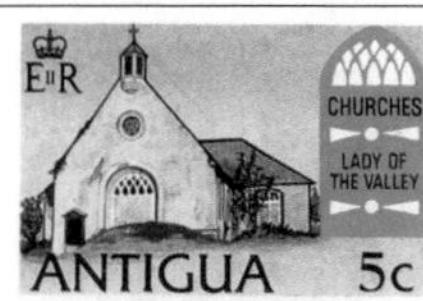

117 Lady of the Valley Church

1975. Antiguan Churches. Multicoloured.
433 5c. Type **117** 10 10
434 20c. Gilbert Memorial 10 10
435 35c. Grace Hill Moravian 15 10
436 50c. St. Phillips 20 20
437 $1 Ebenezer Methodist 35 50
MS438 91 × 101 mm. Nos. 435/7 65 1·25

118 Map of 1721 and Sextant of 1640

1975. Maps of Antigua. Multicoloured.
439 5c. Type **118** 30 15
440 20c. Map of 1775 and galleon 55 15
441 35c. Maps of 1775 and 1955 70 15
442 $1 1973 maps of Antigua and English Harbour 1·40 2·25
MS443 130 × 89 mm. Nos. 439/42 3·00 3·25

119 Scout Bugler

1975. World Scout Jamboree, Norway. Mult.
444 15c. Type **119** 25 15
445 20c. Scouts in camp 30 15
446 35c. "Lord Baden-Powell" (D. Jagger) 50 20
447 $2 Scout dancers from Dahomey 1·50 2·25
MS448 145 × 107 mm. Nos. 444/7 3·25 3·50

120 "Eurema elathea"

1975. Butterflies. Multicoloured.
449 ½c. Type **120** 10 30
450 1c. "Danaus plexippus" 10 30
451 2c. "Phoebis philea" 10 30
452 5c. "Hypolimnas misippus" 20 10
453 20c. "Eurema proterpia" 75 40
454 35c. "Battus polydamas" 1·40 50
455 $2 "Cynthia cardui" 4·00 9·00
MS456 147 × 94 mm. Nos. 452/5 6·00 11·00
No. 452 is incorrectly captioned "Marpesia petreus thetys".

121 "Madonna and Child" (Correggio) **122** Vivian Richards

1975. Christmas. "Madonna and Child" paintings by artists named. Multicoloured.
457 ½c. Type **121** 10 10
458 1c. El Greco 10 10
459 2c. Durer 10 10
460 3c. Antonello 10 10
461 5c. Bellini 10 10
462 10c. Durer (different) 10 10
463 35c. Bellini (different) 40 10
464 $2 Durer (different again) 1·00 1·00
MS465 138 × 119 mm. Nos. 461/4 1·50 1·60

1975. World Cricket Cup Winners. Multicoloured.
466 5c. Type **122** 1·25 20
467 35c. Andy Roberts 2·25 60
468 $2 West Indies team (horiz) 4·25 8·00

123 Antillean Crested Hummingbird

1976. Multicoloured.
469A ½c. Type **123** 40 50
470A 1c. Imperial amazon ("Imperial Parrot") 1·40 50
471A 2c. Zenaida dove 1·40 50
472A 3c. Loggerhead kingbird 1·40 60
473A 4c. Red-necked pigeon 1·40 1·50
474A 5c. Rufous-throated solitaire 2·00 10
475A 6c. Orchid tree 30 1·50
476A 10c. Bougainvillea 30 10
477A 15c. Geiger tree 35 10
478A 20c. Flamboyant 35 35
479A 25c. Hibiscus 40 15
480A 35c. Flame of the wood 40 40
481A 50c. Cannon at Fort James 55 60
482A 75c. Premier's Office 60 1·50
483A $1 Potworks Dam 75 1·00
484A $2.50 Diamond irrigation scheme (44 × 28 mm) 1·00 4·50
485B $5 Government House (44 × 28 mm) 1·50 7·00
486A $10 Coolidge International Airport (44 × 28 mm) 3·50 8·00

124 Privates, Clark's Illinois Regiment

1976. Bicentenary of American Revolution. Mult.
487 ½c. Type **124** 10 10
488 1c. Rifleman, Pennsylvania Militia 10 10
489 2c. Powder horn 10 10
490 5c. Water bottle 10 10
491 35c. American flags 50 10
492 $1 "Montgomery" (American brig) 1·00 40
493 $5 "Ranger" (privateer sloop) 1·75 2·25
MS494 71 × 84 mm. $2.50, Congress flag 1·00 1·40

125 High Jump

1976. Olympic Games, Montreal.
495 **125** ½c. brown, yellow & black 10 10
496 – 1c. violet, blue and black 10 10
497 – 2c. green and black 10 10
498 – 15c. blue and black 15 10
499 – 30c. brown, yell & blk 20 15
500 – $1 orange, red and black 40 40
501 – $2 red and black 60 80
MS502 88 × 138 mm. Nos. 498/501 1·75 1·25
DESIGNS: 1c. Boxing; 2c. Pole vault; 15c. Swimming; 30c. Running; $1 Cycling; $2 Shot put.

126 Water Skiing

1976. Water Sports. Multicoloured.
503 ½c. Type **126** 10 10
504 1c. Sailing 10 10
505 2c. Snorkeling 10 10
506 20c. Deep sea fishing 50 10
507 50c. Scuba diving 75 35
508 $2 Swimming 1·25 1·25
MS509 89 × 114 mm. Nos. 506/8 1·75 1·75

127 French Angelfish

1976. Fishes. Multicoloured.
510 15c. Type **127** 50 15
511 30c. Yellow-finned grouper 75 30
512 50c. Yellow-tailed snapper 95 50
513 90c. Shy hamlet 1·25 1·50

128 The Annunciation **130** Royal Family

129 Mercury and U.P.U. Emblem

1976. Christmas. Multicoloured.
514 8c. Type **128** 10 10
515 10c. The Holy Family 10 10
516 15c. The Magi 10 10
517 50c. The Shepherds 20 25
518 $1 Epiphany scene 30 50

1976. Special Events, 1976. Multicoloured.
519 ½c. Type **129** 10 10
520 1c. Alfred Nobel 10 10
521 10c. Space satellite 30 10
522 50c. Viv Richards and Andy Roberts 3·50 1·75
523 $1 Bell and telephones 1·00 2·00
524 $2 Yacht "Freelance" 2·25 4·50
MS525 127 × 101 mm. Nos. 521/4 7·50 13·00

1977. Silver Jubilee. Multicoloured. (a) Perf.
526 10c. Type **130** 10 10
527 30c. Royal Visit, 1966 10 10
528 50c. The Queen enthroned 15 15
529 90c. The Queen after Coronation 15 25
530 $2.50 Queen and Prince Charles 30 55
MS531 116 × 78 mm. $5 Queen and Prince Philip 65 85

(b) Roul × imperf. Self-adhesive.
532 50c. As 90c. 35 75
533 $5 The Queen and Prince Philip 2·00 3·75
Nos. 532/3 come from booklets.

131 Making Camp

1977. Caribbean Scout Jamboree, Jamaica. Mult.
534 ½c. Type **131** 10 10
535 1c. Hiking 10 10
536 2c. Rock-climbing 10 10
537 10c. Cutting logs 15 10
538 30c. Map and sign reading 40 10
539 50c. First aid 65 25
540 $2 Rafting 1·25 2·50
MS541 127 × 114 mm. Nos. 538/40 3·00 4·00

132 Carnival Costume **134** "Virgin and Child Enthroned" (Tura)

1977. 21st Anniv of Carnival. Multicoloured.
542 10c. Type **132** 10 10
543 30c. Carnival Queen 25 10
544 50c. Butterfly costume 30 15
545 90c. Queen of the band 40 25
546 $1 Calypso King and Queen 40 30
MS547 140 × 120 mm. Nos. 542/6 1·10 1·60

1977. Royal Visit. Nos. 526/30 optd **ROYAL VISIT 28TH OCTOBER 1977.**
548 10c. Type **130** 10 10
549 30c. Royal Visit, 1966 15 10
550 50c. The Queen enthroned 20 10
551 90c. The Queen after Coronation 30 20
552 $2.50 Queen and Prince Charles 50 35
MS553 116 × 178 mm. $5 Queen and Prince Philip 1·00 1·00

1977. Christmas. Paintings by artists listed. Mult.
554 ½c. Type **134** 10 20
555 1c. Crivelli 10 20
556 2c. Lotto 10 20
557 8c. Pontormo 15 10
558 10c. Tura (different) 15 10
559 25c. Lotto (different) 30 10
560 $2 Crivelli (different) 85 1·00
MS561 144 × 118 mm. Nos. 557/60 1·75 2·75

135 Pineapple

1977. 10th Anniv of Statehood. Multicoloured.
562 10c. Type **135** 10 10
563 15c. State flag 60 20
564 50c. Police band 2·50 80
565 90c. Premier V. C. Bird 55 80
566 $2 State Coat of Arms 90 2·00
MS567 129 × 99 mm. Nos. 563/6 3·50 3·00

136 Wright Glider III, 1902

1978. 75th Anniv of Powered Flight. Mult.
568 ½c. Type **136** 10 10
569 1c. Wright Flyer I, 1903 10 10
570 2c. Launch system and engine 10 10
571 10c. Orville Wright (vert) 30 10
572 50c. Wright Flyer III, 1905 60 15
573 90c. Wilbur Wright (vert) 80 30
574 $2 Wright Type B, 1910 1·00 80
MS575 90 × 75 mm. $2.50, Wright Flyer I on launch system 1·25 2·75

137 Sunfish Regatta **138** Queen Elizabeth and Prince Philip

1978. Sailing Week. Multicoloured.
576 10c. Type **137** 20 10
577 50c. Fishing and work boat race 35 20
578 90c. Curtain Bluff race 60 35
579 $2 Power boat rally 1·10 1·25
MS580 110 × 77 mm. $2.50, Guadeloupe–Antigua race 1·50 1·75

1978. 25th Anniv of Coronation. Mult. (a) Perf.
581 10c. Type **138** 10 10
582 30c. Crowning 10 10
583 50c. Coronation procession 15 10
584 90c. Queen seated in St. Edward's Chair 20 15
585 $2.50 Queen wearing Imperial State Crown 40 40
MS586 114 × 104 mm. $5 Queen and Prince Philip 80 80

(b) Roul × imperf. Self-adhesive. Horiz designs as Type **138**.
587 25c. Glass Coach 15 30
588 50c. Irish State Coach 25 50
589 $5 Coronation Coach 1·75 3·00
Nos. 587/9 come from booklets.

140 Player running with Ball **141** Petrea

1978. World Cup Football Championship, Argentina. Multicoloured.
590 10c. Type **140** 15 10
591 15c. Players in front of goal 15 10

592 $3 Referee and player . . . . 2·00 1·75
MS593 126×88 mm. 25c. Player crouching with ball; 30c. Players heading ball; 50c. Players running with ball; $2 Goalkeeper diving. All horiz . . . . 3·25 2·50

1978. Flowers. Multicoloured.
594 25c. Type **141** 25 10
595 50c. Sunflower 35 20
596 90c. Frangipani 60 30
597 $2 Passion flower . . . . . 1·25 2·00
MS598 118×85 mm. $2.50, Hibiscus 1·40 1·60

142 "St. Ildefonso receiving the Chasuble from the Virgin" (Rubens)

1978. Christmas. Multicoloured.
599 8c. Type **142** 10 10
600 25c. "The Flight of St. Barbara" (Rubens) . . 20 10
601 $2 "Madonna and Child, with St. Joseph, John the Baptist and Donor" . . . 65 55
MS602 170×113 mm. $4 "The Annunciation" (Rubens) . . . 1·25 1·50
The painting shown on No. 601 is incorrectly attributed to Rubens on the stamp. The artist was Sebastiano del Piombo.

143 1d. Stamp of 1863 **144** "The Deposition from the Cross" (painting)

1979. Death Centenary of Sir Rowland Hill. Mult.
603 25c. Type **143** 10 10
604 50c. 1840 Penny Black . . . 20 15
605 $1 Mail coach and woman posting letter, c. 1840 . . . 30 20
606 $2 Modern transport . . . . 1·10 60
MS607 108×82 mm. $2.50, Sir Rowland Hill 80 90

1979. Easter. Works by Durer.
608 **144** 10c. multicoloured 10 10
609 – 50c. multicoloured 35 20
610 – $4 black, mauve and yellow . . . . 1·00 90
MS611 – 114×99 mm. $2.50, multicoloured 80 80
DESIGNS: 50c., $2.50, "Christ on the Cross–The Passion" (wood engravings) (both different); $4 "Man of Sorrows with Hands Raised" (wood engraving).

145 Toy Yacht and Child's Hand **147** Cook's Birthplace, Marton

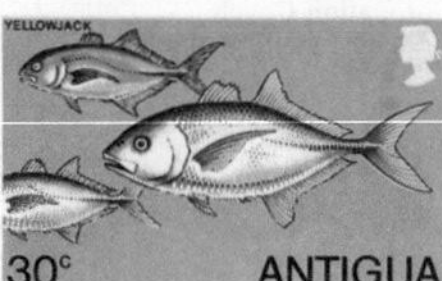

146 Yellow Jack

1979. International Year of the Child. Mult.
612 25c. Type **145** 10 10
613 50c. Rocket 25 15
614 90c. Car 40 25
615 $2 Toy train . . . . 1·00 90
MS616 80×112 mm. $5 Aeroplane 1·10 1·10
Nos. 612/16 also show the hands of children of different races.

1979. Fishes. Multicoloured.
617 30c. Type **146** 40 15
618 50c. Blue-finned tuna 50 25
619 90c. Sailfish 75 40
620 $3 Wahoo . . . . 2·25 1·75
MS621 122×75 mm. $2.50, Great barracuda . . . . 1·50 1·40

1979. Death Bicentenary of Captain Cook. Mult.
622 25c. Type **147** 65 25
623 50c. H.M.S. "Endeavour" . . 1·00 60
624 90c. Marine chronometer . . 75 80
625 $3 Landing at Botany Bay 1·60 3·00
MS626 110×85 mm. $2.50, H.M.S. "Resolution" . . . . 2·25 1·50

148 The Holy Family **149** Javelin Throwing

1979. Christmas. Multicoloured.
627 8c. Type **148** 10 10
628 25c. Virgin and Child on ass 15 10
629 50c. Shepherd and star . . . 25 35
630 $4 Wise Men with gifts . . . 85 2·50
MS631 113×94 mm. $3 Angel with trumpet . . . . 1·00 1·50

1980. Olympic Games, Moscow. Multicoloured.
632 10c. Type **149** 20 10
633 25c. Running 20 10
634 $1 Pole vault 50 60
635 $2 Hurdles . . . . 70 2·00
MS636 127×96 mm. $3 Boxing (horiz) 80 90

150 Mickey Mouse and Airplane

1980. International Year of the Child. Walt Disney Cartoon Characters. Multicoloured.
637 ½c. Type **150** 10 10
638 1c. Donald Duck driving car (vert) 10 10
639 2c. Goofy driving taxi . . . 10 10
640 3c. Mickey and Minnie Mouse on motorcycle . . . 10 10
641 4c. Huey, Dewey and Louie on a bicycle for three . . . 10 10
642 5c. Grandma Duck and truck of roosters 10 10
643 10c. Mickey Mouse in jeep (vert) 10 10
644 $1 Chip and Dale in yacht 1·75 2·00
645 $4 Donald Duck riding toy train (vert) . . . . 3·75 6·50
MS646 101×127 mm. $2.50, Goofy flying biplane . . . . 4·50 3·25

1980. "London 1980" International Stamp Exhibition. Nos. 603/6 optd **LONDON 1980**.
647 25c. Type **143** 25 15
648 50c. Penny Black 35 35
649 $1 Stage-coach and woman posting letter, c. 1840 . . . 60 70
650 $2 Modern mail transport . . 3·25 3·00

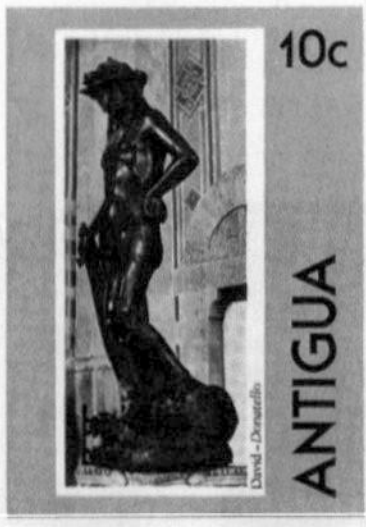

152 "David" (statue, Donatello)

1980. Famous Works of Art. Multicoloured.
651 10c. Type **152** 10 10
652 30c. "The Birth of Venus" (painting, Botticelli) (horiz) 30 15
653 50c. "Reclining Couple" (sarcophagus), Cerveteri (horiz) 40 40
654 90c. "The Garden of Earthly Delights" (painting by Bosch) (horiz) 55 65
655 $1 "Portinari Altarpiece" (painting, van der Goes) (horiz) 65 75
656 $4 "Eleanora of Toledo and her Son, Giovanni de'Medici" (painting, Bronzino) . . . . 1·75 3·00
MS657 99×124 mm. $5 "The Holy Family" (painting, Rembrandt) 2·50 1·75

153 Anniversary Emblem and Headquarters, U.S.A.

1980. 75th Anniv of Rotary International. Mult.
658 30c. Type **153** 30 30
659 50c. Rotary anniversary emblem and Antigua Rotary Club banner . . . 40 50
660 90c. Map of Antigua and Rotary emblem 60 70
661 $3 Paul P. Harris (founder) and Rotary emblem . . . 2·00 3·50
MS662 102×78 mm. $5 Antiguan flags and Rotary emblems . . 1·25 2·00

154 Queen Elizabeth the Queen Mother **155** Ringed Kingfisher

1980. 80th Birthday of The Queen Mother.
663 **154** 10c. multicoloured 40 10
664 $2.50 multicoloured . . . 1·50 1·75
MS665 68×90 mm. As T **154**. $3 multicoloured . . . . 1·75 2·25

1980. Birds. Multicoloured.
666 10c. Type **155** 70 30
667 30c. Plain pigeon . . . . . . 1·00 50
668 $1 Green-throated carib . . . 1·50 2·00
669 $2 Black-necked stilt . . . . 2·00 4·00
MS670 73×73 mm. $2.50, Roseate tern . . . . 7·00 4·50

1980. Christmas. Walt Disney's "Sleeping Beauty". As T **150**. Multicoloured.
671 ½c. The Bad Fairy with her raven 10 10
672 1c. The good fairies 10 10
673 2c. Aurora 10 10
674 4c. Aurora pricks her finger 10 10
675 8c. The prince 10 10
676 10c. The prince fights the dragon 15 10
677 25c. The prince awakens Aurora with a kiss 20 20
678 $2 The prince and Aurora's betrothal . . . . 2·25 2·25
679 $2.50 The prince and princess 2·50 2·50
MS680 126×101 mm. $4 multicoloured (vert) . . . . . 5·00 3·25

156 Diesel Locomotive No. 15

1981. Sugar Cane Railway Locomotives. Mult.
681 25c. Type **156** 15 15
682 50c. Narrow-gauge steam locomotive 30 30
683 90c. Diesel locomotives Nos. 1 and 10 . . . . . . 55 60
684 $3 Steam locomotive hauling sugar cane . . . . . . 2·00 2·25
MS685 82×111 mm. $2.50, Antiguan sugar factory, railway yard and sheds . . . . 1·75 1·75

1981. Independence. Nos. 475/6 and 478/86 optd **"INDEPENDENCE 1981"**.
686B 6c. Orchid tree 10 30
687B 10c. Bougainvillea 10 10
688B 20c. Flamboyant 10 10
689B 25c. Hibiscus 15 15
690B 35c. Flame of the wood . . 20 20
691B 50c. Cannon at Fort James 35 35
692B 75c. Premier's Office . . . 40 60
693B $1 Potworks Dam 55 70
694B $2.50 Irrigation scheme, Diamond Estate . . . . 75 1·75
695B $5 Government House . . . 1·40 3·00
696B $10 Coolidge International Airport . . . . 3·25 5·50

158 "Pipes of Pan"

1981. Birth Centenary of Picasso. Multicoloured.
697 10c. Type **158** 10 10
698 50c. "Seated Harlequin" . . 30 30
699 90c. "Paulo as Harlequin" . . 55 55
700 $4 "Mother and Child" . . . 2·00 2·00
MS701 115×140 mm. $5 "Three Musicians" (detail) . . . . . . 1·75 2·75

159 Prince Charles and Lady Diana Spencer **160** Prince of Wales at Investiture, 1969

1981. Royal Wedding (1st issue). Multicoloured.
702 25c. Type **159** 10 10
703 50c. Glamis Castle 10 10
704 $4 Prince Charles skiing . . . 80 80
MS705 96×82 mm. $5 Glass coach 80 80

1981. Royal Wedding (2nd issue). Multicoloured. Roul×imperf. Self-adhesive.
706 25c. Type **160** 15 25
707 25c. Prince Charles as baby, 1948 . . . . 15 25
708 $1 Prince Charles at R.A.F. College, Cranwell, 1971 . . 25 50
709 $1 Prince Charles attending Hill House School, 1956 25 50
710 $2 Prince Charles and Lady Diana Spencer 50 75
711 $2 Prince Charles at Trinity College, 1967 . . . . . 50 75
712 $5 Prince Charles and Lady Diana (different) . . . . . 1·00 1·50

161 Irene Joshua (founder)

1981. 50th Anniv of Antigua Girl Guide Movement. Multicoloured.
713 10c. Type **161** 15 10
714 50c. Campfire sing-song . . . 45 35
715 90c. Sailing 75 65
716 $2.50 Animal tending . . . . 1·75 2·00
MS717 110×85 mm. $5 Raising the flag . . . . 4·50 3·00

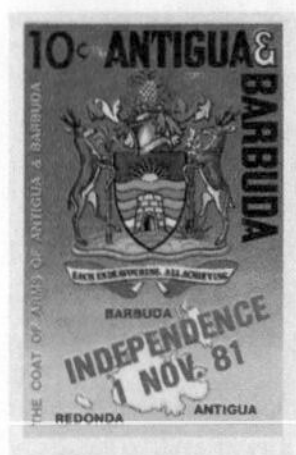

162 Antigua and Barbuda Coat of Arms **163** "Holy Night" (Jacques Stella)

1981. Independence. Multicoloured.
718 10c. Type **162** 25 10
719 50c. Pineapple, with Antigua and Barbuda flag and map 1·50 40
720 90c. Prime Minister Vere Bird 55 55
721 $2.50 St. John's Cathedral (38×25 mm) . . . . . . 1·50 3·50
MS722 105×79 mm. $5 Map of Antigua and Barbuda (42×42 mm) . . . . 4·00 2·75

1981. Christmas. Paintings. Multicoloured.
723 8c. Type **163** 15 10
724 30c. "Mary with Child" (Julius Schnorr von Carolfeld) 40 15

725 $1 "Virgin and Child" (Alonso Cano) 75 90
726 $3 "Virgin and Child" (Lorenzo di Credi) . . . . 1·10 3·75
MS727 77×111 mm. $5 "Holy Family" (Pieter von Avon) . . 2·50 4·50

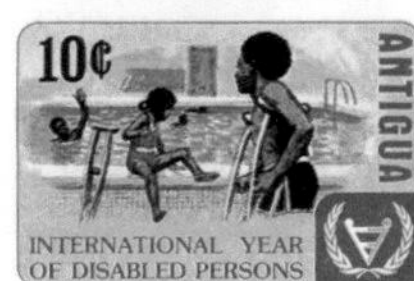

164 Swimming

1981. International Year of Disabled People. Sports for the Disabled. Multicoloured.
728 10c. Type **164** 10 10
729 50c. Discus-throwing 20 30
730 90c. Archery 40 55
731 $2 Baseball . . . . 1·00 1·40
MS732 108×84 mm. $4 Basketball 5·00 2·75

165 Scene from Football Match

1982. World Cup Football Championship, Spain.
733 **165** 10c. multicoloured 30 10
734 – 50c. multicoloured 60 35
735 – 90c. multicoloured . . . . 1·10 70
736 – $4 multicoloured . . . . 3·50 3·50
MS737 – 75×92 mm. $5 multicoloured . . . . 8·50 10·00
DESIGNS: 50c. to $5, Scenes from various matches.

166 Airbus Industrie A300

167 Cordia

1982. Coolidge International Airport. Mult.
738 10c. Type **166** 10 10
739 50c. Hawker-Siddeley H.S.748 . . . . 30 30
740 90c. De Havilland D.H.C.6 Twin Otter 60 60
741 $2.50 Britten Norman Islander . . . . 1·75 1·75
MS742 99×73 mm. $5 Boeing 747-100 (horiz) . . . . 2·75 4·00

1982. Death Centenary of Charles Darwin. Fauna and Flora. Multicoloured.
743 10c. Type **167** 25 10
744 50c. Small Indian mongoose (horiz) 55 40
745 90c. Corallita 85 75
746 $2 Mexican bulldog bat (horiz) . . . . 2·25 3·25
MS747 107×85 mm. $5 Carribbean monk seal . . . . 7·50 8·00

168 Queen's House, Greenwich

1982. 21st Birthday of Princess of Wales. Mult.
748 90c. Type **168** 45 45
749 $1 Prince and Princess of Wales 65 50
750 $4 Princess Diana . . . . . 2·75 2·00
MS751 102×75 mm. $5 Type **169** 3·75 2·50

170 Boy Scouts decorating Streets for Independence Parade

1982. 75th Anniv of Boy Scout Movement. Multicoloured.
752 10c. Type **170** 25 10
753 50c. Boy Scout giving helping hand during street parade 60 40
754 90c. Boy Scouts attending H.R.H. Princess Margaret at Independence Ceremony 1·00 75
755 $2.20 Cub Scout giving directions to tourists . . . 1·90 2·75
MS756 102×72 mm. $5 Lord Baden-Powell . . . . 5·50 5·50

1982. Birth of Prince William of Wales. Nos. 748/50 optd **ROYAL BABY 21.6.82.**
757 90c. Type **168** 45 45
758 $1 Prince and Princess of Wales 50 50
759 $4 Princess Diana . . . . . 2·00 1·50
MS760 102×75 mm. $5 Type **169** 2·40 2·50

172 Roosevelt in 1940

1982. Birth Centenary of Franklin D. Roosevelt. (Nos. 761, 763 and 765/6) and 250th Birth Anniv of George Washington (others). Multicoloured.
761 10c. Type **172** 20 10
762 25c. Washington as blacksmith 45 15
763 45c. Churchill, Roosevelt and Stalin at Yalta Conference 1·25 40
764 60c. Washington crossing the Delaware (vert) . . . . . 1·00 40
765 $1 "Roosevelt Special" train (vert) . . . . 1·50 90
766 $3 Portrait of Roosevelt (vert) . . . . 1·40 2·40
MS767 92×87 mm. $4 Roosevelt and Wife . . . . 2·00 1·75
MS768 92×87 mm. $4 Portrait of Washington (vert) . . . . . . 2·00 1·75
No. **MS**768 also exists imperf.

173 "Annunciation"

1982. Christmas. Religious Paintings by Raphael. Multicoloured.
769 10c. Type **173** 10 10
770 30c. "Adoration of the Magi" 15 15
771 $1 "Presentation at the Temple" 50 50
772 $4 "Coronation of the Virgin" . . . . 2·10 2·25
MS773 95×124 mm. $5 "Marriage of the Virgin" . . . . 2·75 2·50

174 Tritons and Dolphins

1983. 500th Birth Anniv of Raphael. Details from "Galatea" Fresco. Multicoloured.
774 45c. Type **174** 20 25
775 50c. Sea nymph carried off by Triton 25 30
776 60c. Winged angel steering dolphins (horiz) 30 35
777 $4 Cupids shooting arrows (horiz) . . . . 1·60 2·00
MS778 101×125 mm. $5 Galatea pulled along by dolphins . . . 1·50 2·25

175 Pineapple Produce

1983. Commonwealth Day. Multicoloured.
779 25c. Type **175** 15 15
780 45c. Carnival 20 25
781 60c. Tourism 30 35
782 $3 Airport . . . . 1·00 1·50

176 T.V. Satellite Coverage of Royal Wedding

1983. World Communications Year. Multicoloured.
783 15c. Type **176** 40 20
784 50c. Police communications 2·25 1·50
785 60c. House-to-train telephone call . . . . 2·25 1·50
786 $3 Satellite earth station with planets Jupiter and Saturn 4·75 5·00
MS787 100×90 mm. $5 "Comsat" satellite over West Indies . . . 2·00 3·75

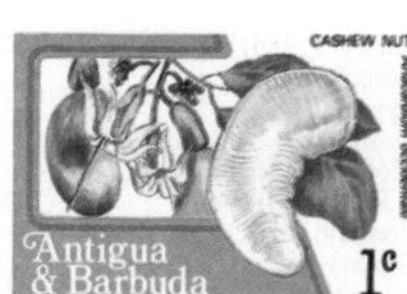

177 Bottle-nosed Dolphin

1983. Whales. Multicoloured.
788 15c. Type **177** 85 20
789 50c. Fin whale . . . . 1·75 1·25
790 60c. Bowhead whale . . . . 2·00 1·25
791 $3 Spectacled porpoise . . . 3·75 4·25
MS792 122×101 mm. $5 Narwhal 8·50 6·00

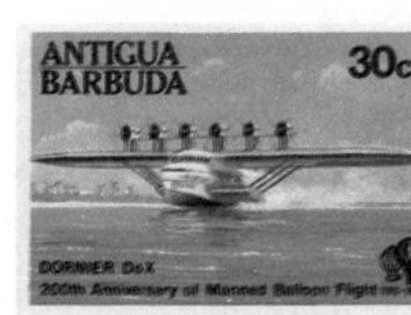

178 Cashew Nut

1983. Fruits and Flowers. Multicoloured.
793 1c. Type **178** . . . . 15 1·00
794 2c. Passion fruit . . . . . . 15 1·00
795 3c. Mango . . . . 15 1·00
796 5c. Grapefruit 20 75
797a 10c. Pawpaw 30 20
798 15c. Breadfruit 75 20
799 20c. Coconut 50 20
800a 25c. Oleander 75 20
801 30c. Banana 60 40
802a 40c. Pineapple 75 30
803a 45c. Cordia 85 40
804 50c. Cassia 90 60
805 60c. Poui . . . . 1·75 1·00
806a $1 Frangipani . . . . . . 2·25 1·50
807a $2 Flamboyant . . . . . . 3·75 4·50
808 $2.50 Lemon . . . . 4·50 6·50
809 $5 Linum vitae . . . . . . 7·00 13·00
810 $10 National flag and coat of arms . . . . 11·00 17·00

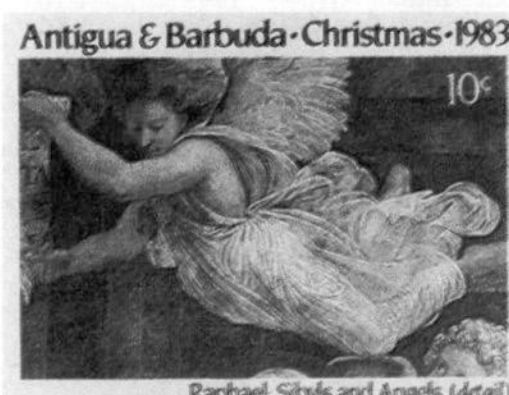

179 Dornier Do-X Flying Boat

1983. Bicentenary of Manned Flight. Mult.
811 30c. Type **179** 85 30
812 50c. Supermarine S.6B seaplane . . . . 1·00 60
813 60c. Curtiss F-9C Sparrowhawk biplane and airship U.S.S. "Akron" . . 1·25 85
814 $4 Hot-air balloon "Pro Juventute" . . . . 3·00 5·00
MS815 80×105 mm. $5 Airship LZ-127 "Graf Zeppelin" . . . 1·75 2·25

180 "Sibyls and Angels" (detail) (Raphael)

1983. Christmas. 500th Birth Anniv of Raphael.
816 **180** 10c. multicoloured 30 20
817 – 30c. multicoloured 65 35
818 – $1 multicoloured . . . . 1·50 1·25
819 – $4 multicoloured . . . . 3·00 5·00
MS820 – 101×103 mm. $5 multicoloured . . . . 1·50 2·25
DESIGNS—HORIZ: 10c. to $4, Different details from "Sibyls and Angels". VERT: $5 "The Vision of Ezekiel".

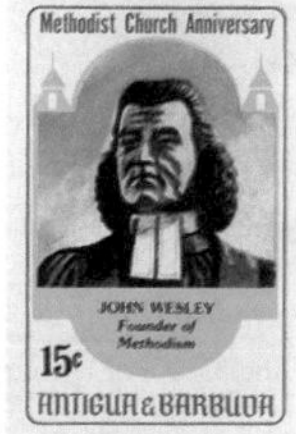

181 John Wesley (founder)

182 Discus

1983. Bicentenary of Methodist Church (1984). Multicoloured.
821 15c. Type **181** 25 15
822 50c. Nathaniel Gilbert (founder in Antigua) . . . 70 50
823 60c. St. John Methodist Church steeple 75 65
824 $3 Ebenezer Methodist Church, St. John's . . . . 2·00 4·00

1984. Olympic Games, Los Angeles. Multicoloured.
825 25c. Type **182** 20 15
826 50c. Gymnastics 35 30
827 90c. Hurdling 65 70
828 $3 Cycling . . . . 2·50 3·75
MS829 82×67 mm. $5 Volleyball 2·75 3·00

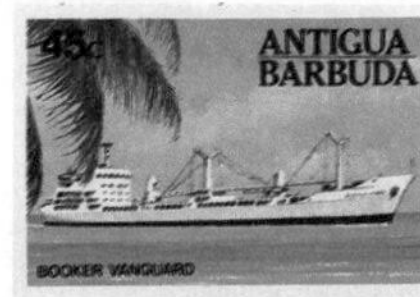

183 "Booker Vanguard" (freighter)

1984. Ships. Multicoloured.
830 45c. Type **183** . . . . 1·00 55
831 50c. S.S. "Canberra" (liner) 1·25 80
832 60c. Yachts . . . . 1·50 1·00
833 $4 "Fairwind" (cargo liner) 3·00 7·00
MS834 107×80 mm. $5 18th-century British man-of-war (vert) . . . . 1·75 3·50

184 Chenille

187 Abraham Lincoln

1984. Universal Postal Union Congress, Hamburg. Multicoloured.
835 15c. Type **184** 40 15
836 50c. Shell flower 80 70
837 60c. Anthurium . . . . . . 85 1·10
838 $3 Angels trumpet . . . . . 2·75 6·50
MS839 100×75 mm. $5 Crown of Thorns . . . . 1·50 3·25

1984. Various stamps surch. (a) Nos. 702/4.
840 $2 on 25c. Type **159** . . . . 2·50 2·50
841 $2 on 50c. Glamis Castle . . 2·50 2·50
842 $2 on $4 Prince Charles skiing . . . . 2·50 2·50
MS843 96×82 mm. $2 on $5 Glass coach . . . . 4·00 4·00

(b) Nos. 748/50.
844 $2 on 90c. Type **168** . . . . 2·00 2·00
845 $2 on $1 Prince and Princess of Wales . . . . 2·00 2·00
846 $2 on $4 Princess Diana . . 2·00 2·00
MS847 102×75 mm. Type **169** 4·00 4·00

(c) Nos. 757/9.
848 $2 on 90c. Type **168** . . . . 2·00 2·00
849 $2 on $1 Prince and Princess of Wales . . . . 2·00 2·00
850 $2 on $4 Princess Diana . . 2·00 2·00
MS851 102×75 mm. $2 on $5 Type **169** . . . . 4·00 4·00

(d) Nos. 779/82.
852 $2 on 25c. Type **175** . . . . 2·75 1·25
853 $2 on 45c. Carnival . . . . 2·75 1·25
854 $2 on 60c. Tourism . . . . . 2·75 1·25
855 $2 on $3 Airport . . . . . . 2·75 1·25

1984. Presidents of the United States of America. Multicoloured.
856 10c. Type **187** 15 10
857 20c. Harry S. Truman . . . 20 15
858 30c. Dwight D. Eisenhower 30 25
859 40c. Ronald W. Reagan . . . 50 30
860 90c. Gettysburg Address, 1863 . . . . 90 75
861 $1.10 Formation of N.A.T.O.,1949 . . . . . . 1·25 1·25
862 $1.50 Eisenhower during the war . . . . 1·60 1·75
863 $2 Reagan and Caribbean Basin Initiative . . . . . 1·75 2·00

188 View of Moravian Mission

1984. 150th Anniv of Abolition of Slavery. Multicoloured.
864 40c. Type **188** 90 50
865 50c. Antigua Courthouse, 1823 . . . . 1·00 65
866 60c. Planting sugar-cane, Monks Hill . . . . 1·10 75
867 $3 Boiling house, Delaps' estate . . . . 4·25 5·50
MS868 95 × 70 mm. $5 Loading sugar, Willoughby Bay . . . . 6·50 4·75

189 Rufous-sided Towhee **190** Grass-skiing

1984. Songbirds. Multicoloured.
869 40c. Type **189** . . . . 1·25 85
870 50c. Parula warbler . . . . . 1·40 1·10
871 60c. House wren . . . . 1·50 1·50
872 $2 Ruby-crowned kinglet . . 2·00 3·75
873 $3 Common flicker ("Yellow-shafted Flicker") . . . . . 2·75 5·00
MS874 76 × 76 mm. $5 Yellow-breasted chat . . . . 2·50 6·00

1984. "Ausipex" International Stamp Exhibition, Melbourne, Australian Sports. Multicoloured.
875 $1 Type **190** . . . . 1·25 1·50
876 $5 Australian football . . . 3·75 5·50
MS877 108 × 78 mm. $5 Boomerang-throwing . . . . 2·50 4·00

191 "The Virgin and Infant with Angels and Cherubs" **192** "The Blue Dancers"

1984. 450th Death Anniv of Correggio (painter). Multicoloured.
878 25c. Type **191** 40 20
879 60c. "The Four Saints" . . . 80 50
880 90c. "St. Catherine" . . . . 1·10 90
881 $3 "The Campori Madonna" 2·25 4·25
MS882 90 × 60 mm. $5 "St. John the Baptist" . . . . 2·00 2·75

1984. 150th Birth Anniv of Edgar Degas (painter). Multicoloured.
883 15c. Type **192** 35 15
884 50c. "The Pink Dancers" . . 80 60
885 70c. "Two Dancers" . . . . 1·10 85
886 $4 "Dancers at the Bar" . . 2·50 4·75
MS887 90 × 60 mm. "The Folk dancers" (40 × 27 mm) . . . . 2·00 2·75

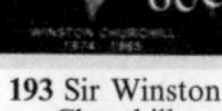

193 Sir Winston Churchill **194** Donald Duck fishing

1984. Famous People. Multicoloured.
888 60c. Type **193** . . . . 1·10 1·50
889 60c. Mahatma Gandhi . . . 1·10 1·50
890 60c. John F. Kennedy . . . 1·10 1·50
891 60c. Mao Tse-tung . . . . . 1·10 1·50
892 $1 Churchill with General De Gaulle, Paris, 1944 (horiz) 1·25 1·75
893 $1 Gandhi leaving London by train, 1931 (horiz) . . . 1·25 1·75
894 $1 Kennedy with Chancellor Adenauer and Mayor Brandt, Berlin, 1963 (horiz) 1·25 1·75
895 $1 Mao Tse-tung with Lin Piao, Peking, 1969 (horiz) 1·25 1·75
MS896 114 × 80 mm. $5 Flags of Great Britain, India, the United States and China . . . . . . 9·00 4·50

1984. Christmas. 50th Birthday of Donald Duck. Walt Disney Cartoon Characters. Multicoloured.
897 1c. Type **194** 10 10
898 2c. Donald Duck lying on beach 10 10
899 3c. Donald Duck and nephews with fishing rods and fishes 10 10
900 4c. Donald Duck and nephews in boat 10 10
901 5c. Wearing diving masks . . 10 10
902 10c. In deckchairs reading books 10 10
903 $1 With toy shark's fin . . . 2·25 1·25
904 $2 In sailing boat . . . . . 2·50 3·00
905 $5 Attempting to propel boat 5·50 6·00
MS906 Two sheets, each 125 × 100 mm. (a) $5 Nephews with crayon and paintbrushes (horiz). (b) $5 Donald Duck in deckchair Set of 2 sheets . . . 9·00 13·00

195 Torch from Statue in Madison Square Park, 1885

1985. Centenary (1986) of Statue of Liberty (1st issue). Multicoloured.
907 25c. Type **195** 30 20
908 30c. Statue of Liberty and scaffolding ("Restoration and Renewal") (vert) . . . 30 20
909 50c. Frederic Bartholdi (sculptor) supervising construction, 1876 . . . . 40 40
910 90c. Close-up of statue . . . 60 75
911 $1 Statue and cadet ship ("Operation Sail", 1976) (vert) . . . . 1·60 1·40
912 $3 Dedication ceremony, 1886 . . . . 1·75 3·00
MS913 110 × 80 mm. $5 Port of New York . . . . 3·75 3·75
See also Nos. 1110/19.

196 Arawak Pot Sherd and Indians making Clay Utensils

1985. Native American Artefacts. Multicoloured.
914 15c. Type **196** 15 10
915 50c. Arawak body design and Arawak Indians tattooing 30 40
916 60c. Head of the god "Yocahu" and Indians harvesting manioc 40 50
917 $3 Carib war club and Carib Indians going into battle 1·25 2·50
MS918 97 × 68 mm. $5 Taino Indians worshipping stone idol 1·50 2·50

197 Triumph 2hp "Jap", 1903

1985. Centenary of the Motorcycle. Multicoloured.
919 10c. Type **197** 65 15
920 30c. "Indian Arrow", 1949 . . 1·10 40
921 60c. BMW "R100RS", 1976 . 1·60 1·25
922 $4 Harley-Davidson "Model II", 1916 . . . . 5·50 9·00
MS923 90 × 93 mm. $5 Laverda "Jota", 1975 . . . . 5·50 7·00

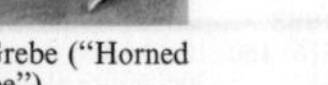

198 Slavonian Grebe ("Horned Grebe")

1985. Birth Bicentenary of John J. Audubon (ornithologist) (1st issue). Multicoloured. Designs showing original paintings.
924 90c. Type **198** . . . . 1·75 1·25
925 $1 British storm petrel ("Least Petrel") . . . . . 2·00 1·25
926 $1.50 Great blue heron . . . 2·50 3·25
927 $3 Double-crested cormorant 3·75 6·50
MS928 103 × 72 mm. $5 White-tailed tropic bird (vert) . . . . . . 7·00 6·00
See also Nos. 990/4.

199 "Anaea cyanea"

1985. Butterflies. Multicoloured.
929 25c. Type **199** . . . . 1·00 30
930 60c. "Leodonta dysoni" . . . 2·25 1·25
931 90c. "Junea doraete" . . . . 2·75 1·50
932 $4 "Prepona pylene" . . . . 7·50 10·50
MS933 132 × 105 mm. $5 "Caerois gerdtrudlus" . . . . 4·50 6·50

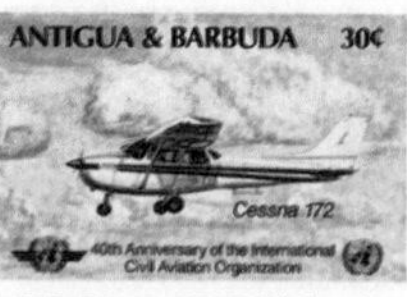

200 Cessna 172D Skyhawk

1985. 40th Anniv of International Civil Aviation Organization. Multicoloured.
934 30c. Type **200** . . . . 1·25 30
935 90c. Fokker D.VII . . . . . 2·75 1·25
936 $1.50 SPAD VII . . . . . . 3·75 3·25
937 $3 Boeing 747-100 . . . . . 5·50 7·50
MS938 97 × 83 mm. $5 De Havilland D.H.C.6 twin otter . . . . . . 4·50 6·50

201 Maimonides **203** The Queen Mother attending Church

202 Young Farmers with Produce

1985. 850th Birth Anniv of Maimonides (physician, philosopher and scholar).
939 **201** $2 green . . . . 4·00 3·25
MS940 70 × 84 mm. Type **201** $5 brown . . . . 7·00 4·50

1985. International Youth Year. Multicoloured.
941 25c. Type **202** 25 20
942 50c. Hotel management trainees 40 50
943 60c. Girls with goat and boys with football ("Environment") . . . . . 1·00 70
944 $3 Windsurfing ("Leisure") 2·75 5·50
MS945 102 × 72 mm. $5 Young people with Antiguan flags . . 2·75 3·25

1985. Life and Times of Queen Elizabeth the Queen Mother. Multicoloured.
946 $1 Type **203** 45 60
947 $1.50 Watching children playing in London garden 60 85
948 $2.50 The Queen Mother in 1979 . . . . 90 1·40
MS949 56 × 85 mm. $5 With Prince Edward at Royal Wedding, 1981 5·50 3·00
Stamps as Nos. 946/8, but with face values of 90c., $1 and $3 exist from additional sheetlets with changed background colours.

204 Magnificent Frigate Bird **206** Bass Trombone

205 Girl Guides Nursing

1985. Marine Life. Multicoloured.
950 15c. Type **204** . . . . 1·00 30
951 45c. Brain coral . . . . . . 2·00 95
952 60c. Cushion star . . . . . 2·25 1·75
953 $3 Spotted moray . . . . . 7·00 9·00
MS954 110 × 80 mm. $5 Elkhorn coral . . . . 9·00 7·00

1985. 75th Anniv of Girl Guide Movement. Multicoloured.
955 15c. Type **205** 75 20
956 45c. Open-air Girl Guide meeting . . . . 1·40 60
957 60c. Lord and Lady Baden-Powell . . . . 1·75 90
958 $3 Girl Guides gathering flowers . . . . 4·25 4·50
MS959 67 × 96 mm. $5 Barn swallow (Nature study) . . . . 6·50 8·50

1985. 300th Birth Anniv of Johann Sebastian Bach (composer).
960 **206** 25c. multicoloured . . . . 1·40 55
961 – 50c. multicoloured . . . . 1·75 1·10
962 – $1 multicoloured . . . . 3·25 1·75
963 – $3 multicoloured . . . . 6·00 7·00
MS964 – 104 × 73 mm. $5 black and grey . . . . 4·50 4·75
DESIGNS: 50c. English horn; $1 Violino piccolo; $3 Bass rackett; $5 Johann Sebastian Bach.

207 Flags of Great Britain and Antigua

1985. Royal Visit. Multicoloured.
965 60c. Type **207** . . . . 1·00 65
966 $1 Queen Elizabeth II (vert) 1·50 1·25
967 $4 Royal Yacht "Britannia" 3·25 7·00
MS968 110 × 83 mm. $5 Map of Antigua . . . . 3·00 3·25

1985. 150th Birth Anniv of Mark Twain (author). As T **118** of Anguilla showing Walt Disney cartoon characters in scenes from "Roughing It". Multicoloured.
969 25c. Donald Duck and Mickey Mouse meeting Indians . . . . 1·00 20
970 50c. Mickey Mouse, Donald Duck and Goofy canoeing 1·50 55
971 $1.10 Goofy as Pony Express rider . . . . 2·50 2·25
972 $1.50 Donald Duck and Goofy hunting buffalo . . 3·00 3·75
973 $2 Mickey Mouse and silver mine . . . . 3·50 4·50
MS974 127 × 101 mm. $5 Mickey Mouse driving stagecoach . . . 8·00 7·50

1985. Birth Bicentenaries of Grimm Brothers (folklorists). As T **119** of Anguilla showing Walt Disney cartoon characters in scenes from "Spindle, Shuttle and Needle". Multicoloured.
975 30c. The Prince (Mickey Mouse) searches for a bride 1·25 40
976 60c. The Prince finds the Orphan Girl (Minnie Mouse) . . . . 1·75 80
977 70c. The Spindle finds the Prince . . . . 2·00 1·40
978 $1 The Needle tidies the Girl's house . . . . 2·50 1·75
979 $3 The Prince proposes . . . 4·75 7·50
MS980 125 × 101 mm. $5 The Orphan Girl and spinning wheel on Prince's horse . . . . . . 8·00 7·50

208 Benjamin Franklin and U.N. (New York) 1953 U.P.U. 5c. Stamp

1985. 40th Anniv of United Nations Organization. Multicoloured.
981 40c. Type **208** . . . . 1·00 70
982 $1 George Washington Carver (agricultural chemist) and 1982 Nature Conservation 28c. stamp 2·00 2·00
983 $3 Charles Lindbergh (aviator) and 1978 I.C.A.O. 25c. stamp . . . . 4·75 7·50
MS984 101 × 77 mm. $5 Marc Chagall (artist) (vert) . . . . 6·50 4·75
Nos. 981/4 each include a United Nations (New York) stamp design.

209 "Madonna and Child" (De Landi) **211** Tug

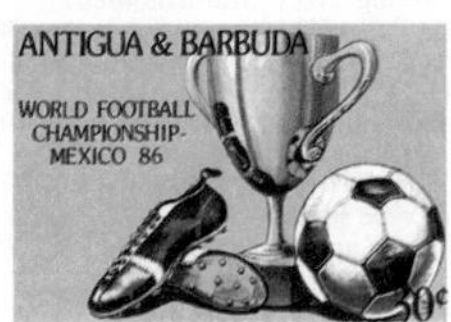

210 Football, Boots and Trophy

1985. Christmas. Religious Paintings. Mult.
985 10c. Type **209** 30 15
986 25c. "Madonna and Child" (Berlinghiero) 55 25
987 60c. "The Nativity" (Fra Angelico) 70 60
988 $4 "Presentation in the Temple" (Giovanni di Paolo) . . . . 1·75 4·25
MS989 113×81 mm. $5 "The Nativity" (Antoniazzo Romano) 3·00 3·75

1986. Birth Bicentenary of John J. Audubon (ornithologist) (2nd issue). As T **198** showing original paintings. Multicoloured.
990 60c. Mallard . . . . 2·25 1·50
991 90c. North American black duck ("Dusky Duck") . . 2·75 2·00
992 $1.50 Pintail ("Common Pintail") . . . . 3·50 4·50
993 $3 American wigeon ("Wigeon") . . . . 4·75 6·50
MS994 102×73 mm. Eider ("Common Eider") . . . . . 7·00 5·50

1986. World Cup Football Championship, Mexico. Multicoloured.
995 30c. Type **210** . . . . 1·50 40
996 60c. Goalkeeper (vert) . . . 2·00 85
997 $1 Referee blowing whistle (vert) . . . . 2·50 1·75
998 $4 Ball in net . . . . 6·50 9·00
MS999 87×76 mm. $5 Two players competing for ball . . . . . . 8·50 7·50

1986. Appearance of Halley's Comet (1st issue). As T **123** of Anguilla. Multicoloured.
1000 5c. Edmond Halley and Old Greenwich Observatory 30 20
1001 10c. Messerschmitt Me 163B Komet (fighter aircraft), 1944 . . . . 30 15
1002 60c. Montezuma (Aztec emperor) and Comet in 1517 (from "Historias de las Indias de Neuva Espana") . . . . 1·50 70
1003 $4 Pocahontas saving Capt. John Smith and Comet in 1607 . . . . 4·50 5·50
MS1004 101×70 mm. $5 Halley's Comet over English Harbour, Antigua . . . . 3·50 3·75
See also Nos. 1047/51.

1986. 60th Birthday of Queen Elizabeth II. As T **125** of Anguilla.
1005 60c. black and yellow . . . 30 35
1006 $1 multicoloured 50 55
1007 $4 multicoloured . . . . . 1·40 1·90
MS1008 120×85 mm. $5 black and brown . . . . 2·00 3·00
DESIGNS: 60c. Wedding photograph, 1947; $1 Queen at Trooping the Colour; $4 In Scotland; $5 Queen Mary and Princess Elizabeth, 1927.

1986. Local Boats. Multicoloured.
1009 30c. Type **211** 25 20
1010 60c. Game fishing boat . . 45 35
1011 $1 Yacht 75 60
1012 $4 Lugger with auxiliary sail 2·50 3·25
MS1013 108×78 mm. $5 Boats under construction . . . . . . 3·00 4·00

212 "Hiawatha" express

1986. "Ameripex '86" International Stamp Exhibition, Chicago. Famous American Trains. Multicoloured.
1014 25c. Type **212** . . . . . . 1·25 50
1015 50c. "Grand Canyon" express . . . . 1·50 80
1016 $1 "Powhattan Arrow" express . . . . 1·75 1·75
1017 $3 "Empire State" express 3·00 7·00
MS1018 116×87 mm. $5 Southern Pacific "Daylight" express . . 6·00 11·00

213 Prince Andrew and Miss Sarah Ferguson **214** Fly-specked Cerith

1986. Royal Wedding. Multicoloured.
1019 45c. Type **213** 70 35
1020 60c. Prince Andrew 80 45
1021 $4 Prince Andrew with Prince Philip . . . . . . 2·75 3·50
MS1022 88×88 mm. $5 Prince Andrew and Miss Sarah Ferguson (different) . . . . 5·00 4·50

1986. Sea Shells. Multicoloured.
1023 15c. Type **214** 75 50
1024 45c. Smooth Scotch bonnet 1·75 1·25
1025 60c. West Indian crown conch . . . . 2·00 2·00
1026 $3 Ciboney murex . . . . . 6·50 10·00
MS1027 109×75 mm. $5 Colourful Atlantic moon (horiz) . . . . 7·50 8·50

215 Water Lily

1986. Flowers. Multicoloured.
1028 10c. Type **215** 20 15
1029 15c. Queen of the night . . 20 15
1030 50c. Cup of gold 55 55
1031 60c. Beach morning glory 70 70
1032 70c. Golden trumpet 80 80
1033 $1 Air plant . . . . 90 1·10
1034 $4 Purple wreath . . . . . 1·75 3·00
1035 $4 Zephyr lily . . . . . . 2·00 3·75
MS1036 Two sheets, each 102×72 mm. (a) $4 Dozakie. (b) $5 Four o'clock flower Set of 2 sheets . . . . 5·00 7·50

1986. World Cup Football Championship Winners, Mexico. Nos. 995/8 optd **WINNERS Argentina 3 W.Germany 2**.
1037 30c. Type **210** . . . . . . 1·25 40
1038 60c. Goalkeeper (vert) . . . 1·75 75
1039 $1 Referee blowing whistle (vert) . . . . 2·25 1·10
1040 $4 Ball in net . . . . 5·50 4·50
MS1041 87×76 mm. $5 Two players competing for ball . . . . . . 5·50 4·00

217 "Hygrocybe occidentalis var. scarletina" **(218)**

1986. Mushrooms. Multicoloured.
1042 10c. Type **217** 30 25
1043 50c. "Trogia buccinalis" . . 70 55
1044 $1 "Collybia subpruinosa" . 1·25 1·25
1045 $4 "Leucocoprinus brebissonii" . . . . . . 3·00 4·50
MS1046 102×82 mm. $5 "Pyrrhoglossum pyrrhum" . . 13·00 11·00

1986. Appearance of Halley's Comet (2nd issue). Nos. 1000/3 optd with T **218**.
1047 5c. Edmond Halley and Old Greenwich Observatory 20 10
1048 10c. Messerschmitt Me 163B Komet (fighter aircraft), 1944 . . . . 50 10
1049 60c. Montezuma (Aztec emperor) and Comet in 1517 (from "Historias de las Indias de Neuva Espana") . . . . 1·25 65
1050 $4 Pocahontas saving Capt. John Smith and Comet in 1607 . . . . 4·50 4·00
MS1051 101×70 mm. $5 Halley's Comet over English Harbour, Antigua . . . . 6·00 6·50

219 Auburn "Speedster" (1933)

1986. Centenary of First Benz Motor Car. Mult.
1052 10c. Type **219** 15 10
1053 15c. Mercury "Sable" (1986) 20 10
1054 50c. Cadillac (1959) 55 30
1055 60c. Studebaker (1950) . . . 70 45
1056 70c. Lagonda "V-12" (1939) 80 55
1057 $1 Adler "Standard" (1930) 1·10 75
1058 $3 DKW (1956) . . . . . . 2·50 2·50
1059 $4 Mercedes "500K" (1936) 3·00 3·00
MS1060 Two sheets, each 99×70 mm. (a) $5 Daimler (1896). (b) $5 Mercedes "Knight" (1921) Set of 2 sheets . . . . 9·00 6·50

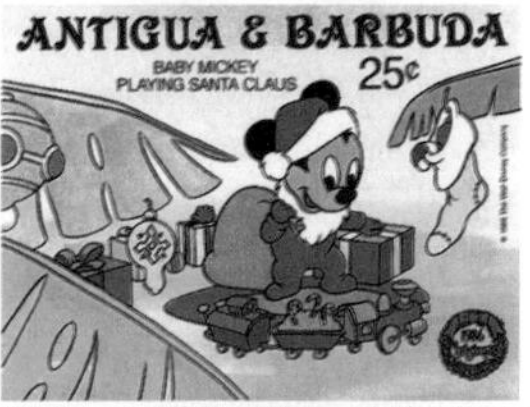

220 Young Mickey Mouse playing Santa Claus

1986. Christmas. Designs showing Walt Disney cartoon characters as babies. Multicoloured.
1061 25c. Type **220** 60 35
1062 30c. Mickey and Minnie Mouse building snowman 70 40
1063 40c. Aunt Matilda and Goofy baking 75 45
1064 60c. Goofy and Pluto . . . 1·00 85
1065 70c. Pluto, Donald and Daisy Duck carol singing 1·10 1·00
1066 $1.50 Donald Duck, Mickey Mouse and Pluto stringing popcorn . . . . 1·75 2·50
1067 $3 Grandma Duck and Minnie Mouse . . . . . 3·00 4·50
1068 $4 Donald Duck and Pete 3·25 4·50
MS1069 Two sheets, each 127×102 mm. (a) $5 Goofy, Donald Duck and Minnie Mouse playing with reindeer. (b) $5 Mickey Mouse, Donald and Daisy Duck playing with toys Set of 2 sheets . . . . 12·00 14·00

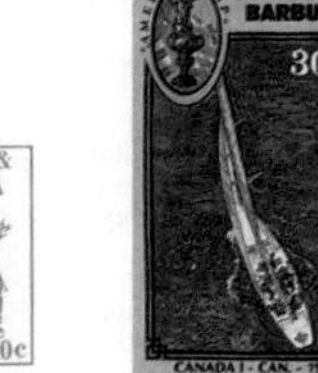

221 Arms of Antigua **222** "Canada I" (1981)

1986.
1070 **221** 10c. blue 50 50
1071 – 25c. red 75 75
DESIGN: 25c. Flag of Antigua.

1987. America's Cup Yachting Championship. Multicoloured.
1072 30c. Type **222** 45 20
1073 60c. "Gretel II" (1970) . . . 60 50
1074 $1 "Sceptre" (1958) . . . . 85 1·00
1075 $3 "Vigilant" (1893) . . . . 2·25 3·00
MS1076 113×84 mm. $5 "Australia II" defeating "Liberty" (1983) (horiz) . . . . 4·00 5·00

223 Bridled Burrfish

1987. Marine Life. Multicoloured.
1077 15c. Type **223** . . . . . . 2·50 50
1078 30c. Common noddy ("Brown Noddy") . . . . 4·50 60
1079 40c. Nassau grouper . . . . 3·00 70
1080 50c. Laughing gull . . . . 5·50 1·50
1081 60c. French angelfish . . . 3·50 1·50
1082 $1 Porkfish . . . . 3·50 1·75
1083 $2 Royal tern . . . . 7·50 6·00
1084 $3 Sooty tern . . . . 7·50 8·00
MS1085 Two sheets, each 120×94 mm. (a) $5 Banded butterflyfish. (b) $5 Brown booby Set of 2 sheets . . . . 17·00 14·00
Nos. 1078, 1080 and 1083/5 are without the World Wildlife Fund logo shown on Type **223**.

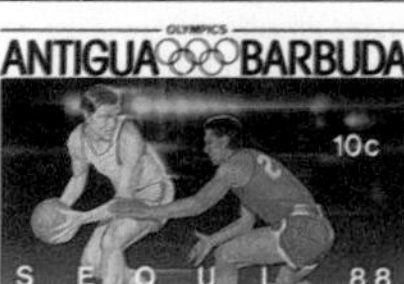

224 Handball

1987. Olympic Games, Seoul (1988) (1st issue). Multicoloured.
1086 10c. Type **224** 60 10
1087 60c. Fencing 85 35
1088 $1 Gymnastics . . . . . . 1·25 75
1089 $3 Football . . . . 2·50 4·00
MS1090 100×72 mm. $5 Boxing gloves . . . . 3·50 4·25
See also Nos. 1222/6.

225 "The Profile"

1987. Birth Centenary of Marc Chagall (artist). Multicoloured.
1091 10c. Type **225** 30 15
1092 30c. "Portrait of the Artist's Sister" 45 30
1093 40c. "Bride with Fan" . . . 50 40
1094 60c. "David in Profile" . . 55 45
1095 90c. "Fiancee with Bouquet" 75 60
1096 $1 "Self Portrait with Brushes" 75 65
1097 $3 "The Walk" . . . . . . 1·75 2·25
1098 $4 "Three Candles" . . . . 2·00 2·50
MS1099 Two sheets, each 110×95 mm. (a) $5 "Fall of Icarus" (104×89 mm). (b) $5 "Myth of Orpheus" (104×89 mm). Imperf Set of 2 sheets . . . . 6·50 6·00

226 "Spirit of Australia" (fastest powerboat), 1978

1987. Milestones of Transportation. Multicoloured.
1100 10c. Type **226** 80 40
1101 15c. Werner von Siemens's electric locomotive, 1879 1·25 50
1102 30c. U.S.S. "Triton" (first submerged circum-navigation), 1960 . . . . 1·25 50
1103 50c. Trevithick's steam carriage (first passenger-carrying vehicle), 1801 . . 1·50 60
1104 60c. U.S.S. "New Jersey" (battleship), 1942 . . . . 1·50 70
1105 70c. Draisaine bicycle, 1818 1·50 80
1106 90c. "United States" (liner) (holder of Blue Riband), 1952 . . . . 1·50 1·00
1107 $1.50 Cierva C.4 (first autogyro), 1923 . . . . . 1·50 2·50
1108 $2 Curtiss NC-4 flying boat (first transatlantic flight), 1919 . . . . 1·75 2·75
1109 $3 "Queen Elizabeth 2" (liner), 1969 . . . . . . 3·00 4·50

227 Lee Iacocca at Unveiling of Restored Statue **228** Grace Kelly

1987. Centenary of Statue of Liberty (1986) (2nd issue). Multicoloured.
1110 15c. Type **227** 15 15
1111 30c. Statue at sunset (side view) 20 20
1112 45c. Aerial view of head . . 30 30
1113 50c. Lee Iacocca and torch 35 35
1114 60c. Workmen inside head of Statue (horiz) 35 35
1115 90c. Restoration work (horiz) 50 50
1116 $1 Head of Statue 55 55

1117 $2 Statue at sunset (front view) . . . . 1·00 1·50
1118 $3 Inspecting restoration work (horiz) . . . . . 1·25 2·00
1119 $5 Statue at night . . . . . 2·00 3·50

1987. Entertainers. Multicoloured.
1120 15c. Type **228** 90 40
1121 30c. Marilyn Monroe . . . 2·75 80
1122 45c. Orson Welles 90 60
1123 50c. Judy Garland 90 65
1124 60c. John Lennon . . . . . 4·25 1·25
1125 $1 Rock Hudson . . . . . 1·40 1·10
1126 $2 John Wayne . . . . . . 2·50 2·00
1127 $3 Elvis Presley . . . . . . 8·50 4·50

229 Scouts around Camp Fire and Red Kangaroo

1987. 16th World Scout Jamboree, Australia. Mult.
1128 10c. Type **229** 65 20
1129 60c. Scouts canoeing and blue-winged kookaburra 1·25 80
1130 $1 Scouts on assault course and ring-tailed rock wallaby . . . . 1·00 85
1131 $3 Field kitchen and koala 1·50 4·25
MS1132 103 × 78 mm. $5 Flags of Antigua, Australia and Scout Movement . . . . 3·25 3·50

230 Whistling Frog

1987. "Capex '87" International Stamp Exhibition, Toronto. Reptiles and Amphibians. Mult.
1133 30c. Type **230** 55 20
1134 60c. Croaking lizard 75 40
1135 $1 Antiguan anole . . . . . 1·00 70
1136 $3 Red-footed tortoise . . . 2·00 3·00
MS1137 106 × 76 mm. $5 Ground lizard . . . . 2·25 2·75

1987. 10th Death Anniv of Elvis Presley (entertainer). No. 1127 optd **10th ANNIVERSARY 16th AUGUST 1987**.
1138 $3 Elvis Presley . . . . . . 7·00 4·50

232 House of Burgesses, Virginia ("Freedom of Speech")

1987. Bicentenary of U.S. Constitution. Mult.
1139 15c. Type **232** 10 10
1140 45c. State Seal, Connecticut 20 25
1141 60c. State Seal, Delaware . . 25 35
1142 $4 Governor Morris (Pennsylvania delegate) (vert) . . . . 1·75 2·25
MS1143 105 × 75 mm. $5 Roger Sherman (Connecticut delegate) (vert) . . . . 2·00 2·75

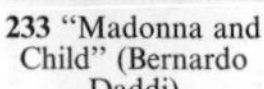

233 "Madonna and Child" (Bernardo Daddi)

234 Wedding Photograph, 1947

1987. Christmas. Religious Paintings. Mult.
1144 45c. Type **233** 50 15
1145 60c. St. Joseph (detail, "The Nativity" (Sano di Pietro)) 65 30
1146 $1 Virgin Mary (detail, "The Nativity" (Sano di Pietro)) 85 55
1147 $4 "Music-making Angel" (Melozzo da Forli) . . . 2·25 3·50
MS1148 99 × 70 mm. $5 "The Flight into Egypt" (Sano di Pietro) 2·25 2·75

1988. Royal Ruby Wedding.
1149 **234** 25c. brown, black and blue 30 15
1150 – 60c. multicoloured . . . 60 40
1151 – $2 brown, black and green . . . . 1·10 1·10
1152 – $3 multicoloured . . . . 1·50 1·60
MS1153 107 × 77 mm. $5 multicoloured . . . . 2·50 2·75
DESIGNS: 60c. Queen Elizabeth II; $2 Princess Elizabeth and Prince Philip with Prince Charles at his christening, 1948; $3 Queen Elizabeth (from photo by Tim Graham), 1980; $5 Royal family, 1952.

235 Great Blue Heron

1988. Birds of Antigua. Multicoloured.
1154 10c. Type **235** 45 50
1155 15c. Ringed kingfisher (horiz) 50 40
1156 50c. Bananaquit (horiz) . . 90 50
1157 60c. American purple gallinule ("Purple Gallinule") (horiz) 90 50
1158 70c. Blue-hooded euphonia (horiz) . . . . 1·00 55
1159 $1 Brown-throated conure ("Caribbean Parakeet") 1·25 75
1160 $3 Troupial (horiz) . . . . 2·50 3·50
1161 $4 Purple-throated carib ("Hummingbird") (horiz) 2·50 3·50
MS1162 Two sheets, each 115 × 86 mm. (a) $5 Greater flamingo. (b) $5 Brown pelican Set of 2 sheets . . . . 4·50 5·50

236 First Aid at Daycare Centre, Antigua

1988. Salvation Army's Community Service. Multicoloured.
1163 25c. Type **236** 80 65
1164 30c. Giving penicillin injection, Indonesia . . . 80 65
1165 40c. Children at daycare centre, Bolivia 90 75
1166 45c. Rehabilitation of the handicapped, India . . . 90 75
1167 50c. Training blind man, Kenya . . . . 1·00 1·25
1168 60c. Weighing baby, Ghana 1·00 1·25
1169 $1 Training typist, Zambia 1·40 1·75
1170 $2 Emergency food kitchen, Sri Lanka . . . . 2·00 3·50
MS1171 152 × 83 mm. $5 General Eva Burrows . . . . 3·75 4·50

237 Columbus's Second Fleet, 1493

1988. 500th Anniv (1992) of Discovery of America by Columbus (1st issue). Multicoloured.
1172 10c. Type **237** 70 40
1173 30c. Painos. Indian village and fleet 70 45
1174 45c. "Santa Mariagalante" (flagship) and Painos. village 80 45
1175 60c. Painos Indians offering Columbus fruit and vegetables 80 50
1176 90c. Painos Indian and Columbus with scarlet macaw . . . . 1·50 1·00
1177 $1 Columbus landing on island . . . . 1·50 1·00
1178 $3 Spanish soldier and fleet 2·25 3·00
1179 $4 Fleet under sail . . . . 2·50 3·00
MS1180 Two sheets, each 110 × 80 mm. (a) $5 Queen Isabella's cross. (b) $5 Gold coin of Ferdinand and Isabella Set of 2 sheets . . . . 6·50 7·00
See also Nos. 1267/71, 1360/8, 1503/11, 1654/60 and 1670/1.

238 "Bust of Christ"

1988. Easter. 500th Birth Anniv of Titian (artist). Multicoloured.
1181 30c. Type **238** 40 20
1182 40c. "Scourging of Christ" 45 25
1183 45c. "Madonna in Glory with Saints" 45 25
1184 50c. "The Averoldi Polyptych" (detail) . . . 45 35
1185 $1 "Christ Crowned with Thorns" 70 55
1186 $2 "Christ Mocked" . . . . 1·10 1·25
1187 $3 "Christ and Simon of Cyrene" . . . . 1·50 1·75
1188 $4 "Crucifixion with Virgin and Saints" . . . . . . 1·75 2·25
MS1189 Two sheets, each 110 × 95 mm. (a) $5 "Ecce Homo" (detail). (b) $5 "Noli me Tangere" (detail) Set of 2 sheets . . . . 7·00 8·50

239 Two Yachts rounding Buoy

1988. Sailing Week. Multicoloured.
1190 30c. Type **239** 35 20
1191 60c. Three yachts 50 40
1192 $1 British yacht under way 60 55
1193 $3 Three yachts (different) 1·10 2·50
MS1194 103 × 92 mm. $5 Two yachts . . . . 1·75 3·25

240 Mickey Mouse and Diver with Porpoise

1988. Disney EPCOT Centre, Orlando, Florida. Designs showing cartoon characters and exhibits. Multicoloured.
1195 1c. Type **240** 10 10
1196 2c. Goofy and Mickey Mouse with futuristic car (vert) 10 10
1197 3c. Mickey Mouse and Goofy as Atlas (vert) . . 10 10
1198 4c. Mickey Mouse and "Eda-phosaurus" (prehistoric reptile) . . . 10 10
1199 5c. Mickey Mouse at Journey into Imagination exhibit 15 10
1200 10c. Mickey Mouse collecting vegetables (vert) 20 10
1201 25c. Type **240** 55 25
1202 30c. As 2c. 55 25
1203 40c. As 3c. 60 30
1204 60c. As 4c. 85 50
1205 70c. As 5c. 95 60
1206 $1.50 As 10c. . . . . 2·00 2·00
1207 $3 Goofy and Mickey Mouse with robot (vert) 2·50 2·75
1208 $4 Mickey Mouse and Clarabelle at Horizons exhibit . . . . 2·50 2·75
MS1209 Two sheets, each 125 × 99 mm. (a) $5 Mickey Mouse and monorail (vert). (b) $5 Mickey Mouse flying over EPCOT Centre Set of 2 sheets . . . . 7·00 6·50

1988. Stamp Exhibitions. Nos. 1083/4 optd.
1210 $2 Royal tern (optd **Praga '88**, Prague) . . . . . . 4·50 2·75
1211 $3 Sooty tern (optd **INDEPENDENCE 40**, Israel) . . . . 4·50 3·50
MS1212 Two sheets, each 120 × 94 mm. (a) $5 Banded butterflyfish (optd **"OLYMPHILEX '88"**, Seoul). (b) $5 brown booby (optd **"FINLANDIA 88"**, Helsinki). Set of 2 sheets 13·00 9·00

242 Jacaranda

243 Gymnastics

1988. Flowering Trees. Multicoloured.
1213 10c. Type **242** 30 20
1214 30c. Cordia 40 20
1215 50c. Orchid tree 60 40
1216 90c. Flamboyant 70 50
1217 $1 African tulip tree 75 55
1218 $2 Potato tree . . . . . . 1·40 1·60
1219 $3 Crepe myrtle . . . . . . 1·60 2·00
1220 $4 Pitch apple . . . . . . 1·75 2·75
MS1221 Two sheets, each 106 × 76 mm. (a) $5 Cassia. (b) $5 Chinaberry Set of 2 sheets . . 5·00 6·00

1988. Olympic Games, Seoul (2nd issue). Mult.
1222 40c. Type **243** 30 25
1223 60c. Weightlifting 40 30
1224 $1 Water polo (horiz) . . . 80 50
1225 $3 Boxing (horiz) . . . . . 1·50 2·25
MS1226 114 × 80 mm. $5 Runner with Olympic torch . . . . . 2·00 3·00

244 "Danaus plexippus"

1988. Caribbean Butterflies. Multicoloured.
1227 1c. Type **244** . . . . . . 60 1·00
1228 2c. "Greta diaphanus" . . 70 1·00
1229 3c. "Calisto archebates" . . 70 1·00
1230 5c. "Hamadryas feronia" 85 1·00
1231 10c. "Mestra dorcas" . . . 1·00 30
1232 15c. "Hypolimnas misippus" . . . . 1·50 30
1233 20c. "Dione juno" . . . . 1·60 30
1234 25c. "Heliconius charithonia" . . . . . . 1·60 30
1235 30c. "Eurema pyro" . . . 1·60 30
1236 40c. "Papilio androgeus" 1·60 30
1237 45c. "Anteos maerula" . . 1·60 30
1238 50c. "Aphrissa orbis" . . . 1·75 45
1239 60c. "Astraptes xagua" . . 2·00 60
1240 $1 "Heliopetes arsalte" . . 2·25 1·00
1241 $2 "Polites baracoa" . . . 3·25 3·75
1242 $2.50 "Phocides pigmalion" 4·00 5·00
1243 $5 "Prepona amphitoe" . . 5·50 7·50
1244 $10 "Oarisma nanus" . . . 7·50 11·00
1244a $20 "Parides lycimenes" . . 14·00 18·00

245 President Kennedy and Family

1988. 25th Death Anniv of John F. Kennedy (American statesman). Multicoloured.
1245 1c. Type **245** 10 10
1246 2c. Kennedy commanding "PT109" 10 10
1247 3c. Funeral cortege 10 10
1248 4c. In motorcade, Mexico City 10 10
1249 30c. As 1c. 35 15
1250 60c. As 4c. 75 40
1251 $1 As 3c. 85 75
1252 $4 As 2c. . . . . 2·75 3·25
MS1253 105 × 75 mm. $5 Kennedy taking presidential oath of office 2·50 3·25

246 Minnie Mouse carol singing

1988. Christmas. "Mickey's Christmas Chorale". Design showing Walt Disney cartoon characters. Multicoloured.
1254 10c. Type **246** 30 30
1255 25c. Pluto 45 45
1256 30c. Mickey Mouse playing ukelele 45 45
1257 70c. Donald Duck and nephew 80 80

1258 $1 Mordie and Ferdie carol singing 80 1·00
1259 $1 Goofy carol singing 80 1·00
1260 $1 Chip n'Dale sliding off roof 80 1·00
1261 $1 Two of Donald Duck's nephews at window 80 1·00
1262 $1 As 10c. 80 1·00
1263 $1 As 25c. 80 1·00
1264 $1 As 30c. 80 1·00
1265 $1 As 70c. 80 1·00
MS1266 Two sheets, each 127 × 102 mm. (a) $7 Donald Duck playing trumpet and Mickey and Minnie Mouse in carriage. (b) $7 Mickey Mouse and friends singing carols on roller skates (horiz) Set of 2 sheets 8·50 8·50

Nos. 1258/65 were printed together, se-tenant, forming a composite design.

247 Arawak Warriors

1989. 500th Anniv of Discovery of America by Columbus (1992) (2nd issue). Pre-Columbian Arawak Society. Multicoloured.

1267 $1.50 Type **247** 1·10 1·40
1268 $1.50 Whip dancers 1·10 1·40
1269 $1.50 Whip dancers and chief with pineapple 1·10 1·40
1270 $1.50 Family and camp fire 1·10 1·40
MS1271 71 × 84 mm. $6 Arawak chief 2·75 3·00

Nos. 1267/70 were printed together, se-tenant, forming a composite design.

248 De Havilland Comet 4 Airliner

1989. 50th Anniv of First Jet Flight. Mult.

1272 10c. Type **248** 90 45
1273 30c. Messerschmitt Me 262 fighter 1·50 45
1274 40c. Boeing 707 airliner 1·50 45
1275 60c. Canadair CL-13 Sabre (inscr "F-86") fighter 1·90 55
1276 $1 Lockheed F-104 Starfighters 2·25 1·10
1277 $2 McDonnell Douglas DC-10 airliner 3·00 3·00
1278 $3 Boeing 747-300/400 airliner 3·25 4·50
1279 $4 McDonnell Douglas F-4 Phantom II fighter 3·25 4·50
MS1280 Two sheets, each 114 × 83 mm. (a) $7 Grumman F-14A Tomcat fighter. (b) $7 Concorde airliner Set of 2 sheets 9·50 12·00

249 "Festivale"

1989. Caribbean Cruise Ships. Multicoloured.

1281 25c. Type **249** 1·50 50
1282 45c. "Southward" 1·75 50
1283 50c. "Sagafjord" 1·75 50
1284 60c. "Daphne" 1·75 60
1285 75c. "Cunard Countess" 1·90 1·00
1286 90c. "Song of America" 2·00 1·10
1287 $3 "Island Princess" 3·50 5·00
1288 $4 "Galileo" 3·50 5·00
MS1289 (a) 113 × 87 mm. $6 "Norway". (b) 111 × 82 mm. $6 "Oceanic" Set of 2 sheets 6·50 9·00

250 "Fish swimming by Duck half-submerged in Stream"

1989. Japanese Art. Paintings by Hiroshige. Mult.

1290 25c. Type **250** 1·00 50
1291 45c. "Crane and Wave" 1·25 50
1292 50c. "Sparrows and Morning Glories" 1·40 50
1293 60c. "Crested Blackbird and Flowering Cherry" 1·50 60
1294 $1 "Great Knot sitting among Water Grass" 1·75 80
1295 $2 "Goose on a Bank of Water" 2·50 2·50
1296 $3 "Black Paradise Flycatcher and Blossoms" 3·00 3·00
1297 $4 "Sleepy Owl perched on a Pine Branch" 3·00 3·00
MS1298 Two sheets, each 102 × 75 mm. (a) $5 "Bullfinch flying near a Clematis Branch". (b) $5 "Titmouse on a Cherry Branch" Set of 2 sheets 9·00 9·50

251 Mickey and Minnie Mouse in Helicopter over River Seine

1989. "Philexfrance 89" International Stamp Exhibition, Paris. Walt Disney cartoon characters in Paris. Multicoloured.

1299 1c. Type **251** 10 10
1300 2c. Goofy and Mickey Mouse passing Arc de Triomphe 10 10
1301 3c. Mickey Mouse painting picture of Notre Dame 10 10
1302 4c. Mickey and Minnie Mouse with Pluto leaving Metro station 10 10
1303 5c. Minnie Mouse as model in fashion show 10 10
1304 10c. Daisy Duck, Minnie Mouse and Clarabelle as Folies Bergere dancers 10 10
1305 $5 Mickey and Minnie Mouse shopping in street market 6·50 6·50
1306 $6 Mickey and Minnie Mouse, Jose Carioca and Donald Duck at pavement cafe 6·50 6·50
MS1307 Two sheets, each 127 × 101 mm. (a) $5 Mickey and Minnie Mouse in hot air balloon. (b) $5 Mickey Mouse at Pompidou Centre cafe (vert) Set of 2 sheets 11·00 13·00

252 Goalkeeper

1989. World Cup Football Championship, Italy (1990). Multicoloured.

1308 15c. Type **252** 85 30
1309 25c. Goalkeeper moving towards ball 90 30
1310 $1 Goalkeeper reaching for ball 2·00 1·25
1311 $4 Goalkeeper saving goal 3·50 5·00
MS1312 Two sheets, each 75 × 105 mm. (a) $5 Three players competing for ball (horiz). (b) $5 Ball and player' legs (horiz) Set of 2 sheets 8·00 10·00

253 "Mycena pura"

1989. Fungi. Multicoloured.

1313 10c. Type **253** 75 50
1314 25c. "Psathyrella tuberculata" (vert) 1·10 40
1315 50c. "Psilocybe cubensis" 1·50 60
1316 60c. "Leptonia caeruleocapitata" (vert) 1·50 70
1317 75c. "Xeromphalina tenuipes" (vert) 1·75 1·10
1318 $1 "Chlorophyllum molybdites" (vert) 1·75 1·25
1319 $3 "Marasmius haematocephalus" 2·75 3·75
1320 $4 "Cantharellus cinnabarinus" 2·75 3·75
MS1321 Two sheets, each 88 × 62 mm. (a) $6 "Leucopaxillus gracillimus" (vert). (b) $6 "Volvariella volvacea" Set of 2 sheets 13·00 15·00

254 Desmarest's Hutia

1989. Local Fauna. Multicoloured.

1322 25c. Type **254** 80 50
1323 45c. Caribbean monk seal 2·50 1·00
1324 80c. Mustache bat (vert) 1·50 1·00
1325 $4 American manatee (vert) 3·50 5·50
MS1326 113 × 87 mm. $5 West Indian giant rice rat 7·00 9·00

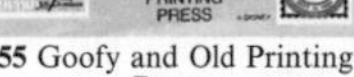

255 Goofy and Old Printing Press

258 Launch of "Apollo II"

256 Mickey Mouse and Donald Duck with Camden and Amboy Locomotive "John Bull", 1831

1989. "American Philately". Walt Disney cartoon characters with stamps and the logo of the American Philatelic Society. Multicoloured.

1327 1c. Type **255** 10 10
1328 2c. Donald Duck cancelling first day cover for Mickey Mouse 10 10
1329 3c. Donald Duck's nephews reading recruiting poster for Pony Express riders 10 10
1330 4c. Morty and Ferdie as early radio broadcasters 10 10
1331 5c. Donald Duck and water buffalo watching television 10 10
1332 10c. Donald Duck with stamp album 10 10
1333 $4 Daisy Duck with computer system 4·75 6·00
1334 $6 Donald's nephews with stereo radio, trumpet and guitar 6·00 7·00
MS1335 Two sheets, each 127 × 102 mm. (a) $5 Donald's nephews donating stamps to charity. (b) $5 Minnie Mouse flying mailplane upside down (horiz) Set of 2 sheets 11·00 13·00

1989. "World Stamp Expo '89" International Stamp Exhibition, Washington. Walt Disney cartoon characters and locomotives. Mult.

1336 25c. Type **256** 80 50
1337 45c. Mickey Mouse and friends with "Atlantic", 1832 1·00 50
1338 50c. Mickey Mouse and Goofy with "William Crooks", 1861 1·00 50
1339 60c. Mickey Mouse and Goofy with "Minnetonka", 1869 1·00 65
1340 $1 Chip n'Dale with "Thatcher Perkins", 1863 1·25 75
1341 $2 Mickey and Minnie Mouse with "Pioneer", 1848 2·00 2·25
1342 $3 Mickey Mouse and Donald Duck with cog railway locomotive "Peppersass", 1869 2·75 4·00
1343 $4 Mickey Mouse with Huey, Dewey and Louie aboard N.Y. World's Fair "Gimbels Flyer", 1939 3·00 4·00
MS1344 Two sheets, each 127 × 101 mm. (a) $6 Mickey Mouse and locomotive "Thomas Jefferson", 1835 (vert). (b) $6 Mickey Mouse and friends at Central Pacific "Golden Spike" ceremony, 1869 Set of 2 sheets 7·50 9·00

1989. 20th Anniv of First Manned Landing on Moon. Multicoloured.

1346 10c. Type **258** 50 30
1347 45c. Aldrin on Moon 1·25 30
1348 $1 Module "Eagle" over Moon (horiz) 1·75 1·10
1349 $4 Recovery of "Apollo II" crew after splashdown (horiz) 2·75 5·00
MS1350 107 × 77 mm. $5 Astronaut Neil Armstrong 4·00 4·75

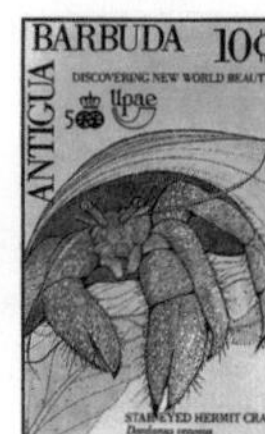

259 "The Small Cowper Madonna" (Raphael)

260 Star-eyed Hermit Crab

1989. Christmas. Paintings by Raphael and Giotto. Multicoloured.

1351 10c. Type **259** 30 15
1352 25c. "Madonna of the Goldfinch" (Raphael) 45 20
1353 30c. "The Alba Madonna" (Raphael) 45 20
1354 50c. Saint (detail, "Bologna Altarpiece") (Giotto) 65 30
1355 60c. Angel (detail, "Bologna Altarpiece") (Giotto) 70 35
1356 70c. Angel slaying serpent (detail, "Bologna Altarpiece") (Giotto) 80 40
1357 $4 Evangelist (detail, "Bologna Altarpiece") (Giotto) 3·00 4·50
1358 $5 "Madonna of Foligno" (detail) (Raphael) 3·00 4·50
MS1359 Two sheets, each 71 × 96 mm. (a) $5 "The Marriage of the Virgin" (detail) (Raphael). (b) $5 Madonna and Child (detail, "Bologna Altarpiece") (Giotto) Set of 2 sheets 9·00 12·00

1990. 500th Anniv (1992) of Discovery of America by Columbus (3rd issue). New World Natural History–Marine Life. Multicoloured.

1360 10c. Type **260** 45 20
1361 20c. Spiny lobster 65 25
1362 25c. Magnificent banded fanworm 65 25
1363 45c. Cannonball jellyfish 80 40
1364 60c. Red-spiny sea star 1·00 60
1365 $2 Peppermint shrimp 2·00 2·50
1366 $3 Coral crab 2·25 3·75
1367 $4 Branching fire coral 2·25 3·75
MS1368 Two sheets, each 100 × 69 mm. (a) $5 Common sea fan. (b) $5 Portuguese man-of-war Set of 2 sheets 8·00 9·00

261 "Vanilla mexicana"

262 Queen Victoria and Queen Elizabeth II

1990. "Expo '90" International Garden and Greenery Exhibition, Osaka. Orchids. Multicoloured.

1369 15c. Type **261** 75 50
1370 45c. "Epidendrum ibaguense" 1·10 50
1371 50c. "Epidendrum secundum" 1·25 55
1372 60c. "Maxillaria conferta" 1·40 55
1373 $1 "Oncidium altissimum" 1·50 1·00
1374 $2 "Spiranthes lanceolata" 2·00 2·50
1375 $3 "Tonopsis utricularioides" 2·25 3·50
1376 $5 "Epidendrum nocturnum" 3·25 4·50
MS1377 Two sheets, each 102 × 70 mm. (a) $6 "Octomeria graminifolia". (b) $6 "Rodriguezia lanceolata" Set of 2 sheets 6·50 8·00

1990. 150th Anniv of the Penny Black.

1378 **262** 45c. green 85 40
1379 – 60c. mauve 1·00 65
1380 – $5 blue 3·50 5·50
MS1381 102 × 80 mm. Type **262** $6 purple 4·75 6·00

DESIGNS: 60c., $5 As Type **262**, but with different backgrounds.

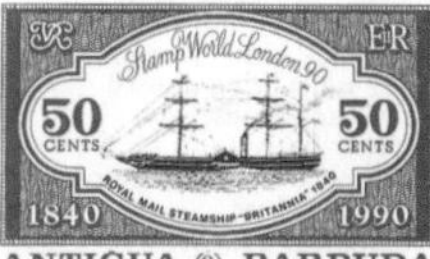

263 "Britannia" (mail paddle-steamer), 1840

1990. "Stamp World London '90" International Stamp Exhibition.
1382 **263** 50c. green and red . . . 85 35
1383 – 75c. brown and red . . . 1·10 90
1384 – $4 blue and red . . . . 3·75 5·50
MS1385 – 104 × 81 mm. $6 brown and red . . . . 3·50 5·00
DESIGNS: 75c. Travelling Post Office sorting van, 1892; $4 Short S.23 Empire "C" Class flying boat "Centaurus", 1938; $6 Post Office underground railway, London, 1927.

264 Flamefish

1990. Reef Fishes. Multicoloured.
1386 10c. Type **264** 65 55
1387 15c. Coney 80 55
1388 50c. Long-spined squirrelfish 1·25 60
1389 60c. Sergeant major . . . . 1·25 60
1390 $1 Yellow-tailed snapper . . 1·50 85
1391 $2 Rock beauty . . . . . . 2·25 2·75
1392 $3 Spanish hogfish . . . . 2·75 3·75
1393 $4 Striped parrotfish . . . . 2·75 3·75
MS1394 Two sheets, each 90 × 70 mm. (a) $5 Black-barred soldierfish. (b) $4 Four-eyed butterflyfish Set of 2 sheets . . 10·00 11·00

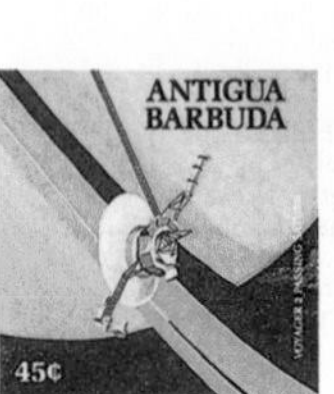

265 "Voyager 2" passing Saturn
266 Queen Mother in Evening Dress

1990. Achievement in Space. Multicoloured.
1395 45c. Type **265** 95 85
1396 45c. "Pioneer 11" photographing Saturn . . 95 85
1397 45c. Astronaut in transporter 95 85
1398 45c. Space shuttle "Columbia" 95 85
1399 45c. "Apollo 10" command module on parachutes . . 95 85
1400 45c. "Skylab" space station 95 85
1401 45c. Astronaut Edward White in space 95 85
1402 45c. "Apollo" spacecraft on joint mission 95 85
1403 45c. "Soyuz" spacecraft on joint mission 95 85
1404 45c. "Mariner 1" passing Venus 95 85
1405 45c. "Gemini 4" capsule . . 95 85
1406 45c. "Sputnik 1" 95 85
1407 45c. Hubble space telescope 95 85
1408 45c. North American X-15 rocket plane 95 85
1409 45c. Bell XS-1 airplane . . . 95 85
1410 45c. "Apollo 17" astronaut and lunar rock formation 95 85
1411 45c. Lunar Rover 95 85
1412 45c. "Apollo 14" lunar module 95 85
1413 45c. Astronaut Buzz Aldrin on Moon 95 85
1414 45c. Soviet "Lunokhod" lunar vehicle 95 85

1990. 90th Birthday of Queen Elizabeth the Queen Mother.
1415 **266** 15c. multicoloured . . . 55 20
1416 – 35c. multicoloured . . . 75 25
1417 – 75c. multicoloured . . . 1·00 85
1418 – $3 multicoloured . . . 2·50 3·50
MS1419 – 67 × 98 mm. mult . . 4·00 4·50
DESIGNS: Nos. 1416/19, Recent photographs of the Queen Mother.

267 Mickey Mouse as Animator

1990. Mickey Mouse in Hollywood. Walt Disney cartoon characters. Multicoloured.
1420 25c. Type **267** 60 25
1421 45c. Minnie Mouse learning lines while being dressed 80 25
1422 50c. Mickey Mouse with clapper board 90 30
1423 60c. Daisy Duck making-up Mickey Mouse . . . . . 1·00 35
1424 $1 Clarabelle Cow as Cleopatra . . . . 1·25 70
1425 $2 Mickey Mouse directing Goofy and Donald Duck 1·75 2·25
1426 $3 Mickey Mouse directing Goofy as birdman . . . . 2·25 3·50
1427 $4 Donald Duck and Mickey Mouse editing film . . . . 2·25 3·50
MS1428 Two sheets, each 132 × 95 mm. (a) $5 Minnie Mouse, Daisy Duck and Clarabelle as musical stars. (b) $5 Mickey Mouse on set as director Set of 2 sheets. . . . . 7·00 9·00

268 Men's 20 Kilometres Walk
269 Huey and Dewey asleep ("Christmas Stories")

1990. Olympic Games, Barcelona (1992) (1st issue). Multicoloured.
1429 50c. Type **268** 75 40
1430 75c. Triple jump . . . . . 1·00 75
1431 $1 Men's 10,000 metres . . 1·25 85
1432 $5 Javelin . . . . 3·50 6·00
MS1433 100 × 70 mm. $6 Athlete lighting Olympic flame at Los Angeles Olympics . . . . . . 5·50 7·00
See also Nos. 1553/61 and 1609/17.

1990. International Literacy Year. Walt Disney cartoon characters illustrating works by Charles Dickens. Multicoloured.
1434 15c. Type **269** 65 35
1435 45c. Donald Duck as Poor Jo looking at grave ("Bleak House") . . . . 1·00 45
1436 50c. Dewey as Oliver asking for more ("Oliver Twist") 1·10 50
1437 60c. Daisy Duck as The Marchioness ("Old Curiosity Shop") . . . . 1·25 55
1438 $1 Little Nell giving nosegay to her grandfather ("Little Nell") . . . . 1·40 85
1439 $2 Scrooge McDuck as Mr. Pickwick ("Pickwick Papers") . . . . 2·00 2·50
1440 $3 Minnie Mouse as Florence and Mickey Mouse as Paul ("Dombey and Son") . . . . 2·25 3·50
1441 $5 Minnie Mouse as Jenny Wren ("Our Mutual Friend") . . . . 2·75 4·50
MS1442 Two sheets, each 126 × 102 mm. (a) $6 Artful Dodger picking pocket ("Oliver Twist"). (b) $6 Unexpected arrivals at Mr. Peggoty's ("David Copperfield") Set of 2 sheets 10·00 12·00

1990. World Cup Football Championship Winners, Italy. Nos. 1308/11 optd **Winners West Germany 1 Argentina 0**.
1443 15c. Type **252** 75 40
1444 25c. Goalkeeper moving towards ball 75 40
1445 $1 Goalkeeper reaching for ball . . . . 1·75 1·60
1446 $4 Goalkeeper saving goal 3·75 5·50
MS1447 Two sheets, each 75 × 105 mm. (a) $5 Three players competing for ball (horiz). (b) $5 Ball and players' legs (horiz) Set of 2 sheets . . . . 9·50 11·00

271 Pearly-eyed Thrasher

1990. Birds. Multicoloured.
1448 10c. Type **271** 45 30
1449 25c. Purple-throated carib 45 35
1450 50c. Common yellowthroat 50 40
1451 60c. American kestrel . . . 1·00 70
1452 $1 Yellow-bellied sapsucker 1·00 80
1453 $2 American purple gallinule ("Purple Gallinule") . . . 2·00 2·25
1454 $3 Yellow-crowned night heron . . . . 2·10 3·00
1455 $4 Blue-hooded euphonia 2·10 3·00
MS1456 Two sheets, each 76 × 60 mm. (a) $6 Brown pelican. (b) $6 Magnificent frigate bird Set of 2 sheets . . . . 14·00 16·00

272 "Madonna and Child with Saints" (detail, Sebastiano del Piombo)

1990. Christmas. Paintings by Renaissance Masters. Multicoloured.
1457 25c. Type **272** 70 30
1458 30c. "Virgin and Child with Angels" (detail, Grunewald) (vert) 80 30
1459 40c. "The Holy Family and a Shepherd" (detail, Titian) 90 30
1460 60c. "Virgin and Child" (detail, Lippi) (vert) . . . 1·25 40
1461 $1 "Jesus, St. John and Two Angels" (Rubens) . . . . 1·50 70
1462 $2 "Adoration of the Shepherds" (detail, Vincenzo Catena) . . . . 2·00 2·50
1463 $4 "Adoration of the Magi" (detail, Giorgione) . . . . 3·50 5·00
1464 $5 "Virgin and Child adored by Warrior" (detail, Vincenzo Catena) . . . . 3·50 5·00
MS1465 Two sheets, each 71 × 101 mm. (a) $6 "Allegory of the Blessings of Jacob" (detail, Rubens) (vert). (b) $6 "Adoration of the Magi" (detail, Fra Angelico) (vert) Set of 2 sheets . . . . . 6·50 7·50

273 "Rape of the Daughters of Leucippus" (detail)

1991. 350th Death Anniv of Rubens. Mult.
1466 25c. Type **273** . . . . . . 1·00 40
1467 45c. "Bacchanal" (detail) . . 1·50 45
1468 50c. "Rape of the Sabine Women" (detail) . . . . 1·50 50
1469 60c. "Battle of the Amazons" (detail) . . . . 1·60 65
1470 $1 "Rape of the Sabine Women" (different detail) 2·00 1·00
1471 $2 "Bacchanal" (different detail) . . . . 2·50 2·50
1472 $3 "Rape of the Sabine Women" (different detail) 3·50 4·25
1473 $4 "Bacchanal" (different detail) . . . . 3·50 5·00
MS1474 Two sheets, each 101 × 71 mm. (a) $6 "Rape of Hippoda-meia" (detail). (b) $6 "Battle of the Amazons" (different detail) Set of 2 sheets . . . . 8·50 10·00

274 U.S. Troops cross into Germany, 1944

1991. 50th Anniv of Second World War. Mult.
1475 10c. Type **274** . . . . . . 1·10 65
1476 15c. Axis surrender in North Africa, 1943 . . . . . . 1·25 50
1477 25c. U.S. tanks invade Kwalajalein, 1944 . . . . 1·25 50
1478 45c. Roosevelt and Churchill meet at Casablanca, 1943 2·50 70
1479 50c. Marshal Badoglio, Prime Minister of Italian anti-fascist government, 1943 . . . . 1·50 70
1480 $1 Lord Mountbatten, Supreme Allied Commander South-east Asia, 1943 . . . . . . 3·00 1·50
1481 $2 Greek victory at Koritza, 1940 . . . . 2·25 2·75
1482 $4 Anglo-Soviet mutual assistance pact, 1941 . . . 3·25 4·25
1483 $5 Operation Torch landings, 1942 . . . . . 3·25 4·25
MS1484 Two sheets, each 108 × 80 mm. (a) $6 Japanese attack on Pearl Harbor, 1941. (b) $6 U.S.A.A.F. daylight raid on Schweinfurt, 1943 Set of 2 sheets 9·00 11·00

275 Locomotive "Prince Regent", Middleton Colliery, 1812

1991. Cog Railways. Multicoloured.
1485 25c. Type **275** . . . . . . 1·25 55
1486 30c. Snowdon Mountain Railway . . . . 1·25 55
1487 40c. First railcar at Hell Gate, Manitou Pike's Peak Railway, U.S.A . . 1·40 65
1488 60c. P.N.K.A. rack railway, Java . . . . 1·60 70
1489 $1 Green Mountain Railway, Maine, 1883 . . 2·00 1·00
1490 $2 Rack locomotive "Pike's Peak", 1891 . . . . . . 3·00 3·00
1491 $4 Vitznau-Rigi Railway, Switzerland, and Mt. Rigi hotel local post stamp . . 3·75 4·75
1492 $5 Leopoldina Railway, Brazil . . . . 3·75 4·75
MS1493 Two sheets, each 100 × 70 mm. (a) $6 Electric towing locomotives, Panama Canal. (b) $6 Gornergracht Railway, Switzerland (vert) Set of 2 sheets . . . . 12·00 13·00

276 "Heliconius charithonia"

1991. Butterflies. Multicoloured.
1494 10c. Type **276** 65 50
1495 35c. "Marpesia petreus" . . 1·10 50
1496 50c. "Anartia amathea" . . 1·25 60
1497 75c. "Siproeta stelenes" . . 1·50 1·00
1498 $1 "Battus polydamas" . . 1·75 1·10
1499 $2 "Historis odius" . . . . 2·25 2·75
1500 $4 "Hypolimnas misippus" 3·25 4·25
1501 $5 "Hamadryas feronia" . . 3·25 4·25
MS1502 Two sheets. (a) 73 × 100 mm. $6 "Vanessa cardui" caterpillar (vert) (b) 100 × 73 mm. $6 "Danaus plexippus" caterpillar (vert) Set of 2 sheets . . . . . 14·00 16·00

277 Hanno the Phoenician, 450 B.C.

1991. 500th Anniv of Discovery of America by Columbus (1992) (4th issue). History of Exploration.
1503 **277** 10c. multicoloured . . . 60 40
1504 – 15c. multicoloured . . . 70 40
1505 – 45c. multicoloured . . . 1·00 50
1506 – 60c. multicoloured . . . 1·25 60
1507 – $1 multicoloured . . . . 1·50 85
1508 – $2 multicoloured . . . . 2·00 2·50
1509 – $4 multicoloured . . . . 2·75 3·75
1510 – $5 multicoloured . . . . 2·75 3·75
MS1511 – Two sheets, each 106 × 76 mm. (a) $6 black and red. (b) $6 black and red Set of 2 sheets 7·00 9·00
DESIGNS—HORIZ: 15c. Pytheas the Greek, 325 B.C.; 45c. Erik the Red discovering Greenland, 985 A.D.; 60c. Leif Eriksson reaching Vinland, 1000 A.D.; $1 Scylax the Greek in the Indian Ocean, 518 A.D.; $2 Marco Polo sailing to the Orient, 1259 A.D.; $4 Ship of Queen Hatshepsut of Egypt, 1493 B.C.; $5 St. Brendan's coracle, 500 A.D. VERT: $6 (No. **MS**1511a) Engraving of Columbus as Admiral; $6 (No. **MS**1511b) Engraving of Columbus bare-headed.

278 "Camille Roulin" (Van Gogh)

1991. Death Centenary (1990) of Vincent van Gogh (artist). Multicoloured.
1512 5c. Type **278** 70 85
1513 10c. "Armand Roulin" . . . 70 60
1514 15c. "Young Peasant Woman with Straw Hat sitting in the Wheat" . . 85 50
1515 25c. "Adeline Ravoux" . . 1·00 50
1516 30c. "The Schoolboy" . . . 1·00 50

1517 40c. "Doctor Gachet" . . . 1·10 50

1518 50c. "Portrait of a Man" . . 1·25 50

1519 75c. "Two Children" . . . 1·75 80

1520 $2 "The Postman Joseph Roulin" . . . . 2·75 2·75

1521 $3 "The Seated Zouave" . . 3·75 4·00

1522 $4 "L'Arlesienne" . . . . . 4·00 4·50

1523 $5 "Self-Portrait, November/ December 1888" . . . . 4·00 4·50

MS1524 Three sheets, each 102×76 mm. (a) $5 "Farmhouse in Provence" (horiz). (b) $5 "Flowering Garden" (horiz). (c) $6 "The Bridge at Trinquetaille" (horiz) Imperf Set of 3 sheets 15·00 16·00

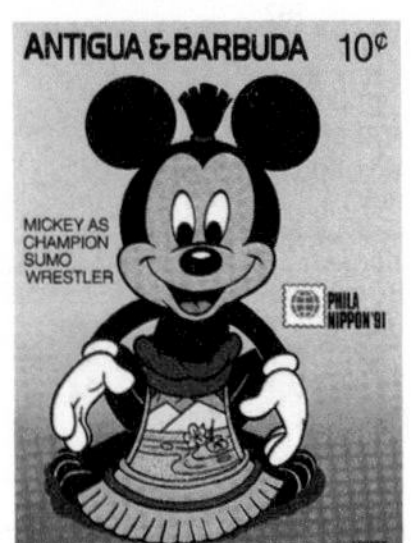

279 Mickey Mouse as Champion Sumo Wrestler

1991. "Philanippon '91" International Stamp Exhibition, Tokyo. Walt Disney cartoon characters participating in martial arts. Multicoloured.

1525 10c. Type **279** 70 20

1526 15c. Goofy using the tonfa (horiz) 85 25

1527 45c. Donald Duck as a Ninja (horiz) . . . . . . 1·40 50

1528 60c. Mickey armed for Kung fu . . . . 1·75 65

1529 $1 Goofy with Kendo sword 2·25 1·25

1530 $2 Mickey and Donald demonstrating Aikido (horiz) . . . . 2·75 2·75

1531 $4 Mickey and Donald in Judo bout (horiz) . . . . 3·50 4·75

1532 $5 Mickey performing Yabusame (mounted archery) . . . . 3·50 4·75

MS1533 Two sheets, each 127×102 mm. (a) $6 Mickey delivering Karate kick (horiz). (b) $6 Mickey demonstrating Tamashiwara Set of 2 sheets 10·00 11·00

280 Queen Elizabeth and Prince Philip in 1976

1991. 65th Birthday of Queen Elizabeth II. Multicoloured.

1534 15c. Type **280** 30 10

1535 20c. The Queen and Prince Philip in Portugal, 1985 30 10

1536 $2 Queen Elizabeth II . . . 1·50 1·50

1537 $4 The Queen and Prince Philip at Ascot, 1986 . . 2·75 3·25

MS1538 68×90 mm. $4 The Queen at National Theatre, 1986, and Prince Philip . . . . 3·25 4·00

1991. 10th Wedding Anniv of Prince and Princess of Wales. As T **280**. Multicoloured.

1539 10c. Prince and Princess of Wales at party, 1986 . . . 40 10

1540 40c. Separate portraits of Prince, Princess and sons 80 25

1541 $1 Prince Henry and Prince William . . . . 1·10 70

1542 $5 Princess Diana in Australia and Prince Charles in Hungary . . . 4·25 4·50

MS1543 68×90 mm. $4 Prince Charles in Hackney and Princess and sons in Majorca, 1987 . . 5·00 5·50

281 Daisy Duck teeing-off

1991. Golf. Walt Disney cartoon characters. Mult.

1544 10c. Type **281** 70 50

1545 15c. Goofy playing ball from under trees 75 50

1546 45c. Mickey Mouse playing deflected shot . . . . . . 1·25 50

1547 60c. Mickey hacking divot out of fairway . . . . . 1·50 65

1548 $1 Donald Duck playing ball out of pond . . . . 1·75 1·10

1549 $2 Minnie Mouse hitting ball over pond . . . . . 2·50 2·75

1550 $4 Donald in a bunker . . . 3·25 4·00

1551 $5 Goofy trying snooker shot into hole . . . . . . 3·25 4·00

MS1552 Two sheets, each 127×102 mm. (a) $6 Grandma Duck in senior tournament. (b) $6 Mickey and Minnie Mouse on course (horiz) Set of 2 sheets 10·00 12·00

282 Moose receiving Gold Medal

1991. 50th Anniv of Archie Comics, and Olympic Games, Barcelona (1992) (2nd issue). Multicoloured.

1553 10c. Type **282** 55 40

1554 25c. Archie playing polo on a motorcycle (horiz) . . . 85 40

1555 40c. Archie and Betty at fencing class . . . . . . 1·10 45

1556 60c. Archie joining girls' volleyball team . . . . . 1·40 65

1557 $1 Archie with tennis ball in his mouth . . . . 1·75 1·10

1558 $2 Archie running marathon 2·50 3·00

1559 $4 Archie judging women's gymnastics (horiz) . . . . 3·75 4·50

1560 $5 Archie watching the cheer-leaders . . . . . . 3·75 4·50

MS1561 Two sheets, each 128×102 mm. (a) $6 Archie heading football. (b) $6 Archie catching baseball (horiz) Set of 2 sheets . . . . 11·00 12·00

283 Presidents De Gaulle and Kennedy, 1961

1991. Birth Centenary of Charles de Gaulle (French statesman). Multicoloured.

1562 10c. Type **283** 70 40

1563 15c. General De Gaulle with President Roosevelt, 1945 (vert) 70 40

1564 45c. President De Gaulle with Chancellor Adenauer, 1962 (vert) . . 1·10 40

1565 60c. De Gaulle at Arc de Triomphe, Liberation of Paris, 1944 (vert) . . . . 1·25 65

1566 $1 General De Gaulle crossing the Rhine, 1945 1·50 1·10

1567 $2 General De Gaulle in Algiers, 1944 . . . . . . 2·25 2·75

1568 $4 Presidents De Gaulle and Eisenhower, 1960 . . . . 3·00 4·00

1569 $5 De Gaulle returning from Germany, 1968 (vert) . . 3·00 4·00

MS1570 Two sheets. (a) 76×106 mm. $6 De Gaulle with crowd. (b) 106×76 mm. $6 De Gaulle and Churchill at Casablanca, 1943 Set of 2 sheets 13·00 13·00

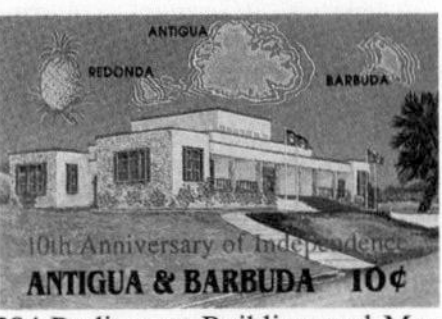

284 Parliament Building and Map

1991. 10th Anniv of Independence.

1571 **284** 10c. multicoloured . . . 75 50

MS1572 87×97 mm. $6 Old Post Office, St. Johns, and stamps of 1862 and 1981 (50×37 mm) 6·00 7·50

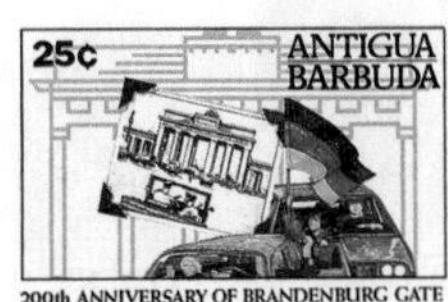

285 Germans celebrating Reunification

1991. Anniversaries and Events. Multicoloured.

1573 25c. Type **285** 30 30

1574 75c. Cubs erecting tent . . . 50 50

1575 $1.50 "Don Giovanni" and Mozart . . . . 4·00 2·75

1576 $2 Chariot driver and Gate at night . . . . 1·10 2·00

1577 $2 Lord Baden-Powell and members of 3rd Antigua Methodist cub pack (vert) 3·00 2·75

1578 $2 Lilienthal's signature and glider "Flugzeug Nr. 5" 3·25 2·75

1579 $2.50 Driver in Class P36 steam locomotive (vert) 5·00 3·75

1580 $3 Statues from podium . . 1·75 3·00

1581 $3.50 Cubs and camp fire 2·25 3·00

1582 $4 St. Peter's Cathedral, Salzburg . . . . 7·50 6·00

MS1583 Two sheets. (a) 100×72 mm. $4 Detail of chariot and helmet; (b) 89×117 mm. $5 Antiguan flag and Jamboree emblem (vert) Set of 2 sheets 8·00 11·00

ANNIVERSARIES AND EVENTS: Nos. 1573, 1576, 1580, **MS**1583a, Bicentenary of Brandenburg Gate, Germany; 1574, 1577, 1581, **MS**1583b, 17th World Scout Jamboree, Korea; 1575, 1582, Death bicentenary of Mozart (composer); 1578, Centenary of Otto Lilienthal's gliding experiments; 1579, Centenary of Trans-Siberian Railway.

286 "Nimitz" Class Carrier and "Ticonderoga" Class Cruiser

1991. 50th Anniv of Japanese Attack on Pearl Harbor. Multicoloured.

1585 $1 Type **286** . . . . 1·75 1·50

1586 $1 Tourist launch . . . . . 1·75 1·50

1587 $1 U.S.S. "Arizona" memorial . . . . 1·75 1·50

1588 $1 Wreaths on water and aircraft . . . . 1·75 1·50

1589 $1 White tern . . . . 1·75 1·50

1590 $1 Mitsubishi A6M Zero-Sen fighters over Pearl City . . . . 1·75 1·50

1591 $1 Mitsubishi A6M Zero-Sen fighters attacking . . 1·75 1·50

1592 $1 Battleship Row in flames 1·75 1·50

1593 $1 U.S.S. "Nevada" (battleship) underway . . 1·75 1·50

1594 $1 Mitsubishi A6M Zero-Sen fighters returning to carriers . . . . 1·75 1·50

287 "The Annunciation"

1991. Christmas. Religious Paintings by Fra Angelico. Multicoloured.

1595 10c. Type **287** 40 30

1596 30c. "Nativity" 65 30

1597 40c. "Adoration of the Magi" 75 30

1598 60c. "Presentation in the Temple" . . . . 1·00 45

1599 $1 "Circumcision" . . . . 1·25 65

1600 $3 "Flight into Egypt" . . . 2·50 3·50

1601 $4 "Massacre of the Innocents" . . . . 2·50 4·00

1602 $5 "Christ teaching in the Temple" . . . . 2·50 4·00

MS1603 Two sheets, each 102×127 mm. (a) $6 "Adoration of the Magi" (Cook Tondo). (b) $6 "Adoration of the Magi" (different) Set of 2 sheets . . . 13·00 14·00

288 Queen Elizabeth II and Bird Sanctuary

1992. 40th Anniv of Queen Elizabeth II's Accession. Multicoloured.

1604 10c. Type **288** 90 40

1605 30c. Nelson's Dockyard . . 1·25 40

1606 $1 Ruins on Shirley Heights 1·25 70

1607 $5 Beach and palm trees . . 2·75 3·75

MS1608 Two sheets, each 75×98 mm. (a) $6 Beach. (b) $6 Hillside foliage Set of 2 sheets 8·50 9·00

289 Mickey Mouse awarding Swimming Gold Medal to Mermaid

1992. Olympic Games, Barcelona (3rd issue). Walt Disney cartoon characters. Multicoloured.

1609 10c. Type **289** 60 30

1610 15c. Huey, Dewey and Louie with kayak 70 30

1611 30c. Donald Duck and Uncle Scrooge in yacht 85 35

1612 50c. Donald and horse playing water polo . . . 1·10 50

1613 $1 Big Pete weightlifting . . 1·75 85

1614 $2 Donald and Goofy fencing . . . . 2·50 2·50

1615 $4 Mickey and Donald playing volleyball . . . . 3·50 3·75

1616 $5 Goofy vaulting . . . . . 3·50 3·75

MS1617 Four sheets, each 123×98 mm. (a) $6 Mickey playing football. (b) $6 Mickey playing basketball (horiz). (c) $6 Minnie Mouse on uneven parallel bars (horiz). (d) $6 Mickey, Goofy and Donald judging gymnastics (horiz) Set of 4 sheets . . . . 14·00 15·00

290 Pteranodon

1992. Prehistoric Animals. Mult.

1618 10c. Type **290** 65 40

1619 15c. Brachiosaurus 65 40

1620 30c. Tyrannosaurus Rex . . 85 40

1621 50c. Parasaurolophus . . . 1·00 50

1622 $1 Deinonychus (horiz) . . 1·50 1·00

1623 $2 Triceratops (horiz) . . . 2·00 2·00

1624 $4 Protoceratops hatching (horiz) . . . . 2·25 2·75

1625 $5 Stegosaurus (horiz) . . . 2·25 2·75

MS1626 Two sheets, each 100×70 mm. (a) $6 Apatosaurus (horiz). (b) $6 Allosaurus (horiz) Set of 2 sheets . . . . 8·50 9·50

291 "Supper at Emmaus" (Caravaggio)

1992. Easter. Religious Paintings. Multicoloured.

1627 10c. Type **291** 55 25

1628 15c. "The Vision of St. Peter" (Zurbaran) . . 65 25

1629 30c. "Christ driving the Money-changers from the Temple" (Tiepolo) 90 40

1630 40c. "Martyrdom of St. Bartholomew" (detail) (Ribera) . . . . 1·00 50

1631 $1 "Christ driving the Money-changers from the Temple" (detail) (Tiepolo) 1·75 1·00

1632 $2 "Crucifixion" (detail) (Altdorfer) . . . . 2·75 2·75

1633 $4 "The Deposition" (detail) (Fra Angelico) . . . . . 3·75 4·50

1634 $5 "The Deposition" (different detail) (Fra Angelico) . . . . 3·75 4·50

MS1635 Two sheets. (a) 102×71 mm. $6 "The Last Supper" (detail, Masip). (b) 71×102 mm. $6 "Crucifixion" (detail, Altdorfer) (vert) Set of 2 sheets . . . . 9·50 12·00

292 "The Miracle at the Well" (Alonso Cano)

1992. "Granada '92" International Stamp Exhibition, Spain. Spanish Paintings. Multicoloured.

1636 10c. Type **292** 50 30
1637 15c. "The Poet Luis de Goingora y Argote" (Velazquez) 65 30
1638 30c. "The Painter Francisco Goya" (Vincente Lopez Portana) 85 40
1639 40c. "Maria de las Nieves Michaela Fourdinier" (Luis Paret y Alcazar) 95 50
1640 $1 "Carlos III eating before his Court" (Alcazar) (horiz) 1·75 1·25
1641 $2 "Rain Shower in Granada" (Antonio Munoz Degrain) (horiz) 2·50 2·75
1642 $4 "Sarah Bernhardt" (Santiago Rusinol i Prats) 3·50 4·00
1643 $5 "The Hermitage Garden" (Joaquim Mir Trinxet) 3·50 4·00
MS1644 Two sheets, each 120 × 95 mm. (a) $6 "The Ascent of Monsieur Boucle's Montgolfier Balloon in the Gardens of Aranjuez" (Antonio Carnicero) (112 × 87 mm). (b) $6 "Olympus: Battle with the Giants" (Francisco Bayeu y Subías) (112 × 87 mm). Imperf Set of 2 sheets 13·00 14·00

293 "Amanita caesarea"

1992. Fungi. Multicoloured.

1645 10c. Type **293** 70 40
1646 15c. "Collybia fusipes" 85 40
1647 30c. "Boletus aereus" 1·25 40
1648 40c. "Laccaria amethystina" 1·25 50
1649 $1 "Russula virescens" 2·00 1·25
1650 $2 "Tricholoma equestre" ("Tricholoma auratum") 2·75 2·75
1651 $4 "Calocybe gambosa" 3·50 3·75
1652 $5 "Lentinus tigrinus" ("Panus tigrinus") 3·50 3·75
MS1653 Two sheets, each 100 × 70 mm. (a) $6 "Clavariadelphus truncatus". (b) $6 "Auricularia auricula-judae" Set of 2 sheets 12·00 13·00

294 Memorial Cross and Huts, San Salvador

1992. 500th Anniv of Discovery of America by Columbus (5th issue). World Columbian Stamp "Expo '92", Chicago. Multicoloured.

1654 15c. Type **294** 30 20
1655 30c. Martin Pinzon with telescope 45 25
1656 40c. Christopher Columbus 65 35
1657 $1 "Pinta" 2·50 1·25
1658 $2 "Nina" 2·75 2·75
1659 $4 "Santa Maria" 3·50 5·50
MS1660 Two sheets, each 108 × 76 mm. (a) $6 Ship and map of West Indies. (b) $6 Sea monster Set of 2 sheets 8·50 11·00

295 Antillean Crested Hummingbird and Wild Plantain

1992. "Genova '92" International Thematic Stamp Exhibition. Hummingbirds and Plants. Multicoloured.

1661 10c. Type **295** 35 50
1662 25c. Green mango and parrot's plantain 50 40
1663 45c. Purple-throated carib and lobster claws 70 45
1664 60c. Antillean mango and coral plant 80 55
1665 $1 Vervain hummingbird and cardinal's guard 1·10 85
1666 $2 Rufous-breasted hermit and heliconia 1·75 2·00
1667 $4 Blue-headed hummingbird and red ginger 3·00 3·25
1668 $5 Green-throated carib and ornamental banana 3·00 3·25
MS1669 Two sheets, each 100 × 70 mm. (a) $6 Bee hummingbird and jungle flame. (b) $6 Western streamertail and bignonia Set of 2 sheets 10·00 12·00

296 Columbus meeting Amerindians

1992. 500th Anniv of Discovery of America by Columbus (6th issue). Organization of East Caribbean States. Multicoloured.

1670 $1 Type **296** 85 65
1671 $2 Ships approaching island 1·40 1·60

297 Ts'ai Lun and Paper

1992. Inventors and Inventions. Mult.

1672 10c. Type **297** 25 25
1673 25c. Igor Sikorsky and "Bolshoi Baltiskii" (first four-engined airplane) 1·25 40
1674 30c. Alexander Graham Bell and early telephone 55 45
1675 40c. Johannes Gutenberg and early printing press 55 45
1676 60c. James Watt and stationary steam engine 3·00 1·25
1677 $1 Anton van Leeuwenhoek and early microscope 1·75 1·40
1678 $4 Louis Braille and hands reading braille 4·25 5·00
1679 $5 Galileo and telescope 4·25 5·00
MS1680 Two sheets, each 100 × 73 mm. (a) $6 Edison and Latimer's phonograph. (b) $6 "Clermont" (first commercial paddle-steamer) Set of 2 sheets 9·50 12·00

298 Elvis looking Pensive

1992. 15th Death Anniv of Elvis Presley. Mult.

1681 $1 Type **298** 1·60 1·00
1682 $1 Wearing black and yellow striped shirt 1·60 1·00
1683 $1 Singing into microphone 1·60 1·00
1684 $1 Wearing wide-brimmed hat 1·60 1·00
1685 $1 With microphone in right hand 1·60 1·00
1686 $1 In Army uniform 1·60 1·00
1687 $1 Wearing pink shirt 1·60 1·00
1688 $1 In yellow shirt 1·60 1·00
1689 $1 In jacket and bow tie 1·60 1·00

299 Madison Square Gardens

1992. Postage Stamp Mega Event, New York. Sheet 100 × 70 mm.

MS1690 $6 multicoloured 4·25 5·50

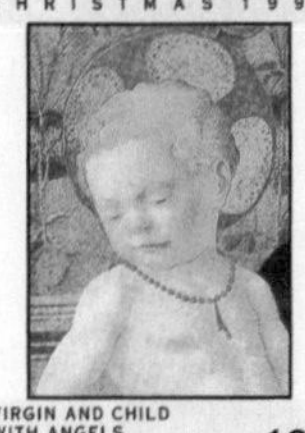

300 "Virgin and Child with Angels" (detail) (School of Piero della Francesca)

301 Russian Cosmonauts

1992. Christmas. Details of the Holy Child from various paintings. Multicoloured.

1691 10c. Type **300** 60 30
1692 25c. "Madonna degli Alberelli" (Giovanni Bellini) 90 30
1693 30c. "Madonna and Child with St. Anthony Abbot and St. Sigismund" (Neroccio) 95 30
1694 40c. "Madonna and the Grand Duke" (Raphael) 1·00 30
1695 60c. "The Nativity" (Georges de la Tour) 1·50 60
1696 $1 "Holy Family" (Jacob Jordaens) 1·75 1·00
1697 $4 "Madonna and Child Enthroned" (Magaritone) 3·75 4·75
1698 $5 "Madonna and Child on a Curved Throne" (Byzantine school) 3·75 4·75
MS1699 Two sheets, each 76 × 102 mm. (a) $6 "Madonna and Child" (Domenco Ghirlando). (b) $6 "The Holy Family" (Pontormo) Set of 2 sheets 9·50 12·00

1992. Anniversaries and Events. Mult.

1700 10c. Type **301** 70 60
1701 40c. "Graf Zeppelin" (airship), 1929 1·50 65
1702 45c. Bishop Daniel Davis 50 40
1703 75c. Konrad Adenauer making speech 65 65
1704 $1 Bus Mosbacher and "Weatherly" (yacht) 1·25 1·25
1705 $1.50 Rain forest 1·40 1·50
1706 $2 Tiger 5·00 3·50
1707 $2 National flag, plant and emblem (horiz) 3·50 2·25
1708 $2 Members of Community Players company (horiz) 1·75 2·25
1709 $2.25 Women carrying pots 1·75 2·50
1710 $3 Lions Club emblem 2·25 3·00
1711 $4 Chinese rocket on launch tower 3·50 3·75
1712 $4 West German and N.A.T.O. flags 3·50 3·75
1713 $6 Hugo Eckener (airship pioneer) 4·00 5·00
MS1714 Four sheets, each 100 × 71 mm. (a) $6 Projected European space station. (b) $6 Airship LZ-129 "Hindenburg", 1936. (c) $6 Brandenburg Gate on German flag. (d) $6 "Danaus plexippus" (butterfly) Set of 4 sheets 17·00 19·00

ANNIVERSARIES AND EVENTS: Nos. 1700, 1711, **MS**1714a, International Space Year; 1701, 1713, **MS**1714b, 75th death anniv of Count Ferdinand von Zeppelin; 1702, 150th anniv of Anglican Diocese of North-eastern Caribbean and Aruba; 1703, 1712, **MS**1714c, 25th death anniv of Konrad Adenauer (German statesman); 1704, Americas Cup yachting championship; 1705/6, **MS**1714d, Earth Summit '92, Rio; 1707, 50th anniv of Inter-American Institute for Agricultural Co-operation; 1708, 40th anniv of Cultural Development; 1709, United Nations World Health Organization Projects; 1710, 75th anniv of International Association of Lions Clubs.

302 Boy Hiker resting

304 Cardinal's Guard

303 Goofy playing Golf

1993. Hummel Figurines. Multicoloured.

1715 15c. Type **302** 35 15
1716 30c. Girl sitting on fence 55 25
1717 40c. Boy hunter 65 35
1718 50c. Boy with umbrella 75 45
1719 $1 Hikers at signpost 1·25 75
1720 $2 Boy hiker with pack and stick 1·75 2·25
1721 $4 Girl with young child and goat 2·75 3·50
1722 $5 Boy whistling 2·75 3·50
MS1723 Two sheets, each 97 × 122 mm. (a) $1.50 × 4, As Nos. 1715/18. (b) $1.50 × 4, As Nos. 1719/22 Set of 2 sheets 13·00 14·00

1993. Opening of Euro-Disney Resort, Paris. Multicoloured.

1724 10c. Type **303** 80 30
1725 25c. Chip and Dale at Davy Crockett's campground 1·00 30
1726 30c. Donald Duck at the Cheyenne Hotel 1·00 35
1727 40c. Goofy at the Santa Fe Hotel 1·10 35
1728 $1 Mickey and Minnie Mouse at the New York Hotel 2·25 1·25
1729 $2 Mickey, Minnie and Goofy in car 2·75 2·75
1730 $4 Goofy at Pirates of the Caribbean 4·00 5·00
1731 $5 Donald at Adventureland 4·00 5·00
MS1732 Four sheets, each 127 × 102 mm. (a) $6 Mickey in bellboy outfit. (b) $6 Mickey on star (vert). (c) $6 Mickey on opening poster (vert). (d) $6 Mickey and balloons on opening poster (vert) Set of 2 sheets 16·00 18·00

1993. Flowers. Multicoloured.

1733 15c. Type **304** 1·00 40
1734 25c. Giant granadilla 1·10 40
1735 30c. Spider flower 1·10 40
1736 40c. Gold vine 1·25 40
1737 $1 Frangipani 2·00 1·25
1738 $2 Bougainvillea 2·75 2·75
1739 $4 Yellow oleander 3·75 4·50
1740 $5 Spicy jatropha 3·75 4·50
MS1741 Two sheets, each 100 × 70 mm. (a) $6 Birdlime tree. (b) Fairy lily Set of 2 sheets 9·00 12·00

305 "The Destiny of Marie de' Medici" (upper detail)

1993. Bicentenary of the Louvre, Paris. Paintings by Peter Paul Rubens. Multicoloured.

1742 $1 Type **305** 95 85
1743 $1 "The Birth of Marie de' Medici" 95 85
1744 $1 "The Education of Marie de' Medici" 95 85
1745 $1 "The Destiny of Marie de' Medici" (lower detail) 95 85
1746 $1 "Henry VI receiving the Portrait of Marie" 95 85
1747 $1 "The Meeting of the King and Marie at Lyons" 95 85
1748 $1 "The Marriage by Proxy" 95 85
1749 $1 "The Birth of Louis XIII" 95 85
1750 $1 "The Capture of Juliers" 95 85
1751 $1 "The Exchange of the Princesses" 95 85
1752 $1 "The Regency" 95 85
1753 $1 "The Majority of Louis XIII" 95 85
1754 $1 "The Flight from Blois" 95 85
1755 $1 "The Treaty of Angouleme" 95 85
1756 $1 "The Peace of Angers" 95 85
1757 $1 "The Reconciliation of Louis and Marie de' Medici" 95 85
MS1758 70 × 100 mm. $6 "Helene Faurment with a Coach" (52 × 85 mm) 5·50 7·00

Nos. 1742/57 depict details from "The Story of Marie de' Medici".

306 St. Lucia Amazon ("St. Lucia Parrot")

1993. Endangered Species. Multicoloured.
1759 $1 Type **306** 90 90
1760 $1 Cahow 90 90
1761 $1 Swallow-tailed kite . . . 90 90
1762 $1 Everglade kite ("Everglades Kite") . . . 90 90
1763 $1 Imperial amazon ("Imperial Parrot") . . . 90 90
1764 $1 Humpback whale 90 90
1765 $1 Plain pigeon ("Puerto Rican Plain Pigeon") . . 90 90
1766 $1 St. Vincent amazon ("St. Vincent Parrot") . . 90 90
1767 $1 Puerto Rican amazon ("Puerto Rican Parrot") 90 90
1768 $1 Leatherback turtle . . . 90 90
1769 $1 American crocodile . . . 90 90
1770 $1 Hawksbill turtle 90 90
MS1771 Two sheets, each 100 × 70 mm. (a) $6 As No. 1764. (b) West Indian manatee Set of 2 sheets . . . . 7·00 8·00
Nos. 1759/70 were printed together, se-tenant, with the background forming a composite design.

307 Queen Elizabeth II at Coronation (photograph by Cecil Beaton)

1993. 40th Anniv of Coronation (1st issue).
1772 **307** 30c. multicoloured . . . 60 60
1773 – 40c. multicoloured . . . 70 70
1774 – $2 blue and black . . . 1·75 2·00
1775 – $4 multicoloured . . . 2·25 2·50
MS1776 70 × 100 mm. $6 multicoloured . . . . 4·75 5·50
DESIGNS: 40c. Queen Elizabeth the Queen Mother's Crown, 1937; $2 Procession of heralds; $4 Queen Elizabeth II and Prince Edward. (28½ × 42½ mm)—$6 "Queen Elizabeth II" (detail) (Dennis Fildes).

308 Princess Margaret and Antony Armstrong-Jones

1993. 40th Anniv of Coronation (2nd issue).
1777/1808 $1 × 32 either grey and black or multicoloured . . . 26·00 28·00
DESIGNS: Various views as Type **308** from each decade of the reign.

309 Edward Stanley Gibbons and Catalogue of 1865

1993. Famous Professional Philatelists (1st series).
1809 **309** $1.50 brown, black & grn . . . . 1·25 1·25
1810 – $1.50 multicoloured . . 1·25 1·25
1811 – $1.50 multicoloured . . 1·25 1·25
1812 – $1.50 multicoloured . . 1·25 1·25
1813 – $1.50 multicoloured . . 1·25 1·25
1814 – $1.50 multicoloured . . 1·25 1·25
MS1815 98 × 69 mm. $3 black; $3 black . . . . 5·50 6·50
DESIGNS: No. 1810, Theodore Champion and France 1849 1f. stamp; 1811, J. Walter Scott and U.S.A. 1918 24c. "Inverted Jenny" error; 1812, Hugo Michel and Bavaria 1849 1k. stamp; 1813, Alberto and Giulio Bolaffi with Sardinia 1851 5c. stamp; 1814, Richard Borek and Brunswick 1865 1gr. stamp; **MS**1815, Front pages of "Mekeel's Weekly Stamp News" in 1891 (misdated 1890) and 1993.
See also No. 1957.

310 Paul Gascoigne

311 Grand Inspector W. Heath

1993. World Cup Football Championship, U.S.A. (1st issue). English Players. Multicoloured.
1816 $2 Type **310** . . . . . . 1·50 1·40
1817 $2 David Platt . . . . . . 1·50 1·40
1818 $2 Martin Peters . . . . . 1·50 1·40
1819 $2 John Barnes . . . . . . 1·50 1·40
1820 $2 Gary Lineker . . . . . 1·50 1·40
1821 $2 Geoff Hurst . . . . . . 1·50 1·40
1822 $2 Bobby Charlton . . . . 1·50 1·40
1823 $2 Bryan Robson . . . . . 1·50 1·40
1824 $2 Bobby Moore . . . . . 1·50 1·40
1825 $2 Nobby Stiles . . . . . 1·50 1·40
1826 $2 Gordon Banks . . . . . 1·50 1·40
1827 $2 Peter Shilton . . . . . 1·50 1·40
MS1828 Two sheets, each 135 × 109 mm. (a) $6 Bobby Moore holding World Cup. (b) $6 Gary Lineker and Bobby Robson Set of 2 sheets . . . . 9·00 10·00
See also Nos. 2039/45.

1993. Anniversaries and Events. Multicoloured.
1829 10c. Type **311** . . . . . . 1·75 1·00
1830 15c. Rodnina and Oulanov (U.S.S.R.) (pairs figure skating) (horiz) . . . . . 1·00 50
1831 30c. Present Masonic Hall, St. John's (horiz) . . . . 2·00 1·00
1832 30c. Willy Brandt with Helmut Schmidt and George Leber (horiz) . . 60 40
1833 30c. "Cat and Bird" (Picasso) (horiz) 60 40
1834 40c. Previous Masonic Hall, St. John's (horiz) . . . . 2·00 1·00
1835 40c. "Fish on a Newspaper" (Picasso) (horiz) 60 50
1836 40c. Early astronomical equipment 60 50
1837 40c. Prince Naruhito and engagement photographs (horiz) 60 50
1838 60c. Grand Inspector J. Jeffery . . . . 2·50 1·25
1839 $1 "Woman combing her Hair" (W. Slewinski) (horiz) . . . . 1·00 1·25
1840 $3 Masako Owada and engagement photographs (horiz) . . . . 2·25 2·75
1841 $3 "Artist's Wife with Cat" (Konrad Kryzanowski) (horiz) . . . . 2·25 2·75
1842 $4 Willy Brandt and protest march (horiz) . . . . . . 2·50 3·25
1843 $4 Galaxy . . . . 2·50 3·25
1844 $5 Alberto Tomba (Italy) (giant slalom) (horiz) . . 2·50 3·25
1845 $5 "Dying Bull" (Picasso) (horiz) . . . . 2·50 3·25
1846 $5 Pres. Clinton and family (horiz) . . . . 2·50 3·25
MS1847 Seven sheets. (a) 106 × 75 mm. $5 Copernicus. (b) 106 × 75 mm. $6 Womens' 1500 metre speed skating medallists (horiz). (c) 106 × 75 mm. $6 Willy Brandt at Warsaw Ghetto Memorial (horiz). (d) 106 × 75 mm. $6 "Woman with a Dog" (detail) (Picasso) (horiz). (e) 106 × 75 mm. $6 Masako Owada. (f) 70 × 100 mm. $6 "General Confusion" (S. I. Witkiewicz). (g) 106 × 75 mm. $6 Pres. Clinton taking the Oath (42½ × 57 mm) Set of 7 sheets . . . . 22·00 25·00
ANNIVERSARIES AND EVENTS: Nos. 1829, 1831, 1834, 1838, 150th anniv of St. John's Masonic Lodge No. 492; 1830, 1844, **MS**1847b, Winter Olympic Games '94, Lillehammer; 1832, 1842, **MS**1847c, 80th birth anniv of Willy Brandt (German politician); 1833, 1835, 1845, **MS**1847d, 20th death anniv of Picasso (artist); 1836, 1843, **MS**1847a, 450th death anniv of Copernicus (astronomer); 1837, 1840, **MS**1847e, Marriage of Crown Prince Naruhito of Japan; 1839, 1841, **MS**1847f, "Polska '93" International Stamp Exhibition, Poznan; 1846, **MS**1847g, Inauguration of U.S. President William Clinton.

312 Hugo Eckener and Dr. W. Beckers with Airship "Graf Zeppelin" over Lake George, New York

1993. Aviation Anniversaries. Multicoloured.
1848 30c. Type **312** . . . . . . 1·00 70
1849 40c. Chicago World's Fair from "Graf Zeppelin" . . 1·00 1·00
1850 40c. Gloster Whittle E.28/39, 1941 . . . . 1·00 1·00
1851 40c. George Washington writing balloon mail letter (vert) . . . . 1·00 1·00
1852 $4 Pres. Wilson and Curtiss JN-4 Jenny . . . . 3·75 4·50
1853 $5 Airship "Hindenburg" over Ebbets Field baseball stadium, 1937 . . . . . 3·75 4·50
1854 $5 Gloster Meteor in dogfight . . . . 3·75 4·50
MS1855 Three sheets. (a) 86 × 105 mm. $6 Hugo Eckener (vert). (b) 105 × 86 mm. $6 Consolidated PBY-5 Catalina flying boat (57 × 42½ mm). (c) 105 × 86 mm. $6 Alexander Hamilton, Washington and John Jay watching Blanchard's balloon, 1793 (horiz) Set of 3 sheets . . 16·00 18·00
ANNIVERSARIES: Nos. 1848/9, 1853, **MS**1855a, 125th birth anniv of Hugo Eckener (airship commander); 1850, 1854, **MS**1855b, 75th anniv of Royal Air Force; 1851/2, **MS**1855c, Bicentenary of first airmail flight.

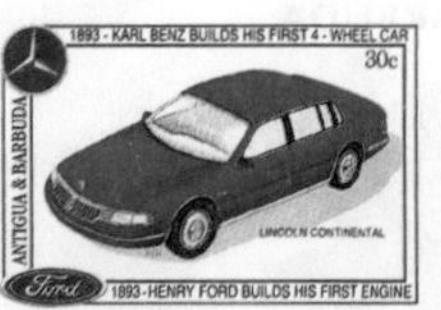

313 Lincoln Continental

1993. Centenaries of Henry Ford's First Petrol Engine (Nos. 1856, 1858), and Karl Benz's First Four-wheeled Car (others). Multicoloured.
1856 30c. Type **313** . . . . . . 1·00 75
1857 40c. Mercedes racing car, 1914 . . . . 1·00 75
1858 $4 Ford "GT40", 1966 . . . 4·00 4·50
1859 $5 Mercedes Benz "gull-wing" coupe, 1954 . . . 4·00 4·50
MS1860 Two sheets. (a) 114 × 87 mm. $6 Ford's Mustang emblem. (b) 87 × 114 mm. $6 Germany 1936 12pf. Benz and U.S.A. 1968 12c. Ford stamps Set of 2 sheets . . . . 9·00 11·00

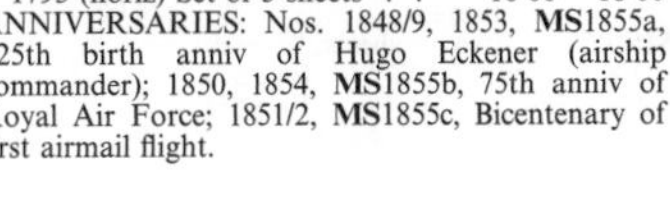

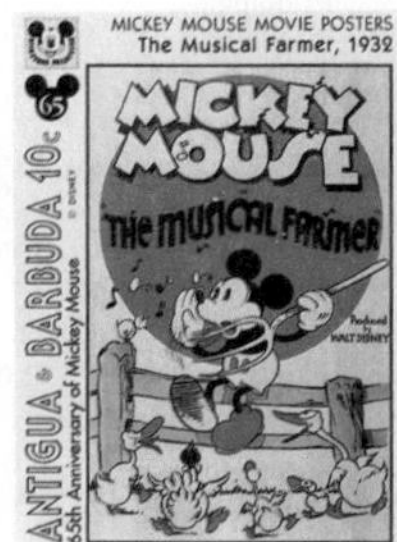

314 "The Musical Farmer", 1932

1993. Mickey Mouse Film Posters. Mult.
1861 10c. Type **314** 60 30
1862 15c. "Little Whirlwind", 1941 . . . . 70 35
1863 30c. "Pluto's Dream House", 1940 . . . . . 80 40
1864 40c. "Gulliver Mickey", 1934 . . . . 80 40
1865 50c. "Alpine Climbers", 1936 . . . . 80 45
1866 $1 "Mr. Mouse Takes a Trip", 1940 . . . . . . 1·25 80
1867 $2 "The Nifty Nineties", 1941 . . . . 1·75 2·00
1868 $4 "Mickey Down Under", 1948 . . . . 2·50 3·50
1869 $5 "The Pointer", 1939 . . 2·50 3·50
MS1870 Two sheets, each 125 × 105 mm. (a) $6 "The Simple Things", 1953. (b) $6 "The Prince and the Pauper", 1990 Set of 2 sheets . . . . 10·00 12·00

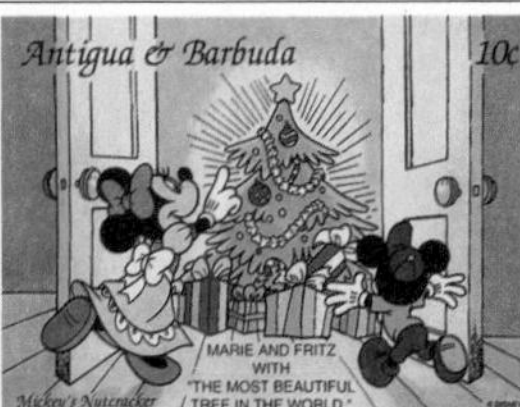

315 Marie and Fritz with Christmas Tree

1993. Christmas. Mickey's Nutcracker. Walt Disney cartoon characters in scenes from "The Nutcracker". Multicoloured.
1871 10c. Type **315** 75 40
1872 15c. Marie receives Nutcracker from Godfather Drosselmeir . . 80 40
1873 20c. Fritz breaks Nutcracker 80 40
1874 30c. Nutcracker with sword 90 40
1875 40c. Nutcracker and Marie in the snow 95 40
1876 50c. Marie and the Prince meet Sugar Plum Fairy 1·00 60
1877 60c. Marie and Prince in Crystal Hall . . . . . . 1·00 60
1878 $3 Huey, Dewey and Louie as Cossack dancers . . . 3·25 4·00
1879 $6 Mother Ginger and her puppets . . . . 4·50 6·50
MS1880 Two sheets, each 127 × 102 mm. (a) $6 Marie and Prince in sleigh. (b) $6 The Prince in sword fight (vert) Set of 2 sheets 8·50 10·00

316 "Hannah and Samuel" (Rembrandt)

1993. Famous Paintings by Rembrandt and Matisse. Multicoloured.
1881 15c. Type **316** 30 30
1882 15c. "Guitarist" (Matisse) 30 30
1883 30c. "The Jewish Bride" (Rembrandt) 40 30
1884 40c. "Jacob wrestling with the Angel" (Rembrandt) 50 30
1885 60c. "Interior with a Goldfish Bowl" (Matisse) 70 50
1886 $1 "Mlle Yvonne Landsberg" (Matisse) . . 1·00 80
1887 $4 "The Toboggan" (Matisse) . . . . 2·75 3·75
1888 $5 "Moses with the Tablets of the Law" (Rembrandt) 2·75 3·75
MS1889 Two sheets. (a) 124 × 99 mm. $6 "The Blinding of Samson by the Philistines" (detail) (Rembrandt). (b) 99 × 124 mm. $6 "The Three Sisters" (detail) (Matisse) Set of 2 sheets . . . 8·50 10·00

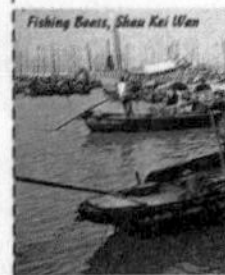
317 Hong Kong 1981 $1 Golden Threadfin Bream Stamp and Sampans, Shau Kei Wan

1994. "Hong Kong '94" International Stamp Exhibition (1st issue). Multicoloured.
1890 40c. Type **317** 80 80
1891 40c. Antigua 1990 $2 Rock beauty stamp and sampans, Shau Kei Wan 80 80
Nos. 1890/1 were printed together, se-tenant, forming a composite design.
See also Nos. 1892/7 and 1898/1905.

318 Terracotta Warriors

1994. "Hong Kong '94" International Stamp Exhibition (2nd issue). Qin Dynasty Terracotta Figures. Multicoloured.
1892 40c. Type **318** 65 65
1893 40c. Cavalryman and horse 65 65
1894 40c. Warriors in armour . . 65 65
1895 40c. Painted bronze chariot and team 65 65

1896 40c. Pekingese dog 65 65
1897 40c. Warriors with horses 65 65

319 Mickey Mouse in Junk

320 Sumatran Rhinoceros lying down

1994. "Hong Kong '94" International Stamp Exhibition (3rd issue). Walt Disney cartoon characters. Multicoloured.

1898 10c. Type **319** 70 30
1899 15c. Minnie Mouse as mandarin 75 35
1900 30c. Donald and Daisy Duck on houseboat . . . 90 45
1901 50c. Mickey holding bird in cage . . . . 1·10 60
1902 $1 Pluto and ornamental dog . . . . 1·75 1·00
1903 $2 Minnie and Daisy celebrating Bun Festival 2·50 2·50
1904 $4 Goofy making noodles 3·50 4·50
1905 $5 Goofy pulling Mickey in rickshaw . . . . 3·50 4·50
MS1906 Two sheets, each 133 × 109 mm. (a) $5 Mickey and Donald on harbour ferry (horiz). (b) $5 Mickey in traditional dragon dance (horiz) Set of 2 sheets . . . . 6·50 8·00

1994. Centenary (1992) of Sierra Club (environmental protection society). Endangered Species. Multicoloured.

1907 $1.50 Type **320** . . . . . . 1·25 1·25
1908 $1.50 Sumatran rhinoceros feeding . . . . 1·25 1·25
1909 $1.50 Ring-tailed lemur on ground . . . . 1·25 1·25
1910 $1.50 Ring-tailed lemur on branch . . . . 1·25 1·25
1911 $1.50 Red-fronted brown lemur on branch . . . . 1·25 1·25
1912 $1.50 Head of red-fronted brown lemur . . . . 1·25 1·25
1913 $1.50 Head of red-fronted brown lemur in front of trunk . . . . 1·25 1·25
1914 $1.50 Sierra Club Centennial emblem . . . . 1·25 1·25
1915 $1.50 Head of Bactrian camel . . . . 1·25 1·25
1916 $1.50 Bactrian camel . . . 1·25 1·25
1917 $1.50 African elephant drinking . . . . 1·25 1·25
1918 $1.50 Head of African elephant . . . . 1·25 1·25
1919 $1.50 Leopard sitting upright . . . . 1·25 1·25
1920 $1.50 Leopard in grass (emblem at right) . . . . 1·25 1·25
1921 $1.50 Leopard in grass (emblem at left) . . . . . 1·25 1·25
MS1922 Four sheets. (a) 100 × 70 mm. $1.50, Sumatran rhinoceros (horiz). (b) 70 × 100 mm. $1.50, Ring-tailed lemur (horiz). (c) 70 × 100 mm. $1.50, Bactrian camel (horiz). (d) 100 × 70 mm. $1.50, African elephant (horiz) Set of 4 sheets 5·50 7·00

321 West Highland White Terrier

1994. Dogs of the World. Chinese New Year ("Year of the Dog"). Multicoloured.

1923 50c. Type **321** 75 65
1924 50c. Beagle 75 65
1925 50c. Scottish terrier 75 65
1926 50c. Pekingese 75 65
1927 50c. Dachshund 75 65
1928 50c. Yorkshire terrier . . . 75 65
1929 50c. Pomeranian 75 65
1930 50c. Poodle 75 65
1931 50c. Shetland sheepdog . . . 75 65
1932 50c. Pug 75 65
1933 50c. Shih Tzu 75 65
1934 50c. Chihuahua 75 65
1935 75c. Mastiff 75 65
1936 75c. Border collie 75 65
1937 75c. Samoyed 75 65
1938 75c. Airedale terrier 75 65
1939 75c. English setter 75 65
1940 75c. Rough collie 75 65
1941 75c. Newfoundland 75 65
1942 75c. Weimarana 75 65
1943 75c. English springer spaniel 75 65
1944 75c. Dalmatian 75 65
1945 75c. Boxer 75 65
1946 75c. Old English sheepdog 75 65
MS1947 Two sheets, each 93 × 58 mm. (a) $6 Welsh corgi. (b) $6 Labrador retriever Set of 2 sheets . . . . 9·00 11·00

322 "Spiranthes lanceolata"

323 Hermann E. Sieger, Germany 1931 1m. Zeppelin Stamp and Airship LZ-127 "Graf Zeppelin"

1994. Orchids. Multicoloured.

1948 10c. Type **322** 70 60
1949 20c. "Ionopsis utricularioides" . . . . . 1·00 50
1950 30c. "Tetramicra canaliculata" . . . . . . 1·25 50
1951 50c. "Oncidium picturatum" 1·50 65
1952 $1 "Epidendrum difforme" 2·00 1·25
1953 $2 "Epidendrum ciliare" . . 3·00 2·75
1954 $4 "Epidendrum ibaguense" 4·00 4·25
1955 $5 "Epidendrum nocturnum" . . . . . . 4·00 4·25
MS1956 Two sheets, each 100 × 73 mm. (a) $6 "Rodriguezia lanceolato". (b) $6 "Encyclia cochleata" Set of 2 sheets . . . 9·00 11·00

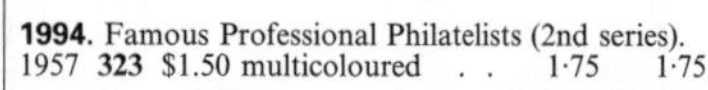

1994. Famous Professional Philatelists (2nd series).

1957 **323** $1.50 multicoloured . . 1·75 1·75

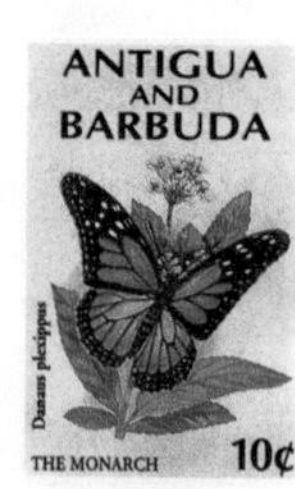

324 "Danaus plexippus"

325 Bottlenose Dolphin

1994. Butterflies. Multicoloured.

1958 10c. Type **324** 85 75
1959 15c. "Appias drusilla" . . . 1·00 45
1960 30c. "Eurema lisa" . . . . 1·25 55
1961 40c. "Anaea troglodyta" . . 1·25 60
1962 $1 "Urbanus proteus" . . . 2·00 1·25
1963 $2 "Junonia evarete" . . . 2·75 2·75
1964 $4 "Battus polydamas" . . 3·50 4·50
1965 $5 "Heliconius charitonia" 3·50 4·50
MS1966 Two sheets, each 102 × 72 mm. (a) $6 "Phoebis sennae". (b) $6 "Hemiargus hanno" Set of 2 sheets . . . . 8·50 10·00

No. 1959 is inscribed "Appisa drusilla" and No. 1965 "Heliconius charitonius", both in error.

1994. Marine Life. Multicoloured.

1967 50c. Type **325** 65 65
1968 50c. Killer whale 65 65
1969 50c. Spinner dolphin 65 65
1970 50c. Oceanic sunfish 65 65
1971 50c. Caribbean reef shark and short fin pilot whale 65 65
1972 50c. Copper-banded butterflyfish 65 65
1973 50c. Mosaic moray 65 65
1974 50c. Clown triggerfish . . . 65 65
1975 50c. Red lobster 65 65
MS1976 Two sheets, each 106 × 76 mm. (a) $6 Seahorse. (b) $6 Swordfish ("Blue Marlin") (horiz) Set of 2 sheets . . . . 11·00 11·00

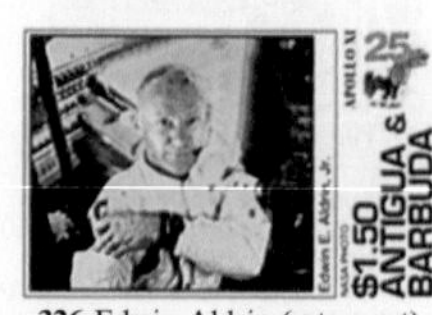

326 Edwin Aldrin (astronaut)

1994. 25th Anniv of First Manned Moon Landing. Multicoloured.

1977 $1.50 Type **326** . . . . . . 1·50 1·50
1978 $1.50 First lunar footprint 1·50 1·50
1979 $1.50 Neil Armstrong (astronaut) . . . . 1·50 1·50
1980 $1.50 Aldrin stepping onto Moon . . . . 1·50 1·50
1981 $1.50 Aldrin and equipment 1·50 1·50
1982 $1.50 Aldrin and U.S.A. flag 1·50 1·50
1983 $1.50 Aldrin at Tranquility Base . . . . 1·50 1·50
1984 $1.50 Moon plaque . . . . . 1·50 1·50
1985 $1.50 "Eagle" leaving Moon 1·50 1·50
1986 $1.50 Command module in lunar orbit . . . . 1·50 1·50
1987 $1.50 First day cover of U.S.A. 1969 10c. First Man on Moon stamp . . 1·50 1·50
1988 $1.50 Pres. Nixon and astronauts . . . . 1·50 1·50
MS1989 72 × 102 mm. $6 Armstrong and Aldrin with postal official 3·50 4·50

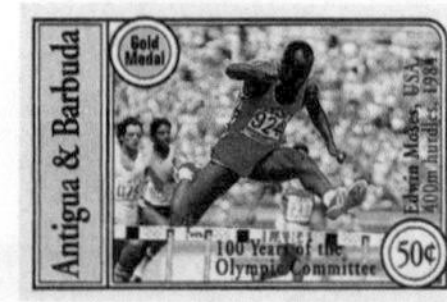

327 Edwin Moses (U.S.A.) (400 m hurdles, 1984)

1994. Centenary of International Olympic Committee. Gold Medal Winners. Multicoloured.

1990 50c. Type **327** 40 30
1991 $1.50 Steffi Graf (Germany) (tennis, 1988) . . . . . 1·50 1·50
MS1992 79 × 110 mm. $6 Johann Olav Koss (Norway) (500, 1500 and 10,000 metre speed skating), 1994 . . . . 4·25 4·50

328 Antiguan Family

1994. International Year of the Family.

1993 **328** 90c. multicoloured . . . 60 60

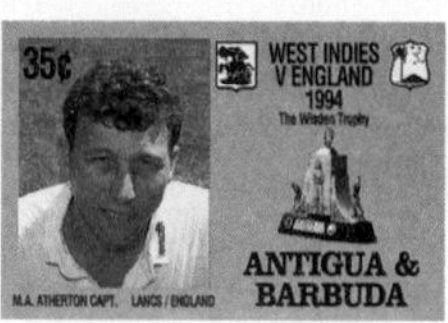

329 Mike Atherton (England) and Wisden Trophy

1994. Centenary (1995) of First English Cricket Tour to the West Indies. Multicoloured.

1994 35c. Type **329** 75 50
1995 75c. Viv Richards (West Indies) (vert) . . . . . . 1·25 80
1996 $1.20 Richie Richardson (West Indies) and Wisden Trophy . . . . 1·50 2·00
MS1997 80 × 100 mm. $3 English team, 1895 (black and brown) 2·25 2·50

330 Entrance Bridge, Songgwangsa Temple

1994. "Philakorea '94" International Stamp Exhibition, Seoul. Multicoloured.

1998 40c. Type **330** 50 40
1999 75c. Long-necked bottle . . 70 75
2000 75c. Punch'ong ware jar with floral decoration . . 70 75
2001 75c. Punch'ong ware jar with blue dragon pattern 70 75
2002 75c. Ewer in shape of bamboo shoot 70 75
2003 75c. Punch'ong ware green jar 70 75
2004 75c. Pear-shaped bottle . . 70 75
2005 75c. Porcelain jar with brown dragon pattern . . 70 75
2006 75c. Porcelain jar with floral pattern 70 75
2007 90c. Song-op Folk Village, Cheju 70 75
2008 $3 Port Sogwipo . . . . . 2·00 2·50
MS2009 104 × 71 mm. $4 Ox herder playing flute (vert) . . . . . . 3·25 3·75

331 Short S.25 Sunderland (flying boat)

1994. 50th Anniv of D-Day. Multicoloured.

2010 40c. Type **331** 90 40
2011 $2 Lockheed P-38 Lightning fighters attacking train . . 2·50 2·50
2012 $3 Martin B-26 Marauder bombers . . . . 3·00 3·50
MS2013 108 × 78 mm. $6 Hawker Typhoon fighter bomber . . . 5·50 6·00

332 Travis Tritt

1994. Stars of Country and Western Music. Multicoloured.

2014 75c. Type **332** 70 70
2015 75c. Dwight Yoakam 70 70
2016 75c. Billy Ray Cyrus 70 70
2017 75c. Alan Jackson 70 70
2018 75c. Garth Brooks 70 70
2019 75c. Vince Gill 70 70
2020 75c. Clint Black 70 70
2021 75c. Eddie Rabbit 70 70
2022 75c. Patsy Cline 70 70
2023 75c. Tanya Tucker 70 70
2024 75c. Dolly Parton 70 70
2025 75c. Anne Murray 70 70
2026 75c. Tammy Wynette 70 70
2027 75c. Loretta Lynn 70 70
2028 75c. Reba McEntire 70 70
2029 75c. Skeeter Davis 70 70
2030 75c. Hank Snow 70 70
2031 75c. Gene Autry 70 70
2032 75c. Jimmie Rodgers 70 70
2033 75c. Ernest Tubb 70 70
2034 75c. Eddy Arnold 70 70
2035 75c. Willie Nelson 70 70
2036 75c. Johnny Cash 70 70
2037 75c. George Jones 70 70
MS2038 Three sheets. (a) 100 × 70 mm. $6 Hank Williams Jr. (b) 100 × 70 mm. $6 Hank Williams Sr. (c) 70 × 100 mm. $6 Kitty Wells (horiz) Set of 3 sheets 14·00 14·00

333 Hugo Sanchez (Mexico)

1994. World Cup Football Championship, U.S.A. (2nd issue). Multicoloured.

2039 15c. Type **333** 75 30
2040 35c. Jurgen Klinsmann (Germany) . . . . 1·25 45
2041 65c. Antiguan player . . . 1·50 55
2042 $1.20 Cobi Jones (U.S.A.) 2·00 1·75
2043 $4 Roberto Baggio (Italy) 3·25 4·00
2044 $5 Bwalya Kalusha (Zambia) . . . . 3·25 4·00
MS2045 Two sheets. (a) 72 × 105 mm. $6 Maldive Islands player (vert). (b) 107 × 78 mm. $6 World Cup trophy (vert) Set of 2 sheets . . . . 8·00 9·00

No. 2040 is inscribed "Klinsman" in error.

334 Sir Shridath Ramphal

1994. 1st Recipients of Order of the Caribbean Community. Multicoloured.

2046 65c. Type **334** 50 40
2047 90c. William Demas 65 60
2048 $1.20 Derek Walcott . . . . 1·75 1·50

335 Pair of Magnificent Frigate Birds

1994. Birds. Multicoloured.

2049 10c. Type **335** 45 45
2050 15c. Bridled quail dove . . . 50 40
2051 30c. Magnificent frigate bird chick hatching 70 70
2052 40c. Purple-throated carib (vert) 70 70
2053 $1 Male magnificent frigate bird in courtship display (vert) . . . . 1·00 1·25
2054 $1 Broad-winged hawk (vert) . . . . 1·00 1·25
2055 $3 Young magnificent frigate bird . . . . . . 2·00 3·00
2056 $4 Yellow warbler . . . . . 2·00 3·00
MS2057 Two sheets. (a) 70 × 100 mm. $6 Female magnificent frigate bird (vert). (b) 100 × 70 mm. $6 Black-billed whistling duck ducklings Set of 2 sheets . . . . 8·00 9·00

Nos. 2049, 2051, 2053 and 2055 also show the W.W.F. Panda emblem.

336 "The Virgin and Child by the Fireside" (Robert Campin) **337** Magnificent Frigate Bird

1994. Christmas. Religious Paintings. Multicoloured.

2058	15c. Type **336**	70	30
2059	35c. "The Reading Madonna" (Giorgione)	95	30
2060	40c. "Madonna and Child" (Giovanni Bellini)	1·00	30
2061	45c. "The Litta Madonna" (Da Vinci)	1·00	30
2062	65c. "The Virgin and Child under the Apple Tree" (Lucas Cranach the Elder)	1·40	55
2063	75c. "Madonna and Child" (Master of the Female Half-lengths)	1·50	70
2064	$1.20 "An Allegory of the Church" (Alessandro Allori)	2·00	1·75
2065	$5 "Madonna and Child wreathed with Flowers" (Jacob Jordaens)	3·50	5·00
MS2066	Two sheets. (a) 123 × 88 mm. $6 "Madonna and Child with Commissioners" (detail) (Palma Vecchio) (b) 88 × 123 mm. $6 "The Virgin Enthroned with Child" (detail) (Bohemian master) Set of 2 sheets	7·50	9·00

1995. Birds. Multicoloured.

2067	15c. Type **337**	10	10
2068	25c. Blue-hooded euphonia	10	15
2069	35c. Eastern meadowlark ("Meadowlark")	15	20
2070	40c. Red-billed tropic bird	15	20
2071	45c. Greater flamingo	20	25
2072	60c. Yellow-faced grassquit	25	30
2073	65c. Yellow-billed cuckoo	25	30
2074	70c. Purple-throated carib	30	35
2075	75c. Bananaquit	30	35
2076	90c. Painted bunting	35	40
2077	$1.20 Red-legged honeycreeper	50	55
2078	$2 Northern jacana ("Jacana")	80	85
2079	$5 Greater Antillean bullfinch	2·00	2·10
2080	$10 Caribbean elaenia	4·00	4·25
2081	$20 Brown trembler ("Trembler")	8·00	8·25

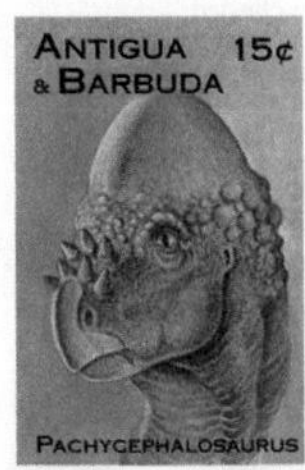

338 Head of Pachycephalosaurus

1995. Prehistoric Animals. Multicoloured.

2082	15c. Type **338**	60	60
2083	20c. Head of afrovenator	60	60
2084	65c. Centrosaurus	80	80
2085	75c. Kronosaurus (horiz)	80	80
2086	75c. Ichthyosaurus (horiz)	80	80
2087	75c. Plesiosaurus (horiz)	80	80
2088	75c. Archelon (horiz)	80	80
2089	75c. Pair of tyrannosaurus (horiz)	80	80
2090	75c. Tyrannosaurus (horiz)	80	80
2091	75c. Parasaurolophus (horiz)	80	80
2092	75c. Pair of parasaurolophus (horiz)	80	80
2093	75c. Oviraptor (horiz)	80	80
2094	75c. Protoceratops with eggs (horiz)	80	80
2095	75c. Pteranodon and protoceratops (horiz)	80	80
2096	75c. Pair of protoceratops (horiz)	80	80
2097	90c. Pentaceratops drinking	1·00	1·00
2098	$1.20 Head of tarbosaurus	1·25	1·25
2099	$5 Head of styracosaurus	3·00	3·75
MS2100	Two sheets, each 101 × 70 mm. (a) $6 Head of Corythosaurus (horiz). (b) $6 Head of Carnotaurus (horiz) Set of 2 sheets	9·50	11·00

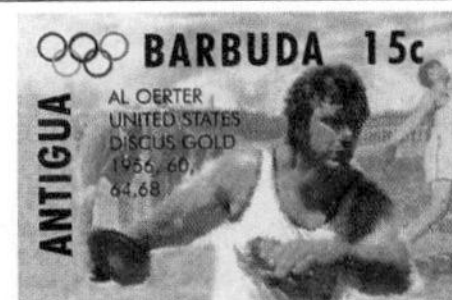

339 Al Oerter (U.S.A.) (discus – 1956, 1960, 1964, 1968)

1995. Olympic Games, Atlanta (1996). Previous Gold Medal Winners (1st issue). Multicoloured.

2101	15c. Type **339**	50	30
2102	20c. Greg Louganis (U.S.A.) (diving – 1984, 1988)	50	30
2103	65c. Naim Suleymanoglu (Turkey) (weightlifting – 1988)	65	50
2104	90c. Louise Ritter (U.S.A.) (high jump – 1988)	90	70
2105	$1.20 Nadia Comaneci (Rumania) (gymnastics – 1976)	1·75	1·10
2106	$5 Olga Bondarenko (Russia) (10,000 metres – 1988)	3·00	4·50
MS2107	Two sheets, each 106 × 76 mm. (a) $6 United States crew (eight-oared shell — 1964). (b) $6 Lutz Hessilch (Germany) (cycling — 1988) (vert) Set of 2 sheets	11·00	11·00

No. 2106 is inscribed "BOLDARENKO" in error.

See also Nos. 2302/23.

340 Map of Berlin showing Russian Advance

1995. 50th Anniv of End of Second World War in Europe. Multicoloured.

2108	$1.20 Type **340**	1·00	1·00
2109	$1.20 Russian tank and infantry	1·00	1·00
2110	$1.20 Street fighting in Berlin	1·00	1·00
2111	$1.20 German tank exploding	1·00	1·00
2112	$1.20 Russian air raid	1·00	1·00
2113	$1.20 German troops surrendering	1·00	1·00
2114	$1.20 Hoisting the Soviet flag on the Reichstag	1·00	1·00
2115	$1.20 Captured German standards	1·00	1·00
MS2116	104 × 74 mm. $6 Gen. Konev (vert)	4·00	4·50

See also Nos. 2132/8.

Antigua & Barbuda

341 Signatures and Earl of Halifax **342** Woman buying Produce from Market

1995. 50th Anniv of United Nations. Multicoloured.

2117	75c. Type **341**	60	80
2118	90c. Virginia Gildersleeve	60	80
2119	$1.20 Harold Stassen	60	80
MS2120	100 × 70 mm. $6 Pres. Franklin D. Roosevelt	3·50	4·00

Nos. 2117/19 were printed together, se-tenant, forming a composite design.

1995. 50th Anniv of F.A.O. Multicoloured.

2121	75c. Type **342**	60	80
2122	90c. Women shopping	60	80
2123	$1.20 Women talking	60	80
MS2124	100 × 70 mm. $6 Tractor	3·00	3·50

Nos. 2121/3 were printed together, se-tenant, forming a composite design.

343 Beach and Rotary Emblem **344** Queen Elizabeth the Queen Mother

1995. 90th Anniv of Rotary International.

2125 **343**	$5 multicoloured	3·50	4·00
MS2126	74 × 104 mm. $6 National flag and emblem	3·50	4·00

1995. 95th Birthday of Queen Elizabeth the Queen Mother.

2127 –	$1.50 brown, light brown and black	1·50	1·50
2128 **344**	$1.50 multicoloured	1·50	1·50
2129 –	$1.50 multicoloured	1·50	1·50
2130 –	$1.50 multicoloured	1·50	1·50
MS2131	100 × 127 mm. $6 multicoloured	5·50	5·50

DESIGNS: No. 2127, Queen Elizabeth the Queen Mother (pastel drawing); 2129, At desk (oil painting); 2130, Wearing green dress; **MS**2131, Wearing blue dress.

1995. 50th Anniv of End of Second World War in the Pacific. As T **340**. Multicoloured.

2132	$1.20 Gen. Chang Kai-Shek and Chinese guerrillas	1·10	1·25
2133	$1.20 Gen. Douglas MacArthur and beach landing	1·10	1·25
2134	$1.20 Gen. Claire Chennault and U.S. fighter aircraft	1·10	1·25
2135	$1.20 Brig. Orde Wingate and supply drop	1·10	1·25
2136	$1.20 Gen. Joseph Stilwell and U.S. supply plane	1·10	1·25
2137	$1.20 Field-Marshal Bill Slim and loading cow into plane	1·10	1·25
MS2138	108 × 76 mm. $3 Admiral Nimitz and aircraft carrier	2·50	3·00

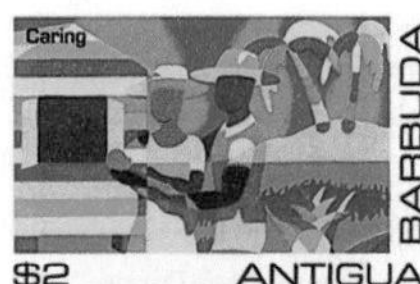

345 Family ("Caring")

1995. Tourism. Sheet 95 × 72 mm, containing T **345** and similar horiz designs. Multicoloured.

MS2139	$2 Type **345**; $2 Market trader ("Marketing"); $2 Workers and housewife ("Working"); $2 Leisure pursuits ("Enjoying Life")	5·50	7·00

346 Purple-throated Carib **347** Original Church, 1845

1995. Birds. Multicoloured.

2140	75c. Type **346**	90	85
2141	75c. Antillean crested hummingbird	90	85
2142	75c. Bananaquit	90	85
2143	75c. Mangrove cuckoo	90	85
2144	75c. Troupial	90	85
2145	75c. Green-throated carib	90	85
2146	75c. Yellow warbler	90	85
2147	75c. Antillean euphonia ("Blue-hooded Euphonia")	90	85
2148	75c. Scaly-breasted thrasher	90	85
2149	75c. Burrowing owl	90	85
2150	75c. Carib grackle	90	85
2151	75c. Adelaide's warbler	90	85
2152	75c. Ring-necked duck	90	85
2153	75c. Ruddy duck	90	85
2154	75c. Green-winged teal	90	85
2155	75c. Wood duck	90	85
2156	75c. Hooded merganser	90	85
2157	75c. Lesser scaup	90	85
2158	75c. Black-billed whistling duck ("West Indian Tree Duck")	90	85
2159	75c. Fulvous whistling duck	90	85
2160	75c. Bahama pintail	90	85
2161	75c. Northern shoveler	90	85
2162	75c. Masked duck	90	85
2163	75c. American wigeon	90	85
MS2164	Two sheets, each 104 × 74 mm. (a) $6 American purple gallinule. (b) $6 Heads of Blue-winged teal Set of 2 sheets	12·00	12·00

Nos. 2140/51 and 2152/63 respectively were printed together, se-tenant, forming composite designs.

1995. 150th Anniv of Greenbay Moravian Church. Multicoloured.

2165	20c. Type **347**	60	30
2166	60c. Church in 1967	90	40
2167	75c. Present church	1·10	50
2168	90c. Revd. John Buckley (first minister of African descent)	1·25	60
2169	$1.20 Bishop John Ephraim Knight (longest-serving minister)	1·50	1·50
2170	$2 As 75c.	2·50	3·00
MS2171	110 × 81 mm. $6 Front of present church	4·25	5·00

348 Mining Bees

1995. Bees. Multicoloured.

2172	90c. Type **348**	90	70
2173	$1.20 Solitary bee	1·25	90
2174	$1.65 Leaf-cutter bee	1·75	1·75
2175	$1.75 Honey bees	1·75	1·75
MS2176	110 × 80 mm. $6 Solitary mining bee	3·50	4·00

349 Narcissus

1995. Flowers. Multicoloured.

2177	75c. Type **349**	65	65
2178	75c. Camellia	65	65
2179	75c. Iris	65	65
2180	75c. Tulip	65	65
2181	75c. Poppy	65	65
2182	75c. Peony	65	65
2183	75c. Magnolia	65	65
2184	75c. Oriental lily	65	65
2185	75c. Rose	65	65
2186	75c. Pansy	65	65
2187	75c. Hydrangea	65	65
2188	75c. Azaleas	65	65
MS2189	80 × 100 mm. $6 Calla lily	4·00	4·50

No. 2186 is inscribed "Pansie" in error.

350 Somali

1995. Cats. Multicoloured.

2190	45c. Type **350**	70	60
2191	45c. Persian and butterflies	70	60
2192	45c. Devon rex	70	60
2193	45c. Turkish angora	70	60
2194	45c. Himalayan	70	60
2195	45c. Maine coon	70	60
2196	45c. Ginger non-pedigree	70	60
2197	45c. American wirehair	70	60
2198	45c. British shorthair	70	60
2199	45c. American curl	70	60
2200	45c. Black non-pedigree and butterfly	70	60
2201	45c. Birman	70	60
MS2202	104 × 74 mm. $6 Siberian kitten (vert)	6·50	6·50

Nos. 2190/2201 were printed together, se-tenant, forming a composite design.

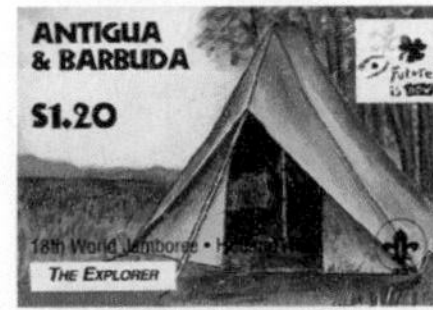

351 The Explorer Tent

1995. 18th World Scout Jamboree, Netherlands. Tents. Multicoloured.

2203	$1.20 Type **351**	1·60	1·60
2204	$1.20 Camper tent	1·60	1·60
2205	$1.20 Wall tent	1·60	1·60
2206	$1.20 Trail tarp	1·60	1·60
2207	$1.20 Miner's tent	1·60	1·60
2208	$1.20 Voyager tent	1·60	1·60
MS2209	Two sheets, each 76 × 106 mm. (a) $6 Scout and camp fire. (b) $6 Scout with back pack (vert) Set of 2 sheets	8·50	10·00

352 Trans-Gabon Diesel-electric Train

1995. Trains of the World. Multicoloured.

2210	35c. Type **352**	1·00	65
2211	65c. Canadian Pacific diesel-electric locomotive	1·50	90
2212	75c. Santa Fe Railway diesel-electric locomotive, U.S.A.	1·60	1·00

2213 90c. High Speed Train, Great Britain 1·60 1·00
2214 $1.20 TGV express train, France 1·60 1·60
2215 $1.20 Diesel-electric locomotive, Australia 1·60 1·60
2216 $1.20 Pendolino "ETR 450" electric train, Italy 1·60 1·60
2217 $1.20 Diesel-electric locomotive, Thailand 1·60 1·60
2218 $1.20 Pennsylvania Railroad Type K4 steam locomotive, U.S.A. 1·60 1·60
2219 $1.20 Beyer-Garratt steam locomotive, East African Railways 1·60 1·60
2220 $1.20 Natal Government steam locomotive 1·60 1·60
2221 $1.20 Rail gun, American Civil War 1·60 1·60
2222 $1.20 Locomotive "Lion" (red livery), Great Britain 1·60 1·60
2223 $1.20 William Hedley's "Puffing Billy" (green livery), Great Britain 1·60 1·60
2224 $6 Amtrak high speed diesel locomotive, U.S.A. 3·75 4·50
MS2225 Two sheets, each 110 × 80 mm. (a) $6 Locomotive "Iron Rooster", China (vert). (b) $6 "Indian-Pacific" diesel-electric locomotive, Australia (vert) Set of 2 sheets 12·00 12·00

353 Dag Hammarskjold (1961 Peace)

1995. Cent of Nobel Prize Trust Fund. Mult.
2226 $1 Type **353** 1·10 1·10
2227 $1 Georg Wittig (1979 Chemistry) 1·10 1·10
2228 $1 Wilhelm Ostwald (1909 Chemistry) 1·10 1·10
2229 $1 Robert Koch (1905 Medicine) 1·10 1·10
2230 $1 Karl Ziegler (1963 Chemistry) 1·10 1·10
2231 $1 Alexander Fleming (1945 Medicine) 1·10 1·10
2232 $1 Hermann Staudinger (1953 Chemistry) 1·10 1·10
2233 $1 Manfred Eigen (1967 Chemistry) 1·10 1·10
2234 $1 Arno Penzias (1978 Physics) 1·10 1·10
2235 $1 Shmuel Agnon (1966 Literature) 1·10 1·10
2236 $1 Rudyard Kipling (1907 Literature) 1·10 1·10
2237 $1 Aleksandr Solzhenitsyn (1970 Literature) 1·10 1·10
2238 $1 Jack Steinberger (1988 Physics) 1·10 1·10
2239 $1 Andrei Sakharov (1975 Peace) 1·10 1·10
2240 $1 Otto Stern (1943 Physics) 1·10 1·10
2241 $1 John Steinbeck (1962 Literature) 1·10 1·10
2242 $1 Nadine Gordimer (1991 Literature) 1·10 1·10
2243 $1 William Faulkner (1949 Literature) 1·10 1·10
MS2244 Two sheets, each 100 × 70 mm. (a) $6 Elie Wiesel (1986 Peace) (vert). (b) $6 The Dalai Lama (1989 Peace) (vert) Set of 2 sheets 8·00 9·50

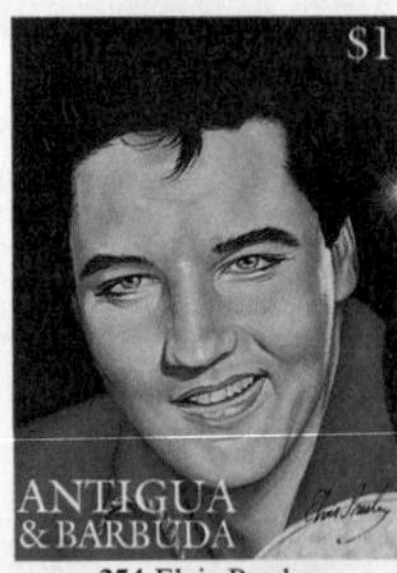

354 Elvis Presley

1995. 60th Birth Anniv of Elvis Presley. Mult.
2245 $1 Type **354** 1·10 85
2246 $1 Holding microphone in right hand 1·10 85
2247 $1 In blue shirt and with neck of guitar 1·10 85
2248 $1 Wearing blue shirt and smiling 1·10 85
2249 $1 On wedding day 1·10 85
2250 $1 In army uniform 1·10 85
2251 $1 Wearing red shirt 1·10 85
2252 $1 Wearing white shirt 1·10 85
2253 $1 In white shirt with microphone 1·10 85
MS2254 101 × 71 mm. $6 "Ghost" image of Elvis amongst the stars 6·00 5·00

355 John Lennon and Signature **357** "Rest on the Flight into Egypt" (Paolo Veronese)

1995. 15th Death Anniv of John Lennon (entertainer). Multicoloured.
2255 45c. Type **355** 50 40
2256 50c. In beard and spectacles 50 50
2257 65c. Wearing sunglasses 55 55
2258 75c. In cap with heart badge 65 65
MS2259 103 × 73 mm. $6 As 75c. 5·50 6·50

1995. Hurricane Relief. Nos. 2203/8 optd **"Hurricane Relief"**.
2260 $1.20 Type **351** 1·25 1·25
2261 $1.20 Camper tent 1·25 1·25
2262 $1.20 Wall tent 1·25 1·25
2263 $1.20 Trail tarp 1·25 1·25
2264 $1.20 Miner's tent 1·25 1·25
2265 $1.20 Voyager tent 1·25 1·25
MS2266 Two sheets, each 76 × 106 mm. (a) $6 Scout and camp fire. (b) $6 Scout with back pack (vert) Set of 2 sheets 11·00 13·00

1995. Christmas. Religious Paintings. Multicoloured.
2267 15c. Type **357** 30 30
2268 35c. "Madonna and Child" (Van Dyck) 40 40
2269 65c. "Sacred Conversation Piece" (Veronese) 60 50
2270 75c. "Vision of St. Anthony" (Van Dyck) 70 60
2271 90c. "Virgin and Child" (Van Eyck) 80 65
2272 $6 "The Immaculate Conception" (Giovanni Tiepolo) 3·00 4·25
MS2273 Two sheets. (a) 101 × 127 mm. $5 "Christ appearing to his Mother" (detail) (Van der Weyden). (b) 127 × 101 mm. $6 "The Infant Jesus and Young St. John" (Murillo) Set of 2 sheets 7·50 9·00

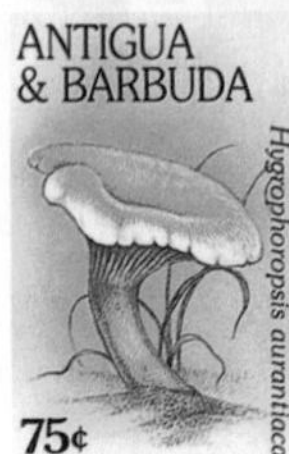

358 "Hygrophoropsis aurantiaca" **360** Florence Griffith Joyner (U.S.A.) (Gold – track, 1988)

359 H.M.S. "Resolution" (Cook)

1996. Fungi. Multicoloured.
2274 75c. Type **358** 60 70
2275 75c. "Hygrophorus bakerensis" 60 70
2276 75c. "Hygrophorus conicus" 60 70
2277 75c. "Hygrophorus miniatus" ("Hygrocybe miniata") 60 70
2278 75c. "Suillus brevipes" 60 70
2279 75c. "Suillus luteus" 60 70
2280 75c. "Suillus granulatus" 60 70
2281 75c. "Suillus caerulescens" 60 70
MS2282 Two sheets, each 105 × 75 mm. (a) $6 "Conocybe filaris". (b) $6 "Hygrocybe flavescens" Set of 2 sheets 7·00 8·00

1996. Sailing Ships. Multicoloured.
2283 15c. Type **359** 60 40
2284 25c. "Mayflower" (Pilgrim Fathers) 60 40
2285 45c. "Santa Maria" (Columbus) 90 40
2286 75c. "Aemilia" (Dutch galleon) 90 90
2287 75c. "Sovereign of the Seas" (English galleon) 90 90
2288 90c. H.M.S. "Victory" (Nelson) 1·00 90
2289 $1.20 As No. 2286 1·25 1·40
2290 $1.20 As No. 2287 1·25 1·40
2291 $1.20 "Royal Louis" (French galleon) 1·25 1·40
2292 $1.20 H.M.S. "Royal George" (ship of the line) 1·25 1·40
2293 $1.20 "Le Protecteur" (French frigate) 1·25 1·40
2294 $1.20 As No. 2288 1·25 1·40
2295 $1.50 As No. 2285 1·40 1·60
2296 $1.50 "Vitoria" (Magellan) 1·40 1·60
2297 $1.50 "Golden Hind" (Drake) 1·40 1·60
2298 $1.50 As No. 2284 1·40 1·60
2299 $1.50 "Griffin" (La Salle) 1·40 1·60
2300 $1.50 Type **359** 1·40 1·60
MS2301 Two sheets. (a) 102 × 72 mm. $6 U.S.S. "Constitution" (frigate). (b) 98 × 67 mm. $6 "Grande" "Hermine" (Cartier) Set of 2 sheets 7·50 9·00

1996. Olympic Games, Atlanta. Previous Medal Winners (2nd issue). Multicoloured.
2302 65c. Type **360** 60 60
2303 75c. Olympic Stadium, Seoul (1988) (horiz) 65 65
2304 90c. Allison Jolly and Lynne Jewell (U.S.A.) (Gold – yachting, 1988) (horiz) 70 70
2305 90c. Wolfgang Nordwig (Germany) (Gold – pole vaulting, 1972) 70 75
2306 90c. Shirley Strong (Great Britain) (Silver – 100 metres hurdles, 1984) 70 75
2307 90c. Sergei Bubka (Russia) (Gold – pole vault, 1988) 70 75
2308 90c. Filbert Bayi (Tanzania) (Silver – 3000 metres steeplechase, 1980) 70 75
2309 90c. Victor Saneyev (Russia) (Gold – triple jump, 1968, 1972, 1976) 70 75
2310 90c. Silke Renk (Germany) (Gold – javelin, 1992) 70 75
2311 90c. Daley Thompson (Great Britain) (Gold – decathlon, 1980, 1984) 70 75
2312 90c. Robert Richards (U.S.A.) (Gold – pole vault, 1952, 1956) 70 75
2313 90c. Parry O'Brien (U.S.A.) (Gold – shot put, 1952, 1956) 70 75
2314 90c. Ingrid Kramer (Germany) (Gold – women's platform diving, 1960) 70 75
2315 90c. Kelly McCormick (U.S.A.) (Silver – women's springboard diving, 1984) 70 75
2316 90c. Gary Tobian (U.S.A.) (Gold – men's springboard diving, 1960) 70 75
2317 90c. Greg Louganis (U.S.A.) (Gold – men's diving, 1984 and 1988) 70 75
2318 90c. Michelle Mitchell (U.S.A.) (Silver – women's platform diving, 1984 and 1988) 70 75
2319 90c. Zhou Jihong (China) (Gold – women's platform diving, 1984) 70 75
2320 90c. Wendy Wyland (U.S.A.) (Bronze – women's platform diving, 1984) 70 75
2321 90c. Xu Yanmei (China) (Gold – women's platform diving, 1988) 70 75
2322 90c. Fu Mingxia (China) (Gold – women's platform diving, 1992) 70 75
2323 $1.20 2000 metre tandem cycle race (horiz) 1·00 1·00
MS2324 Two sheets, each 106 × 76 mm. (a) $5 Bill Toomey (U.S.A.) (Gold—Decathlon, 1968) (horiz). (b) $6 Mark Lenzi (U.S.A.) (Gold—Men's springboard diving, 1992) Set of 2 sheets 7·00 8·00

Nos. 2305/13 and 2314/22 respectively were printed together, se-tenant, with the background forming a composite design.

361 Black Skimmer

1996. Sea Birds. Multicoloured.
2325 75c. Type **361** 60 70
2326 75c. Black-capped petrel 60 70
2327 75c. Sooty tern 60 70
2328 75c. Royal tern 60 70
2329 75c. Pomarine skua ("Pomarine Jaegger") 60 70
2330 75c. White-tailed tropic bird 60 70
2331 75c. Northern gannet 60 70
2332 75c. Laughing gull 60 70
MS2333 Two sheets, each 105 × 75 mm. (a) $5 Magnificent frigate bird ("Great Frigate Bird"). (b) $6 Brown pelican Set of 2 sheets 7·50 9·00

362 Mickey and Goofy on Elephant ("Around the World in Eighty Days")

1996. Novels of Jules Verne. Walt Disney cartoon characters in scenes from the books. Multicoloured.
2334 1c. Type **362** 10 10
2335 2c. Mickey, Donald and Goofy entering cave ("A Journey to the Centre of the Earth") 10 10
2336 5c. Mickey and Minnie driving postcart ("Michel Strogoff") 15 15
2337 10c. Mickey, Donald and Goofy in space rocket ("From the Earth to the Moon") 20 15
2338 15c. Mickey and Goofy in balloon ("Five Weeks in a Balloon") 20 15
2339 20c. Mickey and Goofy in China ("Around the World in Eighty Days") 20 15
2340 $1 Mickey, Goofy and Pluto on island ("The Mysterious Island") 1·75 85
2341 $2 Mickey, Pluto, Goofy and Donald on Moon ("From the Earth to the Moon") 2·25 2·25
2342 $3 Mickey being lifted by bird ("Captain Grant's Children") 2·75 3·00
2343 $5 Mickey with seal and squid ("Twenty Thousand Leagues Under the Sea") 4·00 4·75
MS2344 Two sheets, each 124 × 99 mm. (a) $6 Mickey on "Nautilus" ("Twenty Thousand Leagues Under the Sea"). (b) $6 Mickey and Donald on raft ("A Journey to the Centre of the Earth") Set of 2 sheets 9·50 10·00

363 Bruce Lee

1996. "CHINA '96" 9th Asian International Stamp Exhibition, Peking. Bruce Lee (actor). Multicoloured.
2345 75c. Type **363** 50 55
2346 75c. Bruce Lee in white shirt and red tie 50 55
2347 75c. In plaid jacket and tie 50 55
2348 75c. In mask and uniform 50 55
2349 75c. Bare-chested 50 55
2350 75c. In mandarin jacket 50 55
2351 75c. In brown jumper 50 55
2352 75c. In fawn shirt 50 55
2353 75c. Shouting 50 55
MS2354 76 × 106 mm. $5 Bruce Lee 3·00 3·25

364 Queen Elizabeth II

1996. 70th Birthday of Queen Elizabeth II. Multicoloured.
2355 $2 Type **364** 1·25 1·50
2356 $2 With bouquet 1·25 1·50
2357 $2 In Garter robes 1·25 1·50
MS2358 96 × 111 mm. $6 Wearing white dress 4·75 5·00

365 Ancient Egyptian Calvaryman

1996. Cavalry through the Ages. Multicoloured.
2359 60c. Type **365** 50 55
2360 60c. 13th-century English knight 50 55
2361 60c. 16th-century Spanish lancer 50 55
2362 60c. 18th-century Chinese cavalryman 50 55
MS2363 100 × 70 mm. $6 19th-century French cuirassier 3·25 3·75

366 Girl in Red Sari

367 Tomb of Zachariah and "Verbascum sinuatum"

1996. 50th Anniv of U.N.I.C.E.F. Multicoloured.
2364 75c. Type **366** 60 60
2365 90c. South American mother and child 70 70
2366 $1.20 Nurse with child . . . 90 1·00
MS2367 114 × 74 mm. $6 Chinese child . . . . 3·25 3·75

1996. 3000th Anniv of Jerusalem. Multicoloured.
2368 75c. Type **367** 65 65
2369 90c. Pool of Siloam and "Hyacinthus orientalis" 75 75
2370 $1.20 Hurva Synagogue and "Ranunculus asiaticus" 1·10 1·10
MS2371 66 × 80 mm. Model of Herrod's Temple and "Cerics siliquastrum" . . . . 4·50 4·50

368 Kate Smith

1996. Cent of Radio. Entertainers. Mult.
2372 65c. Type **368** 50 50
2373 75c. Dinah Shore 60 60
2374 90c. Rudy Vallee 70 70
2375 $1.20 Bing Crosby . . . . . 90 1·00
MS2376 72 × 104 mm. $6 Jo Stafford (28 × 42 mm) . . . . 3·25 3·75

369 "Madonna Enthroned"

1996. Christmas. Religious Paintings by Filippo Lippi. Multicoloured.
2377 60c. Type **369** 60 40
2378 90c. "Adoration of the Child and Saints" 70 55
2379 $1 "The Annunciation" . . 85 65
2380 $1.20 "Birth of the Virgin" 90 90
2381 $1.60 "Adoration of the Child" . . . . 1·25 1·50
2382 $1.75 "Madonna and Child" 1·40 1·60
MS2383 Two sheets, each 76 × 106 mm. (a) $6 "Madonna and Child" (different). (b) $6 "The Circumcision" Set of 2 sheets 9·00 9·50

370 Robert Preston ("The Music Man")

1997. Broadway Musical Stars. Multicoloured.
2384 $1 Type **370** 75 75
2385 $1 Michael Crawford ("Phantom of the Opera") 75 75
2386 $1 Zero Mostel ("Fiddler on the Roof") 75 75
2387 $1 Patti Lupone ("Evita") 75 75
2388 $1 Raul Julia ("Threepenny Opera") 75 75
2389 $1 Mary Martin ("South Pacific") 75 75
2390 $1 Carol Channing ("Hello Dolly") 75 75
2391 $1 Yul Brynner ("The King and I") 75 75
2392 $1 Julie Andrews ("My Fair Lady") 75 75
MS2393 106 × 76 mm. $6 Mickey Rooney ("Sugar Babies") . . . 3·75 4·50

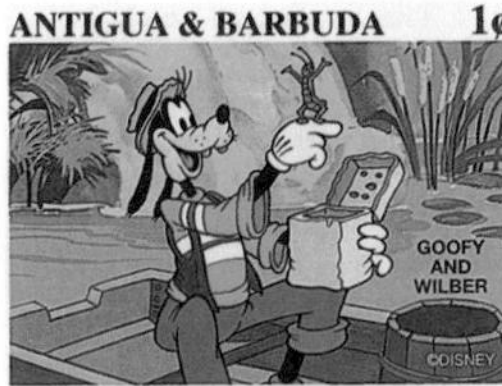

371 Goofy and Wilbur

1997. Walt Disney Cartoon Characters. Mult.
2394 1c. Type **371** 10 10
2395 2c. Donald and Goofy in boxing ring 10 10
2396 5c. Donald, Panchito and Jose Carioca 10 10
2397 10c. Mickey and Goofy playing chess 20 15
2398 15c. Chip and Dale with acorns 20 15
2399 20c. Pluto and Mickey . . . 20 15
2400 $1 Daisy and Minnie eating ice-cream 90 75
2401 $2 Daisy and Minnie at dressing table . . . . . . 1·50 1·75
2402 $3 Gus Goose and Donald 2·00 2·50
MS2403 Two sheets. (a) 102 × 127 mm. $6 Goofy. (b) 127 × 102 mm. Donald Duck playing guitar (vert) Set of 2 sheets 7·00 8·00

372 Charlie Chaplin as Young Man

1997. 20th Death Anniv of Charlie Chaplin (film star). Multicoloured.
2404 $1 Type **372** 70 70
2405 $1 Pulling face 70 70
2406 $1 Looking over shoulder 70 70
2407 $1 In cap 70 70
2408 $1 In front of star 70 70
2409 $1 In "The Great Dictator" 70 70
2410 $1 With movie camera and megaphone 70 70
2411 $1 Standing in front of camera lens 70 70
2412 $1 Putting on make-up . . . 70 70
MS2413 76 × 106 mm. $6 Charlie Chaplin . . . . 4·00 4·25
Nos. 2404/12 were printed together, se-tenant, with the backgrounds forming a composite design.

373 "Charaxes porthos"

1997. Butterflies. Multicoloured.
2414 90c. Type **373** 65 50
2415 $1.10 "Charaxes protoclea protoclea" 70 80
2416 $1.10 "Byblia ilithyia" . . . 70 80
2417 $1.10 Black-headed tchagra (bird) 70 80
2418 $1.10 "Charaxes nobilis" . . 70 80
2419 $1.10 "Pseudacraea boisduvali trimeni" . . . 70 80
2420 $1.10 "Charaxes smaragdalis" 70 80
2421 $1.10 "Charaxes lasti" . . . 70 80
2422 $1.10 "Pseudacrea poggei" 70 80
2423 $1.10 "Graphium colonna" 70 80
2424 $1.10 Carmine bee eater (bird) 70 80
2425 $1.10 "Pseudacraea eurytus" 70 80
2426 $1.10 "Hypolimnas monteironis" 70 80
2427 $1.10 "Charaxes anticlea" 70 80
2428 $1.10 "Graphium leonidas" 70 80
2429 $1.10 "Graphium illyris" . . 70 80
2430 $1.10 "Nephronia argia" . . 70 80
2431 $1.10 "Graphium policenes" 70 80
2432 $1.10 "Papilio dardanus" . . 70 80
2433 $1.20 "Aethiopana honorius" 75 80
2434 $1.60 "Charaxes hadrianus" 1·00 1·10
2435 $1.75 "Precis westermanni" 1·25 1·40
MS2436 Three sheets, each 106 × 76 mm. (a) $6 "Charaxes lactitinctus" (horiz). (b) $6 "Eupheadra neophron". (c) $6 "Euxanthe tiberius" (horiz) Set of 3 sheets . . . . 11·00 13·00
Nos. 2415/23 and 2424/32 respectively were printed together, se-tenant, with the backgrounds forming a composite design.
No. 2430 is inscribed "Nepheronia argia" in error.

374 Convent of The Companions of Jesus, Morelia, Mexico

1997. 50th Anniv of U.N.E.S.C.O. Multicoloured.
2437 60c. Type **374** 60 35
2438 90c. Fortress at San Lorenzo, Panama (vert) 70 50
2439 $1 Canaima National Park, Venezuela (vert) 80 55
2440 $1.10 Aerial view of church with tower, Guanajuato, Mexico (vert) 80 90
2441 $1.10 Church facade, Guanajuato, Mexico (vert) 80 90
2442 $1.10 Aerial view of churches with domes, Guanajuato, Mexico (vert) 80 90
2443 $1.10 Jesuit Missions of the Chiquitos, Bolivia (vert) 80 90
2444 $1.10 Huascaran National Park, Peru (vert) 80 90
2445 $1.10 Jesuit Missions of La Santisima, Paraguay (vert) 80 90
2446 $1.10 Cartagena, Colombia (vert) 80 90
2447 $1.10 Fortification, Havana, Cuba (vert) 80 90
2448 $1.20 As No. 2444 (vert) . . 85 90
2449 $1.60 Church of San Fransico, Guatemala (vert) . . . . 1·25 1·40
2450 $1.65 Tikal National Park, Guatemala . . . . 1·50 1·60
2451 $1.65 Rio Platano Reserve, Honduras . . . . 1·50 1·60
2452 $1.65 Ruins of Copan, Honduras . . . . 1·50 1·60
2453 $1.65 Antigua ruins, Guatemala . . . . 1·50 1·60
2454 $1.65 Teotihuacan, Mexico 1·50 1·60
2455 $1.75 Santo Domingo, Dominican Republic (vert) 1·60 1·75
MS2456 Two sheets, each 127 × 102 mm. (a) $6 Tikal National Park, Guatemala. (b) $6 Teotihuacan pyramid, Mexico Set of 2 sheets . . . . 9·00 9·50
No. 2446 is inscribed "Columbia" in error.

375 Red Bishop

1997. Endangered Species. Multicoloured.
2457 $1.20 Type **375** . . . . . . 1·00 1·10
2458 $1.20 Yellow baboon . . . 1·00 1·10
2459 $1.20 Superb starling . . . 1·00 1·10
2460 $1.20 Ratel . . . . 1·00 1·10
2461 $1.20 Hunting dog . . . . 1·00 1·10
2462 $1.20 Serval . . . . 1·00 1·10
2463 $1.65 Okapi . . . . 1·10 1·25
2464 $1.65 Giant forest squirrel 1·10 1·25
2465 $1.65 Lesser masked weaver 1·10 1·25
2466 $1.65 Small-spotted genet 1·10 1·25
2467 $1.65 Yellow-billed stork . . 1·10 1·25
2468 $1.65 Red-headed agama . . 1·10 1·25
MS2469 Three sheets, each 106 × 76 mm. (a) $6 South African crowned crane. (b) $6 Bat-eared fox. (c) $6 Malachite kingfisher Set of 3 sheets . . . . 13·00 14·00
Nos. 2457/62 and 2463/8 respectively were printed together, se-tenant, with the backgrounds forming composite designs.

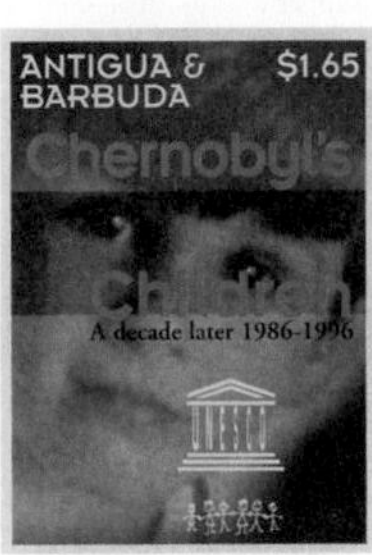

376 Child's Face and U.N.E.S.C.O. Emblem

1997. 10th Anniv of Chernobyl Nuclear Disaster. Multicoloured.
2470 $1.65 Type **376** . . . . . . 1·00 1·10
2471 $2 As Type **376**, but inscr "CHABAD'S CHILDREN OF CHERNOBYL" at foot 1·25 1·40

377 Paul Harris and James Grant

1997. 50th Death Anniv of Paul Harris (founder of Rotary International).
2472 $1.75 Type **377** . . . . . . 1·00 1·25
MS2473 78 × 107 mm. $6 Group study exchange, New Zealand 3·00 3·50

378 Queen Elizabeth II

1997. Golden Wedding of Queen Elizabeth and Prince Philip. Multicoloured.
2474 $1 Type **378** 80 85
2475 $1 Royal coat of arms . . . 80 85
2476 $1 Queen Elizabeth and Prince Philip at reception 80 85
2477 $1 Queen Elizabeth and Prince Philip in landau . . 80 85
2478 $1 Balmoral 80 85
2479 $1 Prince Philip 80 85
MS2480 100 × 71 mm. $6 Queen Elizabeth with Prince Philip in naval uniform . . . . 3·75 4·25

379 Kaiser Wilhelm I and Heinrich von Stephan

1997. "Pacific '97" International Stamp Exhibition, San Francisco. Death Centenary of Heinrich von Stephan (founder of the U.P.U.).
2481 **379** $1.75 blue . . . . 1·00 1·25
2482 – $1.75 brown . . . . . . 1·00 1·25

2483 – $1.75 mauve . . . . . 1·00 1·25
MS2484 82 × 119 mm. $6 violet 3·50 4·00
DESIGNS: No. 2482, Von Stephan and Mercury; 2483, Carrier pigeon and loft; MS2484, Von Stephan and 15th-century Basle messenger.
No. 2483 is inscribed "PIDGEON" in error.

380 The Two Ugly Sisters and their Mother

1997. 175th Anniv of Brothers Grimm's Third Collection of Fairy Tales. Cinderella. Multicoloured.
2485 $1.75 Type **380** . . . . . . 1·00 1·25
2486 $1.75 Cinderella and her Fairy Godmother . . . . 1·00 1·25
2487 $1.75 Cinderella and the Prince . . . . 1·00 1·25
MS2488 124 × 96 mm. $6 Cinderella trying on slipper . . . . 3·50 4·00

381 "Marasmius rotula"

1997. Fungi. Multicoloured.
2489 45c. Type **381** 50 30
2490 65c. "Cantharellus cibarius" 60 40
2491 70c. "Lepiota cristata" . . . 60 40
2492 90c. "Auricularia mesenteric" 70 50
2493 $1 "Pholiota alnicola" . . . 75 55
2494 $1.65 "Leccinum aurantiacum" . . . . . . 1·10 1·25
2495 $1.75 "Entoloma serrulatum" . . . . . . 1·25 1·40
2496 $1.75 "Panaeolus sphinctrinus" . . . . . . 1·25 1·40
2497 $1.75 "Volvariella bombycina" . . . . . . 1·25 1·40
2498 $1.75 "Conocybe percincta" . 1·25 1·40
2499 $1.75 "Pluteus cervinus" . . 1·25 1·40
2500 $1.75 "Russula foetens" . . 1·25 1·40
MS2501 Two sheets, each 106 × 76 mm. (a) $6 "Amanita cothurnata". (b) $6 "Panellus serotinus" Set of 2 sheets . . . 7·50 8·50

382 "Odontoglossum cervantesii"

1997. Orchids of the World. Multicoloured.
2502 45c. Type **382** 50 30
2503 65c. "Phalaenopsis" Medford Star 60 40
2504 75c. "Vanda Motes" Resplendent 65 45
2505 90c. "Odontonia" Debutante 70 50
2506 $1 "Iwanagaara" Apple Blossom 75 55
2507 $1.65 "Cattleya" Sophia Martin . . . . 1·10 1·25
2508 $1.65 Dogface Butterfly . . 1·10 1·25
2509 $1.65 "Laeliocattleya" Mini Purple . . . . 1·10 1·25
2510 $1.65 "Cymbidium" Showgirl . . . . 1·10 1·25
2511 $1.65 "Brassolaeliocattleya" Dorothy Bertsch . . . . 1·10 1·25
2512 $1.65 "Disa Blackii" . . . . 1·10 1·25
2513 $1.65 "Paphiopedilum leeanum" . . . . 1·10 1·25
2514 $1.65 "Paphiopedilum macranthum" . . . . . . 1·10 1·25
2515 $1.65 "Brassocattleya" Angel Lace . . . . 1·10 1·25
2516 $1.65 "Saphrolae liocattleya" Precious Stones . . . . 1·10 1·25
2517 $1.65 Orange Theope Butterfly . . . . 1·10 1·25
2518 $1.65 "Promenaea xanthina" 1·10 1·25
2519 $1.65 "Lycasle macrobulbon" . . . . . 1·10 1·25
2520 $1.65 "Amestella philippinensis" . . . . . 1·10 1·25
2521 $1.65 "Masdevallia" Machu Picchu . . . . 1·10 1·25
2522 $1.65 "Phalaenopsis" Zuma Urchin . . . . 1·10 1·25
2523 $2 "Dendrobium victoria-reginae" . . . . 1·40 1·60
MS2524 Two sheets, each 76 × 106 mm. (a) "Mitonia" Seine. (b) "Pouphiopedilum gratrixanum" Set of 2 sheets 7·50 8·50
Nos. 2507/14 and 2515/22 respectively were printed together, se-tenant, with the backgrounds forming composite designs.

383 Maradona holding World Cup Trophy, 1986

1997. World Cup Football Championship, France (1998).
2525 **383** 60c. multicoloured . . . 50 35
2526 – 75c. brown 60 45
2527 – 90c. multicoloured . . . 70 50
2528 – $1 brown 75 75
2529 – $1 brown 75 75
2530 – $1 brown 75 75
2531 – $1 black 75 75
2532 – $1 brown 75 75
2533 – $1 brown 75 75
2534 – $1 brown 75 75
2535 – $1 brown 75 75
2536 – $1.20 multicoloured . . 75 80
2537 – $1.65 multicoloured . . 1·10 1·25
2538 – $1.75 multicoloured . . 1·10 1·40
MS2539 Two sheets, each 102 × 127 mm. (a) $6 multicoloured. (b) $6 mult Set of 2 sheets . . . . 7·50 8·50
DESIGNS—HORIZ: No. 2526, Fritzwalter, West Germany, 1954; 2527, Zoff, Italy, 1982; 2536, Moore, England, 1966; 2537, Alberto, Brazil, 1970; 2538, Matthaus, West Germany, 1990; MS2539 (b) West German players celebrating, 1990. VERT: No. 2528, Ademir, Brazil, 1950; 2529, Eusebio, Portugal, 1966; 2530, Fontaine, France, 1958; 2531, Schillaci, Italy, 1990; 2532, Leonidas, Brazil, 1938; 2533, Stabile, Argentina, 1930; 2534, Nejedly, Czechoslovakia, 1934; 2535, Muller, West Germany, 1970; MS2539 (a) Bebeto, Brazil.

384 Scottish Fold Kitten

1997. Cats and Dogs. Multicoloured.
2540 $1.65 Type **384** . . . . . . 1·10 1·10
2541 $1.65 Japanese bobtail . . . 1·10 1·10
2542 $1.65 Tabby manx . . . . 1·10 1·10
2543 $1.65 Bicolor American shorthair . . . . 1·10 1·10
2544 $1.65 Sorrel Abyssinian . . 1·10 1·10
2545 $1.65 Himalayan blue point 1·10 1·10
2546 $1.65 Dachshund . . . . . 1·10 1·10
2547 $1.65 Staffordshire terrier 1·10 1·10
2548 $1.65 Shar-pei . . . . . . 1·10 1·10
2549 $1.65 Beagle . . . . 1·10 1·10
2550 $1.65 Norfolk terrier . . . 1·10 1·10
2551 $1.65 Golden retriever . . . 1·10 1·10
MS2552 Two sheets, each 107 × 77 mm. (a) $6 Red tabby (vert). (b) $6 Siberian husky (vert) Set of 2 sheets . . . . 7·50 8·50

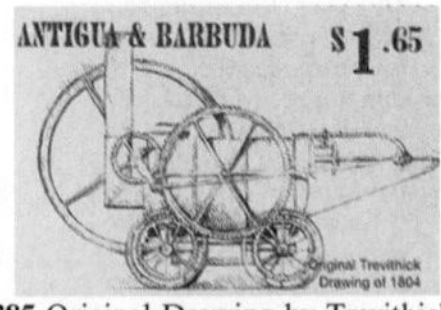

385 Original Drawing by Trevithick, 1803

1997. Railway Locomotives of the World. Multicoloured.
2553 $1.65 Type **385** . . . . . 1·10 1·10
2554 $1.65 William Hedley's "Puffing Billy", (1813–14) 1·10 1·10
2555 $1.65 Crampton locomotive of French Nord Railway, 1858 . . . . 1·10 1·10
2556 $1.65 Lawrence Machine Shop locomotive, U.S.A., 1860 . . . . 1·10 1·10
2557 $1.65 Natchez and Hamburg Railway steam locomotive "Mississippi", U.S.A., 1834 . . . . 1·10 1·10
2558 $1.65 Bury "Coppernob" locomotive, Furness Railway, 1846 . . . . 1·10 1·10
2559 $1.65 David Joy's "Jenny Lind", 1847 . . . . . 1·10 1·10
2560 $1.65 Schenectady Atlantic locomotive, U.S.A., 1899 1·10 1·10
2561 $1.65 Kitsons Class 1800 tank locomotive, Japan, 1881 . . . . 1·10 1·10
2562 $1.65 Pennsylvania Railroad express frieght . . . . . 1·10 1·10
2563 $1.65 Karl Golsdorf's 4 cylinder locomotive, Austria . . . . 1·10 1·10
2564 $1.65 Series "E" locomotive, Russia, 1930 . . . . . . 1·10 1·10
MS2565 Two sheets, each 72 × 100 mm. (a) $6 George Stephenson "Patentee" type locomotive, 1843. (b) $6 Brunel's trestle bridge over River Lynher, Cornwall Set of 2 sheets . . . 7·50 8·50
No. 2554 is dated "1860" in error.

386 "The Angel leaving Tobias and his Family" (Rembrandt)

1997. Christmas. Religious Paintings. Multicoloured.
2566 15c. Type **386** 20 15
2567 25c. "The Resurrection" (Martin Knoller) 30 20
2568 60c. "Astronomy" (Raphael) 50 40
2569 75c. "Music-making Angel" (Melozzo da Forli) . . . 60 55
2570 90c. "Amor" (Parmigianino) 70 60
2571 $1.20 "Madonna and Child with Saints" (Rosso Fiorentino) 80 85
MS2572 Two sheets, each 105 × 96 mm. (a) $6 "The Wedding of Tobias" (Gianantonio and Francesco Guardi) (horiz). (b) $6 "The Portinari Altarpiece" (Hugo van der Goes) (horiz) Set of 2 sheets . . . . 7·50 8·50

387 Diana, Princess of Wales

1998. Diana, Princess of Wales Commemoration. Multicoloured (except Nos. 2574 and 2581/2).
2573 $1.65 Type **387** . . . . . . 95 1·00
2574 $1.65 Wearing hoop earrings (red and black) . . . . . 95 1·00
2575 $1.65 Carrying bouquet . . 95 1·00
2576 $1.65 Wearing floral hat . . 95 1·00
2577 $1.65 With Prince Harry . . 95 1·00
2578 $1.65 Wearing white jacket 95 1·00
2579 $1.65 In kitchen . . . . . 95 1·00
2580 $1.65 Wearing black and white dress . . . . 95 1·00
2581 $1.65 Wearing hat (brown and black) . . . . . . 95 1·00
2582 $1.65 Wearing floral print dress (brown and black) 95 1·00
2583 $1.65 Dancing with John Travolta . . . . 95 1·00
2584 $1.65 Wearing white hat and jacket . . . . 95 1·00
MS2585 Two sheets, each 70 × 100 mm. (a) $6 Wearing red jumper. (b) $6 Wearing black dress for papal audience (brown and black) Set of 2 sheets . . . . . 6·50 7·50

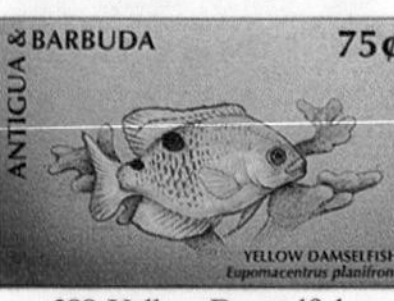

388 Yellow Damselfish

1998. Fishes. Multicoloured.
2586 75c. Type **388** 55 40
2587 90c. Barred hamlet 65 50
2588 $1 Yellow-tailed damselfish ("Jewelfish") 70 55
2589 $1.20 Blue-headed wrasse . . 75 60
2590 $1.50 Queen angelfish . . . 85 85
2591 $1.65 Jackknife-fish 90 95
2592 $1.65 Spot-finned hogfish . . 90 95
2593 $1.65 Sergeant major . . . 90 95
2594 $1.65 Neon goby 90 95
2595 $1.65 Jawfish 90 95
2596 $1.65 Flamefish 90 95
2597 $1.65 Rock beauty 90 95
2598 $1.65 Yellow-tailed snapper 90 95
2599 $1.65 Creole wrasse 90 95
2600 $1.65 Slender filefish 90 95
2601 $1.65 Long-spined squirrelfish 90 95
2602 $1.65 Royal gramma ("Fairy Basslet") 90 95
2603 $1.75 Queen triggerfish . . . 1·00 1·10
MS2604 Two sheets, each 80 × 110 mm. (a) $6 Porkfish. (b) $6 Black-capped basslet Set of 2 sheets . . . . 7·50 8·50
Nos. 2591/6 and 2597/2602 respectively were printed together, se-tenant, with the backgrounds forming composite designs.

389 First Church and Manse, 1822–40

1998. 175th Anniv of Cedar Hall Moravian Church. Multicoloured.
2605 20c. Type **389** 20 20
2606 45c. Cedar Hall School, 1840 . . . . 35 30
2607 75c. Hugh A. King, minister 1945–53 . . . . 55 45
2608 90c. Present Church building 65 50
2609 $1.20 Water tank, 1822 . . 75 75
2610 $2 Former Manse, demolished 1978 . . . . 1·25 1·50
MS2611 100 × 70 mm. $6 Present church building (different) (50 × 37 mm.) . . . . 3·25 4·00

390 Europa Point Lighthouse, Gibraltar

391 Pooh and Tigger (January)

1998. Lighthouses of the World. Multicoloured.
2612 45c. Type **390** 20 25
2613 65c. Tierra del Fuego, Argentina (horiz) 25 30
2614 75c. Point Loma, California, U.S.A. (horiz) 30 35
2615 90c. Groenpoint, Cape Town, South Africa . . . 35 40
2616 $1 Youghal, Cork, Ireland 40 45
2617 $1.20 Launceston, Tasmania, Australia . . . 50 55
2618 $1.65 Point Abino, Ontario, Canada (horiz) 65 70
2619 $1.75 Great Inagua, Bahamas 70 75
MS2620 99 × 70 mm. $6 Cap Hatteras, North Carolina, U.S.A. 2·40 2·50
No. 2613 is inscribed "Terra Del Fuego" in error.

1998. Through the Year with Winnie the Pooh. Multicoloured.
2621 $1 Type **391** 75 75
2622 $1 Pooh and Piglet indoors (February) 75 75
2623 $1 Piglet hang-gliding with scarf (March) 75 75
2624 $1 Tigger, Pooh and Piglet on pond (April) 75 75
2625 $1 Kanga and Roo with posy of flowers (May) . . 75 75
2626 $1 Pooh on balloon and Owl (June) 75 75
2627 $1 Pooh, Eeyore, Tigger and Piglet gazing at stars (July) 75 75
2628 $1 Pooh and Piglet by stream (August) 75 75
2629 $1 Christopher Robin going to school (September) . . 75 75
2630 $1 Eeyore in fallen leaves (October) 75 75
2631 $1 Pooh and Rabbit gathering pumpkins (November) 75 75
2632 $1 Pooh and Piglet skiing (December) 75 75
MS2633 Four sheets, each 126 × 101 mm. (a) $6 Pooh, Rabbit and Piglet with blanket (Spring). (b) $6 Pooh by pond (Summer). (c) $6 Pooh sweeping fallen leaves (Autumn). (d) $6 Pooh and Eeyore on ice (Winter) Set of 4 sheets 13·00 14·00

392 Miss Nellie Robinson (founder)

1998. Centenary of Thomas Oliver Robinson Memorial School.
2634 **392** 20c. green and black . . 10 15
2635 – 45c. multicoloured . . . 20 25
2636 – 65c. green and black . . 25 30
2637 – 75c. multicoloured . . . 30 35
2638 – 90c. multicoloured . . . 35 40
2639 – $1.20 brown, green and black 50 55
MS2640 106 × 76 mm. $6 brown 2·40 2·50
DESIGNS—HORIZ: 45c. School photo, 1985; 65c. Former school building, 1930–49; 75c. Children with Mrs. Natalie Hurst (present headmistress); $1.20, Present school building, 1950. VERT: 90c. Miss Ina Loving (former teacher); $6 Miss Nellie Robinson (different).

393 Spotted Eagle Ray

1998. International Year of the Ocean. Multicoloured.
2641/65 40c. × 25 Type **393**; Manta ray; Hawksbill turtle; Jellyfish; Queen angelfish; Octopus; Emperor angelfish; Regal angelfish; Porkfish; Racoon butterflyfish; Atlantic barracuda; Sea horse; Nautilus; Trumpetfish; White tip shark; Sunken Spanish galleon; Black-tip shark; Long-nosed butterflyfish; Green moray eel; Captain Nemo; Treasure chest; Hammerhead shark; Divers; Lionfish; Clownfish . . . . . .
2666/77 75c. × 12 Maroon-tailed conure; Cocoi heron; Common tern; Rainbow lory ("Rainbow Lorikeet"); Saddleback butterflyfish; Goatfish and cat shark; Blue shark and stingray; Majestic snapper; Nassau grouper; Black-cap gramma and blue tang; Stingrays; Stingrays and giant starfish . . . . . .
2641/77 Set of 37 . . . . 7·75 8·00
MS2678 Two sheets. (a) 68 × 98 mm. $6 Humpback whale. (b) 98 × 68 mm. $6 Fiddler ray Set of 2 sheets . . . . . . 4·75 5·00
Nos. 2641/65 and 2666/77 respectively were printed together, se-tenant, with the backgrounds forming composite designs.

394 "Savannah" (paddle-steamer)

1998. Ships of the World. Multicoloured.
2679 $1.75 Type **394** 70 75
2680 $1.75 Viking longship . . . 70 75
2681 $1.75 Greek galley 70 75
2682 $1.75 Sailing clipper 70 75
2683 $1.75 Dhow 70 75
2684 $1.75 Fishing catboat . . . 70 75
MS2685 Three sheets, each 100 × 70 mm. (a) $6 13th-century English warship (41 × 22 mm). (b) $6 Sailing dory (22 × 41 mm). (c) $6 Baltimore clipper (41 × 22 mm) Set of 3 sheets . . . . 7·25 7·50

395 Flags of Antigua and CARICOM

1998. 25th Anniv of Caribbean Community.
2686 **395** $1 multicoloured 40 45

396 Ford, 1896

1998. Classic Cars. Multicoloured.
2687 $1.65 Type **396** 65 70
2688 $1.65 Ford A, 1903 . . . . 65 70
2689 $1.65 Ford T, 1928 . . . . 65 70
2690 $1.65 Ford T, 1922 . . . . 65 70
2691 $1.65 Ford Blackhawk, 1929 65 70
2692 $1.65 Ford Sedan, 1934 . . 65 70
2693 $1.65 Torpedo, 1911 . . . . 65 70
2694 $1.65 Mercedes 22, 1913 . . 65 70
2695 $1.65 Rover, 1920 . . . . . 65 70
2696 $1.65 Mercedes-Benz, 1956 65 70
2697 $1.65 Packard V-12, 1934 65 70
2698 $1.65 Opel, 1924 . . . . . 65 70
MS2699 Two sheets, each 70 × 100 mm. (a) $6 Ford, 1908 (60 × 40 mm). (b) $6 Ford, 1929 (60 × 40 mm) Set of 2 sheets . . 4·75 5·00

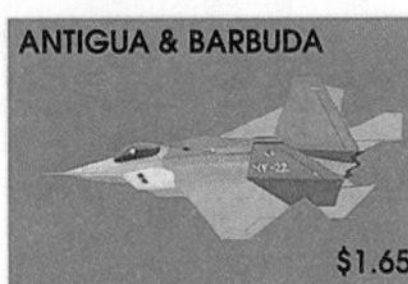

397 Lockheed-Boeing General Dynamics Yf-22

1998. Modern Aircraft. Multicoloured.
2700 $1.65 Type **397** 65 70
2701 $1.65 Dassault-Breguet Rafale BO 1 . . . . . . 65 70
2702 $1.65 MiG 29 . . . . . . 65 70
2703 $1.65 Dassault-Breguet Mirage 2000D 65 70
2704 $1.65 Rockwell B-1B "Lancer" 65 70
2705 $1.65 McDonnell-Douglas C-17A 65 70
2706 $1.65 Space Shuttle 65 70
2707 $1.65 SAAB "Grippen" . . 65 70
2708 $1.65 Eurofighter EF-2000 65 70
2709 $1.65 Sukhoi SU 27 . . . . 65 70
2710 $1.65 Northrop B-2 . . . . 65 70
2711 $1.65 Lockheed F-117 "Nighthawk" 65 70
MS2712 Two sheets, each 110 × 85 mm. (a) $6 F18 Hornet. (b) $6 Sukhoi SU 35 Set of 2 sheets 4·75 5·00
No. **MS**2712b is inscribed "Sukhi" in error.

398 Karl Benz (internal-combustion engine)

399 Stylized Americas

1998. Millennium Series. Famous People of the Twentieth Century. Inventors. Multicoloured.
2713 $1 Type **398** 40 45
2714 $1 Early Benz car and Mercedes-Benz racing car (53 × 38 mm) 40 45
2715 $1 Atom bomb mushroom cloud (53 × 38 mm) . . . 40 45
2716 $1 Albert Einstein (theory of relativity) 40 45
2717 $1 Leopold Godowsky Jr. and Leopold Damrosch Mannes (Kodachrome film) 40 45
2718 $1 Camera and transparencies (53 × 38 mm) 40 45
2719 $1 Heinkel He 178 (first turbo jet plane) (53 × 38 mm) 40 45
2720 $1 Dr. Hans Pabst von Ohain (jet turbine engine) 40 45
2721 $1 Rudolf Diesel (diesel engine) 40 45
2722 $1 Early Diesel engine and forms of transport (53 × 38 mm) 40 45
2723 $1 Zeppelin airship (53 × 38 mm) 40 45
2724 $1 Count Ferdinand von Zeppelin (airship pioneer) 40 45
2725 $1 Wilhelm Conrad Rontgen (X-rays) 40 45
2726 $1 X-ray of hand (53 × 38 mm) 40 45
2727 $1 Launch of Saturn rocket (53 × 38 mm) 40 45
2728 $1 Wernher von Braun (rocket research) 40 45
MS2729 Two sheets, each 106 × 76 mm. (a) $6 Hans Geiger (Geiger counter). (b) $6 William Shockley (research into semi-conductors) Set of 2 sheets . . 4·75 5·00
No. 2713 is inscribed "CARL BENZ" in error.

1998. 50th Anniv of Organization of American States.
2730 **399** $1 multicoloured 40 45

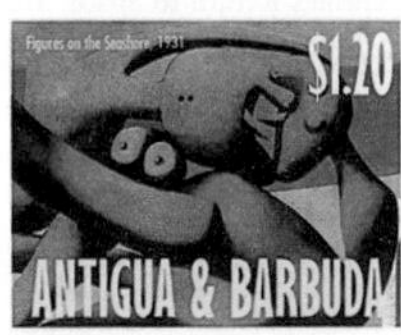

400 "Figures on the Seashore"

1998. 25th Death Anniv of Pablo Picasso (painter). Multicoloured.
2731 $1.20 Type **400** 50 55
2732 $1.65 "Three Figures under a Tree" (vert) 65 70
2733 $1.75 "Two Women running on the Beach" 70 75
MS2734 126 × 102 mm. $6 "Bullfight" . . . . 2·40 2·50

401 Dino 246 GT-GTS

1998. Birth Centenary of Enzo Ferrari (car manufacturer). Multicoloured.
2735 $1.75 Type **401** . . . . . . 2·25 2·25
2736 $1.75 Front view of Dino 246 GT-GTS . . . . . 2·25 2·25
2737 $1.75 365 GT4 BB . . . . 2·25 2·25
MS2738 104 × 72 mm. $6 Dino 246 GT-GTS (91 × 34 mm) . . . . 6·00 6·00

402 Scout Handshake

1998. 19th World Scout Jamboree, Chile. Multicoloured.
2739 90c. Type **402** 35 40
2740 $1 Scouts hiking 40 45
2741 $1.20 Scout salute 50 55
MS2742 68 × 98 mm. $6 Lord Baden-Powell . . . . 2·40 2·50

403 Mahatma Gandhi

405 Diana, Princess of Wales

404 McDonnell Douglas Phantom F-GR1

1998. 50th Death Anniv of Mahatma Gandhi. Multicoloured.
2743 90c. Type **403** 35 40
2744 $1 Gandhi seated 40 45
2745 $1.20 As young man 50 55
2746 $1.65 At primary school in Rajkot, aged 7 . . . . . 65 70
MS2747 100 × 70 mm. $6 Gandhi with staff . . . . 2·40 2·50

1998. 80th Anniv of Royal Air Force. Multicoloured.
2748 $1.75 Type **404** 70 75
2749 $1.75 Two Sepecat Jaguar GR1As 70 75
2750 $1.75 Panavia Tornado F3 70 75
2751 $1.75 McDonnell Douglas Phantom F-GR2 . . . . 70 75
MS2752 Two sheets, each 90 × 68 mm. (a) $6 Golden eagle (bird) and Bristol F2B Fighter. (b) $6 Hawker Hurricane and EF-2000 Eurofighter Set of 2 sheets . . . . 4·75 5·00

1998. 1st Death Anniv of Diana, Princess of Wales.
2753 **405** $1.20 multicoloured . . 50 55

406 Brown Pelican

1998. Sea Birds of the World. Multicoloured.
2754 15c. Type **406** 10 10
2755 25c. Dunlin 10 15
2756 45c. Atlantic puffin 20 25
2757 75c. King eider 30 35
2758 75c. Inca tern 30 35
2759 75c. Little auk ("Dovekie") 30 35
2760 75c. Ross's gull 30 35
2761 75c. Common noddy ("Brown Noddy") 30 35
2762 75c. Marbled murrelet . . . 30 35
2763 75c. Northern gannet . . . 30 35
2764 75c. Razorbill 30 35
2765 75c. Long-tailed skua ("Long-tailed Jaegar") . . 30 35
2766 75c. Black guillemot 30 35
2767 75c. Whimbrel 30 35
2768 75c. American oystercatcher ("Oystercatcher") 30 35
2769 90c. Pied cormorant 35 40
MS2770 Two sheets, each 100 × 70 mm. (a) $6 Black skimmer. (b) $6 Wandering albatross Set of 2 sheets . . . 4·75 5·00
Nos. 2757/68 were printed together, se-tenant, with the backgrounds forming a composite design.
No. 2760 is inscribed "ROSS' BULL" in error.

407 Border Collie

1998. Christmas. Dogs. Multicoloured.
2771 15c. Type **407** 10 10
2772 25c. Dalmatian 10 15
2773 65c. Weimaraner 25 30
2774 75c. Scottish terrier 30 35
2775 90c. Long-haired dachshund 35 40
2776 $1.20 Golden retriever . . . 50 55
2777 $2 Pekingese 80 85
MS2778 Two sheets, each 75 × 66 mm. (a) $6 Dalmatian. (b) $6 Jack Russell terrier Set of 2 sheets . . . . 4·75 5·00

408 Mickey Mouse Sailing

1999. 70th Birthday of Mickey Mouse. Walt Disney characters participating in water sports. Multicoloured.
2779 $1 Type **408** 80 80
2780 $1 Mickey and Goofy sailing 80 80
2781 $1 Goofy windsurfing . . . 80 80
2782 $1 Mickey sailing and seagull 80 80
2783 $1 Goofy sailing 80 80
2784 $1 Mickey windsurfing . . . 80 80
2785 $1 Goofy running with surfboard 80 80
2786 $1 Mickey surfing 80 80
2787 $1 Donald Duck holding surfboard 80 80
2788 $1 Donald on surfboard (face value at right) . . . 80 80
2789 $1 Minnie Mouse surfing in green shorts 80 80
2790 $1 Goofy surfing 80 80

2791 $1 Goofy in purple shorts waterskiing 80 80
2792 $1 Mickey waterskiing . . . 80 80
2793 $1 Goofy waterskiing with Mickey 80 80
2794 $1 Donald on surfboard (face value at left) 80 80
2795 $1 Goofy in yellow shorts waterskiing 80 80
2796 $1 Minnie in pink shorts surfing 80 80
MS2797 Four sheets, each 127×102 mm. (a) $6 Goofy (horiz). (b) $6 Donald Duck. (c) $6 Minnie Mouse. (d) $6 Mickey Mouse Set of 4 sheets . . . . 14·00 15·00

409 Hell's Gate Steel Orchestra, 1996

1999. 50th Anniv of Hell's Gate Steel Orchestra. Multicoloured.
2798 20c. Type **409** 10 15
2799 60c. Orchestra members, New York, 1992 . . . . 25 30
2800 75c. Orchestra members with steel drums, 1950 . . 30 35
2801 90c. Eustace Henry, 1964 . . 35 40
2802 $1.20 Alston Henry playing double tenor 50 55
MS2803 Two sheets. (a) 100×70 mm. $4 Orchestra members, 1950 (vert). (b) 70×100 mm. $4 Eustace Henry, 1964 (vert) Set of 2 sheets . . . 3·25 3·50

410 Tulips

411 Elle Macpherson

1999. Flowers. Multicoloured.
2804 60c. Type **410** 25 30
2805 75c. Fuschia 30 35
2806 90c. Morning glory (horiz) 35 40
2807 90c. Geranium (horiz) . . . 35 40
2808 90c. Blue hibiscus (horiz) . . 35 40
2809 90c. Marigolds (horiz) . . . 35 40
2810 90c. Sunflower (horiz) . . . 35 40
2811 90c. Impatiens (horiz) . . . 35 40
2812 90c. Petunia (horiz) 35 40
2813 90c. Pansy (horiz) 35 40
2814 90c. Saucer magnolia (horiz) 35 40
2815 $1 Primrose (horiz) 40 45
2816 $1 Bleeding heart (horiz) . . 40 45
2817 $1 Pink dogwood (horiz) . . 40 45
2818 $1 Peony (horiz) 40 45
2819 $1 Rose (horiz) 40 45
2820 $1 Hellebores (horiz) . . . 40 45
2821 $1 Lily (horiz) 40 45
2822 $1 Violet (horiz) 40 45
2823 $1 Cherry blossom (horiz) 40 45
2824 $1.20 Calla lily 50 55
2825 $1.65 Sweet pea 65 70
MS2826 Two sheets. (a) 76×100 mm. $6 Sangria lily. (b) 106×76 mm. $6 Zinnias Set of 2 sheets . . . . 4·75 5·00
Nos. 2806/14 and 2815/23 respectively were each printed together, se-tenant, forming composite designs

1999. "Australia '99" International Stamp Exhibition, Melbourne (1st issue). Elle Macpherson (model). Multicoloured.
2827 $1.20 Type **411** 50 55
2828 $1.20 Lying on couch . . . 50 55
2829 $1.20 In swimsuit 50 55
2830 $1.20 Looking over shoulder 50 55
2831 $1.20 Wearing cream shirt 50 55
2832 $1.20 Wearing stetson . . . 50 55
2833 $1.20 Wearing black T-shirt 50 55
2834 $1.20 Holding tree branch 50 55
See also Nos. 2875/92.

412 "Luna 2" Moon Probe

413 John Glenn entering "Mercury" Capsule, 1962

1999. Satellites and Spacecraft. Multicoloured.
2835 $1.65 Type **412** 65 70
2836 $1.65 "Mariner 2" space probe 65 70
2837 $1.65 "Giotto" space probe 65 70
2838 $1.65 Rosat satellite 65 70
2839 $1.65 International Ultraviolet Explorer . . . 65 70
2840 $1.65 "Ulysses" space probe 65 70
2841 $1.65 "Mariner 10" space probe 65 70
2842 $1.65 "Luna 9" Moon probe 65 70
2843 $1.65 Advanced X-ray Astrophysics Facility . . 65 70
2844 $1.65 "Magellan" space probe 65 70
2845 $1.65 "Pioneer – Venus 2" space probe 65 70
2846 $1.65 Infra-red Astronomy Satellite 65 70
MS2847 Two sheets, each 106×76 mm. (a) $6 "Salyut 1" space station (horiz). (b) $6 "MIR" space station (horiz) Set of 2 sheets . . . . 4·75 5·00
Nos. 2835/40 and 2841/46 repectively were each printed together, se-tenant, with the backgrounds forming composite designs.

1999. John Glenn's Return to Space. Multicoloured.
2848 $1.75 Type **413** 70 75
2849 $1.75 Glenn in "Mercury" mission spacesuit 70 75
2850 $1.75 Fitting helmet for "Mercury" mission . . . 70 75
2851 $1.75 Outside pressure chamber 70 75

414 Brachiosaurus

1999. Prehistoric Animals. Multicoloured.
2852 65c. Type **414** 25 30
2853 75c. Oviraptor (vert) 30 35
2854 $1 Homotherium 40 45
2855 $1.20 Macrauchenia (vert) 50 55
2856 $1.65 Struthiomimus 65 70
2857 $1.65 Corythosaurus 65 70
2858 $1.65 Dsungaripterus . . . 65 70
2859 $1.65 Compsognathus . . . 65 70
2860 $1.65 Prosaurolophus . . . 65 70
2861 $1.65 Montanoceratops . . 65 70
2862 $1.65 Stegosaurus 65 70
2863 $1.65 Deinonychus 65 70
2864 $1.65 Ouranosaurus 65 70
2865 $1.65 Leptictidium 65 70
2866 $1.65 Ictitherium 65 70
2867 $1.65 Plesictis 65 70
2868 $1.65 Hemicyon 65 70
2869 $1.65 Diacodexis 65 70
2870 $1.65 Stylinodon 65 70
2871 $1.65 Kanuites 65 70
2872 $1.65 Chriacus 65 70
2873 $1.65 Argyrolagus 65 70
MS2874 Two sheets, each 110×85 mm. (a) $6 Eurhinodelphis. (b) $6 Pteranodon Set of 2 sheets . . . . . . 4·75 5·00
Nos. 2856/64 and 2865/73 respectively were each printed together, se-tenant, with the backgrounds forming composite designs.

415 Two White Kittens

1999. "Australia '99" International Stamp Exhibition, Melbourne (2nd issue). Cats. Mult.
2875 35c. Type **415** 15 20
2876 45c. Kitten with string . . . 20 25
2877 60c. Two kittens under blanket 25 30
2878 75c. Two kittens in basket 30 35
2879 90c. Kitten with ball 35 40
2880 $1 White kitten 40 45
2881 $1.65 Two kittens playing 65 70
2882 $1.65 Black and white kitten 65 70
2883 $1.65 Black kitten and sleeping cream kitten . . 65 70
2884 $1.65 White kitten with green string 65 70
2885 $1.65 Two sleeping kittens 65 70
2886 $1.65 White kitten with black tip to tail 65 70
2887 $1.65 Kitten with red string 65 70
2888 $1.65 Two long-haired kittens 65 70
2889 $1.65 Ginger kitten 65 70
2890 $1.65 Kitten playing with mouse 65 70
2891 $1.65 Kitten asleep on blue cushion 65 70
2892 $1.65 Tabby kitten 65 70
MS2893 Two sheets, each 70×100 mm. (a) $6 Cat carrying kitten in mouth. (b) $6 Kitten in tree Set of 2 sheets . . . . . . 4·75 5·00

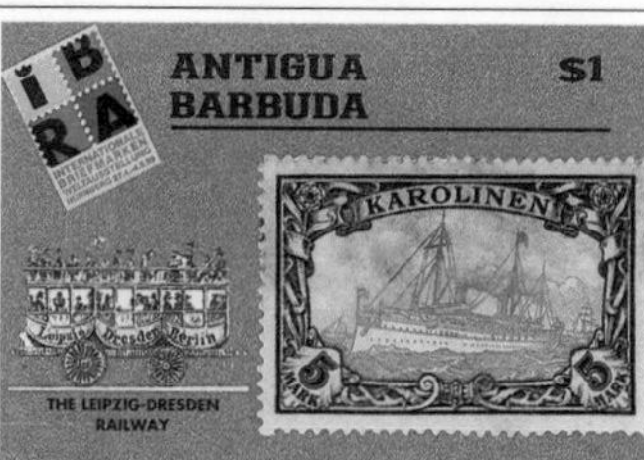

416 Early Leipzig–Dresden Railway Carriage and Caroline Islands 1901 Yacht Type 5m. Stamp

1999. "iBRA '99" International Stamp Exhibition, Nuremberg. Multicoloured.
2894 $1 Type **416** 40 45
2895 $1.20 Golsdorf steam locomotive and Caroline Islands 1901 Yacht type 1m. 50 55
2896 $1.65 Early Leipzig–Dresden Railway carriage and Caroline Islands 1899 20pf. optd on Germany 65 70
2897 $1.90 Golsdorf steam locomotive and Caroline Islands 1901 Yacht type 5pf. and 20pf. 75 80
MS2898 165×110 mm. $6 Registration label for Ponape, Caroline Islands . . . . 2·40 2·50

417 "People on Balcony of Sazaido" (Hokusai)

1999. 150th Death Anniv of Katsushika Hokusai (Japanese artist). Multicoloured.
2899 $1.65 Type **417** 65 70
2900 $1.65 "Nakahara in Sagami Province" 65 70
2901 $1.65 "Defensive Positions" (two wrestlers) 65 70
2902 $1.65 "Defensive Positions" (three wrestlers) 65 70
2903 $1.65 "Mount Fuji in Clear Weather" 65 70
2904 $1.65 "Nihonbashi in Edo" 65 70
2905 $1.65 "Asakusa Honganji" 65 70
2906 $1.65 "Dawn at Isawa in Kai Province" 65 70
2907 $1.65 "Samurai with Bow and Arrow" (with arrows on ground) 65 70
2908 $1.65 "Samurai with Bow and Arrow" (trees in background) 65 70
2909 $1.65 "Kajikazawa in Kai Province" 65 70
2910 $1.65 "A Great Wave" . . 65 70
MS2911 Two sheets, each 100×71 mm. (a) $6 "A Netsuke Workshop" (vert). (b) $6 "Gotenyama at Shinagawa on Tokaido Highway" (vert) Set of 2 sheets . . . . 4·75 5·00
No. 2903 is inscribed "MOUNT FUGI" in error.

418 Sophie Rhys-Jones

419 Three Children

1999. Royal Wedding. Multicoloured.
2912 $3 Type **418** . . . . 1·25 1·40
2913 $3 Sophie and Prince Edward . . . . 1·25 1·40
2914 $3 Prince Edward . . . . . 1·25 1·40
MS2915 108×78 mm. $6 Prince Edward with Sophie Rhys-Jones and Windsor Castle (horiz) . . 2·40 2·50

1999. 10th Anniv of United Nations Rights of the Child Convention. Multicoloured.
2916 $3 Type **419** . . . . 1·25 1·40
2917 $3 Adult hand holding child's hand . . . . . . 1·25 1·40
2918 $3 Dove and U.N. Headquarters . . . . . . 1·25 1·40
MS2919 112×70 mm. $6 Dove 2·40 2·50
Nos. 2916/18 were printed together, se-tenant, forming a composite design.

420 Crampton Type Railway Locomotive, 1855–69

1999. "PhilexFrance '99" International Stamp Exhibition, Paris. Railway Locomotives. Two sheets, each 106×81 mm, containing T **420** and similar design. Multicoloured.
MS2920 (a) $6 Type **420**. (b) $6 Compound type No. 232-U1 steam locomotive, 1949 Set of 2 sheets . . . . 4·75 5·00

421 Three Archangels from "Faust"

1999. 250th Birth Anniv of Johann von Goethe (German writer).
2921 **421** $1.75 purple, mauve and black 70 75
2922 – $1.75 blue, violet and black 70 75
2923 – $1.75 green and black . . 70 75
MS2924 – 79×101 mm. $6 black and brown . . . . 2·40 2·50
DESIGNS: No. 2922, Von Goethe and Von Schiller; 2923, Faust reclining with spirits; **MS**2924 Wolfgang von Goethe.

422 "Missa Ferdie" (fishing launch)

423 Fiery Jewel

1999. Local Ships and Boats. Multicoloured.
2925 25c. Type **422** 10 15
2926 45c. Yachts in 32nd Annual Antigua International Sailing Week 20 25
2927 60c. "Jolly Roger" (tourist ship) 25 30
2928 90c. "Freewinds" (cruise liner) (10th anniv of first visit) 35 40
2929 $1.20 "Monarch of the Seas" (cruise liner) . . . 50 55
MS2930 98×62 mm. $4 "Freewinds" (11th anniv of maiden voyage) (50×37 mm) 1·60 1·75

1999. Butterflies. Multicoloured.
2931 65c. Type **423** 25 30
2932 75c. Hewitson's blue hairstreak 30 35
2933 $1 California dog face (horiz) 40 45
2934 $1 Small copper (horiz) . . 40 45
2935 $1 Zebra swallowtail (horiz) 40 45
2936 $1 White "M" hairstreak (horiz) 40 45
2937 $1 Old world swallowtail (horiz) 40 45
2938 $1 Buckeye (horiz) 40 45
2939 $1 Apollo (horiz) 40 45
2940 $1 Sonoran blue (horiz) . . 40 45
2941 $1 Purple emperor (horiz) 40 45
2942 $1.20 Scarce bamboo page (horiz) 50 55
2943 $1.65 Paris peacock (horiz) 65 70
MS2944 Two sheets. (a) 85×110 mm. $6 Monarch. (b) 110×85 mm. $6 Cairns birdwing (horiz) Set of 2 sheets . . . . 4·75 5·00
Nos. 2933/41 were printed together, se-tenant, forming a composite design.

424 "Madonna and Child in Wreath of Flowers" (Rubens)

1999. Christmas. Religious Paintings.
2945 **424** 15c. multicoloured . . . 10 10
2946 – 25c. black, stone & yellow 10 15
2947 – 45c. multicoloured . . . 20 25
2948 – 60c. multicoloured . . . 25 30
2949 – $2 multicoloured 80 85
2950 – $4 black, stone & yell . . 1·60 1·75
MS2951 – 76 × 106 mm. $6 multicoloured . . . . 2·40 2·50
DESIGNS: 25c. "Shroud of Christ held by Two Angels" (Durer); 45c. "Madonna and Child enthroned between Two Saints" (Raphael); 60c. "Holy Family with Lamb" (Raphael); $2 "The Transfiguration" (Raphael); $4 "Three Putti holding Coat of Arms (Durer); $6 "Coronation of St. Catharine" (Rubens).

425 Katharine Hepburn (actress)

2000. Senior Celebrities of the 20th Century. Mult.
2952 90c. Type **425** 35 40
2953 90c. Martha Graham (dancer) 35 40
2954 90c. Eubie Blake (jazz pianist) 35 40
2955 90c. Agatha Christie (novelist) 35 40
2956 90c. Eudora Welty (American novelist) . . . 35 40
2957 90c. Helen Hayes (actress) 35 40
2958 90c. Vladimir Horowitz (concert pianist) 35 40
2959 90c. Katharine Graham (newspaper publisher) . . 35 40
2960 90c. Pablo Casals (cellist) . . 35 40
2961 90c. Pete Seeger (folk singer) 35 40
2962 90c. Andres Segovia (guitarist) 35 40
2963 90c. Frank Lloyd Wright (architect) 35 40

426 Sir Cliff Richard

2000. 60th Birthday of Sir Cliff Richard (entertainer).
2964 **426** $1.65 multicoloured . . 65 70

427 Charlie Chaplin

2000. Charlie Chaplin (actor and director) Commemoration. Showing film scenes. Mult.
2965 $1.65 Standing in street (*Modern Times*) 65 70
2966 $1.65 Hugging man (*The Gold Rush*) 65 70
2967 $1.65 Type **427** 65 70
2968 $1.65 Wielding tools (*Modern Times*) 65 70
2969 $1.65 With hands on hips (*The Gold Rush*) 65 70
2970 $1.65 Wearing cape (*The Gold Rush*) 65 70

428 Streamertail

2000. "The Stamp Show 2000" International Stamp Exhibition, London. Birds of the Caribbean. Mult.
2971 75c. Type **428** 30 35
2972 90c. Yellow-bellied sapsucker 35 40
2973 $1.20 Rufous-tailed jacamar 50 55
2974 $1.20 Scarlet macaw 50 55
2975 $1.20 Yellow-crowned amazon ("Yellow-fronted Amazon") 50 55
2976 $1.20 Golden conure ("Queen-of-Bavaria") . . 50 55
2977 $1.20 Nanday conure . . . 50 55
2978 $1.20 Jamaican tody 50 55
2979 $1.20 Smooth-billed ani . . 50 55
2980 $1.20 Puerto Rican woodpecker 50 55
2981 $1.20 Ruby-throated hummingbird 50 55
2982 $1.20 Common ground dove 50 55
2983 $1.20 American wood ibis ("Wood Stork") 50 55
2984 $1.20 Saffron finch 50 55
2985 $1.20 Green-backed heron 50 55
2986 $1.20 Lovely cotinga 50 55
2987 $1.20 St. Vincent amazon ("St. Vincent Parrot") . . 50 55
2988 $1.20 Cuban grassquit . . . 50 55
2989 $1.20 Red-winged blackbird 50 55
2990 $2 Spectacled owl 80 85
MS2991 Two sheets, each 80 × 106 mm. (a) $6 Vermillion flycatcher (50 × 37 mm). (b) $6 Red-capped manakin (37 × 50 mm) Set of 2 sheets . . 4·75 5·00
Nos. 2974/81 and 2982/9 were each printed together, se-tenant, with the backgrounds forming composite designs.
No. 2981 is inscribed "Arhilochus colubria" in error.

429 "Arthur Goodwin"

2000. 400th Birth Anniv of Sir Anthony Van Dyck (Flemish painter). Multicoloured.
2992 $1.20 Type **429** 50 55
2993 $1.20 "Sir Thomas Wharton" 50 55
2994 $1.20 "Mary Villiers, Daughter of Duke of Buckingham" 50 55
2995 $1.20 "Christina Bruce, Countess of Devonshire" 50 55
2996 $1.20 "James Hamilton, Duke of Hamilton" . . . 50 55
2997 $1.20 "Henry Danvers, Earl of Danby" 50 55
2998 $1.20 "Marie de Raet, Wife of Philippe le Roy" . . . 50 55
2999 $1.20 "Jacomo de Cachiopin" 50 55
3000 $1.20 "Princess Henrietta of Lorraine attended by a Page" 50 55
3001 $1.20 "Portrait of a Man" 50 55
3002 $1.20 "Portrait of a Woman" 50 55
3003 $1.20 "Philippe le Roy, Seigneur de Ravels" . . . 50 55
3004 $1.20 "Charles I in State Robes" 50 55
3005 $1.20 "Queen Henrietta Maria" (in white dress) 50 55
3006 $1.20 "Queen Henrietta Maria with Sir Jeffrey Hudson" 50 55
3007 $1.20 "Charles I in Armour" 50 55
3008 $1.20 "Queen Henrietta Maria in Profile facing right" 50 55
3009 $1.20 "Queen Henrietta Maria" (in black dress) 50 55
MS3010 Six sheets. (a) 102 × 128 mm. $5 "Charles I on Horseback". (b) 102 × 128 mm. $5 "Charles I Hunting". (c) 128 × 102 mm. $5 "Charles I with Queen Henrietta Maria". (d) 128 × 102 mm. $5 "Charles I" (from Three Aspects portrait). (e) 102 × 128 mm. $6 "William, Lord Russell". (f) 102 × 128 mm. $6 "Two Sons of Duke of Lennox" Set of 6 sheets . . . . 13·00 14·00
No. 2994 is inscribed "Mary Villers", 3002 "Portrait of a Women", 3005 "Henrieta Maria" and **MS**3010f "Duke of Lenox", all in error.

430 *Eupolea miniszeki*

2000. Butterflies. Multicoloured.
3011 $1.65 Type **430** 65 70
3012 $1.65 *Heliconius doris* . . . 65 70
3013 $1.65 *Evenus coronata* . . . 65 70
3014 $1.65 *Papilio anchisiades* . . 65 70
3015 $1.65 *Syrmatia dorilas* . . . 65 70
3016 $1.65 *Morpho patroclus* . . 65 70
3017 $1.65 *Mesosemia loruhama* 65 70
3018 $1.65 *Bia actorion* 65 70
3019 $1.65 *Anteos clorinde* . . . 65 70
3020 $1.65 *Menander menande* . . 65 70
3021 $1.65 *Catasticta manco* . . . 65 70
3022 $1.65 *Urania leilus* 65 70
3023 $1.65 *Theope eudocia* (vert) 65 70
3024 $1.65 *Uranus sloanus* (vert) 65 70
3025 $1.65 *Helicopis cupido* (vert) 65 70
3026 $1.65 *Papilio velovis* (vert) 65 70
3027 $1.65 *Graphium androcles* (vert) 65 70
3028 $1.65 *Mesene phareus* (vert) 65 70
MS3029 Three sheets. (a) 110 × 85 mm. $6 *Graphium encelades*. (b) 110 × 85 mm. $6 *Graphium milon*. (c) 85 × 110 mm. $6 *Hemlargus isola* (vert) Set of 3 sheets . . . . 7·25 7·50
Nos. 3011/16, 3017/22 and 3023/8 were each printed together, se-tenant, with the backgrounds forming composite designs.

431 Boxer

432 *Epidendrum pseudepidendrum*

2000. Cats and Dogs. Multicoloured.
3030 90c. Type **431** 35 40
3031 $1 Alaskan malamute . . . 40 45
3032 $1.65 Bearded collie 65 70
3033 $1.65 Cardigan Welsh corgi 65 70
3034 $1.65 Saluki (red) 65 70
3035 $1.65 Basset hound 65 70
3036 $1.65 White standard poodle 65 70
3037 $1.65 Boston terrier 65 70
3038 $1.65 Long-haired blue and white cat (horiz) 65 70
3039 $1.65 Snow shoe (horiz) . . 65 70
3040 $1.65 Persian (horiz) 65 70
3041 $1.65 Chocolate lynx point (horiz) 65 70
3042 $1.65 Brown and white sphynx (horiz) 65 70
3043 $1.65 White tortoiseshell (horiz) 65 70
3044 $2 Wirehaired pointer . . . 80 85
3045 $4 Saluki (black) . . . . . 1·60 1·75
MS3046 Two sheets. (a) 106 × 71 mm. $6 Cavalier King Charles spaniel. (b) 111 × 81 mm. $6 Lavender tortie Set of 2 sheets 4·75 5·00

2000. Flowers of the Caribbean. Multicoloured.
3047 45c. Type **432** 20 25
3048 65c. *Odontoglossum cervantesii* 25 30
3049 75c. *Cattleya dowiana* . . . 30 35
3050 90c. *Beloperone guttata* . . . 35 40
3051 $1 *Colliandra haematocephala* 40 45
3052 $1.20 *Brassavola nodosa* . . 50 55
3053 $1.65 *Pseudocalymna alliaceum* 65 70
3054 $1.65 *Datura candida* . . . 65 70
3055 $1.65 *Ipomoea tuberosa* . . 65 70
3056 $1.65 *Allamanda cathartica* 65 70
3057 $1.65 *Aspasia epidendroides* 65 70
3058 $1.65 *Maxillaria cucullata* 65 70
3059 $1.65 *Anthurium andreanum* 65 70
3060 $1.65 *Doxantha unguiscati* 65 70
3061 $1.65 *Hibiscus rosa-sinensis* 65 70
3062 $1.65 *Canna indica* 65 70
3063 $1.65 *Heliconius umilis* . . . 65 70
3064 $1.65 *Strelitzia reginae* . . . 65 70
3065 $1.65 *Masdevallia coccinea* 65 70
3066 $1.65 *Paphinia cristata* . . . 65 70
3067 $1.65 *Vanilla planifolia* . . . 65 70
3068 $1.65 *Cattleya forbesii* . . . 65 70
3069 $1.65 *Lycaste skinneri* . . . 65 70
3070 $1.65 *Cattleya percivaliana* 65 70
MS3071 Three sheets, each 74 × 103 mm. (a) $6 *Cattleya leopoldiie*. (b) $6 *Strelitzia reginae*. (c) $6 *Rossioglossum grande* Set of 3 sheets . . . . 7·25 7·50
No. 3061 is inscribed "rosa-senensis" and **MS**3071b "regenae", both in error.

433 Prince William

2000. 18th Birthday of Prince William. Multicoloured.
3072 $1.65 Prince William waving 65 70
3073 $1.65 Wearing Eton school uniform 65 70
3074 $1.65 Wearing grey suit . . 65 70
3075 $1.65 Type **433** 65 70
MS3076 100 × 80 mm. $6 Princess Diana with Princes William and Harry (37 × 50 mm) . . . . . 2·40 2·50

434 "Sputnik I"

2000. "EXPO 2000" World Stamp Exhibition, Anaheim, U.S.A. Space Satellites. Multicoloured.
3077 $1.65 Type **434** 65 70
3078 $1.65 "Explorer I" 65 70
3079 $1.65 "Mars Express" . . . 65 70
3080 $1.65 "Lunik I Solnik" . . 65 70
3081 $1.65 "Ranger 7" 65 70
3082 $1.65 "Mariner 4" 65 70
3083 $1.65 "Mariner 10" 65 70
3084 $1.65 "Soho" 65 70
3085 $1.65 "Mariner 2" 65 70
3086 $1.65 "Giotto" 65 70
3087 $1.65 "Exosat" 65 70
3088 $1.65 "Pioneer Venus" . . . 65 70
MS3089 Two sheets, each 106 × 76 mm. (a) $6 "Vostok I". (b) $6 Hubble Space Telescope Set of 2 sheets . . . . 4·75 5·00
Nos. 3077/82 and 3083/8 were each printed together, se-tenant, with the backgrounds forming composite designs.

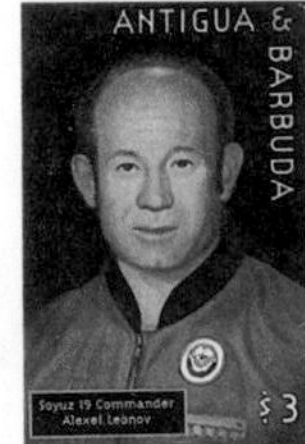

435 Alexei Leonov (Commander of "Soyuz 19")

436 Anna Karina in *Une Femme est Une Femme*, 1961

2000. 25th Anniv of "Apollo–Soyuz" Joint Project. Multicoloured.
3090 $3 Type **435** . . . . 1·25 1·40
3091 $3 "Soyuz 19" . . . . . . 1·25 1·40
3092 $3 Valeri Kubasov ("Soyuz 19" engineer) . . . . . . 1·25 1·40
MS3093 71 × 88 mm. $6 Alexei Leonov and Thomas Stafford (Commander of "Apollo 18") 2·40 2·50

2000. 50th Anniv of Berlin Film Festival. Designs showing actors, directors and film scenes. Mult.
3094 $1.65 Type **436** 65 70
3095 $1.65 *Carmen Jones*, 1955 . . 65 70
3096 $1.65 *Die Ratten*, 1955 . . . 65 70
3097 $1.65 *Die Vier im Jeep*, 1951 65 70
3098 $1.65 Sidney Poitier in *Lilies of the Field*, 1963 . . . . 65 70
3099 $1.65 *Invitation to the Dance*, 1956 . . . . . . 65 70
MS3100 97 × 103 mm. $6 Kate Winslet in *Sense and Sensibility*, 1996 . . . . 2·40 2·50
No. 3096 is inscribed "GOLDER BERLIN BEAR" and **MS**3100 shows the award date "1966" in error.

437 George Stephenson and *Locomotion No. 1*, 1825

2000. 175th Anniv of Stockton and Darlington Line (first public railway). Multicoloured.
3101 $3 Type **437** . . . . 1·25 1·40
3102 $3 Camden and Amboy Railroad locomotive *John Bull*, 1831 . . . . 1·25 1·40

438 Statue of Johann Sebastian Bach

439 Albert Einstein

2000. 250th Death Anniv of Johann Sebastian Bach (German composer). Sheet 77 × 88 mm.
MS3103 $6 multicoloured . . . . 2·40 2·50

2000. Election of Albert Einstein (mathematical physicist) as *Time Magazine* "Man of the Century". Sheet 117 × 91 mm.
MS3104 $6 multicoloured . . . . 2·40 2·50

440 LZ-1 Airship, 1900

2000. Centenary of First Zeppelin Flight.
3105 **440** $3 brown, black and blue . . . . 1·25 1·40
3106 – $3 brown, black and blue . . . . 1·25 1·40
3107 – $3 multicoloured . . . . 1·25 1·40
MS3108 – 93 × 66 mm. $6 multicoloured . . . . 2·40 2·50
DESIGNS: No. 3106, LZ-2, 1906; 3107, LZ-3, 1906. (50 × 37 mm)—No. **MS**3108, LZ-7 *Deutschland*, 1910.
Nos. 3105/7 were printed together, se-tenant, with the backgrounds forming a composite design.

441 Marcus Latimer Hurley (cycling), St. Louis (1904)

2000. Olympic Games, Sydney. Multicoloured.
3109 $2 Type **441** 80 85
3110 $2 Diving 80 85
3111 $2 Flaminio Stadium, Rome (1960) and Italian flag . . 80 85
3112 $2 Ancient Greek javelin thrower 80 85

442 Richie Richardson

2000. West Indies Cricket Tour and 100th Test Match at Lord's. Multicoloured.
3113 90c. Type **442** 35 40
3114 $5 Viv Richards . . . . . . 2·00 2·10
MS3115 121 × 104 mm. $6 Lord's Cricket Ground (horiz) . . . . 2·40 2·50
No. 3114 is inscribed "Viv Richard" in error.

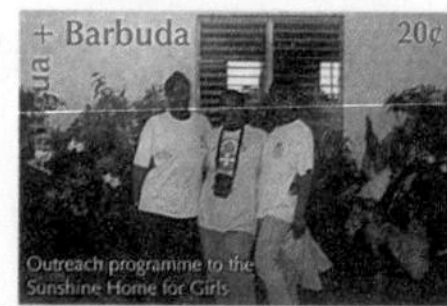

443 Outreach Programme at Sunshine Home for Girls

2000. Girls Brigade. Multicoloured.
3116 20c. Type **443** 10 15
3117 60c. Ullida Rawlins Gill (International Vice President) (vert) 25 30
3118 75c. Officers and girls . . . 30 35
3119 90c. Girl with flag (vert) . . 35 40
3120 $1.20 Members of 8th Antigua Company with flag (vert) 50 55
MS3121 102 × 124 mm. $5 Girl Brigade badge (vert) . . . . . 2·00 2·10

444 Lady Elizabeth Bowes-Lyon as Young Girl

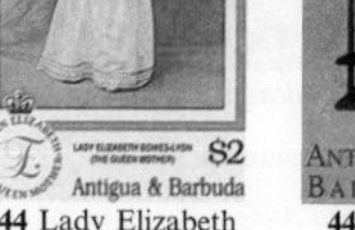

445 Thumbscrew (Expansion of Inquisition, 1250)

2000. "Queen Elizabeth the Queen Mother's Century".
3122 **444** $2 multicoloured 80 85
3123 – $2 black and gold . . . 80 85
3124 – $2 black and gold . . . 80 85
3125 – $2 multicoloured 80 85
MS3126 – 153 × 157 mm. $6 multicoloured . . . . 2·40 2·50
DESIGNS: No. 3123, Queen Elizabeth in 1940; 3124, Queen Mother with Princess Anne, 1951; 3125, Queen Mother in Canada, 1989; **MS**3126, Queen Mother inspecting guard of honour.
No. **MS**3126 also shows the Royal Arms embossed in gold.

2000. New Millennium. People and Events of Thirteenth Century (1250–1300). Multicoloured (except No. 3127).
3127 60c. Type **445** (black and red) 25 30
3128 60c. Chartres Cathedral (completed, 1260) 25 30
3129 60c. Donor's sculpture, Naumberg (completed, 1260) 25 30
3130 60c. Delegates (Simon de Montfort's Parliament, 1261) 25 30
3131 60c. "Maesta" (Cimabue) (painted 1270) 25 30
3132 60c. Marco Polo (departure from Venice, 1271) . . . 25 30
3133 60c. "Divine Wind" (Kamikaze wind saves Japan from invasion, 1274) 25 30
3134 60c. St. Thomas Aquinas (died 1274) 25 30
3135 60c. Arezzo Cathedral (completed 1277) 25 30
3136 60c. Margrethe ("The Maid of Norway") (crowned Queen of Scotland, 1286) 25 30
3137 60c. Jewish refugees (Expulsion of Jews from England, 1290) 25 30
3138 60c. Muslim horseman (capture of Acre, 1291) 25 30
3139 60c. Moshe de Leon (compiles *The Zohar*, 1291) 25 30
3140 60c. Knights in combat (German Civil War, 1292–98) 25 30
3141 60c. Kublai Khan (died 1294) 25 30
3142 60c. Dante (writes *La Vita Nuova*, 1295) (59 × 39 mm) 25 30
3143 60c. "Autumn Colours on Quiao and Hua Mountains" (Zhan Mengfu) (painted 1296) 25 30

446 "Admonishing the Court Ladies" (after Ku K'ai-Chih)

2000. New Millennium. Two Thousand Years of Chinese Paintings. Multicoloured.
3144 25c. Type **446** 10 15
3145 25c. Ink on silk drawing from Zhan Jadashan . . . 10 15
3146 25c. Ink and colour on silk drawing from Mawangdui Tomb 10 15
3147 25c. "Scholars collating Texts" (attr Yang Zihua) 10 15
3148 25c. "Spring Outing" (attr Zhan Ziqian) 10 15
3149 25c. "Portrait of the Emperors" (attr Yen Liben) 10 15
3150 25c. "Sailing Boats and Riverside Mansion" (attr Li Sixun) 10 15
3151 25c. "Two Horses and Groom" (Han Kan) . . . 10 15
3152 25c. "King's Portrait" (attr Wu Daozi) 10 15
3153 25c. "Court Ladies wearing Flowered Headdresses" (attr Zhou Fang) 10 15
3154 25c. "Distant Mountain Forest" (mountain) (Juran) 10 15
3155 25c. "Mount Kuanglu" (Jiang Hao) 10 15
3156 25c. "Pheasant and Small Birds" (Huang Jucai) . . 10 15
3157 25c. "Deer among Red Maples" (anon) 10 15
3158 25c. "Distant Mountain Forest" (river and fields) (Juran) 10 15
3159 25c. "Literary Gathering" (Han Huang) (57 × 39 mm) 10 15
3160 25c. "Birds and Insects" (Huang Quan) 10 15
No. 3148 is inscribed "SPRINTING", No. 3150 "MASION" and No. 3153 "HEADRESSES", all in error.

447 King Donald III of Scotland

2000. Monarchs of the Millennium.
3161 **447** $1.65 black, stone and brown 65 70
3162 – $1.65 black, stone and brown 65 70
3163 – $1.65 black, stone and brown 65 70
3164 – $1.65 black, stone and brown 65 70
3165 – $1.65 black, stone and brown 65 70
3166 – $1.65 black, stone and brown 65 70
3167 – $1.65 multicoloured . . 65 70
3168 – $1.65 multicoloured . . 65 70
3169 – $1.65 multicoloured . . 65 70
3170 – $1.65 multicoloured . . 65 70
3171 – $1.65 multicoloured . . 65 70
3172 – $1.65 multicoloured . . 65 70
MS3173 – Two sheets, each 115 × 135 mm. (a) $6 mult. (b) $6 mult Set of 2 sheets . . . . . 4·75 5·00
DESIGNS: No. 3162, King Duncan I of Scotland; 3163, King Duncan II of Scotland; 3164, King Macbeth of Scotland; 3165, King Malcolm III of Scotland; 3166, King Edgar of Scotland; 3167, King Charles I of England and Scotland; 3168, King Charles II of England and Scotland; 3169, Prince Charles Edward Stuart ("The Young Pretender"); 3170, King James II of England and VII of Scotland; 3171, King James II of Scotland; 3172, King James III of Scotland; **MS**3173a, King Robert I of Scotland; **MS**3173b, Queen Anne of Great Britain.
No. 3169 is inscribed "George III 1760–1820 Great Britain" in error.

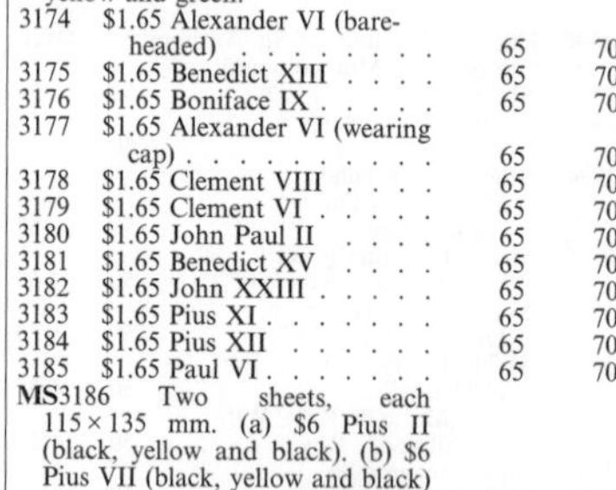

2000. Popes of the Millennium. As T **447**. Each black, yellow and green.
3174 $1.65 Alexander VI (bare-headed) 65 70
3175 $1.65 Benedict XIII 65 70
3176 $1.65 Boniface IX 65 70
3177 $1.65 Alexander VI (wearing cap) 65 70
3178 $1.65 Clement VIII 65 70
3179 $1.65 Clement VI 65 70
3180 $1.65 John Paul II 65 70
3181 $1.65 Benedict XV 65 70
3182 $1.65 John XXIII 65 70
3183 $1.65 Pius XI 65 70
3184 $1.65 Pius XII 65 70
3185 $1.65 Paul VI 65 70
MS3186 Two sheets, each 115 × 135 mm. (a) $6 Pius II (black, yellow and black). (b) $6 Pius VII (black, yellow and black) Set of 2 sheets . . . . . . 4·75 5·00
No. 3181 is inscribed "BENIDICT XV" in error.

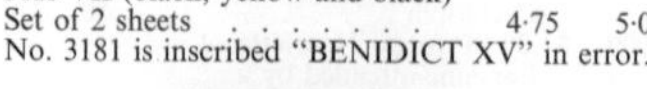

448 Agouti

2000. Fauna of the Rain Forest. Multicoloured.
3187 75c. Type **448** 30 35
3188 90c. Capybara 35 40
3189 $1.20 Basilisk lizard 50 55
3190 $1.65 Green violetear ("Green Violet-Ear Hummingbird") 65 70
3191 $1.65 Harpy eagle 65 70
3192 $1.65 Three-toed sloth . . . 65 70
3193 $1.65 White uakari monkey 65 70
3194 $1.65 Anteater 65 70
3195 $1.65 Coati 65 70
3196 $1.75 Red-eyed tree frog . . 70 75
3197 $1.75 Black spider monkey 70 75
3198 $1.75 Emerald toucanet . . 70 75
3199 $1.75 Kinkajou 70 75
3200 $1.75 Spectacled bear . . . 70 75
3201 $1.75 Tapir 70 75
3202 $2 Heliconid butterfly . . . 80 85
MS3203 Two sheets. (a) 90 × 65 mm. $6 Keel-billed toucan (horiz). (b) 65 × 90 mm. $6 Scarlet macaw Set of 2 sheets . . . . . . 4·75 5·00
Nos. 3190/5 and 3196/201 were printed together, se-tenant, forming composite designs.

449 "Sea Cliff" Submarine

2000. Submarines. Multicoloured.
3204 65c. Type **449** 25 30
3205 75c. "Beaver Mark IV" . . 30 35
3206 90c. "Reef Ranger" 35 40
3207 $1 "Cubmarine" 40 45
3208 $1.20 "Alvin" 50 55
3209 $2 H.M.S. *Revenge* 80 85
3210 $2 *Walrus*, Netherlands . . 80 85
3211 $2 U.S.S. *Los Angeles* . . . 80 85
3212 $2 *Daphne*, France 80 85
3213 $2 U.S.S. *Ohio* 80 85
3214 $2 U.S.S. *Skipjack* 80 85
3215 $3 "Argus", Russia . . . . 1·25 1·40
MS3216 Two sheets, each 107 × 84 mm. (a) $6 "Trieste". (b) $6 Type 209 U-boat, Germany Set of 2 sheets . . . . 4·75 5·00
Nos. 3209/14 were printed together, se-tenant, with the backgrounds forming a composite design.

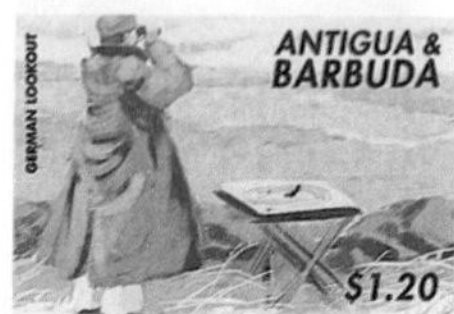

450 German Lookout

2000. 60th Anniv of Battle of Britain. Multicoloured (except No. 3222).
3217 $1.20 Type **450** 50 55
3218 $1.20 Children's evacuation train 50 55
3219 $1.20 Evacuating hospital patients 50 55
3220 $1.20 Hawker Hurricane (fighter) 50 55
3221 $1.20 Rescue team 50 55
3222 $1.20 Churchill cartoon (black) 50 55
3223 $1.20 King George VI and Queen Elizabeth inspecting bomb damage 50 55
3224 $1.20 Barrage balloon above Tower Bridge 50 55
3225 $1.20 Bristol Blenheim (bomber) 50 55
3226 $1.20 Prime Minister Winston Churchill 50 55
3227 $1.20 Bristol Blenheim and barrage balloons 50 55
3228 $1.20 Heinkel (fighter) . . . 50 55
3229 $1.20 Supermarine Spitfire (fighter) 50 55
3230 $1.20 German rescue launch 50 55
3231 $1.20 Messerschmitt 109 (fighter) 50 55
3232 $1.20 R.A.F. rescue launch 50 55
MS3233 Two sheets, each 90 × 60 mm. (a) $6 Junkers 87B (dive bomber). (b) $6 Supermarine Spitfires at dusk Set of 2 sheets 4·75 5·00
No. **MS**3233a is inscribed "JUNKERS 878" in error.

451 "The Defence of Cadiz" (Zurbaran)

2000. "Espana 2000" International Stamp Exhibition, Madrid. Paintings from the Prado Museum. Mult.
3234 $1.65 Type **451** 65 70
3235 $1.65 "The Defence of Cadiz" (General and galleys) 65 70
3236 $1.65 "The Defence of Cadiz" (officers) 65 70
3237 $1.65 "Vulcan's Forge" (Vulcan) (Velazquez) . . . 65 70
3238 $1.65 "Vulcan's Forge" (working metal) 65 70
3239 $1.65 "Vulcan's Forge" (workers with hammers) 65 70
3240 $1.65 "Family Portrait" (three men) (Adriaen Key) 65 70

3241 $1.65 "Family Portrait" (one man) 65 70
3242 $1.65 "Family Portrait" (three women) 65 70
3243 $1.65 "The Devotion of Rudolf I" (horseman with lantern) (Rubens and Jan Wildens) 65 70
3244 $1.65 "The Devotion of Rudolf I" (priest on horseback) 65 70
3245 $1.65 "The Devotion of Rudolf I" (huntsman) . . 65 70
3246 $1.65 "The Concert" (lute player) (Vincente Gonzalez) 65 70
3247 $1.65 "The Concert" (lady with fan) 65 70
3248 $1.65 "The Concert" (two gentlemen) 65 70
3249 $1.65 "The Adoration of the Magi" (Wise Man) (Juan Maino) 65 70
3250 $1.65 "The Adoration of the Magi" (two Wise Men) 65 70
3251 $1.65 "The Adoration of the Magi" (Holy Family) . . 65 70
MS3252 Three sheets. (a) 115 × 90 mm. $6 "The Deliverance of St. Peter" (Jose de Ribera) (horiz). (b) 110 × 90 mm. $6 "The Fan Seller" (Jose del Castillo). (c) 110 × 90 mm. $6 "Family in a Garden" (Jan van Kessel the Younger) Set of 3 sheets . . . 7·25 7·50

Nos. 3246/8 are inscribed "Gonzlez" with No.3248 additionally inscribed "Francisco Rizi", all in error.

452 Two Angels

2000. Christmas and Holy Year. Multicoloured.

3253 25c. Type **452** 10 15
3254 45c. Heads of two angels looking down 20 25
3255 90c. Heads of two angels, one looking up 35 40
3256 $1.75 Type **452** 70 75
3257 $1.75 As 45c. 70 75
3258 $1.75 As 90c. 70 75
3259 $1.75 As $5 . . . . 70 75
3260 $5 Two angels with drapery 2·00 2·10
MS3261 110 × 120 mm. $6 Holy Child . . . . 2·40 2·50

453 "Dr. Ephraim Bueno" (Rembrandt)

2000. Bicentenary of Rijksmuseum, Amsterdam. Dutch Paintings. Multicoloured.

3262 $1 Type **453** 40 45
3263 $1 "Woman writing a Letter" (Frans van Meris de Oude) 40 45
3264 $1 "Mary Magdalen" (Jan van Scorel) 40 45
3265 $1 "Anna Coddle" (Maerten van Heemskerck) 40 45
3266 $1 "Cleopatra's Banquet" (Gerard Laìresse) 40 45
3267 $1 "Titus in Friar's Habit" (Rembrandt) 40 45
3268 $1.20 "Saskia" (Rembrandt) 50 55
3269 $1.20 "In the Month of July" (Paul Joseph Constantin Gabriel) . . . 50 55
3270 $1.20 "Maria Trip" (Rembrandt) 50 55
3271 $1.20 "Still Life with Flowers" (Jan van Huysum) 50 55
3272 $1.20 "Haesje van Cleyburgh" (Rembrandt) 50 55
3273 $1.20 "Girl in a White Kimono" (George Hendrick Breitner) . . . 50 55
3274 $1.65 "Man and Woman at a Spinning Wheel" (Pieter Pietersz) 65 70
3275 $1.65 "Self-portrait" (Rembrandt) 65 70
3276 $1.65 "Jeremiah lamenting the Destruction of Jerusalem" (Rembrandt) 65 70
3277 $1.65 "The Jewish Bride" (Rembrandt) 65 70
3278 $1.65 "Anna accused by Tobit of stealing a Kid" (Rembrandt) 65 70
3279 $1.65 "The Prophetess Anna" (Rembrandt) . . . 65 70
MS3280 Three sheets, each 118 × 88 mm. (a) $6 "Doubting Thomas" (Hendrick ter Brugghen). (b) $6 "Still Life with Cheeses" (Floris van Dijck); (c) $6 "Isaac Blessing Jacob" (Govert Flinck) Set of 3 sheets . . . . 7·25 7·50

454 "Starmie No. 121"

2001. Characters from "Pokemon" (children's cartoon series). Multicoloured.

3281 $1.75 Type **454** 70 75
3282 $1.75 "Misty" 70 75
3283 $1.75 "Brock" 70 75
3284 $1.75 "Geodude No. 74" . . 70 75
3285 $1.75 "Krabby No. 98" . . 70 75
3286 $1.75 "Ash" 70 75
MS3287 74 × 114 mm. $6 "Charizard No. 6" . . . . 2·40 2·50

455 Blue-toothed Entoloma

456 Map and Graphs

2001. "Hong Kong 2001" Stamp Exhibition. Tropical Fungi. Multicoloured.

3288 25c. Type **455** 10 15
3289 90c. Common morel 35 40
3290 $1 Red cage fungus 40 45
3291 $1.65 Copper trumpet . . . 65 70
3292 $1.65 Field mushroom ("Meadow Mushroom") 65 70
3293 $1.65 Green gill ("Green-gilled Parasol") 65 70
3294 $1.65 The panther 65 70
3295 $1.65 Death cap 65 70
3296 $1.65 Royal boletus ("King Bolete") 65 70
3297 $1.65 Lilac fairy helmet ("Lilac Bonnet") 65 70
3298 $1.65 Silky volvar 65 70
3299 $1.65 Agrocybe mushroom ("Poplar Field Cap") . . 65 70
3300 $1.65 Saint George's mushroom 65 70
3301 $1.65 Red-stemmed tough shank 65 70
3302 $1.65 Fly agaric 65 70
3303 $1.75 Common fawn agaric ("Fawn Shield-Cap") . . 70 75
MS3304 Two sheets, each 70 × 90 mm. (a) $6 Yellow parasol. (b) $6 Mutagen milk cap Set of 2 sheets . . . . 4·75 5·00

Nos. 3291/6 and 3297/302 were each printed together, se-tenant, with the backgrounds forming composite designs.

2001. Population and Housing Census.

3305 **456** 15c. multicoloured . . . 10 10
3306 – 25c. multicoloured . . . 10 15
3307 – 65c. multicoloured . . . 25 30
3308 – 90c. multicoloured . . . 35 40
MS3309 – 55 × 50 mm. $6 multicoloured (Map and census logo) . . . . 2·40 2·50

DESIGNS: 25c. to 90c. Map and different form of graph.

457 "Yuna (Bath-house Women)" (detail)

2001. "PHILANIPPON 2001" International Stamp Exhibition, Tokyo. Traditional Japanese Paintings. Multicoloured.

3310 45c. Type **457** 20 25
3311 60c. "Yuna (Bath-house Women)" (different detail) 25 30
3312 65c. "Yuna (Bath-house Women)" (different detail) 25 30
3313 75c. "The Hikone Screen" (detail) 30 35
3314 $1 "The Hikone Screen" (different detail) 40 45
3315 $1.20 "The Hikone Screen" (different detail) 50 55
3316 $1.65 Galleon and Dutch merchants with horse . . 65 70
3317 $1.65 Galleon and merchants with tiger . . . 65 70
3318 $1.65 Merchants unpacking goods 65 70
3319 $1.65 Merchants with parasol and horse 65 70
3320 $1.65 Women packing food 65 70
3321 $1.65 Picnic under the cherry tree 65 70
3322 $1.65 Palanquins and resting bearers 65 70
3323 $1.65 Women dancing . . . 65 70
3324 $1.65 Three samurai 65 70
3325 $1.65 One samurai 65 70
MS3326 Three sheets, each 80 × 110 mm. (a) $6 "Harunobu Suzuki" (Shiba Kokani) (38 × 50 mm). (b) $6 "Daruma" (Tsujo Kako) (38 × 50 mm). (c) $6 "Visiting a Shrine on a Rainy Night" (Harunobu Suziki) (38 × 50 mm) Set of 3 sheets . . 7·25 7·50

Nos. 3316/19 ("The Namban Screen" by Kano Nizen) and Nos. 3320/5 ("Merry-making under the Cherry Blossoms" by Kano Naganobu) were each printed together, se-tenant, with both sheetlets forming the entire painting.

458 Lucille Ball leaning on Mantelpiece

2001. Scenes from *I Love Lucy* (American T.V. comedy series). Eight sheets each containing multicoloured design as T **458**.

MS3327 (a) 118 × 92 mm. $6 Type **458**. (b) 98 × 120 mm. $6 Desi Arnaz laughing. (c) 93 × 130 mm. $6 William Frawley at table. (d) 114 × 145 mm. $6 Lucille Ball with William Frawley. (e) 114 × 145 mm. $6 Lucille Ball in blue dress. (f) 119 × 111 mm. $6 Lucille Ball sitting at table. (g) 128 × 100 mm. $6 Lucille Ball as scarecrow. (h) 93 × 125 mm. $6 William Frawley shouting at Desi Arnaz (horiz) Set of 8 sheets 19·00 20·00

459 *Hintleya burtii*

2001. Caribbean Orchids. Multicoloured.

3328 45c. Type **459** 20 25
3329 75c. *Neomoovea irrovata* . . 30 35
3330 90c. *Comparettia speciosa* . . 35 40
3331 $1 *Cypredium crapeanum* 40 45
3332 $1.20 *Trichoceuos muralis* (vert) 50 55
3333 $1.20 *Dracula rampira* (vert) 50 55
3334 $1.20 *Psychopsis papilio* (vert) 50 55
3335 $1.20 *Lycaste clenningiana* (vert) 50 55
3336 $1.20 *Telipogon nevuosus* (vert) 50 55
3337 $1.20 *Masclecallia ayahbacana* (vert) 50 55
3338 $1.65 *Cattleya dowiana* (vert) 65 70
3339 $1.65 *Dendiobium cruentum* (vert) 65 70
3340 $1.65 *Bulbophyllum lobb* (vert) 65 70
3341 $1.65 *Chysis laevis* (vert) . . 65 70
3342 $1.65 *Ancistrochilus rothschildicanus* (vert) . . 65 70
3343 $1.65 *Angraecum sororium* (vert) 65 70
3344 $1.65 *Rhyncholaelia glanca* (vert) 65 70
3345 $1.65 *Oncidium barbatum* (vert) 65 70
3346 $1.65 *Phaius tankervillege* (vert) 65 70
3347 $1.65 *Ghies brechtiana* (vert) 65 70
3348 $1.65 *Angraecum leonis* (vert) 65 70
3349 $1.65 *Cycnoches loddigesti* (vert) 65 70
MS3350 Two sheets. (a) 68 × 104 mm. $6 *Symphalossum sanquinem* (vert). (b) 104 × 68 mm. $6 *Trichopilia fragrans* (vert) Set of 2 sheets . . . . 4·75 5·00

460 Yellowtail Damselfish

2001. Tropical Marine Life. Multicoloured.

3351 25c. Type **460** 10 15
3352 45c. Indigo hamlet 20 25
3353 65c. Great white shark . . . 25 30
3354 90c. Bottle-nose dolphin . . 35 40
3355 90c. Palette surgeonfish . . 35 40
3356 $1 Octopus 40 45
3357 $1.20 Common dolphin . . 50 55
3358 $1.20 Franklin's gull 50 55
3359 $1.20 Rock beauty 50 55
3360 $1.20 Bicoloured angelfish 50 55
3361 $1.20 Beaugregory 50 55
3362 $1.20 Banded butterflyfish 50 55
3363 $1.20 Common tern 50 55
3364 $1.20 Flying fish 50 55
3365 $1.20 Queen angelfish . . . 50 55
3366 $1.20 Blue-striped grunt . . 50 55
3367 $1.20 Porkfish 50 55
3368 $1.20 Blue tang 50 55
3369 $1.65 Red-footed booby . . 65 70
3370 $1.65 Bottle-nose dolphin 65 70
3371 $1.65 Hawksbill turtle . . . 65 70
3372 $1.65 Monk seal 65 70
3373 $1.65 Great white shark (inscr "Bull Shark") . . . 65 70
3374 $1.65 Lemon shark 65 70
3375 $1.65 Dugong 65 70
3376 $1.65 White-tailed tropicbird 65 70
3377 $1.65 Bull shark 65 70
3378 $1.65 Manta ray 65 70
3379 $1.65 Green turtle 65 70
3380 $1.65 Spanish grunt 65 70
MS3381 Four sheets. (a) 68 × 98 mm. $5 Sailfish. (b) 68 × 98 mm. $5 Brown pelican and beaugregory (vert). (c) 98 × 68 mm. $6 Queen triggerfish. (d) 96 × 68 mm. $6 Hawksbill turtle Set of 4 sheets . . . . . 9·00 9·25

Nos. 3357/62, 3363/8, 3369/74 and 3375/80 were each printed together, se-tenant, the backgrounds forming composite designs.

461 *Freewinds* (liner) and Police Band, Antigua

2001. Work of *Freewinds* (Church of Scientology flagship) in Caribbean. Multicoloured.

3382 30c. Type **461** 15 20
3383 45c. At anchor off St. Barthelemy 20 25
3384 75c. At sunset 30 35
3385 90c. Off Bonaire 35 40
3386 $1.50 *Freewinds* anchored off Bequia 60 65
MS3387 Two sheets, each 85 × 60 mm. (a) $4 *Freewinds* alongside quay, Curacao. (b) $4 Decorated with lights Set of 2 sheets . . . . 3·25 3·50

462 Young Queen Victoria in Blue Dress

2001. Death Centenary of Queen Victoria. Multicoloured.

3388 $2 Type **462** 80 85
3389 $2 Queen Victoria wearing red head-dress 80 85
3390 $2 Queen Victoria with jewelled hair ornament . . 80 85
3391 $2 Queen Victoria, after Chalon, in brooch 80 85
MS3392 70 × 82 mm. $5 Queen Victoria in old age . . . . . . 2·00 2·10

463 "Water Lilies"

2001. 75th Death Anniv of Claude-Oscar Monet (French painter). Multicoloured.

3393 $2 Type **463** 80 85
3394 $2 "Rose Portals, Giverny" 80 85
3395 $2 "Water Lily Pond, Harmony in Green" . . . 80 85
3396 $2 "Artist's Garden, Irises" 80 85
MS3397 136 × 111 mm. $5 "Jerusalem Artichoke Flowers" (vert) . . . . 2·00 2·10
No. 3396 is inscribed "Artists's" in error.

464 Duchess of York with Baby Princess Elizabeth (1926)

465 Verdi in Top Hat

2001. 75th Birthday of Queen Elizabeth II. Multicoloured.

3398 $1 Type **464** 40 45
3399 $1 Queen in Coronation robes (1953) 40 45
3400 $1 Young Princess Elizabeth (1938) 40 45
3401 $1 Queen Elizabeth in Garter robes (1956) . . . 40 45
3402 $1 Princess Elizabeth with pony (1939) 40 45
3403 $1 Queen Elizabeth in red dress and pearls (1985) . . 40 45
MS3404 90 × 72 mm. $6 Princess Elizabeth and Queen Elizabeth (1940) . . . . 2·40 2·50

2001. Death Centenary of Giuseppe Verdi (Italian composer). Multicoloured.

3405 $2 Type **465** 80 85
3406 $2 Don Carlos and part of opera score 80 85
3407 $2 Conductor and score for *Aida* 80 85
3408 $2 Musicians and score for *Rigoletto* 80 85
MS3409 77 × 117 mm. $5 Verdi in evening dress . . . . 2·00 2·25
Nos. 3405/8 were printed together, se-tenant, the backgrounds forming a composite design.

466 "Georges-Henri Manuel"

2001. Death Centenary of Henri de Toulouse-Lautrec (French painter). Multicoloured.

3410 $2 Type **466** 80 85
3411 $2 "Louis Pascal" 80 85
3412 $2 "Romain Coolus" . . . 80 85
3413 $2 "Monsieur Fourcade" . . 80 85
MS3414 67 × 84 mm. $5 "Dancing at the Moulin de la Galette" . . 2·00 2·25
No 3412 is inscribed "ROMAN" in error.

467 Marlene Dietrich smoking

2001. Birth Centenary of Marlene Dietrich (actress and singer).

3415 **467** $2 black, purple and red 80 85
3416 – $2 black, purple and red 80 85
3417 – $2 multicoloured 80 85
3418 – $2 black, purple and red 80 85
DESIGNS: No. 3416, Marlene Dietrich, in evening gown, sitting on settee; 3417, In black dress; 3418, Sitting on piano.

468 Collared Peccary

2001. Vanishing Fauna of the Caribbean. Multicoloured.

3419 25c. Type **468** 10 15
3420 30c. Baird's tapir 10 15
3421 45c. Agouti 20 25
3422 75c. Bananaquit 30 35
3423 90c. Six-banded armadillo 35 40
3424 $1 Roseate spoonbill . . . 40 45
3425 $1.80 Mouse opossum . . . 75 80
3426 $1.80 Magnificent black frigate bird 75 80
3427 $1.80 Northern jacana . . . 75 80
3428 $1.80 Painted bunting . . . 75 80
3429 $1.80 Haitian solenodon . . 75 80
3430 $1.80 St. Lucia iguana . . . 75 80
3431 $2.50 West Indian iguana 1·00 1·10
3432 $2.50 Scarlet macaw . . . . 1·00 1·10
3433 $2.50 Cotton-topped tamarin . . . . 1·00 1·10
3434 $2.50 Kinkajou . . . . . . 1·00 1·10
MS3435 Two sheets. (a) 117 × 85 mm. $6 Ocelot (vert). (b) 162 × 116 mm. $6 King vulture (vert) Set of 2 sheets . . . . . 4·75 5·00

469 Sara Crewe (*The Little Princess*) reading a Letter

2001. Shirley Temple Films. Multicoloured. Showing film scenes. (a) *The Little Princess*. Multicoloured.

3436 $1.50 Type **469** 60 65
3437 $1.50 Sara in pink dressing gown 60 65
3438 $1.50 Sara cuddling doll . . 60 65
3439 $1.50 Sara as Princess on throne 60 65
3440 $1.50 Sara talking to man in frock coat 60 65
3441 $1.50 Sara blowing out candles 60 65
3442 $1.80 Sara with Father (horiz) 75 80
3443 $1.80 Sara scrubbing floor (horiz) 75 80
3444 $1.80 Sara and friend with Headmistress (horiz) . . . 75 80
3445 $1.80 Sara with Queen Victoria (horiz) 75 80
MS3446 106 × 76mm. $6 Sara with wounded Father . . . . . . 2·40 2·50

(b) *Baby, Take a Bow*.

3447 $1.65 Shirley in dancing class (horiz) 65 70
3448 $1.65 Shirley cuddling Father (horiz) 65 70
3449 $1.65 Shirley at bedtime with parents (horiz) . . . 65 70
3450 $1.65 Shirley in yellow dress with Father (horiz) . . . 65 70
3451 $1.65 Shirley and Father at Christmas party (horiz) 65 70
3452 $1.65 Shirley and gangster looking in cradle (horiz) 65 70
3453 $1.65 Shirley in spotted dress 65 70
3454 $1.65 Shirley on steps with gangster 65 70
3455 $1.65 Shirley with gangster holding gun 65 70
3456 $1.65 Shirley with Mother 65 70
MS3457 106 × 76 mm. $6 Shirley in spotted dress . . . . 2·40 2·50

470 Rudolph Valentino in *Blood and Sand*, 1922

2001. 75th Death Anniv of Rudolph Valentino (Italian film actor).

3458 **470** $1 brown and black . . 40 45
3459 – $1 lilac and black . . . 40 45
3460 – $1 brown and black . . 40 45
3461 – $1 brown and black . . 40 45
3462 – $1 red and black 40 45
3463 – $1 lilac and black . . . 40 45
3464 – $1 multicoloured 40 45
3465 – $1 multicoloured 40 45
3466 – $1 multicoloured 40 45
3467 – $1 multicoloured 40 45
3468 – $1 multicoloured 40 45
3469 – $1 multicoloured 40 45
MS3470 Two sheets. (a) 90 × 125 mm. $6 multicoloured. (b) 68 × 95 mm. $6 multicoloured Set of 2 sheets . . . . . . 4·75 5·00
DESIGNS: No. 3459, In *Eyes of Youth* with Clara Kimbal Young, 1919; 3460, In *All Night Long* with Carmel Meyers, 1918; 3461, Valentino in 1926; 3462, In *Camille* with Alla Nazimova, 1921; 3463, In *Cobra* with Nita Naldi, 1925; 3464, In *The Son of the Sheik* with Vilma Banky, 1926; 3465, In *The Young Rajah*, 1922; 3466, In *The Eagle* with Vilma Banky, 1925; 3467, In *The Sheik* with Agnes Ayres, 1921; 3468, In *A Sainted Devil*, 1924; 3469, In *Monsieur Beaucaire*, 1924; **MS**3470, (a) Valentino with Natacha Rambova. (b) In *The Four Horseman of the Apocalypse*, 1921.
Nos. 3464 and 3466 are inscribed "BLANKY" and No. 3467 "AYERS", all in error.

471 Queen Elizabeth

472 Melvin Calvin, 1961

2001. Golden Jubilee (1st issue).

3471 **471** $1 multicoloured 40 45
No. 3471 was printed in sheetlets of 8, containing two vertical rows of four, separated by a large illustrated central gutter. Both the stamp and the illustration on the central gutter are made up of a collage of miniature flower photographs.
See also Nos. 3535/8.

2001. Centenary of Nobel Prizes. Chemistry Winners. Multicoloured.

3472 $1.50 Type **472** 60 65
3473 $1.50 Linus Pauling, 1954 60 65
3474 $1.50 Vincent du Vigneaud, 1955 . . . . 60 65
3475 $1.50 Richard Synge, 1952 60 65
3476 $1.50 Archer Martin, 1952 60 65
3477 $1.50 Alfred Werner, 1913 60 65
3478 $1.50 Robert Curl Jr., 1996 60 65
3479 $1.50 Alan Heeger, 2000 . . 60 65
3480 $1.50 Michael Smith, 1993 60 65
3481 $1.50 Sidney Altman, 1989 60 65
3482 $1.50 Elias Corey, 1990 . . 60 65
3483 $1.50 William Giauque, 1949 . . . . 60 65
MS3484 Three sheets, each 107 × 75 mm. (a) $6 Ernest Rutherford, 1908. (b) $6 Ernst Fischer, 1973. (c) $6 American volunteers, International Red Cross (Peace Prize, 1944) Set of 3 sheets . . . . 7·25 7·50

473 "Madonna and Child with Angels" (Filippo Lippi)

474 Final between Uruguay and Brazil, Brazil 1950

2001. Christmas. Italian Religious Paintings. Multicoloured.

3485 25c. Type **473** 10 15
3486 45c. "Madonna of Corneto Tarquinia" (Lippi) . . . 20 25
3487 50c. "Madonna and Child" (Domenico Ghirlandaio) 20 25
3488 75c. "Madonna and Child" (Lippi) 30 35
3489 $4 "Madonna Delceppo" (Lippi) . . . . 1·60 1·75
MS3490 106 × 136 mm. $6 "Madonna enthroned with Angels and Saints" (Lippi) . . . . . 2·40 2·50

2001. World Cup Football Championship, Japan and Korea (2002). Multicoloured.

3491 $1.50 Type **474** 60 65
3492 $1.50 Ferenc Puskas (Hungary), Switzerland 1954 . . . . 60 65
3493 $1.50 Raymond Kopa (France), Sweden 1958 . . 60 65
3494 $1.50 Mauro (Brazil), Chile 1962 . . . . 60 65
3495 $1.50 Gordon Banks (England), England 1966 60 65
3496 $1.50 Pele (Brazil), Mexico 1970 . . . . 60 65
3497 $1.50 Daniel Passarella (Argentina), Argentina 1978 . . . . 60 65
3498 $1.50 Karl-Heinz Rummenigge (Germany), Spain 1982 . . . . 60 65
3499 $1.50 World Cup Trophy, Mexico 1986 . . . . . . 60 65
3500 $1.50 Diego Maradona (Argentina), Italy 1990 . . 60 65
3501 $1.50 Roger Milla (Cameroun), U.S.A. 1994 60 65
3502 $1.50 Zinedine Zidane (France), France 1998 . . 60 65
MS3503 Two sheets, each 88 × 75 mm. (a) $6 Detail of Jules Rimet Trophy, Uruguay, 1930. (b) $6 Detail of World Cup Trophy, Japan/Korea, 2002 Set of 2 sheets 4·75 5·00
No. 3500 is inscribed "Deigo" in error.

475 Battle of Nashville, 1864

2002. American Civil War. Multicoloured.

3504 45c. Type **475** 20 25
3505 45c. Capture of Atlanta, 1864 . . . . 20 25
3506 45c. Battle of Spotsylvania, 1864 . . . . 20 25
3507 45c. Battle of The Wilderness, 1864 . . . . 20 25
3508 45c. Battle of Chickamauga Creek, 1863 . . . . . . 20 25
3509 45c. Battle of Gettysburg, 1863 . . . . 20 25
3510 45c. Lee and Jackson at Chancellorsville, 1863 . . 20 25
3511 45c. Battle of Fredericksburg, 1862 . . 20 25
3512 45c. Battle of Antietam, 1862 . . . . 20 25
3513 45c. Second Battle of Bull Run, 1862 . . . . . . 20 25
3514 45c. Battle of Five Forks, 1865 . . . . 20 25
3515 45c. Seven Days' Battles, 1862 . . . . 20 25
3516 45c. First Battle of Bull Run, 1861 . . . . . . 20 25
3517 45c. Battle of Shiloh, 1862 20 25
3518 45c. Battle of Seven Pines, 1862 . . . . 20 25
3519 45c. Bombardment of Fort Sumter, 1861 . . . . . . 20 25
3520 45c. Battle of Chattanooga, 1863 . . . . 20 25
3521 45c. Grant and Lee at Appomattox, 1865 . . . 20 25
3522 50c. General Ulysses S. Grant (vert) 20 25
3523 50c. President Abraham Lincoln (vert) 20 25
3524 50c. President Jefferson Davis (vert) 20 25
3525 50c. General Robert E. Lee (vert) 20 25
3526 50c. General George Custer (vert) 20 25
3527 50c. Admiral Andrew Hull Foote (vert) 20 25
3528 50c. General "Stonewall" Jackson (vert) 20 25

3529 50c. General Jeb Stuart (vert) 20 25
3530 50c. General George Meade (vert) 20 25
3531 50c. General Philip Sheridan (vert) 20 25
3532 50c. General James Longstreet (vert) 20 25
3533 50c. General John Mosby (vert) 20 25
MS3534 Two sheets, each 105 × 76 mm. (a) $6 Confederate ironclad *Merrimack* attacking *Cumberland* (Federal sloop) (51 × 38 mm). (b) $6 *Monitor* (Federal ironclad) Set of 2 sheets 4·75 5·00

476 Queen Elizabeth presenting Rosettes

2002. Golden Jubilee (2nd issue). Multicoloured.
3535 $2 Type **476** 80 85
3536 $2 Queen Elizabeth at garden party 80 85
3537 $2 Queen Elizabeth in evening dress 80 85
3538 $2 Queen Elizabeth in cream coat 80 85
MS3539 76 × 108 mm. $6 Princesses Elizabeth and Margaret as bridesmaids 2·40 2·50

477 U.S. Flag as Statue of Liberty and Antigua & Barbuda Flag

478 Sir Vivian Richards waving Bat

2002. "United We Stand". Support for Victims of 11 September 2001 Terrorist Attacks.
3540 **477** $2 multicoloured 80 85

2002. 50th Birthday of Sir Vivian Richards (West Indian cricketer). Multicoloured.
3541 25c. Type **478** 10 15
3542 30c. Sir Vivian Richards receiving presentation from Antigua Cricket Association 10 15
3543 50c. Sir Vivian Richards wearing sash 20 25
3544 75c. Sir Vivian Richards batting 30 35
3545 $1.50 Sir Vivian Richards and Lady Richards 60 65
3546 $1.80 Sir Vivian Richards with enlarged action photograph of himself 75 80
MS3547 Two sheets, each 68 × 95 mm. (a) $6 Sir Vivian Richards with guard of honour. (b) $6 Sir Vivian Richards in Indian traditional dress Set of 2 sheets 4·75 5·00

479 Thick-billed Parrot

2002. Flora and Fauna. Multicoloured.
3548 50c. Type **479** 20 25
3549 75c. Lesser long-nosed bat 30 35
3550 90c. Quetzal 35 40
3551 90c. Two-toed sloth 35 40
3552 90c. Lovely cotinga 35 40
3553 90c. *Pseudolycaena marsyas* (butterfly) 35 40
3554 90c. Magenta-throated woodstar 35 40
3555 90c. *Automeris rubrescens* (moth) 35 40
3556 90c. *Bufo periglenes* (toad) 35 40
3557 90c. Collared peccary 35 40
3558 90c. Tamandua anteater 35 40
3559 $1 St. Lucia parrot 40 45
3560 $1 Cuban kite 40 45
3561 $1 West Indian whistling-duck 40 45
3562 $1 *Eurema amelia* (butterfly) 40 45
3563 $1 Scarlet ibis 40 45
3564 $1 Black-capped petrel 40 45
3565 $1 *Cnemidophorus vanzoi* (lizard) 40 45
3566 $1 Cuban solenodon 40 45
3567 $1 *Papilio thersites* (butterfly) 40 45
3568 $1.50 Montserrat oriole 60 65
3569 $1.80 *Leptotes perkinsae* (butterfly) 75 80
MS3570 Two sheets, each 110 × 85 mm. (a) $6 Olive Ridley turtle. (b) $6 Margay Set of 2 sheets 4·75 5·00
Nos. 3550/8 and 3559/67 were each printed together, se-tenant, with the backgrounds forming composite designs.

480 Community Players wearing Straw Hats

2002. 50th Anniv of Community Players. Multicoloured. Showing scenes from various productions.
3571 20c. Type **480** 10 15
3572 25c. Men in suits with women in long dresses 10 15
3573 30c. In *Pirates of Penzance* 10 15
3574 75c. Female choir 30 35
3575 90c. In Mexican dress 35 40
3576 $1.50 Members at a reception 60 65
3577 $1.80 Production in the open air 75 80
MS3578 Two sheets, each 76 × 84 mm. (a) $4 Mrs. Edie Hill-Thibou (former President) (vert). (b) $4 Miss Yvonne Maginley (Acting President and Director of Music) (vert) Set of 2 sheets 3·25 3·50

481 Mount Fuji, Japan

482 Cross-country Skiing

2002. International Year of Mountains. Mult.
3579 $2 Type **481** 80 85
3580 $2 Machu Picchu, Peru 80 85
3581 $2 The Matterhorn, Switzerland 80 85

2002. Winter Olympic Games, Salt Lake City. Multicoloured.
3582 $2 Type **482** 80 85
3583 $2 Pairs figure skating 80 85
MS3584 84 × 114 mm. Nos. 3582/3 1·60 1·60

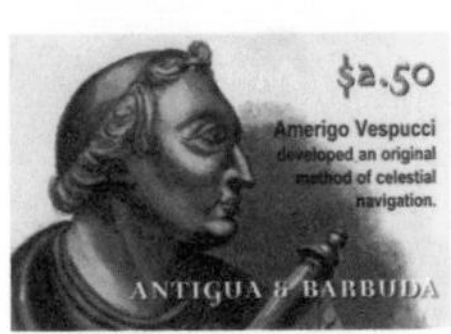

483 Amerigo Vespucci wearing Skullcap

2002. 500th Anniv of Amerigo Vespucci's Third Voyage. Multicoloured.
3585 $2.50 Type **483** 1·00 1·10
3586 $2.50 Vespucci as an old man 1·00 1·10
3587 $2.50 16th-century map 1·00 1·10
MS3588 49 × 68 mm. $5 Vespucci holding dividers (vert) 2·00 2·10

484 *Spirit of St. Louis* and Charles Lindbergh (pilot)

2002. 75th Anniv of First Solo Transatlantic Flight. Multicoloured.
3589 $2.50 Type **484** 1·00 1·10
3590 $2.50 *Spirit of St. Louis* at Le Bourget, Paris, 1927 1·00 1·10
3591 $2.50 Charles Lindbergh in New York ticker-tape parade, 1927 1·00 1·10
MS3592 80 × 110 mm. $6 Charles Lindbergh wearing flying helmet 2·40 2·50

485 Princess Diana

2002. 5th Death Anniv of Diana, Princess of Wales. Multicoloured.
3593 $1.80 Type **485** 75 80
3594 $1.80 Princess Diana in tiara (looking left) 75 80
3595 $1.80 Wearing hat 75 80
3596 $1.80 Princess Diana wearing pearl drop earrings and black dress 75 80
3597 $1.80 Wearing tiara (facing front) 75 80
3598 $1.80 Princess Diana wearing pearl drop earrings 75 80
MS3599 91 × 106 mm. $6 Princess Diana 2·40 2·50

486 Kennedy Brothers

2002. Presidents John F. Kennedy and Ronald Reagan Commemoration. Multicoloured.
3600 $1.50 Type **486** 60 65
3601 $1.50 John Kennedy with Danny Kaye (American entertainer) 60 65
3602 $1.50 Delivering Cuban Blockade speech, 1962 60 65
3603 $1.50 With Jacqueline Kennedy 60 65
3604 $1.50 Meeting Bill Clinton (future president) 60 65
3605 $1.50 Family at John Kennedy's funeral 60 65
3606 $1.50 President and Mrs. Reagan with Pope John Paul II, 1982 60 65
3607 $1.50 As George Gipp in *Knute Rockne - All American*, 1940 60 65
3608 $1.50 With General Matthew Ridgeway, Bitburg Military Cemetery, Germany, 1985 60 65
3609 $1.50 With George H. Bush and Secretary Mikhail Gorbachev of U.S.S.R., 1988 60 65
3610 $1.50 Presidents Reagan, Ford, Carter and Nixon at the White House, 1981 60 65
3611 $1.50 Horse riding with Queen Elizabeth, Windsor, 1982 60 65
MS3612 Two sheets, each 88 × 22 mm. (a) $6 President Kennedy at press conference (vert). (b) $6 President Reagan (vert) Set of 2 sheets 4·75 5·00

487 Red-billed Tropicbird

2002. Endangered Species of Antigua. Multicoloured.
3613 $1.50 Type **487** 60 65
3614 $1.50 Brown pelican 60 65
3615 $1.50 Magnificent frigate bird 60 65
3616 $1.50 Ground lizard 60 65
3617 $1.50 West Indian whistling duck 60 65
3618 $1.50 Antiguan racer snake 60 65
3619 $1.50 Spiny lobster 60 65
3620 $1.50 Hawksbill turtle 60 65
3621 $1.50 Queen conch 60 65

488 Elvis Presley

2002. 25th Death Anniv of Elvis Presley (American entertainer).
3622 **488** $1 multicoloured 40 45

489 Cheerleader Teddy

2002. Centenary of the Teddy Bear. Girl Teddies. Multicoloured.
3623 $2 Type **489** 80 85
3624 $2 Figure skater 80 85
3625 $2 Ballet dancer 80 85
3626 $2 Aerobics instructor 80 85

490 "Croconaw No. 159"

2002. Pokemon (children's cartoon series). Mult.
3627 $1.50 Type **490** 60 65
3628 $1.50 "Mantine No. 226" 60 65
3629 $1.50 "Feraligatr No. 160" 60 65
3630 $1.50 "Qwilfish No. 211" 60 65
3631 $1.50 "Remoraid No. 223" 60 65
3632 $1.50 "Quagsire No. 195" 60 65
MS3633 80 × 106 mm. $6 "Chinchou No. 170" 2·40 2·50

491 Charlie Chaplin

492 Bob Hope

2002. 25th Death Anniv of Charlie Chaplin (British actor). Each black, grey and light grey.
3634 $1.80 Type **491** 75 80
3635 $1.80 Wearing waistcoat and spotted bow-tie 75 80
3636 $1.80 In top hat 75 80
3637 $1.80 Wearing coat and bowler hat 75 80
3638 $1.80 Charlie Chaplin in old age 75 80
3639 $1.80 With finger on chin 75 80
MS3640 90 × 105 mm. $6 Charlie Chaplin as The Tramp 2·40 2·50

2002. Bob Hope (American entertainer) Commemoration. Designs showing him entertaining American troops. Multicoloured.
3641 $1.50 Type **492** 60 65
3642 $1.50 Wearing bush hat,Vietnam, 1972 60 65
3643 $1.50 On board U.S.S. *John F. Kennedy* (aircraft carrier) 60 65
3644 $1.50 With hawk badge on sleeve, Berlin, 1948 60 65
3645 $1.50 Wearing desert fatigues 60 65
3646 $1.50 In white cap and stars on collar 60 65

493 Lee Strasberg **494** Marlene Dietrich

2002. 20th Death Anniv of Lee Strasberg (pioneer of "Method Acting").

3647 **493** $1 black and stone . . . 40 45

2002. 10th Death Anniv of Marlene Dietrich (actress and singer). Each black and grey.

3648 $1.50 Type **494** 60 65
3649 $1.50 Wearing top hat . . . 60 65
3650 $1.50 In chiffon dress . . . 60 65
3651 $1.50 Resting chin on left hand 60 65
3652 $1.50 In cloche hat 60 65
3653 $1.50 Wearing black evening gloves 60 65
MS3654 83 × 108 mm. $6 Marlene Dietrich wearing chiffon scarf 2·40 2·50

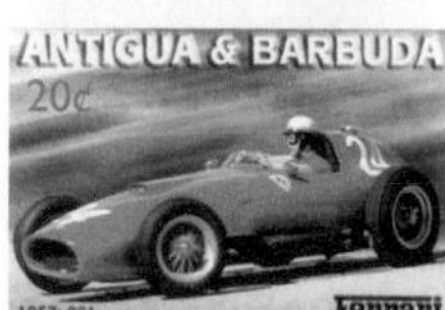

495 Ferrari 801, 1957

2002. Ferrari Racing Cars. Multicoloured.

3655 20c. Type **495** 10 15
3656 25c. Ferrari 256, 1959 . . 10 15
3657 30c. Ferrari 246 P, 1960 . . 10 15
3658 90c. Ferrari 246, 1966 . . . 35 40
3659 $1 Ferrari 312 B2, 1971 . . 40 45
3660 $1.50 Ferrari 312, 1969 . . 60 65
3661 $2 Ferrari F310 B, 1997 . . 80 85
3662 $4 Ferrari F2002, 2002 . . . 1·60 1·75

496 Antigua & Barbuda Flag

2002. 21st Anniv of Independence. Multicoloured.

3663 25c. Type **496** 10 15
3664 30c. Antigua & Barbuda coat of arms (vert) . . . 10 15
3665 $1.50 Mount St. John's Hospital under construction 60 65
3666 $1.80 Parliament Building, St. John's 75 80
MS3667 Two sheets, each 77 × 81 mm. (a) $6 Sir Vere Bird (Prime Minister, 1967–94) (38 × 51 mm). (b) $6 Lester Bird (Prime Minister since 1994) (38 × 51 mm) Set of 2 sheets . . 4·75 5·00

497 Juan Valeron (Spain)

2002. World Cup Football Championship, Japan and Korea. Multicoloured.

3668 $1.65 Type **497** 65 70
3669 $1.65 Iker Casillas (Spain) 65 70
3670 $1.65 Fernando Hierro (Spain) 65 70
3671 $1.65 Gary Kelly (Ireland) 65 70
3672 $1.65 Damien Duff (Ireland) 65 70
3673 $1.65 Matt Holland (Ireland) 65 70
3674 $1.65 Pyo Lee (South Korea) 65 70
3675 $1.65 Ji Sung Park (South Korea) 65 70
3676 $1.65 Jung Hwan Ahn (South Korea) 65 70
3677 $1.65 Filippo Inzaghi (Italy) 65 70
3678 $1.65 Paolo Maldini (Italy) 65 70
3679 $1.65 Dammiano Tommasi (Italy) 65 70
MS3680 Four sheets, each 82 × 82 mm. (a) $3 Jose Camacho (Spanish coach); $3 Raul Gonzales Blanco (Spain). (b) $3 Robbie Keane (Ireland); $3 Mick McCarthy (Irish coach). (c) $3 Guus Hiddink (South Korean coach); $3 Chul Sang Yoo (South Korea). (d) $3 Francesco Totti (Italy); $3 Giovanni Trapattoni (Italian coach) Set of 4 sheets 9·75 10·00

No. **MS**3680a is inscribed "Carlos Gamarra" in error.

498 "Coronation of the Virgin" (Domenico Ghirlandaio)

2002. Christmas. Religious Paintings. Multicoloured.

3681 25c. Type **498** 10 15
3682 45c. "Adoration of the Magi" (detail) (D. Ghirlandaio) 20 25
3683 75c. "Annunciation" (Simone Martini) (vert) 30 35
3684 90c. "Adoration of the Magi" (different detail) (D. Ghirlandaio) 35 40
3685 $5 "Madonna and Child" (Giovanni Bellini) . . . . 2·00 2·10
MS3686 76 × 110 mm. $6 "Madonnna and Child" (S. Martini) . . . . 2·40 2·50

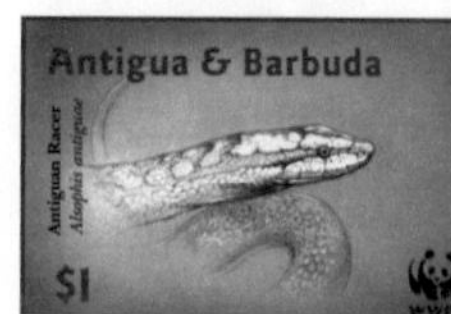

499 Antiguan Racer Snake Head

2002. Endangered Species. Antiguan Racer Snake. Multicoloured.

3687 $1 Type **499** 40 45
3688 $1 Coiled Antiguan racer snake with tail at right . . 40 45
3689 $1 Antiguan racer snake with pebbles and leaves 40 45
3690 $1 Coiled Antiguan racer snake with tail at left . . 40 45

500 Magnificent Frigate Bird

2002. Fauna and Flora. Multicoloured.

3691 $1.50 Type **500** 60 65
3692 $1.50 Sooty tern 60 65
3693 $1.50 Bananaquit 60 65
3694 $1.50 Yellow-crowned night heron 60 65
3695 $1.50 Greater flamingo . . . 60 65
3696 $1.50 Belted kingfisher . . . 60 65
3697 $1.50 Killer whale 60 65
3698 $1.50 Sperm whale 60 65
3699 $1.50 Minke whale 60 65
3700 $1.50 Blainville's beaked whale 60 65
3701 $1.50 Blue whale 60 65
3702 $1.50 Cuvier's beaked whale 60 65
3703 $1.80 *Epidendrum fragans* 75 80
3704 $1.80 *Dombeya wallichii* . . 75 80
3705 $1.80 *Abebuia serratifolia* . . 75 80
3706 $1.80 *Cryptostegia grandiflora* 75 80
3707 $1.80 *Hylocereus undatus* . . 75 80
3708 $1.80 *Rodriguezia lanceolata* 75 80
3709 $1.80 *Diphthera festiva* . . . 75 80
3710 $1.80 *Hypocrita dejanira* . . 75 80
3711 $1.80 *Eupseudosoma involutum* 75 80
3712 $1.80 *Composia credula* . . 75 80
3713 $1.80 *Citherania magnifica* 75 80
3714 $1.80 *Divana diva* 75 80
MS3715 Four sheets, each 75 × 45 mm. (a) $5 Snowy egret. (b) $5 *Rothschildia orizaba* (moth). (c) $6 Humpback whale. (d) $6 *Ionopsis utricularioides* (flower) Set of 4 sheets . . . . 9·00 9·25

Nos. 3691/6 (birds), 3697/702 (whales), 3703/8 (moths) and 3709/14 (flowers) were each printed together, se-tenant, with the backgrounds forming composite designs.

501 Dr. Margaret O'garro **502** Antiguan Brownie

2002. Centenary of Pan American Health Organization. Health Professionals. Multicoloured.

3716 $1.50 Type **501** 60 65
3717 $1.50 Ineta Wallace (nurse) 60 65
3718 $1.50 Vincent Edwards (public health official) . . 60 65

2002. 20th World Scout Jamboree, Thailand. Each lilac and brown (Nos. 3719/21) or multicoloured (others).

3719 $3 Type **502** . . . . 1·25 1·40
3720 $3 Brownie with badge on cap . . . . 1·25 1·40
3721 $3 Brownie without badge on cap . . . . 1·25 1·40
3722 $3 Robert Baden-Powell on horseback, 1896 (horiz) 1·25 1·40
3723 $3 Ernest Thompson Seton (founder, Boy Scouts of America), 1910, and American scout badge (horiz) . . . . 1·25 1·40
3724 $3 First black scout troop, Virginia, 1928 (horiz) . . 1·25 1·40
MS3725 Two sheets. (a) 80 × 113 mm. $6 Ernest Thompson Seton. (b) 110 × 83 mm. $6 Scout salute Set of 2 sheets . . . . . 4·75 5·00

Nos. 3719/21 were printed together, se-tenant, forming a composite design.

503 Scene from *2001: A Space Odyssey* (Arthur C. Clarke)

2002. Famous Science Fiction Authors. Three sheets, each 150 × 108 mm, containg vert designs as T **503**. Multicoloured

MS3726 Three sheets. (a) $6 Type **503**. (b) $6 Scene from *The Monuments of Mars* (Richard C. Hoagland). (c) $6 Nostradamus with globe Set of 3 sheets . . . 7·25 7·50

504 "Goat and Kids" (Liu Jiyou)

2003. Chinese New Year ("Year of the Goat").

3727 **504** $1.80 multicoloured . . 75 80

505 "Lucretia"

2003. 450th Death Anniv of Lucas Cranach the Elder (artist). Multicoloured.

3728 75c. Type **505** 30 35
3729 90c. "Venus and Cupid" (detail) 35 40
3730 $1 "Judith with Head of Holofernes" (c. 1530) . . 40 45
3731 $1.50 "Portrait of a Young Lady" (detail) 60 65
MS3732 152 × 188mm. $2 "Portrait of the Wife of a Jurist"; $2 "Portrait of a Jurist"; $2 "Johannes Cuspinian"; $2 "Portrait of Anna Cuspinian" 2·40 2·50
MS3733 120 × 100mm. $6 "Judith with Head of Holofernes" (c. 1532) . . . . 2·40 2·50

506 "A High Class Maid training in a Samurai Household"

2003. Japanese Art of Taiso Yoshitoshi. Multicoloured.

3734 25c. Type **506** 10 10
3735 50c. "A Castle-Toppler known as a Keisei" . . . 20 25
3736 $1 "Stylish Young Geisha battling a Snowstorm on her Way to Work" . . . 40 45
3737 $5 "A Lady in Distress being treated with Moxa" 2·00 2·10
MS3738 178 × 140mm. $2 "A Lady of the Imperial Court wearing Four Layers of Robes"; $2 "Young Mother adoring her Infant Son"; $2 "Lady-in-Waiting looking amused over a Veranda in the Household of a Great Lord"; $2 "A High Ranking Courtesan known as an "Oiran", waiting for a Private Assignation" . . . . 3·25 3·50
MS3739 135 × 67mm. $6 "A Girl teasing her Cat" . . . . 2·40 2·50

507 "Boats at Martigues"

2003. 50th Death Anniv of Raoul Dufy (artist). Multicoloured.

3740 90c. Type **507** 35 40
3741 $1 "Harvesting" 40 45
3742 $1.80 "Sailboats in the Port of Le Havre" 75 80
3743 $5 "The Big Bather" (vert) 2·00 2·10
MS3744 173 × 124mm. $2 "The Beach and the Pier at Trouville"; $2 "Port with Sailing Ships"; $2 "Black Cargo"; $2 "Nice, The Bay of Anges" . . . . 3·25 3·50
MS3745 Two sheets, each 95 × 76mm. (a) $6 "Vence". (b) $6 "The Interior with an Open Window". Both Imperf . . . . 4·75 5·00

508 Queen Elizabeth II at Trooping the Colour **509** Prince William

2003. 50th Anniv of Coronation. Multicoloured.

MS3746 155 × 93mm. $3 Type **508**; $3 Queen wearing fawn beret with single feather; $3 Queen wearing feathered hat . . . . 4·25 4·50
MS3747 105 × 75mm. $6 Princess Elizabeth . . . . 2·40 2·50

2003. 21st Birthday of Prince William of Wales. Multicoloured.

MS3748 147 × 77mm. $3 Type **509**; $3 Prince william wearing polo helmet; $3 Wearing blue T-shirt 4·25 4·50
MS3749 67 × 97mm. $6 As teenager holding bouquet . . . . 2·40 2·50

510 Tamarind Tree, Parham

2003. Centenary of Salvation Army in Antigua. Multicoloured.
3750 30c. Type **510** 10 10
3751 90c. Salvation Army pre-school 35 40
3752 $1 Meals on wheels (horiz) 40 45
3753 $1.50 St. John Citadel band (horiz) 60 65
3754 $1.80 Salvation Army Citadel (horiz) 75 80
MS3755 146 × 78mm. $6 As Type **510** but without badge and centenary inscription . . . . . 2·40 2·50

511 First Anglican Scout Troop, 1931

512 Cesar Garin (1903)

2003. 90th Anniv of Antigua and Barbuda Scouts Association. Multicoloured (except No. 3756).
3756 30c. Type **511** (black and brown) 10 15
3757 $1 National Scout Camp, 2002 . . . . 40 45
3758 $1.50 Woodbadge Training course, 2000 (horiz) . . . 60 65
3759 $1.80 Visitors to National Camp, 1986 (horiz) . . . 75 80
MS3760 136 × 96mm. 90c. Edris George; 90c. Theodore George; 90c. Edris James (all Deputy Commissioners) . . . . 1·10 1·25
MS3761 74 × 101 mm. $6 Scout leader demonstrating semaphore 2·40 2·50

2003. Centenary of Tour de France Cycle Race. Past winners. Multicoloured.
MS3762 160 × 100mm. $2 Type **512**; $2 Caricature of Henri Cornet (1904); $2 Louis Trousselier (1905); $2 Rene Pottier (1906) 3·25 3·40
MS3763 160 × 100mm. $2 Lucien Petit-Breton (1907); $2 Lucien Petit-Breton (1908); $2 Francois Faber (1909); $2 Octave Lapize (1910) . . . . 3·25 3·40
MS3764 160 × 100mm. $2 Gustave Garrigou (1911); $2 Odile Defraye (1912); $2 Phillipe Thys (1913); $2 Phillipe Thys (1914) . . . . . 3·25 3·40
MS3765 Three sheets, each 100 × 70mm. (a) $6 Henri Desgranges (editor of *L'Auto*). (b) $6 Pierre Giffard (editor of *Le Velo*). (c) $6 Le Compte de Dion (sponsor) Set of 3 sheets . . . 7·25 7·50

513 Frigate Bird and Emblem

2003. 30th Anniv of CARICOM.
3766 **513** $1 multicoloured 40 45

514 Cadillac Eldorado Convertible (1955)

2003. Centenary of General Motors Cadillac. Multicoloured.
MS3767 110 × 150 mm. $2 Type **514**; $2 Cadillac Series 60 (1937); $2 Cadillac Eldorado (1959); $2 Cadillac Eldorado (2002) . . . 3·25 3·50
MS3768 102 × 76 mm. $6 Cadillac Eldorado (1953) . . . . 2·40 2·50

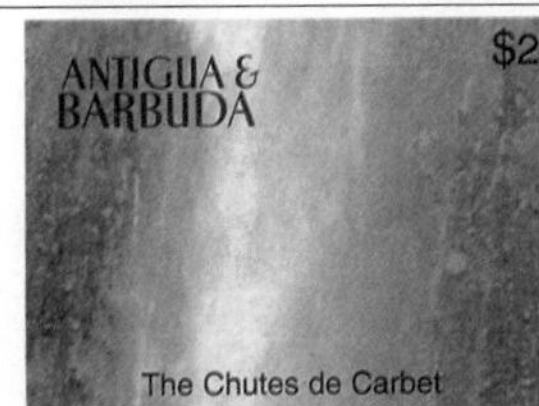

515 Chutes de Carbet Waterfall, Guadeloupe

2003. International Year of Freshwater. Multicoloured.
MS3769 94 × 180 mm. $2 Type **515**; $2 Foot of Chutes de Carbet waterfall; $2 Rapids at foot of Chutes de Carbet waterfall . . 2·40 2·50
MS3770 96 × 67 mm. $6 Waterfall, Ocho Rios, Jamaica (vert) . . 2·40 2·50

516 Corvette Convertible (1954)

2003. 50th Anniv of General Motors Chevrolet Corvette. Multicoloured.
MS3771 110 × 151 mm. $2 Type **516**; $2 Corvette Sting Ray (1964); $2 Corvette Sting Ray Convertible (1964); $2 Corvette Convertible (1998) . . . . 3·25 3·50
MS3772 102 × 74 mm. $6 Corvette Convertible (1956) . . . . . . 2·40 2·50

517 *Flyer I* (first manned powered flight), 1903

2003. Centenary of Powered Flight. Multicoloured.
MS3773 176 × 106 mm. $2 Type **517**; $2 Paul Cornu's helicopter on first helicopter flight, 1907; $2 E.B. Ely's biplane making first landing on ship, 1911; $2 Curtiss A-1 (first seaplane), 1911 . . . . . . 3·25 3·50
MS3774 176 × 106 mm. $2 Bell X-5 research aircraft with variable wings, 1951; $2 Convair XFY-1 vertical take-off and landing; $2 North American X-15 rocket aircraft, 1959; $2 Alexei Leonov on first spacewalk, 1965 . . . 3·25 3·50
MS3775 176 × 106 mm. $2 Concorde, 1969; $2 Martin X-24 Lifting Body Vehicle Pre-Space Shuttle, 1969; $2 Apollo-Soyuz, 1975; $2 Viking Robot Mars Expedition, 1976 . . . . . . 2·40 2·40
MS3776 Three sheets, each 106 × 76 mm. (a) $6 Boeing Model 200 Monomail with retractable landing gear, 1930. (b) $6 Bell XS-1 rocket plane breaking sound barrier, 1947. (c) $6 Grumman X-29 with forward swept wings, 1984 . . . . 2·40 2·50

518 *Psychopsis papilio*

2003. Orchids. Multicoloured.
MS3779 96 × 138 mm. $2.50 Type **518**; $2.50 *Amesiella philippinensis*; $2.50 *Maclellanara* "Pagan Dove Song"; $2.50 *Phalaenopsis* "Little Hal" . . . 4·00 4·25
MS3780 205 × 124 mm. $2.50 *Daeliocattleya* "Amber Glow"; $2.50 *Hygrochilus parishii*; $2.50 *Dendrobium crystallinum*; $2.50 *Disa* hybrid (all horiz) . . . . 4·00 4·25
MS3781 98 × 68 mm. $5 *Cattleya deckeri* (horiz) . . . . 2·00 2·10

519 Bull Shark

2003. Sharks. Multicoloured.
MS3782 128 × 128 mm. $2 Type **519**; $2 Grey reef shark; $2 Black tip shark; $2 Leopard shark . . . 3·25 3·50
MS3783 88 × 88 mm. $5 Great white shark . . . . 2·00 2·10

520 Esmeralda

2003. Butterflies. Multicoloured.
MS3784 105 × 86 mm. $2 Type **520**; $2 Tiger pierid; $2 Blue night butterfly; $2 *Charaxes nobilis* 3·25 3·50
MS3785 205 × 132 mm. $2.50 Orange-barred sulphur; $2.50 Scarce bamboo page; $2.50 *Charaxes latona*; $2.50 Hewitson's blue hairstreak . . . . 4·00 4·25
MS3786 98 × 68 mm. $5 *Diaethia merdionalis* . . . . 2·00 2·10

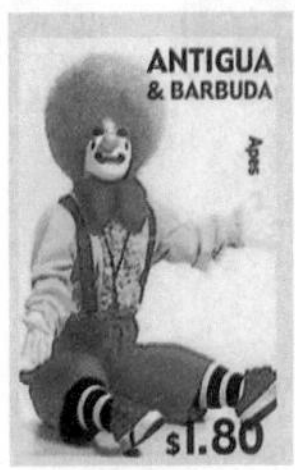

521 Apes

2003. Centenary of Circus Clowns. Multicoloured.
MS3787 119 × 195 mm. $1.80 Type **521**; $1.80 Mo Lite; $1.80 Gigi; $1.80 "Buttons" M. C. Bride 3·00 3·25
MS3788 145 × 218 mm. $1.80 Chun Group; $1.80 Casselly Sisters (acrobats); $1.80 Oliver Groszer; $1.80 Keith Nelson (sword swallower) . . . . 3·25 3·50

No. **MS**3787 is cut in the shape of a clown on a bicycle and No. **MS**3788 in the shape of a circus elephant.

522 "Madonna and Child" (detail) (Bartolommeo Vivarini)

2003. Christmas. Multicoloured.
3789 25c. Type **522** 10 10
3790 30c. "Holy Family" (detail) (Pompeo Girolano Batoni) 10 15
3791 45c. "Madonna and Child" (detail) (Benozzo Gozzoli) 20 25
3792 50c. "Madonna and Child" (detail) (Benozzo Gozzoli), Calci Parish Church . . . 20 25
3793 75c. "Madonna and Child giving Blessings" (Benozzo Gozzoli) 30 35
3794 90c. "Madonna and Child" (detail) (Master of the Female Half-Figures) . . 35 40
3795 $2.50 "The Benois Madonna" (detail) (da Vinci) . . . . 1·00 1·10
MS3796 70 × 110 mm. $6 "The Virgin and Child with Angels" (Rosso Fiorentino) . . . . . . 2·40 2·50

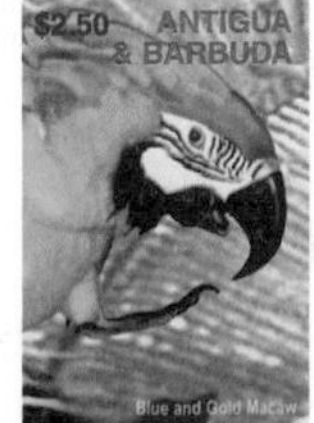

523 Blue and Yellow Macaw ("Blue and Gold Macaw")

2003. Birds. Multicoloured.
MS3797 96 × 137 mm. $2.50 Type **523**; $2.50 Green-winged macaw; $2.50 Rainbow lory ("Green-naped Lorikeet"); $2.50 Lesser sulphur-crested cockatoo 4·00 4·25
MS3798 205 × 133 mm. $2.50 Chestnut-fronted macaw ("Severe Macaw"); $2.50 Blue-headed parrot; $2.50 Budgerigar; $2.50 Sun conure (all horiz) . . . . 4·00 4·25
MS3799 98 × 68 mm. $5 Waldrapp ("Bald Ibis") (horiz) . . . . . 2·00 2·10

524 Diana Monkey

2004. Chinese New Year ("Year of the Monkey"). Multicoloured.
MS3800 152 × 95 mm. $1.50 Type **524**; $1.50 Mandrill; $1.50 Lar gibbon; $1.50 Red howler monkey . . . . 2·40 2·50

525 Mountain Landscape

2004. Hong Kong 2004 International Stamp Exhibition. Paintings by Ren Xiong. Multicoloured.
MS3801 131 × 138 mm. $1.50 Type **525**; $1.50 "Myriad Bamboo in Misty Rain"; $1.50 Winter landscape; $1.50 House and tree 2·40 2·50
MS3802 170 × 137 mm. $1.50 "Myriad Sceptres worshipping Heaven"; $1.50 Misty mountain landscape; $1.50 Myriad cherry trees; $1.50 Mountain landscape with two streams; $1.50 "Myriad Valleys with competing Streams"; $1.50 Myriad lights . . . . . 3·75 4·00
MS3803 74 × 153 mm. $2.50 Bird singing from flowering cherry branch; $2.50 Bird in maple tree 2·00 2·10

Nos. **MS**3801/2 show paintings from *The Ten Myriads* album and No. **MS**3803 paintings from *Album after the Poems of Yao Xie*.

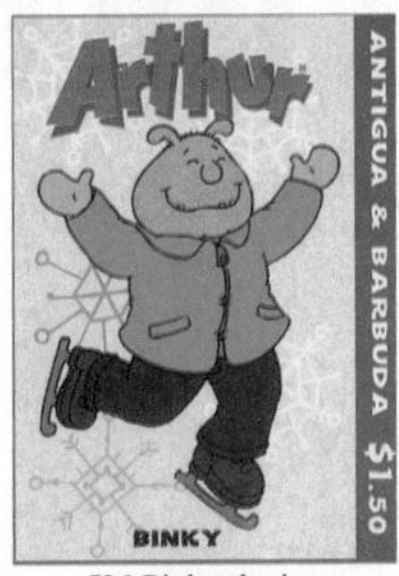

526 Binky skating

2004. *Arthur the Aardvark* by Marc Brown (children's books and TV programme). T **526** and similar vert designs. Multicoloured.

MS3804 150 × 183 mm. $1.50 Type **526**; $150 Buster skating; $1.50 Francine skating; $1.50 D.W.; $1.50 Sue Ellen; $1.50 Muffy skating . . . . 3·75 4·00
MS3805 150 × 183 mm. $1.80 Binky in baseball game; $1.80 Muffy with bat; $1.80 Francine running; $1.80 Buster catching ball . . . 3·00 3·25
MS3806 150 × 183 mm. $2.50 Arthur hitting ball; $2.50 Sue Ellen with bat; $2.50 Binky holding bat; $2.50 Arthur with bat raised 3·00 3·25

No. **MS**3804 shows Arthur characters skating and **MS**3805/6 show them playing baseball.

527 "Freedom of Speech"

2004. 25th Death Anniv of Norman Rockwell (artist) (2003). T **527** and similar vert designs. Multicoloured.

MS3807 135 × 145 mm. $2 Type **527**; $2 "Freedom to Worship"; $2 "Freedom from Want"; $2 "Freedom from Fear" . . . . 3·25 3·50
MS3808 62 × 82 mm. $6 "Do Unto Others as you would have them Do Unto You". Imperf . . . . 3·25 3·50

No. **MS**3807 shows a series of posters and **MS**3808 a painting for Saturday Evening Post cover, 1961.

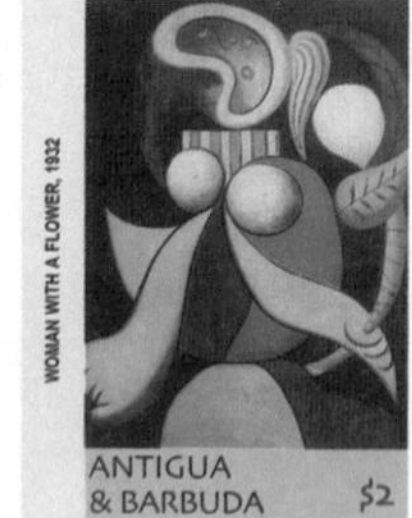

528 "Woman with a Flower"

2004. 30th Death Anniv of Pablo Picasso (artist). T **528** and similar vert designs. Multicoloured.

MS3809 177 × 127 mm. $2 Type **528**; $2 "Marie-Therese Seated"; $2 The Red Armchair (Marie-Therese) Seated"; $2 "The Dream (Marie-Therese) Seated" . . . 3·25 3·50
MS3810 58 × 69 mm. $5 "Bust of a Girl (Marie-Therese)". Imperf 2·00 2·10

ANTIOQUIA Pt. 20

One of the states of the Granadine Confederation. A department of Colombia from 1886, now uses Colombian stamps.

100 centavos = 1 peso.

1 5 6

1868. Various arms designs. Imperf.

1 **1** 2½c. blue £450 £225
2 – 5c. green £350 £200
3 – 10c. lilac £850 £385
4 – 1p. red £300 £185

1869. Various frames. Imperf.

5 **5** 2½c. blue . . . . 2·50 2·00
6 5c. green . . . . 3·25 3·00
8 10c. mauve . . . . 4·00 2·00
9 20c. brown . . . . 4·50 3·00
10 **6** 1p. red . . . . 7·50 7·50

7 15

1873. Arms designs inscr "E.S." (or "Eo. So." or "Estado Soberano") "de Antioquia". Imperf.

11 **7** 1c. green . . . . 2·00 1·50
12 – 5c. green . . . . 2·50 1·60
13 – 10c. mauve . . . . 16·00 12·00
14 – 20c. brown . . . . 4·00 2·50
15 – 50c. blue . . . . 1·00 80
16 – 1p. red . . . . 2·50 2·50
17 – 2p. black on yellow . . . . 5·00 5·00
18 – 5p. black on red . . . . . 25·00 20·00

The 5p. is larger (25½ × 31½ mm).

1875. Imperf.

20 **15** 1c. black on green 60 60
43 1c. mauve . . . . 1·00 1·00
21 1c. black 60 60
52 1c. green . . . . 1·00 1·00
22 – 2½c. blue (Arms) 80 80
23 – 5c. green ("Liberty") . . . 6·00 5·00
25 – 10c. mauve (J. Berrio) . . . 8·00 7·00

20 Condor

21 Liberty

23 Liberty

25 Liberty

1879. Imperf.

30 **20** 2½c. blue . . . . 3·00 3·00
38 2½c. green . . . . 80 1·00
45 2½c. black on buff . . . . . 3·00 3·00
39 **21** 5c. green . . . . 85 1·00
40 5c. violet . . . . 1·75 1·00
32 – 10c. violet (Arms) £250 £200
36 **23** 10c. violet . . . . 50·00 16·00
41 10c. red . . . . 1·00 1·00
42 **21** 20c. brown . . . . 1·25 1·25

1883. Various frames. Head of Liberty to left. Imperf.

53 **25** 5c. brown . . . . 4·00 2·00
47 5c. yellow . . . . 3·00 2·50
48 5c. green . . . . 55·00 40·00
49 10c. green . . . . 2·00 2·00
50 10c. mauve . . . . 3·50 3·50
55 10c. blue . . . . 4·00 3·50
51 20c. blue . . . . 2·50 2·50

28

31

1886. Imperf.

57 **28** 1c. green on pink 50 50
65 1c. red on lilac 30 30
58 2½c. black on orange 35 40
66 2½c. mauve on pink 50 40
59 5c. blue on buff . . . . . . 2·00 75
67 5c. red on green . . . . . . 2·25 2·25
68 5c. lake on buff . . . . . . 1·00 80
60 10c. red on buff . . . . . . 1·00 60
69 10c. brown on green . . . . . 1·00 80
61 20c. purple on buff . . . . . 1·00 60
62 50c. yellow on buff . . . . . 2·00 2·00
63 1p. yellow on green . . . . . 4·00 4·00
64 2p. green on lilac . . . . . 4·00 4·00

1888. Various sizes and frames. Inscr "MEDELLIN". Imperf.

70 **31** 2½c. black on yellow . . . . 15·00 12·00
71 2½c. red on white . . . . . 2·50 2·50
72 5c. black on yellow . . . . . 2·00 2·00
73 5c. red on orange . . . . . 1·75 1·75

34 35

1889. Arms in various frames.

74 **34** 1c. black on red 10 10
75 2½c. black on blue 20 15
76 5c. black on yellow 45 25
77 10c. black on green 50 40
95 10c. brown 25 25
78 20c. blue . . . . 1·00 1·00
79 50c. brown . . . . 2·00 2·00
80 50c. green . . . . 1·75 1·75
81 1p. red . . . . 1·00 1·00
82 2p. black on mauve . . . . . 7·50 6·00
83 5p. black on red . . . . . . 10·00 7·50

1890. Perf.

84 **35** 2½c. black on buff . . . . . 1·00 1·00
85 5c. black on yellow . . . . . 1·00 1·00
86 10c. black on buff . . . . . 4·75 4·75
87 10c. black on red . . . . . 5·00 5·00
88 20c. black on yellow . . . . 5·00 5·00

36 37

1892.

89 **36** 1c. brown on buff 50 40
90 1c. blue 20 20
91 2½c. violet on lilac 30 30
92 2½c. green 30 30
93 5c. black 80 60
94 5c. red 20 20

1896.

96 **37** 2c. grey 40 40
107 2c. red 25 40
97 2½c. brown 40 40
108 2½c. blue 25 40
98 3c. red 50 50
109 3c. olive 25 40
99 5c. green 25 20
110 5c. yellow 20 30
100 10c. lilac 45 45
111 10c. brown 50 60
101 20c. brown 70 70
112 20c. blue . . . . 75 1·00
102 50c. sepia 90 90
113 50c. red . . . . 1·00 1·40
103 1p. black and blue . . . . . 10·00 10·00
114 1p. black and red . . . . . 10·00 10·00
104 2p. black and orange . . . . 40·00 40·00
115 2p. black and green . . . . 35·00 35·00
105 5p. black and mauve . . . . 50·00 50·00

39 Gen. Cordoba 43

1899.

118 **39** ½c. blue 10 10
119 1c. blue 10 10
120 2c. black 10 10
121 3c. red 10 10
122 4c. brown 10 10
123 5c. green 10 10
124 10c. red 10 10
125 20c. violet 10 10
126 50c. yellow 10 10
127 1p. green 10 15
128 2p. green 10 20

1901. Various frames.

132 **43** 1c. red 10 15
133 1c. brown 25 25
134 1c. blue 25 25

Nos. 132 and 134 also exist with "CENTAVO" inside the rectangle below figure "1".

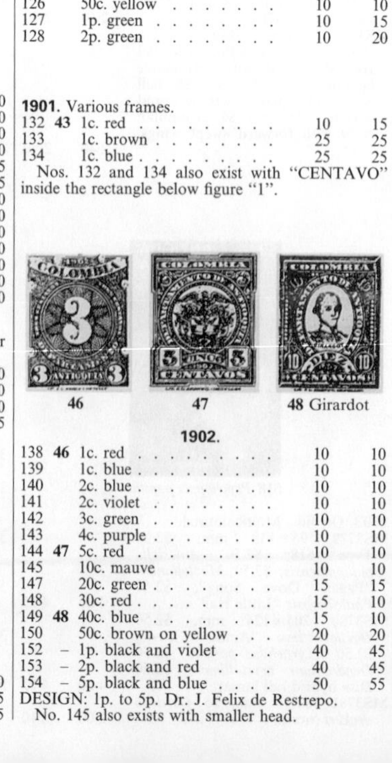

46 47 48 Girardot

1902.

138 **46** 1c. red 10 10
139 1c. blue 10 10
140 2c. blue 10 10
141 2c. violet 10 10
142 3c. green 10 10
143 4c. purple 10 10
144 **47** 5c. red 10 10
145 10c. mauve 10 10
147 20c. green 15 15
148 30c. red 15 10
149 **48** 40c. blue 15 10
150 50c. brown on yellow 20 20
152 – 1p. black and violet 40 45
153 – 2p. black and red 40 45
154 – 5p. black and blue 50 55

DESIGN: 1p. to 5p. Dr. J. Felix de Restrepo.

No. 145 also exists with smaller head.

54

55

56 Zea

1903.

159 **54** 4c. brown 10 10
160 5c. blue 10 10
161 **55** 10c. yellow 10 10
162 20c. lilac 10 10
163 30c. brown 30 30
164 40c. green 30 30
165 50c. red 10 15
166 **56** 1p. green 25 20
167 2p. mauve (Rovira) 25 20
168 3p. blue (La Pola) 30 30
169 4p. red (Restrepo) 50 30
170 5p. brown (Madrid) 50 40
171 10p. red (Corral) . . . . . 2·25 2·25

ACKNOWLEDGEMENT OF RECEIPT STAMPS

AR 53

1902.

AR157 **AR 53** 5c. black on red . . 30 20
AR158 5c. green 10 10

REGISTRATION STAMPS

R 38

1896.

R106 **R 38** 2½c. pink 50 50
R117 2½c. blue 60 60

R 41 Gen. Cordoba

R 42

1899.

R130 **R 41** 2½c. blue 10 10
R131 **R 42** 10c. red 10 10

R 52

1902.

R156 **R 52** 10c. violet on green . . 10 10

TOO LATE STAMPS

L 40 Gen. Cordoba

L 51

1899.

L129 **L 40** 2½c. green 10 10

1901. As T **43**, but inscr "RETARDO" at sides.

L137a 2½c. purple 60 60

1902.

L155 **L 51** 2½c. lilac 10 10

ARBE Pt. 8

During the period of D'Annunzio's Italian Regency of Carnaro (Fiume), separate issues were made for Arbe (now Rab).

100 centesimi = 1 lira.

1920. No. 148, etc of Fiume optd **ARBE**.
1B 5c. green 4·50 5·25
2B 10c. red 10·50 11·50
3B 20c. brown 24·00 18·00
4B 25c. blue 14·50 18·00
5 50c. on 20c. brown 26·00 18·00
6 55c. on 5c. green 26·00 18·00

EXPRESS LETTER STAMPS

1920. Nos. E163/4 of Fiume optd **ARBE**.
E7 30c. on 20c. brown 95·00 55·00
E8 50c. on 5c. green 95·00 55·00

ARGENTINE REPUBLIC Pt. 20

A republic in the S.E. of S. America formerly part of the Spanish Empire.

1858. 100 centavos = 1 peso.
1985. 100 centavos = 1 austral.
1992. 100 centavos = 1 peso.

1 Argentine Confederation
3 Argentine Confederation

1858. Imperf.
1 **1** 5c. red 1·60 9·50
2 10c. green 2·25 55·00
3 15c. blue 16·00 £140

1862. Imperf.
10 **3** 5c. red 20·00 24·00
8 10c. green £160 75·00
9 15c. blue £325 £250

5 Rivadavia
6 Rivadavia

1864. Imperf.
24 **5** 5c. red £250 65·00
14 **6** 10c. green £1700 £1000
15 **5** 15c. blue £8000 £3500

1864. Perf.
16 **5** 5c. red 35·00 14·00
17 **6** 10c. green 80·00 35·00
18 **5** 15c. blue £160 75·00

9 Rivadavia
10 Gen. Belgrano
11 Gen. San Martin

1867. Perf.
28 **9** 5c. red 12·00 75
29 **10** 10c. green 35·00 5·00
30a **11** 15c. blue 50·00 15·00

12 Balcarce
22 Sarsfield
24 Lopez

1873. Portraits. Perf.
31 **12** 1c. violet 4·00 2·25
32 – 4c. brown (Moreno) 5·50 45
33 – 30c. orange (Alvear) £120 17·00
34 – 60c. black (Posadas) £120 5·50
35 – 90c. blue (Saavedra) 28·00 2·50

1877. Surch with large figure of value.
37 **9** 1 on 5c. red 55·00 17·00
38 2 on 5c. red £110 70·00
39 **10** 8 on 10c. green £140 35·00

1876. Roul.
36 **9** 5c. red £170 70·00
40 8c. lake 28·00 30
41 **10** 16c. green 9·00 1·25
42 **22** 20c. blue 9·50 3·50
43 **11** 24c. blue 19·00 3·50

1877. Perf.
46 **24** 2c. green 4·75 1·00
44 **9** 8c. lake 4·75 15
45 **11** 24c. blue 8·50 50
47 – 25c. lake (Alvear) 25·00 7·00

1882. Surch **1/2 (PROVISORIO)**.
51 **9** ½ on 5c. red 1·00 90

29
33

1882.
52 **29** ½c. brown 1·60 90
55 1c. red 4·00 1·25
54 12c. blue 65·00 10·00

1884. Surch **1884** and value in figures or words.
90 **9** ½c. on 5c. red 3·00 2·25
92 **11** ½c. on 15c. blue 2·25 1·75
94 1c. on 15c. blue 7·00 5·50
100 **9** 4c. on 5c. red 10·00 6·00

1884.
101 **33** ½c. brown 1·00 50
102 1c. red 6·00 50
103 12c. blue 28·00 1·40

34 Urquiza
45 Mitre

1888. Portrait types, inscr "CORREOS ARGENTINOS".
108 **34** ½c. blue 55 50
110 – 2c. green (Lopez) 10·00 7·00
111 – 3c. green (Celman) 1·90 70
113 – 5c. red (Rivadavia) 9·00 65
114 – 6c. red (Sarmiento) 24·00 16·00
115 – 10c. brown (Avellaneda) 16·00 1·25
116 – 15c. orange (San Martin) 16·00 1·75
117a – 20c. green (Roca) 13·00 1·40
118 – 25c. violet (Belgrano) 16·00 1·75
119 – 30c. brown (Dorrego) 24·00 2·75
120a – 40c. grey (Moreno) 24·00 3·25
121 **45** 50c. blue 85·00 9·00

60 Paz
51 Rivadavia

1888. Portrait types, inscr "CORREOS Y TELEGRAFOS" except No. 126.
137 **60** ½c. green 10 15
122 – ½c. blue (Urquiza) 30 15
123 – 1c. brown (Sarsfield) 95 20
125 – 2c. violet (Derqui) 95 15
126 – 3c. green (Celman) 2·25 45
127 **51** 5c. red 3·00 20
129 – 6c. blue (Sarmiento) 1·60 60
130 – 10c. brown (Avellaneda) 1·90 30
131 – 12c. blue (Alberti) 4·75 1·25
132 – 40c. grey (Moreno) 4·50 90
133 – 50c. orange (Mitre) 4·50 90
134 – 60c. black (Posadas) 17·00 3·00

1890. No. 131 surch **1/4** and bars.
135 ¼ on 12c. blue 40 35

52 Rivadavia
63 La Madrid
61 Rivadavia

1890.
128a **52** 5c. red 2·25 15

1891. Portraits.
139 – 1p. blue (San Martin) 45·00 6·50
140 **63** 5p. blue £225 24·00
141 – 20p. green (G. Brown) £325 70·00

1891.
138 **61** 8c. red 1·40 25

65 Rivadavia
66 Belgrano
67 San Martin

1892.
142 **65** ½c. blue 20 15
143 1c. brown 40 15
144 2c. green 25 15
145 3c. orange 70 15
146 5c. red 70 15
147 **66** 10c. red 5·50 15
148 12c. blue 2·75 15
149 16c. slate 6·50 60
150 24c. sepia 11·00 60
257 30c. orange 8·00 50
151 50c. green 10·00 50
188 80c. lilac 12·00 50
152a **67** 1p. red 10·00 80
190 1p.20 black 9·50 4·00
153 2p. green 17·00 8·00
154 5p. blue 42·00 3·00

70 Fleet of Columbus
71 "Liberty" and Shield

1892. 4th Centenary of Discovery of America by Columbus.
219 **70** 2c. blue 12·50 4·50
220 5c. blue 26·00 5·00

1899.
221 **71** ½c. brown 15 15
222 1c. green 10 10
223 2c. grey 10 10
224 3c. orange 95 15
225 4c. yellow 1·75 15
226 5c. red 10 10
227 6c. black 1·10 20
228 10c. green 1·75 15
229a 12c. blue 1·10 30
230 12c. green 1·10 30
231 15c. blue 3·00 15
232 16c. orange 8·50 4·25
233 20c. red 2·25 15
234 24c. purple 4·00 80
235 30c. red 4·25 20
237 50c. blue 5·50 15
238 1p. black and blue 16·00 80
239 5p. black and orange 65·00 11·00
240 10p. black and green 60·00 11·00
241 20p. black and red £225 32·00

The peso values are larger (19 × 32 mm).

73 Port Rosario
74 Gen. San Martin

1902. Completion of Port Rosario Docks.
290 **73** 5c. blue 80 2·00

1908.
291 **74** ½c. violet 15 10
292 1c. brown 20 10
293 2c. brown 60 10
294 3c. green 75 35
295 4c. mauve 1·50 35
296 5c. red 35 10
297 6c. green 85 25
298 10c. green 1·75 10
299 12c. brown 45 40
300 12c. blue 1·40 10
301 15c. green 1·90 90
302 20c. blue 1·40 10
303 24c. red 3·75 70
304 30c. red 6·00 70
305 50c. black 5·50 45
306 1p. red and blue 13·00 1·90

The 1p. is larger (21½ × 27 mm) with portrait at upper left.

76 Pyramid of May
80 Saavedra
78 Azcuenaga and Alberti

1910. Cent of Deposition of the Spanish Viceroy.
366 **76** ½c. blue and grey 40 10
367 – 1c. black and green 40 10
368 – 2c. black and green 30 10
369 **78** 3c. green 85 10
370 – 4c. green and blue 85 15
371 **80** 5c. red 70 10
372 – 10c. black and brown 2·00 15
373 – 12c. blue 1·60 25
374 – 20c. black and brown 3·75 40
375 – 24c. blue and brown 2·00 1·00
376 – 30c. black and lilac 2·00 75
377 – 50c. black and red 5·00 1·00
378 – 1p. blue 12·00 3·50
379 – 5p. purple and orange 80·00 35·00
380 – 10p. black and orange £100 75·00
381 – 20p. black and blue £170 £100

DESIGNS—VERT: 50c. Crowds on 25 May 1810; 10p. Centenary Monument; 20p. San Martin. HORIZ: 1c. Pena and Vieytes; 2c. Meeting at Pena's house; 4c. Fort of the Viceroys, Buenos Aires; 10c. Distribution of cockades; 12c. Congress Building; 20c. Castelli and Matheu; 24c. First National Council; 30c. Belgrano and Larrea; 1p. Moreno and Paso; 5p. "Oath of the Junta".

90 Sarmiento
91 Ploughman

1911. Birth Centenary of Pres. Sarmiento.
382 **90** 5c. black and brown 70 40

1911.
383 **91** 5c. red 40 15
384 12c. blue 4·50 20

92 Ploughman
94

1911.
395 **92** ½c. violet 20 20
396 1c. brown 20 15
397 2c. brown 40 15
398 3c. green 50 20
399 4c. purple 40 20
400 5c. red 20 15
401 10c. green 60 15
402 12c. blue 1·60 15
403 20c. blue 5·00 1·25
404 24c. brown 3·75 20
405 30c. red 2·00 70
406 50c. black 6·00 70
408 **94** 1p. red and blue 7·00 1·10
409 5p. green and grey 22·00 7·00
410 10p. blue and violet 85·00 10·00
411 20p. red and blue £200 70·00

95 Dr. F. N. Laprida
97 San Martin
96 Declaration of Independence

1916. Centenary of Independence.
417 **95** ½c. violet 20 15
418 1c. brown 25 15
419 2c. brown 20 15
420 3c. green 50 15
421 4c. purple 75 15
422 **96** 5c. red 35 15
423 10c. green 1·60 15
424 **97** 12c. blue 75 15
425 20c. blue 1·25 15
426 24c. red 2·00 85
427 30c. red 2·00 40
428 50c. black 3·75 50
429 1p. red and blue 11·00 4·50
430 5p. green and grey £130 45·00
431 10p. blue and violet £130 85·00
432 20p. red and grey £190 75·00

98 San Martin **100** Dr. Juan Pujol

1917.
433 **98** ½c. violet 20 15
434 1c. buff 20 15
435 2c. brown 20 15
436 3c. green 70 15
454 4c. purple 30 15
455 5c. red 15 15
456 10c. green 1·75 15
457 – 12c. blue 1·40 15
458 – 20c. blue 1·75 15
459 – 24c. red 5·00 2·25
460 – 30c. red 5·00 70
461 – 50c. black 4·50 70
445 – 1p. red and blue 4·50 20
446 – 5p. green and grey 19·00 3·50
447 – 10p. blue and violet 45·00 11·00
448 – 20p. red and grey 81·00 17·00
The 12c. to 20p. values are larger (21×27 mm).

1918. Birth Centenary of Juan Pujol, 1st P.M.G. of Argentina.
449 **100** 5c. grey and bistre 80 30

102 Mausoleum of Belgrano **103** Creation of Argentine Flag

1920. Death Centenary of Gen. Manuel Belgrano.
478 **102** 2c. red 50 15
479 **103** 5c. blue and red 50 15
480 – 12c. blue and green 1·00 75
DESIGN—VERT: 12c. Gen. Belgrano.

106 General Urquiza **107** General Mitre **108**

1920. Gen. Urquiza's Victory at Cepada.
488 **106** 5c. blue 30 10

1921. Birth Centenary of Gen. Mitre.
490 **107** 2c. brown 35 10
491 5c. blue 35 10

1921. 1st Pan-American Postal Congress.
492 **108** 3c. lilac 1·50 65
493 5c. blue 2·00 20
494 10c. brown 2·50 90
495 12c. red 4·50 1·90

1921. As T **108**, but smaller. Inscr "BUENOS AIRES AGOSTO DE 1921".
496 5c. red 2·25 25

1921. As No. 496, but inscr "REPUBLICA ARGENTINA" at foot.
511 5c. red 1·75 25

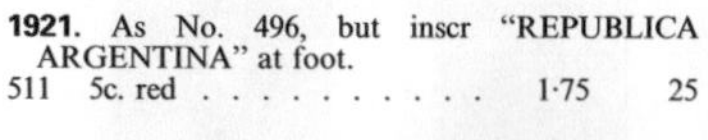

112 **114B.** Rivadavia

1923. With or without stop below "c".
513 **112** ½c. purple 15 15
530 1c. brown 15 15
515 2c. brown 35 15
532 3c. green 15 15
533 4c. red 50 15
518 5c. red 15 15
535 10c. green 35 15
520 12c. blue 45 15
537 20c. blue 85 15
538 24c. brown 2·00 1·00
539 25c. violet 1·00 15
540 30c. red 2·00 15
541 50c. black 2·00 15
542 – 1p. red and blue 2·25 15
543 – 5p. green and lilac 17·00 70
544 – 10p. blue and red 38·00 3·75
545 – 20p. lake and slate 55·00 8·50
The peso values are larger (21×27 mm).

1926. Rivadavia Centenary.
546 **114** 5c. red 50 15

115 Rivadavia **116** San Martin

117 G.P.O., 1926 **118** G.P.O., 1826

1926. Postal Centenary.
547 **115** 3c. green 15 15
548 **116** 5c. red 10 15
549 **117** 12c. blue 1·00 20
550 **118** 25c. brown 1·75 15

120 Biplane and Globe **122**

1928. Air.
558 **120** 5c. red 1·75 50
559 10c. blue 2·75 85
560 – 15c. brown 2·50 90
561 **120** 18c. violet 4·25 3·25
562 – 20c. blue 2·75 90
563 – 24c. blue 4·25 3·00
564 **122** 25c. violet 4·25 1·40
565 30c. red 5·50 1·00
566 – 35c. red 4·25 1·25
567a **120** 36c. brown 3·25 1·40
568 – 50c. black 4·50 65
569 – 54c. brown 4·25 2·10
570 – 72c. green 5·50 2·10
571 **122** 90c. purple 10·00 1·90
572 1p. red and blue 12·00 70
573 1p.08 blue and red 17·00 4·75
574 – 1p.26 green and violet 23·00 9·00
575 – 1p.80 red and blue 23·00 9·00
576 – 3p.60 blue and grey 48·00 21·00
DESIGNS—VERT: 15, 20, 24, 54, 72c. Yellow-headed Caracara over sea. HORIZ: 35, 50c., 1p.26, 1p.80, 3p.60, Andean Condor on mountain top.

124 Arms of Argentina and Brazil **125** Torch illuminating New World

1928. Centenary of Peace with Brazil.
577 **124** 5c. red 1·00 35
578 12c. blue 1·60 70

1929. "Day of the Race" issue.
579 **125** 2c. brown 85 20
580 – 5c. red 95 15
581 – 12c. blue 2·25 75
DESIGNS: 5c. Symbolical figures, Spain and Argentina; 12c. American offering laurels to Columbus.

(128)

1930. Air. "Zeppelin" Europe–Pan-America Flight. Optd with T **128**.
587 – 20c. blue (No. 562) 10·00 5·50
588 – 50c. black (No. 568) 18·00 8·50
589 **122** 90c. purple 9·00 6·50
584 1p. red and blue 20·00 13·00
585 – 1p.80 (No. 575) 60·00 32·00
586 – 3p.60 (No. 576) £170 95·00

129 Soldier and Civilian Insurgents **130** The Victorious March, 6 September 30

1930. Revolution of 6 September 1930.
592 **129** ½c. violet 20 15
611 **130** ½c. mauve 15 10
593 **129** 1c. green 25 15
612 **130** 1c. black 1·00 40
594 2c. lilac 35 15
595 **129** 3c. green 50 25
613 **130** 3c. green 50 25
596 **129** 4c. violet 40 25
614 **130** 4c. lake 40 20
597 **129** 5c. red 20 15
615 **130** 5c. red 15 10
598 **129** 10c. black 85 35
616 **130** 10c. green 1·00 25
599 12c. blue 85 25
600 20c. buff 85 20
601 **130** 24c. brown 3·25 1·50
602 25c. green 4·25 1·50
603 30c. violet 6·00 2·00
604 50c. black 9·00 2·75
605 1p. red and blue 17·00 10·00
606 2p. orange and black 30·00 10·00
607 5p. black and green 90·00 40·00
608 10p. blue and lake £120 50·00
609 20p. blue and green £325 £120
610 50p. violet and green £900 £650

1931. 1st Anniv of 1930 Revolution. Optd **6 Septembre 1930 - 1931.**
617 **112** 3c. green (postage) 25 25
618 10c. green 70 70
619 30c. red 3·75 3·75
620 50c. black 3·75 3·75
621 1p. red and blue 4·25 3·75
623 **130** 2p. orange and black 15·00 8·50
622 **112** 5p. green and lilac 75·00 23·00
624 **129** 18c. violet (air) 2·25 1·75
625 – 72c. green (No. 570) 21·00 13·00
626 **122** 90c. purple 16·00 12·00
627 – 1p.80 red & bl (No. 575) 40·00 30·00
628 – 3p.60 bl & grey (No. 576) 60·00 45·00

1932. Zeppelin Air stamps. Optd **GRAF ZEPPELIN 1932.**
629 **120** 5c. red 2·50 1·60
630 18c. violet 12·00 7·50
631 **122** 90c. purple 35·00 20·00

134 Refrigerating Plant **135** Port La Plata

1932. 6th International Refrigerating Congress.
632 **134** 3c. green 50 25
633 10c. red 1·25 15
634 12c. blue 3·50 1·40

1933. 50th Anniv of La Plata City.
635 **135** 3c. brown and green 1·00 25
636 – 10c. purple and orange 60 20
637 – 15c. blue 4·00 2·00
638 – 20c. brown and lilac 2·00 1·00
639 – 30c. red and green 16·00 6·00
DESIGNS: 10c. President J. A. Roca; 15c. Municipal buildings; 20c. La Plata Cathedral; 30c. Dr. D. Rocha.

139 Christ of the Andes **141** "Liberty" with Arms of Brazil and Argentina

1934. 32nd Int Eucharistic Congress, Buenos Aires.
640 **139** 10c. red 85 25
641 – 15c. blue 1·60 55
DESIGN—HORIZ: 15c. Buenos Aires Cathedral.

1935. Visit of President Vargas of Brazil. Inscr "MAYO DE 1935".
642 **141** 10c. red 85 25
643 – 15c. blue 1·60 55
DESIGN: 15c. Clasped hands and flags.

143 D. F. Sarmiento **146** Prize Bull **151** With Boundary Lines

1935. Portraits.
644 ½c. purple (Belgrano) 15 10
645 1c. brown (Type **143**) 15 10
646 2c. brown (Urquiza) 15 10
647 3c. green (San Martin) 15 10
648 4c. grey (G. Brown) 10 10
653b 5c. brown (Moreno) 60 10
650 6c. green (Alberdi) 15 10
653d 10c. red (Rivadavia) 25 10
651 12c. purple (Mitre) 10 10
708 15c. grey (Martin Guemes) 80 10
652 20c. blue (Juan Martin Guemes) 80 10
653 20c. blue (Martin Guemes) 80 10
See also Nos. 671 etc.

1936. Production and Industry.
676 **146** 15c. blue 60 15
677a 20c. blue (19½×26 mm) 15 15
755 20c. blue (22×33 mm) 1·50 15
656 – 25c. red and pink 40 15
757 – 30c. brown and yellow 40 15
658 – 40c. purple and mauve 35 15
659 – 50c. red and salmon 25 15
660 **151** 1p. blue and brown 19·00 75
760 – 1p. blue and brown 3·00 15
661 – 2p. blue and purple 85 15
662 – 5p. green and blue 11·50 75
763 – 10p. black and purple 11·50 1·60
764 – 20p. brown and blue 11·00 1·60
DESIGNS—VERT: 25c. Ploughman; 50c. Oil well; 1p. (No. 760) as Type **151** but without country boundaries; 5p. Iguazu Falls; 10p. Grapes; 20p. Cotton plant. HORIZ: 30c. Patagonian ram; 40c. Sugar cane and factory; 2p. Fruit products.

157 **158** Pres. Sarmiento

1936. Pan-American Peace Conference.
665 **157** 10c. red 50 15

1938. President's 50th Death Anniv.
666 **158** 3c. green 40 40
667 5c. red 40 40
668 15c. blue 75 40
669 50c. orange 2·25 80

159 "Presidente Sarmiento" **160** Allegory of the Post

1939. Last Voyage of Cadet Ship "Presidente Sarmiento".
670 **159** 5c. green 85 10

1939. Portraits as T **143**.
671 – 2½c. black 15 10
672 – 3c. grey (San Martin) 40 10
672a – 3c. grey (Moreno) 15 10
673 – 4c. green 10 10
894 – 5c. brown (16½×22½ mm) 10 10
674 – 8c. orange 10 10
678 – 10c. purple 15 10
675 – 12c. red 10 10
895 – 20c. lilac (21×27 mm) 20 10
895b – 20c. lilac (19½×25½ mm) 15 10
PORTRAITS: 2½c. L. Braille; 4c. G. Brown; 5c. Jose Hernandez; 8c. N. Avellaneda; 10c. B. Rivadavia; 12c. B. Mitre; 20c. G. Brown.

1939. 11th U.P.U. Congress, Buenos Aires.
679 **160** 5c. red 15 10
680 – 15c. grey 40 25
681 – 20c. blue 40 10
682 – 25c. green 85 35
683 – 50c. brown 2·25 80
684 – 1p. purple 4·50 1·75
685 – 2p. mauve 20·00 11·50
686 – 5p. violet 46·00 23·00
DESIGNS—VERT: 20c. Seal of Argentina; 1p. Symbols of postal communications; 2p. Argentina, "Land of Promise" from a pioneer painting. HORIZ: 15c. G.P.O.; 25c. Iguazu Falls; 50c. Mt. Bonete; 5p. Lake Frias.

165 Working-class Family and New Home **167** North and South America

1939. 1st Pan-American Housing Congress.
687 **165** 5c. green 20 10

1940. 50th Anniv of Pan-American Union.
688 **167** 15c. blue 35 10

169 Airplane and Envelope

1940. Air.
689 **169** 30c. orange . . . . 7·00 10
690 – 50c. brown . . . . 9·50 15
691 **169** 1p. red . . . . 3·50 10
692 – 1p.25 green 80 10
693 **169** 2p.50 blue . . . . 2·75 40
DESIGNS—VERT: 50c. "Mercury"; 1p.25, Douglas DC-2 in clouds.

172 Gen. French, Col. Beruti and Rosette of the "Legion de Patricios"

1941. 131st Anniv of Rising against Spain.
694 **172** 5c. blue 40 10

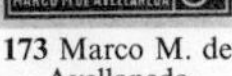

173 Marco M. de Avellaneda
174 Statue of Gen. J. A. Roca

1941. Death Centenary of Avellaneda (patriot).
695 **173** 5c. blue 40 10

1941. Dedication of Statue of Gen. Roca.
696 **174** 5c. green 40 10

175 Pellegrini (founder) and National Bank
176 Gen. Juan Lavalle

1941. 50th Anniv of National Bank.
697 **175** 5c. lake 40 10

1941. Death Centenary of Gen. Lavalle.
698 **176** 5c. blue 40 10

177 New P.O. Savings Bank
178 Jose Manuel Estrada

1942. Inauguration of P.O. Savings Bank.
699 **177** 1c. green 40 10

1942. Birth Centenary of Estrada (patriot).
700 **178** 5c. purple 50 10

180 G.P.O., Buenos Aires
181 Proposed Columbus Lighthouse

1942. Postage and Express Stamps.
717 **180** 35c. blue . . . . 5·50 15
746 35c. blue . . . . 1·10 15
No. 717 is inscr "PALACIO CENTRAL DE CORREOS Y TELEGRAFOS" and No. 746 "PALACIO CENTRAL DE CORREOS Y TELECOMUNICACIONES".

1942. 450th Anniv of Discovery of America by Columbus.
721 **181** 15c. blue . . . . 4·00 15

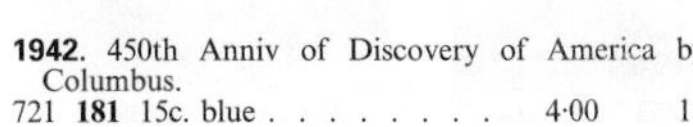

182 Dr. Paz (founder of "La Prensa")
183 Flag of Argentina and Books
184 Arms of Argentina

1942. Birth Centenary of Dr. Jose C. Paz.
722 **182** 5c. blue 40 15

1943. 1st National Book Fair.
723 **183** 5c. blue 20 15

1943. Revolution of 4 June 1943.
724 **184** 5c. red 20 15
725 15c. green 60 15
726 20c. blue (larger) 80 15

185 National Independence House
186 Head of Liberty, Money-box and Laurels

1943. Restoration of Tucuman Museum.
727 **185** 5c. green 35 15

1943. 1st Savings Bank Conference.
728 **186** 5c. brown 40 10

187 Buenos Aires in 1800

1944. Export Day.
729 **187** 5c. black 40 10

188 Postal Union of the Americas and Spain
189 Alexander Graham Bell
191 Liner, Warship and Yacht

1944. Postmen's Benefit Fund. Inscr "PRO-CARTERO".
730 – 3c.+2c. black and violet 1·10 1·10
731 **188** 5c.+5c. black and red . . 85 20
732 **189** 10c.+5c. black and orge 1·10 35
733 – 25c.+15c. black and brn 2·40 75
734 – 1p.+50c. black and green 10·00 7·75
DESIGNS: 3c. Samuel Morse; 25c. Rowland Hill; 1p. Columbus landing in America.

1944. Naval Week.
735 **191** 5c. blue 75 10

192 Argentina
193 Arms of Argentina

1944. San Juan Earthquake Relief Fund.
736 **192** 5c.+10c. black & olive . . 60 50
737 5c.+50c. black and red . . 3·50 1·10
738 5c.+1p. black & orange 7·00 5·50
739 5c.+20p. black & blue . . 28·00 23·00

1944. 1st Anniv of Revolution of 4 June 1943.
740 **193** 5c. blue 40 15

194 Archangel Gabriel
195 Cross of Palermo
196 Allegory of Savings

1944. 4th National Eucharistic Congress.
741 **194** 3c. green 50 15
742 **195** 5c. red 50 15

1944. 20th Anniv of Universal Savings Day.
743 **196** 5c. black 40 15

197 Reservists

1944. Reservists' Day.
744 **197** 5c. blue 40 15

198 Bernardino Rivadavia
199 Rivadavia's Mausoleum

1945. Rivadavia's Death Centenary.
770 **198** 3c. green 15 15
771 – 5c. red 15 15
772 **199** 20c. blue 15 15
DESIGN—As Type **198**: 5c. Rivadavia and Scales of Justice.

200 San Martin
201 Monument to Andes Army, Mendoza

1945.
773 **200** 5c. red 10 10

1946. "Homage to the Unknown Soldier of Independence".
776 **201** 5c. purple 15 15

202 Pres. Roosevelt
203 "Affirmation"

1946. 1st Death Anniv of Pres. Franklin Roosevelt.
777 **202** 5c. grey 10 10

1946. Installation of Pres. Juan Peron.
778 **203** 5c. blue 15 15

204 Airplane over Iguazu Falls

1946. Air.
779 **204** 15c. red 15 10
780 – 25c. green 20 10
DESIGN: 25c. Airplane over Andes.

205 "Flight"

1946. Aviation Week.
781 **205** 15c. green on green . . . 55 10
782 – 60c. purple on buff . . . 55 15
DESIGN: 60c. Hand upholding globe.

207 "Argentina and Populace"

1946. 1st Anniv of Peron's Defeat of Counter-revolution.
783 **207** 5c. mauve 20 10
784 10c. green 30 10
785 15c. blue 60 25
786 50c. brown 60 40
787 1p. red . . . . 1·25 1·10

208 Money-box and Map
209 Industry

1946. Annual Savings Day.
788 **208** 30c. red 35 10

1946. Industrial Exhibition.
789 **209** 5c. purple 10 10

210 Argentine–Brazil International Bridge
211 South Pole

1947. Opening of Bridge between Argentina and Brazil.
790 **210** 5c. green 25 25

1947. 43rd Anniv of 1st Argentine Antarctic Mail.
791 **211** 5c. violet 60 15
792 20c. red . . . . 1·25 15

212 "Justice"
213 Icarus Falling

1947. 1st Anniv of Col. Juan Peron's Presidency.
793 **212** 5c. purple and buff . . . 10 10

1947. "Week of the Wing".
794 **213** 15c. purple 15 10

214 "Presidente Sarmiento"
215 Cervantes and "Don Quixote"

1947. 50th Anniv of Launching of Cadet Ship "Presidente Sarmiento".
795 **214** 5c. blue 50 10

1947. 400th Birth Anniv of Cervantes.
796 **215** 5c. green 10 10

216 Gen. San Martin and Urn

1947. Arrival from Spain of Ashes of Gen. San Martin's Parents.
797 **216** 5c. green 10 10

217 Young Crusaders
218 Statue of Araucarian Indian

1947. Educational Crusade for Universal Peace.

No.	Type	Description	Unused	Used
798	**217**	5c. green	10	10
799		20c. brown	30	10

1948. American Indian Day.

No.	Type	Description	Unused	Used
801	**218**	25c. brown	25	10

219 Phrygian Cap and Sprig of Wheat

220 "Stop"

1948. 5th Anniv of Anti-isolationist Revolution of 4 June 1943.

No.	Type	Description	Unused	Used
802	**219**	5c. blue	10	10

1948. Safety First Campaign.

No.	Type	Description	Unused	Used
803	**220**	5c. yellow and brown	15	10

221 Posthorn and Oak Leaves

222 Argentine Farmers

1948. Bicent of Postal Service in Rio de la Plata.

No.	Type	Description	Unused	Used
804	**221**	5c. mauve	15	15

1948. Agriculture Day.

No.	Type	Description	Unused	Used
805	**222**	10c. brown	15	15

223 "Liberty and Plenty"

225 Statue of Atlas

226 Map, Globe and Compasses

1948. Re-election of President Peron.

No.	Type	Description	Unused	Used
806	**223**	25c. red	15	15

1948. Air. 4th Meeting of Pan-American Cartographers.

No.	Type	Description	Unused	Used
807	**225**	45c. brown	35	10
808	**226**	70c. green	65	15

227 Winged Railway Wheel

1949. 1st Anniv of Nationalization of Argentine Railways.

No.	Type	Description	Unused	Used
809	**227**	10c. blue	25	10

228 Head of Liberty

1949. Constitution Day.

No.	Type	Description	Unused	Used
810	**228**	1p. purple and red	80	15

229 Trophy and Target

230 "Intercommunication"

1949. Air. International Shooting Championship.

No.	Type	Description	Unused	Used
811	**229**	75c. brown	65	15

1949. 75th Anniv of U.P.U.

No.	Type	Description	Unused	Used
812	**230**	25c. green and olive	20	15

231 San Martin

233 Stamp Designer

232 San Martin at Boulogne

1950. San Martin's Death Cent. Dated "1850 1950".

No.	Type	Description	Unused	Used
813	–	10c. purple and blue	15	10
814	**231**	20c. brown and red	15	10
815	**232**	25c. brown	15	10
816	–	50c. blue and green	40	10
817	–	75c. green and brown	40	10
818	–	1p. green	1·00	20
819	–	2p. purple	85	35

DESIGNS—As Type **231**: 10, 50, 75c. Portraits of San Martin; 2p. San Martin Mausoleum. As Type **232**: 1p. House where San Martin died.

1950. Int Philatelic Exhibition, Buenos Aires.

No.	Type	Description	Unused	Used
820	**233**	10c.+10c. violet (postage)	15	15
821	–	45c.+45c. blue (air)	40	25
822	–	70c.+70c. brown	60	40
823	–	1p.+1p. red	1·75	1·60
824	–	2p.50+2p.50 olive	9·50	7·00
825	–	5p.+5p. green	11·00	8·50

DESIGNS: 45c. Engraver; 70c. Proofing; 1p. Printer; 2p.50, Woman reading letter; 5p. San Martin.

234 S. America and Antarctic

235 Douglas DC-3 and Andean Condor

1951.

No.	Type	Description	Unused	Used
826	**234**	1p. blue and brown	50	15

1951. Air. 10th Anniv of State Airlines.

No.	Type	Description	Unused	Used
827	**235**	20c. olive	30	20

236 Pegasus and Steam Locomotive

1951. Five-year Plan.

No.	Type	Description	Unused	Used
828	**236**	5c. brown (postage)	15	15
829	–	25c. green	45	10
830	–	40c. purple	40	15
831	–	20c. blue (air)	25	15

DESIGNS—HORIZ: 25c. "President Peron" (liner) and common dolphin. VERT: 20c. Douglas DC-4 and Andean condor; 40c. Head of Mercury and telephone.

237 Woman Voter and "Argentina"

238 "Piety"

1951. Women's Suffrage in Argentina.

No.	Type	Description	Unused	Used
832	**237**	10c. purple	10	10

1951. Air. Eva Peron Foundation Fund.

No.	Type	Description	Unused	Used
833	**238**	2p.45+7p.55 olive	20·00	13·50

239 Eva Peron

240 Eva Peron

1952. (a) Size 20 × 26 mm.

No.	Type	Description	Unused	Used
834	**239**	1c. brown	10	10
835		5c. grey	10	10
836		10c. red	10	10
837		20c. red	10	10
838		25c. green	10	10
839		40c. purple	15	10
841		45c. blue	25	10
840		50c. bistre	25	10

(b) Size 22 × 33 mm. Without inscr "EVA PERON".

No.	Type	Description	Unused	Used
842	**240**	1p. brown	35	10
843		1p.50 green	1·75	10
844		2p. red	50	10
845		3p. blue	85	15

(c) Size 22 × 33 mm. Inscr "EVA PERON".

No.	Type	Description	Unused	Used
846	**240**	1p. brown	35	10
847		1p.50 green	1·10	10
848		2p. red	1·25	10
849		3p. blue	1·75	45

(d) Size 30½ × 40 mm. Inscr "EVA PERON".

No.	Type	Description	Unused	Used
850	**240**	5p. brown	1·75	40
851	**239**	10p. red	4·75	1·40
852	**240**	20p. green	8·00	3·25
853	**239**	50p. blue	14·00	7·75

241 Indian Funeral Urn

242 Rescue Ship "Uruguay"

1953. 4th Centenary of Santiago del Estero.

No.	Type	Description	Unused	Used
854	**241**	50c. green	15	10

1953. 50th Anniv of Rescue of the "Antarctic".

No.	Type	Description	Unused	Used
855	**242**	50c. blue	1·25	40

243 Planting Flag in S. Orkneys

244 "Telegraphs"

1954. 50th Anniv of Argentine P.O. in South Orkneys.

No.	Type	Description	Unused	Used
856	**243**	1p.45 blue	85	40

1954. International Telecommunications Conference. Symbolical designs inscr as in T **244**.

No.	Type	Description	Unused	Used
857	**244**	1p.50 purple	40	15
858	–	3p. blue	1·10	25
859	–	5p. red	1·60	35

DESIGNS—VERT: 3p. "Radio". HORIZ: 5p. "Television".

245 Pediment, Buenos Aires Stock Exchange

246 Eva Peron

1954. Centenary of Argentine Stock Exchange.

No.	Type	Description	Unused	Used
860	**245**	1p. green	30	10

1954. 2nd Death Anniv of Eva Peron.

No.	Type	Description	Unused	Used
861	**246**	3p. red	1·60	20

247 San Martin

249 Wheat

250 Mt. Fitz Roy

248 "Prosperity"

1954.

No.	Type	Description	Unused	Used
862	**247**	20c. red	10	10
863		40c. red	30	10
868	–	50c. blue (33 × 22 mm)	60	10
869	–	50c. blue (32 × 21 mm)	70	10
870	**249**	80c. brown	25	10
871	–	1p. brown	30	10
872	–	1p.50 blue	25	10
873	–	2p. red	35	10
874	–	3p. purple	35	10
875a	–	5p. green	6·25	10
876	–	10p. green and grey	6·25	10
877	**250**	20p. violet	9·25	40
1018	–	22p. blue	1·40	10
878	–	50p. indigo and blue (30½ × 40½ mm)	8·00	80
1023	–	50p. blue (29½ × 40 mm)	6·25	40
1287	–	50p. blue (22½ × 32½ mm)	1·00	10

DESIGNS—As Type **249**: HORIZ: 50c. Port of Buenos Aires; 1p. Cattle; 2p. Eva Peron Foundation; 3p. El Nihuil Dam. As Type **250**: VERT: 1p.50, 22p. Industrial Plant; 5p. Iguazu Falls; 50p. San Martin. HORIZ: 10p. Humahuaca Ravine.

For 43p. in the design of the 1p.50 and 22p. see No. 1021.

For 65c. in same design see No. 1313.

1954. Centenary of Argentine Corn Exchange.

No.	Type	Description	Unused	Used
867	**248**	1p.50 grey	65	10

251 Clasped Hands and Congress Emblem

252 Father and Son with Model Airplane

1955. Productivity and Social Welfare Congress.

No.	Type	Description	Unused	Used
879	**251**	3p. brown	90	10

1955. 25th Anniv of Commercial Air Services.

No.	Type	Description	Unused	Used
880	**252**	1p.50 grey	80	10

253 "Liberation"

254 Forces Emblem

1955. Anti-Peronist Revolution of 16 Sept. 1955.
881 **253** 1p.50 olive 20 10

1955. Armed Forces Commemoration.
882 **254** 3p. blue 35 10

255 Gen. Urquiza (after J. M. Blanes) **256** Detail from "Antiope" (Correggio)

1956. 104th Anniv of Battle of Caseros.
883 **255** 1p.50 green 25 10

1956. Infantile Paralysis Relief Fund.
884 **256** 20c.+30c. grey 20 10

257 Coin and Die **258** Corrientes Stamp of 1856

259 Dr. J. G. Pujol **260** Cotton, Chaco

1956. 75th Anniv of National Mint.
885 **257** 2p. brown and sepia . . . 20 10

1956. Centenary of 1st Argentine Stamps.
886 **258** 40c. blue and green . . . 15 10
887 2p.40 mauve and brown 20 10
888 **259** 4p.40 blue 50 15
The 40c. shows a 1r. stamp of 1856.

1956. New Provinces.
889 – 50c. blue 10 10
890 **260** 1p. lake 20 10
891 – 1p.50 green 30 10
DESIGNS—HORIZ: 50c. Lumbering, La Pampa. VERT: 1p.50, Mate tea plant, Misiones.

261 "Liberty" **262** Detail from "Virgin of the Rocks" (Leonardo)

1956. 1st Anniv of Revolution.
892 **261** 2p.40 mauve 25 10

1956. Air. Infantile Paralysis Victims, Gratitude for Help.
893 **262** 1p. purple 30 10

264 Esteban Echeverria (writer) **265** F. Ameghino (anthropologist)

266 Roque Saenz Pena (statesman) **267** Franklin

1956.
896 **264** 2p. purple 20 10
897 **265** 2p.40 brown 30 10
898 **266** 4p.40 green 45 10

1956. 250th Birth Anniv of Benjamin Franklin.
899 **267** 40c. blue 25 10

268 "Hercules" (sail frigate) **269** Admiral G. Brown

1957. Death Cent of Admiral Guillermo Brown.
900 **268** 40c. blue (postage) . . . 50 10
901 – 2p.40 green 40 10
902 – 60c. grey (air) 75 10
903 – 1p. mauve 20 10
904 **269** 2p. brown 25 10
DESIGNS—HORIZ: 60c. "Zefiro" and "Nancy" (sail warships) at Battle of Montevideo; 1p. L. Rosales and T. Espora. VERT: 2p.40, Admiral Brown in later years.

270 Church of Santo Domingo **271** Map of the Americas and Badge of Buenos Aires

1957. 150th Anniv of Defence of Buenos Aires.
905 **270** 40c. green 10 10

1957. Air. Inter-American Economic Conference.
906 **271** 2p. purple 35 10

272 "La Portena", 1857 **273** Globe, Flag and Compass Rose

1957. Centenary of Argentine Railways.
907 **272** 40c. sepia (postage) . . . 45 10
908 – 60c. grey (air) 45 10
DESIGN: 60c. Diesel locomotive.

1957. Air. Int Tourist Congress, Buenos Aires.
909 **273** 1p. brown 15 10
910 – 2p. turquoise 20 10
DESIGN: 2p. Symbolic key of tourism.

274 Head of Liberty **275**

1957. Reform Convention.
911 **274** 40c. red 10 10

1957. Air. International Correspondence Week.
912 **275** 1p. blue 15 10

276 "Wealth in Oil" **277** La Plata Museum

1957. 50th Anniv of Argentine Oil Industry.
913 **276** 40c. blue 15 10

1958. 75th Anniv of Founding of La Plata.
914 **277** 40c. black 15 10

278 Health Emblem and Flower

1958. Air. Child Welfare.
915 **278** 1p.+50c. red 20 20

279 Stamp of 1858 and River Ferry **280** Stamp of 1858

1958. Centenary of Argentine Confederation Stamps and Philatelic Exhibition, Buenos Aires.
916 **279** 40c.+20c. purple and green (postage) 45 20
917 – 2p.40+1p.20 blue and black 40 25
918 – 4p.40+2p.20 pur & bl . . 60 40
919 **280** 1p.+50c. blue and olive (air) 40 35
920 2p.+1p. violet and red . . 55 45
921 3p.+1p.50 brown & grn 60 55
922 5p.+2p.50 red and olive 1·00 85
923 10p.+5p. sepia & olive . . 1·50 1·40
DESIGNS—HORIZ: 2p.40, Magnifier, stamp album and stamp of 1858; 4p.40, P.O. building of 1858.

281 Steam Locomotive and Arms of Argentina and Bolivia **282** Douglas DC-6 over Map of Argentine-Bolivian Frontier

1958. Argentine–Bolivian Friendship.
(a) Inauguration of Yacuiba–Santa Cruz Railway.
924 **281** 40c. red and slate 35 10
(b) Exchange of Presidential Visits.
925 **282** 1p. brown 15 10

283 "Liberty and Flag" **284** Farman H.F.20 Biplane

1958. Transfer of Presidential Mandate. Head of "Liberty" in grey; inscr black; flag yellow and blue; background colours given.
926 **283** 40c. buff 10 10
927 1p. salmon 15 10
928 2p. green 25 10

1958. 50th Anniv of Argentine Aero Club.
929 **284** 2p. brown 20 10

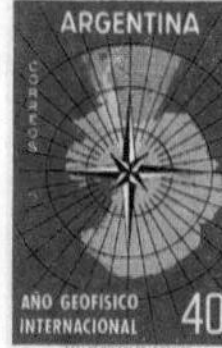

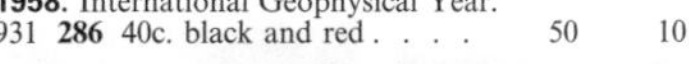

285 National Flag Monument, Rosario **286** Map of Antarctica

1958. 1st Anniv of Inauguration of National Flag Monument.
930 **285** 40c. grey and blue 10 10

1958. International Geophysical Year.
931 **286** 40c. black and red 50 10

287 Confederation Stamp and "The Santa Fe Mail" (after J. L. Palliere)

1958. Cent of Argentine Confederation Stamps.
932 – 40c. grn & blue (postage) 15 10
933 – 80c. blue & yellow (air) 40 10
934 **287** 1p. blue and orange . . . 20 10
DESIGNS: 40c. First local Cordoba 5c. stamp of 1858 and mail coach; 80c. Buenos Aires Type **1** of 1858 and "View of Buenos Aires" (after Deroy).

288 Aerial view of Flooded Town

1958. Flood Disaster Relief Fund. Inscr as in T **288**.
935 **288** 40c.+20c. brn (postage) 15 10
936 – 1p.+50c. plum (air) . . . 20 10
937 – 5p.+2p.50 blue 50 20
DESIGNS—HORIZ: 1p. Different aerial view of flooded town; 5p. Truck in flood water and garage.

289 Child receiving Blood **290** U.N. Emblem and "Dying Captive" (after Michelangelo)

1958. Leukaemia Relief Campaign.
938 **289** 1p.+50c. red and black . . 15 10

1959. 10th Anniv of Declaration of Human Rights.
939 **290** 40c. grey and brown . . . 10 10

291 Hawker Siddeley Comet 4

1959. Air. Inauguration of Comet Jet Airliners by Argentine National Airlines.
940 **291** 5p. black and green . . . 25 10

292 Orchids and Globe **293** Pope Pius XII

1959. 1st Int Horticultural Exn, Buenos Aires.
941 **292** 1p. purple 15 10

1959. Pope Pius XII Commemoration.
942 **293** 1p. black and yellow . . . 15 10
PORTRAITS: 1p. Claude Bernard; 1p.50, Ivan P. Pavlov.

294 William Harvey

1959. 21st International Physiological Science Congress. Medical Scientists.
943 **294** 50c. green 10 10
944 – 1p. red 15 10
945 – 1p.50 brown 20 10

295 Creole Horse

296 Tierra del Fuego

1959.
946 – 10c. green 10 10
947 – 20c. purple 10 10
948 – 50c. ochre 10 10
950 **295** 1p. red 10 10
1016 – 1p. brown 10 10
1027 – 1p. brown 10 10
1035 – 2p. red 35 10
951 – 3p. blue 10 10
1036 – 4p. red 40 10
952 **296** 5p. brown 25 10
1037 – 8p. red 25 10
1286 – 10p. brown 50 10
1038 – 10p. red 70 10
1017 – 12p. purple 90 10
954 – 20p. green . . . . 2·40 10
1039 – 20p. red 30 10
1019 – 23p. green . . . . 4·00 10
1020 – 25p. lilac . . . . 1·25 10
1021 – 43p. lake . . . . 5·50 10
1022 – 45p. brown . . . . . . 3·25 10
1025 – 100p. blue . . . . 6·25 20
1026 – 300p. violet . . . . . . 3·25 10
1032 – 500p. green . . . . . . 1·60 30
1290 – 1000p. blue . . . . . . 4·50 90
DESIGNS—As Type **295**—HORIZ: 10c. Spectacled caiman; 20c. Llama; 25c. Puma. VERT: 2, 4, 8, 10p. (No 1038), 20p. (No. 1039) San Martin. As Type **296**—HORIZ: 3p. Zapata Hill, Catamarca; 300p. Mar del Plata (40 × 29½ mm). VERT: 1p. (No. 1016) Sunflowers; 1p. (No. 1027) Sunflower (22 × 32 mm); 10p. (No. 1286) Inca Bridge, Mendoza; 12, 23, 25p. Red quebracho tree; 20p. (No. 954) Lake Nahuel Huapi; 43, 45p. Industrial plant (30 × 39½ mm); 100p. Ski-jumper; 500p. Red deer (stag); 1,000p. Leaping salmon.
For these designs with face values in revalued currency, see Nos. 1300 etc.

298 Runner

299

1959. 3rd Pan-American Games, Chicago. Designs embody torch emblem. Centres and torch in black.
955 **298** 20c.+10c. green (postage) 10 10
956 – 50c.+20c. yellow 15 15
957 – 1p.+50c. purple 15 15
958 – 2p.+1p. blue (air) 30 15
959 – 3p.+1p.50 olive 45 30
DESIGNS—VERT: 50c. Basketball; 1p. Boxing. HORIZ: 2p. Rowing; 3p. High-diving.

1959. Red Cross Hygiene Campaign.
960 **299** 1p. red, blue and black 10 10

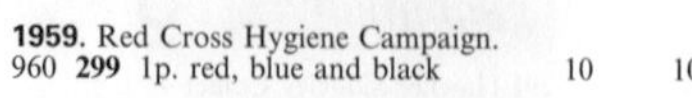

300 Child with Toys

1959. Mothers' Day.
961 **300** 1p. red and black 10 10

301 Buenos Aires 1p. stamp of 1859

1959. Stamp Day.
962 **301** 1p. blue and grey 10 10

302 B. Mitre and J. J. de Urquiza

303 Andean Condor

1959. Centenary of Pact of San Jose de Flores.
963 **302** 1p. plum 10 10

1960. Child Welfare. Birds.
964 **303** 20c.+10c. blue (postage) 70 15
965 – 50c.+20c. violet 70 15
966 – 1p.+50c. brown . . . . . 1·00 25
967 – 2p.+1p. mauve (air) . . . 70 30
968 – 3p.+1p.50 green 70 50
BIRDS: 50c. Fork-tailed flycatcher; 1p. Magellanic woodpecker; 2p. Red-winged tinamou; 3p. Greater rhea.

304 "Uprooted Tree"

305 Abraham Lincoln

1960. World Refugee Year.
969 **304** 1p. red and brown . . . 10 10
970 4p.20 purple and green . . 15 10

1960. 150th Birth Anniv of Abraham Lincoln.
972 **305** 5p. blue 25 15

306 Saavedra and Chapter Hall, Buenos Aires

307 Dr. L. Drago

1960. 150th Anniv of May Revolution.
973 **306** 1p. purple (postage) . . . 10 10
974 – 2p. green 10 10
975 – 4p.20 green and grey . . 20 10
976 – 10p.70 blue and slate . . 40 15
977 – 1p.80 brown (air) 10 10
978 – 5p. purple and brown . . 30 10
DESIGNS—Chapter Hall and: 1p.80, Moreno; 2p. Paso; 4p.20, Alberti and Azcuenaga; 5p. Belgrano and Castelli; 10p.70, Larrea and Matheu.

1960. Birth Centenary of Drago.
980 **307** 4p.20 brown 15 10

308 "Five Provinces"

309 "Market Place 1810" (Buenos Aires)

1960. Air. New Argentine Provinces.
981 **308** 1p.80 blue and red . . . 10 10

1960. Air. Inter-American Philatelic Exhibition, Buenos Aires ("EFIMAYO") and 150th Anniv of Revolution. Inscr "EFIMAYO 1960".
982 **309** 2p.+1p. lake 15 10
983 – 6p.+3p. grey 35 20
984 – 10p.70+5p.30 blue . . . 60 35
985 – 20p.+10p. turquoise . . . 75 60
DESIGNS: 6p. "The Water Carrier"; 10p.70, "The Landing Place"; 20p. "The Fort".

310 J. B. Alberdi

311 Seibo (Argentine National Flower)

1960. 150th Birth Anniv of J. B. Alberdi (statesman).
986 **310** 1p. green 10 10

1960. Air. Chilean Earthquake Relief Fund. Inscr "AYUDA CHILE".
987 **311** 6p.+3p. red 30 25
988 – 10p.70+5p.30 red 40 35
DESIGN: 10p.70, Copihue (Chilean national flower).

312 Map of Argentina

313 Galleon

1960. Census.
989 **312** 5p. lilac 40 10

1960. 8th Spanish-American P.U. Congress.
990 **313** 1p. green (postage) . . . 40 10
991 5p. brown 85 20
992 1p.80 purple (air) 40 10
993 10p.70 turquoise . . . . 1·10 30

1960. Air. U.N. Day. Nos. 982/5 optd **DIA DE LAS NACIONES UNIDAS 24 DE OCTUBRE**.
994 **309** 2p.+1p. red 20 15
995 – 6p.+3p. black 25 25
996 – 10p.70+5p.30 blue 50 40
997 – 20p.+10p. turquoise . . . 70 65

315 Blessed Virgin of Lujan

316 Jacaranda

1960. 1st Inter-American Marian Congress.
998 **315** 1p. blue 10 10

1960. International Thematic Stamp Exhibition ("TEMEX"). Inscr "TEMEX-61".
999 **316** 50c.+50c. blue 10 10
1000 – 1p.+1p. turquoise . . . 10 10
1001 – 3p.+3p. brown 30 20
1002 – 5p.+5p. brown 50 30
FLOWERS: 1p. Passion flowers; 3p. Hibiscus; 5p. Black lapacho.

317 Argentine Scout Badge

318 "Shipment of Cereals" (after B. Q. Martin)

1961. International Scout (Patrol) Camp.
1003 **317** 1p. red and black . . . 15 10

1961. Export Campaign.
1004 **318** 1p. brown 15 10

319 Emperor Penguin and Chick

320 "America"

1961. Child Welfare. Inscr "PRO-INFANCIA".
1005 – 4p.20+2p.10 brown (postage) . . . . . . 1·00 75
1006 **319** 1p.80+90c. black (air) . . 60 50
DESIGN: 4p.20, Blue-eyed cormorant.

1961. 150th Anniv of Battle of San Nicolas.
1007 **320** 2p. black 55 10

321 Dr. M. Moreno

322 Emperor Trajan

1961. 150th Death Anniv of Dr. M. Moreno.
1008 **321** 2p. blue 15 10

1961. Visit of President of Italy.
1009 **322** 2p. green 15 10

1961. Americas Day. Nos. 999/1002 optd **14 DE ABRIL DE LAS AMERICAS**.
1010 **316** 50c.+50c. blue 10 10
1011 – 1p.+1p. turquoise . . . 15 10
1012 – 3p.+3p. brown 20 20
1013 – 5p.+5p. brown 40 35

324 Tagore

325 San Martin Monument, Madrid

1961. Birth Centenary of Rabindranath Tagore (Indian poet).
1014 **324** 2p. violet on green . . . 20 10

1961. Inaug of Spanish San Martin Monument.
1015 **325** 1p. black 15 10

331a Gen. Belgrano (after monument by Rocha, Buenos Aires)

1961. Gen. Manuel Belgrano Commemoration.
1034 **331a** 2p. blue 15 10

333 Antarctic Scene

1961. 10th Anniv of San Martin Antarctic Base.
1044 **333** 2p. black 50 10

334 Conquistador and Sword

335 Sarmiento Statue (Rodin)

1961. 4th Centenary of Jujuy City.
1045 **334** 2p. red and black . . . 15 10

1961. 150th Birth Anniv of Sarmiento.
1046 **335** 2p. violet 15 10

336 Cordoba Cathedral

343 15c. Stamp of 1862

1961. "Argentina 62" International Philatelic Exn.
1047 **336** 2p.+2p. purple (postage) 20 15
1048 – 3p.+3p. green 30 15
1049 – 10p.+10p. blue 85 50
1059 **343** 6p.50+6p.50 blue and turquoise (air) 40 30

DESIGNS—HORIZ: 10p. Buenos Aires Cathedral. VERT: 3p. As Type **343** but showing 10c. value and different inscr.

337 | **338** "The Flight into Egypt" (after Ana Maria Moncalvo)

1961. World Town-planning Day.
1052 **337** 2p. blue and yellow . . . 15 10

1961. Child Welfare.
1053 **338** 2p.+1p. brown & lilac 15 10
1054 10p.+5p. purple & mve 50 15

339 Belgrano Statue (C. Belleuse) | **340** Mounted Grenadier

1962. 150th Anniv of National Flag.
1055 **339** 2p. blue 15 10

1962. 150th Anniv of Gen. San Martin's Mounted Grenadiers.
1056 **340** 2p. red 15 10

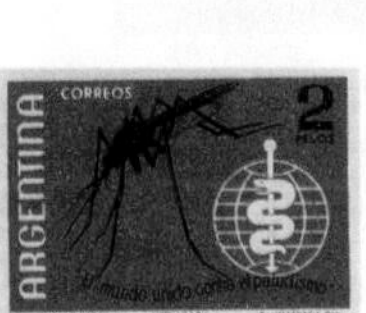

341 Mosquito and Emblem | **342** Lujan Basilica

1962. Malaria Eradication.
1057 **341** 2p. black and red . . . 10 10

1962. 75th Anniv of Coronation of the Holy Virgin of Lujan.
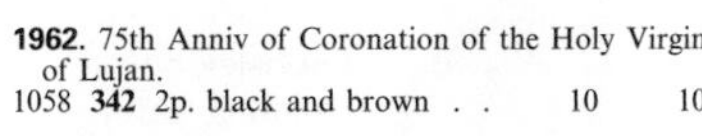
1058 **342** 2p. black and brown . . 10 10

344 Juan Jufre (founder) | **345** U.N.E.S.C.O. Emblem

1962. 400th Anniv of San Juan.
1060 **344** 2p. blue 10 10

1962. Air. 15th Anniv of U.N.E.S.C.O.
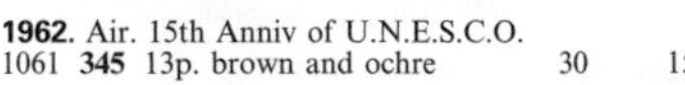
1061 **345** 13p. brown and ochre 30 15

346 "Flight" | **347** Juan Vucetich (fingerprints pioneer)

1962. 50th Anniv of Argentine Air Force.
1062 **346** 2p. blue, black & purple 15 10

1962. Vucetich Commem.
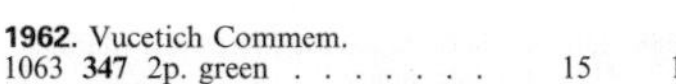
1063 **347** 2p. green 15 10

348 19th-century Mail Coach | **350** U.P.A.E. Emblem

1962. Air. Postman's Day.
1064 **348** 5p.60 black and drab . . 15 10

1962. Air. Surch **AEREO** and value.
1065 **296** 5p.60 on 5p. brown . . 30 15
1066 18p. on 5p. brn on grn 1·00 20

1962. Air. 50th Anniv of Postal Union of Latin America.
1067 **350** 5p.60 blue 10 10

351 Pres. Sarmiento | **352** Chalk-browed Mockingbird

1962.
1073 **351** 2p. green 45 10
1069 – 4p. red 60 10
1075 – 6p. red . . . . 1·40 10
1071 – 6p. brown 10 10
1072 – 90p. bistre . . . . . . 2·00 15
PORTRAITS: 4, 6p. Jose Hernandez; 90p. G. Brown.

1962. Child Welfare.
1076 **352** 4p.+2p. sepia, turquoise and brown . . . . . 1·25 75
1077 – 12p.+6p. brown, yellow and slate . . . . . . 2·00 1·25
DESIGN—VERT: 12p. Rufous-collared sparrow.
See also Nos. 1101/2, 1124/5, 1165/6, 1191/2, 1214/15, 1264/5, 1293/4, 1394/5, 1415/16 and 1441/2.

353 Skylark 3 Glider | **354** "20 de Febrero" Monument, Salta

1963. Air. 9th World Gliding Championships, Junin.
1078 **353** 5p.60 black and blue . . 20 10
1079 – 11p. black, red and blue 40 10
DESIGN: 11p. Super Albatross glider.

1963. 150th Anniv of Battle of Salta.
1080 **354** 2p. green 15 10

355 Cogwheels | **356** National College

1963. 75th Anniv of Argentine Industrial Union.
1081 **355** 4p. red and grey 10 10

1963. Centenary of National College, Buenos Aires.
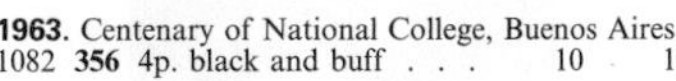
1082 **356** 4p. black and buff . . . 10 10

357 Child drinking Milk | **358** "Flight"

1963. Freedom from Hunger.
1083 **357** 4p. ochre, black and red 15 10

1963. Air. (a) As T **358**.
1084 **358** 5p.60 green, mve & pur 35 10
1085 7p. black & yellow (I) 45 10
1086 7p. black & yellow (II) 4·25 75
1087 11p. purple, green & blk 45 15
1088 18p. blue, red and mauve 1·10 25
1089 21p. grey, red and brown 1·50 35
Two types of 7p. I, "ARGENTINA" reads down, and II, "ARGENTINA" reads up as in Type **358**.

(b) As T **358** but inscr "REPUBLICA ARGENTINA" reading down.
1147 12p. lake and brown . . . . 1·50 15
1148 15p. blue and red . . . . . 1·50 15
1291 26p. ochre 25 15
1150 27p.50 green and black . . 2·25 30
1151 30p.50 brown and blue . . . 2·25 35
1292 40p. lilac . . . . 2·25 15
1153 68p. green . . . . 2·75 25
1154 78p. blue 55 35
See also Nos. 1374/80 in revalued currency.

359 Football | **360** Frigate "La Argentina" (after Bouchard)

1963. 4th Pan-American Games, Sao Paulo.
1090 **359** 4p.+2p. green, black and pink (postage) 20 10
1091 – 12p.+6p. purple, black and salmon 30 25
1092 – 11p.+5p. red, black and green (air) 35 25
DESIGNS: 11p. Cycling; 12p. Show-jumping.

1963. Navy Day.
1093 **360** 4p. blue 80 10

361 Assembly House and Seal

1963. 150th Anniv of 1813 Assembly.
1094 **361** 4p. black and blue . . . 15 10

362 Battle Scene

1963. 150th Anniv of Battle of San Lorenzo.
1095 **362** 4p. black & green on grn 20 10

363 Queen Nefertari (bas-relief)

1963. U.N.E.S.C.O. Campaign for Preservation of Nubian Monuments.
1096 **363** 4p. black, green & buff 25 10

364 Government House | **365** "Science"

1963. Presidential Installation.
1097 **364** 5p. brown and pink . . 15 10

1963. 10th Latin-American Neurosurgery Congress.
1098 **365** 4p. blue, black & brown 20 10

366 Blackboards | **367** F. de las Carreras (President of Supreme Court)

1963. "Alliance for Progress".
1099 **366** 5p. red, black and blue 15 10

1963. Centenary of Judicial Power.
1100 **367** 5p. green 15 10

1963. Child Welfare. As T **352**. Mult.
1101 4p.+2p. Vermilion flycatcher (postage) 35 25
1102 11p.+5p. Great kiskadee (air) 75 75

368 Kemal Ataturk | **369** "Payador" (after Castagnino)

1963. 25th Death Anniv of Kemal Ataturk.
1103 **368** 12p. grey 30 10

1964. 4th National Folklore Festival.
1104 **369** 4p. black, blue & ultram 15 10

370 Map of Antarctic Islands

1964. Antarctic Claims Issue.
1105 **370** 2p. bl & ochre (postage) 80 30
1106 – 4p. bistre and blue . . . 1·25 35
1107 – 18p. bl & bistre (air) . . 2·25 55
DESIGNS—VERT: (30 × 39½ mm): 4p. Map of Argentina and Antarctica. HORIZ: (as Type **291**): 18p. Map of "Islas Malvinas" (Falkland Islands).

371 Jorge Newbery in Airplane

1964. 50th Death Anniv of Jorge Newbery (aviator).
1108 **371** 4p. green 15 10

372 Pres. Kennedy | **373** Father Brochero

1964. President Kennedy Memorial Issue.
1109 **372** 4p. blue and mauve . . 15 10

1964. 50th Death Anniv of Father J. G. Brochero.
1110 **373** 4p. brown 15 10

374 U.P.U. Monument, Berne | **375** Soldier of the Patricios Regiment

1964. Air. 15th U.P.U. Congress, Vienna.
1111 **374** 18p. purple and red . . 50 20

1964. Army Day.
1112 **375** 4p. multicoloured . . . 50 15
See also Nos. 1135, 1170, 1201, 1223, 1246, 1343, 1363, 1399, 1450, 1515, 1564, 1641 and 1678.

376 Pope John XXIII **377** Olympic Stadium

1964. Pope John Commemoration
1113 **376** 4p. black and orange . . 20 10

1964. Olympic Games, Tokyo.
1114 **377** 4p.+2p. brown, yellow and red (postage) . . 15 15
1115 – 12p.+6p. black & green 30 30
1116 – 11p.+5p. blk & bl (air) 40 40
DESIGNS—VERT: 11p. Sailing; 12p. Fencing.

378 University Arms **379** Olympic Flame and Crutch

1964. 350th Anniv of Cordoba University.
1117 **378** 4p. yellow, blue & black 15 10

1964. Air. Invalids Olympic Games, Tokyo.
1118 **379** 18p.+9p. multicoloured 35 45

380 "The Discovery of America" (Florentine woodcut) **381** Pigeons and U.N. Headquarters

1964. Air. "Columbus Day" (or "Day of the Race").
1119 **380** 13p. black and drab . . 35 15

1964. United Nations Day.
1120 **381** 4p. ultramarine and blue 15 10

382 J. V. Gonzalez (medallion) **383** Gen. J. Roca

1964. Birth Centenary of J. V. Gonzalez.
1121 **382** 4p. red 15 10

1964. 50th Death Anniv of General Julio Roca.
1122 **383** 4p. blue 15 10

384 "Market-place, Montserrat Square" (after C. Morel) **385** Icebreaker "General San Martin" and Bearded Penguin

1964. "Argentine Painters".
1123 **384** 4p. sepia 25 10

1964. Child Welfare. As T **352**. Multicoloured.
1124 4p.+2p. Red-crested cardinal (postage) 65 35
1125 18p.+9p. Chilean swallow (air) . . . . 1·25 80

1965. "National Territory of Tierra del Fuego, Antarctic and South Atlantic Isles".
1126 – 2p. purple (postage) . . 50 10
1127 **385** 4p. blue . . . . 2·00 40
1128 – 11p. red (air) 85 15
DESIGNS: 2p. General Belgrano Base (inscr "BASE DE EJERCITO" etc); 11p. Teniente Matienzo Joint Antarctic Base (inscr "BASE CONJUNTA" etc).

1965. Air. 1st Rio Plata Philatelists' Day. Optd **PRIMERAS JORNADAS FILATELICAS RIOPLATENSES.**
1129 **358** 7p. black & yellow (II) 15 15

387 Young Saver **388** I.T.U. Emblem

1965. 50th Anniv of National Postal Savings Bank.
1130 **387** 4p. black and red . . . 10 10

1965. Air. Centenary of I.T.U.
1131 **388** 18p. multicoloured . . . 40 15

389 I.Q.S.Y. Emblem **390** Soldier of the "Pueyrredon Hussars"

1965. Int Quiet Sun Year and Space Research.
1132 **389** 4p. black, orange and blue (postage) 15 10
1133 – 18p. red (air) 55 20
1134 – 50p. blue 80 35
DESIGNS—VERT: 18p. Rocket launching. HORIZ: 50p. Earth, trajectories and space phenomena (both inscr "INVESTIGACIONES ESPACIALES").

1965. Army Day (29 May).
1135 **390** 8p. multicoloured . . . 70 15
See also Nos. 1170, 1201, 1223, 1246, 1343, 1363, 1399, 1450, 1515, 1564 and 1641.

391 Ricardo Guiraldes **392** H. Yrigoyen (statesman)

1965. Argentine Writers (1st series). Each brown.
1136 8p. Type **391** 35 10
1137 8p. E. Larreta 35 10
1138 8p. L. Lugones 35 10
1139 8p. R. J. Payro 35 10
1140 8p. R. Rojas 35 10
See also Nos 1174/8.

1965. Hipolito Yrigoyen Commemoration
1141 **392** 8p. black and red . . . 15 10

393 "Children looking through a Window"

1965. International Mental Health Seminar.
1142 **393** 8p. black and brown . . 15 10

394 Ancient Map and Funeral Urn **395** Mgr. Dr. J. Cagliero

1965. 400th Anniv of San Miguel de Tucuman.
1143 **394** 8p. multicoloured . . . 15 10

1965. Cagliero Commemoration
1144 **395** 8p. violet 15 10

396 Dante (statue in Church of the Holy Cross, Florence) **397** Sail Merchantman "Mimosa"

1965. 700th Birth Anniv of Dante.
1145 **396** 8p. blue 15 10

1965. Centenary of Welsh Colonisation of Chubut and Foundation of Rawson.
1146 **397** 8p. black and red . . . 65 20

398 Police Emblem on Map of Buenos Aires

1965. Federal Police Day.
1155 **398** 8p. red 15 10

399 Schoolchildren

1965. 81st Anniv of Law 1420 (Public Education).
1156 **399** 8p. black and green . . 15 10

400 St. Francis's Church, Catamarca **401** R. Dario (Nicaraguan poet)

1965. Brother Mamerto Esquiu Commemoration.
1157 **400** 8p. brown and yellow . . 15 10

1965. 50th Death Anniv of Ruben Dario.
1158 **401** 15p. violet on grey . . . 15 10

402 "The Orange-seller" (detail)

1966. Prilidiano Pueyrredon's Paintings. Designs show details from the original works, each green.
1159 8p. Type **402** 55 45
1160 8p. "A Halt at the Village Grocer's Shop" 55 45
1161 8p. "San Fernando Landscape" 75 45
1162 8p. "Bathing Horses on the Banks of the River Plate" 55 45

403 Rocket "Centaur" and Antarctic Map **404** Dr. Sun Yat-sen

1966. Air. Rocket Launches in Antarctica.
1163 **403** 27p.50 red, black & blue 65 25

1966. Birth Centenary of Dr. Sun Yat-sen.
1164 **404** 8p. brown 45 25

1966. Child Welfare. As T **352**, inscr "R. ARGENTINA". Multicoloured.
1165 8p.+4p. Southern lapwing (postage) . . . . 1·00 55
1166 27p.50+12p.50 Rufous hornero (air) . . . . . . 1·25 85

406 "Human Races"

1966. Inaug of W.H.O. Headquarters, Geneva.
1168 **406** 8p. black and brown . . 15 10

407 Magellan Gull

1966. Air. 50th Anniv of Naval Aviation School, Puerto Militar.
1169 **407** 12p. multicoloured . . . 40 25

1966. Army Day (29 May). As T **390**.
1170 8p. multicoloured 65 15
DESIGN: 8p. Militiaman of Guemes's "Infernals".

408 Arms of Argentina

1966. Air. "Argentina '66" Philatelic Exhibition, Buenos Aires.
1171 **408** 10p.+10p. multicoloured 1·50 1·10

410 "Charity" Emblem

1966. Argentine Charities.
1173 **410** 10p. blue, black & green 25 15

1966. Argentine Writers (2nd series). Portraits as T **391**. Each green.
1174 10p. H. Ascasubi 40 10
1175 10p. Estanislao del Campo 40 10
1176 10p. M. Cane 40 10
1177 10p. Lucio V. Lopez 40 10
1178 10p. R. Obligado 40 10

411 Anchor

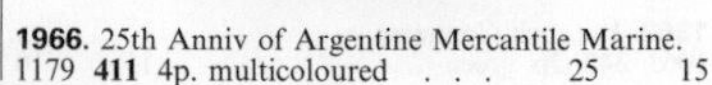

1966. 25th Anniv of Argentine Mercantile Marine.
1179 **411** 4p. multicoloured . . . 25 15

412 L. Agote

413 Map and Flags of the American States

1966. Argentine Scientists. Each violet.
1180 10p. Type **412** 40 10
1181 10p. J. B. Ambrosetti . . . 40 10
1182 10p. M. I. Lillo 40 10
1183 10p. F. P. Moreno 40 10
1184 10p. F. J. Muniz 40 10

1966. 7th American Armies Conf, Buenos Aires.
1185 **413** 10p. multicoloured . . . 15 10

414 Bank Facade

415 La Salle Statue and College

1966. 75th Anniv of Argentine National Bank.
1186 **414** 10p. green 10 10

1966. 75th Anniv of La Salle College, Buenos Aires.
1187 **415** 10p. black and brown . . 10 10

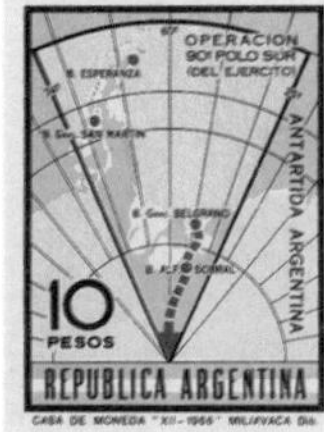

416 Antarctic Map with Expedition Route

417 Gen. J. M. de Pueyrredon

1966. Argentine South Pole Expedition, 1965–66.
1188 **416** 10p. multicoloured . . . 80 50

1966. Gen. J. M. de Pueyrredon Commemoration
1189 **417** 10p. red 10 10

418 Gen. J. G. de Las Heras

419 Ancient Pot

1966. Gen. Juan G. de Las Heras Commemoration.
1190 **418** 10p. black 10 10

1967. Child Welfare. As T **352**, inscr "R. ARGENTINA". Multicoloured.
1191 10p.+5p. Scarlet-headed blackbird (horiz) (postage) 80 60
1192 15p.+7p. Blue and yellow tanager (air) . . . . . . 1·25 90

1967. 20th Anniv of U.N.E.S.C.O.
1193 **419** 10p. multicoloured . . . 15 10

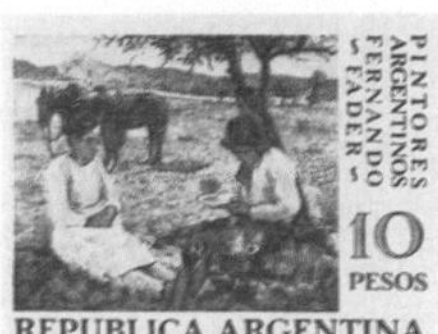

420 "The Meal" (after F. Fader)

1967. Fernando Fader (painter).
1194 **420** 10p. brown 15 10

421 Juana Azurduy de Padilla

422 Schooner "Invencible"

1967. Famous Argentine Women. Each sepia.
1195 6p. Type **421** 30 10
1196 6p. J. M. Gorriti 30 10
1197 6p. C. Grierson 30 10
1198 6p. J. P. Manson 30 10
1199 6p. A. Storni 30 10

1967. Navy Day.
1200 **422** 20p. multicoloured . . . 1·25 20

1967. Army Day (29 May). As T **390**.
1201 20p. multicoloured 75 15
DESIGN: 20p. Soldier of the Arribenos Regiment.

424 Suitcase and Dove

425 PADELAI Emblem and Sun

1967. International Tourist Year.
1203 **424** 20p. multicoloured . . . 15 10

1967. 75th Anniv of PADELAI (Argentine Children's Welfare Association).
1204 **425** 20p. multicoloured . . . 15 10

426 Teodoro Fels's Bleriot XI

427 Ferreyra's Oxwagon and Skyscrapers

1967. Air. 50th Anniv of 1st Argentine–Uruguay Airmail Flight.
1205 **426** 26p. brown, olive & blue 30 10

1967. Centenary of Villa Maria.
1206 **427** 20p. multicoloured . . . 15 10

428 "General San Martin" (from statue by M. P. Nunez de Ibarra)

429 Interior of Museum

1967. 150th Anniv of Battle of Chacabuco.
1207 **428** 20p. brown and yellow 45 15
1208 – 40p. blue 70 15
DESIGN—(48 × 31 mm)—HORIZ: 40p. "Battle of Chacabuco" (from painting by P. Subercaseaux).

1967. 10th Anniv of Government House Museum.
1209 **429** 20p. blue 15 10

430 Pedro Zanni and "Provincia de Buenos Aires"

1967. Aeronautics Week.
1210 **430** 20p. multicoloured . . . 15 10

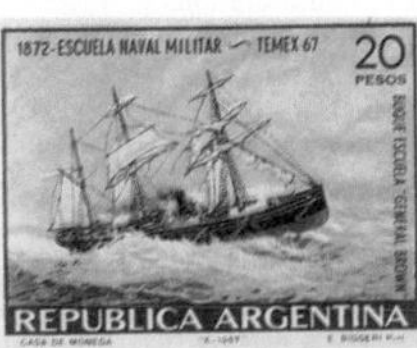

431 Cadet Ship "General Brown" (from painting by E. Biggeri)

432 Ovidio Lagos and Front Page of "La Capital" (newspaper)

1967. "Temex 67" Stamp Exhibition and 95th Anniv of Naval Military School.
1211 **431** 20p. multicoloured . . . 1·00 20

1967. Centenary of "La Capital".
1212 **432** 20p. brown 15 10

433 St. Barbara (from altar-painting, Segovia, Spain)

434 "Sivori's Wife"

1967. Artillery Day (4 Dec).
1213 **433** 20p. red 15 10

1967. Child Welfare. Bird designs as T **352**. Multicoloured.
1214 20p.+10p. Amazon kingfisher (postage) . . . 75 40
1215 26p.+13p. Toco toucan (air) 1·00 60

1968. 50th Death Anniv of Eduardo Sivori (painter).
1216 **434** 20p. green 15 10

435 "Almirante Brown" Scientific Station

436 Man in Wheelchair

1968. "Antarctic Territories".
1217 – 6p. multicoloured . . . 60 15
1218 **435** 20p. multicoloured . . . 85 20
1219 – 40p. multicoloured . . . 1·10 55
DESIGNS—VERT (22½ × 32 mm): 6p. Map of Antarctic radio-postal stations. HORIZ (as Type **435**): 40p. Aircraft over South Pole ("Trans-Polar Round Flight").

1968. Rehabilitation Day for the Handicapped.
1220 **436** 20p. black and green . . 20 10

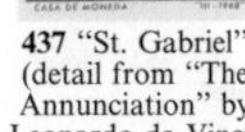

437 "St. Gabriel" (detail from "The Annunciation" by Leonardo da Vinci)

438 Children and W.H.O. Emblem

1968. St. Gabriel (patron saint of army communications).
1221 **437** 20p. mauve 15 10

1968. 20th Anniv of W.H.O.
1222 **438** 20p. blue and red . . . 15 10

1968. Army Day (29 May). As T **390**.
1223 20p. multicoloured 85 15
DESIGN: 20p. Iriarte's artilleryman.

439 Full-rigged Cadet Ship "Libertad" (E. Biggeri)

1968. Navy Day.
1224 **439** 20p. multicoloured . . . 65 15

440 G. Rawson and Hospital

1968. Centenary of Guillermo Rawson Hospital.
1225 **440** 6p. bistre 15 10

441 Vito Dumas and "Legh II"

1968. Air. Vito Dumas' World Voyage in Yacht "Legh II".
1226 **441** 68p. multicoloured . . . 60 20

442 Children using Zebra crossing

1968. Road Safety.
1227 **442** 20p. multicoloured . . . 20 10

443 "O'Higgins greeting San Martin" (P. Subercaseaux)

1968. 150th Anniv of Battle of the Maipu.
1228 **443** 40p. blue 55 20

444 Dr. O. Magnasco (lawyer)

445 "The Sea" (E. Gomez)

446 "Grandmother's Birthday" (P. Lynch)

1968. Magnasco Commemoration.
1229 **444** 20p. brown 20 10

1968. Children's Stamp Design Competition.
1230 **445** 20p. multicoloured . . . 20 15
1231 **446** 20p. multicoloured . . . 20 15

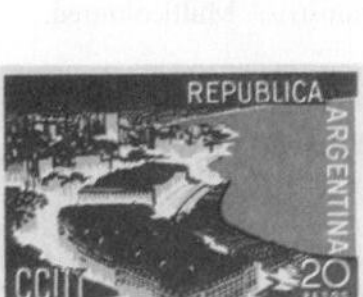

447 Mar del Plata at Night

448 Mounted Gendarme

1968. 4th Plenary Assembly of Int Telegraph and Telephone Consultative Committee, Mar del Plata.
1232 **447** 20p. black, yellow and blue (postage) 25 15
1233 – 40p. black, mauve and blue (air) 35 15
1234 – 68p. multicoloured . . . 50 25

DESIGNS (as Type **447**): 40p. South America in Assembly hemisphere. (Larger, 40×30 mm): 68p. Assembly emblem.

1968. National Gendarmerie.
1235 **448** 20p. multicoloured . . . 30 10

449 Coastguard Cutter "Lynch"
450 A. de Anchorena and "Pampero"

1968. National Maritime Prefecture (Coastguard).
1236 **449** 20p. black, grey and blue 65 10

1968. Aeronautics Week.
1237 **450** 20p. multicoloured . . . 30 10

451 St. Martin of Tours (A. Guido)
452 Bank Emblem

1968. St. Martin of Tours (patron saint of Buenos Aires).
1238 **451** 20p. brown and lilac . . 15 10

1968. Municipal Bank of Buenos Aires.
1239 **452** 20p. black, green & yell 15 10

453 Anniversary and A.L.P.I. Emblems

1968. 25th Anniv of "Fight Against Polio Association" (A.L.P.I.).
1240 **453** 20p. green and red . . . 20 10

454 "My Grandmother's Birthday" (Patricia Lynch)

1968. 1st "Solidarity" Philatelic Exn, Buenos Aires.
1241 **454** 40p.+20p. multicoloured 75 30

455 "The Potter Woman" (Ramon Gomez Cornet)
456 Emblem of State Coalfields

1968. Cent of Whitcomb Gallery, Buenos Aires.
1242 **455** 20p. red 15 10

1968. Coal and Steel Industries. Multicoloured.
1243 20p. Type **456** 15 10
1244 20p. Ladle and emblem of Military Steel-manufacturing Agency ("FM") 15 10

457 Illustration from Schmidl's book "Journey to the River Plate and Paraguay"

1969. Ulrich Schmidl Commemoration.
1245 **457** 20p. yellow, red & black 15 10

1969. Army Day (29 May). As T **390**.
1246 20p. Sapper, Buenos Aires Army, 1856 . . . . . . 70 15

459 Sail Frigate "Hercules"

1969. Navy Day.
1247 **459** 20p. multicoloured . . . 1·00 20

460 "Freedom and Equality" (from poster by S. Zagorski)
461 I.L.O. Emblem within Honeycomb

1969. Human Rights Year.
1254 **460** 20p. black and yellow . . 15 10

1969. 50th Anniv of I.L.O.
1255 **461** 20p. multicoloured . . . 15 10

462 P. N. Arata (biologist)

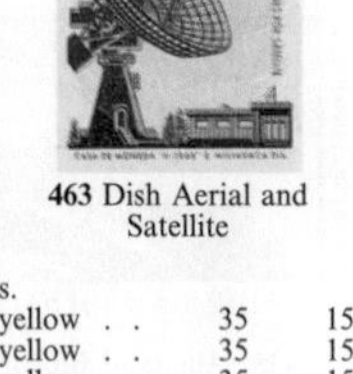

463 Dish Aerial and Satellite

1969. Argentine Scientists.
1256 **462** 6p. brown on yellow . . 35 15
1257 – 6p. brown on yellow . . 35 15
1258 – 6p. brown on yellow . . 35 15
1259 – 6p. brown on yellow . . 35 15
1260 – 6p. brown on yellow . . 35 15
PORTRAITS: No. 1257, M. Fernandez (zoologist); 1258, A. P. Gallardo (biologist); 1259, C. M. Hicken (botanist); 1260, E. L. Holmberg (botanist).

1969. Satellite Communications.
1261 **463** 20p. blk & yell (postage) 25 15
1262 – 40p. blue (air) 55 20
DESIGN—HORIZ: 40p. Earth station and dish aerial.

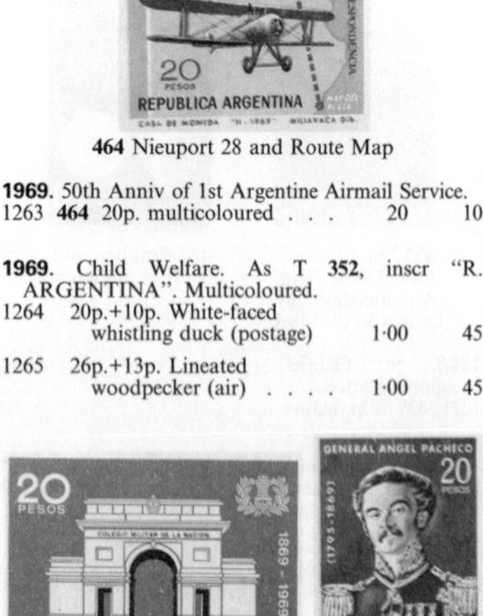

464 Nieuport 28 and Route Map

1969. 50th Anniv of 1st Argentine Airmail Service.
1263 **464** 20p. multicoloured . . . 20 10

1969. Child Welfare. As T **352**, inscr "R. ARGENTINA". Multicoloured.
1264 20p.+10p. White-faced whistling duck (postage) 1·00 45
1265 26p.+13p. Lineated woodpecker (air) . . . . 1·00 45

465 College Entrance

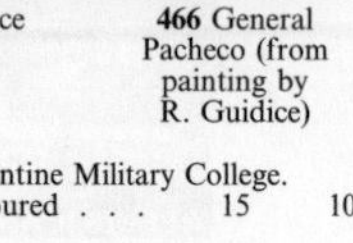

466 General Pacheco (from painting by R. Guidice)

1969. Centenary of Argentine Military College.
1266 **465** 20p. multicoloured . . . 15 10

1969. Death Centenary of General Angel Pacheco.
1267 **466** 20p. green 15 10

467 Bartolome Mitre and Logotypes of "La Nacion"

468 J. Aguirre

1969. Centenary of Newspapers "La Nacion" and "La Prensa".
1268 **467** 20p. black, emer & grn 50 15
1269 – 20p. black orange & yell 50 15
DESIGN: No. 1269 "The Lantern" (masthead) and logotypes of "La Prensa".

1969. Argentine Musicians.
1270 **468** 6p. green and blue . . . 65 15
1271 – 6p. green and blue . . . 65 15
1272 – 6p. green and blue . . . 65 15
1273 – 6p. green and blue . . . 65 15
1274 – 6p. green and blue . . . 65 15
MUSICIANS: No. 1271, F. Boero; 1272, C. Gaito; 1273, C. L. Buchardo; 1274, A. Williams.

469 Hydro-electric Project on Rivers Limay and Neuquen

1969. National Development Projects. Mult.
1275 6p. Type **469** (postage) . . . 50 10
1276 20p. Parana–Santa Fe river tunnel 60 15
1277 26p. Atomic power plant, Atucha (air) . . . . . . 1·00 40

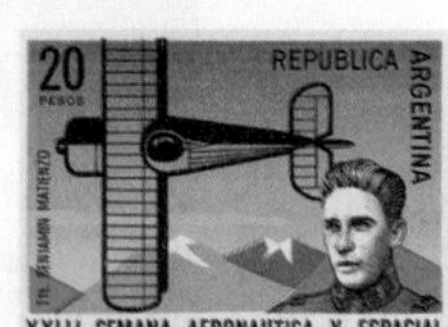

470 Lieut. B. Matienzo and Nieuport 28 Biplane

1969. Aeronautics Week.
1278 **470** 20p. multicoloured . . . 50 10

471 Capital "L" and Lions Emblem

1969. 50th Anniv of Lions International.
1279 **471** 20p. olive, orge & green 50 10

472 "Madonna and Child" (after R. Soldi)

1969. Christmas.
1280 **472** 20p. multicoloured . . . 55 15

1970. Child Welfare. As T **352**, but differently arranged and inscr "REPUBLICA ARGENTINA". Multicoloured.
1293 20c.+10c. Slender-tailed woodstar (postage) . . . 85 55
1294 40c.+20c. Chilean flamingo (air) 90 70
See also Nos. 1394/5, 1415/16 and 1441/2.

474 "General Belgrano" (lithograph by Gericault)

1970. Birth Bicent of General Manuel Belgrano.
1295 **474** 20c. brown 45 15
1296 – 50c. black, flesh & blue 80 25
DESIGN—HORIZ (56×15 mm): 50c. "Monument to the Flag" (bas-relief by Jose Fioravanti).

475 Early Fire Engine

1970. Air. Centenary of Buenos Aires Fire Brigade.
1297 **475** 40c. multicoloured . . . 60 10

476 Naval Schooner "Juliet", 1814

1970. Navy Day.
1298 **476** 20c. multicoloured . . . 1·25 20

477 San Jose Palace
478 General Belgrano

1970. President Justo de Urquiza Commemoration.
1299 **477** 20c. multicoloured . . . 15 10

1970. Revalued currency. Previous designs with values in centavos and pesos as T **478**. Inscr "REPUBLICA ARGENTINA" or "ARGENTINA".
1300 1c. green (No. 1016) . . 15 10
1301 – 3c. red (No. 951) . . . 15 10
1302 **296** 5c. blue 15 10
1303 **478** 6c. blue 15 10
1304 8c. green 15 10
1305 – 10c. brown (No. 1286)* 45 10
1306 – 10c. red (No. 1286) . . 1·25 10
1307 – 10c. brown (No. 1286)* 55 10
1308 **478** 10c. brown 20 10
1309 – 25c. brown 40 10
1310 **478** 30c. purple 10 10
1311 – 50c. red 80 10
1312 **478** 60c. yellow 10 10
1313 – 65c. brown (No. 878) 85 10
1314 – 70c. blue 10 10
1315 – 90c. green (No. 878) . . 2·00 10
1316a – 1p. brown (as No. 1027, but 23×29 mm) 40 10
1317 – 1p.15 blue (No. 1072) 80 10
1318 – 1p.20 orange (No. 878) 80 10
1319 – 1p.20 red 35 10
1320 – 1p.80 brn (as No. 1072) 30 10
1321 **478** 1p.80 blue 20 10
1322 – 2p. brown 20 10
1323 – 2p.70 bl (as No. 878) 25 10
1323a **478** 3p. grey 15 10
1392 – 4p.50 green (as No. 1288) (G. Brown) 40 10
1325 – 5p. green (as No. 1032) 95 10
1326 – 6p. red 25 10
1327 – 6p. green 25 10
1328 – 7p.50 grn (as No. 878) 85 10
1329 – 10p. blue (as No. 1033) 1·25 10
1329a – 12p. green 25 10
1329b – 12p. red 25 10
1330 – 13p.50 red (as No. 1288) . . . . 1·00 10
1331 – 13p.50 red (as No. 1072 but larger, 16×24 mm) 40 10
1332 – 15p. red 25 10
1333 – 15p. blue 25 10
1334 – 20p. red 40 10
1335 – 22p.50 blue (as No. 878) (22×32½ mm) . . . 1·00 10
1393 – 22p.50 blue (as No. 878) (26×39 mm) 40 10

1336 – 30p. red 40 10
1337 **478** 40p. green 70 15
1338 – 40p. red 40 10
1339 **478** 60p. blue 80 20
1340 – 70p. blue . . . . . . 1·00 20
1340a **478** 90p. green 55 30
1340b – 100p. red 55 25
1340c – 110p. red 35 15
1340d – 120p. red 30 20
1340e – 130p. red 40 25
DESIGNS—VERT (as Type **478**): 25, 50, 70c., 1p.20, 2, 6, 12, 15p. (No. 1332), 20, 30, 40p. (No. 1338), 100, 110, 120, 130p. General Jose de San Martin; 15p. (No. 1333), 70p. Guillermo Brown.

*No. 1307 differs from Nos. 1305/6 in being without imprint. It also has "CORREOS" at top right.

482 Wireless Set of 1920 and Radio "Waves"

1970. 50th Anniv of Argentine Radio Broadcasting.
1341 **482** 20c. multicoloured . . . 15 10

483 Emblem of Education Year

485 "United Nations"

484 "Liberation Fleet leaving Valparaiso" (A. Abel)

1970. Air. International Education Year.
1342 **483** 68c. black and blue . . . 30 15

1970. Military Uniforms. As T **390**. Multicoloured.
1343 20c. Military courier, 1879 75 25

1970. 150th Anniv of Peruvian Liberation.
1344 **484** 26c. multicoloured . . . 1·40 20

1970. 25th Anniv of U.N.
1345 **485** 20c. multicoloured . . . 15 10

486 Cordoba Cathedral

1970. 400th Anniv of Tucuman Diocese.
1346 **486** 50c. blk & grey (postage) 85 10
1347 – 40c. multicoloured (air) 85 20
DESIGN—HORIZ: 40c. Chapel, Sumampa.

487 Planetarium

1970. Air. Buenos Aires Planetarium.
1348 **487** 40c. multicoloured . . . 40 15

488 "Liberty" and Mint Building

1970. 25th Anniv of State Mint Building, Buenos Aires.
1349 **488** 20c. black, green & gold 15 10

489 "The Manger" (H. G. Gutierrez) (½-size illustration)

1970. Christmas.
1350 **489** 20c. multicoloured . . . 25 10

490 Jorge Newbery and Morane Saulnier Type L Airplane

1970. Air. Aeronautics Week.
1351 **490** 26c. multicoloured . . . 40 15

491 St. John Bosco and College Building

1970. Salesian Mission in Patagonia.
1352 **491** 20c. black and green . . 15 10

492 "Planting the Flag"

1971. 5th Anniv of Argentine Expedition to the South Pole.
1353 **492** 20c. multicoloured . . . 1·25 35

493 Dorado (½-size illustration)

1971. Child Welfare. Fishes. Multicoloured.
1354 20c.+10c. Type **493** (postage) 65 45
1355 40c.+20c. River Plate pejerry (air) 55 35

494 Einstein and Scanners

495 E. I. Alippi

1971. Electronics in Postal Development.
1356 **494** 25c. multicoloured . . . 30 10

1971. Argentine Actors and Actresses. Each black and brown.
1357 15c. Type **495** 40 10
1358 15c. J. A. Casaberta 40 10
1359 15c. R. Casaux 40 10
1360 15c. Angelina Pagano . . . 40 10
1361 15c. F. Parravicini 40 10

496 Federation Emblem

1971. Inter-American Regional Meeting of International Roads Federation.
1362 **496** 25c. black and blue . . . 15 10

1971. Army Day. As T **390**.
1363 25c. multicoloured . . . . . 1·00 15
DESIGN: 25c. Artilleryman of 1826.

1971. Navy Day. As T **476**.
1364 25c. multicoloured . . . . . 1·75 20
DESIGN: Sloop "Carmen".

498 "General Guemes" (L. Gigli)

1971. 150th Death Anniv of General M. de Guemes. Multicoloured.
1365 25c. Type **498** 55 20
1366 25c. "Death of Guemes" (A. Alice) (84 × 29 mm) 55 20

499 Order of the Peruvian Sun

1971. 150th Anniv of Peruvian Independence.
1367 **499** 31c. yellow, black & red 40 10

500 Stylized Tulip

501 Dr. A. Saenz (founder) (after Jose Gut)

1971. 3rd Int and 8th Nat Horticultural Exhibition.
1368 **500** 25c. multicoloured . . . 25 15

1971. 150th Anniv of Buenos Aires University.
1369 **501** 25c. multicoloured . . . 20 15

502 Arsenal Emblem

1971. 30th Anniv of Fabricaciones Militares (Arsenals).
1370 **502** 25c. multicoloured . . . 20 15

503 Road Transport

1971. Nationalized Industries.
1371 **503** 25c. mult (postage) . . . 35 10
1372 – 65c. multicoloured . . . 90 35
1373 – 31c. yell, blk & red (air) 45 25
DESIGNS: 31c. Refinery and formula ("Petrochemicals"); 65c. Tree and paper roll ("Paper and Cellulose").

1971. Air. Revalued currency. Face values in centavos.
1374 **358** 45c. brown . . . . . . 2·50 15
1375 68c. red 30 15

1376a 70c. blue . . . . 1·60 15
1377 90c. green . . . . . . 1·75 15
1378 1p.70 blue 55 10
1379 1p.95 green 55 15
1380 2p.65 purple 55 15

504 Constellation and Telescope

1971. Centenary of Cordoba Observatory.
1381 **504** 25c. multicoloured . . . 25 15

505 Capt. D. L. Candelaria and Morane Saulnier Type P Airplane

1971. 25th Aeronautics and Space Week.
1382 **505** 25c. multicoloured . . . 40 10

506 "Stamps" (Mariette Lydis)

507 "Christ in Majesty" (tapestry by Butler)

1971. 2nd Charity Stamp Exhibition.
1383 **506** 1p.+50c. multicoloured 35 35

1971. Christmas.
1384 **507** 25c. multicoloured . . . 20 10

1972. Child Welfare. As T **352**, but differently arranged and inscr "REPUBLICA ARGENTINA".
1394 25c.+10c. Saffron finch (vert) 90 40
1395 65c.+30c. Rufous-bellied thrush (horiz) . . . . . . 1·10 50

508 "Maternity" (J. Castagnino)

1972. 25th Anniv of U.N.I.C.E.F.
1396 **508** 25c. black and brown . . 20 15

509 Treaty Emblem, "Libertad" (liner) and Almirante Brown Base

1972. 10th Anniv of Antarctic Treaty.
1397 **509** 25c. multicoloured . . . 1·25 20

510 Postman's Mail Pouch

1972. Bicentenary of 1st Buenos Aires Postman.
1398 **510** 25c. multicoloured . . . 15 10

1972. Army Day. As T **390**. Multicoloured.
1399 25c. Sergeant of Negro and Mulatto Battalion (1806–7) 65 15

1972. Navy Day. As T **476**. Multicoloured.
1400 25c. Brigantine "Santisima Trinidad" . . . . 1·40 20

512 Sonic Balloon **513** Oil Pump

1972. National Meteorological Service.
1401 **512** 25c. multicoloured . . . 25 15

1972. 50th Anniv of State Oilfields (Y.P.F.).
1402 **513** 45c. black, blue & gold 80 10

514 Forest Centre

1972. 7th World Forestry Congress, Buenos Aires.
1403 **514** 25c. black, blue & lt bl 45 10

515 Arms and Cadet Ship "Presidente Sarmiento"

1972. Centenary of Naval School.
1404 **515** 25c. multicoloured . . . 1·25 20

516 Baron A. de Marchi, Balloon and Voisin "Boxkite" **517** Bartolome Mitre

1972. Aeronautics Week.
1405 **516** 25c. multicoloured . . . 40 10

1972. 150th Birth Anniv of General Bartolome Mitre.
1406 **517** 25c. blue 20 10

518 Heart and Flower **519** "Martin Fierro" (J. C. Castignino)

1972. World Health Day.
1407 **518** 90c. blk, violet & blue 45 15

1972. Int Book Year and Cent of "Martin Fierro" (poem by Jose Hernandez). Multicoloured.
1408 50c. Type **519** 25 15
1409 90c. "Spirit of the Gaucho" (V. Forte) 50 20

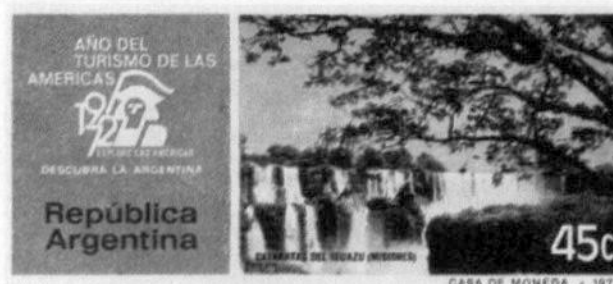

520 Iguazu Falls

1972. American Tourist Year.
1410 **520** 45c. multicoloured . . . 30 10

521 "Wise Man on Horseback" (18th-century wood-carving) **522** Cockerel Emblem

1972. Christmas.
1411 **521** 50c. multicoloured . . . 40 10

1973. 150th Anniv of Federal Police Force.
1412 **522** 50c. multicoloured . . . 20 10

523 Bank Emblem and First Coin **525** Presidential Chair

524 Douglas DC-3 Aircraft and Polar Map

1973. 150th Anniv of Provincial Bank of Buenos Aires.
1413 **523** 50c. multicoloured . . . 15 10

1973. 10th Anniv of 1st Argentine Flight to South Pole.
1414 **524** 50c. multicoloured . . . 90 20

1973. Child Welfare. As T **473**, but differently arranged and inscr "R. ARGENTINA". Mult.
1415 50c.+25c. Crested screamer (vert) 85 50
1416 90c.+45c. Saffron-cowled blackbird (horiz) . . . . 1·25 75

1973. Presidential Inauguration
1417 **525** 50c. multicoloured . . . 20 10

526 San Martin and Bolivar

1973. San Martin's Farewell to People of Peru. Multicoloured.
1418 50c. Type **526** 25 15
1419 50c. "San Martin" (after Gil de Castro) (vert) 25 15

527 "Eva Peron – Eternally with her People"

1973. Eva Peron Commemoration.
1420 **527** 70c. multicoloured . . . 20 15

528 "House of Viceroy Sobremonte" (H. de Virgilio)

1973. 4th Centenary of Cordoba.
1421 **528** 50c. multicoloured . . . 20 10

529 "Woman" (L. Spilimbergo)

1973. Philatelists' Day. Argentine Paintings. Mult.
1422 15c.+15c. "Nature Study" (A. Guttero) (horiz) . . . 50 10
1423 70c. Type **529** 80 15
1424 90c.+90c. "Nude" (M. C. Victorica) (horiz) 85 70
See also Nos. 1434/6 and 1440.

530 "La Argentina" (sail frigate) **531** Early and Modern Telephones

1973. Navy Day.
1425 **530** 70c. multicoloured . . . 1·25 20

1973. 25th Anniv of National Telecommunications Enterprise (E.N.T.E.L.).
1426 **531** 70c. multicoloured . . . 35 10

532 Quill Pen of Flags **533** Lujan Basilica

1973. 12th International Latin Notaries Congress.
1427 **532** 70c. multicoloured . . . 25 15

1973.
1428 **533** 18c. brown and yellow 15 10
1429 50c. purple and black 15 10
1429a 50c. blue and brown . . 15 10
1430 50c. purple 15 10

1973. Transfer of Presidency of General Juan Peron. No. 1318 optd **TRANSMISION DEL MANDO PRESIDENCIAL 12 OCTUBRE 1973.**
1431 1p.20 orange 80 15

535 "Virgin and Child" (stained-glass window)

1973. Christmas. Multicoloured.
1432 70c. Type **535** 30 10
1433 1p.20 "The Manger" (B. Venier) 60 15

1974. Argentine Paintings. As T **529**. Mult.
1434 50c. "Houses" (E. Daneri) (horiz) 30 10
1435 70c. "The Lama" (J. B. Planas) 35 15
1436 90c. "Homage to the Blue Grotto" (E. Pettoruti) (horiz) 50 20

536 View of Mar del Plata

1974. Centenary of Mar del Plata.
1437 **536** 70c. multicoloured . . . 30 10

537 "Fray Justo Santa Maria de Oro" (anon.) **538** Weather Contrasts

1974. Birth Bicentenary of Fray Justo Santa Maria de Oro.
1438 **537** 70c. multicoloured . . . 20 10

1974. Cent of World Meteorological Organization.
1439 **538** 1p.20 multicoloured . . 40 10

1974. "Prenfil 74" Philatelic Press Exhibition, Buenos Aires. As No. 1435.
1440 70c.+30c. multicoloured . . 20 20

1974. Child Welfare. As T **352** but differently arranged and inscr "REPUBLICA ARGENTINA". Multicoloured.
1441 70c.+30c. Double-collared seedeater 65 45
1442 1p.20+60c. Hooded siskin 1·10 65

539 B. Roldan **540** O.E.A. Member Countries

1974. Birth Centenary of Belisario Roldan (writer).
1443 **539** 70c. brown and blue . . 10 10

1974. 25th Anniv of Organization of American States' Charter.
1444 **540** 1p.38 multicoloured . . 15 10

541 Posthorn Emblem

1974. Creation of State Posts and Telecommunications Enterprise (E.N.C.O.T.E.L.).
1445 **541** 1p.20 blue, black & gold 40 10

542 Flags of Member Countries **543** El Chocon Hydro-electric Complex

1974. 6th Meeting of River Plate Countries' Foreign Ministers.
1446 **542** 1p.38 multicoloured . . 15 15

1974. Nationalized Industries. Multicoloured.
1447 70c. Type **543** 35 10
1448 1p.20 Blast furnace, Somisa steel mills 55 25
1449 4p.50 General Belgrano Bridge (61 × 25 mm) . . . 2·75 60

1974. Army Day. As T **390**. Multicoloured.
1450 1p.20 Mounted Grenadier 70 15
See also Nos. 1515 and 1564.

544 A. Mascias and Bleriot XI

1974. Air Force Day.
1451 **544** 1p.20 multicoloured . . 75 15

545 Brigantine "Belgrano"

1974. 150th Anniv of San Martin's Departure into Exile.
1452 **545** 1p.20 multicoloured . . 1·25 20

546 San Francisco Convent, Santa Fe

1974. 400th Anniv of Santa Fe.
1453 **546** 1p.20 multicoloured . . 45 10

547 Symbolic Posthorn

1974. Centenary of U.P.U.
1454 **547** 2p.65 multicoloured . . 70 10

549 Congress Building, Buenos Aires

1974.
1456 **549** 30p. purple and yellow 1·50 10

550 Boy examining Stamp

1974. International Year of Youth Philately.
1457 **550** 1p.70 black and yellow 40 10

551 "Christmas in Peace" (V. Campanella)

1974. Christmas. Multicoloured.
1458 1p.20 Type **551** 35 10
1459 2p.65 "St. Anne and the Virgin Mary" 40 15

552 "Space Monsters" (R. Forner)

1975. Contemporary Argentine Paintings. Mult.
1460 2p.70 Type **552** 80 15
1461 4p.50 "Sleep" (E. Centurion) . . . . . 1·50 25

553 Cathedral and Weaver, Catamarca (½-size illustration)

1975. Tourist Views (1st series). Multicoloured.
1462 1p.20 Type **553** 25 15
1463 1p.20 Street scene and carved pulpit, Jujuy . . . 25 15
1464 1p.20 Monastery and tree-felling, Salta 25 15
1465 1p.20 Dam and vase, Santiago del Estero . . . 25 15
1466 1p.20 Colombres Museum and farm cart, Tucuman 25 15
See also Nos. 1491/3.

554 "We're Vaccinated Now" (M. L. Alonso)

555 "Don Quixote" (Zuloaga)

1975. Children's Vaccination Campaign.
1467 **554** 2p. multicoloured 50 15

1975. Air. "Espana 75" International Stamp Exhibition, Madrid.
1468 **555** 2p.75 black, yell & red 60 15

556 Hugo S. Acuna and South Orkneys Base (¾-size illustration)

1975. Antarctic Pioneers. Multicoloured.
1469 2p. Type **556** 45 10
1470 2p. Francisco P. Moreno and Quetrihue Peninsula 45 10
1471 2p. Capt. Carlos M. Moyano and Cerra Torre, Santa Cruz 45 10
1472 2p. Lt. Col. Luis Piedra Buena and naval cutter "Luisito" in the Antarctic 1·40 25
1473 2p. Ensign Jose M. Sobral and "Snow Hill" House 45 10

557 Valley of the Moon, San Juan Province

559 Eduardo Bradley and Balloon

1975.
1474 **557** 50p. multicoloured . . 1·75 10
1474a 300p. multicoloured . . 2·10 40
1474b – 500p. multicoloured . . 4·25 85
1474c – 1000p. multicoloured 3·75 1·00
DESIGNS—HORIZ: 500p. Admiral Brown Antarctic Station; 1000p. San Francisco Church, Salta.

1975. Air. Surch.
1475 **358** 9p.20 on 5p.60 green, mauve and purple . . 90 10
1476 19p.70 on 5p.60 green, mauve and purple . . 1·10 20
1477 100p. on 5p.60 green, mauve and purple . . 2·75 40

1975. Air Force Day.
1478 **559** 6p. multicoloured . . . 60 15

560 Sail Frigate "25 de Mayo"

1975. Navy Day.
1479 **560** 6p. multicoloured . . . 90 20

561 "Oath of the 33 Orientales on the Beach of La Agraciada" (J. Blanes)

1975. 150th Anniv of Uruguayan Independence.
1480 **561** 6p. multicoloured . . . 30 15

1975. Air. Surch. **REVALORIZADO** and value.
1481 **358** 9p.20 on 5p.60 green, mauve and purple . . 85 15
1482 19p.70 on 5p.60 green, mauve and purple . . 1·00 30

563 Flame Emblem

1975. 30th Anniv of Pres. Peron's Seizure of Power.
1483 **563** 6p. multicoloured . . . 35 15

1975. Surch **REVALORIZADO** and value.
1484 **533** 5p. on 18c. brown & yell 45 10

565 Bridge and Flags of Argentina and Uruguay

1975. "International Bridge" between Colon (Argentina) and Paysandu (Uruguay).
1485 **565** 6p. multicoloured . . . 50 15

566 Posthorn Emblem

568 "The Nativity" (stained-glass window)

1975. Introduction of Postal Codes.
1486 **566** 10p. on 20c. yellow, black and green . . . 35 10

1975. Nos. 951 and 1288 surch **REVALORIZADO** and value.
1487 6c. on 3p. blue 15 10
1488 30c. on 90p. bistre 15 10

1975. Christmas.
1489 **568** 6p. multicoloured . . . 30 15

569 Stylized Nurse and Child

570 "Numeral"

1975. Centenary of Children's Hospital.
1490 **569** 6p. multicoloured . . . 35 10

1975. Tourist Views (2nd series). As T **553**. Mult.
1491 6p. Mounted patrol and oil rig, Chubut 55 15
1492 6p. Glacier and sheep-shearing, Santa Cruz . . 55 15
1493 6p. Lake Lapataia, Tierra del Fuego, and Antarctic scene 55 15

1976.
1494 **570** 12c. grey and black . . . 10 10
1495 50c. slate and green . . 10 10
1496 1p. red and black . . . 10 10
1497 4p. blue and black . . . 15 10
1498 5p. yellow and black . . 15 10
1499 6p. brown and black . . 15 10
1500 10p. grey and violet . . 20 10
1501 27p. green and black . . 55 10
1502 30p. blue and black . . 75 10
1503 45p. yellow and black . . 75 10
1504 50p. green and black . . 75 10
1505 100p. green and red . . 1·10 10

571 Airliner in Flight

1976. 25th Anniv of "Aerolineas Argentinas".
1513 **571** 30p. multicoloured . . . 90 15

572 Sail Frigate "Heroina" and Map of Malvinas

1976. Argentine Claims to Falkland Islands (Malvinas).
1514 **572** 6p. multicoloured . . . 85 20

1976. Army Day. As T **390**. Multicoloured.
1515 12p. Infantryman of Conde's 7th Regiment . . 50 15

573 Louis Braille

574 Plush-crested Jay

1976. Louis Braille (inventor of characters for the Blind) Commemoration.
1516 **573** 19p.70 blue 30 15

1976. Argentine Philately. Multicoloured.
1517 7p.+3p.50 Type **574** 60 35
1518 13p.+6p.50 Yellow-collared macaw 80 35
1519 20p.+10p. "Begonia micranthera" 65 40
1520 40p.+20p. "Echinopsis shaferi" (teasel) 90 55

575 Schooner "Rio de la Plata"

1976. Navy Day.
1521 **575** 12p. multicoloured . . . 1·00 20

576 Dr. Bernardo Houssay (Medicine)

1976. Argentine Nobel Prize Winners.
1522 **576** 10p. black, orge & grey 30 10
1523 – 15p. black, yell & grey 35 15
1524 – 20p. black, brn & grey 50 25
DESIGNS: 15p. Dr. Luis Leloir (chemistry); 20p. Dr. Carlos Lamas (peace).

577 Bridge and Ship

1976. "International Bridge" between Unzue (Argentina) and Fray Bentos (Uruguay).
1525 **577** 12p. multicoloured . . . 30 10

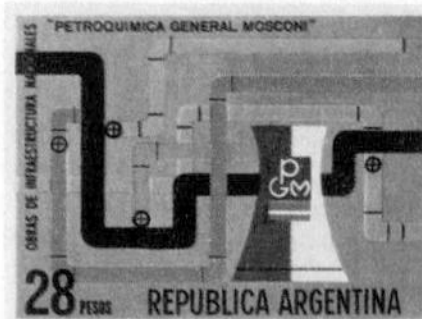

578 Cooling Tower and Pipelines

1976. General Mosconi Petrochemical Project.
1526 **578** 28p. multicoloured . . . 45 15

579 Teodoro Fels and Bleriot XI

1976. Air Force Day.
1527 **579** 15p. multicoloured . . . 40 10

580 "Nativity" (E. Chiapetto)

1976. Christmas.
1528 **580** 20p. multicoloured . . . 50 10

581 Dr. D. Velez Sarsfield (statesman) **582** Conference Emblem

1977. Death Cent (1975) of Dr. D. V. Sarsfield.
1529 **581** 50p. brown and red . . 60 15

1977. United Nations Water Conference.
1530 **582** 70p. multicoloured . . . 45 25

583 "The Visit" (Horacio Butler)

1977. Plastic Arts. Multicoloured.
1531 50p. Type **583** 50 15
1532 70p. "Consecration" (M. P. Caride) (vert) 70 25

584 World Cup Emblem **585** City of La Plata Museum

1977. World Cup Football Championship, Argentina. Multicoloured.
1533 30p. Type **584** 50 15
1534 70p. Stadium and flags (vert) 65 30

1977.
1535 **585** 5p. black and brown 10 10
1536 – 10p. black and blue . . 10 10
1538 – 20p. black and yellow 10 10
1539 – 40p. black and blue . . 20 10
1540 – 50p. black and yellow 40 10
1541 – 50p. black and brown 25 10
1542 – 100p. black and pink 35 10
1543 – 100p. black and orange 10 10
1544 – 100p. black and green 10 10
1545 – 200p. black and blue 25 20
1546 – 280p. black and lilac 4·50 15
1547b – 300p. black and yellow 85 10
1548 – 480p. black and yellow 80 20
1549b – 500p. black and green 60 15
1550 – 520p. black and orange 90 20
1551 – 800p. black and purple 1·10 25
1552a – 1000p. black and gold 1·60 35
1553 – 1000p. black and yellow 1·25 35
1554 – 2000p. multicoloured 1·00 35

DESIGNS—HORIZ: 10p. House of Independence, Tucuman; 20p. Type **585**; 50p. (No. 1541), Cabildo, Buenos Aires; 100p. (Nos. 1542/3), Columbus Theatre, Buenos Aires; 280p., 300p. Rio Grande Museum Chapel, Tierra del Fuego; 480p., 520p., 800p. San Ignacio Mission Church ruins; 500p. Candonga Chapel; 1000p. General Post Office, Buenos Aires (No. 1552 39 × 29 mm, No. 1553 32 × 21 mm); 2000p. Civic Centre, Bariloche. VERT: 40p. Cabildo, Salta; 50p. (No. 1540), Cabildo, Buenos Aires; 200p. Monument to the Flag, Rosario.

586 Morse Key and Satellite

1977. "Argentine Philately". Multicoloured.
1560 10p.+5p. Type **586** 25 15
1561 20p.+10p. Old and modern mail vans 45 25
1562 60p.+30p. Old and modern ships . . . . 1·25 75
1563 70p.+35p. SPAD XIII and Boeing 707 aircraft . . . 85 60

1977. Army Day. As T **390**. Multicoloured.
1564 30p. Trooper of 16th Lancers 50 15

587 Schooner "Sarandi"

1977. Navy Day.
1565 **587** 30p. multicoloured . . . 1·25 20

1977. 150th Anniv of Uruguay Post Office. As No. 1325 but colour changed. Surch **100 PESOS 150 ANIV. DEL CORREO NACIONAL DEL URUGUAY.**
1566 100p. on 5p. brown 90 40

1977. "Argentina '77" Exhibition. As No. 1474c, but inscr "EXPOSICION ARGENTINA '77".
1567 160p.+80p. multicoloured 1·60 1·25

589 Admiral Guillermo Brown

1977. Birth Bicent of Admiral Guillermo Brown.
1568 **589** 30p. multicoloured . . . 40 15

590 Civic Centre, Santa Rosa (La Pampa)

1977. Provinces of the Argentine. Multicoloured.
1569 30p. Type **590** 40 20
1570 30p. Sierra de la Ventana (Buenos Aires) 40 20
1571 30p. Skiers at Chapelco, San Martin de los Andes (Neuquen) 40 20
1572 30p. Lake Fonck (Rio Negro) 40 20

591 Savoia S.16 ter Flying Boat over Rio de la Plata

1977. Air Force and 1926 Buenos Aires–New York Flight Commemoration.
1573 **591** 40p. multicoloured . . . 35 15

592 Jet Fighter Outline

1977. 50th Anniv of Military Aviation Factory.
1574 **592** 30p. blue, pale blue and black 30 10

593 "The Adoration of the Kings" (stained-glass window, Holy Sacrament Basilica, Buenos Aires)

1977. Christmas.
1575 **593** 100p. multicoloured . . 75 20

595 World Cup Emblem

1978. World Cup Football Championship, Argentina.
1577 **595** 200p. green and blue . . 55 20

596 Rosario

1978. World Cup Football Championship (3rd issue). Match Sites. Multicoloured.
1578 50p. Type **596** 20 15
1579 100p. Cordoba 40 15
1580 150p. Mendoza 50 15
1581 200p. Mar del Plata 50 25
1582 300p. Buenos Aires . . . . 2·00 75

597 Children and Institute Emblem

1978. 50th Anniv of Inter-American Children's Institute.
1583 **597** 100p. multicoloured . . 40 15

598 "The Working Day" (B. Quinquela Martin) **600** Hooded Siskin

599 Players from Argentina, Hungary, France and Italy (Group One)

1978. Argentine Art. Multicoloured.
1584 100p. Type **598** 65 15
1585 100p. "Bust of an Unknown Woman" (Orlando Pierri) 2·00 75

1978. World Cup Football Championship (4th issue).
1586 **599** 100p. multicoloured . . 35 10
1587 – 200p. multicoloured . . 40 15
1588 – 300p. multicoloured . . 65 20
1589 – 400p. multicoloured . . 1·00 30

DESIGNS: 200p. Group Two players; 300p. Group Three players; 400p. Group Four players.

1978. Inter-American Philatelic Exhibition. Mult.
1591 50p.+50p. Type **600** . . . . 1·75 1·50
1592 100p.+100p. Double-collared seedeater . . . . 2·00 2·00
1593 150p.+150p. Saffron-cowled blackbird . . . . 2·50 2·10
1594 200p.+200p. Vermilion flycatcher . . . . 2·75 2·40
1595 500p.+500p. Great kiskadee 7·00 5·75

601 Young Tree with Support

1978. Technical Co-operation among Developing Countries Conference, Buenos Aires.
1596 **601** 100p. multicoloured . . 30 15

603 Bank Emblems of 1878 and 1978

1978. Centenary of Bank of Buenos Aires.
1598 **603** 100p. multicoloured . . 30 15

604 General Manuel Savio and Steel Production

1978. 30th Death Anniv of General Manuel Savio (director of military manufacturing).
1599 **604** 100p. multicoloured . . 30 15

605 San Martin **606** Numeral

1978. Birth Bicentenary of Gen. San Martin.
1600 **605** 2000p. green . . . . . 3·25 30
1600a 10000p. blue . . . . . 3·00 35

1978.
1601 **606** 150p. blue and light blue 40 20
1602 180p. blue and light blue 40 10
1603 200p. blue and light blue 30 15

607 Chessboard, Pawn and Queen

608 Argentine Flag supporting Globe

1978. 23rd Chess Olympiad, Buenos Aires.
1604 **607** 200p. multicoloured . . 2·00 65

1978. 12th Int Cancer Congress, Buenos Aires.
1605 **608** 200p. multicoloured . . 80 20

609 "Correct Franking"

1978. Postal Publicity.
1606 **609** 20p. blue 15 10
1607 – 30p. green 15 10
1608 – 50p. red 25 10
DESIGN—VERT: 30p. "Collect postage stamps". HORIZ: 50p. "Indicate the correct post code".

610 Push-pull Tug

1978. 20th Anniv of Argentine River Fleet. Mult.
1609 100p. Type **610** 40 15
1610 200p. Tug "Legador" . . . 90 25
1611 300p. Tug "Rio Parana Mini" 95 30
1612 400p. River passenger ship "Ciudad de Parana" . . . 1·25 25

611 Bahia Blanca and Arms

1978. 150th Anniv of Bahia Blanca.
1613 **611** 200p. multicoloured . . 45 15

612 "To Spain" (Arturo Dresco)

1978. Visit of King and Queen of Spain.
1614 **612** 300p. multicoloured . . 1·75 25

613 Stained-glass Window, San Isidro Cathedral, Buenos Aires

1978. Christmas.
1615 **613** 200p. multicoloured . . 60 15

614 "Chacabuco Slope" (Pedro Subercaseaux)

1978. Birth Bicent of General Jose de San Martin.
1616 500p. Type **614** . . . . . . 1·25 35
1617 1000p. "The Embrace of Maipo" (Pedro Subercaseaux) (vert) . . . 2·25 50

615 San Martin Stamp of 1877 and U.P.U. Emblem

1979. Cent of Argentine Membership of U.P.U.
1618 **615** 200p. blue, black & brn 35 15

616 Mariano Moreno (revolutionary)

1979. Celebrities.
1619 **616** 200p. yellow, blk & red 45 15
1620 – 200p. blue, blk & dp bl 45 15
DESIGNS: No. 1620, Adolfo Alsina (statesman).

617 "Still Life" (Ernesto de la Carcova)

1979. Argentine Paintings. Multicoloured.
1621 200p. Type **617** 60 15
1622 300p. "The Washer-woman" (F. Brughetti) 80 20

618 Balcarce Antenna and Radio Waves

1979. 3rd Inter-American Telecommunications Conference.
1623 **618** 200p. multicoloured . . 35 15

619 Rosette

620 Olives

1979.
1624 **619** 240p. blue and brown 35 10
1625 260p. blue and black 35 10
1626 290p. blue and brown 40 10
1627 310p. blue and purple 45 10
1628 350p. blue and red . . 60 15
1629 450p. blue and ultram 55 15
1630 600p. blue and green 50 20
1631 700p. blue and black 50 20
1632 800p. blue and orange 45 10
1632a 1100p. blue and grey 65 10
1632b 1500p. blue and black 40 10
1632c 1700p. blue and green 50 10

1979. Agricultural Products. Multicoloured.
1633 100p. Type **620** 25 10
1634 200p. Tea 50 25
1635 300p. Sorghum 65 40
1636 400p. Flax . . . . 1·00 55

621 "75" and Symbol

1979. 75th Anniv of Argentine Automobile Club.
1637 **621** 200p. multicoloured . . 35 15

622 Laurel Leaves and Army Emblem

1979. Naming of Village Subteniente Berdina, Tucuman.
1638 **622** 200p. multicoloured . . 30 15

623 Wheat Exchange and Emblem

1979. 125th Anniv of Wheat Exchange, Buenos Aires.
1639 **623** 200p. blue, gold & black 30 15

624 "Uruguay" (sail/steam gunboat)

1979. Navy Day.
1640 **624** 250p. multicoloured . . 1·00 20

1979. Army Day. As T **390**. Multicoloured.
1641 200p. Trooper of Mounted Chasseurs, 1817 . . . . . 1·00 20

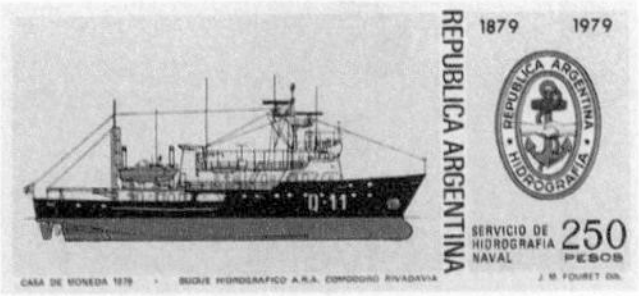

625 "Comodoro Rivadavia" (hydrographic survey ship)

1979. Naval Hydrographic Service.
1642 **625** 250p. multicoloured . . 1·00 20

626 Tree and Man Symbol

1979. Ecology Day.
1643 **626** 250p. multicoloured . . 55 15

627 SPAD XIII and Vicente Almandos

1979. Air Force Day.
1644 **627** 250p. multicoloured . . 80 20

628 "Military Occupation of Rio Negro by Gen. Julio A. Roca's Expedition" (detail, J. M. Blanes)

1979. Centenary of Conquest of the Desert.
1645 **628** 250p. multicoloured . . 70 20

629 Caravel "Magdalena"

1979. "Buenos Aires '80" International Stamp Exhibition. Multicoloured.
1646 400p.+400p. Type **629** . . . 2·50 2·10
1647 500p.+500p. Three-masted sailing ship . . . . 8·50 4·50
1648 600p.+600p. Corvette "Descubierta" . . . . . 8·00 6·75
1649 1500p.+1500p. Yacht "Fortuna" . . . . 17·00 8·75

630 Rowland Hill

631 Francisco de Viedma y Narvaez Monument (A. Funes and J. Agosta)

1979. Death Centenary of Sir Rowland Hill.
1650 **630** 300p. black, grey & red 45 20

1979. Bicentenary of Founding of Viedma and Carmen de Patagones Towns.
1651 **631** 300p. multicoloured . . 45 20

632 Pope Paul VI

633 Molinas Church

1979. Election of Pope John Paul I.
1652 **632** 500p. black 80 35
1653 – 500p. black 80 35
DESIGN: No. 1653, Pope John Paul I.

1979. Churches. Multicoloured.
1654 100p.+50p. Purmamarca Church 30 15
1655 200p.+100p. Type **633** . . . 45 20
1656 300p.+150p. Animana Church 50 35
1657 400p.+200p. San Jose de Lules Church 75 50

1979. 75th Anniv of Rosario Philatelic Society. No. 1545 optd **75 ANIV. SOCIEDAD FILATELICA DE ROSARIO**.
1658 200p. blue and black . . . 70 20

635 Children's Faces, and Sun on Map of Argentina

1979. Resettlement Policy.
1659 **635** 300p. yellow, black & bl . . 50 20

636 Stained-glass Window, Salta Cathedral

1979. Christmas.
1660 **636** 300p. multicoloured . . 55 20

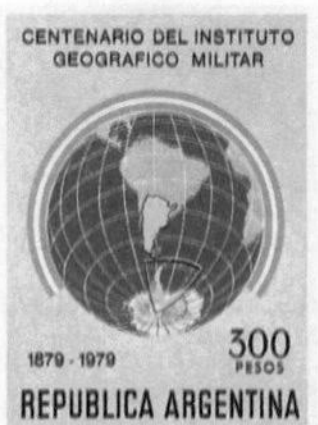

637 Institute Emblem

1979. Centenary of Military Geographical Institute.
1661 **637** 300p. multicoloured . . 70 20

638 General Mosconi and Oil Rig

1979. Birth Centenary of General Enrique Mosconi.
1662 **638** 1000p. blue and black . . 1·75 50

640 Rotary Emblem and Globe

1979. 75th Anniv of Rotary International.
1664 **640** 300p. multicoloured . . 1·00 25

641 Girl with Ruddy Ground Doves

642 Guillermo Brown

1979. International Year of the Child.
1665 **641** 500p. brown, blue & blk . . 90 40
1666 – 1000p. multicoloured . . 1·25 30
DESIGN: 1000p. "Family".

1980.
1667 **642** 5000p. black . . . . . . 2·75 20
1668 30000p. black and blue . . 2·00 50

643 I.T.U. Emblem and Microphone

1980. Regional Administrative Conference on Broadcasting, Buenos Aires.
1669 **643** 500p. blue, gold & ultram 80 30

644 Organization of American States Emblem

1980. Day of the Americas.
1670 **644** 500p. multicoloured . . 50 20

645 Angel

1980. Centenary of Argentinian Red Cross.
1671 **645** 500p. multicoloured . . 60 20

646 Salto Grande Hydro-electric Complex

1980. National Development Projects. Mult.
1672 300p. Type **646** 90 35
1673 300p. Zarate-Brazo Largo bridge 90 35
1674 300p. Dish aerials, Balcarce 50 20

647 Hipolito Bouchard and Sail Frigate "La Argentina"

1980. Navy Day.
1675 **647** 500p. multicoloured . . 1·25 30

648 "Villarino" and Woodcut of San Martin Theodore by Gericault

1980. Centenary of Return of General Jose de San Martin's Remains.
1676 **648** 500p. multicoloured . . 1·25 30

649 "Gazeta de Buenos-Ayres" and Signature of Dr. Mariano Moreno (first editor)

1980. Journalists' Day.
1677 **649** 500p. multicoloured . . 60 20

651 Soldier feeding Dove

1980. Army Day.
1679 **651** 500p. green, blk & gold . . 60 30

652 Lt. Gen. Aramburu

1980. 10th Death Anniv of Lt. Gen. Pedro Eugenio Aramburu.
1680 **652** 500p. yellow and black . . 50 20

653 Gen. Juan Gregorio de Las Heras

1980. National Heroes.
1681 **653** 500p. stone and black . . 60 20
1682 – 500p. yellow, blk & pur . . 60 20
1683 – 500p. mauve and black . . 60 20
DESIGNS: No. 1682, Bernardino Rivadavia; 1683, Brigadier-General Jose Matias Zapiola.

654 University of La Plata

1980. 75th Anniv of La Plata University.
1684 **654** 500p. multicoloured . . 60 20

655 Major Francisco de Arteaga and Avro 504K

1980. Air Force Day.
1685 **655** 500p. multicoloured . . 75 20

656 Flag and "Pencil" Figure

658 Congress Emblem

1980. National Census.
1686 **656** 500p. black and blue . . 1·25 20

657 King Penguin

1980. 75th Anniv of Argentine Presence in South Orkneys and 150th Anniv of Political and Military Command for the Malvinas. Multicoloured.
1687a 500p. Type **657** . . . . 1·00 85
1687b 500p. Bearded penguin . . 1·00 85
1687c 500p. Adelie penguin . . . 1·00 85
1687d 500p. Gentoo penguin . . 1·00 85
1687e 500p. Southern elephant seals . . . . 1·00 85
1687f 500p. Kerguelen fur seals 1·00 85
1687g 500p. South Orkney Naval Station . . . . 1·00 85
1687h 500p. South Orkney Naval Station (different) . . . 1·00 85
1687i 500p. "Puerto Soledad, Falkland Islands, 1829" by Luisa Vernet . . . . 1·00 85
1687j 500p. "Puerto Soledad, Falkland Islands, 1829" by Luisa Vernet (different) . . . . . 1·00 85
1687k 500p. Giant petrel . . . . 1·00 85
1687l 500p. Blue-eyed cormorant 1·00 85
1687m 500p. Snow petrel . . . . 1·00 85
1687n 500p. Snow sheathbill . . 1·00 85

1980. National Marian Congress, Mendoza.
1688 **658** 700p. multicoloured . . 50 15

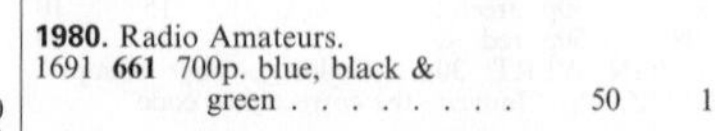

659 Heart pierced by Cigarette

661 Radio Antenna and Call Sign

1980. Anti-smoking Campaign.
1689 **659** 700p. multicoloured . . 60 20

1980. Radio Amateurs.
1691 **661** 700p. blue, black & green 50 15

662 Academy Emblem

663 Commemorative Medallion

1980. 50th Anniv of Technical Military Academy.
1692 **662** 700p. multicoloured . . 50 15

1980. Christmas. 150th Anniv of Appearance of Holy Virgin to St. Catherine Laboure.
1693 **663** 700p. multicoloured . . 50 15

664 Plan of Lujan Cathedral and Outline of Virgin

665 Simon Bolivar

1980. Christmas. 350th Anniv of Appearance of Holy Virgin at Lujan.
1694 **664** 700p. green and brown . . 50 15

1980. 150th Death Anniv of Simon Bolivar.
1695 **665** 700p. multicoloured . . 50 15

666 Football and Flags of Competing Nations

1981. Gold Cup Football Competition, Montevideo.
1696 **666** 1000p. multicoloured . . 85 20

667 "Lujan Landscape" (Marcos Tiglio)

1981. Paintings. Multicoloured.
1697 1000p. Type **667** 70 20
1698 1000p. "Effect of Light on Lines" (Miguel Angel Vidal) 70 20

668 Congress Emblem

1981. International Congress on Medicine and Sciences applied to Sport.
1699 **668** 1000p. blue, brown & blk 45 15

669 Esperanza Army Base, Antarctica

1981. 20th Anniv of Antarctic Treaty. Mult.
1700 1000p. Type **669** . . . . . 1·50 50
1701 2000p. Map of Vicecomodoro Marambio Island and De Havilland Twin Otter airplane (59½ × 25 mm) . . . . . 2·00 80
1702 2000p. Icebreaker "Almirante Irizar" . . . 3·00 95

670 Military Club

1981. Centenary of Military Club. Multicoloured.
1703 1000p. Type **670** 60 20
1704 2000p. Blunderbusses . . . 80 25

671 "Minuet" (Carlos E. Pellegrini)

1981. "Espamer '81" International Stamp Exhibition, Buenos Aires (1st issue).
1705 **671** 500p.+250p. purple, gold and brown 60 45
1706 – 700p.+350p. green, gold and brown 80 70
1707 – 800p.+400p. brown, gold and deep brown . . . 1·00 80
1708 – 1000p.+500p. mult . . . 1·25 1·10
DESIGNS: 700p. "La Media Cana" (Carlos Morel); 800p. "Cielito" (Carlos E. Pellegrini); 1000p. "El Gato" (Juan Leon Palliere).
See also Nos. 1719 and 1720/1.

672 Juan A. Alvarez de Arenales

1981. Celebrities' Anniversaries.
1709 **672** 1000p. black, yell & brn 70 20
1710 – 1000p. blk, pink & lilac 70 20
1711 – 1000p. black, pale green and green 70 20
DESIGNS: No. 1709, Type **672** (patriot, 150th death anniv); 1710, Felix G. Frias (writer and politician, death centenary); 1711, Jose E. Uriburu (statesman, 150th birth centenary).

1981. 50th Anniv of Bahia Blanca Philatelic and Numismatic Society. No. 1553 optd **50 ANIV DE LA ASOCIACION FILATELICA Y NUMISMATICA DE BAHIA BLANCA.**
1712 1000p. black and yellow . . 1·60 65

674 World Map divided into Time Zones and Sun

1981. Centenary of Naval Observatory.
1713 **674** 1000p. multicoloured . . 55 30

675 "St. Cayetano" (detail, stained-glass window, San Cayetano Basilica)

1981. 500th Death Anniv of St. Cayetano (founder of Teatino Order).
1714 **675** 1000p. multicoloured . . 45 20

676 Pablo Castaibert and Bleriot XI

1981. Air Force Day.
1715 **676** 1000p. multicoloured . . 75 20

677 First Argentine Blast Furnace, Sierra de Palpala

1981. 22nd Latin American Steel-makers Congress, Buenos Aires.
1716 **677** 1000p. multicoloured . . 45 20

678 Emblem of National Directorate for Special Education

680 "Espamer 81" Emblem and 15th-century Caravel

1981. International Year of Disabled People.
1717 **678** 1000p. multicoloured . . 50 20

1981. Campaign against Indiscriminate Whaling.
1718 **679** 1000p. multicoloured . . 2·25 25

1981. "Espamer 81" International Stamp Exhibition, Buenos Aires (2nd issue).
1719 **680** 1300p. pink, brn & blk 95 20

681 "San Martin at the Battle of Bailen" (equestrian statuette)

682 Argentine Army Emblem

1981. "Espamer 81" International Stamp Exhibition, Buenos Aires (3rd issue).
1720 **681** 1000p. multicoloured . . 20 15
1721 1500p. multicoloured . . 60 15

1981. Argentine Army. 175th Anniv of Infantry Regiment No. 1 "Patricios". Multicoloured.
1722 1500p. Type **682** 55 20
1723 1500p. "Patricios" badge . . 55 20

1981. Philatelic Services Course, Postal Union of the Americas and Spain Technical Training School, Buenos Aires. Optd **CURSO SUPERIOR DE ORGANIZACION DE SERVICIOS FILATELICOS-UPAE-BUENOS AIRES-1981.**
1724 **680** 1300p. pink, brn & blk 1·10 20

685 "Patacon" (one peso piece)

1981. Centenary of First Argentine Coins.
1726 **685** 2000p. silver, blk & pur 55 15
1727 – 3000p. gold, black & bl 70 20
DESIGN: 3000p. Argentine oro (five pesos piece).

686 Stained-glass Window, Church of Our Lady of Mercy, Tucuman

1981. Christmas.
1728 **686** 1500p. multicoloured . . 75 20

687 "Drive Carefully"

688 Francisco Luis Bernardez

679 Sperm Whale and Map of Argentina and Antarctica

1981. Road Safety. Multicoloured.
1729 1000p. "Observe traffic lights" . . . . 1·40 20
1730 2000p. Type **687** 90 25
1731 3000p. Zebra Crossing ("Cross at the white lines") (horiz) . . . . . . 1·00 35
1732 4000p. Headlights ("Don't dazzle") (horiz) . . . . . 1·25 45

1982. Authors. Multicoloured.
1733 1000p. Type **688** . . . . . 1·25 20
1734 2000p. Lucio V. Mansilla 85 25
1735 3000p. Conrado Nale Roxlo 1·10 35
1736 4000p. Victoria Ocampo . . 1·25 45

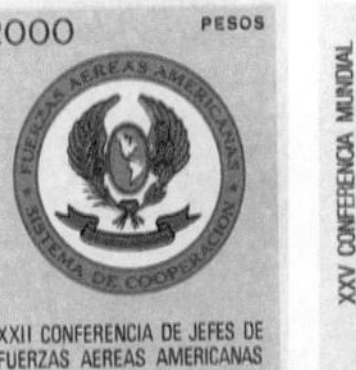

689 Emblem

690 Dr. Robert Koch

1982. 22nd American Air Force Commanders Conference, Buenos Aires.
1737 **689** 2000p. multicoloured . . 85 25

1982. 25th World Tuberculosis Conf, Buenos Aires.
1738 **690** 2000p. brown, red & blk 60 25

691 Pre-Columbian Artwork and Signature of Hernando de Lerma (founder)

1982. 400th Anniv of Salta City.
1739 **691** 2000p. green, blk & gold 80 25

1982. Argentine Invasion of the Falkland Islands. Optd **LAS MALVINAS SON ARGENTINAS.**
1741 **619** 1700p. blue and green 60 20

693 "Poseidon with Trophies of War" (sculpture) and Naval Centre Arms

1982. Centenary of Naval Centre.
1742 **693** 2000p. multicoloured . . 90 25

694 "Chorisia speciosa"

695 Juan C. Sanchez

1982. Flowers. Multicoloured.
1743 200p. "Zinnia peruviana" 10 10
1744 300p. "Ipomoea purpurea" 10 10
1745 400p. "Tillandsia aeranthos" 10 10
1746 500p. Type **694** 10 10
1747 800p. "Oncidium bifolium" 10 10
1748 1000p. "Erythrina crista-galli" 10 10
1749 2000p. "Jacaranda mimosifolia" 15 10
1750 3000p. "Bauhinia candicans" 50 10
1751 5000p. "Tecoma stans" . . 60 10
1752 10000p. "Tabebuia ipe" . . 90 15
1753 20000p. "Passiflora coerulea" . . . . 1·00 20
1754 30000p. "Aristolochia littoralis" . . . . 1·25 30
1755 50000p. "Oxalis enneaphylla" . . . . . . 2·40 40

1982. 10th Death Anniv of Lt. Gen. Juan C. Sanchez.
1761 **695** 5000p. multicoloured . . 80 25

696 Don Luis Verne (first Commander)

1982. 153rd Anniv of Political and Military Command for the Malvinas.
1762 **696** 5000p. black and brown 1·25 50
1763 – 5000p. light bl, blk & bl 90 35
DESIGN (82 × 28 mm): No. 1763, Map of the South Atlantic Islands.

697 Pope John Paul II

698 San Martin

1982. Papal Visit.
1764 **697** 5000p. multicoloured . . 1·00 55

1982.
1765 **698** 50000p. brown and red 4·00 50

699 "The Organ Player" (detail, Aldo Severi)
700 "Gen. de Sombras" (Sylvia Sieburger)

1982. Paintings. Multicoloured.
1766 2000p. Type **699** 65 20
1767 3000p. "Flowers" (Santiago Cogorno) 70 25

1982. "Argentine Philately". Tapestries. Mult.
1768 1000p.+500p. Type **700** . . 20 15
1769 2000p.+1000p. "Interpretation of a Rectangle" (Silke Haupt) 30 20
1770 3000p.+1500p. "Canal" (detail, Beatriz Bongliani) (horiz) . . . . 1·10 40
1771 4000p.+2000p. "Pueblito de Tilcara" (Tana Sachs) (horiz) 75 55

701 Petrol Pump and Sugar Cane
704 Map of Africa showing Namibia

703 Belt Buckle with Argentine Scout Emblem

1982. Alconafta (petrol-alcohol mixture) Campaign.
1772 **701** 2000p. multicoloured . . 40 10

1982. 50th Anniv of Tucuman Philatelic Society. No. 1751 optd **50 ANIVERSARIO SOCIEDAD FILATELICA DE TUCUMAN**.
1773 5000p. multicoloured . . . 1·60 90

1982. 75th Anniv of Boy Scout Movement.
1774 **703** 5000p. multicoloured . . 1·00 25

1982. Namibia Day.
1775 **704** 5000p. multicoloured . . 55 15

705 Rio Tercero Nuclear Power Station

1982. Atomic Energy. Multicoloured.
1776 2000p. Type **705** 40 10
1777 2000p. Control room of Rio Tercero power station . . 40 10

706 Our Lady of Itati, Corrientes
707 "Sidereal Tension" (M. A. Agatiello)

1982. Churches and Cathedrals of the North-east Provinces.
1778 **706** 2000p. green and black 50 15
1779 – 3000p. grey and purple 60 15
1780 – 5000p. blue and purple 80 20
1781 – 10000p. brown and black 1·25 40
DESIGNS—VERT: 3000p. Resistencia Cathedral, Chaco. HORIZ: 5000p. Formosa Cathedral; 10000p. Ruins of San Ignacio, Misiones.

1982. Art. Multicoloured.
1782 2000p. Type **707** 60 20
1783 3000p. "Sugerencia II" (E. MacEntyre) 70 20
1784 5000p. "Storm" (Carlos Silva) . . . . 1·00 25

708 Games Emblem and Santa Fe Bridge

1982. 2nd "Southern Cross" Games, Rosario and Santa Fe.
1785 **708** 2000p. blue and black 45 10

709 Volleyball

1982. 10th Men's Volleyball World Championship.
1786 **709** 2000p. multicoloured . . 30 10
1787 5000p. multicoloured . . 60 20

710 Road Signs

1982. 50th Anniv of National Roads Administration.
1788 **710** 5000p. multicoloured . . 60 20

711 Monument to the Army of the Andes

1982. Centenary of "Los Andes" Newspaper.
1789 **711** 5000p. multicoloured . . 50 20

712 La Plata Cathedral
714 Dr. Carlos Pellegrini (founder) (after J. Sorolla y Bastida)

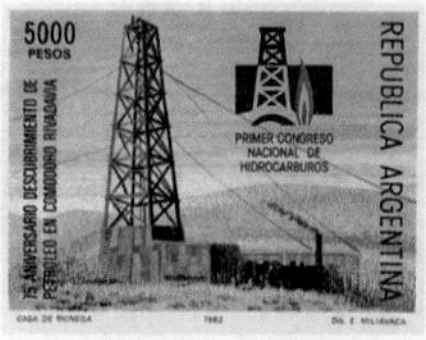

713 First Oil Rig

1982. Centenary of La Plata. Multicoloured.
1790 5000p. Type **712** 50 20
1791 5000p. Municipal Palace . . 50 20

1982. 75th Anniv of Discovery of Oil in Comodoro Rivadavia.
1793 **713** 5000p. multicoloured . . 50 25

1982. Cent of Buenos Aires Jockey Club. Mult.
1794 5000p. Jockey Club emblem 55 20
1795 5000p. Type **714** 55 20

715 Cross of St. Damian, Assisi
716 "St. Vincent de Paul" (stained-glass window, Our Lady of the Miraculous Medal, Buenos Aires)

1982. 800th Birth Anniv of St. Francis of Assisi.
1796 **715** 5000p. multicoloured . . 1·00 20

1982. Christmas.
1797 **716** 3000p. multicoloured . . 1·40 40

717 Pedro B. Palacios

1982. Authors. Each red and green.
1798 1000p. Type **717** 15 10
1799 2000p. Leopoldo Marechal 20 10
1800 3000p. Delfina Bunge de Galvez 25 10
1801 4000p. Manuel Galvez . . . 50 15
1802 5000p. Evaristo Carriego . . 65 15

718 Argentine Flag and Map of South Atlantic Islands ($\frac{1}{2}$-size illustration)

1983. 1st Anniv of Argentine Invasion of Falkland Islands.
1803 **718** 20000p. multicoloured 95 35

719 Sitram (automatic message transmission service) Emblem

1983. Information Technology. Multicoloured
1804 5000p. Type **719** . . . . . 1·00 20
1805 5000p. Red Arpac (data communications system) emblem . . . . 1·00 20

720 Naval League Emblem

1983. Navy Day. 50th Anniv of Naval League.
1806 **720** 5000p. multicoloured . . 50 15

721 Allegorical Figure (Victor Rebuffo)

1983. 25th Anniv of National Arts Fund.
1807 **721** 5000p. multicoloured . . 45 15

722 Golden Saloon

1983. 75th Anniv of Columbus Theatre, Buenos Aires. Multicoloured.
1808 5000p. Type **722** 70 15
1809 10000p. Stage curtain . . . 90 20

(Currency reform. 10000 (old) pesos = 1 (new) peso.)

723 Marbles

1983. Argentine Philately. Children's Games (1st series). Multicoloured.
1810 20c.+10c. Type **723** 15 10
1811 30c.+15c. Skipping 30 15
1812 50c.+25c. Hopscotch 40 25
1813 1p.+50c. Boy with kite . . . 60 40
1814 2p.+1p. Boy with spinning top 70 55
See also Nos. 1870/4.

724 Maned Wolf

1983. Protected Animals (1st series). Mult.
1815 1p. Type **724** 35 10
1816 1p.50 Pampas deer 55 15
1817 2p. Giant anteater 60 15
1818 2p.50 Jaguar 75 25
See also Nos 1883/87.

1983. Flowers. As T **694** but inscr in new currency. Multicoloured.
1819 5c. Type **694** 40 10
1820 10c. "Erythrina crista-galli" 10 10
1821 20c. "Jacaranda mimosifolia" 10 10
1822 30c. "Bauhinia candicans" . . 35 10
1823 40c. "Eichhornia crassipes" 10 10
1824 50c. "Tecoma stans" . . . 10 10
1825 1p. "Tabebuia ipe" 10 10
1826 1p.80 "Mutisia retusa" . . . 15 10
1827 2p. "Passiflora coerulea" . . 20 10
1828 3p. "Aristolochia littoralis" 30 10
1829 5p. "Oxalis enneaphylla" . . 50 10
1830 10p. "Alstroemeria aurantiaca" 40 10
1831 20p. "Ipomoea purpurea" 40 10
1832 30p. "Embothrium coccineum" 40 15
1833 50p. "Tillandsia aeranthos" 45 15
1834 100p. "Oncidium bifolium" 65 15
1835 300p. "Cassia carnaval" . . 1·60 45

725 "Founding of City of Catamarca" (detail, Luis Varela Lezana)

1983. 300th Anniv of San Fernando del Valle de Catamarca.
1836 **725** 1p. multicoloured . . . 30 10

726 Brother Mamerto Esquiu

727 Bolivar (painting by Herrera Toro after engraving by C. Turner)

1983. Death Centenary of Brother Mamerto Esquiu, Bishop of Cordoba.
1837 **726** 1p. black, red and grey 30 10

1983. Birth Bicentenary of Simon Bolivar.
1838 **727** 1p. multicoloured . . . 30 10
1839 – 2p. red and black . . . 60 15
DESIGN: 2p. Bolivar (engraving by Kepper).

728 San Martin

729 Gen. Toribio de Luzuriaga

1983.
1840 **728** 10p. green and black . . 2·50 45
1841 – 20p. blue and black . . 90 40
1842 **728** 50p. brown and blue . . 2·00 45
1843 – 200p. black and blue . . 1·25 45
1844 – 500p. blue and brown . . 1·75 25
DESIGNS: 20, 500p. Guillermo Brown; 200p. Manuel Belgrano.

1983. Birth Bicentenary (1982) of Gen. Toribio de Luzuriaga.
1845 **729** 1p. multicoloured . . . 30 10

730 Grand Bourg House, Buenos Aires

1983. 50th Anniv of Sanmartinian National Institute.
1846 **730** 2p. brown and black . . 55 15

731 Dove and Rotary Emblem

1983. Rotary International South American Regional Conference, Buenos Aires.
1847 **731** 1p. multicoloured . . . 55 20

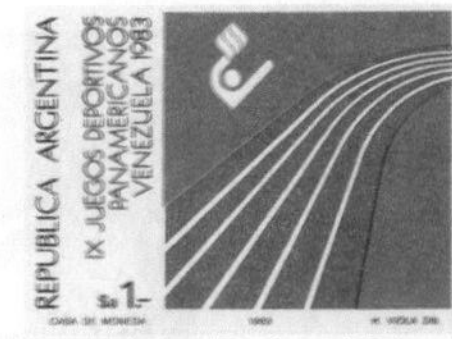
732 Running Track and Games Emblem

1983. 9th Pan-American Games, Venezuela.
1848 **732** 1p. red, green & black 35 15
1849 – 2p. multicoloured . . . 60 25
DESIGN: 2p. Games emblem.

733 W.C.Y. Emblem

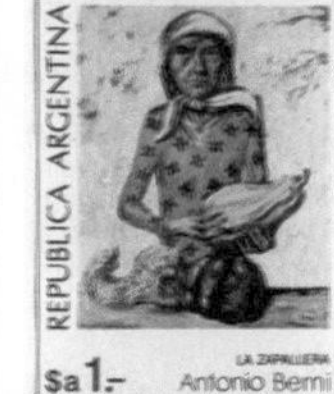
734 "The Squash Peddler" (Antonio Berni)

1983. World Communications Year (1st issue).
1850 **733** 2p. multicoloured . . . 55 20
See also Nos. 1853/6 and 1857.

1983. Argentine Paintings. Multicoloured.
1851 1p. Type **734** 35 10
1852 2p. "Figure in Yellow" (Luis Seoane) 55 20

735 Ox-drawn Wagon

736 "Central Post Office, Buenos Aires" (Lola Frexas)

1983. World Communications Year (2nd issue). Mail Transport. Multicoloured.
1853 1p. Type **735** 45 10
1854 2p. Horse-drawn mail cart 50 15
1855 4p. Locomotive "La Portena" . . . . 1·25 50
1856 5p. Tram . . . . 1·25 50

1983. World Communications Year (3rd issue).
1857 **736** 2p. multicoloured . . . 35 15

737 Rockhopper Penguin

738 Coin of 1813

1983. Fauna and Pioneers of Southern Argentina. Multicoloured.
1858a 2p. Type **737** 40 25
1858b 2p. Wandering albatross 40 25
1858c 2p. Black-browed albatross 40 25
1858d 2p. Macaroni penguin . . 40 25
1858e 2p. Luis Piedra Buena (after Juan R. Mezzadra) 40 15
1858f 2p. Carlos Maria Moyano (after Mezzadra) 40 15
1858g 2p. Luis Py (after Mezzadra) 40 15
1858h 2p. Augusto Lasserre (after Horacio Alvarez Boero) 40 15
1858i 2p. Light-mantled sooty albatross 40 25
1858j 2p. Leopard seal 40 15
1858k 2p. Crabeater seal 40 15
1858l 2p. Weddell seal 40 15

1983. Transfer of Presidency.
1859 **738** 2p. silver, black and blue 35 15

739 "Christmas Manger" (tapestry by Silke)

1983. Christmas. Multicoloured.
1860 2p. Type **739** 35 15
1861 3p. Stained-glass window, San Carlos de Bariloche Church 55 20

740 Printing Cylinder and Newspaper

1984. Centenary of "El Dia" Newspaper.
1862 **740** 4p. multicoloured . . . 40 15

741 Compass Rose

1984. "Espana 84" (Madrid) and "Argentina 85" (Buenos Aires) International Stamp Exhibitions (1st issue). Multicoloured.
1863 5p.+2p.50 Type **741** 50 15
1864 5p.+2p.50 Arms of Spain and Argentine Republic 50 15
1865 5p.+2p.50 Arms of Christopher Columbus . . 50 15
1866 5p.+2p.50 "Nina" . . . . . 1·25 45
1867 5p.+2p.50 "Pinta" . . . . . 1·25 45
1868 5p.+2p.50 "Santa Maria" 1·25 45
See also Nos. 1906/10, 1917/18 and 1920/4.

742 College

1984. Centenary of Alejandro Carbo Teacher Training College, Cordoba.
1869 **742** 10p. multicoloured . . . 40 15

1984. Argentine Philately. Children's Games (2nd series). As T **723**. Multicoloured.
1870 2p.+1p. Blind man's buff . . 20 15
1871 3p.+1p.50 Girls throwing hoop 30 25
1872 4p.+2p. Leap frog 40 35
1873 5p.+2p.50 Boy rolling hoop 55 45
1874 6p.+3p. Ball and stick . . . 60 55

743 Rowing and Basketball

1984. Olympic Games, Los Angeles. Mult.
1875 5p. Type **743** 25 15
1876 5p. Weightlifting and discus 25 15
1877 10p. Cycling and swimming 45 20
1878 10p. Pole vault and fencing 45 20

744 Wheat

1984. Food Supplies. Multicoloured.
1879 10p. Type **744** (18th F.A.O. Latin American Regional Conference, Buenos Aires) 40 20
1880 10p. Sunflowers (World Food Day) 40 20
1881 10p. Maize (3rd National Maize Congress, Pergamino) 40 20

745 Stock Exchange

1984. Centenary of Rosario Stock Exchange.
1882 **745** 10p. multicoloured . . . 40 20

1984. Protected Animals (2nd series). As T **724**. Multicoloured.
1883 20p. Brazilian merganser . . 65 20
1884 20p. Black-fronted piping guan 65 20
1885 20p. Hooded grebes 65 20
1886 20p. Vicunas 65 20
1887 20p. Chilean guemal 65 20

746 Festival Emblem

1984. 1st Latin American Theatre Festival, Cordoba.
1888 **746** 20p. multicoloured . . . 25 15

747 "Apostles' Communion" (detail, Fra Angelico)

1984. 50th Anniv of Buenos Aires International Eucharist Congress.
1889 **747** 20p. multicoloured . . . 25 15

748 Antonio Oneto and Railway Station (Puerto Deseado)

1984. City Centenaries. Multicoloured.
1890 20p. Type **748** 75 25
1891 20p. 19th-century view and sail/steam corvette "Parana" (Ushuaia) . . . 1·25 35

749 Glacier

1984. World Heritage Site. Los Glaciares National Park. Multicoloured.
1892 20p. Glacier (different) . . . 30 10
1893 30p. Type **749** 40 15

1984. 50th Anniv of Buenos Aires Philatelic Centre. No. 1830 optd **1934–50°ANIVERSARIO-1984 CENTRO FILATELICO BUENOS-AIRES**.
1894 10p. multicoloured 20 15

751 "Jesus and the Star" (Diego Aguero)

1984. Christmas. Multicoloured.
1895 20p. Type **751** 30 15
1896 30p. "The Three Kings" (Leandro Ruiz) 40 15
1897 50p. "The Holy Family" (Maria Castillo) (vert) . . 60 20

752 "Sheds (La Boca)" (Marcos Borio)
753 Angel J. Carranza (historian, 150th)

1984. Argentine Paintings. Multicoloured.
1898 20p. Type **752** 30 20
1899 20p. "View of the Zoo" (Fermin Eguia) (horiz) . . 35 20
1900 20p. "Floodlit Congress Building" (Francisco Travieso) 30 20

1985. Birth Anniversaries.
1901 **753** 10p. deep blue & blue 40 10
1902 – 20p. deep brown & brn 40 10
1903 – 30p. deep blue & blue 45 15
1904 – 40p. black and green . . 70 15
DESIGNS: 20p. Estanislao del Campo (poet, 150th); 30p. Jose Hernandez (journalist, 150th); 40p. Vicente Lopez y Planes (President of Argentine Confederation 1827–28, birth bicent).

754 Guemes and "Infernal" (soldier)

1985. Birth Bicentenary of General Martin Miguel de Guemes (Independence hero).
1905 **754** 30p. multicoloured . . . 30 15

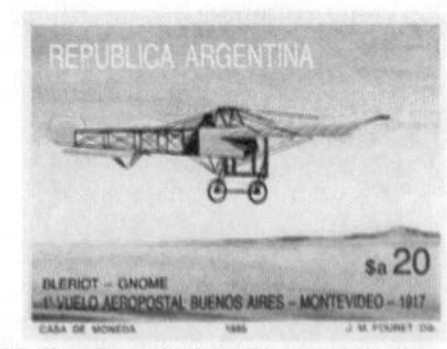

755 Teodoro Fels's Bleriot XI Gnome

1985. "Argentina '85" International Stamp Exhibition, Buenos Aires (2nd issue). First Airmail Flights. Multicoloured.
1906 20p. Type **755** (Buenos Aires–Montevideo, 1917) 30 10
1907 40p. Junkers F-13L (Cordoba–Villa Dolores, 1925) 50 15
1908 60p. Saint-Exupery's Latecoere 25 (first Bahia Blanca-Comodoro Rivadavia, 1929) 75 25
1909 80p. "Graf Zeppelin" airship (Argentina-Germany, 1934) . . . . . 1·10 45
1910 100p. Consolidated PBY-5A Catalina amphibian (to Argentine Antarctic, 1952) 1·25 60

756 Central Bank

1985. 50th Anniv of Central Bank, Buenos Aires.
1911 **756** 80p. multicoloured . . . 40 20

757 Jose A. Ferreyra and "Munequitas Portenas"

1985. Argentine Film Directors. Multicoloured.
1912 100p. Type **757** 45 25
1913 100p. Leopoldo Torre Nilsson and "Martin Fierro" 45 25

758 "Carlos Gardel" (Hermenegildo Sabat)

1985. 50th Death Anniv of Carlos Gardel (entertainer). Multicoloured.
1914 200p. Type **758** 65 25
1915 200p. "Carlos Gardel" (Carlos Alonso) 65 25
1916 200p. "Carlos Gardel" (Aldo Severi and Martiniano Arce) 65 25

759 "The Arrival" (Pedro Figari)

1985. "Argentina '85" International Stamp Exhibition (3rd issue). Multicoloured.
1917 20c. Type **759** 65 25
1918 30c. "Mail Coach Square" (detail, Cesareo B. de Quiros) 75 25

760 Cover of 1917 Teodoro Fels Flight

1985. "Argentina '85" International Stamp Exhibition (4th issue). Multicoloured.
1920 10c. Type **760** 40 15
1921 10c. Cover of 1925 Cordoba–Villa Dolores flight 40 15
1922 10c. Cover of 1929 Saint-Exupery flight 40 15
1923 10c. Cover of 1934 "Graf Zeppelin" flight 40 15
1924 10c. Cover of 1952 Antarctic flight 40 15

1985. Flowers. As T **694** but with currency expressed as "A". Multicoloured.
1930 ½c. "Oxalis enneaphylla" 40 10
1931 1c. "Alstroemeria aurantiaca" 10 10
1932 2c. "Ipomoea purpurea" 10 10
1933 3c. "Embothrium coccineum" 10 10
1934a 5c. "Tillandsia aeranthos" 10 10
1927 8½c. "Erythrina crista-galli" 25 10
1935a 10c. "Oncidium bifolium" 40 10
1936a 20c. "Chorisia speciosa" 35 10
1937 30c. "Cassia carnaval" . . 40 10
1938 50c. "Zinnnia peruviana" 65 10
1941 1a. "Begonia micranthera var. Hieronymi" 80 10
1941a 2a. "Bauhinia candicans" 10 10
1942 5a. "Gymnocalyciun bruchii" 10 10
1942a 10a. "Eichhornia crassipes" 10 10
1942b 20a. "Mutisia retusa" . . . 10 10
1942c 50a. Passion flower 10 10
1943 100a. "Alstroemeria aurantiaca" 10 10
1943a 300a. "Ipomoea purpurea" 10 10
1943b 500a. "Embothrium coccineum" 10 10
1943c 1000a. "Aristolochia littoralis" 20 10
1943d 5000a. "Erythrina crista-galli" . . . . 1·25 10
1943e 10000a. "Jacaranda mimosifolia" . . . . . 4·00 55
No. 1927 is 15 × 23 mm, the remainder 22 × 32 mm.

761 "Woman with Bird" (Juan del Prete)
762 Musical Bow

1985. Argentine Paintings. Multicoloured.
1944 20c. Type **761** 75 30
1945 30c. "Illuminated Fruits" (Fortunato Lacamera) . . 75 30

1985. Traditional Musical Instruments. Mult.
1946 20c. Type **762** 60 20
1947 20c. Long flute with drum accompaniment 60 20
1948 20c. Frame drum 60 20
1949 20c. Pan's flute 60 20
1950 20c. Jew's harp 60 20

763 Juan Bautista Alberdi (writer)

1985. Anniversaries.
1951 10c. Type **763** (death centenary (1984)) 25 15
1952 20c. Nicolas Avellaneda (President 1874–80, death centenary) 50 25
1953 30c. Brother Luis Beltran (Independence hero, birth bicentenary (1984)) . . . 75 25
1954 40c. Ricardo Levene (historian) (birth centenary) 90 25

764 Roller Skaters

1985. International Youth Year.
1955 **764** 20c. black and blue . . . 60 20
1956 – 30c. multicoloured . . . 65 30
DESIGN: 30c. "Disappointment".

765 "Rothschildia jacobaeae"

1985. Argentine Philately. Butterflies.
1958 5c.+2c. Type **765** 35 10
1959 10c.+5c. "Heliconius erato phyllis" 55 20
1960 20c.+10c. "Precis evarete hilaris" . . . . 1·10 40
1961 25c.+13c. "Cyanopepla pretiosa" . . . . 1·40 55
1962 40c.+20c. "Papilio androgeus" . . . . 1·75 90

766 Forclaz Windmill (Entre Rios)
768 "Birth of Our Lord" (Carlos Cortes)

767 Hand holding White Stick

1985. Tourism. Argentine Provinces. Mult.
1963 10c. Type **766** 40 10
1964 10c. Sierra de la Ventana (Buenos Aires) 40 10
1965 10c. Potrero de los Funes artificial lake (San Luis) 40 10
1966 10c. Church belfry (North-west Argentina) 40 10
1967 10c. Magellanic penguins, Punta Tombo (Chubut) 1·00 30
1968 10c. Sea of Mirrors (Cordoba) 40 10

1985. National Campaign for the Prevention of Blindness.
1969 **767** 10c. multicoloured . . . 40 10

1985. Christmas. Multicoloured.
1970 10c. Type **768** 30 15
1971 20c. "Christmas" (Hector Viola) 80 25

769 Rio Gallegos Cathedral

1985. Centenary of Rio Gallegos.
1972 **769** 10c. multicoloured . . . 50 10

770 Grape Harvesting

1986. 50th Anniv of Grape Harvest Nat Festival.
1973 **770** 10c. multicoloured . . . 40 10

771 House of Valentin Alsina (Italian Period)

1986. Buenos Aires Architecture, 1880–1930. Mult.
1974 20c. Type **771** 55 20
1975 20c. 1441 Calle Cerrito (French period) 55 20
1976 20c. Customs House (Academic period) (horiz) 55 20
1977 20c. House, Avenido de Mayo (Art Nouveau) . . 55 20
1978 20c. Isaac Fernandez Blanco Museum (National Restoration period) (horiz) 55 20

772 Jubany Base
773 "Foundation of Nereid" (detail, Lola Mora)

1986. Argentine Antarctic Research. Mult.
1979 10c. Type **772** 60 20
1980 10c. Kerguelen fur seal . . . 60 20
1981 10c. Southern sealion . . . 60 20
1982 10c. General Belgrano Base 60 20
1983 10c. Pintado petrel . . . . 1·00 40

1984 10c. Black-browed albatross 1·00 40
1985 10c. King penguin . . . . . 1·00 40
1986 10c. Giant petrel . . . . . 1·00 40
1987 10c. Hugo Alberto Acuna (explorer) 60 20
1988 10c. Magellanic penguin . . 1·00 40
1989 10c. Magellan snipe . . . . 1·00 40
1990 10c. Capt. Augustin Servando del Castillo (explorer) 60 20

1986. Sculpture. Multicoloured.
1991 20c. Type **773** 85 25
1992 30c. "Work Song" (detail, Rogelio Yrurtia) . . . . 1·25 40

774 Dr. Alicia Moreau de Justo (suffragist, d. 1986)
775 Dr. Francisco Narciso Laprida

1986. Anniversaries.
1993 **774** 10c. black, yellow & brn 30 10
1994 – 10c. black, turq & blue 30 10
1995 – 30c. black, red & mauve 65 30
DESIGNS: No. 1994, Dr. Emilio Ravignani (historian, birth centenary); 1995, Indira Gandhi (Prime Minister of India, 1st death anniv).

1986. Birth Bicentenaries of Independence Heroes. Each brown, yellow and black.
1996 20c. Type **775** 50 45
1997 20c. Brig. Gen. Estanislao Lopez 50 45
1998 20c. Gen. Francisco Ramirez 50 45

776 Namuncura
777 Drawing by Nazarena Pastor

1986. Birth Centenary of Ceferino Namuncura (first Indian seminary student).
1999 **776** 20c. multicoloured . . . 25 15

1986. Argentine Philately. Children's Drawings. Multicoloured.
2000 5c.+2c. Type **777** 15 15
2001 10c.+5c. Girl and boy holding flowers and balloon (Tatiana Valleistein) (horiz) 20 20
2002 20c.+10c. Boy and girl (Juan Manel Flores) 70 70
2003 25c.+13c. Town and waterfront (Marcelo E. Pezzuto) (horiz) . . . 85 85
2004 40c.+20c. Village (Esteban Diehl) (horiz) . . . . . . 1·00 1·00

1986. No. 1825 surch **A0,10**.
2005 10c. on 1p. "Tabebuia ipe" 65 30

779 Argentine Team (value top left)

1986. Argentina, World Cup Football Championship (Mexico) Winners. Multicoloured.
2006 75c. Type **779** . . . . . . 1·10 1·10
2007 75c. Argentine team (value top right) . . . . . . 1·10 1·10
2008 75c. Argentine team (value bottom left) . . . . . . 1·10 1·10
2009 75c. Argentine team (value bottom right) . . . . . . 1·10 1·10
2010 75c. Player shooting for goal 1·10 1·10
2011 75c. Player tackling and goalkeeper on ground . . 1·10 1·10
2012 75c. Player number 11 . . . 1·10 1·10
2013 75c. Player number 7 . . . 1·10 1·10
2014 75c. Crowd and Argentina player . . . . 1·10 1·10
2015 75c. West German player . . 1·10 1·10
2016 75c. Goalkeeper on ground 1·10 1·10
2017 75c. Footballers' legs . . . 1·10 1·10
2018 75c. Hand holding World Cup trophy . . . . . . 1·10 1·10
2019 75c. Raised arm and crowded stadium . . . . 1·10 1·10
2020 75c. People with flags and cameras . . . . 1·10 1·10
2021 75c. Player's body and crowd . . . . 1·10 1·10
Nos. 2006/13 were printed together se-tenant in a sheetlet of eight stamps arranged in two blocks, each block forming a composite design. Nos. 2014/21 were similarly arranged in a second sheetlet.

780 Municipal Building

1986. Centenary of San Francisco City.
2022 **780** 20c. multicoloured . . . 50 20

781 Old Railway Station

1986. Centenary of Trelew City.
2023 **781** 20c. multicoloured . . . 1·00 45

782 Emblem and Colours

1986. Mutualism Day.
2024 **782** 20c. multicoloured . . . 25 15

783 "Primitive Retable" (Aniko Szabo)

1986. Christmas. Multicoloured.
2025 20c. Type **783** 50 10
2026 30c. "Everybody's Tree" (Franca Delacqua) . . . 60 15

784 St. Rosa of Lima
785 Municipal Building

1986. 400th Birth Anniv of St. Rosa de Lima.
2027 **784** 50c. multicoloured . . . 80 20

1986. Anniversaries. Multicoloured.
2028 20c. Type **785** (bicentenary of Rio Cuarto city) . . . 40 10
2029 20c. Palace of Justice, Cordoba (50th anniv) . . 40 10

786 Marine Biology

1987. 25th Anniv of Antarctic Treaty. Mult.
2030 20c. Type **786** 80 20
2031 30c. Study of native birds 1·75 30

787 Emblem

1987. Centenary of National Mortgage Bank.
2033 **787** 20c. yellow, brown & blk 20 15

788 Stylized Pine Trees

1987. Argentine Co-operative Movement.
2034 **788** 20c. multicoloured . . . 20 15

789 Pope

1987. 2nd Visit of Pope John Paul II.
2035 **789** 20c. blue and red 40 10
2036 – 80c. brown and green . . 1·00 55
DESIGN: 80c. Pope in robes with Crucifix.

790 Flag forming "PAZ" (peace)

1987. International Peace Year.
2038 **790** 20c. blue, dp blue & blk 45 15
2039 – 30c. multicoloured . . . 55 20
DESIGN: 30c. "Pigeon" (sculpture, Victor Kaniuka).

791 "Polo Players" (Alejandro Moy)
792 "Supplicant" (Museum of Natural Sciences, La Plata)

1987. World Polo Championships, Palermo.
2040 **791** 20c. multicoloured . . . 80 15

1987. 14th International Museums Council General Conference, Buenos Aires. Multicoloured.
2041 25c. Conference emblem . . 45 15
2042 25c. Shield of Potosi (National History Museum, Buenos Aires) 45 15
2043 25c. Statue of St. Bartholomew (Enrique Larreta Spanish Art Museum, Buenos Aires) 45 15
2044 25c. Cudgel with animal design (Patagonia Museum, San Carlos de Bariloche) 45 15
2045 25c. Type **792** 45 15
2046 25c. Grate from Argentine Confederation House (Entre Rios Historical Museum, Parana) 45 15
2047 25c. Statue of St. Joseph (Northern Historical Museum, Salta) 45 15
2048 25c. Funeral urn (Provincial Archaeological Museum, Santiago del Estero) . . . 45 15

793 Pillar Box
794 Spotted Metynis ("Metynnis maculatus")

1987. No value expressed. (a) Inscr "C" and "TARIFA INTERNA/HASTA 10 GRAMOS".
2049 **793** (18c.) red, black & yell 1·25 15

(b) Inscr "C" and "TARIFA INTERNA/DE 11 A 20 GRAMOS".
2050 **793** (33c.) black, yell & grn 1·60 15

1987. Argentine Philately. River Fishes. Mult.
2051 10c.+5c. Type **794** 35 10
2052 10c.+5c. Black-finned pearlfish ("Cynolebias nigripinnis") 35 10
2053 10c.+5c. Solar's leporinus ("Leporinus solarii") . . 35 10
2054 10c.+5c. Red-flanked bloodfin ("Aphyocharax rathbuni") 35 10
2055 10c.+5c. Bronze catfish ("Corydoras aeneus") . . 35 10
2056 10c.+5c. Giant hatchetfish ("Thoracocharax securis") 35 10
2057 10c.+5c. Black-striped pearlfish ("Cynolebias melanotaenia") 35 10
2058 10c.+5c. Chanchito cichlid ("Cichlasoma facetum") 35 10
2059 20c.+10c. Silver tetra ("Tetragonopterus argente") 65 25
2060 20c.+10c. Buenos Aires tetra ("Hemigrammus caudovittatus") 65 25
2061 20c.+10c. Two-spotted astyanax ("Astyanax bimaculatus") 65 25
2062 20c.+10c. Black widow tetra ("Gymnocorymbus ternetzi") 65 25
2063 20c.+10c. Trahira ("Hoplias malabaricus") 65 25
2064 20c.+10c. Blue-finned tetra ("Aphyocharax rubripinnis") 65 25
2065 20c.+10c. Agassiz's dwarf cichlid ("Apistogramma agassizi") 65 25
2066 20c.+10c. Fanning pyrrhulina ("Pyrrhulina rachoviana") 65 25

796 Jorge Luis Borges (writer)

1987. Anniversaries. Multicoloured.
2068 20c. Type **796** (1st death anniv) 25 10
2069 30c. Armando Discepolo, (dramatist and theatre director, birth cent) . . . 40 15
2070 50c. Dr Carlos Alberto Pueyrredon (historian, birth centenary) 65 20

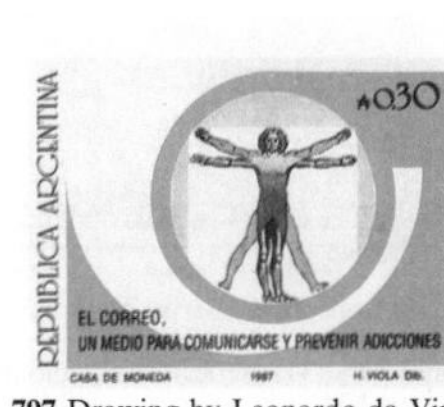

797 Drawing by Leonardo da Vinci

1987. "The Post, a Medium for Communication and Prevention of Addictions".
2071 **797** 30c. multicoloured . . . 40 15

798 "The Sower" (Julio Vanzo)

1987. 75th Anniv of Argentine Farmers' Union.
2072 **798** 30c. multicoloured . . . 40 15

799 Basketball **800** Col. Maj. Ignacio Alvarez Thomas

1987. 10th Pan-American Games, Indianapolis. Multicoloured.
2073 20c. Type **799** 40 10
2074 30c. Rowing 45 15
2075 50c. Dinghies 65 15

1987. Anniversaries. Multicoloured.
2076 25c. Type **800** (birth bicent) 35 10
2077 25c. Col. Manuel Dorrego (birth bicentenary) 35 10
2078 50c. 18th-century Spanish map of Falkland Islands (death bicentenary of Jacinto de Altolaguirre, governor of Islands) (horiz) 60 20
2079 50c. "Signing the Accord" (Rafael del Villar) (50th anniv of House of Accord Museum, San Nicolas) (horiz) 60 20

801 Children as Nurse and Mother

1987. U.N.I.C.E.F. Child Vaccination Campaign.
2080 **801** 30c. multicoloured . . . 40 15

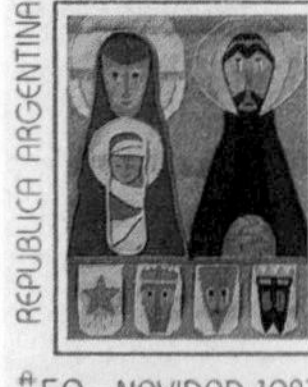

802 Balloon **803** "Nativity" (tapestry, Alisia Frega)

1987. Anniversaries. Multicoloured.
2081 50c. Type **802** (50th anniv of LRA National Radio) . . 40 20
2082 50c. Celendonio Galvan Moreno (first editor) (50th anniv of "Postas Argentinas" magazine) . . 40 20
2083 1a. Dr. Jose Marco del Pont (founder) (centenary of Argentine Philatelic Society) 60 25

1987. Christmas. Multicoloured.
2084 50c. Type **803** 35 25
2085 1a. Doves and flowers (tapestry, Silvina Trigos) 45 25

804 Crested Oropendola, Baritu National Park

1987. National Parks (1st series). Multicoloured.
2086 50c. Type **804** . . . . . 1·00 40
2087 50c. Otter, Nahuel Huapi National Park 65 30
2088 50c. Night monkey, Rio Pilcomayo National Park 65 30
2089 50c. Kelp goose, Tierra del Fuego National Park . . 1·00 40
2090 50c. Alligator, Iguazu National Park 65 30
See also Nos. 2150/4, 2222/6 and 2295/9.

805 "Caminito" (Jose Canella)

1988. Historical and Tourist Sites. Multicoloured.
2090a 3a. "Purmamarca" (Nestor Martin) (33 × 22 mm) . . 60 20
2091 5a. Type **805** . . . . . . 1·75 30
2092 10a. "Old Almacen" (Jose Canella) (A) . . . . . . 3·25 1·50
2092a 10a. "Old Almacen" (Jose Canella) (B) . . . . . . 1·00 45
2095 20a. "Ushuaia" (Nestor Martin) (vert) . . . . . 2·75 1·10
2099 50a. Type **805** 75 10
10a. A. Inscr "Viejo Almacen". B. Inscr "El Viejo Almacen".

806 "Minstrel singing in a Grocer's Shop" (Carlos Morel)

1988. Argentine Paintings. Multicoloured.
2105 1a. Type **806** 50 15
2106 1a. "Curuzu" (detail, Candido Lopez) 50 15

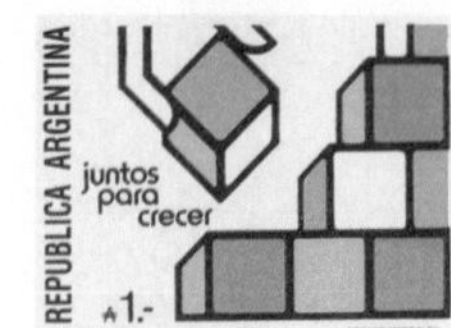

807 Hand arranging Coloured Cubes

1988. Argentine–Brazil Economic Co-operation.
2107 **807** 1a. multicoloured . . . 45 15

808 St. Anne's Chapel, Corrientes

1988. 400th Annivs of Corrientes and Alta Gracia. Multicoloured.
2108 1a. Type **808** 45 15
2109 1a. Alta Gracia church . . . 45 15

809 Men Stacking Sacks

1988. Labour Day. Details of mural "Cereals" (Nueve de Julio station, Buenos Aires underground railway). Multicoloured.
2110 50c. Type **809** 70 70
2111 50c. Sacks 70 70
2112 50c. Men unloading truck 70 70
2113 50c. Horse and cart 70 70
Nos. 2110/13 were printed together, se-tenant, forming a composite design.

810 Steam Locomotive "Yatay" and Tender, 1888 (½-size illustration)

1988. "Prenfil '88" Philatelic Literature Exhibition, Buenos Aires (1st issue). Railways. Multicoloured.
2114 1a.+50c. Type **810** 35 35
2115 1a.+50c. Electric passenger coach, 1914 . . . . . 35 35
2116 1a.+50c. Type B-15 locomotive and tender, 1942 35 35
2117 1a.+50c. Type GT-22 diesel locomotive, 1988 . . . . 35 35
See also Nos. 2134/7.

811 Running

1988. Olympic Games, Seoul. Multicoloured.
2118 1a. Type **811** 35 10
2119 2a. Football 45 15
2120 3a. Hockey 55 20
2121 4a. Tennis 65 35

812 Bank Facade

1988. Centenary of Bank of Mendoza.
2122 **812** 2a. multicoloured . . . 20 15

813 Arms of Guemes and National Guard Emblem **814** "St. Cayetano (patron saint of workers)" (C. Quaglia)

1988. 50th Anniv of National Guard.
2123 **813** 2a. multicoloured . . . 20 15

1988. Philatelic Anniversaries and Events. Mult.
2124 2a. Type **814** (50th anniv of Liniers (Buenos Aires) Philatelic Circle) 45 15
2125 3a. "Our Lady of Carmen (patron saint of Cuyo)" (window, Carlos Quaglia) (50th anniv of West Argentina Philatelic Society) 60 20

815 Sarmiento (after Mario Chierico) and Cathedral of the North School

1988. Death Centenary of Domingo Faustino Sarmiento (President, 1868–74).
2127 **815** 3a. multicoloured . . . 35 20

816 "San Isidro" (Enrique Castro)

1988. Horse Paintings. Multicoloured.
2128 2a.+1a. Type **816** 60 60
2129 2a.+1a. "Waiting" (Gustavo Solari) 60 60
2130 2a.+1a. "Beside the Pond" (F. Romero Carranza) . . 60 60
2131 2a.+1a. "Mare and Colt" (Enrique Castro) 60 60
2132 2a.+1a. "Under the Tail" (Enrique Castro) 60 60

1988. 21st International Urological Society Congress. No. 2091 optd **XXI CONGRESO DE LA SOCIEDAD INTERNACIONAL DE UROLOGIA SIU 88**.
2133 **805** 5a. multicoloured . . . 2·00 1·50

818 Cover of "References de la Poste" **821** "Virgin of Tenderness"

820 Underground Train

1988. "Prenfil '88" Philatelic Literature Exhibition, Buenos Aires (2nd issue). Designs showing magazine covers. Multicoloured.
2134 1a.+1a. Type **818** 60 30
2135 1a.+1a. "Cronaca Filatelica" 55 20
2136 1a.+1a. "Co Fi" 75 35
2137 2a.+2a. "Postas Argentinas" 55 20

1988. 75th Anniv of Buenos Aires Underground Railway.
2139 **820** 5a. multicoloured . . . 1·25 75

1988. Christmas. Virgins in Ucrania Cathedral, Buenos Aires. Multicoloured.
2140 5a. Type **821** 60 40
2141 5a. "Virgin of Protection" 60 40

822 Ushuaia and St. John

1989. Death Centenary (1988) of St. John Bosco (founder of Salesian Brothers).
2142 **822** 5a. multicoloured . . . 35 10

823 "Rincon de los Areneros" (Justo Lynch)

1989. Paintings. Multicoloured.
2143 5a. Type **823** 35 10
2144 5a. "Blancos" (Fernando Fader) 35 10

824 "Crowning with Thorns" and Church of Our Lady of Carmen, Tandil

1989. Holy Week. Multicoloured.
2145 2a. Type **824** 15 10
2146 2a. "Jesus of Nazareth" and Buenos Aires Cathedral 15 10
2147 3a. "Our Lady of Sorrows" and Humahuaca Church, Jujuy 15 10
2148 3a. "Jesus Meets His Mother" (statue) and La Quebrada Church, San Luis 15 10

825 Shattering Drinking Glass

1989. Anti-alcoholism Campaign.
2149 **825** 5a. multicoloured . . . 25 10

1989. National Parks (2nd series). As T **804**. Mult.
2150 5a. Crested gallito ("Gallito Capeton"), Lihue Calel National Park 75 20
2151 5a. Lizard, El Palmar National Park 50 20
2152 5a. Tapirs, Calilegua National Park 60 20
2153 5a. Howler monkey, Chaco National Park 65 20
2154 5a. Magellanic woodpecker ("Carpintero Negro Patagonico"), Los Glaciares National Park 75 20

826 Emblem

1989. Cent of Argentine Membership of I.T.U.
2155 **826** 10a. multicoloured . . . 40 10

827 Class 1A Glider Entries

1989. World Model Airplane Championships, La Cruz-Embals-Cordoba. Multicoloured.
2156 5a. Type **827** 35 10
2157 5a. Class 1B rubber-powered entries 35 10
2158 10a. Class 1C petrol-engined entries 35 10

828 Otuno ("Diplomystes viedmensis")

1989. Argentine Philately. Fishes. Multicoloured.
2159 10a.+5a. Type **828** 30 25
2160 10a.+5a. Striped galaxiid ("Haplochiton taeniatus") 30 25
2161 10a.+5a. Creole perch ("Jenyns percichthys tucha") 30 25
2162 10a.+5a. River Plate galaxiid ("Galaxias platei") 30 25
2163 10a.+5a. Brown trout ("Salmo fario") 30 25

829 "All Men are Born Free and Equal"

1989. Bicentenary of French Revolution.
2164 **829** 10a. red, blue and black 35 10
2165 – 15a. black, red and blue 35 10
DESIGN: 15a. "Marianne" (Gandon) and French flag.

830 "Weser" (steamer)

1989. Immigration. Multicoloured.
2167 150a. Type **830** 90 35
2168 200a. Immigrants' hostel . . 40 35

831 "Republic" (bronze bust)

1989. Transference of Presidency. Unissued stamp surch as in T **831**.
2170 **831** 300a. on 50a. mult . . . 60 55

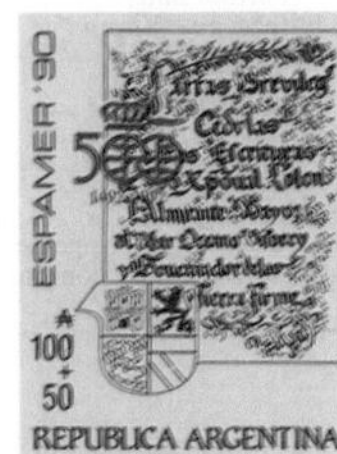

832 Arms of Columbus and Title Page of "Book of Privileges"

1989. "Espamer '90" Spain–Latin America Stamp Exhibition. Chronicles of Discovery. Each yellow, black and red.
2171 100a.+50a. Type **832** . . . 30 30
2172 150a.+50a. Illustration from "New Chronicle and Good Government" (Guaman Poma de Ayala) 40 40
2173 200a.+100a. Illustration from "Discovery and Conquest of Peru" (Pedro de Cieza de Leon) 60 60
2174 250a.+100a. Illustration from "A Journey to the River Plate" (Ulrico Schmidl) 70 70

833 Fr. Guillermo Furlong and Title Page of "Los Jesuitas"

1989. Birth Anniversaries.
2175 **833** 150a. black, light green and green (centenary) 30 25
2176 – 150a. black, buff and brown (centenary) . . 30 25
2177 – 200a. black, light blue and blue (bicentenary) 40 35
DESIGNS: No. 2176, Dr. Gregorio Alvarez (physician) and title page of "Canto A Chos Mala"; 2177, Brigadier Gen. Enrique Martinez and "Battle of Maipu" (detail of lithograph, Theodore Gericault).

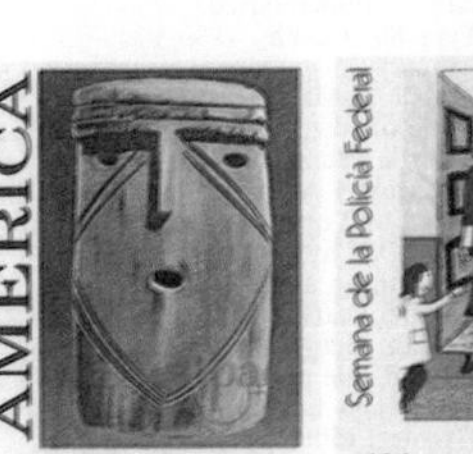

834 Wooden Mask from Atajo
835 "Policewoman with Children" (Diego Molinari)

1989. America. Pre-Columbian Artefacts. Mult.
2178 200a. Type **834** 65 35
2179 300a. Urn from Punta de Balastro 85 55

1989. Federal Police Week. Winning entries in a schools' painting competition.
2180 100a. Type **835** 20 15
2181 100a. "Traffic policeman" (Carlos Alberto Sarago) 20 15
2182 150a. "Adults and child by traffic lights" (Roxana Andrea Osuna) 30 25
2183 150a. "Policeman and child stopping traffic at crossing" (Pablo Javier Quaglia) 30 25

836 "Dream of Christmas" (Maria Carballido)

1989. Christmas. Multicoloured.
2184 200a. Type **836** 40 35
2185 200a. "Cradle Song for Baby Jesus" (Gato Frias) 40 35
2186 300a. "Christ of the Hills" (statue, Chipo Cespedes) (vert) 85 55

837 "Battle of Vuelta de Obligado" (Ulde Todo)

1989.
2187 **837** 300a. multicoloured . . 1·25 45

838 Port Building

1990. Cent of Buenos Aires Port. Multicoloured.
2188 200a. Type **838** . . . . . . 1·50 75
2189 200a. Crane and bows of container and sailing ships 1·50 75
2190 200a. Truck on quay and ships in dock . . . . . . 1·50 75
2191 200a. Van and building . . 1·50 75
Nos. 2188/91 were printed together, se-tenant, forming a composite design.

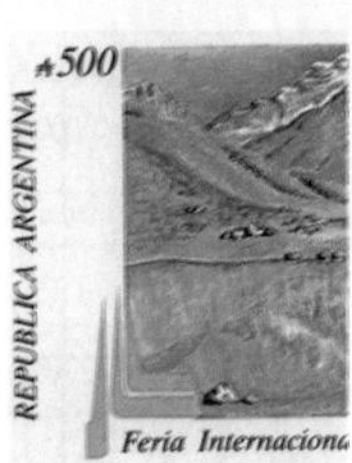

839 Aconcagua Peak and Los Horcones Lagoon

1990. Aconcagua International Fair. Mult.
2192 500a. Type **839** 60 35
2193 500a. Aconcagua Peak and Los Horcones Lagoon (right-hand detail) 60 35
Nos. 2192/3 were printed together, se-tenant, forming a composite design.

840 "75" and Girl with Savings Box

1990. 75th Anniv of National Savings and Insurance Fund.
2194 **840** 1000a. multicoloured . . 20 15

841 Footballer in Striped Shirt

1990. World Cup Football Championship, Italy. Multicoloured.
2195 2500a. Type **841** . . . . . 1·25 1·00
2196 2500a. Upper body of footballer in blue shirt . . . . 1·25 1·00
2197 2500a. Ball and footballers' legs . . . . 1·25 1·00
2198 2500a. Lower body of footballer . . . . 1·25 1·00
Nos. 2195/8 were printed together, se-tenant, forming a composite design.

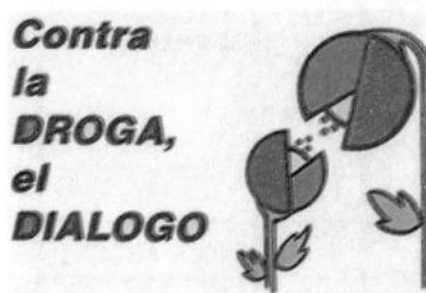

842 Flowers

1990. Anti-drugs Campaign.
2199 **842** 2000a. multicoloured . . 85 30

843 School Emblem and Pellegrini

1990. Centenary of Carlos Pellegrini Commercial High School.
2200 **843** 2000a. multicoloured . . 65 30

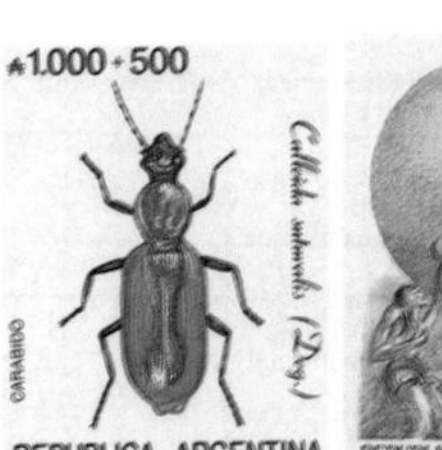

844 "Calleida suturalis"
847 Players

845 Letters and Globe

1990. Argentine Philately. Insects. Multicoloured.
2201 1000a.+500a. Type **844** . . 60 35
2202 1000a.+500a. "Adalia bipunctata" 60 35
2203 1000a.+500a. "Hippodamia convergens" 60 35
2204 1000a.+500a. "Nabis punctipennis" 60 35
2205 1000a.+500a. "Podisus nigrispinus" 60 35

1990. International Literacy Year.
2206 **845** 2000a. multicoloured . . 85 30

1990. World Basketball Championship. Mult.
2208 **847** 2000a. multicoloured . . 85 30

848 Junkers Ju 52/3m

1990. Air. 50th Anniv of LADE (airline). Mult.
2210 2500a. Type **848** . . . . . 1·25 45
2211 2500a. Grumman SA-16 Albatross flying boat . . 1·25 45
2212 2500a. Fokker Friendship 1·25 45
2213 2500a. Fokker Fellowship 1·25 45

849 Arms of West Indies Maritime Post

1990. 14th Postal Union of the Americas and Spain Congress, Buenos Aires.
2214 **849** 3000a. brown & black . . . 85 50
2215 – 3000a. multicoloured . . 1·50 75
2216 – 3000a. multicoloured . . 1·50 75
2217 – 3000a. multicoloured . . 1·25 50
DESIGNS: No. 2215, Sailing packet and despatch boat; 2216, "Rio Carcarana" (cargo liner); 2217, Boeing 707 airplane and mail van.

851 "Hamelia erecta" and Iguazu Falls

1990. America. Natural World. Multicoloured.
2219 3000a. Type **851** . . . . . 1·50 45
2220 3000a. Sea cow, Puerto Deseado . . . . 1·50 45

852 U.P.U. Emblem on "Stamp"

1990. World Post Day.
2221 **852** 3000a. multicoloured . . 95 45

1990. National Parks (3rd series). As T **804**. Mult.
2222 3000a. Anteater, El Rey National Park . . . . . 1·25 45
2223 3000a. Black-necked swans ("Cisne de Cuello Negro"), Laguna Blanca National Park . . . . . 2·00 70
2224 3000a. Black-chested buzzard eagle ("Aguila Mora"), Lanin National Park . . . . 2·00 70
2225 3000a. Armadillo, Perito Moreno National Park . . 1·25 45
2226 3000a. Pudu, Puelo National Park . . . . 1·25 45

853 Hands (after Michelangelo) and Army Emblem

1990. Cent of Salvation Army in Argentina (2227) and Nat University of the Littoral (2228). Mult.
2227 3000a. Type **853** . . . . . 1·10 50
2228 3000a. University building and emblem . . . . . . 1·10 50

854 Archangel Gabriel

856 "Landscape" (Pio Collivadino)

1990. Christmas. Stained-glass windows by Carlos Quaglia from Church of Immaculate Conception, Villaguay. Multicoloured.
2229 3000a. Dove's wing and hand 85 50
2230 3000a. Dove and Mary . . 85 50
2231 3000a. Type **854** 85 50
2232 3000a. Lower half of Mary and open book 85 50
2233 3000a. Joseph 85 50
2234 3000a. Star, shepherds and head of Mary 85 50
2235 3000a. Manger 85 50
2236 3000a. Baby Jesus in Mary's arms 85 50
2237 3000a. Joseph with two doves and Mary 85 50
2238 3000a. Simeon 85 50
2239 3000a. Lower halves of Joseph and Mary 85 50
2240 3000a. Lower half of Simeon and altar 85 50
Nos. 2229/32, 2233/6 and 2237/40 were printed together in se-tenant sheetlets of four stamps, each sheetlet forming a composite design of stained glass windows entitled "Incarnation of Son of God", "The Birth of Christ" and "Presentation of Jesus in the Temple".

1991. Paintings. Multicoloured.
2242 4000a. Type **856** 90 45
2243 4000a. "Weeping Willows" (Atilio Malinverno) (horiz) 90 45

858 Rosas **860** "Hernan, the Pirate" (Jose Salinas)

1991. Return of Remains of Brig. Gen. Juan Manuel de Rosas.
2245 **858** 4000a. multicoloured . . 80 35

1991. Comic Strips. Each black and blue.
2247 4000a. Type **860** . . . . . 1·40 70
2248 4000a. "Don Fulgencio" (Lino Palacio) . . . . . 1·40 70
2249 4000a. "Tablas Medicas de Salerno" (Oscar Conti) . . 1·40 70
2250 4000a. "Buenos Aires en Camiseta" (Alejandro del Prado) . . . . 1·40 70
2251 4000a. "Girls!" (Jose Divito) 1·40 70
2252 4000a. "Langostino" (Eduardo Ferro) . . . . 1·40 70
2253 4000a. "Mafalda" (Joaquin Lavado) . . . . 1·40 70
2254 4000a. "Mort Cinder" (Alberto Breccia) . . . . 1·40 70

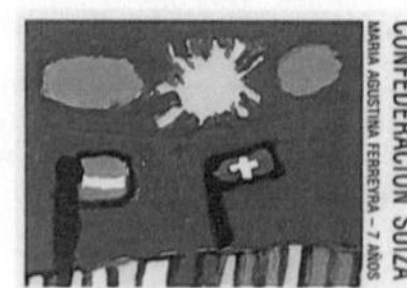

861 "Flags" (Maria Augustina Ferreyra)

1991. 700th Anniv of Swiss Confederation.
2255 **861** 4000a. multicoloured . . 80 30

862 Divine Child Mayor

1991. 400th Anniv of La Rioja City.
2256 **862** 4000a. multicoloured . . 80 30

863 Eduardo Bradley, Angel Zuloaga and Balloon "Eduardo Newbery"

1991. 75th Anniv of Crossing of Andes by Balloon.
2257 **863** 4000a. multicoloured . . 90 35

864 "Vitoria" (Magellan's galleon)

1991. America. Voyages of Discovery. Mult.
2258 4000a. Type **864** . . . . . 1·25 40
2259 4000a. Juan Diaz de Solis's fleet . . . . 1·25 40

865 "Virgin of the Valley, Catamarca" (top half)

1991. Christmas. Stained-glass Windows from Church of Our Lady of Lourdes, Santos Lugares, Buenos Aires. Multicoloured.
2260 4000a. Type **865** . . . . . 1·10 40
2261 4000a. "Virgin of the Valley" (bottom half) . . 1·10 40
2262 4000a. Church and "Virgin of the Rosary of the Miracle, Cordoba" (top half) . . . . 1·10 40
2263 4000a. "Virgin of the Rosary of the Miracle" (bottom half) . . . . . . 1·10 40
Nos. 2260/3 were issued together, se-tenant, Nos. 2260/1 and 2262/3 forming composite designs.

866 Enrique Pestalozzi (editor) and Masthead

1991. Centenaries. Multicoloured.
2264 4000a. Type **866** ("Argentinisches Tageblatt" (1989)) 85 40
2265 4000a. Leandro Alem (founder) and flags (Radical Civic Union) . . 85 40
2266 4000a. Marksman (Argentine Shooting Federation) 85 40
2267 4000a. Dr. Nicasio Etchepareborda (first professor) and emblem (Buenos Aires Faculty of Odontology) 85 40
2268 4000a. Dalmiro Huergo and emblem (Graduate School of Economics) 85 40

867 Gen. Juan Lavalle and Medal

1991. Anniversaries. Multicoloured.
2269 4000a. Type **867** (150th death anniv) 85 40
2270 4000a. Gen. Jose Maria Paz and Battle of Ituzaingo medal (birth bicentenary) 85 40
2271 4000a. Dr. Marco Avellaneda and opening words of "Ode to the 25th May" (politician and writer, 150th death anniv) 85 40
2272 4000a. William Henry Hudson and title page of "Far Away and Long Ago" (writer, 150th birth anniv) 85 40

868 "Castor" (rocket)

1991. "Iberoprenfil '92" Iberia–Latin America Philatelic Literature Exhibition, Buenos Aires (1st issue). Multicoloured.
2273 4000a.+4000a. Type **868** . . 2·00 1·00
2274 4000a.+4000a. "Lusat-1" satellite . . . . 2·00 1·00
See also Nos. 2313/14 and 2325/8.

869 Guiana Crested Eagle ("Morphnu guianensis") **871** Golden Tops

1991. Birds. Multicoloured.
2275 4000a. Type **869** . . . . . 1·50 1·00
2276 4000a. Green-winged macaw ("Ara chloroptera") . . . 1·50 1·00
2277 4000a. Lesser rhea ("Pterocnemia pennata") 1·50 1·00

1992. Fungi.
2279 10c. Type **871** 50 10
2280 25c. Common ink cap . . . 70 20
2281 38c. Type **871** . . . . . . 1·75 25
2282 48c. As 25c. . . . . 1·75 30
2283 50c. Granulated boletus . . 1·75 30
2284 51c. Common morel . . . . 1·75 40
2285 61c. Fly agaric . . . . . . 2·25 45
2286 68c. Lawyer's wig . . . . . 2·25 40
2289 1p. As 61c. . . . . 3·00 40
2290 1p.25 As 50c. . . . . . . 3·25 40
2293 2p. As 51c. . . . . 6·50 60
For redrawn, smaller, designs see Nos. 2365/77.

1992. National Parks (4th series). As T **804**. Multicoloured.
2295 38c. Chucao tapaculo ("Chucao"), Los Alerces National Park . . . . . 1·25 85
2296 38c. Opossum, Los Arrayanes National Park 1·00 40
2297 38c. Giant armadillo, Formosa Nature Reserve 1·00 40
2298 38c. Cavy, Petrified Forests Natural Monument . . . 1·00 40
2299 38c. James's flamingo ("Parina chica"), Laguna de los Pozuelos Natural Monument . . . . 1·25 85

872 Soldier and Truck

1992. National Heroes Commem. Multicoloured.
2300 38c. Type **872** 75 40
2301 38c. "General Belgrano" (cruiser) 90 40
2302 38c. FMA Pucara fighter . . 90 40

873 "Carnotaurus sastrei" **874** "Tileforo Areco"

1992. Dinosaurs. Multicoloured.
2303 38c.+38c. Type **873** . . . 2·25 1·25
2304 38c.+38c. "Amargasaurus cazaui" . . . . 2·25 1·25

1992. Birth Centenary (1991) of Florencio Molina Campios (painter). Multicoloured.
2305 38c. Type **874** . . . . . . 1·10 45
2306 38c. "In the Shade" (horiz) 1·10 45

876 General Lucio N. Mansilla and "San Martin" (frigate)

1992. Birth Anniversaries. Multicoloured.
2308 38c. Type **876** (bicentenary) 1·10 50
2309 38c. Jose Manuel Estrada (historian, 150th) 85 40
2310 38c. General Jose I. Garmendia (150th) . . 85 40

877 Hearts as Flowers

1992. Anti-drugs Campaign.
2311 **877** 38c. multicoloured . . . 85 40

878 Steam Pump Fire Engine and Calaza

1992. 140th Birth Anniv of Col. Jose Calaza (founder of fire service).
2312 **878** 38c. multicoloured . . . 1·10 50

879 "The Party"

1992. "Iberoprenfil '92" Iberia–Latin America Philatelic Literature Exhibition, Buenos Aires (2nd issue). Paintings by Raul Soldi. Multicoloured.
2313 76c.+76c. Type **879** . . . . 3·50 1·75
2314 76c.+76c. "Church of St. Anne of Glew" . . . 3·50 1·75

880 Columbus, European Symbols and "Santa Maria"

1992. America. 500th Anniv of Discovery of America by Columbus. Multicoloured.
2315 38c. Type **880** . . . . . . 1·25 40
2316 38c. American symbols and Columbus . . . . 1·25 40

1992. 50th Anniv of Neuquen and Rio Negro Philatelic Centre. Unissued stamp as T **871** optd **50°ANIVERSARIO CENTRO FILATELICO DE NEUQUEN Y RIO NEGRO**. Multicoloured.
2317 1p.77 Verdigris agaric . . . 4·50 2·50

882 "God Pays You" 883 Flags of Paraguay and Argentina as Stamps

1992. Argentine Films. Advertising posters. Mult.
2318 38c. Type **882** . . . . . . 1·00 40
2319 38c. "The Turbid Waters" 1·00 40
2320 38c. "Un Guapo del 900" 1·00 40
2321 38c. "The Truce" . . . . . 1·00 40
2322 38c. "The Official Version" 1·00 40

1992. "Parafil '92" Paraguay–Argentina Stamp Exhibition, Buenos Aires.
2323 **883** 76c.+76c. mult . . . . . 3·00 1·50

884 Angel and Baby Jesus 885 Punta Mogotes Lighthouse

1992. Christmas.
2324 **884** 38c. multicoloured . . . 1·00 40

1992. "Iberoprenfil '92" Iberia–Latin America Philatelic Literature Exhibition, Buenos Aires (3rd issue). Lighthouses. Multicoloured.
2325 38c. Type **885** . . . . . . 1·00 50
2326 38c. Rio Negro . . . . . . 1·00 50
2327 38c. San Antonio . . . . . 1·00 50
2328 38c. Cabo Blanco . . . . . 1·00 50

886 Campaign Emblem 887 "Sac-B" Research Satellite

1992. Anti-AIDS Campaign.
2329 **886** 10c. black, red and blue 80 15
2330 – 26c. multicoloured . . . 1·60 25
DESIGN: 26c. AIDS cloud over house of life.

1992. International Space Year.
2331 **887** 38c. multicoloured . . . 80 40

889 Footballers and Emblem

1993. Centenary of Argentine Football Assn.
2333 **889** 38c. multicoloured . . . 1·25 60

890 Arquebusier and Arms of Francisco de Arganaras (founder) 892 Order of San Martin

1993. 400th Anniv of Jujuy.
2334 **890** 38c. multicoloured . . . 1·00 40

1993. Anniversaries. Multicoloured.
2336 38c. Type **892** (50th anniv) 85 45
2337 38c. Entrance to and emblem of National History Academy (centenary) 85 45

893 Flag-bearer and Arms of Gendarmerie 895 Snowy Egret ("Egretta thula")

894 Luis Candelaria and Morane Saulnier Type P Monoplane

1993. National Heroes Commemoration. Mult.
2338 38c. Type **893** . . . . . . 1·00 40
2339 38c. "Rio Iguazu" (coastguard corvette) . . 1·00 40

1993. 75th Anniv of First Flight over the Andes.
2340 **894** 38c. multicoloured . . . 1·25 40

1993. Paintings of Birds by Axel Amuchastegui. Multicoloured.
2341 38c.+38c. Type **895** . . . . 1·60 1·60
2342 38c.+38c. Scarlet-headed blackbird ("Amblyramphus holosericeus") . . . . . 1·60 1·60
2343 38c.+38c. Red-crested cardinal ("Paroaria coronata") . . . . 1·60 1·60
2344 38c.+38c. Amazon kingfisher ("Chloroceryle amazona") 1·60 1·60

896 "Coming Home" (Adriana Zaefferer)

1993. Paintings. Multicoloured.
2345 38c. Type **896** 90 40
2346 38c. "The Old House" (Norberto Russo) 90 40

897 Pato

1993. 40th Anniv of Declaration of Pato as National Sport.
2347 **897** 1p. multicoloured . . . 2·40 65

898 Segurola's Pacara ("Enterolobium contortisiliquum")

1993. Old Trees in Buenos Aires. Multicoloured.
2348 75c. Type **898** (Puan and Baldomero Fernandez Moreno Streets) . . . . . 1·25 40
2349 75c. Pueyrredon's carob tree ("Prosopis alba") (Pueyrredon Square) . . . 1·25 40
2350 1p.50 Alvear's coral tree ("Erythrina falcata") (Lavalle Square) . . . . 2·50 80
2351 1p.50 Avellaneda's magnolia ("Magnolia grandiflora") (Adolfo Berro Avenue) . . 2·50 80

899 Southern Right Whale

1993. America. Endangered Animals. Mult.
2352 50c. Type **899** . . . . . . 1·25 55
2353 75c. Commerson's dolphin 1·75 80

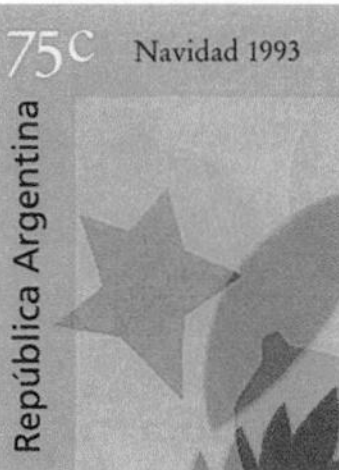
900 Star, Leaf and Bell (Christmas)

1993. Christmas and New Year. Festive Symbols. Multicoloured.
2354 75c. Type **900** . . . . . . 1·25 40
2355 75c. Leaf, sun and moon (New Year) . . . . . . 1·25 40
2356 75c. Leaf and fir tree (Christmas) . . . . 1·25 40
2357 75c. Fish and moon (New Year) . . . . 1·25 40
Nos. 2354/7 were issued together, se-tenant, forming a composite design.

901 Cave Painting

1993. Cave of Hands, Santa Cruz.
2358 **901** 1p. multicoloured . . . 2·00 40

902 Emblem

1994. New Argentine Post Emblem.
2359 **902** 75c. multicoloured . . . 1·25 40

903 Brazil Player 904 Golden Tops

1994. World Cup Football Championship, U.S.A. (1st issue). Multicoloured.
2360 25c. German player 30 20
2361 50c. Type **903** 90 45
2362 75c. Argentine player . . . 1·40 50
2363 1p. Italian player . . . . . 1·90 75
See also Nos. 2380/3.

1994. Fungi. Multicoloured.
2365 10c. Type **904** 20 10
2366 25c. Common ink cap . . . 55 20
2369 50c. Granulated boletus . . 1·25 50
2374 1p. Fly agaric . . . . . . 2·75 1·10
2377 2p. Common morel . . . . 5·25 2·25

905 Argentine Player with Ball (Matias Taylor)

1994. World Cup Football Championship, U.S.A. (2nd issue). Winning entries in children's competition. Multicoloured.
2380 75c. Type **905** . . . . . . 1·40 50
2381 75c. Tackle (Torcuato Santiago Gonzalez Agote) 1·40 50
2382 75c. Players (Julian Lisenberg) (horiz) . . . . 1·40 50
2383 75c. Match scene (Maria Paula Palma) (horiz) . . . 1·40 50

906 Black-throated Finch

1994. Animals of the Falkland Islands (Islas Malvinas). Multicoloured.

2384 25c. Type **906** 55 40
2385 50c. Gentoo penguins . . . 1·10 75
2386 75c. Falkland Islands flightless steamer ducks 1·60 1·10
2387 1p. Southern elephant-seal 1·75 60

907 Town Arms

1994. Anniversaries. Multicoloured.

2388 75c. Type **907** (400th anniv of San Luis) . . . . . . 1·25 50
2389 75c. Arms (3rd anniv of provincial status of Tierra del Fuego, Antarctica and South Atlantic Islands) . . 1·25 50

908 Ladislao Jose Biro

1994. Inventors. Multicoloured.

2390 75c. Type **908** (ball-point pen) . . . . 1·25 50
2391 75c. Raul Pateras de Pescara (helicopter) . . . . 1·25 50
2392 75c. Quirino Cristiani (animated films) . . . . . 1·25 50
2393 75c. Enrique Finochietto (surgical instruments) . . 1·25 50

909 Star, Purple Bauble and Bell

1994. U.N.I.C.E.F. Children's Fund in Argentina. Multicoloured.

2394 50c. Type **909** 85 45
2395 75c. Bell, red bauble and star . . . . 1·25 50

910 Children holding Globe (Ivana Mirna de Caro)

1994. "Care of the Planet". Children's Painting Competition. Multicoloured.

2396 25c. Type **910** 30 20
2397 25c. Girl polishing sunbeam and boy tending tree (Elena Tsouprik) 30 20
2398 50c. Children of all races around globe (Estefania Navarro) (horiz) 60 45
2399 50c. Globe as house (Maria Belen Gidoni) (horiz) . . 60 45

911 Star and Angel (The Annunciation)

1994. Christmas. Multicoloured.

2400 50c. Type **911** 60 45
2401 75c. Madonna and Child (Nativity) . . . . 1·25 50

912 Running

1995. 12th Pan-American Games, Mar del Plata. Multicoloured.

2402 75c. Type **912** . . . . . . 1·25 45
2403 75c. Cycling . . . . 1·25 45
2404 75c. Diving . . . . 1·25 45
2405 1p.25 Football (vert) . . . . 2·00 60
2406 1p.25 Gymnastics (vert) . . 2·00 60

913 Postal Emblem

1995. Self-adhesive.

2407 **913** 25c. yellow, blue & black 3·75 50
2408 75c. yellow, blue & black 1·25 50

914 National Congress Building and "The Republic Triumphant" (statue, detail)

1995. New Constitution, August 1994.

2409 **914** 75c. multicoloured . . . 1·25 40

915 Letters and Disk

1995. 21st International Book Fair.

2410 **915** 75c. multicoloured . . . 1·25 50

916 Bay-winged Cowbird

1995. Birds. Multicoloured.

2412 5p. Hooded siskin . . . . . 10·50 7·50
2413 9p.40 Type **916** . . . . . . 21·00 15·00
2414 10p. Rufous-collared sparrow . . . . 20·00 13·50

917 Clouds seen through Atrium

1995. Centenary of Argentine Engineers' Centre, Buenos Aires.

2420 **917** 75c. multicoloured . . . 1·25 45

920 Jose Marti

1995. Revolutionaries' Anniversaries. Mult.

2423 1p. Type **920** (death cent) 1·60 45
2424 1p. Antonio de Sucre (birth bicentenary) . . . . . . 1·60 45

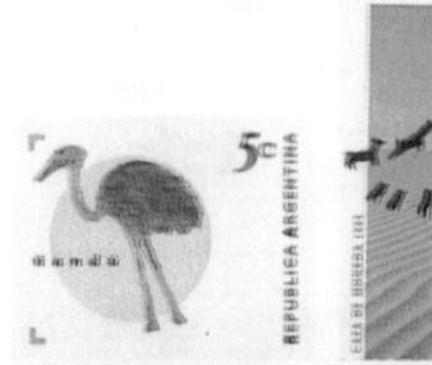

921 Greater Rhea

922 Cave Painting (Patagonia)

1995. Birds. Multicoloured.

2425 5c. Type **921** 15 10
2425a 10c. Giant wood rail ("ipecae") 15 10
2426 25c. King penguin 45 20
2427 50c. Toco toucan 85 45
2428 75c. Andean condor . . . 1·40 75
2429 1p. Barn owl . . . . . . 1·75 1·00
2430 2p. Olivaceous cormorant 3·50 2·00
2431 2p.75 Southern lapwing . . 5·00 2·75
2432 3p.25 Southern lapwing . . 4·00 3·00

1995. Animals. As T **921**. Multicoloured.

2436 25c. Alligator 30 20
2437 50c. Red fox 60 45
2438 75c. Anteater . . . . 1·25 75
2439 75c. Vicuna . . . . 1·25 75
2440 75c. Sperm whale . . . . . 1·25 75

1995. Archaeology. Multicoloured.

2441 75c. Type **922** . . . . . . 1·25 40
2442 75c. Stone mask (Tafi culture, Tucuman) . . . . 1·25 40
2443 75c. Anthropomorphic vase (Catamarca) . . . . . . 1·25 40
2444 75c. Woven cloth (North Patagonia) . . . . 1·25 40

923 Peron

1995. Birth Centenary of Juan Peron (President, 1946–55 and 1973–74).

2445 **923** 75c. blue and bistre . . . 1·25 40

924 Postal Emblem on Sunflower

1995.

2446 **924** 75c. multicoloured . . . 1·25 40

926 Christmas Tree

1995. Christmas. Multicoloured.

2448 75c. Type **926** . . . . . . 1·25 40
2449 75c. "1996" . . . . 1·25 40
2450 75c. Glasses of champagne 1·25 40
2451 75c. Present . . . . 1·25 40
2452 75c. Type **926** . . . . . . 1·25 40

927 "Les 400 Coups" (dir. Francois Truffaut)

1995. Centenary of Motion Pictures. Each black, grey and orange.

2453 75c. "Battleship Potemkin" (dir. Sergei Eisenstein) . . 1·25 40
2454 75c. "Casablanca" (dir. Michael Curtiz) . . . . . 1·25 40
2455 75c. "Bicycle Thieves" (dir. Vittorio de Sica) . . . . 1·25 40
2456 75c. Charlie Chaplin in "Limelight" . . . . . . 1·25 40
2457 75c. Type **927** . . . . . . 1·25 40
2458 75c. "Chronicle of an Only Child" (dir. Leonardo Favio) . . . . 1·25 40

928 Horse-drawn Mail Coach

1995. America (1994). Postal Transport. Mult.

2459 75c. Type **928** . . . . . . 1·25 40
2460 75c. Early postal van . . . 1·25 40

929 Dirigible Airship

1995. The Sky. Multicoloured.

2461 25c. Type **929** 55 20
2462 25c. Kite 55 20
2463 25c. Hot-air balloon 55 20
2464 50c. Balloons 85 45
2465 50c. Paper airplane 85 45
2466 75c. Airplane . . . . 1·25 45
2467 75c. Helicopter . . . . . . 1·25 45
2468 75c. Parachute . . . . . . 1·25 45

930 Ancient Greek and Modern Runners

1996. Multicoloured. (a) Centenary of Modern Olympic Games. Horiz designs.

2471 75c. Type **930** . . . . . . 1·25 35
2472 1p. "The Discus Thrower" (ancient Greek statue, Miron) and modern thrower . . . . 1·60 50

(b) Olympic Games. Vert designs.

2473 75c. Torch bearer (Buenos Aires, 2004) . . . . . . 1·25 35
2474 1p. Rowing (Atlanta, 1996) 1·60 50

931 Francisco Muniz (founder of Academy of Medicine and Public Hygiene Council)

1996. Physicians' Anniversaries. Multicoloured.

2475 50c. Type **931** (birth bicentenary (1995)) . . . 85 45
2476 50c. Ricardo Gutierrez (founder of Children's Hospital and co-founder of periodical "La Patria Argentina", death centenary) 85 45
2477 50c. Ignacio Pirovano (death centenary (1995)) 85 45
2478 50c. Esteban Maradona (birth centenary (1995) and first death anniv) . . 85 45

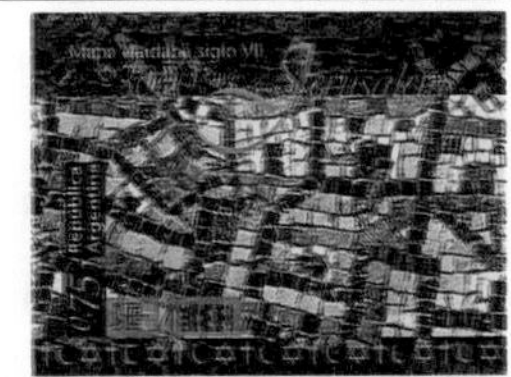

932 Mosaic Map of Jerusalem (left-hand detail)

1996. 3000th Anniv of Jerusalem. Multicoloured.
2479 75c. Type **932** . . . . . . 1·25 40
2480 75c. Map (right-hand detail) 1·25 40
Nos. 2479/80 were issued together, se-tenant, forming a composite design.

933 Capybaras

1996. America. Endangered Species. Mult.
2481 75c. Type **933** . . . . . . 1·50 45
2482 75c. Guanacos . . . . . . 1·50 45

934 Ramon Franco's Seaplane "Plus Ultra"

1996. "Aerofila '96" Latin American Airmail Exhibition. Aircraft. Multicoloured.
2483 25c.+25c. Type **934** . . . . 1·25 60
2484 25c.+25c. Alberto Santos-Dumont's biplane "14 bis" . . . . 1·25 60
2485 50c.+50c. Charles Lindbergh's "Spirit of St. Louis" . . . . 2·50 1·25
2486 50c.+50c. Eduardo Olivero's biplane "Buenos Aires" 2·50 1·25

1996. As Nos. 2407/8. Self-adhesive. Imperf.
2486a **913** 25c. yellow and blue . . 3·75 50
2486b 75c. yellow and blue . . 1·25 70

935 Dusky-legged Guan, Diamante National Park

1996. National Parks. Multicoloured.
2487 75c. Type **935** . . . . . . 1·25 45
2488 75c. Mountain viscacha, El Leoncito Nature Reserve 1·60 70
2489 75c. Marsh deer, Otamendi Nature Reserve . . . . . 1·25 45
2490 75c. Red-spectacled amazon, San Antonio Nature Reserve . . . . 1·60 70

936 Dragon

1996. Murals from Buenos Aires Underground Railway. Multicoloured.
2491 1p.+50c. Type **936** . . . . 3·00 1·75
2492 1p.50+1p. Bird . . . . . . 5·00 2·50

937 "San Antonio" (tank landing ship)

1996. Cent of Port Belgrano Naval Base. Mult.
2493 25c. Type **937** 65 20
2494 50c. "Rosales" (corvette) . . 1·25 45
2495 75c. "Hercules" (destroyer) 1·75 70
2496 1p. "25 de Mayo" (aircraft carrier) . . . . 2·50 1·00

938 Decorative Panel

1996. Carousel. Multicoloured.
2497 25c. Type **938** 55 20
2498 25c. Child on horse 55 20
2499 25c. Carousel 55 20
2500 50c. Fairground horses . . . 85 20
2501 50c. Child in airplane . . . 85 20
2502 50c. Pig 85 20
2503 75c. Child in car . . . . . 1·25 45

939 Head Post Office, Buenos Aires

940 "Adoration of the Wise Men" (Gladys Rinaldi)

1996. Size 24½ × 34½ mm. Self-adhesive. Imperf.
2504 **939** 75c. multicoloured . . . 90 70
See also Nos. 2537/8.

1996. Christmas. Tapestries. Multicoloured.
2505 75c. Type **940** . . . . . . 1·25 45
2506 1p. Abstract (Norma Bonet de Maekawa) (horiz) . . 1·60 70

941 Melchior Base

1996. Argentinian Presence in Antarctic. Mult.
2507 75c. Type **941** . . . . . . 1·40 45
2508 1p.25 "Irizar" (ice-breaker) 2·75 70

942 "Vahine no te Miti" (Gauguin)

1996. Cent of National Gallery of Fine Arts. Mult.
2509 75c. Type **942** . . . . . . 1·25 45
2510 1p. "The Nymph surprised" (Edouard Manet) . . . . 1·60 65
2511 1p. "Figure of Woman" (Amedeo Modigliani) . . 1·60 65
2512 1p.25 "Woman lying down" (Pablo Picasso) (horiz) . . 2·00 75

943 Granite Mining, Cordoba

1997. Mining Industry. Multicoloured.
2513 75c. Type **943** . . . . . . 1·25 45
2514 1p.25 Borax mining, Salta 2·00 65

944 "They amuse Themselves in Dancing" (Raul Soldi)

1997. America (1996). National Costume.
2515 **944** 75c. multicoloured . . . 1·25 45

945 Arms, Sabre and Shako

1997. Centenary of Repatriation of General San Martin's Sabre.
2516 **945** 75c. multicoloured . . . 1·25 45

946 Match Scene

1997. 29th World Rugby Youth Championship, Argentina.
2517 **946** 75c. multicoloured . . . 1·25 45

947 "Fortuna" (yacht)

1997. 50th Anniv of Buenos Aires to Rio de Janeiro Regatta.
2518 **947** 75c. multicoloured . . . 90 30

948 Ceres Design, France (1849–52)

1997. "Mevifil '97" First Int Exn of Philatelic Audio-visual and Computer Systems. Mult.
2519 50c.+50c. Type **948** . . . . 1·60 1·25
2520 50c.+50c. Queen Isabella II design, Spain (1851) . . . 1·60 1·25
2521 50c.+50c. Rivadavia design, Argentine Republic (1864) 1·60 1·25
2522 50c.+50c. Paddle-steamer design, Buenos Aires (1858) . . . . 1·60 1·25
Nos. 2519/22 were issued together, se-tenant, with the centre of the block forming the composite design of an eye.

949 Museum

1997. Centenary of National History Museum, Buenos Aires.
2523 **949** 75c. multicoloured . . . 1·25 45

950 Seal and Oak Leaf

951 Carcano (after Dolores Capdevila)

1997. Centenary of La Plata National University.
2524 **950** 75c. multicoloured . . . 1·25 45

1997. 50th Death Anniv (1996) of Ramon Carcano (postal reformer).
2525 **951** 75c. multicoloured . . . 1·25 45

952 Cabo Virgenes Lighthouse

1997. Lighthouses. Multicoloured.
2526 75c. Type **952** . . . . . . 1·25 45
2527 75c. Isla Pinguino . . . . . 1·25 45
2528 75c. San Juan de Salvamento . . . . 1·25 45
2529 75c. Punta Delgada . . . . 1·25 45

953 Condor and Olympic Rings

1997. Inclusion of Buenos Aires in Final Selection Round for 2004 Olympic Games.
2530 **953** 75c. multicoloured . . . 1·25 45

954 Lacroze Company Suburban Service, 1912

1997. Centenary of First Electric Tramway in Buenos Aires. Illustrations from "History of the Tram" by Marcelo Mayorga. Multicoloured.
2531 75c. Type **954** . . . . . . 1·40 70
2532 75c. Lacroze Company urban service, 1907 . . . 1·40 70
2533 75c. Anglo Argentina Company tramcar, 1930 1·40 70
2534 75c. City of Buenos Aires Transport Corporation tramcar, 1942 . . . . . . 1·40 70
2535 75c. Fabricaciones Militares tramcar, 1956 . . . . . . 1·40 70
2536 75c. Electricos de Sur Company tramcar, 1908 1·40 70
Nos. 2531/6 were issued together, se-tenant, showing a composite design of a tram in a city street.

1997. As No. 2504 but size 23 × 35 mm. Self-adhesive. Imperf.
2537 **939** 25c. multicoloured . . . 70 20
2538 75c. multicoloured . . . 1·40 20

955 Monument (by Mauricio Molina)

1997. Inauguration of Monument to Joaquin Gonzalez (politician) at La Rioja.
2539 **955** 75c. multicoloured . . . 1·25 45

956 Alberto Ginastera (after Carlos Nine)

1997. Composers. Multicoloured.
2540 75c. Type **956** . . . . . . 1·25 45
2541 75c. Astor Piazzolla (after Carlos Alonso) . . . . . 1·25 45
2542 75c. Anibal Troilo (after Hermenegildo Sabat) . . 1·25 45
2543 75c. Atahualpa Yupanqui (after Luis Scafati) . . . 1·25 45

957 "Tren a las Nubes", Salta

1997. Trains. Multicoloured.
2544 50c.+50c. Type **957** . . . . 1·60 80
2545 50c.+50c. Preserved steam locomotive, Buenos Aires 1·60 80
2546 50c.+50c. Patagonian express "La Trochita" Rio Negro–Chubut . . . 1·60 80
2547 50c.+50c. Austral Fueguino Railway locomotive No. 2, Tierra del Fuego 1·60 80

958 Eva Peron (after Raul Manteola)

1997. 50th Anniv of Women's Suffrage.
2548 **958** 75c. pink and grey . . . 1·25 45

959 Jorge Luis Borges and Maze

1997. Writers. Multicoloured.
2549 1p. Type **959** . . . . 1·60 50
2550 1p. Julio Cortazar and hopscotch grid . . . . . 1·60 50

961 Members' Flags and Southern Cross

1997. Mercosur (South American Common Market).
2552 **961** 75c. multicoloured . . . 1·25 45

962 "Presidente Sarmiento" (Hugo Leban)

1997. Centenary of Launch of "Presidente Sarmiento" (cadet ship).
2553 **962** 75c. multicoloured . . . 2·00 55

963 Guevara

1997. 30th Death Anniv of Ernesto "Che" Guevara (revolutionary).
2555 **963** 75c. brown, red & black 1·25 45

964 Vicuna (Julian Chiapparo)

1997. "Draw an Ecostamp" Children's Competition Winners. Multicoloured.
2556 50c. Type **964** 80 20
2557 50c. Vicuna (Leandro Lopez Portal) 80 20
2558 75c. Seal (Andres Lloren) (horiz) . . . . 1·25 45
2559 75c. Ashy-headed goose (Jose Saccone) (horiz) . . 1·25 45

965 "Nativity" (Mary Jose)

1997. Christmas. Tapestries of the Nativity. Designs by artists named. Mult. (a) Size 45 × 34 mm.
2560 75c. Type **965** . . . . . . 1·25 45

(b) Size 44 × 27 mm. Self-adhesive. Imperf.
2561 25c. Elena Aguilar 40 20
2562 25c. Silvia Pettachi 40 20
2563 50c. Ana Escobar 80 20
2564 50c. Alejandra Martinez . . 80 20
2565 75c. As No. 2560 but with inscriptions differently arranged . . . . 1·25 45
2566 75c. Nidia Martinez . . . . 1·25 45

966 Mother Teresa

1997. Mother Teresa (founder of the Missionaries of Charity) Commemoration.
2567 **966** 75c. multicoloured . . . 1·25 45

967 Houssay

1998. 50th Anniv (1997) of Award to Bernardo Houssay of Nobel Prize for Medicine and Physiology.
2568 **967** 75c. multicoloured . . . 90 70

968 Mountaineers

1998. Cent of First Ascent of Mt. Aconcagua.
2569 **968** 1p.25 multicoloured . . 1·25 1·00

969 San Martin de los Andes and Lake Lacar

1998. Centenary of San Martin de los Andes.
2570 **969** 75c. multicoloured . . . 90 70

970 Grenadier Monument (Juan Carlos Ferraro)

1998. Declaration as National Historical Monument of Palermo Barracks of General San Martin Horse Grenadiers. Multicoloured.
2571 75c. Type **970** 90 70
2572 75c. Sevres urn with portrait of San Martin 90 70
2573 75c. Regiment coat of arms 90 70
2574 75c. Main facade of barracks 90 70

971 Globe and Baby

1998. Protection of Ozone Layer.
2575 **971** 75c. multicoloured . . . 90 70

972 Postman, 1920

1998. America. The Postman. Multicoloured.
2576 75c. Type **972** 90 70
2577 75c. Postman, 1998 . . . . 90 70

973 "El Reino del Reves"

1998. Stories by Maria Elena Walsh. Illustrations by Eduardo and Ricardo Fuhrmann. Multicoloured. Self-adhesive.
2578 75c. Type **973** 90 70
2579 75c. "Zoo Loco" 90 70
2580 75c. "Dailan Kifki" 90 70
2581 75c. "Manuelita" 90 70

974 St Peter's, Fiambala, Catamarca

1998. Historic Chapels. Multicoloured.
2582 75c. Type **974** 90 70
2583 75c. Huacalera, Jujuy . . . 90 70
2584 75c. St. Dominic's, La Rioja 90 70
2585 75c. Tumbaya, Jujuy . . . 90 70

975 Raised Hands

1998. White Helmets (volunteer humanitarian workers).
2586 **975** 1p. multicoloured . . . 1·25 1·00

976 Argentine Player

1998. World Cup Football Championship, France. Multicoloured.
2587 75c. Type **976** 90 70
2588 75c. Croatian player 90 70
2589 75c. Jamaican player 90 70
2590 75c. Japanese player 90 70

977 Typewriter, Camera, Pen, Computer and Satellite

1998. Journalism Day.
2591 **977** 75c. multicoloured . . . 90 70

978 Corrientes 1860 3c. Stamps and Postal Emblem

1998. 250th Anniv of Establishment of Regular Postal Service in Rio de la Plata (Spanish dominion in South America). Multicoloured.
2592 75c. Type **978** 90 70
2593 75c. Buenos Aires Post Office and pillar box . . . 90 70

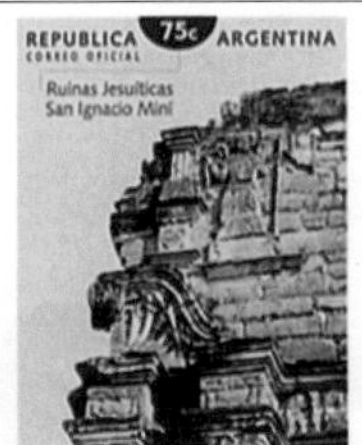

979 Jesuit Ruins, San Ignacio Mini

1998. Mercosur Missions.
2594 **979** 75c. multicoloured . . . 90 70

980 Aberdeen Angus

1998. Cattle. Multicoloured.
2595 25c. Type **980** 30 20
2596 25c. Brahman 30 20
2597 50c. Hereford 60 45
2598 50c. Criolla 60 45
2599 75c. Holando-Argentina . . 90 70
2600 75c. Shorthorn 90 70

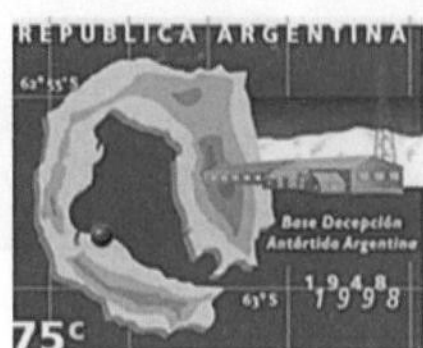

981 Map and Base

1998. 50th Anniv of Decepcion Antarctic Base.
2601 **981** 75c. multicoloured . . . 90 70

982 Anniversary Emblem

1998. 50th Anniv of State of Israel.
2602 **982** 75c. multicoloured . . . 90 70

983 Bridge in Japanese Garden, Buenos Aires

1998. Cent of Argentina–Japan Friendship Treaty.
2603 **983** 75c. multicoloured . . . 90 70

984 Facade and clock

1998. 70th Anniv of Head Post Office, Buenos Aires. Multicoloured.
2604 75c. Type **984** 90 70
2605 75c. Capital and bench . . . 90 70

985 Patoruzu (Quinterno)

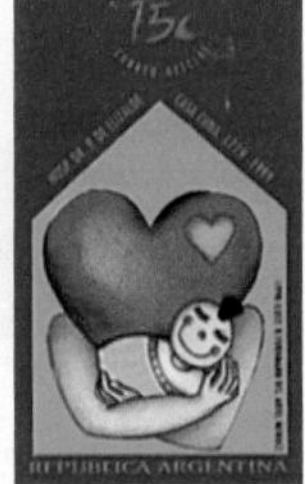

986 Heart with Arms holding Baby

1998. Comic Strip Characters. Multicoloured.
2606 75c. Type **985** 90 70
2607 75c. Matias (Sendra) 90 70
2608 75c. Clemente (Caloi) . . . 90 70
2609 75c. El Eternauta (Oesterheld Solano Lopez) 90 70
2610 75c. Loco Chavez (Trillo Altuna) 90 70
2611 75c. Inodoro Pereyra (Fontanarrosa) 90 70
2612 75c. Tia Vicenta (Landru) 90 70
2613 75c. Gaturro (Nik) 90 70

1998. 220th Anniv of Dr. Pedro de Elizalde Children's Hospital.
2614 **986** 75c. multicoloured . . . 90 70

987 Post Banner and Pennant, 1785, and Arms of Maritime Post

1998. "Espamer '98" Iberian–Latin American Stamp Exhibition, Buenos Aires. Mult. Self-adhesive.
2615 25c. Type **987** 30 20
2616 75c. Mail brigantine . . . . 1·25 70
2617 75c.+75c. Mail brigantine (different) . . . . 2·50 1·75
2618 1p.25+1p.25 Mail brig . . . 4·25 3·00

988 Passport and Wallenberg

1998. Raoul Wallenberg (Swedish diplomat in Hungary who helped Jews escape, 1944–45) Commemoration.
2619 **988** 75c. multicoloured . . . 90 70

989 Aguada Culture Bird

1998. 50th Anniv of Organization of American States.
2620 **989** 75c. multicoloured . . . 90 70

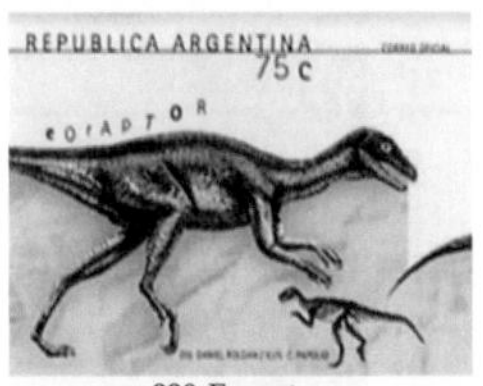

990 Eoraptor

1998. Prehistoric Animals. Multicoloured.
2621 75c. Type **990** 90 70
2622 75c. Gasparinisaura 90 70
2623 75c. Giganotosaurus 90 70
2624 75c. Patagosaurus 90 70
Nos. 2621/4 were issued together, se-tenant, forming a composite design.

991 Child as Angel, Stars and Score

993 Postman

992 Juan Figueroa (founder) and First Issue

1998. Christmas.
2625 **991** 75c. multicoloured . . . 90 70

1998. Centenary of "El Liberal" (newspaper).
2626 **992** 75c. multicoloured . . . 90 70

1998. Postmen. Size 25 × 35 mm. Multicoloured. Self-adhesive.
2627 25c. Type **993** 30 20
2628 75c. Modern postman . . . 90 70
For 75c. in reduced size see No. 2640.

1998. Birds. As T **921**. Multicoloured. Self-adhesive.
2629 60c. Red-tailed comet . . . 75 60

994 Child (painting, Francisco Ramirez)

1998. 50th Anniv of Universal Declaration of Human Rights.
2635 **994** 75c. multicoloured . . . 90 70

995 Enrique Julio (founder) and Newspaper Offices

1998. Cent of "La Nueva Provincia" (newspaper).
2636 **995** 75c. multicoloured . . . 90 70

996 "Haggadah" of Pessah (exhibit) and Carving on Cathedral

1998. Permanent Exhibition commemorating Holocaust Victims, Buenos Aires Cathedral.
2637 **996** 75c. multicoloured . . . 90 70

1999. Postmen. Size 21 × 27 mm. Mult. Self-adhesive.
2638 15c. Type **993** 30 20
2639 50c. Postman, 1950 . . . . 60 45
2640 75c. As No. 2628 . . . . . 90 70

997 Oil-smeared Magellanic Penguin

1999. International Year of the Ocean. Mult.
2641 50c. Type **997** 60 45
2642 75c. Dolphins (horiz) . . . 90 70

998 Buildings and Draughtsman's Instruments

1999. National Arts Fund.
2643 **998** 75c. multicoloured . . . 90 70

999 Computer and Book

1999. 25th Book Fair, Buenos Aires. Multicoloured.
2644 75c. Type **999** 90 70
2645 75c. Obelisk, compact disk case and readers 90 70
Nos. 2644/5 were issued together, se-tenant, forming a composite design.

1000 Rugby Balls and Player

1999. Centenary of Argentine Rugby Union.
2646 **1000** 75c. multicoloured . . . 90 70

1001 Glass, La Giralda

1002 Pierre de Coubertin, 1924 Olympic Gold Medal and Olympic Rings

1999. Cafes. Multicoloured. Self-adhesive.
2648 25c. Type **1001** 30 20
2649 75c. Two glasses, Cafe Homero Manzi 90 70
2650 75c. Hatstand, Confitenia Ideal 90 70
2651 1p.25 Cup and saucer, Cafe Tortoni . . . . 1·50 1·00

1999. 75th Anniv of Argentine Olympic Committee.
2652 **1002** 75c. multicoloured . . . 90 70

1003 Enrico Caruso (Italian tenor)

1999. Opera. Multicoloured.
2653 75c. Type **1003** (125th birth anniv and centenary of American debut) 90 70
2654 75c. Singer and musical instruments 90 70
2655 75c. Buenos Aires Opera House 90 70
2656 75c. Scene from "El Matrero" (Felipe Boero) 90 70

1004 Rosario Vera Penaloza (educationist)

1999. America (1998). Famous Women. Mult.
2659 75c. Type **1004** 90 70
2660 75c. Julieta Lanteri (women's rights campaigner) 90 70

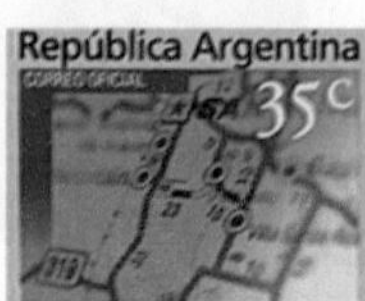

1006 Local Road Network

1999. Bulk Mailing Stamps. Mult. Self-adhesive.
2662 35c. Type **1006** 40 30
2663 40c. Town plan 50 40
2664 50c. Regional map 60 45

1007 Carrier Pigeon

1999.
2665 **1007** 75c. multicoloured . . . 90 70

1008 Boxer

1999. Dogs. Multicoloured.
2666 25c. Type **1008** 20 20
2667 25c. Old English sheepdog 30 20
2668 50c. Welsh collie 60 45
2669 50c. St. Bernard 60 45
2670 75c. German shepherd . . . 90 70
2671 75c. Siberian husky 90 70

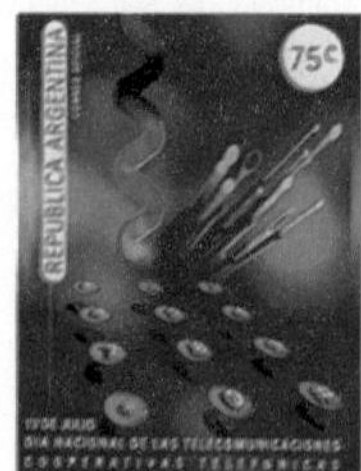

1009 Telephone Keypad

1999. National Telecommunications Day.
2672 **1009** 75c. multicoloured . . . 90 70

1010 College Gates

1999. 150th Anniv of Justo Jose de Urquiza College, Concepcion del Uruguay.
2673 **1010** 75c. multicoloured . . . 90 70

1011 Krause (engineer) and Industrial Instruments

1999. Centenary of Technical School No. 1 Otto Krause.
2674 **1011** 75c. multicoloured . . . 90 70

1012 Nativity

1999. Bethlehem 2000.
2675 **1012** 75c. blue, gold and red 90 70

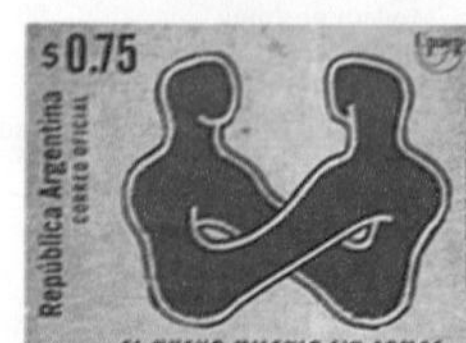

1013 Brotherhood among Men

1999. America. A New Millennium without Arms. Multicoloured.
2676 75c. Type **1013** 90 70
2677 75c. Liberty Tree (vert) . . 90 70

1014 Coypu ("Myocastor coypus"), Mburucuya National Park

1999. National Parks. Multicoloured.
2678 50c. Type **1014** 60 50
2679 50c. Andean condor, Quebrada de los Condoritos National Park 60 50
2680 50c. Vicuna, San Guillermo National Park 60 50
2681 75c. Puma, Sierra de las Quijadas National Park 90 70
2682 75c. Argentine grey fox ("Dusicyon griseus"), Talampaya National Park 90 70

1015 Map of the Americas, Road Network and Wickerwork

1999. 40th Anniv of Inter-American Development Bank.
2683 **1015** 75c. multicoloured . . . 90 70

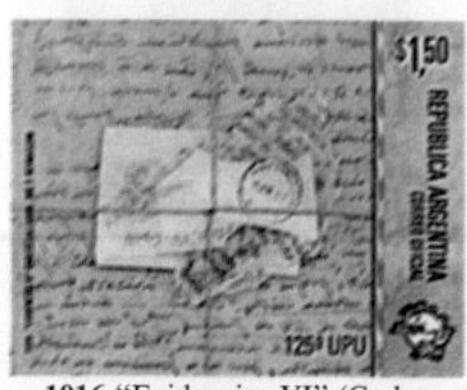

1016 "Evidencias VI" (Carlos Gallardo)

1999. 125th Anniv of Universal Postal Union.
2684 **1016** 1p.50 multicoloured . . 1·75 1·40

1017 "Fournier" and Map

1999. 50th Anniv of Sinking of the "Fournier" (minesweeper) in Antarctica.
2685 **1017** 75c. multicoloured . . . 90 70

1018 "Nothofagus pumillio"

1999. Trees (1st series). Multicoloured.
2686 75c. Type **1018** 90 70
2687 75c. "Prosopis caldenia" . . 90 70
2688 75c. "Schinopsis balansae" 90 70
2689 75c. "Cordia trichotoma" 90 70
Nos. 2686/9 were issued together, se-tenant, forming a composite design.

1019 Latecoere 25 Mailplane

1999. 50th Anniv of World Record for Consecutive Parachute Jumps. Multicoloured.
2690 75c. Type **1019** 90 70
2691 75c. Parachutists 90 70

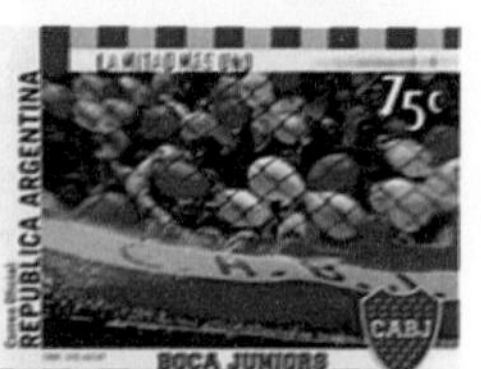

1021 Boca Juniors Club Supporters

1999. Football. Multicoloured. (a) Size 42 × 33 mm.
2693 75c. Type **1021** 90 70
2694 75c. River Plate Club supporters 90 70

(b) Size 37 × 34 mm (1p.50) or 37 × 27 mm (others)

(i) Boca Juniors

2695 25c. Two players and ball 30 25
2696 50c. Club badge 60 50
2697 50c. Players hugging 60 50
2698 75c. Supporters and balloons 90 70
2699 75c. Club banner 90 70
2700 75c. Players 90 70
2701 1p.50 Player making high kick . . . . 1·75 1·40

(ii) River Plate

2702 25c. Stadium 30 25
2703 50c. Players arriving on pitch 60 50
2704 50c. Supporters waving flags 60 50
2705 75c. Club badge 90 70
2706 75c. Trophy 90 70
2707 75c. Supporters with banner 90 70
2708 1p.50 Player preparing to kick ball . . . . 1·75 1·40
Nos. 2695/708 are self-adhesive.

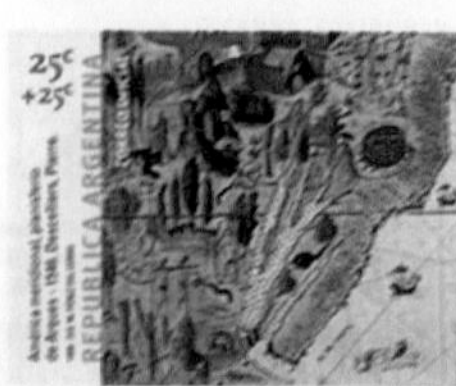

1022 Planisphere of Central South America (Pierre Descelliers, 1546)

1999. Maps. Multicoloured.
2709 25c.+25c. Type **1022** 60 60
2710 50c.+50c. 17th-century map of estuary of the River Plate (Claes Voogt) . . . 1·25 1·25
2711 50c.+50c. Buenos Aires (Military Geographical Institute, 1910) . . . . . 1·25 1·25
2712 75c.+75c. Mouth of Riachuelo river and Buenos Aires harbour (satellite picture, 1999) . . 1·75 1·75

1023 Valdivielso and St. Peter's Cathedral, Rome

1999. Canonization of Hector Valdivielso Saez (Brother of the Christian Schools).
2713 **1023** 75c. multicoloured . . . 90 70

1024 "San Francisco Xavier" (brig)

1999. Bicentenary of Manuel Belgrano Naval Academy.
2714 **1024** 75c. multicoloured . . . 90 70

1026 Holy Family

1999. Christmas. Multicoloured.
2716 25c. Wise Man (29 × 29 mm) 30 25
2717 25c. Bell (29 × 29 mm) . . . 30 25
2718 50c. Two kings and camels (39 × 29 mm) 60 50
2719 50c. Holly leaf (39 × 29 mm) 60 50
2720 75c. Angel with star (39 × 30 mm) 90 70
2721 75c. Star (29 × 30 mm) . . . 90 70
2722 75c. Nativity (39 × 29 mm) 90 70
2723 75c. Tree decorations (29 × 29 mm) 90 70
2724 75c. Type **1026** 90 70

1027 Grape on Vine

2000. Wine Making. Multicoloured.
2725 25c. Type **1027** 35 30
2726 25c. Glass and bottle of wine . . . . 35 [illegible]
2727 50c. Wine bottles 70 55
2728 50c. Cork screw and cork 70 55

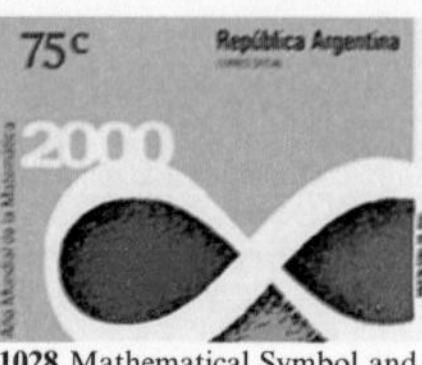

1028 Mathematical Symbol and "2000"

2000. International Mathematics Year.
2729 **1028** 75c. multicoloured . . . 1·00 80

1029 White-fronted Dove

2000. Doves and Pigeon. Mult. Self-adhesive.
2730 75c. Type **1029** . . . . . . 1·00 80
2731 75c. Picazuro pigeon (*Columba picazuro*) . . . 1·00 80

2732 75c. Picui dove (*Columbina picui*) . . . . 1·00 80
2733 75c. Eared dove (*Fenaida auriculata*) . . . . 1·00 80

1031 Open Book (CONABIP Library)

2000. Libraries. Multicoloured.
2735 25c. Type **1031** 35 35
2736 50c. Building facade (Jujuy library) 70 55
2737 75c. Hands and braille book (Argentine Library for the Blind) . . . . 1·00 80
2738 $1 Open book and building (National Library) . . . 2·10 1·60
No. 2737 has an inscription in braille across the stamp.

1032 Caravel, Compass Rose and Letter

2000. 500th Anniv of the Discovery of Brazil. Multicoloured.
2739 25c. Type **1032** 35 30
2740 75c. Pedro Alvares Cabral (discoverer) and map of South America . . . . . 1·00 80

1033 Lieutenant General Luis Maria Campos (founder)

2000. Centenary of the Higher Military Academy.
2741 **1033** 75c. multicoloured . . . 1·00 80

1035 Convention Emblem

2000. 91st Rotary International Convention, Buenos Aires.
2743 **1035** 75c. multicoloured . . . 1·00 80

1036 Futuristic Houses and Emblems (Rocio Casado)

2000. "Stampin' the Future". Winning Entries in Children's International Painting Competition. Mult.
2744 25c. Type **1036** 35 30
2745 50c. Sea and clouds (Carolina Cacerez) (vert) 70 55
2746 75c. Flower (Valeria A. Pizarro) . . . . 1·00 80
2747 $1 Flying cars (Cristina Ayala Castro) (vert) . . . 1·40 1·10

1037 Ribbon

2000. America. AIDS Awareness. Multicoloured.
2748 75c. Type **1037** . . . . . . 1·00 80
2749 75c. Arms circling faces . . 1·00 80

1038 Potez 25 Biplane

2000. Birth Centenary of Antoine de Saint-Exupery (novelist and pilot). Multicoloured.
2750 25c. Type **1038** 35 30
2751 50c. Late 28 . . . . 70 55

1039 Potez 25 Biplane

2000. "Aerofila 2000" Mercosur Air Philately Exhibition, Buenos Aires. Multicoloured.
2752 25c. As Type **1039** 35 30
2753 25c. Antoine de Saint-Exupery (novelist and pilot) (29 × 29 mm) . . . 35 30
2754 50c. Late 28 . . . . 70 55
2755 50c. Henri Guillaumet, Almonacid and Jean Mermoz (aviation pioneers) (29 × 29 mm) . . 70 55
2756 50c. Map of South America and tail of Late 25 (39 × 39 mm) 70 55
2757 $1 Late 25 and cover (39 × 29 mm) . . . . . . 1·40 1·10

1040 Illia

2000. Birth Centenary of Arturo U. Illia (President, 1963–66).
2758 **1040** 75c. multicoloured . . . 1·00 80

1041 San Martin **1042** Siku Pipes

2000. 150th Death Anniv of General Jose de San Martin.
2759 **1041** 75c. multicoloured . . . 1·00 80

2000. Argentine Culture. Multicoloured.
2760 10c. Ceremonial axe 15 10
2761 25c. Type **1042** 35 30
2762 50c. Andean loom 70 55
2763 60c. Pampeana poncho . . 80 60
2764 75c. Funeral mask . . . . . 1·00 80
2765 $1 Basket . . . . 1·40 1·10
2766 $2 Kultun ritual drum . . . 2·75 2·25
2767 $3.25 Ceremonial tiger mask 4·50 3·50
2768 $5 Funeral urn . . . . . . 7·00 5·50
2770 $9.40 Suri ceremonial costume . . . . 13·00 10·00

1043 Sarsfield, Signature and Cordoba Province Arms

2000. Birth Bicentenary of Dalmacio Velez Sarsfield (lawyer).
2775 **1043** 75c. multicoloured . . . 1·00 80

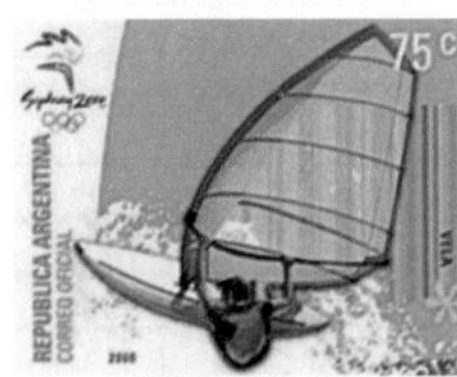

1044 Windsurfing

2000. Olympic Games, Sydney. Multicoloured.
2776 75c. Type **1044** . . . . . . 1·00 80
2777 75c. Hockey . . . . 1·00 80
2778 75c. Volleyball . . . . . . 1·00 80
2779 75c. High jump and pole vault . . . . 1·00 80

1045 Argentine Petiso

2000. "Espana 2000" International Stamp Exhibition, Madrid. Horses. Multicoloured.
2780 25c. Type **1045** 35 30
2781 25c. Carriage horse 35 30
2782 50c. Peruvian horse 70 55
2783 50c. Criolla 70 55
2784 75c. Saddle horse . . . . . 1·00 80
2785 75c. Polo horse . . . . . . 1·00 80

1046 Man on Bicycle and Las Nereidas Fountain

2000. Transportation. Multicoloured.
2787 25c.+25c. Type **1046** 70 55
2788 50c.+50c. *Graf Zeppelin* over Buenos Aires . . . . . . 1·25 1·00
2789 50c.+50c. *Ganz* (diesel locomotive) . . . . . . 1·40 1·10
2790 75c.+75c. Tram . . . . . . 2·10 1·75

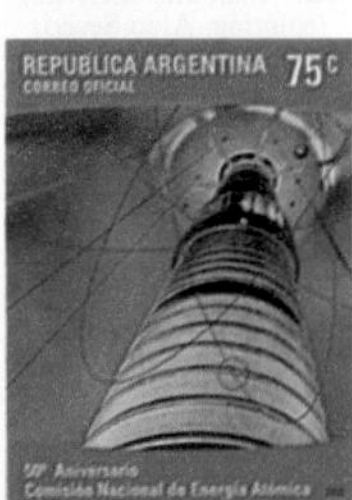

1047 Nuclear Reactor

2000. 50th Anniv of National Commission for Atomic Energy.
2791 **1047** 75c. multicoloured . . . 1·00 80

1048 "Filete" (left-hand detail)

2000. Fileteado (painting genre) (Nos. 2792/3) and Tango (dance) (Nos. 2794/5). Multicoloured.
2792 75c. Type **1048** . . . . . . 1·00 80
2793 75c. "Filete" (right-hand detail) (Brunetti brothers) 1·00 80
2794 75c. Tango orchestra . . . 1·00 80
2795 75c. Couple dancing . . . . 1·00 80

1049 Human Bodies on Jigsaw

2000. 40th Anniv of Organ Donation Publicity Campaign.
2796 **1049** 75c. multicoloured . . . 1·00 60

1050 "Birth of Jesus" (stained glass window, Sanctuary of Our Lady of the Rosary, New Pompeii)

2000. Christmas.
2797 **1050** 75c. multicoloured . . . 1·00 60

1051 *Commelina erecta*

2000. Medicinal Plants. Multicoloured.
2798 75c. Type **1051** . . . . . . 1·00 60
2799 75c. *Senna corymbosa* . . . 1·00 60
2800 75c. *Mirabilis jalapa* . . . . 1·00 60
2801 75c. *Eugenia uniflora* . . . . 1·00 60

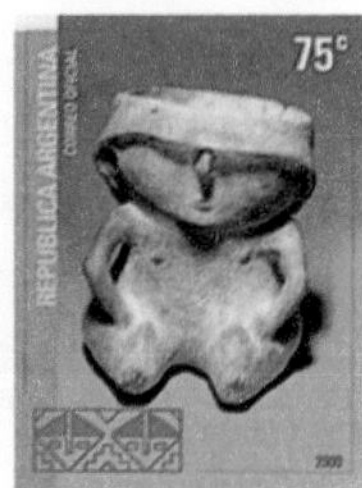

1052 Human-shaped Vessel, Cienaga

2000. Traditional Crafts. Multicoloured.
2802 75c. Type **1052** . . . . . . 1·00 60
2803 75c. Painted human-shaped vase, Vaquerias . . . . . 1·00 60
2804 75c. Animal-shaped vessel, Condorhuasi . . . . . . 1·00 60
2805 75c. Human-shaped vase, Candelaria . . . . 1·00 60

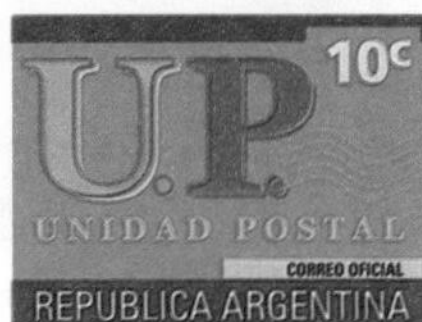

1053 "U. P." Unidad Postal

2001. Postal Agents' Stamps. Multicoloured, background colours given. Self-adhesive gum.
2806 **1053** 10c. turquoise 15 10
2807 25c. green 35 20
2808 60c. yellow 80 45
2809 75c. red . . . . 1·00 60
2810 $1 blue . . . . 1·40 80
2811 $3 red . . . . 4·00 2·40
2812 $3.25 yellow . . . . . 4·50 2·75
2813 $5.50 mauve . . . . . . 7·50 4·50
Nos. 2806/13 were issued for use by Postal Agents as opposed to branches of the Argentine Post Office.

1054 *Megatherium americanum* ("Megaterio")

2001. Cainozoic Mammals. Multicoloured.

2820 75c. Type **1054** 80 45
2821 75c. *Doedicurus clavcaudatus* ("Gliptodonte") 80 45
2822 75c. *Macrauchenia patachonica* ("Macrauqueria") 80 45
2823 75c. *Toxodon platensis* ("Toxodonte") 80 45

1055 Map, South Polar Skua and San Martin Base

2001. 50th Anniv of San Martin and Brown Antarctic Bases. Multicoloured.

2824 75c. Type **1055** 80 45
2825 75c. Blue-eyed cormorant, map and Brown Base . . 80 45

1056 Bees on Clover Flower

2001. Apiculture. Multicoloured.

2826 75c. Type **1056** 80 45
2827 75c. Bees on honeycomb . . 80 45
2828 75c. Bees and bee-keeper attending hives 80 45
2829 75c. Jar of honey and swizzle 80 45

Nos. 2826/9 were issued together, se-tenant, forming a composite design.

1058 Dornier Do-j Wal Flying Boat *Plus Ultra* and Route Map

2001. 75th Anniv of Major Ramon Franco's Flight from Spain to Argentina.

2831 **1058** 75c. multicoloured . . . 80 45

1059 Horse's Bridle Fittings

2001. Silver Work. Each blue, silver and black.

2832 75c. Type **1059** 80 45
2833 75c. Stirrups 80 45
2834 75c. Spurs 80 45
2835 75c. Rastra (gaucho belt decoration) 80 45

1061 Goalkeeper catching Ball

2001. Under 20's World Youth Football Championship, Argentine Republic. Multicoloured.

2837 75c. Type **1061** 80 45
2838 75c. Player kicking ball . . 80 45

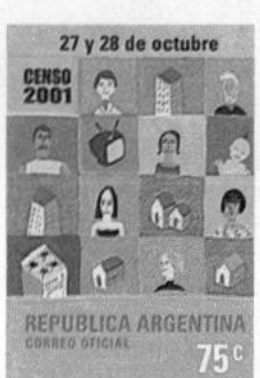

1062 People and Buildings

2001. National Census.

2839 **1062** 75c. multicoloured . . . 80 45

1063 SAC-C Satellite, Seagulls and Sunflowers

2001. Environmental Protection. Satellite Tracking Project.

2840 **1063** 75c. multicoloured . . . 80 45

1064 Puma

2001. Wild Cats. Multicoloured.

2841 25c. Type **1064** 35 20
2842 25c. Jaguar 35 20
2843 50c. Jaguarundi 70 50
2844 50c. Ocelot 70 50
2845 75c. Geoffroy's Cat 80 45
2846 75c. Kodkod 80 45

1065 "Bandoneon Recital" (painting, Aldo Severi)

2001.

2847 **1065** 75c. multicoloured . . . 80 45

1067 Discepolo

2001. Birth Centenary of Enriques Santos Discepolo (actor and lyric writer).

2849 **1067** 75c. multicoloured . . . 80 45

1068 Courtyard, Caroya Estancia, Angel and Chapel, Estancia Santa Catalina

2001. U.N.E.S.C.O. World Heritage Sites. Mult.

2850 75c. Type **1068** 80 45
2851 75c. Emblem and chapel, Estancia La Candelaria, dome of Estancia Alta Gracia and belfry, Estancia Jesus Maria . . 80 45

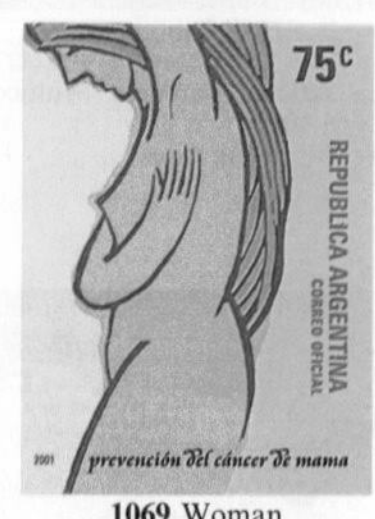

1069 Woman

2001. Breast Cancer Awareness.

2852 **1069** 75c. multicoloured . . . 80 45

1070 Burmeister's Porpoise

2001. Marine Mammals. Multicoloured.

2853 25c.+25c. Type **1070** 70 70
2854 50c.+50c. La Plata River dolphin . . . . 1·40 1·40
2855 50c.+50c. Minke whale . . . 1·40 1·40
2856 75c.+75c. Humpback whale 2·10 2·10

1071 Alfa Romeo 159 Alfetta, Spain, 1951

2001. Formula 1 Racing Cars driven by Juan Manuel Fangio. Multicoloured.

2857 75c. Type **1071** . . . . . . 1·00 60
2858 75c. Mercedes Benz W 196, France, 1954 . . . . . . 1·00 60
2859 75c. Lancia-Ferrari D50, Monaco, 1956 . . . . . 1·00 60
2860 75c. Maserati 250 F, Germany, 1957 . . . . . 1·00 60

1072 Palo Santo Tree

2001. Mercosur (South American Common Market).

2861 **1072** 75c. multicoloured . . . 1·00 60

1073 Justo Jose de Urquiza

2001. Birth Anniversaries. Multicoloured.

2862 75c. Type **1073** (politician) (bicentenary) . . . . . . 1·00 60
2863 75c. Roque Saenz Pena (President 1910—14) (150th anniv) . . . . . . 1·00 60

1075 "La Pobladora" Carriage (Enrique Udaondo Graphic Museum Complex)

2001. Museums. Multicoloured.

2865 75c. Type **1075** . . . . . . 1·00 60
2866 75c. Ebony and silver crucifix (Brigadier General Juan Martin de Pueyrredon Museum) (vert) . . . . 1·00 60
2867 75c. Funerary urn (Emilio and Duncan Wagner Museum of Anthropological and Natural Sciences) (vert) 1·00 60
2868 75c. Skeleton of Carnotaurus sastrei (Argentine Natural Science Museum) . . . . 1·00 60

1076 "The Power of the Most High will Overshadow You" (Martin La Spina)

2001. Christmas.

2869 **1076** 75c. multicoloured . . . 1·00 60

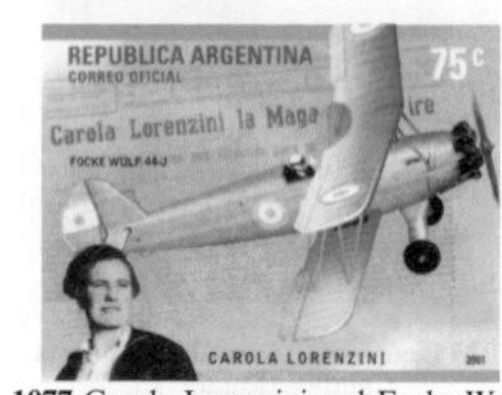

1077 Carola Lorenzini and Focke Wulf 44-J

2001. Aviation. Multicoloured.

2870 75c. Type **1077** . . . . . . 1·00 60
2871 75c. Jean Mermoz and Arc-en-Ciel . . . . 1·00 60

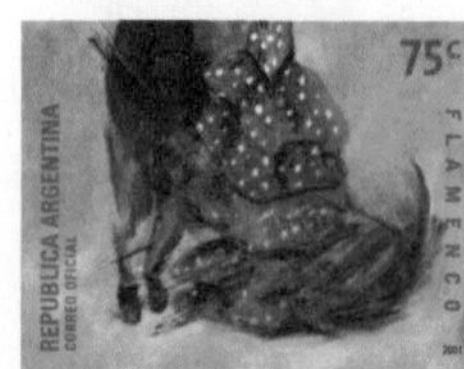

1078 Dancers (Flamenco)

2001. Dances. Multicoloured.

2872 75c. Type **1078** . . . . . . 1·00 60
2873 75c. Dancers (purple skirt) (Vals) . . . . 1·00 60
2874 75c. Dancers (orange skirt) (Zamba) . . . . 1·00 60
2875 75c. Dancers (Tango) . . . 1·00 60

1079 Scene from "Apollon Musagete" (Igor Stravinsky)

2001. National Day of the Dancer.

2876 **1079** 75c. multicoloured . . . 1·00 60

1080 Television Set, Camera and Microphone

2001. 50th Anniv of Television in Argentina. Multicoloured.

2877 75c. Type **1080** . . . . . . 1·00 60
2878 75c. Television set and video tapes . . . . 1·00 60
2879 75c. Satellite dish and astronaut . . . . 1·00 60
2880 75c. Colour television cables and remote control . . . 1·00 60

1081 Consolidated PBY-5A Catalina (amphibian) and Cancellation

2002. 50th Anniv of Argentine Antarctic Programme. Multicoloured.

2881 75c. Type **1081** (first air and sea courier service) . . . 1·00 60
2882 75c. *Chiriguano* (minesweeper) and buildings (foundation of Esparanza Base) . . . . 1·00 60

1082 House and Flag

2002. America. Education and Literacy Campaign. Multicoloured

2883 75c. Type **1082** . . . . . . 1·00 60
2884 75c. Children playing hopscotch . . . . 1·00 60

1083 Two-banded Plover (*Charadrius falklandicus*)

2002. Birds. Multicoloured.

2885 50c. Type **1083** 70 40
2886 50c. Dolphin gull (*Larus scoresbii*) 70 40
2887 75c. Ruddy-headed goose (*Chloephaga rubidiceps*) (vert) . . . . 1·00 60
2888 75c. King penguin (*Aptenodytes patagonicus*) (vert) . . . . 1·00 60

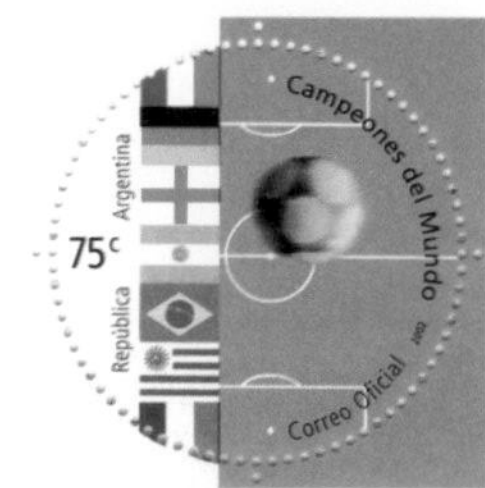

1084 Flags of Championship Winners and Football

2002. 20th-century World Cup Football Champions. Multicoloured.

2889 75c. Type **1084** . . . . . . 1·00 60
2890 75c. Argentine footballer . . 1·00 60

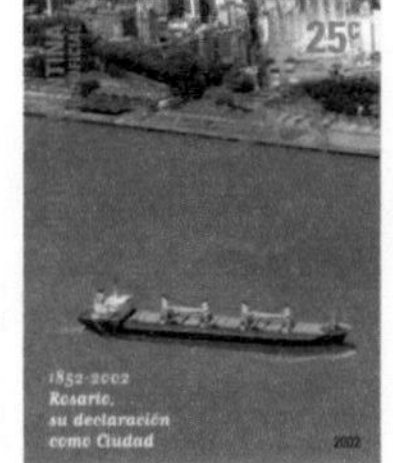

1085 Parana River and Emblem

2002. Anniversaries. Multicoloured.

2891 25c. Type **1085** (150th anniv of Rosario City) 35 20
2892 25c. National flag and monument 35 20
2893 50c. Mount Fitzroy (150th birth anniv of Francisco Pascasio Moreno (Perito) (explorer and founder of Argentine Scouts movement)) 70 40
2894 50c. Dr. Moreno 70 40
2895 75c. Flower and view of city (centenary of foundation San Carlos de Bariloche) 1·00 60
2896 75c. Capilla San Eduardo (St. Edward's chapel) and city plan . . . . 1·00 60

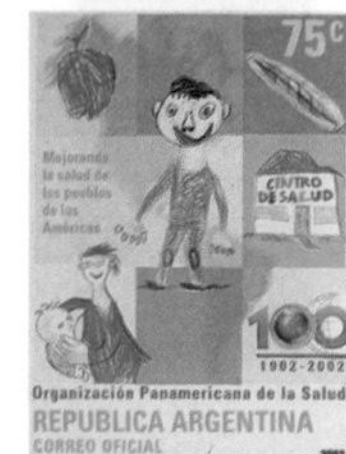

1086 Fruit, Mother, Boy, Bread and Health Centre

2002. Centenary of Pan-American Health Organization.

2897 **1086** 75c. multicoloured . . . 90 55

1087 Cosme Mariano Argerich, 1758–1820

2002. Doctors. Multicoloured.

2898 50c. Type **1087** 55 30
2899 50c. Jose Maria Ramos Mejia, 1849–1914 . . . . 55 30
2900 50c. Salvador Mazza, 1886–1946 . . . . 55 30
2901 50c. Carlos Arturo Giananonio, 1926–1995 55 30

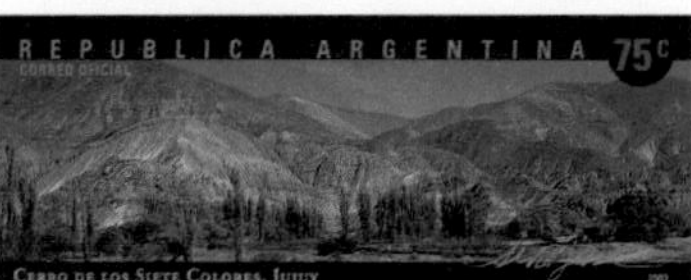

1088 Hill of Seven Colours, Jujuy

2002. Landscapes. Multicoloured.

2902 75c. Type **1088** 90 55
2903 75c. Iguazu waterfall, Misiones 90 55
2904 75c. Talampaya National Park 90 55
2905 75c. Agoncagua mountain, Mendoza 90 55
2906 75c. Rosedal Park, Buenos Aires 90 55
2907 75c. San Jorge lighthouse, Chubut 90 55
2908 75c. Perito Moreno glacier, Santa Cruz 90 55
2909 75c. Lapataia Bay, Tierra del Fuego 90 55

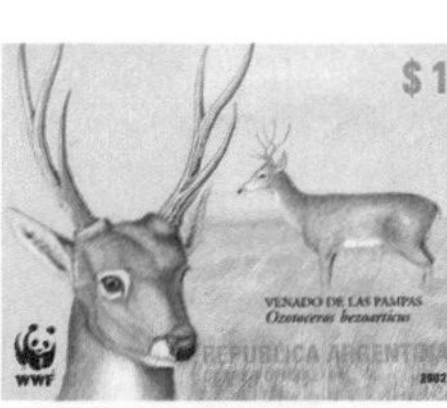

1089 Pampas Deer (*Ozotoceros bezoarticus*)

2002. Endangered Species. Multicoloured.

2910 $1 Type **1089** . . . . 1·10 65
2911 $1 Vicuna (*Vicugna vicugna*) 1·10 65
2912 $1 Southern pudu (*Pudu pudu*) . . . . 1·10 65
2913 $1 Chaco peccary (*Catgonus wagneri*) . . . . 1·10 65

1090 Eva Peron

2002. 50th Death Anniv of Eva Peron. Multicoloured.

2914 75c. Type **1090** 90 55
2915 75c. In cameo 90 55
2916 75c. At microphone 90 55
2917 75c. In profile wearing earrings 90 55

1091 Argentine Footballer

2002. Philakorea 2002 International Stamp Exhibition. Sheet 100 × 75 mm containing T **1091** and similar horiz design. Multicoloured.

MS2918 $1.50 Type **1091**; $1.50 Korean footballer . . . . . . 3·25 3·25

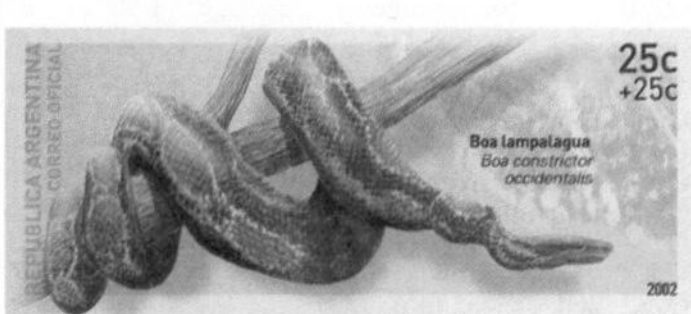

1092 Boa Constrictor (*Boa lampalagua*)

2002. Reptiles. Multicoloured.

2919 25c.+25c. Type **1092** 55 55
2920 50c.+50c. Caiman (*Caiman yacare*) . . . . 1·10 1·10
2921 50c.+50c. Argentine black and white tegu (*Tupinambis merianae*) . . 1·10 1·10
2922 75c.+75c. Red-footed tortoise (*Chelonoidis carbonaria*) . . . . . . 1·60 1·60

1093 Whale's Head

2002. Mercosur (South American Common Market). Multicoloured.

2923 75c. Type **1093** 90 55
2924 75c. Whale's tail 90 55

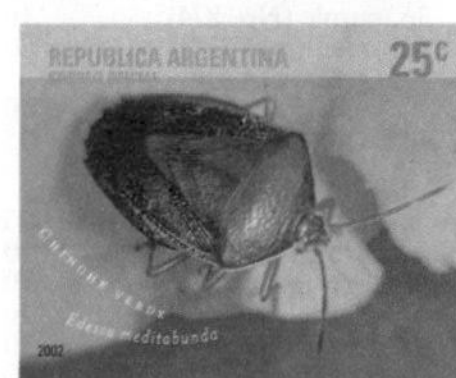

1094 *Edessa meditabunda*

2002. Insects. Multicoloured.

2925 25c. Type **1094** 25 10
2926 50c. *Elaeochlora viridis* . . . 55 30
2927 75c. *Chrysodina aurata* . . . 90 55
2928 75c. *Steirastoma breve* . . . 1·10 65

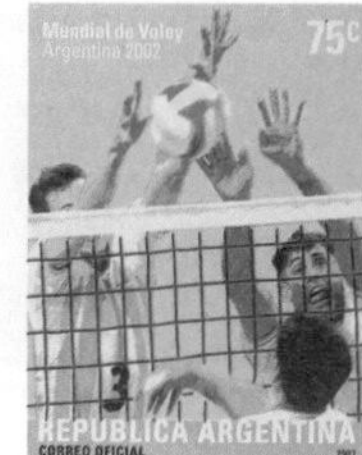

1095 Players, Ball and Net

2002. World Men's Volleyball Championships. Multicoloured.

2929 75c. Type **1095** 90 55
2930 75c. Two players ball and net 90 55
2931 75c. Hands, net, ball and head 90 55
2932 75c. Players congratulating one another 90 55

1096 Roadway

2002. 50th Anniv of Argentine Highways Department.

2933 **1096** 75c. multicoloured . . . 90 55

1097 Roberto Arlt

2002. Death Anniversaries. Multicoloured.

2934 75c. Type **1097** (writer, 60th) 90 55
2935 75c. Luis Sandrini (actor and director, 22nd) . . . 90 55
2936 75c. Nini Marshall (actor, 6th) 90 55
2937 75c. Beatriz Guido (writer, 14th) 90 55

1098 Immigrant Hotel, Mother and Child

2002. Immigration. Multicoloured.

2938 75c. Type **1098** 90 55
2939 75c. Two men and ship . . 90 55
2940 75c. Two men and immigrant hotel 90 55
2941 75c. Horse-drawn farm implement and family . . 90 55

Nos. 2938/41 were issued in horizontal *se-tenant* strips of four stamps within the sheet, each pair (2938/9 and 2940/1) forming a composite design.

1099 Envelope, Horse-drawn Coach and Head

2002. 50th Anniv of Argentine Federation of Philatelic Entities (FAEF). Multicoloured.

2942 75c. Type **1099** . . . . . .
2943 75c. Flag, figure, ship and arms 90 55

1100 Joseph leading Donkey carrying Mary and Jesus

2002. Christmas.
2944 **1100** 75c. multicoloured . . . 90 55

1101 Andres Chazarreta (composer)

2002. Folklorists. Multicoloured.
2945 75c. Type **1101** 90 55
2946 75c. Gustavo "Cuchi" Leguizamon (songwriter) 90 55
2947 75c. Carlos Vega (guitarist) 90 55
2948 75c. Armando Tejada Gomez (poet and songwriter) 90 55

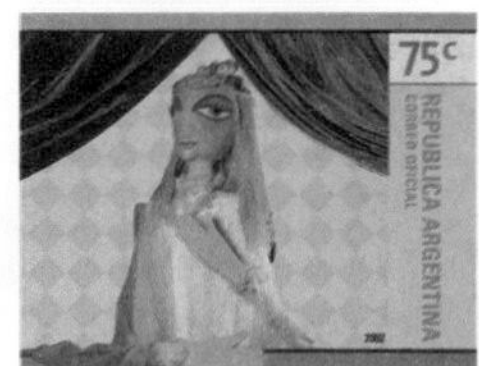

1102 Girl (rod puppet)

2002. Puppets. Multicoloured.
2949 75c. Type **1102** 90 55
2950 75c. Fish and king (marionettes) 90 55
2951 75c. Man (marote puppet) 90 55
2952 75c. Figures (shadow puppets) 90 55

BULK MAIL STAMPS

BP **999** Post Office Building, Buenos Aires

1999. Bulk Mail. Self-adhesive. Imperf.
BP2644 BP **999** $7 black and blue 8·50 8·50
BP2645 $11 black and red 14·00 14·00
BP2646 $16 black and yellow . . . . 20·00 20·00
BP2647 $23 black and green . . . . . 28·00 28·00

BP **1069**

2001. Bulk Mail. Additionally overprinted **UP**. Imperf.
BP2853 BP **1069** $7 black and blue . . . . . . 8·50 8·50
BP2854 $11 black and red . . . . . 14·00 14·00

EXPRESS SERVICE MAIL

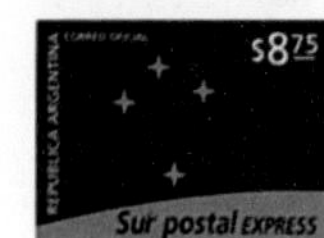

E **999** Express Service Emblem

1999. Self-adhesive.
E2644 E **999** 8p.75 blue and silver 12·00 9·50
E2645 – 17p.50 blue and gold 24·00 19·00
DESIGN: 24-hour service emblem.

No. E2644 was for express service mail and No. E2645 for use on 24-hour express service mail.

OFFICIAL STAMPS

1884. Optd **OFICIAL**.
O66 **33** $\frac{1}{2}$c. brown . . . . 8·00 6·00
O69 1c. red 45 15
O70 **24** 2c. green 45 15
O71 – 4c. brown (No. 32) . . . 45 15
O72 **9** 8c. red 45 15
O73 **10** 10c. green . . . . 42·00 22·00
O76 **33** 12c. blue 70 60
O77 **10** 16c. green . . . . 1·90 75
O78 **22** 20c. blue . . . . 8·00 6·00
O79 **11** 24c. blue (roul) . . . . . 1·40 85
O80 24c. blue (perf) . . . . . 1·25 70
O81 – 25c. red (No. 47) . . . . 9·50 6·50
O82 – 30c. orange (No. 33) . . . 17·00 12·00
O83 – 60c. black (No. 34) . . . 12·00 7·50
O84 – 90c. blue (No. 35) . . . . 8·50 6·50

O 73

1901.
O275 O **73** 1c. grey 25 10
O276 2c. brown 35 15
O277 5c. red 45 15
O278 10c. green 50 15
O279 30c. blue . . . . . . 3·50 85
O280 50c. orange . . . . . . 1·90 65

1938. (a) Optd **SERVICIO OFICIAL** in two lines.
O668 **143** 1c. brown (No. 645) . . 10 10
O669 – 2c. brown (No. 646) . . 10 10
O670 – 3c. green (No. 647) . . 10 10
O679 – 3c. grey (No. 672) . . . 10 10
O771 – 3c. grey (No. 672a) . . 3·00 1·25
O671 – 5c. brown (No. 653b) 10 10
O782 **200** 5c. red (No. 773) . . . 10 10
O667 – 10c. red (No. 653d) . . 10 10
O773 – 10c. purple (No. 678) 10 10
O681 **146** 15c. blue (No. 676) . . 10 10
O774 – 15c. grey (No. 708) . . 10 10
O683 **146** 20c. blue ($19\frac{1}{2} \times 26$ mm) 50 10
O872 **247** 20c. red 10 10
O813 – 25c. (No. 673) 10 10
O674 – 40c. (No. 658) 10 10
O675 – 50c. (No. 659) 10 10
O676 **152** 1p. (No. 760) 10 10
O827 **234** 1p. (No. 826) 35 10
O778 – 2p. (No. 661) 10 10
O779 – 5p. (No. 662) 15 10
O780 – 10p. (No. 763) 25 10
O781 – 20p. (No. 764) 80 20

(b) Optd **SERVICIO OFICIAL** in one line.
O897 – 20c. lilac (No. 895) . . . 15 10

1953. Eva Peron stamps optd **SERVICIO OFICIAL**.
O854 **239** 5c. grey 10 10
O855 10c. red 10 10
O856 20c. red 10 10
O857 25c. green 10 10
O858 40c. purple 10 10
O859 45c. blue 15 10
O860 50c. bistre 10 10
O862 **240** 1p. brown (No. 846) . . 10 10
O863 1p.50 green (No. 847) 25 10
O864 2p. red (No. 848) . . . 20 10
O865 3p. blue (No. 849) . . . 45 15
O866 5p. brown 70 40
O867 **239** 10p. red . . . . 4·00 3·00
O868 **240** 20p. green . . . . . . 32·00 20·00

1955. Stamps of 1954 optd **SERVICIO OFICIAL** in one line.
O869 **247** 20c. red 10 10
O870 40c. red 10 10
O880 – 1p. brown (No. 871) . . 10 10
O882 – 3p. purple (No. 874) . . 10 10
O883 – 5p. green (No. 875) . . 30 10
O884 – 10p. green and grey (No. 876) 40 10
O886 **250** 20p. violet 75 15

1955. Various stamps optd. (a) Optd **S. OFICIAL**.
O 896 – 5c. brown (No. 894) 10 10
O 955 – 10c. green (No. 946) 10 10
O 956 – 20c. purple (No. 947) 10 10
O 879 – 50c. blue (No. 868) . . 20 10
O 957 – 50c. ochre (No. 948) 10 10
O1034 – 1p. brn (No. 1016) . . 10 10
O 899 **264** 2p. purple 10 10
O1050 – 2p. red (No. 1035) . . 10 10
O 959 – 3p. blue (No. 951) . . 15 10
O1051 – 4p. red (No. 1036) . . 15 10
O 961 **296** 5p. brown 20 10
O1052 – 8p. red (No. 1037) . . 15 10
O 962 – 10p. brown (No. 1286) 15 10
O1053 – 10p. red (No. 1038) . . 15 10
O1036 – 12p. dull purple (No. 1028) 40 10
O 964 – 20p. green (No. 954) 50 10
O1055 – 20p. red (No. 1039) . . 20 10
O1037 – 22p. blue (No. 1018) 50 10
O1038 – 23p. green (No. 1019) 95 10
O1039 – 25p. lilac (No. 1020) 50 10
O1040 – 43p. lake (No. 1021) 1·40 65
O1041 – 45p. brn (No. 1022) . . 1·40 65
O1042 – 50p. blue (No. 1023) 2·40 95
O1043 – 50p. blue (No. 1287) 3·25 95
O1045 – 100p. blue (No. 1289) 1·60 65
O1046 – 300p. violet (No. 1026) 4·75 2·25

(b) Optd **SERVICIO OFICIAL**.
O 900 **265** 2p.40 brown 20 10
O 958 – 3p. blue (No. 951) . . 15 10
O 901 **266** 4p.40 green 25 10
O 960 **296** 5p. brown 20 10
O 887 – 50p. ind & bl (No. 878) 1·60 65
O1049 – 500p. grn (No. 1032) 7·75 3·75

For lists of stamps optd **M.A., M.G., M.H., M.I., M.J.I., M.M., M.O.P.** or **M.R.C.** for use in ministerial offices see the Stanley Gibbons Catalogue Part 20 (South America).

1963. Nos. 1068, etc., optd **S. OFICIAL**.
O1076 **351** 2p. green 20 10
O1080 – 4p. red (No. 1069) . . 15 10
O1081 – 6p. red (No. 1070) . . 25 10
O1078 – 90p. bistre (No. 1288) 4·00 2·00

RECORDED MESSAGE STAMPS

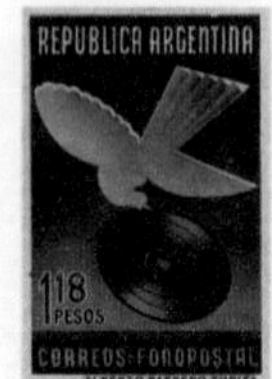

RM **166** Winged Messenger

1939. Various symbolic designs inscr "CORREOS FONOPOSTAL".
RM688 RM **166** 1p.18 blue . . . 16·00 8·00
RM689 – 1p.32 blue . . . 16·00 8·00
RM690 – 1p.50 brown . . 48·00 24·00
DESIGNS—VERT: 1p.32, Head of Liberty and National Arms. HORIZ: 1p.50, Record and winged letter.

TELEGRAPH STAMPS USED FOR POSTAGE

PT **34**

PT **35** (Sun closer to "NACIONAL")

1887.
PT104 PT **34** 10c. red 50 10
PT105 PT **35** 10c. red 50 10
PT106 PT **34** 40c. blue 60 10
PT107 PT **35** 40c. blue 60 15

ARMENIA Pt. 10

Formerly part of Transcaucasian Russia. Temporarily independent after the Russian revolution of 1917. From 12 March 1922, Armenia, Azerbaijan and Georgia formed the Transcaucasian Federation. Issues for the federation were superseded by those of the Soviet Union in 1924.

With the dissolution of the Soviet Union in 1991 Armenia once again became independent.

NOTE. Only one price is given for Nos. 3/245, which applies to unused or cancelled to order. Postally used copies are worth more.

All the overprints and surcharges were handstamped and consequently were applied upright or inverted indiscriminately, some occurring only inverted.

1919. 100 kopeks = 1 rouble.
1994. 100 luma = 1 dram.

NATIONAL REPUBLIC

28 May 1918 to 2 December 1920 and 18 February to 2 April 1921.

1919. Arms type of Russia and unissued Postal Savings Bank stamp (No. 6) surch. Imperf or perf.
(a) Surch thus **k. 60 k** with or without stops.
3 **22** 60k. on 1k. orange 40
6 – 60k. on 1k. red on buff . . . 10·00

(b) Surch in figures only.
7 **22** 60k. on 1k. orange . . . . . 30·00
8 120k. on 1k. orange . . . . 30·00

(6)

(8)

1919. Stamps of Russia optd as T **6** in various sizes, with or without frame. Imperf or perf. (a) Arms types.
53B **22** 1k. orange . . . . 13·00
54B 2k. green 50
55B 3k. red 50
11B **23** 4k. red 25
12B **22** 5k. red 25
13B **23** 10k. blue 40
14B **22** 10k. on 7k. blue 30
15B **10** 15k. blue and purple . . . 35
16B **14** 20k. red and blue 30
17 **10** 25k. mauve and green . . 60
45B 35k. green and purple . . 50
19B **14** 50k. green and purple . . 20
30B **22** 60k. on 1k. orange (No. 3) 50
31B **10** 70k. orange and brown . . 30
32B **15** 1r. orange and brown . . 50
33B **11** 3r.50 green and brown . . 1·00
23B **20** 5r. green and blue . . . . 1·40
62 **11** 7r. yellow and black . . . 25·00
24B 7r. pink and green . . . . 2·50
52B **20** 10r. grey, red and yellow 3·00

(b) Romanov type.
63B 4k. red (No. 129) . . . . . 2·00

(c) Unissued Postal Savings Bank stamp.
64A 1k. red on buff . . . . . . 3·50

1920. Stamps of Russia surch as T **8** in various types and sizes. Imperf or perf. (a) Arms types.
94B **22** 1r. on 60k. on 1k. orange (No. 3) . . . 80
65B 1r. on 1k. orange . . . 50
66B 3r. on 3k. red 50
67B 3r. on 4k. red . . . . . 6·00
97B 5r. on 2k. green 60
69B **23** 5r. on 4k. red . . . . . 1·00
70B **22** 5r. on 5k. red 50
71B 5r. on 7k. blue . . . . 1·00
72B **23** 5r. on 10k. blue 40
73B **22** 5r. on 10 on 7k. blue . . 90
74B **10** 5r. on 14k. red and blue 2·25
75B 5r. on 15k. blue and purple 75
76B **14** 5r. on 20k. red and blue 1·25
76aB **10** 5r. on 20 on 14k. red and blue . . . . . . 7·00
77B 5r. on 25k. mauve and green . . . . 7·00
111B **22** 5r. on 3 r .on 5k. red . . 7·50
78B **10** 10r. on 25k. mauve and green . . . . 1·00
79B 10r. on 35k. green and purple 65
80B **14** 10r. on 50k. green and purple . . . . 1·00
80aB **9** 25r. on 1k. orange . . . 35·00
80bB 25r. on 3k. red . . . . 35·00
80cB 25r. on 5k. purple . . . 35·00
80dB **22** 25r. on 10 on 7k. blue 35·00
80eB **10** 25r. on 15k. blue and purple . . . . 35·00
81B **14** 25r. on 20k. red and blue . . . . 4·00
82B **10** 25r. on 25k. mauve and green . . . . 4·00
83B 25r. on 35k. green and purple . . . . 3·50
84B **14** 25r. on 50k. green and purple . . . . 3·50
85B **10** 25r. on 70k. orange and brown . . . . 4·00
104aB **9** 50r. on 1k. orange . . . 32·00
104bB 50r. on 3k. red . . . . 32·00
85bB **10** 50r. on 4k. red . . . . 38·00
104cB **14** 50r. on 5k. purple . . . 32·00
85cB **10** 50r. on 15k. blue and purple . . . . 38·00
85dB **14** 50r. on 20k. red and blue . . . . 38·00
85eB **10** 50r. on 35k. green & purple . . . . 38·00
85fB **14** 50r. on 50k. green & purple . . . . 20·00
105B **10** 50r. on 70k. orange and brown . . . . 4·50
106B **15** 50r. on 1r. orange and brown . . . . 1·10
107B 100r. on 1r. orange and brown . . . . 6·50
108B **11** 100r. on 3r.50 green and brown . . . . 4·50
88B **20** 100r. on 5r. green and blue . . . . 5·00
89B **11** 100r. on 7r. yellow and black . . . . 20·00
90B 100r. on 7r. pink and green . . . . 6·75
93B **20** 100r. on 10r. grey, red and yellow . . . . . 6·00

(b) Romanov issue of 1913.
112 1r. on 1k. orange . . . . . 7·00
113 3r. on 3k. red . . . . 5·00
114 5r. on 4k. red . . . . 3·50
115 5r. on 10 on 7k. brown . . 3·50
116 5r. on 14k. green . . . . . 22·00
117 5r. on 20 on 14k. green . . 5·00
118 25r. on 4k. red . . . . . . 5·00
118a 100r. on 1k. orange . . . . 50·00
119 100r. on 2k. green . . . . . 50·00
120 100r. on 3r. violet . . . . . 55·00

(c) War Charity issues of 1914 and 1915.
121 **15** 25r. on 1k. green and red on yellow . . . . 38·00
122 25r. on 3k. green and red on rose . . . . 30·00
123 50r. on 7k. green and brown on buff . . . . . 24·00
124 50r. on 10k. brown and blue . . . . 24·00
125 100r. on 1k. green and red on yellow . . . . 24·00
126 100r. on 1k. grey and brown . . . . 24·00
127 100r. on 3k. green and red on rose . . . . 24·00
128 100r. on 7k. green and brown on buff . . . . . 24·00
129 100r. on 10k. brown and blue . . . . 24·00

1920. Arms types of Russia optd as T **6** in various sizes with or without frame, and surch as T **8** or with value only in various types and sizes. Imperf or perf.
155B **22** 1r. on 60k. on 1k. orange (No. 3) . . . 1·10
156A 3r. on 3k. red . . . . . 1·50
157A 5r. on 2k. green 90
141A **23** 5r. on 4k. red . . . . . 3·00
158A **22** 5r. on 5k. red . . . . . 2·75
142A **23** 5r. on 10k. blue . . . . 3·00
143A **22** 5r. on 10 on 7k. blue . . . 3·00
144A **10** 5r. on 15k. blue & pur 1·25
145A **14** 5r. on 20k. red and blue 1·25
132B **10** 10r. on 15k. blue & pur 7·50
145aB **14** 10r. on 20k. red & blue 9·00
146A **10** 10r. on 25k. mauve and green . . . . 1·25
147B 10r. on 35k. green and purple . . . . 1·00
148A **14** 10r. on 50k. green and purple . . . . 2·50
159A **10** 10r. on 70k. orange and brown . . . . 8·75
163A **22** 10r. on 5r. on 5k. red 18·00
164A **10** 10r. on 5r. on 25k. mauve and green . . 20·00
165A 10r. on 5r. on 35k. green and purple . . 6·50
138A 25r. on 70k. orange and brown . . . . 5·00
161B **15** 50r. on 1r. orange and brown . . . . 1·75
135B **11** 100r. on 3r.50 green and brown . . . . 1·75
151A **20** 100r. on 5r. green & bl 6·00
136A **11** 100r. on 7r. pink and green . . . . 5·00
154aA **20** 100r. on 10r. grey, red and yellow . . . . . 8·00
166A 100r. on 25r. on 5r. green and blue . . . 18·00

1920. Stamps of Russia optd as T **6** in various sizes, with or without frame and surch **10**. Perf. (a) Arms types.
168 **14** 10 on 20k. red and blue . . 18·00
169 **10** 10 on 25k. mauve and green . . . . 18·00
170 10 on 35k. green and purple . . . . 12·00
171 **14** 10 on 50k. green and purple . . . . 14·00

(b) Romanov type.
172 10 on 4k. red (No. 129) . . . 30·00

1920. Stamps of Russia optd with monogram as in T **8** in various types and sizes and surch **10**. Imperf or perf. (a) Arms types.
173 **23** 10 on 4k. red . . . . . . 30·00
174 **22** 10 on 5k. red . . . . . . 30·00
175 **10** 10 on 15k. blue & purple 30·00
176 **14** 10 on 20k. red and blue 28·00
176a **10** 10 on 20 on 14k. red and blue . . . . 14·00
177 10 on 25k. mauve & green 14·00
178 10 on 35k. green & purple 14·00
179 **14** 10 on 50k. green & purple 14·00

(b) Romanov type.
181 10 on 4k. red (No. 129) . . . 38·00

11

12 Mt. Ararat

Stamps in Types **11**, **12** and a similar horizontal type showing a woman spinning were printed in Paris to the order of the Armenian National Government, but were not issued in Armenia as the Bolshevists had assumed control. (Price 10p. each).

SOVIET REPUBLIC

2 December 1920 to 18 February 1921 and 2 April 1921 to 12 March 1922.

(13)

1921. Arms types of Russia surch with T **13**. Perf.
182 **15** 5000r. on 1r. orange and brown . . . . 5·00
183 **11** 5000r. on 3r.50 grn & brn 5·00
184 **20** 5000r. on 5r. green & blue 5·00
185 **11** 5000r. on 7r. pink and green . . . . 5·00
186 **20** 5000r. on 10r. grey, red & yellow . . . . 5·00

14 Common Crane

16 Village Scene

1922. Unissued stamps surch in gold kopeks. Imperf.
187 **14** 1 on 250r. red . . . . . . 13·50
188 1 on 250r. slate . . . . . 21·00
189 **16** 2 on 500r. red . . . . . 4·50
190 3 on 500r. slate . . . . . 1·50
191 – 4 on 1000r. red . . . . . 2·75
192 – 4 on 1000r. slate . . . . . 6·00
193 – 5 on 2000r. slate . . . . . 24·00
194 – 10 on 2000r. red . . . . . 24·00
195 – 15 on 5000r. red . . . . . 12·00
196 – 20 on 5000r. slate . . . . 3·00

DESIGNS (sizes in mm): 1000r. Woman at well (17 × 26); 2000r. Erivan railway station (35 × 24½); 5000r. Horseman and Mt. Ararat (39½ × 24½).

17 Soviet Emblems

18 Wall Sculpture at Ani

19 Mt. Aragatz

1922. Unissued stamps as T **17/19** surch in gold kopeks in figures. Imperf or perf.
210 **17** 1 on 1r. green . . . . . 3·00
198 **18** 2 on 2r. slate . . . . . . 7·50
212 – 3 on 3r. red . . . . 12·00
213 – 4 on 25r. green . . . . . 2·50
201 – 5 on 50r. red . . . . . . 3·00
215 – 10 on 100r. orange . . . 4·00
203 – 15 on 250r. blue . . . . 2·00
204a **19** 20 on 500r. purple . . . 2·50
205 – 35 on 20,000r. red . . . . 18·00
206a – 50 on 25,000r. green . . . 28·00
209 – 50r. on 25,000r. blue . . . 4·00

DESIGNS (sizes in mm): 3r. (29 × 22) and 250r. (21 × 35) Soviet emblems; 25r. (30 × 22½); 100r. (34½ × 23) and 20,000r. (43 × 27) Mythological sculptures, Ani. 50r. (25½ × 37). Armenian soldier; 25,000r. (45½ × 27½) Mt. Ararat.

The above and other values were not officially issued without the surcharges.

TRANSCAUCASIAN FEDERATION ISSUES FOR ARMENIA

1923. As T **19**, etc., surch in gold kopeks in figures. Imperf or perf.
219 – 1 on 250r. blue . . . . . 3·00
217 **19** 2 on 500r. purple . . . . 3·00
218 – 3 on 20000r. lake . . . . 8·50

26 Mt. Ararat and Soviet Emblems

28 Ploughing

1923. Unissued stamps in various designs as T **26/28** surch in Transcaucasian roubles in figures. Perf.
227 **26** 10,000r. on 50r. green and red . . . . 1·50
228 – 15,000r. on 300r. blue and buff . . . . 1·50
229 – 25,000r. on 400r. blue and pink . . . . 1·50
240B – 30,000r. on 500r. violet and lilac . . . . 1·50
231 – 50,000r. on 1000r. blue 1·50
232 – 75,000r. on 3000r. black and green . . . . 1·75
233 – 100,000r. on 2000r. black and grey . . . . 2·00
243 – 200,000r. on 4000r. black and brn . . . . 1·00
235 – 300,000r. on 5000r. black and red . . . . 2·75
245 **28** 500,000r. on 10,000r. black and red . . . . 1·25

DESIGNS (sizes in mm): 300r. (26 × 35) Star over Mt. Ararat; 400r. (26 × 34½) Soviet emblems; 500r. (26 × 34½) Crane (bird); 1000r. (19 × 25) Peasant in print; 2000r. (26 × 31) Human-headed bird from old bas-relief; 3000r. (26½ × 36) Sower; 4000r. (26 × 31½) Star and dragon; 5000r. (26 × 32) Blacksmith.

INDEPENDENT REPUBLIC

31 Mount Ararat and National Colours

1992. Independence Day.
246 **31** 20k. multicoloured 15 15
247 2r. multicoloured 90 90
248 5r. multicoloured . . . . . 2·10 2·10
MS249 80 × 80 mm. 7r. multicoloured (Mt. Ararat and eagle) . . . . 27·00 27·00

32 Dish Aerial and World Map

1992. Inauguration of International Direct-dial Telephone System.
250 **32** 50k. multicoloured . . . . 1·25 1·25

33 Ancient Greek Wrestling **34** National Flag

1992. Olympic Games, Barcelona. Multicoloured.
251 40k. Type **33** 10 10
252 3r.60 Boxing 30 30
253 5r. Weightlifting 35 35
254 12r. Gymnastics (ring exercises) 75 75

1992.
255 **34** 20k. multicoloured (postage) 10 10
256 – 1r. black 10 10
257 – 3r. brown 25 25
258 – 3r. brown 10 10
259 – 5r. black 40 40

260 – 20r. grey 25 25
261 – 2r. blue (air) 35 35

DESIGNS: 1r. Goddess Waroubini statuette from Orgov radio-optical telescope; 2r. Zvartnots Airport, Yerevan; 3r. (No. 257) Goddess Anahit; 3r. (No. 258) Runic inscription Karmir-Blour; 5r. U.P.U. Monument, Berne, Switzerland; 20r. Silver cup from Karashamb.

See also Nos. 275/82.

35 "Noah's Descent from Mt. Ararat"

1993. 175th Birth Anniv of Hovhannes Aivazovsky (painter). Sheet 95 × 63 mm.
MS262 35 7r. multicoloured . . . 2·40 2·40

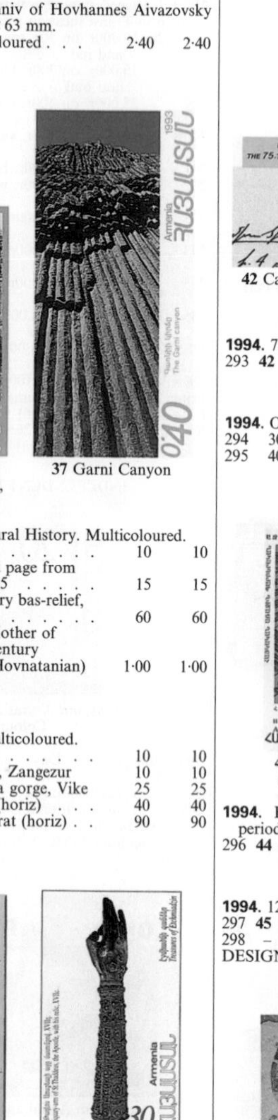

36 Engraved 10th-century Tombstone, Makenis

37 Garni Canyon

1993. Armenian Cultural History. Multicoloured.
263 40k. Type **36** 10 10
264 80k. Illuminated page from Gospel of 1295 . . . . . 15 15
265 3r.60 13th-century bas-relief, Gandzasar 60 60
266 5r. "Glorious Mother of God" (18th-century painting, H. Hovnatanian) 1·00 1·00

1993. Landscapes. Multicoloured.
268 40k. Type **37** 10 10
269 80k. Shaki Falls, Zangezur 10 10
270 3r.60 River Arpa gorge, Vike 25 25
271 5r. Lake Sevan (horiz) . . . 40 40
272 12r. Mount Ararat (horiz) . . 90 90

38 Temple of Garni

39 Reliquary for Arm of St. Thaddeus (17th century)

1993. "YEREVAN '93" International Stamp Exn.
273 **38** 10r. red, black and brown 35 35
MS274 133 × 111 mm. No. 273 × 6 plus two labels . . . . 2·10 2·10

1994. As T **34** but new currency.
275 10l. agate and brown 10 10
277 50l. deep brown and brown 10 10
280 10d. brown and grey 25 25
282 25d. gold and red 75 75

DESIGNS: 10l. Shivini, Sun God (Karmir-Blour); 50l. Tayshaba, God of the Elements (Karmir-Blour); 10d. Khaldi, Supreme God (Karmir-Blour); 25d. National arms.

1994. Treasures of Etchmiadzin (seat of Armenian church). Multicoloured.
286 3d. Descent from the Cross (9th-century wooden panel) 10 10
287 5d. Gilded silver reliquary of Holy Cross of Khotakerats (1300) 10 10
288 12d. Cross with St. Karapet's right hand (14th century) 20 20
289 30d. Type **39** 65 65
290 50d. Gilded silver chrism vessel (1815) 90 90

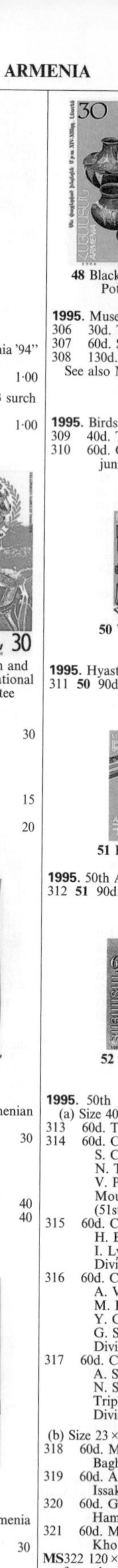

(40) (41)

1994. Stamp Exhibitions, Yerevan. (a) "Armenia '94" National Exn. No. 273 surch with T **40**.
291 **38** 40d. on 10r. red, blk & brn 1·00 1·00

(b) "Armenia–Argentina" Exhibition. No. 273 surch with T **41**.
292 **38** 40d. on 10r. red, blk & brn 1·00 1·00

42 Cancelled Stamps of 1919

43 Stadium and Arms of National Committee

1994. 75th Anniv of First Stamp Issue.
293 **42** 16d. multicoloured 30 30

1994. Olympic Committees. Multicoloured.
294 30d. Type **43** 15 15
295 40d. Olympic rings (centenary of Int Olympic Committee) 20 20

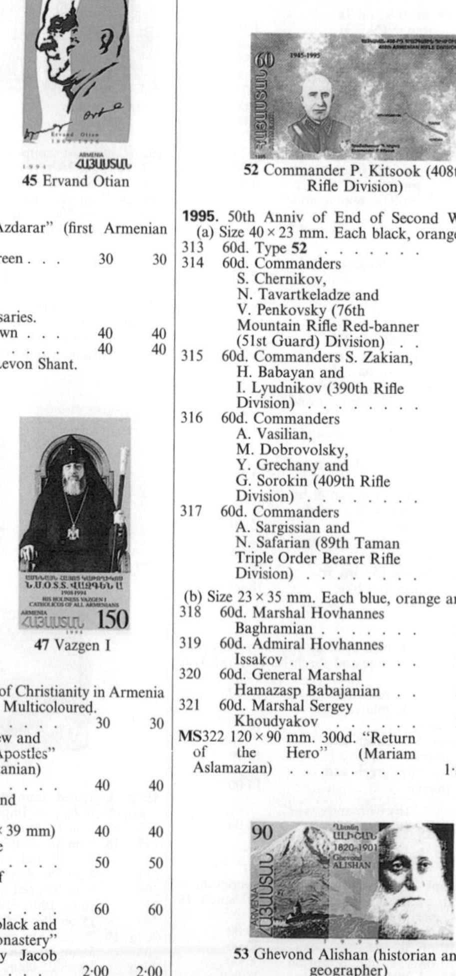

44 Haroutune Shmavonian

45 Ervand Otian

1994. Bicentenary of "Azdarar" (first Armenian periodical).
296 **44** 30d. brown and green . . . 30 30

1994. 125th Birth Anniversaries.
297 **45** 50d. drab and brown . . . 40 40
298 – 50d. brown 40 40

DESIGN—HORIZ: 50d. Levon Shant.

46 "Cross" (from Gospel)

47 Vazgen I

1995. 1700th Anniv (2001) of Christianity in Armenia (1st issue). Works of art. Multicoloured.
299 60d. Type **46** 30 30
300 70d. "St. Bartholomew and St. Thaddeus the Apostles" (Hovnatan Hovnatanian) (45 × 39 mm) 40 40
301 70d. "Kings Abhar and Trdat" (Mkrtoum Hovnatanian) (45 × 39 mm) 40 40
302 80d. "St. Gregory the Illuminator" 50 50
303 90d. "The Baptism of Armenian People" (H. Aivazovsky) 60 60
MS304 97 × 71 mm. 400d. black and ochre ("Echmiadzin Monastery" (detail of engraving by Jacob Peeters)) . . . . 2·00 2·00

See also Nos. **MS**331, 362/**MS**367, 382/**MS**387 and **MS**401.

1995. 1st Death Anniv of Vazgen I (Patriarch of Armenian Orthodox Church).
305 **47** 150d. black and grey . . . 70 70

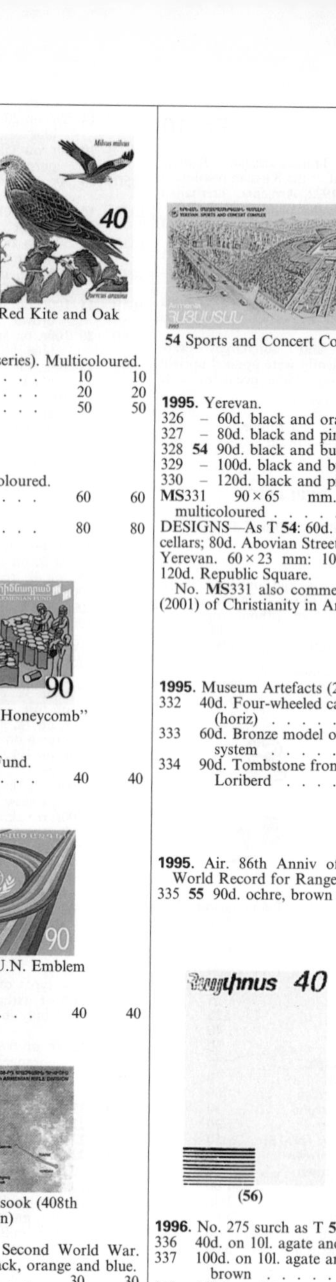

48 Black-polished Pottery

49 Red Kite and Oak

1995. Museum Artefacts (1st series). Multicoloured.
306 30d. Type **48** 10 10
307 60d. Silver horn 20 20
308 130d. Gohar carpet 50 50

See also Nos. 332/4.

1995. Birds and Trees. Multicoloured.
309 40d. Type **49** 60 60
310 60d. Golden eagle and juniper 80 80

50 Workers building "Honeycomb" Map

1995. Hyastan All-Armenian Fund.
311 **50** 90d. multicoloured 40 40

51 Rainbows around U.N. Emblem

1995. 50th Anniv of U.N.O.
312 **51** 90d. multicoloured 40 40

52 Commander P. Kitsook (408th Rifle Division)

1995. 50th Anniv of End of Second World War. (a) Size 40 × 23 mm. Each black, orange and blue.
313 60d. Type **52** 30 30
314 60d. Commanders S. Chernikov, N. Tavartkeladze and V. Penkovsky (76th Mountain Rifle Red-banner (51st Guard) Division) . . 30 30
315 60d. Commanders S. Zakian, H. Babayan and I. Lyudnikov (390th Rifle Division) 30 30
316 60d. Commanders A. Vasilian, M. Dobrovolsky, Y. Grechany and G. Sorokin (409th Rifle Division) 30 30
317 60d. Commanders A. Sargissian and N. Safarian (89th Taman Triple Order Bearer Rifle Division) 30 30

(b) Size 23 × 35 mm. Each blue, orange and brown.
318 60d. Marshal Hovhannes Baghramian 35 35
319 60d. Admiral Hovhannes Issakov 35 35
320 60d. General Marshal Hamazasp Babajanian . . 35 35
321 60d. Marshal Sergey Khoudyakov 35 35
MS322 120 × 90 mm. 300d. "Return of the Hero" (Mariam Aslamazian) . . . . 1·50 1·50

53 Ghevond Alishan (historian and geographer)

1995. Writers' Anniversaries.
323 **53** 90d. green and black . . . 45 45
324 – 90d. sepia, brown & yellow 45 45
325 – 90d. blue and red 45 45

DESIGNS: No. 323, Type **53** (175th birth); 324, Grigor Artsruni (journalist, 150th birth); 325, Franz Werfel (50th death).

54 Sports and Concert Complex

55 Katsian and Spectators watching Flight

1995. Yerevan.
326 – 60d. black and orange . . 20 20
327 – 80d. black and pink . . . 25 25
328 **54** 90d. black and buff 30 30
329 – 100d. black and buff . . . 35 35
330 – 120d. black and pink . . . 45 45
MS331 90 × 65 mm. 400d. multicoloured . . . . 1·50 1·50

DESIGNS—As T **54**: 60d. Brandy distillery and wine cellars; 80d. Abovian Street; 400d. Panoramic view of Yerevan. 60 × 23 mm: 100d. Baghramian Avenue; 120d. Republic Square.

No. **MS**331 also commemorates the 1700th anniv (2001) of Christianity in Armenia.

1995. Museum Artefacts (2nd series). As T **48**. Mult.
332 40d. Four-wheeled carriages (horiz) 10 10
333 60d. Bronze model of solar system 20 20
334 90d. Tombstone from Loriberd 35 35

1995. Air. 86th Anniv of Artiom Katsian's 1909 World Record for Range and Altitude.
335 **55** 90d. ochre, brown and blue 50 50

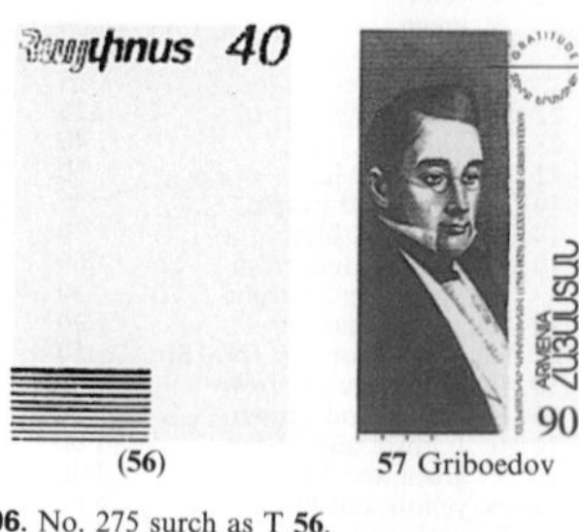

(56)

57 Griboedov

1996. No. 275 surch as T **56**.
336 40d. on 10l. agate and brown 50 50
337 100d. on 10l. agate and brown . . . . 1·40 1·40
338 150d. on 10l. agate and brown . . . . 1·90 1·90
339 200d. on 10l. agate and brown . . . . 2·50 2·50

1996. Birth Bicentenary of Aleksandr Griboedov (historian).
340 **57** 90d. stone, brown and red 35 35

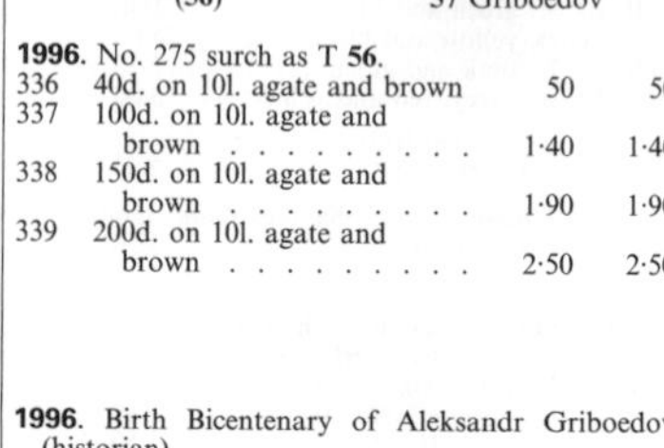

58 Hayrik Khrimian (patriarch of Armenian Orthodox Church, 175th birth anniv (1995))

1996. Anniversaries.
341 **58** 90d. blue & brn (postage) 35 35
342 – 90d. multicoloured 35 35
343 – 90d. grey, blue & red (air) 35 35

DESIGNS—HORIZ: No. 342, Lazar Serebryakov (Admiral of the Fleet, and 19th-century Russian warships, birth bicentenary (1995)). VERT: No. 343, Nelson Stepanian (Second World War pilot, 50th death anniv (1994)).

59 Opening Frame from First Armenian Film

1996. Centenary of Motion Pictures.
344 **59** 60d. black, grey and blue 50 75

60 Angel and Red Cross **61** Wild Goats

1996. 75th Anniv of Armenian Red Cross Society.
345 **60** 60d. multicoloured 30 30

1996. Mammals. Multicoloured.
346 40d. Type **61** 25 25
347 60d. Leopards 30 30

62 Nansen and "Fram"

1996. Centenary of Return of Fridtjof Nansen's Arctic Expedition.
348 **62** 90d. multicoloured 40 40

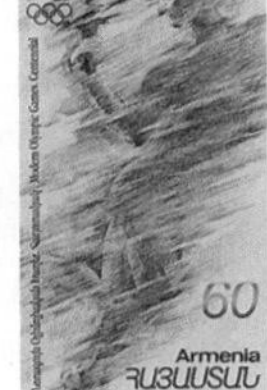

63 Cycling **64** Torch Bearer

1996. Olympic Games, Atlanta. Multicoloured.
349 40d. Type **63** 20 20
350 60d. Triple jumping 30 30
351 90d. Wrestling 40 40
Nos. 349/51 were issued together, se-tenant, the backgrounds forming a composite design showing ancient Greek athletes.

1996. Centenary of Modern Olympic Games.
352 **64** 60d. multicoloured 30 30

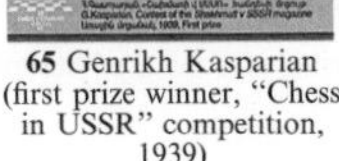

65 Genrikh Kasparian (first prize winner, "Chess in USSR" competition, 1939) **66** Tigran Petrosian (World chess champion, 1963–69) and Tigran Petrosian Chess House, Yerevan

1996. 32nd Chess Olympiad, Yerevan. Designs showing positions from previous games. Mult.
353 40d. Type **65** 40 40
354 40d. Tigran Petrosian v. Mikhail Botvinnik (World Championship, Moscow, 1963) 40 40
355 40d. Gary Kasparov v. Anatoly Karpov (World Championship, Leningrad, 1986) 40 40
356 40d. Olympiad emblem . . . 40 40

1996.
357 **66** 90d. multicoloured 50 50

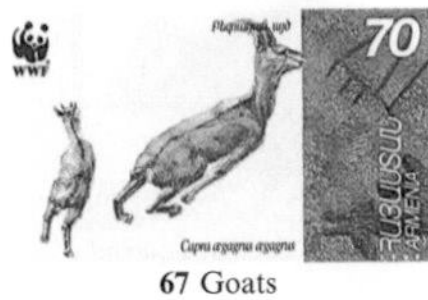

67 Goats

1996. The Wild Goat. Multicoloured.
358 70d. Type **67** 30 30
359 100d. Lone female 40 40
360 130d. Lone male 50 50
361 350d. Heads of male and female . . . . 1·40 1·40

68 Church of the Holy Mother, Samarkand, Uzbekistan

1997. 1700th Anniv (2001) of Christianity in Armenia (2nd issue). Armenian Apostolic Overseas Churches. Multicoloured.
362 100d. Type **68** 35 35
363 100d. Church of the Holy Mother, Kishinev, Moldova 35 35
364 100d. St. Hripsime's Church, Yalta, Ukraine 35 35
365 100d. St. Catherine's Church, St. Petersburg, Russia . . . 35 35
366 100d. Church, Lvov, Ukraine 35 35
MS367 92 × 66 mm. 500d St. George of Echmiadzin's Church, Tbilisi, Georgia . . . . 2·00 2·00

69 Man operating Printing Press

1997. 225th Anniv of First Printing Press in Armenia.
368 **69** 70d. multicoloured 35 35

70 Jivani and Mount Ararat

1997. 150th Birth Anniv of Jivani (folk singer).
369 **70** 90d. multicoloured 35 35

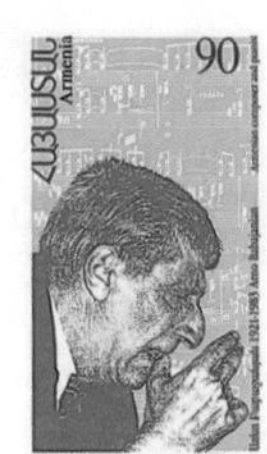

71 Babajanian and Score of "Heroic Ballad"

1997. 75th Birth Anniv (1996) of Arno Babajanian (composer and pianist).
370 **71** 90d. black, lilac & purple 35 35

72 Countryside (Gevorg Bashinjaghian)

1997. Exhibits in National Gallery of Armenia (1st series). Multicoloured.
371 150d. Type **72** 50 50
372 150d. "One of My Dreams" (Eghishe Tadevossian) . . 50 50
373 150d. "Portrait of Natalia Tehumian" (Hakob Hovnatanian) (vert) . . . 50 50
374 150d. "Salome" (Vardges Sureniants) (vert) 50 50
See also Nos. 390/2 and 512/13.

73 Mamulian **74** St. Basil's Cathedral, Moscow

1997. Birth Centenary of Rouben Mamulian (film director).
375 **73** 150d. multicoloured . . . 45 45

1997. "Moscow 97" Int Stamp Exhibition.
376 **74** 170d. multicoloured . . . 55 55

75 Hayk and Bel **76** Charents

1997. Europa. Tales and Legends. Multicoloured.
377 170d. Type **75** 55 55
378 250d. The Song of Vahagn 75 75

1997. Birth Centenary of Eghishe Charents (poet).
379 **76** 150d. brown and red . . . 45 45

77 "Iris lycotis" **78** St. Gregory the Illuminator Cathedral, Anthelias, Libya

1997. Irises. Multicoloured.
380 40d. Type **77** 15 15
381 170d. "Iris elegantissima" . . 55 55

1997. 1700th Anniv (2001) of Christianity in Armenia (3rd issue). Armenian Overseas Educational Centres. Multicoloured.
382 100d. Type **78** 30 30
383 100d. St. Khach Armenian Church, Nakhijevan, Rostov-on-Don 30 30
384 100d. St. James's Monastery, Jerusalem (horiz) 30 30
385 100d. Nercissian School, Tblisi, Georgia (60 × 21 mm) 30 30
386 100d. San Lazzaro Mekhitarian Congregation, Venice (horiz) 30 30
MS387 90 × 45 mm. 500d. Lazarian Seminary, Moscow (horiz) . . 1·50 1·50

79 Baby Jesus, Angel and Mary **80** Eagle and Demonstrator with Flag

1997. Christmas.
388 **79** 40d. multicoloured 15 15

1998. 10th Anniv of Karabakh Movement.
389 **80** 250d. multicoloured . . . 75 75

1998. Exhibits in National Gallery of Armenia (2nd series). As T **72**. Multicoloured.
390 150d. "Family. Generations" (Yervand Kochar) (vert) 45 45
391 150d. "Tartar Women's Dance" (Alexander Bazhbeouk-Melikian) . . . 45 45
392 150d. "Spring in Our Yard" (Haroutiun Kalents) (vert) 45 45

81 Diana, Princess of Wales **82** Eiffel Tower, Ball and Pitch

1998. Diana, Princess of Wales Commemoration.
393 **81** 250d. multicoloured . . . 75 75

1998. World Cup Football Championship, France.
394 **82** 250d. multicoloured . . . 75 75

83 Couple leaping through Flames (Trndez)

1998. Europa. National Festivals. Multicoloured.
395 170d. Type **83** 55 55
396 250d. Girls in traditional costume (Ascension) . . . 75 75

84 Southern Swallowtail **85** Ayrarat Couple

1998. Insects. Multicoloured.
397 170d. Type **84** 55 55
398 250d. "Rethera komarovi" (moth) 75 75

1998. Traditional Costumes (1st series). Mult.
399 170d. Type **85** 55 55
400 250d. Vaspurakan family . . 75 75
See also Nos. 408/9.

86St. Forty Children's Church, Milan

1998. 1700th Anniv (2001) of Christianity in Armenia (4th issue). Sheet 143 × 71 mm. Multicoloured.
MS401 100d. Type **86**; 100d. St. Sargis's Church, London; 100d. St. Vardan's Cathedral, New York; 100d. St. Hovhannes's Cathedral, Paris; 100d. St. Gregory the Illuminator's Cathedral, Buenos Aires . . . 1·50 1·50

87 Fissure in Earth's Surface

1998. 10th Anniv of Armenian Earthquake.
402 **87** 250d. black, red and lilac 75 75

88 Pyrite

1998. Minerals. Multicoloured.
403 170d. Type **88** 55 55
404 250d. Agate 75 75

89 Briusov **90** Parajanov

1998. 125th Birth Anniv of Valery Briusov (Russian translator of Armenian works).
405 **89** 90d. multicoloured 35 35

1999. 75th Birth Anniv of Sergei Parajanov (film director and artist). Sheet 74 × 65 mm.
MS406 **90** 500d. multicoloured 1·25 1·25
MS407 As No. **MS**406 but with emblem in margin of "iBRA" International Stamp Exhibition, Nuremberg, Germany . . . . 1·25 1·25

1999. Traditional Costumes (2nd series). As T **85**.
408 170d. Mother and child from Karin 40 40
409 250d. Zangezour couple . . . 60 60

91 Khosrov Reserve

1999. Europa. Parks and Gardens. Multicoloured.
410 170d. Type **91** 40 40
411 250d. Dilijan Reserve 60 60

92 Anniversary Emblem on Flag

1999. 50th Anniv of Council of Europe.
412 **92** 170d. multicoloured . . . 40 40

93 Medieval Kogge and Map

1999. Ships of the Armenian Kingdom of Cilicia (11–14th centuries). Multicoloured.
413 170d. Type **93** 40 40
414 250d. Medieval single-masted sailing ships 60 60
415 250d. As No. 414 but with emblem of "Philexfrance 99" International Stamp Exhibition, Paris, France, in lower right corner . . . 60 60

94 Armenian Gampr

1999. Domestic Pets. Multicoloured.
416 170d. Type **94** 40 40
417 250d. Turkish van cat . . . 60 60
418 250d. As No. 417 but with emblem of "China 1999" International Stamp Exhibition, Peking, China, in lower right corner . . . 60 60

95 Obverse and Reverse of Medal

1999. 1st Pan-Armenian Games, Yerevan. Sheet 58 × 40 mm.
MS419 **95** 250d. multicoloured 60 60

96 St. Gregory the Illuminator's Church, Cairo

1999. 1700th Anniv (2001) of Christianity in Armenia (5th issue). Sheet 121 × 65 mm containing T **96** and similar horiz designs. Multicoloured.
MS420 70d. Type **96**; 70d. St. Gregory the Illuminator's Church, Singapore; 70d. St. Khach's Church, Suchava; 70d. St. Saviour's Church, Worcester; 70d. Church of the Holy Mother, Madras . . . . 85 1·30

97 House made of Envelopes

1999. 125th Anniv of Universal Postal Union.
421 **97** 270d. multicoloured . . . 65 65

98 Karen Demirchyan (Speaker of the National Assembly)

2000. Commemoration of Victims of Attack on National Assembly. Multicoloured.
422 250d. Type **98** 60 60
423 250d. Vazgen Sargsyan (Prime Minister) 60 60
MS424 60 × 40 mm. 540d. Demirchyan Sargsyan, Yuri Bakshyan, Ruben Mirochyan, Henrik Abrahamyan, Armenak Armenakyan, Leonard Petrossyan and Mikael Kotanyan . . . . 1·30 1·30

99 Sevan Trout

101 "Building Europe"

100 The Liar Hunter

2000. Fishes. Multicoloured.
425 50d. Type **99** 10 10
426 270d. Sevan barbel 70 70

2000. National Fairy Tales. Multicoloured.
427 70d. Type **100** 15 15
428 130d. The King and the Peddler 30 30

2000. Europa.
429 **101** 40d. multicoloured . . . 10 10
430 500d. multicoloured . . . 1·25 1·25

102 St. Gayane Church, Vagharshapat

2000. 1700th Anniv (2001) of Christianity in Armenia (6th issue). Sheet 121 × 65 mm containing T **102** and similar horiz designs. Multicoloured.
MS431 70d. Type **102**; 70d. Etchmiadzin Cathedral, Vagharshapat; 70d. Church of the Holy Mother, Khor Virap; 70d. St. Shoghakat Church, Vagharshapat; 70d. St. Hrip'sime Church, Vagharshapat 65 65

103 Basketball

2000. Olympic Games, Sydney. Multicoloured.
432 10d. Type **103** 10 10
433 30d. Tennis 10 10
434 500d. Weightlifting . . . . . 1·25 1·25

104 Quartz

2000. Minerals. Multicoloured.
435 170d. Type **104** 40 40
436 250d. Molybdenite 60 60

105 Shnorhali

106 Adoration of the Magi

2000. 900th Birth Anniv of Nerses Shnorhali (writer and musician).
437 **105** 270d. multicoloured . . . 70 70

2000. Christmas.
438 **106** 170d. multicoloured . . . 40 40

107 Issahakian

2000. 125th Birth Anniv of Avetik Issahakian (poet).
439 **107** 130d. multicoloured . . . 30 30

108 Dhol

109 Viktor Hambartsoumian (astrophysicist)

2000. Musical Instruments. Multicoloured.
440 170d. Type **108** 40 40
441 250d. Duduk (wind instrument) 60 60

2000. New Millennium. Famous Armenians. Mult.
442 110d. Type **109** 25 25
443 110d. Abraham Alikhanov (physicist) 25 25
444 110d. Andranik Iossifan (electrical engineer) 25 25
445 110d. Sargis Saltikov (metallurgist) 25 25
446 110d. Samval Kochariants (electrical engineer) 25 25
447 110d. Artem Mikoyan (aircraft designer) 25 25
448 110d. Norayr Sisisakian (biochemist) 25 25
449 110d. Ivan Knunyants (chemist) 25 25
450 110d. Nikoghayos Yenikolopian (physical chemist) 25 25
451 110d. Nikoghayos Adonts (historian) 25 25
452 110d. Manouk Abeghian (folklore scholar) 25 25
453 110d. Hovhannes Toumanian (poet) 25 25
454 110d. Hrachya Ajarian (linguist) 25 25
455 110d. Gevorg Emin (poet) . . 25 25
456 110d. Yervand Lalayan (anthropologist) 25 25
457 110d. Daniel Varoujan (poet) 25 25
458 110d. Paruyr Sevak (poet) . . 25 25
459 110d. William Saroyan (dramatist and novelist) . . 25 25
460 110d. Hamo Beknazarian (film director) 25 25
461 110d. Alexandre Tamanian (architect) 25 25
462 110d. Vahram Papazian (actor) 25 25
463 110d. Vasil Tahirov (viticulturist) 25 25
464 110d. Leonid Yengibarian (mime artist) 25 25
465 110d. Haykanoush Danielian (singer) 25 25
466 110d. Sergo Hambartsoumian (weight lifter) 25 25
467 110d. Hrant Shahinian (gymnast) 25 25
468 110d. Toros Toramanian (architect) 25 25
469 110d. Komitas (composer) . . 25 25
470 110d. Aram Khachatourian (composer) 25 25
471 110d. Martiros Sarian (artist) 25 25
472 110d. Avet Terterian (composer) 25 25
473 110d. Alexandre Spendiarian (composer) 25 25
474 110d. Arshile Gorky (artist) 25 25
475 110d. Minas Avetissian (artist) 25 25
476 110d. (Levon Orbeli physiologist) 25 25
477 110d. Hripsimeh Simonian (ceramics artist) 25 25

110 Soldiers

2001. 1550th Anniv of Battle of Avarayr. Sheet 90 × 65 mm containing T **110** and similar vert design. Multicoloured.
MS478 170d. Type **110**; 270d. Vardan Mamikonian 65 65

111 Narekatsi and Text

2001. Millenary of A Record of Lamentations by Grigor Narekatsi.
479 **111** 25d. multicoloured . . . 10 10

112 Lake Sevan

2001. Europa. Water Resources. Multicoloured.
480 50d. Type **112** 10 10
481 500d. Spandarian Reservoir 1·25 1·25

113 Emblem

2001. Armenian Membership of Council of Europe.
482 **113** 240d. multicoloured . . . 55 55

114 Trophy

2001. 2nd Pan-Armenian Games. Sheet 58 × 40 mm.
MS483 **114** 300d. multicoloured 70 70

115 Persian Squirrel

2001. Endangered Species. Persian Squirrel (*Sciurus persicus*). Multicoloured.
484 40d. Type **115** 10 10
485 50d. Adult sitting on branch with young in tree hole . . 10 10
486 80d. Head of squirrel 20 20
487 120d. On ground 30 30

116 Cathedral Facade

2001. 1700th Anniv of Christianity in Armenia (7th issue). St. Gregory the Illuminator Cathedral, Yerevan. Multicoloured.
488 50d. Type **116** 10 10
489 205d. Interior elevation of Cathedral (44 × 30 mm) . . 50 50
490 240d. Exterior elevation of Cathedral (44 × 30 mm) . . 55 55

117 Lazarian and Institute

2001. Death Bicentenary of Hovhannes Lazarian (founder of Institute of Oriental Languages, Moscow).
491 **117** 300d. multicoloured . . . 75 75
A stamp in a similar design was issued by Russia.

2001. Traditional Costumes (3rd series). As T **85**. Multicoloured.
492 50d. Javakhch couple 10 10
493 250d. Artzakh couple 60 60

118 Emblem

119 Children encircling Globe

2001. 6th World Wushu Championships, Yerevan.
494 **118** 180d. black 40 40

2001. United Nations Year of Dialogue among Civilizations.
495 **119** 275d. multicoloured . . . 65 65

120 Emblem

2001. 10th Anniv of Commonwealth of Independent States.
496 **120** 205d. multicoloured . . . 50 50

121 Profiles

2001. European Year of Languages.
497 **121** 350d. multicoloured . . . 85 85

122 Flag

2001. 10th Anniv of Independence.
498 **122** 300d. multicoloured . . . 70 70

123 Cart

2001. Transport. Multicoloured.
499 180d. Type **123** 40 40
500 205d. Phaeton 50 50

124 *Hypericum perforatum*

125 Eagle

2001. Medicinal Plants. Multicoloured.
501 85d. Type **124** 20 20
502 205d. *Thymus serpyllum* . . . 50 50

2002.
503 **125** 10d. brown 10 10
504 25d. green 10 10
506 50d. blue 10 10

126 Calendar Belt (2000 B.C.) and Copper Works

2002. Traditional Production. Multicoloured.
510 120d. Type **126** 25 25
511 350d. Beer vessels (7th century B.C.) and modern brewing equipment 75 75

2002. Exhibits in National Gallery of Armenia (3rd series). Vert designs as T **72**.
512 200d. black, grey and green 40 40
513 200d. black, grey and red . . 40 40
DESIGNS: No. 512, "Lily" (Edgar Chahine); 513, "Salome" (sculpture, Hakob Gurjian).

127 Football and Maps of Japan and South Korea

2002. World Cup Football Championships, Japan and South Korea.
514 **127** 350d. multicoloured . . . 75 75

128 Pushman and "The Silent Order" (detail, painting)

2002. 125th Birth Anniv of Hovsep Pushman (artist). Sheet 75 × 65 mm.
MS515 multicoloured . . . . . 1·40 1·40

129 Technical Drawings, Tevossian and Factory

2002. Birth Centenary of Hovhannes Tevossian (metallurgical engineer).
516 **129** 350d. multicoloured . . . 75 75

130 Birds, Playing Cards, Ribbons and Magician's Hat

132 Ani Cathedral

131 Aivazian

2002. Europa. Circus. Multicoloured.
517 70d. Type **130** 15 15
518 500d. Clown juggling . . . . 1·10 1·10

2002. Birth Centenary of Artemy Aivazian (composer).
519 **131** 600d. multicoloured . . . 1·25 1·25

2002. Sheet 90 × 60 mm.
MS520 **132** 550d. multicoloured 1·25 1·25

133 Kaputjugh Mountain

2002. International Year of Mountains.
521 **133** 350d. multicoloured . . . 75 75

134 Armenian Lizard (*Lacerta armeniaca*)

2002. Reptiles. Multicoloured.
522 170d. Type **134** 35 35
523 220d. Radde's viper (*Vipera raddei*) 50 50

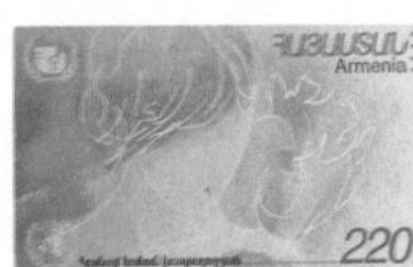

135 Woman and Dove

2002. United Nations Development Fund for Women.
524 **135** 220d. multicoloured . . . 40 40

136 Steam Locomotive

2002. Centenary of Alexandrapol–Yerevan Railway.
525 **136** 350d. multicoloured . . . 70 70

137 *Galanthus artjuschenkoae*

2002. Flowers. Multicoloured.
526 150d. Type **137** 30
527 200d. *Merendera mirzoevae* 40

138 Research Station, Yerevan Physics Institute

2002. Space Research. Multicoloured.
528 120d. Type **138** 25 25
529 220d. Orion 1 and Orion 2 space observatories 40 40

139 "Handle with Care" (Artak Baghdassaryan)

140 Aram Khachatourian

2003. Europa. Poster Art. Multicoloured.
530 170d. Type **139** 35 35
531 250d. "Armenia our Home" (Kearen Kojoyan) 50 50

2003. Birth Centenary of Aram Khachatourian (composer).
532 **140** 350d. multicoloured . . . 70 70

141 Armenian Gull (*Larus Armenicus*)

2003. World Environment Day. Rehabilitation of Lake Gilli.
533 **141** 220d. multicoloured . . . 40 40

142 Viaduct and Emblem

2003. 10th Anniv of TRACEA (transport corridor Europe–Caucasus–Asia) Programme. Sheet 74 × 55 mm.
MS534 **142** 480d. multicoloured 95 95

143 Horse-drawn Cart, Map of Route and First Postal Seal

2003. 175th Anniv of First Armenian Postal Dispatch.
535 **143** 70d. multicoloured . . . 15 15

144 Siamanto and Script

146 Vahan Tekeyan

145 Coins and Currency Notes

2003. 125th Birth Anniv of Siamanto (Atom Yarchanyan) (writer).
536 **144** 350d. multicoloured . . . 70 70

2003. 10th Anniv of Armenian Currency.
537 **145** 170d. multicoloured . . . 35 35

2003. 125th Birth Anniv of Vahan Tekeyan (writer).
538 **146** 200d. multicoloured . . . 40 40

147 Profile showing Brain

2003. Neurophysiology.
539 **147** 120d. multicoloured . . . 25 25

148 Sports and Culture Complex, Yerevan

2003. 3rd Armenian Games. Sheet 58 × 40 mm.

MS540 **148**	350d. multicoloured	70	70

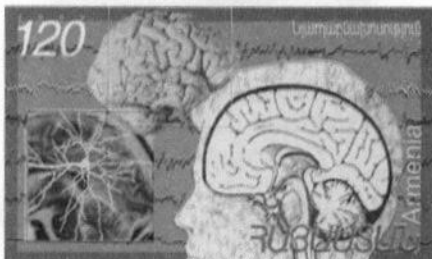

149 "The Baptism" (6–7th century), Gospel of Ejmiatsin

2003. Armenian Miniatures. Sheet 65 × 74 mm.

MS541 **149**	550d. multicoloured	1·10	1·10

ARUBA Pt. 4

An island in the Caribbean, formerly part of Netherlands Antilles. In 1986 became an autonomous country within the Kingdom of the Netherlands.

100 cents = 1 gulden.

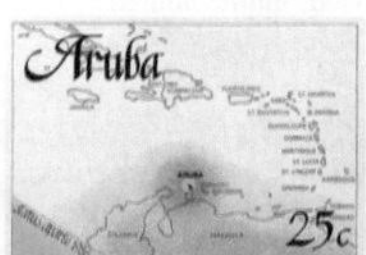

1 Map

1986. New Constitution.

1	**1**	25c. yellow, blue and black	70	35
2	–	45c. multicoloured	90	70
3	–	55c. black, grey and red	1·10	75
4	–	100c. multicoloured	1·75	1·60

DESIGNS—VERT: 45c. Aruban arms; 55c. National anthem. HORIZ: 100c. Aruban flag.

2 House

1986.

5	**2**	5c. black and yellow	10	10
6	–	15c. black and blue	35	20
7	–	20c. black and grey	20	15
8	–	25c. black and violet	30	30
9	–	30c. black and red	65	45
10	–	35c. black and bistre	65	45
12	–	45c. black and blue	65	35
14	–	55c. black and grey	75	45
15	–	60c. black and blue	90	65
16	–	65c. black and blue	1·00	85
18	–	75c. black and brown	90	70
20	–	85c. black and orange	1·00	75
21	–	90c. black and green	1·10	80
22	–	100c. black and brown	1·10	85
23	–	150c. black and green	2·00	1·50
24	–	250c. black and green	3·25	2·75

DESIGNS: 15c. Clock tower; 20c. Container crane; 25c. Lighthouse; 30c. Snake; 35c. Burrowing owl; 45c. Caribbean vase (shell); 55c. Frog; 60c. Water-skier; 65c. Fisherman casting net; 75c. Hurdy-gurdy; 85c. Pot; 90, 250c. Different cacti; 100c. Maize; 150c. Watapana Tree.

3 People and Two Ropes

1986. "Solidarity". Multicoloured.

25	30c.+10c. Type **3**	85	55
26	35c.+15c. People and three ropes	1·00	65
27	60c.+25c. People and one rope	1·40	1·00

4 Dove between Scenes of Peace and War

1986. International Peace Year. Multicoloured.

28	60c. Type **4**	1·00	75
29	100c. Doves flying over broken barbed wire	1·50	1·10

5 Boy and Caterpillar

6 Engagement Picture

1986. Child Welfare. Multicoloured.

30	45c.+20c. Type **5**	1·10	75
31	70c.+25c. Boy and shell	1·60	1·10
32	100c.+40c. Girl and butterfly	2·10	1·50

1987. Golden Wedding of Princess Juliana and Prince Bernhard.

33	**6**	135c. orange, black and gold	2·10	1·40

7 Queen Beatrix and Prince Claus

1987. Royal Visit. Multicoloured.

34	55c. Type **7**	90	55
35	60c. Prince Willem-Alexander	1·00	65

8 Woman looking at Beach

1987. Tourism. Multicoloured.

36	60c. Type **8**	1·10	80
37	100c. Woman looking at desert landscape	1·75	1·10

9 Child with Book on Beach

10 Plantation

1987. Child Welfare. Multicoloured.

38	25c.+10c. Type **9**	80	45
39	45c.+20c. Children drawing Christmas tree	1·10	70
40	70c.+30c. Child gazing at Nativity crib	1·60	1·10

1988. "Aloe vera". Multicoloured.

41	45c. Type **10**	80	55
42	60c. Stem and leaves of plant	1·00	70
43	100c. Harvesting aloes	1·60	1·00

11 25c. Coin

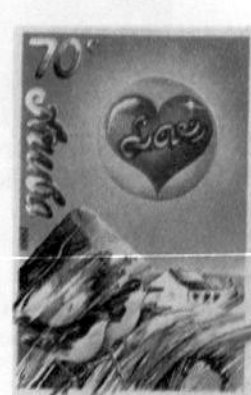

12 Bananaquits, Country Scene and "Love"

1988. Coins. Multicoloured.

44	25c. Type **11**	55	35
45	55c. Square 50c. coin	1·00	70
46	65c. 5c. and 10c. coins	1·25	80
47	150c. 1 gulden coin	2·10	1·50

1988. Greetings Stamps. Multicoloured.

48	70c. Type **12**	90	65
49	135c. West Indian crown conch, West Indian chank (shells), seaside scene and "Love"	1·75	1·25

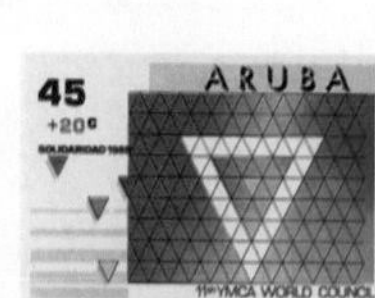

13 White Triangle on Shaded Background

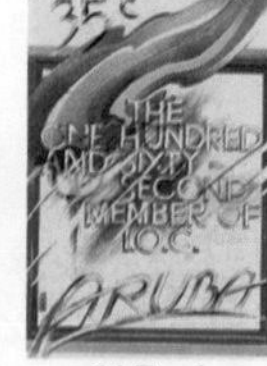

14 Torch

1988. "Solidarity". 11th Y.M.C.A. World Council. Multicoloured.

50	45c.+20c. Type **13**	1·00	70
51	60c.+25c. Interlocking triangles	1·40	1·00
52	100c.+50c. Shaded triangle on white background	1·90	1·40

1988. Olympic Games, Seoul. Multicoloured.

53	35c. Type **14**	70	35
54	100c. Games and Olympic emblems	1·40	1·10

15 Jacks

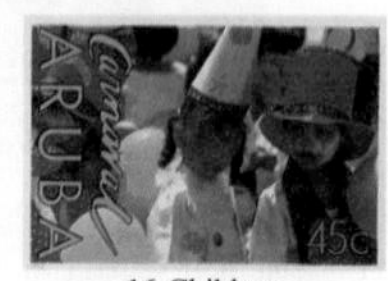

16 Children

1988. Child Welfare. Toys. Multicoloured.

55	45c.+20c. Type **15**	1·00	70
56	70c.+30c. Spinning top	70	1·00
57	100c.+50c. Kite	2·00	1·40

1989. Carnival. Multicoloured.

58	45c. Type **16**	85	55
59	60c. Girl in costume	1·00	70
60	100c. Lights	1·90	1·10

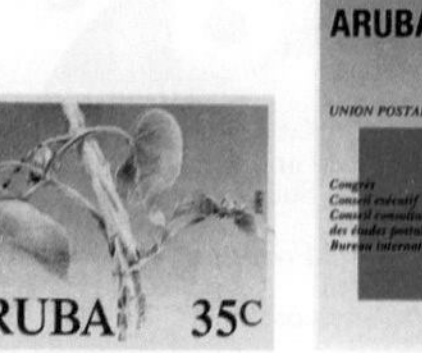

17 Maripampun

18 Emblem

1989. Maripampun. Multicoloured.

61	35c. Type **17**	70	45
62	55c. Seed pods	1·00	70
63	200c. Pod distributing seeds	2·75	2·10

1989. Universal Postal Union.

64	**18**	250c. multicoloured	3·50	2·25

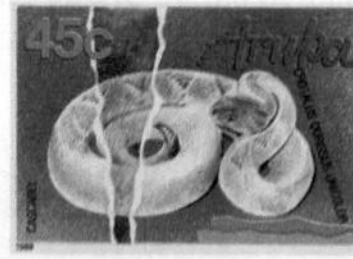

19 Snake

1989. South American Rattlesnake.

65	**19**	45c. multicoloured	70	45
66	–	55c. multicoloured	80	55
67	–	60c. multicoloured	1·00	65

DESIGNS: 55, 60c. Snake (different).

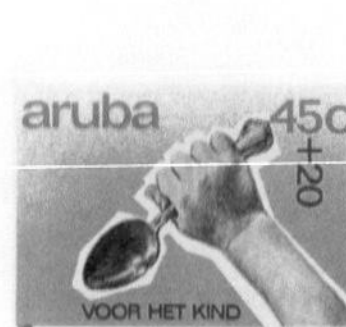

20 Spoon in Child's Hand

21 Violin, Tambour and Cuatro Players

1989. Child Welfare. Multicoloured.

68	45c +20c. Type **20**	90	65
69	60c.+30c. Child playing football	1·10	80
70	100c.+50c. Child's hand in adult's hand (vert)	2·00	1·40

1989. New Year. Dande Musicians. Multicoloured.

71	25c. Type **21**	55	30
72	70c. Guitar and cuatro players and singer with hat	90	65
73	150c. Cuatro, accordion and wiri players	1·75	1·40

22 Tractor and Natural Vegetation

1990. Environmental Protection. Multicoloured.

74	45c. Type **22**	75	55
75	55c. Face and wildlife (vert)	90	65
76	100c. Marine life	1·60	1·10

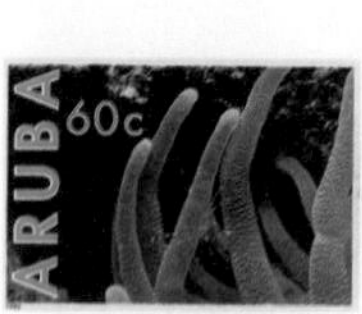

23 Giant Caribbean Anemone and Pederson's Cleaning Shrimp

24 Ball

1990. Marine Life. Multicoloured.

77	60c. Type **23**	1·00	70
78	70c. Queen angelfish and red coral	1·10	1·00
79	100c. Banded coral shrimp, fire sponge and yellow boring sponge	1·90	1·50

1990. World Cup Football Championship, Italy. Multicoloured.

80	35c. Type **24**	65	35
81	200c. Mascot	2·75	2·10

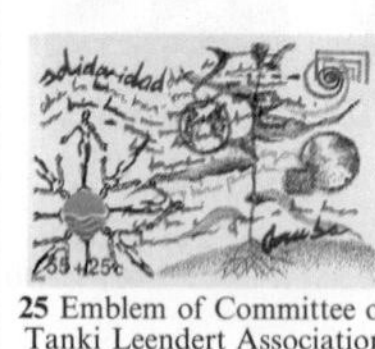

25 Emblem of Committee of Tanki Leendert Association Youth Centre

26 Clay Painting Stamps

1990. "Solidarity". Multicoloured.

82	55c.+25c. Type **25**	1·40	1·10
83	100c.+50c. Emblem of Foundation for Promotion of Responsible Parenthood	2·40	1·90

1990. Archaeology. Multicoloured.

84	45c. Type **26**	70	55
85	60c. Stone figure	90	70
86	100c. Dabajuroid-style jar	1·60	1·25

27 Sailboards and Fishes

28 Mountain and Shoreline

1990. Child Welfare. Multicoloured.

87	45c.+20c. Type **27**	1·00	75
88	60c.+30c. Parakeets and coconut trees	1·25	1·10
89	100c.+50c. Kites and lizard	2·10	1·75

1991. Landscapes. Multicoloured.

90	55c. Type **28**	90	65
91	65c. Cacti and Haystack mountain	1·00	1·25
92	100c. House, mountain and ocean, Jaburibari	1·60	1·25

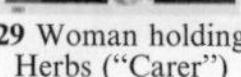

29 Woman holding Herbs ("Carer")

30 "Ocimum sanctum"

1991. Women and Work. Multicoloured.
93 35c. Type **29** 65 35
94 70c. Women and kitchen ("Housewife") . . . . . . 1·00 85
95 100c. Women and telephone ("Woman in the World") 1·40 2·25

1991. Medicinal Plants. Multicoloured.
96 65c. Type **30** 85 75
97 75c. "Jatropha gossypifolia" 1·00 90
98 95c. "Croton flavens" . . . . 1·40 1·10

31 Fishing Net, Float and Needle

32 Child's Hand taking Book from Shelf

1991. Traditional Crafts.
99 **31** 35c. black, ultram & blue 65 35
100 – 250c. black, lilac & purple 3·50 2·75
DESIGNS: 250c. Hat, straw and hat-block.

1991. Child Welfare. Multicoloured.
101 45c.+25c. Type **32** . . . . . 1·00 80
102 60c.+35c. Child's finger pointing to letter "B" . . . 1·50 1·10
103 100c.+50c. Child reading . . 2·10 1·75

33 Toucan saying "Welcome"

34 Government Decree of 1892 establishing first Aruban Post Office

1991. Tourism. Multicoloured.
104 35c. Type **33** 65 45
105 70c. Aruban youth welcoming tourist . . . . 1·00 80
106 100c. Windmill and Bubali swamp . . . . 1·50 1·25

1992. Centenary of Postal Service (1st issue). Mult.
107 60c. Type **34** 90 75
108 75c. Lt.-Governor's building (mail service office, 1892–1908) (horiz) . . . . . . 1·10 80
109 80c. Present Oranjestad P.O. (horiz) . . . . 1·40 1·00
See also Nos. 117/19.

35 Equality of Sexes

1992. Equality. Multicoloured.
110 100c. Type **35** . . . . 1·50 1·10
111 100c. People of different races (equality of nations) . . . 1·50 1·10

36 Aruban Flag, Guide Emblem and Girl Guides

37 Columbus, Map and Clouds

1992. "Solidarity". Multicoloured.
112 55c.+30c. Type **36** . . . . . 1·50 1·10
113 100c.+50c. Open hand with Cancer Fund emblem . . . 2·10 1·00

1992. 500th Anniv of Discovery of America by Columbus. Multicoloured.
114 30c. Type **37** 55 35
115 40c. Caravel (from navigation chart, 1525) 65 50
116 50c. Indians, queen conch shell and 1540 map . . . . 1·00 65

38 "I Love Post" (Jelissa Boekhoudt)

1992. Child Welfare. Centenary of Postal Service (2nd issue). Children's Drawings. Multicoloured.
117 50c.+30c. Type **38** . . . . . 1·25 95
118 70c.+35c. Airplane dropping letters (Marianne Fingal) 1·40 1·10
119 100c.+50c. Pigeon carrying letter in beak (Minorenti Jacobs) (vert) . . . . . . 2·10 1·75

39 Seroe Colorado Bridge

41 Rocks at Ayo

1992. Natural Bridges. Multicoloured.
120 70c. Type **39** . . . . 1·00 75
121 80c. Natural Bridge . . . . 1·25 90

1993. Rock Formations. Multicoloured.
123 50c. Type **41** 75 65
124 60c. Casibari 80 75
125 100c. Ayo (different) . . . . 1·25 1·10

42 Traditional Instruments

43 Sailfish dinghy

1993. Cock's Burial (part of St. John's Feast celebrations). Multicoloured.
126 40c. Type **42** 65 55
127 70c. "Cock's Burial" (painting, Leo Kuiperi) . . 95 80
128 80c. Verses of song, yellow flag, and calabashes . . . 1·10 1·00

1993. Sports. Multicoloured.
129 50c. Type **43** 70 65
130 65c. Land sailing 90 80
131 75c. Sailboard . . . . 1·00 90

44 Young Iguana

1993. The Iguana. Multicoloured.
132 35c. Type **44** 55 50
133 60c. Young adult 80 70
134 100c. Adult (vert) . . . . . 1·25 1·10

45 Aruban House, Landscape and Cacti

1993. Child Welfare. Multicoloured.
135 50c.+30c. Type **45** . . . . . 1·00 90
136 75c.+40c. Face, bridge and sea (vert) . . . . 1·50 1·40
137 100c.+50c. Bridge, buildings and landscape . . . . . . 1·90 1·75

46 Owls

47 Athlete

1994. The Burrowing Owl. Multicoloured.
138 5c. Type **46** 30 20
139 10c. Pair with young 50 35
140 35c. Owl with locust in claw (vert) 85 70
141 40c. Owl (vert) . . . . 1·00 90

1994. Centenary of Int Olympic Committee. Mult.
142 50c. Type **47** 70 65
143 90c. Baron Pierre de Coubertin (founder) . . . 90 1·10

48 Family in House

49 Flags of U.S.A. and Aruba, Ball and Players

1994. "Solidarity". Int Year of The Family. Mult.
144 50c.+35c. Type **48** . . . . . 1·10 1·00
145 100c.+50c. Family outside house . . . . 2·00 1·90

1994. World Cup Football Championship, U.S.A. Multicoloured.
146 65c. Type **49** 90 80
147 150c. Mascot . . . . 2·00 1·75

50 West Indian Cherry

51 Children with Umbrella sitting on Anchor (shelter and security)

1994. Wild Fruits. Multicoloured.
148 40c. Type **50** 70 55
149 70c. Geiger tree 95 80
150 85c. "Pithecellobium unguis-cati" . . . . 1·25 1·10
151 150c. Sea grape . . . . . . 2·25 1·75

1994. Child Welfare. Influence of the Family. Mult.
152 50c.+30c. Type **51** . . . . . 1·10 1·00
153 80c.+35c. Children in smiling sun (warmth of nurturing home) . . . . 1·50 1·40
154 100c.+50c. Child flying on owl (wisdom guiding the child) . . . . 1·90 1·75

52 Government Building, 1888

53 Dove, Emblem and Flags

1995. Historic Buildings. Multicoloured.
155 35c. Type **52** 50 45
156 60c. Ecury Residence, 1929 (vert) 85 70
157 100c. Protestant Church, 1846 (vert) . . . . 1·25 1·10

1995. 50th Anniv of U.N.O. Multicoloured.
158 30c. Type **53** 55 45
159 200c. Emblem, flags, globe and doves . . . . 2·50 2·40

54 Casanova II and Rosettes

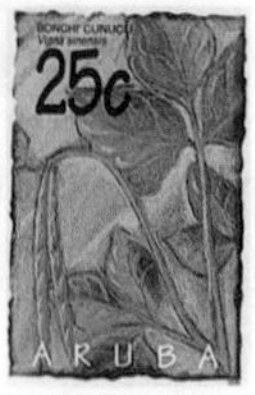

55 Cowpea

1995. Interpaso Horses. Multicoloured.
160 25c. Type **54** 50 35
161 75c. Horse performing Paso Fino . . . . 1·10 90
162 80c. Horse performing Figure 8 (vert) . . . . 1·10 1·00
163 90c. Girl on horseback (vert) 1·25 1·10

1995. Vegetables. Multicoloured.
164 25c. Type **55** 40 35
165 50c. Apple cucumber 80 65
166 70c. Okra 95 80
167 85c. Pumpkin . . . . 1·25 1·00

56 Hawksbill Turtle

57 Children holding Balloons outside House (Christina Trejo)

1995. Turtles. Multicoloured.
168 15c. Type **56** 50 20
169 50c. Green turtle 80 50
170 95c. Loggerhead turtle . . . 1·50 1·10
171 100c. Leatherback turtle . . . 1·60 1·10

1995. Child Welfare. Children's Drawings. Mult.
172 50c.+25c. Type **57** . . . . . 1·10 80
173 70c.+35c. Children at seaside (Julysses Tromp) . . . . . 1·40 1·10
174 100c.+50c. Children and adults gardening (Ronald Tromp) . . . . 2·10 1·60

58 Henry Eman

59 Woman

1996. 10th Anniv of Internal Autonomy. Politicians. Multicoloured.
175 100c. Type **58** . . . . 1·25 1·10
176 100c. Juancho Irausquin . . 1·25 1·10
177 100c. Shon Eman . . . . . 1·25 1·10
178 100c. Betico Croes . . . . . 1·25 1·10

1996. America. Traditional Costumes. Mult.
179 65c. Type **59** 90 70
180 70c. Man 95 70
181 100c. Couple dancing (horiz) 1·40 1·10

60 Running

61 Mathematical Instruments, "G" and Rising Sun

1996. Olympic Games, Atlanta. Multicoloured.
182 85c. Type **60** . . . . 1·10 90
183 130c. Cycling . . . . 1·75 1·60

1996. "Solidarity". 75th Anniv of Freemasons' Lodge El Sol Naciente. Multicoloured.
184 60c.+30c. Type **61** . . . . . 1·25 1·00
185 100c.+50c. Globes on top of columns and doorway . . 1·90 1·75

62 Livia Ecury (teacher and nurse)

63 Rabbits at Bus-stop

1996. Anniversaries. Multicoloured.
186 60c. Type **62** (5th death) . . 90 80
187 60c. Laura Wernet-Paskel (teacher and politician, 85th birth) 90 80
188 60c. Lolita Euson (poet, 2nd death) 90 80

1996. Child Welfare. Comic Strips. Multicoloured.
189 50c.+25c. Type **63** . . . . . 1·00 80
190 70c.+35c. Mother accompanying young owl to school . . . . 1·40 1·25
191 100c.+50c. Boy flying kite with friend . . . . 1·75 1·60

64 Children at the Seaside and Words on Signpost

65 Postman on Bicycle, 1936–57

1997. "Year of Papiamento" (Creole language). Multicoloured.
192 50c. Type **64** 75 60
193 140c. Sunrise over ocean . . 1·90 2·10

1997. America. The Postman. Multicoloured.
194 60c. Type **65** 90 80
195 70c. Postman delivering package by jeep, 1957–88 1·00 80
196 80c. Postman delivering letter from motor scooter, 1995 1·25 1·00

66 Decorated Cunucu House

1997. Aruban Architecture. Multicoloured.
197 30c. Type **66** 45 40
198 65c. Bannistered steps . . . . 1·00 80
199 100c. Arends Building (vert) 1·40 1·25

67 Merlin and Lighthouse

68 Passengers approaching Cruise Liner

1997. "Pacific 97" International Stamp Exhibition, San Francisco. Multicoloured.
200 90c. Type **67** . . . . 1·10 1·10
201 90c. Windswept trees and dolphin . . . . 1·10 1·10
202 90c. Iguana on rock and cacti 1·10 1·10
203 90c. Three types of fishes and one dolphin . . . . 1·10 1·10
204 90c. Two dolphins and fishes 1·10 1·10
205 90c. Burrowing owl on shore, turtle and lionfish . . . . 1·10 1·10
206 90c. Stingray, rock beauty, angelfishes, squirrelfish and coral reef . . . . 1·10 1·10
207 90c. Diver and stern of shipwreck . . . . 1·10 1·10
208 90c. Shipwreck, reef and fishes . . . . 1·10 1·10

Nos. 200/8 were issued together, se-tenant, forming a composite design.

1997. Cruise Tourism. Multicoloured.
209 35c. Type **68** 50 40
210 50c. Passengers disembarking 70 60
211 150c. Cruise liner at sea and launch at shore . . . . . 2·00 1·75

69 Coral Tree

1997. Trees. Multicoloured.
212 50c. Type **69** 70 60
213 60c. "Cordia dentata" . . . 90 80
214 70c. "Tabebuia billbergii" . . 1·00 80
215 130c. Lignum vitae . . . . . 1·75 1·60

70 Girl among Aloes

1997. Child Welfare. Child and Nature. Mult.
216 50c.+25c. Type **70** . . . . . 1·00 85
217 70c.+35c. Boy and butterfly (vert) . . . . 1·40 1·25
218 100c.+50c. Girl swimming underwater by coral reef 1·90 1·75

71 Fort Zoutman

72 Stages of Eclipse

1998. Bicentenary of Fort Zoutman.
219 **71** 30c. multicoloured 50 40
220 250c. multicoloured . . . . 3·00 2·75

Each design consists of alternating strips in brown tones or black and white. When the 250c. is laid on top of the 30c., the brown strips form a composite design of the fort in its early years and the black and white strips a composite design of the fort after 1929, when various alterations were made.

1998. Total Solar Eclipse. Multicoloured.
221 85c. Type **72** . . . . 1·10 1·00
222 100c. Globe showing path of eclipse and map of Aruba plotting duration of total darkness . . . . 1·40 1·25

73 Globe, Emblem and Wheelchair balanced on Map of Aruba

1998. "Solidarity" Anniversaries. Multicoloured.
223 60c.+30c. Type **73** (50th anniv of Lions Club of Aruba) . . . . 1·25 1·00
224 100c.+50c. Boy reading, emblem and grandmother in rocking chair (60th anniv of Rotary Club of Aruba) . . . . 1·90 1·75

74 Tropical Mockingbird

1998. Birds. Multicoloured.
225 50c. Type **74** 70 65
226 60c. American kestrel (vert) 95 80
227 70c. Troupial (vert) . . . . . 1·10 90
228 150c. Bananaquit . . . . . 2·10 1·90

75 Villagers processing Corn

76 Ribbon Dance

1998. World Stamp Day.
229 **75** 225c. multicoloured . . . . 3·25 2·75

1998. Child Welfare. Multicoloured.
230 50c.+25c. Type **76** . . . . . 1·00 90
231 80c.+40c. Boy playing cuarta (four-string guitar) . . . . 1·75 1·60
232 100c. + 50c. Basketball . . . 2·00 1·75

77 Two Donkeys

1999. The Donkey. Multicoloured.
233 40c. Type **77** 60 50
234 65c. Two adults and foal . . 1·00 90
235 100c. Adult and foal . . . . 1·40 1·40

78 "Opuntia wentiana"

79 Creole Dog

1999. Cacti. Multicoloured.
236 50c. Type **78** 70 65
237 60c. "Lemaireocereus griseus" 95 80
238 70c. "Cephalocereus lanuginosus" ("Cadushi di carona") . . . . 1·00 90
239 75c. "Cephalocereus lanuginosus" ("Cadushi") 1·10 1·00

1999. Creole Dogs ("Canis familiaris"). Mult.
240 40c. Type **79** 60 50
241 60c. White dog standing on rock 90 80
242 80c. Dog sitting by sea . . . 1·10 1·00
243 165c. Black and tan dog sitting on rock . . . . . . 2·10 2·00

80 Indian Cave Drawings and Antique Map

1999. 500 Years of Cultural Diversity. Mult.
244 150c. Type **80** . . . . 1·75 1·60
245 175c. Indian cave drawings and carnival headdress . . 2·10 2·00
MS246 90 × 60 mm. Nos. 244/5 4·00 4·00

81 Public Library and Children

1999. 50th Anniv of Public Library Service. Mult.
247 70c. Type **81** 90 80
248 100c. Library, Santa Cruz . . 1·25 1·25

82 Boy with Fisherman

83 Three Wise Men

1999. Child Welfare. Multicoloured.
249 60c.+30c. Type **82** . . . . . 1·00 1·00
250 80c.+40c. Man reading to children . . . . 1·50 1·40
251 100c.+50c. Woman with child (vert) . . . . 1·90 1·75

1999. Christmas. Multicoloured. Self-adhesive.
252 40c. Type **83** 50 45
253 70c. Shepherds 95 90
254 100c. Holy Family . . . . . 1·40 1·25

84 *Norops lineatus*

2000. Reptiles. Multicoloured.
255 40c. Type **84** 55 50
256 60c. Greeen iguana (vert) . . 90 80
257 75c. Annulated snake (vert) 1·00 90
258 150c. Racerunner . . . . . 1·75 1·75

85 Flags

2000. America. A.I.D.S. Awareness. Multicoloured.
259 75c. Type **85** 95 90
260 175c. Ribbon on globe (vert) 2·10 2·00

86 Bank Facade

2000. Anniversaries. Multicoloured.
261 150c. Type **86** (75th anniv of Aruba Bank) . . . . 1·90 1·75
262 165c. Chapel (250th anniv of Alto Vista Chapel) . . . . 2·25 2·00

87 West Indian Top Shell

2000. Aspects of Aruba. Multicoloured.
263 15c. Type **87** 20 20
264 25c. Guadirikiri cave 40 35
265 35c. Mud-house (vert) . . . 50 50
267 55c. Cacti 75 70
269 85c. Hooiberg . . . . 1·00 1·00
271 100c. Gold smelter, Balashi (vert) . . . . 1·25 1·25
272 250c. Rock crystal . . . . . 3·25 3·25
275 500c. Conchi . . . . 5·75 5·50

88 Children at Beach Playground

2000. "Solidarity". Multicoloured.
280 75c.+35c. Type **88** . . . . . 1·40 1·25
281 100c.+50c. Children building sandcastles . . . . 2·10 1·90

89 "Solar Energy" (Nikki Johanna Teresia Willems)

2000. Child Welfare. "Stampin' the Future". Winning Entries in Children's International Painting Competition. Multicoloured.
282 60c.+30c. Type **89** . . . . . 1·25 1·25
283 80c.+40c. "Environmental Protection" (Samantha Jeanne Tromp) . . . . . . 1·50 1·40
284 100c.+50c. "Future Vehicles" (Jennifer Huntington) . . . 2·10 1·90

90 Cat

2001. Domestic Animals. Multicoloured.
285 5c. Type **90** 15 15
286 30c. Tortoise 35 35
287 50c. Rabbit 60 60
288 200c. Brown-throated conure 2·40 2·40

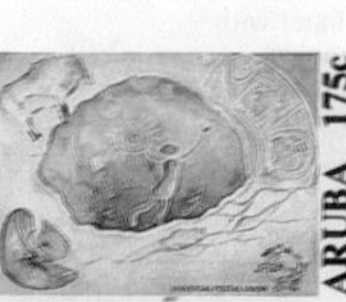

91 Shaman preparing for Sun Ceremony

2001. 40 Years of Mascaruba (amateur theatre group). Depicting scenes from *Macuarima*, History or Legend? (musical play). Mult.
289 60c. Type **91** 70 70
290 150c. Love scene between Guadarikiri and Blanco . . 1·75 1·75

92 Ford Model A Roadster, 1930

2001. Motor Cars. Multicoloured.
291 25c. Type **92** 30 30
292 40c. Citroen Comerciale saloon, 1933 . . . . 45 45
293 70c. Plymouth Pick-up, 1948 90 90
294 75c. Edsel corsair convertable, 1959 . . . . 1·00 1·00

93 Rock Drawings

94 Pedestrians using Crossing

2001. Universal Postal Union. United Nations Year of Dialogue among Civilizations.
295 93 175c. multicoloured . . . . 2·40 2·40

2001. Child Welfare. International Year of Volunteers. Multicoloured.
296 40c. + 20c. Type **94** 80 80
297 60c. + 30c. Boys walking dogs . . . . 1·10 1·10
298 100c. + 50c. Children putting litter in bin . . . . 2·00 2·00

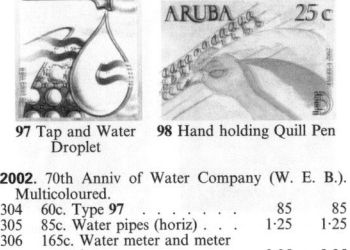

95 Dakota Airport, 1950

2002. Queen Beatrix Airport. Multicoloured.
299 30c. Type **95** 45 45
300 75c. Queen Beatrix Airport, 1972 . . . . 1·10 1·10
301 175c. Queen Beatrix Airport, 2000 . . . . 2·50 2·50

Dakota Airport was re-named Princess Beatrix Airport in 1955 and Queen Beatrix Airport in 1972.

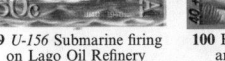

96 Prince Willem-Alexander and Princess Maxima

2002. Wedding of Crown Prince Willem-Alexander to Maxima Zorreguieta. Multicoloured.
302 60c. Type **96** 85 85
303 300c. Prince Willem-Alexander and Princess Máxima facing right . . . 4·25 4·25

97 Tap and Water Droplet

98 Hand holding Quill Pen

2002. 70th Anniv of Water Company (W. E. B.). Multicoloured.
304 60c. Type **97** 85 85
305 85c. Water pipes (horiz) . . . 1·25 1·25
306 165c. Water meter and meter reader . . . . 2·25 2·25

2002. America. Literacy Campaign. Multicoloured.
307 25c. Type **98** 35 35
308 100c. Alphabet on wall and boy on step-ladder . . . . 1·40 1·40

99 *U-156* Submarine firing on Lago Oil Refinery

100 Boy, Iguana and Goat

2002. Second World War. Multicoloured.
309 60c. Type **99** 85 85
310 75c. *Pedernales* (oil-tanker) in flames . . . . 1·00 1·00
311 150c. "Boy" Ecury (resistance fighter) (statue) (vert) . . . 2·10 2·10

2002. Child Welfare. Animals. Multicoloured
312 40c.+20c. Type **100** 85 85
313 60c.+30c. Girl, turtle and crab (horiz) . . . . 1·00 1·00
314 100c.+50c. Pelicans, boy and parakeet . . . . 2·10 2·10

101 House at Fontein

2003. Mud Houses. Multicoloured.
315 40c. Type **101** 30 30
316 60c. House at Ari Kok 45 45
317 75c. House at Fontein . . . 55 55

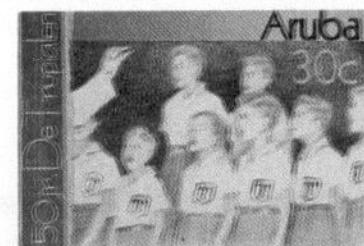

102 The Trupialen Boys Choir

2003. 50th Anniv of "De Trupialen" (boys' organization). Multicoloured.
318 30c. Type **102** 10 10
319 50c. Puppet theatre posters 20 20
320 100c. Organization emblems 35 35

103 *Schomburgkia humboldtii*

2003. Orchids. Multicoloured.
321 75c. Type **103** 25 25
322 500c. *Brassavola nodosa* . . . 1·80 1·80

104 Orange-barred Sulphur Butterfly

105 Hawksbill Turtle (*Eretmochelys imbricate*)

2003. Butterflies. Multicoloured.
323 40c. Type **104** 15 15
324 75c. Monarch 30 30
325 85c. Hairstreak 30 30
326 175c. Gulf fritillary 60 60

2003. Endangered Species. Turtles. Multicoloured.
327 25c. Type **105** 10 10
328 60c. Leatherback turtle (*Dermochelys coricea*) (horiz) 20 20
329 75c. Green turtle (*Chelonia mydas*) 30 30
330 150c. Loggerhead turtle (*Caretta caretta*) (horiz) . . 55 55

EXPRESS MAIL SERVICE

E **40** Globe, Planets and Aruban Arms

1993.
E122 E **40** 200c. multicoloured . . 2·75 2·10

ASCENSION Pt. 1

An island in South Atlantic. A dependency of St. Helena.

1922. 12 pence = 1 shilling;
20 shillings = 1 pound.
1971. 100 pence = 1 pound.

1922. Stamps of St. Helena of 1912 optd ASCENSION.
1 ½d. black and green . . . . . 4·50 17·00
2 1d. green . . . . 4·50 16·00
3 1½d. red . . . . 15·00 48·00
4 2d. black and slate . . . . . 15·00 13·00
5 3d. blue . . . . 13·00 17·00
6 8d. black and purple . . . . . 26·00 48·00
9 1s. black on green . . . . . . 28·00 48·00
7 2s. black and blue on blue . . . 85·00 £120
8 3s. black and violet £120 £160

2 Badge of St. Helena

1924.
10 **2** ½d. black . . . . 3·50 13·00
11 1d. black and green . . . . 5·50 8·50
12 1½d. red . . . . 7·50 26·00
13 2d. black and grey . . . . 14·00 7·50
14 3d. blue . . . . 8·00 14·00
15 4d. black on yellow . . . . 48·00 80·00
15d 5d. purple and green . . . 10·00 21·00
16 6d. black and purple . . . 48·00 90·00
17 8d. black and violet . . . . 15·00 42·00
18 1s. black and brown . . . . 20·00 50·00
19 2s. black and blue on blue 55·00 85·00
20 3s. black on blue . . . . . 80·00 90·00

3 Georgetown

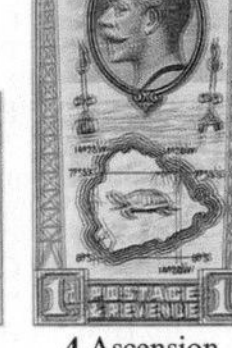

4 Ascension Island

1934. Medallion portrait of King George V (except 1s.).
21 **3** ½d. black and violet 90 80
22 **4** 1d. black and green . . . . 1·75 1·25
23 – 1½d. black and red . . . . . 1·75 2·25
24 **4** 2d. black and orange . . . . 1·75 2·50
25 – 3d. black and blue . . . . . 1·75 1·50
26 – 5d. black and blue . . . . . 2·25 3·25
27 **4** 8d. black and brown . . . . 4·25 4·75
28 – 1s. black and red . . . . . 18·00 7·00
29 **4** 2s.6d. black and purple . . . 45·00 35·00
30 – 5s. black and brown . . . . 45·00 55·00

DESIGNS—HORIZ: 1½d. The Pier; 3d. Long Beach; 5d. Three Sisters; 1s. Sooty tern ("Wideawake Fair"); 5s. Green mountain.

1935. Silver Jubilee. As T **13** of Antigua.
31 1½d. blue and red . . . . . . 3·50 7·00
32 2d. blue and grey . . . . . . 11·00 23·00
33 5d. green and blue . . . . . 17·00 24·00
34 1s. grey and purple . . . . . 23·00 27·00

1937. Coronation. As T **2** of Aden.
35 1d. green . . . . 50 1·25
36 2d. orange . . . . 1·00 50
37 3d. blue . . . . 1·00 50

10 The Pier

1938.
38b A ½d. black and violet . . . 70 1·75
39 B 1d. black and green . . . 40·00 8·00
39b 1d. black and orange . . . 45 60
39d C 1d. black and green . . . 60 1·00
40b **10** 1½d. black and red 85 80
40d 1½d. black and pink . . . 55 80
41a B 2d. black and orange . . . 80 40
41c 2d. black and red . . . . 1·00 1·25
42 D 3d. black and blue . . . . £100 27·00
42b 3d. black and grey 70 80
42d B 4d. black and blue . . . . 4·50 3·00
43 C 6d. black and blue . . . . 9·00 2·00
44a A 1s. black and brown . . . 4·75 2·00
45 **10** 2s.6d. black and red . . . 42·00 9·50
46a D 5s. black and brown . . . 38·00 27·00
47a C 10s. black and purple . . . 42·00 55·00

DESIGNS: A, Georgetown; B, Green Mountain; C, Three Sisters; D, Long Beach.

1946. Victory. As T **9** of Aden.
48 2d. orange 40 65
49 4d. blue 40 50

1948. Silver Wedding. As T **10/11** of Aden.
50 3d. black 50 30
51 10s. mauve . . . . 45·00 42·00

1949. U.P.U. As T **20/23** of Antigua.
52 3d. red . . . . 1·00 1·75
53 4d. blue . . . . 3·50 1·25
54 6d. olive . . . . 2·00 3·75
55 1s. black . . . . 2·00 1·50

1953. Coronation. As T **13** of Aden.
56 3d. black and grey . . . . . 1·00 1·50

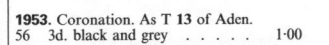

19 Water Catchment

1956.
57 **19** ½d. black and brown 10 50
58 – 1d. black and mauve . . . 2·50 1·00
59 – 1½d. black and orange . . . 50 70
60 – 2d. black and red . . . . 2·50 1·50
61 – 2½d. black and brown . . . 1·00 1·75
62 – 3d. black and blue . . . . 4·00 1·25
63 – 4d. black and turquoise . . 1·25 2·00
64 – 6d. black and blue . . . . 1·25 1·75
65 – 7d. black and olive . . . . 1·25 1·25
66 – 1s. black and red . . . . . 1·00 1·25
67 – 2s.6d. black and purple . . 27·00 6·50
68 – 5s. black and green . . . . 35·00 17·00
69 – 10s. black and purple . . . 48·00 35·00

DESIGNS: 1d. Map of Ascension; 1½d. Georgetown; 2d. Map showing Atlantic cables; 2½d. Mountain road; 3d. White-tailed tropic bird ("Boatswain Bird"); 4d. Yellow-finned tuna; 6d. Rollers on seashore; 7d. Turtles; 1s. Land crab; 2s.6d. Sooty tern ("Wideawake"); 5s. Perfect Crater; 10s. View of Ascension from north-west.

28 Brown Booby

1963. Birds. Multicoloured.
70 1d. Type **28** . . . . 1·25 30
71 1½d. White-capped noddy ("Black Noddy") . . . . . 1·25 1·00
72 2d. White tern ("Fairy Tern") 1·25 30
73 3d. Red-billed tropic bird . . 1·50 30
74 4½d. Common noddy ("Brown Noddy") . . . . 1·50 30
75 6d. Sooty tern ("Wideawake Tern") . . . . 1·25 30
76 7d. Ascension frigate bird ("Frigate bird") . . . . . 1·25 30
77 10d. Blue-faced booby ("White Booby") . . . . 1·25 30
78 1s. White-tailed tropic bird ("Yellow-billed Tropicbird") 1·25 30
79 1s.6d. Red-billed tropic bird 4·50 1·75
80 2s.6d. Madeiran storm petrel 8·50 10·00
81 5s. Red-footed booby (brown phase) . . . . 8·50 10·00
82 10s. Ascension frigate birds ("Frigate birds") . . . . . 13·00 11·00
83 £1 Red-footed booby (white phase) . . . . 20·00 13·00

1963. Freedom from Hunger. As T **28** of Aden.
84 1s.6d. red 75 40

1963. Centenary of Red Cross. As T **33** of Antigua.
85 3d. red and black . . . . . . 2·00 1·25
86 1s.6d. red and blue . . . . . 4·00 2·25

1965. Centenary of I.T.U. As T **36** of Antigua.
87 3d. mauve and violet 50 65
88 6d. turquoise and brown . . . 75 65

1965. I.C.Y. As T **37** of Antigua.
89 1d. purple and turquoise . . . 40 60
90 6d. green and lavender 60 90

1966. Churchill Commemoration. As T **38** of Antigua.
91 1d. blue 50 75
92 3d. green . . . . 2·75 1·25
93 6d. brown . . . . 3·50 1·50
94 1s.6d. violet . . . . 4·50 2·00

1966. World Cup Football Championship. As T **40** of Antigua.
95 3d. multicoloured . . . . . . 1·25 60
96 6d. multicoloured . . . . . . 1·50 80

1966. Inauguration of W.H.O. Headquarters, Geneva. As T **41** of Antigua.
97 3d. black, green and blue . . . 1·75 1·00
98 1s.6d. black, purple and ochre 4·25 2·00

36 Satellite Station

44 Human Rights Emblem and Chain Links

37 B.B.C. Emblem

1966. Opening of Apollo Communication Satellite Earth Station.
99 **36** 4d. black and violet . . . 10 10
100 8d. black and green . . . 15 15
101 1s.3d. black and brown . . 15 20
102 2s.6d. black and blue . . . 15 20

1966. Opening of B.B.C. Relay Station.
103 **37** 1d. gold and blue 10 10
104 3d. gold and green 15 15

105 6d. gold and violet 15 15
106 1s.6d. gold and red 15 15

1967. 20th Anniv of U.N.E.S.C.O. As T **54/56** of Antigua.
107 3d. multicoloured 2·00 1·25
108 6d. yellow, violet and olive 2·75 1·75
109 1s.6d. black, purple and orange 4·50 2·25

1968. Human Rights Year.
110 **44** 6d. orange, red and black 15 15
111 1s.6d. blue, red and black 20 25
112 2s.6d. green, red and black 20 30

45 Black Durgon ("Ascension Black-Fish")

1968. Fishes (1st series).
113 **45** 4d. black, grey and blue 30 40
114 – 8d. multicoloured 35 70
115 – 1s.9d. multicoloured 40 80
116 – 2s.3d. multicoloured 40 85
DESIGNS: 8d. Scribbled filefish ("Leather-jacket"); 1s.9d. Yellow-finned tuna; 2s.3d. Short-finned mako.
See also Nos. 117/20 and 126/9.

1969. Fishes (2nd series). As T **45**. Multicoloured.
117 4d. Sailfish 75 90
118 6d. White seabream ("Old wife") 1·00 1·25
119 1s.6d. Yellowtail 1·50 2·50
120 2s.11d. Rock hind ("Jack") 2·00 3·00

46 H.M.S. "Rattlesnake"

1969. Royal Navy Crests (1st series).
121 **46** 4d. multicoloured 60 30
122 – 9d. multicoloured 75 35
123 – 1s.9d. blue and gold 1·10 45
124 – 2s.3d. multicoloured 1·25 55
MS125 165 × 105 mm. Nos. 121/4 6·50 12·00
DESIGNS: 9d. H.M.S. "Weston"; 1s.9d. H.M.S. "Undaunted"; 2s.3d. H.M.S. "Eagle".
See also Nos. 130/3, 149/52, 154/7 and 166/9.

1970. Fishes (3rd series). As T **45**. Multicoloured.
126 4d. Wahoo 4·50 2·75
127w 9d. Ascension jack ("Coalfish") 3·00 1·25
128 1s.9d. Pompouno dolphin 5·50 3·50
129w 2s.3d. Squirrelfish ("Soldier") 5·50 3·50

1970. Royal Navy Crests (2nd series). As T **46**. Multicoloured.
130 4d. H.M.S. "Penelope" 1·00 1·00
131 9d. H.M.S. "Carlisle" 1·25 1·50
132 1s.6d. H.M.S. "Amphion" 1·75 2·00
133 2s.6d. H.M.S. "Magpie" 1·75 2·00
MS134 159 × 96 mm. Nos. 130/3 11·00 14·00

50 Early Chinese Rocket
51 Course of the "Quest"

1971. Decimal Currency. Evolution of Space Travel. Multicoloured.
135 ½p. Type **50** 15 20
136 1p. Medieval Arab astronomers 20 20
137 1½p. Tycho Brahe's observatory, quadrant and supernova (horiz) 30 30
138 2p. Galileo, Moon and telescope (horiz) 40 30
139 2½p. Isaac Newton, instruments and apple (horiz) 1·00 70
140 3½p. Harrison's chronometer and H.M.S. "Deptford" (frigate), 1735 (horiz) 2·00 70
141 4½p. Space rocket taking off 1·25 70
142 5p. World's largest telescope, Palomar (horiz) 1·00 70
143 7½p. World's largest radio telescope, Jodrell Bank (horiz) 4·00 1·60
144 10p. "Mariner VII" and Mars (horiz) 3·50 1·75
145 12½p. "Sputnik II" and Space dog, Laika (horiz) 5·00 2·00
146 25p. Walking in Space 6·00 2·25
147 50p. "Apollo XI" crew on Moon (horiz) 5·00 2·50
148 £1 Future Space Research station (horiz) 5·00 4·50

1971. Royal Navy Crests (3rd series). As T **46**. Mult.
149 2p. H.M.S. "Phoenix" 1·00 30
150 4p. H.M.S. "Milford" 1·25 55
151 9p. H.M.S. "Pelican" 1·50 80
152 15p. H.M.S. "Oberon" 1·50 1·00
MS153 151 × 104 mm. Nos. 149/52 4·75 15·00

1972. Royal Navy Crests (4th series). As T **46**. Mult.
154 1½p. H.M.S. "Lowestoft" 50 50
155 3p. H.M.S. "Auckland" 55 75
156 6p. H.M.S. "Nigeria" 60 1·25
157 17½p. H.M.S. "Bermuda" 90 2·50
MS158 157 × 93 mm. Nos. 154/7 2·25 7·50

1972. 50th Anniv of Shackleton's Death. Mult.
159 2½p. Type **51** 30 60
160 4p. Shackleton and "Quest" (horiz) 35 60
161 7½p. Shackleton's cabin and "Quest" (horiz) 35 65
162 11p. Shackleton statue and memorial 40 80
MS163 139 × 114 mm. Nos. 159/62 1·25 6·00

52 Land Crab and Short-finned Mako

1972. Royal Silver Wedding. Multicoloured.
164 **52** 2p. violet 15 10
165 16p. red 35 30

1973. Royal Naval Crests (5th series). As T **46**. Multicoloured.
166 2p. H.M.S. "Birmingham" 2·00 1·50
167 4p. H.M.S. "Cardiff" 2·25 1·50
168 9p. H.M.S. "Penzance" 3·00 1·75
169 13p. H.M.S. "Rochester" 3·25 1·75
MS170 109 × 152 mm. Nos. 166/9 28·00 10·00

53 Green Turtle

1973. Turtles. Multicoloured.
171 4p. Type **53** 2·75 1·50
172 9p. Loggerhead turtle 3·00 1·75
173 12p. Hawksbill turtle 3·25 2·00

54 Sergeant, R.M. Light Infantry, 1900

1973. 50th Anniv of Departure of Royal Marines from Ascension. Multicoloured.
174 2p. Type **54** 1·50 1·25
175 6p. R.M. Private, 1816 2·25 1·75
176 12p. R.M. Light Infantry Officer, 1880 2·50 2·25
177 20p. R.M. Artillery Colour Sergeant, 1910 3·00 2·50

1973. Royal Wedding. As T **47** of Anguilla. Multicoloured. Background colours given.
178 2p. brown 15 10
179 18p. green 20 20

55 Letter and H.Q., Berne

1974. Centenary of Universal Postal Union. Mult.
180 2p. Type **55** 20 30
181 9p. Hermes and U.P.U. monument 30 45

56 Churchill as a Boy, and Birthplace, Blenheim Palace

1974. Birth Centenary of Sir Winston Churchill. Multicoloured.
182 5p. Type **56** 20 35
183 25p. Churchill as statesman, and U.N. Building 30 75
MS184 93 × 87 mm. Nos. 182/3 1·00 2·50

57 "Skylab 3" and Photograph of Ascension

1975. Space Satellites. Multicoloured.
185 2p. Type **57** 20 30
186 18p. "Skylab 4" Command module and photograph 30 40

58 U.S.A.F. Lockheed C-141A Starlifter

1975. Wideawake Airfield. Multicoloured.
187 2p. Type **58** 1·00 65
188 5p. R.A.F. Lockheed C-130 Hercules 1·00 85
189 9p. Vickers Super VC-10 1·00 1·40
190 24p. U.S.A.F. Lockheed C-5A Galaxy 1·50 2·50
MS191 144 × 99 mm. Nos. 187/90 17·00 22·00

1975. "Apollo-Soyuz" Space Link. Nos. 141 and 145/6 optd **APOLLO-SOYUZ LINK 1975**.
192 4½p. multicoloured 15 20
193 12½p. multicoloured 15 25
194 25p. multicoloured 25 40

60 Arrival of Royal Navy, 1815

1975. 160th Anniv of Occupation. Multicoloured.
195 2p. Type **60** 25 25
196 5p. Water supply, Dampiers Drip 25 40
197 9p. First landing, 1815 25 60
198 15p. The garden on Green Mountain 35 85

61 Yellow Canaries ("Canary")

1976. Multicoloured.
199 1p. Type **61** 40 1·50
200 2p. White tern ("Fairy Tern") (vert) 50 1·50
201 3p. Common waxbill ("Waxbill") 50 1·50
202 4p. White-capped noddy ("Black Noddy") (vert) 50 1·50
203 5p. Common noddy ("Brown Noddy") 70 1·50
204 6p. Common mynah 70 1·50
205 7p. Madeiran storm petrel (vert) 70 1·50
206 8p. Sooty tern 70 1·50
207 9p. Blue-faced booby ("White Booby") (vert) 70 1·50
208 10p. Red-footed booby 70 1·50
209 15p. Red-necked spurfowl ("Red-throated Francolin") (vert) 85 1·50
210 18p. Brown booby (vert) 85 1·50
211 25p. Red-billed tropic bird ("Red-billed Bo'sun Bird") 90 1·50
212 50p. White-tailed tropic bird ("Yellow-billed Tropic Bird") 1·25 2·25
213 £1 Ascension frigate-bird (vert) 1·25 2·75
214 £2 Boatswain Bird Island Sanctuary (50 × 38 mm) 2·25 5·50

63 G.B. Penny Red with Ascension Postmark

1976. Festival of Stamps, London.
215 **63** 5p. red, black and brown 15 15
216 – 9p. green, black and brown 15 20
217 – 25p. multicoloured 25 45
MS218 133 × 121 mm. No. 217 with St. Helena No. 318 and Tristan da Cunha No. 206 1·50 2·00
DESIGNS—VERT: 9p. ½d. stamp of 1922. HORIZ: 25p. "Southampton Castle" (liner).

64 U.S. Base, Ascension

1976. Bicentenary of American Revolution. Multicoloured.
219 8p. Type **64** 30 40
220 9p. NASA Station at Devils Ashpit 30 45
221 25p. "Viking" landing on Mars 40 80

65 Visit of Prince Philip, 1957
66 Tunnel carrying Water Pipe

1977. Silver Jubilee. Multicoloured.
222 8p. Type **65** 15 15
223 12p. Coronation Coach leaving Buckingham Palace (horiz) 20 20
224 25p. Coronation Coach (horiz) 35 40

1977. Water Supplies. Multicoloured.
225 3p. Type **66** 15 15
226 5p. Breakneck Valley wells 20 20
227 12p. Break tank (horiz) 30 35
228 25p. Water catchment (horiz) 45 65

67 Mars Bay Location, 1877

1977. Centenary of Visit of Professor Gill (astronomer). Multicoloured.
229 3p. Type **67** 15 20
230 8p. Instrument sites, Mars Bay 15 25
231 12p. Sir David and Lady Gill 20 40
232 25p. Maps of Ascension 60 70

68 Lion of England

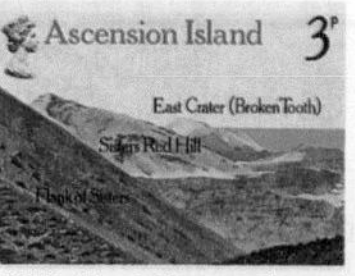

70 Flank of Sisters, Sisters' Red Hill and East Crater

1978. 25th Anniv of Coronation.
233 **68** 25p. yellow, brown and silver 35 50
234 – 25p. multicoloured 35 50
235 – 25p. yellow, brown and silver 35 50
DESIGNS: No 234, Queen Elizabeth II; No 235, Green turtle.

1978. Ascension Island Volcanic Rock Formations. Multicoloured.
236 3p. Type **70** 15 20
237 5p. Holland's Crater (Hollow Tooth) 20 30
238 12p. Street Crater, Lower Valley Crater and Bear's Back 25 40
239 15p. Butt Crater, Weather Post and Green Mountain 30 45
240 25p. Flank of Sisters, Thistle Hill and Two Boats Village 35 50
MS241 185 × 100 mm. Nos. 236/40, each × 2 . . . . 2·00 5·00
Nos. 236/40 were issued as a se-tenant strip within the sheet, forming a composite design.

71 "The Resolution" (H. Roberts)

72 St. Mary's Church, Georgetown

1979. Bicentenary of Captain Cook's Voyages, 1768–79. Multicoloured.
242 3p. Type **71** 25 25
243 8p. Cook's chronometer . . . 25 40
244 12p. Green turtle 30 50
245 25p. Flaxman/Wedgwood medallion of Cook 30 70

1979. Ascension Day. Muticoloured.
246 8p. Type **72** 10 20
247 12p. Map of Ascension . . . 15 30
248 50p. "The Ascension" (painting by Rembrandt) 30 90

73 Landing Cable, Comfortless Cove

1979. 80th Anniv of Eastern Telegraph Company's Arrival on Ascension.
249 **73** 3p. black and red 10 10
250 – 8p. black and green . . . 15 15
251 – 12p. black and yellow . . . 20 20
252 – 15p. black and violet . . . 20 25
253 – 25p. black and brown . . . 25 35
DESIGNS—HORIZ: 8p. C.S. "Anglia"; 15p. C.S. "Seine"; 25p. Cable and Wireless earth station. VERT: 12p. Map of Atlantic cable network.

74 1938 6d. Stamp

1979. Death Centenary of Sir Rowland Hill.
254 **74** 3p. black and blue 10 10
255 – 8p. black, green and pale green 15 20
256 – 12p. black, blue and pale blue 15 25
257 – 50p. black and red 40 90
DESIGNS—HORIZ: 8p. 1956 5s. definitive. VERT: 12p. 1924 3s. stamp; 50p. Sir Rowland Hill.

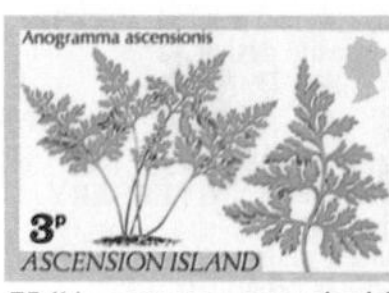

75 "Anogramma ascensionis"

1980. Ferns and Grasses. Multicoloured.
258 3p. Type **75** 10 15
259 6p. "Xiphopteris ascensionense" 10 20
260 8p. "Sporobolus caespitosus" 10 20
261 12p. "Sporobolus durus" (vert) 15 30
262 18p. "Dryopteris ascensionis" (vert) 15 40
263 24p. "Marattia purpurascens" (vert) 20 55

76 17th-Century Bottle Post

1980. "London 1980" International Stamp Exhibition. Multicoloured.
264 8p. Type **76** 15 20
265 12p. 19th-century chance calling ship 20 25
266 15p. "Garth Castle" (regular mail service from 1863) . . 20 30
267 50p. "St. Helena" (mail services, 1980) 60 90

77 H.M. Queen Elizabeth the Queen Mother

1980. 80th Birthday of The Queen Mother.
269 **77** 15p. multicoloured 40 40

78 Lubbock's Yellowtail

1980. Fishes. Multicoloured.
270 3p. Type **78** 25 25
271 10p. Resplendent angelfish . . 30 25
272 25p. Bicoloured butterflyfish 35 55
273 40p. Marmalade razorfish . . 50 75

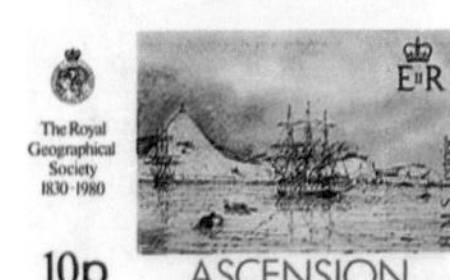

79 H.M.S. "Tortoise"

1980. 150th Anniv of Royal Geographical Society. Multicoloured.
274 10p. Type **79** 20 40
275 15p. "Wideawake Fair" . . . 30 45
276 60p. Mid-Atlantic Ridge (38 × 48 mm) . . . . . . 65 1·25

80 Green Mountain Farm, 1881

1981. Green Mountain Farm. Multicoloured.
277 12p. Type **80** 15 35
278 15p. Two Boats, 1881 . . . . 15 40
279 20p. Green Mountain and Two Boats, 1981 . . . . . 20 50
280 30p. Green Mountain Farm, 1981 . . . . 30 70

81 Cable and Wireless Earth Station

1981. "Space Shuttle" Mission and Opening of 2nd Earth Station.
281 **81** 15p. black, blue and pale blue 30 35

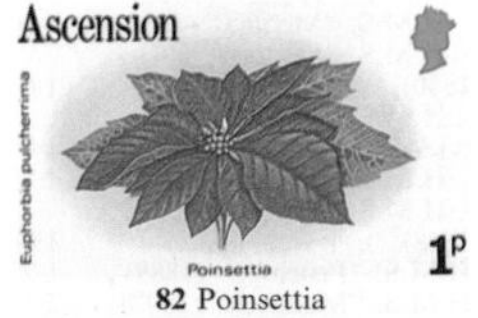

82 Poinsettia

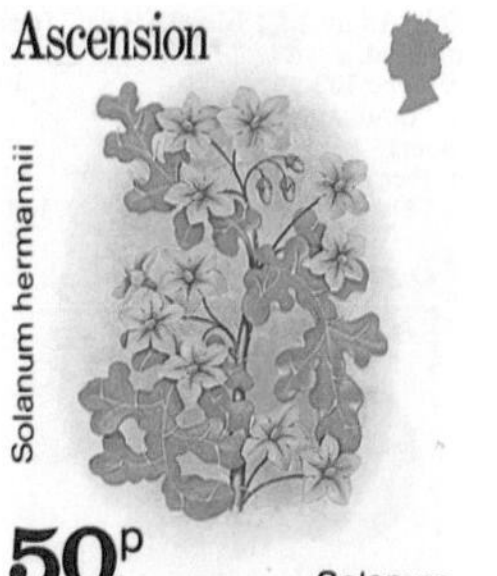

83 Solanum

1981. Flowers. Multicoloured.
282A 1p. Type **82** . . . . 70 1·00
283B 2p. Clustered wax flower . . 50 1·00
284B 3p. Kolanchoe (vert) . . . 50 1·00
285A 4p. Yellow pops . . . . . 80 1·00
286A 5p. Camels foot creeper . . 80 1·00
287A 8p. White oleander . . . . 80 1·00
288B 10p. Ascension lily (vert) 45 75
289A 12p. Coral plant (vert) . . 1·50 85
290B 15p. Yellow allamanda . . 50 75
291B 20p. Ascension euphorbia 1·00 75
292A 30p. Flame of the forest (vert) . . . . 1·25 1·25
293A 40p. Bougainvillea "King Leopold" . . . . 1·25 2·75
294A 50p. Type **83** . . . . 1·25 3·00
295B £1 Ladies petticoat . . . . 2·00 3·00
296A £2 Red hibiscus . . . . . 3·75 6·00
Nos. 294/6 are as Type **83**.

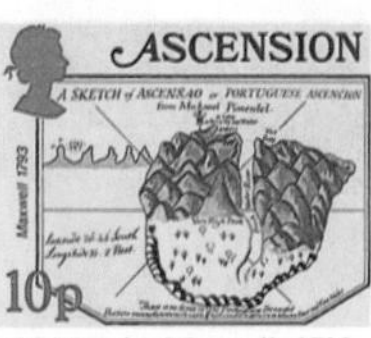

84 Map by Maxwell, 1793

1981. Early Maps of Ascension.
297 **84** 10p. black, gold and blue 20 35
298 – 12p. black, gold and green 20 35
299 – 15p. black, gold and stone 20 35
300 – 40p. black, gold and yellow 50 70
MS301 – 79 × 64 mm. 5p. × 4 multicoloured 60 75
DESIGNS: 12p. Maxwell, 1793 (different); 15p. Ekeberg and Chapman, 1811; 40p. Campbell, 1819; miniature sheet, Linschoten, 1599.
Stamps from **MS**301 form a composite design.

85 Wedding Bouquet from Ascension

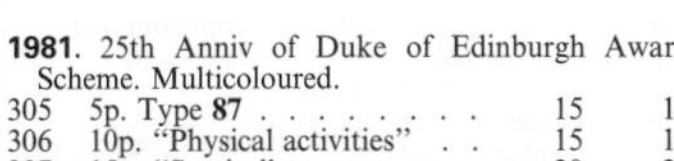

87 "Interest"

1981. Royal Wedding. Multicoloured.
302 10p. Type **85** 15 15
303 15p. Prince Charles in Fleet Air Arm flying kit 30 30
304 50p. Prince Charles and Lady Diana Spencer 65 90

1981. 25th Anniv of Duke of Edinburgh Award Scheme. Multicoloured.
305 5p. Type **87** 15 15
306 10p. "Physical activities" . . 15 15
307 15p. "Service" 20 20
308 40p. Duke of Edinburgh . . 45 45

88 Scout crossing Rope Bridge

1982. 75th Anniv of Boy Scout Movement.
309 **88** 10p. black, blue and light blue 15 35
310 – 15p. black, brown and yellow 15 50
311 – 25p. black, mve & lt mve 20 60
312 – 40p. black, red and orange 30 85
MS313 – 121 × 121 mm. 10, 15, 25, 40p. As Nos. 309/12 (each diamond 40 × 40 mm) . . . . 1·00 2·50
DESIGNS: 15p. 1st Ascension Scout Group flag; 25p. Scouts learning to use radio; 40p. Lord Baden-Powell.

89 Charles Darwin

1982. 150th Anniv of Charles Darwin's Voyage. Multicoloured.
314 10p. Type **89** 20 40
315 12p. Darwin's pistols 20 50
316 15p. Rock crab 25 55
317 40p. H.M.S. "Beagle" . . . 60 95

90 Fairey Swordfish Torpedo Bomber

1982. 40th Anniv of Wideawake Airfield. Multicoloured.
318 5p. Type **90** . . . . 1·00 35
319 10p. North American B-25C Mitchell . . . . 1·25 40
320 15p. Boeing EC-135N Aria 1·50 55
321 50p. Lockheed C-130 Hercules . . . . 2·25 1·10

91 Ascension Coat of Arms

1982. 21st Birthday of Princess of Wales. Mult.
322 12p. Type **91** 25 25
323 15p. Lady Diana Spencer in Music Room, Buckingham Palace 25 25
324 25p. Bride and Earl Spencer leaving Clarence House . . 40 40
325 50p. Formal portrait 75 75

1982. Commonwealth Games, Brisbane. Nos. 290/1 optd **1st PARTICIPATION COMMONWEALTH GAMES 1982**.
326 15p. Yellow allamanda . . . 30 40
327 20p. Ascension euphorbia . . 40 45

94 Bush House, London

1982. Christmas. 50th Anniv of B.B.C. External Broadcasting. Multicoloured.
328 5p. Type **94** 15 20
329 10p. Atlantic relay station . . 20 30
330 25p. Lord Reith, first Director-General 30 60
331 40p. King George V making his first Christmas broadcast, 1932 . . . . . 45 75

95 "Marasmius echinosphaerus"

1983. Fungi. Multicoloured.
332 7p. Type **95** 40 30
333 12p. "Chlorophyllum molybdites" 50 45
334 15p. "Leucocoprinus cepaestripes" 60 50
335 20p. "Lycoperdon marginatum" 70 65
336 50p. "Marasmiellus distantifolius" . . . . 90 1·25

96 Aerial View of Georgetown

1983. Island Views (1st series). Multicoloured.
337 12p. Type **96** 15 25
338 15p. Green Mountain farm 15 25
339 20p. Boatswain Bird Island 20 40
340 60p. Telemetry Hill by night 40 80
See also Nos. 367/70.

97 Westland Wessex 5 Helicopter of No. 845 Naval Air Squadron

1983. Bicentenary of Manned Flight. British Military Aircraft. Multicoloured.
341 12p. Type **97** 50 65
342 15p. Avro Vulcan B.2 of No. 44 Squadron 60 75
343 20p. Hawker Siddeley Nimrod M.R.2P of No. 20 Squadron 65 85
344 60p. Handey Page Victor K2 of No. 55 Squadron . . . 85 2·00

98 Iguanid

1983. Introduced Species. Multicoloured.
345 12p. Type **98** 30 30
346 15p. Common rabbit 35 35
347 20p. Cat 45 45
348 60p. Donkey . . . . 1·10 1·40

99 Speckled Tellin

1983. Sea Shells. Multicoloured.
349 7p. Type **99** 15 20
350 12p. Lion's paw scallop . . . 15 30
351 15p. Lurid cowrie 15 35
352 20p. Ascension nerite 20 45
353 50p. Miniature melo . . . . 40 1·10

100 1922 1½d. Stamp **101** Prince Andrew

1984. 150th Anniv of St. Helena as a British Colony. Multicoloured.
354 12p. Type **100** 15 45
355 15p. 1922 2d. stamp 15 50
356 20p. 1922 8d. stamp 20 55
357 60p. 1922 1s. stamp . . . . 50 1·40

1984. Visit of Prince Andrew. Sheet 124 × 90 mm.
MS358 12p. Type **101**; 70p. Prince Andrew in naval uniform . . . 1·00 1·60

102 Naval Semaphore

1984. 250th Anniv of "Lloyd's List" (newspaper). Multicoloured.
359 12p. Type **102** 40 30
360 15p. "Southampton Castle" (liner) 40 35
361 20p. Pier head 45 45
362 70p. "Dane" (screw steamer) 1·00 1·50

103 Penny Coin and Yellow-finned Tuna

1984. New Coinage. Multicoloured.
363 12p. Type **103** 35 35
364 15p. Twopenny coin and donkey 40 40
365 20p. Fifty pence coin and green turtle 45 50
366 70p. Pound coin and sooty tern . . . . 80 1·75

1984. Island Views (2nd series). As T **96**. Mult.
367 12p. The Devil's Riding-school 20 30
368 15p. St. Mary's Church . . . 25 35
369 20p. Two Boats Village . . . 25 45
370 70p. Ascension from the sea 80 1·50

104 Bermuda Cypress **105** The Queen Mother with Prince Andrew at Silver Jubilee Service

1985. Trees. Multicoloured.
371 7p. Type **104** 25 20
372 12p. Norfolk Island pine . . 30 30
373 15p. Screwpine 30 35
374 20p. Eucalyptus 30 45
375 65p. Spore tree . . . . . . 80 1·40

1985. Life and Times of Queen Elizabeth the Queen Mother. Multicoloured.
376 12p. With the Duke of York at Balmoral, 1924 . . . . 25 35
377 15p. Type **105** 25 40
378 20p. The Queen Mother at Ascot 30 55
379 70p. With Prince Henry at his christening (from photo by Lord Snowdon) . . . . . 80 1·75
MS380 91 × 73 mm. 75p. Visiting the "Queen Elizabeth 2" at Southampton, 1968 . . . . . 1·10 1·60

106 32 Pdr. Smooth Bore Muzzle-loader, c. 1820, and Royal Marine Artillery Hat Plate, c. 1816

1985. Guns on Ascension Island. Multicoloured.
381 12p. Type **106** 50 90
382 15p. 7 inch rifled muzzle-loader, c. 1866, and Royal Cypher on barrel . . . . . 50 1·00
383 20p. 7 pdr rifled muzzle-loader, c. 1877, and Royal Artillery Badge . . . . . 50 1·25
384 70p. 5.5 inch gun, 1941, and crest from H.M.S. "Hood" 1·25 3·50

107 Guide Flag **108** "Clerodendrum fragrans"

1985. 75th Anniv of Girl Guide Movement and International Youth Year. Multicoloured.
385 12p. Type **107** 50 70
386 15p. Practising first aid . . . 50 80
387 20p. Camping 50 90
388 70p. Lady Baden-Powell . . 1·25 2·50

1985. Wild Flowers. Multicoloured.
389 12p. Type **108** 35 75
390 15p. Shell ginger 40 90
391 20p. Cape daisy 45 90
392 70p. Ginger lily . . . . . . 1·00 2·50

109 Newton's Reflector Telescope **110** Princess Elizabeth in 1926

1986. Appearance of Halley's Comet. Mult.
393 12p. Type **109** . . . . 40 1·10
394 15p. Edmond Halley and Old Greenwich Observatory . . 40 1·25
395 20p. Short's Gregorian telescope and comet, 1759 40 1·25
396 70p. Ascension satellite tracking station and ICE spacecraft . . . . 1·25 3·50

1986. 60th Birthday of Queen Elizabeth II. Mult.
397 7p. Type **110** 15 25
398 15p. Queen making Christmas broadcast, 1952 20 40
399 20p. At Garter ceremony, Windsor Castle, 1983 . . . 25 50
400 35p. In Auckland, New Zealand, 1981 . . . . . . 35 80
401 £1 At Crown Agents' Head Office, London, 1983 . . . 1·00 2·25

111 1975 Space Satellites 2p. Stamp

1986. "Ameripex '86" International Stamp Exhibition, Chicago. Designs showing previous Ascension stamps. Multicoloured.
402 12p. Type **111** 25 60
403 15p. 1980 "London 1980" International Stamp Exhibition 50p. 25 70
404 20p. 1976 Bicentenary of American Revolution 8p. 30 90
405 70p. 1982 40th anniv of Wideawake Airfield 10p. 70 2·00
MS406 60 × 75 mm. 75p. Statue of Liberty . . . . 2·00 2·75

112 Prince Andrew and Miss Sarah Ferguson

1986. Royal Wedding. Multicoloured.
407 15p. Type **112** 25 35
408 35p. Prince Andrew aboard H.M.S. "Brazen" 50 75

113 H.M.S. "Ganymede" (c. 1811)

1986. Ships of the Royal Navy. Multicoloured.
409 1p. Type **113** . . . . 55 1·50
410 2p. H.M.S. "Kangaroo" (c.1811) . . . . 60 1·50
411 4p. H.M.S. "Trinculo" (c.1811) . . . . 60 1·50
412 5p. H.M.S. "Daring" (c.1811) 60 1·50
413 9p. H.M.S. "Thais" (c.1811) 70 1·50
414 10p. H.M.S. "Pheasant" (1819) . . . . 70 1·50
415 15p. H.M.S. "Myrmidon" (1819) . . . . 80 1·75
416 18p. H.M.S. "Atholl" (1825) 90 1·75
417 20p. H.M.S. "Medina" (1830) 90 1·75
418 25p. H.M.S. "Saracen" (1840) . . . . 1·00 2·00
419 30p. H.M.S. "Hydra" (c.1845) . . . . 1·00 2·00
420 50p. H.M.S. "Sealark" (1849) 1·00 2·50
421 70p. H.M.S. "Rattlesnake" (1868) . . . . 1·00 3·00
422 £1 H.M.S. "Penelope" (1889) 1·25 3·75
423 £2 H.M.S. "Monarch" (1897) 2·50 6·50

114 Cape Gooseberry

1987. Edible Bush Fruits. Multicoloured.
424 12p. Type **114** 65 90
425 15p. Prickly pear . . . . . . 65 1·00
426 20p. Guava . . . . 70 1·10
427 70p. Loquat . . . . 1·10 2·75

115 Ignition of Rocket Motors **116** Captains in Full Dress raising Red Ensign

1987. 25th Anniv of First American Manned Earth Orbit. Multicoloured.
428 15p. Type **115** 55 75
429 18p. Lift-off 60 80
430 25p. Re-entry 75 95
431 £1 Splashdown . . . . . . 2·50 3·25
MS432 92 × 78 mm. 70p. "Friendship 7" capsule . . . . 1·75 2·00

1987. 19th-century Uniforms (1st series). Royal Navy, 1815–20. Multicoloured.
433 25p. Type **116** 50 60
434 25p. Surgeon and seamen . . 50 60
435 25p. Seaman with water-carrying donkey 50 60
436 25p. Midshipman and gun . . 50 60
437 25p. Commander in undress uniform surveying 50 60
See also Nos. 478/82.

117 "Cynthia cardui"

1987. Insects (1st series). Multicoloured.
438 15p. Type **117** 65 65
439 18p. "Danaus chrysippus" . . 70 75
440 25p. "Hypolimnas misippus" 85 85
441 £1 "Lampides boeticus" . . . 2·25 2·50
See also Nos. 452/5 and 483/6.

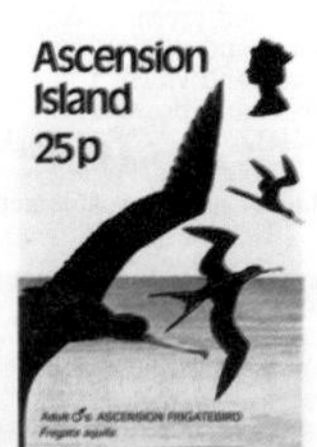

118 Male Ascension Frigate Birds

1987. Sea Birds (1st series). Multicoloured.
442 25p. Type **118** . . . . 1·60 1·90
443 25p. Juvenile Ascension frigate bird, brown booby and blue-faced boobies . . 1·60 1·90
444 25p. Male Ascension frigate bird and blue-faced boobies 1·60 1·90
445 25p. Female Ascension frigate bird . . . . 1·60 1·90
446 25p. Adult male feeding juvenile Ascension frigate bird . . . . 1·60 1·90
Nos. 442/6 were printed together, se-tenant, forming a composite design.
See also Nos. 469/73.

1987. Royal Ruby Wedding. Nos. 397/401 optd **40TH WEDDING ANNIVERSARY**.
447 7p. Type **110** 15 15
448 15p. Queen making Christmas broadcast, 1952 20 20
449 20p. At Garter ceremony, Windsor Castle, 1983 . . . 25 25
450 35p. In Auckland, New Zealand, 1981 . . . . . . 40 45
451 £1 At Crown Agents' Head Office, London, 1983 . . . 1·00 1·10

1988. Insects (2nd series). As T **117**. Multicoloured.
452 15p. "Gryllus bimaculatus" (field cricket) 50 50
453 18p. "Ruspolia differeus" (bush cricket) 55 55

454 25p. "Chilomenus lunata" (ladybird) 70 70
455 £1 "Diachrysia orichalcea" (moth) . . . . 2·25 2·25

120 Bate's Memorial, St. Mary's Church

1988. 150th Death Anniv of Captain William Bate (garrison commander, 1828–38). Multicoloured.
456 9p. Type **120** 35 35
457 15p. Commodore's Cottage 45 45
458 18p. North East Cottage . . 50 50
459 25p. Map of Ascension . . . 70 70
460 70p. Captain Bate and marines . . . . 1·75 1·75

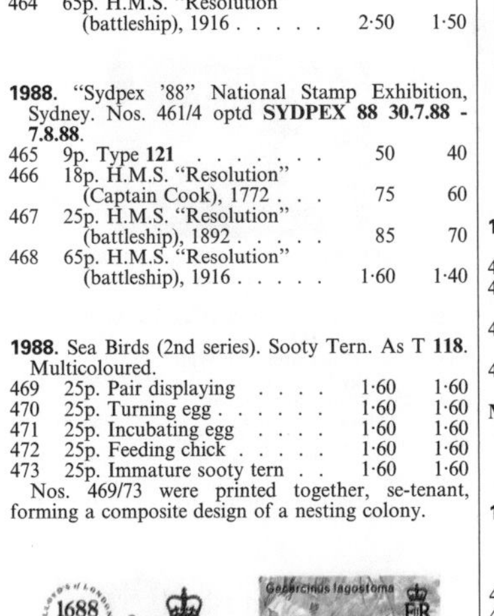

121 H.M.S. "Resolution" (ship of the line), 1667

1988. Bicentenary of Australian Settlement. Ships of the Royal Navy. Multicoloured.
461 9p. Type **121** . . . . 1·00 45
462 18p. H.M.S. "Resolution" (Captain Cook), 1772 . . . 1·50 70
463 25p. H.M.S. "Resolution" (battleship), 1892 . . . . . 1·50 85
464 65p. H.M.S. "Resolution" (battleship), 1916 . . . . . 2·50 1·50

1988. "Sydpex '88" National Stamp Exhibition, Sydney. Nos. 461/4 optd **SYDPEX 88 30.7.88 - 7.8.88.**
465 9p. Type **121** 50 40
466 18p. H.M.S. "Resolution" (Captain Cook), 1772 . . . 75 60
467 25p. H.M.S. "Resolution" (battleship), 1892 . . . . . 85 70
468 65p. H.M.S. "Resolution" (battleship), 1916 . . . . . 1·60 1·40

1988. Sea Birds (2nd series). Sooty Tern. As T **118**. Multicoloured.
469 25p. Pair displaying . . . . 1·60 1·60
470 25p. Turning egg . . . . . . 1·60 1·60
471 25p. Incubating egg . . . . 1·60 1·60
472 25p. Feeding chick . . . . 1·60 1·60
473 25p. Immature sooty tern . . 1·60 1·60
Nos. 469/73 were printed together, se-tenant, forming a composite design of a nesting colony.

123 Lloyd's Coffee House, London, 1688

124 Two Land Crabs

1988. 300th Anniv of Lloyd's of London. Mult.
474 8p. Type **123** 25 35
475 18p. "Alert IV" (cable ship) (horiz) 65 70
476 25p. Satellite recovery in space (horiz) 80 90
477 65p. "Good Hope Castle" (cargo liner) on fire off Ascension, 1973 . . . . . 1·75 2·00

1988. 19th-century Uniforms (2nd series). Royal Marines 1821–34. As T **116**. Multicoloured.
478 25p. Marines landing on Ascension, 1821 . . . . . 1·10 1·60
479 25p. Officer and Marine at semaphore station, 1829 . . 1·10 1·60
480 25p. Sergeant and Marine at Octagonal Tank, 1831 . . 1·10 1·60
481 25p. Officers at water pipe tunnel, 1833 . . . . . . 1·10 1·60
482 25p. Officer supervising construction of barracks, 1834 . . . . 1·10 1·60

1989. Insects (3rd series). As T **117**. Mult.
483 15p. "Trichoptilus wahlbergi" (moth) 75 50
484 18p. "Lucilia sericata" (fly) 80 55
485 25p. "Alceis ornatus" (weevil) 1·10 70
486 £1 "Polistes fuscatus" (wasp) 3·00 2·40

1989. Ascension Land Crabs. Multicoloured.
487 15p. Type **124** 40 45
488 18p. Crab with claws raised 45 50
489 25p. Crab on rock 60 70
490 £1 Crab in surf . . . . . . 2·25 2·50
MS491 98 × 101 mm. Nos. 487/90 3·50 3·75

125 1949 75th Anniversary of U.P.U. 1s. Stamp

1989. "Philexfrance '89" International Stamp Exhibition, Paris, and "World Stamp Expo '89", Washington (1st issue). Sheet 104 × 86 mm.
MS492 75p. multicoloured . . . 1·50 1·75
See also Nos. 498/503.

126 "Apollo 7" Tracking Station, Ascension

127 "Queen Elizabeth 2" (liner) and U.S.S. "John F. Kennedy" (aircraft carrier) in New York Harbour

1989. 20th Anniv of First Manned Landing on Moon. Multicoloured.
493 15p. Type **126** 65 45
494 18p. Launch of "Apollo 7" (30 × 30 mm) 70 50
495 25p. "Apollo 7" emblem (30 × 30 mm) 90 70
496 70p. "Apollo 7" jettisoning expended Saturn rocket . . 1·75 1·75
MS497 101 × 83 mm. £1 Diagram of "Apollo 11" mission . . . . . 2·00 2·10

1989. "Philexfrance 89" International Stamp Exhibition, Paris, and "World Stamp Expo '89", Washington (2nd issue). Designs showing Statue of Liberty and Centenary celebrations. Multicoloured.
498 15p. Type **127** 50 50
499 15p. Cleaning statue 50 50
500 15p. Statue of Liberty . . . 50 50
501 15p. Crown of statue . . . 50 50
502 15p. Warships and New York skyline 50 50
503 15p. "Jean de Vienne" (French destroyer) and skyscrapers 50 50

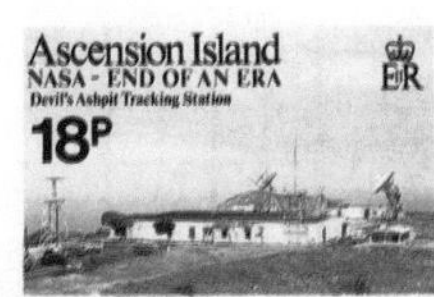

128 Devil's Ashpit Tracking Station

1989. Closure of Devil's Ashpit Tracking Station, Ascension. Multicoloured.
504 18p. Type **128** 80 50
505 25p. Launch of shuttle "Atlantis" 80 55

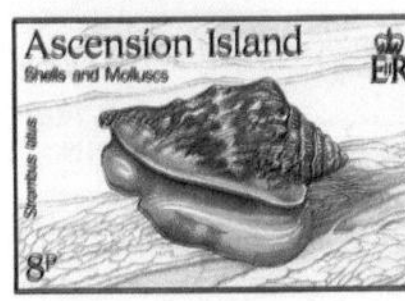

129 Bubonian Conch

1989. Sea Shells. Multicoloured.
506 8p. Type **129** 40 30
507 18p. Giant tun 70 50
508 25p. Doris loup 90 65
509 £1 Atlantic trumpet triton . . 2·75 2·50

130 Donkeys

131 Seaman's Pistol, Hat and Cutlass

1989. Ascension Wildlife. Multicoloured.
510 18p. Type **130** 75 75
511 25p. Green turtle 75 85

1990. Royal Navy Equipment, 1815–20. Mult.
512 25p. Type **131** 70 70
513 25p. Midshipman's belt plate, button, sword and hat . . 70 70
514 25p. Surgeon's hat, sword and instrument chest . . . 70 70
515 25p. Captain's hat, telescope and sword 70 70
516 25p. Admiral's epaulette, megaphone, hat and pocket 70 70
See also Nos. 541/5.

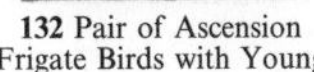

132 Pair of Ascension Frigate Birds with Young

134 "Queen Elizabeth, 1940" (Sir Gerald Kelly)

133 Penny Black and Twopence Blue

1990. Endangered Species. Ascension Frigate Bird. Multicoloured.
517 9p. Type **132** . . . . 1·50 1·00
518 10p. Fledgeling . . . . . . 1·50 1·00
519 11p. Adult male in flight . . 1·50 1·00
520 15p. Female and immature birds in flight . . . . . . 1·75 1·25

1990. "Stamp World London 90" International Stamp Exhibition. Multicoloured.
521 9p. Type **133** 50 40
522 18p. Ascension postmarks used on G.B. stamps . . . 70 60
523 25p. Unloading mail at Wideawake Airfield 95 85
524 £1 Mail van and Main Post Office . . . . 2·25 2·75

1990. 90th Birthday of Queen Elizabeth the Queen Mother.
525 **134** 25p. multicoloured . . . 75 75
526 – £1 black and lilac . . . . 2·25 2·25
DESIGN—29 × 37mm: £1 King George VI and Queen Elizabeth with Bren-gun carrier.

136 "Madonna and Child" (sculpture, Dino Felici)

137 "Garth Castle" (mail steamer), 1910

1990. Christmas. Works of Art. Multicoloured.
527 8p. Type **136** 70 70
528 18p. "Madonna and Child" (anon) . . . . 1·25 1·25
529 25p. "Madonna and Child with St. John" (Johann Gebhard) . . . . 1·75 1·75
530 65p. "Madonna and Child" (Giacomo Gritti) . . . . . 3·00 4·00

1990. Maiden Voyage of "St. Helena II". Mult.
531 9p. Type **137** 90 90
532 18p. "St. Helena I" during Falkland Islands campaign, 1982 . . . . 1·25 1·25
533 25p. Launch of "St. Helena II" . . . . 1·75 1·75
534 70p. Duke of York launching "St. Helena II" . . . . . 3·00 4·25
MS535 100 × 100 mm. £1 "St. Helena II" and outline map of Ascension . . . . 3·50 5·00

1991. 175th Anniv of Occupation. Nos. 418, 420 and 422 optd **BRITISH FOR 175 YEARS**.
536 25p. H.M.S. "Saracen" (1840) . . . . 2·00 2·50
537 50p. H.M.S. "Sealark" (1849) 2·50 3·25
538 £1 H.M.S. "Penelope" (1889) 3·75 4·75

139 Queen Elizabeth II at Trooping the Colour

1991. 65th Birthday of Queen Elizabeth II and 70th Birthday of Prince Philip. Multicoloured.
539 25p. Type **139** . . . . 1·25 1·60
540 25p. Prince Philip in naval uniform . . . . 1·25 1·60

1991. Royal Marines Equipment, 1821–1844. As T **131**. Multicoloured.
541 25p. Officer's shako, epaulettes, belt plate and button . . . . 1·10 1·60
542 25p. Officer's cap, sword, epaulettes and belt plate . . 1·10 1·60
543 25p. Drum major's shako and staff . . . . 1·10 1·60
544 25p. Sergeant's shako, chevrons, belt plate and canteen . . . . 1·10 1·60
545 25p. Drummer's shako and side-drum . . . . 1·10 1·60

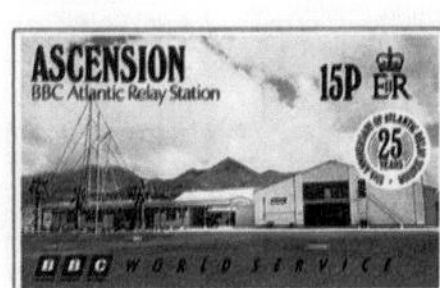

140 B.B.C. World Service Relay Station

1991. 25th Anniv of B.B.C. Atlantic Relay Station. Multicoloured.
546 15p. Type **140** . . . . 90 1·10
547 18p. Transmitters at English Bay . . . . 1·00 1·25
548 25p. Satellite receiving station (vert) . . . . 1·25 1·40
549 70p. Antenna support tower (vert) . . . . 2·50 4·00

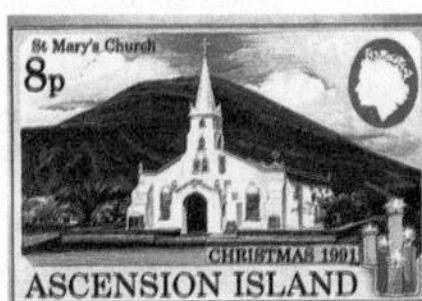

141 St. Mary's Church

1991. Christmas. Ascension Churches. Mult.
550 8p. Type **141** 55 55
551 18p. Interior of St. Mary's Church . . . . 1·00 1·00
552 25p. Our Lady of Ascension Grotto . . . . 1·25 1·25
553 65p. Interior of Our Lady of Ascension Grotto . . . . 2·75 5·00

142 Black Durgon ("Blackfish")

1991. Fishes. Multicoloured.
554 1p. Type **142** 85 60
555 2p. Sergeant major ("Five finger") . . . . 1·00 60
556 4p. Resplendent angelfish . . 1·25 70
557 5p. Derbio ("Silver fish") . . 1·25 70
558 9p. Spotted scorpionfish ("Gurnard") . . . . 1·50 80
559 10p. St. Helena parrotfish ("Blue dad") . . . . . . 1·50 80
560 15p. St. Helena butterflyfish ("Cunning fish") . . . . . 1·75 1·00
561 18p. Rock hind ("Grouper") 1·75 1·00
562 20p. Spotted moray . . . . 1·75 1·25
563 25p. Squirrelfish ("Hardback soldierfish") . . . . 1·75 1·25
564 30p. Blue marlin . . . . . . 1·75 1·40
565 50p. Wahoo . . . . 2·25 2·00
566 70p. Yellow-finned tuna . . . 2·25 2·75

567 £1 Blue shark 2·75 3·50
568 £2.50 Bottlenose dolphin 6·50 7·00

143 Holland's Crater

1992. 40th Anniv of Queen Elizabeth II's Accession. Multicoloured.
569 9p. Type **143** 30 30
570 15p. Green Mountain 50 50
571 18p. Boatswain Bird Island 60 60
572 25p. Three portraits of Queen Elizabeth 80 80
573 70p. Queen Elizabeth II 2·00 2·00

The portraits shown on the 25p. are repeated from the three lower values of the set.

144 Compass Rose and "Eye of the Wind" (cadet brig)

1992. 500th Anniv of Discovery of America by Columbus and Re-enactment Voyages. Mult.
574 9p. Type **144** 1·10 70
575 18p. Map of re-enactment voyages and "Soren Larsen" (cadet brigantine) 1·60 1·00
576 25p. "Santa Maria", "Pinta" and "Nina" 2·00 1·25
577 70p. Columbus and "Santa Maria" 3·50 2·75

145 Control Tower, Wideawake Airfield

146 Hawker Siddeley Nimrod

1992. 50th Anniv of Wideawake Airfield. Multicoloured.
578 15p. Type **145** 65 65
579 18p. Nose hangar 70 70
580 25p. Site preparation by U.S. Army engineers 90 90
581 70p. Laying fuel pipeline 2·25 2·25

1992. 10th Anniv of Liberation of Falkland Islands. Aircraft. Multicoloured.
582 15p. Type **146** 1·25 1·25
583 18p. Vickers VC-10 landing at Ascension 1·25 1·25
584 25p. Westland Wessex HU Mk 5 helicopter lifting supplies 1·75 1·50
585 65p. Avro Vulcan B.2 over Ascension 3·00 4·25
MS586 116×116 mm. 15p.+3p. Type **146**; 18p.+4p. As No. 583; 25p.+5p. As No. 584; 65p.+13p. As No. 585 4·75 6·00

The premiums on No. **MS**586 were for the S.S.A.F.A.

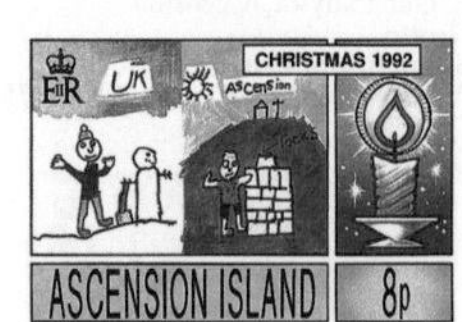

147 "Christmas in Great Britain and Ascension"

1992. Christmas. Children's Paintings. Mult.
587 8p. Type **147** 80 1·00
588 18p. "Santa Claus riding turtle" 1·25 1·50
589 25p. "Nativity" 1·50 1·75
590 65p. "Nativity with rabbit" 2·75 5·00

148 Male Canary Singing

1993. Yellow Canary. Multicoloured.
591 15p. Type **148** 75 70
592 18p. Adult male and female 85 80
593 25p. Young birds calling for food 95 95
594 70p. Adults and young birds on the wing 2·50 3·75

149 Sopwith Snipe

1993. 75th Anniv of Royal Air Force. Multicoloured.
595 20p. Type **149** 1·75 1·75
596 25p. Supermarine Southampton 1·75 1·75
597 30p. Avro Type 652 Anson 1·90 1·90
598 70p. Vickers-Armstrong Wellington 3·00 4·00
MS599 110×77 mm. 25p. Westland Lysander; 25p. Armstrong-Whitworth Meteor ("Gloster Meteor"); 25p. De Havilland D.H.106 Comet; 25p. Hawker Siddeley H.S.801 Nimrod 3·00 4·00

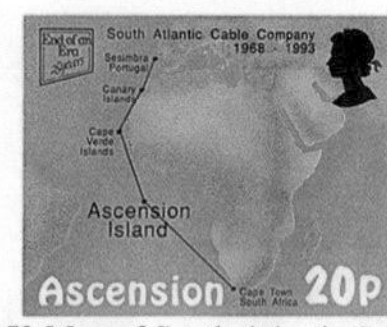

150 Map of South Atlantic Cable

1993. 25th Anniv of South Atlantic Cable Company. Multicoloured.
600 20p. Type **150** 80 80
601 25p. "Sir Eric Sharpe" laying cable 90 90
602 30p. Map of Ascension 1·00 1·00
603 70p. "Sir Eric Sharpe" (cable ship) off Ascension 2·25 2·50

151 Lanatana Camara

1993. Local Flowers. Multicoloured.
604 20p. Type **151** 1·25 80
605 25p. Moonflower 1·40 85
606 30p. Hibiscus 1·40 90
607 70p. Frangipani 2·75 2·50

152 Posting Christmas Card to Ascension

153 Ichthyosaurus

1993. Christmas. Multicoloured.
608 12p. Type **152** 45 45
609 20p. Loading mail onto R.A.F. Lockheed TriStar at Brize Norton 75 55
610 25p. TriStar over South Atlantic 85 65
611 30p. Unloading mail at Wideawake Airfield 1·10 75
612 65p. Receiving card and Georgetown Post Office 1·60 2·50
MS613 161×76 mm. Nos. 608/12 8·50 8·50

1994. Prehistoric Aquatic Reptiles. Mult.
614 12p. Type **153** 70 1·10
615 20p. Metriorhynchus 85 1·25
616 25p. Mosasaurus 90 1·40
617 30p. Elasmosaurus 90 1·50
618 65p. Plesiosaurus 1·75 2·75

1994. "Hong Kong '94" International Stamp Exhibition. Nos. 614/18 optd **HONG KONG '94** and emblem.
619 12p. Type **153** 85 1·40
620 20p. Metriorhynchus 1·10 1·50
621 25p. Mosasaurus 1·10 1·75
622 30p. Elasmosaurus 1·25 1·90
623 65p. Plesiosaurus 2·25 3·50

155 Young Green Turtles heading towards Sea

1994. Green Turtles. Multicoloured.
624 20p. Type **155** 1·75 1·75
625 25p. Turtle digging nest 1·75 1·75
626 30p. Turtle leaving sea 1·90 1·90
627 65p. Turtle swimming 3·00 4·50
MS628 116×90 mm. 30p. Turtle leaving sea (different); 30p. Turtle digging nest (different); 30p. Young turtles heading towards sea (different); 30p. Young turtle leaving nest 8·50 9·00

156 "Yorkshireman" (tug)

1994. Civilian Ships used in Liberation of Falkland Islands, 1982. Multicoloured.
629 20p. Type **156** 1·75 1·75
630 25p. "St. Helena I" (minesweeper support ship) 1·75 1·75
631 30p. "British Esk" (tanker) 1·90 1·90
632 65p. "Uganda" (hospital ship) 3·00 4·50

157 Sooty Tern Chick

1994. Sooty Tern. Multicoloured.
633 20p. Type **157** 90 1·50
634 25p. Juvenile bird 95 1·50
635 30p. Brooding adult 1·10 1·60
636 65p. Adult male performing courting display 1·75 2·75
MS637 77×58 mm. £1 Flock of sooty terns 3·50 5·50

158 Donkey Mare with Foal

159 "Leonurus japonicus"

1994. Christmas. Donkeys. Multicoloured.
638 12p. Type **158** 1·00 1·00
639 20p. Juvenile 1·40 1·40
640 25p. Foal 1·40 1·40
641 30p. Adult and cattle egrets 1·50 1·50
642 65p. Adult 2·75 3·75

1995. Flowers. Multicoloured.
643 20p. Type **159** 2·25 2·00
644 25p. "Catharanthus roseus" (horiz) 2·25 2·00
645 30p. "Mirabilis jalapa" 2·50 2·25
646 65p. "Asclepias curassavica" (horiz) 3·25 4·50

160 Two Boats and Green Mountain

1995. Late 19th-century Scenes. Each in cinnamon and brown.
647 12p. Type **160** 50 80
648 20p. Island Stewards' Store 70 90
649 25p. Navy headquarters and barracks 90 1·10
650 30p. Police office 1·75 1·75
651 65p. Pierhead 2·00 3·50

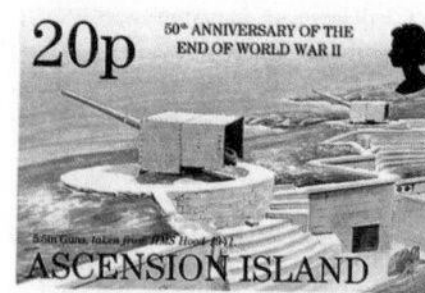

161 5.5-inch Coastal Battery

1995. 50th Anniv of End of Second World War. Multicoloured.
652 20p. Type **161** 1·00 1·75
653 25p. Fairey Swordfish aircraft 1·25 1·75
654 30p. H.M.S. "Dorsetshire" (cruiser) 1·50 2·00
655 65p. H.M.S. "Devonshire" (cruiser) 2·50 4·00
MS656 75×85 mm. £1 Reverse of 1939–45 War Medal (vert) 2·50 3·25

162 Male and Female "Lampides boeticus"

1995. Butterflies. Multicoloured.
657 20p. Type **162** 1·00 1·00
658 25p. "Vanessa cardui" 1·10 1·10
659 30p. Male "Hypolimnas misippus" 1·25 1·25
660 65p. "Danaus chrysippus" 2·25 2·75
MS661 114×85 mm. £1 "Vanessa atalanta" 3·50 3·25

No. **MS**661 includes the "Singapore '95" International Stamp Exhibition logo on the sheet margin.

163 "Santa Claus on Boat" (Phillip Stephens)

1995. Christmas. Children's Drawings. Mult.
662 12p. Type **163** 1·00 1·00
663 20p. "Santa sitting on Wall" (Kelly Lemon) 1·40 1·40
664 25p. "Santa in Chimney" (Mario Anthony) 1·50 1·50
665 30p. "Santa riding Dolphin" (Verena Benjamin) 1·50 1·50
666 65p. "Santa in Sleigh over Ascension" (Tom Butler) 2·75 3·75

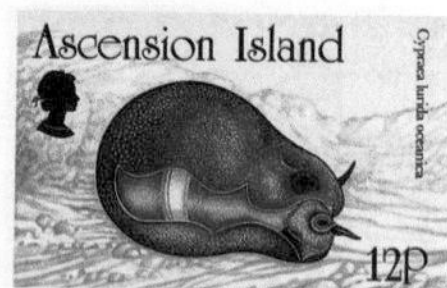

164 "Cypraea lurida oceanica"

1996. Molluscs. Multicoloured.
667 12p. Type **164** 2·00 2·25
668 25p. "Cypraea spurca sanctaehelenae" 2·25 2·50
669 30p. "Harpa doris" 2·25 2·50
670 65p. "Umbraculum umbraculum" 2·75 3·00

Nos. 667/70 were printed together, se-tenant, forming a composite design.

165 Queen Elizabeth II and St. Mary's Church

1996. 70th Birthday of Queen Elizabeth II. Mult.
671 20p. Type **165** 55 60
672 25p. The Residency 60 60
673 30p. The Roman Catholic Grotto 70 70
674 65p. The Exiles' Club 1·75 1·75

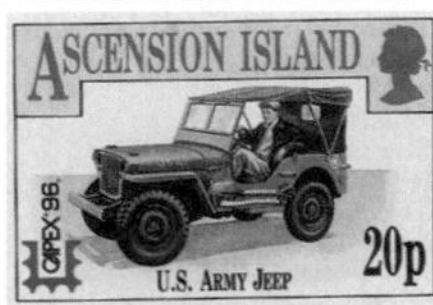

166 American Army Jeep

1996. "CAPEX '96" International Stamp Exhibition, Toronto. Island Transport. Multicoloured.

675 20p. Type **166** 75 80
676 25p. Citroen 7.5hp two-seater car, 1924 80 85
677 30p. Austin ten tourer car, 1930 90 95
678 65p. Series 1 Land Rover 1·75 2·25

167 Madeiran Storm Petrel **168** Pylons

1996. Birds and their Young. Multicoloured.

679 1p. Type **167** 50 60
680 2p. Red-billed tropic bird 50 60
681 4p. Common mynah 50 60
682 5p. House sparrow 50 60
683 7p. Common waxbill 65 65
684 10p. White tern 70 70
685 12p. Red-necked spurfowl 80 80
686 15p. Common noddy ("Brown Noddy") 90 90
687 20p. Yellow canary 1·00 1·00
688 25p. White-capped noddy ("Black Noddy") 1·00 1·00
689 30p. Red-footed booby 1·25 1·25
690 40p. White-tailed tropic bird ("Yellow-billed Tropicbird") 1·50 1·50
691 65p. Brown booby 2·00 2·25
692 £1 Blue-faced booby ("Masked Booby") 2·50 2·75
693 £2 Sooty tern 4·50 5·00
694 £3 Ascension frigate bird 6·50 7·00

See also Nos. 726/7.

1996. 30th Anniv of B.B.C. Atlantic Relay Station. Multicoloured.

695 20p. Type **168** 65 65
696 25p. Pylons (different) 70 70
697 30p. Pylons and station buildings 80 80
698 65p. Dish aerial, pylon and beach 1·75 1·75

169 Santa Claus on Dish Aerial

1996. Christmas. Santa Claus. Multicoloured.

699 12p. Type **169** 35 35
700 20p. Playing golf 65 65
701 25p. In deck chair 65 65
702 30p. On top of aircraft 75 75
703 65p. On funnel of "St. Helena II" (mail ship) 1·75 2·00

170 Date Palm **171** Red Ensign and "Maersk Ascension" (tanker)

1997. "Hong Kong '97" International Stamp Exhibition. Trees. Multicoloured.

704 20p. Type **170** 55 55
705 25p. Mauritius hemp 65 65
706 30p. Norfolk Island pine 75 75
707 65p. Dwarf palm 1·50 1·60

1997. "HONG KONG '97" International Stamp Exhibition. Sheet 130 × 90 mm containing design as No. 691. Multicoloured.

MS708 65p. Brown booby 1·50 1·50

1997. Flags. Multicoloured.

709 12p. Type **171** 60 60
710 25p. R.A.F. flag and Tristar airliner 90 90
711 30p. N.A.S.A. emblem and Space Shuttle "Atlantis" landing 1·00 1·00
712 65p. White Ensign and H.M.S. "Northumberland" (frigate) 1·75 1·75

172 "Solanum sodomaeum"

1997. Wild Herbs. Multicoloured.

713 30p. Type **172** 90 1·10
714 30p. "Ageratum conyzoides" 90 1·10
715 30p. "Leonurus sibiricus" 90 1·10
716 30p. "Cerastium vulgatum" 90 1·10
717 30p. "Commelina diffusa" 90 1·10

Nos. 713/17 were printed together, se-tenant, with the backgrounds forming a composite design.

1997. Return of Hong Kong to China. Sheet 130 × 90 mm containing design as No. 692, but with "1997" imprint date.

MS718 £1 Blue-faced booby 2·00 2·10

173 Queen Elizabeth II

1997. Golden Wedding of Queen Elizabeth and Prince Philip. Multicoloured.

719 20p. Type **173** 1·40 1·60
720 20p. Prince Philip on horseback 1·40 1·60
721 25p. Queen Elizabeth with polo pony 1·40 1·60
722 25p. Prince Philip in Montserrat 1·40 1·60
723 30p. Queen Elizabeth and Prince Philip 1·40 1·60
724 30p. Prince William and Prince Harry on horseback 1·40 1·60

MS725 110 × 70 mm. $1.50, Queen Elizabeth and Prince Philip in landau (horiz) 3·50 3·50

Nos. 719/20, 721/2 and 723/4 respectively were printed together, se-tenant, with the backgrounds forming composite designs.

1997. Birds and their Young. As Nos. 683 and 687, but smaller, size 20 × 24 mm. Multicoloured.

726 15p. Common waxbill 1·00 1·25
727 35p. Yellow canary 1·25 1·50

174 Black Marlin

1997. Gamefish. Multicoloured.

728 12p. Type **174** 40 50
729 20p. Atlantic sailfish 65 75
730 25p. Swordfish 75 80
731 30p. Wahoo 85 90
732 £1 Yellowfin tuna 2·25 2·75

175 Interior of St. Mary's Church **176** "Cactoblastis cactorum" (caterpillar and moth)

1997. Christmas. Multicoloured.

733 15p. Type **175** 45 45
734 35p. Falklands memorial window showing Virgin and child 85 85
735 40p. Falklands memorial window showing Archangel 95 1·10
736 50p. Pair of stained glass windows 1·25 1·40

1998. Biological Control using Insects. Mult.

737 15p. Type **176** 1·00 1·00
738 35p. "Teleonemia scrupulosa" (lace-bug) 1·50 1·60
739 40p. "Neltumius arizonensis" (beetle) 1·50 1·60
740 50p. "Algarobius prosopis" (beetle) 1·60 1·75

177 Diana, Princess of Wales, 1985

1998. Diana, Princess of Wales Commemoration. Sheet 145 × 70 mm, containing T **177** and similar vert designs. Multicoloured.

MS741 35p. Type **177**; 35p. Wearing yellow blouse, 1992; 35p. Wearing grey jacket, 1984; 35p. Carrying bouquets (sold at £1.40 + 20p. charity premium) 3·75 3·75

178 Fairey Fawn

1998. 80th Anniv of Royal Air Force. Mult.

742 15p. Type **178** 65 65
743 35p. Vickers Vernon 1·25 1·25
744 40p. Supermarine Spitfire F.22 1·40 1·40
745 50p. Bristol Britannia C.2 1·60 1·60

MS746 110 × 77 mm. 50p. Blackburn Kangaroo; 50p. S.E.5a; 50p. Curtiss Kittyhawk III; 50p. Boeing Fortress II 4·75 4·75

179 Barn Swallow **180** Cricket

1998. Migratory Birds. Multicoloured.

747 15p. Type **179** 60 70
748 25p. House martin 80 90
749 35p. Cattle egret 1·00 1·40
750 40p. Eurasian swift ("Swift") 1·00 1·50
751 50p. Allen's gallinule 1·10 1·75

1998. Sporting Activities. Multicoloured.

752 15p. Type **180** 1·75 1·00
753 35p. Golf 2·50 1·50
754 40p. Football 1·50 1·50
755 50p. Shooting 1·50 1·50

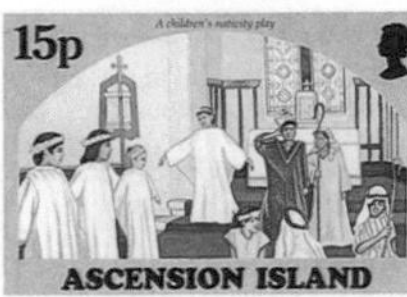

181 Children in Nativity Play

1998. Christmas. Multicoloured.

756 15p. Type **181** 75 75
757 35p. Santa Claus arriving on Ascension 1·25 1·25
758 40p. Santa Claus on carnival float 1·25 1·25
759 50p. Carol singers 1·25 1·25

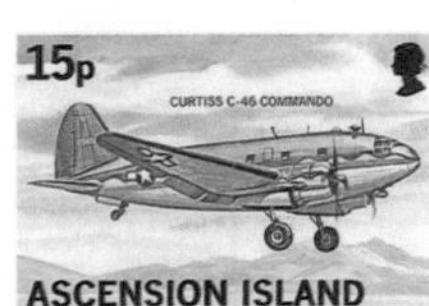

182 Curtiss C-46 Commando

1999. Aircraft. Multicoloured.

760 15p. Type **182** 85 1·10
761 35p. Douglas C-47 Dakota 1·40 1·90
762 40p. Douglas C-54 Skymaster 1·40 1·90
763 50p. Consolidated Liberator Mk. V 1·40 1·90

MS764 120 × 85 mm. $1.50, Consolidated Liberator LB-30 7·00 7·50

No. **MS**764 also commemorates the 125th birth anniv of Sir Winston Churchill.

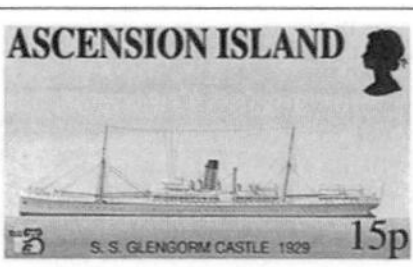

183 "Glengorm Castle" (mail ship), 1929

1999. "Australia '99" World Stamp Exhibition, Melbourne. Ships. Multicoloured.

765 15p. Type **183** 85 1·10
766 35p. "Gloucester Castle" (mail ship), 1930 1·40 1·75
767 40p. "Durham Castle" (mail ship), 1930 1·40 1·75
768 50p. "Garth Castle" (mail ship), 1930 1·40 1·75

MS769 121 × 82 mm. £1 H.M.S. "Endeavour" (Cook) 2·75 3·00

184 Pair of White Terns ("Fairy Terns")

1999. Endangered Species. White Tern ("Fairy Tern"). Multicoloured.

770 10p. Type **184** 30 45
771 10p. On branch 30 45
772 10p. Adult and fledgeling 30 45
773 10p. In flight 30 45

185 Prince Edward and Miss Sophie Rhys-Jones **186** Command and Service Modules

1999. Royal Wedding. Multicoloured.

774 50p. Type **185** 1·25 1·50
775 £1 Engagement photograph 2·25 2·75

1999. 30th Anniv of First Manned Landing on Moon. Multicoloured.

776 15p. Type **186** 75 1·10
777 35p. Moon from "Apollo 11" 1·25 1·60
778 40p. Devil's Ashpit Tracking Station and command module 1·25 1·60
779 50p. Lunar module leaving Moon 1·25 1·60

MS780 90 × 80 mm. $1.50, Earth as seen from Moon (circular, 40 mm diam) 3·75 5·00

187 King George VI, Queen Elizabeth and Prime Minister Winston Churchill, 1940

1999. "Queen Elizabeth the Queen Mother's Century". Multicoloured.

781 15p. Type **187** 75 1·00
782 35p. With Prince Charles at Coronation, 1953 1·25 1·50
783 40p. On her 88th Birthday, 1988 1·25 1·50
784 50p. With Guards' drummers, 1988 1·25 1·50

MS785 145 × 70 mm. £1.50, Lady Elizabeth Bowes-Lyon, and "Titanic" (liner) (black) 3·50 5·00

188 Babies with Toys

1999. Christmas. Multicoloured.
786 15p. Type **188** . . . . 75 1·00
787 35p. Children dressed as clowns . . . . 1·25 1·50
788 40p. Getting ready for bed 1·25 1·50
789 50p. Children dressed as pirates . . . . 1·25 1·50

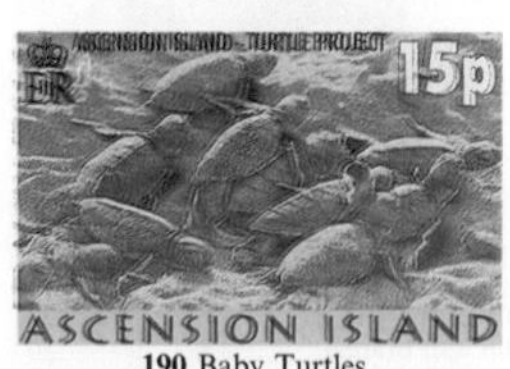

189 "Anglia" (cable ship), 1900

1999. Centenary of Cable & Wireless Communications plc on Ascension.
790 **189** 15p. black, brown and bistre . . . . 1·00 1·10
791 – 35p. black, brown and bistre . . . . 1·50 1·75
792 – 40p. multicoloured . . . 1·50 1·75
793 – 50p. black, brown and bistre . . . . 1·60 1·75
MS794 – 105 × 90 mm. £1.50, multicoloured . . . . 3·50 4·00
DESIGNS: 35p. "Cambria" (cable ship), 1910; 40p. Cable network map; 50p. "Colonia" (cable ship), 1910; £1.50, "Seine" (cable ship), 1899.

190 Baby Turtles

2000. Turtle Project on Ascension. Multicoloured.
795 15p. Type **190** . . . . 75 1·00
796 35p. Turtle on beach . . . . 1·25 1·50
797 40p. Turtle with tracking device . . . . 1·25 1·50
798 50p. Turtle heading for sea 1·40 1·50
MS799 197 × 132 mm. 25p. Head of turtle; 25p. Type **190**; 25p. Turtle on beach; 25p. Turtle entering sea (each 40 × 26 mm) . . . . . . 3·00 3·50

2000. "The Stamp Show 2000" International Stamp Exhibition, London. As No. **MS**799, but with "The Stamp Show 2000" added to the bottom right corner of the margin.
MS800 197 × 132 mm. 25p. Head of turtle; 25p. Type **190**; 25p. Turtle on beach; 25p. Turtle entering sea (each 40 × 26 mm) . . . . . . 2·75 3·25

191 Prince William as Toddler, 1983

2000. 18th Birthday of Prince William. Mult.
801 15p. Type **191** . . . . 75 1·00
802 35p. Prince William in 1994 1·25 1·50
803 40p. Skiing at Klosters, Switzerland (horiz) . . . . 1·25 1·50
804 50p. Prince William in 1997 (horiz) . . . . 1·40 1·50
MS805 175 × 95 mm. 10p. As baby with toy mouse (horiz) and Nos. 801/4 . . . . 5·00 5·50

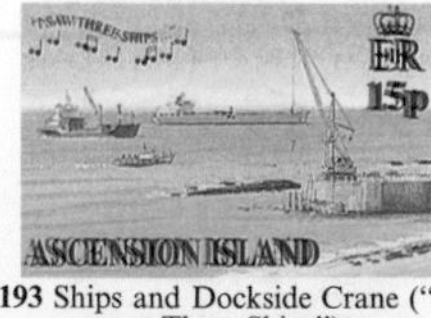

192 Royal Marine and Early Fort, 1815

2000. Forts. Multicoloured
806 15p. Type **192** . . . . 1·00 1·10
807 35p. Army officer and Fort Thornton, 1817 . . . . . 1·50 1·75
808 40p. Soldier and Fort Hayes, 1860 . . . . 1·50 1·75
809 50p. Naval lieutenant and Fort Bedford, 1940 . . . . 1·60 1·75

193 Ships and Dockside Crane ("I saw Three Ships")

2000. Christmas. Carols. Multicoloured.
810 15p. Type **193** 85 75
811 25p. Choir and musicians on beach ("Silent Night") . . 1·00 90
812 40p. Donkeys and church ("Away in a Manger") . . 1·75 1·50
813 90p. Carol singers outside church ("Hark the Herald Angels Sing") . . . . . . 2·75 3·50

194 Green Turtle

2001. "Hong Kong 2001" Stamp Exhibition. Sheet 150 × 90 mm, containing T **194**. Multicoloured.
MS814 25p. Type **194**; 40p. Loggerhead turtle . . . . . . 2·00 2·25

195 Captain William Dampier

196 Alfonso de Albuquerque

2001. Centenary of Wreck of the *Roebuck*. Mult.
815 15p. Type **195** 80 85
816 35p. Construction drawing (horiz) . . . . 1·25 1·50
817 40p. Cave dwelling at Dampier's Drip (horiz) . . 1·25 1·50
818 50p. Map of Ascension . . . 1·50 1·60

2001. 500th Anniv of the Discovery of Ascension Island. Multicoloured.
819 15p. Type **196** . . . . 1·00 1·00
820 35p. Portuguese caravel . . . 1·50 1·50
821 40p. Cantino map . . . . . 1·50 1·50
822 50p. Rear Admiral Sir George Cockburn . . . . 1·75 1·75

197 Great Britain 1d. Stamp used on Ascension, 1855

2001. Death Centenary of Queen Victoria. Mult.
823 15p. Type **197** 65 65
824 25p. Navy church parade, 1901 (horiz) 80 80
825 35p. H.M.S. *Phoebe* (cruiser) (horiz) . . . . 1·00 1·25
826 40p. The Red Lion, 1863 (horiz) . . . . 1·10 1·40
827 50p. "Queen Victoria" . . . 1·25 1·50
828 65p. Sir Joseph Hooker (botanist) . . . . 1·50 2·00
MS829 105 × 80 mm. £1.50, Queen Victoria's coffin on the steps of St. George's Chapel, Windsor (horiz) . . . . 3·50 4·50

198 Islander Hostel

2001. "BELGICA 2001" International Stamp Exhibition, Brussels. Tourism. Multicoloured.
830 35p. Type **198** . . . . 1·10 1·25
831 35p. The Residency . . . . 1·10 1·25
832 40p. The Red Lion . . . . . 1·25 1·40
833 40p. Turtle Ponds . . . . . 1·25 1·40

199 Female Ascension Frigate Bird

2001. Birdlife World Bird Festival (1st series). Ascension Frigate Birds. Multicoloured.
834 15p. Type **199** 75 75
835 35p. Fledgeling . . . . . . 1·10 1·25
836 40p. Male bird in flight (horiz) . . . . 1·10 1·25
837 50p. Male bird with pouch inflated (horiz) . . . . . . 1·25 1·40
MS838 175 × 80 mm. 10p. Male and female birds on rock (horiz) and Nos. 834/7 . . . . 4·00 4·50
See also Nos. 889/94.

200 Princess Elizabeth and Dog

2002. Golden Jubilee.
839 **200** 15p. agate, mauve and gold 85 85
840 – 35p. multicoloured . . . 1·25 1·40
841 – 40p. multicoloured . . . 1·25 1·40
842 – 50p. multicoloured . . . 1·40 1·50
MS843 – 162 × 95 mm. Nos. 839/42 and 60p. multicoloured . . . . 5·00 6·00
DESIGNS—HORIZ: 35p. Queen Elizabeth wearing tiara, 1978; 40p. Princess Elizabeth, 1946; 50p. Queen Elizabeth visiting Henley-on-Thames, 1998. VERT: (38 × 51 mm)—50p. Queen Elizabeth after Annigoni.

201 Royal Marines landing at English Bay

2002. 20th Anniv of Liberation of the Falkland Islands. Multicoloured.
844 15p. Type **201** 80 85
845 35p. Weapons testing . . . . 1·25 1·40
846 40p. H.M.S. *Hermes* (aircraft carrier) . . . . 1·25 1·40
847 50p. R.A.F. Vulcan at Wideawake Airfield . . . . 1·25 1·50

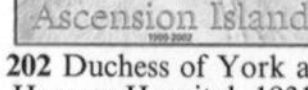

202 Duchess of York at Harrow Hospital, 1931

204 "Ecce Ancilla Dominii" (Dante Rossetti)

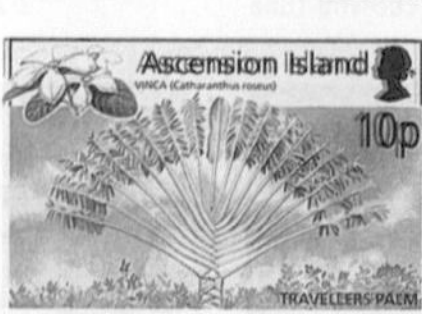

203 Travellers Palm and Vinca

2002. Queen Elizabeth the Queen Mother Commemoration.
848 **202** 35p. black, gold and purple 70 75
849 – 40p. multicoloured . . . 80 85
MS850 – 145 × 70 mm. 50p. brown and gold; £1 multicoloured . . 3·25 3·75
DESIGNS: 40p. Queen Mother on her birthday, 1997; 50p. Duchess of York, 1925; £1 Queen Mother, Scrabster, 1992.

2002. Island Views. Multicoloured.
851 10p. Type **203** 20 25
852 15p. Broken Tooth (volcanic crater) and Mexican poppy 30 35
853 20p. St. Mary's Church and Ascension lily 40 45
854 25p. Boatswain Bird Island and goatweed 50 55
855 30p. Cannon and Mauritius hemp 60 65
856 35p. The Guest House and frangipani 70 75
857 40p. Wideawake tern and Ascension spurge 80 85
858 50p. The Pier Head and lovechaste . . . . 1·00 1·10
859 65p. Sisters' Peak and yellowboy . . . . 1·25 1·40
860 90p. Two Boats School and Persian lilac . . . . 1·75 1·90
861 £2 Green turtle and wild currant . . . . 4·00 4·25
862 £5 Wideawake Airfield and coral tree . . . . 10·00 10·50

2002. Christmas. Religious Paintings. Multi.
863 15p. Type **204** 50 55
864 25p. "The Holy Family and Shepherd" (Titian) (horiz) 75 80
865 35p. "Christ carrying the Cross" (A. Bergognone) . . 95 1·00
866 75p. Sketch for "The Ascension" (Benjamin West) . . . . 2·00 2·50

205 Ariane 4 Rocket on Gantry

207 Queen Elizabeth II

206 Coronation Coach in Procession

2003. Ariane Downrange Station. Multicoloured.
867 35p. Type **205** . . . . 1·10 1·10
868 40p. Map of Ariane Downrange stations (horiz) 1·25 1·25
869 65p. Automated Transfer Vehicle (ATV) in Space (horiz) . . . . 1·90 2·00
870 90p. Launch of Ariane 5 . . 3·00 3·25
MS871 170 × 88 mm. Nos. 867/70 6·50 7·00

2003. 50th Anniv of Coronation. Multicoloured.
872 40p. Type **206** 40 45
873 £1 Newly crowned Queen with bishops and peers . . 2·00 2·10
MS874 95 × 115 mm. As Nos. 872/3 2·40 2·50
Nos. 872/3 have red frame; stamps from **MS**874 have no frame and country name in mauve panel.

2003.
875 **207** £3 black, green and myrtle . . . . 6·00 6·25

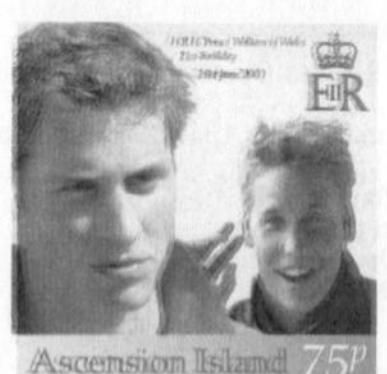

208 Prince William at Tidworth Polo Club and on Skiing Holiday, 2002

2003. 21st Birthday of Prince William of Wales. Multicoloured.
876 75p. Type **208** . . . . 1·50 1·60
877 75p. On Raleigh International Expedition, 2000 and at Queen Mother's 101st Birthday, 2001 . . . . . . 1·50 1·60

209 Bleriot XI

2003. Centenary of Powered Flight. Multicoloured.
878 15p. Type **209** 30 35
879 20p. Vickers VC-10 . . . . . 40 45
880 35p. BAe Harrier FRS Mk1 70 75
881 40p. Westland Sea King HAS Mk. 4 helicopter 80 85
882 50p. Rockwell Space Shuttle 1·00 1·25
883 90p. General Dynamics F-16 Fighting Falcon . . . . . 1·80 1·90
MS884 115 × 65 mm. £1.50 Fairey Swordfish Mk II. . . . . . . 3·00 3·25

210 Casting Vote into Ballot Box

2003. Christmas. First Anniv of Democracy on Ascension. Multicoloured.
885 15p. Type **210** 30 35
886 25p. Island Council session 50 55
887 40p. Students ("HIGHER EDUCATION") 80 85
888 £1 Government Headquarters 1·00 2·25

211 Adult with Fledgling

2004. Bird Life International (2nd series). Masked Booby. Multicoloured.
889 15p. Type **211** 30 35
890 35p. Pair (vert) 70 75
891 40p. In flight (vert) 80 85
892 50p. Adult calling . . . . . 1·00 1·00
893 90p. Masked booby . . . . 1·80 1·90
MS894 175 × 80 mm. Nos. 889/93

POSTAGE DUE STAMPS

D 1 Outline Map of Ascension

1986.
D1 D 1 1p. deep brown and brown 15 20
D2 2p. brown and orange . . 15 20
D3 5p. brown and orange . . 15 20
D4 7p. black and violet . . . 20 30
D5 10p. black and blue . . . 25 35
D6 25p. black and green . . 65 75

AUSTRALIA Pt. 1

An island continent to the S.E. of Asia. A Commonwealth consisting of the states of New S. Wales, Queensland, S. Australia, Tasmania, Victoria and W. Australia.

1913. 12 pence = 1 shilling;
20 shillings = 1 pound.
1966. 100 cents = 1 dollar.

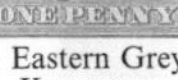
1 Eastern Grey Kangaroo

3

1913.
1 1 ½d. green . . . . 6·00 3·50
2 1d. red . . . . 8·50 1·00
35 2d. grey . . . . 27·00 6·50
36 2½d. blue . . . . 23·00 10·00
37 3d. green . . . . 28·00 4·50
6 4d. orange . . . . 50·00 22·00
8 5d. brown . . . . 40·00 32·00
38 6d. blue . . . . 55·00 7·50
73 6d. brown . . . . 24·00 1·75
133 9d. violet . . . . 28·00 1·25
40 1s. green . . . . 35·00 3·75
41 2s. brown . . . . £180 13·00
134 2s. purple . . . . 5·00 60
135 5s. grey and yellow . . . . £120 12·00
136 10s. grey and pink £250 £100
15 £1 brown and blue £1200 £1300
137 £1 grey £450 £160
138 £2 black and pink £1900 £350

1913.
20 3 ½d. green . . . . 3·75 1·00
94 ½d. orange . . . . 2·25 1·40
17 1d. red . . . . 2·50 4·50
57 1d. violet . . . . 6·00 1·50
125 1d. green . . . . 1·75 20
59a 1½d. brown . . . . 6·50 60
61 1½d. green . . . . 4·00 80
77 1½d. red . . . . 2·25 40
62 2d. orange . . . . 15·00 1·00
127 2d. red . . . . 1·75 10
98 2d. brown . . . . 8·00 9·00
128 3d. blue . . . . 18·00 1·25
22 4d. orange . . . . 27·00 2·50
64 4d. violet . . . . 13·00 15·00
65 4d. blue . . . . 48·00 8·50
129 4d. green . . . . 18·00 1·25
92 4½d. violet . . . . 18·00 3·75
130 5d. brown . . . . 15·00 20
131 1s.4d. blue . . . . 50·00 3·50

4 Laughing Kookaburra

8 Parliament House, Canberra

1913.
19 4 6d. purple . . . . 65·00 38·00

1927. Opening of Parliament House.
105 8 1½d. red 50 50

1928. National Stamp Exhibition, Melbourne.
106 4 3d. blue . . . . 4·25 5·00
MS106a 65 × 70 mm. No. 106 × 4 £110 £200

9 De Havilland Hercules and Pastoral Scene

10 Black Swan

1929. Air.
115 9 3d. green . . . . 8·00 4·00

1929. Centenary of Western Australia.
116 10 1½d. red . . . . 1·25 1·60

11 "Capt. Chas Sturt" (J. H. Crossland)

13 The "Southern Cross" above Hemispheres

1930. Centenary of Sturt's Exploration of River Murray.
117 11 1½d. red . . . . 1·00 1·00
118 3d. blue . . . . 3·25 6·50

1930. Surch in words.
119 3 2d. on 1½d. red . . . . . . 1·50 1·00
120 5d. on 4½d. violet . . . . . 6·00 9·50

1931. Kingsford Smith's Flights.
121 13 2d. red (postage) . . . . . 1·00 1·00
122 3d. blue . . . . 4·50 5·00
123 6d. purple (air) . . . . . 5·50 13·00

1931. Air. As T **13** but inscr "AIR MAIL SERVICE".
139 6d. brown . . . . 13·00 12·00

1931. Air. No. 139 optd **O S**.
139a 6d. brown . . . . 35·00 55·00

17 Superb Lyrebird

18 Sydney Harbour Bridge

1932.
140 17 1s. green . . . . 42·00 2·00

1932. Opening of Sydney Harbour Bridge.
144 18 2d. red . . . . 2·00 1·40
142 3d. blue . . . . 4·50 7·00
143 5s. green £375 £180

19 Laughing Kookaburra

20 Melbourne and River Yarra

1932.
146 19 6d. red . . . . 25·00 55

1934. Centenary of Victoria.
147 20 2d. red . . . . 2·50 1·75
148 3d. blue . . . . 4·00 5·50
149 1s. black . . . . 50·00 20·00

21 Merino Ram

22 Hermes

1934. Death Centenary of Capt. John Macarthur (founder of Australian sheep-farming).
150 21 2d. red . . . . 4·50 1·50
151 3d. blue . . . . 10·00 12·00
152 9d. purple . . . . 27·00 45·00

1934.
153b 22 1s.6d. purple . . . . . . 2·00 1·40

23 Cenotaph, Whitehall

24 King George V on "Anzac"

1935. 20th. Anniv of Gallipoli Landing.
154 23 2d. red . . . . 1·50 30
155 1s. black . . . . 42·00 38·00

1935. Silver Jubilee.
156 24 2d. red . . . . 1·50 30
157 3d. blue . . . . 5·00 8·00
158 2s. violet . . . . 27·00 42·00

25 Amphitrite and Telephone Cable

26 Site of Adelaide, 1836; Old Gum Tree, Glenelg; King William Street, Adelaide

1936. Opening of Submarine Telephone Cable to Tasmania.
159 25 2d. red 75 50
160 3d. blue . . . . 2·75 2·75

1936. Centenary of South Australia.
161 26 2d. red . . . . 1·25 40
162 3d. blue . . . . 4·00 3·50
163 1s. green . . . . 10·00 8·50

27 Wallaroo

28 Queen Elizabeth

29 King George VI

30 King George VI

31 King George VI

33 Merino Ram

38 Queen Elizabeth

40 King George VI and Queen Elizabeth

1937.
228 27 ¼d. orange 20 10
165 28 1d. green 70 40
180 – 1d. green . . . . 3·00 30
181 – 1d. purple . . . . 1·50 30
182 29 1½d. purple . . . . 4·75 8·50
183 1½d. green . . . . 1·00 1·50
167 30 2d. red 60 20
184 – 2d. red . . . . 3·00 10
185 30 2d. purple . . . . 50 1·50
186 31 3d. blue . . . . 45·00 3·25
187 3d. brown 40 10
188 – 4d. green . . . . 1·00 10

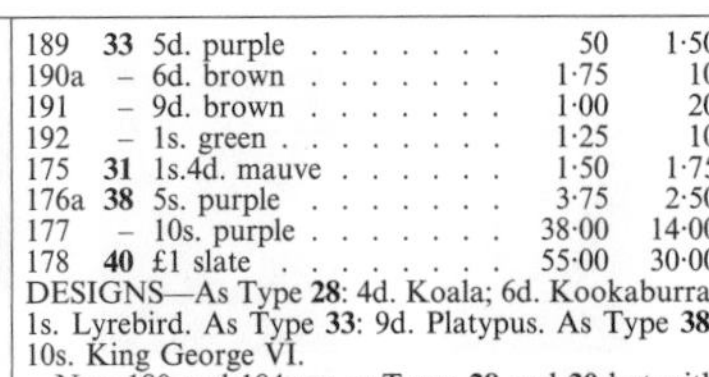
189 33 5d. purple . . . . 50 1·50
190a – 6d. brown . . . . 1·75 10
191 – 9d. brown . . . . 1·00 20
192 – 1s. green . . . . 1·25 10
175 31 1s.4d. mauve . . . . . . 1·50 1·75
176a 38 5s. purple . . . . 3·75 2·50
177 – 10s. purple . . . . 38·00 14·00
178 40 £1 slate . . . . 55·00 30·00
DESIGNS—As Type **28**: 4d. Koala; 6d. Kookaburra; 1s. Lyrebird. As Type **33**: 9d. Platypus. As Type **38**: 10s. King George VI.
Nos. 180 and 184 are as Types **28** and **30** but with completely shaded background.

41 Governor Phillip at Sydney Cove (J. Alcott)

42 A.I.F. and Nurse

1937. 150th Anniv of New South Wales.
193 41 2d. red . . . . 2·25 30
194 3d. blue . . . . 6·00 2·25
195 9d. purple . . . . 16·00 10·00

1940. Australian Imperial Forces.
196 42 1d. green . . . . 1·75 2·25
197 2d. red . . . . 1·75 1·00
198 3d. blue . . . . 12·00 9·00
199 6d. purple . . . . 22·00 16·00

1941. Surch with figures and bars.
200 30 2½d. on 2d. red 75 90
201 31 3½d. on 3d. blue . . . . . 1·00 2·00
202 33 5½d. on 5d. purple . . . . 4·00 5·00

46a Queen Elizabeth

47 King George VI

48 King George VI

49 King George VI

50 Emu

1942.
203 46a 1d. purple . . . . 1·25 10
204 1½d. green . . . . 1·25 10
205 47 2d. purple . . . . 65 1·25
206 48 2½d. red 40 10
207 49 3½d. blue 70 50
208 50 5½d. grey . . . . 1·25 10

52 Duke and Duchess of Gloucester

53 Star and Wreath

1945. Royal Visit.
209 52 2½d. red 10 10
210 3½d. blue 15 80
211 5½d. grey 20 80

1946. Victory. Inscr "PEACE 1945".
213 53 2½d. red 10 10
214 – 3½d. blue . . . . 30 1·00
215 – 5½d. green 35 65
DESIGNS—HORIZ: 3½d. Flag and dove. VERT: 5½d. Angel.

56 Sir Thomas Mitchell and Queensland

1946. Centenary of Mitchell's Central Queensland Exploration.
216 56 2½d. red 10 10
217 3½d. blue . . . . 40 1·25
218 1s. green 40 50

57 Lt. John Shortland, R.N. 58 Steel Foundry

1947. 150th Anniv of City of Newcastle.

No.	Type	Description	Unused	Used
219	**57**	2½d. lake	10	10
220	**58**	3½d. blue	40	1·00
221	–	5½d. green	40	55

DESIGNS—As Type **58**: HORIZ: 5½d. Coal carrier cranes.

60 Queen Elizabeth II when Princess

1947. Wedding of Princess Elizabeth.

No.	Type	Description	Unused	Used
222a	**60**	1d. purple	10	10

61 Hereford Bull **61a** Hermes and Globe

62 Aboriginal Art **62a** Commonwealth Coat of Arms

1948.

No.	Type	Description	Unused	Used
223	**61**	1s.3d. brown	1·75	1·10
223a	**61a**	1s.6d. brown	70	10
224	**62**	2s. brown	2·00	10
224a	**62a**	5s. red	2·75	10
224b		10s. purple	14·00	70
224c		£1 blue	30·00	3·50
224d		£2 green	80·00	14·00

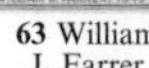

63 William J. Farrer **64** Ferdinand von Mueller

1948. W. J. Farrer (wheat research) Commem.

No.	Type	Description	Unused	Used
225	**63**	2½d. red	20	10

1948. Sir Ferdinand von Mueller (botanist) Commemoration.

No.	Type	Description	Unused	Used
226	**64**	2½d. red	20	10

65 Boy Scout **66** "Henry Lawson" (Sir Lionel Lindsay)

1948. Pan-Pacific Scout Jamboree, Wonga Park.

No.	Type	Description	Unused	Used
227	**65**	2½d. lake	20	10

For 3½d. value dates "1952–53", see No. 254.

1949. Henry Lawson (poet) Commemoration.

No.	Type	Description	Unused	Used
231	**66**	2½d. purple	20	10

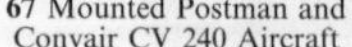

67 Mounted Postman and Convair CV 240 Aircraft **68** John, Lord Forrest of Bunbury

1949. 75th Anniv of U.P.U.

No.	Type	Description	Unused	Used
232	**67**	3½d. blue	30	60

1949. John, Lord Forrest (explorer and politician) Commemoration.

No.	Type	Description	Unused	Used
233	**68**	2½d. red	20	10

69 Queen Elizabeth **70** King George VI

81 King George VI **80** King George VI

71 Aborigine **82** King George VI

1950.

No.	Type	Description	Unused	Used
236	**69**	1½d. green	40	40
237		2d. green	15	10
234	**70**	2½d. red	10	10
237c		2½d. brown	15	35
235		3d. red	15	25
237d		3d. green	15	10
247	**81**	3½d. purple	10	10
248		4½d. red	15	1·25
249		6½d. brown	15	70
250		6½d. green	10	25
251	**80**	7½d. blue	15	80
238	**71**	8½d. brown	15	60
252	**82**	1s.0½d. blue	60	60
253	**71**	2s.6d. brown (21 × 25½ mm)	1·50	70

72 Reproduction of First Stamp of N.S.W. **73** Reproduction of First Stamp of Victoria

1950. Centenary of Australian States Stamps.

No.	Type	Description	Unused	Used
239	**72**	2½d. purple	25	10
240	**73**	2½d. purple	25	10

75 Sir Henry Parkes **77** Federal Parliament House, Canberra

1951. 50th Anniv of Commonwealth. Inscr as in T **75** and **77**.

No.	Type	Description	Unused	Used
241	**75**	3d. lake	40	10
242	–	3d. lake	40	10
243	–	5½d. blue	20	2·25
244	**77**	1s.6d. brown	35	50

DESIGNS—As Type **70**: No. 242, Sir Edmund Barton. As Type **77**: No. 243, Opening first Federal Parliament.

78 E. H. Hargraves **79** C. J. Latrobe

1951. Centenaries. Discovery of Gold in Australia and of Responsible Government in Victoria.

No.	Type	Description	Unused	Used
245	**78**	3d. purple	30	10
246	**79**	3d. purple	30	10

1952. Pan-Pacific Scout Jamboree, Greystanes. As T **65** but dated "1952–53".

No.	Type	Description	Unused	Used
254	**65**	3½d. lake	20	10

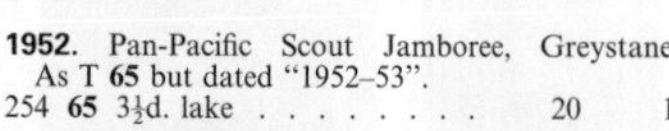

83 Butter **86** Queen Elizabeth II

1953. Food Production. Inscr "PRODUCE FOOD!".

No.	Type	Description	Unused	Used
255	**83**	3d. green	30	10
256	–	3d. green (Wheat)	30	10
257	–	3d. green (Beef)	30	10
258	**83**	3½d. red	30	10
259	–	3½d. red (Wheat)	30	10
260	–	3½d. red (Beef)	30	10

1953.

No.	Type	Description	Unused	Used
261	**86**	1d. purple	15	15
261a		2½d. blue	20	15
262		3d. green	20	10
263		3½d. red	20	10
263a		6½d. orange	2·00	50

87 Queen Elizabeth II

1953. Coronation.

No.	Type	Description	Unused	Used
264	**87**	3½d. red	40	10
265		7½d. violet	75	1·25
266		2s. turquoise	2·50	1·25

88 Young Farmers and Calf

1953. 25th Anniv of Australian Young Farmers' Clubs.

No.	Type	Description	Unused	Used
267	**88**	3½d. brown and green	10	10

89 Lt.-Gov. D. Collins **90** Lt.-Gov. W. Paterson

91 Sullivan Cove, Hobart, 1804 **92** Stamp of 1853

1953. 150th Anniv of Settlement in Tasmania.

No.	Type	Description	Unused	Used
268	**89**	3½d. purple	30	10
269	**90**	3½d. purple	30	10
270	**91**	2s. green	1·25	2·75

1953. 1st Centenary of Tasmania Postage Stamps.

No.	Type	Description	Unused	Used
271	**92**	3d. red	10	40

93 Queen Elizabeth II and Duke of Edinburgh

94 Queen Elizabeth II **95** "Telegraphic Communications"

1954. Royal Visit.

No.	Type	Description	Unused	Used
272	**93**	3½d. red	20	10
273	**94**	7½d. purple	30	1·25
274	**93**	2s. green	60	65

1954. Centenary of Telegraph.

No.	Type	Description	Unused	Used
275	**95**	3½d. brown	10	10

96 Red Cross and Globe **97** Mute Swan

1954. 40th Anniv of Australian Red Cross Society.

No.	Type	Description	Unused	Used
276	**96**	3½d. blue and red	10	10

1954. Centenary of Western Australian Stamps.

No.	Type	Description	Unused	Used
277	**97**	3½d. black	20	10

98 Locomotives of 1854 and 1954

1954. Centenary of Australian Railways.

No.	Type	Description	Unused	Used
278	**98**	3½d. purple	30	10

99 Territory Badge **100** Olympic Games Symbol

1954. Australian Antarctic Research.

No.	Type	Description	Unused	Used
279	**99**	3½d. black	15	10

1954. Olympic Games Propaganda.

No.	Type	Description	Unused	Used
280	**100**	2s. blue	70	1·00
280a		2s. green	1·75	2·00

101 Rotary Symbol, Globe and Flags **103** American Memorial, Canberra

1955. 50th Anniv of Rotary International.

No.	Type	Description	Unused	Used
281	**101**	3½d. red	10	10

1955. Australian–American Friendship.

No.	Type	Description	Unused	Used
283	**103**	3½d. blue	10	10

101a Queen Elizabeth II **102** Queen Elizabeth II

1955.

No.	Type	Description	Unused	Used
282a	**101a**	4d. lake	20	10
282b		7½d. violet	60	1·40
282c		10d. blue	60	85
282	**102**	1s.0½d. blue	1·50	1·00
282d		1s.7d. brown	1·50	35

104 Cobb & Co. Coach (from etching by Sir Lionel Lindsay)

1955. Mail-coach Pioneers Commemoration.

No.	Type	Description	Unused	Used
284	**104**	3½d. sepia	25	10
285		2s. brown	50	1·40

105 Y.M.C.A. Emblem and Map of the World

1955. World Centenary of Y.M.C.A.

No.	Type	Description	Unused	Used
286	**105**	3½d. green and red	10	10

106 Florence Nightingale and Young Nurse **107** Queen Victoria

1955. Nursing Profession Commemoration.
287 **106** 3½d. lilac 10 10

1955. Centenary of South Australian Postage Stamps.
288 **107** 3½d. green 10 10

108 Badges of N.S.W., Victoria and Tasmania

1956. Centenary of Responsible Government in N.S.W., Victoria and Tasmania.
289 **108** 3½d. lake 10 10

109 Arms of Melbourne

110 Olympic Torch and Symbol

111 Collins Street, Melbourne

1956. Olympic Games, Melbourne.
290 **109** 4d. red 25 10
291 **110** 7½d. blue . . . . 50 1·40
292 **111** 1s. multicoloured 60 30
293 – 2s. multicoloured . . . . 85 1·40
DESIGN—As Type **111**: 2s. Melbourne across River Yarra.

115 South Australia Coat of Arms

116 Map of Australia and Caduceus

1957. Centenary of Responsible Government in South Australia.
296 **115** 4d. brown 10 10

1957. Royal Flying Doctor Service of Australia.
297 **116** 7d. blue 15 10

117 "The Spirit of Christmas" (after Sir Joshua Reynolds)

1957. Christmas.
298 **117** 3½d. red 10 20
299 4d. purple 10 10

118 Lockheed Super Constellation Airliner

1958. Inaug of Australian "Round-the-World" Air Service.
301 **118** 2s. blue . . . . 75 1·00

119 Hall of Memory, Sailor and Airman

1958.
302 **119** 5½d. lake 40 30
303 – 5½d. lake 40 30
No. 303 shows a soldier and servicewoman instead of the sailor and airman.

120 Sir Charles Kingsford Smith and the "Southern Cross"

122 The Nativity

121 Silver Mine, Broken Hill

1958. 30th Anniv of 1st Air Crossing of the Tasman Sea.
304 **120** 8d. blue . . . . 60 1·00

1958. 75th Anniv of Founding of Broken Hill.
305 **121** 4d. brown 30 10

1958. Christmas Issue.
306 **122** 3½d. red 20 20
307 4d. violet 20 10

124 Queen Elizabeth II

126 Queen Elizabeth II

127 Queen Elizabeth II

128 Queen Elizabeth II

129 Queen Elizabeth II

1959.
308 – 1d. purple 10 10
309 **124** 2d. brown 50 20
311 **126** 3d. turquoise 15 10
312 **127** 3½d. green 15 15
313 **128** 4d. red . . . . 1·75 10
314 **129** 5d. blue . . . . 1·00 10
No. 308 shows a head and shoulders portrait as in Type **128** and is vert.

131 Numbat

137 Christmas Bells

142 Aboriginal Stockman

1959.
316 **131** 6d. brown . . . . 2·00 10
317 – 8d. red 75 10
318 – 9d. sepia . . . . 1·75 55
319 – 11d. blue . . . . 1·25 15
320 – 1s. green . . . . 3·00 40
321 – 1s.2d. purple . . . . . 1·25 15
322 **137** 1s.6d. red on yellow . . 2·00 90
323 – 2s. blue 70 10
324 – 2s.3d. green on yellow . . 1·00 10
324a – 2s.3d. green . . . . . . 4·00 1·50
325 – 2s.5d. brown on yellow . . 5·00 75
326 – 3s. red . . . . 1·00 20
327 **142** 5s. brown . . . . 22·00 1·25
DESIGNS—As Type **131**: VERT: 8d. Tiger Cat; 9d. Eastern grey kangaroo; 11d. Common rabbit bandicoot; 1s. Platypus. HORIZ: 1s.2d. Thylacine. As Type **137**: 2s. Flannel flower; 2s.3d. Wattle; 2s.5d. Banksia (plant); 3s. Waratah.

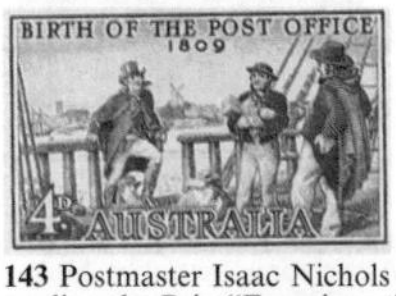

143 Postmaster Isaac Nichols boarding the Brig "Experiment"

1959. 150th Anniv of Australian P.O.
331 **143** 4d. slate 15 10

144 Parliament House, Brisbane, and Arms of Queensland

145 "The Approach of the Magi"

1959. Centenary of Queensland Self-Government.
332 **144** 4d. lilac and green 10 10

1959. Christmas.
333 **145** 5d. violet 10 10

146 Girl Guide and Lord Baden-Powell

147 "The Overlanders" (after Sir Daryl Lindsay)

1960. 50th Anniv of Girl Guide Movement.
334 **146** 5d. blue 30 15

1960. Centenary of Northern Territory Exploration.
335 **147** 5d. mauve 30 15

148 "Archer" and Melbourne Cup

149 Queen Victoria

1960. 100th Melbourne Cup Race Commemoration.
336 **148** 5d. sepia 20 10

1960. Centenary of Queensland Stamps.
337 **149** 5d. green 25 10

150 Open Bible and Candle

151 Colombo Plan Bureau Emblem

1960. Christmas Issue.
338 **150** 5d. lake 10 10

1961. Colombo Plan.
339 **151** 1s. brown 10 10

152 Melba (after bust by Sir Bertram Mackennal)

153 Open Prayer Book and Text

1961. Birth Centenary of Dame Nellie Melba (singer).
340 **152** 5d. blue 30 15

1961. Christmas Issue.
341 **153** 5d. brown 10 10

154 J. M. Stuart

155 Flynn's Grave and Nursing Sister

1962. Centenary of Stuart's South to North Crossing of Australia.
342 **154** 5d. red 15 10

1962. 50th Anniv of Australian Inland Mission.
343 **155** 5d. multicoloured 30 15

156 "Woman"

157 "Madonna and Child"

1962. "Associated Country Women of the World" Conference, Melbourne.
344 **156** 5d. green 10 10

1962. Christmas.
345 **157** 5d. violet 15 10

158 Perth and Kangaroo Paw (plant)

160 Queen Elizabeth II

1962. British Empire and Commonwealth Games, Perth. Multicoloured.
346 5d. Type **158** 40 10
347 2s.3d. Arms of Perth and running track . . . . . . 1·50 2·75

1963. Royal Visit.
348 **160** 5d. green 35 10
349 – 2s.3d. lake . . . . 1·50 3·00
DESIGN: 2s.3d. Queen Elizabeth II and Duke of Edinburgh.

162 Arms of Canberra and W. B. Griffin (architect)

163 Centenary Emblem

1963. 50th Anniv of Canberra.
350 **162** 5d. green 15 10

1963. Centenary of Red Cross.
351 **163** 5d. red, grey and blue . . 40 10

164 Blaxland, Lawson and Wentworth on Mount York

1963. 150th Anniv of First Crossing of Blue Mountains.
352 **164** 5d. blue 15 10

165 "Export"

1963. Export Campaign.
353 **165** 5d. red 10 10

1963. As T **160** but smaller 17½ × 21½ mm "5D" at top right replacing "ROYAL VISIT 1963" and oak leaves omitted.
354 5d. green 75 10
354c 5d. red 55 10

167 Tasman and "Heemskerk"

173 "Peace on Earth ..."

1963. Navigators.
355 **167** 4s. blue . . . . 3·00 55
356 – 5s. brown . . . . 3·25 1·75
357 – 7s.6d. olive . . . . . . 19·00 16·00
358 – 10s. purple . . . . . . 25·00 4·75
359 – £1 violet . . . . 30·00 16·00
360 – £2 sepia . . . . 55·00 75·00

DESIGNS—As Type **167**: 7s.6d. Captain Cook; 10s. Flinders and "Investigator". $20\frac{1}{2} \times 5\frac{1}{2}$ mm: 5s. Dampier and "Roebuck"; £1 Bass and "Tom Thumb" (whale boat); £2 Admiral King and "Mermaid" (survey cutter).

1963. Christmas.

361	**173**	5d. blue	10	10

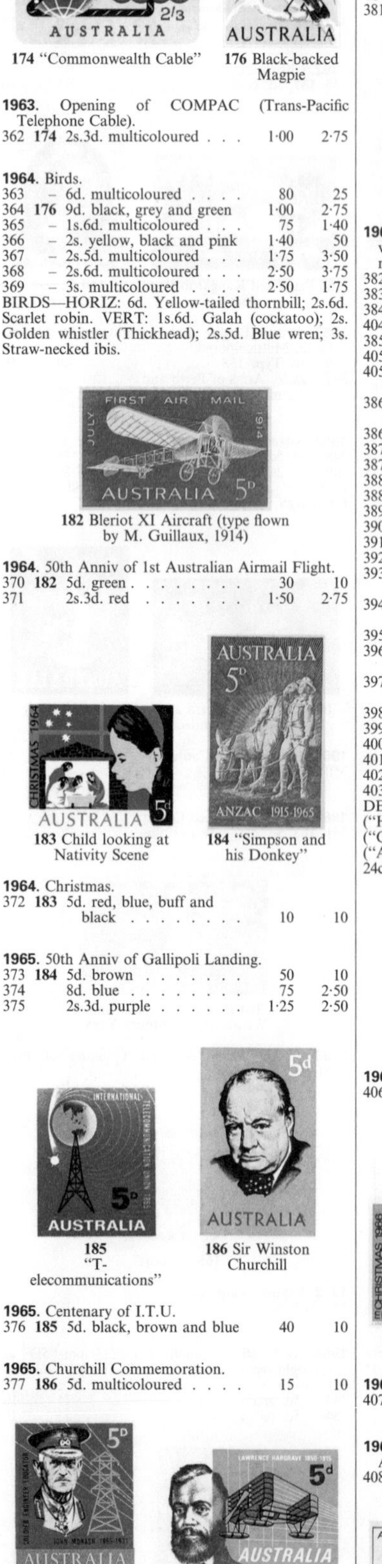

174 "Commonwealth Cable" **176** Black-backed Magpie

1963. Opening of COMPAC (Trans-Pacific Telephone Cable).

362	**174**	2s.3d. multicoloured	1·00	2·75

1964. Birds.

363	–	6d. multicoloured	80	25
364	**176**	9d. black, grey and green	1·00	2·75
365	–	1s.6d. multicoloured	75	1·40
366	–	2s. yellow, black and pink	1·40	50
367	–	2s.5d. multicoloured	1·75	3·50
368	–	2s.6d. multicoloured	2·50	3·75
369	–	3s. multicoloured	2·50	1·75

BIRDS—HORIZ: 6d. Yellow-tailed thornbill; 2s.6d. Scarlet robin. VERT: 1s.6d. Galah (cockatoo); 2s. Golden whistler (Thickhead); 2s.5d. Blue wren; 3s. Straw-necked ibis.

182 Bleriot XI Aircraft (type flown by M. Guillaux, 1914)

1964. 50th Anniv of 1st Australian Airmail Flight.

370	**182**	5d. green	30	10
371		2s.3d. red	1·50	2·75

183 Child looking at Nativity Scene **184** "Simpson and his Donkey"

1964. Christmas.

372	**183**	5d. red, blue, buff and black	10	10

1965. 50th Anniv of Gallipoli Landing.

373	**184**	5d. brown	50	10
374		8d. blue	75	2·50
375		2s.3d. purple	1·25	2·50

185 "T-elecommunications" **186** Sir Winston Churchill

1965. Centenary of I.T.U.

376	**185**	5d. black, brown and blue	40	10

1965. Churchill Commemoration.

377	**186**	5d. multicoloured	15	10

187 General Monash **188** Hargrave and "Multiplane" Seaplane (1902)

1965. Birth Centenary of General Sir John Monash (engineer and soldier).

378	**187**	5d. multicoloured	15	10

1965. 50th Death Anniv of Lawrence Hargrave (aviation pioneer).

379	**188**	5d. multicoloured	15	10

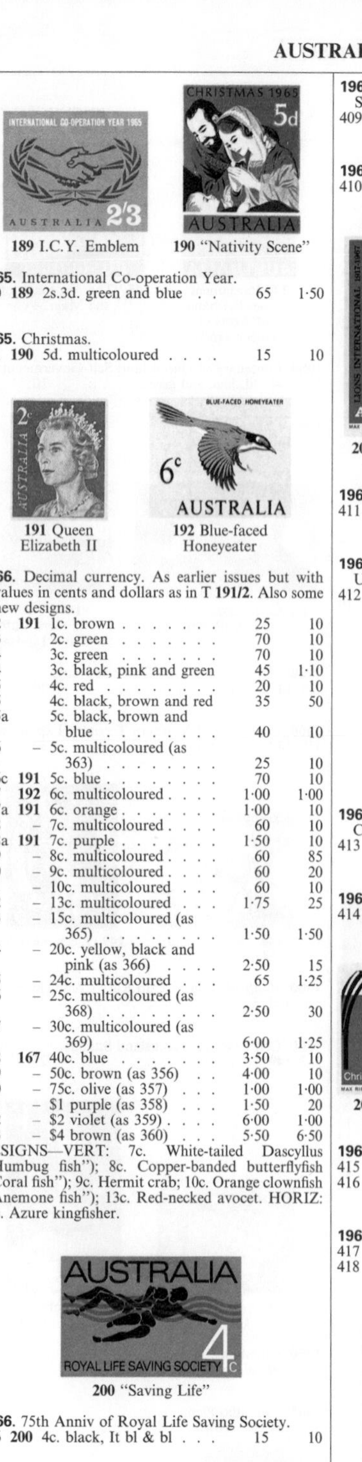

189 I.C.Y. Emblem **190** "Nativity Scene"

1965. International Co-operation Year.

380	**189**	2s.3d. green and blue	65	1·50

1965. Christmas.

381	**190**	5d. multicoloured	15	10

191 Queen Elizabeth II **192** Blue-faced Honeyeater

1966. Decimal currency. As earlier issues but with values in cents and dollars as in T **191/2**. Also some new designs.

382	**191**	1c. brown	25	10
383		2c. green	70	10
384		3c. green	70	10
404		3c. black, pink and green	45	1·10
385		4c. red	20	10
405		4c. black, brown and red	35	50
405a		5c. black, brown and blue	40	10
386	–	5c. multicoloured (as 363)	25	10
386c	**191**	5c. blue	70	10
387	**192**	6c. multicoloured	1·00	1·00
387a	**191**	6c. orange	1·00	10
388	–	7c. multicoloured	60	10
388a	**191**	7c. purple	1·50	10
389	–	8c. multicoloured	60	85
390	–	9c. multicoloured	60	20
391	–	10c. multicoloured	60	10
392	–	13c. multicoloured	1·75	25
393	–	15c. multicoloured (as 365)	1·50	1·50
394	–	20c. yellow, black and pink (as 366)	2·50	15
395	–	24c. multicoloured	65	1·25
396	–	25c. multicoloured (as 368)	2·50	30
397	–	30c. multicoloured (as 369)	6·00	1·25
398	**167**	40c. blue	3·50	10
399	–	50c. brown (as 356)	4·00	10
400	–	75c. olive (as 357)	1·00	1·00
401	–	$1 purple (as 358)	1·50	20
402	–	$2 violet (as 359)	6·00	1·00
403	–	$4 brown (as 360)	5·50	6·50

DESIGNS—VERT: 7c. White-tailed Dascyllus ("Humbug fish"); 8c. Copper-banded butterflyfish ("Coral fish"); 9c. Hermit crab; 10c. Orange clownfish ("Anemone fish"); 13c. Red-necked avocet. HORIZ: 24c. Azure kingfisher.

200 "Saving Life"

1966. 75th Anniv of Royal Life Saving Society.

406	**200**	4c. black, lt bl & bl	15	10

201 "Adoration of the Shepherds" **202** "Eendracht"

1966. Christmas.

407	**201**	4c. black and olive	10	10

1966. 350th Anniv of Dirk Hartog's Landing in Australia.

408	**202**	4c. multicoloured	10	10

203 Open Bible **204** Ancient Keys and Modern Lock

1967. 150th Anniv of British and Foreign Bible Society in Australia.

409	**203**	4c. multicoloured	10	10

1967. 150th Anniv of Australian Banking.

410	**204**	4c. black, blue and green	10	10

205 Lions Badge and 50 Stars **206** Y.W.C.A. Emblem

1967. 50th Anniv of Lions International.

411	**205**	4c. black, gold and blue	10	10

1967. World Y.W.C.A. Council Meeting, Monash University, Melbourne.

412	**206**	4c. multicoloured	10	10

207 Anatomical Figures

1967. 5th World Gynaecology and Obstetrics Congress, Sydney.

413	**207**	4c. black, blue and violet	10	10

1967. No. 385 surch.

414	**191**	5c. on 4c. red	35	10

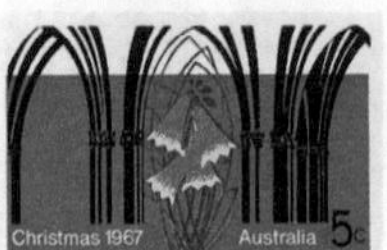

209 Christmas Bells and Gothic Arches **211** Satellite in Orbit

1967. Christmas. Multicoloured.

415	5c. Type **209**	20	10
416	25c. Religious symbols (vert)	1·00	1·90

1968. World Weather Watch. Multicoloured.

417	5c. Type **211**	30	10
418	20c. World weather map	1·10	2·75

213 Radar Antenna **214** Kangaroo Paw (Western Australia)

1968. World Telecommunications via Intelsat II.

419	**213**	25c. blue, black and green	1·25	2·50

1968. State Floral Emblems. Multicoloured.

420	6c. Type **214**	45	1·25
421	13c. Pink Heath (Victoria)	50	60
422	15c. Tasmanian Blue Gum (Tasmania)	70	30
423	20c. Sturt's Desert Pea (South Australia)	1·50	75
424	25c. Cooktown Orchid (Queensland)	1·10	60
425	30c. Waratah (New South Wales)	50	10

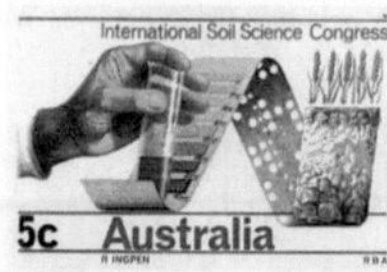

220 Soil Sample Analysis

1968. International Soil Science Congress and World Medical Association Assembly. Mult.

426	5c. Type **220**	10	10
427	5c. Rubber-gloved hands, syringe and head of Hippocrates	10	10

222 Athlete carrying Torch and Sunstone Symbol **224** Houses and Dollar Signs

1968. Olympic Games, Mexico City. Mult.

428	5c. Type **222**	30	10
429	25c. Sunstone symbol and Mexican flag	40	1·50

1968. Building and Savings Societies Congress.

430	**224**	5c. multicoloured	10	40

225 Church Window and View of Bethlehem **226** Edgeworth David (geologist)

1968. Christmas.

431	**225**	5c. multicoloured	10	10

1968. Famous Australians (1st series).

432	**226**	5c. green on myrtle	35	20
433	–	5c. black on blue	35	20
434	–	5c. brown on buff	35	20
435	–	5c. violet on lilac	35	20

DESIGNS: No. 433, A. B. Paterson (poet); No. 434, Albert Namatjira (artist); No. 435, Caroline Chrisholm (social worker).

Nos. 432/5 were only issued in booklets and exist with one or two sides imperf.

See also Nos. 446/9, 479/82, 505/8, 537/40, 590/5, 602/7 and 637/40.

230 Macquarie Lighthouse **231** Pioneers and Modern Building, Darwin

1968. 150th Anniv of Macquarie Lighthouse.

436	**230**	5c. black and yellow	30	60

1969. Centenary of Northern Territory Settlement.

437	**231**	5c. brown, olive and ochre	10	10

232 Melbourne Harbour

1969. 6th Biennial Conference of International Association of Ports and Harbours, Melbourne.

438	**232**	5c. multicoloured	15	10

233 Concentric Circles (symbolizing Management, Labour and Government)

1969. 50th Anniv of I.L.O.

439	**233**	5c. multicoloured	15	10

234 Sugar Cane **238** "The Nativity" (stained glass window)

1969. Primary Industries. Multicoloured.

440	7c. Type **234**	60	1·50
441	15c. Timber	1·00	2·50
442	20c. Wheat	35	60
443	25c. Wool	60	1·50

1969. Christmas. Multicoloured.

444	5c. Type **238**	20	10
445	25c. "Tree of Life", Christ in crib and Christmas Star (abstract)	1·00	2·00

240 Edmund Barton

244 Capt. Ross Smith's Vickers Vimy, 1919

1969. Famous Australians (2nd series). Prime Ministers.

446 **240**	5c. black on green	40	20
447 –	5c. black on green	40	20
448 –	5c. black on green	40	20
449 –	5c. black on green	40	20

DESIGNS: No. 447, Alfred Deakin; 448, J. C. Watson; 449, G. H. Reid.

Nos. 446/9 were only issued in booklets and only exist with one or two adjacent sides imperf.

1969. 50th Anniv of 1st England–Australia Flight.

450 **244**	5c. multicoloured	15	10
451 –	5c. red, black and green	15	10
452 –	5c. multicoloured	15	10

DESIGNS: No. 451, Lt. H. Fysh and Lt. P. McGinness on 1919 survey with Ford Model T runabout; 452, Capt. Wrigley and Sgt. Murphy in Royal Aircraft Factory B.E.2E taking off to meet the Smiths.

247 Symbolic Track and Diesel Locomotive

1970. Sydney–Perth Standard Gauge Railway Link.

453 **247**	5c. multicoloured	15	10

248 Australian Pavilion, Osaka

1970. World Fair, Osaka.

454 **248**	5c. multicoloured	15	10
455 –	20c. red and black	35	65

DESIGN: 20c., "Southern Cross" and "from the Country of the south with warm feelings" (message).

251 Australian Flag

1970. Royal Visit.

456 –	5c. black and ochre	35	15
457 **251**	30c. multicoloured	1·25	2·50

DESIGN: 5c. Queen Elizabeth II and Duke of Edinburgh.

252 Lucerne Plant, Bull and Sun

1970. 11th International Grasslands Congress, Queensland.

458 **252**	5c. multicoloured	10	60

253 Captain Cook and H.M.S. "Endeavour"

259 Sturt's Desert Rose

1970. Bicentenary of Captain Cook's Discovery of Australia's East Coast. Multicoloured.

459	5c. Type **253**	25	10
460	5c. Sextant and H.M.S. "Endeavour"	25	10
461	5c. Landing at Botany Bay	25	10
462	5c. Charting and exploring	25	10
463	5c. Claiming possession	25	10
464	30c. Captain Cook, H.M.S. "Endeavour", sextant, aborigines and kangaroo (63 × 30 mm)	1·00	2·50
MS465	157 × 129 mm. Nos. 459/64. Imperf	7·50	9·00

Nos. 459/63 were issued together, se-tenant, forming a composite design.

1970. Coil Stamps. Multicoloured.

465a	2c. Type **259**	40	20
466	4c. Type **259**	85	1·50
467	5c. Golden wattle	20	10
468	6c. Type **259**	1·25	1·00
468b	7c. Sturt's desert pea	40	60
468d	10c. As 7c.	60	60

264 Snowy Mountains Scheme

265 Rising Flames

1970. National Development (1st series). Mult.

469	7c. Type **264**	20	80
470	8c. Ord River scheme	10	15
471	9c. Bauxite to aluminium	15	15
472	10c. Oil and natural gas	30	10

See also Nos. 541/4.

1970. 16th Commonwealth Parliamentary Association Conference, Canberra.

473 **265**	6c. multicoloured	10	10

266 Milk Analysis and Dairy Herd

267 "The Nativity"

1970. 18th International Dairy Congress, Sydney.

474 **266**	6c. multicoloured	10	10

1970. Christmas.

475 **267**	6c. multicoloured	10	10

268 U.N. "Plant" and Dove of Peace

269 Boeing 707 and Avro 504

1970. 25th Anniv of United Nations.

476 **268**	6c. multicoloured	15	10

1970. 50th Anniv of QANTAS Airline.

477 **269**	6c. multicoloured	30	10
478 –	30c. multicoloured	70	1·50

DESIGN: 30c. Avro 504 and Boeing 707.

1970. Famous Australians (3rd series). As T **226**.

479	6c. blue	65	20
480	6c. black on brown	65	20
481	6c. purple on pink	65	20
482	6c. red on pink	65	20

DESIGNS: No. 479, The Duigan brothers (pioneer aviators); 480, Lachlan Macquarie (Governor of New South Wales); 481, Adam Lindsay Gordon (poet); 482, E. J. Eyre (explorer).

271 "Theatre"

1971. "Australia–Asia". 28th International Congress of Orientalists, Canberra. Multicoloured.

483	7c. Type **271**	45	60
484	15c. "Music"	70	1·00
485	20c. "Sea Craft"	65	90

272 The Southern Cross

273 Market "Graph"

1971. Centenary of Australian Natives' Association.

486 **272**	6c. black, red and blue	10	10

1971. Centenary of Sydney Stock Exchange.

487 **273**	6c. multicoloured	10	10

274 Rotary Emblem

275 Dassault Mirage Jets and De Havilland D.H.9A Biplane

1971. 50th Anniv of Rotary International in Australia.

488 **274**	6c. multicoloured	15	10

1971. 50th Anniv of R.A.A.F.

489 **275**	6c. multicoloured	50	10

276 Draught-horse, Cat and Dog

277 Bark Painting

1971. Animals. Multicoloured.

490	6c. Type **276**	20	10
491	12c. Vet and lamb ("Animal Science")	45	20
492	18c. Red Kangaroo ("Fauna Conservation")	80	35
493	24c. Guide-dog ("Animals Aid to Man")	80	1·50

The 6c. commemorates the Centenary of the Australian R.S.P.C.A.

1971. Aboriginal Art. Multicoloured.

494	20c. Type **277**	20	20
495	25c. Body decoration	20	55
496	30c. Cave painting (vert)	40	20
497	35c. Grave posts (vert)	30	15

278 The Three Kings and the Star

280 Cameo Brooch

1971. Christmas. Colours of star and colour of "AUSTRALIA" given.

498 **278**	7c. blue, mauve and brown	50	15
499	7c. mauve, brown and white	50	15
500	7c. mauve, white and black	2·75	80
501	7c. black, green and black	50	15
502	7c. lilac, green and mauve	50	15
503	7c. black, brown and white	50	15
504	7c. blue, mauve and green	14·00	2·25

1972. Famous Australians. (4th series). As T **240**. Prime Ministers.

505	7c. blue	30	20
506	7c. blue	30	20
507	7c. red	30	20
508	7c. red	30	20

DESIGNS: No. 505, Andrew Fisher; 506, W. M. Hughes; 507, Joseph Cook; 508, S. M. Bruce.

1972. 50th Anniv of Country Women's Association.

509 **280**	7c. multicoloured	20	10

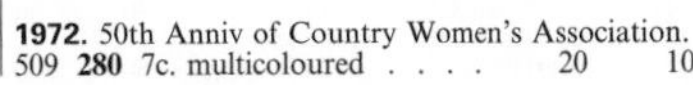

281 Fruit

282 Worker in Wheelchair

1972. Primary Industries. Multicoloured.

510	20c. Type **281**	1·00	2·50
511	25c. Rice	1·00	4·00
512	30c. Fish	1·00	1·00
513	35c. Beef	2·25	75

1972. Rehabilitation of the Disabled.

514 **282**	12c. brown and green	10	10
515 –	18c. green and orange	85	35
516 –	24c. blue and brown	15	10

DESIGNS—HORIZ: 18c. Patient and teacher. VERT: 24c. Boy playing with ball.

283 Telegraph Line

284 Athletics

1972. Centenary of Overland Telegraph Line.

517 **283**	7c. multicoloured	15	15

1972. Olympic Games, Munich. Multicoloured.

518	7c. Type **284**	20	25
519	7c. Rowing	20	25
520	7c. Swimming	20	25
521	35c. Equestrian	1·25	3·50

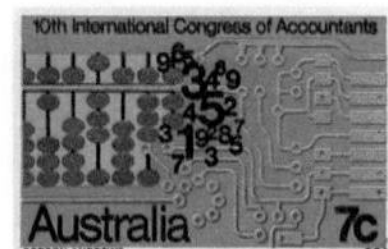

285 Numerals and Computer Circuit

1972. 10th Int Congress of Accountants, Sydney.

522 **285**	7c. multicoloured	15	15

286 Australian-built Harvester

1972. Pioneer Life. Multicoloured.

523	5c. Pioneer family (vert)	10	10
524	10c. Water-pump (vert)	20	10
525	15c. Type **286**	15	10
526	40c. House	15	30
527	50c. Stage-coach	35	20
528	60c. Morse key (vert)	30	80
529	80c. "Gem" (paddle-steamer)	30	80

287 Jesus with Children

288 "Length"

1972. Christmas. Multicoloured.

530	7c. Type **287**	30	10
531	35c. Dove and spectrum motif (vert)	2·75	5·00

1973. Metric Conversion. Multicoloured.

532	7c. Type **288**	40	55
533	7c. "Volume"	40	55
534	7c. "Mass"	40	55
535	7c. "Temperature" (horiz)	40	55

289 Caduceus and Laurel Wreath **291** Shipping

1973. 25th Anniv of World Health Organization.
536 **289** 7c. multicoloured 30 15

1973. Famous Australians (5th series). As T **226**.
537 7c. brown and black 35 45
538 7c. lilac and black 35 45
539 7c. brown and black 35 45
540 7c. lilac and black 35 45
PORTRAITS: No. 537, William Wentworth (statesman and explorer); 538, Isaac Issacs (1st Australian-born Governor-General); 539, Mary Gilmore (writer); 540, Marcus Clarke (author).

1973. National Development (2nd series). Mult.
541 20c. Type **291** . . . . 1·50 2·75
542 25c. Iron ore and steel . . . 1·50 2·75
543 30c. Beef roads . . . . . . 1·50 2·75
544 35c. Mapping . . . . 2·25 2·75

292 Banded Coral Shrimp **293** Children at Play

1973. Marine Life and Gemstones. Multicoloured.
545 1c. Type **292** 10 10
546 2c. Fiddler crab 10 10
547 3c. Coral crab 10 10
548 4c. Mauve stinger 15 55
549 6c. Chrysoprase (vert) . . . 15 40
550 7c. Agate (vert) 20 10
551 8c. Opal (vert) 20 10
552 9c. Rhodonite (vert) 50 15
552a 10c. Star sapphire (vert) . . 75 10

1973. 50th Anniv of Legacy (welfare organization).
553 **293** 7c. brown, red and green 30 10

294 John baptizing Jesus **295** Sydney Opera House

1973. Christmas. Multicoloured.
554 7c. Type **294** 35 10
555 30c. The Good Shepherd . . 1·75 2·25

1973. Architecture.
556 **295** 7c. blue and pale blue . . 30 15
557 – 10c. ochre and brown . . 60 70
558 – 40c. grey, brown and black . . . . 1·00 2·50
559 – 50c. multicoloured . . . . 1·00 2·50
DESIGNS—HORIZ: 10c. Buchanan's Hotel, Townsville; 40c. Como House, Melbourne. VERT: 50c. St. James's Church, Sydney.

296 Wireless Receiver and Speaker **297** Common Wombat

1973. 50th Anniv of Regular Radio Broadcasting.
560 **296** 7c. blue, red and black . . 15 10

1974. Animals. Multicoloured.
561 20c. Type **297** 25 10
562 25c. Short-nosed echidna (inscr "Spiny Anteater") 60 60
563 30c. Brush-tailed possum . . 40 15
564 75c. Pygmy (inscr "Feather-tailed") glider . . . . . 80 1·00

298 "Sergeant of Light Horse" (G. Lambert) **299** Supreme Court Judge

1974. Australian Paintings. Multicoloured.
565 $1 Type **298** . . . . 1·00 10
566 $2 "Red Gums of the Far North" (H. Heysen) (horiz) . . . . 1·25 25
566a $4 "Shearing the Rams" (Tom Roberts) (horiz) . . 2·00 2·25
567 $5 "McMahon's Point" (Sir Arthur Streeton) . . . . 5·00 2·25
567a $10 "Coming South" (Tom Roberts) . . . . 5·50 3·50

1974. 150th Anniv of Australia's Third Charter of Justice.
568 **299** 7c. multicoloured 20 10

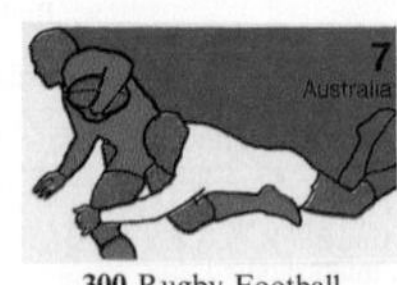

300 Rugby Football

1974. Non-Olympic Sports. Multicoloured.
569 7c. Type **300** 40 45
570 7c. Bowls 40 45
571 7c. Australian football (vert) 40 45
572 7c. Cricket (vert) 40 45
573 7c. Golf (vert) 40 45
574 7c. Surfing (vert) 40 45
575 7c. Tennis (vert) 40 45

301 "Transport of Mails" **302** Letter "A" and W. C. Wentworth (co-founder)

1974. Centenary of U.P.U. Multicoloured.
576 7c. Type **301** 40 20
577 30c. Three-part version of T **301** (vert) . . . . . . 85 1·90

1974. 150th Anniv of First Independent Newspaper, "The Australian".
578 **302** 7c. black and brown . . . 40 40

1974. No. 551 surch.
579 9c. on 8c. multicoloured . . . 15 15

304 "The Adoration of the Magi" **305** "Pre-school Education"

1974. Christmas. Woodcuts by Durer.
580 **304** 10c. black on cream . . . 25 10
581 – 35c. black on cream . . . 80 1·00
DESIGN: 35c. "The Flight into Egypt".

1974. Education in Australia. Multicoloured.
582 5c. Type **305** 25 40
583 11c. "Correspondence Schools" 25 50
584 15c. "Science Education" . . 40 40
585 60c. "Advanced Education" (vert) . . . . 50 2·00

306 "Road Safety" **307** Australian Women's Year Emblem

1975. Environment Dangers. Multicoloured.
586 10c. Type **306** 50 50
587 10c. "Pollution" (horiz) . . . 50 50
588 10c. "Bush Fires" (horiz) . . 50 50

1975. International Women's Year.
589 **307** 10c. blue, green and violet 20 15

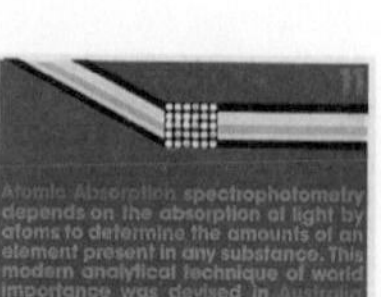

308 J. H. Scullin **309** Atomic Absorption Spectrophotometry

1975. Famous Australians (6th series). Prime Ministers. Multicoloured.
590 10c. Type **308** 25 35
591 10c. J. A. Lyons 25 35
592 10c. Earle Page 25 35
593 10c. Arthur Fadden 25 35
594 10c. John Curtin 25 35
595 10c. J. B. Chifley 25 35

1975. Scientific Development. Multicoloured.
596 11c. Type **309** 70 60
597 24c. Radio astronomy . . . 1·25 1·75
598 33c. Immunology . . . . . 1·25 1·75
599 48c. Oceanography . . . . . 1·50 2·75

310 Logo of Australian Postal Commission

1975. Inauguration of Australian Postal and Telecommunications Commissions.
600 **310** 10c. black, red and grey 25 10
601 – 10c. black, orange and grey 25 10
DESIGN: No. 601, Logo of Australian Telecommunications Commission.

311 Edith Cowan **312** "Helichrysum thomsonii"

1975. Famous Australians (7th series). Australian Women. Multicoloured.
602 10c. Type **311** 40 55
603 10c. Louisa Lawson 40 55
604 10c. "Henry Richardson" (pen name of Ethel Richardson) 40 55
605 10c. Catherine Spence . . . 40 55
606a 10c. Constance Stone . . . 35 55
607 10c. Truganini 40 55

1975. Wild Flowers. Multicoloured.
608 18c. Type **312** 25 10
609 45c. "Callistemon teretifolius" (horiz) 50 10

313 "Tambaran" House and Sydney Opera House **314** Epiphany Scene

1975. Independence of Papua New Guinea. Mult.
610 18c. Type **313** 20 10
611 25c. "Freedom" (bird in flight) (horiz) . . . . . . 50 1·50

1975. Christmas.
612 **314** 15c. multicoloured 35 10
613 – 45c. violet, blue and silver 90 2·75
DESIGN—HORIZ: 45c. "Shining Star".

315 Australian Coat of Arms

1976. 75th Anniv of Nationhood.
614 **315** 18c. multicoloured 40 20

316 Telephone-user, c. 1878

1976. Centenary of Telephone.
615 **316** 18c. multicoloured 20 15

317 John Oxley

1976. 19th Century Explorers. Multicoloured.
616 18c. Type **317** 35 50
617 18c. Hume and Hovell . . . 35 50
618 18c. John Forrest 35 50
619 18c. Ernest Giles 35 50
620 18c. William Gosse 35 50
621 18c. Peter Warburton 35 50

318 Measuring Stick, Graph and Computer Tape

1976. 50th Anniv of Commonwealth Scientific and Industrial Research Organization.
622 **318** 18c. multicoloured 20 15

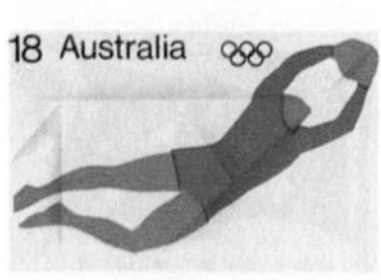

319 Football

1976. Olympic Games, Montreal. Multicoloured.
623 18c. Type **319** 20 20
624 18c. Gymnastics (vert) . . . 20 20
625 25c. Diving (vert) 35 80
626 40c. Cycling . . . . 90 1·25

320 Richmond Bridge, Tasmania **321** Blamire Young (designer of first Australian stamp)

1976. Australian Scenes. Multicoloured.
627 5c. Type **320** 20 10
628 25c. Broken Bay, N.S.W . . 65 20
629 35c. Wittenoom Gorge, W.A 45 20
630 50c. Mt. Buffalo, Victoria (vert) 90 30
631 70c. Barrier Reef . . . . . 1·25 1·25
632 85c. Ayers Rock, N.T . . . 1·50 2·00

1976. National Stamp Week.
633 **321** 18c. multicoloured 15 15
MS634 101 × 112 mm. Nos. 633 × 4 75 2·00

322 "Virgin and Child" (detail, Simone Contarini)

1976. Christmas.
635 **322** 15c. mauve and blue 20 10
636 – 45c. multicoloured 50 90
DESIGN: 45c. Toy koala bear and decorations.

323 John Gould

1976. Famous Australians. (8th series). Scientists. Multicoloured.
637 18c. Type **323** 35 50
638 18c. Thomas Laby 35 50
639 18c. Sir Baldwin Spencer 35 50
640 18c. Griffith Taylor 35 50

324 "Music" 325 Queen Elizabeth II

1977. Performing Arts. Multicoloured.
641 20c. Type **324** 15 25
642 30c. Drama 20 35
643 40c. Dance 25 40
644 60c. Opera 1·25 1·75

1977. Silver Jubilee. Multicoloured.
645 18c. Type **325** 30 10
646 45c. The Queen and Duke of Edinburgh 70 90

326 Fielder and Wicket Keeper 327 Parliament House

1977. Centenary of Australia–England Test Cricket.
647 18c. Type **326** 40 65
648 18c. Umpire and batsman 40 65
649 18c. Fielders 40 65
650 18c. Batsman and umpire 40 65
651 18c. Bowler and fielder 40 65
652 45c. Batsman facing bowler 50 1·25

1977. 50th Anniv of Opening of Parliament House, Canberra.
653 **327** 18c. multicoloured 15 10

328 Trade Union Workers 329 Surfing Santa

1977. 50th Anniv of Australian Council of Trade Unions.
654 **328** 18c. multicoloured 15 10

1977. Christmas. Multicoloured.
655 15c. Type **329** 25 10
656 45c. Madonna and Child 75 1·25

330 National Flag

1978. Australia Day.
657 **330** 18c. multicoloured 20 15

331 Harry Hawker and Sopwith Atlantic

1978. Early Australian Aviators. Multicoloured.
658 18c. Type **331** 30 50
659 18c. Bert Hinkler and Avro Type 581 Avian 30 50
660 18c. Sir Charles Kingsford Smith and "Southern Cross" 30 50
661 18c. Charles Ulm and "Southern Cross" 30 50
MS662 100 × 112 mm. Nos. 658/61 × 2. Imperf 75 1·75

332 Piper PA-31 Navajo landing at Station Airstrip

1978. 50th Anniv of Royal Flying Doctor Service.
663 **332** 18c. multicoloured 20 15

333 Illawarra Flame Tree 334 Sturt's Desert Rose and Map

1978. Trees. Multicoloured.
664 18c. Type **333** 20 15
665 25c. Ghost gum 35 1·40
666 40c. Grass tree 45 2·00
667 45c. Cootamundra wattle 45 70

1978. Establishment of State Government for the Northern Territory.
668 **334** 18c. multicoloured 20 15

335 Hooded Plover 336 1928 3d. National Stamp Exhibition Commemorative

1978. Birds (1st series). Multicoloured.
669 1c. Spotted-sided ("Zebra") finch 10 20
670 2c. Crimson finch 10 20
671 5c. Type **335** 50 10
672 15c. Forest kingfisher (vert) 20 20
673 20c. Australian dabchick ("Little Grebe") 70 10
674 20c. Yellow robin ("Eastern Yellow Robin") 60 10
675 22c. White-tailed kingfisher (22 × 29 mm) 30 10
676 25c. Masked ("Spur-wing") plover 90 1·25
677 30c. Pied oystercatcher 1·00 25
678 40c. Variegated ("Lovely") wren (vert) 30 45
679 50c. Flame robin (vert) 85 50
680 55c. Comb-crested jacana ("Lotus-Bird") 1·40 60
See also Nos. 734/40.

1978. 50th Anniv of National Stamp Week, and National Stamp Exhibition.
694 **336** 20c. multicoloured 15 15
MS695 78 × 113 mm. No. 694 × 4 75 1·75

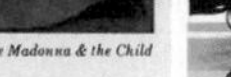

337 "The Madonna and the Child" (after van Eyck) 338 "Tulloch"

1978. Christmas. Multicoloured.
696 15c. Type **337** 30 10
697 25c. "The Virgin and Child" (Marmion) 45 55
698 55c. "The Holy Family" (del Vaga) 70 90

1978. Horse-racing. Multicoloured.
699 20c. Type **338** 30 10
700 35c. "Bernborough" (vert) 45 85
701 50c. "Phar Lap" (vert) 60 1·25
702 55c. "Peter Pan" 60 1·10

339 Raising the Flag, Sydney Cove, 26 January 1788 340 "Canberra" (paddle-steamer)

1979. Australia Day.
703 **339** 20c. multicoloured 15 15

1979. Ferries and Murray River Steamers. Mult.
704 20c. Type **340** 25 10
705 35c. "Lady Denman" 45 1·00
706 50c. "Murray River Queen" (paddle-steamer) 65 1·40
707 55c. "Curl Curl" (hydrofoil) 70 1·25

341 Port Campbell, Victoria

1979. National Parks. Multicoloured.
708 20c. Type **341** 30 30
709 20c. Uluru, Northern Territory 30 30
710 20c. Royal, New South Wales 30 30
711 20c. Flinders Ranges, South Australia 30 30
712 20c. Nambung, Western Australia 30 30
713 20c. Girraween, Queensland (vert) 30 30
714 20c. Mount Field, Tasmania (vert) 30 30

342 "Double Fairlie" Type Locomotive, Western Australia

1979. Steam Railways. Multicoloured.
715 20c. Type **342** 30 10
716 35c. Locomotive, Puffing Billy Line, Victoria 60 70
717 50c. Locomotive, Pichi Richi Line, South Australia 70 1·50
718 55c. Locomotive, Zig Zag Railway, New South Wales 80 1·40

343 Symbolic Swan

1979. 150th Anniv of Western Australia.
719 **343** 20c. multicoloured 15 15

344 Children playing on Slide 345 Letters and Parcels

1979. International Year of the Child.
720 **344** 20c. multicoloured 15 10

1979. Christmas. Multicoloured.
721 15c. "Christ's Nativity" (Eastern European icon) 15 10
722 25c. Type **345** 15 65
723 55c. "Madonna and Child" (Buglioni) 25 80

346 Fly-fishing 347 Matthew Flinders

1979. Fishing.
724 **346** 20c. multicoloured 15 10
725 – 35c. blue and violet 25 70
726 – 50c. multicoloured 35 90
727 – 55c. multicoloured 35 85
DESIGNS: 35c. Spinning; 50c. Deep sea game-fishing; 55c. Surf-fishing.

1980. Australia Day.
728 **347** 20c. multicoloured 20 10

348 Dingo

1980. Dogs. Multicoloured.
729 20c. Type **348** 35 10
730 25c. Border collie 35 50
731 35c. Australian terrier 40 70
732 50c. Australian cattle dog 70 1·75
733 55c. Australian kelpie 70 1·40

1980. Birds (2nd series). As T **335**. Multicoloured.
734 10c. Golden-shouldered parrot (vert) 50 10
734b 18c. Spotted catbird (vert) 50 1·25
735 28c. Australian bee eater ("Rainbow Bird") (vert) 50 20
736 35c. Regent bower bird (vert) 50 10
737 45c. Masked wood swallow 50 10
738 60c. Australian king parrot ("King Parrot") (vert) 50 15
739 80c. Rainbow pitta 1·00 75
740 $1 Black-backed magpie ("Western Magpie") (vert) 1·00 10

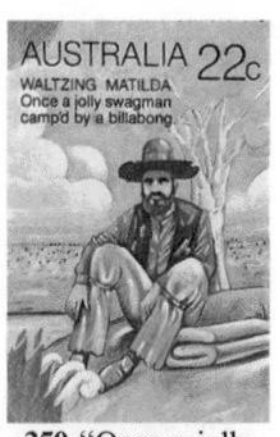

349 Queen Elizabeth II 350 "Once a jolly Swagman camp'd by a Billabong"

1980. Birthday of Queen Elizabeth II.
741 **349** 22c. multicoloured 30 20

1980. Folklore. "Waltzing Matilda". Multicoloured.
742 22c. Type **350** 30 20
743 22c. "And he sang as he shoved that jumbuck in his tuckerbag" 30 20
744 22c. "Up rode the squatter mounted on his thoroughbred" 30 20
745 22c. "Down came the troopers one, two, three" 30 20
746 22c. "And his ghost may be heard as you pass by that billabong" 30 20

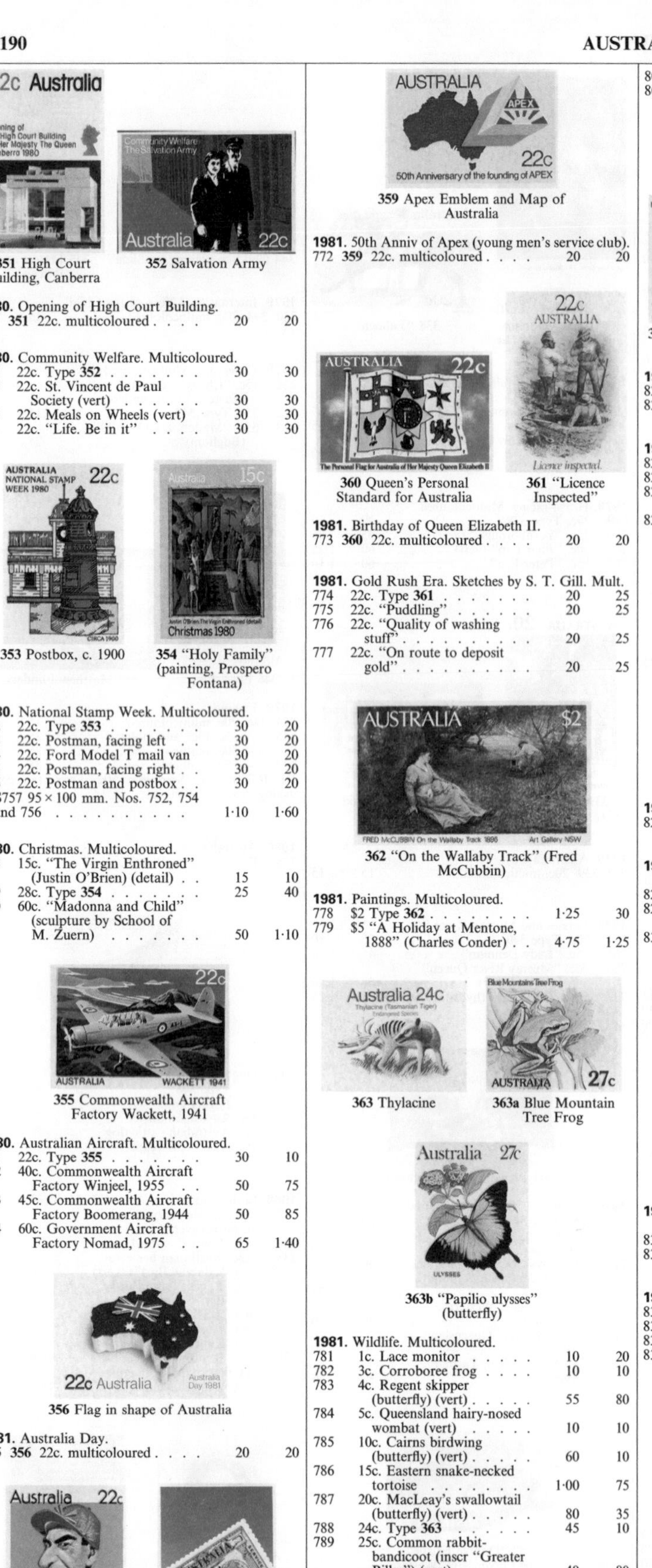

351 High Court Building, Canberra

352 Salvation Army

1980. Opening of High Court Building.
747 **351** 22c. multicoloured 20 20

1980. Community Welfare. Multicoloured.
748 22c. Type **352** 30 30
749 22c. St. Vincent de Paul Society (vert) 30 30
750 22c. Meals on Wheels (vert) 30 30
751 22c. "Life. Be in it" 30 30

353 Postbox, c. 1900

354 "Holy Family" (painting, Prospero Fontana)

1980. National Stamp Week. Multicoloured.
752 22c. Type **353** 30 20
753 22c. Postman, facing left . . 30 20
754 22c. Ford Model T mail van 30 20
755 22c. Postman, facing right . . 30 20
756 22c. Postman and postbox . . 30 20
MS757 95 × 100 mm. Nos. 752, 754 and 756 . . . . 1·10 1·60

1980. Christmas. Multicoloured.
758 15c. "The Virgin Enthroned" (Justin O'Brien) (detail) . . 15 10
759 28c. Type **354** 25 40
760 60c. "Madonna and Child" (sculpture by School of M. Zuern) . . . . 50 1·10

355 Commonwealth Aircraft Factory Wackett, 1941

1980. Australian Aircraft. Multicoloured.
761 22c. Type **355** 30 10
762 40c. Commonwealth Aircraft Factory Winjeel, 1955 . . 50 75
763 45c. Commonwealth Aircraft Factory Boomerang, 1944 50 85
764 60c. Government Aircraft Factory Nomad, 1975 . . 65 1·40

356 Flag in shape of Australia

1981. Australia Day.
765 **356** 22c. multicoloured 20 20

357 Caricature of Darby Munro (jockey)

358 1931 Kingsford Smith's Flights 6d. Commemorative

1981. Sporting Personalities. Caricatures. Mult.
766 22c. Type **357** 20 10
767 35c. Victor Trumper (cricket) 40 60
768 55c. Sir Norman Brookes (tennis) . . . . 40 1·00
769 60c. Walter Lindrum (billiards) . . . . 40 1·25

1981. 50th Anniversary of Official Australia–U.K. Airmail Service.
770 **358** 22c. lilac, red and blue . . 15 10
771 – 60c. lilac, red and blue . . 40 90
DESIGN—HORIZ: 60c. As T **358**, but format changed.

359 Apex Emblem and Map of Australia

1981. 50th Anniv of Apex (young men's service club).
772 **359** 22c. multicoloured 20 20

360 Queen's Personal Standard for Australia

361 "Licence Inspected"

1981. Birthday of Queen Elizabeth II.
773 **360** 22c. multicoloured 20 20

1981. Gold Rush Era. Sketches by S. T. Gill. Mult.
774 22c. Type **361** 20 25
775 22c. "Puddling" 20 25
776 22c. "Quality of washing stuff" 20 25
777 22c. "On route to deposit gold" 20 25

362 "On the Wallaby Track" (Fred McCubbin)

1981. Paintings. Multicoloured.
778 $2 Type **362** . . . . 1·25 30
779 $5 "A Holiday at Mentone, 1888" (Charles Conder) . . 4·75 1·25

363 Thylacine

363a Blue Mountain Tree Frog

363b "Papilio ulysses" (butterfly)

1981. Wildlife. Multicoloured.
781 1c. Lace monitor 10 20
782 3c. Corroboree frog 10 10
783 4c. Regent skipper (butterfly) (vert) 55 80
784 5c. Queensland hairy-nosed wombat (vert) 10 10
785 10c. Cairns birdwing (butterfly) (vert) 60 10
786 15c. Eastern snake-necked tortoise . . . . 1·00 75
787 20c. MacLeay's swallowtail (butterfly) (vert) 80 35
788 24c. Type **363** 45 10
789 25c. Common rabbit-bandicoot (inscr "Greater Bilby") (vert) 40 80
790 27c. Type **363a** . . . . . 1·25 20
791 27c. Type **363b** . . . . . 1·00 30
792 30c. Bridle nail-tailed wallaby (vert) 90 20
792a 30c. Chlorinda hairstreak (butterfly) (vert) . . . . . 1·00 20
793 35c. Blue tiger (butterfly) (vert) . . . . 1·00 30
794 40c. Smooth knob-tailed gecko 45 30
795 45c. Big greasy (butterfly) (vert) . . . . 1·00 30
796 50c. Leadbeater's possum 50 10
797 55c. Stick-nest rat (vert) . . 50 30
798 60c. Wood white (butterfly) (vert) . . . . 1·10 30
799 65c. Yellow-faced whip snake . . . . 1·75 1·50
800 70c. Crucifix toad . . . . . 65 1·75
801 75c. Eastern water dragon 1·25 90
802 80c. Amaryllis azure (butterfly) (vert) . . . . . 1·40 2·00
803 85c. Centralian blue-tongued lizard . . . . 1·10 1·25
804 90c. Freshwater crocodile 1·60 1·25
805 95c. Thorny devil . . . . . 1·60 2·00
806 $1 Sword-grass brown (butterfly) (vert) . . . . . 1·40 30

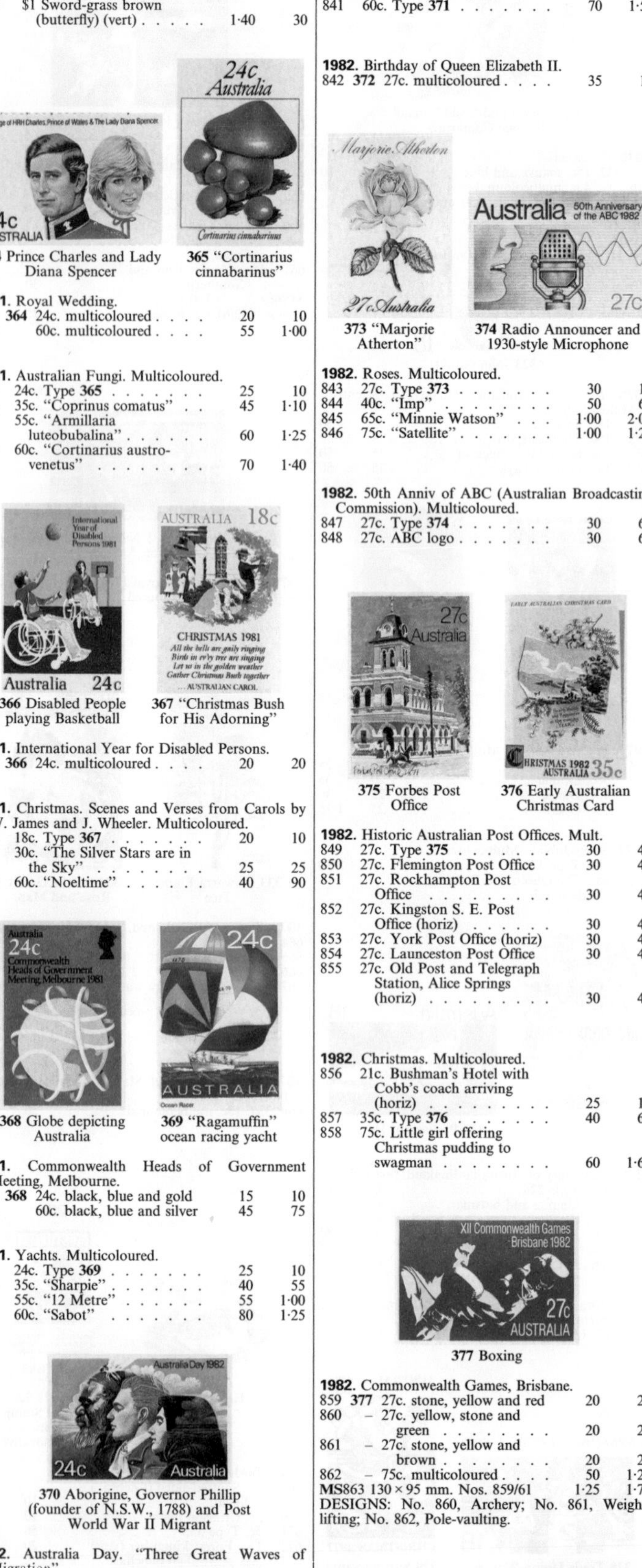

364 Prince Charles and Lady Diana Spencer

365 "Cortinarius cinnabarinus"

1981. Royal Wedding.
821 **364** 24c. multicoloured 20 10
822 60c. multicoloured . . . . 55 1·00

1981. Australian Fungi. Multicoloured.
823 24c. Type **365** 25 10
824 35c. "Coprinus comatus" . . 45 1·10
825 55c. "Armillaria luteobubalina" . . . . . . 60 1·25
826 60c. "Cortinarius austro-venetus" . . . . 70 1·40

366 Disabled People playing Basketball

367 "Christmas Bush for His Adorning"

1981. International Year for Disabled Persons.
827 **366** 24c. multicoloured 20 20

1981. Christmas. Scenes and Verses from Carols by W. James and J. Wheeler. Multicoloured.
828 18c. Type **367** 20 10
829 30c. "The Silver Stars are in the Sky" 25 25
830 60c. "Noeltime" 40 90

368 Globe depicting Australia

369 "Ragamuffin" ocean racing yacht

1981. Commonwealth Heads of Government Meeting, Melbourne.
831 **368** 24c. black, blue and gold 15 10
832 60c. black, blue and silver 45 75

1981. Yachts. Multicoloured.
833 24c. Type **369** 25 10
834 35c. "Sharpie" 40 55
835 55c. "12 Metre" . . . . . . 55 1·00
836 60c. "Sabot" . . . . 80 1·25

370 Aborigine, Governor Phillip (founder of N.S.W., 1788) and Post World War II Migrant

1982. Australia Day. "Three Great Waves of Migration".
837 **370** 24c. multicoloured 35 25

371 Humpback Whale

372 Queen Elizabeth II

1982. Whales. Multicoloured.
838 24c. Sperm whale 30 10
839 35c. Black (inscr "Southern") right whale (vert) 40 60
840 55c. Blue whale (vert) . . . . 60 1·50
841 60c. Type **371** . . . . 70 1·50

1982. Birthday of Queen Elizabeth II.
842 **372** 27c. multicoloured 35 15

373 "Marjorie Atherton"

374 Radio Announcer and 1930-style Microphone

1982. Roses. Multicoloured.
843 27c. Type **373** 30 15
844 40c. "Imp" 50 60
845 65c. "Minnie Watson" . . . 1·00 2·00
846 75c. "Satellite" . . . . 1·00 1·25

1982. 50th Anniv of ABC (Australian Broadcasting Commission). Multicoloured.
847 27c. Type **374** 30 65
848 27c. ABC logo 30 65

375 Forbes Post Office

376 Early Australian Christmas Card

1982. Historic Australian Post Offices. Mult.
849 27c. Type **375** 30 40
850 27c. Flemington Post Office 30 40
851 27c. Rockhampton Post Office 30 40
852 27c. Kingston S. E. Post Office (horiz) 30 40
853 27c. York Post Office (horiz) 30 40
854 27c. Launceston Post Office 30 40
855 27c. Old Post and Telegraph Station, Alice Springs (horiz) 30 40

1982. Christmas. Multicoloured.
856 21c. Bushman's Hotel with Cobb's coach arriving (horiz) 25 10
857 35c. Type **376** 40 60
858 75c. Little girl offering Christmas pudding to swagman . . . . 60 1·60

377 Boxing

1982. Commonwealth Games, Brisbane.
859 **377** 27c. stone, yellow and red 20 25
860 – 27c. yellow, stone and green 20 25
861 – 27c. stone, yellow and brown 20 25
862 – 75c. multicoloured . . . . 50 1·25
MS863 130 × 95 mm. Nos. 859/61 1·25 1·75
DESIGNS: No. 860, Archery; No. 861, Weight-lifting; No. 862, Pole-vaulting.

378 Sydney Harbour Bridge 5s. Stamp of 1932

379 "Yirawala" Bark Painting

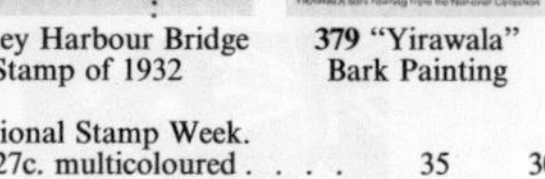

1982. National Stamp Week.
864 **378** 27c. multicoloured 35 30

1982. Opening of Australian National Gallery.
865 **379** 27c. multicoloured 30 25

380 Mimi Spirits Dancing **381** "Eucalyptus calophylla" "Rosea"

1982. Aboriginal Culture. Music and Dance.
866 **380** 27c. multicoloured 20 10
867 – 40c. multicoloured 30 60
868 – 65c. multicoloured . . . . 45 1·00
869 – 75c. multicoloured . . . . 50 1·00
DESIGN: 40c. to 75c. Aboriginal bark paintings of Mimi Spirits.

1982. Eucalyptus Flowers. Multicoloured.
870 1c. Type **381** 10 30
871 2c. "Eucalyptus casia" . . . 10 30
872 3c. "Eucalyptus ficifolia" . . 1·25 2·00
873 10c. "Eucalyptus globulus" 1·25 2·00
874 27c. "Eucalyptus forrestiana" 30 40

382 Shand Mason Steam Fire Engine, 1891

1983. Historic Fire Engines. Multicoloured.
875 27c. Type **382** 35 10
876 40c. Hotchkiss fire engine, 1914 . . . . 45 75
877 65c. Ahrens-Fox fire engine, 1929 . . . . 70 1·60
878 75c. Merryweather manual fire appliance, 1851 . . . . 70 1·40

383 H.M.S. "Sirius" **384** Stylized Kangaroo and Kiwi

1983. Australia Day. Multicoloured.
879 27c. Type **383** 40 75
880 27c. H.M.S. "Supply" . . . 40 75

1983. Closer Economic Relationship Agreement with New Zealand.
881 **384** 27c. multicoloured 30 30

385 Equality and Dignity **386** R.Y. "Britannia" passing Sydney Opera House

1983. Commonwealth Day. Multicoloured.
882 27c. Type **385** 20 25
883 27c. Liberty and Freedom . . 20 25
884 27c. Social Justice and Co-operation 20 25
885 75c. Peace and Harmony . . 50 1·50

1983. Birthday of Queen Elizabeth II.
886 **386** 27c. multicoloured 50 30

387 "Postal and Telecommunications Services" **388** Badge of the Order of St. John

1983. World Communications Year.
887 **387** 27c. multicoloured 30 30

1983. Centenary of St. John Ambulance in Australia.
888 **388** 27c. black and blue . . . 35 30

389 Jaycee Members and Badge **390** "The Bloke"

1983. 50th Anniv of Australian Jaycees.
889 **389** 27c. multicoloured 30 30

1983. Folklore. "The Sentimental Bloke" (humorous poem by C. J. Dennis). Multicoloured.
890 27c. Type **390** 40 50
891 27c. "Doreen—The Intro" . . 40 50
892 27c. "The Stror' at Coot" . . 40 50
893 27c. "Hitched" 40 50
894 27c. "The Mooch o' Life" . . 40 50

391 Nativity Scene

1983. Christmas. Children's Paintings. Mult.
895 24c. Type **391** 20 10
896 35c. Kookaburra 35 45
897 85c. Father Christmas in sleigh over beach . . . . . 90 1·40

392 Sir Paul Edmund de Strzelecki

1983. Explorers of Australia. Multicoloured.
898 30c. Type **392** 35 40
899 30c. Ludwig Leichhardt . . . 35 40
900 30c. William John Wills and Robert O'Hara Burke . . . 35 40
901 30c. Alexander Forrest . . . 35 40

393 Cook Family Cottage, Melbourne

1984. Australia Day.
902 **393** 30c. black and stone . . . 30 35

394 Charles Ulm, "Faith in Australia" and Trans-Tasman Cover

1984. 50th Anniv of First Official Airmail Flights. New Zealand–Australia and Australia–Papua New Guinea. Multicoloured.
903 45c. Type **394** . . . . 1·00 1·40
904 45c. As Type **394** but showing flown cover to Papua New Guinea . . . . 1·00 1·40

395 Thomson "Steamer", 1898

1984. Veteran and Vintage Cars. Multicoloured.
905 30c. Type **395** 50 65
906 30c. Tarrant two seater, 1906 50 65
907 30c. Gordon & Co "Australian Six" two seater, 1919 . . . . 50 65
908 30c. Summit tourer, 1923 . . 50 65
909 30c. Chic two seater, 1924 . . 50 65

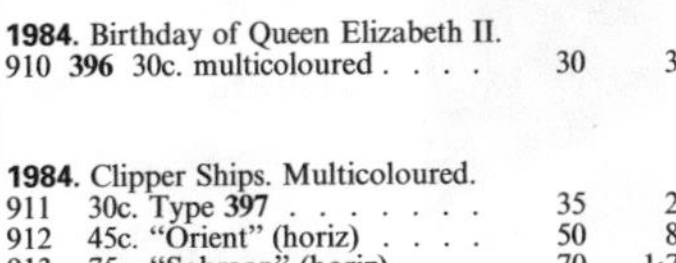

396 Queen Elizabeth II **397** "Cutty Sark"

1984. Birthday of Queen Elizabeth II.
910 **396** 30c. multicoloured 30 35

1984. Clipper Ships. Multicoloured.
911 30c. Type **397** 35 25
912 45c. "Orient" (horiz) 50 80
913 75c. "Sobraon" (horiz) . . . 70 1·75
914 85c. "Thermopylae" . . . . 70 1·50

398 Freestyle **399** Coral Hopper

1984. Skiing. Multicoloured.
915 30c. Type **398** 30 45
916 30c. Downhill racer 30 45
917 30c. Slalom (horiz) 30 45
918 30c. Nordic (horiz) 30 45

1984. Marine Life. Multicoloured.
919 2c. Type **399** 10 30
920 3c. Jimble 40 30
921 5c. Tasselled frogfish ("Anglerfish") 15 10
922 10c. Rough stonefish 80 40
923 20c. Red handfish 65 40
924 25c. Orange-lipped cowrie . . 45 40
925 30c. Choat's wrasse 45 40
926 33c. Leafy seadragon 65 10
927 40c. Red velvetfish . . . . . 85 1·50
928 45c. Textile or cloth of gold cone . . . . 1·50 50
929 50c. Clown surgeonfish . . . 80 50
930 55c. Bennet's nudibranch . . 80 50
931 60c. Zebra lionfish . . . . . 1·50 70
932 65c. Banded stingray . . . . 1·50 2·00
933 70c. Southern blue-ringed octopus . . . . 1·50 1·75
934 80c. Pineconefish ("Pineapple fish") . . . . 1·25 1·75
935 85c. Royal angelfish 90 70
936 90c. Crab-eyed goby . . . . 1·60 75
937 $1 Crown of thorns starfish 1·50 80

400 Before the Event **401** Australian 1913 1d. Kangaroo Stamp

1984. Olympic Games, Los Angeles. Multicoloured.
941 30c. Type **400** 25 40
942 30c. During the event 25 40
943 30c. After the event (vert) . . 25 40

1984. "Ausipex '84" International Stamp Exhibition, Melbourne.
944 **401** 30c. multicoloured 35 30
MS945 126 × 175 mm. 30c. × 7, Victoria 1850 3d. "Half Length"; New South Wales 1850 1d. "Sydney View"; Tasmania 1853 1d.; South Australia 1855 1d.; Western Australia 1854 1d. "Black Swan"; Queensland 1860 6d.; Type **401** . . . . 3·50 4·50

402 "Angel" (stained-glass window, St. Francis's Church, Melbourne) **403** "Stick Figures" (Cobar Region)

1984. Christmas. Stained-glass Windows. Mult.
946 24c. "Angel and Child" (Holy Trinity Church, Sydney) 20 10
947 30c. "Veiled Virgin and Child" (St. Mary's Catholic Church, Geelong) 25 10
948 40c. Type **402** 40 70
949 50c. "Three Kings" (St. Mary's Cathedral, Sydney) 50 85
950 85c. "Madonna and Child" (St. Bartholomew's Church, Norwood) . . . . 60 1·40

1984. Bicentenary (1988) of Australian Settlement (1st issue). The First Australians. Multicoloured.
951 30c. Type **403** 20 45
952 30c. "Bunjil" (large figure), Grampians 20 45
953 30c. "Quikans" (tall figures), Cape York 20 45
954 30c. "Wandjina Spirit and Baby Snakes" (Gibb River) 20 45
955 30c. "Rock Python" (Gibb River) 20 45
956 30c. "Silver Barramundi" (fish) (Kakadu National Park) 20 45
957 30c. Bicentenary emblem . . 20 45
958 85c. "Rock Possum" (Kakadu National Park) 50 1·40
See also Nos. 972/5, 993/6, 1002/7, 1019/22, 1059/63, 1064/6, 1077/81, 1090/2, 1110, 1137/41, 1145/8 and 1149.

404 Yellow-tufted Honeyeater **405** "Musgrave Ranges" (Sidney Nolan)

1984. 150th Anniv of Victoria.
959 30c. Type **404** 40 65
960 30c. Leadbeater's possum . . 40 65

1985. Australia Day. Birth Bicentenary of Dorothea Mackellar (author of poem "My Country"). Multicoloured.
961 30c. Type **405** 50 80
962 30c. "The Walls of China" (Russell Drysdale) 50 80

406 Young People of Different Races and Sun **407** Royal Victorian Volunteer Artillery

1985. International Youth Year.
963 **406** 30c. multicoloured 40 30

1985. 19th-Century Australian Military Uniforms. Multicoloured.
964 33c. Type **407** 50 65
965 33c. Western Australian Pinjarrah Cavalry 50 65
966 33c. New South Wales Lancers 50 65
967 33c. New South Wales Contingent to the Sudan 50 65
968 33c. Victorian Mounted Rifles 50 65

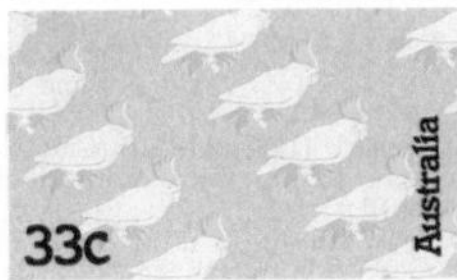

408 District Nurse of early 1900s **410** Abel Tasman and Journal Entry

409 Sulphur-crested Cockatoos

1985. Centenary of District Nursing Services.
969 **408** 33c. multicoloured 45 35

1985. Multicoloured, background colour given.
970 **409** 1c. flesh 1·50 2·50
971 33c. turquoise 45 55

1985. Bicentenary (1988) of Australian Settlement (2nd issue). Navigators. Multicoloured.
972 33c. Type **410** 45 35
973 33c. Dirk Hartog's "Eendracht" (detail, Aert Anthonisz) 45 35
974 33c. "William Dampier" (detail, T. Murray) 45 35
975 90c. Globe and hand with extract from Dampier's journal 1·00 2·50
MS976 150×115 mm. As Nos. 972/5, but with cream-coloured margins 3·25 4·50

411 Sovereign's Badge of Order of Australia
412 Tree, and Soil running through Hourglass ("Soil")

1985. Queen Elizabeth II's Birthday.
977 **411** 33c. multicoloured 40 30

1985. Conservation. Multicoloured.
978 33c. Type **412** 25 20
979 50c. Washing on line and smog ("air") 50 85
980 80c. Tap and flower ("water") 65 1·50
981 90c. Chain encircling flames ("energy") 80 2·00

413 "Elves and Fairies" (Annie Rentoul and Ida Rentoul Outhwaite)
414 Dish Aerials

1985. Classic Australian Children's Books. Mult.
982 33c. Type **413** 50 75
983 33c. "The Magic Pudding" (Norman Lindsay) 50 75
984 33c. "Ginger Meggs" (James Charles Bancks) 50 75
985 33c. "Blinky Bill" (Dorothy Wall) 50 75
986 33c. "Snugglepot and Cuddlepie" (May Gibbs) 50 75

1985. Electronic Mail Service.
987 **414** 33c. multicoloured 35 30

415 Angel in Sailing Ship

1985. Christmas. Multicoloured.
988 27c. Angel with holly wings 25 10
989 33c. Angel with bells 30 10
990 45c. Type **415** 40 35
991 55c. Angel with star 50 70
992 90c. Angel with Christmas tree bauble 75 1·75

416 Astrolabe ("Batavia", 1629)
417 Aboriginal Wandjina Spirit, Map of Australia and Egg

1985. Bicentenary (1988) of Australian Settlement (3rd issue). Relics from Early Shipwrecks. Multicoloured.
993 33c. Type **416** 35 15
994 50c. German beardman jug ("Vergulde Draeck", 1656) 60 1·00
995 90c. Wooden bobbins ("Batavia", 1629) and encrusted scissors ("Zeewijk", 1727) 1·25 3·00
996 $1 Silver and brass buckle ("Zeewijk", 1727) 1·25 2·25

1986. Australia Day.
997 **417** 33c. multicoloured 40 30

418 AUSSAT Satellite, Moon and Earth's Surface
419 H.M.S. "Buffalo"

1986. AUSSAT National Communications Satellite System. Multicoloured.
998 33c. Type **418** 40 15
999 80c. AUSSAT satellite in orbit 1·00 2·25

1986. 150th Anniv of South Australia. Mult.
1000 33c. Type **419** 70 1·00
1001 33c. "City Sign" sculpture (Otto Hajek), Adelaide 70 1·00
Nos. 1000/1 were printed together se-tenant, the background of each horiz pair showing an extract from the colony's Letters Patent of 1836.

420 "Banksia serrata"
421 Radio Telescope, Parkes, and Diagram of Comet's Orbit

1986. Bicentenary (1988) of Australian Settlement (4th issue). Cook's Voyage to New Holland. Multicoloured.
1002 33c. Type **420** 60 35
1003 33c. "Hibiscus meraukensis" 60 35
1004 50c. "Dillenia alata" 90 1·10
1005 80c. "Correa reflexa" 1·75 2·50
1006 90c. "Joseph Banks" (botanist) (Reynolds) and Banks with Dr. Solander 2·25 2·50
1007 90c. "Sydney Parkinson" (self-portrait) and Parkinson drawing 2·25 2·50

1986. Appearance of Halley's Comet.
1008 **421** 33c. multicoloured 50 35

422 Queen Elizabeth II
423 Brumbies (wild horses)

1986. 60th Birthday of Queen Elizabeth.
1009 **422** 33c. multicoloured 55 35

1986. Australian Horses. Multicoloured.
1010 33c. Type **423** 60 15
1011 80c. Mustering 1·50 2·25
1012 90c. Show-jumping 1·50 2·50
1013 $1 Child on pony 1·75 2·25

424 "The Old Shearer stands"
425 "King George III" (A. Ramsay) and Convicts

1986. Folklore. Scenes and Verses from the Folksong "Click go the Shears". Multicoloured.
1014 33c. Type **424** 55 80
1015 33c. "The ringer looks around" 55 80
1016 33c. "The boss of the board" 55 80
1017 33c. "The tar-boy is there" 55 80
1018 33c. "Shearing is all over" 55 80
Nos. 1014/18 were printed together, se-tenant, forming a composite design.

1986. Bicentenary (1988) of Australian Settlement (5th issue). Convict Settlement in New South Wales. Multicoloured.
1019 33c. Type **425** 80 65
1020 33c. "Lord Sydney" (Gilbert Stuart) and convicts 80 65
1021 33c. "Captain Arthur Phillip" (F. Wheatley) and ship 80 65
1022 $1 "Captain John Hunter" (W. B. Bennett) and aborigines 3·25 5·50

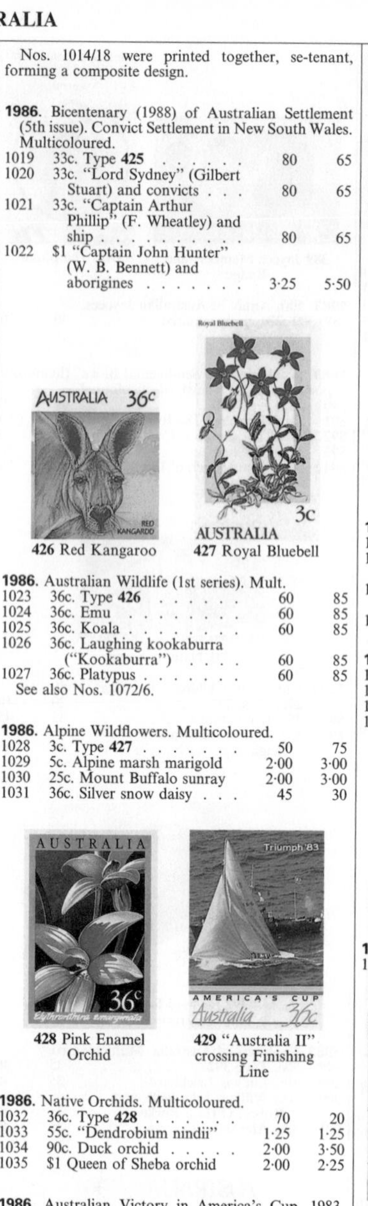

426 Red Kangaroo
427 Royal Bluebell

1986. Australian Wildlife (1st series). Mult.
1023 36c. Type **426** 60 85
1024 36c. Emu 60 85
1025 36c. Koala 60 85
1026 36c. Laughing kookaburra ("Kookaburra") 60 85
1027 36c. Platypus 60 85
See also Nos. 1072/6.

1986. Alpine Wildflowers. Multicoloured.
1028 3c. Type **427** 50 75
1029 5c. Alpine marsh marigold 2·00 3·00
1030 25c. Mount Buffalo sunray 2·00 3·00
1031 36c. Silver snow daisy 45 30

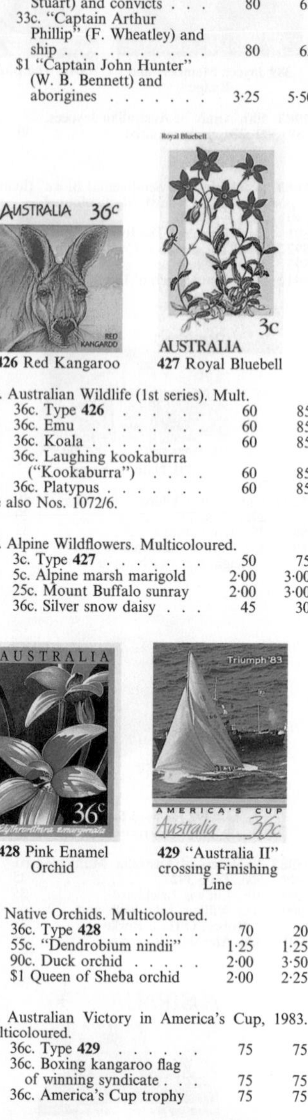

428 Pink Enamel Orchid
429 "Australia II" crossing Finishing Line

1986. Native Orchids. Multicoloured.
1032 36c. Type **428** 70 20
1033 55c. "Dendrobium nindii" 1·25 1·25
1034 90c. Duck orchid 2·00 3·50
1035 $1 Queen of Sheba orchid 2·00 2·25

1986. Australian Victory in America's Cup, 1983. Multicoloured.
1036 36c. Type **429** 75 75
1037 36c. Boxing kangaroo flag of winning syndicate 75 75
1038 36c. America's Cup trophy 75 75

430 Dove with Olive Branch and Sun
431 Mary and Joseph

1986. International Peace Year.
1039 **430** 36c. multicoloured 65 40

1986. Christmas. Scenes from children's nativity play. Multicoloured.
1040 30c. Type **431** 40 30
1041 36c. Three Wise Men leaving gifts 50 45
1042 60c. Angels (horiz) 90 1·50
MS1043 147×70 mm. 30c. Three angels and shepherd (horiz); 30c. Kneeling shepherds (horiz); 30c. Mary, Joseph and three angels; 30c. Innkeeper and two angels; 30c. Three Wise Men (horiz) 3·50 3·75

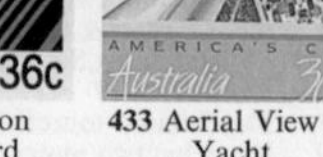

432 Australian Flag on Printed Circuit Board
433 Aerial View of Yacht

1987. Australia Day. Multicoloured.
1044 36c. Type **432** 55 75
1045 36c. "Australian Made" Campaign logos 55 75

1987. America's Cup Yachting Championship. Multicoloured.
1046 36c. Type **433** 40 20
1047 55c. Two yachts tacking 90 1·25
1048 90c. Two yachts beating 1·40 2·50
1049 $1 Two yachts under full sail 1·50 1·75

434 Grapes and Melons
435 Livestock

1987. Australian Fruit. Multicoloured.
1050 36c. Type **434** 40 20
1051 65c. Tropical and sub-tropical fruits 1·00 1·50
1052 90c. Citrus fruit, apples and pears 1·40 2·50
1053 $1 Stone and berry fruits 1·40 1·60

1987. Agricultural Shows. Multicoloured.
1054 36c. Type **435** 60 20
1055 65c. Produce 1·25 1·75
1056 90c. Sideshows 1·75 2·75
1057 $1 Competitions 1·90 2·40

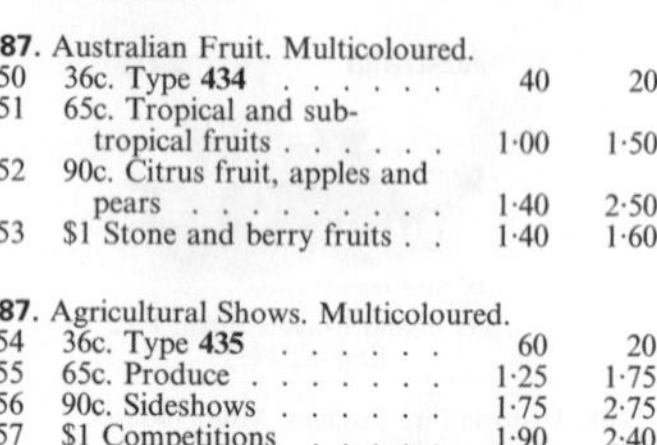

436 Queen Elizabeth in Australia, 1986

1987. Queen Elizabeth II's Birthday.
1058 **436** 36c. multicoloured 55 60

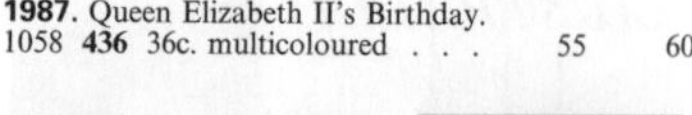

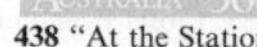

437 Convicts on Quay
438 "At the Station"

1987. Bicentenary (1988) of Australian Settlement (6th issue). Departure of the First Fleet. Multicoloured.
1059 36c. Type **437** 80 1·10
1060 36c. Royal Marines officer and wife 80 1·10
1061 36c. Sailors loading supplies 80 1·10
1062 36c. Officers being ferried to ships 80 1·10
1063 36c. Fleet in English Channel 80 1·10
See also Nos. 1064/6, 1077/81 and 1090/2.

1987. Bicentenary (1988) of Australian Settlement (7th issue). First Fleet at Tenerife. As T **437**. Multicoloured.
1064 36c. Ferrying supplies, Santa Cruz 70 1·00
1065 36c. Canary Islands fishermen and departing fleet 70 1·00
1066 $1 Fleet arriving at Tenerife 1·75 2·25
Nos. 1064/5 were printed together, se-tenant, forming a composite design.

1987. Folklore. Scenes and Verses from Poem "The Man from Snowy River". Multicoloured.
1067 36c. Type **438** 70 1·00
1068 36c. "Mountain bred" 70 1·00
1069 36c. "That terrible descent" 70 1·00
1070 36c. "At their heels" 70 1·00
1071 36c. "Brought them back" 70 1·00
Nos. 1067/71 were printed together, se-tenant, forming a composite background design of mountain scenery.

1987. Australian Wildlife (2nd series). As T **426**. Multicoloured.
1072 37c. Common brushtail possum 55 80
1073 37c. Sulphur-crested cockatoo ("Cockatoo") 55 80
1074 37c. Common wombat 55 80
1075 37c. Crimson rosella ("Rosella") 55 80
1076 37c. Echidna 55 80

1987. Bicentenary (1988) of Australian Settlement (8th issue). First Fleet at Rio de Janeiro. As T **437**. Multicoloured.
1077 37c. Sperm whale and fleet 80 1·00
1078 37c. Brazilian coast 80 1·00

1079 37c. British officers in market . . . . 80 1·00
1080 37c. Religious procession . . 80 1·00
1081 37c. Fleet leaving Rio . . . 80 1·00
Nos. 1077/81 were printed together, se-tenant, forming a composite design.

439 Bionic Ear
440 Catching Crayfish

1987. Australian Achievements in Technology. Mult.
1082 37c. Type **439** 40 35
1083 53c. Microchips 75 60
1084 63c. Robotics 85 70
1085 68c. Ceramics 95 75

1987. "Aussie Kids". Multicoloured.
1086 37c. Type **440** 40 35
1087 55c. Playing cat's cradle . . 75 75
1088 90c. Young football supporters . . . . 1·25 2·00
1089 $1 Children with kangaroo 1·25 1·50

1987. Bicentenary (1988) of Australian Settlement (9th issue). First Fleet at Cape of Good Hope. As T **437**. Multicoloured.
1090 37c. Marine checking list of livestock . . . . 65 1·00
1091 37c. Loading livestock . . . 65 1·00
1092 $1 First Fleet at Cape Town 1·50 2·25
Nos. 1090/1 were printed together, se-tenant, forming a composite design.

441 Detail of Spearthrower, Western Australia

1987. Aboriginal Crafts. Multicoloured.
1093 3c. Type **441** . . . . 1·10 1·50
1094 15c. Shield pattern, New South Wales . . . . . . 5·00 7·00
1095 37c. Basket weave, Queensland . . . . 1·10 1·50
1096 37c. Bowl design, Central Australia . . . . 90 1·25
1097 37c. Belt pattern, Northern Territory . . . . 1·10 1·50

442 Grandmother and Granddaughters with Candles
443 Koala with Stockman's Hat and Eagle dressed as Uncle Sam

1987. Christmas. Designs showing carol singing by candlelight. Multicoloured.
1098 30c. Type **442** 50 65
1099 30c. Father and daughters 50 65
1100 30c. Four children 50 65
1101 30c. Family 50 65
1102 30c. Six teenagers 50 65
1103 37c. Choir (horiz) 50 65
1104 63c. Father and two children (horiz) . . . . . 85 1·25

1988. Bicentenary of Australian Settlement (10th issue). Arrival of First Fleet. As T **437**. Mult.
1105 37c. Aborigines watching arrival of Fleet, Botany Bay 65 90
1106 37c. Aborigine family and anchored ships 65 90
1107 37c. Fleet arriving at Sydney Cove 65 90
1108 37c. Ship's boat 65 90
1109 37c. Raising the flag, Sydney Cove, 26 January 1788 . . 65 90
Nos. 1105/9 were printed together, se-tenant, forming a composite design.

1988. Bicentenary of Australian Settlement (11th issue). Joint issue with U.S.A.
1110 **443** 37c. multicoloured . . . 60 35

444 "Religion" (A. Horner)
445 "Government House, Sydney, 1790" (George Raper)

1988. "Living Together". Designs showing cartoons. Multicoloured (except 30c.).
1111 1c. Type **444** 50 60
1112 2c. "Industry" (P. Nicholson) 50 50
1113 3c. "Local Government" (A. Collette) 50 50
1114 4c. "Trade Unions" (Liz Honey) 10 20
1115 5c. "Parliament" (Bronwyn Halls) 50 50
1116 10c. "Transport" (Meg Williams) 30 40
1117 15c. "Sport" (G. Cook) . . 70 60
1118 20c. "Commerce" (M. Atcherson) 70 70
1119 25c. "Housing" (C. Smith) 45 40
1120 30c. "Welfare" (R. Tandberg) (black and lilac) 55 80
1121 37c. "Postal Services" (P. Viska) 60 50
1121b 39c. "Tourism" (J. Spooner) 60 50
1122 40c. "Recreation" (R. Harvey) 70 70
1123 45c. "Health" (Jenny Coopes) . . . . 70 1·00
1124 50c. "Mining" (G. Haddon) 70 50
1125 53c. "Primary Industry" (S. Leahy) . . . . . . 1·75 1·50
1126 55c. "Education" (Victoria Roberts) . . . . 1·50 1·50
1127 60c. "Armed Forces" (B. Green) . . . . . . 1·50 70
1128 63c. "Police" (J. Russell) 2·00 1·10
1129 65c. "Telecommunications" (B. Petty) . . . . 1·50 2·00
1130 68c. "The Media" (A. Langoulant) . . . . 2·00 2·75
1131 70c. "Science and Technology" (J. Hook) 1·75 1·25
1132 75c. "Visual Arts" (G. Dazeley) . . . . . 1·00 1·00
1133 80c. "Performing Arts" (A. Stitt) . . . . 1·25 1·00
1134 90c. "Banking" (S. Billington) . . . . . 1·50 1·00
1135 95c. "Law" (C. Aslanis) . . 1·00 1·75
1136 $1 "Rescue and Emergency" (M. Leunig) 1·10 1·00

1988. Bicentenary of Australian Settlement (12th issue). "The Early Years, 1788–1809". Mult.
1137 37c. Type **445** . . . . . . 65 1·00
1138 37c. "Government Farm, Parramatta, 1791" ("The Port Jackson Painter") . . 65 1·00
1139 37c. "Parramatta Road, 1796" (attr Thomas Watling) . . . . 65 1·00
1140 37c. "View of Sydney Cove, c. 1800" (detail) (Edward Dayes) . . . . . 65 1·00
1141 37c. "Sydney Hospital, 1803", (detail) (George William Evans) . . . . . 65 1·00
Nos. 1137/41 were printed together, se-tenant, forming a composite background design from the painting "View of Sydney from the East Side of the Cove, c. 1808" by John Eyre.

446 Queen Elizabeth II (from photo by Tim Graham)

1988. Queen Elizabeth II's Birthday.
1142 **446** 37c. multicoloured . . . 50 40

447 Expo '88 Logo

1988. "Expo '88" World Fair, Brisbane.
1143 **447** 37c. multicoloured . . . 50 40

448 New Parliament House

1988. Opening of New Parliament House, Canberra.
1144 **448** 37c. multicoloured . . . 50 40

449 Early Settler and Sailing Clipper

1988. Bicentenary of Australian Settlement (13th issue). Multicoloured.
1145 37c. Type **449** . . . . . . 75 1·00
1146 37c. Queen Elizabeth II with British and Australian Parliament Buildings . . . 75 1·00
1147 $1 W. G. Grace (cricketer) and tennis racquet . . . . 1·50 2·25
1148 $1 Shakespeare, John Lennon (entertainer) and Sydney Opera House . . 1·50 2·25
Stamps in similar designs were also issued by Great Britain.

450 Kiwi and Koala at Campfire

1988. Bicentenary of Australian Settlement (14th issue).
1149 **450** 37c. multicoloured . . . 65 40
A stamp in a similar design was also issued by New Zealand.

451 "Bush Potato Country" (Turkey Tolsen Tjupurrula and David Corby Tjapaltjarri)

1988. Art of the Desert. Aboriginal Paintings from Central Australia. Multicoloured.
1150 37c. Type **451** 30 30
1151 55c. "Courtship Rejected" (Limpi Puntungka Tjapangati) 55 70
1152 90c. "Medicine Story" (artist unknown) . . . . 75 2·40
1153 $1 "Ancestor Dreaming" (Tim Leura Tjapaltjarri) 80 1·50

452 Basketball

1988. Olympic Games, Seoul. Multicoloured.
1154 37c. Type **452** 50 40
1155 65c. Athlete crossing finish line . . . . 60 1·50
1156 $1 Gymnast with hoop . . . 85 1·75

453 Rod and Mace

1988. 34th Commonwealth Parliamentary Conference, Canberra.
1157 **453** 37c. multicoloured . . . 50 60

454 Necklace by Peter Tully

1988. Australian Crafts. Multicoloured.
1158 2c. Type **454** . . . . 3·75 5·00
1159 5c. Vase by Colin Levy . . 3·75 5·00
1160 39c. Teapot by Frank Bauer 50 35

455 Pinnacles Desert

1988. Panorama of Australia. Multicoloured.
1161 39c. Type **455** 60 40
1162 55c. Flooded landscape, Arnhem Land . . . . . 90 1·00
1163 65c. Twelve Apostles, Victoria . . . . 1·25 2·00
1164 70c. Mountain Ash wood 1·25 2·00

456 "The Nativity" (Danielle Hush)

1988. Christmas. Multicoloured.
1165 32c. Type **456** 50 20
1166 39c. "Koala as Father Christmas" (Kylie Courtney) 55 25
1167 63c. "Christmas Cockatoo" (Benjamin Stevenson) . . 1·10 1·60

457 Sir Henry Parkes
458 Bowls

1989. Australia Day. Centenary of Federation Speech by Sir Henry Parkes (N.S.W. Prime Minister).
1168 **457** 39c. multicoloured . . . 45 40

1989. Sports. Multicoloured.
1169 1c. Type **458** 10 30
1170 2c. Tenpin-bowling 10 10
1171 3c. Australian football . . . 60 70
1172 5c. Kayaking and canoeing 15 10
1174 10c. Sailboarding 15 15
1176 20c. Tennis 20 25
1179 39c. Fishing 45 40
1180 41c. Cycling 40 35
1181 43c. Skateboarding 50 40
1184 55c. Kite-flying 50 45
1186 65c. Rock-climbing 80 60
1187 70c. Cricket . . . . 1·25 80
1188 75c. Netball . . . . 55 1·00
1189 80c. Squash . . . . 1·00 65
1190 85c. Diving . . . . 1·75 80
1191 90c. Soccer . . . . 1·75 1·00
1192 $1 Fun-run . . . . 1·00 70
1193 $1.10 Golf . . . . 1·75 90
1194 $1.20 Hang-gliding . . . . 3·75 1·10

459 Merino

1989. Sheep in Australia. Multicoloured.
1195 39c. Type **459** 70 45
1196 39c. Poll Dorset 70 45
1197 85c. Polwarth . . . . 1·40 2·50
1198 $1 Corriedale . . . . 1·40 1·50

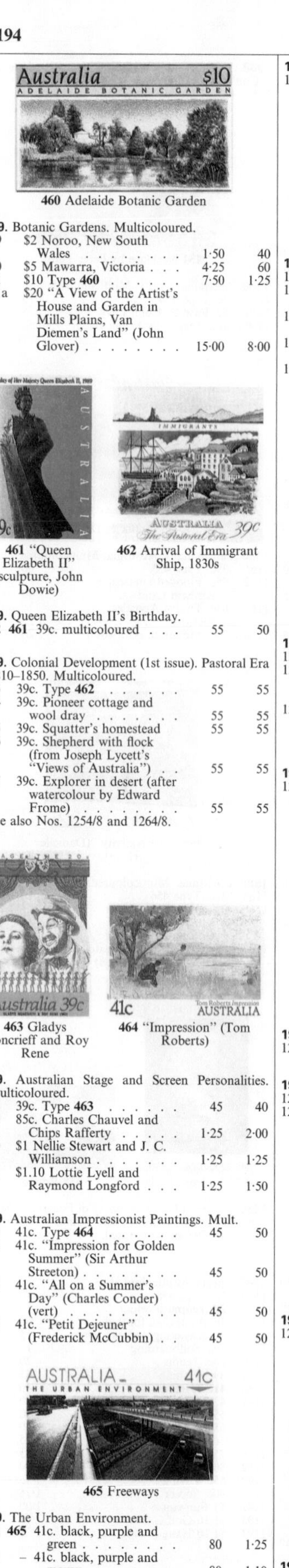

460 Adelaide Botanic Garden

1989. Botanic Gardens. Multicoloured.
1199 $2 Noroo, New South Wales . . . . 1·50 40
1200 $5 Mawarra, Victoria . . . 4·25 60
1201 $10 Type **460** . . . . . . 7·50 1·25
1201a $20 "A View of the Artist's House and Garden in Mills Plains, Van Diemen's Land" (John Glover) . . . . 15·00 8·00

461 "Queen Elizabeth II" (sculpture, John Dowie)
462 Arrival of Immigrant Ship, 1830s

1989. Queen Elizabeth II's Birthday.
1202 **461** 39c. multicoloured . . . 55 50

1989. Colonial Development (1st issue). Pastoral Era 1810–1850. Multicoloured.
1203 39c. Type **462** 55 55
1204 39c. Pioneer cottage and wool dray 55 55
1205 39c. Squatter's homestead 55 55
1206 39c. Shepherd with flock (from Joseph Lycett's "Views of Australia") . . 55 55
1207 39c. Explorer in desert (after watercolour by Edward Frome) 55 55
See also Nos. 1254/8 and 1264/8.

463 Gladys Moncrieff and Roy Rene
464 "Impression" (Tom Roberts)

1989. Australian Stage and Screen Personalities. Multicoloured.
1208 39c. Type **463** 45 40
1209 85c. Charles Chauvel and Chips Rafferty . . . . 1·25 2·00
1210 $1 Nellie Stewart and J. C. Williamson . . . . . . 1·25 1·25
1211 $1.10 Lottie Lyell and Raymond Longford . . . 1·25 1·50

1989. Australian Impressionist Paintings. Mult.
1212 41c. Type **464** 45 50
1213 41c. "Impression for Golden Summer" (Sir Arthur Streeton) 45 50
1214 41c. "All on a Summer's Day" (Charles Conder) (vert) 45 50
1215 41c. "Petit Dejeuner" (Frederick McCubbin) . . 45 50

465 Freeways

1989. The Urban Environment.
1216 **465** 41c. black, purple and green . . . . 80 1·25
1217 – 41c. black, purple and mauve . . . . 80 1·10
1218 – 41c. black, purple and blue . . . . 80 1·25
DESIGNS: No. 1217, City buildings, Melbourne; No. 1218, Commuter train at platform.

466 Hikers outside Youth Hostel

1989. 50th Anniv of Australian Youth Hostels.
1219 **466** 41c. multicoloured . . . 55 50

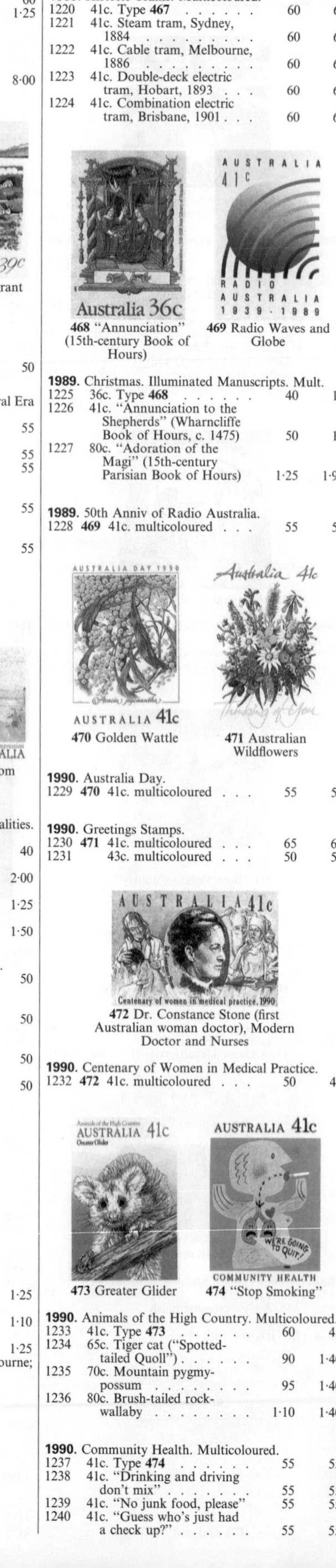

467 Horse Tram, Adelaide, 1878

1989. Historic Trams. Multicoloured.
1220 41c. Type **467** 60 60
1221 41c. Steam tram, Sydney, 1884 . . . . 60 60
1222 41c. Cable tram, Melbourne, 1886 . . . . 60 60
1223 41c. Double-deck electric tram, Hobart, 1893 . . . 60 60
1224 41c. Combination electric tram, Brisbane, 1901 . . . 60 60

468 "Annunciation" (15th-century Book of Hours)
469 Radio Waves and Globe

1989. Christmas. Illuminated Manuscripts. Mult.
1225 36c. Type **468** 40 15
1226 41c. "Annunciation to the Shepherds" (Wharncliffe Book of Hours, c. 1475) 50 15
1227 80c. "Adoration of the Magi" (15th-century Parisian Book of Hours) 1·25 1·90

1989. 50th Anniv of Radio Australia.
1228 **469** 41c. multicoloured . . . 55 50

470 Golden Wattle
471 Australian Wildflowers

1990. Australia Day.
1229 **470** 41c. multicoloured . . . 55 50

1990. Greetings Stamps.
1230 **471** 41c. multicoloured . . . 65 65
1231 43c. multicoloured . . . 50 50

472 Dr. Constance Stone (first Australian woman doctor), Modern Doctor and Nurses

1990. Centenary of Women in Medical Practice.
1232 **472** 41c. multicoloured . . . 50 45

473 Greater Glider
474 "Stop Smoking"

1990. Animals of the High Country. Multicoloured.
1233 41c. Type **473** 60 45
1234 65c. Tiger cat ("Spotted-tailed Quoll") . . . . . . 90 1·40
1235 70c. Mountain pygmy-possum . . . . 95 1·40
1236 80c. Brush-tailed rock-wallaby . . . . 1·10 1·40

1990. Community Health. Multicoloured.
1237 41c. Type **474** 55 55
1238 41c. "Drinking and driving don't mix" 55 55
1239 41c. "No junk food, please" 55 55
1240 41c. "Guess who's just had a check up?" 55 55

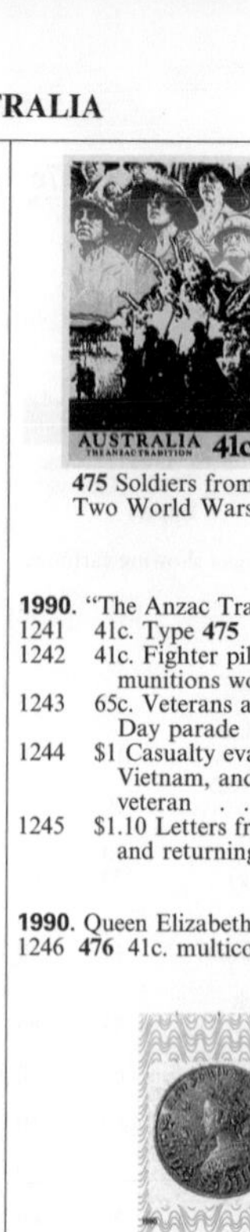

475 Soldiers from Two World Wars
476 Queen at Australian Ballet Gala Performance, London, 1988

1990. "The Anzac Tradition". Multicoloured.
1241 41c. Type **475** 50 40
1242 41c. Fighter pilots and munitions worker 50 40
1243 65c. Veterans and Anzac Day parade 85 90
1244 $1 Casualty evacuation, Vietnam, and disabled veteran . . . . 1·25 1·40
1245 $1.10 Letters from home and returning troopships 1·40 1·50

1990. Queen Elizabeth II's Birthday.
1246 **476** 41c. multicoloured . . . 65 45

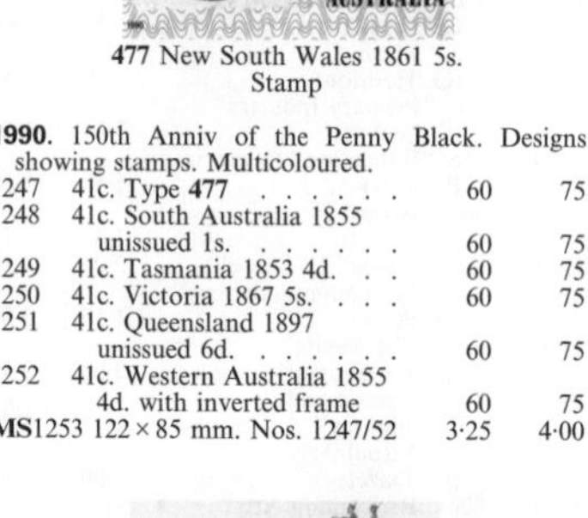

477 New South Wales 1861 5s. Stamp

1990. 150th Anniv of the Penny Black. Designs showing stamps. Multicoloured.
1247 41c. Type **477** 60 75
1248 41c. South Australia 1855 unissued 1s. 60 75
1249 41c. Tasmania 1853 4d. . . 60 75
1250 41c. Victoria 1867 5s. . . . 60 75
1251 41c. Queensland 1897 unissued 6d. 60 75
1252 41c. Western Australia 1855 4d. with inverted frame 60 75
MS1253 122 × 85 mm. Nos. 1247/52 3·25 4·00

478 Gold Miners on Way to Diggings

1990. Colonial Development (2nd issue). Gold Fever. Multicoloured.
1254 41c. Type **478** 80 90
1255 41c. Mining camp 80 90
1256 41c. Panning and washing for gold 80 90
1257 41c. Gold Commissioner's tent 80 90
1258 41c. Moving gold under escort 80 90

479 Glaciology Research

1990. Australian–Soviet Scientific Co-operation in Antarctica. Multicoloured.
1261 41c. Type **479** 65 40
1262 $1.10 Krill (marine biology research) . . . . 1·60 1·50
MS1263 85 × 65 mm. Nos. 1261/2 2·25 2·25
Stamps in similar designs were also issued by Russia.

480 Auctioning Building Plots

1990. Colonial Development (3rd series). Boomtime. Multicoloured.
1264 41c. Type **480** 55 55
1265 41c. Colonial mansion . . . 55 55
1266 41c. Stock exchange 55 55
1267 41c. Fashionable society . . 55 55
1268 41c. Factories 55 55

481 "Salmon Gums" (Robert Juniper)

482 "Adelaide Town Hall" (Edmund Gouldsmith)

1990. "Heidelberg and Heritage" Art Exhibition. Multicoloured.
1269 28c. Type **481** . . . . . . 2·50 3·25
1270 43c. "The Blue Dress" (Brian Dunlop) 40 45

1990. 150th Anniv of Local Government.
1271 **482** 43c. multicoloured . . . 75 50

483 Laughing Kookaburras and Gifts

1990. Christmas. Multicoloured.
1272 38c. Type **483** 50 25
1273 43c. Baby Jesus with koalas and wallaby (vert) 50 25
1274 80c. Possum on Christmas tree . . . . 1·50 2·50

484 National Flag
485 Black-necked Stork

1991. Australia Day. 90th Anniv of Australian Flag.
1275 **484** 43c. blue, red and grey 50 40
1276 – 90c. multicoloured . . . . 1·10 1·25
1277 – $1 multicoloured . . . . 1·25 1·40
1278 – $1.20 red, blue and grey 1·60 1·75
DESIGNS: 90c. Royal Australian Navy ensign; $1 Royal Australian Air Force standard; $1.20, Australian merchant marine ensign.

1991. Waterbirds. Multicoloured.
1279 43c. Type **485** 75 40
1280 43c. Black swan (horiz) . . 75 40
1281 85c. Cereopsis goose ("Cape Barren") . . . . 1·75 2·25
1282 $1 Chestnut-breasted teal ("Chestnut Teal") (horiz) 1·90 1·75

486 Recruitment Poster (Women's Services)

1991. Anzac Day. 50th Anniversaries.
1283 **486** 43c. multicoloured . . . 60 40
1284 – 43c. black, green & brn 60 40
1285 – $1.20 multicoloured . . 2·25 2·00
DESIGNS: 43c. (No. 1284) Patrol (Defence of Tobruk); $1.20, "V-P Day Canberra" (Harold Abbot) (Australian War Memorial).

487 Queen Elizabeth at Royal Albert Hall, London

489 "Bondi" (Max Dupain)

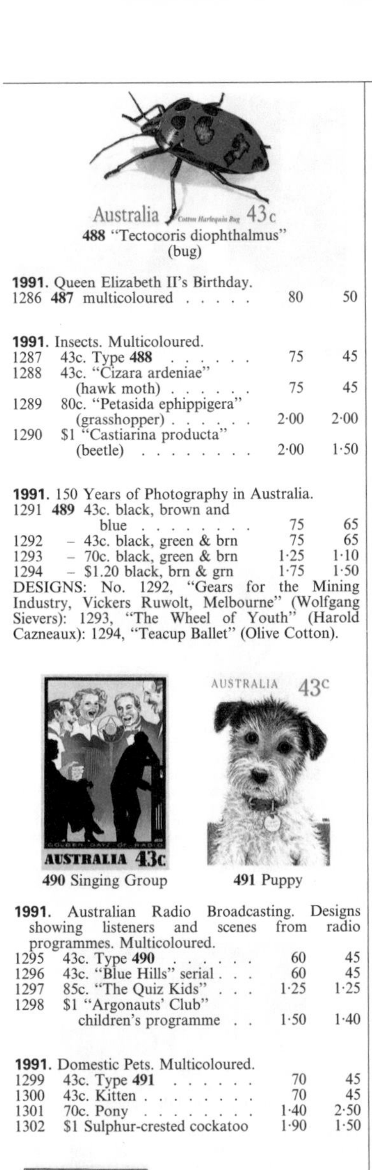

488 "Tectocoris diophthalmus" (bug)

1991. Queen Elizabeth II's Birthday.
1286 **487** multicoloured 80 50

1991. Insects. Multicoloured.
1287 43c. Type **488** 75 45
1288 43c. "Cizara ardeniae" (hawk moth) 75 45
1289 80c. "Petasida ephippigera" (grasshopper) . . . . . . 2·00 2·00
1290 $1 "Castiarina producta" (beetle) . . . . 2·00 1·50

1991. 150 Years of Photography in Australia.
1291 **489** 43c. black, brown and blue 75 65
1292 – 43c. black, green & brn 75 65
1293 – 70c. black, green & brn 1·25 1·10
1294 – $1.20 black, brn & grn 1·75 1·50
DESIGNS: No. 1292, "Gears for the Mining Industry, Vickers Ruwolt, Melbourne" (Wolfgang Sievers): 1293, "The Wheel of Youth" (Harold Cazneaux): 1294, "Teacup Ballet" (Olive Cotton).

490 Singing Group

491 Puppy

1991. Australian Radio Broadcasting. Designs showing listeners and scenes from radio programmes. Multicoloured.
1295 43c. Type **490** 60 45
1296 43c. "Blue Hills" serial . . . 60 45
1297 85c. "The Quiz Kids" . . . 1·25 1·25
1298 $1 "Argonauts' Club" children's programme . . 1·50 1·40

1991. Domestic Pets. Multicoloured.
1299 43c. Type **491** 70 45
1300 43c. Kitten 70 45
1301 70c. Pony . . . . 1·40 2·50
1302 $1 Sulphur-crested cockatoo 1·90 1·50

492 George Vancouver (1791) and Edward Eyre (1841)

493 "Seven Little Australians" (Ethel Turner)

1991. Exploration of Western Australia.
1303 **492** $1.05 multicoloured . . 1·00 1·10
MS1304 100 × 65 mm. No. 1303 1·25 1·40

1991. Australian Writers of the 1890s. Multicoloured.
1305 43c. Type **493** 50 45
1306 75c. "On Our Selection" (Steele Rudd) . . . . . . 80 1·00
1307 $1 "Clancy of the Overflow" (poem, A. B. Paterson) (vert) . . . . 1·10 1·00
1308 $1.20 "The Drover's Wife" (short story, Henry Lawson) (vert) . . . . . 1·25 1·60

494 Shepherd

1991. Christmas. Multicoloured.
1309 38c. Type **494** 40 15
1310 43c. Infant Jesus 45 15
1311 90c. Wise Man . . . . . . 1·50 1·75

495 Parma Wallaby

1992. Threatened Species. Multicoloured.
1312 45c. Type **495** 70 65
1313 45c. Ghost bat 70 65
1314 45c. Long-tailed dunnart . . 70 65
1315 45c. Little pygmy-possum 70 65
1316 45c. Dusky hopping-mouse 70 65
1317 45c. Squirrel glider 70 65

496 Basket of Wild Flowers

1992. Greetings Stamp.
1318 **496** 45c. multicoloured . . . 50 50

497 Noosa River, Queensland

1992. Wetlands and Waterways. Multicoloured.
1319 20c. Type **497** . . . . . . 1·75 2·25
1320 45c. Lake Eildon, Victoria 40 45

498 "Young Endeavour" (brigantine)

1992. Australia Day and 500th Anniv of Discovery of America by Columbus (**MS**1337). Multicoloured. Sailing Ships.
1333 45c. Type **498** 80 50
1334 45c. "Britannia" (yacht) (vert) 80 50
1335 $1.05 "Akarana" (cutter) (vert) . . . . 1·75 2·75
1336 $1.20 "John Louis" (pearling lugger) . . . . 2·00 2·00
MS1337 147 × 64 mm. Nos. 1333/6 4·75 5·25

499 Bombing of Darwin

1992. 50th Anniv of Second World War Battles. Multicoloured.
1338 45c. Type **499** 70 45
1339 75c. Anti-aircraft gun and fighters, Milne Bay . . . 1·25 1·50
1340 75c. Infantry on Kokoda Trail . . . . 1·25 1·50
1341 $1.05 H.M.A.S. "Australia" (cruiser) and U.S.S. "Yorktown" (aircraft carrier), Coral Sea . . . . 1·50 1·75
1342 $1.20 Australians advancing, El Alamein . . . . 1·75 1·60

500 "Helix Nebula"

1992. International Space Year. Multicoloured.
1343 45c. Type **500** 70 45
1344 $1.05 "The Pleiades" . . . 1·75 1·25
1345 $1.20 "Spiral Galaxy, NGC 2997" . . . . 2·00 1·50
MS1346 133 × 70 mm. Nos. 1343/5 4·50 4·50

501 Hunter Valley, New South Wales

1992. Vineyard Regions. Multicoloured.
1347 45c. Type **501** 60 75
1348 45c. North-east Victoria . . 60 75
1349 45c. Barossa Valley, South Australia 60 75
1350 45c. Coonawarra, South Australia 60 75
1351 45c. Margaret River, Western Australia 60 75

502 3½d. Stamp of 1953

503 Salt Action

1992. Queen Elizabeth II's Birthday.
1352 **502** 45c. multicoloured . . . 80 50

1992. Land Conservation. Multicoloured.
1353 45c. Type **503** . . . . . . 85 1·00
1354 45c. Farm planning . . . . 85 1·00
1355 45c. Erosion control . . . . 85 1·00
1356 45c. Tree planting . . . . . 85 1·00
1357 45c. Dune care . . . . . . 85 1·00

504 Cycling

1992. Olympic Games and Paralympic Games (No. 1359), Barcelona. Multicoloured.
1358 45c. Type **504** 60 45
1359 $1.20 High jumping . . . . 1·50 1·60
1360 $1.20 Weightlifting . . . . 1·50 1·60

505 Echidna

506 Sydney Harbour Tunnel (value at left)

1992. Australian Wildlife (1st series). Multicoloured.
1361 30c. Saltwater crocodile . . 25 20
1362 35c. Type **505** 50 30
1363 40c. Platypus . . . . . . 1·25 25
1364 50c. Koala 60 35
1365 60c. Common bushtail possum . . . . 1·00 1·25
1366 70c. Laughing kookaburra ("Kookaburra") . . . . 1·75 1·00
1367 85c. Australian pelican ("Pelican") 75 70
1368a 90c. Eastern grey kangaroo 1·50 1·50
1369 95c. Common wombat . . 1·00 2·00
1370a $1.20 Major Mitchell's cockatoo ("Pink Cockatoo") . . . . . . 1·25 1·10
1371 $1.35 Emu . . . . 1·00 2·00
See also Nos. 1453/8.

1992. Opening of Sydney Harbour Tunnel. Mult.
1375b 45c. Type **506** . . . . . . 1·75 1·75
1376b 45c. Sydney Harbour Tunnel (value at right) 1·75 1·75
Nos. 1375/6 were printed together, se-tenant, forming a composite design.

507 Warden's Courthouse, Coolgardie

508 Bowler of 1892

1992. Centenary of Discovery of Gold at Coolgardie and Kalgoorlie. Multicoloured.
1377 45c. Type **507** 70 45
1378 45c. Post Office, Kalgoorlie 70 45
1379 $1.05 York Hotel, Kalgoorlie . . . . 1·60 1·60
1380 $1.20 Town Hall, Kalgoorlie 1·90 1·90

1992. Centenary of Sheffield Shield Cricket Tournament. Multicoloured.
1381 45c. Type **508** 85 50
1382 $1.20 Batsman and wicket-keeper . . . . 1·90 2·50

509 Children's Nativity Play

1992. Christmas. Multicoloured.
1383 40c. Type **509** 55 25
1384 45c. Child waking on Christmas Day 60 25
1385 $1 Children carol singing . . 1·90 2·00

510 "Ghost Gum, Central Australia" (Namatjira)

1993. Australia Day. Paintings by Albert Namatjira. Multicoloured.
1386 45c. Type **510** . . . . . . 90 1·40
1387 45c. "Across the Plain to Mount Giles" . . . . . . 90 1·40

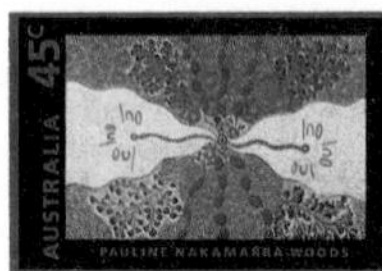

511 "Wild Onion Dreaming" (Pauline Nakamarra Woods)

1993. "Dreamings". Paintings by Aboriginal Artists. Multicoloured.
1388 45c. Type **511** 60 30
1389 75c. "Yam Plants" (Jack Wunuwun) (vert) . . . . 1·10 95
1390 85c. "Goose Egg Hunt" (George Milpurrurru) (vert) . . . . 1·25 1·40
1391 $1 "Kalumpiwarra-Ngulalintji" (Rover Thomas) . . . . 1·40 1·40

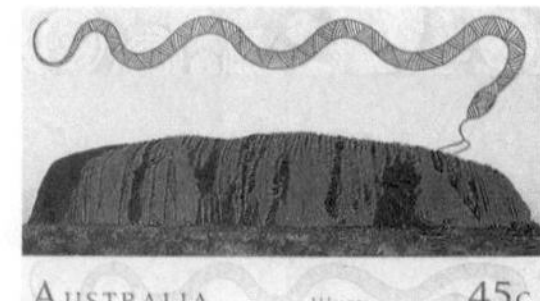

512 Uluru (Ayers Rock) National Park

1993. World Heritage Sites (1st series). Multicoloured.
1392 45c. Type **512** 80 30
1393 85c. Rain forest, Fraser Island . . . . 2·00 1·60
1394 95c. Beach, Shark Bay . . . 2·00 1·60
1395 $2 Waterfall, Kakadu . . . 3·00 2·25
See also Nos. 1582/5.

513 Queen Elizabeth II on Royal Visit, 1992

514 H.M.A.S. "Sydney" (cruiser, launched 1934) in Action

1993. Queen Elizabeth II's Birthday.
1396 **513** 45c. multicoloured . . . 70 60

1993. Second World War Naval Vessels. Mult.
1397 45c. Type **514** 80 45
1398 85c. H.M.A.S. "Bathurst" (mine-sweeper) . . . . . 1·60 1·75
1399 $1.05 H.M.A.S. "Arunta" (destroyer) . . . . 1·75 2·75
1400 $1.20 "Centaur" (hospital ship) and tug . . . . . . 2·00 2·75

515 "Work in the Home"

516 "Centenary Special", Tasmania, 1971

1993. Working Life in the 1890s. Mult.
1401 45c. Type **515** 55 50
1402 45c. "Work in the Cities" . . 55 50
1403 $1 "Work in the Country" 1·10 1·25
1404 $1.20 Trade Union banner 1·50 2·00

1993. Australian Trains. Multicoloured.
1405 45c. Type **516** 65 80
1406 45c. "Spirit of Progress", Victoria 65 80
1407 45c. "Western Endeavour", Western Australia, 1970 65 80

1408 45c. "Silver City Comet", New South Wales 65 80
1409 45c. Cairns–Kuranda tourist train, Queensland 65 80
1410 45c. "The Ghan", Northern Territory 65 80
Nos. 1405/10 also come self-adhesive.

517 "Black Cockatoo Feather" (Fiona Foley)
518 Conference Emblem

1993. International Year of Indigenous Peoples. Aboriginal Art. Multicoloured
1417 45c. Type **517** 55 30
1418 75c. "Ngarrgooroon Country" (Hector Jandany) (horiz) . . . . 1·10 1·50
1419 $1 "Ngak Ngak" (Ginger Riley Munduwalawala) (horiz) . . . . 1·25 1·60
1420 $1.05 "Untitled" (Robert Cole) . . . . 1·50 2·50

1993. Inter-Parliamentary Union Conference and 50th Anniv of Women in Federal Parliament. Multicoloured.
1421 45c. Type **518** . . . . . . 1·00 1·40
1422 45c. Dame Enid Lyons and Senator Dorothy Tangney 1·00 1·40

519 Ornithocheirus

520 "Goodwill"

1993. Prehistoric Animals. Multicoloured.
1423 45c. Type **519** 60 50
1424 45c. Leaellynasaura (25 × 30 mm) 60 50
1425 45c. Timimus (26 × 33 mm) 60 50
1426 45c. Allosaurus (26 × 33 mm) 60 50
1427 75c. Muttaburrasaurus (30 × 50 mm) . . . . . . 1·00 90
1428 $1.05 Minmi (50 × 30 mm) 1·50 1·50
MS1429 166 × 73 mm. Nos. 1423/8 5·50 6·50
Nos. 1423/4 also come self-adhesive.

1993. Christmas. Multicoloured.
1432 40c. Type **520** 50 25
1433 45c. "Joy" 55 25
1434 $1 "Peace" . . . . 1·90 2·00

521 "Shoalhaven River Bank—Dawn" (Arthur Boyd)

1994. Australia Day. Landscape Paintings. Mult.
1435 45c. Type **521** 60 30
1436 85c. "Wimmera" (Sir Sidney Nolan) . . . . 1·40 1·40
1437 $1.05 "Lagoon, Wimmera" (Nolan) . . . . 1·60 1·60
1438 $2 "White Cockatoos with Flame Trees" (Boyd) (vert) . . . . 2·50 2·75

522 Teaching Lifesaving Techniques

1994. Centenary of Organized Life Saving in Australia. Multicoloured.
1439 45c. Type **522** 60 45
1440 45c. Lifeguard on watch . . 60 45
1441 95c. Lifeguard team . . . . 1·25 1·40
1442 $1.20 Lifeguards on surf boards . . . . 1·60 1·75
Nos. 1439/40 also come self-adhesive.

523 Rose

524 Bridge and National Flags

1994. Greetings Stamps. Flower photographs by Lariane Fonseca. Multicoloured.
1445 45c. Type **523** 40 45
1446 45c. Tulips 40 45
1447 45c. Poppies 40 45

1994. Opening of Friendship Bridge between Thailand and Laos.
1448 **524** 95c. multicoloured . . . 1·25 1·40

525 "Queen Elizabeth II" (Sir William Dargie)

526 "Family in Field" (Bobbie-Lea Blackmore)

1994. Queen Elizabeth II's Birthday.
1449 **525** 45c. multicoloured . . . 70 70

1994. International Year of the Family. Children's Paintings. Multicoloured.
1450 45c. Type **526** 55 30
1451 75c. "Family on Beach" (Kathryn Teoh) . . . . . 1·00 1·25
1452 $1 "Family around Fire" (Maree McCarthy) . . . . 1·25 1·50

1994. Australian Wildlife (2nd series). As T **505**. Multicoloured. Ordinary or self-adhesive gum.
1453 45c. Kangaroo 80 55
1454 45c. Female kangaroo with young 80 55
1455 45c. Two kangaroos 80 55
1456 45c. Family of koalas on branch 80 55
1457 45c. Koala on ground . . . 80 55
1458 45c. Koala asleep in tree . . 80 55

527 Suffragettes

1994. Centenary of Women's Emancipation in South Australia.
1465 **527** 45c. multicoloured . . . 60 60

528 Bunyip from Aboriginal Legend

1994. The Bunyip (mythological monster). Mult.
1466 45c. Type **528** 70 70
1467 45c. Nature spirit bunyip . . 70 70
1468 90c. "The Bunyip of Berkeley's Creek" (book illustration) . . . . 1·75 1·75
1469 $1.35 Bunyip as natural history . . . . 2·25 2·25

529 "Robert Menzies" (Sir Ivor Hele)

530 Lawrence Hargrave and Box Kites

1994. Wartime Prime Ministers. Multicoloured.
1470 45c. Type **529** . . . . . . 1·00 1·25
1471 45c. "Arthur Fadden" (William Dargie) . . . . 1·00 1·25
1472 45c. "John Curtin" (Anthony Dattilo-Rubbo) 1·00 1·25
1473 45c. "Francis Forde" (Joshua Smith) . . . . . 1·00 1·25
1474 45c. "Joseph Chifley" (A. D. Colquhoun) . . . . . . 1·00 1·25

1994. Aviation Pioneers.
1475 **530** 45c. brown, green and cinnamon 80 50
1476 – 45c. brown, red and lilac 80 50
1477 – $1.35 brown, violet and blue . . . . 2·50 3·25
1478 – $1.80 brown, deep green and green . . . . . . 2·75 3·50
DESIGNS: No. 1476, Ross and Keith Smith with Vickers Vimy (first England–Australia flight); 1477, Ivor McIntyre, Stanley Goble and Fairey IIID seaplane (first aerial circumnavigation of Australia); 1478, Freda Thompson and De Havilland Moth Major "Christopher Robin" (first Australian woman to fly solo from England to Australia).

531 Scarlet Macaw

532 "Madonna and Child" (detail)

1994. Australian Zoos. Endangered Species. Mult.
1479 45c. Type **531** 75 55
1480 45c. Cheetah (25 × 30 mm) 75 55
1481 45c. Orang-utan (26 × 37 mm) 75 55
1482 45c. Fijian crested iguana (26 × 37 mm) 75 55
1483 $1 Asian elephants (49 × 28 mm) . . . . . . 2·00 1·60
MS1484 166 × 73 mm. Nos. 1479/83 4·50 4·50
Nos. 1479/80 also come self-adhesive.

1994. Christmas. "The Adoration of the Magi" by Giovanni Toscani. Multicoloured.
1487 40c. Type **532** 60 25
1488 45c. "Wise Man and Horse" (detail) (horiz) 60 25
1489 $1 "Wise Man and St. Joseph" (detail) (horiz) 1·50 1·40
1490 $1.80 Complete painting (49 × 29 mm) . . . . . . 2·00 2·75

533 Yachts outside Sydney Harbour

534 Symbolic Kangaroo

1994. 50th Sydney to Hobart Yacht Race. Mult.
1491 45c. Type **533** 90 80
1492 45c. Yachts passing Tasmania coastline . . . 90 80
Nos. 1491/92 also come self-adhesive.

1994. Self-adhesive. Automatic Cash Machine Stamps.
1495 **534** 45c. gold, emerald and green 80 80
1496 45c. gold, green and blue 80 80
1497 45c. gold, green and lilac 80 80
1498 45c. gold, emerald and green 80 80
1499 45c. gold, emerald and green 80 80
1500 45c. gold, green and pink 80 80
1501 45c. gold, green and red 80 80
1502 45c. gold, green and brown 80 80

535 "Back Verandah" (Russell Drysdale)

1995. Australia Day. Paintings. Multicoloured.
1503 45c. Type **535** 60 45
1504 45c. "Skull Springs Country" (Guy Grey-Smith) 60 45
1505 $1.05 "Outcamp" (Robert Juniper) . . . . 1·60 1·50
1506 $1.20 "Kite Flying" (Ian Fairweather) . . . . . . 1·75 1·50

536 Red Heart and Rose

537 "Endeavour" Replica at Sea

1995. St. Valentine's Day. Multicoloured.
1507 45c. Type **536** 55 55
1508 45c. Gold and red heart with rose 55 55
1509 45c. Gold heart and roses 85 85

1995. Completion of "Endeavour" Replica. Mult.
1510 45c. Type **537** . . . . . . 1·25 1·25
1511 45c. "Captain Cook's Endeavour" (detail) (Oswald Brett) . . . . . 1·25 1·25

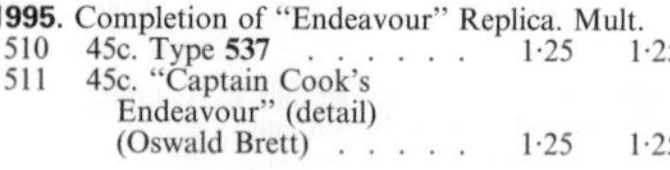

538 Coalport Plate and Bracket Clock, Old Government House, Parramatta

1995. 50th Anniv of Australian National Trusts.
1514 **538** 45c. blue and brown . . 45 45
1515 – 45c. green and brown . . 45 45
1516 – $1 red and blue . . . . 1·00 95
1517 – $2 green and blue . . . 1·90 1·90
DESIGNS: No. 1515, Steiner doll and Italian-style chair, Ayers House, Adelaide; 1516, "Advance Australia" teapot and parian-ware statuette, Victoria; 1517, Silver bowl and china urn, Old Observatory, Perth.

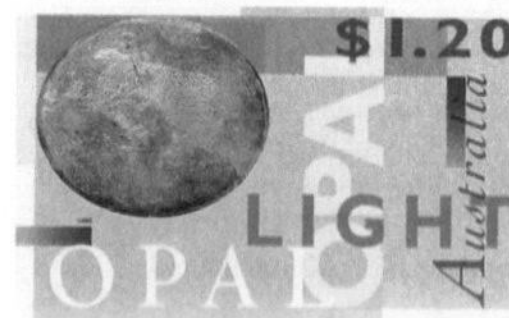

539 Light Opal (hologram)

1995. Opals. Multicoloured.
1518 $1.20 Type **539** . . . . . . 2·50 1·25
1519 $2.50 Black opal (hologram) 4·00 3·75

540 Queen Elizabeth II at Gala Concert, 1992

541 Sir Edward Dunlop and P.O.W. Association Badge

1995. Queen Elizabeth II's Birthday.
1520 **540** 45c. multicoloured . . . 75 75

1995. Australian Second World War Heroes (1st series). Mult. Ordinary or self-adhesive gum.
1521 45c. Type **541** 60 60
1522 45c. Mrs. Jessie Vasey and War Widows' Guild badge 60 60
1523 45c. Sgt. Tom Derrick and Victoria Cross 60 60
1524 45c. Flt. Sgt. Rawdon Middleton and Victoria Cross 60 60
See also Nos. 1545/8.

542 Children and Globe of Flags

543 "The Story of the Kelly Gang"

1995. 50th Anniv of United Nations.
1529 **542** 45c. multicoloured . . . 75 75

1995. Centenary of Cinema. Scenes from Films. Multicoloured. (a) Size 23 × 35 mm.
1530 45c. Type **543** . . . . . . 1·25 1·25
1531 45c. "On Our Selection" . . 1·25 1·25
1532 45c. "Jedda" . . . . 1·25 1·25

1533 45c. "Picnic at Hanging Rock" . . . . 1·25 1·25
1534 45c. "Strictly Ballroom" . . 1·25 1·25

(b) Self-adhesive. Size $19 \times 30\frac{1}{2}$ mm.
1535 45c. Type **543** . . . . . . 1·40 1·50
1536 45c. "On Our Selection" . . 1·40 1·50
1537 45c. "Jedda" . . . . 1·40 1·50
1538 45c. "Picnic at Hanging Rock" . . . . 1·40 1·50
1539 45c. "Strictly Ballroom" . . 1·40 1·50

544 Man in Wheelchair flying Kite **545** Koala with Cub

1995. People with Disabilities. Multicoloured.
1540 45c. Type **544** . . . . . . 1·10 1·10
1541 45c. Blind woman playing violin . . . . 1·10 1·10

1995. 50th Anniv of Peace in the Pacific. Designs as 1946 Victory Commemoration (Nos. 213/15) redrawn with new face values.
1542 **53** 45c. red 75 60
1543 – 45c. green 75 60
1544 – $1.50 blue . . . . 1·90 2·25
DESIGNS—VERT: No. 1543, Angel. HORIZ: No. 1544, Flag and dove.

1995. Australian Second World War Heroes (2nd series). As T **541**. Multicoloured.
1545 45c. Sister Ellen Savage and George Medal . . . . . 1·00 1·00
1546 45c. Chief Petty Officer Percy Collins and Distinguished Service Medal and Bar . . . . . 1·00 1·00
1547 45c. Lt-Comm. Leon Goldsworthy and George Cross . . . . 1·00 1·00
1548 45c. Warrant Officer Len Waters and R.A.A.F. wings . . . . 1·00 1·00

1995. Australia–China Joint Issue. Endangered Species. Multicoloured.
1549 45c. Type **545** . . . . . . 70 1·00
1550 45c. Giant panda with cubs 70 1·00
MS1551 Two sheets, each 106 × 70 mm. (a) No. 1549. (b) No. 1550 Set of 2 sheets . . . 1·60 2·00

546 Father Joseph Slattery, Thomas Lyle and Walter Filmer (Radiology)

1995. Medical Scientists. Multicoloured.
1552 45c. Type **546** . . . . . . 1·10 1·10
1553 45c. Dame Jean Macnamara and Sir Macfarlane Burnet (viruses) . . . . . 1·10 1·10
1554 45c. Fred Hollows (ophthalmology) (vert) . . 1·10 60
1555 $2.50 Sir Howard Florey (antibiotics) (vert) . . . . 5·00 5·50

547 Flatback Turtle **548** "Madonna and Child"

1995. Marine Life. Multicoloured. Ordinary or self-adhesive gum.
1556 45c. Type **547** 55 55
1557 45c. Flame angelfish and nudibranch 55 55
1558 45c. Potato grouper ("Potato cod") and hump-headed wrasse ("Maori wrasse") 55 55
1559 45c. Giant trevally 55 55
1560 45c. Black marlin 55 55
1561 45c. Mako and tiger sharks 55 55
MS1562 166 × 73 mm. Nos. 1556/61 3·50 3·00

1995. Christmas. Stained-glass Windows from Our Lady Help of Christians Church, Melbourne. Multicoloured.
1569 40c. Type **548** 70 25
1570 45c. "Angel carrying the Gloria banner" 70 25
1571 $1 "Rejoicing Angels" . . . 2·25 2·50
No. 1569 also comes self-adhesive.

549 "West Australian Banksia" (Margaret Preston)

1996. Australia Day. Paintings. Multicoloured.
1573 45c. Type **549** 80 30
1574 85c. "The Babe is Wise" (Lina Bryans) . . . . . 1·75 2·00
1575 $1 "The Bridge in Curve" (Grace Cossington Smith) (horiz) . . . . 2·00 2·00
1576 $1.20 "Beach Umbrellas" (Vida Lahey) (horiz) . . . 2·25 2·75

550 Gold Heart and Rose

1996. St. Valentine's Day.
1577 **550** 45c. multicoloured . . . 75 75

551 Bristol Type 156 Beaufighter and Curtiss P-40E Kittyhawk I

1996. Military Aviation. Multicoloured.
1578 45c. Type **551** . . . . . . 1·25 1·25
1579 45c. Hawker Sea Fury and Fairey Firefly . . . . . . 1·25 1·25
1580 45c. Bell Kiowa helicopters 1·25 1·25
1581 45c. Government Aircraft Factory Hornets . . . . 1·25 1·25

552 Tasmanian Wilderness

1996. World Heritage Sites (2nd series). Mult.
1582 45c. Type **552** 65 45
1583 75c. Willandra Lakes . . . 1·25 1·25
1584 95c. Naracoorte Fossil Cave 1·75 1·75
1585 $1 Lord Howe Island . . . 1·75 1·60

553 Australian Spotted Cuscus **555** North Melbourne Players

554 Head of Queen Elizabeth II

1996. Australia–Indonesia Joint Issue. Mult.
1586 45c. Type **553** . . . . . . 1·25 1·25
1587 45c. Indonesian bear cuscus 1·25 1·25
MS1588 106 × 70 mm. Nos. 1586/7 2·50 2·75

1996. Queen Elizabeth II's Birthday.
1589 **554** 45c. multicoloured . . . 85 65

1996. Centenary of Australian Football League. Players from different teams. Multicoloured. Ordinary or self-adhesive gum.
1590 45c. Type **555** 80 90
1591 45c. Brisbane (red and yellow shirt) 80 90
1592 45c. Sydney (red and white shirt) 80 90
1593 45c. Carlton (black shirt with white emblem) . . . 80 90
1594 45c. Adelaide (black, red and yellow shirt) 80 90
1595 45c. Fitzroy (yellow, red and blue shirt) 80 90
1596 45c. Richmond (black shirt with yellow diagonal stripe) 80 90
1597 45c. St. Kilda (red, white and black shirt) 80 90
1598 45c. Melbourne (black shirt with red top) 80 90
1599 45c. Collingwood (black and white vertical striped shirt) 80 90
1600 45c. Fremantle (green, red, white and blue shirt) . . . 80 90
1601 45c. Footscray (blue, white and red shirt) 80 90
1602 45c. West Coast (deep blue shirt with yellow stripes) 80 90
1603 45c. Essendon (black shirt with red stripe) 80 90
1604 45c. Geelong (black and white horizontal striped shirt) 80 90
1605 45c. Hawthorn (black and yellow vertical striped shirt) 80 90

556 Leadbeater's Possum

1996. Fauna and Flora (1st series). Central Highlands Forest, Victoria. Multicoloured.
1622 5c. Type **556** 10 10
1623 10c. Powerful owl 10 10
1624 $2 Blackwood wattle . . . 1·40 1·50
1625 $5 Soft tree fern and mountain ash (30 × 50 mm) . . . . . . 3·50 3·75
See also Nos. 1679/90, 1854/66, 2126/9, 2200/3 and 2272/6.

1996. "China '96" 9th Asian International Stamp Exhibition, Peking. Sheet 120 × 65 mm, containing Nos. 1453b, 1454b and 1455b. Multicoloured.
MS1626 45c. Kangaroo; 45c. Female kangaroo with young; 45c. Two kangaroos . . . . 1·75 1·90

557 Edwin Flack (800 and 1500 metres gold medal winner, 1896)

1996. Centennial Olympic Games and 10th Paralympic Games, Atlanta. Multicoloured.
1627 45c. Type **557** 70 70
1628 45c. Fanny Durack (100 metres freestyle swimming gold medal winner, 1912) 70 70
1629 $1.05 Wheelchair athletes . . 1·60 1·60

558 "Animalia" (Graeme Base)

1996. 50th Anniv of Children's Book Council Awards. Designs taken from book covers. Ordinary or self-adhesive gum. Multicoloured.
1630 45c. Type **558** 60 60
1631 45c. "Greetings from Sandy Beach" (Bob Graham) . . 60 60
1632 45c. "Who Sank the Boat?" (Pamela Allen) 60 60
1633 45c. "John Brown, Rose and the Midnight Cat" (Jenny Wagner, illustrated by Ron Brooks) 60 60

559 American Bald Eagle, Kangaroo and Olympic Flame **560** Margaret Windeyer

1996. Passing of Olympic Flag to Sydney.
1638 **559** 45c. multicoloured . . . 55 50

1996. Centenary of the National Council of Women.
1639 **560** 45c. purple and yellow 50 50
1640 – $1 blue and yellow . . . 1·25 2·00
DESIGN: $1 Rose Scott.

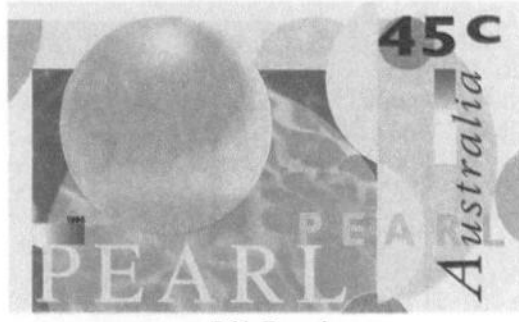

561 Pearl

1996. Pearls and Diamonds. Multicoloured.
1641 45c. Type **561** 60 50
1642 $1.20 Diamond . . . . . . 1·40 1·50
The pearl on the 45c. is shown as an exelgram (holographic printing on ultra thin plastic film) and the diamond on the $1.20 as a hologram, each embossed on to the stamp.

562 Silhouettes of Female Dancer and Musician on Rural Landscape

1996. 50th Anniv of Arts Councils. Multicoloured.
1643 20c. Type **562** . . . . . . 1·60 2·00
1644 45c. Silhouettes of musician and male dancer on landscape 35 40

563 Ginger Cats

1996. Australian Pets. Multicoloured.
1645 45c. Type **563** 75 75
1646 45c. Blue heeler dogs . . . 75 75
1647 45c. Sulphur-crested cockatoo (30 × 25 mm) . . 75 75
1648 45c. Duck with ducklings (25 × 30 mm) 75 75
1649 45c. Dog and cat (25 × 30 mm) 75 75
1650 45c. Ponies (30 × 50 mm) . . 75 75
MS1651 166 × 73 mm. Nos. 1645/50 4·00 4·00
Nos. 1645/6 also come self-adhesive.

564 Ferdinand von Mueller

1996. Australia–Germany Joint Issue. Death Centenary of Ferdinand von Mueller (botanist).
1654 **564** $1.20 multicoloured . . 1·25 1·40

565 Willem de Vlamingh **566** Madonna and Child

1996. 300th Anniv of the Visit of Willem de Vlamingh to Western Australia.
1655 **565** 45c. multicoloured . . . 75 75

1996. Christmas. Multicoloured.
1656 40c. Type **566** 55 30
1657 45c. Wise man with gift . . 55 30
1658 $1 Shepherd boy with lamb 1·25 1·75
No. 1656 also comes self-adhesive.

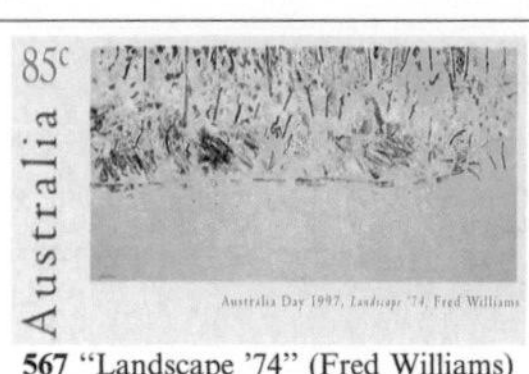

567 "Landscape '74" (Fred Williams)

1997. Australia Day. Contemporary Paintings. Multicoloured.

1660 85c. Type **567** . . . . . . 1·10 1·10
1661 90c. "The Balcony 2" (Brett Whiteley) . . . . 1·10 1·10
1662 $1.20 "Fire Haze at Gerringong" (Lloyd Rees) 1·40 1·40

568 Sir Donald Bradman **569** Red Roses

1997. Australian Legends (1st series). Sir Donald Bradman (cricketer). Multicoloured.

1663 45c. Type **568** 55 55
1664 45c. Bradman playing stroke 55 55

See also Nos. 1731/42, 1838/9, 1947/50, 2069/70, 2160/4, 2264/7 and 2348/9.

1997. St. Valentine's Day. Ordinary or self-adhesive gum.

1665 **569** 45c. multicoloured . . . 50 50

570 Ford Coupe Utility, 1934 **571** May Wirth and Horse

1997. Classic Cars. Multicoloured. Ordinary or self-adhesive gum.

1667 45c. Type **570** 60 70
1668 45c. Holden 48-215 (FX) sedan, 1948 . . . . . . 60 70
1669 45c. Austin Lancer sedan, 1958 . . . . 60 70
1670 45c. Chrysler Valiant "R" Series sedan, 1962 . . . . 60 70

1997. 150th Anniv of the Circus in Australia. Multicoloured.

1675 45c. Type **571** 55 65
1676 45c. Con Colleano on tightrope 55 65
1677 45c. Clowns 55 65
1678 45c. Acrobats 55 65

1997. Fauna and Flora (2nd series). Kakadu Wetlands, Northern Territory. As T **556**. Mult.

1679 20c. Saltwater crocodile . . 15 20
1680 25c. Northern dwarf tree frog 20 25
1681 45c. Comb-crested jacana ("Jacana") 75 75
1682 45c. Mangrove kingfisher ("Little Kingfisher") . . . 75 75
1683 45c. Brolga 75 75
1684 45c. Black-necked stork ("Jabiru") 75 75
1685 $1 "Cressida cressida" (butterfly) 70 75
1686 $10 Kakadu Wetlands (50 × 30 mm) . . . . . . 7·00 7·25
MS1686a 106 × 70 mm. No. 1686 11·00 11·00

Nos. 1681/84 also come self-adhesive.

572 Royal Wedding 1d. Stamp of 1947 **573** Hand holding Globe and Lion's Emblem

1997. Queen Elizabeth II's Birthday.

1691 **572** 45c. purple 60 60

1997. 50th Anniv of First Australian Lions Club.

1692 **573** 45c. blue, brown and purple 50 50

574 Doll holding Teddy Bear (Kaye Wiggs) **575** Police Rescue Helicopter

1997. Dolls and Teddy Bears. Multicoloured.

1693 45c. Type **574** 45 50
1694 45c. Teddy bear standing (Jennifer Laing) 45 50
1695 45c. Doll wearing white dress with teddy bear (Susie McMahon) 45 50
1696 45c. Doll in brown dress and bonnet (Lynda Jacobson) 45 50
1697 45c. Teddy bear sitting (Helen Williams) 45 50

1997. Emergency Services. Multicoloured.

1698 45c. Type **575** . . . . . . 1·00 1·00
1699 45c. Emergency Service volunteers carrying victim 1·00 1·00
1700 $1.05 Fire service at fire . . 1·90 2·25
1701 $1.20 Loading casualty into ambulance . . . . 2·00 2·00

576 George Peppin Jnr (breeder) and Merino Sheep

1997. Bicentenary of Arrival of Merino Sheep in Australia. Multicoloured.

1702 45c. Type **576** 70 90
1703 45c. Pepe chair, cloth and wool logo 70 90

577 Dumbi the Owl

1997. "The Dreaming". Cartoons from Aboriginal Stories. Multicoloured.

1704 45c. Type **577** 85 30
1705 $1 The Two Willy-Willies 1·75 1·10
1706 $1.20 How Brolga became a Bird . . . . 2·00 2·00
1707 $1.80 Tuggan-Tuggan . . . 2·75 3·25

578 "Rhoetosaurus brownei" **579** Spotted-tailed Quoll

1997. Prehistoric Animals. Multicoloured.

1708 45c. Type **578** 50 60
1709 45c. "Mcnamaraspis kaprios" 50 60
1710 45c. "Ninjemys oweni" . . 50 60
1711 45c. "Paracyclotosaurus davidi" 50 60
1712 45c. "Woolungasaurus glendowerensis" 50 60

1997. Nocturnal Animals. Multicoloured.

1713 45c. Type **579** 90 90
1714 45c. Barking owl 90 90
1715 45c. Platypus (30 × 25 mm) 90 90
1716 45c. Brown antechinus (30 × 25 mm) 90 90
1717 45c. Dingo (30 × 25 mm) . . 90 90
1718 45c. Yellow-bellied glider (50 × 30 mm) 90 90
MS1719 166 × 78 mm. Nos. 1713/18 4·75 4·75

Nos. 1713/14 also come self-adhesive.

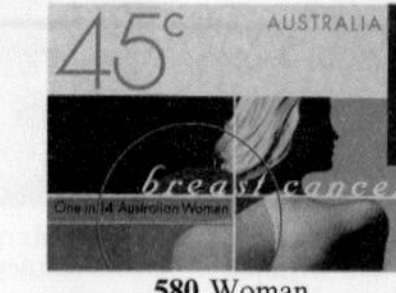

580 Woman

1997. Breast Cancer Awareness Campaign.

1722 **580** 45c. multicoloured . . . 1·00 60

581 Two Angels

1997. Christmas. Children's Nativity Play. Mult.

1723 40c. Type **581** 50 30
1724 45c. Mary 55 30
1725 $1 Three Kings . . . . . . 1·25 1·75

No. 1723 also comes self-adhesive.

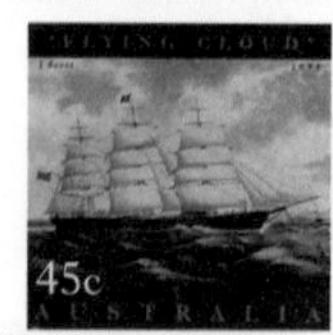

582 "Flying Cloud" (clipper) (J. Scott)

1998. Ship Paintings. Multicoloured.

1727 45c. Type **582** 60 30
1728 85c. "Marco Polo" (full-rigged ship) (T. Robertson) . . . . . 1·00 1·00
1729 $1 "Chusan I" (steamship) (C. Gregory) . . . . . . 1·25 1·10
1730 $1.20 "Heather Belle" (clipper) . . . . 1·50 1·75

583 Betty Cuthbert (1956) **584** "Champagne" Rose

1998. Australian Legends (2nd series). Olympic Gold Medal Winners. Multicoloured. Ordinary or self-adhesive gum.

1731 45c. Type **583** 55 65
1732 45c. Betty Cuthbert running 55 65
1733 45c. Herb Elliott (1960) . . 55 65
1734 45c. Herb Elliott running . . 55 65
1735 45c. Dawn Fraser (1956, 1960 and 1964) 55 65
1736 45c. Dawn Fraser swimming 55 65
1737 45c. Marjorie Jackson (1952) 55 65
1738 45c. Marjorie Jackson running 55 65
1739 45c. Murray Rose (1956) . . 55 65
1740 45c. Murray Rose swimming 55 65
1741 45c. Shirley Strickland (1952 and 1956) 55 65
1742 45c. Shirley Strickland hurdling 55 65

1998. Greeting Stamp. Ordinary or self-adhesive gum.

1755 **584** 45c. multicoloured . . . 55 50

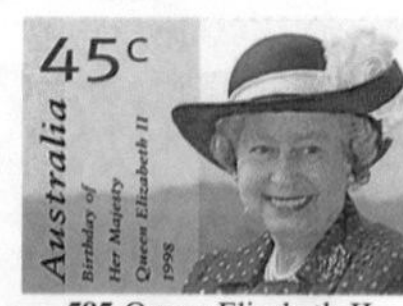

585 Queen Elizabeth II

1998. Queen Elizabeth II's Birthday.

1757 **585** 45c. multicoloured . . . 50 50

586 Sea Hawk (helicopter) landing on Frigate

1998. 50th Anniv of Royal Australian Navy Fleet Air Arm.

1758 **586** 45c. multicoloured . . . 50 50

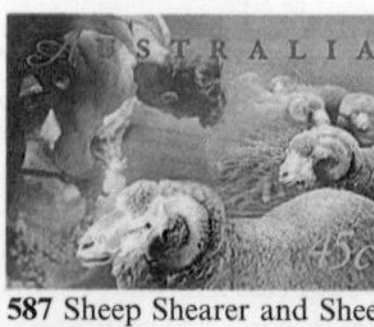

587 Sheep Shearer and Sheep

1998. Farming. Multicoloured. Ordinary or self-adhesive gum.

1759 45c. Type **587** 45 50
1760 45c. Barley and silo 45 50
1761 45c. Farmers herding beef cattle 45 50
1762 45c. Sugar cane harvesting 45 50
1763 45c. Two dairy cows 45 50

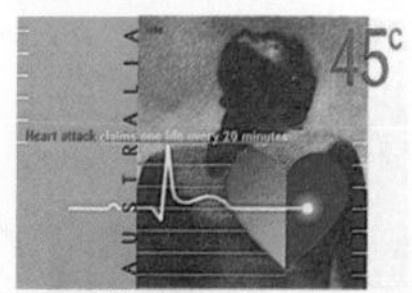

588 Cardiograph Trace and Heart

1998. Heart Disease Awareness.

1769 **588** 45c. multicoloured . . . 50 50

589 Johnny OKeefe ("The Wild One", 1958)

1998. Australian Rock and Roll. Multicoloured. Ordinary or self-adhesive gum.

1770 45c. Type **589** 55 50
1771 45c. Col Joye ("Oh Yeah Uh Huh", 1959) 55 50
1772 45c. Little Pattie ("He's My Blonde Headed Stompie Wompie Real Gone Surfer Boy", 1963) . . . 55 50
1773 45c. Normie Rowe ("Shakin all Over", 1965) 55 50
1774 45c. Easybeats ("She's so Fine", 1965) 55 50
1775 45c. Russell Morris ("The Real Thing", 1969) . . . 55 50
1776 45c. Masters Apprentices ("Turn Up Your Radio", 1970) 55 50
1777 45c. Daddy Cool ("Eagle Rock", 1971) 55 50
1778 45c. Billy Thorpe and the Aztecs ("Most People I know think I'm Crazy", 1972) 55 50
1779 45c. Skyhooks ("Horror Movie", 1974) 55 50
1780 45c. AC/DC ("It's a Long Way to the Top", 1975) 55 50
1781 45c. Sherbet ("Howzat", 1976) 55 50

590 Yellow-tufted Honeyeater ("Helmeted Honeyeater")

1998. Endangered Species. Multicoloured.

1794 5c. Type **590** 45 45
1795 5c. Orange-bellied parrot . . 45 45
1796 45c. Red-tailed cockatoo ("Red-tailed Black-Cockatoo") 80 80
1797 45c. Gouldian finch 80 80

591 French Horn and Cello Players

1998. Youth Arts, Australia. Multicoloured.

1798 45c. Type **591** 50 50
1799 45c. Dancers 50 50

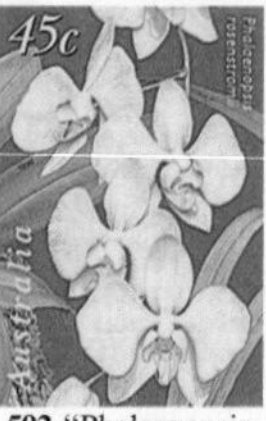

592 "Phalaenopsis rosenstromii"

1998. Australia–Singapore Joint Issue. Orchids. Multicoloured.

1800 45c. Type **592** 55 40
1801 85c. "Arundina graminifolia" . . . . . . 1·00 1·00
1802 $1 "Grammatophyllum speciosum" . . . . 1·40 1·25
1803 $1.20 "Dendrobium phalaenopsis" . . . . . 1·50 1·60
MS1804 138 × 72 mm. Nos. 1800/3 4·00 3·75

593 Flying Angel with Teapot (cartoon by Michael Leunig)

1998. "The Teapot of Truth" (cartoons by Michael Leunig). Multicoloured.

1805 45c. Type **593** 50 55
1806 45c. Two birds in heart-shaped tree 50 55
1807 45c. Pouring tea 50 55
1808 $1 Mother and child (29 × 24 mm) . . . . . . 1·25 1·25
1809 $1.20 Cat with smiling face (29 × 24 mm) . . . . . . 1·50 1·60

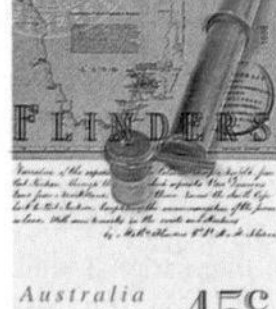

594 Red Lacewing **595** Flinders' Telescope and Map of Tasmania

1998. Butterflies. Multicoloured. Ordinary or self-adhesive gum.

1810 45c. Type **594** 75 75
1811 45c. Dull oakblue 75 75
1812 45c. Meadow argus 75 75
1813 45c. Ulysses butterfly . . . 75 75
1814 45c. Common red-eye . . . 75 75

1998. Bicentenary of the Circumnavigation of Tasmania by George Bass and Matthew Flinders. Multicoloured.

1820 45c. Type **595** 65 50
1821 45c. Sextant and letter from Bass 65 50

596 Weedy Seadragon **597** Rose of Freedom

1998. International Year of the Ocean. Multicoloured.

1822 45c. Type **596** 65 65
1823 45c. Bottlenose dolphin . . 65 65
1824 45c. Fiery squid (24 × 29 mm) 65 65
1825 45c. Manta ray (29 × 24 mm) 65 65
1826 45c. White pointer shark (29 × 49 mm) 65 65
1827 45c. Southern right whale (49 × 29 mm) 65 65
MS1828 166 × 73 mm. Nos. 1822/7 2·75 2·75

Nos. 1822/3 also come self-adhesive.

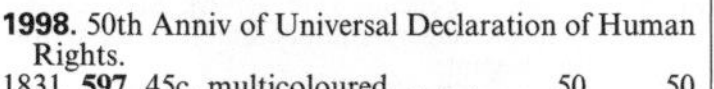

1998. 50th Anniv of Universal Declaration of Human Rights.

1831 **597** 45c. multicoloured . . . 50 50

598 Three Kings

1998. Christmas. Multicoloured.

1832 40c. Type **598** 40 25
1833 45c. Nativity scene 40 25
1834 $1 Mary and Joseph . . . . 1·10 1·50

No. 1832 also comes self-adhesive.

599 Australian Coat of Arms

1999. 50th Anniv of Australian Citizenship. Ordinary or self-adhesive gum.

1836 **599** 45c. multicoloured . . . 50 50

600 Arthur Boyd

1999. Australian Legends (3rd series). Arthur Boyd (painter). Multicoloured. Ordinary or self-adhesive gum.

1838 45c. Type **600** 50 50
1839 45c. "Nebuchadnezzer on fire falling over Waterfall" (Arthur Boyd) 50 50

601 Red Roses

1999. Greetings Stamp. Romance. Ordinary or self-adhesive gum.

1842 **601** 45c. multicoloured . . . 50 50

602 Elderly Man and Grandmother with Boy

1999. International Year of Older Persons. Mult.

1844 45c. Type **602** 50 50
1845 45c. Elderly woman and grandfather with boy . . 50 50

603 "Polly Woodside" (barque) **604** Olympic Torch and 1956 7½d. Stamp

1999. Sailing Ships. Multicoloured.

1846 45c. Type **603** 60 35
1847 85c. "Alma Doepel" (topsail schooner) . . . . 1·00 1·10
1848 $1 "Enterprize" replica (topsail schooner) . . . . 1·25 1·10
1849 $1.05 "Lady Nelson" replica (topsail schooner) . . . . 1·40 1·90

1999. Australia—Ireland Joint Issue. "Polly Woodside" (barque). Sheet 137 × 72 mm. Mult.

MS1850 45c. Type **603**; 30p. Type **374** of Ireland (No. **MS**1850 was sold at $1.25 in Australia) 1·25 1·40

1999. Australia—Canada. Joint Issue. "Marco Polo" (emigrant ship). Sheet 160 × 95 mm. Mult.

MS1851 85c. As No. 1728; 46c. Type **701** of Canada (No. **MS**1851 was sold at $1.30 in Australia) 1·25 1·40

1999. "Australia '99" International Stamp Exhibition, Melbourne. Two sheets, each 142 × 76 mm, containing designs as Nos. 398/403 and all with face value of 45c.

MS1852 (a) 45c. ultramarine (Type **167**); 45c. grey (Captain Cook); 45c. brown (Flinders). (b) 45c. red (Type **168**); 45c. brown (Bass); 45c. purple (King) Set of 2 sheets . . . . 2·50 2·75

1999. Olympic Torch Commemoration.

1853 **604** $1.20 multicoloured . . 1·10 1·10

605 "Correa reflexa" (native fuchsia) **607** "Here's Humphrey"

606 Queen Elizabeth II with The Queen Mother

1999. Fauna and Flora (3rd series). Coastal Environment. Multicoloured. Ordinary or self-adhesive gum.

1854 45c. Type **605** 50 50
1855 45c. "Hibbertia scandens" (guinea flower) 50 50
1856 45c. "Ipomoea pre-caprae" (beach morning glory) . . 50 50
1857 45c. "Wahlenbergia stricta" (Australian bluebells) . . 50 50
1858 70c. Humpback whales and zebra volute shell (29 × 24 mm) 60 70
1859 90c. Brahminy kite and checkerboard helmet shell (29 × 24 mm) 65 70
1860 90c. Fraser Island and chambered nautilus (29 × 24 mm) 65 70
1861 $1.05 Loggerhead turtle and melon shell (29 × 24 mm) 75 80
1862 $1.20 White-bellied sea eagle and Campbell's stromb shell (29 × 24 mm) 85 90

Nos. 1859/60 were printed together, se-tenant, forming a composite design.

1999. Queen Elizabeth II's Birthday.

1870 **606** 45c. multicoloured . . . 50 50

1999. Children's Television Programmes. Multicoloured. Ordinary or self-adhesive gum.

1871 45c. Type **607** 45 45
1872 45c. "Bananas in Pyjamas" 45 45
1873 45c. "Mr. Squiggle" 45 45
1874 45c. "Play School" (teddy bears) 45 45
1875 45c. "Play School" (clock, toy dog and doll) 45 45

608 Obverse and Reverse of 1899 Sovereign

1999. Centenary of the Perth Mint.

1881 **608** $2 gold, blue and green 2·00 1·75

609 Lineout against New Zealand **610** Drilling at Burn's Creek and Rock Bolting in Tumut 2 Power Station Hall

1999. Centenary of Australian Test Rugby. Mult.

1882 45c. Type **609** 50 40
1883 45c. Kicking the ball against England 50 40
1884 $1 Try against South Africa (horiz) . . . . 1·00 85
1885 $1.20 Passing the ball against Wales (horiz) . . 1·10 1·25

Nos. 1882/3 also come self-adhesive.

1999. 50th Anniv of Snowy Mountain Scheme (hydro-electric project). Multicoloured. Ordinary or self-adhesive gum.

1888 45c. Type **610** 65 65
1889 45c. English class for migrant workers, Cooma 65 65
1890 45c. Tumut 2 Tailwater Tunnel and Eucumbene Dam 65 65
1891 45c. German carpenters and Island Bend Dam 65 65

611 Calligraphy Pen and Letter **612** Sydney Olympic Emblem

1999. Greetings Stamps. Multicoloured.

1896 45c. Type **611** 65 65
1897 45c. Wedding rings 65 65
1898 45c. Birthday cake 65 65
1899 45c. Christmas decoration 65 65
1900 45c. Teddy bear 65 65
1901 $1 Koala . . . . 1·25 1·25

See also No. 1921.

1999. Olympic Games, Sydney (2000) (1st issue).

1902 **612** 45c. multicoloured . . . 75 50

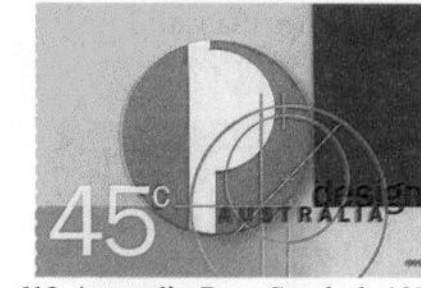

613 Australia Post Symbol, 1975

1999. "Sydney Design '99" International Congress and Exhibition. Multicoloured.

1903 45c. Type **613** 45 30
1904 90c. Embryo chair, 1988 . . 80 80
1905 $1.35 Possum skin textile, c.1985 . . . . 1·25 1·25
1906 $1.50 Storey Hall, R.M.I.T. University, 1995 . . . . 1·25 1·50

614 Magnificent Tree Frog **615** Madonna and Child

1999. National Stamp Collecting Month, Small Pond Life. Multicoloured. Ordinary or self-adhesive gum.

1907 45c. Type **614** 55 55
1908 45c. Sacred kingfisher . . . 55 55
1909 45c. Roth's tree frog (29 × 24 mm) 55 55
1910 45c. Dragonfly (29 × 24 mm) 55 55
1911 50c. Javelin frog (24 × 29 mm) 65 65
1912 50c. Northern dwarf tree frog (24 × 29 mm) 65 65
MS1913 166 × 73 mm. Nos. 1907/12 3·00 3·00

1999. Christmas. Multicoloured.

1918 40c. Type **615** 50 30
1919 $1 Tree of Life (horiz) . . . 1·00 1·00

No. 1918 also comes self-adhesive.

616 Fireworks and Hologram **617** Rachel Thomson (college administrator)

1999. Millennium Greetings stamp.

1921 **616** 45c. multicoloured . . . 50 50

2000. New Millennium. "Face of Australia". Mult.

1922 45c. Nicholle and Meghan Triandis (twin babies) . . 50 60
1923 45c. David Willis (cattleman) 50 60
1924 45c. Natasha Bramley (scuba diver) 50 60
1925 45c. Cyril Watson (Aborigine boy) 50 60
1926 45c. Mollie Dowdall (wearing red hat) (vineyard worker) 50 60
1927 45c. Robin Dicks (flying instructor) 50 60
1928 45c. Mary Simons (retired nurse) 50 60
1929 45c. Peta and Samantha Nieuwerth (mother and baby) 50 60
1930 45c. John Matthews (doctor) 50 60
1931 45c. Edith Dizon-Fitzimmons (wearing drop earrings) (music teacher) 50 60
1932 45c. Philippa Weir (wearing brown hat) (teacher) . . . 50 60
1933 45c. John Thurgar (in bush hat and jacket) (farmer) 50 60
1934 45c. Miguel Alzona (with face painted) (schoolboy) 50 60
1935 45c. Type **617** 50 60
1936 45c. Necip Akarsu (wearing blue shirt) (postmaster) 50 60
1937 45c. Justin Allan (R.A.N. sailor) 50 60
1938 45c. Wadad Dennaoui (wearing checked shirt) (student) 50 60
1939 45c. Jack Laity (market gardener) 50 60
1940 45c. Kelsey Stubbin (wearing cricket cap) (schoolboy) 50 60

1941 45c. Gianna Rossi (resting chin on hand) (church worker) 50 60
1942 45c. Paris Hansch (toddler) 50 60
1943 45c. Donald George Whatham (in blue shirt and tie) (retired teacher) 50 60
1944 45c. Stacey Coull (wearing pendant) 50 60
1945 45c. Alex Payne (wearing cycle helmet) (schoolgirl) 50 60
1946 45c. John Lodge (Salvation Army member) 50 60

618 Walter Parker

2000. Australian Legends (4th series). "The Last Anzacs". Multicoloured.
1947 45c. Type **618** 55 55
1948 45c. Roy Longmore 55 55
1949 45c. Alec Campbell 55 55
1950 45c. 1914–15 Star (medal) 55 55
Nos. 1947/50 also come self-adhesive.

619 Scenes from "Cloudstreet" (play) (Perth Festival)

620 Coast Banksia, False Sarsaparilla and Swamp Bloodwood (plants)

2000. Arts Festivals. Multicoloured.
1955 45c. Type **619** 55 55
1956 45c. Belgian dancers from Rosas Company (Adelaide Festival) 55 55
1957 45c. "Guardian Angel" (sculpture) and dancer (Sydney Festival) 55 55
1958 45c. Musician and Balinese dancer (Melbourne Festival) 55 55
1959 45c. Members of Vusa Dance Company of South Africa (Brisbane Festival) 55 55

2000. Gardens. Multicoloured. Ordinary or self-adhesive gum.
1960 45c. Type **620** 45 50
1961 45c. Eastern spinebill on swamp bottlebrush in foreground 45 50
1962 45c. Border of cannas . . . 45 50
1963 45c. Roses, lake and ornamental bridge 45 50
1964 45c. Hibiscus with bandstand in background 45 50

621 Queen Elizabeth II in 1996

2000. Queen Elizabeth II's Birthday.
1970 **621** 45c. multicoloured . . . 65 50

622 Medals and Korean Landscape

2000. 50th Anniv of Korean War.
1971 **622** 45c. multicoloured . . . 50 50

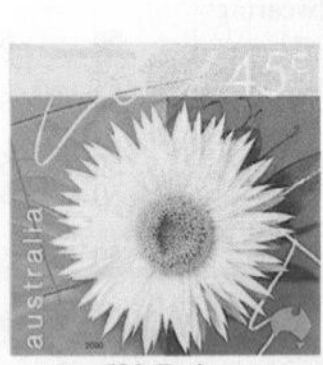
623 Daisy

624 Taking the Vote, New South Wales

2000. Nature and Nation. Greeting stamps. Mult.
1972 45c. Type **623** 45 50
1973 45c. Australia on globe . . 45 50
1974 45c. Red kangaroo and flag 45 50
1975 45c. Sand, sea and sky . . . 45 50
1976 45c. Rainforest 45 50

2000. Centenary of Commonwealth of Australia Constitution Act. Multicoloured.
1977 45c. Type **624** 45 40
1978 45c. Voters waiting for results, Geraldton, Western Australia 45 40
1979 $1.50 Queen Victoria (29 × 49 mm) . . . . . . 1·40 1·40
1980 $1.50 Women dancing ("The Fair New Nation") (29 × 49 mm) . . . . . . 1·40 1·40
MS1981 155 × 189 mm. Nos. 1977/80 3·25 3·25

625 Sydney Opera House, New South Wales

2000. International Stamps. Views of Australia (1st series). Multicoloured.
1982 50c. Type **625** 90 40
1983 $1 Nandroya Falls, Queensland . . . . 1·60 80
1984 $1.50 Sydney Harbour Bridge, New South Wales 2·00 1·25
1985 $2 Cradle Mountain, Tasmania . . . . 2·25 1·50
1986 $3 The Pinnacles, Western Australia . . . . 2·50 2·25
1987 $4.50 Flinders Ranges, South Australia (51 × 24 mm) . . . . . . 3·25 3·50
1988 $5 Twelve Apostles, Victoria (51 × 24 mm) . . . . . . 3·50 3·75
1989 $10 Devils Marbles, Northern Territory (51 × 24 mm) . . . . . . 7·25 7·50
Nos. 1982/9 were intended for international postage which, under changes in Australian tax laws from 1 July 2000, remained exempt from General Sales Tax.
See also Nos. 2121/4, 2195/7 and 2219/22.

626 Tennis Player in Wheelchair

627 Sir Neville Howse (first Australian recipient of Victoria Cross, 1900)

2000. Paralympic Games, Sydney (1st issue). Multicoloured. Ordinary or self-adhesive gum.
1990 45c. Type **626** 50 50
1991 45c. Amputee sprinting . . 50 50
1992 49c. Basketball player in wheelchair 50 50
1993 49c. Blind cyclist 50 50
1994 49c. Amputee putting the shot 50 50
See also Nos. 2053/4.

2000. Cent of Australia's First Victoria Cross Award.
2000 **627** 45c. multicoloured . . . 50 50
2001 – 45c. brown, gold and black 50 50
2002 – 45c. multicoloured . . . 50 50
2003 – 45c. multicoloured . . . 50 50
2004 – 45c. brown, gold and black 50 50
DESIGNS: No. 2001, Sir Roden Cutler, 1941; 2002, Victoria Cross; 2003, Private Edward Kenna, 1945; 2004, Warrant Officer Keith Payne, 1969.

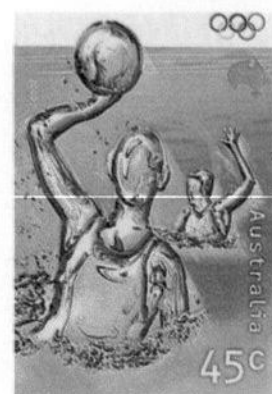

628 Water Polo

629 Olympic Flag, Flame and Parthenon

2000. Olympic Games, Sydney. Multicoloured. Ordinary or self-adhesive gum. Competitors highlighted in varnish.
2005 45c. Type **628** 50 50
2006 45c. Hockey 50 50
2007 45c. Swimming 50 50
2008 45c. Basketball 50 50
2009 45c. Cycling (triathlon) . . . 50 50
2010 45c. Horse riding 50 50
2011 45c. Tennis 50 50
2012 45c. Gymnastics 50 50
2013 45c. Running 50 50
2014 45c. Rowing 50 50
Nos. 2005/14 were printed together, se-tenant, with the backgrounds forming a composite design.

2000. Transfer of Olympic Flag from Sydney to Athens. Joint issue with Greece. Multicoloured.
2025 45c. Type **629** 50 40
2026 $1.50 Olympic Flag, Flame and Sydney Opera House 1·50 1·50
Stamps in similar designs were issued by Greece.

630 Ian Thorpe (Men's 400m Freestyle Swimming)

631 Martian Terrain

2000. Australian Gold Medal Winners at Sydney Olympic Games. Multicoloured.
2027A 45c. Type **630** 45 45
2028A 45c. Australian team (Men's 4 × 100 m Freestyle Swimming Relay) . . . 45 45
2029A 45c. Michael Diamond (Men's Trap Shooting) 45 45
2030A 45c. Australian team (Three Day Equestrian Event) 45 45
2031A 45c. Susie O'Neill (Women's 200 m Freestyle Swimming) 45 45
2032A 45c. Australian team (Men's 4 × 200 m Freestyle Swimming Relay) . . . 45 45
2033A 45c. Simon Fairweather (Men's Individual Archery) 45 45
2034A 45c. Australian team (Men's Madison Cycling) 45 45
2035A 45c. Grant Hackett (Men's 1500 m Freestyle Swimming) 45 45
2036A 45c. Australian team (Women's Water Polo) 45 45
2037A 45c. Australian team (Women's Beach Volleyball) 45 45
2038A 45c. Cathy Freeman (Women's 400 m Athletics) 45 45
2039A 45c. Lauren Burns (Women's under 49 kg Taekwondo) 45 45
2040A 45c. Australian team (Women's Hockey) . . 45 45
2041A 45c. Australian crew (Women's 470 Dinghy Sailing) 45 45
2042A 45c. Australian crew (Men's 470 Dinghy Sailing) 45 45

2000. Stamp Collecting Month. Exploration of Mars. Multicoloured. (a) Ordinary gum.
2043 45c. Type **631** 45 45
2044 45c. Astronaut using thruster 45 45
2045 45c. Spacecraft (50 × 30 mm) 45 45
2046 45c. Flight crew (30 × 25 mm) 45 45
2047 45c. Launch site (30 × 50 mm) 45 45
2048 45c. Robots on kelp rod (25 × 30 mm) 45 45
MS2049 166 × 73 mm. Nos. 2043/8 2·50 2·50

(b) Self-adhesive. Designs 21 × 32 mm.
2050 45c. Type **631** 45 45
2051 45c. Astronaut using thruster 45 45

632 Cathy Freeman with Olympic Torch and Ring of Flames

2000. Opening Ceremony, Olympic Games, Sydney.
2052 **632** 45c. multicoloured . . . 50 50

633 Blind Athlete carrying Olympic Torch

2000. Paralympic Games, Sydney (2nd issue). Multicoloured.
2053 45c. Type **633** 55 50
2054 45c. Paralympic Games logo 55 50

634 Siobhan Paton (swimmer)

635 "Sleep in Heavenly Peace"

2000. Siobhan Paton, Paralympian of the Year.
2055 **634** 45c. multicoloured . . . 50 50

2000. Christmas. "Silent Night" (carol). Multicoloured. (a) Ordinary gum.
2056 40c. Type **635** 50 25
2057 45c. "All is Calm, All is Bright" 50 25
MS2058 165 × 75 mm. Nos. 2056/7 1·00 1·00

(b) Self-adhesive.
2059 40c. Type **635** 45 35

(c) International Mail. As T **625** inscr "Season's Greetings".
2060 80c. Byron Bay, New South Wales 70 85

2001. International Mail. No. 1901 optd **International POST**.
2061 $1 Koala . . . . 1·25 80

637 Parade passing Federation Arch, Sydney

2001. Centenary of Federation. Multicoloured. (a) Ordinary gum.
2062 49c. Type **637** 45 40
2063 49c. Edmund Barton (first Federal Prime Minister) 45 40
2064 $2 "Australia For Ever" (song sheet) and celebration picnic (50 × 30 mm) . . . . . . 1·75 2·00
2065 $2 State Banquet, Sydney (30 × 50 mm) . . . . . . 1·75 2·00
MS2066 166 × 73 mm. Nos. 2062/5 4·25 4·75

(b) Self-adhesive.
2067 49c. Type **637** 60 60
2068 49c. Edmund Barton (first Federal Prime Minister) 60 60

638 Slim Dusty with Guitar in 1940s

2001. Australian Legends (5th series). Slim Dusty (country music singer). Multicoloured. Ordinary or self-adhesive gum.
2069 45c. Type **638** 50 50
2070 45c. Slim Dusty wearing "Sundowner" hat 50 50

639 Light Horse Parade, 1940, and Command Post, New Guinea, 1943

2001. Centenary of Australian Army. Multicoloured.
2073 45c. Type **639** 50 50
2074 45c. Soldier carrying Rwandan child and officers on the Commando Selection Course 50 50

640 Entry Canopy, Skylights and Site Plan

2001. Opening of the National Museum, Canberra. Multicoloured.
2075 49c. Type **640** 50 50
2076 49c. Skylights and "Pangk" (wallaby sculpture) . . . 50 50

2001. Sir Donald Bradman (cricketer) Commemoration. Nos. 1663/4 additionally inscribed "1908–2001" in red. Multicoloured.
2077 45c. Type **568** 50 50
2078 45c. Bradman playing stroke 50 50

641 "Khe Sanh" (Cold Chisel), 1978

2001. Australian Rock and Pop Music. Multicoloured. Ordinary or self-adhesive gum.
2079 45c. Type **641** 60 45
2080 45c. "Down Under" (Men at Work), 1981 . . . . . 60 45
2081 45c. "Power and the Passion" (Midnight Oil), 1983 . . . . 60 45
2082 45c. "Original Sin" (INXS), 1984 . . . . 60 45
2083 45c. "You're the Voice" (John Farnham), 1986 . . 60 45
2084 45c. "Don't Dream it's Over" (Crowded House), 1986 . . . . 60 45
2085 45c. "Treaty" (Yothu Yindi), 1991 . . . . . . 60 45
2086 45c. "Tomorrow" (Silverchair), 1994 . . . . 60 45
2087 45c. "Confide in Me" (Kylie Minogue), 1994 . . . . . 60 45
2088 45c. "Truly, Madly, Deeply" (Savage Garden), 1997 . . 60 45

642 Queen Elizabeth II holding Bouquet

643 Party Balloons

2001. Queen Elizabeth II's Birthday.
2099 **642** 45c. multicoloured . . . 75 55

2001. "Colour My Day". Greetings Stamps. (a) Domestic Mail.
2100 45c. Type **643** 30 35
2101 45c. Smiling Flower 30 35
2102 45c. Hologram and party streamers 30 35

(b) International Mail.
2103 $1 Kangaroo and joey . . . 1·00 80
2104 $1.50 The Bayulu Banner 1·40 1·75

644 "Opening of the First Federal Parliament" (Charles Nuttall)

2001. Centenary of Federal Parliament. Paintings. Multicoloured.
2105 45c. Type **644** 50 40
2106 $2.45 "Prince George opening the First Parliament of the Commonwealth of Australia" (Tom Roberts) 2·25 2·50
MS2107 Two sheets, each 166 × 75 mm. (a) No. 2105. (b) No. 2106 Set of 2 sheets . . . 2·50 2·75

645 Telecommunications Tower

2001. Outback Services. Multicoloured. Ordinary or self-adhesive gum.
2108 45c. Type **645** 45 45
2109 45c. Road train 45 45
2110 45c. School of the Air pupil 45 45
2111 45c. Outback family and mail box 45 45
2112 45c. Royal Flying Doctor Service aircraft and ambulance 45 45

646 Dragon Boat and Hong Kong Convention and Exhibition Centre

2001. Joint Issue with Hong Kong. Dragon Boat Racing. Multicoloured. (a) Domestic Mail.
2118 45c. Type **646** 50 45

(b) International Mail.
2119 $1 Dragon boat and Sydney Opera House . . . . . . 1·00 1·00
MS2120 115 × 70 mm. Nos. 2118/19 1·40 1·40

2001. International Stamps. Views of Australia (2nd series). As T **625**. Multicoloured.
2121 50c. The Three Sisters, Blue Mountains, New South Wales 55 40
2122 $1 The Murrumbidgee River, Australian Capital Territory . . . . 1·00 75
2123 $1.50 Four Mile Beach, Port Douglas, Queensland . . 1·50 1·25
2124 $20 Uluru Rock at dusk, Northern Territory (52 × 24 mm) . . . . . . 14·50 15·00
No. 2121 also comes self-adhesive.

647 Variegated Wren ("Variegated Fairy-Wren")

649 Christmas Tree

648 Daniel Solander (Swedish botanist) and Mango Tree

2001. Fauna and Flora (4th series). Desert Birds. Multicoloured. Ordinary or self-adhesive gum.
2126 45c. Type **647** 40 40
2127 45c. Painted finch ("Painted Firetail") 40 40
2128 45c. Crimson chat 40 40
2129 45c. Budgerigar 40 40

2001. Australia–Sweden Joint Issue. Daniel Solander's Voyage with Captain Cook. Multicoloured. (a) Domestic Mail.
2134 45c. Type **648** 50 50

(b) International Mail.
2135 $1.50 H.M.S. *Endeavour* on reef and Kapok tree . . . 1·75 1·75

2001. Christmas (1st issue). Multicoloured. (a) Domestic Mail.
2136 40c. Type **649** 40 35

(b) International Mail.
2137 80c. Star . . . . 1·00 1·00
See also Nos. 2157/8.

650 Australia on Globe

2001. Commonwealth Heads of Government Meeting (No. 2138) and Commonwealth Parliamentary Conference (No. 2139). Mult.
2138 45c. Type **650** 50 50
2139 45c. Southern Cross 50 50

651 Wedge-tailed Eagle

2001. Centenary of Birds of Australia. Birds of Prey. Multicoloured.
2140 49c. Type **651** 50 50
2141 49c. Australian kestrel ("Nankeen Kestrel") . . . 50 50
2142 98c. Red goshawk (vert) . . 95 1·10
2143 98c. Spotted harrier (vert) 95 1·10

652 Cockatoos dancing to Animal Band

653 "Adoration of the Magi"

2001. National Stamp Collecting Month. "Wild Babies" (cartoons). Multicoloured. Ordinary or self-adhesive gum.
2144 45c. Type **652** 45 45
2145 45c. Kevin Koala with birthday cake 45 45
2146 45c. Ring-tailed possums eating 45 45
2147 45c. Bilbies at foot of tree 45 45
2148 45c. James Wombat on rope ladder 45 45
2149 45c. Wallaby, echidna and platypus on rope ladder 45 45

2001. Christmas (2nd issue). Miniatures from "Wharncliffe Hours Manuscript". Multicoloured.
2157 40c. Type **653** 50 30
2158 45c. "Flight into Egypt" . . 50 35
No. 2157 also comes self-adhesive.

654 Sir Gustav Nossal (immunologist)

2002. Australian Legends. (6th series). Medical Scientists. Ordinary or self-adhesive gum. Multicoloured.
2160 45c. Type **654** 45 45
2161 45c. Nancy Millis (microbiologist) 45 45
2162 45c. Peter Doherty (immunologist) 45 45
2163 45c. Fiona Stanley (epidemiologist) 45 45
2164 45c. Donald Metcalf (haematologist) 45 45

655 Queen Elizabeth in 1953

2002. Golden Jubilee. Multicoloured.
2170 45c. Type **655** 50 35
2171 $2.45 Queen Elizabeth in Italy, 2000 . . . . 2·25 2·25

656 Steven Bradbury (Men's 1000m Short Track Speed Skating)

2002. Australian Gold Medal Winners at Salt Lake City Winter Olympic Games. Multicoloured.
2173 45c. Type **656** 50 50
2174 45c. Alisa Camplin (Women's Aerials Freestyle Skiing) 50 50

657 Austin 7 and Bugatti Type 40, Australian Grand Prix, Phillip Island, 1928

658 Macquarie Lighthouse

2002. Centenary of Motor Racing in Australia and New Zealand. Ordinary or self-adhesive gum. Multicoloured.
2181 45c. Type **657** 45 45
2182 45c. Jaguar Mark II, Australian Touring Car Championship, Mallala, 1963 . . . . 45 45
2183 45c. Repco-Brabham, Tasman Series, Sandown, 1966 . . . . 45 45
2184 45c. Holden Torana and Ford Falcon, Hardie-Ferodo 500, Bathurst, 1972 . . . . 45 45
2185 45c. William's Ford, Australian Grand Prix, Calder, 1980 . . . . . . 45 45
2186 45c. Benetton-Renault, Australian Grand Prix, Albert Park, 2001 . . . . 45 45

2002. Lighthouses. Multicoloured.
2187 45c. Type **658** 50 35
2188 49c. Cape Naturaliste . . . 65 65
2189 49c. Troubridge Island . . . 65 65
2190 $1.50 Cape Bruny . . . . . 1·50 1·60
Nos. 2188/9 also come self-adhesive.

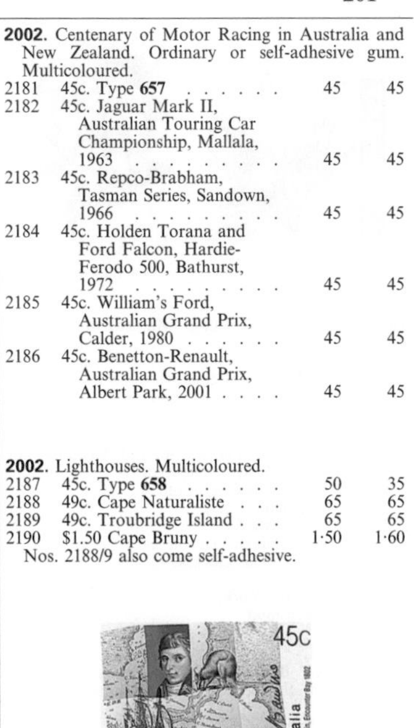

659 Nicolas Baudin, Kangaroo, *Geographe* (ship) and Map

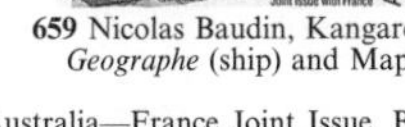

2002. Australia—France Joint Issue. Bicentenary of Flinders—Baudin Meeting at Encounter Bay. Multicoloured. (a) Domestic Mail.
2193 45c. Type **659** 50 40

(b) International Mail.
2194 $1.50 Matthew Flinders, Port Lincoln Parrot, *Investigator* (ship) and Map . . . . 1·75 1·75

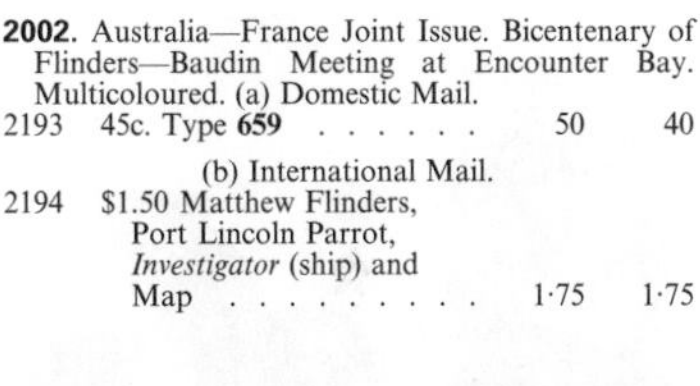

2002. International Stamps. Views of Australia (3rd series). As T **625**. Multicoloured.
2195 50c. Walker Flat, River Murray, South Australia 35 40
2196 $1 Mt. Roland, Tasmania 80 75
2197 $1.50 Cape Leveque, Western Australia . . . . 1·25 1·25
Nos. 2195/6 also come self-adhesive.

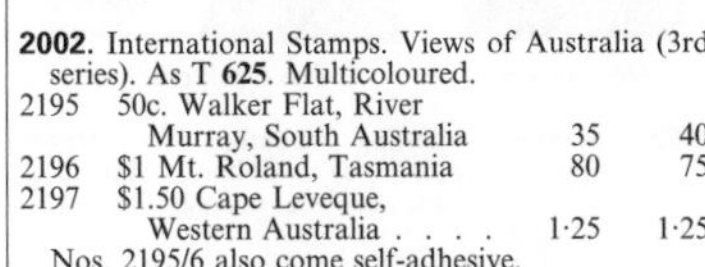

660 Desert Star Flower

2002. Flora and Fauna (5th series). Great Sandy Desert. Multicoloured.
2200 50c. Type **660** 35 40
2201 $1 Bilby 70 75
2202 $1.50 Thorny Devil . . . . 1·10 1·25
2203 $2 Great Sandy Desert landscape (50 × 30 mm) 1·40 1·50
No. 2200 also comes self-adhesive.

661 "Ghost Gum, Mt Sonder" (Albert Namatjira)

2002. Birth Centenary of Albert Namatjira (artist). Multicoloured. Nos. 2204/7, ordinary or self-adhesive gum.
2204 45c. Type **661** 40 40
2205 45c. "Mt Hermannsburg" 40 40
2206 45c. "Glen Helen Country" 40 40
2207 45c. "Simpsons Gap" . . . 40 40
MS2208 133 × 70 mm. Nos. 2205/8 1·40 1·40

662 *Nelumbo nucifera*

2002. Australia–Thailand Joint Issue. 50th Anniv of Diplomatic Relations. Water Lilies. Multicoloured. (a) Domestic Mail.
2213 45c. Type **662** 40 35

(b) International Mail.
2214 $1 *Nymphaea immutabilis* . . 85 75
MS2215 107 × 70 mm. Nos. 2214/15 1·25 1·40

663 Star, Presents and Baubles

664 Lilly-pilly

2002. International Greetings. Multicoloured.

2216 90c. Type **663** 65 70
2217 $1.10 Koala 80 85
2218 $1.65 "Puja" (painting by Ngarralja Tommy May) 1·10 1·25

2002. International Stamps. Views of Australia (4th series). As T **625**. Multicoloured.

2219 $1.10 Coonawarra, South Australia 80 85
2220 $1.65 Gariwerd (Grampians), Victoria . . 1·10 1·25
2221 $2.20 National Library, Canberra . . . . 1·50 1·60
2222 $3.30 Cape York, Queensland . . . . 2·10 2·40

2002. "Bush Tucker". Edible Plants from the Outback. Multicoloured. Ordinary or self-adhesive gum.

2228 49c. Type **664** 45 50
2229 49c. Honey Grevillea . . . 45 50
2230 49c. Quandong 45 50
2231 49c. Acacia seeds 45 50
2232 49c. Murnong 45 50

665 Bunyip

666 "Wakeful"

2002. Stamp Collecting Month. *The Magic Rainforest*, (book by John Marsden). Multicoloured. Nos. 2233/8, ordinary or self-adhesive gum.

2233 45c. Type **665** 40 40
2234 45c. Fairy on branch . . . 40 40
2235 45c. Gnome with sword . . 40 40
2236 45c. Goblin with stock whip 40 40
2237 45c. Wizard 40 40
2238 45c. Sprite 40 40
MS2239 170 × 90 mm. Nos. 2234/9 2·25 2·25

2002. Champion Racehorses. Multicoloured.

2246 45c. Type **666** 50 50
2247 45c. "'Rising Fast" 50 50
2248 45c. "Manikato" 50 50
2249 45c. "Might and Power" . . 50 50
2250 45c. "Sunline" 50 50

667 Nativity

2002. Christmas. Multicoloured. Ordinary or self-adhesive gum.

2253 40c. Type **667** 40 35
2252 45c. The Three Wise Men 50 35

668 Two Daisies

2003. Greetings Stamps. Some adapted from previous issues. Multicoloured.

2254 50c. Type **668** 35 40
2255 50c. Wedding rings and yellow roses 35 40
2256 50c. Hearts and pink roses 35 40
2257 50c. Birthday cake and present 35 40
2258 50c. Seated teddy bear . . . 35 40
2259 50c. Balloons 35 40
2260 50c. Red kangaroo and flag 35 40
2261 50c. Australia on globe . . 35 40
2262 50c. Sports car 35 40
2263 $1 Wedding rings and pink rose 70 75

669 Margaret Court with Wimbledon Trophy

2003. Australian Legends (7th series). Tennis Players. Ordinary or self-adhesive gum. Multicoloured.

2268 50c. Type **669** 45 50
2269 50c. Margaret Court in action 45 50
2270 50c. Rod Laver with Wimbledon Trophy . . . 45 50
2271 50c. Rod Laver in action . . 45 50

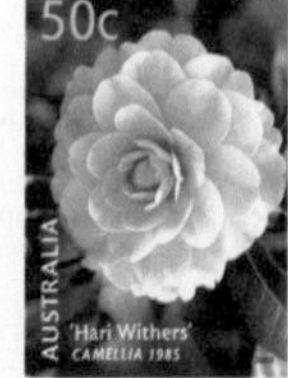

670 Blue Orchid

672 "Hari Withers" Camellia

671 Snapper and Fishing from Beach

2003. Flora and Fauna (6th series). Rainforest, Daintree National Park. Multicoloured. Ordinary or self-adhesive gum.

2272 50c. Orange-thighed tree frog 40 45
2273 50c. Green-spotted triangle (butterfly) 40 45
2274 50c. Striped possum 40 45
2275 50c. Yellow-bellied sunbird 40 45
2276 $1.45 Type **670** . . . . . . 1·00 1·10

2003. Angling in Australia. Multicoloured.

2282 50c. Type **671** 45 50
2283 50c. Murray cod and flooded wood 45 50
2284 50c. Brown trout and fly-fishing 45 50
2285 50c. Yellow-finned tuna and sea-fishing from launch 45 50
2286 50c. Barramundi and anglers in mangrove swamp . . . 45 50

2003. Australian Horticulture. Multicoloured. (a) Size 25 × 36 mm. Ordinary gum.

2287 50c. Type **672** 35 40
2288 50c. "Victoria Gold" rose 35 40
2289 50c. "Superb" grevillea . . 35 40
2290 50c. "Bush Tango" kangaroo paw 35 40
2291 50c. "Midnight" rhododendron 35 40

(b) Size 21 × 33 mm. Self-adhesive.

2292 50c. Type **672** 35 40
2293 50c. "Victoria Gold" rose 35 40
2294 50c. "Superb" grevillea . . 35 40
2295 50c. "Bush Tango" kangaroo paw 35 40
2296 50c. "Midnight" rhododendron 35 40

673 "Ned Kelly" (Sir Sidney Nolan)

2003. Australian Paintings (1st series). Multicoloured.

2297 $1 Type **673** 75 80
2298 $1 "Family Home, Suburban Exterior" (Howard Arkley) 75 80
2299 $1.45 "Cord Long Drawn, Expectant" (Robert Jacks) 1·00 1·10
2300 $2.45 "Girl" (Joy Hester) 1·75 2·00

674 Queen Elizabeth II, 1953 (photograph by Cecil Beaton)

2003. 50th Anniv of Coronation. Multicoloured.

2301 50c. Type **674** 40 45
2302 $2.45 St. Edward's Crown 2·10 2·25
MS2303 105 × 70 mm. Nos. 2301/2

No. 2301 also comes self-adhesive.

675 Untitled Painting by Ningura Napurrula

2003. International Stamps. Art of Papunya Tula Movement. Showing untitled paintings by Aboriginal artists. Multicoloured.

2305 $1.10 Type **675** . . . . . . 95 1·00
2306 $1.65 Naata Nungurrayi . . 1·40 1·50
2307 $2.20 Graham Tjupurrula (55 × 24 mm) . . . . . . 1·90 2·00
2308 $3.30 Dini Campbell Tjampitjinpa (55 × 24 mm) 2·75 3·00

676 Kangaroo Chromosomes

2003. 50th Anniv of Discovery of DNA. Multicoloured.

2309 50c. Type **676** 40 45
2310 50c. DNA double helix . . 40 45

677 *Oscar W* (paddle-steamer)

2003. 150th Anniv of Murray River Shipping. Multicoloured. Ordinary or self-adhesive gum.

2311 50c. Type **677** 40 45
2312 50c. *Marion* (paddle-steamer) 40 45
2313 50c. *Ruby* (paddle-steamer) 40 45
2314 50c. *Pyap* (cruise vessel) . . 40 45
2315 50c. *Adelaide* (paddle-steamer) 40 45

678 Christmas Tree

2003. Greetings Stamps. Peace and Goodwill. Design, adapted from Christmas 2001 (1st issue) (Nos. 2136/7). Multicoloured. (a) Domestic Mail

2321 50c. Type **678** 40 45

(b) International Mail.

2322 90c. Star 75 80

679 Sir Samuel Griffith (first Chief Justice)

2003. Centenary of High Court of Australia.

2323 **679** 50c. purple, black and red 40 45
2324 – $1.45 vermilion, red and black . . . . 1·25 1·40
MS2325 105 × 70 mm. Nos. 2323/4 1·60 1·75

DESIGN: $1.45, "JUSTICE".

680 Ulysses Butterfly

2003. Stamp Collecting Month. Bugs and Butterflies. Multicoloured. Ordinary or self-adhesive gum.

2326 50c. Type **680** 40 45
2327 50c. Leichhardt's grasshopper 40 45
2328 50c. Vedalia ladybird . . . 40 45
2329 50c. Green mantid and captured damselfly . . . 40 45
2330 50c. Emperor gum moth caterpillar 40 45
2331 50c. Fiddler beetle 40 45
MS2332 170 × 85 mm. Nos. 2326/31 2·25 2·50

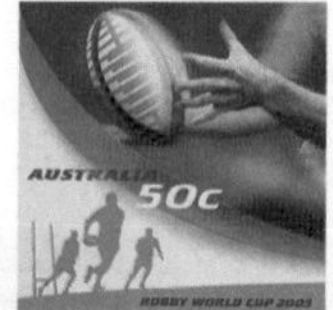

681 Hands passing Ball and Players

2003. Rugby World Cup Championship, Australia. Multicoloured. (a) Domestic Mail.

2339 50c. Type **681** 40 45

(b) International Mail.

2340 $1.10 Trophy (Webb Ellis Cup) and Telstra Stadium 90 1·00
2341 $1.65 Hand grasping ball and player taking shot at goal . . . . 1·40 1·50
MS2342 115 × 70 mm. Nos. 2339/41 2·25 2·50

682 "Active with ASTHMA" and Silhouettes of Sportspeople

2003. National Asthma Week Campaign.

2343 **682** 50c. multicoloured . . . 40 45

683 Mary, Baby Jesus and Angels

2003. Christmas. Multicoloured.

2344 45c. Type **683** 40 45
2345 50c. Three Wise Men . . . 40 45
2346 90c. Angel appearing to shepherds 75 80

No. 2344 also comes self-adhesive.

684 Joan Sutherland as *Lucia di Lammermoor*, 1980

2004. Australian Legends (8th series). Dame Joan Sutherland (opera singer). Multicoloured. Ordinary or self-adhesive gum.

2348 50c. Type **684** 40 45
2349 50c. Joan Sutherland . . . 40 45

685 Aboriginal shell necklace and bracelet

2004. Bicentenary of Settlement of Hobart, Tasmania. Multicoloured.

2352 50c. Type **685** 40 45
2353 50c. Cheshunt House, Deloraine 40 45
2354 $1 "Mount Wellington and Hobart Town from Kangaroo Point" (John Glover) . . . . 90 1·00
2355 $1 Mountains, south west Tasmania . . . . 90 1·00
MS2356 135 × 72 mm. Nos. 2352/5 2·60 2·75

686 Ross Bridge, Tasmania, 1836

2004. Landmark Bridges. Multicoloured. Ordinary or self-adhesive gum.

2357 50c. Type **686** 40 45
2358 50c. Lockyer Creek Bridge, Queensland, 1911 . . . . 40 45
2359 50c. Sydney Harbour Bridge, 1932 . . . . . . 40 45

2360	50c. Birkenhead Bridge, Adelaide, 1940	40	45
2361	50c. Bolte Bridge, Melbourne, 1999	40	45

687 Stylized "Southern Cross"

689 Queen Elizabeth II (from photo by Dorothy Wilding)

688 Solar Systems CS500 Dish ("solar")

2004. Greetings Stamp.

2367 **687**	50c. multicoloured	40	45

2004. Renewable Energy. Multicoloured. Ordinary or self-adhesive gum.

2368	50c. Type **688**	40	45
2369	50c. Wind turbines ("wind")	40	45
2370	50c. Snowy Mountains Hydro-electric Scheme ("hydro")	40	45
2371	50c. Sugar cane field, bagasse (waste plant fibre) and sugar mill ("biomass")	40	45

2004. 50th Anniv of Royal Tour to Australia.

2376 **689**	50c. purple, black and grey	40	45

OFFICIAL STAMPS

1931. Optd **O.S.** (a) Kangaroo issue.

O133 **1**	6d. brown	22·00	20·00
	(b) King George V issue.		
O128 **3**	½d. orange	4·75	1·50
O129	1d. green	3·25	45
O130	2d. red	9·00	55
O131	3d. blue	7·50	4·00
O126	4d. olive	16·00	3·75
O132	5d. brown	35·00	27·00
	(c) Various issues.		
O123 **13**	2d. red	55·00	18·00
O134 **18**	2d. red	5·00	2·00
O124 **13**	3d. blue	£200	32·00
O135 **18**	3d. blue	14·00	5·00
O136 **17**	1s. green	40·00	27·00

POSTAGE DUE STAMPS

D 1 D 3

1902. White space below value at foot.

D1 **D 1**	½d. green	3·25	4·50
D2	1d. green	12·00	7·00
D3	2d. green	35·00	8·00
D4	3d. green	30·00	21·00
D5	4d. green	42·00	12·00
D6	6d. green	55·00	9·50
D7	8d. green	95·00	75·00
D8	5s. green	£180	70·00

1902. White space filled in.

D22 **D 3**	½d. green	8·00	7·50
D23	1d. green	7·50	2·75
D24	2d. green	22·00	2·75
D25	3d. green	65·00	14·00
D26	4d. green	55·00	9·00
D17	5d. green	48·00	9·50
D28	6d. green	55·00	10·00
D29	8d. green	£120	50·00
D18	10d. green	75·00	17·00
D19	1s. green	55·00	12·00
D20	2s. green	£100	18·00
D33	5s. green	£190	22·00
D43	10s. green	£1600	£1400
D44	20s. green	£3500	£2250

1908. As Type D 3, but stroke after figure of value, thus "5/-".

D58 **D 3**	1s. green	75·00	8·50
D60	2s. green	£900	£2000
D59	5s. green	£225	48·00
D61	10s. green	£2250	£3000
D62	20s. green	£5500	£8000

D 7 D 10

1909.

D132 **D 7**	½d. red and green	2·00	2·00
D133	1d. red and green	3·00	3·50
D 93	1½d. red and green	1·50	9·00
D121	2d. red and green	4·50	1·25
D134	3d. red and green	1·75	3·00
D109	4d. red and green	6·50	2·75
D124	5d. red and green	12·00	3·50
D137	6d. red and green	2·75	3·25
D126	7d. red and green	4·25	8·50
D127	8d. red and green	10·00	26·00
D139	10d. red and green	3·75	3·25
D128	1s. red and green	18·00	1·75
D 70	2s. red and green	70·00	11·00
D 71	5s. red and green	90·00	13·00
D 72	10s. red and green	£250	£150
D 73	£1 red and green	£475	£275

1953.

D140 **D 10**	1s. red and green	6·50	3·00
D130	2s. red and green	18·00	12·00
D131a	5s. red and green	12·00	70

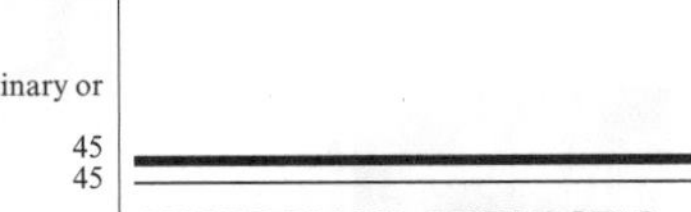

AUSTRALIAN ANTARCTIC TERRITORY Pt. 1

By an Order in Council of 7 February 1933, the territory S. of latitude 60°S. between 160th and 145th meridians of East longitude (excepting Adelie Land) was placed under Australian administration. Until 1957 stamps of Australia were used from the base.

1957. 12 pence = 1 shilling;
20 shillings = 1 pound.
1966. 100 cents = 1 dollar.

1 1954 Expedition at Vestfold Hills and Map

1957.

1 **1**	2s. blue	80	50

2 Members of Shackleton Expedition at S. Magnetic Pole, 1909

3 Weazel and Team

1959.

2 **2**	5d. on 4d. black and sepia	60	15
3 **3**	8d. on 7d. black and blue	1·75	2·25
4 –	1s. myrtle	2·25	2·00
5 –	2s.3d. green	7·00	4·00

DESIGNS—VERT (as Type 3): 1s. Dog-team and iceberg; 2s.3d. Map of Antarctica and emperor penguins.

6

7 Sir Douglas Mawson (Expedition leader)

1961.

6 **6**	5d. blue	1·00	20

1961. 50th Anniv of 1911–14 Australian Antarctic Expedition.

7 **7**	5d. myrtle	35	20

8 Aurora and Camera Dome

11 Sastrugi (Snow Ridges)

1966. Multicoloured.

8	1c. Type **8**	70	30
9	2c. Emperor penguins	3·00	80
10	4c. Ship and iceberg	90	90
11	5c. Banding southern elephant-seals	2·75	1·75
12	7c. Measuring snow strata	80	80
13	10c. Wind gauges	1·00	1·10
14	15c. Weather balloon	5·00	2·00
15	20c. Bell Trooper helicopter (horiz)	6·00	2·50
16	25c. Radio operator (horiz)	2·00	2·25
17	50c. Ice-compression tests (horiz)	2·75	4·00
18	$1 Parahelion ("mock sun") (horiz)	19·00	12·00

1971. 10th Anniv of Antarctic Treaty.

19 **11**	6c. blue and black	75	1·00
20 –	30c. multicoloured	2·75	6·00

DESIGN: 30c. Pancake ice.

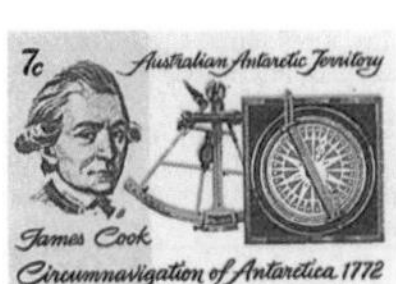

12 Capt. Cook, Sextant and Compass

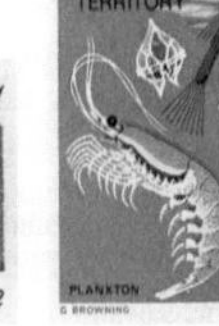

13 Plankton

1972. Bicentenary of Cook's Circumnavigation of Antarctica. Multicoloured.

21	7c. Type **12**	1·00	75
22	35c. Chart and H.M.S. "Resolution"	3·50	3·00

1973. Multicoloured.

23	1c. Type **13**	30	15
24	5c. Mawson's De Havilland Gipsy Moth, 1931	55	70
25	7c. Adelie penguin	1·50	70
26	8c. De Havilland Fox Moth, 1934–37	60	90
27	9c. Leopard seal (horiz)	40	90
28	10c. Killer whale (horiz)	2·25	2·00
29	20c. Wandering albatross ("Albatross") (horiz)	1·25	1·00
30	25c. Wilkins's Lockheed Vega "San Francisco", 1928 (horiz)	55	1·00
31	30c. Ellsworth's Northrop Gamma "Polar Star", 1935	55	1·00
32	35c. Christensen's Avro Type 581 Avian, 1934 (horiz)	55	1·00
33	50c. Byrd's Ford Trimotor "Floyd Bennett", 1929	55	1·00
34	$1 Sperm whale	75	1·40

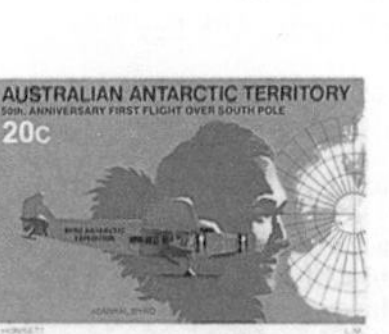

14 Admiral Byrd (expedition leader), Ford Trimotor "Floyd Bennett" and Map of South Pole

15 "Thala Dan" (supply ship)

1979. 50th Anniv of First Flight over South Pole. Multicoloured.

35	20c. Type **14**	25	60
36	55c. Admiral Byrd, aircraft and Antarctic terrain	50	1·25

1979. Ships. Multicoloured.

37	1c. "Aurora" (horiz)	15	10
38	2c. "Penola" (Rymill's ship)	40	10
39	5c. Type **15**	30	40
40	10c. H.M.S. "Challenger" (survey ship) (horiz)	50	75
41	15c. "Morning" (bow view) (whaling ship) (horiz)	2·00	3·00
42	15c. "Nimrod" (stern view) (Shackleton's ship) (horiz)	1·40	1·00
43	20c. "Discovery II" (supply ship) (horiz)	1·50	1·50
44	22c. "Terra Nova" (Scott's ship)	1·00	1·25
45	25c. "Endurance" (Shackleton's ship)	60	1·00
46	30c. "Fram" (Amundsen's ship) (horiz)	60	1·75
47	35c. "Nella Dan" (supply ship) (horiz)	80	1·75
48	40c. "Kista Dan" (supply ship)	1·25	1·50
49	45c. "L'Astrolabe" (D'Urville's ship) (horiz)	70	1·50
50	50c. "Norvegia" (supply ship) (horiz)	70	70
51	55c. "Discovery" (Scott's ship)	1·00	2·00
52	$1 H.M.S. "Resolution" (Cook's ship)	1·75	2·50

No. 41 is incorrectly inscr "S.Y. Nimrod".

16 Sir Douglas Mawson in Antarctic Terrain

17 Light-mantled Sooty Albatross

1982. Birth Centenary of Sir Douglas Mawson (Antarctic explorer). Multicoloured.

53	27c. Type **16**	25	25
54	75c. Sir Douglas Mawson and map of Australian Antarctic Territory	75	1·50

1983. Regional Wildlife. Multicoloured.

55	27c. Type **17**	60	90
56	27c. King cormorant ("Macquarie Island shag")	60	90
57	27c. Southern elephant seal	60	90
58	27c. Royal penguin	60	90
59	27c. Dove prion ("Antarctic prion")	60	90

18 Antarctic Scientist

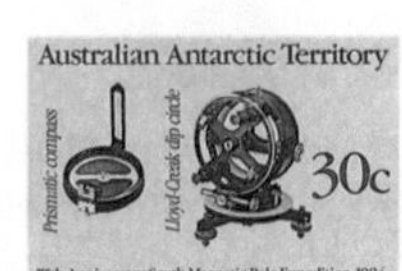

19 Prismatic Compass and Lloyd-Creak Dip Circle

1983. 12th Antarctic Treaty Consultative Meeting. Canberra.

60 **18**	27c. multicoloured	55	75

1984. 75th Anniv of Magnetic Pole Expedition. Multicoloured.

61	30c. Type **19**	30	30
62	85c. Aneroid barometer and theodolite	70	1·25

20 Dog Team pulling Sledge

21 Prince Charles Mountains near Mawson Station

1984. Antarctic Scenes. Multicoloured.

63	2c. Summer afternoon, Mawson Station	10	50
64	5c. Type **20**	15	30
65	10c. Late summer evening, MacRobertson Land	15	30
66	15c. Prince Charles Mountains	15	30
67	20c. Summer morning, Wilkesland	15	70
68	25c. Sea-ice and iceberg	60	1·50
69	30c. Mount Coates	25	50
70	33c. "Iceberg Alley", Mawson	25	60
71	36c. Early winter evening, Casey Station	30	35
72	45c. Brash ice (vert)	70	2·00
73	60c. Midwinter shadows, Casey Station	50	55
74	75c. Coastline	2·25	2·75
75	85c. Landing strip	2·50	3·00
76	90c. Pancake ice (vert)	75	80
77	$1 Emperor penguins	2·75	1·25

1986. 25th Anniv of Antarctic Treaty.

78 **21**	36c. multicoloured	1·25	1·10

22 Hourglass Dolphins and "Nella Dan"

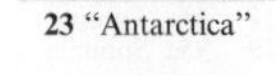

23 "Antarctica"

1988. Environment, Conservation and Technology. Multicoloured.
79 37c. Type **22** . . . . 1·10 1·25
80 37c. Emperor penguins and Davis Station . . . . 1·10 1·25
81 37c. Crabeater seal and Hughes 500D helicopters . . 1·10 1·25
82 37c. Adelie penguins and tracked vehicle . . . . . . 1·10 1·25
83 37c. Grey-headed albatross and photographer . . . . . 1·10 1·25

1989. Antarctic Landscape Paintings by Sir Sidney Nolan. Multicoloured.
84 39c. Type **23** . . . . 1·25 1·50
85 39c. "Iceberg Alley" . . . . . 1·25 1·50
86 60c. "Glacial Flow" . . . . . 2·00 2·25
87 80c. "Frozen Sea" . . . . . . 2·50 2·75

24 "Aurora Australis"

1991. 30th Anniv of Antarctic Treaty (43c.) and Maiden Voyage of "Aurora Australis" (research ship) ($1.20). Multicoloured.
88 43c. Type **24** 75 60
89 $1.20 "Aurora Australis" off Heard Island . . . . 2·75 4·25

25 Adelie Penguin and Chick **26** Head of Husky

1992. Antarctic Wildlife. Multicoloured.
90 45c. Type **25** 30 35
91 75c. Elephant seal with pup 55 60
92 85c. Hall's giant petrel ("Northern giant petrel") on nest with fledgeling 60 65
93 95c. Weddell seal and pup . . 70 75
94 $1 Royal penguin 70 75
95 $1.20 Emperor penguins with chicks (vert) 85 90
96 $1.40 Fur seal . . . . 1·00 1·10
97 $1.50 King penguin (vert) . . 1·10 1·25

1994. Departure of Huskies from Antarctica. Multicoloured.
104 45c. Type **26** . . . . 1·50 75
105 75c. Dogs pulling sledge (horiz) . . . . 1·75 2·00
106 85c. Husky in harness . . . 2·00 2·25
107 $1.05 Dogs on leads (horiz) 2·25 2·50

27 Humpback Whale with Calf

1995. Whales and Dolphins. Multicoloured.
108 45c. Type **27** . . . . 1·25 80
109 45c. Pair of hourglass dolphins (vert) . . . . . . 1·25 1·25
110 45c. Pair of minke whales (vert) . . . . 1·25 1·25
111 $1 Killer whale . . . . 2·50 2·50
MS112 146 × 64 mm. Nos. 108/11 5·50 5·50
Nos. 109/10 were printed together, se-tenant, forming a composite design.

28 "Rafting Sea Ice" (Christian Clare Robertson) **29** Apple Huts

1996. Paintings by Christian Clare Robertson. Multicoloured.
113 45c. Type **28** 90 70
114 45c. "Shadow on the Plateau" 90 70
115 $1 "Ice Cave" . . . . 1·90 1·40
116 $1.20 "Twelve Lake" . . . . 2·25 1·60

1997. 50th Anniv of Australian National Antarctic Research Expeditions (A.N.A.R.E.). Multicoloured.
117 45c. Type **29** 85 85
118 45c. Tuning a radio receiver 85 85
119 95c. Summer surveying . . . 1·40 1·50
120 $1.05 Scientists in cage above sea ice . . . . 1·50 1·60
121 $1.20 Scientists and tents . . 1·60 1·75

30 "Aurora Australis" (research ship)

1998. Antarctic Transport. Multicoloured.
122 45c. Type **30** . . . . 1·40 1·40
123 45c. "Skidoo" . . . . 1·40 1·40
124 $1 Helicopter lifting quad motorcycle (vert) . . . . . 2·50 2·25
125 $2 Hagglunds tractor and trailer (vert) . . . . 2·50 2·75

31 Sir Douglas Mawson (expedition leader, 1911–14) and "Aurora" (research ship)

1999. Restoration of Mawson's Huts, Cape Denison. Each including a background drawing of a hut. Multicoloured.
126 45c. Type **31** . . . . 1·25 1·25
127 45c. Huts in blizzard . . . . 1·25 1·25
128 90c. Husky team . . . . . . 2·00 2·00
129 $1.35 Conservation in progress . . . . 2·00 2·00

32 Emperor Penguins

2000. Penguins. Multicoloured.
130 45c. Type **32** . . . . 1·25 1·25
131 45c. Adelie penguins . . . . 1·25 1·25

33 Adelie Penguins with Egg

2001. Centenary of Australian Antarctic Exploration. Multicoloured.
132 5c. Type **33** 45 45
133 5c. Louis Bernacchi (physicist) 45 45
134 5c. *Nimrod* (Shackleton) . . . 45 45
135 5c. Mackay, Edgeworth David and Mawson at South Magnetic Pole, 1909 45 45
136 5c. Taylor and Debenham (geologists) 45 45
137 10c. Early radio set 45 45
138 10c. Lockheed-Vega aircraft and husky team 45 45
139 10c. Sir Douglas Mawson . . 45 45
140 10c. Members of BANZARE Expedition, 1929–31 . . . 45 45
141 10c. Hoisting Union Jack . . 45 45
142 25c. Hoisting Australian flag, 1948 . . . . 50 50
143 25c. Hagglund vehicle and helicopter 50 50
144 25c. *Aurora australis* over Casey 50 50
145 25c. Scientist with weather balloon 50 50
146 25c. Modern Antarctic clothing and "apple" hut 50 50
147 45c. *Nella Dan* (supply ship) and emperor penguins . . 55 55
148 45c. Male and female scientists taking ice sample 55 55
149 45c. Scientist using satellite phone 55 55
150 45c. Weddell seal and tourists 55 55
151 45c. Satellite photograph of Antarctica 55 55
Nos. 132/51 were printed together, se-tenant, with the backgrounds forming a composite design.
Each stamp carries an inscription on the reverse, printed over the gum.

34 Female Leopard Seal and Pup

2001. Endangered Species. Leopard Seal. Mult.
152 45c. Type **34** 70 70
153 45c. Male seal on ice floe chasing adelie penguins . . 70 70
154 45c. Female seal and pup swimming underwater . . . 70 70
155 45c. Adult seal chasing adelie penguins underwater . . . 70 70

35 Light Detection and Ranging Equipment, Davis Base

2002. Antarctic Research. Multicoloured.
156 45c. Type **35** 70 70
157 45c. Magnified diatom and coastline, Casey Base . . . 70 70
158 45c. Wandering albatross, Macquarie Base 70 70
159 45c. Adelie penguin, Mawson Base 70 70

36 *Kista Dan* in Heavy Seas

2003. Antarctic Supply Ships. Multicoloured.
160 50c. Type **36** 70 70
161 50c. *Magga Dan* entering pack ice 70 70
162 $1 *Thala Dan* and iceberg (vert) . . . . 1·10 1·10
163 $1.45 *Nella Dan* unloading in Antarctic (vert) . . . . . 1·40 1·40

37 Naming Ceremony, 1954

2004. 50th Anniv of Mawson Station. Multicoloured.
164 50c. Type **37** 40 45
165 50c. Mawson Station, 2004 40 45
166 $1 Accomodation "caravan", 1950s . . . . 90 1·00
167 $1.45 Emperor Penguin rookery . . . . 90 1·00

AUSTRIA Pt. 2

A state of Central Europe, part of the Austro-Hungarian Monarchy and Empire until 1918. At the end of the First World War the Empire was dismembered and German-speaking Austria became a Republic.

Austria was absorbed into the German Reich in 1938 and remained part of Germany until 1945. Following occupation by the four Allied Powers the Austrian Republic was re-established on 14 May 1945.

1850. 60 kreuzer = 1 gulden.
1858. 100 kreuzer = 1 gulden.
1899. 100 heller = 1 krone.
1925. 100 groschen = 1 schilling.
1938. 100 pfennig = 1 German reichsmark.
1945. 100 groschen = 1 schilling.
2002. 100 cents = 1 euro.

1 Arms of Austria **4** **5**

1850. Imperf.
6a **1** 1k. yellow £1700 £100
7 2k. black . . . . £1300 65·00
8a 3k. red . . . . £750 3·50
9 6k. brown . . . . £1000 5·25
10 9k. blue . . . . £1300 2·75
For stamps in Type **1** with values in "CENTES", see Lombardy and Venetia.

1858.
22 **5** 2k. yellow . . . . £1100 48·00
23 **4** 3k. black £1500 £200
24 3k. green £1300 £140
25 **5** 5k. red . . . . £400 2·75
26 10k. brown . . . . £800 2·40
27 15k. blue . . . . £700 1·70
For stamps in Types **4** and **5** with values in "SOLDI", see Lombardy and Venetia.
The portraits on Austrian stamps to 1906 are of the Emperor Francis Joseph I.

10 **12** Arms of Austria

1860.
33 **10** 2k. yellow . . . . £375 28·00
34 3k. green . . . . £325 22·00
35 5k. red £250 75
36 10k. brown . . . . £325 1·50
37 15k. blue . . . . £400 1·00

1863.
45 **12** 2k. yellow . . . . £225 35·00
46 3k. green . . . . £275 37·00
47 5k. red . . . . 46·00 30
48 10k. blue . . . . 95·00 1·90
49 15k. brown . . . . £170 1·30

A H **14** A H **16** **20**

1867.
59 A H **14** 2k. yellow . . . . . 10·50 70
60 3k. green . . . . . . 42·00 60
62 5k. red . . . . 1·90 20
63 10k. blue . . . . . . 95·00 30
64 15k. brown . . . . . 12·50 3·25
56a 25k. grey . . . . . . 36·00 11·50
66 A H **16** 50k. brown . . . . . 23·00 65·00

1883.
70 **20** 2k. brown . . . . 6·50 45
71 3k. green . . . . 6·25 30
72 5k. red . . . . 24·00 25
73 10k. blue . . . . 4·25 35
74 20k. grey . . . . 47·00 4·00
75a 50k. mauve . . . . £350 60·00

23 **24** **25**

1890.
79 **23** 1k. grey . . . . 2·00 25
80 2k. brown 25 20
81 3k. green 40 20
82 5k. red 40 20
83 10k. blue . . . . 1·20 25
84 12k. purple . . . . 2·50 30
85 15k. purple . . . . 2·30 30
86 20k. green . . . . 30·00 1·90
87 24k. blue . . . . 2·75 1·00
88 30k. brown . . . . 2·75 60
89 50k. mauve . . . . 6·75 6·50
90 **24** 1g. blue . . . . 2·30 2·00
105 1g. lilac . . . . 41·00 4·75
91 2g. red . . . . 3·50 14·50
106 2g. green . . . . 16·00 45·00

1891. Figures in black.
92 **25** 20k. green . . . . 1·30 20
93 24k. blue . . . . 2·75 65
94 30k. brown . . . . 1·50 20
95 50k. mauve . . . . 1·60 30

27 **28**

29 **30**

1899. Corner numerals in black on heller values.
107 **27** 1h. mauve . . . . 1·40 15
108 2h. grey . . . . 2·75 35
140 3h. brown 80 15
141 5h. green 60 15
142 6h. orange 60 15
143 **28** 10h. red 75 15
144 20h. brown . . . . 1·20 15
145 25h. blue . . . . 1·20 20

146 30h. mauve 3·00 95
147 29 35h. green 1·50 30
148 40h. green 3·25 4·25
149 50h. blue 7·25 7·75
150 60h. brown 3·25 85
119a 30 1k. red 5·25 15
120 2k. lilac 55·00 40
121 4k. green 8·00 8·25

33 35

1904. Types as before, but with corners containing figures altered as T **33** and **35**. Figures in black on white on 10h. to 30h. only.
169 **33** 1h. purple 20 35
170 2h. black 20 25
171 3h. brown 35 15
183 5h. green 30 15
173 6h. orange 40 15
160 **28** 10h. red 2·75 15
161 20h. brown 29·00 80
162 25h. blue 30·00 80
163 30h. mauve 39·00 1·60
178 **35** 35h. green 3·50 30
179 40h. purple 3·50 80
180 50h. blue 3·50 2·75
181 60h. brown 3·50 55
168 72h. red 2·75 1·40

1906. Figures on plain white ground and stamps printed in one colour.
184 **28** 10h. red 40 15
185 12h. violet 1·30 60
186 20h. brown 3·75 15
187 25h. blue 3·75 35
188 30h. red 7·75 25

37 Francis Joseph I
38 Francis Joseph I

41 Schonbrunn

42 Francis Joseph I

1908. 60th Anniv of Emperor's Accession.
189 – 1h. black 30 15
190 – 2h. violet 30 15
191 – 3h. purple 50 15
192 **37** 5h. green 30 15
193 – 6h. brown 70 80
194 **37** 10h. red 25 15
195 – 12h. red 1·40 1·00
196 – 20h. brown 6·75 30
197 **37** 25h. blue 3·00 20
198 – 30h. green 11·00 30
199 – 35h. grey 2·75 25
200 **38** 50h. green 65 25
201 – 60h. red 30 15
202 **38** 72h. brown 2·00 30
203 – 1k. violet 9·75 20
204 **41** 2k. green and red 20·00 55
205 – 5k. purple and brown 40·00 5·00
206 **42** 10k. brown, blue & ochre £140 65·00
DESIGNS—As Type **37**: 1h. Charles VI; 2h. Maria Theresa; 3h. Joseph II; 6h. Leopold II; 12h. Francis I; 20h. Ferdinand; 30h. Francis Joseph I in 1848; 35h. Same in 1878. As Type **38**: 60h. Francis Joseph I on horseback; 1k. Same in ceremonial robes. As Type **41**: 5k. Hofburg.

45

47

1910. 80th Birthday of Francis Joseph I. As issue of 1908 but with dates added as T **45**.
223 1h. black 4·25 8·75
224 2h. violet 5·50 10·00
225 3h. purple 5·50 11·00
226 5h. green 70 55
227 6h. brown 4·25 8·75
228 10h. red 30 55
229 12h. red 4·25 9·00
230 20h. brown 9·00 10·25
231 25h. blue 1·90 2·75
232 30h. green 4·75 7·75
233 35h. grey 4·75 7·75
234 50h. green 7·00 9·50
235 60h. red 7·00 9·50
236 1k. violet 8·00 11·00
237 2k. green and red £140 £225
238 5k. purple and brown £120 £180
239 10k. brown, blue and ochre £200 £350

1914. War Charity Funds.
240 **47** 5h.+(2h.) green 20 40
241 10h.+(2h.) red 30 35

48 Cavalry

1915. War Charity Funds.
242 – 3h.+1h. brown 15 45
243 **48** 5h.+2h. green 15 15
244 – 10h.+2h. red 15 15
245 – 20h.+3h. green 75 2·10
246 – 35h.+3h. blue 2·20 5·00
DESIGNS: 3h. Infantry; 10h. Artillery; 20h. Battleship "Viribus Unitas" (Navy); 35h. Lohner Pfeilflieger B-1 biplane (Air Force).

49 Imperial Austrian Crown

50 Francis Joseph I

51 Arms of Austria
52

1916.
247 **49** 3h. violet 10 10
248 5h. green 10 10
249 6h. orange 30 65
250 10h. red 15 10
251 12h. blue 35 1·10
252 **50** 15h. red 40 10
253 20h. brown 3·00 15
254 25h. blue 4·75 30
255 30h. slate 4·00 55
256 **51** 40h. olive 15 25
257 50h. green 20 15
258 60h. blue 20 15
259 80h. brown 35 15
260 90h. purple 35 15
261 1k. red on yellow 30 15
262aa **52** 2k. blue 15 40
263aa 3k. red 30 1·00
264a 4k. green 2·00 1·60
265aa 10k. violet 12·50 29·00
On Nos. 254/5 the portrait is full face. The 1k. has floral sprays each side of the coat-of-arms.

60 Charles I

1917.
290 **60** 15h. red 15 10
291a 20h. green 15 10
292 25h. blue 55 15
293 30h. violet 40 15

1918. Air. Optd **FLUGPOST** or surch also.
296 **52** 1k.50 on 2k. mauve 3·75 5·00
297 2k.50 on 3k. brown 11·00 25·00
298 4k. grey 5·75 14·50

1918. Optd **Deutschosterreich**.
299 **49** 3h. violet 15 20
300 5h. green 15 20
301 6h. orange 30 1·30
302 10h. red 15 10
303 12h. blue 30 2·10
304 **60** 15h. red 30 80
305 20h. green 15 15
306 25h. blue 30 20
307 30h. violet 20 20
308 **51** 40h. olive 20 20
309 50h. green 70 1·00
310 60h. blue 70 1·00
311 80h. brown 35 35
312 90h. red 35 40
313 1k. red on yellow 35 35
314 **52** 2k. blue 30 25
315 3k. red 40 85
316 4k. green 1·40 1·90
317 10k. violet 9·00 24·00

64 Posthorn
65 Republican Arms
66 "New Republic"

1919. Imperf or perf.
336 **64** 3h. grey 15 15
337 **65** 5h. green 15 15
338 5h. grey 15 15
339 **64** 6h. orange 30 45
340 **65** 10h. red 15 15
342 **64** 12h. blue 15 70
343a 15h. brown 15 15
344 **66** 20h. green 15 15
346 **65** 25h. blue 15 15
347 **64** 25h. violet 15 15
348 **66** 30h. brown 15 15
349 40h. violet 15 15
350 40h. red 15 15
351 **65** 45h. green 15 80
352 **66** 50h. blue 15 15
353 **64** 60h. green 15 15
354 **65** 1k. red on yellow 15 15
355 1k. blue 15 15

67 Parliament Building
71 Republican Arms

1919.
356 **67** 2k. black and red 30 65
357 2½k. bistre 30 40
358 3k. brown and blue 30 30
359 4k. black and red 30 30
360 5k. black 30 30
361 7½k. purple 50 55
362 10k. brown and green 50 55
363 20k. brown and violet 35 60
364 50k. violet on yellow 70 1·30

1920.
402 **71** 80h. red 15 15
403 1k. brown 15 15
404 1½k. green 30 15
405 2k. blue 15 15
406 3k. black and green 15 25
407 4k. claret and red 15 15
408 5k. red and lilac 15 15
409 7½k. brown and orange 30 30
410 10k. blue and violet 30 30
The frames of the 3 to 10k. differ.

1920. Issues for Carinthian Plebiscite. Optd **Karnten Abstimmung** (T **65/7** in new colours). (a) Perf.
411 **65** 5h. (+10h.) grey on yell 65 1·60
412 10h. (+20h.) red on pink 65 1·20
413 **64** 15h. (+30h.) brn on yell 40 1·10
414 **66** 20h. (+40h.) green on bl 40 1·10
415 **64** 25h. (+50h.) pur on pink 40 90
416 **66** 30h. (+60h.) brn on buff 1·40 3·50
417 40h. (+80h.) red on yell 40 1·10
418 50h. (+100h.) indigo on blue 40 70
419 **64** 60h. (+120h.) green on bl 1·70 4·00
420 **71** 80h. (+160h.) red 40 1·00
421 1k. (+2k.) brown 40 1·10
422 2k. (+4k.) blue 40 1·10

(b) Imperf.
423 **67** 2½k. (+5k.) brown 40 1·20
424 3k. (+6k.) green & blue 55 1·50
425 4k. (+8k.) violet & red 90 1·80
426 5k. (+10k.) blue 90 1·60
427 7½k. (+15k.) green 90 1·60
428 10k. (+20k.) red & green 90 1·60
429 20k. (+40k.) brn & lilac 1·00 2·20
The plebiscite was to decide whether Carinthia should be part of Austria or Yugoslavia, and the premium was for a fund to promote a vote in favour of remaining in Austria. The result was a vote for Austria.

1921. Flood Relief Fund. Optd **Hochwasser 1920** (colours changed).
430 **65** 5h. (+10h.) grey on yell 30 60
431 10h. (+20h.) brown 30 60
432 **64** 15h. (+30h.) grey 30 60
433 **66** 20h. (+40h.) green on yell 30 60
434 **64** 25h. (+50h.) blue on yell 30 60
435 **66** 30h. (+60h.) purple on bl 65 1·20
436 40h. (+80h.) brn on red 70 1·30
437 50h. (+100h.) green on bl 1·50 2·30
438 **64** 60h. (+120h.) pur on yell 30 1·20
439 **71** 80h. (+160h.) blue 55 1·10
440 1k. (+2k.) orange on blue 40 95
441 1½k. (+3k.) green on yell 30 55
442 2k. (+4k.) brown 30 55
443 **67** 2½k. (+5k.) blue 30 55
444 3k. (+6k.) red & green 30 55
445 4k. (+8k.) brown & lilac 85 1·90
446 5k. (+10k.) green 30 70
447 7½k. (+15k.) red 35 90
448 10k. (+20k.) green & blue 30 95
449 20k. (+40k.) pur & red 70 1·30

80 Pincers and Hammer

81 Ear of Corn

1922.
461 **81** ½k. brown 10 55
462 **80** 1k. brown 20 25
463 2k. blue 10 15
464 **81** 2½k. brown 10 15
465 **80** 4k. purple 10 1·10
466 5k. green 10 15
467 **81** 7½k. violet 10 15
468 **80** 10k. red 10 10
469 **81** 12½k. green 10 15
470 15k. turquoise 10 15
471 20k. blue 10 10
472 25k. red 10 10
473 **80** 30k. grey 10 20
474 45k. red 10 20
475 50k. brown 10 10
476 60k. green 15 15
477 75k. blue 10 10
478 80k. yellow 10 10
479 **81** 100k. grey 10 10
480 120k. brown 10 15
481 150k. orange 10 10
482 160k. green 10 10
483 180k. red 15 15
484 200k. pink 10 10
485 240k. violet 15 10
486 300k. blue 15 10
487 400k. green 85 15
488 500k. yellow 15 10
489 600k. slate 15 10
490 700k. brown 1·70 15
491 800k. violet 1·10 1·80
492 **80** 1000k. mauve 1·70 15
493 1200k. red 1·40 40
494 1500k. orange 1·70 15
495 1600k. slate 5·00 2·30
496 2000k. blue 4·75 1·30
497 3000k. blue 16·00 1·75
498 4000k. blue on blue 7·00 3·75

82

85 Mozart

1922.
499 **82** 20k. sepia 15 15
500 25k. blue 15 15
501 50k. red 15 15
502 100k. green 15 15
503 200k. purple 15 15
504 500k. orange 30 95
505 1000k. violet on yellow 15 10
506 2000k. green on yellow 15 15
507 3000k. red 11·75 65
508 5000k. black 3·00 1·50
509 10,000k. brown 4·00 5·25

1922. Musicians' Fund.
519 – 2½k. brown 9·00 14·00
520 **85** 5k. blue 1·25 2·20
521 – 7½k. black 2·10 3·50
522 – 10k. purple 2·50 4·75
523 – 25k. green 5·00 8·25
524 – 50k. red 2·40 4·50
525 – 100k. green 7·00 11·75
COMPOSERS: 2½k. Haydn; 7½k. Beethoven; 10k. Schubert; 25k. Bruckner; 50k. J. Strauss; 100k. Wolf.

87 Hawk

88 W. Kress

1922. Air.
546 **87** 300k. red 40 1·40
547 400k. green 5·00 15·00
548 600k. olive 35 1·20
549 900k. red 35 1·30
550 **88** 1200k. purple 35 1·30
551 2400k. slate 35 1·40
552 3000k. brown 3·75 9·00
553 4800k. blue 3·75 9·00

89 Bregenz

90 "Art the Comforter"

1923. Artists' Charity Fund.
554 **89** 100k. green 2·75 10·00
555 – 120k. blue 3·00 6·75
556 – 160k. purple 3·00 6·75
557 – 180k. purple 3·00 6·75

558 – 200k. red . . . . 3·00 6·75
559 – 240k. brown . . . . 3·75 7·00
560 – 400k. brown . . . . 3·25 7·00
561 – 600k. green . . . . 3·25 8·00
562 – 1000k. black . . . . 4·00 9·00
DESIGNS: 120k. Salzburg; 160k. Eisenstadt; 180k. Klagenfurt; 200k. Innsbruck; 240k. Linz; 400k. Graz; 600k. Melk; 1000k. Vienna.

1924. Artists' Charity Fund.
563 **90** 100k.+300k. green . . . . 4·00 7·75
564 – 300k.+900k. brown . . . . 4·00 8·00
565 – 500k.+1500k. purple . . . 4·00 8·00
566 – 600k.+1800k. turquoise . . 4·75 15·00
567 – 1000k.+3000k. brown . . . 8·50 21·00
DESIGNS: 300k. "Agriculture and Handicraft"; 500k. "Mother Love"; 600k. "Charity"; 1000k. "Fruitfulness".

91

92 Plains

93 Minorite Church, Vienna

1925.
568 **91** 1g. grey 40 15
569 2g. red 60 15
570 3g. red 70 15
571 4g. blue . . . . 1·40 15
572 5g. brown . . . . 2·40 15
573 6g. blue . . . . 2·50 15
574 7g. brown . . . . 2·30 15
575 8g. green . . . . 4·50 15
576 **92** 10g. brown 60 15
577 15g. red 60 15
578 16g. blue 60 15
579 18g. green . . . . 1·10 30
580 – 20g. violet 90 15
581 – 24g. red . . . . 1·10 40
582 – 30g. brown 90 15
583 – 40g. blue . . . . 1·10 15
584 – 45g. brown . . . . 1·30 15
585 – 50g. grey . . . . 1·70 30
586 – 80g. blue . . . . 6·00 4·50
587 **93** 1s. green . . . . 28·00 1·30
588 – 2s. red . . . . 9·00 10·75
DESIGN—As T **92**—20g. to 80g. Golden eagle on mountains.

96 Airman and Hansa Brandenburg C-1

97 De Havilland D.H.34 and Common Crane

1925. Air
616 **96** 2g. brown 65 90
617 5g. red 35 30
618 6g. blue . . . . 1·30 1·50
619 8g. green . . . . 1·60 1·90
620 **97** 10g. red . . . . 95 2·75
621 **96** 10g. orange . . . . . . 1·10 2·10
622 **97** 15g. red . . . . 85 1·30
623 **96** 15g. mauve 80 90
624 20g. brown . . . . 12·00 7·50
625 25g. violet . . . . 5·75 8·00
626 **97** 30g. purple . . . . 1·10 2·75
627 **96** 30g. bistre . . . . 10·50 9·25
628 **97** 50g. grey . . . . 1·90 3·00
629 **96** 50g. blue . . . . 21·00 13·50
630 80g. green . . . . 3·00 3·75
631 **97** 1s. blue . . . . 11·00 7·75
632 2s. green . . . . 2·40 4·00
633 3s. brown . . . . 55·00 60·00
634 5s. blue . . . . 14·00 24·00
635 10s. brown on grey (25 × 32 mm) . . . . . 9·00 19·00

98 Siegfried and Dragon

99 Dr. Michael Hainisch

1926. Child Welfare. Scenes from the Nibelung Legend.
636 **98** 3g.+2g. brown 65 85
637 – 8g.+2g. blue 15 45
638 – 15g.+5g. red 30 45
639 – 20g.+5g. green 30 70
640 – 24g.+6g. violet 30 70
641 – 40g.+10g. brown . . . . . 3·75 4·00
DESIGNS: 8g. Gunther's voyage; 15g. Kriemhild and Brunhild; 20g. Hagen and the Rhine maidens; 24g. Rudiger and the Nibelungs; 40g. Dietrich's fight with Hagen.

1928. 10th Anniv of Republic and War Orphans and Invalid Children's Fund.
642 **99** 10g. (+10g.) brown . . . . 3·75 9·50
643 15g. (+15g.) red . . . . 3·75 9·50
644 30g. (+30g.) black . . . 3·75 9·50
645 40g. (+40g.) blue . . . . 3·75 9·50

100 Gussing

101 National Library, Vienna

1929. Views. Size $25\frac{1}{2} \times 21\frac{1}{2}$ mm.
646 **100** 10g. orange . . . . . . 1·10 15
647 10g. brown . . . . 1·10 15
648 – 15g. purple . . . . 65 1·30
649 – 16g. black 40 15
650 – 18g. green 80 50
651 – 20g. black 85 10
653 – 24g. purple . . . . 7·00 60
654 – 30g. violet . . . . 7·00 30
655 – 40g. blue . . . . 12·00 15
656 – 50g. violet . . . . 33·00 20
657 – 60g. green . . . . 22·00 25
658 **101** 1s. brown . . . . 6·25 30
659 – 2s. green . . . . 11·00 8·75
VIEWS—As T **100**: 15g. Hochosterwitz; 16, 20g. Durnstein; 18g. Traunsee; 24g. Salzburg; 30g. Seewiesen; 40g. Innsbruck; 50g. Worthersee; 60g. Hohenems. As T **101**: 2s. St. Stephen's Cathedral, Vienna.
See also Nos. 678/91.

102 Pres. Wilhelm Miklas

104 Johann Nestroy

1930. Anti-tuberculosis Fund.
660 **102** 10g. (+10g.) brown . . . 7·00 14·50
661 20g. (+20g.) red . . . . 7·00 14·50
662 30g. (+30g.) purple . . . 7·00 14·50
663 40g. (+40g.) blue . . . . 7·00 14·50
664 50g. (+50g.) green . . . 7·00 14·50
665 1s. (+1s.) brown . . . . 7·00 14·50

1930. Rotarian Congress. Optd with Rotary Int emblem and **CONVENTION WIEN 1931**.
666 **100** 10g. (+10g.) brown . . . 34·00 46·00
667 – 20g. (+20g.) grey (No. 651) . . . . . . 34·00 46·00
668 – 30g. (+30g.) vio (No. 654) 34·00 46·00
669 – 40g. (+40g.) bl (No. 655) 34·00 46·00
670 – 50g. (+50g.) vio (No. 656) 34·00 46·00
671 **101** 1s. (+1s.) brown . . . . 34·00 46·00

1931. Austrian Writers and Youth Unemployment Fund.
672 – 10g. (+10g.) purple . . . 12·50 24·00
673 – 20g. (+20g.) grey . . . . 12·50 24·00
674 **104** 30g. (+30g.) red . . . . 12·50 24·00
675 – 40g. (+40g.) blue . . . . 12·50 24·00
676 – 50g. (+50g.) green . . . 12·50 24·00
677 – 1s. (+1s.) brown . . . . 12·50 24·00
DESIGNS: 10g. F. Raimund; 20g. E. Grillparzer; 40g. A Stifter; 50g. L. Anzengruber; 1s. P. Rosegger.

105

106 Dr. Ignaz Seipel

1932. Designs as No. 646 etc, but size reduced to $20\frac{1}{2} \times 16$ mm as T **105**.
678 **105** 10g. brown 90 15
679 – 12g. green . . . . 2·00 15
680 – 18g. green . . . . 2·00 2·30
681 – 20g. black . . . . 1·40 10
682 – 24g. red . . . . 5·75 15
683 – 24g. violet . . . . 3·50 15
684 – 30g. violet . . . . 16·00 15
685 – 30g. red . . . . 6·00 15
686 – 40g. blue . . . . 22·00 90
687 – 40g. violet . . . . 7·75 25
688 – 50g. violet . . . . 23·00 30
689 – 50g. blue . . . . 8·00 30
690 – 60g. green . . . . 50·00 2·75
691 – 64g. green . . . . 14·50 30
DESIGNS (new values): 12g. Traunsee; 64g. Hohenems.

1932. Death of Dr. Seipel (Chancellor), and Ex-servicemen's Fund.
692 **106** 50g. (+50g.) blue . . . . 11·50 18·00

107 Hans Makart

108 The Climb

1932. Austrian Painters.
693 – 12g. (+12g.) green . . . . 15·00 27·00
694 – 24g. (+24g.) purple . . . 15·00 24·00
695 – 30g. (+30g.) red . . . . 15·00 24·00
696 **107** 40g. (+40g.) grey . . . . 15·00 26·00
697 – 64g. (+64g.) brown . . . 15·00 26·00
698 – 1s. (+1s.) red . . . . . . 15·00 35·00
DESIGNS: 12g. F. G. Waldmuller; 24g. Von Schwind; 30g. Alt; 64g. Klimt; 1s. A. Egger-Lienz.

1933. International Ski Championship Fund.
699 **108** 12g. (+12g.) green . . . . 7·50 14·00
700 – 24g. (+24g.) violet . . . 95·00 £160
701 – 30g. (+30g.) red . . . . 12·50 26·00
702 – 50g. (+50g.) blue . . . . 95·00 £150
DESIGNS: 24g. Start; 30g. Race; 50g. Ski jump.

109 "The Honeymoon" (M. von Schwind)

111 John Sobieski

1933. International Philatelic Exn, Vienna (WIPA).
703 **109** 50g. (+50g.) blue £130 £180
MS705 127 × 105 mm. As No. 703 (+1s.60 admission) in block of four £2750 £3000

1933. 250th Anniv of Relief of Vienna and Pan-German Catholic Congress.
706 – 12g. (+12g.) green . . . . 23·00 34·00
707 – 24g. (+24g.) violet . . . . 21·00 27·00
708 – 30g. (+30g.) red . . . . 21·00 27·00
709 **111** 40g. (+40g.) grey . . . . 34·00 49·00
710 – 50g. (+50g.) blue . . . . 22·00 28·00
711 – 64g. (+64g.) brown . . . 26·00 60·00
DESIGNS—VERT: 12g. Vienna in 1683; 24g. Marco d'Aviano; 30g. Count von Starhemberg; 50g. Charles of Lorraine; 64g. Burgomaster Liebenberg.

1933. Winter Relief Fund. Surch with premium and **Winterhilfe** (5g.) or **WINTERHILFE** (others).
712 **91** 5g.+2g. green 15 70
713 – 12g.+3g. blue (as 679) . . 30 75
714 – 24g.+6g. brn (as 682) . . 15 70
715 **101** 1s.+50g. red . . . . . . 31·00 43·00

114

115

1934.
716 **114** 1g. violet 15 15
717 3g. red 15 15
718 – 4g. green 15 15
719 – 5g. purple 15 15
720 – 6g. blue 45 25
722 – 8g. green 30 15
723 – 12g. brown 30 10
724 – 20g. brown 30 15
725 – 24g. turquoise 30 15
726 – 25g. violet 35 30
727 – 30g. red 35 15
728 – 35g. red 60 40
729 **115** 40g. grey 95 25
730 45g. brown 75 20
731 – 60g. blue . . . . 1·10 35
732 – 64g. brown . . . . 1·60 15
733 – 1s. purple . . . . 1·90 55
735 – 2s. green . . . . 3·50 5·75
736 – 3s. orange . . . . 17·00 20·00
737 – 5s. black . . . . 28·00 49·00
DESIGNS (Austrian costumes of the districts named)—As Type **114**: 1, 3g. Burgenland; 4, 5g. Carinthia; 6, 8g. Lower Austria; 12, 20g. Upper Austria; 24, 25g. Salzburg; 30, 35g. Styria (Steiermark). As Type **115**: 40, 45g. Tyrol; 60, 64g. Vorarlberg; 1s. Vienna; 2s. Army officer and soldiers. 30 × 31 mm: 3s. Harvesters; 5s. Builders.

117 Chancellor Dollfuss

118 Anton Pilgram

1934. Dollfuss Mourning Stamp.
738 **117** 24g. black 55 30
See also No. 762.

1934. Welfare Funds. Austrian Architects.
739 **118** 12g. (+12g.) black . . . . 10·00 19·00
740 – 24g. (+24g.) violet . . . 10·00 19·00
741 – 30g. (+30g.) red . . . . 10·00 19·00
742 – 40g. (+40g.) brown . . . 10·00 19·00
743 – 60g. (+60g.) blue . . . . 10·00 19·00
744 – 64g. (+64g.) green . . . 10·00 19·00
DESIGNS: 24g. Fischer von Erlach; 30g. J. Prandtauer; 40g. A. von Siccardsburg and E. van der Null; 60g. H. von Ferstel; 64g. Otto Wagner.

119 "Mother and Child" (J. Danhauser)

1935. Mothers Day.
745 **119** 24g. blue 40 25

1935. 1st Anniv of Assassination of Dr. Dollfuss.
762 **117** 24g. blue 90 85

121 Maria Worth Castle, Carinthia

122 Zugspitze Aerial Railway

1935. Air. Designs showing Junkers airplane (except 10s.) and landscape.
763 – 5g. purple 45 60
764 **121** 10g. orange 45 50
765 – 15g. green . . . . 70 1·50
766 – 20g. blue 20 55
767 – 25g. purple 40 35
768 – 30g. red 40 45
769 – 40g. green 40 45
770 – 50g. blue 45 70
771 – 60g. sepia . . . . 40 1·40
772 – 80g. brown . . . . 55 1·40
773 – 1s. red . . . . 40 1·20
774 – 2s. green . . . . 3·25 6·75
775 – 3s. brown . . . . 9·25 19·00
776 **122** 5s. green . . . . 4·75 16·00
777 – 10s. blue . . . . 55·00 95·00
DESIGNS—As T **121**: 5g. Gussing Castle; 15g. Durnstein; 20g. Hallstatt; 25g. Salzburg; 30g. Dachstein Mts.; 40g. Wettersee; 50g. Stuben am Arlberg; 60g. St. Stephen's Cathedral, Vienna; 80g. Minorite Church, Vienna. As T **122**: 1s. River Danube; 2s. Tauern railway viaduct; 3s. Grossglockner mountain roadway; 10s. Glider and yachts on the Attersee.

1935. Winter Relief Fund. As Nos. 719, 723, 725 and 733, but colours changed, surch **Winterhilfe** (778/80) or **WINTERHILFE** (781) and premium.
778 5g.+2g. green 35 80
779 12g.+3g. blue . . . . 35 1·10
780 24g.+6g. brown 35 90
781 1s.+50g. red . . . . 19·00 33·00

123 Prince Eugene of Savoy (born 1663, not 1667 as given)

124 Slalom Course Skier

1935. Welfare Funds. Austrian Heroes.
782 **123** 12g. (+12g.) brown . . . 9·00 17·00
783 – 24g. (+24g.) green . . . . 9·00 17·00
784 – 30g. (+30g.) purple . . . 9·00 17·00
785 – 40g. (+40g.) blue . . . . 9·00 17·00
786 – 60g. (+60g.) blue . . . . 9·00 17·00
787 – 64g. (+64g.) violet . . . 9·00 17·00
PORTRAITS: 24g. Baron von Laudon; 30g. Archduke Charles; 40g. Field-Marshal Radetzky; 60g. Vice-Admiral von Tegetthoff; 64g. Field-Marshal Conrad von Hotzendorff.

1936. International Ski Championship Fund. Inscr "WETTKAMPFE 1936".
788 **124** 12g. (+12g.) green . . . . 2·50 3·75
789 – 24g. (+24g.) violet . . . . 4·50 5·00
790 – 35g. (+35g.) red . . . . 25·00 44·00
791 – 60g. (+60g.) blue . . . . 25·00 44·00
DESIGNS: 24g. Skier on mountain slope; 35g. Woman slalom course skier; 60g. View of Maria Theresienstrasse, Innsbruck.

125 Madonna and Child

1936. Mothers' Day.
792 **125** 24g. blue 30 30

126 Chancellor Dollfuss

127 "St. Martin sharing Cloak"

1936. 2nd Anniv of Assassination of Dr. Dollfuss.
793 **126** 10s. blue £900 £1000

1936. Winter Relief Fund. Inscr "WINTERHILFE 1936/37".
794 **127** 5g.+2g. green 20 55
795 – 12g.+3g. violet 20 55
796 – 24g.+6g. blue 20 55
797 – 1s.+1s. red . . . . . . 6·00 11·50
DESIGNS: 12g. "Healing the sick"; 24g. "St. Elizabeth feeding the hungry"; 1s. "Warming the poor".

128 J. Ressel

129 Mother and Child

1936. Welfare Funds. Austrian Inventors.
798 **128** 12g. (+12g.) brown . . . 4·00 6·25
799 – 24g. (+24g.) violet . . . . 4·00 6·25
800 – 30g. (+30g.) red . . . . 4·00 6·25
801 – 40g. (+40g.) black . . . . 4·00 6·25
802 – 60g. (+60g.) blue . . . . 4·00 6·25
803 – 64g. (+64g.) green . . . . 4·00 6·25
PORTRAITS: 24g. Karl Ritter von Ghega; 30g. J. Werndl; 40g. Carl Freih. Auer von Welsbach; 60g. R. von Lieben; 64g. V. Kaplan.

1937. Mothers' Day.
804 **129** 24g. red 30 30

130 "Maria Anna"

131 "Child Welfare"

1937. Centenary of Regular Danube Services of Danube Steam Navigation Co. Paddle-steamers.
805 **130** 12g. red 85 35
806 – 24g. blue 85 35
807 – 64g. green 85 75
DESIGNS: 24g. "Helios"; 64g. "Oesterreich".

1937. Winter Relief Fund. Inscr "WINTERHILFE 1937 1938".
808 **131** 5g.+2g. green 20 55
809 – 12g.+3g. brown 20 55
810 – 24g.+6g. blue 20 55
811 – 1s.+1s. red . . . . . . 3·00 7·50
DESIGNS: 12g. "Feeding the Children"; 24g. "Protecting the Aged"; 1s. "Nursing the Sick."

132 Steam Locomotive "Austria", 1837

133 Dr. G. Van Swieten

1937. Railway Centenary.
812 **132** 12g. brown . . . . 1·80 15
813 – 25g. violet . . . . 1·80 1·20
814 – 35g. red . . . . 1·80 2·50
DESIGNS: 25g. Steam locomotive, 1936; 35g. Electric locomotive.

1937. Welfare Funds. Austrian Doctors.
815 **133** 5g. (+5g.) brown . . . . 1·80 4·25
816 – 8g. (+8g.) red . . . . . . 1·80 4·25
817 – 12g. (+12g.) brown . . . . 1·80 4·25
818 – 20g. (+20g.) green . . . . 1·80 4·25
819 – 24g. (+24g.) violet . . . . 1·80 4·25
820 – 30g. (+30g.) red . . . . 1·80 4·25
821 – 40g. (+40g.) olive . . . . 1·80 4·25
822 – 60g. (+60g.) blue . . . . 1·80 4·25
823 – 64g. (+64g.) purple . . . 1·80 4·25
DESIGNS: 8g. L. A. von Auenbrugg; 12g. K. von Rokitansky; 20g. J. Skoda; 25g. F. von Hebra; 30g. F. von Arlt; 40g. J. Hyrtl; 60g. T. Billroth; 64g. T. Meynert.

134 Nosegay and Signs of the Zodiac

1937. Christmas Greetings.
824 **134** 12g. green 15 20
825 24g. red 15 20

ALLIED OCCUPATION. Nos. 826/905 were issued in the Russian Zone of occupation and Nos. 906/22 were a joint issue for use in the British, French and American zones.

1945. Hitler portrait stamps of Germany optd.
(a) Optd **Osterreich** only.
826 **173** 5pf. green 20 85
827 8pf. red 25 70

(b) Optd **Osterreich** and bar.
828 **173** 6pf. violet . . . . 25 1·20
829 12pf. red . . . . 25 1·20

(137)

(140)

1945. 1941 and 1944 Hitler stamps of Germany optd as T **137**.
830 **137** 1pf. grey . . . . 3·25 5·50
831 3pf. brown . . . . 2·20 4·75
832 4pf. grey . . . . 11·50 27·00
833 5pf. green . . . . 2·50 4·75
834 6pf. violet 35 55
835 8pf. red . . . . 1·10 1·40
836 10pf. brown . . . . . . 3·00 4·25
837 12pf. red 45 95
838 15pf. red . . . . 1·40 2·75
839 16pf. green . . . . . . 25·00 60·00
840 20pf. blue . . . . 3·00 5·75
841 24pf. brown . . . . . . 26·00 75·00
842 **173** 25pf. blue . . . . 2·50 4·75
843 30pf. green . . . . . . 2·50 4·75
844 40pf. mauve . . . . . . 2·75 5·25
845 **225** 42pf. green . . . . . . 5·25 10·50
846 **173** 50pf. green . . . . . . 4·00 7·50
847 60pf. brown . . . . . . 4·50 11·75
848 80pf. blue . . . . 3·75 9·75
853 **182** 1rm. green . . . . . . 21·00 43·00
850 2rm. violet . . . . . . 22·00 42·00
855 3rm. red . . . . 39·00 85·00
856 5rm. blue £275 £600

1945. Stamps of Germany surch **OSTERREICH** and new value.
857 **186** 5pf. on 12+88pf. green . . 70 2·10
858 – 6pf. on 6+14pf. brown and blue (No. 811) . . 7·25 14·00
859 **220** 8pf. on 42+108pf. brn . . 1·00 3·00
860 – 12pf. on 3+7pf. blue (No. 810) . . . . . . 85 2·00

1948. 1941 and 1944 Hitler stamps of Germany optd as T **140**.
862 **173** 5pf. green . . . . 85 3·75
863 6pf. violet . . . . 50 2·20
864 8pf. red . . . . 35 2·50
865 12pf. red . . . . 50 3·00
866 30pf. green . . . . . . 8·75 18·00
867a **225** 42pf. green . . . . . . 22·00 41·00

141 New National Arms

142 New National Arms

1945.
868 **141** 3pf. brown 15 20
869 4pf. blue 15 45
870 5pf. green 15 25
871 6pf. purple 15 25
872 8pf. orange 15 25
873 10pf. brown 15 25
874 12pf. red 15 25
875 15pf. orange 15 25
876 16pf. green 15 60
877 20pf. blue 15 30
878 24pf. orange 15 35
879 25pf. blue 15 30
880 30pf. green 15 25
881 38pf. blue 15 35
882 40pf. purple 15 35
883 42pf. grey 25 35
884 50pf. green 15 35

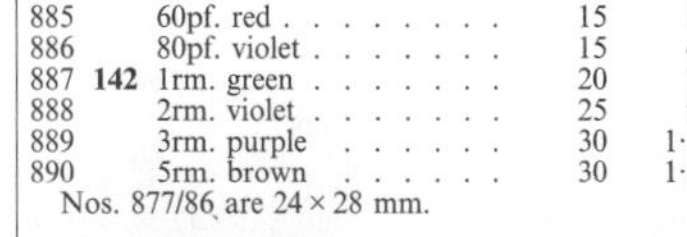
885 60pf. red 15 50
886 80pf. violet 15 40
887 **142** 1rm. green 20 70
888 2rm. violet 25 90
889 3rm. purple . . . . 30 1·10
890 5rm. brown . . . . 30 1·50
Nos. 877/86 are 24 × 28 mm.

144 Allegorical of the Home Land

145 Posthorn

1945. Austrian Welfare Charities.
905 **144** 1s.+10s. green . . . . . 90 2·75

1945.
906 **145** 1g. blue 15 65
907 3g. orange 15 25
908 4g. brown 15 25
909 5g. green 15 20
910 6g. purple 15 20
911 8g. red 15 20
912 10g. grey 15 20
913 12g. brown 15 20
914 15g. red 15 25
915 20g. brown 15 25
916 25g. blue 15 25
917 30g. mauve 15 25
918 40g. blue 15 25
919 60g. olive 15 30
920 1s. violet 20 70
921 2s. yellow . . . . 35 1·60
922 5s. blue . . . . 45 1·60

146 Salzburg

148 Durnstein

1945. Views as T **146/8**.
923 – 3g. blue 15 15
924 – 4g. red 15 15
925 – 5g. red 15 15
926 **146** 6g. green 15 15
927 – 8g. brown 15 15
928 – 8g. purple 15 15
929 – 8g. green 15 15
930 – 10g. green 15 15
931 – 10g. purple 15 15
932 – 12g. brown 15 15
933 – 15g. blue 15 15
934 – 16g. brown 15 15
935 – 20g. blue 15 15
936 – 24g. green 15 15
937 – 25g. grey 15 15
938 – 30g. red 15 15
939 – 30g. blue 35 40
940 – 35g. red 15 15
941 – 38g. green 15 15
942 – 40g. grey 15 15
943 – 42g. red 15 15
944 – 45g. blue 25 45
945 – 50g. blue 20 15
946 – 50g. purple 50 50
947 – 60g. blue 25 25
948 – 60g. violet . . . . . . 2·40 3·00
949 – 70g. blue 30 45
950 – 80g. brown 35 65
951 – 90g. green . . . . . . 1·50 2·20
952 **148** 1s. brown 65 95
953 – 2s. grey . . . . 3·00 4·50
954 – 3s. green . . . . 1·00 1·40
955 – 5s. red . . . . 1·60 2·75
DESIGNS—As Type **146**: 3g. Lermoos; 4g. Iron-ore mine, Erzberg; 5g. Leopoldsberg, Vienna; 8g. (927), Prater Woods, Vienna; 8g. (928/9), Town Hall Park, Vienna; 10g. (930/1), Hochosterwitz; 12g. Schafberg; 15g. Forchtenstein; 16g. Gesauseeingang. 23½ × 29 mm: 20g. Gebhartsberg; 24g. Holdrichsmuhle, near Modling; 25g. Vent im Otztal; 30g. (938/9), Neusiedler Lake; 35g. Belvedere Palace, Vienna; 38g. Langbath Lake; 40g. Mariazell; 42g. Traunstein; 45g. Burg Hartenstein; 50g. (945/6), Silvretta Peaks, Vorarlberg; 60g. (947/8), Semmering; 70g. Badgastein; 80g. Kaisergebirge; 90g. Wayside shrine near Tragoss. As T **148**: 2s. St. Christof; 3s. Heiligenblut; 5s. Schonbrunn Palace, Vienna.
See also Nos. 1072/86a.

1946. 1st Anniv of U.N.O. No. 938 surch **26. JUNI 1945+20 g 26. JUNI 1946** and globe.
971 30g.+20g. red . . . . 2·10 5·25

151 Dr. Karl Renner

1946. 1st Anniv of Establishment of Renner Government.
972 **151** 1s.+1s. green . . . . . . 2·30 6·00
973 2s.+2s. violet . . . . . . 2·30 6·00
974 3s.+3s. purple . . . . . 2·30 6·00
975 5s.+5s. brown . . . . . 2·30 6·00
MS976 Four sheets, each 180 × 155 mm, each with block of 8 of one value (972/5) and Arms in centre. Imperf Set 4 sheets . . £1700

152 Dagger and Map

(153)

1946. "Anti-Fascist" Exhibition.
977 **152** 5g.+3g. sepia . . . . . . 50 1·20
978 – 6g.+4g. green 35 90
979 – 8g.+6g. orange 35 90
980 – 12g.+12g. blue 50 90
981 – 30g.+30g. violet 35 85
982 – 42g.+42g. brown . . . . 35 1·00
983 – 1s.+1s. red . . . . 50 1·40
984 – 2s.+2s. red . . . . . . 1·00 2·25
DESIGNS: 6g. Broom sweeping Nazi and Fascist emblems; 8g. St. Stephen's Cathedral in flames; 12g. Hand and barbed wire; 30g. Hand strangling snake; 42g. Hammer and broken column; 1s. Hand and Austrian flag; 2s. Eagle and smoking Nazi emblem.

1946. Congress of Society for Promotion of Cultural and Economic Relations with the Soviet Union. No. 932 optd with T **153**.
985 12g. brown 15 50

154 Mare and Foal

155 Ruprecht's Church, Vienna

1946. Austria Prize Race Fund.
986 **154** 16g.+16g. red . . . . . . 2·50 5·25
987 – 24g.+24g. violet . . . . . 2·10 4·25
988 – 60g.+60g. green . . . . . 2·10 4·25
989 – 1s.+1s. blue . . . . . . 2·10 4·50
990 – 2s.+2s. brown . . . . . 3·00 7·00
DESIGNS: 24g. Two horses' heads; 60g. Racehorse clearing hurdle; 1s. Three racehorses; 2s. Three horses' heads.

1946. 950th Anniv of First recorded use of name "Osterreich".
991 **155** 30g.+70g. red 30 95

156 Statue of Duke Rudolf

157 Franz Grillparzer (dramatic poet)

1946. St. Stephen's Cathedral Reconstruction Fund. Architectural and Sculptural designs.
992 **156** 3g.+12g. brown 20 65
993 – 5g.+20g. purple 20 70
994 – 6g.+24g. blue 20 70
995 – 8g.+32g. green 20 70
996 – 10g.+40g. blue 20 85
997 – 12g.+48g. violet . . . . 50 1·50
998 – 30g.+1s.20 red . . . . . 1·20 2·10
999 – 50g.+1s.80 blue . . . . 1·40 3·75
1000 – 1s.+5s. purple . . . . . 1·70 5·00
1001 – 2s.+10s. brown . . . . . 3·25 9·00
DESIGNS: 5g. Tomb of Frederick III; 6g. Pulpit; 8g. Statue of St. Stephen; 10g. Statue of Madonna and Child; 12g. Altar; 30g. Organ; 50g. Anton Pilgram; 1s. N.E. Tower; 2s. S.W. Spire.

1947. Famous Austrians.
1002 – 12g. green 25 15
1003 **157** 18g. purple 20 15
1004 – 20g. green 45 25
1005 – 40g. brown . . . . 8·50 5·25
1006 – 40g. green . . . . 7·00 7·25
1007 – 60g. lake 45 30
PORTRAITS: 12g. Franz Schubert (composer); 20g. Carl Michael Ziehrer (composer); 40g. (No. 1005), Adalbert Stifter (poet); 40g. (No. 1006), Anton Bruckner (composer); 60g. Friedrich Amerling (painter).

158 Harvesting **159** Airplane over Hinterstoder

1947. Vienna Fair Fund.
1009 **158** 3g.+2g. brown . . . . . 45 1·20
1010 – 8g.+2g. green 40 80
1011 – 10g.+5g. slate 40 80
1012 – 12g.+8g. violet 40 80
1013 – 18g.+12g. olive 40 80
1014 – 30g.+10g. purple 40 85
1015 – 35g.+15g. red 40 90
1016 – 60g.+20g. blue . . . . . 40 1·10
DESIGNS: 8g. Logging; 10g. Factory; 12g. Pithead; 18g. Oil wells; 30g. Textile machinery; 35g. Foundry; 60g. Electric cables.

1947. Air.
1017 – 50g. brown 20 95
1018 – 1s. purple 25 80
1019 – 2s. green . . . . . . 30 1·10
1020 **159** 3s. brown . . . . . . 2·50 5·00
1021 – 4s. green . . . . . . 1·80 4·75
1022 – 5s. blue . . . . . . 1·80 4·75
1023 – 10s. blue . . . . . . 85 8·00
DESIGNS—Airplane over: 50g. Windmill at St. Andra; 1s. Heidentor; 2s. Gmund; 4s. Pragraten; 5s. Torsaule; 10s. St. Charles's Church, Vienna.

160 Beaker (15th century) **161** Racehorse

1947. National Art Exhibition Fund.
1024 **160** 3g.+2g. brown 25 65
1025 – 8g.+2g. green 25 65
1026 – 10g.+5g. red 25 65
1027 – 12g.+8g. violet 25 65
1028 – 18g.+12g. brown 25 75
1029 – 20g.+10g. violet 25 70
1030 – 30g.+10g. green 25 70
1031 – 35g.+15g. red 30 85
1032 – 48g.+12g. purple 30 85
1033 – 60g.+20g. blue 30 95
DESIGNS: 8g. Statue of "Providence" (Donner); 10g. Benedictine Monastery, Melk; 12g. "Wife of Dr. Brante of Vienna"; 18g. "Children in a Window" (Waldmuller); 20g. Belvedere Palace Gateway; 30g. Figure of "Egeria" on fountain at Schonbrunn; 35g. National Library, Vienna; 48g. "Copper Printer's (Ernst Rohm) Workshop" (Ferdinand Schmutzer); 60g. "Girl in Straw Hat" (Amerling).

1947. Vienna Prize Race Fund.
1034 **161** 60+20g. blue on pink . . 20 60

163 Prisoner-of-war **165** Globe and Tape Machine

1947. Prisoners-of-war Relief Fund.
1063 **163** 8g.+2g. green 15 50
1064 – 12g.+8g. brown 15 55
1065 – 18g.+12g. black 15 60
1066 – 35g.+15g. purple 15 60
1067 – 60g.+20g. blue 15 60
1068 – 1s.+40g. brown 15 80
DESIGNS: 12g. Letter from home; 18g. Gruesome camp visitor; 35g. Soldier and family reunited; 60g. Industry beckons returned soldier; 1s. Soldier sowing.

1947. Nos. 934 and 941 surch.
1069 75g. on 38g. green 30 95
1070 1s.40 on 16g. brown 15 45

1947. Telegraph Centenary.
1071 **165** 40g. violet 25 35

1947. Currency Revaluation. (a) As T **146**.
1072 3g. red (Lermoos) 25 30
1073 5g. red (Leopoldsberg) . . . 25 15
1074 10g. red (Hochosterwitz) . . 25 15
1075 15g. red (Forchtenstein) . . 2·00 1·90
(b) As T **146** but larger (23½ × 29 mm).
1076 20g. red (Gebhartsberg) . . . 35 15
1077 30g. red (Neusiedler Lake) . . 60 25
1078 40g. red (Mariazell) 60 15
1079 50g. red (Silvretta Peaks) . . 70 15
1080 60g. red (Semmering) . . . 8·50 1·70
1081 70g. red (Badgastein) . . . 3·00 20
1082 80g. red (Kaisergebirge) . . 3·00 20
1083 90g. red (Wayside shrine, Tragoss) . . . . 3·50 90
(c) As T **148**.
1084 1s. violet (Durnstein) . . . 60 15
1085 2s. violet (St. Christof) . . . 75 25
1086 3s. violet (Heiligenblut) . . 12·50 1·30
1086a 5s. violet (Schonbrunn) . . 12·50 1·90
Nos. 1072/86a in new currency replaced previous issue at rate of 3s. (old) = 1s. (new).

166 Sacred Olympic Flame **167** Laabenbach Viaduct, Neulenbach

1948. Fund for Entries to 5th Winter Olympic Games, St. Moritz.
1087 **166** 1s.+50g. blue 25 40

1948. Reconstruction Fund.
1088 **167** 10g.+5g. grey 20 30
1089 – 20g.+10g. violet 20 30
1090 – 30g.+10g. green 40 50
1091 – 40g.+20g. green 20 25
1092 – 45g.+20g. blue 20 25
1093 – 60g.+30g. red 20 25
1094 – 75g.+35g. purple 20 30
1095 – 80g.+40g. purple 20 30
1096 – 1s.+50g. blue 20 30
1097 – 1s.40+70g. lake 50 70
DESIGNS (showing reconstruction): 20g. Vermunt Lake Dam; 30g. Danube Port, Vienna; 40g. Erzberg open-cast mine; 45g. Southern Railway Station, Vienna; 60g. Flats; 75g. Vienna Gas Works; 80g. Oil refinery; 1s. Mountain roadway; 1s.40, Parliament Building.

169 Violets **170** Vorarlberg Montafon

1948. Anti-tuberculosis Fund.
1098 **169** 10g.+5g. violet, mauve and green 25 25
1099 – 20g.+10g. green, light green and yellow . . . 25 25
1100 – 30g.+10g. brown, yellow and green . . . . . . 3·00 3·00
1101 – 40g.+20g. green, yellow and orange 65 70
1102 – 45g.+20g. purple, mauve and yellow 20 25
1103 – 60g.+30g. red, mauve and green 20 25
1104 – 75g.+35g. green, pink and yellow 20 25
1105 – 80g.+40g. blue, pink and green 35 35
1106 – 1s.+50g. blue, ultramarine and green 35 30
1107 – 1s.40+70g. green, blue and yellow . . . . 1·80 1·75
FLOWERS: 20g. Anemone; 30g. Crocus; 40g. Primrose; 45g. Pasque flower; 60g. Rhododendron; 75g. Wild rose; 80g. Cyclamen; 1s. Gentian; 1s.40, Edelweiss.

1948. Provincial Costumes.
1108 – 3g. grey . . . . 65 1·10
1109 – 5g. green 20 15
1110 – 10g. blue 20 15
1111 – 15g. brown 40 15
1112 **170** 20g. green 20 15
1113 – 25g. brown 20 15
1114 – 30g. red . . . . 2·00 15
1115 – 30g. violet 40 15
1116 – 40g. violet . . . . . . 2·10 15
1117 – 40g. green 40 15
1118 – 45g. blue . . . . 1·90 50
1119 – 50g. brown 50 15
1120 – 60g. red 40 15
1121 – 70g. green 60 15
1122 – 75g. blue 40 50
1123 – 80g. rose 60 15
1124 – 90g. purple . . . . . . 25·00 30
1125 – 1s. blue . . . . 6·00 15
1126 – 1s. red . . . . 50·00 15
1127 – 1s. green 35 15
1128 – 1s.20 violet 50 15
1129 – 1s.40 brown . . . . . 2·75 25
1130 – 1s.45 red 90 15
1131 – 1s.50 blue 90 15
1132 – 1s.60 red 40 15
1133 – 1s.70 blue . . . . . . 2·10 60
1134 – 2s. green 70 15
1135 – 2s.20 slate . . . . . . 5·25 15
1136 – 2s.40 blue . . . . . . 1·00 15
1137 – 2s.50 brown . . . . . 2·40 1·50
1138 – 2s.70 brown 55 85
1139 – 3s. lake . . . . 1·80 15
1140 – 3s.50 green . . . . . . 17·00 15
1141 – 4s.50 purple 65 75
1142 – 5s. purple . . . . 1·00 15
1143 – 7s. olive . . . . 4·75 1·00
1144 – 10s. grey . . . . 30·00 5·25
DESIGNS—As T **170**: 3g. "Tirol Inntal"; 5 g "Salzburg Pinzgau"; 10, 75g. "Steiermark Salzkammergut" (different designs); 15 g "Burgenland Lutzmannsburg"; 25g., 1s.60, "Wien 1850" (two different designs); 30g. (2) "Salzburg Pongau"; 40g. (2) "Wien 1840"; 45 g "Karnten Lesachtal"; 50g. "Vorarlberg Bregenzerwald"; 60g. "Karnten Lavanttal"; 70g. "Niederosterreich Wachau"; 80 g "Steiermark Ennstal"; 90g. "Steiermark Mittelsteier"; 1s. (3) "Tirol Pustertal"; 1s.20, "Niederosterreich Wienerwald"; 1s.40, "Oberosterreich Innviertel"; 1s.45, "Wilter bei Innsbruck"; 1s.50, "Wien 1853"; 1s.70, "Ost Tirol Kals"; 2s. "Oberosterreich"; 2s.20, "Ischl 1820"; 2s.40, "Kitzbuhel"; 2s.50, "Obersteiermark 1850"; 2s.70, "Kleines Walsertal"; 3s. "Burgenland"; 3s.50, "Niederosterreich 1850"; 4s.50, "Gailtal"; 5s. "Zillertal"; 7s. "Steiermark Sulmtal". 25 × 35 mm: 10s. "Wien 1850".

172 Kunstlerhaus **173** Hans Makart

1948. 80th Anniv of Creative Artists' Association.
1145 **172** 20g.+10g. green . . . . 6·25 5·50
1146 **173** 30g.+15g. brown . . . . 2·40 2·50
1147 – 40g.+20g. blue . . . . 2·40 2·50
1148 – 50g.+25g. violet . . . . 4·00 4·50
1149 – 60g.+30g. red . . . . . 5·50 4·00
1150 – 1s.+50g. blue . . . . . 5·50 5·75
1151 – 1s.40+70g. brown . . . 16·00 13·00
PORTRAITS: 40g. K. Kundmann; 50g. A. von Siccardsburg; 60g. H. Canon; 1s. W. Unger; 1s.40, Friedr. Schmidt.

174 St. Rupert **175** Pres. Renner

1948. Salzburg Cathedral Reconstruction Fund.
1152 **174** 20g.+10g. green . . . . 7·00 7·25
1153 – 30g.+15g. brown . . . . 2·25 2·50
1154 – 40g.+20g. green . . . . 2·10 2·30
1155 – 50g.+25g. brown 50 60
1156 – 60g.+30g. red 50 60
1157 – 80g.+40g. purple 50 60
1158 – 1s.+50g. blue 65 85
1159 – 1s.40+70g. green . . . . 2·10 1·90
DESIGNS: 30, 40, 50, 80g. Views of Salzburg Cathedral; 60g. St. Peter's; 1s. Cathedral and Fortress; 1s.40, Madonna.

1948. 30th Anniv of Republic.
1160 **175** 1s. blue . . . . 2·00 1·50
See also Nos. 1224 and 1333.

176 F. Gruber and J. Mohr **177** Boy and Hare

1948. 130th Anniv of Composition of Carol "Silent Night, Holy Night".
1161 **176** 60g. brown . . . . . . 5·00 5·00

1949. Child Welfare Fund.
1162 **177** 40g.+10g. purple . . . . 12·50 18·00
1163 – 60g.+20g. red . . . . . 12·50 18·00
1164 – 1s.+25g. blue . . . . . 12·50 18·00
1165 – 1s.40+35g. green . . . . 15·00 19·00
DESIGNS: 60g. Two girls and apples in boot; 1s. Boy and birthday cake; 1s.40, Girl praying before candle.

178 Boy and Dove **179** Johann Strauss

1949. U.N. Int. Children's Emergency Fund.
1166 **178** 1s. blue . . . . 8·75 1·10

1949. 50th Death Anniv of Johann Strauss the Younger (composer).
1167 **179** 1s. blue . . . . 2·50 2·10
See also Nos. 1174, 1207 and 1229.

180 Esperanto Star **181** St. Gebhard

1949. Esperanto Congress, Vienna.
1168 **180** 20g. green 65 60

1949. Birth Millenary of St. Gebhard (Bishop of Vorarlberg).
1169 **181** 30g. violet . . . . 1·75 1·30

182 Seal of Duke Friedrich II, 1230 **183** Allegory of U.P.U.

1949. Prisoners-of-war Relief Fund. Arms.
1170 **182** 40g.+10g. yell & brn . . 6·75 6·75
1171 – 60g.+15g. pink & pur . . 5·50 6·00
1172 – 1s.+25g. red & blue . . 5·50 6·00
1173 – 1s.60+40g. pink and green . . . . 7·75 7·50
ARMS: 60g. Princes of Austria, 1450; 1s. Austria, 1600; 1s.60, Austria, 1945.

1949. Death Centenary of Johann Strauss the Elder (composer). Portrait as T **179**.
1174 30g. purple . . . . 1·70 1·70

1949. 75th Anniv of U.P.U.
1175 **183** 40g. green . . . . 2·50 2·75
1176 – 60g. red . . . . 3·00 2·75
1177 – 1s. blue . . . . 7·25 5·75
DESIGNS: 60g. Children holding "75"; 1s. Woman's head.

185 Magnifying Glass and Covers **186** M. M. Daffinger

1949. Stamp Day.
1206 **185** 60g.+15g. brown . . . . 2·25 1·70

1949. 50th Death Anniv of Karl Millocker (composer). Portrait as T **179**.
1207 1s. blue . . . . 12·00 7·75

1950. 160th Birth Anniv of Moritz Michael Daffinger (painter).
1208 **186** 60g. brown . . . . . . 5·75 5·25

187 A. Hofer

1950. 140th Death Anniv of Andreas Hofer (patriot).
1209 **187** 60g. violet . . . . . . 9·75 8·75
See also Nos. 1211, 1223, 1232, 1234, 1243, 1253, 1288 and 1386.

188 Stamp of 1850 **189** Arms of Austria and Carinthia

1950. Austrian Stamp Centenary.
1210 **188** 1s. black on yellow . . . 1·40 1·10

1950. Death Centenary of Josef Madersperger (sewing machine inventor). Portrait as T **187**.
1211 60g. violet . . . . 4·75 3·50

1950. 30th Anniv of Carinthian Plebiscite.
1212 **189** 60g.+15g. grn & brn . . 25·00 26·00
1213 – 1s.+25g. red & orange 29·00 30·00
1214 – 1s.70+40g. blue and turquoise . . . . . . 30·00 35·00
DESIGNS: 1s. Carinthian waving Austrian flag; 1s.70, Hand and ballot box.

190 Rooks **191** Philatelist

1950. Air.
1215 **190** 60g. violet . . . . 4·00 2·75
1216 – 1s. violet (Barn swallows) . . . . . . 23·00 20·00
1217 – 2s. blue (Black-headed gulls) . . . . 19·00 7·25
1218 – 3s. turquoise (Great cormorants) . . . . . £120 85·00
1219 – 5s. brown (Common buzzard) . . . . . . £120 85·00
1220 – 10s. purple (Grey heron) 52·00 43·00
1221 – 20s. sepia (Golden eagle) 8·50 3·25

1950. Stamp Day.
1222 **191** 60g.+15g. green . . . . 5·75 6·50

1950. Birth Centenary of Alexander Girardi (actor). Portrait as T **187**.
1223 30g. blue . . . . 1·40 1·10

192 Dr. Renner **193** Miner

1951. Death of Pres. Karl Renner.
1224 **192** 1s. black on lemon . . . 1·20 45

1951. Reconstruction Fund.
1225 **193** 40g.+10g. purple . . . . 11·00 13·00
1226 – 60g.+15g. green . . . . 11·00 13·00
1227 – 1s.+25g. brown . . . . 11·00 13·00
1228 – 1s.70+40g. blue . . . . 11·00 13·00
DESIGNS: 60g. Bricklayer; 1s. Bridge-builder; 1s.70, Telegraph engineer.

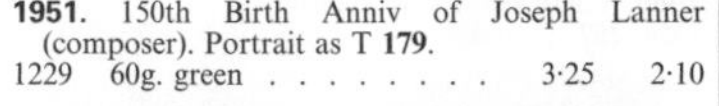

1951. 150th Birth Anniv of Joseph Lanner (composer). Portrait as T **179**.
1229 60g. green . . . . 3·25 2·10

194 Martin Johann Schmidt **195** Scout Badge

1951. 150th Death Anniv of Schmidt (painter).
1230 **194** 1s. red . . . . 4·75 2·75

1951. Boy Scout Jamboree.
1231 **195** 1s. red, yellow & green 4·00 3·25

1951. 10th Death Anniv of Wilhelm Kienzl (composer). Portrait as T **187**.
1232 1s.50 blue . . . . 2·75 1·10

196 Laurel Branch and Olympic Emblem **197** Schrammel

1952. 6th Winter Olympic Games, Oslo.
1233 **196** 2s.40+60g. green . . . . 14·00 17·00

1952. 150th Birth Anniv of Karl Ritter von Ghega (railway engineer). Portrait as T **187**.
1234 1s. green . . . . 6·00 1·60

1952. Birth Cent of Josef Schrammel (composer).
1235 **197** 1s.50 blue . . . . 5·50 1·70
See also No. 1239.

198 Cupid and Letter **199** Breakfast Pavilion

1952. Stamp Day.
1236 **198** 1s.50+35g. purple . . . 15·00 18·00

1952. Bicentenary of Schonbrunn Menagerie.
1237 **199** 1s.50 green . . . . . . 5·00 1·70

200 **202**

1952. Int Union of Socialist Youth Camp, Vienna.
1238 **200** 1s.50 blue . . . . 5·25 1·00

1952. 150th Birth Anniv of Nikolaus Lenau (writer). Portrait as T **197**.
1239 1s. green . . . . 5·50 1·70

1952. International Children's Correspondence.
1240 **202** 2s.40 blue . . . . 8·75 2·30

203 "Christus Pantocrator" (sculpture) **204** Hugo Wolf

1952. Austrian Catholics' Day.
1241 **203** 1s.+25g. olive . . . . . 8·75 12·00

1953. 50th Death Anniv of Wolf (composer).
1242 **204** 1s.50 blue . . . . 7·50 1·40

1953. President Korner's 80th Birthday. As T **187** but portrait of Korner.
1243 1s.50 blue . . . . 5·25 1·10
For 1s.50 black, see No. 1288.

1953. 60th Anniv of Austrian Trade Union Movement. As No. 955 (colour changed) surch **GEWERKSCHAFTS BEWEGUNG 60 JAHRE 1s+25g.**
1244 1s.+25g. on 5s. blue . . . . 2·10 2·50

206 Linz National Theatre **207** Meeting-house, Steyr

1953. 150th Anniv of Linz National Theatre.
1245 **206** 1s.50 turquoise . . . . . 13·50 2·50

1953. Vienna Evangelical School Rebuilding Fund.
1246 **207** 70g.+15g. purple 20 30
1247 – 1s.+25g. blue 25 40
1248 – 1s.50+40g. brown . . . 35 75
1249 – 2s.40+60g. green . . . . 2·75 3·25
1250 – 3s.+75g. lilac . . . . . 8·00 7·25
DESIGNS: 1s. J. Kepler (astronomer); 1s.50, Lutheran Bible, 1534; 2s.40, T. von Hansen (architect); 3s. School after reconstruction.

208 Child and Christmas Tree **209**

1953. Christmas
1251 **208** 1s. green . . . . 1·90 25
See also No. 1266.

1953. Stamp Day.
1252 **209** 1s.+25g. brown . . . . 6·00 5·00

1954. 150th Birth Anniv of M. Von Schwind (painter). As T **187** but portrait of Von Schwind.
1253 1s.50 lilac . . . . 7·75 2·10

210 Baron K. von Rokitansky **212** Surgeon with Microscope

1954. 150th Birth Anniv of Von Rokitansky (anatomist).
1254 **210** 1s.50 violet . . . . . . 15·00 2·40
See also No. 1264.

1954. Avalanche Fund. As No. 953 (colour changed) surch **LAWINENOPFER 1954 1s+20g.**
1255 1s.+20g. blue 20 25

1954. Health Service Fund.
1256 – 30g.+10g. violet . . . . 1·00 1·40
1257 **212** 70g.+15g. brown 35 30
1258 – 1s.+25g. blue 40 35
1259 – 1s.45+35g. green 40 60
1260 – 1s.50+35g. red . . . . . 4·50 5·75
1261 – 2s.40+60g. purple . . . 5·25 6·75
DESIGNS: 30g. Boy patient and sun-ray lamp; 1s. Mother and children; 1s.45, Operating theatre; 1s.50, Baby on scales; 2s.40, Red Cross nurse and ambulance.

213 Esperanto Star **214** J. M. Rottmayr von Rosenbrunn

1954. 50th Anniv of Esperanto in Austria.
1262 **213** 1s. green and brown . . 3·25 30

1954. Birth Tercentenary of Rottmayr von Rosenbrunn (painter).
1263 **214** 1s. green . . . . 8·50 3·25

1954. 25th Death Anniv of Dr. Auer von Welsbach (inventor). Portrait as T **210**.
1264 1s.50 blue . . . . 25·00 2·75

216 Great Organ, Church of St. Florian **217** 18th-century River Boat

1954. 2nd International Congress of Catholic Church Music, Vienna.
1265 **216** 1s. brown . . . . 1·60 30

1954. Christmas. As No. 1251, but colour changed.
1266 **208** 1s. blue . . . . 4·00 50

1954. Stamp Day.
1267 **217** 1s.+25g. green . . . . . 4·75 5·75

218 Arms of Austria and Newspapers

1954. 150th Anniv of State Printing Works and 250th Anniv of "Wiener-Zeitung" (newspaper).
1268 **218** 1s. black and red . . . . 2·00 25

219 "Freedom"

1955. 10th Anniv of Re-establishment of Austrian Republic.
1269 – 70g. purple . . . . . . 1·60 30
1270 – 1s. blue . . . . 6·25 30
1271 **219** 1s.45 red . . . . 7·75 3·50
1272 – 1s.50 brown . . . . . . 23·00 40
1273 – 2s.40 green . . . . . . 7·75 4·75
DESIGNS: 70g. Parliament Buildings; 1s. Western Railway terminus, Vienna; 1s.50, Modern houses; 2s.40, Limberg Dam.

1955. Austrian State Treaty. As No. 888, but colour changed, optd **STAATSVERTRAG 1955**.
1274 **142** 2s. grey . . . . 2·00 30

221 "Strength through Unity"

1955. 4th World Trade Unions Congress, Vienna.
1275 **221** 1s. blue . . . . 2·10 1·80

222 "Return to Work"

1955. Returned Prisoners-of-war Relief Fund.
1276 **222** 1s.+25g. brown . . . . 1·90 1·70

223 Burgtheater, Vienna

1955. Re-opening of Burgtheater and State Opera House, Vienna.
1277 **223** 1s.50 brown . . . . . . 3·25 25
1278 – 2s.40 blue (Opera House) 4·25 2·40

224 Globe and Flags **225** Stamp Collector

1955. 10th Anniv of U.N.O.
1279 **224** 2s.40 green . . . . . . 7·50 2·50

1955. Stamp Day.
1280 **225** 1s.+25g. brown . . . . 2·50 3·00

226 Mozart

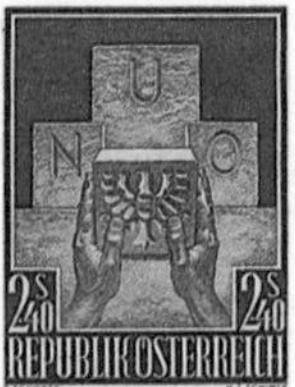

227

1956. Birth Bicentenary of Mozart (composer).
1281 **226** 2s.40 blue . . . . 3·00 1·10

1956. Admission of Austria into U.N.
1282 **227** 2s.40 brown . . . . . . 8·25 1·80

228

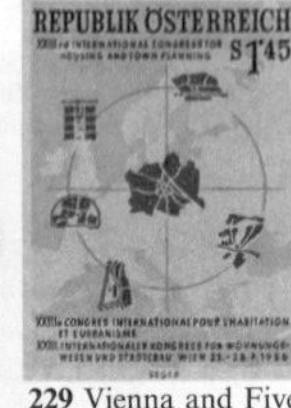

229 Vienna and Five New Towns

1956. 5th World Power Conference, Vienna.
1283 **228** 2s.40 blue . . . . 7·75 1·90

1956. 23rd International Town Planning Congress.
1284 **229** 1s.45 red, black & green 2·40 70

230 J. B. Fischer von Erlach

231 "Stamp Day"

1956. Birth Tercentenary of Fischer von Erlach (architect).
1285 **230** 1s.50 brown . . . . . . 80 1·10

1956. Stamp Day.
1286 **231** 1s.+25g. red . . . . . . 2·30 2·40

1956. Hungarian Relief Fund. As No. 1173, but colours changed, surch **1956 1.50 +50 UNGARNHILFE**.
1287 1s.50+50g. on 1s.60+40g. red and grey 40 40

1957. Death of Pres. Korner. As No. 1243, but colour changed.
1288 1s.50 black . . . . 1·40 1·40

233 J. Wagner von Jauregg

234 Anton Wildgans

1957. Birth Centenary of Wagner von Jauregg (psychiatrist).
1289 **233** 2s.40 brown . . . . . . 3·25 1·80

1957. 25th Death Anniv of Anton Wildgans (poet).
1290 **234** 1s. blue 35 25

235 Daimber (1907), Graf and Stift (1957) Post Buses

1957. 50th Anniv of Postal Coach Service.
1291 **235** 1s. black on yellow . . . 35 25

237 Mt. Gasherbrum II

236 Mariazell Basilica

1957. Austrian Himalaya–Karakorum Expedition, 1956.
1293 **237** 1s.50 blue 45 40

1957. Buildings. (a) Size 20½ × 24½ mm.
1295 – 20g. purple 20 25
1296 – 30g. green 35 25
1297 – 40g. red 20 15
1298 – 50g. grey 80 15
1299 – 60g. brown 35 15
1300 – 70g. blue 25 15
1301 – 80g. brown 25 15
1302 **236** 1s. brown 90 15
1303 – 1s. brown 85 15
1304 – 1s.20 purple 65 25
1305 – 1s.30 green 40 15
1306 – 1s.40 blue 40 25
1307 – 1s.50 red 60 15
1308 – 1s.80 blue 70 15
1309 – 2s. blue . . . . . . 4·00 15
1310 – 2s. blue 80 15
1311 – 2s.20 green 90 25
1312 – 2s.50 violet . . . . . . 1·10 30
1313 – 3s. blue 80 15
1314 – 3s.40 green . . . . . . 1·00 75
1315 – 3s.50 mauve 85 15
1316 – 4s. violet . . . . . . 1·30 15
1317 – 4s.50 green . . . . . . 1·60 30
1318 – 5s.50 green 90 20
1319 – 6s. violet . . . . . . 1·30 15
1320 – 6s.40 blue . . . . . . 1·30 95
1321 – 8s. purple . . . . . . 2·00 25

(b) Larger.
1322 – 10s. green . . . . . . 3·25 40
1323 – 20s. purple . . . . . . 3·50 60

(c) Smaller, size 17½ × 21 mm.
1324 – 50g. grey 25 20
1325 **236** 1s. brown 25 20
1326 – 1s.50 purple 25 20

DESIGNS: 20g. Old Courtyard, Morbisch; 30g. Vienna Town Hall; 40g. Porcia Castle, Spittal; 50g. Heiligenstadt flats; 60g. Lederer Tower, Wells; 70g. Archbishop's Palace, Salzburg; 80g. Old farmhouse, Pinzgau; 1s. (1303) Millstatt; 1s.20, Corn Measurer's House, Bruck-on-the-Mur; 1s.30, Schattenburg Castle; 1s.40, Klagenfurt Town Hall; 1s.50, "Rabenhof" Flats, Erdberg, Vienna; 1s.80, Mint Tower, Hall-in-Tyrol; 2s. (1309) Christkindl Church; 2s. (1310) Dragon Fountain, Klagenfurt; 2s.20, Beethoven's House, Heiligenstadt, Vienna; 2s.50, Danube Bridge, Linz; 3s. "Swiss Portal", Imperial Palace, Vienna; 3s.40, Stein Gate, Krems-on-the-Danube; 3s.50, Esterhazy Palace, Eisenstadt; 4s. Vienna Gate, Hainburg; 4s.50, Schwechat Airport; 5s.50, Chur Gate, Feldkirch; 6s. Graz Town Hall; 6s.40, "Golden Roof", Innsbruck; 8s. Steyr Town Hall. 22 × 28½ mm: 10s. Heidenreichstein Castle. 28½ × 37½ mm: 20s. Melk Abbey.

238 Post Office, Linz

1957. Stamp Day.
1327 **238** 1s.+25g. green . . . . . 2·30 2·75

239 Badgastein

1958. International Alpine Ski Championships, Badgastein.
1328 **239** 1s.50 blue 25 25

240 Vickers Viscount 800

241 Mother and Child

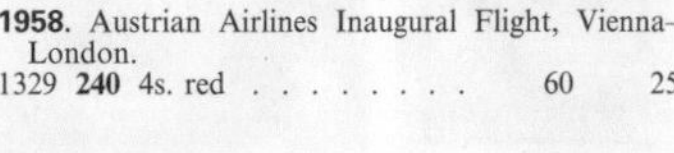

1958. Austrian Airlines Inaugural Flight, Vienna–London.
1329 **240** 4s. red 60 25

1958. Mothers' Day.
1330 **241** 1s.50 blue 25 25

242 Walther von der Vogelweide (after 12th-century manuscript)

243 Dr. O. Redlich

1958. 3rd Austrian Choir Festival, Vienna.
1331 **242** 1s.50 multicoloured . . . 35 25

1958. Birth Cent of Dr. Oswald Redlich (historian).
1332 **243** 2s.40 blue 40 40

1958. 40th Anniv of Republic. As T **175** but inscr "40 JAHRE".
1333 **175** 1s.50 green 50 70

244 Post Office, Kitzbuhel

1958. Stamp Day.
1334 **244** 2s.40+60g. blue 75 90

245 "E" building on Map of Europe

246 Monopoly Emblem and Cigars

1959. Europa.
1335 **245** 2s.40 green 40 25

1959. 175th Anniv of Austrian Tobacco Monopoly.
1336 **246** 2s.40 brown 35 25

247 Archduke Johann

248 Western Capercailie

1959. Death Cent of Archduke Johann of Austria.
1337 **247** 1s.50 green 25 25

1959. International Hunting Congress, Vienna.
1338 **248** 1s. purple 50 25
1339 – 1s.50 blue (Roebuck) . . 40 20
1340 – 2s.40 grn (Wild boar) . . 65 85
1341 – 3s.50 brown (Red deer family) 50 55

249 Haydn

250 Tyrolean Eagle

1959. 150th Death Anniv of Haydn.
1342 **249** 1s.50 purple 65 35

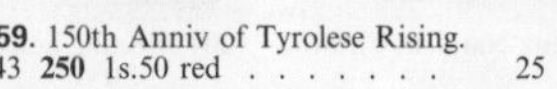

1959. 150th Anniv of Tyrolese Rising.
1343 **250** 1s.50 red 25 25

251 Microwave Transmitting Aerial, Zugspitze

252 Handball Player

1959. Inaug of Austrian Microwave Network.
1344 **251** 2s.40 blue 35 25

1959. Sports.
1345 – 1s. violet 25 25
1346 **252** 1s.50 green 65 25
1347 – 1s.80 red 40 35
1348 – 2s. purple 25 35
1349 – 2s.20 blue 25 25

DESIGNS: 1s. Runner; 1s.80, Gymnast; 2s. Hurdling; 2s.20, Hammer thrower.

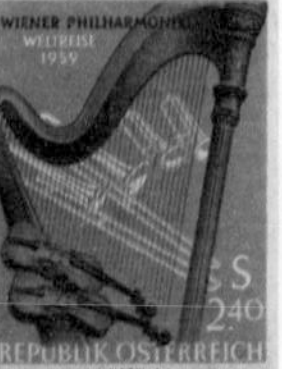

253 Orchestral Instruments

254 Roman Coach

1959. Vienna Philharmonic Orchestra's World Tour.
1350 **253** 2s.40 black and blue . . 45 25

1959. Stamp Day.
1351 **254** 2s.40+60g. blk & mve . . 65 75

255 Refugees

256 Pres. Adolf Scharf

1960. World Refugee Year.
1352 **255** 3s. turquoise 40 40

1960. President's 70th Birthday.
1353 **256** 1s.50 green 40 30

257 Youth Hostellers

258 Dr. Eiselsberg

1960. Youth Hostels Movement.
1354 **257** 1s. red 25 25

1960. Birth Cent of Dr. Anton Eiselsberg (surgeon).
1355 **258** 1s.50 sepia and cream . . 60 25

259 Gustav Mahler

260 Jakob Prandtauer

1960. Birth Centenary of Gustav Mahler (composer).
1356 **259** 1s.50 brown 65 30

1960. 300th Birth Anniv of Jakob Prandtauer (architect).
1357 **260** 1s.50 brown 50 25

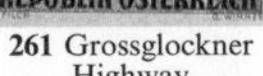

261 Grossglockner Highway **262** Ionic Capital

1960. 25th Anniv of Grossglockner Alpine Highway.
1358 **261** 1s.80 blue 50 40

1960. Europa.
1359 **262** 3s. black . . . . 1·20 85

263 Griffen, Carinthia

1960. 40th Anniv of Carinthian Plebiscite.
1360 **263** 1s.50 green 35 25

264 Examining Proof of Engraved Stamp **265** "Freedom"

1960. Stamp Day.
1361 **264** 3s.+70g. brown 70 90

1961. Austrian Freedom Martyrs' Commem.
1362 **265** 1s.50 red 25 25

266 Hansa Brandenburg C-1 **267** Transport and Multi-unit Electric Train

1961. "LUPOSTA" Exhibition, Vienna, and 1st Austrian Airmail Service Commemoration.
1363 **266** 5s. blue 80 40

1961. European Transport Ministers' Meeting.
1364 **267** 3s. olive and red 55 40

268 "Mower in the Alps" (Detail, A. Egger-Lienz) **269** Observatory on Sonnblick Mountain

1961. Centenary of Kunstlerhaus, Vienna. Inscr as in T **268**.
1365 **268** 1s. purple and brown . . 25 25
1366 – 1s.50 lilac and brown . . 35 35
1367 – 3s. green and brown . . 1·00 90
1368 – 5s. violet and brown . . 80 70
PAINTINGS: 1s.50, "The Kiss" (after A. von Pettenkofen). 3s. "Portrait of a Girl" (after A. Romako). 5s. "The Triumph of Ariadne" (detail of Ariadne, after Hans Makart).

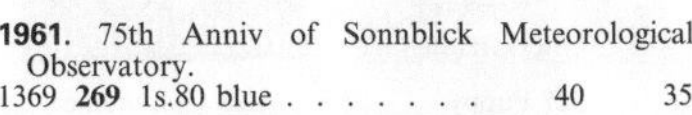

1961. 75th Anniv of Sonnblick Meteorological Observatory.
1369 **269** 1s.80 blue 40 35

270 Lavanttaler Colliery **271** Mercury

1961. 15th Anniv of Nationalized Industries. Inscr "JAHRE VERSTAATLICHTE UNTERNEHMUNGEN".
1370 **270** 1s. black 20 20
1371 – 1s.50 green 25 30
1372 – 1s.80 red 65 60
1373 – 3s. mauve 90 60
1374 – 5s. blue . . . . 1·40 1·10
DESIGNS: 1s.50, Turbine; 1s.80, Industrial plant; 3s. Steelworks, Linz; 5s. Oil refinery, Schwechat.

1961. World Bank Congress, Vienna.
1375 **271** 3s. black 50 45

272 Arms of Burgenland **273** Liszt

1961. 40th Anniv of Burgenland.
1376 **272** 1s.50 red, yellow & sepia 40 25

1961. 150th Birth Anniv of Franz Liszt (composer).
1377 **273** 3s. brown 60 45

274 Rust Post Office

1961. Stamp Day.
1378 **274** 3s.+70g. green 80 90

275 Court of Accounts

1961. Bicentenary of Court of Accounts.
1379 **275** 1s. sepia 20 25

276 Glockner-Kaprun Power Station

1962. 15th Anniv of Electric Power Nationalization. Inscr as in T **276**.
1380 **276** 1s. blue 25 20
1381 – 1s.50 purple 35 35
1382 – 1s.80 green 90 85
1383 – 3s. brown 50 45
1384 – 4s. red 50 55
1385 – 6s.40 black . . . . . . 1·40 1·60
DESIGNS: 1s.50, Ybbs-Persenbeug (Danube); 1s.80, Luner See; 3s. Grossraming (Enns River); 4s. Bisamberg Transformer Station; 6s.40, St. Andra Power Stations.

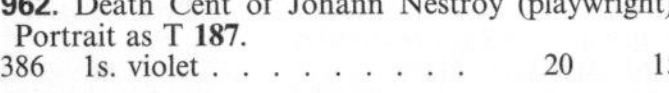

1962. Death Cent of Johann Nestroy (playwright). Portrait as T **187**.
1386 1s. violet 20 15

277 F. Gauermann **278** Scout Badge and Handclasp

1962. Death Cent of Friedrich Gauermann (painter).
1387 **277** 1s.50 blue 25 25

1962. 50th Anniv of Austrian Scout Movement.
1388 **278** 1s.50 green 35 30

279 Forest and Lake

1962. "The Austrian Forest".
1389 **279** 1s. grey 25 20
1390 – 1s.50 brown 40 35
1391 – 3s. myrtle . . . . 1·20 90
DESIGNS: 1s.50, Deciduous forest; 3s. Fir and larch forest.

280 Electric Locomotive and Steam Locomotive "Austria" (1837)

1962. 125th Anniv of Austrian Railways.
1392 **280** 3s. black and buff . . . 1·00 65

281 Engraving Die **282** Postal Officials of 1863

1962. Stamp Day.
1393 **281** 3s.+70g. violet . . . . . 1·00 1·20

1963. Centenary of Paris Postal Conference.
1394 **282** 3s. sepia and yellow . . 40 50

283 Hermann Bahr **284** St. Florian (statue)

1963. Birth Centenary of Hermann Bahr (writer).
1395 **283** 1s.50 sepia and blue . . 25 25

1963. Cent of Austrian Voluntary Fire Brigade.
1396 **284** 1s.50 black and pink . . 65 25

285 Flag and Emblem

1963. 5th Austrian Trade Unions Federation Congress.
1397 **285** 1s.50 red, sepia & grey 25 15

286 Crests of Tyrol and Austria

1963. 600th Anniv of Tyrol as an Austrian Province.
1398 **286** 1s.50 multicoloured . . . 25 15

287 Prince Eugene of Savoy **288** Centenary Emblem

1963. Birth Tercent of Prince Eugene of Savoy.
1399 **287** 1s.50 violet 25 25

1963. Centenary of Red Cross.
1400 **288** 3s. silver, red and black 50 45

289 Skiing (slalom)

1963. Winter Olympic Games, Innsbruck, 1964. Centres black; inscr gold; background colours given.
1401 **289** 1s. grey 20 20
1402 – 1s.20 blue 20 25
1403 – 1s.50 grey 25 30
1404 – 1s.80 purple 35 35
1405 – 2s.20 green 80 75
1406 – 3s. slate 40 40
1407 – 4s. blue 90 90
DESIGNS: 1s.20, Skiing (biathlon); 1s.50, Ski jumping; 1s.80, Figure skating; 2s.20, Ice hockey; 3s. Tobogganing; 4s. Bobsleighing.

290 Vienna "101" P.O. and Railway Shed **291** "The Holy Family" (Josef Stammel)

1963. Stamp Day.
1408 **290** 3s.+70g. black & drab 65 80

1963. Christmas.
1409 **291** 2s. green 35 25

292 Nasturtium

1964. Int Horticultural Exn, Vienna. Mult.
1410 1s. Type **292** 25 15
1411 1s.50 Peony 25 20
1412 1s.80 Clematis 40 30
1413 2s.20 Dahlia 65 60
1414 3s. Convolvulus 60 35
1415 4s. Mallow 80 75

293 Gothic Statue and Stained-glass Window

1964. Romanesque Art Exhibition, Vienna.
1416 **293** 1s.50 blue and black . . 25 25

294 Pallas Athene and Interior of Assembly Hall, Parliament Building

1964. 2nd Parliamentary and Scientific Conference, Vienna.
1417 **294** 1s.80 black and green . . 25 25

295 "The Kiss" (Gustav Klimt)

1964. Re-opening of "Viennese Secession" Exn Hall.
1418 **295** 3s. multicoloured 50 40

296 "Comforting the Sick"

1964. 350th Anniv of Order of Brothers of Mercy in Austria.
1419 **296** 1s.50 blue 25 25

297 "Bringing News of the Victory at Kunersdorf" (Bellotto)

1964. 15th U.P.U. Congress, Vienna. Paintings.
1420 **297** 1s. purple 20 15
1421 – 1s.20 brown 25 25
1422 – 1s.50 blue 25 20
1423 – 1s.80 violet 35 35
1424 – 2s.20 black 35 45
1425 – 3s. purple 45 25
1426 – 4s. green 50 70
1427 – 6s.40 purple . . . . . 1·30 1·40
PAINTINGS: 1s.20, "Changing Horses" (Hormann); 1s.50, "The Wedding Trip" (Schwind); 1s.80, "Postboys returning Home" (Raffalt); 2s.20, "The Vienna Mail Coach" (Klein); 3s. "Changing Horses" (Gauermann); 4s. "Postal Tracked-vehicle in Mountain Village" (Pilch); 6s.40, "Saalbach Post Office and Post-bus" (Pilch).

298 Vienna, from the Hochhaus (N.) 299 "Workers"

1964. "WIPA" Stamp Exhibition, Vienna (1965) (1st issue). Multicoloured.
1428 1s.50+30g. Type **298** . . . 35 30
1429 1s.50+30g. N.E. 35 30
1430 1s.50+30g. E. 35 30
1431 1s.50+30g. S.E. 35 30
1432 1s.50+30g. S. 35 30
1433 1s.50+30g. S.W. 35 30
1434 1s.50+30g. W. 35 30
1435 1s.50+30g. N.W. 35 30
The designs show a panoramic view of Vienna, looking to different points of compass (indicated on stamps). The inscription reads "Vienna welcomes you to WIPA 1965".
See also Nos. 1447/52.

1964. Centenary of Austrian Workers' Movement.
1436 **299** 1s. black 20 25

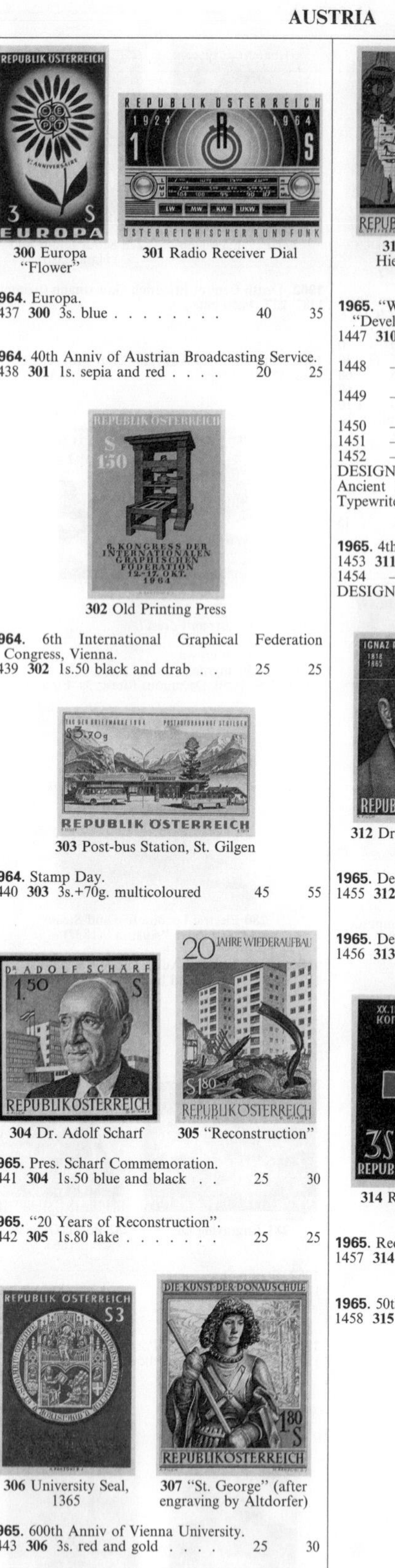

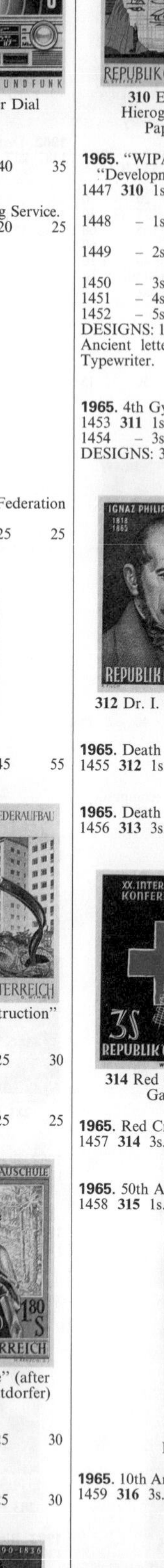

300 Europa "Flower" 301 Radio Receiver Dial

1964. Europa.
1437 **300** 3s. blue 40 35

1964. 40th Anniv of Austrian Broadcasting Service.
1438 **301** 1s. sepia and red 20 25

302 Old Printing Press

1964. 6th International Graphical Federation Congress, Vienna.
1439 **302** 1s.50 black and drab . . 25 25

303 Post-bus Station, St. Gilgen

1964. Stamp Day.
1440 **303** 3s.+70g. multicoloured 45 55

304 Dr. Adolf Scharf 305 "Reconstruction"

1965. Pres. Scharf Commemoration.
1441 **304** 1s.50 blue and black . . 25 30

1965. "20 Years of Reconstruction".
1442 **305** 1s.80 lake 25 25

306 University Seal, 1365 307 "St. George" (after engraving by Altdorfer)

1965. 600th Anniv of Vienna University.
1443 **306** 3s. red and gold 25 30

1965. Danubian Art.
1444 **307** 1s.80 blue 25 30

308 I.T.U. Emblem, Morse Key and T.V. Aerial 309 F. Raimund

1965. Centenary of I.T.U.
1445 **308** 3s. violet 25 25

1965. 175th Birth Anniv of Ferdinand Raimund (actor and playwright).
1446 **309** 3s. purple 25 25

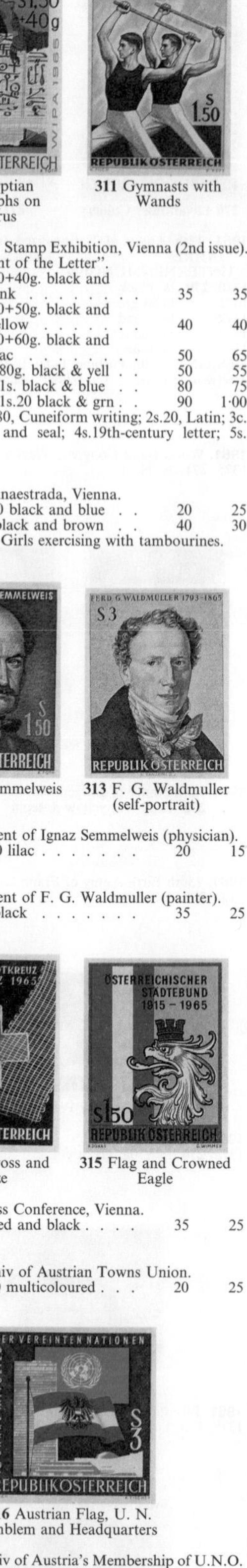

310 Egyptian Hieroglyphs on Papyrus 311 Gymnasts with Wands

1965. "WIPA" Stamp Exhibition, Vienna (2nd issue). "Development of the Letter".
1447 **310** 1s.50+40g. black and pink 35 35
1448 – 1s.80+50g. black and yellow 40 40
1449 – 2s.20+60g. black and lilac 50 65
1450 – 3s.+80g. black & yell . . 50 55
1451 – 4s.+1s. black & blue . . 80 75
1452 – 5s.+1s.20 black & grn . . 90 1·00
DESIGNS: 1s.80, Cuneiform writing; 2s.20, Latin; 3c. Ancient letter and seal; 4s.19th-century letter; 5s. Typewriter.

1965. 4th Gymnaestrada, Vienna.
1453 **311** 1s.50 black and blue . . 20 25
1454 – 3s. black and brown . . 40 30
DESIGNS: 3s. Girls exercising with tambourines.

312 Dr. I. Semmelweis 313 F. G. Waldmuller (self-portrait)

1965. Death Cent of Ignaz Semmelweis (physician).
1455 **312** 1s.50 lilac 20 15

1965. Death Cent of F. G. Waldmuller (painter).
1456 **313** 3s. black 35 25

314 Red Cross and Gauze 315 Flag and Crowned Eagle

1965. Red Cross Conference, Vienna.
1457 **314** 3s. red and black 35 25

1965. 50th Anniv of Austrian Towns Union.
1458 **315** 1s.50 multicoloured . . . 20 25

316 Austrian Flag, U. N. Emblem and Headquarters

1965. 10th Anniv of Austria's Membership of U.N.O.
1459 **316** 3s. sepia, red and blue 40 30

317 University Building 318 Bertha von Suttner

1965. 150th Anniv of University of Technology, Vienna.
1460 **317** 1s.50 violet 20 15

1965. 60th Anniv of Nobel Peace Prize Award to Bertha von Suttner (writer).
1461 **318** 1s.50 black 20 25

319 Postman delivering Mail

1965. Stamp Day.
1462 **319** 3s.+70g. green 45 60

320 Postal Code Map

1966. Introduction of Postal Code System.
1463 **320** 1s.50 black, red & yell 20 15

321 P.T.T. Headquarters 322 M. Ebner-Eschenbach

1966. Centenary of Austrian Posts and Telegraphs Administration.
1464 **321** 1s.50 black on cream . . 20 25

1966. 50th Death Anniv of Maria Ebner-Eschenbach (writer).
1465 **322** 3s. purple 35 25

323 Big Wheel 324 Josef Hoffmann

1966. Bicentenary of Vienna Prater.
1466 **323** 1s.50 green 20 25

1966. 10th Death Anniv of Josef Hoffmann (architect).
1467 **324** 3s. brown 35 25

325 Bank Emblem

1966. 150th Anniv of Austrian National Bank.
1468 **325** 3s. brown, grn & drab 35 25

326 Arms of Wiener Neustadt

1966. "Wiener Neustadt 1440–93" Art Exhibition.
1469 **326** 1s.50 multicoloured . . . 20 15

327 Puppy 328 Columbine

1966. 120th Anniv of Vienna Animal Protection Society.
1470 **327** 1s.80 black and yellow . . . 25 25

1966. Alpine Flora. Multicoloured.
1471 1s.50 Type **328** 25 20
1472 1s.80 Turk's cap 35 25
1473 2s.20 Wulfenia 40 35
1474 3s. Globe flower 45 40
1475 4s. Orange lily 65 55
1476 5s. Alpine anemone 80 60

329 Fair Building

1966. Wels International Fair.
1477 **329** 3s. blue 35 25

330 Peter Anich

1966. Death Bicent of Peter Anich (cartographer).
1478 **330** 1s.80 black 25 15

331 "Suffering"

1966. 15th International Occupational Health Congress, Vienna.
1479 **331** 3s. black and red 35 25

332 "Eunuchus" by Terence (engraving, Johann Gruninger)

1966. Austrian National Library, Vienna. Mult.
1480 1s.50 Type **332** (Theatre collection) 25 25
1481 1s.80 Detail of title page of Willem Blaeu's atlas (Cartography collection) 25 30
1482 2s.20 "Herrengasse, Vienna" (Anton Stutzinger (Pictures and portraits collection)) 40 40
1483 3s. Illustration from Rene of Anjou's "Livre du Cuer d'Amours Espris" (Manuscripts collection) 45 40

333 Young Girl

1966. Austrian "Save the Children" Fund.
1484 **333** 3s. black and blue . . . 35 25

334 Strawberries

335 16th-century Postman

1966. Fruits. Multicoloured.
1485 50g. Type **334** 15 20
1486 1s. Grapes 20 15
1487 1s.50 Apple 25 20
1488 1s.80 Blackberries 35 30
1489 2s.20 Apricots 40 35
1490 3s. Cherries 45 30

1966. Stamp Day.
1491 **335** 3s.+70g. multicoloured . . 40 55

336 Arms of Linz University

337 Skater of 1867

1966. Inauguration of Linz University.
1492 **336** 3s. multicoloured 35 25

1967. Centenary of Vienna Skating Assn.
1493 **337** 3s. indigo and blue . . . 35 25

338 Dancer with Violin

339 Dr. Schonherr

1967. Centenary of "Blue Danube" Waltz.
1494 **338** 3s. purple 65 30

1967. Birth Cent of Dr. Karl Schonherr (poet).
1495 **339** 3s. brown 35 25

340 Ice Hockey Goalkeeper

341 Violin and Organ

1967. World Ice Hockey Championships, Vienna.
1496 **340** 3s. blue and green . . . 35 25

1967. 125th Anniv of Vienna Philharmonic Orchestra.
1497 **341** 3s.50 blue 45 25

342 "Mother and Children" (aquarelle, Peter Fendi)

1967. Mother's Day.
1498 **342** 2s. multicoloured 25 25

343 "Madonna" (Gothic wood-carving)

1967. "Gothic Art in Austria" Exhibition, Krems.
1499 **343** 3s. green 35 25

344 Jewelled Cross

345 "The White Swan" (from Kokoschkas tapestry "Cupid and Psyche")

1967. "Salzburg Treasures" Exhibition, Salzburg Cathedral.
1500 **344** 3s.50 multicoloured . . . 35 25

1967. "Art of the Nibelungen District" Exhibition, Pochlarn.
1501 **345** 2s. multicoloured 25 25

346 Vienna

1967. 10th European Talks, Vienna.
1502 **346** 3s. black and red 35 25

347 Champion Bull

1967. Centenary of Ried Fair.
1503 **347** 2s. purple 15 35

348 Colorado Potato Beetle

1967. 6th Int Plant Protection Congress, Vienna.
1504 **348** 3s. multicoloured 20 25

349 Locomotive No. 671

350 "Christ" (fresco detail)

1967. Centenary of Brenner Railway.
1505 **349** 3s.50 green and brown . . 35 25

1967. Lambach Frescoes.
1506 **350** 2s. multicoloured 60 30

351 Prater Hall, Vienna

352 Rector's Medallion and Chain

1967. International Trade Fairs Congress, Vienna.
1507 **351** 2s. purple and cream . . 20 25

1967. 275th Anniv of Fine Arts Academy, Vienna.
1508 **352** 2s. brown, yellow & blue 20 15

353 Bible on Rock (from commemorative coin of 1717)

355 Memorial, Vienna

354 Forest Trees

1967. 450th Anniv of the Reformation.
1509 **353** 3s.50 blue 35 25

1967. 100 Years of Austrian University Forestry Studies.
1510 **354** 3s.50 green 40 25

1967. 150th Anniv of Land Registry.
1511 **355** 2s. green 20 25

356 "St. Leopold" (stained-glass window, Heiligenkreuz Monastery)

357 "Music and Art"

1967. Margrave Leopold the Holy.
1512 **356** 1s.80 multicoloured . . . 25 25

1967. 150th Anniv of Academy of Music and Dramatic Art, Vienna.
1513 **357** 3s.50 black and violet . . 50 25

358 St. Mary's Altar, Nonnberg Convent, Salzburg

359 "The Letter-carrier" (from playing-card)

1967. Christmas.
1514 **358** 2s. green 25 25

1967. Stamp Day.
1515 **359** 3s.50+80g. mult 40 50

360 Ski Jump, Stadium and Mountains

1968. Winter University Games, Innsbruck.
1516 **360** 2s. blue 35 30

361 C. Sitte **362** Mother and Child

1968. 125th Birth Anniv of Camillo Sitte (architect).
1517 **361** 2s. brown 20 25

1968. Mothers' Day.
1518 **362** 2s. olive 20 25

363 "Veterinary Medicine" **364** Bride with Lace Veil

1968. Bicentenary of Vienna Veterinary College.
1519 **363** 3s.50 gold, pur & drab 35 25

1968. Centenary of Vorarlberg Lace.
1520 **364** 3s.50 blue 45 30

365 Etrich Limousine

1968. "IFA Wien 1968" Airmail Stamp Exhibition, Vienna.
1521 **365** 2s. brown 40 45
1522 – 3s.50 green 65 55
1523 – 5s. blue . . . . 80 1·00
DESIGNS: 3s.50, Sud Aviation Caravelle; 5s. Douglas DC-8.

366 Horse-racing

1968. Centenary of Freudenau Gallop Races.
1524 **366** 3s.50 brown 45 30

367 Landsteiner **368** P. Rosegger

1968. Birth Centenary of Dr. Karl Landsteiner (physician and pathologist).
1525 **367** 3s.50 blue 40 35

1968. 50th Death Anniv of Peter Rosegger (writer).
1526 **368** 2s. green 25 25

369 A. Kauffmann (self-portrait) **370** Statue of Young Man (Helenenberg site)

1968. Exhibition of Angelica Kauffmann's Paintings, Bregenz.
1527 **369** 2s. violet 25 25

1968. Magdalensberg Excavations, Carinthia.
1528 **370** 2s. black and green . . . 20 25

371 "The Bishop" (Romanesque carving) **372** K. Moser

1968. 750th Anniv of Graz-Seckau Diocese.
1529 **371** 2s. grey 20 25

1968. 50th Death Anniv of Koloman Moser (graphic artist).
1530 **372** 2s. brown and red . . . 20 25

373 Human Rights Emblem **374** Arms and Provincial Shields

1968. Human Rights Year.
1531 **373** 1s.50 red, green & grey 20 25

1968. 50th Anniv of Republic. Multicoloured.
1532 2s. Type **374** 25 35
1533 2s. Karl Renner (first President of Second Republic) 35 35
1534 2s. First Article of Constitution 35 35

375 Crib, Oberndorf, Salzburg **376** Mercury

1968. 150th Anniv of "Silent Night, Holy Night" (carol).
1535 **375** 2s. green 25 25

1968. Stamp Day.
1536 **376** 3s.50+80g. green 40 55

377 Fresco (Troger), Melk Monastery **378** "Madonna and Child"

1968. Baroque Frescoes. Designs showing frescoes in locations given. Multicoloured.
1537 2s. Type **377** 35 45
1538 2s. Altenburg Monastery . . 35 45
1539 2s. Rohrenbach-Greillenstein 35 45
1540 2s. Ebenfurth Castle 35 45
1541 2s. Halbthurn Castle 35 45
1542 2s. Maria Treu Church, Vienna 35 45
Nos. 1537/9 are the work of Anton Troger and Nos. 1540/2 that of Franz Maulbertsch.

1969. 500th Anniv of Vienna Diocese. Statues in St. Stephen's Cathedral, Vienna.
1543 **378** 2s. blue 35 45
1544 – 2s. grey 35 45
1545 – 2s. green 35 45
1546 – 2s. purple 35 45
1547 – 2s. black 35 45
1548 – 2s. brown 35 45
DESIGNS: No. 1544, "St. Christopher"; No. 1545, "St. George"; No. 1546, "St. Paul"; No. 1547, "St. Sebastian"; No. 1548, "St. Stephen".

379 Parliament Building, Vienna

1969. Interparliamentary Union Meeting, Vienna.
1549 **379** 2s. green 20 25

380 Colonnade

1969. Europa.
1550 **380** 2s. multicoloured 25 30

381 "Council Members" **382** Soldiers

1969. 20th Anniv of Council of Europe.
1551 **381** 3s.50 multicoloured . . . 40 40

1969. Austrian Armed Forces.
1552 **382** 2s. brown and red . . . 25 25

383 "Don Giovanni"

1969. Centenary of State Opera, Vienna. Sheet 182 × 212 mm. T **383** and similar scenes.
MS1553 2s. × 8 each brown, red and gold . . . . 5·00 5·00
DESIGNS—Scenes from Opera and Ballet: "Don Giovanni" (Mozart), "The Magic Flute" (Mozart), "Fidelio" (Beethoven), "Lohengrin" (Wagner), "Don Carlos" (Verdi), "Carmen" (Bizet), "Der Rosenkavlier" (R. Strauss) and "Swan Lake" (Tchaikovsky).

384 Maximilian's Armour **385** Viennese "Privilege" Seal

1969. "Maximilian I" Exhibition, Innsbruck.
1554 **384** 2s. black 25 25

1969. 19th International Union of Local Authorities Congress, Vienna.
1555 **385** 2s. red, brown & ochre 20 25

386 Young Girl **387** Hands clasping Spanner

1969. 20th Anniv of "SOS" Children's Villages Movement.
1556 **386** 2s. brown and green . . 20 25

1969. 50th Anniv of Int Labour Organization.
1557 **387** 2s. green 20 25

388 Austrian "Flag" encircling Globe **389** "El Cid killing a Bull" (Goya)

1969. "Austrians Living Abroad" Year.
1558 **388** 3s.50 red and green . . . 35 25

1969. Bicentenary of Albertina Art Collection, Vienna. Multicoloured.
1559 2s. Type **389** 35 35
1560 2s. "Young Hare" (Durer) 35 35
1561 2s. "Madonna with Pomegranate" (Raphael) 35 35
1562 2s. "The Painter and the Amateur" (Bruegel) . . . 35 35
1563 2s. "Rubens's Son, Nicholas" (Rubens) . . . 35 35
1564 2s. "Self-portrait" (Rembrandt) 35 35
1565 2s. "Madame de Pompadour" (detail, Guerin) 35 35
1566 2s. "The Artist's Wife" (Schiele) 35 35

390 Pres. Jonas **391** Posthorn and Lightning over Globe

1969. Pres. Franz Jonas's 70th Birthday.
1567 **390** 2s. blue and grey 20 25

1969. 50th Anniv of Post and Telegraph Employees Union.
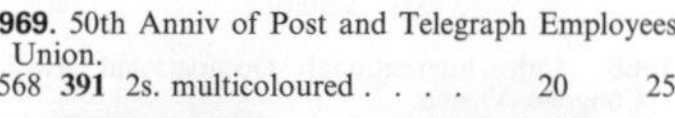
1568 **391** 2s. multicoloured 20 25

392 Savings Bank (c. 1450) **393** "The Madonna" (Egger-Lienz)

1969. 150th Anniv of Austrian Savings Bank.
1569 **392** 2s. green and silver . . . 20 25

1969. Christmas.
1570 **393** 2s. purple and yellow . . 20 25

394 Unken, Salzburg, Post-house Sign (after F. Zeller) **395** J. Schoffel

1969. Stamp Day.
1571 **394** 3s.50+80g. black, red and stone 40 60

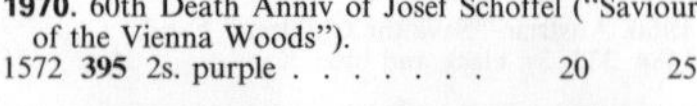
1970. 60th Death Anniv of Josef Schoffel ("Saviour of the Vienna Woods").
1572 **395** 2s. purple 20 25

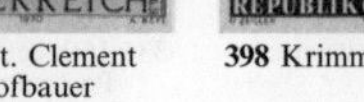
396 St. Clement Hofbauer **398** Krimml Waterfalls

397 Chancellor Leopold Figl

1970. 150th Death Anniv of St. Clement Hofbauer (theologian).
1573 **396** 2s. brown and green . . 20 25

1970. 25th Anniv of Austrian Republic.
1574 **397** 2s. olive 25 35
1575 – 2s. brown 25 35
DESIGN: No. 1575, Belvedere Castle.

1970. Nature Conservation Year.
1576 **398** 2s. green 40 25

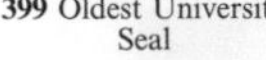
399 Oldest University Seal **401** Tower Clock, 1450–1550

400 "Musikverein" Organ

1970. 300th Anniv of Leopold Franz University, Innsbruck.
1577 **399** 2s. black and red 20 25

1970. Centenary of "Musikverein" Building.
1578 **400** 2s. purple and gold . . . 35 30

1970. Antique Clocks.
1579 **401** 1s.50 brown and cream 35 35
1580 – 1s.50 green & lt green . . 35 35
1581 – 2s. blue and pale blue . . 40 35
1582 – 2s. red and purple . . . 40 35
1583 – 3s.50 brown and buff . . 50 55
1584 – 3s.50 purple and lilac . . 50 60
DESIGNS: No. 1580, Empire "lyre" clock, 1790–1815; No. 1581, Pendant ball clock, 1600–50; No. 1582, Pocket-watch and signet, 1800–30; No. 1583, Bracket clock, 1720–60; No. 1584, "Biedermeier" pendulum clock and musical-box, 1820–50.

402 "The Beggar Student" (Millocker) **403** Scene from "The Gipsy Baron" (J. Strauss)

1970. Famous Operettas.
1585 **402** 1s.50 turquoise & green 40 35
1586 – 1s.50 blue and yellow . . 40 35
1587 – 2s. purple and pink . . . 50 45
1588 – 2s. brown and green . . 50 45
1589 – 3s.50 blue and light blue 50 70
1590 – 3s.50 blue and buff . . . 65 70
OPERETTAS: No. 1586, "Die Fledermaus" (Johann Strauss the younger); 1587, "A Waltz Dream" (O. Straus); 1588, "The Birdseller" (C. Zeller); 1589, "The Merry Widow" (F. Lehar); 1590, "Two Hearts in Waltz-time" (R. Stoiz).

1970. 25th Anniv of Bregenz Festival.
1591 **403** 3s.50 blue, buff & ult . . 40 35

404 Festival Emblem **405** T. Koschat

1970. 50th Anniv of Salzburg Festival.
1592 **404** 3s.50 multicoloured . . . 40 40

1970. 125th Birth Anniv of Thomas Koschat (composer and poet).
1593 **405** 2s. brown 35 25

406 "Head of St. John", from sculpture "Mount of Olives", Ried Church (attributed to T. Schwanthaler)

1970. 13th World Veterans Federation General Assembly.
1594 **406** 3s.50 sepia 35 25

407 Climbers and Mountains

1970. "Walking and Mountaineering".
1595 **407** 2s. blue and mauve . . . 25 25

408 A. Cossmann

1970. Birth Cent of Alfred Cossmann (engraver).
1596 **408** 2s. brown 20 25

409 Arms of Carinthia **410** U.N. Emblem

1970. 50th Anniv of Carinthian Plebiscite.
1597 **409** 2s. multicoloured 20 25

1970. 25th Anniv of United Nations.
1598 **410** 3s.50 blue and black . . 35 25

411 "Adoration of the Shepherds" (carving, Garsten Monastery)

1970. Christmas.
1599 **411** 2s. blue 20 25

412 Saddle, Harness and Posthorn **413** Pres. K. Renner

1970. Stamp Day.
1600 **412** 3s.50+80g. black, yellow and grey 40 60

1970. Birth Centenary of Pres. Renner.
1601 **413** 2s. purple 20 25

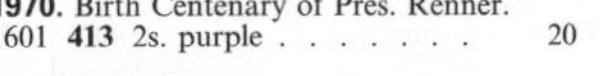

414 Beethoven (after painting by Waldmuller) **415** E. Handel-Mazzetti

1970. Birth Bicentenary of Beethoven.
1602 **414** 3s.50 black and stone . . 80 40

1971. Birth Centenary of Enrica Handel-Mazzetti (novelist).
1603 **415** 2s. brown 20 25

416 "Safety for Children"

1971. Road Safety.
1604 **416** 2s. multicoloured 35 25

417 Florentine Bowl, c. 1580

1971. Austrian Art Treasures (1st series). Sculpture and Applied Art.
1605 **417** 1s.50 green and grey . . 35 25
1606 – 2s. purple and grey . . . 35 35
1607 – 3s.50 yellow, brn & grey 60 65
DESIGNS: 2s. Ivory equestrian statuette of Joseph I, 1693 (Matthias Steinle); 3s.50, Salt-cellar, c. 1570 (Cellini).
See also Nos. 1609/11, 1632/4 and 1651/3.

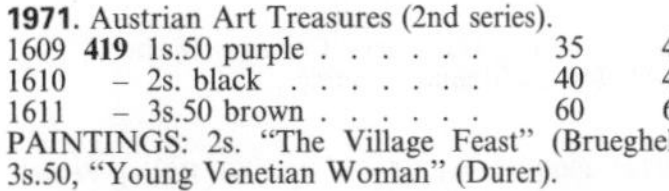
418 Shield of Trade Association **419** "Jacopo de Strada" (Titian)

1971. 23rd International Chamber of Commerce Congress, Vienna.
1608 **418** 3s.50 multicoloured . . . 35 25

1971. Austrian Art Treasures (2nd series).
1609 **419** 1s.50 purple 35 40
1610 – 2s. black 40 40
1611 – 3s.50 brown 60 65
PAINTINGS: 2s. "The Village Feast" (Brueghel); 3s.50, "Young Venetian Woman" (Durer).

420 Notary's Seal **421** "St. Matthew" (altar sculpture)

1971. Austrian Notarial Statute Cent Congress.
1612 **420** 3s.50 purple and brown 35 40

1971. "Krems Millennium of Art" Exhibition.
1613 **421** 2s. brown and purple . . 20 25

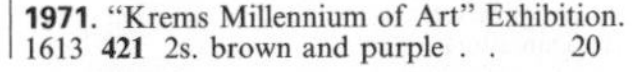

422 Dr. A. Neilreich **423** Singer with Lyre

1971. Death Cent of Dr. August Neilreich (botanist).
1614 **422** 2s. brown 20 25

1971. International Choir Festival, Vienna.
1615 **423** 4s. blue, gold & lt blue 70 40

424 Arms of Kitzbuhel

1971. 700th Anniv of Kitzbuhel.
1616 **424** 2s.50 multicoloured . . . 25 25

425 Stock Exchange Building

1971. Bicentenary of Vienna Stock Exchange.
1617 **425** 4s. brown 40 25

426 Old and New Fair Halls **427** O.G.B. Emblem

1971. "50 Years of Vienna International Fairs".
1618 **426** 2s.50 purple 25 25

1971. 25th Anniv of Austrian Trade Unions Federation.
1619 **427** 2s. multicoloured 20 25

428 Arms and Insignia **429** "Marcus" Veteran Car

1971. 50th Anniv of Burgenland Province.
1620 **428** 4s. multicoloured 25 30

1971. 75th Anniv of Austrian Automobile, Motor Cycle and Touring Club.
1621 **429** 4s. black and green . . . 60 35

430 Europa Bridge, Brenner Highway **431** Iron-ore Workings, Erzberg

1971. Inauguration of Brenner Highway.
1622 **430** 4s. blue 60 30

1971. 25 Years of Nationalized Industries.
1623 **431** 1s.50 brown 25 30
1624 – 2s. blue 35 35
1625 – 4s. green 60 55
DESIGNS: 2s. Nitrogen Works, Linz; 4s. Iron and Steel works, Linz.

432 Electric Train on the Semmering Line

433 E. Tschermak-Seysenegg

1971. Railway Anniversaries.
1626 **432** 2s. purple 65 30

1971. Birth Centenary of Dr. E. Tshermak-Seysenegg (biologist).
1627 **433** 2s. purple and grey . . . 20 25

434 Angling

435 "The Infant Jesus as Saviour" (from miniature by Durer)

1971. Sports.
1628 **434** 2s. brown 25 25

1971. Christmas.
1629 **435** 2s. multicoloured 25 25

436 "50 Years"

1971. 50th Anniv of Austrian Philatelic Clubs Association.
1630 **436** 4s.+1s.50 pur & gold . . 65 85

437 Franz Grillparzer (from miniature by Daffinger)

438 Roman Fountain, Friesach

1972. Death Centenary of Grillparzer (dramatist).
1631 **437** 2s. black, brown & stone 25 25

1972. Austrian Art Treasures (3rd series). Fountains.
1632 **438** 1s.50 purple 25 35
1633 – 2s. brown 40 35
1634 – 2s.50 green 50 55
DESIGNS: 2s. Lead Fountain, Heiligenkreuz Abbey; 2s.50. Leopold Fountain, Innsbruck.

439 Hofburg Palace

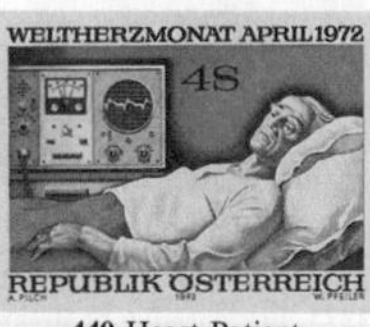

440 Heart Patient

1972. 4th European Postal Ministers' Conf, Vienna.
1635 **439** 4s. violet 50 45

1972. World Heart Month.
1636 **440** 4s. brown 50 40

441 "Woman's Head" (sculpture, Gurk Cathedral)

442 Vienna Town Hall and Congress Emblem

1972. 900th Anniv of Gurk Diocese.
1637 **441** 2s. purple and gold . . . 25 25

1972. 9th International Public and Co-operative Economy Congress, Vienna.
1638 **442** 4s. black, red and yellow 45 25

443 Lienz–Pelos Pylon Line

1972. 25th Anniv of Electric Power Nationalization.
1639 **443** 70g. violet and grey . . 15 20
1640 – 2s.50 brown and grey . . 35 35
1641 – 4s. blue and grey 50 40
DESIGNS: 2s.50, Vienna-Semmering Power Station; 4s. Zemm Dam and lake.

444 Runner with Torch

445 "Hermes" (C. Laib)

1972. Passage of the Olympic Torch through Austria.
1642 **444** 2s. brown and red . . . 25 25

1972. "Late Gothic Art" Exhibition, Salzburg.
1643 **445** 2s. purple 25 25

446 Pears 448 University Arms

447 "Spanish Walk"

1972. Amateur Gardeners' Congress, Vienna.
1644 **446** 2s.50 multicoloured . . . 35 25

1972. 400th Anniv of the Spanish Riding School, Vienna. Sheet 136 × 181 mm containing T **447** and similar square designs each in purple, red and gold.
MS1645 2s. Type **447**; 2s. "Piaffe"; 2s.50 "Levade"; 2s.50 "On the long rein"; 4s. "Capriole"; 4s. "Courbette" . . . . 3·00 3·00

1972. Cent of University of Agriculture, Vienna.
1646 **448** 2s. multicoloured 25 25

449 Old University Buildings (after F. Danreiter)

450 C. M. Ziehrer

1972. 350th Anniv of Paris Lodron University, Salzburg.
1647 **449** 4s. brown 50 25

1972. 50th Death Anniv of Carl M. Ziehrer (composer and conductor).
1648 **450** 2s. red 45 25

451 "Virgin and Child", Inzersdorf Church

1972. Christmas.
1649 **451** 2s. purple and green . . 25 25

452 18th-century Viennese Postman

1972. Stamp Day.
1650 **452** 4s.+1s. green 65 80

453 State Sledge of Maria Theresa

1972. Austrian Art Treasures (4th series). Carriages from the Imperial Coach House.
1651 **453** 1s.50 brown and bistre 35 25
1652 – 2s. green and bistre . . . 40 35
1653 – 2s.50 purple and bistre 45 50
DESIGNS: 2s. Coronation landau; 2s.50, Hapsburg State Coach.

454 Telephone Network

456 A. Petzold

455 "Drug Addict"

1972. Completion of Austrian Telephone System Automation.
1654 **454** 2s. black and yellow . . 25 25

1973. Campaign against Drug Abuse.
1655 **455** 2s. multicoloured 65 55

1973. 50th Death Anniv of Alfons Petzold (writer).
1656 **456** 2s. purple 25 25

457 Korner 458 Douglas DC-9-80 Super Eighty

1973. Birth Centenary of Pres. Theodor Korner (President, 1951–57).
1657 **457** 2s. purple and grey . . . 25 25

1973. Austrian Aviation Anniversaries.
1658 **458** 2s. blue and red 40 30

459 Otto Loewi

460 "Succour"

1973. Birth Cent of Otto Loewi (pharmacologist).
1659 **459** 4s. violet 50 40

1973. 25th Anniv of National Federation of Austrian Social Insurance Institutes.
1660 **460** 2s. blue 25 25

461 Telephone Dial within Posthorn

463 Military Pentathlon

462 Fair Emblem

1973. Europa.
1661 **461** 2s.50 black, yell & orge 45 30

1973. 25th Dornbirn Fair.
1662 **462** 2s. multicoloured 25 25

1973. 25th Anniv of International Military Sports Council and 23rd Military Pentathlon Championships, Wiener Neustadt.
1663 **463** 4s. green 60 45

464 Leo Slezak

465 Main Entrance, Hofburg Palace

1973. Birth Centenary of Leo Slezak (operatic tenor).
1664 **464** 4s. brown 65 50

1973. 39th International Statistical Institute's Congress, Vienna.
1665 **465** 2s. brown, red and grey 25 25

466 "Admiral Tegetthof Icebound" (J. Payer)

467 I.U.L.C.S. Arms

1973. Centenary of Discovery of Franz Josef Land.
1666 **466** 2s.50 green 65 30

1973. 13th International Union of Leather Chemists' Societies Congress, Vienna.
1667 **467** 4s. multicoloured 50 40

468 "Academy of Sciences, Vienna" (B. Bellotto)

469 Max Reinhardt

1973. Cent of Int Meteorological Organization.
1668 **468** 2s.50 violet 40 25

1973. Birth Centenary of Max Reinhardt (theatrical director).
1669 **469** 2s. purple 40 30

470 F. Hanusch

1973. 50th Death Anniv of Ferdinand Hanusch (politician).
1670 **470** 2s. purple 25 25

471 Light Harness Racing

1973. Centenary of Vienna Trotting Assn.
1671 **471** 2s. green 45 35

472 Radio Operator

1973. 50th Anniv of International Criminal Police Organization (Interpol).
1672 **472** 4s. violet 65 45

473 Petzval Camera Lens

1973. "Europhot" (professional photographers) Congress, Vienna.
1673 **473** 2s.50 multicoloured . . . 40 30

474 Aqueduct, Hollen Valley

1973. Centenary of Vienna's 1st Mountain-spring Aqueduct.
1674 **474** 2s. brown, red & blue . . 35 25

475 Almsee

476 "The Nativity" (stained-glass window, St. Erhard Church, Bretenau)

1973. Views. (a) Size 23 × 29 mm.

No.	Type	Description	Unused	Used
1674a	–	20g. blue and light blue	35	30
1675	–	50g. green & lt green	15	15
1676	–	1s. sepia and brown . .	20	15
1677	–	1s.50 purple and pink	35	15
1678	–	2s. indigo and blue . .	25	15
1679	–	2s.50 deep lilac & lilac	40	15
1680	–	3s. ultramarine & blue	40	15
1680a	–	3s.50 brown & orange	65	20
1681	**475**	4s. violet and lilac . . .	65	15
1681a	–	4s.20 black and grey . .	65	60
1682	–	4s.50 dp green & green	80	20
1683	–	5s. violet and lilac . . .	80	15
1683a	–	5s.50 blue and violet . .	80	55
1683b	–	5s.60 olive and green	1·10	1·10
1684	–	6s. lilac and pink . . .	1·10	15
1684a	–	6s.50 blue & turquoise	1·00	25
1685	–	7s. deep green & green	1·20	15
1685a	–	7s.50 purple & mauve	1·20	35
1686	–	8s. brown and pink . .	1·20	25
1686a	–	9s. red and pink . . .	1·40	60
1687	–	10s. myrtle and green	1·30	15
1688	–	11s. red and orange . .	1·60	30
1688a	–	12s. sepia and brown	1·60	35
1688b	–	14s. myrtle and green	1·75	35
1688c	–	16s. brown and orange	2·00	40
1688d	–	20s. green and bistre . .	2·50	50

(b) Size 28 × 37 mm.
1689 – 50s. violet and grey . . . . 6·50 2·10

(c) Size 17 × 20 mm.
1690 – 3s. ultramarine and blue 50 35

DESIGNS: 20g. Friedstadt Keep, Muhlviertel; 50g. Zillertal; 1s. Kahlenbergerdorf, Vienna; 1s.50, Bludenz; 2s. Old bridge, Finstermunz; 2s.50, Murau, Styria; 3s. Bischofsmutze and Alpine farm; 3s.50, Osterkirche, Oberwart; 4s.20, Hirschegg, Kleinwalsertal; 4s.50, Windmill, Retz; 5s. Ruins of Aggstein Castle; 5s.50, Peace Chapel, Stoderzinken; 5s.60, Riezlern, Kleinwalsertal; 6s. Lindauer Hut, Ratikon Massif; 6s.50, Villach, Carinthia; 7s. Falkenstein Castle; 7s.50, Hohensalzburg Fortress; 8s. Votive column, Reiteregg, Styria; 9s. Asten valley; 10s. Neusiedlersee; 11s. Enns; 12s. Kufstein Fortress; 14s. Weiszsee, Salzburg; 16s. Bad Tatzmannsdorf open-air museum; 20s. Myra Falls, Muggendorf; 50s. Hofburg, Vienna.

1973. Christmas.
1691 **476** 2s. multicoloured 35 25

477 "Archangel Gabriel" (carving by Lorenz Luchsperger)

478 Dr. Fritz Pregl

1973. Stamp Day.
1692 **477** 4s.+1s. purple 65 65

1973. 50th Anniv of Award of Nobel Prize for Chemistry to Fritz Pregl.
1693 **478** 4s. blue 35 25

479 Telex Machine and Globe

480 Hugo Hofmannsthal

1974. 50th Anniv of Radio Austria.
1694 **479** 2s.50 blue & ultramarine 35 25

1974. Birth Cent of Hugo Hofmannsthal (writer).
1695 **480** 4s. blue 50 35

481 Anton Bruckner (composer)

1974. Inaug of Bruckner Memorial Centre, Linz.
1696 **481** 4s. brown 90 55

482 Vegetables

1974. 2nd Int Horticultural Show, Vienna. Mult.
1697 2s. Type **482** 65 25
1698 2s.50 Fruit 60 30
1699 4s. Flowers 65 55

483 Head from Ancient Seal

484 Karl Kraus

1974. 750th Anniv of Judenburg.
1700 **483** 2s. multicoloured 35 30

1974. Birth Centenary of Karl Kraus (poet).
1701 **484** 4s. red 50 40

485 "St. Michael" (wood-carving, Thomas Schwanthaler)

486 "King Arthur" (statue, Innsbruck)

1974. "Sculptures by the Schwanthaler Family" Exhibition, Reichersberg.
1702 **485** 2s.50 green 40 30

1974. Europa.
1703 **486** 2s.50 blue and brown . . 40 30

487 Early De Dion-Bouton Motor-tricycle

489 I.R.U. Emblem

488 Mask of Satyr's Head

1974. 75th Anniv of Austrian Association of Motoring, Motor Cycling and Cycling.
1704 **487** 2s. brown and grey . . . 40 30

1974. "Renaissance in Austria" Exhibition, Schallaburg Castle.
1705 **488** 2s. black, brown & gold 25 25

1974. 14th International Road Haulage Union Congress, Innsbruck.
1706 **489** 4s. black and orange . . 50 40

490 F. A. Maulbertsch

491 Gendarmes of 1849 and 1974

1974. 205th Birth Anniv of Franz Maulbertsch (painter).
1707 **490** 2s. brown 25 25

1974. 125th Anniv of Austrian Gendarmerie.
1708 **491** 2s. multicoloured 45 30

492 Fencing

1974. Sports.
1709 **492** 2s.50 black and orange 40 25

493 Transport Emblems

1974. European Transport Ministers' Conference, Vienna.
1710 **493** 4s. multicoloured 60 40

494 "St. Virgilius" (wood-carving)

495 Pres. F. Jonas

1974. 1200 Years of Christianity in Salzburg.
1711 **494** 2s. blue 25 25

1974. Pres. Franz Jonas Commemoration.
1712 **495** 2s. black 20 25

496 F. Stelzhamer

497 Diving

1974. Death Cent of Franz Stelzhamer (poet).
1713 **496** 2s. blue 25 25

1974. 13th European Swimming, Diving and Water-polo Championships.
1714 **497** 4s. brown and blue . . . 65 40

498 F. R. von Hebra (founder of German scientific dermatology)

499 A. Schonberg

1974. 30th Meeting of German-speaking Dermatologists Association, Graz.
1715 **498** 4s. brown 50 40

1974. Birth Cent of Arnold Schonberg (composer).
1716 **499** 2s.50 purple 50 30

500 Broadcasting Studios, Salzburg

501 E. Eysler

1974. 50th Anniv of Austrian Broadcasting.
1717 **500** 2s. multicoloured 35 25

1974. 25th Death Anniv of Edmund Eysler (composer).
1718 **501** 2s. green 40 25

502 19th-century Postman and Mail Transport

1974. Centenary of U.P.U.
1719 **502** 2s. brown and mauve . . 40 30
1720 – 4s. blue and grey 50 45
DESIGN: 4s. Modern postman and mail transport.

503 Sports Emblem

1974. 25th Anniv of Football Pools in Austria.
1721 **503** 70g. red, black and green 20 15

504 Steel Gauntlet grasping Rose

1974. Nature Protection.
1722 **504** 2s. multicoloured 40 30

505 C. D. von Dittersdorf   **506** Mail Coach and P.O., 1905

1974. 175th Death Anniv of Carl Ditters von Dittersdorf (composer).
1723 **505** 2s. green 40 25

1974. Stamp Day.
1724 **506** 4s.+2s. blue 80 95

507 "Virgin Mary and Child" (wood-carving)   **508** F. Schmidt

1974. Christmas.
1725 **507** 2s. brown and gold . . . 35 25

1974. Birth Centenary of Franz Schmidt (composer).
1726 **508** 4s. black and stone . . . 50 40

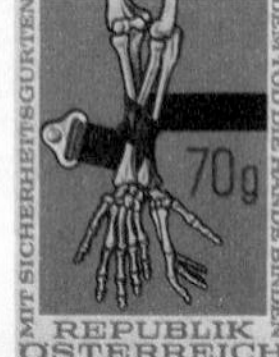

509 "St. Christopher and Child" (altarpiece)   **511** Seat-belt around Skeletal Limbs

510 Slalom

1975. European Architectural Heritage Year and 125th Anniv of Austrian Commission for Preservation of Monuments.
1727 **509** 2s.50 brown and grey . . 65 40

1975. Winter Olympics, Innsbruck (1976) (1st issue). Multicoloured.
1728 1s.+50g. Type **510** 25 25
1729 1s.50+70g. Ice hockey . . . 40 40
1730 2s.+90g. Ski-jumping . . . 50 55
1731 4s.+1s.90 Bobsleighing . . . 80 95
See also Nos. 1747/50.

1975. Car Safety-belts Campaign.
1732 **511** 70g. multicoloured . . . 20 15

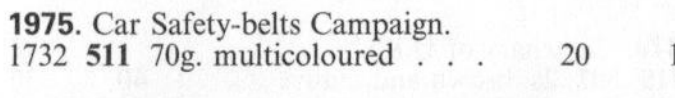

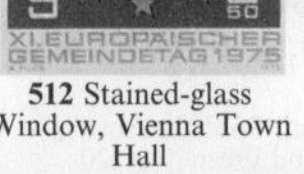

512 Stained-glass Window, Vienna Town Hall   **513** "The Buffer State"

1975. 11th European Communities' Day.
1733 **512** 2s.50 multicoloured . . . 40 30

1975. 30th Anniv of Foundation of Austrian Second Republic.
1734 **513** 2s. black and brown . . 25 25

514 Forest Scene

1975. 50th Anniv of Foundation of Austrian Forests Administration.
1735 **514** 2s. green 50 30

515 "The High Priest" (M. Pacher)   **516** Gosaukamm Cable-way

1975. Europa.
1736 **515** 2s.50 multicoloured . . . 40 30

1975. 4th International Ropeways Congress, Vienna.
1737 **516** 2s. blue and red 35 25

517 J. Misson

1975. Death Centenary of Josef Misson (poet).
1738 **517** 2s. brown and red . . . 35 25

518 "Setting Sun"   **520** L. Fall

519 F. Porsche

1975. Nat Pensioners' Assn Meeting, Vienna.
1739 **518** 1s.50 multicoloured . . . 25 25

1975. Birth Centenary of Prof. Ferdinand Porsche (motor engineer).
1740 **519** 1s.50 purple & green . . 25 20

1975. 50th Death Anniv of Leo Fall (composer).
1741 **520** 2s. violet 40 25

521 Judo "Shoulder Throw"   **522** Heinrich Angeli

1975. World Judo Championships, Vienna.
1742 **521** 2s.50 multicoloured . . . 35 25

1975. 50th Death Anniv of Heinrich Angeli (court painter).
1743 **522** 2s. purple 35 25

523 J. Strauss

1975. 150th Birth Anniv of Johann Strauss the Younger (composer).
1744 **523** 4s. brown and ochre . . 80 45

524 "The Cellist"   **525** "One's Own House"

1975. 75th Anniv of Vienna Symphony Orchestra.
1745 **524** 2s.50 blue and silver . . 50 30

1975. 50th Anniv of Austrian Building Societies.
1746 **525** 2s. multicoloured 25 25

1975. Winter Olympic Games, Innsbruck (1976) (2nd issue). As T **510**. Multicoloured.
1747 70g.+30g. Figure-skating (pairs) 20 25
1748 2s.+1s. Cross-country skiing 40 45
1749 2s.50+1s. Tobogganing . . . 50 60
1750 4s.+2s. Rifle-shooting (biathlon) . . . . 80 1·00

526 Scene on Folding Fan

1975. Bicentenary of Salzburg State Theatre.
1751 **526** 1s.50 multicoloured . . . 50 30

527 Austrian Stamps of 1850, 1922 and 1945   **528** "Virgin and Child" (Schottenaltar, Vienna)

1975. Stamp Day. 125th Anniv of Austrian Postage Stamps.
1752 **527** 4s.+2s. multicoloured . . 80 1·00

1975. Christmas.
1753 **528** 2s. lilac and gold 35 25

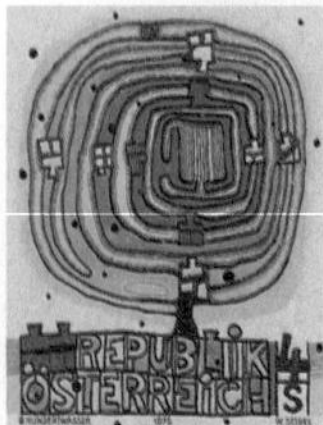

529 "Spiralbaum" (F. Hundertwasser)   **531** Dr. R. Barany

530 Old Theatre Building

1975. Modern Austrian Art.
1754 **529** 4s. multicoloured . . . . 1·00 60

1976. Bicentenary of the Burgtheatre, Vienna. Sheet 130 × 60 mm containing T **530** and similar horiz design.
MS1755 3s. blue (Type **530**); 3s. brown (Interior of the modern theatre) . . . . 1·20 1·20

1976. Birth Centenary of Dr. Robert Barany (Nobel prizewinner for Medicine, 1915).
1756 **531** 3s. brown and blue . . . 45 35

532 Ammonite Fossil   **533** 9th-century Coronation Throne

1976. Cent Exn, Vienna Natural History Museum.
1757 **532** 3s. multicoloured 50 30

1976. Millenary of Carinthia.
1758 **533** 3s. black and yellow . . 40 30

534 Stained-glass Window, Klosterneuburg   **535** "The Siege of Linz" (contemporary engraving)

1976. Babenberg Exhibition, Lilienfeld.
1759 **534** 3s. multicoloured 50 30

1976. 350th Anniv of the Peasants' War in Upper Austria.
1760 **535** 4s. black and green . . . 65 50

536 Bowler delivering Ball

1976. 11th World Skittles Championships, Vienna.
1761 **536** 4s. black and orange . . 65 45

537 "St. Wolfgang" (altar painting by Michael Pacher)   **538** Tassilo Cup, Kremsmunster

1976. International Art Exhibition, St. Wolfgang.
1762 **537** 6s. purple 90 60

1976. Europa.
1763 **538** 4s. multicoloured 60 55

539 Fair Emblem   **540** Constantin Economo

1976. 25th Austrian Timber Fair, Klagenfurt.
1764 **539** 3s. multicoloured 40 30

1976. Birth Centenary of Constantin Economo (brain specialist).
1765 **540** 3s. brown 45 30

541 Bohemian Court Chancellery, Vienna

542 Arms of Lower Austria

1976. Centenary of Administrative Court.
1766 **541** 6s. brown 80 70

1976. Millenary of Austria. Sheet 135×180 mm containing T **542** and similar vert designs showing provincial arms.
MS1767 2s. ×9 multicoloured . . 3·25 3·25
DESIGNS: Arms of Lower Austria, Upper Austria, Styria, Carinthia, Vorarlberg, Salzberg, Burgenland and Vienna.

543 Cancer the Crab

544 U.N. Emblem and Bridge

1976. Fight against Cancer.
1768 **543** 2s.50 multicoloured . . . 40 30

1976. 10th Anniv of U.N. Industrial Development Organization.
1769 **544** 3s. blue and gold 40 30

545 Punched Tapes and Map of Europe

1976. 30th Anniv of Austrian Press Agency.
1770 **545** 1s.50 multicoloured . . . 20 15

546 V. Kaplan

1976. Birth Centenary of Viktor Kaplan (inventor of turbine).
1771 **546** 2s.50 multicoloured . . . 35 25

547 "The Birth of Christ" (Konrad von Friesach)

1976. Christmas.
1772 **547** 3s. multicoloured 45 30

548 Postilion's Hat and Posthorn

1976. Stamp Day.
1773 **548** 6s.+2s. black & lilac . . 1·00 1·20

549 R. M. Rilke

550 "Augustin the Piper" (Arik Brauer)

1976. 50th Death Anniv of Rainer Maria Rilke (poet).
1774 **549** 3s. violet 40 30

1976. Austrian Modern Art.
1775 **550** 6s. multicoloured 90 70

551 City Synagogue

552 N. J. von Jacquin

1976. 150th Anniv of Vienna City Synagogue.
1776 **551** 1s.50 multicoloured . . . 35 20

1977. 250th Birth Anniv of Nikolaus Joseph Freiherrn von Jacquin (botanist).
1777 **552** 4s. brown 50 35

553 Oswald von Wolkenstein

555 A. Kubin

554 Handball

1977. 600th Birth Anniv of Oswald von Wolkenstein (poet).
1778 **553** 3s. multicoloured 50 30

1977. World Indoor Handball Championships, Group B, Austria.
1779 **554** 1s.50 multicoloured . . . 20 20

1977. Birth Centenary of Alfred Kubin (writer and illustrator).
1780 **555** 6s. blue 80 55

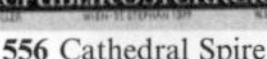

556 Cathedral Spire

558 I.A.E.A. Emblem

557 F. Herzmanovsky-Orlando

1977. 25th Anniv of Re-opening of St. Stephen's Cathedral, Vienna.
1781 **556** 2s.50 brown 40 30
1782 – 3s. blue 50 50
1783 – 4s. purple 80 75
DESIGNS: 3s. West front; 4s. Interior.

1977. Birth Centenary of Fritz Herzmanovsky-Orlando (writer).
1784 **557** 6s. green and gold . . . 80 55

1977. 20th Anniv of Int Atomic Energy Agency.
1785 **558** 3s. lt blue, gold & blue 40 30

559 Arms of Schwanenstadt

561 Globe (Vincenzo Coronelli)

560 Attersee

1977. 350th Anniv of Schwanenstadt.
1786 **559** 3s. multicoloured 50 30

1977. Europa.
1787 **560** 6s. green 80 60

1977. 5th International Symposium and 25th Anniv of Coronelli World Federation of Globe Friends.
1788 **561** 3s. black and stone . . . 45 30

562 Canoeist

1977. World "White Water" Canoe Championships.
1789 **562** 4s. multicoloured 60 40

563 "The Samaritan" (Francesco Bassano)

1977. 50th Anniv of Austrian Workers' Samaritan Federation.
1790 **563** 1s.50 multicoloured . . . 25 25

564 Papermakers' Arms

565 "Freedom"

1977. 17th Conference of European Committee of Pulp and Paper Technology.
1791 **564** 3s. multicoloured 40 25

1977. Martyrs for Austrian Freedom.
1792 **565** 2s.50 blue and red . . . 35 30

566 Steam Locomotive, "Austria", 1837

1977. 140th Anniv of Austrian Railways. Mult.
1793 1s.50 Type **566** 35 30
1794 2s.50 Type 214 steam locomotive, 1928 . . . . 65 40
1795 3s. Type 1044 electric locomotive, 1974 . . . . 85 65

567 "Madonna and Child" (wood carving, Mariastein Pilgrimage Church)

1977. Christmas.
1796 **567** 3s. multicoloured 40 25

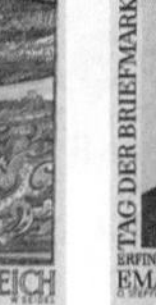

568 "Danube Maiden" (Wolfgang Hutter)

569 Emanuel Herrmann (inventor of postcard)

1977. Austrian Modern Art.
1797 **568** 6s. multicoloured 90 55

1977. Stamp Day.
1798 **569** 6s.+2s. brown and cinnamon . . . . . . 1·00 1·40

570 Egon Friedell

1978. Birth Centenary of Egon Friedell (writer).
1799 **570** 3s. black and blue . . . 40 30

571 Underground Train

1978. Opening of Vienna Underground Railway.
1800 **571** 3s. multicoloured 90 40

572 Rifleman and Skier

1978. Biathlon World Championships, Hochfilzen.
1801 **572** 4s. multicoloured 60 40

573 Aztec Feather Shield

1978. 30th Anniv of Museum of Ethnology, Vienna.
1802 **573** 3s. multicoloured 40 30

574 Leopold Kunschak

575 "Mountain Peasants"

1978. 25th Death Anniv of Leopold Kunschak (politician).
1803 **574** 3s. blue 40 25

1978. Birth Centenary of Suitbert Lobisser (wood engraver).
1804 **575** 3s. brown and stone . . 40 30

576 Black Grouse, Hunting Satchel and Fowling Piece

577 Map of Europe and Austrian Parliament Building

1978. International Hunting Exn, Marchegg.
1805 **576** 6s. blue, brown & turq 80 50

1978. 3rd Interparliamentary European Security Conference, Vienna.
1806 **577** 4s. multicoloured 60 40

578 Riegersburg Castle, Styria

1978. Europa.
1807 **578** 6s. purple 80 70

579 "Admont Pieta" (Salzburg Circle Master)

580 Ort Castle

1978. "Gothic Art in Styria" Exhibition.
1808 **579** 2s.50 black and ochre . . 40 30

1978. 700th Anniv of Gmunden Town Charter.
1809 **580** 3s. multicoloured 45 30

581 Face surrounded by Fruit and Flowers

582 Franz Lehar and Villa at Bad Ischl

1978. 25th Anniv of Austrian Association for Social Tourism.
1810 **581** 6s. multicoloured 80 60

1978. International Lehar Congress.
1811 **582** 6s. blue . . . . 1·00 60

583 Tools and Globe

1978. 15th Congress of International Federation of Building and Wood Workers.
1812 **583** 1s.50 black, yellow & red 20 20

584 Knights Jousting

1978. 700th Anniv of Battle of Durnkrut and Jedenspeigen.
1813 **584** 3s. multicoloured 40 30

585 Bridge over River Drau

586 City Seal, 1440

1978. 1100th Anniv of Villach.
1814 **585** 3s. multicoloured 40 30

1978. 850th Anniv of Graz.
1815 **586** 4s. brown, green & grey 50 40

587 Angler

588 Distorted Pattern

1978. 25th Sport Fishing Championships, Vienna.
1816 **587** 4s. multicoloured 60 40

1978. Handicapped People.
1817 **588** 6s. black and brown . . 80 55

589 Concrete Chain

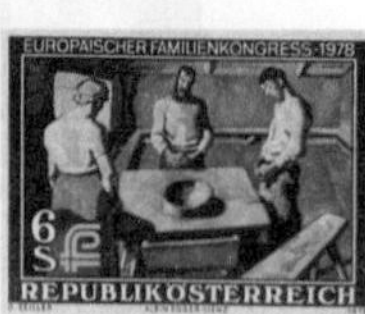

590 "Grace" (Albin Egger-Lienz)

1978. 9th International Concrete and Prefabrication Industry Congress, Vienna.
1818 **589** 2s.50 multicoloured . . . 35 25

1978. European Family Congress.
1819 **590** 6s. multicoloured 80 55

591 Lise Meitner

592 Victor Adler (bust, Anton Hamek)

1978. Birth Centenary of Lise Meitner (physicist).
1820 **591** 6s. violet 80 55

1978. 60th Death Anniv of Victor Adler (statesman).
1821 **592** 3s. black and red 40 30

593 Franz Schubert (after Josef Kriehuber)

594 "Madonna and Child" (Martino Altomonte, Wilhering Collegiate Church)

1978. 150th Death Anniv of Franz Schubert (composer).
1822 **593** 6s. brown . . . . 1·30 70

1978. Christmas.
1823 **594** 3s. multicoloured 40 25

595 Postbus, 1913

1978. Stamp Day.
1824 **595** 10s.+5s. multicoloured 2·00 1·90

596 "Archduke Johann Hut, Grossglockner" (E. T. Compton)

1978. Centenary of Austrian Alpine Club.
1825 **596** 1s.50 violet and gold . . 25 20

597 "Adam" (Rudolf Hausner)

598 Bound Hands

1978. Austrian Modern Art.
1826 **597** 6s. multicoloured 90 55

1978. 30th Anniv of Declaration of Human Rights.
1827 **598** 6s. purple 80 55

599 "CCIR"

1979. 50th Anniv of International Radio Consultative Committee.
1828 **599** 6s. multicoloured 80 45

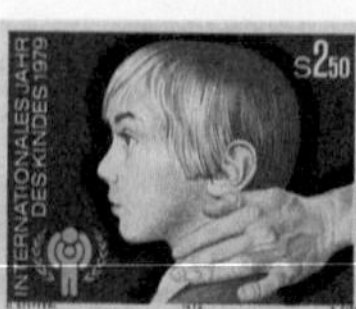

600 Adult protecting Child

1979. International Year of the Child.
1829 **600** 2s.50 multicoloured . . . 35 30

601 Air Rifle, Pistol and Target

1979. Centenary of Austrian Shooting Club, and European Air Rifle and Air Pistol Shooting Championships.
1830 **601** 6s. multicoloured 80 45

602 "Franz I" (paddle-steamer)

1979. 150th Anniv of Danube Steam Navigation Company.
1831 **602** 1s.50 blue 25 25
1832 – 2s.50 brown 50 35
1833 – 3s. red 35 25
DESIGNS: 2s.50, Pusher tug "Linz"; 3s. "Theodor Korner" (passenger vessel).

603 Skater

1979. World Ice Skating and Dancing Championships. Vienna.
1834 **603** 4s. multicoloured 60 45

604 Fashion Drawing by Theo Zache, 1900

605 Wiener Neustadt Cathedral

1979. 50th Viennese Int Ladies' Fashion Week.
1835 **604** 2s.50 multicoloured . . . 35 30

1979. 700th Anniv of Wiener Neustadt Cathedral.
1836 **605** 4s. blue and grey 35 30

606 Relief from Emperor Joseph II Monument, Vienna

607 Population Graph

1979. Bicentenary of Education for the Deaf.
1837 **606** 2s.50 green, black & gold 80 40

1979. 150th Anniv of Austrian Central Statistical Office.
1838 **607** 2s.50 multicoloured . . . 50 35

608 Laurenz Koschier (postal reformer)

609 Section through Diesel Engine

1979. Europa.
1839 **608** 6s. brown and ochre . . 40 40

1979. 13th Congress of International Combustion Engine Council.
1840 **609** 4s. multicoloured 40 30

610 Town Arms of Ried, Braunau and Scharding

1979. Bicentenary of Innviertel District.
1841 **610** 3s. multicoloured 40 25

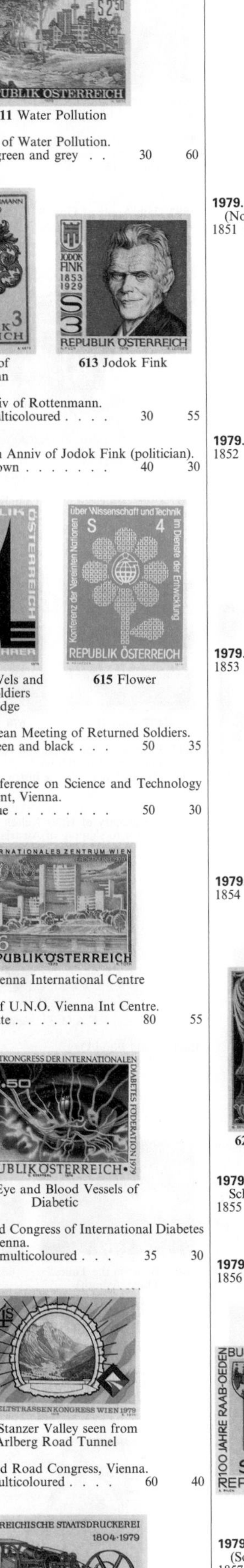
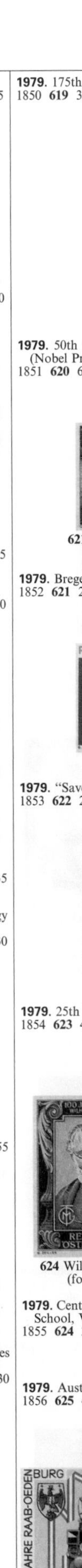
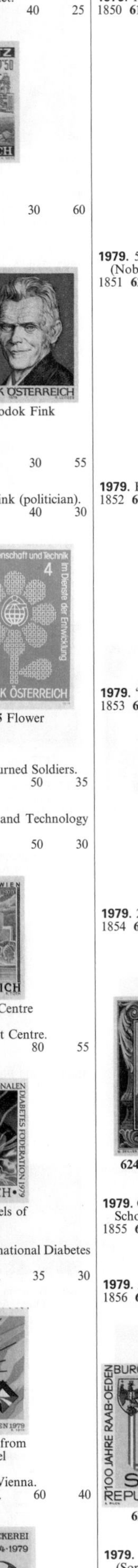
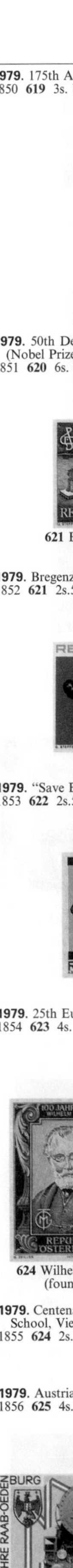

611 Water Pollution

1979. Prevention of Water Pollution.
1842 **611** 2s.50 green and grey . . 30 60

612 Arms of Rottenmann **613** Jodok Fink

1979. 700th Anniv of Rottenmann.
1843 **612** 3s. multicoloured 30 55

1979. 50th Death Anniv of Jodok Fink (politician).
1844 **613** 3s. brown 40 30

614 Arms of Wels and Returned Soldiers League Badge **615** Flower

1979. 5th European Meeting of Returned Soldiers.
1845 **614** 4s. green and black . . . 50 35

1979. U.N. Conference on Science and Technology for Development, Vienna.
1846 **615** 4s. blue 50 30

616 Vienna International Centre

1979. Opening of U.N.O. Vienna Int Centre.
1847 **616** 6s. slate 80 55

617 Eye and Blood Vessels of Diabetic

1979. 10th World Congress of International Diabetes Federation, Vienna.
1848 **617** 2s.50 multicoloured . . . 35 30

618 Stanzer Valley seen from Arlberg Road Tunnel

1979. 16th World Road Congress, Vienna.
1849 **618** 4s. multicoloured 60 40

619 Steam-driven Printing Press

1979. 175th Anniv of State Printing Works.
1850 **619** 3s. black and stone . . . 40 40

620 Richard Zsigmondy

1979. 50th Death Anniv of Dr. Richard Zsigmondy (Nobel Prize winner for Chemistry).
1851 **620** 6s. brown 80 45

621 Bregenz Festival and Congress Hall

1979. Bregenz Festival and Congress Hall.
1852 **621** 2s.50 lilac 35 35

622 Burning Match

1979. "Save Energy".
1853 **622** 2s.50 multicoloured . . . 35 25

623 Lions Emblem

1979. 25th European Lions Forum, Vienna.
1854 **623** 4s. yellow, gold and lilac 50 35

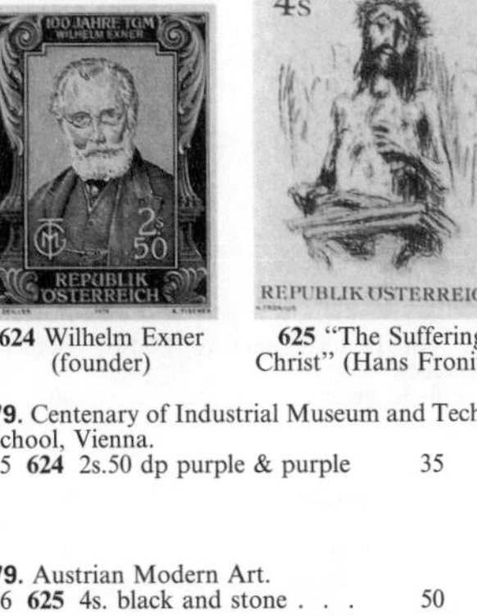

624 Wilhelm Exner (founder) **625** "The Suffering Christ" (Hans Fronius)

1979. Centenary of Industrial Museum and Technical School, Vienna.
1855 **624** 2s.50 dp purple & purple 35 30

1979. Austrian Modern Art.
1856 **625** 4s. black and stone . . . 50 40

626 Series 52 Goods Locomotive **627** August Musger

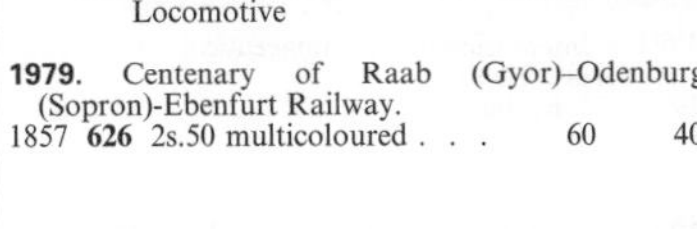

1979. Centenary of Raab (Gyor)–Odenburg (Sopron)-Ebenfurt Railway.
1857 **626** 2s.50 multicoloured . . . 60 40

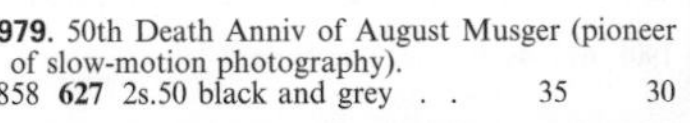

1979. 50th Death Anniv of August Musger (pioneer of slow-motion photography).
1858 **627** 2s.50 black and grey . . 35 30

628 "Nativity" (detail of icon by Moses Subotic, St. Barbara Church, Vienna)

1979. Christmas.
1859 **628** 4s. multicoloured 50 25

629 Neue Hofburg, Vienna

1979. "WIPA 1981" International Stamp Exhibition, Vienna (1st issue). Inscr "1. Phase".
1860 **629** 16s.+8s. multicoloured 3·00 3·25
See also No. 1890.

630 Arms of Baden **631** Loading Exports

1980. 500th Anniv of Baden.
1861 **630** 4s. multicoloured 50 35

1980. Austrian Exports.
1862 **631** 4s. blue, red and black 50 35

632 Rheumatic Hand holding Stick

1980. Fight against Rheumatism.
1863 **632** 2s.50 red and blue . . . 40 30

633 Emblems of 1880 and 1980

1980. Centenary of Austrian Red Cross.
1864 **633** 2s.50 multicoloured . . . 40 25

634 Kirchschlager **635** Robert Hamerling

1980. Pres. Rudolf Kirchschlager's 65th Birthday.
1865 **634** 4s. brown and red . . . 50 40

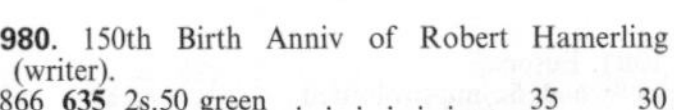

1980. 150th Birth Anniv of Robert Hamerling (writer).
1866 **635** 2s.50 green 35 30

636 Town Seal **637** "Maria Theresa as a Young Woman" (Andreas Moller)

1980. 750th Anniv of Hallein.
1867 **636** 4s. black and red 50 40

1980. Death Bicentenary of Empress Maria Theresa.
1868 **637** 2s.50 purple 65 35
1869 – 4s. blue . . . . 1·00 55
1870 – 6s. brown . . . . 1·50 90
DESIGNS: 4s. "Maria Theresa with St. Stephen's Crown" (Martin van Meytens); 6s. "Maria Theresa as Widow" (Joseph Ducreux).

638 Flags of Treaty Signatories **639** St. Benedict (statue, Meinrad Guggenbichler)

1980. 25th Anniv of Austrian State Treaty.
1871 **638** 4s. multicoloured 50 35

1980. Congress of Austrian Benedictine Orders, Mariazell.
1872 **639** 2s.50 green 35 30

640 "Hygieia" (Gustav Klimt) **641** Dish Aerial, Aflenz

1980. 175th Anniv of Hygiene Education.
1873 **640** 4s. multicoloured 50 35

1980. Inauguration of Aflenz Satellite Communications Earth Station.
1874 **641** 6s. multicoloured 80 45

642 Steyr (copperplate engraving, 1693)

1980. Millenary of Steyr.
1875 **642** 4s. brown, black & gold 60 35

643 Oil Driller **644** Town Seal of 1267

1980. 50th Anniv of Oil Production in Austria.
1876 **643** 2s.50 multicoloured . . . 35 30

1980. 800th Anniv of Innsbruck.
1877 **644** 2s.50 yellow, blk & red 35 30

645 Ducal Crown

1980. 800th Anniv of Elevation of Styria to Dukedom.
1878 **645** 4s. multicoloured 50 35

646 Leo Ascher

647 "Abraham" (illustration from "Viennese Genesis")

1980. Birth Cent of Leo Ascher (composer).
1879 **646** 3s. violet 65 40

1980. 10th Congress of International Organization for Study of the Old Testament.
1880 **647** 4s. multicoloured 50 40

648 Robert Stolz

649 Falkenstein Railway Bridge

1980. Europa and Birth Centenary of Robert Stolz (composer).
1881 **648** 6s. red . . . . 1·00 70

1980. 11th International Association of Bridge and Structural Engineering Congress, Vienna.
1882 **649** 4s. multicoloured 50 40

650 "Moon Figure" (Karl Brandstatter)

651 Customs Officer

1980. Austrian Modern Art.
1883 **650** 4s. multicoloured 50 40

1980. 150th Anniv of Customs Service.
1884 **651** 2s.50 brown and red . . 35 30

652 Masthead of 1810

1980. 350th Anniv of "Linzer Zeitung" (Linz newspaper).
1885 **652** 2s.50 black, red & gold 35 30

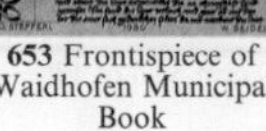

653 Frontispiece of Waidhofen Municipal Book

654 Heads

1980. 750th Anniv of Waidhofen.
1886 **653** 2s.50 multicoloured . . . 40 30

1980. 25th Anniv of Federal Army.
1887 **654** 2s.50 green and red . . . 35 25

655 Alfred Wegener

656 Robert Musil

1980. Birth Centenary of Alfred Wegener (explorer and geophysicist).
1888 **655** 4s. blue 50 35

1980. Birth Centenary of Robert Musil (writer).
1889 **656** 4s. brown 50 40

1980. "WIPA 1981" International Stamp Exhibition, Vienna (2nd issue). Inscr "2. Phase".
1890 **629** 16s.+8s. mult . . . . . 3·00 3·25

657 "Adoration of the Kings" (stained-glass window, Viktring Collegiate Church)

658 Ribbon in National Colours

1980. Christmas.
1891 **657** 4s. multicoloured 50 25

1981. 25th Anniv of General Social Insurance Act.
1892 **658** 2s.50 red, green & black 35 25

659 Unissued Design for 1926 Child Welfare Stamps

660 Disabled Person operating Machine Tool

1981. Birth Centenary of Wilhelm Dachauer (artist).
1894 **659** 3s. brown 40 25

1981. 3rd European Regional Conference of Rehabilitation International.
1895 **660** 6s. brown, blue and red 80 60

661 Sigmund Freud

662 Long-distance Heating System

1981. 125th Birth Anniv of Sigmund Freud (psychoanalyst).
1896 **661** 3s. purple 40 35

1981. 20th International Union of Long-distance Heat Distributors Congress, Vienna.
1897 **662** 4s. multicoloured 50 40

663 "Azzo and his Vassals" (cover of Monastery's "bearskin" Manuscript)

664 Maypole

1981. Kuenring Exhibition, Zwettl Monastery.
1898 **663** 3s. multicoloured 40 30

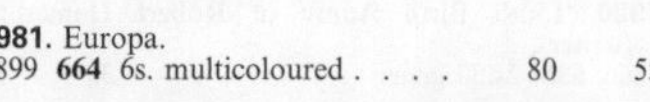

1981. Europa.
1899 **664** 6s. multicoloured 80 55

665 Early Telephone

1981. Centenary of Austrian Telephone System.
1900 **665** 4s. multicoloured 50 40

666 "The Frog King"

1981. Art Education in Schools.
1901 **666** 3s. multicoloured 50 30

667 Research Centre

1981. 25th Anniv of Seibersdorf Research Centre.
1902 **667** 4s. blue, dp blue & orge 60 40

668 Town Hall and Seal

669 Johann Florian Heller (chemist)

1981. 850th Anniv of St. Veit-on-Glan.
1903 **668** 4s. yellow, brown & red 50 40

1981. 11th Int Clinical Chemistry Congress, Vienna.
1904 **669** 6s. brown 80 55

670 Boltzmann

671 Otto Bauer

1981. 75th Death Anniv of Ludwig Boltzmann (physicist).
1905 **670** 3s. green 40 30

1981. Birth Centenary of Otto Bauer (writer and politician).
1906 **671** 4s. multicoloured 50 35

672 Chemical Balance

673 Impossible Construction (M. C. Escher)

1981. International Pharmaceutical Federation Congress, Vienna.
1907 **672** 6s. black, brown and red 80 45

1981. 10th International Austrian Mathematicians' Congress, Innsbruck.
1908 **673** 4s. lt blue, blue & dp blue 50 40

674 "Coronation of Virgin Mary" (detail)

675 Compass Rose

1981. 500th Anniv of Michael Pacher's Altarpiece at St. Wolfgang, Abersee.
1909 **674** 3s. blue 45 30

1981. 75th Anniv of Graz S.E. Exhibition.
1910 **675** 4s. multicoloured 50 45

676 "Holy Trinity" (illuminated MS, 12th century)

1981. 16th International Congress of Byzantine Scholars, Vienna.
1911 **676** 6s. multicoloured 80 45

677 Josef II

678 Hans Kelsen

1981. Bicentenary of Toleration Act (giving freedom of worship to Protestants).
1912 **677** 4s. black, blue & bistre 50 45

1981. Bicentenary of Hans Kelsen (law lecturer and contributor to shaping of Austrian Constitution).
1913 **678** 3s. red 40 30

679 Full and Empty Bowls and F.A.O. Emblem

1981. World Food Day.
1914 **679** 6s. multicoloured 80 55

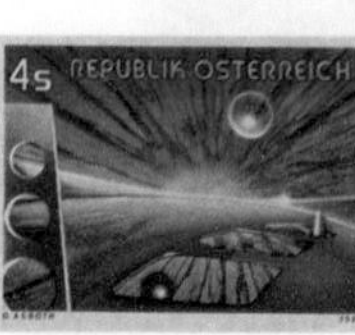

680 "Between the Times" (Oscar Asboth)

681 Workers and Emblem

1981. Austrian Modern Art.
1915 **680** 4s. multicoloured 50 40

1981. 7th International Catholic Employees' Meeting, Vienna-Lainz.
1916 **681** 3s. multicoloured 40 30

682 Hammer-Purgstall

1981. 125th Death Anniv of Josef Hammer-Purgstall (orientalist).
1917 **682** 3s. multicoloured 40 30

683 Julius Raab   684 Stefan Zweig

1981. 90th Birth Anniv of Julius Raab (politician).
1918 **683** 6s. purple 80 45

1981. Birth Centenary of Stefan Zweig (writer).
1919 **684** 4s. lilac 50 40

685 Christmas Crib, Burgenland

1981. Christmas.
1920 **685** 4s. multicoloured 50 40

686 Arms of St. Nikola

1981. 800th Anniv of St. Nikola-on-Danube.
1921 **686** 4s. multicoloured 50 45

687 Volkswagen Transporter Ambulance

1981. Cent of Vienna's Emergency Medical Service.
1922 **687** 3s. multicoloured 40 30

688 Skier   689 Dorotheum Building

1982. Alpine Skiing World Championship, Schladming-Haus.
1923 **688** 4s. multicoloured 50 40

1982. 275th Anniv of Dorotheum Auction, Pawn and Banking Society.
1924 **689** 4s. multicoloured 50 40

690 Lifesaving   691 St. Severin

1982. 25th Anniv of Austrian Water Lifesaving Service.
1925 **690** 5s. blue, red & light blue 65 55

1982. "St. Severin and the End of the Roman Period" Exhibition, Enns.
1926 **691** 3s. multicoloured 40 30

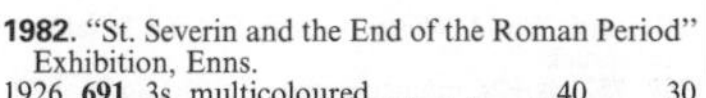

692 Sebastian Kneipp (pioneer of holistic medicine)   693 Printers' Coat-of-arms

1982. International Kneipp Congress, Vienna.
1927 **692** 4s. multicoloured 50 40

1982. 500th Anniv of Printing in Austria.
1928 **693** 4s. multicoloured 50 40

694 Urine Analysis from "Canon Medicinae" by Avicenna   695 St. Francis preaching to Animals (miniature)

1982. 5th European Union for Urology Congress, Vienna.
1929 **694** 6s. multicoloured 80 70

1982. "Franciscan Art and Culture in the Middle Ages" Exhibition, Krems-Stein.
1930 **695** 3s. multicoloured 40 30

696 Haydn and Birthplace, Rohrau   697 Globe within Milk Churn

1982. "Joseph Haydn and His Time" Exhibition, Eisenstadt.
1931 **696** 3s. green 65 40

1982. World Dairying Day.
1932 **697** 7s. multicoloured 80 70

698 Town Arms (1804 flag)   699 Tennis Player

1982. 800th Anniv of Gfohl.
1933 **698** 4s. multicoloured 50 40

1982. 80th Anniv of Austrian Lawn Tennis Assn.
1934 **699** 3s. multicoloured 40 35

700 Main Square, Langenlois   701 Town Arms

1982. 900th Anniv of Langenlois.
1935 **700** 4s. multicoloured 50 45

1982. 800th Anniv of Weiz.
1936 **701** 4s. multicoloured 45 40

702 Linz–Freistadt–Budweis Horse-drawn Railway

1982. Europa.
1937 **702** 6s. brown 85 70

703 Ignaz Seipel   704 Postbus

1982. 50th Death Anniv of Ignaz Seipel (Federal Chancellor).
1938 **703** 3s. purple 35 30

1982. 75th Anniv of Post-bus Service.
1939 **704** 4s. multicoloured 65 40

705 Rocket Launch

1982. Second U.N. Conference on the Exploration and Peaceful Uses of Outer Space, Vienna.
1940 **705** 4s. multicoloured 50 40

706 Globe (Federal Office for Standardization and Surveying, Vienna)

1982. Geodesists' Day.
1941 **706** 3s. multicoloured 40 30

707 Great Bustard ("Grosstrappe")

1982. Endangered Animals. Multicoloured.
1942 3s. Type **707** 60 50
1943 4s. Eurasian beaver 65 65
1944 6s. Western capercaillie ("Auerhahn") 90 95

708 Institute Building, Laxenburg

1982. 10th Anniv of International Institute for Applied Systems Analysis.
1945 **708** 3s. black and brown . . 40 30

709 St. Apollonia (patron saint of dentists)

1982. 70th International Dentists Federation Congress, Vienna.
1946 **709** 4s. multicoloured 50 40

710 Emmerich Kalman   711 Max Mell

1982. Birth Cent of Emmerich Kalman (composer).
1947 **710** 3s. blue 65 40

1982. Birth Centenary of Max Mell (writer).
1948 **711** 3s. multicoloured 40 30

712 Christmas Crib, Damuls Church   713 Aerial View of Bosphorus

1982. Christmas.
1949 **712** 4s. multicoloured 50 40

1982. Centenary of St. George's Austrian College, Istanbul.
1950 **713** 4s. multicoloured 50 40

714 "Mainz-Weber" Mailbox, 1870

1982. Stamp Day.
1951 **714** 6s.+3s. multicoloured . . 1·20 1·40

715 "Muse of the Republic" (Ernst Fuchs)   716 Bank, Vienna

1982. Austrian Modern Art.
1952 **715** 4s. red and violet 50 45

1983. Centenary of Postal Savings Bank.
1953 **716** 4s. yellow, black and blue 50 40

717 Hildegard Burjan

1983. Birth Centenary of Hildegard Burjan (founder of Caritas Socialis (religious sisterhood)).
1954 **717** 4s. red 50 40

718 Linked Arms

1983. World Communications Year.
1955 **718** 7s. multicoloured 80 70

719 Young Girl **720** Josef Matthias Hauer

1983. 75th Anniv of Children's Friends Organization.
1956 **719** 4s. black, blue and red 50 40

1983. Birth Centenary of Josef Matthias Hauer (composer).
1957 **720** 3s. purple 50 40

721 Douglas DC-9-80 Super Eighty

1983. 25th Anniv of Austrian Airlines.
1958 **721** 6s. multicoloured 80 60

722 Hands protecting Workers

1983. Cent of Government Work Inspection Law.
1959 **722** 4s. grn, dp grn & brn . . 50 40

723 Wels (engraving, Matthaeus Merian)

1983. "Millenary of Upper Austria" Exn, Wels.
1960 **723** 3s. multicoloured 40 30

724 Human Figure, Heart and Electrocardiogram **725** Monastery Arms

1983. 7th World Symposium on Pacemakers.
1961 **724** 4s. red, mauve and blue 60 50

1983. 900th Anniv of Gottweig Monastery.
1962 **725** 3s. multicoloured 40 30

726 Weitra

1983. 800th Anniv of Weitra.
1963 **726** 4s. black, red and gold 60 40

727 Cap, Stick, Ribbon and Emblems

1983. 50th Anniv of MKV and CCV Catholic Students' Organizations.
1964 **727** 4s. multicoloured 55 40

728 Glopper Castle and Town Arms **729** Hess

1983. 650th Anniv of Hohenems Town Charter.
1965 **728** 4s. multicoloured 55 40

1983. Europa. Birth Centenary of Viktor Franz Hess (physicist and Nobel Prize winner).
1966 **729** 6s. green 80 70

730 Vienna City Hall **731** Kiwanis Emblem and View of Vienna

1983. 25th Anniv of Vienna City Hall.
1967 **730** 4s. multicoloured 55 40

1983. Kiwanis International, World and European Conference, Vienna.
1968 **731** 5s. multicoloured 60 55

732 Congress Emblem **733** Hasenauer and Natural History Museum, Vienna

1983. 7th World Psychiatry Congress, Vienna.
1969 **732** 4s. multicoloured 55 40

1983. 150th Birth Anniv of Carl Freiherr von Hasenauer (architect).
1970 **733** 3s. brown 40 30

734 Institute for Promotion of Trade and Industry, Linz

1983. 27th International Professional Competition for Young Skilled Workers, Linz.
1971 **734** 4s. multicoloured 55 40

735 Symbols of Penicillin V Efficacy and Cancer **736** Pope John Paul II

1983. 13th Int Chemotherapy Congress, Vienna.
1972 **735** 5s. red and green 70 60

1983. Papal Visit.
1973 **736** 6s. black, red and gold 90 70

737 "Relief of Vienna, 1683" (Franz Geffels)

1983. 300th Anniv of Relief of Vienna. Sheet 90 × 70 mm.
MS1974 **737** 6s. multicoloured . . 1·00 1·00

738 Spectrum around Cross **739** Vienna Town Hall

1983. Austrian Catholics' Day.
1975 **738** 3s. multicoloured 40 30

1983. Centenary of Vienna Town Hall.
1976 **739** 4s. multicoloured 60 40

740 Karl von Terzaghi

1983. Birth Centenary of Karl von Terzaghi (soil mechanics and foundations engineer).
1977 **740** 3s. blue 40 30

741 Initials of Federation

1983. 10th Austrian Trade Unions Federation Congress.
1978 **741** 3s. red and black 40 30

742 "Evening Sun in Burgenland" (Gottfried Kumpf) **743** Tram No. 5, 1883

1983. Austrian Modern Art.
1979 **742** 4s. multicoloured 60 55

1983. Centenary of Modling–Hinterbruhl Electric Railway.
1980 **743** 3s. multicoloured 60 40

744 Boy looking at Stamped Envelope

1983. Stamp Day.
1981 **744** 6s.+3s. multicoloured . . 1·30 1·50

745 Francisco Carolinum Museum, Linz

1983. 150th Anniv of Upper Austrian Provincial Museum.
1982 **745** 4s. multicoloured 55 40

746 Crib by Johann Giner the Elder, Kitzbuhel Church

1983. Christmas.
1983 **746** 4s. multicoloured 70 40

747 Parliament Building **748** "St. Nicholas" (Maria Freund)

1983. Centenary of Parliament Building, Vienna.
1984 **747** 4s. blue 55 40

1983. Youth Stamp.
1985 **748** 3s. multicoloured 40 30

749 Wolfgang Pauli

1983. 25th Death Anniv of Wolfgang Pauli (Nobel Prize winner for Physics).
1986 **749** 6s. brown 80 55

750 Gregor Mendel

1984. Death Cent of Gregor Mendel (geneticist).
1987 **750** 4s. ochre and brown . . 55 35

751 Hanak at Work

1984. 50th Death Anniv of Anton Hanak (sculptor).
1988 **751** 3s. brown and black . . 40 30

752 Disabled Skier

1984. 3rd World Winter Games for the Disabled, Innsbruck.
1989 **752** 4s.+2s. multicoloured . . 80 1·00

753 Memorial, Wollersdorf

1984. 50th Anniv of 1934 Insurrections.
1990 **753** 4s.50 red and black . . . 55 40

754 Founders' Stone **755** Geras Monastery

1984. 900th Anniv of Reichersberg Monastery.
1991 **754** 3s.50 stone, brown & bl 45 35

1984. Monasteries and Abbeys.

1992	–	50g. yellow, black & grey	15	25
1993	–	1s. yellow, black & mve	15	15
1994	–	1s.50 yellow, red & blue	25	25
1995	–	2s. yellow, green & black	35	25
1996	**755**	3s.50 yellow, sep & brn	45	15
1997	–	4s. yellow, purple & red	65	15
1998	–	4s.50 yellow, lilac & blue	60	15
1999	–	5s. yellow, purple & orge	70	15
2000	–	5s.50 yell, dp vio & vio	1·00	30
2001	–	6s. yellow, green & emer	90	15
2002	–	7s. yellow, green & blue	95	20
2003	–	7s.50 yell, dp brn & brn	1·00	35
2004	–	8s. yellow, blue and red	1·10	35
2005	–	10s. yellow, red & grey	1·40	25
2006	–	11s. yellow, black & brn	1·50	55
2007	–	12s. yellow, brn & orge	1·60	1·00
2008	–	17s. yellow, ultram & bl	2·30	75
2009	–	20s. yellow, brown & red	3·00	1·20

DESIGNS: 50g. Vorau Monastery; 1s. Wettingen Abbey, Mehrerau; 1s.50, Monastery of Teutonic Order, Vienna; 2s. Michaelbeuern Benedictine Monastery, Salzburg; 4s. Stams Monastery; 4s.50, Schlagl Monastery; 5s. St. Paul's Monastery, Lavanttal; 5s.50, St. Gerold's Priory, Vorarlberg; 6s. Rein Monastery; 7s. Loretto Monastery; 7s.50, Dominican Monastery, Vienna; 8s. Cistercian Monastery, Zwettl; 10s. Premonstratensian Monastery, Wilten; 11s. Trappist Monastery, Engelszell; 12s. Monastery of the Hospitallers, Eisenstadt; 17s. St. Peter's Abbey, Salzburg; 20s. Wernberg Convent, Carinthia.

756 Cigar Band showing Tobacco Plant **757** Kostendorf

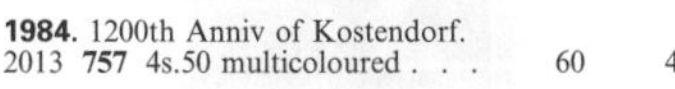

1984. Bicentenary of Tobacco Monopoly.
2012 **756** 4s.50 multicoloured . . . 60 40

1984. 1200th Anniv of Kostendorf.
2013 **757** 4s.50 multicoloured . . . 60 40

758 Wheel Bearing

1984. 20th International Federation of Automobile Engineers' Associations World Congress, Vienna.
2014 **758** 5s. multicoloured 70 55

759 Bridge **760** Archduke Johann (after Schnorr von Carolsfeld)

1984. Europa. 25th Anniv of E.P.T. Conference.
2015 **759** 6s. blue and ultramarine 80 50

1984. 125th Death Anniv of Archduke Johann.
2016 **760** 4s.50 multicoloured . . . 60 40

761 Aragonite **762** Binding of "Das Buch vom Kaiser", by Max Herzig

1984. "Ore and Iron in the Green Mark" Exhibition, Eisenerz.
2017 **761** 3s.50 multicoloured . . . 45 35

1984. Lower Austrian "Era of Emperor Franz Joseph: From Revolution to Grunderzeit" Exhibition, Grafenegg Castle.
2018 **762** 3s.50 red and gold . . . 55 40

763 Upper City Tower and Arms **764** Dionysus (Virunum mosaic)

1984. 850th Anniv of Vocklabruch.
2019 **763** 4s.50 multicoloured . . . 60 40

1984. Centenary of Carinthia Provincial Museum, Klagenfurt.
2020 **764** 3s.50 stone, brn & grey 45 35

765 "Meeting of Austrian Army with South Tyrolean Reserves" (detail, Schnorr von Carolsfeld) **766** Ralph Benatzky

1984. "Jubilee of Tyrol Province" Exhibition.
2021 **765** 3s.50 multicoloured . . . 45 35

1984. Birth Cent of Ralph Benatzky (composer).
2022 **766** 4s. brown 80 55

767 Flood Control Barriers **768** Christian von Ehrenfels

1984. Centenary of Flood Control Systems.
2023 **767** 4s.50 green 60 50

1984. 125th Death Anniv of Christian von Ehrenfels (philosopher).
2024 **768** 3s.50 multicoloured . . . 45 35

769 Models of European Monuments

1984. 25th Anniv of Minimundus (model world), Worthersee.
2025 **769** 4s. yellow and black . . 55 40

770 Blockheide Eibenstein National Park

1984. Natural Beauty Spots.
2026 **770** 4s. pink and olive . . . 70 55

771 Electric Train on Schanatobel Bridge (Arlberg Railway Centenary)

1984. Railway Anniversaries.
2027 **771** 3s.50 brown, gold & red 70 55
2028 – 4s.50 blue, silver and red 75 55
DESIGN: 4s.50, Electric train on Falkenstein Bridge (75th anniv of Tauern Railway).

772 Johann Georg Stuwer's Ascent in Montgolfier Balloon

1984. Bicentenary of First Manned Balloon Flight in Austria.
2029 **772** 6s. multicoloured 80 60

773 Lake Neusiedl

1984. Natural Beauty Spots.
2030 **773** 4s. purple and blue . . . 75 55

774 Palace of Justice, Vienna **775** "Joseph Hyrtl" (window, Innsbruck Anatomy Institute)

1984. 20th Int Bar Assn Congress, Vienna.
2031 **774** 7s. multicoloured 80 70

1984. 7th European Anatomists' Congress, Innsbruck.
2032 **775** 6s. multicoloured 80 60

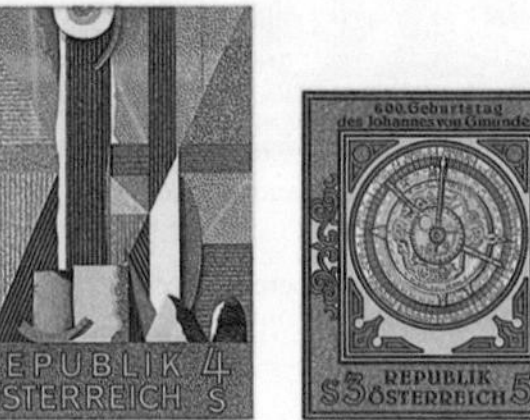

776 "Window" (Karl Korab) **777** Clock of Imms (astrolabe)

1984. Austrian Modern Art.
2033 **776** 4s. multicoloured 60 40

1984. 600th Birth Anniv of Johannes von Gmunden (astronomer and mathematician).
2034 **777** 3s.50 multicoloured . . . 45 40

778 Quill **779** Fanny Elssler

1984. 125th Anniv of Concordia Press Club.
2035 **778** 4s.50 black, gold & red 55 40

1984. Death Centenary of Fanny Elssler (dancer).
2036 **779** 4s. multicoloured 55 40

780 "Holy Family" (detail, Aggsbach Old High Altar)

1984. Christmas.
2037 **780** 4s.50 multicoloured . . . 60 40

781 Detail from Burial Chamber Wall of Seschemnofer III **782** Coat of Arms

1984. Stamp Day.
2038 **781** 6s.+3s. multicoloured . . 1·30 1·50

1985. 400th Anniv of Graz University.
2039 **782** 3s.50 multicoloured . . . 45 40

783 Dr. Lorenz Bohler

1985. Birth Centenary of Prof. Dr. Lorenz Bohler (surgeon).
2040 **783** 4s.50 purple 55 40

784 Ski Jumping, Skiing and Emblem

1985. World Nordic Skiing Championship, Seefeld.
2041 **784** 4s. multicoloured 60 40

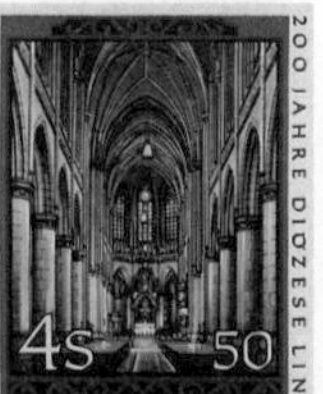

785 Linz Cathedral **786** Alban Berg

1985. Bicentenary of Linz Diocese.
2042 **785** 4s.50 multicoloured . . . 70 50

1985. Birth Centenary of Alban Berg (composer).
2043 **786** 6s. blue . . . . 1·10 75

787 Institute Emblem **788** Stylized "B" and Clouds

1985. 25th Anniv of Institute for Vocational Advancement.
2044 **787** 4s.50 multicoloured . . . 55 40

1985. 2000th Anniv of Bregenz.
2045 **788** 4s. black, ultram & blue 45 45

789 1885 Registration Label **790** Josef Stefan

1985. Centenary of Registration Labels in Austria.
2046 **789** 4s.50 black, yell & grey 60 40

1985. 150th Birth Anniv of Josef Stefan (physicist).
2047 **790** 6s. brown, stone and red 80 60

791 St. Leopold (Margrave and patron saint) **792** "The Story-teller"

1985. Lower Austrian Provincial Exhibition, Klosterneuburg Monastery.
2048 **791** 3s.50 multicoloured . . . 55 40

1985. 150th Birth Anniv of Franz Defregger (artist).
2049 **792** 3s.50 multicoloured . . . 55 40

793 Barbed Wire, Broken Tree and New Shoot **794** Johann Joseph Fux (composer)

1985. 40th Anniv of Liberation.
2050 **793** 4s.50 multicoloured . . . 60 55

1985. Europa. Music Year.
2051 **794** 6s. brown and grey . . . 1·20 75

795 Flags and Caduceus **797** Bishop's Gate, St. Polten

796 Town and Arms

1985. 25th Anniv of European Free Trade Association.
2052 **795** 4s. multicoloured 60 55

1985. Millenary of Boheimkirchen.
2053 **796** 4s.50 multicoloured . . . 60 55

1985. Bicentenary of St. Polten Diocese.
2054 **797** 4s.50 multicoloured . . . 60 40

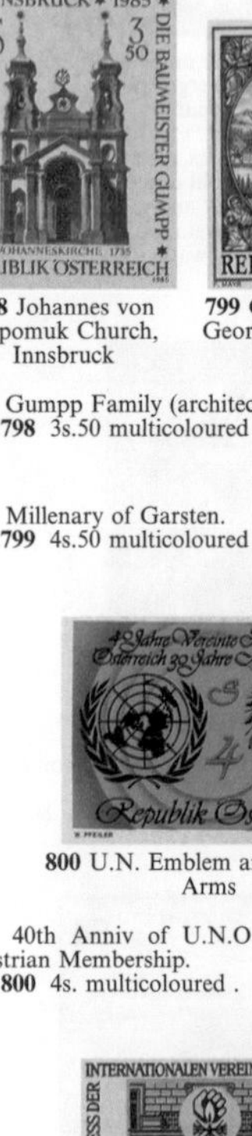

798 Johannes von Nepomuk Church, Innsbruck **799** Garsten (copperplate, George Matthaus Fischer)

1985. Gumpp Family (architects) Exn, Innsbruck.
2055 **798** 3s.50 multicoloured . . . 55 40

1985. Millenary of Garsten.
2056 **799** 4s.50 multicoloured . . . 70 55

800 U.N. Emblem and Austrian Arms

1985. 40th Anniv of U.N.O. and 30th Anniv of Austrian Membership.
2057 **800** 4s. multicoloured 60 55

801 Association Headquarters, Vienna

1985. 13th International Suicide Prevention Association Congress, Vienna.
2058 **801** 5s. brown, lt yell & yell 70 55

802 Woodland

1985. Forestry Year. Sheet 90 × 70 mm.
MS2059 **802** 6s. multicoloured . . 1·10 1·10

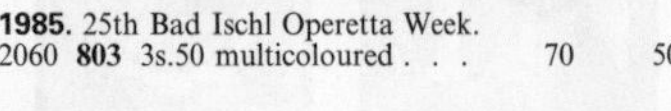

803 Operetta Emblem and Spa Building **804** Fireman and Emblem

1985. 25th Bad Ischl Operetta Week.
2060 **803** 3s.50 multicoloured . . . 70 50

1985. 8th International Fire Brigades Competition, Vocklabruck.
2061 **804** 4s.50 black, green & red 95 65

805 Grossglockner Mountain Road

1985. 50th Anniv of Grossglockner Mountain Road.
2062 **805** 4s. multicoloured 60 45

806 Chessboard as Globe **807** "Founding of Konigstetten" (August Stephan)

1985. World Chess Association Congress, Graz.
2063 **806** 4s. multicoloured 70 45

1985. Millenary of Konigstetten.
2064 **807** 4s.50 multicoloured . . . 70 45

808 Webern Church and Arms of Hofkirchen and Taufkircher

1985. 1200th Anniversaries of Hofkirchen, Weibern and Taufkirchen.
2065 **808** 4s.50 multicoloured . . . 70 55

809 Dr. Adam Politzer

1985. 150th Birth Anniv of Dr. Adam Politzer (otologist).
2066 **809** 3s.50 violet 45 40

810 Emblem and View of Vienna

1985. International Association of Forwarding Agents World Congress, Vienna.
2067 **810** 6s. multicoloured 75 60

811 "Clowns Riding High Bicycles" (Paul Flora)

1985. Austrian Modern Art.
2068 **811** 4s. multicoloured 80 60

812 St. Martin, Patron Saint of Burgenland

1985. 25th Anniv of Eisenstadt Diocese.
2069 **812** 4s.50 black, bistre & red 70 50

813 Roman Mounted Courier

1985. 50th Anniv of Stamp Day.
2070 **813** 6s.+3s. multicoloured . . 1·40 1·60

814 Hanns Horbiger **815** "Adoration of the Christ Child" (marble relief)

1985. 125th Birth Anniv of Hanns Horbiger (design engineer).
2071 **814** 3s.50 purple and gold . . 45 40

1985. Christmas.
2072 **815** 4s.50 multicoloured . . . 70 30

816 Aqueduct

1985. 75th Anniv of Second Vienna Waterline.
2073 **816** 3s.50 black, red & blue 45 40

818 Chateau de la Muette (headquarters)

1985. 25th Anniv of Organization of Economic Co-operation and Development.
2080 **818** 4s. black, gold & mauve 55 40

819 Johann Bohm

1986. Birth Centenary of Johann Bohm (founder of Austrian Trade Unions Federation).
2081 **819** 4s.50 black and red . . . 60 45

820 Dove and Globe

1986. International Peace Year.
2082 **820** 6s. multicoloured 80 60

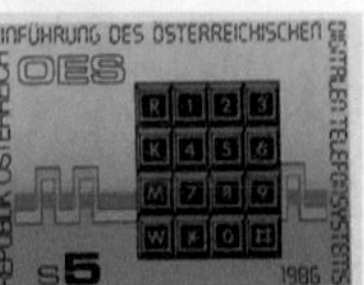

821 Push-button Dialling

1986. Introduction of Digital Preselection Telephone System.
2083 **821** 5s. multicoloured 70 45

822 Albrechtsberger and Organ

1986. 250th Birth Anniv of Johann Georg Albrechtsberger (composer).
2084 **822** 3s.50 multicoloured . . . 80 45

823 Main Square and Arms

1986. 850th Anniv of Korneuburg.
2085 **823** 5s. multicoloured 70 45

824 Kokoschka (self-portrait) 825 Council Flag

1986. Birth Centenary of Oskar Kokoschka (artist).
2086 **824** 4s. black and pink . . . 55 40

1986. 30th Anniv of Membership of Council of Europe.
2087 **825** 6s. black, red and blue 80 60

826 Holzmeister and Salzburg Festival Hall

1986. Birth Centenary of Professor Clemens Holzmeister (architect).
2088 **826** 4s. grey, brown & lt brn 55 40

827 Road, Roll of Material, and Congress Emblem

1986. 3rd International Geotextile Congress, Vienna.
2089 **827** 5s. multicoloured 70 50

828 Schlosshof Palace (after Bernardo Bellotto) and Prince Eugene

1986. "Prince Eugene and the Baroque Era" Exhibition, Schlosshof and Niederweiden.
2090 **828** 4s. multicoloured 60 45

829 St. Florian Monastery

1986. Upper Austrian "World of Baroque" Exhibition, St. Florian Monastery.
2091 **829** 4s. multicoloured 60 45

830 Herberstein Castle and Styrian Arms

1986. "Styria – Bridge and Bulwark" Exhibition, Herberstein Castle, near Stubenberg.
2092 **830** 4s. multicoloured 60 45

831 Large Pasque Flower

1986. Europa.
2093 **831** 6s. multicoloured . . . . 1·00 75

832 Wagner and Scene from Opera "Lohengrin"

1986. International Richard Wagner (composer) Congress, Vienna.
2094 **832** 4s. multicoloured 95 60

833 Antimonite Crystal

1986. Burgenland "Mineral and Fossils" Exhibition, Oberpullendorf.
2095 **833** 4s. multicoloured 60 55

834 Martinswall, Zirl

1986. Natural Beauty Spots.
2096 **834** 5s. brown and blue . . . 80 60

835 Waidhofen

1986. 800th Anniv of Waidhofen on Ybbs.
2097 **835** 4s. multicoloured 55 50

836 Tschauko Falls, Ferlach

1986. Natural Beauty Spots.
2098 **836** 5s. green and brown . . 80 60

837 19th-century Steam and Modern Articulated Trams

1986. Cent of Salzburg Local Transport System.
2099 **837** 4s. multicoloured 95 60

838 Enns and Seals of Signatories

1986. 800th Anniv of Georgenberg Treaty (between Duke Leopold V of Austria and Duke Otakar IV of Styria).
2100 **838** 5s. multicoloured 70 55

839 Tandler 840 "Observatory, 1886" (A. Heilmann)

1986. 50th Death Anniv of Julius Tandler (social reformer).
2101 **839** 4s. multicoloured 55 40

1986. Centenary of Sonnblick Observatory.
2102 **840** 4s. black, blue and gold 55 40

841 Man collecting Mandragora (from "Codex Tacuinum Sanitatis") 842 Fire Assistant

1986. 7th European Anaesthesia Congress, Vienna.
2103 **841** 5s. multicoloured 70 45

1986. 300th Anniv of Vienna Fire Brigade.
2104 **842** 4s. multicoloured 80 60

843 Stoessl 844 Viennese Hunting Tapestry (detail)

1986. 50th Death Anniv of Otto Stoessl (writer).
2105 **843** 4s. multicoloured 55 45

1986. 5th International Oriental Carpets and Tapestry Conference, Vienna and Budapest.
2106 **844** 5s. multicoloured 70 55

845 Minister in Pulpit 846 "Decomposition" (Walter Schmogner)

1986. 125th Anniv of Protestants Act and 25th Anniv of Protestants Law.
2107 **845** 5s. black and violet . . . 70 55

1986. Austrian Modern Art.
2108 **846** 4s. multicoloured 60 45

847 Liszt, Birthplace and Score

1986. 175th Birth Anniv of Franz Liszt (composer).
2109 **847** 5s. green and brown . . 1·10 65

848 Aerial View of Vienna (½-size illustration)

1986. European Security and Co-operation Conference Review Meeting, Vienna. Sheet 90 × 70 mm.
MS2110 **848** 6s. multicoloured . . 1·00 1·00

849 Strettweg Religious Carriage

1986. 175th Anniv of Styrian Joanneum Museum.
2111 **849** 4s. multicoloured 60 45

850 "Nuremberg Letter Messenger" (16th century woodcut) 852 Headquarters

851 "Adoration of the Shepherds" (woodcut, Johann Georg Schwanthaler)

1986. Stamp Day.
2112 **850** 6s.+3s. multicoloured . . 1·40 1·60

1986. Christmas.
2113 **851** 5s. brown and gold . . . 75 45

1986. 40th Anniv of Federal Chamber of Trade and Industry.
2114 **852** 5s. multicoloured 70 55

853 Foundry Worker

1986. Austrian World of Work (1st series).
2115 **853** 4s. multicoloured 60 45
See also Nos. 2144, 2178, 2211, 2277, 2386, 2414, 2428, 2486, 2520, 2572 and 2605.

854 "The Educated Eye"

1987. Centenary of Adult Education in Vienna.
2116 **854** 5s. multicoloured 70 55

855 "Large Blue Madonna" (Anton Faistauer)

1987. Painters' Birth Centenaries. Multicoloured.
2117 4s. Type **855** 70 45
2118 6s. "Self-portrait" (Albert Paris Gutersloh) 80 70

856 Hundertwasser House, Vienna

1987. Europa and "Europalia 1987 Austria" Festival, Belgium.
2119 **856** 6s. multicoloured . . . . 1·10 1·20

857 Ice Hockey Players

1987. World Ice Hockey Championships, Vienna, and 75th Anniv of Austrian Ice Hockey Association.
2120 **857** 5s. multicoloured 75 60

858 Austria Centre

1987. Inaug of Austria Conference Centre, Vienna.
2121 **858** 5s. multicoloured 70 55

859 Salzburg

860 Machine Shop, 1920

1987. 700th Anniv of Salzburg Town Charter.
2122 **859** 5s. multicoloured 70 55

1987. Upper Austrian "Work–Men–Machines, the Route to Industrialized Society" Exhibition, Steyr.
2123 **860** 4s. black and red 55 40

861 Man and Woman

862 "Adele Bloch-Bauer I" (detail, Gustav Klimt)

1987. Equal Rights for Men and Women.
2124 **861** 5s. multicoloured 70 55

1987. Lower Austrian "Era of Emperor Franz Joseph: Splendour and Misery" Exhibition, Grafenegg Castle.
2125 **862** 4s. multicoloured 70 55

863 Archbishop and Salzburg

1987. 400th Anniv of Election of Prince Wolf Dietrich von Raitenau as Archbishop of Salzburg.
2126 **863** 4s. multicoloured 60 40

864 Schnitzler

865 Lace and Arms

1987. 125th Birth Anniv of Arthur Schnitzler (dramatist).
2127 **864** 6s. multicoloured 80 60

1987. 1100th Anniv of Lustenau.
2128 **865** 5s. multicoloured 70 55

866 Anniversary Emblem (William Slattery)

1987. 150th Anniv of Austrian Railways. Sheet 90 × 70 mm.
MS2129 **866** 6s. silver, red and black 1·00 1·00

867 Dachstein Giant Ice Cave

1987. Natural Beauty Spots.
2130 **867** 5s. green and black . . . 95 60

868 Engraver at Work

869 Dr. Karl Josef Bayer (chemist)

1987. 8th European Association of Engravers and Flexographers International Congress, Vienna.
2131 **868** 5s. brown, pink and grey 70 55

1987. 8th International Light Metal Meeting, Leoben and Vienna.
2132 **869** 5s. multicoloured 70 55

870 Passenger Ferry

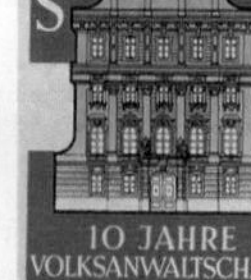

871 Office Building, Vienna

1987. Centenary of 1st Achensee Steam Service.
2133 **870** 4s. multicoloured 60 55

1987. 10th Anniv of Office of Ombudsmen.
2134 **871** 5s. black, yellow and red 70 55

872 Schrodinger

873 Freistadt Town Square

1987. Birth Cent of Erwin Schrodinger (physicist).
2135 **872** 5s. brown, cream and bistre 70 55

1987. 125th Anniv of Freistadt Exhibitions.
2136 **873** 5s. multicoloured 75 55

874 Arbing Church

1987. 850th Anniv of Arbing.
2137 **874** 5s. multicoloured 75 55

875 Gauertal and Montafon Valleys, Voralberg

1987. Natural Beauty Spots.
2138 **875** 5s. brown and yellow . . 95 55

876 Cyclist

877 Emblem

1987. World Cycling Championship, Vienna and Villach.
2139 **876** 5s. multicoloured 80 50

1987. World Congress of International Institute of Savings Banks, Vienna.
2140 **877** 5s. multicoloured 70 45

878 Hofhaymer at Organ

880 Lammergeier ("Bartgeier")

879 Haydn and Salzburg

1987. 450th Death Anniv of Paul Hofhaymer (composer and organist).
2141 **878** 4s. blue, black and gold 85 55

1987. 250th Birth Anniv of Michael Haydn (composer).
2142 **879** 4s. lilac 85 55

1987. 25th Anniv of Alpine Zoo, Innsbruck.
2143 **880** 4s. multicoloured 70 55

881 Woman using Word Processor

1987. Austrian World of Work (2nd series).
2144 **881** 4s. multicoloured 55 50

882 "Tree Goddesses" (Arnulf Neuwirth)

1987. Austrian Modern Art.
2145 **882** 5s. multicoloured 80 60

883 Lottery Wheel

884 Helmer

1987. Bicentenary of Gambling Monopoly.
2146 **883** 5s. multicoloured 70 45

1987. Birth Centenary of Oskar Helmer (politician).
2147 **884** 4s. multicoloured 55 40

885 Gluck

886 Stagecoach and Passengers (lithograph, Carl Schuster)

1987. Death Bicentenary of Christoph Willibald Gluck (composer).
2148 **885** 5s. brown and ochre . . 75 60

1987. Stamp Day.
2149 **886** 6s.+3s. multicoloured . . 1·40 1·60

887 Josef Mohr and Franz Xaver Gruber (composers of "Silent Night")

1987. Christmas.
2150 **887** 5s. multicoloured . . . . 1·00 55

888 Bosco and Boys **889** Cross-country Sledging

1988. International Educational Congress of St. John Bosco's Salesian Brothers, Vienna.
2151 **888** 5s. purple and orange . . 70 45

1988. 4th World Winter Games for the Disabled, Innsbruck.
2152 **889** 5s.+2s.50 multicoloured 1·00 1·30

890 Mach **891** "Village with Bridge"

1988. 150th Birth Anniv of Ernst Mach (physicist and philosopher).
2153 **890** 6s. multicoloured 80 60

1988. 25th Death Anniv of Franz von Zulow (artist).
2154 **891** 4s. multicoloured 60 55

892 "The Confiscation" (Ferdinand Georg Waldmuller)

1988. "Patriotism and Protest: Viennese Biedermeier and Revolution" Exhibition, Vienna.
2155 **892** 4s. multicoloured 60 55

893 Barbed Wire, Flag and Crosses

1988. 50th Anniv of Annexation of Austria by Germany.
2156 **893** 5s. green, brown and red 70 45

894 Steam Locomotive "Aigen", Muhlkreis Railway, 1887 **895** European Bee Eater

1988. Railway Centenaries. Multicoloured.
2157 4s. Type **894** 75 75
2158 5s. Modern electric tram and Josefsplatz stop (Viennese Local Railways Stock Corporation) . . . 85 60

1988. 25th Anniv of World Wildlife Fund, Austria.
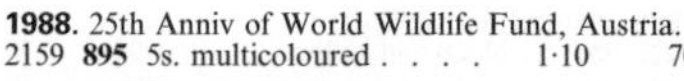
2159 **895** 5s. multicoloured . . . . 1·10 70

896 Decanter and Beaker **897** Late Gothic Silver Censer

1988. Styrian "Glass and Coal" Exn, Barnbach.

2160 **896** 4s. multicoloured 55 45

1988. Lower Austrian "Art and Monastic Life at the Birth of Austria" Exhibition, Seitenstetten Benedictine Monastery.
2161 **897** 4s. multicoloured 55 40

898 Taking Casualty to Volkswagen Transporter Ambulance and Red Cross **900** Mattsee Monastery

899 Dish Aerials, Aflenz

1988. 125th Anniv of Red Cross.
2162 **898** 12s. black, red and green 1·50 1·10

1988. Europa. Telecommunications.
2163 **899** 6s. multicoloured 80 60

1988. Salzburg "Bajuvars from Severin to Tassilo" Exhibition, Mattsee Monastery.
2164 **900** 4s. multicoloured 60 50

901 Weinberg Castle **902** Horvath

1988. Upper Austrian "Muhlviertel: Nature, Culture, Life" Exhibition, Weinberg Castle, near Kefermarkt.
2165 **901** 4s. multicoloured 55 50

1988. 50th Death Anniv of Odon von Horvath (writer).
2166 **902** 6s. black and bistre . . . 75 55

903 Stockerau Town Hall

1988. 25th Anniv of Stockerau Festival.
2167 **903** 5s. multicoloured 70 50

904 Motorway **905** Brixlegg

1988. Completion of Tauern Motorway.
2168 **904** 4s. multicoloured 55 40

1988. 1200th Anniv of Brixlegg.
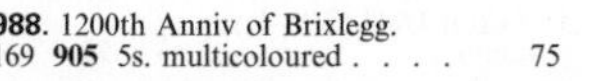
2169 **905** 5s. multicoloured 75 50

906 Klagenfurt (after Matthaus Merian)

1988. 400th Anniv of Regular Postal Services in Carinthia.
2170 **906** 5s. multicoloured 70 45

907 Parish Church and Dean's House

1988. 1200th Anniv of Brixen im Thale, Tyrol.
2171 **907** 5s. multicoloured 70 45

908 Krimml Waterfalls, Upper Tauern National Park

1988. Natural Beauty Spots.
2172 **908** 5s. black and blue . . . 95 60

909 Town Arms

1988. 1100th Anniv of Feldkirchen, Carinthia.
2173 **909** 5s. multicoloured 70 45

910 Feldbach

1988. 800th Anniv of Feldbach.
2174 **910** 5s. multicoloured 70 55

911 Ansfelden **912** Hologram of Export Emblem

1988. 1200th Anniv of Ansfelden.
2175 **911** 5s. multicoloured 70 45

1988. Federal Economic Chamber Export Congress.
2176 **912** 8s. multicoloured . . . . 2·00 2·00

913 Concert Hall

1988. 75th Anniv of Vienna Concert Hall.
2177 **913** 5s. multicoloured 70 45

914 Laboratory Assistant

1988. Austrian World of Work (3rd series).
2178 **914** 4s. multicoloured 55 55

915 "Guards" (Giselbert Hoke) **916** Schonbauer

1988. Austrian Modern Art.
2179 **915** 5s. multicoloured 70 45

1988. Birth Centenary of Dr. Leopold Schonbauer (neurosurgeon and politician).
2180 **916** 4s. multicoloured 55 50

917 Carnation **918** Loading Railway Mail Van at Pardubitz Station, 1914

1988. Cent of Austrian Social Democratic Party.
2181 **917** 4s. multicoloured 55 50

1988. Stamp Day.
2182 **918** 6s.+3s. multicoloured . . 1·40 1·60

919 "Nativity" (St. Barbara's Church, Vienna) **920** "Madonna" (Lucas Cranach)

1988. Christmas.
2183 **919** 5s. multicoloured 70 40

1989. 25th Anniv of Diocese of Innsbruck.
2184 **920** 4s. multicoloured 55 50

921 Margrave Leopold II leading Abbot Sigibold and Monks to Melk (detail of fresco, Paul Troger)

1989. 900th Anniv of Melk Benedictine Monastery.
2185 **921** 5s. multicoloured 70 45

922 Marianne Hainisch **923** Glider and Paraskier

1989. 150th Birth Anniv of Marianne Hainisch (women's rights activist).
2186 **922** 6s. multicoloured 75 55

1989. World Gliding Championships, Wiener Neustadt, and World Paraskiing Championships, Damuls.
2187 **923** 6s. multicoloured 80 60

924 "The Painting" **926** Wittgenstein

925 "Bruck an der Leitha" (17th-century engraving, Georg Vischer)

1989. 50th Death Anniv of Rudolf Jettmar (painter).
2188 **924** 5s. multicoloured 70 45

1989. 750th Anniv of Bruck an der Leitha.
2189 **925** 5s. multicoloured 70 55

1989. Birth Centenary of Ludwig Wittgenstein (philosopher).
2190 **926** 5s. multicoloured 60 45

927 Holy Trinity Church, Stadl-Paura **928** Suess (after Josef Kriehuber) and Map

1989. 250th Death Anniv of Johann Michael Prunner (architect).
2191 **927** 5s. multicoloured 70 45

1989. 75th Death Anniv of Eduard Suess (geologist and politician).
2192 **928** 6s. multicoloured 80 70

929 "Judenburg" (17th-century engraving, Georg Vischer) **930** Steam Engine (Vinzenz Prick)

1989. Upper Styrian "People, Coins, Markets" Exhibition, Judenburg.
2193 **929** 4s. multicoloured 55 55

1989. Lower Austrian "Magic of Industry" Exhibition, Pottenstein.
2194 **930** 4s. blue and gold 55 55

931 Radstadt

1989. 700th Anniv of Radstadt.
2195 **931** 5s. multicoloured 70 45

932 Wooden Salt Barge from Viechtau

1989. Europa. Children's Toys.
2196 **932** 6s. multicoloured 80 75

933 "St. Adalbero and Family before Madonna and Child" (Monastery Itinerary Book) **935** Hansa Brandenburg C-1 Mail Biplane at Vienna, 1918

934 "Gisela" (paddle-steamer)

1989. Upper Austrian "Graphic Art" Exhibition and 900th Anniv of Lambach Monastery Church.
2197 **933** 4s. multicoloured 60 55

1989. 150th Anniv of Passenger Shipping on Traunsee.
2198 **934** 5s. multicoloured 75 55

1989. Stamp Day.
2199 **935** 6s.+3s. multicoloured . . 1·20 1·50

936 St. Andra (after Matthaus Merian)

1989. 650th Anniv of St. Andra.
2200 **936** 5s. multicoloured 70 45

937 Strauss **938** Locomotive

1989. 125th Birth Anniv of Richard Strauss (composer).
2201 **937** 6s. red, brown and gold 1·00 85

1989. Centenary of Achensee Steam Rack Railway.
2202 **938** 5s. multicoloured . . . . 1·00 70

939 Parliament Building, Vienna

1989. Centenary of Interparliamentary Union.
2203 **939** 6s. multicoloured 75 60

940 Anniversary Emblem

1989. Centenary of National Insurance in Austria.
2204 **940** 5s. multicoloured 60 50

941 U.N. Building, Vienna

1989. 10th Anniv of U.N. Vienna Centre.
2205 **941** 8s. multicoloured . . . . 1·00 75

942 Lusthaus Water, Prater Woods, Vienna

1989. Natural Beauty Spots.
2206 **942** 5s. black and buff . . . 90 60

943 Wildalpen and Hammerworks

1989. 850th Anniv of Wildalpen.
2207 **943** 5s. multicoloured 70 55

944 Emblem **946** "Tree of Life" (Ernst Steiner)

945 Palace of Justice, Vienna

1989. 33rd Congress of European Organization for Quality Control, Vienna.
2208 **944** 6s. multicoloured 75 70

1989. 14th Congress of Int Assn of Criminal Law.
2209 **945** 6s. multicoloured 80 60

1989. Austrian Modern Art.
2210 **946** 5s. multicoloured 70 55

947 Bricklayer **948** Ludwig Anzengruber (150th birth anniv)

1989. Austrian World of Work (4th series).
2211 **947** 5s. multicoloured 60 55

1989. Writers' Anniversaries. Multicoloured.
2212 4s. Type **948** 55 45
2213 4s. Georg Trakl (75th death anniv) 55 45

949 Fried **950** "Adoration of the Shepherds" (detail, Johann Carl von Reslfeld)

1989. 125th Birth Anniv of Alfred Fried (Peace Movement worker).
2214 **949** 6s. multicoloured 80 75

1989. Christmas.
2215 **950** 5s. multicoloured 70 40

951 "Courier" (Albrecht Durer) **952** Streif Downhill and Ganslern Slalom Runs

1990. 500th Anniv of Regular European Postal Services.
2216 **951** 5s. chocolate, cinnamon and brown 60 45

1990. 50th Hahnenkamm Ski Championships, Kitzbuhel.
2217 **952** 5s. multicoloured 70 45

953 Sulzer **954** Emich

1990. Death Centenary of Salomon Sulzer (creator of modern Synagogue songs).
2218 **953** 4s.50 multicoloured . . . 95 60

1990. 50th Death Anniv of Friedrich Emich (microchemist).
2219 **954** 6s. purple and green . . 75 65

955 Emperor Friedrich III (miniature by Ulrich Schreier)

1990. 500th Anniv of Linz as Capital of Upper Austria.
2220 **955** 5s. multicoloured 75 55

956 University Seals

1990. 625th Anniv of Vienna University and 175th Anniv of Vienna University of Technology.
2221 **956** 5s. red, gold and lilac . . 60 55

957 South Styrian Vineyards

1990. Natural Beauty Spots.
2222 **957** 5s. black and yellow . . 95 70

958 Parish Church

959 1897 May Day Emblem

1990. 1200th Anniv of Anthering.
2223 **958** 7s. multicoloured . . . . 1·30 85

1990. Centenary of Labour Day.
2224 **959** 4s.50 multicoloured . . . 60 55

960 "Our Dear Housewife of Seckau" (relief)

961 Ebene Reichenau Post Office

1990. 850th Anniv of Seckau Abbey.
2225 **960** 4s.50 blue 60 50

1990. Europa. Post Office Buildings.
2226 **961** 7s. multicoloured . . . . 1·10 85

962 Thematic Stamp Motifs

963 Makart (self-portrait)

1990. Stamp Day.
2227 **962** 7s.+3s. multicoloured . . 1·70 1·70

1990. 150th Birth Anniv of Hans Makart (painter).
2228 **963** 4s.50 multicoloured . . . 60 50

964 Schiele (self-portrait)

965 Raimund

1990. Birth Centenary of Egon Schiele (painter).
2229 **964** 5s. multicoloured 65 50

1990. Birth Bicentenary of Ferdinand Raimund (actor and playwright).
2230 **965** 4s.50 multicoloured . . . 60 50

966 "The Hundred Guilden Note" (Rembrandt)

1990. 2nd Int Christus Medicus Congress, Bad Ischl.
2231 **966** 7s. multicoloured . . . . 1·10 85

967 Hardegg

1990. 700th Anniv of Hardegg's Elevation to Status of Town.
2232 **967** 4s.50 multicoloured . . . 60 60

968 Oberdrauburg (copperplate engraving, Freiherr von Valvasor)

970 Zdarsky skiing

969 Church and Town Hall

1990. 750th Anniv of Oberdrauburg.
2233 **968** 5s. multicoloured 70 55

1990. 850th Anniv of Gumpoldskirchen.
2234 **969** 5s. multicoloured 70 55

1990. 50th Death Anniv of Mathias Zdarsky (developer of alpine skiing).
2235 **970** 5s. multicoloured 70 65

971 "Telegraph", 1880, and "Anton Chekhov", 1978

1990. 150th Anniv of Modern (metal) Shipbuilding in Austria.
2236 **971** 9s. multicoloured . . . . 1·50 1·20

972 Perkonig

973 "Man of Rainbows" (Robert Zeppel-Sperl)

1990. Birth Centenary of Josef Friedrich Perkonig (writer).
2237 **972** 5s. sepia, brown & gold 70 55

1990. Austrian Modern Art.
2238 **973** 5s. multicoloured 75 55

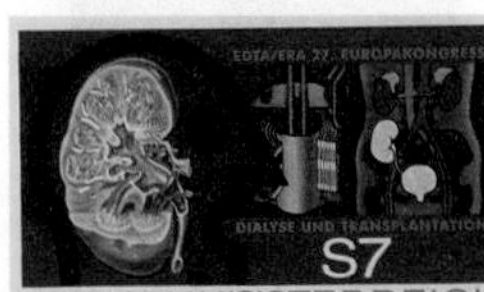

974 Kidney, Dialysis Machine and Anatomical Diagram

1990. 27th European Dialysis and Transplantation Federation Congress, Vienna.
2239 **974** 7s. multicoloured . . . . 1·10 75

975 Werfel

1990. Birth Centenary of Franz Werfel (writer).
2240 **975** 5s. multicoloured 70 55

976 U.N. and Austrian Flags

1990. 30th Anniv of Austrian Participation in U.N. Peace-keeping Forces.
2241 **976** 7s. multicoloured . . . . 1·00 90

977 Arms of Provinces

1990. 45th Anniv of First Provinces Conference (established Second Republic as Federal State).
2242 **977** 5s. multicoloured 70 55

978 University Seal

979 Vogelsang

1990. 150th Anniv of Mining University, Leoben.
2243 **978** 4s.50 black, red & green 60 55

1990. Death Centenary of Karl von Vogelsang (Christian social reformer).
2244 **979** 4s.50 multicoloured . . . 60 50

980 Metal Workers

1990. Centenary of Metal, Mining and Energy Trade Union.
2245 **980** 5s. multicoloured 70 55

981 Player

982 Greenhouse

1990. 3rd World Ice Curling Championships, Vienna.
2246 **981** 7s. multicoloured . . . . 1·10 80

1990. Re-opening of Schonbrunn Greenhouse.
2247 **982** 5s. multicoloured 70 65

983 "Birth of Christ"

984 Grillparzer

1990. Christmas. Detail of Altarpiece by Master Nikolaus of Verdun, Klosterneuburg Monastery.
2248 **983** 5s. multicoloured 70 45

1991. Birth Bicent of Franz Grillparzer (dramatist).
2249 **984** 4s.50 multicoloured . . . 60 55

985 Skier

986 Kreisky

1991. World Alpine Skiing Championships, Saalbach-Hinterglemm.
2250 **985** 5s. multicoloured 70 55

1991. 80th Birth Anniv of Bruno Kreisky (Chancellor, 1970–82).
2251 **986** 5s. multicoloured 60 55

987 Schmidt and Vienna Town Hall

1991. Death Centenary of Friedrich von Schmidt (architect).
2252 **987** 7s. multicoloured . . . . 1·10 85

988 Fountain, Vienna

1991. Anniversaries. Multicoloured.
2253 4s.50 Type **988** (250th death anniv of Georg Raphael Donner (sculptor)) . . . 60 55
2254 5s. "Kitzbuhel in Winter" (birth centenary of Alfons Walde (artist and architect)) 70 55
2255 7s. Vienna Stock Exchange (death centenary of Theophil von Hansen (architect)) 95 85
See also No. 2269.

989 M. von Ebner-Eschenbach

1991. 75th Death Anniv of Marie von Ebner-Eschenbach (writer).
2256 **989** 4s.50 purple 60 50

990 Mozart

1991. Death Bicentenary of Wolfgang Amadeus Mozart (composer). Sheet 115×69 mm containing T **990** and similar vert design, each purple, mauve and gold.
MS2257 5s. Type **990**; 5s. "The Magic Flute" (statue, Vienna) 1·60 1·60

991 Obir Stalactite Caverns, Eisenkappel

1991. Natural Beauty Spots.
2258 **991** 5s. multicoloured 90 70

992 Spittal an der Drau (after Matthaus Merian)

1991. 800th Anniv of Spittal an der Drau.
2259 **992** 4s.50 multicoloured . . . 60 55

993 "ERS-1" European Remote Sensing Satellite

1991. Europa. Europe in Space.
2260 **993** 7s. multicoloured . . . . 1·00 1·00

994 "Garden Party" (Anthoni Bays)

1991. Vorarlberg "Clothing and People" Exhibition, Hohenems.
2261 **994** 5s. multicoloured 70 55

995 Grein

1991. 500th Anniv of Grein Town Charter.
2262 **995** 4s.50 multicoloured . . . 60 55

996 Bedding Plants forming Arms

1991. 1200th Anniv of Tulln.
2263 **996** 5s. multicoloured 70 55

997 Military History Museum

1991. Vienna Museum Centenaries. Multicoloured.
2264 5s. Type **997** 70 60
2265 7s. Museum of Art History 95 85

998 "B" and "P"

999 Tunnel Entrance

1991. Stamp Day.
2266 **998** 7s.+3s. brown, sepia and black . . . . 1·40 2·00

This is the first of a series of ten annual stamps, each of which will illustrate two letters. The complete series will spell out the words "Briefmarke" and "Philatelie".

1991. Opening of Karawanken Road Tunnel between Carinthia and Slovenia.
2267 **999** 7s. multicoloured 95 90

1000 Town Hall

1991. 5th Anniv of St. Polten as Capital of Lower Austria.
2268 **1000** 5s. multicoloured . . . 70 55

1991. 150th Birth Anniv of Otto Wagner (architect). As T **988**. Multicoloured.
2269 4s.50 Karlsplatz Station, Vienna City Railway . . 60 55

1001 Rowing

1991. Junior World Canoeing Championships and World Rowing Championships, Vienna.
2270 **1001** 5s. multicoloured . . . 70 55

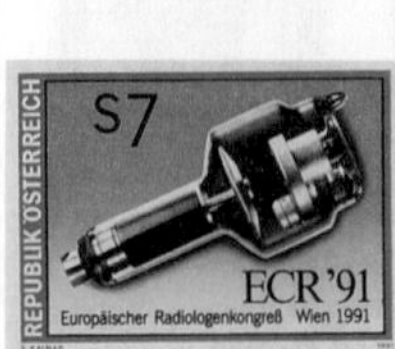

1002 X-ray Tube

1003 Paracelsus

1991. European Radiology Congress, Vienna.
2271 **1002** 7s. multicoloured . . . 95 85

1991. 450th Death Anniv of Theophrastus Bombastus von Hohenheim (Paracelsus) (physician and scientist).
2272 **1003** 4s. black, red & brown 60 50

1004 "Mir" Space Station

1005 Almabtrieb (driving cattle from mountain pastures) (Zell, Tyrol)

1991. "Austro Mir 91" Soviet–Austrian Space Flight.
2273 **1004** 9s. multicoloured . . . 1·30 1·60

1991. Folk Customs and Art (1st series). Mult.
2274 4s.50 Type **1005** 60 55
2275 5s. Vintage Crown (Neustift, Vienna) 75 70
2276 7s. Harvest monstrance (Nestelbach, Styria) . . . 1·00 90

See also Nos. 2305/7, 2349/51, 2363/5, 2393/5, 2418, 2432/3, 2450, 2482, 2491, 2500/1, 2508, 2524, 2546, 2550, 2552, 2568, 2581, 2587 and 2595.

1006 Weaver

1991. Austrian World of Work (5th series).
2277 **1006** 4s.50 multicoloured . . 60 55

1007 "The General" (Rudolf Pointner)

1008 Raab

1991. Austrian Modern Art.
2278 **1007** 5s. multicoloured . . . 70 50

1991. Birth Centenary of Julius Raab (Chancellor, 1953–61).
2279 **1008** 4s.50 brown & chestnut 60 50

1009 "Birth of Christ" (detail of fresco, Baumgartenberg Church)

1991. Christmas.
2280 **1009** 5s. multicoloured . . . 70 55

1010 Clerks

1992. Centenary of Trade Union of Clerks in Private Enterprise.
2281 **1010** 5s.50 multicoloured . . 65 55

1011 Emblems of Games and Olympic Rings

1992. Winter Olympic Games, Albertville, and Summer Games, Barcelona.
2282 **1011** 7s. multicoloured . . . 1·10 95

1012 Competitor

1992. 8th World Toboggan Championships on Natural Runs, Bad Goisern.
2283 **1012** 5s. multicoloured . . . 70 55

1013 Hollow Stone, Klostertal

1992. Natural Beauty Spots.
2284 **1013** 5s. multicoloured . . . 90 65

1014 Saiko

1015 "Athlete with Ball" (Christian Attersee)

1992. Birth Centenary of George Saiko (writer).
2285 **1014** 5s.50 brown 70 55

1992. Centenary of Workers' Sport Movement.
2286 **1015** 5s.50 multicoloured . . 75 60

1016 Franz Joseph Muller (chemist and mineralogist)

1992. Scientific Anniversaries. Multicoloured.
2287 5s. Type **1016** (250th birth anniv) 60 55
2288 5s.50 Paul Kitaibel (botanist, 175th death anniv) 70 70
2289 6s. Christian Doppler (physicist) (150th anniv of observation of Doppler Effect) 75 80
2290 7s. Richard Kuhn (chemist, 25th death anniv) 95 80

1017 Angels playing Instruments

1992. 150th Death Anniv of Vienna Philharmonic Orchestra. Sheet 90 × 70 mm.
MS2291 **1017** 5s.50 black, brown and gold 80 80

1018 First and Present Emblems

1992. Centenary of Railway Workers' Trade Union.
2292 **1018** 5s.50 red and black . . 80 60

1019 Hanrieder

1020 Scenes from "The Birdseller" (Zeller) and "The Beggar Student" (Millocker)

1992. 150th Birth Anniv of Norbert Hanrieder (writer).
2293 **1019** 5s.50 lilac & brown . . 70 55

1992. 150th Birth Anniversaries of Carl Zeller and Karl Millocker (composers).
2294 **1020** 6s. multicoloured . . . 1·00 95

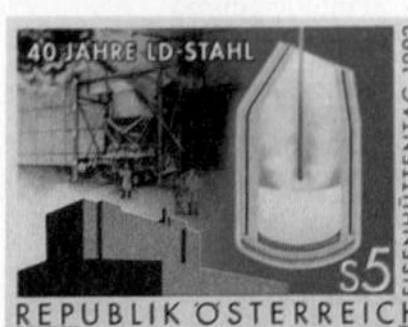

1021 Foundry and Process

1992. Ironworks Day. 40th Anniv of First LD-Process Steel Works, Linz.
2295 **1021** 5s. multicoloured . . . 65 55

1022 Woodcut of the Americas by Sebastian Munster (from "Geographia Universalis" by Claudius Ptolomaus)

1992. Europa. 500th Anniv of Discovery of America by Columbus.
2296 **1022** 7s. multicoloured . . . 1·10 90

1023 Dredger 1024 Rieger

1992. Centenary of Treaty for International Regulation of the Rhine.
2297 **1023** 7s. multicoloured . . . 1·00 90

1992. Centenary of Adoption of Pseudonym Reimmichl by Sebastian Rieger (writer).
2298 **1024** 5s. brown 60 55

1025 Flags and Alps 1026 Dr. Anna Dengel

1992. Alpine Protection Convention.
2299 **1025** 5s.50 multicoloured . . 95 70

1992. Birth Centenary of Dr. Anna Dengel (founder of Medical Missionary Sisters).
2300 **1026** 5s.50 multicoloured . . 70 55

1027 "R" and "H"

1992. Stamp Day.
2301 **1027** 7s.+3s. multicoloured 1·20 1·70
See note below No. 2266.

1028 Town Hall

1992. 750th Anniv of First Documentation of Lienz as a Town.
2302 **1028** 5s. multicoloured . . . 70 55

1029 "Billroth in Lecture Room" (A. F. Seligmann) 1030 Waldheim

1992. Austrian Surgery Society International Congress, Eisenstadt.
2303 **1029** 6s. multicoloured . . . 75 80

1992. Presidency of Dr. Kurt Waldheim.
2304 **1030** 5s.50 black, red & grey 70 60

1992. Folk Customs and Art (2nd series). As T **1005**. Multicoloured.
2305 5s. Target with figure of Zieler, Lower Austria, 1732 . . . . 80 70
2306 5s.50 Chest, Carinthia . . . 90 85
2307 7s. Votive tablet from Venser Chapel, Vorarlberg 95 85

1031 Bridge over Canal

1992. Completion of Marchfeld Canal System.
2308 **1031** 5s. multicoloured . . . 70 55

1032 "The Purification of Sea Water" (Peter Pongratz)

1992. Austrian Modern Art.
2309 **1032** 5s.50 multicoloured . . 75 65

1033 Gateway, Hofburg Palace (venue)

1992. 5th Int Ombudsmen's Conference, Vienna.
2310 **1033** 5s.50 multicoloured . . 70 55

1034 Academy Seal 1035 "The Annunciation"

1992. 300th Anniv of Academy of Fine Arts, Vienna.
2311 **1034** 5s. blue and red 70 65

1992. Death Bicentenary of Veit Koniger (sculptor).
2312 **1035** 5s. multicoloured . . . 75 60

1036 "Birth of Christ" (Johann Georg Schmidt)

1992. Christmas.
2313 **1036** 5s.50 multicoloured . . 75 45

1037 Earth and Satellite

1992. Birth Centenary of Hermann Potocnik (alias Noordung) (space travel pioneer).
2314 **1037** 10s. multicoloured . . . 1·30 1·50

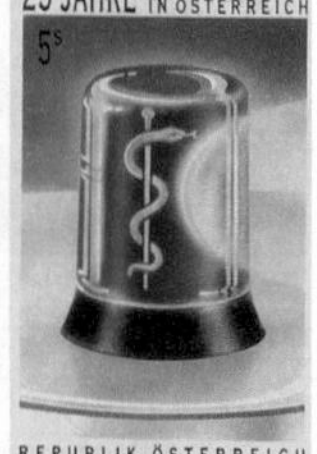
1038 Dome of Michael Wing, Hofburg Palace, Vienna 1039 Emergency Vehicle's Flashing Lantern

1993. Architects' Anniversaries. Multicoloured.
2315 5s. Type **1038** (Joseph Emanuel Fischer von Erlach, 300th birth) . . . 60 55
2316 5s.50 Kinsky Palace, Vienna (Johann Lukas von Hildebrandt, 325th birth) 75 60
2317 7s. State Opera House, Vienna (Eduard van der Null and August Siccard von Siccardsburg, 125th death annivs) 95 90

1993. 25th Anniv of Radio-controlled Emergency Medical Service.
2318 **1039** 5s. multicoloured . . . 70 55

1040 Wilder Kaiser Massif, Tyrol

1993. Natural Beauty Spots.
2319 **1040** 6s. multicoloured . . . 95 90

1041 Mitterhofer Typewriter

1993. Death Centenary of Peter Mitterhofer (typewriter pioneer).
2320 **1041** 17s. multicoloured . . . 2·20 2·20

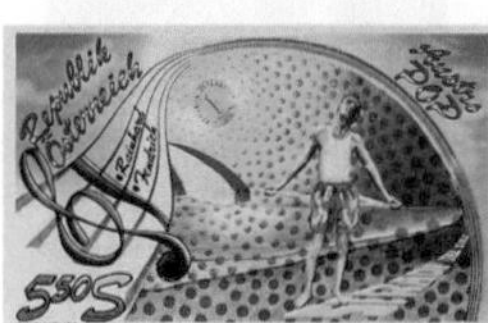
1042 "Strada del Sole" (record sleeve)

1993. "Austro Pop" (1st series). Rainhard Fendrich (singer).
2321 **1042** 5s.50 multicoloured . . 75 55
See also Nos. 2356 and 2368.

1043 Games Emblem

1993. Winter Special Olympics, Salzburg and Schladming.
2322 **1043** 6s.+3s. multicoloured 1·20 1·60

1044 Sealsfield 1045 Girl realizing her Rights

1993. Birth Bicent of Charles Sealsfield (novelist).
2323 **1044** 10s. red, blue and gold 1·30 1·10

1993. Ratification of U.N. Convention on Children's Rights.
2324 **1045** 7s. multicoloured . . . 95 90

1046 "Death" (detail of sculpture, Josef Stammel), Admont Monastery, Styria 1047 "Flying Harlequin" (Paul Flora)

1993. Monasteries and Abbeys.

2325	–	1s. brown, black & grn	15	15
2328	**1046**	5s.50 black, yell & grn	75	30
2329	–	6s. black, mauve & yell	80	25
2330	–	7s. brown, black & grey	95	40
2331	–	7s.50 brown, bl & blk	1·00	45
2332	–	8s. orange, black & bl	1·10	65
2334	–	10s. black, blue & orge	1·40	30
2339	–	20s. black, blue & yell	1·90	55
2340	–	26s. orange, black & bis	3·50	2·00
2341	–	30s. red, yellow & black	3·75	1·30

DESIGNS: 1s. The Annunciation (detail of crosier of Abbess), St. Gabriel Benedictine Abbey, Bertholdstein; 6s. St. Benedict of Nursia (glass painting), Mariastern Abbey, Gwiggen; 7s. Marble lion, Franciscan Monastery, Salzburg; 7s.50, Virgin Mary (detail of cupola painting by Paul Troger), Altenburg Monastery; 8s. Early Gothic doorway, Wilhering Monastery; 10s. "The Healing of St. Peregrinus" (altarpiece), Maria Luggau Monastery; 20s. Hartmann Crosier, St. Georgenberg Abbey, Fiecht; 26s. "Master Dolorosa" (sculpture), Franciscan Monastery, Schwaz; 30s. Madonna and Child, Monastery of the Scottish Order, Vienna.

1993. Europa. Contemporary Art.
2345 **1047** 7s. multicoloured . . . 95 90

1048 Silhouette, Script and Signature 1049 "Hohentwiel" (lake steamer) and Flags

1993. 150th Birth Anniv of Peter Rosegger (writer and newspaper publisher).
2346 **1048** 5s.50 black and green 70 55

1993. Lake Constance European Region.
2347 **1049** 6s. multicoloured . . . 95 70

1050 Knights in Battle and "I"s 1051 Human Rights Emblem melting Bars

1993. Stamp Day.
2348 **1050** 7s.+3s. gold, black and blue . . . . 1·40 1·50
See note below No. 2266.

1993. Folk Customs and Art (3rd series). As T **1005**. Multicoloured.
2349 5s. Corpus Christi Day procession, Hallstatt, Upper Austria 80 60
2350 5s.50 Drawing the block (log), Burgenland 70 60
2351 7s. Aperschnalzen (whipping the snow away), Salzburg 95 90

1993. U.N. World Conf on Human Rights, Vienna.
2352 **1051** 10s. multicoloured . . . 1·30 1·20

1052 Jagerstatter 1053 Train approaching Wolfgangsee

1993. 50th Death Anniv of Franz Jagerstatter (conscientious objector).
2353 **1052** 5s.50 multicoloured . . 70 55

1993. Centenary of Schafberg Cog Railway.
2354 **1053** 6s. multicoloured . . . 1·00 85

1054 "Self-portrait with Doll"

1993. Birth Centenary of Rudolf Wacker (artist).
2355 **1054** 6s. multicoloured . . . 75 70

1993. "Austro Pop" (2nd series). Ludwig Hirsch (singer and actor). As T **1042**. Multicoloured.
2356 5s.50 "Die Omama" (record sleeve) 75 65

1055 "Concert in Dornbacher Park" (Balthasar Wigand)

1993. 150th Anniv of Vienna Male Choral Society.
2357 **1055** 5s. multicoloured . . . 75 60

1056 "Easter" (Max Weiler)

1057 "99 Heads" (detail, Friedensreich Hundertwasser)

1993. Austrian Modern Art.
2358 **1056** 5s.50 multicoloured . . 75 60

1993. Council of Europe Heads of State Conference, Vienna.
2359 **1057** 7s. multicoloured . . . 1·10 95

1058 Statue of Athene, Parliament Building

1060 "Birth of Christ" (Krainburg Altar, Styria)

1059 Workers

1993. 75th Anniv of Austrian Republic.
2360 **1058** 5s. multicoloured . . . 75 65

1993. Cent of 1st Austrian Trade Unions Congress.
2361 **1059** 5s.50 multicoloured . . 70 55

1993. Christmas.
2362 **1060** 5s.50 multicoloured . . 75 50

1994. Folk Customs and Art (4th series). As T **1005**. Multicoloured.
2363 5s.50 Rocking cradle, Vorarlberg 75 70
2364 6s. Carved sleigh, Styria . . 80 70
2365 7s. Godparent's bowl and lid, Upper Austria . . . . 1·00 1·00

1061 Winter Sports

1994. Winter Olympic Games, Lillehammer, Norway.
2366 **1061** 7s. multicoloured . . . 95 95

1062 Early Production of Coins

1994. 800th Anniv of Vienna Mint.
2367 **1062** 6s. multicoloured . . . 75 75

1994. "Austro Pop" (3rd series). Falco (Johann Holzel) (singer). As T **1042**. Multicoloured.
2368 6s. "Rock Me Amadeus" (record sleeve) 80 75

1063 "Reclining Lady" (detail, Herbert Boeckl)

1994. Birth Centenary of Herbert Boeckl (painter).
2369 **1063** 5s.50 multicoloured . . 75 60

1064 N.W. Tower of City Wall

1994. 800th Anniv of Wiener Neustadt.
2370 **1064** 6s. multicoloured . . . 80 60

1065 Lurgrotte (caves), Styria

1994. Natural Beauty Spots.
2371 **1065** 6s. multicoloured . . . 95 85

1066 Lake Rudolf (Teleki–Hohnel expedition to Africa, 1887)

1994. Europa. Discoveries.
2372 **1066** 7s. multicoloured . . . 95 90

1067 "E" and "L" as Ruins in Landscape

1994. Stamp Day.
2373 **1067** 7s.+3s. multicoloured 1·40 1·70
See note below No. 2266.

1068 "Allegory of Theology, Justice, Philosophy and Medicine" (detail of fresco, National Library)

1994. 300th Birth Anniv of Daniel Gran (artist).
2374 **1068** 20s. multicoloured . . . 2·30 2·20

1069 Scene from "The Prodigal Son" (opera, Benjamin Britten)

1994. 25th Anniv of Carinthian Summer Festival, Ossiach and Villach.
2375 **1069** 5s.50 gold and red . . 75 60

1070 Steam Locomotive and Diesel Railcar (Gailtal)

1994. Railway Centenaries. Multicoloured.
2376 5s.50 Type **1070** 75 70
2377 6s. Steam locomotive and diesel railcar (Murtal) . . 90 85

1071 Gmeiner and Children

1072 Seitz (bust, G. Ambrosi)

1994. 75th Birth Anniv of Hermann Gmeiner (founder of S.O.S. children's villages).
2378 **1071** 7s. multicoloured . . . 80 90

1994. 125th Birth Anniv of Karl Seitz (acting President, 1920).
2379 **1072** 5s.50 multicoloured . . 60 70

1073 Bohm

1075 Franz Theodor Csokor (dramatist and poet)

1074 Ethnic Minorities on Map

1994. Birth Centenary of Karl Bohm (conductor).
2380 **1073** 7s. blue and gold . . . 1·00 1·00

1994. Legal and Cultural Protection of Ethnic Minorities.
2381 **1074** 5s.50 multicoloured . . 70 80

1994. Writers' Anniversaries. Multicoloured.
2382 6s. Type **1075** (25th death anniv) 75 85
2383 7s. Joseph Roth (novelist, birth cent) . . . . 90 1·30

1076 "Head" (Franz Ringel)

1077 Money Box

1994. Austrian Modern Art.
2384 **1076** 6s. multicoloured . . . 80 70

1994. 175th Anniv of Savings Banks in Austria.
2385 **1077** 7s. multicoloured . . . 80 90

1078 Air Hostess and Child

1994. Austrian World of Work (6th series).
2386 **1078** 6s. multicoloured . . . 75 80

1079 Coudenhove-Kalergi and Map of Europe

1994. Birth Cent of Richard Coudenhove-Kalergi (founder of Paneuropa Union).
2387 **1079** 10s. multicoloured . . . 1·30 1·30

1080 "Birth of Christ" (Anton Wollenek)

1081 Map and Austrian and E.U. Flags

1994. Christmas.
2388 **1080** 6s. multicoloured . . . 75 55

1995. Austria's Entry into E.U.
2389 **1081** 7s. multicoloured . . . 95 95

1082 Loos House, Michaelerplatz, Vienna

1995. 125th Birth Anniv of Adolf Loos (architect).
2390 **1082** 10s. multicoloured . . . 1·30 1·30

1083 Sporting Activities

1995. 50th Anniv of Austrian Gymnastics and Sports Association.
2391 **1083** 6s. multicoloured . . . 80 70

1084 Workers

1995. 75th Anniv of Workers' and Employees' Chambers (advisory body).
2392 **1084** 6s. multicoloured . . . 80 70

1995. Folk Costumes and Art (5th series). As T **1005**. Multicoloured.
2393 5s.50 Belt, Carinthia 75 65
2394 6s. Costume of Hiata (vineyard guard), Vienna 90 70
2395 7s. Gold bonnet, Wachau 1·00 95

1085 State Seal **1086** Heft Ironworks

1995. 50th Anniv of Second Republic.
2396 **1085** 6s. multicoloured . . . 80 65

1995. Carinthian "History of Mining and Industry" Exhibition, Heft, Huttenberg.
2397 **1086** 5s.50 multicoloured . . 75 65

1087 Hiker in Mountains

1995. Centenary of Friends of Nature.
2398 **1087** 5s.50 multicoloured . . 75 65

1088 Heidenreichstein National Park

1995. Natural Beauty Spots.
2399 **1088** 6s. multicoloured . . . 95 75

1089 Woman and Barbed Wire around Skull **1090** Map, Woman and Child and Transport

1995. Europa. Peace and Freedom.
2400 **1089** 7s. multicoloured . . . 80 90

1995. Meeting of European Ministers of Transport Conference, Vienna.
2401 **1090** 7s. multicoloured . . . 95 95

1091 "F" and "A" on Vase of Flowers **1093** St. Gebhard (stained-glass window, Martin Hausle)

1092 Set for "The Flying Dutchman"

1995. Stamp Day.
2402 **1091** 10s.+5s. mult . . . . . 1·90 2·40
See note below No. 2266.

1995. 50th Bregenz Festival.
2403 **1092** 6s. multicoloured . . . 80 70

1995. Death Millenary of St. Gebhard, Bishop of Konstanz (patron saint of Vorarlberg chuches).
2404 **1093** 7s.50 multicoloured . . 1·00 90

1094 Members' Flags **1095** Loschmidt

1995. 50th Anniv of U.N.O.
2405 **1094** 10s. multicoloured . . . 1·30 1·10

1995. Death Centenary of Josef Loschmidt (physical chemist).
2406 **1095** 20s. black, stone & brn 2·50 2·30

1096 K. Leichter **1097** Scene from "Jedermann" (Hugo von Hofmannsthal)

1995. Birth Cent of Kathe Leichter (sociologist).
2407 **1096** 6s. cream, black & red 80 60

1995. 75th Anniv of Salzburg Festival.
2408 **1097** 6s. multicoloured . . . 80 65

1098 "European Scene" (Adolf Frohner)

1995. Austrian Modern Art.
2409 **1098** 6s. multicoloured . . . 80 70

1099 Franz von Suppe and "The Beautiful Galatea"

1995. Composers' Anniversaries. Scenes from operettas. Multicoloured.
2410 6s. Type **1099** (death cent) 80 75
2411 7s. Nico Dostal and "The Hungarian Wedding" (birth centenary) 95 90

1100 University Building

1995. 25th Anniv of Klagenfurt University.
2412 **1100** 5s.50 multicoloured . . 75 65

1101 Hollenburg Castle

1995. 75th Anniv of Carinthian Referendum.
2413 **1101** 6s. multicoloured . . . 80 75

1102 Postman

1995. Austrian World of Work (7th series).
2414 **1102** 6s. multicoloured . . . 80 75

1103 Anton von Webern (50th death) **1104** Christ Child

1995. Composers' Anniversaries.
2415 **1103** 6s. blue and orange . . 90 65
2416 – 7s. red and orange . . 80 90
DESIGN: 7s. Ludwig van Beethoven (225th birth).

1995. Christmas. 300th Anniv of Christkindl Church.
2417 **1104** 6s. multicoloured . . . 80 70

1996. Folk Customs and Art (6th series). As T **1005**.
2418 6s. multicoloured 80 55
DESIGN: 6s. Masked figures Roller and Scheller (Imst masquerades, Tyrol).

1105 Empress Maria Theresia and Academy Building

1996. 250th Anniv of Theresian Academy, Vienna.
2419 **1105** 6s. multicoloured . . . 80 65

1106 Ski Jumping

1996. World Ski Jumping Championships, Tauplitz and Bad Mitterndorf.
2420 **1106** 7s. multicoloured . . . 95 90

1107 Terminal

1996. Completion of West Terminal, Vienna International Airport.
2421 **1107** 7s. multicoloured . . . 95 90

1108 Hohe Tauern National Park

1996. Natural Beauty Spots.
2422 **1108** 6s. multicoloured . . . 80 70

1109 "Mother and Child" (Peter Fendi) **1110** Organ and Music

1996. Artists' Birth Bicentenaries. Multicoloured.
2423 6s. Type **1109** 80 70
2424 7s. "Self-portrait" (Leopold Kupelwieser) . . . . . . 95 1·00

1996. Death Cent of Anton Bruckner (composer).
2425 **1110** 5s.50 multicoloured . . 95 90

1111 Kollmitz Castle (from copper engraving)

1996. 300th Death Anniv of Georg Vischer (cartographer and engraver).
2426 **1111** 10s. black and stone . . 1·30 1·30

1112 Old Market Square

1996. 800th Anniv of Klagenfurt.
2427 **1112** 6s. multicoloured . . . 80 75

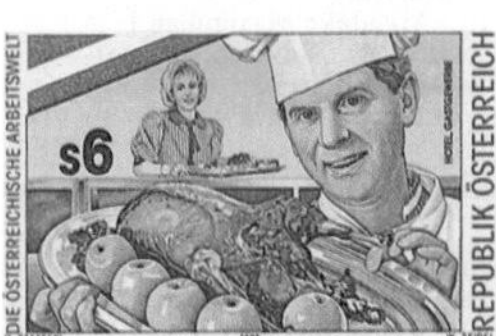

1113 Hotel Chef and Waitress

1996. Austrian World of Work (8th series).
2428 **1113** 6s. multicoloured . . . 80 85

1114 Paula von Preradovic (writer)

1115 "M" and "T" and Bluebirds (mosaic)

1996. Europa. Famous Women.
2429 **1114** 7s. stone, brown & grey . . . 95 95

1996. Stamp Day.
2430 **1115** 10s.+5s. mult . . . . . 2·00 2·30
See note below No. 2266.

1116 Mascot with Olympic Flag

1996. Olympic Games, Atlanta.
2431 **1116** 10s. multicoloured . . . 1·40 1·40

1996. Folk Customs and Art (7th series). As T **1005**.
2432 5s.50 Flower-bedecked poles, Salzburg 95 85
2433 7s. Tyrol militia . . . . . . 1·10 1·10

1117 Landscape

1996. 75th Anniv of Burgenland.
2434 **1117** 6s. multicoloured . . . 80 85

1118 Mountaineers

1119 Deed of Otto III, 996

1996. Cent of Austrian Mountain Rescue Service.
2435 **1118** 6s. multicoloured . . . 80 75

1996. Millenary of Austria. Multicoloured.
2436 6s. Type **1119** 90 85
2437 6s. Archduke Joseph II (after Georg Weikert) and Archduchess Maria Theresia (after Martin van Meytens) 90 85
2438 7s. "Duke Heinrich II" (stained-glass window, Monastery of the Holy Cross) . . . . 95 1·00
2439 7s. Arms in flames (1848 Revolution) . . . . . . 95 1·00
2440 7s. Rudolf IV, the Founder 95 1·10
2441 7s. Karl Renner (first Federal Republic president) . . . . 95 1·10
2442 10s. Archduke Maximilian I (Holy Roman Emperor) (miniature from Statute Book of Order of the Golden Fleece) . . . . . 1·20 1·40
2443 10s. Seal and signature of Leopold Figl (State Treaty of 1955) . . . . . 1·20 1·40
2444 20s. Imperial crown of Rudolf II . . . . 2·75 3·00
2445 20s. State arms, stars of Europe and "The Horsebreaker" (bronze by Josef Lax) (Austria and Europe) . . . . 2·75 3·00

1120 "Power Station" (Reinhard Artberg)

1996. Austrian Modern Art.
2446 **1120** 7s. multicoloured . . . 95 1·00

1121 Children of Different Nations

1996. 50th Anniv of U.N.I.C.E.F.
2447 **1121** 10s. multicoloured . . . 1·30 1·30

1122 Nativity and Vienna Town Hall

1996. Christmas.
2448 **1122** 6s. multicoloured . . . 80 75

1123 Kramer

1997. Birth Centenary of Theodor Kramer (poet).
2449 **1123** 5s.50 blue 80 60

1997. Folk Customs and Art (8th series). As T **1005**. Multicoloured.
2450 7s. Epiphany carol singers, Eisenstadt Burgenland . . 80 90

1124 Vineyards on the Nussberg, Vienna

1997. Natural Beauty Spots.
2451 **1124** 6s. multicoloured . . . 75 70

1125 Academy and Light

1997. 150th Anniv of Austrian Academy of Sciences, Vienna.
2452 **1125** 10s. multicoloured . . . 75 1·00

1126 Emblem

1997. 50th Anniv of Verbund Electricity Company.
2453 **1126** 6s. multicoloured . . . 1·20 75

1127 The Cruel Rosalia of Forchtenstein

1128 Stage Set for "Die tote Stadt"

1997. Myths and Legends.
2459 – 6s.50 grn, pink & blk 75 70
2460 **1127** 7s. black, stone & brn 80 75
2461 – 8s. orange, blk & lilac 1·00 1·10
2462 – 9s. black, stone & pur 1·20 1·40
2462a – 10s. black, grey & red 60 1·70
2463 – 13s. black, brn & pur 1·50 1·70
2464 – 14s. black, lt blue & bl 1·60 2·00
2465 – 20s. green, blk & stone 2·50 2·75
2466 – 22s. black, bl & stone 3·00 2·75
2467 – 23s. black, ochre and green . . . . 3·00 2·75
2468 – 25s. stone, black and yellow . . . . . . 3·75 3·25
2469 – 32s. black, brn & pink 4·50 4·00
DESIGNS: 6s.50, Lindworm of Klagenfurt; 8s. The Black Lady of Hardegg; 9s. Charming Augustin; 10s. Basilisk of Vienna; 13s. The Pied Piper of Korneuburg; 14s. The Strudengau Water-nymph; 20s. St. Notburga; 22s. Witches Whirl; 23s. Loaf Agony; 25s. St. Konrad and Altems Castle; 32s. The Discovery of Erzberg (Mountain of Ore).

1997. Birth Cent of Erich Korngold (composer).
2470 **1128** 20s. black, blue & gold 2·40 1·90

1129 Stadium, Badge and Players

1997. Rapid Vienna, National Football Champions, 1995–96.
2471 **1129** 7s. multicoloured . . . 80 90

1130 Red Deer

1997. Hunting and the Environment. Deer Feeding in Winter.
2472 **1130** 7s. multicoloured . . . 80 90

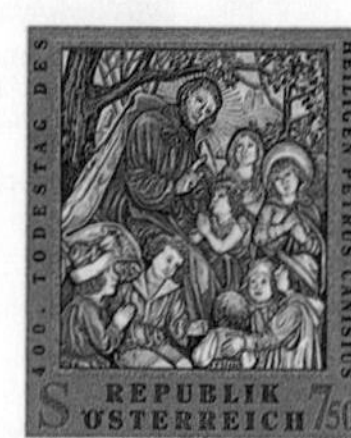

1131 Canisius and Children (altar by Josef Bachlechner in Innsbruck Seminary)

1997. 400th Death Anniv of St. Petrus Canisius (patron saint of Innsbruck).
2473 **1131** 7s.50 multicoloured . . 90 1·00

1132 Johannes Brahms (after L. Michalek)

1997. Composers' Anniversaries.
2474 **1132** 6s. violet and gold . . . 80 90
2475 – 10s. purple and gold . . 1·20 1·30
DESIGNS: 6s. Type **1132** (death centenary); 10s. Franz Schubert (birth bicentenary).

1133 "A" and "E"

1134 The Four Friends

1997. Stamp Day.
2476 **1133** 7s. multicoloured . . . 80 1·00
See note below No. 2266.

1997. Europa. Tales and Legends. "The Town Band of Bremen" by the Brothers Grimm.
2477 **1134** 7s. multicoloured . . . 80 1·00

1135 1850 9k. Stamp and Postman

1997. "WIPA 2000" International Stamp Exhibition, Vienna (1st issue).
2478 **1135** 27s.+13s. mult . . . . 4·75 5·25
See also Nos. 2521, 2543/**MS**2551 and **MS**2564.

1136 Train on Hochschneeberg Line

1997. Railway Anniversaries. Multicoloured.
2479 6s. Type **1136** (centenary of Hochschneeberg rack-railway) 70 85
2480 7s.50 Steam locomotive "Licaon" and viaduct near Mattersburg (150th anniv of Odenburg–Wiener Neustadt line) . . 90 1·10

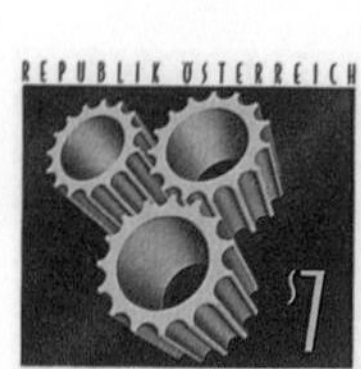

1137 Cogwheels

1138 Waggerl (self-portrait)

1997. 125th Anniv of Austrian Technical Supervisory Association.
2481 **1137** 7s. multicoloured . . . 95 95

1997. Folk Customs and Art (9th series). As T **1005**. Multicoloured.
2482 6s.50 Tyrolean brass band 95 95

1997. Birth Centenary of Karl Waggerl (writer).
2483 **1138** 7s. green, yellow & blue 80 90

1139 Adolf Lorenz (founder of German Society of Orthopaedia)

1997. Orthopaedics Congress, Vienna.
2484 **1139** 8s. multicoloured . . . 95 1·10

1140 Emblem

1142 Blind Man with Guide Dog

1141 Patient, Nurse and Doctor

1997. 125th Anniv of College of Agricultural Sciences, Vienna.
2485 **1140** 9s. multicoloured . . . 1·00 1·20

1997. Austrian World of Work (9th series).
2486 **1141** 6s.50 multicoloured . . 75 70

1997. Cent of Austrian Association for the Blind.
2487 **1142** 7s. multicoloured . . . 80 90

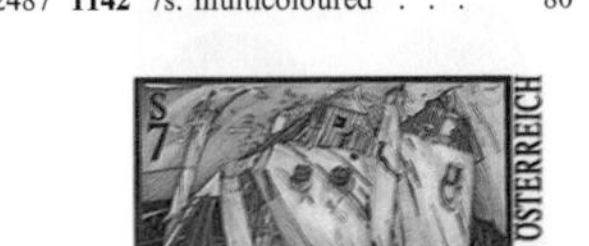

1143 "House in Wind" (Helmut Schickhofer)

1997. Austrian Modern Art.
2488 **1143** 7s. multicoloured . . . 80 90

1144 Klestil

1145 Werner

1997. 65th Birthday of Pres. Thomas Klestil.
2489 **1144** 7s. multicoloured . . . 80 95

1997. 75th Birth Anniv of Oskar Werner (actor).
2490 **1145** 7s. black, orge & grey 80 90

1997. Folk Customs and Art (10th series). As T **1005**. Multicoloured.
2491 6s.50 Tower wind-band, Upper Austria 90 90

1146 Glowing Light

1997. 25th Anniv of Light in Darkness (umbrella organization of children's charities).
2492 **1146** 7s. blue 80 95

1147 "Mariazell Madonna"

1997. Christmas.
2493 **1147** 7s. multicoloured . . . 80 90

1148 Kalkalpen National Park

1998. Natural Beauty Spots.
2494 **1148** 7s. multicoloured . . . 80 90

1149 Courting Pair

1998. Hunting and the Environment. Preservation of Breeding Habitat of the Black Grouse.
2495 **1149** 9s. multicoloured . . . 1·00 1·30

1150 Ice Skaters

1998. Winter Olympic Games, Nagano, Japan.
2496 **1150** 14s. multicoloured . . . 1·70 2·00

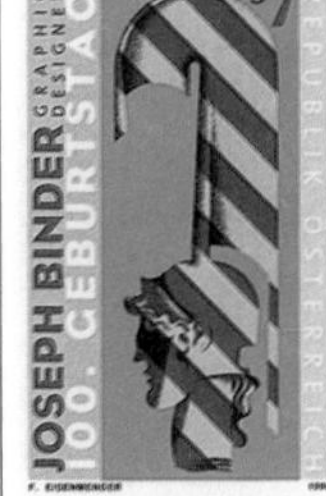

7s Republik Österreich

200 Jahre Steindruck

1151 Austrian Poster Exposition Advertising Poster, 1928

1152 Alois Senefelder (inventor) on Lithographic Stone

1998. Birth Cent of Joseph Binder (designer).
2497 **1151** 7s. multicoloured . . . 80 1·00

1998. Bicentenary of Invention of Lithography (printing process).
2498 **1152** 7s. blue, yellow & black 80 85

1153 Facade

1155 "St. Florian" (glass painting)

1154 Player and Team Emblem

1998. Centenary of Vienna Secession (exn hall).
2499 **1153** 8s. brown, gold & blue 95 90

1998. Folk Customs and Art (11th series). As T **1005**. Multicoloured.
2500 6s.50 Fiacre, Vienna . . . . 1·10 90
2501 7s. Palm Sunday procession, Thaur, Tyrol . . . . . . 1·20 1·00

1998. Austria Memphis Football Club.
2502 **1154** 7s. multicoloured . . . 80 95

1998. St. Florian, Patron Saint of Firemen.
2503 **1155** 7s. multicoloured . . . 80 95

1156 Rupertus Cross

1998. 1200th Anniv of Salzburg Archdiocese.
2504 **1156** 7s. multicoloured . . . 80 90

1157 Series Yv Locomotive No. 2, 1895

1998. Centenary of Completion of Ybbs Valley Railway.
2505 **1157** 6s.50 multicoloured . . 95 1·00

1158 "Tyrolia" (Ferdinand Cosandier)

1159 Vienna Town Hall (Viennese festive weeks)

1998. 175th Anniv of Tyrol Ferdinandeum (state museum), Innsbruck.
2506 **1158** 7s. multicoloured . . . 80 95

1998. Europa. National Festivals.
2507 **1159** 7s. multicoloured . . . 80 95

1998. Folk Customs and Art (12th series). As T **1005**. Multicoloured.
2508 6s.50 Samson and the dwarves, Salzburg 90 95

1160 Christine Lavant

1998. 25th Death Anniv of Christine Lavant (poet).
2509 **1160** 7s. multicoloured . . . 80 1·00

1161 Electric Railcar No. 1

1162 "R" and "L"

1998. Centenary of Postlingberg Railway.
2510 **1161** 6s.50 multicoloured . . 80 95

1998. Stamp Day.
2511 **1162** 7s. multicoloured . . . 80 1·20
See note below No. 2266.

1163 Presidency Emblem

1164 Railcar No. 5090

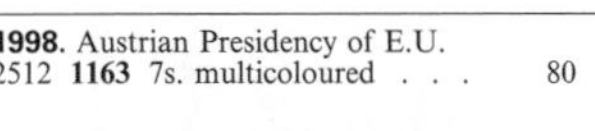

1998. Austrian Presidency of E.U.
2512 **1163** 7s. multicoloured . . . 80 90

1998. Centenary of Pinzgau Railway.
2513 **1164** 6s.50 multicoloured . . 95 1·10

1165 Volksoper, Vienna

1998. Centenary of Volksoper (theatre) and 50th Death Anniv of Franz Lehar (composer).
2514 **1165** 6s.50 multicoloured . . 75 1·00

1166 Empress Elisabeth (after Franz Winterhalter)

1998. Death Centenary of Empress Elisabeth.
2515 **1166** 7s. multicoloured . . . 80 1·00

1167 School Building

1998. Centenary of Vienna Business School.
2516 **1167** 7s. multicoloured . . . 80 1·00

1168 Kudlich and Farmers

1169 "My Garden" (Hans Staudacher)

1998. 175th Birth Anniv of Hans Kudlich (promoter of 1848 "Peasants' Liberation" Law).
2517 **1168** 6s.50 multicoloured . . 95 1·00

1998. Austrian Modern Art.
2518 **1169** 7s. multicoloured . . . 95 1·00

1170 Town Hall and Arms

1998. 350th Anniv of Declaration of Eisenstadt as a Free Town.
2519 **1170** 7s. multicoloured . . . 95 90

1171 Photographer and Reporter

1998. Austrian World of Work (10th series). Art, Media and Freelances.
2520 **1171** 6s.50 multicoloured . . 85 85

1172 1929 2s. Stamp and Post Van

1998. "WIPA 2000" International Stamp Exhibition, Vienna (2nd issue).
2521 **1172** 32s.+13s. mult . . . . 5·50 6·75

1173 "Nativity" (fresco, Tainach Church)
1174 Cross-country Skiing

1998. Christmas.
2522 **1173** 7s. multicoloured . . . 95 90

1999. World Nordic Skiing Championships, Ramsau.
2523 **1174** 7s. multicoloured . . . 95 90

1999. Folk Customs and Art (13th series). As T **1005**. Multicoloured.
2524 6s.50 Walking pilgrimage to Mariazell 85 85

1175 Stingl Rock, Bohemian Forest

1999. Natural Beauty Spots.
2525 **1175** 7s. multicoloured . . . 95 90

1176 Books and Compact Disc

1999. Centenary of Austrian Patent Office.
2526 **1176** 7s. multicoloured . . . 95 90

1177 Player and Club Emblem

1999. SK Puntigamer Sturm Graz Football Club.
2527 **1177** 7s. multicoloured . . . 95 90

1178 Palace Facade

1999. World Heritage Site. Schonbrunn Palace, Vienna.
2528 **1178** 13s. multicoloured . . . 1·80 1·70

1179 Partridges

1999. Hunting and the Environment. Living Space for Grey Partridges.
2529 **1179** 6s.50 multicoloured . . 95 90

1180 Snowboarder

1999. 50th Anniv of Austrian General Sport Federation.
2530 **1180** 7s. multicoloured . . . 95 95

1181 Council Building, Strasbourg

1999. 50th Anniv of Council of Europe.
2531 **1181** 14s. multicoloured . . . 1·80 1·80
No. 2531 is denominated both in Austrian schillings and in euros.

1182 Steyr Type 50 Baby Saloon

1999. Birth Centenary of Karl Jenschke (engineer and car manufacturer).
2532 **1182** 7s. multicoloured . . . 95 90

1183 "St. Martin" (marble relief, Peuerbach Church)

1999. Ancient Arts and Crafts (1st series).
2533 **1183** 8s. brown, blue & orange . . . . 1·10 1·10
See also Nos. 2542, 2575, 2600 and 2602.

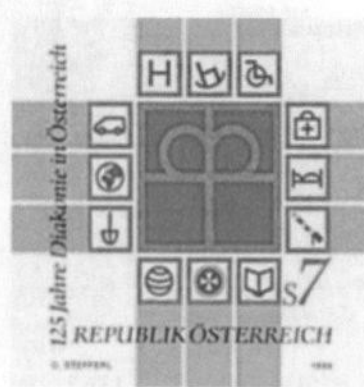

1184 Symbols of Aid and Emblem

1999. 125th Anniv of Diakonie (professional charitable services).
2534 **1184** 7s. multicoloured . . . 95 95

1185 Johann Strauss, the Younger

1999. Composers' Death Anniversaries. Mult.
2535 7s. Type **1185** (centenary) 95 90
2536 8s. Johann Strauss, the Elder (150th anniv) . . . 1·00 1·00

1186 Rural Gendarmes
1188 "K" and "I"

1187 Donau-auen National Park

1999. 150th Anniv of National Gendarmerie.
2537 **1186** 7s. multicoloured . . . 95 90

1999. Europa. Parks and Gardens.
2538 **1187** 7s. multicoloured . . . 95 90

1999. Stamp Day.
2539 **1188** 7s. multicoloured . . . 95 90
See note below No. 2266.

1189 Iron Stage Curtain

1999. Centenary of Graz Opera.
2540 **1189** 6s.50 multicoloured . . 95 90

1190 Couple on Bench

1999. International Year of the Elderly.
2541 **1190** 7s. multicoloured . . . 95 90

1191 "St. Anne with Mary and Child Jesus" (wood-carving, St. George's Church, Purgg)

1999. Ancient Arts and Crafts (2nd series).
2542 **1191** 9s. multicoloured . . . 1·20 1·30

1192 1949 25g. Stamp and Vienna Airport

1999. "WIPA 2000" International Stamp Exhibition, Vienna (3rd issue).
2543 **1192** 32s.+16s. mult . . . . 5·50 7·00

1193 "Security throughout Life"
1194 "Cafe Girardi" (Wolfgang Herzig)

1999. 14th Congress of Federation of Austrian Trade Unions.
2544 **1193** 6s.50 multicoloured . . 95 90

1999. Austrian Modern Art.
2545 **1194** 7s. multicoloured . . . 95 90

1999. Folk Customs and Art (14th series). As T **1005**. Multicoloured.
2546 8s. Pumpkin Festival, Lower Austria . . . . 1·10 1·20

1999. Folk Customs and Art (15th series). As T **1005**. Multicoloured.
2547 7s. The Pummerin (great bell of St. Stephen's Cathedral) ringing in the New Year 95 90

1195 Institute and Fossils

1999. 150th Anniv of National Institute of Geology.
2548 **1195** 7s. multicoloured . . . 95 90

1196 "Nativity" (altar painting, Pinkafeld Church)

1999. Christmas.
2549 **1196** 7s. multicoloured . . . 95 90

2000. Folk Customs and Art (16th series). As T **1005**. Multicoloured.
2550 7s. Chapel procession, Carinthia . . . . 95 1·10

2000. "WIPA 2000" International Stamp Exhibition, Vienna (4th issue). Sheet 150 × 95 mm.
MS2551 27s.+13s. No. 2478; 32s.+13s. No. 2521; 32s.+16s. No. 2543 . . . . 12·00 12·00

2000. Folk Customs and Art (17th series). As T **1005**. Multicoloured.
2552 6s.50 Three men wearing masks (Cavalcade of Beautiful Masks, Telfs) 85 95

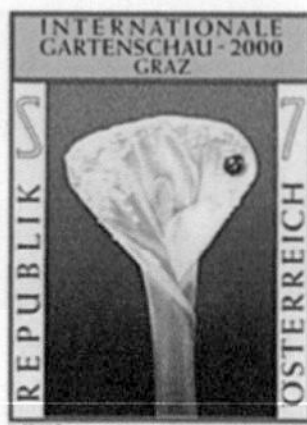

1197 *Zantadeschica aethiopica*

2000. International Garden Show, Graz.
2553 **1197** 7s. multicoloured . . . 95 1·10

1198 Ibex

2000. Hunting and the Environment. Return of Ibex to Austrian Mountains.
2554 **1198** 7s. multicoloured . . . 95 1·10

1199 Players

2000. F.C. Tirol Innsbruck, National Football Champion 2000.
2555 **1199** 7s. multicoloured . . . 95 1·10

1200 Mt. Grossglockner and Viewing Point

2000. Bicentenary of First Ascent of Mt. Grossglockner.
2556 **1200** 7s. multicoloured . . . 95 1·10

1201 Weisssee Lake

2000. Natural Beauty Spots.
2557 **1201** 7s. multicoloured . . . 95 1·10

1202 "Building Europe"

1203 Junkers Airplane and Air Traffic Control Tower

2000. Europa.
2558 **1202** 7s. multicoloured . . . 95 1·10

2000. 75th Anniv of Civil Aviation at Klagenfurt Airport.
2559 **1203** 7s. multicoloured . . . 95 1·10

1204 Madonna of Altenmarkt (statue) and Glass Roof, Palm House, Burggarten, Vienna

2000. 150th Anniv of Protection of Historic Monuments.
2560 **1204** 8s. multicoloured . . . 1·00 1·20

1205 Illuminated Letter and Text

2000. Life of St. Malachy (treatise) by St. Bernard of Clairvaux.
2561 **1205** 9s. multicoloured . . . 1·20 1·40

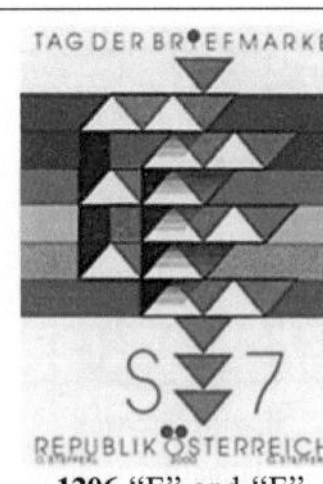
1206 "E" and "E"

2000. Stamp Day.
2562 **1206** 7s. multicoloured . . . 95 1·10
See note below No. 2266.

1207 1850 9 Kreuzer and 2000 Stamp Day Stamps

2000. 150th Anniv of Austrian Stamps.
2563 **1207** 7s. multicoloured . . . 95 1·10

2000. "WIPA 2000" International Stamp Exhibition, Vienna (5th series). Sheet 65 × 90 mm.
MS2564 10s. As No. 2458 . . . 12·00 12·00

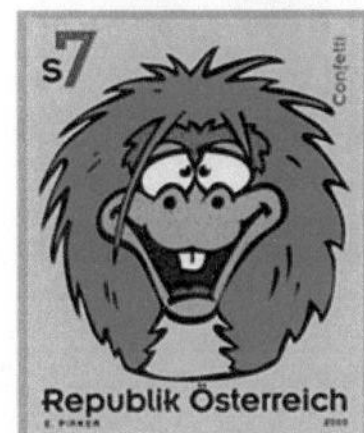
1208 "Confetti"

2000. *Confetti* (children's television programme).
2565 **1208** 7s. multicoloured . . . 95 1·10

1209 "Blue Blues"

2000. Death Commemoration of Friedensreich Hundertwasser (artist). Sheet 129 × 126 mm, containing four versions of T **1209** identified by the colours of the vertical strips at the top of the design.
MS2566 7s. silver; 7s. red; 7s. mauve; 7s. black . . . . 3·25 3·25

1210 Blood Droplets

2000. Centenary of Discovery of Blood Groups by Karl Landsteiner (pathologist).
2567 **1210** 8s. pink, silver & black 90 1·20

1211 Daimler Cannstatter Bus

2000. Centenary of First Regular Bus Route between Purkersdorf and Gablitz.
2568 **1211** 9s. black, blue and light blue . . . . 1·10 1·30

2000. Folk Customs and Art (18th series). As T **1005**. Multicoloured.
2569 7s. Men on raft (International Rafting Meeting, Carinthia) . . . 95 1·10

1212 Dachstein River and Hallstatt

2000. Natural Beauty Spots.
2570 **1212** 7s. multicoloured . . . 95 1·10

1213 String Instrument and Emblem

2000. Centenary of Vienna Symphony Orchestra.
2571 **1213** 7s. multicoloured . . . 95 1·10

1214 Dinghies

2000. Olympic Games, Sydney.
2572 **1214** 9s. multicoloured . . . 1·20 1·30

1215 Old and Modern Paper Production Methods

2000. Austrian World of Work (11th series). Printing and Paper.
2573 **1215** 6s.50 multicoloured . . 85 1·00

1216 "Turf Turkey" (Ida Szigethy)

2000. Austrian Modern Art.
2574 **1216** 7s. multicoloured . . . 95 1·10

1217 Codex 965 (National Library)

2000. Ancient Arts and Crafts (3rd series).
2575 **1217** 8s. multicoloured . . . 1·00 1·20
See also Nos. 2600 and 2602.

1218 Child receiving Vaccination

2000. Bicentenary of Vaccination in Austria.
2576 **1218** 7s. black and cinnamon 95 1·10

1219 Urania Building, Vienna

2000. 50th Anniv of Adult Education Association.
2577 **1219** 7s. brown, grey & gold 95 1·10

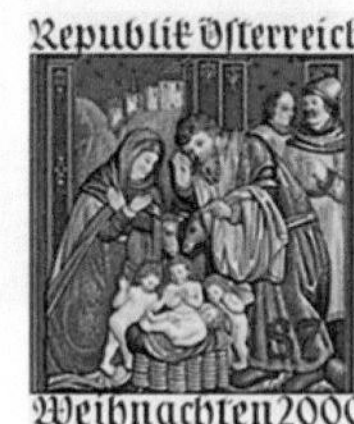
1220 The Nativity (altar piece, Ludesch Church)

2000. Christmas.
2578 **1220** 7s. multicoloured . . . 95 1·10

1221 Downhill Skier

2000. World Skiing Championship (2001), St. Anton am Arlberg.
2579 **1221** 7s. multicoloured . . . 95 1·20

1222 Pair of Mallards

2001. Hunting and the Environment. Protection of Wetlands.
2580 **1222** 7s. multicoloured . . . 95 1·10

2001. Folk Customs and Art (19th series). As T **1005**. Multicoloured.
2581 8s. Boat mill, Mureck, Styria . . . . 95 1·20

1223 Steam Locomotive No. 3

2001. Centenary of Zillertal Railway.
2582 **1223** 7s. multicoloured . . . 95 1·10

1224 Players and Club Emblem

2001. SV Casino Salzburg, National Football Champion.
2583 **1224** 7s. multicoloured . . . 95 1·10

1225 Rolf Rudiger

2001. *Confetti* (children's television programme).
2584 **1225** 7s. multicoloured . . . 95 1·10

1226 Monoplane and Airport

2001. 75th Anniv of Salzburg Airport.
2585 **1226** 14s. multicoloured . . . 1·70 1·90

1227 Baerenschuetz Gorge

2001. Natural Beauty Spots.
2586 **1227** 7s. multicoloured . . . 95 1·10

2001. Folk Customs and Art (20th series). As T **1005**. Multicoloured.
2587 7s. Lent season cloth from Eastern Tyrol . . . . . . 95 1·10

1228 Water Droplet **1230** Air Balloon

1229 Post Office Railway Car

2001. Europa. Water Resources.
2588 **1228** 15s. multicoloured . . . 1·90 1·80

2001. Stamp Day.
2589 **1229** 20s.+10s. mult . . . . 4·00 4·50

2001. Centenary of Austrian Flying Club.
2590 **1230** 7s. multicoloured . . . 95 85

1231 Refugee

2001. 50th Anniv of United Nations High Commissioner for Refugees.
2591 **1231** 21s. multicoloured . . . 3·75 2·40

1232 Kalte Rinne Viaduct

2001. U.N.E.S.C.O. World Heritage Site. The Semmering Railway.
2592 **1232** 35s. multicoloured . . . 4·50 5·75

1233 "Seppl" (mascot) (Michelle Schneeweiss)

2001. 7th International Hiking Olympics, Seefeld.
2593 **1233** 7s. multicoloured . . . 95 1·10

1234 Field Post Office at Famagusta

2001. Army Postal Services Abroad.
2594 **1234** 7s. multicoloured . . . 85 1·10

2001. Folk Customs and Art (21st series). As T **1005**. Multicoloured.
2595 7s. Rifle and Clubhouse, Preberschiessen, Salzburg (Rifleman's gathering) . . 95 1·10

1235 "Taurus" (Railway Engine)

2001. Conversion of East–West Railway to Four-tracked Railway.
2596 **1235** 7s. multicoloured . . . 95 1·10

1236 19th-century Theatrical Scene

2001. Birth Bicentenary of Johann Nestroy (playwright and actor).
2597 **1236** 7s. multicoloured . . . 95 1·10

1237 "The Continents" (detail Helmut Leherb)

2001. Austrian Modern Art.
2598 **1237** 7s. multicoloured . . . 95 1·10

1238 "False Friends" (Von Fuehrich)

2001. 125th Death Anniv of Joseph Ritter von Fuehrich (artist and engraver).
2599 **1238** 8s. deep green & green 1·10 1·20

1239 Pluviale (embroidered religious robe) **1240** Dobler

2001. Ancient Arts and Crafts (4th series).
2600 **1239** 10s. multicoloured . . . 1·40 1·50

2001. Birth Bicentenary of Leopold Ludwig Dobler (magician and inventor).
2601 **1240** 7s. multicoloured . . . 95 1·10

1241 Dalmatik (religious vestment) (Carmelite Monastery, Silbergrasse, Vienna)

2001. Ancient Arts and Crafts (5th series).
2602 **1241** 7s. multicoloured . . . 95 1·10

1242 Building and Scientific Equipment

2001. 150th Anniv of the Central Institute for Meteorology and Geodynamics, Vienna.
2603 **1242** 12s. multicoloured . . . 1·70 1·60

1243 Cat

2001.
2604 **1243** 19s. multicoloured . . . 2·30 3·00

1244 Civil Servants

2001. Austrian World of Work (12th series). Civil Service.
2605 **1244** 7s. multicoloured . . . 95 1·10

1245 Figure of Infant Jesus **1246** House of the Basilisk, Vienna

2001. Christmas. Glass Shrine, Fitzmoos Church.
2606 **1245** 7s. multicoloured . . . 95 1·10

New Currency

2002. Tourism.

2607	–	4c. multicoloured . . .	10	10
2608	–	7c. blue and black . . .	10	10
2609	–	13c. multicoloured . . .	20	20
2610	–	17c. violet and black . .	25	25
2611	–	20c. multicoloured . . .	30	30
2612	–	25c. multicoloured . . .	35	35
2613	–	27c. blue and black . .	35	35
2614	–	45c. multicoloured . . .	60	60
2615	**1246**	51c. multicoloured . . .	70	70
2616	–	55c. multicoloured . . .	75	75
2617	–	58c. multicoloured . . .	1·10	1·20
2618	–	73c. multicoloured . . .	1·40	1·50
2619	–	75c. multicoloured . . .	1·00	1·00
2620	–	87c. multicoloured . . .	5·25	5·25
2621	–	€1 multicoloured . . .	1·70	1·70
2622	–	€1.25 multicoloured	1·50	1·40
2623	–	€2.03 multicoloured	3·50	4·00
2626	–	€3.75 multicoloured	5·00	5·00

DESIGNS: 4c. As No. 2615; 7c. As No. 2623; 13c. As No. 2620; 17c. As No. 2617; 20c. Yachts, Worthersee, Carintha; 25c. Crucifixes on rock, Mondsee, Upper Austria; 27c. As No. 2618; 45c. Snow covered chalet, Jungholz, Kleinwasler; 55c. Gothic houses, Steyr, Upper Austria; 58c. Wine cellars, Hadres, Lower Austria; 73c. Alpine chalet, Salzburg; 87c. Alpach Valley, Tyrol; €1 Farmhouse, Rossegg, Styria; €1.25 Wine press building, Eisenburg, Burgenland; €2.03 Heligenkreuz, Lower Austria; €3.75 Gothic shrine, Hochhosterwitz, Carinthia.

1247 Stars, Map of Europe and €1 Coin

2002. Euro Currency.
2630 **1247** €3.27 multicoloured 5·25 5·25
No. 2630 is printed on the back under the gum with examples of Austrian schilling coins.

1248 Skiers and Olympic Rings

2002. Winter Olympic Games, Salt Lake City, U.S.A.
2631 **1248** 73c. multicoloured . . . 1·40 1·40

1249 Bouquet of Flowers

2002.
2632 **1249** 87c. multicoloured . . . 1·50 1·40

1250 Woman and Skyline

2002. Women's Day.
2633 **1250** 51c. multicoloured . . . 95 1·10

1251 Mel and Lucy

2002. "Philis" (children's stamp awareness programme) (1st issue).
2634 **1251** 58c. multicoloured . . . 1·10 1·10
See also Nos. 2639 and 2662.

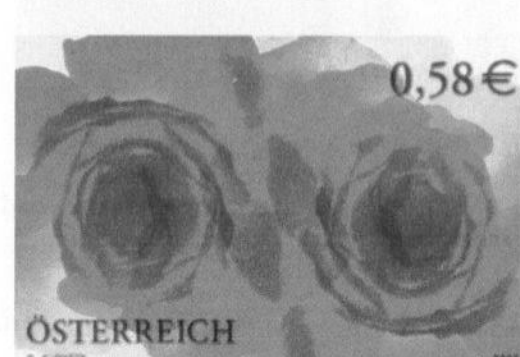

1252 Red Roses

2002. Greetings Stamp.
2635 **1252** 58c. multicoloured . . . 1·10 1·00

1253 Kubin

2002. 125th Birth Anniv of Alfred Kubin (artist).
2636 **1253** 87c. black and buff . . 1·60 1·40

1254 St. Elizabeth of Thuringia and Sick Man

2002. Caritas (Catholic charity organization).
2637 **1254** 51c. multicoloured . . . 95 1·00

1255 Tiger, Clown and Circus Tent

2002. Europa. The Circus.
2638 **1255** 87c. multicoloured . . . 1·40 95

1256 Sisko and Mauritius

2002. "Philis" (children's stamp awareness programme) (2nd issue).
2639 **1256** 58c. multicoloured . . . 1·10 75

1257 The Nativity

2002. 800th Anniv of Lilienfeld Abbey.
2640 **1257** €2.03 multicoloured 3·25 1·90

1258 Mimi

2002. *Confetti* (children's television programme).
2641 **1258** 51c. multicoloured . . . 90 65

1259 Railway Carriage, 1919

2002. Stamp Day.
2642 **1259** €1.60+80c. multicoloured . . . . 3·75 4·00

1260 Cheetah, Zebra and Orang-utan

2002. 250th Anniv of Schonbrunn Zoo. Mult.
2643 51c. Type **1260** 95 70
2644 58c. Gulls, flamingos and pelicans . . . . 1·10 65
2645 87c. Lion, turtle and crocodile . . . . 1·40 95
2646 €1.38 Elephant, birds and fish . . . . 2·30 1·30
Nos. 2643/6 were issued together, se-tenant, forming a composite design.

1261 Teddy Bears

2002. Centenary of the Teddy Bear.
2647 **1261** 51c. multicoloured . . . 95 65

1262 Chair No. 14 (Michael Thonet)

2002. 75th Anniv of "Design Austria" (design group) (1st issue).
2648 **1262** €1.38 multicoloured 2·40 1·40
See also Nos. 2661 and 2670.

1263 Crystal Cup

2002. Ancient Arts and Crafts.
2649 **1263** €1.60 multicoloured 2·40 1·60

1264 Museum Buildings

2002. Museumsquartier (MQ), Messepalast, Vienna.
2650 **1264** 58c. multicoloured . . . 1·10 65

1265 Figures supporting Emblem

2002. 50th Anniv of Union of Austrians Abroad.
2651 **1265** €2.47 multicoloured 3·00 2·75

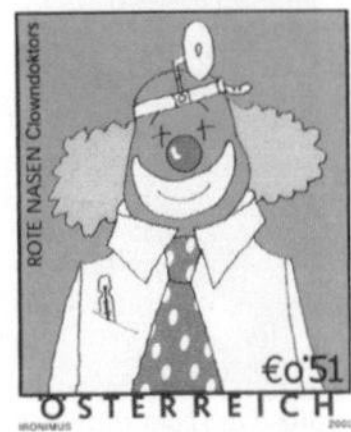

1266 Clown Doctor

2002. "Rote Nasen" (Red Noses (charity)).
2652 **1266** 51c. multicoloured . . . 75 65

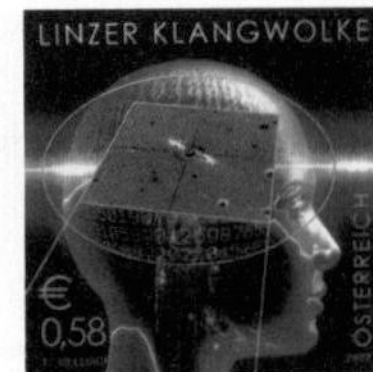

1267 Head

2002. Linzer Klangwolke (sound and light performance), Linz.
2653 **1267** 58c. multicoloured . . . 95 60

1268 Graf & Stift Typ 40/45

2002.
2654 **1268** 51c. multicoloured . . . 85 50

1269 Dog

2002.
2655 **1269** 51c. multicoloured . . . 85 50

1270 Steam Locomotive 109

2002.
2656 **1270** 51c. multicoloured . . . 85 50

1271 "Schutzenhaus" (Karl Goldammer)

2002. Austrian Modern Art.
2657 **1271** 51c. multicoloured . . . 85 50

1272 Lottery Ball

2002. 250th Anniv of Austrian Lottery. Sheet 72 × 90 mm.
MS2658 **1272** 87c. multicoloured 1·60 1·60

1273 Thayatal National Park

2002.
2659 **1273** 58c. multicoloured . . . 1·10 65

1274 Puch 175 SV

2002.
2660 **1274** 58c. multicoloured . . . 1·10 90

1275 "Eye"

2002. 75th Anniv of "Design Austria" (design group) (2nd issue). Winning Entry in Design Competition.
2661 **1275** €1.38 multicoloured 2·75 2·10

1276 Edison and Gogo

2002. "Philis" (children's stamp awareness programme) (3rd issue).
2662 **1276** 58c. multicoloured . . . 1·10 90

1277 Crib Aureola, Thaur, Tyrol

2002. Christmas.
2663 **1277** 51c. multicoloured . . . 95 65

1278 Emblem

2003. Make-up Rate Stamp.
2664 **1278** 45c. yellow, silver and black 60 60

1279 Amphitheatre on River Mur

2003. Graz, Cultural Capital of Europe, 2003.
2665 **1279** 58c. multicoloured . . . 80 80

1280 Billy Wilder

1281 Heart, Linked Rings and Doves

2003. 1st Death Anniv of Billy Wilder (film director).
2666 **1280** 58c. multicoloured . . . 80 80

2003. Greetings Stamp. Wedding.
2667 **1281** 58c. multicoloured . . . 80 80

1282 Kasperl

2003. Confetti (children's television programme). 45th Anniv of Kasperl (puppet).
2668 **1282** 51c. multicoloured . . . 70 70

1283 Emblem

1284 Carafe and Glasses (Adolf Loos)

2003. 10th Anniv of Recycling Enterprise.
2669 **1283** 55c. multicoloured . . . 75 75

2003. 75th Anniv of "Design Austria" (design group) (3rd issue).
2670 **1284** €1.38 blue, black and orange . . . . 1·90 1·90

1285 Seated Pandas

2003. Schönbrunn Zoo's Acquisition of Pandas from People's Republic of China. Sheet 110 × 76 mm containing T **1285** and similar multicoloured design.
MS2671 75c. Pandas nuzzling (40 × 34 mm) (horiz); €1 Type **1285** . . . . 2·40 2·40

1286 St. George's Monastery

2003. Millenary of St. George's Monastery, Carintha.
2672 **1286** 87c. multicoloured . . . 1·20 1·20

1287 Marcel Prawy

2003. Marcel Prawy Commemoration (musician). Sheet 100 × 100 mm.
MS2673 **1287** €1.75 multicoloured 2·40 2·40

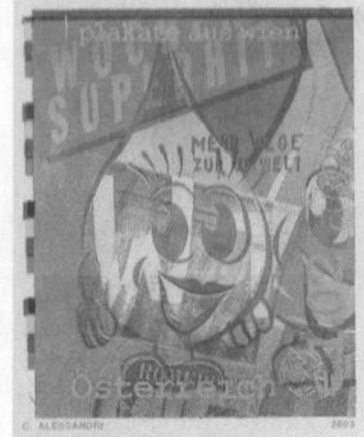
1288 Face

2003. Europa. Poster Art.
2674 **1288** €1.02 multicoloured 1·40 1·40

1289 Siemens M 320 Postal Wagon

2003. Stamp Day.
2675 **1289** €2.54+€1.26 multicoloured . . . . 5·00 5·00

1290 Series 5045 Locomotive "Blue Flash"

2003.
2676 **1290** 75c. multicoloured . . . 1·00 1·00

1291 Bridge over Salzach River

2003. Centenary of Oberndorf–Laufen Bridge.
2677 **1291** 55c. multicoloured . . . 75 75
A stamp of the same design was issued by Germany.

1292 Ford Model T

2003. Centenary of Ford Motor Company. Sheet 150 × 81 mm containing T **1292** and similar horiz designs. Multicoloured. .
MS2678 Type **1292**; 55c. Henry Ford; 55c. Ford Streetka . . . 1·50 1·50

1293 Keith Richards

2003. Rolling Stones. Sheet 101 × 101 mm containing T **1291** and similar vert designs. Multicoloured.
MS2679 Type **1293**; 55c. Mick Jagger; 55c. Charlie Watts; 55c. Ronnie Woods . . . . 2·25 2·25

1294 Panther Airport Fire Appliance

2003.
2688 **1294** 55c. multicoloured . . . 75 75

1295 Apostle and Scribe

1296 "Prenez le temps d'aimer" (Take time to enjoy) (Kiki Kogelnik)

2003. Year of the Bible.
2689 **1295** 55c. multicoloured . . . 75 75

2003.
2690 **1296** 55c. multicoloured . . . 75 75

1297 Lake

2003. UNESCO World Heritage Site. Lake Neusiedlersee.
2691 **1297** €1 multicoloured . . . 1·40 1·40

1298 Geisha and Samurai

2003. Japan Exhibition, Leoben.
2692 **1298** 55c. multicoloured . . . 75 75

1299 Princess Turandot

2003. Performance of Puccini's Opera *Turandot*, St. Margarethen Roman Quarry.
2693 **1299** 55c. multicoloured . . . 75 75

1300 Family (Eva Wallner)

1301 Water Tower

2003. Children's Stamp.
2694 **1300** 55c. multicoloured . . . 75 75

2003. 50th Anniv Local Government Conference, Wiener Neustadt.
2695 **1301** 55c. multicoloured . . . 75 75

1302 TomTom (cartoon character) and Bouquet

2003. Greetings stamp.
2696 **1302** 55c. multicoloured . . . 75 75

1303 TomTom throwing Parcel from Hot Air Balloon

2003.
2697 **1303** 55c. multicoloured . . . 75 75

1304 Werner Schlager

2003. Werner Schlager, World Table Tennis Champion, 2003.
2698 **1304** 55c. multicoloured . . . 75 75

1305 Stylized Head (Cornelia Zell)

2003. Jugend-Phila '03 International Youth Stamp Exhibition, Graz.
2699 **1305** 55c. multicoloured . . . 75 75

1306 Fan and "Elisabeth"

2003. Elisabeth, the Musical (musical based on life of Empress Elisabeth).
2700 **1306** 55c. multicoloured . . . 75 75

1307 "Judith"

1309 Grand Piano

1308 Hands enclosing Light

2003. 185th Death Anniv of Gustav Klimt (artist). Sheet 80 × 100 mm.
MS2701 **1308** €2.10 multicoloured 3·00 3·00

2003. 30th Anniv of "Licht ins Dunkel" (Bringing light into darkness) (fund raising campaign).
2702 **1308** 55c. multicoloured . . . 75 75

2003. 175th Anniv of Bosendorfer (piano manufacturer).
2703 **1309** 75c. multicoloured . . . 1·00 1·00

1310 Oscar Peterson

2003. 78th Birth Anniv of Oscar Peterson (pianist).
2704 **1310** €1.25 multicoloured 1·70 1·70

1311 Stained Glass Window

2003. Christmas.
2705 **1311** 55c. multicoloured . . . 75 75

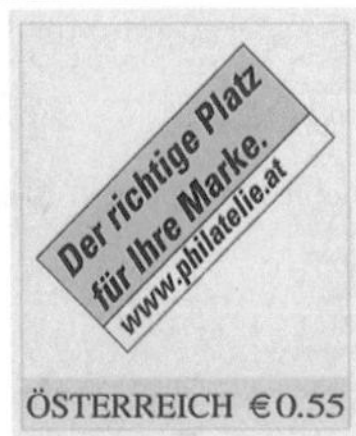

1312 Postal Emblem

2003. Greeting Stamps. T **1312** and similar design. Each yellow, black and gold.
2706 55c. Type **1312** 75 75
2707 55c. Postal emblem (horiz) 75 75
Nos. 2706/7 could be personalised by the addition of photograph or logo, replacing the design shown on the stamp.

1313 Ricardo Muti

2004. Vienna Philharmonic Orchestra's New Year Concert conducted by Ricardo Muti (principal conductor, La Scala Milan).
2708 **1313** €1 multicoloured . . . 1·30 1·30

1314 Seiji Ozawa

2004. 2nd Anniv of Seija Ozawa's Appointment as Musical Director of Vienna State Opera House.
2709 **1314** €1 multicoloured . . . 1·30 1·30

1315 Jose Carreras

2004. 30th Anniv of Jose Carreras Association with Vienna State Opera House.
2710 **1315** €1 multicoloured . . . 1·30 1·30

1316 Gerard Hanappi

2004. Centenary of Austrian Football. Sheet 196 × 113 mm containing T **1316** and similar vert designs. Multicoloured.
MS2711 55c. × 10, Type **1316**; Mathias Sindelar; Football and anniversary emblem; Bruno Pezzey; Ernst Ocwirk; Walter Zeman; Herbert Prohaska; Hans Krankl; Andreas Herzog; Anton Polster . . . . 7·25 7·25

1317 Crucifixion (Werner Berg)

2004. Easter.
2712 **1317** 55c. multicoloured . . . 75 75

1318 Dancers

2004. Life Ball (AIDS charity).
2713 **1318** 55c. multicoloured . . . 75 75

1319 Cardinal Franz Konig

2004. Cardinal Franz Konig Commemoration.
2714 **1319** €1 multicoloured . . . 1·30 1·30

1320 Emperor Franz Joseph and Empress Elisabeth

2004. 150th Anniv of the Marriage of Emperor Franz Joseph and Empress Elisabeth. Sheet 157 × 109 mm containing T **1320** and similar vert designs. Multicoloured.
MS2715 €1.25 Type **1320**; €1.50 Wedding procession; €1.75 Emperor Franz Joseph and Empress Elisabeth (35 × 42 mm) 4·75 4·75

1321 Catholics' Day Emblem

2004. Catholics' Day. Sheet 110 × 160 mm containing T **1321** and similar vert designs. Multicoloured.
MS2716 55c. Type **1321**; €1.25 Pope John Paul II; €1.25 Magna Mater Austriae (Romanesque statue) (Chapel of Grace, Basilica, Mariazell); €1.25 Mother of God on Column of the Blessed Virgin (Basilica, Mariazell); €1.25 Virgin Mary (Treasury Altar, Basilica, Mariazell); €1.25 Crucifix (High Altar, Basilica, Mariazell) . . . 9·00 9·00

IMPERIAL JOURNAL STAMPS

J 18 **J 21** Arms of Austria **J 22** Arms of Austria

1853. Imperf.
J67 1k. blue . . . . 38·00 5·25
J15 2k. green . . . . £1800 70·00
J68 2k. brown . . . . 33·00 7·50
J32 4k. brown £425 £1400
The 2k. green has different corner ornaments.
For similar values in black or red, see Lombardy and Venetia Imperial Journal stamps, Nos. J22/4.

1890. Imperf.
J76 **J 21** 1k. brown . . . . 11·50 1·60
J77 2k. green . . . . 11·50 2·75

1890. Perf.
J78 **J 22** 25k. red £100 £225

NEWSPAPER STAMPS

N 2 Mercury **N 8** Francis Joseph I **N 11** Francis Joseph I

1851. Imperf.
N11b **N 2** (0.6k.) blue £160 £100
N12 (6k.) yellow £21000 £9000
N13 (6k.) red £43000 £49000
N14 (30k.) red £16000 £13000

1858. Imperf.
N28 **N 8** (1k.05) blue £500 £650
N29 (1k.05) lilac £750 £350

1861. Imperf.
N38 **N 11** (1k.05) grey £180 £170

N 13 Arms of Austria **AHN 17** Mercury **N 19** Mercury

1863. Imperf.
N44 **N 13** (1k.05) lilac . . . . . 40·00 15·00

1867. Imperf.
AHN58b **AHN 17** (1k.) lilac . . . 55 30

1880. Imperf.
N69 **N 19** ½k. green . . . . 7·00 1·10

N 31 Mercury **N 43** Mercury

1899. Imperf.
N122 **N 31** 2h. blue 20 15
N123 6h. orange . . . . . 1·90 2·20
N124 10h. brown . . . . . 1·40 1·00
N125 20h. pink . . . . . . 1·40 1·80

1908. Imperf.
N207 **N 43** 2h. blue 95 20
N208 6h. orange . . . . . 4·25 65
N209 10h. red . . . . . . 4·25 65
N210 20h. brown . . . . . 4·25 50

N 53 Mercury **N 54** Mercury

1916. Imperf.
N266 **N 53** 2h. brown 10 20
N267 4h. green . . . . . . 40 1·20
N268 6h. blue . . . . 40 1·10
N269 10h. orange . . . . . 65 1·30
N270 30h. red . . . . 40 1·10

1916. For Express. Perf.
N271 **N 54** 2h. red on yellow . . 95 2·00
N272 5h. green on yellow . . 95 2·00

N 61 Mercury **N 68** Mercury

1917. For Express. Perf.
N294 **N 61** 2h. red on yellow . . 20 35
N295 5h. green on yellow . . 20 35

1919. Optd **Deutschosterreich**. Imperf.
N318 **N 53** 2h. brown 10 15
N319 4h. green 30 85
N320 6h. blue 20 90
N321 10h. orange . . . . . 30 1·30
N322 30h. red 20 55

1919. For Express. Optd **Deutschosterreich**. Perf.
N334 **N 61** 2h. red on yellow . . 10 25
N335 5h. green on yellow . . 10 25

1920. Imperf.
N365 **N 68** 2h. violet 10 15
N366 4h. brown 10 25
N367 5h. slate 10 15
N368 6h. blue 10 15
N369 8h. green 10 35
N370 9h. bistre 10 15
N371 10h. red 10 15
N372 12h. blue 10 45
N373 15h. mauve 10 20
N374 18h. turquoise 10 30
N375 20h. orange 10 30
N376 30h. brown 10 15
N377 45h. green 10 65
N378 60h. red 20 20
N379 72h. brown 30 65
N380 90h. violet 30 85
N381 1k.20 red 30 95
N382 2k.40 green 30 95
N383 3k. grey 30 55

1921. For Express. No. N334 surch **50 50**.
N450 **N 61** 50 on 2h. red on yell 20 25

N 78 Mercury **N 79** Posthorn and Arrow

1921. Imperf.
N452 **N 78** 45h. grey 10 30
N453 75h. red 10 50
N454 1k.50 green 10 75
N455 1k.80 blue 10 80
N456 2k.25 brown . . . . . 20 1·10
N457 3k. green 20 70
N458 6k. purple 20 90
N459 7k.50 brown . . . . . 30 1·30

1921. For Express. Perf.
N460 **N 79** 50h. lilac on yellow . . 20 2·10

POSTAGE DUE STAMPS

D 26 **D 44**

1894. Perf.
D 96 **D 26** 1k. brown . . . . . . 2·50 1·10
D 97 2k. brown . . . . . . 3·25 2·20
D 98 3k. brown . . . . . . 3·75 1·20
D 99 5k. brown . . . . . . 3·50 65
D100 6k. brown . . . . . . 3·00 5·75
D101 7k. brown . . . . . . 1·40 5·75
D102 10k. brown . . . . . 4·00 60
D103 20k. brown . . . . . 1·00 6·00
D104 50k. brown . . . . . 32·00 60·00

1899. As Type D **26**, but value in heller. Perf or imperf.
D126 **D 26** 1h. brown 40 30
D127 2h. brown 45 35
D128 3h. brown 40 30
D129 4h. brown 95 50
D130 5h. brown 80 45
D131 6h. brown 65 30
D132 10h. brown 75 30
D133 12h. brown 80 90
D134 15h. brown . . . . . 1·25 1·10
D135 20h. brown . . . . . 1·90 60
D136 40h. brown . . . . . 2·75 75
D137 100h. brown . . . . . 5·25 2·30

1908. Perf.
D210 **D 44** 1h. red . . . . 2·75 1·90
D211 2h. red 35 40
D212 4h. red 30 25
D213 6h. red 30 30
D214 10h. red 50 25
D215 14h. red . . . . . . 4·25 2·30
D216 20h. red . . . . . . 9·00 15
D217 25h. red . . . . . . 8·25 5·00
D218 30h. red . . . . . . 8·50 30
D219 50h. red . . . . . . 16·00 40
D220 100h. red . . . . . . 22·00 65
D221 5k. violet . . . . . . 70·00 12·00
D222 10k. violet . . . . . . £250 3·50

D 55 **D 56**

1916.
D273 **D 55** 5h. red 10 15
D274 10h. red 10 15
D275 15h. red 10 15
D276 20h. red 10 15
D277 25h. red 30 90
D278 30h. red 15 30
D279 40h. red 20 30
D280 50h. red . . . . . . 1·10 2·00
D281 **D 56** 1k. blue 25 20

D282 5k. blue . . . . 2·40 3·00
D283 10k. blue . . . . . . 3·00 1·40

1916. Nos. 189/90 optd **PORTO** or surch **15 15** also.
D284 1h. black 10 15
D285 15 on 2h. violet 30 50

1917. Unissued stamps as T **50** surch **PORTO** and value.
D286 **50** 10 on 24h. blue . . . . 1·80 50
D287 15 on 36h. violet . . . 45 20
D288 20 on 54h. orange . . . 35 40
D289 50 on 42h. brown . . . 35 30

The above differ from Type **50** by showing a full-face portrait.

1919. Optd **Deutschosterreich**.
D323 **D 55** 5h. red 15 20
D324 10h. red 15 20
D325 15h. red 30 50
D326 20h. red 30 40
D327 25h. red . . . . . . 8·50 17·00
D328 30h. red 15 30
D329 40h. red 30 65
D330 50h. red . . . . . . 30 1·50
D331 **D 56** 1k. blue . . . . . . 5·00 12·00
D332 5k. blue . . . . . . 8·75 13·00
D333 10k. blue . . . . . . 9·25 4·25

D 69 D 70

1920. Imperf or perf (D **69**), perf (D **70**).
D384 **D 69** 5h. pink 15 30
D385 10h. pink 10 40
D386 15h. pink . . . . . . 15 1·10
D387 20h. pink 10 45
D388 25h. pink . . . . . . 25 1·10
D389 30h. pink 10 30
D390 40h. pink 10 25
D391 50h. pink 10 30
D392 80h. pink 10 40
D393 **D 70** 1k. blue 10 20
D394 1½k. blue 10 25
D395 2k. blue 10 30
D396 3k. blue 15 55
D397 4k. blue 10 85
D398 5k. blue 15 45
D399 8k. blue 30 90
D400 10k. blue 20 40
D401 20k. blue . . . . . . 60 1·40

1921. No. 343a surch **Nachmarke 7½ K.** Perf.
D451 **64** 7½k. on 15h. brown . . . 15 25

D 83 D 86

1921.
D510 **D 83** 1k. brown 10 30
D511 2k. brown 10 35
D512 4k. brown 10 70
D513 5k. brown 10 30
D514 7½k. brown . . . . . . 15 1·10
D515 – 10k. blue 10 30
D516 – 15k. blue 15 55
D517 – 20k. blue 15 55
D518 – 50k. blue 10 50

The 10k. to 50k. are larger (22 × 30 mm).

1922.
D526 **D 83** 10k. turquoise 15 35
D527 15k. turquoise 10 75
D528 20k. turquoise 15 50
D529 25k. turquoise . . . . 10 1·30
D530 40k. turquoise 10 35
D531 50k. turquoise . . . . 15 1·30
D532 **D 86** 100k. purple 15 20
D533 150k. purple 15 20
D534 200k. purple 15 20
D535 400k. purple 15 20
D536 600k. purple 25 55
D537 800k. purple 15 20
D538 1000k. purple 15 20
D539 **D 86** 1200k. purple . . . . 1·60 3·00
D540 1500k. purple 25 30
D541 1800k. purple . . . . 3·00 7·50
D542 2000k. purple 65 95
D543 3000k. purple . . . . 9·75 18·00
D544 4000k. purple . . . . 8·25 15·00
D545 6000k. purple . . . . 10·00 26·00

D 94 D 120

1925.
D589 **D 94** 1g. red 15 15
D590 2g. red 15 15
D591 3g. red 20 15
D592 4g. red 20 15
D593 5g. red 15 10
D594 6g. red 35 50
D595 8g. red 35 25
D596 10g. blue 35 10
D597 12g. blue 20 15
D598 14g. blue 20 15
D599 15g. blue 15 10
D600 16g. blue 40 20
D601 18g. blue . . . . . . 1·50 4·25
D602 20g. blue 35 10
D603 23g. blue . . . . . . 1·10 20
D604 24g. blue . . . . . . 3·25 15
D605 28g. blue . . . . . . 2·75 30
D606 30g. blue 90 15
D607 31g. blue . . . . . . 3·25 30
D608 35g. blue . . . . . . 3·50 20
D609 39g. blue . . . . . . 3·75 15
D610 40g. blue . . . . . . 2·75 2·40
D611 60g. blue . . . . . . 1·70 2·10
D612 – 1s. green . . . . . . 4·75 1·20
D613 – 2s. green . . . . . . 29·00 4·00
D614 – 5s. green . . . . . . £130 43·00
D615 – 10s. green . . . . . . 55·00 4·50

DESIGN: 1 to 10s. Horiz bands of colour.

1935.
D746 **D 120** 1g. red 20 20
D747 2g. red 30 25
D748 3g. red 20 20
D749 5g. red 20 20
D750 – 10g. blue 20 20
D751 – 12g. blue 20 15
D752 – 15g. blue 30 55
D753 – 20g. blue 40 15
D754 – 24g. blue 65 15
D755 – 30g. blue 65 15
D756 – 39g. blue . . . . . . 1·00 15
D757 – 60g. blue . . . . . . 1·30 1·20
D758 – 1s. green . . . . . . 1·80 30
D759 – 2s. green . . . . . . 3·75 95
D760 – 5s. green . . . . . . 5·25 4·25
D761 – 10s. green . . . . . . 7·00 80

DESIGNS: 10 to 60g. As Type D **120** but with background of horizontal lines; 1 to 10s. As last, but with positions of figures, arms and inscriptions reversed.

D 143 D 162

1945.
D891 **D 143** 1pf. red 10 20
D892 2pf. red 10 20
D893 3pf. red 10 20
D894 5pf. red 10 20
D895 10pf. red 10 20
D896 12pf. red 10 25
D897 20pf. red 10 25
D898 24pf. red 10 35
D899 30pf. red 10 55
D900 60pf. red 10 45
D901 1rm. violet 10 50
D902 2rm. violet 10 80
D903 5rm. violet . . . . . . 10 1·00
D904 10rm. violet . . . . . . 10 1·20

1946. Optd **PORTO**.
D956 **145** 3g. orange 10 15
D957 5g. green 10 15
D958 6g. purple 10 15
D959 8g. red 10 15
D960 10g. grey 10 25
D961 12g. brown 10 15
D962 15g. red 10 20
D963 20g. brown 10 15
D964 25g. blue 10 20
D965 30g. mauve 10 15
D966 40g. blue 10 20
D967 60g. green 10 20
D968 1s. violet 15 30
D969 2s. yellow . . . . . . 60 1·00
D970 5s. blue 60 65

1947.
D1035 **D 162** 1g. brown 10 15
D1036 2g. brown 10 15
D1037 3g. brown 10 15
D1038 5g. brown 10 15
D1039 8g. brown 10 15
D1040 10g. brown 10 15
D1041 12g. brown 10 15
D1042 15g. brown 10 15
D1043 16g. brown 40 90
D1044 17g. brown 30 90
D1045 18g. brown 30 90
D1046 20g. brown 80 15
D1047 24g. brown . . . . . 30 1·20
D1048 30g. brown 15 30
D1049 36g. brown . . . . . 65 1·20
D1050 40g. brown 10 15
D1051 **D 162** 42g. brown . . . . . 85 1·40
D1052 48g. brown . . . . . 85 1·40
D1053 50g. brown 65 15
D1054 60g. brown 20 25
D1055 70g. brown 10 25
D1056 80g. brown . . . . . 4·50 2·00
D1057 1s. blue 15 15
D1058 1s.15 blue . . . . . 3·25 30
D1059 1s.20 blue . . . . . 3·25 1·50
D1060 2s. blue 30 25
D1061 5s. blue 35 25
D1062 10s. blue 45 25

D 184 D 817

1949.
D1178 **D 184** 1g. red 20 15
D1179 2g. red 25 20
D1180 4g. red 45 45
D1181 5g. red . . . . . . 1·80 50
D1182 8g. red . . . . . . 2·30 2·10
D1183 10g. red 40 15
D1184 20g. red 45 15
D1185 30g. red 35 15
D1186 40g. red 20 15
D1187 50g. red 40 15
D1188 60g. red . . . . . . 11·50 50
D1189 63g. red . . . . . . 4·25 5·00
D1190 70g. red 35 15
D1191 80g. red 35 15
D1192 90g. red 45 30
D1193 1s. violet 85 15
D1194 1s.20 violet 50 30
D1195 1s.35 violet 40 30
D1196 1s.40 violet 80 55
D1197 1s.50 violet 70 15
D1198 1s.65 violet 45 40
D1199 1s.70 violet 45 45
D1200 2s. violet 85 15
D1201 2s.50 violet 80 15
D1202 3s. violet 80 25
D1203 4s. violet 95 80
D1204 5s. violet . . . . . . 2·00 30
D1205 10s. violet . . . . . . 2·00 30

1985.
D2074 **D 817** 10g. yellow & black . . 10 15
D2075 20g. red and black . . 10 15
D2076 50g. orange & black . . 10 15
D2077 1s. blue and black . . 15 20
D2078 2s. brown & black . . 30 40
D2079 3s. violet and black . . 40 50
D2080 5s. yellow & black . . 90 85
D2081 10s. green & black . . 1·60 1·40

AUSTRIAN TERRITORIES ACQUIRED BY ITALY Pt. 2

Italian territory acquired from Austria at the close of the war of 1914–18, including Trentino and Trieste.

1918. 100 heller = 1 krone.
1918. 100 centesimi = 1 lira.
1919. 100 centesimi = 1 corona.

TRENTINO

1918. Stamps of Austria optd **Regno d'Italia Trentino 3 nov 1918.**
1 **49** 3h. purple . . . . 1·90 2·10
2 5h. green . . . . 1·50 1·50
3 6h. orange . . . . 30·00 25·00
4 10h. red . . . . 2·00 1·50
5 12h. green . . . . 85·00 80·00
6 **60** 15h. brown . . . . 2·50 2·50
7 20h. green . . . . 1·50 1·75
8 25h. blue . . . . 23·00 21·00
9 30h. violet . . . . 6·75 6·75
10 **51** 40h. green . . . . 32·00 32·00
11 50h. green . . . . 18·00 17·00
12 60h. blue . . . . 23·00 25·00
13 80h. brown . . . . 35·00 40·00
14 90h. red £850 £850
15 1k. red on yellow . . . . 35·00 38·00
16 **52** 2k. blue £180 £190
17 4k. green £1400 £1300
18 10k. violet £65000

1918. Stamps of Italy optd **Venezia Tridentina**.
19 **30** 1c. brown . . . . 40 1·25
20 **31** 2c. brown . . . . 40 1·25
21 **37** 5c. green . . . . 70 1·25
22 10c. red . . . . 70 1·25
23 **41** 20c. orange . . . . 1·10 1·90
24 **39** 40c. brown . . . . 35·00 35·00
25 **33** 45c. olive . . . . 17·00 24·00
26 **39** 50c. mauve . . . . 21·00 26·00
27 **34** 1l. brown and green . . . . 21·00 26·00

1919. Stamps of Italy surch **Venezia Tridentina** and value.
28 **37** 5h. on 5c. green . . . . . 70 1·10
29 10h. on 10c. red . . . . . 70 1·10
30 **41** 20h. on 20c. orange . . . . 70 1·10

VENEZIA GIULIA

For use in Trieste and territory, Gorizia and province, and in Istria.

1918. Stamps of Austria optd **Regno d'Italia Venezia Giulia 3. XI. 18.**
31 **49** 3h. purple 90 90
32 5h. green 90 90
33 6h. orange . . . . 1·10 1·10
34 10h. red 55 55
35 12h. green . . . . 1·10 1·10
36 **60** 15h. brown 55 55
37 20h. green 55 55
38 25h. blue . . . . 3·50 3·50
39 30h. purple . . . . 1·50 1·50
40 **51** 40h. green . . . . 40·00 60·00
41 50h. green . . . . 2·10 3·00
42 60h. blue . . . . 11·00 11·00
43 80h. brown . . . . 3·50 5·50
44 1k. red on yellow . . . . 3·50 6·75
45 **52** 2k. blue . . . . 85·00 £110
46 3k. red £140 £160
47 4k. green £210 £250
48 10k. violet £23000 £24000

1918. Stamps of Italy optd **Venezia Giulia**.
49 **30** 1c. brown . . . . 55 1·00
50 **31** 2c. brown . . . . 55 1·00
51 **37** 5c. green 55 55
52 10c. red 55 55
53 **41** 20c. orange 55 55
54 **39** 25c. blue 55 55
55 40c. brown . . . . 4·25 5·50
56 **33** 45c. green . . . . 75 1·25
57 **39** 50c. mauve . . . . 1·75 2·50
58 60c. red . . . . 27·00 30·00
59 **34** 1l. brown and green . . . . 14·00 14·00

1919. Stamps of Italy surch **Venezia Giulia** and value.
60 **37** 5h. on 5c. green 90 90
61 **41** 20h. on 20c. orange 70 70

EXPRESS LETTER STAMPS

1919. Express Letter stamp of Italy optd **Venezia Giulia**.
E60 **E 35** 25c. red . . . . 21·00 23·00

POSTAGE DUE STAMPS

1918. Postage Due Stamps of Italy optd **Venezia Giulia**.
D60 **D 12** 5c. mauve and orange . . 15 55
D61 10c. mauve & orange . . 15 55
D62 20c. mauve & orange . . 70 1·10
D63 30c. mauve & orange . . 1·50 1·90
D64 40c. mauve & orange . . 14·00 16·00
D65 50c. mauve & orange . . 35·00 45·00
D66 1l. mauve and blue . . £110 £120

GENERAL ISSUE

For use throughout the liberated area of Trentino, Venezia Giulia and Dalmatia.

1919. Stamps of Italy surch in new currency.
62 **30** 1ce. di cor on 1c. brown . . 90 90
64 **31** 2ce. di cor on 2c. brown . . 90 90
65 **37** 5ce. di cor on 5c. green . . 90 90
67 10ce. di cor on 10c. red . . 90 90
68 **41** 20ce. di cor on 20c. orange 90 90
70 **39** 25ce. di cor on 25c. blue . . 90 90
71 40ce. di cor on 40c. brown 90 90
72 **33** 45ce. di cor on 45c. green 90 90
73 **39** 50ce. di cor on 50c. mauve 90 90
74 60ce. di cor on 60c. red . . 90 1·50
75 **34** 1cor. on 1l. brown & green 90 1·50
76 una corona on 1l. brn & grn 2·00 5·50
82 5cor. on 5l. blue and red . . 21·00 25·00
83 10cor. on 10l. green & red 21·00 25·00

EXPRESS LETTER STAMPS

1919. Express Letter stamps of Italy surch in new currency.
E76 **E 35** 25ce. di cor on 25c. red 70 1·10
E77 **E 41** 30ce. di cor on 30c. red and blue . . . . . . 70 1·10

POSTAGE DUE STAMPS

1919. Postage Due stamps of Italy surch in new currency.
D76 **D 12** 5ce. di cor on 5c. mauve and orange . . 40 90
D77 10ce. di cor. on 10c. mauve and orange . . 40 90
D78 20ce. di cor on 20c. mauve and orange . . 40 90
D79 30ce. di cor on 30c. mauve and orange . . 40 90
D80 40ce. di cor on 40c. mauve and orange . . 40 90
D81 50ce. di cor on 50c. mauve and orange . . 40 90
D82 una corona on 1l. mauve and blue . . . 40 1·50
D86 1cor. on 1l. mve & blue 3·00 3·50
D83 due corona on 2l. mauve and blue . . . 35·00 48·00
D87 2cor. on 2l. mve & blue 17·00 26·00
D84 cinque corona on 5l. mauve and blue . . . 35·00 45·00
D88 5cor. on 5l. mve & blue 18·00 26·00

AUSTRO-HUNGARIAN MILITARY POST Pt. 2

A. GENERAL ISSUES

100 heller = 1 krone.

1915. Stamps of Bosnia and Herzegovina optd **K.U.K. FELDPOST.**
1 **25** 1h. olive 40 80
2 2h. blue 40 80
3 3h. lake 40 80
4 5h. green 40 40
5 6h. black 40 80
6 10h. red 25 45
7 12h. olive . . . . 40 1·00
8 20h. brown 50 75
9 25h. blue . . . . 50 1·00
10 30h. red . . . . 2·75 9·50
11 **26** 35h. green . . . . 1·90 7·00
12 40h. violet . . . . 1·90 7·00
13 45h. brown . . . . 1·90 7·00

14 26 50h. blue . . . . 1·90 7·00
15 60h. purple . . . . 50 4·00
16 72h. blue . . . . 2·00 7·13
17 25 1k. brown on cream . . . . 2·00 6·75
18 2k. indigo on blue . . . . . 2·00 7·50
19 26 3k. red on green . . . . . 21·00 60·00
20 5k. lilac on grey . . . . . 18·00 55·00
21 10k. blue on grey £170 £375

2 Francis Joseph

1915.

22 2 1h. green 15 25
23 2h. blue 10 30
24 3h. red 15 25
25 5h. green 15 25
26 6h. black 15 35
27 10h. red 15 27
28 10h. blue 10 30
29 12h. green 15 40
30 15h. red 15 20
31 20h. brown 25 50
32 20h. green 25 60
33 25h. blue 15 30
34 30h. red 20 60
35 35h. green 25 85
36 40h. violet 25 85
37 45h. brown 25 85
38 50h. deep green 25 85
39 60h. purple 30 85
40 72h. blue 35 85
41 80h. brown 25 35
42 90h. red . . . . 65 1·90
43 – 1k. purple on cream . . . . 1·25 3·72
44 – 2k. green on blue . . . . . 90 1·75
45 – 3k. red on green . . . . . 70 1·00
46 – 4k. violet on grey . . . . 70 1·00
47 – 5k. violet on grey . . . . . 21·00 25·00
48 – 10k. blue on grey . . . . . 2·75 10·50
The kronen values are larger, with profile portrait.

1917. As 1917 issue of Bosnia, but inscr "K.u.K. FELDPOST".
49 1h. blue 90 20
50 2h. orange 90 20
51 3h. grey 90 20
52 5h. green 90 20
53 6h. violet 15 25
54 10h. brown 10 20
55 12h. blue 10 20
56 15h. red 15 20
57 20h. brown 15 20
58 25h. blue 20 45
59 30h. grey 15 20
60 40h. bistre 15 20
61 50h. green 10 20
62 60h. red 15 30
63 80h. blue 15 20
64 90h. purple 25 85
65 2k. red on buff 15 25
66 3k. green on blue . . . . . 70 2·10
67 4k. red on green . . . . . . 14·50 26·00
68 10k. violet on grey . . . . . 1·10 7·50
The kronen values are larger and the border is different.

1918. Imperial and Royal Welfare Fund. As 1918 issue of Bosnia, but inscr "K. UND K. FELDPOST".
69 40 10h. (+10h.) green 25 90
70 – 20h. (+10h.) red 25 90
71 40 45h. (+10h.) blue 25 90

NEWSPAPER STAMPS

N 4 Mercury

1916.

N49 N 4 2h. blue 15 30
N50 6h. orange . . . . . . 35 1·40
N51 10h. red . . . . 60 1·40
N52 20h. brown . . . . . . 75 1·40

B. ISSUES FOR ITALY

100 centesimi = 1 lira.

1918. General Issue stamps of 1917 surch in figs and words.
1 2c. on 1h. blue 10 25
2 3c. on 2h. orange 10 25
3 4c. on 3h. grey 10 25
4 6c. on 5h. green 10 25
5 7c. on 6h. violet 10 25
6 11c. on 10h. brown 10 25
7 13c. on 12h. blue 10 25
8 16c. on 15h. red 10 25
9 22c. on 20h. brown 10 25
10 27c. on 25h. blue 30 65
11 32c. on 30h. grey 10 50
12 43c. on 40h. bistre 15 55
13 53c. on 50h. green 15 30
14 64c. on 60h. red 20 65
15 85c. on 80h. blue 15 35
16 95c. on 90h. purple 15 35
17 2l.11 on 2k. red on buff . . . 25 55
18 3l.16 on 3k. green on blue . . 60 1·40
19 4l.22 on 4k. red on green . . . 75 1·60

NEWSPAPER STAMPS

1918. Newspaper stamps of General Issue surch in figs and words.
N20 N 4 3c. on 2h. blue 15 40
N21 7c. on 6h. orange . . . 35 1·00
N22 11c. on 10h. red 35 95
N23 22c. on 20h. brown . . . 30 95

1918. For Express. Newspaper stamps of Bosnia surch in figs and words.
N24 N 35 3c. on 2h. red on yell 5·50 11·50
N25 6c. on 5h. green on yell 5·50 11·50

POSTAGE DUE STAMPS

1918. Postage Due stamps of Bosnia surch in figs and words.
D20 D 35 6c. on 5h. red . . . . 3·50 5·50
D21 11c. on 10h. red . . . . 2·10 4·50
D22 16c. on 15h. red . . . . 80 2·25
D23 27c. on 25h. red . . . . 80 2·25
D24 32c. on 30h. red . . . . 80 2·25
D25 43c. on 40h. red . . . . 80 2·25
D26 53c. on 50h. red . . . . 80 2·25

C. ISSUES FOR MONTENEGRO

100 heller = 1 krone.

1917. Nos. 28 and 30 of General Issues optd **K.U.K. MILIT. VERWALTUNG MONTENEGRO**.
1 2 10h. blue . . . . 9·50 9·00
2 15h. red . . . . 11·50 9·00

D. ISSUES FOR RUMANIA

100 bani = 1 leu.

1917. General Issue stamps of 1917 optd **BANI** or **LEI**.
1 3b. grey . . . . 1·90 2·40
2 5b. green . . . . 1·90 2·00
3 6b. violet . . . . 1·90 1·90
4 10b. brown 15 75
5 12b. blue . . . . 1·10 1·50
6 15b. red . . . . 1·10 1·90
7 20b. brown 15 75
8 25b. blue 15 30
9 30b. grey 40 65
10 40b. bistre 15 65
11 50b. green 40 70
12 60b. red 40 70
13 80b. blue 15 45
14 90b. purple 40 65
15 2l. red on buff 50 90
16 3l. green on blue . . . . . . 65 1·10
17 4l. red on green . . . . . . 65 1·10

3 Charles I

1918.

18 3 3b. grey 15 70
19 5b. green 15 55
20 6b. violet 20 45
21 10b. brown 25 60
22 12b. blue 20 60
23 15b. red 20 50
24 20b. brown 20 45
25 25b. blue 20 45
26 30b. grey 20 42
27 40b. bistre 20 45
28 50b. green 25 60
29 60b. red 25 65
30 80b. blue 15 50
31 90b. purple 25 75
32 2l. red on buff 25 90
33 3l. green on blue 35 90
34 4l. red on green . . . . . . 40 1·00

E. ISSUES FOR SERBIA

100 heller = 1 krone.

1916. Stamps of Bosnia optd **SERBIEN**.
22 25 1h. olive . . . . 2·00 3·50
23 2h. blue . . . . 2·00 3·50
24 3h. lake . . . . 1·90 3·25
25 5h. green 25 75
26 6h. black . . . . 1·25 2·10
27 10h. red 25 70
28 12h. olive . . . . 1·25 2·10
29 20h. brown . . . . 65 1·40
30 25h. blue . . . . 65 1·25
31 30h. red . . . . 65 1·25
32 26 35h. green . . . . 65 1·25
33 40h. violet . . . . 65 1·25
34 45h. brown . . . . 65 1·25
35 50h. blue . . . . 65 1·25
36 60h. brown . . . . 65 1·25
37 72h. blue . . . . 65 1·25
38 25 1k. brown on cream . . . . 70 1·50
39 2k. indigo on blue . . . . . 70 1·50
40 26 3k. red on green . . . . . 70 1·60
41 5k. lilac on grey . . . . . 1·00 1·25
42 10k. blue on grey . . . . . 10·25 25·00

AUSTRO-HUNGARIAN POST OFFICES IN THE TURKISH EMPIRE Pt. 2

Various Austro-Hungarian P.O.s in the Turkish Empire. Such offices had closed by 15 December 1914 except for several in Albania which remained open until 1915.

A. LOMBARDY AND VENETIA CURRENCY

100 soldi = 1 florin.

1 2 3

1867.

1 1 2s. yellow . . . . 1·90 2·50
9 3s. green . . . . 1·25 23·00
10 5s. red . . . . 40 17·00
11 10s. blue . . . . 90 1·10
5 15s. brown . . . . 30 7·00
6 25s. lilac . . . . 25 35·00
7a 2 50s. brown . . . . 1·40 50·00

1883.

14 3 2s. black and brown 20 £120
15 3s. black and green . . . . 1·25 28·00
16 5s. black and red . . . . . 20 17·00
17 10s. black and blue 80 65
18 20s. black and grey . . . . 5·75 7·00
19 50s. black and mauve . . . . 1·25 17·00

B. TURKISH CURRENCY

40 paras = 1 piastre.

1886. Surch **10 PARA 10**.
21a 3 10p. on 3s. green . . . . . 40 8·00

1888. Nos. 71/75a of Austria surch.
22 20 10pa. on 3k. green . . . . 3·75 8·50
23 20pa. on 5k. red . . . . . 55 7·50
24 1pi. on 10k. blue . . . . . 65·00 1·00
25 2pi. on 20k. grey . . . . . 2·00 3·50
26 5pi. on 50k. purple . . . . 2·00 14·00

1890. Stamps of Austria of 1890, the kreuzer values with lower figures of value removed, surch at foot.
27 23 8pa. on 2k. brown 15 40
28 10pa. on 3k. green 55 50
29 20pa. on 5k. red 30 45
30 1pi. on 10k. blue 40 15
31 2pi. on 20k. olive . . . . . 7·25 25·00
32 5pi. on 50k. mauve . . . . 12·00 75·00
33 24 10pi. on 1g. blue . . . . . 12·50 30·00
37 10pi. on 1g. lilac . . . . . 10·75 25·00
34 20pi. on 2g. red . . . . . . 14·00 50·00
38 20pi. on 2g. green . . . . . 40·00 80·00

1890. Stamps of Austria of 1891, with lower figures of value removed, surch at foot.
35 25 2pi. on 20k. green . . . . 4·75 1·40
36 5pi. on 50k. mauve . . . . 2·75 2·75

1900. Stamps of Austria of 1899, the heller values with lower figures of value removed, surch at foot.
46 27 10pa. on 5h. green . . . . 2·00 3·00
40 28 20pa. on 10h. red . . . . . 5·75 1·00
48 1pi. on 25h. blue . . . . . 1·40 50
49 29 2pi. on 50h. blue . . . . . 3·00 5·75
43 30 5pi. on 1k. red 85 35
44 10pi. on 2k. lavender . . . 2·10 2·75
45 20pi. on 4k. green . . . . . 1·60 6·50

1903. Stamps of Austria of 1899, with all figures of value removed, surch at top and at foot.
55 27 10pa. green . . . . 55 1·50
56 28 20pa. red . . . . 1·25 80
57 30pa. mauve . . . . 65 3·25
58 1pi. blue 70 45
59 29 2pi. blue 75 80

11 Francis Joseph I

12 Francis Joseph I

1908. 60th Anniv of Emperor's Accession.
60 11 10pa. green on yellow . . . 15 25
61 20pa. red on pink 25 25
62 30pa. brown on buff 35 90
63 60pa. purple on blue . . . . 55 3·50
64 1pi. ultramarine on blue . . 55 50
65 12 2pi. red on yellow 35 25
66 5pi. brown on grey 65 85
67 10pi. green on yellow . . . 1·10 1·60
68 20pi. blue on grey . . . . . 2·40 1·50

POSTAGE DUE STAMPS

1902. Postage Due stamps as Type D 32 of Austria, but with value in heller, surch with new value.
D50 D 32 10pa. on 5h. green . . 1·40 2·75
D51 20pa. on 10h. green . . 1·50 3·25
D52 1pi. on 20h. green . . . 1·90 4·00
D53 2pi. on 40h. green . . . 1·75 3·75
D54 5pi. on 100h. green . . 2·10 3·50

D 13

1908.

D71 D 13 ¼pi. green . . . . . . 3·25 8·75
D72 ½pi. green . . . . . . 1·90 6·50
D73 1pi. green . . . . . . 2·25 8·00
D74 1½pi. green . . . . . . 1·40 16·00
D75 2pi. green . . . . . . 2·25 17·00
D76 5pi. green . . . . . . 2·25 10·50
D77 10pi. green . . . . . . 16·00 £130
D78 20pi. green . . . . . . 12·50 £150
D79 30pi. green . . . . . . 18·00 15·00

C. FRENCH CURRENCY

100 centimes = 1 franc.

1903. Stamps of Austria surch **CENTIMES** or **FRANC**.
F1 27 5c. on 5h. green and black 1·50 5·25
F2 28 10c. on 10h. red and black (No. 143) . . . . 1·10 5·75
F3 25c. on 25h. blue and black (No. 145) . . . . 34·00 34·00
F4 29 50c. on 50h. blue and black 15·00 £225
F5 30 1f. on 1k. red . . . . . . 1·40 £150
F6 2f. on 2k. lilac . . . . . . 10·50 £375
F7 4f. on 4k. green . . . . . 13·50 £600

1904. Stamps of Austria surch **CENTIMES**.
F14 33 5c. on 5h. green . . . . . 2·25 8·25
F13 28 10c. on 10h. red and black (No. 160) . . . . . . 28·00 46·00
F10 25c. on 25h. blue and black (No. 176) . . . . 1·80 £150
F11 35 50c. on 50h. blue 75 £500

1906. Type of Austria surch **CENTIMES**.
F15 28 10c. on 10h. red (No. 184) 1·20 46·00
F16 15c. on 15h. violet and black (as No. 185) . . . 90 42·00
No. F16 was not issued without the surch.

1908. 60th Anniv of Emperor's Accession. As T **11/12** but in centimes or franc.
F17 11 5c. green on yellow . . . 20 1·10
F18 10c. red on pink . . . . . 40 1·50
F19 15c. brown on buff . . . . 55 7·75
F20 25c. blue on blue . . . . 14·50 7·00
F21 12 50c. red on yellow . . . . 2·10 38·00
F22 1f. brown on grey . . . . 3·00 55·00

AZERBAIJAN Pt. 10

Formerly part of the Russian Empire. Became independent on 27 May 1918, following the Russian Revolution. Soviet troops invaded the country on 27 April 1920, and a Soviet Republic followed. From 1 October 1923 stamps of the Transcaucasian Federation were used but these were superseded by those of the Soviet Union in 1924.

With the dissolution of the Soviet Union in 1991, Azerbaijan once again became an independent state.

1919. 100 kopeks = 1 rouble.
1992. 100 qopik = 1 manat.

1 Standard-bearer

6 Famine Supplies

3 "Labour"

4 Petroleum Well

1919. Imperf. Various designs.
1 1 10k. multicoloured 40 50
2 – 20k. multicoloured 30 50
3 – 40k. olive, black and yellow 25 30
4 – 60k. orange, black & yellow 25 30
5 – 1r. blue, black and yellow . . 25 30
6 – 2r. red, black and yellow . . 25 30
7 – 5r. blue, black and yellow . . 25 40
8 – 10r. olive, black & yellow . . 50 75

9 – 25r. blue, black and red . . . 50 1·00
10 – 50r. olive, black and red . . 75 1·50
DESIGNS—HORIZ: 40k. to 1r. Reaper; 2r. to 10r. Citadel, Baku; 25r., 50r. Temple of Eternal Fires.

1921. Imperf.
11 **3** 1r. green 30 40
12 **4** 2r. brown 30 40
13 – 5r. brown 30 40
14 – 10r. grey 50 50
15 – 25r. orange 30 40
16 – 50r. violet 30 70
17 – 100r. orange 30 70
18 – 150r. blue 30 40
19 – 250r. violet and buff 30 40
20 – 400r. blue 30 60
21 – 500r. black and lilac 30 60
22 – 1000r. red and blue 30 50
23 – 2000r. black and blue 30 60
24 – 3000r. brown and blue . . . 30 60
25 – 5000r. green on olive 30 50
DESIGNS—HORIZ: 5r., 3000r. Bibi Eibatt Oilfield; 100r., 5000r. Goukasoff House (State Museum of Arts); 400r., 1000r. Hall of Judgment, Khan's Palace. VERT: 10r., 2000r. Minaret of Friday Mosque, Khan's Palace, Baku; 25r., 250r. Globe and Workers; 50r. Malden's Tower, Baku; 150r., 500r. Blacksmiths.

1921. Famine Relief. Imperf.
26 **6** 500r. blue . . . . 50 1·50
27 – 1000r. brown . . . . 85 2·50
DESIGN—VERT: 1000r. Starving family.
For stamps of the above issues surch with new values, see Stanley Gibbons Part 10 (Russia) Catalogue.

13 Azerbaijan Map and Flag
16 Maiden's Tower, Baku

1992. Independence.
83 **13** 35q. multicoloured 85 85

1992. Unissued stamp showing Caspian Sea surch **AZARBAYCAN** and new value.
84 25q. on 15k. multicoloured . . 20 20
85 35q. on 15k. multicoloured . . 30 30
86 50q. on 15k. multicoloured . . 50 50
87 1m.50 on 15k. multicoloured 1·40 1·40
88 2m.50 on 15k. multicoloured 2·25 2·25

1992. Dated "1992".
89 **16** 10q. green and black . . . 10 10
90 20q. red and black . . . 10 10
91 50q. yellow and black . . . 10 10
92 1m.50 blue and black . . . 50 50
See also Nos. 101/4.

17 Akhalteka Horse

1993. Horses. Multicoloured.
93 20q. Type **17** 10 10
94 30q. Kabarda horse 10 10
95 50q. Qarabair horse 10 10
96 1m. Don horse 10 10
97 2m.50 Yakut horse 30 30
98 5m. Orlov horse 55 55
99 10m. Diliboz horse . . . . . 1·10 1·10
MS100 80 × 60 mm. 8m. Qarabag horse 75 75

1993. Dated "1993"
101 **16** 50q. blue and black . . . 10 10
102 1m. mauve and black . . . 10 10
103 2m.50 yellow and black . . 10 10
104 5m. green and black . . . 50 50

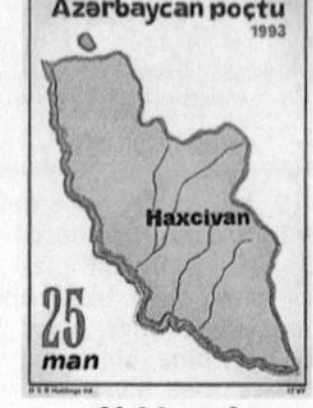

18 "Tulipa eichleri"
20 Map of Nakhichevan

19 Russian Sturgeon

1993. Flowers. Multicoloured.
105 25q. Type **18** 10 10
106 50q. "Puschkinia scilloides" . . 10 10
107 1m. "Iris elegantissima" . . . 10 10
108 1m.50 "Iris acutiloba" . . . 25 25
109 5m. "Tulipa florenskyii" . . 70 70
110 10m. "Iris reticulata" . . . . 1·25 1·25
MS111 78 × 58 mm. 10m. *Muscari elecostomum* (31 × 39 mm) . . 1·10 1·10

1993. Fishes. Multicoloured.
112 25q. Type **19** 10 10
113 50q. Stellate sturgeon 10 10
114 1m. Iranian roach 20 20
115 1m.50 Caspian roach 25 25
116 5m. Caspian trout 55 55
117 10m. Black-backed shad . . . 1·25 1·25
MS118 76 × 58 mm. 10m. Beluga (*Huso huso*) (39 × 31 mm) . . . 1·25 1·25

1993. 70th Birthday of President Heydar Aliev.
119 – 25m. black and red . . . . 1·10 1·10
120 **20** 25m. multicoloured . . . . 1·10 1·10
MS121a 110 × 90 mm. Nos. 119/20 (map inscr "Naxcivan") . . . . 4·00 4·00
DESIGN: No. 119, President Aliev.

21 Government Building, Baku
22 Flags, and Dish Aerials on Maps

1993.
122 **21** 25q. black and yellow . . . 10 10
123 30q. black and green . . . 15 15
124 50q. black and blue . . . 20 20
125 1m. black and red 40 40

1993. Azerbaijan–Iran Telecommunications Co-operation.
126 **22** 15q. multicoloured 70 70

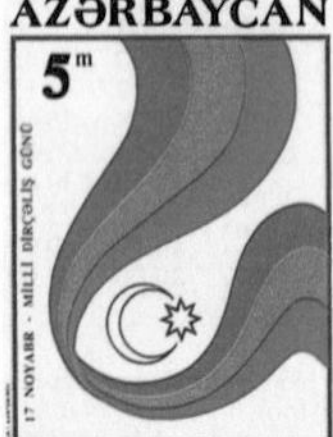

23 National Colours and Islamic Crescent
24 State Arms

1994. National Day.
127 **23** 5m. multicoloured 40 40

1994.
128 **24** 8m. multicoloured 40 40

25 Sirvan Palace
26 Fuzuli

1994. Baku Architecture.
129 **25** 2m. red, silver and black 10 10
130 – 4m. green, silver and black 20 20
131 – 8m. blue, silver and black 45 45
DESIGNS: 4m. 15th-century tomb; 8m. Divan-Khana.

1994. 500th Birth Anniv (1992) of Mohammed ibn Suleiman Fuzuli (poet).
132 **26** 10m. multicoloured 25 25

1994. No. 126 surch **IRAN–AZERBAYGAN** and value.
133 **22** 2m. on 15q. multicoloured 10 10
134 20m. on 15q. multicoloured 30 30
135 25m. on 15q. multicoloured 50 50
136 50m. on 15q. multicoloured 1·00 1·00

1994. Nos. 122/5 surch.
137 **21** 5m. on 1m. black and red 20 20
138 10m. on 30q. black & grn 20 20
139 15m. on 30q. black & grn 20 20
140 20m. on 50q. black & blue 20 20
141 25m. on 1m. black & red 25 25
142 40m. on 50q. black & blue 30 30
143 50m. on 25q. black & yell 45 45
144 100m. on 25q. black & yell 95 95

29 Rasulzade

1994. 110th Birth Anniv of Mammed Amin Rasulzade (politician).
145 **29** 15m. brown, ochre & black 55 55

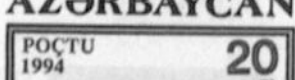

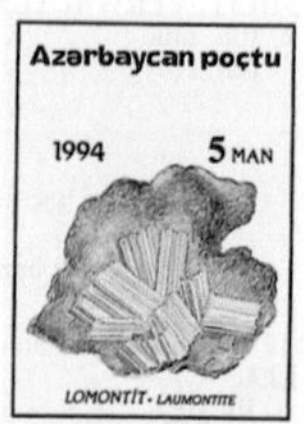

30 Mamedquluzade
32 Laumontite

31 Temple of the Fire Worshippers of Atashgah

1994. 125th Birth Anniv of Jalil Mamedquluzade (writer).
146 **30** 20m. black, gold and blue 55 55

1994. 115th Anniv of Nobel Partnership to Exploit Black Sea Oil. Multicoloured.
147 15m. Type **31** 20 20
148 20m. Oil wells 25 25
149 25m. "Zoroastr" (first oil tanker in Caspian Sea) . . 40 40
150 50m. Nobel brothers and Petr Bilderling (partners) . . . 75 75
MS151 110 × 73 mm. No. 150 . . 80 80

1994. Minerals. Multicoloured.
152 5m. Type **32** 20 20
153 10m. Epidot calcite 45 45
154 15m. Andradite 70 70
155 20m. Amethyst 95 95
MS156 120 × 110 mm. Nos. 152/5 1·60 1·60

33 Players

1994. World Cup Football Championship, U.S.A.
157 **33** 5m. multicoloured 10 10
158 – 10m. multicoloured 10 10
159 – 20m. multicoloured 20 20
160 – 25m. multicoloured 25 25
161 – 30m. multicoloured 30 30
162 – 50m. multicoloured 55 55
163 – 80m. multicoloured 70 70
MS164 90 × 65 mm. 100m. multicoloured (31 × 39 mm) . . 1·50 1·50
DESIGNS: 10m. to 100m. Match scenes.

34 Posthorn

1994.
165 **34** 5m. red and black 10 10
166 10m. green and black . . . 10 10
167 20m. blue and black . . . 20 20
168 25m. yellow and black . . 20 20
169 40m. brown and black . . 25 25

35 Coelophysis and Segisaurus

1994. Prehistoric Animals. Multicoloured.
170 5m. Type **35** 10 10
171 10m. Pentaceratops and tyrannosaurids 10 10
172 20m. Segnosaurus and oviraptor 20 20
173 25m. Albertosaurus and corythosaurus 25 25
174 30m. Igaunodons 25 25
175 50m. Stegosaurus and allosaurus 40 40
176 80m. Tyrannosaurus and saurolophus 65 65
MS177 81 × 61 mm. 100m. Phobetor (39 × 31 mm) . . . . 1·25 1·25

36 Nesting Grouse

1994. The Caucasian Black Grouse. Multicoloured.
178 50m. Type **36** 20 20
179 80m. Grouse on mountain . . 40 40
180 100m. Pair of grouse 55 55
181 120m. Grouse in spring meadow 90 90

1994. No. 84 further surch **400 M.**
182 400m. on 25q. on 15k. mult 35 35

38 "Kapitan Razhabov" (tug)

1994. Ships. Multicoloured.
183 50m. Type **38** 25 25
184 50m. "Azerbaijan" (ferry) . . 25 25
185 50m. "Merkuri 1" (ferry) . . 25 25
186 50m. "Tovuz" (container ship) 25 25
187 50m. "Ganzha" (tanker) . . 25 25
Nos. 183/7 were issued together, se-tenant, the backgrounds of which form a composite design of a map.

39 Pres. Aliev

1994. President Haidar Aliev. Sheet 102 × 72 mm.
MS188 **39** 150m. multicoloured 2·00 2·00

40 White-tailed Sea Eagle

1994. Birds of Prey. Multicoloured.
189 10m. Type **40** 25 25
190 15m. Imperial eagle 30 30
191 20m. Tawny eagle 45 45
192 25m. Lammergeier (vert) . . 50 50
193 50m. Saker falcon (vert) . . . 1·00 1·00
MS194 83 × 64 mm. 100m. Golden eagle (*Aquila chrysaetos*) (39 × 31 mm) . . . . . . 1·60 1·60
Nos. 190/1 and **MS**194 are wrongly inscr "Aguila".

41 "Felis libica caudata"

1994. Wild Cats. Multicoloured.
195 10m. Type **41** 25 25
196 15m. Manul cat 30 30
197 20m. Lynx 45 45
198 25m. Leopard (horiz) 50 50
199 50m. Tiger (horiz) . . . . . 1·25 1·25
MS200 64 × 56 mm. 100m. Tiger with cub (31 × 39 mm) . . . . 1·60 1·60
No. 197 is wrongly inscribed "Felis lyns lyns".

42 Ancient Greek and Modern Javelin Throwers

1994. Centenary of Int Olympic Committee. Mult.
201 100m. Type **42** 45 45
202 100m. Ancient Greek and modern discus throwers . . 45 45
203 100m. Baron Pierre de Coubertin (founder of modern games) and flame 45 45

1995. Nos. 89/92 and 101/4 surch.
204 **15** 250m. on 10q. green & blk 30 30
205 250m. on 20q. red & black 30 30
206 250m. on 50q. yell & blk 30 30
207 250m. on 1m.50 bl & blk 30 30
208 500m. on 50q. blue & blk 65 65
209 500m. on 1m. mve & blk 65 65
210 500m. on 2m.50 yellow and black 65 65
211 500m. on 5m. green & blk 65 65

44 Apollo

1995. Butterflies. Multicoloured.
212 10m. Type **44** 20 20
213 25m. "Zegris menestho" . . 30 30
214 50m. "Manduca atropos" . . 50 50
215 60m. "Pararge adrastoides" 70 70
MS216 103 × 157 mm. Nos. 212/15 1·75 1·75

45 Aleksei Urmanov (Russia) (gold, men's figure skating)

46 Mary Cleave

1995. Winter Olympic Games, Lillehammer, Norway, Medal Winners. Multicoloured.
217 10m. Type **45** 10 10
218 25m. Nancy Kerrigan (U.S.A.) (silver, women's figure skating) 20 20
219 40m. Bonnie Blair (U.S.A.) (gold, women's 500m. speed skating) (horiz) . . . 25 25
220 50m. Takanori Kano (Japan) (gold, men's ski jumping) (horiz) 30 30
221 80m. Philip Laros (Canada) (silver, men's freestyle skiing) 50 50
222 100m. German team (gold, three-man bobsleigh) . . . 70 70
MS223 102 × 71 mm. 200m. Katya Seizinger (Germany) (gold, women's skiing) . . . . 1·00 1·00

1995. 25th Anniv (1994) of First Manned Moon Landing. Female Astronauts. Two sheets, each 137 × 78 mm, containing T **46** and similar vert designs. Multicoloured.
MS224 (a) 100m. Type **46**; 100m. Valentina Tereshkova; 100m. Tamara Jernigen; 100m. Wendy Lawrence. (b) 100m. Mae Jemison; 100m. Cathy Coleman; 100m. Ellen Shulman; 100m. Mary Weber . . . . 2·25 2·25

1995. Nos. 165/7 surch.
225 **34** 100m. on 5m. red & black 10 10
226 250m. on 10m. grn & blk 25 25
227 500m. on 20m. blue & blk 45 45

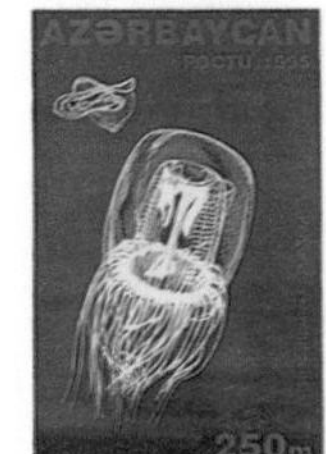

48 "Polyorchis karafutoensis"

1995. Marine Animals. Multicoloured.
228 50m. "Loligo vulgaris" (horiz) 10 10
229 100m. "Orchistoma pileus" (horiz) 25 25
230 150m. "Pegea confoederata" (horiz) 40 40
231 250m. Type **48** 70 70
232 300m. "Agalma okeni" . . . 85 85
MS233 89 × 60 mm. 500m. *Corolla spectabilis* (39 × 31 mm) . . . 1·50 1·50

49 Matamata Turtle

1995. Tortoises and Turtles. Multicoloured.
234 50m. Type **49** 10 10
235 100m. Loggerhead turtle . . 25 25
236 150m. Leopard tortoise . . . 40 40
237 250m. Indian star tortoise . . 70 70
238 300m. Hermann's tortoise . . 85 85
MS239 79 × 65 mm. 500m. Alligator-snapping turtle (*Macroclemys temmincki*) (31 × 39 mm) . . . 1·50 1·50

50 Uzeyir Hacibeyov (composer, 110th)

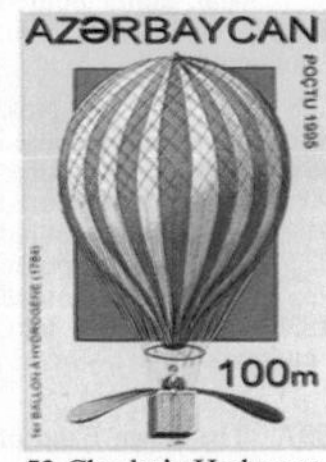

53 Charles's Hydrogen Balloon, 1783

1995. Birth Anniversaries.
240 **50** 250m. silver and black . . 40 40
241 – 400m. gold and black . . . 75 75
DESIGN: 400m. Vakhid (poet, centenary).

1995. Nos. 84/88 surch.
242 200m. on 2m.50 on 15k. mult 25 25
243 400m. on 25q. on 15k. mult 50 50
244 600m. on 35q. on 15k. mult 85 85
245 800m. on 50q. on 15k. mult 1·10 1·10
246 1000m. on 1m.50 on 15k. multicoloured . . . . . . 1·40 1·40

1995. Nos. 168/9 surch.
247 **34** 400m. on 25m. yell & blk 25 25
248 900m. on 40m. brn & blk 60 60

1995. History of Airships. Multicoloured.
249 100m. Type **53** 10 10
250 150m. Tissandier Brothers' electrically-powered airship, 1883 . . . . 25 25
251 250m. J.-B. Meusnier's elliptical balloon design, 1784 (horiz) 40 40
252 300m. Baldwin's dirigible airship, 1904 (horiz) . . . 50 50
253 400m. U.S. Navy dirigible airship, 1917 (horiz) . . . 60 60
254 500m. Pedal-powered airship, 1909 (horiz) 70 70
MS255 79 × 62 mm. 800m. First rigid dirigible airship by Hugo Eckener, 1924 (horiz) . . . . 1·10 1·10
No. 249 is wrongly dated.

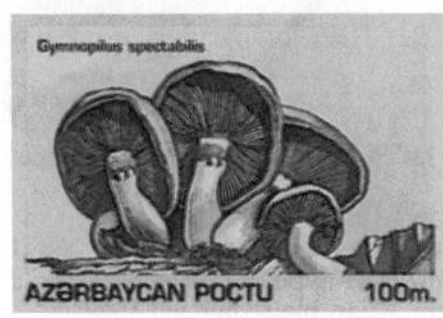

54 "Gymnopilus spectabilis"

1995. Fungi. Multicoloured.
256 100m. Type **54** 25 25
257 250m. Fly agaric 65 65
258 300m. Parasol mushroom . . 70 70
259 400m. "Hygrophorus spectosus" . . . . 1·00 1·00
MS260 110 × 80 mm. 500m. Fly agaric (different) . . . . 1·25 1·25
The 250m. and 500m. are wrongly inscr "agaris".

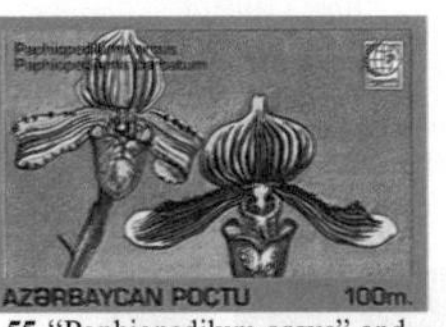

55 "Paphiopedilum argus" and "Paphiopedilum barbatum"

1995. "Singapore '95" International Stamp Exhibition. Orchids. Multicoloured.
261 100m. Type **55** 25 25
262 250m. "Maxillaria picta" . . 65 65
263 300m. "Laeliocattleya" . . . 70 70
264 400m. "Dendrobium nobile" 1·00 1·00
MS265 110 × 80 mm. 500m. *Cattleya gloriette* . . . . 1·25 1·25

56 Pres. Aliev and U.N. Secretary-General Boutros Boutros Ghali

1995. 50th Anniv of U.N.O.
266 **56** 250m. multicoloured . . . 1·25 1·25

57 Players

58 American Bald Eagle

1995. World Cup Football Championship, France (1998). Multicoloured.
267 100m. Type **57** 20 20
268 150m. Dribbling 40 40
269 250m. Tackling 60 60
270 300m. Preparing to kick ball 65 65
271 400m. Contesting for ball . . 90 90
MS272 79 × 60 mm. 600m. Goalkeeper diving for ball . . 1·25 1·25

1995. Air.
273 **58** 2200m. multicoloured . . . 1·50 1·50

59 Persian

60 Horse

1995. Cats. Multicoloured
274 100m. Type **59** 10 10
275 150m. Chartreux 25 25
276 250m. Somali 30 30
277 300m. Longhair Scottish fold 45 45
278 400m. Cymric 50 50
279 500m. Turkish angora . . . 70 70
MS280 85 × 75 mm. 800m. Birman (31 × 39 mm) . . . . 1·10 1·10

1995. Flora and Fauna. Multicoloured.
281 100m. Type **60** 10 10
282 200m. Grape hyacinths (vert) 20 20
283 250m. Beluga 25 25
284 300m. Golden eagle 30 30
285 400m. Tiger 30 30
286 500m. Georgian black grouse nesting 50 50
287 1000m. Georgian black grouse in meadow . . . . 1·00 1·00

61 Lennon and Signature

1995. 15th Death Anniv of John Lennon (entertainer).
288 **61** 500m. multicoloured . . . 55 55

62 Early Steam Locomotive, U.S.A.

1996. Railway Locomotives. Multicoloured.
289 100m. Type **62** 40 40
290 100m. New York Central Class J3 locomotive . . . 40 40
291 100m. Steam locomotive on bridge 40 40
292 100m. Steam locomotive No. 1959, Germany . . . 40 40
293 100m. Steam locomotive No. 4113, Germany . . . 40 40
294 100m. Steam locomotive, Italy 40 40
295 100m. Class 59 steam locomotive, Japan 40 40
296 100m. Class QJ steam locomotive, China 40 40
297 100m. Class Sn 23 steam locomotive, China 40 40
MS298 110 × 80 mm. 500m. Electric train (vert) . . . . 2·00 2·00

63 Operating Theatre and Topcubasov

1996. Birth Centenary of M. Topcubasov (surgeon).
299 **63** 300m. multicoloured . . . 65 65

64 Feast and Woman wearing Traditional Costume

1996. New Year.
300 **64** 250m. multicoloured . . . 65 65

65 Carl Lewis (athletics, Los Angeles, 1984)

1996. Olympic Games, Atlanta. Previous Gold Medallists. Multicoloured.
301 50m. Type **65** (wrongly inscr "1994") 10 10
302 100m. Mohammed Ali (Cassius Clay) (boxing, Rome, 1960) 20 20
303 150m. Li Ning (gymnastics, Los Angeles, 1984) 40 40
304 200m. Said Aouita (5000m, Los Angeles, 1984) 50 50
305 250m. Olga Korbut (gymnastics, Munich, 1972) 65 65

306 300m. Nadia Comaneci (gymnastics, Montreal, 1976) 85 85
307 400m. Greg Louganis (diving, Los Angeles, 1984) . . . . 1·00 1·00
MS308 74 × 104 mm. 500m. Nazim Goussinev (bantamweight boxing, Barcelona, 1992) (vert) . . . . 1·25 1·25

66 "Maral-Gol"

1996. 5th Death Anniv of G. Aliev (painter). Mult.
309 100m. "Reka Cura" 50 50
310 200m. Type **66** . . . . 1·00 1·00

67 Behbudov and Globe

1996. 7th Death Anniv of Resid Behbudov (singer).
311 **67** 100m. multicoloured . . . 65 65

68 Mammadaliev and Flasks
69 National Flag and Government Building

1996. 1st Death Anniv of Yusif Mammadaliev (scientist).
312 **68** 100m. multicoloured . . . 65 65

1996. 5th Anniv of Republic.
313 **69** 250m. multicoloured . . . 65 65

70 Dome of the Rock

1996. 3000th Anniv of Jerusalem. Multicoloured.
314 100m. Praying at the Wailing Wall 40 40
315 250m. Interior of church . . 1·00 1·00
316 300m. Type **70** . . . . 1·10 1·10
MS317 73 × 104 mm. 500m. Montefiore Windmill . . . . . 1·50 1·50

71 German Shepherd

1996. Dogs. Multicoloured.
318 50m. Type **71** 10 10
319 100m. Basset hounds 25 25
320 150m. Collies 35 35
321 200m. Bull terriers 50 50
322 300m. Boxers 70 70
323 400m. Cocker spaniels . . . 1·10 1·10
MS324 70 × 80 mm. 500m. Shar-pei (38 × 30 mm) . . . . 1·10 1·10

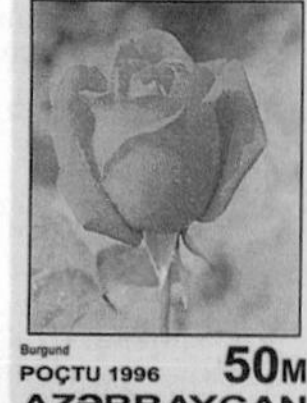

72 Shaft-tailed Whydah
73 "Burgundy"

1996. Birds. Multicoloured.
325 50m. Type **72** 10 10
326 100m. Blue-naped mousebird 25 25
327 150m. Asian black-headed oriole 35 35
328 200m. Golden oriole 50 50
329 300m. Common starling . . . 70 70
330 400m. Yellow-fronted canary 1·00 1·00
MS331 60 × 80 mm. 500m. European bee eater (*Merops apaister*) (31 × 39 mm) . . . . 1·50 1·50

1996. Roses. Multicoloured.
332 50m. Type **73** 10 10
333 100m. "Virgo" 20 20
334 150m. "Rose Gaujard" . . . 30 30
335 200m. "Luna" 45 45
336 300m. "Lady Rose" 70 70
337 400m. "Landora" . . . . . 1·00 1·00
MS338 90 × 70 mm. 500m. "Luxor" (39 × 31 mm) . . . . 1·10 1·10

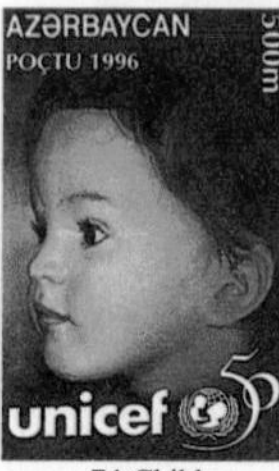

74 Child
75 Spain v. Bulgaria

1996. 50th Anniv of U.N.I.C.E.F.
339 **74** 500m. multicoloured . . . 1·00 1·00

1996. European Football Championship, England. Multicoloured.
340 100m. Type **75** 20 20
341 150m. Rumania v. France . . 30 30
342 200m. Czech Republic v. Germany 45 45
343 250m. England v. Switzerland 55 55
344 300m. Croatia v. Turkey . . 70 70
345 400m. Italy v. Russia . . . . 1·00 1·00
MS346 110 × 80 mm. 500m. Detail of cup . . . . 1·10 1·10

76 Chinese Junk

1996. Ships. Multicoloured.
347 100m. Type **76** 25 25
348 150m. "Danmark" (Danish full-rigged cadet ship) . . . 40 40
349 200m. "Nippon-Maru II" (Japanese cadet ship) . . . 45 45
350 250m. "Mircea" (Rumanian barque) 55 55
351 300m. "Kruzenshtern" (Russian cadet barque) . . 85 85
352 400m. "Ariadne" (German cadet schooner) . . . . . 1·10 1·10
MS353 107 × 77 mm. 500m. *Tovarishch* (Russian four-masted cadet barque) (vert) . . . . . 1·40 1·40

77 Baxram Gur killing Dragon (fountain by A. Shulgin at Baku)
82 Dog

78 Nariman Narimanov (politician and writer)

1997.
354 **77** 100m. purple and black . . 55 55
356 250m. black and yellow . . 20 20
357 400m. black and red . . . 40 40
358 500m. black and green . . 45 45
359 1000m. black and blue . . 75 75

1997. Anniversaries. Multicoloured.
365 250m. Type **78** (125th birth anniv (1995)) 55 55
366 250m. Fatali Xoyskin (politician, 120th birth anniv (1995)) 55 55
367 250m. Aziz Mammed-Kerim ogli Aliyev (politician, birth centenary) 55 55
368 250m. Ilyas Afendiyev (writer, 1st death anniv) . . 55 55

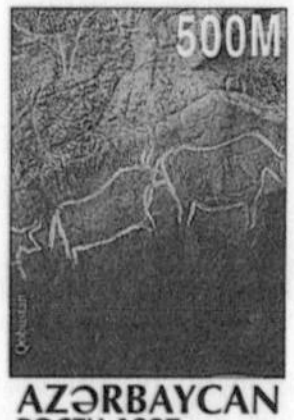

79 Bulls

1997. Qobustasn Rock Carvings. Sheet 127 × 84 mm containing T **79** and similar vert designs. Multicoloured.
MS369 500m. Type **79**; 500m. Goats; 500m. Dancers . . . . 2·75 2·75

1997. Red Cross. Various stamps optd **Red Cross** and cross. (a) Nos. 93/99.
370 20q. multicoloured 50 50
371 30q. multicoloured 50 50
372 50q. multicoloured 50 50
373 1m. multicoloured 75 75
374 2m.50 multicoloured 75 75
375 5m. multicoloured . . . . . 1·60 1·60
376 10m. multicoloured . . . . . 4·25 4·25
MS377 80 × 60 mm. 8m. multicoloured 75 75

(b) Nos. 195/9.
378 10m. multicoloured 70 70
379 15m. multicoloured . . . . . 1·00 1·00
380 20m. multicoloured . . . . . 1·40 1·40
381 25m. multicoloured . . . . . 1·60 1·60
382 50m. multicoloured . . . . . 3·00 3·00
MS383 64 × 56 mm. 100m. multicoloured . . . . 5·50 5·50

1997. 50th Anniv of Rotary Club International in Azerbaijan. Various stamps optd **50th Anniversary of the Rotary Club** and emblem. (a) Nos. 314/16.
384 100m. multicoloured 90 90
385 250m. multicoloured . . . . 3·00 3·00
386 300m. multicoloured . . . . 3·50 3·50
MS387 74 × 103 mm. 500m. multicoloured . . . . 2·00 2·00

(b) Nos. 347/52.
388 100m. multicoloured 30 30
389 150m. multicoloured 55 55
390 200m. multicoloured 70 70
391 250m. multicoloured . . . . 1·00 1·00
392 300m. multicoloured . . . . 1·10 1·10
393 400m. multicoloured . . . . 1·40 1·40
MS394 106 × 76 mm. 500m. multicoloured . . . . 2·00 2·00

1997. "The Town Band of Bremen" by the Brothers Grimm. Multicoloured.
395 250m. Type **82** . . . . 1·10 1·10
396 250m. Donkey and cat . . . 1·10 1·10
397 250m. Rooster . . . . 1·10 1·10
MS398 125 × 96 mm. 500m. Animals frightening robbers from hideaway 1·60 1·60
Nos. 395/7 were issued together, se-tenant, forming a composite design.

83 Seal Pup

1997. The Caspian Seal. Multicoloured.
399 250m. Type **83** 65 65
400 250m. Bull and mountain peak 65 65
401 250m. Bull and gull 65 65
402 250m. Cow (profile) 65 65
403 250m. Cow (full face) 65 65
404 250m. Young seal (three-quarter face) 65 65
MS405 106 × 77 mm. 500m. Cow (vert) . . . . 1·00 1·00

Nos. 399/404 were issued together, se-tenant, forming a composite design.

84 Tanbur

1997. Traditional Musical Instruments. Mult.
406 250m. Type **84** 50 50
407 250m. Gaval (tambourine) . . 50 50
408 500m. Jang (harp) . . . . . 1·00 1·00

85 19th-century Oil Derricks, Aspheron Peninsula
86 Sirvani

1997. 125th Anniv of First Industrial Oil Well in Azerbaijan. Sheet 115 × 91 mm containing T **85** and similar vert design. Multicoloured.
MS409 500m. Type **85**; 500m. Modern drilling platform, Caspian Sea . . . . 2·50 2·50

1997. 870th Birth Anniv (1996) of Xanqani Sirvani (poet).
410 **86** 250m. multicoloured . . . 90 90

87 Taza-pir Mosque, Baku

1997. Mosques. Multicoloured.
411 250m. Type **87** 70 70
412 250m. Momuna-Xatun Mosque, Nakhichevan . . 70 70
413 250m. Govharaga Mosque, Shusha 70 70

88 Rasulbekov and Baku T.V. Tower
90 Katarina Wit, East Germany

89 Italy, 1938

1997. 80th Birth Anniv of G. D. Rasulbekov (former Minister of Telecommunications).
414 **88** 250m. multicoloured . . . 65 65

1997. World Cup Football Championship, France (1998).
415 **89** 250m. black 55 55
416 – 250m. multicoloured . . . 55 55
417 – 250m. black 55 55
418 – 250m. multicoloured . . . 55 55
419 – 250m. multicoloured . . . 55 55
420 – 250m. multicoloured . . . 55 55
MS421 85 × 90 mm. 1500m. black and blue (Tofiq Bahramov (referee)) . . . . 2·40 2·40
DESIGNS—World Champion Teams: No. 416, Argentina, 1986; 417, Uruguay, 1930 (wrongly inscr "1980"); 418, Brazil, 1994; 419, England, 1966; 420, West Germany, 1990.

1997. Winter Olympic Games, Nagano, Japan. Mult.
422 250m. Type **90** (figure skating gold medal, 1984 and 1988) 50 50
423 250m. Elvis Stoyko, Canada (figure skating silver medal, 1994) 50 50

424 250m. Midori Ito, Japan (figure skating silver medal, 1992) 50 50
425 250m. Azerbaijan flag and silhouettes of sports . . . 50 50
426 250m. Olympic torch and mountain 50 50
427 250m. Kristin Yamaguchi, U.S.A. (figure skating gold medal, 1992) 50 50
428 250m. John Curry, Great Britain (figure skating gold medal, 1976) 50 50
429 250m. Cen Lu, China (figure skating bronze medal, 1994) 50 50
MS430 76 × 106 mm. 500m. Yekaterina Gordeyeva and Sergi Grinkov, Russia (figure skating gold medal, 1984 and 1988) . . 1·10 1·10

91 Diana, Princess of Wales

1998. Diana, Princess of Wales Commem. Mult.
431 400m. Type **91** 40 40
432 400m. Wearing black polo-neck jumper 40 40

92 Aliyev and Mountain Landscape

1998. 90th Birth Anniv of Hasan Aliyev (ecologist).
433 **92** 500m. multicoloured . . . 65 65

93 Tourist Map, Flag and Pres. Aliev

1998. 75th Birthday of President Haidar Aliev. Sheet 114 × 89 mm.
MS434 **93** 500m. multicoloured 2·00 2·00

1998. "Israel 98" International Stamp Exhibition, Tel Aviv. No. **MS**369 optd **98** and emblem on each stamp and "Israel 98–WORLD STAMP EXHIBITION TEL–AVIV 13–21 MAY 1998" in margin.
MS435 500m. × 3 multicoloured 4·00 4·00

95 Ashug Alesker (singer)

1998. Birth Anniversaries. Multicoloured.
436 250m. Type **95** (175th anniv) 65 65
437 250m. Magomedhuseyn Shakhriyar (poet, 90th anniv) 65 65
438 250m. Qara Qarayev (composer, 80th anniv) . . 65 65

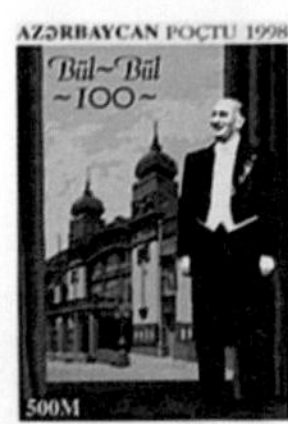

96 Bul-Bul

1998. Birth Centenary of Bul-Bul (Murtuz Meshadirza ogli Mamedov) (singer).
439 **96** 500m. multicoloured . . . 75 75

97 Mickey and Minnie Mouse playing Chess

1998. World Rapid Chess Championship, Georgia. Multicoloured.
440 250m. Type **97** 40 40
441 500m. Mickey, Minnie, pawn and rook 70 70
442 500m. Goofy, bishop and knight 70 70
443 500m. Donald Duck, king and bishop 70 70
444 500m. Pluto, rook, pawn and clockwork pawn 70 70
445 500m. Minnie and queen . . 70 70
446 500m. Daisy Duck, bishop and king 70 70
447 500m. Goofy, Donald and pawn 70 70
448 500m. Mickey, queen and rook 70 70
MS449 Two sheets, each 127 × 101 mm. (a) 4000m. Mickey, Minnie, Pluto and queen; (b) 4000m. Donald, Mickey and pawn 4·50 4·50

98 Preparing Pastries

1998. Europa. National Festivals: New Year. Mult.
450 1000m. Type **98** 85 85
451 3000m. Acrobat and wrestlers 2·40 2·40

1999. "iBRA" International Stamp Exhibition, Nuremberg, Germany. Nos. 450/1 optd with exhibition emblem.
452 1000m. multicoloured 90 90
453 3000m. multicoloured . . . . 2·75 2·75

100 Greater Flamingo, Gizilagach National Park

101 14th-century Square Tower

1999. Europa. Parks and Gardens. Multicoloured.
454 1000m. Type **100** 90 90
455 3000m. Stag, Girkan National Park . . . . . . 2·75 2·75

1999. Towers at Mardakyan.
456 **101** 1000m. black and blue . . 50 50
457 – 3000m. black and red . . 1·40 1·40
DESIGN: 3000m. 13th-century round tower.

102 President Aliev and Flag

1999. 75th Anniv of Nakhichevan Autonomous Region. Multicoloured.
460 1000m. Type **102** 75 75
461 1000m. Map of Nakhichevan 75 75
MS462 110 × 90 mm. Nos. 460/1 2·60 2·50

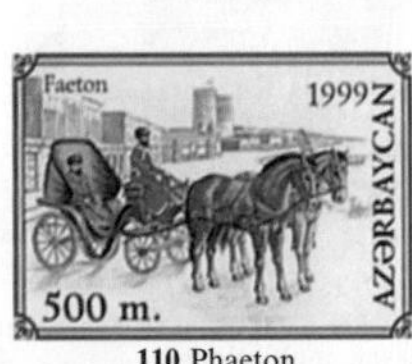

103 Cabbarli

1999. Birth Centenary of Cafar Cabbarli (dramatist).
463 **103** 250m. multicoloured . . . 1·10 1·10

104 40k. Stamp

1999. 80th Anniv of First Azerbaijani Stamps. Sheet 131 × 106 mm containing T **104** and similar multicoloured designs showing stamps of 1919.
MS464 500m. 10k. stamp (Type **1**) (25 × 35 mm); 500m. Type **104**; 500m. 5r. stamp; 500m. 50r. stamp (Type **2**) . . . . 2·75 2·75

105 Flag, Pigeon and Emblem on Scroll

106 Caravanserai Inner Court and Maiden's Tower, Baku

1999. 125th Anniv of Universal Postal Union. Multicoloured.
465 250m. Type **105** 10 10
466 300m. Satellite, computer and emblem . . . . 2·00 2·00

1999. 19th-century Caravanserais. Multicoloured.
467 500m. Type **106** 95 95
468 500m. Camels outside caravanserai, Sheki 95 95

107 Anniversary Emblem

1999. 50th Anniv of Council of Europe.
469 **107** 1000m. multicoloured . . 1·00 1·00

108 Beybur Khan's Son fighting Camel

1999. 1300th Anniv of Kitabi Dada Qorqud (folk epic). Sheet 90 × 125 mm containing T **108** and similar horiz designs. Multicoloured.
MS470 1000m. Type **108**; 1000m. Wounded Tural slumped on horse; 1000m. Gaza Khan asleep beside horse . . . . 2·75 2·75

109 "Building Europe"

111 14th-century Square Tower, Ramana

110 Phaeton

2000. Europa.
471 **109** 1000m. multicoloured . . 90 90
472 3000m. multicoloured . . 2·75 2·75

2000. Baku City Transport. Sheet 111 × 88 mm containing T **110** and similar horiz designs. Multicoloured.
MS473 500m. Type **110**; 500m. Konka; 500m. Electric tram; 500m. Trolleybus . . . . . . 3·25 3·25

2000. Towers of Mardakyan.
474 **111** 100m. black and orange 25 25
475 – 250m. black and green . . 55 55
DESIGN: 250m. 14th-century round tower, Nardaran.
See also Nos. 499/500.

112 Wrestling

2000. Olympic Games, Sydney. Multicoloured.
476 500m. Type **112** 65 65
477 500m. Weightlifting 65 65
478 500m. Boxing 65 65
479 500m. Relay 65 65

113 Duck flying

2000. The Ferruginous Duck. Multicoloured.
480 500m. Type **113** 45 45
481 500m. Ducks in water and standing on rocks 45 45
482 500m. Duck standing on rock and others swimming by grasses 45 45
483 500m. Ducks at sunset . . . 45 45

114 Satellite Picture of Azerbaijan and Emblem

115 Quinces

2000. 50th Anniv of World Meteorological Organization.
484 **114** 1000m. multicoloured . . 65 65

2000. Fruits. Multicoloured.
485 500m. Type **115** 55 55
486 500m. Pomegranates (*Punica granatum*) 55 55
487 500m. Peaches (*Persica*) . . . 55 55
488 500m. Figs (*Ficus carica*) . . 55 55

116 Ringed-necked Pheasant

117 Rasul-Rza

2000. The Ringed-necked Pheasant (*Phasanus colchicus*). Sheet 102 × 72 mm.
MS489 **116** 2000m. multicoloured 2·10 2·10

2000. 90th Birth Anniv of Rasul-Rza (poet).
490 **117** 250m. multicoloured . . . 50 50

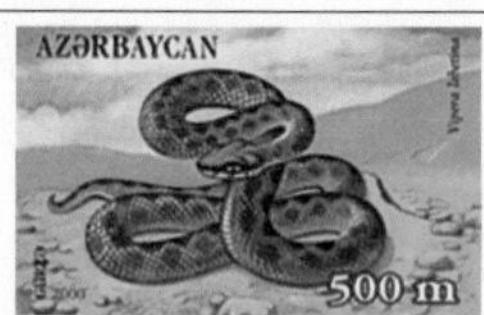

118 Levantine Viper

2000. Reptiles. Multicoloured.
491 500m. Type **118** 75 75
492 500m. Rock lizard (*Lacerta saxicola*) (wrongly inscr "Laserta saxcola") 75 75
493 500m. Ottoman viper (*Vipera xanthina*) 75 75
494 500m. Toad-headed agama (*Phrynocephalus mystaceus*) 75 75
MS495 90 × 63 mm. 500m. Watersnake (*Natrix tessellate*) and sunwatcher (*Phrynocephalus helioscopus*) (vert) . . . . . . 1·25 1·25

119 Rahman

2000. 90th Birth Anniv of Sabit Rahman (writer).
496 **119** 1000m. multicoloured . . 45 45

120 Emblem

2000. U.N.E.S.C.O. International Year of Culture and Peace.
497 **120** 3000m. multicoloured . . 1·40 1·40

121 Namig Abullayev (gold, freestyle flyweight wrestling)

2001. Olympic Games, Sydney. Medal Winners. Sheet 99 × 127 mm containing T **121** and similar horiz designs. Multicoloured.
MS498 1000m. Type **121**; 1000m. Zemifira Meftahaddinova (gold, skeet shooting); 1000m. Vugar Alakbarov (bronze, middle-weight boxing) . . . . 2·75 2·75

122 Seal, Lesser White-fronted Goose and Oil Rig

2001. Europa. Water Resources. The Caspian Sea. Multicoloured.
499 1000m. Type **122** 55 55
500 3000m. Sturgeon, crab and oil rig . . . . 1·60 1·60

123 Building and Flags

2001. Admission of Azerbaijan to Council of Europe.
501 **123** 1000m. multicoloured . . 55 55

2001. Towers of Sheki. As T **111**
502 100m. black and lilac 10 10
503 250m. black and yellow . . . 25 25
DESIGNS: 100m. 18th-century round tower; 250m. Ruin of 12th-century tower.

124 Refugee Camp

2001. 50th Anniv of United Nations High Commissioner for Refugees. Sheet 100 × 73 mm.
MS504 **124** 3000m. black and blue 2·50 2·50

125 Tusi, Globe and Books

2001. 800th Birth Anniv of Nasraddin Tusi (mathematician and astronomer). Sheet 110 × 78 mm.
MS505 **125** 3000m. multicoloured 1·40 1·40

126 Handshake and Emblem

127 Yuri Gagarin, "Vostok 1" and Globe

128 Short-eared Owl (*Asio flammeus*)

2001. 10th Anniv of Union of Independent States.
506 **126** 1000m. multicoloured . . 45 45

2001. 40th Anniv of First Manned Space Flight. Sheet 83 × 56 mm.
MS507 **127** 3000m. multicoloured 1·40 1·40

2001. Owls. Multicoloured.
508 1000m. Type **128** 45 45
509 1000m. Tawny owl (*Strix aluco*) 45 45
510 1000m. Scops owl (*Otus scops*) 45 45
511 1000m. Long-eared owl (*Asio otus*) 45 45
512 1000m. Eagle owl on branch (*Bubo bubo*) 45 45
513 1000m. Little owl (*Athene noctua*) 45 45
MS514 91 × 68 mm. 1000 m. Eagle owl (*Bubo bubo*) in flight . . . 45 45

129 Pres. Heydar Aliyev

2001. 10th Anniv of Independence.
515 **129** 5000m. multicoloured . . 2·25 2·25

130 Pres. Vladimir Putin and Pres. Heydar Aliyev

2001. Visit of President Putin to Azerbaijan.
516 **130** 1000m. multicoloured . . 45 45

131 Emblem and Athletes

2002. 10th Anniv of National Olympic Committee.
517 **131** 3000m. multicoloured . . 1·40 1·40

132 Circus Performers

2002. Europa. Circus. Multicoloured.
518 1000m. Type **132** 45 45
519 3000m. Equestrian juggler and trapeze artist . . . . 1·40 1·40

133 Presidents Heydar Aliyev and Jiang Zemin

2002. 10th Anniv of Azerbaijan--China Diplomatic Relations.
520 **133** 1000m. multicoloured . . 45 45

134 Molla Panah Vagif's Mausoleum, Susa

136 Emblem

2002. Towers of Karabakh.
521 **134** 100m. black and green . . 10 10
522 – 250m. black and cinnamon 10 10
DESIGNS: 250m. 19th-century mosque, Aghdam.

2002. 10th Anniv of Azermarka Stamp Company. No. 83 surch **Azermarka 1992–2002 1000m.**
523 **13** 1000m. on 35q. multicoloured 45 45

2002. 10th Anniv of New Azerbaijan Party.
524 **136** 3000m. multicoloured . . 1·40 1·40

137 African Monarch (*Danaus chrysippus*)

2002. Butterflies and Moths. Multicoloured.
525 1000m. Type **137** (inscr "Danais") 45 45
526 1000m. Southern swallowtail (*Papilio alexanor*) 45 45
527 1000m. *Thaleropis jonia* . . . 45 45
528 1000m. Red admiral (*Vanessa atalanta*) 45 45
529 1000m. *Argynnis alexandra* 45 45
530 1000m. *Brahmaea christoph* (moth) 45 45

138 Pres. Heydar Aliyev and Pope John Paul II

2002. Pope John Paul II's Visit to Azerbaijan. Sheet 80 × 65 mm.
MS531 **138** 1500m. multicoloured 55 55

139 Telegraph Machine, Building Facade and Emblem

2002. 70th Anniv of Baku Telegraph Office.
532 **139** 3000m. multicoloured . . 1·10 1·10

140 Gadjiyev and Piano

2002. 80th Birth Anniv of Ruaf Gadjiyev (composer).
533 **140** 5000m. multicoloured . . 1·90 1·90

141 Bearded Men with Swords, Black Pawns, White Pawn and White Rook

2002. European Junior Chess Championships, Baku. Showing chess board and views of Baku. Multicoloured.
534 1500m. Type **141** 55 55
535 1500m. Two knights on horseback 55 55
536 1500m. Two elephants . . . 55 55
537 1500m. Black rook, black pawn, bearded men with swords and fallen knight 55 55
Nos. 534/7 were issued together, se-tenant, forming a composite design showing a chess game and views of ancient Baku.

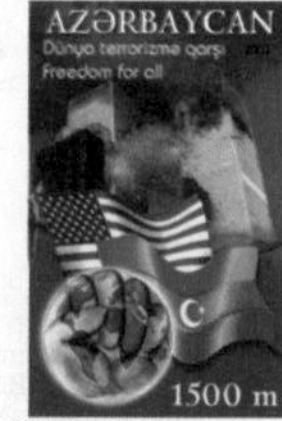

142 World Trade Centre, New York, U.S.A. and Azerbaijan Flags and Globe

2002. 1st Anniv of Attack on World Trade Centre, New York. Sheet 130 × 65 mm containing vert design as T **142**. Multicoloured.
MS538 1500m. × 3 Type **142** . . 1·60 1·60

143 Turkish Football Team

2002. Football World Cup Championship, Japan and South Korea. Sheet 102 × 110 mm.
MS539 **143** 5000m. multicoloured 1·90 1·90

144 Dove, Woman, Flag and Emblems

145 Siamese Fighting Fish (*Betta splendens*)

2002. United Nations Development Fund for Women.
540 **144** 3000m. multicoloured 1·10 1·10

2002. Aquarium Fish. Multicoloured.
541 100m. Type **145** 10 10
542 100m. Blue discus (*Symphysodon aequifasciatus*) 10 10
543 100m. Freshwater angelfish (*Pterophyllum scalare*) 10 10
544 100m. Black moor (*Carassius auratus auratus*) 10 10
545 100m. Boeseman's rainbowfish (*Melanotaenia boesemani*) 10 10
546 1000m. Firemouth cichlid (*Cichlasoma meeki*) 35 35

AZORES Pt. 9

A group of islands in the Atlantic Ocean.

1868. 1000 reis = 1 milreis.
1912. 100 centavos = 1 escudo.
2002. 100 cents = 1 euro.

NOTE. Except where otherwise stated, Nos. 1/393 are all stamps of Portugal optd **ACORES**.

1868. Curved value labels. Imperf.
1 **14** 5r. black £2250 £1900
2 10r. yellow £13000 £9000
3 20r. bistre £170 £150
4 50r. green £170 £150
5 80r. orange £190 £160
6 100r. purple £190 £160

1868. Curved value labels. Perf.
7 **14** 5r. black 60·00 60·00
9 10r. yellow 80·00 60·00
10 20r. bistre 60·00 55·00
11 25r. pink 65·00 9·50
12 50r. green £180 £170
13 80r. orange £180 £170
14 100r. lilac £180 £170
16 120r. blue £150 £100
17 240r. lilac £550 £350

1871. Straight value labels.
38 **15** 5r. black 11·50 7·75
39 10r. yellow 37·00 29·00
73 10r. green 70·00 60·00
29 15r. brown 15·00 14·00
31 20r. bistre 26·00 15·00
109 20r. red 90·00 75·00
32 25r. pink 14·50 3·75
33 50r. green 75·00 30·00
54 50r. blue £130 75·00
101b 80r. orange 65·00 50·00
103 100r. mauve 50·00 45·00
25 120r. blue £140 £120
49 150r. blue 75·00 55·00
104 150r. yellow 50·00 45·00
26 240r. lilac £750 £600
50 300r. lilac 75·00 55·00
94 1000r. black £120 £100

1880.
58 **16** 5r. black 23·00 11·00
61 25r. grey 46·00 45·00
61b 25r. brown 46·00 45·00
60 **17** 25r. grey £120 37·00
67 **16** 50r. blue £140 34·00

1882.
136 **19** 5r. grey 26·00 9·00
125 10r. green 24·00 11·50
139 20r. red 12·00 1·80
126 25r. brown 24·00 3·50
141 25r. mauve 28·00 2·40
142 50r. blue 21·00 3·50
128 500r. black £150 £130
129 500r. mauve £120 85·00

1894. Prince Henry the Navigator.
143 **32** 5r. orange 2·75 2·40
144 10r. red 2·75 2·40
145 15r. brown 3·50 3·25
146 20r. lilac 3·50 3·25
147 25r. green 4·00 3·50
148 50r. blue 9·75 5·50
149 75r. red 18·00 7·50
150 80r. green 21·00 8·00
151 100r. brown on buff 21·00 6·50
152 150r. red 28·00 15·00
153 300r. blue on buff 33·00 23·00
154 500r. purple 60·00 35·00
155 1000r. black on buff £180 90·00

1895. St. Anthony of Padua.
156 **35** 2½r. black 2·40 95
157 – 5r. orange 7·50 2·30
158 – 10r. mauve 7·50 3·50
159 – 15r. brown 11·50 5·50
160 – 20r. grey 12·50 7·50
161 – 25r. purple and green 8·00 2·30
162 **37** 50r. brown and blue 26·00 11·50
163 75r. brown and red 38·00 32·00
164 80r. brown and green 43·00 38·00
165 100r. black and brown 43·00 34·00
166 – 150r. red and brown 90·00 80·00
167 – 200r. blue and brown 95·00 85·00
168 – 300r. black and brown £120 85·00
169 – 500r. brown & green £170 £120
170 – 1000r. lilac and green £275 £350

1898. Vasco da Gama stamps as Nos. 378/385 of Portugal but inscr "ACORES".
171 2½r. green 2·75 1·00
172 5r. red 5·00 1·20
173 10r. purple 5·50 2·30
174 25r. green 5·50 2·30
175 50r. blue 7·75 7·50
176 75r. brown 16·00 11·00
177 100r. brown 21·00 11·50
178 150r. bistre 34·00 23·00

1906. "King Carlos" key-type inscr "ACORES" and optd with letters **A**, **H** and **PD** in three of the corners.
179 S 2½r. grey 35 30
180 5r. orange 35 30
181 10r. green 35 30
182 20r. lilac 55 40
183 25r. red 55 30
184 50r. blue 4·75 3·75
185 75r. brown on yellow 1·70 1·00
186 100r. blue on blue 1·60 1·10
187 200r. purple on pink 1·80 1·10
188 300r. blue on pink 5·25 4·50
189 500r. black on blue 12·50 11·00

7 King Manoel

1910.
190 **7** 2½r. lilac 35 30
191 5r. black 35 30
192 10r. green 35 30
193 15r. brown 70 50
194 20r. red 95 80
195 25r. brown 35 35
196 50r. blue 2·40 1·20
197 75r. brown 2·40 1·20
198 80r. grey 2·40 1·20
199 100r. brown on green 2·40 3·00
200 200r. green on pink 3·75 3·00
201 300r. black on blue 3·75 2·20
202 500r. brown and olive 2·40 8·00
203 1000r. black and blue 7·50 15·00

1910. Optd **REPUBLICA.**
204 **7** 2½r. lilac 30 25
205 5r. black 30 25
206 10r. green 35 25
207 15r. brown 1·50 1·10
208b 20r. red 1·50 1·10
209 25r. brown 30 20
210a 50r. blue 1·00 95
211 75r. brown 1·10 75
212 80r. grey 1·10 75
213 100r. brown on green 95 75
214 200r. green on orange 95 75
215 300r. black on blue 2·75 1·80
216 500r. brown and green 3·50 2·50
217 1000r. black and blue 8·75 5·50

1911. Vasco da Gama stamps of Azores optd **REPUBLICA**, some surch also.
218 2½r. green 50 35
219 15r. on 5r. red 50 35
220 25r. green 50 35
221 50r. blue 1·70 1·20
222 75r. brown 1·50 1·40
223 80r. on 150r. brown 1·50 1·50
224 100r. brown 1·70 1·50
225 1000r. on 10r. purple 21·00 12·00

1911. Postage Due stamps optd or surch **REPUBLICA ACORES.**
226 D **48** 5r. black 1·00 90
227 10r. mauve 2·20 90
228 20r. orange 4·25 3·00
229 200r. brown on buff 18·00 16·00
230 300r. on 50r. grey 17·00 15·00
231 500r. on 100r. red on pink 17·00 14·50

1912. "Ceres" type.
250 **56** ¼c. brown 45 35
273 ½c. black 45 40
252 1c. green 85 65
274 1c. brown 45 40
254 1½c. brown 85 65
255 1½c. green 45 40
256 2c. red 65 50
257 2c. orange 45 40
258 2½c. lilac 65 50
259 3c. red 45 40
278 3c. blue 35 25
260 3½c. green 45 40
261 4c. green 45 40
401 4c. orange 45 35
262 5c. blue 65 50
280 5c. brown 45 40
264 6c. purple 45 40
282 6c. brown 45 40
403 6c. red 30 20
265 7½c. brown 5·25 3·00
266 7½c. blue 1·50 1·40
267 8c. grey 65 50
283 8c. green 65 45
284 8c. orange 80 75
268 10c. brown 5·25 2·20
285 10c. red 95 70
286 12c. blue 2·10 1·50
287 12c. green 70 60
288 13½c. blue 2·10 1·50
249 14c. blue on yellow 1·80 1·50
269 15c. purple 65 50
289 15c. black 45 40
290 16c. blue 75 70
243 20c. brown on green 9·75 5·50
291 20c. brown 70 60
292 20c. green 95 75
293 20c. drab 65 50
294 24c. blue 70 45
295 25c. pink 55 40
244 30c. brown on pink 60·00 48·00
245 30c. brown on yellow 1·80 1·50
296 30c. brown 1·50 1·30
406 32c. green 2·20 1·50
298 36c. red 65 50
299 40c. blue 80 55
300 40c. brown 1·50 80
407 40c. green 1·20 60
408 48c. pink 2·75 2·30
246 50c. orange on orange 5·25 1·50
247 50c. orange on yellow 5·00 2·20
302 50c. yellow 1·50 90
410 50c. red 2·75 2·30
303 60c. blue 1·40 1·20
304 64c. blue 4·00 2·10
411 64c. red 3·75 2·10
305 75c. pink 4·00 3·00
412 75c. red 3·75 2·75
306 80c. purple 2·00 1·60
307 80c. lilac 2·10 1·50
413 80c. green 3·75 2·30
308 90c. blue 2·00 1·60
309 96c. red 6·00 2·75
248 1e. green on blue 13·50 6·00
310 1e. lilac 2·00 1·60
314 1e. purple 3·00 2·50
414 **56** 1e. red 32·00 22·00
311 1e.10 brown 2·20 1·60
312 1e.20 green 2·50 1·60
315 1e.20 buff 6·50 4·75
415 1e.25 blue 2·10 1·80
316 1e.50 purple 7·75 5·25
317 1e.50 lilac 6·75 5·50
400 1e.60 blue 3·25 1·40
313 2e. green 8·00 5·25
319 2e.40 green 55·00 24·00
320 3e. pink 65·00 39·00
321 3e.20 green 7·75 7·50
322 5e. green 14·50 8·00
323 10e. pink 39·00 22·00
324 20e. blue 95·00 65·00

1925. C. C. Branco Centenary.
325 **65** 2c. orange 20 20
326 3c. green 20 20
327 4c. blue 20 20
328 5c. red 20 20
329 – 10c. blue 20 20
330 – 16c. orange 30 20
331 **67** 25c. red 30 20
332 – 32c. green 40 40
333 **67** 40c. black and green 40 40
334 48c. purple 95 95
335 – 50c. green 95 80
336 – 64c. brown 95 80
337 – 75c. grey 95 80
338 **67** 80c. brown 95 80
339 – 96c. red 1·10 95
340 – 1e.50 blue on blue 1·10 95
341 **67** 1e.60 blue 1·20 1·10
342 – 2e. green on green 2·00 1·70
343 – 2e.40 red on orange 2·75 1·90
344 – 3e.20 black on green 4·75 4·25

1926. 1st Independence Issue.
345 **76** 2c. black and orange 30 25
346 – 3c. black and blue 30 25
347 **76** 4c. black and green 30 25
348 – 5c. black and brown 30 25
349 **76** 6c. black and orange 30 25
350 – 15c. black and green 60 60
351 **77** 20c. black and violet 60 60
352 – 25c. black and red 60 60
353 **77** 32c. black and green 60 60
354 – 40c. black and brown 60 60
355 – 50c. black and olive 1·30 1·30
356 – 75c. black and red 1·40 1·40
357 – 1e. black and violet 1·70 1·70
358 – 4e.50 black and green 7·00 7·00

1927. 2nd Independence Issue.
359 **80** 2c. black and brown 35 35
360 – 3c. black and blue 25 25
361 **80** 4c. black and orange 25 25
362 – 5c. black and brown 25 25
363 – 6c. black and brown 25 25
364 – 15c. black and brown 25 25
365 **80** 25c. black and grey 1·00 1·00
366 – 32c. black and green 1·00 1·00
367 – 40c. black and green 60 60
368 – 96c. black and red 2·50 2·50
369 – 1e.60 black and blue 2·75 2·75
370 – 4e.50 black and yellow 7·00 2·50

1928. 3rd Independence Issue.
371 – 2c. black and blue 25 20
372 **84** 3c. black and green 25 20
373 – 4c. black and red 25 20
374 – 5c. black and olive 25 20
375 – 6c. black and brown 25 20
376 **84** 15c. black and grey 50 50
377 – 16c. black and purple 60 60
378 – 25c. black and blue 60 60
379 – 32c. black and green 65 65
380 – 40c. black and brown 65 65
381 – 50c. black and red 1·40 1·30
382 **84** 80c. black and grey 1·40 1·30
383 – 96c. black and red 3·50 2·50
384 – 1e. black and mauve 3·50 2·50
385 – 1e.60 black and blue 3·50 2·50
386 – 4e.50 black and yellow 9·50 6·75

1929. "Ceres" type surch **ACORES** and new value.
387 **56** 4c. on 25c. pink 60 60
388 4c. on 60c. blue 1·20 1·10
389 10c. on 25c. pink 1·20 1·10
390 12c. on 25c. pink 1·10 1·10
391 15c. on 25c. pink 1·10 1·10
392 20c. on 25c. pink 1·90 1·90
393 40c. on 1e.10 brown 3·75 3·75

14 10r. Stamp of 1868

1980. 112th Anniv of First Azores Stamps.
416 **14** 6e.50 black, yellow & red 20 10
417 – 19e.50 blk, purple & blue 95 60
MS418 140×115 mm. Nos. 416/17 (sold at 30e.) 3·25 3·75
DESIGN: 19e.50, 100r. stamp of 1868.

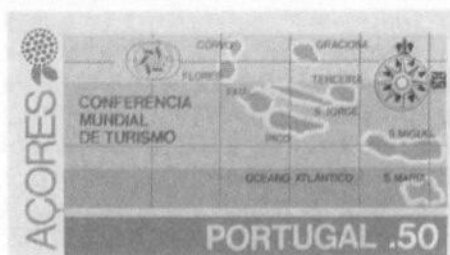

15 Map of the Azores

1980. World Tourism Conference, Manila, Philippines. Multicoloured.

419	50c. Type **15**	10	10
420	1e. Church	10	10
421	5e. Windmill	50	10
422	6e.50 Traditional costume	55	15
423	8e. Coastal scene	80	35
424	30e. Coastal village	1·80	65

16 St. Peter's Cavalcade, Sao Miguel Island

1981. Europa. Folklore.

425 **16**	22e. multicoloured	1·40	70
MS426	140 × 116 mm. No. 425 × 2	9·75	1·50

17 Bulls attacking Spanish Soldiers

1981. 400th Anniv of Battle of Salga. Mult.

427	8e.50 Type **17**	50	10
428	33e.50 Friar Don Pedro leading attack	1·90	80

18 "Myosotis azorica"

1981. Regional Flowers. Multicoloured.

429	4e. Type **18**	15	10
430	7e. "Tolpis azorica"	25	15
431	8e.50 "Ranunculus azoricus"	40	15
432	10e. "Lactuca watsoniana"	55	15
433	12e.50 "Hypericum foliosum"	25	10
434	20e. "Platanthera micranta"	70	40
435	27e. "Vicia dennesiana"	2·50	1·10
436	30e. "Rubus hochstetterorum"	80	30
437	33e.50 "Azorina vidalii"	3·25	1·00
438	37e.50 "Vaccinium cylindraceum"	1·10	60
439	50e. "Laurus azorica"	1·60	80
440	100e. "Juniperus brevifolia"	2·20	85

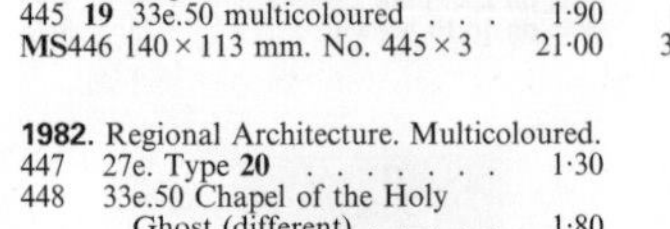

19 Embarkation of the Heroes of Mindelo

20 Chapel of the Holy Ghost

1982. Europa. Multicoloured.

445 **19**	33e.50 multicoloured	1·90	75
MS446	140 × 113 mm. No. 445 × 3	21·00	3·75

1982. Regional Architecture. Multicoloured.

447	27e. Type **20**	1·30	65
448	33e.50 Chapel of the Holy Ghost (different)	1·80	90

21 Geothermal Power Station, Pico Vermeilho, Sao Miguel

1983. Europa.

449 **21**	37e.50 multicoloured	1·50	65
MS450	114 × 140 mm. No. 449 × 3	22·00	3·75

22 Flag of Azores

1983. Flag.

451 **22**	12e.50 multicoloured	75	10

23 Two "Holy Ghost" Jesters, Sao Miguel

1984. Traditional Costumes. Multicoloured.

452	16e. Type **23**	55	10
453	51e. Two women wearing Terceira cloak	1·90	1·20

23a Bridge

1984. Europa.

454 **23a**	51e. multicoloured	2·00	1·10
MS455	114 × 139 mm. No. 454 × 3	21·00	3·75

24 "Megabombus ruderatus"

1984. Insects (1st series). Multicoloured.

456	16e. Type **24**	35	10
457	35e. Large white (butterfly)	1·00	55
458	40e. "Chrysomela banksi" (leaf beetle)	1·40	50
459	51e. "Phlogophora interrupta" (moth)	1·60	90

1985. Insects (2nd series). As T **24**. Multicoloured.

460	20e. "Polyspilla polyspilla" (leaf beetle)	35	10
461	40e. "Sphaerophoria nigra" (hover fly)	1·00	45
462	46e. Clouded yellow (butterfly)	1·40	65
463	60e. Southern grayling (butterfly)	1·60	75

25 Drummer

26 Jeque

1985. Europa. Music Year.

464 **25**	60e. multicoloured	2·20	95
MS465	140 × 114 mm. No. 464 × 3	24·00	4·50

1985. Traditional Boats. Multicoloured.

466	40e. Type **26**	1·30	70
467	60e. Bote	1·80	80

27 Northern Bullfinch

28 Alto das Covas Fountain, Terceira

1986. Europa.

468 **27**	68e.50 multicoloured	2·40	1·00
MS469	140 × 114 mm. No. 468 × 3	16·00	3·75

1986. Regional Architecture. Drinking Fountains. Multicoloured.

470	22e.50 Type **28**	55	10
471	52e.50 Faja de Baixo, Sao Miguel	1·80	80
472	68e.50 Portoes de S. Pedro, Terceira	2·50	1·00
473	100e. Agua d'Alto, Sao Miguel	3·50	90

29 Ox Cart, Santa Maria

1986. Traditional Carts. Multicoloured.

474	25e. Type **29**	55	10
475	75e. Ram cart, Sao Miguel	2·50	1·30

30 Regional Assembly Building (Correia Fernandes and Luis Miranda)

1987. Europa. Architecture.

476 **30**	74e.50 multicoloured	2·30	1·00
MS477	140 × 114 mm. No. 476 × 4	22·00	4·50

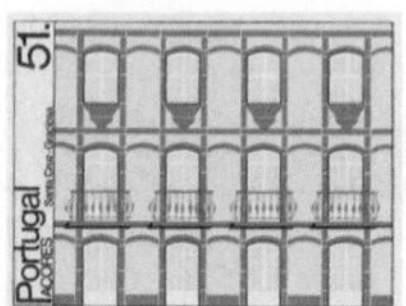

31 Santa Cruz, Graciosa

1987. Windows and Balconies. Multicoloured.

478	51e. Type **31**	1·60	80
479	74e.50 Ribeira Grande, Sao Miguel	2·00	80

32 A. C. Read's Curtiss NC-4 Flying Boat, 1919

1987. Historic Airplane Landings in the Azores. Multicoloured.

480	25e. Type **32**	50	10
481	57e. E. F. Christiansen's Dornier Do-X flying boat, 1932	1·80	1·00
482	74e.50 Italo Balbo's Savoia Marchetti S-55X flying boat, 1933	2·50	95
483	125e. Charles Lindbergh's Lockheed 8 Sirius seaplane "Tingmissartoq", 1933	3·00	1·30

33 19th-century Mule-drawn Omnibus

1988. Europa. Transport and Communications.

484 **33**	80e. multicoloured	2·40	85
MS485	140 × 112 mm. As No. 484 × 4 but with cream background	16·00	5·25

34 Wood Pigeon

1988. Nature Protection. Birds (1st series). Mult.

486	27e. Type **34**	55	15
487	60e. Eurasian woodcock	1·80	80
488	80e. Roseate tern	1·90	85
489	100e. Common buzzard	2·50	90

See also Nos. 492/5 and 500/3.

35 Azores Arms

1988. Coats-of-arms. Multicoloured.

490	55e. Type **35**	1·50	70
491	80e. Bettencourt family arms	2·00	90

1989. Nature Protection (2nd series). Goldcrest. As T **34**. Multicoloured.

492	30e. Goldcrest perched on branch	80	20
493	30e. Pair	80	20
494	30e. Goldcrest on nest	80	20
495	30e. Goldcrest with outspread wings	80	20

36 Boy in Boat

1989. Europa. Children's Games and Toys.

496 **36**	80e. multicoloured	2·00	90
MS497	139 × 112 mm. 80e. × 2, Type **36**; 80e. × 2, Boy with toy boat	19·00	10·50

37 Pioneers

1989. 550th Anniv of Portuguese Settlement in Azores. Multicoloured.

498	29e. Type **37**	50	15
499	87e. Settler breaking land	2·20	1·00

1990. Nature Protection (3rd series). Northern Bullfinch. As T **34**. Multicoloured.

500	32e. Two bullfinches	1·00	25
501	32e. Bullfinch on branch	1·00	25
502	32e. Bullfinch landing on twig	1·00	25
503	32e. Bullfinch on nest	1·00	25

38 Vasco da Gama P.O.

1990. Europa. P.O. Buildings.

504 **38**	80e. multicoloured	1·50	80
MS505	139 × 111 mm. 80e. × 2, Type **38**; 80e. × 2, Maia Post Office	18·00	6·00

39 Cart Maker

1990. Traditional Occupations. Multicoloured.

506	5e. Type **39**	15	10
507	10e. Viol maker	15	10
508	32e. Potter	50	20
509	35e. Making roof tiles	50	15
510	38e. Carpenter	50	20
511	60e. Tinsmith	1·50	65
512	65e. Laying pavement mosaics	1·20	60
513	70e. Quarrying	1·30	65
514	85e. Basket maker	1·30	55
515	100e. Cooper	2·10	95
516	110e. Shaping stones	1·30	65
517	120e. Boat builders	1·60	80

40 "Hermes" Spaceplane

1991. Europa. Europe in Space.
520 **40** 80e. multicoloured . . . . 1·50 85
MS521 140 × 112 mm. 80e. × 2, Type **40**; 80e. × 2, "Sanger" spaceplane . . . . 16·00 6·75

41 "Helena" (schooner)

1991. Inter-island Transport. Multicoloured.
522 35e. Type **41** 50 10
523 60e. Beech Model 18 airplane, 1947 . . . . . . 95 45
524 80e. "Cruzeiro do Canal" (ferry), 1987 . . . . 1·50 75
525 110e. British Aerospace ATP airliner, 1991 . . . . . . 1·80 80

42 "Santa Maria" off Azores

1992. Europa. 500th Anniv of Discovery of America by Columbus.
526 **42** 85e. multicoloured . . . . 1·30 65

43 "Insulano" (steamer, 1868)

1992. The Empresa Insulana de Navegacao Shipping Fleet. Multicoloured.
527 38e. Type **43** 50 15
528 65e. "Carvalho Araujo" (ferry, 1930) 95 50
529 85e. "Funchal" (ferry, 1961) 1·20 65
530 120e. "Terceirense" (freighter, 1948) . . . . 1·60 70

44 Ox-mill

1993. Traditional Grinders. Multicoloured.
531 42e. Type **44** 50 20
532 130e. Hand-mill . . . . . . 1·90 90

45 "Two Sirens at the Entrance of a Grotto" (Antonio Dacosta)

46 Main Entrance, Praia da Vitoria Church, Terceira

1993. Europa. Contemporary Art.
533 **45** 90e. multicoloured . . . . 1·40 65
MS534 140 × 112 mm. 90e. × 2, Type **45**; 90e. × 2, "Acorinan III" 5·50 5·50

1993. Doorways. Multicoloured.
535 42e. Type **46** 50 20
536 70e. South door, Praia da Vitoria Church 90 45
537 90e. Main door, Ponta Delgada Church, Sao Miguel . . . . 1·20 50
538 130e. South door, Ponta Delgada Church . . . . . 1·60 65

47 Floral Decoration, Our Lady of Sorrows, Caloura, Sao Miguel

1994. Tiles. Multicoloured.
539 40e. Type **47** 40 20
540 70e. Decoration of crosses, Our Lady of Sorrows, Caloura, Sao Miguel . . . 90 40
541 100e. "Adoration of the Wise Men", Our Lady of Hope Monastery, Ponta Delgada, Sao Miguel . . . . 1·20 60
542 150e. "St. Bras" (altar frontal), Our Lady of Anjos, Santa Maria . . . 1·70 80

48 Monkey and Explorer with Model Caravel

49 Doorway, St. Barbaras Church, Cedros, Faial

1994. Europa. Discoveries. Multicoloured.
543 **48** 100e. multicoloured . . . . 1·20 60
MS544 140 × 112 mm. 100e. × 2, Type **48**; 100e. × 2, Armadilo and explorer with model caravel . . 4·50 4·50

1994. Manoeline Architecture. Multicoloured.
545 45e. Type **49** 45 20
546 140e. Window, Ribeira Grande, Sao Miguel . . . 1·50 80

50 Aristides Moreira da Motta

1995. Centenary of Decree decentralizing Government of the Azores and Madeira Islands. Pro-autonomy activists. Multicoloured.
547 42e. Type **50** 45 20
548 130e. Gil Mont' Alverne de Sequeira . . . . 1·40 65

51 Santana Palace, Ponta Delgada

1995. Architecture of Sao Miguel. Multicoloured.
549 45e. Type **51** 45 20
550 80e. Chapel of Our Lady of the Victories, Furnas . . . 80 35
551 95e. Hospital, Ponta Delgada 95 40
552 135e. Ernesto do Canto's villa, Furnas . . . . 1·20 60

52 Contendas Lighthouse, Terceira (½-size illustration)

1996. Lighthouses. Multicoloured.
553 47e. Type **52** 40 20
554 78e. Molhe Lighthouse, Sao Miguel 85 45
555 98e. Arnel Lighthouse, Sao Miguel 95 50
556 140e. Santa Clara Lighthouse, Sao Miguel . . 1·30 65
MS557 110 × 140 mm. 200e. Ponta da Barca Lighthouse, Graciosa 3·00 3·00

53 Natalia Correia (poet)

1996. Europa. Famous Women.
558 **53** 98e. multicoloured 95 50
MS559 140 × 112 mm. No. 558 × 3 1·60 1·60

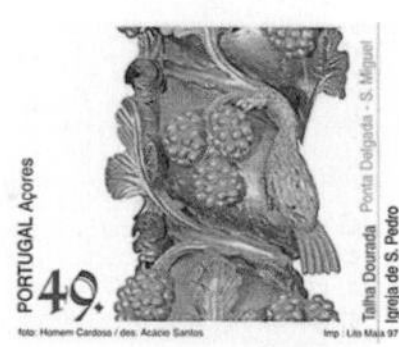

54 Bird eating Grapes (St. Peter's Church, Ponta Delgada)

1997. Gilded Wooden Altarpieces. Multicoloured.
560 49e. Type **54** 45 20
561 80e. Cherub (St. Peter of Alcantara Convent, Sao Roque) 80 30
562 100e. Cherub with wings (All Saints Church, Jesuit College, Ponta Delgada) 90 50
563 140e. Caryatid (St. Joseph's Church, Ponta Delgada) 1·30 70

55 Island of the Seven Cities

1997. Europa. Tales and Legends.
564 **55** 100e. multicoloured . . . . 1·00 50
MS565 140 × 106 mm. No. 564 × 3 3·00 3·00

56 Emperor and Empress and young Bulls (Festival of the Holy Spirit)

1998. Europa. National Festivals.
566 **56** 100e. multicoloured 90 45
MS567 140 × 109 No. 566 × 3 . . 2·50 2·50

57 Spotted Dolphin

1998. "Expo '98" World's Fair, Lisbon. Marine Life. Multicoloured.
568 50e. Type **57** 45 20
569 140e. Sperm whale (79 × 30 mm) . . . . . . 1·20 65

58 Mt. Pico Nature Reserve

1999. Europa. Parks and Gardens.
570 **58** 100e. multicoloured 85 45
MS571 154 × 109mm. No. 570 × 3 3·00 3·00

59 "Emigrants" (Domingos Rebelo)

1999. Paintings. Multicoloured.
572 51e. Type **59** 45 20
573 95e. "Portrait of Vitorino Nemesio" (Antonio Dacosta) (vert) 80 45
574 100e. "Cattle loose on the Alto das Covas" (Ze van der Hagen Bretao) 85 45
575 140e. "Vila Franca Island" (Duarte Maia) . . . . . . 1·10 65

60 "Building Europe"

2000. Europa.
576 **60** 100e. multicoloured 85 45
MS577 154 × 108 mm. No. 576 × 3 2·50 2·50

61 Fishermen retrieving Mail Raft

2000. History of Mail Delivery in the Azores. Mult.
578 85e. Type **61** 70 35
579 140e. Zeppelin airship dropping mail sacks . . . 1·10 60

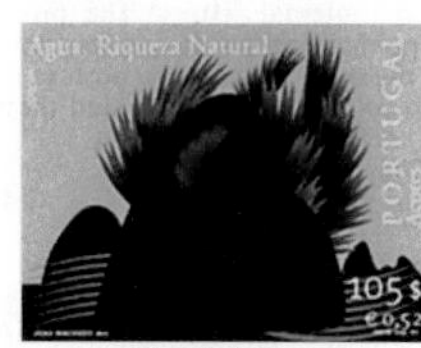

62 Coast Line

2001. Europa. Water Resources.
580 **62** 105e. multicoloured 85 45
MS581 140x110 mm. No. 580 × 3 2·20 2·20

63 Arch and Town

2001. U.N.E.S.C.O. World Heritage Site, Angra do Heroismo. Multicoloured.
582 53e. Type **63** 40 20
583 85e. Monument and town . . 70 35
584 140e. Balcony and view over town . . . . 1·10 60
MS585 140 × 112 mm. 350e. Map of town . . . . 2·40 2·40

64 Clown

2002. Europa. Circus.
586 **64** 54c. multicoloured 85 40
MS587 140 × 110 mm. No. 586 × 3 3·00 3·00

65 Faial Island, Azores

2002. Windmills. Multicoloured.
588 43c. Type **65** 65 30
589 54c. Onze-Lieve-Vrouw-Lombeek, Roosdaal . . . 80 40

Stamps of a similar design were issued by Belgium.

66 Birds (Sebastiao Rodrigues)

2003. Europa. Poster Art.
590 **66** 55c. multicoloured 85 85
MS591 140×113mm. No. 591×2 75 40

67 Pineapple Groves

2003. Sao Miguel Island. Multicoloured.
592 30c. Type **67** 45 25
593 43c. Vineyards and grapes . . 55 30
594 55c. Date growing 75 40
595 70c. Coffee growing 90 45
MS596 140×112 mm. €1 Dancers and ceramic figure; €2 Fruit and ceramic bird (Espirito Santos festival) . . . . 4·00 4·00

CHARITY TAX STAMPS

Used on certain days of the year as an additional postal tax on internal letters. The proceeds were devoted to public charities. If one was not affixed in addition to the ordinary postage, postage due stamps were used to collect the deficiency and the fine.

1911. No. 206 optd **ASSISTENCIA**.
C218a **7** 10r. green . . . . 1·40 90

1913. No. 252 optd **ASSISTENCIA**.
C250 **56** 1c. green . . . . 3·75 2·75

1915. For the Poor. Charity stamp of Portugal optd **ACORES**.
C251 **C 58** 1c. red 50 35

1925. No. C251 surch **15 ctvs**.
C325 **C 58** 15c. on 1c. red 65 65

1925. Portuguese Army in Flanders issue of Portugal optd **ACORES**.
C345 **C 71** 10c. red 90 90
C346 10c. green 90 90
C347 10c. blue 90 90
C348 10c. brown 90 90

1925. As Marquis de Pombal issue of Portugal, inscr "ACORES".
C349 **C 73** 20c. green 90 90
C350 – 20c. green 90 90
C351 **C 75** 20c. green 90 90

NEWSPAPER STAMPS

1876. Stamps of Portugal optd **ACORES**.
N146 **N 16** 2r. black . . . . . . 4·25 2·20
N150b **N 17** 2½r. green . . . . . 4·25 2·20
N150a 2½r. brown . . . . . 4·25 2·20

PARCEL POST STAMPS

1921. Stamps of Portugal optd **ACORES**.
P325 **P 59** 1c. brown 70 65
P326 2c. orange 70 65
P327 5c. brown 65 65
P328 10c. brown 70 65
P329 20c. blue 70 65
P330 40c. red 70 60
P331 50c. black 80 60
P332 60c. blue 80 70
P333 70c. brown . . . . . . 1·80 1·80
P334 80c. blue . . . . . . 1·80 1·80
P335 90c. violet . . . . . . 1·80 1·80
P336 1e. green . . . . . . 1·80 1·80
P337 2e. lilac . . . . . . 2·75 2·75
P338 3e. olive . . . . . . 5·00 2·75
P339 4e. blue . . . . . . 5·25 2·75
P340 5e. lilac . . . . . . 5·25 35
P341 10e. brown . . . . . . 27·00 15·00

POSTAGE DUE STAMPS

Nos. D179/351 are stamps of Portugal overprinted **ACORES**.

1904.
D179 **D 49** 5r. brown . . . . . . 1·00 90
D180 10r. orange . . . . . 1·00 90
D181 20r. mauve . . . . . . 1·60 1·20
D182 30r. green . . . . . . 1·60 1·20
D183 40r. lilac . . . . . . 2·75 1·80
D184 50r. red . . . . 4·25 3·25
D185 100r. blue . . . . . . 5·50 4·75

1911. As last, optd **REPUBLICA**.
D218 **D 49** 5r. brown 45 45
D219 10r. orange 45 45
D220 20r. mauve 70 60
D221 30r. green 70 60
D222 40r. lilac . . . . . 1·10 70
D223 50r. red . . . . . . 5·25 5·25
D224 100r. blue . . . . . . 1·90 1·90

1918. Value in centavos.
D325 **D 49** ½c. brown 55 50
D326 1c. orange 55 50
D327 2c. purple 55 50
D328 3c. green 55 50
D329 4c. lilac 55 50
D330 5c. red 55 50
D331 10c. blue 55 50

1922.
D332 **D 49** ½c. green 30 30
D333 1c. green 45 30
D334 2c. green 45 35
D335 3c. green 70 35
D336 8c. green 70 35
D337 10c. green 70 35
D338 12c. green 70 35
D339 16c. green 75 35
D340 20c. green 50 35
D341 24c. green 75 35
D342 32c. green 75 35
D343 36c. green 75 50
D344 40c. green 75 50
D345 48c. green 75 50
D346 50c. green 75 50
D347 60c. green 80 55
D348 72c. green 80 55
D349 80c. green . . . . . . 4·00 3·25
D350 1e.20 green . . . . . 4·50 3·75

1925. Portuguese Army in Flanders.
D351 **D 72** 20c. brown 90 75

1925. As Nos. C349/51, optd **MULTA**.
D352 **D 73** 40c. green 90 85
D353 – 40c. green 90 85
D354 **D 75** 40c. green 90 85

BADEN Pt. 7

In S.W. Germany. Formerly a Grand Duchy, now part of the German Federal Republic.

60 kreuzer = 1 gulden.

1

3

1851. Imperf.
1 1 1k. black on buff £250 £200
8 1k. black on white . . . . . . £140 21·00
3 3k. black on yellow . . . . . £120 12·00
9 3k. black on green . . . . . £140 5·25
10 3k. black on blue . . . . . . £550 27·00
5 6k. black on green . . . . . £400 40·00
11 6k. black on orange . . . . . £250 19·00
6 9k. black on red . . . . . . 75·00 19·00

1860. Shaded background behind Arms. Perf.
13 **2** 1k. black . . . . 70·00 19·00
16 3k. blue . . . . 75·00 14·00
17 6k. orange . . . . 90·00 55·00
22 6k. blue . . . . 95·00 60·00
19 9k. red £200 £150
25 9k. brown . . . . 75·00 60·00

1862. Uncoloured background behind Arms.
27 1k. black . . . . 40·00 10·00
28 3k. red . . . . 38·00 1·50
30 6k. blue . . . . 6·75 20·00
33 9k. brown . . . . 12·00 25·00
36 18k. green £350 £500
38 30k. orange . . . . . . 26·00 £1300

1868. "K R." instead of "KREUZER".
39 1k. green . . . . 3·50 4·00
41 3k. red . . . . 2·00 1·50
44 7k. blue . . . . 17·00 32·00

For issues of 1947 to 1964 see Germany: Allied Occupation (French Zone).

RURAL POSTAGE DUE STAMPS

D 4

1862.
D39 D 4 1k. black on yellow . . . . 3·75 £275
D40 3k. black on yellow . . . . 2·00 95·00
D41 12k. black on yellow . . . 30·00 £10000

BAGHDAD Pt. 1

A city in Iraq. Special stamps issued during British occupation in the War of 1914–18.

16 annas = 1 rupee.

1917. Various issues of Turkey surch **BAGHDAD IN BRITISH OCCUPATION** and new value in annas.

A. Pictorial issues of 1913.
1 **32** ½a. on 2pa. red £120 £140
2 **34** ½a. on 5pa. purple . . . . . 85·00 90·00
3 – ½a. on 10pa. green (No. 516) £550 £650
4 **31** ½a. on 10pa. green £950 £1100
5 – 1a. on 20pa. red (No. 504) £375 £400
6 – 2a. on 1pi. blue (No. 518) . . £150 £180

B. As last, but optd with small star.
7 – 1a. on 20pa. red £200 £250
8 – 2a. on 1pi. blue £3000 £3500

C. Postal Jubilee issue.
9 **60** ½a. on 10pa. red £400 £425
10b 1a. on 20pa. blue £850 £1000
11b 2a. on 1pi. black & violet 85·00 95·00

D. Optd with Turkish letter "B".
12 **30** 2a. on 1pi. blue £350 £475

E. Optd with star and Arabic date within crescent.
13 **30** ½a. on 10pa. green . . . . 85·00 90·00
14 1a. on 20pa. red £350 £375
15 **23** 1a. on 20pa. red £400 £425
16 **21** 1a. on 20pa. red (No. N185) £3250 £4000
17 **30** 2a. on 1pi. blue . . . . . . 95·00 £110
18 **21** 2a. on 1pi. blue £160 £170

F. Optd as last, but with date between star and crescent.
19 **23** ½a. on 10pa. green £100 £110
20 **60** ½a. on 10pa. red £150 £160
21 **30** 1a. on 20pa. red £100 £120
22 **28** 1a. on 20pa. red £375 £425
23 **15** 1a. on 10pa. on 20pa. red £170 £170
24 **30** 2a. on 1pi. blue £160 £170
25 **28** 2a. on 1pi. blue £1300 £1500

BAHAMAS Pt. 1

A group of islands in the Br. W. Indies, S.E. of Florida. Self-Government introduced on 7 January 1964. The islands became an independent member of the British Commonwealth on 10 July 1973.

1859. 12 pence = 1 shilling;
20 shillings = 1 pound.
1966. 100 cents = 1 dollar.

1

2

3

1859. Imperf.
2 **1** 1d. red . . . . 55·00 £1500

1860. Perf.
33 **1** 1d. red . . . . 50·00 15·00
26 **2** 4d. red . . . . £275 60·00
31 6d. violet . . . . £160 60·00
39b **3** 1s. green . . . . 8·00 7·00

1883. Surch **FOURPENCE**.
45 **2** 4d. on 6d. violet £550 £400

5

6 Queen's Staircase, Nassau

1884.
48 **5** 1d. red . . . . 7·00 2·50
52 2½d. blue . . . . 9·50 2·25
53 4d. yellow . . . . 9·50 4·00
54 6d. mauve . . . . 6·00 26·00
56 5s. green . . . . 65·00 75·00
57 £1 red £275 £225

1901.
111 **6** 1d. black and red . . . . 1·00 1·75
76a 3d. purple on buff . . . 5·50 4·50
77 3d. black and brown . . . 2·00 2·25
59 5d. black and orange . . . 8·50 48·00
78 5d. black and mauve . . . 2·75 5·50
113 2s. black and blue . . . . 19·00 22·00
61 3s. black and green . . . 38·00 60·00

7 8

1902.
71 **7** ½d. green . . . . 5·00 3·00
62 1d. red . . . . 1·50 2·50
63 2½d. blue . . . . 6·50 1·25
64 4d. yellow . . . . 15·00 60·00
66 6d. brown . . . . 3·50 20·00
67 1s. black and red . . . . . 20·00 50·00
69 5s. purple and blue . . . . 65·00 80·00
70 £1 green and black £250 £325

1912.
115 **8** ½d. green 50 40
116 1d. red . . . . 1·00 15
117 1½d. red . . . . 5·00 1·00
118 2d. grey . . . . 1·25 2·75
119 2½d. blue . . . . 1·00 2·75
120 3d. purple on yellow . . . 6·50 16·00
121 4d. yellow . . . . 1·50 5·00
122 6d. brown . . . . 70 1·25
123 1s. black and red . . . . . 2·75 5·50
124 5s. purple and blue . . . . 35·00 65·00
125 £1 green and black £170 £325

1917. Optd **1.1.17.** and Red Cross.
90 **6** 1d. black and red . . . . . 40 2·00

1918. Optd **WAR TAX** in one line.
96 **8** ½d. green . . . . 1·75 1·75
97 1d. red . . . . 1·00 35
93 **6** 1d. black and red . . . . . 3·50 4·25
98 3d. purple on yellow . . . 1·00 1·50
100 3d. black and brown . . . 50 4·00
99 **8** 1s. black and red . . . . . 9·00 2·75

1919. Optd **WAR CHARITY 3.6.18.**
101 **6** 1d. black and red . . . . . 30 2·50

1919. Optd **WAR TAX** in two lines.
102 **8** ½d. green . . . . 30 1·25
103 1d. red . . . . 1·50 1·50
105 **6** 3d. black and brown . . . . 75 8·00
104 **8** 1s. black and red . . . . . 18·00 32·00

16

17 Seal of the Colony

1920. Peace Celebration.
106 **16** ½d. green . . . . 1·00 5·50
107 1d. red . . . . 2·75 1·00
108 2d. grey . . . . 2·75 7·50
109 3d. brown . . . . 2·75 9·00
110 1s. green . . . . 12·00 35·00

1930. Tercentenary of the Colony.
126 **17** 1d. black and red . . . . 2·00 2·75
127 3d. black and brown . . . 4·00 15·00
128 5d. black and violet . . . 4·00 15·00
129 2s. black and blue . . . . 18·00 48·00
130 3s. black and green . . . 42·00 85·00

1931. As T **17**, but without dates at top.
131b 2s. black and blue . . . . . 8·00 3·75
132a 3s. black and green . . . . 8·00 2·50

1935. Silver Jubilee. As T **13** of Antigua.
141 1½d. blue and red . . . . . 1·00 3·00
142 2½d. brown and blue . . . . 5·00 9·00
143 6d. blue and olive . . . . . 7·00 13·00
144 1s. grey and purple . . . . . 7·00 10·00

19 Greater Flamingo (in flight)

1935.
145 **19** 8d. blue and red . . . . . 6·00 3·25

1937. Coronation. As T **2** of Aden.
146 ½d. green 15 15
147 1½d. brown . . . . 30 1·10
148 2½d. blue . . . . 50 1·10

20 King George VI

21 Sea Garden, Nassau

1938.
149 **20** ½d. green . . . . 1·00 1·25
149e ½d. purple . . . . 1·00 2·50
150 1d. red . . . . 8·50 3·00
150ab 1d. grey 60 70
151 1½d. brown . . . . 1·50 1·25
152 2d. grey . . . . 18·00 4·00
152b 2d. red . . . . 1·00 65
152c 2d. green . . . . 1·00 80
153 2½d. blue . . . . 3·25 1·50
153a 2½d. violet . . . . 1·25 1·25
154 3d. violet . . . . 16·00 3·00
154a 3d. blue . . . . 60 1·25
154b 3d. red . . . . 60 3·25

158 **21** 4d. blue and orange 1·00 1·00
159 – 6d. green and blue 60 1·00
160 – 8d. blue and red 6·75 2·25
154c **20** 10d. orange 2·50 20
155c 1s. black and red 12·00 75
156b 5s. purple and blue 28·00 18·00
157a £1 green and black 60·00 50·00
DESIGNS—As Type **21**: 6d. Fort Charlotte; 8d. Greater flamingos.

1940. Surch **3d.**
161 **20** 3d. on 2½d. blue 1·50 1·75

1942. 450th Anniv of Landing of Columbus. Optd **1492 LANDFALL OF COLUMBUS 1942**.
162 **20** ½d. green 30 60
163 1d. grey 30 60
164 1½d. brown 40 60
165 2d. red 50 65
166 2½d. blue 50 65
167 3d. blue 30 65
168 **21** 4d. blue and orange 40 90
169 – 6d. green & blue (No. 159) 40 1·75
170 – 8d. blue and red (No. 160) 1·50 70
171 **20** 1s. black and red 6·50 4·00
172a **17** 2s. black and blue 8·00 10·00
173 3s. black and green 7·00 6·50
174a **20** 5s. purple and blue 20·00 14·00
175a £1 green and black 30·00 25·00

1946. Victory. As T **9** of Aden.
176 1½d. brown 10 60
177 3d. blue 10 60

26 Infant Welfare Clinic

1948. Tercentenary of Settlement of Island of Eleuthera. Inscr as in T **26**.
178 **26** ½d. orange 30 90
179 – 1d. olive 30 35
180 – 1½d. yellow 30 80
181 – 2d. red 30 40
182 – 2½d. brown 70 75
183 – 3d. blue 2·50 85
184 – 4d. black 60 70
185 – 6d. green 2·25 80
186 – 8d. violet 1·00 70
187 – 10d. red 1·00 35
188 – 1s. brown 2·00 50
189 – 2s. purple 4·00 8·50
190 – 3s. blue 8·50 8·50
191 – 5s. mauve 13·00 4·50
192 – 10s. grey 10·00 10·00
193 – £1 red 9·50 15·00
DESIGNS: 1d. Agriculture; 1½d. Sisal; 2d. Straw work; 2½d. Dairy; 3d. Fishing fleet; 4d. Island settlement; 6d. Tuna fishing; 8d. Paradise Beach; 10d. Modern hotels; 1s. Yacht racing; 2s. Water sports—skiing; 3s. Shipbuilding; 5s. Transportation; 10s. Salt production; £1 Parliament Buildings.

1948. Silver Wedding. As T **10/11** of Aden.
194 1½d. brown 20 25
195 £1 grey 32·00 32·00

1949. 75th Anniv of U.P.U. As T **20/23** of Antigua.
196 2½d. violet 35 50
197 3d. blue 2·25 2·75
198 6d. blue 55 2·50
199 1s. red 55 75

1953. Coronation. As T **13** of Aden.
200 6d. black and blue 60 60

42 Infant Welfare Clinic

43 Queen Elizabeth II

1954. Designs as Nos. 178/93 but with portrait of Queen Elizabeth II and without commemorative inscr as in T **42**.
201 **42** ½d. black and red 10 1·50
202 – 1d. olive and brown 10 30
203 – 1½d. blue and black 15 80
204 – 2d. brown and green 15 30
205 – 3d. black and red 65 1·25
206 – 4d. turquoise and purple 30 30
207 – 5d. brown and blue 1·40 2·25
208 – 6d. blue and black 2·25 20
209 – 8d. black and lilac 70 40
210 – 10d. black and blue 30 10
211 – 1s. blue and brown 1·50 10
212 – 2s. orange and black 2·00 70
213 – 2s.6d. black and blue 3·50 2·00
214 – 5s. green and orange 19·00 75
215 – 10s. black and slate 22·00 2·50
216 – £1 black and violet 21·00 6·50
DESIGNS: 1½d. Hatchet Bay, Eleuthera; 4d. Water sports—skiing; 5d. Dairy; 6d. Transportation; 2s. Sisal; 2s.6d. Shipbuilding; 5s. Tuna fishing. Other values the same as for the corresponding values in Nos. 178/93.

1959. Centenary of 1st Bahamas Postage Stamp.
217 **43** 1d. black and red 35 20
218 2d. black and green 35 1·00
219 6d. black and blue 45 40
220 10d. black and brown 50 1·00

44 Christ Church Cathedral

1962. Centenary of Nassau.
221 **44** 8d. green 45 55
222 – 10d. violet 45 25
DESIGN: 10d. Nassau Public Library.

1963. Freedom from Hunger. As T **28** of Aden.
223 8d. sepia 40 40

1963. Bahamas Talks. Nos. 209/10 optd **BAHAMAS TALKS 1962**.
224 8d. black and lilac 40 75
225 10d. black and blue 50 75

1963. Centenary of Red Cross. As T **33** of Antigua.
226 1d. red and black 50 50
227 10d. red and blue 1·75 2·50

1964. New Constitution. Nos. 201/16 optd **NEW CONSTITUTION 1964**.
228 **42** ½d. black and red 15 1·50
229 – 1d. olive and brown 15 15
230 – 1½d. blue and black 70 1·50
231 – 2d. brown and green 15 20
232 – 3d. black and red 2·00 1·75
233 – 4d. turquoise and purple 70 55
234 – 5d. brown and blue 70 1·50
235 – 6d. blue and black 2·75 30
236 – 8d. black and lilac 70 30
237 – 10d. black and blue 30 15
238 – 1s. blue and brown 1·50 15
239 – 2s. brown and black 2·00 1·75
240 – 2s.6d. black and blue 3·00 2·75
241 – 5s. green and orange 7·00 3·25
242 – 10s. black and slate 7·00 5·50
243 – £1 black and violet 7·50 18·00

1964. 400th Birth Anniv of Shakespeare. As T **34** of Antigua.
244 6d. turquoise 20 10

1964. Olympic Games, Tokyo. No. 211 surch **8d.** and Olympic rings.
245 8d. on 1s. blue and brown 45 15

49 Colony's Badge

1965.
247 **49** ½d. multicoloured 15 2·00
248 – 1d. slate, blue and orange 30 1·00
249 – 1½d. red, green and brown 15 2·50
250 – 2d. slate, green and blue 15 10
251 – 3d. red, blue and purple 3·50 20
252 – 4d. green, blue and brown 4·25 2·50
253 – 6d. green, blue and red 1·00 10
254 – 8d. purple, blue & bronze 50 30
255 – 10d. brown, green and violet 25 10
256a – 1s. multicoloured 30 10
257 – 2s. brown, blue and green 1·00 1·25
258 – 2s.6d. olive, blue and red 2·50 3·00
259 – 5s. brown, blue and green 2·75 1·00
260 – 10s. red, blue and brown 16·00 3·50
261 – £1 brown, blue and red 19·00 9·00
DESIGNS: 1d. Out Island regatta; 1½d. Hospital; 2d. High School; 3d. Greater flamingo; 4d. R.M.S. "Queen Elizabeth"; 6d. "Development"; 8d. Yachting; 10d. Public square; 1s. Sea garden; 2s. Old cannons at Fort Charlotte; 2s.6d. Sikorsky S-38 flying boat, 1929, and Boeing 707 airliner; 5s. Williamson film project, 1914, and undersea post office, 1939; 10s. Queen or pink conch; £1 Columbus's flagship.

1965. Centenary of I.T.U. As T **36** of Antigua.
262 1d. green and orange 15 10
263 2s. purple and olive 65 45

1965. No. 254 surch **9d.**
264 9d. on 8d. purple, blue & bronze 30 15

1965. I.C.Y. As T **37** of Antigua.
265 ½d. purple and turquoise 10 1·10
266 1s. green and lavender 30 40

1966. Churchill Commemoration. As T **38** of Antigua.
267 ½d. blue 10 75
268 2d. green 40 30
269 10d. brown 75 85
270 1s. violet 75 1·40

1966. Royal Visit. As T **39** of Antigua but inscr "to the Caribbean" omitted.
271 6d. black and blue 75 50
272 1s. black and mauve 1·25 1·25

1966. Decimal currency. Nos. 247/61 surch.
273 **49** 1c. on ½d. multicoloured 10 30
274 – 2c. on 1d. slate, blue and orange 75 30
275 – 3c. on 2d. slate, green and blue 10 10
276 – 4c. on 3d. red, blue and purple 2·00 20
277 – 5c. on 4d. green, blue and brown 2·00 3·00
278 – 8c. on 6d. green, blue and red 20 20
279 – 10c. on 8d. purple, blue and bronze 30 75
280 – 11c. on 1½d. red, green and brown 15 30
281 – 12c. on 10d. brown, green and violet 15 10
282 – 15c. on 1s. multicoloured 25 10
283 – 22c. on 2s. brown, blue and green 60 1·25
284 – 50c. on 2s.6d. olive, blue and red 1·00 1·40
285 – $1 on 5s. brown, blue and green 1·75 1·50
286 – $2 on 10s. red, blue and brown 7·50 4·50
287 – $3 on £1 brown, blue and red 7·50 4·50

1966. World Cup Football Championships. As T **36** of Antigua.
288 8c. multicoloured 25 15
289 15c. multicoloured 30 25

1966. Inauguration of W.H.O. Headquarters, Geneva. As T **41** of Antigua.
290 11c. black, green and blue 50 90
291 15c. black, purple and ochre 50 50

1966. 20th Anniv of U.N.E.S.C.O. As T **54/6** of Antigua.
292 3c. multicoloured 10 10
293 15c. yellow, violet and olive 35 20
294 $1 black, purple and orange 1·10 2·00

1967. As Nos. 247/51, 253/9 and 261 but values in decimal currency, and new designs for 5c. and $2.
295 **49** 1c. multicoloured 10 3·25
296 – 2c. slate, blue and green 50 60
297 – 3c. slate, green and violet 10 10
298 – 4c. red, light blue and blue 4·75 50
299 – 5c. black, blue and purple 1·00 3·50
300 – 8c. green, blue and brown 25 10
301 – 10c. purple, blue and red 30 70
302 – 11c. red, green and blue 25 80
303 – 12c. brown, green and olive 25 10
304 – 15c. multicoloured 55 10
305 – 22c. brown, blue and red 70 65
306 – 50c. olive, blue and green 2·00 1·00
307 – $1 maroon, blue and purple 2·00 60
308 – $2 multicoloured 13·00 3·00
309 – $3 brown, blue and purple 3·75 2·00
NEW DESIGNS: 5c. "Oceanic"; $2 Conch shell (different).

69 Bahamas Crest

1967. Diamond Jubilee of World Scouting. Mult.
310 3c. Type **69** 35 15
311 15c. Scout badge 40 15

71 Globe and Emblem

1968. Human Rights Year. Multicoloured.
312 3c. Type **71** 10 10
313 12c. Scales of Justice and emblem 20 10
314 $1 Bahamas Crest and emblem 70 80

74 Golf

1968. Tourism. Multicoloured.
315 5c. Type **74** 1·75 1·75
316 11c. Yachting 1·25 40
317 15c. Horse-racing 1·75 45
318 50c. Water-skiing 2·50 6·50

78 Racing Yacht and Olympic Monument

1968. Olympic Games, Mexico City.
319 **78** 5c. brown, yellow and green 40 75
320 – 11c. multicoloured 40 25
321 – 50c. multicoloured 60 1·75
322 **78** $1 grey, blue and violet 2·00 3·75
DESIGNS: 11c. Long jumping and Olympic Monument; 50c. Running and Olympic Monument.

81 Legislative Building

1968. 14th Commonwealth Parliamentary Conference. Multicoloured.
323 3c. Type **81** 10 30
324 10c. Bahamas Mace and Westminster Clock Tower (vert) 15 30
325 12c. Local straw market (vert) 15 25
326 15c. Horse-drawn surrey 20 35

85 Obverse and reverse of $100 Gold Coin

1968. Gold Coins commemorating the first General Election under the New Constitution.
327 **85** 3c. red on gold 40 40
328 – 12c. green on gold 45 50
329 – 15c. purple on gold 50 60
330 – $1 black on gold 1·25 3·25
OBVERSE AND REVERSE OF: 12c. $50 gold coin; 15c. $20 gold coins; $1, $10 gold coin.

89 First Flight Postcard of 1919

1969. 50th Anniv of Bahamas Airmail Services.
331 **89** 12c. multicoloured 50 50
332 – 15c. multicoloured 60 1·75
DESIGN: 15c. Sikorsky S-38 flying boat of 1929.

91 Game-fishing Boats

1969. Tourism. One Millionth Visitor to Bahamas. Multicoloured.
333 3c. Type **91** 25 10
334 11c. Paradise Beach 35 15

335 12c. "Sunfish" sailing boats 35 15
336 15c. Rawson Square and parade 45 25
MS337 130 × 96 mm. Nos. 333/6 3·00 4·50

92 "The Adoration of the Shepherds" (Louis le Nain)

1969. Christmas. Multicoloured.
338 3c. Type **92** 10 20
339 11c. "The Adoration of the Shepherds" (Poussin) 15 30
340 12c. "The Adoration of the Kings" (Gerard David) 15 20
341 15c. "The Adoration of the Kings" (Vincenzo Foppa) 20 65

93 Badge of Girl Guides

1970. Diamond Jubilee of Girl Guides' Association. Multicoloured.
342 3c. Type **93** 30 10
343 12c. Badge of Brownies 45 20
344 15c. Badge of Rangers 50 35

94 New U.P.U. Headquarters and Emblem

1970. New U.P.U. Headquarters Building.
345 **94** 3c. multicoloured 10 40
346 15c. multicoloured 20 60

95 Coach and Globe

1970. "Goodwill Caravan". Multicoloured.
347 3c. Type **95** 75 20
348 11c. Diesel train and globe 1·50 60
349 12c. "Canberra" (liner), yacht and globe 1·50 60
350 15c. B.A.C. One Eleven airliner and globe 1·50 1·75
MS351 165 × 125 mm. Nos. 347/50 9·50 17·00

96 Nurse, Patients and Greater Flamingo

1970. Centenary of British Red Cross. Multicoloured.
352 3c. Type **96** 75 50
353 15c. Hospital and blue marlin 75 1·75

97 "The Nativity" (detail, Pittoni)

1970. Christmas. Multicoloured.
354 3c. Type **97** 15 15
355 11c. "The Holy Family" (detail, Anton Raphael Mengs) 20 25
356 12c. "The Adoration of the Shepherds" (detail, Giorgione) 20 20
357 15c. "The Adoration of the Shepherds" (detail, School of Seville) 30 75
MS358 114 × 140 mm. Nos. 354/7 1·40 4·00

98 International Airport

1971. Multicoloured.
359 1c. Type **98** 10 30
360 2c. Breadfruit 15 35
361 3c. Straw market 15 30
362 4c. Hawksbill turtle 1·75 10·00
363 5c. Nassau grouper 60 60
364 6c. As 4c. 45 1·25
365 7c. Hibiscus 2·00 5·00
366 8c. Yellow elder 60 1·50
367 10c. Bahamian sponge boat 55 30
368 11c. Greater flamingos 2·50 3·25
369 12c. As 7c. 2·00 3·00
370 15c. Bonefish 55 55
466 16c. As 7c. 70 35
371 18c. Royal poinciana 65 65
467a 21c. As 2c. 80 1·25
372 22c. As 18c. 2·75 15·00
468 25c. As 4c. 90 40
469 40c. As 10c. 7·00 75
470 50c. Post Office, Nassau 1·50 1·75
471 $1 Pineapple (vert) 1·50 2·50
399 $2 Crawfish (vert) 1·50 6·00
473 $3 Junkanoo (vert) 1·50 9·00

99 Snowflake

101 Shepherd

100 High Jumping

1971. Christmas.
377 **99** 3c. purple, orange and gold 10 10
378 – 11c. blue and gold 20 15
379 – 15c. multicoloured 20 20
380 – 18c. blue, ultram & gold 25 25
MS381 126 × 95 mm. Nos. 377/80 1·25 1·50
DESIGNS: 11c. "Peace on Earth" (doves); 15c. Arms of Bahamas and holly; 18c. Starlit lagoon

1972. Olympic Games, Munich. Multicoloured.
382 10c. Type **100** 35 60
383 11c. Cycling 1·50 75
384 15c. Running 60 75
385 18c. Sailing 95 1·25
MS386 127 × 95 mm. Nos. 382/5 3·25 3·00

1972. Christmas. Multicoloured.
387 3c. Type **101** 10 10
388 6c. Bells 10 10
389 15c. Holly and Cross 15 20
390 20c. Poinsettia 25 45
MS391 108 × 140 mm. Nos. 387/90 80 2·75

102 Northerly Bahama Islands

1972. Tourism Year of the Americas. Sheet 133 × 105 mm, containing T **102**.
MS392 11, 15, 18 and 50c. multicoloured 3·00 3·25

The four designs are printed, se-tenant in **MS**392, forming a composite map design of the Bahamas.

1972. Royal Silver Wedding. As T **52** of Ascension, but with mace and galleon in background.
393 11c. pink 15 15
394 18c. violet 15 20

104 Weather Satellite

1973. Centenary of I.M.O./W.M.O. Multicoloured.
410 15c. Type **104** 50 25
411 18c. Weather radar 60 35

105 C. A. Bain (national hero)

106 "The Virgin in Prayer" (Sassoferrato)

1973. Independence. Multicoloured.
412 3c. Type **105** 10 10
413 11c. Coat of arms 15 10
414 15c. Bahamas flag 20 15
415 $1 Governor-General, M. B. Butler 65 1·00
MS416 86 × 121 mm. Nos. 412/15 1·75 1·75

1973. Christmas. Multicoloured.
417 3c. Type **106** 10 10
418 11c. "Virgin and Child with St. John" (Filippino Lippi) 15 15
419 15c. "A Choir of Angels" (Simon Marmion) 15 15
420 18c. "The Two Trinities" (Murillo) 25 25
MS421 120 × 99 mm. Nos. 417/20 1·75 1·40

107 "Agriculture and Sciences"

1974. 25th Anniv of University of West Indies. Multicoloured.
422 15c. Type **107** 20 25
423 18c. "Arts, Engineering and General Studies" 25 30

108 U.P.U. Monument, Berne

1974. Centenary of U.P.U.
424 **108** 3c. multicoloured 10 15
425 – 13c. multicoloured (vert) 20 25
426 – 14c. multicoloured 20 30
427 – 18c. multicoloured (vert) 25 40
MS428 128 × 95 mm. Nos. 424/7 80 1·60
DESIGNS—As Type **108** but showing different arrangements of the U.P.U. Monument.

109 Roseate Spoonbills

1974. 15th Anniv of Bahamas National Trust. Mult.
429 13c. Type **109** 1·60 1·10
430 14c. White-crowned pigeon 1·60 75
431 21c. White-tailed tropic birds 2·00 1·25
432 36c. Cuban amazon ("Bahamian parrot") 2·50 6·50
MS433 123 × 120 mm. Nos. 429/32 9·50 13·00

110 "The Holy Family" (Jacques de Stella)

1974. Christmas. Multicoloured.
434 8c. Type **110** 10 10
435 10c. "Madonna and Child" (16th-century Brescian School) 15 15
436 12c. "Virgin and Child with St. John the Baptist and St. Catherine" (Previtali) 15 15
437 21c. "Virgin and Child with Angels" (Previtali) 25 30
MS438 126 × 105 mm. Nos. 434/7 1·00 1·40

111 "Anteos maerula"

1975. Butterflies. Multicoloured.
439 3c. Type **111** 25 15
440 14c. "Eurema nicippe" 80 50
441 18c. "Papilio andraemon" 95 65
442 21c. "Euptoieta hegesia" 1·10 85
MS443 194 × 94 mm. Nos. 439/42 7·50 6·50

112 Sheep Husbandry

1975. Economic Diversification. Multicoloured.
444 3c. Type **112** 10 10
445 14c. Electric-reel fishing (vert) 20 15
446 18c. Farming 25 20
447 21c. Oil refinery (vert) 80 35
MS448 127 × 94 mm. Nos. 444/7 1·25 1·50

113 Rowena Rand (evangelist)

1975. International Women's Year.
449 **113** 14c. brown, lt blue & bl 20 50
450 – 18c. yellow, grn & brn 25 75
DESIGN: 18c. I.W.Y. symbol and harvest symbol.

114 "Adoration of the Shepherds" (Perugino)

1975. Christmas. Multicoloured.
451 3c. Type **114** 15 60
452 8c. "Adoration of the Magi" (Ghirlandaio) 20 10
453 18c. As 8c. 55 90
454 21c. Type **114** 60 95
MS455 142 × 107 mm. Nos. 451/4 2·25 4·50

115 Telephones, 1876 and 1976

1976. Centenary of Telephone. Multicoloured.
456 3c. Type **115** 20 50
457 16c. Radio-telephone link, Deleporte 40 50
458 21c. Alexander Graham Bell 50 65
459 25c. Satellite 60 1·00

116 Map of North America

1976. Bicentenary of American Revolution. Mult.
475 16c. Type **116** 30 30
476 $1 John Murray, Earl of Dunmore . . . . 1·50 1·75
MS477 127 × 100 mm. Nos. 476 × 4 6·00 7·50

117 Cycling **118** "Virgin and Child" (detail, Lippi)

1976. Olympic Games, Montreal.
478 **117** 8c. mauve, blue and light blue . . . . 1·25 20
479 – 16c. orange, brown and light blue 35 30
480 – 25c. blue, mauve and light blue 45 50
481 – 40c. brown, orange and blue . . . . 55 1·60
MS482 100 × 126 mm. Nos. 478/81 3·00 3·00
DESIGNS: 16c. Jumping; 25c. Sailing; 40c. Boxing.

1976. Christmas. Multicoloured.
483 3c. Type **118** 10 10
484 21c. "Adoration of the Shepherds" (School of Seville) 20 15
485 25c. "Adoration of the Kings" (detail, Foppa) . . 20 20
486 40c. "Virgin and Child" (detail, Vivarini) 35 40
MS487 107 × 127 mm. Nos. 483/6 1·00 2·00

119 Queen beneath Cloth of Gold Canopy

1977. Silver Jubilee. Multicoloured.
488 8c. Type **119** 10 10
489 16c. The Crowning 15 15
490 21c. Taking the Oath 15 15
491 40c. Queen with sceptre and orb 25 30
MS492 122 × 90 mm. Nos. 488/91 80 1·25

120 Featherduster

1977. Marine Life. Multicoloured.
493 3c. Type **120** 40 15
494 8c. Porkfish and cave 60 20
495 16c. Elkhorn coral 70 40
496 21c. Soft coral and sponge 80 55
MS497 119 × 93 mm. Nos. 493/6 2·75 4·50

121 Scouts around Campfire and Home-made Shower

1977. 6th Caribbean Scout Jamboree. Multicoloured.
498 16c. Type **121** 75 30
499 21c. Boating scenes 85 35

1977. Royal Visit. Nos. 488/91 optd **Royal Visit October 1977**.
500 8c. Type **119** 15 10
501 16c. The Crowning 20 15
502 21c. Taking the Oath 25 25
503 40c. Queen with sceptre and orb 30 40
MS504 122 × 90 mm. Nos. 500/3 1·25 1·50

123 Virgin and Child **124** Public Library, Nassau (Colonial)

1977. Christmas. Multicoloured.
505 3c. Type **123** 10 10
506 16c. The Magi 20 25
507 21c. Nativity scene 25 40
508 25c. The Magi and star . . . 30 45
MS509 136 × 74 mm. Nos. 505/8 75 1·75

1978. Architectural Heritage.
510 **124** 3c. black and green . . . 10 10
511 – 8c. black and blue 15 10
512 – 16c. black and mauve . . 20 20
513 – 18c. black and pink . . . 25 30
MS514 91 × 91 mm. Nos. 510/13 70 1·60
DESIGNS: 8c. St. Matthew's Church (Gothic); 16c. Government House (Colonial); 18c. Hermitage, Cat Island (Spanish).

125 Sceptre, St. Edward's Crown and Orb **127** Child reaching for Adult

126 Coat of Arms within Wreath and Three Ships

1978. 25th Anniv of Coronation. Multicoloured.
515 16c. Type **125** 15 10
516 $1 Queen in Coronation regalia 50 65
MS517 147 × 96 mm. Nos. 515/16 1·25 1·00

1978. Christmas.
532 **126** 5c. gold, lake and red . . 15 10
533 – 21c. gold, deep blue and blue 30 25
MS534 95 × 95 mm. Nos. 532/3 1·50 5·00
DESIGN: 21c. Three angels with trumpets.

1979. International Year of the Child. Multicoloured.
535 5c. Type **127** 20 15
536 16c. Boys playing leapfrog . . 40 45
537 21c. Girls skipping 50 60
538 25c. Bricks with I.Y.C. emblem 50 75
MS539 101 × 125 mm. Nos. 535/8 1·40 3·25

128 Sir Rowland Hill and Penny Black

1979. Death Centenary of Sir Rowland Hill. Multicoloured.
540 10c. Type **128** 30 10
541 21c. Printing press, 1840, and 6d. stamp of 1862 . . . . 40 30
542 25c. Great Britain 1856 6d. with "A 05" (Nassau) cancellation, and 1840 2d. Blue 40 50
543 40c. Early mailboat and 1d. stamp of 1859 . . . . . . 45 70
MS544 115 × 80 mm. Nos. 540/3 2·00 3·25

129 Commemorative Plaque and Map of Bahamas

1979. 250th Anniv of Parliament. Multicoloured.
545 16c. Type **129** 35 10
546 21c. Parliament buildings . . 40 15
547 25c. Legislative Chamber . . 40 15
548 $1 Senate Chamber . . . . . 80 1·00
MS549 116 × 89 mm. Nos. 545/8 1·75 3·75

130 Goombay Carnival Headdress **132** Virgin and Child

131 Landfall of Columbus, 1492

1979. Christmas.
550 **130** 5c. multicoloured 10 10
551 – 10c. multicoloured 15 10
552 – 16c. multicoloured 20 10
553 – 21c. multicoloured 20 20
554 – 25c. multicoloured 25 20
555 – 40c. multicoloured 30 45
MS556 50 × 88 mm. Nos. 550/5 2·00 3·00
DESIGNS: 10c. to 40c. Various Carnival costumes.

1980. Multicoloured.
557 1c. Type **131** . . . . 1·25 2·50
558 3c. Blackbeard the pirate . . 30 2·50
559 5c. Eleutheran Adventurers (Articles and Orders, 1647) 30 1·25
560 10c. Ceremonial mace 20 40
561 12c. The Loyalists, 1783–88 30 2·00
562 15c. Slave trading, Vendue House . . . . 5·50 1·25
563 16c. Wrecking in the 1800s 1·75 1·25
564 18c. Blockade running (American Civil War) . . . 2·25 2·50
565 21c. Bootlegging, 1919–29 . . 60 2·50
566 25c. Pineapple cultivation . . 40 2·50
567 40c. Sponge clipping . . . . 70 1·50
568 50c. Tourist development . . 75 1·50
569 $1 Modern agriculture . . . 75 4·25
570 $2 Modern air and sea transport . . . . 4·25 5·50
571 $3 Banking (Central Bank) 1·25 4·00
572 $5 Independence, 10 July 1973 . . . . 1·50 6·00

1980. Christmas. Straw-work. Multicoloured.
573 5c. Type **132** 10 10
574 21c. Three Kings 25 10
575 25c. Angel 25 15
576 $1 Christmas tree 75 85
MS577 168 × 105 mm. Nos. 573/6 1·25 2·25

133 Disabled Persons with Walking Stick

1981. International Year of Disabled People. Mult.
578 5c. Type **133** 10 10
579 $1 Disabled person in wheelchair . . . . 1·25 1·25
MS580 120 × 60 mm. Nos. 578/9 1·40 2·50

134 Grand Bahama Tracking Site

1981. Space Exploration. Multicoloured.
581 10c. Type **134** 30 15
582 20c. Satellite view of Bahamas (vert) 60 50
583 25c. Satellite view of Eleuthera 65 60
584 50c. Satellite view of Andros and New Province (vert) 1·00 1·25
MS585 115 × 99 mm. Nos. 581/4 2·25 2·25

135 Prince Charles and Lady Diana Spencer

1981. Royal Wedding. Multicoloured.
586 30c. Type **135** . . . . 1·50 30
587 $2 Prince Charles and Prime Minister Pindling . . . . . 1·50 1·25
MS588 142 × 120 mm. Nos. 586/7 5·00 1·25

136 Bahamas Pintail ("Bahama Duck")

1981. Wildlife (1st series). Birds. Multicoloured.
589 5c. Type **136** . . . . 1·50 60
590 20c. Reddish egret . . . . . 2·25 60
591 25c. Brown booby . . . . . 2·25 65
592 $1 Black-billed whistling duck ("West Indian Tree Duck") 4·00 7·00
MS593 100 × 74 mm. Nos. 589/92 8·50 7·50
See also Nos. 626/30, 653/7 and 690/4.

1981. Commonwealth Finance Ministers' Meeting. Nos. 559/60, 566 and 568 optd **COMMONWEALTH FINANCE MINISTERS' MEETING 21–23 SEPTEMBER 1981**.
594 5c. Eleutheran Adventures (Articles and Orders, 1647) 15 15
595 10c. Ceremonial mace 20 20
596 25c. Pineapple cultivation . . 50 60
597 50c. Tourist development . . 85 1·50

138 Poultry

1981. World Food Day. Multicoloured.
598 5c. Type **138** 20 10
599 20c. Sheep 35 35
600 30c. Lobsters 45 50
601 50c. Pigs . . . . 75 1·50
MS602 115 × 63 mm. Nos. 598/601 1·50 3·25

139 Father Christmas **141** Greater Flamingo (male)

140 Robert Koch

1981. Christmas. Multicoloured.
603 5c. Type **139** 55 85
604 5c. Mother and child 55 85
605 5c. St. Nicholas, Holland . . 55 85
606 25c. Lussibruden, Sweden . . 70 95
607 25c. Mother and child (different) 70 95
608 25c. King Wenceslas, Czechoslovakia 70 95
609 30c. Mother with child on knee 70 95
610 30c. Mother carrying child 70 95
611 $1 Christkindl Angel, Germany . . . . 1·00 1·50

1982. Centenary of Discovery of Tubercle Bacillus by Robert Koch.
612 **140** 5c. black, brown and lilac 70 50
613 – 16c. black, brown & orge 1·25 50
614 – 21c. multicoloured . . . . 1·40 55
615 – $1 multicoloured . . . . 3·00 7·50
MS616 94 × 97 mm. Nos. 612/15 6·00 7·50

DESIGNS: 16c. Stylised infected person; 21c. Early and modern microscopes; $1 Mantoux test.

1982. Greater Flamingos. Multicoloured.
617 25c. Type **141** . . . . 1·60 1·00
618 25c. Female . . . . 1·60 1·00
619 25c. Female with nestling . . 1·60 1·00
620 25c. Juvenile . . . . 1·60 1·00
621 25c. Immature bird . . . . . 1·60 1·00

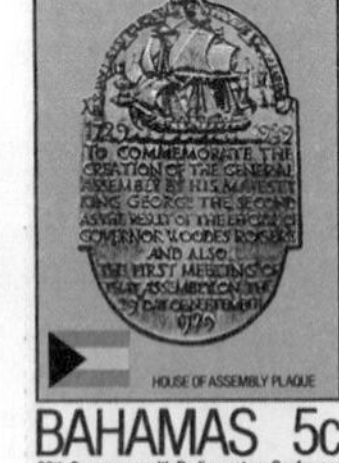

142 Lady Diana Spencer at Ascot, June, 1981 **143** House of Assembly Plaque

1982. 21st Birthday of Princess of Wales. Mult.
622 16c. Bahamas coat of arms 20 10
623 25c. Type **142** 45 15
624 40c. Bride and Earl Spencer arriving at St. Paul's . . . 60 20
625 $1 Formal portrait . . . . . 1·00 1·25

1982. Wildlife (2nd series). Mammals. As T **136**. Multicoloured.
626 10c. Buffy flower bat . . . . 1·00 15
627 16c. Bahamian hutia . . . . 1·25 25
628 21c. Common racoon . . . . 1·50 55
629 $1 Common dolphin . . . . 3·25 1·75
MS630 115 × 76 mm. Nos. 626/9 6·00 3·50

1982. 28th Commonwealth Parliamentary Association Conference. Multicoloured.
631 5c. Type **143** 15 10
632 25c. Association coat of arms 50 35
633 40c. Coat of arms 80 60
634 50c. House of Assembly . . . 1·10 75

144 Wesley Methodist Church, Baillou Hill Road

1982. Christmas. Churches. Multicoloured.
635 5c. Type **144** 10 20
636 12c. Centreville Seventh Day Adventist Church 15 20
637 15c. The Church of God of Prophecy, East Street . . . 15 30
638 21c. Bethel Baptist Church, Meeting Street 15 30
639 25c. St. Francis Xavier Catholic Church, Highbury Park 15 50
640 $1 Holy Cross Anglican Church, Highbury Park . . 60 3·00

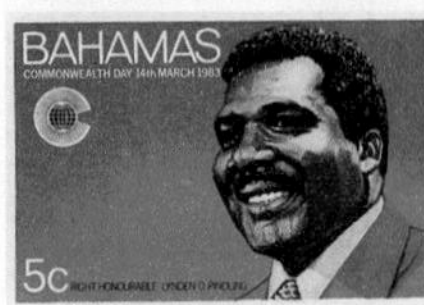

145 Prime Minister Lyndon O. Pindling

1983. Commonwealth Day. Multicoloured.
641 5c. Type **145** 10 10
642 25c. Bahamian and Commonwealth flags . . . 50 40
643 35c. Map showing position of Bahamas 50 50
644 $1 Ocean liner . . . . 1·10 1·40

1983. Nos. 562/5 surch.
645 20c. on 15c. Slave trading, Vendue House 50 35
646 31c. on 21c. Bootlegging, 1919–29 . . . . 60 55
647 35c. on 16c. Wrecking in the 1800s 70 60
648 80c. on 18c. Blockade running (American Civil War) . . . . 80 1·40

147 Customs Officers and "Queen Elizabeth 2" (liner) **148** Raising the National Flag

1983. 30th Anniv of Customs Co-operation Council. Multicoloured.
649 31c. Type **147** . . . . 1·50 45
650 $1 Customs officers and Lockheed JetStar airliner 3·50 2·75

1983. 10th Anniv of Independence.
651 **148** $1 multicoloured . . . . 1·00 1·40
MS652 105 × 65 mm. No. 651 . . 1·00 1·40

1983. Wildlife (3rd series). Butterflies. As T **136**.
653 5c. multicoloured . . . . . . 1·25 20
654 25c. multicoloured . . . . . . 2·00 40
655 31c. black, yellow and red . . 2·00 55
656 50c. multicoloured . . . . . 2·25 85
MS657 120 × 80 mm. Nos. 653/6 5·50 6·00
DESIGNS: 5c. "Atalopedes carteri"; 25c. "Ascia monuste"; 31 c. "Phoebis agarithe"; 50c. "Dryas julia"

149 "Loyalist Dreams" **151** "Christmas Bells" (Monica Pinder)

150 Consolidated Catalina

1983. Bicentenary of Arrival of American Loyalists in the Bahamas. Multicoloured.
658 5c. Type **149** 10 10
659 31c. New Plymouth, Abaco (horiz) 30 50
660 35c. New Plymouth Hotel (horiz) 40 70
661 50c. "Island Hope" 45 90
MS662 111 × 76 mm. Nos. 658/61 1·25 2·50

1983. Air. Bicentenary of Manned Flight. Mult.
663 10c. Type **150** 55 15
664 25c. Avro Tudor IV 75 30
665 31c. Avro Lancastrian . . . 85 45
666 35c. Consolidated Commodore . . . . 1·00 50
For these stamps without the Manned Flight logo, see Nos. 699/702.

1983. Christmas. Children's Paintings. Multicoloured.
667 5c. Type **151** 15 10
668 20c. "Flamingo" (Cory Bullard) 35 30
669 25c. "Yellow Hibiscus with Christmas Candle" (Monique Bailey) 45 40
670 31c. "Santa goes-a-sailing" (Sabrina Seiler) (horiz) . . 55 45
671 35c. "Silhouette scene with Palm Trees" (James Blake) 60 50
672 50c. "Silhouette scene with Pelicans" (Erik Russell) (horiz) 70 70

152 1861 4d. Stamp **153** "Trent I" (paddle-steamer)

1984. 125th Anniv of First Bahamas Postage Stamp. Multicoloured.
673 5c. Type **152** 25 10
674 $1 1859 1d. stamp . . . . . 1·75 1·50

1984. 250th Anniv of "Lloyd's List" (newspaper). Multicoloured.
675 5c. Type **153** 50 10
676 31c. "Orinoco II" (mail ship), 1886 . . . . 1·00 60
677 35c. Cruise liners in Nassau harbour . . . . 1·10 75
678 50c. "Oropesa" (container ship) . . . . 1·40 1·60

154 Running **155** Bahamas and Caribbean Community Flags

1984. Olympic Games, Los Angeles.
679 **154** 5c. green, black and gold 15 20
680 – 25c. blue, black and gold 50 50
681 – 31c. red, black and gold 55 60
682 – $1 brown, black and gold 5·50 6·50
MS683 115 × 80 mm. Nos. 679/82 6·00 8·00
DESIGNS: 25c. Shot-putting; 31c. Boxing; $1 Basketball.

1984. 5th Conference of Caribbean Community Heads of Government.
684 **155** 50c. multicoloured . . . . 1·00 1·00

156 Bahama Woodstar **157** "The Holy Virgin with Jesus and Johannes" (19th-century porcelain plaque after Titian)

1984. 25th Anniv of National Trust. Multicoloured.
685 31c. Type **156** . . . . 3·50 3·50
686 31c. Belted kingfishers, greater flamingos and "Eleutherodactylus planirostris" (frog) . . . . 3·50 3·50
687 31c. Black-necked stilts, greater flamingos and "Phoebis sennae" (butterfly) . . . . 3·50 3·50
688 31c. "Urbanus proteus" (butterfly) and "Chelonia mydas" (turtle) . . . . . 3·50 3·50
689 31c. Osprey and greater flamingos . . . . 3·50 3·50
Nos. 685/9 were printed together in horiz strips of 5 forming a composite design.

1984. Wildlife (4th series). Reptiles and Amphibians. As T **136**.
690 5c. Allens' Cay iguana . . . 75 20
691 25c. Curly-tailed lizard . . . 1·50 60
692 35c. Greenhouse frog . . . . 1·75 85
693 50c. Atlantic green turtle . . 2·00 3·00
MS694 112 × 82 mm. Nos. 690/3 5·50 7·50

1984. Christmas. Religious Paintings. Multicoloured.
695 5c. Type **157** 30 10
696 31c. "Madonna with Child in Tropical Landscape" (aquarelle, Anais Colin) . . 80 60
697 35c. "The Holy Virgin with the Child" (miniature on ivory, Elena Caula) . . . . 1·00 65
MS698 116 × 76 mm. Nos. 695/7 2·25 4·00

1985. Air. As Nos. 663/6, but without Manned Flight logo.
699 10c. Type **150** 70 50
700 25c. Avro Tudor IV 85 50
701 31c. Avro Lancastrian . . . 85 60
702 35c. Consolidated Commodore . . . . 1·25 1·10

158 Brownie Emblem and Queen or Pink Conch

1985. International Youth Year. 75th Anniv of Girl Guide Movement. Multicoloured.
703 5c. Type **158** 60 50
704 25c. Tents and coconut palm 1·25 1·00
705 31c. Guide salute and greater flamingos . . . . 1·90 1·50
706 35c. Ranger emblem and marlin . . . . 1·90 1·50
MS707 95 × 74 mm. Nos. 703/6 5·50 7·50

159 Killdeer Plover

1985. Birth Bicent of John J. Audubon (ornithologist). Multicoloured.
708 5c. Type **159** . . . . 1·00 60
709 31c. Mourning dove (vert) . . 2·25 60
710 35c. "Mourning dove" (John J. Audubon) (vert) . . . . 2·25 65
711 $1 "Killdeer Plover" (John J. Audubon) . . . . 4·00 4·50

160 The Queen Mother at Christening of Peter Phillips, 1977 **162** Queen Elizabeth II

161 Ears of Wheat and Emblems

1985. Life and Times of Queen Elizabeth the Queen Mother. Multicoloured.
712 5c. Visiting Auckland, New Zealand, 1927 . . . . . . 45 20
713 25c. Type **160** 70 40
714 35c. The Queen Mother attending church 75 55
715 50c. With Prince Henry at his christening (from photo by Lord Snowdon) . . . . . 1·50 2·00
MS716 91 × 73 mm. $1.25, In horse-drawn carriage, Sark . . . . . 2·75 1·90

1985. 40th Anniv of U.N.O. and F.A.O.
717 **161** 25c. multicoloured 85 60

1985. Commonwealth Heads of Government Meeting, Nassau. Multicoloured.
718 31c. Type **162** . . . . 2·75 3·50
719 35c. Bahamas Prime Minister's flag and Commonwealth emblem . . 2·75 3·50

163 "Grandma's Christmas Bouquet" (Alton Roland Lowe)

1985. Christmas. Paintings by Alton Roland Lowe. Multicoloured.
736 5c. Type **163** 60 40
737 25c. "Junkanoo Romeo and Juliet" (vert) . . . . 1·50 1·00
738 31c. "Bunce Gal" (vert) . . . 1·75 1·50
739 35c. "Home for Christmas" 1·75 2·75
MS740 110 × 68 mm. Nos. 736/9 2·75 3·25

1986. 60th Birthday of Queen Elizabeth II. As T **110** of Ascension. Multicoloured.
741 10c. Princess Elizabeth aged one, 1927 . . . . 15 15
742 25c. The Coronation, 1953 30 30
743 35c. Queen making speech at Commonwealth Banquet, Bahamas, 1985 . . . . . . 35 40
744 40c. In Djakova, Yugoslavia, 1972 . . . . 35 45
745 $1 At Crown Agents Head Office, London, 1983 . . . 80 1·40

164 1980 1c. and 18c. Definitive Stamps

1986. "Ameripex '86" International Stamp Exn, Chicago.
746 **164** 5c. multicoloured 80 50
747 – 25c. multicoloured . . . . 1·75 50
748 – 31c. multicoloured . . . . 1·90 60
749 – 50c. multicoloured . . . . 2·75 4·50
750 – $1 black, green and blue 3·00 5·50
MS751 80 × 80 mm. No. 750 . . 4·00 4·00
DESIGNS—HORIZ: (showing Bahamas stamps)—25c. 1969 50th Anniv of Bahamas Airmail Service pair; 31c. 1976 Bicentenary of American Revolution 16c., 50c. 1981 Space Exploration miniature sheet. VERT: $1 Statue of Liberty.
No. 750 also commemorates the Centenary of the Statue of Liberty.

1986. Royal Wedding. As T **112** of Ascension. Mult.
756 10c. Prince Andrew and Miss Sarah Ferguson 20 20
757 $1 Prince Andrew . . . . . 1·25 2·10

165 Rock Beauty (juvenile)

1986. Fishes. Multicoloured.
758A 5c. Type **165** 75 75
759A 10c. Stoplight parrotfish . . 80 1·00
760A 15c. Jackknife-fish . . . . 1·50 1·50
761A 20c. Flamefish . . . . . . 1·25 1·25
762A 25c. Peppermint basslet ("Swissguard basslet") . . 1·50 1·50
763A 30c. Spot-finned butterflyfish . . . . . . 1·10 1·50
764A 35c. Queen triggerfish . . . 1·10 2·50
765B 40c. Four-eyed butterflyfish 1·10 1·60
766A 45c. Royal gramma ("Fairy basslet") . . . . 1·50 1·25
767A 50c. Queen angelfish . . . 2·00 3·50
797 60c. Blue chromis . . . . . 2·25 5·00
769B $1 Spanish hogfish . . . . 2·75 3·00
799 $2 Harlequin bass . . . . 3·00 7·50
771A $3 Black-barred soldierfish 6·00 7·00
772A $5 Cherub angelfish ("Pygmy angelfish") . . . 6·50 8·00
773A $10 Red hind . . . . . . 17·00 22·00

166 Christ Church Cathedral, Nassau, 1861

1986. 125th Anniv of City of Nassau. Diocese and Cathedral. Multicoloured.
774 10c. Type **166** 30 20
775 40c. Christ Church Cathedral, 1986 . . . . 70 80
MS776 75 × 100 mm. Nos. 774/5 4·00 6·00

167 Man and Boy looking at Crib

1986. Christmas. International Peace Year. Mult.
777 10c. Type **167** 35 20
778 40c. Mary and Joseph journeying to Bethlehem 85 75
779 45c. Children praying and Star of Bethlehem . . . . 95 1·00
780 50c. Children exchanging gifts 1·00 2·50
MS781 95 × 90 mm. Nos. 777/80 8·50 11·00

168 Great Isaac Lighthouse **169** Anne Bonney

1987. Lighthouses. Multicoloured.
782 10c. Type **168** . . . . 2·50 85
783 40c. Bird Rock lighthouse . . 4·75 1·75
784 45c. Castle Island lighthouse 4·75 2·00
785 $1 "Hole in the Wall" lighthouse . . . . 7·50 12·00

1987. Pirates and Privateers of the Caribbean. Multicoloured.
786 10c. Type **169** . . . . 3·00 1·25
787 40c. Edward Teach ("Blackbeard") . . . . . 5·00 3·50
788 45c. Captain Edward England . . . . 5·00 3·50
789 50c. Captain Woodes Rogers 5·50 6·50
MS790 75 × 95 mm. $1.25, Map of Bahamas and colonial coat of arms . . . . 10·00 4·50

170 Boeing 737

1987. Air. Aircraft. Multicoloured.
800 15c. Type **170** . . . . 2·50 1·50
801 40c. Boeing 757-200 . . . . 3·25 2·25
802 45c. Airbus Industrie A300 B4-200 . . . . 3·25 2·25
803 50c. Boeing 747-200 . . . . 3·25 4·00

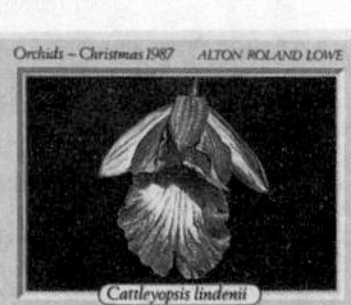

171 "Norway" (liner) and Catamaran **172** "Cattleyopsis lindenii"

1987. Tourist Transport. Multicoloured.
804 40c. Type **171** . . . . 2·00 2·00
805 40c. Liners and speedboat . . 2·00 2·00
806 40c. Game fishing boat and cruising yacht . . . . . . 2·00 2·00
807 40c. Game fishing boat and racing yachts . . . . . . 2·00 2·00
808 40c. Fishing boat and schooner . . . . 2·00 2·00
809 40c. Hawker Siddeley H.S.748 airliner . . . . . 2·00 2·00
810 40c. Boeing 737 and Boeing 727-200 airliners . . . . 2·00 2·00
811 40c. Beech 200 Super King Air aircraft and radio beacon . . . . 2·00 2·00
812 40c. Aircraft and Nassau control tower . . . . . . 2·00 2·00
813 40c. Helicopter and parked aircraft . . . . 2·00 2·00
Nos. 804/8 and 809/13 were each printed together, se-tenant, forming composite design.

1987. Christmas. Orchids. Multicoloured.
814 10c. Type **172** . . . . 1·75 60
815 40c. "Encyclia lucayana" . . 3·00 1·50
816 45c. "Encyclia hodgeana" . . 3·00 1·50
817 50c. "Encyclia lleidae" . . . 3·00 3·00
MS818 120 × 92 mm. Nos. 814/17 9·50 10·00

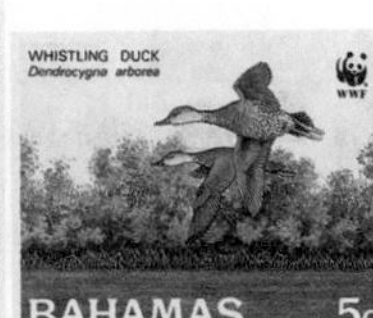

173 King Ferdinand and Queen Isabella of Spain **174** Whistling Ducks in Flight

1988. 500th Anniv (1992) of Discovery of America by Columbus (1st issue). Multicoloured.
819 10c. Type **173** 85 60
820 40c. Columbus before Talavera Committee . . . 1·75 1·75
821 45c. Lucayan village . . . . 1·90 1·90
822 50c. Lucayan potters . . . . 2·00 3·25
MS823 65 × 50 mm. $1.50, Map of Antilles, c. 1500 . . . . . . 6·00 3·75
See also Nos. 844/8, 870/4, 908/12 and 933/7.

1988. Black-billed Whistling Duck. Multicoloured.
824 5c. Type **174** . . . . 2·25 1·75
825 10c. Whistling duck in reeds 2·25 1·75
826 20c. Pair with brood . . . . 4·00 2·75
827 45c. Pair wading . . . . . . 6·00 3·25

175 Grantstown Cabin, c.1820 **177** "Oh Little Town of Bethlehem"

176 Olympic Flame, High Jumping, Hammer throwing, Basketball and Gymnastics

1988. 150th Anniv of Abolition of Slavery. Multicoloured.
828 10c. Type **175** 50 30
829 40c. Basket-making, Grantstown . . . . 1·25 95

1988. Olympic Games, Seoul. Designs taken from painting by James Martin. Multicoloured.
830 10c. Type **176** 90 50
831 40c. Athletics, archery, swimming, long jumping, weightlifting and boxing . . 90 60
832 45c. Javelin throwing, gymnastics, hurdling and shot put 90 60
833 $1 Athletics, hurdling, gymnastics and cycling . . 3·50 5·00
MS834 113 × 85 mm. Nos. 830/3 5·00 3·00

1988. 300th Anniv of Lloyd's of London. As T **123** of Ascension. Multicoloured.
835 10c. "Lloyd's List" of 1740 30 15
836 40c. Freeport Harbour (horiz) 1·75 60
837 45c. Space shuttle over Bahamas (horiz) . . . . . 1·75 60
838 $1 "Yarmouth Castle" (freighter) on fire . . . . . 2·75 1·90

1988. Christmas. Carols. Multicoloured.
839 10c. Type **177** 55 30
840 40c. "Little Donkey" . . . . 1·50 75
841 45c. "Silent Night" . . . . . 1·50 90
842 50c. "Hark the Herald Angels Sing" . . . . 1·60 2·25
MS843 88 × 108 mm. Nos. 839/42 2·75 2·75

1989. 500th Anniv (1992) of Discovery of America by Columbus (2nd issue). As T **173**. Multicoloured.
844 10c. Columbus drawing chart 2·25 75
845 40c. Types of caravel . . . . 3·25 1·50
846 45c. Early navigational instruments . . . . 3·25 1·50
847 50c. Arawak artefacts . . . . 3·25 4·50
MS848 64 × 64 mm. $1.50, Caravel under construction (from 15th-cent "Nuremburg Chronicles") . . . . 2·50 2·50

178 Cuban Emerald **179** Teaching Water Safety

1989. Hummingbirds. Multicoloured.
849 10c. Type **178** . . . . 1·75 1·25
850 40c. Ruby-throated hummingbird . . . . . . 3·00 2·00
851 45c. Bahama woodstar . . . 3·00 2·00
852 50c. Rufous hummingbird . . 3·25 4·50

1989. 125th Anniv of Int Red Cross. Mult.
853 10c. Type **179** . . . . 1·75 50
854 $1 Henri Dunant (founder) and Battle of Solferino . . 3·75 4·50

1989. 20th Anniv of First Manned Landing on Moon. As T **126** of Ascension. Multicoloured.
855 10c. "Apollo 8" Communications Station, Grand Bahama . . . . . 1·00 50
856 40c. Crew of "Apollo 8" (30 × 30 mm) . . . . . . 1·75 90
857 45c. "Apollo 8" emblem (30 × 30 mm) . . . . . . 1·75 90
858 $1 The Earth seen from "Apollo 8" . . . . 2·50 4·50
MS859 100 × 83 mm. $2 "Apollo 11" astronauts in training, Manned Spacecraft Centre, Houston . . 4·50 5·00

180 Church of the Nativity, Bethlehem

1989. Christmas. Churches of the Holy Land. Multicoloured.
860 10c. Type **180** . . . . 1·00 30
861 40c. Basilica of the Annunciation, Nazareth . . 2·00 70
862 45c. Tabgha Church, Galilee 2·00 70
863 $1 Church of the Holy Sepulchre, Jerusalem . . . 3·75 6·00
MS864 92 × 109 mm. Nos. 860/3 8·50 9·00

181 1974 U.P.U. Centenary 13c. Stamp and Globe

1989. "World Stamp Expo '89" International Stamp Exhibition, Washington. Multicoloured.
865 10c. Type **181** 70 40
866 40c. New U.P.U. Headquarters Building 3c. and building . . . . 1·40 85
867 45c. 1986 "Ameripex '86" $1 and Capitol, Washington 1·40 90
868 $1 1949 75th anniv of U.P.U. 2½d. and Boeing 737 airliner . . . . 5·50 7·00
MS869 107 × 80 mm. $2 Map showing route of Columbus, 1492 (30 × 38 mm) . . . . 10·00 14·00

1990. 500th Anniv (1992) of Discovery of America by Columbus (3rd issue). As T **173**. Multicoloured.
870 10c. Launching caravel . . . 1·75 80
871 40c. Provisional ship . . . . 2·75 2·00
872 45c. Shortening sail . . . . . 2·75 2·00
873 50c. Lucayan fisherman . . . 2·75 4·00
MS874 70 × 61 mm. $1.50, Departure of Columbus, 1492 5·50 7·00

182 Bahamas Flag, O.A.S. Headquarters and Centenary Logo

1990. Centenary of Organization of American States.
875 **182** 40c. multicoloured . . . . 2·00 2·25

183 Supermarine Spitfire Mk I "Bahamas I"

1990. "Stamp World London 90" International Stamp Exhibition, London. Presentation Fighter Aircraft. Sheet 107 × 78 mm. containing T **183**. Multicoloured.
MS876 $1 Type **183**; $1 Hawker Hurricane Mk IIc "Bahamas V" 7·50 7·50

184 Teacher with Boy

1990. International Literacy Year. Multicoloured.
877 10c. Type **184** . . . . 1·00 50
878 40c. Three boys in class . . . 1·75 1·25
879 50c. Teacher and children with books . . . . 1·75 5·00

1990. 90th Birthday of Queen Elizabeth the Queen Mother. As T **134** of Ascension.
880 40c. multicoloured . . . . . 1·50 50
881 $1.50 black and ochre . . . 2·75 4·50
DESIGNS—21 × 36 mm: 40c. "Queen Elizabeth 1938" (Sir Gerald Kelly); 29 × 37 mm: $1.50, Queen Elizabeth at garden party, France, 1938.

185 Cuban Amazon preening **186** The Annunciation

1990. Cuban Amazon ("Bahamian Parrot"). Mult.
882 10c. Type **185** . . . . . . 1·25 85
883 40c. Pair in flight . . . . . . 2·25 1·50
884 45c. Cuban amazon's head . . . 2·25 1·50
885 50c. Perched on branch . . . 2·50 3·75
MS886 73 × 63 mm. $1.50, Feeding on berries . . . . 8·00 10·00

1990. Christmas. Multicoloured.
887 10c. Type **186** 65 50
888 40c. The Nativity . . . . . 1·25 70
889 45c. Angel appearing to Shepherds . . . . 1·25 70
890 $1 The Three Kings . . . . 3·00 5·50
MS891 94 × 110 mm. Nos. 887/90 11·00 11·00

187 Green-backed Heron ("Green Heron") **189** The Annunciation

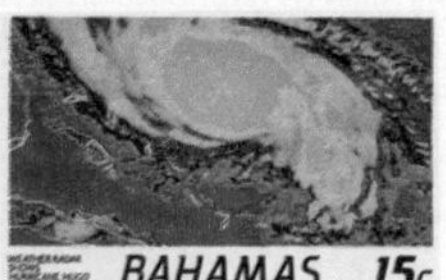

188 Radar Plot of Hurricane Hugo

1991. Birds. Multicoloured.
892 5c. Type **187** . . . . 85 1·25
893 10c. Turkey vulture . . . . . 1·50 1·50
976 15c. Osprey 80 70
895 20c. Clapper rail . . . . . . 1·00 80
978 25c. Royal tern 60 70
979 30c. Key West quail dove . . 2·25 90
898 40c. Smooth-billed ani . . . 1·75 55
899 45c. Burrowing owl . . . . . 2·75 80
900 50c. Hairy woodpecker . . . 2·25 80
983 55c. Mangrove cuckoo . . . 2·00 80
902 60c. Bahama mockingbird . . 2·00 1·75
903 70c. Red-winged blackbird . 2·00 1·75
904 $1 Thick-billed vireo . . . . 2·50 1·50
905 $2 Bahama yellowthroat . . 5·50 6·50
988 $5 Stripe-headed tanager . . 6·50 8·50
907 $10 Greater Antillean bullfinch . . . . 13·00 16·00

1991. 500th Anniv (1992) of Discovery of America by Columbus (4th issue). As T **173**. Multicoloured.
908 15c. Columbus navigating by stars . . . . 1·75 85
909 40c. Fleet in mid-Atlantic . . 2·50 2·25
910 55c. Lucayan family worshipping at night . . . 2·50 2·50
911 60c. Map of First Voyage . . 3·25 5·00
MS912 56 × 61 mm. $1.50, "Pinta"'s look-out sighting land . . . . 6·00 7·00

1991. 65th Birthday of Queen Elizabeth II and 70th Birthday of Prince Philip. As T **139** of Ascension. Multicoloured.
913 15c. Prince Philip . . . . . 1·00 1·50
914 $1 Queen Elizabeth II . . . 1·75 2·00

1991. International Decade for Natural Disaster Reduction. Multicoloured.
915 15c. Type **188** . . . . 1·25 65
916 40c. Diagram of hurricane . . 1·75 1·50
917 55c. Flooding caused by Hurricane David, 1979 . . 2·00 2·25
918 60c. U.S. Dept of Commerce weather reconnaissance Lockhead WP-3D Orion 2·75 4·00

1991. Christmas. Multicoloured.
919 15c. Type **189** 80 30
920 55c. Mary and Joseph travelling to Bethlehem . . 1·75 1·00
921 60c. Angel appearing to the shepherds . . . . 1·75 1·50
922 $1 Adoration of the kings . . 2·75 4·00
MS923 92 × 108 mm. Nos. 919/22 9·00 9·50

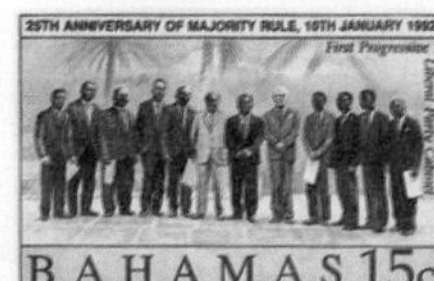

190 First Progressive Liberal Party Cabinet

1992. 25th Anniv of Majority Rule. Multicoloured.
924 15c. Type **190** 60 40
925 40c. Signing of Independence Constitution . . . . 1·40 1·10
926 55c. Prince of Wales handing over Constitutional Instrument (vert) . . . . 1·50 1·50
927 60c. First Bahamian Governor-General, Sir Milo Butler (vert) . . . . 1·75 3·00

1992. 40th Anniv of Queen Elizabeth II's Accession. As T **143** of Ascension. Multicoloured.
928 15c. Queen Elizabeth with bouquet 60 30
929 40c. Queen Elizabeth with flags . . . . 1·10 70
930 55c. Queen Elizabeth at display . . . . 1·10 90
931 60c. Three portraits of Queen Elizabeth . . . . 1·25 1·50
932 $1 Queen Elizabeth II . . . 1·50 2·50

1992. 500th Anniv of Discovery of America by Columbus (5th issue). As T **173**. Multicoloured.
933 15c. Lucayans sighting fleet 1·75 1·00
934 40c. "Santa Maria" and dolphins . . . . 2·50 1·75
935 55c. Lucayan canoes approaching ships . . . . 2·50 2·25
936 60c. Columbus giving thanks for landfall . . . . . . 3·00 4·25
MS937 61 × 57 mm. $1.50, Children at Columbus Monument . . . 3·50 6·00

191 Templeton, Galbraith and Hansberger Ltd Building

1992. 20th Anniv of Templeton Prize for Religion.
938 **191** 55c. multicoloured . . . . 1·50 1·75

192 Pole Vaulting **194** Mary visiting Elizabeth

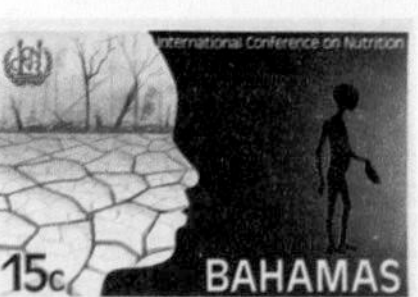

193 Arid Landscape and Starving Child

1992. Olympic Games, Barcelona. Multicoloured.
939 15c. Type **192** 60 50
940 40c. Javelin . . . . 1·00 90
941 55c. Hurdling . . . . 1·10 1·25
942 60c. Basketball . . . . 6·00 5·00
MS943 70 × 50 mm. $2 Sailing 7·50 9·00

1992. International Conference on Nutrition, Rome. Multicoloured.
944 15c. Type **193** . . . . . . 1·25 75
945 55c. Seedling, cornfield and child . . . . 2·00 2·00

1992. 500th Anniv of Discovery of America by Columbus (6th issue). Sheet 65 × 65 mm, containing vert design as T **173**. Multicoloured.
MS946 $2 Columbus landing in Bahamas . . . . 7·50 8·00

1992. Christmas. Multicoloured.
947 15c. Type **194** 40 20
948 55c. The Nativity . . . . . 1·10 1·00
949 60c. Angel and shepherds . . 1·25 1·50
950 70c. Wise Men and star . . . 1·40 2·50
MS951 95 × 110 mm. Nos. 947/50 6·50 8·50

1992. Hurricane Relief. No. **MS**876 showing each stamp surch **HURRICANE RELIEF+$1**.
MS952 $1+$1 Type **183**; $1+$1 Hawker Hurricane Mk IIc "Bahamas V" . . . . 12·00 15·00

196 Flags of Bahamas and U.S.A. with Agricultural Worker

1993. 50th Anniv of The Contract (U.S.A.–Bahamas farm labour programme). Each including national flags. Multicoloured.
953 15c. Type **196** . . . . 1·75 70
954 55c. Onions . . . . 2·25 1·50
955 60c. Citrus fruit . . . . . . 2·50 2·50
956 70c. Apples . . . . 2·75 3·25

1993. 75th Anniv of Royal Air Force. As T **149** of Ascension. Multicoloured.
957 15c. Westland Wapiti IIA . . 1·50 85
958 40c. Gloster Gladiator I . . . 2·00 1·00
959 55c. De Havilland Vampire F.3 . . . . 2·25 1·75
960 70c. English Electric Lightning F.3 . . . . . . 2·75 4·50
MS961 110 × 77 mm. 60c. Avro Shackleton M.R.2; 60c. Fairey Battle; 60c. Douglas Boston III; 60c. De Havilland D.H.9a . . 8·50 9·50

197 1978 Coronation Anniversary Stamps **198** "Lignum vitae" (national tree)

1993. 40th Anniv of Coronation. Multicoloured.
962 15c. Type **197** 70 50
963 55c. Two examples of 1953 Coronation stamp . . . . 1·75 1·75
964 60c. 1977 Silver Jubilee 8c. and 16c. stamps . . . . 1·75 2·00
965 70c. 1977 Silver Jubilee 21c. and 40c. stamps . . . . . 2·00 2·75

1993. 20th Anniv of Independence. Mult.
966 15c. Type **198** 30 20
967 55c. Yellow elder (national flower) 90 90
968 60c. Blue marlin (national fish) . . . . 1·25 1·25
969 70c. Greater flamingo (national bird) . . . . . . 2·00 3·00

199 Cordia **200** The Annunciation

1993. Environment Protection (1st series). Wildflowers. Multicoloured.
970 15c. Type **199** . . . . 1·25 50
971 55c. Seaside morning glory . 2·75 1·25
972 60c. Poinciana . . . . 3·00 2·25
973 70c. Spider lily . . . . 3·50 4·00
See also Nos. 1017/21, 1035/8, 1084/7, 1121/4, 1149/53 and 1193/6.

1993. Christmas. Multicoloured.
990 15c. Type **200** . . . . 1·25 50
991 55c. Angel and shepherds . . 3·00 1·75
992 60c. Holy Family . . . . . 3·25 2·50
993 70c. Three Kings . . . . . . 3·50 4·00
MS994 86 × 106 mm. $1 Virgin Mary and Child . . . . 6·50 8·50

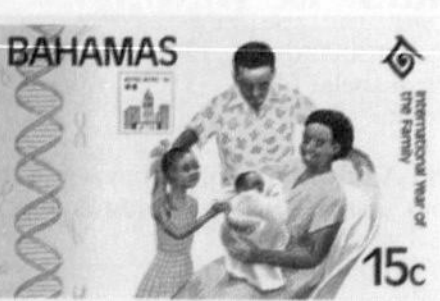

201 Family

1994. "Hong Kong '94" International Stamp Exhibition. International Year of the Family. Multicoloured.
995 15c. Type **201** . . . . . . 1·25 40
996 55c. Children doing homework . . . . 2·25 1·25
997 60c. Grandfather and grandson fishing . . . . . 2·50 1·75
998 70c. Grandmother teaching grandchildren the Lord's Prayer . . . . 3·00 4·50

202 Flags of Bahamas and Great Britain

1994. Royal Visit. Multicoloured.
999 15c. Type **202** . . . . . . 1·00 50
1000 55c. Royal Yacht "Britannia" . . . . 2·25 1·75
1001 60c. Queen Elizabeth II . . 2·25 1·90
1002 70c. Queen Elizabeth and Prince Philip . . . . . . 2·25 4·00

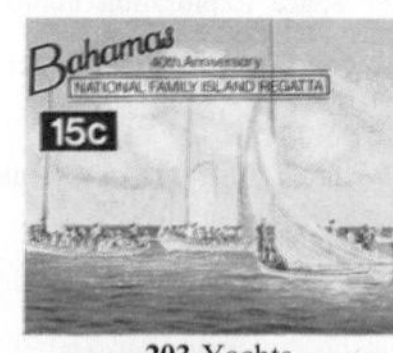

203 Yachts

1994. 40th Anniv of National Family Island Regatta. Multicoloured.
1003 15c. Type **203** 80 40
1004 55c. Dinghies racing . . . . 1·75 1·25
1005 60c. Working boats . . . . 1·75 1·75
1006 70c. Sailing sloop . . . . . 2·25 4·00
MS1007 76 × 54 mm. $2 Launching sloop (vert) . . . . 8·00 9·00

204 Logo and Bahamas 1968 Olympic Games Stamp

1994. Centenary of International Olympic Committee. Multicoloured.
1008 15c. Type **204** . . . . . . 1·50 50
1009 55c. 1976 Olympic Games stamps (vert) . . . . . . 2·50 1·25
1010 60c. 1984 Olympic Games stamps . . . . 2·50 2·25
1011 70c. 1992 Olympic Games stamps (vert) . . . . . . 2·75 4·00

205 Star of Order

1994. First Recipients of Order of the Caribbean Community. Sheet 90 × 69 mm.
MS1012 **205** $2 multicoloured . . 5·50 6·50

206 "Calpodes ethlius" and Canna **207** Spot-finned Hogfish and Spanish Hogfish

1994. Butterflies and Flowers. Multicoloured.
1013 15c. Type **206** . . . . . . 1·10 55
1014 55c. "Phoebis sennae" and cassia . . . . 2·00 1·50
1015 60c. "Anartia jatrophae" and passion flower . . . . 2·25 2·25
1016 70c. "Battus devilliersi" and calico flower . . . . . . 2·25 3·00

1994. Environment Protection (2nd series). Marine Life. Multicoloured.
1017 40c. Type **207** . . . . . . 1·00 1·25
1018 40c. Tomate and long-spined squirrelfish . . . . 1·00 1·25
1019 40c. French angelfish . . . 1·00 1·25
1020 40c. Queen angelfish . . . . 1·00 1·25
1021 40c. Rock beauty . . . . . 1·00 1·25
MS1022 57 × 55 mm. $2 Rock beauty, Queen angelfish and windsurfer . . . . 6·00 7·00

Nos. 1017/21 were printed together, se-tenant, with the backgrounds forming a composite design.

208 Angel

1994. Christmas. Multicoloured.
1023 15c. Type **208** 30 30
1024 55c. Holy Family . . . . . 90 1·10
1025 60c. Shepherds . . . . . . 1·10 1·40
1026 70c. Wise Men . . . . . . 1·25 2·50
MS1027 73 × 85 mm. Jesus in manger . . . . 3·50 5·00

209 Lion and Emblem

210 Kirtlands Warbler on Nest

1995. 20th Anniv of the College of the Bahamas. Multicoloured.
1028 15c. Type **209** 30 30
1029 70c. Queen Elizabeth II and College building . . . . 1·25 1·75

1995. 50th Anniv of End of Second World War. As T **161** of Ascension. Multicoloured.
1030 15c. Bahamian infantry drilling 75 50
1031 55c. Consolidated PBY-5A Catalina flying boat . . . 2·00 1·25
1032 60c. Bahamian women in naval operations room . . 2·00 2·25
1033 70c. Consolidated B-24 Liberator bomber . . . . 2·50 3·75
MS1034 75 × 85 mm. $2 Reverse of 1939–45 War Medal (vert) . . 3·00 4·00

1995. Environment Protection (3rd series). Endangered Species. Kirtland's Warbler. Mult.
1035 15c. Type **210** 55 75
1036 15c. Singing on branch . . . 55 75
1037 25c. Feeding chicks 55 75
1038 25c. Catching insects 55 75
MS1039 73 × 67 mm. $2 On branch 7·50 8·50

No. **MS**1039 does not show the W.W.F. Panda emblem.

211 Eleuthera Cliffs

1995. Tourism. Multicoloured.
1040 15c. Type **211** . . . . . . 1·25 50
1041 55c. Clarence Town, Long Island . . . . 2·25 1·25
1042 60c. Albert Lowe Museum 2·50 2·50
1043 70c. Yachts . . . . 2·75 4·25

212 Pigs and Chick

1995. 50th Anniv of F.A.O. Multicoloured.
1044 15c. Type **212** . . . . . . 1·25 50
1045 55c. Seedling and hand holding seed . . . . . . 1·75 1·10
1046 60c. Family with fruit and vegetables . . . . 2·25 2·25
1047 70c. Fishes and crustaceans 3·00 4·00

213 Sikorsky S-55 Helicopter, Sinai, 1957

1995. 50th Anniv of United Nations. Multicoloured.
1048 15c. Type **213** 70 50
1049 55c. Ferret armoured car, Sinai, 1957 . . . . 1·25 1·25
1050 60c. Fokker F.27 Friendship (airliner), Cambodia, 1991–93 . . . . 1·50 1·75
1051 70c. Lockheed C-130 Hercules (transport) . . . 1·60 2·50

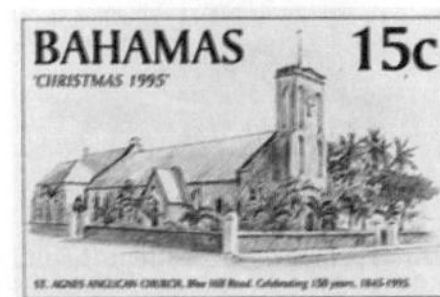

214 St. Agnes Anglican Church

1995. Christmas. Churches. Multicoloured.
1052 15c. Type **214** 30 25
1053 55c. Church of God, East Street 90 90
1054 60c. Sacred Heart Roman Catholic Church . . . . 95 1·25
1055 70c. Salem Union Baptist Church . . . . 1·10 1·75

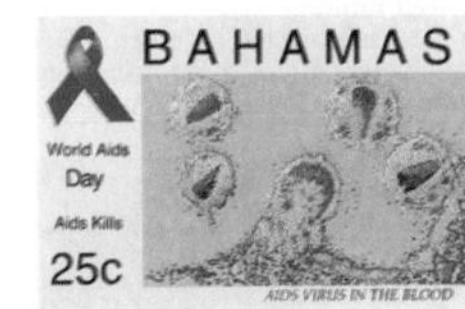

215 Microscopic View of AIDS Virus

1995. World AIDS Day. Multicoloured.
1056 25c. Type **215** 60 50
1057 70c. Research into AIDS . . 1·00 1·50

216 Sunrise Tellin

1996. Sea Shells. Multicoloured.
1098 5c. Type **216** 50 75
1099 10c. Queen conch 50 60
1100 15c. Angular triton 55 25
1101 20c. True tulip 60 45
1102 25c. Reticulated cowrie-helmet 70 40
1063 30c. Sand dollar . . . . . 1·00 55
1103a 35c. As 30c. . . . . 1·00 55
1104 40c. Lace short-frond murex . . . . 1·00 70
1065 45c. Inflated sea biscuit . . 1·25 60
1106 50c. West Indian top shell 1·25 85
1067 55c. Spiny oyster . . . . . 1·50 75
1108 60c. King helmet . . . . . 1·75 90
1108a 65c. As 45c. . . . . 1·75 1·25
1109 70c. Lion's paw . . . . . 1·75 1·50
1109a 80c. As 55c. . . . . 1·75 1·50
1110 $1 Crown cone . . . . . 2·50 2·00
1111 $2 Atlantic partridge tun 5·00 5·00
1112 $5 Wide-mouthed purpura 9·00 10·00
1113 $10 Atlantic trumpet triton 17·00 18·00

217 East Goodwin Lightship with Marconi Apparatus on Mast

1996. Centenary of Radio. Multicoloured.
1074 15c. Type **217** . . . . . . 1·75 80
1075 55c. Newspaper headline concerning Dr. Crippen 2·25 1·25
1076 60c. "Philadelphia" (liner) and first readable transatlantic message . . 2·25 2·00
1077 70c. Guglielmo Marconi and "Elettra" (yacht) . . . . 2·75 3·50
MS1078 80 × 47 mm. $2 "Titanic" and "Carpathia" (liners) . . . 6·50 8·00

218 Swimming

219 Green Anole

1996. Centenary of Modern Olympic Games. Multicoloured.
1079 15c. Type **218** 40 35
1080 55c. Running 90 80
1081 60c. Basketball . . . . . . 1·75 1·75
1082 70c. Long jumping . . . . 1·40 2·50
MS1083 73 × 86 mm. $2 Javelin throwing . . . . 3·00 4·00

1996. Environment Protection (4th series). Reptiles. Multicoloured.
1084 15c. Type **219** 55 50
1085 55c. Little Bahama bank boa . . . . 1·10 1·00
1086 60c. Inagua freshwater turtle 1·50 1·75
1087 70c. Acklins rock iguana . . 1·75 2·75
MS1088 85 × 105 mm. Nos. 1084/7 4·50 5·50

220 The Annunciation

221 Department of Archives Building

1996. Christmas. Multicoloured.
1089 15c. Type **220** . . . . . . 1·00 40
1090 55c. Joseph and Mary travelling to Bethlehem 2·25 1·00
1091 60c. Shepherds and angel . . 2·25 1·50
1092 70c. Adoration of the Magi 2·50 3·25
MS1093 70 × 87 mm. $2 Presentation in the Temple . . . . 3·00 3·75

1996. 25th Anniv of Archives Department.
1094 **221** 55c. multicoloured . . . 1·25 1·00
MS1095 83 × 54 mm. $2 multicoloured . . . . 4·75 6·50

1997. "HONG KONG '97" International Stamp Exhibition. Sheet 130 × 90 mm, containing design as No. 1070, but with "1997" imprint date. Multicoloured.
MS1096 $1 Crown cone . . . . 2·75 3·00

1997. Return of Hong Kong to China. Sheet 130 × 90 mm, containing design as No. 1069, but with "1997" imprint date.
MS1097 70c. Lion's paw . . . . 2·00 2·50

1997. Golden Wedding of Queen Elizabeth and Prince Philip. As T **173** of Ascension. Multicoloured.
1114 50c. Queen Elizabeth II in Bonn, 1992 . . . . 1·75 2·00
1115 50c. Prince Philip and Prince Charles at Trooping the Colour . . . . 1·75 2·00
1116 60c. Prince Philip . . . . . 1·75 2·00
1117 60c. Queen at Trooping the Colour . . . . 1·75 2·00
1118 70c. Queen Elizabeth and Prince Philip at polo, 1970 . . . . 1·75 2·00
1119 70c. Prince Charles playing polo . . . . 1·75 2·00
MS1120 110 × 70 mm. $2 Queen Elizabeth and Prince Philip in landau (horiz) . . . . 5·50 6·00

222 Underwater Scene

1997. Environment Protection (5th series). International Year of the Reefs.
1121 **222** 15c. multicoloured . . . 1·25 60
1122 – 55c. multicoloured . . . 2·25 1·00
1123 – 60c. multicoloured . . . 2·25 1·75
1124 – 70c. multicoloured . . . 2·50 3·00

DESIGNS: 55c. to 70c. Different children's paintings of underwater scenes.

223 Angel

223a Wearing Grey Jacket, 1988

1997. Christmas. Multicoloured.
1125 15c. Type **223** . . . . . . 1·00 40
1126 55c. Mary and Baby Jesus 1·60 80
1127 60c. Shepherd . . . . . . 1·75 1·25
1128 70c. King . . . . 2·25 3·25
MS1129 74 × 94 mm. $2 Baby Jesus wrapped in swaddling-bands. 6·00 7·00

1998. Diana, Princess of Wales Commemoration.
1130 **223a** 15c. multicoloured . . . 50 50
MS1131 145 × 70 mm. 15c. As No. 1130; 55c. Wearing striped jacket, 1983; 60c. In evening dress, 1983; 70c. Meeting crowds, 1993 2·50 2·75

1998. 80th Anniv of the Royal Air Force. As T **178** of Ascension. Multicoloured.
1132 15c. Handley Page Hyderabad 55 40
1133 55c. Hawker Demon . . . . 1·00 85
1134 60c. Gloster Meteor F.8 . . 1·10 1·25
1135 70c. Lockheed Neptune MR.1 . . . . 1·40 2·25
MS1136 110 × 76 mm. 50c. Sopwith Camel; 50c. Short 184 (seaplane); 50c. Supermarine Spitfire PR.19; 50c. North American Mitchell III 4·00 4·25

224 Newsletters

1998. 50th Anniv of Organization of American States. Multicoloured.
1137 15c. Type **224** 30 30
1138 55c. Headquarters building and flags, Washington . . 70 80

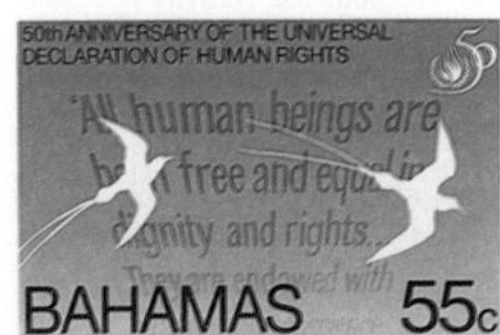

225 Start of Declaration and Birds

1998. 50th Anniv of Universal Declaration of Human Rights.
1139 **225** 55c. blue and black . . . 1·50 1·00

226 University Arms and Graduates

1998. 50th Anniv of University of the West Indies.
1140 **226** 55c. multicoloured . . . 1·50 1·00

227 Supreme Court Building

1998. 25th Anniv of Independence. Multicoloured.
1141 15c. Type **227** 75 50
1142 55c. Nassau Library . . . . 1·50 1·00
1143 60c. Government House . . 1·60 1·50
1144 70c. Gregory Arch . . . . 1·75 2·50
MS1145 70 × 55 mm. $2 Island Regatta, George Town . . . . 3·50 5·00

228 "Disney Magic" (cruise liner) at Night

1998. Disney Cruise Line's Castaway Cay Holiday Development. Multicoloured.
1146 55c. Type **228** . . . . . . 1·50 1·50
1147 55c. "Disney Magic" by day 1·50 1·50

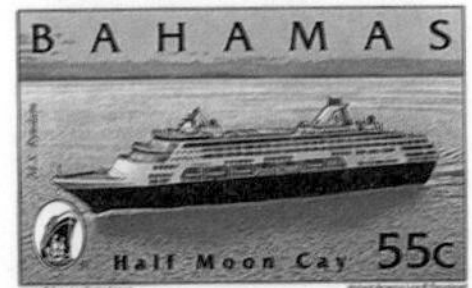

229 "Ryndam" (cruise liner)

1998. Holland America Line's Half Moon Cay Holiday Development.
1148 **229** 55c. multicoloured 1·75 1·25

230 Barrel Pink Rose

1998. Environment Protection (6th series). Roses. Multicoloured.
1149 55c. Type **230** 1·25 1·40
1150 55c. Yellow cream 1·25 1·40
1151 55c. Seven sisters 1·25 1·40
1152 55c. Big red 1·25 1·40
1153 55c. Island beauty 1·25 1·40
MS1154 100 × 70 mm. No. 1153 1·25 1·50

231 The Annunciation

1998. Christmas. Multicoloured.
1155 15c. Type **231** 50 30
1156 55c. Shepherds 1·00 70
1157 60c. Three Kings 1·25 1·10
1158 70c. The Flight into Egypt 1·50 2·50
MS1159 87 × 67 mm. The Nativity 3·00 4·00

232 Killer Whale and other Marine Life

1998. International Year of the Ocean. Multicoloured.
1160 15c. Type **232** 65 50
1161 55c. Tropical fish 85 90

233 Timothy Gibson (composer)

1998. 25th Anniv of "March on Bahamaland" (national anthem).
1162 **233** 60c. multicoloured 1·00 1·25

234 Head of Greater Flamingo and Chick

1999. 40th Anniv of National Trust (1st issue). Inagua National Park. Multicoloured.
1163 55c. Type **234** 1·25 1·40
1164 55c. Pair with two chicks 1·25 1·40
1165 55c. Greater flamingos asleep or stretching wings 1·25 1·40
1166 55c. Greater flamingos feeding 1·25 1·40
1167 55c. Greater flamingos in flight 1·25 1·40
Nos. 1163/7 were printed together, se-tenant, with the backgrounds forming a composite design.
See also Nos. 1173/7, 1198/1202 and 1207/11.

235 Arawak Indian Canoe

1999. "Australia '99" World Stamp Exhibition, Melbourne. Maritime History. Multicoloured.
1168 15c. Type **235** 30 30
1169 55c. "Santa Maria" (Columbus), 1492 1·50 1·00
1170 60c. "Queen Anne's Revenge" (Blackbeard), 1716 1·60 1·25
1171 70c. "The Banshee" (Confederate paddle-steamer) running blockade 1·75 2·50
MS1172 110 × 66 mm. $2 Firing on American ships, 1776 3·25 4·25

1999. 40th Anniv of National Trust (2nd issue). Exuma Cays Land and Sea Park. As T **234**. Mult.
1173 55c. Dolphin 1·00 1·40
1174 55c. Angelfish and parrotfish 1·00 1·40
1175 55c. Queen triggerfish 1·00 1·40
1176 55c. Turtle 1·00 1·40
1177 55c. Lobster 1·00 1·40
Nos. 1173/7 were printed together, se-tenant, with the backgrounds forming a composite design.

236 Society Headquarters Building

1999. 40th Anniv of Bahamas Historical Society.
1178 **236** $1 multicoloured 1·50 2·00

1999. 30th Anniv of First Manned Landing on Moon. As T **186** of Ascension. Multicoloured.
1179 15c. Constructing ascent module 45 40
1180 65c. Diagram of command and service module 1·25 1·25
1181 70c. Lunar module descending 1·25 1·75
1182 80c. Lunar module preparing to dock with service module 1·25 2·00
MS1183 90 × 80 mm. $2 Earth as seen from Moon (circular, 40 mm diam) 3·25 4·25

1999. "Queen Elizabeth the Queen Mother's Century". As T **187** of Ascension. Multicoloured.
1184 15c. Visiting Herts Hospital, 1940 60 35
1185 65c. With Princess Elizabeth, Hyde Park, 1944 1·50 1·00
1886 70c. With Prince Andrew, 1997 1·50 1·50
1887 80c. With Irish Guards' mascot, 1997 1·50 2·25
MS1188 145 × 70 mm. $2 Lady Elizabeth Bowes-Lyon with her brother David, 1904, and England World Cup team celebrating, 1966. 4·50 5·00

237 "Delaware" (American mail ship), 1880

1999. 125th Anniv of U.P.U. Ships. Multicoloured.
1189 15c. Type **237** 1·00 50
1190 65c. "Atlantis" (liner), 1923 2·00 1·25
1191 70c. "Queen of Bermuda 2" (liner), 1937 2·00 1·75
1192 80c. U.S.S. "Saufley" (destroyer), 1943 2·25 2·50

238 "Turtle Pond" (Green Turtle)

1999. Environment Protection (7th series). Marine Life Paintings by Ricardo Knowles. Multicoloured.
1193 15c. Type **238** 50 35
1194 65c. "Turtle Cliff" (Loggerhead turtle) 1·25 1·00
1195 70c. "Barracuda" 1·40 1·40
1196 80c. "Coral Reef" 1·50 2·25
MS1197 90 × 75 mm. $2 "Atlantic Bottle-nosed Dolphins" 3·25 4·50
The 65c. is inscribed "GREEN TURTLES" in error.

1999. 40th Anniv of National Trust (3rd issue). Birds. As T **234**. Multicoloured.
1198 65c. Bridled tern and white-tailed tropic bird 1·50 1·50
1199 65c. Louisiana heron 1·50 1·50
1200 65c. Bahama woodstar 1·50 1·50
1201 65c. Black-billed whistling duck 1·50 1·50
1202 65c. Cuban amazon 1·50 1·50
Nos. 1198/1202 were printed together, se-tenant, with the backgrounds forming a composite design.

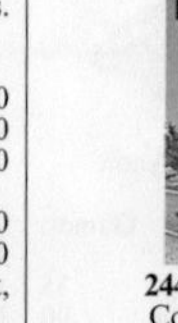

239 Man on Elephant Float

1999. Christmas. Junkanoo Festival. Multicoloured.
1203 15c. Type **239** 50 30
1204 65c. Man in winged costume 1·00 1·00
1205 70c. Man in feathered mask 1·25 1·25
1206 80c. Man blowing conch shell 1·50 2·00

1999. 40th Anniv of National Trust (4th issue). Flora and Fauna. As T **234**. Multicoloured.
1207 65c. Foxglove 1·60 1·60
1208 65c. Vole 1·60 1·60
1209 65c. Cuban amazon 1·60 1·60
1210 65c. Lizard 1·60 1·60
1211 65c. Red hibiscus 1·60 1·60
Nos. 1207/11 were printed together, se-tenant, with the backgrounds forming a composite design.

240 New Plymouth

2000. Historic Fishing Villages. Multicoloured.
1212 15c. Type **240** 75 40
1213 65c. Cherokee Sound 1·60 1·00
1214 70c. Hope Town 1·75 1·60
1215 80c. Spanish Wells 2·00 2·50

241 Gold Medal Winning Bahamas Women's Relay Team

2000. "The Golden Girls" winners of 4 × 100 metre Relay at I.A.A.F. World Track and Field Championship '99, Spain. Sheet 100 × 55 mm.
MS1216 **241** $2 multicoloured 3·00 3·50

242 Prickly Pear

2000. Medicinal Plants (1st series). Multicoloured.
1217 15c. Type **242** 35 30
1218 65c. Buttercup 1·25 1·25
1219 70c. Shepherd's needle 1·25 1·50
1220 80c. Five fingers 1·40 2·00
See also Nos. 1282/5 and 1324/7.

243 Re-arming and Re-fuelling Spitfire

2000. "The Stamp Show 2000" International Stamp Exhibition, London. 60th Anniv of Battle of Britain. Multicoloured.
1221 15c. Type **243** 70 45
1222 65c. Sqdn. Ldr. Stanford-Tuck's Hurricane Mk I 1·40 1·40
1223 70c. Dogfight between Spitfires and Heinkel IIIs 1·60 1·75
1224 80c. Flight of Spitfires attacking 1·60 2·00
MS1225 90 × 70 mm. $2 Presentation Spitfire Bahamas 3·50 4·00

244 Teachers' and Salaried Workers' Co-operative Credit Union Building

2000. Co-operatives Movement in Bahamas. Sheet 90 × 50 mm.
MS1226 $2 multicoloured 3·50 4·00

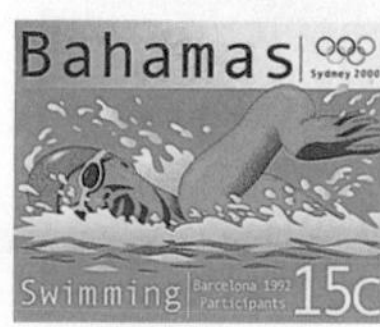

245 Swimming

2000. Olympic Games, Sydney. Each inscribed with details of previous Bahamian participation. Mult.
1227 15c. Type **245** 50 30
1228 65c. Triple jump 1·40 1·25
1229 70c. Women's 4 × 100 m relay 1·40 1·40
1230 80c. Sailing 1·50 2·00

246 *Encyclia cochleata*

2000. Christmas. Orchids. Multicoloured.
1231 15c. Type **246** 55 30
1232 65c. *Encyclia plicata* 1·40 1·25
1233 70c. *Bletia purpurea* 1·60 1·60
1234 80c. *Encyclia gracilis* 1·75 2·00

247 Cuban Amazon and Primary School Class

2000. Bahamas Humane Society. Multicoloured.
1235 15c. Type **247** 80 45
1236 65c. Cat and Society stall 1·75 1·25
1237 70c. Dogs and veterinary surgery 2·00 1·75
1238 80c. Goat and animal rescue van 2·00 2·25

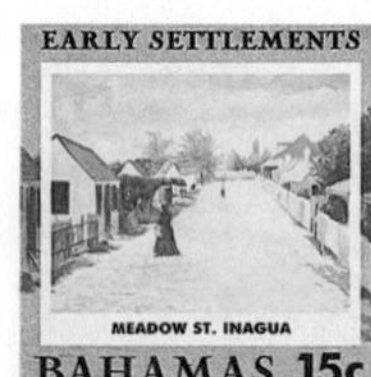

248 "Meadow Street, Inagua"

2001. Early Settlements. Paintings by Ricardo Knowles. Multicoloured.
1239 15c. Type **248** 40 30
1240 65c. "Bain Town" 1·25 1·00
1241 70c. "Hope Town, Abaco" 1·40 1·40
1242 80c. "Blue Hills" 1·50 2·00

249 Lynden Pindling presenting Independence Constitution, 1972

2001. Sir Lynden Pindling (former Prime Minister) Commemoration. Multicoloured.
1243 15c. Type **249** 35 25
1244 65c. Sir Lynden Pindling with Bahamas flag 1·40 1·50

250 "Cocoaplum"

2001. Edible Wild Fruits. Paintings by Alton Roland Lowe. Multicoloured.
1245 15c. Type **250** 35 25
1246 65c. "Guana Berry" 1·25 1·10
1247 70c. "Mastic" 1·25 1·25
1248 80c. "Seagrape" 1·50 2·00

251 Reddish Egret

2001. Birds and their Eggs. Multicoloured.
1249 5c. Type **251** 10 10
1250 10c. American purple gallinule 10 15
1251 15c. Antillean nighthawk . . 15 20
1252 20c. Wilson's plover 20 25
1253 25c. Killdeer plover 25 30
1254 30c. Bahama woodstar . . 35 40
1255 40c. Bahama swallow . . . 45 50
1256 50c. Bahama mockingbird 55 60
1257 60c. Black-cowled oriole . . 65 70
1258 65c. Great lizard cuckoo 70 75
1259 70c. Audubon's shearwater 75 80
1260 80c. Grey kingbird 90 95
1261 $1 Bananaquit . . . . . . 1·10 1·25
1262 $2 Yellow warbler . . . . 2·25 2·40
1263 $5 Greater Antillean bullfinch . . . . 5·50 5·75
1264 $10 Roseate spoonbill . . . 11·00 11·50

252 H.M.S. *Norfolk* (cruiser), 1933

2001. Royal Navy Ships connected to Bahamas. Multicoloured.
1265 15c. Type **252** 50 30
1266 25c. H.M.S. *Scarborough* (sloop), 1930s 65 50
1267 50c. H.M.S. *Bahamas* (frigate), 1944 . . . . . 1·00 1·00
1268 65c. H.M.S. *Battleaxe* (frigate), 1979 . . . . . 1·25 1·25
1269 70c. H.M.S. *Invincible* (aircraft carrier), 1997 . . 1·25 1·50
1270 80c. H.M.S. *Norfolk* (frigate), 2000 . . . . . 1·25 1·75

253 "Adoration of the Shepherds"

2001. Christmas. Paintings by Rubens. Mult.
1271 15c. Type **253** 35 25
1272 65c. "Adoration of the Magi" (with Van Dyck) 1·10 95
1273 70c. "Holy Virgin in Wreath of Flowers" (with Breughel) . . . . 1·25 1·25
1274 80c. "Holy Virgin adored by Angels" . . . . 1·25 1·75

2002. Golden Jubilee. As T **200** of Ascension.
1275 15c. black, green and gold 35 25
1276 65c. multicoloured . . . . . 1·10 95
1277 70c. multicoloured . . . . . 1·25 1·25
1278 80c. multicoloured . . . . . 1·25 1·75
MS1279 162 × 95 mm. Nos. 1275/8 and $2 multicoloured . . . . . 5·50 5·50
DESIGNS—HORIZ: 15c. Princess Elizabeth; 65c. Queen Elizabeth in Bonn, 1992; 70c. Queen Elizabeth with Prince Edward, 1965; 80c. Queen Elizabeth at Sandringham, 1996. VERT (38 × 51 mm)—$2 Queen Elizabeth after Annigoni.

254 Avard Moncur (athlete)

2002. Award of BAAA Most Outstanding Male Athlete Title to Avard Moncur. Sheet 65 × 98 mm.
MS1280 **254** $2 multicoloured . . 3·25 3·50

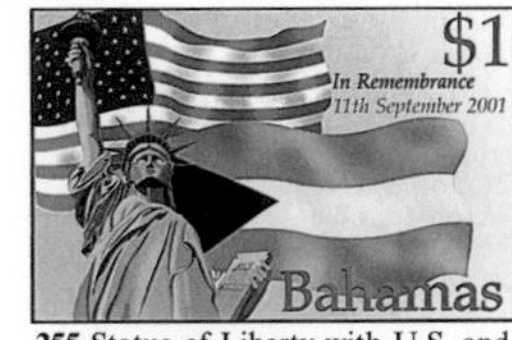
255 Statue of Liberty with U.S. and Bahamas Flags

2002. In Remembrance. Victims of Terrorist Attacks on U.S.A. (11 September 2001).
1281 **255** $1 multicoloured . . . . 3·00 3·00

2002. Medicinal Plants (2nd series). As T **242**. Multicoloured.
1282 15c. Wild sage 50 35
1283 65c. Seaside maho . . . . 1·40 1·10
1284 70c. Sea ox-eye . . . . . . 1·50 1·40
1285 80c. Mexican poppy . . . . 1·50 1·75

2002. Queen Elizabeth the Queen Mother Commemoration. As T **202** of Ascension.
1286 15c. brown, gold and purple 40 30
1287 65c. multicoloured . . . . . 1·25 1·25
MS1288 145 × 70 mm. 70c. black and gold; 80c. multicoloured 2·75 2·75
DESIGNS: 15c. Queen Elizabeth at American Red Cross Club, London, 1944; 65c. Queen Mother at Remembrance Service, 1989; 70c. Queen Elizabeth, 1944; 80c. Queen Mother at Cheltenham Races, 2000.

256 Rice Bird and Rice

2002. Illustrations from *The Natural History of Carolina, Florida and the Bahama Islands* by Mark Catesby (1747). Multicoloured.
1289 15c. Type **256** 50 35
1290 25c. Alligator and red mangrove 60 40
1291 50c. Parrot fish . . . . . . 1·00 90
1292 65c. Ilathera duck and sea ox-eye . . . . 1·25 1·25
1293 70c. Flamingo and gorgonian coral . . . . 1·40 1·40
1294 80c. Crested bittern and inkberry . . . . 1·50 1·75

257 "While Shepherds watched their Flocks"

2002. Christmas. Scenes from Carols. Multicoloured.
1295 15c. Type **257** 40 25
1296 65c. "We Three Kings" . . 1·10 90
1297 70c. "Once in Royal David's City" . . . . 1·25 1·25
1298 80c. "I saw Three Ships" . . 1·40 1·60

258 Flamingo on Nest

2003. Inagua National Park Wetlands. Flamingos. Multicoloured.
1299 15c. Type **258** 40 35
1300 25c. Flock of flamingos feeding 60 45
1301 50c. Group of flamingos . . 1·00 90
1302 65c. Group of flamingos walking . . . . 1·25 1·25
1303 70c. Flamingos taking-off 1·25 1·40
1304 80c. Flamingos in flight . . 1·40 1·60

259 Captain Edward Teach ("Blackbeard")

260 Dinghies

2003. Pirates. Multicoloured.
1305 15c. Type **259** 40 35
1306 25c. Captain "Calico Jack" Rackham 60 45
1307 50c. Anne Bonney . . . . . 1·00 90
1308 65c. Captain Woodes Rogers . . . . 1·25 1·25
1309 70c. Sir John Hawkins . . . 1·25 1·40
1310 80c. Captain Bartholomew Roberts ("Black Bart") 1·40 1·60

2003. 50th Anniv of Family Island Regatta. Multicoloured.
1311 15c. Type **260** 10 10
1312 65c. *New Courageous* (racing sloop) 25 30
1313 70c. *New Susan Chase* (racing sloop) 30 35
1314 80c. *Tida Wave* (racing sloop) 35 40

2003. 50th Anniv of Coronation. As T **206** of Ascension. Multicoloured.
1315 65c. Queen with crown, orb and sceptre 25 30
1316 80c. Royal family on Buckingham Palace balcony 35 40
MS1317 95 × 115 mm. 15c. As 65c.; 70c. As 80c. 35 40
Nos. 1315/16 have red frame; stamps from **MS**874 have no frame and country name in mauve panel.

2003. Medicinal Plants (3rd series). As T **242**.
1318 15c. *Asystasia* 10 10
1319 65c. *Cassia* 25 30
1320 70c. *Lignum vitae* 30 35
1321 80c. Snowberry 35 40

2003. Centenary of Powered Flight. As T **209** of Ascension. Multicoloured.
1322 15c. Piper Cub 10 10
1323 25c. De Havilland Tiger Moth 10 15
1324 50c. Lockheed SR-71A Blackbird 20 25
1325 65c. Supermarine S6B . . . 25 30
1326 70c. North American P-51D Mustang "Miss America" 30 35
1327 80c. Douglas DC-3 Dakota 35 40

261 Interior with Stained Glass Window

2003. Christmas. St. Matthew's Church, Nassau. Multicoloured.
1328 15c. Type **261** 10 10
1329 65c. Church interior (horiz) 25 30
1330 70c. St. Matthew's Church (horiz) 30 35
1331 80c. Church tower 35 40

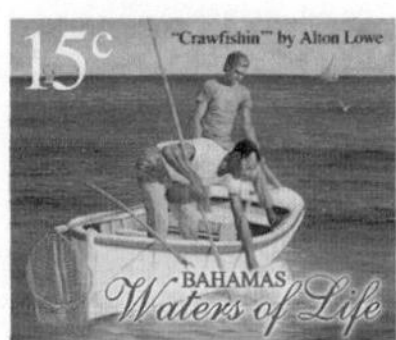
262 "Crawfishin"

2003. "Waters of Life". Paintings by Alton Lowe. Multicoloured.
1332 15c. Type **262** 10 10
1333 65c. "Summer" 25 30
1334 70c. "The Whelkers" . . . 30 35
1335 80c. "Annual Visit" 35 40

263 Egrets on Dead Tree

2004. Wetlands (2nd series). Harrold and Wilson Ponds, New Providence Island. Multicoloured.
1336 15c. Type **263** 15 20
1337 25c. Green-backed heron and duck 25 30
1338 50c. Birdwatchers in canoes 55 55
1339 65c. Egret and Bahama pintail ducks 70 75
1340 70c. Egret and Louisiana heron 75 80
1341 80c. Birdwatchers with binoculars and telescope 90 95

SPECIAL DELIVERY STAMPS

1916. Optd **SPECIAL DELIVERY**.
S2 **6** 5d. black and orange . . . . 45 7·50
S3 5d. black and mauve . . . . 30 2·75

BAHAWALPUR Pt. 1

A former Indian Feudatory state which joined Pakistan in 1947 and continued to use its own stamps until 1953.

12 pies = 1 anna, 16 annas = 1 rupee.

(1)

2 Amir Muhammad Bahawal Khan I Abbasi

1947. Nos. 265/8, 269a/77 and 259/62 of India optd with Type **1**.
1 **100a** 3p. slate . . . . 20·00
2 ½a. purple . . . . 20·00
3 9p. green . . . . 20·00
4 1a. red . . . . 20·00
5 **101** 1½a. violet . . . . 20·00
6 2a. red . . . . 20·00
7 3a. violet . . . . 20·00
8 3½a. blue . . . . 20·00
9 **102** 4a. brown . . . . 20·00
10 6a. green . . . . 20·00
11 8a. violet . . . . 20·00
12 12a. lake . . . . 20·00
13 – 14a. purple . . . . 60·00
14 **93** 1r. grey and brown . . . 23·00
15 2r. purple and brown . . £1200
16 5r. green and blue £1200
17 10r. purple and red . . . £1200

1948. Bicentenary Commemoration.
18 **2** ½a. black and red . . . . . 2·50 3·00

4 H. H. the Amir of Bahawalpur
5 The Tombs of the Amirs

1948.
19 **4** 3p. black and blue . . . . . 1·75 20·00
20 ½a. black and red . . . . . 1·75 20·00
21 9p. black and green . . . . 1·75 20·00
22 1a. black and red . . . . . 1·75 20·00
23 1½a. black and violet . . . . 1·75 16·00
24 **5** 2a. green and red . . . . . 2·00 20·00
25 – 4a. orange and brown . . . 2·25 20·00
26 – 6a. violet and blue . . . . . 2·25 20·00
27 – 8a. red and violet . . . . . 2·25 20·00
28 – 12a. green and red . . . . . 2·75 30·00
29 – 1r. violet and brown . . . . 19·00 42·00
35 – 1r. green and orange . . . . 1·50 18·00
30 – 2r. green and red . . . . . . 45·00 70·00
36 – 2r. black and red . . . . . . 1·75 22·00
31 – 5r. black and violet . . . . . 45·00 85·00
37 – 5r. brown and blue . . . . . 1·90 40·00
32 – 10r. red and black . . . . . 32·00 £100
38 – 10r. brown and green . . . . 2·00 45·00
DESIGNS—HORIZ: 6a. Fort Derawar from the lake; 8a. Nur-Mahal Palace; 12a. Sadiq-Garh Palace. 46 × 32 mm: 10r. Three generations of Rulers. VERT (As Type **5**): 4a. Mosque in Sadiq-Garh; 1, 2, 5r. H.H. the Amir of Bahawalpur.

12 H.H. the Amir of Bahawalpur and Mohammed Ali Jinnah

1948. 1st Anniv of Union with Pakistan.
33 **12** 1½a. red and green . . . . 1·50 3·00

13 Soldiers of 1848 and 1948
14 Irrigation

1948. Centenary of Multan Campaign.
34 **13** 1½a. black and red . . . . 1·25 9·00

1949. Silver Jubilee of Accession of H.H. the Amir of Bahawalpur.
39 **14** 3p. black and blue . . . . 10 8·00
40 – ½a. black and orange . . . 10 8·00

41 – 9p. black and green . . . . 10 8·00
42 – 1a. black and red . . . . . 10 8·00
DESIGNS: ½a. Wheat; 9p. Cotton; 1a. Sahiwal bull.

17 U.P.U. Monument, Berne

1949. 75th Anniv of U.P.U.
43 **17** 9p. black and green . . . 20 1·25
44 1a. black and mauve . . . . 20 1·25
45 1½a. black and orange . . . 20 1·25
46 2½a. black and blue . . . . 20 1·25

OFFICIAL STAMPS

O 4 Eastern White Pelicans

1945. As Type O 4 with Arabic opt.
O1 – ½a. black and green . . . 3·75 13·00
O2 – 1a. black and red . . . . 3·75 7·50
O7 – 1a. black and brown . . . 40·00 55·00
O3 – 2a. black and violet . . . 3·25 11·00
O4 **O 4** 4a. black and olive . . . 12·00 26·00
O5 – 8a. black and brown . . . 22·00 15·00
O6 – 1r. black and orange . . . 22·00 15·00
DESIGNS: ½a. Panjnad Weir; 1a. (No. O2), Camel and calf; 1a. (No. O7), Baggage camels; 2a. Blackbuck antelopes; 8a. Friday Mosque, Fort Derawar; 1r. Temple at Pattan Munara.

(O 8)

1945. Types as Nos. O1, etc., in new colours and without Arabic opt. (a) Surch as Type **O 8**.
O11 ½a. on 8a. black and purple (as No. O5) . . . . 5·50 4·50
O12 1½a. on 5r. black and orange (as No. O6) . . . . 40·00 11·00
O13 1½a. on 2r. black and blue (as No. O1) . . . . £120 8·00
(b) Optd **SERVICE** and Arabic inscription.
O14 ½a. black and red (as No. O1) . . . . 1·25 11·00
O15 1a. black and red (as No. O2) . . . . 2·00 13·00
O16 2a. black and orange (as No. O3) . . . . 3·25 45·00

1945. As Type 4 but inscr "SERVICE" at left.
O17 3p. black and blue . . . . . 3·50 8·00
O18 1½a. black and violet . . . . 20·00 8·00

O 11 Allied Banners

1946. Victory.
O19 **O 11** 1½a. green and grey . . 3·00 4·00

1948. Stamps of 1948 with Arabic opt as in Type **O 4**.
O20 **4** 3p. black and blue . . . . 80 12·00
O21 1a. black and red . . . . . 80 11·00
O22 **5** 2a. green and red . . . . 80 12·00
O23 – 4a. orange and brown . . . 80 16·00
O24 – 1r. green and orange . . . 80 18·00
O25 – 2r. black and red . . . . 80 24·00
O26 – 5r. chocolate and blue . . . 80 40·00
O27 – 10r. brown and green . . . 80 40·00

1949. 75th Anniv of U.P.U. optd as in Type O 4.
O28 **17** 9p. black and green . . . 15 4·50
O29 1a. black and mauve . . . . 15 4·50
O30 1½a. black and orange . . . 15 4·50
O31 2½a. black and blue . . . 15 4·50

BAHRAIN Pt. 1, Pt. 19

An archipelago in the Persian Gulf on the Arabian coast. An independent shaikhdom with Indian and later British postal administration. The latter was closed on 1 January 1966, when the Bahrain Post Office took over.

1933. 12 pies = 1 anna; 16 annas = 1 rupee.
1957. 100 naya paise = 1 rupee.

Stamps of India optd **BAHRAIN**.

1933. King George V.
1 **55** 3p. grey . . . . 3·50 45
2 **56** ½a. green . . . . 7·50 3·25
15 **79** ½a. green . . . . 4·50 1·25
3 **80** 9p. green . . . . 3·75 2·25
4 **57** 1a. brown . . . . 7·00 2·50
16 **81** 1a. brown . . . . 10·00 40
5 **82** 1a.3p. mauve . . . . 6·50 1·75
6 **70** 2a. orange . . . . 16·00 15·00
17 **59** 2a. orange . . . . 42·00 7·50
7 **62** 3a. blue . . . . 19·00 50·00
18 3a. red . . . . 4·75 50
8 **83** 3a.6p. blue . . . . 3·75 30
9 **71** 4a. green . . . . 18·00 48·00
19 **63** 4a. olive . . . . 4·75 40
10 **65** 8a. mauve . . . . 6·00 30
11 **66** 12a. red . . . . 7·50 1·25
12 **67** 1r. brown and green . . . . 16·00 7·50
13 2r. red and orange . . . . 28·00 35·00
14 5r. blue and violet £130 £140

1938. King George VI.
20 **91** 3p. slate . . . . 12·00 4·00
21 ½a. brown . . . . 7·00 10
22 9p. green . . . . 7·00 6·50
23 1a. red . . . . 7·00 10
24 **92** 2a. red . . . . 5·00 2·00
26 – 3a. green (No. 253) . . . 12·00 5·50
27 – 3a.6p. blue (No. 254) . . . 6·00 3·50
28 – 4a. brown (No. 255) . . . £130 70·00
30 – 8a. violet (No. 257) . . . £160 35·00
31 – 12a. red (No. 258) . . . £110 45·00
32 **93** 1r. slate and brown . . . 3·50 1·75
33 2r. purple and brown . . . 13·00 6·50
34 5r. green and blue . . . . 15·00 13·00
35 10r. purple and red . . . 65·00 35·00
36w 15r. brown and green . . . 50·00 55·00
37 25r. slate and purple . . . £100 85·00

1942. King George VI.
38 **100a** 3p. slate . . . . 2·50 1·50
39 ½a. mauve . . . . 4·25 2·00
40 9p. green . . . . 13·00 16·00
41 1a. red . . . . 4·50 60
42 **101** 1a.3p. bistre . . . . . . 8·50 18·00
43 1½a. violet . . . . 5·00 5·50
44 2a. red . . . . 6·00 1·50
45 3a. violet . . . . 18·50 5·50
46 3½a. blue . . . . 4·75 18·00
47 **102** 4a. brown . . . . 3·00 1·50
48 6a. green . . . . 14·00 9·00
49 8a. violet . . . . 4·50 3·00
50 12a. purple . . . . 7·50 4·25

Stamps of Great Britain surch **BAHRAIN** and new value in Indian currency.

1948. King George VI.
51 **128** ½a. on ½d. green . . . . 50 1·25
71 ½a. on ½d. orange . . . . 2·50 2·25
52 1a. on 1d. red . . . . . 50 1·75
72 1a. on 1d. blue . . . . . 3·00 20
53 1½a. on 1½d. brown . . . 50 2·50
73 1½a. on 1½d. green . . . 3·00 13·00
54 2a. on 2d. orange 50 20
74 2a. on 2d. brown . . . . 1·50 30
55 2½a. on 2½d. blue . . . . 50 3·25
75 2½a. on 2½d. red . . . . 3·00 13·00
56 3a. on 3d. violet 50 10
76 **129** 4a. on 4d. blue . . . . 3·00 1·50
57 6a. on 6d. purple 50 10
58 **130** 1r. on 1s. brown . . . . 1·25 10
59 **131** 2r. on 2s.6d. green . . . 5·50 4·75
60 5r. on 5s. red . . . . . 5·50 4·75
60a – 10r. on 10s. blue (No. 478a) . . . . . . 70·00 48·00

1948. Silver Wedding.
61 **137** 2½a. on 2½d. blue . . . . 1·00 1·00
62 **138** 15r. on £1 blue . . . . 30·00 48·00

1948. Olympic Games.
63 **139** 2½a. on 2½d. blue . . . . 1·00 3·25
64 **140** 3a. on 3d. violet . . . . 1·00 3·00
65 – 6a. on 6d. purple . . . . 1·50 3·00
66 – 1r. on 1s. brown . . . . 2·00 3·00

1949. U.P.U.
67 **143** 2½a. on 2½d. blue . . . . 40 2·25
68 **144** 3a. on 3d. violet . . . . 60 2·75
69 – 6a. on 6d. purple . . . . 50 3·00
70 – 1r. on 1s. brown . . . . 1·25 2·00

1951. Pictorial stamps (Nos. 509/11).
77 **147** 2r. on 2s.6d. green . . . 24·00 8·50
78 – 5r. on 5s. red . . . . . 13·00 3·75
79 – 10r. on 10s. blue . . . . 29·00 7·50

1952. Queen Elizabeth II.
97 **154** ½a. on ½d. orange 10 15
81 1a. on 1d. blue 10 10
82 1½a. on 1½d. green 10 30
83 2a. on 2d. brown 10 10
84 **155** 2½a. on 2½d. red . . . . 20 1·75
85 3a. on 3d. lilac . . . . . 3·00 10
86 4a. on 4d. blue . . . . . 9·50 30
99 **157** 6a. on 6d. purple 50 50
88 **160** 12a. on 1s.3d. green . . . 3·25 20
89 1r. on 1s.6d. blue . . . . 3·25 10

1953. Coronation.
90 **161** 2½a. on 2½d. red . . . . . 1·25 75
91 – 4a. on 4d. blue . . . . . 2·25 5·00
92 **163** 12a. on 1s.3d. green . . . 3·25 4·50
93 – 1r. on 1s.6d. blue . . . . 7·50 50

1955. Pictorial stamps (Nos. 595a/598a).
94 **166** 2r. on 2s.6d. brown . . . 5·50 2·00
95 – 5r. on 5s. red . . . . . . 13·00 2·75
96 – 10r. on 10s. blue . . . . . 20·00 2·75

1957. Queen Elizabeth II.
102 **157** 1n.p. on 5d. brown . . . 10 10
103 **154** 3n.p. on ½d. orange . . . 50 2·50
104 6n.p. on 1d. blue . . . . 50 2·50
105 9n.p. on 1½d. green . . . 50 2·75
106 12n.p. on 2d. pale brown 30 60
107 **155** 15n.p. on 2½d. red . . . 30 15
108 20n.p. on 3d. lilac 30 10
109 25n.p. on 4d. blue . . . . 1·25 2·50
110 **157** 40n.p. on 6d. purple . . . 40 10
111 50n.p. on 9d. olive . . . 3·75 4·50
112 75n.p. on 1s.3d. green . . 2·50 50

1957. World Scout Jubilee Jamboree.
113 **170** 15n.p. on 2½d. red 25 35
114 **171** 25n.p. on 4d. blue 30 35
115 – 75n.p. on 1s.3d. green . . 40 45

16 Shaikh Sulman bin Hamed al-Khalifa

1960.
117 **16** 5n.p. blue 10 10
118 15n.p. orange 10 10
119 20n.p. violet 10 10
120 30n.p. bistre 10 10
121 40n.p. grey 15 10
122 50n.p. green 15 10
123 75n.p. brown 30 15
124 – 1r. black . . . . 2·50 30
125 – 2r. red . . . . 3·00 2·25
126 – 5r. blue . . . . 5·00 3·00
127 – 10r. green . . . . 12·00 5·50
The rupee values are larger, 27 × 32½ mm.

18 Shaikh Isa bin Sulman al-Khalifa
19 Air Terminal, Muharraq

1964.
128 **18** 5n.p. blue 10 10
129 15n.p. orange 10 30
130 20n.p. violet 10 10
131 30n.p. bistre 10 10
132 40n.p. slate 15 10
133 50n.p. green 15 75
134 75n.p. brown 25 10
135 **19** 1r. black . . . . 9·00 2·25
136 2r. red . . . . 9·00 2·50
137 – 5r. blue . . . . 14·00 14·00
138 – 10r. myrtle . . . . 14·00 14·00
DESIGN—As Type **19**: 5r., 10r. Deep water harbour.

21 Sheikh Isa bin Sulman al-Khalifa
22 Ruler and Bahrain Airport

1966.
139 **21** 5f. green 10 10
140 10f. red 15 15
141 15f. blue 20 15
142 20f. purple 20 15
143 **22** 30f. black and green . . . 25 15
144 40f. black and blue 30 15
145 – 50f. black and red 55 25
146 – 75f. black and violet . . . 70 35
147 – 100f. blue and yellow . . . 2·00 90
148 – 200f. green and orange . . 8·00 1·90
149 – 500f. brown and yellow . . 6·75 3·25
150 – 1d. multicoloured . . . . 14·00 7·00
DESIGNS—As Type **22**: 50f., 75f. Ruler and Mina Sulman deep-water harbour. VERT (26½ × 42½ mm): 100f. Pearl-diving; 200f. Lanner falcon and horse-racing; 500f. Serving coffee, and ruler's palace. LARGER (37 × 52½ mm): 1d. Ruler, crest, date palm, horse, dhow, pearl necklace, mosque, coffee-pot and Bab-al-Bahrain (gateway).

23 Produce
24 W.H.O. Emblem and Map of Bahrain

1966. Trade Fair and Agricultural Show.
151 **23** 10f. turquoise and red . . 30 15
152 20f. lilac and green 65 35
153 40f. blue and brown . . . 1·40 50
154 200f. red and blue . . . . 6·50 3·75

1968. 20th Anniv of W.H.O.
155 **24** 20f. black and grey 60 45
156 40f. black and turquoise 2·00 1·10
157 150f. black and red . . . . 8·00 4·25

25 View of Isa Town

1968. Inauguration of Isa New Town. Mult.
158 50f. Type **25** . . . . 3·00 90
159 80f. Shopping centre . . . . 4·50 1·75
160 120f. Stadium . . . . . . 7·00 3·25
161 150f. Mosque . . . . 8·00 4·00

26 Symbol of Learning

1969. 50th Anniv of School Education in Bahrain.
162 **26** 40f. multicoloured . . . . 1·25 75
163 60f. multicoloured . . . . 2·40 1·25
164 150f. multicoloured . . . . 6·50 3·25

27 Dish Aerial and Map of Persian Gulf

1969. Opening of Satellite Earth Station, Ras Abu Jarjour. Multicoloured.
165 20f. Type **27** . . . . 2·00 50
166 40f. Dish aerial and palms (vert) . . . . 4·00 80
167 100f. Type **27** . . . . 9·00 3·25
168 150f. As 40f. . . . . 13·00 4·75

28 Arms, Map and Manama Municipality Building

1970. 2nd Arab Cities Organization Conf, Manama.
169 **28** 30f. multicoloured . . . . 1·25 1·25
170 150f. multicoloured . . . . 5·25 5·25

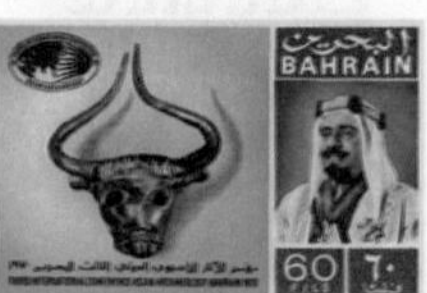

29 Copper Bull's Head, Barbar

1970. 3rd International Asian Archaeology Conference, Bahrain. Multicoloured.
171 60f. Type **29** . . . . 2·50 1·60
172 80f. Palace of Dilmun excavations . . . . 3·25 2·00
173 120f. Desert gravemounds . . 4·75 2·75
174 150f. Dilmun seal . . . . . 6·00 3·50

30 Vickers Super VC-10 Airliner, Big Ben, London, and Bahrain Minaret

1970. 1st Gulf Aviation Vickers Super VC-10 Flight, Doha–London.
175 **30** 30f. multicoloured . . . . 2·00 70
176 60f. multicoloured . . . . 4·50 1·50
177 120f. multicoloured . . . . 8·50 4·50

31 I.E.Y. Emblem and Open Book

1970. International Education Year. Multicoloured.
178 60f. Type **31** . . . . 1·75 1·40
179 120f. Emblem and Bahraini children . . . . 4·25 3·75

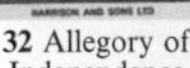

32 Allegory of Independence **34** Human Heart

33 Arab Dhow with Arab League and U.N. Emblems

1971. Independence Day and 10th Anniv of Ruler's Accession. Multicoloured.
180 30f. Type **32** . . . . 1·75 90
181 60f. Government House . . . 3·25 1·75
182 120f. Arms of Bahrain . . . 8·00 4·00
183 150f. Arms of Bahrain (gold background) . . . . 11·00 5·50

1972. Bahrain's Membership of Arab League and U.N. Multicoloured.
184 30f. Type **33** . . . . 3·00 95
185 60f. Type **33** . . . . 5·00 1·90
186 120f. Dhow sails (vert) . . . 6·00 4·00
187 150f. As 120f. . . . . 11·00 5·50

1972. World Health Day.
188 **34** 30f. multicoloured . . . . 2·00 2·00
189 60f. multicoloured . . . . 5·00 5·00

35 F.A.O. and U.N. Emblems

1973. 10th Anniv of World Food Programme.
190 **35** 30f. brown, red and green 2·75 2·75
191 60f. brown, lt brown & grn 5·00 5·00

36 "Races of the World"

1973. 25th Anniv of Declaration of Human Rights.
192 **36** 30f. blue, brown and black 2·00 1·00
193 60f. red, brown and black 3·50 2·50

38 Flour Mill

1973. National Day. "Progress in Bahrain". Mult.
195 30f. Type **38** . . . . 1·00 75
196 60f. Muharraq Airport . . . 2·50 1·00
197 120f. Sulmaniya Medical Centre . . . . 3·00 1·75
198 150f. Aluminium Smelter . . 3·50 3·00

39 U.P.U. Emblem within Letters

1974. Admission of Bahrain to U.P.U. Mult.
199 30f. Type **39** . . . . 1·50 55
200 60f. U.P.U. emblem on letters 2·50 90
201 120f. Ruler and emblem on dove with letter in beak (37×28 mm) . . . . . . 2·25 1·90
202 150f. As 120f. (37×28 mm) 3·25 2·75

40 Traffic Lights and Directing Hands

1974. International Traffic Day.
203 **40** 30f. multicoloured . . . . 1·75 1·60
204 60f. multicoloured . . . . 4·00 3·50

41 U.P.U. "Stamp" and Mail Transport

1974. Centenary of U.P.U.
205 **41** 30f. multicoloured 70 50
206 60f. multicoloured . . . . 1·25 90
207 120f. multicoloured . . . . 2·25 1·60
208 150f. multicoloured . . . . 2·75 1·90

42 Emblem and Sitra Power Station **43** Costume and Headdress

1974. National Day. Multicoloured.
209 30f. Type **42** 55 50
210 60f. Type **42** 95 85
211 120f. Emblem and Bahrain Dry Dock . . . . 2·50 2·00
212 150f. As 120f. . . . . 3·25 2·50

1975. Bahrain Women's Costumes.
213 **43** 30f. multicoloured 60 50
214 – 60f. multicoloured . . . . 1·25 1·10
215 – 120f. multicoloured . . . . 2·00 1·90
216 – 150f. multicoloured . . . . 2·50 2·40
DESIGNS: Nos. 214/16, Costumes as Type **43**.

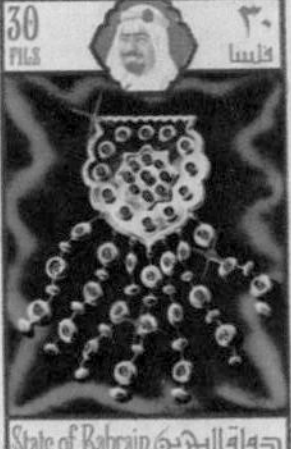

44 Jewelled Pendant **45** Women planting "Flower"

1975. Costume Jewellery. Multicoloured.
217 30f. Type **44** 60 50
218 60f. Gold crown . . . . . . 1·25 1·10
219 120f. Jewelled necklace . . . 2·00 1·90
220 150f. Gold necklace . . . . 2·50 2·40

1975. International Women's Year. Multicoloured.
221 30f. Type **45** . . . . 1·50 75
222 60f. Woman holding I.W.Y. emblem . . . . 3·00 1·75

46 Head of Horse

1975. Horses. Multicoloured.
223a 60f. Type **46** . . . . 4·00 4·00
223b 60f. Grey . . . . 4·00 4·00
223c 60f. Grey with foal (horiz) 4·00 4·00
223d 60f. Close-up of Arab with grey . . . . 4·00 4·00
223e 60f. Grey and herd of browns (horiz) . . . . . 4·00 4·00
223f 60f. Grey and brown (horiz) 4·00 4·00
223g 60f. Arabs riding horses (horiz) . . . . 4·00 4·00
223h 60f. Arab leading grey beside sea (horiz) . . . . 4·00 4·00

47 National Flag **48** Map of Bahrain within Cog and Laurel

1976.
224 **47** 5f. red, pink and blue . . 15 10
225 10f. red, pink & green . . 15 10
226 15f. red, pink & black . . 15 15
227 20f. red, pink & brown 15 15
227a **48** 25f. black and grey . . . 20 15
228 40f. black and blue . . . 20 15
228a 50f. green, black & olive 25 15
228b 60f. black and green . . . 30 20
229 80f. black and mauve . . 45 30
229b 100f. black and red . . . 55 45
230 150f. black and yellow . . 90 85
231 200f. black and yellow . . 1·10 1·00

49 Concorde Taking off

1976. 1st Commercial Flight of Concorde. Mult.
232 80f. Type **49** . . . . 2·25 2·00
233 80f. Concorde landing . . . 2·25 2·00
234 80f. Concorde en route . . . 2·25 2·00
235 80f. Concorde on runway . . 2·25 2·00

50 Soldier, Crest and Flag **52** Shaikh Isa bin Sulman al-Khalifa

51 King Khalid of Saudi Arabia and Shaikh of Bahrain with National Flags

1976. Defence Force Cadets' Day.
237 **50** 40f. multicoloured . . . . 1·40 1·25
238 80f. multicoloured . . . . 2·50 2·25

1976. Visit to Bahrain of King Khalid of Saudi Arabia.
239 **51** 40f. multicoloured . . . . 1·50 1·25
240 80f. multicoloured . . . . 3·00 2·50

1976.
241 **52** 300f. green and pale green 2·25 1·60
242 400f. purple and pink . . 3·00 2·25
243 500f. blue and pale blue 3·75 3·00
244 1d. black and grey . . . 7·50 4·75
244a 2d. violet and lilac . . . 15·00 11·00
244b 3d. brown and pink . . . 23·00 17·00

53 Ministry of Housing Emblem, Designs for Houses and Mosque **54** A.P.U. Emblem

1976. National Day.
245 **53** 40f. multicoloured . . . . 1·25 1·00
246 80f. multicoloured . . . . 2·75 1·75

1977. 25th Anniv of Arab Postal Union.
247 **54** 40f. multicoloured . . . . 1·25 1·00
248 80f. multicoloured . . . . 2·75 1·75

55 Dogs on Beach

1977. Saluki Dogs. Multicoloured.
249a 80f. Type **55** . . . . 2·40 2·40
249b 80f. Dog and dromedaries 2·40 2·40
249c 80f. Dog and antelope . . . 2·40 2·40
249d 80f. Dog on lawn of building . . . . 2·40 2·40
249e 80f. Head of dog . . . . . 2·40 2·40
249f 80f. Heads of two dogs . . 2·40 2·40
249g 80f. Dog in scrubland . . . 2·40 2·40
249h 80f. Dogs fighting . . . . . 2·40 2·40

56 Arab Students and Candle

1977. International Literacy Day.
250 **56** 40f. multicoloured . . . . 1·25 1·00
251 80f. multicoloured . . . . 2·75 1·75

57 Shipyard Installations and Arab Flags

1977. Inauguration of Arab Shipbuilding and Repair Yard Co.
252 **57** 40f. multicoloured 1·25 1·00
253 80f. multicoloured 2·75 1·75

58 Microwave Antenna

1978. 10th World Telecommunications Day.
254 **58** 40f. multicoloured 1·25 1·00
255 80f. silver, dp blue & blue 2·75 1·75

59 Child being helped to Walk

60 Boom Dhow

1979. International Year of the Child. Mult.
256 50f. Type **59** 1·00 80
257 100f. Hands protecting child 2·50 1·60

1979. Dhows. Multicoloured.
258 100f. Type **60** 2·60 2·40
259 100f. Baghla 2·60 2·40
260 100f. Shu'ai (horiz) 2·60 2·40
261 100f. Ghanja (horiz) 2·60 2·40
262 100f. Kotia 2·60 2·40
263 100f. Sambuk 2·60 2·40
264 100f. Jaliboot (horiz) 2·60 2·40
265 100f. Zarook (horiz) 2·60 2·40

61 Dome of Mosque, Mecca

1980. 1400th Anniv of Hejira.
266 **61** 50f. multicoloured 65 40
267 100f. multicoloured 1·60 1·25
268 150f. multicoloured 1·90 1·50
269 200f. multicoloured 2·50 2·00

62 Arab with Gyr Falcon

1980. Falconry. Multicoloured.
271 100f. Type **62** 2·75 1·60
272 100f. Arab looking at Lanner falcon on wrist 2·75 1·60
273 100f. Peregrine falcon resting with outstretched wings 2·75 1·60
274 100f. Peregrine falcon in flight 2·75 1·60
275 100f. Gyr falcon on pillar (with camels in background) (vert) 2·75 1·60
276 100f. Gyr falcon on pillar (closer view) (vert) 2·75 1·60
277 100f. Close-up of gyr falcon facing right (vert) 2·75 1·60
278 100f. Close-up of Lanner falcon full-face (vert) 2·75 1·60

63 Map and I.Y.D.P. Emblem

1981. International Year for Disabled Persons.
279 **63** 50f. multicoloured 1·25 75
280 100f. multicoloured 2·25 1·75

64 Jubilee Emblem

1981. 50th Anniv of Electrical Power in Bahrain.
281 **64** 50f. multicoloured 1·25 75
282 100f. multicoloured 2·25 1·75

65 Carving

66 Mosque

1981. Handicrafts. Multicoloured.
283 50f. Type **65** 55 45
284 100f. Pottery 1·00 90
285 150f. Weaving 1·90 1·60
286 200f. Basket-making 2·25 2·10

1981. Mosques.
287 **66** 50f. multicoloured 70 55
288 – 100f. multicoloured 1·40 1·10
289 – 150f. multicoloured 2·00 1·75
290 – 200f. multicoloured 2·75 2·50
DESIGNS: 100f. to 200f. As Type **66** but showing different mosques.

67 Shaikh Isa bin Sulman al-Khalifa

69 Flags and Clasped Hands encircling Emblem

68 Dorcas Gazelle

1981. 20th Anniv of Coronation of Shaikh Isa bin Sulman al-Khalifa.
291 **67** 15f. gold, grey and mauve 25 20
292 50f. gold, grey and red 55 45
293 100f. gold, grey and brown 1·10 95
294 150f. gold, grey and blue 1·75 1·40
295 200f. gold, grey and blue 2·10 2·10

1982. Al-Areen Wildlife Park. Multicoloured.
296 100f. Goitred gazelle 1·75 1·75
297 100f. Type **68** 1·75 1·75
298 100f. Dhub lizard 1·75 1·75
299 100f. Brown hares 1·75 1·75
300 100f. Arabian oryx 1·75 1·75
301 100f. Addax 1·75 1·75

1982. 3rd Supreme Council Session of Gulf Co-operation Council.
302 **69** 50f. multicoloured 65 50
303 – 100f. multicoloured 1·40 1·10

70 Madinat Hamad

1983. Opening of Madinat Hamad New Town. Multicoloured.
304 50f. Type **70** 65 50
305 100f. View of Madinat Hamad (different) 1·40 1·10

71 Shaikh Isa bin Sulman al-Khalifa

1983. Bicentenary of Al-Khalifa Dynasty. Mult.
306 100f. Type **71** 70 70
307 100f. Cartouche of Ali bin Khalifa al-Khalifa 70 70
308 100f. Isa bin Ali al-Khalifa 70 70
309 100f. Hamad bin Isa al-Khalifa 70 70
310 100f. Salman bin Hamad al-Khalifa 70 70
311 100f. Cartouche of Ahmed bin Mohammed al-Khalifa 70 70
312 100f. Cartouche of Salman bin Ahmed al-Khalifa 70 70
313 100f. Cartouche of Abdullah bin Ahmed al-Khalifa 70 70
314 100f. Cartouche of Mohammed bin Khalifa al-Khalifa 70 70

72 G.C.C. and Traffic and Licensing Directorate Emblems

1984. Gulf Co-operation Council Traffic Week.
316 **72** 15f. multicoloured 25 20
317 50f. multicoloured 80 40
318 100f. multicoloured 1·25 75

73 Hurdling

1984. Olympic Games, Los Angeles. Multicoloured.
319 15f. Type **73** 20 20
320 50f. Show-jumping 70 55
321 100f. Swimming 1·25 1·10
322 150f. Fencing 1·75 1·50
323 200f. Shooting 2·40 2·25

74 Manama and Emblem

1984. Centenary of Postal Services.
324 **74** 15f. multicoloured 35 20
325 50f. multicoloured 1·00 50
326 100f. multicoloured 1·75 95

75 Narrow-barred Spanish Mackerel

1985. Fishes. Multicoloured.
327 100f. Type **75** 1·40 1·00
328 100f. Crocodile needlefish (three fishes) 1·40 1·00
329 100f. Sombre sweetlips (fish swimming to left, blue and lilac background) 1·40 1·00
330 100f. White-spotted rabbitfish (two fishes, blue and lilac background) 1·40 1·00
331 100f. Grey mullet (two fishes, green and pink background) 1·40 1·00
332 100f. Two-banded seabream (green and grey background) 1·40 1·00
333 100f. River seabream (blue background) 1·40 1·00
334 100f. Malabar grouper (green background) 1·40 1·00
335 100f. Small-toothed emperor (pink anemone background) 1·40 1·00
336 100f. Golden trevally (fish swimming to right, blue and lilac background) 1·40 1·00

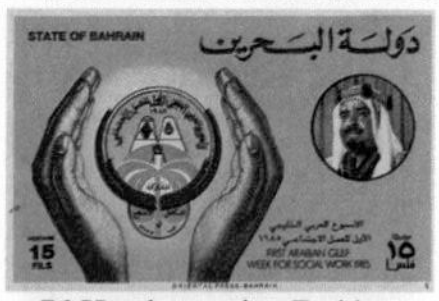

76 Hands cupping Emblem

1985. Arabian Gulf States Social Work Week.
337 **76** 15f. multicoloured 20 15
338 50f. multicoloured 60 40
339 100f. multicoloured 1·00 70

77 I.Y.Y. Emblem

1986. International Youth Year.
340 **77** 15f. multicoloured 20 15
341 50f. multicoloured 60 40
342 100f. multicoloured 1·00 70

78 Aerial View of Causeway

1986. Opening of Saudi–Bahrain Causeway. Mult.
343 15f. Type **78** 25 20
344 50f. Aerial view of island 60 40
345 100f. Aerial view of road bridge 1·00 70

79 Shaikh Isa bin Sulman al-Khalifa

1986. 25th Anniv of Accession of Shaikh Isa bin Sulman al-Khalifa.
346 **79** 15f. multicoloured 25 20
347 50f. multicoloured 60 40
348 100f. multicoloured 1·00 70

80 Emblem

1988. 40th Anniv of W.H.O.
350 **80** 50f. multicoloured 40 25
351 150f. multicoloured 1·25 90

81 Centre

1988. Opening of Ahmed al-Fateh Islamic Centre.
352 **81** 50f. multicoloured 40 25
353 150f. multicoloured 1·25 90

82 Running

1988. Olympic Games, Seoul. Multicoloured.
354 50f. Type **82** 30 20
355 80f. Dressage 60 40
356 150f. Fencing 1·10 80
357 200f. Football 1·90 1·40

83 Emblem in "1988"

1988. 9th Supreme Council Meeting of Gulf Co-operation Council.

No.	Type	Description	Unused	Used
358	83	50f. multicoloured	35	25
359		150f. multicoloured	1·25	90

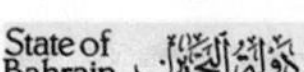

84 Arab leading Camel

85 Shaikh Isa bin Sulman al-Khalifa

1989. Camels. Multicoloured.

No.	Type	Description	Unused	Used
360		150f. Type **84**	1·00	1·00
361		150f. Arab leading camel (different)	1·00	1·00
362		150f. Head of camel and pump-head	1·00	1·00
363		150f. Close-up of Arab on camel	1·00	1·00
364		150f. Arab riding camel	1·00	1·00
365		150f. Two Arab camel-riders	1·00	1·00
366		150f. Head of camel and camel-rider (horiz)	1·00	1·00
367		150f. Camels at rest in camp (horiz)	1·00	1·00
368		150f. Camels with calf (horiz)	1·00	1·00
369		150f. Heads of three camels (horiz)	1·00	1·00
370		150f. Camel in scrubland (horiz)	1·00	1·00
371		150f. Arab on camel (horiz)	1·00	1·00

1989. Multicoloured, colour of frame given.

No.	Type	Description	Unused	Used
372	85	25f. green	20	10
373		40f. grey	30	10
374		50f. pink	30	10
375		60f. brown	40	15
376		75f. mauve	50	15
377		80f. green	50	15
378		100f. orange	70	25
379		120f. violet	80	25
380		150f. grey	1·00	35
381		200f. blue	1·25	45

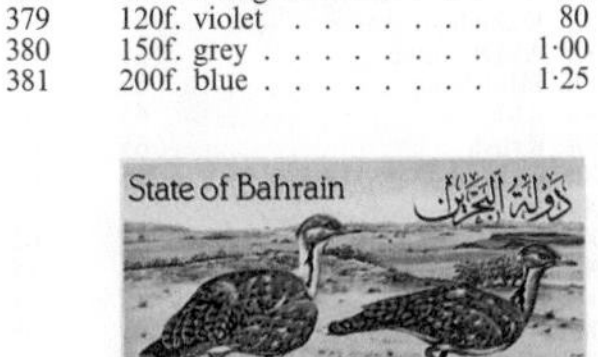

86 Houbara Bustards

1990. The Houbara Bustard. Multicoloured.

No.	Type	Description	Unused	Used
383		150f. Type **86**	1·00	1·00
384		150f. Two bustards (facing each other)	1·00	1·00
385		150f. Chicks and eggs	1·00	1·00
386		150f. Adult and chick	1·00	1·00
387		150f. Adult (vert)	1·00	1·00
388		150f. In flight	1·00	1·00
389		150f. Adult (facing right)	1·00	1·00
390		150f. Young bird (vert)	1·00	1·00
391		150f. Adult (facing left)	1·00	1·00
392		150f. Bird in display plumage	1·00	1·00
393		150f. Two bustards in display plumage	1·00	1·00
394		150f. Two bustards with bridge in background	1·00	1·00

87 Anniversary Emblem

1990. 40th Anniv of Gulf Air.

No.	Type	Description	Unused	Used
395	87	50f. multicoloured	35	25
396		80f. multicoloured	55	35
397		150f. multicoloured	1·00	75
398		200f. multicoloured	1·40	95

88 Anniversary Emblem

1990. 50th Anniv of Bahrain Chamber of Commerce and Industry.

No.	Type	Description	Unused	Used
399	88	50f. multicoloured	30	20
400		80f. multicoloured	50	35
401		150f. multicoloured	95	65
402		200f. multicoloured	1·25	85

89 I.L.Y. Emblem

1990. International Literacy Year.

No.	Type	Description	Unused	Used
403	89	50f. multicoloured	30	20
404		80f. multicoloured	50	35
405		150f. multicoloured	95	65
406		200f. multicoloured	1·25	85

90 Crested Lark

1991. Birds. Multicoloured.

No.	Type	Description	Unused	Used
407		150f. Type **90**	90	90
408		150f. Hoopoe ("Upupa epops")	90	90
409		150f. White-cheeked bulbul ("Pycnonotus leucogenys")	90	90
410		150f. Turtle dove ("Streptopelia turtur")	90	90
411		150f. Collared dove ("Streptopelia decaocto")	90	90
412		150f. Common kestrel ("Falco tinnunculus")	90	90
413		150f. House sparrow ("Passer domesticus") (horiz)	90	90
414		150f. Great grey shrike ("Lanius excubitor") (horiz)	90	90
415		150f. Rose-ringed parakeet ("Psittacula krameri")	90	90

91 Shaikh Isa bin Sulman al-Khalifa

1991. 30th Anniv of Amir's Coronation.

No.	Type	Description	Unused	Used
416	91	50f. multicoloured	30	20
417	A	50f. multicoloured	30	20
418	91	80f. multicoloured	45	30
419	A	80f. multicoloured	45	30
420	91	150f. multicoloured	90	60
421	A	150f. multicoloured	90	60
422	91	200f. multicoloured	1·10	75
423	A	200f. multicoloured	1·10	75

DESIGN: A, The Amir and sunburst.

92 White Stork ("Ciconia ciconia")

1992. Migratory Birds. Multicoloured.

No.	Type	Description	Unused	Used
425		150f. Type **92**	80	80
426		150f. European bee eater ("Merops apiaster")	80	80
427		150f. Common starling ("Sturnus vulgaris")	80	80
428		150f. Grey hypocolius ("Hypocolius ampelinus")	80	80
429		150f. European cuckoo ("Cuculus canorus")	80	80
430		150f. Mistle thrush ("Turdus viscivorus")	80	80
431		150f. European roller ("Coracias garrulus")	80	80
432		150f. Eurasian goldfinch ("Carduelis carduelis")	80	80
433		150f. Red-backed shrike ("Lanius collurio")	80	80
434		150f. Redwing ("Turdus iliacus") (horiz)	80	80
435		150f. Pied wagtail ("Motacilla alba") (horiz)	80	80
436		150f. Golden oriole ("Oriolus oriolus") (horiz)	80	80
437		150f. European robin ("Erithacus rubecula")	80	80
438		150f. Nightingale ("Luscinia luscinia")	80	80
439		150f. Spotted flycatcher ("Muscicapa striata")	80	80
440		150f. Barn swallow ("Hirundo rustica")	80	80

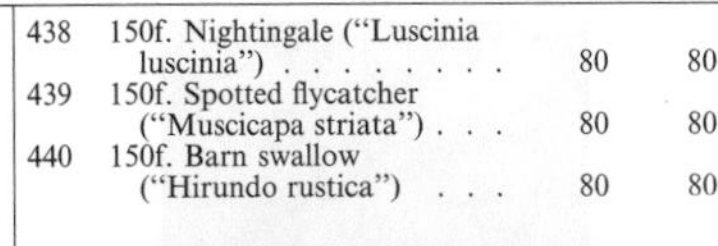

93 Start of Race

1992. Horse-racing. Multicoloured.

No.	Type	Description	Unused	Used
441		150f. Type **93**	80	80
442		150f. Parading in paddock	80	80
443		150f. Galloping around bend	80	80
444		150f. Galloping past national flags	80	80
445		150f. Galloping past spectator stand	80	80
446		150f. Head-on view of horses	80	80
447		150f. Reaching winning post	80	80
448		150f. A black and a grey galloping	80	80

94 Show-jumping

1992. Olympic Games, Barcelona. Multicoloured.

No.	Type	Description	Unused	Used
449		50f. Type **94**	30	20
450		80f. Running	45	30
451		150f. Karate	85	55
452		200f. Cycling	1·10	75

95 Airport

1992. 60th Anniv of Bahrain International Airport.

No.	Type	Description	Unused	Used
453	95	50f. multicoloured	30	20
454		80f. multicoloured	45	30
455		150f. multicoloured	85	55
456		200f. multicoloured	1·10	75

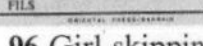

96 Girl skipping **98** Artillery Gun Crew

97 Cable-cars and Pylons

1992. Children's Paintings. Multicoloured.

No.	Type	Description	Unused	Used
457		50f. Type **96**	30	20
458		80f. Women	45	30
459		150f. Women preparing food (horiz)	85	55
460		200f. Pearl divers (horiz)	1·40	75

1992. Expansion of Aluminium Industry. Mult.

No.	Type	Description	Unused	Used
461		50f. Type **97**	30	20
462		80f. Worker in aluminium plant	45	30
463		150f. Aerial view of aluminium plant	85	55
464		200f. Processed aluminium	1·10	75

1993. 25th Anniv of Bahrain Defence Force. Mult.

No.	Type	Description	Unused	Used
465		50f. Type **98**	25	15
466		80f. General Dynamics Fighting Falcon jet fighters, tanks and patrol boat	40	25
467		150f. "Ahmed al Fatah" (missile corvette) (horiz)	75	50
468		200f. Fighting Falcon over Bahrain (horiz)	1·00	65

99 Satellite View of Bahrain **100** Purple Heron

1993. World Meteorological Day. Multicoloured.

No.	Type	Description	Unused	Used
469		50f. Type **99**	30	20
470		150f. Satellite picture of world (horiz)	75	60
471		200f. Earth seen from space	1·25	85

1993. Water Birds. Multicoloured.

No.	Type	Description	Unused	Used
472		150f. Type **100**	90	90
473		150f. Moorhen ("Gallinula chloropus")	90	90
474		150f. Socotra cormorant ("Phalacrocorax nigrogularis")	90	90
475		150f. Crab plover ("Dromas ardeola")	90	90
476		150f. River kingfisher ("Alcedo atthis")	90	90
477		150f. Northern lapwing ("Vanellus vanellus")	90	90
478		150f. Oystercatcher ("Haematopus ostralegus") (horiz)	90	90
479		150f. Black-crowned night heron ("Nycticorax nycticorax")	90	90
480		150f. Caspian tern ("Sterna caspia") (horiz)	90	90
481		150f. Ruddy turnstone ("Arenaria interpres") (horiz)	90	90
482		150f. Water rail ("Rallus aquaticus") (horiz)	90	90
483		150f. Mallard ("Anas platyrhyncos) (horiz)	90	90
484		150f. Lesser black-backed gull ("Larus fuscus") (horiz)	90	90

101 Fawn

1993. The Goitered Gazelle. Multicoloured.

No.	Type	Description	Unused	Used
485		25f. Type **101**	15	10
486		50f. Doe walking	25	15
487		50f. Doe with ears pricked	25	15
488		150f. Male gazelle	75	60

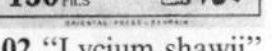

102 "Lycium shawii" **103** Children and Silhouettes of Parents' Heads

1993. Wild Flowers. Multicoloured.

No.	Type	Description	Unused	Used
489		150f. Type **102**	75	75
490		150f. "Alhagi maurorum"	75	75
491		150f. Caper-bush ("Caparis spinosa")	75	75
492		150f. "Cistanche phelypae"	75	75
493		150f. "Asphodelus tenuifolius"	75	75
494		150f. "Limonium axillare"	75	75
495		150f. "Cynomorium coccineum"	75	75
496		150f. "Calligonum polygonoides"	75	75

1994. International Year of the Family.

No.	Type	Description	Unused	Used
497	103	50f. multicoloured	20	15
498		80f. multicoloured	30	20
499		150f. multicoloured	65	45
500		200f. multicoloured	80	55

104 "Lepidochrysops arabicus" **105** Anniversary Emblem

1994. Butterflies. Multicoloured.
501 50f. Type **104** 20 20
502 50f. "Ypthima bolanica" . . 20 20
503 50f. Desert grass yellow ("Eurema brigitta") . . . 20 20
504 50f. "Precis limnoria" 20 20
505 50f. Small tortoiseshell ("Aglais urticae") 20 20
506 50f. Protomedia ("Colotis protomedia") 20 20
507 50f. Clouded mother-of-pearl (Salamis anacardii") . . . 20 20
508 50f. "Byblia ilithyia" 20 20
509 150f. Swallowtail ("Papilio machaon") (horiz) 65 65
510 150f. Blue ("Agrodiaetus loewii") (horiz) 65 65
511 150f. Painted lady ("Vanessa cardui") (horiz) 65 65
512 150f. Chequered swallowtail ("Papilio demoleus") (horiz) 65 65
513 150f. Guineafowl ("Hamanumida daedalus") (horiz) 65 65
514 150f. "Funonia orithya" (horiz) 65 65
515 150f. "Funonia chorimine" (horiz) 65 65
516 150f. "Colias croceus" (horiz) 65 65

1994. 75th Anniv of International Red Cross and Red Crescent.
517 **105** 50f. multicoloured 20 15
518 80f. multicoloured 30 20
519 150f. multicoloured . . . 65 45
520 200f. multicoloured . . . 80 55

106 Goalkeeper

1994. World Cup Football Championship, U.S.A. Multicoloured.
521 50f. Type **106** 20 15
522 80f. Players 30 20
523 150f. Players' legs 65 45
524 200f. Player on ground . . . 80 55

107 Earth Station

1994. 25th Anniv of Ras Abu Jarjour Satellite Earth Station.
525 **107** 50f. multicoloured 20 15
526 80f. multicoloured 30 20
527 150f. multicoloured . . . 65 45
528 200f. multicoloured . . . 80 55

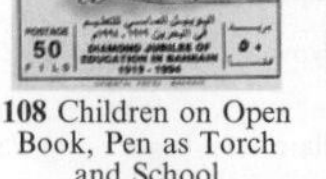

108 Children on Open Book, Pen as Torch and School **109** Dove with "Olive Branch" of Members' Flags

1994. 75th Anniv of Education in Bahrain.
529 **108** 50f. multicoloured 20 15
530 80f. multicoloured 30 20
531 150f. multicoloured . . . 65 45
532 200f. multicoloured . . . 80 55

1994. 15th Gulf Co-operation Council Supreme Council Session, Bahrain.
533 **109** 50f. multicoloured 20 15
534 80f. multicoloured 30 20
535 150f. multicoloured . . . 65 45
536 200f. multicoloured . . . 80 55

110 Date Palm in Bloom

1995. The Date Palm.
537 80f. Type **110** 25 15
538 100f. Date palm with unripened dates 35 25
539 200f. Dates ripening 65 45
540 250f. Date palm trees with ripened dates 80 55

111 Campaign Emblem

1995. World Health Day. Anti-poliomyelitis Campaign.
542 **111** 80f. multicoloured 25 15
543 200f. multicoloured . . . 65 45
544 250f. multicoloured . . . 80 55

112 Exhibition Emblem **114** Headquarters, Cairo

113 Crops

1995. 1st National Industries Exhibition.
545 **112** 80f. multicoloured 25 15
546 200f. multicoloured . . . 65 45
547 250f. multicoloured . . . 80 55

1995. 50th Anniv of F.A.O. Multicoloured.
548 80f. Type **113** 25 15
549 200f. Field of crops 65 45
550 250f. Field of cabbages . . . 80 55

1995. 50th Anniv of Arab League.
551 **114** 80f. multicoloured 25 15
552 200f. multicoloured . . . 65 45
553 250f. multicoloured . . . 80 55

115 U.N. Headquarters and Map of Bahrain

1995. 50th Anniv of U.N.O.
554 **115** 80f. multicoloured 25 15
555 100f. multicoloured . . . 35 25
556 200f. multicoloured . . . 65 45
557 250f. multicoloured . . . 80 55

116 Tower

1995. Traditional Architecture. Multicoloured.
558 200f. Type **116** 65 65
559 200f. Balcony 65 65
560 200f. Doorway 65 65
561 200f. Multi-storied facade . . 65 65
562 200f. Entrance flanked by two windows 65 65
563 200f. Three arched windows 65 65

117 National Flag and Shaikh Isa Bin Sulman al-Khalifa **118** Bookcase and Open Book

1995. National Day.
564 **117** 80f. multicoloured 25 15
565 100f. multicoloured . . . 35 25
566 200f. multicoloured . . . 65 45
567 250f. multicoloured . . . 85 55

1996. 50th Anniv of Public Library.
568 **118** 80f. multicoloured 25 15
569 200f. multicoloured . . . 65 45
570 250f. multicoloured . . . 85 55

119 Divers on Dhow

1996. Pearl Diving. Multicoloured.
571 80f. Type **119** 40 15
572 100f. Divers 70 25
573 200f. Diver on sea-bed and dhow . . . . 1·00 45
574 250f. Diver with net 85 55

120 Globe, Ship and Olympic Rings

1996. Olympic Games, Atlanta.
576 **120** 80f. multicoloured 25 15
577 100f. multicoloured . . . 35 25
578 200f. multicoloured . . . 65 45
579 250f. multicoloured . . . 85 55

121 Interpol Emblem and Map, Arms and Flag of Bahrain

1996. 24th Anniv of Membership of International Criminal Police (Interpol).
580 **121** 80f. multicoloured 25 15
581 100f. multicoloured . . . 35 25
582 200f. multicoloured . . . 65 45
583 250f. multicoloured . . . 85 55

122 Anniversary Emblems in English and Arabic

1996. 25th Anniv of Aluminium Bahrain.
584 **122** 80f. multicoloured 25 15
585 100f. multicoloured . . . 30 20
586 200f. multicoloured . . . 65 45
587 250f. multicoloured . . . 80 55

123 National Flag, Map and Shaikh Isa bin Sulman al-Khalifa

1996. 35th Anniv of Amir's Accession.
588 **123** 80f. multicoloured 25 15
589 100f. multicoloured . . . 30 20
590 200f. multicoloured . . . 65 45
591 250f. multicoloured . . . 80 55

124 Tanker, Refinery and Storage Tanks

1997. 60th Anniv of Bahrain Refinery.
592 **124** 80f. multicoloured 25 20
593 200f. multicoloured . . . 65 50
594 250f. multicoloured . . . 85 70

125 Kuheilaan Weld umm Zorayr

1997. Arab Horses at Amiri Stud. Multicoloured.
595 200f. Musannaan (white horse), Al-Jellabieh and Rabdaan 65 65
596 200f. Type **125** 65 65
597 200f. Al-Jellaby 65 65
598 200f. Musannaan (brown horse) 65 65
599 200f. Kuheilaan Aladiyat . . 65 65
600 200f. Kuheilaan Aafas . . . 65 65
601 200f. Al-Dhahma 65 65
602 200f. Mlolshaan 65 65
603 200f. Al-Kray 65 65
604 200f. Krush 65 65
605 200f. Al Hamdaany 65 65
606 200f. Hadhfaan 65 65
607 200f. Rabda 65 65
608 200f. Al-Suwaitieh 65 65
609 200f. Al-Obeyah 65 65
610 200f. Al-Shuwaimeh 65 65
611 200f. Al-Ma'anaghieh 65 65
612 200f. Al-Tuwaisah 65 65
613 200f. Wadhna 65 65
614 200f. Al-Saqlawieh 65 65
615 200f. Al-Shawafah 65 65

126 Championship Emblem

1997. 9th World Men's Junior Volleyball Championship.
616 **126** 80f. multicoloured 25 15
617 100f. multicoloured . . . 30 20
618 200f. multicoloured . . . 65 45
619 250f. multicoloured . . . 80 55

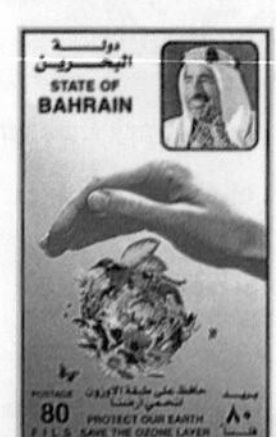

127 Emblem

1997. 10th Anniv of Montreal Protocol (on reduction of use of chlorofluorocarbons).
620 **127** 80f. multicoloured 25 15
621 100f. multicoloured . . . 30 20
622 200f. multicoloured . . . 65 45
623 250f. multicoloured . . . 80 55

128 Close-up of Support

1997. Inauguration of Shaikh Isa bin Salman Bridge between Manama and Muharraq. Multicoloured.
624 80f. Type **128** 25 15
625 200f. Distant view of middle section 65 45
626 250f. View of complete bridge (75 × 26 mm) 80 55

129 Complex at Night

1998. Inauguration of Urea Plant at Gulf Petrochemical Industries Co Complex. Mult.
628 80f. Type **129** 25 15
629 200f. Refining towers 65 45
630 250f. Aerial view of complex 80 55

130 Map of Bahrain and Anniversary Emblem

1998. 50th Anniv of W.H.O.
631 **130** 80f. multicoloured 25 15
632 200f. multicoloured . . . 65 45
633 250f. multicoloured . . . 80 55

131 Emblem

1998. World Cup Football Championship, France. Multicoloured.
634 80f. Type **131** 25 15
635 200f. Globes and football forming "98" (vert) 65 45
636 250f. Footballers and globe (vert) 80 55

132 Football

1998. 14th Arabian Gulf Cup Football Championship, Bahrain. Multicoloured.
637 80f. Type **132** 25 15
638 200f. Close-up of football . . 65 45
639 250f. As No. 638 . . . . . . 85 55

133 Emblem and Koran

1999. Holy Koran Reading Competition.
640 **133** 100f. multicoloured . . . 30 20
641 200f. multicoloured . . . 65 45
642 250f. multicoloured . . . 85 55

134 Shaikh Isa bin Sulman al-Khalifa and State Flag

1999. Shaikh Isa bin Sulman al-Khalifa Commemoration. Multicoloured.
643 100f. Type **134** 30 20
644 200f. Shaikh and map of Bahrain (41 × 31 mm) . . . 65 45
645 250f. Shaikh, map of Bahrain and state flag 80 55

135 Emblem

1999. International Year of the Elderly. Mult.
647 100f. Type **135** 30 20
648 200f. Emblem and flame . . 65 45
649 250f. Emblem (different) . . 80 55

136 Emblem

1999. 10th Anniv of Bahrain Stock Exchange. Multicoloured.
650 100f. Type **136** 30 20
651 200f. Shaikh Isa bin Salman Bridge and emblem 65 40
652 250f. Globe and emblem . . 80 55

137 Shaikh Isa bin Salman and Shaikh Hamad bin Isa holding Flag

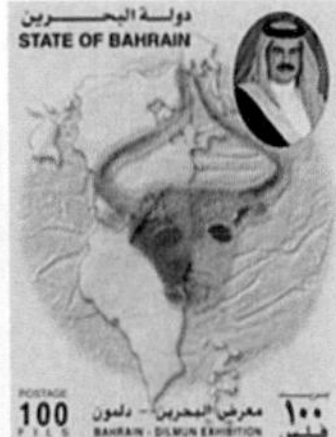
138 Map of Bahrain and Animal Skull

1999. National Day. Multicoloured.
653 100f. Type **137** 30 20
654 200f. Shaikh Hamad bin Isa and flag 65 40
655 250f. Shaikh Hamad bin Isa and globe 80 55

2000. Dilmun Exhibition. Multicoloured.
657 100f. Type **138** 35 25
658 200f. Map of Bahrain superimposed over animal skull 75 50
659 250f. Map of Bahrain and artefact 90 60

139 Map of Bahrain and Emblem

2000. 50th Anniv of Gulf Air. Multicoloured.
660 100f. Type **139** 35 25
661 200f. Map of Bahrain and emblem in circle 75 50
662 250f. Map of Bahrain, emblem and eagles 90 60

140 Emblem

2000. "Made in Bahrain 2000" Exhibition. Multicoloured.
663 100f. Type **140** 45 25
664 200f. Type **140** 75 50
665 250f. Oil refinery 90 60

141 Minarets and Fort

2000. Millennium. Multicoloured.
666 100f. Type **141** 45 25
667 100f. Dhows and factories . . 45 25
668 100f. Man harvesting dates 45 25
669 100f. Fort, globe and dish aerial 45 25
670 200f. Lake and bridge . . . 75 50
671 200f. Modern building and woman 75 50
672 200f. Dhows, jug and wicker basket 75 50
673 200f. Horseman and falconer 75 50
674 250f. Pearl divers 90 60
675 250f. Opening clams 90 60
676 250f. Fishermen 90 60
677 250f. Man mending fishing nets 90 60

142 Emblem

2000. 21st Gulf Co-operation Council Supreme Council Session, Bahrain. Multicoloured.
678 100f. Type **142** 35 20
679 200f. Members' flags 70 40

143 Stained-glass Window

2001. 10th Anniv of Beit Al Qur'an (Islamic institution). Multicoloured.
680 100f. Type **143** 35 20
681 200f. Beit Al Qur'an by night 70 40
682 250f. Facade 90 55

144 Building

2001. 25th Anniv of Ministry of Housing and Agriculture. Multicoloured.
684 100f. Type **144** 35 20
685 150f. Sculpture and building 55 35
686 200f. Building viewed through arch 70 40
687 250f. Tall, arched building . . 90 55

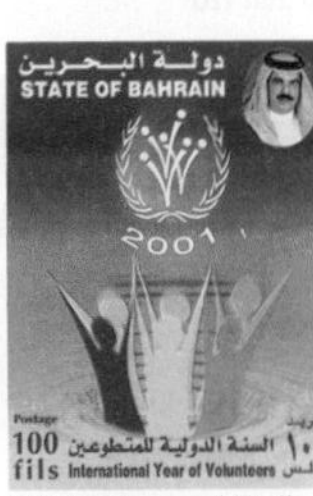
145 Emblem and Stylized Figures

2001. International Year of Volunteers. Multicoloured.
688 100f. Type **145** 35 20
689 150f. Hands encircling emblem 55 35
690 200f. Star pattern and emblem 70 40
691 250f. Paper cut figures . . . 90 55

146 Emblem

2002. Arab Women's Day. Multicoloured.
692 100f. Type **146** 35 20
693 200f. Elliptical shapes and emblem 65 40
694 250f. Women (horiz) 80 45

147 Football and Emblem

148 Shaikh Hamad Bin Isa Al Khalifa

2002. World Cup Football Championship, Japan and South Korea. Sheet 124 × 64 mm containing T **147** and similar vert designs. Multicoloured.
MS695 100f. Type **147**; 200f. Earth, football and emblem; 250f. Football and white peaks . . . 1·75 1·75

2002. Multicoloured, background colour given.
(a) Size 22 × 28 mm.
696 **148** 25f. brown 10 10
697 40f. purple 15 10
698 50f. grey 15 10
699 60f. blue 20 15
700 80f. blue 25 15
701 100f. orange 30 20
702 125f. mauve 40 25
703 150f. orange 45 25
704 200f. green 60 35
705 250f. pink 80 50
706 300f. brown . . . . . . 1·00 60
707 400f. green . . . . . . 1·25 75

(b) 26 × 36 mm.
708 500f. mauve . . . . 1·60 95
709 1d. orange 30 20
710 2d. blue 60 35
711 3d. brown . . . . 1·00 60
MS712 246 × 162 mm. Nos. 696/711 9·25 9·50

149 Stylized Teacher, Child and Symbols of Communication

2002. World Teacher's Day.
713 **149** 100f. multicoloured . . . 30 20
714 200f. multicoloured . . . 60 35

150 Emblem

2002. Parliamentary Election, 2002. Multicoloured.
715 100f. Type **150** 30 20
716 200f. Hand posting voting slip (vert) 60 35

151 Shaikh Hamad Bin Isa Al Khalifa and Flag

2002. National Day. Multicoloured.
717 100f. Type **151** 30 20
718 200f. Shaikh Hamad Bin Isa and flag (different) (vert) 60 35
719 250f. As No. 718 but with maroon background (vert) 80 45

152 Bahrain

2003. Arab Summit Conference, Sharm el-Sheikh, Egypt. Designs representing landmarks from each state.
720 100f. Type **152** 30 30
721 100f. Sudan 30 30
722 100f. Saudi Arabia 30 30
723 100f. Djibouti 30 30
724 100f. Algeria 30 30
725 100f. Tunisia 30 30
726 100f. UAE 30 30
727 100f. Jordan 30 30
728 200f. Comoros 60 60
729 200f. Qatar 60 60
730 200f. Palestine 60 60
731 200f. Oman 60 60
732 200f. Iraq 60 60
733 200f. Somalia 60 60
734 200f. Syria 60 60
735 250f. Yemen 70 70
736 250f. Mauritania 70 70
737 250f. Egypt 70 70
738 250f. Libya 70 70
739 250f. Lebanon 70 70
740 250f. Kuwait 70 70
MS741 120 × 103 mm. 500f. Buildings surrounding Holy Kabba. Imperf . . . . 1·40 1·40

153 Children, Emblem and Flowers

2003. World Health Day. Multicoloured.
742 100f. Type **153** 30 20
743 200f. Stylized figures and emblem 60 35

154 Swan

2003. World Environment Day. Flora and Fauna. Multicoloured.
744 100f. Type **154** 30 30
745 100f. Peacock 30 30
746 100f. Flamingos 30 30
747 100f. Ostrich 30 30
748 200f. *Rumex vesicarius* . . . 60 60
749 200f. *Arnebia hispidissima* . . 60 60
750 200f. *Capparis spinosa* . . . 60 60
751 200f. *Cassia italica* 60 60
752 250f. Crab 70 70
753 250f. Turtle 70 70
754 250f. Sting ray 70 70
755 250f. Shark 70 70

WAR TAX STAMPS

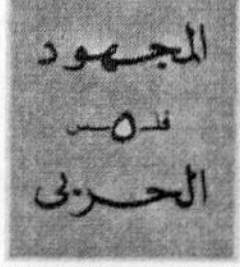

T **36** "War Effort"

T **37** "War Effort"

1973.
T192 T **36** 5f. blue and cobalt . .

1973.
T194a T **37** 5f. blue . . . . 1·00 10

BAMRA Pt. 1

A state in India. Now uses Indian stamps.

12 pies = 1 anna; 16 annas = 1 rupee.

BAMRA
postage

1

8

1888.
1 **1** ¼a. black on yellow £375
2 ½a. black on red . . . . . . 75·00
3 1a. black on blue . . . . . 50·00
4 2a. black on green . . . . . 75·00 £275
5 4a. black on yellow . . . . . 65·00 £275
6 8a. black on red . . . . . . 40·00

1890. Imperf.
10 **8** ¼a. black on red . . . . . . 1·90 2·50
11 ½a. black on green . . . . . 2·50 2·75
30 1a. black on yellow . . . . . 3·75 3·00
16 2a. black on green . . . . . 4·00 4·50
19 4a. black on red . . . . . . 8·50 5·50
22 8a. black on red . . . . . . 13·00 16·00
25 1r. black on red . . . . . . 17·00 20·00

BANGLADESH Pt. 1

Formerly the Eastern wing of Pakistan. Following a landslide victory at the Pakistan General Election in December 1970 by the Awami League party the National Assembly was suspended. Unrest spread throughout the eastern province culminating in the intervention of India on the side of the East Bengalis. The new state became effective after the surrender of the Pakistan army in December 1971.

1971. 100 paisa = 1 rupee.
1972. 100 paisa = 1 taka.

1 Map of Bangladesh

3 "Martyrdom"

1971.
1 **1** 10p. indigo, orange and blue 10 10
2 – 20p. multicoloured 10 10
3 – 50p. multicoloured 10 10
4 – 1r. multicoloured 10 10
5 – 2r. turquoise, blue and red . . 25 35
6 – 3r. light green, green and blue 30 55
7 – 5r. multicoloured . . . . . 50 1·00
8 – 10r. gold, red and blue . . . . 1·00 2·00
DESIGNS: 20p. "Dacca University Massacre"; 50p. "75 Million People"; 1r. Flag of Independence; 2r. Ballot box; 3r. Broken chain; 5r. Shaikh Majibur Rahman; 10r. "Support Bangla Desh" and map.

1971. Liberation. Nos. 1 and 7/8 optd **BANGLADESH LIBERATED**.
9 10p. indigo, orange and blue 20 10
10 5r. multicoloured . . . . . . 2·25 2·75
11 10r. gold, red and blue . . . . 2·75 3·50
The remaining values of the original issue were also overprinted and placed on sale in Great Britian but were not issued in Bangladesh.
On 1 February 1972 the Agency placed on sale a further issue in the flag, map and Sheikh Mujib designs in new colours and new currency (100 paisa = 1 taka). This issue proved to be unacceptable to the Bangladesh authorities who declared them to be invalid for postal purposes, no supplies being sold within Bangladesh. The values comprise 1, 2, 3, 5, 7, 10, 15, 20, 25, 40, 50, 75p., 1, 2 and 5t.

1972. In Memory of the Martyrs.
12 **3** 20p. green and red 30 50

4 Flames of Independence

5 Doves of Peace

1972. 1st Anniv of Independence.
13 **4** 20p. lake and red 25 10
14 60p. blue and red 40 45
15 75p. violet and red 45 55

1972. Victory Day.
16 **5** 20p. multicoloured 25 10
17 60p. multicoloured 40 70
18 75p. multicoloured 45 70

6 "Homage to Martyrs"

7 Embroidered Quilt

8 Court of Justice

9 Flame Emblem

1973. In Memory of the Martyrs.
19 **6** 20p. multicoloured 15 10
20 60p. multicoloured 30 40
21 1t.35 multicoloured . . . . . 65 1·75

1973.
22 **7** 2p. black . . . . 10 1·00
23 – 3p. green . . . . 20 1·00
24 – 5p. brown 20 10
25 – 10p. black 20 10
26 – 20p. green 50 10
27 – 25p. mauve . . . . 3·25 10
28 – 50p. purple . . . . 2·25 30
29 – 60p. grey . . . . 1·25 1·00
30 – 75p. orange . . . . 1·25 1·00
31 – 90p. brown . . . . 1·50 1·75
32 **8** 1t. violet . . . . 6·00 30
33 – 2t. green . . . . 6·00 65
34 – 5t. blue . . . . 7·00 2·25
35 – 10t. pink . . . . 7·50 4·50
DESIGNS—As Type **7**: 3p. Jute field; 5p. Jack fruit; 10p. Bullocks ploughing; 20p. Rakta jaba (flower); 25p. Tiger; 60p. Bamboo grove; 75p. Plucking tea; 90p. Handicrafts. (28 × 22 mm): 50p. Hilsa (fish). As Type **8**. VERT: 2t. Date tree. HORIZ: 5t. Fishing boat; 10t. Sixty-dome mosque, Bagerhat.
See also Nos. 49/51a, 64/75 and 711.

1973. 25th Anniv of Declaration of Human Rights.
36 **9** 10p. multicoloured 10 10
37 1t.25 multicoloured 20 20

10 Family, Map and Graph

11 Copernicus and Heliocentric System

1974. First Population Census.
38 **10** 20p. multicoloured 10 10
39 25p. multicoloured 10 10
40 75p. multicoloured 20 20

1974. 500th Birth Anniv of Copernicus.
41 **11** 25p. orange, violet and black 10 10
42 75p. orange, green and black 25 50

12 U.N. H.Q. and Bangladesh Flag

13 U.P.U. Emblem

1974. Bangladesh's Admission to the U.N.
43 **12** 25p. multicoloured 10 10
44 1t. multicoloured 35 40

1974. Centenary of Universal Postal Union. Mult.
45 25p. Type **13** 10 10
46 1t.25 Mail runner 20 15
47 1t.75 Type **13** 20 25
48 5t. As 1t.25 . . . . 80 1·60

14 Courts of Justice

1974. As Nos. 32/5 with revised inscriptions.
49 **14** 1t. violet . . . . 1·50 10
50 – 2t. olive . . . . 2·00 2·00
51 – 5t. blue . . . . 7·00 70
51a – 10t. pink . . . . 17·00 13·00
For these designs redrawn to 32 × 20 mm or 20 × 32 mm, see Nos. 72/5 and, to 35 × 22 mm, see No. 711.

15 Tiger

16 Symbolic Family

1974. Wildlife Preservation. Multicoloured.
52 25p. Type **15** 70 10
53 50p. Tiger cub . . . . 1·00 70
54 2t. Tiger in stream . . . . . 1·75 3·50

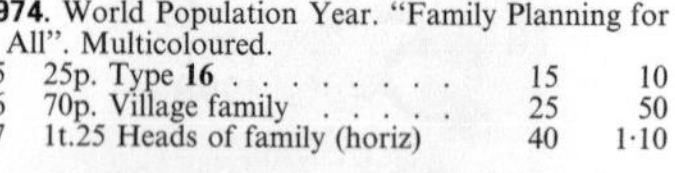

1974. World Population Year. "Family Planning for All". Multicoloured.
55 25p. Type **16** 15 10
56 70p. Village family 25 50
57 1t.25 Heads of family (horiz) 40 1·10

17 Radar Antenna

19 Telephones of 1876 and 1976

18 Woman's Head

1975. Inauguration of Betbunia Satellite Earth Station.
58 **17** 25p. black, silver and red . . 10 10
59 1t. black, silver and blue . . 20 70

1975. International Women's Year.
60 **18** 50p. multicoloured 10 10
61 2t. multicoloured . . . . . 25 1·00

1976. As Nos. 24/31 and 49/51a but redrawn in smaller size.
64 – 5p. green 20 10
65 – 10p. black 20 10
66 – 20p. green . . . . 1·00 10
67 – 25p. mauve . . . . 3·75 10
68 – 50p. purple . . . . 3·50 10
69 – 60p. grey 40 20
70 – 75p. green . . . . 1·75 3·00
71 – 90p. brown 40 20
72 **14** 1t. violet . . . . 2·00 10
73 – 2t. green . . . . 8·50 10
74 – 5t. blue . . . . 3·25 3·00
75 – 10t. red . . . . 8·50 4·00
Nos. 64/71 are 23 × 18 mm (50p.) or 18 × 23 mm (others) and Nos. 72/75 are 20 × 32 mm (2t.) or 32 × 20 mm (others).
For the 10t. redrawn to 35 × 22 mm, see No. 711.

1976. Centenary of Telephone.
76 **19** 2t.25 multicoloured 25 20
77 – 5t. red, green and black . . 55 65
DESIGN: 5t. Alexander Graham Bell.

20 Eye and Nutriments

1976. Prevention of Blindness.
78 **20** 30p. multicoloured 50 10
79 2t.25 multicoloured . . . . 1·40 2·25

21 Liberty Bell

1976. Bicentenary of American Revolution. Mult.
80 30p. Type **21** 10 10
81 2t.25 Statue of Liberty 20 25
82 5t. "Mayflower" 55 50
83 10t. Mount Rushmore 55 80
MS84 167 × 95 mm. No. 83 . . . 1·50 3·00

22 Industry, Science, Agriculture and Education
23 Hurdling

1976. 25th Anniv of Colombo Plan.
85 **22** 30p. multicoloured 15 10
86 2t.25 multicoloured . . . . 35 1·00

1976. Olympic Games, Montreal. Multicoloured.
87 25p. Type **23** 10 10
88 30p. Running (horiz) 10 10
89 1t. Pole vaulting 15 10
90 2t.25 Swimming (horiz) . . . 30 45
91 3t.50 Gymnastics . . . . . . 55 1·25
92 5t. Football . . . . 1·00 2·00

24 The Blessing
25 Qazi Nazrul Islam (poet)

1977. Silver Jubilee. Multicoloured.
93 30p. Type **24** 10 10
94 2t.25 Queen Elizabeth II . . . 20 25
95 10t. Queen Elizabeth and Prince Philip 70 85
MS96 114 × 127 mm. Nos. 93/5 80 1·50

1977. Qazi Nazrul Islam Commemoration.
97 **25** 40p. green and black . . . 10 10
98 – 2t.25 brown, red & lt brn 30 30
DESIGN—HORIZ: 2t.25, Head and shoulders portrait.

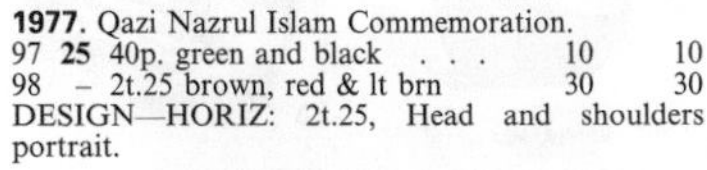

26 Bird with Letter

1977. 15th Anniv of Asian–Oceanic Postal Union.
99 **26** 30p. red, blue and grey . . 10 10
100 2t.25 red, blue and grey . . 20 25

27 Sloth Bear
28 Campfire and Tent

1977. Animals. Multicoloured.
101 40p. Type **27** 15 10
102 1t. Spotted deer 15 10
103 2t.25 Leopard (horiz) 30 20
104 3t.50 Gaur (horiz) 30 35
105 4t. Indian elephant (horiz) . . 80 50
106 5t. Tiger (horiz) 90 75
The Bengali numerals on the 40p. resemble "80", and that on the 4t. resembles "8".

1978. First National Scout Jamboree.
107 **28** 40p. red, blue and pale blue 30 10
108 – 3t.50 lilac, green and blue 1·25 30
109 – 5t. green, blue and red . . 1·40 45
DESIGNS—HORIZ: 3t.50, Scout stretcher-team. VERT: 5t. Scout salute.

29 "Michelia champaca"

1978. Flowers. Multicoloured.
110 40p. Type **29** 20 10
111 1t. "Cassia fistula" 30 15
112 2t.25 "Delonix regia" 40 30
113 3t.50 "Nymphaea nouchali" 45 60
114 4t. "Butea monosperma" . . 45 80
115 5t. "Anthocephalus indicus" 45 85

30 St. Edward's Crown and Sceptres
32 Fenchuganj Fertiliser Factory

31 Sir Alan Cobham's De Havilland D.H.50

1978. 25th Anniv of Coronation. Multicoloured.
116 40p. Type **30** 10 10
117 3t.50 Balcony scene 15 30
118 5t. Queen Elizabeth and Prince Philip 25 50
119 10t. Coronation portrait by Cecil Beaton 45 80
MS120 89 × 121 mm. Nos. 116/19 1·10 1·50

1978. 75th Anniv of Powered Flight.
121 **31** 40p. multicoloured 15 10
122 – 2t.25 brown and blue . . . 30 45
123 – 3t.50 brown and yellow . . 35 65
124 – 5t. multicoloured . . . . . 3·00 3·50
DESIGNS: 2t.25, Captain Hans Bertram's seaplane "Atlantis"; 3t.50, Wright brothers' Flyer III; 5t. Concorde.

1978.
125 – 5p. brown 10 10
126 **32** 10p. blue 10 10
127 – 15p. orange 10 10
128 – 20p. red 10 10
129 – 25p. blue 15 10
130 – 30p. green . . . . 2·50 10
131 – 40p. purple 30 10
132 – 50p. black . . . . 4·50 1·50
134 – 80p. brown 20 10
136 – 1t. violet . . . . 6·50 10
137 – 2t. blue . . . . 2·25 3·00
DESIGNS—HORIZ: 5p. Lalbag Fort; 25p. Jute on a boat; 40, 50p. Baitul Mukarram Mosque; 1t. Dotara (musical instrument); 2t. Karnaphuli Dam. VERT: 15p. Pineapple; 20p. Bangladesh gas; 30p. Banana tree; 80p. Mohastan Garh.

33 Tawaf-E-Ka'aba, Mecca
35 Moulana Abdul Hamid Khan Bhashani

34 Jasim Uddin

1978. Pilgrimage to Mecca. Multicoloured.
140 40p. Type **33** 20 10
141 3t. Pilgrims in Wuquf, Arafat (horiz) 60 45

1979. 3rd Death Anniv of Jasim Uddin (poet).
142 **34** 40p. multicoloured 20 50

1979. 3rd Death Anniv of Moulana Abdul Hamid Khan Bhashani (national leader).
143 **35** 40p. multicoloured 40 30

36 Sir Rowland Hill
37 Children with Hoops

1979. Death Centenary of Sir Rowland Hill.
144 **36** 40p. blue, red and light blue 10 10
145 – 3t.50 multicoloured 35 30
146 – 10t. multicoloured . . . . 80 1·00
MS147 176 × 96 mm. Nos. 144/6 2·00 2·75
DESIGNS: 3t.50, Sir Rowland Hill and first Bangladesh stamp; 10t. Sir Rowland Hill and Bangladesh U.P.U. stamp.

1979. International Year of the Child. Multicoloured.
148 40p. Type **37** 10 10
149 3t.50 Boy with kite 35 35
150 5t. Children jumping 50 50
MS151 170 × 120 mm. Nos. 148/50 1·50 2·75

38 Rotary International Emblem
40 A. K. Fazlul Huq

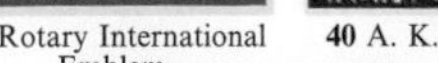

39 Canal Digging

1980. 75th Anniv of Rotary International.
152 **38** 40p. black, red and yellow 20 10
153 – 5t. gold and blue 65 45
DESIGN: 5t. Rotary emblem (different).

1980. Mass Participation in Canal Digging.
154 **39** 40p. multicoloured 40 30

1980. 18th Death Anniv of A. K. Fazlul Huq (national leader).
155 **40** 40p. multicoloured 30 30

41 Early Forms of Mail Transport

1980. "London 1980" International Stamp Exhibition. Multicoloured.
156 1t. Type **41** 15 10
157 10t. Modern forms of mail transport . . . . 1·25 90

42 Dome of the Rock
43 Outdoor Class

1980. Palestinian Welfare.
159 **42** 50p. lilac 70 30

1980. Education.
160 **43** 50p. multicoloured 40 30

44 Beach Scene

1980. World Tourism Conference, Manila. Mult.
161 50p. Type **44** 35 50
162 5t. Beach scene (different) . . 65 1·10
MS163 140 × 88 mm. Nos. 161/2 1·00 1·50

45 Mecca
46 Begum Roquiah

1980. Moslem Year 1400 A. H. Commemoration.
164 **45** 50p. multicoloured 20 20

1980. Birth Centenary of Begum Roquiah (campaigner for women's rights).
165 **46** 50p. multicoloured 10 10
166 2t. multicoloured 35 20

47 Spotted Deer and Scout Emblem
49 Queen Elizabeth the Queen Mother

1981. 5th Asia–Pacific and 2nd Bangladesh Scout Jamboree.
167 **47** 50p. multicoloured 40 15
168 5t. multicoloured . . . . . 1·25 2·50

1981. 2nd Population Census. Nos. 38/40 optd **2nd. CENSUS 1981**.
169 **10** 20p. multicoloured 10 10
170 25p. multicoloured 10 10
171 75p. multicoloured 20 30

1981. 80th Birthday of the Queen Mother.
172 **49** 1t. multicoloured 15 15
173 15t. multicoloured . . . . . 1·75 2·50
MS174 95 × 73 mm. Nos. 172/3 2·40 2·50

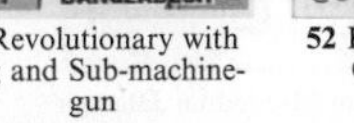

50 Revolutionary with Flag and Sub-machine-gun
52 Kemal Ataturk in Civilian Dress

51 Bangladesh Village and Farm Scenes

1981. 10th Anniv of Independence. Mult.
175 50p. Type **50** 15 10
176 2t. Figures on map symbolizing Bangladesh life style 25 45

1981. U.N. Conference on Least Developed Countries, Paris.
177 **51** 50p. multicoloured 35 15

1981. Birth Centenary of Kemal Ataturk (Turkish statesman).
178 50p. Type **52** 45 30
179 1t. Kemal Ataturk in uniform 80 1·25

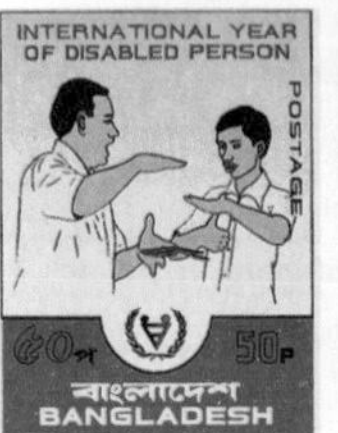

53 Deaf People using Sign Language **54** Farm Scene and Wheat Ear

1981. Int Year for Disabled Persons. Mult.
180 50p. Type **53** 40 20
181 2t. Disabled person writing (horiz) . . . . 85 2·50

1981. World Food Day.
182 **54** 50p. multicoloured . . . . 50 1·00

55 River Scene **56** Dr. M. Hussain

1982. 10th Anniv of Human Environment Conference.
183 **55** 50p. multicoloured . . . . 50 1·00

1982. 1st Death Anniv of Dr. Motahar Hussain (educationist).
184 **56** 50p. multicoloured . . . . 50 1·00

57 Knotted Rope surrounding Bengali "75"

1982. 75th Anniv of Boy Scout Movement and 125th Birth Anniv of Lord Baden-Powell. Multicoloured.
185 50p. Type **57** 75 30
186 2t. Lord Baden-Powell (vert) 2·25 4·50

সম্মিলিত
সশস্ত্র বাহিনী দিবস
২১ নভেম্বর,৮২
(58)

60 Metric Scales

59 Captain Mohiuddin Jahangir

1982. Armed Forces' Day. No. 175 optd with T **58**.
187 50p. Type **50** . . . . 3·00 3·00

1983. Heroes and Martyrs of the Liberation. Multicoloured, background colour of commemorative plaque given.
188 50p. Type **59** (orange) . . . 30 45
189 50p. Sepoy Hamidur Rahman (green) 30 45
190 50p. Sepoy Mohammed Mustafa Kamal (red) . . . 30 45
191 50p. Muhammed Ruhul Amin (yellow) 30 45
192 50p. Flt. Lt. M. Matiur Rahman (brown) 30 45
193 50p. Lance-Naik Munshi Abdur Rob (brown) . . . 30 45
194 50p. Lance-Naik Nur Mouhammad (green) . . . 30 45

1983. Introduction of Metric Weights and Measures. Multicoloured.
195 50p. Type **60** 40 30
196 2t. Weights, jug and tape measure (horiz) . . . . . 1·75 2·75

61 Dr. Robert Koch **63** Dr. Muhammed Shahidulla

62 Open Stage Theatre

1983. Centenary (1982) of Robert Koch's Discovery of Tubercle Bacillus. Multicoloured.
197 50p. Type **61** . . . . 1·00 40
198 1t. Microscope, slide and X-ray . . . . 2·25 3·50

1983. Commonwealth Day. Multicoloured.
199 1t. Type **62** 10 15
200 3t. Boat race 20 30
201 10t. Snake dance 50 90
202 15t. Picking tea . . . . . . 60 1·50

1983. Dr. Muhammed Shahidulla (Bengali scholar) Commemoration.
203 **63** 50p. multicoloured . . . . 75 1·00

64 Magpie Robin

1983. Birds of Bangladesh. Multicoloured.
204 50p. Type **64** . . . . 1·00 40
205 2t. White-throated kingfisher (vert) . . . . 1·50 2·25
206 3t.75 Lesser flame-backed woodpecker (vert) . . . . 1·50 2·75
207 5t. White-winged wood duck 1·75 3·25
MS208 165 × 110 mm. Nos. 240/7 (sold at 13t.) . . . . 6·50 13·00

65 "Macrobrachium rosenbergii"

1983. Marine Life. Multicoloured.
209 50p. Type **65** 60 30
210 2t. White pomfret . . . . . 80 1·50
211 3t.75 Rohu . . . . 90 1·75
212 5t. Climbing perch . . . . . 1·00 2·50
MS213 119 × 98 mm. Nos. 209/12 (sold at 13t.) . . . . 3·00 6·00

1983. Visit of Queen Elizabeth II. No. 95 optd **Nov. '83 Visit of Queen.**
214 10t. Queen Elizabeth and Prince Philip . . . . . . 4·50 6·00

67 Conference Hall, Dhaka

1983. 14th Islamic Foreign Ministers' Conference, Dhaka. Multicoloured.
215 50p. Type **67** 35 30
216 5t. Old Fort, Dhaka . . . . 1·25 3·00

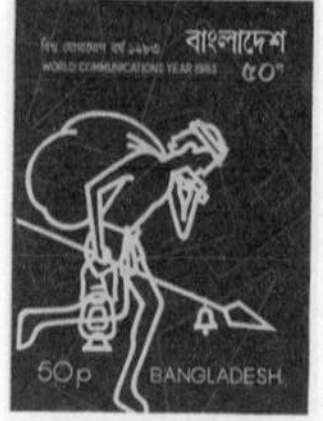

68 Early Mail Runner **69** Carrying Mail by Boat

1983. World Communications Year. Multicoloured.
217 50p. Type **68** 30 15
218 5t. Sailing ship, steam train and Boeing 707 airliner . . 2·00 1·50
219 10t. Mail runner and dish aerial (horiz) . . . . . . 2·75 4·50

1983. Postal Communications.
220 **69** 5p. blue 10 30
221 – 10p. purple 10 30
222 – 15p. blue 20 30
223 – 20p. black 65 30
224 – 25p. grey 20 30
225 – 30p. brown 20 30
226 – 50p. brown 65 10
227 – 1t. blue 65 10
228 – 2t. green 65 10
228a – 3t. brown . . . . 2·50 70
229 – 5t. purple . . . . 2·00 80
DESIGNS—HORIZ (22 × 17 mm): 10p. Counter, Dhaka G.P.O.; 15p. I.W.T.A. Terminal, Dhaka; 20p. Inside railway travelling post office; 30p. Emptying pillar box; 50p. Mobile post office van. (30 × 19 mm): 1t. Kamalapur Railway Station, Dhaka; 2t. Zia International Airport; 3t. Sorting mail by machine; 5t. Khulna G.P.O. VERT (17 × 22 mm): 25p. Delivering a letter.

প্রথম বাংলাদেশ জাতীয় ডাকটিকিট প্রদর্শনী - ১৯৮৪
(70)

1984. 1st National Stamp Exhibition (1st issue). Nos. 161/2 optd with T **70** (5t.) or **First Bangladesh National Philatelic Exhibition—1984** (50p.)
230 **44** 50p. multicoloured . . . . 1·25 1·75
231 – 5t. multicoloured . . . . . 1·75 2·50

71 Girl with Stamp Album (¾-size illustration)

1984. 1st National Stamp Exhibition (2nd issue). Multicoloured.
232 50p. Type **71** . . . . 65 1·25
233 7t.50 Boy with stamp album 1·10 2·00
MS234 98 × 117 mm. Nos. 232/3 (sold at 10t.) . . . . 3·00 4·00

72 Sarus Crane and Gavial **73** Eagle attacking Hen with Chicks

1984. Dhaka Zoo. Multicoloured.
235 1t. Type **72** . . . . 1·75 85
236 2t. Common peafowl and tiger . . . . 2·50 4·25

1984. Centenary of Postal Life Insurance. Mult.
237 1t. Type **73** 50 25
238 5t. Bangladesh family and postman's hand with insurance cheque . . . . . 1·50 2·25

74 Abbasuddin Ahmad

খুলনাপেক্স—৮৪
(75)

1984. Abbasuddin Ahmad (singer) Commemoration.
239 **74** 3t. multicoloured . . . . . 70 1·00

1984. "Khulnapex-84" Stamp Exhibition. No. 86 optd with T **75**.
240 **22** 2t.25 multicoloured . . . . 1·00 1·75

76 Cycling

1984. Olympic Games, Los Angeles. Multicoloured.
241 1t. Type **76** . . . . 1·75 30
242 5t. Hockey . . . . 2·50 2·25
243 10t. Volleyball . . . . 2·75 4·25

77 Farmer with Rice and Sickle

1985. 9th Annual Meeting of Islamic Development Bank, Dhaka. Multicoloured.
244 1t. Type **77** 35 15
245 5t. Citizens of four races . . 1·25 2·25

78 Mother and Baby **80** Women working at Traditional Crafts

উপজেলা নির্বাচন ১৯৮৫
(79)

1985. Child Survival Campaign. Multicoloured.
246 1t. Type **78** 30 10
247 10t. Young child and growth graph . . . . 2·50 3·25

1985. Local Elections. Nos. 110/15 optd with T **79**.
248 40p. Type **29** 35 50
249 1t. "Cassia fistula" 40 30
250 2t.25 "Delonix regia" 60 65
251 3t.50 "Nymphaea nouchali" 70 1·00
252 4t. "Butea monosperma" . . 70 1·00
253 5t. "Anthocephalus indicus" 75 1·40

1985. U.N. Decade for Women. Multicoloured.
254 1t. Type **80** 25 10
255 10t. Women with microscope, computer terminal and in classroom . . . . 1·25 2·25

81 U.N. Building, New York, Peace Doves and Flags

1985. 40th Anniv of United Nations Organization and 11th Anniv of Bangladesh Membership. Multicoloured.
256 1t. Type **81** 10 10
257 10t. Map of world and Bangladesh flag . . . . . 80 1·40

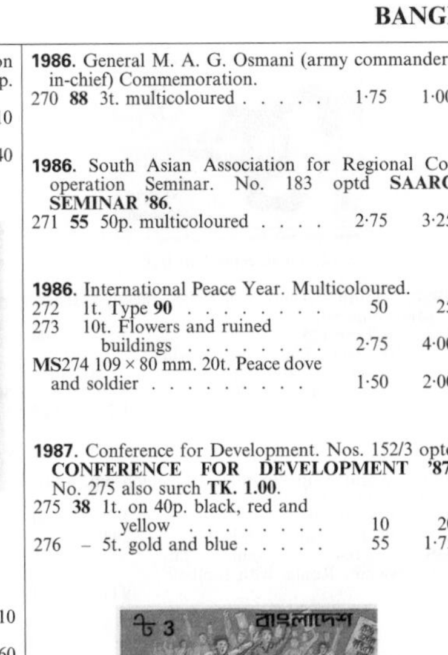

82 Head of Youth, Flowers and Symbols of Commerce and Agriculture

83 Emblem and Seven Doves

1985. International Youth Year. Multicoloured.
258 1t. Type **82** 10 10
259 5t. Head of youth, flowers and symbols of industry . . 40 60

1985. 1st Summit Meeting of South Asian Association for Regional Co-operation, Dhaka. Multicoloured.
260 1t. Type **83** 10 10
261 5t. Flags of member nations and lotus blossom . . . . 1·25 90

84 Zainul Abedin

তৃতীয় বাংলাদেশ
জাতীয় জাম্বুরী
১৯৮৫-৮৬

(85)

1985. 10th Death Anniv of Zainul Abedin (artist).
262 **84** 3t. multicoloured 75 30

1985. 3rd National Scout Jamboree. No. 109 optd with T **85**.
263 5t. green, blue and red . . . 2·50 3·50

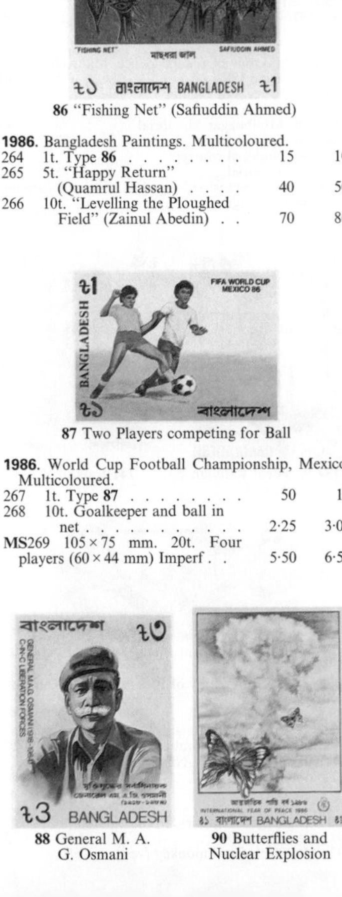

86 "Fishing Net" (Safiuddin Ahmed)

1986. Bangladesh Paintings. Multicoloured.
264 1t. Type **86** 15 10
265 5t. "Happy Return" (Quamrul Hassan) 40 50
266 10t. "Levelling the Ploughed Field" (Zainul Abedin) . . 70 80

87 Two Players competing for Ball

1986. World Cup Football Championship, Mexico. Multicoloured.
267 1t. Type **87** 50 10
268 10t. Goalkeeper and ball in net . . . . 2·25 3·00
MS269 105 × 75 mm. 20t. Four players (60 × 44 mm) Imperf . . 5·50 6·50

88 General M. A. G. Osmani

90 Butterflies and Nuclear Explosion

1986. General M. A. G. Osmani (army commander-in-chief) Commemoration.
270 **88** 3t. multicoloured . . . . . 1·75 1·00

1986. South Asian Association for Regional Co-operation Seminar. No. 183 optd **SAARC SEMINAR '86**.
271 **55** 50p. multicoloured . . . . 2·75 3·25

1986. International Peace Year. Multicoloured.
272 1t. Type **90** 50 25
273 10t. Flowers and ruined buildings . . . . 2·75 4·00
MS274 109 × 80 mm. 20t. Peace dove and soldier . . . . 1·50 2·00

1987. Conference for Development. Nos. 152/3 optd **CONFERENCE FOR DEVELOPMENT '87**, No. 275 also surch **TK. 1.00**.
275 **38** 1t. on 40p. black, red and yellow 10 20
276 – 5t. gold and blue . . . . . 55 1·75

92 Demonstrators with Placards

1987. 35th Anniv of Bangla Language Movement. Multicoloured.
277 3t. Type **92** . . . . 1·40 2·50
278 3t. Martyrs' Memorial . . . 1·40 2·50
Nos. 277/8 were printed together, se-tenant, forming a composite design.

93 Nurse giving Injection

94 Pattern and Bengali Script

1987. World Health Day.
279 **93** 1t. black and blue . . . . 1·75 2·00
See also No 295.

1987. Bengali New Year Day. Multicoloured.
280 1t. Type **94** 10 10
281 10t. Bengali woman 40 60

95 Jute Shika

96 Ustad Ayet Ali Khan and Surbahar

1987. Export Products. Multicoloured.
282 1t. Type **95** 10 10
283 5t. Jute carpet (horiz) 30 35
284 10t. Cane table lamp 45 70

1987. 20th Death Anniv of Ustad Ayet Ali Khan (musician and composer).
285 **96** 5t. multicoloured . . . . . 1·50 70

97 Palanquin

1987. Transport. Multicoloured.
286 2t. Type **97** 20 15
287 3t. Bicycle rickshaw 60 20
288 5t. River steamer . . . . . . 1·00 45
289 7t. Express diesel train . . . 3·00 60
290 10t. Bullock cart 60 85

98 H. S. Suhrawardy

1987. Hossain Shadid Suhrawardy (politician) Commemoration.
291 **98** 3t. multicoloured 20 30

99 Villagers fleeing from Typhoon

1987. International Year of Shelter for the Homeless. Multicoloured.
292 5t. Type **99** 20 30
293 5t. Villagers and modern houses 20 30

100 President Ershad addressing Parliament

1987. 1st Anniv of Return to Democracy.
294 **100** 10t. multicoloured 40 60

1988. World Health Day. As T **93**.
295 25p. brown 30 20
DESIGN: 25p. Oral rehydration.

101 Woman planting Palm Saplings

1988. I.F.A.D. Seminar on Agricultural Loans for Rural Women. Multicoloured.
296 3t. Type **101** 15 20
297 5t. Village woman milking cow 20 40

102 Basketball

1988. Olympic Games, Seoul. Multicoloured.
298 5t. Type **102** . . . . 1·00 80
299 5t. Weightlifting . . . . . . 1·00 80
300 5t. Tennis . . . . 1·00 80
301 5t. Rifle-shooting . . . . . . 1·00 80
302 5t. Boxing . . . . 1·00 80

103 Interior of Shait Gumbaz Mosque, Bagerhat

1988. Historical Buildings. Multicoloured.
303 1t. Type **103** 35 10
304 4t. Paharpur Monastery . . . 60 20
305 5t. Kantanagar Temple, Dinajpur 60 20
306 10t. Lalbag Fort, Dhaka . . 85 60

104 Henri Dunant (founder), Red Cross and Crescent

105 Dr. Qudrat-i-Khuda in Laboratory

1988. 125th Anniv of International Red Cross and Red Crescent. Multicoloured.
307 5t. Type **104** . . . . 1·10 30
308 10t. Red Cross workers with patient . . . . 1·75 95

1988. Dr. Qudrat-i-Khuda (scientist) Commem.
309 **105** 5t. multicoloured 30 30

106 Wicket-keeper

107 Labourers, Factory and Technician

1988. Asia Cup Cricket. Multicoloured.
310 1t. Type **106** 80 90
311 5t. Batsman . . . . 1·00 1·00
312 10t. Bowler . . . . 1·75 2·00

1988. 32nd Meeting of Colombo Plan Consultative Committee, Dhaka.
313 **107** 3t. multicoloured 10 10
314 10t. multicoloured 40 45

108 Dhaka G.P.O. Building

1988. 25th Anniv of Dhaka G.P.O. Building. Multicoloured.
315 1t. Type **108** 15 10
316 5t. Post Office counter . . . 30 30

৫ম জাতীয় রোভার মুট
১৯৮৮-৮৯

(109)

1988. 5th National Rover Scout Moot. No. 168 optd with T **109**.
317 **47** 5t. multicoloured . . . . . 2·50 2·00

110 Bangladesh Airport

1989. Bangladesh Landmarks.
318 **110** 3t. black and blue . . . 10 10
318a – 4t. blue 10 10
710 – 5t. black and brown . . 10 15
320 – 10t. red . . . . 3·00 35
321 – 20t. multicoloured . . . 35 40
DESIGNS—VERT (22 × 33 mm): 5t. Curzon Hall. (19½ × 31½ mm): 10t. Fertiliser factory, Chittagong. HORIZ (33 × 23 mm): 4t. Chittagong port; 20t. Postal Academy, Rajshahi.

চতুর্থ দ্বিবার্ষিক এশীয়
চারুকলা প্রদর্শনী
বাংলাদেশ ১৯৮৯

(111)

1989. 4th Biennial Asian Art Exhibition. No. 266 optd with T **111**.
322 10t. "Levelling the Ploughed Field" (Zainul Abedin) . . 50 50

112 Irrigation Methods and Student with Telescope

113 Academy Logo

1989. 12th National Science and Technology Week.
323 **112** 10t. multicoloured 50 50

1989. 75th Anniv of Police Academy, Sardah.
324 **113** 10t. multicoloured 50 50

114 Rejoicing Crowds, Paris, 1789

1989. Bicentenary of French Revolution. Mult.
325 17t. Type **114** 70 75
326 17t. Storming the Bastille, 1789 . . . . 70 75
MS327 125 × 125 mm 5t. Men with pickaxes; 10t. "Liberty guiding the People" (detail) (Delacroix); 10t. Crowd with cannon. P 14 . . . 2·00 3·00
MS328 152 × 88 mm. 25t. Storming the Bastille. Imperf . . . . . 2·00 3·00
The design of No. **MS**328 incorporates the three scenes featured on No. **MS**327.

115 Sowing and Harvesting

1989. 10th Anniv of Asia–Pacific Integrated Rural Development Centre. Multicoloured.
329 5t. Type **115** 45 45
330 10t. Rural activities 55 55
Nos. 329/30 were printed together, se-tenant, forming a composite design.

116 Helper and Child playing with Baby

1989. 40th Anniv of S.O.S. International Children's Village. Multicoloured.
331 1t. Type **116** 15 10
332 10t. Foster mother with children 55 55

117 U.N. Soldier on Watch

118 Festival Emblem

1989. 1st Anniv of Bangladesh Participation in U.N. Peace-keeping Force. Multicoloured.
333 4t. Type **117** 50 30
334 10t. Two soldiers checking positions . . . . 1·00 70

1989. 2nd Asian Poetry Festival, Dhaka.
335 **118** 2t. red, deep red and green 15 10
336 – 10t. multicoloured 60 65
DESIGN: 10t. Festival emblem and hall.

119 State Security Printing Press

1989. Inauguration of State Security Printing Press, Gazipur.
337 **119** 10t. multicoloured 65 65

120 Water Lilies and T.V. Emblem

1989. 25th Anniv of Bangladesh Television. Multicoloured.
338 5t. Type **120** 35 30
339 10t. Central emblem and water lilies 65 80

121 Gharial in Shallow Water

1990. Endangered Wildlife. Gharial. Multicoloured.
340 50p. Type **121** 80 45
341 2t. Gharial feeding . . . . . 1·00 60
342 4t. Gharials basking on sand bank . . . . 1·40 70
343 10t. Two gharials resting . . 1·75 95

122 Symbolic Family

124 Boy learning Alphabet

123 Justice S. M. Murshed

1990. Population Day.
344 **122** 6t. multicoloured 55 35

1990. 10th Death Anniv of Justice Syed Mahbub Murshed.
345 **123** 5t. multicoloured . . . . 2·00 1·25

1990. International Literacy Year. Multicoloured.
346 6t. Type **124** . . . . 1·00 50
347 10t. Boy teaching girl to write 1·50 1·00

125 Penny Black with "Stamp World London 90" Exhibition Emblem

127 Mango

126 Goalkeeper and Ball

1990. 150th Anniv of the Penny Black. Multicoloured.
348 7t. Type **125** . . . . 1·50 2·00
349 10t. Penny Black, 1983 World Communications Year stamp and Bengali mail runner . . . . 1·75 2·25

1990. World Cup Football Championship, Italy. Multicoloured.
350 8t. Type **126** . . . . 1·75 1·50
351 10t. Footballer with ball . . 2·00 1·75
MS352 104 × 79 mm. 25t. Colosseum, Rome, with football. Imperf . . . . 9·00 9·00

1990. Fruit. Multicoloured.
353 1t. Type **127** 30 10
354 2t. Guava 30 10
355 3t. Water melon 35 15
356 4t. Papaya 40 25
357 5t. Bread fruit 65 50
358 10t. Carambola . . . . 1·25 1·25

128 Man gathering Wheat

1990. U.N. Conference on Least Developed Countries, Paris.
359 **128** 10t. multicoloured . . . . 1·25 1·00

129 Map of Asia with Stream of Letters

131 Lalan Shah

130 Canoe Racing

1990. 20th Anniv of Asia–Pacific Postal Training Centre. Multicoloured.
360 2t. Type **129** . . . . 1·50 1·50
361 6t. Map of Pacific with stream of letters . . . . . 1·50 1·50
Nos. 360/1 were printed together, se-tenant, forming a composite map design.

1990. Asian Games, Beijing. Multicoloured.
362 2t. Type **130** 80 20
363 4t. Kabaddi . . . . 1·00 25
364 8t. Wrestling . . . . 1·60 1·25
365 10t. Badminton . . . . . . 2·75 1·75

1990. 1st Death Anniv of Lalan Shah (poet).
366 **131** 6t. multicoloured . . . . 1·50 1·00

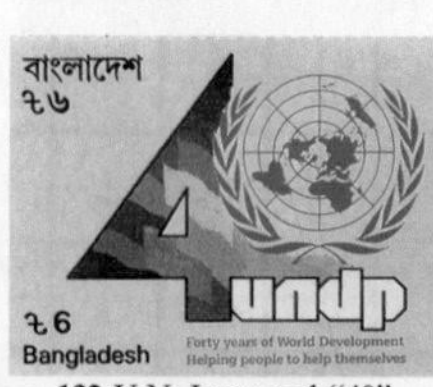
132 U.N. Logo and "40"

1990. 40th Anniv of United Nations Development Programme.
367 **132** 6t. multicoloured 80 35

133 Baby

134 "Danaus chrysippus"

1990. Immunization.
368 **133** 1t. green 10 10
369 2t. brown 10 10

1990. Butterflies. Multicoloured.
370 6t. Type **134** . . . . 1·60 1·60
371 6t. "Precis almana" . . . . . 1·60 1·60
372 10t. "Ixias pyrene" . . . . . 1·75 1·75
373 10t. "Danaus plexippus" . . 1·75 1·75

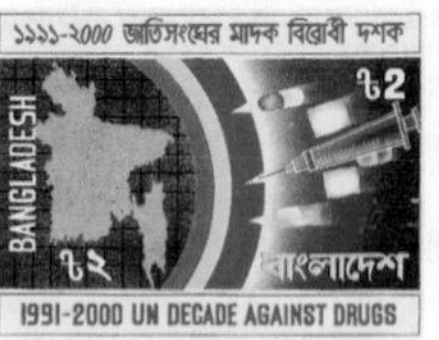
135 Drugs attacking Bangladesh

1991. U.N. Anti-drugs Decade. Multicoloured.
374 2t. Type **135** . . . . 1·00 50
375 4t. "Drug" snake around globe . . . . 1·25 1·25

136 Salimullah Hall

1991.
376 **136** 6t. blue and yellow . . . 10 15

137 Silhouetted People on Map

138 "Invincible Bangla" (statue)

1991. 3rd National Census.
382 **137** 4t. multicoloured . . . . 1·25 1·00

1991. 20th Anniv of Independence. Multicoloured.
383 4t. Type **138** 75 90
384 4t. "Freedom Fighter" (statue) 75 90
385 4t. Mujibnagar Memorial . . 75 90
386 4t. Eternal flame 75 90
387 4t. National Martyrs' Memorial 75 90
Nos. 383/7 were issued together, se-tenant, forming a composite design.

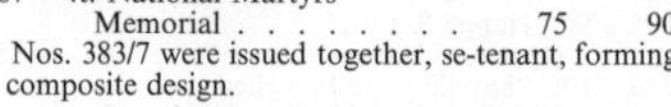

139 President Rahman Seated

141 Kaikobad

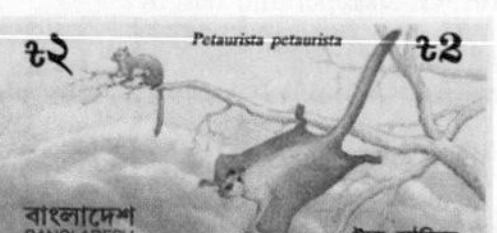
140 Red Giant Flying Squirrel

1991. 10th Death Anniv of President Ziaur Rahman. Multicoloured.
388 50p. Type **139** 20 15
389 2t. President Rahman's head in circular decoration . . . 80 1·10
MS390 146 × 75 mm. Nos. 388/9 (sold at 10t.) . . . . 1·60 2·50

1991. Endangered Species. Multicoloured.
391 2t. Type **140** . . . . 1·60 1·75
392 4t. Black-faced monkey (vert) 1·60 1·75

393 6t. Great Indian hornbill (vert) . . . . 1·60 1·75
394 10t. Armoured pangolin . . . 1·60 1·75

1991. 40th Death Anniv of Kaikobad (poet).
395 **141** 6t. multicoloured . . . . 1·00 60

142 Rabindranath Tagore and Temple

1991. 50th Death Anniv of Rabindranath Tagore (poet).
396 **142** 4t. multicoloured 70 55

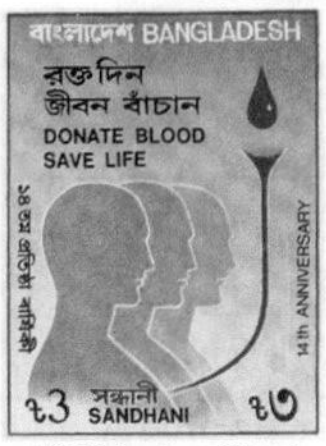

143 Voluntary Blood Programme

144 Shahid Naziruddin and Crowd

1991. 14th Anniv of "Sandhani" (medical students' association).
397 **143** 3t. black and red 90 50
398 – 5t. multicoloured . . . . 1·60 2·00
DESIGN: 5t. Blind man and eye.

1991. 1st Death Anniv of Shahid Naziruddin Jahad (democrat).
399 **144** 2t. black, green and brown . . . . 1·00 60

145 Shaheed Noor Hossain with Slogan on Chest

1991. 4th Death Anniv of Shaheed Noor Hossain (democrat).
400 **145** 2t. multicoloured . . . . 1·00 55

146 Bronze Stupa

1991. Archaeological Relics from Mainamati. Multicoloured.
401 4t. Type **146** . . . . 1·50 1·60
402 4t. Earthenware and bronze pitchers . . . . 1·50 1·60
403 4t. Remains of Salban Vihara Monastery . . . . 1·50 1·60
404 4t. Gold coins . . . . 1·50 1·60
405 4t. Terracotta plaque . . . . 1·50 1·60

147 Demostrators

1991. 1st Anniv of Mass Uprising.
406 **147** 4t. multicoloured . . . . 1·25 80

148 Munier Chowdhury

1991. 20th Anniv of Independence. Martyred Intellectuals (1st series). Each black and brown.
407 2t. Type **148** 45 45
408 2t. Ghyasuddin Ahmad . . . 45 45
409 2t. Rashidul Hasan 45 45
410 2t. Muhammad Anwar Pasha 45 45
411 2t. Dr. Muhammad Mortaza 45 45
412 2t. Shahid Saber 45 45
413 2t. Fazlur Rahman Khan . . 45 45
414 2t. Ranada Prasad Saha . . 45 45
415 2t. Adhyaksha Joges Chandra Ghose 45 45
416 2t. Santosh Chandra Bhattacharyya 45 45
417 2t. Dr. Gobinda Chandra Deb 45 45
418 2t. A. Muniruzzaman 45 45
419 2t. Mufazzal Haider Chaudhury 45 45
420 2t. Dr. Abdul Alim Choudhury 45 45
421 2t. Sirajuddin Hossain . . . 45 45
422 2t. Shahidulla Kaiser 45 45
423 2t. Altaf Mahmud 45 45
424 2t. Dr. Jyotirmay Guha Thakurta 45 45
425 2t. Dr. Muhammad Abul Khair 45 45
426 2t. Dr. Serajul Haque Khan 45 45
427 2t. Dr. Mohammad Fazle Rabbi 45 45
428 2t. Mir Abdul Quyyum . . . 45 45
429 2t. Golam Mostafa 45 45
430 2t. Dhirendranath Dutta . . 45 45
431 2t. S. Mannan 45 45
432 2t. Nizamuddin Ahmad . . . 45 45
433 2t. Abul Bashar Chowdhury 45 45
434 2t. Selina Parveen 45 45
435 2t. Dr. Abul Kalam Azad . . 45 45
436 2t. Saidul Hassan 45 45
See also Nos. 483/92, 525/40, 568/83, 620/35, 656/71, 691/706, 731/46 and 779/94.

149 "Penaeus monodon"

1991. Shrimps. Multicoloured.
437 6t. Type **149** . . . . 2·00 2·25
438 6t. "Metapenaeus monoceros" . . . . 2·00 2·25

150 Death of Raihan Jaglu

1992. 5th Death Anniv of Shaheed Mirze Abu Raihan Jaglu.
439 **150** 2t. multicoloured . . . . 1·00 60

151 Rural and Urban Scenes

152 Nawab Sirajuddaulah

1992. World Environment Day. Multicoloured.
440 4t. Type **151** 75 25
441 10t. World Environment Day logo (horiz) . . . . 1·75 2·50

1992. 235th Death Anniv of Nawab Sirajuddaulah of Bengal
442 **152** 10t. multicoloured . . . . 1·25 1·75

153 Syed Ismail Hossain Sirajee

1992. 61st Death Anniv of Syed Ismail Hossain Sirajee
443 **153** 4t. multicoloured . . . . 1·00 60

154 Couple planting Seedling

1992. Plant Week. Multicoloured.
444 2t. Type **154** . . . . 1·00 80
445 4t. Birds on tree (vert) . . . 1·75 95

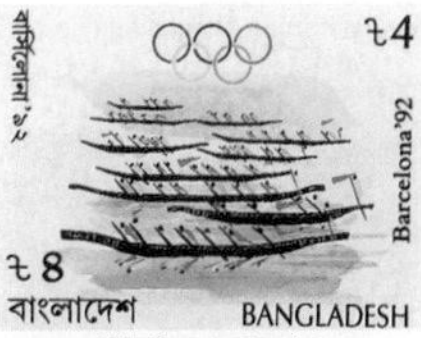

155 Canoe Racing

1992. Olympic Games, Barcelona. Multicoloured.
446 4t. Type **155** . . . . 1·25 1·50
447 6t. Hands holding torch with Olympic rings . . . . . . 1·25 1·50
448 10t. Olympic rings and doves 1·25 1·50
449 10t. Olympic rings and multiracial handshake . . . 1·25 1·50

1992. "Banglapex '92", National Philatelic Exhibition (1st issue). No. 290 optd **Banglapex '92** in English and Bengali.
450 10t. Bullock cart . . . . . . 2·00 2·50
See also Nos. 452/3.

157 Masnad-e-Ala Isa Khan

1992. 393rd Death Anniv of Masnad-e-Ala Isa Khan.
451 **157** 4t. multicoloured . . . . 1·00 60

158 Ceremonial Elephant (19th-century ivory carving)

1992. "Banglapex '92" National Philatelic Exhibition (2nd issue). Multicoloured.
452 10t. Type **158** . . . . 1·40 2·00
453 10t. Victorian pillarbox between early and modern postmen . . . . 1·40 2·00
MS454 145 × 92 mm. Nos. 452/3. Imperf (sold at 25t.) . . . . . 3·25 4·00

159 Star Mosque

1992. Star Mosque, Dhaka.
455 **159** 10t. mutlicoloured . . . . 1·75 1·75

160 Meer Nisar Ali Titumeer and Fort

1992. 161st Death Anniv of Meer Nisar Ali Titumeer.
456 **160** 10t. multicoloured . . . . 1·50 1·50

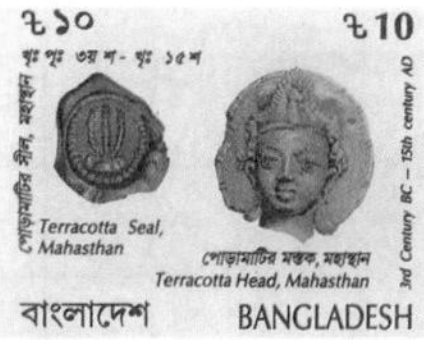

161 Terracotta Head and Seal

1992. Archaeological Relics from Mahasthangarh. Multicoloured.
457 10t. Type **161** . . . . 1·75 1·90
458 10t. Terracotta panel showing swan . . . . 1·75 1·90
459 10t. Terracotta statue of Surya . . . . 1·75 1·90
460 10t. Gupta stone column . . 1·75 1·90

162 Young Child and Food

1992. Int Conference on Nutrition, Rome.
461 **162** 4t. multicoloured . . . . 1·00 55

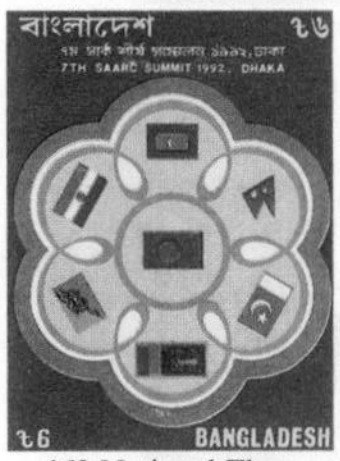

163 National Flags

164 Syed Abdus Samad

1992. 7th South Asian Association for Regional Co-operation Summit Conference, Dhaka. Mult.
462 6t. Type **163** . . . . 1·00 75
463 10t. S.A.A.R.C. emblem . . . 1·40 1·75

1993. Syed Abdus Samad (footballer) Commem.
464 **164** 2t. multicoloured . . . . 1·25 60

165 Haji Shariat Ullah

1993. Haji Shariat Ullah Commemoration.
465 **165** 2t. multicoloured . . . . 1·25 60

166 People digging Canal

1993. Irrigation Canals Construction Project. Mult.
466 2t. Type **166** 80 80
467 2t. Completed canal and paddy-fields 80 80

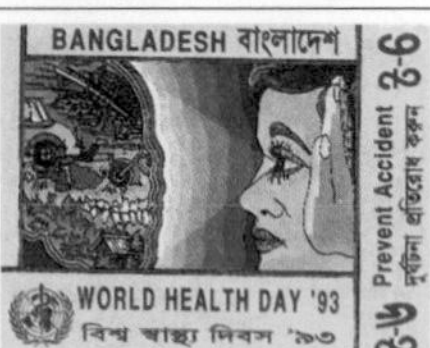

167 Accident Prevention

1993. World Health Day. Multicoloured.
468 6t. Type **167** . . . . 1·75 75
469 10t. Satellite photograph and symbols of trauma (vert) 2·00 2·50

168 National Images

169 Schoolchildren and Bengali Script

1993. 1400th Year of Bengali Solar Calendar.
470 **168** 2t. multicoloured . . . . 1·00 50

1993. Compulsory Primary Education. Mult.
471 2t. Type **169** 80 80
472 2t. Books and slate (horiz) 80 80

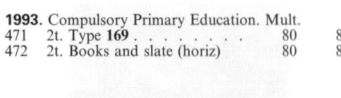

170 Nawab Sir Salimullah and Palace

1993. 122nd Birth Anniv of Nawab Sir Salimullah.
473 **170** 4t. multicoloured . . . . 1·00 55

171 Fish Production

1993. Fish Fortnight.
474 **171** 2t. multicoloured 50 40

172 Sunderban

1993. Natural Beauty of Bangladesh. Mult.
475 10t. Type **172** . . . . 85 1·10
476 10t. Kuakata beach . . . . . 85 1·10
477 10t. Madhabkunda waterfall (vert) . . . . 85 1·10
478 10t. River Piyain, Jaflang (vert) . . . . 85 1·10
MS479 174 × 102 mm. Nos. 475/8. Imperf (sold at 50t.) . . . . . 3·25 3·75

173 Exhibition Emblem

175 Burdwan House

174 Foy's Lake

1993. 6th Asian Art Biennale.
480 **173** 10t. multicoloured . . . . 80 1·00

1993. Tourism Month.
481 **174** 10t. multicoloured . . . . 1·00 1·25

1993. Foundation Day, Bangla Academy.
482 **175** 2t. brown and green . . . 60 40

1993. Martyred Intellectuals (2nd series). As T **148**. Each black and brown.
483 2t. Lt. Cdr. Moazzam Hussain 20 30
484 2t. Muhammad Habibur Rahman 20 30
485 2t. Khandoker Abu Taleb . . 20 30
486 2t. Moshiur Rahman 20 30
487 2t. Md. Abdul Muktadir . . 20 30
488 2t. Nutan Chandra Sinha . . 20 30
489 2t. Syed Nazmul Haque . . . 20 30
490 2t. Dr. Mohammed Amin Uddin 20 30
491 2t. Dr. Faizul Mohee 20 30
492 2t. Sukha Ranjan Somaddar 20 30

176 Throwing the Discus

1993. 6th South Asian Federation Games, Dhaka. Multicoloured.
493 2t. Type **176** 20 20
494 4t. Running (vert) 35 35

177 Tomb of Sultan Ghiyasuddin Azam Shah

1993. Muslim Monuments.
495 **177** 10t. multicoloured . . . . 75 1·00

178 Scouting Activities and Jamboree Emblem

179 Emblem and Mother giving Solution to Child

1994. 14th Asian–Pacific and 5th Bangladesh National Scout Jamboree.
496 **178** 2t. multicoloured 40 30

1994. 25th Anniv of Oral Rehydration.
497 **179** 2t. multicoloured 40 30

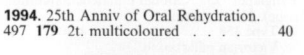

180 Interior of Chhota Sona Mosque, Nawabgonj

1994. Ancient Mosques. Multicoloured.
498 4t. Type **180** 40 20
499 6t. Exterior of Chhota Sona Mosque 50 65
500 6t. Exterior of Baba Adam's Mosque, Munshigonj . . . 50 65

181 Agricultural Workers and Emblem

1994. 75th Anniv of I.L.O. Multicoloured.
501 4t. Type **181** 25 20
502 10t. Worker turning cog (vert) . . . . 1·00 1·50

182 Priest releasing Peace Doves

184 Family, Globe and Logo

183 Scenes from Baishakhi Festival

1994. 1500th Year of Bengali Solar Calendar.
503 **182** 2t. multicoloured 35 25

1994. Folk Festivals. Multicoloured.
504 4t. Type **183** 35 35
505 4t. Scenes from Nabanna and Paush Parvana Festivals 35 35

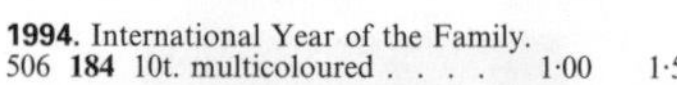

1994. International Year of the Family.
506 **184** 10t. multicoloured . . . . 1·00 1·50

185 People planting Saplings

186 Player kicking Ball

1994. Tree Planting Campaign. Multicoloured.
507 4t. Type **185** 50 25
508 6t. Hands holding saplings 75 45

1994. World Cup Football Championship, U.S.A. Multicoloured.
509 20t. Type **186** . . . . . . 2·25 3·00
510 20t. Player heading ball . . . 2·25 3·00

187 Traffic on Bridge

1994. Inauguration of Jamuna Multi-purpose Bridge Project.
511 **187** 4t. multicoloured . . . . 1·50 45

188 Asian Black-headed Oriole

190 Nawab Faizunnessa Chowdhurani

189 Dr. Mohammad Ibrahim and Hospital

1994. Birds. Multicoloured.
512 4t. Type **188** 40 40
513 6t. Greater racquet-tailed drongo 60 80
514 6t. Indian tree pie 60 80
515 6t. Red junglefowl 60 80

1994. 5th Death Anniv of Dr. Mohammad Ibrahim (diabetes treatment pioneer).
517 **189** 2t. multicoloured 40 20

1994. 160th Birth Anniv of Nawab Faizunnessa Chowdhurani (social reformer).
518 **190** 2t. muticoloured 50 20

191 Boxing

1994. Asian Games, Hiroshima, Japan.
519 **191** 4t. multicoloured . . . . 1·25 50

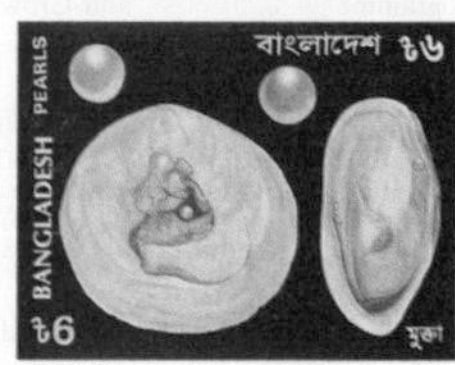

192 Pink and White Pearls with Windowpane Oysters

1994. Sea Shells. Multicoloured.
520 6t. Type **192** . . . . 1·10 1·40
521 6t. Tranquelous scallop and other shells . . . . 1·10 1·40
522 6t. Lister's conch, Asiatic Arabian cowrie, bladder moon and woodcock murex . . . . 1·10 1·40
523 6t. Spotted tun, spiny frog shell, spiral melongena and gibbous olive (vert) . . . . 1·10 1·40

193 Dr. Milon and Demonstrators

1994. 4th Death Anniv of Dr. Shamsul Alam Khan Milon (medical reformer).
524 **193** 2t. multicoloured 25 20

1994. Martyred Intellectuals (3rd series). As T **148**. Each black and brown.
525 2t. Dr. Harinath Dey 25 30
526 2t. Dr. A. F. Ziaur Rahman 25 30
527 2t. Mamun Mahmud 25 30
528 2t. Mohsin Ali Dewan 25 30
529 2t. Dr. N. A. M. Jahangir . . 25 30
530 2t. Shah Abdul Majid 25 30
531 2t. Muhammad Akhter . . . 25 30
532 2t. Meherunnesa 25 30
533 2t. Dr. Kasiruddin Talukder 25 30
534 2t. Fazlul Haque Choudhury 25 30
535 2t. Md. Shamsuzzaman . . . 25 30
536 2t. A. K. M. Shamsuddin . . 25 30
537 2t. Lt. Mohammad Anwarul Azim 25 30
538 2t. Nurul Amin Khan . . . 25 30
539 2t. Mohammad Sadeque . . 25 30
540 2t. Md. Araz Ali 25 30

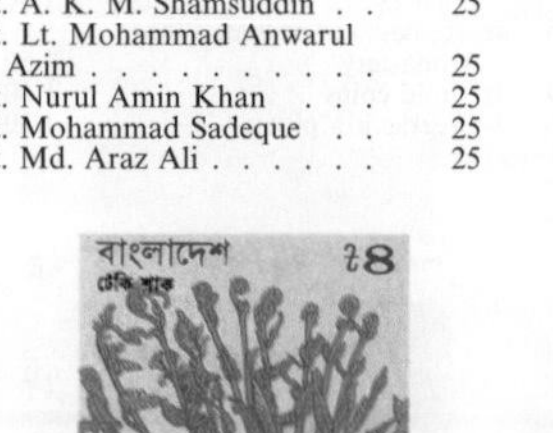

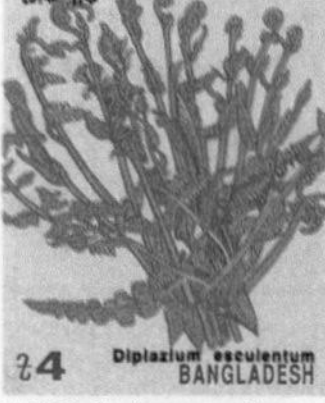

194 "Diplazium esculentum"

1994. Vegetables. Multicoloured.
541 4t. Type **194** 60 40
542 4t. "Momordica charantia" 60 40
543 6t. "Lagenaria siceraria" . . 80 60
544 6t. "Trichosanthes dioica" . . 80 60
545 10t. "Solanum melongena" 1·25 1·75
546 10t. "Cucurbita maxima" (horiz) . . . . 1·25 1·75

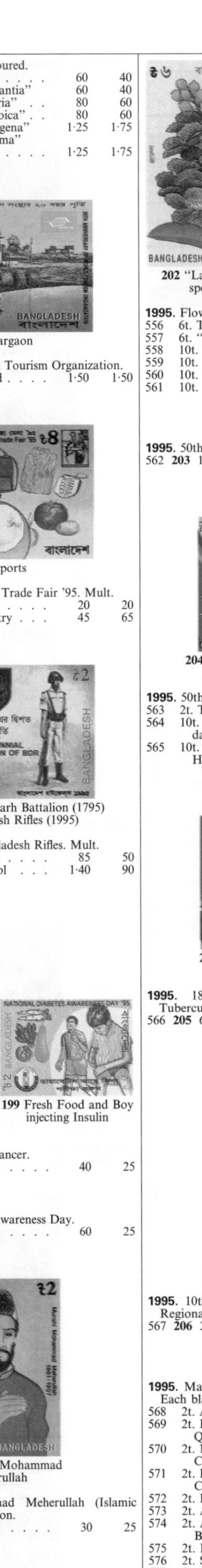

195 Sonargaon

1995. 20th Anniv of World Tourism Organization.
547 **195** 10t. multicoloured . . . . 1·50 1·50

196 Exports

1995. Dhaka International Trade Fair '95. Mult.
548 4t. Type **196** 20 20
549 6t. Symbols of industry . . . 45 65

197 Soldiers of Ramgarh Battalion (1795) and of Bangladesh Rifles (1995)

1995. Bicentenary of Bangladesh Rifles. Mult.
550 2t. Type **197** 85 50
551 4t. Riflemen on patrol . . . 1·40 90

198 Surgical Equipment and Lightning attacking Crab (cancer)

199 Fresh Food and Boy injecting Insulin

1995. Campaign against Cancer.
552 **198** 2t. multicoloured 40 25

1995. National Diabetes Awareness Day.
553 **199** 2t. multicoloured 60 25

200 Munshi Mohammad Meherullah

1995. Munshi Mohammad Meherullah (Islamic educator) Commemoration.
554 **200** 2t. multicoloured 30 25

রাজশাহীপেক্স-৯৫

(**201**)

1995. "Rajshahipex '95" National Philatelic Exhibition. No. 499 optd with T **201**.
555 6t. Exterior of Chhota Sona Mosque . . . . 1·75 2·00

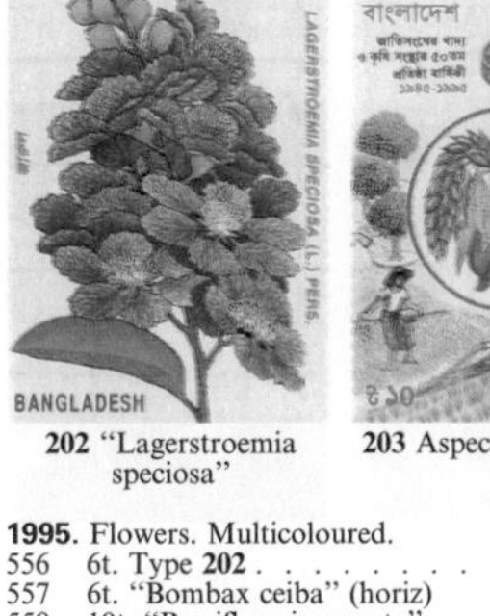

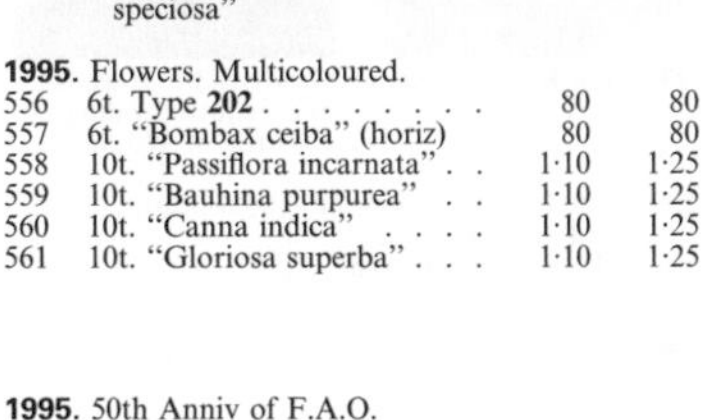

202 "Lagerstroemia speciosa"

203 Aspects of Farming

1995. Flowers. Multicoloured.
556 6t. Type **202** 80 80
557 6t. "Bombax ceiba" (horiz) 80 80
558 10t. "Passiflora incarnata" . . 1·10 1·25
559 10t. "Bauhinia purpurea" . . 1·10 1·25
560 10t. "Canna indica" . . . . 1·10 1·25
561 10t. "Gloriosa superba" . . . 1·10 1·25

1995. 50th Anniv of F.A.O.
562 **203** 10t. multicoloured 60 85

204 Anniversary Emblem, Peace Dove and U.N. Headquarters

1995. 50th Anniv of United Nations. Multicoloured.
563 2t. Type **204** 30 20
564 10t. Peace doves circling dates and Globe . . . . . 90 1·40
565 10t. Clasped hands and U.N. Headquarters . . . . . . 90 1·40

205 Diseased Lungs, Microscope, Family and Map

1995. 18th Eastern Regional Conference on Tuberculosis, Dhaka.
566 **205** 6t. multicoloured . . . . 1·10 80

206 Peace Doves, Emblem and National Flags

1995. 10th Anniv of South Asian Association for Regional Co-operation.
567 **206** 2t. multicoloured . . . . 1·00 35

1995. Martyred Intellectuals (4th series). As T **148**. Each black and brown.
568 2t. Abdul Ahad 25 30
569 2t. Lt. Col. Mohammad Qadir 25 30
570 2t. Mozammel Hoque Chowdhury 25 30
571 2t. Rafiqul Haider Chowdhury 25 30
572 2t. Dr. Azharul Haque . . . 25 30
573 2t. A. K. Shamsuddin . . . 25 30
574 2t. Anudwaipayan Bhattacharjee 25 30
575 2t. Lutfunnahar Helena . . . 25 30
576 2t. Shaikh Habibur Rahman 25 30
577 2t. Major Naimul Islam . . . 25 30
578 2t. Md. Shahidullah 25 30
579 2t. Ataur Rahman Khan Khadim 25 30
580 2t. A. B. M. Ashraful Islam Bhuiyan 25 30
581 2t. Dr. Md. Sadat Ali 25 30
582 2t. Sarafat Ali 25 30
583 2t. M. A. Sayeed 25 30

207 Aspects of COMDECA Projects

1995. 2nd Asia–Pacific Community Development Scout Camp.
584 **207** 2t. multicoloured 60 35

208 Volleyball Players

1995. Centenary of Volleyball.
585 **208** 6t. multicoloured 60 45

209 Man in Punjabi and Lungi

1995. Traditional Costumes. Multicoloured.
586 6t. Type **209** 80 80
587 6t. Woman in sari 80 80
588 10t. Christian bride and groom . . . . 1·10 1·25
589 10t. Muslim bride and groom 1·10 1·25
590 10t. Buddhist bride and groom (horiz) . . . . . . 1·10 1·25
591 10t. Hindu bride and groom (horiz) . . . . 1·10 1·25

210 Shaheed Amanullah Mohammad Asaduzzaman

1996. 27th Death Anniv of Shaheed Amanullah Mohammad Asaduzzaman (student leader).
592 **210** 2t. multicoloured 30 25

211 Bowler and Map

1996. World Cup Cricket Championship. Multicoloured.
593 4t. Type **211** . . . . 1·00 45
594 6t. Batsman and wicket keeper . . . . 1·25 65
595 10t. Match in progress (horiz) 1·75 2·00

212 Liberation Struggle, 1971

1996. 25th Anniv of Independence. Multicoloured.
596 4t. Type **212** 55 60
597 4t. National Martyrs Memorial 55 60
598 4t. Education 55 60
599 4t. Health 55 60
600 4t. Communications 55 60
601 4t. Industry 55 60

213 Michael Madhusudan Dutt

214 Gymnastics

1996. Michael Madhusudan Dutt (poet) Commemoration.
602 **213** 4t. multicoloured 50 20

1996. Olympic Games, Atlanta. Multicoloured.
603 4t. Type **214** 30 20
604 6t. Judo 40 30
605 10t. Athletics (horiz) 45 60
606 10t. High jumping (horiz) . . 45 60
MS607 165 × 110 mm. Nos. 603/6 (sold at 40t.) . . . . 1·50 2·00

1996. 25th Anniv of Bangladesh Stamps. No. **MS**234 optd "**Silver Jubilee Bangladesh Postage Stamps 1971-96**" on sheet margin.
MS608 98 × 117 mm. Nos. 232/3 (sold at 10t.) . . . . 80 1·00

215 Bangabandhu Sheikh Mujibur Rahman

1996. 21st Death Anniv of Bangabandhu Sheikh Mujibur Rahman.
609 **215** 4t. multicoloured 40 25

216 Maulana Mohammad Akrum Khan

1996. 28th Death Anniv of Maulana Mohammad Akrum Khan.
610 **216** 4t. multicoloured 30 20

217 Ustad Alauddin Khan

1996. 24th Death Anniv of Ustad Alauddin Khan (musician).
611 **217** 4t. multicoloured 50 20

218 "Kingfisher" (Mayeesha Robbani)

1996. Children's Paintings. Multicoloured.
612 2t. Type **218** 45 35
613 4t. "River Crossing" (Iffat Panchlais) (horiz) 55 35

219 Syed Nazrul Islam

1996. 21st Death Anniv of Jail Martyrs. Multicoloured.
614 4t. Type **219** 30 40
615 4t. Tajuddin Ahmad 30 40
616 4t. M. Monsoor Ali 30 40
617 4t. A. H. M. Quamaruzzaman 30 40

220 Children receiving Medicine

1996. 50th Anniv of U.N.I.C.E.F. Multicoloured.
618 4t. Type **220** 40 25
619 10t. Mother and child . . . 85 1·25

1996. Martyred Intellectuals (5th series). As T **148**. Each black and brown.
620 2t. Dr. Jekrul Haque 35 35
621 2t. Munshi Kabiruddin Ahmed 35 35
622 2t. Md. Abdul Jabbar 35 35
623 2t. Mohammad Amir 35 35
624 2t. A. K. M. Shamsul Huq Khan 35 35
625 2t. Dr. Siddique Ahmed . . . 35 35
626 2t. Dr. Soleman Khan . . . 35 35
627 2t. S. B. M. Mizanur Rahman 35 35
628 2t. Aminuddin 35 35
629 2t. Md. Nazrul Islam 35 35
630 2t. Zahirul Islam 35 35
631 2t. A. K. Lutfor Rahman . . 35 35
632 2t. Afsar Hossain 35 35
633 2t. Abul Hashem Mian 35 35
634 2t. A. T. M. Alamgir 35 35
635 2t. Baser Ali 35 35

221 Celebrating Crowds

1996. 25th Anniv of Victory Day. Multicoloured.
636 4t. Type **221** 25 25
637 6t. Soldiers and statue (vert) 40 60

222 Paul P. Harris

1997. 50th Death Anniv of Paul Harris (founder of Rotary International).
638 **222** 4t. multicoloured 30 25

223 Shaikh Mujibur Rahman making Speech

1997. 25th Anniv of Shaikh Mujibur's Speech of 7 March (1996).
639 **223** 4t. multicoloured 30 25

224 Sheikh Mujibur Rahman

226 Heinrich von Stephan

225 Sheikh Mujibur Rahman and Crowd with Banners

1997. 77th Birth Anniv of Sheikh Mujibur Rahman (first President).
640 **224** 4t. multicoloured 30 25

1997. 25th Anniv (1996) of Independence.
641 **225** 4t. multicoloured 30 25

1997. Death Centenary of Heinrich von Stephan (founder of U.P.U.).
642 **226** 4t. multicoloured 30 25

227 Sheep

1997. Livestock. Multicoloured.
643 4t. Type **227** 55 55
644 4t. Goat 55 55
645 6t. Buffalo bull 75 75
646 6t. Cow 75 75

228 "Tilling the Field - 2" (S. Sultan)

1997. Bangladesh Paintings. Multicoloured.
647 6t. Type **228** 40 30
648 10t. "Three Women" (Quamrul Hassan) . . . . 60 1·25

229 Trophy, Flag and Cricket Ball

1997. 6th International Cricket Council Trophy Championship, Malaysia.
649 **229** 10t. multicoloured . . . . 2·00 1·75

230 Kusumba Mosque, Naogaon

1997. Historic Mosques. Multicoloured.
650 4t. Type **230** 50 25
651 6t. Atiya Mosque, Tangail . . 70 35
652 10t. Bagha Mosque, Rajshahi 1·00 1·50

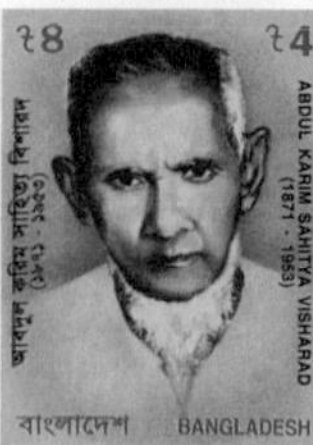

231 Adul Karim Sahitya Vishard

232 River Moot Emblem and Scouts standing on top of World

1997. 126th Birth Anniv of Abdul Karim Sahitya Vishard (scholar).
653 **231** 4t. multicoloured 30 25

1997. 9th Asia-Pacific and 7th Bangladesh Rover Moot, Lakkatura.
654 **232** 2t. multicoloured 50 25

233 Officers and Flag

1997. 25th Anniv of Armed Forces.
655 **233** 2t. multicoloured . . . . 1·00 45

1997. Martyred Intellectuals (6th series). As T **148**. Each black and brown.
656 2t. Dr. Shamsuddin Ahmed 60 60
657 2t. Mohammad Salimullah 60 60
658 2t. Mohiuddin Haider . . . 60 60
659 2t. Abdur Rahin 60 60
660 2t. Nitya Nanda Paul 60 60
661 2t. Abdel Jabber 60 60
662 2t. Dr. Humayun Kabir . . . 60 60
663 2t. Khaja Nizamuddin Bhuiyan 60 60
664 2t. Gulam Hossain 60 60
665 2t. Ali Karim 60 60
666 2t. Md. Moazzem Hossain 60 60
667 2t. Rafiqul Islam 60 60
668 2t. M. Nur Husain 60 60
669 2t. Captain Mahmood Hossain Akonda 60 60
670 2t. Abdul Wahab Talukder 60 60
671 2t. Dr. Hasimoy Hazra . . . 60 60

234 Mohammad Mansooruddin

1998. Professor Mohammad Mansooruddin (folklorist) Commemoration.
672 **234** 4t. multicoloured . . . . 1·10 45

235 Standard-bearer and Soldiers

1998. 50th Anniv of East Bengal Regiment.
673 **235** 2t. multicoloured 60 30

236 Bulbul Chowdhury

1998. Bulbul Chowdhury (traditional dancer) Commemoration.
674 **236** 4t. multicoloured 30 20

237 World Cup Trophy

1998. World Cup Football Championship, France. Multicoloured.
675 6t. Type **237** 50 30
676 18t. Footballer and trophy 1·50 2·25

238 Eastern Approach Road, Bangabandhu Bridge

1998. Opening of Bangabandhu Bridge. Mult.
677 4t. Type **238** 55 25
678 6t. Western approach road 65 35
679 8t. Embankment . . . . . . 85 1·10
680 10t. Main span, Bangabandhu Bridge . . . 1·10 1·25

239 Diana, Princess of Wales

1998. Diana, Princess of Wales Commemoration. Multicoloured.
681 8t. Type **239** 85 60
682 18t. Wearing pearl choker . . 1·50 1·50
683 22t. Wearing pendant necklace . . . . 1·50 1·75

240 Means of collecting Solar Energy

1998. World Solar Energy Programme Summit.
684 **240** 10t. multicoloured . . . . 1·00 1·00

241 World Habitat Day Emblem and City Scene

1998. World Habitat Day.
685 **241** 4t. multicoloured . . . . 1·00 45

242 Farmworkers, Sunflower and "20"

1998. 20th Anniv of International Fund for Agricultural Development. Multicoloured.

686 6t. Type **242** 50 25
687 10t. Farmworker with baskets and harvested crops . . . 90 1·25

243 Batsman

1998. Wills International Cricket Cup, Dhaka.

688 **243** 6t. multicoloured . . . . 1·50 1·00

244 Begum Rokeya

1998. Begum Rokeya (campaigner for women's education) Commemoration.

689 **244** 4t. multicoloured . . . . 1·00 45

245 Anniversary Logo

1998. 50th Anniv of Universal Declaration of Human Rights.

690 **245** 10t. multicoloured . . . . 1·00 1·00

1998. Martyred Intellectuals (7th series). As T **148**. Each black and brown.

691 2t. Md. Khorshed Ali Sarker 40 40
692 2t. Abu Yakub Mahfuz Ali 40 40
693 2t. S. M. Nural Huda 40 40
694 2t. Nazmul Hoque Sarker . . 40 40
695 2t. Md. Taslim Uddin . . . 40 40
696 2t. Gulam Mostafa 40 40
697 2t. A. H. Nural Alam 40 40
698 2t. Timir Kanti Dev 40 40
699 2t. Altaf Hossain 40 40
700 2t. Aminul Hoque 40 40
701 2t. S. M. Fazlul Hoque . . . 40 40
702 2t. Mozammel Ali 40 40
703 2t. Syed Akbar Hossain . . . 40 40
704 2t. Sk. Abdus Salam 40 40
705 2t. Abdur Rahman 40 40
706 2t. Dr. Shyamal Kanti Lala 40 40

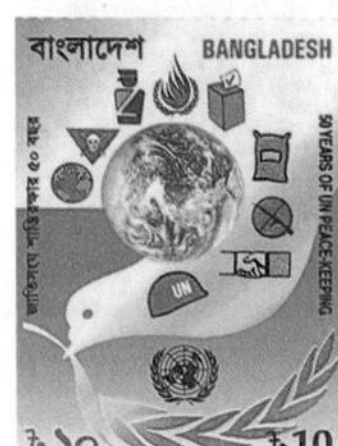

246 Dove of Peace and U.N. Symbols

1998. 50th Anniv of U.N. Peace-keeping Operations.

707 **246** 10t. multicoloured . . . . 1·00 1·25

247 Kazi Nazrul Islam

1998. Birth Centenary (1999) of Kazi Nazrul Islam (poet).

708 **247** 6t. multicoloured . . . . 1·00 60

248 Jamboree Emblem and Scout Activities

1999. 6th Bangladesh National Scout Jamboree.

709 **248** 2t. multicoloured 75 35

1999. As No. 75 but redrawn. Size 35 × 22 mm.

711 10t. red 20 25

No. 711 has been redrawn so that "SIXTY-DOME MOSQUE" appears above the face value at bottom right instead of below the main inscription at top left.

249 Surjya Sen and Demonstrators

1999. Surjya Sen (revolutionary) Commemoration.

715 **249** 4t. multicoloured . . . . 1·00 45

250 Dr. Fazlur Rahman Khan and Sears Tower

1999. 70th Birth Anniv of Dr. Fazlur Rahman Khan (architect).

716 **250** 4t. multicoloured 85 40

251 National Team Badges

1999. Cricket World Cup, England. Multicoloured.

717 8t. Type **251** . . . . 1·50 1·75
718 10t. Bangladesh cricket team badge and flag . . . . . . 1·75 2·00
MS719 139 × 89 mm. Nos. 717/18 (sold at 30t.) . . . . 3·25 3·75

252 Mother Teresa

253 Sheikh Mujibur Rahman, New York Skyline and Dove

1999. Mother Teresa Commemoration.

720 **252** 4t. multicoloured . . . . 1·00 45

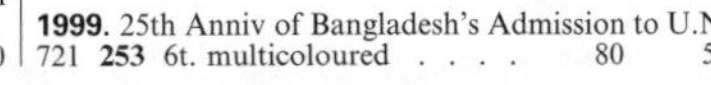

1999. 25th Anniv of Bangladesh's Admission to U.N.

721 **253** 6t. multicoloured 80 50

254 Shaheed Mohammad Maizuddin

1999. 15th Death Anniv of Shaheed Mohammad Maizuddin (politician).

722 **254** 2t. multicoloured 50 30

255 Faces in Tree

1999. International Year of the Elderly.

723 **255** 6t. multicoloured 80 45

256 Shanty Town and Modern Buildings between Hands

1999. World Habitat Day.

724 **256** 4t. multicoloured 75 35

257 Mobile Post Office

1999. 125th Anniv of U.P.U. Multicoloured.

725 4t. Type **257** 60 50
726 4t. Postman on motorcycle 60 50
727 6t. Postal motor launch . . . 70 70
728 6t. Two Bangladesh airliners 70 70
MS729 141 × 90 mm. Nos. 725/8 (sold at 25t.) . . . . 2·00 2·50

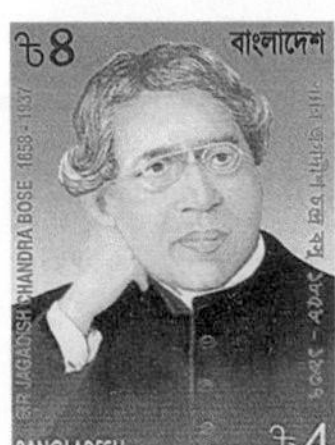

258 Sir Jagadis Chandra Bose

1999. Sir Jagadis Chandra Bose (physicist and botanist) Commemoration.

730 **258** 4t. multicoloured . . . . 1·00 40

1999. Martyred Intellectuals (8th series). As T **148**. Each black and brown.

731 2t. Dr. Mohammad Shafi . . 30 30
732 2t. Maulana Kasimuddin Ahmed 30 30
733 2t. Quazi Ali Imam 30 30
734 2t. Sultanuddin Ahmed . . . 30 30
735 2t. A. S. M. Ershadullah . . 30 30
736 2t. Mohammad Fazlur Rahman 30 30
737 2t. Captain A. K. M. Farooq 30 30
738 2t. Md. Latafot Hossain Joarder 30 30
739 2t. Ram Ranjan Bhattacharjya 30 30
740 2t. Abani Mohan Dutta . . . 30 30
741 2t. Sunawar Ali 30 30
742 2t. Abdul Kader Miah . . . 30 30
743 2t. Major Rezaur Rahman 30 30
744 2t. Md. Shafiqul Anowar . . 30 30
745 2t. A. A. M. Mozammel Hoque 30 30
746 2t. Khandkar Abul Kashem 30 30

259 Bangladesh Flag and Monument

2000. New Millennium. Multicoloured.

747 4t. Type **259** 60 35
748 6t. Satellite, computer and dish aerial (vert) 80 90

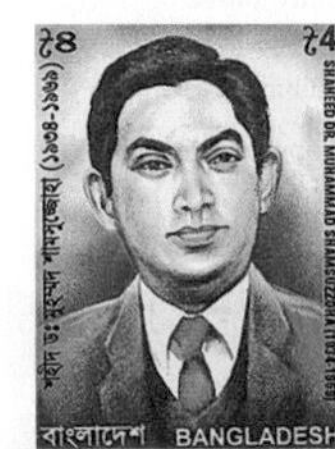

260 Cub Scouts, Globe and Flag

2000. 5th Bangladesh Cub Camporee.

749 **260** 2t. multicoloured 40 30

261 Jibananada Das

2000. Death Centenary (1999) of Jibananada Das (poet).

750 **261** 4t. multicoloured 60 30

262 Dr. Muhammad Shamsuzzoha

2000. 30th Death Anniv (1999) of Dr. Muhammad Shamsuzzoha.

751 **262** 4t. multicoloured 60 30

263 Shafiur Rahman

2000. International Mother Language Day. Mult.

752 4t. Type **263** 45 55
753 4t. Abul Barkat 45 55
754 4t. Abdul Jabbar 45 55
755 4t. Rafiq Uddin Ahmad . . . 45 55

264 Meteorological Equipment

2000. 50th Anniv of World Meteorological Organization.

756 **264** 10t. multicoloured . . . . 1·00 1·00

265 Cricket Week Logo and Web Site Address

266 Wasp

2000. International Cricket Week.
757 **265** 6t. multicoloured . . . . 1·00 60

2000. Insects. Multicoloured.
758 2t. Type **266** 25 20
759 4t. Grasshopper 40 25
760 6t. Bumble bee 55 45
761 10t. Silkworms . . . . 90 1·25

267 Gecko

2000. Native Fauna. Multicoloured.
762 4t. Type **267** 45 45
763 4t. Indian crested porcupine 45 45
764 6t. Indian black-tailed python 60 70
765 6t. Bengal monitor 60 70

268 Batsman

2000. Pepsi 7th Asia Cricket Cup.
766 **268** 6t. multicoloured . . . . 1·25 65

269 Water Cock

2000. Birds. Multicoloured.
767 4t. Type **269** 55 50
768 4t. White-breasted waterhen (*Amaurornis phoenicurus*) 55 50
769 6t. Javanese cormorant (*Phalacrocorax niger*) (vert) 70 70
770 6t. Indian pond heron (*Ardeola grayii*) (vert) . . . 70 70

270 Women's Shotput

2000. Olympic Games, Sydney. Multicoloured.
771 6t. Type **270** 65 30
772 10t. Men's Shotput . . . . . 95 1·25

271 Clasped Hands, Landmarks and Flags

2000. 25th Anniv of Diplomatic Relations with People's Republic of China.
773 **271** 6t. multicoloured 70 35

272 Idrakpur Fort, Munshigonj

2000. Archaeology. Multicoloured.
774 4t. Type **272** 50 30
775 6t. Statue of Buddha, Mainamati (vert) 75 60

273 Year Emblem

2000. International Volunteers' Year.
776 **273** 6t. multicoloured 70 35

274 Hason Raza

2000. 80th Death Anniv of Hason Raza (mystic poet).
777 **274** 6t. multicoloured 70 35

275 U.N.H.C.R. Logo

2000. 50th Anniv of United Nations High Commissioner for Refugees (U.N.H.C.R.).
778 **275** 10t. multicoloured . . . . 80 1·00

2000. Martyred Intellectuals (9th series). As T **148**. Each black and brown.
779 2t. M. A. Gofur 30 30
780 2t. Faizur Rahman Ahmed 30 30
781 2t. Muslimuddin Miah . . . 30 30
782 2t. Sgt. Shamsul Karim Khan 30 30
783 2t. Bhikku Zinananda . . . 30 30
784 2t. Abdul Jabber 30 30
785 2t. Sekander Hayat Chowdhury 30 30
786 2t. Chishty Shah Helalur Rahman 30 30
787 2t. Birendra Nath Sarker . . 30 30
788 2t. A. K. M. Nurul Haque 30 30
789 2t. Sibendra Nath Mukherjee 30 30
790 2t. Zahir Raihan 30 30
791 2t. Ferdous Dowla Bablu . . 30 30
792 2t. Capt A. K. M. Nurul Absur 30 30
793 2t. Mizanur Rahman Miju 30 30
794 2t. Dr. Shamshad Ali 30 30

276 Map of Faces

2001. Population and Housing Census.
795 **276** 4t. multicoloured 75 35

277 Producing Food

2001. "Hunger-free Bangladesh" Campaign.
796 **277** 6t. multicoloured 75 40

278 "Peasant Women" (Rashid Chowdbury)

2001. Bangladesh Paintings.
797 **278** 10t. multicoloured . . . . 1·00 1·00

279 Lalbagh Kella Mosque

2001. Historic Buildings. Multicoloured.
798 6t. Type **279** 40 45
799 6t. Uttara Ganabhavan, Natore 40 45
800 6t. Armenian Church, Armanitola 40 45
801 6t. Panam Nagar, Sonargaon 40 45

280 Smoking Accessories, Globe and Paper People

2001. World No Tobacco Day.
802 **280** 10t. multicoloured . . . . 1·00 1·00

281 Ustad Gul Mohammad Khan

282 Begum Sufia Kamal

2001. Artists. Multicoloured.
803 6t. Type **281** 45 50
804 6t. Ustad Khadem Hossain Khan 45 50
805 6t. Gouhar Jamil 45 50
806 6t. Abdul Alim 45 50

2001. Begum Sufia Kamal (poet) Commemoration.
807 **282** 4t. multicoloured 50 25

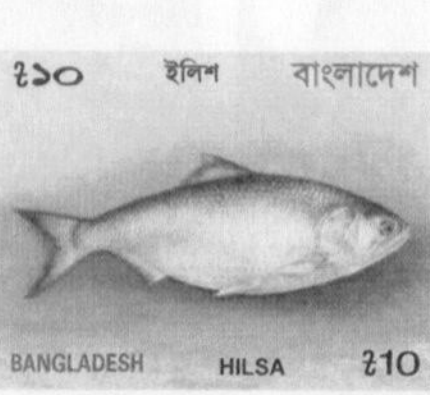

283 Hilsa

2001. Fish. Multicoloured.
808 10t. Type **283** 70 80
809 10t. Tengra 70 80
810 10t. Punti 70 80
811 10t. Khalisa 70 80

284 Parliament House, Dhaka

2001. Completion of First Full National Parliamentary Term.
812 **284** 10t. multicoloured . . . . 1·50 1·50

285 Parliament House, Dhaka

2001. 8th Parliamentary Elections.
813 **285** 2t. multicoloured 50 35

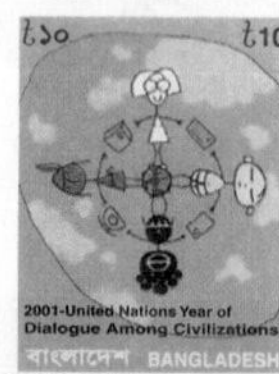

286 "Children encircling Globe" (Urska Golob)

2001. U.N. Year of Dialogue among Civilizations.
814 **286** 10t. multicoloured . . . . 1·00 1·00
MS815 95×65 mm. **286** 10t. multicoloured (sold at 30t.) . . 1·50 1·75

287 Meer Mosharraf Hossain

2001. Meer Mosharraf Hossain (writer) Commemoration.
816 **287** 4t. black, red and crimson 50 30

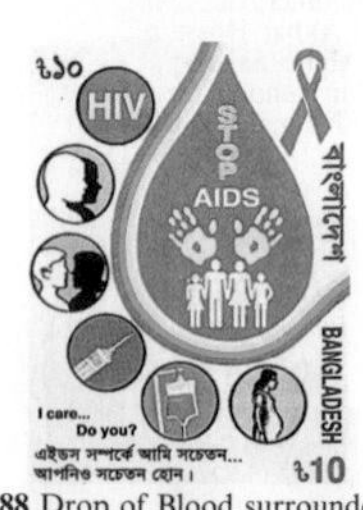

288 Drop of Blood surrounded by Images

2001. World AIDS Day.
817 **288** 10t. multicoloured . . . . 1·25 1·25

289 Sreshto Medal

2001. 30th Anniv of Independence. Gallantry Medals. Multicoloured.
818 10t. Type **289** . . . . 1·00 1·25
819 10t. Uttom medal . . . . . 1·00 1·25
820 10t. Bikram medal . . . . . 1·00 1·25
821 10t. Protik medal . . . . . 1·00 1·25

290 Publicity Poster

2002. 10th Asian Art Biennale, Dhaka.
822 **290** 10t. multicoloured . . . . 1·00 1·00

291 Letters from Bengali Alphabet

2002. 50th Anniv of Amar Ekushey (language movement). International Mother Language Day.
823 **291** 10t. black, gold and red 80 1·00
824 – 10t. black, gold and red 80 1·00
825 – 10t. black, gold and red 80 1·00
MS826 96 × 64 mm. 30t. multicoloured . . . . 2·00 2·25
DESIGNS—HORIZ: No. 824, Language Martyrs' Monument, Dhaka; 825, Letters from Bengali alphabet ("INTERNATIONAL MOTHER LANGUAGE DAY" inscr at right). VERT: No. **MS**826, Commemorative symbol of Martyrs' Monument.

292 Rokuon-Ji Temple, Japan

2002. 30th Anniv of Diplomatic Relations with Japan.
827 **292** 10t. multicoloured . . . . 1·00 1·00

293 Silhouetted Goats

2002. Goat Production.
828 **293** 2t. multicoloured 30 20

294 Children

2002. U.N. Special Session on Children.
829 **294** 10t. multicoloured . . . . 1·00 1·00

295 Mohammad Nasiruddin

2002. Mohammad Nasiruddin (journalist) Commemoration.
830 **295** 4t. black and brown . . . 50 30

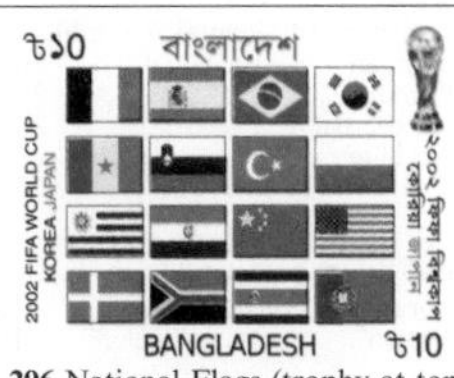

296 National Flags (trophy at top right)

2002. World Cup Football Championship, Japan and Korea. Multicoloured.
831 10t. Type **296** . . . . 90 1·00
832 10t. Pitch markings on world map . . . . 90 1·00
833 10t. National flags (trophy at top left) . . . . 90 1·00

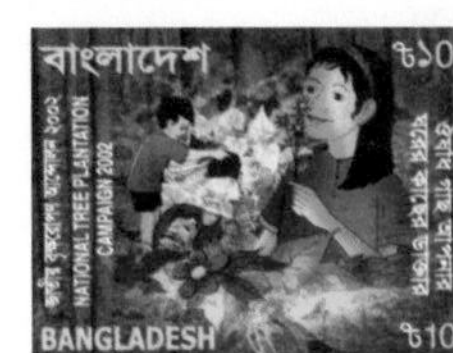

297 Children tending Saplings

2002. National Tree Planting Campaign. Mult.
834 10t. Type **297** . . . . 90 1·00
835 10t. Citrus fruit . . . . . . 90 1·00
836 10t. Trees within leaf symbol (vert) . . . . 90 1·00

298 Children inside Symbolic House

2002. 30th Anniv of S.O.S. Children's Village in Bangladesh.
837 **298** 6t. multicoloured 70 35

299 Rural Family

2002. World Population Day.
838 **299** 6t. multicoloured 70 35

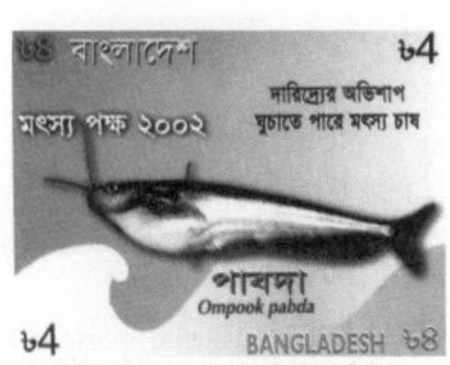

300 Ompook Pabda (fish)

2002. Fish. Multicoloured.
839 4t. Type **300** 50 50
840 4t. *Labeo gonius* 50 50

301 Bangladesh–U.K. Friendship Bridge, Bhairab

2002. Opening of Bangladesh–U.K. Friendship Bridge, Bhairab.
841 **301** 4t. multicoloured 55 30

302 Dhaka City Centre

2002. World Habitat Day.
842 **302** 4t. multicoloured 55 30

303 Dariabandha (Tag)

2002. Rural Games. Multicoloured.
843 4t. Type **303** 50 50
844 4t. Kanamachee (Blind-man's buff) 50 50

304 Jasimuddin

2003. Birth Centenary of Jasimuddin (poet).
845 **304** 5t. multicoloured 10 10

305 Books

2003. National Book Year.
846 **305** 6t. multicoloured 10 10

OFFICIAL STAMPS

1973. Nos. 22, etc. optd **SERVICE**.
O 1 **7** 2p. black . . . . 10 1·50
O 2 – 3p. green . . . . 10 1·50
O 3 – 5p. brown 20 10
O 4 – 10p. black 20 10
O 5 – 20p. green . . . . 1·75 10
O 6 – 25p. mauve . . . . 4·00 10
O 7 – 60p. grey . . . . 4·00 2·25
O 8 – 75p. orange . . . . 1·50 30
O 9 **8** 1t. violet . . . . 12·00 5·50
O10 – 5t. blue . . . . 5·00 9·00

1974. Nos. 49/51 optd **SERVICE**.
O11 **14** 1t. violet . . . . 5·00 50
O12 – 2t. olive . . . . 7·00 2·25
O13 – 5t. blue . . . . 12·00 12·00

1976. Nos. 64/70 and 72/4 optd **SERVICE**.
O14 – 5p. green . . . . 1·50 1·00
O15 – 10p. black . . . . 2·00 1·00
O16 – 20p. green . . . . 2·25 1·00
O17 – 25p. mauve . . . . 3·25 1·00
O18 – 50p. purple . . . . 3·75 60
O19 – 60p. grey . . . . 30 2·75
O20 – 75p. olive . . . . 30 3·50
O21 **14** 1t. blue . . . . 2·75 50
O22 – 2t. green . . . . 35 2·25
O23 – 5t. blue . . . . 30 2·25

1981. Nos. 125/37 optd **SERVICE**.
O24 – 5p. brown . . . . 1·75 2·50
O25 **32** 10p. blue . . . . 1·75 2·75
O26 – 15p. orange . . . . 1·75 2·50
O27 – 20p. red . . . . 1·50 2·50
O28 – 25p. blue . . . . 80 2·50
O29 – 30p. green . . . . 3·25 3·00
O30 – 40p. purple . . . . 2·75 2·50
O31 – 50p. black 30 10
O32 – 80p. brown . . . . 2·25 50
O33 – 1t. violet 30 10
O34 – 2t. blue . . . . 35 2·75

1983. Nos. 220/9, 318a and 710 (1989) optd **Service**.
O35 **69** 5p. blue 10 10
O36 – 10p. purple 10 10
O37 – 15p. blue 10 10
O38 – 20p. black 10 10
O39 – 25p. grey 10 10
O40 – 30p. brown 10 10
O41 – 50p. brown 10 10
O42 – 1t. blue . . . . 1·25 10
O43 – 2t. green 10 10
O44 – 3t. black and blue 10 10
O45 – 4t. blue 10 15
O46 – 5t. purple . . . . 2·00 80

সার্ভিস (O 5) (O 6) সার্ভিস (O 7)

1989. Nos. 227 and 710 (1989) optd with Type O **5**.
O47 1t. blue 20 10
O48 5t. black and brown 80 90

1990. Nos. 368/9 (Immunization) optd with Type O **6**.
O49 **133** 1t. green 10 10
O50 2t. brown 10 10

1992. No. 376 optd as Type O **6** but horiz.
O51 **136** 6t. blue and yellow . . . 10 15

1995. No. 553 (National Diabetes Awareness Day) optd as Type O **6** but horiz.
O52 **199** 2t. multicoloured . . . . 1·00 1·00

1996. Nos. 221 and 223 optd with Type O **7**.
O53 10p. purple 50 50
O54 20p. black 75 75

1999. No. 710 optd as Type O **5** but vert.
O56 5t. black and brown 10 15

BARBADOS Pt. 1

An island in the Br. West Indies, E. of the Windward Islands, attained self-government on 16 October 1961 and achieved independence within the Commonwealth on 30 November 1966.

1852. 12 pence = 1 shilling;
20 shillings = 1 pound.
1950. 100 cents = 1 West Indian, later Barbados, dollar.

1 Britannia

2

1852. Imperf.
8 **1** (½d.) green £130 £200
10 (1d.) blue . . . . 32·00 60·00
4a (2d.) slate £250 £1200
5 (4d.) red . . . . 90·00 £275
11 **2** 6d. red £700 £120
12a 1s. black . . . . £200 75·00

1860. Perf.
21 **1** (½d.) green . . . . 16·00 13·00
24 (1d.) blue . . . . 35·00 3·50
25 (4d.) red . . . . 85·00 40·00
31 **2** 6d. red . . . . 85·00 21·00
33 6d. orange . . . . £110 30·00
35 1s. black . . . . 55·00 7·00

1873. Perf.
72 **2** ½d. green . . . . 11·00 50
74 1d. blue . . . . 60·00 65
63 3d. brown £325 £110
75 3d. mauve . . . . £110 6·50
76 4d. red . . . . £110 8·50
79 6d. yellow . . . . £120 1·00
81 1s. purple . . . . £140 3·50

3

4

1873.
64 **3** 5s. red £950 £300

1878. Half of No. 64 surch **1D**.
86 **3** 1d. on half 5s. red £4250 £650

1882.
90 **4** ½d. green . . . . 16·00 1·50
92 1d. red . . . . 19·00 1·00
93 2½d. blue . . . . 90·00 1·50
96 3d. purple . . . . 4·25 17·00
97 4d. grey . . . . £250 3·25
99 4d. brown . . . . 5·00 1·50
100 6d. brown . . . . 75·00 42·00
102 1s. brown . . . . 27·00 21·00
103 5s. bistre £150 £190

1892. Surch **HALF-PENNY**.
104 **4** ½d. on 4d. brown . . . . . 2·25 4·50

6 Seal of Colony 7

1892.
105 6 ½d. grey and red 2·50 10
163 ½d. brown 8·00 30
106 ½d. green 2·50 10
107 1d. red 4·75 10
108 2d. black and orange 8·00 75
166 2d. grey 7·50 11·00
139 2½d. blue 18·00 15
110 5d. olive 7·00 4·50
111 6d. mauve and red 16·00 2·00
168 6d. deep purple and purple 10·00 15·00
112 8d. orange and blue 4·00 22·00
113 10d. green and red 8·00 6·50
169 1s. black on green 10·00 14·00
114 2s.6d. black and orange 48·00 48·00
144 2s.6d. violet and green 42·00 95·00

1897. Diamond Jubilee.
116 7 ¼d. grey and red 4·00 60
117 ½d. green 4·00 60
118 1d. red 4·00 60
119 2½d. blue 7·50 85
120 5d. brown 18·00 16·00
121 6d. mauve and red 24·00 22·00
122 8d. orange and blue 9·50 24·00
123 10d. green and red 48·00 55·00
124 2s.6d. black and orange 70·00 55·00

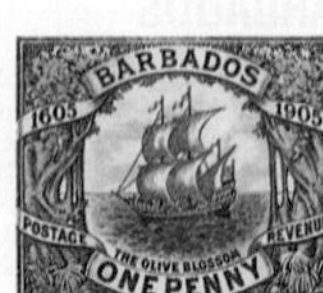

8 Nelson Monument 9 "Olive Blossom", 1650

1906. Death Centenary of Nelson.
145 8 ¼d. black and grey 8·50 1·75
146 ½d. black and green 9·50 15
147 1d. black and red 12·00 15
148 2d. black and yellow 1·75 4·50
149 2½d. black and blue 3·75 1·25
150 6d. black and mauve 18·00 25·00
151 1s. black and red 21·00 50·00

1906. Tercentenary of Annexation of Barbados.
152 9 1d. black, blue and green 10·00 25

1907. Surch **Kingston Relief Fund. 1d.**
153 6 1d. on 2d. black and orange 2·75 6·50

11 14

1912.
170 11 ¼d. brown 1·50 1·50
171 ½d. green 3·75 10
172 1d. red 9·00 10
173 2d. grey 3·00 14·00
174 2½d. blue 1·50 50
175 3d. purple on yellow 1·50 14·00
176 4d. red and black on yellow 1·75 18·00
177 6d. deep purple and purple 12·00 12·00
Larger type, with portrait at top centre.
178 1s. black on green 8·50 14·00
179 2s. blue and purple on blue 42·00 48·00
180 3s. violet and green 90·00 £100

1916.
181 14 ¼d. brown 75 40
182 ½d. green 1·10 15
183a 1d. red 2·50 15
184 2d. grey 4·75 22·00
185 2½d. blue 3·50 2·50
186 3d. purple on yellow 2·50 7·00
187 4d. red on yellow 1·00 14·00
199 4d. black and red 80 3·75
188 6d. purple 4·00 4·50
189 1s. black on green 7·00 11·00
190 2s. purple on blue 16·00 7·50
191 3s. violet 50·00 £130
200 3s. green and violet 20·00 70·00

1917. Optd **WAR TAX**.
197 11 1d. red 50 15

16 18

1920. Victory. Inscr "VICTORY 1919".
201 16 ¼d. black and brown 30 70
202 ½d. black and green 1·00 15
203 1d. black and red 4·00 10
204 2d. black and grey 2·25 8·00
205 2½d. indigo and blue 2·75 18·00
206 3d. black and purple 3·00 6·50
207 4d. black and green 3·25 7·00
208 6d. black and orange 3·75 15·00
209 – 1s. black and green 10·00 29·00
210 – 2s. black and brown 28·00 42·00
211 – 3s. black and orange 32·00 50·00
The 1s. to 3s. show Victory full-face.

1921.
217 18 ¼d. brown 25 10
219 ½d. green 1·50 10
220 1d. red 80 10
221 2d. grey 1·75 20
222 2½d. blue 1·50 8·00
213 3d. purple on yellow 2·00 6·50
214 4d. red on yellow 1·75 15·00
225 6d. purple 3·50 5·50
215 1s. black on green 5·50 15·00
227 2s. purple on blue 10·00 19·00
228 3s. violet 14·00 60·00

19 21 Badge of the Colony

20 King Charles I and King George V

1925. Inscr "POSTAGE & REVENUE".
229 19 ¼d. brown 25 10
230 ½d. green 50 10
231 1d. red 50 10
231ba 1½d. orange 2·00 1·00
232 2d. grey 50 3·25
233 2½d. blue 50 80
234 3d. purple on yellow 1·00 45
235 4d. red on yellow 75 1·00
236 6d. purple 1·00 90
237 1s. black on green 2·00 6·50
238 2s. purple on blue 7·00 6·50
238a 2s.6d. red on blue 22·00 28·00
239 3s. violet 11·00 13·00

1927. Tercentenary of Settlement of Barbados.
240 20 1d. red 1·00 75

1935. Silver Jubilee. As T **13** of Antigua.
241 1d. blue and red 50 20
242 1½d. blue and grey 3·75 6·00
243 2½d. brown and blue 2·25 4·00
244 1s. grey and purple 17·00 18·00

1937. Coronation. As T **2** of Aden.
245 1d. red 30 15
246 1½d. brown 40 65
247 2½d. blue 70 75

1938. "POSTAGE & REVENUE" omitted.
248 21 ½d. green 6·00 15
248c ½d. bistre 15 30
249a 1d. red 16·00 10
249c 1d. green 15 10
250 1½d. orange 15 40
250c 2d. purple 50 2·50
250d 2d. red 20 70
251 2½d. blue 50 60
252b 3d. brown 20 60
252c 3d. blue 20 1·75
253 4d. black 20 10
254 6d. violet 80 40
254a 8d. mauve 55 2·00
255a 1s. green 1·00 10
256 2s.6d. purple 7·00 1·50
256a 5s. blue 3·25 7·00

22 Kings Charles I, George VI, Assembly Chamber and Mace

1939. Tercentenary of General Assembly.
257 22 ½d. green 2·75 1·00
258 1d. red 2·75 35
259 1½d. orange 2·75 60
260 2½d. blue 2·75 4·50
261 3d. brown 2·75 3·00

1946. Victory. As T **9** of Aden.
262 1½d. orange 15 15
263 3d. brown 15 15

1947. Surch **ONE PENNY**.
264 17 1d. on 2d. red 1·75 2·50

1948. Silver Wedding. As T **10/11** of Aden.
265 1½d. orange 30 10
266 5s. blue 10·00 8·00

1949. U.P.U. As T **20/23** of Antigua.
267 1½d. orange 30 75
268 3d. blue 2·00 2·50
269 4d. grey 35 2·50
270 1s. olive 35 60

24 Dover Fort

35 Seal of Barbados

1950.
271 24 1c. blue 30 2·75
272 – 2c. green 15 2·00
273 – 3c. brown and green 1·25 3·00
274 – 4c. red 15 40
275 – 6c. blue 15 2·25
276 – 8c. blue and purple 1·25 2·50
277 – 12c. blue and olive 1·00 1·00
278 – 24c. red and black 1·00 50
279 – 48c. violet 8·50 6·50
280 – 60c. green and lake 9·50 9·00
281 – $1.20 red and olive 9·50 4·00
282 35 $2.40 black 17·00 18·00
DESIGNS—As Type **24**: HORIZ: 2c. Sugar cane breeding; 3c. Public buildings; 6c. Casting net; 8c. "Frances W. Smith" (schooner); 12c. Four-winged flyingfish; 24c. Old Main Guard Garrison; 60c. Careenage. VERT: 4c. Statue of Nelson; 48c. St. Michael's Cathedral; $1.20, Map and wireless mast.

1951. Inauguration of B.W.I. University College. As T **24/25** of Antigua.
283 3c. brown and blue 30 30
284 12c. blue and olive 55 2·00

36 King George VI and Stamp of 1852

1952. Centenary of Barbados Stamps.
285 36 3c. green and slate 25 40
286 4c. blue and red 25 1·00
287 12c. slate and green 30 1·00
288 24c. brown and sepia 30 55

37 Harbour Police

1953. As 1950 issue but with portrait or cypher (No. 301) of Queen Elizabeth II as in T **37**.
289 24 1c. blue 10 80
290 – 2c. orange and turquoise 15 60
291 – 3c. black and green 1·00 90
292 – 4c. black and orange 20 20
293 37 5c. blue and red 1·00 60
294 – 6c. brown 50 60
314 – 8c. black and blue 60 35
296 – 12c. blue and olive 1·00 10
297 – 24c. red and black 50 10
298 – 48c. violet 6·00 1·00
318 – 60c. green and purple 10·00 4·00
300 – $1.20 red and olive 19·00 3·75
319 35 $2.40 black 1·25 1·75

1953. Coronation. As T **13** of Aden.
302 4c. black and orange 40 10

1958. British Caribbean Federation. As T **28** of Antigua.
303 3c. green 35 20
304 6c. blue 50 2·25
305 12c. red 50 30

38 Deep Water Harbour, Bridgetown

1961. Opening of Deep Water Harbour.
306 38 4c. black and orange 25 50
307 8c. black and blue 25 60
308 24c. red and black 25 60

39 Scout Badge and Map of Barbados

1962. Golden Jubilee of Barbados Boy Scout Association.
309 39 4c. black and orange 50 10
310 12c. blue and brown 80 15
311 $1.20 red and green 1·50 3·75

1965. Centenary of I.T.U. As T **36** of Antigua.
320 2c. lilac and red 20 40
321 48c. yellow and drab 45 1·00

40 Deep Sea Coral

1965.
342 40 1c. black, pink and blue 10 20
323 – 2c. brown, yell & mve 20 15
324 – 3c. brown and orange 45 60
344 – 3c. brown and orange 30 2·75
325 – 4c. blue and green 15 10
326 – 5c. sepia, red and lilac 30 20
327 – 6c. multicoloured 45 20
328 – 8c. multicoloured 25 10
329 – 12c. multicoloured 35 10
330 – 15c. black, yellow and red 1·50 30
331 – 25c. blue and ochre 95 30
332 – 35c. red and green 1·50 15
333 – 50c. blue and green 2·00 40
334 – $1 multicoloured 3·00 1·75
335 – $2.50 multicoloured 2·75 3·75
355a – $5 multicoloured 13·00 8·00
DESIGNS—HORIZ: 2c. Lobster; 3c. (No. 324) Lined seahorse (wrongly inscribed "Hippocanpus"); 3c. (No. 344) (correctly inscribed "Hippocampus"); 4c. Sea urchin; 5c. Staghorn coral; 6c. Spot-finned butterflyfish; 8c. Rough file shell; 12c. Porcupinefish ("Balloon fish"); 15c Grey angel-fish; 25c. Brain coral; 35c. Brittle star; 50c. Four-winged flyingfish: $1 Queen or pink conch shell; $2.50, Fiddler crab. VERT: $5 Dolphin.

1966. Churchill Commemoration. As T **38** of Antigua.
336 1c. blue 10 2·50
337 4c. green 30 10
338 25c. brown 70 50
339 35c. violet 80 60

1966. Royal Visit. As T **39** of Antigua.
340 3c. black and blue 35 1·00
341 35c. black and mauve 1·40 1·00

54 Arms of Barbados 58 Policeman and Anchor

1966. Independence. Multicoloured.
356 4c. Type **54** 10 10
357 25c. Hilton Hotel (horiz) 15 10
358 35c. G. Sobers (Test cricketer) 1·50 65
359 50c. Pine Hill Dairy (horiz) 70 1·10

1967. 20th Anniv of U.N.E.S.C.O. As T **54/56** of Antigua.
360 4c. multicoloured 20 10
361 12c. yellow, violet and olive 45 50
362 25c. black, purple and orange 75 1·25

1967. Centenary of Harbour Police. Multicoloured.
363 4c. Type **58** 25 10
364 25c. Policeman and telescope 40 15

365 35c. "BPI" (police launch) (horiz) 45 15
366 50c. Policeman outside H.Q. 60 1·60

62 Governor-General Sir Winston Scott G.C.M.G

67 Radar Antenna

66 U.N. Building, Santiago, Chile

1967. 1st Anniv of Independence. Multicoloured.
367 4c. Type **62** 10 10
368 25c. Independence Arch (horiz) 20 10
369 35c. Treasury Building (horiz) 25 10
370 50c. Parliament Building (horiz) 35 90

1968. 20th Anniv of Economic Commission for Latin America.
371 **66** 15c. multicoloured 10 10

1968. World Meteorological Day. Multicoloured.
372 3c. Type **67** 10 10
373 25c. Meteorological Institute (horiz) 25 10
374 50c. Harp Gun and Coat of Arms 30 90

70 Lady Baden-Powell and Guide at Campfire

1968. Golden Jubilee of Girl Guiding in Barbados.
375 **70** 3c. blue, black and gold . . 20 60
376 – 25c. blue, black and gold 30 60
377 – 35c. yellow, black and gold 35 60
DESIGNS: 25c. Lady Baden-Powell and Pax Hill; 35c. Lady Baden-Powell and Guides' Badge.

73 Hands breaking Chain, and Human Rights Emblem

1968. Human Rights Year.
378 **73** 4c. violet, brown and green 10 20
379 – 25c. black, blue and yellow 10 25
380 – 35c. multicoloured 15 25
DESIGNS: 25c. Human Rights emblem and family enchained; 35c. Shadows of refugees beyond opening fence.

76 Racehorses in the Paddock

1969. Horse Racing. Multicoloured.
381 4c. Type **76** 25 15
382 25c. Starting-gate 25 15
383 35c. On the flat 30 15
384 50c. The winning-post . . . 35 2·00
MS385 117 × 85 mm. Nos. 381/4 2·00 2·75

80 Map showing "CARIFTA" Countries

1969. 1st Anniv of "CARIFTA". Multicoloured.
386 5c. Type **80** 10 10
387 12c. "Strength in Unity" (horiz) 10 10
388 25c. Type **80** 10 10
389 50c. As 12c. 15 20

82 I.L.O. Emblem and "1919–1969"

1969. 50th Anniv of I.L.O.
390 **82** 4c. black, green and blue 10 10
391 25c. black, mauve and red 20 10

1969. No. 363 surch **ONE CENT**.
392 **58** 1c. on 4c. multicoloured . . 10 10

84 National Scout Badge

1969. Independence of Barbados Boy Scouts Association and 50th Anniv of Barbados Sea Scouts. Multicoloured.
393 5c. Type **84** 15 10
394 25c. Sea Scouts rowing . . . 45 10
395 35c. Scouts around campfire 55 10
396 50c. Scouts and National Scout H.Q. . . . . 80 1·25
MS397 155 × 115 mm. Nos. 393/6 12·00 13·00

1970. No. 346 surch **4**.
398 4c. on 5c. sepia, red and lilac 10 10

89 Lion at Gun Hill

1970. Multicoloured.
399 1c. Type **89** . . . . 10 1·50
400 2c. Trafalgar Fountain . . . 30 1·25
401 3c. Montefiore Drinking Fountain . . . . 10 1·00
402a 4c. St. James' Monument . . 30 10
403 5c. St. Ann's Fort 10 10
404 6c. Old Sugar Mill, Morgan Lewis . . . . 35 3·00
405 8c. The Cenotaph 10 10
406a 10c. South Point Lighthouse 1·25 15
407 12c. Barbados Museum (horiz) . . . . 1·50 10
408 15c. Sharon Moravian Church (horiz) 30 15
409 25c. George Washington House (horiz) 25 15
410 35c. Nicholas Abbey (horiz) 30 85
411 50c. Bowmanston Pumping Station (horiz) . . . . . 40 1·00
412 $1 Queen Elizabeth Hospital (horiz) . . . . 70 2·50
413 $2.50 Suger Factory (horiz) 1·50 4·00
467 $5 Seawell International Airport (horiz) . . . . . 4·50 5·50

105 Primary Schoolgirl

1970. 25th Anniv of U.N. Multicoloured.
415 4c. Type **105** 10 10
416 5c. Secondary schoolboy . . 10 10
417 25c. Technical student . . . 35 10
418 50c. University building . . . 55 1·50

106 Minnie Root

1970. Flowers of Barbados. Multicoloured.
419 1c. Barbados Easter lily (vert) 10 2·00
420 5c. Type **106** 40 10
421 10c. Eyelash orchid . . . . . 1·75 30
422 25c. Pride of Barbados (vert) 1·25 75
423 35c. Christmas hope . . . . 1·25 85
MS424 162 × 101 mm. Nos. 419/23. Imperf . . . . 2·00 6·00

107 "Via Dolorosa" Window, St. Margaret's Church, St. John

109 S. J. Prescod (politician)

108 "Sailfish" Dinghy

1971. Easter. Multicoloured.
425 4c. Type **107** 10 10
426 10c. "The Resurrection" (Benjamin West) 10 10
427 35c. Type **107** 15 10
428 50c. As 10c. . . . . 30 1·50

1971. Tourism. Multicoloured.
429 1c. Type **108** 10 40
430 5c. Tennis 40 10
431 12c. Horse-riding 60 10
432 25c. Water-skiing 40 20
433 50c. Scuba-diving 50 80

1971. Death Centenary of Samuel Jackman Prescod.
434 **109** 3c. multicoloured 10 15
435 35c. multicoloured 15 15

110 Arms of Barbados

1971. 5th Anniv of Independence. Multicoloured.
436 4c. Type **110** 20 10
437 15c. National flag and map 45 10
438 25c. Type **110** 45 10
439 50c. As 15c. . . . . 90 1·60

111 Transmitting "Then and Now"

1972. Centenary of Cable Link. Multicoloured.
440 4c. Type **111** 10 10
441 10c. Cable Ship "Stanley Angwin" 20 10
442 35c. Barbados Earth Station and "Intelsat 4" 35 20
443 50c. Mt. Misery and Tropospheric Scatter Station . . . . 50 1·75

112 Map and Badge

1972. Diamond Jubilee of Scouts. Multicoloured.
444 5c. Type **112** 15 10
445 15c. Pioneers of scouting (horiz) 15 10
446 25c. Scouts (horiz) 30 15
447 50c. Flags (horiz) . . . . . 60 1·00

113 Mobile Library

1972. Int Book Year. Multicoloured.
448 4c. Type **113** 20 10
449 15c. Visual-aids van 25 10
450 25c. Public library 25 10
451 $1 Codrington College . . . 1·00 1·50

114 Potter's Wheel

1973. Pottery in Barbados. Multicoloured.
468 5c. Type **114** 10 10
469 15c. Kilns 20 10
470 25c. Finished products . . . 25 10
471 $1 Market scene . . . . . . 90 1·10

115 First Flight, 1911

1973. Aviation.
472 **115** 5c. multicoloured 30 10
473 – 15c. multicoloured 90 10
474 – 25c. blue, blk & cobalt . . 1·25 20
475 – 50c. multicoloured . . . . 2·00 1·90
DESIGNS: 15c. De Havilland Cirrus Moth on first flight to Barbados, 1928; 25c. Lockheed Super Electra, 1939; 50c. Vickers Super VC-10 airliner, 1973.

116 University Chancellor

1973. 25th Anniv of University of West Indies. Multicoloured.
476 5c. Type **116** 10 10
477 25c. Sherlock Hall 25 15
478 35c. Cave Hill Campus . . . 30 25

1974. No. 462 surch **4c.**
479 4c. on 25c. multicoloured . . 15 15

118 Old Sail Boat

1974. Fishing Boats of Barbados. Multicoloured.
480 15c. Type **118** 30 15
481 35c. Rowing-boat 55 25
482 50c. Motor fishing-boat . . . 70 70
483 $1 "Calamar" (fishing boat) 1·10 1·40
MS484 140 × 140 mm. Nos. 480/3 3·50 3·00

119 "Cattleya gaskelliana alba"

1974. Orchids. Multicoloured.

510 1c. Type **119** . . . . . . 15 1·25
511 2c. "Renanthera storiei" (vert) . . . . 15 1·25
512 3c. "Dendrobium" "Rose Marie" (vert) . . . . . . 15 1·00
488 4c. "Epidendrum ibaguense" (vert) . . . . 1·75 90
514 5c. "Schomburgkia humboldtii" (vert) 35 15
490 8c. "Oncidium ampliatum" (vert) . . . . 1·50 90
515 10c. "Arachnis maggie oei" (vert) 35 10
492 12c. "Dendrobium aggregatum" (vert) . . . 45 2·75
517 15c. "Paphiopedilum puddle" (vert) 70 15
493b 20c. "Spathoglottis" "The Gold" . . . . 4·75 4·75
518 25c. "Epidendrum ciliare" (Eyelash) 70 10
550 35c. "Bletia patula" (vert) 2·00 1·75
519 45c. "Phalaenopsis schilleriana" "Sunset Glow" (vert) 60 15
496 50c. As 45c. (vert) . . . . . 6·00 4·50
497 $1 "Ascocenda" "Red Gem" (vert) . . . . . . 9·00 3·25
498 $2.50 "Brassolaeliocattleya" "Nugget" . . . . 3·00 7·00
499 $5 "Caularthron bicornutum" . . . . . . 3·00 6·00
500 $10 "Vanda" "Josephine Black" (vert) . . . . . . 3·50 13·00

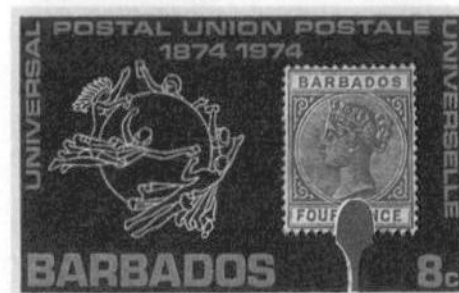

120 4d. Stamp of 1882, and U.P.U. Emblem

1974. Centenary of Universal Postal Union.

501 **120** 8c. mauve, orange & grn 10 10
502 – 35c. red, orge & brown 20 10
503 – 50c. ultram, bl & silver 25 35
504 – $1 blue, brown & black 55 1·00
MS505 126 × 101 mm. Nos. 501/4 1·75 2·25

DESIGNS: 35c. Letters encircling the globe; 50c. U.P.U. emblem and arms of Barbados; $1 Map of Barbados, sailing ship and Boeing 747 airliner.

121 Royal Yacht "Britannia"

1975. Royal Visit. Multicoloured.

506 8c. Type **121** 85 30
507 25c. Type **121** . . . . . . 1·40 30
508 35c. Sunset and palms . . . 60 35
509 $1 As 35c. . . . . 1·75 4·00

122 St. Michael's Cathedral

1975. 150th Anniv of Anglican Diocese. Mult.

526 5c. Type **122** 10 10
527 15c. Bishop Coleridge 15 10
528 50c. All Saints' Church . . . 45 50
529 $1 "Archangel Michael and Satan" (stained glass window, St. Michael's Cathedral, Bridgetown) . . 70 80

123 Pony Float

1975. Crop-over Festival. Multicoloured.

531 8c. Type **123** 10 10
532 25c. Man on stilts 10 10
533 35c. Maypole dancing . . . 15 10
534 50c. Cuban dancers 30 80
MS535 127 × 85 mm. Nos. 531/4 1·00 1·60

124 Barbados Coat of Arms

125 17th-Century Sailing Ship

1975. Coil Definitives.

536 **124** 5c. blue 15 80
537 25c. violet . . . . 25 1·10

1975. 350th Anniv of First Settlement. Multicoloured.

538 4c. Type **125** 50 20
539 10c. Bearded fig tree and fruit 30 15
540 25c. Ogilvy's 17th-century map . . . . 1·00 30
541 $1 Captain John Powell . . . 1·00 5·00
MS542 105 × 115 mm. Nos. 538/41 2·50 7·00

126 Map of Caribbean

1976. West Indian Victory in World Cricket Cup.

559 **126** 25c. multicoloured . . . . 1·00 1·00
560 – 45c. black and purple . . 1·00 2·00

DESIGN—VERT: 45c. The Prudential Cup.

127 Flag and Map of South Carolina

1976. Bicentenary of American Revolution. Mult.

561 15c. Type **127** 45 15
562 25c. George Washington and map of Bridgetown 45 15
563 50c. Independence Declaration . . . . 60 1·00
564 $1 Prince Hall . . . . 75 3·00

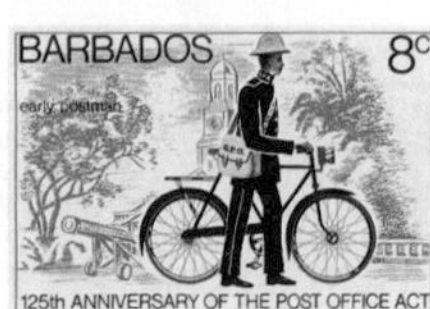

128 Early Postman

1976. 125th Anniv of Post Office Act. Multicoloured.

565 8c. Type **128** 10 10
566 35c. Modern postman . . . 25 10
567 50c. Early letter 30 75
568 $1 Delivery van . . . . . . 50 1·75

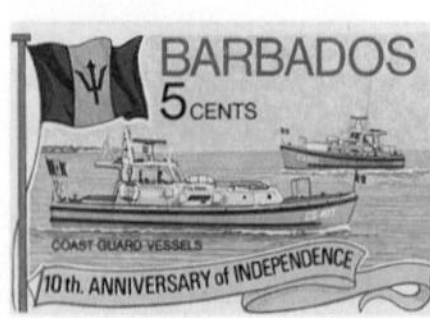

129 Coast Guard "Commander Marshall" and "T. T. Lewis" launches

1976. 10th Anniv of Independence. Multicoloured.

569 5c. Type **129** 30 20
570 15c. Reverse of currency note 30 10
571 25c. Barbados national anthem 30 20
572 $1 Independence Day parade 1·10 3·00
MS573 90 × 125 mm. Nos. 569/72 2·75 3·75

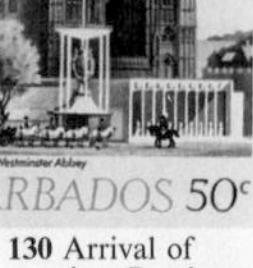

130 Arrival of Coronation Coach at Westminster Abbey

132 Maces of the House of Commons

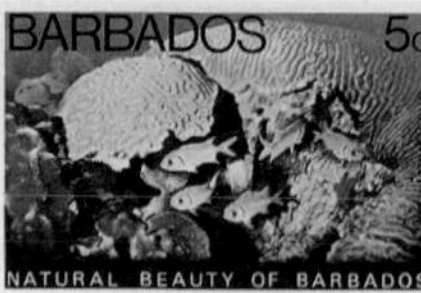

131 Underwater Park

1977. Silver Jubilee. Multicoloured.

574 15c. Queen knighting Garfield Sobers, 1975 . . . . 30 25
575 50c. Type **130** 30 40
576 $1 Queen entering Abbey . . 30 70

1977. Natural Beauty of Barbados. Multicoloured.

577 5c. Type **131** 15 10
578 35c. Royal palms (vert) . . . 30 10
579 50c. Underwater caves . . . 40 50
580 $1 Stalagmite in Harrison's Cave (vert) . . . . . . 70 1·10
MS581 138 × 92 mm. Nos. 577/80 2·25 2·75

1977. 13th Regional Conference of Commonwealth Parliamentary Association.

582 **132** 10c. orange, yellow & brn 10 10
583 – 25c. green, orge & dp grn 10 10
584 – 50c. multicoloured 20 20
585 – $1 blue, orange and dp bl 55 75

DESIGNS—VERT: 25c. Speaker's Chair; 50c. Senate Chamber. HORIZ: $1 Sam Lord's Castle.

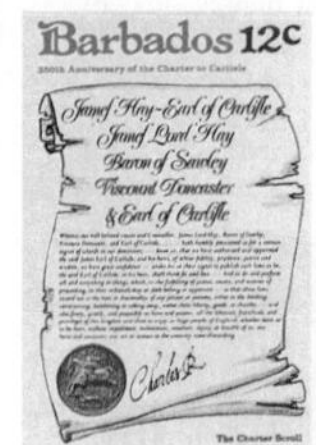

133 The Charter Scroll

135 Brown Pelican

134 Gibson's Map of Bridgtown, 1766

1977. 350th Anniv of Granting of Charter to Earl of Carlisle. Multicoloured.

586 12c. Type **133** 15 10
587 25c. The earl receiving charter 15 10
588 45c. The earl and Charles I (horiz) 30 35
589 $1 Ligon's map, 1657 (horiz) 50 1·00

1977. Royal Visit. As Nos. 574/6 but inscr "SILVER JUBILEE ROYAL VISIT".

590 15c. Garfield Sobers being knighted, 1975 . . . . . . 60 50
591 50c. Type **130** 20 75
592 $1 Queen entering Abbey . . 30 1·25

1978. 350th Anniv of Founding of Bridgetown.

593 **134** 12c. multicoloured 15 10
594 – 25c. black, green & gold 15 10
595 – 45c. multicoloured 20 15
596 – $1 multicoloured 30 60

DESIGNS: 25c. "A Prospect of Bridgetown in Barbados" (engraving by S. Copens, 1695); 45c. "Trafalgar Square, Bridgetown" (drawing by J. M. Carter, 1835); $1 The Bridges, 1978.

1978. 25th Anniv of Coronation.

597 – 50c. olive, black & blue 25 50
598 – 50c. multicoloured 25 50
599 **135** 50c. olive, black & blue 25 50

DESIGNS: No. 597, Griffin of Edward III. No. 598, Queen Elizabeth II.

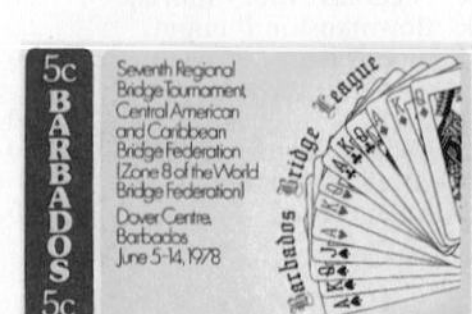

136 Barbados Bridge League Logo

1978. 7th Regional Bridge Tournament, Barbados. Multicoloured.

600 5c. Type **136** 10 10
601 10c. Emblem of World Bridge Federation 15 10
602 45c. Central American and Caribbean Bridge Federation emblem 25 10
603 $1 Playing cards on map of Caribbean 40 60
MS604 134 × 83 mm. Nos. 600/3 2·00 2·50

137 Camp Scene

1978. Diamond Jubilee of Guiding. Multicoloured.

605 12c. Type **137** 25 15
606 28c. Community work . . . 40 15
607 50c. Badge and "60" (vert) 55 30
608 $1 Guide badge (vert) . . . . 75 1·00

138 Garment Industry

1978. Industries of Barbados. Multicoloured.

609 12c. Type **138** 15 10
610 28c. Cooper (vert) 25 25
611 45c. Blacksmith (vert) 35 95
612 50c. Wrought iron working 40 95

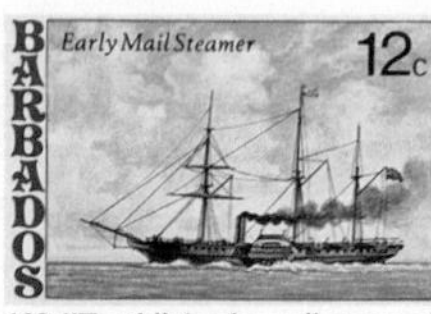

139 "Forth" (early mail steamer)

1979. Ships. Multicoloured.

613 12c. Type **139** 35 10
614 25c. "Queen Elizabeth 2" in Deep Water Harbour . . . 55 15
615 50c. "Ra II" nearing Barbados . . . . 75 1·00
616 $1 Early mail paddle-steamer 1·00 2·50

140 1953 1c. Definitive Stamp

1979. Death Cent of Sir Rowland Hill. Mult.

617 12c. Type **140** 15 15
618 28c. 1975 350th anniv of first settlement 25c. commemorative (vert) . . . 20 30
619 45c. Penny Black with Maltese Cross postmark (vert) 30 45
MS620 137 × 90 mm. 50c. Unissued "Brittannia" blue 55 50

1979. St. Vincent Relief Fund. No. 495 surch **28c+4c ST. VINCENT RELIEF FUND.**

621 28c.+4c. on 35c. "Bletia patula" 50 60

142 Grassland Yellow Finch ("Grass Canary")

1979. Birds. Multicoloured.

622 1c. Type **142** . . . . 10 1·25
623 2c. Grey kingbird ("Rainbird") . . . . . . 10 1·25
624 5c. Lesser Antillean bullfinch ("Sparrow") . . 10 70
625 8c. Magnificent frigate bird ("Frigate Bird") . . . . 75 2·25
626 10c. Cattle egret 10 40
627 12c. Green-backed heron ("Green Gaulin") . . . . 50 1·50
627a 15c. Carib grackle ("Blackbird") . . . . . . 4·50 5·00
628 20c. Antillean crested hummingbird ("Humming Bird") 20 55
629 25c. Scaly-breasted ground dove ("Ground Dove") 20 60
630 28c. As 15c. . . . . 2·00 2·00
631 35c. Green-throated carib 70 70
631b 40c. Red-necked pigeon ("Ramier") . . . . 4·50 5·50
632 45c. Zenaida dove ("Wood Dove") . . . . 1·50 1·50

633 50c. As 40c. . . . . 1·50 2·00
633a 55c. American golden plover ("Black breasted Plover") 4·00 3·50
633b 60c. Bananaquit ("Yellow Breasted") . . . . 4·50 6·00
634 70c. As 60c. . . . . 2·00 3·50
635 $1 Caribbean elaenia ("Peer whistler") . . . . 2·00 1·50
636 $2.50 American redstart ("Christmas Bird") . . . 2·00 6·00
637 $5 Belted kingfisher ("Kingfisher") . . . . . 3·25 9·00
638 $10 Moorhen ("Red-seal Coot") . . . . 4·50 14·00

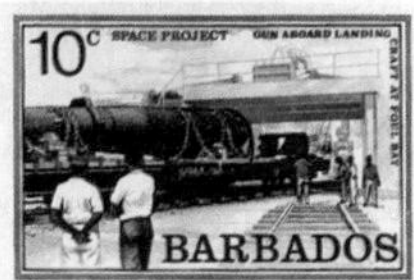

143 Unloading H.A.R.P. Gun on Railway Wagon at Foul Bay

1979. Space Projects Commemorations. Mult.
639 10c. Type **143** 15 10
640 12c. H.A.R.P. gun on railway wagon under tow (vert) . . 15 15
641 20c. Firing launcher (vert) . . 15 20
642 28c. Bath Earth Station and "Intelsat" 15 30
643 45c. "Intelsat" over Caribbean 25 50
644 50c. "Intelsat" over Atlantic (vert) 25 60
MS645 118 × 90 mm. $1 Lunar module descending on to Moon 1·00 80

144 Family

146 Private, Artillery Company, Barbados Volunteer Force, c.1909

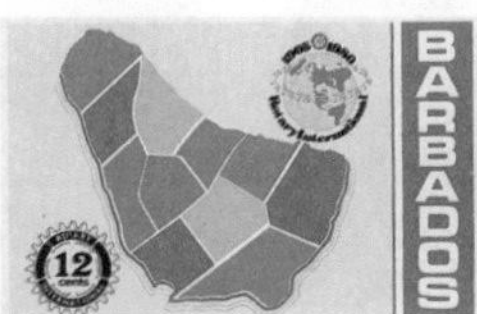

145 Map of Barbados

1979. International Year of the Child. Multicoloured.
646 12c. Type **144** 10 10
647 28c. Ring of children and map of Barbados 15 15
648 45c. Child with teacher . . . 20 20
649 50c. Children playing 20 20
650 $1 Children and kite 35 45

1980. 75th Anniv of Rotary International. Multicoloured.
651 12c. Type **145** 15 10
652 28c. Map of Caribbean . . . 15 15
653 50c. Rotary anniversary emblem 20 35
654 $1 Paul P. Harris (founder) 30 95

1980. Barbados Regiment. Multicoloured.
655 12c. Type **146** 25 10
656 35c. Drum Major, Zouave uniform 35 15
657 50c. Sovereign's and Regimental Colours . . . 40 30
658 $1 Barbados Regiment Women's Corps 55 70

147 Early Postman

1980. "London 1980" International Stamp Exhibition. Two sheets each 122 × 125 mm containing T **147** or similar vert design. Multicoloured.
MS659 (a) 28c. × 6, Type **147**. (b) 50c. × 6, Modern postwoman and Inspector Set of 2 sheets . . . 1·00 1·25

148 Yellow-tailed Snapper

1980. Underwater Scenery. Multicoloured.
660 12c. Type **148** 20 10
661 28c. Banded butterflyfish . . 35 15
662 50c. Male and female blue-headed wrasse and princess parrotfish 45 25
663 $1 French grunt and French angelfish 70 70
MS664 136 × 110 mm. Nos. 660/3 2·50 3·75

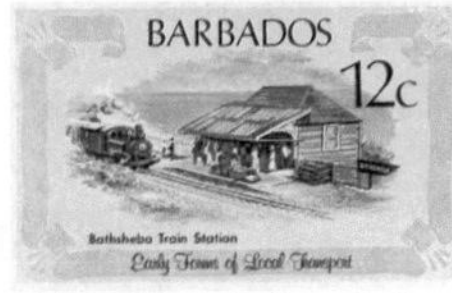

149 Bathsheba Railway Station

1981. Early Transport. Multicoloured.
665 12c. Type **149** 30 10
666 28c. Cab stand at The Green 20 15
667 45c. Animal-drawn tram . . 30 30
668 70c. Horse-drawn bus 45 60
669 $1 Railway Station, Fairchild Street 70 95

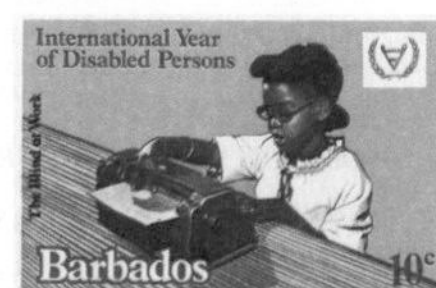

150 The Blind at Work

1981. Int Year for Disabled Persons. Mult.
670 10c. Type **150** 20 10
671 25c. Sign Language (vert) . . 25 15
672 45c. "Be alert to the white cane" (vert) 40 25
673 $2.50 Children at play . . . 80 3·00

151 Prince Charles dressed for Polo

152 Landship Manoeuvre

1981. Royal Wedding. Multicoloured.
674 28c. Wedding bouquet from Barbados 15 10
675 50c. Type **151** 20 15
676 $2.50 Prince Charles and Lady Diana Spencer . . . 55 1·25

1981. Carifesta (Caribbean Festival of Arts), Barbados. Multicoloured.
677 15c. Type **152** 15 15
678 20c. Yoruba dancers 15 15
679 40c. Tuk band 20 25
680 55c. Sculpture by Frank Collymore 25 35
681 $1 Harbour scene 50 75

1981. Nos. 630, 632 and 634 surch.
682 15c. on 28c. Carib grackle . . 30 15
683 40c. on 45c. Zenaida dove . . 30 35
684 60c. on 70c. Bananaquit . . . 30 45

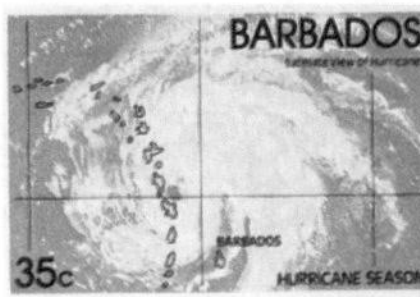

154 Satellite View of Hurricane

1981. Hurricane Season.
685 **154** 35c. black and blue . . . 35 20
686 – 50c. multicoloured 45 35
687 – 60c. multicoloured 70 50
688 – $1 multicoloured 85 90
DESIGNS: 50c. Hurricane "Gladys" from "Apollo 7"; 60c. Police Department on hurricane watch; $1 McDonnell Banshee "hurricane chaser" aircraft.

155 Twin Falls

1981. Harrison's Cave. Multicoloured.
689 10c. Type **155** 10 10
690 20c. Stream in Rotunda Room 20 15
691 55c. Formations in Rotunda Room 25 30
692 $2.50 Cascade Pool . . . . . 60 2·25

156 Black Belly Ram

1982. Black Belly Sheep. Multicoloured.
693 40c. Type **156** 15 20
694 50c. Black belly ewe 15 20
695 60c. Ewe with lambs 20 45
696 $1 Ram and ewe, with map of Barbados . . . . 35 1·50

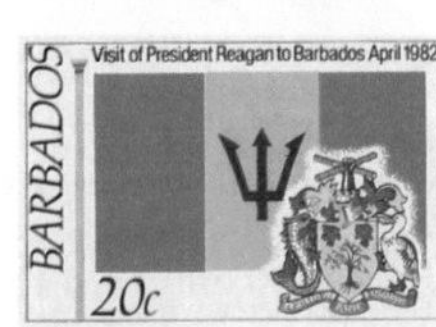

157 Barbados Coat of Arms and Flag

1982. President Reagan's Visit. Multicoloured.
697 20c. Type **157** . . . . 40 1·25
698 20c. U.S.A. coat of arms and flag . . . . 40 1·25
699 55c. Type **157** . . . . 50 1·50
700 55c. As No. 698 . . . . . . 50 1·50

158 Lighter

1982. Early Marine Transport. Multicoloured.
701 20c. Type **158** 20 15
702 35c. Rowing boat 35 25
703 55c. Speightstown schooner 50 40
704 $2.50 Inter-colonial schooner 1·75 2·50

159 Bride and Earl Spencer Proceeding up the Aisle

160 "To Help other People"

1982. 21st Birthday of Princess of Wales. Mult.
705 20c. Barbados coat of arms 20 15
706 60c. Princess at Llanelwedd, October, 1981 . . . . . . 45 50
707 $1.20 Type **159** . . . . . . 75 1·10
708 $2.50 Formal portrait . . . . 1·25 1·90

1982. 75th Anniv of Boy Scout Movement. Mult.
709 15c. Type **160** 50 10
710 40c. "I Promise to do my Best" (horiz) 80 30
711 55c. "To do my Duty to God, the Queen and my Country" (horiz) 90 65
712 $1 National and Troop flags 1·40 1·75
MS713 119 × 93 mm. $1.50, The Scout Law . . . . 3·50 3·00

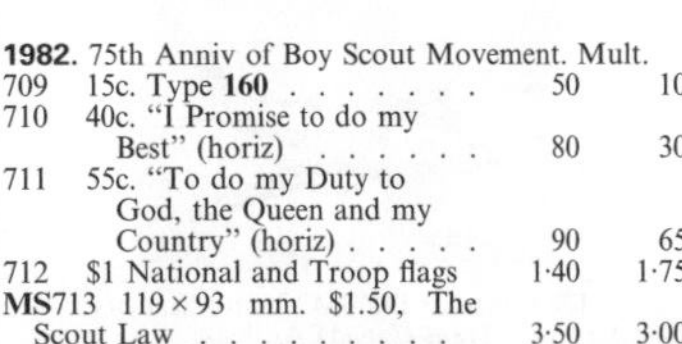

161 Arms of George Washington

1982. 250th Birth Anniv of George Washington. Multicoloured.
714 10c. Type **161** 10 10
715 55c. Washington House, Barbados 25 30
716 60c. Washington with troops 25 35
717 $2.50 Washington taking Oath . . . . 75 1·60

162 "Agraulis vanillae"

1983. Butterflies. Multicoloured.
718 20c. Type **162** . . . . 1·00 40
719 40c. "Danaus plexippus" . . 1·50 40
720 55c. "Hypolimnas misippus" 1·50 45
721 $2.50 "Hemiargus hanno" . . 3·25 3·75

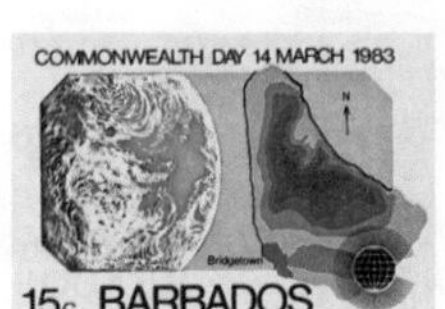

163 Map of Barbados and Satellite View

1983. Commonwealth Day. Multicoloured.
722 15c. Type **163** 20 10
723 40c. Tourist beach 25 20
724 60c. Sugar cane harvesting 35 40
725 $1 Cricket match . . . . . . 1·25 1·10

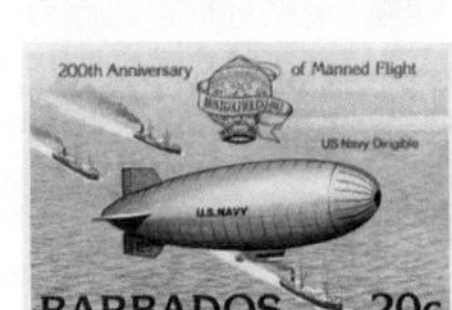

164 U.S. Navy "M" Class Airship M-20

1983. Bicentenary of Manned Flight.
726 20c. Type **164** 35 15
727 40c. Douglas DC-3 . . . . . 40 40
728 55c. Vickers Viscount 837 . . 40 50
729 $1 Lockheed TriStar 500 . . 65 2·50

165 Nash 600, 1934 (inscr "1941")

1983. Classic Cars. Multicoloured.
730 25c. Type **165** 35 20
731 45c. Dodge D-8 coupe, 1938 40 30
732 75c. Ford Model A tourer, 1930 . . . . 60 1·50
733 $2.50 Dodge Four tourer, 1918 . . . . 1·25 4·50

166 Game in Progress

167 Angel playing Lute (detail "The Virgin and Child") (Masaccio)

1983. Table Tennis World Cup Competition. Multicoloured.
734 20c. Type **166** 25 20
735 65c. Map of Barbados . . . 50 55
736 $1 World Table Tennis Cup 75 1·00

1983. Christmas. 50th Anniv of Barbados Museum.
737 **167** 10c. multicoloured 30 10
738 – 25c. multicoloured 60 20
739 – 45c. multicoloured 90 40
740 – 75c. black and gold . . . 1·40 1·60
741 – $2.50 multicoloured . . . 4·50 6·00
MS742 59 × 98 mm. $2 multicoloured . . . . 1·75 2·00
DESIGNS—HORIZ: 45c. "The Barbados Museum" (Richard Day); 75c. "St. Ann's Garrison" (W. S. Hedges); $2.50, Needham's Point, Carlisle Bay. VERT: 25c., $2 Different details from "The Virgin and Child" (Masaccio).

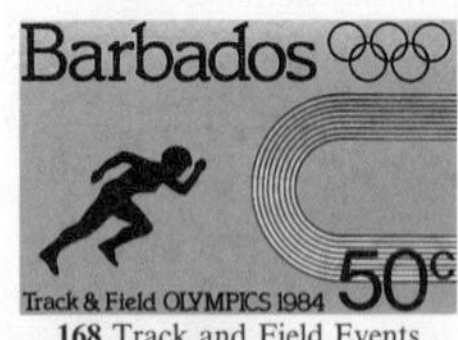

168 Track and Field Events

1984. Olympic Games, Los Angeles.
745 **168** 50c. green, black and brown 60 45
746 – 65c. orange, blk & brn . . 80 60
747 – 75c. blue, black & dp bl 1·00 85
748 – $1 brown, black and yellow . . . . 2·50 1·75
MS749 115 × 97 mm. Nos. 745/8 8·00 9·00
DESIGNS: 65c. Shooting; 75c. Sailing; $1 Cycling.

169 Global Coverage **171** Local Junior Match

170 U.P.U. 1943 3d. Stamp and Logo

1984. 250th Anniv of "Lloyd's List" (newspaper). Multicoloured.
750 45c. Type **169** 80 40
751 50c. Bridgetown harbour . . 90 50
752 75c. "Philosopher" (full-rigged ship), 1857 . . . . 1·40 1·25
753 $1 "Sea Princess" (liner), 1984 . . . . 1·40 1·60

1984. Universal Postal Union Congress, Hamburg. Sheet 90 × 75 mm.
MS754 **170** $2 multicoloured . . 2·50 2·50

1984. 60th Anniv of International Chess Federation. Multicoloured.
755 25c. Type **171** . . . . 1·50 30
756 45c. Staunton and 19th-century knights . . . 1·75 50
757 65c. Staunton queen and 18th-century queen from Macao . . . . 2·00 1·75
758 $2 Staunton and 17th-century rooks . . . . 3·75 6·50

172 Poinsettia **174** The Queen Mother at Docks

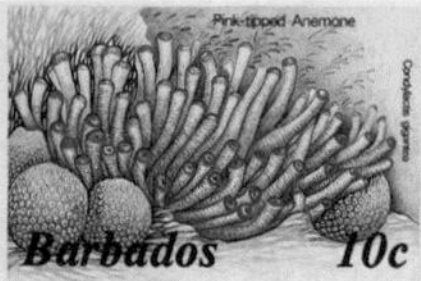

173 Pink-tipped Anemone

1984. Christmas. Flowers. Multicoloured.
759 50c. Type **172** . . . . 1·75 90
760 65c. Snow-on-the-Mountain 2·00 1·75
761 75c. Christmas Candle . . . 2·25 3·25
762 $1 Christmas Hope . . . . . 2·50 3·75

1985. Marine Life. Multicoloured.
794B 1c. Bristle worm . . . . . 30 2·50
795B 2c. Spotted trunkfish . . . 30 2·50
796A 5c. Coney . . . . 65 1·50
797B 10c. Type **173** 30 30
798B 20c. Christmas tree worm 30 40
799B 25c. Hermit crab 40 40
800A 35c. Animal flower . . . . 1·00 1·50
801B 40c. Vase sponge 50 50
802B 45c. Spotted moray 60 50
803B 50c. Ghost crab 60 60
804B 65c. Flamingo tongue snail 65 70
805B 75c. Sergeant major 70 75
806B $1 Caribbean warty anemone 85 85
807B $2.50 Green turtle . . . . 1·50 6·00
808B $5 Rock beauty (fish) . . . 1·75 8·00
809B $10 Elkhorn coral . . . . 2·75 8·00

1985. Life and Times of Queen Elizabeth the Queen Mother. Multicoloured.
779 25c. In the White Drawing Room, Buckingham Palace, 1930s 50 20
780 65c. With Lady Diana Spencer at Trooping the Colour, 1981 . . . . . . 2·50 1·00
781 75c. Type **174** . . . . 80 1·00
782 $1 With Prince Henry at his christening (from photo by Lord Snowdon) . . . . . 85 1·25
MS783 91 × 73 mm. $2 In Land Rover Series I opening Syon House Garden Centre . . . . 2·50 1·50

175 Peregrine Falcon

1985. Birth Bicentenary of John J. Audubon (ornithologist). Designs showing original paintings. Multicoloured.
784 45c. Type **175** . . . . 2·25 80
785 65c. Prairie warbler (vert) . . 2·50 2·25
786 75c. Great blue heron (vert) 2·75 3·00
787 $1 Yellow warbler (vert) . . 3·00 4·00

176 Intelsat Satellite orbiting Earth

1985. 20th Anniv of Intelsat Satellite System.
788 **176** 75c. multicoloured . . . . 1·00 70

BARBADOS
150th ANNIVERSARY OF THE ROYAL BARBADOS POLICE
25c

177 Traffic Policeman

1985. 150th Anniv of Royal Barbados Police. Multicoloured.
789 25c. Type **177** 80 20
790 50c. Police band on bandstand . . . . 1·40 80
791 65c. Dog handler . . . . . . 1·60 1·40
792 $1 Mounted policeman in ceremonial uniform . . . . 1·75 2·00
MS793 85 × 60 mm. $2 Police Band on parade (horiz). . . . . . . 1·50 2·75

1986. 60th Birthday of Queen Elizabeth II. As T **110** of Ascension. Multicoloured.
810 25c. Princess Elizabeth aged two, 1928 . . . . 40 20
811 50c. At University College of West Indies, Jamaica, 1953 50 40
812 65c. With Duke of Edinburgh, Barbados, 1985 70 50
813 75c. At banquet in Sao Paulo, Brazil, 1968 . . . . 70 60
814 $2 At Crown Agents Head Office, London, 1983 . . . 1·10 1·50

178 Canadair DC-4M2 North Star of Trans-Canada Airlines

1986. "Expo '86" World Fair, Vancouver. Mult.
815 50c. Type **178** 75 50
816 $2.50 "Lady Nelson" (cargo liner) . . . . 2·00 2·50

1986. "Ameripex '86" International Stamp Exhibition, Chicago. As T **164** of Bahamas, showing Barbados stamps. Multicoloured.
817 45c. 1976 Bicentenary of American Revolution 25c. 70 35
818 50c. 1976 Bicentenary of American Revolution 50c. 80 55
819 65c. 1981 Hurricane Season $1 . . . . 90 1·00
820 $1 1982 Visit of President Reagan 55c. . . . . 1·00 1·75
MS821 90 × 80 mm. $2 Statue of Liberty and liner "Queen Elizabeth 2" . . . . 8·00 11·00
No. **MS**821 also commemorates the Centenary of the Statue of Liberty.

1986. Royal Wedding. As T **112** of Ascension. Multicoloured.
822 45c. Prince Andrew and Miss Sarah Ferguson 75 35
823 $1 Prince Andrew in midshipman's uniform . . 1·25 75

179 Transporting Electricity Poles, 1923 **180** "Alpinia purpurata" and Church Window

1986. 75th Anniv of Electricity in Barbados. Multicoloured.
824 10c. Type **179** 15 10
825 25c. Heathman Ladder, 1935 (vert) 25 20
826 65c. Transport fleet, 1941 . . 60 60
827 $2 Bucket truck, 1986 (vert) 1·60 2·00

1986. Christmas. Multicoloured.
828 25c. Type **180** 20 20
829 50c. "Anthurium andraeanum" 45 45
830 75c. "Heliconia rostrata" . . 75 80
831 $2 "Heliconia × psittacorum" 1·50 4·00

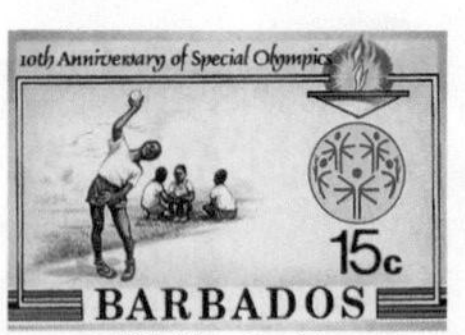

181 Shot Putting

1987. 10th Anniv of Special Olympics. Multicoloured.
832 15c. Type **181** 25 15
833 45c. Wheelchair racing . . . 45 30
834 65c. Long jumping 60 65
835 $2 Logo and slogan . . . . 1·25 2·50

75th Anniversary of Scouting in Barbados
BARBADOS 10c

182 Barn Swallow **183** Sea Scout saluting

1987. "Capex '87" International Stamp Exhibition, Toronto. Birds. Multicoloured.
836 25c. Type **182** . . . . 2·00 50
837 50c. Yellow warbler . . . . 2·25 1·75
838 65c. Audubon's shearwater 2·25 1·75
839 75c. Black-whiskered vireo 2·50 3·25
840 $1 Scarlet tanager . . . . . 2·75 4·00

1987. 75th Anniv of Scouting in Barbados. Multicoloured.
841 10c. Type **183** 20 10
842 25c. Scout jamboree 30 20
843 65c. Scout badges 65 45
844 $2 Scout band . . . . 1·60 1·75

184 Bridgetown Synagogue

1987. Restoration of Bridgetown Synagogue. Multicoloured.
845 50c. Type **184** . . . . 2·00 1·75
846 65c. Interior of Synagogue 2·25 2·25
847 75c. Ten Commandments (vert) . . . . 2·50 2·50
848 $1 Marble laver (vert) . . . 2·75 3·25

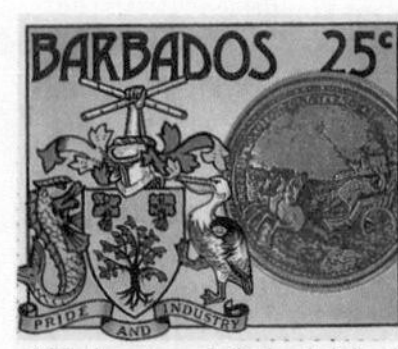

185 Arms and Colonial Seal

1987. 21st Anniv of Independence. Mult.
849 29c. Type **185** 40 20
850 45c. Flags of Barbados and Great Britain . . . . . . 1·00 35
851 65c. Silver dollar and one penny coins . . . . 1·00 55
852 $2 Colours of Barbados Regiment . . . . 2·50 2·75
MS853 94 × 56 mm. $1.50, Prime Minister E. W. Barrow (vert) 1·00 1·25

186 Herman C. Griffith

1988. West Indian Cricket. Each showing portrait, cricket equipment and early belt buckle. Multicoloured.
854 15c. E. A. (Manny) Martindale . . . . 2·50 75
855 45c. George Challenor . . . 3·25 75
856 50c. Type **186** . . . . 3·50 2·25
857 75c. Harold Austin . . . . . 3·75 3·50
858 $2 Frank Worrell . . . . . 4·50 11·00

187 "Kentropyx borckianus" **188** Cycling

1988. Lizards of Barbados. Multicoloured.
859 10c. Type **187** . . . . 1·75 50
860 50c. "Hemidactylus mabouia" 3·00 70
861 65c. "Anolis extremus" . . . 3·00 1·25
862 $2 "Gymnophthalmus underwoodii" . . . . . . 6·00 10·00

1988. Olympic Games, Seoul. Multicoloured.
863 25c. Type **188** . . . . 1·50 40
864 45c. Athletics 60 30
865 75c. Relay swimming 75 65
866 $2 Yachting . . . . 1·75 2·50
MS867 114 × 63 mm. Nos. 863/6 4·25 3·00

1988. 300th Anniv of Lloyd's of London. As T **123** of Ascension.
868 40c. multicoloured 55 30
869 50c. multicoloured 65 35
870 65c. multicoloured . . . . . 1·50 45
871 $2 blue and red . . . . . . 4·25 2·00
DESIGNS—VERT: 40c. Royal Exchange, 1774; $2 Sinking of "Titanic", 1912. HORIZ: 50c. Early sugar mill; 65c. "Author" (container ship).

189 Harry Bayley and Observatory

1988. 25th Anniv of Harry Bayley Observatory. Multicoloured.
872 25c. Type **189** 60 20
873 65c. Observatory with North Star and Southern Cross constellations . . . . . . 1·25 75
874 75c. Andromeda galaxy . . . 1·50 90
875 $2 Orion constellation . . . 2·75 5·50

190 L.I.A.T. Hawker Siddeley H.S.748

1989. 50th Anniv of Commercial Aviation in Barbados. Multicoloured.
876 25c. Type **190** . . . . 2·25 40
877 65c. Pan Am Douglas DC-8-62 . . . . 3·00 1·25
878 75c. British Airways Concorde at Grantley Adams Airport . . . . . 3·00 1·25
879 $2 Caribbean Air Cargo Boeing 707-351C . . . . . 4·75 7·00

191 Assembly Chamber

1989. 350th Anniv of Parliament.
880 **191** 25c. multicoloured 40 20
881 – 50c. multicoloured 60 35
882 – 75c. blue and black . . . 1·00 50
883 – $2.50 multicoloured . . . 2·50 2·25
DESIGNS: 50c. The Speaker; 75c. Parliament Buildings, c. 1882; $2.50, Queen Elizabeth II and Prince Philip in Parliament.

192 Brown Hare

193 Bread 'n Cheese

1989. Wildlife Preservation. Multicoloured.
884 10c. Type **192** 70 30
885 50c. Red-footed tortoise (horiz) . . . . 1·50 70
886 65c. Savanna ("Green") monkey . . . . 1·75 1·25
887 $2 "Bufo marinus" (toad) (horiz) . . . . 3·25 6·50
MS888 87 × 97 mm. $1 Small Indian mongoose . . . . 1·00 1·25

1989. 35th Commonwealth Parliamentary Conference. Square design as T **191**. Mult.
MS889 108 × 69 mm. $1 Barbados Mace . . . . 1·00 1·50

1989. Wild Plants. Multicoloured.
921 2c. Type **193** . . . . 40 1·50
891 5c. Scarlet cordia . . . . . 50 1·00
892 10c. Columnar cactus . . . 50 30
893 20c. Spiderlily 50 30
925 25c. Rock balsam 55 20
895 30c. Hollyhock 70 25
895a 35c. Red sage . . . . 1·25 1·00
927 45c. Yellow shak-shak . . . 65 35
928 50c. Whitewood 70 40
898 55c. Bluebell . . . . 1·00 55
930 65c. Prickly sage 80 55
900 70c. Seaside samphire . . . 1·25 1·25
901 80c. Flat-hand dildo . . . . 1·75 1·40
901a 90c. Herringbone . . . . . 1·75 2·25
902 $1.10 Lent tree . . . . . . 1·50 2·25
934 $2.50 Rodwood . . . . . . 1·90 4·00
935 $5 Cowitch . . . . 3·25 6·00
936 $10 Maypole . . . . 6·50 9·00

194 Water Skiing

195 Barbados 1852 1d. Stamp

1989. "World Stamp Expo '89" International Stamp Exn., Washington. Watersports. Mult.
906 25c. Type **194** . . . . 1·25 40
907 50c. Yachting . . . . 2·25 1·00
908 65c. Scuba diving . . . . . 2·25 1·75
909 $2.50 Surfing . . . . 6·00 11·00

1990. 150th Anniv of the Penny Black and "Stamp World London '90" International Stamp Exn.
910 **195** 25c. green, black and yellow . . . . 1·25 40
911 – 50c. multicoloured . . . . 1·75 1·00
912 – 65c. multicoloured . . . . 1·75 1·50
913 – $2.50 multicoloured . . . 4·00 8·00
MS914 90 × 86 mm. 50c. multicoloured; 50c. multicoloured 1·75 2·75
DESIGNS: 50c. 1882 1d. Queen Victoria stamp; 65c. 1899 2d. stamp; $2.50, 1912 3d. stamp; miniature sheet, 50c. Great Britain Penny Black, 50c. Barbados "1906" Nelson Centenary 1s.

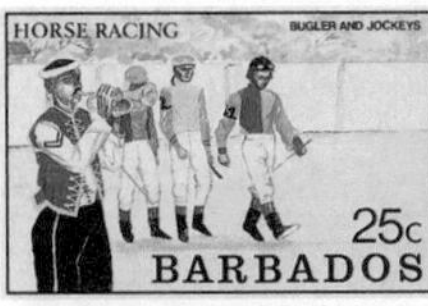
196 Bugler and Jockeys

1990. Horse Racing. Multicoloured.
915 25c. Type **196** 45 30
916 45c. Horse and jockey in parade ring 70 50
917 75c. At the finish 90 85
918 $2 Leading in the winner (vert) . . . . 2·50 4·75

1990. 90th Birthday of Queen Elizabeth the Queen Mother. As T **134** of Ascension.
919 75c. multicoloured 75 60
920 $2.50 black and green . . . . 2·25 3·25
DESIGNS—21 × 36 mm: 75c. Lady Elizabeth Bowes-Lyon, April 1923 (from painting by John Lander). 29 × 37 mm: $2.50, Lady Elizabeth Bowes-Lyon on her engagement, January 1923.

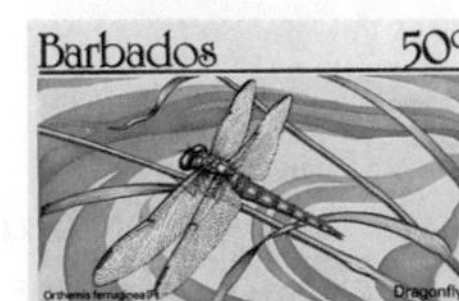
197 "Orthemis ferruginea" (dragonfly)

1990. Insects. Multicoloured.
937 50c. Type **197** . . . . 1·50 80
938 65c. "Ligyrus tumulosus" (beetle) . . . . 1·75 1·00
939 75c. "Neoconocephalus sp." (grasshopper) . . . . . . 2·00 1·25
940 $2 "Bostra maxwelli" (stick-insect) . . . . 3·50 5·50

1990. Visit of the Princess Royal. Nos. 925, 901 and 903 optd **VISIT OF HRH THE PRINCESS ROYAL OCTOBER 1990**.
941 25c. Rock balsam . . . . . 1·75 50
942 80c. Flat-hand dildo . . . . 3·00 2·00
943 $2.50 Rodwood . . . . . . 7·00 9·00

199 Star

201 Sorting Daily Catch

200 Adult Male Yellow Warbler

1990. Christmas. Multicoloured.
944 20c. Type **199** 65 20
945 50c. Figures from crib . . . 1·00 50
946 $1 Stained glass window . . . 2·00 1·50
947 $2 Angel (statue) . . . . . . 3·00 5·50

1991. Endangered Species. Yellow Warbler. Multicoloured.
948 10c. Type **200** . . . . 1·40 80
949 20c. Pair feeding chicks in nest . . . . 2·00 80
950 45c. Female feeding chicks in nest . . . . 2·50 80
951 $1 Male with fledgeling . . . 4·00 5·25

1991. Fishing in Barbados. Multicoloured.
952 5c. Type **201** 50 50
953 50c. Line fishing (horiz) . . . 1·75 90
954 75c. Fish cleaning (horiz) . . 2·25 1·25
955 $2.50 Game fishing . . . . . 4·50 6·50

202 Masonic Building, Bridgetown

1991. 250th Anniv of Freemasonry in Barbados (1990).
956 **202** 25c. multicoloured . . . . 1·25 50
957 – 65c. multicoloured . . . . 2·00 1·25
958 – 75c. black, yellow & brn 2·00 1·25
959 – $2.50 multicoloured . . . 4·75 7·00
DESIGNS: 65c. Compass and square (masonic symbols); 75c. Royal Arch jewel; $2.50, Ceremonial apron, columns and badge.

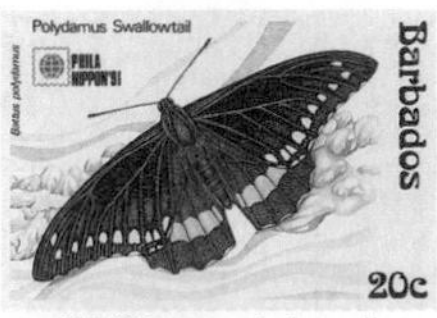
203 "Battus polydamus"

1991. "Phila Nippon '91" International Stamp Exhibition, Tokyo. Butterflies. Multicoloured.
960 20c. Type **203** . . . . 1·00 40
961 50c. "Urbanus proteus" (vert) 1·50 65
962 65c. "Phoebis sennae" . . . 1·60 95
963 $2.50 "Junonia evarete" (vert) . . . . 4·00 6·00
MS964 87 × 86 mm. $4 "Vanessa cardui" . . . . 8·00 9·00

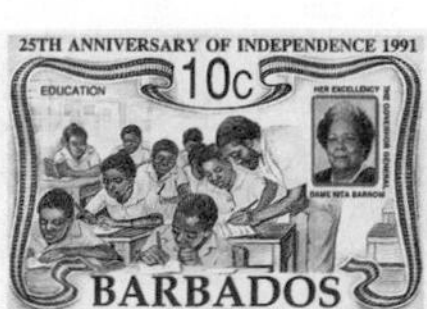
204 School Class

1991. 25th Anniv of Independence. Multicoloured.
965 10c. Type **204** 20 20
966 25c. Barbados Workers' Union Labour College . . 30 30
967 65c. Building a house 70 90
968 75c. Sugar cane harvesting 80 1·00
969 $1 Health clinic . . . . . . 1·00 2·00
MS970 123 × 97 mm. $2.50, Gordon Greenidge and Desmond Haynes (cricketers) (vert) . . . . . . 9·00 10·00

205 Jesus carrying Cross

1992. Easter. Multicoloured.
971 35c. Type **205** 80 30
972 70c. Crucifixion . . . . . . 1·40 90
973 90c. Descent from the Cross 1·50 1·25
974 $3 Risen Christ . . . . . . 4·00 6·50

206 Cannon Ball

1992. Conservation. Flowering Trees. Multicoloured.
975 10c. Type **206** 60 40
976 30c. Golden shower tree . . . 1·00 50
977 80c. Frangipani . . . . . . 2·25 2·50
978 $1.10 Flamboyant . . . . . 2·75 3·00

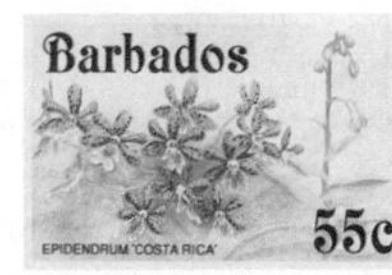
207 "Epidendrum" "Costa Rica"

1992. Orchids. Multicoloured.
979 55c. Type **207** 85 65
980 65c. "Cattleya guttaca" . . . 1·00 1·00
981 70c. "Laeliacattleya" "Splashing Around" . . . 1·00 1·00
982 $1.40 "Phalaenopsis" "Kathy Saegert" . . . . 1·60 3·00

208 Mini Moke and Gun Hill Signal Station, St. George

1992. Transport and Tourism. Multicoloured.
983 5c. Type **208** 50 50
984 35c. Tour bus and Bathsheba Beach, St. Joseph . . . . 1·00 30
985 90c. B.W.I.A. McDonnell Douglas MD-83 over Grantley Adams Airport 2·50 2·25
986 $2 "Festivale" (liner) and Bridgetown harbour . . . 3·75 5·50

209 Barbados Gooseberry

212 Sailor's Shell-work Valentine and Carved Amerindian

211 18 pdr Culverin of 1625, Denmark Fort

1993. Cacti and Succulents. Multicoloured.
987 10c. Type **209** 55 30
988 35c. Night-blooming cereus 1·25 35
989 $1.40 Aloe . . . . 3·00 3·50
990 $2 Scrunchineel . . . . . . 3·50 5·50

1993. 75th Anniv of Royal Air Force. As T **149** of Ascension. Multicoloured.
991 10c. Hawker Hunter F.6 . . 65 40
992 30c. Handley Page Victor K2 1·00 40
993 70c. Hawker Typhoon IB . . 1·50 1·50
994 $3 Hawker Hurricane Mk I 3·50 6·00
MS995 110 × 77 mm. 50c. Armstrong Whitworth Siskin IIIA; 50c. Supermarine S6B; 50c. Supermarine Walrus Mk I; 50c. Hawker Hart . . . . 2·25 2·75

1993. 14th World Orchid Conference, Glasgow. Nos. 979/82 optd **WORLD ORCHID CONFERENCE 1993**.
996 55c. Type **207** . . . . 1·25 1·25
997 65c. "Cattleya guttaca" . . . 1·40 1·40
998 70c. "Laeliacattleya" "Splashing Around" . . . 1·40 1·40
999 $1.40 "Phalaenopsis" "Kathy Saegert" . . . . 2·25 3·50

1993. 17th-century English Cannon. Mult.
1000 5c. Type **211** 30 50
1001 45c. 6 pdr of 1649–60, St. Ann's Fort 85 50
1002 $1 9 pdr demi-culverin of 1691, The Main Guard 1·75 2·00
1003 $2.50 32 pdr demi-cannon of 1693–94, Charles Fort 2·75 4·50

1993. 60th Anniv of Barbados Museum. Mult.
1004 10c. Type **212** 50 50
1005 75c. "Barbados Mulatto Girl" (Agostino Brunias) 1·50 1·50
1006 90c. Morris Cup and soldier of West India Regiment, 1858 . . . . 2·00 2·50
1007 $1.10 Ogilby's map of Barbados, 1679, and Ashanti gold weights . . 2·25 3·00

213 Plesiosaurus

214 Cricket

1993. Prehistoric Aquatic Animals. Mult.
1008 90c. Type **213** 2·00 2·75
1009 90c. Ichthyosaurus 2·00 2·75
1010 90c. Elasmosaurus 2·00 2·75
1011 90c. Mosasaurus 2·00 2·75
1012 90c. Archelon 2·00 2·75
Nos. 1008/12 were printed together, se-tenant, with the background forming a composite design.

1994. Sports and Tourism. Multicoloured.
1013 10c. Type **214** 1·25 75
1014 35c. Rally driving 1·40 50
1015 50c. Golf 2·25 1·75
1016 70c. Long distance running 1·75 2·50
1017 $1.40 Swimming 2·00 3·50

215 Whimbrel

1994. "Hong Kong '94" Int Stamp Exhibition. Migratory Birds. Multicoloured.
1018 10c. Type **215** 50 50
1019 35c. Pacific golden plover ("American Golden Plover") 1·00 50
1020 70c. Ruddy turnstone 1·50 1·50
1021 $3 Louisiana heron ("Tricoloured Heron") 3·50 5·50

216 Bathsheba Beach and Logo

1994. 1st United Nations Conference of Small Island Developing States. Multicoloured.
1022 10c. Type **216** 25 15
1023 65c. Pico Tenneriffe 90 70
1024 90c. Ragged Point Lighthouse 3·00 2·00
1025 $2.50 Consett Bay 2·75 4·50

217 William Demas

219 Private, 2nd West India Regt, 1860

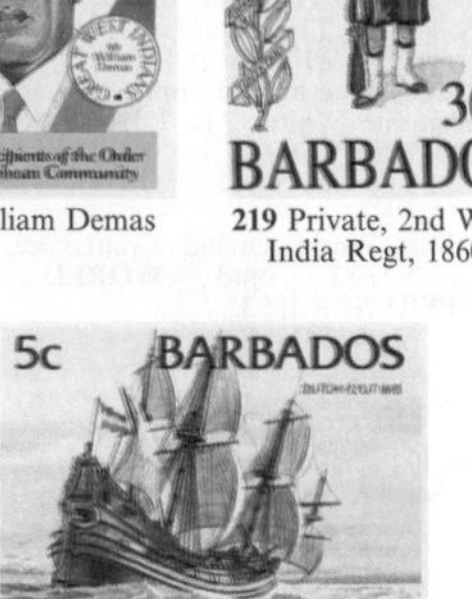

218 Dutch Flyut, 1695

1994. First Recipients of Order of the Caribbean Community. Multicoloured.
1026 70c. Type **217** 70 1·00
1027 70c. Sir Shridath Ramphal 70 1·00
1028 70c. Derek Walcott 70 1·00

1994. Ships. Multicoloured.
1075 5c. Type **218** 75 1·00
1076 10c. "Geestport" (freighter), 1994 75 40
1031B 25c. H.M.S. "Victory" (ship of the line), 1805 50 40
1078 30c. "Royal Viking Queen" (liner), 1994 50 30
1079 35c. H.M.S. "Barbados" (frigate), 1945 50 30
1080 45c. "Faraday" (cable ship), 1924 50 35
1081 50c. U.S.C.G. "Hamilton" (coastguard cutter), 1974 3·00 75
1082 65c. H.M.C.S. "Saguenay" (destroyer), 1939 75 70
1083 70c. "Inanda" (cargo liner), 1928 75 70
1084 80c. H.M.S. "Rodney" (battleship), 1944 75 70
1085 90c. U.S.S. "John F. Kennedy" (aircraft carrier), 1982 75 70
1086 $1.10 "William and John" (immigrant ship), 1627 1·00 1·00
1087 $5 U.S.C.G. "Champlain" (coastguard cutter), 1931 4·00 5·00
1042B $10 "Artist" (full-rigged ship), 1877 7·00 9·00

1995. Bicentenary of Formation of West India Regiment. Multicoloured.
1043 30c. Type **219** 55 35
1044 50c. Light Company private, 4th West India Regt, 1795 70 55
1045 70c. Drum Major, 3rd West India Regt, 1860 85 1·10
1046 $1 Privates in undress and working dress, 5th West India Regt, 1815 1·00 1·40
1047 $1.10 Troops from 1st and 2nd West India Regts in Review Order, 1874 1·25 1·75

1995. 50th Anniv of End of Second World War. As T **161** of Ascension. Multicoloured.
1048 10c. Barbadian Bren gun crew 60 50
1049 35c. Avro Type 683 Lancaster bomber 90 50
1050 55c. Supermarine Spitfire 1·25 75
1051 $2.50 "Davisian" (cargo liner) 3·00 4·75
MS1052 75 × 85 mm. $2 Reverse of 1939–45 War Medal (vert) 1·50 2·25

220 Member of 1st Barbados Combermere Scout Troop, 1912

1995. 300th Anniv of Combermere School. Mult.
1053 5c. Type **220** 25 40
1054 20c. Violin and sheet of music 45 30
1055 35c. Sir Frank Worrell (cricketer) (vert) 1·50 55
1056 $3 Painting by pupil 2·25 4·50
MS1057 174 × 105 mm. Nos. 1053/6 and 90c. 1981 Carifesta 55c. stamp 4·00 4·75

1995. 50th Anniv of United Nations. As T **213** of Bahamas. Multicoloured.
1058 30c. Douglas C-124 Globemaster (transport), Korea, 1950–53 70 40
1059 45c. Royal Navy Sea King helicopter 1·00 50
1060 $1.40 Westland Wessex helicopter, Cyprus, 1964 1·50 2·00
1061 $2 Sud Aviation SA 341 Gazelle helicopter, Cyprus, 1964 1·50 2·75

221 Blue Beauty **223** Football

222 Magnifying Glass, Tweezers and 1896 Colony Seal ½d. Stamp

1995. Water Lilies. Multicoloured.
1062 10c. Type **221** 35 30
1063 65c. White water lily 1·00 60
1064 70c. Sacred lotus 1·00 60
1065 $3 Water hyacinth 2·75 4·50

1996. Centenary of Barbados Philatelic Society. Each showing magnifying glass, tweezers and stamp. Multicoloured.
1066 10c. Type **222** 30 30
1067 55c. 1906 Tercentenary of Annexation 1d. 65 45
1068 $1.10 1920 Victory 1s. 1·25 1·40
1069 $1.40 1937 Coronation 2½d. 1·60 2·50

1996. Cent of Modern Olympic Games. Mult.
1070 20c. Type **223** 40 30
1071 30c. Relay running 45 30
1072 55c. Basketball 1·60 60
1073 $3 Rhythmic gymnastics 2·25 4·00
MS1074 68 × 89 mm. $2.50, "The Discus Thrower" (Myron) 2·00 3·25

224 Douglas DC-10 of Canadian Airlines

1996. "CAPEX '96" International Stamp Exhibition, Toronto. Aircraft. Multicoloured.
1089 10c. Type **224** 55 30
1090 90c. Boeing 767 of Air Canada 1·25 80
1091 $1 Airbus Industrie A320 of Air Canada 1·25 1·25
1092 $1.40 Boeing 767 of Canadian Airlines 1·60 2·75

225 Chattel House

1996. Chattel Houses.
1093 **225** 35c. multicoloured 40 25
1094 – 70c. multicoloured 70 60
1095 – $1.10 multicoloured 90 1·10
1096 – $2 multicoloured 1·60 3·00
DESIGNS: 70c. to $2, Different houses.

226 "Going to Church"

1996. Christmas. 50th Anniv of U.N.I.C.E.F. Children's Paintings. Multicoloured.
1097 10c. Type **226** 35 15
1098 30c. "The Tuk Band" 55 25
1099 55c. "Singing carols" 70 40
1100 $2.50 "Decorated house" 1·75 3·50

227 Doberman Pinscher

1997. "HONG KONG '97" International Stamp Exhibition. Dogs. Multicoloured.
1101 10c. Type **227** 75 40
1102 30c. German shepherd 1·50 40
1103 90c. Japanese akita 2·00 1·25
1104 $3 Irish red setter 4·25 6·50

228 Barbados Flag and State Arms

1997. Visit of President Clinton of U.S.A. Multicoloured.
1105 35c. Type **228** 75 75
1106 90c. American flag and arms 1·00 1·10

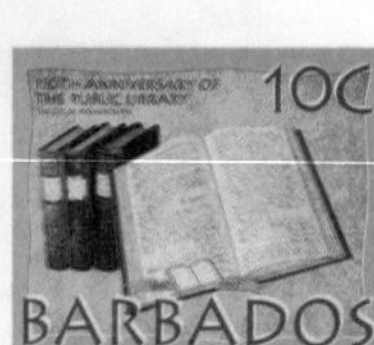

229 Measled Cowrie **230** Lucas Manuscripts

1997. Shells. Multicoloured.
1107 5c. Type **229** 30 30
1108 35c. Trumpet triton 75 25
1109 90c. Scotch bonnet 1·40 90
1110 $2 West Indian murex 2·00 3·25
MS1111 71 × 76 mm. $2.50, Underwater scene 2·50 3·75

1997. 150th Anniv of the Public Library Service. Multicoloured.
1112 10c. Type **230** 25 15
1113 30c. Librarian reading to children 50 25
1114 70c. Mobile library van 1·10 60
1115 $3 Man using computer 2·50 4·00

231 Barbados Cherry

1997. Local Fruits. Multicoloured.
1116 35c. Type **231** 45 30
1117 40c. Sugar apple 50 30
1118 $1.15 Soursop 1·10 1·25
1119 $1.70 Pawpaw 1·75 2·50

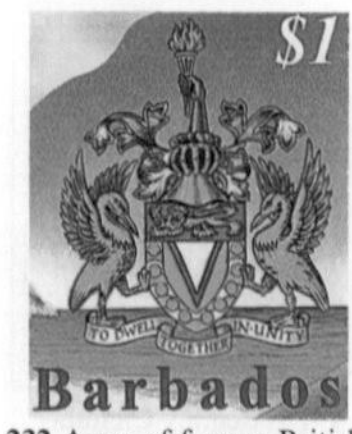

232 Arms of former British Caribbean Federation

1998. Birth Centenary of Sir Grantley Adams (statesman). Sheet 118 × 74 mm, containing T **232** and similar vert designs. Multicoloured.
MS1120 $1 Type **232**; $1 Sir Grantley Adams; $1 Flag of former British Caribbean Federation 4·50 4·75

1998. Diana, Princess of Wales Commemoration. Sheet 145 × 70 mm, containing vert designs as T **177** of Ascension. Multicoloured.
MS1121 $1.15, Wearing blue hat, 1985; $1.15, Wearing red jacket, 1981; $1.15, Wearing tiara, 1987; $1.15, Wearing black jacket 3·25 3·75

233 Environment Regeneration

1998. 50th Anniv of Organization of American States. Multicoloured.
1122 15c. Type **233** 20 15
1123 $1 Stilt dancing 70 80
1124 $2.50 Judge and figure of Justice 1·75 2·75

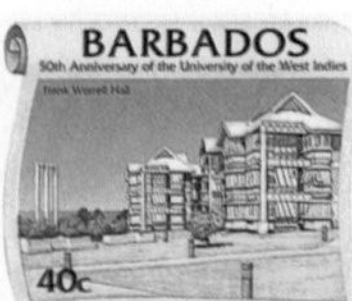

234 Frank Worrell Hall

1998. 50th Anniv of University of West Indies. Multicoloured.
1125 40c. Type **234** 50 30
1126 $1.15 Student graduating 1·25 1·25
1127 $1.40 50th anniversary plaque 1·50 2·00
1128 $1.75 Quadrangle 2·75 4·00

235 Catamaran **236** Racing Yacht

1998. Tourism. Multicoloured.
1129 10c. Type **235** 45 30
1130 45c. "Jolly Roger" (tourist schooner) (horiz) 1·00 35
1131 70c. "Atlantis" (tourist submarine) (horiz) 1·50 1·10
1132 $2 "Harbour Master" (ferry) 3·25 4·00

1999. "Australia '99" World Stamp Exhibition, Melbourne. Sheet 90 × 90 mm.
MS1133 **236** $4 multicoloured 3·25 4·50

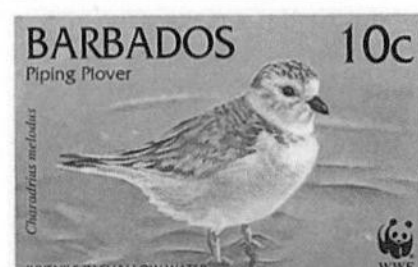

237 Juvenile Piping Plover in Shallow Water

1999. Endangered Species. Piping Plover. Mult.
1134 10c. Type **237** 20 20
1135 45c. Female with eggs . . . 55 55
1136 50c. Male and female with fledglings 55 75
1137 70c. Male in shallow water 65 95

1999. 30th Anniv of First Manned Landing on Moon. As T **186** of Ascension. Multicoloured.
1138 40c. Astronaut in training 55 45
1139 45c. 1st stage separation . . 55 45
1140 $1.15 Lunar landing module 1·40 1·25
1141 $1.40 Docking with service module . . . . 1·50 2·00
MS1142 90 × 80 mm. $2.50, Earth as seen from Moon (circular, 40 mm diam) . . . . 2·25 3·25

238 Hare running

1999. "China '99" International Stamp Exhibition, Beijing. Hares. Multicoloured.
1143 70c. Type **238** . . . . . . 1·10 1·25
1144 70c. Head of hare . . . . . 1·10 1·25
1145 70c. Baby hares suckling . . 1·10 1·25
1146 70c. Hares boxing . . . . . 1·10 1·25
1147 70c. Two leverets . . . . . 1·10 1·25
Nos. 1143/7 were printed together, se-tenant, forming a composite background design.

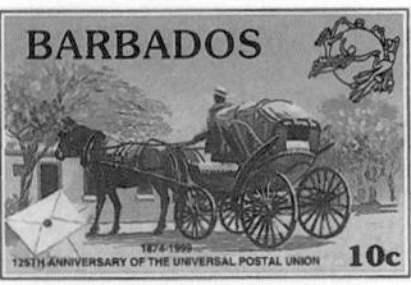

239 Horse-drawn Mail Cart

1999. 125th Anniv of U.P.U. Multicoloured.
1148 10c. Type **239** 75 35
1149 45c. Mail van . . . . 1·00 40
1150 $1.75 Sikorsky S42 flying boat . . . . 1·50 2·00
1151 $2 Computer and fax machine . . . . 1·50 2·25

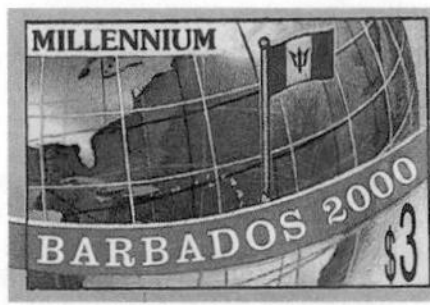

240 Globe and Barbados Flag

2000. New Millennium. Sheet 90 × 80 mm.
MS1152 **240** $3 multicoloured . . 3·00 3·50

241 Drax Hall House

2000. Pride of Barbados. Multicoloured.
1153 5c. Type **241** 10 10
1154 10c. Reaping sugar cane (vert) 10 10
1155 40c. Needham's Point Lighthouse (vert) 20 25
1156 45c. Port St. Charles . . . 25 30
1157 65c. Interior of Jewish synagogue 35 40
1158 70c. Bridgetown Port (I) 40 45
1158a 70c. Bridgetown Port (II) 40 45
1159 90c. Harrison's Cave . . . 50 55
1160 $1.15 Villa Nova 65 70
1161 $1.40 Cricket at Kensington Oval 75 80
1162 $1.75 Sunbury House . . . 95 1·00
1163 $2 Bethel Methodist Church . . . . 1·10 1·25
1164 $3 Peacock, Barbados Wildlife Reserve (vert) 1·60 1·75
1165 $5 Royal Westmoreland Golf Course (vert) . . . 2·75 3·00
1166 $10 Grantley Adams International Airport . . 5·50 5·75

Two types of 50c. :
I. Central design reversed. The bows of three of the four liners shown point to the right.
II. Design corrected. The bows of three of the four liners point to the left.

242 Sir Conrad Hunte batting

2000. West Indies Cricket Tour and 100th Test Match at Lord's. Multicoloured.
1167 45c. Type **242** 60 35
1168 90c. Malcolm Marshall bowling . . . . 1·25 75
1169 $2 Sir Garfield Sobers batting . . . . 2·00 2·50
MS1170 121 × 104 mm. $2.50, Lord's Cricket Ground (horiz) 2·25 2·75

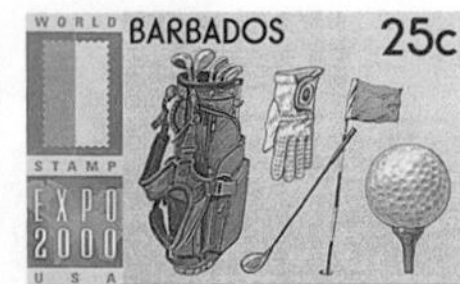

243 Golf Clubs, Flag and Ball on Tee Peg

2000. "EXPO 2000" World Stamp Exhibition, Anaheim, U.S.A. Golf. Multicoloured.
1171 25c. Type **243** 50 35
1172 40c. Golfer teeing off on top of giant ball 70 35
1173 $1.40 Golfer on green . . . 1·50 1·60
1174 $2 Golfer putting . . . . . 2·00 2·75

244 Bentley Mk VI Drophead Coupe, 1947

2000. Vintage Cars. Multicoloured.
1175 10c. Type **244** 25 15
1176 30c. Vanden Plas Princess Limousine, 1964 . . . . 50 25
1177 90c. Austin Atlantic, 1952 1·00 70
1178 $3 Bentley Special, 1950 . . 3·00 3·75

245 Thread Snake

2001. "HONG KONG 2001" Stamp Exhibition. Sheet 125 × 80 mm.
MS1179 **245** $3 multicoloured . . 3·00 3·50

246 Lizardfish

2001. Deep Sea Creatures. Multicoloured.
1180 45c. Type **246** 50 55
1181 45c. Golden-tailed moray . . 50 55
1182 45c. Black-barred soldierfish 50 55
1183 45c. Golden zoanthid . . . 50 55
1184 45c. Sponge brittle star . . 50 55
1185 45c. Magnificent feather duster 50 55
1186 45c. Bearded fireworm . . . 50 55
1187 45c. Lima shell 50 55
1188 45c. Yellow tube sponge . . 50 55

247 Octagonal, Fish and Butterfly Kites

2001. "Philanippon '01" International Stamp Exhibition, Tokyo. Kites. Multicoloured.
1189 10c. Type **247** 20 15
1190 65c. Hexagonal, bird and geometric kites 60 45
1191 $1.40 Policeman, Japanese and butterfly kites . . . . 1·40 1·50
1192 $1.75 Anti-drug, geisha and eagle kites . . . . 1·60 1·75

248 George Washington on the Quay, 1751

249 Shaggy Bear(Traditional Carnival Character)

2001. 250th Anniv of George Washington's Visit to Barbados. Multicoloured.
1193 45c. Type **248** 50 40
1194 50c. George Washington in Barbados 50 40
1195 $1.15 George Washington superimposed on Declaration of Independence, 1776 . . . 1·00 1·00
1196 $2.50 Needham's Point Fort, 1750 . . . . 2·25 2·50
MS1197 110 × 90 mm. $3 George Washington as President of U.S.A. 2·25 2·75

2001. 35th Anniv of Independence. Multicoloured.
1198 25c. Type **249** 30 20
1199 45c. Tuk band 50 30
1200 $1 Landship Dancers . . . 85 65
1201 $2 Guitar, saxophone and words of National Anthem . . . . 1·75 2·00

2002. Golden Jubilee. As T **200** of Ascension.
1202 10c. black, violet and gold 30 15
1203 70c. multicoloured 70 50
1204 $1 black, violet and gold . . 1·00 1·00
1205 $1.40 multicoloured . . . . 1·25 1·60
MS1206 162 × 95 mm. Nos. 1202/5 and $3 multicoloured . . . . . 4·75 5·00
DESIGNS—HORIZ: 10c. Princess Elizabeth; 70c. Queen Elizabeth in cerise hat; $1 Queen Elizabeth wearing Imperial State Crown, Coronation, 1953; $1.40, Queen Elizabeth in purple feathered hat. VERT (38 × 51 mm)—$3 Queen Elizabeth after Annigoni.
Designs as Nos. 1202/5 in **MS**1206 omit the gold frame around each stamp and "Golden Jubilee 1952–2002" inscription.

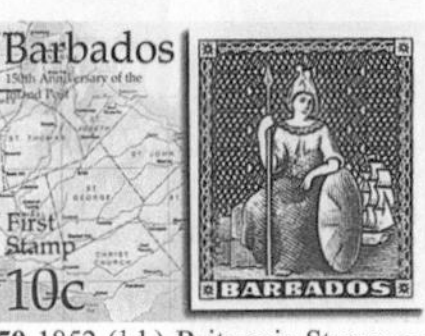

250 1852 (½d.) Britannia Stamp and Map

2002. 150th Anniv of Inland Postal Service. Multicoloured.
1207 10c. Type **250** 20 15
1208 45c. Early twentieth-century postman delivering letter 45 35
1209 $1.15 *Esk* (mail steamer) . . 1·25 1·25
1210 $2 B.W.I.A. Tri-Star airliner 1·60 2·00

251 *Alpinia purpurata*

252 Drax Hall Windmill, St. George

2002. Flowers. Multicoloured.
1211 10c. Type **251** 20 20
1212 40c. *Heliconia caribaea* . . . 40 30
1213 $1.40 *Polianthes tuberosa* (horiz) . . . . 1·25 1·25
1214 $2.50 *Anthurium* (horiz) . . 2·00 2·50

2002. 375th Anniv of First Settlement.
1215 **252** 10c. brown, agate and blue 25 15
1216 – 45c. brown, agate and blue 50 35
1217 – $1.15 multicoloured . . 1·25 1·25
1218 – $3 multicoloured . . . . 2·50 2·75
DESIGNS: 45c. Donkey cart; $1.15, Cattle Mill ruins, Gibbons; $3, Morgan Lewis windmill, St. Andrew.

253 Traditional Christmas Fare

2002. Christmas. Multicoloured.
1219 45c. Type **253** 50 35
1220 $1.15 Christmas morning in the park . . . . 1·00 1·00
1221 $1.40 Nativity scene from float parade . . . . . . 1·10 1·10

254 AIDS Ribbon

2002. Centenary of Pan American Health Organization. Multicoloured.
1222 10c. Type **254** 30 15
1223 70c. Amateur athletes . . . 70 50
1224 $1.15 Sir George Alleyne (Director-General of P.A.H.O.) . . . . 1·00 1·00
1225 $2 Pregnant woman . . . . 1·50 1·75

255H.M.S. *Tartar*, 1764

2003. Royal Navy Connections. Multicoloured.
1226 10c. Type **255** 10 10
1227 70c. H.M.S. *Barbadoes*, 1803 30 35
1228 $1.15 H.M.S. *Valerian*, 1926 45 50
1229 $2.50 H.M.S. *Victorious*, 1941 . . . . 1·00 1·10

256 Broad Street, c. 1900

2003. 375th Anniv of the Settlement of Bridgetown. Multicoloured.
1230 10c. Type **256** 10 10
1231 $1.15 Swan Street, 1900 . . 45 55
1232 $1.40 Roebuck Street, c. 1880 . . . . . 60 65
1233 $2 Chamberlain Bridge . . 80 85
MS1234 160 × 120 mm. Nos. 1230/3 2·00 2·10

2003. Centenary of Powered Flight. As T **209** of Ascension. Multicoloured.
1235 10c. McDonnell F2H-2P Banshee 10 10
1236 45c. Vickers Viscount 700 20 25
1237 50c. Douglas DC-9-30 . . . 20 25
1238 $1.15 Short Sunderland Mk II 45 55
1239 $1.40 North American P-51D Mustang 60 65
1240 $2.50 Concorde . . . . . . 1·00 1·10

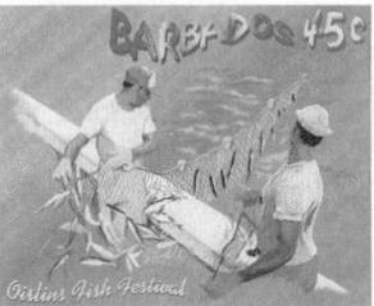

257 Fishermen (Oistins Fish Festival)

2003. Barbados Festivals. Multicoloured.
MS1241 127 × 105 mm. 45c. Type **257**; 45c. Saxophone player (Barbados Jazz Festival); 45c. Man and woman in traditional costume (Crop Over Festival); 45c. Actresses (National Independence Festival of Creative Arts); 45c. School choir (National Independence Festival of Creative Arts); 45c. Carnival dancers (Crop Over Festival); 45c. Bass player (Barbados Jazz Festival); 45c. Competitor in fish boning competition (Oistins Fish Festival) 1·20 1·40

POSTAGE DUE STAMPS

D 1

D 2

1934.

D1 D 1 ½d. green . . . . 1·25 8·50
D2 1d. black . . . . 1·25 1·25
D3 3d. red . . . . 20·00 20·00

1950. Values in cents.

D4a D 1 1c. green . . . . 30 3·00
D8 2c. black . . . . 30 5·00
D9 6c. red . . . . 50 7·00

1976.

D14a D 2 1c. mauve and pink . . 10 10
D15a – 2c. blue and light blue 10 10
D16a – 5c. brown and yellow 10 15
D17a – 10c. blue and lilac . . . 15 20
D18a – 25c. deep green and green 20 30
D19 – $1 red and deep red . . 75 1·25

DESIGNS: Nos. D15/19 show different floral backgrounds.

BARBUDA Pt. 1

One of the Leeward Is., Br. W. Indies. Dependency of Antigua. Used stamps of Antigua and Leeward Is. concurrently. The issues from 1968 are also valid for use in Antigua. From 1971 to 1973 the stamps of Antigua were again used.

1922. 12 pence = 1 shilling;
20 shillings = 1 pound.
1951. 100 cents = 1 West Indian dollar.

1922. Stamps of Leeward Islands optd **BARBUDA**.

1 11 ½d. green . . . . 1·50 9·50
2 1d. red . . . . 1·50 9·50
3 2d. grey . . . . 1·50 7·00
4 2½d. blue . . . . 1·50 7·50
9 3d. purple on yellow . . . . 1·75 12·00
5 6d. purple . . . . 2·00 18·00
10 1s. black on green . . . . . 1·50 8·00
6 2s. purple and blue on blue 14·00 48·00
7 3s. green and violet . . . . 32·00 75·00
8 4s. black and red . . . . . 38·00 75·00
11 5s. green and red on yellow 65·00 £130

2 Map of Barbuda

3 Greater Amberjack

1968.

12 2 ½c. brown, black and pink 20 1·50
13 1c. orange, black and flesh 30 10
14 2c. brown, red and rose . . 1·00 10
15 3c. brown, yellow and lemon 30 10
16 4c. black, green & lt green 1·00 1·50
17 5c. turquoise and black . . 30 10
18 6c. black, purple and lilac 40 1·50
19 10c. black, blue and cobalt 30 1·00
20 15c. black, green & turq . . 30 1·75
20a – 20c. multicoloured . . . . . 1·50 2·00
21 3 25c. multicoloured 60 25
22 – 35c. multicoloured 80 25
23 – 50c. multicoloured 80 55
24 – 75c. multicoloured 80 80
25 – $1 multicoloured . . . . . 85 2·00
26 – $2.50 multicoloured . . . . 1·50 5·00
27 – $5 multicoloured . . . . . 2·25 7·50

DESIGNS: As T 3—20c. Great barracuda; 35c. French angelfish; 50c. Porkfish; 75c. Princess parrotfish; $1, Long-spined squirrelfish; $2.50, Bigeye; $5, Blue chromis.

10 Sprinting and Aztec Sun-stone

1968. Olympic Games. Mexico. Multicoloured.

28 25c. Type **10** 45 25
29 35c. High-jumping and Aztec statue 50 25
30 75c. Dinghy-racing and Aztec lion mask 55 45
MS31 87 × 76 mm. $1 Football and engraved plate . . . . 1·75 3·25

14 "The Ascension" (Orcagna)
18 "Sistine Madonna" (Raphael)

15 Scout Enrolment Ceremony

1969. Easter Commemoration.

32 14 25c. black and blue 15 45
33 35c. black and red 15 50
34 75c. black and lilac 15 55

1969. 3rd Caribbean Scout Jamboree. Multicoloured.

35 25c. Type **15** 45 55
36 35c. Scouts around camp fire 60 65
37 75c. Sea Scouts rowing boat 75 85

1969. Christmas.

38 18 ½c. multicoloured 10 10
39 25c. multicoloured 10 15
40 35c. multicoloured 10 20
41 35c. multicoloured 20 35

19 William I (1066–87)
21 "The Way to Calvary" (Ugolino)

1970. English Monarchs. Multicoloured.

42 35c. Type **19** 30 15
43 35c. William II (1087–1100) 10 15
44 35c. Henry I (1100–35) 10 15
45 35c. Stephen (1135–54) 10 15
46 35c. Henry II (1154–89) . . . 10 15
47 35c. Richard I (1189–99) . . . 10 15
48 35c. John (1199–1216) 10 15
49 35c. Henry III (1216–72) . . . 10 15
50 35c. Edward I (1272–1307) . . 10 15
51 35c. Edward II (1307–27) . . 10 15
52 35c. Edward III (1327–77) . . 10 15
53 35c. Richard II (1377–99) . . 10 15
54 35c. Henry IV (1399–1413) . . 10 15
55 35c. Henry V (1413–22) . . . 10 15
56 35c. Henry VI (1422–61) . . . 10 15
57 35c. Edward IV (1462–83) . . 10 15
58 35c. Edward V (April–June 1483) 10 15
59 35c. Richard III (1483–85) . . 10 15
60 35c. Henry VII (1485–1509) 10 15
61 35c. Henry VIII (1509–47) . . 10 15
62 35c. Edward VI (1547–53) . . 10 15
63 35c. Lady Jane Grey (1553) . . 10 15
64 35c. Mary I (1553–8) 10 15
65 35c. Elizabeth I (1558–1603) 10 15
66 35c. James I (1603–25) 10 15
67 35c. Charles I (1625–49) . . . 10 15
68 35c. Charles II (1649–1685) . . 10 15
69 35c. James II (1685–1688) . . 10 15
70 35c. William III (1689–1702) 10 15
71 35c. Mary II (1689–1694) . . 10 15
72 35c. Anne (1702–1714) 15 15
73 35c. George I (1714–1727) . . 15 15
74 35c. George II (1727–1760) . . 15 15
75 35c. George III (1760–1820) 15 15
76 35c. George IV (1820–1830) 15 15
77 35c. William IV (1830–1837) 15 60
78 35c. Victoria (1837–1901) . . . 15 60

See also Nos. 710/5.

1970. No. 12 surch **20c**.

79 2 20c. on ½c. brn, blk & pink 10 20

1970. Easter. Paintings. Multicoloured.

80 25c. Type **21** 15 30
81 35c. "The Deposition from the Cross" (Ugolino) 15 30
82 75c. Crucifix (The Master of St. Francis) 15 35

22 Oliver is introduced to Fagin ("Oliver Twist")

1970. Death Centenary of Charles Dickens. Mult.

83 20c. Type **22** 20 25
84 75c. Dickens and scene from "The Old Curiosity Shop" 45 65

23 "Madonna of the Meadows" (G. Bellini)

1970. Christmas. Multicoloured.

85 20c. Type **23** 10 25
86 50c. "Madonna, Child and Angels" (from Wilton diptych) 15 30
87 75c. "The Nativity" (della Francesca) 15 35

24 Nurse with Patient in Wheelchair
25 "Angel with Vases"

1970. Centenary of British Red Cross. Multicoloured.

88 20c. Type **24** 15 30
89 35c. Nurse giving patient magazines (horiz) 20 40
90 75c. Nurse and mother weighing baby (horiz) . . . 25 70

1971. Easter. "Mond" Crucifixion by Raphael. Multicoloured.

91 35c. Type **25** 15 85
92 50c. "Christ crucified" 15 95
93 75c. "Angel with vase" . . . 15 1·00

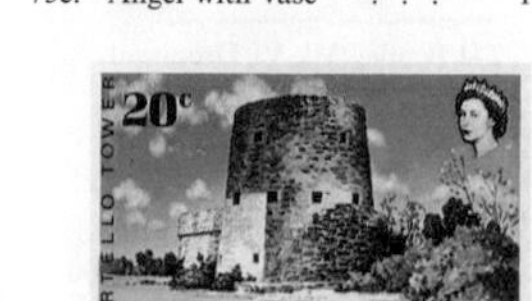

26 Martello Tower

1971. Tourism. Multicoloured.

94 20c. Type **26** 15 35
95 25c. "Sailfish" dinghy 25 40
96 50c. Hotel bungalows 25 45
97 75c. Government House and Mystery Stone 25 55

27 "The Granducal Madonna" (Raphael)

1971. Christmas. Multicoloured.

98 ½c. Type **27** 10 10
99 35c. "The Ansidei Madonna" (Raphael) 10 20
100 50c. "The Madonna and Child" (Botticelli) 15 25
101 75c. "The Madonna of the Trees" (Bellini) 15 30

Four stamps to commemorate the 500th Birth Anniv of Durer were prepared in late 1971, but their issue was not authorised by the Antigua Government.

1973. Royal Wedding. Nos. 370/1 of Antigua optd **BARBUDA** twice.

102 106 25c. multicoloured . . . . 3·25 2·00
103 $2 multicoloured . . . . 1·25 1·25

1973. Ships. Nos. 269/85 of Antigua optd **BARBUDA**.

116 92 ½c. multicoloured 15 20
104 – 1c. multicoloured 15 30
105 – 2c. multicoloured 25 30
117 – 3c. multicoloured 25 25
106 – 4c. multicoloured 30 30
107 – 5c. multicoloured 40 40
108 – 6c. multicoloured 40 40
109 – 10c. multicoloured 45 45
118 – 15c. multicoloured 45 50
110 – 20c. multicoloured 55 60
111 – 25c. multicoloured 55 60
112 – 35c. multicoloured 55 70
113 – 50c. multicoloured 55 70
114 – 75c. multicoloured 55 70
119 – $1 multicoloured 55 70
115 – $2.50 multicoloured . . . 75 1·50
121 – $5 multicoloured . . . . . 1·10 2·50

1973. Military Uniforms. Nos. 353, 355 and 357 of Antigua optd **BARBUDA**.

122 ½c. multicoloured 10 10
123 20c. multicoloured 15 10
124 75c. multicoloured 40 15
MS125 127 × 145 mm. Nos. 353/7 of Antigua . . . . 2·00 3·50

1973. Carnival. Nos. 360/3 of Antigua optd **BARBUDA**.

126 20c. multicoloured 10 10
127 35c. multicoloured 10 10
128 75c. multicoloured 20 25
MS129 134 × 95 mm. Nos. 359/62 of Antigua . . . . 1·00 2·25

1973. Christmas. Nos. 364/69 of Antigua optd **BARBUDA**.

130 105 3c. multicoloured 10 10
131 – 5c. multicoloured 10 10
132 – 20c. multicoloured 10 10
133 – 35c. multicoloured 15 15
134 – $1 multicoloured 30 30
MS135 130 × 128 mm. Nos. 130/4 2·25 9·00

1973. Honeymoon Visit. Nos. 373/4 of Antigua additionally optd **BARBUDA**.

136 35c. multicoloured 30 20
137 $2 multicoloured 70 60
MS138 78 × 100 mm. Nos. 136/7 1·10 1·00

1974. University of West Indies. Nos. 376/9 of Antigua optd **BARBUDA**.

139 5c. multicoloured 10 10
140 20c. multicoloured 10 10
141 35c. multicoloured 15 15
142 75c. multicoloured 15 15

1974. Military Uniforms. Nos. 380/4 of Antigua optd **BARBUDA**.

143 ½c. multicoloured 10 10
144 10c. multicoloured 15 10
145 20c. multicoloured 25 10
146 35c. multicoloured 25 10
147 75c. multicoloured 45 25

1974. Centenary of U.P.U. (1st issue). Nos. 386/92 of Antigua optd with either a or b. (a) **BARBUDA 13 JULY 1992**.

148 ½c. multicoloured 10 10
150 1c. multicoloured 10 10
152 2c. multicoloured 20 15
154 5c. multicoloured 50 15
156 20c. multicoloured 40 70
158 35c. multicoloured . . . . . 80 1·50
160 $1 multicoloured . . . . . . 1·75 4·00

(b) **BARBUDA 15 SEPT. 1874 G.P.U.** ("General Postal Union").

149 ½c. multicoloured 10 10
151 1c. multicoloured 10 10
153 2c. multicoloured 20 15
155 5c. multicoloured 50 15
157 20c. multicoloured 40 70
159 35c. multicoloured . . . . . 80 1·50
161 $1 multicoloured . . . . . . 1·75 4·00
MS162 141 × 164 mm. No. **MS**393 of Antigua optd **BARBUDA** 3·50 6·00

1974. Antiguan Steel Bands. Nos. 394/98 of Antigua optd **BARBUDA**.

163 5c. deep red, red and black 10 10
164 20c. brown, lt brown & blk 10 10
165 35c. light green, green and black 10 10
166 75c. deep blue, blue and black 20 20
MS167 115 × 108 mm. Nos. 163/6 65 80

39 Footballers

1974. World Cup Football Championships (1st issue).

168 39 35c. multicoloured 10 10
169 – $1.20 multicoloured . . . 25 35
170 – $2.50 multicoloured . . . 35 50
MS171 70 × 128 mm. Nos. 168/70 85 90

DESIGNS: $1.20, $2.50, Footballers in action similar to Type **39**.

1974. World Cup Football Championships (2nd issue). Nos. 399/403 of Antigua optd **BARBUDA**.

172 111 5c. multicoloured 10 10
173 – 35c. multicoloured 20 10
174 – 75c. multicoloured 25 15
175 – $1 multicoloured 25 25
MS176 135 × 130 mm. Nos. 172/5 75 1·25

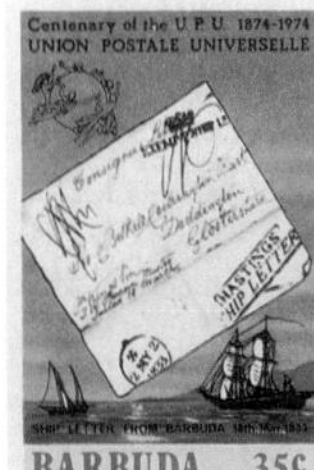

41 Ship Letter of 1833

1974. Cent of Universal Postal Union (2nd issue). Multicoloured.
177 35c. Type **41** 10 10
178 $1.20 Stamps and postmarks of 1922 . . . . 25 50
179 $2.50 Britten Norman Islander mailplane over map of Barbuda 35 75
MS180 128 × 97 mm. Nos. 177/9 1·00 2·00

42 Greater Amberjack

1974. Multicoloured.
181 ½c. Oleander, Rose Bay (vert) 10 40
182 1c. Blue petrea (vert) . . . 15 40
183 2c. Poinsettia (vert) 15 40
184 3c. Cassia tree (vert) 15 40
185 4c. Type **42** . . . . 1·75 40
186 5c. Holy Trinity School . . 15 15
187 6c. Snorkeling 15 30
188 10c. Pilgrim Holiness Church 15 20
189 15c. New Cottage Hospital 15 20
190 20c. Post Office and Treasury 15 20
191 25c. Island jetty and boats (vert) 30 30
192 35c. Martello Tower 30 30
193 50c. Warden's House . . . 30 30
194 75c. Britten Norman Islander aircraft . . . . . 2·25 1·00
195 $1 Tortoise 70 80
196 $2.50 Spiny lobster . . . . 80 1·75
197 $5 Magnificent frigate bird 4·00 2·50
197b $10 Hibiscus (vert) . . . . 1·50 4·50

The 50c. to $1 are 39 × 25 mm, $2.50 and $5 45 × 29 mm, $10 34 × 48 mm.

1974. Birth Centenary of Sir Winston Churchill (1st issue). Nos. 408/12 of Antigua optd **BARBUDA**.
198 **113** 5c. multicoloured 15 10
199 – 35c. multicoloured 25 15
200 – 75c. multicoloured 40 45
201 – $1 multicoloured 75 70
MS202 107 × 82 mm. Nos. 198/201 7·00 14·00

43 Churchill making Broadcast

1974. Birth Centenary of Sir Winston Churchill (2nd issue). Multicoloured.
203 5c. Type **43** 10 10
204 35c. Churchill and Chartwell 10 10
205 75c. Churchill painting . . . 20 20
206 $1 Churchill making "V" sign 25 30
MS207 146 × 95 mm. Nos. 203/6 75 2·50

1974. Christmas. Nos. 413/21 of Antigua optd **BARBUDA**.
208 **114** ½c. multicoloured 10 10
209 – 1c. multicoloured 10 10
210 – 2c. multicoloured 10 10
211 – 3c. multicoloured 10 10
212 – 5c. multicoloured 10 10
213 – 20c. multicoloured 10 10
214 – 35c. multicoloured 15 15
215 – 75c. multicoloured 30 30
MS216 139 × 126 mm. Nos. 208/15 80 1·40

1975. Nelson's Dockyard. Nos. 427/32 of Antigua optd **BARBUDA**.
217 **116** 5c. multicoloured 15 15
218 – 15c. multicoloured 40 25
219 – 35c. multicoloured 55 35
220 – 50c. multicoloured 60 50
221 – $1 multicoloured 65 80
MS222 130 × 134 mm. As Nos. 217/21, but larger format; 43 × 28 mm . . . . 1·75 2·75

45 Ships of the Line

1975. Sea Battles. Battle of the Saints, 1782. Mult.
223 35c. Type **45** 40 65
224 50c. H.M.S. "Ramillies" . . 40 75
225 75c. "Bonhomme Richard" (American frigate) firing broadside 50 90
226 95c. "L'Orient" (French ship of the line) burning . . . . 50 1·25

1975. "Apollo–Soyuz" Space Project. No. 197 optd **U.S.A.-U.S.S.R SPACE COOPERATION 1975** with **APOLLO** (No. 227) or **SOYUZ** (No. 228).
227 $5 multicoloured . . . . . . 3·25 6·00
228 $5 multicoloured . . . . . . 3·25 6·00

47 Officer, 65th Foot, 1763

1975. Military Uniforms. Multicoloured.
229 35c. Type **47** 60 60
230 50c. Grenadier, 27th Foot 1701–10 . . . . 75 75
231 75c. Officer, 21st Foot, 1793–6 . . . . 80 80
232 95c. Officer, Royal Regiment of Artillery, 1800 . . . . . 90 90

1975. 25th Anniv of United Nations. Nos. 203/6 optd **30TH ANNIVERSARY UNITED NATIONS 1945–1975**.
233 **43** 5c. multicoloured 10 10
234 – 35c. multicoloured 10 15
235 – 75c. multicoloured 15 20
236 – $1 multicoloured 20 30

1975. Christmas. Nos. 457/65 of Antigua optd **BARBUDA**.
237 **121** ½c. multicoloured 10 15
238 – 1c. multicoloured 10 15
239 – 2c. multicoloured 10 15
240 – 3c. multicoloured 10 15
241 – 5c. multicoloured 10 15
242 – 10c. multicoloured 10 15
243 – 35c. multicoloured 15 20
244 – $2 multicoloured . . . . 60 1·00
MS245 138 × 119 mm. Nos. 241/4 1·10 2·25

1975. World Cup Cricket Winners. Nos. 466/8 of Antigua optd **BARBUDA**.
246 **122** 5c. multicoloured . . . . 90 1·25
247 – 35c. multicoloured . . . . 1·75 2·00
248 – $2 multicoloured . . . . 3·25 4·50

51 Surrender of Cornwallis at Yorktown (Trumbull)

1976. Bicentenary of American Revolution.
249 **51** 15c. multicoloured 10 15
250 – 15c. multicoloured 10 15
251 – 15c. multicoloured 10 15
252 – 35c. multicoloured 10 15
253 – 35c. multicoloured 10 15
254 – 35c. multicoloured 10 15
255 – $1 multicoloured 15 25
256 – $1 multicoloured 15 25
257 – $1 multicoloured 15 25
258 – $2 multicoloured 25 40
259 – $2 multicoloured 25 40
260 – $2 multicoloured 25 40
MS261 140 × 70 mm. Nos. 249/54 and 255/60 (two sheets) . . . . 1·40 9·00

DESIGNS—As Type **51**: Nos. 249/51; 252/4, The Battle of Princeton; 255/7, Surrender of General Burgoyne at Saratoga; 258/60, Jefferson presenting Declaration of Independence.

Type **51** shows the left-hand stamp of the 15c. design.

52 Bananaquits

1976. Birds. Multicoloured.
262 35c. Type **52** 45 50
263 50c. Blue-hooded euphonia 45 60
264 75c. Royal tern 45 80
265 95c. Killdeer plover ("Killdeer") 55 85
266 $1.25 Shiney-headed cowbird ("Glossy Cowbird") . . . 55 1·00
267 $2 American purple gallinule ("Purple Gallinule") . . . 60 1·25

1976. Royal Visit to the U.S.A. Nos. 249/60 additionally inscr "H.M. QUEEN ELIZABETH ROYAL VISIT 6TH JULY 1976 H.R.H. DUKE OF EDINBURGH".
268 15c. multicoloured 10 15
269 15c. multicoloured 10 15
270 15c. multicoloured 10 15
271 35c. multicoloured 10 20
272 35c. multicoloured 10 20
273 35c. multicoloured 10 20
274 $1 multicoloured 15 50
275 $1 multicoloured 15 50
276 $1 multicoloured 15 50
277 $2 multicoloured 25 70
278 $2 multicoloured 25 70
279 $2 multicoloured 25 70
MS280 143 × 81 mm. Nos. 268/73 and 274/9 (two sheets) . . . . 1·50 9·00

1976. Christmas. Nos. 514/18 of Antigua optd **BARBUDA**.
281 **128** 8c. multicoloured 10 10
282 – 10c. multicoloured 10 10
283 – 15c. multicoloured 10 10
284 – 50c. multicoloured 15 15
285 – $1 multicoloured 25 30

1976. Olympic Games, Montreal. Nos. 495/502 of Antigua optd **BARBUDA**.
286 **125** ½c. brown, yellow and black 10 10
287 – 1c. violet and black . . . 10 10
288 – 2c. green and black . . . 10 10
289 – 15c. blue and black . . . 10 10
290 – 30c. brown, yellow & blk 10 10
291 – $1 orange, red and black 20 20
292 – $2 red and black 35 35
MS293 88 × 138 mm. Nos. 289/92 1·75 2·40

55 P.O. Tower, Telephones and Alexander Graham Bell

1977. Cent of First Telephone Transmission. Mult.
294 75c. Type **55** 15 35
295 $1.25 T.V. transmission by satellite 20 55
296 $2 Globe showing satellite transmission scheme . . . 30 75
MS297 96 × 144 mm. Nos. 294/6 70 2·00

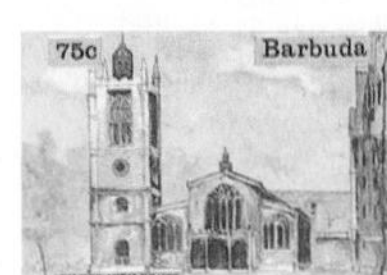

56 St. Margaret's Church, Westminster

1977. Silver Jubilee (1st issue). Multicoloured.
298 75c. Type **56** 10 15
299 75c. Street decorations . . . 10 15
300 75c. Westminster Abbey . . 10 15
301 $1.25 Household Cavalry . . 15 20
302 $1.25 Coronation Coach . . 15 20
303 $1.25 Postillions 15 20
MS304 148 × 83 mm. As Nos. 298/303, but with silver borders. . . . . 75 1·50

Nos. 298/300 and 301/3 were printed together, se-tenant, forming composite designs.

See also Nos. 323/30 and 375/8.

1977. Nos. 469/86 of Antigua optd **BARBUDA**.
305 ½c. Antillean crested hummingbird 75 75
306 1c. Imperial amazon ("Imperial Parrot") 75 75
307 2c. Zenaida dove 75 75
308 3c. Loggerhead kingbird . . 75 75
309 4c. Red-necked pigeon . . . 75 75
310 5c. Rufous throated solitaire 75 75
311 6c. Orchid tree 50 50
312 10c. Bougainvillea 30 20
313 15c. Geiger tree 30 25
314 20c. Flamboyant 30 25
315 25c. Hibiscus 30 25
316 35c. Flame of the Wood . . 35 30
317 50c. Cannon at Fort James 40 40
318 75c. Premier's Office 40 40
319 $1 Potworks Dam 50 60
320 $2.50 Irrigation scheme . . . 75 1·60
321 $5 Government House . . . 1·25 3·25
322 $10 Coolidge Airport . . . . 3·50 7·50

1977. Silver Jubilee (2nd issue). Nos. 526/31 of Antigua optd **BARBUDA**. (a) Ordinary gum.
323 10c. Royal Family 10 15
324 30c. Royal visit, 1966 . . . . 10 20
325 50c. The Queen enthroned . . 15 30
326 90c. The Queen after Coronation 15 40
327 $2.50 The Queen and Prince Charles . . . . 45 1·25
MS328 116 × 78 mm. $5 Queen Elizabeth and Prince Philip . . 80 1·25

(b) Self-adhesive.
329 50c. Queen after Coronation 40 70
330 $5 The Queen and Prince Philip . . . . 3·00 9·00

1977. Caribbean Scout Jamboree, Jamaica. Nos. 534/40 of Antigua optd **BARBUDA**.
331 ½c. Type **131** 10 10
332 1c. Hiking 10 10
333 2c. Rock-climbing 10 10
334 10c. Cutting logs 10 10
335 30c. Map and sign reading 30 40
336 50c. First aid 35 65
337 $2 Rafting . . . . 75 2·25
MS338 127 × 114 mm. Nos. 335/7 2·50 4·00

1977. 21st Anniv of Carnival. Nos. 542/47 of Antigua optd **BARBUDA**.
339 10c. Type **312** 10 10
340 30c. Carnival Queen 10 10
341 50c. Butterfly costume . . . 15 20
342 90c. Queen of the Band . . . 20 35
343 $1 Calypso King and Queen 25 45
MS344 140 × 120 mm. Nos. 339/43 1·00 1·75

61 Royal Yacht "Britannia"

1977. Royal Visit (1st issue). Multicoloured.
345 50c. Type **61** 10 20
346 $1.50 Jubilee emblem 25 35
347 $2.50 Union Jack and flag of Antigua 35 55
MS348 77 × 124 mm. Nos. 345/7 85 2·25

1977. Royal Visit (2nd issue). Nos. 548/53 of Antigua optd **BARBUDA**.
349A 10c. Royal Family 10 10
350B 30c. Queen Elizabeth and Prince Philip in car . . . 10 15
351B 50c. Queen enthroned . . . 15 20
352B 90c. Queen after Coronation 20 30
353B $2.50 The Queen and Prince Charles 45 80
MS354A 116 × 78 mm. $5 Queen and Prince Philip . . . . . . 1·75 4·00

1977. Christmas. Nos. 554/61 of Antigua optd **BARBUDA**.
355 ½c. Type **134** 10 10
356 1c. Crivelli 10 10
357 2c. Lotto 10 10
358 8c. Pontormo 10 10
359 10c. Tura (different) 10 10
360 25c. Lotto (different) 15 10
361 $2 Crivelli (different) 45 45
MS362 144 × 118 mm. Nos. 358/61 1·00 1·75

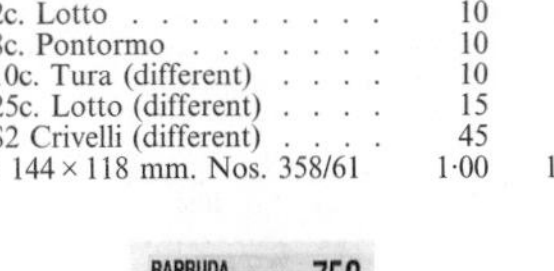

64 Airship LZ-1

1977. Special Events, 1977. Multicoloured.
363 75c. Type **64** 30 30
364 75c. German battleship and German Navy airship L-31 30 30
365 75c. "Graf Zeppelin" in hangar 30 30
366 75c. Gondola of military airship 30 30
367 95c. Sputnik 1 . . . . 35 35
368 95c. Vostok rocket 35 35
369 95c. Voskhod rocket 35 35
370 95c. Space walk 35 35
371 $1.25 Fuelling for flight . . . 40 45
372 $1.25 Leaving New York . . 40 45
373 $1.25 "Spirit of St. Louis" . . 40 45
374 $1.25 Welcome to England 40 45
375 $2 Lion of England 50 70
376 $2 Unicorn of Scotland . . . 50 70
377 $2 Yale of Beaufort 50 70
378 $2 Falcon of Plantagenets . . 50 70
379 $5 "Daniel in the Lion's Den" (Rubens) . . . . . 50 1·25
380 $5 Different detail of painting 50 1·25
381 $5 Different detail of painting 50 1·25
382 $5 Different detail of painting 50 1·25
MS383 132 × 156 mm. Nos. 362/82 6·00 17·00

EVENTS: 75c. 75th anniv of navigable airships; 95c. 20th anniv of U.S.S.R. space programme; $1.25, 50th anniv of Lindbergh's transatlantic flight; $2 Silver Jubilee of Queen Elizabeth II; $5 400th birth anniv of Rubens.

Nos. 379/82 form a composite design.

1978. 10th Anniv of Statehood. Nos. 562/7 of Antigua optd **BARBUDA**.
384 10c. Type **135** 10 10
385 15c. State flag 15 10
386 50c. Police band 1·25 70
387 90c. Premier V. C. Bird 20 40
388 $2 State Coat of Arms 40 80
MS389 122 × 99 mm. Nos. 385/88 6·50 4·00

66 "Pieta" (sculpture) (detail)

1978. Easter. Paintings and Sculptures by Michelangelo. Multicoloured.
390 75c. Type **66** 15 15
391 95c. "The Holy Family" 15 20
392 $1.25 "Libyan sibyl" (from the Sistine Chapel) 15 35
393 $2 "The Flood" (from the Sistine Chapel) 20 45
MS394 117 × 85 mm. Nos. 390/3 1·90 2·00

1978. 75th Anniv of Powered Flight. Nos. 568/75 of Antigua optd **BARBUDA**.
395 ½c. Wright Glider No. III, 1902 10 10
396 1c. Wright Flyer I, 1903 10 10
397 2c. Launch system and engine 10 10
398 10c. Orville Wright (vert) 10 10
399 50c. Wright Flyer III, 1905 25 20
400 90c. Wilbur Wright (vert) 35 25
401 $2 Wright Type B, 1910 60 45
MS402 90 × 75 mm. $2.50, Wright Flyer I on launch system 1·50 2·50

1978. Sailing Week. Nos. 576/80 of Antigua optd **BARBUDA**.
403 10c. Sunfish regatta 20 10
404 50c. Fishing and work boat race 40 25
405 90c. Curtain Bluff race 55 35
406 $2 Power boat rally 85 75
MS407 110 × 77 mm. $2.50, Guadeloupe–Antigua race 1·25 1·60

68 St. Edward's Crown

1978. 25th Anniv of Coronation (1st issue). Multicoloured.
408 75c. Type **68** 15 20
409 75c. Imperial State Crown 15 20
410 $1.50 Queen Mary's Crown 20 30
411 $1.50 Queen Mother's Crown 20 30
412 $2.50 Queen Consort's Crown 35 50
413 $2.50 Queen Victoria's Crown 35 50
MS414 123 × 117 mm. Nos. 408/13 1·10 1·75

1978. 25th Anniv of Coronation (2nd issue). Nos. 581/5 of Antigua optd **BARBUDA**.
415 10c. Queen Elizabeth and Prince Philip 10 10
416 30c. The Crowning 10 10
417 50c. Coronation procession 10 15
418 90c. Queen seated in St. Edward's Chair 15 20
419 $2.50 Queen wearing Imperial State Crown 30 60
MS420 114 × 103 mm. $5 Queen Elizabeth and Prince Philip 1·00 1·50

1978. 25th Anniv of Coronation (3rd issue). As Nos. 587/9 of Antigua, additionally inscr "BARBUDA".
421 25c. Glass Coach 30 70
422 50c. Irish State Coach 30 70
423 $5 Coronation Coach 1·00 2·25

1978. World Cup Football Championship, Argentina. Nos. 590/3 of Antigua optd **BARBUDA**.
424 10c. Player running with ball 10 10
425 15c. Players in front of goal 10 10
426 $3 Referee and player 1·00 1·25
MS427 126 × 88 mm. 25c. Player crouching with ball; 30c. Players heading ball; 50c. Players running with ball; $2 Goalkeeper diving 80 90

1978. Flowers. As Nos. 594/7 of Antigua optd **BARBUDA**.
428 25c. Petrea 15 20
429 50c. Sunflower 25 40
430 90c. Frangipani 35 45
431 $2 Passion flower 60 90
MS432 118 × 85 mm. $2.50, Hibiscus 1·00 1·50

1978. Christmas. As Nos. 599/601 of Antigua optd **BARBUDA**.
433 8c. "St. Ildefonso receiving the Chasuble from the Virgin" 10 10
434 25c. "The Flight of St. Barbara" 15 15
435 $2 "Madonna and Child, with St. Joseph, John the Baptist and Donor" 60 1·25
MS436 170 × 113 mm. $4 "The Annuciation" 1·00 1·25

70 Black-barred Soldierfish

1978. Flora and Fauna. Multicoloured.
437 25c. Type **70** 65 1·50
438 50c. "Cynthia cardui" (butterfly) 1·00 2·25
439 75c. Dwarf poinciana 65 2·25
440 95c. "Heliconius charithonia" (butterfly) 1·25 2·50
441 $1.25 Bougainvillea 75 2·50

71 Footballers and World Cup **72** Sir Rowland Hill

1978. Anniversaries and Events.
442 75c. Type **71** 30 30
443 95c. Wright Brothers and Flyer I (horiz) 30 40
444 $1.25 Balloon "Double Eagle II" and map of Atlantic (horiz) 40 45
445 $2 Prince Philip paying homage to the Queen 40 60
MS446 122 × 90 mm. Nos. 442/5. Imperf 4·25 6·00
EVENTS: 75c. Argentina—Winners of World Cup Football Championship; 95c. 75th anniv of powered flight; $1.25, First Atlantic crossing by balloon; $2 25th anniv of Coronation.

1979. Death Centenary of Sir Rowland Hill (1st issue). Multicoloured.
447 75c. Type **72** 25 45
448 95c. Mail coach, 1840 (horiz) 25 50
449 $1.25 London's first pillar box, 1855 (horiz) 30 60
450 $2 Mail leaving St. Martin's Le Grand Post Office, London 45 85
MS451 129 × 104 mm. Nos. 447/50. Imperf 1·40 2·25

1979. Death Centenary of Sir Rowland Hill (2nd issue). Nos. 603/6 of Antigua optd **BARBUDA**.
452 25c. 1d. Stamp of 1863 15 15
453 50c. Penny Black 20 20
454 $1 Stage-coach and woman posting letter, c. 1840 35 30
455 $2 Modern mail transport 80 60
MS456 108 × 82 mm. $2.50, Sir Rowland Hill 75 80

1979. Easter. Works of Durer. Nos. 608/11 of Antigua optd **BARBUDA**.
457 10c. multicoloured 10 10
458 50c. multicoloured 20 20
459 $4 black, mauve and yellow 90 1·10
MS460 114 × 99 mm. $2.50, multicoloured 55 75

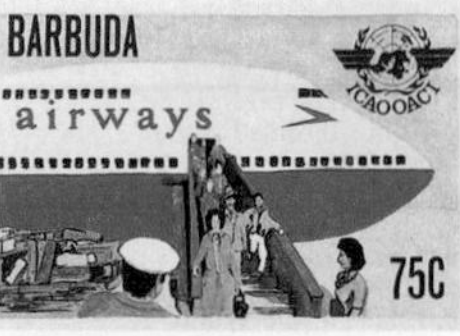

74 Passengers alighting from British Airways Boeing 747

1979. 30th Anniv of International Civil Aviation Organization. Multicoloured.
461 75c. Type **74** 25 50
462 95c. Air traffic control 25 50
463 $1.25 Ground crew-man directing Douglas DC-8 on runway 25 50

1979. International Year of the Child (1st issue). Nos. 612/15 of Antigua optd **BARBUDA**.
464 25c. Yacht 20 15
465 50c. Rocket 30 25
466 90c. Car 40 35
467 $2 Toy train 80 60
MS468 80 × 112 mm. $5 Airplane 1·10 1·10

1979. Fishes. Nos. 617/21 of Antigua optd **BARBUDA**.
469 30c. Yellow jack 20 15
470 50c. Blue-finned tuna 25 20
471 90c. Sailfish 30 30
472 $3 Wahoo 65 1·10
MS473 122 × 75 mm. $2.50, Great barracuda 1·00 1·25

1979. Death Bicentenary of Captain Cook. Nos. 622/6 of Antigua optd **BARBUDA**.
474 25c. Cook's Birthplace, Marton 25 25
475 50c. H.M.S. "Endeavour" 70 35
476 90c. Marine chronometer 70 40
477 $3 Landing at Botany Bay 1·50 1·25
MS478 110 × 85 mm. $2.50, H.M.S. "Resolution" 1·25 1·50

77 "Virgin with the Pear"

1979. International Year of the Child (2nd issue). Paintings by Durer. Multicoloured.
479 25c. Type **77** 15 15
480 50c. "Virgin with the Pink" (detail) 20 25
481 75c. "Virgin with the Pear" (different detail) 25 30
482 $1.25 "Nativity" (detail) 25 40
MS483 86 × 118 mm. Nos. 479/82 1·00 1·75

1979. Christmas. Nos. 627/31 of Antigua optd **BARBUDA**.
484 8c. The Holy Family 10 10
485 25c. Mary and Jesus on donkey 15 10
486 50c. Shepherd looking at star 25 15
487 $4 The Three Kings 85 80
MS488 113 × 94 mm. $3 Angel with trumpet 80 1·10

1980. Olympic Games, Moscow. Nos. 632/6 of Antigua optd **BARBUDA**.
489 10c. Javelin 10 10
490 25c. Running 15 10
491 $1 Pole vault 35 20
492 $2 Hurdles 55 40
MS493 127 × 96 mm. $3 Boxing 70 1·10

1980. "London 1980" International Stamp Exhibition. Nos. 452/5 optd **LONDON 1980**.
494 25c. 1d. stamp of 1863 35 20
495 50c. Penny Black 45 40
496 $1 Stage-coach and woman posting letter, c. 1840 85 65
497 $2 Modern mail transport 2·75 1·50

80 "Apollo 11" Crew Badge

1980. 10th Anniv of "Apollo 11" Moon Landing. Multicoloured.
498 75c. Type **80** 50 25
499 95c. Plaque left on Moon 50 30
500 $1.25 Rejoining the mother-ship 65 50
501 $2 Lunar module 75 75
MS502 118 × 84 mm. Nos. 498/501 1·40 2·50

81 American Wigeon ("American Widgeon")

1980. Birds. Multicoloured.
503 1c. Type **81** 70 1·25
504 2c. Snowy plover 70 70
505 4c. Rose-breasted grosbeak 75 70
506 6c. Mangrove cuckoo 75 70
507 10c. Adelaide's warbler 75 70
508 15c. Scaly-breasted thrasher 80 70
509 20c. Yellow-crowned night heron 80 70
510 25c. Bridled quail dove 80 70
511 35c. Carib grackle 85 1·25
512 50c. Northern pintail 90 55
513 75c. Black-whispered vireo 1·00 55
514 $1 Blue-winged teal 1·25 80
515 $1.50 Green-throated carib (vert) 1·50 80
516 $2 Red-necked pigeon (vert) 2·25 1·25
517 $2.50 Wied's crested flycatcher ("Stolid Flycatcher") (vert) 2·75 1·50
518 $5 Yellow-bellied sapsucker (vert) 4·00 3·50
519 $7.50 Caribbean elaenia (vert) 5·00 6·00
520 $10 Great egret (vert) 5·00 5·00

1980. Famous Works of Art. Nos. 651/8 of Antigua optd **BARBUDA**.
521 10c. "David" (statue, Donatello) 10 10
522 30c. "The Birth of Venus" (painting, Sandro Botticelli) 15 15
523 50c. "Reclining Couple" (sarcophagus), Cerveteri 15 20
524 90c. "The Garden of Earthly Delights" (painting, Hieronymus Bosch) 20 25
525 $1 "Portinari Altarpiece" (painting, Hugo van der Goes) 20 25
526 $4 "Eleanora of Toledo and her Son Giovanni de'Medici" (painting, Agnolo Bronzino) 60 80
MS527 99 × 124 mm. $5 "The Holy Family" (painting, Rembrandt) 1·50 1·75

1980. 75th Anniv of Rotary International. Nos. 658/62 of Antigua optd **BARBUDA**.
528 30c. Rotary Headquarters 15 15
529 50c. Antigua Rotary banner 20 20
530 90c. Map of Antigua 25 25
531 $3 Paul P. Harris (founder) 65 65
MS532 102 × 77 mm. $5 Antigua flags and Rotary emblems 1·50 2·25

1980. 80th Birthday of the Queen Mother. Nos. 663/5 of Antigua optd **BARBUDA**.
533 10c. multicoloured 50 15
534 $2.50 multicoloured 1·25 1·50
MS535 68 × 88 mm. $3 multicoloured 2·50 1·75

1980. Birds. Nos. 666/70 of Antigua optd **BARBUDA**.
536 10c. Ringed kingfisher 3·00 1·00
537 30c. Plain pigeon 3·50 1·10
538 $1 Green-throated carib 4·50 2·75
539 $2 Black necked stilt 5·50 5·25
MS540 73 × 73 mm. $2.50, Roseate tern 5·50 2·75

1981. Sugar Cane Railway Locomotives. Nos. 681/5 of Antigua optd **BARBUDA**.
541 25c. Diesel locomotive No. 15 1·00 25
542 50c. Narrow-gauge steam locomotive 1·25 35
543 90c. Diesel locomotive Nos. 1 and 10 1·75 45
544 $3 Steam locomotive hauling sugar cane 3·25 1·40
MS545 82 × 111 mm. $2.50, Antigua sugar factory, railway yard and sheds 1·50 1·75

84 Florence Nightingale

1981. Famous Women.
546 **84** 50c. multicoloured 15 30
547 – 90c. multicoloured 40 55
548 – $1 multicoloured 35 60
549 – $4 black, brown and lilac 50 1·75
DESIGNS: 90c. Marie Curie; $1 Amy Johnson; $4 Eleanor Roosevelt.

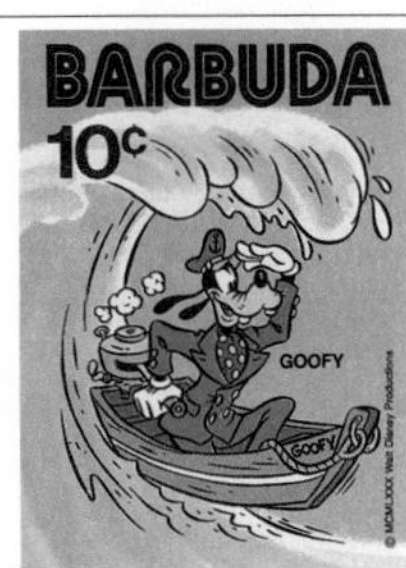

85 Goofy in Motor-boat

1981. Walt Disney Cartoon Characters. Mult.
550 10c. Type **85** 85 15
551 20c. Donald Duck reversing car into sea 1·00 20
552 25c. Mickey Mouse asking tug-boat to take on more than it can handle 1·10 30
553 30c. Porpoise turning tables on Goofy 1·10 35
554 35c. Goofy in sailing boat 1·10 35
555 40c. Mickey Mouse and boat being lifted out of water by fish 1·25 40
556 75c. Donald Duck fishing for flying-fish with butterfly net 1·75 60
557 $1 Minnie Mouse in brightly decorated sailing boat 1·75 80
558 $2 Chip and Dale on floating ship-in-bottle 2·25 1·40
MS559 127 × 101 mm. $2.50, Donald Duck 4·50 3·00

1981. Birth Centenary of Picasso. Nos. 697/701 of Antigua optd with **BARBUDA**.
560 10c. "Pipes of Pan" 10 10
561 50c. "Seated Harlequin" 25 15
562 90c. "Paulo as Harlequin" 35 30
563 $4 "Mother and Child" 90 1·00
MS564 115 × 140 mm. $5 "Three Musicians" (detail) 1·50 1·50

87/8 Buckingham Palace (½-size illustration)

1981. Royal Wedding (1st issue). Buildings. Each printed in black on either pink, green or lilac backgrounds.
565 $1 Type **87** 25 40
566 $1 Type **88** 25 40
567 $1.50 Caernarvon Castle (right) 30 50
568 $1.50 Caernarvon Castle (left) 30 50
569 $4 Highgrove House (right) 55 90
570 $4 Highgrove House (left) 55 90
MS571 75 × 90 mm. $5 black and yellow (St. Paul's Cathedral—26 × 32 mm) 80 1·25
Same prices for any background colour. The two versions of each value form composite designs.

1981. Royal Wedding (2nd issue). Nos. 702/5 of Antigua optd **BARBUDA**.
572 25c. Prince Charles and Lady Diana Spencer 15 15
573 50c. Glamis Castle 25 25
574 $4 Prince Charles skiing 75 1·00
MS575 95 × 85 mm. $5 Glass coach 90 90

89 "Integration and Travel"

1981. International Year of Disabled Persons (1st issue).
576 **89** 50c. multicoloured 25 20
577 – 90c. black, orange and green 25 25
578 – $1 black, blue and green 30 30
579 – $4 black, yellow and brown 45 85
DESIGNS: 90c. Braille and sign language; $1 "Helping hands"; $4 "Mobility aids for disabled".
See also Nos. 603/6.

1981. Royal Wedding (3rd issue). Nos. 706/12 of Antigua optd **BARBUDA**.
580 25c. Prince of Wales at Investiture, 1969 40 70
581 25c. Prince Charles as baby, 1948 40 70
582 $1 Prince Charles at R.A.F. College, Cranwell, 1971 50 85
583 $1 Prince Charles attending Hill House School, 1956 50 85
584 $2 Prince Charles and Lady Diana Spencer 75 1·00
585 $2 Prince Charles at Trinity College, 1967 75 1·00
586 $5 Prince Charles and Lady Diana 3·75 5·00

1981. Independence. No. 686/96 of Antigua additionally optd **BARBUDA**.
587 6c. Orchid tree 50 15
588 10c. Bougainvillea 55 15
589 20c. Flamboyant 70 20
590 25c. Hibiscus 80 25
591 35c. Flame of the wood 90 30
592 50c. Cannon at Fort James 1·10 45
593 75c. Premier's Office 1·25 75
594 $1 Potworks Dam 1·50 80
595 $2.50 Irrigation scheme, Diamond Estate 2·50 2·75
596 $5 Government House and Gardens 2·75 3·75
597 $10 Coolidge International Airport 4·50 6·00

1981. 50th Anniv of Antigua Girl Guide Movement. Nos. 713/16 of Antigua optd **BARBUDA**.
598 10c. Irene Joshua (founder) 55 10
599 50c. Campfire sing-song 1·25 30
600 90c. Sailing 1·75 45
601 $2.50 Animal tending 3·00 1·40
MS602 170 × 113 mm. $4 "The Annunciation" (Rubens) 1·25 1·50

1981. International Year of Disabled Persons (2nd issue). Sport for the Disabled. Nos. 728/32 of Antigua optd **BARBUDA**.
603 10c. Swimming 15 15
604 50c. Discus throwing 20 25
605 90c. Archery 45 45
606 $2 Baseball 60 1·50
MS607 108 × 84 mm. $4 Basketball 2·00 1·75

1981. Christmas. Paintings. Nos. 723/7 of Antigua optd **BARBUDA**.
608 8c. "Holy Night" (Jacques Stella) 10 10
609 30c. "Mary with Child" (Julius Schnorr von Carolfeld) 20 20
610 $1 "Virgin and Child" (Alsono Cano) 40 40
611 $3 "Virgin and Child" (Lorenzo di Credi) 1·10 1·10
MS612 77 × 111 mm. $5 "Holy Family" (Pieter von Avon) 1·75 2·25

93 Princess of Wales

97 Vincenzo Lunardi's Balloon Flight, London, 1785

1982. Birth of Prince William of Wales (1st issue).
613 **93** $1 multicoloured 50 50
614 $2.50 multicoloured 70 1·10
615 $5 multicoloured 1·25 1·75
MS616 88 × 108 mm. $4 multicoloured 2·00 2·10

1982. South Atlantic Fund. Nos. 580/6 surch **S. Atlantic Fund + 50c.**
617 25c.+50c. Prince of Wales at Investiture, 1969 30 50
618 25c.+50c. Prince Charles as baby, 1948 30 50
619 $1+50c. Prince Charles at R.A.F. College, Cranwell, 1971 50 75
620 $1+50c. Prince Charles attending Hill House School, 1956 50 75
621 $2+50c. Prince Charles and Lady Diana Spencer 75 1·10
622 $2+50c. Prince Charles at Trinity College, 1967 75 1·10
623 $5+50c. Prince Charles and Lady Diana Spencer 3·00 3·50

1982. 21st Birthday of Princess of Wales (1st issue). As Nos. 613/16 but inscr "Twenty First Birthday Greetings to H.R.H. The Princess of Wales."
624 $1 multicoloured 1·50 45
625 $2.50 multicoloured 2·25 1·25
626 $5 multicoloured 3·00 2·40
MS627 88 × 108 mm. $4 multicoloured 2·75 2·25

1982. 21st Birthday of Princess of Wales (2nd issue). Nos. 748/51 of Antigua optd **BARBUDA MAIL**.
628 90c. Queen's House, Greenwich 80 45
629 $1 Prince and Princess of Wales 1·25 50
630 $4 Princess of Wales 3·00 1·50
MS631 114 × 94 mm. $3 Angel with trumpet 1·00 1·50

1982. Birth of Prince William of Wales (2nd issue). Nos. 757/60 of Antigua further optd **BARBUDA MAIL**.
632 90c. Queen's House, Greenwich 70 45
633 $1 Prince and Princess of Wales 1·25 50
634 $4 Princess of Wales 3·25 2·00
MS635 102 × 75 mm. $5 Princess of Wales (different) 4·25 2·50

1982. Birth Centenary of Franklin D. Roosevelt and 250th Birth Anniv of George Washington. Nos. 761/8 of Antigua optd **BARBUDA MAIL**.
636 10c. Roosevelt in 1940 10 10
637 25c. Washington as blacksmith 15 15
638 45c. Churchill, Roosevelt and Stalin at Yalta Conference 1·50 25
639 60c. Washington crossing Delaware 20 25
640 $1 "Roosevelt Special" train 1·50 40
641 $3 Portrait of Roosevelt 60 90
MS642 92 × 87 mm. $4 Roosevelt and wife 1·00 1·75
MS643 92 × 87 mm. $4 Portrait of Washington 1·00 1·75

1982. Christmas. Religious Paintings by Raphael. Nos. 769/73 of Antigua optd **BARBUDA MAIL**.
644 10c. "Annunciation" 10 10
645 30c. "Adoration of the Magi" 15 15
646 $1 "Presentation at the Temple" 40 40
647 $4 "Coronation of the Virgin" 1·00 1·00
MS648 95 × 142 mm. $5 "Marriage of the Virgin" 1·25 2·00

1983. 500th Birth Anniv of Raphael. Details from "Galatea" Fresco. Nos. 774/8 of Antigua optd **BARBUDA MAIL**.
649 45c. Tritons and dolphins 20 20
650 50c. Sea Nymph carried off by Triton 20 20
651 60c. Winged angel steering dolphins (horiz) 25 25
652 $4 Cupids shooting arrows 1·00 1·00
MS653 101 × 102 mm. $5 Galatea pulled along by dolphins 1·25 2·00

1983. Commonwealth Day. Nos. 779/82 of Antigua optd **BARBUDA MAIL**.
654 25c. Pineapple produce 45 55
655 45c. Carnival 50 70
656 60c. Tourism 70 1·25
657 $3 Airport 2·00 3·50

1983. World Communications Year. Nos. 783/6 of Antigua optd **BARBUDA MAIL**.
658 15c. T.V. satellite coverage of Royal Wedding 1·75 20
659 50c. Police communications 3·00 90
660 60c. House-to-diesel train telephone call 2·50 90
661 $3 Satellite earth station with planets Jupiter and Saturn 3·75 2·50
MS662 100 × 90 mm. $5 "Comsat" satellite over West Indies 1·75 2·25

1983. Bicent of Manned Flight (1st issue). Mult.
663 $1 Type **97** 25 35
664 $1.50 Montgolfier brothers' balloon flight, Paris, 1783 40 55
665 $2.50 Blanchard and Jeffries' Cross-Channel balloon flight, 1785 60 90
MS666 111 × 111 mm. $5 Maiden flight of airship LZ-127 "Graf Zeppelin", 1928 2·00 2·75
See also Nos. 672/6.

1983. Whales. Nos. 788/93 of Antigua optd **BARBUDA MAIL**.
667 15c. Bottlenose dolphin 1·25 40
668 50c. Finback whale 4·00 1·60
669 60c. Bowhead whale 4·50 1·75
670 $3 Spectacled porpoise 5·50 4·25
MS671 122 × 101 mm. $5 Narwhal 6·00 4·50

1983. Bicentenary of Manned Flight (2nd issue). Nos. 811/15 of Antigua optd **BARBUDA MAIL**.
672 30c. Dornier Do-X flying boat 85 35
673 50c. Supermarine S6B seaplane 1·10 60
674 60c. Curtiss Sparrowhawk biplane and airship U.S.S. "Akron" 1·25 70
675 $4 Hot-air balloon "Pro-Juventute" 4·50 4·00
MS676 80 × 105 mm. $5 Airship LZ-127 "Graf Zeppelin" 3·75 4·25

1983. Nos. 565/70 surch.
677 45c. on $1 Type **87** 25 45
678 45c. on $1 Type **88** 25 45
679 50c. on $1.45 Caernarvon Castle (right) 25 45
680 50c. on $1.45 Caernarvon Castle (left) 25 45
681 60c. on $4 Highgrove House (left) 25 45
682 60c. on $4 Highgrove House (right) 25 45

1983. Nos. 793/810 of Antigua optd **BARBUDA MAIL**.
683 1c. Cashew nut 10 10
684 2c. Passion fruit 15 10
685 3c. Mango 15 10
686 5c. Grapefruit 15 10
687 10c. Pawpaw 20 10
688 15c. Breadfruit 40 10
689 20c. Coconut 50 15
690 25c. Oleander 50 15
691 30c. Banana 55 20
692 40c. Pineapple 65 25
693 45c. Cordia 70 30
694 50c. Cassia 80 30
695 60c. Poui 80 30
696 $1 Frangipani 1·10 50
697 $2 Flamboyant 1·75 1·25
698 $2.50 Lemon 2·00 1·75
699 $5 Lignum vitae 3·00 2·75
700 $10 National flag and coat of arms 4·50 5·50

1983. Christmas. 500th Birth Anniv of Raphael. Nos. 816/20 of Antigua optd **BARBUDA MAIL**.
701 10c. multicoloured 10 10
702 30c. multicoloured 10 20
703 $1 multicoloured 30 50
704 $4 multicoloured 1·00 1·50
MS705 101 × 131 mm. $5 multicoloured 1·40 2·50

1983. Bicentenary (1984) of Methodist Church. Nos. 821/4 of Antigua optd **BARBUDA MAIL**.
706 15c. Type **181** 20 15
707 50c. Nathaniel Gilbert (founder in Antigua) 30 25
708 60c. St. John Methodist Church steeple 30 30
709 $3 Ebenezer Methodist Church, St John's 80 1·00

100 Edward VII

1984. Members of British Royal Family. Mult.
710 $1 Type **100** 55 1·10
711 $1 George V 55 1·10
712 $1 George VI 55 1·10
713 $1 Elizabeth II 55 1·10
714 $1 Charles, Prince of Wales 55 1·10
715 $1 Prince William of Wales 55 1·10

1984. Olympic Games, Los Angeles (1st issue). Nos. 825/9 of Antigua optd **BARBUDA MAIL**.
716 25c. Discus 25 20
717 50c. Gymnastics 40 40
718 90c. Hurdling 50 60
719 $3 Cycling 2·75 1·50
MS720 82 × 67 mm. $5 Volleyball 2·75 3·25

1984. Ships. Nos. 830/4 of Antigua optd **BARBUDA MAIL**.
721 45c. "Booker Vanguard" (freighter) 1·50 45
722 50c. "Canberra" (liner) 1·50 50
723 60c. Yachts 1·75 60
724 $4 "Fairwind" (cargo liner) 4·25 2·75
MS725 101 × 80 mm. $5 18th-century British man-o-war (vert) 4·50 4·25

1984. Universal Postal Union Congress, Hamburg. Nos. 835/8 of Antigua optd **BARBUDA MAIL**.
726 15c. Chenille 25 15
727 50c. Shell flower 30 30
728 60c. Anthurium 40 40
729 $3 Angels trumpet 75 1·25
MS730 100 × 75 mm. $5 Crown of Thorns 2·00 2·50

101 Olympic Stadium, Athens, 1896

1984. Olympic Games, Los Angeles (2nd issue). Multicoloured.
731 $1.50 Type **101** 50 90
732 $2.50 Olympic stadium, Los Angeles, 1984 70 1·50
733 $5 Athlete carrying Olympic torch 1·10 2·25
MS734 121 × 95 mm. No. 733 1·50 2·50

1984. Presidents of the United States of America. Nos. 856/63 of Antigua optd **BARBUDA MAIL**.
735 10c. Abraham Lincoln 10 10
736 20c. Harry Truman 15 15
737 30c. Dwight Eisenhower 20 25
738 40c. Ronald Reagan 25 30
739 90c. Gettysburg Address, 1863 40 55
740 $1.10 Formation of N.A.T.O., 1949 40 65
741 $1.50 Eisenhower during Second World War 45 70
742 $2 Reagan and Caribbean Basin Initiative 50 1·00

1984. Abolition of Slavery. Nos. 864/8 of Antigua optd **BARBUDA MAIL**.
743 40c. View of Moravian Mission 30 30
744 50c. Antigua Courthouse, 1823 40 40

745 60c. Planting sugar-cane, Monks Hill 45 45
746 $3 Boiling house, Delaps' Estate . . . . 1·40 1·40
MS747 95 × 70 mm. $5 Loading sugar, Willoughby Bay . . . . 2·00 2·50

1984. Songbirds. Nos. 869/74 of Antigua optd **BARBUDA MAIL.**
748 40c. Rufous-sided towhee . . 1·75 45
749 50c. Parula warbler . . . . . 1·90 50
750 60c. House wren . . . . . . 2·00 55
751 $2 Ruby-crowned kinglet . . 3·25 1·50
752 $3 Common flicker ("Yellow-shafted Flicker") . . . . . 3·50 2·25
MS753 76 × 76 mm. $5 Yellow-breasted chat . . . . 4·00 4·50

1984. 450th Death Anniv of Correggio (painter). Nos. 878/82 of Antigua optd **BARBUDA MAIL.**
754 25c. "The Virgin and Infant with Angels and Cherubs" . . . 15 20
755 60c. "The Four Saints" . . . 40 45
756 90c. "St. Catherine" 50 55
757 $3 "The Campori Madonna" . 1·25 1·75
MS758 90 × 60 mm. $5 "St. John the Baptist" . . . . 1·75 3·25

1984. "Ausipex" International Stamp Exhibition Melbourne. Australian Sports. Nos. 875/7 of Antigua optd **BARBUDA MAIL.**
759 $1 Grass-skiing 50 60
760 $5 Australian Football . . . 2·00 3·00
MS761 108 × 78 mm. Boomerang-throwing . . . . 2·00 3·25

1984. 150th Birth Anniv of Edgar Degas (painter). Nos. 883/7 of Antigua optd **BARBUDA MAIL.**
762 15c. "The Blue Dancers" . . 10 10
763 50c. "The Pink Dancers" . . 30 40
764 70c. "Two Dancers" 45 55
765 $4 "Dancers at the Bar" . . 1·25 3·50
MS766 90 × 60 mm. $5 "The Folk Dancers" (40 × 27 mm) . . . . 1·75 2·75

1985. Famous People. Nos. 888/96 of Antigua optd **BARBUDA MAIL.**
767 60c. Winston Churchill . . . 4·00 1·75
768 60c. Mahatma Gandhi . . . 4·00 1·75
769 60c. John F. Kennedy . . . 4·00 1·75
770 60c. Mao Tse-tung . . . . . 4·00 1·75
771 $1 Churchill with General De Gaulle, Paris, 1944 (horiz) 4·00 1·75
772 $1 Gandhi leaving London by train, 1931 (horiz) . . . 4·00 1·75
773 $1 Kennedy with Chancellor Adenauer and Mayor Brandt, Berlin, 1963 (horiz) 4·00 1·75
774 $1 Mao Tse-tung with Lin Piao, Peking, 1969 (horiz) 4·00 1·75
MS775 114 × 80 mm. $5 Flags of Great Britain, India, the United States and China . . . . . . 6·00 6·00

103 Lady Elizabeth Bowes-Lyon, 1907, and Camellias

104 Roseate Tern

1985. Life and Times of Queen Elizabeth the Queen Mother. Multicoloured.
776 15c. Type **103** 35 20
777 45c. Duchess of York, 1926, and "Elizabeth of Glamis" roses 45 25
778 50c. The Queen Mother after the Coronation, 1937 . . . 45 25
779 60c. In Garter robes, 1971, and dog roses 45 30
780 90c. Attending Royal Variety Show, 1967, and red Hibiscus 60 45
781 $1 The Queen Mother in 1982, and blue plumbago 75 1·10
782 $3 Receiving 82nd birthday gifts from children, and morning glory . . . . . . 95 2·25

1985. Birth Bicentenary of John J. Audubon (ornithologist) (1st issue). Designs showing original paintings. Multicoloured.
783 45c. Type **104** 25 30
784 50c. Mangrove cuckoo . . . 25 30
785 60c. Yellow-crowned night heron 30 40
786 $5 Brown pelican . . . . . 1·40 3·50
See also Nos. 794/7 and 914/17.

1985. Centenary (1986) of Statue of Liberty (1st issue). Nos. 907/13 of Antigua optd **BARBUDA MAIL.**
787 25c. Torch from statue in Madison Square Park, 1885 . . . . 20 20
788 30c. Statue of Liberty and scaffolding ("Restoration and Renewal") (vert) . . . 20 20
789 50c. Frederic Bartholdi (sculpture) supervising construction, 1876 . . . . 30 30
790 90c. Close-up of Statue . . 55 55
791 $1 Statue and sailing ship ("Operation Sail", 1976) (vert) 60 60
792 $3 Dedication ceremony, 1886 (vert) . . . . 1·75 1·75
MS793 110 × 80 mm. $5 Port of New York . . . . 4·75 4·75
See also Nos. 987/96.

1985. Birth Bicentenary of John J. Audubon (ornithologist) (2nd issue). Nos. 924/8 of Antigua optd **BARBUDA MAIL.**
794 90c. Slavonian grebe ("Horned Grebe") . . . . 8·50 4·25
795 $1 British storm petrel ("Least Petrel") . . . . . 8·50 4·50
796 $1.50 Great blue heron . . . 9·50 7·50
797 $3 Double-crested cormorant (white phase) . . . . . 13·00 12·00
MS798 103 × 72 mm. $5 White-tailed tropic bird (vert) . . . . . . 27·00 11·00

1985. Butterflies. Nos. 929/33 of Antigua optd **BARBUDA MAIL.**
799 25c. "Anaea cyanea" . . . . 5·00 1·25
800 60c. "Leodonta dysoni" . . . 7·00 2·00
801 90c. "Junea doraete" . . . . 8·00 2·50
802 $4 "Prepona pylene" . . . . 14·00 15·00
MS803 132 × 105 mm. $5 "Caervois gerdtrudtus" . . . . 16·00 9·00

1985. Centenary of Motorcycle. Nos. 919/23 of Antigua optd **BARBUDA MAIL.**
804 10c. Triumph 2hp "Jap", 1903 . . . . 40 10
805 30c. Indian "Arrow", 1949 70 20
806 60c. BMW "R100RS", 1976 1·10 40
807 $4 Harley Davidson "Model II", 1916 . . . . 3·50 2·75
MS808 90 × 93 mm. $5 Laverda "Jota", 1975 . . . . 4·00 4·00

1985. 85th Birthday of Queen Elizabeth the Queen Mother. Nos. 776/82 optd **4TH AUG 1900–1985.**
809 15c. Type **103** 75 50
810 45c. Duchess of York, 1926 and "Elizabeth of Glamis" roses . . . . 1·10 60
811 50c. The Queen Mother after the Coronation, 1937 . . . 1·10 60
812 60c. In Garter robes, 1971, and dog roses . . . . . . 1·25 1·00
813 90c. Attending Royal Variey Show, 1967, and red hibiscus . . . . 1·25 1·25
814 $2 The Queen Mother in 1982, and blue plumbago 1·40 3·75
815 $3 Receiving 82nd birthday gifts from children, and morning glory . . . . . . 1·50 3·75

1985. Native American Artefacts. Nos. 914/18 of Antigua optd **BARBUDA MAIL.**
816 15c. Arawak pot sherd and Indians making clay utensils 15 10
817 50c. Arawak body design and Arawak Indians tattooing 25 25
818 60c. Head of the god "Yocahu" and Indians harvesting manioc 35 35
819 $3 Carib war club and Carib Indians going into battle 1·25 1·50
MS820 97 × 68 mm. $5 Taino Indians worshiping stone idol 2·00 3·00

1985. 40th Anniv of International Civil Aviation Organization. Nos. 934/8 of Antigua optd **BARBUDA MAIL.**
821 30c. Cessna Skyhawk . . . . 2·00 75
822 90c. Fokker D.VII . . . . . 3·00 1·25
823 $1.50 SPAD VII . . . . . . 3·50 4·50
824 $3 Boeing 747 . . . . 4·75 7·00
MS825 97 × 83 mm. De Havilland D.H.C.6 Twin Otter . . . . . 3·25 3·50

1985. Life and Times of Queen Elizabeth the Queen Mother (2nd series). Nos. 946/9 of Antigua optd **BARBUDA MAIL.**
826 $1 The Queen Mother attending church . . . . . 5·50 2·50
827 $1.50 Watching children playing in London garden 6·50 3·00
828 $2.50 The Queen Mother in 1979 . . . . 7·50 3·50
MS829 56 × 85 mm. $5 With Prince Edward at Royal Wedding, 1981 17·00 11·00

1985. 850th Birth Anniv of Maimonides (physician philosopher and scholar). Nos. 939/40 of Antigua optd **BARBUDA MAIL.**
830 $2 green . . . . 4·50 3·75
MS831 70 × 84 mm. $5 brown . . 4·25 4·25

1985. Marine Life. Nos. 950/4 of Antigua optd **BARBUDA MAIL.**
832 15c. Magnificent frigate bird 6·50 1·25
833 45c. Brain coral . . . . . . 6·50 80
834 60c. Cushion star . . . . . 6·50 1·25
835 $3 Spotted moray . . . . . 12·00 5·50
MS836 110 × 80 mm. $5 Elkhorn coral . . . . 17·00 6·50

1986. International Youth Year. Nos. 941/5 of Antigua optd **BARBUDA MAIL.**
837 25c. Young farmers with produce 15 15
838 50c. Hotel management trainees 25 30
839 60c. Girls with goat and boys with football ("Environment") 30 35
840 $3 Windsurfing ("Leisure") 1·50 1·60
MS841 102 × 72 mm. $5 Young people with Antiguan flag . . . 2·75 3·25

1986. Royal Visit. Nos. 965/8 of Antigua optd **BARBUDA MAIL.**
842 60c. Flags of Great Britain and Antigua . . . . 2·50 50
843 $1 Queen Elizabeth II (vert) 2·50 65
844 $4 Royal Yacht "Britannia" 6·00 2·50
MS845 110 × 83 mm. $5 Map of Antigua . . . . 8·50 4·00

1986. 75th Anniv of Girl Guide Movement. Nos. 955/9 of Antigua optd **BARBUDA MAIL.**
846 15c. Girl Guides nursing . . 1·50 80
847 45c. Open-air Girl Guide meeting . . . . 2·75 1·75
848 60c. Lord and Lady Baden-Powell . . . . 2·75 2·50
849 $3 Girl Guides gathering flowers . . . . 7·50 9·50
MS850 67 × 96 mm. $5 Barn swallow (Nature study) . . . . 28·00 19·00

1986. 300th Birth Anniv of Johann Sebastian Bach (composer). Nos. 960/4 of Antigua optd **BARBUDA MAIL.**
851 25c. multicoloured . . . . . 3·00 70
852 50c. multicoloured . . . . . 3·25 1·40
853 $1 multicoloured . . . . . . 4·25 2·00
854 $3 multicoloured . . . . . . 7·50 8·50
MS855 104 × 73 mm. $5 black and grey . . . . 24·00 12·00

1986. Christmas. Religious Paintings. Nos. 985/8 of Antigua optd **BARBUDA MAIL.**
856 10c. "Madonna and Child" (De Landi) 40 30
857 25c. "Madonna and Child" (Berlinghiero) 80 50
858 60c. "The Nativity" (Fra Angelico) . . . . 1·50 1·00
859 $4 "Presentation in the Temple" (Giovanni di Paolo) . . . . 4·00 7·00
MS860 113 × 81 mm. $5 "The Nativity" (Antoniazzo Romano) 4·25 5·50

108 Queen Elizabeth II meeting Members of Legislature

1986. 60th Birthday of Queen Elizabeth II (1st issue). Multicoloured.
861 $1 Type **108** . . . . 50 1·00
862 $2 Queen with Headmistress of Liberta School . . . . 60 1·10
863 $2.50 Queen greeted by Governor-General of Antigua . . . . 60 1·25
MS864 95 × 75 mm. $5 Queen Elizabeth in 1928 and 1986 (33 × 27 mm) . . . . 6·00 8·50
See also Nos. 872/5.

109 Halley's Comet over Barbuda Beach

1986. Appearance of Halley's Comet (1st issue). Multicoloured.
865 $1 Type **109** . . . . 60 1·25
866 $2.50 Early telescope and dish aerial (vert) . . . . . 80 2·25
867 $5 Comet and world map . . 1·40 3·75
See also Nos. 886/9.

1986. 40th Anniv of United Nations Organization. Nos. 981/4 of Antigua optd **BARBUDA MAIL.**
868 40c. Benjamin Franklin and U.N. (New York) 1953 U.P.U. 5c. stamp . . . . 1·50 1·00
869 $1 George Washington Carver (agricultural chemist) and 1982 Nature Conservation 28c. stamp 2·25 2·25
870 $3 Charles Lindbergh (aviator) and 1978 I.C.A.O. 25c. stamp . . . . . . 4·00 5·00
MS871 101 × 77 mm. $5 Marc Chagell (artist) (vert) . . . . . 11·00 12·00

1986. 60th Birthday of Queen Elizabeth II (2nd issue). Nos. 1005/8 of Antigua optd **BARBUDA MAIL.**
872 60c. black and yellow . . . . 2·50 1·25
873 $1 multicoloured . . . . . . 2·75 1·75
874 $4 muticoloured . . . . . . 4·25 4·25
MS875 120 × 85 mm. $5 black and brown . . . . 7·00 8·00

1986. World Cup Football Championship, Mexico. Nos. 995/9 of Antigua optd **BARBUDA MAIL.**
876 30c. Football, boots and trophy . . . . 3·50 1·00
877 60c. Goalkeeper (vert) . . . 4·75 2·00
878 $1 Referee blowing whistle (vert) . . . . 5·00 2·25
879 $4 Ball in net . . . . 10·00 7·00
MS880 87 × 76 mm. $5 Two players competing for ball . . . . . . 17·00 13·00

1986. "Ameripex '86" International Stamp Exhibition, Chicago. Famous American Trains. Nos. 1014/18 of Antigua optd **BARBUDA MAIL.**
881 25c. "Hiawatha" express . . 2·00 1·50
882 50c. "Grand Canyon" express 2·75 2·25
883 $1 "Powhattan Arrow" express . . . . 3·50 3·00
884 $3 "Empire State" express . . 6·00 7·00
MS885 117 × 87 mm. $5 Southern Pacific "Daylight" express . . 8·50 9·00

1986. Appearance of Halley's Comet (2nd issue). Nos. 1000/4 of Antigua optd **BARBUDA MAIL.**
886 5c. Edmond Halley and Old Greenwich Observatory . . 1·75 85
887 10c. Messerschmitt Me 163B Komet (fighter aircraft), 1944 . . . . 1·75 85
888 60c. Montezuma (Aztec Emperor) and Comet in 1517 (from "Historias de las Indias de Neuva Espana") . . . . 3·25 2·00
889 $4 Pocahontas saving Capt. John Smith and Comet in 1607 . . . . 11·00 7·50
MS890 101 × 70 mm. $5 Halley's Comet over English Harbour, Antigua . . . . 4·75 4·75

1986. Royal Wedding. Nos. 1019/22 of Antigua optd **BARBUDA MAIL.**
891 45c. Prince Andrew and Miss Sarah Ferguson 75 50
892 60c. Prince Andrew 90 65
893 $4 Prince Andrew with Prince Philip . . . . 3·50 4·00
MS894 88 × 88 mm. $5 Prince Andrew and Miss Sarah Ferguson (different) . . . . 7·50 8·00

1986. Sea Shells. Nos. 1023/7 of Antigua optd **BARBUDA MAIL.**
895 15c. Fly-specked cerith . . . 2·50 2·00
896 45c. Smooth Scotch bonnet 2·75 2·25
897 60c. West Indian crown conch . . . . 3·50 2·75
898 $3 Criboney murex . . . . . 8·00 12·00
MS899 109 × 75 mm. $5 Colourful Atlantic moon (horiz) . . . . 20·00 18·00

1986. Flowers. Nos. 1028/36 of Antigua optd **BARBUDA MAIL.**
900 10c. "Nymphaea ampla" (water lily) 20 30
901 15c. Queen of the night . . . 30 30
902 50c. Cup of gold 50 70
903 60c. Beach morning glory . . 55 70
904 70c. Golden trumpet 70 90
905 $1 Air plant 85 90
906 $3 Purple wreath . . . . . . 2·25 3·50
907 $4 Zephyr lily . . . . 2·75 3·75
MS908 Two sheets, each 102 × 72 mm. (a) $4 Dozakie. (b) $5 Four o'clock flower Set of 2 sheets . . . . 22·00 22·00

1986. Mushrooms. Nos. 1042/6 of Antigua optd **BARBUDA MAIL.**
909 10c. "Hygrocybe occidentalis var scarletina" 90 50
910 50c. "Trogia buccinalis" . . 3·25 1·75
911 $1 "Collybia subpruinosa" 4·75 2·75
912 $4 "Leucocoprinus brebissonii" . . . . 9·50 8·00
MS913 102 × 82 mm. $5 Pyrrhoglossum pyrrhum . . . 22·00 13·00

1986. Birth Bicentenary of John J. Audubon (ornithologist) (3rd issue). Nos. 990/3 of Antigua optd **BARBUDA MAIL.**
914 60c. Mallard . . . . 6·00 2·50
915 90c. North American black duck ("Dusky Duck") . . 8·00 2·75
916 $1.50 American pintail ("Common Pintail") . . . 10·00 8·00
917 $3 American wigeon ("Wigeon") . . . . 14·00 13·00

1987. Local Boats. Nos. 1009/13 of Antigua optd **BARBUDA MAIL.**
918 30c. Tugboat . . . . 1·00 60
919 60c. Game fishing boat . . . 1·50 80
920 $1 Yacht . . . . 2·00 1·25
921 $4 Lugger with auxiliary sail 4·25 6·00
MS922 108 × 78 mm. $5 Boats under construction . . . . 18·00 15·00

1987. Centenary of First Benz Motor Car. Nos. 1052/60 of Antigua optd **BARBUDA MAIL.**
923 10c. Auburn "Speedster" (1933) 90 45
924 15c. Mercury "Sable" (1986) 1·00 50
925 50c. Cadillac (1959) . . . . 1·60 70
926 60c. Studebaker (1950) . . . 1·60 70
927 70c. Lagonda "V-12" (1939) 1·75 1·00
928 $1 Adler "Standard" (1930) 2·25 1·00

929 $3 DKW (1956) 3·00 3·75
930 $4 Mercedes "500K" (1936) 3·00 3·75
MS931 Two sheets, each 99×70 mm. (a) $5 Daimler (1896). (b) $5 Mercedes "Knight" (1921) Set of 2 sheets 24·00 15·00

1987. World Cup Football Championship Winners, Mexico. Nos. 1037/40 of Antigua optd **BARBUDA MAIL**.
932 30c. Football, boots and trophy 3·50 1·00
933 60c. Goalkeeper (vert) 4·00 1·50
934 $1 Referee blowing whistle (vert) 4·50 2·25
935 $4 Ball in net 9·00 10·00

1987. America's Cup Yachting Championship. Nos. 1072/6 of Antigua optd **BARBUDA MAIL**.
936 30c. "Canada I" (1981) 90 40
937 60c. "Gretel II" (1970) 1·25 50
938 $1 "Sceptre" (1958) 1·60 80
939 $3 "Vigilant" (1893) 2·25 3·50
MS940 113×84 mm. $5 "Australia II" defeating "Liberty" (1983) (horiz) 4·00 4·50

1987. Marine Life. Nos. 1077/85 of Antigua optd **BARBUDA MAIL**.
941 15c. Bridled burrfish 5·00 1·00
942 30c. Common noddy ("Brown Noddy") 7·00 1·00
943 40c. Nassau grouper 5·50 1·00
944 50c. Laughing gull 9·00 1·75
945 60c. French angelfish 8·00 1·50
946 $1 Porkfish 8·00 2·25
947 $2 Royal tern 16·00 9·00
948 $3 Sooty tern 16·00 10·00
MS949 Two sheets, each 120×94 mm. (a) $5 Banded butterflyfish. (b) $5 Brown booby Set of 2 sheets 50·00 23·00

1987. Milestones of Transportation. Nos. 1100/9 of Antigua optd **BARBUDA MAIL**.
950 10c. "Spirit of Australia" (fastest powerboat), 1978 2·50 1·00
951 15c. Werner von Siemens's electric locomotive, 1879 3·50 90
952 30c. U.S.S. "Triton" (first submerged circumnavigation), 1960 3·50 90
953 50c. Trevithick's steam carriage (first passenger-carrying vehicle), 1801 3·75 1·75
954 60c. U.S.S. "New Jersey" (battleship), 1942 4·25 1·50
955 70c. Draisine bicycle, 1818 4·50 2·25
956 90c. "United States" (liner) (holder of the Blue Riband), 1952 5·00 1·75
957 $1.50 Cierva C.4 (first autogyro), 1923 5·00 5·50
958 $2 Curtiss NC-4 flying boat (first transatlantic flight), 1919 6·00 7·00
959 $3 "Queen Elizabeth 2" (liner), 1969 8·50 8·50

110 Shore Crab

1987. Marine Life. Multicoloured.
960 5c. Type **110** 10 20
961 10c. Sea cucumber 10 20
962 15c. Stop-light parrotfish 10 20
963 25c. Banded coral shrimp 15 20
964 35c. Spotted drum 15 20
965 60c. Thorny starfish 25 40
966 75c. Atlantic trumpet triton 25 60
967 90c. Feather star and yellow beaker sponge 25 65
968 $1 Blue gorgonian (vert) 25 65
969 $1.25 Slender filefish (vert) 30 85
970 $5 Barred hamlet (vert) 60 4·00
971 $7.50 Royal gramma ("Fairy basslet") (vert) 80 5·50
972 $10 Fire coral and banded butterflyfish (vert) 1·00 6·50

1987. Olympic Games, Seoul (1988). Nos. 1086/90 of Antigua optd **BARBUDA MAIL**.
973 10c. Handball 85 50
974 60c. Fencing 1·75 80
975 $1 Gymnastics 2·00 1·40
976 $3 Football 3·75 5·00
MS977 100×77 mm. $5 Boxing gloves 6·00 4·75

1987. Birth Centenary of Marc Chagall (artist). Nos. 1091/9 of Antigua optd **BARBUDA MAIL**.
978 10c. "The Profile" 10 20
979 30c. "Portrait of the Artist's Sister" 15 15
980 40c. "Bride with Fan" 20 30
981 60c. "David in Profile" 25 30
982 90c. "Fiancee with Bouquet" 40 50
983 $1 "Self Portrait with Brushes" 45 55
984 $3 "The Walk" 1·40 2·00
985 $4 "Three Candles" 1·75 2·25
MS986 Two sheets, each 110×95 mm. (a) $5 "Fall of Icarus" (104×89 mm). (b) $5 "Myth of Orpheus" (104×89 mm) Set of 2 sheets 4·50 5·50

1987. Centenary (1986) of Statue of Liberty (2nd issue). Nos. 1110/19 of Antigua optd **BARBUDA MAIL**.
987 15c. Lee Iacocoa at unveiling of restored statue 10 10
988 30c. Statue at sunset (side view) 15 15
989 45c. Aerial view of head 20 25
990 50c. Lee Iacocoa and torch 25 30
991 60c. Workmen inside head of statue (horiz) 25 30
992 90c. Restoration work (horiz) 40 50
993 $1 Head of statue 45 55
994 $2 Statue at sunset (front view) 90 1·40
995 $3 Inspecting restoration work (horiz) 1·40 2·00
996 $5 Statue at night 2·25 3·00

1987. Entertainers. Nos. 1120/7 of Antigua optd **BARBUDA MAIL**.
997 15c. Grace Kelly 2·00 70
998 30c. Marilyn Monroe 4·25 1·25
999 45c. Orson Welles 2·00 75
1000 50c. Judy Garland 2·00 1·00
1001 60c. John Lennon 9·00 2·00
1002 $1 Rock Hudson 2·75 1·75
1003 $1 John Wayne 4·00 3·50
1004 $3 Elvis Presley 19·00 9·50

1987. "Capex '87" International Stamp Exhibition, Toronto. Reptiles and Amphibians. Nos. 1133/7 of Antigua optd **BARBUDA MAIL**.
1005 30c. Whistling frog 4·50 1·75
1006 60c. Croaking lizard 5·00 1·75
1007 $1 Antiguan anole 6·00 2·50
1008 $3 Red-footed tortoise 12·00 13·00
MS1009 106×76 mm. $5 Ground lizard 25·00 11·00

1988. Christmas. Religious Paintings. Nos. 1144/8 of Antigua optd **BARBUDA MAIL**.
1010 45c. "Madonna and Child" (Bernardo Daddi) 1·75 30
1011 60c. St. Joseph (detail, "The Nativity" (Sano di Pietro)) 1·75 55
1012 $1 Virgin Mary (detail, "The Nativity" (Sano di Pietro)) 2·00 1·00
1013 $4 "Music-making Angel" (Melozzo da Forli) 5·00 7·00
MS1014 90×70 mm. $5 "The Flight into Egypt" (Sano di Pietro) 9·00 6·50

1988. Salvation Army's Community Service. Nos. 1163/71 of Antigua optd **BARBUDA MAIL**.
1015 25c. First aid at daycare centre, Antigua 1·50 1·00
1016 30c. Giving penicillin injection, Indonesia 1·50 1·00
1017 40c. Children at daycare centre, Bolivia 1·50 1·00
1018 45c. Rehabilitation of the handicapped, India 1·50 1·00
1019 50c. Training blind man, Kenya 2·00 1·50
1020 60c. Weighing baby, Ghana 2·00 1·50
1021 $1 Training typist, Zambia 2·50 2·50
1022 $2 Emergency food kitchen, Sri Lanka 3·00 3·75
MS1023 152×83 mm. $5 General Eva Burrows 23·00 23·00

1988. Bicentenary of U.S. Constitution. Nos. 1139/43 of Antigua optd **BARBUDA MAIL**.
1024 15c. House of Burgesses, Virginia ("Freedom of Speech") 10 15
1025 45c. State Seal, Connecticut 20 25
1026 60c. State Seal, Delaware 25 40
1027 $4 Gouverneur Morris (Pennsylvania delegate) (vert) 1·75 3·25
MS1028 105×75 mm. $5 Roger Sherman (Connecticut delegate) (vert) 2·75 3·25

1988. Royal Ruby Wedding. Nos. 1149/53 of Antigua optd **BARBUDA MAIL**.
1029 25c. brown, black and blue 2·00 40
1030 60c. multicoloured 2·50 65
1031 $2 brown, black and green 5·00 2·50
1032 $3 multicoloured 6·00 3·00
MS1033 102×77 mm. $5 multicoloured 12·00 6·00

1988. Birds of Antigua. Nos. 1154/62 of Antigua optd **BARBUDA MAIL**.
1034 10c. Great blue heron 3·50 1·75
1035 15c. Ringed kingfisher (horiz) 3·75 1·75
1036 50c. Bananaquit (horiz) 4·50 1·75
1037 60c. American purple gallinule ("Purple Gallinule") (horiz) 4·50 1·75
1038 70c. Blue-hooded euphonia (horiz) 4·75 2·75
1039 $1 Brown-throated concure ("Caribbean Parakeet") 5·00 2·75
1040 $3 Troupial (horiz) 9·00 8·50
1041 $4 Purple-throated carib (horiz) 9·00 8·50
MS1042 Two sheets, each 115×86 mm. (a) $5 Greater flamingo. (b) $5 Brown pelican Set of 2 sheets 30·00 17·00

1988. 500th Anniv (1992) of Discovery of America by Columbus (1st issue). Nos. 1172/80 of Antigua optd **BARBUDA MAIL**.
1043 10c. Columbus's second fleet, 1493 2·25 1·00
1044 30c. Painos Indian village and fleet 2·25 80
1045 45c. "Santa Mariagalante" (flagship) and Painos village 3·00 80
1046 60c. Painos Indians offering Columbus fruit and vegetables 2·25 85
1047 90c. Painos Indian and Columbus with scarlet macaw 4·75 1·75
1048 $1 Columbus landing on island 4·25 1·75
1049 $3 Spanish soldier and fleet 5·00 4·50
1050 $4 Fleet under sail 5·00 4·50
MS1051 Two sheets, each 110×80 mm. (a) $5 Queen Isabella's cross. (b) $5 Gold coin of Ferdinand and Isabella Set of 2 sheets 10·00 11·00
See also Nos. 1112/16, 1177/85, 1285/93, 1374/80 and 1381/2.

1988. 500th Birth Anniv of Titian. Nos. 1181/9 of Antigua optd **BARBUDA MAIL**.
1052 30c. "Bust of Christ" 25 20
1053 40c. "Scourging of Christ" 30 25
1054 45c. "Madonna in Glory with Saints" 35 25
1055 50c. "The Averoldi Polyptych" (detail) 35 30
1056 $1 "Christ Crowned with Thorns" 55 55
1057 $2 "Christ Mocked" 90 1·25
1058 $3 "Christ and Simon of Cyrene" 1·40 2·00
1059 $4 "Crucifixion with Virgin and Saints" 1·75 2·50
MS1060 Two sheets, each 110×95 mm. (a) $5 "Ecce Homo" (detail). (b) $5 "Noli me Tangere" (detail) Set of 2 sheets 5·00 6·50

1988. 16th World Scout Jamboree, Australia. Nos. 1128/32 of Antigua optd **BARBUDA MAIL**.
1061 10c. Scouts around campfire and red kangaroo 2·00 1·00
1062 60c. Scouts canoeing and blue-winged kookaburra 6·00 1·50
1063 $1 Scouts on assault course and ring-tailed rock wallaby 3·00 1·75
1064 $3 Field kitchen and koala 6·00 6·50
MS1065 103×78 mm. $5 Flags of Antigua, Australia and Scout Movement 4·75 4·50

1988. Sailing Week. Nos. 1190/4 of Antigua optd **BARBUDA MAIL**.
1066 30c. Two yachts rounding buoy 60 35
1067 60c. Three yachts 1·00 70
1068 $1 British yacht under way 1·25 1·10
1069 $3 Three yachts (different) 2·25 2·75
MS1070 103×92 mm. $5 Two yachts 7·50 4·50

1988. Flowering Trees. Nos. 1213/21 of Antigua optd **BARBUDA MAIL**.
1071 10c. Jacaranda 10 10
1072 30c. Cordia 15 15
1073 50c. Orchid tree 20 25
1074 90c. Flamboyant 40 45
1075 $1 African tulip tree 45 50
1076 $2 Potato tree 80 1·25
1077 $3 Crepe myrtle 1·25 1·75
1078 $4 Pitch apple 1·60 2·25
MS1079 Two sheets, each 106×76 mm. (a) $5 Cassia. (b) $5 Chinaberry Set of 2 sheets 4·25 5·00

1988. Olympic Games, Seoul. Nos. 1222/6 of Antigua optd **BARBUDA MAIL**.
1080 40c. Gymnastics 1·25 40
1081 60c. Weightlifting 1·50 55
1082 $1 Water polo (horiz) 1·75 1·00
1083 $3 Boxing (horiz) 2·50 3·00
MS1084 114×80 mm. $5 Runner with Olympic torch 2·10 2·40

1988. Caribbean Butterflies. Nos. 1227/44 of Antigua optd **BARBUDA MAIL**.
1085 1c. "Danaus plexippus" 30 60
1086 2c. "Greta diaphanus" 30 60
1087 3c. "Calisto archebates" 40 60
1088 5c. "Hamadryas feronia" 40 60
1089 10c. "Mestra dorcas" 50 50
1090 15c. "Hypolimnas misippus" 60 40
1091 20c. "Dione juno" 70 50
1092 25c. "Heliconius charithonia" 75 50
1093 30c. "Eurema pyro" 85 50
1094 40c. "Papilio androgeus" 90 50
1095 45c. "Anteos maerula" 90 50
1096 50c. "Aphrissa orbis" 1·10 75
1097 60c. "Astraptes xagua" 1·10 60
1098 $1 "Heliopetes arsalte" 1·40 1·00
1099 $2 "Polites baracoa" 3·00 3·50
1100 $2.50 "Phocides pigmalion" 3·25 4·00
1101 $5 "Prepona amphitoe" 4·50 5·50
1102 $10 "Oarisma nanus" 7·50 8·50
1102a $20 "Parides lycimenes" 12·00 13·00

1989. 25th Death Anniv of John F. Kennedy (American statesman). Nos. 1245/53 of Antigua optd **BARBUDA MAIL**.
1103 1c. President Kennedy and family 10 40
1104 2c. Kennedy commanding "PT109" 10 40
1105 3c. Funeral cortege 10 40
1106 4c. In motorcade, Mexico 10 40
1107 30c. As 1c. 75 40
1108 60c. As 4c. 2·25 55
1109 $1 As 3c. 2·25 1·50
1110 $4 As 2c. 6·50 7·00
MS1111 105×75 mm. $5 Kennedy taking presidential oath of office 3·75 5·00

1989. 500th Anniv (1992) of Discovery of America by Columbus (2nd issue). Pre-Columbian Arawak Society. Nos. 1267/71 of Antigua optd **BARBUDA MAIL**.
1112 $1.50 Arawak warriors 3·25 3·50
1113 $1.50 Whip dancers 3·25 3·50
1114 $1.50 Whip dancers and chief with pineapple 3·25 3·50
1115 $1.50 Family and camp fire 3·25 3·50
MS1116 71×84 mm. $6 Arawak chief 3·50 4·50

1989. 50th Anniv of First Jet Flight. Nos. 1272/80 of Antigua optd **BARBUDA MAIL**.
1117 10c. Hawker Siddeley Comet 4 airliner 3·00 1·50
1118 30c. Messerschmitt Me 262 fighter 3·50 1·25
1119 40c. Boeing 707 airliner 3·75 1·00
1120 60c. Canadair CL-13 Sabre fighter 4·50 1·00
1121 $1 Lockheed Starfighters 5·00 2·00
1122 $2 Douglas DC-10 airliner 6·50 5·50
1123 $3 Boeing 747-300/400 airliner 7·50 8·00
1124 $4 McDonnell Douglas Phantom II fighter 7·50 8·00
MS1125 Two sheets, each 114×83 mm. (a) $7 Grumman F-14 Tomcat fighter. (b) $7 Concorde airliner Set of 2 sheets 45·00 30·00

1989. Caribbean Cruise Ships. Nos. 1281/9 of Antigua optd **BARBUDA MAIL**.
1126 25c. "Festivale" 2·50 1·00
1127 45c. "Southward" 2·75 1·00
1128 50c. "Sagafjord" 2·75 1·25
1129 60c. "Daphne" 3·00 1·25
1130 75c. "Cunard Countess" 3·00 2·75
1131 90c. "Song of America" 3·25 2·75
1132 $3 "Island Princess" 6·50 7·00
1133 $4 "Galileo" 6·50 7·00
MS1134 (a) 113×87 mm. $6 "Norway". (b) 111×82 mm. $6 "Oceanic" Set of 2 sheets 45·00 32·00

1989. Japanese Art. Paintings by Hiroshige. Nos. 1290/8 of Antigua optd **BARBUDA MAIL**.
1135 25c. "Fish swimming by Duck half-submerged in Stream" 3·00 70
1136 45c. "Crane and Wave" 3·50 70
1137 50c. "Sparrows and Morning Glories" 3·75 1·00
1138 60c. "Crested Blackbird and Flowering Cherry" 3·75 1·00
1139 $1 "Great Knot sitting among Water Grass" 4·00 1·25
1140 $2 "Goose on a Bank of Water" 5·50 3·50
1141 $3 "Black Paradise Fly-catcher and Blossoms" 6·50 4·00
1142 $4 "Sleepy Owl perched on a Pine Branch" 7·00 4·50
MS1143 Two sheets, each 102×75 mm. (a) $5 "Bullfinch flying near a Clematis Branch". (b) $5 "Titmouse on a Cherry Branch" Set of 2 sheets 38·00 20·00

1989. World Cup Football Championship, Italy (1990). Nos. 1308/12 of Antigua optd **BARBUDA MAIL**.
1144 15c. Goalkeeper 1·75 50
1145 25c. Goalkeeper moving towards ball 1·75 50
1146 $1 Goalkeeper reaching for ball 3·50 1·75
1147 $4 Goalkeeper saving goal 6·50 8·00
MS1148 Two sheets, each 75×105 mm. (a) $5 Three players competing for ball (horiz). (b) $5 Ball and players' legs (horiz) Set of 2 sheets 28·00 27·00

1989. Christmas. Paintings by Raphael and Giotto. Nos. 1351/9 of Antigua optd **BARBUDA MAIL**.
1149 10c. "The Small Cowper Madonna" (Raphael) 15 20
1150 25c. "Madonna of the Goldfinch" (Raphael) 20 20
1151 30c. "The Alba Madonna" (Raphael) 20 20
1152 50c. Saint (detail, "Bologna Altarpiece") (Giotto) 35 30
1153 60c. Angel (detail, "Bologna Altarpiece") (Giotto) 45 45
1154 70c. Angel slaying serpent (detail, "Bologna Altarpiece") (Giotto) 50 50

1155 $4 Evangelist (detail, "Bologna Altarpiece") (Giotto) . . . . 2·25 3·50
1156 $5 "Madonna of Foligno" (Raphael) . . . . 2·50 3·50
MS1157 Two sheets, each 71×96 mm. (a) $5 "The Marriage of the Virgin" (detail) (Raphael). (b) $5 Madonna and Child (detail, "Bologna Altarpiece") (Giotto) Set of 2 sheets . . . . 10·00 12·00

1990. Fungi. Nos. 1313/21 of Antigua optd **BARBUDA MAIL.**
1158 10c. "Mycena pura" . . . . 1·75 75
1159 25c. Psathyrella turberculata" (vert) . . . 2·00 65
1160 50c. "Psilocybe cubensis" . . 2·50 1·00
1161 60c. "Leptonia caeruleocapitata" (vert) 2·50 1·00
1162 75c. "Xeromphalina tenuipes" (vert) . . . . . 2·50 1·40
1163 $1 "Chlorophyllum molybdites" (vert) . . . . 2·50 1·40
1164 $3 "Marasmius haematocephalus" . . . . 5·00 6·00
1165 $4 "Cantharellus cinnabarinus" . . . . . 5·00 6·00
MS1166 Two sheets, each 88×62 mm. (a) $6 "Leucopaxillus gracillimus" (vert). (b) $6 "Volvariella volvacea" Set of 2 sheets . . . . 35·00 22·00

1990. Local Fauna. Nos. 1322/6 optd **BARBUDA MAIL.**
1167 25c. Desmarest's hutia . . . 75 60
1168 45c. Caribbean monk seal 2·00 1·00
1169 60c. Mustache bat (vert) . . 1·50 1·00
1170 $4 American manatee (vert) 4·00 6·00
MS1171 113×87 mm. $5 West Indian giant rice rat . . . . . 18·00 19·00

1990. 20th Anniv of First Manned Landing on Moon. Nos. 1346/50 optd **BARBUDA MAIL.**
1172 10c. Launch of "Apollo 11" 2·00 1·50
1173 45c. Aldrin on Moon . . . 3·50 80
1174 $1 Module "Eagle" over Moon (horiz) . . . . . . 4·75 2·50
1175 $4 Recovery of "Apollo 11" crew after splashdown (horiz) . . . . 10·00 12·00
MS1176 107×77 mm. $5 Astronaut Neil Armstrong . . . . 18·00 19·00

1990. 500th Anniv (1992) of Discovery of America by Columbus (3rd issue). New World Natural History – Marine Life. Nos. 1360/8 of Antigua optd **BARBUDA MAIL.**
1177 10c. Star-eyed hermit crab 1·50 1·50
1178 20c. Spiny lobster . . . . . 1·75 1·50
1179 25c. Magnificent banded fanworm . . . . 1·75 1·50
1180 45c. Cannonball jellyfish . . 2·50 75
1181 60c. Red-spiny sea star . . . 2·75 75
1182 $2 Peppermint shrimp . . . 4·00 4·25
1183 $3 Coral crab . . . . 4·25 4·75
1184 $4 Branching fire coral . . . 4·25 4·75
MS1185 Two sheets, each 101×69 mm. (a) $5 Common sea fan. (b) Portuguese man-o-war Set of 2 sheets . . . . 23·00 23·00

1990. "EXPO 90" International Gardens and Greenery Exhibition, Osaka. Orchids. Nos. 1369/77 of Antigua optd **BARBUDA MAIL.**
1186 15c. "Vanilla mexicana" . . 1·75 80
1187 45c. "Epidendrum ibaguense" . . . . 2·25 80
1188 50c. "Epidendrum secundum" . . . . 2·25 90
1189 60c. "Maxillaria conferta" 2·50 1·10
1190 $1 "Onicidium altissimum" 2·75 1·75
1191 $2 "Spiranthes lanceolata" 5·00 5·00
1192 $3 "Tonopsis utricularioides" . . . . . 5·50 6·50
1193 $5 "Epidendrum nocturnum" . . . . . . 7·00 8·50
MS1194 Two sheets, each 101×69 mm. (a) $6 "Octomeria graminifolia". (b) $6 "Rodriguezia lanceolata" Set of 2 sheets . . 32·00 21·00

1990. Reef Fishes. Nos. 1386/94 of Antigua optd **BARBUDA MAIL.**
1195 10c. Flamefish . . . . . . 2·25 1·50
1196 15c. Coney . . . . 2·25 1·50
1197 50c. Long-spined squirrelfish 3·00 1·25
1198 60c. Sergeant major . . . . 3·00 1·25
1199 $1 Yellow-tailed snapper . . 3·75 2·25
1200 $2 Rock beauty . . . . . . 6·00 6·00
1201 $3 Spanish hogfish . . . . 7·50 8·00
1202 $4 Striped parrotfish . . . . 7·50 8·00
MS1203 Two sheets, each 99×70 mm. (a) $5 Black-barred soldierfish. (b) $5 Four-eyed butterflyfish Set of 2 sheets . . 32·00 28·00

1990. 1st Anniv of Hurricane Hugo. Nos. 971/2 surch **1st Anniversary Hurricane Hugo 16th September, 1989-1990** and new value.
1204 $5 on $7.50 Fairy basslet (vert) . . . . 10·00 11·00
1205 $7.50 on $10 Fire coral and butterfly fish (vert) . . . 11·00 13·00

1990. 90th Birthday of Queen Elizabeth the Queen Mother. Nos. 1415/19 of Antigua optd **BARBUDA MAIL.**
1206 15c. multicoloured . . . . . 6·00 1·75
1207 35c. multicoloured . . . . . 9·00 1·50
1208 75c. multicoloured . . . . . 15·00 3·25
1209 $3 multicoloured . . . . . 26·00 17·00
MS1210 67×98 mm. $6 multicoloured . . . . 50·00 25·00

1990. Achievements in Space. Nos. 1395/414 of Antigua optd **BARBUDA MAIL.**
1211 45c. "Voyager 2" passing Saturn . . . . 3·00 2·25
1212 45c. "Pioneer 11" photographing Saturn . . 3·00 2·25
1213 45c. Astronaut in transporter . . . . 3·00 2·25
1214 45c. Space shuttle "Columbia" . . . . . . 3·00 2·25
1215 45c. "Apollo 10" command module on parachutes . . 3·00 2·25
1216 45c. "Skylab" space station 3·00 2·25
1217 45c. Astronaut Edward White in space . . . . . 3·00 2·25
1218 45c. "Apollo" spacecraft on joint mission . . . . . . 3·00 2·25
1219 45c. "Soyuz" spacecraft on joint mission . . . . . . 3·00 2·25
1220 45c. "Mariner 1" passing Venus . . . . 3·00 2·25
1221 45c. "Gemini 4" capsule . . 3·00 2·25
1222 45c. "Sputnik 1" . . . . . 3·00 2·25
1223 45c. Hubble space telescope 3·00 2·25
1224 45c. North American X-15 rocket plane . . . . . 3·00 2·25
1225 45c. Bell XS-1 airplane . . . 3·00 2·25
1226 45c. "Apollo 17" astronaut and lunar rock formation 3·00 2·25
1227 45c. Lunar rover . . . . . 3·00 2·25
1228 45c. "Apollo 14" lunar module . . . . 3·00 2·25
1229 45c. Astronaut Buzz Aldrin on Moon . . . . 3·00 2·25
1230 45c. Soviet "Lunokhod" lunar vehicle . . . . . . 3·00 2·25

1990. Christmas. Paintings by Renaissance Masters. Nos. 1457/65 of Antigua optd **BARBUDA MAIL.**
1231 25c. "Madonna and Child with Saints" (detail, Sebastiano del Piombo) 1·60 60
1232 30c. "Virgin and Child with Angels" (detail, Grunewald) (vert) . . . . 1·75 60
1233 40c. "The Holy Family and a Shepherd" (detail, Titian) . . . . 1·75 60
1234 60c. "Virgin and Child" (detail, Lippi) (vert) . . . 2·25 1·10
1235 $1 "Jesus, St. John and Two Angels" (Rubens) . . . . 3·00 1·50
1236 $2 "Adoration of the Shepherds" (detail, Vincenzo Catena) . . . . 4·50 4·75
1237 $4 "Adoration of the Magi" (detail, Giorgione) . . . . 6·50 7·50
1238 $5 "Virgin and Child adored by Warriors" (detail, Vincenzo Catena) . . . 6·50 7·50
MS1239 Two sheets, each 71×101 mm. (a) $6 "Allegory of the Blessings of Jacob" (detail, Rubens) (vert). (b) $6 "Adoration of the Magi" (detail, Fra Angelico) (vert) Set of 2 sheets . . . . . 18·00 21·00

1991. 150th Anniv of the Penny Black. Nos. 1378/81 of Antigua optd **BARBUDA MAIL.**
1240 45c. green . . . . 3·50 80
1241 60c. mauve . . . . 3·50 85
1242 $5 blue . . . . 12·00 13·00
MS1243 102×80 mm. $6 purple 13·00 13·00

1991. "Stamp World London 90" International Stamp Exhibition. Nos. 1382/4 of Antigua optd **BARBUDA MAIL.**
1244 50c. green and red . . . . 3·50 85
1245 75c. brown and red . . . . 3·50 1·25
1246 $4 blue and red . . . . . . 12·00 13·00
MS1247 104×81 mm. $6 black and red . . . . 17·00 17·00

119 Troupial

1991. Wild Birds. Multicoloured.
1248 60c. Type **119** . . . . . . 2·00 65
1249 $2 Adelaide's warbler ("Christmas Bird") . . . 3·50 3·00
1250 $4 Rose-breasted grosbeak 5·00 6·00
1251 $7 Wied's crested flycatcher ("Stolid Flycatcher") . . 7·00 10·00

1991. Olympic Games, Barcelona (1992). Nos. 1429/33 of Antigua optd **BARBUDA MAIL.**
1252 50c. Men's 20 kilometres walk . . . . 2·00 90
1253 75c. Triple jump . . . . . 2·25 1·00
1254 $1 Men's 10,000 metres . . 2·50 1·75
1255 $5 Javelin . . . . 9·00 11·00
MS1256 100×70 mm. $6 Athlete lighting Olympic flame at Los Angeles Olympics . . . . . . 11·00 13·00

1991. Birds. Nos. 1448/56 of Antigua optd **BARBUDA MAIL.**
1257 10c. Pearly-eyed thrasher . . 2·75 1·50
1258 25c. Purple-throated carib 3·50 80
1259 50c. Common yellowthroat 4·00 1·00
1260 60c. American kestrel . . . 4·00 1·10
1261 $1 Yellow-bellied sapsucker 4·25 2·00
1262 $2 American purple gallinule ("Purple Gallinule") . . . 5·50 5·50
1263 $3 Yellow-crowned night heron . . . . 6·00 7·50
1264 $4 Blue-hooded euphonia 6·00 7·50
MS1265 Two sheets, each 76×60 mm. (a) $6 Brown pelican. (b) Magnificent frigate bird Set of 2 sheets . . . . 24·00 22·00

1991. 350th Death Anniv of Rubens. Nos. 1466/74 of Antigua optd **BARBUDA MAIL.**
1266 25c. "Rape of the Daughters of Leucippus" (detail) . . 1·75 70
1267 45c. "Bacchanal" (detail) . . 2·00 70
1268 50c. "Rape of the Sabine Women" (detail) . . . . 2·00 75
1269 60c. "Battle of the Amazons" (detail) . . . . 2·25 85
1270 $1 "Rape of the Sabine Women" (different detail) 2·75 1·75
1271 $2 "Bacchanal" (different detail) . . . . 4·50 4·75
1272 $3 "Rape of the Sabine Women" (different detail) 6·50 7·50
1273 $4 "Bacchanal" (different detail) . . . . 6·50 7·50
MS1274 Two sheets, each 111×71 mm. (a) $6 "Rape of Hippodameia" (detail). (b) "Battle of the Amazons" (different detail) Set of 2 sheets . . . . 19·00 22·00

1991. 50th Anniv of Second World War. Nos. 1475/88 of Antigua optd **BARBUDA MAIL.**
1275 10c. U.S. troops cross into Germany, 1944 . . . . . 2·50 1·75
1276 15c. Axis surrender in North Africa, 1943 . . . . . . 3·00 1·75
1277 25c. U.S. tanks invade Kwalajalein, 1944 . . . . 3·25 1·25
1278 45c. Roosevelt and Churchill meet at Casablanca, 1943 7·00 1·75
1279 50c. Marshall Badoglio, Prime Minister of Italian anti-facist government, 1943 . . . . 3·25 1·75
1280 $1 Lord Mountbatten, Supreme Allied Commander South-east Asia, 1943 . . . . 9·00 3·75
1281 $2 Greek victory at Koritza, 1940 . . . . 8·50 8·50
1282 $4 Anglo-Soviet mutual assistance pact, 1941 . . . 10·00 10·00
1283 $5 Operation Torch landings, 1942 . . . . . 10·00 10·00
MS1284 Two sheets, each 108×80 mm. (a) $6 Japanese attack on Pearl Harbor, 1941. (b) $6 U.S.A.A.F. daylight raid on Schweinfurt, 1943 Set of 2 sheets 40·00 29·00

1991. 500th Anniv (1992) of Discovery of America by Columbus (4th issue). History of Exploration. Nos. 1503/11 of Antigua optd **BARBUDA MAIL.**
1285 10c. multicoloured . . . . . 1·25 1·00
1286 15c. multicoloured . . . . . 1·50 1·00
1287 45c. multicoloured . . . . . 2·00 80
1288 60c. multicoloured . . . . . 2·25 1·00
1289 $1 multicoloured . . . . . 3·00 1·75
1290 $2 multicoloured . . . . . 4·00 4·00
1291 $4 multicoloured . . . . . 6·50 7·50
1292 $5 multicoloured . . . . . 6·50 7·50
MS1293 Two sheets, each 106×76 mm. (a) $6 black and red. (b) $6 black and red Set of 2 sheets 23·00 22·00

1991. Butterflies. Nos. 1494/502 of Antigua optd **BARBUDA MAIL.**
1294 10c. "Heliconius charithonia" . . . . . . 2·50 1·75
1295 35c. "Marpesia petreus" . . 3·25 1·25
1296 50c. "Anartia amathea" . . 3·75 1·40
1297 75c. "Siproeta stelenes" . . 4·25 1·75
1298 $1 "Battus polydamas" . . 4·25 2·00
1299 $2 "Historis odius" . . . . 6·50 6·50
1300 $4 "Hypolimnas misippus" 8·50 9·00
1301 $5 "Hamadryas feronia" . . 8·50 9·00
MS1302 Two sheets. (a) 73×100 mm. $6 "Vanessa cardui" (caterpillar) (vert). (b) 100×73 mm. $6 "Danaus plexippus" (caterpillar) (vert) Set of 2 sheets . . . . 26·00 24·00

1991. 65th Birthday of Queen Elizabeth II. Nos. 1534/8 of Antigua optd **BARBUDA MAIL.**
1303 15c. Queen Elizabeth and Prince Philip in 1976 . . 3·25 85
1304 20c. The Queen and Prince Philip in Portugal, 1985 3·25 85
1305 $2 Queen Elizabeth II . . . 10·00 5·50
1306 $4 The Queen and Prince Philip at Ascot, 1986 . . 17·00 14·00
MS1307 68×90 mm. $4 The Queen at National Theatre, 1986 and Prince Philip . . . . 28·00 15·00

1991. 10th Wedding Anniv of Prince and Princess of Wales. Nos. 1539/43 of Antigua optd **BARBUDA MAIL.**
1308 10c. Prince and Princess of Wales at party, 1986 . . . 3·00 1·75
1309 40c. Separate portraits of Prince, Princess and sons 7·50 1·00
1310 $1 Prince Henry and Prince William . . . . 8·50 3·00
1311 $5 Princess Diana in Australia and Prince Charles in Hungary . . . 17·00 14·00
MS1312 68×90 mm. $4 Prince Charles in Hackney and Princess and sons in Majorca, 1987 . . 28·00 15·00

1991. Christmas. Religious Paintings by Fra Angelico. Nos. 1595/1602 of Antigua optd **BARBUDA MAIL.**
1313 10c. "The Annunciation" . . 2·00 1·00
1314 30c. "Nativity" . . . . . . 2·50 70
1315 40c. "Adoration of the Magi" . . . . 2·50 70
1316 60c. "Presentation in the Temple" . . . . 3·25 70
1317 $1 "Circumcision" . . . . 4·00 1·75
1318 $3 "Flight into Egypt" . . . 7·00 7·50
1319 $4 "Massacre of the Innocents" . . . . 7·00 8·00
1320 $5 "Christ teaching in the Temple" . . . . 7·00 8·00

1992. Death Centenary (1990) of Vincent van Gogh (artist). Nos. 1512/24 of Antigua optd **BARBUDA MAIL.**
1321 5c. "Camille Roulin" . . . 1·40 1·50
1322 10c. "Armand Roulin" . . . 1·50 1·50
1323 15c. "Young Peasant Woman with Straw Hat sitting in the Wheat" . . 1·75 1·50
1324 25c. "Adeline Ravoux" . . . 1·75 1·50
1325 30c. "The Schoolboy" . . . 1·75 1·00
1326 40c. "Doctor Gachet" . . . 2·00 1·00
1327 50c. "Portrait of a Man" . . 2·00 1·50
1328 75c. "Two Children" . . . 3·25 2·00
1329 $2 "The Postman Joseph Roulin" . . . . 5·50 5·50
1330 $3 "The Seated Zouave" . . 6·50 7·00
1331 $4 "L'Arlesienne" . . . . . 7·00 8·00
1332 $5 "Self-Portrait, November/ December 1888" . . . . 7·00 8·00
MS1333 Three sheets, each 102×76 mm. (a) $5 "Farmhouse in Provence" (horiz). (b) $5 "Flowering Garden" (horiz). (c) $6 "The Bridge at Trinquetaille" (horiz). Imperf Set of 3 sheets 28·00 28·00

1992. Birth Centenary of Charles de Gaulle (French statesman). Nos. 1562/70 of Antigua optd **BARBUDA MAIL.**
1334 10c. Pres. De Gaulle and Kennedy, 1961 . . . . . 2·00 1·50
1335 15c. General De Gaulle with Pres. Roosevelt, 1945 (vert) . . . . 2·00 1·50
1336 45c. President De Gaulle with Chancellor Adenauer, 1962 (vert) . . 3·00 80
1337 60c. De Gaulle at Arc de Triomphe, Liberation of Paris, 1944 (vert) . . . . 3·25 1·00
1338 $1 General De Gaulle crossing the Rhine, 1945 4·00 2·00
1339 $2 General De Gaulle in Algiers, 1944 . . . . . 6·00 6·00
1340 $4 Presidents De Gaulle and Eisenhower, 1960 . . . . 8·00 9·50
1341 $5 De Gaulle returning from Germany, 1968 (vert) . . 8·00 9·50
MS1342 Two sheets. (a) 76×106 mm. $6 De Gaulle with crowd. (b) 106×76 mm. $6 De Gaulle and Churchill at Casablanca, 1943 Set of 2 sheets 27·00 25·00

1992. Easter. Religious Paintings. Nos. 1627/35 of Antigua optd **BARBUDA MAIL.**
1343 10c. "Supper at Emmaus" (Caravaggio) . . . . . . 1·25 1·00
1344 15c. "The Vision of St. Peter" (Zurbaran) . . 1·50 1·00
1345 30c. "Christ driving the Money-changers from the Temple" (Tiepolo) . . . . 1·75 70
1346 40c. "Martyrdom of St. Bartholomew" (detail) (Ribera) . . . . 1·75 70
1347 $1 "Christ driving the Money-changers from the Temple" (detail) (Tiepolo) 3·25 1·75
1348 $2 "Crucifixion" (detail) (Altdorfer) . . . . 4·50 5·00
1349 $4 "The Deposition" (detail) (Fra Angelico) . . . . . 6·50 8·00
1350 $5 "The Deposition" (different detail) (Fra Angelico) . . . . 6·50 8·00
MS1351 Two sheets. (a) 102×71 mm. $6 "The Last Supper" (detail) (Masip). (b) 71×102 mm. $6 "Crucifixion" (detail) (vert) (Altdorfer) Set of 2 sheets . . . . 22·00 22·00

1992. Anniversaries and Events. Nos. 1573/83 of Antigua optd **BARBUDA MAIL.**
1352 25c. Germans celebrating Reunification . . . . . . 1·00 70
1353 75c. Cubs erecting tent . . . 2·25 1·50

1354 $1.50 "Don Giovanni" and Mozart 8·50 3·75
1355 $2 Chariot driver and Gate at night 2·75 3·00
1356 $2 Lord Baden-Powell and members of the 3rd Antigua Methodist cub pack (vert) 2·75 3·00
1357 $2 Lilienthal's signature and glider "Flugzeug Nr. 5" 2·75 3·00
1358 $2.50 Driver in Class P36 steam locomotive (vert) 7·00 4·25
1359 $3 Statues from podium 3·00 4·25
1360 $3.50 Cubs and campfire 4·00 5·00
1361 $4 St. Peter's Cathedral, Salzburg 10·00 10·00
MS1362 Two sheets. (a) 100 × 72 mm. $4 Detail of chariot and helmet. (b) 89 × 117 mm. $5 Antiguan flag and Jamboree emblem (vert) Set of 2 sheets 23·00 24·00

1992. 50th Anniv of Japanese Attack on Pearl Harbor. Nos. 1585/94 of Antigua optd **BARBUDA MAIL.**
1364 $1 "Nimitz" class carrier and "Ticonderoga" class cruiser 5·00 3·25
1365 $1 Tourist launch 5·00 3·25
1366 $1 U.S.S. "Arizona" memorial 5·00 3·25
1367 $1 Wreaths on water and aircraft 5·00 3·25
1368 $1 White tern 5·00 3·25
1369 $1 Japanese torpedo bombers over Pearl City 5·00 3·25
1370 $1 Zeros attacking 5·00 3·25
1371 $1 Battleship Row in flames 5·00 3·25
1372 $1 U.S.S. "Nevada" (battleship) underway 5·00 3·25
1373 $1 Zeros returning to carriers 5·00 3·25

1992. 500th Anniv of Discovery of America by Columbus (5th issue). World Columbian Stamp "Expo '92", Chicago. Nos. 1654/60 of Antigua optd **BARBUDA MAIL.**
1374 15c. Memorial cross and huts, San Salvador 75 80
1375 30c. Martin Pinzon with telescope 90 90
1376 40c. Christopher Columbus 1·25 90
1377 $1 "Pinta" 3·75 2·50
1378 $2 "Nina" 5·00 5·00
1379 $4 "Santa Maria" 7·50 8·50
MS1380 Two sheets, each 108 × 76 mm. (a) $6 Ship and map of West Indies. (b) $6 Sea monster Set of 2 sheets 22·00 23·00

1992. 500th Anniv of Discovery of America by Columbus (6th issue). Organization of East Caribbean States. Nos. 1670/1 of Antigua optd **BARBUDA MAIL.**
1381 $1 Columbus meeting Amerindians 2·50 1·50
1382 $2 Ships approaching island 6·50 4·75

1992. Postage Stamp Mega Event, New York. No. **MS**1690 of Antigua optd **BARBUDA MAIL.**
MS1383 $6 multicoloured 11·00 13·00

1992. 40th Anniv of Queen Elizabeth II's Accession. Nos. 1604/8 of Antigua optd **BARBUDA MAIL.**
1384 10c. Queen Elizabeth II and bird sanctuary 5·00 1·75
1385 30c. Nelson's Dockyard 6·00 1·25
1386 $1 Ruins on Shirley Heights 8·00 2·75
1387 $5 Beach and palm trees 16·00 14·00
MS1388 Two sheets, each 75 × 98 mm. (a) $6 Beach. (b) $6 Hillside foliage Set of 2 sheets 40·00 25·00

1992. Prehistoric Animals. Nos. 1618/26 of Antigua optd **BARBUDA MAIL.**
1389 10c. Pteranodon 2·00 1·50
1390 15c. Brachiosaurus 2·50 1·50
1391 30c. Tyrannosaurus Rex 3·00 1·25
1392 50c. Parasaurolophus 3·00 1·50
1393 $1 Deinonychus (horiz) 3·75 2·25
1394 $2 Triceratops (horiz) 6·00 5·00
1395 $4 Protoceratops hatching (horiz) 7·00 8·00
1396 $5 Stegosaurus (horiz) 7·00 8·00
MS1397 Two sheets, each 100 × 70 mm. (a) $6 Apatosaurus (horiz). (b) $6 Allosaurus (horiz) Set of 2 sheets 25·00 21·00

1992. Christmas. Nos. 1691/9 of Antigua optd **BARBUDA MAIL.**
1398 10c. "Virgin and Child with Angels" (School of Piero della Francesca) 1·75 75
1399 25c. "Madonna degli Alberelli" (Giovanni Bellini) 1·75 75
1400 30c. "Madonna and Child with St. Anthony Abbot and St. Sigismund" (Neroccio) 1·75 75
1401 40c. "Madonna and the Grand Duke" (Raphael) 2·00 75
1402 60c. "The Nativity" (Georges de la Tour) 2·25 75
1403 $1 "Holy Family" (Jacob Jordaens) 2·75 1·50
1404 $4 "Madonna and Child Enthroned" (Magaritone) 6·50 8·50
1405 $5 "Madonna and Child on a Curved Throne" (Byzantine school) 6·50 8·50
MS1406 Two sheets, each 76 × 102 mm. (a) $6 "Madonna and Child" (Domenco Ghirlando). (b) $6 "The Holy Family" (Pontormo) Set of 2 sheets 23·00 22·00

1993. Fungi. Nos. 1645/53 of Antigua optd **BARBUDA MAIL.**
1407 10c. "Amanita caesarea" 1·75 1·25
1408 15c. "Collybia fusipes" 2·00 1·25
1409 30c. "Boletus aereus" 2·25 1·50
1410 40c. "Laccaria amethystina" 2·25 1·50
1411 $1 "Russula virescens" 3·25 2·00
1412 $2 "Tricholoma equestre" ("Tricholoma auratum") 4·50 4·00
1413 $4 "Calocybe gambosa" 5·50 6·50
1414 $5 "Lentinus tigrinus" ("Panus tigrinus") 5·50 6·50
MS1415 Two sheets, each 100 × 70 mm. (a) $6 "Clavariadelphus truncatus". (b) $6 "Auricularia auricula-judae" Set of 2 sheets 24·00 21·00

1993. "Granada '92" International Stamp Exhibition, Spain. Spanish Paintings. Nos. 1636/44 of Antigua optd **BARBUDA MAIL.**
1416 10c. "The Miracle at the Well" (Alonzo Cano) 1·25 1·00
1417 15c. "The Poet Luis de Goingora y Argote" (Velazquez) 1·50 1·00
1418 30c. "The Painter Francisco Goya" (Vincente Lopez Portana) 1·75 1·00
1419 40c. "Maria de las Nieves Michaela Fourdinier" (Luis Paret y Alcazar) 1·75 1·00
1420 $1 "Carlos III eating before his Court" (Alcazar) (horiz) 3·00 2·25
1421 $2 "Rain Shower in Granada" (Antonio Munoz Degrain) (horiz) 4·75 4·75
1422 $4 "Sarah Bernhardt" (Santiago Ruisnol i Prats) 6·50 7·50
1423 $5 "The Hermitage Garden" (Joaquim Mir Trinxet) 6·50 7·50
MS1424 Two sheets, each 120 × 95 mm. (a) $6 "The Ascent of Monsieur Boucle's Montgolfier Balloon in the Gardens of Aranjuez" (Antonio Carnicero) (112 × 87 mm). (b) $6 "Olympus: Battle with the Giants" (Francisco Bayeu y Subias) (112 × 87 mm). Imperf Set of 2 sheets 17·00 18·00

1993. "Genova '92" International Thematic Stamp Exhibition. Hummingbirds and Plants. Nos. 1661/9 of Antigua optd **BARBUDA MAIL.**
1425 10c. Antillean crested hummingbird and wild plantain 2·00 1·50
1426 25c. Green mango and parrot's plantain 2·25 1·00
1427 45c. Purple-throated carib and lobster claws 2·50 1·25
1428 60c. Antillean mango and coral plant 2·75 1·50
1429 $1 Vervain hummingbird and cardinal's guard 3·25 2·25
1430 $2 Rufous-breasted hermit and heliconia 4·75 4·75
1431 $4 Blue-headed hummingbird and reed ginger 6·50 7·00
1432 $5 Green-throated carib and ornamental banana 6·50 7·00
MS1433 Two sheets, each 100 × 70 mm. (a) $6 Bee hummingbird and jungle flame. (b) $6 Western streamertail and bignonia Set of 2 sheets 25·00 19·00

1993. Inventors and Inventions. Nos. 1672/80 of Antigua optd **BARBUDA MAIL.**
1434 10c. Ts'ai Lun and paper 65 85
1435 25c. Igor Sikorsky and "Bolshoi Baltiskii" (first four-engined airplane) 2·25 80
1436 30c. Alexander Graham Bell and early telephone 1·25 80
1437 40c. Johannes Gutenberg and early printing press 1·25 80
1438 60c. James Watt and stationary steam engine 5·00 1·60
1439 $1 Anton van Leeuwenhoek and early microscope 3·50 2·25
1440 $4 Louis Braille and hands reading braille 6·00 7·00
1441 $5 Galileo and telescope 6·00 7·00
MS1442 Two sheets, each 100 × 71 mm. (a) $6 Edison and Latimer's phonograph. (b) $6 "Clermont" (first commercial paddle-steamer) Set of 2 sheets 16·00 17·00

1993. Anniversaries and Events. Nos. 900/14 of Antigua optd **BARBUDA MAIL.**
1443 10c. Russian cosmonauts 1·75 1·40
1444 40c. "Graf Zeppelin" (airship), 1929 3·00 1·00
1445 45c. Bishop Daniel Davis 80 70
1446 75c. Konrad Adenauer making speech 1·00 1·00
1447 $1 Bus Mosbacher and "Weatherly" (yacht) 2·25 1·75
1448 $1.50 Rain forest 2·50 2·50
1449 $2 Tiger 9·00 5·50
1450 $2 National flag, plant and emblem (horiz) 5·50 3·50
1451 $2 Members of Community Players company (horiz) 3·50 3·50
1452 $2.25 Women carrying pots 3·50 4·00
1453 $3 Lions Club emblem 3·75 4·25
1454 $4 Chinese rocket on launch tower 5·50 5·50
1455 $4 West German and N.A.T.O. flags 5·50 5·50
1456 $6 Hugo Eckener (airship pioneer) 6·50 7·00
MS1457 Four sheets, each 100 × 71 mm. (a) $6 Projected European space station. (b) $6 Airship LZ-129 "Hindenburg", 1936. (c) $6 Brandenburg Gate on German flag. (d) $6 "Danaus plexippus" (butterfly) Set of 4 sheets 38·00 32·00

1993. Flowers. Nos. 1733/41 of Antigua optd **BARBUDA MAIL.**
1458 15c. Cardinal's guard 1·75 1·25
1459 25c. Giant granadilla 1·90 1·10
1460 30c. Spider flower 2·00 1·25
1461 40c. Gold vine 2·25 1·40
1462 $1 Frangipani 3·50 2·25
1463 $2 Bougainvillea 4·50 4·50
1464 $4 Yellow oleander 6·00 7·00
1465 $5 Spicy jatropha 6·00 7·00
MS1466 Two sheets, each 100 × 70 mm. (a) $6 Bird lime tree. (b) $6 Fairy lily Set of 2 sheets 21·00 21·00

1993. World Bird Watch. Nos. 1248/51 optd **WORLD BIRDWATCH 9-10 OCTOBER 1993.**
1467 60c. Type **119** 4·00 1·75
1468 $2 Adelaide's warbler 7·00 4·50
1469 $4 Rose-breasted grosbeak 9·50 10·00
1470 $7 Wied's crested flycatcher 12·00 13·00

1993. Endangered Species. Nos. 1759/71 of Antigua optd **BARBUDA MAIL.**
1471 $1 St. Lucia amazon ("St. Lucia Parrot") 5·50 4·00
1472 $1 Cahow 5·50 4·00
1473 $1 Swallow-tailed kite 5·50 4·00
1474 $1 Everglade kite ("Everglades Kite") 5·50 4·00
1475 $1 Imperial amazon ("Imperial Parrot") 5·50 4·00
1476 $1 Humpback whale 5·50 4·00
1477 $1 Plain pigeon ("Puerto Rican Plain Pigeon") 5·50 4·00
1478 $1 St. Vincent amazon ("St. Vincent Parrot") 5·50 4·00
1479 $1 Puerto Rican amazon ("Puerto Rican Parrot") 5·50 4·00
1480 $1 Leatherback turtle 5·50 4·00
1481 $1 American crocodile 5·50 4·00
1482 $1 Hawksbill turtle 5·50 4·00
MS1483 Two sheets, each 100 × 70 mm. (a) $6 As No. 1476. (b) $6 West Indian manatee Set of 2 sheets. 28·00 26·00

1994. Bicentenary of the Louvre, Paris. Paintings by Peter Paul Rubens. Nos. 1742/9 and **MS**1758 of Antigua optd **BARBUDA MAIL.**
1484 $1 "The Destiny of Marie de' Medici" (upper detail) 4·00 3·25
1485 $1 "The Birth of Marie de' Medici" 4·00 3·25
1486 $1 "The Education of Marie de' Medici" 4·00 3·25
1487 $1 "The Destiny of Marie de' Medici" (lower detail) 4·00 3·25
1488 $1 "Henry VI receiving the Portrait of Marie" 4·00 3·25
1489 $1 "The Meeting of the King and Marie at Lyons" 4·00 3·25
1490 $1 "The Marriage by Proxy" 4·00 3·25
1491 $1 "The Birth of Louis XIII" 4·00 3·25
MS1492 70 × 100 mm. $6 "Helene Fourment with a Coach" (52 × 85 mm) 15·00 16·00

1994. World Cup Football Championship, 1994, U.S.A. (1st Issue). Nos. 1816/28 of Antigua optd **BARBUDA MAIL.**
1493 $2 Paul Gascoigne 3·50 2·50
1494 $2 David Platt 3·50 2·50
1495 $2 Martin Peters 3·50 2·50
1496 $2 John Barnes 3·50 2·50
1497 $2 Gary Lineker 3·50 2·50
1498 $2 Geoff Hurst 3·50 2·50
1499 $2 Bobby Charlton 3·50 2·50
1500 $2 Bryan Robson 3·50 2·50
1501 $2 Bobby Moore 3·50 2·50
1502 $2 Nobby Stiles 3·50 2·50
1503 $2 Gordon Banks 3·50 2·50
1504 $2 Peter Shilton 3·50 2·50
MS1505 Two sheets, each 135 × 109 mm. (a) $6 Bobby Moore holding World Cup. (b) $6 Gary Lineker and Bobby Robson Set of 2 sheets 23·00 19·00
See also Nos. 1573/9.

1994. Anniversaries and Events. Nos. 1829/38, 1840 and 1842/7 of Antigua optd **BARBUDA MAIL.**
1506 10c. Grand Inspector W.Heath 3·00 1·75
1507 15c. Rodnina and Oulanov (U.S.S.R.) (pairs figure skating) (horiz) 1·75 1·50
1508 30c. Present Masonic Hall, St. John's (horiz) 4·00 1·50
1509 30c. Willy Brandt with Helmut Schmidt and George Leber (horiz) 1·25 1·00
1510 30c. "Cat and Bird" (Picasso) (horiz) 1·25 1·00
1511 40c. Previous Masonic Hall, St. John's (horiz) 4·00 1·50
1512 40c. "Fish on a Newspaper" (Picasso) (horiz) 1·25 1·00
1513 40c. Early astronomical equipment 1·25 1·00
1514 40c. Prince Naruhito and engagement photographs (horiz) 1·25 1·00
1515 60c. Grand Inspector J.Jeffery 4·50 1·75
1516 $3 Masako Owada and engagement photographs (horiz) 3·00 4·00
1517 $4 Willy Brandt and protest march (horiz) 4·00 4·50
1518 $4 Galaxy 4·00 4·50
1519 $5 Alberto Tomba (Italy) (giant slalom) (horiz) 4·00 4·50
1520 $5 "Dying Bull" (Picasso) (horiz) 4·00 4·50
1521 $5 Pres. Clinton and family (horiz) 4·00 4·50
MS1522 Six sheets. (a) 106 × 75 mm. $5 Copernicus. (b) 106 × 75 mm. $6 Womens' 1500 metre speed skating medallists (horiz). (c) 106 × 75 mm. $6 Willy Brandt at Warsaw Ghetto Memorial (horiz). (d) 106 × 75 mm. $6 "Woman with a Dog" (detail) (Picasso) (horiz). (e) 106 × 75 mm. $6 Masako Owada. (f) 106 × 75 mm. $6 Pres. Clinton taking the Oath (42½ × 57 mm) Set of 6 sheets 40·00 40·00

1994. Aviation Anniversaries. Nos. 1848/55 of Antigua optd **BARBUDA MAIL.**
1523 30c. Hugo Eckener and Dr. W. Beckers with airship "Graf Zeppelin" over Lake George, New York 2·50 1·50
1524 40c. Chicago World's Fair from "Graf Zeppelin" 2·50 1·50
1525 40c. Gloster Whittle E28/39, 1941 2·50 1·50
1526 40c. George Washington writing balloon mail letter (vert) 2·50 1·50
1527 $4 Pres. Wilson and Curtiss "Jenny" 6·50 7·50
1528 $5 Airship LZ-129 "Hindenburg" over Ebbets Field baseball stadium, 1937 6·50 7·50
1529 $5 Gloster Meteor in dogfight 6·50 7·50
MS1530 Three sheets. (a) 86 × 105 mm. $6 Hugo Eckener (vert). (b) 105 × 86 mm. $6 Consolidated Catalina PBY-5 flying boat (57 × 42½ mm). (c) 105 × 86 mm. $6 Alexander Hamilton, Washington and John Jay watching Blanchard's balloon, 1793 (horiz) Set of 3 sheets 28·00 25·00

1994. Centenaries of Henry Ford's First Petrol Engine (Nos. 1531, 1533, 1533a) and Karl Benz's First Four-wheeled Car (others). Nos. 1856/60 of Antigua optd **BARBUDA MAIL.**
1531 30c. Lincoln Continental 2·00 1·25
1532 40c. Mercedes racing car, 1914 2·00 1·25
1533 $4 Ford "GT40", 1966 7·00 7·50
1534 $5 Mercedes Benz "gull-wing" coupe, 1954 7·00 7·50
MS1535 Two sheets. (a) 114 × 87 mm. $6 Ford's Mustang emblem. (b) 87 × 114 mm. $6 Germany 1936 12pf. Benz and U.S.A. 1968 12c. Ford stamps Set of 2 sheets 19·00 19·00

1994. Famous Paintings by Rembrandt and Matisse. Nos. 1881/9 of Antigua optd **BARBUDA MAIL.**
1536 15c. "Hannah and Samuel" (Rembrandt) 1·75 1·50
1537 15c. "Guitarist" (Matisse) 1·75 1·50
1538 30c. "The Jewish Bride" (Rembrandt) 2·00 1·10
1539 40c. "Jacob wrestling with the Angel" (Rembrandt) 2·00 1·10
1540 60c. "Interior with a Goldfish Bowl" (Matisse) 2·50 1·25
1541 $1 "Mlle. Yvonne Landsberg" (Matisse) 3·25 1·75
1542 $4 "The Toboggan" (Matisse) 6·50 7·50
1543 $5 "Moses with the Tablets of the Law" (Rembrandt) 6·50 7·50
MS1544 Two sheets. (a) 124 × 99 mm. $6 "The Blinding of Samson by the Philistines" (detail) (Rembrandt). (b) 99 × 124 mm. $6 "The Three Sisters" (detail) (Matisse) Set of 2 sheets 19·00 19·00

1994. "Polska '93" International Stamp Exhibition, Poznan. Nos. 1839, 1841 and **MS**1847f of Antigua optd **BARBUDA MAIL.**
1545 $1 "Woman Combing her Hair" (W. Slewinski) (horiz) 3·25 2·50
1546 $3 "Artist's Wife with Cat" (Konrad Kryzanowski) (horiz) 6·00 7·00
MS1547 70 × 100 mm. $6 "General Confusion" (S. I. Witkiewicz) 10·00 12·00

1994. Orchids. Nos. 1949/56 of Antigua optd **BARBUDA MAIL.**
1548 10c. "Spiranthes lanceolata" 2·00 1·50
1549 20c. "Ionopsis utricularioides" 3·00 1·50
1550 30c. "Tetramicra canaliculata" 3·25 1·25
1551 50c. "Oncidium picturatum" 3·75 1·50

1552 $1 "Epidendrum difforme" . . 4·50 2·25
1553 $2 "Epidendrum ciliare" . . 6·50 5·00
1554 $4 "Epidendrum ibaguense" 7·50 8·00
1555 $5 "Epidendrum nocturnum" . . . . . . 7·50 8·00
MS1556 Two sheets, each 100 × 73 mm. (a) $6 "Rodriguezia lanceolata". (b) $6 "Encyclia cochleata" Set of 2 sheets . . . 26·00 25·00

1994. Centenary of Sierra Club (environmental protection society) (1992). Endangered Species. Nos. 1907/22 of Antigua optd **BARBUDA MAIL.**
1557 $1.50 Sumatran rhinoceros lying down . . . . 3·00 2·50
1558 $1.50 Sumatran rhinoceros feeding . . . . 3·00 2·50
1559 $1.50 Ring-tailed lemur on ground . . . . 3·00 2·50
1560 $1.50 Ring-tailed lemur on branch . . . . 3·00 2·50
1561 $1.50 Red-fronted brown lemur on branch . . . . 3·00 2·50
1562 $1.50 Head of red-fronted brown lemur . . . . . 3·00 2·50
1563 $1.50 Head of red-fronted brown lemur in front of trunk . . . . 3·00 2·50
1564 $1.50 Sierra Club Centennial emblem . . . . 1·75 1·60
1565 $1.50 Head of bactrian camel . . . . 3·00 2·50
1566 $1.50 Bactrian camel . . . 3·00 2·50
1567 $1.50 African elephant drinking . . . . 3·00 2·50
1568 $1.50 Head of African elephant . . . . 3·00 2·50
1569 $1.50 Leopard sitting upright . . . . 3·00 2·50
1570 $1.50 Leopard in grass (emblem at right) . . . . 3·00 2·50
1571 $1.50 Leopard in grass (emblem at left) . . . . . 3·00 2·50
MS1572 Four sheets. (a) 100 × 70 mm. $1.50, Sumatran rhinoceros (horiz). (b) 70 × 100 mm. $1.50, Ring-tailed lemur (horiz). (C) 70 × 100 mm. $1.50, Bactrian camel (horiz) (d) 100 × 70 mm. $1.50, African elephant (horiz) Set of 4 sheets 11·00 11·00

1995. World Cup Football Championship, U.S.A. (2nd issue). Nos. 2039/45 of Antigua optd **BARBUDA MAIL.**
1573 15c. Hugo Sanchez (Mexico) 1·75 1·25
1574 35c. Jurgen Klinsmann (Germany) . . . . 2·25 1·25
1575 65c. Antiguan player . . . 2·25 1·25
1576 $1.20 Cobi Jones (U.S.A.) 3·25 2·75
1577 $4 Roberto Baggio (Italy) 6·00 6·50
1578 $5 Bwalya Kalusha (Zambia) . . . . 6·00 6·50
MS1579 Two sheets. (a) 72 × 105 mm. $6 Maldive Islands player (vert). (b) 107 × 78 mm. $6 World Cup trophy (vert) Set of 2 sheets . . . . 15·00 14·00

1995. Christmas. Religious Paintings. Nos. 2058/66 of Antigua optd **BARBUDA MAIL.**
1580 15c. "Virgin and Child by the Fireside" (Robert Campin) . . . . 1·25 75
1581 35c. "The Reading Madonna" (Giorgione) 1·75 70
1582 40c. "Madonna and Child" (Giovanni Bellini) . . . . 1·75 70
1583 45c. "The Little Madonna" (Da Vinci) . . . . 1·75 70
1584 65c. "The Virgin and Child under the Apple Tree" (Lucas Cranach the Elder) 2·25 1·00
1585 75c. "Madonna and Child" (Master of the Female Half-lengths) . . . . . . 2·25 1·25
1586 $1.20 "An Allegory of the Church" (Alessandro Allori) . . . . 3·25 3·50
1587 $5 "Madonna and Child wreathed with Flowers" (Jacob Jordaens) . . . . 6·00 8·50
MS1588 Two sheets. (a) 123 × 88 mm. $6 "Madonna and Child with Commissioners" (detail) (Palma Vecchio). (b) 88 × 123 mm. $6 "The Virgin Enthroned with Child" (detail) (Bohemian master) Set of 2 sheets 15·00 15·00

1995. "Hong Kong '94" International Stamp Exhibition (1st issue). Nos. 1890/1 of Antigua optd **BARBUDA MAIL.**
1589 40c. Hong Kong 1981 $1 Fish stamp and sampans, Shau Kei Wan . . . . . 2·50 2·00
1590 40c. Antigua 1990 $2 Reef fish stamp and sampans, Shau Kei Wan . . . . . 2·50 2·00
See also Nos. 1591/6.

1995. "Hong Kong '94" International Stamp Exhibition (2nd issue). Nos. 1892/7 of Antigua optd **BARBUDA MAIL.**
1591 40c. Terracotta warriors . . 50 60
1592 40c. Cavalryman and horse 50 60
1593 40c. Warriors in armour . . 50 60
1594 40c. Painted bronze chariot and team 50 60
1595 40c. Pekingese dog 50 60
1596 40c. Warriors with horses 50 60

1995. Centenary of International Olympic Committee. Nos. 1990/2 of Antigua optd **BARBUDA MAIL.**
1597 50c. Edwin Moses (U.S.A.) (400 metres hurdles), 1984 75 75
1598 $1.50 Steffi Graf (Germany) (tennis), 1988 . . . . . . 5·00 3·50
MS1599 79 × 110 mm. $6 Johann Olav Koss (Norway) (500, 1500 and 10,000 metre speed skating), 1994 . . . . 6·00 7·00

1995. Dogs of the World. Chinese New Year ("Year of the Dog"). Nos. 1923/47 of Antigua optd **BARBUDA MAIL.**
1600 50c. West Highland white terrier . . . . 1·25 95
1601 50c. Beagle . . . . 1·25 95
1602 50c. Scottish terrier . . . . 1·25 95
1603 50c. Pekingese . . . . . . 1·25 95
1604 50c. Dachshund . . . . . . 1·25 95
1605 50c. Yorkshire terrier . . . 1·25 95
1606 50c. Pomeranian . . . . . 1·25 95
1607 50c. Poodle . . . . 1·25 95
1608 50c. Shetland sheepdog . . 1·25 95
1609 50c. Pug . . . . 1·25 95
1610 50c. Shih tzu . . . . 1·25 95
1611 50c. Chihuahua . . . . . . 1·25 95
1612 50c. Mastiff . . . . 1·25 95
1613 50c. Border collie . . . . . 1·25 95
1614 50c. Samoyed . . . . 1·25 95
1615 50c. Airedale terrier . . . . 1·25 95
1616 50c. English setter . . . . . 1·25 95
1617 50c. Rough collie . . . . . 1·25 95
1618 50c. Newfoundland . . . . 1·25 95
1619 50c. Weimarana . . . . . . 1·25 95
1620 50c. English springer spaniel 1·25 95
1621 50c. Dalmatian . . . . . . 1·25 95
1622 50c. Boxer . . . . 1·25 95
1623 50c. Old English sheepdog 1·25 95
MS1624 Two sheets, each 93 × 58 mm. (a) $6 Welsh corgi. (b) $6 Labrador retriever Set of 2 sheets . . . . 27·00 19·00

1995. Centenary of First English Cricket Tour to the West Indies (1995). Nos. 1994/7 of Antigua optd **BARBUDA MAIL.**
1625 35c. Mike Atherton (England) and Wisden Trophy . . . . 3·00 1·25
1626 75c. Viv Richards (West Indies) (vert) . . . . . . 4·00 2·75
1627 $1.20 Richie Richardson (West Indies) and Wisden Trophy . . . . 5·00 4·00
MS1628 80 × 100 mm. $3 English team, 1895 (black and brown) 10·00 9·00

1995. "Philakorea '94" International Stamp Exhibition (1st issue). Nos. 1998/2009 of Antigua optd **BARBUDA MAIL.**
1629 40c. Entrance bridge, Songgwangsa Temple . . 1·00 80
1630 75c. Long-necked bottle . . 1·25 1·25
1631 75c. Punch'ong ware jar with floral decoration . . 1·25 1·25
1632 75c. Punch'ong ware jar with blue dragon pattern 1·25 1·25
1633 75c. Ewer in shape of bamboo shoot . . . . . . 1·25 1·25
1634 75c. Punch'ong ware green jar . . . . 1·25 1·25
1635 75c. Pear-shaped bottle . . 1·25 1·25
1636 75c. Porcelain jar with brown dragon pattern . . 1·25 1·25
1637 75c. Porcelain jar with floral pattern . . . . 1·25 1·25
1638 90c. Song-op Folk Village, Cheju . . . . 1·25 1·25
1639 $3 Port Sogwipo . . . . . 3·00 3·50
MS1640 104 × 71 mm. $4 Ox herder playing flute (vert) . . . . . . 4·00 5·50

1995. 1st Recipients of Order of the Caribbean Community. Nos. 2046/8 of Antigua optd **BARBUDA MAIL.**
1641 65c. Sir Shridath Ramphal 50 55
1642 90c. William Demas 70 75
1643 $1.20 Derek Walcott . . . 2·25 2·25

1995. 25th Anniv of First Moon Landing. Nos. 1977/89 of Antigua optd **BARBUDA MAIL.**
1644 $1.50 Edwin Aldrin (astronaut) . . . . 2·75 2·25
1645 $1.50 First lunar footprint 2·75 2·25
1646 $1.50 Neil Armstrong (astronaut) . . . . 2·75 2·25
1647 $1.50 Aldrin stepping onto Moon . . . . 2·75 2·25
1648 $1.50 Aldrin and equipment 2·75 2·25
1649 $1.50 Aldrin and U.S.A. flag 2·75 2·25
1650 $1.50 Aldrin at Tranquility Base . . . . 2·75 2·25
1651 $1.50 Moon plaque . . . . 2·75 2·25
1652 $1.50 "Eagle" leaving Moon 2·75 2·25
1653 $1.50 Command module in lunar orbit . . . . 2·75 2·25
1654 $1.50 First day cover of U.S.A. 1969 10c. First Man on Moon stamp . . 2·75 2·25
1655 $1.50 Pres. Nixon and astronauts . . . . 2·75 2·25
MS1656 72 × 102 mm. $6 Armstrong and Aldrin with postal official 15·00 15·00

1995. International Year of the Family. No. 1993 of Antigua optd **BARBUDA MAIL.**
1657 90c. Antiguan family . . . 1·50 1·50

1995. 50th Anniv of D-Day. Nos. 2010/13 of Antigua optd **BARBUDA MAIL.**
1658 40c. Short S.25 Sunderland flying boat . . . . 2·50 1·00
1659 $2 Lockheed P-38 Lightning fighters attacking train . . 8·00 4·75
1660 $3 Martin B-26 Marauder bombers . . . . 8·00 5·50
MS1661 108 × 78 mm. $6 Hawker Typhoon fighter bomber . . . 11·00 13·00

122 Queen Elizabeth the Queen Mother (95th birthday)

1995. Anniversaries. Multicoloured.
1662 $7.50 Type **122** . . . . . . 11·00 11·00
1663 $8 German bombers over St. Paul's Cathedral, London (horiz) (50th anniv of end of Second World War) . . . . . . 20·00 14·00
1664 $8 New York skyline with U.N. and national flags (horiz) (50th anniv of United Nations) . . . . . 8·00 9·00

1995. Hurricane Relief. Nos. 1662/4 surch **HURRICANE RELIEF** and premium.
1665 $7.50+$1 Type **122** (90th birthday) . . . . 7·50 8·50
1666 $8+$1 German bombers over St. Paul's Cathedral, London (horiz) (50th anniv of end of Second World War) . . . . . . 10·00 11·00
1667 $8+$1 New York skyline with U.N. and national flags (horiz) (50th anniv of United Nations) . . . 7·50 8·50

1996. Marine Life. Nos. 1967/76 of Antigua optd **BARBUDA MAIL.**
1668 50c. Bottlenose dolphin . . 90 85
1669 50c. Killer whale 90 85
1670 50c. Spinner dolphin 90 85
1671 50c. Oceanic sunfish 90 85
1672 50c. Caribbean reef shark and short fin pilot whale 90 85
1673 50c. Copper-banded butterflyfish 90 85
1674 50c. Mosaic moray 90 85
1675 50c. Clown triggerfish . . . 90 85
1676 50c. Red lobster 90 85
MS1677 Two sheets, each 106 × 76 mm. (a) $6 Seahorse. (b) $6 Swordfish ("Blue Marlin") (horiz) Set of 2 sheets . . . 12·00 14·00

1996. Christmas. Religious Paintings. Nos. 2267/73 of Antigua optd **BARBUDA MAIL.**
1678 15c. "Rest on the Flight into Egypt" (Paolo Veronese) 65 40
1679 35c. "Madonna and Child" (Van Dyck) 75 40
1680 65c. "Sacred Conversation Piece" (Veronese) . . . . 1·00 55
1681 75c. "Vision of St. Anthony" (Van Dyck) 1·25 60
1682 90c. "Virgin and Child" (Van Eyck) . . . . 1·40 75
1683 $6 "The Immaculate Conception" (Giovanni Tiepolo) . . . . 4·75 7·00
MS1684 Two sheets. (a) 101 × 127 mm. $5 "Christ appearing to his Mother" (detail) (Van der Weyden). (b) 127 × 101 mm. $6 "The Infant Jesus and the Young St. John" (Murillo) Set of 2 sheets . . . 10·00 13·00

1996. Stars of Country and Western Music. Nos. 2014/38 of Antigua optd **BARBUDA MAIL.**
1685 75c. Travis Tritt 80 75
1686 75c. Dwight Yoakam . . . 80 75
1687 75c. Billy Ray Cyrus 80 75
1688 75c. Alan Jackson 80 75
1689 75c. Garth Brooks 80 75
1690 75c. Vince Gill 80 75
1691 75c. Clint Black 80 75
1692 75c. Eddie Rabbit 80 75
1693 75c. Patsy Cline 80 75
1694 75c. Tanya Tucker 80 75
1695 75c. Dolly Parton 80 75
1696 75c. Anne Murray 80 75
1697 75c. Tammy Wynette . . . 80 75
1698 75c. Loretta Lynn 80 75
1699 75c. Reba McEntire 80 75
1700 75c. Skeeter Davis 80 75
1701 75c. Hank Snow 80 75
1702 75c. Gene Autry 80 75
1703 75c. Jimmie Rodgers 80 75
1704 75c. Ernest Tubb 80 75
1705 75c. Eddy Arnold 80 75
1706 75c. Willie Nelson 80 75
1707 75c. Johnny Cash 80 75
1708 75c. George Jones 80 75
MS1709 Three sheets. (a) 100 × 70 mm. $6 Hank Williams Jr. (b) 100 × 70 mm. $6 Hank Williams Sr. (c) 70 × 100 mm. $6 Kitty Wells (horiz) Set of 3 sheets 15·00 15·00

1996. Birds. Nos. 2067/81 of Antigua optd **BARBUDA MAIL.**
1710 15c. Magnificent frigate bird 70 70
1711 25c. Antillean euphonia ("Blue-hooded Euphonia") 80 50
1712 35c. Eastern meadowlark ("Meadowlark") 90 60
1713 40c. Red-billed tropic bird 90 60
1714 45c. Greater flamingo . . . 1·00 60
1715 60c. Yellow-faced grassquit 1·10 1·00
1716 65c. Yellow-billed cuckoo 1·25 1·25
1717 70c. Purple-throated carib 1·25 1·25
1718 75c. Bananaquit . . . . . 1·25 1·00
1719 90c. Painted bunting . . . . 1·40 1·00
1720 $1.20 Red-legged honeycreeper . . . . . . 1·75 2·00
1721 $2 Northern jacana ("Jacana") . . . . 2·25 2·75
1722 $5 Greater Antillean bullfinch . . . . 4·00 4·50
1723 $10 Caribbean elaenia . . 6·50 8·00
1724 $20 Brown trembler ("Trembler") . . . . . . 11·00 13·00

1996. Birds. Nos. 2050, 2052 and 2054/7 of Antigua optd **BARBUDA MAIL.**
1725 15c. Bridled quail dove . . 1·25 80
1726 40c. Purple-throated carib (vert) . . . . 1·75 60
1727 $1 Broad-winged hawk ("Antigua Broad-winged Hawk") (vert) . . . . . 2·75 2·00
1728 $4 Yellow warbler . . . . . 4·50 6·50
MS1729 Two sheets. (a) 70 × 100 mm. $6 Female magnificent frigate bird (vert). (b) 100 × 70 mm. $6 Black-billed whistling duck ducklings Set of 2 sheets . . . . 12·00 14·00

1996. Prehistoric Animals. Nos. 2082/100 of Antigua optd **BARBUDA MAIL.**
1730 15c. Head of pachycephalosaurus . . . . 1·40 1·40
1731 20c. Head of afrovenator . . 1·40 1·40
1732 65c. Centrosaurus . . . . . 1·40 1·40
1733 75c. Kronosaurus (horiz) . . 1·40 1·40
1734 75c. Ichthyosaurus (horiz) 1·40 1·40
1735 75c. Plesiosaurus (horiz) . . 1·40 1·40
1736 75c. Archelon (horiz) . . . 1·40 1·40
1737 75c. Pair of tyrannosaurus (horiz) . . . . 1·40 1·40
1738 75c. Tyrannosaurus (horiz) 1·40 1·40
1739 75c. Parasaurolophus (horiz) 1·40 1·40
1740 75c. Pair of parasaurolophus (horiz) . . . . 1·40 1·40
1741 75c. Oviraptor (horiz) . . . 1·40 1·40
1742 75c. Protoceratops with eggs (horiz) . . . . 1·40 1·40
1743 75c. Pteranodon and protoceratops (horiz) . . . 1·40 1·40
1744 75c. Pair of protoceratops (horiz) . . . . 1·40 1·40
1745 90c. Pentaceratops drinking 1·75 1·50
1746 $1.20 Head of tarbosaurus 2·25 2·00
1747 $5 Head of styracosaurus 5·50 6·50
MS1748 Two sheets, each 101 × 70 mm. (a) $6 Head of Corythosaurus (horiz). (b) $6 Head of Carnotaurus (horiz) Set of 2 sheets . . . . 13·00 15·00

1996. Olympic Games, Atlanta (1st issue). Previous Gold Medal Winners. Nos. 2101/7 of Antigua optd **BARBUDA MAIL.**
1749 15c. Al Oerter (U.S.A.) (discus – 1956, 1960, 1964, 1968) . . . . 1·00 80
1750 20c. Greg Louganis (U.S.A.) (diving – 1984, 1988) . . 1·00 80
1751 65c. Naim Suleymanoglu (Turkey) (weightlifting – 1988) . . . . 1·50 80
1752 90c. Louise Ritter (U.S.A.) (high jump – 1988) . . . 2·00 1·10
1753 $1.20 Nadia Comaneci (Rumania) (gymnastics – 1976) . . . . 3·25 2·25
1754 $5 Olga Bondarenko (Russia) (10,000 m – 1988) . . . . 5·00 6·50
MS1755 Two sheets, each 106 × 76 mm. (a) $6 United States crew (eight-oared shell – 1964). (b) $6 Lutz Hessilch (Germany) (cycling – 1988) (vert) Set of 2 sheets . . . . 12·00 12·00
See also Nos. 1922/44.

1996. 18th World Scout Jamboree, Netherlands. Tents. Nos. 2203/9 of Antigua optd **BARBUDA MAIL.**
1756 $1.20 The Explorer Tent . . 1·00 1·25
1757 $1.20 Camper tent . . . . . 1·00 1·25
1758 $1.20 Wall tent . . . . . . 1·00 1·25
1759 $1.20 Trail tent . . . . . . 1·00 1·25

1760 $1.20 Miner's tent . . . . . 1·00 1·25
1761 $1.20 Voyager tent . . . . 1·00 1·25
MS1762 Two sheets, each 76×106 mm. (a) $6 Scout and camp fire. (b) $6 Scout with back pack Set of 2 sheets . . . . . 8·00 10·00

1996. Centenary of Nobel Prize Trust Fund. Nos. 2226/44 of Antigua optd **BARBUDA MAIL**.
1763 $1 Dag Hammarskjold (1961 Peace) . . . . . . 1·00 75
1764 $1 Georg Wittig (1979 Chemistry) . . . . 1·00 75
1765 $1 Wilhelm Ostwold (1909 Chemistry) . . . . 1·00 75
1766 $1 Robert Koch (1905 Medicine) . . . . 1·00 75
1767 $1 Karl Ziegler (1963 Chemistry) . . . . 1·00 75
1768 $1 Alexander Fleming (1945 Medicine) . . . . 1·00 75
1769 $1 Hermann Staudinger (1953 Chemistry) . . . . 1·00 75
1770 $1 Manfred Eigen (1967 Chemistry) . . . . 1·00 75
1771 $1 Arno Penzias (1978 Physics) . . . . 1·00 75
1772 $1 Shumal Agnon (1966 Literature) . . . . 1·00 75
1773 $1 Rudyard Kipling (1907 Literature) . . . . 1·00 75
1774 $1 Aleksandr Solzhenitsyn (1970 Literature) . . . . 1·00 75
1775 $1 Jack Steinburger (1988 Physics) . . . . 1·00 75
1776 $1 Andrei Sakharov (1975 Peace) . . . . 1·00 75
1777 $1 Otto Stern (1943 Physics) 1·00 75
1778 $1 John Steinbeck (1962 Literature) . . . . 1·00 75
1779 $1 Nadine Gordimer (1991 Literature) . . . . 1·00 75
1780 $1 William Faulkner (1949 Literature) . . . . 1·00 75
MS1781 Two sheets, each 100×70 mm. (a) $6 Elie Wiesel (1986 Peace) (vert). (b) $6 Dalai Lama (1989 Peace) (vert) Set of 2 sheets . . . . 11·00 13·00

1996. 70th Birthday of Queen Elizabeth II. Nos. 2355/8 of Antigua optd **BARBUDA MAIL**.
1782 $2 Queen Elizabeth II in blue dress . . . . 1·75 1·75
1783 $2 With bouquet . . . . . 1·75 1·75
1784 $2 In Garter robes . . . . 1·75 1·75
MS1785 96×111 mm. $6 Wearing white dress . . . . 7·00 6·00

1997. Christmas. Religious Paintings by Filippo Lippi. Nos. 2377/83 of Antigua optd **BARBUDA MAIL**.
1786 60c. "Madonna Enthroned" 50 35
1787 90c. "Adoration of the Child and Saints" 75 55
1788 $1 "The Annunciation" . . 90 80
1789 $1.20 "Birth of the Virgin" 1·10 1·10
1790 $1.60 "Adoration of the Child" . . . . 1·40 1·60
1791 $1.75 "Madonna and Child" 1·60 2·00
MS1792 Two sheets, each 76×106 mm. (a) $6 "Madonna and Child" (different). (b) $6 "The Circumcision" Set of 2 sheets 10·00 12·00

1997. 50th Anniv of F.A.O. Nos. 2121/4 of Antigua optd **BARBUDA MAIL**.
1793 75c. Woman buying produce from market . . . . . . 1·00 1·00
1794 90c. Women shopping . . . 1·10 1·10
1795 $1.20 Women talking . . . 1·40 1·75
MS1796 100×70 mm. $6 Tractor 5·50 7·00

1997. 90th Anniv of Rotary International (1995). No. 2126 of Antigua optd **BARBUDA MAIL**.
1797 $5 Beach and rotary emblem 3·25 4·25
MS1798 74×104 mm. $6 National flag and emblem . . . . 4·50 5·50

1997. 50th Anniv of End of Second World War in Europe and the Pacific. Nos. 2108/16 and 2132/8 of Antigua optd **BARBUDA MAIL**.
1799 $1.20 Map of Berlin showing Russian advance 75 80
1800 $1.20 Russian tank and infantry 75 80
1801 $1.20 Street fighting in Berlin 75 80
1802 $1.20 German tank exploding 75 80
1803 $1.20 Russian air raid . . . 75 80
1804 $1.20 German troops surrendering 75 80
1805 $1.20 Hoisting the Soviet flag on the Reichstag . . 75 80
1806 $1.20 Captured German standards 75 80
1807 $1.20 Gen. Chiang Kai-shek and Chinese guerrillas . . 75 80
1808 $1.20 Gen. Douglas MacArthur and beach landing 75 80
1809 $1.20 Gen. Claire Chennault and U.S. fighter aircraft 75 80
1810 $1.20 Brig. Orde Wingate and supply drop 75 80
1811 $1.20 Gen. Joseph Stilwell and U.S. supply plane . . 75 80
1812 $1.20 Field-Marshal Bill Slim and loading cow onto plane 75 80
MS1813 Two sheets, each 100×70 mm. (a) $3 Admiral Nimitz and aircraft carrier. (b) $6 Gen. Konev (vert) Set of 2 sheets 6·50 8·00

1997. Bees. Nos. 2172/6 of Antigua optd **BARBUDA MAIL**.
1814 90c. Mining bees 75 50
1815 $1.20 Solitary bee . . . . . 1·00 80
1816 $1.65 Leaf-cutter bee . . . 1·40 1·60
1817 $1.75 Honey bees . . . . . 1·60 1·75
MS1818 110×80 mm. $6 Solitary mining bird . . . . 4·50 5·00

1997. Flowers. Nos. 2177/89 of Antigua optd **BARBUDA MAIL**.
1819 75c. Narcissus 55 60
1820 75c. Camellia 55 60
1821 75c. Iris 55 60
1822 75c. Tulip 55 60
1823 75c. Poppy 55 60
1824 75c. Peony 55 60
1825 75c. Magnolia 55 60
1826 75c. Oriental lily 55 60
1827 75c. Rose 55 60
1828 75c. Pansy 55 60
1829 75c. Hydrangea 55 60
1830 75c. Azaleas 55 60
MS1831 80×110 mm. $6 Calla lily 5·00 6·00

1997. Cats. Nos. 2190/202 of Antigua optd **BARBUDA MAIL**.
1832 45c. Somali 50 50
1833 45c. Persian and butterflies 50 50
1834 45c. Devon rex 50 50
1835 45c. Turkish angora 50 50
1836 45c. Himalayan 50 50
1837 45c. Maine coon 50 50
1838 45c. Ginger non-pedigree . . 50 50
1839 45c. American wirehair . . 50 50
1840 45c. British shorthair . . . 50 50
1841 45c. American curl 50 50
1842 45c. Black non-pedigree and butterfly 50 50
1843 45c. Birman 50 50
MS1844 104×74 mm. $6 Siberian kitten (vert) . . . . 5·50 6·50

1997. 95th Birthday of Queen Elizabeth the Queen Mother. Nos. 2127/31 of Antigua optd **BARBUDA MAIL**.
1845 $1.50 brown, lt brown & black . . . . 4·00 3·00
1846 $1.50 multicoloured . . . . 4·00 3·00
1847 $1.50 multicoloured . . . . 4·00 3·00
1848 $1.50 multicoloured . . . . 4·00 3·00
MS1849 102×27 mm. $6 multicoloured . . . . 6·50 5·50

1997. 50th Anniv of United Nations. Nos. 2117/18 of Antigua optd **BARBUDA MAIL**.
1850 75c. Signatures and Earl of Halifax 60 60
1851 90c. Virginia Gildersleeve 70 70
1852 $1.20 Harold Stassen . . . 90 1·10
MS1853 100×70 mm. $6 Pres. Franklin D. Roosevelt . . . . 4·00 5·50

1997. Trains of the World. Nos. 2210/25 of Antigua optd **BARBUDA MAIL**.
1854 35c. Trans-Gabon diesel-electric train 75 30
1855 65c. Canadian Pacific diesel-electric locomotive 80 40
1856 75c. Santa Fe Railway diesel-electric locomotive, U.S.A. 80 50
1857 90c. High Speed Train, Great Britain 80 60
1858 $1.20 TGV express train, France 80 90
1859 $1.20 Diesel-electric locomotive, Australia . . 80 90
1860 $1.20 Pendolino "ETR 450" electric train, Italy 80 90
1861 $1.20 Diesel-electric locomotive, Thailand . . 80 90
1862 $1.20 Pennsylvania Railroad Type 4 steam locomotive, U.S.A. 80 90
1863 $1.20 Beyer-Garratt steam locomotive, East African Railways 80 90
1864 $1.20 Natal Govt steam locomotive 80 90
1865 $1.20 Rail gun, American Civil War 80 90
1866 $1.20 Locomotive "Lion" (red livery), Great Britain 80 90
1867 $1.20 William Hedley's "Puffing Billy" (green livery), Great Britain . . 80 90
1868 $6 Amtrak high speed diesel locomotive, U.S.A. . . . 3·50 4·50
MS1869 Two sheets, each 110×80 mm. (a) $6 Locomotive "Iron Rooster", China (vert). (b) $6 "Indian-Pacific" diesel-electric locomotive, Australia (vert) Set of 2 sheets . . . . 10·00 12·00

1997. Golden Wedding of Queen Elizabeth II and Prince Philip (1st issue). Nos. 1662/3 optd **Golden Wedding of H.M. Queen Elizabeth II and Prince Philip 1947-1997.**
1870 $7.50 Type **122** . . . . . . 6·00 7·00
1871 $8 German bombers over St. Paul's Cathedral, London (horiz) . . . . . 7·00 8·00
See also Nos. 1925/30.

1997. Fungi. Nos. 2274/82 of Antigua optd **BARBUDA MAIL**.
1872 75c. "Hygrophoropsis aurantiaca" 90 90
1873 75c. "Hygrophorus bakerensis" 90 90
1874 75c. "Hygrophorus conicus" 90 90
1875 75c. "Hygrophorus miniatus" ("Hygrocybe miniata") 90 90
1876 75c. "Suillus brevipes" . . . 90 90
1877 75c. "Suillus luteus" 90 90
1878 75c. "Suillus granulatus" . . 90 90
1879 75c. "Suillus caerulescens" 90 90
MS1880 Two sheets, each 106×76 mm. (a) $6 "Conocybe filaris". (b) $6 "Hygrocybe flavescens" Set of 2 sheets . . 11·00 12·00

1997. Birds. Nos. 2140/64 of Antigua optd **BARBUDA MAIL**.
1881 75c. Purple-throated carib 65 70
1882 75c. Antillean crested hummingbird 65 70
1883 75c. Bananaquit 65 70
1884 75c. Mangrove cuckoo . . . 65 70
1885 75c. Troupial 65 70
1886 75c. Green-throated carib 65 70
1887 75c. Yellow warbler 65 70
1888 75c. Antillean euphonia ("Blue-hooded Euphonia") 65 70
1889 75c. Scaly-breasted thrasher 65 70
1890 75c. Burrowing owl 65 70
1891 75c. Carib grackle 65 70
1892 75c. Adelaide's warbler . . 65 70
1893 75c. Ring-necked duck . . . 65 70
1894 75c. Ruddy duck 65 70
1895 75c. Green-winged teal . . . 65 70
1896 75c. Wood duck 65 70
1897 75c. Hooded merganser . . 65 70
1898 75c. Lesser scaup 65 70
1899 75c. Black-billed whistling duck ("West Indian Tree Duck") 65 70
1900 75c. Fulvous whistling duck 65 70
1901 75c. Bahama pintail 65 70
1902 75c. Northern shoveler ("Shoveler") 65 70
1903 75c. Masked duck 65 70
1904 75c. American wigeon . . . 65 70
MS1905 Two sheets, each 104×74 mm. (a) $6 Head of purple gallinule. (b) $6 Heads of blue-winged teals Set of 2 sheets 9·00 11·00

1997. Sailing Ships. Nos. 2283/301 of Antigua optd **BARBUDA MAIL**.
1906 15c. H.M.S. "Resolution" (Cook) 65 60
1907 25c. "Mayflower" (Pilgrim Fathers) 65 45
1908 45c. "Santa Maria" (Columbus) 65 40
1909 75c. "Aemilia" (Dutch galleon) 70 60
1910 75c. "Sovereign of the Seas" (English galleon) 70 60
1911 90c. H.M.S. "Victory" (Nelson) 75 60
1912 $1.20 As No. 1909 . . . . 75 85
1913 $1.20 As No. 1910 . . . . 75 85
1914 $1.20 "Royal Louis" (French galleon) 75 85
1915 $1.20 H.M.S. "Royal George" (ship of the line) 75 85
1916 $1.20 "Le Protecteur" (French frigate) 75 85
1917 $1.20 As No. 1911 . . . . 75 85
1918 $1.50 As No. 1908 . . . . 85 95
1919 $1.50 "Victoria" (Magellan) 85 95
1920 $1.50 "Golden Hind" (Drake) 85 95
1921 $1.50 As No. 1907 . . . . 85 95
1922 $1.50 "Griffin" (La Salle) 85 95
1923 $1.50 As No. 1906 . . . . 85 95
MS1924 (a) 102×72 mm. $6 U.S.S. "Constitution" (frigate). (b) 98×67 mm. $6 "Grande Hermine" (Cartier) Set of 2 sheets 7·00 8·00

1997. Golden Wedding of Queen Elizabeth and Prince Philip (2nd issue). Nos. 2474/80 of Antigua optd **BARBUDA MAIL**.
1925 $1 Queen Elizabeth II . . . 1·75 1·75
1926 $1 Royal coat of arms . . . 1·75 1·75
1927 $1 Queen Elizabeth and Prince Philip at reception 1·75 1·75
1928 $1 Queen Elizabeth and Prince Philip in landau . . 1·75 1·75
1929 $1 Balmoral . . . . 1·75 1·75
1930 $1 Prince Philip . . . . . . 1·75 1·75
MS1931 100×71 mm. $6 Queen Elizabeth with Prince Philip in naval uniform . . . . 8·50 9·00

1997. Christmas. Religious Paintings. Nos. 2566/72 of Antigua optd **BARBUDA MAIL**.
1932 15c. "The Angel leaving Tobias and his Family" (Rembrandt) 80 35
1933 25c. "The Resurrection" (Martin Knoller) 90 35
1934 60c. "Astronomy" (Raphael) 1·25 65
1935 75c. "Music-making Angel" (Melozzo da Forli) . . . 1·40 1·00
1936 90c. "Amor" (Parmigianino) 1·60 1·10
1937 $1.20 "Madonna and Child with Saints" (Rosso Fiorentino) . . . . 1·75 1·90
MS1938 Two sheets, each 105×96 mm. (a) $6 "The Wedding of Tobias" (Gianantonio and Francesco Guardi) (horiz). (b) $6 "The Portinari Altarpiece" (Hugo van der Goes) (horiz) Set of 2 sheets . . . . 8·00 9·00

1998. Sea Birds. Nos. 2325/33 of Antigua optd **BARBUDA MAIL**.
1939 75c. Black skimmer . . . . 1·25 1·25
1940 75c. Black-capped petrel . . 1·25 1·25
1941 75c. Sooty tern . . . . . . 1·25 1·25
1942 75c. Royal tern . . . . . . 1·25 1·25
1943 75c. Pomarine skua ("Pomarine Jaegger") . . 1·25 1·25
1944 75c. White-tailed tropic bird 1·25 1·25
1945 75c. Northern gannet . . . 1·25 1·25
1946 75c. Laughing gull . . . . 1·25 1·25
MS1947 Two sheets, each 105×75 mm. (a) $5 Great frigate bird. (b) $6 Brown pelican Set of 2 sheets . . . . 7·50 8·00

1998. Centenary of Radio. Entertainers. Nos. 2372/6 of Antigua optd **BARBUDA MAIL**.
1948 65c. Kate Smith 65 55
1949 75c. Dinah Shore 75 70
1950 90c. Rudy Vallee 90 80
1951 $1.20 Bing Crosby . . . . 1·10 1·25
MS1952 72×104 mm. $6 Jo Stafford (28×42 mm) . . . . 4·50 5·50

1998. Olympic Games, Atlanta (2nd issue). Previous Medal Winners. Nos. 2302/23 of Antigua optd **BARBUDA MAIL**.
1953 65c. Florence Griffith Joyner (U.S.A.) (Gold – track, 1988) 75 75
1954 75c. Olympic Stadium, Seoul (1988) (horiz) 75 75
1955 90c. Allison Jolly and Lynne Jewell (U.S.A.) (Gold – yachting, 1988) (horiz) . . 75 75
1956 90c. Wolfgang Nordwig (Germany) (Gold – pole vaulting, 1972) 75 75
1957 90c. Shirley Strong (Great Britain) (Silver – 100 m hurdles, 1984) . . 75 75
1958 90c. Sergei Bubka (Russia) (Gold – pole vault, 1988) 75 75
1959 90c. Filbert Bayi (Tanzania) (Silver – 3000 m steeplechase, 1980) 75 75
1960 90c. Victor Saneyev (Russia) (Gold – triple jump, 1968, 1972, 1976) 75 75
1961 90c. Silke Renk (Germany) (Gold – javelin, 1992) . . 75 75
1962 90c. Daley Thompson (Great Britain) (Gold – decathlon, 1980, 1984) . . 75 75
1963 90c. Robert Richards (U.S.A.) (Gold – pole vault, 1952, 1956) 75 75
1964 90c. Parry O'Brien (U.S.A.) (Gold – shot put, 1952, 1956) 75 75
1965 90c. Ingrid Kramer (Germany) (Gold – Women's platform diving, 1960) 75 75
1966 90c. Kelly McCormick (U.S.A.) (Silver – Women's springboard diving, 1984) 75 75
1967 90c. Gary Tobian (U.S.A.) (Gold – Men's springboard diving, 1960) 75 75
1968 90c. Greg Louganis (U.S.A.) (Gold – Men's diving, 1984 and 1988) 75 75
1969 90c. Michelle Mitchell (U.S.A.) (Silver – Women's platform diving, 1984 and 1988) 75 75
1970 90c. Zhou Jihong (China) (Gold – Women's platform diving, 1984) . . 75 75
1971 90c. Wendy Wyland (U.S.A.) (Bronze – Women's platform diving, 1984) 75 75
1972 90c. Xu Yanmei (China) (Gold – Women's platform diving, 1988) . . 75 75

1973 90c. Fu Mingxia (China) (Gold – Women's platform diving, 1992) 75 75
1974 $1.20 2000 m tandem cycle race (horiz) 2·00 1·75
MS1975 Two sheets, each 106×76 mm. (a) $5 Bill Toomey (U.S.A.) (Gold – decathlon, 1968) (horiz). (b) $6 Mark Lenzi (U.S.A.) (Gold – Men's springboard diving, 1992) Set of 2 sheets 8·00 9·00

1998. World Cup Football Championship, France. Nos. 2525/39 of Antigua optd **BARBUDA MAIL**.
1976 60c. multicoloured 75 60
1977 75c. brown 75 60
1978 90c. multicoloured 80 65
1979 $1 brown 80 80
1980 $1 brown 80 80
1981 $1 brown 80 80
1982 $1 black 80 80
1983 $1 brown 80 80
1984 $1 brown 80 80
1985 $1 brown 80 80
1986 $1 brown 80 80
1987 $1.20 multicoloured 1·00 1·00
1988 $1.65 multicoloured 1·25 1·40
1989 $1.75 multicoloured 1·40 1·60
MS1990 Two sheets, each 102×127 mm. (a) $6 multicoloured. (b) $6 multicoloured Set of 2 sheets 8·00 9·00

1998. Cavalry through the Ages. Nos. 2359/63 of Antigua optd **BARBUDA MAIL**.
1991 60c. Ancient Egyptian cavalryman 90 90
1992 60c. 13th-century English knight 90 90
1993 60c. 16th-century Spanish lancer 90 90
1994 60c. 18th-century Chinese cavalryman 90 90
MS1995 100×70 mm. $6 19th-century French cuirassier (vert) 5·00 6·00

1998. 50th Anniv of U.N.I.C.E.F. Nos. 2364/7 of Antigua optd **BARBUDA MAIL**.
1996 75c. Girl in red sari 75 75
1997 90c. South American mother and child 85 85
1998 $1.20 Nurse with child 95 1·10
MS1999 114×74 mm. $6 Chinese child 4·50 5·50

1998. 3000th Anniv of Jerusalem. Nos. 2368/71 of Antigua optd **BARBUDA MAIL**.
2000 75c. Tomb of Zachariah and "Verbascum sinuatum" 1·00 80
2001 90c. Pool of Siloam and "Hyacinthus orientalis" 1·25 90
2002 $1.20 Hurva Synagogue and "Ranunculus asiaticus" 1·50 1·50
MS2003 66×80 mm. $6 Model of Herod's Temple and "Cercis siliquastrum" 5·50 5·50

1998. Diana, Princess of Wales Commemoration. Nos. 2573/85 of Antigua optd **BARBUDA MAIL**.
2004 $1.65 Diana, Princess of Wales 1·10 1·00
2005 $1.65 Wearing hoop earrings (red and black) 1·10 1·00
2006 $1.65 Carrying bouquet 1·10 1·00
2007 $1.65 Wearing floral hat 1·10 1·00
2008 $1.65 With Prince Harry 1·10 1·00
2009 $1.65 Wearing white jacket 1·10 1·00
2010 $1.65 In kitchen 1·10 1·00
2011 $1.65 Wearing black and white dress 1·10 1·00
2012 $1.65 Wearing hat (brown and black) 1·10 1·00
2013 $1.65 Wearing floral print dress (brown and black) 1·10 1·00
2014 $1.65 Dancing with John Travolta 1·10 1·00
2015 $1.65 Wearing white hat and jacket 1·10 1·00
MS2016 Two sheets, each 70×100 mm. (a) $6 Wearing red jumper. (b) $6 Wearing black dress for Papal audience (brown and black) Set of 2 sheets 8·00 9·00

1998. Broadway Musical Stars. Nos. 2384/93 of Antigua optd **BARBUDA MAIL**.
2017 $1 Robert Preston ("The Music Man") 75 75
2018 $1 Michael Crawford ("Phantom of the Opera") 75 75
2019 $1 Zero Mostel ("Fiddler on the Roof") 75 75
2020 $1 Patti Lupone ("Evita") 75 75
2021 $1 Raul Julia ("Threepenny Opera") 75 75
2022 $1 Mary Martin ("South Pacific") 75 75
2023 $1 Carol Channing ("Hello Dolly") 75 75
2024 $1 Yul Brynner ("The King and I") 75 75
2025 $1 Julie Andrews ("My Fair Lady") 75 75
MS2026 106×76 mm. $6 Mickey Rooney ("Sugar Babies") 5·00 6·00

1998. 20th Death Anniv of Charlie Chaplin (film star). Nos. 2404/13 of Antigua optd **BARBUDA MAIL**.
2027 $1 Charlie Chaplin as young man 85 75
2028 $1 Pulling face 85 75
2029 $1 Looking over shoulder 85 75
2030 $1 In cap 85 75
2031 $1 In front of star 85 75
2032 $1 In "The Great Dictator" 85 75
2033 $1 With movie camera and megaphone 85 75
2034 $1 Standing in front of camera lens 85 75
2035 $1 Putting on make-up 85 75
MS2036 76×106 mm. $6 Charlie Chaplin 6·00 6·00

1998. Butterflies. Nos. 2414/36 of Antigua optd **BARBUDA MAIL**.
2037 90c. "Charaxes porthos" 1·00 70
2038 $1.10 "Charaxes protoclea protoclea" 1·00 1·00
2039 $1.10 "Byblia ilithyia" 1·00 1·00
2040 $1.10 Black-headed tchagra (bird) 1·00 1·00
2041 $1.10 "Charaxes nobilis" 1·00 1·00
2042 $1.10 "Pseudacraea boisduvali trimeni" 1·00 1·00
2043 $1.10 "Charaxes smaragdalis" 1·00 1·00
2044 $1.10 "Charaxes lasti" 1·00 1·00
2045 $1.10 "Pseudacraea poggei" 1·00 1·00
2046 $1.10 "Graphium colonna" 1·00 1·00
2047 $1.10 Carmine bee eater (bird) 1·00 1·00
2048 $1.10 "Pseudacraea eurytus" 1·00 1·00
2049 $1.10 "Hypolimnas monteironis" 1·00 1·00
2050 $1.10 "Charaxes anticlea" 1·00 1·00
2051 $1.10 "Graphium leonidas" 1·00 1·00
2052 $1.10 "Graphium illyris" 1·00 1·00
2053 $1.10 "Nephronia argia" 1·00 1·00
2054 $1.10 "Graphium policenes" 1·00 1·00
2055 $1.10 "Papilio dardanus" 1·00 1·00
2056 $1.20 "Aethiopana honorius" 1·00 1·10
2057 $1.60 "Charaxes hadrianus" 1·25 1·40
2058 $1.75 "Precis westermanni" 1·40 1·60
MS2059 Three sheets, each 107×76 mm. (a) $6 "Charaxes lactincus" (horiz). (b) $6 "Eupheadra reophron". (c) "Euxantha tiberius") (horiz) Set of 3 sheets 13·00 15·00

1998. Christmas. Dogs. Nos. 2771/8 of Antigua optd **BARBUDA MAIL**.
2060 15c. Border collie 45 35
2061 25c. Dalmatian 55 35
2062 65c. Weimaraner 90 60
2063 75c. Scottish terrier 95 65
2064 90c. Long-haired dachshund 1·00 70
2065 $1.20 Golden retriever 1·25 1·10
2066 $2 Pekingese 1·75 2·25
MS2067 Two sheets, each 75×66 mm. (a) $6 Dalmatian. (b) $6 Jack Russell terrier Set of 2 sheets 11·00 11·00

1999. Lighthouses of the World. Nos. 2612/20 of Antigua optd **BARBUDA MAIL**.
2068 45c. Europa Point Lighthouse, Gibraltar 75 50
2069 65c. Tierra del Fuego, Argentina (horiz) 80 70
2070 75c. Point Loma, California, U.S.A. (horiz) 85 70
2071 90c. Groenpoint, Cape Town, South Africa 95 80
2072 $1 Youghal, Cork, Ireland 1·10 90
2073 $1.20 Launceston, Tasmania, Australia 1·25 1·25
2074 $1.65 Point Abino, Ontario, Canada (horiz) 1·50 1·75
2075 $1.75 Great Inagua, Bahamas (horiz) 1·50 1·75
MS2076 99×70 mm. $6 Cape Hatteras, North Carolina, U.S.A. 6·50 6·50

1999. Endangered Species. Nos. 2457/69 of Antigua optd **BARBUDA MAIL**.
2077 $1.20 Red bishop 1·00 1·10
2078 $1.20 Yellow baboon 1·00 1·10
2079 $1.20 Superb starling 1·00 1·10
2080 $1.20 Ratel 1·00 1·10
2081 $1.20 Hunting dog 1·00 1·10
2082 $1.20 Serval 1·00 1·10
2083 $1.65 Okapi 1·10 1·25
2084 $1.65 Giant forest squirrel 1·10 1·25
2085 $1.65 Lesser masked weaver 1·10 1·25
2086 $1.65 Small-spotted genet 1·10 1·25
2087 $1.65 Yellow-billed stork 1·10 1·25
2088 $1.65 Red-headed agama 1·10 1·25
MS2089 Three sheets, each 106×76 mm. (a) $6 South African crowned crane. (b) $6 Bat-eared fox. (c) $6 Malachite kingfisher Set of 3 sheets 12·00 14·00

1999. "Pacific 97" International Stamp Exhibition, San Francisco. Death Centenary of Heinrich von Stephan (founder of the U.P.U.). Nos. 2481/4 of Antigua optd **BARBUDA MAIL**.
2090 $1.75 blue 1·25 1·50
2091 $1.75 brown 1·25 1·50
2092 $1.75 mauve 1·25 1·50
MS2093 82×119 mm. $6 violet 3·75 4·50
DESIGNS: No. 2090, Kaiser Wilhelm I and Heinrich von Stephan; 2091, Von Stephan and Mercury; 2092, Carrier pigeon and loft; **MS**2093 Von Stephan and 15th-century Basel messenger.

1999. 175th Anniv of Brothers Grimm's Third Collection of Fairy Tales. *Cinderella*. Nos. 2485/8 of Antigua optd **BARBUDA MAIL**.
2094 $1.75 The Ugly Sisters and their Mother 1·50 1·75
2095 $1.75 Cinderella and her Fairy Godmother 1·50 1·75
2096 $1.75 Cinderella and the Prince 1·50 1·75
MS2097 124×96 mm. $6 Cinderella trying on slipper 4·50 4·75

1999. Orchids of the World. Nos. 2502/24 of Antigua optd **BARBUDA MAIL**.
2098 45c. *Odontoglossum cervantesii* 65 35
2099 65c. *Phalaenopsis* Medford Star 75 65
2100 75c. *Vanda* Motes Resplendent 85 65
2101 90c. *Odontonia* Debutante 90 70
2102 $1 *Iwanagaara* Apple Blossom 1·00 80
2103 $1.65 *Cattleya* Sophia Martin 1·25 1·40
2104 $1.65 Dogface Butterfly 1·25 1·40
2105 $1.65 *Laeliocattleya* Mini Purple 1·25 1·40
2106 $1.65 *Cymbidium* Showgirl 1·25 1·40
2107 $1.65 *Brassolaeliocattleya* Dorothy Bertsch 1·25 1·40
2108 $1.65 *Disa blackii* 1·25 1·40
2109 $1.65 *Paphiopedilum leeanum* 1·25 1·40
2110 $1.65 *Paphiopedilum macranthum* 1·25 1·40
2111 $1.65 *Brassocattleya* Angel Lace 1·25 1·40
2112 $1.65 *Saphrolae liocattleya* Precious Stones 1·25 1·40
2113 $1.65 Orange Theope Butterfly 1·25 1·40
2114 $1.65 *Promenaea xanthina* 1·25 1·40
2115 $1.65 *Lycasle macrobulbon* 1·25 1·40
2116 $1.65 *Amestella philippinensis* 1·25 1·40
2117 $1.65 *Masdevallia* Machu Picchu 1·25 1·40
2118 $1.65 *Phalaenopsis* Zuma Urchin 1·25 1·40
2119 $2 *Dendrobium victoria-reginae* 1·50 2·00
MS2120 Two sheets, each 76×106 mm. (a) $6 *Miltonia* Seine. (b) $6 *Paphiopedilum gratrixanum* Set of 2 sheets 9·00 9·50

1999. 50th Death Anniv of Paul Harris (founder of Rotary International). No. 2472/3 of Antigua optd **BARBUDA MAIL**.
2121 $1.65 Paul Harris and James Grant 2·00 2·50
MS2122 78×107 mm. $6 Group study exchange, New Zealand 4·00 5·00

1999. Royal Wedding. Nos. 2912/16 of Antigua optd **BARBOUDA MAIL**.
2123 $3 Sophie Rhys-Jones 2·00 2·25
2124 $3 Sophie and Prince Edward 2·00 2·25
2125 $3 Prince Edward 2·00 2·25
MS2126 108×78 mm. $6 Prince Edward with Sophie Rhys-Jones and Windsor Castle 4·75 4·75
All examples of Nos. 2123/5 show the incorrect country overprint as above.

1999. Fungi. Nos. 2489/501 of Antigua optd **BARBUDA MAIL**.
2127 45c. *Marasmius rotula* 80 35
2128 65c. *Cantharellus cibarius* 95 55
2129 70c. *Lepiota cristata* 1·10 60
2130 90c. *Auricularia mesenterica* 1·25 70
2131 $1 *Pholiota alnicola* 1·25 1·00
2132 $1.65 *Leccinum aurantiacum* 1·40 1·50
2133 $1.75 *Entoloma serrulatum* 1·40 1·50
2134 $1.75 *Panaeolus sphinctrinus* 1·40 1·50
2135 $1.75 *Volvariella bombycina* 1·40 1·50
2136 $1.75 *Conocybe percincta* 1·40 1·50
2137 $1.75 *Pluteus cervinus* 1·40 1·50
2138 $1.75 *Russula foetens* 1·40 1·50
MS2139 Two sheets, each 106×76 mm. (a) $6 *Amanita cothurnata*. (b) $6 *Panellus serotinus* Set of 2 sheets 9·00 9·50

1999. 1st Death Anniv of Diana, Princess of Wales. No. 2753 of Antigua optd **BARBUDA MAIL**.
2140 $1.20 Diana, Princess of Wales 1·00 1·00

1999. Railway Locomotives of the World. Nos. 2553/65 of Antigua optd **BARBUDA MAIL**.
2141 $1.65 Original drawing by Richard Trevithick, 1803 1·10 1·10
2142 $1.65 William Hedley's *Puffing Billy*, (1813–14) 1·10 1·10
2143 $1.65 Crampton locomotive of French Nord Railway, 1858 1·10 1·10
2144 $1.65 Lawrence Machine Shop locomotive, U.S.A., 1860 1·10 1·10
2145 $1.65 Natchez and Hamburg Railway steam locomotive *Mississippi*, U.S.A., 1834 1·10 1·10
2146 $1.65 Bury "Coppernob" locomotive, Furness Railway, 1846 1·10 1·10
2147 $1.65 David Joy's *Jenny Lind*, 1847 1·10 1·10
2148 $1.65 Schenectady Atlantic locomotive, U.S.A., 1899 1·10 1·10
2149 $1.65 Kitson Class 1800 tank locomotive, Japan, 1881 1·10 1·10
2150 $1.65 Pennsylvania Railroad express freight 1·10 1·10
2151 $1.65 Karl Golsdorf's 4 cylinder locomotive, Austria 1·10 1·10
2152 $1.65 Series "E" locomotive, Russia, 1930 1·10 1·10
MS2153 Two sheets, each 72×100 mm. (a) $6 George Stephenson's "Patentee" Type locomotive, 1843. (b) $6 Brunel's trestle bridge over River Lynher, Cornwall 7·50 8·00

1999. 175th Anniv of Cedar Hall Moravian Church. Nos. 2605/11 of Antigua optd **BARBUDA MAIL**.
2154 20c. First Church and Manse, 1822–40 35 35
2155 45c. Cedar Hall School, 1840 45 30
2156 75c. Hugh A. King, minister, 1945–53 65 45
2157 90c. Present Church building 75 50
2158 $1.20 Water tank, 1822 1·00 1·00
2159 $2 Former Manse, demolished 1978 1·40 2·00
MS2160 100×70 mm. $6 Present church building (different) (50×37 mm) 3·75 4·50

1999. Christmas. Religious Paintings. Nos. 2945/51 of Antigua optd **BARBUDA MAIL**.
2161 15c. multicoloured 25 20
2162 25c. black, stone and yellow 30 20
2163 45c. multicoloured 45 30
2164 60c. multicoloured 70 35
2165 $2 multicoloured 1·50 2·00
2166 $4 black, stone and yellow 2·50 3·50
MS2167 76×106 mm. $6 multicoloured 3·50 4·00

1999. Centenary of Thomas Oliver Robinson Memorial School. Nos. 2634/40 of Antigua optd **BARBUDA MAIL**.
2168 20c. green and black 25 25
2169 45c. multicoloured 45 30
2170 65c. green and black 65 40
2171 75c. multicoloured 70 50
2172 90c. multicoloured 80 60
2173 $1.20 brown, green and black 90 1·25
MS2174 106×76 mm. $6 brown 3·75 4·50

2000. Cats and Dogs. Nos. 2540/52 of Antigua optd **BARBUDA MAIL**.
2175 $1.65 Scottish fold kitten 1·25 1·25
2176 $1.65 Japanese bobtail 1·25 1·25
2177 $1.65 Tabby manx 1·25 1·25
2178 $1.65 Bicolor American shorthair 1·25 1·25
2179 $1.65 Sorel Abyssinian 1·25 1·25
2180 $1.65 Himalayan blue point 1·25 1·25
2181 $1.65 Dachshund 1·25 1·25
2182 $1.65 Staffordshire terrier 1·25 1·25
2183 $1.65 Shar-pei 1·25 1·25
2184 $1.65 Beagle 1·25 1·25
2185 $1.65 Norfolk terrier 1·25 1·25
2186 $1.65 Golden retriever 1·25 1·25
MS2187 Two sheets, each 107×77 mm. (a) $6 Red tabby (vert). (b) $6 Siberian husky (vert) 9·50 9·50

2000. Fishes. Nos. 2586/604 of Antigua optd **BARBUDA MAIL**.
2188 75c. Yellow damselfish 75 50
2189 90c. Barred hamlet 80 55
2190 $1 Yellow-tailed damselfish ("Jewelfish") 90 70
2191 $1.20 Blue-headed wrasse 1·10 1·00
2192 $1.50 Queen angelfish 1·25 1·25
2193 $1.65 Jackknife-fish 1·25 1·25
2194 $1.65 Spot-finned hogfish 1·25 1·25
2195 $1.65 Sergeant major 1·25 1·25
2196 $1.65 Neon goby 1·25 1·25
2197 $1.65 Jawfish 1·25 1·25
2198 $1.65 Flamefish 1·25 1·25
2199 $1.65 Rock beauty 1·25 1·25
2200 $1.65 Yellow-tailed snapper 1·25 1·25
2201 $1.65 Creole wrasse 1·25 1·25
2202 $1.65 Slender filefish 1·25 1·25
2203 $1.65 Long-spined squirrelfish 1·25 1·25
2204 $1.65 Royal gramma ("Fairy Basslet") 1·25 1·25
2205 $1.75 Queen triggerfish 1·40 1·40
MS2206 Two sheets, each 80×110 mm. (a) $6 Porkfish. (b) $6 Black-capped basslet 9·00 10·00

2000. Ships of the World. Nos. 2679/85 of Antigua optd **BARBUDA MAIL**.
2207 $1.75 *Savannah* (paddle-steamer) 1·25 1·25
2208 $1.75 Viking longship 1·25 1·25
2209 $1.75 Greek galley 1·25 1·25
2210 $1.75 Sailing clipper 1·25 1·25
2211 $1.75 Dhow 1·25 1·25
2212 $1.75 Fishing catboat 1·25 1·25
MS2213 Three sheets, each 100×70 mm. (a) $6 13th-century English warship (41×22 mm). (b) $6 Sailing dory (22×41 mm). (c) $6 Baltimore clipper (41×22 mm) 11·00 13·00

2000. Modern Aircraft. Nos. 2700/12 of Antigua optd **BARBUDA MAIL**.
2214 $1.65 Lockheed-Boeing General Dynamics Yf-22 1·25 1·25
2215 $1.65 Dassault-Breguet Rafale BO 1 1·25 1·25
2216 $1.65 MiG 29 1·25 1·25
2217 $1.65 Dassault-Breguet Mirage 2000D 1·25 1·25
2218 $1.65 Rockwell B-1B "Lancer" 1·25 1·25
2219 $1.65 McDonnell-Douglas C-17A 1·25 1·25
2220 $1.65 Space Shuttle 1·25 1·25

2221 $1.65 SAAB "Grippen" . . 1·25 1·25
2222 $1.65 Eurofighter EF-2000 1·25 1·25
2223 $1.65 Sukhoi SU 27 . . . . 1·25 1·25
2224 $1.65 Northrop B-2 . . . . 1·25 1·25
2225 $1.65 Lockheed F-117 "Nighthawk" . . . . . . 1·25 1·25
MS2226 Two sheets, each 110×85 mm. (a) $6 F18 Hornet. (b) $6 Sukhoi SU 35 . . . . . 9·50 10·00

BARWANI Pt. 1

A State of Central India. Now uses Indian stamps.

12 pies = 1 anna; 16 annas = 1 rupee.

1 Rana Ranjit Singh

2

1921.
5 **1** ¼a. green . . . . 20·00 65·00
19 ¼a. blue . . . . 1·00 11·00
37 B ¼a. black . . . . 3·75 29·00
18 ¼a. pink . . . . 1·75 12·00
4 ½a. blue . . . . 17·00 £140
29 ½a. green . . . . 2·75 12·00
10 **2** 1a. red . . . . 2·25 19·00
39 B 1a. brown . . . . 11·00 24·00
11 2a. purple . . . . 2·25 22·00
41 B 2a. red . . . . 24·00 95·00
31 4a. orange . . . . 65·00 £170
42Ba – 4a. green . . . . 13·00 40·00
DESIGN: 4a. Another portrait of Rana Ranjit Singh.

4 Rana Devi Singh

5

1932.
32A **4** ¼a. slate . . . . 1·75 19·00
33A ½a. green . . . . 2·75 19·00
34A 1a. brown . . . . 3·00 18·00
35A 2a. purple . . . . 3·50 32·00
36A 4a. olive . . . . 6·00 35·00

1938.
43 **5** 1a. brown . . . . 30·00 55·00

BASUTOLAND Pt. 1

An African territory under British protection, N.E. of Cape Province. Self-Government introduced on 1 April 1965. Attained independence on 4 October 1966, when the country was renamed Lesotho.

1933. 12 pence = 1 shilling;
20 shillings = 1 pound.
1961. 100 cents = 1 rand.

1 King George V, Nile Crocodile and Mountains

1933.
1 **1** ½d. green . . . . 1·00 1·75
2 1d. red . . . . 75 1·25
3 2d. purple . . . . 1·00 80
4 3d. blue . . . . 75 1·25
5 4d. grey . . . . 2·00 7·00
6 6d. yellow . . . . 2·25 1·75
7 1s. orange . . . . 2·25 4·50
8 2s.6d. brown . . . . 21·00 45·00
9 5s. violet . . . . 50·00 70·00
10 10s. olive £130 £140

1935. Silver Jubilee. As T **13** of Antigua.
11 1d. blue and red . . . . . . 55 1·00
12 2d. blue and grey . . . . . . 65 1·25
13 3d. brown and blue . . . . . 3·75 4·25
14 6d. grey and purple . . . . . 3·75 4·25

1937. Coronation. As T **2** of Aden.
15 1d. red . . . . 35 1·00
16 2d. purple . . . . 50 1·00
17 3d. blue . . . . 60 1·00

1938. As T **1**, but portrait of King George VI.
18 ½d. green . . . . 30 1·25
19 1d. red 50 70
20 1½d. blue 40 50
21 2d. purple 30 60
22 3d. blue . . . . 30 1·25
23 4d. grey . . . . 1·50 3·50
24 6d. yellow . . . . 60 1·50
25 1s. orange . . . . 60 1·00
26 2s.6d. brown . . . . 9·00 8·50
27 5s. violet . . . . 24·00 9·50
28 10s. olive . . . . 24·00 17·00

1945. Victory. Stamps of South Africa optd **Basutoland**. Alternate stamps inscr in English or Afrikaans.
29 **55** 1d. brown and red 40 80
30 2d. blue and violet 40 50
31 3d. blue 40 70
Prices are for bi-lingual pairs.

5 King George VI and Queen Elizabeth

1947. Royal Visit.
32 – 1d. red 10 10
33 **5** 2d. green 10 10
34 – 3d. blue 10 10
35 – 1s. mauve 15 10
DESIGNS—VERT: 1d. King George VI. HORIZ: 3d. Queen Elizabeth II as Princess and Princess Margaret; 1s. The Royal Family.

1948. Silver Wedding. As T **10/11** of Aden.
36 1½d. blue 20 10
37 10s. green . . . . 30·00 27·00

1949. U.P.U. As T **20/23** of Antigua.
38 1½d. blue . . . . 20 1·50
39 3d. blue . . . . 1·75 2·00
40 6d. orange . . . . 1·00 2·50
41 1s. brown . . . . 50 1·25

1953. Coronation. As T **13** of Aden.
42 2d. black and purple 55 50

8 Qiloane

9 Mohair (Shearing Goats)

1954.
43 **8** ½d. black and sepia 10 10
44 – 1d. black and green 10 10
45 – 2d. blue and orange 60 10
46 – 3d. sage and red 80 30
47 – 4½d. indigo and blue 70 15
48 – 6d. brown and green . . . . 1·25 15
49 – 1s. bronze and purple . . . . 1·25 30
50 – 1s.3d. brown and turquoise 18·00 5·50
51 – 2s.6d. blue and red . . . . . 18·00 7·50
52 – 5s. black and red . . . . . . 5·50 8·50
53 **9** 10s. black and purple . . . . 20·00 23·00
DESIGNS—HORIZ: 1d. Orange River; 2d. Mosuto horseman; 3d. Basuto household; 4½d. Maletsunyane Falls; 6d. Herd-boy playing lesiba; 1s. Pastoral scene; 1s.3d. De Havilland Comet 1 airplane over Lancers' Gap; 2s.6d. Old Fort, Leribe; 5s. Mission cave house.

1959. No. 45 Surch ½**d.** and bar.
54 ½d. on 2d. blue and orange . . 10 15

20 "Chief Moshoeshoe I" (engraving by Delangle)

26 Basuto Household

1959. Inauguration of National Council.
55 **20** 3d. black and olive 30 10
56 – 1s. red and green 30 10
57 – 1s.3d. blue and orange . . . 50 45
DESIGNS: 1s. Council house; 1s.3d. Mosuto horseman.

1961. Nos. 43/53 surch.
58 **8** ½c. on ½d. black and sepia 10 10
59 – 1c. on 1d. black and green 10 10
60 – 2c. on 2d. blue and orange 10 10
61 – 2½c. on 3d. green and red 10 10
62 – 3½c. on 4½d. indigo and blue 10 10
63 – 5c. on 6d. brown and green 10 10
64 – 10c. on 1s. green and purple 10 10
65 – 12½c. on 1s.3d. brown and turquoise . . . . 2·00 30
66 – 25c. on 2s.6d. blue and red 30 30
67a – 50c. on 5s. black and red . . 1·00 1·60
68b **9** 1r. on 10s. black and purple 11·00 12·00

1961. As 1954 but value in new currency as in T **26**.
69 **8** ½c. black and brown 10 20
70 – 1c. black and green (as 1d.) 10 40
71 – 2c. blue and orange (as 2d.) 50 1·40
86 **26** 2½c. green and red 15 15
73 – 3½c. indigo and blue (as 4½d.) . . . . 30 1·50
88 – 5c. brown and green (as 6d.) 30 40
75 – 10c. green and purple (as 1s.) 30 40
90 – 12½c. brown & grn (as 1s.3d.) . . . . 3·00 1·50
77 – 25c. blue and red (as 2s.6d.) 6·50 6·50
92 – 50c. black and red (as 5s.) 7·25 11·00
79 **9** 1r. black and purple . . . . 29·00 13·00

1963. Freedom from Hunger. As T **28** of Aden.
80 12½c. violet 40 15

1963. Centenary of Red Cross. As T **33** of Antigua.
81 2½c. red and black 20 10
82 12½c. red and blue 80 60

28 Mosotho Woman and Child

1965. New Constitution. Inscr "SELF GOVERNMENT 1965". Multicoloured.
94 2½c. Type **28** 20 10
95 3½c. Maseru border post . . . 25 20
96 5c. Mountain scene 25 20
97 12½c. Legislative Buildings . . 45 70

1965. Centenary of I.T.U. As T **36** of Antigua.
98 1c. red and purple 15 10
99 20c. blue and brown 35 30

1965. I.C.Y. As T **37** of Antigua.
100 ½c. purple and turquoise . . . 10 10
101 12½c. green and lavender . . 45 35

1966. Churchill Commemoration. As T **38** of Antigua.
102 1c. blue 15 30
103 2½c. green 35 10
104 10c. brown 55 30
105 22½c. violet 80 60

OFFICIAL STAMPS

1934. Nos. 1/3 and 6 optd **OFFICIAL**.
O1 **1** ½d. green £4000 £3500
O2 1d. red £1600 £1000
O3 2d. purple £1000 £550
O4 6d. yellow £11000 £4750

POSTAGE DUE STAMPS

1933. As Type D **1** of Barbados.
D1b 1d. red . . . . 1·00 2·25
D2a 2d. violet . . . . 30 12·00

D 2

1956.
D3 **D 2** 1d. red . . . . 30 3·00
D4 2d. violet . . . . 30 6·00

1961. Surch.
D5 **D 2** 1c. on 1d. red 10 35
D6 1c. on 2d. violet 10 35
D7 5c. on 2d. violet 15 45
D8 – 5c. on 2d. violet (No. D2a) . . . . 1·00 6·50

1964. As Type D **2**, but value in decimal currency.
D 9 1c. red . . . . 2·50 15·00
D10 5c. violet . . . . 2·50 15·00

For later issues see **LESOTHO**.

BATUM Pt. 1

Batum, a Russian port on the Black Sea, had been taken by Turkish troops during the First World War. Following the Armistice, British Forces occupied the town on 1 December 1918. Batum was handed over to the National Republic of Georgia on 7 July 1920.

100 kopeks = 1 rouble.

1 Aloe Tree

БАТУМ. ОБ.

Руб 10 Руб

(2)

1919. Imperf.
1 **1** 5k. green . . . . 6·50 13·00
2 10k. blue . . . . 6·50 13·00
3 50k. yellow . . . . 2·75 4·00
4 1r. brown . . . . 4·25 4·25
5 3r. violet . . . . 9·50 15·00
6 5r. brown . . . . 10·00 22·00

1919. Arms types of Russia surch as T **2**. Imperf (Nos. 7/8), perf (Nos. 9/10).
7 10r. on 1k. orange . . . . . 48·00 60·00
8 10r. on 3k. red . . . . 20·00 25·00
9 10r. on 5k. purple £375 £375
10 10r. on 10 on 7k. blue £325 £325

1919. T **1** optd **BRITISH OCCUPATION**.
11 **1** 5k. green . . . . 13·00 12·00
12 10k. blue . . . . 13·00 12·00
13 25k. yellow . . . . 13·00 12·00
14 1r. blue . . . . 3·75 11·00
15 2r. pink . . . . 1·00 4·00
16 3r. violet . . . . 1·00 4·00
17 5r. brown . . . . 1·25 4·00
18 7r. red . . . . 4·25 7·00

1919. Arms types of Russia surch with Russian inscr, **BRITISH OCCUPATION** and new value.
19 10r. on 3k. red . . . . 16·00 20·00
20a 15r. on 1k. orange . . . . . 42·00 48·00
29 25r. on 5k. purple . . . . . 40·00 42·00
30a 25r. on 10 on 7k. blue . . . 65·00 70·00
31a 25r. on 20 on 14k. red and blue . . . . 65·00 70·00
32a 25r. on 25k. purple and green 90·00 95·00
33 25r. on 50k. green and purple 60·00 70·00
21 50r. on 1k. orange £375 £400
34 50r. on 2k. green . . . . . . 95·00 £100
35 50r. on 3k. red . . . . 95·00 £100
36 50r. on 4k. red . . . . 85·00 90·00
37 50r. on 5k. purple . . . . . 65·00 70·00
27 50r. on 10k. blue £1100 £1200
28 50r. on 15k. blue and brown £475 £550

1920. Romanov type of Russia surch with Russian inscr, **BRITISH OCCUPATION** and new value.
41 50r. on 4k. red . . . . 55·00 70·00

1920. Nos. 11, 13 and 3 surch with new value (50r. with **BRITISH OCCUPATION** also).
42 **1** 25r. on 5k. green . . . . . 29·00 30·00
43 25r. on 25k. yellow . . . . 23·00 24·00
44a 50r. on 50k. yellow . . . . 14·00 15·00

1920. T **1** optd **BRITISH OCCUPATION**.
45 **1** 1r. brown . . . . 1·00 8·00
46 2r. blue . . . . 1·00 8·00
47 3r. pink . . . . 1·25 8·00
48 5r. black . . . . 1·00 8·00
49 7r. yellow . . . . 1·00 8·00
50 10r. green . . . . 1·00 8·00
51 15r. violet . . . . 1·50 9·50
52 25r. red . . . . 1·10 9·00
53 50r. blue . . . . 1·50 12·00

BAVARIA Pt. 7

In S. Germany. A kingdom till 1918, then a republic. Incorporated into Germany in 1920.

1849. 60 kreuzer = 1 gulden.
1874. 100 pfennig = 1 mark.

1

2 (Circle cut)

1849. Imperf.
1 **1** 1k. black £650 £1600

1849. Imperf. Circle cut by labels.
3 **2** 3k. blue . . . . 38·00 2·75
23 3k. red . . . . 38·00 4·50
7 6k. brown £5500 £170

1850. Imperf. As T **2**, but circle not cut.
8a **2** 1k. red . . . . 70·00 16·00
21 1k. yellow . . . . 50·00 17·00
11 6k. brown . . . . 40·00 2·25
25 6k. blue . . . . 50·00 7·00
16 9k. green . . . . 50·00 11·50
28 9k. brown . . . . 90·00 11·50
18 12k. red £100 £120
31 12k. green . . . . 75·00 50·00
19 18k. yellow £100 £180
32 18k. red £120 £375

3

6

8

1867. Imperf.
34 **3** 1k. green . . . . 50·00 8·40
37 3k. red . . . . 46·00 1·75
39 6k. blue . . . . 35·00 17·00
41 6k. brown . . . . 65·00 38·00
43 7k. blue . . . . £325 9·00
46 9k. brown . . . . 40·00 27·00
48 12k. mauve . . . . £300 80·00

50 18k. red £110 £150
65 6 1m. mauve £550 65·00

1870. Perf.
51A 3 1k. green 10·00 1·25
69 3k. red 70 3·50
55A 6k. brown 26·00 25·00
56A 7k. blue 2·40 2·10
59A 9k. brown 4·00 3·25
60A 10k. yellow 4·50 10·00
61A 12k. mauve £300 £950
63A 18k. red 8·00 10·00

1876. Perf.
120 8 2pf. grey 1·25 40
103 3pf. green 8·25 1·75
121 3pf. brown 15 20
122 5pf. green 15 20
107 5pf. mauve 14·50 1·25
123 10pf. red 30 20
124 20pf. blue 30 20
114 25pf. brown 25·00 5·25
125 25pf. orange 20 40
126 30pf. olive 35 60
127 40pf. yellow 35 70
86 50pf. red 40·00 4·50
117 50pf. brown 50·00 3·25
128 50pf. purple 25 85
129 80pf. mauve 1·75 2·75
100 6 1m. mauve 2·00 70
101a 2m. orange 3·00 3·75
136 3m. brown 6·75 28·00
137 5m. green 6·75 28·00

11 13 Prince Luitpold

1911. Prince Regent Luitpold's 90th Birthday.
138c 11 3pf. brown on drab 20 20
139c 5pf. green on green 20 20
140d 10pf. red on buff 20 20
141b 20pf. blue on blue 1·75 40
142a 25pf. deep brown on buff 2·40 1·25
143a – 30pf. orange on buff 1·40 75
144a – 40pf. olive on buff 2·40 70
145a – 50pf. red on drab 2·25 1·40
146 – 60pf. green on buff 2·25 1·40
147a – 80pf. violet on drab 7·75 4·00
148a 13 1m. brown on drab 2·25 1·00
149a 2m. green on green 2·25 6·00
150a 3m. red on buff 12·00 17·00
151 5m. blue on buff 17·00 22·00
152 10m. orange on yellow 27·00 40·00
153 20m. brown on yellow 17·00 19·00
The 30 pf. to 80 pf. values are similar to Type **11**, but larger.

14

1911. 25th Anniv of Regency of Prince Luitpold.
154 14 5pf. yellow, green & black 50 70
155 10pf. yellow, red & black 65 1·40

15 King Ludwig III 16

1914. Imperf or perf.
171A 15 2pf. slate 15 70
172A 2½ on 2pf. slate 15 70
173A 3pf. brown 15 65
175A 5pf. green 15 65
176A 7½pf. green 15 70
178A 10pf. red 20 65
179A 15pf. red 20 65
181A 20pf. blue 20 90
183A 25pf. grey 30 70
184A 30pf. orange 30 70
185A 40pf. olive 30 70
186A 50pf. brown 25 70
187A 60pf. green 2·00 70
188A 80pf. violet 20 90
189A 16 1m. brown 30 90
190A 2m. violet 40 1·60
191A 3m. red 55 3·75
192A – 5m. blue 80 7·00
193A – 10m. green 2·75 38·00
194A – 20m. brown 5·25 48·00
The 5, 10 and 20m. are larger.

1919. Peoples' State Issue. Overprinted **Volksstaat Bayern**. Imperf or perf.
195A 15 3pf. brown 20 65
196A 5pf. green 25 65
197A 7½pf. green 25 65
198A 10pf. lake 25 65
199A 15pf. red 25 65
200A 20pf. blue 25 65
201A 25pf. grey 25 65
202A 30pf. orange 25 65
203A 35pf. orange 25 1·40
204A 40pf. olive 25 75
205A 50pf. brown 25 75
206A 60pf. turquoise 25 1·00
207A 75pf. brown 25 85
208A 80pf. violet 25 70
209A 16 1m. brown 25 90
210A 2m. violet 45 1·40
211A 3m. red 65 4·00
212A – 5m. blue (No. 192) 1·40 10·50
213A – 10m. green (No. 193) 1·75 21·00
214A – 20m. brown (No. 194) 2·75 28·00

1919. 1st Free State Issue. Stamps of Germany (inscr "DEUTSCHES REICH") optd **Freistaat Bayern**.
215 24 2½pf. grey 30 55
216 10 3pf. brown 30 55
217 5pf. green 30 55
218 24 7½pf. orange 30 55
219 10 10pf. red 30 90
220 24 15pf. violet 30 70
221 10 20pf. blue 30 55
222 25pf. black & red on yell 30 1·25
223 24 35pf. brown 30 1·40
224 10 40pf. black and red 30 1·40
225 75pf. black and green 70 2·10
226 80pf. black & red on rose 70 2·50
227 12 1m. red 85 4·75
228 13 2m. blue 2·00 7·00
229 14 3m. black 2·00 11·00
230 15 5m. red and black 1·75 11·00

1919. 2nd Free State Issue. Stamps of Bavaria overprinted **Freistaat Bayern**. Imperf or perf.
231A 15 3pf. brown 15 1·10
232A 5pf. green 15 60
233A 7½pf. green 15 12·00
234A 10pf. lake 15 60
235A 15pf. red 15 60
236A 20pf. blue 15 60
237A 25pf. grey 15 1·10
238A 30pf. orange 15 2·00
239A 40pf. olive 15 11·50
240A 50pf. brown 15 1·40
241A 60pf. turquoise 30 11·50
242A 75pf. brown 55 11·50
243A 80pf. violet 30 2·75
244A 16 1m. brown 30 2·10
245A 2m. violet 40 4·25
246A 3m. red 55 6·00
247A – 5m. blue (No. 192) 70 15·00
248A – 10m. green (No. 193) 70 27·00
249A – 20m. brown (No. 194) 3·00 55·00

1919. War Wounded. Surch **5 Pf. fur Kriegsbeschadigte Freistaat Bayern**. Perf.
250 15 10pf.+5pf. lake 45 1·90
251 15pf.+5pf. red 45 2·00
252 20pf.+5pf. blue 45 2·50

1920. Surch **Freistaat Bayern** and value. Imperf or perf.
253A 16 1m.25pf. on 1m. green 25 90
254A 1m.50pf. on 1m. orange 35 2·40
255A 2m.50pf. on 1m. slate 50 3·50

1920. No. 121 surch **20** in four corners.
256 8 20 on 3pf. brown 15 1·10

26 27 28

29 30

1920.
257 26 5pf. green 15 55
258 10pf. orange 15 55
259 15pf. red 15 55
260 27 20pf. violet 15 55
261 30pf. blue 15 1·50
262 40pf. brown 15 1·50
263 28 50pf. red 15 1·60
264 60pf. turquoise 15 1·90
265 75pf. red 15 2·40
266 29 1m. red and grey 55 2·40
267 1¼m. blue and brown 35 2·40
268 1½m. green and grey 35 2·75
269 2½m. black and grey 45 15·00
270 30 3m. blue 80 12·00
271 5m. orange 95 13·50
272 10m. green 1·75 18·00
273 20m. black 2·00 28·00

OFFICIAL STAMPS

O 18

1916.
O195 O 18 3pf. brown 15 35
O196 5pf. green 15 35
O197 7½pf. green on green 20 50
O198 7½pf. green 15·00 15
O199 10pf. red 15 15
O200 15pf. red on buff 15 15
O201 15pf. red 45 1·60
O202 20pf. blue on blue 1·10 2·00
O203 20pf. blue 40 15
O204 25pf. grey 50 15
O205 30pf. orange 15 15
O206 60pf. turquoise 45 50
O207 1m. purple on buff 1·25 2·00
O208 1m. purple 4·25 £450

1919. Optd **Volksstaat Bayern**.
O215 O 18 3pf. brown 20 5·25
O216 5pf. green 20 70
O217 7½pf. green 20 65
O218 10pf. red 20 65
O219 15pf. red 25 60
O220 20pf. blue 20 65
O221 25pf. grey 20 85
O222 30pf. orange 20 85
O223 35pf. orange 20 85
O224 50pf. olive 20 85
O225 60pf. turquoise 20 2·75
O226 75pf. brown 25 1·75
O227 1m. purple on buff 70 70
O228 1m. purple 3·00 £350

O 31 O 32 O 33

1920.
O274 O 31 5pf. green 15 2·50
O275 10pf. orange 15 2·50
O276 15pf. red 15 2·50
O277 20pf. violet 15 2·50
O278 30pf. blue 15 8·00
O279 40pf. brown 15 8·00
O280 O 32 50pf. red 15 20·00
O281 60pf. green 15 10·00
O282 70pf. lilac 15 23·00
O283 75pf. red 15 27·00
O284 80pf. blue 15 27·00
O285 90pf. olive 15 45·00
O286 O 33 1m. brown 15 35·00
O287 1¼m. green 15 50·00
O288 1½m. red 15 50·00
O289 2½m. blue 15 55·00
O290 3m. lake 55 80·00
O291 5m. green 4·75 90·00

POSTAGE DUE STAMPS

D 6

1862. Inscr "Bayer. Posttaxe" at top. Imperf.
D34 D 6 3k. black £110 £325

1870. As Type D 6, but inscr "Bayr. Posttaxe" at top. Perf.
D65B D 6 1k. black 10·50 £650
D66B 3k. black 10·50 £400

1876. Optd **Vom Empfanger zahlbar.**
D130a 8 2pf. grey 60 2·00
D131a 3pf. grey 40 1·40
D132a 5pf. grey 85 3·25
D133a 10pf. grey 55 70

1895. No. D131a surch **2** in each corner.
D134 8 2 on 3pf. grey † £40000

RAILWAY OFFICIALS' STAMPS

1908. Stamps of 1876 optd **E.**
R133 8 3pf. brown 1·75 3·50
R134 5pf. green 40 30
R135 10pf. red 40 15
R136 20pf. blue 70 70
R137 50pf. purple 7·75 7·00

BECHUANALAND Pt. 1

A colony and protectorate in Central S. Africa. British Bechuanaland (colony) was annexed to Cape of Good Hope in 1895. Internal Self-Government in the protectorate was introduced on 1 March 1965. Attained independence on 30 September 1966, when the country was renamed Botswana.

1885. 12 pence = 1 shilling;
20 shillings = 1 pound.
1961. 100 cents = 1 rand.

A. BRITISH BECHUANALAND

1885. Stamps of Cape of Good Hope ("Hope" seated) optd **British Bechuanaland.**
4 6 ½d. black 7·00 12·00
38 1d. red 2·25 2·25
32 2d. bistre 3·25 2·25
2 3d. red 35·00 45·00
3 4d. blue 55·00 65·00
7 6d. purple £100 38·00
8 1s. green £250 £150

1887. Stamp of Great Britain (Queen Victoria) optd **BRITISH BECHUANALAND.**
9 71 ½d. red 1·25 1·25

3 4

1887.
10 3 1d. lilac and black 15·00 1·75
11a 2d. lilac and black 55·00 23·00
12 3d. lilac and black 3·50 5·50
13 4d. lilac and black 45·00 2·25
14 6d. lilac and black 55·00 2·50
15 4 1s. green and black 29·00 5·50
16 2s. green and black 50·00 35·00
17 2s.6d. green and black 60·00 60·00
18 5s. green and black 90·00 £150
19 10s. green and black £180 £350
20 – £1 lilac and black £800 £700
21 – £5 lilac and black £3000 £1500
Nos. 20/1 are as Type **4** but larger, 23 × 39½ mm.

1888. Surch.
22 3 "1d." on 1d. lilac and black 7·50 6·50
23 "2d." on 2d. lilac and black 23·00 3·00
25 "4d." on 4d. lilac and black £250 £350
26 "6d." on 6d. lilac and black £100 10·00
28 4 "1s." on 1s. green and black £150 80·00

1888. Surch **ONE HALF PENNY** and bars.
29 3 ½d. on 3d. lilac and black £150 £160

1891. Stamps of Great Britain (Queen Victoria) optd **BRITISH BECHUANALAND.**
33 57 1d. lilac 6·00 1·50
34 73 2d. green and red 10·00 4·00
35 76 4d. green and brown 2·50 50
36 79 6d. purple on red 3·50 2·00
37 82 1s. green 13·00 16·00

B. BECHUANALAND PROTECTORATE

1888. No. 9 to 19 optd **Protectorate** or surch also.
40 71 ½d. red 3·75 27·00
41 3 1d. on 1d. lilac and black 8·00 14·00
42 2d. on 2d. lilac and black 25·00 17·00
43 3d. on 3d. lilac and black £130 £180
51 4d. on 4d. lilac and black 75·00 32·00
45 6d. on 6d. lilac and black 70·00 40·00
46 4 1s. green and black 80·00 50·00
47 2s. green and black £600 £900
48 2s.6s. green and black £550 £800
49 5s. green and black £1200 £2000
50 10s. green and black £3750 £5500

1889. Stamp of Cape of Good Hope ("Hope" seated) optd **Bechuanaland Protectorate.**
52 6 ½d. black 2·75 40·00

1889. No. 9 surch **Protectorate Fourpence.**
53 71 4d. on ½d. red 22·00 3·50

1897. Stamp of Cape of Good Hope ("Hope" seated) optd **BRITISH BECHUANALAND.**
56 6 ½d. green 2·50 10·00

1897. Queen Victoria stamps of Great Britain optd **BECHUANALAND PROTECTORATE.**
59 71 ½d. red 1·00 2·25
60 ½d. green 1·40 3·50
61 57 1d. lilac 4·00 75
62 73 2d. green and red 3·25 3·50
63 75 3d. purple on yellow 5·50 8·50
64 76 4d. green and brown 15·00 12·00
65 79 6d. purple on red 23·00 11·00

1904. King Edward VII stamps of Great Britain optd **BECHUANALAND PROTECTORATE.**
66 83 ½d. turquoise 2·00 2·00
68 1d. red 7·50 30
69 2½d. blue 7·50 5·00
70 – 1s. green and red (No. 314) 35·00 £130

1912. King George V stamps of Great Britain optd **BECHUANALAND PROTECTORATE.**
73 105 ½d. green 1·25 1·75
72 102 1d. red 2·00 60
92 104 1d. red 2·00 70
75 105 1½d. brown 3·00 3·00
93 106 2d. orange 1·75 1·00
78 104 2½d. blue 3·50 20·00
79 106 3d. violet 6·00 12·00
80 4d. grey 6·50 20·00
81 107 6d. purple 7·00 16·00
82 108 1s. brown 9·50 20·00
88 109 2s.6d. brown 85·00 £160
89 5s. red £110 £275

22 King George V, Baobab Tree and Cattle drinking

1932.
99 **22** ½d. green . . . . 1·00 30
100 1d. red . . . . 1·00 25
101 2d. brown . . . . 1·00 30
102 3d. blue . . . . 1·00 2·25
103 4d. orange . . . . 1·25 5·50
104 6d. purple . . . . 2·50 4·00
105 1s. black and olive . . . . 3·00 7·00
106 2s. black and orange . . . 24·00 45·00
107 2s.6d. black and red . . . 19·00 30·00
108 3s. black and purple . . . 35·00 42·00
109 5s. black and blue . . . . 65·00 75·00
110 10s. black and brown . . . £120 £130

1935. Silver Jubilee. As T **13** of Antigua.
111 1d. blue and red . . . . . . 30 3·25
112 2d. blue and black . . . . . 1·00 3·25
113 3d. brown and blue . . . . 2·50 3·50
114 6d. grey and purple . . . . 4·00 3·50

1937. Coronation. As T **2** of Aden.
115 1d. red 45 40
116 2d. brown . . . . 60 1·00
117 3d. blue . . . . 60 1·25

1938. As T **22**, but portrait of King George VI.
118 ½d. green . . . . 2·00 2·50
119 1d. red 75 50
120a 1½d. blue . . . . 1·00 1·00
121 2d. brown 75 50
122 3d. blue . . . . 1·00 2·50
123 4d. orange . . . . 2·00 3·50
124a 6d. purple . . . . 4·00 2·50
125 1s. black and olive . . . . 4·00 5·00
126 2s.6d. black and red . . . . 14·00 14·00
127 5s. black and blue . . . . . 30·00 17·00
128 10s. black and brown . . . 14·00 21·00

1945. Victory. Stamps of South Africa optd **Bechuanaland**. Alternate stamps inscr in English or Afrikaans.
129 **55** 1d. brown and red . . . . 50 1·00
130 2d. blue and violet (No. 109) . . . . 50 1·25
131 3d. blue (No. 110) . . . . 50 1·25
Prices for bi-lingual pairs.

1947. Royal Visit. As Nos. 32/5 of Basutoland.
132 1d. red 10 10
133 2d. green 10 10
134 3d. blue 10 10
135 1s. mauve 10 10

1948. Silver Wedding. As T **10/11** of Aden.
136 1½d. blue 30 10
137 10s. grey . . . . 27·00 35·00

1949. U.P.U. As T **20/23** of Antigua.
138 1½d. blue . . . . 30 1·25
139 3d. blue . . . . 1·25 2·50
140 6d. mauve . . . . 45 1·50
141 1s. olive . . . . 45 1·50

1953. Coronation. As T **13** of Aden.
142 2d. black and brown 30 30

1955. As T **22** but portrait of Queen Elizabeth II, facing right.
143 ½d. green 50 30
144 1d. red 80 10
145 2d. brown . . . . 1·25 30
146 3d. blue . . . . 3·00 70
146b 4d. orange . . . . 6·50 7·00
147 4½d. blue . . . . 1·50 35
148 6d. purple . . . . 1·25 60
149 1s. black and olive . . . . 1·25 80
150 1s.3d. black and lilac . . . 14·00 9·50
151 2s.6d. black and red . . . . 10·00 9·50
152 5s. black and blue . . . . . 15·00 7·00
153 10s. black and brown . . . 29·00 15·00

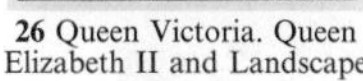

26 Queen Victoria. Queen Elizabeth II and Landscape

28 African Golden Oriole ("Golden Oriole")

1960. 75th Anniv of Protectorate.
154 **26** 1d. sepia and black 40 50
155 3d. mauve and black . . . 40 30
156 6d. blue and black 40 50

1961. Stamps of 1955 surch.
157 1c. on 1d. red 30 10
158 2c. on 2d. brown 20 10
159 2½c. on 2d. brown 30 10
160 2½c. on 3d. blue . . . . . 2·00 4·50
161d 3½c. on 4d. orange 20 60
162a 5c. on 6d. purple 20 10
163 10c. on 1s. black and olive 20 10
164 12½c. on 1s.3d. black and lilac 65 20
165 25c. on 2s.6d. black and red 2·00 50
166 50c. on 5s. black and blue 3·00 2·00
167b 1r. on 10s. black and brown 7·50 4·75

1961.
168 **28** 1c. multicoloured . . . . . 1·50 40
169 – 2c. orange, black and olive 2·00 3·00
170 – 2½c. multicoloured . . . . 1·75 10
171 – 3½c. multicoloured . . . . 2·50 2·50
172 – 5c. multicoloured . . . . . 3·25 1·00
173 – 7½c. multicoloured . . . . 2·25 2·25
174 – 10c. multicoloured . . . . 2·25 60
175 – 12½c. multicoloured . . . . 18·00 5·50
176 – 20c. brown and drab . . . 1·25 1·50
177 – 25c. sepia and lemon . . . 1·75 1·00
178 – 35c. blue and orange . . . 1·25 2·25
179 – 50c. sepia and olive . . . . 1·00 2·25
180 – 1r. black and brown . . . 3·00 2·50
181 – 2r. brown and turquoise 18·00 9·00
DESIGNS—VERT: 2c. Hoopoe ("African Hoopoe"); 2½c. Scarlet-chested sunbird; 3½c. Yellow-rumped bishop ("Cape Widow-bird"); 5c. Swallow-tailed bee eater; 7½c. African grey hornbill ("Grey Hornbill"); 10c. Red-headed weaver; 12½c. Brown-hooded kingfisher; 20c. Woman musician; 35c. Woman grinding maize; 1r. Lion; 2r. Police camel patrol. HORIZ: 25c. Baobab tree; 50c. Bechuana ox.

1963. Freedom from Hunger. As T **28** of Aden.
182 12½c. green 30 15

1963. Centenary of Red Cross. As T **33** of Antigua.
183 2½c. red and black 20 10
184 12½c. red and blue 40 50

1964. 400th Birth Anniv of Shakespeare. As T **34** of Antigua.
185 12½c. brown 15 15

C. BECHUANALAND

42 Map and Gaberones Dam

1965. New Constitution.
186 **42** 2½c. red and gold 20 10
187 5c. blue and gold 20 40
188 12½c. brown and gold . . . 30 40
189 25c. green and gold 40 55

1965. Centenary of I.T.U. As T **36** of Antigua.
190 2½c. red and yellow 20 10
191 12½c. mauve and brown . . . 45 30

1965. I.C.Y. As T **37** of Antigua.
192 1c. purple and turquoise . . 10 10
193 12½c. green and lavender . . 60 55

1966. Churchill Commemoration. As T **38** of Antigua.
194 1c. blue 15 30
195 2½c. green 35 10
196 12½c. brown 70 30
197 20c. violet 75 50

43 Haslar Smoke Generator

1966. Bechuanaland Royal Pioneer Corps.
198 **43** 2½c. blue, red and green . . 25 10
199 – 5c. brown and blue 25 20
200 – 15c. blue, red and green . . 30 25
201 – 35c. multicoloured 30 80
DESIGNS: 5c. Bugler; 15c. Gun-site; 35c. Regimental cap badge.

POSTAGE DUE STAMPS

1926. Postage Due stamps of Great Britain optd **BECHUANALAND PROTECTORATE**.
D1 **D 1** ½d. green . . . . 4·50 70·00
D2 1d. red . . . . 4·50 50·00
D3 2d. black . . . . 6·00 85·00

D 3

1932.
D4 **D 3** ½d. green . . . . 6·00 40·00
D5a 1d. red . . . . 1·00 16·00
D6b 2d. violet . . . . 1·50 20·00

1961. Surch.
D7 **D 3** 1c. on 1d. red 25 50
D8 2c. on 2d. violet . . . . . 25 1·50
D9 5c. on ½d. green 20 60

1961. As Type D **3** but value in decimal currency.
D10 1c. red . . . . 20 1·75
D11 2c. violet . . . . 20 1·75
D12 5c. green . . . . 40 2·00

For later issues see **BOTSWANA**.

BELARUS Pt. 10

Formerly a constituent republic of the Soviet Union, Belarus became independent in 1991.

100 kopeks = 1 rouble.

1 12th-century Cross

1992.
1 **1** 1r. multicoloured 15 15

2 Shyrma

3 Arms of Polotsk

1992. Birth Cent of R. R. Shyrma (composer).
2 **2** 20k. lt blue, blue and black . . 15 15

1992.
3 **3** 2r. multicoloured 15 15
See also Nos. 63 and 89/90.

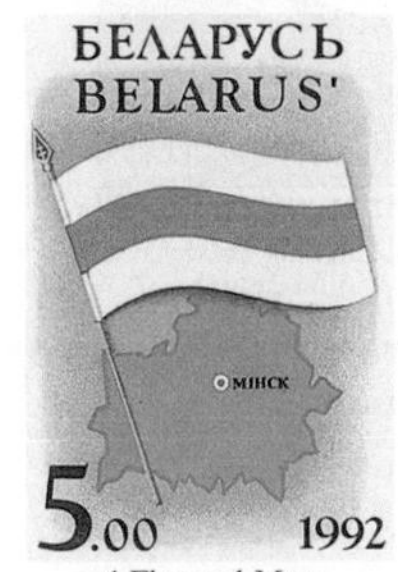

4 Flag and Map

(5)

1992.
4 **4** 5r. multicoloured 15 15
5 – 5r. black, yellow and red . . . 15 15
DESIGN: No. 5, State arms.

1992. Millenary of Orthodox Church in Belarus. (a) No. 1 optd with T **5**.
6 **1** 1r. multicoloured 15 15

(b) Sheet 91 × 66 mm.
MS7 5r. multicoloured 15 15
DESIGN: 24 × 36 mm.—5r. Cross of Polotsk.

6 Kamen Tower

7 State Arms

1992. Ancient Buildings and Monuments. Mult.
8 2r. Type **6** 10 10
9 2r. Calvinist church, Zaslavl 10 10
10 2r. St. Euphrosyne's church, Polotsk 10 10
11 2r. St. Boris Gleb church, Grodno (horiz) 10 10
12 2r. Mir castle (horiz) 10 10
13 2r. Nesvizh castle (horiz) . . . 10 10

1992.
14 **7** 30k. blue 10 10
15 45k. green 10 10
16 50k. green 10 10
17 1r. brown 10 10
18 2r. brown 10 10
19 3r. yellow 10 10
20 5r. blue 15 15
21 10r. red 15 15
22 15r. violet 20 20
23 25r. green 20 20
24 50r. mauve 25 25
25 100r. red 25 25
26 150r. purple 25 25
27 200r. green 10 10
28 300r. red 15 15
29 600r. mauve 20 25
30 1000r. red 25 25
31 3000r. blue 50 50

8 Jug and Bowl

1992. Pottery. Multicoloured.
40 1r. Type **8** 10 10
41 1r. Vases and jug on jug tree 10 10
42 1r. Flagon 10 10
43 1r. Jugs 10 10

9 Chickens

1993. Corn Dollies. Multicoloured.
44 5r. Type **9** 10 10
45 10r. Woman and gunman (vert) 15 15
46 15r. Woman (vert) 25 25
47 25r. Man and woman (vert) 50 50

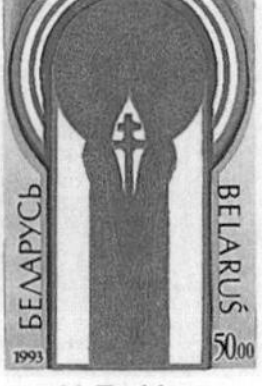

10 Harezki

11 Emblem

1993. Birth Centenary of M. I. Harezki (author).
48 **10** 50r. purple 15 15

1993. World Belarussian Congress, Minsk.
49 **11** 50r. red, gold and black . . 60 60

12 "Man Over Vitebsk"

1993. Europa. Contemporary Art. Paintings by Marc Chagall. Multicoloured.
50 1500r. Type **12** . . . . . . 2·25 2·25
51 1500r. "Promenade" (vert) . . 2·25 2·25
MS52 142 × 103 mm. 2500r. "Allegory" (50 × 37 mm) . . . 23·00 23·00

(13)

ЧЭМПІЯНАТ СВЕТУ
ПА ФУТБОЛУ.
ЗША. 1994

1500

(14)

1993. Sports Events. Nos. 4/5 variously surch. (a) Winter Olympic Games, Lillehammer, Norway (1994). Surch **Winter Pre-Olympic Games Lillehammer, Norway 1500** (in capitals on No. 44) or in Cyrillic as T **13**.

53 **4** 1500r. on 5r. mult (in Cyrillic) . . . . 2·50 2·50
54 1500r. on 5r. mult (in English) . . . . 2·50 2·50
55 – 1500r. on 5r. black, yellow and red (in Cyrillic) . . . 2·50 2·50
56 – 1500r. on 5r. black, yellow and red (in English) . . . 2·50 2·50

(b) World Cup Football Championship, U.S.A. (1994). **Surch WORLD CUP USA 94 1500** or in Cyrillic as T **14**.

58 **4** 1500r. on 5r. mult (in Cyrillic) . . . . 2·50 2·50
59 1500r. on 5r. mult (in English) . . . . 2·50 2·50
60 – 1500r. on 5r. black, yellow and red (in Cyrillic) . . . 2·50 2·50
61 – 1500r. on 5r. black, yellow and red (in English) . . . 2·50 2·50
MS62 Two sheets. (a) 1500r. on 5r. multicoloured (in Cyrillic); (b) 1500r. on 5r. multicoloured (in English) . . . . 5·00 5·00

1993. Town Arms. As T **3**. Multicoloured.
63 25r. Minsk 15 15

15 St. Stanislav's Church, Mogilev

1993.
64 **15** 150r. multicoloured 40 40

16 Kastus Kalinowski (leader)

1993. 130th Anniv of Peasants' Uprising.
65 **16** 50r. multicoloured 20 20

17 Princess Ragneda **18** Statue of Budny

1993. 10th-century Rulers of Polotsk. Mult.
66 75r. Type **17** 30 30
67 75r. Prince Ragvalod and map 30 30

1993. 400th Death Anniv of Simon Budny (poet).
68 **18** 100r. multicoloured 50 50

19 Golden Eagle

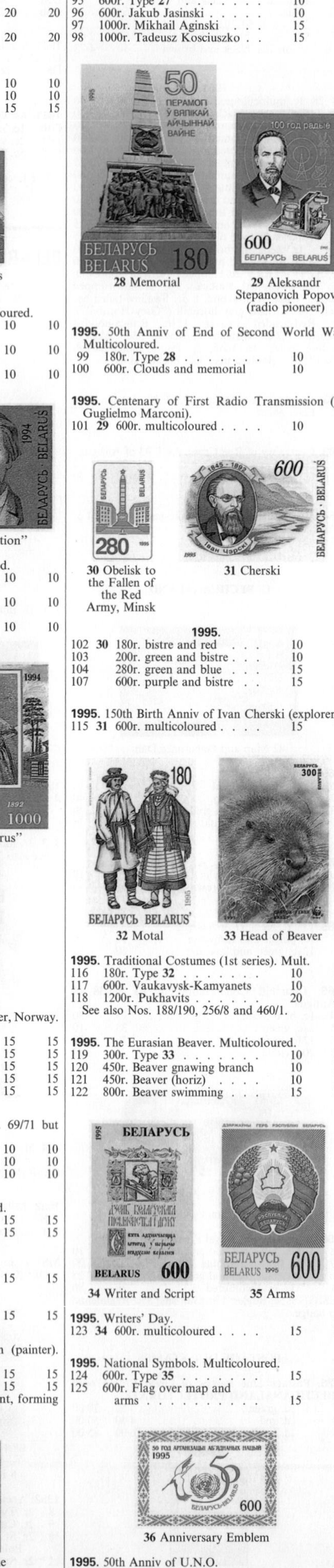

1994. Birds in the Red Book. Multicoloured.
69 20r. Type **19** 10 10
70 40r. Mute swan ("Cygnus olor") 20 20
71 40r. River kingfisher ("Alcedo atthis") 20 20

1994. Nos. 14/16 surch.
72 **7** 15r. on 30k. blue 10 10
73 25r. on 45k. green 10 10
74 50r. on 50k. green 15 15
See also Nos. 86/8.

21 Map and Rocket Launchers (Liberation of Russia)

1994. 50th Anniv of Liberation. Multicoloured.
75 500r. Type **21** 10 10
76 500r. Map and airplanes (Ukraine) 10 10
77 500r. Map, tank and soldiers (Byelorussia) 10 10

22 Yasev Drazdovich and "Persecution"

1994. Artists and Paintings. Multicoloured.
78 300r. Type **22** 10 10
79 300r. Pyotr Sergievich and "The Path through Life" . . 10 10
80 300r. Ferdinand Rushchyts and "The Land" 10 10

23 Figure Skating **26** "Belarus"

25 Church, Synkavichai (16th-century)

1994. Winter Olympic Games, Lillehammer, Norway. Multicoloured.
81 1000r. Type **23** 15 15
82 1000r. Biathlon 15 15
83 1000r. Cross-country skiing . . 15 15
84 1000r. Speed skating 15 15
85 1000r. Ice hockey 15 15

1994. Birds in the Red Book. As Nos. 69/71 but values changed. Multicoloured.
86 300r. As Type **19** 10 10
87 400r. As No. 70 . . . . 10 10
88 400r. As No. 71 . . . . 10 10

1994. Town Arms. As T **3**. Multicoloured.
89 700r. Grodno 15 15
90 700r. Vitebsk 15 15

1994. Religious Buildings. Multicoloured.
91 700r. Type **25** 15 15
92 700r. Sts. Peter and Paul's Cathedral, Gomel (19th-century) 15 15

1994. 150th Birth Anniv of Ilya Repin (painter). Multicoloured.
93 1000r. Type **26** 15 15
94 1000r. Repin Museum 15 15
Nos. 93/4 were issued together, se-tenant, forming a composite design.

27 Tomasz Wojshezki and Battle Scene

1995. Bicentenary (1994) of Polish Insurrection. Multicoloured.
95 600r. Type **27** 10 10
96 600r. Jakub Jasinski 10 10
97 1000r. Mikhail Aginski . . . 15 15
98 1000r. Tadeusz Kosciuszko . . 15 15

28 Memorial **29** Aleksandr Stepanovich Popov (radio pioneer)

1995. 50th Anniv of End of Second World War. Multicoloured.
99 180r. Type **28** 10 10
100 600r. Clouds and memorial 10 10

1995. Centenary of First Radio Transmission (by Guglielmo Marconi).
101 **29** 600r. multicoloured 10 10

30 Obelisk to the Fallen of the Red Army, Minsk **31** Cherski

1995.
102 **30** 180r. bistre and red . . . 10 10
103 200r. green and bistre . . . 10 10
104 280r. green and blue . . . 15 15
107 600r. purple and bistre . . 15 15

1995. 150th Birth Anniv of Ivan Cherski (explorer).
115 **31** 600r. multicoloured 15 15

32 Motal **33** Head of Beaver

1995. Traditional Costumes (1st series). Mult.
116 180r. Type **32** 10 10
117 600r. Vaukavysk-Kamyanets 10 10
118 1200r. Pukhavits 20 20
See also Nos. 188/190, 256/8 and 460/1.

1995. The Eurasian Beaver. Multicoloured.
119 300r. Type **33** 10 10
120 450r. Beaver gnawing branch 10 10
121 450r. Beaver (horiz) 10 10
122 800r. Beaver swimming . . . 15 15

34 Writer and Script **35** Arms

1995. Writers' Day.
123 **34** 600r. multicoloured 15 15

1995. National Symbols. Multicoloured.
124 600r. Type **35** 15 15
125 600r. Flag over map and arms 15 15

36 Anniversary Emblem

1995. 50th Anniv of U.N.O.
126 **36** 600r. blue, black and gold 15 15

37 Mstislavl Church

1995. Churches. Multicoloured.
127 600r. Type **37** 15 15
128 600r. Kamai Church 15 15
See also Nos. 227/8.

1995
125 год
з дня нараджэння

(38)

1995. 125th Birth Anniv of Ferdinand Rushchyts (artist). No. 80 optd with T **38**.
129 300r. multicoloured 55 55

39 Sukhoi and Aircraft **40** Red Deer (*Cervus elaphus*)

1995. Birth Centenary of P. V. Sukhoi (aircraft designer).
130 **39** 600r. multicoloured 15 15

1995. Nature. Sheet 100 × 64 mm. Imperf.
MS131 **40** 10000r. multicoloured 1·25 1·25

41 Leu Sapega (statesman)

1995. 17th-century Belarussians. Multicoloured.
132 600r. Type **41** 10 10
133 1200r. Kazimir Semyanovich (military scholar) 15 15
134 1800r. Simyaon Polatski (writer) 20 20

42 Lynx

1996. Mammals. Multicoloured.
135 1000r. Type **42** 10 10
136 2000r. Roe deer (vert) . . . 15 15
137 2000r. Brown bear 15 15
138 3000r. Elk (vert) 30 30
139 5000r. European bison . . . 55 55

1996. Nos. 17 and 23 optd with capital letter.
140 **7** B (200r.) on 1r. brown . . . 10 10
141 A (400r.) on 25r. green . . 10 10

44 Krapiva

1996. Birth Centenary of Kandrat Krapiva (writer).
142 **44** 1000r. multicoloured . . . 15 15

45 Beaver

1996. The Eurasian Beaver (*Castor fiber*). Sheet 90 × 70 mm.
MS143 **45** 1200r. multicoloured 20 20

46 Purple Emperor ("Apatura iris")

1996. Butterflies and Moths. Multicoloured.
144 300r. Type **46** 45 45
145 300r. "Lopinga achine" . . . 45 45
146 300r. Scarlet tiger moth ("Callimorpha dominula") 45 45
147 300r. Clifden's nonpareil ("Catocala fraxini") . . . 45 45
148 300r. Swallowtail ("Papilio machaon") 45 45
149 300r. Apollo ("Parnassius apollo") 45 45
150 300r. "Ammobiota hebe" . . 45 45
151 300r. Palaeno sulphur yellow ("Colias palaeno") 45 45
MS152 Two sheets, each 100×70 mm. (a) 1000r. *Vacciniina optilete*; (b) 1000r. Willow-herb hawk moth (*Proserpinus proserpina*) . . . . 7·00 7·00

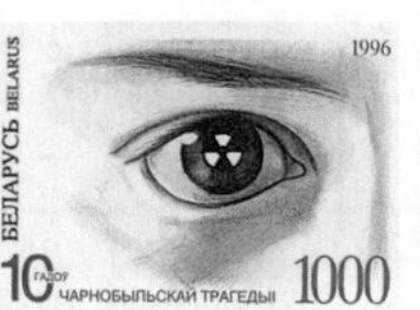

47 Radioactivity Symbol within Eye
48 State Arms

1996. 10th Anniv of Chernobyl Nuclear Disaster. Multicoloured.
153 1000r. Type **47** 15 15
154 1000r. Radioactivity symbol on diseased leaf 15 15
155 1000r. Radioactivity symbol on boarded-up window . . 15 15

1996. Arms and value in black, background colours given.
159 **48** 100r. blue 10 10
160 200r. grey 10 10
161 400r. brown 10 10
162 500r. green 10 10
163 600r. red 10 10
164 800r. blue 10 10
165 1000r. orange 10 10
166 1500r. mauve 10 10
167 1500r. blue 10 10
168 1800r. violet 10 10
169 2000r. green 10 10
170 2200r. mauve 10 10
171 2500r. blue 10 10
172 3000r. brown 15 15
173 3300r. yellow 15 15
174 5000r. blue 20 20
175 10000r. green 45 45
176 30000r. brown . . . . . 1·25 1·25
177 50000r. purple . . . . . 2·10 2·10

49 Russian and Belarussian Flags

1996. Russian–Belarussian Treaty.
182 **49** 1500r. multicoloured . . . 15 15

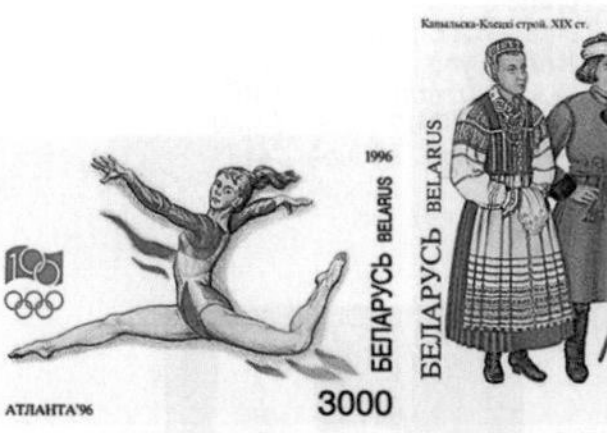

50 Gymnastics
51 Kapyl-Kletski

1996. Olympic Games, Atlanta. Multicoloured.
183 3000r. Type **50** 15 15
184 3000r. Throwing the discus 15 15
185 3000r. Weightlifting 15 15
186 3000r. Wrestling 15 15
MS187 100×71 mm. 5000r. Rifle-shooting. Imperf 40 40

1996. Traditional Costumes (2nd series). Mult.
188 1800r. Type **51** 10 10
189 2200r. David-Garadots Turau 10 10
190 3300r. Kobryn 15 15
MS191 95×71 mm. 5000r. Naraulyanski. Imperf 40 40
See also Nos. 256/8 and 460/1.

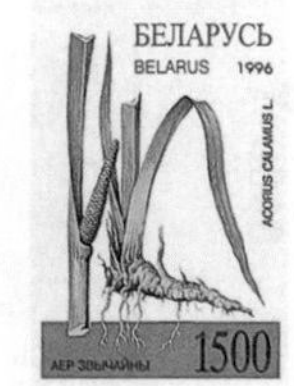

52 "Acorus calamus"

1996. Medicinal Plants. Multicoloured.
192 1500r. Type **52** 10 10
193 1500r. "Sanguisorba officinalis" 10 10
194 2200r. "Potentilla erecta" . . 10 10
195 3300r. "Frangula alnus" . . 15 15
MS196 96×71 mm. 5000r. *Menyanthes trifoliate*. Imperf 35 35

53 Grey Heron ("Ardea cinerea")

1996. Birds. Multicoloured.
197 400r. Type **53** 25 25
198 400r. Black storks ("Ciconia nigra") 25 25
199 400r. Great cormorant ("Phalacrocorax carbo") 25 25
200 400r. White stork ("Ciconia ciconia") 25 25
201 400r. Black-headed gulls ("Larus ridibundus") . . . 25 25
202 400r. Common snipe ("Gallinago gallinago") . . 25 25
203 400r. White-winged black tern ("Chlidonias leucopterus") 25 25
204 400r. Penduline tit ("Remiz pendulinus") 25 25
205 400r. Eurasian bittern ("Botaurus stellaris") . . . 25 25
206 400r. Black coot ("Fulica atra") 25 25
207 400r. Little bittern ("Ixobrychus minutus") . . 25 25
208 400r. River kingfisher ("Alcedo atthis") 25 25
209 400r. Green-winged teals ("Anas crecca") 25 25
210 400r. Gadwalls ("Anas strepera") 25 25
211 400r. Northern pintails ("Anas acuta") 25 25
212 400r. Mallards ("Anas platyrhynchos") 25 25
213 400r. Greater scaups ("Aythya marila") 25 25
214 400r. Long-tailed duck ("Clangula hyemalis") . . 25 25
215 400r. Northern shovelers ("Anas clypeata") 25 25
216 400r. Garganeys ("Anas querquedula") 25 25
217 400r. European wigeon ("Anas penelope") 25 25
218 400r. Ferruginous ducks ("Aythya nyroca") 25 25
219 400r. Common goldeneyes ("Bucephala clangula") . . 25 25
220 400r. Goosander ("Mergus merganser") 25 25
221 400r. Smew ("Mergus albellus") 25 25
222 400r. Tufted duck ("Aythya fuligula") 25 25
223 400r. Red-breasted merganser ("Mergus serrator") . . . 25 25
224 400r. Common pochard ("Aythya ferina") 25 25
MS225 Two sheets, each 100×70 mm. (a) 1000r. Common snipe (*Gallinago gallinago*); (b) 1000r. European pochards (*Aythya farina*) . . . . 4·50 4·50

54 Title Page
55 Shchakatsikhin

1996. 400th Anniv of Publication of First Belarussian Grammar.
226 **54** 1500r. multicoloured . . . 10 10

1996. Churches. As T **37**. Multicoloured.
227 3300r. St. Nicholas's Church, Mogilev 10 10
228 3300r. Franciscan church, Pinsk 10 10

1996. Birth Centenary of Mikola Shchakatsikhin (artist).
229 **55** 2000r. multicoloured . . . 10 10

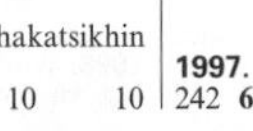

56 Old and New Telephones

1996. Cent of Telephone Service in Minsk.
230 **56** 2000r. multicoloured . . . 10 10

57 Lukashenka

1996. President Alyaksandr Rygoravich Lukashenka.
231 **57** 2500r. multicoloured . . . 10 10

58 Kiryla Turovski (12th-century Bishop of Turov)
59 Decorated Tree, Minsk

1996. Multicoloured.
232 3000r. Type **58** 15 15
233 3000r. Mikolaj Radziwill (16th-century Chancellor of Lithuania) 15 15
234 3000r. Mikola Gusovski (15th-16th century writer) 15 15

1996. New Year. Multicoloured.
235 1500r. Type **59** 10 10
236 2000r. Winter landscape (horiz) 10 10

60 "Paraskeva"

1996. Icons in National Museum, Minsk. Multicoloured.
237 3500r. Type **60** 15 15
238 3500r. "Illya" (17th-century) 15 15
239 3500r. "Three Holy Men" (Master of Sharashov) . . 15 15
240 3500r. "Madonna of Smolensk" 15 15
MS241 70×100 mm. 5000r. "Birth of the Madonna" (Patr Yavseevich) 35 35

61 Zhukov

1997. Birth Cent of Marshal G. K. Zhukov.
242 **61** 2000r. black, gold and red 10 10

62 Theatre

1997. Kupala National Theatre, Minsk.
243 **62** 3500r. black and gold . . . 20 20

63 Byalnitsky-Birulya

1997. 125th Birth Anniv of W. K. Byalnitsky-Birulya (painter).
244 **63** 2000r. black and brown . . 10 10

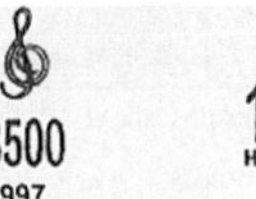

(64)

1997. 105th Birth Anniv of R. R. Shyrma (composer). No. 2 surch with T **64**.
245 **2** 3500r. on 20k. light blue, blue and black 20 20

65 Salmon

1997. Fishes. Multicoloured.
246 2000r. Type **65** 10 10
247 3000r. Vimba 15 15
248 4500r. Barbel ("Barbus barbus") 20 20
249 4500r. European grayling ("Thymallus thymallus") 20 20
MS250 90×60 mm. 5000r. Sterlet (*Acipenser ruthenus*) 35 35

66 "SOS" on Globe

1997. International Conference on Developing Countries, Minsk. Multicoloured.
251 3000r. Type **66** 10 10
252 4500r. Protective hand over ecosystem 15 15
Nos. 251/2 were issued together, se-tenant, with intervening label showing the Conference emblem, the whole strip forming a composite design.

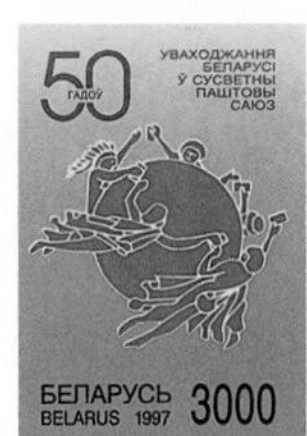

67 Emblem
69 Map, National Flag and Monument to the Fallen of Second World War, Minsk

1997. 50th Anniv of Belarussian Membership of Universal Postal Union.
253 **67** 3000r. multicoloured . . . 10 10

1997. No. 18 surch **100 1997**.
254 **7** 100r. on 2r. brown 10 10

1997. Independence Day.
255 **69** 3000r. multicoloured . . . 20 20

1997. Traditional Costumes (3rd series). As T **51**. Multicoloured.
256 2000r. Dzisensk 10 10
257 3000r. Navagrydsk 20 20
258 4500r. Bykhaisk 30 30

70 Page from Skorina Bible and Vilnius

1997. 480th Anniv of Printing in Belarus. Each red, black and grey.
259 3000r. Type **70** 20 20
260 3000r. Page from Skorina Bible and Prague 20 20
261 4000r. Franzisk Skorina and Polotsk 25 25
262 7500r. Skorina and Cracow 40 40

71 Jesuit College

1997. 900th Anniv of Pinsk.
263 **71** 3000r. multicoloured . . . 20 20

72 Books and Entrance

1997. 75th Anniv of National Library.
264 **72** 3000r. multicoloured . . . 20 20

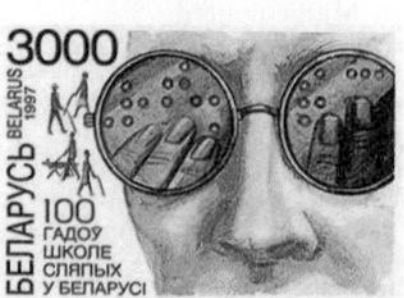

73 Dark Glasses reflecting Hands reading Braille

1997. Cent of Schools for the Blind in Belarus.
265 **73** 3000r. multicoloured . . . 20 20

74 Child in Hand "Flower"

1997. World Children's Day.
266 **74** 3000r. multicoloured . . . 20 20

75 Red Ribbon and Crowd

1997. Red Ribbon AIDS Solidarity Campaign.
267 **75** 4000r. multicoloured . . . 20 20

76 Model 1221

1997. Belarussian Tractors. Multicoloured.
268 3300r. Type **76** 20 20
269 4400r. First Belarussian tractor, 1953 . . . . . . 25 25
270 7500r. Model 680 . . . . . 40 40
271 7500r. Model 952 . . . . . 40 40

3000
УЗВОЎЛЕНЬЫ І АСВЕЧАНЫ Ў ВЕРАСНІ 1997

(77)

1997. Restoration of Cross of St. Ephrosina of Polotsk. No. 1 surch with T **77**.
272 **1** 3000r. on 1r. multicoloured 20 20

78 St. Nicholas hang-gliding over Houses (New Year)

1997. Greetings Stamps. Multicoloured.
273 1400r. Type **78** 10 10
274 4400r. Procession of musicians (Christmas) . . . 25 25

79 Cross-country Skiing

1998. Winter Olympic Games, Nagano, Japan. Multicoloured.
275 2000r. Type **79** 15 15
276 3300r. Ice hockey 20 20
277 4400r. Biathlon 30 30
278 7500r. Freestyle skiing . . . 55 55

80 Mashcherov

1998. 80th Birth Anniv of P. M. Mashcherov (writer).
279 **80** 2500r. multicoloured . . . 15 15

81 MAZ-205 Lorry, 1947

1998. Tipper Trucks. Multicoloured.
280 1400r. Type **81** 10 10
281 2000r. MAZ-503, 1968 . . . 15 15
282 3000r. MAZ-5549, 1977 . . . 20 20
283 4400r. MAZ-5551, 1985 . . . 30 30
284 7500r. MAZ-5516, 1994 . . . 50 50

82 Entrance to Nyasvizh Castle

БЕЛАРУСЬ 1998 BELARUS 8600
АДАМ МІЦКЕВІЧ
1798-1855

83 Mickiewicz

1998. Europa. National Festivals.
285 **82** 15000r. multicoloured . . . 55 55

1998. Birth Bicentenary of Adam Mickiewicz (political writer).
286 **83** 8600r. multicoloured . . . 35 35

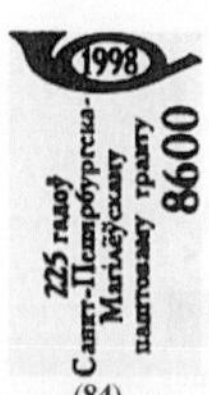

(84)

Варакушка
Luscinia svecica
БЕЛАРУСЬ
BELARUS 1998 1500

85 Bluethroat

1998. 225th Anniv of Postal Service between Mogilov and St. Petersburg. No. 64 surch with T **84**.
287 **15** 8600r. on 150r. mult . . . 35 35

1998. Birds. Multicoloured.
288 1500r. Type **85** 10 10
289 3200r. Penduline tit 15 15
290 3800r. Aquatic warbler . . . 15 15
291 5300r. Savi's warbler 20 20
292 8600r. Azure tit 35 35

86 Watermill

1500 БЕЛАРУСЬ
BELARUS 1998

87 Bulldozer Model 7821

1998.
293 **86** 100r. black and green . . . 10 10
294 – 200r. black and brown . . 10 10
295 – 500r. black and blue . . . 10 10
296 – 800r. black and violet . . . 10 10
297 – 1000r. black and green . . 10 10
298 – 1000r. black and brown . . 10 10
299 – 2000r. black and blue . . . 10 10
300 – 3000r. black and yellow . . 15 15
301 – 3200r. black and green . . 15 15
302 – 5000r. black and blue . . . 25 25
303 – 5300r. black and yellow . . 25 25
304 – 10000r. black and orange 45 45
305 **86** 30000r. black and blue . . 40 40
306 – 50000r. black, orange and deep orange 60 60
308 – 100000r. black and mauve 1·40 1·40
309 – 500000r. black and brown 3·00 3·00

DESIGNS—VERT: 200, 50000r. Windmill; 500r. Stork; 800r. Cathedral of the Holy Trinity, Ishkold; 1000r. Bison; 1500, 3200r. Dulcimer; 2000r. Star; 3000, 5300r. Lute; 5000r. Church; 10000r. Flaming wheel; 500000r. Lyavoniha (folk dance). HORIZ: 100000r. Exhibition centre, Minsk.

1998. 50th Anniv of Belaz Truck Works. Mult.
310 1500r. Type **87** 10 10
311 3200r. Tipper Model 75131 15 15
312 3800r. Tipper Model 75303 15 15
313 5300r. Tipper Model 75483 20 20
314 8600r. Tipper Model 7555 . . 35 35

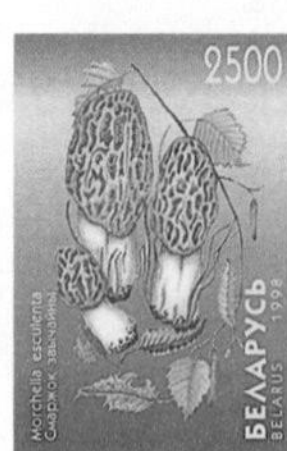

88 Common Morel

89 Lion's Head

1998. Fungi. Multicoloured.
315 2500r. Type **88** 10 10
316 3800r. "Morchella conica" 15 15
317 4600r. Shaggy parasol . . . 20 20
318 5800r. Parasol mushroom . . 25 25
319 9400r. Shaggy ink cap . . . 45 45

1998. Wood Sculptures. Multicoloured.
320 3400r. Type **89** 20 20
321 3800r. Archangel Michael . . 20 20
322 5800r. Prophet Zacharias . . 30 30
323 9400r. Madonna and Child 50 50

90 Emblem and Belarussian Stamps

1998. World Post Day.
324 **90** 5500r. multicoloured . . . 30 30

91 "Kalozha" (V. K. Tsvirka)

1998. Paintings. Multicoloured.
325 3000r. Type **91** 20 20
326 3500r. "Hotel Lounge" (S. Yu. Zhukoiski) 20 20
327 5000r. "Winter Sleep" (V. K. Byalynitski-Birulya) . . . 30 30
328 5500r. "Portrait of a Girl" (I. I. Alyashkevich) (vert) 30 30
329 10000r. "Portrait of an Unknown Woman" (I. F. Khrutski) (vert) 60 60

92 Anniversary Emblem

93 Girl, Rabbit and Fir Trees

1998. 50th Anniv of Universal Declaration of Human Rights.
330 **92** 7100r. multicoloured . . . 35 35

1998. Christmas and New Year. Multicoloured.
331 5500r. Type **93** 30 30
332 5500r. Girl, rabbit and house 30 30

94 Pushkin and Adam Mickiewicz Monument, St. Petersburg (A. Anikeichyk)

1999. Birth Bicentenary of Aleksandr Pushkin (writer).
333 **94** 15300r. multicoloured . . . 1·00 1·00

95 MAZ Model 8007 Truck and Excavator

1999. Minsk Truck and Military Works. Mult.
334 10000r. Type **95** 15 15
335 15000r. MAZ model 543M and Smerch rocket system 20 20
336 30000r. MAZ model 7907 crane 35 35
337 30000r. MAZ model 543M Rubezh missile launcher . . 35 35
MS338 175 × 120 mm. Nos. 334/7; 5000r. Model 7917 and Topol missile; 150000r. Model 74135 low-loader . . . . 2·75 2·75

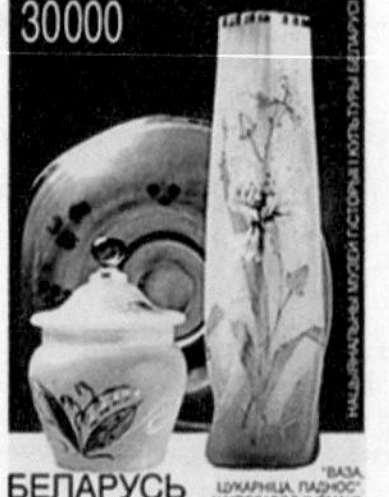

96 Dish, Jar and Vase

1999. Glasswork. Multicoloured.
339 30000r. Type **96** 40 40
340 30000r. Chalice 40 40
341 100000r. Oil lamp . . . . . 1·40 1·40

(97)

1999. "iBRA '99" International Stamp Exhibition, Nuremberg. Nos. 69/71 surch with T **97**.
342 500000 on 20r. multicoloured (Type **19**) 10 10
343 500000 on 40r. multicoloured (No. 70) 35 35
344 500000 on 40r. multicoloured (No. 71) 35 35

98 Belavezhskaya Pushcha Reserve

1999. Europa. Parks and Gardens. Multicoloured.
345 150000r. Type **98** 55 55
346 150000r. Beaver in Byarezinski Reserve . . . 55 55

99 Well

1999. Wooden Buildings. Multicoloured.
347 50000r. Type **99** 20 20
348 50000r. Public house 20 20
349 100000r. Windmill 40 40

100 "Portrait of Yu. M. Pen" (A. M. Brazer)

1999. Vitebsk Art School. Paintings. Multicoloured.
350 30000r. Type **100** 15 15
351 60000r. "St. Anthony's Church, Vitebsk" (S. B.Yudovin) 25 25
352 100000r. "Street in Vitebsk" (Yu. M. Pen) 30 30
353 100000r. "Kryvaya Street, Vitebsk" (M. P. Mikhalap) (horiz) 30 30
MS354 104 × 82 mm. 200000r. "The World is a River without Banks" (Marc Chagall) . . . . 1·00 1·00

101 Karvat

1999. 3rd Death Anniv of Wing Commander Karvat.
355 **101** 25000r. multicoloured . . 10 10

102 Main Post Office, Minsk, 1954

1999. 125th Anniv of Universal Postal Union. Mult.
356 150000r. Type **102** 50 50
357 150000r. First post office in Minsk, 1800 . . . . 50 50

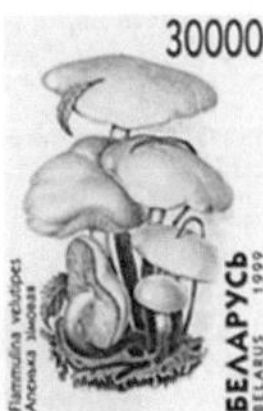

103 Golden Mushroom

1999. Fungi. Multicoloured.
358 30000r. Type **103** 10 10
359 50000r. Changeable agaric . . 15 15
360 75000r. *Lyophyllum connatum* 20 20
361 100000r. *Lyophyllum decastes* 30 30
MS362 97 × 79 mm. 150000r. Bootlace fungus (*Armillariella mellea*) 75 75

104 East and West Belarussians Embracing

1999. 60th Anniv of Re-unification of Republic of Byelorussia.
363 **104** 29000r. multicoloured . . 10 10

105 MAZ MA3-6430, 1998

1999. Minsk Truck and Military Works. Lorries. Multicoloured.
364 51000r. Type **105** 15 15
365 86000r. Lorry Model MAZ MA3-4370 . . . . 30 30

106 Landscape (Olya Smantser)

1999. Children's Painting Competition Winners. Mult.
366 32000r. Type **106** 10 10
367 59000r. Girl (Masha Dudarenko) (vert) 15 15

107 Teddybear in Snow (Mitya Kutas)

1999. Christmas and New Year. Children's Paintings. Multicoloured.
368 30000r. Type **107** 10 10
369 30000r. Children building snowman and ice-skating (Yulya Yakubovich) . . . 10 10

Currency Revaluation

108 Spasa-Praabrazhenskaya Church, Polatsk

110 Bison

109 Our Lady Oranta (mosaic, Spohia Catherdral, Kiev, Ukraine)

2000. Birth Bimillenary of Jesus Christ (1st issue). Mult.
370 50r. Type **108** 25 25
371 75r. St. Atsistratsiga Cathedral, Slutsk 40 40
372 100r. The Reverend Serafim Sarovskaga Church, Belaazersk 55 55

2000. Birth Bimillenary of Jesus Christ (2nd issue). Sheet 150 × 100 mm containing T **109** and similar vert designs. Multicoloured.
MS373 100r. Type **109**; 100r. Jesus Christ (fresco, Spasa-Praabrazhenskaya Church, Polatsk); 100r. Our Lady Volodimirska (icon, National Tretyakov Gallery, Moscow, Russia) . . . . 1·50 1·50

2000.
374 **110** 1r. black and green . . . 10 10
375 – 2r. black and blue 10 10
376 – 3r. black and yellow . . . 10 10
377 – 5r. black and blue 10 10
378 – 10r. black and orange . . 10 10
380 – 20r. black and mauve . . 10 10
382 – 30r. black and green . . . 15 15
383 – 50r. black and yellow . . . 55 55
387 – 100r. black and mauve . . 1·00 1·10
DESIGNS—VERT: 2r. Star; 3r. Lyre; 5r. Synkovichy Church; 10r. Flaming wheel; 20r. Type **111**; 30r. Watermill; 50r. Windmill. HORIZ: 100r. Exhibition Centre.

111 Kryzhachok (folk dance)
112 Su-24 Bomber

2000. Self-adhesive.
391 **111** 20r. black and red 10 10

2000. 25th Death Anniv of Pavel Sukhoi (aircraft designer). Multicoloured.
392 50r. Type **112** 50 50
393 50r. Su-27 fighter 50 50
394 50r. Su-25 battle fighter 50 50
MS395 120 × 83 mm. 150r. Type **112**; 150r. As No. 394; 150r. As No. 393 . . . . 1·50 1·50

113 Kupala Holiday

114 Stone-Curlew

2000.
396 **113** A black and blue 15 15
No. 396 was for Inland Letter Post rate.

2000. Birds in the Red Book. Multicoloured.
397 50r. Type **114** 25 25
398 50r. Smew (*Mergellus albellus*) 25 25
399 75r. Willow grouse 40 40
400 100r. Lesser spotted eagle (vert) 55 55

115 "The Partisan Madonna of Minsk" (M. Savitsky)

116 "Building Europe"

2000. 55th Anniv of End of Second World War.
401 **115** 100r. multicoloured . . . 55 55

2000. Europa.
402 **116** 250r. multicoloured . . . 1·10 1·10

117 Scene from "Creation of the World"
118 Hands holding Lifebelt

2000. National Ballet Company. Multicoloured.
403 100r. Type **117** 55 55
MS404 77 × 73 mm. 150r. Scene from "Passions" 55 55

2000. 50th Anniv of United Nations High Commission for Refugees.
405 **118** 50r. multicoloured 25 25

119 Head of Lynx
120 People wearing National Costumes

2000. Endangered Species. The Lynx. Multicoloured.
406 100r. Type **119** 55 55
407 100r. On branch 55 55
408 150r. Walking through woodland 80 80
409 150r. Adult and cub 80 80

2000. International Year of Culture.
410 **120** 100r. multicoloured . . . 55 55

121 Rings

122 Amber

2000. Olympic Games, Sydney. Multicoloured.
411 100r. Type **121** 55 55
412 100r. Kayaking 55 55
413 100r. Rhythmic gymnastics . . 55 55
MS414 77 × 74 mm. 400r. Athletes . . 2·25 2·25

2000. Minerals. Multicoloured.
415 200r. Type **122** . . . . . . 1·10 1·10
416 200r. Galit . . . . 1·10 1·10
417 200r. Flint . . . . 1·10 1·10
418 200r. Silvin . . . . 1·10 1·10

123 People around decorated Tree
124 Nativity Scene

2000. New Year.
419 **123** 200r. multicoloured . . . 1·10 1·10

2000. Christmas.
420 **124** 100r. multicoloured . . . 55 55

125 "Connection of Times" (Roman Zabello)

2000. New Millennium. Children's Paintings. Multicoloured.
421 100r. Type **125** 55 55
422 100r. "Festival of Life" (Alena Emeliyanova) 55 55

126 Euphrosiniya Polotskaya and Church

2001. 900th Birth Anniv of St. Euphrosiniya Polotskaya (Saint Euphrosyne). Imperf.
423 **126** 500r. multicoloured . . . 95 95

127 Brest

128 Runner

2001. Town Arms (1st series). Multicoloured.
424 200r. Type **127** 35 35
425 200r. Gomel 35 35
426 200r. Borisov 35 35
427 300r. Minsk 35 35
428 300r. David-Gorodok 35 35

2001. Byelorussian Medal Winners, Olympic Games, Sydney. Sheet 78 × 75 mm.
MS435 **128** 1000r. multicoloured 1·90 1·90
No. **MS**435 is as No. **MS**414 but with face value changed and design altered to include list of winners.

129 Tupolev ANT-25 RD

2001. 25th Death Anniv of Pavel Sukhoy (aircraft designer). Multicoloured.
436 250r. Type **129** 50 50
437 250r. Tupolev ANT-37 Rodina 50 50

2001. As T **86**.
438 1r. black and green (inscr "2002") 10 10
439 2r. black and blue (inscr "2002") 10 10
440 3r. black and yellow (inscr "2002") 10 10
441 5r. black and blue (inscr "2002") 10 10
442 10r. black and brown (inscr "2002") 10 10
442a 20r. black and mauve (inscr "2002") 10 10
442b 30r. black and green (inscr "2002") 10 10
442c 50r. black and yellow (inscr "2002") 10 10
442d 100r. black and mauve (inscr "2002") 20 20
443 200r. black and green . . . 40 40
444 500r. black and brown . . . 1·10 1·10
DESIGNS: 1r. Bison; 2r. Star; 3r. Lyre; 5r. Synkovichy Church; 10r. Flaming wheel; 20r. Dancers; 50r. Windmill; 100r. Exhibition centre; 200r. 18th-century town house, Vitebsk; 500r. As No. 309.

130 Stag Beetle (*Lucanus cervus*)

2001. Beetles. Multicoloured.
445 300r. Type **130** 65 65
446 300r. European rhinoceros beetle (*Oryctes nasicornis*) 65 65

2001. As T **110**. Self-adhesive.
447 100r. black and mauve . . . 15 15
448 200r. black and green (vert) 40 40
DESIGNS: 100r. As No. 387; 200r. As No. 438.

131 *Nymphaea alba*

132 Swans and Lake, Narochanskyi Nature Reserve

2001. Endangered Species. Flowers. Multicoloured.
455 200r. Type **131** 40 40
456 400r. *Cypripedium calceolus* 1·40 1·40

2001. Europa. Water Resources. Multicoloured.
457 400r. Geese and lake, Pripjatiskyi Nature Reserve 90 90
458 1000r. Type **132** . . . . . . 2·25 2·25

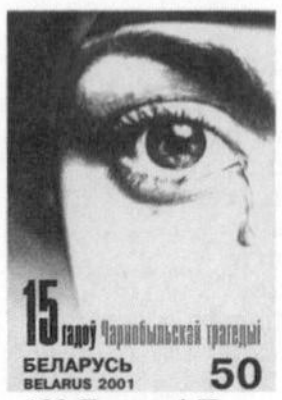

133 Eye and Tear

134 National Arms

2001. 15th Anniv of Chernobyl Nuclear Disaster.
459 **133** 50r. black and rose . . . 10 10

2001. Traditional Costumes (4th series). As T **51**. Multicoloured.
460 200r. 19th-century, Slutsk region 40 40
461 1000r. 19th-century, Pinsk region . . . . 1·90 1·90

2001. 10th Anniv of State Sovereignty.
462 **134** 500r. multicoloured . . . 95 95

135 Union Emblem

138 Figures encircling Globe

137 King and Courtier ("The blue suit made inside out")

2001. 10th Anniv of Union of Independent States.
463 **135** 195r. multicoloured . . . 30 30

2001. No. 166 surch **400**.
464 400r. on 1500r. mauve . . . 60 60

2001. Folk Tales. Multicoloured.
465 100r. Type **137** 15 15
466 200r. Horse-drawn coach ("Okh and the golden snuff-box") 35 35

2001. United Nations Year of Dialogue among Civilizations.
467 **138** 400r. multicoloured . . . 60 60

139 Otto Schmidt

141 Wind-surfer

2001. 110th Birth Anniv of Otto Yulievich Schmidt (scientist and Arctic explorer). Sheet 78 × 74 mm.
MS468 **139** 3000r. multicoloured 4·50 4·50

2001. Surch.
469 400r. on 100r. blue (No. 159) 55 55
470 400r. on 600r. red (No. 163) 55 55
471 400r. on 1500r. blue (No. 167) 55 55
472 400r. on 3300r. yellow (No. 173) 55 55
473 1000r. on 100r. black and green (No. 293) . . . . . 1·40 1·40
474 1000r. on 180r. brown and red (No. 102) . . . . . . 1·40 1·40
475 1000r. on 280r. green and blue (No. 104) . . . . . . 1·40 1·40

2001. Aquatic Sports. Multicoloured.
476 200r. Type **141** 25 25
MS477 102 × 66 mm. 1000r. Water-skier . . . . 1·40 1·40

142 Arms of Francisk Skorina

144 Calligraphy

143 Building Facade

2001. Architecture and Arms. Multicoloured.
478 1000r. Type **142** . . . . . . 1·25 1·25
479 2000r. City Hall, Minsk . . . 2·50 2·50
480 3000r. City Hall, Nesvizh . . 4·00 4·00
481 5000r. City Hall, Cherchersk 6·50 6·50

2001. House of Mercy (Orthodox Church humanitarian centre), Minsk.
495 **143** 200r. multicoloured . . . 25 25

2001. Christmas (496) and New Year (497). Multicoloured.
496 100r. Type **144** 15 15
497 100r. Snowy scene contained in bauble 15 15

145 E. V. Klumov

2001. 125th Birth Anniv of E. V. Klumov (surgeon and resistance worker).
498 **145** 100r. multicoloured . . . 15 15

146 Ski Slalom

2002. Winter Olympics, Salt Lake City, USA (1st issue). Multicoloured.
499 300r. Type **146** 35 35
500 300r. Figure skating 35 35
501 500r. Biathlon 70 70
502 500r. Ski jumping 70 70
See also No. **MS**507.

147 *Formica rufa*

2002. Ants. Multicoloured.
503 200r. Type **147** 25 25
504 1000r. Grubs and worker ants (vert) . . . . 1·25 1·25
MS505 100 × 72 mm. 1000r. No. 504 plus label (vert) forming a composite design . . . . . . 1·25 1·25

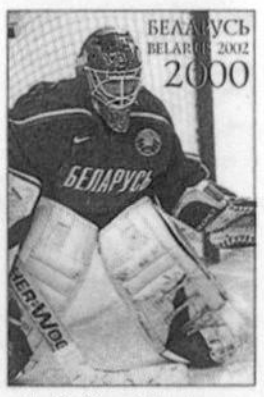

148 Woman carrying Corn (Dozhinki Feast)

149 Ice Hockey Player

2002.
506 **148** B (55r.) black and yellow 15 15

2002. Winter Olympic Games, Salt Lake City, USA (2nd issue). Sheet 100 × 70 mm.
MS507 **149** 2000r. multicoloured 2·40 2·40

2002. As T **113** but inscr "2002".
508 **113** A black and blue 10 10
No. 508 was for use on inland letters.

150 Clown riding Unicycle

151 Yanka Kupala

2002. Europa. Circus. Multicoloured.
509 400r. Type **150** 60 60
510 500r. Horse 80 80

2002. 120th Birth Annivs of Poets. Multicloured.
511 100r. Type **151** 10 10
512 100r. Yacub Kolas 10 10
MS513 100 × 70 mm. 500r. × 2 Nos. 511/12 . . . . 1·10 1·10

152 Church, Polotsk

153 Clover *Trifolium*

2002. No value expressed. Multicoloured.
514 H (236r.) Type **152** 30 30
515 C (314r.) Railway Station, Brest 35 35
No. 514 was for use on letters up to 20 grams to Russia, Lithuania, Latvia, Uzbekistan, Tadjikistan and Turkmenistan.
No. 515 was for use on air-mail letters up to 20 grams to the same countries.

2002. Flowers. Multicoloured. Self-adhesive gum.
516 30r. Type **153** 10 10
517 50r. Matricaria 10 10
518 B (75r.) Flax (*Linium*) . . . 10 10
519 A (90r.) Cornflower (*Centaurea cyanus*) 15 15
520 100r. Pasque flower (*Pulsatilla patens*) 20 20
521 200r. Yellow water lily (Nuphar lutea) 25 25
522 H (236r.) Campanula 30 30
523 C (314r.) Rhododendron . . 35 35
524 500r. Fireweed (*Chamaenerion angustifolium*) 60 60
No. 518 was for use on post cards within Belarus.
No. 519 was for use on letters up to 20 grams within Belarus.
No. 522 was for use on letters up to 20 grams to Russia, Lithuania, Latvia, Uzbekistan, Tadjikistan and Turkmenistan.
No. 523 was for use on airmail letters up to 20 grams to Russia, Lithuania, Latvia, Uzbekistan, Tadjikistan and Turkmenistan.

154 Go-Kart

2002. Children's Activities. Multicoloured.
525 90r. Type **154** 10 10
526 239r. Model aircraft 30 30

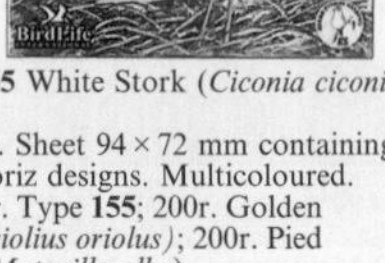

155 White Stork (*Ciconia ciconia*)

2002. Birds. Sheet 94 × 72 mm containing T **155** and similar horiz designs. Multicoloured.
MS527 200r. Type **155**; 200r. Golden oriole (*Oriolius oriolus*); 200r. Pied wagtail (*Matacilla alba*) 90 90

156 Bridge over River Svisloch, Minsk

2002. Bridges.
528 **156** 200r. black, mauve and blue 15 15
529 – 300r. multicoloured . . . 35 35
530 – 500r. black, blue and green 55 55
DESIGNS: 200r. Type **156**; 300r. Bridge over River Sozh, Gomel; 500r. Bridge over River Zapadnaja Dvina, Vitebsk.

157 Lake, Braslav

2002. International Year of Eco-Tourism.
531 **157** 300r. multicoloured . . . 30 30

158 "By the Church" (F. Rushchits)

2002. Art. Multicoloured.
532 300r. Type **158** 25 25
533 300r. "Battle at Nemiga" (M. Philippovich) (horiz) 25 25

159V. V. Kovalyonok and P. I. Klimuk (cosmonauts)

2002. 45th Anniv of Space Exploration. Sheet 131 × 71 mm.
MS534 **159** 3000r. multicoloured 1·90 1·90

160 Father Christmas

161 Ksimir Malevich and "Black Square"

2002. Christmas and New Year. Multicoloured.
535 300r. Type **160** 30 30
536 300r. Angel 30 30

2003. 125th Birth Anniv of Kasimir Malevich (artist). Sheet 82 × 54 mm.
MS537 **161** 3000r. multicoloured 3·00 3·00

162 Smooth Snake (*Coronella austriaca*)

163 Glass containing Land and Water

2003. Reptiles. Multicoloured.
538 300r. Type **162** 25 25
539 600r. European pond turtle (*Emys orbicularis*) 55 55

2003. International Year of Freshwater.
540 **163** 370r. multicoloured . . . 40 40

164 House Sparrow **165** In-line Skates

2003.
541 **164** 630r. multicoloured . . . 55 55

2003. Children's Sports. Multicoloured.
542 300r. Type **165** 25 25
543 300r. Scooter (vert) 25 25

166 "Europa"

2003. Europa. Poster Art. Multicoloured.
544 400r. Type **166** 35 35
545 700r. Painted wooden panels 65 65

167 Globeflower (*Trollius europaeus*)

168 Women's Costumes, Polesye

2003. Endangered Flora. Multicoloured.
546 270r. Type **167** 15 15
547 740r. Siberian iris (*Iris sibirica*) 55 55

2003. Traditional Costumes. Multicoloured.
548 380r. Type **168** 40 40
549 430r. Men and women's costumes, Mogilyov . . . 45 45

169 470 Class Sailing Dinghy

2003. Dinghy Sailing. Sheet 128 × 78 mm, containing T **169** and similar multicoloured design.
MS550 1000r. Type **169**; 1000r. Laser dinghy (vert) . . . . . 1·75 1·75

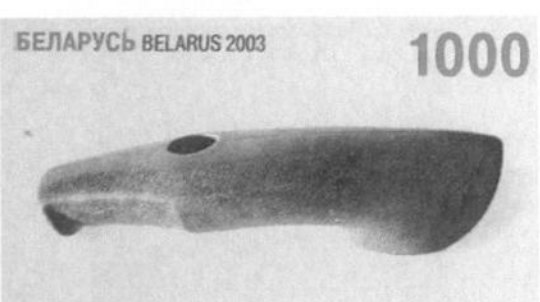

170 Bronze Age Axe Head

2003. National Museum of Natural History and Culture, Minsk. Three sheets, each 82 × 52 mm, containing T **170** and similar multicoloured designs.
MS551 (a) 1000r. Type **170**; (b) 1500r. Bronze age pot (28 × 30 mm); (c) 1500r. 14th-century bowl (28 × 30 mm) 3·50 3·50

171 Horse Stall, Povitie (19th-century)

2003. Architecture. Multicoloured.
552 270r. Type **171** 15 10
553 430r. Church, Sinkevichi (1724) 20 15
554 740r. Watermill, Volma (19th-century) 35 20
MS555 97 × 112 mm. Nos. 552/4 70 70

172 Golden Retriever

173 Young Player holding Ball

2003. Dogs. Multicoloured.
556 270r. Type **172** 15 10
557 380r. Great dane 20 15
558 430r. German shepherd . . . 20 15

2003. Centenary of FIFA (Federation Internationale de Football Association). Multicoloured.
559 380r. Type **173** 20 15
560 380r. Five players (horiz) . . 20 15
561 460r. Three players (horiz) 20 15
562 780r. Player holding ball . . 40 25

174 Angel

2003. Christmas. Multicoloured.
563 380r. Type **174** 20 10
564 780r. Grandfather Frost . . . 40 25

BELGIAN CONGO Pt. 4

A Belgian colony in Central Africa. Became independent in July 1960. For later issues see Congo, Zaire, Democratic Republic of Congo, Katanga and South Kasai.

100 centimes = 1 franc.

INDEPENDENT STATE OF THE CONGO

The Independent State of the Congo was established in 1885, with King Leopold II of the Belgians as ruler.

1 Leopold II

5 Leopold II

1886. Various frames.
1 **1** 5c. green . . . . 8·25 14·50
2 10c. red . . . . 2·75 3·00
3 25c. blue . . . . 32·00 25·00
4 50c. green . . . . 5·50 6·50
5 5f. lilac £375 £190

1887. Surch **COLIS-POSTAUX Fr. 3.50**.
6 **1** 3f.50 on 5f. lilac £300 £600

1887.
7 **5** 5c. green 45 70
8 10c. red . . . . 1·00 85
9 25c. blue 90 90
10 50c. brown . . . . 40·00 14·50
11 50c. grey . . . . 2·25 11·50
12 5f. lilac £800 £300
13 5f. grey . . . . 90·00 75·00
14 10f. orange £350 £225

1887. Surch **COLIS-POSTAUX Fr. 3.50**.
15 **5** 3f.50 on 5f. violet £700 £400

1889. Surch **COLIS-POSTAUX Fr. 3.50** in frame.
16 **5** 3f.50 on 5f. violet £500 £275
17 3f.50 on 5f. grey . . . . . . £100 90·00

7 Port of Matadi

8 Stanley Falls

13 Oil Palms

14 Native Canoe

1894. Inscr "ETAT INDEPENDANT DU "CONGO".
18 **7** 5c. black and blue . . . . . 13·00 13·50
24 5c. black and brown . . . . 2·40 95
30 5c. black and green . . . . 1·25 35
19 **8** 10c. black and brown . . . 13·00 15·00
25 10c. black and blue . . . . 1·60 95
31 10c. black and red . . . . 2·40 50
26 **13** 15c. black and brown . . . 3·75 60
20 – 25c. black and orange . . . 3·25 1·90
32 – 25c. black and blue . . . 3·50 1·25
27 **14** 40c. black and green . . . . 4·75 2·10
21 – 50c. black and green . . . 1·75 1·00
33 – 50c. black and brown . . . 4·75 65
22 – 1f. black and violet . . . . 24·00 10·50
35 – 1f. black and red . . . . . £190 4·25
28 – 3f.50 black and red . . . . £120 70·00
23 – 5f. black and red . . . . . 38·00 19·00
29 – 10f. black and green . . . . £100 16·00
DESIGNS—HORIZ: 25c. Inkissi Falls; 50c. Railway Bridge over the M'pozo; 1f. African elephant hunt; 3f.50 Congo village; 10f. "Deliverance" (stern wheel paddle-steamer). VERT: 5f. Bangala Chief Morangi and wife.

BELGIAN CONGO

The Congo was annexed to Belgium in 1908 and was renamed the Belgian Congo.

1909. Nos. 23, 26/29 and 30/33 optd **CONGO BELGE**.
36A **7** 5c. black and green . . . 2·40 1·40
37A **8** 10c. black and red . . . . 3·00 1·40
38A **13** 15c. black and brown . . 5·00 2·50
49 – 25c. black and blue . . . 50 1·75
50 **14** 40c. black and green . . . 2·40 2·10
51 – 50c. black and brown . . 5·00 1·75
52 – 1f. black and red . . . . 24·00 8·50
53 – 3f.50 black and red . . . 24·00 14·50
54 – 5f. black and red . . . . 42·00 20·00
55b – 10f. black and green . . . 85·00 21·00

1909. As 1894 issue but inscr "CONGO BELGE".
56 **7** 5c. black and green 75 85
57 **8** 10c. black and red 60 65
58 **13** 15c. black and brown . . . 19·00 11·00
59 – 50c. black and bistre . . . . 3·25 2·75

1910. As 1894 issue but inscr "CONGO BELGE BELGISCH-CONGO" with values in French and Flemish.
60 **7** 5c. black and green 40 20
61 **8** 10c. black and red 50 15
62 **13** 15c. black and brown . . . 35 10
63 – 25c. black and blue . . . . 1·40 25
64 **14** 40c. black and green . . . . 1·75 1·90
65 – 50c. black and bistre . . . . 3·00 1·60
66 – 1f. black and red . . . . . 4·50 2·10
68 – 3f. black and red . . . . . 21·00 12·50
67 – 5f. black and red . . . . . 20·00 19·00
69 – 10f. black and green . . . . 32·00 18·00

32 Port of Matadi

33 Stanley Falls

34 Inkissi Falls

1915. New types as **32** to **34** (with value in words at top) and other types as 1910 all inscr "CONGO BELGE" and "BELGISCH-CONGO".
70 **32** 5c. black and green 30 15
71 **33** 10c. black and red 45 35
72b **13** 15c. black and green 55 35
73 **34** 25c. black and blue . . . . 1·00 25

74 14 40c. black and red . . . . 3·75 1·90
75 – 50c. black and red . . . . 7·00 1·50
76 – 1f. black and olive . . . . 2·75 65
77 – 5f. black and orange . . . 1·90 1·00

1918. Types as before, surch with red cross and premium.
78 32 5c.+10c. blue and green . . 25 90
79 33 10c.+15c. blue and red . . . 30 85
80 13 15c.+20c. blue and green . . 35 85
81 34 25c.+25c. blue 45 95
82 14 40c.+40c. blue and red . . . 50 1·25
83 – 50c.+50c. blue and red . . . 45 1·50
84 – 1f.+1f. blue and olive . . . 2·25 2·50
85 – 5f.+5f. blue and orange . . 10·50 14·00
86 – 10f.+10f. blue and green . . 85·00 90·00

38 Congo Wharf

1920. Air.
87 38 50c. black and orange . . . 40 10
88 – 1f. black and violet 40 10
89 – 2f. black and blue 65 35
90 – 5f. black and green . . . . 1·00 50
DESIGNS—HORIZ: 1f. District stores; 2f. Native canoes on beach. VERT: 5f. Provincial prison.

1921. Stamps of 1910 surch.
91 14 5c. on 40c. black and green 30 95
92 – 10c. on 5c. black and green 30 35
93 – 15c. on 50c. black and olive 30 80
94 13 25c. on 15c. black & yellow 1·60 95
95 8 30c. on 10c. black and red 30 45
96 – 50c. on 25c. black and blue 1·50 55

1921. Stamps of 1910 optd **1921**.
97 1f. black and red . . . . . . 1·00 75
98 3f. black and red . . . . . . 2·50 2·50
99 5f. black and lake . . . . . 7·00 7·50
100 10f. black and green . . . . 5·75 4·00

1922. Stamps of previous issues variously surch without bars.
101 – 5c. on 50c. black and lake (No. 75) 35 60
102 32 10c. on 5c. black and green (No. 70) 30 25
114 8 0.25 on 30c. on 10c. black and red (No. 95) . . . . 13·00 13·50
115 33 0.25 on 30c. on 10c. black and red (No. 104) . . . 9·50 13·00
103 14 25c. on 40c. black and lake (No. 74) . . . . 2·00 30
104 33 30c. on 10c. black and red (No. 71) 25 30
105 34 50c. on 25c. black and blue (No. 73) 40 25

1922. Stamps of 1915 surch with new value and two bars through old values.
108 32 10c. on 5c. black & green 90 95
110 – 10c. on 1f. black & olive 1·00 1·40
112 14 25c. on 40c. black & lake 60 60
113 – 25c. on 5f. blk & orange 1·90 2·40

46 Wood Carver 56 Native Cattle

1923.
117 A 5c. yellow 15 10
118 B 10c. green 15 10
119 C 15c. brown 15 10
120 D 20c. olive 15 10
121 E 20c. green 15 10
122 F 25c. brown 15 10
123 46 30c. red . . . . 45 1·40
124 30c. olive 25 45
125 35c. green . . . . 3·00 1·90
126 D 40c. purple 20 10
142 56 45c. purple 45 25
127 G 50c. blue 25 30
128 50c. orange 35 10
143 56 60c. red 30 20
129 E 75c. orange 20 20
130 75c. blue 40 85
131 46 75c. red 60 15
132 H 1f. brown 30 20
133 1f. blue 30 10
134 1f. red 65 10
135 D 1f.25 blue 30 35
136 1f.50 blue 30 35
137 1f.75 blue . . . . 3·25 2·75
138 I 3f. brown . . . . 4·00 2·50
139 J 5f. grey . . . . 8·25 5·00
140 K 10f. black . . . . 20·00 9·00
DESIGNS: A, Ubangi woman; B, Baluba woman; C, Babuende woman; D, Ubangi man; E, Weaver; F, Basketmaker; G. Archer; H, Potter; I, Rubber worker; J, Palm oil; K, African elephant.

55 Native Canoe 58 H. M. Stanley

1925. Great War Colonial Memorial Fund. Inscr in French or in Flemish.
141a 55 25c.+25c. black and red 45 2·25

1927. No. 136 surch **1.75**.
144 1.75 on 1f. 50 blue 45 35

1928. 50th Anniv of Stanley's Exploration of the Congo.
145 58 5c. olive 10 10
146 10c. violet 10 10
147 20c. red 10 10
148 35c. green 85 95
149 40c. brown 45 40
150 60c. sepia 45 20
151 1f. red 40 10
152 1f.60 grey . . . . 4·75 5·00
153 1f.75 blue 85 55
154 2f. brown 70 40
155 2f.75 purple . . . . . . 3·25 35
156 3f.50 red . . . . 1·10 55
157 5f. turquoise 65 45
158 10f. blue 85 45
159 20f. red . . . . 6·50 4·00

59 Nurse weighing Children 60 Doctor and Tent Surgery

1930. Congo Natives Protection Fund.
160 59 10c.+5c. red . . . . . . 60 1·50
161 – 20c.+10c. brown . . . . 80 1·90
162 60 35c.+15c. green . . . . 1·90 3·00
163 – 60c.+30c. purple . . . . 1·75 3·00
164 – 1f.+50c. red . . . . . . 3·50 4·50
165 – 1f.75+75c. blue . . . . 4·75 8·00
166 – 3f.50+1f.50 red . . . . 7·25 17·00
167 – 5f.+2f.50 brown . . . . 9·00 13·00
168 – 10f.+5f. black . . . . . 11·00 18·00
DESIGNS—VERT: 20c. Missionary and child; 1f. Dispenser attending patients. HORIZ: 60c. View of local hospital; 1f.75, Nurses and patients; 3f.50, Nurse bathing baby; 5f. Operating theatre in local hospital; 10f. Children in school.

61 Native Kraal

1930. Air.
169 61 15f. black and sepia . . . 4·25 1·75
170 – 30f. black and purple . . . 5·75 3·75
DESIGN: 30f. Native porters.

1931. Surch.
171 40c. on 35c. grn (No. 148) . . 1·25 95
177 40c. on 35c. green (125) . . 3·50 8·00
178 50c. on 45c. purple (142) . . 1·90 1·25
172 1f.25 on 1f. red (151) . . . 1·40 10
173 2f. on 1f.60 grey (152) . . . 80 25
174 2f. on 1f.75 blue (153) . . . 70 25
179 2f. on 1f.75 blue (137) . . . 7·25 9·50
175 3f.25 on 2f.75 purple (155) 2·25 1·60
180 3f.25 on 3f. brown (138) . . 6·25 7·50
176 3f.25 on 3f.50 red (156) . . 4·25 6·00

67 Sankuru River 68 Flute Players

1931.
181 67 10c. brown 10 30
182 – 15c. grey 10 10
183 – 20c. mauve 15 35
184 – 25c. blue 35 10
185 68 40c. green 35 60
186 – 50c. violet 45 10
187 – 60c. purple 40 60
188 – 75c. red 40 15
189 – 1f. red 85 15
190 – 1f.25 brown 75 10
190b – 1f.50 black . . . . 1·00 65
191 – 2f. blue . . . . 1·00 30
191a – 2f.50 blue . . . . 1·25 1·00
192 – 3f.25 grey . . . . 1·25 1·25
193 – 4f. lilac 80 55
194 – 5f. purple . . . . 1·50 30
195 – 10f. orange . . . . 1·40 1·40
196 – 20f. sepia . . . . 2·40 2·10
DESIGNS—HORIZ: 15c., 25c. Native kraals (different views); 20c. Waterfall; 50c. Native musicians (seated); 1f.50, 2f., Riverside dwellings; 2f.50, 3f.25, Okapi; 4f. Canoes on river shore. VERT: 60c. Native musicians (standing); 75c. Mangbethu woman; 1f. Elephant transport; 1f.25., Native chief; 5f. Pressing out tapioca; 10f. Witch doctor; 20f. Woman carrying latex.

69 Fokker F.VIIb/3m over Congo 70 King Albert I

1934. Air
197 69 50c. black 60 65
198 1f. red 85 30
199 1f.50 green 70 15
200 3f. brown 30 20
201 4f.50 blue 90 10
202 5f. red 95 10
203 15f. purple . . . . 2·10 85
204 30f. red . . . . 2·50 2·40
205 50f. violet . . . . 7·00 2·25

1934. Death of King Albert.
206 70 1f.50 black 90 55

71 The Kings of Belgium

1935. 50th Anniv of Independent State of the Congo.
207 71 50c. green . . . . 1·10 1·10
208 1f.25 red . . . . 1·10 15
209 1f.50 purple . . . . 1·10 15
210 2f.40 orange . . . . 2·75 3·25
211 2f.50 blue . . . . 2·75 1·75
212 4f. violet . . . . 3·00 1·90
213 5f. brown . . . . 3·00 3·25

1936. Air. Surch **3.50F**.
214 69 3f.50 on 3f. brown 25 10

1936. King Albert Memorial Fund. Surch **+ 50 c**.
215 71 1f.50+50c. purple . . . . 2·75 6·75
216 2f.50+50c. blue . . . . . 1·90 5·00

74 Queen Astrid and Congo Children 76 R. Molindi

75 Mitumba Forest

1936. Queen Astrid Fund for Congo Children.
217 74 1f.25+5c. brown . . . . . 70 1·25
218 1f.50+10c. red . . . . . . 80 1·75
219 2f.50+25c. blue . . . . . 1·25 2·50

1937. Promotion of National Parks. (a) Sheet (140 × 111 mm) comprising block of four
MS219a 75 4f.50 black and red 3·75 6·25

(b) As T **76**.
220 76 5c. black and violet 10 15
221 – 90c. brown and red 55 75
222 – 1f.50 black and purple . . 35 20
223 – 2f.40 brown and grey . . . 20 30
224 – 2f.50 black and blue . . . 40 40
225 – 4f.50 brown and green . . 80 65
DESIGNS—VERT: 90c. Bamboo-canes; 1f.50, R. Suza; 2f.40, R. Rutshuru. HORIZ: 2f.50, Mt. Karisimbi; 4f.50, Mitumba Forest.

1938. Tourism Congress, Costermansville. Sheet 140 × 120 mm containing Nos. 220/5 but all printed in brown and blue
MS225a 5c. to 4f.50 . . . . . . 24·00 27·00

77 Marabou Stork and Ruppels Griffon

1939. Leopoldville Zoological Gardens.
226 77 1f.+1f. purple . . . . . . 9·75 11·00
227 – 1f.25+1f.25 red . . . . . 8·50 11·00
228 – 1f.50+1f.50 violet . . . . 9·50 11·00
229 – 4f.50+4f.50 green . . . . 7·50 11·00
230 – 5f.+5f. brown . . . . . . 9·50 11·00
DESIGNS: 1f.25, Kob; 1f.50, Young chimpanzees; 4f.50, Crocodiles; 5f. Lioness.

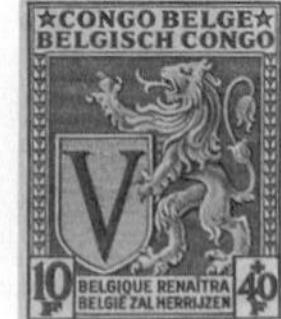
78 King Albert Memorial, Leopoldville 81 "Belgium Shall Rise Again"

1941.
231 78 10c. grey . . . . 1·25 1·40
232 15c. brown 25 20
233 25c. blue 75 35
234 50c. lilac . . . . 1·25 30
235 75c. pink . . . . 1·60 50
236 1f.25 brown . . . . 1·10 35
237 1f.75 orange . . . . 3·00 3·00
238 2f.50 red . . . . 1·60 15
239 2f.75 blue . . . . 1·75 60
240 5f. olive . . . . 3·75 2·75
241 10f. red . . . . 4·00 2·75

1941. Surch.
242 – 5c. on 1f.50 black & purple (No. 222) (postage) . . . 15 1·10
243 78 75c. on 1f.75 orange . . . 1·75 2·25
244 – 2f.50 on 2f.40 brown and grey (No. 223) . . . . . 1·40 1·25
245 69 50c. on 1f.50 green (air) . . 90 80

1942. War Relief Fund.
246 81 10f.+40f. green . . . . . 2·25 2·40
247 10f.+40f. blue . . . . . . 2·25 2·40

82 Oil Palms 84 Leopard

1942. (a) Inscr "BELGISCH CONGO BELGE".
248 82 5c. red 10 10
249 – 50f. black and blue . . . . 5·00 1·25
250 – 100f. black and red . . . . 8·75 1·60

(b) Inscr "CONGO BELGE BELGISCH CONGO", or vice versa.
251 82 10c. olive 10 10
252 15c. brown 10 20
253a 20c. blue 10 15
254 25c. purple 10 10
255a 30c. blue 20 10
256 50c. green 35 10
257 60c. brown 30 15
258 – 75c. black and violet . . . 50 10
259a – 1f. black and brown . . . 45 10
260 – 1f.25 black and red . . . 45 10
261 84 1f.75 brown . . . . 1·10 50
262 2f. yellow . . . . 1·25 10
263a 2f.50 red 80 10
264 – 3f.50 olive 60 10
265 – 5f. orange 95 10
266a – 6f. blue . . . . 1·00 10
267a – 7f. black . . . . 1·00 10
268 – 10f. brown 85 10
269a – 20f. black and red . . . . 7·00 9·50
DESIGNS—As Type **82**: 75c. to 1f.25, Head of a native woman; 3f.50 to 10f. Askari sentry. As Type **84**: 20f. Okapi; 28 × 33 mm: 50 f. Head of woman; 100f. Askari sentry.

1944. Red Cross Fund. Surch **Au profit de la Croix Rouge Ten voordeele van het Roode Kruis** (or with French and Flemish reversed) and additional value.
269aa 82 50c.+50f. green . . . . 1·90 1·90
269b – 1f.25+100f. black and red (No. 260) . . . . 7·00 9·50
269c 84 1f.75+100f. brown . . . 7·00 9·50
269d – 3f.50+100f. green (No. 264) . . . . . . 7·00 9·50

87 Driving Slaves to Market
88 Leopold II

1947. 50th Anniv of Abolition of Slavery in Belgian Congo.
270 **87** 1f.25 brown 40 15
270a – 1f.50 violet . . . . 2·25 85
270b – 3f. brown . . . . 2·10 10
271 – 3f.50 blue 30 10
272 **88** 10f. orange 60 20
PORTRAITS–As Type **88**: 1f.50, Lavigerie. 3f. Dhanis. 3f.50, Lambermont.

89 Seated Figure
90 Railway Train and Map

1947. Native masks and carvings as T **89**.
273 **89** 10c. orange 10 10
274 A 15c. blue 10 10
275 B 20c. blue 10 10
276 C 25c. red 20 10
277 D 40c. purple 20 10
278 **89** 50c. brown 55 10
279 A 70c. green 10 20
280 B 75c. purple 25 10
281 C 1f. purple and orange . . 1·50 10
281a A 1f.20 brown and grey . . 85 60
282 D 1f.25 purple and green . . 35 20
282a E 1f.50 red and green . . . 17·00 4·50
282b B 1f.60 blue and grey . . . 1·10 70
283 **89** 2f. red and orange . . . 80 10
283a C 2f.40 green and turquoise 1·00 20
284 A 2f.50 green and brown . . 45 10
284a E 3f. indigo and blue . . . 5·00 10
285 B 3f.50 green and blue . . . 4·00 20
286 C 5f. purple and bistre . . . 1·75 10
287 D 6f. green and orange . . . 1·60 10
287a F 6f.50 brown and red . . . 2·40 10
287b D 8f. green and blue . . . . 2·40 20
288 E 10f. brown and violet . . 12·50 10
289 F 20f. brown and red . . . 30 10
290 E 50f. black and brown . . 4·25 25
291 F 100f. black and red . . . 6·50 85
DESIGNS: A, Seated figure (different); B, Kneeling figure; C, Double mask; D, Mask; E, Mask with tassels; F, Mask with horns.

1948. 50th Anniv of Matadi–Leopoldville Railway.
292 **90** 2f.50 green and blue . . . 1·50 25

91 Globe and 19th-century Full-rigged Ship
92 Allegorical Figure and Map

1949. 75th Anniv of U.P.U.
293 **91** 4f. blue 55 70

1950. 50th Anniv of "Comite Special du Katanga" (Chartered Company).
294 **92** 3f. slate and blue . . . . . 1·90 1·25
295 6f.50 sepia and red . . . . 2·00 75

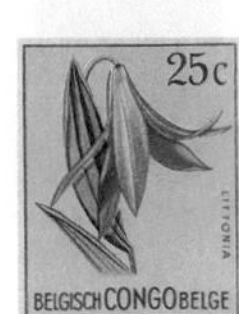

93 "Littonia"
94 St. Francis Xavier

1952. Flowers. Multicoloured.
296 10c. "Dissotis" 10 10
297 15c. "Protea" 10 10
298 20c. "Vellozia" 10 10
299 25c. Type **93** 10 10
300 40c. "Ipomoea" 25 10
301 50c. "Angraecum" 25 10
302 60c. "Euphorbia" 30 20
303 75c. "Ochna" 30 11
304 1f. "Hibiscus" 55 10
305 1f.25 "Protea" . . . . 1·60 1·40
306 1f.50 "Schizoglossum" . . . 45 10
307 2f. "Ansellia" . . . . 1·00 10
308 3f. "Costus" 95 10
309 4f. "Nymphaea" . . . . . . 1·25 10
310 5f. "Thunbergia" . . . . . . 1·60 10
311 6f.50 "Thonningia" . . . . . 1·40 10
312 7f. "Gerbera" . . . . 1·60 10
313 8f. "Gloriosa" . . . . 2·75 30
314 10f. "Silene" . . . . 4·00 20
315 20f. "Aristolochia" . . . . . 5·00 25
316 50f. "Eulophia" . . . . . . 12·50 1·00
317 100f. "Cryptosepalum" . . . 14·50 2·50
SIZES: Nos. 296/315, 21 × 25½ mm. Nos. 316/17, 22½ × 32½ mm.

1953. 400th Death Anniv of St. Francis Xavier.
318 **94** 1f.50c. black and blue . . 1·60 50

95 Lake Kivu

1953. Kivu Festival.
319 **95** 3f. black and red . . . . . 2·25 55
320 7f. brown and blue . . . . 2·50 30

96 Medallion

1954. 25th Anniv of Belgian Royal Colonial Institute. No. 322 has different frame.
321 **96** 4f.50 grey and blue 80 35
322 6f.50 brown and green . . 55 15

97 King Baudouin and Mountains
98 Badge and Map

1955. Inscr "CONGO BELGE . BELGISCH CONGO" or vice versa.
323 **97** 1f.50 black and red . . . . 9·00 1·90
324 – 3f. black and green . . . . 5·75 90
325 – 4f.50 black and blue . . . 5·75 90
326 – 6f.50 black & purple . . . 8·00 30
DESIGNS: 3f. Forest; 4f.50, River; 6f.50, Grassland.

1955. 5th Int Congress of African Tourism. Inscr in Flemish or French.
327 **98** 6f.50 blue . . . . 2·50 1·40

1956. Birth Bicentenary of Mozart. As T **316/17** of Belgium.
328 **316** 4f.50+1f.50 violet . . . . 4·75 5·00
329 **317** 6f.50+2f.50 blue . . . . . 7·00 6·50

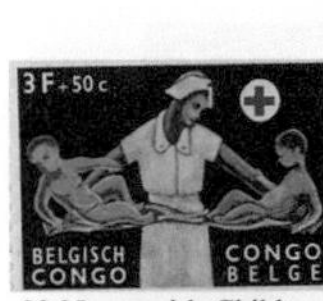

99 Nurse with Children
101 Roan Antelope

100 Belgian Monarchs

1957. Red Cross Fund. Cross in red.
330 **99** 3f.+50c. blue . . . . . . 2·10 2·25
331 – 4f.50+50c. green . . . . . 2·40 2·40
332 – 6f.50+50c. brown . . . . 2·25 2·40
DESIGNS—HORIZ: 4f.50, Doctor inoculating patient; 6f.50, Nurse in tropical kit bandaging patient.

1958. 50th Anniv of Belgian Annexation of the Congo.
333 **100** 1f. red 40 10
334 1f.50 blue 45 10
335 3f. red 95 10
336 5f. green . . . . 1·60 60
337 6f.50 brown . . . . 1·40 25
338 10f. violet . . . . 1·40 55

1959. Wild Animals.
339 **101** 10c. brown, sepia & blue 10 40
340 – 20c. blue and red 10 70
341 – 40c. brown and blue . . . 25 85
342 – 50c. multicoloured 50 60
343 – 1f. black, green & brown 55 45
344 – 1f.50 black and yellow . . 80 40
345 – 2f. black, brown and red 1·00 55
346 – 3f. black, purple & slate 1·00 55
347 – 5f. brown, green & sepia 1·25 50
348 – 6f.50 brn, yellow & blue 1·10 55
349 – 8f. bistre, violet & brown 1·40 80
350 – 10f. multicoloured . . . . 1·50 1·25
DESIGNS—HORIZ: 20c. White rhinoceros; 50c. Demidoff's galago; 1f.50, African buffaloes; 3f. African elephants; 6f.50, Impala; 10f. Eland and common zebras. VERT: 40c. Giraffe; 1f. Gorilla; 2f. Eastern Black and White Colobus monkey; 5f. Okapis; 8f. Giant ground pangolin.

102 Madonna and Child
103 "African Resources"

1959. Christmas.
351 **102** 50c. brn, ochre & chestnut 15 20
352 1f. brown, violet & blue 10 15
353 2f. brown, blue and grey 20 25

1960. 10th Anniv of African Technical Co-operation Commission. Inscr in French or Flemish.
354 **103** 3f. orange and grey . . . 75 1·25

104 High Jumping

1960. Child Welfare Fund.
355 **104** 50c.+25c. blue and red . . 55 1·10
356 – 1f.50+50c. red & green . . 85 1·10
357 – 2f.+1f. green and red . . 90 1·25
358 – 3f.+1f.25 purple & bl . . 1·40 1·75
359 – 6f.50+3f.50 brn & red . . 1·60 2·25
DESIGNS: 1f.50, Hurdling; 2f. Football; 3f. Throwing the javelin; 6f.60, Throwing the discus.

POSTAGE DUE STAMPS

D 54
D 86

1923.
D141 **D 54** 5c. sepia 10 65
D142a 10c. red 10 60
D143 15c. violet 15 60
D144 30c. green 25 30
D145 50c. blue 35 45
D146 1f. grey 40 40

1943.
D270a **D 86** 10c. olive 30 75
D271a 20c. blue 25 70
D272a 50c. green 30 55
D273a 1f. brown 25 65
D274a 2f. orange 30 50

D 99

1957.
D330 **D 99** 10c. brown . . . . . 60 1·00
D331 20c. purple . . . . . 70 1·00
D332 50c. green . . . . . . 1·00 1·00
D333 1f. blue . . . . 1·10 1·10
D334 2f. red . . . . 1·40 1·50
D335 4f. violet . . . . . . 1·50 1·75
D336 6f. blue . . . . 1·90 2·00

For later issues see **CONGO (KINSHASA), ZAIRE REPUBLIC** and **DEMOCRATIC REPUBLIC OF CONGO**.

BELGIAN OCCUPATION OF GERMANY Pt. 7

Stamps used in German territory occupied by Belgian Forces at the end of the War of 1914/18, and including the districts of Eupen and Malmedy, now incorporated in Belgium.

100 centimes = 1 Belgian franc.

1919. Stamps of Belgium optd **ALLEMAGNE DUITSCHLAND**.
1 **51** 1c. orange 45 30
2 2c. brown 45 30
3 3c. grey . . . . 90 1·10
4 5c. green . . . . 1·00 65
5 10c. red . . . . 3·00 1·50
6 15c. violet . . . . 1·25 60
7 20c. purple . . . . 1·90 85
8 25c. blue . . . . 2·75 1·40
9 **63** 25c. blue . . . . 6·50 6·25
10 **52** 35c. black and brown . . . . 2·50 85
11 – 40c. black and green . . . . 3·00 1·50
12 – 50c. black and red . . . . . 11·50 8·25
13 – 65c. black and red . . . . . 4·00 6·50
14 **55** 1f. violet . . . . 30·00 19·00
15 – 2f. grey . . . . 90·00 45·00
16 – 5f. blue (FRANK, No. 194) . 15·00 7·50
17 – 10f. sepia . . . . 90·00 55·00

1920. Stamps of Belgium surch **EUPEN & MALMEDY** and value.
18 **51** 5pf. on 5c. green 75 35
19 10pf. on 10c. red 90 45
20 15pf. on 15c. violet . . . . 1·10 60
21 20pf. on 20c. purple . . . . 1·25 85
22 30pf. on 25c. blue . . . . . 1·90 1·00
23 – 75pf. on 50c. black and red . 28·00 18·00
24 **55** 1m.25 on 1f. violet . . . . . 42·00 21·00

1920. Stamps of Belgium optd **Eupen**.
25 **51** 1c. orange 45 25
26 2c. brown 45 25
27 3c. grey 65 90
28 5c. green 75 65
29 10c. red . . . . 1·50 1·25
30 15c. violet . . . . 1·60 85
31 20c. purple . . . . 2·50 1·60
32 25c. blue . . . . 2·50 2·10
33 **63** 25c. blue . . . . 6·00 6·25
34 **52** 35c. black and brown . . . . 2·50 1·40
35 – 40c. black and green . . . . 3·00 1·90
36 – 50c. black and red . . . . . 9·75 7·00
37 – 65c. black and red . . . . . 4·25 6·75
38 **55** 1f. violet . . . . 30·00 17·00
39 – 2f. grey . . . . 60·00 42·00
40 – 5f. blue (FRANK, No. 194) . 16·00 8·00
41 – 10f. sepia . . . . 80·00 50·00

1920. Stamps of Belgium optd **Malmedy**.
42 **51** 1c. orange 35 30
43 2c. brown 35 30
44 3c. grey 55 90
45 5c. green 80 65
46 10c. red . . . . 1·40 1·10
47 15c. violet . . . . 1·90 1·40
48 20c. purple . . . . 2·75 1·90
49 25c. blue . . . . 2·50 2·00
50 **63** 25c. blue . . . . 6·00 6·00
51 **52** 35c. black and brown . . . . 2·40 1·75
52 – 40c. black and green . . . . 2·75 1·90
53 – 50c. black and red . . . . . 11·00 7·25
54 – 65c. black and red . . . . . 4·25 6·75
55 **55** 1f. violet . . . . 30·00 15·00
56 – 2f. grey . . . . 65·00 42·00
57 – 5f. blue (FRANK, No. 194) . 16·00 10·50
58 – 10f. sepia . . . . 85·00 55·00

POSTAGE DUE STAMPS

1920. Postage Due stamps of Belgium, 1919. (a) Optd **Eupen**.
D1 5c. green . . . . 1·40 1·10
D2 10c. red . . . . 2·40 1·40
D3 20c. green . . . . 7·25 5·75
D4 30c. blue . . . . 6·00 4·50
D5 50c. grey . . . . 24·00 16·50

(b) Optd **Malmedy**.
D 6 5c. green . . . . 2·40 1·10
D 7 10c. red . . . . 4·50 1·40
D 8 20c. green . . . . 24·00 16·00
D 9 30c. blue . . . . 9·25 5·75
D10 50c. grey . . . . 24·00 14·00

BELGIUM Pt. 4

An independent Kingdom of N.W. Europe.

1849. 100 centimes = 1 franc.
2002. 100 cents = 1 euro.

1 "Epaulettes"
3 "Medallions"

1849. Imperf.
1 **1** 10c. brown . . . . £1800 65·00
2a 20c. blue . . . . £1900 45·00

1861. Imperf.
12 **3** 1c. green £150 £100
13 10c. brown . . . . £325 6·00

No.	Type	Description	Unused	Used
14		20c. blue	£350	6·00
15		40c. red	£2750	55·00

1863. Perf.

No.	Type	Description	Unused	Used
24	3	1c. green	38·00	22·00
25		10c. brown	50·00	2·75
26		20c. blue	50·00	3·00
27		40c. red	£325	21·00

5 — 8 — 10 "Small Lion"

1865. Various frames.

No.	Type	Description	Unused	Used
34	5	10c. grey	£120	1·60
35		20c. blue	£190	1·75
36		30c. brown	£425	8·50
37	8	40c. red	£500	15·00
38	5	1f. lilac	£1300	75·00

1866.

No.	Type	Description	Unused	Used
43	10	1c. grey	32·00	10·50
44		2c. blue	£110	70·00
45		5c. brown	£140	65·00

11 — 13 — 14

15 — 20

Types **13** to **20** and all later portraits to Type **38** are of Leopold II.

1869. Various frames.

No.	Type	Description	Unused	Used
46	11	1c. green	7·50	35
59a		2c. blue	15·00	2·00
60		5c. buff	38·00	80
49		8c. lilac	65·00	45·00
50	13	10c. green	26·00	50
51b	14	20c. blue	£100	1·00
62	15	25c. bistre	80·00	1·40
53a	13	30c. buff	65·00	2·40
54b		40c. red	90·00	6·50
55a	15	50c. grey	£180	9·00
56	13	1f. mauve	£325	14·50
57a	20	5f. brown	£1300	£1200

21 — 25

1883. Various frames.

No.	Type	Description	Unused	Used
63	21	10c. red	22·00	1·75
64	–	20c. grey	£140	5·50
65	–	25c. blue	£225	24·00
66	–	50c. violet	£250	25·00

1884. Various frames.

No.	Type	Description	Unused	Used
67	11	1c. olive	13·00	55
68		1c. grey	3·25	30
69		2c. brown	11·00	1·50
70		5c. green	32·00	35
71	25	10c. red	9·00	25
72	–	20c. olive	£140	1·10
73	–	25c. blue on red	11·50	60
74	–	35c. brown	12·50	2·25
75	–	50c. bistre	9·00	1·40
76	–	1f. brown on green	£550	12·50
77	–	2f. lilac	60·00	28·00

32 — 33 — 34 Arms of Antwerp

1893.

No.	Type	Description	Unused	Used
78a	32	1c. grey	65	30
79		2c. yellow	70	85
80		2c. brown	1·25	20
81		5c. green	3·75	30
82	33	10c. brown	1·50	20
83		10c. red	2·25	25
84		20c. olive	12·00	35
85		25c. blue	11·00	25
86a		35c. brown	17·00	1·50
87		50c. brown	40·00	9·50
88		50c. grey	45·00	1·50
89		1f. red on green	55	14·00
90		1f. orange	70·00	4·50
91		2f. mauve	75·00	45·00

The prices for the above and all following issues with the tablet are for stamps with the tablet attached. Without tablet, the prices will be about half those quoted.

See also Nos. 106/8.

1894. Antwerp Exhibition.

No.	Type	Description	Unused	Used
93	34	5c. green on red	5·25	2·50
94		10c. red on blue	2·50	1·75
95		25c. blue on red	95	80

35 St. Michael encountering Satan — 36

1896. Brussels Exhibition of 1897.

No.	Type	Description	Unused	Used
96	35	5c. violet	45	45
97	36	10c. red	7·50	2·75
98		10c. brown	20	25

37 — 38 — 40 St. Martin and the Beggar (from altarpiece by Van Dyck)

1905. Various frames.

No.	Type	Description	Unused	Used
99	37	10c. red	1·10	30
100		20c. olive	22·00	60
101		25c. blue	9·75	60
102		35c. purple	22·00	1·40
103	38	50c. grey	75·00	1·50
104		1f. orange	£100	5·75
105		2f. mauve	65·00	13·50

1907. As T **32** but no scroll pattern between stamps and labels.

No.	Type	Description	Unused	Used
106		1c. grey	1·25	25
107		2c. red	14·00	5·50
108		5c. green	12·00	55

1910. Brussels Exhibition. A. Unshaded background. B. Shaded background. A.

No.	Type	Description	Unused	Used
109	40	1c. (+1c.) grey	85	90
110		2c. (+2c.) purple	7·50	7·00
111		5c. (+5c.) green	2·10	1·90
112		10c. (+5c.) red	2·10	1·90

B.

No.	Type	Description	Unused	Used
113	40	1c. (+1c.) green	2·10	1·90
114		2c. (+2c.) purple	5·25	5·00
115		5c. (+5c.) green	2·10	1·90
116		10c. (+5c.) red	2·10	1·90

1911. Nos. 109/16 optd **1911**.A.

No.	Type	Description	Unused	Used
117	40	1c. (+1c.) grey	20·00	15·00
118		2c. (+2c.) purple	80·00	50·00
119		5c. (+5c.) green	6·50	6·25
120		10c. (+5c.) red	6·50	6·25

B.

No.	Type	Description	Unused	Used
121	40	1c. (+1c.) green	30·00	23·00
122		2c. (+2c.) purple	38·00	21·00
123		5c. (+5c.) green	6·50	6·75
124		10c. (+5c.) red	6·50	6·75

1911. Charleroi Exhibition. Nos. 109/16 optd **CHARLEROI–1911**. A.

No.	Type	Description	Unused	Used
125	40	1c. (+1c.) grey	4·75	2·75
126		2c. (+2c.) purple	12·50	11·50
127		5c. (+5c.) green	7·50	7·75
128		10c. (+5c.) red	7·50	7·75

B.

No.	Type	Description	Unused	Used
129	40	1c. (+1c.) green	4·75	2·75
130		2c. (+2c.) purple	13·00	9·00
131		5c. (+5c.) green	7·50	6·25
132		10c. (+5c.) red	7·50	6·25

42 — 43 — 44

45 Albert I — 46 (Larger head)

1912.

No.	Type	Description	Unused	Used
133	42	1c. orange	10	15
134	43	2c. brown	20	20
135	44	5c. green	10	10
136	45	10c. red	55	40
137		20c. olive	12·50	4·00
138		35c. brown	50	45
139		40c. green	13·50	13·00
140		50c. grey	70	50
141		1f. orange	3·00	2·75
142		2f. violet	15·00	16·00
143	–	5f. purple	70·00	23·00

The 5f. is as Type **45** but larger (23 × 35 mm).

1912. Large head.

No.	Type	Description	Unused	Used
148	46	10c. red	10	15
145		20c. olive	25	30
150		25c. blue	20	25
147		40c. green	35	45

47 Merode Monument — 48 Albert I

1914. Red Cross.

No.	Type	Description	Unused	Used
151	47	5c. (+5c.) red & green	2·25	3·00
152		10c. (+10c.) red & pink	3·75	4·75
153		20c. (+20c.) red & vio	40·00	42·00

1914. Red Cross.

No.	Type	Description	Unused	Used
154	48	5c. (+5c.) red and green	3·25	3·25
155		10c. (+10c.) red	40	30
156		20c. (+20c.) red & violet	9·50	9·75

49 Albert I

1915. Red Cross.

No.	Type	Description	Unused	Used
157	49	5c. (+5c.) red and green	6·25	2·40
158		10c. (+10c.) red and pink	18·00	10·50
159		20c. (+20c.) red & violet	32·00	14·50

51 Albert I — 52 Cloth Hall, Ypres

55 Freeing of the Scheldt

1915.

No.	Type	Description	Unused	Used
170	51	1c. orange	20	15
171		2c. brown	15	15
179		3c. grey	30	20
172		5c. green	65	15
173		10c. red	90	15
174		15c. violet	1·00	20
187		20c. purple	1·90	25
176		25c. blue	45	30
188	52	35c. black and brown	45	20
189	–	40c. black and green	45	20
190	–	50c. black and red	4·00	20
191	55	1f. violet	28·00	65
192	–	2f. grey	18·00	1·50
193	–	5f. blue (FRANKEN)	£250	£110
194	–	5f. blue (FRANK)	1·10	90
195	–	10f. brown	17·00	18·00

DESIGNS: As T **52**: 40c. Dinant; 50c. Louvain. As T **55**: 2f. Annexation of the Congo; 5f. King Albert at Furnes; 10f. The Kings of Belgium.

1918. Red Cross. Surch with new value and cross. Some colours changed.

No.	Type	Description	Unused	Used
222	51	1c.+1c. orange	25	25
223		2c.+2c. brown	35	35
224		5c.+5c. green	1·00	95
225		10c.+10c. red	2·10	1·90
226		15c.+15c. purple	4·50	4·25
227		20c.+20c. brown	9·25	8·00
228		25c.+25c. blue	18·00	17·00
229	52	35c.+35c. black & violet	9·00	8·50
230	–	40c.+40c. black & brown	9·00	8·50
231	–	50c.+50c. black and blue	9·00	8·50
232	55	1f.+1f. grey	28·00	32·00
233	–	2f.+2f. green	65·00	60·00
234	–	5f.+5f. brn (FRANKEN)	£160	£140
235	–	10f.+10f. blue	£500	4·25

63 "Perron" at Liege — 64 Albert I

1919.

No.	Type	Description	Unused	Used
236a	63	25c. blue	2·00	30

1919.

No.	Type	Description	Unused	Used
237	64	1c. brown	15	10
238		2c. olive	15	10
239		5c. green	25	25
240		10c. red	20	25
241		15c. violet	25	20
242		20c. sepia	1·00	1·00
243		25c. blue	1·50	1·25
244		35c. brown	1·90	1·40
245		40c. red	5·75	5·25
246		50c. brown	11·50	9·00
247		1f. orange	38·00	35·00
248		2f. purple	£300	£275
249		5f. red	90·00	75·00
250		10f. red	£110	£100

SIZES: 1c., 2c., $18\frac{1}{2} \times 21\frac{1}{2}$ mm. 5c. to 2f., $22\frac{1}{2} \times 26\frac{1}{2}$ mm. 5f., 10f., $27\frac{1}{2} \times 33$ mm.

67 Discus thrower — 68 Charioteer

1920. Olympic Games, Antwerp.

No.	Type	Description	Unused	Used
256	67	5c. (+5c.) green	1·75	1·40
257	68	10c. (+5c.) red	1·40	1·25
258	–	15c. (+5c.) brown	1·50	1·60

DESIGN—VERT: 15c. Runner.

73 Hotel de Ville, Termonde — 76 Albert I

1920.

No.	Type	Description	Unused	Used
308b	73	65c. black and purple	65	25

1921. Nos. 256/8 surch **20c. 20c.**

No.	Type	Description	Unused	Used
309	67	20c. on 5c. green	50	20
310	68	20c. on 10c. red	30	20
311	–	20c. on 15c. brown	50	25

1921.

No.	Type	Description	Unused	Used
313	76	50c. blue	25	10
314		75c. red	25	25
315		75c. blue	35	10
316		1f. sepia	50	10
317		1f. blue	30	15
318		2f. green	70	20
319		5f. purple	10·50	11·00
320		5f. brown	6·50	7·00
321		10f. red	7·25	5·25

1921. Surch **55c 55c.**

No.	Type	Description	Unused	Used
322	73	55c. on 65c. black & pur	2·00	35

80 — 81 Albert I

1922. War Invalids Fund.

No.	Type	Description	Unused	Used
348	80	20c.+20c. brown	1·40	1·25

1922.

No.	Type	Description	Unused	Used
349	81	1c. orange	10	10
350		2c. olive	15	20
351		3c. brown	10	10
352		5c. slate	10	10
353		10c. green	10	10
354		15c. plum	10	10
355		20c. brown	15	10
356		25c. purple	15	20
357		25c. violet	45	10
358		30c. red	35	10
359		30c. mauve	25	10
360		35c. brown	30	30
361		35c. green	90	30

362 40c. red 35 15
363 50c. bistre 40 15
364 60c. olive . . . . 2·75 10
365 75c. violet 85 55
366 1f. yellow 40 35
367 1f. red 85 15
368 1f.25 blue . . . . 1·10 1·10
369 1f.50 blue . . . . 1·75 40
370 1f.75 blue . . . . 1·50 10
371 2f. blue . . . . 2·25 30
372 5f. green . . . . 25·00 1·40
373 10f. brown . . . . 60·00 7·75

83 Wounded Soldier

1923. War Invalids Fund.
374 **83** 20c.+20c. slate . . . . . . 1·60 1·90

87 Leopold I and Albert I

1925. 75th Anniv of 1st Belgian Stamps.
410 **87** 10c. green . . . . 6·50 6·50
411 15c. violet . . . . 3·00 3·00
412 20c. brown . . . . 3·00 3·00
413 25c. slate . . . . 3·00 3·00
414 30c. red . . . . 3·00 3·00
415 35c. blue . . . . 3·00 3·00
416 40c. sepia . . . . 3·00 3·00
417 50c. brown . . . . 3·00 3·00
418 75c. blue . . . . 3·00 3·00
419 1f. purple . . . . 5·50 5·75
420 2f. blue . . . . 3·50 4·00
421 5f. black . . . . 3·25 3·25
422 10f. red . . . . 6·50 5·75

88 **90**

1925. Anti-T.B. Fund.
423 **88** 15c.+5c. red and mauve . . 20 20
424 30c.+5c. red and grey . . . 20 15
425 1f.+10c. red and blue . . . 85 1·10

1926. Flood Relief. Type of 1922 surch **Inondations 30 c Watersnood**.
426 **81** 30c.+30c. green 70 75

1926. Flood Relief Fund. A. Shaded background. B. Solid background. A.
427 **90** 1f.+1f. blue . . . . 4·25 5·50
B.
428 **90** 1f.+1f. blue . . . . 1·00 1·10

91

92 Queen Elisabeth and King Albert

1926. War Tuberculosis Fund.
429 **91** 5c.+5c. brown 10 15
430 20c.+5c. brown 35 35
431 50c.+5c. violet 20 20
432 **92** 1f.50+25c. blue 55 55
433 5f.+1f. red . . . . 5·50 5·00

1927. Stamps of 1922 surch.
434 **81** 3c. on 2c. olive 10 10
435 10c. on 15c. plum 10 10
436 35c. on 40c. red 20 10
437 1f.75 on 1f.50 blue 90 65

94 Rowing Boat

1927. Anti-T.B. Fund.
438 **94** 25c.+10c. brown 85 75
439 35c.+10c. green 55 75
440 60c.+10c. violet 20 25
441 1f.75+25c. blue . . . . . 1·10 1·00
442 5f.+1f. purple . . . . . . 4·25 4·00

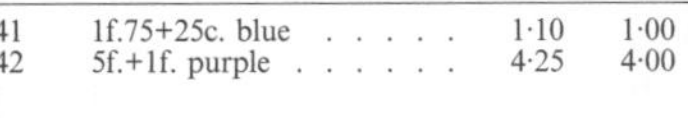

96 Ogives

97 Ruins of Orval Abbey

1928. Orval Abbey Restoration Fund. Inscr "ORVAL 1928" or "ORVAL".
461 **96** 5c.+5c. red and gold . . . 15 20
462 – 25c.+5c. violet and gold . . 30 35
463 – 35c.+10c. green 70 75
464 – 60c.+15c. brown 55 20
465 – 1f.75+25c. blue . . . . . 2·10 1·50
466 – 2f.+40c. purple . . . . . 14·00 14·00
467 – 3f.+1f. red . . . . 13·50 13·00
468 **97** 5f.+5f. lake . . . . 11·00 10·00
469 – 10f.+10f. sepia . . . . . . 11·00 10·00
DESIGNS—VERT: 35c., 2f. Cistercian monk stone-carving; 60c., 1f.75, 3f. Duchess Matilda retrieving her ring.

99 Mons Cathedral

101 Malines Cathedral

1928. Anti-T.B. Fund.
472 **99** 5c.+5c. red 20 20
473 – 25c.+15c. sepia 20 20
474 **101** 35c.+10c. green 85 90
475 – 60c.+15c. brown 25 35
476 – 1f.75+25c. violet . . . . 6·50 6·25
477 – 5f.+5f. purple . . . . . . 14·00 16·00
DESIGNS—As Type **99**: 25c. Tournai Cathedral. As Type **101**: 60c. Ghent Cathedral; 1f.75, St. Gudule Cathedral, Brussels; 5f. Louvain Library.

1929. Surch **BRUXELLES 1929 BRUSSEL 5 c** in frame.
478 **81** 5c. on 30c. mauve 15 10
479 5c. on 75c. violet 20 15
480 5c. on 1f.25c. blue 10 10
The above cancellation, whilst altering the original face value of the stamps, also constitutes a precancel, although stamps also come with additional ordinary postmark. The unused prices are for stamps with full gum and the used prices are for stamps without gum, with or without postmarks. We do not list precancels where there is no change in face value.

104 The Belgian Lion

105 Albert I

1929.
487 **104** 1c. orange 10 10
488 2c. green 35 45
489 3c. brown 10 10
490 5c. green 10 10
491 10c. bistre 10 10
492 20c. mauve 85 25
493 25c. red 30 10
494 35c. green 40 10
495 40c. purple 30 10
496 50c. blue 30 10
497 60c. mauve . . . . 1·60 20
498 70c. brown 90 10
499 75c. blue . . . . 1·40 10
500 75c. brown . . . . 4·75 10
501 **105** 10f. brown . . . . 13·50 3·25
502 20f. green . . . . 75·00 18·00
503a 50f. purple . . . . 22·00 13·00
504a 100f. red . . . . 16·00 17·00

1929. Laying of first Stone towards Restoration of Orval Abbey. Nos. 461/9 optd with crown over ornamental letter "L" and **19-8-29**.
543 5c.+5c. red and gold . . . . 60·00 55·00
544 25c.+5c. violet and gold . . . 60·00 55·00
545 35c.+10c. green . . . . . . 60·00 55·00
546 60c.+15c. brown . . . . . . 60·00 55·00
547 1f.75c.+25c. blue . . . . . . 60·00 55·00
548 2f.+40c. purple . . . . . . 60·00 55·00
549 3f.+1f. red . . . . 60·00 55·00
550 5f.+5f. lake . . . . 60·00 55·00
551 10f.+10f. sepia . . . . 60·00 55·00

109 Canal and Belfry, Bruges

1929. Anti-T.B. Fund.
552 – 5c.+5c. brown 20 25
553 – 25c.+15c. grey . . . . . 75 1·10
554 – 35c.+10c. green 70 75
555 – 60c.+15c. lake 30 35
556 – 1f.75+25c. blue . . . . . 4·50 5·00
557 **109** 5f.+5f. purple . . . . . . 22·00 22·00
DESIGNS—HORIZ: 5c. Waterfall at Coo; 35c. Menin Gate, Ypres; 60c. Promenade d'Orleans, Spa; 1f.75, "Aquitania" and "Dinteldyk" (liners), Antwerp Harbour. VERT: 25c. Bayard Rock, Dinant.

110 Paul Rubens

111 Zenobe Gramme

1930. Antwerp and Liege Exns.
558 **110** 35c. green 40 15
559 **111** 35c. green 40 15

112 Ostend

113 "Leopold II" by Jef Lempoels

1930. Air.
560 **112** 50c. blue 35 25
561 – 1f.50 brown (St. Hubert) 2·00 2·10
562 – 2f. green (Namur) . . . . 2·25 75
563 – 5f. red (Brussels) . . . . 1·50 95
564 – 5f. violet (Brussels) . . . 23·00 23·00

1930. Centenary of Independence.
565 – 60c. purple 30 20
566 **113** 1f. red . . . . 1·10 55
567 – 1f.75 blue . . . . 2·25 2·50
PORTRAITS: 60c. "Leopold I" by Lievin de Winne. 1f.75, King Albert I.

114 Antwerp City Arms

1930. International Philatelic Exhibition, Antwerp. Sheet 138 × 136 mm.
MS568 **114** 4f. (+6f.) green . . . £225 £170

1930. I.L.O. Congress. Nos. 565/7 optd **B.I.T. OCT. 1930.**
569 60c. purple . . . . 1·75 1·90
570 1f. red . . . . 7·25 8·00
571 1f.75 blue . . . . 13·50 15·00

116 Wynendaele **117** Gaesbeek

1930. Anti-T.B. Fund.
572 – 10c.+5c. mauve 20 25
573 **116** 25c.+15c. sepia 55 60
574 – 40c.+10c. purple 60 70
575 – 70c.+15c. slate 45 55
576 – 1f.+25c. red . . . . . . 3·75 4·75
577 – 1f.75+25c. blue . . . . . 3·25 3·25
578 **117** 5f.+5f. green . . . . . . 26·00 29·00
DESIGNS: 10c. Bornhem; 40c. Beloeil; 70c. Oydonck, 1f. Ghent; 1f.75, Bouillon.

1931. Surch **2c**.
579 **104** 2c. on 3c. brown 10 20

1931. Surch **BELGIQUE 1931 BELGIE 10c**.
580 **104** 10c. on 60c. mauve . . . 40 20
See note below No. 480.

121 Albert I

123

1931.
582 **121** 75c. brown (18 × 22 mm) 1·10 10
583 1f. lake (21 × 23½ mm) . . 20 15
584 **123** 1f.25 black 50 35
585 1f.50 purple . . . . . . 1·10 35
586 1f.75 blue 50 10
587 2f. brown 75 15
588 2f.45 violet . . . . . . 2·10 30
589 2f.50 sepia . . . . 8·00 50
590 5f. green . . . . 22·00 85
591 10f. red . . . . 38·00 10·00
See also No. 654.

124 Prince Leopold

1931. Disabled Soldiers' Relief Fund. Brussels National Philatelic Exhibition. Sheet 123 × 161 mm.
MS592 **124** 2f.45+55c. red (sold at 5f.) £200 £140

125 Queen Elisabeth

126 Reaper

127 Mercury

1931. Anti-Tuberculosis Fund.
593 **125** 10c.+5c. brown 25 25
594 25c.+15c. violet 90 55
595 50c.+10c. green 55 45
596 75c.+15c. sepia 45 20
597 1f.+25c. lake . . . . . . 6·00 5·75
598 1f.75+25c. blue . . . . . 4·75 3·50
599 5f.+5f. purple . . . . . . 45·00 45·00

1932. Surch **BELGIQUE 1932 BELGIE 10c**.
600 **104** 10c. on 40c. mauve . . . 2·50 25
601 10c. on 70c. brown . . . 2·50 20
See Note below No. 480.

1932.
602 **126** 2c. green 35 35
603 **127** 5c. red 10 10
604 **126** 10c. green 15 10
605 **127** 20c. lilac 65 15
606 **126** 25c. red 45 10
607 **127** 35c. green . . . . 1·90 10

129 Cardinal Mercier

132

1932. Cardinal Mercier Memorial Fund.
609 **129** 10c.+10c. purple 25 25
610 50c.+30c. mauve . . . . 1·50 1·60
611 75c.+25c. brown . . . . 1·10 1·40
612 1f.+2f. red . . . . 5·00 5·00
613 – 1f.75+75c. blue . . . . . 70·00 60·00
614 – 2f.50+2f.50 brown . . . . 70·00 60·00
615 – 3f.+4f.50 green . . . . . 70·00 60·00
616 – 5f.+20f. purple . . . . . 75·00 60·00
617 – 10f.+40f. red £130 £130
DESIGNS: 1f.75, 3f. Mercier protecting refugees at Malines; 2f.50, 5f. Mercier with busts of Aristotle and Thomas Aquinas; 10f. Mercier when Professor at Louvain University.

1932. Infantry Memorial.
618 **132** 75c.+3f.25 red . . . . . 50·00 50·00
619 1f.75+4f.25 blue . . . . . 50·00 50·00

133 Prof Piccard's Stratosphere Balloon "F.N.R.S.", 1931

134 Hulpe-Waterloo Sanatorium

1932. Scientific Research Fund.
621 **133** 75c. brown . . . . 2·00 25
622 1f.75 blue . . . . 11·00 95
623 2f.50 violet . . . . 13·50 8·75

1932. Anti-T.B. Fund.
624 **134** 10c.+5c. violet 25 25
625 25c.+15c. mauve . . . . 1·40 95
626 50c.+10c. red . . . . . . 1·40 55
627 75c.+15c. brown . . . . 1·00 25
628 1f.+25c. red . . . . . . 9·50 9·00
629 1f.75+25c. blue . . . . . 7·75 7·00
630 5f.+5f. green . . . . . . 70·00 70·00

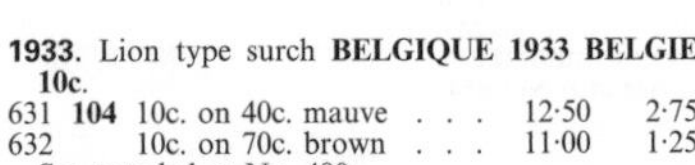

1933. Lion type surch **BELGIQUE 1933 BELGIE 10c**.
631 **104** 10c. on 40c. mauve . . . 12·50 2·75
632 10c. on 70c. brown . . . 11·00 1·25
See note below No. 480.

135 The Transept

138 Anti-T.B. Symbol

1933. Orval Abbey Restoration Fund. Inscr "ORVAL".
633 – 5c.+5c. green . . . . . . 42·00 42·00
634 – 10c.+15c. green . . . . . 40·00 38·00
635 – 25c.+15c. brown . . . . 32·00 30·00
636 **135** 50c.+25c. lake . . . . . 32·00 30·00
637 – 75c.+50c. green . . . . . 32·00 30·00
638 – 1f.+1f.25 lake . . . . . . 32·00 30·00
639 – 1f.25+1f.75 sepia . . . . 32·00 30·00
640 – 1f.75+2f.75 blue . . . . . 48·00 45·00
641 – 2f.+3f. mauve . . . . . 48·00 45·00
642 – 2f.50+5f. brown . . . . . 48·00 45·00
643 – 5f.+20f. purple . . . . . 48·00 45·00
644 – 10f.+40f. blue £180 £170
DESIGNS—VERT: 10c. Abbey Ruins; 75c. Belfry, new abbey; 1f. Fountain, new abbey. HORIZ: 5c. The old abbey; 25c. Guests' Courtyard, new abbey; 1f.25, Cloister, new abbey; 1f.75, Foundation of Orval Abbey in 1131; 2f. Restoration of the abbey, XVI and XVII centuries; 2f.50, Orval Abbey, XVIII century; 5f. Prince Leopold laying foundation stone of new abbey; 10f. The Virgin Mary (30 × 45 mm).

1933. Anti-tuberculosis Fund.
646 **138** 10c.+5c. grey 55 45
647 25c.+15c. mauve . . . . 1·90 2·00
648 50c.+10c. brown . . . . 1·60 1·50
649 75c.+15c. sepia . . . . . 20·00 35
650 1f.+25c. red . . . . . . 9·75 11·50
651 1f.75+25c. blue . . . . . 14·00 16·00
652 5f.+5f. purple . . . . . . 95·00 £100

1934. Lion type surch **BELGIQUE 1934 BELGIE 10c**.
653 **104** 10c. on 40c. mauve . . . 11·00 1·25
See note below No. 480.

1934. King Albert's Mourning Stamp.
654 **121** 75c. black 20 10

140 Peter Benoit

141 Brussels Palace

1934. Benoit Centenary Memorial Fund.
658 **140** 75c.+25c. brown . . . . 4·50 4·00

1934. International Exhibition, Brussels.
659 – 35c. green 75 20
660 **141** 1f. red . . . . 1·40 30
661 – 1f.50 brown . . . . . . 3·75 80
662 – 1f.75 blue . . . . . . 4·00 20
DESIGNS: 35c. Congo Palace; 1f.50, Old Brussels; 1f.75, Grand Palace of the Belgian section.

142 King Leopold III

143 King Leopold III

1934. War Invalids' Fund. (a) Size 18 × 22 mm. (b) Size 21 × 24 mm. (i) Exhibition Issue.
663 **142** 75c.+25c. green (a) . . . 14·50 14·00
664 1f.+25c. purple (b) . . . 14·00 13·00

(ii) Ordinary postage stamps.
665 **142** 75c.+25c. purple (a) . . . 3·25 3·25
666 1f.+25c. red (b) . . . . . 5·50 5·00

1934.
667 **142** 70c. green 30 10
668 75c. brown 40 25
669 **143** 1f. red . . . . 3·00 30

144 Health Crusader

1934. Anti-tuberculosis Fund. Cross in red.
670 **144** 10c.+5c. black 20 25
671 25c.+15c. brown . . . . 2·00 2·10
672 50c.+10c. green . . . . 1·25 1·40
673 75c.+15c. purple 70 65
674 1f.+25c. red . . . . . . 9·00 9·00
675 1f.75+25c. blue . . . . . 7·25 6·75
676 5f.+5f. purple . . . . . . 90·00 95·00

145 The Royal Children

1935. Queen Astrid's Appeal.
680 **145** 35c.+15c. green 75 85
681 70c.+30c. purple 75 80
682 1f.75+50c. blue . . . . . 3·25 3·50

146 "Mail-diligence"

1935. Brussels Int Exn.
683 **146** 10c.+10c. olive 35 45
684 25c.+25c. brown . . . . 1·75 1·75
685 35c.+25c. green . . . . . 2·50 2·50

1935. Air. Surch with new value twice.
686 **112** 1f. on 1f.50 brown . . . 35 45
687 4f. on 5f. red . . . . . . 7·00 6·50

148 Francis of Taxis

151 Queen Astrid

1935. Brussels Philatelic Exhibition (SITEB). Sheet 93 × 118 mm.
MS688 **148** 5f.+5f. grey £200 £120

1935. Death of Queen Astrid. Mourning Stamp.
713 **151** 70c.+5c. black 10 15

1935. Anti-tuberculosis Fund. Black borders.
714 **151** 10c.+5c. olive 10 15
715 25c.+15c. brown 20 25
716 35c.+5c. green 20 20
717 50c.+10c. mauve 30 30
718 1f. +25c. red 80 90
719 1f.75+25c. blue . . . . . 1·40 1·50
720 2f.45+55c. violet . . . . 2·40 2·75

152 State arms

153

155 King Leopold III

1936.
727 **152** 2c. green 10 10
728 5c. orange 10 10
729 10c. olive 10 10
730 15c. blue 10 10
731 20c. violet 10 10
732 25c. red 10 10
733 25c. yellow 10 10
734 30c. brown 10 10
735 35c. green 10 10
736 40c. lilac 20 10
737 50c. blue 25 10
738 60c. grey 15 10
739 65c. mauve . . . . 1·75 15
740 70c. green 30 15
741 75c. mauve 50 15
742 80c. green . . . . 7·25 75
743 90c. violet 45 10
744 1f. brown 50 10

1936. Various frames. (a) Size 17$\frac{1}{2}$ × 22 mm.
745 **153** 70c. brown 25 10
746 75c. olive 25 10
747 1f. red 15 10

(b) Size 21 × 24 mm.
748 **153** 1f. red 30 10
749 1f.20 brown . . . . . . 1·60 20
750 1f.50 mauve 35 30
751 1f.75 blue 15 20
752 1f.75 red 20 10
753 2f. violet 95 95
754 2f.25 black 15 15
755 2f.50 red . . . . 5·50 40
756 3f.25 brown 25 20
757 5f. green . . . . 1·10 40
Nos. 746/7, 751/2, 754/5 and 757 are inscribed "BELGIE BELGIQUE".

1936.
760 **155** 1f.50 mauve 50 10
761 1f.75 blue 20 15
762 2f. violet 40 20
763 2f.25 violet 25 20
764 2f.45 black . . . . . . 32·00 55
765 2f.50 black . . . . . . 3·50 25
770 3f. brown . . . . 1·25 25
766 3f.25 brown 30 20
771 4f. blue . . . . 3·50 10
767 5f. green . . . . 2·00 40
772 6f. red . . . . 5·00 50
768 10f. purple 35 20
769 20f. red . . . . 1·10 30
See also No. 2775.

156 Borgerhout Town Hall

1936. Borgerhout Philatelic Exhibition. Sheet 95 × 119 mm.
MS775 **156** 70c.+30c. brown . . 90·00 55·00

157 Charleroi Town Hall

1936. Charleroi Philatelic Exhibition. Sheet 95 × 119 mm.
MS776 **157** 2f.45+55c. blue . . . 65·00 42·00

158 Prince Baudouin

159 Queen Astrid and Prince Baudouin

1936. Anti-tuberculosis Fund.
777 **158** 10c.+5c. brown 10 10
778 25c.+5c. violet 15 15
779 35c.+5c. green 15 10
780 50c.+5c. brown 25 25
781 70c.+5c. olive 15 15
782 1f.+25c. red . . . . . . 1·10 1·25
783 1f.75+25c. blue . . . . . 1·50 1·75
784 2f.45+2f.55 purple . . . . 3·50 4·25

1937. Stamp of 1929 surch **BELGIQUE 1937 BELGIE 10c**.
785 **104** 10c. on 40c. purple . . . 20 20
See note below No. 480.

1937. International Stamp Day.
786 **158** 2f.45c.+2f.55c. slate . . . 1·60 1·75

1937. Queen Astrid Public Utility Fund.
787 **159** 10c.+5c. purple 10 10
788 25c.+5c. olive 10 15
789 35c.+5c. green 10 15
790 50c.+5c. violet 20 25
791 70c.+5c. black 10 10
792 1f.+25c. red 90 95
793 1f.75c.+25c. blue . . . . 1·90 2·00
794 2f.45c.+1f.55c. brown . . 4·50 4·75

160 Queen Elisabeth

161 Princess Josephine Charlotte

1937. Eugene Ysaye Memorial Fund.
795 **160** 70c.+5c. black 20 25
796 1f.75+25c. blue 55 70
MS797 113 × 146 mm. **160** 1f.50+2f.50 red (2); 2f.45+3f.55, violet (2) . . . . 40·00 16·00
See also **MS**1963.

1937. Anti-tuberculosis Fund.
798 **161** 10c.+5c. green 15 10
799 25c.+5c. brown 20 20
800 35c.+5c. green 15 20
801 50c.+5c. olive 25 25
802 70c.+5c. purple 15 10
803 1f.+25c. red . . . . . . 1·10 1·10
804 1f.75+25c. blue . . . . . 85 1·10
805 2f.45+2f.55 purple . . . . 3·50 3·00

163 King Albert Memorial, Nieuport

1938. King Albert Memorial Fund. Sheet 138 × 115 mm.
MS809 **163** 2f.45+7f.55 red . . . 13·00 13·00

164 King Leopold

1938. Aeronautical Propaganda.
810 **164** 10c.+5c. purple 15 10
811 35c.+5c. green 25 25
812 70c.+5c. black 40 30
813 1f.75+25c. blue . . . . . 2·40 2·25
814 2f.45+2f.55 violet . . . . 35 3·50

165 Basilica of the Sacred Heart, Koekelberg

1938. Building (Completion) Fund.
815 **165** 10c.+5c. brown 10 15
816 – 35c.+5c. green 10 15
817 **165** 70c.+5c. grey 10 15
818 – 1f.+25c. red 45 40
819 **165** 1f.75+25c. blue 45 40
820 – 2f.45+2f.55 red . . . . . 3·25 3·00
821 – 5f.+5f. green . . . . . . 8·50 9·00
MS822 95 × 120 mm. 5f.+5f. violet (as 821) . . . . 12·50 12·00
DESIGNS—HORIZ: 35c., 1f., 2f.45, Front view of Basilica. VERT: 5f. Interior view.

1938. Surch **2F50**.
823 **155** 2f.50 on 2f.45 black . . . 9·50 25

167 Exhibition Pavilion

170 Prince Albert of Liege

1938. International Exhibition, Liege (1939). Inscr "LIEGE 1939 LUIK".
824 – 35c. green 10 15
825 **167** 1f. red 25 20
826 – 1f.50 brown . . . . . . 1·25 45
827 – 1f.75 blue . . . . 1·25 10

DESIGNS—VERT: 35c. View of Liege. HORIZ: 1f.50, R. Meuse at Liege; 1f.75, Albert Canal and King Albert.

1938. Koekelberg Basilica Completion Fund. Surch.
828 – 40c. on 35c.+5c. green (No. 816) 40 50
829 **165** 75c. on 70c.+5c. grey . . 30 35
830 – 2f.50+2f.50 on 2f.45+2f.55 red (No. 820) . . . . . 5·50 5·00

1938. Anti-tuberculosis Fund.
831 **170** 10c.+5c. brown 10 15
832 30c.+5c. purple 10 15
833 40c.+5c. olive 10 15
834 75c.+5c. grey 10 15
835 1f.+25c. red 95 90
836 1f.75+25c. blue 95 85
837 2f.50+2f.50 green . . . . 4·25 4·25
838 5f.+5f. purple . . . . . . 8·50 8·50

171 King Leopold and Royal Children

1939. 5th Anniv of Int Red Cross Society.
839 – 10c.+5c. brown 10 10
840 – 30c.+5c. red 10 15
841 – 40c.+5c. olive 10 15
842 **171** 75c.+5c. black 20 20
843 – 1f.+25c. red . . . . . . 1·50 1·50
844 **171** 1f.75+25c. blue 95 90
845 – 2f.50+2f.50 violet . . . . 1·60 1·75
846 – 5f.+5f. green . . . . . . 5·00 5·25
DESIGNS—VERT: 10c. H. Dunant; 30c. Florence Nightingale; 40c. and 1f. Queen Elisabeth and Royal children; 2f.50, Queen Astrid. HORIZ: 5f. Queen Elisabeth and wounded soldier (larger).

173 Rubens's House (after engraving by Harrewijn)

175 Portrait by Memling

1939. Rubens's House Restoration Fund.
847 **173** 10c.+5c. brown 10 10
848 – 40c.+5c. purple 15 15
849 – 75c.+5c. green 25 30
850 – 1f.+25c. red . . . . . . 1·40 1·40
851 – 1f.50+25c. brown . . . . 1·75 1·75
852 – 1f.75+25c. blue . . . . . 2·75 2·75
853 – 2f.50+2f.50 purple . . . . 10·50 10·50
854 – 5f.+5f. grey . . . . . . 13·50 15·00
DESIGNS—As Type **173**: VERT: 40c. "Rubens's Sons, Albert and Nicholas"; 1f. "Helene Fourment (2nd wife) and Children"; 1f.50, "Rubens and Isabella Brant" (1st wife); 1f.75, Rubens (after engraving by Pontius); 2f.50, "Straw Hat" (Suzanne Fourment). HORIZ: 75c. Arcade of Rubens's house. 35 × 45 mm: 5f. "The Descent from the Cross".

1939. Exn of Memling's Paintings, Bruges.
855 **175** 75c.+75c. olive . . . . . 1·40 1·40

177 Orval Abbey Cloisters and Belfry

180 Thuin

1939. Orval Abbey Restoration Fund. Inscr "ORVAL".
861 – 75c.+75c. olive . . . . . 3·50 3·50
862 **177** 1f.+1f. red . . . . 1·25 1·25
863 – 1f.50+1f.50 brown . . . . 1·25 1·25
864 – 1f.75+1f.75 blue . . . . . 2·25 2·25
865 – 2f.50+2f.50 mauve . . . . 6·25 6·75
866 – 5f.+5f. purple . . . . . . 6·75 6·75
DESIGNS—As Type **177**: VERT: 75c. Monks in laboratory. HORIZ: 1f.50, Monks harvesting; 1f.75, Aerial view of Orval Abbey; 52½ × 35½ mm: 2f.50, Cardinal Van Roey, Statue of the Madonna and Abbot of Orval; 5f. Kings Albert and Leopold III and shrine.

1939. Anti-tuberculosis Fund. Belfries.
868 – 10c.+5c. olive 10 10
869 **180** 30c.+5c. brown 10 10
870 – 40c.+5c. purple 10 15
871 – 75c.+5c. grey 10 10
872 – 1f.+25c. red . . . . . . 95 1·10
873 – 1f.75+25c. blue 70 70
874 – 2f.50+2f.50 brown . . . . 7·25 7·25
875 – 5f.+5f. violet . . . . . . 8·50 8·25
DESIGNS—As Type **180**: 10c. Bruges; 40c. Lier; 75c. Mons. LARGER (21½ × 34 mm): 1f. Furnes; 1f.75, Namur; 2f.50, Alost; 5f. Tournai.

182 Arms of Mons

183 Painting

184 Monks studying Plans of Orval Abbey

1940. Winter Relief Fund.
901 **182** 10c.+5c. black, red and green 10 10
902 – 30c.+5c. multicoloured . . 10 10
903 – 40c.+10c. multicoloured 10 10
904 – 50c.+10c. multicoloured 10 10
905 – 75c.+15c. multicoloured 10 10
906 – 1f.+25c. multicoloured . . 35 35
907 – 1f.75c.+50c. mult 40 35
908 – 2f.50c.+2f.50c. olive, red and black . . . . . . 1·40 1·10
909 – 5f.+5f. multicoloured . . 1·60 1·25
MS910 103 × 145 mm. Nos. 901/9 each in first colour given, together with red . . . . 13·00 13·00
DESIGNS: 30c. to 5f. Arms of Ghent, Arlon, Bruges, Namur, Hasselt, Brussels, Antwerp and Liege, respectively.

1941. Orval Abbey Restoration Fund.
935 **183** 10c.+15c. brown 35 35
936 – 30c.+30c. grey 35 35
937 – 40c.+60c. brown 35 35
938 – 50c.+65c. violet 35 35
939 – 75c.+1f. mauve 35 35
940 – 1f.+1f.50 red 35 35
941 **183** 1f.25+1f.75 green 35 35
942 – 1f.75+2f.50 blue 35 35
943 – 2f.+3f.50 mauve 35 35
944 – 2f.50+4f.50 brown 35 35
945 – 3f.+5f. green 35 35
946 **184** 5f.+10f. brown . . . . . 1·40 1·10
MS947 183 × 165 mm. 5f.+15f. blue (as 946) . . . . 8·25 8·25
DESIGNS—As Type **183**. 30c., 1f., 2f.50, Sculpture; 40c., 2f. Goldsmiths (Monks carrying candlesticks and cross); 50c., 1f.75, Stained glass (Monk at prayer); 75c., 3f. Sacred music.

1941. Surch.
955 **152** 10c. on 30c. brown . . . 10 10
956 10c. on 40c. lilac 10 10
957 **153** 10c. on 70c. brown . . . 10 10
958 50c. on 75c. olive 20 20
959 **155** 2f.25 on 2f.50 black . . . 40 45

189 Maria Theresa

190 St. Martin, Dinant

1941. Soldiers' Families Relief Fund.
960 **189** 10c.+5c. black 10 10
961 – 35c.+5c. green 10 10
962 – 50c.+10c. brown 10 10
963 – 60c.+10c. violet 10 10
964 – 1f.+15c. red 10 10
965 – 1f.50+1f. mauve 20 20
966 – 1f.75+1f.75 blue 20 20
967 – 2f.25+2f.25 brown 20 25
968 – 3f.25+3f.25 brown 40 45
969 – 5f.+5f. green 65 70
PORTRAITS: 35c. to 5f. Charles of Lorraine, Margaret of Parma, Charles V, Johanna of Castile, Philip the Good, Margaret of Austria, Charles the Bold, Archduke Albert and Archduchess Isabella respectively.

1941. Winter Relief Fund. Statues.
970 **190** 10c.+5c. brown 15 10
971 – 35c.+5c. green 15 10
972 – 50c.+10c. violet 15 10
973 – 60c.+10c. brown 15 10
974 – 1f.+15c. red 15 10
975 **190** 1f.50+25c. green 25 25
976 – 1f.75+50c. blue 25 25
977 – 2f.25+2f.25 mauve 30 30
978 – 3f.25+3f.25 brown 30 30
979 – 5f.+5f. green 50 50
MS980 105 × 139 mm. 5f.+20f. purple (as 979) . . . . . . 15·00 15·00
DESIGNS (Statues of St. Martin in churches)—As Type **190**: 35c., 1f. Lennick, St. Quentin; 50c., 3f. Beck, Limberg; 60c., 2f.25, Dave on the Meuse; 1f.75, Hal, Brabant. 35 × 50 mm: 5f. St. Trond.

192 Concert Hall, Argenteuil

1941. Fund for Queen Elisabeth's Concert Hall. Two sheets, each 103 × 133 mm.
MS981 **192** 10f.+15f. green . . . 5·50 5·50
MS982 As last with perforated crown and monogram with violet control number on back . . . 5·50 5·50

193 Mercator

198 Prisoner writing Letter

1942. Anti-tuberculosis Fund. Portraits.
986 – 10c.+5c. brown 10 10
987 – 35c.+5c. green 10 10
988 – 50c.+10c. brown 10 10
989 – 60c.+10c. green 10 10
990 – 1f.+15c. red 10 10
991 **193** 1f.75+50c. blue 10 10
992 – 3f.25+3f.25 purple 15 10
993 – 5f.+5f. violet 20 20
994 – 10f.+30f. orange . . . . . 1·10 1·10
MS995 77 × 59 mm. 3f.25+6f.75 green (as 968); 5f.+10f. red (as 969) . . . . 10·00 10·00
SCIENTISTS—As T **193**: 10c. Bolland. 35c. Versale. 50c. S. Stevin. 60c. Van Helmont. 1f. Dodoens. 3f.25, Oertell. 5f. Juste Lipse. 25½ × 28½ mm: 10f. Plantin.

1942. Prisoners of War Fund.
1000 **198** 5f.+45f. grey . . . . . 4·50 4·50

199 St. Martin

200 St. Martin sharing his cloak

1942. Winter Relief Fund.
1001 **199** 10c.+5c. orange 10 10
1002 – 35c.+5c. green 10 10
1003 – 50c.+10c. brown 10 10
1004 – 60c.+10c. black (horiz) 10 10
1005 – 1f.+15c. red 10 10
1006 – 1f.50+25c. green 20 25
1007 – 1f.75+50c. blue 20 25
1008 – 2f.25+2f.25 brn (horiz) 20 25
1009 – 3f.25+3f.25 purple (horiz) 35 40
1010 **200** 5f.+10f. brown . . . . . 1·00 1·10
1011 10f.+20f. brown & vio 1·00 1·10
1012 10f.+20f. red & violet . . 90 1·00

201 Soldiers and Vision of Home

1943. Prisoners of War Relief Fund.
1013 **201** 1f.+30f. red . . . . . . 1·90 1·90
1014 – 1f.+30f. brown . . . . . 1·50 1·60
DESIGN: No. 1014, Soldiers emptying parcel of books and vision of home.

202 Tiler

1943. Anti-tuberculosis Fund. Trades.
1015 **202** 10c.+5c. brown 10 10
1016 – 35c.+5c. green 10 10
1017 – 50c.+10c. brown 10 10
1018 – 60c.+10c. green 10 10
1019 – 1f.+15c. red 25 20
1020 – 1f.75+75c. blue 25 20
1021 – 3f.25+3f.25 purple . . . 40 35
1022 – 5f.+25f. violet 75 65
DESIGNS: 35c. Blacksmith; 50c. Coppersmith; 60c. Gunsmith; 1f. Armourer; 1f.75, Goldsmith; 3f.25, Fishmonger; 5f. Clockmaker.

203 Ornamental Letter

204 Ornamental Letters (⅔-size illustration)

1943. Orval Abbey Restoration Fund. Designs showing single letters forming "ORVAL".
1023 **203** 50c.+1f. black 30 30
1024 – 60c.+1f.90 violet 20 20
1025 – 1f.+3f. red 20 20
1026 – 1f.75+5f.25 blue 20 20
1027 – 3f.25+16f.75 green . . . 50 40
1028 **204** 5f.+30f. brown 85 65

205 St. Leonard's Church, Leon, and St. Martin

206 Church of Notre Dame, Hal, and St. Martin

207 St. Martin and River Scheldt

1943. Winter Relief Fund.
1029 **205** 10c.+5c. brown 10 10
1030 – 35c.+5c. green 10 10
1031 – 50c.+15c. green 10 10
1032 – 60c.+20c. purple 10 10
1033 – 1f.+1f. red 20 25
1034 – 1f.75+4f.25 blue 60 65
1035 – 3f.25+11f.75 mauve . . . 90 85
1036 **206** 5f.+25f. blue . . . . . 1·40 1·40
1037 **207** 10f.+30f. green . . . . . 1·25 1·10
1038 – 10f.+30f. brown . . . . 1·25 1·10
DESIGNS: (Various churches and statues of St. Martin sharing his cloak). As Type **205**: HORIZ: 35c. Dion-le-Val; 50c. Alost; 60c. Liege; 3f.25, Loppem. VERT: 1f. Courtrai; 1f.75, Angre. As Type **207**: 10f. brown Meuse landscape.

208 "Daedalus and Icarus"

209 Jan van Eyck

1944. Red Cross.
1039 **208** 35c.+1f.65 green 25 25
1040 – 50c.+2f.50 grey 25 25
1041 – 60c.+3f.40 brown . . . 25 45

1042 – 1f.+5f. red 35 40
1043 – 1f.75+8f.25 blue 30 35
1044 – 5f.+30f. brown 45 50
DESIGNS: 50c. "The Good Samaritan" (Jacob Jordsen); 60c. "Christ healing the Paralytic" (detail); 1f. "Madonna and Child"; 1f.75, "Self-portrait"; 5f. "St. Sebastian".
Nos. 1039 and 1041/4 depict paintings by Anthony van Dyck.

1944. Prisoners of War Relief Fund.
1045 **209** 10c.+15c. violet 20 20
1046 – 35c.+15c. green 20 20
1047 – 50c.+25c. brown 20 20
1048 – 60c.+40c. olive 20 30
1049 – 1f.+50c. red 20 25
1050 – 1f.75+4f.25 blue 20 30
1051 – 2f.25+8f.25 slate 50 50
1052 – 3f.25+11f.25 brown . . . 25 30
1053 – 5f.+35f. grey 50 60
PORTRAITS: 35c. "Godefroid de Bouillon". 50c. "Jacob van Maerlant". 60c. "Jean Joses de Dinant". 1f. "Jacob van Artevelde". 1f.75, "Charles Joseph de Ligne". 2f.25, "Andre Gretry". 3f.25, "Jan Moretus-Plantin". 5f. "Ruusbroeck".

210 "Bayard and Four Sons of Aymon", Namur

211 Lion Rampant

1944. Anti-tuberculosis Fund. Provincial legendary types.
1054 **210** 10c.+5c. brown 10 10
1055 – 35c.+5c. green 10 10
1056 – 50c.+10c. violet 10 10
1057 – 60c.+10c. brown 10 10
1058 – 1f.+15c. red 10 10
1059 – 1f.75+5f.25 blue 10 20
1060 – 3f.25+11f.75 green . . . 20 25
1061 – 5f.+25f. blue 25 35
DESIGNS—VERT: 35c. "Brabo severing the giant's hand", Antwerp; 60c. "Thyl Ulenspiegel" and "Nele", Flanders; 1f. "St. George and the Dragon", Hainaut; 1f.75, "Genevieve of Brabant, with the Child and the Hind", Brabant. HORIZ: 50c. "St. Hubert encounters the Hind with the Cross", Luxemburg; 3f.25, "Tchantches wrestling with the Saracen", Liege; 5f. "St. Gertrude rescuing the Knight with the cards", Limburg.

1944. Inscr "BELGIQUE-BELGIE" or "BELGIE-BELGIQUE".
1062A **211** 5c. brown 10 10
1063A 10c. green 10 10
1064A 25c. blue 10 10
1065A 35c. brown 10 10
1066A 50c. green 10 10
1067B 75c. violet 10 20
1068B 1f. red 10 15
1069B 1f.25 brown 15 20
1070B 1f.50 orange 25 30
1071A 1f.75 blue 10 10
1072B 2f. blue . . . . . . 90 1·10
1073A 2f.75 mauve 10 10
1074B 3f. red 10 15
1075B 3f.50 grey 10 15
1076B 5f. brown . . . . . . 2·10 2·25
1077B 10f. black 45 45

1944. Overprinted with large **V**.
1078 **152** 2c. green 10 10
1079 15c. blue 10 10
1080 20c. violet 10 10
1081 60c. grey 10 10

213 King Leopold III and "V"

214 War Victims

215 Rebuilding Homes

1944.
1082 **213** 1f. red 15 10
1083 1f.50 mauve 15 10
1084 1f.75 blue 25 40
1085 2f. violet 45 15
1086 2f.25 green 35 35
1087 3f.25 brown 20 10
1088 5f. green 75 15

1945. War Victims' Relief Fund.
1114 **214** 1f.+30f. red 75 65
1115 **215** 1½f.+30f. blue 75 65
Nos. 1114/15 measure 50 × 35 mm.

1945. Post Office Employers' Relief Fund.
1119 **214** 1f.+9f. red 15 15
1120 **215** 1f.+9f. red 15 15

217 Resister

218 Group of Resisters

1945. Prisoners of War Relief Fund.
1121 **217** 10c.+15c. orange 10 10
1122 – 20c.+20c. violet 10 10
1123 – 60c.+25c. brown 10 10
1124 – 70c.+30c. green 10 10
1125 **217** 75c.+50c. brown 10 10
1126 – 1f.+75c. green 15 15
1127 – 1f.50+1f. red 15 15
1128 – 3f.50+3f.50 blue . . . . 1·00 80
1129 **218** 5f.+40f. brown . . . . . 1·50 90
DESIGNS—VERT: 20c., 1f. Father and child; 60c., 1f.50, Victim tied to stake. HORIZ: 70c., 3f.50, Rifleman.

219 West Flanders

222 Douglas DC-4

1945. Anti-tuberculosis Fund.
1130 **219** 10c.+15c. green 20 10
1131 – 20c.+20c. red 20 10
1132 – 60c.+25c. brown 20 10
1133 – 70c.+30c. green 20 10
1134 – 75c.+50c. brown 20 10
1135 – 1f.+75c. violet 20 10
1136 – 1f.50+1f. red 20 15
1137 – 3f.50+1f.50 blue 35 30
1138 – 5f.+45f. mauve . . . . . 2·50 2·00
ARMS DESIGNS—VERT: 20c. to 5f. Arms of Luxemburg, East Flanders, Namur, Limburg Hainaut, Antwerp, Liege and Brabant respectively.

1946. Air.
1165 **222** 6f. blue 30 20
1166 8f.50 red 45 40
1167 50f. green . . . . 3·75 65
1168 100f. grey . . . . 6·50 1·60

1946. Surch **-10%**, reducing the original value by 10%.
1171 **213** "-10%" on 1f.50 mauve 60 15
1172 "-10%" on 2f. violet . . 1·40 60
1173 "-10%" on 5f. green . . 1·25 15

224 "Marie Henriette" (paddle-steamer)

1946. Ostend–Dover Mail-boat Service Centenary.
1174a – 1f.35 blue 30 15
1175 **224** 2f.25 green 30 25
1176 – 3f.15 grey 25 25
DESIGNS—21½ × 18½ or 21 × 17 mm: 1f.35, "Prince Baudouin" (mail steamer). As T **224**: 3f.15, "Diamant" (paddle-steamer), formerly "Le Chemin de Fer".

225 Paratrooper

1946. Air. Bastogne Monument Fund.
1177 **225** 17f.50+62f.50 green . . . 1·00 75
1178 17f.50+62f.50 purple . . 1·00 75

226 Father Damien

227 E. Vandervelde

228 Francois Bovesse

1946. Belgian Patriots. (a) Father Damien.
1179 **226** 65c.+75c. blue . . . . . 1·40 95
1180 – 1f.35+2f. brown . . . . 1·40 85
1181 – 1f.75+18f. lake . . . . . 1·40 95
DESIGNS—HORIZ: 1f.35, Molokai Leper Colony. VERT: 1f.75, Damien's statue.

(b) Emile Vandervelde.
1182 **227** 65c.+75c. green . . . . 1·40 85
1183 – 1f.35+2f. blue . . . . . 1·40 85
1184 – 1f.75+18f. red . . . . . 1·40 95
DESIGNS—HORIZ: 1f.35, Vandervelde, miner, mother and child. VERT: 1f.75, Sower.

(c) Francois Bovesse.
1185 – 65c.+75c. violet . . . . 1·40 85
1186 **228** 1f.35+2f. brown . . . . 1·40 85
1187 – 1f.75+18f. red . . . . . 1·40 85
DESIGNS—VERT: 65c. Symbols of Patriotism and Learning; 1f.75, Draped memorial figures holding wreath and torch.

229 Pepin d'Herstal

230 Allegory of "Flight"

1946. War Victims' Relief Fund.
1188 **229** 75c.+25c. green 50 20
1189 – 1f.+50c. violet 50 35
1190 – 1f.50+1f. purple 65 35
1191 – 3f.50+1f.50 blue 80 50
1192 – 5f.+45f. mauve . . . . . 8·00 8·00
1194 – 5f.+45f. orange . . . . 8·25 8·00
DESIGNS: 1f. Charlemagne; 1f.50, Godfrey of Bouillon; 3f.50, Robert of Jerusalem; 5f. Baudouin of Constantinople.
See also Nos. 1207/11, 1258/9 and 1302/6.

1946. Air.
1193 **230** 2f.+8f. violet 40 40

231 Malines

232 Joseph Plateau

1946. Anti-tuberculosis Fund. No date.
1195 **231** 65c.+35c. red 50 25
1196 – 90c.+60c. olive 55 25
1197 – 1f.35+1f.15 green 55 30
1198 – 3f.15+1f.85 blue 75 35
1199 – 4f.50+45f.50 brown . . . 10·50 9·50
DESIGNS—(Arms and Industries): 90c. Dinant; 1f.35, Ostend; 3f.15, Verviers; 4f.50, Louvain.
See also Nos. 1212/16.

1947. Air. "Cipex" International Stamp Exhibition, New York. Nos. 1179/87 surch **LUCHTPOST POSTE AERIENNE** or **POSTE AERIENNE LUCHTPOST** and new value. (a) Father Damien.
1199a 1f.+2f. on 65c. +75c. blue 55 45
1199b 1f.+50+2f.50 on 1f.35+2f. brown 55 45
1199c 2f.+45f. on 1f.75+18f. red 55 45

(b) Emile Vandervelde.
1199d 1f.+2f. on 65c.+75c. green 55 45
1199e 1f.50+2f.50 on 1f.35+2f. blue 55 45
1199f 2f.+45f. on 1f.75+18f. red 55 45

(c) Francois Bovesse.
1199g 1f.+2f. on 65c.+75c. vio . . 55 45
1199h 1f.50+2f.50 on 1f.35+2f. brown 55 45
1199i 2f.+45f. on 1f.75+18f. red 55 45

1947. Int Film and Belgian Fine Arts Festival.
1200 **232** 3f.15 blue 65 20

233 Adrien de Gerlache

234 Explorers landing from "Belgica"

1947. 50th Anniv of Belgian Antarctic Expedition.
1201 **233** 1f.35 red 25 10
1202 **234** 2f.25 grey . . . . 2·50 60

1947. War Victims' Relief Fund. Mediaeval Princes as T **229**.
1207 65c.+35c. blue 85 45
1208 90c.+60c. green . . . . . 1·40 55
1209 1f.35+1f.15 red . . . . . 2·40 80
1210 3f.15+1f.85 blue . . . . . 2·50 95
1211 20f.+20f. purple . . . . . 60·00 30·00
DESIGNS: 65c. John II, Duke of Brabant; 90c. Philippe of Alsace; 1f.35, William the Good; 3f.15, Notger, Bishop of Liege; 20f. Philip the Noble.

1947. Anti-Tuberculosis Fund. Arms designs as T **231**, but dated "1947".
1212 65c.+35c. orange 35 35
1213 90c.+60c. purple 35 35
1214 1f.35+1f.15 brown 35 35
1215 3f.15+1f.85 blue . . . . . 1·75 65
1216 20f.+20f. green . . . . . . 16·00 12·00
DESIGNS (Arms and Industries): 65c. Nivelles; 90c. St. Truiden; 1f.35, Charleroi; 3f.15, St. Nicholas; 20f. Bouillon.

237 Chemical Industry

240 Textile Machinery

239 Antwerp Docks

1948. National Industries.
1217 **237** 60c. blue 15 15
1218 1f.20 brown . . . . . . 1·60 15
1219 – 1f.35 brown 15 15
1220 – 1f.75 green 35 15
1221 – 1f.75 red 25 25
1222 **239** 2f.25 grey . . . . 1·10 65
1223 – 2f.50 mauve . . . . . . 5·75 45
1224 **239** 3f. purple . . . . 9·50 35
1225 **240** 3f.15 blue . . . . 1·10 50
1226 4f. blue . . . . 8·00 35
1227 – 6f. blue . . . . 17·00 40
1228 – 6f.30 purple . . . . . . 2·25 4·25
DESIGNS—As Type **237**: 1f.35, 1f.75 green, Woman making lace; 1f.75 red, 2f.50, Agricultural produce. As Type **239**: 6f., 6f.30, Steel works.

242 St. Benedict and King Totila

243 St. Bega and Chevremont Castle

1948. Achel Abbey Fund. Inscr "ACHEL"
1232 **242** 65c.+65c. brown 65 45
1233 – 1f.35+1f.35 green 75 50
1234 – 3f.15+2f.85 blue . . . . 2·40 1·25
1235 – 10f.+10f. purple . . . . 8·50 7·00
DESIGNS—HORIZ: 1f.35, Achel Abbey. VERT: 3f.15, St. Benedict as Law-Giver; 10f. Death of St. Benedict.

1948. Chevremont Abbey Fund. Inscr "CHEVREMONT".
1236 **243** 65c.+65c. blue 60 45
1237 – 1f.35+1f.35 red 65 50
1238 – 3f.15+2f.85 blue . . . . 2·00 1·25
1239 – 10f.+10f. brown . . . . 8·25 6·25
DESIGNS—HORIZ: 1f.35, Chevremont Basilica and Convent. VERT: 3f.15, Madonna of Chevremont and Chapel; 10f. Monk and Madonna of Mt. Carmel.

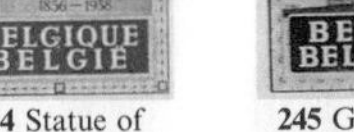

244 Statue of Anseele — 245 Ghent and E. Anseele

1948. Inauguration of Edward Anseele (Socialist Leader) Statue.
1245 **244** 65c.+35c. red . . . . . 1·75 1·00
1246 **245** 90c.+60c. grey . . . . . 2·40 1·50
1247 – 1f.35+1f.15 brn . . . . 1·50 1·00
1248 – 3f.15+1f.85 blue . . . . 5·00 3·25
MS1249 82 × 145 mm. Nos. 1245/8 £140 65·00
DESIGNS: 1f.35, Statue and Ed. Anseele; 3f.15, Reverse side of statue.

247 "Liberty" — 248 "Resistance"

1948. Antwerp and Liege Monuments Funds.
1253 **247** 10f.+10f. green . . . . . 30·00 15·00
1254 **248** 10f.+10f. brown . . . . 13·00 8·50

249 Cross of Lorraine

1948. Anti-tuberculosis Fund.
1255 **249** 20c.+5c. green 15 10
1256 1f.20+30c. purple . . . 70 35
1257 1f.75+25c. red 85 45
1258 – 4f.+3f.25 blue . . . . . 5·50 3·50
1259 – 20f.+20f. green . . . . . 30·00 21·00
DESIGNS—As Type **229**: 4f. Isabel of Austria; 20f. Albert, Archduke of Austria.

250 (½-size illustration)

1949. Social and Cultural Funds. Sheets 140 × 90 mm sold at 50f. each incl premium (a) Paintings by R. van der Weyden.
MS1260 90c. brown (T **250** "Madonna and Child"); 1f.75 purple ("Crucifixion"); 4f. blue ("Mary Magdalene") £140 £120

(b) Paintings by J. Jordaens.
MS1261 90c. violet ("Woman Reading"); 1f.75 red ("Flute-player"); 4f. blue ("Old Woman and Letter") £140 £120

1949. Surch **1-1-49** at top, **31-XII-49** and value at bottom with posthorn in between. (a) Arms type.
1262 **152** 5c. on 15c. blue 10 10
1263 5c. on 30c. brown . . . 10 10
1264 5c. on 40c. lilac 10 10
1265 20c. on 70c. green . . . 10 10
1266 20c. on 75c. mauve . . . 10 10

(b) Anseele Statue.
1267 **244** 10c. on 65c.+35c. red . . 1·90 1·75
1268 **245** 40c. on 90c.+60c. grey 1·10 1·10
1269 – 80c. on 1f.35+1f.15 brown 50 45
1270 – 1f.20 on 3f.15+1f.85 blue 1·10 1·10

251 King Leopold I — 253 St. Madeleine from "The Baptism of Christ"

252 Forms of Postal Transport

1949. Belgian Stamp Cent.
1271 **251** 90c. green (postage) . . 45 30
1272 1f.75 brown 25 15
1273 3f. red . . . . 5·25 2·50
1274 4f. blue . . . . 4·25 60
1275 **252** 50f. brown (air) . . . . 38·00 14·00

1949. Exhibition of Paintings by Gerard David, Bruges.
1276 **253** 1f.75 brown 55 20

255 Hemispheres and Allegorical Figure

1949. 75th Anniv of U.P.U.
1296 **255** 4f. blue . . . . 3·00 1·75

256 Guido Gezelle — 257 Arnica

1949. 50th Death Anniv of Gezelle (poet).
1297 **256** 1f.75+75c. green . . . . 1·10 85

1949. Anti-tuberculosis and other Funds. (a) Flowers.
1298 **257** 20c.+5c. black, yellow and green 20 10
1299 – 65c.+10c. black, green and buff 85 45
1300 – 90c.+10c. black, blue and red . . . . 1·25 75
1301 – 1f.20+30c. mult . . . . 1·40 75
FLOWERS: 65c. Thistle. 90c. Periwinkle. 1f.20, Poppy.

(b) Portraits as T **229**.
1302 1f.75+25c. orange 55 25
1303 3f.+1f.50 red . . . . . . 7·00 5·00
1304 4f.+2f. blue . . . . 7·00 5·25
1305 6f.+3f. brown . . . . . . 13·50 7·50
1306 8f.+4f. green . . . . . . 15·00 9·25
PORTRAITS: 1f.75, Philip the Good. 3f. Charles V. 4f. Maria Christina. 6f. Charles of Lorraine. 8f. Maria Theresa.

260 Anglo-Belgian Monument, Hertain — 261 Allegory of Saving

1950. Anglo-Belgian Union and other Funds.
1307 – 80c.+20c. green 80 40
1308 – 2f.50+50c. red . . . . . 4·00 2·40
1309 **260** 4f.+2f. blue . . . . . . 5·75 4·50
DESIGNS—HORIZ: 80c. Arms of Great Britain and Belgium; 2f.50, British tanks at Tournai.

1950. National Savings Bank Centenary.
1310 **261** 1f.75 sepia 40 20

262 Hurdling — 263 Sikorsky S-51 Helicopter and Douglas DC-4 leaving Melsbroeck

1950. European Athletic Championships. Inscr "HEYSEL 1950".
1311 **262** 20c.+5c. green 30 20
1312 – 90c.+10c. purple . . . . 2·75 1·40
1313 – 1f.75+25c. red . . . . . 4·50 1·40
1314 – 4f.+2f. blue . . . . . . 26·00 15·00
1315 – 8f.+4f. green . . . . . 28·00 18·00
MS1316 70 × 119 mm. 1f.75+25c. (+18f.) (No. 1313) . . . . . . 60·00 40·00
DESIGNS—HORIZ: 1f.75, Relay racing. VERT: 90c. Javelin throwing; 4f. Pole vaulting; 8f. Sprinting.

1950. Air. Inauguration of Helicopter Airmail Services and Aeronautical Committee's Fund.
1317 **263** 7f.+3f. blue . . . . . . 6·50 4·00

265 Gentian — 266 Sijsele Sanatorium

1950. Anti-tuberculosis and other Funds. Cross in red.
1326 **265** 20c.+5c. blue, green and purple 20 15
1327 – 65c.+10c. green and brown 80 40
1328 – 90c.+10c. light green and green . . . . 1·00 75
1329 – 1f.20+30c. blue, green and ultramarine . . . 1·25 75
1330 **266** 1f.75+25c. red . . . . . 1·50 1·00
1331 – 4f.+2f. blue . . . . . . 11·50 6·50
1332 – 8f.+4f. green . . . . . 19·00 13·50
DESIGNS—Flowers as Type **265**: 65c. Rushes; 90c. Foxglove; 1f.20, Sea lavender. Sanatoria as Type **266**: HORIZ: 4f. Jauche. VERT: 8f. Tombeek.

267 The Belgian Lion — 268 "Science"

1951. (a) 17½ × 20½ mm.
1334 **267** 2c. brown 10 10
1335 3c. violet 10 10
1336 5c. lilac 15 15
1336a 5c. pink 10 10
1337 10c. orange 10 15
1338 15c. mauve 10 10
1333 20c. blue 10 10
1339 20c. red 10 15
1340 25c. green . . . . . 1·75 45
1341 25c. blue 10 10
1342 30c. green 10 10
1343 40c. brown 10 15
1344a 50c. blue 15 25
1345 60c. mauve 10 10
1346 65c. purple . . . . . 8·25 40
1347 75c. lilac 10 10
1348 80c. green 55 15
1349 90c. blue 85 30
1350 1f. red 10 15
1351 1f.50 grey 10 10
1353 2f. green 10 10
1354 2f.50 brown 10 10
1355 3f. mauve 10 10
1355a 4f. purple 15 10
1355b 4f.50 blue 25 10
1355c 5f. purple 25 10

(b) 20½ × 24½ mm.
1356 **267** 50c. blue 20 15
1357 60c. purple 70 55
1358a 1f. red 10 10

(c) Size 17½ × 22 mm.
1359 **267** 50c. blue 10 10
1360 1f. pink . . . . 1·40 65
1361 2f. green . . . . 3·50 20

1951. U.N.E.S.C.O. Fund. Inscr "UNESCO".
1365 **268** 80c.+20c. green . . . . 1·25 45
1366 – 2f.50+50c. brown . . . 7·25 4·75
1367 – 4f.+2f. blue . . . . . 9·00 6·00
DESIGNS—HORIZ: 2f.50, "Education". VERT: 4f. "Peace".

269 Fairey Tipsy Belfair Trainer I

1951. Air. 50th Anniv of National Aero Club.
1368 – 6f. blue . . . . 19·00 30·00
1369 **269** 7f. red . . . . 19·00 30·00
DESIGN: 6f. Arsenal Air 100 glider.

1951. Air.
1370 – 6f. brown (glider) . . . 3·50 20
1371 **269** 7f. green . . . . 4·50 55

270 Monument — 272 Queen Elisabeth

1951. Political Prisoners' National Monument Fund.
1372 **270** 1f.75+25c. brown . . . 1·75 45
1373 – 4f.+2f. blue . . . . . . 22·00 11·50
1374 – 8f.+4f. green . . . . . 22·00 13·00
DESIGNS—HORIZ: 4f. Breendonk Fort. VERT: 8f. Side view of monument.

1951. Queen Elisabeth Medical Foundation Fund.
1376 **272** 90c.+10c. grey . . . . . 2·75 60
1377 1f.75+25c. red . . . . . 3·75 1·25
1378 3f.+1f. green . . . . . 22·00 9·50
1379 4f.+2f. blue . . . . . . 21·00 10·00
1380 8f.+4f. sepia . . . . . . 26·00 13·00

273 Lorraine Cross and Dragon — 274 Beersel Castle

1951. Anti-tuberculosis and other Funds.
1381 **273** 20c.+5c. red 20 10
1382 65c.+10c. blue 35 15
1383 90c.+10c. brown 45 30
1384 1f.20+30c. violet 90 40
1385 **274** 1f.75+75c. brown . . . 3·00 1·00
1386 – 3f.+1f. green . . . . . 9·25 5·25
1387 – 4f.+2f. blue . . . . . . 11·00 7·00
1388 – 8f.+4f. black . . . . . 17·00 9·50
CASTLES—As Type **274**: VERT: 3f. Horst Castle. 8f. Veves Castle. HORIZ: 4f. Lavaux St. Anne Castle.
For stamps as Type **273** but dated "1952" see Nos. 1416/19 and for those dated "1953" see Nos. 1507/10.

276 Consecration of the Basilica

1952. 25th Anniv of Cardinalate of Primate of Belgium and Koekelberg Basilica Fund.
1389 – 1f.75+25c. brown . . . 95 35
1390 – 4f.+2f. blue . . . . . . 11·00 5·50
1391 **276** 8f.+4f. purple . . . . . 14·00 7·50
MS1392 120 × 72 mm. Nos. 1389/91 (10f.) £275 £140
DESIGNS—24 × 35 mm: 1f.75, Interior of Koekelberg Basilica; 4f. Exterior of Koekelberg Basilica.

277 King Baudouin — 278 King Baudouin

1952.
1393 **277** 1f.50 grey . . . . . . 1·10 15
1394 2f. red 35 15
1395 4f. blue . . . . 3·75 30
1396a **278** 50f. purple . . . . . . 2·75 25
1397a 100f. red . . . . 4·00 25

279 Francis of Taxis — 281 A. Vermeylen

1952. 13th U.P.U. Congress, Brussels. Portraits of Members of the House of Thurn and Taxis.
1398 **279** 80c. green 10 15
1399 – 1f.75 orange 10 10
1400 – 2f. brown 40 20
1401 – 2f.50 red 95 30
1402 – 3f. olive 95 15

1403 – 4f. blue 95 10
1404 – 5f. brown . . . . 2·50 40
1405 – 5f.75 violet . . . . . . 3·00 90
1406 – 8f. black . . . . 13·00 2·50
1407 – 10f. purple . . . . . . 18·00 6·25
1408 – 20f. grey . . . . 65·00 32·00
1409 – 40f.+10f. turquoise . . . £130 85·00
DESIGNS—VERT: 1f.75, John Baptist; 2f. Leonard; 2f.50, Lamoral; 3f. Leonard Francis; 4f. Lamoral Claud; 5f. Eugene Alexander; 5f.75, Anselm Francis; 8f. Alexander Ferdinand; 10f. Charles Anselm; 20f. Charles Alexander; 40f. Beaulieu Chateau.

1952. Culture Fund. Writers.
1410 **281** 65c.+30c. lilac . . . . . 3·50 1·75
1411 – 80c.+40c. green . . . . 3·50 1·75
1412 – 90c.+45c. olive . . . . . 3·50 1·75
1413 – 1f.75+75c. lake . . . . 6·25 3·50
1414 – 4f.+2f. blue . . . . . . 24·00 13·00
1415 – 8f.+4f. sepia . . . . . . 25·00 14·00
PORTRAITS: 80c. K. van de Woestijne. 90c. C. de Coster. 1f.75, M. Maeterlinck. 4f. E. Verhaeren. 8f. H. Conscience.
A 4f. blue as No. 1414 and an 8f. lake as No. 1415 each se-tenant with a label showing a laurel wreath and bearing a premium "+ 9 fr." were put on sale by subscription only.

282 Arms, Malmedy

284 Dewe and Monument at Liege

1952. Anti-tuberculosis and other Funds. As T **273** but dated "1952" and designs as T **282**.
1416 **273** 20c.+5c. brown 10 10
1417 80c.+20c. green 55 30
1418 1f.20+30c. purple . . . 1·25 60
1419 1f.50+50c. olive . . . . 1·25 60
1420 **282** 2f.+75c. red . . . . . 1·60 70
1421 – 3f.+1f.50 brown . . . . 15·00 10·00
1422 – 4f.+2f. blue . . . . . . 14·00 8·50
1423 – 8f.+4f. purple . . . . . 15·00 10·00
DESIGNS—HORIZ: 3f. Ruins, Burgreuland. VERT: 4f. Dam, Eupen; 8f. Saint and lion, St. Vith.

1953. Walthere Dewe Memorial Fund.
1435 **284** 2f.+1f. lake . . . . . . 2·00 1·10

285 Princess Josephine Charlotte

286 Fishing Boats "Marcel", "De Meeuw" and "Jacqueline Denise"

1953. Red Cross National Disaster Fund. Cross in red.
1436 **285** 80c.+20c. green . . . . 2·25 90
1437 1f.20+30c. brown . . . 1·90 80
1438 2f.+50c. lake . . . . . 1·90 80
1439 2f.50+50c. red . . . . . 12·00 7·00
1440 4f.+1f. blue . . . . . . 11·00 6·00
1441 5f.+2f. black . . . . . 12·00 6·25

1953. Tourist Propaganda and Cultural Funds.
1442 **286** 80c.+20c. green . . . . 1·60 65
1443 – 1f.20+30c. brown . . . 4·75 2·10
1444 – 2f.+50c. sepia . . . . . 4·75 2·10
1445 – 2f.50+50c. mauve . . . 12·50 5·50
1446 – 4f.+2f. blue . . . . . . 16·00 9·00
1447 – 8f.+4f. green . . . . . 19·00 11·00
DESIGNS—HORIZ: 1f.20, Bridge Bouillon; 2f. Antwerp. VERT: 2f.50, Namur; 4f. Ghent; 8f. Freyr Rocks and River Meuse.

289 King Baudouin

290

1953. (a) 21 × 24½ mm.
1453 **289** 1f.50 black 15 10
1454 2f. red . . . . 6·25 10
1455 2f. green 25 10
2188 2f.50 brown 30 10
1457 3f. purple 25 10
1458 3f.50 green 75 10
1459 4f. blue . . . . 1·75 10
1460 4f.50 brown . . . . . . 1·10 10
1462 5f. violet 85 10
1463 6f. mauve . . . . 1·75 10
1464 6f.50 grey . . . . 70·00 12·00
2189 7f. blue 35 25
1466 7f.50 brown . . . . . . 65·00 14·50
1467 8f. blue 40 10
1468 8f.50 purple . . . . . . 12·50 40
1469 9f. olive . . . . 70·00 1·25
1470 12f. turquoise 70 10
1471 30f. orange . . . . . . 7·50 35

(b) 17½ × 22 mm.
1472 **289** 1f.50 black 30 20
1473 2f.50 brown . . . . . . 6·00 5·00
1474 3f. mauve 40 10
1475 3f.50 green 35 10
1476 4f.50 brown . . . . . . 1·50 60

1953. European Child Welfare Fund.
1482 **290** 80c.+20c. green . . . . 3·75 2·10
1483 2f.50+1f. red . . . . . 21·00 14·00
1484 4f.+1f.50 blue . . . . . 24·00 16·00

293 Ernest Malvoz

296 King Albert Statue

1953. Anti-tuberculosis and other Funds. As T **273** but dated "1953" and portraits as T **293**.
1507 **273** 20c.+5c. blue 25 20
1508 80c.+20c. purple . . . . 1·10 45
1509 1f.20+30c. brown . . . 1·25 70
1510 1f.50+50c. slate . . . . 1·60 95
1511 **293** 2f.+75c. green . . . . . 2·00 1·25
1512 – 3f.+1f.50 red . . . . . 12·00 6·75
1513 – 4f.+2f. blue . . . . . . 14·00 8·00
1514 – 8f.+4f. brown . . . . . 16·00 9·25
PORTRAITS—VERT: 3f. Carlo Forlanini. 4f. Albert Calmette. HORIZ: 8f. Robert Koch.

1954. Surch **20c** and **I-I-54** at top, **31-XII-54** at bottom and bars in between.
1515 **267** 20c. on 65c. purple . . . 1·25 20
1516 20c. on 90c. blue . . . . 1·25 20
See note below No. 480.

1954. King Albert Memorial Fund.
1520 **296** 2f.+50c. brown . . . . 5·25 2·40
1521 – 4f.+2f. blue . . . . . . 19·00 10·50
1522 – 9f.+4f.50 black . . . . 18·00 10·50
DESIGNS—HORIZ: 4f. King Albert Memorial. VERT: 9f. Marche-les-Dames Rocks and medallion portrait.

298 Monument

299 Breendonk Camp and Fort

1954. Political Prisoners' National Monument Fund.
1531 **298** 2f.+1f. red . . . . . . 15·00 8·00
1532 **299** 4f.+2f. brown . . . . . 30·00 16·00
1533 – 9f.+4f.50 green . . . . 35·00 19·00
DESIGN—VERT: 9f. As Type **298** but viewed from different angle.

300 Entrance to Beguinal House

1954. Beguinage of Bruges Restoration Fund.
1534 **300** 80c.+20c. green 80 50
1535 – 2f.+1f. red . . . . . . 9·00 5·50
1536 – 4f.+2f. violet . . . . . 12·50 7·00
1537 – 7f.+3f.50 purple . . . . 26·00 15·00
1538 – 8f.+4f. brown . . . . . 26·00 15·00
1539 – 9f.+4f.50 blue . . . . . 45·00 24·00
DESIGNS—HORIZ: 2f. River scene. VERT: 4f. Convent Buildings; 7f. Cloisters; 8f. Doorway; 9f. Statue of our Lady of the Vineyard (larger, 35 × 53 mm).

302 Map of Europe and Rotary Symbol

1954. 50th Anniv of Rotary International and 5th Regional Conference, Ostend.
1540 **302** 20c. red 10 10
1541 – 80c. green 25 20
1542 – 4f. blue . . . . 1·25 35
DESIGNS: 80c. Mermaid, "Mercury" and Rotary symbol; 4f. Rotary symbol and hemispheres.

303 Child

304 "The Blind Man and the Paralytic" (after Anto-Carte)

1954. Anti-T.B. and other Funds.
1543 **303** 20c.+5c. green 15 20
1544 80c.+20c. black 65 40
1545 1f.20+30c. brown . . . 1·40 1·00
1546 1f.50+50c. violet . . . . 2·75 1·60
1547 **304** 2f.+75c. red . . . . . . 4·25 2·75
1548 4f.+1f. blue . . . . . . 15·00 9·50

305 Begonia and the Rabot

1955. Ghent Flower Show.
1549 **305** 80c. red 35 20
1550 – 2f.50 sepia . . . . . . 5·25 1·90
1551 – 4f. lake . . . . 3·00 65
DESIGNS—VERT: 2f.50, Azaleas and Chateau des Comtes; 4f. Orchid and the "Three Towers".

306 "Homage to Charles V" (A. De Vriendt)

307 "Charles V" (Titian)

1955. Emperor Charles V Exhibition, Ghent.
1552 **306** 20c. red 15 10
1553 **307** 2f. green 70 10
1554 – 4f. blue . . . . 3·25 95
DESIGN—As Type **306**: 4f. "Abdication of Charles V" (L. Gallait).

308 Emile Verhaeren (after C. Montald)

309 "Textile Industry"

1955. Birth Centenary of Verhaeren (poet).
1555 **308** 20c. black 10 10

1955. 2nd Int Textile Exhibition, Brussels.
1556 **309** 2f. purple 75 20

310 "The Foolish Virgin" (R. Wouters)

311 "The Departure of the Liege Volunteers in 1830" (Soubre)

1955. 3rd Biennial Sculpture Exn, Antwerp.
1557 **310** 1f.20 green 70 30
1558 2f. violet . . . . 1·25 15

1955. Liege Exn. 125th Anniv of 1830 Revolution.
1559 **311** 20c. green 10 10
1560 2f. brown 65 10

312 Ernest Solvay

1955. Cultural Fund. Scientists.
1561 **312** 20c.+5c. brown 15 20
1562 – 80c.+20c. violet 95 35
1563 – 1f.20+30c. blue . . . . 4·50 2·40
1564 – 2f.+50c. red . . . . . . 4·00 2·10
1565 – 3f.+1f. green . . . . . 10·00 5·75
1566 – 4f.+2f. brown . . . . . 10·00 5·75
PORTRAITS—VERT: 80c. Jean-Jacques Dony. 2f. Leo H. Baekeland. 3f. Jean-Etienne Lenoir. HORIZ: 1f.20, Egide Walschaerts. 4f. Emile Fourcault and Emile Gobbe.

313 "The Joys of Spring" (E. Canneel)

314 E. Holboll (Danish postal official)

1955. Anti-T.B. and other Funds.
1567 **313** 20c.+5c. mauve 15 20
1568 80c.+20c. green 45 30
1569 1f.20+30c. brown . . . 2·00 85
1570 1f.50+50c. violet . . . . 1·60 70
1571 **314** 2f.+50c. red . . . . . . 7·00 3·25
1572 – 4f.+2f. blue . . . . . . 17·00 9·25
1573 – 8f.+4f. sepia . . . . . . 18·00 9·75
PORTRAITS—As Type **314**: 4f. J. D. Rockefeller (philanthropist). 8f. Sir R. W. Philip (physician).

315 Blood Donors Emblem

316 Mozart when a Child

317 Queen Elisabeth and Mozart Sonata

1956. Blood Donors.
1574 **315** 2f. red 30 10

1956. Birth Bicentenary of Mozart. Inscr as in T **316**.
1575 – 80c.+20c. green 40 15
1576 **316** 2f.+1f. purple . . . . . 3·00 1·60
1577 **317** 4f.+2f. lilac . . . . . . 6·50 3·50
DESIGN—As Type **316**: 80c. Palace of Charles de Lorraine, Brussels.

318

319 Queen Elisabeth Medallion (Courtens)

1956. "Scaldis" Exhibitions in Tournai, Ghent and Antwerp.
1578 **318** 2f. blue 20 10

1956. 80th Birthday of Queen Elisabeth and Foundation Fund.
1579 **319** 80c.+20c. green 40 20
1580 2f.+1f. lake . . . . . . 2·75 1·40
1581 4f.+2f. sepia . . . . . . 3·50 2·40

320

321 Electric Train Type 122 and Railway Bridge

1956. Europa.
1582 **320** 2f. green . . . . 1·40 10
1583 4f. violet . . . . 6·50 30

1956. Electrification of Brussels–Luxembourg Railway Line.
1584 **321** 2f. blue 30 10

322 E. Anseele

1956. Birth Centenary of Anseele (statesman).
1588 **322** 20c. purple 10 10

323 Medieval Ship **324** Weighing a Baby

1956. Anti-tuberculosis and other Funds.
1589 **323** 20c.+5c. brown 10 10
1590 80c.+20c. green 50 25
1591 1f.20+30c. purple . . . 55 30
1592 1f.50+50c. slate 80 50
1593 **324** 2f.+50c. green . . . . . 1·40 95
1594 – 4f.+2f. purple . . . . . 3·75 5·75
1595 – 8f.+4f. red . . . . . . 10·00 7·00
DESIGNS—As Type **324**: HORIZ: 4f. X-ray examination. VERT: 8f. Convalescence and rehabilitation.

325 "Atomium" and Exhibition Emblem **327** Emperor Maximilian I, with Messenger

1957. Brussels International Exhibition.
1596 **325** 2f. red 15 10
1597 2f.50 green 25 20
1598 4f. violet 55 20
1599 5f. purple . . . . 1·00 35

1957. Stamp Day.
1603 **327** 2f. red 30 15

328 Charles Plisnier and Albrecht Rodenbach (writers)

1957. Cultural Fund. Belgian Celebrities.
1604 **328** 20c.+5c. violet 10 10
1605 – 80c.+20c. brown 30 15
1606 – 1f.20+30c. sepia 60 35
1607 – 2f.+50c. red . . . . . . 1·60 95
1608 – 3f.+1f. green . . . . . 2·00 1·75
1609 – 4f.+2f. blue . . . . . . 2·40 2·00
DESIGNS: 80c. Professors Emiel Vliebergh and Maurice Wilmotte; 1f.20, Paul Pastur and Julius Hoste; 2f. Lodewijk de Raet and Jules Destree (politicians); 3f. Constantin Meunier and Constant Permeke (artists); 4f. Lieven Gevaert and Edouard Empain (industrialists).

329 Sikorsky S-58 Helicopter

1957. Conveyance of 100,000th Passenger by Belgian Helicopter Service.
1610 **329** 4f. blue, green and grey 70 30

330 Steamer entering Zeebrugge Harbour

1957. 50th Anniv of Completion of Zeebrugge Harbour.
1611 **330** 2f. blue 30 10

331 King Leopold I entering Brussels (after Simonau) **332** Scout and Guide Badges

1957. 126th Anniv of Arrival of King Leopold I in Belgium.
1612 **331** 20c. green 15 10
1613 – 2f. mauve 40 10
DESIGN—HORIZ: 2f. King Leopold I at frontier (after Wappers).

1957. 50th Anniv of Boy Scout Movement and Birth Centenary of Lord Baden-Powell.
1614 **332** 80c. brown 25 15
1615 – 4f. green 95 40
DESIGN—VERT: 4f. Lord Baden-Powell.

333 "Kneeling Woman" (after Lehmbruck) **334** "Agriculture and Industry"

1957. 4th Biennial Sculpture Exn, Antwerp.
1616 **333** 2f.50 green 75 55

1957. Europa.
1617 **334** 2f. purple 45 10
1618 4f. blue . . . . 1·10 35

335 Sledge-dog Team

1957. Belgian Antarctic Expedition, 1957–58.
1619 **335** 5f.+2f.50 orange, brown and grey . . . . . . 2·40 1·75
MS1620 115 × 83 mm. Block of four of No. 1619 in new colours, brown, red and blue £250 £100

336 General Patton's Grave at Hamm **337** Adolphe Max

1957. General Patton Memorial Issue.
1621 **336** 1f.+50c. black . . . . . 1·25 55
1622 – 2f.50+50c. green . . . . 1·50 65
1623 – 3f.+1f. brown . . . . . 3·00 1·60
1624 – 5f.+2f.50 slate . . . . . 5·75 3·50
1625 – 6f.+3f. red . . . . . . 7·75 5·75
DESIGNS—HORIZ: 2f.50, Patton Memorial project at Bastogne; 3f. Gen. Patton decorating Brig.-General A. MacAuliffe; 6f. (51 × 35½ mm) Tanks in action. VERT: 5f. General Patton.

1957. 18th Death Anniv of Burgomaster Adolphe Max (patriot).
1626 **337** 2f.50+1f. blue 90 55

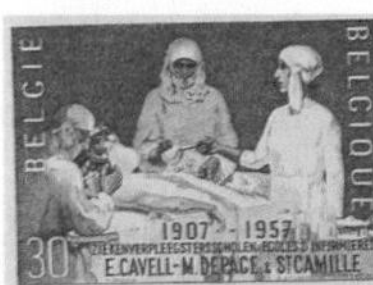
338 Queen Elisabeth with Doctors Depage and Debaisieux at a surgical operation

1957. 50th Anniv of "Edith Cavell-Marie Depage" and "St. Camille" Nursing Schools.
1627 **338** 30c. red 20 10

339 "Carnival Kings of Fosses" (Namur) **340** "Infanta Isabella with Crossbow" (Brussels)

1957. Anti-tuberculosis and other Funds. Provincial Legends.
1628 **339** 30c.+20c. pur & yell . . 20 15
1629 – 1f.+50c. sepia & blue . . 25 20
1630 – 1f.50+50c. grey & red . . 45 25
1631 – 2f.+1f. black & green . . 45 30
1632 **340** 2f.50+1f. grn & mve . . 1·50 90
1633 – 5f.+2f. black & blue . . 3·00 2·45
1634 – 6f.+2f.50 lake & red . . 3·50 3·25
DESIGNS: As Type **339**—HORIZ: 1f.50, "St. Remacle and the Wolf" (Liège). VERT: 1f. "Op Signoorken" (Antwerp); 2f. "The Long Man and the Pea Soup" (Limburg). As Type **340**—HORIZ: 6f. "Carnival Kings of Binche" (Hainaut). VERT: 5f. "The Virgin with the Inkwell" (West Flanders).

341 Posthorn and Postilion's Badges

1958. Postal Museum Day.
1635 **341** 2f.50 grey 20 10

342 Benelux Gate

1958. Inauguration of Brussels International Exhibition. Inscr as in T **342**.
1636 **342** 30c.+20c. sepia, brown and violet 10 10
1637 – 1f.+50c. purple, slate and green 10 10
1638 – 1f.50+50c. violet, turquoise and green 20 15
1639 – 2f.50+1f. red, blue and vermilion 30 20
1640 – 3f.+1f.50 blue, black and red 60 50
1641 – 5f.+3f. mauve, black and blue . . . . 1·00 90
DESIGNS—HORIZ: 1f. Civil Engineering Pavilion; 1f.50, Belgian Congo and Ruanda-Urundi Pavilion; 2f.50, "Belgium, 1900"; 3f. Atomium; 5f. (49 × 33½ mm) Telexpo Pavilion.

343 "Food and Agriculture Organization"

1958. United Nations Commemoration.
1642 – 50c. grey (postage) . . . 1·90 1·75
1643 **343** 1f. red 15 25
1644 – 1f.50 blue 20 20
1645 – 2f. purple 35 40
1646 – 2f.50 green 15 25
1647 – 3f. turquoise 40 40
1648 – 5f. mauve 20 25
1649 – 8f. brown 50 50
1650 – 11f. lilac . . . . 1·00 1·00
1651 – 20f. red . . . . 1·90 1·75
1652 – 5f. blue (air) 15 10
1653 – 6f. green 20 15
1654 – 7f.50 violet 20 15
1655 – 8f. sepia 25 25
1656 – 9f. red 35 40
1657 – 10f. brown 40 40
DESIGNS (Emblems and symbols)—HORIZ: 50c. I.L.O. 2f.50, U.N.E.S.C.O. 3f. U.N. Pavilion, Brussels Int Exn; 6f. World Meteorological Organization; 8f. (No. 1649), Int Monetary Fund; 8f. (No. 1655), General Agreement on Tariffs and Trade; 10f. Atomic Energy Agency; 11f. W.H.O. 20f. U.P.U. VERT: 1f.50, U.N.O. 2f. World Bank; 5f. (No. 1648), I.T.U. 5f. (No. 1652), I.C.A.O. 7f.50, Protection of Refugees; 9f. UNICEF.

344 Eugene Ysaye **345** "Europa"

1958. Birth Centenary of Ysaye (violinist).
1658 **344** 30c. blue and red 10 10

1958. Europa.
1659 **345** 2f.50 blue and red . . . 80 10
1660 5f. red and blue . . . . 1·50 30

346 "Marguerite Van Eyck" (after Jan Van Eyck)

1958. Cultural Relief Funds. Paintings as T **346**. Frames in brown and yellow.
1661 **346** 30c.+20c. myrtle 10 20
1662 – 1f.+50c. lake 55 35
1663 – 1f.+50+50c. blue 85 65
1664 – 2f.50+1f. sepia . . . . . 1·60 1·40
1665 – 3f.+1f.50 red . . . . . 2·10 1·75
1666 – 5f.+3f. blue . . . . . . 3·75 3·50
PAINTINGS—HORIZ: 1f. "Carrying the Cross" (Hieronymus Bosch). 3f. "The Rower" (James Ensor). VERT: 1f.50, "St. Donatien" (Jan Gossaert). 2f.50, Self-portrait (Lambert Lombard). 5f. "Henriette with the Large Hat" (Henri Evenepoel).

347 "Hoogstraten" **348** Pax—"Creche vivante"

1958. Anti-tuberculosis and other Funds. Provincial Legends.
1667 **347** 40c.+10c. blue & grn . . 10 15
1668 – 1f.+50c. sepia & yell . . 20 20
1669 – 1f.50+50c. pur & grn . . 40 20
1670 – 2f.+1f. brown & red . . 45 25
1671 **348** 2f.50+1f. red and green 1·40 75
1672 – 5f.+2f. purple & blue . . 3·00 2·75
1673 – 6f.+2f. blue & red . . . 3·50 3·25
DESIGNS: As Type **347**—VERT: 1f. "Jean de Nivelles"; 1f.50, "Jeu de Saint Evermare a Russon". HORIZ: 2f. "Les penitents de Furnes". As Type **348**—HORIZ: "Marches de l'Entre Sambre et Meuse". VERT: 6f. "Pax—Vierge".

349 "Human Rights" **350** "Europe of the Heart"

1958. 10th Anniv of Human Rights Declaration.
1674 **349** 2f.50 slate 25 10

1959. "Heart of Europe". Fund for Displaced Persons.
1675 **350** 1f.+50c. purple 25 20
1676 2f.50+1f. green 65 50
1677 5f.+2f.50 brown . . . . 1·10 85

351 J. B. de Taxis taking the oath at the hands of Charles V (after J.-E. Van den Bussche) **352** N.A.T.O. Emblem

1959. Stamp Day.
1680 **351** 2f.50 green 35 10

1959. 10th Anniv of N.A.T.O.
1681 **352** 2f.50 blue and red . . . 30 10
1682 5f. blue and green . . . 75 55
On the 5f. value the French and Flemish inscriptions are transposed.
For similar design but inscr "1969", see No. 2112.

353 "Blood Transfusion"

354 J. H. Dunant and battle scene at Solferino, 1859

1959. Red Cross Commem. Inscr "1859 1959".

No.	Type	Description	Mint	Used
1683	353	40c.+10c. red & grey	15	15
1684		1f.+50c. red & sepia	80	35
1685		1f.50+50c. red and lilac	1·75	1·10
1686	–	2f.50+1f. red & grn	2·10	1·40
1687	–	3f.+1f.50 red and blue	3·75	2·45
1688	354	5f.+3f. red and sepia	6·75	4·00

DESIGN—As Type **353**—HORIZ: 2f.50, 3f. Red Cross and broken sword ("Aid for the wounded").

355 Philip the Good **356** Arms of Philip the Good

1959. Royal Library of Belgium Fund. Mult.

No.	Type	Description	Mint	Used
1689		40c.+10c. Type **355**	10	20
1690		1f.+50c. Charles the Bold	30	30
1691		1f.50+50c. Maximillian of Austria	95	45
1692		2f.50+1f. Philip the Fair	1·75	1·50
1693		3f.+1f.50 Charles V	2·40	2·25
1694		5f.+3f. Type **355**	3·50	3·25

358 Town Hall, Oudenarde **359** Pope Adrian VI

1959. Oudenarde Town Hall Commem.

No.	Type	Description	Mint	Used
1699	358	2f.50 purple	25	10

1959. 500th Birth Anniv of Pope Adrian VI.

No.	Type	Description	Mint	Used
1700	359	2f.50 red	15	10
1701		5f. blue	30	30

360 "Europa" **361** Boeing 707

1959. Europa.

No.	Type	Description	Mint	Used
1702	360	2f.50 red	25	10
1703		5f. turquoise	45	35

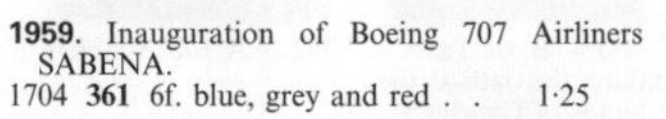

1959. Inauguration of Boeing 707 Airliners by SABENA.

No.	Type	Description	Mint	Used
1704	361	6f. blue, grey and red	1·25	50

362 Antwerp fish (float) **363** Stavelot "Blancs Moussis" (carnival figures)

1959. Anti-tuberculosis and other Funds. Carnival scenes.

No.	Type	Description	Mint	Used
1705	362	40c.+10c. green, red and bistre	10	15
1706	–	1f.+50c. green, violet and olive	30	20
1707	–	2f.+50c. yellow, purple and brown	35	25
1708	363	2f.50+1f. blue, violet and grey	55	25
1709	–	3f.+1f. purple, yellow and grey	1·40	85
1710	–	6f.+2f. blue, red and olive	3·25	3·00
1711	–	7f.+3f. blk, yell, & bl	3·75	3·25

DESIGNS—As Type **362**—HORIZ: 1f. Mons dragon (float); 2f. Eupen and Malmedy clowns in chariot. As Type **363**—VERT: 3f. Ypres jester. HORIZ: 6f. Holy Family; 7f. Madonna and child.

364 Countess Alexandrine of Taxis (tapestry) **365** Indian Azalea

1960. Stamp Day.

No.	Type	Description	Mint	Used
1712	364	3f. blue	45	10

1960. Ghent Flower Show. Inscr as in T **365**.

No.	Type	Description	Mint	Used
1713	365	40c. red and purple	10	10
1714	–	3f. yellow, red and green	45	10
1715	–	6f. red, green and blue	1·10	50

FLOWERS: 3f. Begonia. 6f. Anthurium and bromelia.

366 Refugee **367** "Labour" (after Meunier)

1960. World Refugee Year. Inscr as in T **366**.

No.	Type	Description	Mint	Used
1716	–	40c.+10c. purple	10	20
1717	366	3f.+1f.50 sepia	40	30
1718	–	6f.+3f. blue	95	80
MS1719		121 × 93 mm. Nos. 1716/18 in new colours, violet, brown and red respectively	27·00	23·00

DESIGNS: 40c. Child refugee; 6f. Woman refugee.

1960. 75th Anniv of Belgian Socialist Party. Inscr as in T **367**.

No.	Type	Description	Mint	Used
1720	367	40c. purple and red	10	15
1721	–	3f. brown and red	45	20

DESIGN—HORIZ: 3f. "Workers" (after Meunier).

369 Parachutist on ground

1960. Parachuting. Designs bearing emblem of National Parachuting Club.

No.	Type	Description	Mint	Used
1726	–	40c.+10c. black & blue	20	20
1727	–	1f.+50c. black & blue	1·00	60
1728	–	2f.+50c. black, blue and green	2·10	1·25
1729	–	2f.50+1f. black, turquoise and green	3·50	2·25
1730	369	3f.+1f. black, blue and green	3·50	2·25
1731		6f.+2f. black, blue and green	3·75	3·00

DESIGNS—HORIZ: 40c., 1f., Parachutists dropping from Douglas DC-4 aircraft. VERT: 2f., 2f.50, Parachutists descending.

370 Ship's Officer and Helmsman

1960. Congo Independence.

No.	Type	Description	Mint	Used
1732	370	10c. red	10	10
1733	–	40c. red	10	10
1734	–	1f. purple	40	20
1735	–	2f. green	35	20
1736	–	2f.50 blue	50	20
1737	–	3f. blue	50	15
1738	–	6f. violet	1·50	60
1739	–	8f. brown	5·50	4·50

DESIGNS—As Type **370**: 40c. Doctor and nurses with patient; 1f. Tree-planting; 2f. Sculptors; 2f.50, Sport (putting the shot); 3f. Broadcasting from studio. (52 × 35½ mm): 6f. Children with doll; 8f. Child with globe.

371 Refugee Airlift

1960. Congo Refugees Relief Fund.

No.	Type	Description	Mint	Used
1740	371	40c.+10c. turquoise	15	20
1741	–	3f.+1f.50 red	1·75	1·10
1742	–	6f.+3f. violet	3·25	2·75

DESIGNS—As Type **371**: 3f. Mother and child. 35 × 51½ mm: 6f. Boeing 707 airplane spanning map of aircraft route.

1960. Surch.

No.	Type	Description	Mint	Used
1743	267	15c. on 30c. green	10	10
1744		15c. on 50c. blue	10	10
1745		20c. on 30c. green	10	10

373 Conference Emblem **374** Young Stamp Collectors

1960. 1st Anniv of E.P.T. Conference.

No.	Type	Description	Mint	Used
1746	373	3f. lake	40	15
1747		6f. green	75	40

1960. "Philately for the Young" Propaganda.

No.	Type	Description	Mint	Used
1748	374	40c. black and bistre	10	10

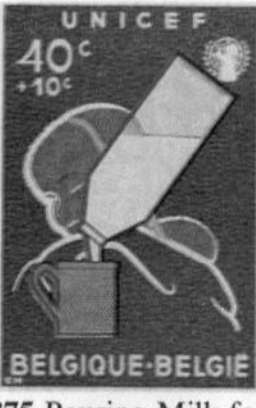

375 Pouring Milk for Child **376** Frere Orban (founder)

1960. United Nations Children's Fund.

No.	Type	Description	Mint	Used
1749	375	40c.+10c. yellow, green and brown	10	20
1750	–	1f.+50c. red, blue and drab	55	45
1751	–	2f.+50c. bistre, green and violet	1·25	1·10
1752	–	2f.50+1f. sepia, blue and red	1·75	1·25
1753	–	3f.+1f. violet, orange and turquoise	1·90	1·50
1754	–	6f.+2f. brown, green and blue	3·00	2·00

DESIGNS: 1f. Nurse embracing children; 2f. Child carrying clothes, and ambulance; 2f.50, Nurse weighing baby; 3f. Children with linked arms; 6f. Refugee worker and child.

1960. Centenary of Credit Communal (Co-operative Bank).

No.	Type	Description	Mint	Used
1755	376	10c. brown and yellow	10	10
1756		40c. brown and green	15	10
1757		1f.50 brown and violet	70	50
1758		3f. brown and red	70	20

377 Tapestry

1960. Anti-T.B. and other Funds. Arts and Crafts.

No.	Type	Description	Mint	Used
1759	377	40c.+10c. ochre, brown and blue	10	20
1760	–	1f.+50c. blue, brown and indigo	65	55
1761	–	2f.+50c. green, black and brown	1·10	85
1762	–	2f.50+1f. yellow and brown	1·90	1·40
1763	–	3f.+1f. black, brown and blue	2·25	1·75
1764	–	6f.+2f. lemon and black	3·25	2·25

DESIGNS—VERT: 1f. Crystalware; 2f. Lace. HORIZ: 2f.50, Brassware; 3f. Diamond-cutting; 6f. Ceramics.

378 King Baudouin and Queen Fabiola **379** Nicolaus Rockox (after Van Dyck)

1960. Royal Wedding.

No.	Type	Description	Mint	Used
1765	378	40c. sepia and green	15	10
1766		3f. sepia and purple	55	10
1767		6f. sepia and blue	1·75	40

1961. Surch in figs and **1961** at top, **1962** at bottom and bars in between.

No.	Type	Description	Mint	Used
1768	267	15c. on 30c. green	60	10
1769		20c. on 30c. green	1·60	10

See note below No. 480.

1961. 400th Birth Anniv of Nicolaus Rockox (Burgomaster of Antwerp).

No.	Type	Description	Mint	Used
1770	379	3f. black, bistre & brn	30	10

380 Seal of Jan Bode **381** K. Kats (playwright) and Father N. Pietkin (poet)

1961. Stamp Day.

No.	Type	Description	Mint	Used
1771	380	3f. sepia and brown	30	10

1961. Cultural Funds. Portrait in purple.

No.	Type	Description	Mint	Used
1772		40c.+10c. lake and pink	10	15
1773		1f.+50c. lake and brown	1·40	1·10
1774		2f.+50c. red and yellow	2·40	2·10
1775		2f.50+1f. myrtle and sage	2·40	2·10
1776		3f.+1f. blue and light blue	2·75	2·25
1777		6f.+2f. blue and lavender	3·50	2·75

PORTRAITS: 40c. Type **381**. 1f. A. Mockel and J. F. Willems (writers). 2f. J. van Rijswijck and X. Neujean (politicians). 2f.50, J. Demarteau (journalist) and A. van de Perre (politician). 3f. J. David (litterateur) and A. du Bois (writer). 6f. H. Vieuxtemps (violinist) and W. de Mol (composer).

382 White Rhinoceros **383** Cardinal A.P. de Granville (first Archbishop)

1961. Philanthropic Funds. Animals of Antwerp Zoo.

No.	Type	Description	Mint	Used
1778		40c.+10c. dp brown & brn	15	15
1779		1f.+50c. brown and green	70	65
1780		2f.+50c. sepia, red and black	1·25	85
1781		2f.50+1f. brown and red	1·25	95
1782		3f.+1f. brown and orange	1·50	1·10
1783		6f.+2f. ochre and blue	1·90	1·40

ANIMALS—VERT: 40c. Type **382**; 1f. Wild horse and foal; 2f. Okapi. HORIZ: 2f.50, Giraffe; 3f. Lesser panda; 6f. Elk.

1961. 400th Anniv of Archbishopric of Malines.

No.	Type	Description	Mint	Used
1784	383	40c.+10c. brown, red and purple	10	10
1785	–	3f.+1f.50 mult	55	35
1786	–	6f.+3f. bistre, violet and purple	90	80

DESIGNS: 3f. Cardinal's Arms; 6f. Symbols of Archbishopric and Malines.

385 "Interparliamentary Union"

1961. 50th Interparliamentary Union Conference, Brussels.
1791 **385** 3f. brown and turquoise . . . 45 10
1792 6f. purple and red . . . 70 40

386 Doves

1961. Europa.
1793 **386** 3f. black and olive . . . 20 10
1794 6f. black and brown . . 40 25

387 Reactor BR 2, Mol
388 "The Mother and Child" (after Paulus)

1961. Euratom Commemoration.
1795 **387** 40c. green 10 10
1796 – 3f. mauve 15 10
1797 – 6f. blue 35 30
DESIGNS—VERT: 3f. Heart of reactor BR 3, Mol. HORIZ: 6f. View of reactor BR 3, Mol.

1961. Anti-T.B. and other Funds. Belgian paintings of mothers and children. Frames in gold.
1798 **388** 40c.+10c. sepia 10 15
1799 – 1f.+50c. blue 40 40
1800 – 2f.+50c. red 80 65
1801 – 2f.50+1f. lake 80 70
1802 – 3f.+1f. violet 75 65
1803 – 6f.+2f. myrtle 95 85
PAINTINGS: 1f. "Maternal Love" (Navez). 2f. "Maternity" (Permeke). 2f.50, "The Virgin and the Child" (Van der Weyden). 3f. "The Virgin with the Apple" (Memling), 6f. "The Myosotis Virgin" (Rubens).

389 Horta Museum
390 Male Castle

1962. Birth Cent of Victor Horta (architect).
1804 **389** 3f. brown 25 10

1962. Cultural and Patriotic Funds. Buildings.
1805 **390** 40c.+10c. green 10 10
1806 – 90c.+10c. mauve 20 20
1807 – 1f.+50c. lilac 40 30
1808 – 2f.+50c. violet 60 55
1809 – 2f.50+1f. brown 80 70
1810 – 3f.+1f. turquoise 90 80
1811 – 6f.+2f. red . . . . . 1·50 1·25
BUILDINGS—HORIZ: 90c. Royal Library, Brussels. 1f. Collegiate Church, Soignies. 6f. Ypres Halls. VERT: 1f. Notre-Dame Basilica, Tongres. 2f.50, Notre-Dame Church, Hanswijk, Malines. 3f. St. Denis-en-Broqueroie Abbey.

391 16th-Century Postilion
392 G. Mercator (after F. Hogenberg)

1962. Stamp Day.
1812 **391** 3f. brown and green . . 25 10
See also No. 1997.

1962. 450th Birth Anniv of Mercator (geographer).
1813 **392** 3f. sepia 25 10

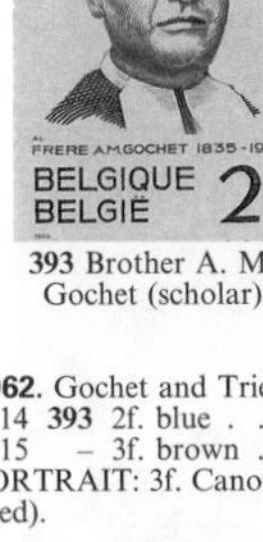

393 Brother A. M. Gochet (scholar)
394 Guianan Cock of the Rock ("Coq de Roch, Rotshann")

1962. Gochet and Triest Commemoration.
1814 **393** 2f. blue 10 15
1815 – 3f. brown 25 15
PORTRAIT: 3f. Canon P.-J. Triest (benefactor of the aged).

1962. Philanthropic Funds. Birds of Antwerp Zoo. Birds, etc., in natural colours; colours of name panel and inscription given.
1816 **394** 40c.+10c. blue 10 20
1817 – 1f.+50c. blue and red . . 35 35
1818 – 2f.+50c. mauve & blk . . 60 60
1819 – 2f.50+1f. turq & red . . 75 80
1820 – 3f.+1f. brown & grn . . 90 1·00
1821 – 6f.+2f. blue and red . . 1·10 1·25
BIRDS: 1f. Red lory ("Rode Lori, Lori Rouge"); 2f. Green turaco ("Touracou du Senegal, Senegal Toerakoe"); 2f.50, Keel-billed toucan ("Kortbek Toecan, Toucan a Bec Court"); 3f. Greater bird of paradise ("Grand Paradijsier, Grosse Paradisvogel"); 6f. Congo peafowl ("Kongo Pauw, Paon du Congo").

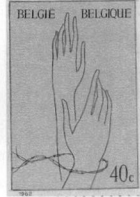

395 Europa "Tree"
396 "Captive Hands" (after sculpture by Ianchelivici)

1962. Europa.
1822 **395** 3f. black, yellow & red . . 20 10
1823 6f. black, yellow & olive . . 40 35

1962. Concentration Camp Victims.
1824 **396** 40c. blue and black . . . 15 10

397 Reading Braille
398 "Adam" (after Michelangelo)

1962. Handicapped Children Relief Funds.
1825 **397** 40c.+10c. brown 10 20
1826 – 1f.+50c. red 30 40
1827 – 2f.+50c. mauve 75 80
1828 – 2f.50+1f. green 70 80
1829 – 3f.+1f. blue 75 75
1830 – 6f.+2f. sepia 65 90
DESIGNS—VERT: 1f. Girl solving puzzle; 2f.50, Crippled child with ball; 3f. Girl walking with crutches. HORIZ: 2f. Child with earphones; 6f. Crippled boys with football.

1962. "The Rights of Man".
1831 **398** 3f. sepia and green . . . 20 15
1832 6f. sepia and brown . . 40 35

399 Queen Louise-Marie
400 Menin Gate, Ypres

1962. Anti-tuberculosis and other Funds. Belgian Queens in green and gold.
1833 40c.+10c. Type **399** 10 10
1834 40c.+10c. As T **399** but inscr "ML" 10 10
1835 1f.+50c. Marie-Henriette . . 45 40
1836 2f.+1f. Elisabeth 80 75
1837 3f.+1f.50 Astrid . . . . . . 1·10 95
1838 8f.+2f.50 Fabiola . . . . . 1·25 1·10

1962. Ypres Millenary.
1839 **400** 1f.+50c. multicoloured . . 30 40
MS1840 113 × 137 mm. Block of eight . . . . 5·00 4·50

401 H. Pirenne
402 "Peace Bell"

1963. Birth Cent of Henri Pirenne (historian).
1841 **401** 3f. blue 30 10

1963. Cultural Funds and Installation of "Peace Bell" in Koekelberg Basilica. Bell in yellow; "PAX" in black.
1842 **402** 3f.+1f.50 green & bl . . 1·25 1·10
1843 6f.+3f. chestnut & brn 65 65
MS1844 82 × 116 mm. No. 1842 (block of four) . . . . 7·00 6·50

403 "The Sower" (after Brueghel)
404 17th-century Duel

1963. Freedom from Hunger.
1845 **403** 2f.+1f. brown, black and green 20 20
1846 – 3f.+1f. brown, black and purple 25 20
1847 – 6f.+2f. yellow, black and brown 40 40
PAINTINGS—HORIZ: 3f. "The Harvest" (Brueghel). VERT: 6f. "The Loaf" (Anto Carte).

1963. 350th Anniv of Royal Guild and Knights of St. Michael.
1848 **404** 1f. red and blue 10 10
1849 – 3f. violet and green . . . 20 10
1850 – 6f. multicoloured 40 30
DESIGNS—HORIZ: 3f. Modern fencing. VERT: 6f. Arms of the Guild.

405 19th-century Mail-coach

1963. Stamp Day.
1851 **405** 3f. black and ochre . . . 25 10
See also No. 1998.

406 Hotel des Postes, Paris, and Belgian 1c. Stamp of 1863
407 Child in Wheatfield

1963. Centenary of Paris Postal Conference.
1852 **406** 6f. sepia, mauve & grn . . 35 35

1963. "8th May" Peace Movement.
1853 **407** 3f. multicoloured 20 15
1854 6f. multicoloured 35 35

408 "Transport"
409 Town Seal

1963. European Transport Ministers' Conference, Brussels.
1855 **408** 6f. black and blue . . . 35 35

1963. Int Union of Towns Congress, Brussels.
1856 **409** 6f. multicoloured 35 35

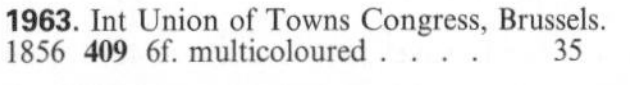

410 Racing Cyclists
411 Sud Aviation SE 210 Caravelle

1963. Belgian Cycling Team's Participation in Olympic Games, Tokyo (1964).
1857 **410** 1f.+50c. multicoloured . . 10 25
1858 – 2f.+1f. multicoloured . . 10 25
1859 – 3f.+1f.50 mult 25 35
1860 – 6f.+3f. multicoloured . . 35 50
DESIGNS—HORIZ: 2f. Group of cyclists; 3f. Cyclists rounding bend. VERT: 6f. Cyclists being paced by motorcyclists.

1963. 40th Anniv of SABENA Airline.
1861 **411** 3f. black and turquoise . . 20 10

412 "Co-operation"
413 Princess Paola with Princess Astrid

1963. Europa.
1862 **412** 3f. black, brown & red . . 65 15
1863 6f. black, brown & blue . . 1·00 40
No. 1863 is inscr with "6 F" on the left, "BELGIE" at foot and "BELGIQUE" on right.

1963. Centenary of Red Cross and Belgian Red Cross Fund. Cross in red.
1864 – 40c.+10c. red & yell . . 10 10
1865 **413** 1f.+50c. grey & yellow . . 20 20
1866 – 2f.+50c. mauve & yell . . 25 25
1867 – 2f.50+1f. blue & yell . . 25 35
1868 – 3f.+1f. brown & yell . . 45 45
1869 – 3f.+1f. bronze & yell . . 1·45 2·00
1870 – 6f.+2f. green & yellow . . 1·10 1·25
DESIGNS—As T **413**: 40c. Prince Philippe; 2f. Princess Astrid; 2f.50, Princess Paola; 6f. Prince Albert; 46 × 35 mm: 3f. (2), Prince Albert and family.

414 J. Destree (writer)

1963. Jules Destree and H. Van de Velde Commems.
1871 **414** 1f. purple 10 10
1872 – 1f. green 10 10
DESIGN: No. 1872, H. Van de Velde (architect).

415 Bas-reliefs from Facade of Postal Cheques Office (after O. Jespars)
416 Balthasar Gerbier's Daughter

1963. 50th Anniv of Belgian Postal Cheques Office.
1873 **415** 50c. black, blue & red . . 10 15

1963. T.B. Relief and Other Funds. Rubens's Drawings. Background buff; inscr in black: designs colour given.
1874 **416** 50c.+10c. blue 10 10
1875 – 1f.+40c. red 20 20
1876 – 2f.+50c. violet 20 20
1877 – 2f.50+1f. green 45 40
1878 – 3f.+1f. brown 45 35
1879 – 6f.+2f. black 75 65
DRAWINGS—VERT: Rubens's children—1f. Nicolas (aged 2). 2f. Franz (aged 4). 2f.50, Nicolas (aged 6). 3f. Albert (aged 3). HORIZ: (46½ × 35½ mm): 6f. Infant Jesus, St. John and two angels.

417 Dr. G. Hansen and Laboratory

1964. Leprosy Relief Campaign.
1880 **417** 1f. black and brown . . 15 20
1881 – 2f. brown and black . . 20 25
1882 – 5f. black and brown . . 45 35
MS1883 135 × 98 mm. Nos. 1880/2 (+4f.) . . . . 2·25 2·25
DESIGNS: 2f. Leprosy hospital; 5f. Father Damien.

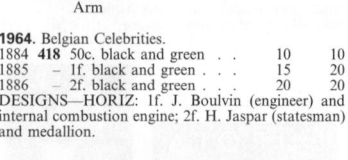

418 A. Vesale (anatomist) with Model of Human Arm **419** Postilion

1964. Belgian Celebrities.
1884 **418** 50c. black and green . . 10 10
1885 – 1f. black and green . . . 15 20
1886 – 2f. black and green . . . 20 20
DESIGNS—HORIZ: 1f. J. Boulvin (engineer) and internal combustion engine; 2f. H. Jaspar (statesman) and medallion.

1964. Stamp Day.
1887 **419** 3f. grey 20 10

420 Admiral Lord Gambier and U.S. Ambassador J. Q. Adams after signing treaty (from painting by Sir A. Forestier)

1964. 150th Anniv of Signing of Treaty of Ghent.
1888 **420** 6f.+3f. blue 50 55

421 Arms of Ostend **422** Ida of Bure (Calvin's wife)

1964. Millenary of Ostend.
1889 **421** 3f. multicoloured 20 10

1964. "Protestantism in Belgium".
1890 – 1f.+50c. blue 15 20
1891 **422** 3f.+1f.50 red 20 25
1892 – 6f.+3f. brown 45 50
PORTRAITS: 1f. P. Marnix of St. Aldegonde (Burgomaster of Antwerp). 6f. J. Jordaens (painter).

423 Globe, Hammer and Flame

424 Infantryman of 1918

1964. Centenary of Socialist International.
1893 **423** 50c. red and blue 10 10
1894 – 1f. red and blue 10 10
1895 – 2f. red and blue 15 25
DESIGNS: 1f. "SI" on Globe; 2f. Flames.

1964. 50th Anniv of German Invasion of Belgium. Multicoloured.
1896 1f.+50c. Type **424** 15 10
1897 2f.+1f. Colour sergeant of the Guides Regt, 1914 . . 15 20
1898 3f.+1f.50 Trumpeter of the Grenadiers & Drummers of the Infantry and Carabiniers, 1914 . . . . 25 30

425 Soldier at Bastogne

426 Europa "Flower"

1964. "Liberation–Resistance". Multicoloured.
1899 3f.+1f. Type **425** 20 20
1900 6f.+3f. Soldier at estuary of the Scheldt 45 50

1964. Europa.
1901 **426** 3f. grey, red and green 20 10
1902 6f. blue, green and red 40 35

427 "Philip the Good"

428 "Descent from the Cross"

1964. Cultural Funds. 500th Death Anniv of R. van der Weyden. Two sheets each 153 × 114 mm showing paintings by Van der Weyden.
MS1903 1f. Type **427**; 2f. "Portrait of a Lady"; 3f. "The Man with the Arrow" (+8f.) . . . . 3·75 3·75
MS1904 **428** 8f. (+8f.) brown . . 3·75 3·75

429 Pand Abbey, Ghent

1964. Pand Abbey Restoration Fund.
1905 **429** 2f.+1f. bl, turq & blk . . 20 25
1906 – 3f.+1f. brown, blue and purple 20 25
DESIGN: 3f. Waterside view of Abbey.

430 King Baudouin, Queen Juliana and Grand Duchess Charlotte

1964. 20th Anniv of "BENELUX".
1907 **430** 3f. purple, blue and olive 30 10

431 "One of Charles I's Children" (Van Dyck)

432 "Diamonds"

1964. T.B. Relief and Other Funds. Paintings of Royalty.
1908 **431** 50c.+10c. purple 15 15
1909 – 1f.+40c. red 15 20
1910 – 2f.+1f. purple 20 25
1911 – 3f.+1f. grey 25 25
1912 – 4f.+2f. violet 30 35
1913 – 6f.+3f. violet 40 50

DESIGNS—VERT: 1f. "William of Orange and his fiancee, Marie" (Van Dyck); 2f. "Portrait of a Little Boy" (E. Quellin and Jan Fyt); 3f. "Alexander Farnese at the age of 12 Years" (A. Moro); 4f. "William II, Prince of Orange" (Van Dyck). HORIZ—LARGER (46 × 35 mm): 6f. "Two Children of Cornelis De Vos" (C. de Vos).

1965. "Diamantexpo" (Diamonds Exn) Antwerp.
1914 **432** 2f. multicoloured 20 20

433 "Textiles"

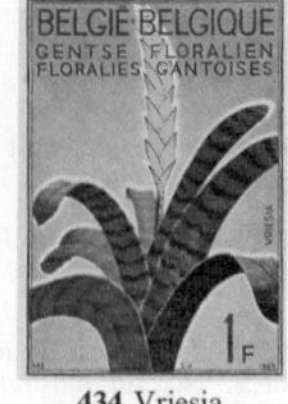
434 Vriesia

1965. "Textirama" (Textile Exn), Ghent.
1915 **433** 1f. black, red and blue 10 10

1965. Ghent Flower Show. Inscr "FLORALIES GANTOISES", etc. Multicoloured.
1916 1f. Type **434** 10 20
1917 2f. Echinocactus 20 25
1918 3f. Stapelia 20 10

435 Paul Hymans

436 Rubens

1965. Birth Cent of Paul Hymans (statesman).
1919 **435** 1f. violet 10 10

1965. Centenary of General Savings and Pensions Funds. Painters.
1920 **436** 1f. sepia and mauve . . 20 10
1921 – 2f. sepia and turquoise 20 10
1922 – 3f. sepia and purple . . 15 10
1923 – 6f. sepia and red 30 25
1924 – 8f. sepia and blue . . . 45 40
PAINTERS: 2f. Franz Snyders. 3f. Adam van Noort. 6f. Anthony van Dyck. 8f. Jakob Jordaens.

437 "Sir Rowland Hill with Young Collectors" (detail from mural by J. Van den Bussche)

438 19th-century Postmaster

1965. "Philately for the Young".
1925 **437** 50c. green 10 10

1965. Stamp Day.
1926 **438** 3f. green 20 10

1965. U.N.W.R.A. Commemoration. Sheet 123 × 89 mm. Nos. 1916/18 in new colours.
MS1927 1f., 2f., 3f. (+14f.) . . . 1·50 1·50

439 Globe and Telephone

1965. Centenary of I.T.U.
1928 **439** 2f. black and purple . . 15 20

440 Handclasp

441 Abbey Staircase

1965. 20th Anniv of Liberation of Prison Camps.
1929 **440** 50c.+50c. purple, black and bistre 10 10
1930 – 1f.+50c. multicoloured 20 20
1931 – 3f.+1f.50 black, purple and green 25 25
1932 – 8f.+5f. multicoloured . . 75 75
DESIGNS—VERT: 1f. Hand reaching for barbed wire. HORIZ: 3f. Tank entering prison camp; 8f. Rose within broken wall.

1965. Affligem Abbey.
1933 **441** 1f. blue 10 10

442 St. Jean Berchmans, Birthplace and Residence

443 Toc H Lamp and Arms of Poperinge

1965. St. Jean Berchmans.
1934 **442** 2f. brown and purple . . 10 10

1965. 50th Anniv of Founding of Toc H Movement at Talbot House, Poperinge.
1935 **443** 3f. multicoloured 20 10

444 Maison Stoclet, Brussels

445 Tractor ploughing

1965. Josef Hoffman (architect) Commemoration.
1936 **444** 3f.+1f. grey and drab . . 20 25
1937 – 6f.+3f. brown 40 45
1938 – 8f.+4f. purple & drab . . 65 65
DESIGNS—Maison Stoclet: VERT: 6f. Entrance hall. HORIZ: 8f. Rear of building.

1965. 75th Anniv of Boerenbond (Belgian Farmers' Association). Multicoloured.
1939 50c. Type **445** 10 10
1940 3f. Horse-drawn plough . . 20 10

446 Europa "Sprig"

1965. Europa.
1941 **446** 1f. black and pink . . . 10 10
1942 3f. black and green . . . 20 10

447 Jackson's Chameleon

1965. Philanthropic Funds. Reptiles of Antwerp Zoo. Multicoloured.
1943 1f.+50c. Type **447** 10 20
1944 2f.+1f. Iguana 20 20
1945 3f.+1f.50 Nile lizard 25 30
1946 6f.+3f. Komodo lizard . . . 45 45
MS1947 118 × 98 mm. 8f.+4f. Soft-shelled turtle (larger) . . . . . 1·10 1·10

448 J. Lebeau (after A. Schollaert)

449 Leopold I (after 30c. and 1f. Stamps of 1865)

1965. Death Cent of Joseph Lebeau (statesman).
1948 **448** 1f. multicoloured 10 10

1965. Death Centenary of King Leopold I.
1949 **449** 3f. sepia 25 10
1950 – 6f. violet 40 35
DESIGN: 6f. As 3f. but with different portrait frame.

450 Huy **451** Guildhouse

1965. Tourist Publicity. Multicoloured.
1951 50c. Type **450** 10 10
1952 50c. Hoeilaart (vert) 10 10
See also Nos. 1995/6, 2025/6, 2083/4, 2102/3, 2123/4, 2159/60, 2240/1 and 2250/1.

1965. T.B. Relief and Other Funds. Public Buildings, Brussels.
1953 **451** 50c.+10c. blue 10 10
1954 – 1f.+40c. turquoise . . . 10 20
1955 – 2f.+1f. purple 20 20
1956 – 3f.+1f.50 violet 25 25
1957 – 10f.+4f.50 sepia and grey 70 70
BUILDINGS—HORIZ: 1f. Brewers' House; 2f. Builders' House; 3f. House of the Dukes of Brabant. VERT: (24½ × 44½ mm): 10f. Tower of Town Hall.

452 Queen Elisabeth (from medallion by A. Courtens) **453** "Peace on Earth"

1965. Queen Elisabeth Commem.
1958 **452** 3f. black 25 10

1966. 75th Anniv of "Rerum Novarum" (papal encyclical). Multicoloured.
1959 50c. Type **453** 10 10
1960 1f. "Building for Tomorrow" (family and new building) 10 10
1961 3f. Arms of Pope Paul VI (vert 24½ × 45 mm) . . . 10 10

1966. Queen Elisabeth. Sheets 82 × 116 mm incorporating old designs, each with se-tenant label showing Crown over "E". (a) In brown, blue, gold and grey.
MS1962 3f. T **125** and 3f. T **317** (sold at 20f.) . . . . 1·25 1·25
(b) In brown, myrtle and green.
MS1963 3f. T **160** and 3f. T **172** (sold at 20f.) . . . . 1·25 1·25

454 Rural Postman **455** High Diving

1966. Stamp Day.
1964 **454** 3f. black, lilac & buff . . 25 10

1966. Swimming.
1965 **455** 60c.+40c. brown, green and blue 10 10
1966 – 10f.+4f. brown, purple and green 80 70
DESIGN: 10f. Diving from block.

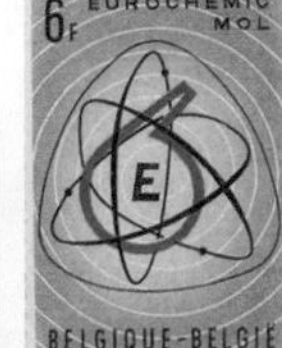

456 Iguanodon Fossil (Royal Institute of Natural Sciences) **457** Eurochemic Symbol

1966. National Scientific Institutions.
1967 **456** 1f. black and green . . . 25 20
1968 – 2f. black, orge & cream 10 20
1969 – 2f. multicoloured 10 20
1970 – 3f. multicoloured 10 10
1971 – 3f. gold, black and red 10 10
1972 – 6f. multicoloured 25 25
1973 – 8f. multicoloured 45 45

DESIGNS—HORIZ: No. 1968, Kasai head (Royal Central African Museum); No. 1969, Snow crystals (Royal Meteorological Institute). VERT: No. 1970, "Scholar" (Royal Library); No. 1971, Seal (General Archives); No. 1972, Arend-Roland comet and telescope (Royal Observatory); No. 1973, Satellite and rocket (Space Aeronomy Inst.).

1966. European Chemical Plant, Mol.
1974 **457** 6f. black, red and drab 35 25

458 A. Kekule **460** Rik Wouters (self-portrait)

1966. Centenary of Professor August Kekule's Benzene Formula.
1975 **458** 3f. brown, black & blue 25 10

1966. 19th World I.P.T.T. Congress, Brussels. Optd **XIXe CONGRES IPTT** and emblem.
1976 **454** 3f. black, lilac and buff 25 10

1966. 50th Death Anniv of Rik Wouters (painter).
1977 **460** 60c. multicoloured . . . 10 10

461 Minorites Convent, Liege

1966. Cultural Series.
1978 **461** 60c.+40c. purple, blue and brown 10 20
1979 – 1f.+50c. blue, purple and turquoise 10 20
1980 – 2f.+1f. red, purple and brown 10 20
1981 – 10f.+4f.50 purple, turquoise and green 70 65
DESIGNS: 1f. Val-Dieu Abbey, Aubel; 2f. Huy and town seal; 10f. Statue of Ambiorix and castle, Tongres.

463 Europa "Ship" **464** Surveying

1966. Europa.
1989 **463** 3f. green 25 10
1990 6f. purple 45 35

1966. Antarctic Expeditions.
1991 **464** 1f.+50c. green 10 10
1992 – 3f.+1f.50 violet 25 25
1993 – 6f.+3f. red 45 50
MS1994 130 × 95 mm. 10f.+5f. multicoloured 90 90
DESIGNS: 3f. Commander A. de Gerlache and "Belgica" (polar barque); 6f. "Magga Dan" (Antarctic supply ship) and meteorological operations. 52 × 35½ mm.—10f. "Magga Dan" and emperor penguins.

1966. Tourist Publicity. As T **450**. Multicoloured.
1995 2f. Bouillon 10 10
1996 2f. Lier (vert) 10 10

1966. 75th Anniv of Royal Federation of Belgian Philatelic Circles. Stamps similar to Nos. 1812 and 1851 but incorporating "1890 1996" and F.I.P. emblem.
1997 **391** 60c. purple and green . . 10 10
1998 **405** 3f. purple and ochre . . 10 10

466 Children with Hoops **467** Lions Emblem

1966. "Solidarity" (Child Welfare).
1999 – 1f.+1f. black & pink . . 10 10
2000 – 2f.+1f. black & green . . 10 10
2001 – 3f.+1f.50 black & lav . . 20 25
2002 **466** 6f.+3f. brown & flesh . . 40 40
2003 – 8f.+3f.50 brown & grn 50 50

DESIGNS—VERT: 1f. Boy with ball and dog; 2f. Girl with skipping-rope; 3f. Boy and girl blowing bubbles. HORIZ: 8f. Children and cat playing "Follow My Leader".

1967. Lions International.
2004 **467** 3f. sepia, blue and olive 25 10
2005 6f. sepia, violet and green 35 35

468 Part of Cleuter Pistol

1967. Arms Museum, Liege.
2006 **468** 2f. black, yellow & red 20 20

469 I.T.Y. Emblem

1967. International Tourist Year.
2007 **469** 6f. blue, red and black 40 25

470 Young Refugee

1967. European Refugee Campaign Fund. Sheet 110 × 77 mm comprising T **470** and similar vert designs.
MS2008 1f. black and yellow (Type **470**); 2f. black and blue; 3f. black and orange (sold at 20f.) 90 1·00

471 Woodland and Trientalis (flowers), Hautes Fagnes

1967. Nature Conservation. Multicoloured.
2009 1f. Type **471** 10 20
2010 1f. Dunes and eryngium (flowers), Westhoek . . . 10 20

472 Paul-Emile Janson (statesman) **473** 19th-century Postman

1967. Janson Commemoration.
2011 **472** 10f. blue 55 35

1967. Stamp Day.
2012 **473** 3f. purple and red . . . 25 10

474 Cogwheels **475** Flax Plant and Shuttle

1967. Europa.
2013 **474** 3f. black, red and blue 25 10
2014 6f. black, yellow & green 45 35

1967. Belgian Linen Industry.
2015 **475** 6f. multicoloured 35 25

476 Kursaal in 19th Century

1967. 700th Anniv of Ostend's Rank as Town.
2016 **476** 2f. sepia, buff and blue 10 10

478 With F.I.T.C.E. Emblem **479** Robert Schuman (statesman)

1967. European Telecommunications Day. "Stamp Day" design of 1967 incorporating F.I.T.C.E. emblem as T **478** in green.
2021 **478** 10f. sepia and blue . . . 55 35
"F.I.T.C.E." "Federation des Ingenieurs des Telecommunications de la Communaute Europeenne."

1967. Charity.
2022 **479** 2f.+1f. green 25 25
2023 – 5f.+2f. brown, yellow and black 40 40
2024 – 10f.+5f. multicoloured 70 75
DESIGNS—HORIZ: 5f. Kongolo Memorial, Gentinnes (Congo Martyrs). VERT: 10f. "Colonial Brotherhood" emblem (Colonial Troops Memorial).

1967. Tourist Publicity. As T **450**. Mult.
2025 1f. Ypres 10 10
2026 1f. Spontin 10 20

480 "Caesar Crossing the Rubicon" (Tournai Tapestry) **481** "Jester in Pulpit" (from Erasmus's "Praise of Folly")

1967. Charles Plisnier and Lodewijk de Raet Foundations.
2028 **480** 1f. multicoloured 10 10
2029 – 1f. multicoloured 10 10
DESIGN No. 2029, "Maximilian hunting boar" (Brussels tapestry).

1967. Cultural Series. "Erasmus and His Time".
2030 1f.+50c. multicoloured . . . 10 10
2031 2f.+1f. multicoloured . . . 20 25
2032 3f.+1f.50 multicoloured . . 25 25
2033 5f.+2f. black, red & carmine 35 40
2034 6f.+3f. multicoloured . . . 45 45
DESIGNS—VERT: 1f. Type **481**. 2f. "Jester declaiming" (from Erasmus' "Praise of Folly"); 3f. Erasmus; 6f. Pierre Gilles ("Aegidius" from painting by Metzijs). HORIZ: 5f. "Sir Thomas More's Family" (Holbein).

482 "Princess Margaret of York" (from miniature) **483** Arms of Ghent University

1967. "British Week".
2035 **482** 6f. multicoloured 40 25

1967. Universities of Ghent and Liege. Mult.
2036 3f. Type **483** 25 10
2037 3f. Liege 25 10

484 Emblem of "Pro-Post" Association

1967. "Postphila" Stamp Exhibition, Brussels. Sheet 110 × 77 mm.
MS2038 **484** 10f.+5f. black, green, red and brown 75 75

485 Our Lady of Virga Jesse, Hasselt

1967. Christmas.
2039 **485** 1f. blue 10 10

486 "Children's Games" (section of Brueghel's painting)

1967. "Solidarity".
2040 **486** 1f.+50c. multicoloured 10 10
2041 – 2f.+50c. multicoloured 10 10
2042 – 3f.+1f. multicoloured . . 25 25
2043 – 6f.+3f. multicoloured . . 45 40
2044 – 10f.+4f. multicoloured 70 65
2045 – 13f.+6f. multicoloured 90 90
Nos. 2040/5 together form the complete painting.

487 Worker in Protective Hand

489 Army Postman (1916)

1968. Industrial Safety Campaign.
2046 **487** 3f. multicoloured 25 10

1968. Stamp Day.
2068 **489** 3f. purple, brown & blue 25 10

490 Belgian 1c. "Small Lion" Stamp of 1866

491 Grammont and Seal of Baudouin VI

1968. Cent of State Printing Works, Malines.
2069 **490** 1f. olive 10 10

1968. "Historical Series". Multicoloured.
2070 2f. Type **491** 25 20
2071 3f. Theux-Franchimont Castle and battle emblems 25 10
2072 6f. Archaeological discoveries, Spiennes . . . 40 25
2073 10f. Roman oil lamp and town crest, Wervik . . . 55 40

492 Europa "Key"

493 Queen Elisabeth and Dr. Depage

1968. Europa.
2074 **492** 3f. gold, black & green 25 15
2075 6f. silver, black and red 45 35

1968. Belgian Red Cross Fund. Cross in red.
2076 **493** 6f.+3f. sepia, black and green 55 50
2077 – 10f.+5f. sepia, black and green 75 70
DESIGN: 10f. Queen Fabiola and baby.

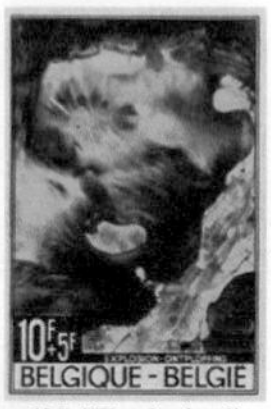

494 Gymnastics

495 "Explosion"

1968. Olympic Games, Mexico. Multicoloured.
2078 1f.+50c. Type **494** 10 10
2079 2f.+1f. Weightlifting 10 20
2080 3f.+1f.50 Hurdling 20 20
2081 6f.+2f. Cycling 25 30
2082 13f.+5f. Sailing (vert 24½ × 45 mm) 45 70
Each design includes the Olympic "rings" and a Mexican cultural motif.

1968. Tourist Publicity. As Type **450**.
2083 2f. multicoloured 10 10
2084 2f. black, blue and green . . 10 10
DESIGNS: No. 2083, Farm-house and windmill, Bokrijk; No. 2084, Bath-house and fountain, Spa.

1968. Belgian Disasters. Victims Fund. Mult.
2085 10f.+5f. Type **495** 55 70
2086 12f.+5f. "Fire" . . . . . . 75 1·00
2087 13f.+5f. "Typhoon" 90 90

496 St. Laurent Abbey, Liege

1968. "National Interest".
2088 **496** 2f. black, bistre & blue 10 20
2089 – 3f. brown, grey & lt brn 25 10
2090 – 6f. black, blue & dp bl 35 20
2091 – 10f. multicoloured . . . 65 35
DESIGNS: 3f. Church, Lissewege; 6f. "Mineral Seraing" and "Gand" (ore carriers), canal-lock, Zandvliet; 10f. Canal-lift, Ronquieres.

497 Undulate Triggerfish

1968. "Solidarity" and 125th Anniv of Antwerp Zoo. Designs showing fish. Multicoloured.
2092 1f.+50c. Type **497** 10 20
2093 3f.+1f.50 Ear-spotted angelfish 20 20
2094 6f.+3f. Lionfish 40 45
2095 10f.+5f. Diagonal butterflyfish 65 70

498 King Albert in Bruges (October, 1918)

499 Lighted Candle

1968. Patriotic Funds.
2096 **498** 1f.+50c. multicoloured 10 20
2097 – 3f.+1f.50 mult 20 25
2098 – 6f.+3f. multicoloured . . 40 45
2099 – 10f.+5f. multicoloured 65 70
DESIGNS—HORIZ: 3f. King Albert entering Brussels (November, 1918); 6f. King Albert in Liege (November, 1918). LARGER (46 × 35 mm): 10f. Tomb of the Unknown Soldier, Brussels.

1968. Christmas.
2100 **499** 1f. multicoloured 10 10

500 "Mineral Seraing" (ore carrier) in Ghent Canal

1968. Ghent Maritime Canal.
2101 **500** 6f. black brown, & blue 35 20

1969. Tourist Publicity. As Type **450**.
2102 1f. black, blue & pur (vert) 10 10
2103 1f. black, olive and blue . . 10 10
DESIGNS. No. 2102, Town Hall, Louvain; No. 2103, Valley of the Ourthe.

501 "Albert Magnis" (detail of wood carving by Quellin, Confessional, St. Paul's Church, Antwerp)

1969. St. Paul's Church, Antwerp, and Aulne Abbey Commemoration.
2104 **501** 2f. sepia 10 10
2105 – 3f. black and mauve . . 10 10
DESIGN: 3f. Aulne Abbey.

502 "The Travellers" (sculpture, Archaeological Museum, Arlon)

503 Broodjes Chapel, Antwerp

1969. 2,000th Anniv of Arlon.
2106 **502** 2f. purple 10 20

1969. "150 Years of Public Education in Antwerp".
2107 **503** 3f. black and grey . . . 25 10

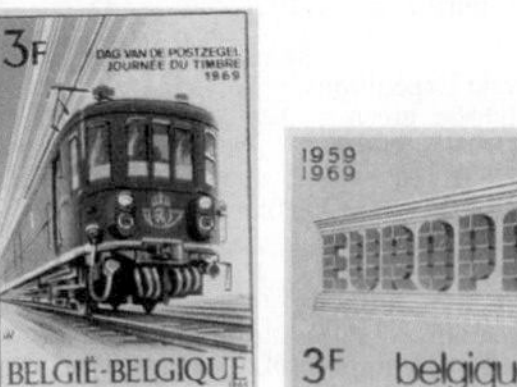

504 Mail Train

505 Colonnade

1969. Stamp Day.
2108 **504** 3f. multicoloured 20 10

1969. Europa.
2109 **505** 3f. multicoloured 20 15
2110 6f. multicoloured 45 35

506 "The painter and the Amateur" (detail, Brueghel)

1969. "Postphila 1969" Stamp Exhibition, Brussels. Sheet 91 × 124 mm.
MS2111 **506** 10f.+5f. brown . . . 90 90

507 NATO Emblem

508 "The Builders" (F. Leger)

1969. 20th Anniv of N.A.T.O.
2112 **507** 6f. blue and brown . . . 35 35

1969. 50th Anniv of I.L.O.
2113 **508** 3f. multicoloured 25 10

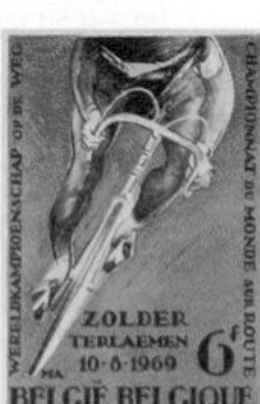

509 "Houses" (I. Dimitrova)

510 Racing Cyclist

1969. U.N.I.C.E.F. "Philanthropy" Funds. Mult.
2114 1f.+50c. Type **509** 10 20
2115 3f.+1f.50 "My Art" (C. Patric) 25 25
2116 6f.+3f. "In the Sun" (H. Rejchlova) 45 40
2117 10f.+5f. "Out for a Walk" (P. Sporn) (horiz) 65 70

1969. World Championship Cycle Races, Zolder.
2118 **510** 6f. multicoloured 40 25

511 Mgr. V. Scheppers

512 National Colours

1969. Monseigneur Victor Scheppers (founder of "Brothers of Mechlin") Commemoration.
2119 **511** 6f.+3f. purple 50 50

1969. 25th Anniv of BENELUX Customs Union.
2120 **512** 3f. multicoloured 25 10

513 Pascali Rose and Annevoie Gardens

1969. Flowers and Gardens. Multicoloured.
2121 2f. Type **513** 10 10
2122 2f. Begonia and Lochristi Gardens 10 10

1969. Tourist Publicity. As Type **450**.
2123 2f. brown, red and blue . . 10 10
2124 2f. black, green and blue . . 10 10
DESIGNS: No. 2123, Veurne Furnes; No. 2124, Vielsalm.

514 "Feats of Arms" from "History of Alexander the Great" (Tournai, 15th century)

516 Wounded Soldier

515 Astronauts and Location of Moon Landing

1969. "Cultural Works" Tapestries. Mult.
2125 1f.+50c. Type **514** 10 20
2126 3f.+1f.50 "The Violinist" from "Festival" (David Teniers II, Oudenarde, c.1700) 35 30
2127 10f.+4f. "The Paralytic", from "The Acts of the Apostles" (Brussels, c.1517) 85 80

1969. 1st Man on the Moon.
2128 **515** 6f. sepia 40 25
MS2129 95 × 130 mm. 20f.+10f. blue 2·25 2·25
DESIGN: **MS**2129 is as T **515**, but in vert format.

1969. 50th Anniv of National War Invalids Works (O.N.I.G.).
2130 **516** 1f. green 10 10

517 "The Postman" (Daniella Sainteney)

519 Count H. Carton de Wiart (from painting by G. Geleyn)

518 John F. Kennedy Motorway Tunnel, Antwerp

1969. "Philately for the Young".
2131 **517** 1f. multicoloured 10 10

1969. Completion of Belgian Road-works. Mult.
2132 3f. Type **518** 25 10
2133 6f. Loncin flyover, Wallonie motorway 40 35

1969. Birth Centenary of Count Henry Carton de Wiart (statesman).
2134 **519** 6f. sepia 35 30

520 "Barbu d'Anvers" (Cockerel)

1969. "The Poultry-yard" (poultry-breeding).
2135 **520** 10f.+5f. multicoloured 90 85

521 "Le Denombrement de Bethleem" (detail, Brueghel)

1969. Christmas.
2136 **521** 1f.50 multicoloured . . . 10 10

522 Emblem, "Coin" and Machinery

523 Window, St. Waudru Church, Mons

1969. 50th Anniv of National Credit Society (S.N.C.I.).
2137 **522** 3f.50 brown and blue . . 25 10

1969. "Solidarity". Musicians in Stained-glass Windows. Multicoloured.
2138 1f.50+50c. Type **523** . . . 15 20
2139 3f.50+1f.50 's-Herenelderen Church 25 25
2140 7f.+3f. St. Jacques Church, Liege 55 60
2141 9f.+4f. Royal Museum of Art and History, Brussels 90 90
No. 2141 is larger, 36 × 52 mm.

524 Camellias

525 Beech Tree in National Botanical Gardens

1970. Ghent Flower Show. Multicoloured.
2142 1f.50 Type **524** 10 10
2143 2f.50 Water-lily 25 20
2144 3f.50 Azaleas 25 10
MS2145 122 × 92 mm. Nos. 2142/4 in slightly different shades . . 1·60 1·60

1970. Nature Conservation Year. Multicoloured.
2146 3f.50 Type **525** 25 10
2147 7f. Birch 35 30

526 Young "Postman"

1970. "Philately for the Young".
2148 **526** 1f.50 multicoloured . . . 10 10

527 New U.P.U. Headquarters Building

1970. New U.P.U. Headquarters Building.
2149 **527** 3f.50 green 25 10

528 "Flaming Sun"

1970. Europa.
2150 **528** 3f.50 cream, blk & lake 30 10
2151 7f. flesh, black and blue 45 35

529 Open-air Museum, Bokrijk

530 Clock-tower, Virton

1970. Cultural Works. Multicoloured.
2152 1f.50+50c. Type **529** . . . 10 20
2153 3f.50+1f.50 Relay Post-house, Courcelles 20 20
2154 7f.+3f. "The Reaper of Trevires" (bas-relief, Virton) 45 50
2155 9f.+4f. Open-air Museum, Middelheim, (Antwerp) 60 60

1970. Historic Towns of Virton and Zelzate.
2156 **530** 2f.50 violet and ochre . . 10 20
2157 – 2f.50 black and blue . . 10 10
DESIGN—HORIZ: No. 2157, "Skaustand" (freighter), canal bridge, Zelzate.

531 Co-operative Alliance Emblem

1970. 75th Anniv of Int Co-operative Alliance.
2158 **531** 7f. black and orange . . 35 20

1970. Tourist Publicity, As Type **450**.
2159 1f.50 green, blue and black 10 10
2160 1f.50 buff, blue & deep blue 10 10
DESIGNS—HORIZ: No. 2159, Kasterlee. VERT: No. 2160, Nivelles.

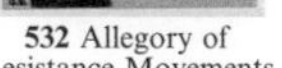
532 Allegory of Resistance Movements

533 King Baudouin

1970. 25th Anniv of Prisoner of War and Concentration Camps Liberation.
2161 **532** 3f.50+1f.50 black, red and green 25 20
2162 – 7f.+3f. black, red and mauve 45 50
DESIGN: 7f. Similar to Type **532**, but inscr "LIBERATION DES CAMPS", etc.

1970. King Baudouin's 40th Birthday.
2163 **533** 3f.50 brown 20 10
See also Nos. 2207/23c and 2335/9b.

534 Fair Emblem

535 U.N. Headquarters, New York

1970. 25th International Ghent Fair.
2164 **534** 1f.50 multicoloured . . . 10 10

1970. 25th Anniv of United Nations.
2165 **535** 7f. blue and black . . . 25 20

536 Queen Fabiola

537 Angler's Rod and Reel

1970. Queen Fabiola Foundation.
2166 **536** 3f.50 black and blue . . 20 10

1970. Sports. Multicoloured.
2167 3f.50+1f.50 Type **537** . . . 30 30
2168 9f.+4f. Hockey stick and ball 45 55

538 Belgian 8c. Stamp of 1870

1970. "Belgica 72" Stamp Exhibition, Brussels (1st issue).
MS2169 1f.50+50c. violet and black; 3f.50+1f.50 lilac and black; 9f.+4f. brown and black . . . . . . 3·50 3·50
DESIGNS: 3f.50, Belgian 1f. stamp of 1870; 9f. Belgian 5f. stamp of 1870.

539 "The Mason" (sculpture by G. Minne)

541 "Madonna and Child" (Jan Gossaert)

540 Man, Woman and Hillside Town

1970. 50th Anniv of National Housing Society.
2170 **539** 3f.50 brown & yell . . . 10 10

1970. 25th Anniv of Belgian Social Security.
2171 **540** 2f.50 multicoloured . . . 10 10

1970. Christmas.
2172 **541** 1f.50 brown 10 10

542 C. Huysmans (statesman)

543 Arms of Eupen, Malmedy and St. Vith

1970. Cultural Works. Famous Belgians.
2173 **542** 1f.50+50c. brown and red 10 10
2174 – 3f.50+1f.50 brown and purple 20 15
2175 – 7f.+3f. brown & green 45 40
2176 – 9f.+4f. brown & blue . . 60 60
PORTRAITS: 3f.50, Cardinal J. Cardijn. 7f. Maria Baers (Catholic social worker). 9f. P. Pastur (social reformer).

1970. 50th Anniv of Annexation of Eupen, Malmedy and St. Vith.
2177 **543** 7f. brown and sepia . . 20 20

544 "The Uneasy Town" (detail, Paul Delvaux)

545 Telephone

1970. "Solidarity". Paintings. Multicoloured.
2178 3f.50+1f.50 Type **544** . . . 25 30
2179 7f.+3f. "The Memory" (Rene Magritte) 45 45

1971. Inaug of Automatic Telephone Service.
2183 **545** 1f.50 multicoloured . . . 10 10

546 "Auto" Car

547 Touring Club Badge

1971. 50th Brussels Motor Show.
2184 **546** 2f.50 black and red . . . 10 10

1971. 75th Anniv of Royal Touring Club of Belgium.
2185 **547** 3f.50 gold, red & blue 20 10

548 Tournai Cathedral

549 "The Letter-box" (T. Lobrichon)

1971. 800th Anniv of Tournai Cathedral.
2186 **548** 7f. blue 35 35

1971. "Philately for the Young".
2187 **549** 1f.50 brown 10 10

550 Notre-Dame Abbey, Marche-les-Dames

1971. Cultural Works.
2190 **550** 3f.50+1f.50 black, green and brown 25 30
2191 – 7f.+3f. black, red and yellow 45 45
DESIGN: 7f. Convent, Turnhout.

552 King Albert I, Jules Destree and Academy

1971. 50th Anniv of Royal Academy of French Language and Literature.
2201 **552** 7f. black and grey . . . 35 35

553 Postman of 1855 (from lithograph, J. Thiriar)

554 Europa Chain

1971. Stamp Day.
2202 **553** 3f.50 multicoloured . . . 20 10

1971. Europa.
2203 **554** 3f.50 brown and black 20 10
2204 7f. green and black . . . 30 30

555 Satellite Earth Station

556 Red Cross

1971. World Telecommunications Day.
2205 **555** 7f. multicoloured 35 25

1971. Belgian Red Cross.
2206 **556** 10f.+5f. red & black . . 70 70

1971. As T **533**, but without dates.
2207 1f.75 green 10 15
2208 2f.25 green 20 15
2208a 2f.50 green 10 10
2209 3f. green 20 10
2209a 3f.25 plum 20 10
2210 3f.50 brown 25 10
2211 4f. blue 25 10
2212 4f.50 purple 30 15
2212a 4f.50 blue 30 10
2213 5f. violet 75 10
2214 6f. red 35 10
2214b 6f.50 violet 35 10
2215 7f. red 30 10
2215b 7f.50 mauve 35 10
2216a 8f. black 45 10
2217 9f. sepia 45 20
2217a 9f. brown 45 10
2218a 10f. mauve 55 10
2218b 11f. sepia 70 10
2219 12f. blue 85 10
2219b 13f. blue 70 10
2219c 14f. green 90 10
2220 15f. violet 75 10
2220b 16f. green 85 10
2220c 17f. purple 85 20
2221 18f. blue 85 20
2221a 18f. turquoise 90 20
2222a 20f. blue 90 10
2222b 22f. black . . . . 1·25 1·10
2222c 22f. turquoise . . . . . . 1·25 25
2222d 25f. purple . . . . 1·25 25
2223a 30f. orange . . . . 1·60 10
2223b 35f. turquoise . . . . . . 1·75 25
2223c 40f. blue . . . . 2·00 20
2223d 45f. brown . . . . 2·50 40
See also Nos. 2335/9.

557 Scientist, Adelie Penguins and "Erika Dan" (polar vessel)

1971. 10th Anniv of Antarctic Treaty.
2230 **557** 10f. multicoloured . . . 50 50

558 "The Discus thrower" and Munich Cathedral

559 G. Hubin (statesman)

1971. Olympic Games, Munich (1972) Publicity.
2231 **558** 7f.+3f. black & blue . . 45 45

1971. Georges Hubin Commemoration.
2232 **559** 1f.50 violet and black . . 10 10

560 Notre-Dame Abbey, Orval

561 Processional Giants, Ath

1971. 900th Anniv of Notre-Dame Abbey, Orval.
2233 **560** 2f.50 brown 10 10

1971. Historic Towns.
2234 **561** 2f.50 multicoloured . . . 10 10
2235 – 2f.50 brown 10 20
DESIGN—HORIZ: (46 × 35 mm): No. 2235, View of Ghent.

562 Test-tubes and Diagram

1971. 50th Anniv of Discovery of Insulin.
2236 **562** 10f. multicoloured . . . 55 40

563 Flemish Festival Emblem

1971. Cultural Works. Festivals. Multicoloured.
2237 3f.50+1f.50 Type **563** . . . 25 25
2238 7f.+3f. Walloon Festival emblem 55 60

564 Belgian Family and "50"

565 Dr. Jules Bordet (medical scientist)

1971. 50th Anniv of "League of Large Families".
2239 **564** 1f.50 multicoloured . . . 10 10

1971. Tourist Publicity. Designs similar to T **450**.
2240 2f.50 black, brown and blue 10 10
2241 2f.50 black, brown and blue 10 10
DESIGNS: No. 2240, St. Martin's Church, Alost; No. 2241, Town Hall and belfry, Mons.

1971. Belgian Celebrities.
2242 **565** 3f.50 green 25 10
2243 – 3f.50 brown 25 10
DESIGN: No. 2242, Type **565** (10th death anniv); No. 2243, "Stijn Streuvels" (Frank Lateur, writer, birth cent.).

566 Achaemenid Tomb, Buzpar

567 Elewijt Chateau

1971. 2500th Anniv of Persian Empire.
2244 **566** 7f. multicoloured 40 30

1971. "Belgica 72" Stamp Exhibition, Brussels (2nd issue).
2245 – 3f.50+1f.50 green 25 25
2246 **567** 7f.+3f. brown 55 50
2247 – 10f.+5f. blue 85 80
DESIGNS—HORIZ: (52 × 35½ mm): 3f. Attre Chateau; 10f. Royal Palace, Brussels.

568 F.I.B./V.B.N. Emblem

569 "The Flight into Egypt" (15th-century Dutch School)

1971. 25th Anniv of Federation of Belgian Industries.
2248 **568** 3f.50 gold, black & blue 25 10

1971. Christmas.
2249 **569** 1f.50 multicoloured . . . 10 10

1971. Tourist Publicity. Designs similar to T **450**.
2250 1f.50 blue and buff 10 10
2251 2f.50 blue and buff 20 10
DESIGNS—HORIZ: 1f.50, Town Hall, Malines. VERT: 2f.50, Basilica, St. Hubert.

570 "Actias luna"

1971. "Solidarity". Insects in Antwerp Zoo. Multicoloured.
2252 1f.50+50c. Type **570** . . . 10 10
2253 3f.50+1f.50 "Tabanus bromius" (horiz) 30 30
2254 7f.+3f. "Polistes gallicus" (horiz) 55 50
2255 9f.+4f. "Cicindela campestris" 65 65

572 Road Signs and Traffic Signals

573 Book Year Emblem

1972. 20th Anniv of "Via Secura" Road Safety Organization.
2263 **572** 3f.50 multicoloured . . . 25 10

1972. International Book Year.
2264 **573** 7f. blue, brown & black 40 30

574 Coins of Belgium and Luxembourg

576 "Auguste Vermeylen" (I. Opsomer)

1972. 50th Anniv of Belgo–Luxembourgeoise Economic Union.
2265 **574** 1f.50 silver, black and orange 10 10

1972. Birth Centenary of Auguste Vemeylen (writer).
2267 **576** 2f.50 multicoloured . . . 10 20

577 "Belgica 72" Emblem

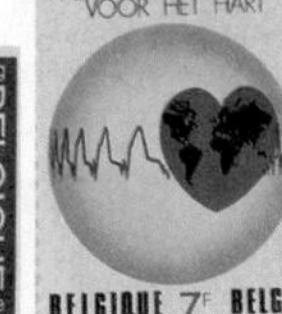

578 Heart Emblem

1972. "Belgica 72" Stamp Exn., Brussels (3rd Issue).
2268 **577** 3f.50 purple, blue & brn 25 10

1972. World Heart Month.
2269 **578** 7f. multicoloured 40 25

579 Astronaut cancelling Letter on Moon

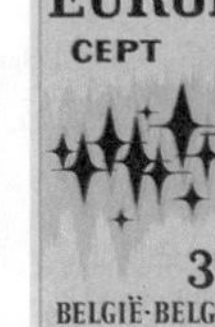

580 "Communications"

1972. Stamp Day.
2270 **579** 3f.50 multicoloured . . . 25 10

1972. Europa.
2271 **580** 3f.50 multicoloured . . . 30 10
2272 7f. multicoloured 50 40

581 Quill Pen and Newspaper

582 "UIC" on Coupled Wagons

1972. "Liberty of the Press". 50th Anniv of Belga News Agency and 25th Congress of International Federation of Newspaper Editors (F.I.E.J.).
2273 **581** 2f.50 multicoloured . . . 20 10

1972. 50th Anniv of Int Railways Union (U.I.C.).
2274 **582** 7f. multicoloured 35 25
See also No. P2266.

583 Couvin

584 Leopold I 10c. "Epaulettes" Stamp of 1849

1972. Tourist Publicity.
2275 **583** 2f.50 purple, blue & grn . . 20 25
2276 – 2f.50 brown and blue . . 20 25
DESIGN—VERT: No. 2276, Aldeneik Church, Maaseik.

1972. "Belgica 72" Stamp Exn, Brussels (4th issue).
2277 **584** 1f.50+50c. brown, black and gold 20 20
2278 – 2f.+1f. red, brown and gold 25 25
2279 – 2f.50+1f. red, brown and gold 30 25
2280 – 3f.50+1f.50 lilac, black and gold 35 35
2281 – 6f.+3f. violet, black and gold 45 45
2282 – 7f.+3f. red, black and gold 55 60
2283 – 10f.+5f. blue, black and gold 85 80
2284 – 15f.+7f.50 green, turquoise and gold . . 1·25 1·25
2285 – 20f.+10f. chestnut, brown and gold . . . 1·75 1·60
DESIGNS: 2f. Leopold I 40c. "Medallion" of 1849; 2f.50, Leopold II 10c. of 1883. 3f.50, Leopold II 50c. of 1883; 6f. Albert I; 2f. "Tin Hat" of 1919; 7f. Albert I 50f. of 1929; 10f. Albert I 1f.75 of 1931; 15f. Leopold III 5f. of 1936; 20f. Baudouin 3f.50 of 1970.

585 "Beatrice" (G. de Smet)

586 Emblem of Centre

1972. "Philately for the Young".
2287 **585** 3f. multicoloured 25 20

1972. Inauguration of William Lennox Epileptic Centre, Ottignies.
2288 **586** 10f.+5f. multicoloured 85 75

587 Dish Aerial and "Intelstat 4" Satellite

588 Frans Masereel (wood-carver and painter)

1972. Inaug of Satellite Earth Station, Lessive.
2289 **587** 3f.50 black, silver & bl 25 10

1972. Masereel Commem.
2290 **588** 4f.50 black and green . . 30 10

589 "Adoration of the Magi" (F. Timmermans)

590 "Empress Maria Theresa" (unknown artist)

1972. Christmas.
2291 **589** 3f.50 multicoloured . . . 25 10

1972. Bicentenary of Belgian Royal Academy of Sciences, Letters and Fine Arts.
2292 **590** 2f. multicoloured 25 10

591 Greylag Goose

592 "Fire"

1972. "Solidarity". Birds from Zwin Nature Reserve. Multicoloured.
2293 2f.+1f. Type **591** 25 25
2294 4f.50+2f. Northern lapwing 40 40
2295 8f.+4f. White stork 65 65
2296 9f.+4f.50 Common kestrel (horiz) 80 80

1973. Industrial Buildings Fire Protection Campaign.
2297 **592** 2f. multicoloured 10 10

593 W.M.O. Emblem and Meteorological Equipment

595 W.H.O. Emblem as Man's "Heart"

594 Bijloke Abbey and Museum, Ghent

1973. Centenary of World Meteorological Organization.
2298 **593** 9f. multicoloured 50 35

1973. Cultural Works. Religious Buildings.
2299 **594** 2f.+1f. green 20 25
2300 – 4f.50+2f. brown 35 35
2301 – 8f.+4f. red 60 60
2302 – 9f.+4f.50 blue 80 75
DESIGNS: 4f.50, Collegiate Church of St. Ursmer, Lobbes; 8f. Park Abbey, Heverlee; 9f. Floreffe Abbey.

1973. 25th Anniv of W.H.O.
2303 **595** 8f. black, yellow & red 40 30

596 Ball in Hands

1973. 1st World Basketball Championships for the Handicapped, Bruges.
2304 **596** 10f.+5f. multicoloured 85 80

597 Europa "Posthorn"

598 Thurn and Taxis Courier (17th-cent)

1973. Europa.
2305 **597** 4f.50 blue, yellow & brn 25 10
2306 8f. blue, yellow & green 45 35

1973. Stamp Day.
2307 **598** 4f.50 brown and red . . 25 10

599 Fair Emblem

600 Arrows encircling Globe

1973. 25th International Fair, Liege.
2308 **599** 4f.50 multicoloured . . . 25 10

1973. 5th World Telecommunications Day.
2309 **600** 3f.50 multicoloured . . . 20 10

601 "Sport" (poster for Ghent Exhibition, 1913)

1973. 60th Anniv of Workers' International Sports Organization.
2310 **601** 4f.50 multicoloured . . . 25 10

602 Douglas DC-10-30CF and De Havilland D.H.9

1973. 50th Anniv of SABENA.
2311 **602** 8f. black, blue and grey 45 40

603 Ernest Tips's Biplane, 1908

1973. 35th Anniv (1972) of "Les Vieilles Tiges de Belgique" (pioneer aviators' association).
2312 **603** 10f. black, blue & green 55 30

604 15th-Century Printing-press

605 "Woman Bathing" (fresco by Lemaire)

1973. Historical Events and Anniversaries.
2313 **604** 2f.+1f. blk, brn & red . . 25 25
2314 – 3f.50+1f.50 mult 25 25
2315 – 4f.50+2f. mult 35 35
2316 – 8f.+4f. multicoloured . . 65 65
2317 – 9f.+4f.50 mult 70 60
2318 – 10f.+5f. multicoloured 90 95
DESIGNS—VERT (As Type **604**): 2f. (500th anniv of first Belgian printed book, produced by Dirk Martens); 3f.50, Head of Amon (Queen Elisabeth Egyptological Foundation. 50th anniv.); 4f.50, "Portrait of a Young Girl" (Petrus Christus, 500th death anniv). HORIZ (36 × 25 mm): 8f. Gold coins of Hadrian and Marcus Aurelius (Discovery of Roman treasure at Luttre-Liberchies); (52 × 35 mm); 9f. "Members of the Great Council" (Coessaert) (Great Council of Malines, 500th anniv.). 10f. "Jong Jacob" (East Indiaman) (Ostend Merchant Company, 250th anniv).

1973. Thermal Treatment Year.
2319 **605** 4f.50 multicoloured . . . 25 10

606 Adolphe Sax and Tenor Saxophone

607 St. Nicholas Church, Eupen

1973. Belgian Musical Instrument Industry.
2320 **606** 9f. multicoloured 45 35

1973. Tourist Publicity.
2321 **607** 2f. multicoloured 10 20

See also Nos. 2328/9, 2368/70, 2394/5, 2452/5, 2508/11, 2535/8, 2573/6, 2595/6 and 2614.

608 "Little Charles" (Evenepoel)

609 J. B. Moens (philatelist) and Perforations

1973. "Philately for the Young".
2322 **608** 3f. multicoloured 25 20

1973. 50th Anniv of Belgian Stamp Dealers Association.
2323 **609** 10f. multicoloured . . . 55 40

610 "Adoration of the Shepherds" (H. van der Goes)

611 Motorway and Emblem

1973. Christmas.
2324 **610** 4f. blue 30 20

1973. 50th Anniv of "Vlaamse Automobilistenbond" (VAB) (motoring organization).
2325 **611** 5f. multicoloured 30 10

612 L. Pierard (after sculpture by Ianchelevici)

613 Early Microphone

1973. 21st Death Anniv of Louis Pierard (politician and writer).
2326 **612** 4f. red and cream . . . 30 10

1973. 50th Anniv of Belgium Radio.
2327 **613** 4f. black and blue . . . 30 20

1973. Tourist Publicity. As T **607**.
2328 3f. grey, brown and blue . . 25 10
2329 4f. grey and green 30 25
DESIGNS—HORIZ: 3f. Town Hall, Leau; 4f. Chimay Castle.

614 F. Rops (self-portrait)

615 Jack of Diamonds

1973. 75th Death Anniv of Felicien Rops (artist and engraver).
2330 **614** 7f. black and brown . . 40 35

1973. "Solidarity". Old Playing Cards. Mult.
2331 5f.+2f.50 Type **615** 40 40
2332 5f.+2f.50 Jack of Spades . . 40 40
2333 5f.+2f.50 Queen of Hearts 40 40
2334 5f.+2f.50 King of Clubs . . 40 40

1973. As Nos. 2207/23 but smaller, 22 × 17 mm.
2335 **583** 3f. green . . . . 1·10 85
2336 4f. blue 20 25
2337 4f.50 blue 25 20
2338 5f. mauve 25 20
2338c 6f. red 35 10
2339 6f.50 violet 25 20
2339b 8f. grey 40 20

616 King Albert (Baron Opsomer) **617** "Blood Donation"

1974. 40th Death Anniv of King Albert I.
2340 **616** 4f. blue and black . . . 25 20

1974. Belgian Red Cross. Multicoloured.
2341 4f.+2f. Type **617** 35 35
2342 10f.+5f. "Traffic Lights" (Road Safety) 85 80

618 "Protection of the Environment" **619** "Armand Jamar" (Self-portrait)

1974. Robert Schuman Association for the Protection of the Environment.
2343 **618** 3f. multicoloured 25 10

1974. Belgian Cultural Celebrities. Multicoloured.
2344 4f.+2f. Type **619** 35 35
2345 5f.+2f.50 Tony Bergmann (author) and view of Lier 40 40
2346 7f.+3f.50 Henri Vieuxtemps (violinist) and view of Verviers 55 60
2347 10f.+5f. "James Ensor" (self-portrait with masks) (35 × 52 mm) 85 85

620 N.A.T.O. Emblem **621** Hubert Krains (Belgian postal administrator)

1974. 25th Anniv of North Atlantic Treaty Organization.
2348 **620** 10f. blue and light blue 55 35

1974. Stamp Day.
2349 **621** 5f. black and grey . . . 25 10

622 "Destroyed Town" (O. Zadkine) **623** Heads of Boy and Girl

1974. Europa. Sculptures.
2350 **622** 5f. black and red 40 10
2351 – 10f. black and blue . . . 75 45
DESIGN: 10f. "Solidarity" (G. Minne).

1974. 10th Lay Youth Festival.
2352 **623** 4f. multicoloured 25 25

625 New Planetarium, Brussels

1974. Historical Buildings.
2354 **625** 3f. brown and blue . . . 20 15
2355 – 4f. brown and red . . . 25 25
2356 – 5f. brown and green . . 35 15
2357 – 7f. brown and yellow . . 40 25
2358 – 10f. brown, orange & bl 55 30
DESIGNS—As T **625**. HORIZ: 4f. Pillory, Braine-le-Chateau. VERT: 10f. Belfry, Bruges. 45 × 25 mm: 5f. Ruins of Soleilmont Abbey; 7f. "Procession" (fountain sculpture, Ghent).

626 "BENELUX"

1974. 30th Anniv of Benelux Customs Union.
2359 **626** 5f. blue, green & lt blue 25 10

627 "Jan Vekemans at the Age of Five" (Cornelis de Vos) **628** Self-portrait and Van Gogh House, Cuesmes

1974. "Philately for the Young".
2360 **627** 3f. multicoloured 25 20

1974. Opening of Vincent Van Gogh House, Cuesmes.
2361 **628** 10f.+5f. multicoloured 85 70

629 Corporal Tresignies and Brule Bridge

1974. 60th Death Anniv of Corporal Leon Tresignies (war hero).
2362 **629** 4f. green and brown . . 25 20

630 Montgomery Blair and U.P.U. Emblem **631** Graph within Head

1974. Centenary of U.P.U.
2363 **630** 5f. black and green . . . 25 10
2364 – 10f. black and red . . . 50 40
DESIGN: 10f. H. von Stephan and U.P.U. Monument.

1974. 25th Anniv of Central Economic Council.
2365 **631** 7f. multicoloured 40 25

632 Rotary Emblem on Belgian Flag **633** Wild Boar

1974. 50th Anniv of Rotary Int in Belgium.
2366 **632** 10f. multicoloured . . . 55 30

1974. 40th Anniv of Granting of Colours to Ardennes Regiment of Chasseurs.
2367 **633** 3f. multicoloured 25 10

1974. Tourist Publicity. As T **607**.
2368 3f. brown and yellow . . . 25 20
2369 4f. green and blue 25 25
2370 4f. green and blue 25 25
DESIGNS—VERT: No. 2368, Aarschot. HORIZ: No. 2369, Meeting of three frontiers, Gemmenich; 2370, Nassogne.

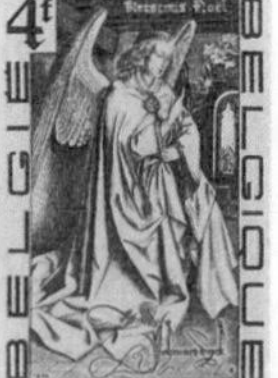

634 "Angel" (detail, "The Mystic Lamb", Brothers Van Eyck) **635** Gentian

1974. Christmas.
2371 **634** 4f. purple 25 20

1974. "Solidarity". Flora and Fauna. Multicoloured.
2372 4f.+2f. Type **635** 35 35
2373 5f.+2f.50 Eurasian badger (horiz) 45 40
2374 7f.+3f.50 "Carabus auratus" (beetle) (horiz) 55 60
2375 10f.+5f. Spotted cat's-ear . . 85 85

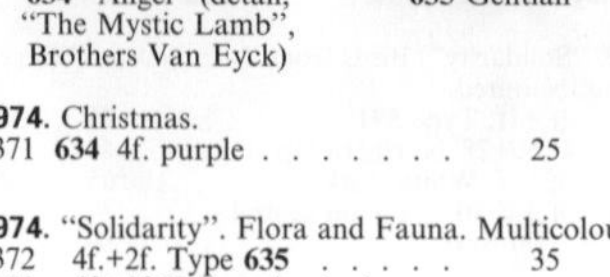

636 Adolphe Quetelet (after J. Odevaere) **637** Exhibition Emblem

1974. Death Centenary of Adolphe Quetelet. (scientist).
2376 **636** 10f. black and brown . . 50 30

1975. "Themabelga" Stamp Exhibition, Brussels (1st issue).
2377 **637** 6f.50 orange, blk & grn 35 10
See also Nos. 2411/16.

638 "Neoregelia carolinae" **639** Student and Young Boy

1975. Ghent Flower Show. Multicoloured.
2378 4f.50 Type **638** 25 25
2379 5f. "Tussilago petasites" . . 35 15
2380 6f.50 "Azalea japonica" . . 35 10

1975. Cent of Charles Buls Normal School.
2381 **639** 4f.50 multicoloured . . . 25 15

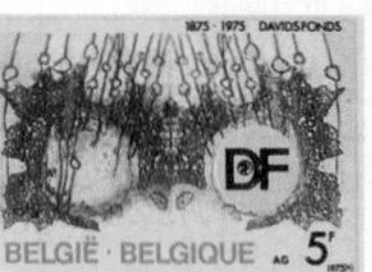

640 Foundation Emblem **641** King Albert I

1975. Centenary of Davids Foundation (Flemish cultural organisation).
2382 **640** 5f. multicoloured 25 10

1975. Birth Centenary of King Albert I.
2383 **641** 10f. black and purple . . 55 30

642 Pesaro Palace, Venice **643** "Postman of 1840" (J. Thiriar)

1975. Cultural Works.
2384 **642** 6f.50+2f.50 brown . . . 45 45
2385 – 10f.+4f.50 purple 80 70
2386 – 15f.+6f.50 blue . . . . . 1·10 1·00
DESIGNS—HORIZ: 10f. Sculpture Museum, St. Bavon Abbey, Ghent. VERT: 15f. "Virgin and Child" (Michelangelo, 500th Birth Anniv.)

1975. Stamp Day.
2387 **643** 6f.50 purple 35 10

644 "An Apostle" (detail, "The Last Supper", Dirk Bouts) **645** Prisoners' Identification Emblems

1975. Europa. Paintings.
2388 **644** 6f.50 black, blue & grn 35 10
2389 – 10f. black, red & orange 70 40
DESIGN: 10f. "The Suppliant's Widow" (detail, "The Justice of Otho", Dirk Bouts).

1975. 30th Anniv of Concentration Camps' Liberation.
2390 **645** 4f.50 multicoloured . . . 25 10

646 St John's Hospice, Bruges

1975. European Architectural Heritage Year.
2391 **646** 4f.50 purple 25 10
2392 – 5f. green 35 20
2393 – 10f. blue 55 35
DESIGNS—VERT: 5f. St. Loup's Church, Namur. HORIZ: 10f. Martyrs Square, Brussels.

1975. Tourist Publicity. As T **607**.
2394 4f.50 brown, buff and red 25 10
2395 5f. multicoloured 25 10
DESIGN—VERT: 4f.50, Church, Dottignies. HORIZ: 5f. Market Square, Saint Truiden.

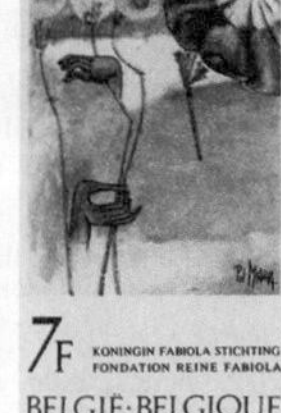

647 G. Ryckmans and L. Cerfaux (founders), and Louvain University Library **648** "Metamorphosis" (P. Mara)

1975. 25th Anniv of Louvain Colloquium Biblicum (Biblical Scholarship Association).
2396 **647** 10f. sepia and blue . . . 50 30

1975. Queen Fabiola Foundation for the Mentally Ill.
2397 **648** 7f. multicoloured 40 25

649 Marie Popelin (women's rights pioneer) and Palace of Justice **650** "Assia" (Charles Despiau)

1975. International Women's Year.
2398 **649** 6f.50 purple and green 40 10

1975. 25th Anniv of Middelheim Open-air Museum, Antwerp.
2399 **650** 5f. black and green . . . 25 15

651 Dr. Hemerijckx and Leprosy Hospital, Zaire

1975. Dr. Frans Hemerijckx (treatment of leprosy pioneer) Commemoration.
2400 **651** 20f.+10f. mult . . . . . 1·75 1·60

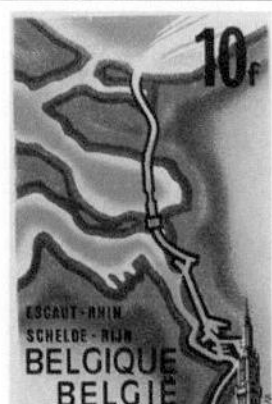

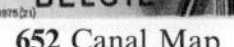

652 Canal Map

653 "Cornelia Vekemans at the Age of Seven" (Cornelis de Vos)

1975. Opening of Rhine–Scheldt Canal.
2401 **652** 10f. multicoloured . . . 50 35

1975. "Philately for the Young".
2402 **653** 4f.50 multicoloured . . . 25 20

654 National Bank and F. Orban (founder)

1975. 125th Anniv of Belgian National Bank.
2403 **654** 25f. multicoloured . . . 1·25 40

655 Edmond Thieffry (pilot) and "Princess Marie-Jose"

656 University Seal

1975. 50th Anniv of First Flight, Brussels–Kinshasa.
2404 **655** 7f. purple and black . . 40 20

1975. 550th Anniv of Louvain University.
2405 **656** 6f.50 black, green & bl 40 10

657 "Angels", (detail, "The Nativity", R. de le Pasture)

658 Emile Moyson (Flemish Leader)

1975. Christmas.
2406 **657** 5f. multicoloured 25 25

1975. "Solidarity".
2407 **658** 4f.50+2f. purple 35 35
2408 – 6f.50+3f. green 55 60
2409 – 10f.+5f. vio, blk & bl . . 85 80
2410 – 13f.+6f. multicoloured 1·10 1·00
DESIGNS—VERT: 6f.50, Dr. Augustin Snellaert (Flemish literature scholar); 13f. Detail of retable, St. Dymphne Church, Geel. HORIZ: 10f. Eye within hand, and Braille characters (150th anniv of introduction of Braille).

659 Cheese Seller

660 "African" Collector

1975. "Themabelga" International Thematic Stamp Exhibition, Brussels (2nd issue). Traditional Belgian Trades. Multicoloured.
2411 4f.50+1f.50 Type **659** . . . 35 35
2412 6f.50+3f. Potato seller . . . 50 50
2413 6f.50+3f. Basket-carrier . . 50 50
2414 10f.+5f. Prawn fisherman and pony (horiz) 80 70
2415 10f.+5f. Knife-grinder and cart (horiz) 80 70
2416 30f.+15f. Milk-woman with dog-cart (horiz) . . . . . 2·25 2·00

1976. Centenary of "Conservatoire Africain" (Charity Organization).
2417 **660** 10f.+5f. multicoloured 85 80

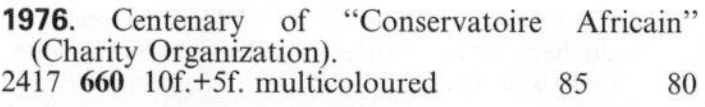

661 Owl Emblem and Flemish Buildings

662 Bicentennial Symbol

1976. 125th Anniv of Wilhems Foundation (Flemish cultural organization).
2418 **661** 5f. multicoloured 25 25

1976. Bicentenary of American Revolution.
2419 **662** 14f. multicoloured . . . 80 50

663 Cardinal Mercier

664 "Vlaams Ekonomisch Verbond"

1976. 50th Death Anniv of Cardinal Mercier.
2420 **663** 4f.50 purple 25 15

1976. 50th Anniv of Flemish Economic Federation.
2421 **664** 6f.50 multicoloured . . . 35 10

665 Swimming

1976. Olympic Games, Montreal. Multicoloured.
2422 4f.50+1f.50 Type **665** . . . 35 35
2423 5f.+2f. Running (vert) . . . 35 35
2424 6f.50+2f.50 Horse jumping 50 50

666 Money Centre Building, Brussels

1976. Stamp Day.
2425 **666** 6f.50 brown 35 10

667 Queen Elisabeth playing Violin

668 Basket-making

1976. 25th Anniv of Queen Elisabeth International Music Competitions.
2426 **667** 14f.+6f. red & black . . 1·00 1·00

1976. Europa. Traditional Crafts. Multicoloured.
2427 6f.50 Type **668** 40 10
2428 14f. Pottery (horiz) 85 40

669 Truck on Motorway

670 Queen Elisabeth

1976. 14th Congress of International Road Haulage Union, Brussels.
2429 **669** 14f. black, red & yellow 70 40

1976. Birth Centenary of Queen Elisabeth.
2430 **670** 14f. green 70 40

672 Jan Olieslagers (aviator), Bleriot XI Monoplane and club Badge

1976. 75th Anniv of Belgian Royal Aero Club. Sheet 82 × 116 mm.
MS2435 **672** 25f.+10f. black, yellow and blue . . . . 2·00 1·00

673 Ardennes Horses

1976. 50th Anniv of Ardennes Draught Horses Society.
2436 **673** 5f. multicoloured 35 25

674 King Baudouin

675 "Madonna and Child" (detail)

1976. 25th Anniv of King Baudouin's Accession. Two sheets each 110 × 62 mm containing stamps as T **674**.
MS2437 (a) 4f.50 grey; 6f.50 yellow; 10f. red (sold at 30f.). (b) 20f. green; 30f. blue (sold at 70f.) 5·50 5·50

1976. 400th Birth Anniv of Peter Paul Rubens (artist) (1st issue). Multicoloured.
2438 4f.50+1f.50 "Descent from the Cross" (detail) 45 45
2439 6f.50+3f. "Adoration of the Shepherds" (detail) (24½ × 35 mm) 55 60
2440 6f.50+3f. "Virgin of the Parrot" (detail) (24½ × 35 mm) 55 60
2441 10f.+5f. "Adoration of the Kings" (detail) (24½ × 35 mm) 95 90
2442 10f.+5f. "Last Communion of St. Francis" (detail) (24½ × 35 mm) 95 90
2443 30f.+15f. Type **675** . . . . 2·50 2·10
See also Nos. 2459 and 2497.

676 William the Silent, Prince of Orange

678 Underground Train

677 Modern Electric Train

1976. 400th Anniv of Pacification of Ghent.
2444 **676** 10f. green 55 25

1976. 50th Anniv of National Belgian Railway Company.
2445 **677** 6f.50 multicoloured . . . 40 10

1976. Opening of Brussels Metro (Underground) Service.
2446 **678** 6f.50 multicoloured . . . 40 10

679 "The Young Musician" (W. C. Duyster)

680 Charles Bernard (writer, birth cent)

1976. "Philately for the Young" and Young Musicians' Movement.
2447 **679** 4f.50 multicoloured . . . 45 10

1976. Cultural Anniversaries.
2448 **680** 5f. purple 25 25
2449 – 5f. red 25 25
2450 – 6f.50 brown 35 20
2451 – 6f.50 green 35 20
DESIGNS—VERT: No. 2449, Fernand Toussaint van Boelaere (writer, birth cent 1975); No. 2450, "St. Jerome in Mountain Landscape" (J. le Patinier) (25th anniv of Charles Plisnier Foundation). HORIZ: No. 2451, "Story of the Blind" (P. Brueghel) (25th anniv of "Vereniging voor Beschaafde Omgangstaal" (Dutch language organisation)).

1976. Tourist Publicity. As T **607**.
2452 4f.50 multicoloured 25 25
2453 4f.50 multicoloured 25 25
2454 5f. brown and blue 25 25
2455 5f. brown and olive 25 25
DESIGNS—HORIZ: No. 2452, Hunnegem Priory, Grammont; No. 2454, River Lys, Sint-Martens-Latem; No. 2455, Chateau. Ham-sur-Heure. VERT: No. 2453, Remouchamps Caves.

681 "Child with Impediment" (Velasquez)

682 "The Nativity" (detail, Master of Flemalle)

1976. National Association for Aid to the Mentally Handicapped.
2456 **681** 14f.+6f. multicoloured 1·00 1·00

1976. Christmas.
2457 **682** 5f. violet 35 25

683 Monogram

1977. 400th Birth Anniv of Peter Paul Rubens (2nd issue).
2459 **683** 6f.50 black and lilac . . 40 15

684 Belgian Lion

1977. (a) Size 17 × 20 mm.
2460 **684** 50c. brown 10 10
2461 65c. red 10 10
2462 1f. mauve 10 10
2463 1f.50 grey 10 10
2464a 2f. orange 10 10
2465 2f.50 green 25 20
2466 2f.75 blue 25 30
2467a 3f. violet 20 10
2468 4f. brown 25 10
2469 4f.50 blue 35 10
2470 5f. green 25 10
2471 6f. red 35 10
2472 7f. red 40 10
2473 8f. blue 40 10
2474 9f. orange 85 20

(b) 17 × 22 mm.
2475 **684** 1f. mauve 10 20
2476 2f. orange 35 20
2477 3f. violet 35 30

685 Dr. Albert Hustin (pioneer of blood transfusion)

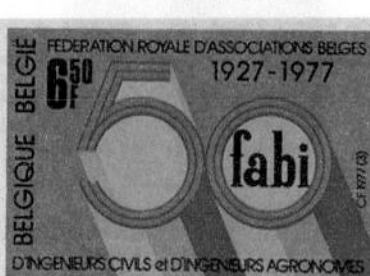

686 "50 Years of F.A.B.I."

1977. Belgian Red Cross.
2478 **685** 6f.50+2f.50 red and black 55 50
2479 – 14f.+7f. red, blue and black . . . . 1·10 1·00
DESIGN: 14f.+7f. Knee joint and red cross (World Rheumatism Year).

1977. 50th Anniv of Federation of Belgian Engineers.
2480 **686** 6f.50 multicoloured . . . 40 10

687 Jules Bordet School, Brussels (bicent)

688 Gulls in Flight

1977. Cultural Anniversaries.
2481 **687** 4f.50+1f. mult 25 25
2482 – 4f.50+1f. mult 25 25
2483 – 5f.+2f. multicoloured . . 35 35
2484 – 6f.50+2f. mult 40 40
2485 – 6f.50+2f. red & black . . 40 40
2486 – 10f.+5 slate 75 75
DESIGNS—VERT: 24 × 37 mm: No. 2482, Marie-Therese College, Herve (bicentenary); 2483, Detail from "La Grande Pyramide Musicale" (E. Tytgat) (50th anniv of Brussels Philharmonic Society). 35 × 45 mm: No. 2486, Camille Lemonnier (75th anniv of Society of Belgian Authors writing in French). HORIZ: 35 × 24 mm: No. 2484, Lucien van Obbergh and stage scene (50th anniv of Union of Artists). 37 × 24 mm: No. 2485, Emblem of Humanist Society (25th anniv).

1977. 25th Anniv of District 112 of Lions International.
2487 **688** 14f. multicoloured . . . 85 35

689 Footballers

690 Pillar Box, 1852

1977. 30th International Youth Tournament of European Football Association.
2488 **689** 10f.+5f. multicoloured 85 80

1977. Stamp Day.
2489 **690** 6f.50 olive 45 10

691 Gileppe Dam, Jalhay

692 "Mars and Mercury Association Emblem"

1977. Europa. Multicoloured.
2490 6f.50 Type **691** 40 20
2491 14f. The Yser, Nieuport . . 80 45

1977. 50th Anniv of Mars and Mercury Association of Reserve and Retired Officers.
2492 **692** 5f. green, black & brown 25 10

693 De Hornes Coat of Arms

694 "Self-Portrait"

1977. Historical Anniversaries.
2493 **693** 4f.50 lilac 25 20
2494 – 5f. red 25 20
2495 – 6f.50 brown 20 15
2496 – 14f. green . . . . 1·10 45
DESIGNS AND EVENTS—VERT: 4f.50, Type **693** (300th anniv of creation of principality of Overijse under Eugene-Maximilien de Hornes); 6f.50, Miniature (600th anniv of Froissart's "Chronicles"); 14f. "The Conversion of St. Hubert" (1250th death anniv). HORIZ: (45 × 24 mm): 5f. Detail from "Oxford Chest" (675th anniv of Battle of Golden Spurs).

1977. 400th Birth Anniv of Peter Paul Rubens (3rd issue).
2497 **694** 5f. multicoloured 35 20
MS2498 100 × 152 mm. As No. 2497 but larger (24 × 37 mm) × 3 (sold at 20f.) . . . . 1·10 1·00

695 "The Mystic Lamb" (detail, Brothers Van Eyck)

1977. 50th Anniv of International Federation of Library Associations and Congress, Brussels.
2499 **695** 10f. multicoloured . . . 55 25

696 Gymnast and Footballer

1977. Sports Events and Anniversaries.
2500 **696** 4f.50 red, black & grn 25 20
2501 – 6f.50 black, violet and brown 35 10
2502 – 10f. turquoise, black and salmon 55 35
2503 – 14f. green, blk & ochre 80 40
DESIGNS—VERT: 4f.50, Type **696** (50th anniv of Workers' Central Sports Association); 10f. Basketball (20th European Championships); 14f. Hockey (International Hockey Cup competition). HORIZ: 6f.50, Disabled fencers (Rehabilitation through sport).

697 Festival Emblem

1977. "Europalia '77" Festival.
2504 **697** 5f. multicoloured 25 10

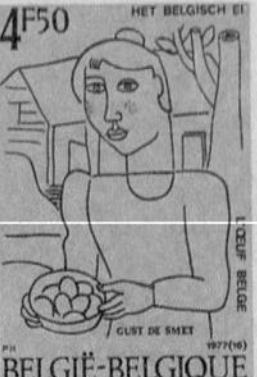

699 "The Egg-seller" (Gustave de Smet)

700 "The Stamp Collectors" (detail, Constant Cap)

1977. Promoting Belgian Eggs.
2506 **699** 4f.50 black and ochre . . 25 20

1977. "Philately for the Young".
2507 **700** 4f.50 sepia 25 10

1977. Tourist Publicity. As T**607**.
2508 4f.50 multicoloured 25 20
2509 4f.50 black, blue and green 25 20
2510 5f. multicoloured 25 20
2511 5f. multicoloured 25 20
DESIGNS—VERT: No. 2508, Bailiff's House, Gembloux; No. 2509, St. Aldegone's Church. HORIZ: No. 2510, View of Liege and statue of Mother and Child; No. 2511, View and statue of St. Nicholas.

701 "Nativity" (detail, R. de la Pasture)

702 Albert-Edouard Janssen (financier)

1977. Christmas.
2512 **701** 5f. red 25 25

1977. "Solidarity".
2513 **702** 5f.+2f.50 black 40 40
2514 – 5f.+2f.50 red 40 40
2515 – 10f.+5f. purple 80 75
2516 – 10f.+5f. grey 80 75
DESIGNS: No. 2514, Joseph Wauters (politician); No. 2516, Jean Capart (egyptologist); No. 2515, August de Boeck (composer).

703 Distressed Girl (Deserted Children)

704 Railway Signal as Arrows on Map of Europe

1978. Philanthropic Works. Multicoloured.
2517 4f.50+1f.50 Type **703** . . . 35 30
2518 6f.+3f. Blood pressure measurement (World Hypertension Month) . . 45 45
2519 10f.+5f. De Mick Sanatorium, Brasschaat (Anti-tuberculosis) (horiz) 85 85

1978. "European Action". Multicoloured.
2520 10f. Type **704** (25th anniv of European Conference of Transport Ministers) . . . 55 25
2521 10f. European Parliament Building, Strasbourg (first direct elections) 55 25
2522 14f. Campidoglio Palace, Rome and map of EEC countries (20th anniv of Treaties of Rome) (horiz) 85 40
2523 14f. Paul Henri Spaak (Belgian Prime Minister) (horiz) 85 40

705 Grimbergen Abbey

1978. 850th Anniv of Premonstratensian Abbey, Grimbergen.
2524 **705** 4f.50 brown 40 25

706 Emblem

707 5f. Stamp of 1878

1978. 175th Anniv of Ostend Chamber of Commerce and Industry.
2525 **706** 8f. multicoloured 40 10

1978. Stamp Day.
2526 **707** 8f. brown, blk & drab 40 10

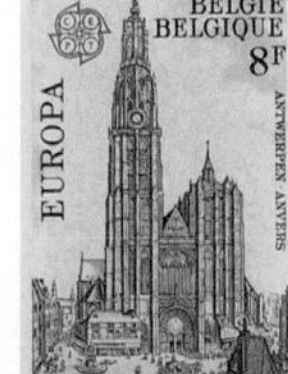

708 Antwerp Cathedral

709 Theatre and Characters from "The Brussels Street Singer"

1978. Europa. Multicoloured.
2527 8f. Type **708** 45 20
2528 14f. Pont des Trous, Tournai (horiz) 90 50

1978. Cultural Anniversaries.
2529 **709** 6f.+3f. multicoloured . . 45 45
2530 – 6f.+3f. multicoloured . . 45 45
2531 – 8f.+4f. brown 60 60
2532 – 10f.+5f. brown 80 75
DESIGNS AND EVENTS: No. 2529, (Type **709**) (Royal Flemish Theatre Cent.); 2530, Arquebusier with standard, arms and Company Gallery, Vise (Royal Company of Crossbowmen of Vise 400th anniv); 2531, Karel van der Woestijne (poet) (birth cent); 2532, Don John of Austria (signing of Perpetual Edict, 400th anniv).

710 "Education"

711 "K.V.I."

1978. Teaching. Multicoloured.
2533 6f. Type **710** (Municipal education in Ghent, 150th anniv) 35 25
2534 8f. Paul Pastur Workers' University, Charleroi (75th anniv) 40 25

1978. Tourist Publicity. As T **607**.
2535 4f.50 sepia, buff and blue 25 25
2536 4f.50 multicoloured 25 25
2537 6f. multicoloured 35 25
2538 6f. multicoloured 35 25
DESIGNS—VERT: No. 2535, Jonathas House, Enghien. HORIZ: No. 2536, View of Wetteren and couple in local costume; 2537, Brussels tourist hostess; 2538, Carnival Prince and church tower.

1978. 50th Anniv of Royal Flemish Association of Engineers.
2539 **711** 8f. black and red 40 10

712 Young Stamp Collector

713 Mountain Scenery

1978. "Philately for the Young".
2540 **712** 4f.50 violet 25 20

1978. Olympic Games (1980) Preparation.
2541 **713** 6f.+2f.50 mult 45 40
2542 – 8f.+3f.50 green, brown and black 55 50
MS2543 150 × 100 mm. 7f. + 3f., 14f.+6f. multicoloured . . . . 1·75 1·60
DESIGNS: 7f. Ancient Greek athletes; 8f. Kremlin Towers, Moscow; 14f. Olympic flame.

714 "The Nativity" (detail, Bethlehem Door, Notre Dame, Huy)

715 Tabernacle, Brussels Synagogue (centenary)

1978. Christmas.
2544 **714** 6f. black 35 25

1978. "Solidarity". Anniversaries.
2545 **715** 6f.+2f. brown, grey and black 45 40
2546 – 8f.+3f. multicoloured . . 65 55
2547 – 14f.+7f. multicoloured 1·10 1·00
DESIGNS—HORIZ: (36×24 mm): 8f. Dancing figures (Catholic Students Action, 50th anniv); 14f. Father Dominique-Georges Pire and African Village (Award of Nobel Peace Prize, 20th anniv).

716 Relief Workers giving First Aid
717 "Till Eulenspiegel" (legendary character)

1978. Belgian Red Cross. Multicoloured.
2548 8f.+3f. Type **716** 55 60
2549 16f.+8f. Skull smoking, bottle and syringe ("Excess kills") . . . . . 1·25 1·25

1979. 10th Anniv of Lay Action Centres.
2550 **717** 4f.50 multicoloured . . . 35 20

718 "European Dove"
719 Millenary Emblem

1979. 1st Direct Elections to European Assembly.
2551 **718** 8f. multicoloured 45 10

1979. Brussels Millenary (1st issue).
2552 **719** 4f.50 brown, blk & red 25 20
2553 8f. turquoise, blk & grn 65 10
See also Nos. 2559/62.

720 Sculpture at N.A.T.O. Headquarters and Emblem
721 Drawing of Monument

1979. 30th Anniv of North Atlantic Treaty Organization.
2554 **720** 30f. blue, gold and light blue . . . . 1·50 45

1979. 25th Anniv of Breendonk Monument.
2555 **721** 6f. orange and black . . 35 25

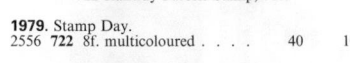

722 Railway Parcels Stamp, 1879

1979. Stamp Day.
2556 **722** 8f. multicoloured 40 10

723 Mail Coach and Renault R4 Post Van

1979. Europa. Multicoloured.
2557 8f. Type **723** 45 10
2558 14f. Semaphore posts, satellite and dish aerial . . 85 45

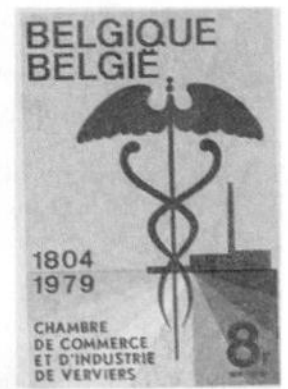

724 "Legend of Our Lady of Sablon" (detail of tapestry, Town Museum of Brussels)
725 Caduceus and Factory

1979. Brussels Millenary (2nd issue). Multicoloured.
2559 6f.+2f. Type **724** 40 40
2560 8f.+3f. Different detail of tapestry 50 55
2561 14f.+7f. "Legend of Our Lady of Sablon" (tapestry) . . . . 1·10 1·10
2562 20f.+10f. Different detail of tapestry . . . . 1·50 1·50
MS2563 100×150 mm. 20f.+10f. Different detail of Town Museum tapestry (48×37 mm) . . . . 1·75 1·75
The tapestry shown on Nos. 2559/60 is from Brussels Town Museum and that on Nos. 2561/2 from the Royal Museum of Art and History.

1979. 175th Anniv of Verviers Chamber of Commerce.
2564 **725** 8f. multicoloured 40 10

726 "50" and Bank Emblem

1979. 50th Anniv of Professional Credit Bank.
2565 **726** 4f.50 blue and gold . . . 25 25

727 Bas-relief

1979. 50th Anniv of Chambers of Trade and Commerce.
2566 **727** 10f. crimson, orange and red 50 25

728 Cambre Abbey

1979. Cultural Anniversaries.
2567 **728** 6f.+2f. multicoloured . . 45 40
2568 – 8f.+3f. multicoloured . . 50 50
2569 – 14f.+7f. black, orange and green . . . . . . 1·10 1·00
2570 – 20f.+10f. brown, red and grey . . . . 1·50 1·50
DESIGNS: 6f. Type **728** (50th anniv of restoration); 8f. Beauvoorde Chateau; 14f. Barthelemy Dumortier (founder) and newspaper "Courrier de L'Escaut" (150th anniv); 20f. Crypt, shrine and Collegiate Church of St. Hermes, Renaix (850th anniv of consecration).

729 "Tintin" with Dog, Stamps and Magnifier

1979. "Philately for the Young".
2571 **729** 8f. multicoloured . . . . 2·00 40

730 Le Grand-Hornu

1979. Le Grand-Hornu Industrial Archaeological Site.
2572 **730** 10f.+5f. black & grey . . 85 80

1979. Tourist Publicity. As T **607**.
2573 5f. multicoloured 25 20
2574 5f. multicoloured 25 20
2575 6f. black, turquoise & green 35 25
2576 6f. multicoloured 35 25
DESIGNS—HORIZ: No. 2573, Royal African Museum, Tervuren, and hunters with hounds; 2575, St. John's Church, Poperinge, and statue of Virgin Mary. VERT: No. 2574, Belfry, Thuin, and men carrying religious image; 2576, St. Nicholas's Church and cattle market, Ciney.

731 Francois Auguste Gevaert
732 Madonna and Child, Foy-Notre-Dame Church

1979. Music. Each brown and ochre.
2577 5f. Type **731** (150th birth anniv) 25 25
2578 6f. Emmanuel Durlet . . . 35 25
2579 14f. Grand piano and string instruments (40th anniv of Queen Elisabeth Musical Chapel) 75 40

1979. Christmas.
2580 **732** 6f. black and blue . . . 35 25

733 H. Heyman (politician, birth centenary)
734 "1830–1980"

1979. "Solidarity".
2581 **733** 8f.+3f. brown, green and black 55 50
2582 – 10f.+5f. multicoloured 75 65
2583 – 16f.+8f. black, green and yellow . . . . 1·25 1·25
DESIGNS—VERT: As Type **733**. 10f. War Invalids Organization medal (50th anniv). HORIZ: (44×24 mm): 16f. Child's head and International Year of the Child emblem.

1980. 150th Anniv of Independence (1st issue).
2584 **734** 9f. mauve & lt mauve . . 45 15
See also Nos. 2597/2601.

735 Frans Van Cauwelaert
736 Spring Flowers

1980. Birth Centenary of Frans Van Cauwelaert (politician).
2585 **735** 5f. black 25 10

1980. Ghent Flower Show. Multicoloured.
2586 5f. Type **736** 25 25
2587 6f.50 Summer flowers . . . 35 30
2588 9f. Autumn flowers 45 10

737 Telephone and Diagram of Satellite Orbit

1980. 50th Anniv of Telegraph and Telephone Office.
2589 **737** 10f. multicoloured . . . 50 25

738 5f. Airmail Stamp of 1930

1980. Stamp Day.
2590 **738** 9f. multicoloured 50 10

739 St. Benedict of Nursia

1980. Europa. Multicoloured.
2591 9f. Type **739** 70 10
2592 14f. Marguerite of Austria 90 45

740 Ivo van Damme
741 Palais de la Nation

1980. Ivo van Damme (athlete) Commemoration.
2593 **740** 20f.+10f. mult . . . . . 1·50 1·50

1980. 4th Interparliamentary Conference on European Co-operation and Security, Brussels.
2594 **741** 5f. blue, lilac and black 25 25

742 Golden Carriage, Mons

1980. Tourist Publicity. Multicoloured.
2595 6f.50 Type **742** 35 25
2596 6f.50 Damme 35 25

743 King Leopold I and Queen Louise-Marie

1980. 150th Anniv of Belgian Independence (2nd issue).
2597 **743** 6f.50+1f.50 pur & blk . . 45 40
2598 – 9f.+3f. blue & black . . 55 50
2599 – 14f.+6f. green & blk . . 1·10 1·00
2600 – 17f.+8f. orange. & blk 1·25 1·25
2601 – 25f.+10f. green & blk . . 1·75 1·75
MS2602 100×150 mm. 50f. black (sold at 75f.) . . . . 3·50 3·25
DESIGNS: 9f. King Leopold II and Queen Marie-Henriette; 14f. King Albert I and Queen Elisabeth; 17f. King Leopold III and Queen Astrid; 25f. King Baudouin and Queen Fabiola; 50f. Royal Mint Theatre, Brussels.

744 King Baudouin
745 "Brewer" (detail, Reliquary of St. Lambert)

1980. King Baudouin's 50th Birthday.
2603 **744** 9f. red 50 15

1980. Millenary of Liege. Multicoloured.
2604 9f.+3f. Type **745** 55 60
2605 17f.+6f. "The Miner" (sculpture by Constantin Meunier) (horiz) . . . . 1·25 1·25
2606 25f.+10f. "Seat of Wisdom" (Madonna, Collegiate Church of St. John, Liege) . . . . 2·00 1·90
MS2607 150×100 mm. 20f.+10f. Seal of Prince Bishop Notger (43×24 mm) . . . . 1·75 1·75

746 Chiny

1980. Tourist Publicity.
2608 **746** 5f. multicoloured 30 25

747 Emblem of Cardiological League of Belgium

748 Rodenbach (statue at Roulers)

1980. Heart Week.
2609 **747** 14f. light blue, red and blue 70 40

1980. Death Cent of Albrecht Rodenbach (poet).
2610 **748** 9f. brown, blue and deep blue 45 10

749 "Royal Procession" (children of Thyl Uylenspiegel Primary School)

1980. "Philately for the Young".
2611 **749** 5f. multicoloured 25 20

750 Emblem

751 "Garland of Flowers and Nativity" (attr. D. Seghers)

1980. 50th Anniv of Belgian Broadcasting Corporation.
2612 **750** 10f. black and grey . . . 50 25

1980. Christmas.
2613 **751** 6f.50 multicoloured . . . 35 25

752 Gateway, Diest

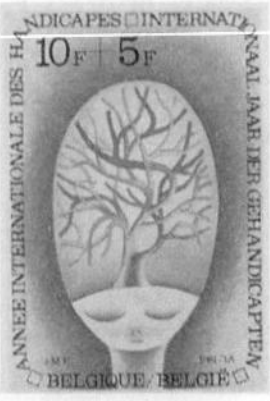

754 Brain

1980. Tourist Publicity.
2614 **752** 5f. multicoloured 25 20
See also Nos. 2648/51 and 2787/92.

1981. International Year of Disabled Persons. Multicoloured.
2637 10f.+5f. Type **754** 85 80
2638 25f.+10f. Eye . . . . 2·00 1·75

755 "Baron de Gerlache" (after F. J. Navez)

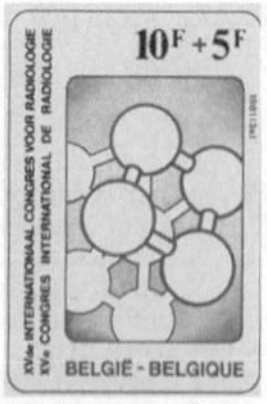

756 Emblem of 15th International Radiology Convention

1981. Historical Anniversaries.
2639 **755** 6f. multicoloured 35 25
2640 – 9f. multicoloured 45 10
2641 – 50f. brown & yellow . . 2·50 65
DESIGNS—As T **755**: 6f. Type **755** (1st President of Chamber of Deputies) (150th anniv of Chamber); 9f. Baron de Stassart (1st President of Senate) (after F. J. Navez) (150th anniv of Senate). 35×51 mm: 50f. Statue of King Leopold I by Geefs (150th anniv of royal dynasty).

1981. Belgian Red Cross.
2642 **756** 10f.+5f. bl, blk & red . . 85 80
2643 – 25f.+10f. blue, red and black . . . . 2·00 1·75
DESIGN: 25f. Dove and globe symbolizing international emergency assistance.

757 Tchantches and Op-Signoorke (puppets)

1981. Europa. Multicoloured.
2644 9f. Type **757** 55 10
2645 14f. D'Artagnan and Woltje (puppets) 90 55

758 Stamp Transfer-roller depicting A. de Cock (founder of Postal Museum)

759 Ovide Decroly

1981. Stamp Day.
2646 **758** 9f. multicoloured 45 10

1981. 110th Birth Anniv of Dr. Ovide Decroly (educational psychologist).
2647 **759** 35f.+15f. brown & bl . . 2·50 2·40

1981. Tourist Publicity. As T **752**. Multicoloured.
2648 6f. Statue of our Lady of Tongre 35 25
2649 6f. Egmont Castle, Zottegem 35 25
2650 6f.50 Dams on Eau d'Heure (horiz) 40 25
2651 6f.50 Tongerlo Abbey, Antwerp (horiz) 40 25

760 Footballer

761 Edouard Remouchamps (Walloon dramatist)

1981. Cent of Royal Antwerp Football Club.
2652 **760** 6f. red, brown & black 40 25

1981. 125th Anniv of Society of Walloon Language and Literature.
2653 **761** 6f.50 brown and stone 35 25

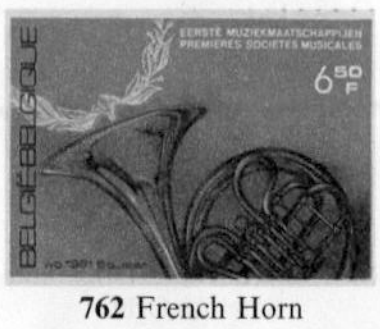

762 French Horn

1981. Centenary of De Vredekring Band, Antwerp.
2654 **762** 6f.50 blue, mve & blk . . 35 25

763 Audit Office

1981. 150th Anniv of Audit Office.
2655 **763** 10f. purple 50 25

764 Pietà

1981. 25th Anniv of Bois du Cazier Mining Disaster. Sheet 150×100 mm.
MS2656 **764** 20f. multicoloured (sold at 30f.) . . . . 1·50 1·50

765 Tombs of Marie of Burgundy and Charles the Bold

1981. Relocation of Tombs of Marie of Burgundy and Charles the Bold in Notre-Dame Church, Bruges.
2657 **765** 50f. multicoloured . . . 2·50 65

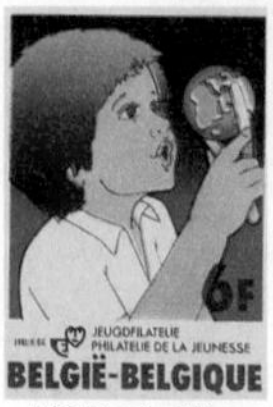

766 Boy holding Globe in Tweezers

767 King Baudouin

1981. "Philately for Youth".
2658 **766** 6f. multicoloured 35 25

1981.
2659 **767** 50f. light blue and blue 3·00 15
2660 65f. mauve and black . . 4·00 75
2661 100f. brown and blue . . 5·50 50

768 Max Waller (founder)

769 Nativity (miniature from "Missale ad usum d. Leodensis")

1981. Cultural Anniversaries.
2672 **768** 6f. multicoloured 35 15
2673 – 6f.50 multicoloured . . . 40 25
2674 – 9f. multicoloured 45 10
2675 – 10f. multicoloured . . . 55 40
2676 – 14f. lt brn & brn 85 50
DESIGNS: 6f. Type **768** (centenary of literary review "La Jeune Belgique"); 6f.50," Liqueur Drinkers" (detail, Gustave van de Woestijne (inscr "Woestyne") (birth centenary); 9f. Fernand Severin (poet, 50th death anniv); 10f. Jan van Ruusbroec (mystic, 600th death anniv); 14f. Owl (La Pensee et les Hommes organization, 25th anniv).

1981. Christmas.
2677 **769** 6f.50 brown and black 35 25

770 Mounted Gendarme, 1832

771 Cellist and Royal Conservatory of Music, Brussels

1981. "Solidarity". Multicoloured.
2678 9f.+4f. Type **770** 70 65
2679 20f.+7f. Carabinier . . . . 1·40 1·25
2680 40f.+20f. Mounted Guide, 1843 . . . . 3·00 2·75

1982. 150th Anniversaries. Multicoloured.
2681 6f.50 Type **771** 35 25
2682 9f. Front of former Law Court, Brussels (anniv of judiciary) 45 10

772 Sectional View of Cyclotron

773 Billiards

1982. Science. Multicoloured.
2683 6f. Type **772** (Installation of cyclotron at National Radio-elements Institute, Fleurus) 35 25
2684 14f. Telescope and galaxy (Royal Observatory) . . . 70 40
2685 50f. Dr. Robert Koch and tubercle bacillus (centenary of discovery) 2·40 50

1982. Sports. Multicoloured.
2686 6f.+2f. Type **773** 70 70
2687 9f.+4f. Cycling 90 95
2688 10f.+5f. Football . . . . . 1·10 1·00
2689 50f.+14f. "Treaty of Rome" (yacht) . . . . 3·00 2·75
MS2690 105×100 mm. 25f. multicoloured (Type **773**); 25f. brown, yellow and black (as No. 2687); 25f. red, yellow and black (as No. 2688); 25f. multicoloured (as No. 2689) . . 5·50 4·75

774 Joseph Lemaire (after Jean Maillard)

775 Voting (Universal Suffrage)

1982. Birth Centenary of Joseph Lemaire (Minister of State and social reformer).
2691 **774** 6f.50 multicoloured . . . 35 45

1982. Europa.
2692 **775** 10f. multicoloured . . . 70 25
2693 – 17f. green, black and grey . . . . 1·25 40
DESIGN: 17f. Portrait and signature of Emperor Joseph II (Edict of Toleration).

1982. Surch **1 F**.
2694 **684** 1f. on 5f. green 10 10

777 17th-century Postal Messenger

778 "Tower of Babel" (Brueghel the Elder)

1982. Stamp Day.
2695 **777** 10f. multicoloured . . . 50 10

1982. World Esperanto Congress, Antwerp.
2696 **778** 12f. multicoloured . . . 70 30

1982. Tourist Publicity. As T **752**.
2697 7f. blue and light blue . . . 45 25
2698 7f. black and green 45 25
2699 7f.50 brown and light brown 45 25

2700 7f.50 violet and lilac 45 25
2701 7f.50 black and grey 45 25
2702 7f.50 black and pink 45 25
DESIGNS—VERT: No. 2697, Gosselies Tower; 2698, Zwijveke Abbey, Termonde; 2701, Entrance gate, Grammont Abbey; 2702, Beveren pillory. HORIZ: No. 2699, Stavelot Abbey; 2700, Abbey ruins, Villers-la-Ville.

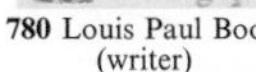

780 Louis Paul Boon (writer) **781** Abraham Hans

1982. Cultural Anniversaries.
2707 **780** 7f. black, red and grey 35 25
2708 – 10f. multicoloured . . . 45 10
2709 – 12f. multicoloured . . . 60 30
2710 – 17f. multicoloured . . . 90 40
DESIGNS: 7f. Type **780** (70th birth anniv); 10f. "Adoration of the Shepherds" (detail of Portinari retable) (Hugo van der Goes, 500th death anniv); 12f. Michel de Ghelderode (dramatist, 20th death anniv); 17f. "Motherhood" (Pierre Paulus, birth centenary (1981)).

1982. Birth Centenary of Abraham Hans (writer).
2711 **781** 17f. black, turquoise and blue 80 25

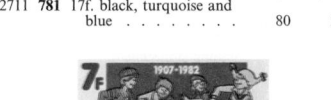

782 Children playing Football

1982. "Philately for the Young". Scout Year.
2712 **782** 7f. multicoloured 45 25

783 Masonic Emblems **784** Star over Village

1982. 150th Anniv of Belgium Grand Orient (Freemasonry Lodge).
2713 **783** 10f. yellow and black . . 55 10

1982. Christmas.
2714 **784** 10f.+1f. multicoloured 70 70

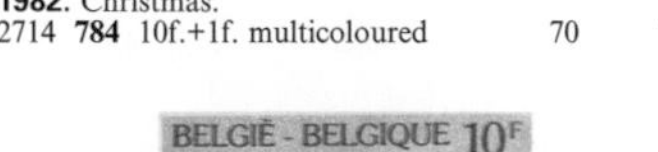

785 Cardinal Cardijn

1982. Birth Centenary of Cardinal Joseph Cardijn.
2715 **785** 10f. multicoloured . . . 55 10

786 King Baudouin **787** King Baudouin

1982.
2716 **786** 10f. blue 55 10
2717 11f. brown 70 10
2718 12f. green 90 10
2719 13f. red 85 10
2720 14f. black 85 10
2721 15f. red 90 30
2722 20f. blue . . . . 1·25 10
2723 22f. purple . . . . . . 2·25 95
2724 23f. green . . . . 2·10 45
2725 24f. grey . . . . 1·40 25
2726 25f. blue . . . . 1·50 20
2727 30f. brown . . . . . . 1·40 10
2728 40f. red . . . . 2·10 20
2729 **787** 50f. light brown, brown and black . . . . 3·50 20
2730 100f. blue, deep blue and black . . . . 9·00 25
2731 200f. light green, green and deep green . . . 18·00 80

788 St. Francis preaching to the Birds **789** Messenger handing Letter to King in the Field

1982. 800th Birth Anniv of St. Francis of Assisi.
2736 **788** 20f. multicoloured . . . 1·00 40

1982. "Belgica 82" Postal History Exhibition. Multicoloured.
2737 7f.+2f. Type **789** 45 45
2738 7f.50+2f.50 Messenger, Basel (vert) 55 60
2739 10f.+3f. Messenger, Nuremburg (vert) 70 70
2740 17f.+7f. Imperial courier, 1750 (vert) . . . . 1·25 1·25
2741 20f.+9f. Imperial courier, 1800 . . . . 1·50 1·50
2742 25f.+10f. Belgian postman, 1886 . . . . 1·75 1·60
MS2743 123 × 89 mm. 50f.+25f. Mail coach (48 × 37 mm) . . . 4·50 4·50

790 Emblem **791** Horse Tram

1983. 50th Anniv of Caritas Catholica Belgica.
2744 **790** 10f.+2f. red and grey . . 70 70

1983. Trams. Multicoloured.
2745 7f.50 Type **791** 45 25
2746 10f. Electric tram 50 10
2747 50f. Tram with trolley (invented by K. van de Poele) . . . . 2·75 50

792 Mountaineer **793** Brussels Buildings, Open Periodicals and Globe

1983. Belgian Red Cross. Multicoloured.
2748 12f.+3f. Type **792** 80 80
2749 20f.+5f. Walker . . . . . . 1·25 1·10

1983. 24th International Periodical Press Federation World Congress, Brussels.
2750 **793** 20f. multicoloured . . . 1·00 30

794 Woman at Work

1983. Women.
2751 **794** 8f. multicoloured 45 25
2752 – 11f. multicoloured . . . 55 10
2753 – 20f. yellow, brown & bl 1·10 40
DESIGNS: 11f. Woman at home; 20f. Woman manager.

795 Graphic Representation of Midi Railway Station, Brussels

1983. Stamp Day. World Communications Year.
2754 **795** 11f. black, red and blue 55 20

796 Procession of the Holy Blood

1983. Procession of the Holy Blood, Bruges.
2755 **796** 8f. multicoloured 45 20

797 "The Man in the Street" **798** Hot-air Balloon over Town

1983. Europa. Paintings by Paul Delvaux. Mult.
2756 11f. Type **797** 80 20
2757 20f. "Night Trains" (horiz) 1·40 45

1983. Bicentenary of Manned Flight. Mult.
2758 11f. Type **798** 55 10
2759 22f. Hot-air balloon over countryside . . . . 1·25 40

799 Church of Our Lady, Hastiere **800** Milkmaid

1983. Tourist Publicity. Multicoloured.
2760 8f. Type **799** 55 25
2761 8f. Tumulus, Landen . . . 55 25
2762 8f. Park, Mouscron 55 25
2763 8f. Wijnendale Castle, Torhout 55 25

1983. Tineke Festival, Heule.
2764 **800** 8f. multicoloured 40 20

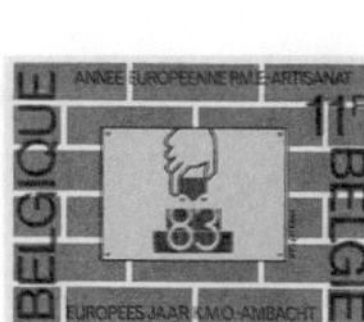

801 Plaque on Wall **802** Rainbow and Child

1983. European Small and Medium-sized Industries and Crafts Year.
2765 **801** 11f. yellow, black & red 55 10

1983. "Philately for the Young". 20th Anniv of Queen Fabiola Village No. 1 (for handicapped people).
2766 **802** 8f. multicoloured 50 20

803 Textiles **804** Conscience (after wood engraving by Nelly Degouy)

1983. Belgian Exports (1st series). Multicoloured.
2767 10f. Type **803** 50 25
2768 10f. Steel beams (metallurgy) 50 25
2769 10f. Diamonds 50 25
See also Nos. 2777/80.

1983. Death Centenary of Hendrik Conscience (writer).
2770 **804** 20f. black and green . . 1·10 25

805 "Madonna" (Jef Wauters) **806** 2nd Foot Regiment

1983. Christmas.
2771 **805** 11f.+1f. multicoloured 70 65

1983. "Solidarity". Military Uniforms. Mult.
2772 8f.+2f. Type **806** 55 60
2773 11f.+2f. Lancer 90 85
2774 50f.+12f. Grenadier . . . . 3·25 3·00

1983. King Leopold III Commemoration.
2775 **155** 11f. black 70 10

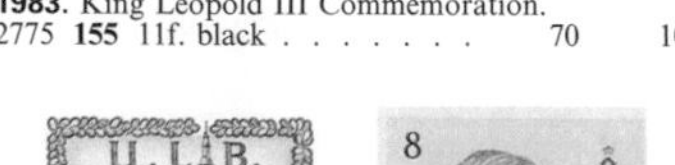

807 Free University of Brussels **808** Albert I

1984. 150th Anniv of Free University of Brussels.
2776 **807** 11f. multicoloured . . . 55 10

1984. Belgian Exports (2nd series). As T **803**. Multicoloured.
2777 11f. Retort and test tubes (chemicals) 55 25
2778 11f. Combine harvester (agricultural produce) . . 55 25
2779 11f. Ship, coach and electric commuter train (transport) 55 25
2780 11f. Atomic emblem and computer terminal (new technology) 55 25

1984. 50th Death Anniv of King Albert I.
2781 **808** 8f. black and stone . . . 50 25

809 Judo **810** Releasing Doves

1984. Olympic Games, Los Angeles. Multicoloured.
2782 8f.+2f. Type **809** 55 50
2783 12f.+3f. Windsurfing (vert) 75 70
MS2784 125 × 90 mm. 10f. Archery; 24f. Dressage . . . . 2·00 2·00

1984. 25th Anniv of Movement without a Name.
2785 **810** 12f. multicoloured . . . 60 10

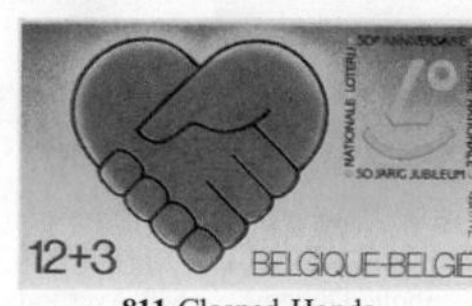

811 Clasped Hands

1984. 50th Anniv of National Lottery.
2786 **811** 12f.+3f. multicoloured 85 80

812 St. John Bosco with Children **813** Bridge

1984. 50th Anniv of Canonization of St. John Bosco (founder of Salesians).
2787 **812** 8f. multicoloured 40 10

1984. Europa. 25th Anniv of European Posts and Telecommunications Conference.
2788 **813** 12f. red and black . . . 65 20
2789 22f. blue and black . . . 1·40 30

814 Leopold II 1884 10c. Stamp

1984. Stamp Day.

2790	**814**	12f. multicoloured	65	10

815 Dove and Pencils

1984. 2nd European Parliament Elections.

2791	**815**	12f. multicoloured	65	10

816 Shako **817** Church of Our Lady of the Chapel, Brussels

1984. 150th Anniv of Royal Military School.

2792	**816**	22f. multicoloured	1·25	40

1984. Tourist Publicity. Multicoloured.

2793	10f. Type **817**	55	20
2794	10f. St. Martin's Church and lime tree, Montigny-le-Tilleul	55	20
2795	10f. Belfry and Town Hall, Tielt (vert)	55	20

818 "Curious Masks" (detail, James Ensor)

1984. Inaug of Brussels Modern Art Museum.

2796	**818**	8f.+2f. multicoloured	55	60
2797	–	12f.+3f. multicoloured	90	95
2798	–	22f.+5f. multicoloured	1·40	1·40
2799	–	50f.+13f. grn, bl & blk	3·25	3·00

DESIGNS: 12f. "The Empire of Lights" (detail, Rene Magritte); 22f. "The End" (detail, Jan Cox); 50f. "Rhythm No. 6" (Jo Delahaut).

819 Symbolic Design **820** Averbode Abbey

1984. 50th Anniv of Chirojeugd (Christian youth movement).

2800	**819**	10f. yellow, violet & bl	50	25

1984. Abbeys.

2801	**820**	8f. green and brown	35	20
2802	–	22f. brown & dp brown	1·10	30
2803	–	24f. green & light green	1·25	45
2804	–	50f. lilac and brown	2·50	60

DESIGNS—VERT: 22f. Chimay; 24f. Rochefort. HORIZ: 50f. Affligem.

821 Smurf as Postman **822** Child collecting Flowers

1984. "Philately for the Young".

2805	**821**	8f. multicoloured	1·25	40

1984. Children.

2806	10f.+2f. Type **822**	70	65
2807	12f.+3f. Children with globe	85	80
2808	15f.+3f. Child on merry-go-round	1·10	1·00

823 Meulemans **824** Three Kings

1984. Birth Cent of Arthur Meulemans (composer).

2809	**823**	12f. black and orange	65	10

1984. Christmas.

2810	**824**	12f.+1f. multicoloured	80	75

825 St. Norbert **826** "Virgin of Louvain" (attr. Jan Gossaert)

1985. 850th Death Anniv of St. Norbert.

2811	**825**	22f. brown & lt brown	1·25	40

1985. "Europalia 85 Espana" Festival.

2812	**826**	12f. multicoloured	65	20

827 Press Card in Hatband **828** Blood System as Tree

1985. Cent of Professional Journalists Association.

2814	**827**	9f. multicoloured	45	25

1985. Belgian Red Cross. Blood Donations.

2815	**828**	9f.+2f. multicoloured	70	70
2816	–	23f.+5f. red, blue and black	1·60	1·50

DESIGN: 23f. Two hearts.

829 "Sophrolaelio cattleya" "Burlingama" **830** Pope John Paul II

1985. Ghent Flower Festival. Orchids. Mult.

2817	12f. Type **829**	65	20
2818	12f. Phalaenopsis "Malibu"	65	20
2819	12f. Tapeu orchid ("Vanda coerulea")	65	20

1985. Visit of Pope John Paul II.

2820	**830**	12f. multicoloured	70	20

831 Rising Sun behind Chained Gates

1985. Centenary of Belgian Workers' Party.

2821	9f. Type **831**	50	30
2822	12f. Broken wall, flag and rising sun	65	20

832 Jean de Bast (engraver)

1985. Stamp Day.

2823	**832**	12f. blue	60	10

834 Class 18 Steam Locomotive, 1896

1985. Public Transport Year. Multicoloured.

2826	9f. Type **834**	55	25
2827	12f. Locomotive "Elephant", 1835	70	20
2828	23f. Class 23 tank engine, 1904	1·40	50
2829	24f. Class I Pacific locomotive, 1935	1·40	50
MS2830	150 × 100 mm. 50f. Class 27 electric locomotive, 1979	3·50	3·50

835 Cesar Franck and Score

1985. Europa. Music Year. Multicoloured.

2831	12f. Type **835**	70	20
2832	23f. Queen and king with viola dressed in music score (Queen Elisabeth International Music Competition)	1·40	40

836 Planned Canal Lock, Strepy-Thieu **837** Church of Our Lady's Assumption, Avernas-le-Bauduin

1985. Permanent International Navigation Congress Association Centenary Congress, Brussels. Multicoloured.

2833	23f. Type **836**	1·40	50
2834	23f. Aerial view of Zeebrugge harbour	1·40	50

1985. Tourist Publicity. Multicoloured.

2835	12f. Type **837**	70	25
2836	12f. Saint Martin's Church, Marcinelle (horiz)	70	25
2837	12f. Roman tower and Church of old beguinage, Tongres	70	25
2838	12f. House, Wachtebeke (horiz)	70	25

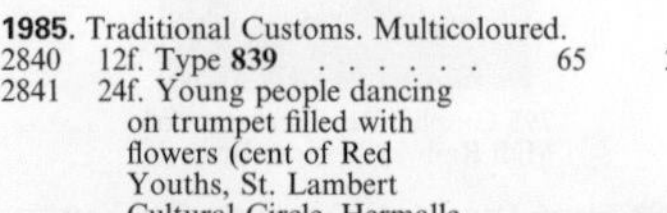

838 Queen Astrid **839** Baking Matton Tart, Grammont

1985. 50th Death Anniv of Queen Astrid.

2839	**838**	12f. lt brown & brown	85	10

1985. Traditional Customs. Multicoloured.

2840	12f. Type **839**	65	25
2841	24f. Young people dancing on trumpet filled with flowers (cent of Red Youths, St. Lambert Cultural Circle, Hermalle-sous-Argenteau)	1·40	45

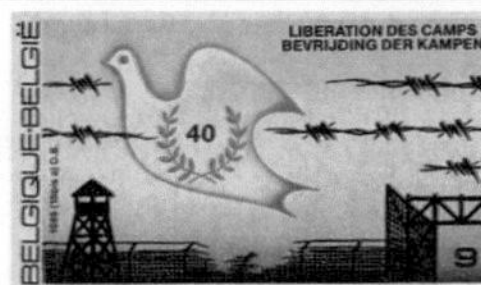

840 Dove and Concentration Camp

1985. 40th Anniv of Liberation. Multicoloured.

2842	9f. Type **840**	55	25
2843	23f. Battle of the Ardennes	1·40	50
2844	24f. Troops landing at Scheldt estuary	1·40	50

841 Hawfinch ("Appelvink – Gros Bec") **842** Claes and Fictional Character

1985. Birds (1st series). Multicoloured.

2845	1f. Lesser spotted woodpecker ("Pic epeichette")	30	10
2846	2f. Eurasian tree sparrow ("Moineau friquet")	25	10
2847	3f. Type **841**	45	10
2847a	3f.50 European robin ("Rouge-gorge")	25	10
2848	4f. Bluethroat ("Gorge-bleue")	35	10
2848a	4f.50 Common stonechat ("Traquet patre")	35	20
2849	5f. Eurasian nuthatch ("Sittelle torche-pot")	35	10
2850	6f. Northern bullfinch ("Bouvreuil")	55	10
2851	7f. Blue tit ("Mesange bleue")	55	20
2852	8f. River kingfisher ("Martin-pecheur")	55	20
2853	9f. Eurasian goldfinch ("Chardonneret")	90	10
2854	10f. Chaffinch ("Pinson")	60	20

See also Nos. 3073/86 and 3306/23.

1985. Birth Centenary of Ernest Claes (writer).

2855	**842**	9f. multicoloured	45	25

843 Youth **844** Trazegnies Castle

1985. "Philately for the Young". International Youth Year.

2856	**843**	9f. multicoloured	45	25

1985. "Solidarity". Castles. Multicoloured.

2857	9f.+2f. Type **844**	70	65
2858	12f.+3f. Laarne	85	80
2859	23f.+5f. Turnhout	1·50	1·40
2860	50f.+12f. Colonster	3·00	3·00

845 Miniature from "Book of Hours of Duc de Berry"

1985. Christmas.

2861	**845**	12f.+1f. multicoloured	85	80

846 King Baudouin and Queen Fabiola

1985. Royal Silver Wedding.

2862	**846**	12f. grey, blue and deep blue	90	20

847 Map and 1886 25c. Stamp

848 Giants and Belfry, Alost

1986. Centenary of First Independent State of Congo Stamp.
2863 **847** 10f. blue, grey & dp blue . . . 90 25

1986. Carnivals. Multicoloured.
2864 9f. Type **848** 45 25
2865 12f. Clown, Binche 70 20

849 Dove as Hand holding Olive Twig

850 Emblem

1986. International Peace Year.
2866 **849** 23f. multicoloured . . . 1·25 45

1986. 10th Anniv of King Baudouin Foundation.
2867 **850** 12f.+3f. blue, light blue and grey . . . . . . 1·25 1·10

851 Virgin Mary

1986. "The Mystic Lamb" (altarpiece, Brothers Van Eyck). Multicoloured.
2868 9f.+2f. Type **851** 70 65
2869 13f.+3f. Christ in Majesty . . . 1·00 1·00
2870 24f.+6f. St. John the Baptist . . . 1·75 1·60
MS2871 92 × 150 mm. 50f.+12f. The Lamb (central panel) (48 × 37 mm) . . . 7·00 7·00

852 Exhibits

1986. Stamp Day. 50th Anniv of Postal Museum, Brussels.
2872 **852** 13f. multicoloured . . . 70 10

853 Living and Dead Fish and Graph

854 Malinois Shepherd Dog

1986. Europa. Multicoloured.
2873 13f. Type **853** 70 20
2874 24f. Living and dead trees and graph . . . . 1·40 50

1986. Belgian Dogs. Multicoloured.
2875 9f. Type **854** 55 30
2876 13f. Tervuren shepherd dog . . . 85 10
2877 24f. Groenendael cattle dog . . . 1·40 50
2878 26f. Flanders cattle dog . . 1·60 50

855 St. Ludger Church, Zele

856 Boy, Broken Skateboard and Red Triangle

1986. Tourist Publicity.
2879 **855** 9f. brown and flesh . . . 50 25
2880 – 9f. red and pink 50 25
2881 – 13f. green & light green . . . 75 25
2882 – 13f. black and green . . 75 25
2883 – 13f. blue and azure . . . 75 25
2884 – 13f. brown & lt brown . . . 75 25

DESIGNS—VERT: No. 2880, Town Hall, Wavre; 2882, Chapel of Our Lady of the Dunes, Bredene. HORIZ: 2881, Water-mills, Zwalm; 2883, Chateau Licot, Viroinval; 2884, Chateau d'Eynebourg, La Calamine.

1986. "Philately for the Young". 25th International Festival of Humour, Knokke.
2885 **856** 9f. black, green & red . . 50 20

857 Constant Permeke (artist)

1986. Celebrities. Multicoloured.
2886 9f. Type **857** (birth centenary) 45 25
2887 13f. Michael Edmond de Selys-Longchamps (naturalist) 70 20
2888 24f. Felix Timmermans (writer) (birth cent) . . . 1·25 40
2889 26f. Maurice Careme (poet) . . . 1·40 40

858 Academy Building, Ghent

1986. Centenary of Royal Academy for Dutch Language and Literature.
2890 **858** 9f. blue 45 25

859 Hops, Glass of Beer and Barley

1986. Belgian Beer.
2891 **859** 13f. multicoloured . . . 70 20

860 Symbols of Provinces and National Colours

1986. 150th Anniv of Provincial Councils.
2892 **860** 13f. multicoloured . . . 65 10

861 Lenoir Hydrocarbon Carriage, 1863

1986. "Solidarity". Cars. Multicoloured.
2893 9f.+2f. Type **861** 70 70
2894 13f.+3f. Pipe de Tourisme saloon, 1911 . . . . . . 1·10 1·00
2895 24f.+6f. Minerva 22 h.p. coupe, 1930 . . . . . . 2·00 1·90
2896 26f.+6f. FN 8 cylinder saloon, 1931 . . . . . . 2·00 1·90

862 Snow Scene

1986. Christmas.
2897 **862** 13f.+1f. multicoloured . . . 90 90

863 Tree and "100"

1986. Centenaries. Multicoloured.
2898 9f. Type **863** (Textile Workers Christian Union) . . . 70 30
2899 13f. Tree and "100" (Christian Unions) . . . 65 20

864 Corneel Heymans

865 Emblem

1987. Belgian Red Cross. Nobel Physiology and Medicine Prize Winners. Each black, red and stone.
2900 13f.+3f. Type **864** . . . . 1·10 1·00
2901 24f.+6f. Albert Claude . . . 2·00 1·75

1987. "Flanders Technology International" Fair.
2902 **865** 13f. multicoloured . . . 65 15

866 Bee Orchid

868 Jakob Wiener (engraver)

867 "Waiting" (detail of mural, Gustav Klimt)

1987. European Environment Year. Multicoloured.
2903 9f.+2f. Type **866** 85 85
2904 24f.+6f. Small horse-shoe bat . . . . 2·00 1·90
2905 26f.+6f. Peregrine falcon ("Slechtvalk–Faucan Pelerin") . . . . 2·00 2·00

1987. "Europalia 87 Austria" Festival.
2906 **867** 13f. multicoloured . . . 65 10

1987. Stamp Day.
2907 **868** 13f. deep green and green 65 10

869 Penitents' Procession, Furnes

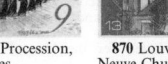

870 Louvain-la-Neuve Church (Jean Cosse)

1987. Folklore Festivals. Multicoloured.
2908 9f. Type **869** 85 35
2909 13f. "John and Alice" (play), Wavre 70 10

1987. Europa. Architecture. Multicoloured.
2910 13f. Type **870** 85 20
2911 24f. St.-Maartensdal (Regional Housing Association tower block), Louvain (Braem, de Mol and Moerkerke) . . . . . 1·10 50

871 Statue of Gretry and Stage Set

872 Virelles Lake

1987. 20th Anniv of Wallonia Royal Opera.
2912 **871** 24f. multicoloured . . . 1·40 45

1987. Tourist Publicity. Multicoloured.
2913 13f. St. Christopher's Church, Racour 85 25
2914 13f. Type **872** 85 25
2915 13f. Heimolen windmill, Keerbergen 85 25
2916 13f. Boondael Chapel . . . 85 25
2917 13f. Statue of Jan Breydel and Pieter de Coninck, Bruges 85 25

873 Rowing

1987. Centenary of Royal Belgian Rowing Association (2918) and European Volleyball Championships (2919). Multicoloured.
2918 9f. Type **873** 45 30
2919 13f. Volleyball (27 × 37 mm) . . . 70 20

874 Emblem

1987. Foreign Trade Year.
2920 **874** 13f. multicoloured . . . 65 10

875 "Leisure Time" (P. Paulus)

1987. Centenary of Belgian Social Law.
2921 **875** 26f. multicoloured . . . 1·40 45

876 Willy and Wanda (comic strip characters)

1987. "Philately for the Young".
2922 **876** 9f. multicoloured . . . . 1·60 30

878 Rixensart Castle

1987. "Solidarity". Castles. Multicoloured.
2928 9f.+2f. Type **878** 70 65
2929 13f.+3f. Westerlo 90 85
2930 26f.+5f. Fallais . . . . . . 2·00 1·90
2931 50f.+12f. Gaasbeek . . . . 3·50 3·25

879 "Madonna and Child" (Remi Lens) **880** Cross and Road

1987. Christmas.
2932 **879** 13f.+1f. multicoloured 90 90

1987. 50th Anniv of Yellow and White Cross (home nursing organization).
2933 **880** 9f.+2f. multicoloured . . 90 90

881 Newsprint ("Le Soir")

1987. Newspaper Centenaries.
2934 **881** 9f. multicoloured 45 25
2935 – 9f. black and brown . . 45 25
DESIGN—VERT: No. 2935, Type characters ("Het Laatste Nieuws" (1988)).

882 Lighthouse, "Snipe" (trawler) and Horse Rider in Sea **883** "Flanders Alive" (cultural activities campaign)

1988. The Sea. Multicoloured.
2936 10f. Type **882** 60 55
2937 10f. "Asannot" (trawler) and people playing on beach 60 55
2938 10f. Cross-channel ferry, yacht and bathing huts . . 60 55
2939 10f. Container ship, spotted redshank and oystercatcher 60 55
Nos. 2936/9 were issued together, se-tenant, forming a composite design.

1988. Regional Innovations.
2940 **883** 13f. multicoloured . . . 70 20
2941 – 13f. black, yellow & red 70 20
DESIGN: No. 2941, "Operation Athena" emblem (technological advancement in Wallonia).

884 19th-century Postman (after James Thiriar) **885** "Bengale Triomphant"

1988. Stamp Day.
2942 **884** 13f. brown and cream 65 10

1988. Philatelic Promotion Fund. Illustrations from "60 Roses for a Queen" by Pierre-Joseph Redoute (1st series). Multicoloured.
2943 13f.+3f. Type **885** . . . . 1·25 1·25
2944 24f.+6f. "Centfeuille cristata" . . . . 2·00 1·90
MS2945 150 × 100 mm. 50f.+12f. White tea rose . . . . . . 6·25 6·25
See also Nos. 2979/**MS**2981, 3009/**MS**3011 and **MS**3025.

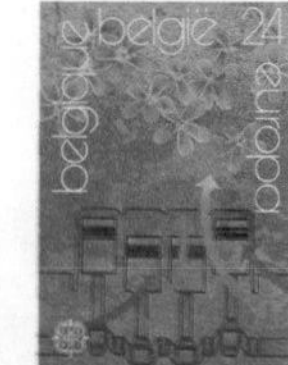

886 Non-polluting Motor

1988. Europa. Transport and Communications. Multicoloured.
2946 13f. Dish aerial 90 20
2947 24f. Type **886** . . . . . . 1·40 60

887 Table Tennis

1988. Olympic Games, Seoul. Multicoloured.
2948 9f.+2f. Type **887** 90 90
2949 13f.+3f. Cycling . . . . . . 1·25 1·25
MS2950 125 × 85 mm. 50f.+12f. Running . . . . 6·75 6·50

888 Amay Tower **889** Monnet

1988. Tourist Publicity.
2951 **888** 9f. black and brown . . 55 25
2952 – 9f. black and blue . . . 55 25
2953 – 9f. black, green and pink 55 25
2954 – 13f. black and pink . . . 80 20
2955 – 13f. black and grey . . . 80 20
DESIGNS—VERT: No. 2952, Lady of Hanswijk Basilica, Malines; 2954, Old Town Hall and village pump, Peer. HORIZ: No. 2953, St. Sernin's Church, Waimes; 2955, Basilica of Our Lady of Bon Secours, Peruwelz.

1988. Birth Centenary of Jean Monnet (statesman).
2956 **889** 13f. black and cream . . 65 20

890 Tapestry (detail) and Academy Building **891** Antwerp Ethnographical Museum Exhibits

1988. 50th Annivs of Royal Belgian Academy of Medicine (2957) and Royal Belgian Academy of Sciences, Literature and Fine Arts (2958). Multicoloured.
2957 9f. Type **890** 45 25
2958 9f. Symbols of Academy and building 45 25

1988. Cultural Heritage. Multicoloured.
2959 9f. Type **891** 45 25
2960 13f. Tomb of Lord Gilles Othon and Jacqueline de Lalaing, St. Martin's Church, Trazegnies . . . 70 20
2961 24f. Organ, St. Bartholomew's Church, Geraardsbergen 1·40 55
2962 26f. St. Hadelin's reliquary, St. Martin's Church, Vise 1·75 45

892 Spirou (comic strip character) and Stamp

1988. "Philately for the Young". 50th Anniv of "Spirou" (comic).
2963 **892** 9f. multicoloured . . . . 1·40 35

893 Jacques Brel (songwriter)

1988. "Solidarity". Death Anniversaries. Mult.
2964 9f.+2f. Type **893** (10th) . . 1·25 1·25
2965 13f.+3f. Jef Denyn (carilloner) (47th) . . . . 1·25 1·25
2966 26f.+6f. Fr. Ferdinand Verbiest (astronomer) (300th) . . . . 2·00 1·90

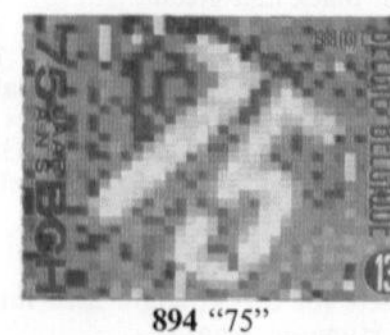

894 "75"

1988. 75th Anniv of Belgian Giro Bank.
2967 **894** 13f. multicoloured . . . 70 20

895 Winter Scene

1988. Christmas.
2968 **895** 9f. multicoloured 50 35

896 Standard Bearer and Guards of Royal Mounted Escort **897** Wooden Press, 1600

1988. 50th Anniv of Royal Mounted Escort.
2969 **896** 13f. multicoloured . . . 70 20

1988. Printing Presses.
2970 **897** 9f. black, pink and blue 45 25
2971 – 24f. brown, pink and deep brown . . . . . 1·25 50
2972 – 26f. green, pink and light green . . . . 1·40 50
DESIGNS—VERT: 24f. 18th-cent Stanhope metal letterpress. HORIZ: 26f. 19th-cent Krause lithographic press.

898 "Crucifixion of Christ" (detail, Rogier van der Weyden)

1989. Belgian Red Cross. Paintings. Mult.
2973 9f.+2f. Type **898** 90 90
2974 13f.+3f. "Virgin and Child" (Gerard David) . . . . . 1·25 1·25
2975 24f.+6f. "The Good Samaritan" (detail, Denis van Alsloot) . . . . . . 2·00 1·90

899 Marche en Famenne

1989. Lace-making Towns.
2976 **899** 9f. green, black & brown 55 35
2977 – 13f. blue, black & grey 70 25
2978 – 13f. red, black & grey . . 70 25
DESIGNS: No. 2977, Bruges; 2978, Brussels.

1989. Philatelic Promotion Fund. "60 Roses for a Queen" by Pierre-Joseph Redoute (2nd series). As T **885**. Multicoloured.
2979 13f.+5f. "Centfeuille unique melee de rouge" . . . . 1·25 1·25
2980 24f.+6f. "Bengale a grandes feuilles" . . . . 2·00 1·90
MS2981 150 × 100 mm. 50f.+17f. "Aime vibere" . . . . 6·50 6·50

900 Post-chaise and Mail Coach

1989. Stamp Day.
2982 **900** 13f. yellow, black & brn 70 20

901 Marbles **902** Palette on Column

1989. Europa. Children's Games and Toys. Multicoloured.
2983 13f. Type **901** 90 25
2984 24f. Jumping-jack . . . . . 1·75 80

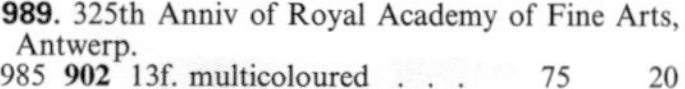

1989. 325th Anniv of Royal Academy of Fine Arts, Antwerp.
2985 **902** 13f. multicoloured . . . 75 20

903 Brussels (½-size illustration)

1989. 3rd Direct Elections to European Parliament.
2986 **903** 13f. multicoloured . . . 75 25

904 Hand (detail, "Creation of Adam", Michelangelo) **905** St. Tillo's Church, Izegem

1989. Bicentenary of French Declaration of Rights of Man.
2987 **904** 13f. black, red and blue 75 25

1989. Tourist Publicity. Multicoloured.
2988 9f. Type **905** 55 35
2989 9f. Logne Castle, Ferrieres (vert) 55 35
2990 13f. Antoing Castle (vert) 85 25
2991 13f. St. Laurentius's Church, Lokeren (vert) 85 25

906 Mallard

1989. Ducks. Multicoloured.
2992 13f. Type **906** . . . . . . 1·10 50
2993 13f. Green-winged teal ("Sarcelle d'Hiver") . . . 1·10 50
2994 13f. Common shoveler ("Canard Souchet") . . . 1·10 50
2995 13f. Pintail ("Canard Pilet") 1·10 50

907 "Shogun Uesugi Shigefusa" (Kamakura period wood figure)

1989. "Europalia 89 Japan" Festival.
2996 **907** 24f. multicoloured . . . 1·40 45

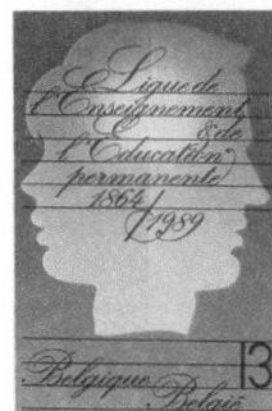

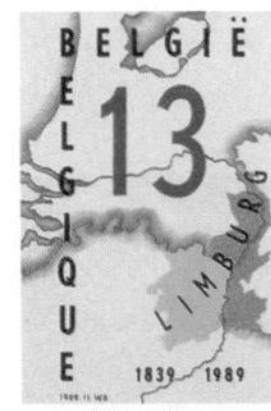

908 Profiles **909** Map

1989. 125th Anniv of League of Teaching and Permanent Education.
2997 **908** 13f. multicoloured . . . 70 15

1989. 150th Anniv of Division of Limburg between Netherlands and Belgium.
2998 **909** 13f. multicoloured . . . 70 15

910 Nibbs (comic strip character) **911** Flower Beds in Greenhouse

1989. "Philately for the Young".
2999 **910** 9f. multicoloured . . . . 1·25 35

1989. "Solidarity". Royal Greenhouses, Laeken. Multicoloured.
3000 9f.+3f. Statue and greenhouses (horiz) . . . 90 85
3001 13f.+4f. Type **911** . . . . 1·00 4·00
3002 24f.+5f. External view of greenhouse . . . . 1·75 1·60
3003 26f.+6f. Trees in greenhouse 2·00 1·75

912 Treble Clef

1989. 50th Anniv of Queen Elisabeth Musical Chapel, Waterloo.
3004 **912** 24f.+6f. multicoloured 2·00 1·90

913 Army Musicians

1989. Christmas. Centenary of Salvation Army in Belgium.
3005 **913** 9f. multicoloured 50 20

914 Fr. Damien and Church **915** Fr. Daens

1989. Death Cent of Fr. Damien (missionary).
3006 **914** 24f. multicoloured . . . 1·75 45

1989. 150th Birth Anniv of Fr. Adolf Daens (social reformer).
3007 **915** 9f. turquoise and green 50 20

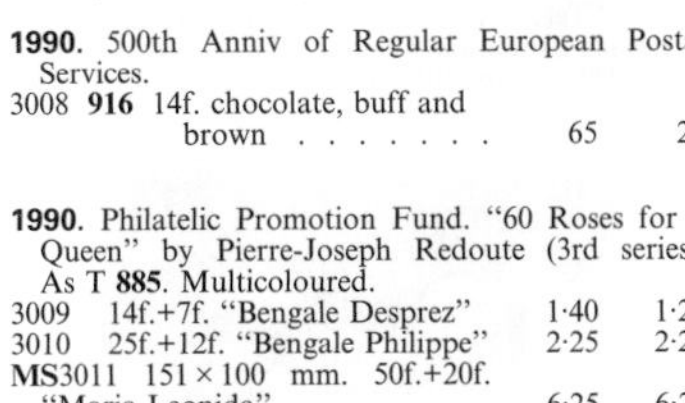

916 "Courier" (Albrecht Durer) **917** "Iris florentina"

1990. 500th Anniv of Regular European Postal Services.
3008 **916** 14f. chocolate, buff and brown 65 20

1990. Philatelic Promotion Fund. "60 Roses for a Queen" by Pierre-Joseph Redoute (3rd series). As T **885**. Multicoloured.
3009 14f.+7f. "Bengale Desprez" 1·40 1·25
3010 25f.+12f. "Bengale Philippe" 2·25 2·25
MS3011 151 × 100 mm. 50f.+20f. "Maria Leonida" . . . . . . 6·25 6·25

1990. Ghent Flower Show. Multicoloured.
3012 10f. Type **917** 55 35
3013 14f. "Cattleya harrisoniana" 85 20
3014 14f. "Lilium bulbiferum" . . 85 20

918 Emilienne Brunfaut (women's rights activist)

1990. International Women's Day.
3015 **918** 25f. red and black . . . 1·40 45

919 Special Olympics **921** "Postman Roulin" (Vincent van Gogh)

920 Water, Tap and Heart

1990. Sporting Events. Multicoloured.
3016 10f. Type **919** 55 25
3017 14f. Football (World Cup football championship, Italy) 85 15
3018 25f. Disabled pictogram and ball (Gold Cup wheelchair basketball championship, Bruges) . . . . 1·40 45

1990. 75th Anniv of Foundation of National Water Supply Society (predecessor of present water-supply companies).
3019 **920** 14f. multicoloured . . . 80 20

1990. Stamp Day.
3020 **921** 14f. multicoloured . . . 80 20

922 Worker and Crowd **923** Liege I Post Office

1990. Centenary of Labour Day.
3021 **922** 25f. brown, pink & black 1·40 50

1990. Europa. Post Office Buildings.
3022 – 14f. black and blue . . . 90 20
3023 **923** 25f. black and red . . . 2·00 50
DESIGN—HORIZ: 14f. Ostend I Post Office.

924 Monument of the Lys, Courtrai

1990. 50th Anniv of the 18 Days Campaign (resistance to German invasion).
3024 **924** 14f. black, yellow & red 85 20

1990. "Belgica 90" International Stamp Exhibition, Brussels. "60 Roses for a Queen" by Pierre-Joseph Rerdoute (4th series). Sheet 189 × 120 mm containing vert designs as T **885**. Multicoloured.
MS3025 14f. Tricoloured rose; 14f. "Belle Rubanee"; 14f. "Mycrophylla"; 25f. "Amelie"; 25f. "Adelaide"; 25f. "Helene" (sold at 220f.) . . . . 35·00 35·00

925 Battle Scene (⅗-size illustration)

1990. 175th Anniv of Battle of Waterloo.
3026 **925** 25f. multicoloured . . . 1·60 1·25

926 Berendrecht Lock, Antwerp **927** King Baudouin

1990. Tourist Publicity. Multicoloured.
3027 10f. Type **926** 65 30
3028 10f. Procession of Bayard Steed, Termonde 65 30
3029 14f. St. Rolende's March, Gerpinnes (vert) 80 25
3030 14f. Lommel (1000th anniv) 80 25
3031 14f. St. Clement's Church, Watermael 80 25

1990.
3032 **927** 14f. multicoloured . . . 90 20

928 Eurasian Perch

1990. Fishes. Multicoloured.
3033 14f. Type **928** . . . . . . 1·75 60
3034 14f. Eurasian minnow ("Vairon") . . . . 1·75 60
3035 14f. European bitterling ("Bouviere") . . . . . . 1·75 60
3036 14f. Three-spined stickle-back ("Epinoche") . . . 1·75 60

929 Orchestra and Children (½-size illustration)

1990. "Solidarity". Multicoloured.
3037 10f.+2f. Type **929** (50th anniv of Jeunesses Musicales) . . . . 1·75 1·60
3038 14f.+3f. Count of Egmont (16th-century campaigner for religious tolerance) and Beethoven (composer of "Egmont" overture) . . 2·10 2·00
3039 25f.+6f. Jozef Cantre (sculptor) and sculptures (birth centenary) . . . . 2·75 2·50

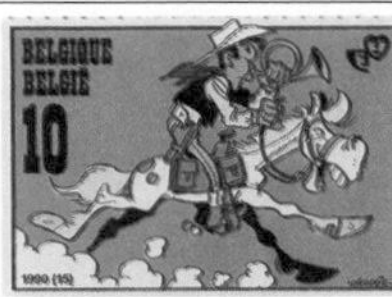

930 Lucky Luke (comic strip character)

1990. "Philately for the Young".
3040 **930** 10f. multicoloured . . . 1·25 35

931 St. Bernard

1990. 900th Birth Anniv of St. Bernard (Abbot of Clairvaux and Church mediator).
3041 **931** 25f. black and flesh . . . 1·40 45

932 "Pepingen, Winter 1977" (Jozef Lucas)

1990. Christmas.
3042 **932** 10f. multicoloured . . . 55 25

933 "Self-portrait"

1990. 300th Death Anniv of David Teniers, the Younger (painter). Multicoloured.
3043 10f. Type **933** 55 25
3044 14f. "Dancers" 85 20
3045 25f. "Peasants playing Bowls outside Village Inn" . . . 1·40 45

934 King Baudouin and Queen Fabiola (photograph by Valeer Vanbeckbergen)

1990. Royal 30th Wedding Anniversary.
3046 **934** 50f.+15f. mult . . . . . 6·50 7·00

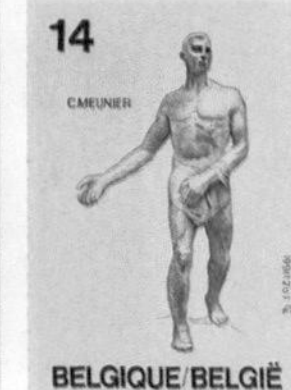

935 "Temptation of St. Anthony" (detail, Hieronymus Bosch) **936** "The Sower" (detail of "Monument to Labour", Brussels) (Constantin Meunier)

1991. Belgian Red Cross. Paintings. Mult.
3047 14f.+3f. Type **935** . . . . 2·10 1·90
3048 25f.+6f. "The Annunciation" (detail, Dirck Bouts) . . . . . . 3·00 3·00

1991. 19th-Century Sculpture.
3049 **936** 14f. black & cinnamon 85 25
3050 – 25f. black and blue . . . 1·40 45

DESIGN: 25f. Detail of Brabo Fountain, Antwerp (Jef Lambeaux).

937 Rhythmic Gymnastics (European Youth Olympic Days, Brussels)

1991. Sports Meetings.
3051 **937** 10f. grey, mauve & blk . . . 55 25
3052 – 10f. grey, green & black . . . 55 25
DESIGN: No. 3052, Korfball (Third World Championship, Belgium).

938 New Stamp Printing Office, Malines (Hugo van Hoecke)

1991. Stamp Day.
3053 **938** 14f. multicoloured . . . 80 20

939 Cogwheels

1991. Centenary of Liberal Trade Union.
3054 **939** 25f. blue, light blue and deep blue . . . . . . 1·40 50

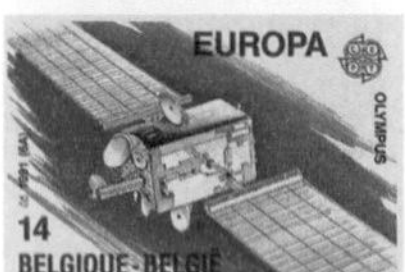

940 "Olympus 1" Communications Satellite

1991. Europa. Europe in Space. Multicoloured.
3055 14f. Type **940** . . . . . . 1·40 20
3056 25f. "Ariane 5" rocket carrying space shuttle "Hermes" . . . . 2·25 50

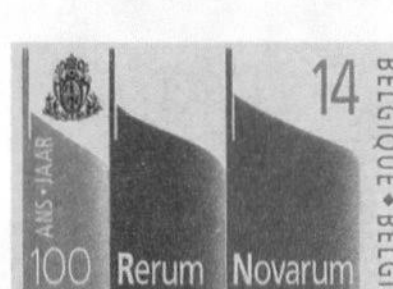

941 Leo XIII's Arms and Standard, and Christian Labour Movement Banners

1991. Centenary of "Rerum Novarum" (encyclical letter from Pope Leo XIII on workers' rights).
3057 **941** 14f. multicoloured . . . 80 20

942 "Isabella of Portugal and Philip the Good" (anon)

1991. "Europalia 91 Portugal" Festival.
3058 **942** 14f. multicoloured . . . 80 20

943 Neptune Grottoes, Couvin

1991. Tourist Publicity. Multicoloured.
3059 14f. Type **943** 80 20
3060 14f. Dieleghem Abbey, Jette 80 20
3061 14f. Niel Town Hall (vert) 80 20
3062 14f. Hautes Fagnes nature reserve 80 20
3063 14f. Giant Rolarius, Roeselare (vert) 80 20

944 King Baudouin (photograph by Dimitri Ardelean)

1991. 60th Birthday (1990) and 40th Anniv of Accession to Throne of King Baudouin.
3064 **944** 14f. multicoloured . . . 1·50 20

945 Academy Building, Caduceus and Leopold I

1991. 150th Anniv of Royal Academy of Medicine.
3065 **945** 10f. multicoloured . . . 55 25

946 "The English Coast at Dover" **948** Hands reaching through Bars

947 Death Cap

1991. 61st Death Anniv of Alfred Finch (painter and ceramic artist).
3066 **946** 25f. multicoloured . . . 1·40 50

1991. Fungi. Multicoloured.
3067 14f. Type **947** . . . . . . 1·50 65
3068 14f. The Blusher (inscr "Golmotte") . . . . . . 1·50 65
3069 14f. Flaky-stemmed witches' mushroom (inscr "Bolet a pied rouge") . . . . . . 1·50 65
3070 14f. "Hygrocybe persistens" (inscr "Hygrophore jaune conique") . . . . 1·50 65

1991. 30th Anniv of Amnesty International (3071) and 11th Anniv of Belgian Branch of Medecins sans Frontieres (3072). Multicoloured.
3071 25f. Type **948** . . . . . . 1·40 50
3072 25f. Doctor examining baby 1·40 55

1991. Birds (2nd series). As T **841**. Mult.
3073 50c. Goldcrest ("Roitelet Huppe") 10 10
3074 1f. Redpoll ("Sizerin Flamme") 15 10
3075 2f. Blackbird ("Merle Noir") 15 10
3076 3f. Reed bunting ("Bruant des Roseaux") 30 10
3077 4f. Pied wagtail ("Bergeronette Grise") 30 10
3078 5f. Barn swallow ("Hirondelle de Cheminee") 30 10
3079 5f.50 Jay ("Geai des Chenes") 40 20
3080 6f. White-throated dipper ("Cincle Plongeur") . . 40 20
3081 6f.50 Sedge-warbler ("Phragmite des Jones") 50 20
3082 7f. Golden oriole ("Loriot") 50 20
3083 8f. Great tit ("Mesange Charbonniere") 65 20
3084 9f. Song thrush ("Grive Musicienne") 65 20
3085 10f. Western greenfinch ("Verdier") 65 20
3086 11f. Winter wren ("Troglodyte Mignon") 85 20
3087 13f. House sparrow ("Moineau Domestique") 85 20
3088 14f. Willow warbler ("Pouillot Fitis") . . . . 1·10 20
3088a 16f. Bohemian waxwing ("Jaseur Boreal") . . . 1·10 20

949 Exhibition Emblem

1991. "Telecom 91" International Telecommunications Exhibition, Geneva.
3089 **949** 14f. multicoloured . . . 75 20

950 Blake and Mortimer in "The Yellow Mark" (Edgar P. Jacobs)

1991. "Philately for the Young". Comic Strips. Multicoloured.
3090 14f. Type **950** . . . . . . 1·50 70
3091 14f. Cori the ship boy in "The Ill-fated Voyage" (Bob de Moor) . . . . . 1·50 70
3092 14f. "Cities of the Fantastic" (Francois Schuiten) . . . . 1·50 70
3093 14f. "Boule and Bill" (Jean Roba) . . . . 1·50 70

951 Charles Dekeukeleire

1991. "Solidarity". Film Makers.
3094 **951** 10f.+2f. black, brown and green 90 85
3095 – 14f.+3f. black, orange and brown . . . . . 1·40 1·25
3096 – 25f.+6f. black, ochre and brown . . . . 2·25 2·25
DESIGNS: 14f. Jacques Ledoux; 25f. Jacques Feyder.

952 Printing Press forming "100" ("Gazet van Antwerpen")

1991. Newspaper Centenaries. Multicoloured.
3097 **952** 10f. black, lt grn & grn 55 25
3098 – 10f. yellow, blue & blk 55 25
DESIGN: No. 3098, Cancellation on "stamp" ("Het Volk").

953 "Our Lady rejoicing in the Child" (icon, Chevetogne Abbey) **955** Speed Skating

954 Mozart and Score

1991. Christmas.
3099 **953** 10f. multicoloured . . . 55 25

1991. Death Bicentenary of Wolfgang Amadeus Mozart (composer).
3100 **954** 25f. purple, bl & ultram 1·60 80

1992. Olympic Games, Albertville and Barcelona. Multicoloured.
3101 10f.+2f. Type **955** . . . . 1·00 1·00
3102 10f.+2f. Baseball . . . . . 1·00 1·10
3103 14f.+3f. Tennis (horiz) . . . 1·40 2·00
3104 25f.+6f. Clay-pigeon shooting . . . . 2·50 2·25

956 Fire Hose and Service Emblem **957** Flames and Silhouette of Man

1992. Fire Service.
3105 **956** 14f. multicoloured . . . 75 20

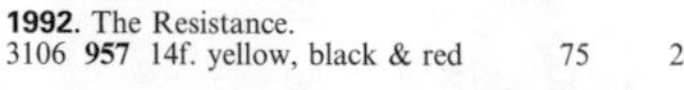

1992. The Resistance.
3106 **957** 14f. yellow, black & red 75 20

958 Tapestry and Carpet **959** Belgian Pavilion and Exhibition Emblem

1992. Prestige Occupations. Multicoloured.
3107 10f. Type **958** 55 25
3108 14f. Chef's hat and cutlery (10th anniv (1991) of Association of Belgian Master Chefs) 75 20
3109 27f. Diamond and "100" (centenary (1993) of Antwerp Diamond Club) 1·75 40

1992. "Expo '92" World's Fair, Seville.
3110 **959** 14f. multicoloured . . . 75 20

960 King Baudouin **961**

1992.
3111 **960** 15f. red 75 10
3115 28f. green . . . . 1·75 50
3120 **961** 100f. green . . . . . . 5·50 65

962 Van Noten at Work **963** "White Magic No. VI"

1992. Stamp Day. 10th Death Anniv of Jean van Noten (stamp designer).
3124 **962** 15f. black and red . . . 80 20

1992. Original Art Designs for Stamps. Mult.
3125 15f. Type **963** 80 25
3126 15f. "Colours" (horiz) . . . 80 25

964 Compass Rose, Setting Sun and Harbour

1992. Europa. 500th Anniv of Discovery of America. Multicoloured.
3127 15f. Type **964** . . . . . . 1·40 25
3128 28f. Globe and astrolabe forming "500" . . . . . 2·75 65

965 Faces of Different Colours

1992. Anti-racism.
3129 **965** 15f. grey, black & pink 75 20

966 "The Hamlet" (Jacob Smits)

1992. Belgian Paintings in Orsay Museum, Paris. Multicoloured.
3130 11f. Type **966** 55 30
3131 15f. "The Bath" (Alfred Stevens) 90 20
3132 30f. "Man at the Helm" (Theo van Rysselberghe) 1·75 45

967 Proud Margaret **968** Mannekin-Pis, Brussels

1992. Folk Tales. Multicoloured.
3133 11f.+2f. Type **967** . . . . 1·25 1·10
3134 15f.+3f. Witches ("Les Macrales") . . . . 1·75 1·60
3135 28f.+6f. Reynard the fox . . 2·75 2·50

1992. Tourist Publicity. Multicoloured.
3136 15f. Type **968** 80 25
3137 15f. Former Landcommandery of Teutonic Order, Alden Biesen (now Flemish cultural centre) (horiz) . . 80 25
3138 15f. Andenne (1300th anniv) 80 25
3139 15f. Carnival revellers on Fools' Monday, Renaix (horiz) 80 25
3140 15f. Great Procession (religious festival), Tournai (horiz) 80 25

969 European Polecat

1992. Mammals. Multicoloured.
3141 15f. Type **969** . . . . . . 1·40 70
3142 15f. Eurasian red squirrel 1·40 70
3143 15f. Eurasian hedgehog . . 1·40 70
3144 15f. Common dormouse . . 1·40 70

970 Henri van der Noot, Jean van der Meersch and Jean Vonck

1992. 203rd Anniv of Brabant Revolution.
3145 **970** 15f. multicoloured . . . 80 20

971 Arms of Thurn and Taxis **972** Gaston Lagaffe (cartoon character)

1992. 500th Anniv of Mention of Thurn and Taxis Postal Services in Lille Account Books.
3146 **971** 15f. multicoloured . . . 80 20

1992. "Philately for the Young".
3147 **972** 15f. multicoloured . . . 1·10 20

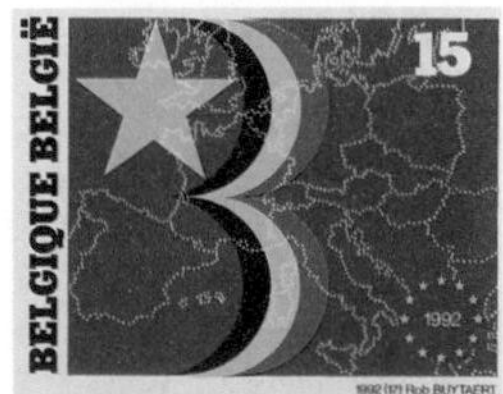

973 Star, "B" and Map

1992. European Single Market.
3148 **973** 15f. multicoloured . . . 80 20

974 Okapi **975** "Place Royale in Winter" (Luc de Decker)

1992. 150th Anniv of Antwerp Zoo. Mult.
3149 15f. Type **974** 80 25
3150 30f. Golden-headed tamarin 1·75 40

1992. Christmas.
3151 **975** 11f. multicoloured . . . 55 25

976 "Man with Pointed Hat" (Adriaen Brouwer)

1993. Belgian Red Cross. Paintings. Mult.
3152 15f.+3f. Type **976** . . . . 1·60 1·60
3153 28f.+7f. "Nereid and Triton" (Peter Paul Rubens) (horiz) . . . . . 3·25 3·25

977 Council of Leptines, 743

1993. Historical Events. Multicoloured.
3154 11f. Type **977** 55 30
3155 15f. Queen Beatrix and King Matthias I Corvinus of Hungary (detail of "Missale Romanum") (77 × 24 mm) 90 20
3156 30f. Battle scene (Battles of Neerwinden, 1673 and 1773) . . . . 1·75 40
MS3157 105 × 155 mm. 28f. Illustration from Matthias I Corvinus's *Missale Romanum*, 1485 (54 × 39 mm) . . . . . . 1·60 1·60

978 Town Hall

1993. Antwerp, European City of Culture. Mult.
3158 15f. Panorama of Antwerp (76 × 24 mm) 90 20
3159 15f. Type **978** 90 20
3160 15f. "Study of Women's Heads and Male Torso" (Jacob Jordaens) 90 20
3161 15f. St. Job's altarpiece, Schoonbroek 90 20
3162 15f. "Angels" (stained glass window by Eugeen Yoors, Mother of God Chapel, Marie-Josee Institute, Elisabethville) (vert) . . . 90 20

979 1893 2f. Stamp **980** "Florence 1960" (Gaston Bertrand)

1993. Stamp Day.
3163 **979** 15f. multicoloured . . . 75 20

1993. Europa. Contemporary Art. Multicoloured.
3164 15f. Type **980** 70 20
3165 28f. "The Gig" (Constant Permeke) . . . . 1·50 55

981 Red Admiral ("Vanessa atalanta")

1993. Butterflies. Multicoloured.
3166 15f. Type **981** 75 30
3167 15f. Purple emperor ("Apatura iris") 75 30
3168 15f. Peacock ("Inachis io") 75 30
3169 15f. Small tortoiseshell ("Aglais urticae") 75 30

982 Knot **983** Mayan Warrior (statuette)

1993. 150th Anniv of Alumni of Free University of Brussels Association.
3170 **982** 15f. blue and black . . . 75 25

1993. "Europalia 93 Mexico" Festival.
3171 **983** 15f. multicoloured . . . 75 20

984 Ommegang, Brussels

1993. Folklore Festivals. Multicoloured.
3172 11f. Type **984** 65 30
3173 15f. Royale Moncrabeau, Namur 75 20
3174 28f. Stilt-walkers, Merchtem (vert) . . . . 1·40 50

985 La Hulpe Castle

1993. Tourist Publicity.
3175 **985** 15f. black and blue . . . 75 20
3176 – 15f. black and lilac . . . 75 20
3177 – 15f. black and grey . . . 75 20
3178 – 15f. black and pink . . . 75 20
3179 – 15f. black and green . . 75 20
DESIGNS—HORIZ: No. 3176, Cortewalle Castle, Beveren; 3177, Jehay Castle; 3179, Raeren Castle. VERT: No. 3178, Arenberg Castle, Heverlee.

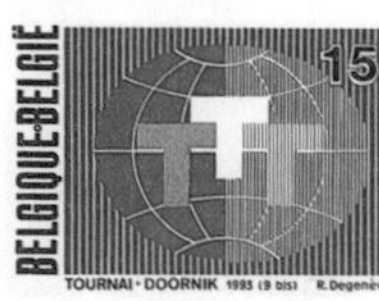

986 Emblem

1993. 2nd International Triennial Textile Exhibition, Tournai.
3180 **986** 15f. blue, red and black 75 20

987 Presidency Emblem

1993. Belgian Presidency of European Community Council.
3181 **987** 15f. multicoloured . . . 75 20

988 Magritte **989** King Baudouin

1993. 25th Death Anniv (1992) of Rene Magritte (artist).
3182 **988** 30f. multicoloured . . . 1·50 50

1993. King Baudouin Commemoration.
3183 **989** 15f. black and blue . . . 90 20

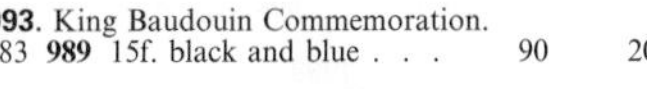

990 Red and White Cat

1993. Cats. Multicoloured.
3184 15f. Type **990** . . . . . . 1·00 50
3185 15f. Tabby and white cat standing on rock . . . . 1·00 50
3186 15f. Silver tabby lying on wall . . . . 1·00 50
3187 15f. Tortoiseshell and white cat sitting by gardening tools . . . . 1·00 50

991 Highlighted Cancer Cell **992** Frontispiece

1993. Anti-cancer Campaign.

3188 **991** 15f.+3f. multicoloured 1·40 1·25

1993. 450th Anniv of "De Humani Corporis Fabrica" (treatise on human anatomy) by Andreas Vesalius.

3189 **992** 15f. black, brown & red 75 20

993 Natacha (cartoon character)

1993. "Philately for the Young".

3190 **993** 15f. multicoloured . . . 1·00 25

994 Sun's Rays

995 "Madonna and Child" (statue, Our Lady of the Chapel, Brussels)

1993. 50th Anniv of Publication of "Le Faux Soir" (resistance newspaper).

3191 **994** 11f. multicoloured . . . 55 40

1993. Christmas.

3192 **995** 11f. multicoloured . . . 55 25

996 Child looking at Globe

1993. Children's Town Councils.

3193 **996** 15f. multicoloured . . . 80 20

997 King Albert II

998 King Albert II

1993.

3194 **997** 16f. multicoloured . . . 1·10 10

3195 16f. turquoise and blue 90 10

3196 20f. brown and stone . . 90 10

3197 30f. purple and mauve 1·25 20

3198 32f. orange and yellow 1·10 20

3199 40f. red and mauve . . . 2·00 20

3200 50f. myrtle and green . . 3·25 25

3201 **998** 100f. multicoloured . . . 4·50 35

3202 200f. multicoloured . . . 9·00 85

999 "Ma Toute Belle" (Serge Vandercam)

1000 Olympic Flames and Rings

1994. Painters' Designs. Multicoloured.

3210 16f. Type **999** 75 20

3211 16f. "The Malleable Darkness" (Octave Landuyt) (horiz) 75 20

1994. Sports. Multicoloured.

3212 16f.+3f. Type **1000** (cent of International Olympic Committee) . . . . . . 1·50 1·50

3213 16f.+3f. Footballers (World Cup Football Championship, U.S.A.) 1·50 1·50

3214 16f.+3f. Skater (Winter Olympic Games, Lillehammer, Norway) . . 1·50 1·50

1001 Hanriot HD-1

1002 Masthead of "Le Jour-Le Courrier" (centenary)

1994. Biplanes. Multicoloured.

3215 13f. Type **1001** 75 30

3216 15f. Spad XIII 90 25

3217 30f. Schrenck FBA.H flying boat . . . . 1·50 50

3218 32f. Stampe SV-4B . . . . 1·75 45

1994. Newspaper Anniversaries. Multicoloured.

3219 16f. Type **1002** 85 20

3220 16f. Masthead of "La Wallonie" (75th anniv) (horiz) 85 20

1003 "Fall of the Golden Calf" (detail, Fernand Allard l'Olivier)

1994. Centenary of Charter of Quaregnon (social charter).

3221 **1003** 16f. multicoloured . . . 85 20

1004 1912 5f. Stamp

1994. Stamp Day. 60th Death Anniv of King Albert I.

3222 **1004** 16f. purple, mauve & bl 85 20

1005 Reconciliation of Duke John I and Arnold, Squire of Wezemaal

1994. 700th Death Anniv of John I, Duke of Brabant. Illustrations from 15th-century "Brabantse Yeesten". Multicoloured.

3223 13f. Type **1005** 70 25

3224 16f. Tournament at wedding of his son John to Margaret of York, 1290 85 20

3225 30f. Battle of Woeringen (77×25 mm) . . . . . . 1·75 55

1006 Georges Lemaitre (formulator of expanding Universe and of "big bang" theory)

1008 St. Peter's Church, Bertem

1007 Father Damien (missionary and leprosy worker)

1994. Europa. Discoveries and Inventions. Mult.

3226 16f. Type **1006** 70 20

3227 30f. Gerardus Mercator (inventor of Mercator projection in cartography) 1·50 50

1994. Visit of Pope John Paul II. Mult.

3228 16f. Type **1007** (beatification) 85 20

3229 16f. St. Mutien-Marie (5th anniv of canonization) . . 85 20

1994. Tourist Publicity. Multicoloured.

3230 16f. Type **1008** 85 20

3231 16f. St. Bavo's Church, Kanegem (vert) 85 20

3232 16f. Royal St. Mary's Church, Schaarbeek . . . 85 20

3233 16f. St. Gery's Church, Aubechies 85 20

3234 16f. Sts. Peter and Paul's Church, St.-Severin en Condroz (vert) 85 20

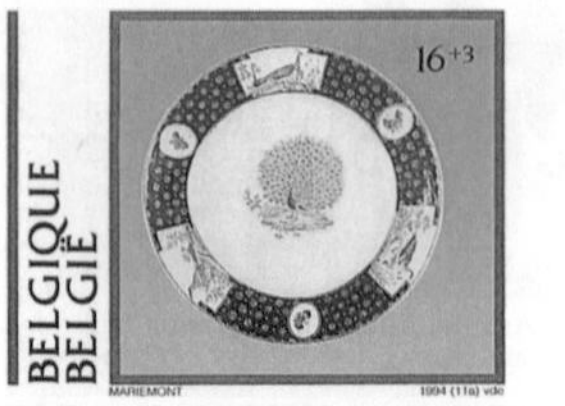

1009 Tournai Porcelain Plate from Duke of Orleans Service (Mariemont Museum)

1994. Museum Exhibits. Multicoloured.

3235 16f.+3f. Type **1009** . . . . 1·40 1·25

3236 16f.+3f. Etterbeek porcelain coffee cup and saucer (Louvain Municipal Museum) . . . . 1·40 1·25

MS3237 125×90 mm. 50f.+11f. Delft containers (Pharmacy Museum, Maaseik . . . . . . 6·25 6·25

1010 Guillame Lekeu (composer)

1994. Anniversaries. Multicoloured.

3238 16f. Type **1010** (death cent) 75 20

3239 16f. Detail of painting by Hans Memling (500th death anniv) 75 20

1011 Generals Crerar, Montgomery and Bradley and Allied Troops (½-size illustration)

1994. 50th Anniv of Liberation.

3240 **1011** 16f. multicoloured . . . 90 30

1012 Marsh Marigold ("Caltha palustris")

1994. Flowers. Multicoloured.

3241 16f. Type **1012** . . . . . . 1·10 55

3242 16f. White helleborine ("Cephalanthera damasonium") . . . . . . 1·10 55

3243 16f. Sea bindweed ("Calystegia soldanella") 1·10 55

3244 16f. Broad-leaved helleborine ("Epipactis helleborine") . . . . 1·10 55

1013 Cubitus (cartoon character)

1014 Simenon and Bridge of Arches, Liege

1994. "Philately for the Young".

3245 **1013** 16f. multicoloured . . . 70 25

1994. 5th Death Anniv of Georges Simenon (novelist).

3246 **1014** 16f. multicoloured . . . 70 20

The depiction of the bridge alludes to Simenon's first novel "Au Pont des Arches".

1015 Deaf Man and Butterfly

1994. "Solidarity".

3247 **1015** 16f.+3f. mult . . . . . 1·00 1·00

1016 Santa Claus on Rooftop

1994. Christmas.

3248 **1016** 13f. multicoloured . . . 70 25

1017 Field and Flax Knife (Flax Museum, Courtrai)

1995. Museums. Multicoloured.

3249 16f.+3f. Type **1017** 90 95

3250 16f.+3f. River and pump (Water and Fountain Museum, Genval) 90 95

MS3251 125×90 mm. 34f.+6f. Mask (International Carnival and Mask Museum, Binche) . . . . . . 2·50 2·50

The premium was for the promotion of philately.

1018 Emblem

1995. Anniversaries. Anniversary emblems.

3252 **1018** 16f. red, blue & black 85 20

3253 – 16f. multicoloured . . . 85 20

3254 – 16f. multicoloured . . . 85 20

3255 – 16f. red, black & brown 85 20

ANNIVERSARIES: No. 3252, 50th anniv of August Vermeylen Fund; 3253, Centenary of Touring Club of Belgium; 3254, Centenary of Federation of Belgian Enterprises; 3255, 50th anniv of Social Security in Belgium.

1019 "Hibiscus rosa-sinensis"

1995. Ghent Flower Show. Multicoloured.

3256 13f. Type **1019** 70 65

3257 16f. Azalea 90 20

3258 30f. Fuchsia . . . . 1·50 40

1020 Crossword Puzzle

1021 Frans de Troyer (promoter of thematic philately)

1995. Games and Pastimes. Multicoloured.

3259 13f. Type **1020** 70 20

3260 16f. King (chess piece) . . . 85 25

3261 30f. Scrabble . . . . 1·50 40
3262 34f. Queen (playing cards) 1·75 65

1995. Post Day.
3263 **1021** 16f. black, stone & orge 85 20

1022 Watch Tower and Barbed Wire Fence

1995. Europa. Peace and Freedom. Mult.
3264 16f. Type **1022** (50th anniv of liberation of concentration camps) . . 1·40 20
3265 30f. Nuclear cloud (25th anniv of Non-Proliferation Treaty) . . . 2·25 50

1023 Soldiers of the Irish Brigade and Memorial Cross

1995. 250th Anniv of Battle of Fontenoy.
3266 **1023** 16f. multicoloured . . . 90 20

1024 U.N. Emblem

1995. 50th Anniv of U.N.O.
3267 **1024** 16f. multicoloured . . . 85 20

1025 "Sauvagemont, Maransart" (Pierre Alechinsky)

1995. Artists' Philatelic Creations.
3268 **1025** 16f. red, black & yellow 85 20
3269 – 16f. multicoloured . . . 85 20
DESIGN: No. 3269, "Telegram-style" (Pol Mara).

1026 Paul Cauchie (Brussels)

1995. Tourist Publicity. Art nouveau house facades by named architects. Multicoloured.
3270 16f. Type **1026** 85 20
3271 16f. Frans Smet-Verhas (Antwerp) 85 20
3272 16f. Paul Jaspar (Liege) . . 85 20

1027 Anniversary Emblem

1995. Cent of Royal Belgian Football Assn.
3273 **1027** 16f.+4f. mult . . . . . 1·10 1·00

1028 "Mercator" (Belgian cadet barque)

1995. Sailing Ships. Multicoloured.
3274 16f. Type **1028** . . . . . . 1·00 55
3275 16f. "Kruzenshern" (Russian cadet barque) (inscr "Kruzenstern") . . . . . 1·00 55
3276 16f. "Sagres II" (Portuguese cadet barque) . . . . . . 1·00 55
3277 16f. "Amerigo Vespucci" (Italian cadet ship) . . . 1·00 55

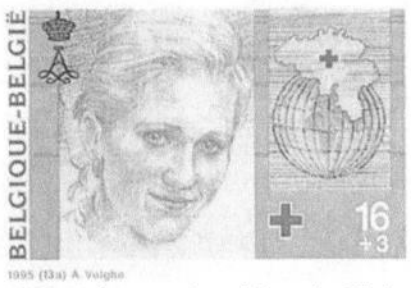

1029 Princess Astrid and Globe

1995. Red Cross. Multicoloured.
3278 16f.+3f. Type **1029** (Chairwoman) . . . . . 1·00 90
3279 16f.+3f. Wilhelm Rontgen (discoverer of X-rays) and X-ray of hand . . . . . 1·00 90
3280 16f.+3f. Louis Pasteur (chemist) and microscope 1·00 90

1030 1908 Minerva

1995. Motorcycles. Multicoloured.
3281 13f. Type **1030** 70 30
3282 16f. 1913 FN (vert) 85 20
3283 30f. 1929 La Mondiale . . . 1·40 50
3284 32f. 1937 Gillet (vert) . . . 1·60 45

1031 Sammy (cartoon character)

1995. "Philately for the Young".
3285 **1031** 16f. multicoloured . . . 1·00 20

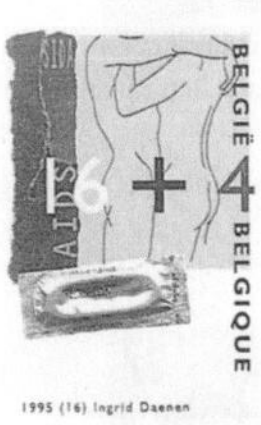

1032 Couple and Condom in Wrapper

1034 "Nativity" (from 15th-century breviary)

1033 King Albert II and Queen Paola (photograph by Christian Louis)

1995. "Solidarity". AIDS Awareness.
3286 **1032** 16f.+4f. mult . . . . . 1·00 90

1995. King's Day.
3287 **1033** 16f. multicoloured . . . 90 20

1995. Christmas.
3288 **1034** 13f. multicoloured . . . 15 15

1035 Puppets, Walloon Museum, Liege

1996. Museums. Multicoloured.
3289 16f.+4f. Type **1035** . . . . 1·00 1·00
3290 16f.+4f. National Gin Museum, Hasselt . . . . 1·00 1·00
MS3291 126 × 90 mm. 34f.+6f. "Fall of Saul" (detail of title panel), Butchers' Guild Hall Museum, Antwerp . . . . 2·40 2·40
The premium was used for the promotion of philately.

1036 "Emile Mayrisch"

1037 "LIBERALISME"

1996. 70th Death Anniv of Theo van Rysselberghe (painter). No value expressed.
3292 **1036** A (16f.) mult 20 20

1996. 150th Anniv of Liberal Party.
3293 **1037** 16f. dp blue, violet & bl 20 20

1038 Oscar Bonnevalle (stamp designer) and "Gelatenheid"

1996. Stamp Day.
3294 **1038** 16f. multicoloured . . . 20 20

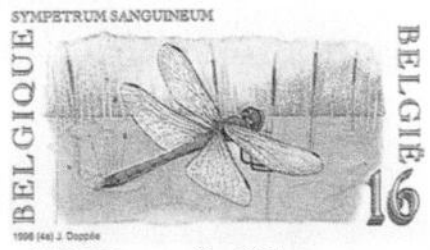

1039 Dragonfly ("Sympetrum sanguineum")

1996. 150th Anniv of Royal Institute of Natural Sciences of Belgium. Insects. Multicoloured.
3295 16f. Type **1039** 60 60
3296 16f. Buff-tailed bumble bee ("Bombus terrestris") . . 60 60
3297 16f. Stag beetle ("Lucanus cervus") 60 60
3298 16f. May beetle ("Melolontha melolontha") 60 60
3299 16f. European field cricket ("Gryllus campestris") . . 60 60
3300 16f. Seven-spotted ladybird ("Coccinella septempunctata") 60 60

1040 Yvonne Nevejean (rescuer of Jewish children)

1042 King Albert II

1996. Europa. Famous Women. Multicoloured.
3301 16f. Type **1040** 20 20
3302 30f. Marie Gevers (poet) . . 50 50

1996. Birds (3rd series). As T **841**. Mult.
3303 1f. Crested tit ("Mesange Huppee") 15 10
3304 2f. Redwing ("Grive mauvis") 20 10
3305 3f. Eurasian skylark ("Alouette des champs") 20 10
3306 4f. Pied flycatcher ("Gore-mouche noir") 30 10
3307 5f. Common starling ("Etourneau sansonnet") 20 10
3308 6f. Spruce siskin ("Tarin des aulnes") 20 20
3309 7f. Yellow wagtail ("Bergeronnette printaniere") 30 20
3310 7f.50 Great grey shrike ("Pie-Grienche Grise") . . 30 20
3311 9f. Green woodpecker ("Pic Vert") 35 20
3312 10f. Turtle dove ("Tourterelle des Bois") 30 20
3313 15f. Willow tit ("Mesange boreale") 65 20
3314 16f. Coal tit ("Mesange noire") 65 20
3315 21f. Fieldfare ("Grive Litorne") (horiz) 90 60
3316 150f. Black-billed magpie ("Pie bavarde") (35 × 25 mm) . . . . . . 6·25 75

1996. 62nd Birthday of King Albert II.
3327 **1042** 16f. multicoloured . . . 85 10

1043 Han sur Lesse Grottoes

1996. Tourist Publicity. Multicoloured.
3328 16f. Type **1043** 85 20
3329 16f. Statue of beguine, Begijnendijk (vert) 85 20

1044 Royal Palace

1996. Brussels, Heart of Europe. Mult.
3330 16f. Type **1044** 85 20
3331 16f. St. Hubert Royal Galleries 85 20
3332 16f. Le Petit Sablon, Egmont Palace (horiz) . . 85 20
3333 16f. Jubilee Park (horiz) . . 85 20

1045 1900 Germain 6CV Voiturette

1996. Cent of Motor Racing at Spa. Mult.
3334 16f. Type **1045** 85 25
3335 16f. 1925 Alfa Romeo P2 85 25
3336 16f. 1939 Mercedes Benz W154 . . . . 85 25
3337 16f. 1967 Ferrari 330P . . . 85 25

1046 Table Tennis

1996. Olympic Games, Atlanta. Mult.
3338 16f.+4f. Type **1046** 90 95
3339 16f.+4f. Swimming 90 95
MS3340 125 × 90 mm. 34f.+6f. High jumping (41 × 34 mm) . . . . 2·10 2·10

1996.

3341 **1042** 16f. blue 70 15
3342 17f. blue 85 10
3343 18f. green 85 20
3344 19f. lilac 85 25
3344a 20f. brown 90 10
3345 25f. brown . . . . . 1·25 20
3346 28f. brown . . . . . 1·25 30
3347 32f. violet . . . . . . 1·40 25
3348 34f. blue . . . . . . 1·25 30
3349 36f. blue . . . . . . 1·50 30
3350 50f. green . . . . . . 2·25 30

1047 "The Straw Hat" (Peter Paul Rubens)   1048 Philip the Fair

1996. Paintings by Belgian Artists in the National Gallery, London. Multicoloured.

3351	14f. "St. Ivo" (Rogier van der Weyden)	70	30
3352	16f. Type **1047**	85	20
3353	30f. "Man in a Turban" (Jan van Eyck)	1·50	45

1996. 500th Anniv of Marriage of Philip the Fair and Joanna of Castile and Procession into Brussels. Details of triptych by the Master of Afflligem Abbey at Zierikzee Town Hall. Multicoloured.

3354	16f. Type **1048**	85	20
3355	16f. Joanna of Castile . . .	85	20

1049 Cloro (cartoon character)

1996. "Philately for the Young".

3356	**1049** 16f. multicoloured . . .	90	20

1050 Title of First Issue and Charles Letellier (founder)

1996. 150th Anniv of "Mons Almanac".

3357	**1050** 16f. black, yell & mve	85	20

1051 Arthur Grumiaux (violinist, 10th death anniv)

1996. Music and Literature Anniversaries.

3358	**1051** 16f. multicoloured . . .	85	20
3359	– 16f. multicoloured . . .	85	20
3360	– 16f. black and brown	85	20
3361	– 16f. multicoloured . . .	85	20

DESIGNS: No. 3359, Flor Peeters (organist, 10th death anniv); 3360, Christian Dotremont (poet, 5th death anniv); 3361, Paul van Ostaijen (writer, birth centenary) and cover drawing by Oscar Jespers for "Bezette Stad".

1052 Globe and Children of Different Races

1996. "Solidarity". 50th Anniv of U.N.I.C.E.F.

3362	**1052** 16f.+4f. mult	85	95

1053 Christmas Trees

1996. Christmas. Sheet 185 × 145 mm containing T **1053** and similar horiz designs. Multicoloured.

MS3363 14f. Type **1053**; 14f. "Happy Christmas" in Flemish, German and French; 14f. Church; 14f. Cake stall; 14f. Stall with cribs; 14f. Meat stall; 14f. Father Christmas; 14f. Crowd including man smoking pipe; 14f. Crowd including man carrying holly   6·00   6·00

1054 Students

1997. Centenary of Catholic University, Mons.

3364	**1054** 17f. multicoloured . . .	85	20

1055 Barbed Wire and Buildings

1997. Museums. Multicoloured.

3365	17f.+4f. Type **1055** (Deportation and Resistance Museum, Dossin Barracks, Malines)	1·10	1·00
3366	17f.+4f. Foundryman pouring molten metal (Fourneau Saint-Michel Iron Museum)	1·10	1·00

MS3367 90 × 125 mm. 41f.+9f. Horta Museum, Saint-Giles . .   4·25   3·50

The premium was used for the promotion of philately.

1056 Deer and Landscape (½-size illustration)

1997. "Cantons of the East" (German-speaking Belgium).

3368	**1056** 17f. black and brown	85	25

1057 Marie Sasse

1997. Opera Singers. Multicoloured.

3369	17f. Type **1057**	85	20
3370	17f. Ernest van Dijck . . .	85	20
3371	17f. Hector Dufranne . . .	85	20
3372	17f. Clara Clairbert	85	20

1058 Soldier on Duty

1997. Belgian Involvement in United Nations Peacekeeping Forces.

3373	**1058** 17f. multicoloured . . .	85	20

1059 The Goat Riders

1997. Europa. Tales and Legends. Mult.

3374	17f. Type **1059**	90	20
3375	30f. Jean de Berneau . . .	1·50	50

1060 Spinoy working on Recess Plate

1997. Stamp Day. 4th Death Anniv of Constant Spinoy (engraver).

3376	**1060** 17f. brown, yell & blk	85	20

1061 "The Man in the Street" (detail)   1062 Flower Arrangement

1997. Birth Centenary of Paul Delvaux (artist). Multicoloured.

3377	15f. Type **1061**	70	30
3378	17f. "The Public Voice" (horiz)	85	20
3379	32f. "The Messenger of the Night"	1·50	55

1997. 2nd International Flower Show, Liege.

3380	**1062** 17f. multicoloured . . .	85	20

1063 Men's Judo

1997. Judo. Each black and red.

3381	17f.+4f. Type **1063**	1·10	1·00
3382	17f.+4f. Women's judo (showing female symbol)	1·10	1·00

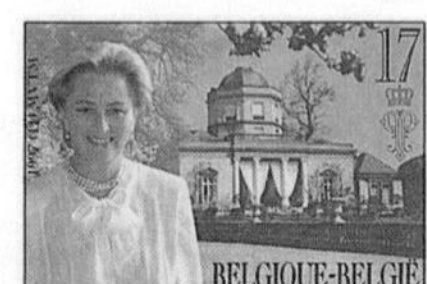

1064 Queen Paola and Belvedere Villa

1997. 60th Birthday of Queen Paola.

3383	**1064** 17f. multicoloured . . .	90	20

1065 Jommeke, Flip and Filiberke (comic strip characters)

1997. "Philately for the Young".

3384	**1065** 17f. multicoloured . . .	90	20

1066 "Rosa damascena" "Coccinea"   1067 St. Martin's Cathedral, Hal

1997. Roses. Illustrations by Pierre-Joseph Redoute. Multicoloured.

3385	17f. Type **1066**	85	20
3386	17f. "Rosa sulfurea"	85	20
3387	17f. "Rosa centifolia" . . .	85	20

1997. Tourist Publicity. Multicoloured.

3388	17f. Type **1067**	85	20
3389	17f. Notre-Dame Church, Laeken (horiz)	85	20
3390	17f. St. Martin's Cathedral, Liege	85	20

1068 Stonecutter

1997. Trades. Multicoloured.

3391	17f. Type **1068**	85	20
3392	17f. Bricklayer	85	20
3393	17f. Carpenter	60	10
3394	17f. Blacksmith	85	20

1069 Queen amidst Workers

1997. Centenary of Apimondia (International Apicultural Association) and 35th Congress, Antwerp. Bees. Multicoloured.

3395	17f. Type **1069**	85	50
3396	17f. Development of egg . .	85	50
3397	17f. Bees emerging from cells	85	50
3398	17f. Bee collecting nectar from flower	85	50
3399	17f. Bee fanning at hive entrance and worker arriving with nectar . . .	85	50
3400	17f. Worker feeding drone	85	50

1070 "Belgica" (polar barque) ice-bound

1997. Cent of Belgian Antarctic Expedition.

3401	**1070** 17f. multicoloured . . .	85	20

1071 Mask   1073 "Fairon" (Pierre Grahame)

1997. Centenary of Royal Central Africa Museum, Tervuren. Multicoloured.

3402	17f. Type **1071**	85	20
3403	17f. Museum (74 × 24 mm)	85	20
3404	34f. Statuette	1·75	60

1997. Christmas.

3408	**1073** 15f. multicoloured . . .	70	25

1074 Disjointed Figure   1075 Azalea "Mrs. Haerens A"

1997. "Solidarity". Multiple Sclerosis.

3409	**1074** 17f.+4f. black & blue	90	90

1997. Willow Tit. As No. 3318 but horiz.

3410	15f. multicoloured	65	60

1997. Self-adhesive.

3411	**1075** (17f.) multicoloured . .	85	20

1076 Female Symbol

1078 Gerard Walschap

1077 Thalys High Speed Train on Antoing Viaduct

1998. 50th Anniv of Women's Suffrage in Belgium.
3412 **1076** 17f. red, brown & sepia 85 25

1998. Paris–Brussels–Cologne–Amsterdam High Speed Rail Network.
3413 **1077** 17f. multicoloured . . . 85 25

1998. Writers' Birth Centenaries. Mult.
3414 17f. Type **1078** 85 25
3415 17f. Norge (Georges Mogin) 85 25

1079 King Leopold III

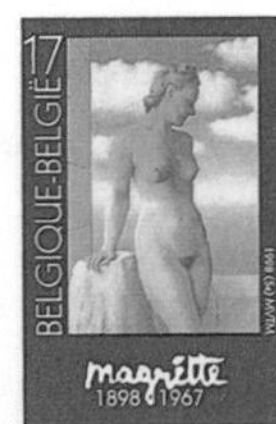

1080 "Black Magic"

1998. Kings of Belgium (1st series).
3416 **1079** 17f.+8f. green . . . . . 1·10 1·10
3417 – 32f.+15f. brown . . . . 2·00 1·90
MS3418 125 × 90 mm. 50f.+25f. red 4·50 4·00
KINGS: 32f. Baudouin I; 50f. Albert II.
The premium was used for the promotion of philately.
See also Nos. 3466/8 ans **MS**3508.

1998. Birth Centenary of Rene-Ghislain Magritte (artist) (1st issue). Multicoloured.
3419 17f. Type **1080** 85 25
3420 17f. "The Sensitive Chord" (horiz) 85 25
3421 17f. "The Castle of the Pyrenees" 85 25
See also No. 3432.

1081 "La Foire aux Amours" (Felicien Rops)

1998. Art Anniversaries. Multicoloured.
3422 17f. Type **1081** (death cent) 85 70
3423 17f. "Hospitality for the Strangers" (Gustave van de Woestijne) (bicentenary of Museum of Fine Arts, Ghent) 85 70
3424 17f. "Man with Beard" (self-portrait of Felix de Boeck, birth centenary) 85 70
3425 17f. "black writing mixed with colours..." (Karel Appel and Christian Dotremont) (50th anniv of Cobra art movement) . . 85 70

1082 Anniversary Emblem

1998. 75th Anniv of Belgian Postage Stamp Dealers' Association.
3426 **1082** 17f. multicoloured . . . 85 25

1083 Avro RJ85 Airplane

1998. 75th Anniv of Sabena Airlines.
3427 **1083** 17f. multicoloured . . . 85 40

1084 Fox

1998. Wildlife of the Ardennes. Mult.
3428 17f. Type **1084** 85 35
3429 17f. Red deer ("Cervus elaphus") 85 35
3430 17f. Wild boar ("Sus scrofa") 85 35
3431 17f. Roe deer ("Capreolus capreolus") 85 35

1085 "The Return" (Magritte)

1998. Birth Centenary of Rene-Ghislain Magritte (artist) (2nd issue).
3432 **1085** 17f. multicoloured . . . 85 25

1086 Struyf

1088 Pelote

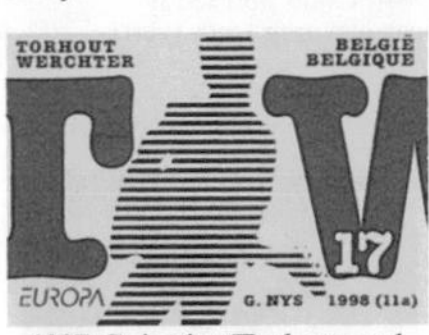

1087 Guitarist (Torhout and Werchter Festival)

1998. Stamp Day. 2nd Death Anniv of Edmond Struyf (founder of Pro-Post (organization for promotion of philately)).
3433 **1086** 17f. black, red & yellow 85 25

1998. Europa. National Festivals.
3434 **1087** 17f. violet and yellow 85 25
3435 – 17f. violet and mauve 85 25
DESIGN: No. 3435, Music conductor (Wallonie Festival).

1998. Sports. Multicoloured.
3436 17f.+4f. Type **1088** 90 85
3437 17f.+4f. Handball 90 85
MS3438 123 × 88 mm. 30f.+7f. Goalkeeper (World Cup Football Championship, France) . . . . 1·75 1·60

1089 Emblem

1090 Marnix van Sint-Aldegonde

1998. European Heritage Days. Mult.
3439 17f. Type **1089** 70 35
3440 17f. Bourla Theatre, Antwerp 70 35
3441 17f. La Halle, Durbuy . . . 70 35
3442 17f. Halletoren, Kortrijk . . 70 35
3443 17f. Louvain Town Hall . . 70 35
3444 17f. Perron, Liege 70 35
3445 17f. Royal Theatre, Namur 70 35
3446 17f. Aspremont-Lynden Castle, Rekem 70 35
3447 17f. Neo-Gothic kiosk, Saint Nicolas 70 35
3448 17f. Saint-Vincent's Chapel, Tournai 70 35
3449 17f. Villers-la-Ville Abbey 70 35
3450 17f. Saint-Gilles Town Hall 70 35

1998. 400th Death Anniv of Philips van Marnix van St. Aldegonde (writer).
3451 **1090** 17f. multicoloured . . . 85 25

1091 Face

1998. Bicentenary of "Amis Philanthropes" (circle of free thinkers).
3452 **1091** 17f. black and blue . . 85 25

1092 Mniszech Palace

1998. Belgium Embassy, Warsaw, Poland.
3453 **1092** 17f. multicoloured . . . 85 25

1093 King Albert II

1096 Chick Bill and Ric Hochet

1094 "The Eighth Day" (dir. Jaco van Dormael)

1998.
3454 **1093** 19f. lilac 85 25
No. 3454 was for use on direct mail by large companies.

1998. 25th Anniv of Brussels and Ghent Film Festivals. Multicoloured.
3455 17f. Type **1094** 85 25
3456 17f. "Daens" (dir. Stijn Coninx) 85 25

1998. "Philately for the Young". Comic Strip Characters.
3460 **1096** 17f. multicoloured . . . 85 25

1097 "Youth and Space"

1998. 14th World Congress of Association of Space Explorers.
3461 **1097** 17f. multicoloured . . . 85 25

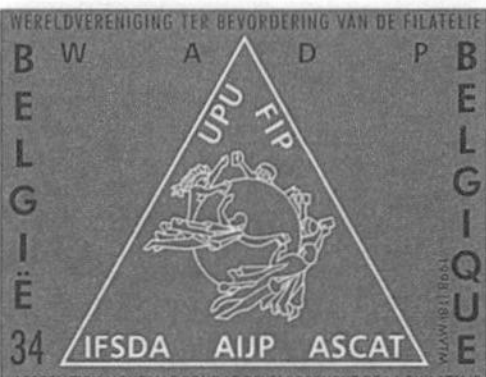

1098 Universal Postal Union Emblem

1998. World Post Day.
3462 **1098** 34f. blue & ultramarine 1·75 40

1099 "The Three Kings" (Michel Provost)

1998. Christmas. No value indicated.
3463 **1099** (17f.) multicoloured . . 85 25

1100 Detail of Triptych by Constant Dratz

1101 Blind Man with Guide Dog

1998. Cent of General Belgium Trade Union.
3464 **1100** 17f. multicoloured . . . 85 25

1998. "Solidarity". Guide Dogs for the Blind.
3465 **1101** 17f.+4f. multicoloured 1·00 1·00
The face value is embossed in Braille.

1999. Kings of Belgium (2nd series). As T **1079**.
3466 17f.+8f. deep green & green 1·10 1·10
3467 32f.+15f. black . . . . . . 2·00 2·00
MS3468 125 × 90 mm. 50f.+25f. brown and purple . . . . . . 3·50 3·50
KINGS: 17f. Albert I; 32f. Leopold II; 50f. Leopold I.
The premium was used for the promotion of philately.

1102 Candle ("Happy Birthday")

1103 Barn Owl

1999. Greetings stamps. No value expressed. Mult.
3469 (17f.) Type **1102** 75 40
3470 (17f.) Stork carrying heart ("Welcome" (new baby)) 75 40
3471 (17f.) Wristwatch ("Take your Time" (retirement)) 75 40
3472 (17f.) Four-leafed clover ("For your pleasure") . . 75 40
3473 (17f.) White doves ("Congratulations" (marriage)) 75 40
3474 (17f.) Arrow through heart ("I love you") 75 40
3475 (17f.) Woman with heart as head ("Happy Mother's Day") 75 40
3476 (17f.) Man with heart as head ("Happy Father's Day") 75 40

1999. Owls. Multicoloured.
3477 17f. Type **1103** 80 50
3478 17f. Little owl ("Athene noctua") 80 50
3479 17f. Tawny owl ("Strix aluco") 80 50
3480 17f. Long-eared owl ("Asio otus") 80 50

1104 Leopard Tank (Army)

1999. 50th Anniv of North Atlantic Treaty Organization. Multicoloured.
3481 17f. Type **1104** 80 25
3482 17f. General Dynamics F-16 jet fighters (Air Force) . . 80 25
3483 17f. "De Wandelaar" (frigate) (Navy) 80 25
3484 17f. Field hospital (Medical Service) 80 25
3485 17f. Display chart of military operations (General Staff) 80 25

1105 Envelopes and World Map

1999. 125th Anniv of U.P.U.
3486 **1105** 34f. multicoloured . . . 1·50 1·00

1106 De Bunt Nature Reserve, Hamme

1999. Europa. Parks and Gardens. Multicoloured.
3487 17f. Type **1106** 80 25
3488 17f. Harchies Marsh 80 25

1107 1849 10c. "Epaulettes" Stamp

1999. Stamp Day. 150th Anniv of First Belgian Postage Stamp. Multicoloured.
3489 17f. Type **1107** 80 25
3490 17f. 1849 20c."Epaulettes" stamp 80 25

1108 Racing

1999. Sport. Belgian Motor Cycling. Multicoloured.
3491 17f.+4f. Type **1108** . . . . 1·10 1·00
3492 17f.+4f. Trial (vert) . . . . 1·10 1·00
MS3493 90 × 125 mm. 30f.+7f. Motocross (vert) . . . . 2·00 1·90

1109 "My Favourite Room"

1999. 50th Death Anniv of James Ensor (artist) (1st issue).
3494 **1109** 17f. mullticoloured . . 80 25
See also Nos. 3501/3.

1110 Giant Family, Geraardsbergen

1111 Harvesting of Cocoa Beans

1999. Tourist Publicity. Multicoloured.
3495 17f. Type **1110** 80 25
3496 17f. Members of Confrerie de la Misericorde in Car d'Or procession, Mons (horiz) 80 25

1999. Belgian Chocolate. Multicoloured.
3497 17f. Type **1111** 80 25
3498 17f. Chocolate manufacture 80 25
3499 17f. Selling product 80 25

1112 Photographs of 1959 and 1999

1999. 40th Wedding Anniv of King Albert and Queen Paola.
3500 **1112** 17f. multicoloured . . . 90 25

1113 "Woman eating Oysters"

1999. 50th Death Anniv of James Ensor (artist) (2nd issue).
3501 **1113** 17f. multicoloured . . . 80 25
3502 – 30f. black, brown and grey . . . . 1·25 90
3503 – 32f. multicoloured . . . 1·60 85
DESIGNS—30f. "Triumph of Death"; 32f. "Old Lady with Masks".

1999. "Bruphila '99" National Stamp Exhibition, Brussels. Kings of Belgium (3rd series). Sheet 191 × 121 mm containing vert designs as T **1079**. Each deep blue and blue.
MS3508 17f. As No. 3466; 17f. Type **1079**; 32f. As No. 3467; 32f. As No. 3417; 50f. As No. **MS**3468; 50f. As No. **MS**3418 . . . . . 13·50 13·00

1115 Henri la Fontaine (President of International Peace Bureau), 1913

1999. Belgian Winners of Nobel Peace Prize.
3509 **1115** 17f. red and gold . . . 80 20
3510 – 21f. blue and gold . . . 85 60
DESIGNS: 3510, Auguste Beernaert (Prime Minister 1884–94), 1909.

DENOMINATION. From No. 3511 Belgian stamps are denominated both in Belgian francs and in euros.

1116 King Albert II

1116a King Albert II

1999.
3511 **1116** 17f. multicoloured . . 80 10
3512 17f. blue 80 10
3513 19f. purple 85 15
3514 20f. brown 90 20
3515 25f. brown . . . . . 1·10 10
3516 30f. purple . . . . . 1·25 10
3517 32f. green . . . . . 1·25 15
3518 34f. blue . . . . . 1·50 20
3519 36f. brown . . . . . 1·50 10
3520 **1116a** 50f. blue . . . . . 2·25 30
3521 200f. lilac . . . . . . 8·00 30

1117 "Corentin" (Paul Cuvelier)

1999. "Philately for the Young". Comic Strips. Sheet 185 × 145 mm containing T **1117** and similar horiz designs. Multicoloured.
MS3525 17f. Type **1117**; 17f. "Jerry Spring" (Jije); 17f. "Gil Jourdan" (Maurice Tillieux); 17f. "Beaver Patrol" (Mitacq); 17f. Entrance Hall, Belgian Comic Strip Centre; 17f. "Hassan and Kadour" (Jacques Laudy); 17f. "Buck Danny" (Victor Hubinon); 17f. "Tif and Tondu" (Fernand Dineur); 17f. "Les Timour" (Sirius) . . . . 7·00 7·00

1118 Geranium "Matador"

1119 Reindeer holding Glass of Champagne

1999. Flowers. No value expressed (geranium) or inscr "ZONE A PRIOR" (tulip). Multicoloured. Self-adhesive.
3528 (17f.) Type **1118** 85 25
3529 (21f.) Tulip (21 × 26 mm) . . 1·10 25
The geranium design was for use on inland letters up to 20g. and the tulip design for letters within the European Union up to 20g.

1999. Christmas.
3530 **1119** 17f. multicoloured . . . 80 25

1120 Child bandaging Teddy Bear

1999. "Solidarity". Red Cross. Multicoloured.
3531 17f.+4f. Type **1120** 90 85
3532 17f.+4f. Child and teddy bear cleaning teeth (vert) 90 85

1121 Prince Philippe and Mathilde d'Udekem d'Acoz

1999. Engagement of Prince Philippe and Mathilde d'Udekem d'Acoz.
3533 17f. Type **1121** . . . . . . 1·10 50
MS3534 120 × 89 mm. 21f. Prince Philippe and Mathilde d'Udekem d'Acoz (different) . . . . . . 1·10 1·00

1122 Pope John Paul XXIII

1999. The Twentieth Century (1st issue). Personalities, Sports and Leisure. Sheet 166 × 200 mm containing T **1122** and similar vert designs. Multicoloured.
MS3535 17f. Type **1122**; 17f. King Baudouin; 17f. Willy Brandt (German statesman); 17f. John F. Kennedy (U.S. President, 1961–3); 17f. Mahatma Gandhi (Indian leader); 17f. Martin Luther King (civil rights leader); 17f. Vladimir Lenin (Prime Minister of Russia, 1917–24; 17f. Che Guevara (revolutionary); 17f. Golda Meir (Prime Minister of Israel, 1969–74); 17f. Nelson Mandela (Prime Minister of South Africa, 1994–99); 17f. Jesse Owens (American athlete) (modern Olympics); 17f. Football; 17f. Eddy Merckx (racing cyclist) (Tour de France); 17f. Edith Piaf (French singer); 17f. The Beatles (English pop band); 17f. Charlie Chaplin (English film actor and director); 17f. Postcards (tourism); 17f. Children around campfire (youth movements); 17f. Tintin and Snowy (comic strip); 17f. Magnifying glass over stamp (hobbies) . . . . 16·00 15·00
See also Nos. **MS**3613 and **MS**3656.

1123 Fireworks and Streamer forming "2000"

2000. New Year.
3536 **1123** 17f. multicoloured . . . 80 25

1124 Red-backed Shrike

1125 Brussels Skyline and Group of People

2000. Birds. Multicoloured.
3537 50c. Goldcrest ("Roitelet Huppe") 10 10
3538 1f. Red crossbill ("Beccroisé des Sapins") 10 10
3539 2f. Short-toed treecreeper ("Grimpereau des Jardins") 10 10
3540 3f. Meadow pipit ("Pipit Farlouse") 10 10
3541 5f. Brambling ("Pinson du Nord") 20 10
3542 7f.50 Great grey shrike ("Pie-Grieche Grise") . . 30 20
3543 8f. Great tit ("Mesange Charbonniere") 40 10
3544 10f. Wood warbler ("Pouillot Siffleur") . . . 40 10
3545 16f. Type **1124** 40 10
3546 16f. Common tern ("Sterne Pierregarin") 40 10
3547 21f. Fieldfare ("Grive Litorne") (horiz) 85 15
3548 150f. Black-billed magpie ("Pie Bavarde") (36 × 25 mm) . . . . . 6·25 20

2000. Brussels, European City of Culture. Mult.
3555 17f. Type **1125** 80 30
3556 17f. Toots Tielmans (jazz musician), Anne Teresa de Keersmaeker (gymnast) and skyline 80 30
3557 17f. Airplane, train and skyline 80 30
Nos. 3555/7 were issued together, se-tenant, forming a composite design showing the Brussels skyline.

1126 Queen Astrid

2000. Queens of Belgium (1st series).
3558 **1126** 17f.+8f. green and deep green . . . . 1·10 1·10
3559 – 32f.+15f. brown and black . . . . 1·60 1·60
MS3560 125 × 89 mm. 50f.+25f. deep purple and purple . . . . . . 2·50 2·50
DESIGNS: 32f. Queen Fabiola; 50f. Queen Paola.
The premium was used for the promotion of philately.
See also Nos. 3615/**MS**3617 and **MS**3618.

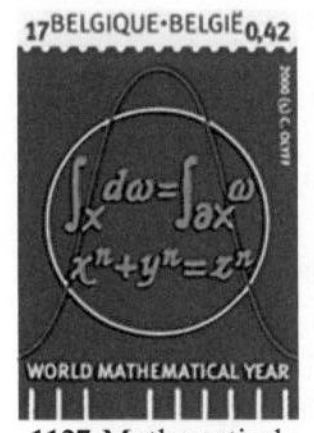

1127 Mathematical Formulae

1128 Globe and Technology (Joachim Beckers)

2000. World Mathematics Year.
3561 **1127** 17f. multicoloured . . . 80 15

2000. "Stampin' the Future". Winning Entries in Children's International Painting Competition.
3562 **1128** 17f. multicoloured . . . 80 15

1129 "Charles V as Sovereign Master of the Order of the Golden Fleece" (anon)

2000. 500th Birth Anniv of Charles V, Holy Roman Emperor. Paintings of Charles V. Multicoloured.
3563 17f. Type **1129** 65 10
3564 21f. "Charles V" (Corneille de la Haye) 75 30
MS3565 125 × 88 mm. 34f. "Charles V on Horseback" (Titian) . . . 2·50 2·50

1130 Common Adder

2000. Amphibians and Reptiles. Multicoloured.
3566 17f. Type **1130** 80 20
3567 17f. Sand lizard (*Lacerta agilis*) (vert) 80 20
3568 17f. Common tree frog (*Hyla arborea*) (vert) . . . 80 20
3569 17f. Spotted salamander (*Salamander salamander*) 80 20

1131 Children flying Kites

2000. Red Cross and Red Crescent Movements.
3570 **1131** 17f.+4f. multicoloured 75 75

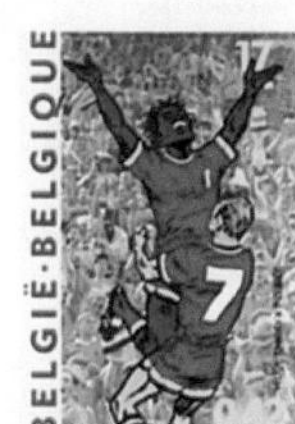

1132 Players Celebrating

2000. European Football Championship, Belgium and The Netherlands. Multicoloured. (a) With face value. Size 26 × 38 mm.
3571 17f. Type **1132** 60 10
3572 21f. Football 65 20

(b) Size 20 × 26 mm. Self-adhesive.
3573 (17f.) As Type **1132** 60 10

Nos. 3571/3 were printed together, se-tenant, with the backgrounds forming the composite design of a crowd of spectators and the Belgian flag.

1133 Cat and Rabbit reading Book

2000. Stamp Day. Winning Entry in Stamp Design Competition.
3574 **1133** 17f. black, blue and red 60 10

1134 Francois de Tassis (detail of tapestry)

1135 *Iris spuria*

2000. "Belgica 2001" Int Stamp Exhibition, Brussels, (1st issue).
3575 **1134** 17f. multicoloured . . . 60 20
See also Nos. 3629/33.

2000. Ghent Flower Show. Multicoloured.
3576 16f. Type **1135** 60 15
3577 17f. Rhododendron (horiz) 65 10
3578 21f. Begonia (horiz) 70 20

1136 Prince Philippe

2000. 2nd Anniv of Prince Philippe (cultural organization).
3579 **1136** 17f. brn, grey & sil . . 60 10

1137 Harpsichord

1139 "Building Europe"

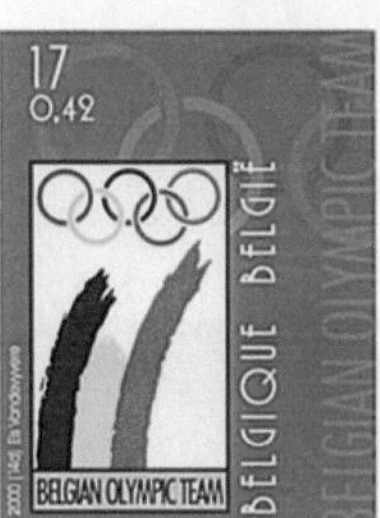

1138 Belgium Team Emblem and Olympic Rings

2000. 250th Death Anniv of Johann Sebastian Bach. No value expressed. Multicoloured.
3580 (17f.) Type **1137** 60 25
3581 (17f.) Violin 60 25
3582 (17f.) Two tenor lutes . . . 60 25
3583 (17f.) Treble viol 60 25
3584 (17f.) Three trumpets . . . 60 25
3585 (17f.) Bach . . . . 3·25 1·40

2000. Olympic Games, Sydney. Multicoloured.
3586 17f. Type **1138** 60 10
3587 17f.+4f. Tae-kwon-do . . . 70 70
3588 17f.+4f. Paralympic athlete (horiz) 70 70
MS3589 125 × 90 mm. 30f.+7f. Swimmer (horiz) . . . . 1·25 1·25

2000. Europa.
3590 **1139** 21f. multicoloured . . . 70 15

1140 Flemish Beguinages

2000. U.N.E.S.C.O. World Heritage Sites in Belgium. Multicoloured.
3591 17f. Type **1140** 60 10
3592 17f. Grand-Place, Brussels 60 10
3393 17f. Four lifts, Centre Canal, Wallonia 50 10

1141 Baroque Organ, Norbertine Abbey Church, Grimbergen

2000. Tourism. Churches and Church Organs. Mult.
3594 17f. Type **1141** 60 15
3595 17f. St. Wandru Abbey, Mons 60 15
3596 17f. O.-L.-V. Hemelvaartkerk (former abbey church), Ninove . . 60 15
3597 17f. St. Peter's Church, Bastogne 60 15

1142 Red-backed Shrike ("Pie grieche ecorcheur")

1143 Marcel, Charlotte, Fanny and Konstantinopel

2000.
3598 **1142** 16f. multicoloured . . . 65 15
3599 – 17f. mult (51 × 21 mm) 70 20
3600 – 23f. lilac 85 20
DESIGNS: 17f. Francois de Tassis (detail of tapestry) and Belgica 2001 emblem; 23f. King Albert II.

2000. "Philately for the Young". Kiekeboe (cartoon series created by Robert Merhottein).
3601 **1143** 17f. multicoloured . . . 60 15

1144 "Springtime"

2000. Hainaut Flower Show.
3602 **1144** 17f. multicoloured . . . 60 15

1145 Pansies **1148** Postman

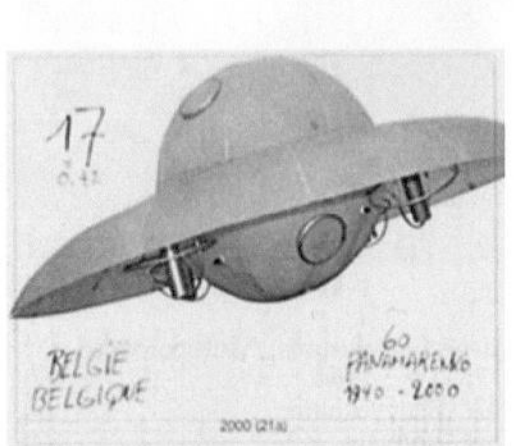

1147 "Bing of the Ferro Lusto X" (Panamarenko)

2000. Flowers. No value expressed. Self-adhesive.
3603 **1145** (17f.) multicoloured . . 60 15

2000. Modern Art. Multicoloured.
3608 17f. Type **1147** 60 15
3609 17f. "Construction" (Anne-Mie van Kerckhoven) (vert) 60 15
3610 17f. "Belgique eternelle" (Jacques Charlier) 60 15
3611 17f. "Les Belles de Nuit" (Marie Jo Lafontaine) . . 60 15

2000. Christmas.
3612 **1148** 17f. multicoloured . . . 60 15

1149 Soldiers at Yser Front, West Flanders (First World War, 1914–18)

2000. The Twentieth Century (2nd issue). War, Peace and Art. Sheet 200 × 166 mm containing T **1149** and similar horiz designs. Multicoloured.
MS3613 17f. Type **1149**; 17f. German concentration camp and prisoners (black and scarlet); 17f. Atomic cloud and Hiroshima (atomic bomb, 1945); 17f. Winston Churchill, Franklin D. Roosevelt and Joseph Stalin (Yalta conference, 1945); 17f. Headquarters (United Nations established, 1945); 17f. Joseph Kasavubu (first President) and map of Africa (independence of Belgian Congo, 1960); 17f. American soldiers and helicopter (Vietnam War); 17f. Collapse of Berlin Wall, 1989; 17f. Campaign for Nuclear Disarmament emblem and crowd; 17f. Dome of the Rock (Middle East conflict); 17f. Rene Magritte (artist); 17f. Le Corbusier (architect) and building; 17f. Bertolt Brecht (dramatist and poet); 17f. Anne Teresa de Keersmaeker (choreographer); 17f. Bila Bartok (composer); 17f. Andy Warhol (artist); 17f. Maria Callas (opera singer); 17f. Henry Moore (sculptor) and sculpture; 17f. Charlie Parker (alto saxophonist and composer) and Toots Thielemans (composer and jazz musician) . . . . 13·00 13·00

1150 Stars

2000. New Year.
3614 **1150** 17f. gold, blue & blk 70 10

2001. Queens of Belgium (2nd series). As T **1126**.
3615 17f.+8f. green & dp green 90 90
3616 32f.+15f. black and green 1·50 1·50
MS3617 126 × 91 mm. 50f.+25f. deep brown and brown . . . . . . 2·40 2·40
DESIGNS: 17f. Queen Elisabeth; 32f. Queen Marie-Henriette; 50f. Queen Louise-Marie.
The premium was used for the promotion of philately.

2001. Queens of Belgium (3rd series). Vert designs as T **1126**. Each blue, deep blue and ochre.
MS3618 190 × 121 mm. 17f. As No. 3615; 17f. As Type **1126**; 32f. As No. 3616; 32f. As No. 3559; 50f. As No. **MS**3617; 50f. As No. **MS**3560 . . . . 10·50 10·50

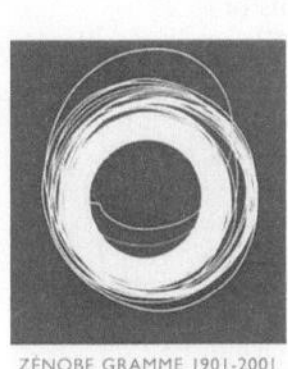

1151 Movement of a Dynamo

1152 Virgin and Child (statue)

2001. Death Centenary of Zenobe Gramme (physicist).
3619 **1151** 17f. black, red & black 60 10

2001. 575th Anniv of Louvain Catholic University.
3620 **1152** 17f. multicoloured . . . 60 10

2001. As T **998** but with face value expressed in francs and euros.
3621 100f. multicoloured . . . . 3·00 35

1153 Willem Elsschot (poet)

2001. Music and Literature.
3622 **1153** 17f. brown and black . . . 60 10
3623 – 17f. grey and black . . 60 10
MS3624 125 × 90 mm. 21f. orange and brown 75 75
DESIGNS—VERT: No. 3623, Albert Ayguesparse (poet). HORIZ: **MS**3624 21f. Queen Elisabeth and emblem (50th anniv of Queen Elisabeth International Music Competition).

1154 Boy washing Hands

2001. Europa. Water Resources.
3625 **1154** 21f. multicoloured . . . 70 20

1155 Type 12 Steam Locomotive

2001. 75th Anniv of National Railway Company. Multicoloured.
3626 17f. Type **1155** 60 15
3627 17f. Series 06 dual locomotive No. 671 . . . 60 15
3628 17f. Series 03 locomotive No. 328 . . . . 60 15
Nos. 3626/8 were issued together, se-tenant, forming a composite design.

1156 16th-century Postman on horseback

2001. "Belgica 2001" International Stamp Exhibition, Brussels (2nd issue). 500th Anniv of European Post. Multicoloured.
3629 17f. Type **1156** 70 20
3630 17f. 17th-century postman with walking staff (vert) 70 20
3631 17f. 18th-century postman and hand using quill (vert) 70 20
3632 17f. Steam locomotive and 19th-century postman (vert) 70 20
3633 17f. 20th-century forms of communication (vert) . . 70 20
MS3634 190 × 120 mm. 150f. Female postal worker (35 × 46 mm) . . 10·50 10·50

1157 Hassan II Mosque, Casablanca

2001. Places of Worship. Multicoloured.
3635 17f. Type **1157** 60 10
3636 34f. Koekelberg Basilica . . 1·25 20

1158 "Winter Landscape with Skaters" (Pieter Bruegel the Elder)

2001. Art. Multicoloured.
3637 17f. Type **1158** 60 25
3638 17f. "Heads of Negros" (Peter Paul Rubens) . . . 60 25
3639 17f. "Sunday" (Frits van den Berghe) 60 25
3640 17f. "Mussels" (Marcel Broodthaers) 60 25

1159 Pottery Vase

1160 Luc Orient

2001. Chinese Pottery. Multicoloured.
3641 17f. Type **1159** 60 10
3642 34f. Teapot . . . . 1·25 20

2001. "Philately for the Young". Cartoon Characters.
3643 **1160** 17f. multicoloured . . . 60 10

1161 Cyclists (World Cycling Championship, Antwerp)

2001. Sports. Multicoloured.
3644 17f.+4f. Type **1161** 70 70
3645 17f.+4f. Gymnast (World Gymnastics Championships, Ghent) 70 70

1162 Emblem

2001. Belgian Presidency of European Union.
3646 **1162** 17f. multicoloured . . . 60 10

1163 Binche

2001. Town Hall Belfries.
3647 **1163** 17f. mauve and black 60 10
3648 – 17f. blue, mauve & blk 60 10
DESIGN: No. 3648, Diksmuide.

1164 Damme

2001. Large Farmhouses. Multicoloured.
3649 17f. Type **1164** 60 10
3650 17f. Beauvechain 60 10
3651 17f. Louvain 60 10
3652 17f. Honnelles 60 10
3653 17f. Hasselt 60 10

1165 Red Cross and Doctor

2001. Red Cross.
3654 **1165** 17f.+4f. multicoloured 65 65

1166 Stam and Pilou

1167 Ovide Decroly (educational psychologist) and Road Sign

2001. Stamp Day. No value expressed. Self-adhesive.
3655 **1166** (17f.) multicoloured . . 50 15
No. 3655 was for use on inland standard letters up to 20g.

2001. The Twentieth Century. Science and Technology. Sheet 166 × 200 mm. Multicoloured.
MS3656 17f. Type **1167**; 17f. Dandelion and windmills (alternative energy sources); 17f. Globe, signature and map (first solo non-stop crossing of North Atlantic by Charles Lindbergh); 17f. Man with head on lap (Sigmund Freud, founder of psychoanalysis); 17f. Astronaut and foot print on moon surface (Neil Armstrong, first man on the moon, 1969); 17f. Claude Levi-Strauss (anthropologist); 17f. DNA double helix and athletes (human genetic code); 1f. Pierre Teilhard de Chardin (theologian palaeontologist and philosopher); 17f. Max Weber (sociologist) and crowd; 17f. Albert Einstein (physicist) (Theory of Relativity); 17f. Knight and jacket of pills (discovery of Penicillin, 1928); 17f. Ilya Prigogine (theoretical chemist and clock face; 17f. Text and Roland Barthes (writer and critic); 17f. Simone de Beauvoir (feminist writer); 17f. Globe and technology highway (computer science); 17f. John Maynard Keynes (economist) and folded paper; 17f. Marc Bloch (historian) and photographs; 17f. Tools and Julius Robert Oppenheimer (nuclear physicist); 17f. Marie and Pierre Curie, discoverers of radioactivity, 1896); 17f. Caricature of Ludwig Josef Wittgenstein (philosopher) 10·50 10·50

1168 Nativity

2001. Christmas.
3657 **1168** 15f. multicoloured . . . 45 10

1169 Sunset

2001. Bereavement. No value expressed.
3658 **1169** (17f.) multicoloured . . 50 15
See also No. 3732.

1170 Daffodil

1171 Tintin

2001. Flowers. No value expressed. Self-adhesive.
(a) Without service indicator. Multicoloured.
3659 (17f.) Type **1170** 50 15
(b) Inscr "ZONE A PRIOR".
3660 (21f.) Tulip "Darwin" (vert) 65 20
No. 3659 was for use on inland letters up to 20g. and No. 3660 was for use on letters within the European Union up to 20g.

2001. 70th Anniv of Tintin in *Congo* (cartoon strip). Multicoloured.
3661 17f. Type **1171** 50 15
MS3662 123 × 88 mm. 34f. Tintin, Snowy and guide in car (48 × 37 mm) . . . . 1·10 1·10

New Currency 100 cents = 1 euro

1172 King Albert II

1173 King Albert II

2002.
3663 **1173** 7c. blue and red 10 10
3666 **1172** 42c. red 55 15
3667 47c. green 60 20
3668 **1173** 49c. red 65 20
3669 52c. blue 65 20
3670 59c. blue 75 25
3672 **1173** 79c. blue and red . . . 1·00 30
3674 €4.21 brown and red 5·75 1·90
Nos. 3663, 3668 and 3672 are inscribed "PRIOR" at left.

1174 Female Tennis Player

2002. Centenary of Royal Belgian Tennis Federation. Multicoloured.
3675 42c. Type **1174** 55 15
3676 42c. Male tennis player . . 55 15

1175 Cyclist

2002. International Cycling Events held at Circuit Zolder. Multicoloured.
3677 42c. Type **1175** (World Cyclo-Cross Championships) 55 15
3678 42c. Cyclist with hand raised (Road Cycling Championships) 55 15

1176 Dinosaur

2002. Winning Entry in Children's Stamp Design Competition at "Belgica 2001".
3679 **1176** 42c.+10c. mult 70 70
The premium was used for the promotion of philately.

1177 Antwerp from River

2002. 150th Anniv of Antwerp University.
3680 **1177** 42c. blue and black . . 55 15

1178 Buildings and Architectural Drawing

2002. "Bruges 2002", European City of Culture. Multicoloured.
3681 42c. Type **1178** 55 15
3682 42c. Organ pipes and xylophone 55 15
3683 42c. Octopus 55 15

1179 16th-century Manuscript (poem, Anna Bijns)

2002. Women and Art. Multicoloured.
3684 42c. Type **1179** 55 15
3685 84c. Woman writing (painting, Anna Boch) (vert) . . . . 1·10 35

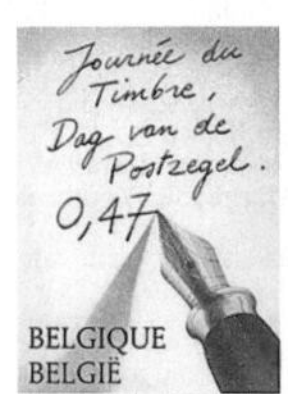
1180 Fountain Pen and Writing

2002. Stamp Day.
3686 **1180** 47c. multicoloured . . . 60 20

1181 Papillon

2002. Centenary of Flanders Canine Society. Multicoloured.
3687 42c. Type **1181** 55 15
3688 42c. Brussels griffon 55 15
3689 42c. Bloodhounds 55 15
3690 42c. Bouvier des Ardennes 55 15
3691 42c. Schipperke 55 15

1182 Stock Dove ("Pigeon Colombin-Holenduif")

1183 Big Top, Ringmaster, Seal and Clown

2002. Birds. Multicoloured.
3692 2c. Snipe ("Becassine des Marais-Watersnip") . . 10 10
3693 7c. Type **1182** 10 10
3698 25c. Oystercatcher ("Scholekster-Huitrier Pie") 30 10
3700 35c. Spotted woodpecker ("Pic Epeiche-Grote Bonte Specht") 45 30
3701 41c. Collared dove ("Touterelle Turque") . . 50 15
3701a 52c. Hoopoe ("Hop-Huppe Fascaie") 60 20
3702 57c. Black tern ("Guifette Noire") 75 20
3704 70c. Redshank ("Chevailer Gambette") 90 25
3705 €1 Wheatear ("Traquet Motteux") (38 × 27 mm) 1·25 40
3706 €2 Ringed plover ("Grand Gravelot") (38 × 27 mm) 2·50 75
3707 €3.72 Moorhen ("Waterhoen-Poule d'eau") (38 × 27 mm) . . 5·00 1·75
3709 €5 Ruff ("Combattant Varie") (38 × 27 mm) . . 6·50 1·90

2002. Europa. Circus. Winning Entry in Children's Drawing Competition.
3710 **1183** 52c. multicoloured . . . 70 20

1184 Paramedic, Patient and Damaged Buildings

2002. Red Cross.
3711 **1184** 84c.+12c. multicoloured 1·25 1·25

1185 Abbey Buildings

2002. 850th Anniv of Leffe Abbey.
3712 **1185** 42c. multicoloured . . . 55 15

1186 Loppem Castle

2002. Tourism. Castles. Sheet 161 × 141 mm containing T **1186** and similar horiz designs showing castles. Multicoloured.
MS3713 42c. Type **1186**; 42c. Horst; 42c. Wissekerke; 42c. Chimay; 42c. Ecaussinnes-Lalaing; 42c. Reinhardstein; 42c. Modave; 42c. Ooidonk; 42c. Corroy-le-Chateau; 42c. Alden Biesen . . . . . . 5·00 5·00

1187 Show Jumping

2002. Horses. Designs showing equestrian events. Multicoloured.
3714 40c. Type **1187** 50 15
3715 42c. Carriage driving (vert) 55 15
MS3716 126 × 91 mm. 52c. Two Brabant draught horses' heads (Centenary of St. Paul's horse procession, Opwijk) (37 × 48 mm) 70 70

1188 Golden Spur and Battle Scene

1189 Onze-Lieve-Vrouw-Lombeek, Roosdaal

2002. 700th Anniv of Battle of the Golden Spurs (Flemish--French battle), Kortrijk. Multicoloured.
3717 42c. Type **1188** 55 15
3718 52c. Broel towers 55 15
MS3719 126 × 91 mm. 57c. Flemish and French soldiers, river and knight on horseback (48 × 38 mm) 70 20

2002. Windmills. Multicoloured.
3720 42c. Type **1189** 55 15
3721 52c. Faial Island, Azores, Portugal 70 20
Stamps of a similar design were issued by Portugal.

1190 Liedekerke Lacework and Statue of Lace-maker

2002. Lace-making. Multicoloured.
3722 42c. Type **1190** 55 15
3723 74c. Pag lacework . . . . . 1·00 1·00
Stamps of a similar design were issued by Croatia.

1191 Bakelandt, Red Zita and Stagecoach

2002. "Philately for the Young". Bakelandt (comic strip created by Hec Leemans).
3724 **1191** 42c. multicoloured . . . 55 15

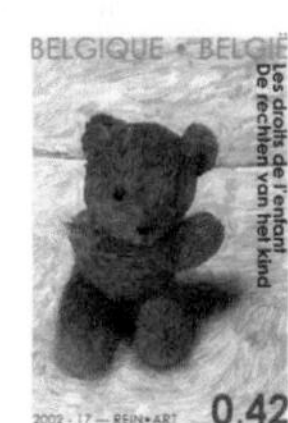

1192 Teddy Bear

1193 Rey

2002. "The Rights of the Child".
3725 **1192** 42c. multicoloured . . . 55 15

2002. Birth Centenary of Jean Rey (politician).
3726 **1193** 52c. blue and cobalt . . 70 20

1194 Princess Elisabeth

1195 Church, Ice Cream Van and Family

2002. 1st Birthday of Princess Elisabeth. Multicoloured.
3727 49c. Type **1194** 65 20
3728 59c. Princess Elisabeth with parents (horiz) 75 25
MS3729 123 × 88 mm. 84c. Princess Elisabeth (different) (59 × 38 mm) 1·10 1·10
No. 3727 was issued with a se-tenant label inscribed "PRIOR".

2002. Christmas. Sheet 166 × 40 mm containing T **1195** and similar vert designs. Multicoloured.
MS3730 41c. Type **1195**; 41c. Skier in snowy fir tree; 41c. Tobogganist and bird wearing hat; 41c. Skier wearing kilt; 41c. Skiers holding candles; 41c. Boy holding snowman-shaped ice cream; 41c. Children throwing snowballs; 41c. Children, snowman, and elderly man; 41c. Brazier, refreshment hut and people; 41c. Hut, robbers, cow and policeman . . . . 2·75 2·75

1196 Bricks

2002. The Twentieth Century. Society. Sheet 200 × 166 mm containing T **1196**.
MS3731 41c. purple, red and pink (Type **1196** (social housing)); 41c. deep purple, orange and purple ("MEI/MAI 68" and rubble (student protests)); 41c. slate, grey and green (telephone telecommunications)); 41c. red, orange and brown (slabs (gap between wealth and poverty)); 41c. brown, bistre and blue (broken crucifix (secularization of society)); 41c. multicoloured (towers of blocks (urbanization)); 41c. pink, violet and purple (combined female and male symbols (universal suffrage)); 41c. blue, orange and grey (enclosed circle (social security)); 41c. grey, green and bistre (schoolbag (equality in education)); 41c. grey, purple and deep purple (elderly man (ageing population)); 41c. blue, green and emerald ("E" (European Union)); 41c. chestnut, brown and yellow (stylized figure (declaration of Human Rights)); 41c. bistre, orange and light orange (pyramid of blocks (growth of consumer society)); 41c. blue, mauve and green (female symbol (feminism)); 41c. brown, sepia and light brown (mechanical arm (de-industrialization)); 41c. brown and green (dripping nozzle (oil crises)); 41c. multicoloured (vehicle (transportation)); 41c. lilac, brown and purple (sperm and egg (contraception)); 41c. green, red and grey (television (growth of television and radio)); 41c. pink, violet and blue (electric plug (increase in home appliances)) 10·50 10·50

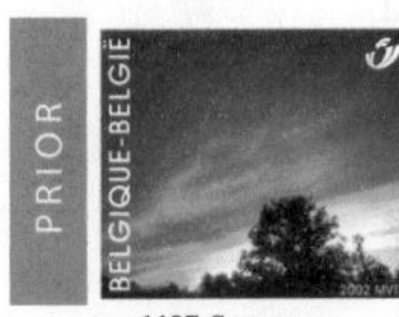
1197 Sunset

2002. Bereavement. No value expressed.
3732 **1197** (49c.) multicoloured . . 65 20

1198 Crocus

1199 Nero and Adhemar (cartoon characters)

2002. Flowers. No value expressed. Ordinary or self-adhesive gum.
3733 **1198** (49c.) multicoloured . . 65 20
No. 3733 was for use on inland letters up to 50 g.

2003. 80th (2002) Birth Anniv of Marc Sleen (cartoonist). Multicoloured.
3735 49c. Type **1199** 65 20
MS3736 121 × 91 mm 82c. Nero and Marc Sleen (49 × 38 mm) . . . 1·10 1·10

1200 Firefighters, Engine and Ladders

2003. Public Services (Nos. 3737/41) and St. Valentine (3742). Multicoloured.
3737 49c. Type **1200** 65 20
3738 49c. Traffic police men and policewoman 65 20
3739 49c. Civil defence workers mending flood defences 65 20
3740 49c. Elderly woman wearing breathing mask, hand holding syringe and theatre nurse 65 20
3741 49c. Postman riding bicycle and obtaining signature for parcel 65 20
3742 49c. Hearts escaping from birdcage 65 20

1201 Van de Velde and New House, Tervuren

2003. 140th Birth Anniv of Henry van de Velde (architect). Multicoloured.
3743 49c. Type **1201** 65 20
3744 59c. Van de Velde and Belgian pavilion, Paris International Exhibition, 1937 (vert) 75 25
3745 59c. Van de Velde and Book Tower, Central Library, Ghent University (vert) 75 25
MS3746 91 × 125 mm 84c. Woman and Art Nouveau newel post 1·10 1·10

1202 Bowls

2003. Traditional Sports. Multicoloured.
3747 49c. Type **1202** 65 20
3748 49c. Archery 65 20
MS3749 91 × 126 mm. 82c. Pigeon racing . . . . 1·10 1·10

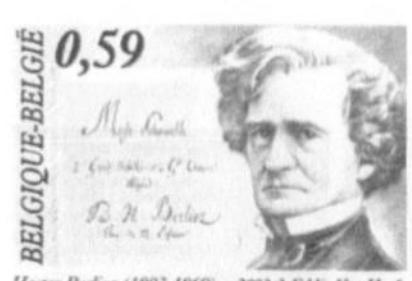
1203 Berlioz

2003. Birth Bicentenary of Hector Berlioz (composer).
3750 **1203** 59c. multicoloured . . . 75 25

1204 Statue of Men Conversing 1205 Papy Ferdinand

2003. Anniversaries. Multicoloured.
3751 49c. Type **1204** (150th anniv of engineers' association) 70 20
3752 49c. Statue of seated man (centenary of Solvay Business School) 70 20

2003. Red Cross. Cartoon characters in rescue attempt. Multicoloured.
3753 41c. + 9c. Type **1205** . . . 75 75
3754 41c. + 9c. Pilou holding light 75 75
3755 41c. + 9c. Stam running for help 75 75
Nos. 3753/5 were issued together, se-tenant, forming a composite design.

1206 Bouquet 1207 "Maigret" (film poster)

2003. 3rd International Flower Show, Liege.
3756 **1206** 49c. multicoloured . . . 70 20

2002. Birth Centenary of Georges Simenon (writer). Multicoloured.
3757 49c. Type **1207** 70 20
3758 59c. "Le chat" (film poster) 80 20
MS3759 91 × 126 mm. 84c. Simenon (38 × 49 mm) . . . . 1·10 1·10

1208 Bells of St. Rumbold's Cathedral, Maline

2003. 150th Anniv of Belgium–Russia Diplomatic Relations. Multicoloured.
3760 59c. Type **1208** 80 20
3761 59c. Bells of St. Peter and Paul's Cathedral, St. Petersburg 80 20

1209 Eternity Symbol and "Mail Art"

2003. Stamp Day. Mail Art.
3762 **1209** 49c. multicoloured . . . 70 20

1210 Roland on Horseback 1212 "Belgium, The Coast" (Leo Marfut)

1211 Calcite

2003. "Philately for the Young". The Valiant Knight (comic strip created by Francois Craenhals).
3763 **1210** 49c. multicoloured . . . 70 20

2003. Minerals. Multicoloured.
3764 49c. Type **1211** 70 20
3765 49c. Quartz 70 20
3766 49c. Barytes 70 20
3767 49c. Galena 70 20
3768 49c. Turquoise 70 20

2003. Europa. Poster Art.
3769 **1212** 59c. multicoloured . . . 80 20

1213 "La Robe de Mariee" (Paul Delvaux, Koksijde) 1214 *Monument to the Seasonal Worker, Rillaar* (Jan Peirelinck)

2003. "This is Belgium" (1st series). Sheet 167 × 200 mm containing T **1213** and similar vert designs showing sites from smaller Belgian towns. Multicoloured.
MS3770 41c. Type **1213**; 41c. Mural, Town Hall, Oudenaarde; 41c. "De viust" (sculpture, Rik Poot) and Town Hall, Vilvoorde; 41c. Turnhout chateau; 41c. Ambiorix (sculpture), Gallo-Roman museum, Tongeren; 41c. Fountain (sculpture, Pol Bury), La Louviere; 41c. Town Hall, Braine; 52c. Mardasson Memorial, Bastogne; 52c. Tower and snow scene, Sankt Vith; 57c. Saxophone and Citadel, Dinant . . . . 10·00 10·00
See also No. **MS**3809.

2003. Tourism. Statues. Multicoloured.
3771 49c. Type **1214** 70 20
3772 49c. La Tionade, Treignes (Yves and Claude Rahir) 70 20
3773 49c. Textile Teut, Town Hall, Hamont-Achel (Teo Groenen) 70 20
3774 49c. The Canal Guy, Brussels (Tom Frantzen) 70 20
3775 49c. The Maca, Wavre (Jean Godart) 70 20

1215 King Baudouin and Prince Albert

2003. 10th Anniv of the Accession of King Albert. Multicoloured.
3776 49c. Type **1215** 70 20
MS3777 90 × 125 mm. 59c. King Baudouin (38 × 48 mm); 84c. King Albert (38 × 48 mm) . . . . . 2·00 2·00

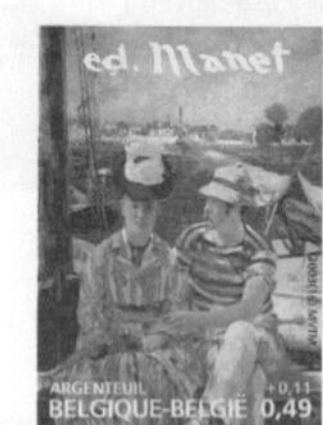
1216 "Argenteuil" (Edouard Manet)

2003. Art.
3778 **1216** 49c. multicoloured . . . 70 20
No. 3778 was issued with a se-tenant label inscribed "PRIOR".

1217 "Still Life" (Giorgio Morandi)

2003. "Europhalia 2003 Italy" Festival. Italian Presidency of European Union. Multicoloured.
3779 49c. Type **1217** 70 20
3780 79c. Cistalia 202 (1947) . . 1·10 25
No. 3779 was issued with a se-tenant label inscribed "PRIOR".
Stamps of the same design were issued by Italy.

1218 Elderly Couple, Family and Young People

2003. Social Cohesion.
3781 **1218** 49c. multicoloured . . . 70 20
No. 3781 was issued with a se-tenant label inscribed "PRIOR".

1219 St. Nichola 1220 King Albert II

2003. Christmas.
3782 **1219** 49c. multicoloured . . . 70 20
No. 3782 was issued with a se-tenant label inscribed "PRIOR".

2003.
3783 **1220** 49c. red 70 20
3784 79c. blue and red . . . 1·10 25
Nos. 3783/4 are inscribed "PRIOR" at left.

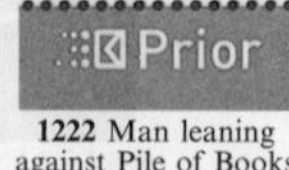
1221 Woman holding Cat ("Jardin extraordinaire") 1222 Man leaning against Pile of Books

2003. 50th Anniv of Belgian Television. Sheet 166 × 140 mm containing T **1221** and similar vert designs. Multicoloured.
MS3795 41c. × 5 Type **1221**; Cameraman and camera; Broadcasting tower; Brothers Cassiers and Jef Burm; Scene from "Schipper naast Mathide" . . 2·75 2·75

2003. The Book. Multicoloured.
3796 49c. Type **1222** 70 20
3797 49c. Man rolling through printing machine (horiz) 70 20
3798 49c. Books on shelves . . . 70 20
Nos. 3796/8 were each issued with an attached label inscribed "Prior".

1223 Maurice Gilliams 1224 Tulip

2003. Writers.
3799 **1223** 49c. brown, sepia and light brown 70 20
3800 – 59c. brown and orange 80 20
DESIGN: 59c. Marguerite Yourcenar (Maugerite de Crayencour).
No. 3799 was issued with an attached label inscribed "Prior".

2003. Flowers. No value expressed. Self-adhesive.
3801 **1224** (59c.) multicoloured . . 80 20
No. 3801 was for use on inland letters up to 50g.

1225 Herbeumont Church

2003. Christmas and New Year.
3802 **1225** 41c. multicoloured . . . 55 15

1226 Justin Henin Hardenne

2003. Belgian Tennis Champions. Multicoloured.
3803 49c. Type **1226** (2003 Roland Garros and U.S. Open champion) 70 20
3804 49c. Kim Clijsters (2002 Masters Cup and 2003 WTA No. 1 champion) (horiz) 70 20
Nos. 3803/4 were each issued with an attached label inscribed "Prior", either at top or bottom (vert) or left or right (horiz).

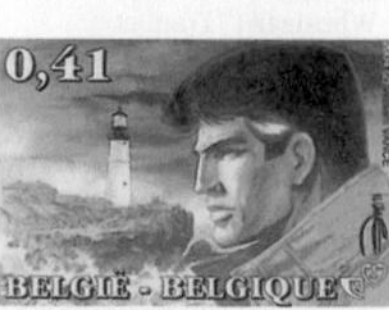
1227 XIII and Lighthouse

2004. "Philately for the Young". XIII (comic strip created by Jean van Damme and William Vance).
3805 **1227** 41c. multicoloured . . . 55 15

1228 "Portrait of Marguerite Khonopff"
1229 Carnation

2004. Fernand Khnopff (artist) Commemoration. Sheet 160 × 140 mm containing T **1228** and similar multicoloured designs.
MS3806 41c. × 4, Type **1228**; "Caresses" (55 × 24 mm); "The Abandoned City"; "Brown Eyes and a Blue Flower" (55 × 24 mm) 2·20 2·20

2004. Flowers. No value expressed. Self-adhesive.
3807 **1229** (49c.) multicoloured . . 70 20
No. 3807 was for use on inland letters up to 50g.

1230 Profile, Stamp and Kiss

2004. Stamp Day.
3808 **1230** 41c. multicoloured . . . 55 15

1231 Peter Piot (AIDS agency director)
1232 Herg and Models of Rocket and Tintin

2004. "This is Belgium" (2nd series). Sheet 166 × 200 mm containing T **1231** and similar vert designs showing Belgian personalities. Multicoloured.
MS3809 57c. × 10, Type **1231**; Nicole Van Goethem (film maker); Dirk Frimout and Frank de Winnie (astronaut and cosmonaut); Jaques Rogge (president, International Olympic Committee); Christian de Duve (winner, Nobel Prize for Medicine); Gabrielle Petit (war heroine); Catherine Verfaillie (director, Stem Cell Institute, Minnesota) and Christine Van Broeckhoven (director, Molecular Biology Laboratory, University of Antwerp); Jaques Stilbe (philatelist); Queen Fabiola; Adrien van der Burch (organizer, Brussels Exhibition, 1935) . . . 7·50 7·50

2004. 75th Anniv of Tintin (cartoon character created by Georges Remi (Herge)). Sheet 163 × 126 mm containing T **1232** and similar vert designs. Multicoloured.
MS3810 41c. × 5, Type **1232**; Technical sketch for Destination Moon; Tintin and Snowy (Bobbie); Tintin climbing up rocket (*Explorers on the Moon*); Tintin, Captain Haddock and Snowy on the moon (cover illustration, *Explorers on the Moon*) . . . . 2·10 2·10

EXPRESS LETTER STAMPS

E 107 Ghent

1929.
E530 – 1f.75 blue 60 25
E531 E **107** 2f.35 red . . . . . . 1·90 35
E581 – 2f.45 green . . . . . 14·00 1·75
E532 – 3f.50 purple . . . . . 11·50 6·00
E533 – 5f.25 olive . . . . . 8·50 7·00

DESIGNS: 1f.75, Town Hall, Brussels; 2f.45, Eupen; 3f.50, Bishop's Palace, Liege; 5f.25, Antwerp Cathedral.

1932. No. E581 surch **2 Fr 50** and cross.
E608 2f.50 on 2f.45 green . . . . 12·00 1·50

MILITARY STAMPS

1967. As T **289** (Baudouin) but with letter "M" within oval at foot.
M2027 1f.50 green 20 15

1971. As No. 2207/8a and 2209a but with letter "M" within oval at foot.
M2224 1f.75 green 35 50
M2225 2f.25 green 35 45
M2226 2f.50 green 10 15
M2227 3f.25 plum 15 20

NEWSPAPER STAMPS

1928. Railway Parcels stamps of 1923 optd **JOURNAUX DAGBLADEN 1928**.
N443 P **84** 10c. red 40 40
N444 20c. green 40 40
N445 40c. olive 40 40
N446 60c. orange 60 40
N447 70c. brown 60 40
N448 80c. violet 75 45
N449 90c. slate . . . . . . 6·50 2·40
N450 – 1f. blue . . . . 1·60 45
N451 – 2f. olive . . . . 3·25 3·00
N452 – 3f. red . . . . 3·25 60
N453 – 4f. red . . . . 3·25 60
N454 – 5f. violet . . . . . . 3·25 60
N455 – 6f. brown . . . . . . 4·50 1·50
N456 – 7f. orange . . . . . . 12·50 2·50
N457 – 8f. brown . . . . . . 8·50 1·00
N458 – 9f. purple . . . . . . 25·00 7·50
N459 – 10f. green . . . . . . 8·75 1·75
N460 – 20f. pink . . . . . . 25·00 9·25

1929. Railway Parcels stamps of 1923 optd **JOURNAUX DAGBLADEN** only.
N505 P **84** 10c. red 70 30
N506 20c. green 40 40
N507 40c. olive 40 30
N508 60c. orange 60 40
N509 70c. brown 45 30
N510 80c. violet 75 65
N511 90c. slate . . . . . . 6·25 4·50
N512 – 1f. blue . . . . 1·10 40
N513 – 1f.10 brown . . . . . 3·50 1·25
N514 – 1f.50 blue . . . . . 3·50 1·25
N515 – 2f. olive . . . . . . 2·40 55
N516 – 2f.10 slate . . . . . 10·50 7·50
N517 – 3f. red . . . . 2·40 50
N518 – 4f. red . . . . 2·40 50
N519 – 5f. violet . . . . . . 2·40 50
N520 – 6f. brown . . . . . . 5·50 1·10
N521 – 7f. orange . . . . . . 16·00 1·10
N522 – 8f. brown . . . . . . 10·50 1·10
N523 – 9f. purple . . . . . . 23·00 12·50
N524 – 10f. green . . . . . . 12·50 2·75
N525 – 20f. pink . . . . . . 30·00 10·00

PARCEL POST STAMPS
Stamps issued at Belgian Post Offices only.

1928. Optd **COLIS POSTAL POSTCOLLO**.
B470 **81** 4f. brown . . . . 4·75 1·25
B471 5f. bistre . . . . 4·75 1·25

B 106 G.P.O., Brussels

1929.
B526 B **106** 3f. sepia . . . . . . 1·25 20
B527 4f. slate . . . . . . 1·25 20
B528 5f. red . . . . 1·25 20
B529 6f. purple . . . . . . 22·00 24·00

1933. Surch **X4 4X**.
B645 B **106** 4f. on 6f. purple . . . 23·00 25

POSTAGE DUE STAMPS

D 21
D 35

1870.
D63 D **21** 10c. green . . . . . . 3·00 1·90
D64 20c. blue . . . . 42·00 3·00

1895.
D 96a D **35** 5c. green 10 10
D 97 10c. brown . . . . . 13·00 4·50
D101 10c. red 10 10
D 98a 20c. green 10 10
D102 30c. blue 20 15
D 99 50c. brown . . . . . 19·00 4·00
D103 50c. grey 40 25
D100 1f. red . . . . 16·00 8·00
D104 1f. yellow . . . . . 4·75 3·50

1919. As Type D **35**, but value in colour on white background.
D 251 D **35** 5c. green 55 25
D 323 5c. grey 10 10
D 252 10c. red . . . . . . 1·00 30
D 324 10c. green 10 10
D 253 20c. green . . . . . 5·50 1·00
D 325 20c. brown 10 10
D 254 30c. blue . . . . . . 2·75 35
D 326 30c. red 60 45
D 327 35c. green 20 10
D 328 40c. brown 15 10
D 330 50c. grey 15 10
D 329 50c. blue . . . . . . 2·75 35
D 331 60c. red 25 20
D1146 65c. green . . . . . 4·75 2·75
D 332 70c. brown 25 10
D 333 80c. grey 25 10
D 334 1f. violet 40 15
D 335 1f. purple 45 20
D 336 1f.20 olive 55 20
D 337 1f.40 green 50 35
D 338 1f.50 olive 55 40
D1147 1f.60 mauve . . . . 9·25 5·25
D1148 1f.80 red . . . . . . 11·50 4·75
D 339 2f. mauve 55 15
D1149 2f.40 lavender . . . 6·25 2·75
D1150 3f. red . . . . 1·40 45
D 340 3f.50 blue 55 15
D1151 4f. blue . . . . . . 7·00 40
D1152 5f. brown . . . . . . 2·40 25
D1153 7f. violet . . . . . . 2·40 1·50
D1154 8f. purple . . . . . . 7·50 8·00
D1155 10f. violet . . . . . 3·50 2·50

D 218
D 462

1945. Inscr "A PAYER" at top and "TE BETALEN" at bottom, or vice versa.
D1130A D **218** 10c. olive 10 10
D1131A 20c. blue 10 10
D1132A 30c. red 10 10
D1133A 40c. blue 10 10
D1134A 50c. green . . . 10 10
D1135A 1f. brown 10 10
D1136A 2f. orange 10 10

1966.
D2812 D **462** 1f. mauve 10 10
D2813 2f. green 10 10
D2814 3f. blue 20 20
D2815 4f. green 20 20
D1985ab 5f. purple 25 20
D2816 5f. lilac 25 25
D1986 6f. brown 70 20
D1987 7f. red 55 30
D2818 7f. orange 40 35
D2819 8f. grey 40 35
D2820 9f. red 40 40
D2821 10f. brown 40 40
D1988 20f. green . . . . 1·10 45
D2822 20f. green 80 80
On No. D1988 the "F" is outside the shield; on No. D2822 it is inside.

RAILWAY PARCELS STAMPS

In Belgium the parcels service is largely operated by the Belgian Railways for which the following stamps were issued.

Certain stamps under this heading were also on sale at post offices in connection with a "small parcels" service. These show a posthorn in the design except for Nos. P1116/18.

P 21

1879.
P63 P **21** 10c. brown . . . . . . 75·00 4·75
P64 20c. blue . . . . . . £190 14·50
P65 25c. green . . . . . . £275 8·50
P66 50c. red . . . . £1300 8·00
P67 80c. yellow . . . . . £1400 55·00
P68 1f. grey . . . . £190 12·50

P 22

1882.
P69 P **22** 10c. brown . . . . . . 20·00 1·40
P73 15c. grey . . . . . . 8·00 7·00
P75 20c. blue . . . . . . 70·00 3·00
P77 25c. green . . . . . 70·00 3·50
P78 50c. red . . . . . . 70·00 65
P81 80c. yellow . . . . . 70·00 85
P84 80c. brown . . . . . 65·00 70
P86 1f. grey . . . . £350 2·50
P87 1f. purple . . . . . . £400 3·50
P88 2f. buff . . . . £170 60·00

P 35

1895. Numerals in black except 1f. and 2f.
P 96 P **35** 10c. brown . . . . . . 11·00 70
P 97 15c. slate . . . . . . 11·00 1·25
P 98 20c. blue . . . . . . 17·00 90
P 99 25c. green . . . . . 17·00 1·25
P100 30c. orange . . . . . 22·00 1·75
P101 40c. green . . . . . 30·00 2·00
P102 50c. red . . . . . . 30·00 80
P103 60c. lilac . . . . . . 55·00 80
P104 70c. blue . . . . . . 55·00 1·25
P105 80c. yellow . . . . . 55·00 1·25
P106 90c. red . . . . . . 85·00 1·75
P107 1f. purple . . . . . . £225 2·75
P108 2f. buff . . . . £275 13·00

P 37 Winged Railway Wheel

1902.
P109a P **35** 10c. slate and brown 15 20
P110 15c. purple and slate 25 25
P111 20c. brown and blue 25 25
P112 25c. red and green . . 35 25
P113 30c. green and orange 25 30
P114 35c. green and brown 25 30
P115 40c. mauve and green 30 30
P116 50c. mauve and pink 25 20
P117 55c. blue and purple 35 30
P118 60c. red and lilac . . . 25 20
P119 70c. red and blue . . 10 20
P120 80c. purple and yellow 10 20
P121 90c. green and red . . 20 20
P122 P **37** 1f. orange and purple 20 20
P123 1f.10 black and red . . 20 20
P124 2f. green and bistre . . 25 20
P125 3f. blue and black . . 25 25
P126 4f. red and green . . . 65 1·25
P127 5f. green and orange 40 70
P128 10f. purple and yellow 75 80

1915. Stamps of 1912–14 optd **CHEMINS DE FER SPOORWEGEN** and Winged Railway Wheel.
P160 **44** 5c. green £130
P161 **46** 10c. red £160
P162 20c. green £170
P163 25c. blue £170
P164 **45** 35c. brown £250
P165 **46** 40c. green £225
P166 **45** 50c. grey £225
P167 1f. orange £200
P168 2f. violet £1300
P169 – 5f. purple (No. 143) . . . £2500

P 59 Winged Railway Wheel
P 60 Steam Locomotive

1915.
P196 P **59** 10c. blue 75 55
P197 15c. olive . . . . . . 1·25 1·40
P198 20c. red . . . . . . 1·10 90
P199 25c. brown . . . . . 1·10 90
P200 30c. mauve . . . . . 1·10 90
P201 35c. grey . . . . . . 1·10 75
P202 40c. orange . . . . . 1·10 75
P203 50c. bistre . . . . . 1·75 1·90
P204 55c. brown . . . . . 1·50 85
P205 60c. lilac . . . . . . 2·00 2·10
P206 70c. green . . . . . 1·00 75
P207 80c. brown . . . . . 1·00 70
P208 90c. blue . . . . . . 1·50 90
P209 P **60** 1f. grey . . . . 1·00 75
P210 1f.10 bl (FRANKEN) 22·00 25·00
P211 1f.10 blue (FRANK) 1·60 70
P212 2f. red . . . . 35·00 1·10
P213 3f. violet . . . . . . 35·00 1·10
P214 4f. green . . . . . . 38·00 2·40
P215 5f. brown . . . . . . 70·00 2·50
P216 10f. orange . . . . . 75·00 2·50

P 69 Winged Railway Wheel
P 70 Steam Train

1920.
P259 P **69** 10c. green . . . . . . 1·40 70
P280 10c. red 30 25
P281 15c. green 40 25
P261 20c. red . . . . . . 1·40 70
P282 20c. green 55 30
P262 25c. brown . . . . . 1·75 85
P283 25c. blue 50 25
P263 30c. mauve . . . . . 24·00 23·00

P284 30c. brown 50 25
P285 35c. brown 50 35
P286 40c. orange 50 25
P265 50c. bistre 7·00 1·25
P287 50c. red 80 20
P266 55c. brown 7·50 6·00
P288 55c. yellow 4·25 4·00
P267 60c. purple 9·00 95
P289 60c. red 50 25
P290 70c. green 2·40 45
P269 80c. brown 42·00 1·50
P291 80c. violet 1·75 35
P270 90c. blue 10·00 1·00
P292 90c. yellow 29·00 26·00
P293 90c. purple 5·25 35
P271 P 70 1f. grey 75·00 1·10
P272 1f.10 blue 13·00 95
P273 1f.20 green 14·00 1·10
P274 1f.40 brown 14·00 1·10
P275 2f. red £110 1·10
P276 3f. mauve £120 80
P277 4f. green £120 1·25
P278 5f. brown £120 80
P279 10f. orange £120 90

On Nos. P271/9 the engine has one head lamp.

1920. Three head lamps on engine.

P294 P 70 1f. brown 5·25 25
P296 1f.10 blue 1·60 25
P297 1f.20 orange 2·10 25
P298 1f.40 yellow 13·00 2·50
P299 1f.60 green 27·00 60
P300 2f. red 26·00 25
P301 3f. red 26·00 25
P302 4f. green 26·00 25
P303 5f. violet 24·00 25
P304 10f. yellow £130 16·00
P305 10f. brown 30·00 25
P306 15f. red 30·00 25
P307 20f. blue £350 3·00

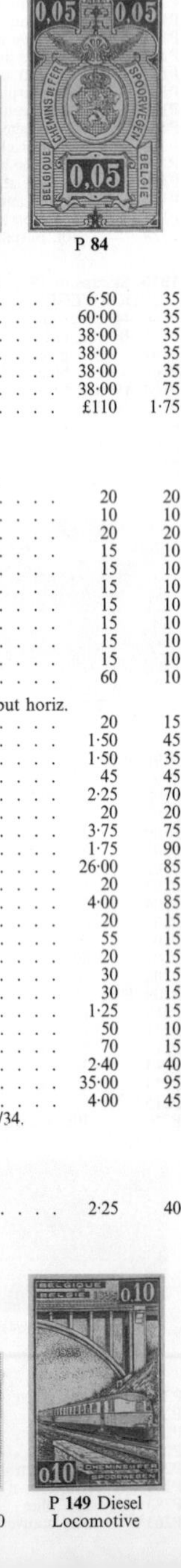

P 76 P 84

1921.

P312 P 76 2f. black 6·50 35
P313 3f. brown 60·00 35
P314 4f. green 38·00 35
P315 5f. red 38·00 35
P316 10f. brown 38·00 35
P317 15f. red 38·00 75
P318 20f. blue £110 1·75

1923.

P375 P 84 5c. brown 20 20
P376 10c. red 10 10
P377 15c. blue 20 20
P378 20c. green 15 10
P379 30c. purple 15 10
P380 40c. olive 15 10
P381 50c. red 15 10
P382 60c. orange 15 10
P383 70c. brown 15 10
P384 80c. violet 15 10
P385 90c. slate 60 10

Similar type, but horiz.

P386 1f. blue 20 15
P388 1f.10 orange 1·50 45
P389 1f.50 green 1·50 35
P390 1f.70 brown 45 45
P391 1f.80 red 2·25 70
P392 2f. olive 20 20
P393 2f.10 green 3·75 75
P394 2f.40 violet 1·75 90
P395 2f.70 grey 26·00 85
P396 3f. red 20 15
P397 3f.30 brown 4·00 85
P398 4f. red 20 15
P399 5f. violet 55 15
P400 6f. brown 20 15
P401 7f. orange 30 15
P402 8f. brown 30 15
P403 9f. purple 1·25 15
P404 10f. green 50 10
P405 20f. pink 70 15
P406 30f. green 2·40 40
P407 40f. slate 35·00 95
P408 50f. bistre 4·00 45

See Nos. P876/7 and P911/34.

1924. No. P394 surch **2F30**.

P409 2f.30 on 2f.40 violet 2·25 40

P 139 Type 5 Steam locomotive "Goliath", 1930

P 149 Diesel Locomotive

1934.

P655 P 139 3f. green 8·00 1·75
P656 4f. mauve 3·25 20
P657 5f. red 45·00 20

1935. Centenary of Belgian Railway.

P 89 P 149 10c. red 35 20
P690 20c. violet 30 20
P691 30c. brown 40 20
P692 40c. blue 50 20
P693 50c. orange 50 15
P694 60c. green 45 15
P695 70c. blue 45 20
P696 80c. black 45 20
P697 90c. red 90 45

Horiz type. Locomotive "Le Belge", 1835.

P698 1f. purple 60 20
P699 2f. black 1·60 20
P700 3f. orange 2·10 20
P701 4f. purple 2·10 20
P702 5f. purple 3·25 20
P703 6f. green 4·50 20
P704 7f. violet 18·00 20
P705 8f. black 18·00 25
P706 9f. blue 20·00 20
P707 10f. red 20·00 20
P708 20f. green 35·00 25
P709 30f. violet £100 3·50
P710 40f. brown £100 35
P711 50f. red £140 3·25
P712 100f. blue £250 48·00

P 162 Winged Railway Wheel and Posthorn

1938.

P 806 P 162 5f. on 3f.50 green 15·00 25
P 807 5f. on 4f.50 purple 10 10
P 808 6f. on 5f.50 red 30 10
P1162 8f. on 5f.50 brown 55 15
P1163 10f. on 5f.50 blue 70 10
P1164 12f. on 5f.50 violet 95 20

P 176 Seal of the International Railway Congress

1939. International Railway Congress, Brussels.

P856 P 176 20c. brown 2·75 2·75
P857 50c. blue 2·75 2·75
P858 2f. red 2·75 2·75
P859 9f. green 2·75 2·75
P860 10f. purple 2·75 2·75

1939. Surch **M. 3Fr.**

P867 P 162 3f. on 5f.50 red 45 30

1940. Optd **B** in oval and two vert bars.

P878 P 84 10c. red 10 10
P879 20c. green 10 10
P880 30c. purple 10 10
P881 40c. olive 10 10
P882 50c. red 10 10
P883 60c. orange 45 50
P884 70c. brown 10 10
P885 80c. violet 10 10
P886 90c. slate 15 20
P887 1f. blue 10 15
P888 2f. olive 15 10
P889 3f. red 15 10
P890 4f. red 15 10
P891 5f. violet 15 10
P892 6f. brown 30 15
P893 7f. orange 30 10
P894 8f. brown 30 15
P895 9f. purple 30 10
P896 10f. green 30 10
P897 20f. pink 50 30
P898 30f. green 65 85
P899 40f. slate 1·60 2·10
P900 50f. bistre 90 1·10

1940. As Type P **84** but colours changed.

P911 P 84 10c. olive 10 15
P912 20c. violet 10 15
P913 30c. red 10 15
P914 40c. blue 10 15
P915 50c. green 10 15
P916 60c. grey 10 15
P917 70c. green 10 15
P918 80c. orange 15 15
P919 90c. lilac 1·75 15

Similar design, but horizontal.

P920 1f. green 20 15
P921 2f. brown 25 15
P922 3f. grey 30 15
P923 4f. olive 35 15
P924 5f. lilac 45 15
P925 5f. black 65 25
P926 6f. red 60 25
P927 7f. violet 60 25
P928 8f. green 60 25
P929 9f. blue 75 25
P930 10f. mauve 75 25
P931 20f. blue 2·00 30
P932 30f. yellow 3·25 70
P933 40f. red 4·25 80
P934 50f. red 6·50 55

No. P925 was for use as a railway pacels tax stamp.

P 195 Engine Driver

P 216 Mercury

1942. Various designs.

P1090 P 195 10c. grey 20 10
P1091 20c. violet 20 15
P1092 30c. red 20 20
P1093 40c. blue 20 10
P1094 50c. blue 20 15
P1095 60c. black 20 15
P1096 70c. green 40 25
P1097 80c. orange 30 25
P1098 90c. brown 35 25
P1099 – 1f. green 20 20
P1100 – 2f. purple 20 20
P1101 – 3f. black 90 30
P1102 – 4f. blue 20 20
P1103 – 5f. brown 20 20
P1104 – 6f. green 90 50
P1105 – 7f. violet 25 20
P1106 – 8f. red 25 20
P1107 – 9f. blue 45 20
P 996 – 9f.20 red 40 35
P1108 – 10f. red 2·10 45
P1109 – 10f. brown 1·50 40
P 997 P 195 12f.30 green 40 25
P 998 – 14f.30 red 40 25
P1110 – 20f. green 70 25
P1111 – 30f. violet 80 25
P1112 – 40f. red 45 20
P1113 – 50f. blue 8·25 50
P 999 – 100f. blue 14·00 14·50

DESIGNS—As Type P **195**: 1f. to 9f.20, Platelayer; 10f. and 14f.30 to 50f. Railway porter; 24½ × 34½ mm: 100f. Electric train.

No. P1109 was for use as a railway parcels tax stamp.

1945. Inscribed "BELGIQUE-BELGIE" or vice-versa.

P1116A P 216 3f. green 10 10
P1117A 5f. blue 10 10
P1118A 6f. red 10 10

P 224 Level Crossing

1947.

P1174 P 224 100f. green 4·75 20

P 230 Archer

1947.

P1193 P 230 8f. brown 70 30
P1194 10f. blue and black 70 15
P1195 12f. violet 1·10 25

1948. Surch.

P1229 P 230 9f. on 8f. brown 75 20
P1230 11f. on 10f. blue and black 75 25
P1231 13f.50 on 12f. violet 1·10 20

P 246 "Parcel Post"

1948.

P1250 P 246 9f. brown 5·75 20
P1251 11f. red 5·00 10
P1252 13f.50 black 8·50 10

P 254 Type 1 Locomotive, 1867 (dated 1862)

1949. Locomotives.

P1277 – ½f. brown 40 25
P1278 P 254 1f. red 50 25
P1279 – 2f. blue 80 20
P1280 – 3f. red (1884) 1·90 20
P1281 – 4f. green (1901) 1·25 20
P1282 – 5f. red (1902) 1·25 20
P1283 – 6f. purple (1904) 1·90 20
P1284 – 7f. green (1905) 2·75 20
P1285 – 8f. blue (1906) 3·25 20
P1286 – 9f. brown (1909) 4·50 20
P1287 – 10f. olive (1910) 6·00 20
P1288 – 10f. black and red (1905) 5·50 1·40
P1289 – 20f. orange (1920) 15·00 20
P1290 – 30f. blue (1928) 22·00 20
P1291 – 40f. red (1930) 38·00 20
P1292 – 50f. mauve (1935) 19·00 20
P1293 – 100f. red (1939) 75·00 30
P1294 – 300f. violet (1951) £100 40

DESIGNS: 50c. Locomotive "Le Belge", 1835; 2f. Type 29 locomotive, 1875; 3f. Type 25 locomotive, 1884; 4f. Type 18 locomotive, 1901; 5f. Type 22 locomotive, 1902; 6f. Type 53 locomotive, 1904; 7f. Type 8 locomotive, 1905; 8f. Type 16 locomotive, 1906; 9f. Type 10 locomotive, 1909; 10f. (P1287) Type 36 locomotive, 1910; 10f. (P 1288) Type 38 locomotive, 1905; 20f. Type 38 locomotive, 1920; 30f. Type 48 locomotive, 1928; 40f. Type 5 locomotive, 1935; 50f. Type 1 Pacific locomotive, 1935; 100f. Type 12 locomotive, 1939; 300f. Two-car electric train, 1951.

The 300f. is larger (37½ × 25 mm).

1949. Electrification of Charleroi–Brussels Line. As Type P**254**.

P1296 60f. brown 19·00 20

DESIGN: 60f. Type 101 electric locomotive, 1945.

P 258 Loading Parcels

1950.

P1307 – 11f. orange 4·00 20
P1308 – 12f. purple 14·00 1·40
P1309 – 13f. green 4·75 15
P1310 – 15f. blue 12·00 20
P1311 P 258 16f. grey 4·00 15
P1312 – 17f. brown 4·75 20
P1313 P 258 18f. red 10·00 80
P1314 – 20f. orange 5·00 20

DESIGNS—HORIZ: 11, 12, 17f. Dispatch counter; 13, 15f. Sorting compartment.

P 271 Mercury

1951. 25th Anniv of National Belgian Railway Society.

P1375 P 271 25f. blue 9·50 7·50

1953. Nos. P1307, P1310 and P1313 surch.

P1442 – 13f. on 15f. blue 48·00 3·25
P1443 – 17f. on 11f. orange 23·00 80
P1444 P 258 20f. on 18f. red 12·50 2·00

P 288 Electric Train and Brussels Skyline

1953. Inauguration of Nord-Midi Junction.

P1451 P 288 200f. green £180 70
P1452 200f. green & brown £190 2·40

P 291 Nord Station

P 292 Central Station

1953. Brussels Railway Stations.

P1485 P 291 1f. ochre 20 10
P1486 2f. black 35 10
P1487 3f. green 40 10
P1488 4f. orange 60 10
P1489 5f. brown 2·00 15
P1490 – 5f. brown 8·00 15
P1491 P 291 6f. purple 85 10
P1492 7f. green 85 10
P1493 8f. red 1·10 10
P1494 9f. blue 1·40 10
P1495 – 10f. green 1·90 10
P1496 – 10f. black 1·10 10
P1497 – 15f. red 10·50 40
P1498 – 20f. blue 3·00 10
P1498a – 20f. green 1·60 30
P1499 – 30f. purple 4·75 10
P1500 – 40f. mauve 6·25 10
P1501 – 50f. mauve 7·75 10
P1501a – 50f. blue 2·50 50
P1502 – 60f. violet 16·00 10
P1503 – 80f. purple 25·00 20

P1504 **P 292** 100f. green 14·00 35
P1505 200f. blue 80·00 60
P1506 300f. mauve £140 1·10

DESIGNS—VERT: 5f. (P1490), 10f. (P1496), 15, 20f. (P1498a), 50f. (P1501a), Congress Station; 10f. (P1495), 20f. (P1498) to 50f. (P1501), Midi Station. HORIZ: 60, 80f. Chapelle Station.

Nos. P1490, P1496/7, P1498a and P1501a were for use as railway parcels tax stamps.

P **295** Electric Train Type 121 and Nord Station, Brussels

P **326** Mercury and Railway Winged Wheel

1953.
P1517 **P 295** 13f. brown 16·00 20
P1518 18f. blue 16·00 20
P1519 21f. mauve 16·00 30

1956. Surch in figures.
P1585 **P 295** 14f. on 13f. brown 5·50 15
P1586 19f. on 18f. blue 5·50 15
P1587 22f. on 21f. mauve 5·50 20

1957.
P1600 **P 326** 14f. green 5·50 15
P1601 19f. sepia 5·50 15
P1602 22f. red 5·50 25

1959. Surch **20 F**.
P1678 **P 326** 20f. on 19f. sepia 20·00 20
P1679 20f. on 22f. red 20·00 55

P **357** Brussels Nord Station, 1861–1954

1959.
P1695 **P 357** 20f. olive 9·00 10
P1696 – 24f. red 3·50 20
P1697 – 26f. blue 3·50 1·75
P1698 – 28f. purple 3·50 1·10

DESIGNS—VERT: 24f. Brussels Midi station, 1869–1949. HORIZ: 26f. Antwerp Central station, 1905; 28f. Ghent St. Pieter's station.

P **368** Congress Seal, Type 202 Diesel and Type 125 Electric Locomotives

1960. 75th Anniv of Int Railway Congress Assn.
P1722 **P 368** 20f. red 35·00 24·00
P1723 50f. blue 35·00 24·00
P1724 60f. purple 35·00 24·00
P1725 70f. green 35·00 24·00

1961. Nos. P1695/8 surch.
P1787 **P 357** 24f. on 20f. olive 40·00 15
P1788 – 26f. on 24f. red 3·50 15
P1789 – 28f. on 26f. blue 3·50 15
P1790 – 35f. on 28f. purple 3·50 15

P **477** Arlon Station

1967.
P2017 **P 477** 25f. ochre 6·75 25
P2018 30f. green 2·00 25
P2019 35f. blue 2·25 25
P2020 40f. red 19·00 25

P **488** Type 122 Electric Train

1968.
P2047 **P 488** 1f. bistre 25 15
P2048 2f. green 25 15
P2049 3f. green 45 15
P2050 4f. orange 45 15
P2051 5f. brown 50 15
P2052 6f. plum 45 15
P2053 7f. green 50 15
P2054 8f. red 65 15
P2055 9f. blue 1·10 15
P2056 – 10f. green 2·25 15
P2057 – 20f. blue 1·25 15
P2058 – 30f. lilac 4·00 15
P2059 – 40f. violet 4·50 15
P2060 – 50f. purple 5·50 15
P2061 – 60f. violet 7·00 20
P2062 – 70f. brown 7·50 20
P2063 – 80f. purple 5·50 20
P2063a – 90f. green 5·00 25
P2064 – 100f. green 8·75 20
P2065 – 200f. violet 11·00 35
P2066 – 300f. mauve 20·00 1·10
P2067 – 500f. yellow 30·00 1·50

DESIGNS: 10f. to 40f. Type 126 electric train; 50, 60, 70, 80, 90f. Type 160 electric train; 100, 200, 300f. Type 205 diesel-electric train; 500f. Type 210 diesel-electric train.

1970. Surch.
P2180 **P 477** 37f. on 25f. ochre 42·00 4·50
P2181 48f. on 35f. blue 4·25 3·50
P2182 53f. on 40f. red 4·25 3·50

P **551** Ostend Station

1971. Figures of value in black.
P2192 **P 551** 32f. ochre 1·25 1·10
P2193 37f. grey 10·50 11·00
P2194 42f. blue 1·75 1·50
P2195 44f. mauve 1·75 1·50
P2196 46f. violet 2·00 1·50
P2197 50f. red 1·75 1·50
P2198 52f. brown 10·50 11·00
P2199 54f. green 5·25 4·00
P2200 61f. blue 2·40 2·00

1972. Nos. P2192/5 and P2198/200 surch in figures.
P2256 **P 551** 34f. on 32f. ochre 1·90 80
P2257 40f. on 37f. grey 1·90 80
P2258 47f. on 44f. mauve 2·10 80
P2259 53f. on 42f. blue 2·75 80
P2260 56f. on 52f. brown 2·50 80
P2261 59f. on 54f. green 2·75 80
P2262 66f. on 61f. blue 3·00 70

P **575** Emblems within Bogie Wheels

1972. 50th Anniv of Int Railways Union (U.I.C.).
P2266 **P 575** 100f. black, red and green 7·00 1·60

See also No. 2274.

P **624** Global Emblem

1974. 4th International Symposium of Railway Cybernetics, Washington.
P2353 **P 624** 100f. black, red and yellow 4·25 1·25

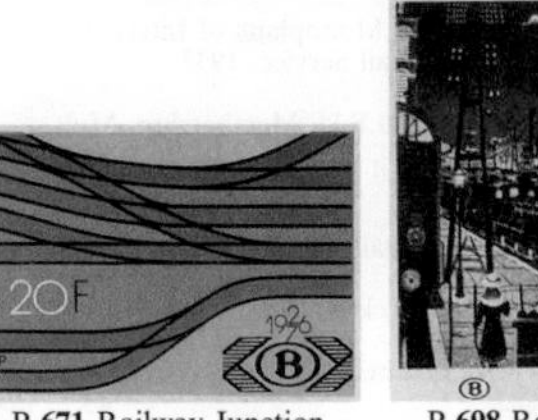

P **671** Railway Junction

P **698** Railway Station at Night

1976.
P2431 **P 671** 20f. black, bl & lilac 95 75
P2432 50f. black, green and turquoise 1·75 75
P2433 100f. black & orange 3·25 1·00
P2434 150f. black, mauve and deep mauve 5·00 1·00

1977.
P2505 **P 698** 1000f. mult 42·00 14·00

P **753** Goods Wagon, Type 2216 A8

1980. Values in black.
P2615 **P 753** 1f. ochre 15 15
P2616 2f. red 15 15
P2617 3f. blue 15 15
P2618 4f. blue 15 15
P2619 5f. brown 20 15
P2620 6f. orange 30 20
P2621 7f. violet 35 20
P2622 8f. black 35 20
P2623 9f. green 40 35
P2624 – 10f. brown 40 30
P2625 – 20f. blue 1·00 35
P2626 – 30f. ochre 1·75 30
P2627 – 40f. mauve 2·10 30
P2628 – 50f. purple 2·40 35
P2629 – 60f. olive 2·75 35
P2630 – 70f. blue 3·50 2·00
P2631 – 80f. purple 4·00 60
P2632 – 90f. mauve 4·50 2·10
P2633 – 100f. red 5·00 85
P2634 – 200f. brown 9·75 1·25
P2635 – 300f. olive 14·50 1·60
P2636 – 500f. purple 26·00 2·75

DESIGNS: 10f. to 40f. Packet wagon, Type 3614 A5; 50f. to 90f. Self-discharging wagon, Type 1000 D; 100f. to 500f. Tanker wagon, Type 2000 G.

P **833** Electric Train entering Station

1985. 150th Anniv of Belgian Railways. Paintings by P. Delvaux. Multicoloured.
P2824 250f. Type P **833** 12·50 5·00
P2825 500f. Electric trains in station 24·00 9·50

RAILWAY PARCEL TAX STAMPS

1940. As Nos. P399 and P404 but colours changed.
P876 **P 84** 5f. brown 25 25
P877 10f. black 3·50 3·50

P **779** Electric Locomotive at Station

P **877** Buildings and Electric Locomotive

1982.
P2703 **P 779** 10f. red & black 1·40 25
P2704 20f. green & blk 1·60 1·25
P2705 50f. brown & blk 3·00 55
P2706 100f. blue & blk 5·50 85

1987.
P2923 **P 877** 10f. red 75 40
P2924 20f. green 1·25 1·10
P2925 50f. brown 3·50 1·25
P2926 100f. purple 6·25 2·50
P2927 150f. brown 9·50 2·75

RAILWAY OFFICIAL STAMPS

For use on the official mail of the Railway Company.

1929. Stamps of 1922 optd with winged wheel.
O481 **81** 5c. slate 25 20
O482 10c. green 30 25
O483 35c. green 35 25
O484 60c. olive 45 15
O485 1f.50 blue 15·00 7·00
O486 1f.75 blue 1·90 50

1929. Stamps of 1929 optd with winged wheel.
O534 **104** 5c. green 15 10
O535 10c. bistre 15 20
O536 25c. red 1·90 45
O537 35c. green 60 20
O538 40c. purple 60 20
O539 50c. blue 35 20
O540 60c. mauve 14·00 7·50
O541 70c. brown 4·00 95
O542 75c. blue 5·25 75

1932. Stamps of 1931–34 optd with winged wheel.
O620 **126** 10c. green 55 50
O677 **127** 35c. green 9·50 50
O678 **142** 70c. green 3·25 30
O679 **121** 75c. brown 1·60 35

1936. Stamps of 1936 optd with winged wheel.
O721 **152** 10c. olive 15 15
O722 35c. green 10 10
O723 40c. lilac 20 20
O724 50c. blue 40 45
O725 **153** 70c. brown 2·75 3·00
O726 75c. olive 45 25

1941. Optd **B** in oval frame.
O948 **152** 10c. green 15 15
O949 40c. lilac 15 15
O950 50c. blue 15 15
O951 **153** 1f. red (No. 747) 15 10
O952a 1f. red (No. 748) 10 15
O953 2f.25 black 35 35
O954 **155** 2f.25 violet 25 35

1942. Nos. O722, O725 and O726 surch.
O983 **152** 10c. on 35c. green 10 10
O984 **153** 50c. on 70c. brown 10 15
O985 50c. on 75c. olive 10 15

O **221**

O **283**

1946. Designs incorporating letter "B".
O1156 **O 221** 10c. green 10 15
O1157 20c. violet 2·40 70
O1158 50c. blue 10 10
O1159 65c. purple 3·00 75
O1160 75c. mauve 15 15
O1161 90c. violet 3·50 25
O1240 – 1f.35 brn (as 1219) 1·75 45
O1241 – 1f.75 green (as 1220) 4·75 45
O1242 **239** 3f. purple 21·00 6·50
O1243 **240** 3f.15 blue 9·25 5·75
O1244 4f. blue 17·00 7·50

1952.
O1424 **O 283** 10c. orange 30 10
O1425 20c. red 2·75 55
O1426 30c. green 1·25 35
O1427 40c. brown 30 15
O1428 50c. blue 25 10
O1429 60c. mauve 55 20
O1430 65c. purple 24·00 17·00
O1431 80c. green 4·00 90
O1432 90c. blue 6·00 85
O1433 1f. red 40 10
O1433a 1f.50 grey 10 10
O1434 2f.50 brown 20 10

1954. As T **289** (King Baudouin) but with letter "B" incorporated in design.
O1523 1f.50 black 30 20
O1524 2f. red 32·00 30
O1525 2f. green 35 20
O1526 2f.50 brown 26·00 50
O1527 3f. mauve 1·40 20
O1528 3f.50 green 65 20
O1529 4f. blue 80 25
O1530 6f. red 1·40 45

1971. As Nos. 2209/20 but with letter "B" incorporated in design.
O2224 3f. green 80 60
O2225 3f.50 brown 25 10
O2226 4f. blue 90 40
O2227 4f.50 purple 25 20
O2228 4f.50 blue 30 20
O2229 5f. violet 30 20
O2230 6f. red 30 10
O2231 6f.50 violet 35 20
O2232a 7f. red 30 15
O2233 8f. black 35 20
O2233a 9f. brown 40 10
O2234 10f. red 40 20
O2235 15f. violet 50 30
O2236 25f. purple 1·10 20
O2237 30f. brown 1·25 25

1977. As T **684** but with letter "B" incorporated in design.
O2455 50c. brown 10 10
O2456 1f. mauve 10 10
O2457 2f. orange 20 15
O2458 4f. brown 25 10
O2459 5f. green 25 25

BELIZE Pt. 1

British Honduras was renamed Belize on 1 June 1973 and the country became independent within the Commonwealth on 21 September 1981.

100 cents = 1 dollar.

1973. Nos. 256/66 and 277/8 of British Honduras optd **BELIZE** and two stars.

347 – ½c. multicoloured 10 20
348 **63** 1c. black, brown and yellow 10 20
349 – 2c. black, green and yellow 10 20
350 – 3c. black, brown and lilac 10 10
351 – 4c. multicoloured 10 20
352 – 5c. black and red 10 20
353 – 10c. multicoloured 15 15
354 – 15c. multicoloured 20 20
355 – 25c. multicoloured 35 35
356 – 50c. multicoloured 65 75
357 – $1 multicoloured . . . . . 75 1·50
358 – $2 multicoloured . . . . . 1·25 2·75
359 – $5 multicoloured . . . . . 1·40 4·75

1973. Royal Wedding. As T **47** of Anguilla. Background colours given. Multicoloured.

360 26c. blue 15 10
361 50c. brown 15 20

82 Mozambique Mouthbrooder

1974. As Nos. 256/66 and 276/78 of British Honduras. Multicoloured.

362 ½c. Type **82** 10 50
363 1c. Spotted jewfish 10 30
364 2c. White-lipped peccary ("Waree") 10 30
365 3c. Misty grouper 10 10
366 4c. Collared anteater 10 30
367 5c. Bonefish 10 30
368 10c. Paca ("Gibnut") 15 15
369 15c. Dolphin 20 20
370 25c. Kinkajou ("Night Walker") 35 35
371 50c. Mutton snapper 60 70
372 $1 Tayra ("Bush Dog") . . . 75 1·50
373 $2 Great barracuda . . . . . 1·25 2·50
374 $5 Puma . . . . 1·50 5·50

83 Deer

1974. Mayan Artefacts (1st series). Pottery Motifs. Multicoloured.

375 3c. Type **83** 10 10
376 6c. Jaguar deity 10 10
377 16c. Sea monster 15 10
378 26c. Cormorant 25 10
379 50c. Scarlet macaw 40 40

See also Nos. 398/402.

84 "Parides arcas"

1974. Butterflies of Belize. Multicoloured.

380 ½c. Type **84** . . . . 1·00 4·50
381 1c. "Evenus regalis" . . . . 1·00 1·75
405 2c. "Colobura dirce" 50 70
406 3c. "Catonephele numilia" . . 1·25 70
407 4c. "Battus belus" . . . . . 3·00 30
408 5c. "Callicore patelina" . . . 3·25 30
386 10c. "Diaethria astala" . . . 1·50 70
410 15c. "Nessaea aglaura" . . . 75 70
388 16c. "Prepona pseudojoiceyi" 5·00 7·50
412 25c. "Papilio thoas" . . . . 6·50 40
390 26c. "Hamadryas arethusa" 2·00 4·25
413 35c. Type **84** . . . . 13·00 4·50
391 50c. "Panthiades bathildis" 3·25 65
392 $1 "Caligo uranus" . . . . . 6·50 6·50
393 $2 "Heliconius sapho" . . . 4·00 1·25
394 $5 "Eurytides philolaus" . . 5·50 6·00
395 $10 "Philaethria dido" . . . 10·00 4·00

85 Churchill when Prime Minister, and Coronation Scene

1974. Birth Centenary of Sir Winston Churchill. Multicoloured.

396 50c. Type **85** 20 20
397 $1 Churchill in stetson, and Williamsburg Liberty Bell 30 30

86 The Actun Balam Vase

1975. Mayan Artefacts (2nd series). Multicoloured.

398 3c. Type **86** 10 10
399 6c. Seated figure 10 10
400 16c. Costumed priest 25 15
401 26c. Head with headdress . . 35 20
402 50c. Layman and priest . . . 45 1·75

87 Musicians

1975. Christmas. Multicoloured.

435 6c. Type **87** 10 10
436 26c. Children and "crib" . . 20 10
437 50c. Dancer and drummers (vert) 30 55
438 $1 Family and map (vert) . . 55 1·60

88 William Wrigley Jr. and Chicle Tapping

1976. Bicent of American Revolution. Mult.

439 10c. Type **88** 10 10
440 35c. Charles Lindbergh . . . 20 40
441 $1 J. L. Stephens (archaeologist) . . . . . . 50 1·50

89 Cycling

1976. Olympic Games, Montreal. Multicoloured.

442 35c. Type **89** 15 10
443 45c. Running 20 15
444 $1 Shooting . . . . 35 1·40

1976. No. 390 surch **20c**.

445 20c. on 26c. multicoloured . . 1·50 1·75

1976. West Indian Victory in World Cricket Cup. As Nos. 559/60 of Barbados.

446 35c. multicoloured 40 50
447 $1 black and purple . . . . 60 2·00

1976. No. 426 surch **5c**.

448 5c. on 15c. multicoloured . . 1·10 2·75

92 Queen and Bishops

1977. Silver Jubilee. Multicoloured.

449 10c. Royal Visit, 1975 . . . 10 10
450 35c. Queen and Rose Window 15 15
451 $2 Type **92** 45 90

93 Red-capped Manakin

94 Laboratory Workers

1977. Birds (1st series). Multicoloured.

452 8c. Type **93** 75 55
453 10c. Hooded oriole 90 30
454 25c. Blue-crowned motmot 1·25 55
455 35c. Slaty-breasted tinamou 1·50 75
456 45c. Ocellated turkey . . . . 1·75 1·25
457 $1 White hawk . . . . . . 3·00 5·50
MS458 110 × 133 mm. Nos. 452/7 8·25 11·00

See also Nos. 467/78, 488/94 and 561/7.

1977. 75th Anniv of Pan-American Health Organization. Multicoloured.

459 35c. Type **94** 20 20
460 $1 Mobile medical unit . . . 40 65
MS461 126 × 95 mm. Nos. 459/60 85 1·40

1978. Nos. 386 and 413 optd **BELIZE DEFENCE FORCE 1ST JANUARY 1978**.

462 10c. "Diaethria astala" . . . 75 1·50
463 35c. Type **84** . . . . 1·50 2·25

96 White Lion of Mortimer

97 "Russelia sarmentosa"

1978. 25th Anniv of Coronation.

464 **96** 75c. brown, red and silver 20 30
465 – 75c. multicoloured 20 30
466 – 75c. brown, red and silver 20 30

DESIGNS: No. 465, Queen Elizabeth II; 466, Jaguar (Maya god of Day and Night).

1978. Birds (2nd series). As T **93**. Multicoloured.

467 10c. White-capped parrot("White-crowned Parrot") 55 30
468 25c. Crimson-collared tanager 80 45
469 35c. Black-headed trogon ("Citreoline Trogon") . . . 1·10 55
470 45c. American finfoot ("Sungrebe") . . . . . . 1·25 1·75
471 50c. Muscovy duck . . . . . 1·40 2·50
472 $1 King vulture . . . . . . 2·00 6·50
MS473 111 × 133 mm. Nos. 467/72 8·00 11·00

1978. Christmas. Wild Flowers and Ferns. Mult.

474 10c. Type **97** 15 10
475 15c. "Lygodium polymorphum" 20 15
476 35c. "Heliconia aurantiaca" 20 20
477 45c. "Adiantum tetraphyllum" 20 40
478 50c. "Angelonia ciliaris" . . 35 50
479 $1 "Thelypteris obliterata" 50 1·25

98 Fairchild Monoplane of Internal Airmail Service, 1937

1979. Centenary of U.P.U. Membership. Mult.

480 5c. Type **98** 25 30
481 10c. "Heron H" (mail boat), 1949 . . . . 25 10
482 35c. Internal mail service, 1920 (canoe) 25 20
483 45c. Steam Creek Railway mail, 1910 . . . . 45 55
484 50c. Mounted mail courier, 1882 . . . . 45 60
485 $1 "Eagle" (mail boat), 1856 80 2·50

1979. No. 413 surch **15c**.

487 **84** 15c. on 35c. multicoloured 2·25 1·75

1979. Birds (3rd series). As T **93**. Multicoloured.

488 10c. Boat-billed heron . . . 65 30
489 25c. Grey-necked wood rail 90 30
490 35c. Lineated woodpecker . . 1·10 55
491 45c. Blue-grey tanager . . . 1·25 70
492 50c. Laughing falcon . . . . 1·25 1·25
493 $1 Long-tailed hermit . . . . 1·60 4·50
MS494 113 × 136 mm. Nos. 488/93 4·75 6·00

101 Paslow Building, Belize G.P.O.

1979. 25th Anniv of Coronation. Multicoloured.

495 25c. Type **101** . . . . 1·50 10
496 50c. Houses of Parliament . . 2·00 10
497 75c. Coronation State Coach 2·50 15
498 $1 Queen on horseback (vert) 3·25 20
499 $2 Prince of Wales (vert) . . 3·25 35
500 $3 Queen and Duke of Edinburgh (vert) . . . . . 3·25 35
501 $4 Portrait of Queen (vert) 3·25 40
502 $5 St. Edward's Crown (vert) 3·50 40
MS503 Two sheets, both 126 × 95 mm: (a) $5 Princess Anne on horseback at Montreal Olympics (vert); $10 Queen at Montreal Olympics (vert). (b) $15 As Type **101** Set of 2 sheets . . 24·00

102 Mortimer and Vaughan "Safety" Airplane, 1910

1979. Death Centenary of Sir Rowland Hill. 60th Anniv of I.C.A.O. (International Civil Aviation Organization), previously Int Commission for Air Navigation. Multicoloured.

504 4c. Type **102** 50 10
505 25c. Boeing 720 . . . . . . 1·50 20
506 50c. Concorde . . . . 4·25 30
507 75c. Handley Page H.P.18 W.8b (1922) . . . . . . 2·00 30
508 $1 Avro Type F (1912) . . . 2·00 30
509 $1.50 Samuel Cody's biplane (1910) . . . . 2·75 30
510 $2 A.V. Roe Triplane I (1909) . . . . 2·75 40
511 $3 Santos Dumont's biplane "14 bis" (1906) . . . . 2·75 45
512 $4 Wright Type A . . . . . 3·00 65
MS513 Two sheets: (a) 115 × 95 mm. $5 Dunne D-5 (1910), $5 G.B. 1969 Concorde stamp; (b) 130 × 95 mm. $10 Boeing 720 (different) Set of 2 sheets . . . 21·00

103 Handball

104 Olympic Torch

1979. Olympic Games, Moscow (1980). Mult.

514 25c. Type **103** 45 10
515 50c. Weightlifting 65 10
516 75c. Athletics 90 15
517 $1 Football . . . . 1·25 20
518 $2 Yachting . . . . 1·75 25
519 $3 Swimming . . . . 2·00 30
520 $4 Boxing . . . . 2·50 30
521 $5 Cycling . . . . 9·00 90
MS522 Two sheets: (a) 126 × 92 mm. $5 Athletics (different), $10 Boxing (different); (b) 92 × 126 mm. $15 As $5 Set of 2 sheets . . . . . 16·00

1979. Winter Olympic Games, Lake Placid (1980). Multicoloured.

523 25c. Type **104** 20 10
524 50c. Giant slalom 45 15
525 75c. Figure-skating 65 15
526 $1 Downhill skiing 80 15
527 $2 Speed-skating . . . . . . 1·60 20
528 $3 Cross-country skiing . . . 2·50 30
529 $4 Shooting . . . . 3·00 40
530 $5 Gold, Silver and Bronze medals . . . . 3·50 45
MS531 Two sheets: (a) 127 × 90 mm. $5 Lighting the Olympic Flame, $10 Gold, Silver and Bronze medals (different); (b) 90 × 127 mm. $15 Olympic Torch (different) Set of 2 sheets . . . 20·00

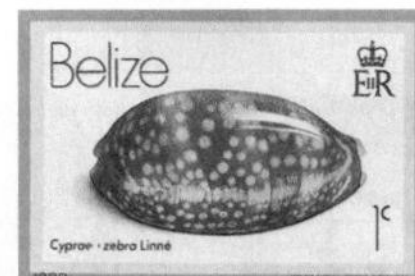

105 Measled Cowrie

1980. Shells. Multicoloured.
532 1c. Type **105** 55 10
533 2c. Callico clam 70 10
534 3c. Altantic turkey wing (vert) 80 10
535 4c. Leafy jewel box (vert) 80 10
536 5c. Trochlear latirus 80 10
537 10c. Alphabet cone (vert) 1·00 10
538 15c. Cabrits murex (vert) 1·40 10
539 20c. Stiff pen shell 1·50 10
540 25c. Little knobbed scallop (vert) 1·50 10
541 35c. Glory of the Atlantic cone (vert) 1·75 10
542 45c. Sunrise tellin (vert) 2·00 10
543 50c. "Leucozonia nassa leucozonalis" 2·00 10
544 85c. Triangular typhis 3·00 10
545 $1 Queen or pink conch (vert) 3·25 10
546 $2 Rooster-tail conch (vert) 5·00 30
547 $5 True tulip 7·50 50
548 $10 Star arene 9·50 90
MS549 Two sheets, each 125 × 90 mm. (a) Nos. 544 and 547. (b) Nos. 546 and 548 40·00 15·00

106 Girl and Flower Arrangement **108** Jabiru

1980. International Year of the Child (1st issue). Multicoloured.
550 25c. Type **106** 45 10
551 50c. Boy holding football 70 10
552 75c. Boy with butterfly 1·00 10
553 $1 Girl holding doll 1·00 10
554 $1.50 Boy carrying basket of fruit 1·50 15
555 $2 Boy holding reticulated cowrie-helmet shell 1·75 20
556 $3 Girl holding posy 2·25 25
557 $4 Boy and girl wrapped in blanket 2·50 30
MS558 130 × 95 mm. $5 Three children of different races. $5 "Madonna with Cat" (A. Dürer) (each 35 × 53 mm). 9·00
MS559 111 × 151 mm. $10 Children and Christmas tree (73 × 110 mm). 9·00
See also Nos. 583/91.

1980. No. 412 surch **10c**.
560 10c. on 25c. "Papilio thoas" 1·25 1·25

1980. Birds (4th series). Multicoloured.
561 10c. Type **108** 7·00 2·75
562 25c. Barred antshrike 8·00 2·75
563 35c. Northern royal flycatcher ("Royal Flycatcher") 8·00 2·75
564 45c. White-necked puffbird 8·00 3·00
565 50c. Ornate hawk-eagle 8·00 3·00
566 $1 Golden-masked tanager 8·50 3·75
MS567 85 × 90 mm. $2 Type **108**, $3 As $1 32·00 18·00

109 Speed Skating **111** Witch in Sky

1980. Winter Olympic Games, Lake Placid. Medal Winners. Multicoloured.
568 25c. Type **109** 30 15
569 50c. Ice-hockey 50 15
570 75c. Figure-skating 60 15
571 $1 Alpine-skiing 85 15
572 $1.50 Giant slalom (women) 1·25 25
573 $2 Speed-skating (women) 1·50 30
574 $3 Cross-country skiing 2·25 40
575 $5 Giant slalom 3·50 55
MS576 Two sheets: (a) 126 × 91 mm. $5 Type **109**; $10 Type **109**; (b) 91 × 126 mm. $10 As 75 c. Set of 2 sheets 16·00

1980. "ESPAMER" International Stamp Exhibition, Madrid. Nos. 560/5 optd **BELIZE ESPAMER '80 MADRID 3-12 OCT 1980** and emblem (Nos. 577/9) or surch also.
577 10c. Type **107** 7·00 2·75
578 25c. Barred antshrike 7·50 3·00
579 35c. Northern royal flycatcher 7·50 3·00
580 40c. on 45c. White-necked puffbird 8·00 3·25
581 40c. on 50c. Ornate hawk eagle 8·00 3·25
582 40c. on $1 Golden-masked tanager 8·50 3·25

1980. International Year of the Child (2nd issue). "Sleeping Beauty".
583 **111** 25c. multicoloured 1·75 15
584 – 40c. multicoloured 2·00 15
585 – 50c. multicoloured 2·25 15
586 – 75c. multicoloured 2·50 20
587 – $1 multicoloured 2·50 25
588 – $1.50 multicoloured 3·00 40
589 – $3 multicoloured 4·00 50
590 – $4 multicoloured 4·00 55
MS591 Two sheets: (a) 82 × 110 mm. $8 "Paumgartner Altar-piece" (Dürer); (b) 110 × 82 mm. $5 Marriage ceremony, $5 Sleeping Beauty and Prince on horseback Set of 2 sheets 21·00
DESIGNS: 40c. to $4, Illustrations from the story.

112 H.M. Queen Elizabeth the Queen Mother

1980. 80th Birthday of H.M. Queen Elizabeth the Queen Mother.
592 **112** $1 multicoloured 3·00 65
MS593 82 × 110 mm, $5 As Type **112** (41 × 32 mm) 14·00 4·75

113 The Annunciation **115** Paul Harris (founder)

1980. Christmas. Multicoloured.
594 25c. Type **113** 65 10
595 50c. Bethlehem 1·25 10
596 75c. The Holy Family 1·50 10
597 $1 The Nativity 1·60 10
598 $1.50 The Flight into Egypt 1·75 15
599 $2 Shepherds following the Star 2·00 20
600 $3 Virgin, Child and Angel 2·25 25
601 $4 Adoration of the Kings 2·25 30
MS602 Two sheets, each 82 × 111 mm: (a) $5 As $1: (b) $10 As $3 Set of 2 sheets 14·00

1981. "WIPA" International Stamp Exhibition, Vienna. Nos. 598 and 601 surch.
603 $1 on $1.50 The Flight into Egypt 8·00 1·90
604 $2 on $4 Adoration of the Kings 9·00 2·75
MS605 82 × 111 mm. $2 on $10 Virgin, Child and Angel 10·00 4·50

1981. 75th Anniv of Rotary International. Mult.
606 25c. Type **115** 2·00 25
607 50c. Emblems of Rotary activities 2·50 35
608 $1 75th Anniversary emblem 3·00 65
609 $1.50 Educational scholarship programme (horiz) 3·75 1·00
610 $2 "Project Hippocrates" 4·25 1·40
611 $3 Emblems 5·50 2·00
612 $5 Emblems and handshake (horiz) 6·50 3·25
MS613 Two sheets: (a) 95 × 130 mm. $10 As 50c. (b) 130 × 95 mm, $5 As $1, $10 As $2 Set of 2 sheets 30·00

116 Coat of Arms of Prince of Wales **118** Athletics

1981. Royal Wedding. Mult. (a) Size 22 × 38 mm.
614 50c. Type **116** 45 50
615 $1 Prince Charles in military uniform 80 90
616 $1.50 Royal couple 1·25 1·50

(b) Size 25 × 42 mm, with gold borders.
617 50c. Type **116** 45 30
618 $1 As No. 615 80 50
619 $1.50 As No. 616 1·25 70
MS620 145 × 85 mm. $3 × 3 As Nos 614/16, but 30 × 47 mm. P 14 2·50 4·25

1981. No. 538 surch **10c**.
621 10c. on 15c. "Murex cabritii" 3·50 3·75

1981. History of the Olympics. Multicoloured.
622 85c. Type **118** 2·25 30
623 $1 Cycling 7·00 50
624 $1.50 Boxing 3·25 50
625 $2 1984 Games–Los Angeles and Sarajevo 4·00 50
626 $3 Baron de Coubertin 4·75 60
627 $5 Olympic Flame 6·00 70
MS628 Two sheets, each 175 × 123 mm: (a) $5 As $3, $10 As $5 (each 35 × 53 mm). P13½; (b) $15 As $2 (45 × 67 mm). P 14½. Set of 2 sheets 38·00

1981. Independence Commemoration (1st issue). Optd **Independence 21 Sept., 1981.** (a) On Nos. 532/44 and 546/8.
629 1c. Type **105** 1·00 10
630 2c. Callico clam 1·00 10
631 3c. Atlantic turkey wing (vert) 1·00 10
632 4c. Leafy jewel box (vert) 1·00 10
633 5c. Trochlear latirus 1·25 10
634 10c. Alphabet cone (vert) 1·50 10
635 15c. Cabrits murex (vert) 2·25 10
636 20c. Stiff pen shell 2·25 15
637 25c. Little knobbed scallop (vert) 2·50 25
638 35c. Glory of the Atlantic cone 2·50 30
639 45c. Sunrise tellin (vert) 3·00 40
640 50c. "Leucozonia nassa leucozonalis" 3·00 40
641 85c. Triangular typhis 4·75 90
642 $2 Rooster-tail conch (vert) 9·00 2·50
643 $5 True tulip 11·00 5·50
644 $10 Star arene 13·00 9·50
MS645 Two sheets, each 126 × 91 mm; (a) Nos. 641 and 643; (b) Nos. 642 and 644 Set of 2 sheets 40·00

(b) On Nos. 606/12.
646 25c. Type **115** 2·50 25
647 50c. Emblems of Rotary activities 2·75 35
648 $1 75th Anniversary emblem 3·25 65
649 $1.50 Educational scholarship programme 4·00 1·25
650 $2 "Project Hippocrates" 4·75 1·60
651 $3 Emblems 6·50 2·50
652 $5 Emblems and hand-shake 7·50 3·75
MS653 Two sheets: (a) 95 × 130 mm. $10 As 50c.; (b) 130 × 95 mm. $5 As $1, $10 As $2 Set of 2 sheets 40·00
See also Nos. 657/63.

1981. "ESPAMER" International Stamp Exhibition, Buenos Aires. No. 609 surch **$1 ESPAMER 81 BUENOS AIRES 13-22 NOV** and emblem.
654 $1 on $1.50 Educational scholarship programme 10·00 3·00
MS655 95 × 130 mm. $1 on $5 75th anniversary emblem, $1 on $10 "Project Hippocrates" 14·00 8·00

(121)

1981. "Philatelia 81" International Stamp Exhibition, Frankfurt. No. **MS**549 surch with T **121**.
MS656 Two sheets, each 125 × 90 mm: (a) $1 on 85c. "Tripterotyphis triangularis", $1 on $5 "Fasciolaria tulipa"; (b) $1 on $2 "Strombus gallus", $1 on $10 "Arene cruentata" Set of 2 sheets 55·00

122 Black Orchid **123** Uruguayan Footballer

1981. Independence Commemoration (2nd issue). Multicoloured.
657 10c. Belize Coat of Arms (horiz) 2·25 20
658 35c. Map of Belize 4·50 40
659 50c. Type **122** 9·00 1·25
660 85c. Baird's tapir (horiz) 3·00 1·25
661 $1 Mahogany tree 2·50 1·25
662 $2 Keel-billed toucan (horiz) 13·00 4·00
MS663 130 × 98 mm. $5 As 10c. 12·00 5·50

1981. World Cup Football Championship, Spain (1st issue). Multicoloured.
664 10c. Type **123** 2·25 20
665 25c. Italian footballer 3·25 20
666 50c. German footballer 4·00 45
667 $1 Brazilian footballer 5·00 70
668 $1.50 Argentinian footballer 6·50 1·50
669 $2 English footballer 7·00 1·75
MS670 Two sheets: (a) 145 × 115 mm. $2 "SPAIN '82" logo; (b) 155 × 115 mm. $3 Footballer (46 × 76 mm) Set of 2 sheets 28·00 7·50
See also Nos. 721/7.

124 H.M.S. "Centurion" (frigate)

1981. Sailing Ships. Multicoloured.
671 10c. Type **124** 3·00 40
672 25c. "Madagascar" (1837) 4·50 50
673 35c. Brig "Whitby" (1838) 5·00 55
674 55c. "China" (1838) 5·50 85
675 85c. "Swiftsure" (1850) 7·00 1·25
676 $2 "Windsor Castle" (1857) 10·00 3·00
MS677 110 × 87 mm. $5 Ships in battle 27·00 8·50

1982. "ESSEN '82" Int Stamp Exn, West Germany. Nos. 662 and 669 surch **$1 ESSEN 82**.
678 $1 on $2 Keel-billed toucan 9·00 2·50
679 $1 on $2 English footballer 9·00 2·50

126 Princess Diana

1982. 21st Birthday of Princess of Wales. (a) Size 22 × 38 mm.
680 **126** 50c. multicoloured 1·60 45
681 – $1 multicoloured 2·00 75
682 – $1.50 multicoloured 2·00 1·50

(b) Size 25 × 43 mm.
683 **126** 50c. multicoloured 1·60 30
684 – $1 multicoloured 2·00 60
685 – $1.50 multicoloured 2·00 1·10
MS686 145 × 85 mm. $3 × 3 As Nos. 680/2, but 30 × 47 mm. 2·75 3·00
DESIGNS: Portraits of Princess of Wales with different backgrounds.

127 Lighting Campfire

1982. 125th Birth Anniv of Lord Baden-Powell. Multicoloured.
687 10c. Type **127** 1·75 20
668 25c. Bird watching 4·50 30
689 35c. Three scouts, one playing guitar 2·75 30
690 50c. Hiking 3·00 55

691 85c. Scouts with flag . . . . 4·25 1·00
692 $2 Saluting . . . . 4·75 2·50
MS693 Two sheets: each 85 × 115 mm: (a) $2 Scout with flag; (b) $3 Portrait of Lord Baden-Powell Set of 2 sheets 32·00 13·00

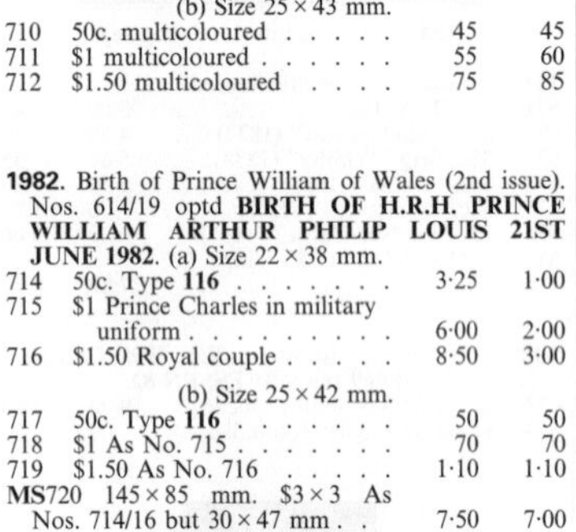

128 "Gorgonia ventalina"

1982. 1st Anniv of Independence. Marine Life. Multicoloured.
694 10c. Type **128** . . . . 2·00 20
695 35c. "Carpiuis corallinus" . . 3·25 20
696 50c. "Plexaura flexuasa" . . 3·75 45
697 85c. "Candylactis gigantea" . 4·00 60
698 $1 "Stenopus hispidus" . . . 5·00 90
699 $2 Sergeant major . . . . . 6·00 1·60
MS700 130 × 98 mm. $5 "Schyllarides aequinoclialis" 27·00 10·00

1982. "BELGICA 82" International Stamp Exhibition, Brussels. Nos. 687/92 optd **BELGICA 82 INT. YEAR OF THE CHILD SIR ROWLAND HILL 1795 1879 Picasso CENTENARY OF BIRTH** and emblems.
701 10c. Type **127** . . . . 2·50 40
702 25c. Bird watching . . . . . 6·50 1·25
703 35c. Three scouts, one playing guitar . . . . . . 3·75 1·00
704 50c. Hiking . . . . 4·00 1·50
705 85c. Scouts with flag . . . . 9·50 2·75
706 $2 Saluting . . . . 10·00 7·50

1982. Birth of Prince William of Wales (1st issue). Nos. 680/5 optd **BIRTH OF H.R.H. PRINCE WILLIAM ARTHUR PHILIP LOUIS 21ST JUNE 1982**. (a) Size 22 × 38 mm.
707 50c. multicoloured 45 45
708 $1 multicoloured 55 60
709 $1.50 multicoloured 75 85

(b) Size 25 × 43 mm.
710 50c. multicoloured 45 45
711 $1 multicoloured 55 60
712 $1.50 multicoloured 75 85

1982. Birth of Prince William of Wales (2nd issue). Nos. 614/19 optd **BIRTH OF H.R.H. PRINCE WILLIAM ARTHUR PHILIP LOUIS 21ST JUNE 1982**. (a) Size 22 × 38 mm.
714 50c. Type **116** . . . . 3·25 1·00
715 $1 Prince Charles in military uniform . . . . 6·00 2·00
716 $1.50 Royal couple . . . . . 8·50 3·00

(b) Size 25 × 42 mm.
717 50c. Type **116** 50 50
718 $1 As No. 715 . . . . 70 70
719 $1.50 As No. 716 . . . . . 1·10 1·10
MS720 145 × 85 mm. $3 × 3 As Nos. 714/16 but 30 × 47 mm . . 7·50 7·00

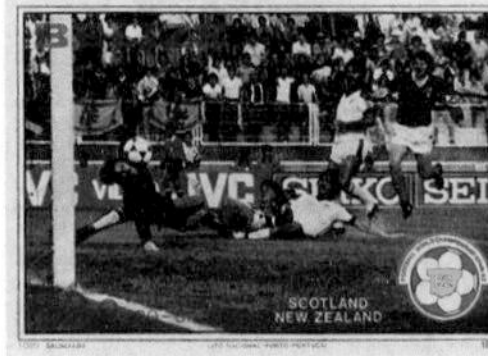

131 Scotland v New Zealand

1982. World Cup Football Championship, Spain (2nd issue). Multicoloured.
721 20c.+10c. Type **131** . . . . 2·50 1·25
722 30c.+15c. Scotland v New Zealand (different) . . . 2·50 1·25
723 40c.+20c. Kuwait v France . 2·75 1·25
724 60c.+50c. Italy v Brazil . . . 3·25 1·60
725 $1+50c. France v Northern Ireland . . . . 4·00 1·75
726 $1.50+75c. Austria v Chile . 4·75 2·25
MS727 Two sheets: (a) 91 × 137 mm. $1+50c. Germany v Italy (50 × 70 mm); (b) 122 × 116 mm. $2+$1 England v France (50 × 70 mm) Set of 2 sheets . . 18·00 9·50

133 Belize Cathedral

1983. Visit of Pope John Paul II.
729 **133** 50c. multicoloured . . . . 2·75 1·50
MS730 135 × 110 mm. $2.50, Pope John Paul II (30 × 47 mm.) . . 22·00 8·00

134 Map of Belize

1983. Commonwealth Day. Multicoloured.
731 35c. Type **134** 35 35
732 50c. "Maya Stella" from Lamanai Indian church (horiz) 40 50
733 85c. Supreme Court Building (horiz) 50 75
734 $2 University Centre, Belize (horiz) . . . . 85 2·50

1983. No. 658 surch **10c.**
735 10c. on 35c. Map of Belize 30·00

136 De Lana-Terzis "Aerial Ship", 1670

1983. Bicentenary of Manned Flight. Multicoloured.
736 10c. Type **136** . . . . 2·50 65
737 25c. De Gusmao's "La Passarole", 1709 . . . . . 3·25 70
738 50c. Guyton de Morveau's balloon with oars, 1784 . . 3·50 1·00
739 85c. Airship . . . . 4·25 1·25
740 $1 Airship "Clement Bayard" 4·50 1·60
741 $1.50 Beardmore airship R-34 5·00 3·25
MS742 Two sheets: (a) 125 × 84 mm. $3 Charles Green's balloon "Royal Vauxhall"; (b) 115 × 128 mm. $3 Montgolfier balloon, 1783 (vert) Set of 2 sheets 27·00 6·00

1983. Nos. 662 and 699 surch **$1.25**.
743 $1.25 on $2 Keel-billed toucan . . . . 14·00 11·00
744 $1.25 on $2 Sergeant major 6·00 8·50

1983. No. 541 surch **10c**.
746 10c. on 35c. Glory of the Atlantic cone . . . . . . 38·00

141 Altun Ha

1983. Maya Monuments. Multicoloured.
747 10c. Type **141** 10 10
748 15c. Xunantunich 10 10
749 75c. Cerros 30 40
750 $3 Lamanal . . . . 70 1·75
MS751 102 × 72 mm. $3 Xunantunich (different) . . . . 1·00 1·75

142 Belmopan Earth Station

1983. World Communications Year. Multicoloured.
752 10c. Type **142** 30 10
753 15c. "Telstar 2" 40 25
754 75c. U.P.U. logo . . . . . . 70 1·75
755 $2 M.V. "Heron H" mail service . . . . 1·25 4·50

143 Jaguar Cub

1983. The Jaguar. Multicoloured.
756 5c. Type **143** 30 75
757 10c. Adult jaguar 35 45
758 85c. Jaguar in river . . . . . 1·40 3·00
759 $1 Jaguar on rock . . . . . 1·50 3·25
MS760 102 × 72 mm. $3 Jaguar in tree (44 × 28 mm). P 13½ × 14 1·50 2·50

144 Pope John Paul II

1983. Christmas.
761 **144** 10c. multicoloured 25 10
762 15c. multicoloured 25 10
763 75c. multicoloured 50 60
764 $2 multicoloured . . . . 80 1·40
MS765 102 × 72 mm. $3 multicoloured . . . . 1·50 4·00

145 Four-eyed Butterflyfish

1984. Marine Life from the Belize Coral Reef. Multicoloured.
766 1c. Type **145** . . . . 25 1·25
767 2c. Cushion star . . . . . . 30 1·00
768 3c. Flower coral . . . . . . 35 1·00
769 4c. Royal gramma ("Fairy basslet") . . . . 40 1·00
770 5c. Spanish hogfish . . . . 45 1·00
771 6c. Star-eyed hermit crab . . 45 1·25
772a 10c. Sea fans and fire sponge 50 35
773a 15c. Blue-headed wrasse . . 70 60
774a 25c. Blue-striped grunt . . . 80 80
775a 50c. Coral crab . . . . . . 1·00 1·75
776a 60c. Tube sponge . . . . . 1·00 1·75
777 75c. Brain coral . . . . . . 1·00 1·50
778 $1 Yellow-tailed snapper . . 1·00 1·25
779 $2 Common lettuce slug . . 1·00 55
780 $5 Three-spotted damselfish 1·25 70
781 $10 Rock beauty . . . . . 1·50 1·10

1984. Visit of the Archbishop of Canterbury. Nos. 772 and 775 optd **VISIT OF THE LORD ARCHBISHOP OF CANTERBURY 8th-11th MARCH 1984**.
782 10c. Sea fans and fire sponge 1·00 50
783 50c. Coral crab . . . . . . 1·75 2·00

147 Shooting

1984. Olympic Games, Los Angeles. Multicoloured. (a) As T **147**.
784 25c. Type **147** 30 25
785 75c. Boxing 50 70
786 $1 Marathon 60 90
787 $2 Cycling . . . . 2·75 2·75
MS788 101 × 72 mm. $3 Statue of discus thrower . . . . 1·60 3·00

(b) Similar designs to T **147** but Royal cypher replaced by Queen's Head.
789 5c. Marathon 20 90
790 20c. Sprinting 25 90
791 25c. Shot-putting 25 90
792 $2 Olympic torch . . . . . 35 1·25

148 British Honduras 1866 1s. Stamp

1984. "Ausipex" International Stamp Exhibition, Melbourne. Multicoloured.
793 15c. Type **148** 25 15
794 30c. British mail coach, 1784 35 25
795 65c. Sir Rowland Hill and Penny Black 65 65
796 75c. British Honduras railway locomotive, 1910 . . . . . 70 75
797 $2 Royal Exhibition Buildings, Melbourne (46 × 28 mm) . . . . 1·00 2·25
MS798 103 × 73 mm. $3 Australia 1932 Sydney Harbour Bridge 5s. and British Honduras 1866 1s. stamps (44 × 28 mm). P 13½ × 14 1·10 2·00

149 Prince Albert

150 White-fronted Amazon ("White-fronted Parrot")

1984. 500th Anniv (1985) of British Royal House of Tudor. Multicoloured.
799 50c. Type **149** 25 45
800 50c. Queen Victoria 25 45
801 75c. King George VI 30 55
802 75c. Queen Elizabeth the Queen Mother 30 55
803 $1 Princess of Wales 40 75
804 $1 Prince of Wales 40 75
MS805 147 × 97 mm. $1.50, Prince Philip; $1.50, Queen Elizabeth II 1·25 2·00

1984. Parrots. Multicoloured.
806 $1 Type **150** . . . . 1·75 2·25
807 $1 White-capped parrot (horiz) . . . . 1·75 2·25
808 $1 Mealy amazon ("Mealy Parrot") (horiz) . . . . . 1·75 2·25
809 $1 Red-lored amazon ("Red-lored Parrot") . . . . . . 1·75 2·25
MS810 102 × 73 mm. $3 Scarlet macaw . . . . 3·25 4·00
Nos. 806/9 were issued together, se-tenant, forming a composite design.

151 Effigy Censer, 1450 (Santa Rita Site)

153 White-tailed Kite

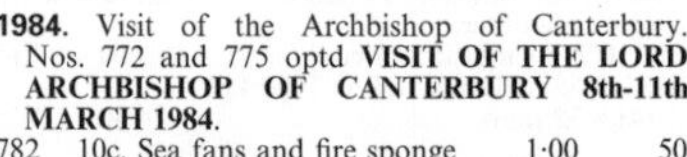

152 Governor-General inspecting Girl Guides

1984. Maya Artefacts. Multicoloured.
811 25c. Type **151** 30 25
812 75c. Vase, 675 (Actun Chapat) 60 80
813 $1 Tripod vase, 500 (Santa Rita site) . . . . 65 1·00
814 $2 Sun god Kinich Ahau, 600 (Altun Ha site) . . . . . 90 2·50

1985. International Youth Year and 75th Anniv of Girl Guides Movement. Multicoloured.
815 25c. Type **152** 30 15
816 50c. Girl Guides camping . . 45 30
817 90c. Checking map on hike 60 45
818 $1.25 Students in laboratory 70 60
819 $2 Lady Baden-Powell (founder) 90 75

1985. Birth Bicentenary of John J. Audubon (ornithologist). Designs showing original paintings. Multicoloured.
820 10c. Type **153** 50 60
821 15c. Ruby-crowned kinglet ("Cuvier's Kinglet") (horiz) 50 60
822 25c. Painted bunting 60 60
822a 60c. As 25c. . . . . 20·00 8·50
823 75c. Belted kingfisher . . . 60 1·40
824 $1 Common cardinal ("Northern Cardinal") . . 60 2·25
825 $3 Long-billed curlew (horiz) . . . . 1·00 3·00
MS826 139 × 99 mm. $5 "John James Audubon" (John Syme) 2·50 2·00

154 The Queen Mother with Princess Elizabeth, 1928

1985. Life and Times of Queen Elizabeth the Queen Mother. Multicoloured.
827 10c. Type **154** 10 10
828 15c. The Queen Mother, 1980 10 10
829 75c. Waving to the crowd, 1982 . . . . 40 40
830 $5 Four generations of Royal Family at Prince William's Christening . . . . 1·50 2·75
MS831 Two sheets, each 138 × 98 mm. (a) $2 The Queen Mother with Prince Henry (from photo by Lord Snowdon) (38 × 50 mm): (b) $5 The Queen Mother, 1984 (38 × 50 mm) Set of 2 sheets . . . . 3·75 4·50

1985. Inauguration of New Government. Nos. 772/3 and 775 optd **INAUGURATION OF NEW GOVERNMENT – 21st. DECEMBER 1984**.
832 10c. Sea fans and fire sponge 1·50 60
833 15c. Blue-headed wrasse . . . 1·50 60
834 50c. Coral crab . . . . . . 2·00 3·50

156 British Honduras 1935 Silver Jubilee 25c. stamp and King George V with Queen Mary in Carriage (½-size illustration)

1985. 50th Anniv of First Commonwealth Omnibus Issue. Designs showing British Honduras/Belize stamps. Multicoloured.
835 50c. Type **156** 45 75
836 50c. 1937 Coronation 3c., and King George VI and Queen Elizabeth in Coronation robes 45 75
837 50c. 1946 Victory 3c. and Victory celebrations . . . 45 75
838 50c. 1948 Royal Silver Wedding 4c. and King George VI and Queen Elizabeth at Westminster Abbey service 45 75
839 50c. 1953 Coronation 4c. and Queen Elizabeth II in Coronation robes 45 75
840 50c. 1966 Churchill 25c., Sir Winston Churchill and fighter aircraft 45 75
841 50c. 1972 Royal Silver Wedding 50c. and 1948 Wedding photograph . . . 45 75
842 50c. 1973 Royal Wedding 50c. and Princess Anne and Capt. Mark Phillips at their Wedding 45 75
843 50c. 1977 Silver Jubilee $2 and Queen Elizabeth II during tour 45 75
844 50c. 1978 25th anniversary of Coronation 75c. and Imperial Crown 45 75
MS845 138 × 98 mm. $5 Queen Elizabeth in Coronation robes (38 × 50 mm) . . . . 4·00 4·00

157 Mounted Postboy and Early Letter to Belize

1985. 350th Anniv of British Post Office. Mult.
846 10c. Type **157** 50 25
847 15c. "Hinchinbrook II" (sailing packet) engaging "Grand Turk" (American privateer) 70 25
848 25c. "Duke of Marlborough II" (sailing packet) 85 30
849 75c. "Diana" (packet) . . . 1·40 1·50
850 $1 Falmouth packet ship . . 1·40 2·00
851 $3 "Conway" (mail paddle-steamer) . . . . 2·25 5·50

1985. Commonwealth Heads of Government Meeting, Nassau, Bahamas. Nos. 827/30 optd **COMMONWEALTH SUMMIT CONFERENCE, BAHAMAS 16th-22nd OCTOBER 1985**.
852 10c. Type **154** 30 30
853 15c. The Queen Mother, 1980 40 35
854 75c. Waving to the crowd, 1982 . . . . 80 80
855 $4 Four generations of Royal Family at Prince William's christening . . . . 2·00 3·75
MS856 Two sheets, each 138 × 98 mm. (a) $2 The Queen Mother with Prince Henry (from photo by Lord Snowdon) (38 × 50 mm): (b) $5 The Queen Mother, 1984 (38 × 50 mm) Set of 2 sheets . . . . 2·75 3·50

1985. 80th Anniv of Rotary International. Nos. 815/19 optd **80TH ANNIVERSARY OF ROTARY INTERNATIONAL**.
857 25c. Type **152** 70 40
858 50c. Girl Guides camping . . 1·25 75
859 90c. Checking map on hike 1·75 2·00
860 $1.25 Students in laboratory 2·25 2·75
861 $2 Lady Baden-Powell (founder) . . . . 2·75 3·50

160 Royal Standard and Belize Flag

1985. Royal Visit. Multicoloured.
862 25c. Type **160** 80 95
863 75c. Queen Elizabeth II . . . 1·25 2·00
864 $4 Royal Yacht "Britannia" (81 × 39 mm) . . . . . . 3·75 3·75
MS865 138 × 98 mm. $5 Queen Elizabeth II (38 × 50 mm). . . 4·50 4·75

161 Mountie in Canoe (Canada)

1985. Christmas. 30th Anniv of Disneyland, U.S.A. Designs showing dolls from "It's a Small World" exhibition. Multicoloured.
866 1c. Type **161** 10 15
867 2c. Indian chief and squaw (U.S.A.) 10 15
868 3c. Incas climbing Andes (South America) 10 15
869 4c. Africans beating drums (Africa) 10 15
870 5c. Snake-charmer and dancer (India and Far East) 10 15
871 6c. Boy and girl with donkey (Belize) 10 15
872 50c. Musician and dancer (Balkans) . . . . 1·75 1·50
873 $1.50 Boys with camel (Egypt and Saudi Arabia) . . . . 2·75 3·50
874 $3 Woman and girls playing with kite (Japan) . . . . . 3·75 5·00
MS875 127 × 102 mm. $4 Beefeater and castle (Great Britain). P 13½ × 14 . . . . 5·50 8·00

1985. World Cup Football Championship, Mexico (1986) (1st issue). Nos. 835/44 optd **PRE "WORLD CUP FOOTBALL" MEXICO 1986** and trophy.
876 50c. Type **156** 75 90
877 50c. 1937 Coronation 3c., and King George VI and Queen Elizabeth in Coronation robes 75 90
878 50c. Victory 3c., and Victory celebrations 75 90
879 50c. 1948 Royal Silver Wedding 4c., and King George VI and Queen Elizabeth at Westminster Abbey service 75 90
880 50c. 1953 Coronation 4c., and Queen Elizabeth II in Coronation robes 75 90
881 50c. 1966 Churchill 25c., Sir Winston Churchill and fighter aircraft 75 90
882 50c. 1972 Royal Silver Wedding 50c. and 1948 wedding photograph . . . 75 90
883 50c. 1973 Royal Wedding 5c., and Princess Anne and Capt. Mark Phillips at their Wedding 75 90
884 50c. 1977 Silver Jubilee $2 and Queen Elizabeth II during tour 75 90
885 50c. 1978 25th anniv of Coronation 75c. and Imperial Crown 75 90
MS886 138 × 98 mm. $5 Queen Elizabeth II in Coronation robes 4·25 4·25
See also Nos. 936/40.

163 Indian Costume

165 Princess Elizabeth aged Three

164 Pope Pius X

1986. Costumes of Belize. Multicoloured.
887 5c. Type **163** 75 30
888 10c. Maya 80 30
889 15c. Garifuna . . . . 1·00 35
890 25c. Creole . . . . 1·25 35
891 50c. Chinese . . . . 1·75 1·25
892 75c. Lebanese . . . . 2·00 2·00
893 $1 European c. 1900 . . . . 2·00 2·50
894 $2 Latin . . . . 2·75 3·75
MS895 139 × 98 mm. Amerindian (38 × 50 mm.) . . . . 6·00 7·00

1986. Easter. 20th-century Popes. Multicoloured.
896 50c. Type **164** . . . . 1·25 1·50
897 50c. Benedict XV . . . . . 1·25 1·50
898 50c. Pius XI . . . . 1·25 1·50
899 50c. Pius XII . . . . 1·25 1·50
900 50c. John XXIII . . . . . . 1·25 1·50
901 50c. Paul VI . . . . 1·25 1·50
902 50c. John Paul I . . . . . . 1·25 1·50
903 50c. John Paul II . . . . . 1·25 1·50
MS904 147 × 92 mm. $4 Pope John Paul II preaching (vert). . . . 10·00 10·00

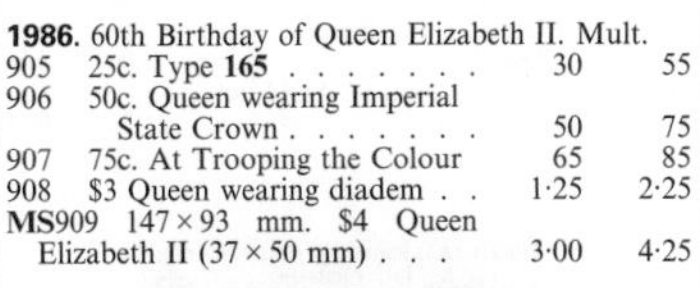

1986. 60th Birthday of Queen Elizabeth II. Mult.
905 25c. Type **165** 30 55
906 50c. Queen wearing Imperial State Crown 50 75
907 75c. At Trooping the Colour 65 85
908 $3 Queen wearing diadem . . 1·25 2·25
MS909 147 × 93 mm. $4 Queen Elizabeth II (37 × 50 mm) . . . 3·00 4·25

166 Halley's Comet and Japanese "Planet A" Spacecraft

1986. Appearance of Halley's Comet. Multicoloured.
910 10c. Type **166** 45 70
911 15c. Halley's Comet, 1910 . . 55 80
912 50c. Comet and European "Giotto" spacecraft 60 90
913 75c. Belize Weather Bureau 80 90
914 $1 Comet and U.S.A. space telescope . . . . 1·10 1·25
915 $2 Edmond Halley . . . . . 1·50 1·75
MS916 147 × 93 mm. $4 Computer enhanced photograph of Comet (37 × 50 mm) . . . . 6·00 8·00

167 George Washington

1986. United States Presidents. Multicoloured.
917 10c. Type **167** 35 60
918 20c. John Adams 35 65
916 30c. Thomas Jefferson . . . 40 70
920 50c. James Madison 50 70
921 $1.50 James Monroe . . . . 80 1·25
922 $2 John Quincy Adams . . . 1·00 1·50
MS923 147 × 93 mm. $4 George Washington (different) . . . . 3·75 5·50

168 Auguste Bartholdi (sculptor) and Statue's Head

1986. Centenary of Statue of Liberty. Multicoloured.
924 25c. Type **168** 40 65
925 50c. Statue's head at U.S. Centennial Celebration, Philadelphia, 1876 . . . . 55 85
926 75c. Unveiling ceremony, 1886 . . . . 55 90
927 $4 Statue of Liberty and flags of Belize and U.S.A. . . . 1·25 2·50
MS928 147 × 92 mm. $4 Statue of Liberty and New York skyline (37 × 50 mm.) . . . . 3·75 5·50

169 British Honduras 1866 1s. Stamp

1986. "Ameripex" International Stamp Exhibition, Chicago. Multicoloured.
929 10c. Type **169** 40 55
930 15c. 1981 Royal Wedding $1.50 stamps 55 75
931 50c. U.S.A. 1918 24c. airmail inverted centre error . . . 75 80
932 75c. U.S.S. "Constitution" (frigate) . . . . 75 1·10
933 $1 Liberty Bell . . . . 80 1·40
934 $2 White House . . . . . . 90 1·60
MS935 147 × 93 mm. $4 Capitol , Washington (37 × 50 mm) . . . 3·25 4·50

170 English and Brazilian Players

1986. World Cup Football Championship, Mexico (2nd issue). Multicoloured.
936 25c. Type **170** . . . . 1·50 1·75
937 50c. Mexican player and Maya statues . . . . . . 1·75 2·00
938 75c. Two Belizean players . . 2·00 2·25
939 $3 Aztec stone calendar . . . 2·25 2·50
MS940 147 × 92 mm. $4 Flags of competing nations on two footballs (37 × 50 mm) . . . . 6·00 8·00

171 Miss Sarah Ferguson

1986. Royal Wedding. Multicoloured.
941 25c. Type **171** 65 40
942 75c. Prince Andrew . . . . . 1·00 90
943 $3 Prince Andrew and Miss Sarah Ferguson (92 × 41 mm) . . . . . . 1·75 2·75
MS944 155 × 106 mm. $1 Miss Sarah Ferguson (different). $3 Prince Andrew (different) . . . . . . 4·00 6·00

1986. World Cup Football Championship Winners, Mexico. Nos. 936/9 optd **ARGENTINA – WINNERS 1986**.
945 25c. Type **170** . . . . 1·75 2·00
946 50c. Mexican player and Maya statues . . . . . . 2·00 2·25
947 75c. Two Belizean players . . 2·25 2·50
948 $3 Aztec stone calendar . . . 3·25 3·50
MS949 147 × 92 mm. $4 Flags of competing nations on two footballs (37 × 50 mm) . . . . 7·50 9·00

1986. "Stockholmia '86" International Stamp Exhibition, Sweden. Nos. 929/34 optd **STOCKHOLMIA 86** and emblem.
950 10c. Type **169** 50 75
951 15c. 1981 Royal Wedding $1.50 stamp 65 90
952 50c. U.S.A. 1918 24c. airmail inverted centre error . . . 80 1·10
953 75c. U.S.S. "Constitution" 1·00 1·50

954 $1 Liberty Bell 1·25 1·60
955 $2 White House 1·60 1·90
MS956 147 × 93 mm. $4 Capitol, Washington (37 × 50 mm) 5·00 7·00

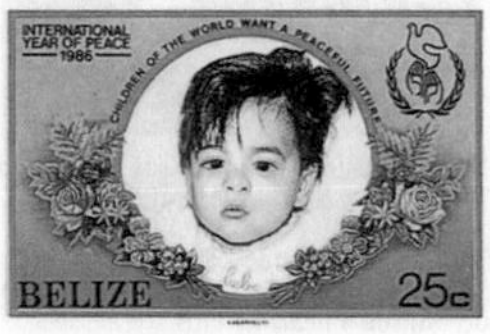

174 Amerindian Girl

1986. International Peace Year. Multicoloured.
957 25c. Type **174** 65 80
958 50c. European boy and girl 80 1·10
959 75c. Japanese girl 1·00 1·60
960 $3 Indian boy and European girl 1·75 2·75
MS961 132 × 106 mm. $4 As 25c. but vert (35 × 47 mm) 5·00 6·50

175 "Amanita lilloi" **176** Jose Carioca

1986. Fungi and Toucans. Multicoloured.
962 5c. Type **175** 1·50 1·25
963 10c. Keel-billed toucan 1·75 1·60
964 20c. "Boletellus cubensis" 2·00 1·75
965 25c. Collared aracari 2·00 1·75
966 75c. "Psilocybe caerulescens" 2·25 2·00
967 $1 Emerald toucanet 2·25 2·00
968 $1.25 Crimson-rumped toucanet ("Crimson-rumped Toucan") 2·50 2·25
969 $2 "Russula puiggarii" 2·50 2·50

1986. Christmas. Designs showing Walt Disney cartoon characters in scenes from "Saludos Amigos". Multicoloured.
970 2c. Type **176** 20 20
971 3c. Jose Carioca, Panchito and Donald Duck 20 20
972 4c. Daisy Duck as Rio Carnival dancer 20 20
973 5c. Mickey and Minnie Mouse as musician and dancer 20 20
974 6c. Jose Carioca using umbrella as flute 20 20
975 50c. Donald Duck and Panchito 1·00 1·75
976 65c. Joe Carioca and Donald Duck playing hide and seek 1·25 2·00
977 $1.35 Donald Duck playing maracas 2·00 3·25
978 $2 Goofy as matador 2·75 3·75
MS979 131 × 111 mm. $4 Donald Duck 8·50 10·00

177 Princess Elizabeth in Wedding Dress, 1947 **179** "Mother and Child"

178 "America II", 1983

1987. Royal Ruby Wedding. Multicoloured.
980 25c. Type **177** 25 20
981 75c. Queen and Duke of Edinburgh, 1972 45 50
982 $1 Queen on her 60th birthday 50 60
983 $4 In Garter robes 1·00 2·00
MS984 171 × 112 mm. $6 Queen and Duke of Edinburgh (44 × 50 mm) 6·00 7·00

1987. America's Cup Yachting Championship. Multicoloured.
985 25c. Type **178** 30 25
986 75c. "Stars and Stripes", 1987 40 50
987 $1 "Australia II", 1983 50 60
988 $4 "White Crusader" 1·00 2·00
MS989 171 × 112 mm. $6 Sails of Australia II" (44 × 50 mm.) 5·00 7·50

1987. Wood Carvings by George Gabb. Mult.
990 25c. Type **179** 15 25
991 75c. "Standing Form" 35 50
992 $1 "Love-doves" 40 60
993 $4 "Depiction of Music" 1·10 2·00
MS994 173 × 114 mm. $6 "African Heritage" (44 × 50 mm.) 4·00 6·50

180 Black-handed Spider Monkey

1987. Primates. Multicoloured.
995 25c. Type **180** 25 20
996 75c. Black howler monkey 40 55
997 $1 Spider monkeys with baby 45 65
998 $4 Two black howler monkeys 1·10 2·25
MS999 171 × 112 mm. $6 Young spider monkey (44 × 50 mm.) 5·00 7·50

181 Guides on Parade

1987. 50th Anniv of Girl Guide Movement in Belize. Multicoloured.
1000 25c. Type **181** 45 20
1001 75c. Brownie camp 80 1·00
1002 $1 Guide camp 1·00 1·25
1003 $4 Olave, Lady Baden-Powell 3·00 5·00
MS1004 173 × 114 mm. $6 As $4 but vert (44 × 50 mm) 4·00 6·50

182 Indian Refugee Camp

1987. Int Year of Shelter for the Homeless. Mult.
1005 25c. Type **182** 50 25
1006 75c. Filipino family and slum 90 90
1007 $1 Family in Middle East shanty town 1·00 1·25
1008 $4 Building modern house in Belize 2·00 4·50

183 "Laelia euspatha"

1987. Christmas. Orchids. Illustrations from Sander's "Reichenbachia". Multicoloured.
1009 1c. Type **183** 95 95
1010 2c. "Cattleya citrina" 95 95
1011 3c. "Masdevallia backhousiana" 95 95
1012 4c. "Cypripedium tautzianum" 95 95
1013 5c. "Trichopilia suavis alba" 95 95
1014 6c. "Odontoglossum hebraicum" 95 95
1015 7c. "Cattleya trianaei schroederiana" 95 95
1016 10c. "Saccolabium giganteum" 95 95
1017 30c. "Cattleya warscewiczii" 1·25 1·25
1018 50c. "Chysis bractescens" 1·50 1·50
1019 70c. "Cattleya rochellensis" 1·75 1·75
1020 $1 "Laellia elegans schilleriana" 1·90 1·90
1021 $1.50 "Laelia anceps percivaliana" 2·00 2·00
1022 $3 "Laelia gouldiana" 2·50 2·50
MS1023 Two sheets, each 171 × 112 mm. (a) $3 "Odontoglossum roezlii" (40 × 47 mm). (b) $5 "Cattleya dowiana aurea" (40 × 47 mm) Set of 2 sheets 11·00 12·00

184 Christ condemned to Death

1988. Easter. The Stations of the Cross. Mult.
1024 40c. Type **184** 35 60
1025 40c. Christ carrying the Cross 35 60
1026 40c. Falling for the first time 35 60
1027 40c. Christ meets Mary 35 60
1028 40c. Simon of Cyrene helping to carry the Cross 35 60
1029 40c. Veronica wiping the face of Christ 35 60
1030 40c. Christ falling a second time 35 60
1031 40c. Consoling the women of Jerusalem 35 60
1032 40c. Falling for the third time 35 60
1033 40c. Christ being stripped 35 60
1034 40c. Christ nailed to the Cross 35 60
1035 40c. Dying on the Cross 35 60
1036 40c. Christ taken down from the Cross 35 60
1037 40c. Christ being laid in the sepulchre 35 60

185 Basketball

1988. Olympic Games, Seoul. Multicoloured.
1038 10c. Type **185** 2·00 75
1039 25c. Volleyball 1·00 30
1040 60c. Table tennis 1·00 60
1041 75c. Diving 1·00 70
1042 $1 Judo 1·25 1·10
1043 $2 Hockey 5·50 4·50
MS1044 76 × 106 mm. $3 Gymnastics 5·50 6·00

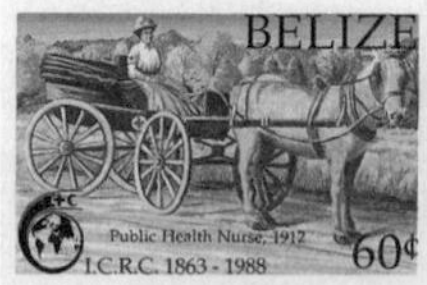

186 Public Health Nurse, c. 1912

1988. 125th Anniv of Int Red Cross. Mult.
1045 60c. Type **186** 2·75 1·25
1046 75c. "Aleda E. Lutz" (hospital ship) and ambulance launch, 1937 3·00 1·50
1047 $1 Ambulance at hospital tent, 1956 3·50 2·00
1048 $2 Auster ambulance plane, 1940 4·50 5·50

187 Collared Anteater ("Ants Bear")

1989. Small Animals of Belize. Multicoloured.
1049 10c. Paca ("Gibnut") 2·50 2·50
1050 25c. Four-eyed opossum (vert) 2·50 1·75
1051 50c. Type **187** 3·00 2·25
1052 60c. As 10c. 3·00 2·50
1053 75c. Red brocket 3·00 2·50
1054 $1 Collared peccary 4·50 6·50

1989. 20th Anniv of First Manned Landing on Moon. As T **126** of Ascension. Multicoloured.
1055 25c. Docking of "Apollo 9" modules 1·50 30
1056 50c. "Apollo 9" command service module in Space (30 × 30 mm) 2·00 75
1057 75c. "Apollo 9" emblem (30 × 30 mm) 2·25 1·25
1058 $1 "Apollo 9" lunar module in space 2·50 2·25
MS1059 83 × 100 mm. $5 "Apollo II" command service module undergoing test 9·00 9·50

1989. No. 771 surch **5c.**
1060 5c. on 6c. Star-eyed hermit crab 8·50 2·50

1989. "World Stamp Expo '89" International Stamp Exhibition, Washington. No. **MS**1059 optd **WORLD STAMP EXPO '89, United States Postal Service Nov 17—20 and Nov 24—Dec 3. 1989 Washington Convention Center Washington, DC** and emblem.
MS1061 83 × 100 mm. $5 "Apollo II" command service module undergoing tests 8·50 9·50

190 Wesley Church **191** White-winged Tanager and "Catonephele numilia"

1989. Christmas. Belize Churches.
1062 **190** 10c. black, pink and brown 20 10
1063 – 25c. black, lilac and mauve 25 20
1064 – 60c. black, turq & bl 50 70
1065 – 75c. black, grn & lt grn 65 90
1066 – $1 black, lt yell & yell 80 1·25
DESIGNS: 25c. Baptist Church; 60c. St. John's Anglican Cathedral; 75c. St. Andrew's Presbyterian Church; $1 Holy Redeemer Roman Catholic Cathedral.

1990. Birds and Butterflies. Multicoloured.
1067A 5c. Type **191** 60 75
1068B 10c. Keel-billed toucan and "Nessaea aglaura" 80 80
1069A 15c. Magnificent frigate bird and "Eurytides philolaus" 80 40
1070A 25c. Jabiru and "Heliconius sapho" 80 40
1071A 30c. Great blue heron and "Colobura dirce" 80 50
1072A 50c. Northern oriole and "Hamadyras arethusia" 1·00 60
1073A 60c. Scarlet macaw and "Evenus regalis" 1·25 70
1074A 75c. Red-legged honey-creeper and "Callicore patelina" 1·25 75
1075A $1 Spectacled owl and "Caligo uranus" 2·25 1·60
1076A $2 Green jay and "Philaethria dido" 2·75 3·50
1077A $5 Turkey vulture and "Battus belus" 4·50 6·50
1078A $10 Osprey and "Papilio thoas" 8·50 11·00

1990. First Belize Dollar Coin. No. 1075 optd **FIRST DOLLAR COIN 1990.**
1079 $1 Spectacled owl and "Caligo uranus" 4·75 2·75

193 Green Turtle

1990. Turtles. Multicoloured.
1080 10c. Type **193** 65 40
1081 25c. Hawksbill turtle 1·00 40
1082 60c. Saltwater loggerhead turtle 1·50 1·50
1083 75c. Freshwater loggerhead turtle 1·60 1·60
1084 $1 Bocatora turtle 2·00 2·00
1085 $2 Hicatee turtle 2·75 5·00

194 Fairey Battle

1990. 50th Anniv of the Battle of Britain. Multicoloured.
1086 10c. Type **194** 1·00 50
1087 25c. Bristol Type 152 Beaufort 1·60 50
1088 60c. Bristol Type 142 Blenheim Mk IV 2·00 2·00
1089 75c. Armstrong-Whitworth Whitley 2·00 2·00
1090 $1 Vickers-Armstrong Wellington Mk 1c 2·00 2·00
1091 $1 Handley Page Hampden 2·50 3·50

195 "Cattleya bowringiana"

1990. Christmas. Orchids. Multicoloured.
1092 25c. Type **195** 85 20
1093 50c. "Rhyncholaelia digbyana" 1·25 50
1094 60c. "Sobralia macrantha" 1·50 1·00
1095 75c. "Chysis bractescens" 1·50 1·00
1096 $1 "Vanilla planifolia" 1·75 1·75
1097 $2 "Epidendrum polyanthum" 2·50 4·00

196 Common Iguana

1991. Reptiles and Mammals. Multicoloured.
1098 25c. Type **196** 80 35
1099 50c. Morelet's crocodile 1·25 90
1100 60c. American manatee 1·50 1·50
1101 75c. Boa constrictor 1·75 1·75
1102 $1 Baird's tapir 2·00 2·00
1103 $2 Jaguar 2·75 3·75

1991. 65th Birthday of Queen Elizabeth II and 70th Birthday of Prince Philip. As T **139** of Ascension. Multicoloured.
1104 $1 Queen Elizabeth II wearing tiara 1·00 1·50
1105 $1 Prince Philip wearing panama 1·00 1·50

197 Weather Radar

1991. International Decade for Natural Disaster Reduction.
1106 **197** 60c. multicoloured 1·50 1·25
1107 – 75c. multicoloured 1·60 1·40
1108 – $1 blue and black 1·75 1·75
1109 – $2 multicoloured 2·50 3·25
DESIGNS: 75c. Weather station; $1 Floods in Belize after Hurricane Hattie, 1961; $2 Satellite image of Hurricane Gilbert.

198 Thomas Ramos and Demonstration

1991. 10th Anniv of Independence. Famous Belizeans (1st series). Multicoloured.
1110 25c. Type **198** 60 30
1111 60c. Sir Isaiah Morter and palm trees 1·25 1·50
1112 75c. Antonio Soberanis and political meeting 1·25 1·75
1113 $1 Santiago Ricalde and cutting sugar-cane 1·50 2·00
See also Nos. 1126/9 and 1148/51.

199 "Anansi the Spider"

1991. Christmas. Folklore. Multicoloured.
1114 25c. Type **199** 1·25 20
1115 60c. "Jack-o-Lantern" 1·75 55
1116 60c. "Tata Duende" (vert) 2·00 1·25
1117 75c. "Xtabai" 2·00 1·25
1118 $1 "Warrie Massa" (vert) 2·25 2·00
1119 $2 "Old Heg" 3·50 6·00

200 "Gongora quinquenervis"

1992. Easter. Orchids. Multicoloured.
1120 25c. Type **200** 90 20
1121 50c. "Oncidium sphacelatum" 1·50 75
1122 60c. "Encyclia bratescens" 1·75 1·75
1123 75c. "Epidendrum ciliare" 1·75 1·75
1124 $1 "Psygmorchis pusilla" 2·00 2·25
1125 $2 "Galeandra batemanii" 2·75 4·50

1992. Famous Belizeans (2nd series). As T **198**, but inscr "EMINENT BELIZEANS" at top. Multicoloured.
1126 25c. Gwendolyn Lizarraga (politician) and High School 75 30
1127 60c. Rafael Fonseca (civil servant) and Government Offices, Belize 1·50 1·50
1128 75c. Vivian Seay (health worker) and nurses 1·75 1·75
1129 $1 Samuel Haynes (U.N.I.A. worker) and words of National Anthem 2·00 2·25

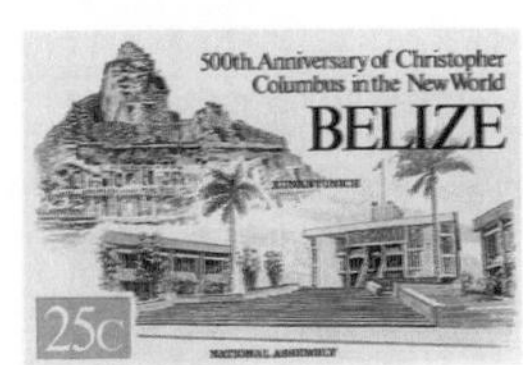

201 Xunantunich and National Assembly

1992. 500th Anniv of Discovery of America by Columbus. Mayan sites and modern buildings. Multicoloured.
1130 25c. Type **201** 1·00 25
1131 60c. Altun Ha and Supreme Court 1·50 1·00
1132 75c. Santa Rita and Tower Hill Sugar Factory 1·60 1·25
1133 $5 Lamanai and Citrus Company works 8·00 11·00

202 Hashishi Pampi

1992. Christmas. Folklore. Multicoloured.
1134 25c. Type **202** 30 20
1135 60c. Cadejo 60 60
1136 $1 La Sucia (vert) 90 1·00
1137 $5 Sisimito 4·00 7·00

1993. 75th Anniv of Royal Air Force. As T **149** of Ascension. Multicoloured.
1138 25c. Sud Aviation SA 330L Puma helicopter 1·00 60
1139 50c. Hawker Siddeley Harrier GR3 1·25 80
1140 60c. De Havilland DH98 Mosquito Mk XVIII 1·40 1·10
1141 75c. Avro Type 683 Lancaster 1·40 1·10
1142 $1 Consolidated Liberator I 1·60 1·40
1143 $3 Short Stirling Mk I 3·25 5·50

203 "Lycaste aromatica"

1993. 14th World Orchid Conference, Glasgow. Multicoloured.
1144 25c. Type **203** 40 25
1145 60c. "Sobralia decora" 75 80
1146 $1 "Maxillaria alba" 1·00 1·25
1147 $2 "Brassavola nodosa" 1·75 3·00

1993. Famous Belizeans (3rd series). As T **198**, but inscr "EMINENT BELIZEANS" at top. Multicoloured.
1148 25c. Herbert Watkin Beaumont, Post Office and postmark 40 25
1149 60c. Dr. Selvyn Walford Young and score of National Anthem 75 85
1150 75c. Cleopatra White and health centre 90 1·25
1151 $1 Dr. Karl Heusner and early car 1·10 1·40

204 Boom and Chime Band

1993. Christmas. Local Customs. Mult.
1152 25c. Type **204** 70 20
1153 60c. John Canoe dance 1·50 75
1154 75c. Cortez dance 1·50 80
1155 $2 Maya musical group 3·75 6·00

1994. "Hong Kong '94" International Stamp Exhibition. No. 1075 optd **HONG KONG '94** and emblem.
1156 $1 Spectacled owl and "Caligo uranus" 2·75 2·50

1994. Royal Visit. As T **202** of Bahamas. Mult.
1157 25c. Flags of Belize and Great Britain 1·25 45
1158 60c. Queen Elizabeth II in yellow coat and hat 1·75 1·00
1159 75c. Queen Elizabeth in evening dress 2·00 1·25
1160 $1 Queen Elizabeth, Prince Philip and Yeomen of the Guard 2·25 2·25

205 "Lonchorhina aurita" (bat)

1994. Bats. Multicoloured.
1161 25c. Type **205** 45 20
1162 60c. "Vampyrodes caraccioli" 75 65
1163 75c. "Noctilio leporinus" 90 80
1164 $2 "Desmodus rotundus" 2·00 3·50

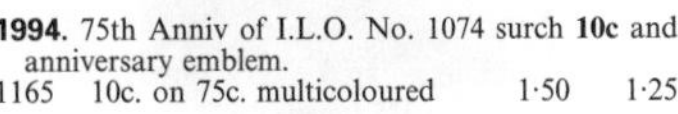
1994. 75th Anniv of I.L.O. No. 1074 surch **10c** and anniversary emblem.
1165 10c. on 75c. multicoloured 1·50 1·25

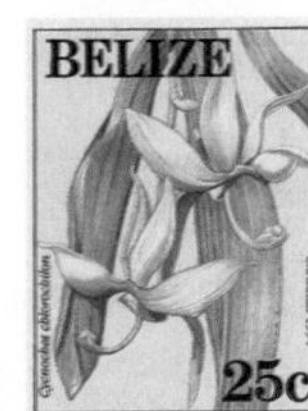

207 "Cycnoches chlorochilon"

1994. Christmas. Orchids. Multicoloured.
1166 25c. Type **207** 45 20
1167 60c. "Brassavola cucullata" 75 70
1168 75c. "Sobralia mucronata" 90 90
1169 $1 "Nidema boothii" 1·10 1·40

208 Ground Beetle

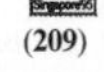

(209)

1995. Insects. Multicoloured.
1170A 5c. Type **208** 45 70
1171A 10c. Harlequin beetle 50 70
1172A 15c. Giant water bug 60 80
1173A 25c. Peanut-head bug 70 20
1174A 30c. Coconut weevil 70 25
1175A 50c. Mantis 85 40
1176B 60c. Tarantula wasp 1·00 50
1177B 75c. Rhinoceros beetle 1·10 60
1178B $1 Metallic wood borer 1·25 1·25
1179B $2 Dobson fly 3·00 3·50
1180B $5 Click beetle 4·75 6·00
1181B $10 Long-horned beetle 7·50 9·50

1995. 50th Anniv of End of Second World War. As T **161** of Ascension. Multicoloured.
1182 25c. War memorial 35 25
1183 60c. Remembrance Day parade 1·00 1·00
1184 75c. British Honduras forestry unit 1·10 1·10
1185 $1 Vickers-Armstrong Wellington bomber 1·40 1·75

1995. "Singapore '95" International Stamp Exhibition. Nos. 1166/9 optd with T **209**.
1186 25c. Type **207** 60 30
1187 60c. "Brassavola cucullata" 1·00 90
1188 75c. "Sobralia mucronata" 1·25 1·10
1189 $1 "Nidema boothii" 1·50 2·00

1995. 50th Anniv of United Nations. As T **213** of Bahamas. Multicoloured.
1190 25c. M113-light reconnaisance vehicle 25 20
1191 60c. Sultan armoured command vehicle 60 65
1192 75c. Leyland-Daf 8 × 4 drop truck 75 80
1193 $2 Warrior infantry combat vehicle 1·50 2·50

210 Male and Female Blue Ground Dove

1995. Christmas. Doves. Multicoloured.
1194 25c. Type **210** 35 20
1195 60c. White-fronted doves 70 70
1196 75c. Pair of ruddy ground doves 85 90
1197 $1 White-winged doves 1·25 1·50

1996. "CHINA '96" 9th Asian International Stamp Exhibition, Peking. Nos. 1172, 1174/5 and 1179 optd **'96 CHINA** and emblem.
1198 15c. Giant water bug 20 15
1199 30c. Coconut weevil 40 30
1200 50c. Mantis 55 50
1201 $2 Dobson fly 1·75 2·50

212 Unloading Banana Train, Commerce Bight Pier

1996. "CAPEX '96" International Stamp Exhibition, Toronto. Railways. Multicoloured.
1202 25c. Type **212** 1·00 40
1203 60c. Locomotive No. 1 Stann Creek station 1·50 1·00
1204 75c. Locomotive No. 4 pulling mahogany log train 1·50 1·10
1205 $3 L.M.S. No. 5602 "British Honduras" locomotive 3·25 5·50

213 "Epidendrum stamfordianum"

214 Red Poll

1996. Christmas. Orchids. Multicoloured.
1206 25c. Type **213** 50 20
1207 60c. "Oncidium carthagenense" 80 70
1208 75c. "Oerstedella verrucosa" 90 90
1209 $1 "Coryanthes speciosa" 1·25 1·50

1997. "HONG KONG '97" International Stamp Exhibition. Chinese New Year ("Year of the Ox"). Cattle Breeds. Multicoloured.
1210 25c. Type **214** 60 25
1211 60c. Brahman 95 90

1212 75c. Longhorn . . . . . . 1·25 1·10
1213 $1 Charbray . . . . 1·40 1·60

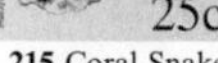

215 Coral Snake
216 Adult Male Howler Monkey

1997. Snakes. Multicoloured.
1214 25c. Type **215** 45 20
1215 60c. Green vine snake . . . 70 70
1216 75c. Yellow-jawed tommygoff 80 80
1217 $1 Speckled racer . . . . . 95 1·25

1997. Endangered Species. Howler Monkey. Multicoloured.
1218 10c. Type **216** 25 20
1219 25c. Female feeding 40 20
1220 60c. Female with young . . 70 70
1221 75c. Juvenile monkey feeding 90 95

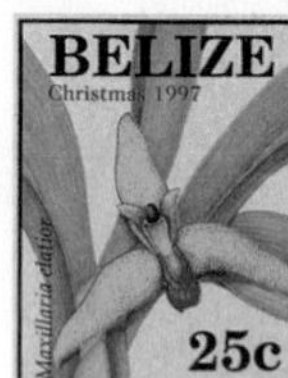
217 "Maxillaria elatior"

1997. Christmas. Orchids. Multicoloured.
1222 25c. Type **217** 40 20
1223 60c. "Dimmerandra emarginata" 75 65
1224 75c. "Macradenia brassavolae" 90 80
1225 $1 "Ornithocephalus gladiatus" . . . . 1·10 1·25

1998. Diana, Princess of Wales Commemoration. Sheet, 145 × 70 mm, containing vert designs as T **177** of Ascension. Multicoloured.
MS1226 $1 Wearing floral dress, 1988; $1 In evening dress, 1981; $1 Wearing pearl drop earrings, 1988; $1 Carrying bouquet, 1983 . . 3·00 3·50

218 School Children using the Internet

1998. 50th Anniv of Organization of American States. Multicoloured.
1227 25c. Type **218** 25 20
1228 $1 Map of Central America 1·00 1·10

219 University Arms

1998. 50th Anniv of University of West Indies.
1229 **219** $1 multicoloured . . . . 1·00 1·00

220 Baymen Gun Flats

1998. Bicentenary of Battle of St. George's Cay. Multicoloured.
1230 10c. Boat moored at quayside (vert) 30 50
1231 10c. Three sentries and cannon (vert) 30 50
1232 10c. Cannon and rowing boats (vert) 30 50
1233 25c. Type **220** 60 25
1234 60c. Baymen sloops 80 80
1235 75c. British schooners . . . 85 85
1236 $1 H.M.S. "Merlin" (sloop) 1·00 1·00
1237 $2 Spanish flagship . . . . 1·75 2·00

221 "Brassia maculata"
222 "Eucharis grandiflora"

1998. Christmas. Orchids. Multicoloured.
1238 25c. Type **221** 35 20
1239 60c. "Encyclia radiata" . . 50 40
1240 75c. "Stanhopea ecornuta" 50 55
1241 $1 "Isochilus carnosiflorus" 60 80

1999. Easter. Flowers. Multicoloured.
1242 10c. Type **222** 20 10
1243 25c. "Hippeastrum puniceum" 30 20
1244 60c. "Zephyranthes citrina" 50 50
1245 $1 "Hymenocallis littoralis" 60 80

223 Postman on Bicycle

1999. 125th Anniv of U.P.U. Multicoloured.
1246 25c. Type **223** 50 30
1247 60c. Postal truck 65 55
1248 75c. "Dee" (mail ship) . . . 85 80
1249 $1 Modern airliner . . . . 1·00 1·25

224 "Holy Family with Jesus and St. John" (School of Rubens)

1999. Christmas. Religious Paintings. Multicoloured.
1250 25c. Type **224** 20 20
1251 60c. "Holy Family with St. John" (unknown artist) 50 45
1252 75c. "Madonna and Child with St. John and Angel" (unknown artist) 55 60
1253 $1 "Madonna with Child and St. John" (Andrea del Salerno) 75 90

225 Iguana

2000. Wildlife. Multicoloured.
1254 5c. Type **225** 10 10
1255 10c. Gibnut 10 10
1256 15c. Howler monkey 10 15
1257 25c. Collared anteater . . . 15 20
1258 30c. Hawksbill turtle 15 20
1259 50c. Red brocket antelope 25 30
1260 60c. Jaguar 35 40
1261 75c. American manatee . . 40 45
1262 $1 Crocodile 55 60
1263 $2 Baird's tapir . . . . . . 1·10 1·25
1264 $5 Collared peccary . . . . 2·75 3·00
1265 $10 Boa constrictor . . . . 5·50 5·75

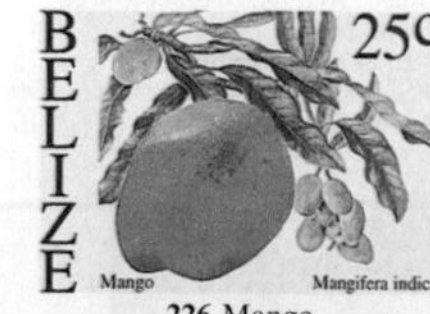
226 Mango

2000. Fruits. Multicoloured.
1266 25c. Type **226** 30 25
1267 60c. Cashew 55 50
1268 75c. Papaya 70 70
1269 $1 Banana . . . . 90 1·25

227 Meeting in Battlefield Park and Supreme Court, 1950

2000. 50th Anniv of People's United Party. Mult.
1270 10c. Type **227** 20 15
1271 25c. Voters queuing, 1954 30 25
1272 60c. Legislative Council and Mace, 1964 . . . . 55 50
1273 75c. National Assembly Building (under construction and completed), Belmopan, 1967–70 . . . . 70 70
1274 $1 Belizean flag in searchlights, Independence, 1981 . . . 1·25 1·50

228 *Bletia purpurea*

2000. Christmas. Orchids. Multicoloured
1275 25c. Type **228** 30 25
1276 60c. *Cyrtopodium punctatum* 55 50
1277 75c. *Cycnoches egertonianum* 70 70
1278 $1 *Catasetum integerrimum* 90 1·25

229 Children at Computers

2001. 20th Anniv of Independence. Multicoloured.
1279 25c. Type **229** 30 25
1280 60c. Shrimp farm 50 45
1281 75c. Privassion Cascade (vert) 65 60
1282 $2 Map of Belize (vert) . . 2·25 2·50

230 *Sobralia fragrans*

2001. Christmas. Orchids. Multicoloured.
1283 25c. Type **230** 40 25
1284 60c. *Encyclia cordigera* . . . 65 50
1285 75c. *Maxillaria fulgens* . . . 80 80
1286 $1 *Epidendrum nocturnum* 1·00 1·25

2002. Golden Jubilee. As T **200** of Ascension.
1287 25c. black, violet and gold 30 25
1288 60c. multicoloured 55 50
1289 75c. black, violet and gold 70 70
1290 $1 multicoloured . . . . . 90 1·00
MS1291 162 × 95 mm. Nos. 1287/90 and $5 multicoloured . . . . . 6·50 7·00
DESIGNS—Horiz: 25c. Princess Elizabeth in pantomime, Windsor, 1943; 60c. Queen Elizabeth in floral hat; 75c. Queen Elizabeth in garden with Prince Charles and Princess Anne, 1952; $1 Queen Elizabeth in South Africa, 1995. VERT (38 × 51 mm)—$5 Queen Elizabeth after Annigoni.

231 *Dichaea neglecta*

2002. Christmas. Orchids. Multicoloured.
1292 25c. Type **231** 40 25
1293 50c. *Epinendrum hawkesii* . . 50 40
1294 60c. *Encyclia belizensis* . . . 60 50
1295 75c. *Eriopsis biloba* 70 60
1296 $1 *Harbenaria monorrhiza* 80 90
1297 $2 *Mormodes buccinator* . . 1·40 1·75

232 B.D.F. Emblem

2003. 25th Anniv of Belize Defence Force.
1298 **232** 25c. multicoloured . . . 50 35

233 Avro Shackleton MK 3

2003. Centenary of Powered Flight. Multicoloured.
1299 25c. Type **233** 40 45
1300 60c. Lockheed L-749 Constellation 60 65
1301 75c. Sepecat Jaguar GR. 1 70 75
1302 $3 British Aerospace Harrier GR. 3 . . . . 2·20 2·40
MS1303 116 × 66 mm. $5 Ryan NYP *Spirit of St. Louis*, Belize, 1927 3·50 3·75

234 Head of Scarlet Macaw

2003. Christmas. Scarlet Macaw. Multicoloured.
1304 25c. Type **234** 40 45
1305 60c. Pair on tree 60 65
1306 75c. Three macaws feeding on clay 70 75
1307 $5 Pair in flight . . . . . . 3·50 3·75

POSTAGE DUE STAMPS

D 2

1976.
D 6 D **2** 1c. red and green . . . . 10 1·00
D 7 – 2c. purple and violet . . 15 1·00
D 8 – 5c. green and brown . . 20 1·25
D 9 – 15c. green and red . . . 30 1·50
D10 – 25c. orange and green 40 1·75
DESIGNS: Nos. D7/10 as Type D **2** but with different frames.

BENIN — Pt. 6; Pt. 12

A French possession on the W. coast of Africa incorporated, in 1899, into the colony of Dahomey.

100 centimes = 1 franc.

A. FRENCH COLONY

1892. Stamps of French Colonies. "Commerce" type, optd **BENIN**.
1 J 1c. black on blue £120 £110
2 2c. brown on yellow £110 £100
3 4c. brown on grey . . . . . . 48·00 45·00
4 5c. green on light green . . . 17·00 15·00
5 10c. black on lilac . . . . . . 65·00 60·00
6 15c. blue on light blue . . . . 35·00 13·00
7 20c. red on green £190 £170
8 25c. black on red . . . . . . 80·00 50·00
9 30c. brown on drab £140 £120
10 35c. black on orange £140 £120
11 40c. red on yellow £120 £110
12 75c. red on pink £250 £225
13 1f. green £275 £225

1892. Nos. 4 and 6 surch.
14 J 01 on 5c. green on lt green . . £220 £170
15 40 on 15c. blue on lt blue . . £130 70·00
16 75 on 15c. blue on lt blue . . £600 £400

1893. "Tablet" key-type inscr "GOLFE DE BENIN" in red (1, 5, 15, 25, 75c., 1f.) or blue (others).
17 D 1c. black on blue . . . . 1·90 4·00
18 2c. brown on buff . . . . . . 2·25 3·75
19 4c. brown on grey . . . . . . 2·00 4·00
20 5c. green on light green . . . . 5·50 7·00
21 10c. black on lilac . . . . . . 6·25 6·50

22 15c. blue . . . . 28·00 21·00
23 20c. red on green . . . . . 8·00 9·25
24 25c. black on pink . . . . . 27·00 14·50
25 30c. brown on drab . . . . 16·00 10·50
26 40c. red on yellow . . . . . 2·50 4·25
27 50c. red on pink . . . . . . 2·25 3·75
28 75c. brown on orange . . . . 9·00 11·00
29 1f. green . . . . 55·00 55·00

1894. "Tablet" key-type inscr "BENIN" in red (1, 5, 15, 25, 75c., 1f.) or blue (others).
33 D 1c. black on blue . . . . . . 2·25 3·25
34 2c. brown on buff . . . . . 2·50 4·00
35 4c. brown on grey . . . . . 1·75 3·75
36 5c. green on light green . . . 3·50 3·75
37 10c. black on lilac . . . . . 4·50 4·25
38 15c. blue . . . . 9·00 2·25
39 20c. red on green . . . . . 7·75 7·25
40 25c. black on pink . . . . . 10·00 3·00
41 30c. brown on drab . . . . . 4·00 6·00
42 40c. red on yellow . . . . . 14·00 9·00
43 50c. red on pink . . . . . . 19·00 15·00
44 75c. brown on orange . . . . 14·00 12·00
45 1f. green . . . . 4·25 5·00

POSTAGE DUE STAMPS

1894. Postage Due stamps of French Colonies optd **BENIN**. Imperf.
D46 U 5c. black . . . . £120 55·00
D47 10c. black . . . . £120 55·00
D48 20c. black . . . . £120 55·00
D49 30c. black . . . . £120 55·00

B. PEOPLE'S REPUBLIC

The Republic of Dahomey was renamed the People's Republic of Benin on 30 November 1975.

185 Celebrations

1976. Republic of Benin Proclamation. Mult.
603 50f. Type **185** 50 30
604 60f. President Kerekou making Proclamation . . . 70 30
605 100f. Benin arms and flag . . 1·25 65

186 Skiing

1976. Air. Winter Olympic Games, Innsbruck. Multicoloured.
606 60f. Type **186** 90 45
607 150f. Bobsleighing (vert) . . 1·60 95
608 300f. Figure-skating . . . . 3·50 2·00

1976. Various Dahomey stamps surch **POPULAIRE DU BENIN** and new value (609/11) or surch only (617/18).
617 **108** 50f. on 1f. multicoloured (postage) 50 25
618 – 60f. on 2f. multicoloured (No. 415) 60 35
609 – 135f. brown, purple and blue (No. 590) (air) . . 1·40 75
610 – 210f. on 300f. brown, red and blue (No. 591) . . 2·10 1·10
611 – 380f. on 500f. brown, red and green (No. 592) . . 3·75 1·90

188 Alexander Graham Bell, Early Telephone and Satellite

1976. Telephone Centenary.
612 **188** 200f. red, violet & brown 2·25 1·50

189 Basketball

1976. Air. Olympic Games, Montreal. Mult.
613 60f. Long jump (horiz) . . . 75 40
614 150f. Type **189** . . . . . . 1·50 90
615 200f. Hurdling (horiz) . . . 2·10 1·25

191 Scouts and Camp-fire

1976. African Scout Jamboree, Jos, Nigeria.
619 **191** 50f. purple, brown & blk 75 60
620 – 70f. brown, green & blk 1·25 70
DESIGN: 70f. "Comradeship".

192 Konrad Adenauer **193** Benin 1c. Stamp, 1893, and Lion Cub

1976. Air. Birth Centenary of Konrad Adenauer (German statesman).
621 **192** 90f. slate, blue and red . . 1·25 50
622 – 250f. blue, red & lt blue 3·25 1·40
DESIGN—HORIZ: 250f. Adenauer and Cologne Cathedral.

1976. Air. "Juvarouen 76" Youth Stamp Exhibition, Rouen.
623 – 60f. blue and turquoise 1·00 40
624 **193** 210f. red, brown & olive 2·25 1·25
DESIGN—HORIZ: 60f. Dahomey 60f. Stamp of 1965, and children's silhouettes.

194 Blood Bank, Cotonou

1976. National Days of Blood Transfusion Service. Multicoloured.
625 5f. Type **194** 20 10
626 50f. Casualty and blood clinic 50 40
627 60f. Donor, patient and ambulance 90 50

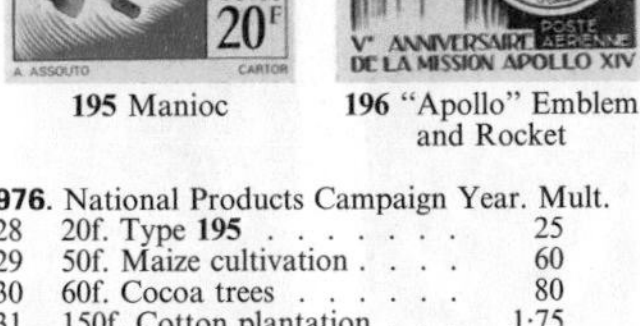

195 Manioc **196** "Apollo" Emblem and Rocket

1976. National Products Campaign Year. Mult.
628 20f. Type **195** 25 15
629 50f. Maize cultivation . . . 60 25
630 60f. Cocoa trees 80 35
631 150f. Cotton plantation . . . 1·75 75

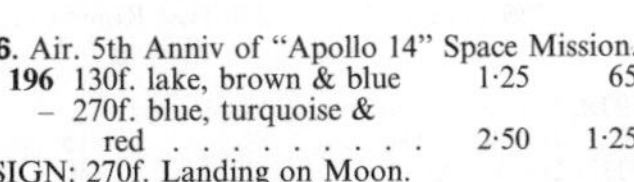

1976. Air. 5th Anniv of "Apollo 14" Space Mission.
632 **196** 130f. lake, brown & blue 1·25 65
633 – 270f. blue, turquoise & red . . . . 2·50 1·25
DESIGN: 270f. Landing on Moon.

197 Classroom **198** Roan Antelope

1976. 3rd Anniv of Bariba Periodical "Kparo".
634 **197** 50f. multicoloured 75 40

1976. Mammals in Pendjari National Park. Multicoloured.
635 10f. Type **198** 40 30
636 30f. African buffalo 75 60
637 50f. Hippopotamus (horiz) 1·25 80
638 70f. Lion . . . . 1·50 1·00

199 "Freedom" **200** "The Annunciation" (Master of Jativa)

1976. 1st Anniv of Proclamation of Republic. Multicoloured.
639 40f. Type **199** 45 25
640 150f. Maize cultivation . . . 1·40 75

1976. Air. Christmas. Multicoloured.
641 50f. Type **200** 65 30
642 60f. "The Nativity" (David) 75 40
643 270f. "Adoration of the Magi" (Dutch school) . . 3·00 1·60
644 300f. "The Flight into Egypt" (Fabriano) (horiz) . . . . 3·25 2·00

201 Table Tennis and Games Emblem

1976. West African University Games, Cotonou. Multicoloured.
645 10f. Type **201** 20 15
646 50f. Sports Hall, Cotonou . . 55 25

202 Loser with Ticket and Winner with Money

1977. Air. 10th Anniv of National Lottery.
647 **202** 50f. multicoloured 65 30

203 Douglas DC-10 crossing Globe

205 Adder

204 Chateau Sassenage, Grenoble

1977. Europafrique.
648 **203** 200f. multicoloured . . . 2·25 2·00

1977. Air. 10th Anniv of International French Language Council.
649 **204** 200f. multicoloured . . . 1·90 95

1977. Reptiles and Domestic Animals. Mult.
650 2f. Type **205** 30 20
651 3f. Tortoise 30 20
652 5f. Zebus 50 30
653 10f. Cats 75 30

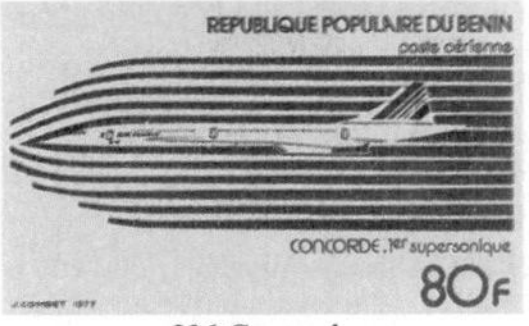

206 Concorde

1977. Air. Aviation.
654 **206** 80f. red and blue 80 45
655 – 150f. red, violet & green 1·75 80
656 – 300f. violet, red & mauve 2·50 1·60
657 – 500f. red, blue & green . . 5·00 2·75
DESIGNS: 150f. "Graf Zeppelin"; 300f. Charles Lindbergh and "Spirit of St. Louis"; 500f. Charles Nungesser and Francois Coli with "L'Oiseau".

207 Footballer heading Ball

208 Rheumatic Patients

1977. Air. World Football Cup Eliminators. Multicoloured.
658 60f. Type **207** 65 25
659 200f. Goalkeeper and players 1·90 90

1977. World Rheumatism Year.
660 **208** 100f. multicoloured . . . 1·25 65

209 Karate

210 Mao Tse-tung

1977. 2nd African Games, Lagos. Multicoloured.
661 90f. Type **209** 95 55
662 100f. Javelin (horiz) . . . . 1·10 70
663 150f. Hurdling . . . . 1·75 1·10

1977. 1st Death Anniv of Mao Tse-tung.
665 **210** 100f. multicoloured . . . 1·25 75

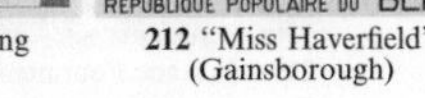

211 Sterilising Scalpels **212** "Miss Haverfield" (Gainsborough)

1977. 150th Birth Anniv of Joseph Lister.
666 **211** 150f. grey, red & carmine 1·60 75
667 – 210f. olive, green & red 2·25 1·10
DESIGN: 210f. Lister and antiseptic spray.

1977. Air. Paintings.
668 **212** 100f. green and brown 1·25 40
669 – 150f. brown, bistre & red 1·90 90
670 – 200f. red and bistre 2·50 1·25
DESIGNS: 150f. "Self-Portrait" (Rubens); 200f. "Study of an Old Man" (da Vinci).

213 "Jarre Trouee" Emblem of King Ghezo (D'Abomey Museum)

214 Atacora Waterfall

1977. Historic Museums of Benin. Mult.
671 50f. Type **213** 55 35
672 60f. Mask (Porto-Novo Museum) (horiz) 80 45
673 210f. D'Abomey Museum 2·10 1·10

1977. Tourism. Multicoloured.
674 50f. Type **214** 50 30
675 60f. Stilt houses, Ganvie (horiz) 75 45
676 150f. Hut village, Savalou 1·90 95

1977. Air. 1st Commercial Concorde Flight. Paris–New York. No. 654 optd **1er VOL COMMERCIAL 22.11.77 PARIS NEW-YORK.**
678 **206** 80f. red and blue 1·25 75

216 "Viking" on Mars ("Operation Viking", 1977)

1977. Air. Space Conquest Anniversaries.
679 **216** 100f. brown, olive & red 90 50
680 – 150f. blue, turq & mve 1·40 75
681 – 200f. brown, blue & red 2·25 95
682 – 500f. blue, brn & olive 5·50 2·75
DESIGNS AND EVENTS: 150f. Sir Isaac Newton, apple and stars (250th death anniv); 200f. Komarov and "Soyuz 2" over Moon (10th death anniv); 500f. Space dog "Laika" and rocket (20th anniv of ascent into Space).

217 Monument, Red Flag Square, Cotonou

218 Mother and Child with Owl of Wisdom

1977. Air. 1st Anniv of Inauguration of Red Flag Square Monument.
683 **217** 500f. multicoloured 5·00 2·25

1977. Fight against Witchcraft. Multicoloured.
684 60f. Type **218** 80 50
685 150f. Felling the tree of sorcery 2·00 1·00

219 "Suzanne Fourment"

1977. Air. 400th Birth Anniv of Rubens.
686 **219** 200f. brown, red & green 2·50 1·10
687 – 380f. orange and brown 4·50 2·00
DESIGN: 380f. "Albert Rubens".

220 Battle Scene

1978. "Victory over Imperialism".
688 **220** 50f. multicoloured 80 40

221 Benin Houses and Map of Heads

223 Abdoulaye Issa

222 Sir Alexander Fleming, Microscope and Drugs

1978. General Population Census.
689 **221** 50f. multicoloured 65 25

1978. 50th Anniv of Discovery of Antibiotics.
690 **222** 300f. multicoloured 3·75 1·90

1978. 1st Death Anniv of Abdoulaye Issa.
691 **223** 100f. multicoloured 90 45

224 El Hadj Omar

1978. Heroes of Anti-colonial Resistance.
692 – 90f. multicoloured 80 40
693 **224** 100f. green, grey & blue 95 55
DESIGN: 90f. Samory Toure.

225 "Communications"

1978. 10th World Telecommunications Day.
694 **225** 100f. multicoloured 1·25 65

226 Footballer and Stadium

1978. World Cup Football Championship, Argentina. Multicoloured.
695 200f. Type **226** 1·60 85
696 300f. Tackling (vert) 2·50 1·40
697 500f. Footballer and world map 4·50 2·10

1978. Argentina's Victory in World Cup Football Championship. Nos. 695/7 optd.
699 **226** 200f. multicoloured 1·75 1·10
700 – 300f. multicoloured 2·50 1·75
701 – 500f. multicoloured 4·50 3·00
OPTS: 200f. **FINALE ARGENTINE: 3 HOLLANDE: 1**; 300f. **CHAMPION 1978 ARGENTINE**; 500f. **3e BRESIL 4e ITALIE.**

228 Map, Olympic Flag and Basketball Players

1978. 3rd African Games, Algiers. Multicoloured.
703 50f. Type **228** 60 30
704 60f. African map and Volleyball 85 50
705 80f. Cyclists and map of Algeria 1·00 60

229 Martin Luther King

230 Bicycle Taxi (Oueme)

1978. 10th Anniv of Martin Luther King's Assassination.
707 **229** 300f. multicoloured 2·75 1·50

1978. Benin Provinces. Multicoloured.
708 50f. Type **230** 60 30
709 60f. Leather work (Borgou) 70 35
710 70f. Drums (Oueme) 90 45
711 100f. Calabash with burnt-work ornamentation (Zou) 1·25 50

231 "Stamps" and Magnifying Glass

1978. Philatelic Exhibition, Riccione, Italy.
712 **231** 200f. multicoloured 1·90 95

232 Parthenon and Frieze showing Horsemen

1978. Air. U.N.E.S.C.O. Campaign for the Preservation of the Acropolis. Multicoloured.
713 70f. Acropolis and Frieze showing Procession 70 30
714 250f. Type **232** 2·10 1·00
715 500f. The Parthenon (horiz) 4·25 1·90

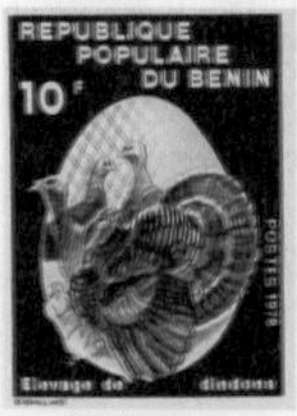

235 Turkeys

236 Post Runner and Boeing 747

1978. Domestic Poultry. Multicoloured.
722 10f. Type **235** 15 15
723 20f. Ducks 30 15
724 50f. Chickens 80 35
725 60f. Helmeted guineafowl 95 45

1978. Centenary of U.P.U. Paris Congress. Mult.
726 50f. Messenger of the Dahomey Kings (horiz) 70 30
727 60f. Pirogue oarsman, boat and post car 80 35
728 90f. Type **236** 1·00 50

237 Red-breasted Merganser and Baden 1851 1k. Stamp

1978. Air. "Philexafrique" Exhibition, Libreville (Gabon) (1st issue) and International Stamp Fair, Essen, West Germany. Multicoloured.
729 100f. Type **237** 2·50 1·25
730 100f. African Buffalo and Dahomey 1966 50f. African Pygmy Goose stamp 2·50 1·25
See also Nos. 747/8.

238 Raoul Follereau

1978. 1st Death Anniv of Raoul Follereau (leprosy pioneer).
731 **238** 200f. multicoloured 1·50 75

239 Wilbur and Orville Wright and Wright Flyer 1

1978. Air. 75th Anniv of First Powered Flight.
732 **239** 500f. blue, yellow & brn 5·00 2·25

240 I.Y.C. Emblem

241 Hydrangea

1979. International Year of the Child. Mult.
733 10f. Type **240** 15 15
734 20f. Children in balloon 20 15
735 50f. Children dancing around globe 40 20

1979. Flowers. Multicoloured.
736 20f. Type **241** 30 30
737 25f. Assangokan 35 30
738 30f. Geranium 50 40
739 40f. Water Lily (horiz) 65 40

242 Flags around Map of Africa

1979. O.C.A.M. Summit Meeting, Cotonou (1st series). Multicoloured.
740 50f. Type **242** 50 30
741 60f. Flags and map of Benin 65 40
742 80f. O.C.A.M. flag and map of member countries . . . 90 45
See also Nos. 754/6.

1979. Various stamps surch.
743 **205** 50f. on 2f. multicoloured (postage) . . . . . .
743a – 50f. on 3f. multicoloured (651) . . . .
743b – 50f. on 70f. brown, green and black (620) . . .
744 **207** 50f. on 60f. mult (air) . .
745 **192** 50f. on 90f. blue, deep blue and red . . . .
746 – 50f. on 150f. mult (607)
747 **189** 50f. on 150f. mult . . .

244 Antenna, Satellite and Wave Pattern

1979. World Telecommunications Day.
748 **244** 50f. multicoloured 65 30

245 Headquarters Building

1979. West African Savings Bank Building Opening.
749 **245** 50f. multicoloured 55 30

246 "Resolution" and "Discovery" in Karakakoa Bay, Hawaii

1979. Air. Death Bicentenary of Capt. James Cook.
750 **246** 20f. blue, green & brown 85 45
751 – 50f. brown, green & blue 1·00 60
DESIGN: 50f. Cook's death at Kowrowa.

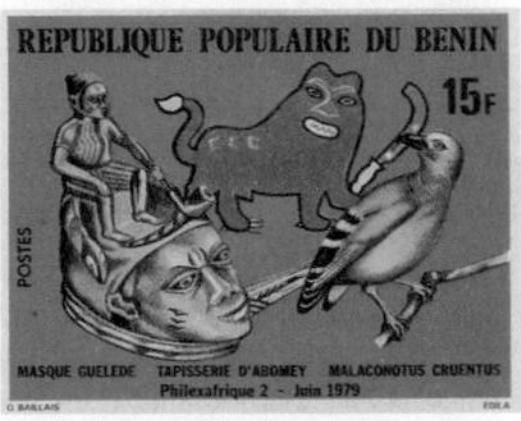

247 Guelede Mask, Abomey Tapestry and Fiery-breasted Bush Shrike

1979. "Philexafrique" Stamp Exhibition, Gabon (2nd issue).
752 **247** 15f. multicoloured 75 20
753 – 50f. orange, yellow & turq 95 55
DESIGN: 50f. Lockheed Tristar 500, satellite, U.P.U. emblem and canoe post.

1979. Common African and Mauritian Organization Summit Conference, Cotonou (2nd issue). Nos. 740/2 optd **26 Au 28 Juin 1979**.
754 50f. Type **242** 55 30
755 60f. Map of Benin and flags of members 70 40
756 80f. OCAM flag and map showing member countries 90 45

249 Olympic Flame, Benin Flags and Pictograms

1979. Pre-Olympic Year. Multicoloured.
757 10f. Type **249** 20 15
758 50f. High jump 65 40

250 Roan Antelope

1979. Endangered Animals. Multicoloured.
759 5f. Type **250** 30 20
760 10f. Giraffes (vert) 40 30
761 20f. Chimpanzee 60 40
762 50f. African elephants (vert) 1·25 40

251 Emblem, Concorde and Map of Africa

252 Post Offices, Antenna, Telephone and Savings Book

1979. 20th Anniv of ASECNA (African Air Safety Organization). Multicoloured.
763 50f. Type **251** 40 20
764 60f. As No. 763 but emblem at bottom right and without dates 50 25

1979. 20th Anniv of Posts and Telecommunications Office. Multicoloured.
765 50f. Type **252** 60 40
766 60f. Collecting, sorting and delivering mail 85 50

253 Rotary Emblem, Symbols of Services and Globe

254 Copernicus and Planetary System

1980. 75th Anniv of Rotary International. Mult.
767 90f. Cotonou Rotary Club banner (vert) 75 40
768 200f. Type **253** . . . . 1·50 75

1980. 50th Anniv of Discovery of Planet Pluto. Multicoloured.
769 70f. Kepler and astrolabe . . 65 40
770 100f. Type **254** 90 50

255 Pharaonic Capital

1980. 20th Anniv of Nubian Monuments Preservation Campaign. Multicoloured.
771 50f. Type **255** 45 25
772 60f. Rameses II, Abu Simbel 55 40
773 150f. Temple, Abu Simbel (horiz) . . . . 1·25 75

256 Lenin in Library

1980. 110th Birth Anniv of Lenin. Mult.
774 50f. Lenin and globe 50 25
775 150f. Type **256** . . . . 1·60 65

257 Monument

1980. Martyrs Square, Cotonou.
776 **257** 50f. multicoloured 40 15
777 – 60f. multicoloured 50 20
778 – 70f. multicoloured 55 25
779 – 100f. multicoloured . . . 80 30
DESIGNS—HORIZ: 60f. to 100f. Different views of the monument.

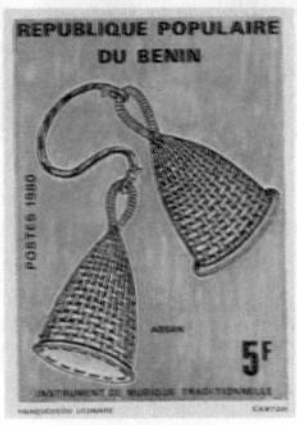

258 Farmer using Telephone

259 Assan

1980. World Telecommunications Day. Mult.
780 50f. Type **258** 40 25
781 60f. Telephone 50 25

1980. Traditional Musical Instruments. Mult.
782 5f. Type **259** 20 10
783 10f. Tinbo (horiz) 20 10
784 15f. Tam-tam sato 25 15
785 20f. Kora (horiz) 25 15
786 30f. Gangan (horiz) 60 35
787 50f. Sinhoun (horiz) 85 50

260 Monument

1980. King Gbehanzin Monument.
788 **260** 1000f. multicoloured . . . 9·50 6·25

261 Dieudonne Costes, Maurice Bellonte and "Point d'Interrogation"

1980. 50th Anniv of First Paris–New York Non-stop Flight.
789 – 90f. red, lt blue & blue . . 1·00 50
790 **261** 100f. red, blue and flesh 1·25 60
DESIGN: 90f. Airplane "Point d'Interrogation" and scenes of New York and Paris.

262 "Lunokhod I"

1980. 10th Anniv of "Lunokhod I".
791 – 90f. brown, blue and violet (postage) 75 50
792 **262** 210f. purple, blue and yellow (air) . . . . . . 2·25 1·10
DESIGN (48 × 36 mm): 90f. Rocket and "Lunokhod I".

263 Show-jumping

1980. Olympic Games, Moscow. Multicoloured.
793 50f. Olympic Flame, running track, emblem and mascot Mischa the bear (horiz) . . 45 20
794 60f. Type **263** 50 30
795 70f. Judo (horiz) 70 40
796 200f. Olympic flag and globe surrounded by sports pictogram . . . . 1·50 75
797 300f. Weightlifting . . . . . 2·50 1·25

264 O.C.A.M. Building

1980. Common African and Mauritian Organization Village, Cotonou. Multicoloured.
798 50f. Entrance to O.C.A.M. village 45 20
799 60f. View of village 50 20
800 70f. Type **264** 70 55

265 Dancers

1980. Agbadja Dance. Multicoloured.
801 30f. Type **265** 50 25
802 50f. Singer and musicians . . 75 40
803 60f. Dancers and musicians 85 50

266 Casting a Net

267 Philippines under Magnifying Glass

1980. Fishing. Multicoloured.
804 5f. Type **266** 10 10
805 10f. Fisherman with catch (vert) 25 15
806 15f. Line fishing 35 20
807 20f. Fisherman emptying eel-pot 40 20
808 50f. Hauling in a net 65 30
809 60f. Fish farm . . . . 1·25 40

1980. World Tourism Conference, Manila. Mult.
810 50f. Type **267** 55 25
811 60f. Conference flag on globe 70 25

268 "Othreis materna" **269** Map of Africa and Posthorn

1980. Insects. Multicoloured.
812 40f. Type **268** 65 30
813 50f. "Othreis fullonia" (butterfly) 90 40
814 200f. "Oryctes" sp. (beetle) 2·75 1·25

1980. 5th Anniv of African Posts and Telecommunications.
815 **269** 75f. multicoloured 80 25

270 Hands freed from Chains **271** "Self-portrait"

1980. 30th Anniv of Signing of Human Rights Convention. Multicoloured.
816 30f. Type **270** 25 15
817 50f. African pushing through bars 45 20
818 60f. Figure holding Human Rights flame 55 20

1980. 90th Death Anniv of Van Gogh (artist). Multicoloured.
819 100f. Type **271** . . . . 1·75 80
820 300f. "The Postman Roulin" 4·25 2·10

272 Offenbach and Scene from "Orpheus in the Underworld"

1980. Death Centenary of Jacques Offenbach (composer).
821 **272** 50f. black, red and green 75 50
822 – 60f. blue, brown & dp brn 1·25 75
DESIGN: 60f. Offenbach and scene from "La Vie Parisienne".

273 Kepler and Astronomical Diagram

1980. 30th Death Anniv of Johannes Kepler (astronomer).
823 **273** 50f. red, blue and grey . . 55 25
824 – 60f. blue, black and green 70 25
DESIGN: 60f. Kepler, satellite and dish aerials.

274 Footballers **275** Disabled Person holding Flower

1981. Air. World Cup Football Championship. Multicoloured.
825 200f. Football and globe . . 1·50 55
826 500f. Type **274** . . . . 3·75 1·60

1981. International Year of Disabled People.
827 **275** 115f. multicoloured . . . 1·00 40

276 Yuri Gagarin

1981. 20th Anniv of First Man in Space.
828 **276** 500f. multicoloured . . . 4·50 2·50

277 I.T.U. and W.H.O. Emblems and Ribbons forming Caduceus **278** Amaryllis

1981. World Telecommunications Day.
829 **277** 115f. multicoloured . . . 90 40

1981. Flowers. Multicoloured.
830 10f. Type **278** 25 20
831 20f. "Eischornia crassipes" 40 30
832 80f. "Parkia biglobosa" . . . 1·25 60

279 Hotel and Map

1981. Opening of Benin Sheraton Hotel.
833 **279** 100f. multicoloured . . . 90 40

1981. Surch **50F.**
834 **216** 50f. on 100f. brown, green and red 45 20
835 **193** 50f. on 210f. red, brown and green 45 20

281 Prince Charles, Lady Diana Spencer and Tower Bridge

1981. Air. British Royal Wedding.
836 **281** 500f. multicoloured . . . 3·75 1·75

282 Guinea Pig

1981. Domestic Animals. Multicoloured.
837 5f. Type **282** 25 20
838 60f. Cat 70 40
839 80f. Dogs . . . . 1·00 60

283 Heinrich von Stephan (founder of U.P.U.)

1981. World Universal Postal Union Day.
840 **283** 100f. slate and red 75 40

284 Heads, Quill, Paper Darts and U.P.U. Emblem

1981. International Letter Writing Week.
841 **284** 100f. blue and purple . . 75 40

285 "The Dance"

1981. Air. Birth Centenary of Pablo Picasso. Multicoloured.
842 300f. Type **285** . . . . 2·75 95
843 500f. "The Three Musicians" 4·75 1·60

286 Globe, Map of Member Countries and Communication Symbols **287** St. Theodore Stratilates (tile painting)

1981. 5th Anniv of E.C.O.W.A.S. (Economic Community of West African States).
844 **286** 60f. multicoloured 65 25

1981. Air. 1300th Anniv of Bulgarian State.
845 **287** 100f. multicoloured . . . 75 35

288 Tractor and Map

1981. 10th Anniv of West African Rice Development Association.
846 **288** 60f. multicoloured 65 25

289 Pope John Paul II

1982. Air. Papal Visit.
847 **289** 80f. multicoloured . . . . 1·50 65

290 John Glenn

1982. Air. 20th Anniv of First United States Manned Space Flight.
848 **290** 500f. multicoloured . . . 4·25 1·90

291 Dr. Robert Koch

1982. Centenary of Discovery of Tubercle Bacillus.
849 **291** 115f. multicoloured . . . 1·25 45

292 Washington, U.S. Flag and Map

1982. 250th Birth Anniv of George Washington.
850 **292** 200f. multicoloured . . . 1·90 75

1982. Red Cross. Surch **Croix Rouge 8 Mai 1982 60f.**
851 **266** 60f. on 5f. multicoloured 50 25

294 Map of Member Countries and Torch **295** Scouts round Campfire

1982. 5th Economic Community of West African States Summit, Cotonou.
852 **294** 60f. multicoloured 50 25

1982. Air. 75th Anniv of Boy Scout Movement.
853 **295** 105f. multicoloured . . . 1·25 75

296 Footballers

1982. World Cup Football Championship, Spain. Multicoloured.
854 90f. Type **296** 75 40
855 300f. Leg with sock formed from flags of participating countries and globe/ football . . . . 2·40 1·10

1982. African Posts and Telegraph Union. Surch **UAPT 1982 60f.**
856 **282** 60f. on 5f. multicoloured 65 30

298 Stamp of Map of France and Magnifying Glass

1982. "Philexfrance 82" International Stamp Exhibition, Paris.
857 **298** 90f. multicoloured 1·00 50

1982. World Cup Football Championship Results. Nos. 854/5 optd.
858 90f. Type **296** 1·00 50
859 300f. Leg with flags of participating countries and football "globe" 2·75 1·25
OVERPRINTS: 90f. **COUPE 82 ITALIE bat RFA 3-1**; 300f. **COUPE 82 1 ITALIE 2 RFA 3 POLOGNE**.

1982. Riccione Stamp Exhibition. Optd **RICCIONE 1982**.
860 **231** 200f. multicoloured 1·50 65

301 Laughing Kookaburra ("Dacelo Gigas")

302 World Map and Satellite

1982. Birds. Multicoloured.
861 5f. Type **301** 30 20
862 10f. Bluethroat ("La Gorge Bleue") (horiz) 45 20
863 15f. Barn swallow ("L'Hirondelle") 45 20
864 20f. Woodland kingfisher ("Martin-Pecheur") and Village weaver ("Tisserin") 70 25
865 30f. Reed warbler ("La Rousserolle") (horiz) 1·10 35
866 60f. Warbler sp. ("Faurette Commoune") (horiz) 1·40 50
867 80f. Eagle owl ("Hibou Grand Doc") 2·50 95
868 100f. Sulphur-crested cockatoo ("Cacatoes") 3·00 1·25

1982. I.T.U. Delegates' Conference, Nairobi.
869 **302** 200f. turq, blue & blk 1·50 65

303 U.P.U. Emblem and Heads

1982. U.P.U. Day.
870 **303** 100f. green, blue & brown 90 40

305 "Claude Monet in his Studio"

1982. Air. 150th Birth Anniv of Edouard Manet (artist).
876 **305** 300f. multicoloured 5·50 2·25

306 "Virgin and Child" (Grunewald)

1982. Air. Christmas. Multicoloured.
877 200f. Type **306** 2·25 1·10
878 300f. "Virgin and Child with Angels and Cherubins" (Correggio) 2·75 1·40

307 Pres. Mitterrand and Pres. Kerekou

1983. Visit of President Mitterrand.
879 **307** 90f. multicoloured 1·10 45

1983. Various stamps surch.
880 – 60f. on 50f. multicoloured (No. 798) (postage) 45 20
881 – 60f. on 70f. multicoloured (No. 778) 45 20
882 **279** 60f. on 100f. mult 45 25
883 – 75f. on 80f. multicoloured (No. 832) 75 40
884 – 75f. on 80f. multicoloured (No. 839) 75 40
885 **262** 75f. on 210f. red, blue and yellow (air) 65 35

309 "Tender Benin" (tug) and "Amazone" (oil rig)

1983. Seme Oilfield.
886 **309** 125f. multicoloured 1·40 60

1983. Various stamps surch.
887 **267** 5f. on 50f. multicoloured 10 10
888 **284** 10f. on 100f. blue & pur 10 10
889 – 10f. on 200f. mult (No. 659) 10 10
890 – 15f. on 200f. red and bistre (No. 670) 10 10
891 – 15f. on 200f. mult (No. 796) 10 10
892 – 15f. on 210f. green, deep green and red (No. 667) 10 10
893 – 15f. on 270f. mult (No. 643) 10 10
894 **219** 20f. on 200f. brown, red and olive 20 10
895 – 25f. on 70f. mult (No. 795) 25 10
896 – 25f. on 210f. mult (No. 673) 20 10
897 – 25f. on 270f. blue, turq & red (No. 633) 20 10
898 – 25f. on 380f. brown and red (No. 687) 25 10
899 – 30f. on 200f. brown, blue and red (No. 681) 30 20
900 **290** 40f. on 500f. mult 40 20
901 **282** 75f. on 5f. multicoloured 55 40
902 – 75f. on 100f. red, blue and pink (No. 790) 55 40
903 – 75f. on 150f. mult (No. 631) 55 40
904 – 75f. on 150f. violet, red and green (No. 655) 65 40
905 **211** 75f. on 150f. grey, orange and red 55 40
906 – 75f. on 150f. dp brown, brown & red (No. 669) 65 40

311 W.C.Y. Emblem

1983. World Communications Year.
907 **311** 185f. multicoloured 1·50 65

312 Stamps of Benin and Thailand and World Map

1983. Air. "Bangkok 1983" International Stamp Exhibition.
908 **312** 300f. multicoloured 2·50 1·25

313 Hand with Tweezers and Stamp

1983. "Riccione 83" Stamp Fair, San Marino.
909 **313** 500f. multicoloured 3·75 1·60

314 First Aid

315 Carved Table and Chairs

1983. 20th Anniv of Benin Red Cross.
910 **314** 105f. multicoloured 95 50

1983. Benin Woodwork. Multicoloured.
911 75f. Type **315** 65 25
912 90f. Rustic table and chairs 90 40
913 200f. Monkeys holding box 1·60 65

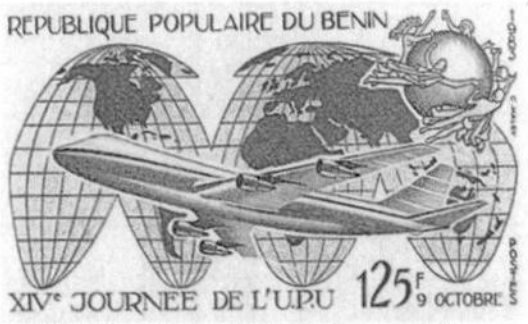

316 Boeing 747, World Map and U.P.U. Emblem

1983. U.P.U. Day.
914 **316** 125f. green, blue & brown 1·25 60

317 Egoun

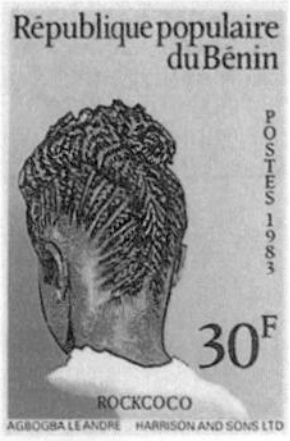

318 Rockcoco

1983. Religious Cults. Multicoloured.
915 75f. Type **317** 65 30
916 75f. Zangbeto 65 30

1983. Hair-styles. Multicoloured.
917 30f. Type **318** 25 20
918 75f. Serpent 65 40
919 90f. Songas 90 45

319 Alfred Nobel

1983. 150th Birth Anniv of Alfred Nobel.
920 **319** 300f. multicoloured 2·75 1·50

320 "Madonna of Lorette" (Raphael)

1983. Air. Christmas.
921 **320** 200f. multicoloured 1·90 95

1984. Various stamps surch.
922 – 5f. on 150f. mult (No. 685) (postage) 15 15
923 **316** 5f. on 125f. green, blue and brown 1·50 1·25
924 **292** 10f. on 200f. mult 15 15
925 – 10f. on 200f. mult (No. 913) 20 20
926 – 15f. on 300f. mult (No. 820) 20 20
927 – 25f. on 300f. mult (No. 644) 25 10
928 **276** 40f. on 500f. mult 1·00 90
929 **314** 75f. on 105f. mult 70 60
930 **275** 75f. on 115f. mult 70 45
931 **277** 75f. on 115f. mult 70 60
932 **291** 75f. on 115f. mult 70 60
933 **311** 75f. on 185f. mult 70 60
934 **302** 75f. on 200f. turquoise, blue and black 70 60
935 **320** 15f. on 200f. mult (air) 10 10
936 **285** 15f. on 300f. mult 10 10
937 **312** 25f. on 300f. mult 25 10
938 **281** 40f. on 500f. mult 30 25
939 **295** 75f. on 105f. mult 1·00 90
940 **306** 90f. on 200f. mult 70 45
941 **305** 90f. on 300f. mult 70 45

322 Flags, Agriculture and Symbol of Unity and Growth

323 U.P.U. Emblem and Magnifying Glass

1984. 25th Anniv of Council of Unity.
942 **322** 75f. multicoloured 65 25
943 90f. multicoloured 75 30

1984. 19th Universal Postal Union Congress, Hamburg.
944 **323** 90f. multicoloured 1·00 40

324 Abomey-Calavi Ground Station

325 Koumboro (Borgou)

1984. Inauguration of Abomy-Calavi Ground Station.
945 **324** 75f. multicoloured 65 40

1984. Traditional Costumes. Multicoloured.
946 5f. Type **325** 25 25
947 10f. Taka (Borgou) 35 30
948 20f. Toko (Atacora Province) 50 40

326 Olympic Mascot

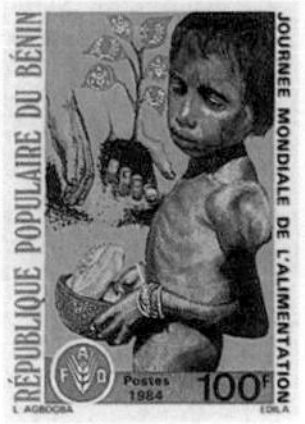

327 Plant and Starving Child

1984. Air. Olympic Games, Los Angeles.
949 **326** 300f. multicoloured 2·50 1·25

1984. World Food Day.
950 **327** 100f. multicoloured 75 35

328 Anatosaurus

1984. Prehistoric Animals. Multicoloured.
951 75f. Type **328** 90 50
952 90f. Brontosaurus 1·25 60

329 "Virgin and Child" (detail, Murillo)

1984. Air. Christmas.
953 **329** 500f. multicoloured . . . 4·25 1·90

1984. Various stamps surch.
954 **203** 75f. on 200f. mult (post) 1·50 1·25
955 **226** 75f. on 200f. mult . . . . 1·25 1·00
956 – 75f. on 300f. mult (No. 696) . . . . . . 1·25 1·00
957 **229** 75f. on 300f. mult 70 45
958 – 90f. on 300f. mult (No. 855) . . . . . . 1·25 1·00
959 – 90f. on 500f. mult (No. 697) . . . . . . 1·25 1·00
960 – 90f. on 500f. mult (No. 701) . . . . . . 1·25 1·00
961 **204** 75f. on 200f. mult (air) . . 55 40
962 – 75f. on 200f. mult (No. 825) . . . . . . 1·25 1·00
963 – 75f. on 300f. violet, red and mauve (No. 656) 1·50 1·25
964 – 75f. on 300f. mult (No. 878) 55 40
965 **239** 90f. on 500f. blue, yellow and brown . . . . . . 1·50 1·25
966 – 90f. on 500f. mult (No. 715) 70 40
967 – 90f. on 500f. mult (No. 843) 70 40

331 Sidon Merchant Ship (2nd century)

1984. Air. Ships.
968 **331** 90f. black, green & blue 1·10 60
969 – 125f. multicoloured . . . 1·75 90
DESIGN—VERT: 125f. Sail merchantman "Wavertree", 1895.

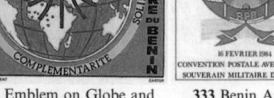

332 Emblem on Globe and Hands reaching for Cultural Symbols

333 Benin Arms

1985. 15th Anniv of Cultural and Technical Co-operation Agency.
970 **332** 300f. multicoloured . . . 2·25 95

1985. Air. Postal Convention between Benin and Sovereign Military Order of Malta. Multicoloured.
971 75f. Type **333** 60 25
972 75f. Arms of Sovereign Military Order 60 25

334 Soviet Flag, Soldier and Tank

335 Teke Dance, Borgou

1985. 40th Anniv of End of Second World War.
973 **334** 100f. multicoloured . . .

1985. Traditional Dances. Multicoloured.
974 75f. Type **335** 75 50
975 100f. Tipen ti dance, Atacora 1·10 60

1985. Various Dahomey Stamps optd **POPULAIRE DU BENIN** (985/6) or **REPUBLIQUE POPULAIRE DU BENIN** (others), Nos. 976/7 and 979/85 surch also.
976 **174** 15f. on 40f. mult (post) 20 10
977 **182** 25f. on 40f. brown, blue and violet (air) 20 10
978 **115** 40f. black, purple & bl 25 10
978a – 75f. on 85f. brown, blue and green (No. 468) 50 25
979 – 75f. on 85f. brown, blue and green (No. 482) 50 25
980 **135** 75f. on 100f. purple, violet and green . . . 50 25
981 – 75f. on 125f. green, blue and purple (No. 509) 50 25
982 **127** 90f. on 20f. brown, blue and green 65 40
983 – 90f. on 150f. purple, blue & brown (No. 456) . . 65 40
984 – 90f. on 200f. green, red and blue (No. 438) . . 65 40
985 – 90f. on 200f. mult (No. 563) 65 40
986 – 150f. mult (No. 562) . . 1·00 65

338 Oil Rig

1985. Air. "Philexafrique" International Stamp Exhibition, Lome, Togo (1st issue). Mult.
987 200f. Type **338** . . . . . . 2·50 1·75
988 200f. Footballers . . . . . . 2·40 1·50
See also Nos. 999/1000.

339 Emblem

1985. International Youth Year.
989 **339** 150f. multicoloured . . . 1·10 55

340 Football between Globes

1985. World Cup Football Championship, Mexico (1986) (1st issue).
990 **340** 200f. multicoloured . . . 1·50 80
See also No. 1015.

341 Boeing 727, Map and Emblem

1985. 25th Anniv of Aerial Navigation Security Agency for Africa and Malagasy.
991 **341** 150f. multicoloured . . . 1·25 90

342 "Boletus edulis"

343 Audubon and Arctic Skua ("Labbe Parasite")

1985. Fungi. Multicoloured.
992 35f. Type **342** . . . . 1·60 60
993 40f. "Amanita phalloides" . . 2·10 1·10
994 100f. "Paxillus involutus" . . 4·75 2·10

1985. Birth Bicentenary of John J. Audubon (ornithologist). Multicoloured.
995 150f. Type **343** . . . . 2·00 1·10
996 300f. Audubon and oystercatcher ("Huitrier Pie") . . . . 4·50 2·40

344 Emblem, Hands and Dove

1985. 40th Anniv of United Nations Organization and 25th Anniv of Benin's Membership.
997 **344** 250f. multicoloured . . . 1·90 90

345 Stamps and Globe

1985. "Italia '85" International Stamp Exhibition, Rome.
998 **345** 200f. multicoloured . . . 1·50 80

1985. "Philexafrique" International Stamp Exhibition, Lome, Togo (2nd issue). As Type **338**. Multicoloured.
999 250f. Forest and hand holding tools . . . . . . 2·50 1·60
1000 250f. Magnifying glass over judo stamp . . . . 2·50 1·60

1985. Various Dahomey stamps optd **Republique Populaire du Benin**. Nos. 1001/9 and 1011 surch also.
1001 – 75f. on 35f. mult (No. 596) (postage) . . 50 25
1002 – 90f. on 70f. multicoloured (No. 419) 70 35
1003 – 90f. on 140f. multicoloured (No. 446) 70 35
1004 **113** 100f. on 40f. red, brown and green 75 40
1005 – 150f. on 45f. multicoloured (No. 597) . . . . . . 1·10 65
1006 – 75f. on 70f. multicoloured (No. 342) (air) . . . . 6·50 6·50
1007 – 75f. on 100f. multicoloured (No. 251) . . . . . . 2·25 60
1008 **59** 75f. on 200f. mult . . . 2·25 60
1009 – 90f. on 250f. multicoloured (No. 272) . . . . . . 2·50 60
1010 **110** 100f. multicoloured . . . 45 40
1011 – 150f. on 500f. multicoloured (No. 252) . . . . . . 3·75 1·40

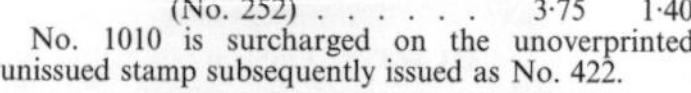
No. 1010 is surcharged on the unoverprinted unissued stamp subsequently issued as No. 422.

349 Church, Children playing and Nativity Scene

1985. Air. Christmas.
1012 **349** 500f. multicoloured . . . 4·00 1·60

350 Emblem

1986. 10th Anniv of African Parliamentary Union and Ninth Conference, Cotonou.
1013 **350** 100f. multicoloured . . . 75 40

351 Halley, Comet and "Giotto" Space Probe

1986. Appearance of Halley's Comet.
1014 **351** 205f. multicoloured . . . 2·25 1·25

352 Footballers

1986. World Cup Football Championship, Mexico (2nd issue). Multicoloured.
1015 **352** 500f. Footballers . . . . 3·75 1·75

353 Dead and Healthy Trees

354 Amazone

1986. Anti-desertification Campaign.
1016 **353** 150f. multicoloured . . . 1·25 65

1986.
1017 **354** 100f. blue 65 20
1018 150f. purple 95 25

355 "Haemanthus"

356 "Inachis io", "Aglais urticae" and "Nymphalis antiopa"

1986. Flowers. Multicoloured.
1019 100f. Type **355** . . . . . . 1·10 75
1020 205f. "Hemerocallis" . . . 2·25 1·25

1986. Butterflies. Multicoloured.
1021 150f. Type **356** . . . . . . 1·75 1·10
1022 150f. "Anthocharis cardamines", "Papilio machaon" and "Cynthia cardui" . . . . 1·75 1·10

1986. Various stamps of Dahomey surch **Republique Populaire du Benin** and new value.
1024 – 150f. on 100f. mult (444) (postage) . . . . . .
1025 – 15f. on 85f. mult (600) (air) . . . .
1026 – 25f. on 200f. mult (432)
1027 **150** 25f. on 200f. deep green, violet and green . . . .
1030 **175** 100f. purple, indigo & bl
1031 **128** 150f. on 100f. blue, violet and red . . . .

358 Statue and Buildings

359 Bust of King Behanzin

1986. Centenary of Statue of Liberty.
1032 **358** 250f. multicoloured . . . 2·25 1·00

1986. King Behanzin.
1033 **359** 440f. multicoloured . . . 3·75 1·90
For design in smaller size, see Nos. 1101/4.

360 Family with Crib, Church and Nativity Scene

1986. Air. Christmas.
1034 **360** 300f. multicoloured . . . 2·50 1·10

361 Rainbow and Douglas DC-10

1986. Air. 25th Anniv of Air Afrique.
1035 **361** 100f. multicoloured . . . 1·00 60

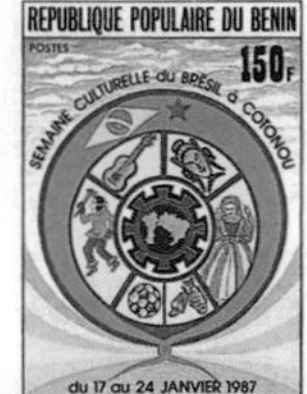

362 Emblem around Map in Cog

1987. Brazil Culture Week, Cotonou.
1036 **362** 150f. multicoloured . . . 1·75 70

363 Cotonou Centre for the Blind and Partially Sighted

1987. Rotary International 910 District Conference, Cotonou.
1037 **363** 300f. multicoloured . . . 2·50 1·10

1987. Various stamps of Dahomey optd **Republique Populaire du Benin**. Nos. 1038/9 and 1042/53 surch also.
1038 **129** 10f. on 65f. black, violet and red (postage) . . . . . .
1039 – 15f. on 100f. red, blue and green (434) . . .
1040 **98** 40f. green, blue and brown . . . .
1042 – 150f. on 200f. mult (560) . . . .
1043 **144** 10f. on 65f. black, yellow & purple (air)
1046 – 25f. on 150f. mult (487)
1047 – 30f. on 300f. mult (602)
1048 **140** 40f. on 15f. purple, green and blue . . .
1049 – 40f. on 100f. mult (453)
1051 – 50f. on 140f. mult (601)
1052 – 50f. on 500f. mult (252)
1053 – 70f. on 250f. mult (462)
1054 – 80f. mult (286) . . . .
1055 – 100f. mult (429) . . . .
1055a – 100f. mult (447) . . . .

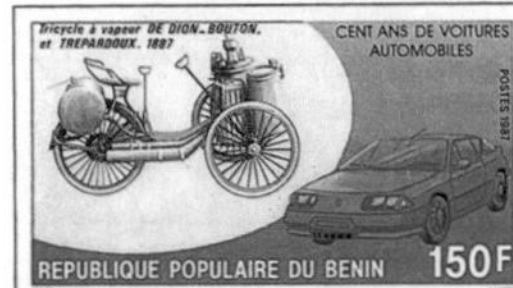

365 De Dion-Bouton and Trepardoux Steam Tricycle and Ford Coupe

1987. Centenary of Motor Car. Multicoloured.
1058 150f. Type **365** . . . . . . 1·50 75
1059 300f. Daimler motor carriage, 1886 and Mercedes Benz W124 series saloon . . . . . . 2·75 1·50

366 Baptism in the Python Temple

368 G. Hansen and R. Follereau (leprosy pioneers) and Patients

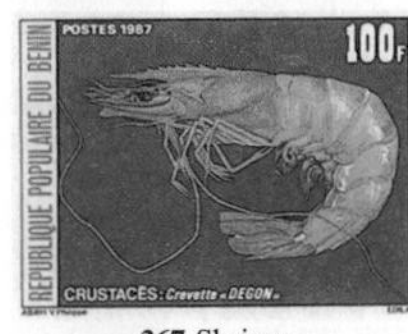

367 Shrimp

1987. Ritual Ceremonies.
1060 **366** 100f. multicoloured . . . 95 50

1987. Shellfish. Multicoloured.
1061 100f. Type **367** . . . . . . 1·10 60
1062 150f. Crab . . . . 1·40 90

1987. Anti-leprosy Campaign.
1063 **368** 200f. multicoloured . . . 1·90 95

369 Crop-spraying and Locusts

1987. Anti-locust Campaign.
1064 **369** 100f. multicoloured . . . 1·10 60

370 Fisherman and Farmer

1987. Air. 10th Anniv of International Agricultural Development Fund.
1065 **370** 500f. multicoloured . . . 3·75 1·90

371 Nativity Scene in Moon and Father Christmas giving Sweets to Crowd

1987. Christmas.
1066 **371** 150f. multicoloured . . . 1·25 75

372 Rally

375 Hands holding Pot Aloft

1988. 15th Anniv (1987) of Start of Benin Revolution.
1067 **372** 100f. multicoloured . . .

1988. Various stamps surch. (a) Stamps of Dahomey surch **Populaire du Benin** (1081c) or **Republique Populaire du Benin** (others).
1068 – 5f. on 3f. black and blue (173) (postage)
1069 – 20f. on 100f. mult (506)
1071 – 25f. on 100f. mult (576)
1073 – 50f. on 45f. mult (320)
1074 **178** 55f. on 200f. olive, brown and green . .
1075a 125f. on 100f. mult (557) . . . .
1076 **116** 10f. on 50f. black, orange and blue (air)
1077 **161** 15f. on 150f. red and black . . . .
1078 – 25f. on 100f. mult (526)
1079 **156** 25f. on 100f. blue, brown and violet . .
1079a **153** 40f. on 35f. mult . . .
1080 – 40f. on 100f. mult (495)
1081 **162** 40f. on 150f. red, brown and blue . . .
1081a **148** 100f. brown and green
1081b **181** 125f. on 75f. lilac, red and green . . . . .
1081c – 125f. on 150f. blue and purple (541) . . . .
1082 – 125f. on 250f. mult (491) . . . .
1082a – 125f. red and brown (540) . . . .
1083 – 190f. on 250f. brown, green and red (594)
1084 – 1000f. on 150f. multicoloured (545)

(b) No. 618 of Benin surch **Republique Populaire du Benin**.
1085 – 10f. on 60f. on 2f. mult . .

(c) Stamps of Benin surch only.
1086 **359** 125f. on 440f. mult (postage) . . . . . .
1087 **338** 125f. on 200f. mult (air)
1088 – 190f. on 250f. mult (999)
1089 – 190f. on 250f. mult (1000) . . . .

1988. 25th Anniv of Organization of African Unity.
1094 **375** 125f. multicoloured . . . 95 40

376 Resuscitation of Man pulled from River

1988. 125th Anniv of Red Cross Movement.
1095 **376** 200f. multicoloured . . . 1·50 1·00

377 King

378 Scout and Camp

1988. 20th Death Anniv of Martin Luther King (Civil Rights leader).
1096 **377** 200f. multicoloured . . . 1·50 75

1988. 1st Benin Scout Jamboree, Savalou.
1097 **378** 125f. multicoloured . . . 1·25 90

379 Healthy Family and Health Care

1988. 40th Anniv of W.H.O. and 10th Anniv of "Health for All by 2000" Declaration.
1098 **379** 175f. multicoloured . . . 1·25 65

380 Dugout Canoes and Houses

1988. Ganvie (lake village). Multicoloured.
1099 125f. Type **380** 95 50
1100 190f. Boatman and houses 1·60 75

1988. As T **359** but smaller (17 × 24 mm).
1101 **359** 40f. black 25 15
1102 125f. red 75 25
1103 190f. blue . . . . 1·25 25
1104 220f. green . . . . . . 1·50 40

381 Adoration of the Magi

1988. Air. Christmas.
1105 **381** 500f. multicoloured . . . 3·75 1·90

382 Offering to Hebiesso, God of Thunder

1988. Ritual Ceremony.
1106 **382** 125f. multicoloured . . . 95 50

383 Roseate Tern

1989. Endangered Animals. Roseate Tern. Mult.
1107 10f. Type **383** 25 15
1108 15f. Tern with fish 50 20
1109 50f. Tern on rocks . . . . 1·00 40
1110 125f. Tern flying . . . . . 2·50 85

384 Eiffel Tower

386 Tractor, Map and Pump

1989. Centenary of Eiffel Tower.
1111 **384** 190f. multicoloured . . . 1·60 1·00

1989. 30th Anniv of Agriculture Development Council.
1113 **386** 75f. multicoloured . . .

387 Symbols of Revolution and France 1950 National Relief Fund Stamps

1989. Bicentenary of French Revolution and "Philexfrance 89" International Stamp Exhibition, Paris.
1114 **387** 190f. multicoloured . . . 1·90 1·25

388 Burbot

1989. Fishes. Multicoloured.
1115 125f. Type **388** . . . . . . 1·50 75
1116 190f. Northern pike and Atlantic salmon . . . . . 2·25 1·25

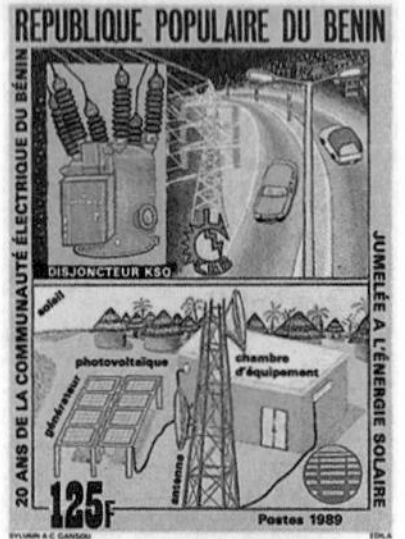

389 Circuit Breaker, Illuminated Road and Solar Energy Complex

1989. 20th Anniv of Benin Electricity Community.
1117 **389** 125f. multicoloured . . . 95 50

390 Lion within Wreath

1989. Death Centenary of King Glele.
1118 **390** 190f. multicoloured . . . 1·40 75

391 Nativity

1989. Christmas.
1119 **391** 200f. multicoloured . . . 1·50 90

392 Anniversary Emblem and Means of Communications

1990. Centenary of Postal and Telecommunications Ministry (1st issue).
1120 **392** 125f. multicoloured . . . 95 50
See also No. 1127.

393 Oranges

1990. Fruit and Flowers. Multicoloured.
1121 60f. Type **393** 45 30
1122 190f. Kaufmannia tulips (vert) . . . . 1·75 90
1123 250f. Cashew nuts (vert) . . 1·90 1·10

394 Launch of "Apollo 11" and Footprint on Moon

1990. 21st Anniv of First Manned Moon Landing.
1124 **394** 190f. multicoloured . . . 1·40 75

395 Footballers

1990. World Cup Football Championship, Italy. Multicoloured.
1125 125f. Type **395** . . . . . . 1·10 60
1126 190f. Mascot holding torch and pennant (vert) . . . 1·75 75

396 Balloons, Emblem and Means of Communication **398** De Gaulle

1990. Centenary of Postal and Telecommunications Ministry (2nd issue).
1127 **396** 150f. multicoloured . . . 1·10 55

1990. World Cup Finalists. No. 1125 optd **FINALE R.F.A.-ARGENTINE 1-0**.
1128 **395** 125f. multicoloured . . . 80 50

1990. Birth Centenary of Charles de Gaulle (French statesman) (1st issue).
1129 **398** 190f. multicoloured . . . 1·50 1·00
See also No. 1160.

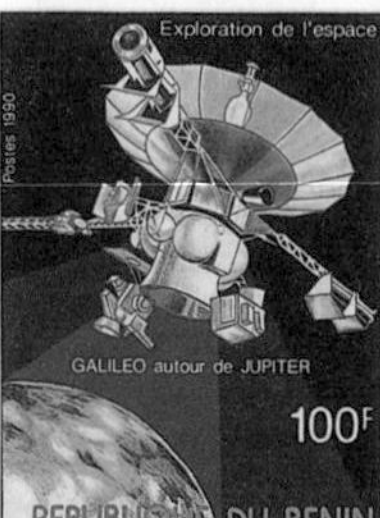

399 "Galileo" Space Probe orbiting Jupiter **400** Nativity

1990. Space Exploration.
1130 **399** 100f. multicoloured . . . 75 50

1990. Christmas.
1131 **400** 200f. multicoloured . . . 1·50 1·00

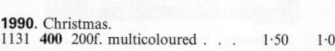

401 Hands pointing to Scales of Justice

1990. National Conference of Active Forces.
1132 **401** 125f. multicoloured . . .

406 Different Cultures and Emblem

1991. African Tourism Year.
1150 **406** 190f. multicoloured . . . 1·50 1·00

407 Tennis Player **408** Flag and Arms

1991. Cent of French Open Tennis Championships.
1151 **407** 125f. multicoloured . . . 1·50 75

1991. 31st Anniv of Independence.
1152 **408** 125f. multicoloured . . . 1·50 75

1991. "Riccione 91" Stamp Fair. No. 1130 optd **"Riccione 91"**.
1153 **399** 100f. multicoloured . . . 1·00 60

410 Adoration of the Magi

1991. Christmas.
1154 **410** 125f. multicoloured . . . 95 40

411 Guelede Dancer **412** Mozart

1991.
1155 **411** 190f. multicoloured . . . 1·50 65

1991. Death Bicentenary of Wolfgang Amadeus Mozart (composer).
1156 **412** 1000f. multicoloured . . 8·00 5·00

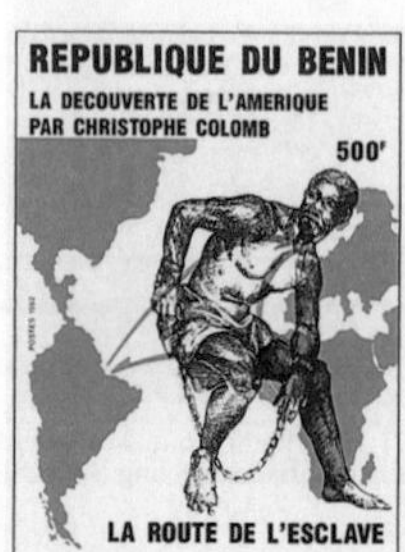

413 Slave in Chains and Route Map

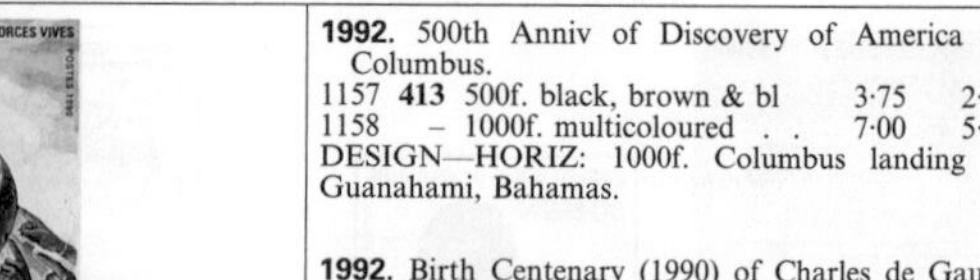

1992. 500th Anniv of Discovery of America by Columbus.
1157 **413** 500f. black, brown & bl 3·75 2·50
1158 – 1000f. multicoloured . . 7·00 5·00
DESIGN—HORIZ: 1000f. Columbus landing at Guanahami, Bahamas.

1992. Birth Centenary (1990) of Charles de Gaulle (French statesman) (2nd issue). As No. 1129 but value changed.
1160 **398** 300f. multicoloured . . . 2·25 1·50

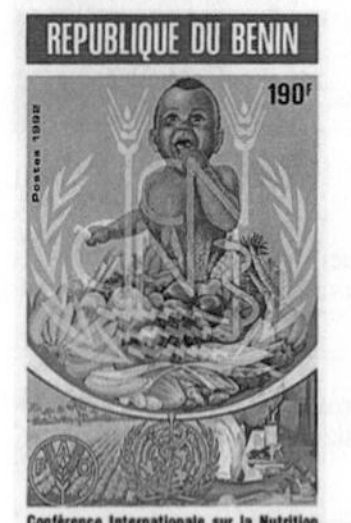

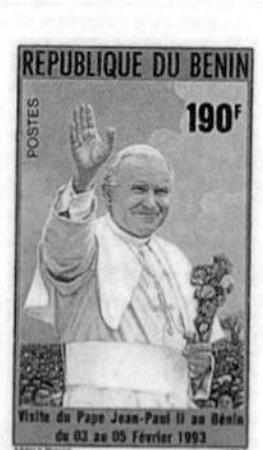

414 Child, Produce and Emblems **415** Pope John Paul II

1992. International Nutrition Conference, Rome.
1161 **414** 190f. multicoloured . . . 1·40 1·00

1993. Papal Visit.
1162 **415** 190f. multicoloured . . . 1·25 90

416 Emblem and Voodoo Culture

1993. "Ouidah 92" Voodoo Culture Festival.
1163 **416** 125f. multicoloured . . . 75 50

417 Well and Blue-throated Roller

1993. Possotome Artesian Well.
1164 **417** 125f. multicoloured . . . 75 50

418 Map, Clasped Hands and Flags of Member Countries

1993. 30th Anniv of Organization of African Unity.
1165 **418** 125f. multicoloured . . . 70 40

419 John F. Kennedy (President of United States, 1961–63)

1993. Death Anniversaries. Multicoloured.
1166 190f. Type **419** (30th anniv) 85 45
1167 190f. Dr. Martin Luther King (American civil rights campaigner, 25th anniv) (vert) 85 45

1993. Stamps of Dahomey variously optd or surch.
(a) **REPUBLIQUE DU BENIN**.
1167a **139** 5f. multicoloured (postage) . . . . . .
1170 **108** 50f. on 1f. multicoloured (617)
1171 **113** 80f. on 40f. red, brown and green . . . . .
1173 135f. on 20f. black, green and red (190)
1175 135f. on 30f. black, brown and violet (472) . . . . . .
1177 **107** 135f. on 40f. mult . . .

1179 – 135f. on 60f. olive, red and purple (181)
1181 – 200f. on 100f. mult (322)
1186 – 15f. on 40f. mult (458) (air)
1190 **126** 100f. multicoloured
1190a **119** 125f. on 40f. mult
1191 – 125f. on 65f. red and blue (552)
1201 – 200f. on 250f. mult (569)

(b) **DU BENIN.**

1207 **60** 5f. on 1f. multicoloured (postage)
1208 – 10f. on 3f. black and blue (173)
1211 – 25f. multicoloured (441)
1220 – 135f. on 3f. mult (274)
1223 – 20f. on 200f. mult (451) (air)
1225 – 25f. on 85f. mult (600)
1227 **140** 30f. on 15f. purple, green and blue
1231 – 125f. on 70f. mult (383)
1235 – 150f. purple, blue and brown (456)
1236 – 150f. multicoloured (527)
1239 **150** 200f. green, violet and emerald
1242 – 200f. on 150f. mult (562)
1243 **179** 300f. multicoloured

(c) **BENIN.**

1257 – 25f. on 500f. brown, red and green (592) (air)
1258 – 30f. on 200f. mult (528)
1260a – 100f. brown, green and blue (522)
1261 **116** 125f. on 50f. black, orange and blue
1263a – 190f. on 200f. mult (478)
1266 – 300f. brn, red & bl (591)

422 Conference Emblem

1994. U.N.E.S.C.O. Conference on the Slave Route, Ouidah.

1275 **422** 300f. multicoloured . . . 75 40

423 World Map

1994. International Year of the Family.

1276 **423** 200f. multicoloured . . . 50 25

425 Water Polo

1995. Olympic Games, Atlanta (1996) (1st issue). Multicoloured.

1278	45f. Type **425**	20	20
1279	50f. Throwing the javelin (vert)	25	20
1280	75f. Weightlifting (vert)	35	25
1281	100f. Tennis (vert)	50	40
1282	135f. Baseball (vert)	60	50
1283	200f. Synchronised swimming (vert)	90	70

See also Nos. 1347/52.

426 Paddle-steamer

1995. Ships. Multicoloured.

1285	40f. Type **426**	20	20
1286	50f. "Charlotte" (paddle steamer)	25	20
1287	75f. "Citta di Catania" (Italian liner)	35	25
1288	100f. "Mountbatten" SR-N4 (hovercraft)	50	40
1289	135f. "Queen Elizabeth 2" (liner)	60	50
1290	200f. "Matsu-Nef" (Japanese nuclear-powered freighter)	90	70

427 Chimpanzee

1995. Primates. Multicoloured.

1292	50f. Type **427**	25	20
1293	75f. Mandrill	35	30
1294	100f. Colobus	50	40
1295	135f. Barbary ape	70	50
1296	200f. Hamadryas baboon	1·00	75

428 Tabby Shorthair

1995. Cats. Multicoloured.

1298	40f. Type **428**	20	20
1299	50f. Sorrel Abyssinian ("Ruddy red")	25	20
1300	75f. White Persian long-hair	35	30
1301	100f. Seal colourpoint	50	40
1302	135f. Tabby point	60	50
1303	200f. Black shorthair	90	70

429 German Shepherd

1995. Dogs. Multicoloured.

1305	40f. Type **429**	20	20
1306	50f. Beagle	25	20
1307	75f. Great dane	35	30
1308	100f. Boxer	50	40
1309	135f. Pointer	60	50
1310	200f. Long-haired fox terrier	90	70

430 Arms  **431** Lion

1995.

1312 **430**	135f. multicoloured	35	20
1313	150f. multicoloured	35	20
1314	200f. multicoloured	50	25

See also Nos. 1458 and 1480/2.

1995. Mammals. Multicoloured.

1315	50f. Type **431**	25	20
1316	75f. African buffalo	35	30
1317	100f. Chimpanzee	50	40
1318	135f. Impala	70	50
1319	200f. Cape ground squirrel (horiz)	1·00	75

432 Hawfinches  **433** "Dracunculus vulgaris"

1995. Birds and their Young. Multicoloured.

1321	40f. Type **432**	20	20
1322	50f. Spotted-necked doves	25	20
1323	75f. Peregrine falcons	35	30
1324	100f. Blackburnian warblers	50	40
1325	135f. Black-headed gulls	60	50
1326	200f. Eastern white pelican	90	70

1995. Flowers. Multicoloured.

1327	40f. Type **433**	20	20
1328	50f. Daffodil	25	20
1329	75f. Amaryllis	35	30
1330	100f. Water-lily	50	40
1331	135f. "Chrysanthemum carinatum"	60	50
1332	200f. Iris	90	70

434 Lynx  **435** "Angraecum sesquipedale"

1995. Big Cats and their Young. Mult.

1333	40f. Type **434**	20	20
1334	50f. Pumas	30	20
1335	75f. Cheetahs	35	20
1336	100f. Leopards	45	25
1337	135f. Tigers	60	30
1338	200f. Lions	85	40

1995. Orchids. Multicoloured.

1339	40f. Type **435**	20	20
1340	50f. "Polystachya virginea"	25	20
1341	75f. "Disa uniflora"	35	30
1342	100f. "Ansellia africana"	50	40
1343	135f. "Angraecum eichlerianum"	60	50
1344	200f. "Jumellea confusa"	90	70

436 Emblem  **437** Diving

1995. 6th Francophone Summit, Cotonou.

1345 **436**	150f. multicoloured	35	20
1346	200f. multicoloured	50	25

1996. Olympic Games, Atlanta (2nd issue). Multicoloured.

1347	40f. Type **437**	20	20
1348	50f. Tennis	25	20
1349	75f. Running	35	30
1350	100f. Gymnastics	50	40
1351	135f. Weightlifting	60	50
1352	200f. Shooting	90	70

438 Player with Ball

1996. World Cup Football Championship, France (1998) (1st issue).

1354 **438**	40f. multicoloured	35	20
1355 –	50f. multicoloured	35	20
1356 –	75f. multicoloured	75	50
1357 –	100f. multicoloured	90	60
1358 –	135f. multicoloured	1·25	1·00
1359 –	200f. multicoloured	1·90	1·50

DESIGNS: 50f. to 200f. Different players.

See also Nos. 1473/8.

439 Small Striped Swallowtail

1996. Butterflies. Multicoloured.

1361	40f. Type **439**	35	20
1362	50f. Red admiral	35	20
1363	75f. Common blue	75	50
1364	100f. African monarch	90	60
1365	135f. Painted lady	1·25	1·00
1366	200f. "Argus celbulina ortbitulus"	1·90	1·50

440 Dancer

1996. "China '96" International Stamp Exhibition, Peking. Multicoloured.

1368	40f. Type **440**	75	50
1369	50f. Exhibition emblem	1·00	75
1370	75f. Water-lily	1·50	1·00
1371	100f. Temple of Heaven, Peking	2·00	1·50

Nos. 1368/71 were issued together, se-tenant, forming a composite design.

441 Emblem

1996. 15th Convention of Lions Club International, Cotonou.

1457 **441**	100f. multicoloured	75	50
1372	135f. multicoloured	1·10	75
1373	150f. multicoloured	1·10	75
1374	200f. multicoloured	1·50	1·00

442 "Holy Family of Rouvre" (Raphael)

1996. Christmas. Multicoloured.

1375	40f. Type **442**	35	20
1376	50f. "The Holy Family" (Raphael)	35	20
1377	75f. "St. John the Baptist" (Bartolome Murillo)	75	60
1378	100f. "The Virgin of the Scales" (Leonardo da Vinci)	95	60
1379	135f. "The Virgin and Child" (Gerhard David)	1·25	1·00
1380	200f. "Adoration of the Magi" (Juan Mayno)	1·90	1·50

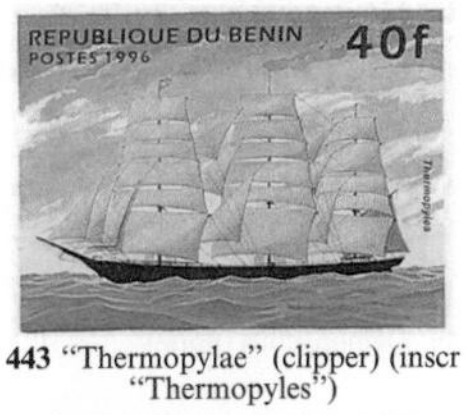

443 "Thermopylae" (clipper) (inscr "Thermopyles")

1996. Ships. Multicoloured.

1382	40f. Type **443**	35	20
1383	50f. Barque	35	20
1384	75f. "Nightingale" (full-rigged ship)	75	50
1385	100f. Opium clipper	90	60
1386	135f. "Torrens" (full-rigged ship)	1·25	1·00
1387	200f. English tea clipper	1·90	1·50

444 Serval  **445** Hurdler and Gold Medal

1996. Big Cats. Multicoloured.
1389 40f. Type **444** 35 20
1390 50f. Golden cat 35 20
1391 75f. Ocelot 75 50
1392 100f. Bobcat 90 60
1393 135f. Leopard cat 1·25 1·00
1394 200f. "Felis euptilura" 1·95 1·50

1996. Centenary of Issue by Greece of First Olympic Stamps. Multicoloured.
1396 40f. Type **445** 1·00 50
1397 50f. Hurdler and Olympic flames 1·00 50
1398 75f. Pierre de Coubertin (founder of modern Olympics) and map showing south-west U.S.A. 1·25 60
1399 100f. Map showing south-east U.S.A. 1·50 75
Nos. 1396/9 were issued together, se-tenant, forming a composite design.

446 Running
447 "Parodia subterranea"

1996. "Olymphilex '96" Olympics and Sports Stamp Exhibition, Atlanta. Multicoloured.
1400 40f. Type **446** 35 20
1401 50f. Canoeing 35 20
1402 75f. Gymnastics 75 50
1403 100f. Football 90 60
1404 135f. Tennis 1·25 1·00
1405 200f. Baseball 1·90 1·50

1996. Flowering Cacti. Multicoloured.
1407 40f. Type **447** 35 20
1408 50f. "Astrophytum senile" 35 20
1409 75f. "Echinocereus melanocentrus" 75 50
1410 100f. "Turbinicarpus klinkerianus" 90 60
1411 135f. "Astrophytum capricorne" 1·25 1·00
1412 200f. "Nelloydia grandiflora" 1·90 1·50

448 Chestnut Horse
449 Longisquama

1996. Horses. Multicoloured.
1413 40f. Type **448** 35 20
1414 50f. Horse on hillside 35 20
1415 75f. Foal by fence 75 50
1416 100f. Mother and foal 95 60
1417 135f. Pair of horses 1·40 1·00
1418 200f. Grey horse (horiz) 2·00 1·50

1996. Prehistoric Animals. Multicoloured.
1419 40f. Type **449** 35 20
1420 50f. Dimorphodon 35 20
1421 75f. Dunkleosteus (horiz) 75 50
1422 100f. Eryops (horiz) 90 60
1423 135f. Peloneustes (horiz) 1·25 1·00
1424 200f. Deinonychus (horiz) 1·90 1·50

450 Ivory-billed Woodpecker
451 Golden Tops

1996. Birds. Multicoloured.
1425 40f. Type **450** 35 20
1426 50f. Grey-necked bald crow 35 20
1427 75f. Kakapo 75 50
1428 100f. Puerto Rican amazon 90 60
1429 135f. Japanese crested ibis 1·25 1·00
1430 200f. California condor 1·90 1·50

1996. Fungi. Multicoloured.
1432 40f. Type **451** 35 20
1433 50f. "Psilocybe zapotecorum" 35 20
1434 75f. "Psilocybe mexicana" 75 50
1435 100f. "Conocybe siligineoides" 90 60
1436 135f. "Psilocybe caerulescens mazatecorum" 1·25 1·00
1437 200f. "Psilocybe caerulescens nigripes" 1·90 1·50

452 Impala

1996. Mammals. Multicoloured.
1439 40f. Type **452** 35 20
1440 50f. Waterbuck 35 20
1441 75f. African buffalo 75 50
1442 100f. Blue wildebeest 90 60
1443 135f. Okapi 1·25 1·00
1444 200f. Greater kudu 1·90 1·40

453 White Whale

1996. Marine Mammals. Multicoloured.
1445 40f. Type **453** 35 20
1446 50f. Bottle-nosed dolphin 35 20
1447 75f. Blue whale 75 50
1448 100f. "Eubalaena australis" 90 60
1449 135f. "Gramphidelphis griseus" 1·25 1·00
1450 200f. Killer whale 1·90 1·40

454 Grey Angelfish
455 Grenadier, Glassenapps Regiment

1996. Fishes. Multicoloured.
1451 50f. Type **454** 10 10
1452 75f. Sail-finned tang (horiz) 15 10
1453 100f. Golden trevally (horiz) 20 10
1454 135f. Pyramid butterflyfish (horiz) 25 15
1455 200f. Racoon butterflyfish (horiz) 40 20

1996. Arms. Dated "1996".
1458 **430** 100f. multicoloured 95 40

1996. Stamps of Benin variously surch.
1469 **311** 15f. on 185f. mult (postage)
1470 **379** 25f. on 175f. mult
1473 **359** 50f. on 220f. green (1104)
1479 **414** 150f. on 190f. mult
1480 **415** 150f. on 190f. mult
1484 **412** 250f. on 1000f. mult
1494 **193** 40f. on 210f. red, brown and green (air)
1495 – 40f. on 210f. purple, blue and yellow (792)
1499 – 150f. on 500f. red, ultramarine and green (657)

1996. Stamps of Dahomey variously optd or surch. (a) **Republique de Benin** (1510, 1516, 1519, 1522, 1526/9, 1535, 1544, 1556, 1558 and 1568) or **REPUBLIQUE DU BENIN** (others).
1510 – 35f. on 85f. brown, orange and green (493) (postage)
1511 – 125f. on 100f. violet, red and black (510)
1516 **85** 150f. on 30f. mult
1519 **113** 150f. on 40f. red, brown and green
1522 – 150f. on 45f. mult (597)
1526 – 35f. on 100f. deep blue and blue (326) (air)
1527 – 35f. on 100f. on 200f. multicoloured (409)
1528 – 35f. on 125f. green, blue and light blue (553)
1529 – 35f. on 300f. brown, red and blue (591)
1535 – 150f. multicoloured (527)
1544 **112** 150f. on 40f. multicoloured
1556 – 150f. on 110f. mult (386)
1558 – 150f. on 120f. mult (404)
1568 – 200f. on 500f. mult (252)

(b) **DU BENIN**.
1578 35f. on 125f. brown and green (540) (air)
1579 125f. on 65f. mult (465)
1580 **168** 135f. on 35f. mult

(c) **BENIN**.
1587 **68** 150f. on 30f. mult (post)
1591 25f. on 85f. mult (600) (air)

1997. Military Uniforms. Multicoloured.
1600 135f. Type **455** 35 20
1601 150f. Officer, Von Groben's Regiment 35 20
1602 200f. Private, Dohna's Regiment 75 50
1603 270f. Artilleryman 90 60
1604 300f. Cavalry trooper 1·25 1·00
1605 400f. Trooper, Mollendorf's Dragoons 1·90 1·40

456 Reid Macleod Gas-turbine Locomotive, 1920

1997. Railway Locomotives. Multicoloured.
1607 135f. Type **456** 25 15
1608 150f. Class O5 steam locomotive, 1935, Germany 30 15
1609 200f. Locomotive "Silver Fox", Great Britain 40 20
1610 270f. Class "Merchant Navy" locomotive, 1941, Great Britain 55 30
1611 300f. Diesel locomotive, 1960, Denmark 60 30
1612 400f. GM Type diesel locomotive, 1960 80 40
No. 1607 is wrongly inscr "Reid Maclead 1920".

457 Footballer and Map
458 Arms

1997. World Cup Football Championship, France (1998) (2nd issue).
1614 **457** 135f. multicoloured 35 20
1615 – 150f. multicoloured 35 20
1616 – 200f. multicoloured 75 50
1617 – 270f. multicoloured 90 60
1618 – 300f. mult (horiz) 1·25 1·00
1619 – 400f. mult (horiz) 1·90 1·50
DESIGNS: 150f. to 400f. Each showing map of France and player.

1997. T **430** redrawn as T **458**. Dated "1997".
1621 **458** 135f. multicoloured 40 25
1622 150f. multicoloured 70 35
1623 200f. multicoloured 90 50

459 Horse's Head

1997. Horses. Multicoloured.
1624 135f. Type **459** 40 25
1625 150f. Bay horse 55 35
1626 200f. Chestnut horse looking forward 70 45
1627 270f. Chestnut horse looking backwards 80 60
1628 300f. Black horse 1·00 70
1629 400f. Profile of horse 1·25 85

460 Irish Setter
461 "Phalaenopsis penetrate"

1997. Dogs. Multicoloured.
1631 135f. Type **460** 40 25
1632 150f. Saluki 55 35
1633 200f. Dobermann pinscher 70 45
1634 270f. Siberian husky 80 60
1635 300f. Basenji 1·00 90
1636 400f. Boxer 1·25 85

1997. Orchids. Multicoloured.
1638 135f. Type **461** 40 25
1639 150f. "Phalaenopsis" "Golden Sands" 55 35
1640 200f. "Phalaenopsis" "Sun Spots" 70 45
1641 270f. "Phalaenopsis fuscata" 80 60
1642 300f. "Phalaenopsis christi floyd" 1·00 70
1643 400f. "Phalaenopsis cayanne" 1·25 85

462 Buick Model C Tourer, 1905

1997. Motor Cars. Multicoloured.
1645 135f. Type **462** 40 25
1646 150f. Ford model A tonneau, 1903 55 35
1647 200f. Stanley steamer tourer, 1913 70 45
1648 270f. Stoddar-Dayton tourer, 1911 80 60
1649 300f. Cadillac convertible sedan, 1934 1·00 70
1650 400f. Cadillac convertible sedan, 1931 1·25 85

463 Northern Bullfinch

1997. Birds. Multicoloured.
1652 135f. Type **463** 40 25
1653 150f. Spruce siskin 50 35
1654 200f. Ring ousel 70 50
1655 270f. Crested tit 90 70
1656 300f. Spotted nutcracker 1·00 75
1657 400f. Nightingale 1·50 1·00

464 "Faucaria lupina"

1997. Cacti. Multicoloured.
1659 135f. Type **464** 40 25
1660 150f. "Conophytum bilobun" 50 35
1661 200f. "Lithops aucampiae" 70 50
1662 270f. "Lithops helmutii" 90 70
1663 300f. "Stapelia grandiflora" 1·00 75
1664 400f. "Lithops fulviceps" 1·50 1·00

465 Egyptian Merchant Ship

1997. Ancient Sailing Ships. Multicoloured.
1666 135f. Type **465** 45 30
1667 150f. Greek merchant ship 45 30
1668 200f. Phoenician galley 75 50
1669 270f. Roman merchant ship 1·00 60
1670 300f. Norman knarr 1·10 70
1671 400f. Mediterranean sailing ship 1·50 90

466 Black-tipped Grouper

1997. Fishes. Multicoloured.

1673 135f. Type **466** 30 15
1674 150f. Cardinal fish 30 15
1675 200f. Indo-Pacific humpheaded parrotfish . . 45 25
1676 270f. Regal angelfish 60 30
1677 300f. Wrasse 65 35
1678 400f. Hawkfish 85 45

REPUBLIQUE DU BENIN 135F
Postes 1997
27 JANVIER 1987 27 JANVIER 1997
APPA
Xe Anniversaire de l'Association des Producteurs de Pétrole Africains (APPA)

467 Emblem

1997. 10th Anniv of African Petroleum Producers' Association.

1680 **467** 135f. multicoloured . . . 50 25
1681 200f. multicoloured . . . 85 35
1682 300f. multicoloured . . . 1·10 50
1683 500f. multicoloured . . . 1·75 70

468 Caesar's Mushroom **470** "Tephrocybe carbonaria"

469 "Puffing Billy", 1813

1997. Fungi. Multicoloured.

1684 135f. Type **468** 40 25
1685 150f. Slimy-banded cort . . 50 35
1686 200f. "Amanita bisporigera" 70 50
1687 270f. The blusher 90 70
1688 300f. Cracked green russula 1·00 75
1689 400f. Strangulated amanita 1·50 1·00

1997. Steam Railway Locomotives. Mult.

1691 135f. Type **469** 30 15
1692 150f. "Rocket", 1829 . . . 30 15
1693 200f. "Royal George", 1827 45 25
1694 270f. "Novelty", 1829 . . . 60 30
1695 300f. "Locomotion", 1825 (vert) 65 35
1696 400f. "Sans Pareil", 1829 (vert) 85 45

1998. Fungi. Multicoloured.

1698 135f. Type **470** 25 15
1699 150f. Butter mushroom . . 30 15
1700 200f. Oyster fungus 40 20
1701 270f. "Hohenbuehelia geogenia" 50 25
1702 300f. Bitter bolete 60 30
1703 400f. "Lepiota leucothites" 80 40

471 Philadelphia or "Double Deck", 1885

1998. Fire Engines. Multicoloured.

1705 135f. Type **471** 25 15
1706 150f. "Veteran", 1850 . . . 30 15
1707 200f. Merryweather, 1894 40 20
1708 270f. 19 th-century Hippomobile 50 25
1709 300f. Jeep "Willy", 1948 . . 60 30
1710 400f. Chevrolet 6400 . . . . 80 40

472 Uranite

1998. Minerals. Multicoloured.

1712 135f. Type **472** 25 15
1713 150f. Quartz 30 15
1714 200f. Aragonite 40 20
1715 270f. Malachite 50 25
1716 300f. Turquoise 60 30
1717 400f. Corundum 80 40

473 Locomotive

1998. Steam Railway Locomotives. Multicoloured.

1719 135f. Type **473** 25 15
1720 150f. Green locomotive . . 30 15
1721 200f. Brown locomotive . . 40 20
1722 270f. Lilac locomotive . . . 50 25
1723 300f. Toledo Furnace Co No. 1 . . . . 60 30
1724 400f. No. 1 "Helvetia" . . . 80 40

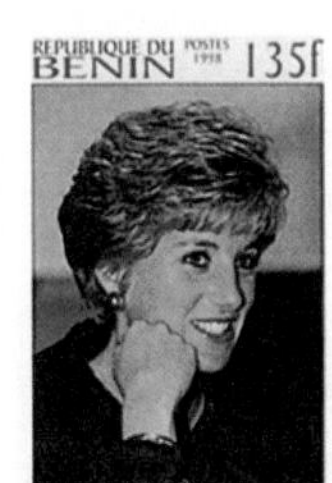

474 Diana, Princess of Wales

1998. 1st Death Anniv of Diana, Princess of Wales. Multicoloured.

1726 135f. Type **474** 25 15
1727 150f. Wearing pink dress . . 25 15
1728 200f. Wearing beige jacket 35 20
1729 270f. Wearing white jacket with revers 50 25
1730 300f. Making speech 55 30
1731 400f. Wearing collarless single-breasted white jacket 70 35
1732 500f. Wearing red jacket . . 90 45
1733 600f. Wearing black jacket 1·10 55
1734 700f. Wearing double-breasted white jacket . . 1·25 65

475 Sordes

1998. Prehistoric Animals. Multicoloured.

1735 135f. Type **475** 25 15
1736 150f. Scaphognatus 25 15
1737 200f. Dsungaripterus 35 20
1738 270f. Brontosaurus 50 25
1739 300f. Diplodocus 55 30
1740 400f. Coelurus and baryonyx 70 35
1741 500f. Kronosaurus and ichthyosaurus 90 45
1742 600f. Ceratosaurus . . . . 1·10 55
1743 700f. Yangchuansaurus . . 1·25 65

Nos. 1735/43 were issued together, se-tenant, forming a composite design.

476 Beagle **477** Abyssinian

1998. Dogs. Multicoloured.

1744 135f. Type **476** 25 15
1745 150f. Dalmatians 25 15
1746 200f. Dachshund 35 20
1747 270f. Cairn terrier 50 25
1748 300f. Shih-tzus 55 30
1749 400f. Pug 70 35

1998. Cats. Multicoloured.

1751 135f. Type **477** 25 15
1752 150f. Striped silver tabby . . 25 15
1753 200f. Siamese 35 20
1754 270f. Red tabby (horiz) . . 50 25
1755 300f. Wild cat (horiz) . . . 55 30
1756 400f. Manx (horiz) 70 35

478 Bugatti 13 Torpedo, 1910

1998. Motor Cars. Multicoloured.

1758 135f. Type **478** 25 15
1759 150f. Clement voiturette, 1903 . . . . 25 15
1760 200f. Stutz Bearcat speedster, 1914 . . . . . 35 20
1761 270f. Darracq phaeton, 1907 50 25
1762 300f. Napier delivery car, 1913 . . . . 55 30
1763 400f. Pierce Arrow roadster, 1911 . . . . 70 35

479 Apollo

1998. Butterflies. Multicoloured.

1765 135f. Type **479** 25 15
1766 150f. Orange-tip 25 15
1767 200f. Camberwell beauty . . 35 20
1768 250f. Speckled wood 40 20
1769 300f. Purple-edged copper 55 30
1770 400f. Chequered skipper . . 70 35

480 Gouldian Finch

1999. Birds. Multicoloured.

1772 135f. Type **480** 25 15
1773 150f. Saffron finch 25 15
1774 200f. Red-billed quelea . . . 35 20
1775 270f. Golden bishop 50 25
1776 300f. Red-crested cardinal 55 30
1777 400f. Golden-breasted bunting 70 35

481 Boat, Ceylon

1999. Sailing Boats. Multicoloured.

1779 135f. Type **481** 25 15
1780 150f. Tanka-Tim, Canton, Macao 25 15
1781 200f. Sampan, Hong Kong 35 20
1782 270f. Outrigger sailing canoe, Polynesia 50 25
1783 300f. Junk, Japan 55 30
1784 400f. Dacca-Pulwar, Bengal 70 35

482 White Rhinoceros

1999. Mammals.

1786 **482** 50f. grey 10 10
1787 – 100f. violet 20 10
1788 – 135f. green 25 15
1789 – 135f. black 25 15
1790 – 150f. blue 25 15
1791 – 150f. green 25 15
1792 – 200f. blue 35 20
1793 – 200f. brown 35 20
1794 – 300f. brown 55 25
1795 – 300f. red 55 35
1796 – 400f. brown 70 35
1797 – 500f. brown 90 45

DESIGNS: No. 1787, Sable antelope; 1788, Warthog (*Phacochoerus aethiopicus*); 1789, Brown hyena (*Hyaena brunnea*); 1790, Eastern black-and-white colobus (*Colobus guereza*); 1791, Hippopotamus (*Hippopotamus amphibius*); 1792, Mountain zebra (*Equus zebra*); 1793, African buffalo (*Synceros caffer*) (wrongly inscr "Cyncerus"); 1794, Lion (*Panthera leo*); 1795, Cheetah (*Acinonyx jubatus*); 1796, Hunting dog; 1797, Potto.

483 Mikhail Tal

1999. Chess Players. Multicoloured.

1798 135f. Type **483** 25 15
1799 150f. Emanuel Lasker . . . 25 15
1800 200f. Jose Raul Capablanca 35 20
1801 270f. Aleksandr Alekhine . . 50 25
1802 300f. Max Euwe 55 25
1803 400f. Mikhail Botvinnik . . 70 35

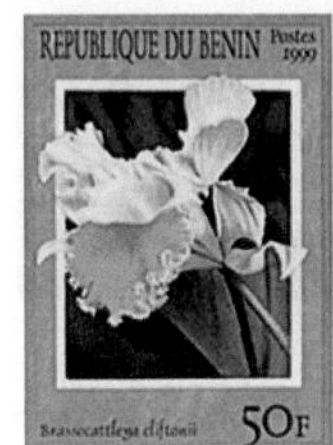

484 *Brassocattleya cliftonii*

1999. Orchids. Multicoloured.

1805 50f. Type **484** 10 10
1806 100f. Wilsonara 20 10
1807 150f. *Cypripedium paeony* 25 15
1808 300f. *Cymbidium babylon* . . 55 25
1809 400f. Cattleya 70 35
1810 500f. *Miltonia minx* 90 45

485 Royal Python

1999. Snakes. Multicoloured.

1812 135f. Type **485** 25 15
1813 150f. Royal python (different) 25 15
1814 200f. African rock python 35 20
1815 2000f. Head of African rock python . . . . 3·50 1·75

486 Clown Knifefish

1999. Fishes. Multicoloured.

1816 135f. Type **486** 25 15
1817 150f. Puntius filamentosus 25 15
1818 200f. *Epalzeorhynchos bicolor* 35 20
1819 270f. Spotted rasbora . . . 50 25
1820 300f. Tigernander 55 25
1821 400f. Siamese fighting fish 70 35

487 A. Murdock's Steam Tricycle, 1786

1999. Steam-powered Vehicles. Multicoloured.

1823 135f. Type **487** 25 15
1824 150f. Richard Trevithick's locomotive, 1800 . . . 25 15
1825 200f. Trevithick's locomotive, 1803 . . . . 35 20
1826 270f. John Blenkinsop's locomotive, 1811 . . . . 50 25
1827 300f. Foster and Rastik's *Stourbridge Lion*, 1829 . . 55 30
1828 400f. Peter Cooper's *Tom Thumb*, 1829 . . . . . . 70 35

488 Aesculapian Snake

1999. Snakes. Multicoloured.

1830	135f. Type **488**	25	15
1831	150f. Common pine snake	25	15
1832	200f. Grass snake	35	20
1833	270f. Green whip snake	50	25
1834	300f. Jamaica boa	55	30
1835	400f. Diamond-back rattlesnake	70	35

489 Testing Chinese Lantern (14th-century)

1999. "China 1999" International Stamp Exhibition, Peking. Multicoloured.

1837	50f. Type **489**	10	10
1838	100f. Satellite launching centre, Jiuquan	20	10
1839	135f. DFH-3 communications satellite	25	15
1840	150f. Satellite launch	25	15
1841	200f. Launch of *Long March* (rocket)	35	20
1842	300f. *Yuan Wang* (passenger ferry) at sea	55	30
1843	400f. Dish aerial	70	35
1844	500f. Items of space post	90	45

Nos. 1837/44 were issued together, se-tenant, with the backgrounds forming a composite design of the Earth.

490 Cheetah

1999. Big Cats. Multicoloured.

1845	135f. Type **490**	25	15
1846	150f. Jaguar	25	15
1847	200f. Snow leopard	35	20
1848	270f. Leopard	50	25
1849	300f. Puma	55	25
1850	400f. Tiger	70	35

PARCEL POST STAMPS

1982. Optd or surch **Colis Postaux**.

P871	– 100f. multicoloured (No. 779) (postage)	75	40
P872	**256** 100f. on 150f. mult	75	40
P873	– 300f. mult (No. 797)	2·25	1·10
P874	**260** 1000f. multicoloured	6·75	3·25
P875	**274** 5000f. on 500f. mult (air)	35·00	17·00

1988. No. 543 of Dahomey surch **Republique Populaire du Benin colis postaux**.

P1089	**174** 5f. on 40f. multicoloured (postage)		
P1093	– 500f. on 200f. mult	3·00	1·90
P1092	– 300f. on 200f. blue, yellow & brown (air)		

POSTAGE DUE STAMPS

D 233 Pineapples

1978. Fruits. Multicoloured.

D716	10f. Type D **233**	30	30
D717	20f. Cashew nuts (vert)	50	40
D718	40f. Oranges	85	70
D719	50f. Breadfruit	1·10	80

D 234 Village Postman on Bicycle

1978. Rural Post.

D720	D **234** 60f. brown, grn & red	95	60
D721	– 80f. blue, brn & red	1·10	75

DESIGN: 80f. River village and postman in canoe.

BERGEDORF Pt. 7

A German city on the Elbe, governed by Hamburg and Lubeck until 1867 when it was purchased by the former. In 1868 became part of North German Confederation.

16 schilling = 1 Hamburg mark.

1

1861. Various sizes. Imperf.

1	**1** ½s. black on lilac	£375	
2	½s. black on blue	35·00	£550
4	1s. black on white	35·00	£250
5	1½s. black on yellow	15·00	£950
6	3s. black on red	£550	
7	3s. blue on red	18·00	£1200
8	4s. black on brown	18·00	£1600

BERMUDA Pt. 1

A group of islands in the W. Atlantic, E. of N. Carolina. Usually regarded by collectors as part of the Br. W. Indies group, though this is not strictly correct.

1865. 12 pence = 1 shilling;
20 shillings = 1 pound.
1970. 100 cents = 1 dollar (U.S.).

9 Queen Victoria

13 Dry Dock

1865. Portrait. Various frames.

19	**9** ½d. stone	2·75	4·25
21a	½d. green	2·50	80
24a	1d. red	9·00	20
25	2d. blue	55·00	4·00
26a	2d. purple	3·50	1·50
27b	2½d. blue	5·50	40
10	3d. yellow	£170	60·00
28	3d. grey	22·00	6·50
20	4d. red	17·00	1·75
28a	4d. brown	3·00	50·00
7	6d. mauve	23·00	12·00
11	1s. green	11·00	£120
29b	1s. brown	13·00	16·00

1874. Surch in words.

15	**9** 1d. on 2d. blue	£700	£375
16	1d. on 3d. yellow	£450	£350
17	1d. on 1s. green	£500	£250
12	3d. on 1d. red	£1600	
14	3d. on 1s. green	£1500	£650

1901. Surch **ONE FARTHING** and bar.

30	**9** ¼d. on 1s. grey	2·00	50

1902.

34	**13** ½d. brown and violet	1·75	1·50
31	½d. black and green	12·00	2·25
36	½d. green	14·00	2·75
32	1d. brown and red	8·00	10
38	1d. red	19·00	10
39	2d. grey and orange	7·50	11·00
40	2½d. brown and blue	16·00	7·00
41	2½d. blue	12·00	6·50
33	3d. mauve and green	3·00	2·00
42	4d. blue and brown	3·00	16·00

14 Badge of the Colony

15

1910.

44a	**14** ¼d. brown	60	1·50
77	½d. green	1·50	15
78d	1d. red	11·00	80
79b	1½d. brown	9·00	35
80	2d. grey	1·50	1·50
82b	2½d. blue	1·75	75
81a	2½d. green	1·75	1·50
84	3d. purple on yellow	4·00	1·00
83	3d. blue	16·00	26·00
85	4d. red on yellow	2·00	1·00
86	6d. purple	1·00	80
51	1s. black on green	4·25	4·00
51b	**15** 2s. purple and blue on blue	18·00	50·00
52	2s.6d. black and red on blue	29·00	80·00
52b	4s. black and red	60·00	£160
53d	5s. green and red on yellow	48·00	£100
92	10s. green and red on green	£130	£250
93	12s.6d. black and orange	£250	£350
55	£1 purple and black on red	£325	£550

1918. Optd **WAR TAX**.

56	**14** 1d. red	50	1·00

18

1920. Tercentenary of Representative Institutions. (a) 1st Issue.

59	**18** ¼d. brown	3·25	19·00
60	½d. green	3·50	10·00
65	1d. red	3·75	30
61	2d. grey	13·00	42·00
66	2½d. blue	13·00	13·00
62	3d. purple on yellow	12·00	40·00
63	4d. black and red on yellow	12·00	35·00
67	6d. purple	26·00	75·00
64	1s. black on green	16·00	48·00

19

(b) 2nd Issue.

74	**19** ¼d. brown	1·50	3·75
75	½d. green	2·75	6·00
76	1d. red	2·50	35
68	2d. grey	6·00	28·00
69	2½d. blue	9·00	3·00
70	3d. purple on yellow	5·50	16·00
71	4d. red on yellow	16·00	21·00
72	6d. purple	12·00	50·00
73	1s. black on green	23·00	50·00

1935. Silver Jubilee. As T **13** of Antigua.

94	1d. blue and red	45	60
95	1½d. blue and grey	70	2·25
96	2½d. brown and blue	1·40	1·25
97	1s. grey and purple	15·00	25·00

20 Hamilton Harbour

22 "Lucie" (yacht)

1936.

98	**20** ½d. green	10	10
99	– 1d. black and red	30	30
100	– 1½d. black and brown	1·00	50
101	**22** 2d. black and blue	5·00	1·50
102	– 2½d. blue	1·00	25
103	– 3d. black and red	2·75	1·40
104	– 6d. red and violet	80	10
105	– 1s. green	5·00	9·50
106	**20** 1s.6d. brown	50	10

DESIGNS—HORIZ: 1d., 1½d. South Shore, near Spanish Rock; 3d. Point House, Warwick Parish. VERT: 2½d., 1s. Grape Bay, Paget Parish; 6d. House at Par-la-Ville, Hamilton.

The 1d., 1½d., 2½d. and 1s. values include a portrait of King George V.

1937. Coronation. As T **2** of Aden.

107	1d. red	50	80
108	1½d. brown	60	1·50
109	2½d. blue	70	1·50

26 Ships in Hamilton Harbour

28 White-tailed Tropic Bird, Arms of Bermuda and Native Flower

1938.

110	**26** 1d. black and red	85	20
111b	1½d. blue and brown	2·25	70
112	**22** 2d. blue and brown	45·00	8·50
112a	2d. blue and red	1·50	1·00
113	– 2½d. blue and deep blue	11·00	1·25
113b	– 2½d. blue and black	2·75	2·00
114	– 3d. black and red	18·00	3·00
114a	– 3d. black and blue	1·75	40
114c	**28** 7½d. black, blue and green	5·50	2·75
115	– 1s. green	2·00	50

DESIGNS—VERT: 3d. St. David's Lighthouse. The 2½d. and 1s. are as 1935, but with King George VI portrait.

1938. As T **15**, but King George VI portrait.

116c	2s. purple and blue on blue	8·00	1·50
117d	2s.6d. black and red on blue	16·00	12·00
118f	5s. green and red on yellow	25·00	20·00
119e	10s. green and red on green	38·00	42·00
120b	12s.6d. grey and orange	95·00	50·00
121d	£1 purple and black on red	50·00	75·00

1940. Surch **HALF PENNY**.

122	**26** ½d. on 1d. black and red	40	1·00

1946. Victory. As T **9** of Aden.

123	1½d. brown	15	15
124	3d. blue	15	15

1948. Silver Wedding. As T **10/11** of Aden.

125	1½d. brown	30	50
126	£1 red	40·00	48·00

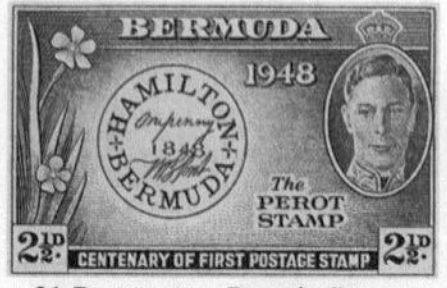

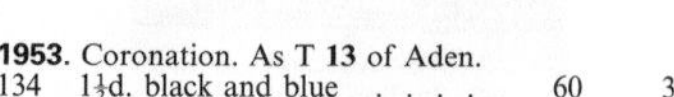

31 Postmaster Perot's Stamp

1949. Centenary of Postmaster Perot's Stamp.

127	**31** 2½d. blue and brown	15	25
128	3d. black and blue	15	15
129	6d. violet and green	15	15

1949. U.P.U. As T **20/23** of Antigua.

130	2½d. black	30	1·25
131	3d. blue	1·40	1·25
132	6d. purple	40	75
133	1s. green	40	1·25

1953. Coronation. As T **13** of Aden.

134	1½d. black and blue	60	30

34 Easter Lily

43 Hog Coin

1953.

135a	– ½d. olive	40	60
136	– 1d. black and red	2·00	50
137	**34** 1½d. green	30	10
138	– 2d. blue and red	50	40
139	– 2½d. red	2·00	50
140	– 3d. purple	30	10
141	– 4d. black and blue	55	75
142	– 4½d. green	1·50	1·00
143	– 6d. black and turquoise	6·00	60
156	– 6d. black and mauve	70	15
143a	– 8d. black and red	3·00	30
143b	– 9d. violet	9·00	2·50
144	– 1s. orange	50	15
145	– 1s.3d. blue	3·50	30
146	– 2s. brown	4·00	85
147	– 2s.6d. red	4·50	45
148	**43** 5s. red	19·00	85
149	– 10s. blue	13·00	5·00
150	– £1 multicoloured	25·00	21·00

DESIGNS—HORIZ: ½d. Easter lilies; 1d., 4d. Postmaster Perot's stamp; 2d. "Victory II" (racing dinghy); 2½d. Sir George Somers and "Sea Venture"; 3d., 1s.3d. Map of Bermuda; 4½d. 9d. "Sea Venture" (galleon), coin and Perot stamp; 6d. (No. 143), 8d. White-tailed tropic bird; 6d. (No. 156), Perot's Post Office; 1s. Early Bermuda coins; 2s. Arms of St. George's 10s. Obverse and reverse of hog coin; £1 Arms of Bermuda. VERT: 2s.6d. Warwick Fort.

No. 156 commemorates the restoration and reopening of Perot's Post Office.

1953. Royal Visit. As No. 143a but inscr "ROYAL VISIT 1953".

151	6d. black and turquoise	50	20

1953. Three Power Talks. Nos. 140 and 145 optd **Three Power Talks December, 1953.**

152	3d. purple	10	10
153	1s.3d. blue	10	10

1956. 50th Anniv of United States-Bermuda Yacht Race. Nos. 143a and 145 optd **50TH ANNIVERSARY US – BERMUDA OCEAN RACE 1956.**

154	8d. black and red	20	45
155	1s.3d. blue	20	55

49 Arms of King James I and Queen Elizabeth II

1959. 350th Anniv of Settlement. Arms in red, yellow and blue. Frame colours given.
157 **49** 1½d. blue 20 10
158 3d. grey 25 50
159 4d. purple 30 55
160 8d. violet 30 15
161 9d. olive . . . . 30 1·25
162 1s.3d. brown 30 30

50 The Old Rectory, St George's, c.1730

1962.
163 **50** 1d. purple, black and orange 10 75
164 – 2d. multicoloured . . . . 1·00 35
165 – 3d. brown and blue 10 10
166 – 4d. brown and mauve . . . 20 40
167 – 5d. blue and red . . . . . 75 2·50
168 – 6d. blue, green & lt blue 30 30
169 – 8d. blue, green and orange 30 35
170 – 9d. blue and brown 30 60
197 – 10d. violet and ochre . . . 75 60
171 – 1s. multicoloured 30 10
172 – 1s.3d. lake, grey and bistre 75 15
173 – 1s.6d. violet and ochre . . 75 1·00
199 – 1s.6d. blue and red . . . . 1·75 50
200 – 2s. brown and orange . . . 1·75 75
175 – 2s.3d. sepia and green . . 1·00 6·50
176 – 2s.6d. sepia, green & yell 55 50
177 – 5s. purple and green . . . 1·25 1·50
178 – 10s. mauve, green and buff 4·50 7·00
179 – £1 black, olive and orange 14·00 14·00
DESIGNS: 2d. Church of St. Peter, St. George's; 3d. Government House, 1892; 4d. The Cathedral. Hamilton, 1894; 5d., 1s.6d. (No. 199) H.M. Dockyard, 1811; 6d. Perot's Post Office, 1848; 8d. G.P.O., Hamilton, 1869; 9d. Library, Par-la-Ville; 10d., 1s.6d. (No. 173) Bermuda cottage, c. 1705; 1s. Christ Church, Warwick, 1719; 1s.3d. City Hall, Hamilton, 1960; 2s. Town of St. George; 2s.3d. Bermuda house, c. 1710; 2s.6d. Bermuda house, early 18th century; 5s. Colonial Secretariat, 1833; 10s. Old Post Office, Somerset, 1890; £1 The House of Assembly, 1815.

1963. Freedom from Hunger. As T **28** of Aden.
180 1s.3d. sepia 60 40

1963. Centenary of Red Cross. As T **33** of Antigua.
181 3d. red and black 50 25
182 1s.3d. red and blue . . . . . 1·00 2·50

67 "Tsotsi in the Bundu" (Finn class yacht)

1964. Olympic Games, Tokyo.
183 **67** 3d. red, violet and blue . . 10 10

1965. Centenary of I.T.U. As T **36** of Antigua.
184 3d. blue and green 35 25
185 2s. yellow and blue . . . . . 65 1·25

68 Scout Badge and St. Edward's Crown

1965. 50th Anniv of Bermuda Boy Scouts Association.
186 **68** 2s. multicoloured 50 50

1965. I.C.Y. As T **37** of Antigua.
187 4d. purple and turquoise . . 40 20
188 2s.6d. green and lavender . . 60 80

1966. Churchill Commemoration. As T **38** of Antigua.
189 3d. blue 25 20
190 6d. green . . . . 50 1·00
191 10d. brown 70 75
192 1s.3d. violet . . . . 80 2·50

1966. World Cup Football Championship. As T **40** of Antigua.
193 10d. multicoloured 60 15
194 2s.6d. multicoloured . . . . 90 1·25

1966. 20th Anniv of U.N.E.S.C.O. As T **54/56** of Antigua.
201 4d. multicoloured 45 15
202 1s.3d. yellow, violet and olive 75 50
203 2s. black, purple and orange 1·00 1·10

69 G.P.O. Building

1967. Opening of New General Post Office.
204 **69** 3d. multicoloured 10 10
205 1s. multicoloured 10 10
206 1s.6d. multicoloured . . . 20 25
207 2s.6d. multicoloured . . . 20 70

70 "Mercury" (cable ship) and Chain Links

1967. Inauguration of Bermuda–Tortola Telephone Service. Multicoloured.
208 3d. Type **70** 15 10
209 1s. Map, telephone and microphone 25 10
210 1s.6d. Telecommunications media 25 25
211 2s.6d. "Mercury" (cable ship) and marine fauna 40 70

74 Human Rights Emblem and Doves

1968. Human Rights Year.
212 **74** 3d. indigo, blue and green 10 10
213 1s. brown, blue and light blue 10 10
214 1s.6d. black, blue and red 10 15
215 2s.6d. green, blue and yellow 15 25

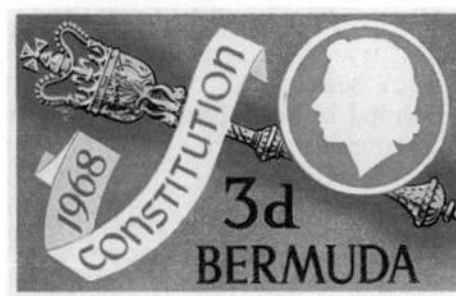

75 Mace and Queen's Profile

1968. New Constitution.
216 **75** 3d. multicoloured 10 10
217 1s. multicoloured 10 10
218 – 1s.6d. yellow, black and blue 10 20
219 – 2s.6d. lilac, black and yellow 15 75
DESIGNS: 1s.6d., 2s.6d., Houses of Parliament, and House of Assembly, Bermuda.

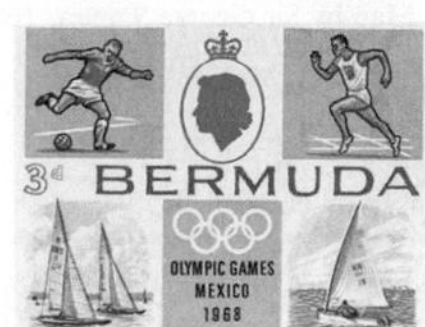

77 Football, Athletics and Yachting

1968. Olympic Games, Mexico.
220 **77** 3d. multicoloured 15 10
221 1s. multicoloured 25 10
222 1s.6d. multicoloured . . . 50 30
223 2s.6d. multicoloured . . . 50 1·40

78 Brownie and Guide

1969. 50th Anniv of Girl Guides. Multicoloured.
224 3d. Type **78** 10 10
225 1s. Type **78** 20 10
226 1s.6d. Guides and Badge . . 25 40
227 2s.6d. As 1s.6d. . . . . . . 35 1·40

80 Emerald-studded Gold Cross and Seaweed

1969. Underwater Treasure. Multicoloured.
228 4d. Type **80** 20 10
229 1s.3d. Emerald-studded gold cross and sea-bed 35 15
230 2s. As Type **80** 45 90
231 2s.6d. As 1s.3d. . . . . . . 45 1·75

1970. Decimal Currency. Nos. 163/79 surch.
232 1c. on 1d. purple, black & orge . . . . 10 1·75
233 2c. on 2d. multicoloured . . 10 10
234 3c. on 3d. brown and blue 10 10
235 4c. on 4d. brown and mauve 10 10
236 5c. on 8d. blue, green & orge 15 2·00
237 6c. on 6d. blue, green & lt blue . . . . 15 1·75
238 9c. on 9d. blue and brown 30 2·75
239 10c. on 10d. violet and ochre 30 25
240 12c. on 1s. multicoloured . . 30 1·00
241 15c. on 1s.3d. lake, grey & bis . . . . 1·50 1·00
242 18c. on 1s.6d. blue and red 80 65
243 24c. on 2s. brown and orange 85 1·75
244 30c. on 2s.6d. sepia, grn & yell . . . . 1·00 2·75
245 36c. on 2s.3d. sepia and green 1·75 7·50
246 60c. on 5s. purple and green 2·25 4·25
247 $1.20 on 10s. mve, grn & buff . . . . 4·00 15·00
248 $2.40 on £1 black, ol & orge 5·50 19·00

83 Spathiphyllum

1970. Flowers. Multicoloured.
249 1c. Type **83** 10 20
250 2c. Bottlebrush 20 25
251 3c. Oleander (vert) 15 10
252 4c. Bermudiana 15 10
253 5c. Poinsettia 30 20
254 6c. Hibiscus 30 30
255 9c. Cereus 20 45
256 10c. Bougainvillea (vert) . . 20 15
257 12c. Jacaranda 80 60
258 15c. Passion flower . . . . 90 1·40
258a 17c. As 15c. . . . . 2·75 4·00
259 18c. Coralita . . . . 2·25 1·75
259a 20c. As 18c. . . . . 2·75 4·00
260 24c. Morning glory . . . . 1·50 4·50
260a 25c. As 24c. . . . . 2·75 4·50
261 30c. Tecoma . . . . 1·00 1·25
262 36c. Angel's trumpet . . . . 1·25 1·75
262a 40c. As 36c. . . . . 2·75 5·50
263 60c. Plumbago . . . . . . 1·75 1·50
263a $1 As 60c. . . . . 3·25 6·50
264 $1.20 Bird of paradise flower . . . . 2·25 2·25
264a $2 As $1.20 . . . . 5·50 8·50
265 $2.40 Chalice cup . . . . . 5·00 5·00
265a $3 As $2.40 . . . . 11·00 11·00

84 The State House, St. George's

1970. 350th Anniv of Bermuda Parliament. Multicoloured.
266 4c. Type **84** 10 10
267 15c. The Sessions House, Hamilton 25 20
268 18c. St. Peter's Church, St. George's 25 25
269 24c. Town Hall, Hamilton . . 35 60
MS270 131 × 95 mm. Nos. 266/9 1·10 1·25

85 Street Scene, St. George's

1971. "Keep Bermuda Beautiful". Multicoloured.
271 4c. Type **85** 20 10
272 15c. Horseshoe Bay 65 65
273 18c. Gibbs Hill Lighthouse 1·50 2·25
274 24c. Hamilton Harbour . . . 1·25 2·50

86 Building of the "Deliverance"

1971. Voyage of the "Deliverance". Multicoloured.
275 4c. Type **86** 60 20
276 15c. "Deliverance" and "Patience" at Jamestown (vert) . . . . 1·50 1·75
277 18c. Wreck of the "Sea Venture" (vert) . . . . . 1·50 2·25
278 24c. "Deliverance" and "Patience" on high seas . . 1·75 2·50

87 Green overlooking Ocean View

1971. Golfing in Bermuda. Multicoloured.
279 4c. Type **87** 70 10
280 15c. Golfers at Port Royal 1·25 65
281 18c. Castle Harbour . . . . 1·25 1·00
282 24c. Belmont . . . . 1·50 2·00

1971. Anglo-American Talks. Nos. 252, 258, 259 and 260 optd **HEATH-NIXON DECEMBER 1971**.
283 4c. Bermudiana 10 10
284 15c. Passion flower 10 20
285 18c. Coralita 15 65
286 24c. Morning glory . . . . . 20 1·00

89 Bonefish

1972. World Fishing Records. Multicoloured.
287 4c. Type **89** 30 10
288 15c. Wahoo 30 50
289 18c. Yellow-finned tuna . . . 35 75
290 24c. Greater amberjack . . . 40 1·25

1972. Silver Wedding. As T **52** of Ascension, but with "Admiralty Oar" and Mace in background.
291 4c. violet 15 10
292 15c. red 15 50

91 Palmetto

1973. Tree Planting Year. Multicoloured.
293 4c. Type **91** 25 10
294 15c. Olivewood bark 65 75
295 18c. Bermuda cedar . . . . 70 1·25
296 24c. Mahogany . . . . . . 75 1·60

1973. Royal Wedding. As T **47** of Anguilla, background colour given. Multicoloured.
297 15c. mauve 15 15
298 18c. blue 15 15

92 Bernard Park, Pembroke, 1973

1973. Centenary of Lawn Tennis. Multicoloured.
299 4c. Type **92** 30 10
300 15c. Clermont Court, 1873 50 65
301 18c. Leamington Spa Court, 1872 . . . . 55 1·75
302 24c. Staten Island Courts, 1874 . . . . 65 2·25

93 Weather Vane, City Hall

1974. 50th Anniv of Rotary in Bermuda. Mult.
320 5c. Type **93** 15 10
321 17c. St. Peter's Church, St. George's 45 35
322 20c. Somerset Bridge . . . . 50 1·50
323 25c. Map of Bermuda, 1626 60 2·25

94 Jack of Clubs and "good bridge hand"

1975. World Bridge Championships, Bermuda. Multicoloured.
324 5c. Type **94** 20 10
325 17c. Queen of Diamonds and Bermuda Bowl 35 50
326 20c. King of Hearts and Bermuda Bowl . . . . . . 40 1·75
327 25c. Ace of Spades and Bermuda Bowl . . . . . . 40 2·50

95 Queen Elizabeth II and the Duke of Edinburgh

1975. Royal Visit.
328 **95** 17c. multicoloured 60 65
329 20c. multicoloured . . . . 65 2·10

96 Short S.23 Flying Boat "Cavalier", 1937

1975. 50th Anniv of Air-mail Service to Bermuda. Multicoloured.
330 5c. Type **96** 40 10
331 17c. U.S. Navy airship "Los Angeles", 1925 . . . . . . 1·25 85
332 20c. Lockheed Constellation, 1946 . . . . 1·40 2·75
333 25c. Boeing 747-100, 1970 . . 1·50 3·50
MS334 128 × 85 mm. Nos. 330/3 11·00 15·00

97 Supporters of American Army raiding Royal Magazine

1975. Bicentenary of Gunpowder Plot, St. George's. Multicoloured.
335 5c. Type **97** 15 10
336 17c. Setting off for raid . . . 30 40
337 20c. Loading gunpowder aboard American ship . . 35 1·40
338 25c. Gunpowder on beach . . 35 1·50
MS339 165 × 138 mm. Nos. 335/8 2·25 7·00

98 Launching "Ready" (bathysphere)

1976. 50th Anniv of Bermuda Biological Station. Multicoloured.
357 5c. Type **98** 30 10
358 17c. View from the sea (horiz) 60 60
359 20c. H.M.S. "Challenger", 1873 (horiz) . . . . . . 65 2·25
360 25c. Beebe's Bathysphere descent, 1934 . . . . . . 70 3·00

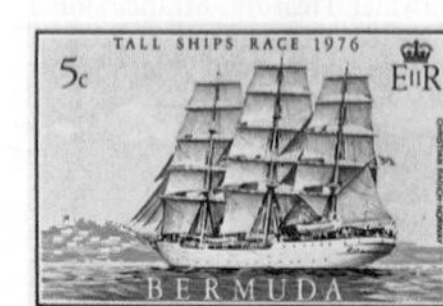

99 "Christian Radich" (cadet ship)

1976. Tall Ships Race. Multicoloured.
361 5c. Type **99** 75 20
362 12c. "Juan Sebastian de Elcano" (Spanish cadet schooner) . . . . 80 2·25
363 17c. "Eagle" (U.S. coastguard cadet ship) . . 80 1·50
364 20c. "Sir Winston Churchill" (cadet schooner) . . . . 80 1·75
365 40c. "Kruzenshtern" (Russian cadet barque) . . . . . . 1·00 2·75
366 $1 "Cutty Sark" trophy . . . 1·25 7·00

100 Silver Trophy and Club Flags

1976. 75th Anniv of St. George's v. Somerset Cricket Cup Match. Multicoloured.
367 5c. Type **100** 30 10
368 17c. Badge and pavilion, St. George's Club 50 65
369 20c. Badge and pavilion, Somerset Club . . . . . . 65 2·75
370 25c. Somerset playing field 1·00 3·75

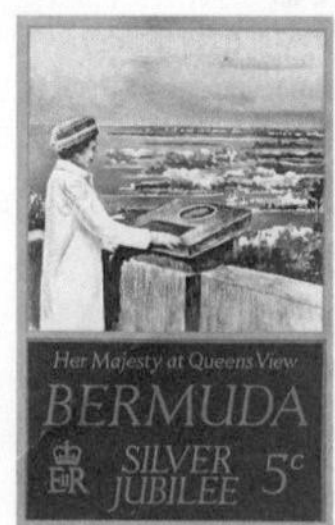

101 Royal Visit, 1975

1977. Silver Jubilee. Multicoloured.
371 5c. Type **101** 10 10
372 20c. St. Edward's Crown . . 15 20
373 $1 The Queen in Chair of Estate . . . . 40 1·25

102 Stockdale House, St. George's, 1784–1812

1977. Centenary of U.P.U. Membership. Mult.
374 5c. Type **102** 15 10
375 15c. Perot Post Office and stamp 25 50
376 17c. St. George's P.O. c. 1860 25 50
377 20c. Old G.P.O., Hamilton, c. 1935 . . . . 30 60
378 40c. New G.P.O., Hamilton, 1967 . . . . 45 1·10

103 17th-Century Ship approaching Castle Island

1977. Piloting. Multicoloured.
379 5c. Type **103** 50 10
380 15c. Pilot leaving ship, 1795 70 60
381 17c. Pilots rowing out to paddle-steamer 80 60
382 20c. Pilot gig and brig "Harvest Queen" . . . . . 85 2·25
383 40c. Modern pilot cutter and R.M.S. "Queen Elizabeth 2" . . . . 1·60 3·75

104 Great Seal of Queen Elizabeth I

1978. 25th Anniv of Coronation. Multicoloured.
384 8c. Type **104** 10 10
385 50c. Great Seal of Queen Elizabeth II 30 30
386 $1 Queen Elizabeth II . . . 60 75

105 White-tailed Tropic Bird

1978. Wildlife. Multicoloured.
387 3c. Type **105** . . . . 2·50 2·50
388 4c. White-eyed vireo . . . . 3·00 3·00
389 5c. Eastern bluebird . . . . 1·25 1·75
390 7c. Whistling frog . . . . . 50 1·50
391 8c. Common cardinal ("Cardinal Redbird") . . . 1·25 55
392 10c. Spiny lobster 20 10
393 12c. Land crab 30 70
394 15c. Lizard (Skink) 30 15
395 20c. Four-eyed butterflyfish 30 30
396 25c. Red hind 30 20
397 30c. "Danaus plexippus" (butterfly) . . . . 2·25 2·50
398 40c. Rock beauty . . . . . 50 1·75
399 50c. Banded butterflyfish . . 55 1·50
400 $1 Blue angelfish . . . . . 2·50 1·75
401 $2 Humpback whale . . . . 2·00 2·75
402 $3 Green turtle . . . . . . 2·50 3·00
403 $5 Cahow . . . . 5·50 6·00

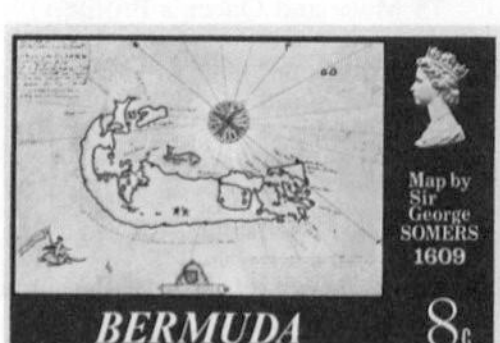

106 Map by Sir George Somers, 1609

1979. Antique Maps. Multicoloured.
404 8c. Type **106** 15 10
405 15c. Map by John Seller, 1685 . . . . 20 15
406 20c. Map by H. Moll, 1729–40 (vert) 25 25
407 25c. Map by Desbruslins, 1740 . . . . 30 30
408 50c. Map by Speed, 1626 . . 45 80

107 Policeman and Policewoman

1979. Centenary of Police Force. Multicoloured.
409 8c. Type **107** 30 10
410 20c. Policeman directing traffic (horiz) 50 55
411 25c. "Blue Heron" (police launch) (horiz) 60 65
412 50c. Police Morris Marina and motorcycle . . . . . 80 1·50

108 1d. "Perot" Stamp of 1848 and 1840 Penny Black

1980. Death Cent of Sir Rowland Hill. Mult.
413 8c. Type **108** 20 10
414 20c. "Perot" and Sir Rowland Hill 30 25
415 25c. "Perot" and early letter 30 30
416 50c. "Perot" and "Paid 1" cancellation 35 70

109 Lockheed TriStar 500 approaching Bermuda

1980. "London 1980" International Stamp Exhibition. Multicoloured.
417 25c. Type **109** 30 15
418 50c. "Orduna I" (liner) at Grassy Bay, 1926 . . . . 45 35
419 $1 "Delta" (screw steamer) at St. George's Harbour, 1856 85 1·00
420 $2 "Lord Sidmouth" (sailing packet) in Old Ship Channel, St. George's . . . 1·40 2·00

110 Gina Swainson ("Miss World 1979–80")

1980. "Miss World 1979–80" Commem. Mult.
421 8c. Type **110** 15 10
422 20c. Miss Swainson after crowning ceremony 20 20
423 50c. Miss Swainson on Peacock Throne 35 35
424 $1 Miss Swainson in Bermuda carriage 70 90

111 Queen Elizabeth the Queen Mother

1980. 80th Birthday of The Queen Mother.
425 **111** 25c. multicoloured . . . . 30 1·00

112 Bermuda from Satellite

1980. Commonwealth Finance Ministers Meeting. Muticoloured.
426 8c. Type **112** 10 10
427 20c. "Camden" 20 40
428 25c. Princess Hotel, Hamilton 20 50
429 50c. Government House . . . 35 1·25

113 Kitchen, 18th-century

1981. Heritage Week. Multicoloured.
430 8c. Type **113** 15 10
431 25c. Gathering Easter lilies, 20th-century 30 35
432 30c. Fishing, 20th-century . . 40 50
433 40c. Stone cutting, 19th-century 40 80
434 50c. Onion shipping, 19th-century 65 90
435 $1 Privateering, 17th-century 1·25 2·50

114 Wedding Bouquet from Bermuda
115 "Service", Hamilton

1981. Royal Wedding. Multicoloured.
436 30c. Type **114** 20 20
437 50c. Prince Charles as Royal Navy Commander 35 40
438 $1 Prince Charles and Lady Diana Spencer 55 80

1981. 25th Anniv of Duke of Edinburgh Award Scheme. Multicoloured.
439 10c. Type **115** 15 10
440 25c. "Outward Bound", Paget Island 20 20
441 30c. "Expedition", St. David's Island 20 30
442 $1 Duke of Edinburgh . . . 55 1·25

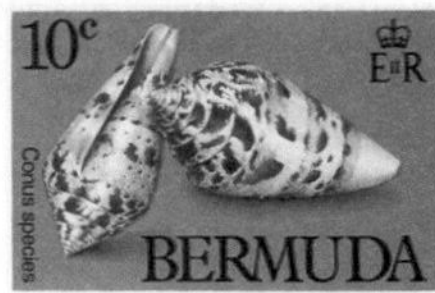

116 Lightbourne's Cone

1982. Sea Shells. Multicoloured.
443 10c. Type **116** 30 10
444 25c. Finlay's frog shell . . . 55 55
445 30c. Royal bonnet 60 60
446 $1 Lightbourne's murex . . . 1·75 3·25

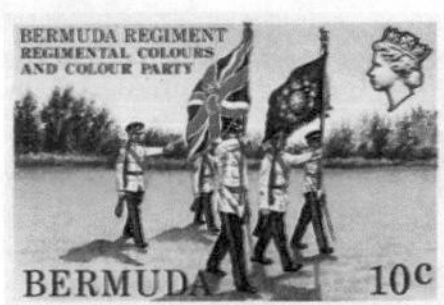

117 Regimental Colours and Colour Party

1982. Bermuda Regiment. Multicoloured.
447 10c. Type **117** 65 10
448 25c. Queen's Birthday Parade 1·10 80
449 30c. Governor inspecting Guard of Honour . . . . 1·40 1·40
450 40c. Beating the Retreat . . . 1·50 1·75
451 50c. Ceremonial gunners . . . 1·50 2·00
452 $1 Guard of Honour, Royal visit, 1975 . . . . 2·25 3·50

118 Charles Fort
119 Arms of Sir Edwin Sandys

1982. Historic Bermuda Forts. Multicoloured.
453 10c. Type **118** 20 20
454 25c. Pembroks Fort 50 85
455 30c. Southampton Fort (horiz) . . . . 60 1·25
456 $1 Smiths Fort and Pagets Fort (horiz) . . . . 1·25 4·50

1983. Coat of Arms (1st series). Multicoloured.
457 10c. Type **119** 45 15
458 25c. Arms of the Bermuda Company . . . . 1·40 1·00
459 50c. Arms of William Herbert, Earl of Pembroke 2·25 3·75
460 $1 Arms of Sir George Somers . . . . 3·00 6·50
See also Nos. 482/5 and 499/502.

120 Early Fitted Dinghy
122 Joseph Stockdale

121 Curtiss N-9 Seaplane

1983. Fitted Dinghies. Multicoloured.
461 12c. Type **120** 45 15
462 30c. Modern dinghy inshore 60 75
463 40c. Early dinghy (different) 70 90
464 $1 Modern dinghy with red and white spinnaker . . . 1·40 3·25

1983. Bicentenary of Manned Flight. Multicoloured.
465 12c. Type **121** (First flight over Bermuda) 60 20
466 30c. Stinson Pilot Radio seaplane (First completed flight between U.S. and Bermuda) . . . . 1·25 1·25
467 40c. S.23 Flying boat "Cavalier" (First scheduled passenger flight) . . . . . 1·50 1·75
468 $1 U.S.N. "Los Angeles" (airship) moored to U.S.S. "Patoka" . . . . 2·75 5·50

1984. Bicentenary of Bermuda's First Newspaper and Postal Service. Multicoloured
469 12c. Type **122** 30 15
470 30c. "The Bermuda Gazette" 60 80
471 40c. Stockdale's postal service (horiz) . . . . 80 1·10
472 $1 "Lady Hammond" (mail boat) (horiz) . . . . 2·50 3·25

123 Sir Thomas Gates and Sir George Somers

1984. 375th Anniv of First Settlement. Mult.
473 12c. Type **123** 20 15
474 30c. Jamestown, Virginia . . 50 1·25
475 40c. Wreck of "Sea Venture" 90 1·25
476 $1 Fleet leaving Plymouth, Devon . . . . 2·00 6·00
MS477 130 × 73 mm. Nos. 474 and 476 . . . . 3·75 9·50

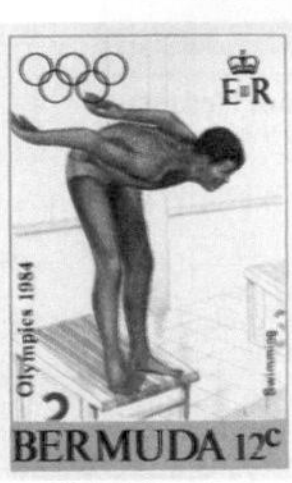

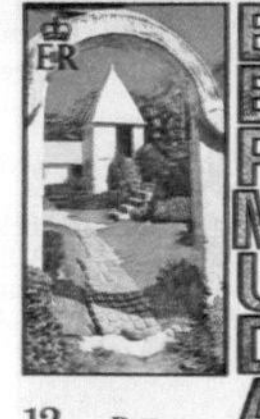

124 Swimming
125 Buttery

1984. Olympic Games, Los Angeles. Multicoloured.
478 12c. Type **124** 40 15
479 30c. Track and field events (horiz) 70 75
480 40c. Equestrian . . . . . . 1·25 1·25
481 $1 Sailing (horiz) . . . . . . 2·50 6·25

1984. Coat of Arms (2nd series). As T **119**. Mult.
482 12c. Arms of Henry Wriothesley, Earl of Southampton 50 15
483 30c. Arms of Sir Thomas Smith . . . . 1·00 85
484 40c. Arms of William Cavendish, Earl of Devonshire . . . . 1·25 1·50
485 $1 Town arms of St. George 2·75 4·50

1985. Bermuda Architecture. Multicoloured.
486 12c. Type **125** 35 15
487 30c. Limestone rooftops (horiz) 80 70
488 40c. Chimneys (horiz) . . . . 95 1·00
489 $1.50 Entrance archway . . . 3·00 3·75

126 Osprey
127 The Queen Mother with Grandchildren, 1980

1985. Birth Bicentenary of John J. Audubon (ornithologist). Designs showing original drawings. Multicoloured.
490 12c. Type **126** . . . . 2·00 65
491 30c. Yellow-crowned night heron . . . . 2·00 95
492 40c. Great egret (horiz) . . . 2·25 1·25
493 $1.50 Eastern bluebird ("Bluebird") . . . . 3·75 6·50

1985. Life and Times of Queen Elizabeth the Queen Mother. Multicoloured.
494 12c. Queen Consort, 1937 . . 35 15
495 30c. Type **127** 60 50
496 40c. At Clarence House on 83rd birthday 70 60
497 $1.50 With Prince Henry at his christening (from photo by Lord Snowdon) . . . . 2·00 2·75
MS498 91 × 73 mm. $1 With Prince Charles at 80th birthday celebrations . . . . 3·50 3·25

1985. Coats of Arms (3rd series). As T **119**. Mult.
499 12c. Hamilton 75 15
500 30c. Paget . . . . 1·40 80
501 40c. Warwick . . . . 1·60 1·40
502 $1.50 City of Hamilton . . . 3·75 4·50

128 Halley's Comet and Bermuda Archipelago

1985. Appearance of Halley's Comet. Multicoloured.
503 15c. Type **128** 85 25
504 40c. Halley's Comet, A.D. 684 (from Nuremberg Chronicles, 1493) . . . . . 1·60 1·75
505 50c. "Halley's Comet, 1531" (from Peter Apian woodcut, 1532) . . . . . 1·90 2·50
506 $1.50 "Halley's Comet, 1759" (Samuel Scott) . . . . . . 3·50 6·00

129 "Constellation" (schooner) (1943)

1986. Ships Wrecked on Bermuda. Multicoloured.
507A 3c. Type **129** . . . . . . 70 1·00
508A 5c. "Early Riser" (pilot boat), 1876 . . . . 20 20
509A 7c. "Madiana" (screw steamer), 1903 . . . . . . 65 2·50
510A 10c. "Curlew" (sail/ steamer), 1856 . . . . . 30 30
511A 12c. "Warwick" (galleon), 1619 . . . . 60 80
512A 15c. H.M.S. "Vixen" (gun-boat), 1890 . . . . . . 40 60
512cA 18c. As 7c. . . . . 5·00 4·25
513A 20c. "San Pedro" (Spanish galleon), 1594 . . . . . 1·10 80
514A 25c. "Alert" (fishing sloop), 1877 . . . . . . 60 3·00
515A 40c. "North Carolina" (barque), 1880 . . . . . . 65 1·25
516A 50c. "Mark Antonie" (Spanish privateer), 1777 1·50 3·25
517A 60c. "Mary Celestia" (Confederate paddle-steamer), 1864 . . . . . 1·50 1·75
517cA 70c. "Caesar" (brig), 1818 5·50 6·50
518B $1 "L'Herminie" (French frigate), 1839 . . . . . 1·50 1·60
519A $1.50 As 70c. . . . . 4·50 6·00
520B $2 "Lord Amherst" (transport), 1778 . . . . 2·50 5·00
521B $3 "Minerva" (sailing ship), 1849 . . . . 4·25 8·00
522A $5 "Caraquet" (cargo liner), 1923 . . . . 4·75 11·00
523A $8 H.M.S. "Pallas" (frigate), 1783 . . . . . 6·00 12·00

1986. 60th Birthday of Queen Elizabeth II. As T **110** of Ascension. Multicoloured.
524 15c. Princess Elizabeth aged three, 1929 . . . . 45 30
525 40c. With Earl of Rosebery at Oaks May Meeting, Epsom, 1954 . . . . . . 80 60
526 50c. With Duke of Edinburgh, Bermuda, 1975 80 75
527 60c. At British Embassy, Paris, 1972 . . . . 90 90
528 $1.50 At Crown Agents Head Office, London, 1983 . . . 2·00 2·50

1986. "Ameripex '86" International Stamp Exhibition, Chicago. As T **164** of Bahamas, showing Bermuda stamps. Multicoloured.
529 15c. 1984 375th Anniv of Settlement miniature sheet 1·50 30
530 40c. 1973 Lawn Tennis Centenary, 24c. . . . . . 2·25 70
531 50c. 1983 Bicentenary of Manned Flight 12c. . . . 2·25 1·00
532 $1 1976 Tall Ships Race 17c. 3·75 3·00
MS533 80 × 80 mm. $1.50, Statue of Liberty and "Monarch of Bermuda" . . . . 7·50 6·50
No. **MS**533 also commemorates the Centenary of the Statue of Liberty.

1986. 25th Anniv of World Wildlife Fund. No. 402 surch **90c**.
534 90c. on $3 Green turtle . . . 3·00 4·25

131 Train in Front Street, Hamilton, 1940

1987. Transport (1st series). Bermuda Railway. Multicoloured.
535 15c. Type **131** . . . . 2·00 25
536 40c. Train crossing Springfield Trestle . . . . 2·50 90
537 50c. "St. George Special" at Bailey's Bay Station . . . 2·50 1·50
538 $1.50 Boat train at St. George . . . . 4·00 3·50
See also Nos. 557/60, 574/7 and 624/9.

132 "Bermuda Settlers", 1901

1987. Bermuda Paintings (1st series). Works by Winslow Homer. Multicoloured.
539 15c. Type **132** 60 25
540 30c. "Bermuda", 1900 . . . 85 45
541 40c. "Bermuda Landscape", 1901 (buff frame) 95 55
544 40c. Type **132** . . . . 1·00 1·75
545 40c. As No. 540 . . . . . . 1·00 1·75
546 40c. As No. 541 (grey frame) 1·00 1·75
547 40c. As No. 542 . . . . . . 1·00 1·75
548 40c. As No. 543 . . . . . . 1·00 1·75
542 50c. "Inland Water", 1901 . . 1·10 70
543 $1.50 "Salt Kettle", 1899 . . 2·50 2·50
See also Nos. 607/10 and 630/3.

133 Sikorsky S-42B Flying Boat "Bermuda Clipper"

1987. 50th Anniv of Inauguration of Bermuda–U.S.A. Air Service. Multicoloured.
549 15c. Type **133** . . . . 2·00 15
550 40c. Short S.23 flying boat "Cavalier" . . . . 3·00 70
551 50c. "Bermuda Clipper" in flight over signpost . . . . 3·25 80
552 $1.50 "Cavalier" on apron and "Bermuda Clipper" in flight . . . . 6·00 4·00

134 19th-century Wagon carrying Telephone Poles

1987. Centenary of Bermuda Telephone Company. Multicoloured.
553 15c. Type **134** 75 15
554 40c. Early telephone exchange 1·40 60
555 50c. Early and modern telephones 1·75 70
556 $1.50 Communications satellite orbiting Earth 2·75 3·50

135 Mail Wagon, c. 1869

1988. Transport (2nd series). Horse-drawn Carts and Wagons. Multicoloured.
557 15c. Type **135** 25 15
558 40c. Open cart, c. 1823 55 55
559 50c. Closed cart, c. 1823 65 65
560 $1.50 Two-wheeled wagon, c. 1930 2·00 2·75

136 "Old Blush"

1988. Old Garden Roses (1st series). Multicoloured.
561 15c. Type **136** 85 25
562 30c. "Anna Olivier" 1·25 45
563 40c. "Rosa chinensis semperflorens" (vert) 1·40 85
564 50c. "Archduke Charles" 1·50 1·25
565 $1.50 "Rosa chinensis viridiflora" (vert) 3·00 5·50

See also Nos. 584/8 and, for designs with the royal cypher instead of the Queen's head, Nos. 589/98 and 683/6.

1988. 300th Anniv of Lloyd's of London. As T **123** of Ascension. Multicoloured.
566 18c. Loss of H.M.S. "Lutine" (frigate), 1799 85 25
567 50c. "Sentinel" (cable ship) (horiz) 1·60 65
568 60c. "Bermuda" (liner), Hamilton, 1931 (horiz) 1·75 75
569 $2 Loss of H.M.S. "Valerian" (sloop) in hurricane, 1926 3·00 3·25

137 Devonshire Parish Militia, 1812

1988. Military Uniforms. Multicoloured.
570 18c. Type **137** 1·50 25
571 50c. 71 st (Highland) Regiment, 1831–34 2·00 1·10
572 60c. Cameron Highlanders, 1942 2·25 1·25
573 $2 Troop of horse, 1774 4·75 7·50

138 "Corona" (ferry)

1989. Transport (3rd series). Ferry Services. Mult.
574 18c. Type **138** 35 25
575 50c. Rowing boat ferry 75 65
576 60c. St. George's barge ferry 85 75
577 $2 "Laconia" 2·50 4·00

139 Morgan's Island

1989. 150 Years of Photography. Multicoloured.
578 18c. Type **139** 85 25
579 30c. Front Street, Hamilton 1·10 45
580 50c. Waterfront, Front Street, Hamilton 1·60 1·25
581 60c. Crow Lane from Hamilton Harbour 1·75 1·40
582 70c. Shipbuilding, Hamilton Harbour 1·90 3·00
583 $1 Dockyard 2·25 3·50

1989. Old Garden Roses (2nd series). As T **136**. Multicoloured.
584 18c. "Agrippina" (vert) 90 25
585 30c. "Smith's Parish" (vert) 1·25 60
586 50c. "Champney's Pink Cluster" 1·75 1·40
587 60c. "Rosette Delizy" 1·75 1·60
588 $1.50 "Rosa bracteata" 2·75 6·00

1989. Old Garden Roses (3rd series). Designs as Nos. 561/5 and 584/8, but with royal cypher at top left instead of Queen's head. Multicoloured.
589 50c. As No. 565 (vert) 1·75 2·25
590 50c. As No. 563 (vert) 1·75 2·25
591 50c. Type **136** 1·75 2·25
592 50c. As No. 562 1·75 2·25
593 50c. As No. 564 1·75 2·25
594 50c. As No. 585 (vert) 1·75 2·25
595 50c. As No. 584 (vert) 1·75 2·25
596 50c. As No. 586 1·75 2·25
597 50c. As No. 587 1·75 2·25
598 50c. As No. 588 1·75 2·25

140 Main Library, Hamilton

1989. 150th Anniv of Bermuda Library. Mult.
599 18c. Type **140** 60 25
600 50c. The Old Rectory, St. George's 1·25 65
601 60c. Somerset Library, Springfield 1·25 75
602 $2 Cabinet Building, Hamilton 3·25 3·25

141 1865 1d. Rose

1989. Commonwealth Postal Conference. Mult.
603 **141** 18c. grey, pink and red 1·50 25
604 – 50c. grey, blue & lt blue 2·00 75
605 – 60c. grey, purple and mauve 2·25 1·25
606 – $2 grey, green and emerald 3·75 6·00

DESIGNS: 50c. 1866 2d. blue; 60c. 1865 6d. purple; $2 1865 1s. green.

142 "Fairylands, c. 1890" (Ross Turner)

1990. Bermuda Paintings (2nd series). Multicoloured.
607 18c. Type **142** 75 25
608 50c. "Shinebone Alley, c. 1953" (Ogden Pleissner) 1·25 1·25
609 60c. "Salt Kettle, 1916" (Prosper Senat) 1·25 1·50
610 $2 "St. George's, 1934" (Jack Bush) 3·25 7·00

1990. "Stamp World London 90" International Stamp Exhibition. Nos. 603/6 optd **Stamp World London 90** and logo.
611 18c. grey, pink and red 1·25 25
612 50c. grey, blue and light blue 1·75 1·50
613 60c. grey, purple and mauve 2·00 1·75
614 $2 grey, green and emerald 3·50 7·00

1990. Nos. 511, 516 and 519 surch.
615 30c. on 12c. "Warwick" (galleon), (1619) 1·50 1·25
616 55c. on 50c. "Mark Antonie" (Spanish privateer), 1777 2·00 2·25
617 80c. on $1.50 "Caesar" (brig), 1818 2·50 4·25

145 The Halifax and Bermudas Cable Company Office, Hamilton

1990. Centenary of Cable and Wireless in Bermuda.
618 **145** 20c. brown and black 70 25
619 – 55c. brown and black 2·00 1·25
620 – 70c. multicoloured 2·00 2·75
621 – $2 multicoloured 4·75 7·50

DESIGNS: 55c. "Westmeath" (cable ship), 1890; 70c. Wireless transmitter station, St. George's, 1928; $2 "Sir Eric Sharp" (cable ship).

1991. President Bush–Prime Minister Major Talks, Bermuda. Nos. 618/19 optd **BUSH-MAJOR 16 MARCH 1991**.
622 **145** 20c. brown and black 2·00 1·50
623 – 55c. brown and black 3·00 3·50

147 Two-seater Pony Cart, 1805

1991. Transport (4th series). Horse-drawn Carriages. Multicoloured.
624 20c. Type **147** 80 30
625 30c. Varnished rockaway, 1830 90 60
626 55c. Vis-a-Vis victoria, 1895 1·60 1·10
627 70c. Semi-formal phaeton, 1900 2·25 2·50
628 80c. Pony runabout, 1905 2·50 3·75
629 $1 Ladies phaeton, 1910 2·75 4·50

148 "Bermuda, 1916" (Prosper Senat)

1991. Bermuda Paintings (3rd series). Multicoloured.
630 20c. Type **148** 1·00 30
631 55c. "Bermuda Cottage" 1930 (Frank Allison) (horiz) 2·00 1·40
632 70c. "Old Maid's Lane", 1934 (Jack Bush) 2·50 3·25
633 $2 "St. George's", 1953 (Ogden Pleissner) (horiz) 5·00 8·50

1991. 65th Birthday of Queen Elizabeth II and 70th Birthday of Prince Philip. As T **139** of Ascension. Multicoloured.
634 55c. Prince Philip in tropical naval uniform 1·25 1·75
635 70c. Queen Elizabeth II in Bermuda 1·25 1·75

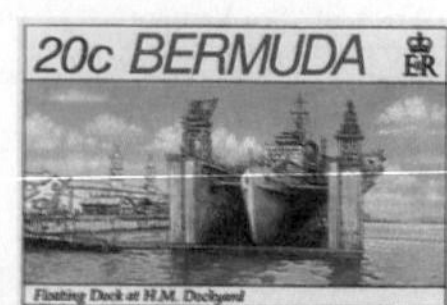

149 H.M.S. "Argonaut" (cruiser) in Floating Dock

1991. 50th Anniv of Second World War. Mult.
636 20c. Type **149** 1·50 40
637 55c. Kindley Airfield 2·25 1·40
638 70c. Boeing 314A flying boat and map of Atlantic route 2·75 3·50
639 $2 Censored trans-Atlantic mail 4·50 8·50

1992. 40th Anniv of Queen Elizabeth II's Accession. As T **143** of Ascension. Multicoloured.
640 20c. Old fort on beach 60 30
641 30c. Public gardens 75 55
642 55c. Cottage garden 1·25 90
643 70c. Beach and hotels 1·60 2·25
644 $1 Queen Elizabeth II 1·90 2·75

150 Rings and Medallion

1992. 500th Anniv of Discovery of America by Columbus. Spanish Artifacts. Multicoloured.
645 25c. Type **150** 1·25 35
646 35c. Ink wells 1·40 75
647 60c. Gold ornaments 2·25 2·00
648 75c. Bishop buttons and crucifix 2·50 3·25
649 85c. Earrings and pearl buttons 2·75 3·75
650 $1 Jug and bowls 3·00 4·25

151 "Wreck of 'Sea Venture' "

1992. Stained Glass Windows. Multicoloured.
651 25c. Type **151** 1·50 40
652 60c. "Birds in tree" 2·75 2·00
653 75c. "St. Francis feeding bird" 3·25 3·00
654 $2 "Shells" 7·00 10·00

152 German Shepherd

1992. 7th World Congress of Kennel Clubs. Mult.
655 25c. Type **152** 1·25 40
656 35c. Irish setter 1·50 70
657 60c. Whippet (vert) 2·25 2·25
658 75c. Border terrier (vert) 2·25 3·25
659 85c. Pomeranian (vert) 2·50 3·75
660 $1 Schipperke (vert) 2·50 4·25

153 Policeman, Cyclist and Cruise Liner

154 "Duchesse de Brabant" and Bee

1993. Tourism Posters by Adolph Treidler. Mult.
679 25c. Type **153** 2·25 80
680 60c. Seaside golf course 3·00 2·75
681 75c. Deserted beach 2·50 2·75
682 $2 Dancers in evening dress and cruise liner 4·50 7·00

1993. Garden Roses (4th series).
683 **154** 10c. multicoloured 75 1·25
684 25c. multicoloured 75 50
685 50c. multicoloured 1·75 2·50
686 60c. multicoloured 1·00 1·50

1993. 75th Anniv of Royal Air Force. As T **149** of Ascension. Multicoloured.
687 25c. Consolidated PBY-5 Catalina 85 35
688 60c. Supermarine Spitfire Mk IX 2·00 2·00
689 75c. Bristol Type 156 Beaufighter Mk X 2·25 2·25
690 $2 Handley Page Halifax Mk III 3·75 6·00

155 Hamilton from the Sea

1993. Bicentenary of Hamilton. Mult.
691 25c. Type **155** 1·00 35
692 60c. Waterfront 2·00 2·00
693 75c. Barrel warehouse 2·00 2·50
694 $2 Sailing ships off Hamilton 5·00 7·00

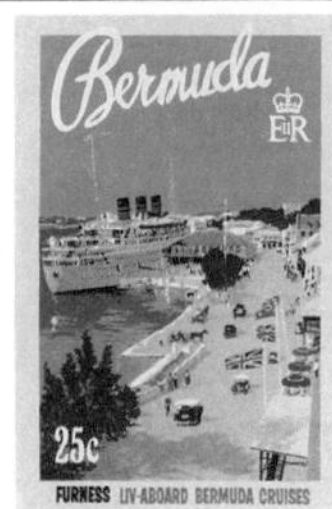

156 "Queen of Bermuda" (liner) at Hamilton

157 Queen Elizabeth II in Bermuda

1994. 75th Anniv of Furness Line's Bermuda Cruises. Adolphe Treidler Posters. Multicoloured.

695 25c. Type **156** 65 35
696 60c. "Monarch of Bermuda" entering port (horiz) . . . 1·50 1·60
697 75c. "Queen of Bermuda" and "Ocean Monarch" (liners) (horiz) . . . . . . 1·60 1·75
698 $2 Passengers on promenade deck at night . . . . . . 3·50 6·00

1994. Royal Visit. Multicoloured.

699 25c. Type **157** 85 35
700 60c. Queen Elizabeth and Prince Philip in open carriage . . . . 1·75 1·75
701 75c. Royal Yacht "Britannia" 3·50 3·00

158 Peach

1994. Flowering Fruits. Multicoloured.

792 5c. Type **158** 30 50
703A 7c. Fig 35 60
704A 10c. Calabash (vert) 35 35
795 15c. Natal plum 50 25
796 18c. Locust and wild honey 50 30
797 20c. Pomegranate 50 35
798 25c. Mulberry (vert) . . . 50 40
709A 35c. Grape (vert) 70 55
710A 55c. Orange (vert) . . . . 1·00 80
711A 60c. Surinam cherry . . . . 1·25 90
802 75c. Loquat . . . . 1·50 1·50
803 90c. Sugar apple . . . . . 1·75 1·75
804 $1 Prickly pear (vert) . . . 2·00 2·50
715A $2 Paw paw . . . . 3·50 3·50
716A $3 Bay grape . . . . 5·00 6·00
717A $5 Banana (vert) . . . . . 7·50 8·00
718A $8 Lemon . . . . 11·00 12·00

159 Nurse with Mother and Baby

1994. Centenary of Hospital Care. Multicoloured.

719 25c. Type **159** . . . . 1·00 35
720 60c. Patient on dialysis machine . . . . 2·00 1·90
721 75c. Casualty on emergency trolley . . . . 2·25 2·25
722 $2 Elderly patient in wheelchair with physiotherapists . . . . . 4·75 7·00

160 Gombey Dancers

1994. Cultural Heritage (1st series). Multicoloured.

723 25c. Type **160** 75 35
724 60c. Christmas carol singers 1·40 1·50
725 75c. Marching band . . . . 2·50 2·00
726 $2 National Dance Group performers . . . . 4·75 7·50

See also Nos. 731/4.

161 Bermuda 1970 Flower 1c. Stamps and 1c. Coin

162 Bermuda Coat of Arms

1995. 25th Anniv of Decimal Currency. Mult.

727 25c. Type **161** 75 35
728 60c. 1970 5c. stamps and coin 1·40 1·50
729 75c. 1970 10c. stamps and coin . . . . 1·75 2·00
730 $2 1970 25c. stamps and coin 4·50 6·50

1995. Cultural Heritage (2nd series). As T **160**. Multicoloured.

731 25c. Kite flying 55 35
732 60c. Majorettes . . . . . . 1·50 1·50
733 75c. Portuguese dancers . . . 1·75 2·00
734 $2 Floral float . . . . 3·75 6·00

1995. 375th Anniv of Bermuda Parliament.

735 **162** 25c. multicoloured . . . . 1·00 35
736 $1 multicoloured . . . . 2·25 3·00

For design as No. 736 but inscr "Commonwealth Finance Ministers Meeting", see No. 765.

163 U.S. Navy Ordnance Island Submarine Base

1995. Military Bases. Multicoloured.

737 20c. Type **163** 50 50
738 25c. Royal Naval Dockyard 60 35
739 60c. U.S.A.F. Fort Bell and Kindley Field . . . . . . 1·25 1·25
740 75c. R.A.F. Darrell's Island flying boat base . . . . . 1·50 1·75
741 90c. U.S. Navy operating base . . . . 1·50 2·50
742 $1 Canadian Forces Communications Station, Daniel's Head . . . . . . 1·60 2·50

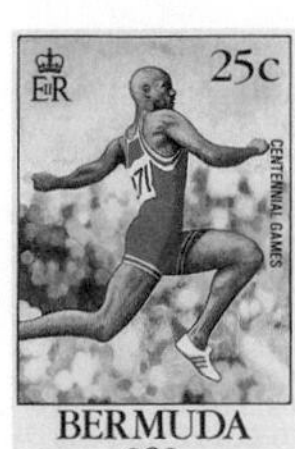

164 Triple Jump

1996. Olympic Games, Atlanta. Multicoloured.

743 25c. Type **164** 70 35
744 30c. Cycling . . . . 2·50 1·00
745 65c. Yachting . . . . 1·75 2·00
746 80c. Show jumping . . . . . 1·75 2·50

165 Jetty and Islets, Hamilton

1996. Panoramic Paintings of Hamilton (Nos. 747/51) and St. George's (Nos. 752/6) by E. J. Holland. Multicoloured.

747 60c. Type **165** . . . . 1·40 1·75
748 60c. End of island and buildings . . . . 1·40 1·75
749 60c. Yachts and hotel . . . . 1·40 1·75
750 60c. Islet, hotel and cathedral 1·40 1·75
751 60c. Cliff and houses by shore . . . . 1·40 1·75
752 60c. Islet and end of main island . . . . 1·40 1·75
753 60c. Yacht and houses on hillside . . . . 1·40 1·75
754 60c. Yacht and St. George's Hotel on hilltop . . . . . 1·40 1·75
755 60c. Shoreline and fishing boats . . . . 1·40 1·75
756 60c. Entrance to harbour channel . . . . 1·40 1·75

166 Somerset Express Mail Cart, c. 1900

1996. "CAPEX '96" International Stamp Exhibition, Toronto. Local Transport. Multicoloured.

757 25c. Type **166** . . . . 1·10 35
758 60c. Victoria carriage and railcar, 1930s . . . . . . 2·50 1·75
759 75c. First bus, 1946 . . . . 2·50 2·00
760 $2 Sightseeing bus, c. 1947 4·75 7·00

167 Hog Fish Beacon

1996. Lighthouses. Multicoloured.

761 30c. Type **167** . . . . 1·25 50
762 65c. Gibbs Hill Lighthouse 1·75 1·25
763 80c. St. David's Lighthouse 2·25 2·00
764 $2 North Rock Beacon . . . 3·75 6·50

See also Nos. 770/3.

1996. Commonwealth Finance Ministers' Meeting. As No. 736, but inscr "Commonwealth Finance Ministers Meeting" at top and with wider gold frame.

765 $1 multicoloured . . . . . . 2·50 2·75

168 Waterville

1996. Architectural Heritage. Multicoloured.

766 30c. Type **168** . . . . 1·00 45
767 65c. Bridge House . . . . . 1·40 1·50
768 80c. Fannie Fox's Cottage . . 1·75 2·00
769 $2.50 Palmetto House . . . . 4·00 7·00

1997. "HONG KONG '97" International Stamp Exhibition. Designs as Nos. 761/4, but incorporating "HONG KONG '97" logo and with some values changed.

770 30c. As Type **167** . . . . . 1·75 50
771 65c. Gibbs Hill Lighthouse 2·50 1·50
772 80c. St David's Lighthouse 2·75 2·00
773 $2.50 North Rock Beacon . . 5·50 8·00

169 White-tailed Tropic Bird

1997. Bird Conservation. Multicoloured.

774 30c. Type **169** 60 50
775 60c. White-tailed tropic bird and chick (vert) . . . . . 1·25 1·25
776 80c. Cahow and chick (vert) 1·75 2·00
777 $2.50 Cahow . . . . 4·00 6·50

170 Queen Elizabeth II with Crowd

1997. Golden Wedding of Queen Elizabeth and Prince Philip. Multicoloured.

778 30c. Type **170** 50 40
779 $2 Queen Elizabeth and Prince Philip . . . . . . 3·25 4·50
MS780 90 × 56 mm. Nos. 778/9 3·75 4·75

171 Father playing with Children

1997. Education. Multicoloured.

781 30c. Type **171** 50 40
782 40c. Teacher and children with map 60 55
783 60c. Boys holding sports trophy . . . . 85 1·25
784 65c. Pupils outside Berkeley Institute . . . . 90 1·25
785 80c. Scientific experiments . . 1·25 2·00
786 90c. New graduates . . . . . 1·40 2·50

1998. Diana, Princess of Wales Commemoration. Sheet, 145 × 170 mm, containing vert designs as T **177** of Ascension. Multicoloured.

MS787 30c. Wearing black hat, 1983; 40c. Wearing floral dress; 65c. Wearing blue evening dress, 1996; 80c. Carrying bouquets, 1993 (sold at $2.15 + 25c. charity premium) . . . . 3·50 4·00

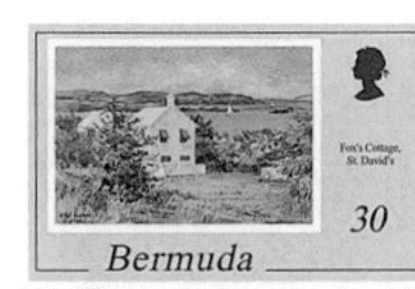

172 "Fox's Cottage, St. Davids" (Ethel Tucker)

1998. Paintings by Catherine and Ethel Tucker. Multicoloured.

788 30c. Type **172** . . . . 1·00 40
789 40c. "East Side, Somerset" 1·25 70
790 65c. "Long Bay Road, Somerset" . . . . 2·00 1·25
791 $2 "Flatts Village" . . . . . 4·50 6·50

173 Horse and Carriage

1998. Hospitality in Bermuda. Multicoloured.

809 25c. Type **173** . . . . 1·00 40
810 30c. Golf club desk . . . . . 1·50 75
811 65c. Chambermaid preparing room . . . . 1·50 1·25
812 75c. Kitchen staff under training . . . . 1·50 1·75
813 80c. Waiter at beach hotel . . 1·50 2·00
814 90c. Nightclub bar . . . . . 1·75 2·75

174 "Agave attenuata"

1998. Centenary of Botanical Gardens. Multicoloured.

815 30c. Type **174** . . . . 1·00 40
816 65c. Bermuda palmetto tree 2·00 90
817 $1 Banyan tree . . . . . . 2·50 2·50
818 $2 Cedar tree . . . . 3·75 6·00

175 Lizard with Fairy Lights (Claire Critchley)

1998. Christmas. Children's Paintings. Mult.

819 25c. Type **175** 75 35
820 40c. "Christmas stairway" (Cameron Rowling) (horiz) 1·00 1·10

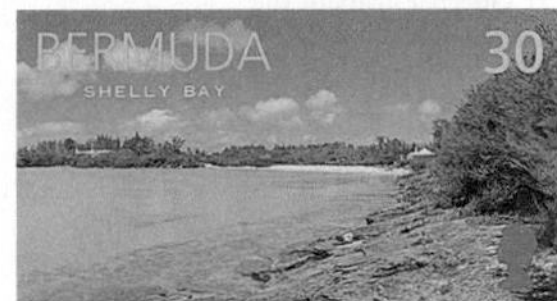

176 Shelly Bay

1999. Bermuda Beaches. Multicoloured.

821 30c. Type **176** 75 40
822 60c. Catherine's Bay . . . . 1·00 90
823 65c. Jobson's Cove . . . . . 1·10 1·00
824 $2 Warwick Long Bay . . . 3·25 4·75

177 Tracking Station

1999. 30th Anniv of First Manned Landing on Moon. Multicoloured.
825 30c. Type **177** 85 40
826 60c. Mission launch (vert) . . 1·25 90
827 75c. Aerial view of tracking station, Bermuda . . . . . 1·50 1·25
828 $2 Astronaut on Moon (vert) 3·50 5·25
MS829 90 × 80 mm. 65c. Earth as seen from Moon (circular, 40 mm diam) . . . . 2·00 2·50

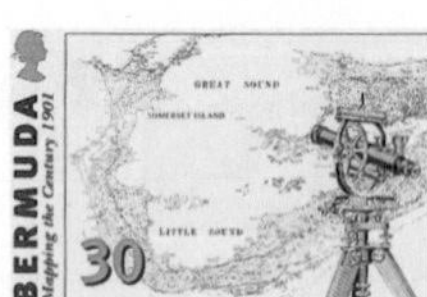

178 Theodolite and Map, 1901

1999. Centenary of First Digital Map of Bermuda.
830 **178** 30c. multicoloured . . . . 1·00 40
831 – 65c. black, stone & silver 1·75 1·40
832 – 80c. multicoloured . . . . 1·90 1·90
833 – $1 multicoloured . . . . 2·00 2·50
DESIGNS: 65c. Street map, 1901; 80c. Street plan and aerial photograph, 1999; $1 Satellite and Bermuda from Space, 1999.

179 Victorian Pillar Box and Bermuda 1865 1s. Stamp

180 Sir Henry Tucker and Meeting of House of Assembly

1999. Bermuda Postal History. Multicoloured.
834 30c. Type **179** 80 40
835 75c. King George V pillar box and 1920 2s. stamp . . 1·75 1·40
836 95c. King George VI wall box and 1938 3d. stamp . . 1·90 2·25
837 $1 Queen Elizabeth II pillar box and 1953 Coronation 1½d. stamp . . . . 1·90 2·25

2000. Pioneers of Progress. Each brown, black and gold.
838 30c. Type **180** 60 80
839 30c. Gladys Morrell and suffragettes 60 80
840 30c. Dr. E. F. Gordon and workers 60 80

181 *Amerigo Vespucci* (full-rigged ship)

182 Prince William

2000. Tall Ships Race. Multicoloured.
841 30c. Type **181** 85 45
842 60c. *Europa* (barque) . . . . 1·25 1·25
843 80c. *Juan Sebastian de Elcano* (schooner) . . . . 1·40 1·75

2000. Royal Birthdays. Multicoloured.
844 35c. Type **182** . . . . 1·00 45
845 40c. Duke of York . . . . . 1·10 50
846 50c. Princess Royal . . . . . 1·25 80
847 70c. Princess Margaret . . . 1·40 2·00
848 $1 Queen Elizabeth the Queen Mother . . . . . . 1·75 2·50
MS849 169 × 90 mm. Nos. 844/8 5·50 5·50

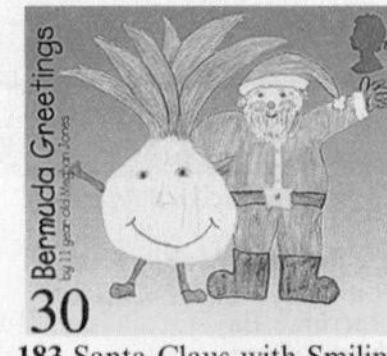

183 Santa Claus with Smiling Vegetable (Meghan Jones)

2000. Christmas. Children's Paintings. Mult.
850 30c. Type **183** 75 45
851 45c. Christmas tree and presents (Carlita Lodge) . . 1·00 80

2001. Endangered Species. Bird Conservation. Designs as Nos. 774/7, but with different face values, inscriptions redrawn and WWF panda emblem added. Multicoloured.
852 15c. As Type **169** 55 60
853 15c. Cahow 55 60
854 20c. White-tailed tropic bird with chick (vert) 55 60
855 20c. Cahow with chick (vert) 55 60
MS856 200 × 190 mm. Nos. 852/5 each × 4 . . . . 6·00 6·50
No. **MS**856 includes the "HONG KONG 2001" logo on the margin.

184 King's Castle

2001. Historic Buildings, St. George's. Multicoloured.
857 35c. Type **184** 85 55
858 50c. Bridge House . . . . . 1·10 75
859 55c. Whitehall . . . . 1·25 1·00
860 70c. Fort Cunningham . . . 1·60 1·75
861 85c. St. Peter's Church . . . 1·90 2·25
862 95c. Water Street . . . . . . 2·00 2·50

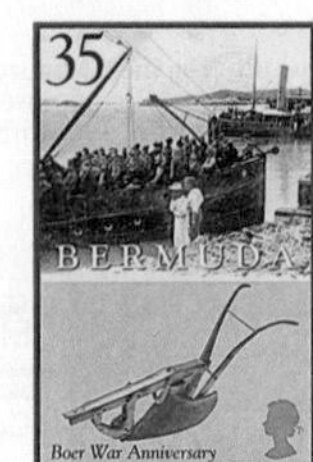

185 Boer Prisoners on Boat and Plough

2001. Centenary of Anglo-Boer War. Multicoloured.
863 35c. Type **185** 75 55
864 50c. Prisoners in shelter and boot 95 75
865 70c. Elderly Boer with children and jewellery . . . 1·40 1·60
866 95c. Bermuda residents and illustrated envelope of 1902 1·90 2·75

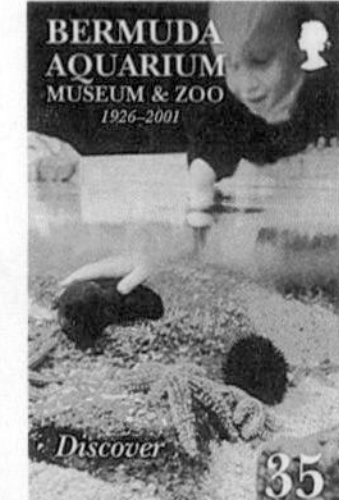

186 Girl touching Underwater Environment

2001. 75th Anniv of Bermuda Aquarium. Multicoloured.
867 35c. Type **186** 70 55
868 50c. Museum exhibits (horiz) 90 75
869 55c. Feeding giant tortoise (horiz) 95 95
870 70c. Aquarium building (horiz) . . . . 1·40 1·40
871 80c. Lesson from inside tank 1·40 1·60
872 95c. Turtle . . . . 1·75 2·00

187 "Fishing Boats" (Charles Lloyd Tucker)

2001. Paintings of Charles Lloyd Tucker. Multicoloured.
873 35c. Type **187** . . . . 1·00 55
874 70c. "Bandstand and City Hall, Hamilton" . . . . . 1·50 1·40
875 85c. "Hamilton Harbour" . . 1·75 1·75
876 $1 "Train in Front Street, Hamilton" . . . . 2·25 2·50

2002. Golden Jubilee. As T **200** of Ascension.
877 10c. black, violet and gold . . 50 50
878 35c. multicoloured . . . . . 1·25 1·10
879 70c. black, violet and gold . . 1·75 1·40
880 85c. multicoloured . . . . . 2·00 2·00
MS881 162 × 95 mm. Nos. 887/80 and $1 multicoloured . . . . . 6·00 6·50
DESIGNS—HORIZ: 10c. Princess Elizabeth with corgi; 35c. Queen Elizabeth in evening dress, 1965; 70c. Queen Elizabeth in car, 1952; 85c. Queen Elizabeth on Merseyside, 1991. VERT (38 × 51 mm)—$2 Queen Elizabeth after Annigoni
Designs as Nos. 877/80 in No. **MS**881 omit the gold frame around each stamp and the "Golden Jubilee 1952–2002" inscription.

188 Fantasy Cave

2002. Caves. Multicoloured.
882 35c. Type **188** . . . . 1·00 55
883 70c. Crystal Cave . . . . . 1·50 1·40
884 80c. Prospero's Cave . . . . 1·75 1·75
885 $1 Cathedral Cave . . . . . 2·00 2·50

189 Fielder and Somerset Club Colours

190 Slit Worm-shell

2002. Centenary of Bermuda Cup Cricket Match. Multicoloured.
886 35c. Type **189** 80 70
887 35c. Batsman and wicketkeeper with St. George's Club colours 80 70
MS888 110 × 85 mm. $1 Batsman (48 × 31 mm) . . . . 2·00 2·25

2002. Queen Elizabeth the Queen Mother Commemoration. As T **202** of Ascension.
889 30c. brown, gold and purple 75 45
890 $1.25 multicoloured . . . . 2·00 2·25
MS891 145 × 70 mm. Nos. 889/90 3·25 3·50
DESIGNS: 30c. Duchess of York, 1923; $1.25, Queen Mother on her birthday, 1995.
Designs as Nos. 889/90 in No. **MS**891 omit the "1900–2002" inscription and the coloured frame.

2002. Shells. Multicoloured.
892 5c. Type **190** 10 10
893 10c. Netted olive 10 15
894 20c. Angular triton (horiz) . . 20 25
895 25c. Frog shell (horiz) . . . 25 30
896 30c. Colourful atlantic moon (horiz) 35 40
897 35c. Noble wentletrap 40 45
898 40c. Atlantic trumpet triton (horiz) 45 50
899 45c. Zigzag scallop 50 55
900 50c. Bermuda cone 55 60
901 75c. Very distorted distorsio (horiz) 80 85
902 80c. Purple sea snail (horiz) 90 95
903 90c. Flame helmet (horiz) . . 1·00 1·10
904 $1 Scotch bonnet (horiz) . . 1·10 1·25
905 $2 Gold mouth triton (horiz) 2·25 2·40
906 $3 Bermuda's slit shell (horiz) 3·25 3·50
907 $4 Reticulated cowrie-helmet (horiz) . . . . 4·50 4·75
908 $5 Dennison's morum (horiz) 5·50 5·75
909 $8 Sunrise tellin . . . . . . 8·75 9·00

191 Dove of Peace

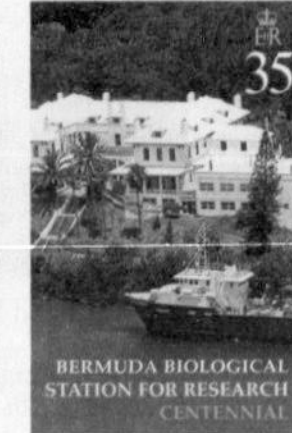

192 Research Station and *Weatherbird II* (research ship)

2002. World Peace Day.
910 **191** 35c. multicoloured 75 50
911 – 70c. multicoloured . . . . 1·50 1·75
DESIGN: 70c. Dove.

2003. Centenary of Bermuda Biological Research Station. Multicoloured.
912 35c. Type **192** 75 50
913 70c. Spotfin butterflyfish (horiz) . . . . 1·40 1·25
914 85c. Collecting coral (horiz) 1·60 1·75
915 $1 Krill . . . . 1·75 1·90

193 Costume Dolls

2003. Heritage "Made in Bermuda". Multicoloured.
916 35c. Type **193** 35 40
917 70c. Model sailing ship . . . 75 80
918 80c. Abstract sculpture in wood 85 90
919 $1 Silverware . . . . 1·10 1·25

2003. 50th Anniv of Coronation. As T **206** of Ascension. Multicoloured.
920 35c. Queen in Coronation Coach 35 40
921 70c. Queen in Coronation chair, flanked by bishops of Durham and Bath & Wells 75 80
MS922 95 × 115 mm. $1.25 As 35c.; $2 As 70c. . . . . 3·50 3·75
Nos. 920/1 have red frame; stamps from **MS**922 have no frame and country name in mauve panel.

194 Red Poinsettias

2003. Christmas Greetings. Poinsettias. Multicoloured.
925 30c. Type **194** 30 35
926 45c. White poinsettias 50 55
927 80c. Pink poinsettias 85 90

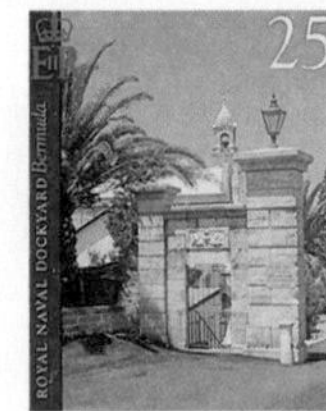

195 Gateway

2004. Royal Naval Dockyard, Bermuda. Multicoloured.
928 25c. Type **195** 25 30
929 35c. Fountain and Clock Tower 40 45
930 70c. Waterside seat and Clock Tower 75 80
931 85c. Marina 85 90
932 95c. Window in ramparts . . 1·00 1·10
933 $1 Boats moored at pontoon and Clocktower Centre . . 1·10 1·25

EXPRESS LETTER STAMP

E **1** Queen Elizabeth II

1996.
E1 E **1** $22 orange and blue . . . 24·00 25·00

2003. As T **207** of Ascension.
E2 $25 black, blue and violet . . 27·00 28·00

BHOPAL Pt. 1

A state of C. India. Now uses Indian stamps.

12 pies = 1 anna; 16 annas = 1 rupee.

3 4

1876. Imperf.
5 **3** ¼a. black . . . . 7·00 12·00
2 ½a. red . . . . 17·00 38·00

1878. Imperf or perf.
7 **4** ¼a. green . . . . 9·00 14·00
15 ¼a. red . . . . 5·50 2·50
8 ½a. red . . . . 6·00 12·00
9 ½a. brown . . . . 24·00 38·00

1881. As T **3**, but larger. Imperf or perf.
29 ¼a. black . . . . 2·00 1·50
37 ½a. red . . . . 1·60 3·25
46 ½a. black . . . . 1·00 1·50
30 1a. brown . . . . 1·75 4·00
31 2a. blue . . . . 1·50 1·75
32 4a. yellow . . . . 2·00 3·25

13 15

1884. Perf.
49 **13** ¼a. green . . . . 4·50 12·00
76 ¼a. black . . . . 1·00 1·00

1884. Imperf or perf.
64 **15** ¼a. green 60 50
65 ¼a. black 30 30
53 ½a. black . . . . 65 2·75
56 ½a. red . . . . 55 1·25

17

1890. Imperf or perf.
71 **17** 8a. greenish black . . . . . 20·00 20·00

19 **20** State Arms

1902. Imperf.
90 **19** ¼a. red . . . . 80 3·75
91 ½a. black . . . . 85 4·50
92 1a. brown . . . . 1·75 5·50
94 2a. blue . . . . 5·00 20·00
96 4a. yellow . . . . 16·00 42·00
97 8a. lilac . . . . 42·00 £110
98 1r. red . . . . 65·00 £150

1908. Perf.
100 **20** 1a. green . . . . 3·75 3·75

OFFICIAL STAMPS

1908. As T **20** but inscr "H.H. BEGUM'S SERVICE" optd **SERVICE**.
O301 ½a. green . . . . 2·25 10
O302 1a. red . . . . 4·25 35
O307 2a. blue . . . . 3·50 50
O304 4a. brown . . . . 11·00 40

O 4

1930. Type O **4** optd **SERVICE**.
O309 O **4** ½a. green . . . . 9·00 1·40
O310 1a. red . . . . 10·00 15

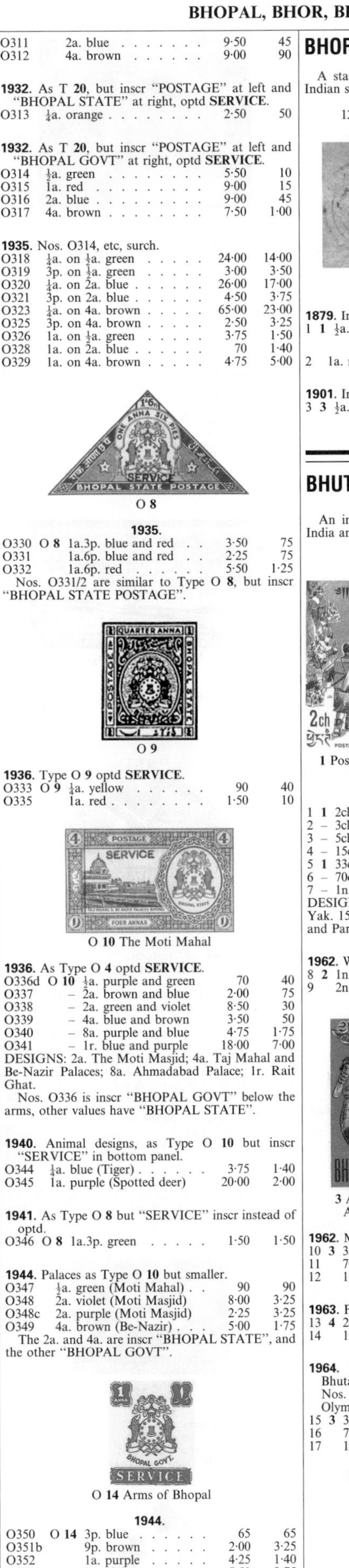

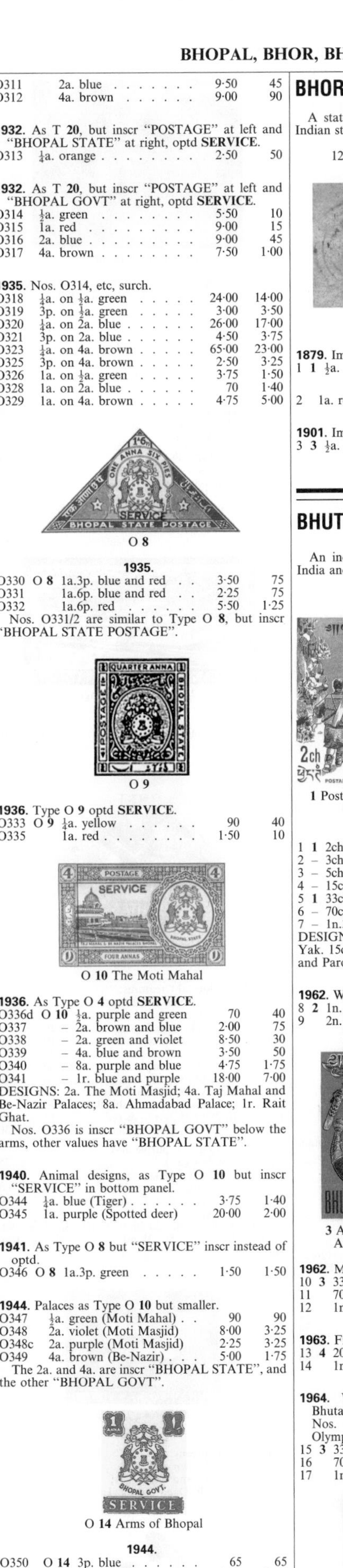

O311 2a. blue . . . . 9·50 45
O312 4a. brown . . . . 9·00 90

1932. As T **20**, but inscr "POSTAGE" at left and "BHOPAL STATE" at right, optd **SERVICE**.
O313 ¼a. orange . . . . 2·50 50

1932. As T **20**, but inscr "POSTAGE" at left and "BHOPAL GOVT" at right, optd **SERVICE**.
O314 ½a. green . . . . 5·50 10
O315 1a. red . . . . 9·00 15
O316 2a. blue . . . . 9·00 45
O317 4a. brown . . . . 7·50 1·00

1935. Nos. O314, etc, surch.
O318 ¼a. on ½a. green . . . . . 24·00 14·00
O319 3p. on ½a. green . . . . . 3·00 3·50
O320 ¼a. on 2a. blue . . . . . 26·00 17·00
O321 3p. on 2a. blue . . . . . 4·50 3·75
O323 ¼a. on 4a. brown . . . . . 65·00 23·00
O325 3p. on 4a. brown . . . . . 2·50 3·25
O326 1a. on ½a. green . . . . . 3·75 1·50
O328 1a. on 2a. blue . . . . . 70 1·40
O329 1a. on 4a. brown . . . . . 4·75 5·00

O 8

1935.
O330 O **8** 1a.3p. blue and red . . 3·50 75
O331 1a.6p. blue and red . . 2·25 75
O332 1a.6p. red . . . . . 5·50 1·25

Nos. O331/2 are similar to Type O **8**, but inscr "BHOPAL STATE POSTAGE".

O 9

1936. Type O **9** optd **SERVICE**.
O333 O **9** ¼a. yellow 90 40
O335 1a. red . . . . 1·50 10

O **10** The Moti Mahal

1936. As Type O **4** optd **SERVICE**.
O336d O **10** ½a. purple and green 70 40
O337 – 2a. brown and blue 2·00 75
O338 – 2a. green and violet 8·50 30
O339 – 4a. blue and brown 3·50 50
O340 – 8a. purple and blue 4·75 1·75
O341 – 1r. blue and purple 18·00 7·00

DESIGNS: 2a. The Moti Masjid; 4a. Taj Mahal and Be-Nazir Palaces; 8a. Ahmadabad Palace; 1r. Rait Ghat.

Nos. O336 is inscr "BHOPAL GOVT" below the arms, other values have "BHOPAL STATE".

1940. Animal designs, as Type O **10** but inscr "SERVICE" in bottom panel.
O344 ¼a. blue (Tiger) . . . . . . 3·75 1·40
O345 1a. purple (Spotted deer) 20·00 2·00

1941. As Type O **8** but "SERVICE" inscr instead of optd.
O346 O **8** 1a.3p. green . . . . . 1·50 1·50

1944. Palaces as Type O **10** but smaller.
O347 ½a. green (Moti Mahal) . . 90 90
O348 2a. violet (Moti Masjid) 8·00 3·25
O348c 2a. purple (Moti Masjid) 2·25 3·25
O349 4a. brown (Be-Nazir) . . . 5·00 1·75

The 2a. and 4a. are inscr "BHOPAL STATE", and the other "BHOPAL GOVT".

O **14** Arms of Bhopal

1944.
O350 O **14** 3p. blue 65 65
O351b 9p. brown . . . . . . 2·00 3·25
O352 1a. purple . . . . . . 4·25 1·40
O352b 1a. violet . . . . . . 7·50 2·75
O353 1½a. red . . . . . . 1·25 75
O354 3a. yellow . . . . . . 9·50 11·00
O354d 3a. brown . . . . . . 90·00 90·00
O355 6a. red . . . . . . 14·00 40·00

1949. Surch **2 As.** and bars.
O356 O **14** 2a. on 1½a. red . . . . 2·50 6·50

1949. Surch **2 As.** and ornaments.
O357 O **14** 2a. on 1½a. red £700 £700

BHOR Pt. 1

A state of W. India, Bombay district. Now uses Indian stamps.

12 pies = 1 anna; 16 annas = 1 rupee.

1 **3** Pandit Shankar Rao

1879. Imperf.
1 **1** ½a. red . . . . 2·75 4·25

Similar to T **1**, but rectangular.
2 1a. red . . . . 4·75 6·50

1901. Imperf.
3 **3** ½a. red . . . . 12·50 35·00

BHUTAN Pt. 21

An independent territory in treaty relations with India and bounded by India, Sikkim and Tibet.

100 chetrum = 1 ngultrum.

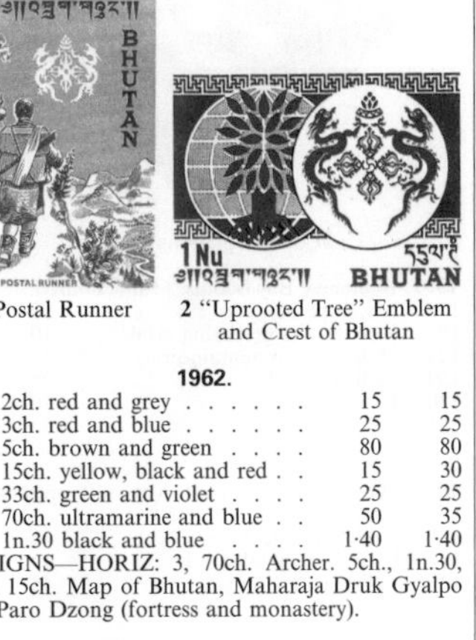

1 Postal Runner **2** "Uprooted Tree" Emblem and Crest of Bhutan

1962.
1 **1** 2ch. red and grey 15 15
2 – 3ch. red and blue 25 25
3 – 5ch. brown and green . . . 80 80
4 – 15ch. yellow, black and red . . 15 30
5 **1** 33ch. green and violet . . . 25 25
6 – 70ch. ultramarine and blue . . 50 35
7 – 1n.30 black and blue . . . 1·40 1·40

DESIGNS—HORIZ: 3, 70ch. Archer. 5ch., 1n.30, Yak. 15ch. Map of Bhutan, Maharaja Druk Gyalpo and Paro Dzong (fortress and monastery).

1962. World Refugee Year.
8 **2** 1n. red and blue . . . . . 2·75 2·75
9 2n. violet and green . . . . 2·50 2·50

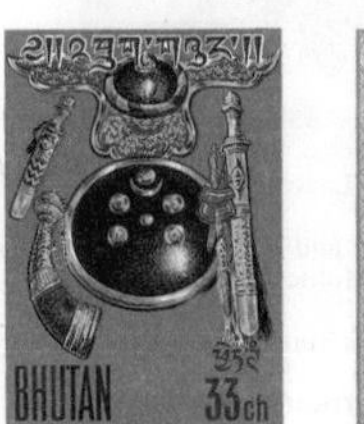

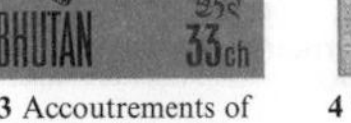

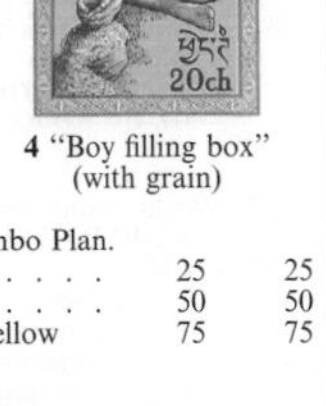

3 Accoutrements of Ancient Warrior **4** "Boy filling box" (with grain)

1962. Membership of Colombo Plan.
10 **3** 33ch. multicoloured 25 25
11 70ch. multicoloured 50 50
12 1n.30 red, brown & yellow 75 75

1963. Freedom from Hunger.
13 **4** 20ch. brown, blue & yellow 25 25
14 1n.50 purple, brown & blue 65 65

1964. Winter Olympic Games, Innsbruck, and Bhutanese Winter Sports Committee Fund. Nos. 10/12 surch **INNSBRUCK 1964 +50 ch**, Olympic rings and emblem.
15 **3** 33ch.+50ch. multicoloured . . 2·40 2·40
16 70ch.+50ch. multicoloured . . 2·40 2·40
17 1n.30+50ch. multicoloured 2·40 2·40

6 Dancer with upraised hands

1964. Bhutanese Dancers. Multicoloured.
18 2ch. Standing on one leg (vert) 10 10
19 3ch. Type **6** 10 10
20 5ch. With tambourine (vert) 10 10
21 20ch. As 2ch. 10 10
22 33ch. Type **6** 10 10
23 70ch. With sword 15 15

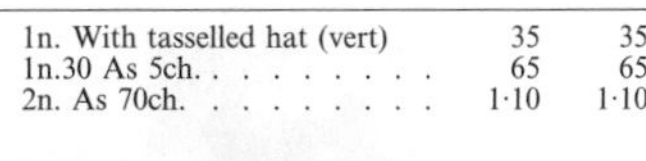

24 1n. With tasselled hat (vert) 35 35
25 1n.30 As 5ch. 65 65
26 2n. As 70ch. . . . . 1·10 1·10

7 Bhutanese Athlete **9** Primula

8 Flags at Half-mast

1964. Olympic Games, Tokyo. Multicoloured.
27 2ch. Type **7** 15 10
28 5ch. Boxing 10 10
29 15ch. Type **7** 10 10
30 33ch. As 5ch. 15 15
31 1n. Archery 35 35
32 2n. Football 70 70
33 3n. As 1n. . . . . 1·30 1·50

1964. Pres. Kennedy Commemoration.
34 **8** 33ch. multicoloured 25 25
35 1n. multicoloured 60 60
36 3n. multicoloured 90 90

1965. Flowers. Multicoloured.
37 2ch. Type **9** 10 10
38 5ch. Gentian 10 10
39 15ch. Type **9** 10 10
40 33ch. As 5ch. 15 15
41 50ch. Rhododendron 25 25
42 75ch. Peony 35 35
43 1n. As 50ch. 35 35
44 2n. As 75ch. 85 85

1965. Churchill Commemoration. Optd **WINSTON CHURCHILL 1874 1965**.
45 **1** 33ch. green and violet . . . 35 35
46 **8** 1n. multicoloured 55 55
47 – 1n. multicoloured (No. 43) 50 50
48 – 2n. multicoloured (No. 44) 85 85
49 **8** 3n. multicoloured . . . . . 1·30 1·30

11 Pavilion and Skyscrapers

1965. New York World's Fair. Mult.
50 1ch. Type **11** 10 10
51 10ch. Buddha and Michelangelo's "Pieta" . . . 10 10
52 20ch. Bhutan houses and New York skyline 10 10
53 33ch. Bhutan and New York bridges 10 10
54 1n.50 Type **11** 50 50
55 2n. As 10ch. 80 80

1965. Surch.
56 **2** 5ch. on 1n. (No. 8) . . . . . 28·00 28·00
57 5ch. on 2n. (No. 9) . . . . . 28·00 28·00
58 – 10ch. on 70ch. (No. 23) . . . 7·75 7·75
59 – 10ch. on 2n. (No. 26) . . . . 7·75 7·75
60 – 15ch. on 70ch. (No. 6) . . . 6·50 6·50
61 – 15ch. on 1n.30 (No. 7) . . . 6·50 6·50
62 – 20ch. on 1n. (No. 24) . . . . 9·25 9·25
63 – 20ch. on 1n.30 (No. 25) . . . 9·25 9·25

13 "Telstar" and Portable Transmitter

1966. Centenary of I.T.U. Multicoloured.
64 35ch. Type **13** 15 15
65 2n. "Telstar" & morse key . . 40 40
66 3n. "Relay" and headphones 75 75

14 Asiatic Black Bear

1966. Animals. Multicoloured.
68 1ch. Type **14** 10 10
69 2ch. Snow leopard 10 10
70 4ch. Pygmy hog 10 10
71 8ch. Tiger 10 10
72 10ch. Dhole 10 10
73 75ch. As 8ch. 25 25
74 1n. Takin 40 40
75 1n.50 As 10ch. 55 55
76 2n. As 4ch. 70 70
77 3n. As 2ch. . . . . 1·00 1·00
78 4n. Type **14** . . . . 1·40 1·40
79 5n. As 1n. . . . . 2·00 2·00

15 Simtoke Dzong (fortress)

1966.
80 – 5c. brown 15 10
81 **15** 15ch. brown 15 15
82 20ch. green 25 25
DESIGN: 5ch. Rinpung Dzong (fortress).

16 King Jigme Dorji Wangchuck (obverse of 50n.p. coin)

1966. 40th Anniv of King Jigme Wangchuck's Accession (father of King Jigme Dorji Wangchuck). Circular designs, embossed on gold foil, backed with multicoloured patterned paper. Imperf. Sizes: (a) Diameter 38 mm; (b) Diameter 50 mm; (c) Diameter 63 mm. (i) 50n.p. Coin
83 **16** 10ch. green (a) 15 15

(ii) 1r. Coin
84 **16** 25ch. green (b) 25 25

(iii) 3r. Coin
85 **16** 50ch. green (c) 45 45

(iv) 1 sertum Coin
86 **16** 1n. red (a) 80 80
87 – 1n.30 red (a) . . . . 1·20 1·20

(v) 2 sertum Coin
88 **16** 2n. red (b) . . . . 1·80 1·80
89 – 3n. red (b) . . . . 2·50 2·50

(vi) 5 sertum Coin
90 **16** 4n. red (c) . . . . 3·25 3·25
91 – 5n. red (c) . . . . 3·75 3·75
Nos. 87, 89 and 91 show the reverse side of the coins (Symbol).

17 "Abominable Snowman"

1966. "Abominable Snowman". Various triangular designs.
92 **17** 1ch. multicoloured 10 10
93 – 2ch. multicoloured 10 10
94 – 3ch. multicoloured 10 10
95 – 4ch. multicoloured 10 10
96 – 5ch. multicoloured 10 10
97 – 15ch. multicoloured . . . 10 10
98 – 30ch. multicoloured . . . 10 10
99 – 40ch. multicoloured . . . 15 15
100 – 50ch. multicoloured . . . 15 15
101 – 1n.25 multicoloured . . . 30 30
102 – 2n.50 multicoloured . . . 50 50
103 – 3n. multicoloured 60 60
104 – 5n. multicoloured 85 85
105 – 6n. multicoloured 85 85
106 – 7n. multicoloured 95 95

1967. Air. Optd **AIR MAIL** and helicopter motif.
107 **6** 33ch. multicoloured . . . 10 15
108 – 50ch. mult (No. 41) . . . 25 25
109 – 70ch. mult (No. 23) . . . 30 30
110 – 75ch. mult (No. 42) . . . 25 25
111 – 1n. mult (No. 24) 35 35
112 – 1n.50 mult (No. 75) . . . 55 55
113 – 2n. mult (No. 76) 80 80
114 – 3n. mult (No. 77) . . . . 1·20 1·20
115 **14** 4n. multicoloured . . . . 1·80 1·80
116 – 5n. mult (No. 79) . . . . 2·30 2·30

20 "Lilium sherriffiae"

1967. Flowers. Multicoloured.
117 3ch. Type **20** 10 10
118 5ch. "Meconopsis" 10 10
119 7ch. "Rhododendron dhwoju" 10 10
120 10ch. "Pleione hookeriana" . . 10 10
121 50ch. Type **20** 15 15
122 1n. As 5ch. 30 30
123 2n.50 As 7ch. 75 75
124 4n. As 10ch. . . . . 1·00 1·00
125 5n. "Rhododendron giganteum" . . . . 1·30 1·30

21 Scouts planting Sapling

1967. Bhutanese Boy Scouts. Multicoloured.
126 5ch. Type **21** 10 10
127 10ch. Scouts preparing meal 10 10
128 15ch. Scout mountaineering 15 15
129 50ch. Type **21** 25 25
130 1n.25. As 10ch. 70 70
131 4n. As 15ch. . . . . 1·70 1·70

1967. World Fair, Montreal. Nos. 53/5 optd **expo67** and emblem.
133 – 33ch. multicoloured . . . 30 30
134 **11** 1n.50 multicoloured . . . 40 40
135 – 2n. multicoloured 45 45

23 Avro Lancaster Bomber

1967. Churchill and Battle of Britain Commemoration. Multicoloured.
137 45ch. Type **23** 20 20
138 2n. Supermarine Spitfire fighter 45 45
139 4n. Hawker Hurricane Mk IIC fighter 90 90

1967. World Scout Jamboree, Idaho. Nos. 126/31 optd **WORLD JAMBOREE IDAHO, U.S.A. AUG. 1-9/67.**
141 **21** 5ch. multicoloured 15 15
142 – 10ch. multicoloured . . . 20 20
143 – 15ch. multicoloured . . . 25 25
144 – 50ch. multicoloured . . . 35 35
145 – 1n.25 multicoloured . . . 70 75
146 – 4n. multicoloured . . . . 1·80 1·80

25 Painting

1967. Bhutan Girl Scouts. Multicoloured.
148 5ch. Type **25** 10 10
149 10ch. Playing musical instrument 10 10
150 15ch. Picking fruit 10 10
151 1n.50 Type **25** 45 45
152 2n.50 As 10ch. . . . . 1·10 1·10
153 5n. As 15ch. . . . . 2·50 2·50

26 Astronaut in Space

1967. Space Achievements. With laminated prismatic-ribbed plastic surface. Multicoloured.
155 3ch. Type **26** (postage) . . . 25 25
156 5ch. Space vehicle and astronaut 25 25
157 7ch. Astronaut and landing vehicle 45 45
158 10ch. Three astronauts in space 50 50
159 15ch. Type **26** 75 75
160 30ch. As 5ch. 90 90
161 50ch. As 7ch. . . . . 1·30 1·30
162 1n.25 As 10ch. . . . . 2·75 2·75

163 2n.50 Type **26** (air) . . . . . 1·90 1·90
164 4n. As 5ch. . . . . 2·75 2·75
165 5n. As 7ch. . . . . 3·75 3·75
166 9n. As 10ch. . . . . 6·50 6·50
The laminated plastic surface gives the stamps a three-dimensional effect.

27 Tashichho Dzong

1968.
168 **27** 10ch. purple and green . . 20 10

28 Elephant

1968. Mythological Creatures.
169 **28** 2ch. red, blue and brown (postage) 10 10
170 – 3ch. pink, blue & green . . 10 10
171 – 4ch. orange, green & blue 10 10
172 – 5ch. blue, yellow & pink 10 10
173 – 15ch. green, purple & blue 10 10
174 **28** 20ch. brown, blk & orge 10 10
175 – 30ch. yellow, black & blue 15 15
176 – 50ch. bistre, green & black 15 15
177 – 1n.25 black, green & red 15 15
178 – 2n. yellow, violet & black 30 30

179 **28** 1n.50 green, purple and yellow (air) 25 25
180 – 2n.50 red, black & blue . . 35 35
181 – 4n. orange, green & black 60 60
182 – 5n. brown, grey & orange 80 80
183 – 10n. violet, grey & black 1·50 1·50
DESIGNS: 3, 30ch., 2n.50, Garuda; 4, 50ch., 4n. Tiger; 5ch., 1n.25, 5n. Wind horse; 15ch., 2, 10n. Snow lion.

29 Tongsa Dzong

1968.
184 **29** 50ch. green 30 15
185 – 75ch. brown and blue . . . 35 20
186 – 1n. blue and violet 40 25
DESIGNS: 75ch. Daga Dzong; 1n. Lhuntsi Dzong.

30 Ward's Trogon

1968. Rare Birds.
187 2ch. Red-faced liocichla ("Crimson-winged Laughing Thrush") (horiz) (postage) 10 10
188 3ch. Type **30** 10 10
189 4ch. Burmese ("Grey") Peacock-pheasant (horiz) 10 10
190 5ch. Rufous-necked hornbill 10 10
191 15ch. Fire-tailed 'myzornis' ("Myzornis") (horiz) . . . 15 15
192 20ch. As No. 187 . . . . . 20 20
193 30ch. Type **30** 20 20
194 50ch. As No. 189 . . . . . 25 25
195 1n.25 As No. 190 . . . . . 35 35
196 2n. As No. 191 . . . . . . 45 45

197 1n.50 As No. 187 (air) . . . 50 50
198 2n.50 Type **30** 60 55
199 4n. As No. 189 . . . . . . 90 90
200 5n. As No. 190 . . . . . . 1·20 1·20
201 10n. As No. 191 . . . . . . 1·80 1·80

31 Mahatma Gandhi

1969. Birth Centenary of Mahatma Gandhi.
202 **31** 20ch. brown and blue . . . 15 15
203 2n. brown and yellow . . . 75 75

1970. Various stamps surch **5 CH** or **20 CH.**
(a) Freedom from Hunger (No. 14).
223 20ch. on 1n.50 purple, brown and blue . . . . 2·75 2·75

(b) Animals (Nos. 75/9).
224 20ch. on 1n.50 multicoloured 2·75 2·75
225 20ch. on 2n. multicoloured 2·75 2·75
204 20ch. on 3n. multicoloured 2·10 2·10
205 20ch. on 4n. multicoloured 2·10 2·10
206 20ch. on 5n. multicoloured 2·10 2·10

(c) Abominable Snowmen (Nos. 101/6).
226 20ch. on 1n.25 multicoloured 2·75 2·75
227 20ch. on 2n.50 multicoloured 2·75 2·75
207 20ch. on 3n. multicoloured 1·90 1·90
208 20ch. on 5n. multicoloured 2·10 2·10
209 20ch. on 6n. multicoloured 2·75 2·75
210 20ch. on 7n. multicoloured 2·75 2·75

(d) Flowers (Nos. 124/5).
211 20ch. on 4n. multicoloured 2·10 2·10
212 20ch. on 5n. multicoloured 2·50 2·50

(e) Boy Scouts (Nos. 130/1).
228 20ch. on 1n.25 multicoloured 2·75 2·75
213 20ch. on 4n. multicoloured 17·00 17·00

(f) Churchill (Nos. 138/9).
229 20ch. on 2n. multicoloured 2·75 2·75
230 20ch. on 4n. multicoloured 2·75 2·75

(g) 1968 Pheasants (Appendix).
231 20ch. on 2n. multicoloured 3·75 3·75
214 20ch. on 4n. multicoloured 2·10 2·10
232 20ch. on 7n. multicoloured 3·75 3·75

(h) Mythological Creatures (Nos. 175/80 and 182/3).
233 5ch. on 30ch. yellow, black and blue (postage) 85 85
234 5ch. on 50ch. bistre, green and black 85 85
235 5ch. on 1n.25 black, green and red 85 85
236 5ch. on 2n. yellow, vio & blk 85 85
215 20ch. on 2n. yellow, violet and black . . . . 3·75 3·75

237 5ch. on 1n.50 green, purple and brown (air) 85 85
238 5ch. on 2n.50 red, black and blue 85 85
216 20ch. on 5n. brown, grey and orange . . . . 2·40 2·40
217 20ch. on 10n. violet, grey and black . . . . 2·10 2·10

(i) Rare Birds (Nos. 193/201).
239 20ch. on 30ch. mult (postage) 3·75 3·75
240 20ch. on 50ch. multicoloured 3·75 3·75
241 20ch. on 1n. 25. multicoloured . . . . . . 3·75 3·75
218 20ch. on 2n. multicoloured 2·75 2·75

242 20ch. on 1n.50. mult (air) . . 3·75 3·75
219 20ch. on 2n.50. multicoloured 2·75 2·75
220 20ch. on 4n. multicoloured 2·10 2·10
221 20ch. on 5n. multicoloured 2·50 2·50
222 20ch. on 10n. multicoloured 3·50 3·50

(j) 1969 U.P.U. (Appendix).
243 20ch. on 1n.05. multicoloured 2·75 2·75
244 20ch. on 1n.40. multicoloured 2·75 2·75
245 20ch. on 4n. multicoloured 2·75 2·75
For stamps surcharged with 55 or 90ch. values, see Nos. 253/65 and for 25ch. surcharges see Nos. 385/410.

33 Wangdiphodrang Dzong and Bridge

34 Book Year Emblem

1971.
246 **33** 2ch. grey 25 10
247 3ch. mauve 35 15
248 4ch. violet 35 25
249 5ch. green 10 10
250 10ch. brown 15 10
251 15ch. blue 20 15
252 20ch. purple 30 15

1971. Various stamps surch **55 CH** or **90 CH**.
I. Dancers (Nos. 25/6).
253 55ch. on 1n.30 multicoloured 85 85
254 90ch. on 2n. multicoloured 85 85

II. Animals (Nos. 77/8).
255 55ch. on 3n. multicoloured 85 85
256 90ch. on 4n. multicoloured 85 85

III. Boy Scouts (No. 131).
257 90ch. on 4n. multicoloured 1·60 1·60

IV. 1968 Pheasants (Appendix).
258 55ch. on 5n. multicoloured 3·00 3·00
259 90ch. on 9n. multicoloured 3·00 3·00

V. Air. Mythological Creatures (No. 181).
260 55ch. on 4n. orange, green and black 55 55

VI. 1968 Mexico Olympics (Appendix).
261 90ch. on 1n.05 multicoloured 1·40 1·40

VII. Rare Birds (No. 196).
262 90ch. on 2n. multicoloured 3·00 3·00

VIII. 1969 U.P.U. (Appendix).
263 55ch. on 60ch. multicoloured 85 85

IX. 1970 New U.P.U. Headquarters (Appendix).
264 90ch. on 2n. 50 gold and red 2·75 2·75

X. 1971 Moon Vehicles (plastic-surfaced) (Appendix).
265 90ch. on 1n. 70 multicoloured 4·00 4·00

1972. International Book Year.
266 **34** 2ch. green and blue 10 10
267 3ch. brown and yellow . . 10 10
268 5ch. brown, orange & red 10 10
269 20ch. brown and blue . . . 10 10

35 Dochi

1972. Dogs. Multicoloured.
270 5ch. Apsoo standing on hind legs (vert) 10 10
271 10ch. Type **35** 10 10
272 15ch. Brown and white damci 10 10
273 25ch. Black and white damci 10 10
274 55ch. Apsoo lying down . . 10 10
275 8n. Two damci . . . . . . 1·40 1·40

36 King and Royal Crest

1974. Coronation of King Jigme Singye Wangchuck. Multicoloured.
277 10ch. Type **36** 10 10
278 25ch. Bhutan Flag 15 15
279 1n.25 Good Luck signs . . . 30 30
280 2n. Punakha Dzong 45 45
281 3n. Royal Crown 60 60

37 Mail Delivery by Horse

1974. Centenary of U.P.U. Multicoloured.
283 1ch. Type **37** (postage) . . . 10 10
284 2ch. Early and modern locomotives 10 10
285 3ch. "Hindoostan" (paddle-steamer) and "Iberia" (liner) 10 10
286 4ch. Vickers Vimy and Concorde aircraft 10 10
287 25ch. Mail runner and four-wheel drive 10 10
288 1n. As 25ch. (air) 20 20
289 1n.40 As 2ch. 45 45
290 2n. As 4ch. 80 80

38 Family and W.P.Y. Emblem

1974. World Population Year.
292 **38** 25ch. multicoloured . . . 10 10
293 50ch. multicoloured . . . 10 10
294 90ch. multicoloured . . . 25 25
295 2n.50 multicoloured . . . 55 55

39 Eastern Courtier

1975. Butterflies. Multicoloured.
297 1ch. Type **39** 10 10
298 2ch. Bamboo forester 10 10
299 3ch. Tailed labyrinth 10 10
300 4ch. Blue duchess 10 10
301 5ch. Cruiser 10 10
302 10ch. Bhutan glory 10 10
303 3n. Bi-coloured commodore 65 65
304 5n. Red-breasted jezebel . . . 1·40 1·40

40 King Jigme Singye Wangchuck

1976. King Jigme's 20th Birthday. Imperf.
(a) Diameter 39 mm.
306 **40** 15ch. green on gold . . . 10 10
307 1n. red on gold 25 25
308 – 1n.30 red on gold 25 25

(b) Diameter 50 mm.
309 **40** 25ch. green on gold . . . 10 10
310 2n. red on gold 45 45
311 – 3n. red on gold 70 70

(c) Diameter 63 mm.
312 **40** 90ch. green on gold . . . 75 75
313 4n. red on gold . . . . . 1·40 1·40
314 – 5n. red on gold . . . . . 1·70 1·70
DESIGN: 1n.30, 3, 5n. Decorative motif.

41 "Apollo"

1976. "Apollo"–"Soyuz" Space Link. Mult.
315 10n. Type **41** . . . . 2·40 2·40
316 10n. "Soyuz" . . . . 2·40 2·40

42 Jewellery

1976. Handicrafts and Craftsmen. Mult.
318 1ch. Type **42** 10 10
319 2ch. Coffee-pot, hand bell and sugar dish 10 10
320 3ch. Powder horns 10 10
321 4ch. Pendants and inlaid box 10 10
322 5ch. Painter 10 10
323 15ch. Silversmith 10 10
324 20ch. Wood carver with tools 10 10
325 1n.50 Textile printer 40 40
326 10n. Printer . . . . 1·90 1·90

43 "Rhododendron cinnabarinum"

45 Dragon Mask

44 Skiing

1976. Rhododendrons. Multicoloured.
328 1ch. Type **43** 10 10
329 2ch. "R. campanulatum" . . 10 10
330 3ch. "R. fortunei" 10 10
331 4ch. "R. arboreum" 10 10
332 5ch. "R. arboreum" (different) 25 10
333 1n. "R. falconeri" 20 40
334 3n. "R. hodgsonii" 55 55
335 5n. "R. keysii" . . . . . . 1·10 1·10

1976. Winter Olympic Games, Innsbruck. Mult.
337 1ch. Type **44** 10 10
338 2ch. Bobsleighing 10 10
339 3ch. Ice hockey 10 10
340 4ch. Cross-country skiing . . 10 10
341 5ch. Women's figure skating 10 10
342 2n. Downhill skiing 25 25
343 4n. Speed skating 60 55
344 10n. Pairs figure skating . . . 1·90 1·70

1976. Ceremonial Masks. Laminated prismatic-ribbed plastic surface.
346 **45** 5ch. mult (postage) 10 10
347 – 10ch. multicoloured . . . 10 10
348 – 15ch. multicoloured . . . 10 10
349 – 20ch. multicoloured . . . 10 10
350 – 25ch. multicoloured . . . 10 10
351 – 30ch. multicoloured . . . 10 10
352 – 35ch. multicoloured . . . 10 10
353 – 1n. multicoloured (air) . . 25 25
354 – 2n. multicoloured 45 45
355 – 2n.50 multicoloured . . . 75 75
356 – 3n. multicoloured 90 90
DESIGNS: 10ch. to 3n. Similar Bhutanese masks.

46 Orchid

1976. Flowers. Multicoloured.
358 1ch. Type **46** 10 10
359 2ch. Orchid (different) . . . 10 10
360 3ch. Orchid (different) . . . 10 10
361 4ch. "Primula denticulata" 10 10
362 5ch. Arum 10 10
363 2n. Orchid (different) 35 35
364 4n. "Leguminosa" 80 80
365 6n. Rhododendron . . . . . 1·20 1·20

47 Double Carp Emblem

1976. 25th Anniv of Colombo Plan.
367 3ch. Type **47** 10 10
368 4ch. Vase emblem 10 10
369 5ch. Geometric design . . . 10 10
370 25ch. Design incorporating animal's face 10 10
371 1n.25 Ornamental design . . 25 25
372 2n. Floral design 40 35
373 2n.50 Carousel design 50 45
374 3n. Wheel design 70 65

48 Bandaranaike Conference Hall

1976. 5th Non-aligned Countries Summit Conference, Colombo.
375 **48** 1n.25 multicoloured . . . 35 35
376 2n.50 multicoloured . . . 75 65

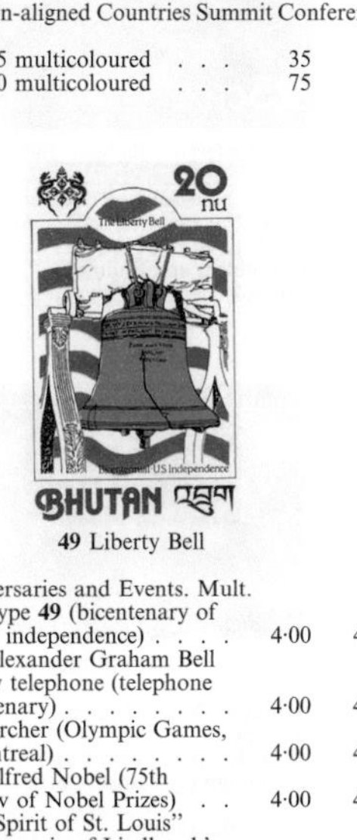

49 Liberty Bell

1978. Anniversaries and Events. Mult.
377 20n. Type **49** (bicentenary of U.S. independence) . . . . 4·00 4·00
378 20n. Alexander Graham Bell early telephone (telephone centenary) . . . . 4·00 4·00
379 20n. Archer (Olympic Games, Montreal) . . . . 4·00 4·00
380 20n. Alfred Nobel (75th anniv of Nobel Prizes) . . 4·00 4·00
381 20n. "Spirit of St. Louis" (50th anniv of Lindbergh's transatlantic flight) . . . . 4·00 4·00
382 20n. Airship LZ3 (75th anniv of Zeppelin) . . . . 4·50 4·50
383 20n. Queen Elizabeth II (25th anniv of Coronation) . . . 4·00 4·00

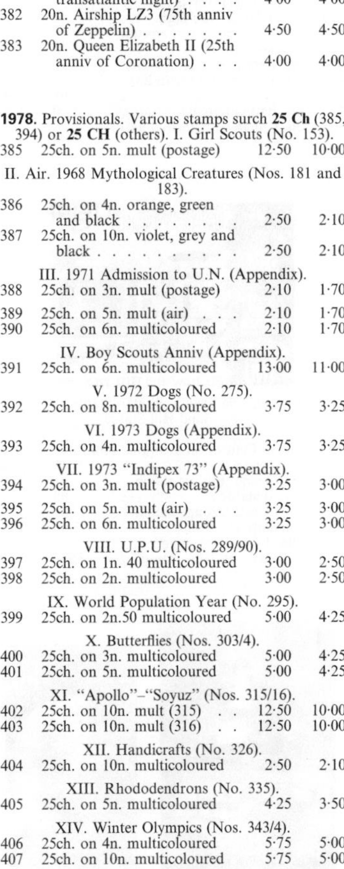

1978. Provisionals. Various stamps surch **25 Ch** (385, 394) or **25 CH** (others). I. Girl Scouts (No. 153).
385 25ch. on 5n. mult (postage) 12·50 10·00

II. Air. 1968 Mythological Creatures (Nos. 181 and 183).
386 25ch. on 4n. orange, green and black . . . . 2·50 2·10
387 25ch. on 10n. violet, grey and black . . . . 2·50 2·10

III. 1971 Admission to U.N. (Appendix).
388 25ch. on 3n. mult (postage) 2·10 1·70
389 25ch. on 5n. mult (air) . . . 2·10 1·70
390 25ch. on 6n. multicoloured 2·10 1·70

IV. Boy Scouts Anniv (Appendix).
391 25ch. on 6n. multicoloured 13·00 11·00

V. 1972 Dogs (No. 275).
392 25ch. on 8n. multicoloured 3·75 3·25

VI. 1973 Dogs (Appendix).
393 25ch. on 4n. multicoloured 3·75 3·25

VII. 1973 "Indipex 73" (Appendix).
394 25ch. on 3n. mult (postage) 3·25 3·00
395 25ch. on 5n. mult (air) . . . 3·25 3·00
396 25ch. on 6n. multicoloured 3·25 3·00

VIII. U.P.U. (Nos. 289/90).
397 25ch. on 1n. 40 multicoloured 3·00 2·50
398 25ch. on 2n. multicoloured 3·00 2·50

IX. World Population Year (No. 295).
399 25ch. on 2n.50 multicoloured 5·00 4·25

X. Butterflies (Nos. 303/4).
400 25ch. on 3n. multicoloured 5·00 4·25
401 25ch. on 5n. multicoloured 5·00 4·25

XI. "Apollo"–"Soyuz" (Nos. 315/16).
402 25ch. on 10n. mult (315) . . 12·50 10·00
403 25ch. on 10n. mult (316) . . 12·50 10·00

XII. Handicrafts (No. 326).
404 25ch. on 10n. multicoloured 2·50 2·10

XIII. Rhododendrons (No. 335).
405 25ch. on 5n. multicoloured 4·25 3·50

XIV. Winter Olympics (Nos. 343/4).
406 25ch. on 4n. multicoloured 5·75 5·00
407 25ch. on 10n. multicoloured 5·75 5·00

XV. Flowers (Nos. 364/5).
408 25ch. on 4n. multicoloured 2·10 1·80
409 25ch. on 6n. multicoloured 2·10 1·80

XVI. Colombo Plan (No. 373).
410 25ch. on 2n.50 multicoloured 2·50 2·10

50 Mother and Child

1979. International Year of the Child. Mult.

411	2n. Type **50**	50	50
412	5n. Mother carrying two children	1·10	95
413	10n. Children at school	1·60	1·50

51 Conference Emblem and Dove

1979. 6th Non-Aligned Countries Summit Conference, Havana. Multicoloured.

415	25ch. Type **51**	15	15
416	10n. Emblem and Bhutanese symbols	2·50	2·20

52 Dorji (rattle)

1979. Antiquities. Multicoloured.

417	5ch. Type **52**	10	10
418	10ch. Dilbu (hand bell) (vert)	10	10
419	15ch. Jadum (cylindrical pot) (vert)	10	10
420	25ch. Jamjee (teapot)	10	10
421	1n. Kem (cylindrical container) (vert)	35	30
422	1n.25 Jamjee (different)	40	40
423	1n.70 Sangphor (ornamental vessel) (vert)	60	60
424	2n. Jamjee (different) (vert)	75	70
425	3n. Yangtho (pot with lid) (vert)	95	90
426	4n. Battha (circular case)	1·20	1·20
427	5n. Chhap (ornamental flask) (vert)	1·70	1·60

53 Rinpiang Dzong, Bhutan Stamp and Rowland Hill Statue

1980. Death Cent of Sir Rowland Hill. Mult.

428	1n. Type **53**	45	40
429	2n. Dzong, Bhutan stamp and statue	80	75
430	5n. Ounsti Dzong, Bhutan stamp and statue	1·30	1·20
431	10n. Lingzi Dzong and British 1912 1d. stamp	2·75	2·50

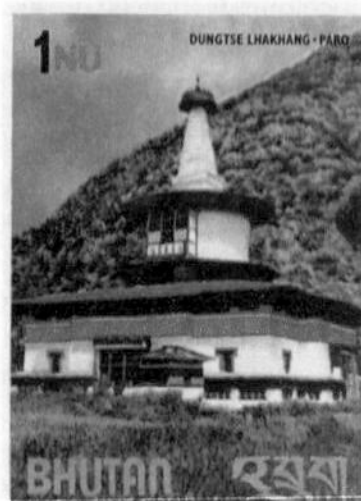

54 Dungtse Lhakhang, Paro

55 St. Paul's Cathedral

1981. Monasteries. Multicoloured.

433	1n. Type **54**	20	15
434	2n. Kich Lhakhang, Paro (horiz)	40	35
435	2n.25 Kurjey Lhakhang (horiz)	55	50
436	3n. Tangu, Thimphu (horiz)	70	65
437	4n. Cheri, Thimphu (horiz)	95	85
438	5n. Chorten, Kora (horiz)	1·50	1·30
439	7n. Tak-Tsang, Paro	2·10	1·90

1981. Wedding of Prince of Wales. Multicoloured.

440	1n. Type **55**	10	10
441	5n. Type **55**	90	75
442	20n. Prince Charles and Lady Diana Spencer	3·25	2·75
443	25n. As No. 442	4·00	3·75

56 Orange-bellied Leafbird ("Orange-billed Chiropsis")

57 Footballers

1982. Birds. Multicoloured.

445	2n. Type **56**	70	65
446	3n. Himalayan monal pheasant ("Monal Pheasant")	1·00	95
447	5n. Ward's trogon	2·00	1·80
448	10n. Mrs. Gould's sunbird	3·25	3·00

1982. World Cup Football Championship, Spain.

450	**57**	1n. multicoloured	20	15
451	–	2n. multicoloured	45	40
452	–	3n. multicoloured	65	60
453	–	20n. multicoloured	3·75	3·25

DESIGNS: 2n. to 20n. Various football scenes.

58 St. James's Palace

59 Lord Baden-Powell (founder)

1982. 21st Birthday of Princess of Wales. Mult.

455	1n. Type **58**	40	35
456	10n. Prince and Princess of Wales	2·20	2·00
457	15n. Windsor Castle	3·75	4·00
458	25n. Princess in wedding dress	5·75	5·25

1982. 75th Anniv of Boy Scout Movement. Multicoloured.

460	3n. Type **59**	55	50
461	5n. Scouts around campfire	1·10	95
462	15n. Map reading	2·75	2·50
463	20n. Pitching tents	4·00	3·75

60 Rama finds Mowgli

1982. "The Jungle Book" (cartoon film). Mult.

465	1ch. Type **60**	10	10
466	2ch. Bagheera leading Mowgli to Man-village	10	10
467	3ch. Kaa planning attack on Bagheera and Mowgli	10	10
468	4ch. Mowgli and elephants	10	10
469	5ch. Mowgli and Baloo	10	10
470	10ch. Mowgli and King Louie	10	10
471	30ch. Kaa and Shere Khan	10	10
472	2n. Mowgli, Baloo and Bagheera	45	35
473	20n. Mowgli carrying jug for girl	4·00	3·50

1982. Birth of Prince William of Wales. Nos. 455/8 optd **ROYAL BABY 21.6.82.**

475	1n. multicoloured	40	40
476	10n. multicoloured	1·40	1·20
477	15n. multicoloured	2·75	2·50
478	25n. multicoloured	4·50	4·00

62 Washington surveying

1982. 250th Birth Anniv of George Washington and Birth Centenary of Franklin D. Roosevelt. Mult.

480	50ch. Type **62**	10	10
481	1n. Roosevelt and Harvard University	10	10
482	2n. Washington at Valley Forge	30	30
483	3n. Roosevelt's mother and family	45	40
484	4n. Washington at Battle of Monmouth	55	50
485	5n. Roosevelt and the White House	80	75
486	15n. Washington and Mount Vernon	2·40	2·20
487	20n. Churchill, Roosevelt and Stalin at Yalta	3·25	3·00

1983. "Druk Air" Bhutan Air Service. Various stamps optd **DRUK AIR** (491) or **Druk Air** (others), No. 489 surch also.

489	**42**	30ch. on 1n. multicoloued (postage)	1·30	1·30
490	–	5n. multicoloured (Scouts, Appendix)	2·40	2·10
491	–	8n. mult (No. 275)	2·50	2·20
492	–	5n. mult ("Indipex 73", Appendix) (air)	3·75	3·50
493	–	7n. mult (Munich Olympics, Appendix)	3·75	3·50

64 "Angelo Doni"

1983. 500th Birth Anniv of Raphael (artist). Multicoloured.

494	1n. Type **64**	15	10
495	4n. "Maddalena Doni"	70	60
496	5n. "Baldassare Castiglione"	1·00	85
497	20n. "Woman with Veil"	4·00	3·50

65 Ta-Gyad-Boom-Zu (the eight luck-bringing symbols)

1983. Religious Offerings. Multicoloured.

499	25ch. Type **65**	10	10
500	50ch. Doeyun Nga (the five sensory symbols)	15	15
501	2n. Norbu Chadun (the seven treasures) (47×41 mm)	35	35
502	3n. Wangpo Nga (the five sensory organs)	60	55
503	8n. Sha Nga (the five kinds of flesh)	1·30	1·10
504	9n. Men-Ra-Tor Sum (the sacrificial cake) (47×41 mm)	1·60	1·60

66 Dornier Wal Flying Boat "Boreas"

1983. Bicentenary of Manned Flight. Mult.

506	50ch. Type **66**	10	10
507	3n. Savoia-Marchetti S.66 flying boat	60	55
508	10n. Hawker Osprey biplane	2·00	1·90
509	20n. Astra airship "Ville de Paris"	4·00	3·75

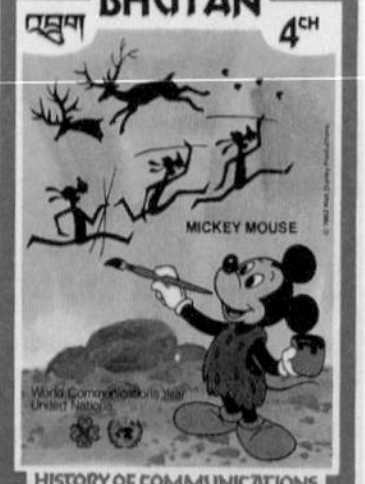

67 Mickey Mouse as Caveman

68 Golden Langur

1984. World Communications Year. Mult.

511	4ch. Type **67**	10	10
512	5ch. Goofy as printer	10	10
513	10ch. Chip 'n' Dale with morse key	10	10
514	20ch. Pluto talks to girlfriend on telephone	10	10
515	25ch. Minnie Mouse pulling record from bulldog	10	10
516	50ch. Morty and Ferdie with microphone and loudhailers	10	10
517	1n. Huey, Dewey, and Louie listening to radio	30	30
518	5n. Donald Duck watching television on buffalo	1·10	1·10
519	20n. Daisy Duck with computers and abacus	4·25	4·00

1984. Endangered Species. Multicoloured.

521	50ch. Type **68**	20	20
522	1n. Golden langur family in tree (horiz)	30	30
523	2n. Male and female Golden langurs with young (horiz)	70	70
524	4n. Group of langurs	1·40	1·30

69 Downhill Skiing

70 "Sans Pareil", 1829

1984. Winter Olympic Games, Sarajevo. Mult.

526	50ch. Type **69**	10	10
527	1n. Cross-country skiing	20	15
528	3n. Speed skating	70	65
529	20n. Four-man bobsleigh	3·50	3·25

1984. Railway Locomotives. Multicoloured.

531	50ch. Type **70**	10	10
532	1n. "Planet", 1830	15	15
533	3n. "Experiment" 1832	65	60
534	4n. "Black Hawk", 1835	85	80
535	5n.50 "Jenny Lind", 1847 (horiz)	1·10	1·10
536	8n. "Bavaria", 1851 (horiz)	1·60	1·50
537	10n. Great Northern locomotive No. 1, 1870 (horiz)	2·10	1·90
538	25n. Steam locomotive Type 110, Prussia, 1880 (horiz)	5·00	4·50

71 Riley Sprite Sports Car, 1936

1984. Cars. Multicoloured.

540	50ch. Type **71**	10	10
541	1n. Lanchester Forty saloon, 1919	15	15
542	3n. Itala 35/45 racer, 1907	55	50
543	4n. Morris Oxford (Bullnose) tourer, 1913	80	70
544	5n.50 Lagonda LG6 drophead coupe, 1939	1·10	95
545	6n. Wolseley four seat tonneau, 1903	1·30	1·10
546	8n. Buick Super convertible, 1952	1·50	1·40
547	20n. Maybach Zeppelin limousine, 1933	4·00	3·50

72 Women's Archery

73 Domkhar Dzong

1984. Olympic Games, Los Angeles. Multicoloured.

549	15ch. Type **72**	10	10
550	25ch. Men's archery	15	10
551	2n. Table tennis	40	35
552	2n.25 Basketball	50	45
553	5n.50 Boxing	1·00	95
554	6n. Running	1·20	1·10
555	8n. Tennis	1·70	1·60

1984. Monasteries.

557	**73**	10ch. blue	10	10
558	–	25ch. red	10	10
559	–	50ch. violet	10	10
560	–	1n. brown	20	20
561	–	2n. red	35	35
562	–	5n. green	85	85

DESIGNS: 25ch. Shemgang Dzong; 50ch. Chapcha Dzong; 1n. Tashigang Dzong; 2n. Pungthang Dzong; 5n. Dechhenphoda Dzong.

74 "Magician Mickey"

1984. 50th Anniv of Donald Duck. Scenes from films. Multicoloured.

563 4ch. Type **74** 10 10
564 5ch. "Slide, Donald, Slide" 10 10
565 10ch. "Donald's Golf Game" 10 10
566 20ch. "Mr. Duck Steps Out" 10 10
567 25ch. "Lion Around" 10 10
568 50ch. "Alpine Climbers" . . 10 10
569 1n. "Flying Jalopy" 10 10
570 5n. "Frank Duck brings 'Em Back Alive" 55 45
571 20n. "Good Scouts" . . . . 2·20 1·80

1984. Various stamps surch. (a) World Cup Football Championship, Spain (Nos. 450/3).

573 5n. on 1n. multicoloured . . 1·60 1·40
574 5n. on 2n. multicoloured . . 1·60 1·40
575 5n. on 3n. multicoloured . . 1·60 1·40
576 5n. on 20n. multicoloured . . 1·60 1·40

(b) 21st Birthday of Princess of Wales (Nos. 455/8).

578 5n. on 1n. multicoloured . . 1·40 1·30
579 5n. on 10n. multicoloured . . 1·40 1·30
580 5n. on 15n. multicoloured . . 1·40 1·30
581 40n. on 25n. multicoloured 11·00 10·00

(c) Birth of Prince William of Wales (Nos. 475/8).

583 5n. on 1n. multicoloured . . 1·30 1·30
584 5n. on 10n. multicoloured . . 1·30 1·30
585 5n. on 15n. multicoloured . . 1·30 1·30
586 40n. on 25n. multicoloured 11·00 10·50

(d) Wedding of Prince of Wales (Nos. 440/3).

588 10n. on 1n. multicoloured . . 2·40 2·20
589 10n. on 5n. multicoloured . . 2·40 2·20
590 10n. on 20n. multicoloured 2·40 2·20
591 10n. on 25n. multicoloured 2·40 2·20

(e) 75th Anniv of Boy Scout Movement (Nos. 460/3).

593 10n. on 3n. multicoloured . . 2·40 2·20
594 10n. on 5n. multicoloured . . 2·40 2·20
595 10n. on 15n. multicoloured 2·40 2·20
596 10n. on 20n. multicoloured 2·40 2·20

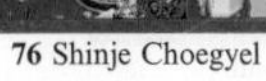

76 Shinje Choegyel

77 Bhutan and U.N. Flags

1985. The Judgement of Death Mask Dance. Multicoloured.

598 5ch. Type **76** 10 10
599 35ch. Raksh Lango 10 10
600 50ch. Druelgo 10 10
601 2n.50 Pago 40 35
602 3n. Telgo 55 50
603 4n. Due Nakcung 75 70
604 5n. Lha Karpo 90 85
605 5n.50 Nyalbum . . . . . . 1·00 95
606 6n. Khimda Pelkyi . . . . . 1·10 1·10

1985. 40th Anniv of U.N.O.

608 **77** 50ch. multicoloured . . . 20 20
609 – 15n. multicoloured . . . . 2·00 1·70
610 – 20n. black and blue . . . . 3·00 2·50

DESIGNS—VERT: 15n. U.N. building, New York. HORIZ: 20n. Veterans' War Memorial Building, San Francisco (venue of signing of charter, 1945).

78 Mickey Mouse tramping through Black Forest

1985. 150th Birth Anniv of Mark Twain (writer) and International Youth Year. Multicoloured.

612 50ch. Type **78** 10 10
613 2n. Mickey Mouse, Donald Duck and Goofy on steamboat trip on Lake Lucerne 35 30
614 5n. Mickey Mouse, Donald Duck and Goofy climbing Rigi-Kulm 85 75
615 9n. Mickey Mouse and Goofy rafting to Heidelberg on River Neckar . . . . 1·60 1·40
616 20n. Mickey Mouse leading Donald Duck on horse back up the Riffelberg . . 3·50 3·25

Nos. 612/16 show scenes from "A Tramp Abroad" (cartoon film of Twain novel).

79 Prince sees Rapunzel

1985. Birth Bicentenaries (1985 and 1986) of Grimm Brothers (folklorists). Multicoloured.

618 1n. Type **79** 10 10
619 4n. Rapunzel (Minnie Mouse) in tower 50 45
620 7n. Mother Gothel calling to Rapunzel to let down her hair . . . . 1·10 95
621 8n. Prince climbing tower using Rapunzel's hair . . . 1·40 1·30
622 15n. Prince proposing to Rapunzel . . . . 2·40 2·10

80 "Brewers Duck" (mallard)

1985. Birth Bicentenary of John J. Audubon (ornithologist). Audubon illustrations. Mult.

624 50ch. Type **80** 10 10
625 1n. "Willow Ptarmigan" (Willow/red Grouse) . . . 15 15
626 2n. "Mountain Plover" . . . 35 30
627 3n. "Red-throated Loon" (Red-throated Diver) . . . 50 50
628 4n. "Spruce Grouse" 80 70
629 5n. "Hooded Merganser" . . 95 90
630 15n. "Trumpeter Swan" (Whooper Swan) . . . . . 2·75 2·50
631 20n. Common goldeneye . . 3·75 3·25

81 Members' Flags around Buddhist Design

1985. South Asian Regional Co-operation Summit, Dhaka, Bangladesh.

634 **81** 50ch. multicoloured . . . 15 15
635 5n. multicoloured 95 85

82 Precious Wheel

85 Mandala of Phurpa (Ritual Dagger)

1986. The Precious Symbols. Multicoloured.

636 30ch. Type **82** 10 10
637 50ch. Precious Gem 10 10
638 1n.25 Precious Queen 15 15
639 2n. Precious Minister 30 30
640 4n. Precious Elephant 55 55
641 6n. Precious Horse 80 80
642 8n. Precious General . . . . 1·10 1·10

1986. Olympic Games Gold Medal Winners. Nos. 549/50 and 552/5 optd.

643 **72** 15ch. **GOLD HYANG SOON SEO SOUTH KOREA** 10 10
644 – 25ch. **GOLD DARRELL PACE USA** 10 10
645 – 2n.25 **GOLD MEDAL USA** 35 35
646 – 5n.50 **GOLD MARK BRELAND USA** . . . 70 70
647 – 6n. **GOLD DALEY THOMPSON ENGLAND** 80 80
648 – 8n. **GOLD STEFAN EDBERG SWEDEN** . . 1·10 1·10

1986. "Ameripex 86" International Stamp Exhibition, Chicago. Various stamps optd **AMERIPEX 86.**

653 8n. mult (No. 621) . . . . . 1·40 1·20
650 9n. mult (No. 615) . . . . . 2·20 1·80
654 15n. mult (No. 622) . . . . 1·90 1·70
651 20n. mult (No. 616) . . . . 3·25 3·00

1986. Kilkhor Mandalas of Mahayana Buddhism. Multicoloured.

656 10ch. Type **85** 10 10
657 25ch. Mandala of Amitayus in Wrathful Form 10 10
658 50ch. Mandala of Overpowering Deities . . . 10 10
659 75ch. Mandala of the Great Wrathful One 10 10
660 1n. Type **85** 15 15
661 3n. As 25ch. 45 45
662 5n. As 50ch. 65 65
663 7n. As 75ch. 85 85

1986. 75th Anniv of Girl Guides. Nos. 460/3 optd **75th ANNIVERSARY GIRL GUIDES.**

664 3n. multicoloured 40 40
665 5n. multicoloured . . . . . 1·00 1·00
666 15n. multicoloured . . . . . 3·00 3·00
667 20n. multicoloured . . . . . 4·00 4·00

87 Babylonian Tablet and Comet over Noah's Ark

1986. Appearance of Halley's Comet. Mult.

669 50ch. Type **87** 10 10
670 1n. 17th-century print 10 10
671 2n. 1835 French silhouette . . 25 25
672 3n. Bayeux tapestry 40 35
673 4n. Woodblock from "Nuremburg Chronicle" 60 50
674 5n. Illustration of Revelation 6, 12–13 from 1650 Bible 80 75
675 15n. Comet in constellation of Cancer . . . . 2·30 2·10
676 20n. Decoration on Delft plate . . . . 3·25 2·75

88 Statue and "Libertad" (Argentine full-rigged cadet ship)

1986. Centenary of Statue of Liberty. Multicoloured.

678 50ch. Type **88** 10 10
679 1n. "Shalom" (Israeli liner) 10 10
680 2n. "Leonardo da Vinci" (Italian liner) 25 25
681 3n. "Mircea" (Rumanian cadet barque) 40 35
682 4n. "France" (French liner) 55 50
683 5n. S.S. "United States" (American liner) 80 75
684 15n. "Queen Elizabeth 2" (British liner) . . . . . . 2·30 2·10
685 20n. "Europa" (West German liner) . . . . . . 3·25 2·75

The descriptions of the ships on Nos. 678 and 681 were transposed in error.

89 "Santa Maria"

1987. 500th Anniv (1992) of Discovery of America by Columbus. Multicoloured.

687 20ch. Type **89** 25 30
688 25ch. Queen Isabella of Spain 25 25
689 50ch. Flying fish 25 25
690 1n. Columbus's coat of arms 50 40
691 2n. Christopher Columbus . . 85 70
692 3n. Columbus landing with Spanish soldiers . . . . . 1·10 1·10

90 Canadian National Class "U1-f" Steam Locomotive No. 6060

1987. "Capex '87" International Stamp Exhibition, Toronto. Canadian Railways. Multicoloured.

695 50ch. Type **90** 10 10
696 1n. Via Rail "L.R.C." electric locomotive No. 6903 . . . 10 10
697 2n. Canadian National GM "GF30t" diesel locomotive No. 5341 . . . . 35 30
698 3n. Canadian National steam locomotive No. 6157 . . . 45 40
699 8n. Canadian Pacific steam locomotive No. 2727 . . . 1·30 1·20
700 10n. Via Express diesel locomotive No. 6524 . . . 1·60 1·40
701 15n. Canadian National "Turbotrain" . . . . . . 2·40 2·10
702 20n. Canadian Pacific diesel-electric locomotive No. 1414 . . . . 3·00 2·75

91 "Two Faces" (sculpture)

1987. Birth Centenary of Marc Chagall (artist). Multicoloured.

704 50ch. Type **91** 15 15
705 1n. "At the Barber's" 25 25
706 2n. "Old Jew with Torai" . . 40 40
707 3n. "Red Maternity" 65 65
708 4n. "Eve of Yom Kippur" . . 1·00 1·00
709 5n. "The Old Musician" . . 1·20 1·20
710 6n. "The Rabbi of Vitebsk" . 1·30 1·30
711 7n. "Couple at Dusk" . . . 1·50 1·50
712 9n. "The Artistes" . . . . . 1·80 1·80
713 10n. "Moses breaking the Tablets" . . . . 2·00 2·00
714 12n. "Bouquet with Flying Lovers" . . . . 2·30 2·30
715 20n. "In the Sky of the Opera" . . . . 4·00 4·00

92 Goofy (slalom)

1988. Winter Olympic Games, Calgary. Mult.

717 50ch. Type **92** 10 10
718 1n. Donald Duck pushing Goofy at start (downhill skiing) 15 15
719 2n. Goofy in goal (ice hockey) 25 25
720 4n. Goofy (biathlon) 55 50
721 7n. Goofy and Donald Duck (speed skating) . . . . . . 1·10 95
722 8n. Minnie Mouse (figure skating) . . . . 1·30 1·20
723 9n. Minnie Mouse (free-style skating) . . . . 1·50 1·30
724 20n. Goofy and Mickey Mouse (two-man bobsleigh) . . . . 3·00 2·75

93 Stephenson's Railway Locomotive "Rocket", 1829

1988. Transport. Multicoloured.

726 50ch. Pullman "Pioneer" sleeper, 1865 . . . . 10 10
727 1n. Type **93** 15 15

728 2n. Pierre Lallement's "Velocipede", 1866 . . . . 25 25
729 3n. Benz "Patent Motor Wagon", 1866 . . . . . . 45 35
730 4n. Volkswagen Beetle . . . 55 50
731 5n. Mississippi paddle-steamers "Natchez" and "Robert E. Lee", 1870 . . 65 60
732 6n. American La France motor fire engine, 1910 . . 80 75
733 7n. Frigate U.S.S. "Constitution", 1797 (vert) 95 85
734 9n. Bell rocket belt, 1961 (vert) . . . . 1·20 1·10
735 10n. Trevithick's railway locomotive, 1804 . . . . 1·30 1·20

No. 731 is wrongly inscribed "Natches" and No. 733 is wrongly dated "1787".

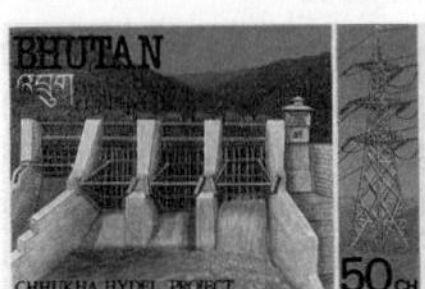

94 Dam and Pylon

1988. Chhukha Hydro-electric Project.
737 **94** 50ch. multicoloured . . . 30 30

1988. World Aids Day. Nos. 411/13 optd **WORLD AIDS DAY.**
738 **50** 2n. multicoloured 40 35
739 – 5n. multicoloured . . . . 1·00 90
740 – 10n. multicoloured . . . . 2·10 1·90

96 "Diana and Actaeon" (detail)

1989. 500th Birth Anniv of Titian (painter). Multicoloured.
741 50ch. "Gentleman with a Book" 10 10
742 1n. "Venus and Cupid, with a Lute Player" (detail) . . 15 15
743 2n. Type **96** 30 30
744 3n. "Cardinal Ippolito dei Medici" 50 45
745 4n. "Sleeping Venus" (detail) 75 70
746 5n. "Venus risen from the Waves" (detail) 90 85
747 6n. "Worship of Venus" (detail) . . . . 1·20 1·10
748 7n. "Fete Champetre" (detail) 1·40 1·30
749 10n. "Perseus and Andromeda" (detail) . . . 1·80 1·70
750 15n. "Danae" (detail) . . . . 2·75 2·50
751 20n. "Venus at the Mirror" 3·75 3·50
752 25n. "Venus and the Organ Player" (detail) . . . . . 4·50 4·25

97 Volleyball

1989. Olympic Games, Seoul (1988). Mult.
754 50ch. Gymnastics 10 10
755 1n. Judo 10 10
756 2n. Putting the shot 25 25
757 4n. Type **97** 55 50
758 7n. Basketball (vert) 95 85
759 8n. Football (vert) . . . . . 1·10 95
760 9n. High jumping (vert) . . . 1·30 1·10
761 20n. Running (vert) . . . . 2·75 2·50

1989. "Fukuoka '89" Asia-Pacific Exhibition. Nos. 598/606 optd **ASIA-PACIFIC EXPOSITION FUKUOKA '89.**
763 5ch. multicoloured 10 10
764 35ch. multicoloured 10 10
765 50ch. multicoloured 10 10
766 2n.50 multicoloured 25 25
767 3n. multicoloured 40 35
768 4n. multicoloured 50 45
769 5n. multicoloured 60 55
770 5n.50 multicoloured 75 65
771 6n. multicoloured 85 80

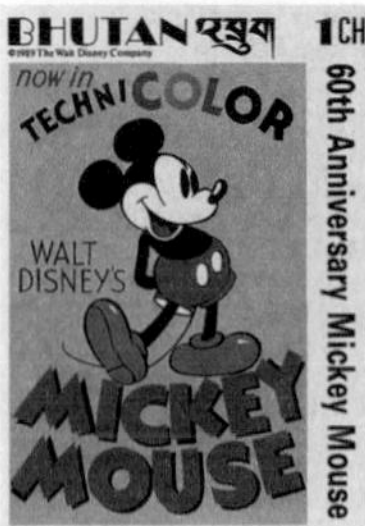

99 Mickey Mouse

1989. 60th Anniv of Mickey Mouse. Film Posters. Multicoloured.
772 1ch. Type **99** 15 15
773 2ch. "Barnyard Olympics" 15 15
774 3ch. "Society Dog Show" . . 15 15
775 4ch. "Fantasia" 15 15
776 5ch. "The Mad Dog" 15 15
777 10ch. "A Gentleman's Gentleman" 15 15
778 50ch. "Symphony hour" . . 15 15
779 10n. "The Moose Hunt" . . 1·50 1·50
780 15n. "Wild Waves" . . . . 2·30 2·30
781 20n. "Mickey in Arabia" . . 3·25 3·25
782 25n. "Tugboat Mickey" . . . 3·75 3·75
783 30n. "Building a Building" 4·75 4·75

100 "Tricholoma pardalotum"

1989. Fungi. Multicoloured.
785 50ch. Type **100** 10 10
786 1n. "Suillus placidus" 10 10
787 2n. Royal boletus 25 25
788 3n. "Gomphidius glutinosus" 45 35
789 4n. Scarlet-stemmed boletus 55 50
790 5n. Elegant boletus 70 65
791 6n. "Boletus appendiculatus" 85 80
792 7n. Griping toadstool . . . . 1·10 95
793 10n. "Macrolepiota rhacodes" . . . . 1·40 1·30
794 15n. The blusher . . . . . . 2·10 1·90
795 20n. Death cap . . . . . . 2·75 2·50
796 25n. False death cap . . . . 3·50 3·25

101 "La Reale" (Spanish galley), 1680

1989. 30th Anniv of International Maritime Organization. Multicoloured.
798 50ch. Type **101** 10 10
799 1n. "Turtle" (submarine), 1776 . . . . 15 15
800 2n. "Charlotte Dundas" (steamship), 1802 . . . . 30 30
801 3n. "Great Eastern" (paddle-steamer), 1858 . . . . . 50 45
802 4n. H.M.S. "Warrior" (armoured ship), 1862 . . 65 60
803 5n. Mississippi river steamer, 1884 . . . . 85 75
804 6n. "Preussen" (full-rigged ship), 1902 . . . . . . 1·00 90
805 7n. U.S.S. "Arizona" (battleship), 1915 . . . . . 1·20 1·10
806 10n. "Bluenose" (fishing schooner), 1921 . . . . . 1·60 1·50
807 15n. Steam trawler, 1925 . . 2·50 2·20
808 20n. "Liberty" freighter, 1943 3·25 3·00
809 25n. "United States" (liner), 1952 . . . . 4·00 3·50

102 Nehru

103 Greater Flamed-backed Woodpecker

1989. Birth Centenary of Jawaharlal Nehru (Indian statesman).
811 **102** 1n. brown 30 30

No. 811 is erroneously inscribed "ch".

1989. Birds. Multicoloured.
812 50ch. Type **103** 10 10
813 1n. Black-naped blue monarch ("Black–naped Monarch") 15 15
814 2n. White-crested laughing thrush 30 30
815 3n. Blood pheasant 50 45
816 4n. Plum-headed ("Blossom-headed") parakeet 65 60
817 5n. Rosy minivet 85 75
818 6n. Chestnut-headed fulvetta ("Tit-Babbler") (horiz) . . 1·00 90
819 7n. Blue pitta (horiz) . . . . 1·20 1·10
820 10n. Black-naped oriole (horiz) . . . . 1·60 1·50
821 15n. Green magpie (horiz) . . 2·50 2·20
822 20n. Three-toed kingfisher ("Indian Three-toed Kingfisher")(horiz) . . . . 3·25 3·00
823 25n. Ibis bill (horiz) . . . . 4·00 3·50

104 "Best Friend of Charleston", 1830, U.S.A.

105 "Charaxes harmodius"

1990. Steam Railway Locomotives. Mult.
825 50ch. Type **104** 10 10
826 1n. Class U locomotive, 1948, France 10 10
827 2n. Consolidation locomotive, 1866, U.S.A. 25 25
828 3n. Luggage engine, 1843, Great Britain 45 35
829 4n. Class 60-3 Shay locomotive No. 18, 1913, U.S.A. 55 50
830 5n. "John Bull", 1831, U.S.A. 70 65
831 6n. "Hercules", 1837, U.S.A. 85 80
832 7n. Locomotive No. 947, 1874, Great Britain . . . . 1·10 95
833 10n. "Illinois", 1852, U.S.A. 1·40 1·30
834 15n. Class O5 locomotive, 1935, Germany . . . . . 2·10 1·90
835 20n. Standard locomotive, 1865, U.S.A. . . . . . . 2·75 2·50
836 25n. Class Ps-4 locomotive, 1936, U.S.A. . . . . . . 3·50 3·25

1990. Butterflies. Multicoloured.
838 50ch. Type **105** 10 10
839 1n. "Prioneris thestylis" . . . 10 10
840 2n. Eastern courtier 25 25
841 3n. "Penthema lisarda" (horiz) 45 35
842 4n. Golden birdwing 55 50
843 5n. Great nawab 70 65
844 6n. "Polyura dolon" (horiz) 85 80
845 7n. Tailed labyrinth (horiz) 1·10 95
846 10n. "Delias descombesi" . . 1·40 1·30
847 15n. "Childreni childrena" (horiz) . . . . 2·10 1·90
848 20n. Leaf butterfly (horiz) . . 2·75 2·50
849 25n. "Elymnias malelas" (horiz) . . . . 3·50 3·25

106 "Renanthera monachica" **107** "Plum Estate, Kameido"

1990. "Expo '90" International Garden and Greenery Exposition, Osaka. Orchids. Mult.
851 10ch. Type **106** 10 10
852 50ch. "Vanda coerulea" . . . 10 10
853 1n. "Phalaenopsis violacea" 15 15
854 2n. "Dendrobium nobile" . . 30 25
855 5n. "Vandopsis lissochiloides" 60 55
856 6n. "Paphiopedilum rothschildianum" 85 75
857 7n. "Phalaenopsis schilleriana" . . . . 1·00 90
858 9n. "Paphiopedilum insigne" 1·30 1·10
859 10n. "Paphiopedilum bellatulum" . . . . 1·40 1·30
860 20n. "Doritis pulcherrima" . . 2·75 2·50
861 25n. "Cymbidium giganteum" 4·25 3·25
862 35n. "Phalaenopsis mariae" 5·00 4·75

1990. Death of Emperor Hirohito and Accession of Emperor Akihito of Japan. "100 Famous Views of Edo" by Ando Hiroshige. Multicoloured.
864 10ch. Type **107** 10 10
865 20ch. "Yatsumi Bridge" . . . 10 10
866 50ch. "Ayase River and Kanegafuchi" 10 10
867 75ch. "View of Shiba Coast" 10 10
868 1n. "Grandpa's Teahouse, Meguro" 15 15
869 2n. "Inside Kameido Tenjin Shrine" 25 25
870 6n. "Yoroi Ferry, Koami-cho" 90 80
871 7n. "Sakasai Ferry" . . . . 1·10 95
872 10n. "Fukagawa Lumberyards" . . . . 1·50 1·40
873 15n. "Suido Bridge and Surugadai" . . . . 2·40 2·10
874 20n. "Meguro Drum Bridge and Sunset Hill" . . . . . 3·00 2·75
875 25n. "Atagoshita and Yabu Lane" . . . . 3·75 3·25

108 Thimphu Post Office

1990.
877 **108** 1n. multicoloured 15 15

109 Giant Panda

1990. Mammals. Multicoloured.
878 50ch. Type **109** 10 10
879 1n. Giant panda in tree . . . 15 15
880 2n. Giant panda with cub . . 30 30
881 3n. Giant panda (horiz) . . . 50 45
882 4n. Giant panda eating (horiz) 65 60
883 5n. Tiger (horiz) 85 75
884 6n. Giant pandas pulling up bamboo (horiz) . . . . . 1·00 90
885 7n. Giant panda and cub resting (horiz) . . . . . . 1·20 1·10
886 10n. Indian elephant (horiz) 1·60 1·50
887 15n. Giant panda beside fallen tree . . . . 2·50 2·20
888 20n. Indian muntjac (inscr "Barking deer") (horiz) . . 3·25 3·00
889 25n. Snow leopard (horiz) . . 4·00 3·50

110 Roim

1990. Religious Musical Instruments. Mult.
891 10ch. Dungchen (large trumpets) 10 10
892 20ch. Dungkar (Indian chank shell) 10 10
893 30ch. Type **110** 10 10
894 50ch. Tinchag (cup cymbals) 10 10
895 1n. Dradu and drilbu (pellet drum and hand bell) . . . 10 10
896 2n. Gya-ling (oboes) 20 15
897 2n.50 Nga (drum) 30 25
898 3n.50 Kang-dung (trumpets) 35 35

111 Penny Black and Bhutan 1962 2ch. Stamp

1990. "Stamp World London 90" International Stamp Exhibition. 150th Anniv of the Penny Black. Multicoloured.
900 50ch. Type **111** 10 10
901 1n. Oldenburg 1852 $\frac{1}{30}$th. stamp 15 15
902 2n. Bergedorf 1861 1½s. stamp 25 25
903 4n. German Democratic Republic 1949 50pf. stamp 50 45
904 5n. Brunswick 1852 1 sgr. stamp 60 55
905 6n. Basel 1845 2½r. stamp . . 85 75
906 8n. Geneva 1843 5c.+5c. stamp . . . . 1·10 1·00
907 10n. Zurich 1843 4r. stamp 1·40 1·30
908 15n. France 1849 20c. stamp 2·10 1·90
909 20n. Vatican City 1929 5c. stamp . . . . 2·75 2·50
910 25n. Israel 1948 3m. stamp 3·50 3·25
911 30n. Japan 1871 48m. stamp 4·25 3·75

Each value also depicts the Penny Black.
No. 901 is wrongly inscribed "Oldenberg".

112 Girls **113** Temple of Artemis, Ephesus

1990. South Asian Association for Regional Co-operation Girl Child Year. Multicoloured.
913 50ch. Type **112** 20 20
914 20n. Girl . . . . 2·75 2·40

1991. Wonders of the World. Designs featuring Walt Disney cartoon characters. Multicoloured.
915 1ch. Type **113** 10 10
916 2ch. Statue of Zeus, Olympia 10 10
917 3ch. Pyramids of Egypt . . . 10 10
918 4ch. Lighthouse of Alexandria, Egypt 10 10
919 5ch. Mausoleum, Halicarnassus 10 10
920 10ch. Colossus of Rhodes . . 10 10
921 50ch. Hanging Gardens of Babylon 10 10
922 5n. Mauna Loa Volcanoes, Hawaii (horiz) 70 65
923 6n. Carlsbad Caverns, New Mexico (horiz) 90 80
924 10n. Rainbow Bridge National Monument, Utah (horiz) . . . . 1·50 1·40
925 15n. Grand Canyon, Colorado (horiz) . . . . . 3·25 1·90
926 20n. Old Faithful, Yellowstone National Park, Wyoming (horiz) . . . . . 2·75 2·50
927 25n. Sequoia National Park, California (horiz) . . . . . 3·75 3·25
928 30n. Crater Lake and Wizard Island, Oregon (horiz) . . 4·50 4·00

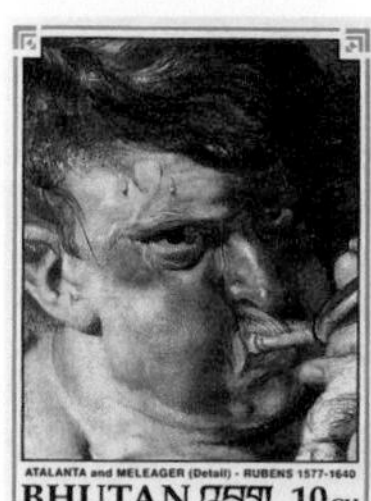

114 "Atalanta and Meleager" (detail)

1991. 350th Death Anniv (1990) of Peter Paul Rubens (painter). Multicoloured.
930 10ch. Type **114** 10 10
931 50ch. "The Fall of Phaeton" (detail) 10 10
932 1n. "Feast of Venus Verticordia" (detail) . . . 15 15
933 2n. "Achilles slaying Hector" (detail) 35 30
934 3n. "Arachne punished by Minerva" (detail) 50 35
935 4n. "Jupiter receives Psyche on Olympus" (detail) . . . 75 55
936 5n. "Atalanta and Meleager" (different detail) 90 85
937 6n. "Atalanta and Meleager" (different detail) . . . . . 1·10 1·00
938 7n. "Venus in Vulcan's Furnace" (detail) . . . . . 1·30 1·20
939 10n. "Atalanta and Meleager" (different detail) 1·70 1·60
940 20n. "Briseis returned to Achilles" (detail) . . . . . 3·50 3·25
941 30n. "Mars and Rhea Sylvia" (detail) . . . . 5·00 4·50

115 "Cottages, Reminiscence of the North"

1991. Death Centenary (1990) of Vincent van Gogh (painter). Multicoloured.
943 10ch. Type **115** 10 10
944 50ch. "Head of a Peasant Woman with Dark Cap" 10 10
945 1n. "Portrait of a Woman in Blue" 15 15
946 2n. "Head of an Old Woman with White Cap (the Midwife)" 45 35
947 8n. "Vase with Hollyhocks" 1·20 1·10
948 10n. "Portrait of a Man with a Skull Cap" . . . . . . 1·40 1·30
949 12n. "Agostina Segatori sitting in the Cafe du Tambourin" . . . . 1·80 1·60
950 15n. "Vase with Daisies and Anemones" . . . . 2·20 2·00
951 18n. "Fritillaries in a Copper Vase" . . . . 2·75 2·40
952 20n. "Woman sitting in the Grass" . . . . 3·00 2·75
953 25n. "On the Outskirts of Paris" (horiz) . . . . . 3·50 3·25
954 30n. "Chrysanthemums and Wild Flowers in a Vase" 4·25 3·75

116 Winning Uruguay Team, 1930

1991. World Cup Football Championship. Mult.
956 50ch. Type **116** 10 10
957 1n. Italy, 1934 . . . . 15 15
958 2n. Italy, 1938 . . . . 25 20
959 3n. Uruguay, 1950 . . . . . 45 30
960 5n. West Germany, 1954 . . 70 65
961 10n. Brazil, 1958 . . . . . . 1·40 1·30
962 20n. Brazil, 1962 . . . . . . 2·75 2·50
963 25n. England, 1966 . . . . . 3·50 3·25
964 29n. Brazil, 1970 . . . . . . 4·00 3·50
965 30n. West Germany, 1974 . . 4·25 3·75
966 31n. Argentina, 1978 . . . . 4·25 3·75
967 32n. Italy, 1982 . . . . . . 4·50 4·00
968 33n. Argentina, 1986 . . . . 4·50 4·00
969 34n. West Germany, 1990 . . 4·50 4·00
970 35n. Stadium, Los Angeles (venue for 1994 World Cup) . . . . 4·50 4·00

117 Bhutan and Japan State Flags

1991. "Phila Nippon '91" International Stamp Exhibition, Tokyo.
972 **117** 15n. multicoloured . . . 2·10 1·80

118 Teachers, Pupils and Hemisphere

1992. "Education for All by Year 2000".
973 **118** 1n. multicoloured 10 10

119 Hurdler **120** "Santa Maria"

1992. Olympic Games, Barcelona. Mult.
974 25n. Type **119** . . . . . . 3·25 3·25
975 25n. Body of hurdler . . . . 3·25 3·25
Nos. 974/5 were issued together, se-tenant, forming a composite design.

1992. 500th Anniv of Discovery of America by Columbus. Multicoloured.
977 15n. Type **120** . . . . . . 1·10 1·10
978 20n. Columbus . . . . . . 1·40 1·40

121 Brandenburg Gate and rejoicing Couple

1992. 2nd Anniv of Reunification of Germany.
980 **121** 25n. multicoloured . . . 1·80 1·80

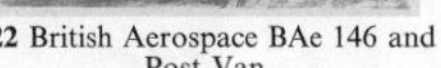

122 British Aerospace BAe 146 and Post Van

1992. 30th Anniv of Bhutan Postal Organization. Multicoloured.
982 1n. Type **122** 10 10
983 3n. Rural letter courier . . . 25 25
984 5n. Emptying post box . . . 40 40

123 Industry and Agriculture

1992. 20th Anniv of Accession of King Jigme Singye Wangchuck. Multicoloured.
985 1n. Type **123** 15 15
986 5n. British Aerospace RJ70 of National Airline 35 35
987 10n. House with water-pump 65 65
988 15n. King Jigme Singye Wangchuk . . . . 1·20 1·20
Nos. 985/8 were issued together, se-tenant, each horizontal pair within the block forming a composite design.

124 Dragon

1992. International Volunteer Day.
990 **124** 1n.50 multicoloured . . . 15 15
991 9n. multicoloured 65 65
992 15n. multicoloured . . . 1·20 1·20

125 "Meconopsis grandis" **127** "The Love Letter" (Jean Honore Fragonard)

1993. Medicinal Flowers. Designs showing varieties of the Asiatic Poppy. Multicoloured.
993 1n.50 Type **125** 15 15
994 7n. "Meconopsis" sp. 60 60
995 10n. "Meconopsis wallichii" 75 75
996 12n. "Meconopsis horridula" 1·00 1·00
997 20n. "Meconopsis discigera" 1·70 1·70

1993. Paintings. Multicoloured.
1000 1ch. Type **127** (postage) . . 15 15
1001 2ch. "The Writer" (Vittore Carpaccio) 15 15
1002 3ch. "Mademoiselle Lavergne" (Jean Etienne Liotard) 15 15
1003 5ch. "Portrait of Erasmus" (Hans Holbein) 15 15
1004 10ch. "Woman writing a Letter" (Gerard Terborch) 15 15
1005 15ch. Type **127** 15 15
1006 25ch. As No. 1001 . . . . 15 15
1007 50ch. As No. 1002 . . . . 15 15
1008 60ch. As No. 1003 . . . . 15 15
1009 80ch. As No. 1004 . . . . 15 15
1010 1n. Type **127** 15 15
1011 1n.25 As No. 1001 . . . . 15 15
1012 2n. As No. 1002 (air) . . . 15 15
1013 3n. As No. 1003 . . . . . 15 15
1014 6n. As No. 1004 . . . . . 15 15

128 Lesser Panda **130** Namtheo-say

1993. Environmental Protection. Multicoloured.
1016 7n. Type **128** 60 60
1017 10n. One-horned rhinoceros 85 85
1018 15n. Black-necked crane and blue poppy . . . . 1·20 1·20
1019 20n. Takin . . . . 1·50 1·50
Nos. 1016/19 were issued together, se-tenant, forming a composite design.

1993. Door Gods. Multicoloured.
1021 1n.50 Type **130** 10 15
1022 5n. Pha-ke-po 40 40
1023 10n. Chen-mi Jang 80 80
1024 15n. Yul-khor-sung . . . . 1·20 1·20

131 "Rhododendron mucronatum" **132** Dog

1994. Flowers. Multicoloured.
1025 1n. Type **131** 15 15
1026 1n.50 "Anemone rupicola" 15 15
1027 2n. "Polemonium coeruleum" 15 15
1028 2n.50 "Rosa marophylla" 15 15
1029 4n. "Paraquilegia microphylla" 35 35
1030 5n. "Aquilegia nivalis" . . . 40 40
1031 6n. "Geranium wallichianum" 50 50
1032 7n. "Rhododendron campanulatum" (wrongly inscr "Rhodendron") . . 60 60
1033 9n. "Viola suavis" 75 75
1034 10n. "Cyananthus lobatus" 90 90

1994. New Year. Year of the Dog. "Hong Kong '94" International Stamp Exhibition.
1036 **132** 11n.50 multicoloured . . 80 80

133 Trophy and Mascot

1994. World Cup Football Championship, U.S.A.
1038 **133** 15n. multicoloured . . . 80 80

134 Tagtshang Monastery (½-size illustration)

135 Relief Map of Bhutan (½-size illustration)

1994. Air. Self-adhesive.
1039 **134** 16n. multicoloured . . . 85 85
1040 **135** 20n. multicoloured . . . 1·00 1·00
The individual stamps are peeled directly from the card backing. Each card contains six different designs with the same face value forming the composite designs illustrated. Each stamp is a horizontal strip with a label indicating the main class of mail covered by the rate at the left, separated by a vertical line of rouletting. The outer edges of the cards are imperforate.

138 Horseman with raised Sword

1994. 350th Anniv of Victory over Tibet-Mongol Army. Multicoloured.

1043	15n. Type **138**	80	80
1044	15n. Archers and hand-to-hand sword fighting	80	80
1045	15n. Horseman with insignia on helmet amongst infantry	80	80
1046	15n. Drummer, piper and troops	80	80

Nos. 1043/6 were issued together, se-tenant, forming a composite design of a battle scene and the Drugyel Dzong.

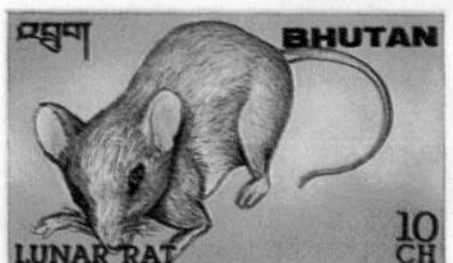

140 Lunar Rat

1995. New Year. Year of the Boar. Mult.

1048	10ch. Type **140**	15	15
1049	20ch. Lunar ox	15	15
1050	30ch. Lunar tiger	15	15
1051	40ch. Lunar rabbit	15	15
1052	1n. Lunar dragon	15	15
1053	2n. Lunar snake	15	15
1054	3n. Lunar horse	15	15
1055	4n. Lunar sheep	15	15
1056	5n. Lunar monkey	15	15
1057	7n. Lunar rooster	25	25
1058	8n. Lunar dog	35	35
1059	9n. Lunar boar	40	40

141 "Pleione praecox" 142 Human Resources Development

1995. Flowers. Multicoloured.

1061	9n. Type **141**	50	50
1062	10n. "Primula calderina"	60	60
1063	16n. "Primula whitei"	1·00	1·00
1064	18n. "Notholirion macrophyllum"	1·10	1·10

1995. 50th Anniv of U.N.O. Multicoloured.

1065	1n.50 Type **142**	15	15
1066	5n. Transport and Communications	35	35
1067	9n. Health and Population	50	50
1068	10n. Water and Sanitation	60	60
1069	11n.50 U.N. in Bhutan	65	65
1070	16n. Forestry and Environment	90	90
1071	18n. Peace and Security	1·00	1·00

143 Greater Pied Kingfisher ("Himalayan Pied Kingfisher") 144 Making Paper

1995. "Singapore '95" International Stamp Exhibition. Birds. Multicoloured.

1072	1n. Type **143**	15	15
1073	2n. Blyth's tragopan	15	15
1074	3n. Long-tailed minivets	15	15
1075	10n. Red junglefowl	60	60
1076	15n. Black-capped sibia	85	85
1077	20n. Red-billed chough	1·00	1·00

1995. Traditional Crafts. Multicoloured.

1079	1n. Type **144**	15	15
1080	2n. Religious painting	15	15
1081	3n. Clay sculpting	15	15
1082	10n. Weaving	60	60
1083	15n. Making boots	85	85
1084	20n. Carving wooden bowls	1·00	1·00

146 "The White Bird" 147 Blue Pansy

1996. Folk Tales. Multicoloured.

1087	1n. Type **146**	15	15
1088	2n. "Sing Sing Lhamo and the Moon"	15	15
1089	3n. "The Hoopoe"	15	15
1090	5n. "The Cloud Fairies"	35	35
1091	10n. "The Three Wishes"	60	60
1092	20n. "The Abominable Snowman"	1·10	1·10

1996. Butterflies. Multicoloured.

1094	2n. Type **147**	15	15
1095	3n. Blue peacock	15	15
1096	5n. Great mormon	25	25
1097	10n. Fritillary	60	60
1098	15n. Blue duke	85	85
1099	25n. Brown gorgon	1·30	1·30

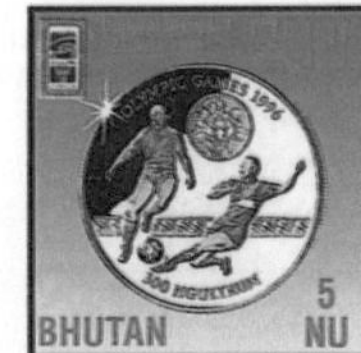

148 300n. Football Coin

1996. Olympic Games, Atlanta. Mult.

1101	5n. Type **148**	25	25
1102	7n. 300n. basketball coin	40	40
1103	10n. 5s. judo coin	60	60

149 Standard Goods Locomotive, India

1996. Trains. Multicoloured.

1105	20n. Type **149**	1·00	1·00
1106	20n. Diesel-electric locomotive, Finland	1·00	1·00
1107	20n. Shunting tank locomotive, Russia	1·00	1·00
1108	20n. Alco PA-1 diesel-electric locomotive, U.S.A.	1·00	1·00
1109	20n. Class C11 passenger tank locomotive, Japan	1·00	1·00
1110	20n. Settebello high speed electric train, Italy	1·00	1·00
1111	20n. Tank locomotive No. 191, Chile	1·00	1·00
1112	20n. Pacific locomotive, France	1·00	1·00
1113	20n. Steam locomotive No. 10, Norway	1·00	1·00
1114	20n. Atlantic express locomotive, Germany	1·00	1·00
1115	20n. Express steam locomotive, Belgium	1·00	1·00
1116	20n. Type 4 diesel-electric locomotive, Great Britain	1·00	1·00

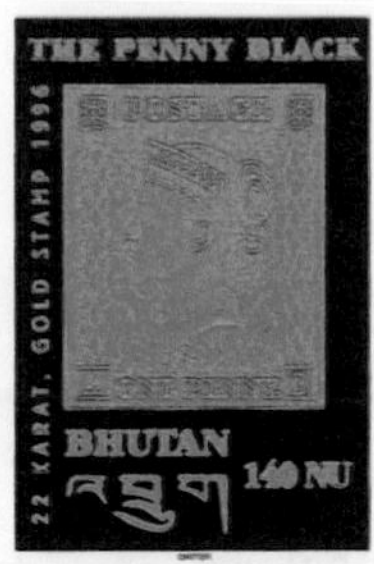

150 Penny Black

1996.

1118	**150** 140n. gold and black	7·25	7·25

151 Vegard Ulvang, Norway 152 Bee

1997. Winter Olympic Gold Medallists. Multicoloured. (a) Without frame.

1119	10n. Type **151** (30km. cross-country skiing, 1992)	60	60
1120	15n. Kristi Yamaguchi, U.S.A. (women's figure skating, 1992)	85	85
1121	25n. Markus Wasmeier, Germany (men's super giant slalom, 1994)	1·50	1·50
1122	30n. Georg Hackl, Germany (luge, 1992)	1·70	1·70

(b) As T **151** but with black frame around design.

1123	15n. Andreas Ostler, West Germany (two-man bobsleighing, 1952)	80	80
1124	15n. East German team (four-man bobsleighing, 1984)	80	80
1125	15n. Stein Eriksen, Norway (men's giant slalom, 1952)	80	80
1126	15n. Alberto Tomba, Italy (men's giant slalom, 1988)	80	80

1997. Insects and Arachnidae. Multicoloured.

1128	1ch. Type **152**	10	10
1129	2ch. "Neptunides polychromus" (beetle)	10	10
1130	3ch. "Conocephalus maculctus" (grasshopper)	10	10
1131	4ch. "Blattidae" sp. (beetle)	10	10
1132	5ch. Great diving beetle	10	10
1133	10ch. Hercules beetle	10	10
1134	15ch. Ladybird	10	10
1135	20ch. "Sarcophaga haemorrhoidalis" (fly)	10	10
1136	25ch. Stag beetle	10	10
1137	30ch. Caterpillar	10	10
1138	35ch. "Lycia hirtaria" (moth)	10	10
1139	40ch. "Clytarius pennatus" (beetle)	10	10
1140	45ch. "Ephemera denica" (mayfly)	10	10
1141	50ch. European field cricket	10	10
1142	60ch. Elephant hawk moth	10	10
1143	65ch. "Gerris" sp. (beetle)	10	10
1144	70ch. Banded agrion	10	10
1145	80ch. "Tachyta nana" (beetle)	10	10
1146	90ch. "Eurydema pulchra" (shieldbug)	10	10
1147	1n. "Hadrurus hirsutus" (scorpion)	10	10
1148	1n.50 "Vespa germanica" (wasp)	10	10
1149	2n. "Pyrops" sp. (beetle)	10	10
1150	2n.50 Praying mantis	10	10
1151	3n. "Araneus diadematus" (spider)	10	10
1152	3n.50 "Atrophaneura" sp. (butterfly)	10	10

153 Polar Bears

1997. "Hong Kong '97" International Stamp Exhibition. Multicoloured.

1154	10n. Type **153**	55	55
1155	10n. Koalas ("Phascolarctos cinereus")	55	55
1156	10n. Asiatic black bear ("Selenarctos thibetanus")	55	55
1157	10n. Lesser panda ("Ailurus fulgens")	55	55

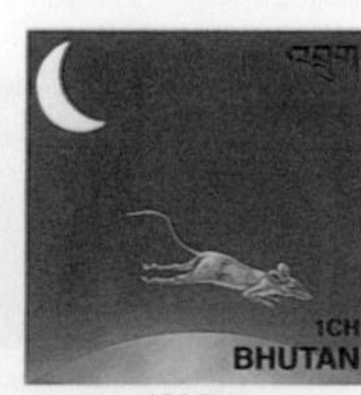

154 Rat

1997. New Year. Year of the Ox. Multicoloured.

1159	1ch. Type **154**	15	15
1160	2ch. Ox	15	15
1161	3ch. Tiger	15	15
1162	4ch. Rabbit	15	15
1163	90ch. Monkey	15	15
1164	5n. Dragon	25	25
1165	6n. Snake	35	35
1166	7n. Horse	40	40
1167	8n. Ram	50	50
1168	10n. Cock	65	65
1169	11n. Dog	75	75
1170	12n. Boar	85	85

155 Lynx

1997. Endangered Species. Multicoloured.

1172	10n. Type **155**	55	55
1173	10n. Lesser ("Red") panda ("Ailurus fulgens")	55	55
1174	10n. Takin ("Budorcas taxicolor")	55	55
1175	10n. Forest musk deer ("Moschus chrysogaster")	55	55
1176	10n. Snow leopard ("Panthera uncia")	55	55
1177	10n. Golden langur ("Presbytis geei")	55	55
1178	10n. Tiger ("Panthera tigris")	55	55
1179	10n. Indian muntjac ("Muntiacus muntjak")	55	55
1180	10n. Bobak marmot ("Marmota bobak")	55	55
1181	10n. Dhole ("Cuon alpinis") running	55	55
1182	10n. Dhole walking	55	55
1183	10n. Mother dhole nursing cubs	55	55
1184	10n. Two dhole	55	55

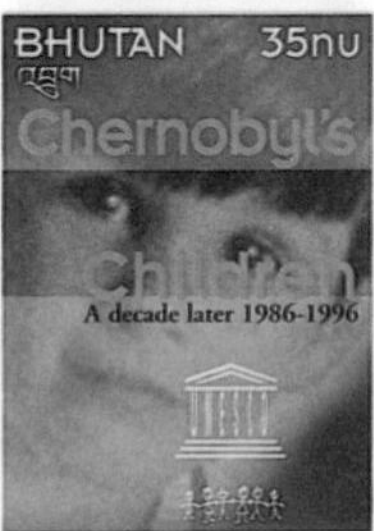

156 Child's Face and U.N.E.S.C.O. Emblem

1997. 10th Anniv of Chernobyl Nuclear Disaster.

1186	**156** 35n. multicoloured	1·90	1·90

157 Mount Huangshah, China

1997. 50th Anniv of U.N.E.S.C.O. World Heritage Sites. Multicoloured.

1187	10n. Type **157**	65	65
1188	10n. Statue of Emperor Qin, China	65	65
1189	10n. Imperial bronze dragon, China	65	65
1190	10n. Pyramids, Tikal National Park, Guatemala	65	65
1191	10n. Fountain, Evora, Portugal	65	65
1192	10n. Forest path, Shirakami-Sanchi, Japan	65	65
1193	10n. View from Eiffel Tower, Paris, France	65	65
1194	10n. Wooden walkway, Valley Below the Falls, Croatia	65	65
1195	15n. Bamberg Cathedral, Germany	1·00	1·00

1196 15n. Aerial view of Bamberg 1·00 1·00
1197 15n. St. Michael's Church, Hildesheim, Germany . . 1·00 1·00
1198 15n. Potsdam Palace, Germany . . . . 1·00 1·00
1199 15n. Church, Potsdam . . . 1·00 1·00
1200 15n. Waterfront, Lubeck, Germany . . . . 1·00 1·00
1201 15n. Quedlinberg, Germany 1·00 1·00
1202 15n. Benedictine church, Lorsch, Germany . . . . 1·00 1·00

158 Turkish Angora   159 Stuart Pearce (England)

1997. Domestic Animals. Mult. (a) Cats.
1204 10n. Type **158** 65 65
1205 15n. Oriental shorthair . . . 90 90
1206 15n. Japanese bobtail . . . 85 85
1207 15n. Ceylon 85 85
1208 15n. Exotic 85 85
1209 15n. Rex 85 85
1210 15n. Ragdoll 85 85
1211 15n. Russian blue 85 85
1212 20n. British shorthair . . . 1·20 1·20
1213 25n. Burmese . . . . 1·40 1·40

(b) Dogs.
1214 10n. Dalmatian 65 65
1215 15n. Siberian husky 90 90
1216 20n. Saluki . . . . 1·20 1·20
1217 20n. Dandie Dinmont terrier 1·20 1·20
1218 20n. Chinese crested . . . . 1·20 1·20
1219 20n. Norwich terrier . . . . 1·20 1·20
1220 20n. Basset hound . . . . . 1·20 1·20
1221 20n. Cardigan Welsh corgi 1·20 1·20
1222 20n. French bulldog . . . . 1·20 1·20
1223 25n. Shar-Pei . . . . 1·40 1·40

Nos. 1206/11 and 1217/22 respectively were issued together, se-tenant, forming composite designs.

1997. World Cup Football Championship, France (1998). Black (Nos. 1225, 1231, 1235, 1237, 1241, 1243) or multicoloured (others).
1225 5n. Type **159** 35 35
1226 10n. Paul Gascoigne (England) 65 65
1227 10n. Diego Maradona (Argentina 1986) (horiz) 65 65
1228 10n. Carlos Alberto (Brazil 1970) (horiz) 65 65
1229 10n. Dunga (Brazil 1994) (horiz) 65 65
1230 10n. Bobby Moore (England 1966) (horiz) 65 65
1231 10n. Fritz Walter (West Germany 1954) (horiz) . . 65 65
1232 10n. Walter Matthaus (Germany 1990) (horiz) 65 65
1233 10n. Franz Beckenbauer (West Germany 1974) (horiz) 65 65
1234 10n. Daniel Passarella (Argentina 1978) (horiz) 65 65
1235 10n. Italy team, 1938 (horiz) 65 65
1236 10n. West Germany team, 1954 (horiz) 65 65
1237 10n. Uruguay team, 1958 (horiz) 65 65
1238 10n. England team, 1966 (horiz) 65 65
1239 10n. Argentina team, 1978 (horiz) 65 65
1240 10n. Brazil team, 1962 (horiz) 65 65
1241 10n. Italy team, 1934 (horiz) 65 65
1242 10n. Brazil team, 1970 (horiz) 65 65
1243 10n. Uruguay team, 1930 (horiz) 65 65
1244 10n. David Beckham (England) . . . . 1·00 1·00
1245 20n. Steve McManaman (England) . . . . 1·20 1·20
1246 25n. Tony Adams (England) 1·50 1·50
1247 30n. Paul Ince (England) . . 1·90 1·90

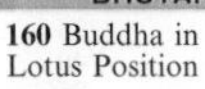

160 Buddha in Lotus Position

161 Jawaharlal Nehru and King Jigme Dorji Wangchuck

1997. "Indepex '97" International Stamp Exhibition, New Delhi. 50th Anniv of Independence of India. Multicoloured.
1249 3n. Type **160** 15 15
1250 7n. Mahatma Gandhi with hands together 35 35
1251 10n. Gandhi (three-quarter face portrait) 50 50
1252 15n. Buddha with feet on footstool 65 65

1997. Int Friendship between India and Bhutan.
1254 **161** 3n. black and pink . . . 15 15
1255 – 10n. multicoloured . . . 55 55
DESIGN: 10n. Prime Minister Rajiv Gandhi of India and King Jigme Singye Wangchuck.

162 Tiger

1998. New Year. Year of the Tiger.
1257 **162** 3n. multicoloured . . . 10 10

163 Safe Motherhood and Anniversary Emblems

1998. 50th Anniv of W.H.O.
1259 **163** 3n. multicoloured . . . 10 10
1260 10n. multicoloured . . . 50 50

164 Mother Teresa

1998. Mother Teresa (founder of Missionaries of Charity) Commemoration. Multicoloured.
1262 10n. Type **164** 50 50
1263 10n. With Diana, Princess of Wales 50 50
1264 10n. Holding child 50 50
1265 10n. Holding baby 50 50
1266 10n. With Sisters 50 50
1267 10n. Smiling 50 50
1268 10n. Praying 50 50
1269 10n. With Pope John Paul II 50 50
1270 10n. Close-up of face . . . 50 50

165 Red-billed Chough

1998. Birds. Multicoloured.
1272 10ch. Type **165** 15 15
1273 30ch. Great Indian hornbill ("Great Hornbill") . . . 15 15
1274 50ch. Western Singing bush lark ("Singing Lark") . . 15 15
1275 70ch. Chestnut-flanked white-eye 15 15
1276 90ch. Magpie robin (wrongly inscr "Megpie-robin") 15 15
1277 1n. Mrs. Gould's sunbird . . 15 15
1278 2n. Long-tailed tailor bird ("Tailorbird") 15 15
1279 3n. Mallard ("Duck") . . . 15 15
1280 5n. Great spotted cuckoo ("Spotted Cuckoo") . . . 15 15
1281 7n. Severtzov's tit warbler ("Goldcrest") 15 15
1282 9n. Common mynah 15 15
1283 10n. Green cochoa 15 15

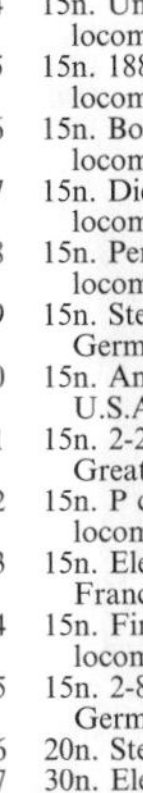

166 Rabbit

1999. New Year. Year of the Rabbit. Multicoloured.
1285 4n. Type **166** 20 20
1286 16n. Rabbit on hillock . . . 70 70

168 King Wangchuck

1999. 25th Anniv of Coronation of King Jigme Singye Wangchuck. Multicoloured.
1289 25n. Type **168** . . . . . . 1·20 1·20
1290 25n. Facing left (yellow background) . . . . . . 1·20 1·20
1291 25n. Facing forwards (orange background) . . 1·20 1·20
1292 25n. With arm raised (green background) . . . . . . 1·20 1·20

169 Early German Steam Locomotive

1999. Trains. Multicoloured.
1294 5n. Type **169** 25 25
1295 10n. Electric locomotive . . 65 65
1296 10n. "Hikari" express train, Japan 60 60
1297 10n. Steam locomotive, South Africa, 1953 . . . 60 60
1298 10n. Super Chief locomotive, U.S.A., 1946 60 60
1299 10n. Magleus Magnet train, Japan, 1991 . . . . . . 60 60
1300 10n. *Flying Scotsman*, Great Britain, 1992 . . . . . . 60 60
1301 10n. Kodama locomotive, Japan, 1958 . . . . . . 60 60
1302 10n. "Blue Train", South Africa, 1969 . . . . . . 60 60
1303 10n. Intercity train, Germany, 1960 . . . . . 60 60
1304 10n. ET 403 high speed electric locomotive, Germany, 1973 . . . . . 60 60
1305 10n. 4-4-0 steam locomotive, U.S.A., 1855 . . . . . . 60 60
1306 10n. Beyer-Garratt steam locomotive, South Africa, 1954 (wrongly inscr "BAYER GARRATT") 60 60
1307 10n. Settebello locomotive, Italy, 1953 . . . . 60 60
1308 15n. Pacific Class 01 steam locomotive, Germany . . 85 85
1309 15n. Neptune Express, Germany 85 85
1310 15n. 4-6-0 steam locomotive, Great Britain 85 85
1311 15n. Shovelnose Streamliner diesel locomotive, U.S.A. 85 85
1312 15n. Electric locomotive, Germany 85 85
1313 15n. Early steam locomotive, Germany . . 85 85
1314 15n. Union Pacific diesel locomotive, U.S.A. . . . 85 85
1315 15n. 1881 Borsig steam locomotive, Germany . . 85 85
1316 15n. Borsig 4-6-4 diesel locomotive, Germany . . 85 85
1317 15n. Diesel-electric locomotive, France . . . 85 85
1318 15n. Pennsylvania Railroad locomotive, U.S.A. . . . 85 85
1319 15n. Steam locomotive, Germany 85 85
1320 15n. Amtrak locomotive, U.S.A. 85 85
1321 15n. 2-2-2 steam locomotive, Great Britain 85 85
1322 15n. P class steam locomotive, Denmark . . 85 85
1323 15n. Electric locomotive, France 85 85
1324 15n. First Japanese locomotive 85 85
1325 15n. 2-8-2 steam locomotive, Germany 85 85
1326 20n. Steam locomotive . . . 1·20 1·20
1327 30n. Electric locomotive . . 1·70 1·70

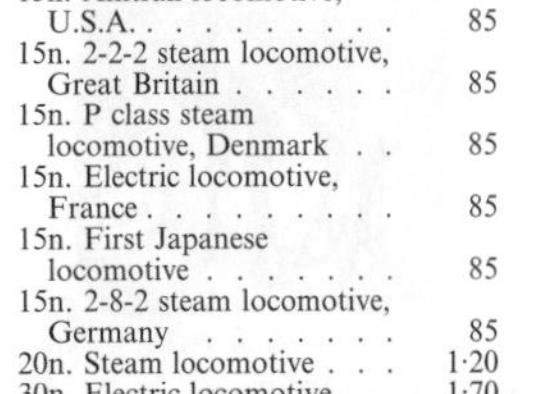

170 "Festive Dancers"

1999. 150th Death Anniv of Katsushika Hokusai (artist). Multicoloured.
1329 15n. Type **170** 75 75
1330 15n. "Drawings of Women" (woman reading) 75 75
1331 15n. "Festive Dancers" (man wearing pointed hat) 75 75
1332 15n. "Festive Dancers" (man looking up) 75 75
1333 15n. "Drawings of Women" (woman sitting on ground) 75 75
1334 15n. "Festive Dancers" (woman) 75 75
1335 15n. "Suspension Bridge between Hida and Etchu" 75 75
1336 15n. "Drawings of Women" (woman dressing hair) . . 75 75
1337 15n. "Exotic Beauty" . . . 75 75
1338 15n. "The Poet Nakamaro in China" 75 75
1339 15n. "Drawings of Women" (woman rolling up sleeve) 75 75
1340 15n. "Chinese Poet in Snow" 75 75
1341 15n. "Mount Fuji seen above Mist on the Tama River" (horiz) 75 75
1342 15n. "Mount Fuji seen from Shichirigahama" (horiz) 75 75
1343 15n. "Sea Life" (turtle) (horiz) 75 75
1344 15n. "Sea Life" (fish) (horiz) 75 75
1345 15n. "Mount Fuji reflected in a Lake" (horiz) 75 75
1346 15n. "Mount Fuji seen through the Piers of Mannenbashi" (horiz) . . 75 75

171 Tyrannosaurus Rex

1999. Prehistoric Animals. Multicoloured.
1348 10n. Type **171** 60 60
1349 10n. Dimorphodon 60 60
1350 10n. Diplodocus 60 60
1351 10n. Pterodaustro 60 60
1352 10n. Tyrannosaurus Rex (different) 60 60
1353 10n. Edmontosaurus 60 60
1354 10n. Apatosaurus 60 60
1355 10n. Deinonychus 60 60
1356 10n. Hypsilophodon 60 60
1357 10n. Oviraptor 60 60
1358 10n. Stegosaurus beside lake 60 60
1359 10n. Head of Triceratops . . 60 60
1360 10n. Pterodactylus and Brachiosaurus 60 60
1361 10n. Pteranodon 60 60
1362 10n. Anurognathus and Tyrannosaurus Rex . . . 60 60
1363 10n. Brachiosaurus 60 60
1364 10n. Corythosaurus 60 60
1365 10n. Iguanodon 60 60
1366 10n. Lesothosaurus 60 60
1367 10n. Allosaurus 60 60
1368 10n. Velociraptor 60 60
1369 10n. Triceratops in water . . 60 60
1370 10n. Stegosaurus in water 60 60
1371 10n. Compsognathus . . . 60 60
1372 20n. Moeritherium 90 90
1373 20n. Platybelodon 90 90
1374 20n. Woolly mammoth . . . 90 90
1375 20n. African elephant . . . 90 90
1376 20n. Deinonychus 90 90
1377 20n. Dimorphodon 90 90
1378 20n. Archaeopteryx 90 90
1379 20n. Common pheasant ("Ring-necked Pheasant") 90 90

Nos. 1348/59 and 1360/71 were issued together, se-tenant, with the backgrounds forming a composite design

172 Siberian Musk Deer

1999. "China '99" World Philatelic Exhibition, Peking. Animals. Multicoloured.

1381 20n. Type **172** . . . . . . 1·00 1·00
1382 20n. Takin (*Budorcas taxicolor*) . . . . 1·00 1·00
1383 20n. Bharal ("Blue sheep") (*Pseudois nayur*) (wrongly inscr "nayour") . . . . . 1·00 1·00
1384 20n. Yak (*Bos gunniens*) . . 1·00 1·00
1385 20n. Common goral (*Nemorhaedus goral*) . . . 1·00 1·00

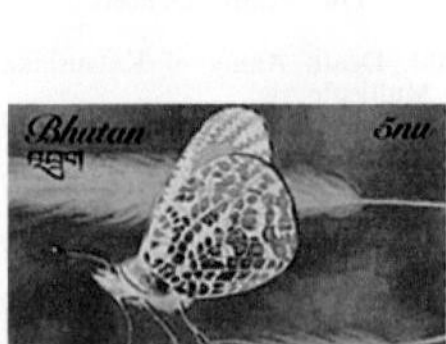

173 Sara Orange-tip

1999. Butterflies. Multicoloured.

1386 5n. Type **173** 35 35
1387 10n. Pipe-vine swallowtail 60 60
1388 15n. Longwings 85 85
1389 20n. Viceroy . . . . 1·10 1·10
1390 20n. Frosted skipper . . . . 1·20 1·20
1391 20n. Fiery skipper . . . . 1·20 1·20
1392 20n. Banded hairstreak . . 1·20 1·20
1393 20n. Cloudless ("Clouded") sulphur . . . . 1·20 1·20
1394 20n. Milbert's tortoiseshell 1·20 1·20
1395 20n. Eastern tailed blue . . 1·20 1·20
1396 20n. Jamaican kite ("Zebra") swallowtail 1·20 1·20
1397 20n. Colorado hairstreak . . 1·20 1·20
1398 20n. Pink-edged sulphur . . 1·20 1·20
1399 20n. Barred sulphur (wrongly inscr "Fairy Yellow") . . . . 1·20 1·20
1400 20n. Red-spotted purple . . 1·20 1·20
1401 20n. Aphrodite . . . . . . 1·20 1·20
1402 25n. Silver-spotted skipper (vert) . . . . 1·40 1·40
1403 30n. Great spangled fritillary (vert) . . . . 1·70 1·70
1404 35n. Little copper (vert) . . 2·00 2·00

Nos. 1390/95 and 1396/1401 were issued together, se-tenant, forming a composite design.

174 Chestnut-breasted Chlorophonia

1999. Birds. Multicoloured.

1406 15n. Type **174** 65 65
1407 15n. Yellow-faced amazon 65 65
1408 15n. White ibis 65 65
1409 15n. Parrotlet sp. ("Caique") 65 65
1410 15n. Green jay 65 65
1411 15n. Tufted coquette 65 65
1412 15n. Troupial 65 65
1413 15n. American purple gallinule ("Purple Gallinule") 65 65
1414 15n. Copper-rumped hummingbird 65 65
1415 15n. Great egret ("Common egret") 65 65
1416 15n. Rufous-browed pepper shrike 65 65
1417 15n. Glittering-throated emerald 65 65
1418 15n. Great kiskadee 65 65
1419 15n. Cuban green woodpecker 65 65
1420 15n. Scarlet ibis 65 65
1421 15n. Belted kingfisher . . . 65 65
1422 15n. Barred antshrike . . . 65 65
1423 15n. Brown-throated conure ("Caribbean Parakeet") 65 65
1424 15n. Rufous-tailed jacamar (vert) 65 65
1425 15n. Scarlet macaw (vert) . . 65 65
1426 15n. Channel-billed toucan (vert) 65 65
1427 15n. Louisiana heron ("Tricolored heron") (vert) 65 65
1428 15n. St. Vincent amazon ("St. Vincent Parrot") (vert) 65 65
1429 15n. Blue-crowned motmot (vert) 65 65
1430 15n. Horned screamer (vert) 65 65
1431 15n. Grey plover ("Black-billed Plover") (vert) . . . 65 65
1432 15n. Eastern meadowlark ("Common meadowlark") (vert) 65 65

Nos. 1406/14, 1415/23 and 1424/32 were issued together, se-tenant, forming a composite design.

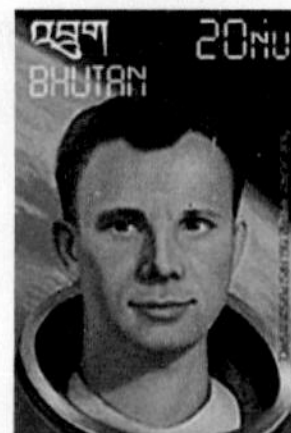

175 Yuri Gagarin (first person in space, 1961)

1999. 30th Anniv of First Manned Moon Landing. Multicoloured.

1434 20n. Type **175** 90 90
1435 20n. Alan Shepard (first American in space, 1961) 90 90
1436 20n. John Glenn (first American to orbit Earth, 1962) 90 90
1437 20n. Valentina Tereshkova (first woman in space, 1963) 90 90
1438 20n. Edward White (first American to walk in space, 1965) 90 90
1439 20n. Neil Armstrong (first person to set foot on Moon, 1969) 90 90
1440 20n. Neil Armstrong (wearing N.A.S.A. suit) 90 90
1441 20n. Michael Collins 90 90
1442 20n. Edwin (Buzz) Aldrin 90 90
1443 20n. *Columbia* (pointing upwards) 90 90
1444 20n. *Eagle* on lunar surface 90 90
1445 20n. Edwin Aldrin on lunar surface 90 90
1446 20n. N.A.S.A. X-15 rocket (1960) 90 90
1447 20n. Gemini 8 (1966) . . . 90 90
1448 20n. Saturn V rocket (1969) 90 90
1449 20n. *Columbia* (pointing downwards) 90 90
1450 20n. *Eagle* above Moon . . 90 90
1451 20n. Edwin Aldrin descending ladder 90 90

Nos. 1434/9, 1440/5 and 1446/51 were issued together, se-tenant, forming a composite design.

176 Tortoiseshell Cat

1999. Animals. Multicoloured.

1453 5n. Type **176** 75 75
1454 5n. Man watching blue and white cat 75 75
1455 10n. Chinchilla golden longhair adult and kittens 1·40 1·40
1456 12n. Russian blue adult and kitten 65 65
1457 12n. Birman 65 65
1458 12n. Devon rex 65 65
1459 12n. Pewter longhair 65 65
1460 12n. Bombay 65 65
1461 12n. Sorrel somali 65 65
1462 12n. Red tabby manx . . . 65 65
1463 12n. Blue smoke longhair 65 65
1464 12n. Oriental tabby shorthair adult and kitten 65 65
1465 12n. Australian silky terrier 65 65
1466 12n. Samoyed 65 65
1467 12n. Basset bleu de Gascogne 65 65
1468 12n. Bernese mountain dog 65 65
1469 12n. Pug 65 65
1470 12n. Bergamasco 65 65
1471 12n. Basenji 65 65
1472 12n. Wetterhoun 65 65
1473 12n. Drever 65 65
1474 12n. Przewalski horse . . . 65 65
1475 12n. Shetland pony 65 65
1476 12n. Dutch gelderlander horse 65 65
1477 12n. Shire horse 65 65
1478 12n. Arab 65 65
1479 12n. Boulonnais 65 65
1480 12n. Falabella 65 65
1481 12n. Orlov trotter 65 65
1482 12n. Suffolk punch 65 65
1483 15n. Lipizzaner 65 65
1484 20n. Andalusian . . . . . 1·20 1·20
1485 25n. Weimaraner (dog) . . . 1·70 1·70
1486 30n. German shepherd dog 3·00 3·00

177 Bharal

1999. Animals and Birds of the Himalayas. Multicoloured. (a) Animals.

1489 20n. Type **177** 90 90
1490 20n. Lynx 90 90
1491 20n. Rat snake 90 90
1492 20n. Indian elephant 90 90
1493 20n. Langur 90 90
1494 20n. Musk deer 90 90
1495 20n. Otter 90 90
1496 20n. Tibetan wolf 90 90
1497 20n. Himalayan black bear 90 90
1498 20n. Snow leopard 90 90
1499 20n. Flying squirrel 90 90
1500 20n. Red fox 90 90
1501 20n. Ibex 90 90
1502 20n. Takin 90 90
1503 20n. Agama lizard 90 90
1504 20n. Marmot 90 90
1505 20n. Red panda 90 90
1506 20n. Leopard cat 90 90

(b) Birds.

1508 20n. Red-crested pochard 90 90
1509 20n. Satyr tragopan 90 90
1510 20n. Lammergeier ("Lammergeier Vulture") 90 90
1511 20n. Kalij pheasant 90 90
1512 20n. Great Indian hornbill 90 90
1513 20n. White stork ("Stork") 90 90
1514 20n. Rufous-necked hornbill (wrongly inscr "Rofous") 90 90
1515 20n. Black drongo ("Drongo") 90 90
1516 20n. Himalayan monal pheasant 90 90
1517 20n. Black-necked crane . . 90 90
1518 20n. Little green bee-eater 90 90
1519 20n. Oriental ibis ("Ibis") 90 90
1520 20n. Crested lark 90 90
1521 20n. Ferruginous duck . . . 90 90
1522 20n. Blood pheasant 90 90
1523 20n. White-crested laughing thrush ("Laughing Thrush") 90 90
1524 20n. Golden eagle 90 90
1525 20n. Siberian rubythroat . . 90 90

178 Elephant, Monkey, Rabbit and Bird (Four Friends)

1999. Year 2000.

1527 **178** 10n. multicoloured . . . 60 60
1528 20n. multicoloured . . . 1·10 1·10

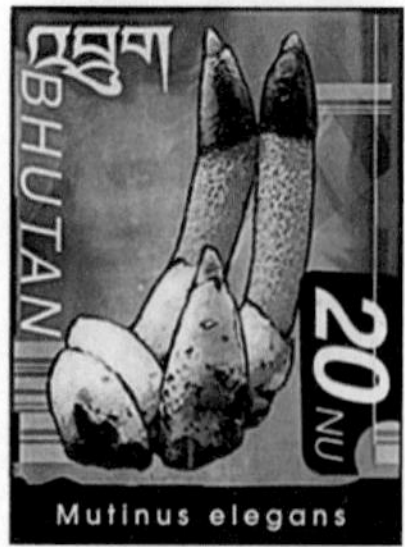

179 Elegant Stink Horn

1999. Fungi. Multicoloured.

1529 20n. Type **179** . . . . . . 1·20 1·20
1530 20n. *Pholiota squarrosoides* 1·20 1·20
1531 20n. Scaly inky cap (*Coprinus quadrifidus*) . . 1·20 1·20
1532 20n. Golden spindles (*Clavulinopsis fusiformis*) 1·20 1·20
1533 20n. *Spathularia velutipes* 1·20 1·20
1534 20n. *Ganoderma lucidum* . . 1·20 1·20
1535 20n. *Microglossum rufum* 1·20 1·20
1536 20n. *Lactarius hygrophoroides* . . . . 1·20 1·20
1537 20n. *Lactarius speciosus complex* . . . . 1·20 1·20
1538 20n. *Calostoma cinnabarina* 1·20 1·20
1539 20n. *Clitocybe clavipes* . . 1·20 1·20
1540 20n. *Microstoma floccosa* 1·20 1·20
1541 20n. Frost's bolete (*Boletus frostii*) . . . . 1·20 1·20
1542 20n. Common morel (*Morchella esculenta*) (wrongly inscr "estculenta") . . . . . . 1·20 1·20
1543 20n. *Hypomyces lactifluorum* 1·20 1·20
1544 20n. *Polyporus auricularius* 1·20 1·20
1545 20n. *Cantharellus lateritius* 1·20 1·20
1546 20n. *Volvariella pusilla* . . 1·20 1·20

180 Green Dragon with Red Flames

2000. New Year. Year of the Dragon. Multicoloured.

1548 3n. Type **180** 15 15
1549 5n. Green dragon encircling moon 25 25
1550 8n. Dragon and symbols of Chinese zodiac 50 50
1552 12n. Brown dragon encircling moon 75 75

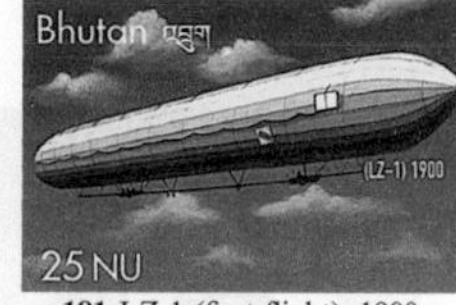

181 LZ-1 (first flight), 1900

2000. Centenary of First Zeppelin Flight. Multicoloured.

1554 25n. Type **181** . . . . . . 1·30 1·30
1555 25n. LZ-2, 1906 . . . . . . 1·30 1·30
1556 25n. LZ-3 over hills (first flight, 1906) . . . . . . 1·30 1·30
1557 25n. LZ-127 *Graf Zeppelin* (first flight, 1928) . . . . 1·30 1·30
1558 25n. LZ-129 *Hindenberg* (first flight, 1936) . . . . 1·30 1·30
1559 25n. LZ-130 *Graf Zeppelin II* (first flight, 1938) . . . 1·30 1·30
1560 25n. LZ-1 over hill with tree 1·30 1·30
1561 25n. LZ-2 over mountains 1·30 1·30
1562 25n. LZ-3 against sky . . . 1·30 1·30
1563 25n. LZ-4 (first flight, 1908) 1·30 1·30
1564 25n. LZ-5 (first flight, 1909) 1·30 1·30
1565 25n. LZ-6 (formation of Deutsche Liftschiffahrts Aktien Gesallschaft (DELAG) (world's first airline), 1909) . . . . . . 1·30 1·30
1566 25n. LZ-1 over grassy hills, 1900 . . . . 1·30 1·30
1567 25n. Z11 *Ersatz*, 1913 . . . 1·30 1·30
1568 25n. LZ-6 exiting hanger, 1909 . . . . 1·30 1·30
1569 25n. LZ-10 *Schwabein* first flight, 1911) . . . . . . 1·30 1·30
1570 25n. LZ-7 *Deutschland* (inscr "Ersatz Deutschland") . . 1·30 1·30
1571 25n. LZ-11 *Viktoria Luise* 1·30 1·30

182 Lunix III

2000. "WORLD STAMP EXPO 2000" International Stamp Exhibition, Anaheim, California. Space. Multicoloured.

1573 25n. Type **182** . . . . . . 1·30 1·30
1574 25n. Ranger 9 . . . . . . 1·30 1·30
1575 25n. Lunar Orbiter . . . . 1·30 1·30
1576 25n. Lunar Prospector spacecraft . . . . 1·30 1·30
1577 25n. *Apollo 11* spacecraft . . 1·30 1·30
1578 25n. Selen satellite . . . . . 1·30 1·30
1579 25n. Space shuttle *Challenger* . . . . 1·30 1·30
1580 25n. North American X-15 experimental rocket aircraft . . . . 1·30 1·30
1581 25n. Space shuttle *Buran* . . 1·30 1·30
1582 25n. Hermes (experimental space plane) . . . . . . 1·30 1·30
1583 25n. X-33 Venturi Star (re-usable launch vehicle) . . 1·30 1·30
1584 25n. Hope (unmanned experimental spacecraft) 1·30 1·30
1585 25n. Victor Patsayev (cosmonaut) . . . . . . 1·30 1·30
1586 25n. Yladislaov Volkov (cosmonaut) . . . . . . 1·30 1·30
1587 25n. Georgi Dobrvolski (cosmonaut) . . . . . . 1·30 1·30
1588 25n. Virgil Grissom (astronaut) . . . . 1·30 1·30
1589 25n. Roger Chaffee (astronaut) . . . . 1·30 1·30
1590 25n. Edward White (astronaut) . . . . 1·30 1·30

183 Trashigang Dzong

2000. "EXPO 2000" World's Fair, Hanover, Germany (1st issue). Monasteries. Multicoloured.

1592 3n. Type **183** 15 15
1593 4n. Lhuentse Dzong 15 15
1594 6n. Gasa Dzong 25 25
1595 7n. Punakha Dzong 35 35
1596 10n. Trashichhoe Dzong . . 40 40
1597 20n. Paro Dzong 85 85

184 Snow Leopard

2000. "EXPO 2000" World's Fair, Hanover, Germany (2nd issue). Wildlife. Multicoloured.
1599 10n. Type **184** 40 40
1600 10n. Common raven ("Raven") 40 40
1601 10n. Golden langur 40 40
1602 10n. Rhododendron 40 40
1603 10n. Black-necked crane . . 40 40
1604 10n. Blue poppy 40 40

185 Jesse Owens (U.S.A.) (Berlin, 1936)

2000. Olympic Games, Sydney. Multicoloured.
1605 20n. Type **185** . . . . . . 1·00 1·00
1606 20n. Kayaking (modern games) . . . . 1·00 1·00
1607 20n. Fulton County Stadium, Atlanta, Georgia (1996 games) . . . . . . 1·00 1·00
1608 20n. Ancient Greek athlete 1·00 1·00

186 G. and R. Stephenson's *Rocket* (first steam locomotive)

2000. 175th Anniv of Opening of Stockton and Darlington Railway. Multicoloured.
1609 50n. Type **186** . . . . . . 2·50 2·50
1610 50n. Steam locomotive (opening of London and Birmingham railway, 1828) . . . . 2·50 2·50
1611 50n. Northumbrian locomotive, 1825 . . . . 2·50 2·50

187 Laird Commercial (biplane), 1929

2000. Airplanes. Multicoloured.
1613 25n. Type **187** . . . . . . 1·20 1·20
1614 25n. Ryan B-5 Brougham, 1927 (wrongly inscr "Broughm") . . . . . . 1·20 1·20
1615 25n. Cessna AW, 1928 . . . 1·20 1·20
1616 25n. Travel Air 4000 biplane, 1927 . . . . . . 1·20 1·20
1617 25n. Fairchild F-71, 1927 . . 1·20 1·20
1618 25n. Command Aire biplane, 1928 . . . . . . 1·20 1·20
1619 25n. Waco YMF biplane, 1935 . . . . 1·20 1·20
1620 25n. Piper J-4 Cub Coupe, 1938 . . . . 1·20 1·20
1621 25n. Ryan ST-A, 1937 . . . 1·20 1·20
1622 25n. Spartan Executive, 1939 . . . . 1·20 1·20
1623 25n. Luscombe 8, 1939 . . . 1·20 1·20
1624 25n. Stinson SR5 Reliant seaplane, 1935 . . . . . 1·20 1·20
1625 25n. Cessna 195 seaplane, 1949 . . . . 1·20 1·20
1626 25n. Waco SRE biplane, 1940 . . . . 1·20 1·20
1627 25n. Erco Ercope, 1948 . . 1·20 1·20
1628 25n. Boeing Stearman biplane, 1941 . . . . . 1·20 1·20
1629 25n. Beech Staggerwing biplane, 1944 . . . . . . 1·20 1·20
1630 25n. Republic Seabee, 1947 1·20 1·20

188 A Kind of Loving, 1962

190 Aquinas

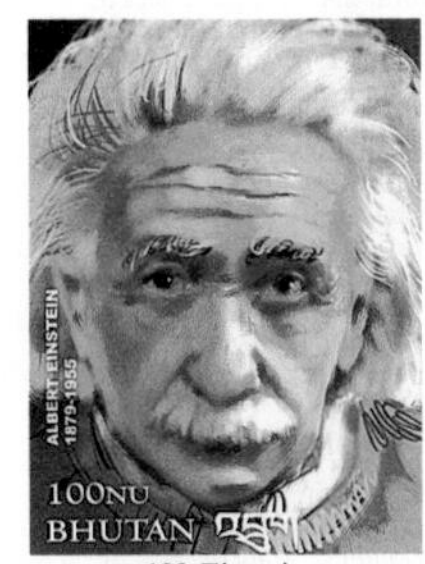

189 Einstein

2000. Berlin Film Festival. Winners of Golden Bear Award. Multicoloured.
1632 25n. Type **188** . . . . . . 1·20 1·20
1633 25n. *Bushido Zankoku Monogatari*, 1963 . . . . 1·20 1·20
1634 25n. *Hobson's Choice*, 1954 1·20 1·20
1635 25n. *El Lazarillo de Tormes*, 1960 . . . . 1·20 1·20
1636 25n. *In the Name of the Father*, 1997 . . . . . . 1·20 1·20
1637 25n. *Les Cousins*, 1959 . . . 1·20 1·20
MS1638 96 × 102 mm. 100n. *Die Ratten*, 1962 . . . . 4·00 4·00

2000. Albert Einstein—*Time* Magazine Man of the Century. Sheet 113 × 83 mm.
MS1639 **189** 100n. multicoloured 4·50 4·50

2000. 775th Birth Anniv of Thomas Aquinas (Catholic philosopher and theologian). Sheet 136 × 76 mm.
MS1640 **190** 25n. × 4 multicoloured 4·00 4·00

191 Pierre de Coubertin

2000. New Millennium. Multicoloured. (a) Centenary of the Modern Olympic Games.
1641 25n. Type **191** (founder of modern games) . . . . . 1·20 1·20
1642 25n. Hand holding baton (first modern Games, Athens, 1896) . . . . . . 1·20 1·20
1643 25n. Jesse Owen (Berlin, 1936) . . . . 1·20 1·20
1644 25n. Handprint and white dove (Munich, 1972) . . . 1·20 1·20
1645 25n. Sydney Opera House (Sydney, 2000) . . . . . 1·20 1·20
1646 25n. Children wearing T-shirts (Greece, 2004) . . 1·20 1·20

(b) Breakthroughs in Modern Medicine.
1647 25n. Albert Calmette (bacteriologist, joint discoverer of B.C.G. vaccine) . . . . 1·20 1·20
1648 25n. Camillo Colgi and S. Ramon y Cajal (discovery of the neurone) 1·20 1·20
1649 25n. Alexander Fleming (bacteriologist, discoverer of penicillin) . . . . . . 1·20 1·20
1650 25n. Jonas Salk (virologist, developer of polio vaccine) . . . . 1·20 1·20
1651 25n. Christiaan Barnard (surgeon, performed first human heart transplant) 1·20 1·20
1652 25n. Luc Mantagnier (A.I.D.S. research) . . . 1·20 1·20

192 Paro Taktsang

193 Christopher Columbus

2000. Sheet 86 × 49 mm.
MS1653 **192** multicoloured . . . 4·00 4·00

2000. Explorers. Two sheets, each 66 × 83 mm. Multicoloured.
MS1654 (a) 100n. Type **193**; (b) 100n. Captain James Cook . . 8·00 8·00

194 *Crinum amoenum*

2000. Flowers of the Himalayan Mountains. Multicoloured.
1655 25n. Type **194** . . . . . . 1·20 1·20
1656 25n. *Beaumontia grandiflora* 1·20 1·20
1657 25n. *Trachelospermum lucidum* . . . . 1·20 1·20
1658 25n. *Curcuma aromatica* . . 1·20 1·20
1659 25n. *Barleria cristata* . . . 1·20 1·20
1660 25n. *Holmskioldia sanguinea* 1·20 1·20
1661 25n. *Meconopsis villosa* . . 1·20 1·20
1662 25n. *Salva hians* . . . . . . 1·20 1·20
1663 25n. *Caltha palustris* . . . . 1·20 1·20
1664 25n. *Anemone polyanthes* . . 1·20 1·20
1665 25n. *Cypripedium cordigerum* 1·20 1·20
1666 25n. *Cryptochilus luteus* . . 1·20 1·20
1667 25n. *Androsace globifera* . . 1·20 1·20
1668 25n. *Tanacetum atkinsonii* 1·20 1·20
1669 25n. *Aster stracheyi* . . . . 1·20 1·20
1670 25n. *Arenaria glanduligera* 1·20 1·20
1671 25n. *Sibbaldia purpurea* . . 1·20 1·20
1672 25n. *Saxifraga parnassifolia* 1·20 1·20
MS1673 Three sheets, each 68 × 98 mm. (a) 100n. *Dendrobium densiflorum* (vert); (b) 100n. *Rhododendron arboreum* (vert); (c) 100n. *Gypsophila cerastioides* 14·50 14·50
Nos. 1655/60, 1661/6 and 1667/72 respectively were issued together, se-tenant, forming a composite design.

195 "The Duke and Duchess of Osuna with their Children" (detail, Francisco de Goya)

2000. "Espana 2000" International Stamp Exhibition, Madrid. Prado Museum Exhibits. Multicoloured.
1674 25n. Type **195** . . . . . . 1·50 1·50
1675 25n. Young child (detail from "The Duke and Duchess of Osuna with their Children") . . . . . 1·50 1·50
1676 25n. Duke (detail from "The Duke and Duchess of Osuna with their Children") . . . . 1·50 1·50
1677 25n. "Isidoro Maiquez" (Francisco de Goya) . . . 1·50 1·50
1678 25n. "Dona Juana Galarza de Goicoechea" (Francisco de Goya) . . . 1·50 1·50
1679 25n. "Ferdinand VII in an Encampment" (Francisco de Goya) . . . . 1·50 1·50
1680 25n. "Portrait of an Old Man" (Joos van Cleve) 1·50 1·50
1681 25n. "Mary Tudor" (Anthonis Mor) . . . . . 1·50 1·50
1682 25n. "Portrait of a Man" (Jan van Scorel) . . . . . 1·50 1·50
1683 25n. "The Court Jester Pejeron" (Anthonis Mor) 1·50 1·50
1684 25n. "Elizabeth of France" (Frans Pourbus the Younger) . . . . 1·50 1·50
1685 25n. "King James I" (Paul van Somer) . . . . 1·50 1·50
1686 25n. "The Empress Isabella of Portugal" (Titian) . . . 1·50 1·50
1687 25n. "Lucrecia di Baccio del Fede, the Painter's Wife" (Andrea del Sarto) . . . 1·50 1·50
1688 25n. "Self-Portrait" (Titian) 1·50 1·50
1689 25n. "Philip II" (Sofonisba Anguisciola) . . . . . . 1·50 1·50
1690 25n. "Portrait of a Doctor" (Lucia Anguisciola) . . . 1·50 1·50
1691 25n. "Anna of Austria" (Sofonisba Anguisciola) 1·50 1·50
MS1692 Three sheets (a) 90 × 110 mm. 100n. Duchess and Duke (detail from "The Duke and Duchess of Osuna with their Children" (Francisco de Goya) (horiz); (b) 90 × 110 mm. 100n. "Charles V at Mühlberg" (Titian); (c) 110 × 90 mm. 100n. "The Relief of Genoa" (Antonio de Pereda) Set of 3 sheets . . . . 13·50 13·50

196 Butterfly

197 Snake

2000. "Indepex Asiana 2000" International Stamp Exhibition, Calcutta. Multicoloured.
1693 5n. Type **196** 15 15
1694 8n. Red jungle fowl 40 40
1695 10n. *Zinnia elegans* 50 50
1696 12n. Tiger 60 60
MS1697 144 × 84 mm. 15n. Spotted deer (28 × 34 mm) 65 65

2001. New Year. Year of the Snake. Multicoloured.
1698 3n. Type **197** 15 15
1699 20n. Snake . . . . 1·10 1·10
MS1700 135 × 135 mm. 3, 10n. As Type **197**; 15, 20n. As No. 1699 2·00 2·00

198 Snow Leopard (*Uncia uncia*)

2001. "Hong Kong 2001" International Stamp Exhibition. Nature Protection. Sheet 195 × 138 mm containing T **198** and similar horiz designs. Multicoloured.
MS1701 15n. Type **198**; 15n. Rufous-necked hornbill (*Aceros nipalensis*); 15n. Black-necked crane (*Grus nigricollis*); 15n. Tiger (*Panthera tigris*) . . . . 2·75 2·75

199 Working in Fields

2001. International Year of Volunteers. Mult.
1702 3n. Type **199** 15 15
1703 4n. Planting crops 25 25
1704 10n. Children and bucket 50 50
1705 15n. Planting seeds and making compost 75 75
MS1706 170 × 120 mm. Nos. 1702/5 1·30 1·30

200 Chenrezig

2001. Buddhist Art, Taksang Monastery. Sheet 120 × 147 mm containing T **200** and similar vert designs. Multicoloured.
MS1707 10n. Type **200**; 15n. Guru Rimpoche; 20n. Sakyamuni . . 2·10 2·10

2001. Nos. 557/60 surch.
1708 4n. on 10ch. blue 40 40
1709 10n. on 25ch. red 50 50
1710 15n. on 50ch. violet 70 70
1711 20n. on 1n. brown 95 95

202 Snow Leopard's Head

203 Horse carrying Treasure Vase (Buddhist symbol)

2001. Snow Leopard (Uncia uncial). Sheet 172 × 140 mm containing T **202** and similar multicoloured design.

MS1712	10n. × 4, each × 2, Type **202**; Two adults; Three juveniles; Crouched adult . . .	4·00	4·00

2002. Year of the Horse. Multicoloured.

1713	20n. Type **203**	1·00	1·00
1714	20n. White horse	1·00	1·00
MS1715	94 × 94 mm. 25n. Horse and Dharma Wheel (horiz)	1·20	1·20

Nos. 1713/14 were issued together, se-tenant forming a composite design.

204 Teri gang

2002. International Year of Mountains. Sheet 144 × 105 mm containing T **204** and similar horiz designs. Multicoloured.

MS1716	20n. Type **204**; 20n. Tsenda gang; 20n. Jomolhari; 20n. Gangeheytag; 20n. Jitchudrake; 20n. Tse-rim Gang	5·75	5·75

205 *Rhomboda lanceolata*

2002. Orchids. Sheet 162 × 131 mm containing T **205** and similar vert designs. Multicoloured.

MS1717	10n. Type **205**; 10n. *Odontochilus lanceolatus*; 10n. *Zeuxine glandulosai*; 10n. *Goodyera schlechtendaliana*; 10n. *Anoectochilus lanceolatus*; 10n. *Goodyera hispida*	3·00	3·00

206 *Rhododendron niveum*

2002. Rhododendrons. Sheet 132 × 132 mm containing T **206** and similar square designs. Multicoloured.

MS1718	15n. Type **206**; 15n. *Rhododendron glaucophyllum*; 15n. *Rhododendron arboretum*; 15n. *Rhododendron grande*; 15n. *Rhododendron dalhousiae*; 15n. *Rhododendron barbatum* . . .	4·00	4·00

207 Kapok Tree (*Bombax ceiba*) **208** Fireman and Flags

2002. Medicinal Plants. Multicoloured.

1719	10n. Type **207**	25	25
1720	10n. Angel's trumpet (*Brugmansia suaveolens*)	25	25
1721	10n. Himalayan mayapple (*Podophyllum hexandrum*)	25	25
1722	10n. Himalayan pokeberry (*Photlacca acinosa*) . . .	25	25
MS1723	85 × 106 mm. 10n. × 4, Nos. 1719/22	4·25	4·25

2002. "United We Stand".

1724	**208** 25n. multicoloured . . .	60	60

209 Zinedine Zidane **210** Queen Elizabeth

2002. World Cup Football Championships, Japan and South Korea. Two sheets containing T **209** and similar vert designs. Multicoloured.

MS1725	(a) 167 × 118 mm. 25n. Type **209**; 25n. Michael Owen; 25n. Miyagi stadium, Japan; 25n. Cuauhtemoc Blanco (inscr "Cuahutemoc"); 25n. Gabriel Batistuta; 25n. Incheon stadium, South Korea; (b) 97 × 112 mm. 150n. Roberto Carlos	7·00	7·00

2002. Golden Jubilee of Queen Elizabeth II. Two sheets containing T **210** and similar square designs. Multicoloured.

MS1726	(a) 133 × 101 mm. 40n. Type **210**; 40n. Wearing green floral hat; 40n. With Duke of Edinburgh; 40n. Wearing white hat; (b) 79 × 108 mm. 90n. Wearing tiara	6·00	6·00

211 Ski Jumping **212** Lotus Flower

2002. Winter Olympic Games, Salt Lake City, USA. Sheet 89 × 120 mm containing T **211** and similar vert design. Multicoloured.

MS1727	50n. Type **211**; 50n. Cross country skiing	2·40	2·40

2002. United Nations Year of Eco-Tourism. Two sheets containing T **212** and similar vert designs. Multicoloured.

MS1728	(a) 117 × 75 mm. 50n. Type **212**; 50n. Northern jungle queen butterfly; 50n. Bengal tiger; (b) 72 × 95 mm. 90n. Peacock	5·75	5·75

213 Cub Scout

2002. World Scout Jamboree, Thailand. Two sheets containing T **213** and similar multicoloured designs.

MS1729	(a) 182 × 142 mm. 50n. Type **213**; 50n. Scouts of different nationalities; 50n. 1908 Scout; (b) 90 × 120 mm. 90n. Dan Beard (founder of American Boy Scouts) (vert)	5·75	5·75

214 Charles Lindbergh and *The Spirit of St Louis*

2002. 75th Anniv of First Solo Trans-Atlantic Flight. Two sheets containing T **214** and similar vert designs. Multicoloured.

MS1730	(a) 171 × 134 mm. 75n. Type **214**; 75n. Lindbergh; (b) 123 × 89 mm. 90n. Lindbergh (different)	5·75	5·75

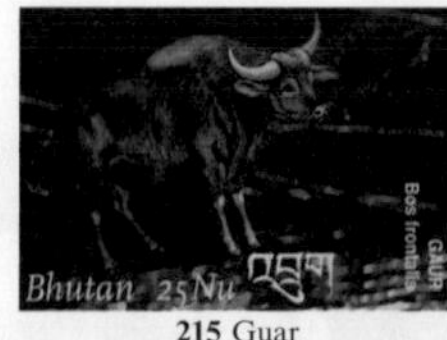

215 Guar

2002. Flora and Fauna. Twelve sheets containing T **215** and similar horiz designs. Multicoloured.

MS1731	(a) 132 × 155 mm. 25n. Type **215**; 25n. Hog badger; 25n. Indian cobra; 25n. Leopard gecko; 25n. Gavial; 25n. Hispid hare; (b) 132 × 155 mm. 25n. Yellow-legged gull; 25n. Sand martin; 25n. Asian open-bill stork; 25n. White stork; 25n. Eurasian oystercatcher; 25n. Indian pitta; (c) 132 × 155 mm. 25n. Blue oak-leaf butterfly (inscr "Dead leaf butterfly") (Kalima horsfieldi); 25n. Golden birdwing (*Troides aeacus*); 25n.*Atrophaneura latrellei*; 25n. Kaiser-I-Hind (*Teinopalpus imperialis*); 25n. *Zeuxidia aurelius*; 25n. *Euploea dufresne*; (d) 137 × 158 mm. 25n. *Primula cawdoriana*; 25n. *Meconopsis aculeate*; 25n.*Primula wigramiana*; 25n. *Primula stuartii*; 25n. *Saxifraga andersonii*; 25n. *Rheum nobile*; (e) 133 × 153 mm. 25n. *Russula integra*; 25n. *Hydgrophorus marzuolus*; 25n. *Trichloma fulvum*; 25n. *Hypholoma fasciculare*; 25n. *Tricholoma populinum*; 25n. *Cortinarius orellanus*; (f) 136 × 161 mm. 25n. *Coelogyne rhodeana*; 25n. *Coelogyne virescens*; 25n. *Phalanopsis schilleriana*; 25n. *Angraecum eburneum*; 25n. *Dendrobium aureum*; 25n. *Dendrobium Ceasar*; (g) 89 × 92 mm. 90n. Esturine crocodile; (h) 89 × 94 mm. 90n. Mandarin duck; (i) 93 × 94 mm. 90n. *Portia philota*; (j) 103 × 101 mm. 90n. *Paris polyphylla*; (k) 101 × 101 mm. 90n.*Clathrus archeri*; (l) 99 × 100 mm. 90n. *Dendrobium chrysotoxum*	35·00	35·00

216 Elvis Presley

2003. Anniversaries in 2002. 25th Death Anniv of Elvis Presley (entertainer) (**MS**1732a/b). 85th Birth Anniv of John Fitzgerald Kennedy (president USA, 1961–1963) (**MS**1732c/d). 5th Death Anniv of Diana, Princess of Wales (**MS**1732e/f). Six sheets containing T **216** and similar vert designs. Multicoloured.

MS1732	Six sheets (a) 110 × 178 mm. 25n. × 4, Type **216**lding guitar at waist; Singing into microphone; Seated holding guitar to side; (b) 195 × 131 mm. 25n. × 6, Wearing shirt and kerchief, 25n. × 6; (c) 132 × 146 mm. 25n. × 6, College graduate, 1935; Walking with John F. Kennedy Jr.; As Congressman, 1946; At the White House, 1961; With Jacqueline Kennedy on tennis court; Jacqueline Kennedy and children at John F.Kennedy's funeral; (d) 76 × 108 mm. 90n. Head and shoulders ; (e) 134 × 118 mm. 25n. × 4, Wearing earrings and red dress; Wearing ball-gown; Wearing jacket and blouse; Wearing tiara; (f) 65 × 98 mm. 90n. Wearing hat with feathers . . .	17·00	17·00

2003. No. 659 surch **8NU**.

1733	8n. on 75ch. Multicoloured	20	10

APPENDIX

The following stamps have either been issued in excess of postal needs or have not been available to the public in reasonable quantities at face value. Such stamps may later be given full listing if there is evidence of regular postal use.

1968.

Bhutan Pheasants, 1, 2, 4, 8, 15ch., 2, 4, 5, 7, 9n.

Winter Olympic Games, Grenoble. Optd on 1966 Abominable Snowmen issue. 40ch., 1n.25, 3, 6n.

Butterflies (plastic-surfaced). Postage 15. 50ch., 1n.25, 2n., Air 3, 4, 5, 6n.

Paintings (relief-printed). Postage 2, 4, 5, 10 45, 80ch., 1n.05, 1n.40, 2, 3, 4, 5n.; Air 1n.50, 2n.50, 6, 8n.

Olympic Games, Mexico. 5, 45, 60, 80ch., 1n.05, 2, 3, 5n.

Human Rights Year. Die-stamped surch on unissued "Coins". 15ch. on 50n.p., 33ch. on 1r., 9n. on 3r.75.

1969.

Flood Relief. Surch on 1968 Mexico Olympics issue. 5ch.+5ch., 80ch.+25ch., 2n.+50ch.

Fish (plastic-surfaced). Postage 15, 20, 30ch.; Air 5, 6, 7n.

Insects (plastic-surfaced). Postage 10, 75ch., 1n.25, 2n.; Air 3, 4, 5, 6n.

Admission of Bhutan to Universal Postal Union. 5, 10, 15, 45, 60ch., 1n.05, 1n.40, 4n.

5000 Years of Steel Industry. On steel foil. Postage 2, 5, 15, 45, 75ch., 1 n 50, 1n.75, 2n.; Air 3, 4, 5, 6n.

Birds (plastic-surfaced). Postage 15, 50ch., 1n.25, 2n.; Air 3, 4, 5, 6n.

Buddhist Prayer Banners. On silk rayon. 15, 75ch., 2, 5, 6n.

Moon Landing of "Apollo 11" (plastic-surfaced). Postage 3, 5, 15, 20, 25, 45, 50ch., 1n.75; Air 3, 4, 5, 6n.

1970.

Famous Paintings (plastic-surfaced). Postage 5, 10, 15ch., 2n.75; Air 3, 4, 5, 6n.

New U.P.U. Headquarters Building, Berne. 3, 10, 20ch., 2n.50.

Flower Paintings (relief-printed). Postage 2, 3, 5, 10, 15, 75ch., 1n., 1n.40; Air 80, 90ch., 1n.10, 1n.40, 1n.60, 1n.70, 3n., 3n.50.

Animals (plastic-surfaced). Postage 5, 10, 20, 25, 30, 40, 65, 75, 85ch.; Air 2, 3, 4, 5n.

Conquest of Space (plastic-surfaced). Postage 2, 5, 15, 25, 30, 50, 75ch., 1n.50; Air 2, 3, 6, 7n.

1971.

History of Sculpture (plastic-moulded). Postage 10, 75ch., 1n.25, 2n.; Air 3, 4, 5, 6n.

Moon Vehicles (plastic-surfaced). Postage 10ch., 1n.70; Air 2n.50, 4n.

History of the Motor Car (plastic-surfaced). Postage 2, 5, 10, 15, 20, 30, 60, 75, 85ch., 1n., 1n.20, 1n.55, 1n.80, 2n., 2n.50; Air 4, 6, 7, 9, 10n.

Bhutan's Admission to United Nations. Postage 5, 10, 20ch., 3 n; Air 2n.50, 5, 6n.

60th Anniv of Boy Scout Movement. 10, 20, 50, 75ch., 2, 6n.

World Refugee Year. Optd on 1971 United Nations issue. Postage 5, 10, 20ch., 3n.; Air 2n.50, 5, 6n.

1972.

Famous Paintings (relief-printed). Postage 15, 20, 90ch., 2n.50; Air 1n.70, 4n.60, 5n.40, 6n.

Famous Men (plastic-moulded). Postage 10, 15, 55ch.; Air 2, 6, 8n.

Olympic Games, Munich. Postage 10, 15, 20, 30, 45ch.; Air 35ch., 1n.35, 7n.

Space Flight of "Apollo 16" (plastic-surfaced). Postage 15, 20, 90ch., 2n.50; Air 1n.70, 4n.60, 5n.40, 6n.

1973.

Dogs. 2, 3, 15, 20, 30, 99ch., 2n.50, 4n.

Roses (on scent-impregnated paper). Postage 15, 25, 30ch., 3n.; Air 6, 7n.

Moon Landing of "Apollo 17" (plastic-surfaced). Postage 10, 15, 55ch. 2n.; Air 7n., 9n.

"Talking Stamps" (miniature records). Postage 10, 25ch., 1n.25, 7, 8n.; Air 3, 9n.

Death of King Jigme Dorji Wangchuck. Embossed on gold foil. Postage 10, 25ch., 3n.; Air 6, 8n.

Mushrooms. 15, 25, 30ch., 3, 6, 7n.

"Indipex 73" Stamp Exhibition, New Delhi. Postage 5, 10, 15, 25ch., 1n.25, 3n.; Air 5, 6n.

BIAFRA Pt. 1

The Eastern Region of Nigeria declared its Independence on 30 May 1967 as the Republic of Biafra. Nigerian military operations against the breakaway Republic commenced in July 1967.

The Biafran postal service continued to use Nigerian stamps when supplies of these became low. In July 1967 "Postage Paid" cachets were used pending the issue of Nos. 1/3.

12 pence = 1 shilling;
20 shillings = 1 pound.

1 Map of Republic **5** Flag and Scientist

1968. Independence. Multicoloured.

1		2d. Type **1**	10	65
2		4d. Arms, flag and date of Independence	10	65
3		1s. Mother and child (17 × 22 mm)	15	1·75

1968. Nos. 172/5 and 177/85 of Nigeria optd **SOVEREIGN BIAFRA** and arms.

4		½d. multicoloured (No. 172)	1·50	4·25
5		1d. multicoloured (No. 173)	1·75	6·50
6		1½d. multicoloured (No. 174)	8·00	13·00
7		2d. multicoloured (No. 175)	25·00	50·00
8		4d. multicoloured (No. 177)	17·00	50·00
9		6d. multicoloured (No. 178)	8·00	13·00
10		9d. blue and red (No. 179)	3·00	3·00
11		1s. multicoloured (No. 180)	60·00	£110
12		1s.3d. multicoloured (No. 181)	35·00	50·00
13		2s.6d. multicoloured (No. 182)	1·75	13·00
14		5s. multicoloured (No. 183)	2·25	12·00
15		10s. multicoloured (No. 184)	10·00	38·00
16		£1 multicoloured (No. 185)	10·00	38·00

The overprint on No. 15 does not include **SOVEREIGN**.

1968. 1st Anniv of Independence. Multicoloured.

17		4d. Type **5**	15	10
18		1s. Victim of atrocity	20	20
19		2s.6d. Nurse and refugees	45	3·00
20		5s. Biafran arms and banknote	60	3·50
21		10s. Orphaned child	1·00	4·00

16 Child in Chains, and Globe

17 Pope Paul VI, Africa, and Papal Arms

1969. 2nd Anniv of Independence. Multicoloured; frame colours given.

35	**16**	2d. orange	1·25	4·25
36		4d. red	1·25	4·25
37		1s. blue	1·75	7·00
38		2s.6d. green	2·00	14·00

1969. Visit of Pope Paul to Africa. Multicoloured; background colours given.

39	**17**	4d. orange	40	3·00
40	–	6d. blue	55	6·50
41	–	9d. green	75	8·50
42	–	3s. mauve	2·25	14·00

DESIGNS: Pope Paul VI, map of Africa and 6d. Arms of Vatican; 9d. St. Peter's Basilica; 3s. Statue of St. Peter.

BIJAWAR Pt. 1

A state of Central India. Now uses Indian stamps.

12 pies = 1 anna; 16 annas = 1 rupee.

1 Maharaja Sarwant Singh

2 Maharaja Sarwant Singh

1935.

6	**1**	3p. brown	4·50	4·00
2		6p. red	5·00	4·50
3		9p. violet	6·50	4·25
4		1a. blue	7·00	4·75
5		2a. green	7·00	4·75

1937.

11	**2**	4a. orange	11·00	70·00
12		6a. lemon	12·00	70·00
13		8a. green	13·00	85·00
14		12a. blue	13·00	85·00
15		1r. violet	32·00	£130

BOHEMIA AND MORAVIA Pt. 5

Following the proclamation of Slovak Independence on 14 March, 1939, the Czech provinces of Bohemia and Moravia became a German Protectorate. The area was liberated in 1945 and returned to Czechoslovakia.

100 haleru = 1 koruna.

1939. Stamps of Czechoslovakia optd **BOHMEN u. MAHREN CECHY a MORAVA**.

1	**34**	5h. blue	10	1·10
2		10h. brown	10	1·10
3		20h. red	20	1·10
4		25h. green	10	1·10
5		30h. purple	10	1·10
6	**59**	40h. blue	2·50	4·50
7	**77**	50h. green	25	1·10
8	**60a**	60h. violet	2·50	4·50
9	**61**	1k. purple (No. 348)	90	1·50
10		1k. purple (No. 395)	30	1·10
11	–	1k.20 purple (No. 354)	3·50	4·50
12	**64**	1k.50 red	3·50	4·50
13	–	1k.60 green (No. 355a)	2·50	4·50
14	–	2k. green (No. 356)	1·25	2·00
15	–	2k.50 blue (No. 357)	3·25	4·50
16	–	3k. brown (No. 358)	3·25	4·50
17	**65**	4k. violet	3·50	6·00
18	–	5k. green (No. 361)	3·50	9·00
19	–	10k. blue (No. 362)	4·25	13·50

2 Linden Leaves and Buds

3 Karluv Tyn Castle

5 Zlin

1939.

20	**2**	5h. blue	10	10
21		10h. brown	10	10
22		20h. red	10	10
23		25h. green	10	10
24		30h. purple	10	10
25	–	40h. blue	10	10
26	**3**	50h. green	10	10
27	–	60h. violet	10	10
28	–	1k. red	10	10
29	–	1k.20 purple	10	40
30	–	1k.50 red	10	10
31	–	2k. green	10	10
32	–	2k.50 blue	10	10
33	**5**	3k. mauve	10	10
34	–	4k. grey	10	10
35	–	5k. green	10	55
36	–	10k. blue	10	85
37	–	20k. brown	30	1·40

DESIGNS—As Type **3**: 40h. Svikov Castle; 60h. St. Barbara's Church, Kutna Hora; 1k. St. Vitus's Cathedral, Prague. As Type **5**—VERT: 1k.20, 1k.50, Brno Cathedral; 2k., 2k.50, Olomouc. HORIZ: 4k. Ironworks, Moravska-Ostrava; 5k., 10k., 20k. Karlsburg, Prague.

1940. As 1939 issue, but colours changed and new values.

38	**2**	30h. brown	10	10
39		40h. orange	10	15
40		50h. green	10	15
44	–	50h. green	10	10
41	**2**	60h. violet	10	10
42		80h. orange	10	15
45	–	80h. blue	10	20
43	**2**	1k. brown	10	10
46	–	1k.20 brown	10	25
47	–	1k.20 red	10	10
48	–	1k.50 pink	10	10
49	–	2k. green	10	10
50	–	2k. blue	10	10
51	–	2k.50 blue	10	10
52	–	3k. green	10	15
53	–	5k. green	10	10
54	–	6k. brown	10	25
55	–	8k. green	10	25
56	–	10k. blue	10	30
57	–	20k. brown	45	1·25

DESIGNS—As Type **3**: 50h. (No. 44), Neuhaus Castle; 80h. (No. 45), 3k. Pernstyn Castle; 1k.20 (No. 46), 2k.50, Brno Cathedral; 1k.20 (No. 47), St. Vitus's Cathedral, Prague; 1k.50 St. Barbara's Church, Kutna Hora; 2k. Pardubitz Castle. As Type **5**—HORIZ: 5k. Bridge at Beching; 6k. Samson Fountain, Budweis; 8k. Kremsier; 10k. Wallenstein Palace, Prague; 20k. Karlsburg, Prague.

6 Red Cross Nurse and Wounded Soldier

7 Patient in Hospital

1940. Red Cross Relief Fund.

58	**6**	60h.+40h. blue	20	1·00
59		1k.20+80h. plum	20	1·00

1941. Red Cross Relief Fund.

60	**7**	60h.+40h. blue	10	65
61		1k.20+80h. plum	10	75

8 Anton Dvorak

9 Harvesting

10 Blast-furnace, Pilsen

1941. Birth Centenary of Dvorak (composer).

62	**8**	60h. violet	10	70
63		1k.20 brown	25	70

1941. Prague Fair.

64	**9**	30h. brown	10	10
65		60h. green	10	10
66	**10**	1k.20 plum	10	25
67		2k.50 blue	10	30

11 "Stande- theater", Prague

12 Mozart

1941. 150th Death Anniv of Mozart.

68	**11**	30h.+30h. brown	10	25
69		60h.+60h. green	10	25
70	**12**	1k.20+1k.20 red	10	50
71		2k.50+2k.50 blue	10	70

15. III. 1939

15. III. 1942

(**13**)

1942. 3rd Anniv of German Occupation. Optd with T **13**.

72		1k.20 red (No. 47)	20	75
73		2k.50 blue (No. 51)	30	90

14 Adolf Hitler

15 Adolf Hitler

1942. Hitler's 53rd Birthday.

74	**14**	30h.+20h. brown	10	10
75		60h.+40h. green	10	10
76		1k.20+80h. purple	10	10
77		2k.50+1k.50 blue	10	40

1942. Various sizes.

78	**15**	10h. black	10	10
79		30h. brown	10	10
80		40h. blue	10	10
81		50h. green	10	10
82		60h. violet	10	10
83		80h. orange	10	10
84		1k. brown	10	10
85		1k.20 red	10	10
86		1k.50 red	10	10
87		1k.60 green	10	35
88		2k. blue	10	10
89		2k.40 brown	10	20
90		2k.50 blue	10	10
91		3k. olive	10	10
92		4k. purple	10	10
93		5k. green	10	10
94		6k. brown	10	10
95		8k. blue	10	10
96		10k. green	10	85
97		20k. violet	10	1·00
98		30k. red	20	1·50
99		50k. blue	25	3·00

SIZES—17½ × 21½ mm: 10h. to 80h.; 18½ × 21 mm: 1k. to 2k.40; 19 × 24 mm: 2k.50 to 8k.; 24 × 30 mm: 10k. to 50k.

16 Nurse and Patient

17 Mounted Postman

1942. Red Cross Relief Fund.

100	**16**	60h.+40h. blue	10	30
101		1k.20+80h. red	10	30

1943. Stamp Day.

102	**17**	60h. purple	10	08

18 Peter Parler

19 Adolf Hitler

1943. Winter Relief Fund.

103	–	60h.+40h. violet	10	10
104	**18**	1k.20+80h. red	10	10
105	–	2k.50+1k.50 blue	10	10

DESIGNS: 60h. Charles IV; 2k.50, King John of Luxembourg.

1943. Hitler's 54th Birthday.

106	**19**	60h.+1k.40 violet	10	20
107		1k.20+3k.80 red	10	25

20 Scene from "The Mastersingers of Nuremberg"

21 Richard Wagner

1943. 130th Birth Anniv of Wagner.

108	**20**	60h. violet	10	10
109	**21**	1k.20 red	10	10
110	–	2k.50 blue	10	10

DESIGN: 2k.50, Blacksmith scene from "Siegfried".

22 Reinhard Heydrich

23 Arms of Bohemia and Moravia and Red Cross

1943. 1st Death Anniv of Reinhard Heydrich (German Governor).

111	**22**	60h.+4k.40 black	10	50

1943. Red Cross Relief Fund.

112	**23**	1k.20+8k.80 blk & red	10	20

24 National Costumes

25 Arms of Bohemia and Moravia

1944. 5th Anniv of German Occupation.

113	**24**	1k.20+3k.80 red	10	10
114	**25**	4k.20+18k.80 brown	10	10
115	**24**	10k.+20k. blue	10	25

26 Adolf Hitler

27 Smetana

1944. Hitler's 55th Birthday.

116	**26**	60h.+1k.40 brown	10	10
117		1k.20+3k.80 green	10	25

1944. 600th Death Anniv of Bedrich Smetana (composer).

118	**27**	60h.+1k.40 green	10	20
119		1k.20+3k.80 red	10	25

28 St. Vitus's Cathedral, Prague

29 Adolf Hitler

1944.

120	**28**	1k.50 purple	10	10
121		2k.50 violet	10	15

1944.

122	**29**	4k.20 green	10	40

NEWSPAPER STAMPS

N 6 Dove

N 19 Dove

1939. Imperf.
N38 N 6 2h. brown 10 25
N39 5h. blue 10 25
N40 7h. red 10 25
N41 9h. green 10 25
N42 10h. red 10 25
N43 12h. blue 10 25
N44 20h. green 10 25
N45 50h. brown 10 40
N46 1k. green 10 65

1940. For bulk postings. No. N42 optd **GD-OT**.
N60 N 6 10h. red 20 60

1943. Imperf.
N106 N 19 2h. brown 10 10
N107 5h. blue 10 10
N108 7h. red 10 10
N109 9h. green 10 10
N110 10h. red 10 10
N111 12h. blue 10 10
N112 20h. green 10 10
N113 50h. brown 10 10
N114 1k. green 10 20

OFFICIAL STAMPS

O 7 Numeral and Laurel Wreath

O 19 Eagle and Numeral

1941.
O60 O 7 30h. brown 10 10
O61 40h. blue 10 10
O62 50h. green 10 10
O63 60h. green 10 10
O64 80h. red 40 15
O65 1k. brown 15 10
O66 1k.20 red 15 10
O67 1k.50 purple 30 25
O68 2k. blue 30 10
O69 3k. green 30 10
O70 4k. purple 45 65
O71 5k. yellow 98 1·00

1943.
O106 O 19 30h. brown 10 20
O107 40h. blue 10 20
O108 50h. green 10 20
O109 60h. violet 10 20
O110 80h. red 10 20
O111 1k. brown 10 20
O112 1k.20 red 10 20
O113 1k.50 brown 10 25
O114 2k. blue 10 25
O115 3k. green 10 25
O116 4k. purple 10 25
O117 5k. green 10 45

PERSONAL DELIVERY STAMPS

P 6

1939.
P38 P 6 50h. blue 40 1·10
P39 50h. red 65 1·25

POSTAGE DUE STAMPS

D 6

1939.
D38 D 6 5h. red 10 10
D39 10h. red 10 10
D40 20h. red 10 10
D41 30h. red 10 10
D42 40h. red 10 10
D43 50h. red 10 10
D44 60h. red 10 10
D45 80h. red 10 10
D46 1k. blue 10 25
D47 1k.20 blue 15 25
D48 2k. blue 40 85
D49 5k. blue 55 95
D50 10k. blue 70 1·40
D51 20k. blue 2·00 3·75

BOLIVAR Pt. 20

One of the states of the Granadine Confederation. A department of Colombia from 1886, now uses Colombian stamps.

1863. 100 centavos = 1 peso.

1 2

3

1863. Imperf.
1 1 10c. green £350 £275
2 10c. red 20·00 20·00
3 1p. red 10·00 10·00

1872. Various frames. Imperf.
4 2 5c. blue 5·00 5·50
5 3 10c. mauve 7·00 7·50
6 – 20c. green 15·00 16·00
7 – 80c. red 38·00 30·00

6 7

8

1874. Imperf.
8 6 5c. blue 12·00 7·50
9 7 5c. blue 6·00 5·00
10 8 10c. mauve 2·00 2·00

9 Simon Bolivar

10 Simon Bolivar

1879. Various frames. Dated "1879". White or blue paper. Perf.
14 9 5c. blue 20 20
12 10c. mauve 20 20
13 20c. red 25 20

1880. Various frames. Dated "1880". White or blue paper.
19 9 5c. blue 15 15
20 10c. mauve 25 25
21 20c. red 25 25
22 80c. green 2·00 2·00
23 1p. orange 2·75 2·75

1882.
30 10 5p. red and blue 1·00 1·00
31 10p. blue and purple 1·00 1·00

11 Simon Bolivar

12 Simon Bolivar

1882. Various frames. Dated "1882".
32 11 5c. blue 20 20
33 10c. mauve 20 20
34 20c. red 25 35
35 80c. green 55 55
36 1p. orange 65 60

1883. Various frames. Dated "1883".
37 11 5c. blue 15 15
38 10c. mauve 20 20
39 20c. red 20 20
40 80c. green 45 55
41 1p. orange 55 80

1884. Various frames. Dated "1884".
42 11 5c. blue 40 40
43 10c. mauve 15 15
44 20c. red 15 15
45 80c. green 20 25
46 1p. orange 45 55

1885. Various frames. Dated "1885".
47 11 5c. blue 10 10
48 10c. mauve 10 10
49 20c. red 10 10
50 80c. green 20 25
51 1p. orange 55 35

1891.
56 12 1c. black 15 20
57 5c. orange 35 25
58 10c. red 55 55
59 20c. blue 65 65
60 50c. green 95 95
61 1p. violet 95 95

13 Simon Bolivar

1903. Various sizes and portraits. Imperf or perf. On paper of various colours.
63 13 50c. green 45 45
64 50c. blue 30 30
65 50c. violet 90 1·00
67 – 1p. red 50 50
68 – 1p. green 70 70
69 – 5p. red 35 35
70b – 10p. blue 50 50
71 – 10p. violet 2·50 2·50
PORTRAITS: 1p. Fernandez Madrid. 5p. Rodriguez Torices. 10p. Garcia de Toledo.

20 J. M. del Castillo

23

1904. Various portraits. Imperf or perf.
77 20 5c. black 15 15
78 – 10c. brown (M. Anguiano) 15 15
80 – 20c. red (P.G. Ribon) 40 40

1904. Figures in various frames. Imperf.
81 23 ¼c. black 30 25
82 1c. blue (horiz) 50 50
83 2c. violet 75 70

ACKNOWLEDGMENT OF RECEIPT STAMPS

AR 19

AR 27

1903. Imperf. On paper of various colours.
AR75 AR 19 20c. orange 60 60
AR76 20c. blue 50 50

1904. Imperf.
AR85 AR 27 2c. red 1·00 1·00

LATE FEE STAMPS

L 18

1903. Imperf. On paper of various colours.
L73 L 18 20c. red 30 30
L74 20c. violet 30 30

REGISTRATION STAMPS

1879. As T 9 but additionally inscr "CERTIFICADA".
R17 9 40c. brown 60 60

1880. As previous issue dated "1880".
R28 9 40c. brown 30 35

1882. As T 11, but additionally inscr "CERTIFICADA". Dated as shown.
R52 11 40c. brown ("1882") 25 40
R53 40c. brown ("1883") 40 40
R54 40c. brown ("1884") 15 15
R55 40c. brown ("1885") 35 40

R 17

1903. Imperf. On paper of various colours.
R72 R 17 20c. orange 50 50

R 26

1904. Imperf.
R84 R 26 5c. black 2·00 2·00

BOLIVIA Pt. 20

A republic of Central South America.

1867. 100 centavos = 1 boliviano.
1963. 100 centavos = 1 peso boliviano ($b).
1987. 100 centavos = 1 boliviano.

1 Condor

4 (9 Stars)

1867. Imperf.
3a 1 5c. green 2·40 3·00
10 5c. mauve £120 90·00
7 10c. brown £140 90·00
8 50c. yellow 12·50 19·00
11 50c. blue £200 £160
9 100c. blue 38·00 48·00
12 100c. green 90·00 85·00

1868. Nine stars below Arms. Perf.
32 4 5c. green 11·00 5·50
33 10c. red 16·00 5·50
34 50c. blue 28·00 16·00
35 100c. orange 28·00 17·00
36 500c. black £300 £225

1871. Eleven stars below Arms. Perf.
37 4 5c. green 6·25 4·00
38 10c. red 8·75 6·25
39 50c. blue 23·00 11·00
40 100c. orange 22·00 11·00
41 500c. black £1100 £1100

7

11

1878. Perf.
42 7 5c. blue 5·75 2·50
43 10c. orange 4·75 1·90
44 20c. green 14·00 2·40
45 50c. red 70·00 7·50

1887. Eleven stars below Arms. Roul.
46 4 1c. red 1·50 1·40
47 2c. violet 1·50 1·40
48 5c. blue 4·50 2·00
49 10c. orange 4·50 2·00

1890. Nine stars below Arms. Perf.
50 4 1c. red 90 50
58 2c. violet 2·75 1·40
52 5c. blue 2·50 50
53 10c. orange 4·00 60
54 20c. green 8·00 1·00
55 50c. red 4·00 1·00
56 100c. yellow 8·00 2·00

1893. Eleven stars below Arms. Perf.
59 4 5c. blue 3·75 1·40

1894.
63 11 1c. bistre 60 60
64 2c. red 60 60
65 5c. green 60 60
66 10c. brown 60 40
67 20c. blue 2·00 85
68 50c. red 4·75 1·25
69 100c. red 11·00 4·00

12 Frias

13

1897.
77 12 1c. green 70 50
78 – 2c. red (Linares) 1·00 90
79 – 5c. green (Murillo) 1·40 40
80 – 10c. purple (Monteagudo) 1·60 40
81 – 20c. black and red (J. Ballivian) 3·00 70
82 – 50c. orange (Sucre) 3·00 1·40

83 – 1b. blue (Bolivar) . . . . . 3·00 3·50
84 **13** 2b. multicoloured . . . . . 23·00 30·00

18 Sucre **19** A. Ballivian **24**

1899.
92 **18** 1c. blue . . . . 1·40 40
93 2c. red . . . . 1·00 25
94 5c. green . . . . 3·75 85
95 5c. red . . . . 1·00 50
96 10c. orange . . . . 1·40 70
97 20c. red . . . . 1·75 30
98 50c. brown . . . . 3·75 1·40
99 1b. lilac . . . . 1·00 1·00

1901.
100 **19** 1c. red 35 15
101 – 2c. green (Camacho) . . . 40 25
102 – 5c. red (Campero) 40 25
103 – 10c. blue (J. Ballivian) . . 1·00 15
104 – 20c. black and purple (Santa Cruz) 45 15
105 **24** 2b. brown . . . . 2·40 1·75

25 **26** Murillo

1909. Issued in La Paz. Centenary of Revolution of July, 1809. Centres in black.
110 **25** 5c. blue . . . . 5·50 3·00
111 **26** 10c. green . . . . 5·50 3·00
112 – 20c. orange (Lanza) . . . 5·50 3·00
113 – 2b. red (Montes) . . . . . 5·50 3·00

37 P. D. Murillo F **8** Figure of Justice

1909. Centenary of Beginning of War of Independence, 1809–25.
115 – 1c. black and brown . . . 25 15
116 – 2c. black and green 35 25
117 **37** 5c. black and red 35 10
118 – 10c. black and blue 35 10
119 – 20c. black and violet . . . 40 25
120 – 50c. black and bistre . . . 60 35
121 – 1b. black and brown . . . 60 50
122 – 2b. black and brown . . . 1·00 70
PORTRAITS: 1c. M. Betanzos. 2c. I. Warnes. 10c. B. Monteagudo. 20c. E. Arze. 50c. A. J. Sucre. 1b. S. Bolivar. 2b. M. Belgrano.

1910. Centenary of Liberation of Santa Cruz, Potosi and Cochabamba. Portraits as T **37**.
123 5c. black and green 25 10
124 10c. black and red 25 10
125 20c. black and blue 55 35
PORTRAITS: 5c. I. Warnes. 10c. M. Betanzos. 20c. E. Arze.

1911. Nos. 101 and 104 surch **5 Centavos 1911**.
127 5c. on 2c. green 40 20
128 5c. on 20c. black & purple 10·00 10·00

1912. Stamps similar to Type F **8** optd **CORREOS 1912.** or surch also.
130 F **8** 2c. green 40 25
131 5c. orange 35 35
132 10c. red 85 50
129 10c. on 1c. blue 35 15

1913. Portraits as 1901 and new types.
133 **19** 1c. pink 35 25
134 – 2c. red 35 20
135 – 5c. green 40 10
136 – 8c. yellow (Frias) 70 30
137 – 10c. grey 70 25
139 – 50c. purple (Sucre) 95 35
140 – 1b. blue (Bolivar) . . . . 1·40 85
141 **24** 2b. black . . . . 2·75 1·75

46 Monolith **47** Mt. Potosi

1916. Various sizes.
142 **46** ½c. brown 20 20
143 **47** 1c. green 25 15
144 – 2c. black and red 30 15
145 – 5c. blue 50 10
147 – 10c. blue and orange . . . 85 10
DESIGNS—HORIZ: 2c. Lake Titicaca; 5c. Mt. Illimani; 10c. Parliament Building, La Paz.

51 **54** Morane Saulnier Type P Airplane

1919.
158a **51** 1c. lake 15 10
158b 2c. violet 25 15
151 5c. green 35 10
152 10c. red 35 10
179 15c. blue 50 15
180 20c. blue 35 15
154 22c. blue 50 45
155 24c. violet 35 25
162 50c. orange . . . . . . 1·75 35
163 1b. brown 40 15
164 2b. brown 25 15
See also Nos. 194/206.

1923. Surch **Habilitada** and value.
165 **51** 5c. on 1c. lake 35 25
169 15c. on 10c. red 40 35
168 15c. on 22c. blue 40 35

1924. Air. Establishment of National Aviation School.
170 **54** 10c. black and red 30 25
171 15c. black and lake . . . . 1·10 70
172 25c. black and blue 55 35
173 50c. black and orange . . 1·10 70
174 – 1b. black and brown . . . 1·10 1·00
175 – 2b. black and brown . . . 2·25 2·00
176 – 5b. black and violet . . . 3·50 3·25
Nos. 174/6 have a different view.

57 Andean Condor

1925. Centenary of Independence.
184 – 5c. red on green 50 25
185 – 10c. red on yellow 85 45
186 – 15c. red 35 10
187 **57** 25c. blue . . . . 2·00 50
188 – 50c. purple 35 10
189 – 1b. red 85 85
190 – 2b. yellow . . . . 1·25 1·25
191 – 5b. brown . . . . 1·40 1·40
DESIGNS—VERT: 5c. Torch of Freedom; 10c. Kantuta (national flower); 15c. Pres. B. Saavedra; 50c. Head of Liberty; 1b. Mounted archer; 5b. Marshal Sucre. HORIZ: 2b. Hermes.

1927. Surch **1927** and value.
192 **51** 5c. on 1c. lake . . . . . . 1·40 50
193 10c. on 24c. violet . . . . 1·40 85

1928.
194 **51** 2c. yellow 35 25
195 3c. pink 40 35
196 4c. red 40 35
197 20c. olive 60 25
198 25c. blue 60 35
199 30c. violet 60 50
200 40c. orange . . . . 1·00 85
201 50c. brown . . . . 1·00 50
202 1b. red . . . . 1·25 85
203 2b. purple . . . . 1·75 1·75
204 3b. green . . . . 1·75 1·60
205 4b. lake . . . . 2·75 2·40
206 5b. brown . . . . 3·25 2·75

1928. Optd **Octubre 1927** and star.
207 **51** 5c. green 25 15
208 10c. grey 35 15
209 15c. red 50 35

1928. Surch **15 cts. 1928.**
211 **51** 15c. on 20c. blue . . . . 5·50 5·50
213 15c. on 24c. violet 95 50
216 15c. on 50c. orange 70 40

66 "L.A.B." (Lloyd Aereo Boliviano) **68** Andean Condor

1928. Air.
217 **66** 15c. green 55 55
218 20c. blue 20 10
219 35c. red 35 35

1928.
221 **68** 5c. green . . . . 2·25 30
222 – 10c. blue 35 10
223 – 15c. red 35 10
DESIGNS: 10c. Pres. Siles; 15c. Map of Bolivia.

1930. Stamps of 1913 and 1916 surch **R. S. 21-4 1930** and value.
224 – 0.01c. on 2c. (No. 134) . . 70 70
225 – 0.03c. on 2c. (No. 144) . . 85 70
226 **46** 25c. on ½c. brown 70 50
227 – 25c. on 2c. (No. 144) . . . 70 50

1930. Air. Optd **CORREO AEREO R. S. 6-V-1930** or surch **5 Cts.** also.
228 **54** 5c. on 10c. black & red . . 8·00 10·00
229 10c. black and red . . . . 8·00 10·00
231 15c. black and lake . . . . 8·00 10·00
232 25c. black and blue . . . . 8·00 10·00
233 50c. black and orange . . 8·00 10·00
235 1b. black and brown . . . £100 £100

1930. "Graf Zeppelin" Air stamps. Stamps of 1928 surch **Z 1930** and value.
241 **66** 1b.50 on 15c. green . . . . 20·00 27·00
242 3b. on 20c. blue . . . . . 20·00 27·00
243 6b. on 35c. red . . . . . 35·00 45·00

75 Junkers F-13 over Bullock Cart **77** Pres. Siles

78 Map of Bolivia **79** Marshal Sucre

1930. Air.
244 **75** 5c. violet . . . . 1·60 65
245 – 15c. red . . . . 1·60 65
246 – 20c. yellow 65 40
247 **75** 35c. green 65 15
248 – 50c. blue 65 15
249 **75** 1b. brown 65 20
250 – 2b. red 65 30
251 **75** 3b. grey . . . . 3·75 1·60
DESIGN: 15, 20, 50c., 2b. Junkers F-13 seaplane over river boat.

1930.
252 **77** 1c. brown 25 25
253 – 2c. green (Potosi) 85 35
254 – 5c. blue (Illimani) 85 15
255 – 10c. red (E. Abaroa) . . . 85 15
256 **78** 15c. violet 70 15
257 35c. red . . . . 1·40 70
258 45c. orange . . . . 1·40 70
259 **79** 50c. slate 70 50
260 – 1b. brown (Bolivar) . . . 35 35

80 Symbols of Revolution

1931. 1st Anniv of Revolution.
263 **80** 15c. red . . . . 1·40 35
264 50c. lilac 45 50

81

1932. Air.
265 **81** 5c. blue 45 50
266 10c. grey 50 25
267 15c. red 45 35
268 25c. orange 45 35
269 30c. green 40 35
270 50c. purple 40 35
271 1b. brown 40 35

1933. Surch **Habilitada D. S. 13-7-1933** and value.
273 **51** 5c. on 1b. red 40 20
274 **78** 15c. on 35c. red 20 20
275 15c. on 45c. orange 20 20
276 **51** 15c. on 50c. brown 85 15
277 25c. on 40c. orange 40 15

83 **84** M. Baptista

1933.
278 **83** 2c. green 25 15
279 5c. blue 15 10
280 10c. red 40 25
281 15c. violet 25 15
282 25c. blue 60 40

1935. Ex-President Baptista Commemoration.
283 **84** 15c. violet 50 20

85 Map of Bolivia **86** Fokker Super Universal

1935.
284 **85** 2c. blue 25 15
285 3c. yellow 25 15
286 5c. green 25 15
287 5c. red 25 15
288 10c. brown 25 15
289 15c. blue 25 15
290 15c. red 25 15
291 20c. green 25 15
292 25c. blue 35 15
293 30c. red 35 25
294 40c. orange 60 20
295 50c. violet 60 15
296 1b. yellow 60 40
297 2b. brown 60 40

1935. Air.
298 **86** 5c. brown 15 15
299 10c. green 15 15
300 20c. violet 15 15
301 30c. blue 15 15
302 50c. orange 35 15
303 1b. brown 35 30
304 1½b. yellow . . . . 1·00 15
305 2b. red . . . . 1·00 45
306 5b. green . . . . 1·25 45
307 10b. brown . . . . 2·10 85

1937. Surch **Comunicaciones D.S. 25-2-37** and value in figures.
308 **83** 5c. on 2c. green 20 20
310 15c. on 25c. blue 25 25
311 30c. on 25c. blue 40 40
312 **51** 45c. on 1b. brown 50 50
313 1b. on 2b. purple 60 60
314 **83** 2b. on 25c. blue 60 60
315 **80** 3b. on 50c. lilac 85 85
316 5b. on 50c. lilac 70 70

1937. Air. Surch **Correo Aereo D. S. 25-2-37** and value in figures.
321 **75** 5c. on 35c. green 35 35
322 **66** 20c. on 35c. red 40 25
323 50c. on 35c. red 75 40
324 1b. on 35c. red 90 50
325 **54** 2b. on 50c. black & orge 1·75 70
317 – 3b. on 50c. pur (No. 188) 90 35
318 – 4b. on 1b. red (No. 189) 75 70
319 **57** 5b. on 2b. orange 95 85
320 10b. on 5b. sepia (No. 191) 2·40 1·75
326 **54** 12b. on 10c. black & red 6·00 3·50
327 15b. on 10c. black & red 6·00 2·25

89 Native School **92** Junkers Ju52/3m over Cornfield

1938.
328 **89** 2c. red (postage) 10 10
329 – 10c. orange 15 10
330 – 15c. green 25 25
331 – 30c. yellow 40 35
332 – 45c. red . . . . 5·25 2·75
333 – 60c. violet 50 35
334 – 75c. blue 70 35
335 – 1b. brown . . . . 1·00 35
336 – 2b. buff 95 35
DESIGNS—VERT: 10c. Oil Wells; 15c. Industrial buildings; 30c. Pincers and torch; 75c. Indian and condor. HORIZ: 45c. Sucre-Camiri railway map; 60c. Natives and book; 1b. Machinery; 2b. Agriculture.

337 – 20c. red (air) 25 20
338 – 30c. grey 25 20
339 – 40c. yellow 25 20
340 **92** 50c. green 35 20
341 – 60c. blue 35 20
342 – 1b. red 50 50
343 – 2b. buff . . . . 1·25 20
344 – 3b. brown 90 20
345 – 5b. violet . . . . 6·00 1·25

DESIGNS—VERT: 20c. Mint, Potosi; 30c. Miner; 40c. Symbolical of women's suffrage; 1b. Pincers, torch and slogan; 3b. New Government emblem; 5b. Junkers aircraft over map of Bolivia. HORIZ: 60c. Airplane and monument; 2b. Airplane over river.

102 Llamas

103 Arms

1939.
346 102 2c. green 70 50
347 4c. brown 70 50
348 5c. mauve 70 35
349 – 10c. black 70 50
350 – 15c. green 70 55
351 – 20c. green 70 35
352 103 25c. yellow 60 25
353 – 30c. blue 60 35
354 – 40c. red 2·75 60
355 – 45c. black 2·50 60
356 – 60c. red 1·40 70
357 – 75c. slate 1·40 70
358 – 90c. orange 4·25 75
359 – 1b. blue 4·25 75
360 – 2b. red 5·50 75
361 – 3b. violet 6·50 1·00
362 – 4b. brown 4·00 1·40
363 – 5b. purple 5·00 1·60
DESIGNS—HORIZ: 10, 15, 20c. Vicuna; 60, 75c. Mountain viscacha; 90c., 1b. Toco toucan; 2, 3b. Andean condor; 4, 5b. Jaguar. VERT: 40, 45c. Cocoi herons.

107 Virgin of Copacabana

111 Workman

1939. Air. 2nd National Eucharistic Congress. Inscr "II° CONGRESO EUCARISTICO NACIONAL".
364 – 5c. violet 25 35
365 107 30c. green 20 20
366 – 45c. blue 60 20
367 – 60c. red 60 40
368 – 75c. red 45 40
369 – 90c. blue 30 25
370 – 2b. brown 50 25
371 – 4b. mauve 70 40
372 107 5b. blue 1·75 25
373 – 10b. yellow 3·50 25
DESIGNS—TRIANGULAR: 5c., 10b. Allegory of the Light of Religion. VERT: 45c., 4b. The "Sacred Heart of Jesus"; 75c., 90c. S. Anthony of Padua. HORIZ: 60c., 2b. Facade of St. Francis's Church, La Paz.

1939. Obligatory Tax. Workers' Home Building Fund.
374 111 5c. violet 35 10

112 Flags of 21 American Republics

1940. 50th Anniv of Pan-American Union.
375 112 9b. red, blue & yellow 70 70

114 Urns of Murillo and Sagarnaga

117 Shadow of Aeroplane on Lake Titicaca

1941. 130th Death Anniv of P. D. Murillo (patriot).
376 – 10c. purple 10 10
377 114 15c. green 15 10
378 – 45c. red 15 15
379 – 1b.05 blue 35 15
DESIGNS—VERT: 10c. Murillo statue; 1b.05 Murillo portrait. HORIZ: 45c. "Murillo dreaming in Prison".

1941. Air.
380 117 10b. green 4·00 50
381 20b. blue 4·50 85
382 – 50b. mauve 9·25 1·75
383 – 100b. brown 18·00 6·00
DESIGN: 50, 100b. Andean condor over Mt. Illimani.

119 1867 and 1941 Issues

120 "Union is Strength"

1942. 1st Students' Philatelic Exn, La Paz.
384 119 5c. mauve 65 55
385 10c. orange 65 55
386 20c. green 1·10 60
387 40c. red 1·25 65
388 90c. blue 2·50 80
389 1b. violet 3·75 2·00
390 10b. brown 12·00 7·50

1942. Air. Chancellors' Meeting, Rio de Janeiro.
391 120 40c. red 35 25
392 50c. blue 35 25
393 1b. brown 40 35
394 5b. mauve 1·40 25
395 10b. purple 1·75 1·60

121 Mt. Potosi

122 Chaquiri Dam

1943. Mining Industry.
396 121 15c. brown 25 15
397 – 45c. blue 25 15
398 – 1b.25 purple 1·40 85
399 – 1b.50 green 35 25
400 – 2b. brown 1·40 85
401 122 2b.10 blue 50 40
402 – 3b. orange 2·50 90
DESIGNS—VERT: 45c. Quechisla (at foot of Mt. Choroloque); 1b.25, Miner Drilling. HORIZ: 1b.50, Dam; 2b. Truck Convoy; 3b. Entrance to Pulacayo Mine.

125 Gen. Ballivian leading Cavalry Charge

1943. Centenary of Battle of Ingavi.
403 125 2c. green 10 10
404 3c. orange 10 10
405 25c. purple 15 10
406 45c. blue 25 15
407 3b. red 25 15
408 4b. purple 40 25
409 5b. sepia 55 35

126 Gen. Ballivian and Trinidad Cathedral

1943. Centenary of Founding of El Beni. Centres in brown.
410 126 5c. green (postage) 10 10
411 10c. purple 15 15
412 30c. red 15 15
413 45c. blue 25 25
414 2b.10 orange 35 35
415 – 10. violet (air) 10 10
416 – 20c. green 15 10
417 – 30c. red 20 15
418 – 3b. blue 25 20
419 – 5b. black 60 35
DESIGN: Nos. 415/19, Gen. Ballivian and mule convoy crossing bridge below airplane.

127 Trans. "Honour-Work-Law/All for the Country"

129 Allegory of "Flight"

1944. Revolution of 20th December, 1943.
420 127 20c. orange (postage) 10 10
421 20c. green 10 10
422 90c. blue 10 10
423 90c. red 10 10
424 – 1b. purple 15 10
425 – 2b.40 brown 20 15
DESIGN—VERT: 1b., 2b.40, Clasped hands and flag.

426 129 40c. mauve (air) 10 10
427 – 1b. violet 15 10
428 – 1b.50 green 15 10
429 – 2b.50 blue 35 15
DESIGN—HORIZ: 1b.50, 2b.50, Lockheed 10 Electra airplane and sun.

131 Posthorn and Envelope

132 Douglas DC-2 and National Airways Route Map

1944. Obligatory Tax.
430 131 10c. red 1·00 25
432 10c. blue 1·00 25

Smaller Posthorn and Envelope.
469 10c. red 1·60 60
470 10c. yellow 1·40 60
471 10c. green 1·40 60
472 10c. brown 1·40 60

1945. Air. Panagra Airways, 10th Anniv of First La Paz–Tacna Flight.
433 132 10c. red 15 10
434 50c. orange 20 10
435 90c. green 30 10
436 5b. blue 45 15
437 20b. brown 1·40 45

133 Lloyd-Aereo Boliviano Air Routes

134 L. B. Vincenti and J. I. de Sanjines, Composers of National Anthem

1945. Air. 20th Anniv of First National Air Service.
438 133 20c. blue, orange & vio 10 10
439 30c. blue, orange & brn 10 10
440 50c. blue, orange & grn 10 10
441 90c. blue, orange & pur 10 10
442 2b. blue and orange 15 10
443 3b. blue, orange & red 20 15
444 4b. blue, orange & bistre 40 15

1946. Centenary of National Anthem.
445 134 5c. black and mauve 10 10
446 10c. black and blue 10 10
447 15c. black and green 10 10
448 30c. brown and red 15 15
449 90c. brown and blue 15 15
450 2b. brown and black 40 15

1947. Surch **1947 Habilitada Bs. 1.40.**
451 1b.40 on 75c. blue (No. 334) (postage) 15 10
452 1b.40 on 75c. slate (No. 357) 15 10
455 1b.40 on 75c. red (No. 368) (air) 15 10

136 Seizure of Government Palace

137 Mt. Iillimani

1947. Popular Revolution of 21 July 1946.
456 136 20c. green (postage) 10 10
457 50c. purple 10 10
458 1b.40 blue 10 10
459 3b.70 orange 15 10
460 4b. violet 25 15
461 10b. olive 30 30
462 137 1b. red (air) 10 10
463 1b.40 green 10 10
464 2b.50 blue 15 15
465 3b. orange 25 20
466 4b. mauve 35 20

138 Arms of Bolivia and Argentina

140 Cross and Child

1947. Meeting of Presidents of Bolivia and Argentina.
467 138 1b.40 orange (postage) 10 10
468 2b.90 blue (air) 25 25

1948. 3rd Inter-American Catholic Education Congress.
473 – 1b.40 bl & yell (postage) 35 10
474 140 2b. green and orange 50 15
475 – 3b. green and blue 55 20
476 – 5b. violet and orange 60 25
477 – 5b. brown and green 75 25
478 – 2b.50 orange & yell (air) 30 35
479 140 3b.70 red and buff 40 35
480 – 4b. mauve and blue 40 25
481 – 4b. blue and orange 40 15
482 – 13b.60 blue and green 50 25
DESIGNS: 1b.40, 2b.50, Christ the Redeemer, Monument; 3b., 4b. (No. 480), Don Bosco; 5b. (No. 476), 4b. (No. 481), Virgin of Copacabana; 5b. (No. 477), 13b.60, Pope Pius XII.

141 Map of S. America and Bolivian Auto Club Badge

142 Posthorn, Globe and Pres. G. Pacheco

1948. Pan-American Motor Race.
483 141 5b. blue & pink (postage) 1·00 20
484 10b. green & cream (air) 1·10 25

1950. 75th Anniv of U.P.U.
485 142 1b.40 blue (postage) 10 10
486 4b.20 red 10 10
487 1b.40 brown (air) 10 10
488 2b.50 orange 10 10
489 3b.30 purple 10 10

1950. Air. Surch **XV ANIVERSARIO PANAGRA 1935–1950** and value.
490 132 4b. on 10c. red 10 10
491 10b. on 20b. brown 25 20

1950. No. 379 surch **Bs. 2.- Habilitada D.S.6.VII.50.**
492 2b. on 1b.05 blue 15 10

145 Apparition at Potosi

146 Douglas DC-2

1950. 400th Anniv of Apparition at El Potosi.
493 145 20c. violet 10 10
494 30c. orange 10 10
495 50c. purple 10 10
496 1b. red 10 10
497 2b. blue 15 10
498 6b. brown 25 10

1950. Air. 25th Anniv of Lloyd Aereo Boliviano.
499 146 20c. orange 15 10
500 30c. violet 15 10
501 50c. green 15 10
502 1b. yellow 15 10
503 3b. blue 15 10
504 15b. red 50 15
505 50b. brown 1·40 40

1950. Air. Surch **Triunfo de la Democracia 24 de Sept. 49 Bs. 1.40.**
506 137 1b.40 on 3b. orange 15 15

148 U.N. Emblem and Globe

150 St. Francis Gate

149 Gate of the Sun, Tiahuanacu

1950. 5th Anniv of U.N.O.
507 148 60c. blue (postage) 70 10
508 2b. green 95 25

509		3b.60 red (air)	35	15
510		4b.70 brown	45	15

1951. 4th Centenary of Founding of La Paz. Centres in black.

511	**149**	20c. green (postage)	10	10
512	**150**	30c. orange	10	10
513	A	40c. brown	10	10
514	B	50c. red	10	10
515	C	1b. purple	10	10
516	D	1b.40 violet	15	15
517	E	2b. purple	15	15
518	F	3b. mauve	20	15
519	G	5b. red	25	15
520	H	10b. sepia	50	25
521	**149**	20c. red (air)	15	15
522	**150**	30c. violet	15	15
523	A	40c. slate	15	15
524	B	50c. green	15	15
525	C	1b. red	20	20
526	D	2b. orange	35	35
527	E	3b. blue	35	35
528	F	4b. red	40	40
529	G	5b. green	40	40
530	H	10b. brown	45	45

DESIGNS—HORIZ: As Type **149**: A, Camacho Avenue; B, Consistorial Palace; C, Legislative Palace; D, G.P.O. E, Arms; F, Pedro de la Casca authorizes plans of City; G, Founding the City; H, City Arms and Captain A. de Mendoza.

151 Tennis

1951. Sports. Centres in black.

531	–	20c. blue (postage)	15	10
532	**151**	50c. red	15	10
533	–	1b. purple	20	10
534	–	1b.40 yellow	20	15
535	–	2b. red	25	15
536	–	3b. brown	55	50
537	–	4b. blue	70	50
538	–	20c. violet (air)	25	10
539	–	30c. purple	35	10
540	–	50c. orange	50	10
541	–	1b. brown	50	10
542	–	2b.50 orange	70	40
543	–	3b. sepia	70	50
544	–	5b. red	1·40	1·00

DESIGNS—Postage: 20c. Boxing; 1b. Diving; 1b.40, Football; 2b. Skiing; 3b. Pelota; 4b. Cycling. Air: 20c. Horse-jumping; 30c. Basketball; 50c. Fencing; 1b. Hurdling; 2b.50, Javelin; 3b. Relay race; 5b. La Paz Stadium.

152 Andean Condor and Flag

1951. 100th National Flag Anniv. Flag in red, yellow and green.

545	**152**	2b. green	10	10
546		3b.50c. blue	10	10
547		5b. violet	15	15
548		7b.50c. grey	35	15
549		15b. red	40	25
550		30b. brown	85	50

153 Posthorn and Envelope

154 E. Abaroa

1951. Obligatory Tax.

551	–	20c. orange	30	15
551b	–	20c. green	30	15
552	–	20c. blue	30	15
553	**153**	50c. green	40	15
553d		50c. red	40	15
553e		3b. green	40	15
553f		3b. bistre	60	45
553g		5b. violet	65	15

DESIGN: 20c. Condor over posthorn and envelope.

1952. 73rd Death Anniv of Abaroa (patriot).

554	**154**	80c. red (postage)	10	10
555		1b. orange	10	10
556		2b. green	15	10
557		5b. blue	20	15
558		10b. mauve	35	15
559		20b. brown	70	40
560		70c. red (air)	10	10
561		2b. yellow	15	15
562		3b. green	15	15
563		5b. blue	15	15
564		50b. purple	70	50
565		100b. black	75	70

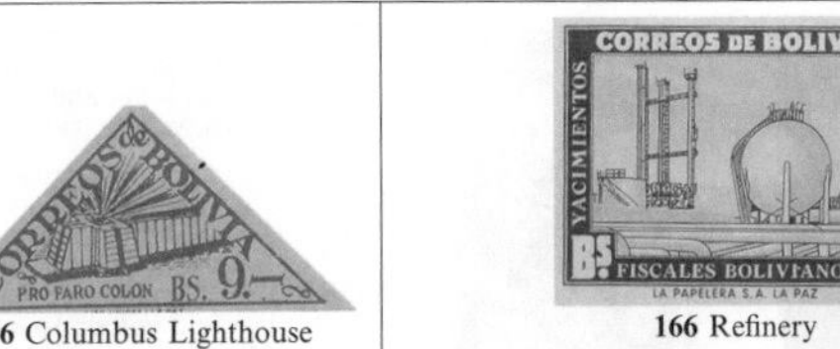

155 Isabella the Catholic

156 Columbus Lighthouse

1952. 500th Birth Anniv of Isabella the Catholic.

566	**155**	2b. blue (postage)	10	10
567		6b.30 red	25	15
568		50b. green (air)	40	25
569		100b. brown	45	35

1952. Columbus Memorial Lighthouse. On tinted papers.

570	**156**	2b. blue (postage)	20	15
571		5b. red	40	20
572		9b. green	65	35
573		2b. purple (air)	15	10
574		3b.70 turquoise	15	10
575		4b.40 orange	20	10
576		20b. brown	45	10

157 Miner

159 Revolutionaries

158 Villarroel, Paz Estenssoro and Siles Zuazo

1953. Nationalization of Mining Industry.

577	**157**	2b.50c. red	10	10
578		8b. violet	15	10

1953. 1st Anniv of Revolution of April 9th, 1952.

579	**158**	50c. mauve (postage)	10	10
580		1b. red	10	10
581		2b. blue	10	10
582		3b. green	10	10
583		4b. yellow	10	10
584		5b. violet	15	10
585		3b.70 brown (air)	15	15
590	**159**	6b. mauve	15	15
586	**158**	9b. red	15	15
587		10b. turquoise	15	15
588		16b. orange	15	15
591	**159**	22b.50 brown	25	20
589	**158**	40b. grey	40	15

1953. Obligatory Tax. No. 551b and similar stamp surch **50 cts.**

592		50c. on 20c. mauve	30	30
593		50c. on 20c. green	15	15

161

162 Ear of Wheat and Map

1954. Obligatory Tax.

594	**161**	1b. lake	25	10
595		1b. brown	25	10

1954. 1st National Agronomical Congress.

596	**162**	25b. blue	15	10
597		85b. brown	35	15

163 Pres. Paz Estenssoro embracing Indian

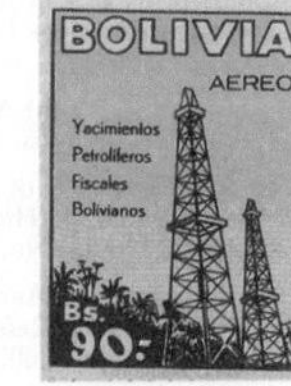

167 Derricks

166 Refinery

1954. Air. 3rd Inter-American Indigenous Congress.

598	**163**	20b. brown	10	10
599		100b. turquoise	25	10

1954. 1st Anniv of Agrarian Reform. As T **162**, but designs inscr "REFORMA AGRARIA".

600		5b. red (postage)	10	10
601		17b. turquoise	10	10
602		27b. mauve (air)	10	15
603		30b. orange	15	10
604		45b. purple	25	10
605		300b. green	70	25

DESIGNS—5b., 17b. Cow's head and map; 27b. to 300b. Indian peasant woman.

1955. Obligatory Tax. Nos. 553e and 553f surch **Bs. 5.—D. S. 21-IV-55.**

606	**153**	5b. on 3b. green	25	10
607		5b. on 3b. bistre	25	10

1955. Development of Petroleum Industry.

608	**166**	10b. blue (postage)	10	10
609		35b. red	10	10
610		40b. green	10	10
611		50b. purple	15	10
612		80b. brown	25	10
613	**167**	55b. blue (air)	10	10
614		70b. black	20	10
615		90b. green	30	10
616		500b. mauve	45	40
617		1000b. brown	85	75

168 Control Tower

169 Douglas DC-6B Aircraft

1957. Obligatory Tax. Airport Building Fund.

618	**168**	5b. blue	50	10
620		5b. red	50	10
619	**169**	10b. green	40	10
620b		20b. brown	55	25

DESIGNS: 5b. (No. 620), Douglas DC-6B over runway; 20b. Lockheed Constellation in flight.

1957. Currency revaluation. Founding of La Paz stamps of 1951 surch. Centres in black.

621	F	50b. on 3b. mauve (post)	10	10
622	E	100b. on 2b. purple	10	10
623	C	200b. on 1b. purple	15	10
624	D	300b. on 1b.40 violet	20	10
625	**149**	350b. on 20c. green	30	10
626	A	400b. on 40c. brown	30	10
627	**150**	600b. on 30c. orange	40	10
628	B	800b. on 50c. red	45	10
629	H	1000b. on 10b. sepia	45	15
630	G	2000b. on 5b. red	50	25
631	E	100b. on 3b. blue (air)	10	10
632	D	200b. on 2b. orange	10	10
633	F	500b. on 4b. red	15	10
634	C	600b. on 1b. red	15	10
635	**149**	700b. on 20c. red	30	15
636	A	800b. on 40c. slate	40	20
637	**150**	900b. on 30c. violet	45	10
638	B	1800b. on 50c. green	45	35
639	G	3000b. on 5b. green	70	30
640	H	5000b. on 10b. brown	1·10	50

172 Congress Buildings (Santiago de Chile and La Paz)

173 "Latin America" on Globe

1957. 7th Latin-America Economic Congress, La Paz.

641	**172**	150b. bl & grey (postage)	10	10
642		350b. grey and brown	20	10
643		550b. sepia and blue	25	10
644		750b. green and red	35	10
645		900b. brown and green	50	15
646	**173**	700b. violet & lilac (air)	15	10
647		1200b. brown	25	15
648		1350b. red and mauve	40	25
649		2700b. olive and turq	75	45
650		4000b. violet and blue	95	50

174 Steam Train and Presidents of Bolivia and Argentina

1957. Yacuiba-Santa Cruz Railway Inauguration.

651	**174**	50b. orange (postage)	55	45
652		350b. blue and light blue	1·75	60
653		1000b. brown & cinna	4·25	1·25
654		600b. purple & pink (air)	1·60	60
655		700b. violet and blue	3·00	1·25
656		900b. green	4·25	75

175 Presidents and Flags of Bolivia and Mexico

1960. Visit of Mexican President to Bolivia.

657	**175**	350b. olive (postage)	15	10
658		600b. brown	25	10
659		1,500b. sepia	50	15
660		400b. red (air)	25	10
661		800b. blue	45	20
662		2,000b. green	70	40

The President's visit to Bolivia did not take place.

176 Indians and Mt. Illimani

177 "Gate of the Sun", Tiahuanacu

1960. Tourist Publicity.

663	**176**	500b. bistre (postage)	30	10
664		1000b. blue	50	15
665		2000b. sepia	1·40	35
666		4000b. green	2·50	1·75
667	**177**	3000b. grey (air)	1·25	75
668		5000b. orange	1·90	75
669		10,000b. purple	3·00	1·75
670		15,000b. violet	4·25	3·00

178 Refugees

179 "Uprooted Tree"

1960. World Refugee Year.

671	**178**	50b. brown (postage)	10	10
672		350b. purple	15	10
673		400b. blue	15	10
674		1000b. sepia	50	15
675		3000b. green	70	70
676	**179**	600b. blue (air)	35	35
677		700b. brown	35	35
678		900b. turquoise	40	35
679		1800b. violet	40	35
680		2000b. black	45	40

180 Jaime Laredo (violinist)

181 Jaime Laredo (violinist)

1960. Jaime Laredo Commem.

681	**180**	100b. green (postage)	10	10
682		350b. lake	20	10
683		500b. blue	25	10
684		1000b. brown	35	15
685		1500b. violet	60	60
686		5000b. black	2·00	2·00
687	**181**	600b. plum (air)	50	25
688		700b. olive	50	35
689		800b. brown	50	35
690		900b. blue	70	35
691		1800b. turquoise	1·00	1·00
692		4000b. grey	2·00	70

182 Rotary Emblem and Nurse with Children

183

1960. Founding of Children's Hospital by La Paz Rotary Club. Wheel in blue and yellow, foreground in yellow; background given.
693 **182** 350b. green (postage) 15 10
694 500b. sepia 25 10
695 600b. violet 35 10
696 1000b. grey 45 15

697 600b. brown (air) 45 25
698 1000b. olive 40 25
699 1800b. purple 70 70
700 5000b. black 2·00 80

1960. Air. Unissued stamp, surch as in T **183**.
701 **183** 1200b. on 10b. orange 2·75 1·75

184 Design from Gate of the Sun

185 Flags of Argentina and Bolivia

1960. Unissued Tiahuanacu Excavation stamps surch as in T **184**. Gold backgrounds.
702 50b. on ½c. red 30 20
703 100b. on 1c. red 35 15
704 200b. on 2c. black 50 15
705 300b. on 5c. green 25 15
706 350b. on 10c. green 25 50
707 400b. on 15c. blue 35 15
708 500b. on 20c. red 35 15
709 500b. on 50c. red 40 15
710 600b. on 22½c. green 30 25
711 600b. on 60c. violet 40 35
712 700b. on 25c. violet 50 20
713 700b. on 1b. green 85 80
714 800b. on 30c. red 40 20
715 900b. on 40c. green 30 25
716 1000b. on 2b. blue 40 35
717 1800b. on 3b. grey 3·25 2·40
718 4000b. on 4b. grey 19·00 16·00
719 5000b. on 5b. grey 5·00 4·75
DESIGNS: Various gods, motifs and ornaments. SIZES: Nos. 702/6, As Type **184**. Nos. 707/17, As Type **184** but horiz. No. 718, 49 × 23 mm. No. 719, 50 × 52½ mm.

1961. Air. Visit of Pres. Frondizi of Argentina.
720 **185** 4000b. multicoloured 70 60
721 – 6000b. sepia and green 1·00 85
DESIGN: 6000b. Presidents of Argentina and Bolivia.

186 Miguel de Cervantes (First Mayor of La Paz)

187 "United in Christ"

1961. M. de Cervantes Commem and 4th Centenary of Santa Cruz de la Sierra (1500b.).
722 **186** 600b. violet and ochre (postage) 40 10
723 – 1500b. blue and orange 60 20
724 – 1400b. brown & green (air) 60 25
DESIGNS: 1400b. Portrait as Type **186** (diamond shape, 30½ × 30½ mm); 1500b. Nuflo de Chaves (vert: as Type **186**).
See also Nos. 755/6.

1962. 4th National Eucharistic Congress, Santa Cruz.
725 **187** 1000b. yellow, red and green (postage) 45 35
726 – 1400b. yellow, pink and brown (air) 45 35
DESIGN: 1400b. Virgin of Cotoca.

1962. Nos. 671/80 surch.
727 **178** 600b. on 50b. brown (postage) 25 15
728 900b. on 350b. purple 30 15
729 1000b. on 400b. blue 25 15
730 2000b. on 1000b. brown 25 30
731 3500b. on 3000b. green 45 45
732 **179** 1200b. on 600b. blue (air) 40 35
733 1300b. on 700b. brown 35 35
734 1400b. on 900b. green 40 35
735 2800b. on 1800b. violet 60 50
736 3000b. on 2000b. black 60 50

189 Hibiscus

190 Infantry

1962. Flowers in actual colours; background colours given.
737 **189** 200b. green (postage) 25 10
738 – 400b. brown 25 10
739 – 600b. deep blue 50 10
740 – 1000b. violet 85 20

741 – 100b. blue (air) 10 10
742 – 800b. green 40 15
743 – 1800b. violet 90 35
744 – 10,000b. deep blue 4·50 2·25
FLOWERS: Nos. 738, 740 Orchids; 739, St. James' lily; 741/4, Types of Kantuta (national flowers).

1962. Armed Forces Commemoration.
745 **190** 400b. mult (postage) 10 10
746 – 500b. multicoloured 15 10
747 – 600b. multicoloured 20 15
748 – 2000b. multicoloured 60 40

749 – 600b. mult (air) 35 15
750 – 1200b. multicoloured 45 20
751 – 2000b. multicoloured 65 35
752 – 5000b. multicoloured 1·75 85
DESIGNS: No. 746, Cavalry; 747, Artillery; 748, Engineers; 749, Parachutists and aircraft; 750, 752, "Overseas Flights" (Lockheed Super Electra airplane over oxen-cart); 751, "Aerial Survey" (Douglas DC-3 airplane photographing ground).

191 Campaign Emblem

192 Goal-Keeper diving to save Goal

1962. Malaria Eradication.
753 **191** 600b. yellow, violet and lilac (postage) 25 15
754 – 2000b. yellow, green and blue (air) 55 50
DESIGN: 2000b. As No. 753 but with laurel wreath and inscription encircling emblem.

1962. Spanish Discoverers. As T **186** but inscribed "1548–1962".
755 600b. mauve on blue (postage) 35 15
756 1200b. brown on yellow (air) 45 20
PORTRAITS: 600b. A. de Mendoza. 1200b. P. de la Gasca.

(Currency reform. 1000 (old) pesos = 1 (new) peso)

1963. 21st South American Football Championships, La Paz. Multicoloured.
757 **192** 60c. Type **192** (postage) 40 10
758 1p. Goalkeeper saving ball (vert) 60 15
759 1p.40 Andean condor on football (vert) (air) 2·40 1·50
760 1p.80 Ball in corner of net (vert) 70 70

193 Globe and Emblem

194 Alliance Emblem

1963. Freedom from Hunger.
761 **193** 60c. yellow, blue and indigo (postage) 25 10
762 – 1p.20 yellow, blue and myrtle (air) 50 50
DESIGN: 1p.20, Ear of wheat across Globe.

1963. Air. "Alliance for Progress".
763 **194** 1p.20 green, blue & bis 55 35

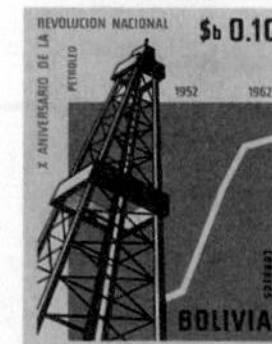

195 Oil Derrick

1963. 10th Anniv of Revolution (1962).
764 **195** 10c. grn & brn (postage) 10 10
765 – 60c. sepia and orange 30 10
766 – 1p. yellow, violet & green 35 15

767 – 1p.20 pink, brown and grey (air) 45 20
768 – 1p.40 green and ochre 55 25
769 – 2p.80 buff and slate 70 50
DESIGNS: 60c. Map of Bolivia; 1p. Students; 1p.20, Ballot box and voters; 1p.40, Peasant breaking chain; 2p.80, Miners.

196 Flags of Argentina and Bolivia

197 Marshal Santa Cruz

1966. Death Centenary of Marshal Santa Cruz.
770 **196** 10c. mult (postage) 10 10
771 60c. multicoloured 20 10
772 1p. multicoloured 35 15
773 2p. multicoloured 50 20

774 **197** 20c. blue (air) 10 10
775 60c. green 20 10
776 1p.20 brown 50 35
777 2p.80 black 65 40

198 Generals Barrientos and Ovando, Bolivian Map and Flag

199 Needy Children

1966. Co-Presidents Commemoration.
778 **198** 60c. mult (postage) 20 10
779 1p. multicoloured 30 10

780 2p.80 mult (air) 95 70
781 10p. multicoloured 1·10 35

1966. Aid for Poor Children.
783 **199** 30c. brown, sepia and ochre (postage) 15 10
784 – 1p.40 black & blue (air) 70 45
DESIGN: 1p.40, Mother and needy children.

1966. Commemorative Issues. Various stamps surch with inscr (as given below) and value. (i) Red Cross Centenary. Surch **Centenario de la Cruz Roja Internacional.**
785 20c. on 150b. (No. 641) (post) 10 10
786 4p. on 4000b. (No. 650) (air) 95 70

(ii) General Azurduy de Padilla. Surch **Homenaje a la Generala J. Azurduy de Padilla.**
787 30c. on 550b. (No. 643) 10 10
788 2p.80 on 750b. (No. 644) 70 35

(iii) Air. Tupiza Cent. Surch **Centenario de Tupiza.**
789 60c. on 1350b. (No. 648) 20 20

(iv) Air. 25th Anniv of Bolivian Motor Club. Surch **XXV Aniversario Automovil Club Boliviano.**
790 2p.80 on 2700b. (No. 649) 1·40 1·10

(v) Air. Cochabamba Philatelic Society Anniv. Surch **Aniversario Centro Filatelico Cochabamba.**
791 1p.20 on 800b. (No. 742) 35 25
792 1p.20 on 1800b. (No. 743) 35 25

(vi) Rotary Help for Children's Hospital. Surch with value only. (a) Postage.
793 1p.60 on 350b. (No. 693) 45 15
794 2p.40 on 500b. (No. 694) 70 25

(b) Air.
795 1p.40 on 1000b. (No. 698) 45 45
796 1p.40 on 1800b. (No. 699) 45 45

(vii) 150th Anniv of Coronilla Heroines. Surch **CL Aniversario Heroinas Coronilla.** (a) Postage.
797 60c. on 350b. (No. 682) 15 10

(b) Air.
798 1p.20 on 800b. (No. 689) 40 35

(viii) Air. Centenary of Hymn La Paz. Surch **Centenario Himno Paceno.**
799 1p.40 on 4000b. (No. 692) 40 35

(ix) Air. 12th Anniv of Agrarian Reform. Surch **XII Aniversario Reforma Agraria.**
800 10c. on 27b. (No. 602) 15 15

(x) Air. 25th Anniv of Chaco Peace Settlement. Surch **XXV Aniversario Paz del Chaco.**
801 10c. on 55b. (No. 613) 15 15

All the following are surch on Revenue stamps. The design shows a beach scene with palms, size 27 × 21½mm.

(xi) Centenary of Rurrenabaque. Surch **Centenario de Rurrenabaque.**
802 1p. on 10b. brown 30 10

(xii) 25th Anniv of Busch Government. Surch **XXV Aniversario Gobierno Busch.**
803 20c. on 5b. red 10 10

(xiii) 20th Anniv of Villarroel Government. Surch **XX Aniversario Gob. Villarroel.**
804 60c. on 2b. green 15 10

(xiv) 25th Anniv of Pando Department. Surch **XXV Aniversario Dpto. Pando.** (a) Postage.
805 1p.60 on 50c. violet 45 15

(b) Air. Surch **Aereo** also.
806 1p.20 on 1b. blue 50 40

201 Sower

202 "Macheteros"

1967. 50th Anniv of Lions International. Mult.
807 **201** 70c. Type **201** (postage) 35 10
808 2p. Lions emblem and Inca obelisks (horiz) (air) 55 45

1968. 9th Congress of the U.P.A.E. (Postal Union of the Americas and Spain). Bolivian Folklore. Designs showing costumed figures. Multicoloured.
810 **202** 30c. Type **202** (postage) 10 10
811 60c. "Chunchos" 15 10
812 1p. "Wiphala" 25 15
813 2p. "Diablada" 50 20

814 1p.20 "Pujllay" (air) 25 15
815 1p.40 "Ujusiris" 35 20
816 2p. "Morenada" 50 25
817 3p. "Auki-aukis" 85 50

203 Arms of Tarija

204 President G. Villarroel

1968. 150th Anniv of Battle of the Tablada (1817).
819 **203** 20c. mult (postage) 10 10
820 30c. multicoloured 10 10
821 40c. multicoloured 15 10
822 60c. multicoloured 20 10

823 – 1p. multicoloured (air) 35 15
824 – 1p.20 multicoloured 40 15
825 – 2p. multicoloured 70 35
826 – 4p. multicoloured 70 50
DESIGNS: Nos. 823/6, Moto Mendez.

1968. 400th Anniv of Cochabamba.
827 **204** 20c. brn & orge (postage) 15 10
828 30c. brown & turquoise 15 10
829 40c. brown and purple 15 10
830 50c. brown and green 15 10
831 1p. brown and bistre 35 10

832 – 1p.40 black & red (air) 35 25
833 – 3p. black and blue 35 40
834 – 4p. black and red 50 50
835 – 5p. black and green 60 40
836 – 10p. black and violet 1·10 75
DESIGN—HORIZ: 1p.40 to 10p. Similar portrait of President.

205 Painted Clay Cup

206 President J. F. Kennedy

1968. 20th Anniv of U.N.E.S.C.O. (1966).
837 **205** 20c. mult (postage) 15 10
838 60c. multicoloured 40 25

839 1p.20 black & blue (air) 40 20
840 2p.80 black and green 45 45
DESIGNS: Nos. 839/40, U.N.E.S.C.O. emblem.

1968. 5th Death Anniv of John F. Kennedy (U.S. President).
841 **206** 10c. black & grn (postage) 15 10
842 4p. black and violet 95 95

843 1p. black and green (air) 35 20
844 10p. black and red 1·90 1·90

207 I.T.U. Emblem **208** Tennis Player

1968. Centenary (1965) of I.T.U.
846 **207** 10c. black grey and yellow (postage) . . . 15 10
847 60c. black, orange & bistre . . . 35 10
848 1p.20 black, grey and yellow (air) . . . 30 10
849 1p.40 black, blue & brn 40 20

1968. South American Tennis Championships, La Paz.
850 **208** 10c. black, brown and grey (postage) . . . 20 10
851 20c. black, brown & yell 20 10
852 30c. black, brown & blue 20 10
853 1p.40 black, brown and orange (air) . . . 45 25
854 2p.80 black, brown & bl 50 50

209 Unofficial 1r. Stamp of 1863 **210** Rifle-shooting

1963. Stamp Centenary.
856 **209** 10c. brown, black and green (postage) . . . 15 10
857 30c. brown, black & blue 15 10
858 2p. brown, black & drab 25 10
859 – 1p.40 green, black and yellow (air) . . . 50 25
860 – 2p.80 green, blk & pink 70 50
861 – 3p. green, black & lilac 70 50
DESIGNS: Nos. 859/61 First Bolivian stamp.

1969. Olympic Games, Mexico (1968).
863 **210** 40c. black, red and orange (postage) . . . 15 10
864 – 50c. black, red and green 15 10
865 – 60c. black, blue & green 25 10
866 – 1p.20 black, green and ochre (air) . . . 40 15
867 – 2p.80 black, red & yell . . 85 35
868 – 5p. multicoloured . . . 1·00 1·00
DESIGNS—HORIZ: 50c. Horse-jumping; 60c. Canoeing; 5p. Hurdling. VERT: 1p.20, Running; 2p.80, Throwing the discus.

211 F. D. Roosevelt **212** "Temensis laothoe violetta"

1969. Air. Franklin D. Roosevelt Commem.
870 **211** 5p. black, orange & brown . . . 1·40 75

1970. Butterflies. Multicoloured.
871 5c. Type **212** (postage) . . . 35 35
872 10c. "Papilio crassus" . . . 70 70
873 20c. "Catagramma cynosura" 70 70
874 30c. "Eunica eurota flora" . . 70 70
875 80c. "Ituna phenarete" . . . 70 70
876 1p. "Metamorpha dido wernichei" (air) . . . 90 50
877 1p.80 "Heliconius felix" . . . 1·25 65
878 2p.80 "Morpho casica" . . . 1·75 1·75
879 3p. "Papilio yuracares" . . . 1·90 1·75
880 4p. "Heliconsus melitus" . . 2·50 2·00

213 Scout mountaineering **214** President A. Ovando and Revolutionaries

1970. Bolivian Scout Movement. Multicoloured.
882 **213** 5c. Type **213** (postage) . . 15 10
883 10c. Girl-scout planting shrub . . . 15 10
884 50c. Scout laying bricks (air) . . . 15 10
885 1p.20 Bolivian scout badge . . . 35 15

1970. Obligatory Tax. Revolution and National Day.
886 **214** 20c. blk & red (postage) 25 15
887 30c. black & green (air) 25 15
DESIGN: 30c. Pres. Ovando, oil derricks and laurel sprig.

1970. "Exfilca 70" Stamp Exhibition, Caracas, Venezuela. No. 706 further surch **EXFILCA 70** and new value.
888 30c. on 350b. on 10c. . . . 15 10

1970. Provisionals. Various stamps surch.
889 **178** 60c. on 900b. on 350b. (postage) . . . 30 10
890 – 1p.20 on 1500b. (No. 723) 50 15
891 **185** 1p.20 on 4000b. (air) . . 35 15

217 Pres. G. Busch and Oil Derrick **218** "Amaryllis escobar uriae"

1971. 32nd Death Anniv of President G. Busch and 25th Death Anniv of Pres. Villarroel.
892 **217** 20c. blk & lilac (postage) 35 10
893 – 30c. black and blue (air) 30 10
DESIGN: 30c. Pres. Villarroel and oil refinery.

1971. Bolivian Flora. Multicoloured.
894 30c. Type **218** (postage) . . . 15 10
895 40c. "Amaryllis evansae" . . 15 10
896 50c. "Amaryllis yungacensis" (vert) . . . 20 15
897 2p. "Gymnocalycium chiquitanum" (vert) . . . 55 35
898 1p.20 "Amaryllis pseudopardina" (air) . . . 45 15
899 1p.40 "Rebutia kruegeri" (vert) . . . 60 15
900 2p.80 "Lobivia pentlandii" 95 25
901 4p. "Rebutia tunariensis" (vert) . . . 1·60 50

219 Sica Sica Cathedral **220** Pres. H. Banzer

1971. "Exfilima" Stamp Exhibition, Lima, Peru.
903 **219** 20c. multicoloured . . . 15 10

1972. "Bolivia's Development".
904 **220** 1p.20 multicoloured . . . 35 15

221 Chiriwano de Achocalla Dance **222** "Virgin and Child" (B. Bitti)

1972. Folk Dances. Multicoloured.
905 20c. Type **221** (postage) . . . 10 10
906 40c. Rueda Chapaca . . . 20 15
907 60c. Kena-Kena . . . 30 15
908 1p. Waca Thokori . . . 40 25
909 1p.20 Kusillo (air) . . . 40 15
910 1p.40 Taquirari . . . 45 15

1972. Bolivian Paintings. Multicoloured.
911 10c. "The Washerwoman" (M. P. Holguin) (postage) 10 10
912 50c. "Coronation of the Virgin" (G. M. Berrio) . . 20 10
913 70c. "Arquebusier" (anon.) 25 10
914 80c. "St. Peter of Alcantara" (M. P. Holguin) . . . 25 15
915 1p. Type **222** . . . 35 15
916 1p.40 "Chola Pacena" (G. de Rojas) (air) . . . 40 10
917 1p.50 "Adoration of the Kings" (G. Gamarra) . . 40 10
918 1p.60 "Pachamama Vision" (A. Borda) . . . 40 10
919 2p. "Idol's Kiss" (G. de Rojas) . . . 40 25

223 Tarija Cathedral

1972. "EXFILIBRA 72" Stamp Exhibition, Rio de Janeiro.
920 **223** 30c. multicoloured . . . 15 10

224 National Arms

1972. Air.
921 **224** 4p. multicoloured . . . 95 35

225 Santos Dumont and "14 bis"

1973. Air. Birth Centenary of Alberto Santos Dumont (aviation pioneer).
922 **225** 1p.40 black and yellow . . 1·25 45

226 "Echinocactus notocactus" **227** Power Station, Santa Isabel

1973. Cacti. Multicoloured.
923 20c. Type **226** (postage) . . . 10 10
924 40c. "Echinocactus lenninghaussii" . . . 15 10
925 50c. "Mammillaria bocasana" 20 10
926 70c. "Echinocactus lenninghaussii" (different) 30 10
927 1p.20 "Mammillaria bocasana" (different) (air) 40 15
928 1p.90 "Opuntia cristata" . . 60 20
929 2p. "Echinocactus rebutia" 85 25

1973. Bolivian Development Multicoloured.
930 10c. Type **227** (postage) . . . 10 10
931 20c. Tin foundry . . . 15 10
932 90c. Bismuth plant . . . 40 10
933 1p. Gas plant . . . 40 10
934 1p.40 Road bridge, Highways 1 and 4 (air) . . . 50 15
935 2p. Inspection car crossing bridge, Al Beni . . . 8·00 2·50

228 "Cattleya nobilior" **229** Morane Saulnier Type P and Emblem

1974. Orchids. Multicoloured.
936 20c. Type **228** (postage) . . . 10 10
937 50c. "Zygopetalum bolivianum" . . . 20 10
938 1p. "Huntleya melagris" . . 35 10
939 2p.50 "Cattleya luteola" (horiz) (air) . . . 90 25
940 3p.80 "Stanhopaea" . . . 1·00 35
941 4p. "Catasetum" (horiz) . . . 1·00 45
942 5p. "Maxillaria" . . . 1·75 50

1974. Air. 50th Anniv of Bolivian Air Force. Multicoloured.
944 3p. Type **229** . . . 75 50
945 3p.80 Douglas DC-3 crossing Andes . . . 1·25 70
946 4p.50 Triplane trainer and Morane Saulnier Paris I aircraft . . . 1·25 70
947 8p. Col. Rafael Pabon and biplane fighter . . . 1·75 1·40
948 15p. Jet airliner on "50" . . 3·75 2·00

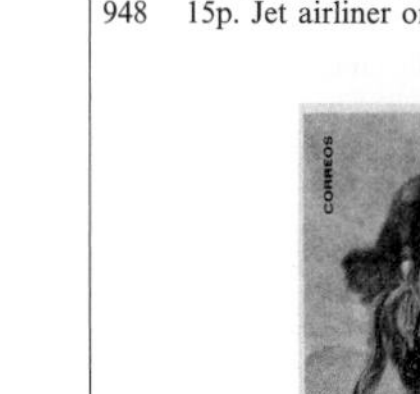

230 General Sucre (after J. Wallpher)

1974. 150th Anniv of Battle of Avacucho.
949 **230** 5p. multicoloured . . . 75 55

231 U.P.U. and Exhibition Emblems

1974. Centenary of U.P.U. and Expo U.P.U. (Montevideo) and Prenfil U.P.U. (Buenos Aires) Stamp Exhibitions.
950 **231** 3p.50 green, black & bl 70 45

232 Lions Emblem and Steles

1975. 50th Anniv of Lions International in Bolivia.
951 **232** 30c. multicoloured . . . 35 10

233 Exhibition Emblem

1975. "Espana 75" International Stamp Exhibition, Madrid.
952 **233** 4p.50 multicoloured . . . 55 35

234 Emblem of Meeting **235** Arms of Pando

1975. Cartagena Agreement. First Meeting of Postal Ministers, Quito, Ecuador.
953 **234** 2p.50 silver, violet & blk 45 30

1975. 150th Anniv of Republic (1st issue). Provincial Arms. Multicoloured.
955 20c. Type **235** (postage) . . . 10 10
956 2p. Chuzuisaca . . . 50 35
957 3p. Cochabamba . . . 70 50
958 20c. Beni (air) . . . 10 10
959 30c. Tarija . . . 10 10
960 50c. Potosi . . . 10 10
961 1p. Oruro . . . 4·50 1·50
962 2p.50 Santa Cruz . . . 50 50
963 3p. La Paz . . . 70 50
See also Nos. 965/78.

236 Presidents Perez and Banzer **237** Pres. Victor Paz Estenssoro

1975. Air. Visit of Pres. Perez of Venezuela.
964 **236** 3p. multicoloured 75 55

1975. 150th Anniv of Republic (2nd issue).
965 30c. Type **237** (postage) . . 10 10
966 60c. Pres. Thomas Frias . . 15 10
966a 1p. Ismael Montes 20 10
967 2p.50 Aniceto Arce 50 25
968 7p. Bautista Saavedra . . . 95 35
969 10p. Jose Manuel Pando . . 1·40 50
970 15p. Jose Maria Linares . . 1·75 1·75
971 50p. Simon Bolivar . . . . 6·25 6·25
972 50c. Rene Barrientos Ortuno (air) 15 10
973 2p. Francisco B. O'Connor 50 25
973a 3p.80 Gualberto Villaroel 70 50
974 4p.20 German Busch . . . 70 70
975 4p.50 Pres. Hugo Banzer Suarez 70 70
976 20p. Jose Ballivian . . . . 2·50 1·40
977 30p. Pres. Andres de Santa Cruz . . . . 3·25 3·25
978 40p. Pres. Antonio Jose de Sucre . . . . 4·25 4·25

Nos. 965/70, 972/4 and 976/78 are smaller, 24 × 33 mm.

238 Laurel Wreath and L.A.B. Emblem

239 "EXFIVIA"

1975. Air. 50th Anniv of Lloyd-Aereo Boliviano (national airline). Multicoloured.
979 1p. Type **238** 15 10
980 1p.50 Douglas DC-9 and L.A.B. route map (horiz) 35 15
981 2p. Guillermo Kyllmann (founder) and Junkers F-13 aircraft (horiz) 45 25

1975. Obligatory Tax. As No. 893 but inscr "XXV ANIVERSARIO DE SU GOBIERNO".
982 30c. black and blue 30 10

1975. "Exfivia 75". Stamp Exhibition.
983 **239** 3p. multicoloured 70 35

240 U.P.U. Emblem

1975. Air. Centenary (1974) of U.P.U.
984 **240** 25p. multicoloured . . . 2·00 2·00

241 Chiang Kai-shek

1976. 1st Death Anniv of President Chiang Kai-shek.
985 **241** 2p.50 multicoloured . . . 60 25

242 Geological Hammer, Lamp and Map

1976. Bolivian Geological Institute.
986 **242** 4p. multicoloured 55 55

243 Naval Insignia

1976. Navy Day.
987 **243** 50c. multicoloured 25 10

244 Douglas DC-10 and Divided Roundel

1976. 50th Anniv of Lufthansa Airline.
988 **244** 3p. multicoloured 90 35

245 Bolivian Boy Scout and Badge

1976. 60th Anniv of Bolivian Boy Scouts.
989 **245** 1p. multicoloured 50 20

246 Battle Scene

247 Brother Vicente Bernedo (missionary)

1976. Bicentenary of American Revolution.
990 **246** 4p.50 multicoloured . . . 95 45

1976. Brother Vincente Bernedo Commemoration.
992 **247** 1p.50 multicoloured . . . 35 15

248 Rainbow over La Paz, Police Handler with Dog

249 Bolivian Family

1976. 150th Anniv of Police Service.
993 **248** 2p.50 multicoloured . . . 40 25

1976. National Census.
994 **249** 2p.50 multicoloured . . . 55 35

250 Pedro Poveda (educator)

1976. Poveda Commemoration.
995 **250** 1p.50 multicoloured . . . 35 15

251 Arms, Bolivar and Sucre

252 "Numeral"

1976. International Bolivarian Societies Congress.
996 **251** 1p.50 multicoloured . . . 55 25

1976.
997 **252** 20c. brown 10 10
998 1p. blue 25 10
999 1p.50 green 40 10

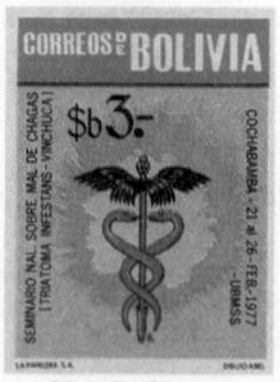

253 Boy and Girl

254 Caduceus

1977. Christmas 1976 and 50th Anniv of Inter-American Children's Institute.
1000 **253** 50c. multicoloured . . . 15 10

1977. National Seminar on "Chagas Disease".
1001 **254** 3p. multicoloured . . . 70 10

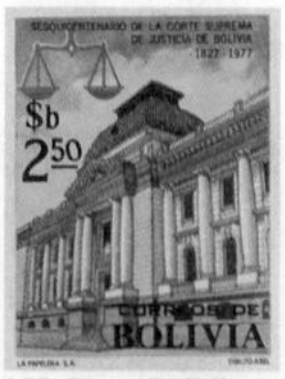

255 Court Buildings, La Paz

256 Tower and Map

1977. 150th Anniv of Bolivian Supreme Court. Multicoloured.
1002 2p.50 Type **255** 30 10
1003 4p. Dr. Manuel M. Urcullu, first President 45 10
1004 4p.50 Dr. Pantaleon Dalence, President, 1883–89 . . . . 50 10

1977. 90th Anniv of Oruro Club.
1005 **256** 3p. multicoloured . . . 50 15

257 Newspaper Mastheads

258 Games Poster

1977. Bolivian Newspapers. Multicoloured.
1006 1p.50 Type **257** 25 10
1007 2p.50 "Ultima Hora" and Alfredo Alexander (horiz) 35 10
1008 3p. "El Diaro" and Jose Carrasco (horiz) 45 15
1009 4p. "Los Tiempos" and Demetrio Canelas 50 15
1010 5p.50 "Presencia" 70 20

1977. 8th Bolivarian Games, La Paz.
1011 **258** 5p. multicoloured . . . 70 20

259 Tin Miner and Mining Corporation Emblem

260 Miners, Globe and Chemical Symbol for Tin

1977. 25th Anniv of Bolivian Mining Corporation.
1012 **259** 3p. multicoloured . . . 4·25 2·00

1977. International Tin Symposium, La Paz.
1013 **260** 6p. multicoloured . . . 55 30

261 Map of Bolivia and Radio Masts

263 "Eye", Compass, Key and Law Book

1977. 50th Anniv of Bolivian Radio.
1014 **261** 2p.50 multicoloured . . 35 10

1977. "Exfivia 77" Philatelic Exhibition, Cochabamba. No. 719 surch **EXFIVIA — 77 $b. 5.—.**
1015 5p. on 5,000b. on $b. 5 grey and gold 85 15

1978. 50th Anniv of Audit Department.
1016 **263** 5p. multicoloured . . . 45 15

264 Aesculapius Staff and Map of Andean Countries

265 Map of the Americas

266 Mt. Illimani

1978. 5th Meeting of Andean Countries' Health Ministers.
1017 **264** 2p. orange and black . . 40 10

1978. World Rheumatism Year (1977).
1018 **265** 2p.50 blue and red . . . 35 15

1978.
1019 **266** 50c. green and blue . . . 10 10
1020 – 1p. yellow and brown . . 15 10
1021 – 1p.50 grey and red . . . 25 10

DESIGNS—HORIZ: 1p.50, Mt. Cerro de Potosi. VERT: 1p. Pre-Columbian monolith.

267 Central Bank

268 Jesus with Children

1978. 50th Anniv of Bank of Bolivia.
1022 **267** 7p. multicoloured . . . 70 25

1979. International Year of the Child.
1023 **268** 8p. multicoloured . . . 60 15

269 Antofagasta Cancellation

270 Antofagasta

1979. Centenary of Loss of Litoral Department to Chile.
1024 **269** 50c. brown and black . . 10 10
1025 – 1p. mauve and black . . 15 10
1026 – 1p.50 green and black 25 10
1027 **270** 5p.50 multicoloured . . 40 15
1028 – 6p.50 multicoloured . . 55 20
1029 – 7p. multicoloured . . . 55 20
1030 – 8p. multicoloured . . . 60 25
1031 – 10p. multicoloured . . . 75 35

DESIGNS—HORIZ: 1p. La Chimba cancel; 1p.50, Mejillonos cancel. VERT: (As Type **270**). 6p.50, Woman in chains; 7p. Eduardo Arbaroa; 8p. Map of Department, 1876; 10p. Arms of Litoral.

271 Map and Radio Club Emblem

272 Runner and Games Emblem

1979. Radio Club of Bolivia.
1032 **271** 3p. multicoloured . . . 40 10

1979. 1st "Southern Cross" Games. Mult.
1033 6p.50 Type **272** 55 20
1034 10p. Gymnast 75 35

273 Bulgarian Stamp of 1879

274 "Exfilmar" Emblem

1979. "Philaserdica 79" Philatelic Exhibition, Sofia, Bulgaria.
1035 **273** 2p.50 black, yellow and light yellow 30 10

1979. "Exfilmar 79" Maritime Philatelic, Exhibition, La Paz.
1036 **274** 2p. blue, black and light blue 20 20

275 O.A.S. Emblem and Map

276 Franz Tamayo (lawyer)

1979. 9th Congress of Organization of American States, La Paz.
1037 **275** 6p. multicoloured . . . 50 20

1979. Anniversaries and Events.
1038 **276** 2p.80 light grey, black and grey 35 10
1039 – 5p. multicoloured . . . 35 20
1040 – 5p. multicoloured . . . 35 20
1041 – 6p. multicoloured . . . 45 20
1042 – 9p.50 multicoloured . . 2·00 80
DESIGNS—VERT: 2p.80, Type **276** (birth centenary); 5p. (No. 1039) U.N. emblem and delegates (18th CEPAL Sessions, La Paz); 5p. (No. 1042), Gastroenterological laboratory (Japanese health co-operation); 6p. Radio mast (50th anniv of national radio). HORIZ: 9p.50, Puerto Suarez iron ore deposits.

277 500c. Stamp of 1871, Exhibition Emblem and Flag

1980. "Exfilmar" Bolivian Maritime Stamp Exhibition, La Paz.
1043 **277** 4p. multicoloured . . . 50 15

278 Juana Azurduy de Padilla

1980. Birth Bicentenary of Juana Azurduy de Padilla (Independence heroine).
1044 **278** 4p. multicoloured . . . 55 15

279 Jean Baptiste de la Salle (founder)

1980. 300th Anniv of Brothers of Christian Schools.
1045 **279** 9p. multicoloured . . . 75 30

280 "Victory in a Chariot", Emblem and Flags

1980. "Espamer 80" International Stamp Exhibition, Madrid.
1046 **280** 14p. multicoloured . . . 1·10 45

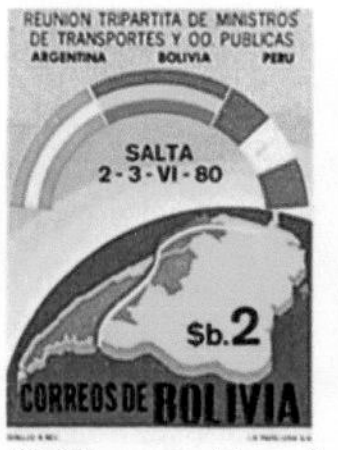

281 Flags over Map of South America

282 Diesel Locomotive

1980. Meeting of Public Works and Transport Ministers of Argentina, Bolivia and Peru.
1047 **281** 2p. multicoloured . . . 25 10

1980. Inauguration of Santa Cruz-Trinidad Railway, Third Section.
1048 **282** 3p. multicoloured . . . 90 50

283 Soldier and Citizen with Flag destroying Communism

284 Scarlet Macaw

1981. 1st Anniv of 17 July Revolution. Mult.
1049 1p. Type **283** 15 10
1050 3p. Flag shattering hammer and sickle on map 35 10
1051 40p. Flag on map of Bolivia showing provinces . . . . 3·25 85
1052 50p. Rejoicing crowd (horiz) 3·75 85

1981. Macaws. Multicoloured.
1053 4p. Type **284** 65 35
1054 7p. Green-winged macaw . . 1·00 50
1055 8p. Blue and yellow macaw 1·25 60
1056 9p. Red-fronted macaw . . 1·40 65
1057 10p. Yellow-collared macaw 1·40 65
1058 12p. Hyacinth macaw . . . 1·90 90
1059 15p. Military macaw . . . . 1·50 1·10
1060 20p. Chestnut-fronted macaw . . . . 3·00 1·25

285 Virgin and Child receiving Flower

286 Emblem

1981. Christmas.
1061 **285** 1p. pink and red 15 10
1062 – 2p. light blue and blue 30 10
DESIGN: 2p. Child and star (horiz).
See also No. 1080.

1982. 22nd American Air Force Commanders' Conference, Buenos Aires.
1063 **286** 14p. multicoloured . . . 1·10 35

287 Cobija

288 Simon Bolivar

1982. 75th Anniv of Cobija City.
1064 **287** 28p. multicoloured . . . 30 20

1982. Birth Bicentenary of Simon Bolivar.
1065 **288** 18p. multicoloured . . . 35 25

289 Dish Antenna

290 Footballers

1982. World Communication Year.
1066 **289** 26p. multicoloured . . . 30 20

1982. World Cup Football Championship, Spain. Multicoloured.
1067 4p. Type **290** 20 10
1068 100p. "The Final Number" (Picasso) . . . . 1·25 65

291 Boy playing Football

1982. Bolivian Youth. Multicoloured.
1069 16p. Type **291** 20 20
1070 20p. Girl playing piano (horiz) 25 30

292 Harvesting

1982. China-Bolivian Agricultural Co-operation.
1071 **292** 30p. multicoloured . . . 50 20

293 Flowers

1982. 1st Bolivian-Japanese Gastroenterological Days.
1072 **293** 22p. multicoloured . . . 25 20

294 Bolivian Stamps

295 Hernando Siles

1982. 10th Anniv of Bolivian Philatelic Federation.
1073 **294** 19p. multicoloured . . . 35 15

1982. Birth Centenary of Hernando Siles (former President).
1074 **295** 20p. buff and brown . . 40 20

296 Baden-Powell

297 "Liberty", Cochabamba

1982. 125th Birth Anniv of Lord Baden-Powell and 75th Anniv of Boy Scout Movement.
1075 **296** 5p. multicoloured . . . 15 10

1982. 25th Anniv of Cochabamba Philatelic Centre.
1076 **297** 3p. buff, black & blue 10 10

298 High Court, Cochabamba

299 Virgin of Copacabana

1982. 150th Anniv of High Court, Cochabamba.
1077 **298** 10p. black, red and bronze 25 10

1982. 400th Anniv of Enthronement of Virgin of Copacabana.
1078 **299** 13p. multicoloured . . . 30 15

300 Puerto Busch Naval Base

1982. Navy Day.
1079 **300** 14p. multicoloured . . . 60 20

1982. Christmas. Design as Type **285**, inscribed "NAVIDAD 1982".
1080 **285** 10p. grey and green . . 20 10

301 Footballer and Emblem

1983. 10th American Youth Football Championships.
1081 **301** 50p. multicoloured . . . 55 45

302 Sun Gate

1983. "Exfivia 83" Stamp Exhibition.
1082 **302** 150p. red 90 35

303 Presidents Figueiredo and Zuazo

1984. Visit of President of Brazil.
1083 **303** 150p. multicoloured . . 40 15

1984. Various stamps surch.
1084 **276** 40p. on 2p.80 light grey, black and grey 15 10
1085 – 60p. on 1p.50 green and black (1026) 15 10
1086 **265** 60p. on 2p.50 blue and red 15 10
1087 **274** 100p. on 2p. blue, black and light blue 30 15
1088 **174** 200p. on 350b. blue and light blue . . . . . . 2·25 90

1984. "Mladost 84" Youth Stamp Exn, Pleven, Bulgaria. No. 1035 surch.
1089 **273** 40p. on 2p.50 black, yellow and light yellow 15 10

306 "Simon Bolivar" (Mulato Gil de Quesada)

308 Pedestrian walking in Road

1984. Birth Bicentenary of Simon Bolivar. Mult.
1090 50p. Type **306** 15 10
1091 200p. "Simon Bolivar entering La Paz" (Carmen Baptista) 35 20

1984. Various stamps surch.
1092 **297** 500p. on 3p. buff, black and blue (postage) . . 45 30
1093 **290** 1000p. on 4p. mult . . . 90 65
1094 **285** 2000p. on 10p. grey and green . . . . 2·00 85
1095 **296** 5000p. on 5p. mult . . . 4·75 2·00

1096 – 10000p. on 3p.80 mult (No. 940) (air) . . . . 6·25 3·75

1984. Road Safety Campaign. Multicoloured.
1097 80p. Type **308** 10 10
1098 120p. Police motorcyclist and patrol car 10 10

309 "Mendezs Birthplace" (Jorge Campos)
310 Legs and Feet on Map and Bata Emblem

1984. Birth Bicentenary of Jose Eustaquio Mendez. Multicoloured.
1099 300p. Type **309** 15 10
1100 500p. "Battle of La Tablada" (M. Villegas) . . 20 10

1984. World Footwear Festival. Mult.
1101 100p. Type **310** 10 10
1102 200p. Legs and feet on map and Power emblem . . . 10 10
1103 600p. Football and globes (World Cup, Mexico, 1986) (horiz) 15 10

311 Inca Postal Runner
312 Vicuna

1985.
1104 **311** 11000p. blue 30 15

1985. Endangered Animals.
1105 **312** 23000p. brown and deep brown 35 15
1106 – 25000p. brown, blue and orange . . . . 1·00 20
1107 – 30000p. red and green 45 20
DESIGNS—VERT: 25000p. Andean condor; 30000p. Marsh deer.

313 National Work Education Service Emblem
314 Hand with Syringe, Victim in Droplet and Campaign Emblem

1985. International Professional Education Year.
1108 **313** 2000p. blue and red . . 10 10

1985. Anti-polio Campaign.
1109 **314** 20000p. blue and violet 30 15

315 Vicenta Juaristi Eguino
316 U.N. Emblem

1985. Birth Bicentenary of Vicenta Juaristi Eguino (Independence heroine).
1110 **315** 300000p. multicoloured 30 15

1985. 40th Anniv of U.N.O.
1111 **316** 1000000p. blue and gold 45 30

317 Emblem
318 Emblem, Envelope and Posthorn

1985. 75th Anniv of "The Strongest" Football Club.
1112 **317** 200000p. multicoloured 20 10

1986. Cent of Bolivian U.P.U. Membership.
1113 **318** 800000p. multicoloured 65 30

319 Bull and Rider
321 Football as Globes

1986. 300th Anniv of Trinidad City.
1114 **319** 1400000p. multicoloured 1·00 45

1986. No. 1108 surch.
1115 **313** 200000p. on 2000p. blue and red 15 10
1116 5000000p. on 2000p. blue and red . . . . . 3·50 1·60

1986. World Cup Football Championship, Mexico.
1117 **321** 300000p. red and black 25 10
1118 – 550000p. multicoloured 45 20
1119 – 1000000p. black and green (horiz) 80 40
1120 – 2500000p. green & yell 1·90 85
DESIGNS—VERT: 550000p. Pique (mascot); 2500000p. Trophy. HORIZ: 1000000p. Azteca Stadium, Mexico City.

322 Alfonso Subieta Viaduct
323 Envelope

1986. 25th Anniv of American Development Bank.
1121 **322** 400000p. blue 35 15

1986. 50th Anniv of Society of Postmen.
1122 **323** 2000000p. brown . . . . 1·60 70

324 Emblem and Dove
325 Emblem

1986. International Peace Year.
1123 **324** 200000p. green 15 10

1986. International Youth Year (1985).
1124 **325** 150000p. red 15 10
1125 500000p. green 45 30
1126 – 3000000p. multicoloured 2·10 1·00
DESIGNS: 3000000p. Child clutching trophy and flag (25th anniv of Enrique Happ Sports Club, Cochabamba).

326 Zampa (after F. Diaz de Ortega)
328 Refinery

327 1870 500c. Stamp

1986. 50th Death Anniv of Friar Jose Antonio Zampa.
1127 **326** 400000p. multicoloured 35 15

1986. 15th Anniv of Bolivian Philatelic Federation.
1128 **327** 600000p. brown 50 20

1986. 50th Anniv of National Petroleum Refining Corporation.
1129 **328** 1000000p. multicoloured 1·00 30

329 Demon Mask
330 Flags

1987. Centenary of 10th February Society, Oruro.
1130 **329** 20c. multicoloured . . . 10 10

1987. State Visit of President Richard von Weizsacker of German Federal Republic.
1131 **330** 30c. multicoloured . . . 15 15

331 National Arms

1987. Visit of King Juan Carlos of Spain.
1132 **331** 60c. multicoloured . . . 60 20

332 Andean ("Condor")
333 Modern View of Potosi

1987. Endangered Animals. Multicoloured.
1133 20c. Type **332** 35 25
1134 20c. Tapir 10 10
1135 30c. Vicuna (new-born) . . 15 15
1136 30c. Armadillo 15 15
1137 40c. Spectacled bear 25 20
1138 60c. Keel-billed toucans ("Tucan") . . . . 1·10 50

1987. "Exfivia 87" Stamp Exhibition, Potosi. Multicoloured.
1139 40c. Type **333** 25 20
1140 50c. 18th-century engraving of Potosi 30 25

334 "Nina" and Stern of "Santa Maria"

1987. "Espamer '87" Stamp Exhibition, La Coruna. Multicoloured.
1141 20c. Type **334** 30 15
1142 20c. "Pinta" and bow of "Santa Maria" 30 15
Nos. 1141/2 were printed together, se-tenant, forming a composite design.

335 Pan-pipes and Indian Flute

1987. Musical Instruments. Multicoloured.
1143 50c. Type **335** 30 20
1144 1b. Indian guitars . . . . . 1·00 35

336 Carabuco Church

1988. Visit of Pope John Paul II. Mult.
1145 20c. Type **336** 10 10
1146 20c. Tihuanacu church . . . 10 10
1147 20c. Cathedral of the Kings, Beni 10 10
1148 30c. St. Joseph church, Chiquitos 15 15
1149 30c. St. Francis's church, Sucre 15 15
1150 40c. Cobija chapel (vert) . . 20 15
1151 50c. Cochabamba cathedral (vert) 25 20
1152 50c. Jayu Kcota church . . 25 20
1153 60c. St. Francis's Basilica, La Paz (vert) 30 25
1154 70c. Church of Jesus, Machaca 60 30
1155 70c. St. Lawrence's church, Potosi (vert) 60 30
1156 80c. Vallegrande church . . 70 35
1157 80c. Copacabana Virgin (vert) 70 35
1158 80c. "The Holy Family" (Peter Paul Rubens) (vert) 70 35
1159 1b.30 Concepcion church . . 1·10 55
1160 1b.30 Tarija cathedral (vert) 1·10 55
1161 1b.50 Pope and Arms of John Paul II and Bolivia 1·40 65

337 Handshake and Flags

1988. Visit of President Jose Sarney of Brazil.
1162 **337** 50c. multicoloured . . . 25 20

338 St. John Bosco
339 La Paz–Beni Steam Locomotive

1988. Death Centenary of St. John Bosco (founder of Salesian Brothers).
1163 **338** 30c. multicoloured . . . 15 15

1988. Centenary of Bolivian Railways.
1164 **339** 1b. multicoloured . . . 2·25 1·10

340 Aguirre
341 "Column of the Future" (Battle of Bahia Monument)

1988. Death Cent of Nataniel Aguirre (writer).
1165 **340** 1b. black and brown . . 80 35

1988. 50th Anniv of Pando Department. Mult.
1166 40c. Type **341** 15 10
1167 60c. Rubber production . . 50 20

342 Athlete
343 Mother Rosa Gattorno

1988. Olympic Games, Seoul.
1168 **342** 1b.50 multicoloured . . 1·25 55

1988. 88th Death Anniv of Mother Rosa Gattorno (Founder of the Daughters of St. Anne).
1169 **343** 80c. multicoloured . . . 70 30

344 Bernardino de Cardenas
345 Ministry Building

1988. 220th Death Anniv of Br. Bernardino de Cardenas (first Bishop of La Paz).
1170 **344** 70c. black and brown . . 60 25

1988. Ministry of Transport and Communications.
1171 **345** 2b. black, green & red 1·60 70

346 Arms  **347** Rally Car

1988. 50th Anniv of Army Communications Corps.
1172 **346** 70c. multicoloured . . . 65 25

1988. 50th Anniv of Bolivian Automobile Club.
1173 **347** 1b.50 multicoloured . . 1·00 55

348 Microphone and Emblem

1989. 50th Anniv of Radio Fides.
1174 **348** 80c. multicoloured . . . 65 30

349 Obverse and Reverse of 1852 Gold Cuartillo

1989. Coins.
1175 **349** 1b. multicoloured . . . 80 35

350 "Bulgaria 89" Stamp Exhibition Emblem and Orchid  **351** Birds

1989. Events and Plants. Multicoloured.
1176 50c. Type **350** 20 15
1177 60c. "Italia '90" World Cup football championship emblem and kantuta (national flower) (horiz) 50 20
1178 70c. "Albertville 1986" emblem and "Heliconia humilis" 55 25
1179 1b. Olympic Games, Barcelona emblem and "Hoffmanseggia" 80 35
1180 2b. Olympic Games, Seoul emblem and bromeliad . . 1·60 70

1989. Bicentenary of French Revolution.
1181 **351** 70c. multicoloured . . . 60 25

352 Clock Tower and Steam Locomotive  **353** Federico Ahlfeld Waterfall, River Pauserna

1989. Centenary of Uyuni.
1182 **352** 30c. grey, black & blue 75 40

1989. Noel Kempff Mercado National Park. Multicoloured.
1183 1b.50 Type **353** . . . . . . 1·25 60
1184 3b. Pampas deer . . . . . 2·40 1·00

354 Making Metal Articles

1989. America. Tiahuanacu Culture. Mult.
1185 50c. Type **354** 20 15
1186 1b. Kalasasaya Temple . . 70 35

355 Dr. Carlos Perez and Jaime Zamora  **356** Cobija Arch

1989. Meeting of Presidents of Bolivia and Venezuela.
1187 **355** 2b. multicoloured . . . 1·40 70

1989. World Heritage Site, Potosi. Mult.
1188 60c. Type **356** 50 15
1189 80c. Mint 60 20

357 "Andean Lake" (Arturo Borda)

1989. Christmas. Paintings. Multicoloured.
1190 40c. Type **357** 15 10
1191 60c. "Virgin of the Roses" (anon) 45 15
1192 80c. "Conquistador" (Jorge de la Reza) 55 20
1193 1b. "Native Harmony" (Juan Rimsa) 70 25
1194 1b.50 "Woman with Pitcher" (Cecilio Guzman de Rojas) . . . . 1·10 40
1195 2b. "Flower of Tenderness" (Gil Imana) . . . . . . 1·40 55

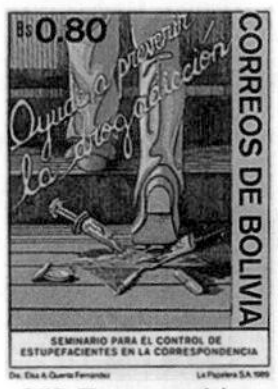

358 Foot crushing Syringe  **359** Map of Americas

1990. Anti-drugs Campaign.
1196 **358** 80c. multicoloured . . . 60 20

1990. Centenary of Organization of American States.
1197 **359** 80c. blue and deep blue 55 20

360 Colonnade  **361** Penny Black, Sir Rowland Hill and Bolivian 5c. Condor Stamp

1990. 450th Anniv of White City.
1198 **360** 1b.20 multicoloured . . 85 35

1990. 150th Anniv of the Penny Black.
1199 **361** 4b. multicoloured . . . 2·75 1·25

362 Giuseppe Meaza Stadium, Milan  **363** Emblem

1990. World Cup Football Championship, Italy. Multicoloured.
1200 2b. Type **362** . . . . 1·40 55
1201 6b. Match scene . . . . . 4·00 1·50

1990. Cent of Bolivian Chamber of Commerce.
1202 **363** 50c. black, blue & gold 40 10

364 Satellite, Map and Globe  **366** Chipaya Village, Oruro

365 Hall

1990. Telecommunications Development Year.
1203 **364** 70c. multicoloured . . . 50 15

1990. Centenary of Cochabamba Social Club.
1204 **365** 40c. multicoloured . . . 15 10

1990. America. Multicoloured.
1205 80c. Type **366** 50 15
1206 1b. Nevado Huayna, Cordillera Real (mountain) (vert) 65 20

367 Emblem  **368** Trees and Mountains

1990. "Meeting of Two Worlds. United towards Progress". 500th Anniv (1992) of Discovery of America by Columbus.
1207 **367** 2b. multicoloured . . . 1·25 40

1990. 400th Anniv of Larecaja District.
1208 **368** 1b.20 multicoloured . . 70 25

369 Dove and German National Colours  **370** Boys playing Football (Omar Espana)

1990. Unification of Germany.
1209 **369** 2b. multicoloured . . . 1·25 55

1990. Christmas. Rights of the Child.
1210 **370** 50c. multicoloured . . . 15 10

371 Arms of Bolivia and Ecuador  **373** Andes

372 Flags and Andes

1990. Visit of Pres. Rodrigo Borja Cevallos of Ecuador.
1211 **371** 80c. multicoloured . . . 60 15

1990. 4th Andean Presidents' Council, La Paz.
1212 **372** 1b.50 multicoloured . . 90 30

1990. "Exfivia 90" National Stamp Exhibition.
1213 **373** 40c. blue 15 10

374 Arms of Bolivia and Mexico  **376** Emblem

375 Emblem, Globe and Flags

1990. Visit of Pres. Carlos Salinas de Gortari of Mexico.
1214 **374** 60c. multicoloured . . . 50 15

1990. Express Mail Service.
1215 **375** 1b. multicoloured . . . 60 20

1991. 50th Anniv of Bolivian Radio Club.
1216 **376** 2b.40 multicoloured . . 1·40 50

377 Head of Bear  **378** National Museum of Archaeology

1991. The Spectacled Bear. Multicoloured.
1217 30c. Type **377** 10 10
1218 30c. Bear on branch 10 10
1219 30c. Bear and cub at water's edge 10 10
1220 30c. Bear and cubs on branches 10 10

1991. "Espamer '91" Spain–Latin America Stamp Exhibition, Buenos Aires. Multicoloured.
1221 50c. Type **378** 15 10
1222 50c. National Art Museum 15 10
1223 1b. National Museum of Ethnography and Folklore 60 20

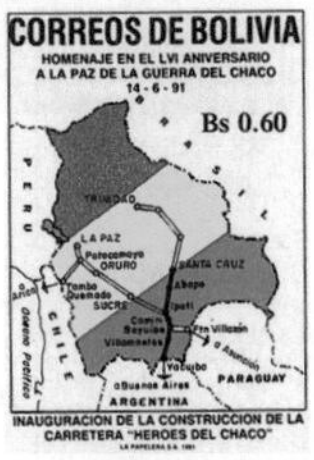

379 Map  **380** Statue of Our Lady of La Paz and Cathedral

1991. 56th Anniv of Ending of Chaco War and Beginning of Construction of "Heroes of Chaco" Road.
1224 **379** 60c. multicoloured . . . 20 15

1991. La Paz Cathedral.
1225 **380** 1b.20 multicoloured . . 80 25

381 Presidents Lacalle and Paz Zamora

1991. Meeting of Uruguayan and Bolivian Presidents.
1226 **381** 1b. multicoloured . . . 60 20

382 Presidents Paz Zamora and Menem

1991. Meeting of Bolivian and Argentine Presidents.
1227 **382** 1b. multicoloured . . . 60 20

383 "Exfivia 83", "87" and "90" Stamps

385 Route Map, Motor Cycle and Rally Car

384 Presidents Fujimori and Paz Zamora

1991. 20th Anniv of Bolivian Philatelic Federation.
1228 **383** 70c. multicoloured . . . 45 10

1991. Presidential Summit of Bolivia and Peru.
1229 **384** 50c. multicoloured . . . 15 10

1991. Pres. Jaime Paz Zamora National Grand Prix Motor Rally, Tarija-Cobija.
1230 **385** 50c. multicoloured . . . 15 10

386 Data Retrieval Systems

1991. "Ecobol" Postal Security.
1231 **386** 1b.40 multicoloured . . 90 30

387 "First Discovery of Chuquiago" (Arturo Reque)

388 Stylized Figures and City Skyline

1991. America. Voyages of Discovery. Mult.
1232 60c. Type **387** 20 10
1233 1b.20 "Foundation of City of Our Lady of La Paz" (J. Rimsa) (vert) 80 30

1991. National Population and Housing Census.
1234 **388** 50c. multicoloured . . . 15 10

389 "Landscape" (Daniel Pena y Sarmiento)

1991. Christmas. Multicoloured.
1235 2b. Type **389** . . . . . . 1·00 40
1236 5b. "Fruit Seller" (Cecilio Guzman de Rojas) . . . 2·50 1·00
1237 15b. "Native Mother" (Crespo Gastelu) . . . . 7·50 3·00

390 Camp-site and Emblem

1992. 75th Anniv (1990) of Bolivian Scout Movement and Los Andes Jamboree, Cochabamba.
1238 **390** 1b.20 multicoloured . . 80 30

391 Simon Bolivar

392 Raising Flag

1992. "Exfilbo 92" National Stamp Exhibition, La Paz.
1239 **391** 1b.20 deep brown, brown and stone . . . 80 30

1992. Creation of Bolivian Free Zone in Ilo, Peru. Multicoloured.
1240 1b.20 Type **392** 65 30
1241 1b.50 Presidents Fujimori (Peru) and Paz Zamora (horiz) 80 30
1242 1b.80 Beach at Ilo (horiz) 95 35

393 Logotype of Pavilion

1992. "Expo '92" World's Fair, Seville, and "Granada '92" Int Stamp Exhibition. Mult.
1243 30c. Type **393** 10 10
1244 50c. Columbus's fleet . . . 30 10

394 Rotary International Emblem and Prize

1992. Rotary Club Miraflores District 4690 "Illimani de Oro" Prize.
1245 **394** 90c. gold, blue & black 30 20

395 School and Perez

1992. Birth Centenary of Elizardo Perez (founder of Ayllu School, Warisata).
1246 **395** 60c. blue, black & yellow 50 10

396 Government Palace

1992. U.N.E.S.C.O. World Heritage Site, Sucre.
1247 **396** 50c. multicoloured . . . 15 10

397 Mario Martinez Guzman

398 Front Page

1992. Olympic Games, Barcelona.
1248 **397** 1b.50 multicoloured . . 80 30

1992. 25th Anniv of "Los Tiempos" (newspaper).
1249 **398** 50c. multicoloured . . . 15 10

399 Canoeing

400 Columbus leaving Palos (after Bejarano)

1992. 1st International River Bermejo Canoeing Championship.
1250 **399** 1b.20 multicoloured . . 75 30

1992. America. 500th Anniv of Discovery of America by Columbus.
1251 **400** 60c. brown and black . . 20 10
1252 – 2b. multicoloured . . . 95 40
DESIGN—HORIZ: 2b. "Columbus meeting the Caribisis Tribe" (Luis Vergara).

401 Football Match

402 "Chenopodium quinoa"

1992. World Cup Football Championship, U.S.A. (1994).
1253 **401** 1b.20 multicoloured . . 1·25 30

1992. 50th Anniv of Interamerican Institute for Agricultural Co-operation.
1254 **402** 1b.20 multicoloured . . 80 30

403 University Arms and Minerals

1992. Cent of Oruro Technical University.
1255 **403** 50c. multicoloured . . . 15 10

404 Mascots

1992. 12th Bolivarian Games, Cochabamba and Santa Cruz (1st issue).
1256 **404** 2b. multicoloured . . . 1·00 40
See also No. 1271.

405 Cayman

1992. Ecology and Conservation. Multicoloured.
1257 20c. Type **405** 10 10
1258 50c. Spotted cavy 15 10
1259 1b. Chinchilla 30 20
1260 2b. Anteater . . . . 1·00 40
1261 3b. Jaguar . . . . 1·50 65
1262 4b. Long-tailed sylph ("Picaflor") (vert) . . . . 3·50 1·60
1263 5b. Piranhas . . . . 2·50 1·10
Each stamp also bears the emblem of an anniversary or event.

406 Battle Scene

1992. 150th Anniv of Battle of Ingavi.
1264 **406** 1b.20 brown and black 65 30

407 Man following Star in Boat

1992. Christmas. Multicoloured.
1265 1b.20 Type **407** 60 20
1266 2b.50 Star over church . . . 1·40 50
1267 6b. Infant in manger and church . . . . 3·00 1·25

408 Nicolas Copernicus (450th death anniv)

409 Mother Nazaria (after Victor Eusebio Choque)

1993. Astronomy.
1268 – 50c. multicoloured . . . 15 10
1269 **408** 2b. black . . . . 1·00 35
DESIGN—HORIZ: 50c. Santa Ana International Astronomical Observatory, Tarija (10th anniv (1992)).

1993. Beatification (1992) of Mother Nazaria Ignacia March Meza.
1270 **409** 60c. multicoloured . . . 40 10

410 Pictograms and Flags of Ecuador, Venezuela, Peru, Bolivia, Colombia and Panama

1993. 12th Bolivarian Games, Cochabamba and Santa Cruz (2nd issue).
1271 **410** 2b.30 multicoloured . . 1·10 35

411 Bolivia 1962 10000b. Kantuta and Brazil 90r. "Bull's Eye" Stamps

1993. 150th Anniv of First Brazilian Stamps.
1272 **411** 2b.30 multicoloured . . 1·10 35

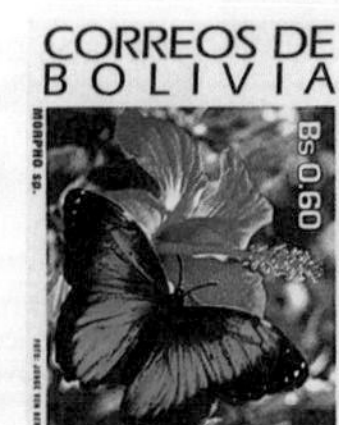

412 "Morpho sp."

1993. Butterflies. Multicoloured.
1273 60c. Type **412** 40 10
1274 60c. "Archaeoprepona demophon" 40 10
1275 80c. "Papilio sp." 45 10

1276 80c. Orion ("Historis odius") 45 10
1277 80c. Mexican fritillary ("Euptoieta hegesia") . . 45 10
1278 1b.80 "Morpho deidamia" 1·10 30
1279 1b.80 Orange swallowtail ("Papilio thoas") . . . . 1·10 30
1280 1b.80 Monarch ("Danaus plexippus") . . . . 1·10 30
1281 2b.30 Scarlet emperor ("Anaea marthesia") . . . 1·25 35
1282 2b.30 "Caligo sp." . . . . 1·25 35
1283 2b.30 "Rothschildia sp." . . 1·25 35
1284 2b.70 "Heliconius sp." . . . 1·50 45
1285 2b.70 "Marpesia corinna" 1·50 45
1286 2b.70 "Prepona chromus" 1·50 45
1287 3b.50 Rusty-tipped page ("Siproeta epaphus") . . 1·90 60
1288 3b.50 "Heliconius sp." . . . 1·90 60

413 "Eternal Father" (wood statuette, Gaspar de la Cueva)

414 "Virgin of Urkupina"

1993.
1289 **413** 1b.80 multicoloured . . 90 30

1993. 400th Anniv of Quillacollo.
1290 **414** 50c. multicoloured . . . 15 10

415 Student, Machinery and Emblem

1993. 50th Anniv (1992) of Pedro Domingo Murillo Technical College.
1291 **415** 60c. multicoloured . . . 15 10

416 Owl (painting, Chuquisaca)

417 Common Squirrel-monkeys

1993. Cave Art. Multicoloured.
1292 80c. Type **416** 20 10
1293 80c. Animals (painting, Cochabamba) 20 10
1294 80c. Geometric patterns (engraving, Chuquisaca) (vert) 20 10
1295 80c. Sun (engraving, Beni) (vert) 20 10
1296 80c. Llama (painting, Oruro) 20 10
1297 80c. Human figure (engraving, Potosi) . . . 20 10
1298 80c. Church and tower (painting, La Paz) (vert) 20 10
1299 80c. Warrior (engraving, Tarija) (vert) 20 10
1300 80c. Religious mask (engraving, Santa Cruz) (vert) 20 10

1993. America. Endangered Animals. Mult.
1301 80c. Type **417** 20 10
1302 2b.30 Ocelot . . . . 1·00 35

418 Emblems and Map

419 Yolanda Bedregal (poet)

1993. 90th Anniv (1992) of Pan-American Health Organization. Anti-AIDS Campaign.
1303 **418** 80c. multicoloured . . . 20 10

1993. Personalities. Each brown.
1304 50c. Type **419** 15 10
1305 70c. Simon Martinic (President of Cochabamba Philatelic Centre) 20 10
1306 90c. Eugenio von Boeck (politician and President of Bolivian Philatelic Federation) 25 15
1307 1b. Marina Nunez del Prado (sculptor) 25 15

420 "Virgin with Child and Saints" (anonymous)

421 Riberalta Square

1993. Christmas. Multicoloured.
1308 2b.30 "Adoration of the Shepherds" (Leonardo Flores) 95 35
1309 3b.50 Type **420** . . . . . . 1·50 60
1310 6b. "Virgin of the Milk" (Melchor Perez de Holguin) . . . . 2·50 1·00

1994. Centenary of Riberalta.
1311 **421** 2b. multicoloured . . . 85 35

422 "Population and Our World" (Mayari Rodriguez)

1994. 2nd Prize-winning Design (6–8 year group) in United Nations Fund for Population Activities International Design Contest.
1312 **422** 2b.30 multicoloured . . 1·00 35

423 Sanchez de Lozada

424 Mascot

1994. Presidency of Gonzalo Sanchez de Lozada.
1313 **423** 2b. multicoloured . . . 85 35
1314 2b.30 multicoloured . . 1·00 35

1994. World Cup Football Championship, U.S.A. Multicoloured.
1315 80c. Type **424** 20 10
1316 1b.80 Bolivia v Uruguay . . 75 30
1317 2b.30 Bolivia v Venezuela 95 35
1318 2b.50 Bolivian team (left half) . . . . 1·00 35
1319 2b.50 Bolivian team (right half) . . . . 1·00 35
1320 2b.70 Bolivia v Ecuador . . 1·10 45
1321 3b.50 Bolivia v Brazil . . . 1·50 60

Nos. 1318/19 were issued together, se-tenant, forming a composite design.

425 Child

427 "Buddleja coriacea"

426 St. Peter's Church and Mgr. Jorge Manrique Hurtado (Archbishop, 1967–87)

1994. S.O.S. Children's Villages.
1322 **425** 2b.70 multicoloured . . 1·10 45

1994. 50th Anniv (1993) of Archdiocese of La Paz. Multicoloured.
1323 1b.80 Type **426** 75 30
1324 2b. Church of the Sacred Heart of Mary and Mgr. Abel Antezana y Rojas (first Archbishop, 1943–67) (vert) 85 35
1325 3b.50 Santo Domingo Church and Mgr. Luis Sainz Hinojosa (Archbishop since 1987) (vert) . . . . 1·50 60

1994. Environmental Protection. Trees. Mult.
1326 60c. Type **427** 15 10
1327 1b.80 "Bertholletia exelsa" 50 30
1328 2b. "Schinus molle" (horiz) 80 35
1329 2b.70 "Polylepis racemosa" 1·00 45
1330 3b. "Tabebuia chrysantha" 1·25 50
1331 3b.50 "Erythrina falcata" (horiz) . . . . 1·40 60

428 Paz

429 Tramcar and Mail Van

1994. Dr. Victor Paz Estenssoro (former President).
1332 **428** 2b. multicoloured . . . 55 35

1994. America. Postal Transport. Mult.
1333 1b. Type **429** . . . . 2·25 1·50
1334 5b. Airplane and ox cart . . 1·25 80

430 Coral Tree

431 Diagram of Eclipse

1994. 300th Anniv of San Borja.
1335 **430** 1b.60 multicoloured . . 40 25

1994. Solar Eclipse.
1336 **431** 3b.50 multicoloured . . 1·40 60

432 1894 100c. Stamp

433 Col. Marzana and Soldiers

1994. Centenary of Arms Issue of 1894.
1337 **432** 1b.80 multicoloured . . 50 30

1994. 62nd Anniv of Defence of Fort Boqueron.
1338 **433** 80c. multicoloured . . . 20 10

434 "Delicate Flower of Tarija"

435 Emblem

1994. Christmas. Pastels of children by Maria Susana Castillo. Multicoloured.
1339 2b. Type **434** 55 35
1340 5b. "Child of the High Plateau" . . . . 1·75 40
1341 20b. "Shoot of the Bolivian East" . . . . 6·75 2·40

1994. Pan-American Scout Jamboree, Cochabamba.
1342 **435** 1b.80 multicoloured . . 50 30

436 Sucre

437 Santa Ana Cathedral

1995. Birth Bicentenary of General Antonio Jose de Sucre. Multicoloured.
1343 1b.80 Type **436** 50 30
1344 3b.50 Sucre and national colours 90 60

1995. Centenary (1994) of Yacuma Province, Beni Department.
1345 **437** 1b.90 multicoloured . . 80 35
1346 2b.90 multicoloured . . 1·10 50

438 "Holy Virgin of Copacabana", Sanctuary and Franciscans

1995. Centenary of Franciscan Presence at Copacabana Sanctuary.
1347 **438** 60c. multicoloured . . . 15 10
1348 80c. multicoloured . . . 20 10

439 Anniversary Emblem

440 Paraguay and Bolivia Flags (Chaco Peace Treaty, 1938)

1995. 25th Anniv of Andean Development Corporation.
1349 **439** 2b.40 multicoloured . . 80 35

1995. Visit of President Juan Carlos Wasmosy of Paraguay and 169th Anniv (1994) of Republic of Bolivia.
1350 **440** 2b. multicoloured . . . 45 30

441 Montenegro

442 Digging Potatoes

1995. 50th Anniv of Publication of "Nationalism and Colonialism" by Carlos Montenegro.
1351 **441** 1b.20 black and pink . . 25 15

1995. 50th Anniv of F.A.O.
1352 **442** 1b. multicoloured . . . 20 10

443 Anniversary Emblem

1995. 50th Anniv of U.N.O.
1353 **443** 2b.90 dp blue, gold & bl 90 40

444 Andean Condor ("Condor")

1995. America. Endangered Species. Mult.
1354 5b. Type **444** . . . . 1·60 70
1355 5b. Llamas . . . . 1·60 70
Nos. 1354/5 were issued together, se-tenant, forming a composite design.

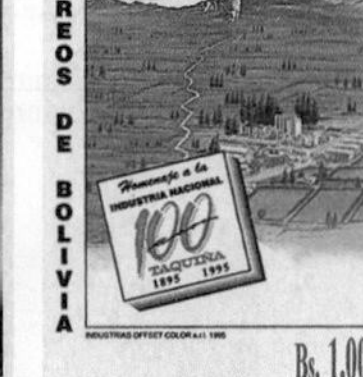

445 Airbus Industrie A320 **447** Brewery Complex

446 Stone Head

1995. 50th Anniv (1994) of I.C.A.O.
1356 **445** 50c. multicoloured . . . 10 10

1995. Archaeology. Samaipata Temple, Florida. Multicoloured.
1357 1b. Type **446** 20 10
1358 1b.90 Stone head (different) 40 25
1359 2b. Excavation and stone head 45 30
1360 2b.40 Entrance and animal-shaped vessel 55 35
Nos. 1357/60 were issued together, se-tenant, forming a composite design.

1995. Centenary of Taquina Brewery.
1361 **447** 1b. multicoloured . . . 20 10

448 "The Annunciation" (Cima da Conegliano)
449 Jose de Sanjines (lyricist)

1995. Christmas. Multicoloured.
1362 1b.20 Type **448** 25 15
1363 3b. "The Nativity" (Hans Baldung) 90 40
1364 3b.50 "Adoration of the Wise Men" (altarpiece, Rogier van der Weyden) 1·10 50

1995. 150th Anniv of National Anthem. Mult.
1365 1b. Type **449** 20 10
1366 2b. Benedetto Vincenti (composer) 45 30
Nos. 1365/6 were issued together, se-tenant, forming a composite design.

450 Flats, Villarroel, Factories, Road and Railway **452** Summit Emblem

1996. 50th Anniv of Decree for Abolition of Enforced Amerindian Labour. Mult.
1367 1b.90 Type **450** . . . . . . 1·25 1·10
1368 2b.90 Pres. Gualberto Villarroel addressing Congress and freed workers . . . . 2·25 1·90
Nos. 1367/8 were issued together, se-tenant, forming a composite design.

1996. Various stamps surch.
1369 – 50c. on 3000000p. multicoloured (No. 1126) (postage) 10 10
1370 **265** 60c. on 2p.50 blue and red 10 10
1371 **313** 60c. on 5000000p. on 2000p. blue and red (No. 1116) 10 10
1372 **319** 60c. on 1400000p. mult 10 10
1373 1b. on 2500000p. green and yellow (No. 1120) 20 10
1374 **311** 1b.50 on 11000p. blue 30 20
1375 **312** 2b.50 on 23000p. brown and sepia 55 35
1376 **316** 3b. on 1000000p. blue and gold 65 40
1377 **272** 3b.50 on 6p.50 mult . . 80 50
1378 **279** 3b.50 on 9p. mult . . . 80 50
1379 **323** 3b.50 on 2000000p. brown 80 50
1380 **298** 20b. on 10p. black, purple and bronze . . 5·00 2·00
1381 **299** 20b. on 13p. mult . . . 5·00 2·00
1382 – 3b.80 on 3p.80 mult (No. 945) (air) 85 55
1383 – 20b. on 3p.80 mult (No. 973a) . . . . . 5·00 2·00

1996. 10th Rio Group Summit Meeting, Cochabamba. Multicoloured.
1384 2b.50 Type **452** 55 35
1385 3b.50 Rio Group emblem 80 50

453 Summit Emblem **454** Facade

1996. Summit of the Americas on Sustainable Development, Santa Cruz de la Sierra.
1386 **453** 2b.50 multicoloured . . 55 35
1387 5b. multicoloured . . . 1·10 70

1996. National Bank.
1388 **454** 50c. black and blue . . . 10 10

455 De Lemoine **456** Family

1996. 220th Birth Anniv of Jose Joaquin de Lemoine (first postal administrator).
1389 **455** 1b. brown and stone . . 20 10

1997. CARE (Co-operative for American Relief Everywhere). Multicoloured.
1390 60c. Type **456** (20th anniv in Bolivia) 10 10
1391 70c. Hands cradling globe (50th anniv) (vert) 15 10

457 Musicians playing Piccolo and Saxophone **458** Casa Dorada (cultural centre)

1997. 50th Anniv of National Symphony Orchestra. "Overture" by G. Rodo Boulanger. Multicoloured.
1392 1b.50 Type **457** 30 20
1393 2b. Musicians playing violin and cello 45 30
Nos. 1392/3 were issued together, se-tenant, forming a composite design of the complete painting.

1997. Tarija. Multicoloured.
1394 50c. Type **458** 10 10
1395 60c. Entre Rios Church and musician 10 10
1396 80c. Narrows of San Luis (horiz) 15 10
1397 1b. Memorial to the Fallen of the Chaco War (territorial dispute with Paraguay) (horiz) 20 10
1398 3b. Virgin and shrine of Chaguaya (horiz) 60 40
1399 20b. Birthplace and statue of Jose Eustaquio Mendez (Independence hero), San Lorenzo (horiz) . . . . . 4·75 1·90

459 La Glorieta, Sucre

1997. Chuquisaca. Multicoloured.
1400 60c. Type **459** 10 10
1401 1b. Government Palace, Sucre (vert) 20 10
1402 1b.50 Footprints and drawing of dinosaur . . . 30 20
1403 1b.50 Interior of House of Freedom 30 20
1404 2b. Man playing traditional wind instrument (vert) . . 40 25
1405 3b. Statue of Juana Azurduy de Padilla (Independence heroine) (vert) 60 40

460 Miners' Monument

1997. Oruro. Multicoloured.
1406 50c. Type **460** 35 25
1407 60c. Demon carnival mask 10 10
1408 1b. Vigin of the Cave (statue) 20 10
1409 1b.50 Sajama (volcano) (horiz) 30 20
1410 2b.50 Chipaya child and belfry 50 30
1411 3b. Moreno (Raul Shaw) (singer and musician) (horiz) 60 40

461 Pres. Gonzalo Sanchez de Lozada of Bolivia and Pres. Chirac

1997. Visit to Bolivia of President Jacques Chirac of France.
1412 **461** 4b. multicoloured . . . 80 50

462 Children playing (Pamela G. Villarroel) **463** St. John Bosco (founder)

1997. 50th Anniv of U.N.I.C.E.F. Children's Drawings. Multicoloured.
1413 50c. Type **462** 10 10
1414 90c. Boy leaping across clifftop (Lidia Acapa) . . 20 10
1415 1b. Children of different races on top of world (Gabriela Philco) 20 10
1416 2b.50 Children and swing (Jessica Grundy) 50 30

1997. Centenary of Salesian Brothers in Bolivia. Multicoloured.
1417 1b.50 Type **463** 30 20
1418 2b. Church and statue of Bosco with child 40 25

464 Chulumani **465** Emblem

1997. La Paz. Multicoloured.
1419 50c. Type **464** 10 10
1420 80c. Inca stone monolith . . 15 10
1421 1b.50 La Paz and Mt. Illimani 30 20
1422 2b. Gate of the Sun, Tiahuanaco (horiz) . . . 40 25
1423 2b.50 Dancers 50 30
1424 10b. "Virgin of Copacabana" and balsa raft on Lake Titicaca (horiz) . . . . 2·50 1·75

1997. Football Events. Multicoloured.
1425 3b. Type **465** (America Cup Latin-American Football Championship, Bolivia) 60 40
1426 5b. Eiffel Tower and trophy (World Cup Football Championship, France (1998) Eliminating Rounds) . . . . 1·00 65

466 Parliamentary Session and Building **467** Valley

1997. National Congress.
1427 **466** 1b. multicoloured . . . 20 10

1997. America. Traditional Costumes. Mult.
1428 5b. Type **467** . . . . 1·00 65
1429 15b. Eastern region . . . . 3·50 1·40

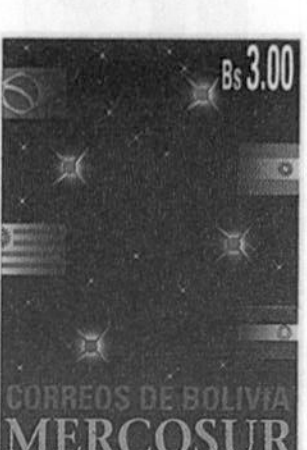

468 Members Flags and Southern Cross **469** "Virgin of the Hill" (anon)

1997. 6th Anniv of Mercosur (South American Common Market).
1430 **468** 3b. multicoloured . . . 60 40

1997. Christmas. Multicoloured.
1431 2b. Type **469** 40 25
1432 5b. "Virgin of the Milk" (anon) . . . . 1·00 65
1433 10b. "Holy Family" (Melchor Perez Holguin) 2·00 1·25

470 Diana, Princess of Wales

1997. Diana, Princess of Wales Commemoration. Multicoloured.
1434 2b. Type **470** 40 25
1435 3b. Diana, Princess of Wales beside minefield warning sign (horiz) 60 40

471 Presidents of Boliva and Spain

1998. State Visit of Prime Minister Jose Maria Aznar of Spain.
1436 **471** 6b. multicoloured . . . 2·00 80

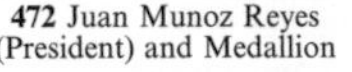

472 Juan Munoz Reyes (President) and Medallion

473 Linked Arms and Globe

1998. 75th Anniv of Bolivian Engineers' Association.
1437 **472** 3b.50 multicoloured . . 60 40

1998. 70th Anniv of Rotary International in Bolivia.
1438 **473** 5b. multicoloured . . . 1·00 60

474 Delivering Letter, 1998

475 Werner Guttentag Tichauer (35th anniv of his bibliography)

1998. America. The Postman. Multicoloured.
1439 3b. Type **474** 60 40
1440 4b. Postmen on parade, 1942 (horiz) 80 50

1998. Anniversaries.
1441 **475** 1b.50 brown 20 10
1442 – 2b. green 40 25
1443 – 3b.50 black 60 40
DESIGNS—VERT: 2b. Martin Cardenas Hermosa (botanist, birth centenary (1999)); 3b. Adrian Patino Carpio (composer, 47th death anniv).

476 Amazon Water-lily

1998. Beni. Multicoloured.
1444 50c. Type **476** 10 10
1445 1b. "Callandria" sp. 20 10
1446 1b.50 White tajibo tree (vert) 20 10
1447 3b.50 Ceremonial mask . . 60 40
1448 5b. European otter . . . . 1·00 60
1449 7b. King vulture ("Tropical Condor") . . . . 1·40 90

477 River Acre

1998. Pando. Multicoloured.
1450 50c. Type **477** 10 10
1451 1b. Pale-throated sloth (vert) 20 10
1452 1b.50 Arroyo Bahia (vert) 20 10
1453 4b. Boa constrictor 80 50
1454 5b. Capybara with young 1·00 60
1455 7b. Palm trees, Cobija (vert) 1·40 90

478 Rural Activities and First Lady

1998. America. Women. Multicoloured.
1456 1b.50 Type **478** 20 10
1457 2b. First Lady, girl at blackboard and woman using computer 40 25
Nos. 1456/7 were issued together, se-tenant, forming a composite design.

479 Town Arms and Church

1998. 450th Anniv of La Paz.
1458 **479** 2b. multicoloured . . . 40 25

480 Emblem

481 Magnifying Glass and 1998 7b. Stamp

1998. 50th Anniv of Organization of American States.
1459 **480** 3b.50 blue and yellow . . 60 40

1998. "Espamer 98" Stamp Exhibition, Buenos Aires and 25th Anniv of Bolivian Philatelic Federation.
1460 **481** 2b. multicoloured . . . 40 25

482 "People going to Church" (Kathia Lucuy Saenz)

1998. Christmas. Multicoloured.
1461 2b. Type **482** 40 25
1462 6b. Pope John Paul II (vert) 1·25 80
1463 7b. Pope John Paul II with Mother Teresa (vert) . . . 1·40 90

483 U.P.U. Monument, Berne

1999. 125th Anniv of Universal Postal Union.
1464 **483** 3b.50 multicoloured . . 70 45

484 Statue of Football Player

1999. 75th Anniv of Cochabamba Football Association.
1465 **484** 5b. multicoloured . . . 1·40 65

485 Red Cross Lorries at Earthquake Site

1999. 50th Anniv of Geneva Conventions.
1466 **485** 5b. multicoloured . . . 1·00 65

486 Bernardo Guarachi and Mt. Everest

1999. 1st Ascent (1998) of Mt. Everest by a Bolivian.
1467 **486** 6b. multicoloured . . . 1·25 85

487 Winners on Podium

1999. 30th Anniv of First Special Olympics. Multicoloured.
1468 2b. Type **487** 40 25
1469 2b.50 Athletes on race track and winners on podium 50 30

488 Golden Palace

1999. Centenary of Japanese Immigration to Bolivia. Multicoloured.
1470 3b. Type **488** 60 40
1471 6b. View over lake and flags (vert) . . . . 1·25 85

489 Children dancing

1999. Anti-drugs Campaign.
1472 **489** 3b.50 multicoloured . . 70 45

490 Route Map and Presidents Hugo Banzer Suarez of Bolivia and Fernando Cardoso of Brazil

1999. Inauguration of Gas Pipeline from Santa Cruz, Bolivia, to Campinas, Brazil. Multicoloured.
1473 3b. Type **490** 60 40
1474 6b. Presidents Hugo Banzer Suarez and Fernando Cardoso embracing . . . 1·25 85

491 Village Scene

493 International Lions Emblem

492 "Hacia la Gloria" (directed Rau Duran, Mario Camacho and Jose Jimenez)

1999. 50th Anniv of S.O.S. Children's Villages.
1475 **491** 3b.50 multicoloured . . 70 45

1999. Centenary of Motion Pictures in Bolivia. Multicoloured.
1476 50c. Type **492** 10 10
1477 50c. "Jonah and the Pink Whale" (dir. J. Carlos Valdivia) 10 10
1478 1b. "Wara Wara" (dir. Jose Velasco) 20 15
1479 1b. "Vuelve Sebastiana" (dir. Jorge Ruiz) 20 15
1480 3b. "The Chaco Campaign" (dir. Juan Penaranda, Jose Velasco and Mario Camacho) 60 40
1481 3b. "The Watershed" (dir. Jorge Ruiz) 60 40
1482 6b. "Yawar Mallku" (dir. Jorge Sanjines) . . . . . 1·25 85
1483 6b. "Mi Socio" (dir. Paolo Agazzi) . . . . 1·25 85

1999. 50th Anniv (1998) of La Paz Lions Club.
1485 **493** 3b.50 multicoloured . . 70 45

494 Mt. Tunari

1999. Cochabamba. Multicoloured.
1486 50c. Type **494** 10 10
1487 1b. Forest, Cochabamba Valley 20 15
1488 2b. Omereque vase and fertility goddess (vert) . . 40 25
1489 3b. Totora 60 40
1490 5b. Teofilo Vargas Candia (composer) and music score (vert) . . . . 1·00 65
1491 6b. "Christ of Harmony" (mountain-top statue) (vert) . . . . 1·25 85

495 Tarapaya Lagoon (Inca spa)

496 Globe with Children, Fish, Flower, Pencil, Heart and Stars

1999. Potosi. Multicoloured.
1492 50c. Type **495** 10 10
1493 1b. First republican coins, minted in 1827 (horiz) . . 20 10
1494 2b. Mt. Chorolque (horiz) 45 30
1495 3b. Green Lagoon (horiz) 65 40
1496 4b. "The Mestizo sitting on a Trunk" (Teofilo Loaiza) 90 60
1497 6b. Alfredo Dominguez Romeo (Tupiceno singer) 1·25 80

1999. America. A New Millennium without Arms. Multicoloured.
1498 3b.50 Type **496** 75 50
1499 3b.50 Globe emerging from flower 75 50

497 Children from S.O.S. Childrens Village

498 Ugarte

1999. Christmas. Multicoloured.
1500 2b. Type **497** 45 30
1501 6b. "The Birth of Jesus" (Gaspar Miguel de Berrios) (vert) . . . . . 1·25 80
1502 7b. "Our Family in the World" (Omar Medina) (vert) . . . . 1·50 1·00

2000. 5th Death Anniv of Victor Agustin Ugarte (football player).
1503 **498** 3b. grey, green and yellow 65 40

499 El Arenal Park

2000. Santa Cruz. Multicoloured.
1504 50c. Type **499** 10 10
1505 1b. Ox cart 20 10
1506 2b. Raul Otero Reiche, Gabriel Rene Moreno and Hernando Sanabria Fernandez (writers) . . . 45 30
1507 3b. Cotoca Virgin (statue) (vert) 65 40
1508 5b. Anthropomorphic vase (vert) . . . . 1·10 70
1509 6b. Bush dog . . . . 1·25 80

500 "The Village of Serinhaem in Brazil" (Frans Post)

2000. 500th Anniv of Discovery of Brazil.
1510 **500** 5b. multicoloured . . . 1·10 70

501 Granado

2000. Javier del Granado (poet) Commemoration.
1511 **501** 3b. grey, blue and red 65 40

502 Cyclists

503 Oriental Clay Figure

2000. "Double Copacabana" Cycle Race.
1512 **502** 1b. multicoloured . . . 20 10
1513 – 3b. multicoloured . . . 65 40
1514 – 5b. multicoloured . . . 1·10 70
1515 – 7b. multicoloured . . . 1·50 1·00
DESIGNS: 3b. to 7b. Various race scenes.

2000. National Archaeology Museum Exhibits. Each brown and gold.
1516 50c. Type **503** 10 10
1517 50c. Clay figure, Potosi . . 10 10
1518 70c. Oriental clay head, Beni 15 10
1519 90c. Clay vase, Tarija . . . 20 10
1520 1b. Clay head, Oruro . . . 20 10
1521 1b. Yampara clay urn . . . 20 10
1522 3b. Inca wood carving . . . 65 40
1523 5b. Oriental anthropomorphic vase . . 1·10 70
1524 20b. Tiwanaku clay mask 4·50 3·00

504 Male and Female Symbols in Red Vortex

2000. America. Anti-A.I.D.S. Campaign. Multicoloured.
1525 3b.50 Type **504** 75 45
1526 3b.50 Couple walking through wall 75 45

505 Soldier's Head and Bird on Laurel Wreath

2000. Centenary of Maximiliano Parades Military School.
1527 **505** 2b.50 multicoloured . . 55 35

506 "Self-portrait"

2000. Birth Centenary of Cecilio Guzman de Rojas (artist). Showing paintings. Multicoloured.
1528 1b. Type **506** 25 15
1529 2b.50 "Triumph of Nature" (horiz) 55 35
1530 5b. "Andina" . . . . 1·10 65
1531 6b. "Students' Quarrel" (horiz) . . . . 1·25 75

507 Crowd and Brandenburg Gate

2000. 50th Anniv of German Federal Republic.
1532 **507** 6b. multicoloured . . . 1·25 75

508 San Francisco Basilica, La Paz

509 Waterfall and Statue

2000. Holy Year 2000. Bolivian Episcopal Conference. Multicoloured.
1533 4b. Type **508** 90 55
1534 6b. Stalks of grain breaking through barbed-wire . . . 1·25 75

2000. New Millennium.
1535 **509** 5b. multicoloured . . . 1·10 65

510 Archangel Gabriel

511 Painting of John the Baptist and Emblem

2000. Christmas. Showing 17th-century paintings of Angels from Calamarca Church. Multicoloured.
1536 3b. Type **510** 65 40
1537 5b. Angel of Virtue . . . . 1·10 65
1538 10b. Angel with ear of corn 2·25 1·40

2000. 900th Anniv of Sovereign Military Order of St. John.
1539 **511** 6b. multicoloured . . . 1·25 75

512 Lobster Claw (*Heliconia rostrata*)

2001. Patriotic Symbols. Multicoloured.
1540 10b. Type **512** (designated national flower, 1990) . . 2·25 1·40
1541 20b. *Periphrangus dependens* (designated national flower 1924) . . . . . 4·50 2·75
1542 30b. First Bolivian coat of arms (adopted 1825) . . . 6·50 4·00
1543 50b. Second Bolivian coat of arms (adopted 1826) . . . 11·00 6·50
1544 100b. Present day Bolivian coat of arms (adopted 1851) . . . . 20·00 12·00

513 Map and Stars of European Union and Map of Bolivia

2001. 25th Anniv of Co-operation between Bolivia and European Union.
1550 **513** 6b. multicoloured . . . 1·25 75

514 Statue of Justice, Lion and Portico

515 Temple of San Francisco, Potosi

2001. 171st Anniv of Faculty of Law and Political Sciences, Universidad de Mayor of San Andres, La Paz.
1551 **514** 6b. multicoloured . . . 1·00 60

2001. America. U.N.E.S.C.O. World Heritage Sites. Multicoloured.
1552 1b.50 Type **515** 25 15
1553 5b. "Fraile" and "Ponce" (monoliths) (horiz) . . . 80 50

516 Man carrying Envelopes up Stairs

518 Family

517 Devil's Molar (mountain)

2001. Philately. Each green.
1554 50c. Type **516** 10 10
1555 1b. Boy with six stamps . . 15 10
1556 1b.50 Man with glasses and stamp album 25 15
1557 2b. Child wearing hat, and three stamps 35 20
1558 2b.50 Humanized stamp lying in tray 40 25

2001.
1559 **517** 1b.50 multicoloured . . 25 15

2001. National Census. Multicoloured.
1560 1b. Type **518** 15 10
1561 1b.50 People surrounding wheelchair user 25 15
1562 1b.50 Aboriginal woman and people of different races 25 15
1563 2b.50 People of different races 40 25
1564 3b. Children 50 30

519 Silver Spot (*Dione juno*)

2001. Butterflies and Insects. Multicoloured.
1565 1b. Type **519** 15 10
1566 1b. *Orthoptera* sp. 15 10
1567 1b.50 Bamboo page (*Philaethria dido*) 25 15
1568 2b.50 Jewel butterfly (*Diaethria clymena*) (inscr "Diathria clymene") . . . 40 25
1569 2b.50 *Mantis religiosa* . . . 40 25
1570 3b. *Tropidacris latreillei* . . 50 30
1571 4b. Hercules beetle (*Dynastes hercules*) (inscr "Escarabajo Hercule") . . 65 40
1572 5b. *Arctiidae* sp. 80 50
1573 5b. *Acrocinus longimanus* . . 80 50
1574 5b. *Lucanidae* sp. 80 50
1575 6b. *Morpho godarti* . . . . 1·00 60
1576 6b. *Caligo idomeneus* ("inscr idomineus") . . . . . . 1·00 60

520 Map of Americas and Emblem

2001. 21st Inter-America Scout Conference, Cochabamba.
1577 **520** 3b.50 multicoloured . . 60 35

521 Woman and Emblem

522 St. Mary Magdalen

2001. Breast Cancer Prevention Campaign.
1578 **521** 1b.50 multicoloured . . 25 15

2001. Christmas. Showing sculptures by Gaspar of La Cueva from Convent of San Francisco, Potosí. Multicoloured.
1579 3b. Type **522** 25 15
1580 5b. St. Apolonia 80 50
1581 10b. St. Teresa of Avila . . 1·75 1·00

523 Portrait and Casa La Laertad, Sucre

2001. Joaquin Gantier Valda Commemoration.
1582 **523** 4b. multicoloured . . . 65 40

524 Flags and Hands enclosing Farmer, Mother, Child and Doctor

2001. 25th Anniv of Co-operation between Bolivia and Belgium.
1583 **524** 6b. multicoloured . . . 65 40

525 Aerial Photograph and Bridge

526 Charangos (guitars) and Musical Score

2002. Bolivia–Peru Presidential Summit. Multicoloured.
1584 50c. Type **525** 10 10
1585 3b. Aerial photograph and bridge (different) 40 25

2001. Birth Centenary of Mauro Nunez (musician). Multicoloured.
1586 1b. Type **526** 15 10
1587 6b. Mauro Nunez 80 50

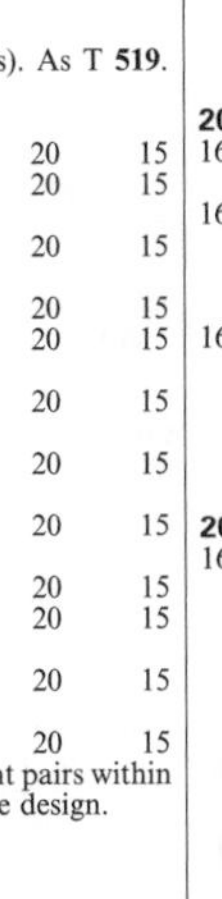

527 Dancers with Horned Head-dresses (Diablada) **528** "El Kusillo" (folk character)

2001. Cultural Heritage. Oruro Carnival. Multicoloured.
1588 50c. Type **527** 10 10
1589 1b.50 Female dancer (Morenada) 20 15
1590 2b.50 Female dancers and man in embroidered clothes (Caporales) . . . 35 20
1591 5b. Male dancers in multicoloured head-dresses (Tobas) 70 40
1592 7b. Woman dancer in elaborate hat and yellow skirt (Suri Sikuri) (vert) 95 55
1593 7b. Dancers wearing bonnets (Pujllay) (vert) 95 55

2002. Butterflies and Insects (2nd series). As T **519**. Multicoloured.
1594 3b. White-tailed page (*Urania leilus*) 20 15
1595 3b. *Tropidacris latreilli* . . . 20 15
1596 3b. *Papilio cresphontes macho* 20 15
1597 3b. Longhorn beetle (*Acrocinus longimanus*) . . 20 15
1598 3b. *Prepona buckleyana* . . 20 15
1599 3b. *Thysannia agripyna cramer* (left wings) 20 15
1600 3b. *Thysannia agripyna cramer* (right wings) . . . 20 15
1601 3b. *Lucanus verde* (inscr "Lucano") 20 15
1602 3b. Butterfly (inscr "Nymphalidae") 20 15
1603 3b. *Escarabajo hercule* . . . 20 15
1604 3b. Butterfly (different) (inscr "Heliconinae") . . 20 15
1605 3b. Grasshopper (inscr "Orthopterdae") 20 15
Nos. 1599/1600 were issued in se-tenant pairs within the sheet, each pair forming a composite design.

2002. 3rd International Theatre Festival, La Paz.
1606 **528** 3b. multicoloured . . . 20 15

529 Mountain Viscachas (rodent), Potosi

2002. International Year of Mountains and Eco-tourism. Multicoloured.
1607 80c. Type **529** 10 10
1608 1b. Polylepis (tree), Cochabamba (vert) . . . 15 10
1609 1b.50 Huayna Potosi mountains, La Paz . . . 20 15
1610 2b.50 Payachatas mountains, Oruro 35 20
1611 2b.50 Sajama mountain, Oruro (vert) 35 20

530 Anniversary Emblem and Rainbow

2002. Centenary of Pan-American Health Organization.
1612 **530** 3b. multicoloured . . . 40 25

531 Gunnar Mendoza

2002. Dr. Gunnar Mendoza (scientist) Commemoration.
1613 **531** 4b. multicoloured . . . 55 35

532 Airliner over Mountains

2002. 50th Anniv of Military Aviation College, Gemán Busch. Multicoloured.
1614 4b. Type **532** 55 35
1615 5b. Acrobatic aeroplanes (vert) 70 45
1616 6b. Three helicopters . . . 80 50

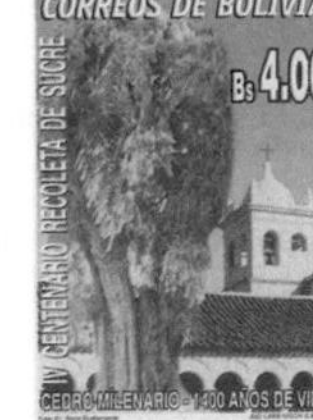

533 Orinoco Goose (*Neochen jubata*) **534** Thousand Year old Cedar Tree and Church Tower

2002. Day of Natural Resources. Multicoloured.
1617 50c. Type **533** (CEFILCO philatelic association) . . 10 10
1618 4b. Orange-breasted falcon (*Falco deiroleucus*) (30th anniv of Bolivian philatelic federation) . . . 55 35
1619 6b. Black-bodied woodpecker (*Dryocopus schulzi*) (PHILAKOREA 2002) 80 50

2002. 400th Anniv of Sucre Monastery.
1620 **534** 4b. multicoloured . . . 55 35

535 Indian Madonna **537** Couple wearing Traditional Costume

536 Potosi and Armando Alba Zambrana

2002. Twentieth-century Art. Multicoloured.
1621 70c. Type **535** (sculpture, Marina Nunez del Prado) 10 10
1622 70c. Mountain (painting, Maria Luisa Pachero) . . 10 10
1623 80c. Indian mother (sculpture, Marina Nunez del Prado) 10 10
1624 80c. "Cordillera" (painting, Maria Luisa Pachero) . . 10 10
1625 5b. Venus Negra (sculpture, Marina Nunez del Prado) 70 45
1626 5b. "Cerros" (painting, Maria Luisa Pachero) (horiz) 70 45

2002. Birth Centenary (2001) of Armando Alba Zambrana (historian).
1627 **536** 3b. multicoloured . . . 40 25

2002. Birth Bicentenary of Alcide d'Orbigny (naturalist and palaeontologist). Multicoloured.
1628 1b. Type **537** 15 10
1629 4b. Boat on river (horiz) . . 55 35
1630 6b. Alcide d'Orbigny . . . 80 50

538 Teacher and Pupils

2002. America. Education and Literacy Campaign. Multicoloured.
1631 1b. Type **538** 15 10
1632 2b.50 Indigenous children and computer 35 20

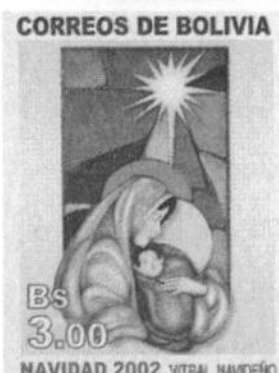

539 Mary and Jesus

2002. Christmas. Multicoloured.
1633 3b. Type **539** 40 25
1634 5b. Nativity 70 45
1635 6b. "The Adoration of the Kings" (painting, 18th-century) 80 50

POSTAGE DUE STAMPS

D 81 D 93 "Youth"

1931.
D265 **D 81** 5c. blue 70 85
D266 10c. red 70 85
D267 15c. yellow . . . . . 1·00 85
D268 30c. green . . . . . . 1·00 85
D269 40c. violet . . . . . . 1·75 1·75
D270 50c. sepia . . . . . . 2·40 2·40

1938. Triangular designs.
D346 **D 93** 5c. red 50 50
D347 – 10c. green 50 50
D348 – 30c. blue 50 50
DESIGNS: 10c. Torch of Knowledge; 30c. Date and Symbol of 17 May 1936 Revolution.

BOPHUTHATSWANA Pt. 1

The republic of Bophuthatswana was established on 6 December 1977 as one of the "black homelands" constructed from the territory of the Republic of South Africa.

Although this independence did not receive international political recognition we are satisfied that the stamps had "de facto" acceptance as valid for the carriage of mail outside Bophuthatswana.

Bophuthatswana was formally re-incorporated into South Africa on 27 April 1994.

100 cents = 1 rand.

1 Hand releasing Dove

1977. Independence. Multicoloured.
1 4c. Type **1** 35 35
2 10c. Leopard (national emblem) 75 60
3 15c. Coat of arms . . . . . . 1·25 1·00
4 20c. National flag . . . . . . 1·50 1·40

2 African Buffalo

1977. Tribal Totems. Multicoloured.
5a 1c. Type **2** 20 15
6a 2c. Bush pig 20 15
7a 3c. Chacma baboon 20 15
8a 4c. Leopard 20 10
9a 5c. Crocodile 20 10
10 6c. Savanna monkey 20 10
11a 7c. Lion 30 15
12a 8c. Spotted hyena 20 15
13 9c. Cape porcupine 25 15
14 10c. Aardvark 25 10
15 15c. Tilapia (fish) . . . . . 1·00 15
16 20c. Hunting dog 25 20
17 25c. Common duiker 40 30
18 30c. African elephant 60 35
19 50c. Python 70 40
20 1r. Hippopotamus . . . . . 1·10 1·00
21 2r. Greater kudu . . . . . . 1·10 1·75

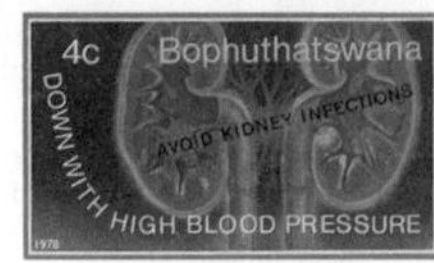

3 Infected Kidney

1978. World Hypertension Month. Multicoloured.
22 4c. Type **3** 50 25
23 10c. Heart and spoon of salt 70 70
24 15c. Spoon reflecting skull, knife and fork . . . . . . 1·25 1·25

4 Skull behind Steering Wheel of Car

1978. Road Safety. Multicoloured.
25 4c. Type **4** 70 40
26 10c. Child knocked off tricycle 90 80
27 15c. Pedestrian stepping in front of car . . . . 1·00 1·10
28 20c. Cyclist ignoring stop sign 1·40 1·75

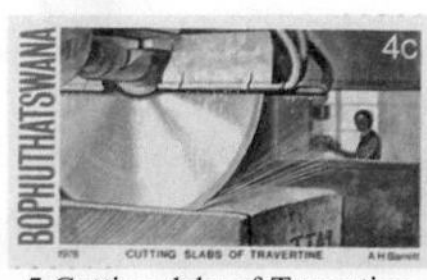

5 Cutting slabs of Travertine

1978. Semi-precious Stones. Multicoloured.
29 4c. Type **5** 65 25
30 10c. Polishing travertine . . . 1·25 85
31 15c. Sorting semi-precious stones . . . . 1·50 1·25
32 20c. Factory at Taung . . . . 2·25 1·60

6 Wright Flyer I

1978. 75th Anniv of First Powered Flight by Wright Brothers.
33 **6** 10c. black, blue and red . . . 1·00 1·00
34 – 15c. black, blue and red . . . 1·40 1·50
DESIGN: 15c. Orville and Wilbur Wright.

7 Pres. Lucas M. Mangope **9** Kallie Knoetze (South Africa)

8 Drying Germinated Wheat Sorghum

1978. 1st Anniv of Independence. Multicoloured.
35 4c. Type **7** 25 20
36 15c. Full face portrait of President 75 60

1978. Sorghum Beer-making. Multicoloured.
37 4c. Type **8** 25 20
38 15c. Cooking the ground grain 65 70
39 20c. Sieving the liquid 70 75
40 25c. Drinking the beer . . . . 80 1·00

1979. Knoetze–Tate Boxing Match. Multicoloured.
41 15c. Type **9** 75 75
42 15c. John Tate (U.S.A.) . . . 75 75

10 Emblem and Drawing of Local Fable (Hendrick Sebapo)

1979. International Year of the Child. Children's Drawings of Local Fables. Multicoloured.
43 4c. Type **10** 20 20
44 15c. Family with animals (Daisy Morapedi) 25 25
45 20c. Man's head and landscape (Peter Tladi) . . . 35 35
46 25c. Old man, boy and donkey (Hendrick Sebapo) 45 60

11 Miner and Molten Platinum

1979. Platinum Industry.
47 **11** 4c. multicoloured 25 10
48 – 15c. multicoloured 35 30
49 – 20c. multicoloured 45 45
50 – 25c. black and grey 60 65
DESIGNS: 15c. Platinum granules and industrial use; 20c. Telecommunications satellite; 25c. Jewellery.

12 Cattle **13** Cigarettes forming Cross

1979. Agriculture. Multicoloured.
51 5c. Type **12** 20 20
52 15c. Picking cotton 25 25
53 20c. Scientist examining maize 30 30
54 25c. Catch of fish 35 35

1979. Anti-smoking Campaign.
55 **13** 5c. multicoloured 40 20

14 "Landolphia capensis" **15** Pied Babbler

1980. Edible Wild Fruits. Multicoloured.
56 5c. Type **14** 15 15
57 10c. "Vangueria infausta" . . 30 30
58 15c. "Bequaertiodendron magalismontanum" 40 40
59 20c. "Sclerocarya caffra" . . . 55 55

1980. Birds. Multicoloured.
60 5c. Type **15** 30 20
61 10c. Carmine bee eater 40 35
62 15c. Shaft-tailed whydah . . . 60 60
63 20c. Brown parrot ("Meyer's Parrot") 70 65

16 Sun City Hotel **17** Deaf Child

1980. Tourism. Sun City. Multicoloured.
64 5c. Type **16** 10 15
65 10c. Gary Player Country Club 40 30
66 15c. Casino 45 50
67 20c. Extravaganza 50 70

1981. Int Year of Disabled Persons. Mult.
68 5c. Type **17** 15 10
69 15c. Blind child 30 20
70 20c. Archer in wheelchair . . 45 35
71 25c. Tuberculosis X-ray . . . 60 60

18 "Behold the Lamb of God ..." **19** Siemens and Halske Wall Telephone, 1885

1981. Easter. Multicoloured.
72 5c. Type **18** 10 10
73 15c. Bread ("I am the bread of life") 25 25
74 20c. Shepherd ("I am the good shepherd") 35 35
75 25c. Wheatfield ("Unless a grain of wheat falls into the earth and dies ...") 45 45

1981. History of the Telephone (1st series). Multicoloured.
76 5c. Type **19** 10 10
77 15c. Ericsson telephone, 1895 25 25
78 20c. Hasler telephone, 1900 . . 35 35
79 25c. Mix and Genest wall telephone, 1904 . . . . . . 45 45
See also Nos. 92/5, 108/11 and 146/9.

20 "Themeda triandra" **21** Boy Scout

1981. Indigenous Grasses (1st series). Multicoloured.
80 5c. Type **20** 10 10
81 15c. "Rhynchelytrum repens" 20 25
82 20c. "Eragrostis capensis" . . 20 30
83 25c. "Monocymbium ceresiiforme" 30 45
See also Nos. 116/19.

1982. 75th Anniv of Boy Scout Movement. Multicoloured.
84 5c. Type **21** 15 10
85 15c. Mafeking siege stamps . . 35 35
86 20c. Original cadet 40 40
87 25c. Lord Baden-Powell . . . 45 45

22 Jesus arriving at Bethany (John 12:1) **23** Ericsson Telephone, 1878

1982. Easter. Multicoloured.
88 15c. Type **22** 25 25
89 20c. Jesus sending disciples for donkey (Matthew 21:1,2) . . 30 30
90 25c. Disciples taking donkey (Mark 11:5,6) 40 40
91 30c. Disciples with donkey and foal (Matthew 21:7) 45 45

1982. History of the Telephone (2nd series). Multicoloured.
92 8c. Type **23** 15 10
93 15c. Ericsson telephone, 1885 20 20
94 20c. Ericsson telephone, 1893 20 20
95 25c. Siemens and Halske telephone, 1898 . . . . . . 30 30

24 Old Parliament Building

1982. 5th Anniv of Independence. Multicoloured.
96 8c. Type **24** 10 10
97 15c. New government offices 20 20
98 20c. University, Mmabatho . . 25 25
99 25c. Civic Centre, Mmabatho 30 30

25 White Rhinoceros

1983. Pilanesberg Nature Reserve. Multicoloured.
100 8c. Type **25** 30 10
101 20c. Common zebras 40 30
102 25c. Sable antelope 40 35
103 40c. Hartebeest 60 60

26 Disciples bringing Donkeys to Jesus (Matthew 21:7)

1983. Easter. Palm Sunday. Multicoloured.
104 8c. Type **26** 10 10
105 20c. Jesus stroking colt (Mark 11:7) 30 30
106 25c. Jesus enters Jerusalem on donkey (Matthew 21:8) 35 35
107 40c. Crowd welcoming Jesus (Mark 11:9) 60 60

1983. History of the Telephone (3rd series). As T **19**. Multicoloured.
108 10c. A.T.M. table telephone c. 1920 . . . . . 15 10
109 20c. A/S Elektrisk wall telephone, c. 1900 . . . . 30 30
110 25c. Ericsson wall telephone c. 1900 . . . . . 35 35
111 40c. Ericsson wall telephone c. 1900 (different) 60 60

27 Kori Bustard

1983. Birds of the Veld. Multicoloured.
112 10c. Type **27** 30 20
113 20c. Black bustard ("Black Korhaan") 45 45
114 25c. Crested bustard ("Red-crested Korhaan") 55 55
115 40c. Denhan's ("Stanley Bustard") 70 80

1984. Indigenous Grasses (2nd series). As T **20**. Multicoloured.
116 10c. "Panicum maximum" . . 15 10
117 20c. "Hyparrhenia dregeana" 20 20
118 25c. "Cenchrus ciliaris" . . . 25 35
119 40c. "Urochloa brachyura" 50 70

28 Money-lenders in the Temple (Mark 11:11)

1984. Easter. Multicoloured.
120 10c. Type **28** 15 10
121 20c. Jesus driving the money-lenders from the Temple (Mark 11:15) 25 20
122 25c. Jesus and fig tree (Matthew 21:9) 35 35
123 40c. The withering of the fig tree (Matthew 21:9) . . . 60 70

29 Car Upholstery, Ga-Rankuwa

1984. Industries. Multicoloured.
124 1c. Textile mill 10 10
125 2c. Sewing sacks, Selosesha 10 10
126 3c. Ceramic tiles, Babelegi 10 10
127 4c. Sheepskin car seat covers 10 10
128 5c. Crossbow manufacture 15 10
129 6c. Automobile parts, Babelegi 15 10
130 7c. Hosiery, Babelegi . . . 15 10
131 8c. Specialised bicycle factory, Babelegi 30 10
132 9c. Lawn mower assembly line 30 15
133 10c. Dress factory, Thaba 'Nchu 20 10
134 11c. Molten platinum . . . 60 20
135 12c. Type **29** 40 15
136 14c. Maize mill, Mafeking 50 15
137 15c. Plastic bags, Babelegi 25 15
137b 16c. Brick factory, Mmabatho 60 15
137c 18c. Cutlery manufacturing, Mogwase 60 15
138 20c. Men's clothing, Babelegi 25 15
138b 21c. Welding bus chassis . . 50 50
138c 21c. Fitting engine to bus chassis 50 50
138d 21c. Bus body construction 50 50
138e 21c. Spraying and finishing bus 50 50
138f 21c. Finished bus 50 50
139 25c. Chromium plating pram parts 30 20
140 30c. Spray painting metal beds 40 25
141 50c. Milk processing plant 50 40
142 1r. Modern printing works 60 75
143 2r. Industrial complex, Babelegi . . . . 1·00 2·50

1984. History of the Telephone (4th series). As T **19**. Multicoloured.
146 11c. Schuchhardt table telephone, 1905 . . . . . 15 10
147 20c. Siemens wall telephone, 1925 . . . . 25 20
148 25c. Ericsson table telephone, 1900 . . . . 30 30
149 30c. Oki table telephone, 1930 . . . . 40 50

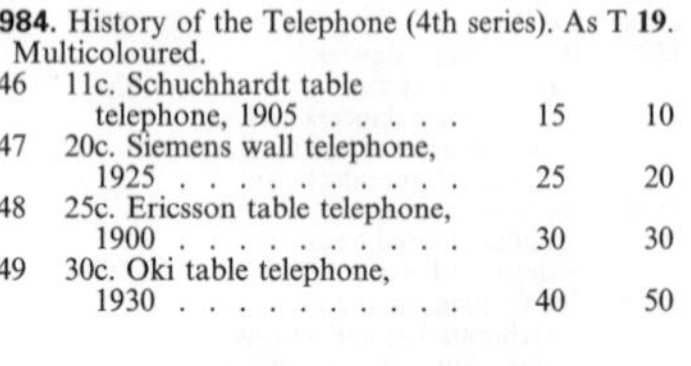

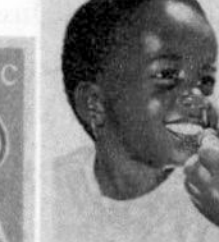

30 Yellow-throated Plated Lizard **31** Giving Oral Vaccine against Polio

1984. Lizards. Multicoloured.
150 11c. Type **30** 20 10
151 25c. Transvaal girdled lizard 30 30
152 30c. Ocellated sand lizard . . 35 40
153 45c. Bibron's thick-toed gecko 50 60

1985. Health. Multicoloured.
154 11c. Type **31** 40 10
155 25c. Vaccinating against measles 50 30
156 30c. Examining child for diphtheria 55 40
157 50c. Examining child for whooping cough 80 90

32 Chief Montshiwa of Barolong booRatshidi **34** "Faurea saligna" and planting Sapling

33 The Sick flock to Jesus in the Temple (Matthew, 21:41)

1985. Centenary of Mafeking.
158 **32** 11c. black, grey and orange 20 10
159 – 25c. black, grey and blue 40 30
DESIGN: 25c. Sir Charles Warren.

1985. Easter. Multicoloured.
160 12c. Type **33** 20 10
161 25c. Jesus cures the sick (Matthew 21:14) 30 20

162 30c. Children praising Jesus (Matthew 21:15) 35 30
163 50c. Community leaders discussing Jesus's acceptance of praise (Matthew 21:15, 16) . . . 50 60

1985. Tree Conservation. Multicoloured.
164 12c. Type **34** 20 10
165 25c. "Boscia albitrunca" and kudu 25 20
166 30c. "Erythrina lysistemon" and mariqua sunbird . . . 35 30
167 50c. "Bequaertiondendron magalismontanum" and bee 55 50

35 Jesus at Mary and Martha's, Bethany (John 12:2)

1986. Easter. Multicoloured.
168 12c. Type **35** 25 10
169 20c. Mary anointing Jesus's feet (John 12:3) 30 20
170 25c. Mary drying Jesus's feet with her hair (John 12:3) 35 25
171 30c. Disciple condemns Mary for anointing Jesus's head with oil (Matthew 26:7) . . 45 50

36 "Wesleyan Mission Station and Residence of Moroka, Chief of the Barolong, 1834" (C. D. Bell)

1986. Paintings of Thaba 'Nchu. Multicoloured.
172 14c. Type **36** 40 15
173 20c. "James Archbell's Congregation, 1834" (Charles Davidson Bell) . . 60 60
174 25c. "Mission Station at Thaba 'Nchu, 1850" (Thomas Baines) 65 80

37 Farmer using Tractor (agricultural development)

1986. Temisano Development Project. Mult.
175 14c. Type **37** 20 10
176 20c. Children at school (community development) 30 20
177 25c. Repairing engine (training) 35 30
178 30c. Grain elevator (secondary industries) . . . 50 50

38 Stewardesses and Cessna Citation II

1986. "B.O.P." Airways. Multicoloured.
179 14c. Type **38** 25 10
180 20c. Passengers disembarking from Boeing 707 . . . . . 40 20
181 25c. Mmabatho International Airport 50 35
182 30c. Cessna Citation II . . . 60 50

39 Netball

40 "Berkheya zeyheri"

1987. Sports. Multicoloured.
183 14c. Type **39** 20 15
184 20c. Tennis 30 30
185 25c. Football 30 30
186 30c. Athletics 45 50

1987. Wild Flowers. Multicoloured.
187 16c. Type **40** 25 15
188 20c. "Plumbago auriculata" 35 35
189 25c. "Pterodiscus speciosus" 35 35
190 30c. "Gazania krebsiana" . . 40 50

41 E. M. Mokgoko Farmer Training Centre

1987. Tertiary Education. Multicoloured.
191 16c. Type **41** 20 15
192 20c. Main lecture block, University of Bophuthatswana 30 35
193 25c. Manpower Centre . . . 30 35
194 30c. Hotel Training School 30 50

42 Posts

1987. 10th Anniv of Independence. Communications. Multicoloured.
195 16c. Type **42** 25 15
196 30c. Telephone 35 35
197 40c. Radio 35 35
198 50c. Television 40 50

43 Jesus entering Jerusalem on Donkey (John 12:12–14)

1988. Easter. Multicoloured.
199 16c. Type **43** 25 15
200 30c. Judas negotiating with chief priests (Mark 14:10–11) 35 35
201 40c. Jesus washing the disciples' feet (John 13:5) 35 35
202 50c. Jesus handing bread to Judas (John 13:26) 40 50

44 Environment Education

1988. National Parks Board. Multicoloured.
203 16c. Type **44** 25 15
204 30c. Rhinoceros (Conservation) 40 40
205 40c. Catering workers 40 40
206 50c. Cheetahs (Tourism) . . 55 65

45 Sunflowers

1988. Crops. Multicoloured.
207 16c. Type **45** 25 15
208 30c. Peanuts 35 35
209 40c. Cotton 45 45
210 50c. Cabbages 60 60

46 Ngotwane Dam

1988. Dams. Multicoloured.
211 16c. Type **46** 30 20
212 30c. Groothoek Dam 50 50
213 40c. Sehujwane Dam 50 50
214 50c. Molatedi Dam 70 70

47 The Last Supper (Matthew 26: 26)

1989. Easter. Multicoloured.
215 16c. Type **47** 40 20
216 30c. Jesus praying in Garden of Gethsemane (Matthew 26:39) 60 55
217 40c. Judas kissing Jesus (Mark 14:45) 70 70
218 50c. Peter severing ear of High Priest's slave (John 18:10) . . . . 85 1·00

48 Cock (Thembi Atong)

49 Black-shouldered Kite

1989. Children's Art. Designs depicting winning entries in National Children's Day Art Competition.
219 18c. Type **48** 30 20
220 30c. Traditional thatched hut (Muhammad Mahri) . . . 40 40
221 40c. Airplane, telephone wires and houses (Tshepo Mashokwi) 45 45
222 50c. City scene (Miles Brown) 50 60

1989. Birds of Prey. Paintings by Claude Finch-Davies. Multicoloured.
223 18c. Type **49** . . . . 1·25 30
224 30c. Pale chanting goshawk 1·40 75
225 40c. Lesser kestrel . . . . . 1·60 1·10
226 50c. Short-toed eagle . . . . 1·75 1·50

50 Bilobial House

1989. Traditional Houses. Multicoloured.
227 18c. Type **50** 25 20
228 30c. House with courtyards at front and side 35 35
229 40c. House with conical roof 35 35
230 50c. House with rounded roof 40 50

51 Early Learning Schemes

1990. Community Services. Multicoloured.
231 18c. Type **51** 25 20
232 30c. Clinics 35 35
233 40c. Libraries 35 35
234 50c. Hospitals 40 45

52 Lesser Climbing Mouse

1990. Small Mammals. Multicoloured.
235 21c. Type **52** 30 20
236 30c. Zorilla 40 40
237 40c. Transvaal elephant shrew 60 60
238 50c. Large-toothed rock hyrax 80 85

53 Variegated Sandgrouse

1990. Sandgrouse. Paintings by Claude Finch-Davies. Multicoloured.
239 21c. Type **53** 90 30
240 35c. Double-banded sandgrouse . . . . 1·10 75
241 40c. Namaqua sandgrouse . . 1·10 90
242 50c. Yellow-throated sandgrouse . . . . 1·40 1·40

54 Basketry

1990. Traditional Crafts. Multicoloured.
243 21c. Type **54** 40 20
244 35c. Training 60 60
245 40c. Beer making 60 65
246 50c. Pottery 65 75

55 Sud Aviation Alouette II Helicopter

56 Wild Custard Apple

1990. Bophuthatswana Air Force. Multicoloured.
247 21c. Type **55** . . . . 1·25 1·10
248 21c. MBB-Kawasaki BK-117 helicopter . . . . 1·25 1·10
249 21c. Pilatus PC-7 turbo trainer . . . . 1·25 1·10
250 21c. Pilatus PC-6 . . . . . . 1·25 1·10
251 21c. CASA C-212 Aviocar . . 1·25 1·10

1991. Edible Wild Fruit. Multicoloured.
252 21c. Type **56** 50 25
253 35c. Spine-leaved monkey orange 65 70
254 40c. Sycamore fig 70 75
255 50c. Kei apple 85 95

57 Arrest of Jesus (Mark 14:46)

1991. Easter. Multicoloured.
256 21c. Type **57** 45 25
257 35c. First trial by the Sanhedrin (Mark 14:53) . . 60 55
258 40c. Assault and derision of Jesus after sentence (Mark 14:65) 70 70
259 50c. Servant girl recognizing Peter (Mark 14:67) 75 90

58 Class 7A Locomotive No. 350, 1897

59 Caneiro Chart, 1502

1991. Steam Locomotives. Multicoloured.
260 25c. Class 6A locomotive No. 194, 1897, trucks and caboose (71 × 25 mm) . . . 95 55
261 40c. Type **58** . . . . 1·25 85
262 50c. Double-boiler Class 6Z locomotives pulling Cecil Rhodes's funeral train (71 × 25 mm) . . . . . . 1·40 1·25
263 60c. Class 8 locomotive at Mafeking station, 1904 . . 1·50 1·75

1991. Old Maps (1st series). Multicoloured.
264 25c. Type **59** . . . . 1·10 40
265 40c. Cantino Chart, 1502 . . 1·50 95

266		50c. Giovanni Contarini's map, 1506	1·75	1·40
267		60c. Martin Waldseemuller's map, 1507	1·75	1·90

See also Nos. 268/71 and 297/300.

60 Fracanzano Map, 1508

1992. Old Maps (2nd series). Multicoloured.

268		27c. Type **60**	1·10	40
269		45c. Martin Waldseemuller's map (from edition of Ptolemy), 1513	1·50	95
270		65c. Section of Waldseemuller's woodcut "Carta Marina Navigatora Portugallan Navigationes", 1516	1·75	1·50
271		85c. Map from Laurent Fries's "Geographia", 1522	1·75	2·00

61 Delivery of Jesus to Pilate (Mark 15:1)

1992. Easter. Multicoloured.

272		27c. Type **61**	25	20
273		45c. Scourging of Jesus (Mark 15:15)	40	40
274		65c. Placing crown of thorns on Jesus's head (Mark 15: 17–18)	50	70
275		85c. Soldiers mocking Jesus (Mark 15:19)	60	90

62 Sweet Thorn

1992. Acacia Trees. Multicoloured.

276		35c. Type **62**	30	25
277		70c. Camel thorn	50	60
278		90c. Umbrella thorn	60	80
279		1r.05 Black thorn	70	1·00

63 View of Palace across Lake

64 Light Sussex

1992. The Lost City Complex, Sun City. Mult.

280		35c. Type **63**	35	45
281		35c. Palace facade	35	45
282		35c. Palace porte cochere	35	45
283		35c. Palace lobby	35	45
284		35c. Tusk Bar, Palace	35	45

1993. Chickens. Multicoloured.

285		35c. Type **64**	50	25
286		70c. Rhode Island red	75	60
287		90c. Brown leghorn	90	1·00
288		1r.05 White leghorn	1·10	1·40

65 Pilate offering Release of Barabbas (Luke 23:25)

1993. Easter. Multicoloured.

289		35c. Type **65**	60	30
290		70c. Jesus falling under cross (John 19:17)	95	75
291		90c. Simon of Cyrene carrying cross (Mark 15:21)	1·25	1·25
292		1r.05 Jesus being nailed to cross (Mark 15:23)	1·40	1·75

66 Mafeking Locomotive Shed, 1933 (⅔-size illustration)

1993. Steam Locomotives (2nd series). Multicoloured.

293		45c. Type **66**	65	55
294		65c. Rhodesian Railways steam locomotive No. 5, 1901 (34 × 25 mm)	75	65
295		85c. Class 16B locomotive pulling "White Train" during visit of Prince George, 1934	95	95
296		1r.05 Class 19D locomotive, 1923 (34 × 25 mm)	1·25	1·40

67 Sebastian Munster's Map (from edition of Ptolemy), 1540

1993. Old Maps (3rd series). Multicoloured.

298		45c. Type **67**	50	40
299		65c. Jacopo Gastaldi's map, 1564	65	65
300		85c. Map from Mercator's "Atlas", 1595	75	90
301		1r.05 Map from Ortelius's "Theatrum Orbis Terrarum", 1570	90	1·25

68 Crucifixion (Luke 23:33)

1994. Easter. Multicoloured.

302		35c. Type **68**	65	45
303		65c. Soldiers and Jews mocking Jesus (Luke 23: 35–36)	95	80
304		85c. Soldier offering Jesus vinegar (Luke 23:36)	1·10	1·25
305		1r.05 Jesus on cross and charge notice (Luke 23:38)	1·60	1·75

BOSNIA AND HERZEGOVINA

Pts. 2, 3

Turkish provinces administered by Austria from 1878 and annexed by her in 1908. In 1918 it became part of Yugoslavia.

In 1992 Bosnia and Herzegovina declared itself independent. Hostilities subsequently broke out between the Croat, Moslem and Serbian inhabitants, which ultimately led to the establishment of three de facto administrations: the mainly Moslem Bosnian government, based in Sarajevo; the Croats in Mostar; and the Serbian Republic in Pale. Under the Dayton Agreement in November 1995 the Republic was split between a Moslem-Croat Federation and the Serbian Republic.

A. AUSTRO-HUNGARIAN MILITARY POST

1879. 100 kreuzer = 1 gulden.
1900. 100 heller = 1 krone.
1993. 100 paras = 1 dinar.
2002. 100 cents = 1 euro.

1 Value at top

2 Value at bottom

1879.

106	**1**	½k. black	11·00	23·00
135		1k. grey	3·00	1·10
136		2k. yellow	1·90	50
137		3k. green	3·00	1·25
146		5k. red	4·00	55
139		10k. blue	4·00	75
140		15k. brown	3·25	3·75
141		20k. green	4·00	4·25
142		25k. purple	5·00	6·00

1900.

148	**2**	1h. black	20	15
149		2h. grey	20	15
151		3h. yellow	20	15
152		5h. green	15	10
154		6h. brown	30	15
155		10h. red	15	10
156		20h. pink	£100	8·00
158		25h. blue	90	35
173		30h. brown	£110	8·25
160		40h. orange	£120	13·00
161		50h. purple	60	45

Larger stamps with value in each corner.

162		1k. red	80	50
163		2k. blue	1·40	1·50
164		5k. green	3·00	4·50

1901. Black figures of value.

177	**2**	20h. pink and black	60	45
178		30h. brown and black	55	45
180		35h. blue and black	1·00	65
181		40h. orange and black	70	65
182		45h. turquoise and black	80	70

4 View of Doboj

5 In the Carshija (business quarter) Sarajevo

1906.

186	**4**	1h. black	10	15
187	–	2h. violet	10	15
188	–	3h. yellow	10	15
189	–	5h. green	35	10
190	–	6h. brown	20	20
191	–	10h. red	40	10
192	–	20h. brown	65	20
193	–	25h. blue	1·40	90
194	–	30h. green	1·40	45
195	–	35h. green	1·40	45
196	–	40h. orange	1·40	45
197	–	45h. red	1·40	75
198	–	50h. brown	1·60	90
199	**5**	1k. red	4·75	3·00
200	–	2k. green	6·25	11·50
201	–	5k. blue	4·75	7·75

DESIGNS—As Type **4**: 2h. Mostar; 3h. The old castle, Jajce; 5h. Naretva pass and Prenz Planina; 6h. Valley of the Rama; 10h. Valley of the Vrbas; 20h. Old Bridge, Mostar; 25h. The Begova Djamia (Bey's Mosque), Sarajevo; 30h. Post by beast of burden; 35h. Village and lake, Jezero; 40h. Mail wagon; 45h. Bazaar at Sarajevo; 50h. Post car. As Type **5**: 2k. St. Luke's Campanile at Jajce; 5k. Emperor Francis Joseph I.

See also Nos. 359/61.

1910. 80th Birthday of Francis Joseph I. As stamps of 1906 but with date-label at foot.

343		1h. black	50	25
344		2h. violet	60	25
345		3h. yellow	60	25
346		5h. green	65	25
347		6h. brown	70	45
348		10h. red	65	15
349		20h. brown	1·60	1·40
350		25h. blue	3·00	2·50
351		30h. green	2·00	2·25
352		35h. green	2·75	2·25
353		40h. orange	3·00	2·25
354		45h. red	5·25	5·50
355		50h. brown	5·25	6·00
356		1k. red	5·25	6·25
357		2k. green	19·00	21·00
358		5k. blue	3·50	6·00

1912. As T **4** (new values and views).

359		12h. blue	4·50	5·00
360		60h. grey	3·25	4·25
361		72h. red	12·50	16·00

DESIGNS: 12h. Jajce; 60h. Konjica; 72h. Vishegrad.

25 Francis Joseph I

26 Francis Joseph I

1912. Various frames. Nos. 378/82 are larger (27 × 22 mm).

362	**25**	1h. olive	30	10
363		2h. blue	30	10
364		3h. lake	30	10
365		5h. green	30	10
366		6h. black	30	10
367		10h. red	30	10
368		12h. green	50	20
369		20h. brown	3·50	10
370		25h. blue	1·75	10
371		30h. red	1·75	10
372	**26**	35h. green	1·75	10
373		40h. violet	6·00	10
374		45h. brown	3·00	20
375		50h. blue	2·50	10
376		60h. brown	2·25	10
377		72h. blue	3·00	3·25
378	**25**	1k. brown on cream	12·00	35
379		2k. blue on blue	7·25	50
380	**26**	3k. red on green	11·00	10·00
381		5k. lilac and grey	21·00	25·00
382		10k. blue on grey	65·00	95·00

1914. Nos. 189 and 191 surch **1914.** and new value.

383		7h. on 5h. green	40	40
384		12h. on 10h. red	40	40

1915. Nos. 189 and 191 surch **1915.** and new value.

385		7h. on 5h. green	9·00	9·00
386		12h. on 10h. red	30	40

1915. Surch **1915.** and new value.

387	**25**	7h. on 5h. green	70	1·75
388		12h. on 10h. red	1·50	1·75

1916. Surch **1916.** and new value.

389	**25**	7h. on 5h. green	60	60
390		12h. on 10h. red	60	65

31

1916. War Invalids' Fund.

391	**31**	5h. (+2h.) green	85	80
392	–	10h. (+2h.) purple	1·40	1·40

DESIGN: 10h. Blind soldier and girl.

See also Nos. 434/5.

33 Francis Joseph I

34 Francis Joseph I

1916.

393	**33**	3h. black	25	25
394		5h. olive	45	50
395		6h. violet	45	50
396		10h. bistre	2·00	2·25
397		12h. grey	45	60
398		15h. red	45	25
399		20h. brown	45	60
400		25h. blue	45	60
401		30h. green	45	60
402		40h. red	45	60
403		50h. green	45	60
404		60h. lake	45	60
405		80h. brown	1·40	40
406		90h. purple	1·60	80
407	**34**	2k. red on yellow	65	1·00
408		3k. green on blue	80	2·10
409		4k. red on green	5·50	10·00
410		10k. violet on grey	28·00	20·00

1917. War Widows' Fund. Optd **WITWEN-UND WAISENWOCHE 1917.**

411	**33**	10h. (+2h.) bistre	10	20
412		15h. (+2h.) pink	10	20

36 Design for Memorial Church, Sarajevo

39 Emperor Charles

1917. Assassination of Archduke Ferdinand. Fund for Memorial Church at Sarajevo.

413	**36**	10h. (+2h.) black	10	30
414	–	15h. (+2h.) red	10	30
415	–	40h. (+2h.) blue	10	30

PORTRAITS—HORIZ: 40h. Francis Ferdinand and Sophie. VERT: 15h. Archduke Francis Ferdinand.

1917.

416	**39**	3h. grey	10	20
417		5h. olive	10	10
418		6h. violet	60	70
419		10h. brown	20	10
420		12h. blue	60	70
421		15h. red	10	10
422		20h. brown	10	10
423		25h. blue	90	65
424		30h. green	25	20
425		40h. bistre	25	20
426		50h. green	90	50
427		60h. red	90	45
428		80h. blue	20	25
429		90h. lilac	1·00	1·40
430	–	2k. red on yellow	60	35
431	–	3k. green on blue	15·00	16·00
432	–	4k. red on green	6·00	8·00
433	–	10k. violet on grey	4·00	6·25

The kronen values are larger (25 × 25 mm) and with different border.

1918. War Invalids' Fund.

434	–	10h. (+2h.) green (as No. 392)	60	70
435	**31**	15h. (+2h.) brown	60	70

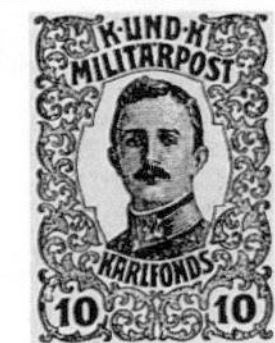
40 Emperor Charles

1918. Emperor's Welfare Fund.

436	40 10h. (+10h.) green	40	85
437	– 15h. (+10h.) brown	40	85
438	40 40h. (+10h.) purple	40	85

DESIGN—15h. Empress Zita.

1918. Optd 1918.

439	– 2h. violet (No. 344)	50	1·00
440	25 2h. blue	50	1·10

NEWSPAPER STAMPS

N 27 Girl in Bosnian Costume

N 35 Mercury

1913. Imperf.

N383	N 27 2h. blue	40	40
N384	6h. mauve	1·40	1·40
N385	10h. red	1·60	1·40
N386	20h. green	2·10	1·60

For these stamps perforated see Yugoslavia, Nos. 25 to 28.

1916. For Express.

N411	N 35 2h. red	25	25
N412	5h. green	45	45

POSTAGE DUE STAMPS

D 4

D 35

1904. Imperf. or perf.

D183	D 4 1h. black, red & yellow	30	10
D184	2h. black, red & yellow	30	15
D185	3h. black, red & yellow	30	10
D186	4h. black, red & yellow	30	10
D187	5h. black, red & yellow	1·40	10
D188	6h. black, red & yellow	25	10
D189	7h. black, red & yellow	2·25	3·25
D190	8h. black, red & yellow	2·25	1·50
D191	10h. black, red & yellow	50	10
D192	15h. black, red & yellow	40	10
D193	20h. black, red & yellow	3·00	25
D194	50h. black, red & yellow	1·10	30
D195	200h. black, red & grn	4·00	2·25

1916.

D411	D 35 2h. red	40	1·00
D412	4h. red	35	60
D413	5h. red	40	60
D414	6h. red	35	85
D415	10h. red	35	50
D416	15h. red	2·75	5·25
D417	20h. red	35	50
D418	25h. red	90	2·00
D419	30h. red	90	2·00
D420	40h. red	7·25	12·50
D421	50h. red	23·00	40·00
D422	1k. blue	2·50	5·25
D423	3k. blue	12·00	23·00

B. INDEPENDENT REPUBLIC

I. SARAJEVO GOVERNMENT

The following issues were used for postal purposes in those areas controlled by the Sarajevo government.

1993. 100 paras = 1 dinar.
1997. 100 fennig = 1 mark.

50 State Arms

51 Games Emblem

1993. Imperf.

450	50 100d. blue, lemon & yellow	10	10
451	500d. blue, yellow & pink	15	15
452	1000d. ultramarine, yellow and blue	25	25
453	5000d. blue, yellow & grn	75	75
454	10000d. blue, lemon & yell	1·50	1·50
455	20000d. blue, yellow & bis	3·00	3·00
456	50000d. blue, yellow & grey	7·50	7·50

1994. 10th Anniv of Winter Olympic Games, Sarajevo. Imperf.

457	51 50000d. black and orange	5·00	5·00
MS458	78 × 65 mm. 100000d. black, orange and lilac; 200000d. black, orange and lilac	10·00	10·00

DESIGNS: 45 × 27 mm—100000d. Four-man bobsleigh; 200000d. Ice hockey.

Currency Reform
10000 (old) dinars = 1 (new) dinar.

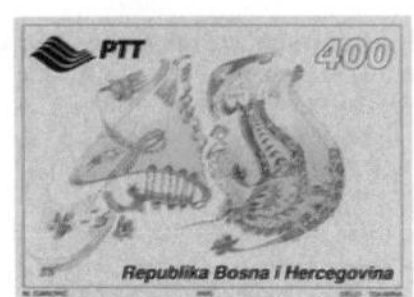
52 Koran Illustration

1995. Bairam Festival. Sheet 105 × 50 mm containing T 52 and similar horiz design. Multicoloured.

MS459	400d. Type 52; 600d. Koran illustration (different)	10·00	10·00

53 Facade

55 Postman and Globe

54 Historical Map, 10th–15th Centuries

1995. Sarajevo Head Post Office. Multicoloured.

460	10d. Type 53	10	10
461	20d. Interior	15	15
462	30d. As No. 461	30	30
463	35d. Before conflict	35	35
464	50d. As No. 463	45	45
465	100d. Present day	90	90
466	200d. As No. 465	1·75	1·75

1995. Bosnian History. Multicoloured.

467	35d. Type 54	30	30
468	100d. 15th-century Bogomil tomb, Oplicici (vert)	80	80
469	200d. Arms of Kotromanic Dynasty (14th-15th centuries) (vert)	1·60	1·60
470	300d. Charter by Ban Kulin of Bosnia, 1189	2·50	2·00

1995. World Post Day.

471	55 100d. multicoloured	95	95

56 Dove with Olive Branch

1995. Europa. Peace and Freedom.

472	56 200d. multicoloured	1·75	1·75

58 Tramcar, 1895

59 "Simphyandra hofmannii"

1995. Centenary of Sarajevo Electric Tram System.

474	58 200d. multicoloured	1·75	1·75

1995. Flowers. Multicoloured.

475	100d. Type 59	95	95
476	200d. Turk's-head lily	1·90	1·90

60 Dalmatian Barbel Gudgeon

1995. Fishes. Multicoloured.

477	100d. Type 60	95	95
478	200d. Adriatic minnow	1·90	1·90

61 Kozija Bridge, Sarajevo

1995. Bridges. Multicoloured.

479	20d. Type 61	15	15
480	30d. Arslanagica Bridge, Trebinje	25	25
481	35d. Latinska Bridge, Sarajevo	35	35
482	50d. Old bridge, Mostar	45	45
483	100d. Visegrad	90	90

62 Visiting Friends

1995. Christmas. Multicoloured.

484	100d. Type 62	1·00	1·00
485	200d. Madonna and Child (vert)	2·00	2·00

63 Queen Jelena of Bosnia and Tomb (600th death anniv)

1995. Multicoloured.

486	30d. Type 63	20	20
487	35d. Husein Kapetan Gradascevic "Dragon of Bosnia" (leader of 1831 uprising against Turkey)	30	30
488	100d. Mirza Safvet Basagic (125th death anniv) (horiz)	95	95

64 Places of Worship and Graveyards

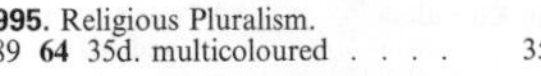
57 Children and Buildings (A. Softic)

1995. Children's Week.

473	57 100d. multicoloured	95	95

1995. Religious Pluralism.

489	64 35d. multicoloured	35	35

65 Stadium and Sports

1995. Destruction of Olympic Stadium, Sarajevo. Multicoloured.

490	35d. Type 65	30	30
491	100d. Stadium ablaze (vert)	95	95

66 Bahrija Hadzic (opera singer)

67 Child's Handprint

1996. Europa. Famous Women. Multicoloured.

492	80d. Type 66	75	75
493	120d. Nasiha Hadzic (children's writer and radio presenter)	1·10	1·10

1996. 50th Anniv of U.N.I.C.E.F. Multicoloured.

494	50d. Child stepping on landmine (P. Mirna and K. Princes)	65	65
495	150d. Type 67	1·25	1·25

68 Bobovac Castle

69 Roofed Fountain and Extract from Holy Koran

1996.

496	68 35d. black, blue and violet	35	35

1996. Bairam Festival.

497	69 80d. multicoloured	75	75

70 Town Hall

1996. Centenary of Sarajevo Town Hall.

498	70 80d. multicoloured	75	75

71 Hands on Computer Keyboard and Title Page of "Bosanki Prijatelj"

1996. 150th Anniv of Journalists' Association.

499	71 100d. multicoloured	95	95

72 Essen

1996. "Essen 96" International Stamp Fair, Essen.

500	72 200d. multicoloured	1·75	1·75

73 Running

74 "Campanula hercegovina"

1996. Centenary of Modern Olympic Games and Olympic Games, Atlanta. Multicoloured.

501 30d. Type **73** 25 25
502 35d. Games emblem 30 30
503 80d. Torch bearer and Olympic flag 75 75
504 120d. Pierre de Coubertin (founder) . . . . 1·10 1·10

Nos. 501/4 were issued together, se-tenant, with the backgrounds forming a composite design of athletes.

1996. Flowers. Multicoloured.

505 30d. Type **74** 30 30
506 35d. "Iris bosniaca" 35 35

75 Barak

1996. Dogs. Multicoloured.

507 35d. Type **75** 35 35
508 80d. Tornjak 85 85

76 Globe, Telephone and Alexander Bell

1996. Anniversaries. Multicoloured.

509 80d. Type **76** (120th anniv of Bell's invention of telephone) 80 80
510 120d. 1910 50h. stamp (cent of post car in Bosnia and Herzegovina) . . . . . . 1·10 1·10

77 Charter with Seal

78 Hot-air Balloons

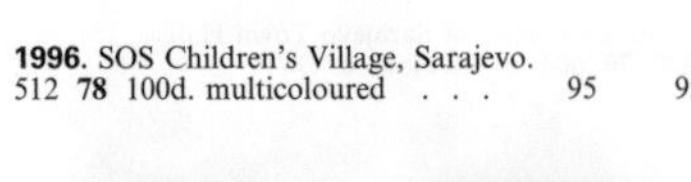

1996. Granting of Privileges to Dubrovnik by Ban Stepan II Kotromanic, 1333.

511 **77** 100d. multicoloured . . . 95 95

1996. SOS Children's Village, Sarajevo.

512 **78** 100d. multicoloured . . . 95 95

79 Muslim Costume of Bjelasnice

80 Bogomil Soldier

1996. Traditional Costumes. Multicoloured.

513 50d. Type **79** 40 40
514 80d. Croatian 75 75
515 100d. Muslim costume of Sarajevo . . . . 1·10 1·10

1996. Military Uniforms. Multicoloured.

516 35d. Type **80** 30 30
517 80d. Austro-Hungarian rifleman 75 75
518 100d. Turkish light cavalryman . . . . 1·10 1·10
519 120d. Medieval Bosnian king 1·25 1·25

81 Mosque

1996. Winter Festival, Sarajevo.

520 **81** 100d. multicoloured . . . 90 90

82 Map and State Arms

1996. Bosnia Day.

521 **82** 120d. multicoloured . . . 1·00 1·00

83 Crowd around Baby Jesus

1996. Christmas.

522 **83** 100d. multicoloured . . . 90 90

84 Pope John Paul II

85 Palaeolithic Rock Carving, Badanj

1996. Papal Visit.

523 **84** 500d. multicoloured . . . 4·00 4·00

1997. Archaeological Finds. Multicoloured.

524 35d. Type **85** 30 30
525 50d. Neolithic ceramic head, Butmir 40 40
526 80d. Bronze Age "birds" wagon, Glasinac 65 65
MS527 100 × 72 mm. 100, 120d. Walls of Illyrian town of Daorson (composite design) . . . . . . 1·75 1·75

86 Ferhad Pasha Mosque, Banja Luka

87 "Clown" (Martina Nokto)

1997. Bairam Festival.

528 **86** 200d. multicoloured . . . 1·50 1·50

1997. Children's Week.

529 **87** 100d. multicoloured . . . 75 75

88 Komadina

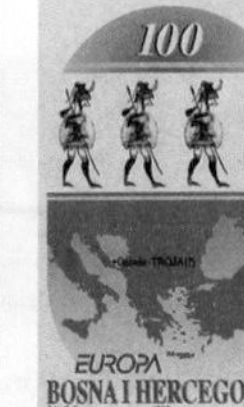

89 Trojan Warriors and Map

1997. 72nd Death Anniv of Mujaga Komadina (developer and Mayor of Mostar).

530 **88** 100d. multicoloured . . . 75 75

1997. Europa. Tales and Legends. Mult.

531 100d. Type **89** (theory of Roberto Prays) 75 75
532 120d. Man on prayer-mat and castle ("The Miraculous Spring of Ajvatovica") 90 90

90 "Rainbow Warrior"

1997. 26th Anniv of Greenpeace (environmental organization). Designs showing the "Rainbow Warrior". Multicoloured.

533 35d. Type **90** 35 35
534 80d. inscr "Dorreboom" . . 80 65
535 100d. inscr "Beltra" . . . . 1·10 1·10
536 120d. inscr "Morgan" . . . 1·40 1·40

91 Open Air Cinema, Sarajevo

1997. 3rd International Film Festival, Sarajevo.

537 **91** 110d. multicoloured . . . 90 90

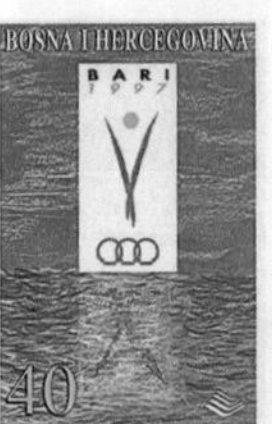

92 Games Emblem

93 Diagram of Electrons

1997. Mediterranean Games, Bari. Mult.

538 40d. Type **92** 35 35
539 130d. Boxing, basketball and kick boxing . . . . 1·10 1·10

1997. Anniversaries and Event. Mult.

540 40d. Type **93** (centenary of discovery of electrons) . . 35 35
541 110d. Vasco da Gama (navigator) and map (500th anniv of science of navigation) (vert) . . . . . 1·75 1·25
542 130d. Airmail envelope and airplane (Stamp Day) . . . 1·40 1·40
543 150d. Steam locomotive "Bosna" (125th anniv of railway in Bosnia and Herzegovina) . . . . . . 1·25 1·25

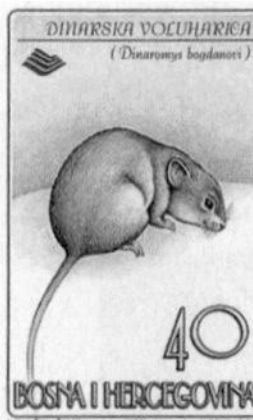

94 Vole

95 Map and Flags

1997. Flora and Fauna. Multicoloured.

544 40d. Type **94** 35 35
545 40d. "Oxytropis prenja" . . . 35 35
546 80d. Alpine newt 65 65
547 110d. "Dianthus freynii" . . 1·10 1·10

1997. International Peace Day. Mult.

548 50d. Type **95** 50 50
549 60d. Flags and right half of globe showing Europe and Africa 55 55
550 70d. Flags and left half of globe showing the Americas 60 60
551 110d. Map and flags (including U.S.A. and U.K.) . . . . 1·10 1·10

Nos. 548/51 were issued together, se-tenant, Nos. 549/50 forming a composite design.

96 House with Attic

1997. Architecture. Multicoloured.

552 40d. Type **96** 35 35
553 50d. Tiled stove and door . . 50 50
554 130d. Three-storey house . . 1·40 1·40

97 Sarajevo in 1697 and 1997

1997. 300th Anniv of Great Fire of Sarajevo.

555 **97** 110d. multicoloured . . . 1·10 1·10

98 Augustin Tin Ujevic

1997. Personalities. Multicoloured.

556 1m.30 Type **98** (lyricist and essayist) 90 90
557 2m. Zaim Imanovic (singer) (vert) . . . . 1·40 1·40

99 Sarajevo and Corps Emblem

1997. Contribution of Italian Pioneer Corps in Reconstruction of Sarajevo.

558 **99** 1m.40 multicoloured . . . 95 95

100 Diana, Princess of Wales, and Roses

1997. Diana, Princess of Wales, Commem.

559 **100** 2m.50 multicoloured . . . 1·90 1·90

101 "Gnijezdo" (Fikret Libovac)

1997. Art. Multicoloured.

560 35f. Type **101** 20 20
561 80f. "Sarajevo Library" (sculpture, Nusret Pasic) 55 55

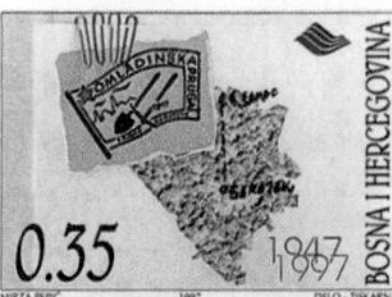

102 Youth Builders Emblem attached to Route Map

1997. 50th Anniv of Samac-Sarajevo Railway.

562 **102** 35f. multicoloured 30 30

103 Nativity (icon)

104 Giant Slalom, Luge, Two-man Bobsleigh and Speed Skating

1997. Religious Events. Multicoloured.

563	50f. Type **103** (Orthodox Christmas)	35	35
564	1m.10 Wreath on door (Christmas)	80	80
565	1m.10 Pupils before teacher (14th-century miniature) (Haggadah)	80	80

1998. Winter Olympic Games, Nagano, Japan. Sheet 78 × 60 mm containing T **104** and similar vert design. Multicoloured.

MS566	35f. Type **104**; 1m. Games emblem	60	60

105 Mosque Fountain

1998. Bairam Festival.

567 **105**	1m. multicoloured	70	70

106 Zvornik

1998. Old Fortified Towns. Multicoloured.

568	35f. Type **106**	25	25
569	70f. Bihac	50	50
570	1m. Pocitelj	70	70
571	1m.20 Gradacac	85	85

107 Muradbegovic

1998. Birth Centenary of Ahmed Muradbegovic (dramatist and actor-director).

572 **107**	1m.50 multicoloured	1·10	1·10

108 Branislav Djurdjev

109 White Storks

1998. Former Presidents of the University of Arts and Science. Multicoloured.

573	40f. Type **108**	30	30
574	70f. Alojz Benac	50	50
575	1m.30 Edhem Camo	95	95

1998. Endangered Species. The White Stork. Multicoloured.

576	70f. Type **109**	50	50
577	90f. Two storks flying	65	65
578	1m.10 Two adult storks on nest	80	80
579	1m.30 Adult stork with young	95	95

110 International Theatre Festival, Sarajevo

112 Emblem

111 Footballs

1998. Europa. National Festivals.

580 **110**	1m.10 multicoloured	80	80

1998. World Cup Football Championship, France. Multicoloured.

581	50f. Type **111**	35	35
582	1m. Map of Bosnia and ball	70	70
583	1m.50 Asim Ferhatovic Hase (footballer)	1·10	1·10

1998. International League of Humanists World Congress, Sarajevo. Sheet 104 × 61 mm containing T **112** and two labels.

MS584 **112**	2m. multicoloured	1·25	1·25

113 Common Morel

114 Tunnel

1998. Fungi. Multicoloured.

585	50f. Type **113**	35	35
586	80f. Chanterelle	55	55
587	1m.10 Edible mushroom	80	80
588	1m.35 Caesar's mushroom	95	95

1998. 5th Anniv of Sarajevo's Supply Tunnels.

589 **114**	1m.10 multicoloured	80	80

115 Eiffel Tower and Underground Train

1998. Paris Metro.

590 **115**	2m. multicoloured	1·40	1·40

116 Henri Dunant (founder of Red Cross)

118 Travnik

117 Vesna Misanovic

1998. Anti-tuberculosis Week.

591 **116**	50f. multicoloured	35	35

1998. Bosnian and Herzegovina Chess Teams. Sheet 109 × 88 mm containing T **117** and similar horiz designs. Multicoloured.

MS592	20f. Type **117** (silver medal, tenth European Team championship, Debrecen, 1992); 40f. Men's team (silver medal winners, 31st Chess Olympiad, Moscow, 1994); 60f. Women's team (32nd Chess Olympiad, Yerevan, 1996); 80f. National team (11th European Team championship, Pula, 1997)	1·00	1·00

1998. Old Towns.

593 **118**	5f. black and green	10	10
597 –	38f. black and brown	25	25

DESIGN: 38f. Sarajevo.

119 Postal Workers in New Uniforms

120 Lutes

1998. World Post Day.

605 **119**	1m. multicoloured	70	70

1998. Musical Instruments.

606 **120**	80f. multicoloured	55	55

121 "The Creation of Adam" (detail of fresco on ceiling of Sistine Chapel, Michelangelo)

1998. World Disabled Day.

607 **121**	1m. multicoloured	70	70

122 Bjelasnica Mountain Range

1998.

608 **122**	1m. multicoloured	70	70

123 People

1998. 50th Anniv of Universal Declaration of Human Rights.

609 **123**	1m.35 multicoloured	90	90

124 Christmas Tree (Lamija Pehilj)

1998. Christmas and New Year. Multicoloured.

610	1m. Type **124**	70	70
611	1m.50 Father Andeo Zvizdovic	1·00	1·00

125 Sarajevo University and "Proportion of Man" (Leonardo da Vinci)

127 Astronaut, Earth and Moon

126 Feral Rock Pigeons

1999. Anniversaries. Multicoloured.

612	40f. Type **125** (50th anniv)	25	25
613	40f. Sarajevo High School (120th anniv) (horiz)	25	25

1999. Flora and Fauna. Multicoloured.

614	80f. Type **126**	55	55
615	1m.10 "Knautia sarajevensis"	75	75

1999. 30th Anniv of First Manned Moon Landing.

616 **127**	2m. multicoloured		

128 Slapovi Une

1999. Europa. Parks and Gardens.

617 **128**	2m. multicoloured	1·40	1·40

129 Gorazde

1999.

618 **129**	40f. multicoloured	25	25

130 Children playing Football in Sun (Pranjkovic Nenad)

1999. Children's Week.

619 **130**	50f. multicoloured	35	35

131 House

1999. World Environment Day.

620 **131**	80f. multicoloured	55	55

132 Church, Mosque and Emblem

1999. "Philexfrance 99" International Stamp Exhibition, Paris, France.

621 **132**	2m. multicoloured	1·40	1·40

133 Sarajevo on Stamp

1999. 120th Anniv of First Bosnia and Herzegovina Stamps.
622 **133** 1m. multicoloured 70 70

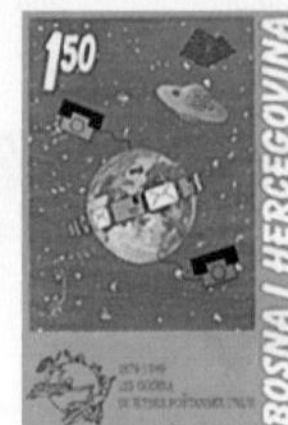

134 Letters encircling Globe and Telephones

1999. 125th Anniv of Universal Postal Union.
623 **134** 1m.50 multicoloured . . . 1·00 1·00

135 Tuzlait from Tuoanj

1999. Minerals. Multicoloured.
624 40f. Type **135** 20 20
625 60f. Siderit from Vitez . . . 40 40
626 1m.20 Hijelofan from Busovaca 80 80
627 1m.80 Quartz from Srebrenica (vert) . . . . . 1·25 1·25

136 Dove and Cathedral

BOSNA I HERCEGOVINA 1,00 KURŠUMLI MEDRESA 1537. g.

137 Kursum Medresa, Sarajevo, 1537 (site of library)

1999. Southern Europe Stability Pact, Sarajevo.
628 **136** 2m. multicoloured . . . . 1·40 1·40

1999. Gazi-Husref Library. Multicoloured.
629 1m. Type **137** 70 70
630 1m.10 Miniature from Hval Codex, 1404 . . . . 75 75

138 Koran, 1550

1999.
631 **138** 1m.50 multicoloured . . . 1·00 1·00

139 X-Ray and Thermal Image of Hands

1999. Centenary of Radiology in Bosnia and Herzegovina.
632 **139** 90f. multicoloured 60 60

140 Kresevljakovic

1999. 40th Death Anniv of Hamdija Kresvljakovic (historian).
633 **140** 1m.30 multicoloured . . . 90 90

141 Chess Emblems and Stars

1999. 15th European Chess Clubs Championship Final, Bugojno.
634 **141** 1m.10 multicoloured . . . 75 75

142 Twipsy (exhibition mascot)

1999. "Expo 2000" World's Fair, Hanover, Germany.
635 **142** 1m. multicoloured 60 60

143 Painting (Afan Ramic)

1999.
636 **143** 1m.20 multicoloured . . . 75 75

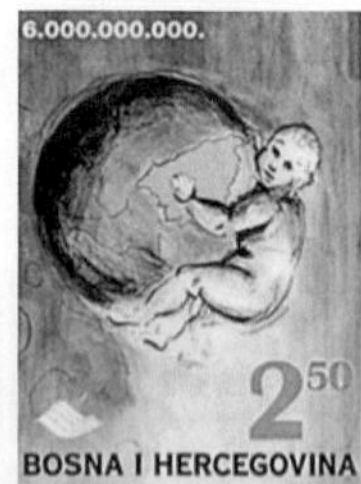

144 Globe and Baby

1999. Birth of World's Six Billionth Inhabitant in Sarajevo.
637 **144** 2m.50 multicoloured . . . 1·50 1·50

145 Bjelasnica Observatory

1999. 105th Anniv of Bjelsnica Meteorological Observatory. Sheet 100 × 60 mm.
MS638 **145** 1m.10 multicoloured 75 75

146 Philharmonic Orchestra Building, Sarajevo

1.10 BOSNA I HERCEGOVINA

147 Woman

1999. International Music Festival, Sarajevo.
639 **146** 40f. black and red 25 25
640 – 1m.10 multicoloured . . . 65 65
DESIGN: 1m.10, Festival poster

2000. Bairam Festival.
641 **147** 1m.10 multicoloured . . . 65 65

148 Map of Bosnia and Herzegovina and Emblem

2000. Olympic Games, Sydney. Sheet 104 × 72 mm containing T **148** and similar horiz design. Multicoloured.
MS642 1m.30 Type **148**; 1m.70 Map of Australia and stylised sailing boats . . . . 2·25 2·25

149 Spaho

1.50 BOSNA I HERCEGOVINA T9 50 godina radioamatera

150 Morse Apparatus

2000. 60th (1999) Death Anniv of Mehmed Spaho (politician).
643 **149** 1m. multicoloured 60 60

2000. 50th Anniv of Amateur Radio in Bosnia and Herzegovina.
644 **150** 1m.50 multicoloured . . . 95 95

151 Illuminated Manuscript

2000. 50th Anniv of Institute of Oriental Studies, Sarajevo University.
645 **151** 2m. multicoloured . . . . 1·25 1·25

152 Boracko River

2000. 15th Anniv of Emerald River Nature Protection Organization. Multicoloured.
646 40f. Type **152** 25 25
647 1m. Figure of woman and river (vert) 60 60

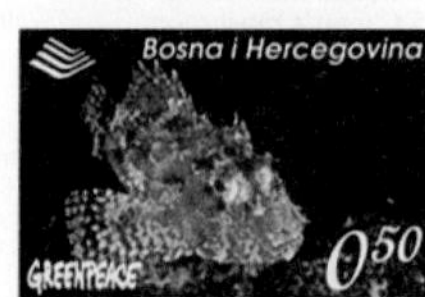

153 Scorpionfish

2000. Greenpeace (environmental organization). Sheet 100 × 72 mm containing T **153** and similar horiz design. Multicoloured.
MS648 50f. Type **153**; 60f. Crayfish; 90f. Crimson anemone; 1m.50 Wreck of *Rainbow Warrior* (campaign ship) . . . . 1·25 1·25

154 Griffon Vulture

2000. Birds. Multicoloured.
649 1m. Type **154** 60 60
650 1m.50 White spoonbill . . . 95 95

2.00 KM 1.02 € BOSNA I HERCEGOVINA EUROPA 2000

155 "Building Europe"

2000. Europa.
651 **155** 2m. multicoloured . . . . 1·25 1·25

156 Count Ferdinand von Zeppelin and LZ-1

2000. Centenary of 1st Zeppelin Flight.
652 **156** 1m.50 multicoloured . . . 95 95

157 Zenica

2000. Towns. Multicoloured.
653 50f. Type **157** 35 35
654 1m. Mostar 65 65
655 1m.10 Bihac 75 75
656 1m.50 Tuzla (vert) . . . . . 1·00 1·00

158 Millennium

2000. New Millennium. Sheet 100 × 72 mm containing T **158** and similar multicoloured design.
MS657 80f. Type **158**; 1m.20, Millennium (57 × 57 mm) . . . 80 80

159 Vranduk

2000. Towns. Multicoloured.
658 1m.30 Type **159** 90 90
659 1m.50 Franciscan Abbey, Kraljeva Sutjeska . . . . 1·00 1·00

160 Tom Sawyer, Huckleberry Finn (characters) and Twain

2000. *The Adventures of Tom Sawyer* (children's book by Mark Twain).
660 **160** 1m.50 multicoloured . . . 1·00 1·00

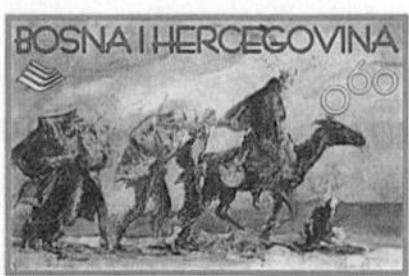

161 People walking (Ismet Mujezinovic)

2000. Paintings. Multicoloured.
661 60f. Type **161** 40 40
662 80f. Trees (Ivo Seremet) . . . 55 55

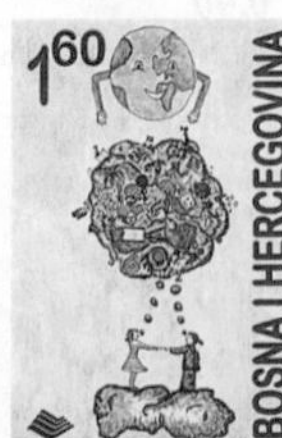

162 Children and Globe

2000. International Children's Week.
663 **162** 1m.60 multicoloured . . . 1·10 1·10

163 Refugees

2000. 50th Anniv of United Nations Commissioner for Refugees.
664 **163** 1m. multicoloured 65 65

164 Tesanj

165 Horse wearing Skirt

2001. Towns. Multicoloured.

665	10f. Type **164**	10	10
666	20f. Bugojno (horiz)	15	15
667	30f. Konjic (horiz)	20	20
668	35f. Zivinice (horiz)	25	25
669	2m. Cazin (horiz)	1·20	1·20

2001. Thelma (cartoon character). Sheet 125 × 170 mm containing T **165** and similar vert designs. Multicoloured.
MS670 30f. Type **165**; 30f. Bear chased by bees; 30f. Cat and boot; 30f. Thelma wet from watering can; 30f. Roast turkey 80 80

166 Kingfisher (*Alcedo athinis*)

167 Disney

2001. Fauna. Multicoloured.

671	90f. Type **166**	60	60
672	1m.10 Bohemian waxwing (*Bombycilla garrulous*) . .	75	75
673	1m.10 Serbian work horse (*Equus caballus*)	75	75
674	1m.90 Head of Serbian horse	1·30	1·30

2001. Birth Centenary of Walt Disney (film maker).
675 **167** 1m.10 multicoloured . . . 75 75

168 Sea Snail

2001. Fossils. Multicoloured.

676	1m.30 Type **168**	90	90
677	1m.80 Ammonite	1·30	1·30

169 Land and Sea Sports

2001. 14th Mediterranean Games, Tunis.
678 **169** 1m.30 multicoloured . . . 90 90

170 Swans on Lake

2001. Europa. Water Resources. Sheet 60 × 81 mm.
MS679 **170** 2m. multicoloured . . 1·20 1·20

2001. Adil Zulfikarpasic Foundation Bosniak Institute (inter-denominational foundation). Sheet 81 × 50 mm.
MS680 **171** 1m.10 multicoloured 75 75

172 Balic

2001. Emir Balic (bridge diving competition winner). Sheet 66 × 47 mm.
MS681 **172** 2m. multicoloured . . 1·20 1·20

173 Ferrari 625 F1 (1954)

2001. Ferrari Racing Cars. Multicoloured.

682	40f. Type **173**	25	25
683	60f. Ferrari 312 B (1970) . .	40	40
684	1m.30 Ferrari 312 T3 (1978)	90	90
685	1m.70 Ferrari 126 C3 (1983)	1·20	1·20

174 Zeljeznicar, Sarajevo Football Team

2001. National Football Champions, 2001.
686 **174** 1m. multicoloured 70 70

175 Ink Well, Quill Pen, Medal and Dove

2001. Centenary of First Nobel Prize.
687 **175** 1m.50 multicoloured . . . 1·00 1·00

176 Charlie Chaplin

2001. Charlie Chaplin Commemoration.
688 **176** 1m.60 multicoloured . . . 1·10 1·10

177 "Traces" (Edin Numankadic)

2001. Art. Multicoloured.

689	80f. Type **177**	55	55
690	2m. David (detail) (sculpture)	1·30	1·30

178 Feeding Bottle enclosed in Stop Sign and Baby at Breast

2001. International Breastfeeding Week.
691 **178** 1m.10 multicoloured . . . 75 75

179 Acropolis, Castle and Pyramid

180 Horse-drawn Tram

2001. United Nations Year of Dialogue Among Civilizations.
692 **179** 1m.30 multicoloured . . . 90 90

2001. Posteurop Plenary, Sarajevo.
693 **180** 1m.10 multicoloured . . .

181 Alija Bejtic and Monument

2001. 20th Death Anniv of Alija Bejtic (cultural historian).
694 **181** 80f. multicoloured 75 75

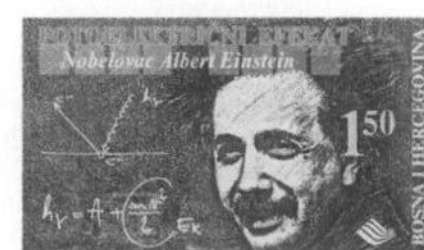

182 Albert Einstein and Formula

2001. 80th Anniv of Albert Einstein's Nobel Prize for Physics (photoelectric effect).
695 **182** 1m.50 multicoloured . . . 55 55

183 Davorin Popovic

2002. 1st Death Anniv of Davorin Popovic (musician).
696 **183** 38f. multicoloured 25 25

184 Bridge, Figure and Books

2002. 350th Birth Anniv of Mustafa Ejubovic (Sejh Jujo) (writer).
697 **184** 1m. multicoloured 70 70

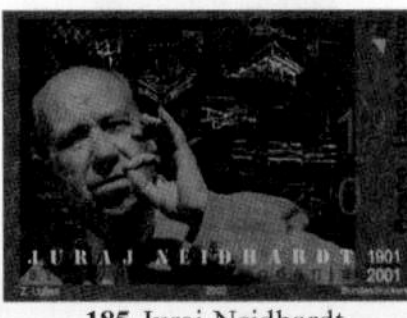

185 Juraj Neidhardt

2002. Birth Centenary (2001) of Juraj Neidhardt (architect).
698 **185** 1m. multicoloured 70 70

186 Sevala Zidzic

187 Skier

2002. Birth Centenary (2003) of Sevala Zidzic (first female Bosnian doctor).
699 **186** 1m.30 multicoloured . . . 90 90

2002. Sarajevo's Candidacy for Winter Olympic Games, 2010.
700 **187** 1m.50 multicoloured . . . 1·00 1·00

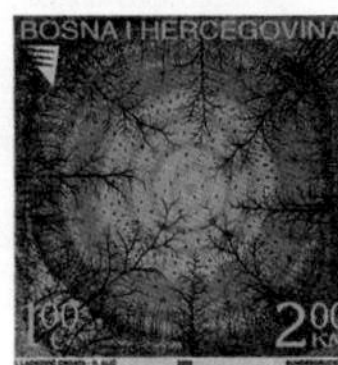

188 Trees

2002. International Earth Day.
701 **188** 2m. multicoloured . . . . 1·30 1·30

189 Scout Camp

2002. 80th Anniv of Bosnian Scouts.
702 **189** 1m. multicoloured 70 70

190 Gentian (*Gentiana dinarica*)

2002. Flora. Multicoloured.

703	1m. Type **190**	70	70
704	1m.50 Aquilegia (*Aquilegia dinarica*)	1·00	1·00

191 "War and Peace" (Asad Nuhanovic)

2002. 10th Anniv of Independence.
705 **191** 2m.50 multicoloured . . . 1·90 1·90

192 Apollo (*Parnassius Apollo*)

193 Firemen fighting Fire

2002. Butterflies. Multicoloured.

706	1m.50 Type **192**	1·00	1·00
707	2m.50 Scarce swallowtail (*Iphiclides podalirius*) . . .	1·90	1·90

2002. 120th Anniv of Sarajevo Fire Brigades. Sheet 68 × 48 mm.
MS708 **193** 2m.20 multicoloured 1·50 1·50

194 Clown 195 Boy wearing Gag

2002. Europa. Circus.
709 **194** 2m.50 multicoloured . . . 1·90 1·90

2002. Letter Writing Campaign. Sheet 120 × 105 mm containing T **195** and similar vert designs showing scenes from "Young Philatelists" (animated film). Multicoloured.
MS710 40f. Type **195**; 40f. Boy with burnt face; 40f. Boy hit by frying pan; 40f. Boy hit by hammer; 40f. Boy hit with saucepan lids . . 1·20 1·20

196 Cevpcici (traditional dish)

2002.
711 **196** 1m.10 multicoloured . . . 75 75

197 Galley

2002. Roman Ships. Sheet 90 × 54 mm containing T **197** and similar horiz design. Multicoloured.
MS712 1m.20 Type **197**; 1m.80 Galleon . . . . 2·10 2·10

198 White Water Rafting

2002. 30th Anniv of Una International Regatta.
713 **198** 1m.30 multicoloured . . . 90 90

199 Association Emblem

2002. Centenary of Napredak (Croatian cultural association).
714 **199** 1m. multicoloured 70 70

200 Mountaineer and Hut

2002. 110th Anniv of Mountaineering Association.
715 **200** 1m. multicoloured 70 70

201 Synagogue

2002. Centenary of Ashkenazi Synagogue, Sarajevo.
716 **201** 2m. multicoloured . . . . 1·20 1·20

202 Metal Worker

2002. Traditional Crafts. Sheet 110 × 75 mm containing T **202** and similar horiz designs. Multicoloured.
MS717 80f. Type **202**; 1m.10 Leather worker; 1m 20 Filigree jewellery; 1m.30 Lace work . . . . . . 3·00 3·00

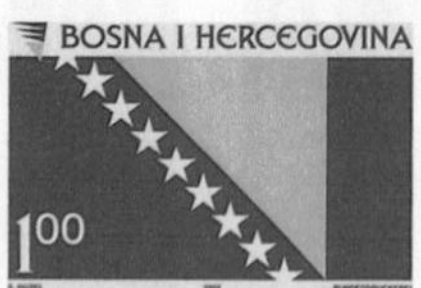

203 Bosnia and Herzegovina Flag

2002.
718 **203** 1m. multicoloured 70 70

204 Coin and Map of Europe

2002. "The Euro" (European currency).
719 **204** 2m. multicoloured . . . . 1·20 1·20

205 Tvrtka I Coin (1376-1391)

2002. Old Coins.
720 **205** 20f. grey, red and black 15 15
721 – 30f. green, red and black 20 20
722 – 50f. blue, red and black 35 35
DESIGNS: 20f. Type **205**; 30f. Stepana Tomasa coin (1443-1461); 50f. Stepana Tomasevita coin (1461-1463).

206 Mother and Child Institute, Sarajevo

2002.
723 **206** 38f. multicoloured 25 25

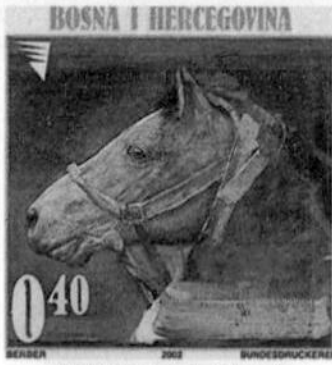

207 Horse's Head

2002. Art. Multicoloured.
724 40f. Type **207** 30 30
725 1m.10 Portrait of a woman (25 × 42 mm) 75 75
726 1m.50 Sculpture and portrait of two women (42 × 25 mm) . . . . . . 1·00 1·00

208 Mak Dizdar

2002. 85th Birth Anniv of Mak Dizdar (poet).
727 **208** 1m. multicoloured 70 70

209 Emaciated Man

2002. Anti-Drugs Campaign.
728 **209** 1m. multicoloured 70 70

II. CROATIAN POSTS

Issues made by the Croat administration in Mostar.

1993. 100 paras = 1 Croatian dinar.
1994. 100 lipa = 1 kuna.

C **1** Statue and Church C **2** Silvije Kranjcevic (poet)

1993. Sanctuary of Our Lady Queen of Peace Shrine, Medugorje.
C1 C **1** 2000d. multicoloured . . . 50 50

1993. Multicoloured.
C2 200d. Type C **2** 10 10
C3 500d. Jajce 15 15
C4 1000d. Mostar (horiz) 20 20

C **3** Medieval Gravestone C **4** "Madonna of the Grand Duke" (Raphael)

1993. 250th Anniv of Census in Bosnia and Herzegovina.
C5 C **3** 100d. multicoloured . . . 10 10

1993. Christmas.
C6 C **4** 6000d. multicoloured . . . 1·25 1·25

C **5** "Uplands in Bloom"

1993. Europa. Contemporary Art. Paintings by Gabrijel Jurkic. Multicoloured.
C7 3500d. Type C **5** . . . . . . 1·75 1·75
C8 5000d. "Wild Poppy" . . . . 2·25 2·25

C **6** Kravica Waterfall

1993.
C9 C **6** 3000d. multicoloured . . . 60 60

C **7** Hrvoje (from "Hrvoje's Missal" by Butko)

1993. 577th Death Anniv of Hrvoje Vukcic Hrvatinic, Duke of Split, Viceroy of Dalmatia and Croatia and Grand Duke of Bosnia.
C10 C **7** 1500d. multicoloured . . 30 30

C **8** Plehan Monastery

1993.
C11 C **8** 2200d. multicoloured . . 45 45

C **9** Arms C **11** "Campanula hercegovina"

C **10** Bronze Cross, Rama-Scit (Mile Blazevic)

1994. Proclamation (August 1993) of Croatian Community of Herceg Bosna.
C12 C **9** 10000d. multicoloured . . 2·00 2·00

1994.
C13 C **10** 2k.80 multicoloured . . 55 55

1994. Flora and Fauna. Multicoloured.
C14 3k.80 Type C **11** 75 75
C15 4k. Mountain dog 80 80

C **12** Hutova Swamp

1994.
C16 C **12** 80l. multicoloured . . . 20 20

C **13** Penny Farthing Bicycles

1994. Europa. Discoveries and Inventions. Mult.
C17 8k. Type C **13** . . . . 1·50 1·50
C18 10k. Mercedes cars, 1901 . . 2·00 2·00

C **14** Views of Town and Fortress

1994. 550th Anniv of First Written Record of Ljubuski.
C19 C **14** 1k. multicoloured . . . 20 20

C **15** Hospital and Christ C **16** Anniversary Emblem

1994. 2nd Anniv of Dr. Nikolic Franciscan Hospital, Nova Bila.
C20 C **15** 5k. multicoloured . . . 1·00 1·00

1995. 50th Anniv of U.N.O. Self-adhesive. Rouletted.
C21 C **16** 1k.50 blue, red & black 30 30

C 17 Crib

1995. Christmas.
C22 C **17** 5k.40 multicoloured . . 1·10 1·10

C 18 Franciscan Monastery, Kraljeva Sutjeska
C **19** Srebrenica

1995.
C23 C **18** 3k. multicoloured . . . 60 60

1995. Towns. Multicoloured.
C24 2k. Type C **19** 40 40
C25 4k. Franciscan Monastery, Mostar 80 80

C **20** Christ on the Cross
C **21** Statue and Church

1995. Europa. Peace and Freedom.
C26 C **20** 6k.50 multicoloured . . 1·25 1·25

1996. 15th Anniv of Sanctuary of Our Lady Queen of Peace Shrine, Medugorje.
C27 C **21** 10k. multicoloured . . . 2·00 2·00

C **22** Queen Katarina Kosaca Kotromanic
C **23** Monastery

1996. Europa. Famous Women.
C28 C **22** 2k.40 multicoloured . . 50 50

1996. 150th Anniv of Franciscan Monastery and Church, Siroki Brijeg.
C29 C **23** 1k.40 multicoloured . . 30 30

C **24** Virgin Mary
C **26** "Madonna and Child" (anon)

1996. Self-adhesive. Rouletted.
C30 C **24** 2k. mult (postage) . . . 40 40
C31 9k. multicoloured (air) 1·75 1·75

1996. "Taipeh '96" International Stamp Exn. Nos. C30/1 surch **1.10** and emblem.
C32 C **24** 1k.10 on 2k. mult (postage) 20 20
C33 1k.10 on 9k. mult (air) 20 20

1996. Christmas.
C34 C **26** 2k.20 multicoloured . . 45 45

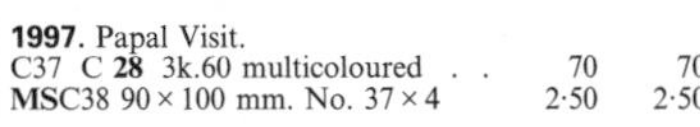
C **27** St. George and the Dragon
C **28** Pope John Paul II

1997. Europa. Tales and Legends. Mult.
C35 2k. Type C **27** 40 40
C36 5k. Zeus as bull and Europa (39 × 34 mm) . . . . . . 1·00 1·00

1997. Papal Visit.
C37 C **28** 3k.60 multicoloured . . 70 70
MSC38 90 × 100 mm. No. 37 × 4 2·50 2·50

C **29** Chapel, Samatorje, Gorica
C **30** Purple Heron

1997.
C39 C **29** 1k.40 multicoloured . . 25 25

1997. Flora and Fauna. Multicoloured.
C40 1k. Type C **30** 20 20
C41 2k.40 "Symphyandra hofmannii" (orchid) . . . 45 45

C **31** "Birth of Christ" (fresco, Giotto)

1997. Christmas.
C42 C **31** 1k.40 multicoloured . . 25 25

C **32** Cats

1998. Europa. Animated Film Festival.
C43 C **32** 6k.50 multicoloured . . 1·10 1·10

C **33** Seal
C **35** "Sibiraea croatica"

C **34** Livno

1998. 550th Anniv of Herzegovina.
C44 C **33** 2k.30 red, black and gold 40 40

1998. 1100th Anniv of Livno.
C45 C **34** 1k.20 multicoloured . . 20 20

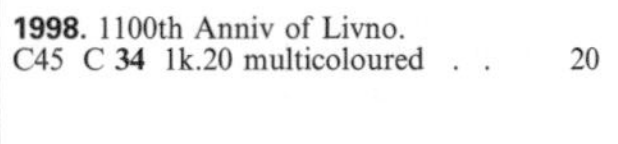
1998.
C46 C **35** 1k.40 multicoloured . . 25 25

C **36** Griffon Vulture
C **37** Adoration of the Wise Men

1998.
C47 C **36** 2k.40 multicoloured . . 40 40

1998. Christmas.
C48 C **37** 5k.40 multicoloured . . 90 90

C **38** Woman, Posavina Region
C **39** Ruins of Bobovac

1999. Regional Costumes.
C49 C **38** 40l. multicoloured . . . 10 10

1999. Old Towns.
C50 C **39** 10l. multicoloured . . . 10 10

C **40** Simic
C **41** Blidinje Nature Park

1999. Birth Centenary (1998) of Antun Simic (writer).
C51 C **40** 30l. multicoloured . . . 10 10

1999. Europa. Parks and Gardens.
C52 C **41** 1k.50 multicoloured . . 25 25

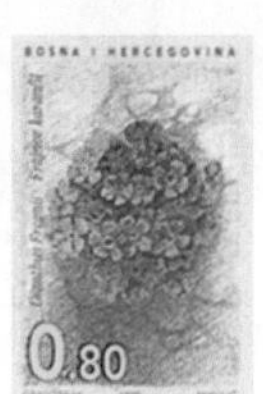
C **42** *Dianthus freynii*

1999.
C53 C **42** 80l. multicoloured . . . 50 50

C **43** Pine Marten

1999.
C54 C **43** 40l. multicoloured . . . 25 25

C **44** Gradina Osanici, Stolac
C **45** The Nativity (mosaic)

1999. Archaeology.
C55 C **44** 10l. multicoloured . . . 10 10

1999. Christmas.
C56 C **45** 30l. multicoloured . . . 20 20

C **46** Sop
C **47** Emblem

2000. 96th Birth Anniv of Nikola Sop (poet).
C57 C **46** 40l. multicoloured . . . 25 25

2000. World Health Day.
C58 C **47** 40l. multicoloured . . . 25 25

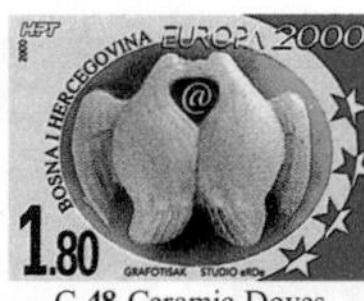
C **48** Ceramic Doves

2000. Europa.
C59 C **48** 1k.80 multicoloured . . 30 30

C **49** Chess Board and Emblem

2000. 40th Anniv of Bosnian Chess Association. Chess Events in 2000. Multicoloured.
C60 80l. Type C **49** (30th Chess Olympiad, Sarajevo) . . . 15 15
C61 80l. Octopus holding pawn and emblem (16th European Chess Club Cup, Neum) 15 15

C **50** Brother Karaula
C **51** Oak Tree (*Quercus sessilis*)

2000. Birth Bicentenary of Brother Lovro Karaula.
C62 C **50** 80l. multicoloured . . . 15 15

2000. Chestnut Oak of Siroki Brijeg.
C63 C **51** 1k.50 multicoloured . . 25 25

C **52** European Eel (*Anguilla anguilla*)

2000.
C64 C **52** 80l. multicoloured . . . 15 15

C **53** Franciscan Monastery, Tomislavgrad

2000.
C65 C **53** 1k.50 multicoloured . . 25 25

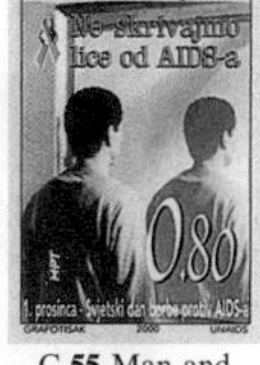
C **54** Woman and Patterned Cloth
C **55** Man and Reflection

2000. Traditional Costume from Kraljeve Sutjeske.
C66 C **54** 40l. multicoloured . . . 10 10

2000. A.I.D.S. Awareness Campaign.
C67 C **55** 80l. multicoloured . . . 15 15

C **56** Nativity C **57** *Chondrostoma phoxinus*

2000. Christmas.
C68 C **56** 40l. multicoloured . . . 10 10

2001. Fishes. Multicoloured.
C69 30l. Type C **57** 10 10
C70 1k.50 *Salmo marmoratus* . . 25 25

C **58** Tihaljina Spring C **59** Petar Zrinski

2001. Europa. Water Resources. Multicoloured.
C71 1k.10 Type C **58** 20 20
C72 1k.80 Pliva Waterfall 30 30

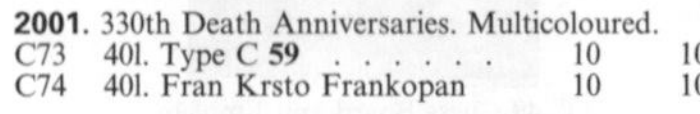

2001. 330th Death Anniversaries. Multicoloured.
C73 40l. Type C **59** 10 10
C74 40l. Fran Krsto Frankopan 10 10

C **60** 16th-century Galley Ship

2001.
C75 C **60** 1k.80 multicoloured . . 30 30

C **61** Boat, Neretva River Valley C **62** Queen of Peace of Medugorje

2001.
C76 C **61** 80l. multicoloured . . . 15 15

2001. 20th Anniv of Medugorje. Sheet 90 × 65 mm.
C77 C **62** 3k.80 multicoloured . . 65 65

C **63** Our Lady of Kondzilo (17th-century painting) C **64** Binary Digits

2001.
C78 C **63** 80l. multicoloured . . . 10 10

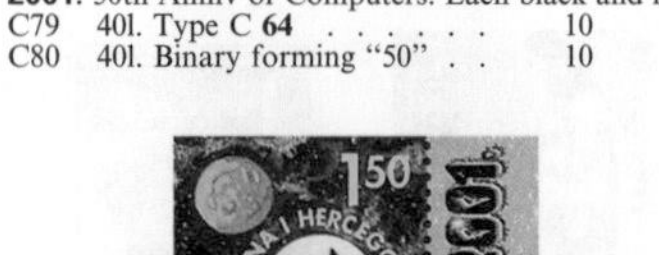

2001. 50th Anniv of Computers. Each black and red.
C79 40l. Type C **64** 10 10
C80 40l. Binary forming "50" . . 10 10

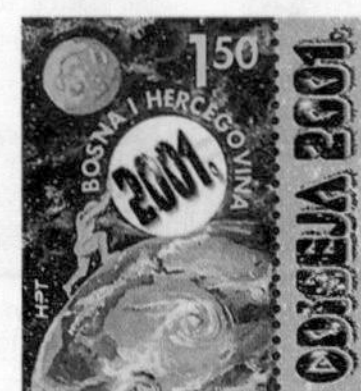

C **65** Mars, Globe and Sisyphus pushing Stone

2001. Millennium.
C81 C **65** 1k.50 multicoloured . . 25 25

C **66** Father Slavko Barbaric

2001. 1st Death Anniv of Father Slavko Barbaric.
C82 C **66** 80l. multicoloured . . . 10 10

C **67** Minnie and Mickey Mouse (Danijela Nedic)

2001. Birth Centenary of Walt Disney (film maker).
C83 C **67** 1k.50 multicoloured . . 25 25

C **68** Nativity

2001. Christmas.
C84 C **68** 40l. multicoloured . . . 10 10

C **69** Alfred Nobel

2001. Centenary of the Nobel Prize.
C85 C **69** 1k.80 multicoloured . . 35 35

C **70** Skier C **71** Vran Mountain

2002. Winter Olympic Games, Salt Lake City, U.S.A.
C86 C **70** 80l. multicoloured . . . 10 10

2002. International Year of Mountains.
C87 C **71** 40l. multicoloured . . . 10 10

C **72** Bridge over River Neretva, Mostar

2002. 550th Anniv of First Written Record of Mostar.
C88 C **72** 30l. multicoloured . . . 10 10

C **73** Clown, Lion and Mouse C **74** Leonardo da Vinci and Designs

2002. Europa. Circus. Multicoloured.
C89 80l. Type C **73** 10 10
C90 1k.50 Big Top and clowns 25 25

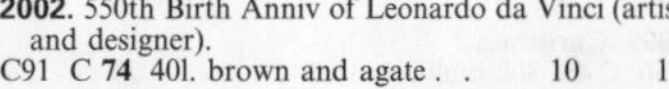

2002. 550th Birth Anniv of Leonardo da Vinci (artist and designer).
C91 C **74** 40l. brown and agate . . 10 10

C **75** Players and Football C **76** Father Bunti and Children

2002. World Cup Football Championships, Japan and South Korea.
C92 C **75** 1k.50 multicoloured . . 25 25

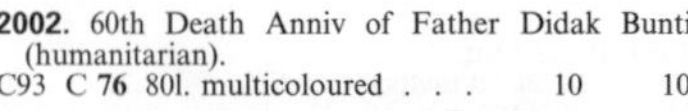

2002. 60th Death Anniv of Father Didak Bunti (humanitarian).
C93 C **76** 80l. multicoloured . . . 10 10

C **77** Inscribed Tablet

2002. 11th-century Inscribed Tablet, Humac.
C94 C **77** 40l. multicoloured . . . 40 40

C **78** Marilyn Monroe C **79** Elvis Presley

2002. 40th Death Anniv of Marilyn Monroe (actor).
C95 C **78** 40l. multicoloured . . . 40 40

2002. 25th Death Anniv of Elvis Presley (entertainer).
C96 C **79** 1k.50 multicoloured . . 25 25

C **80** Transmitter Tower C **82** 1929 Calendar

C **81** 1905 Postcard

2002. 50th Anniv of Television.
C97 C **80** 1k.50 multicoloured . . 25 25

2002. Stamp Day.
C98 C **81** 80l. multicoloured . . . 10 10

2002. Centenary of "Naprodak" (cultural association).
C99 C **82** 40l. multicoloured . . . 10 10

C **83** Stylized Player C **84** *Viola beckiana*

2002. European Bowling Championships, Grude.
C100 C **83** 1k.50 multicoloured . . 25 25

2002. Flowers.
C101 C **84** 30l. multicoloured . . 10 10

C **85** Red Admiral (*Vanessa atalanta*) C **86** Madonna and Child (painting, Bernardino Luini)

2002. Butterflies.
C102 C **85** 80l. multicoloured . . 10 10

2002. Christmas.
C103 C **86** 40l. multicoloured . . 10 10

C **87** School Buildings

2002. 120th Anniv of Society of Jesuits High School, Travnik.
C104 C **87** 80l. multicoloured . . 10 10

III. REPUBLIKA SRPSKA

Issued by the Serb administration based in Pale.

100 paras = 1 dinar.
1998. 100 fennig = 1 mark.

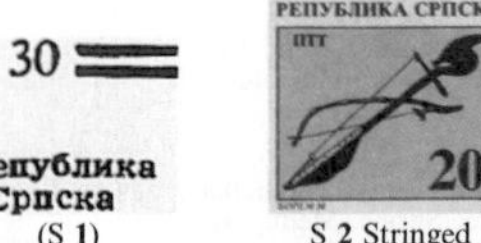

(S 1) S **2** Stringed Instrument

1992. Nos. 2587/98 of Yugoslavia surch as Type S **1**.
S 1 5d. on 10p. violet and green 10 10
S 2 30d. on 3d. blue and red . . 60·00 60·00
S 3a 50d. on 40p. green & purple 50 50
S 4 60d. on 20p. red and yellow 60 60
S 5 60d. on 30p. green & orange 60 60
S 6 100d. on 1d. blue and purple . . . . 1·00 1·00
S 7a 100d. on 2d. blue and red 1·00 1·00
S 8 100d. on 3d. blue and red 1·00 1·00
S 9a 300d. on 5d. ultram & blue 3·00 3·00
S10 500d. on 50p. green & violet 5·00 5·00
S11 500d. on 60p. mauve & red 5·00 5·00

1993. Dated "1992".
S12 S **2** 10d. black and yellow . . 10 10
S13 20d. black and blue . . . 25 25
S14 30d. black and pink . . . 35 35
S15 – 50d. black and red . . . 60 60
S16 – 100d. black and red . . . 1·25 1·25
S17 – 500d. black and blue . . . 6·25 6·25
DESIGNS—VERT: 50, 100d. Coat of arms. HORIZ: 500d. Monastery.

1993. Dated "1993".
S18 S **2** 5000d. black and lilac . . 10 10
S19 6000d. black and yellow 15 15
S20 10000d. black and blue . . 25 25
S21 – 20000d. black and red . . 55 55
S22 – 30000d. black and red . . 85 85
S23 – 50000d. black and lilac . . 1·40 1·40
DESIGNS—VERT: 20000, 30000d. Coat of arms. HORIZ: 50000d. Monastery.

(S 3)

S **4** Symbol of St. John the Evangelist

1993. Referendum. Nos. S15/16 surch as Type S 3.
S24 7500d. on 50d. black and red . . . 60 60
S25 7500d. on 100d. black and red . . . 60 60
S26 9000d. on 50d. black and red . . . 80 80

1993. No value expressed.
S27 S **4** A red . . . 40 40
No. S27 was sold at the rate for internal letters.

Currency Reform

S **5** Icon of St. Stefan

1994. Republic Day.
S28 S **5** 1d. multicoloured . . . 4·00 4·00

S **6** King Petar I

1994. 150th Birth Anniv of King Petar I of Serbia.
S29 S **6** 80p. sepia and brown . . 2·50 2·50

S **7** Banja Luka

1994. 500th Anniv of Banja Luka.
S30 S **7** 1d.20 multicoloured . . . 2·00 2·50

1994. Issued at Doboj. Surch with letter. (a) On Nos. S13/16.
S31 S **2** A on 20d. black and blue
S32 R on 20d. black and blue
S33 R on 30d. black and pink
S34 – R on 50d. black and red
S35 – R on 100d. black and red

(b) On Nos. S18/19 and S21/2.
S36 S **2** R on 5000d. black and lilac . . .
S37 R on 6000d. black and yellow . . .
S38 – A on 20000d. black and red . . .
S39 – R on 20000d. black and red . . .
S40 – R on 30000d. black and red . . .
Set of 10 . . . 65·00

Stamps surcharged "A" were sold at the current rate for internal letters and those surcharged "R" at the rate for internal registered letters. The "R" on No. S32 is reversed.

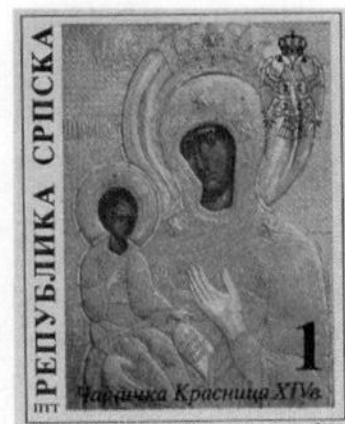

S **9** "Madonna and Child" (icon)

1994. Cajnicka Church.
S41 S **9** 1d. multicoloured . . . 2·00 2·00

1994. Nos. S18/20 and S23 surch (Nos. 542/3 with letter).
S42 S **2** A on 5000d. black & lilac 1·10 1·10
S43 R on 6000d. black & yell 1·10 1·10
S44 40p. on 10000d. blk & bl 1·10 1·10
S45 – 2d. on 50000d. black and lilac . . . 1·10 1·10
No. S42 was sold at the current rate for internal letters and No. S43, which shows the surcharge as the cyrillic letter resembling "P", at the rate for internal registered letters.

S **11** Tavna Monastery

1994. Monasteries. Multicoloured.
S46 60p. Type S **11** . . . 2·00 2·00
S47 1d. Mostanica (horiz) . . . 2·00 2·00
S48 1d.20 Zitomislic . . . 2·25 2·25

S **12** "Aquilegia dinarica"

S **14** Relay Station, Mt. Kozara

1996. Nature Protection. Multicoloured.
S49 1d.20 Type S **12** . . . 1·25 1·25
S50 1d.20 "Edraianthus niveus" (plant) . . . 1·25 1·25
S51 1d.20 Shore lark . . . 1·25 1·25
S52 1d.20 "Dinaromys bogdanovi" (dormouse) . . 1·25 1·25

1996. Nos. S14/16, S19 and S22 surch.
S53 S **2** 70p. on 30d. black and pink . . . 30 30
S54 – 1d. on 100d. black & red 40 40
S55 – 2d. on 30000d. blk & red 80 80
S56 – 3d. on 50d. black and red 1·25 1·25
S57 S **2** 5d. on 6000d. black and yellow . . . 2·25 2·25

1996.
S58 S **14** A green and bistre . . .
S59 – R purple and brown . .
S60 – 1d.20 violet and blue . .
S61 – 2d. lilac and mauve . .
S62 – 5d. purple and blue . .
S63 – 10d. brown and sepia
Set of 6 . . . 6·50 6·50
DESIGNS—VERT: R, Kraljica relay station, Mt. Ozren; 2d. Relay station, Mt. Romanija; 5d. Stolice relay station, Mt. Maljevica. HORIZ: 1d.20, Bridge over river Drina at Srbinje; 10d. Bridge at Visegrad.
No. S58 was sold at the current rate for an internal letter and No. S59 at the rate for an internal registered letter.

S **15** Orthodox Church, Bascarsiji

1997.
S64 S **15** 2d.50 multicoloured . . 1·00 1·00

S **16** Pupin

S **17** "Primula kitaibeliana"

1997. 62nd Death Anniv of Michael Pupin (physicist and inventor).
S65 S **16** 2d.50 multicoloured . . 1·00 1·00

1997. Flowers. Multicoloured.
S66 3d.20 Type S **17** . . . 85 85
S67 3d.20 "Pedicularis hoermanniana" . . . 85 85
S68 3d.20 "Knautia sarajevensis" 85 85
S69 3d.20 "Oxytropis campestris" 85 85

S **18** Robert Koch

S **19** Branko Copic

1997. Obligatory Tax. Anti-tuberculosis Week. Self-adhesive
S70 S **18** 15f. red and blue . . . 10 10

1997. Writers. Each mauve and yellow.
S71 A (60p.) Type S **19** . . . 25 25
S72 R (90p.) Jovan Ducic . . . 35 35
S73 1d.50 Mesa Selimovic . . . 35 35
S74 3d. Aleksa Santic . . . 85 85
S75 5d. Petar Kocic . . . 1·25 1·25
S76 10d. Ivo Andric . . . 2·50 2·50

S **20** European Otter

S **21** Two Queens

1997. Nature Protection. Multicoloured.
S77 2d.50 Type S **20** . . . 50 50
S78 4d.50 Roe deer . . . 1·10 1·10
S79 6d.50 Brown bear . . . 1·75 1·75

1997. Europa. Tales and Legends. Multicoloured.
S80 2d.50 Type S **21** . . . 1·00 1·00
S81 6d.50 Prince on horseback . . 2·50 2·50

S **22** Diana, Princess of Wales

1998. Diana, Princess of Wales Commemoration.
S82 S **22** 3d.50 multicoloured ("DIANA" in Roman alphabet) . . . 1·25 1·25
S83 3d.50 multicoloured ("DIANA" in Cyrillic alphabet) . . . 1·25 1·25

S **23** Cross and Globe

S **24** Brazil

1998. Obligatory Tax. Red Cross. Self-adhesive.
S84 S **23** 90f. red, blue and ultram 60 60

1998. World Cup Football Championship, France. Showing flags and players of countries in final rounds. Multicoloured.
S 85 90f. Type S **24** . . . 60 60
S 86 90f. Morocco . . . 60 60
S 87 90f. Norway . . . 60 60
S 88 90f. Scotland . . . 60 60
S 89 90f. Italy . . . 60 60
S 90 90f. Chile . . . 60 60
S 91 90f. Austria . . . 60 60
S 92 90f. Cameroun . . . 60 60
S 93 90f. France . . . 60 60
S 94 90f. Saudi Arabia . . . 60 60
S 95 90f. Denmark . . . 60 60
S 96 90f. South Africa . . . 60 60
S 97 90f. Spain . . . 60 60
S 98 90f. Nigeria . . . 60 60
S 99 90f. Paraguay . . . 60 60
S100 90f. Bulgaria . . . 60 60
S101 90f. Netherlands . . . 60 60
S102 90f. Belgium . . . 60 60
S103 90f. Mexico . . . 60 60
S104 90f. South Korea . . . 60 60
S105 90f. Germany . . . 60 60
S106 90f. United States of America . . . 60 60
S107 90f. Yugoslavia . . . 60 60
S108 90f. Iran . . . 60 60
S109 90f. Rumania . . . 60 60
S110 90f. England (U.K. flag) . . 60 60
S111 90f. Tunisia . . . 60 60
S112 90f. Colombia . . . 60 60
S113 90f. Argentina . . . 60 60
S114 90f. Jamaica . . . 60 60
S115 90f. Croatia . . . 60 60
S116 90f. Japan . . . 60 60

S **26** Family walking in Countryside

1998. Obligatory Tax. Anti-tuberculosis Week.
S119 S **26** 75f. multicoloured . . . 50 50

S **27** St. Pantelejmon

S **28** Bijelijna

1998. 800th Anniv of Hilandar Monastery. Icons. Multicoloured.
S120 50f. Type S **27** . . . 35 35
S121 70f. Jesus Christ . . . 45 45
S122 1m.70 St. Nikola . . . 1·10 1·10
S123 2m. St. John of Rila . . . 1·40 1·40

1999. Towns. Multicoloured. (a) With face value.
S124 15f. Type S **28** . . . 10 10
S125 20f. Sokolac . . . 15 15
S126 75f. Prijedor . . . 50 50
S127 2m. Brcko . . . 1·40 1·40
S128 4m.50 Zvornik . . . 3·00 3·00
S129 10m. Doboj . . . 6·75 6·75

(b) Face value expressed by letter.
S130 A (50f.) Banja Luka . . . 35 35
S131 R (1m.) Trebinje . . . 70 70
No. S130 was sold at the current rate for an internal letter and No. S131 at the rate for an internal registered letter.

S **29** Airliner over Lake

1999. Founding of Air Srpska (state airline). Multicoloured.
S132 50f. Type S **29** . . . 35 35
S133 50f. Airliner above clouds 35 35
S134 75f. Airliner over beach . . 50 50
S135 1m.50 Airliner over lake (different) . . . 1·00 1·00

S **30** Table Tennis Ball as Globe

1999. International Table Tennis Championships, Belgrade. Multicoloured.
S136 1m. Type S **30** . . . 70 70
S137 2m. Table tennis table, bat and ball . . . 1·40 1·40

S **31** Kozara National Park

S **32** Open Hands

1999. Europa. National Parks. Multicoloured.
S138 1m.50 Type S **31** . . . 1·00 1·00
S139 2m. Perucica National Park 1·40 1·40

1999. Obligatory Tax. Red Cross.
S140 S **32** 10f. multicoloured . . . 10 10

S **25** Couple and Musical Instrument

1998. Europa. National Festivals. Multicoloured.
S117 7m.50 Type S **25** . . . 5·00 5·00
S118 7m.50 Couple from Neretva and musical instrument . . . 5·00 5·00

S 33 Manuscript

1999. 780th Anniv of Bosnia and Herzegovina Archbishopric (S142, S144/8) and 480th Anniv of Garazole Printing Works (S141, S143). Mult.
S141 50f. Type **S 33** 30 30
S142 50f. Dobrun Monastery 30 30
S143 50f. "G" 30 30
S144 50f. Zhitomislib Monastery 30 30
S145 50f. Gomionitsa Monastery 30 30
S146 50f. Madonna and Child with angels and prophets (icon, 1578) 30 30
S147 50f. St. Nicolas (icon) 30 30
S148 50f. Wise Men (icon) 30 30

S **34** Brown Trout
S **35** Lunar Module on Moon's Surface

1999. Fishes. Multicoloured.
S149 50f. Type **S 34** 30 30
S150 50f. Lake trout (*Salmo trutta morpha lacustris*) 30 30
S151 75f. Huchen 45 45
S152 1m. European grayling 65 65

1999. 30th Anniv of First Manned Landing on Moon. Multicoloured.
S153 1m. Type **S 35** 65 65
S154 2m. Astronaut on Moon 1·25 1·25

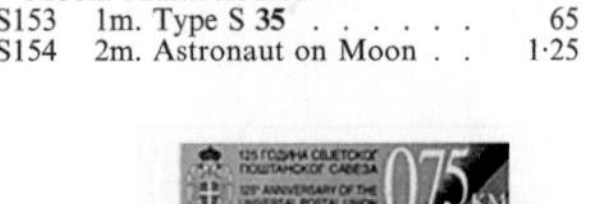

S 36 Pencil and Emblem

1999. 125th Anniv of Universal Postal Union. Mult.
S155 75f. Type **S 36** 45 45
S156 1m.25 Earth and emblem 75 75

BOTSWANA Pt. 1

Formerly Bechuanaland Protectorate, attained independence on 30 September 1966, and changed its name to Botswana.

1966. 100 cents = 1 rand.
1976. 100 thebe = 1 pula.

47 National Assembly Building

1966. Independence. Multicoloured.
202 2½c. Type **47** 15 10
203 5c. Abattoir, Lobatsi 20 10
204 15c. National Airways Douglas DC-3 65 20
205 35c. State House, Gaberones 40 30

1966. Nos. 168/81 of Bechuanaland optd **REPUBLIC OF BOTSWANA.**
206 **28** 1c. multicoloured 25 10
207 – 2c. orange, black and olive 30 1·75
208 – 2½c. multicoloured 30 10
209 – 3½c. multicoloured 70 20
210 – 5c. multicoloured 70 1·50
211 – 7½c. multicoloured 50 1·75
212 – 10c. multicoloured 1·00 20
213 – 12½c. multicoloured 2·00 2·75
214 – 20c. brown and drab 30 1·00
215 – 25c. sepia and lemon 30 2·00
216 – 35c. blue and orange 40 2·25
217 – 50c. sepia and olive 30 70
218 – 1r. black and brown 40 1·25
219 – 2r. brown and turquoise 75 2·50

52 Golden Oriole

1967. Multicoloured.
220 1c. Type **52** 30 15
221 2c. Hoopoe ("African Hoopese") 40 70
222 3c. Groundscraper thrush 55 10
223 4c. Cordon-bleu ("Blue Waxbill") 55 10
224 5c. Secretary bird 55 10
225 7c. Southern yellow-billed hornbill ("Yellow-billed Hornbill") 60 90
226 10c. Burchell's gonolek ("Crimson-breasted Strike") 60 15
227 15c. Malachite kingfisher 7·50 3·00
228 20c. African fish eagle ("Fish Eagle") 7·50 2·00
229 25c. Go-away bird ("Grey Loerie") 4·00 1·50
230 35c. Scimitar-bill 6·00 2·25
231 50c. Comb duck ("Knob-Billed Duck") 2·75 2·75
232 1r. Levaillant's barbet ("Crested Barbet") 5·00 3·50
233 2r. Didric cuckoo ("Diederick Cuckoo") 7·00 16·00

66 Students and University

1967. 1st Conferment of University Degrees.
234 **66** 3c. sepia, blue and orange 10 10
235 7c. sepia, blue and turquoise 10 10
236 15c. sepia, blue and red 10 10
237 35c. sepia, blue and violet 20 20

67 Bushbuck

1967. Chobe Game Reserve. Multicoloured.
238 3c. Type **67** 10 20
239 7c. Sable Antelope 15 30
240 35c. Fishing on the Chobe River 80 1·10

70 Arms of Botswana and Human Rights Emblem

1968. Human Rights Year.
241 **70** 3c. multicoloured 10 10
242 – 15c. multicoloured 25 45
243 – 25c. multicoloured 25 60
The designs of Nos. 242/3 are similar, but are arranged differently.

73 Eland and Giraffe Rock Paintings, Tsodilo Hills

1968. Opening of National Museum and Art Gallery. Multicoloured.
244 3c. Type **73** 20 20
245 7c. Girl wearing ceremonial beads (31 × 48 mm) 25 40
246 10c. "Baobab Trees" (Thomas Baines) 25 30
247 15c. National Museum and art gallery (72 × 19 mm) 40 1·50
MS248 132 × 82 mm. Nos. 244/7 1·00 2·25

77 African Family, and Star over Village

1968. Christmas.
249 **77** 1c. multicoloured 10 10
250 2c. multicoloured 10 10
251 5c. multicoloured 10 10
252 25c. multicoloured 15 50

78 Scout, Lion and Badge in frame

1969. 22nd World Scout Conference, Helsinki. Mult.
253 3c. Type **78** 30 30
254 15c. Scouts cooking over open fire (vert) 35 1·00
255 25c. Scouts around camp fire 35 1·00

81 Woman, Child and Christmas Star
82 Diamond Treatment Plant, Orapa

1969. Christmas.
256 **81** 1c. blue and brown 10 10
257 2c. olive and brown 10 10
258 4c. yellow and brown 10 10
259 35c. brown and violet 20 20
MS260 86 × 128 mm. Nos. 256/9 70 1·10

1970. Developing Botswana. Multicoloured.
261 3c. Type **82** 70 20
262 7c. Copper-nickel mining 95 20
263 10c. Copper-nickel mine, Selebi-Pikwe (horiz) 1·25 15
264 35c. Orapa Diamond mine and diamonds (horiz) 2·75 1·25

83 Mr. Micawber ("David Copperfield")

1970. Death Centenary of Charles Dickens. Mult.
265 3c. Type **83** 20 10
266 7c. Scrooge ("A Christmas Carol") 25 10
267 15c. Fagin ("Oliver Twist") 45 40
268 25c. Bill Sykes ("Oliver Twist") 70 60
MS269 114 × 81 mm. Nos. 265/8 2·75 4·00

84 U.N. Building and Emblem

1970. 25th Anniv of United Nations.
270 **84** 15c. blue, brown and silver 70 30

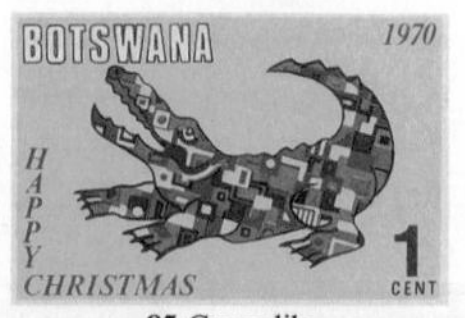

85 Crocodile

1970. Christmas. Multicoloured.
271 1c. Type **85** 10 10
272 2c. Giraffe 10 10
273 7c. Elephant 15 15
274 25c. Rhinoceros 60 80
MS275 128 × 90 mm. Nos. 271/4 1·00 3·00

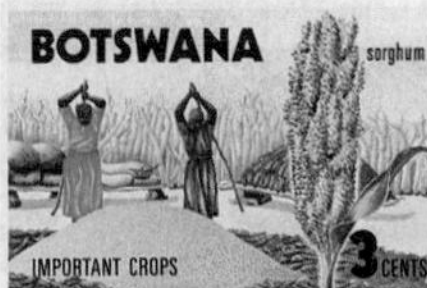

86 Sorghum

1971. Important Crops. Multicoloured.
276 3c. Type **86** 15 10
277 7c. Millet 20 10
278 10c. Maize 20 10
279 35c. Groundnuts 70 1·00

87 Map and Head of Cow
88 King bringing Gift of Gold

1971. 5th Anniv of Independence.
280 **87** 3c. black, brown and green 10 10
281 – 4c. black, light blue and blue 10 10
282 – 7c. black and orange 20 15
283 – 10c. multicololured 20 15
284 – 20c. multicoloured 55 2·25
DESIGNS: 4c. Map and cogs; 7c. Map and common zebra; 10c. Map and sorghum stalk crossed by tusk; 20c. Arms and map of Botswana.

1971. Christmas. Multicoloured.
285 2c. Type **88** 10 10
286 3c. King bringing frankincense 10 10
287 7c. King bringing myrrh 10 10
288 20c. Three Kings behold the star 35 65
MS289 85 × 128 mm. Nos. 285/8 1·00 3·50

89 Orion
90 Postmark and Map

1972. "Night Sky".
290 **89** 3c. blue, black and red 75 30
291 – 7c. blue, black and yellow 1·10 80
292 – 10c. green, black and orange 1·25 85
293 – 20c. blue, black and green 1·75 3·25
CONSTELLATIONS: 7c. The Scorpion; 10c. The Centaur; 20c. The Cross.

1972. Mafeking-Gubulawayo Runner Post. Mult.
294 3c. Type **90** 30 10
295 4c. Bechuanaland stamp and map 30 35
296 7c. Runners and map 45 50
297 20c. Mafeking postmark and map 1·10 1·50
MS298 84 × 216 mm. Nos. 294/7 vertically se-tenant, forming a composite map design 11·00 15·00
For these designs with changed inscription see Nos. 652/5.

91 Cross, Map and Bells
92 Thor

1972. Christmas. Each with Cross and Map. Mult.
299 2c. Type **91** 10 75
300 3c. Cross, map and candle 10 10
301 7c. Cross, map and Christmas tree 15 25
302 20c. Cross, map, star and holly 40 85
MS303 96 × 119 mm. Nos. 299/302 1·25 3·25

1973. Centenary of I.M.O./W.M.O. Norse Myths. Multicoloured.
304 3c. Type **92** 20 10
305 4c. Sun God's chariot (horiz) 25 15

306 7c. Ymir, the frost giant . . 30 15
307 20c. Odin and Sleipnir (horiz) 75 70

93 Livingstone and River Scene

1973. Death Centenary of Dr. Livingstone. Mult.
308 3c. Type **93** 20 10
309 20c. Livingstone meeting Stanley 90 90

94 Donkey and Foal at Village Trough

1973. Christmas. Multicoloured.
310 3c. Type **94** 10 10
311 4c. Shepherd and flock (horiz) 10 10
312 7c. Mother and Child 10 10
313 20c. Kgotla meeting (horiz) 40 85

95 Gaborone Campus

1974. 10th Anniv of University of Botswana, Lesotho and Swaziland. Multicoloured.
314 3c. Type **95** 10 10
315 7c. Kwaluseni Campus . . . 10 10
316 20c. Roma Campus 15 20
317 35c. Map and flags of the three countries 20 35

96 Methods of Mail Transport

1974. Centenary of U.P.U. Multicoloured.
318 2c. Type **96** 55 35
319 3c. Post Office, Palapye, circa 1889 . . . . 55 35
320 7c. Bechuanaland Police Camel Post, circa 1900 . . 95 70
321 20c. Hawker Siddeley H.S.748 and De Havilland D.H.9 mail planes of 1920 and 1974 . . . . 2·75 2·50

97 Amethyst

1974. Botswana Minerals. Multicoloured.
322 1c. Type **97** . . . . 60 2·00
323 2c. Agate-"Botswana Pink" 60 2·00
324 3c. Quartz 65 80
325 4c. Copper nickel 70 60
326 5c. Moss agate . . . . . . 70 1·00
327 7c. Agate . . . . 80 1·00
328 10c. Stilbite . . . . 1·60 65
329 15c. Moshaneng banded marble . . . . 2·00 4·00
330 20c. Gem diamonds . . . . 4·00 4·50
331 25c. Chrysotile . . . . 5·00 2·50
332 35c. Jasper . . . . 5·00 5·50
333 50c. Moss quartz . . . . . 4·50 7·00
334 1r. Citrine . . . . 7·50 10·00
335 2r. Chalcopyrite . . . . . 20·00 20·00

98 "Stapelia variegata" 99 President Sir Seretse Khama

1974. Christmas. Multicoloured.
336 2c. Type **98** 20 40
337 7c. "Hibiscus lunarifolius" . . 40 20
338 15c. "Ceratotheca triloba" . . 60 1·00
339 20c. "Nerine laticoma" . . . 70 1·25
MS340 85 × 130 mm. Nos. 336/9 2·00 4·25

1975. 10th Anniv of Self-Government.
341 **99** 4c. multicoloured 10 10
342 10c. multicoloured 15 10
343 20c. multicoloured 25 25
344 35c. multicoloured 45 50
MS345 93 × 130 mm. Nos. 341/4 1·00 1·50

100 Ostrich

1975. Rock Paintings, Tsodilo Hills. Multicoloured.
346 4c. Type **100** 60 10
347 10c. White rhinoceros . . . . 1·00 10
348 25c. Spotted hyena . . . . . 2·00 55
349 35c. Scorpion . . . . 2·00 1·10
MS350 150 × 150 mm. Nos. 346/9 11·00 7·50

101 Map of British Bechuanaland, 1885 102 "Aloe marlothii"

1975. Anniversaries. Multicoloured.
351 6c. Type **101** 30 20
352 10c. Chief Khama, 1875 . . . 40 15
353 25c. Chiefs Sebele, Bathoen and Khama, 1895 (horiz) 80 75

EVENTS: 6c. 90th anniv of Protectorate; 10c. Centenary of Khama's accession; 25c. 80th anniv of Chiefs' visit to London.

1975. Christmas. Aloes. Multicoloured.
354 3c. Type **102** 20 10
355 10c. "Aloe lutescens" 40 20
356 15c. "Aloe zebrina" . . . . 60 1·50
357 25c. "Aloe littoralis" . . . . 75 2·50

103 Drum

1976. Traditional Musical Instruments. Mult.
358 4c. Type **103** 15 10
359 10c. Hand piano 20 10
360 15c. Segankuru (violin) . . . 25 50
361 25c. Kudu signal horn . . . 30 1·25

104 One Pula Note

1976. 1st National Currency. Multicoloured.
362 4c. Type **104** 15 10
363 10c. Two pula note 20 10
364 15c. Five pula note 35 20
365 25c. Ten pula note 45 45
MS366 163 × 107 mm. Nos. 362/5 1·00 3·50

1976. Nos. 322/35 surch in new currency.
367 1t. on 1c. multicoloured . . . 2·00 70
368 2t. on 2c. multicoloured . . . 2·00 1·75
369 3t. on 3c. multicoloured . . . 1·50 60
370 4t. on 4c. multicoloured . . . 2·50 40
371 5t. on 5c. multicoloured . . . 2·50 40
372 7t. on 7c. multicoloured . . . 1·25 2·75
373 10t. on 10c. multicoloured . . 1·25 80
374 15t. on 15c. multicoloured . . 4·25 3·25
375 20t. on 20c. multicoloured . . 7·50 80
376 25t. on 25c. multicoloured . . 5·00 1·25
377 35t. on 35c. multicoloured . . 4·50 5·00
378 50t. on 50c. multicoloured . . 7·00 9·00
379 1p. on 1r. multicoloured . . 8·00 9·50
380 2p. on 2r. multicoloured . . 11·00 11·00

106 Botswana Cattle

1976. 10th Anniv of Independence. Multicoloured.
381 4t. Type **106** 15 10
382 10t. Antelope, Okavango Delta (vert) 20 10
383 15t. School and pupils . . . 20 40
384 25t. Rural weaving (vert) . . 20 50
385 35t. Miner (vert) 75 85

107 "Colophospermum mopane"

1976. Christmas. Trees. Multicoloured.
386 3t. Type **107** 15 10
387 4t. "Baikiaea plurijuga" . . . 15 10
388 10t. "Sterculia rogersii" . . . 20 10
389 25t. "Acacia nilotica" 45 50
390 40t. "Kigelia africana" . . . 75 1·25

108 Coronation Coach

1977. Silver Jubilee. Multicoloured.
391 4t. The Queen and Sir Seretse Khama 10 10
392 25t. Type **108** 20 15
393 40t. The Recognition 35 90

109 African Clawless Otter

1977. Diminishing Species. Multicoloured.
394 3t. Type **109** . . . . 4·25 40
395 4t. Serval . . . . 4·25 40
396 10t. Bat-eared fox . . . . . 4·75 40
397 25t. Temminck's ground pangolin . . . . 11·00 2·00
398 40t. Brown hyena . . . . . 13·00 7·50

110 Cwihaba Caves

1977. Historical Monuments. Multicoloured.
399 4t. Type **110** 20 10
400 5t. Khama Memorial 20 10
401 15t. Green's Tree 30 40
402 20t. Mmajojo Ruins 30 45
403 25t. Ancient morabaraba board 30 50
404 35t. Matsieng's footprint . . 40 60
MS405 154 × 105 mm. Nos. 399/404 2·50 3·25

111 "Hypoxis nitida" 112 Black Bustard

1977. Christmas. Lilies. Multicoloured.
406 3t. Type **111** 15 10
407 5t. "Haemanthus magnificus" 15 10
408 10t. "Boophane disticha" . . 20 10
409 25t. "Vellozia retinervis" . . 40 55
410 40t. "Ammocharis coranica" 55 1·25

1978. Birds. Multicoloured.
411 1t. Type **112** . . . . 70 1·25
412 2t. Marabou stork . . . . . 90 1·25
413 3t. Green wood hoopoe ("Red Billed Hoopoe") . . 70 85
414 4t. Carmine bee eater . . . . 90 1·00
415 5t. African jacana 70 40
416 7t. African paradise flycatcher ("Paradise Flycatcher) . . 1·00 3·00
417 10t. Bennett's woodpecker . . 2·00 60
418 15t. Red bishop . . . . . . 1·50 3·00
419 20t. Crowned plover . . . . 1·75 2·00
420 25t. Giant kingfisher . . . . 70 3·00
421 30t. White-faced whistling duck ("White-faced Duck") 70 70
422 35t. Green-backed heron . . 70 3·25
423 45t. Black-headed heron . . . 1·00 3·00
424 50t. Spotted eagle owl . . . 5·00 4·50
425 1p. Gabar goshawk . . . . 2·50 4·50
426 2p. Martial eagle . . . . . . 3·00 8·00
427 5p. Saddle-bill stork . . . . 6·50 16·00

113 Tawana making Kaross

1978. Okavango Delta. Multicoloured.
428 4t. Type **113** 10 30
429 5t. Tribe localities 10 10
430 15t. Bushman collecting roots 25 40
431 20t. Herero woman milking 35 70
432 25t. Yei poling "mokoro" (canoe) 40 60
433 35t. Mbukushu fishing . . . 45 1·75
MS434 150 × 98 mm. Nos. 428/33 1·50 3·75

114 "Caralluma lutea" 115 Sip Well

1978. Christmas. Flowers. Multicoloured.
435 5t. Type **114** 35 10
436 10t. "Hoodia lugardii" . . . 50 15
437 15t. "Ipomoea transvaalensis" 90 55
438 25t. "Ansellia gigantea" . . . 1·10 70

1979. Water Development. Multicoloured.
439 3t. Type **115** 10 10
440 5t. Watering pit 10 10
441 10t. Hand dug well 15 10
442 22t. Windmill 20 30
443 50t. Modern drilling rig . . . 40 55

116 Pottery

1979. Handicrafts. Multicoloured.
444 5t. Type **116** 10 10
445 10t. Clay modelling 10 10
446 25t. Basketry 20 25
447 40t. Beadwork 40 50
MS448 123 × 96 mm. Nos. 444/7 1·00 2·50

117 British Bechuanaland 1885 1d. Stamp and Sir Rowland Hill

1979. Death Centenary of Sir Rowland Hill. Mult.
449 5t. Type **117** 20 10
450 25t. Bechuanaland Protectorate 1932 2d. stamp 45 50
451 45t. 1967 Hoopoe 2c. definitive stamp . . . . . 55 1·25

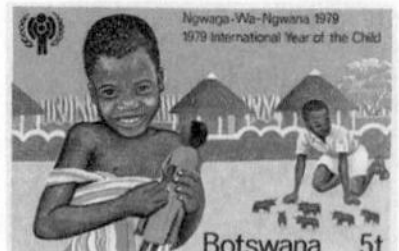

118 Children Playing

1979. International Year of the Child. Multicoloured.
452 5t. Type **118** 20 10
453 10t. Child playing with doll (vert) 30 20

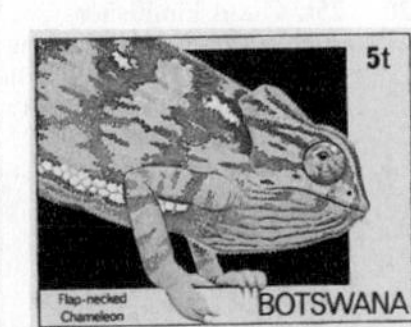

119 "Ximenia caffra" 120 Flap-necked Chameleon

1979. Christmas. Flowers. Multicoloured.
454 5t. Type **119** 10 10
455 10t. "Sclerocarya caffra" . . 20 20
456 15t. "Hexalobus monopetalus" 35 35
457 25t. "Ficus soldanella" . . . 45 45

1980. Reptiles. Multicoloured.
458 5t. Type **120** 30 10
459 10t. Leopard tortoise 30 15
460 25t. Puff adder 50 65
461 40t. White-throated monitor 60 2·50

121 Rock Breaking

1980. Early Mining. Multicoloured.
462 5t. Type **121** 25 15
463 10t. Ore hoisting 30 15
464 15t. Ore transport 70 60
465 20t. Ore crushing 75 90
466 25t. Smelting 80 90
467 35t. Tool and products . . . 1·00 1·75

122 "Chiwele and the Giant"

1980. Folktales. Multicoloured.
468 5t. Type **122** 10 10
469 10t. "Kgori is not deceived" (vert) 15 10
470 30t. "Nyambi's wife and Crocodile" (vert) 45 45
471 45t. "Clever Hare" (horiz) . . 60 60
The 10t. and 30t. are 28 × 37 mm and the 45t. 44 × 27 mm.

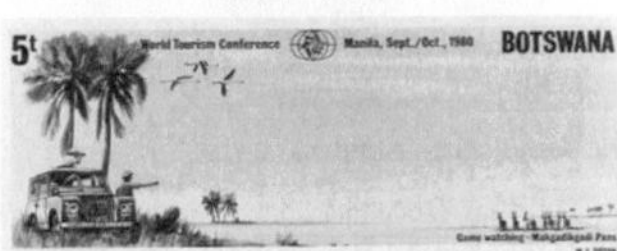

123 Game watching, Makgadikgadi Pans

1980. World Tourism Conference, Manila.
472 **123** 5t. multicoloured 45 20

124 "Acacia gerrardii" 126 "Anax imperator" (dragonfly)

125 Heinrich von Stephan and Botswana 3d. and 3c. U.P.U. Stamps

1980. Christmas. Multicoloured.
473 6t. Type **124** 10 10
474 1t. "Acacia nilotica" 20 10
475 25t. "Acacia erubescens" . . 45 30
476 40t. "Dichrostachys cinerea" 70 70

1981. 150th Birth Anniv of Heinrich von Stephan (founder of Universal Postal Union). Multicoloured.
477 6t. Type **125** 75 30
478 20t.6d. and 7c. U.P.U. stamps . . . . 1·75 2·25

1981. Insects. Multicoloured.
479 6t. Type **126** 15 10
480 7t. "Sphodromantis gastrica" (mantid) 15 20
481 10t. "Zonocerus elegans" (grasshopper) 15 20
482 20t. "Kheper nigroaeneus" (beetle) 25 50
483 30t. "Papilio demodocus" (butterfly) 35 70
484 45t. "Acanthocampa belina" (moth larva) . . . . 40 1·10
MS485 180 × 89 mm. Nos. 479/84 3·25 8·50

127 Camphill Community Rankoromane, Otse

1981. International Year for Disabled Persons. Multicoloured.
486 6t. Type **127** 20 10
487 20t. Resource Centre for the Blind, Mochudi 55 35
488 30t. Tlamelong Rehabilitation Centre, Tlokweng 75 45

128 Woman reading Letter

1981. Literacy Programme. Multicoloured.
489 6t. Type **128** 20 10
490 7t. Man filling in form . . . 20 15
491 20t. Boy reading newspaper 60 35
492 30t. Child being taught to read 80 45

129 Sir Seretse Khama and Building

1981. 1st Death Anniv of Sir Seretse Khama (former President). Multicoloured.
493 6t. Type **129** 15 10
494 10t. Seretse Khama and building (different) 25 15
495 30t. Seretse Khama and Botswana flag 40 45
496 45t. Seretse Khama and building (different) 55 70

1981. Nos. 417 and 422 surch.
497 25t. on 35t. Green-backed heron . . . . 3·75 2·00
498 30t. on 10t. Bennett's woodpecker . . . . 3·75 2·00

131 Traditional Ploughing

1981. Cattle Industry. Multicoloured.
499 6t. Type **131** 10 10
500 20t. Agricultural show . . . 30 50
501 30t. Botswana Meat Commission 35 60
502 45t. Vaccine Institute, Botswana . . . . 50 1·00

132 "Nymphaea caerulea"

1981. Christmas. Flowers. Multicoloured.
503 6t. Type **132** 20 10
504 10t. "Nymphoides indica" . . 25 10
505 25t. "Nymphaea lotus" . . . 60 90
506 40t. "Ottelia kunenensis" . . 80 2·25

133 "Cattle Post Scene" (Boitumelo Golaakwena)

1982. Children's Art. Multicoloured.
507 6t. Type **133** 40 10
508 10t. "Kgotla Meeting" (Reginald Klinck) 50 15
509 30t. "Village Water Supply" (Keronmemang Matswiri) 1·75 1·25
510 45t. "With the Crops" (Kennedy Balemoge) . . . 1·75 2·75

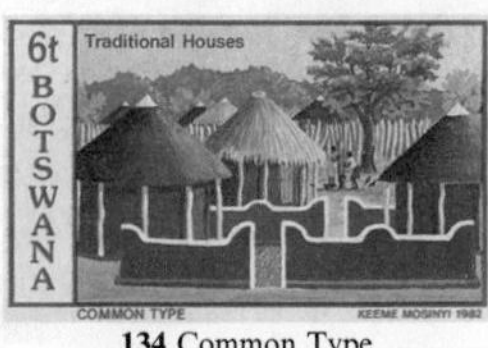

134 Common Type

1982. Traditional House. Multicoloured.
511 6t. Type **134** 40 15
512 10t. Kgatleng type 50 15
513 30t. North Eastern type . . . 2·00 1·10
514 45t. Sarwa type . . . . 2·00 3·00

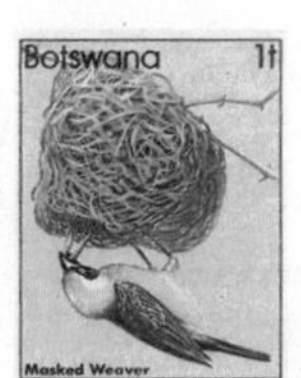

135 African Masked Weaver 136 "Coprinus comatus"

1982. Birds. Multicoloured.
515 1t. Type **135** . . . . 80 1·50
516 2t. Miombo double-collared sunbird ("Lesser double-collared Sunbird") . . . . 90 1·60
517 3t. Red-throated bee eater . . 1·00 1·60
518 4t. Ostrich . . . . 1·00 1·60
519 5t. Grey-headed gull . . . . 1·00 1·60
520 6t. African pygmy ("Pygmy Goose") . . . . 1·00 40
521 7t. Cattle egret . . . . 1·00 15
522 8t. Lanner falcon . . . . . . 2·50 1·50
523 10t. Yellow-billed stork . . . 1·00 20
524 15t. Red-billed pintail ("Red-billed Teal") (horiz) . . 2·75 25
525 20t. Barn owl (horiz) . . . . 5·50 3·50
526 25t. Hammerkop ("Hammerkop") (horiz) . . 3·25 70
527 30t. South African stilt ("Stilt") (horiz) . . . . . 3·75 90
528 35t. Blacksmith plover (horiz) 3·75 80
529 45t. Senegal wattled plover ("Watted Plover") (horiz) 3·75 1·75
530 50t. Helmeted guineafowl ("Crowned Guineafowl") (horiz) . . . . 4·75 2·50
531 1p. Cape vulture (horiz) . . . 9·00 12·00
532 2p. Augur buzzard (horiz) . . 11·00 16·00

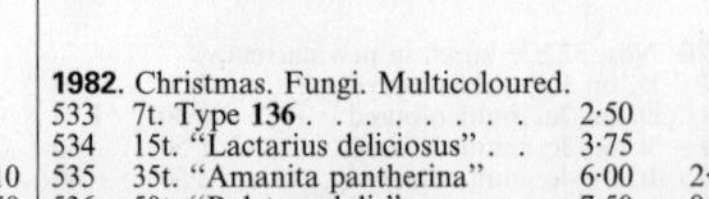

1982. Christmas. Fungi. Multicoloured.
533 7t. Type **136** . . . . 2·50 20
534 15t. "Lactarius deliciosus" . . 3·75 65
535 35t. "Amanita pantherina" . . 6·00 2·00
536 50t. "Boletus edulis" . . . . 7·50 8·00

137 President Quett Masire

1983. Commonwealth Day. Multicoloured.
537 7t. Type **137** 10 10
538 15t. Native dancers 15 20
539 35t. Melbourne conference centre 45 55
540 45t. Meeting of Heads of State, Melbourne 55 80

138 Wattled Crane 139 Wooden Spoons

1983. Endangered Species. Multicoloured.
541 7t. Type **138** . . . . 3·00 55
542 15t. "Aloe lutescens" . . . . 2·50 80
543 35t. Roan antelope . . . . . 3·00 3·25
544 50t. Ivory palm . . . . 3·50 6·00

1983. Traditional Artifacts. Multicoloured.
545 7t. Type **139** 25 10
546 15t. Personal ornaments . . . 45 30
547 35t. Ox-hide milk bag 75 65
548 50t. Decorated knives . . . . 1·00 1·10
MS549 115 × 102 mm. Nos. 545 × 8 4·25 5·00

140 "Pantala flavescens"

1983. Christmas. Dragonflies. Multicoloured.
550 6t. Type **140** 85 10
551 15t. "Anax imperator" . . . 1·75 50
552 25t. "Trithemis arteriosa" . . 2·00 85
553 45t. "Chlorolestes elegans" . . 2·75 4·75

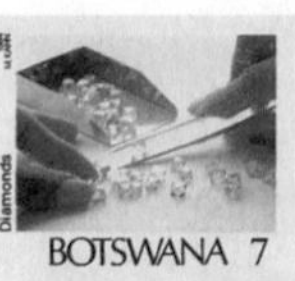

141 Sorting Diamonds 142 Riding Cattle

1984. Mining Industry. Multicoloured.
554 7t. Type **141** . . . . 2·00 50
555 15t. Lime kiln . . . . 2·00 75
556 35t. Copper-nickel smelter plant (vert) . . . . . . 3·25 3·25
557 60t. Stockpiled coal (vert) . . 3·75 10·00

1984. Traditional Transport. Multicoloured.
558 7t. Type **142** 20 10
559 25t. Sledge 65 60
560 35t. Wagon . . . . 85 1·50
561 50t. Two-wheeled donkey cart 1·25 4·50

143 Avro 504 Aircraft 144 "Papilio demodocus"

1984. 40th Anniv of International Civil Aviation Organization. Multicoloured.
562 7t. Type **143** 75 20
563 10t. Westland Wessex trimotor . . . . 1·00 35
564 15t. Junkers Ju 52/3m . . . . 1·40 95
565 25t. De Havilland Dominie . 2·00 1·75
566 35t. Douglas DC-3 "Wenala" 2·25 3·50
567 50t. Fokker Friendship . . . 2·50 7·00

1984. Christmas. Butterflies. Multicoloured.
568 7t. Type **144** . . . . 2·00 30
569 25t. "Byblia anavatara" . . . 2·25 1·50
570 35t. "Danaus chrysippus" . . 3·50 3·00
571 50t. "Graphium taboranus" 4·75 11·00
No. 570 is incorrectly inscr "Hypolimnas misippus".

145 Seswaa (meat dish)

146 1885 British Bechuanaland Overprint on Cape of Good Hope ½d.

1985. 5th Anniv of Southern African Development Co-ordination Conference. Traditional Foods. Multicoloured.
572 7t. Type **145** 50 10
573 15t. Bogobe (cereal porridge) 75 35
574 25t. Madila (soured coagulated cow's milk) . . 1·00 55
575 50t. Phane (caterpillars) . . . 1·50 2·25
MS576 117 × 103 mm. Nos. 572/5 7·00 10·00

1985. Centenary of First Bechuanaland Stamps.
577 **146** 7t. black, grey and red . . 1·00 20
578 – 15t. black, brown yell . . 1·75 50
579 – 25t. black and red . . . . 2·25 80
580 – 35t. black, blue and gold 2·50 2·00
581 – 50t. multicoloured . . . . 2·75 3·75
DESIGNS—VERT: 15t. 1897 Bechuanaland Protectorate overprint on G.B. 3d.; 25t. Bechuanaland Protectorate 1932 1d. definitive. HORIZ: 35t. Bechuanaland 1965 Internal Self-Government 5c.; 50t. Botswana 1966 Independence 2½c.

147 Bechuanaland Border Police, 1885–95

1985. Centenary of Botswana Police. Multicoloured.
582 7t. Type **147** . . . . 2·25 50
583 10t. Bechuanaland Mounted Police, 1895–1902 . . . . 2·50 50
584 25t. Bechuanaland Protectorate Police, 1903–66 . . . . 3·50 2·00
585 50t. Botswana Police, from 1966 . . . . 5·00 7·50

148 "Cucumis metuliferus"

1985. Christmas. Edible Wild Cucumbers. Mult.
586 7t. Type **148** . . . . 1·25 10
587 15t. "Acanthosicyos naudinianus" . . . . . 2·25 70
588 25t. "Coccinia sessifolia" . . 3·50 1·25
589 50t. "Momordica balsamina" 5·00 9·50

149 Mr. Shippard and Chief Gaseitsiwe of the Bangwaketse

150 Halley's Comet over Serowe

1985. Centenary of Declaration of Bechuanaland Protectorate. Multicoloured.
590 7t. Type **149** 35 10
591 15t. Sir Charles Warren and Chief Sechele of the Bakwena 70 45
592 25t. Revd. Mackenzie and Chief Khama of the Bamangwato . . . . . . 1·25 85
593 50t. Map showing Protectorate . . . . . . 2·75 2·75
MS594 130 × 133 mm. Nos. 590/3 11·00 13·00

1986. Appearance of Halley's Comet. Multicoloured.
595 7t. Type **150** 80 15
596 15t. Comet over Bobonong at sunset . . . . 1·50 70
597 35t. Comet over Gomare at dawn . . . . 2·00 1·50
598 50t. Comet over Thamaga and Letlhakeng . . . . . 2·25 3·75

151 Milk Bag

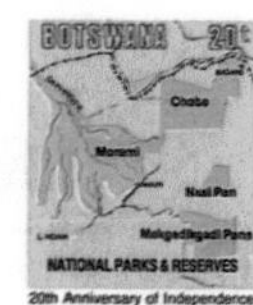

152 Map showing National Parks and Reserves

1986. Traditional Milk Containers. Multicoloured.
599 8t. Type **151** 30 10
600 15t. Clay pot and calabashes 45 30
601 35t. Wooden milk bucket . . 75 65
602 50t. Milk churn . . . . . . 1·00 1·40

1986. 20th Anniv of Independence. Sheet 100 × 120 mm. Multicoloured.
MS603 20t. Type **152**; 20t. Morupule power station; 20t. Cattle breeding in Kgalagadi; 20t. National Assembly Building . . . . . . 3·75 2·50

153 "Ludwigia stogonifera"

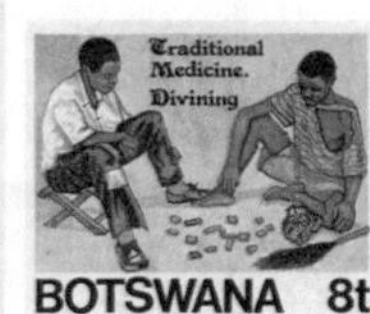

154 Divining

1986. Christmas. Flowers of Okavango. Mult.
604 8t. Type **153** . . . . 1·25 10
605 15t. "Sopubia mannii" . . . 2·25 1·10
606 35t. "Commelina diffusa" . . 3·50 3·00
607 50t. "Hibiscus diversifolius" . . 4·00 12·00

1987. Traditional Medicine. Multicoloured.
608 8t. Type **154** 80 10
609 15t. Lightning prevention . . 1·50 80
610 35t. Rain making . . . . . 2·25 2·50
611 50t. Blood letting . . . . . 2·75 8·50

1987. Nos. 520, 523 and 530 surch.
612 3t. on 6t. African pygmy goose . . . . 2·25 60
613 5t. on 10t. Yellow-billed stork 2·25 60
614 20t. on 50t. Helmeted guineafowl (horiz) . . . . 4·25 1·40

156 Oral Rehydration Therapy

157 Cape Fox

1987. U.N.I.C.E.F. Child Survival Campaign. Multicoloured.
615 8t. Type **156** 35 10
616 15t. Growth monitoring . . . 60 55
617 35t. Immunization . . . . . 1·25 2·00
618 50t. Breast feeding . . . . . 1·50 5·00

1987. Animals of Botswana. Multicoloured.
619 1t. Type **157** 10 70
620 2t. Lechwe . . . . 50 1·50
621 3t. Zebra 15 70
622 4t. Duiker . . . . 15 1·75
623 5t. Banded mongoose . . . . 20 1·75
624 6t. Rusty-spotted genet . . . 20 1·75
625 8t. Hedgehog 30 10
626 10t. Scrub hare 30 10
627 12t. Hippopotamus . . . . . 3·00 3·50
628 15t. Suricate . . . . 2·50 2·25
629 20t. Caracal 70 65
630 25t. Steenbok . . . . 70 1·50
631 30t. Gemsbok . . . . 1·50 1·50
632 35t. Square-lipped rhinoceros 2·00 2·00
633 40t. Mountain reedbuck . . . 1·75 1·50
634 50t. Rock dassie . . . . . . 90 1·75
635 1p. Giraffe . . . . 2·50 3·75
636 2p. Tsessebe . . . . 2·50 5·50
637 3p. Side-striped jackal . . . 3·75 7·00
638 5p. Hartebeest . . . . . . 6·00 11·00

158 "Cyperus articulatus"

159 Planting Seeds with Digging Stick

1987. Christmas. Grasses and Sedges of Okavango. Multicoloured.
639 8t. Type **158** 40 10
640 15t. Broomgrass 60 40
641 30t. "Cyperus alopurcides" 1·25 75
642 1p. Bulrush sedge . . . . . 2·50 5·00
MS643 88 × 99 mm. Nos. 639/42 4·25 4·75

1988. Early Cultivation. Multicoloured.
644 8t. Type **159** 40 10
645 15t. Using iron hoe 60 35
646 35t. Wooden ox-drawn plough . . . . 1·00 1·00
647 50t. Villagers working in lesotlas communal field . . 1·40 2·00

160 Red Lechwe at Water-hole

161 Gubulawayo Postmark and Route Southwards to Tati

1988. Red Lechwe. Multicoloured.
648 10t. Type **160** 90 15
649 15t. Red lechwe and early morning sun . . . . 1·75 65
650 35t. Female and calf . . . . 2·50 1·75
651 75t. Herd on the move . . . 3·75 8·50

1988. Cent of Mafeking–Gubalawayo Runner Post. Designs as Nos. 294/7, but redrawn smaller with changed inscriptions as in T **161**. Multicoloured.
652 10t. Type **161** 35 10
653 15t. Bechuanaland 1888 6d. on 6d. stamp and route from Tati southwards . . . 55 30
654 30t. Runners and twin routes south from Shoshong . . . 95 75
655 60t. Mafeking postmark and routes to Bechuanaland and Transvaal . . . . . . 1·60 2·75
MS656 81 × 151 mm. Nos. 652/5 vertically se-tenant, forming a composite map design . . . . 6·00 6·50

162 Pope John Paul II and Outline Map of Botswana

163 National Museum and Art Gallery, Gaborone

1988. Visit of Pope John Paul II. Multicoloured.
657 10t. Type **162** . . . . 1·75 20
658 15t. Pope John Paul II . . . 2·00 30
659 30t. Pope giving blessing and outline map . . . . 2·50 70
660 80t. Pope John Paul II (different) . . . . 3·25 2·75

1988. 20th Anniv of National Museum and Art Gallery, Gaborone. Multicoloured.
661 8t. Type **163** 15 10
662 15t. Pottery 20 25
663 30t. Blacksmith's buffalo bellows 35 40
664 60c. Children and land rover mobile museum van . . . 70 1·00

164 "Grewia flava" 165 Basket Granary

1988. Flowering Plants of South-eastern Botswana. Multicoloured.
665 8t. Type **164** 20 10
666 15t. "Cienfuegosia digitata" 30 25
667 40t. "Solanum seaforthianum" 60 55
668 75t. "Carissa bispinosa" . . . 1·00 1·40

1989. Traditional Grain Storage. Multicoloured.
669 8t. Type **165** 75 10
670 15t. Large letlole granary . . 1·25 40
671 30t. Pot granary . . . . . . 1·75 60
672 60t. Two types of serala . . . 2·50 2·25

166 Female with Eggs

1989. Slaty Egret. Multicoloured.
673 8t. Type **166** 55 15
674 15t. Chicks in nest 75 40
675 30t. In flight . . . . 1·00 75
676 60t. Pair building nest . . . 1·40 1·60
MS677 119 × 89 mm. Nos. 673/6 3·25 2·75

167 "My Work at Home" (Ephraim Seeletso)

1989. Children's Paintings. Multicoloured.
678 10t. Type **167** 35 10
679 15t. "My Favourite Game" (hopscotch) (Neelma Bhatia) (vert) 50 35
680 30t. "My Favourite Toy" (clay animals) (Thabo Habana) 75 70
681 1p. "My School Day" (Thabo Olesitse) . . . . . 2·00 3·25

168 "Eulophia angolensis"

171 Telephone Engineer

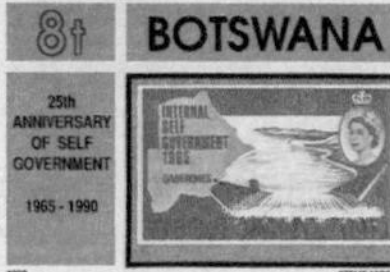

169 Bechuanaland 1965 New Constitution 25c. Stamp (25th anniv of Self-Government)

1989. Christmas. Orchids. Multicoloured.
682 8t. Type **168** 70 10
683 15t. "Eulophia hereroensis" 1·25 60
684 30t. "Eulophia speciosa" . . 1·75 1·00
685 60t. "Eulophia petersii" . . . 2·50 7·00

1990. Anniversaries.
686 **169** 8t. multicoloured 70 15
687 – 15t. multicoloured 75 50
688 – 30t. multicoloured . . . . 2·75 1·60
689 – 60t. black, blue and yellow . . . . 3·25 6·50
DESIGNS: 15t. Casting vote in ballot box (25th anniv of First Elections); 30t. Outline map and flags of Southern Africa Development Co-ordination Conference countries (10th anniv); 60t. Penny Black (150th anniv of first postage stamp).

1990. Nos. 619, 624 and 627 surch.
690 10t. on 1t. Type **157** 45 20
691 20t. on 6t. Rusty-spotted genet 60 80
692 50t. on 12t. Hippopotamus 2·00 3·50

1990. "Stamp World London 90" International Stamp Exhibition. Multicoloured.
693 8t. Type **171** 35 10
694 15t. Transmission pylon . . . 65 40
695 30t. Public telephone . . . . 1·00 75
696 2p. Testing circuit board . . 3·00 6·50

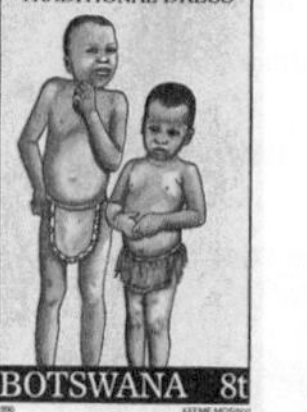

172 Young Children

173 "Acacia nigrescens"

1990. Traditional Dress. Multicoloured.
697 8t. Type **172** 35 10
698 15t. Young woman 65 40

699 30t. Adult man . . . . . . 1·00 70
700 2p. Adult woman . . . . . . 3·00 6·50
MS701 104 × 150 mm. Nos. 697/700 4·50 6·50

1990. Christmas. Flowering Trees. Multicoloured.
702 8t. Type **173** 50 10
703 15t. "Peltophorum africanum" 85 35
704 30t. "Burkea africana" . . . 1·50 75
705 2p. "Pterocarpus angolensis" 3·50 7·50

174 Children running in front of Hatchback

1990. 1st National Road Safety Day. Multicoloured.
706 8t. Type **174** . . . . 2·25 30
707 15t. Careless overtaking . . . 2·75 1·00
708 30t. Cattle on road . . . . . 3·50 2·75

175 Cattle **176** Children

1991. Rock Paintings. Multicoloured.
709 8t. Type **175** . . . . 2·00 40
710 15t. Cattle, drying frames and tree . . . . 2·50 85
711 30t. Animal hides . . . . . 3·00 1·50
712 2p. Family herding cattle . . 5·50 9·50

1991. National Census. Multicoloured.
713 8t. Type **176** . . . . 1·25 20
714a 15t. Village . . . . 1·75 55
715 30t. School . . . . 2·00 90
716 2p. Hospital . . . . 7·00 9·50

177 Tourists viewing Elephants

1991. African Tourism Year. Okavango Delta. Mult.
717 8t. Type **177** . . . . 1·50 70
718 15t. Crocodiles basking on river bank . . . . 1·75 90
719 35t. Fish eagles and De Havilland D.H.C.7 Dash Seven aircraft . . . . . . 3·50 3·25
720 2p. Okavango wildlife (26 × 44 mm) . . . . . . 5·50 8·50

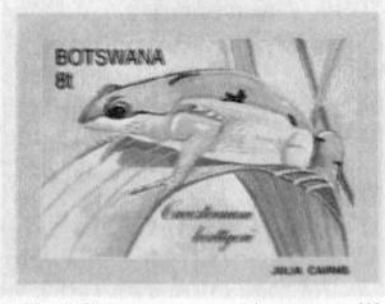

178 "Harpagophytum procumbens" **179** "Cacosternum boettgeri"

1991. Christmas. Seed Pods. Multicoloured.
721 8t. Type **178** 60 10
722 15t. "Tylosema esculentum" 1·00 40
723 30t. "Abrus precatorius" . . 1·75 80
724 2p. "Kigelia africana" . . . 4·00 8·00

1992. Nos. 621, 624 and 627 surch.
725 8t. on 12t. Hippopotamus . . 1·00 70
726 10t. on 12t. Hippopotamus 1·00 70
727 25t. on 6t. Rusty-spotted genet . . . . 1·25 1·50
728 40t. on 3t. Zebra . . . . . . 2·25 4·00

1992. Climbing Frogs. Multicoloured.
729 8t. Type **179** 70 30
730 10t. "Hyperolius marmoratus angolensis" (vert) 70 30
731 40t. "Bufo fenoulheti" . . . 2·25 1·50
732 1p. "Hyperolius sp." (vert) 4·00 6·00

180 Air-conditioned Carriages

1992. Deluxe Railway Service. Multicoloured.
733 10t. Type **180** . . . . 1·25 40
734 25t. Diesel locomotive No. BD001 (vert) . . . . . . 2·00 80
735 40t. Carriage interior (vert) 2·25 1·25
736 2p. Diesel locomotive No. BD028 . . . . 3·50 7·50
MS737 127 × 127 mm. Nos. 733/6 11·00 11·00

181 Cheetah **182** Boxing

1992. Animals. Multicoloured.
738 1t. Type **181** . . . . 30 1·75
739 2t. Spring hare . . . . 30 1·75
740 4t. Blackfooted cat . . . . . 40 1·75
741 5t. Striped mouse . . . . . 40 1·50
742 10t. Oribi 55 10
743 12t. Pangolin . . . . 1·00 2·50
744 15t. Aardwolf . . . . 1·00 40
745 20t. Warthog . . . . 1·00 40
746 25t. Ground squirrel . . . . 1·00 20
747 35t. Honey badger . . . . . 1·25 30
748 40t. Common mole rat . . . 1·25 30
749 45t. Wild dog . . . . 1·25 30
750 50t. Water mongoose . . . . 1·25 35
751 80t. Klipspringer . . . . . . 1·75 1·75
752 1p. Lesser bushbaby . . . . 1·75 1·75
753 2p. Bushveld elephant shrew 2·50 4·00
754 5p. Zorilla . . . . 4·25 7·00
755 10p. Vervet monkey . . . . 6·50 10·00

1992. Olympic Games, Barcelona. Multicoloured.
756 10t. Type **182** 60 10
757 50t. Running . . . . 1·50 50
758 1p. Boxing (different) . . . . 2·00 2·50
759 2p. Running (different) . . . 2·50 5·00
MS760 87 × 117 mm. Nos. 756/9 4·50 8·00

183 "Adiantum incisum" **184** Helping Blind Person (Lions Club International)

1992. Christmas. Ferns. Multicoloured.
761 10t. Type **183** 40 10
762 25t. "Actiniopteris radiata" 70 35
763 40t. "Ceratopteris cornuta" 1·00 55
764 1p.50 "Pellaea calomelanos" 3·00 6·50

1993. Charitable Organizations in Botswana. Mult.
765 10t. Type **184** 80 20
766 15t. Nurse carrying child (Red Cross Society) (horiz) 90 40
767 25t. Woman watering seedling (Ecumenical Decade) 90 50
768 35t. Deaf children (Round Table) (horiz) . . . . . 1·25 1·50
769 40t. Crowd of people (Rotary International) . . . . . 1·25 1·75
770 50t. Hands at prayer (Botswana Christian Council) (horiz) . . . . . 1·50 2·50

185 Bechuanaland Railways Class "6" Locomotive No. 1 **186** Long-crested Eagle

1993. Railway Centenary. Multicoloured.
771 10t. Type **185** 75 40
772 40t. Class "19" locomotive No. 317 . . . . 1·40 75
773 50t. Class "12" locomotive No. 256 . . . . 1·40 90
774 1p.50 Class "7" locomotive No. 71 . . . . 2·00 4·50
MS775 190 × 100 mm. Nos. 771/4 4·50 6·00

1993. Endangered Eagles. Multicoloured.
776 10t. Type **186** 70 35
777 25t. Short-toed eagle ("Snake eagle") . . . . 1·25 65
778 50t. Bateleur ("Bateleur Eagle") . . . . 1·60 1·75
779 1p.50 Secretary bird . . . . 2·50 6·00

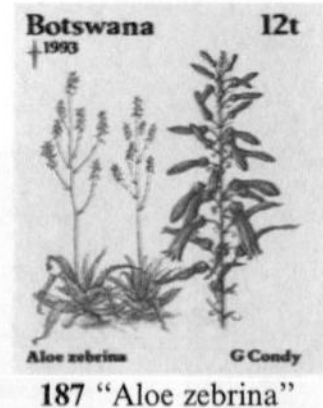

187 "Aloe zebrina"

1993. Christmas. Flora. Multicoloured.
780 12t. Type **187** 40 10
781 25t. "Croton megalobotrys" 60 25
782 50t. "Boophane disticha" . . 85 70
783 1p. "Euphoria davyi" . . . . 1·25 3·25

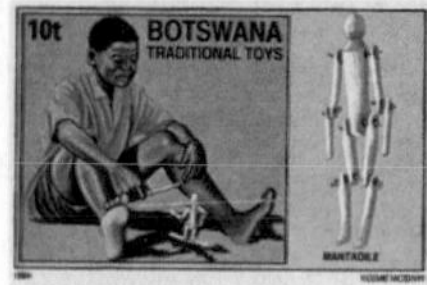

188 Boy with String Puppet

1994. Traditional Toys. Multicoloured.
784 10t. Type **188** 20 10
785 40t. Boys with clay cattle . . 45 30
786 50t. Boy with spinner 50 50
787 1p. Girls playing in make-believe houses . . . . . . 1·10 2·75

189 Interior of Control Tower, Gaborone Airport

1994. 50th Anniv of I.C.A.O. Multicoloured.
788 10t. Type **189** 40 10
789 25t. Crash fire tender 55 30
790 40t. Loading supplies onto airliner (vert) 75 75
791 50t. Control tower, Gaborone (vert) . . . . 80 1·50

1994. No. 743 surch **10t.**
792 10t. on 12t. Pangolin . . . . 5·00 75

191 Lesser Flamingos at Sua Pan **192** "Ziziphus mucronata"

1994. Environment Protection. Makgadikgadi Pans. Multicoloured.
793 10t. Type **191** 75 40
794 35t. Baobab trees (horiz) . . 50 40
795 50t. Zebra and palm trees . . 65 80
796 2p. Map of area (horiz) . . . 2·50 5·00

1994. Christmas. Edible Fruits. Multicoloured.
797 10t. Type **192** 25 10
798 25t. "Strychnos cocculoides" 40 30
799 40t. "Bauhinia petersiana" 60 70
800 50t. "Schinziphyton rautoneii" . . . . 70 1·40

193 Fisherman with Bow and Arrow **194** Boys watering Horses (F.A.O.)

1995. Traditional Fishing. Multicoloured.
801 15t. Type **193** 35 20
802 40t. Men in canoe and boy with fishing rod 60 40
803 65t. Fisherman with net . . . 80 75
804 80t. Fisherman with basket fish trap . . . . 1·00 1·75

1995. 50th Anniv of United Nations. Multicoloured.
805 20t. Type **194** 20 10
806 50t. Schoolchildren queueing for soup (W.F.P.) 35 30
807 80t. Policeman conducting census (U.N.D.P.) 60 80
808 1p. Weighing baby (U.N.I.C.E.F.) . . . . . . 70 1·75

195 Brown Hyena

1995. Endangered Species. Brown Hyena. Mult.
809 20t. Type **195** 45 60
810 50t. Pair of hyenas 65 75
811 80t. Hyena stealing ostrich eggs . . . . 1·10 1·50
812 1p. Adult hyena and cubs . . 1·25 2·00

196 "Adenia glauca" **198** Spears

1995. Christmas. Plants. Multicoloured.
813 20t. Type **196** 35 10
814 50t. "Pterodiscus ngamicus" 60 30
815 80t. "Sesamothamnus lugardii" . . . . 1·00 1·00
816 1p. "Fockea multiflora" . . . 1·10 1·75

1996. Nos. 738/40 surch.
817 20t. on 2t. Spring hare . . . 65 30
818 30t. on 1t. Type **181** 80 30
819 70t. on 4t. Blackfooted cat 1·40 2·75

1996. Traditional Weapons. Multicoloured.
820 20t. Type **198** 20 10
821 50t. Axes 35 30
822 80t. Shield and knobkerries 55 65
823 1p. Knives and sheaths . . . 60 1·25

199 Child with Basic Radio **200** Olympic Flame, Rings and Wreath

1996. Centenary of Radio. Multicoloured.
824 20t. Type **199** 25 10
825 50t. Radio Botswana's mobile transmitter 40 30
826 80t. Police radio control . . . 60 70
827 1p. Listening to radio . . . . 70 1·40

1996. Centenary of Modern Olympic Games. Mult.
828 20t. Type **200** 25 10
829 50t. Pierre de Coubertin (founder of modern Olympics) 40 30
830 80t. Map of Botswana with flags and athletes 75 75
831 1p. Ruins of ancient stadium at Olympia . . . . 75 1·40

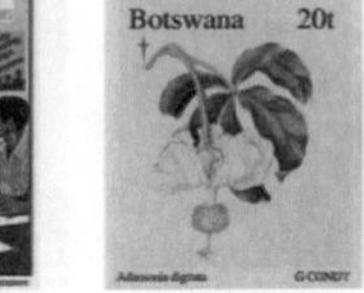

201 Family Planning Class (Botswana Family Welfare Association) **202** "Adansonia digitata" Leaf and Blossom

1996. Local Charities. Multicoloured.
832 20t. Type **201** 20 10
833 30t. Blind workers (Pudulogong Rehabilitation Centre) 20 15
834 50t. Collecting seeds (Forestry Association of Botswana) 30 30
835 70t. Secretarial class (Y.W.C.A.) 40 70
836 80t. Children's day centre (Botswana Council of Women) 50 75
837 1p. Children's village, Tlokweng (S.O.S. Children's village) . . . . 60 1·25

1996. Christmas. Parts of Life Cycle for "Adansonia digitata". Multicoloured.
838 20t. Type **202** 25 10
839 50t. Fruit 40 25

840 80t. Tree in leaf 60 75
841 1p. Tree with bare branches 70 1·40

203 Tati Hotel

204 Steam Locomotive, Bechuanaland Railway, 1897

1997. Francistown Centenary. Multicoloured.
842 20t. Type **203** 15 10
843 50t. Railway Station 55 35
844 80t. Company Manager's House 60 75
845 1p. Monarch Mine . . . . . 80 1·40

1997. Railway Centenary. Multicoloured.
846 35t. Type **204** 40 20
847 50t. Elephants crossing railway line 60 35
848 80t. First locomotive in Bechuanaland, 1897 . . . 70 45
849 1p. Beyer-Garratt type steam locomotive No. 352 . . . 75 75
850 2p. Diesel locomotive No. BD339 . . . . 1·00 1·75
851 2p.50 Fantuzzi container stacker . . . . 1·25 2·25

205 Pel's Fishing Owl

206 "Combretum zeyheri"

1997. Birds. Multicoloured.
852 5t. Type **205** 50 75
853 10t. African harrier hawk ("Gymnogene") (horiz) . . 50 75
854 15t. Brown parrot ("Meyer's Parrot") 50 60
855 20t. Harlequin quail (horiz) 60 60
856 25t. Mariqua sunbird ("Marico Sunbird") (horiz) 60 60
857 30t. Kurrichane thrush (horiz) 65 60
858 40t. Paradise sparrow ("Redheaded Finch") . . . 70 60
859 50t. Red-billed buffalo weaver ("Buffalo Weaver") 80 40
860 60t. Sacred ibis (horiz) . . . 90 70
861 70t. Cape shoveler (horiz) . . 90 80
862 80t. Black-throated honeyguide ("Greater Honeyguide") (horiz) . . . 90 70
863 1p. Woodland kingfisher (horiz) . . . . 1·10 80
864 1p.25 Purple heron . . . . . 1·40 1·40
865 1p.50 Yelllow-billed oxpecker (horiz) . . . . 1·40 1·75
866 2p. Shaft-tailed whydah . . . 1·60 2·00
867 2p.50 White stork . . . . . 1·75 2·00
868 5p. Ovampo sparrow hawk ("Sparrowhawk") . . . . 2·25 2·75
869 10p. Spotted crake . . . . . 3·25 4·50
No. 861 is inscribed "Shoveller" in error.

1997. Golden Wedding of Queen Elizabeth and Prince Philip. As T **173** of Ascension. Multicoloured.
870 35t. Prince Philip with carriage 20 55
871 35t. Queen Elizabeth with binoculars 20 55
872 2p. Queen Elizabeth with horse team . . . . 90 1·50
873 2p. Prince Philip and horse 90 1·50
874 2p.50 Queen Elizabeth and Prince Philip . . . . . . 1·10 1·50
875 2p.50 Princess Anne and Prince Edward . . . . . . 1·10 1·50
MS876 110 × 70 mm. 10p. Queen Elizabeth and Prince Philip in landau (horiz) . . . . 4·00 5·50

1997. Christmas. Plants. Multicoloured.
877 35t. Type **206** 45 10
878 1p. "Combretum apiculatum" 1·00 35
879 2p. "Combretum molle" . . 1·75 1·90
880 2p.50 "Combretum imberbe" 2·00 2·50

207 Baobab Trees

1998. Tourism (1st series). Multicoloured.
881 35t. Type **207** 25 15
882 1p. Crocodile 50 40
883 2p. Stalactites (vert) . . . . 85 1·10
884 2p.50 Tourists and rock paintings (vert) . . . . . 1·10 1·60
See also Nos. 899/902.

1998. Diana, Princess of Wales Commemoration. As T **223a** of Bahamas. Multicoloured.
885 35t. Princess Diana, 1990 . . 25 15
886 1p. In green hat, 1992 . . . 40 35
887 2p. In white blouse, 1993 . . 75 1·10
888 2p.50 With crowd, Cambridge, 1993 . . . . . 90 1·50
MS889 145 × 70 mm. As Nos. 885/8, but each with a face value of 2p.50 3·75 4·50

208 "Village Life" (tapestry)

209 "Ficus ingens"

1998. Botswana Weavers. Multicoloured.
890 35t. Type **208** 30 15
891 55t. Weaver dyeing threads 35 20
892 1p. "African wildlife" (tapestry) . . . . 1·10 80
893 2p. Weaver at loom . . . . 1·25 2·00
MS894 68 × 58 mm. 2p.50, "Elephants" (tapestry) (horiz) 2·25 2·50

1998. Christmas. Plants. Multicoloured.
895 35t. Type **209** 40 10
896 55t. "Ficus pygmaea" 60 20
897 1p. "Ficus abutilifolia" . . . 1·00 55
898 2p.50 "Ficus sycomorus" . . 1·90 2·75

1999. Tourism (2nd series). As T **207**. Multicoloured.
899 35t. Rock painting of men and cattle 35 10
900 55t. Expedition at Salt Pan 40 20
901 1p. Rock painting of elephant and antelope (vert) 65 65
902 2p. Tourists under Baobab tree (vert) . . . . 80 1·75

210 Road Map

1999. Southern African Development Community Day. Sheet 77 × 84 mm.
MS903 **210** 5p. multicoloured . . 2·75 3·00

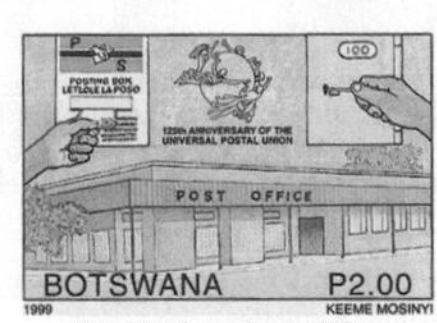

211 Modern Post Office

1999. 125th Anniv of Universal Postal Union.
904 **211** 2p. multicoloured . . . . 1·50 1·50

212 Mpule Kwelagobe winning contest

1999. Mpule Kwelagobe ("Miss Universe 1999"). Multicoloured.
905 35t. Type **212** 35 10
906 1p. In traditional dress (horiz) 75 30
907 2p. In traditional dancing costume with lion . . . . 1·10 60
908 2p.50 Wearing "Botswana" sash (horiz) . . . . . . 1·25 75
909 15p. With leopard in background (horiz) . . . . 7·00 10·00
MS910 175 × 80 mm. Nos. 905/9 9·50 12·00

213 Saddle-bill Stork and Limpopo River

2000. Scenic Rivers. Multicoloured.
911 35t. Type **213** 25 10
912 1p. Hippopotamuses in water lilies (vert) 50 30
913 2p. African skimmer and makoro (dugout canoe) . . 85 1·00
914 2p.50 African elephant at sunset, Chobe River (vert) 1·00 1·60

214 Mopane Moth

2000. Moths. Multicoloured.
915 35t. Type **214** 15 10
916 70t. Wild silk moth 25 20
917 1p. Crimson speckled footman ("Tiger Moth") 35 30
918 2p. African lunar moth . . . 65 60
919 15p. Speckled emperor moth 4·75 7·00
MS920 175 × 135 mm. Nos. 915/19 5·50 7·00
No. **MS**920 is in the shape of a moth.

215 Mother reading Medicine Label with Child ("Protect Your Children")

2000. United Nations Literacy Decade. Mult.
921 35t. Type **215** 15 10
922 70t. Adult literacy class ("Never Too Old To Learn") 25 20
923 2p. Man smoking next to petrol pump ("Be Aware Of Danger") 65 85
924 2p.50 Man at Automatic Teller Machine ("Be Independent") . . . . . . 85 1·40

216 Pres. Sir Seretse Khama

217 Doctor giving Eye Test

2000. Chiefs and Presidents.
925 **216** 35t. black, red and gold 30 10
926 – 1p. multicoloured 45 25
927 – 2p. multicoloured 75 85
928 – 2p.50 multicoloured . . . 1·00 1·50
DESIGNS—HORIZ (60 × 40 mm): 35t. Chiefs Sebele I of Bakwena, Bathoen I of Bangwaketse and Khama III of Bangato, 1895. VERT (as T **216**): 2p. Pres. Sir Ketumile Masire; 2p.50, Pres. Festus Mogae.

2000. Airborne Medical Service. Multicoloured.
929 35t. Type **217** 25 10
930 1p. Medical team and family 55 30
931 2p. Aircraft over canoes . . . 1·00 1·10
932 2p.50 Donkeys and mule cart on airstrip . . . . 1·25 1·75

218 Hippopotamus

2000. Wetlands (1st series). Okavango Delta. Mult.
933 35t. Type **218** 35 20
934 1p. Tiger fish and tilapia . . 55 30
935 1p.75 Painted reed frog and wattled crane (vert) . . . . 1·25 1·50
936 2p. Pels fishing owl and vervet monkey (vert) . . . 1·50 1·75
937 2p.50 Nile crocodile, Sitatunga and red lechwe 1·50 1·75
MS938 175 × 80 mm. Nos. 933/7 4·50 4·75
See also Nos. 958/62.

2001. "HONG KONG 2001" Stamp Exhibition. No. **MS**938 overprinted with exhibition logo on sheet margin.
MS939 175 × 80 mm. Nos. 933/7 4·50 5·50

219 Diamonds

2001. Diamonds. Multicoloured. Self-adhesive.
940 35t. Type **219** 35 20
941 1p.75 J.C.B. in open-cast mine . . . . 1·10 1·25
942 2p. Quality inspector . . . . 1·25 1·40
943 2p.50 Diamonds in jewellery 1·50 1·60

220 African Pygmy Falcon

2001. Kgalagadi Transfrontier Wildlife Park. Joint Issue with South Africa. Multicoloured.
944 35t. Type **220** 45 20
945 1p. Leopard 60 25
946 2p. Gemsbok . . . . 1·00 1·10
947 2p.50 Bat-eared fox . . . . 1·25 1·50
MS948 115 × 80 mm. Nos. 945 and 947 . . . . 1·75 2·00

221 Shallow Basket

2001. Traditional Baskets. Multicoloured.
949 35t. Type **221** 20 15
950 1p. Tall basket 35 25
951 2p. Woman weaving basket 60 75
952 2p.50 Spherical basket . . . 65 85
MS953 177 × 92 mm. Nos. 949/52 2·00 2·50

222 Boys by River at Sunset

2001. Scenic Skies. Multicoloured.
954 50t. Type **222** 20 15
955 1p. Woman with baby at sunset 40 25
956 2p. Girls carrying firewood at sunset 60 70
957 10p. Traditional village at sunset near huts . . . . . 2·25 3·00

2001. Wetlands (2nd series). Chobe River. As T **218**. Multicoloured.
958 50t. Water monitor and carmine bee-eater 40 15
959 1p.75 Buffalo 65 50
960 2p. Savanna baboons (vert) 80 90
961 2p.50 Lion (vert) . . . . . . 1·00 1·25
962 3p. African elephants in river 1·60 1·75
MS963 175 × 80 mm. Nos. 958/62 4·00 4·25

223 Black Mamba

2002. Snakes. Multicoloured.
964 50t. Type **223** 35 15
965 1p.75 Spitting cobra (vert) . . 65 45
966 2p.50 Puff adder . . . . . . 75 1·00
967 3p. Boomslang (vert) . . . . 90 1·25

224 Mbukushu Pots

2002. Botswana Pottery. Multicoloured.

968	50t. Type **224**	30	10
969	2p. Sekgatla pots	60	65
970	2p.50 Setswana pots	70	85
971	3p. Kalanga pots	80	1·10

225 Queen Elizabeth in Evening Dress and Commonwealth Emblem

2002. Golden Jubilee. Multicoloured.

972	55t. Type **225**	30	15
973	2p.75 Queen Elizabeth with bouquet (vert)	1·10	1·40

226 Tree Squirrel

227 Tebelopele (counselling and testing centres) Symbol

2002. Mammals. Multicoloured.

974	5t. Type **226**	10	10
975	10t. Black-backed jackal	10	10
976	20t. African wild cat	10	10
977	30t. Slender mongoose (horiz)	10	10
978	40t. African civet (horiz)	10	10
979	55t. Elephant	10	15
980	90t. Reedbuck	20	25
981	1p. Kudu	20	25
982	1p.45 Waterbuck	30	35
983	1p.95 Sable (horiz)	45	50
984	2p.20 Sitatunga (horiz)	50	55
985	2p.75 Porcupine (horiz)	60	65
986	3p.30 Serval (horiz)	75	80
987	4p. Antbear (horiz)	90	95
988	5p. Bushpig (horiz)	1·10	1·25
989	15p. Chakma baboon	3·25	3·50

2002. AIDS Awareness. Multicoloured.

990	55t. Type **227**	30	15
991	1p.10 AIDS ribbon and mother and baby badge	50	25
992	2p.75 Hands and male gender symbol	90	1·10
993	3p.30 Orphans with foster parent	1·10	1·25

2002. Wetlands (3rd series). The Makgadikgadi Pans. As T **218**. Multicoloured.

994	55t. Aardwolf	20	15
995	1p.10 Blue wildebeest and zebra	35	25
996	2p.50 Zebra (vert)	80	80
997	2p.75 Flamingo (vert)	1·00	1·25
998	3p.30 Pelican in flight	1·25	1·40
MS999	175 × 80 mm. Nos. 994/8	3·25	3·50

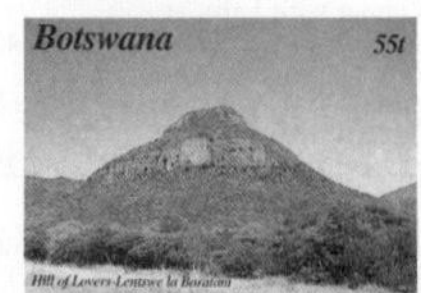

228 Lentswe la Baratani ("Hill of Lovers")

2003. Natural Places of Interest. Multicoloured.

1000	55t. Type **228**	10	15
1001	2p.20 Sand dunes	50	55
1002	2p.75 Moremi Waterfalls (vert)	60	65
1003	3p.30 Gcwihaba Cave	75	80

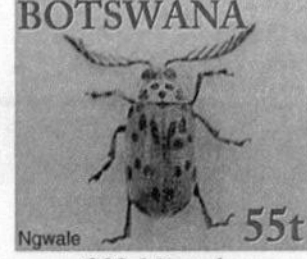

229 Ngwale

2003. Beetles. Multicoloured.

1004	55t. Type **229**	10	15
1005	2p.20 Kgomo-ya-buru	50	55
1006	2p.75 Kgomo-ya-pula	60	64
1007	3p.30 Lebitse	75	80
MS1008	69 × 59 mm. 5p.50 Kgaladuwa	1·20	1·30

POSTAGE DUE STAMPS

1967. Nos. D10/12 of Bechuanaland optd **REPUBLIC OF BOTSWANA**.

D13	D 1	1c. red	15	1·75
D14		2c. violet	15	1·75
D15		5c. green	20	1·75

D **5** African Elephant

D **6** Common Zebra

1971.

D16	D 5	1c. red	1·10	3·25
D17		2c. violet	1·40	3·50
D18		6c. brown	1·75	5·50
D19		14c. green	2·00	7·50

1977.

D25a	D 6	1t. black and red	40	1·25
D26a		2t. black and green	40	1·25
D27a		4t. black and red	40	1·25
D28a		10t. black and blue	40	1·25
D29a		16t. black and brown	50	1·50

BOYACA Pt. 20

One of the states of the Granadine Confederation. A Department of Colombia from 1886, now uses Colombian stamps.

100 centavos = 1 peso.

1 Mendoza Perez

1899. Imperf or perf.

1	1	5c. green	60	1·50

2

6 Battle of Boyaca Monument

1903. Imperf or perf.

3	2	10c. grey	15	15
4		10c. blue	60	60
12	–	10c. orange	20	15
5	2	20c. brown	20	20
5a		20c. lake	25	25
6	–	50c. turquoise	15	15
8	–	1p. red	20	15
9	–	1p. red	1·40	1·40
10	6	5p. black on red	50	35
11	–	10p. black on buff	50	40

DESIGNS—As Type **2**: 10c. orange, Building; 50c. Gen. Pinzon; 1p. Figure of value. As Type **6**: 10p. Pres. Marroquin.

BRAZIL Pt. 20

A country in the N.E. of S. America. Portuguese settlement, 1500. Kingdom, 1815. Empire, 1822. Republic from 1889.

1843. 1000 reis = 1 milreis.
1942. 100 centavos = 1 cruzeiro.
1986. 100 centavos = 1 cruzado.
1990. 100 centavos = 1 cruzeiro.
1994. 100 centavos = 1 real.

1 "Bull's Eye"

1843. Imperf.

4	1	30r. black	£2250	£375
5		60r. black	£600	£200
6		90r. black	£2250	£950

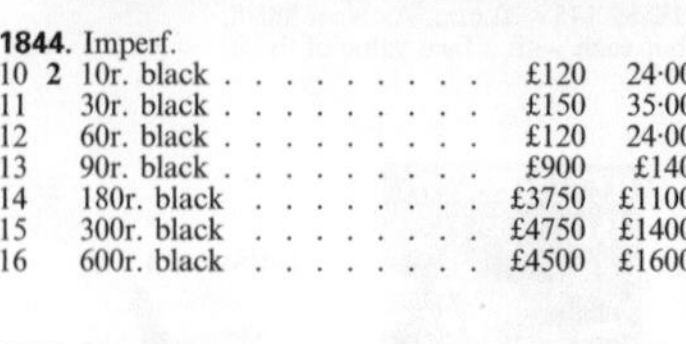

2 **3** **4**

1844. Imperf.

10	2	10r. black	£120	24·00
11		30r. black	£150	35·00
12		60r. black	£120	24·00
13		90r. black	£900	£140
14		180r. black	£3750	£1100
15		300r. black	£4750	£1400
16		600r. black	£4500	£1600

1850. Imperf.

17	3	10r. black	30·00	26·00
18		20r. black	90·00	£110
19		30r. black	12·00	3·50
20		60r. black	12·00	2·50
21		90r. black	95·00	12·00
22		180r. black	£120	55·00
23		300r. black	£350	70·00
24		600r. black	£450	80·00

1854. Imperf.

25	3	10r. blue	12·00	9·00
26		30r. blue	35·00	55·00
27	4	280r. red	£120	85·00
28		430r. yellow	£190	£120

5 **6**

17 Emperor Dom Pedro II

1866. Various frames, but in T **5** the Emperor has a dark beard. Perf or roul.

43	5	10r. red	9·00	5·25
44a	6	20r. purple	12·00	3·00
45	5	50r. blue	20·00	1·75
46a		80r. purple	55·00	4·75
47a		100r. green	20·00	1·25
55	6	200r. black	48·00	4·75
67	17	300r. green and orange	90·00	24·00
56	5	500r. orange	£160	24·00

12 **13**

1878. Various frames, but in T **13** the Emperor's beard is white. Roulette.

57	12	10r. red	9·00	3·00
58	13	20r. mauve	12·00	2·40
59	12	50r. blue	18·00	1·75
60		80r. red	20·00	9·50
61		100r. green	20·00	1·25
62		200r. black	£110	15·00
63		260r. brown	60·00	20·00
64		300r. brown	60·00	6·00
65		700r. red	£130	80·00
66		1000r. grey	£140	35·00

21

27 Pedro II

1881. Various frames. Perf.

71	21	10r. black	12·00	26·00
72		10r. orange	3·00	1·75
73		50r. blue	30·00	3·00
74		100r. olive	50·00	3·00
77		100r. lilac	£175	1·75
75a		200r. red	42·00	3·50

No. 77 is inscr "CORREIO".

1884.

81	27	100r. lilac	£175	3·50

25 **26** **29**

30 Southern Cross **31** **32**

33 Entrance to Bay of Rio de Janeiro

35 Southern Cross

1884.

78	25	20r. green	24·00	3·50
80	26	50r. blue	20·00	5·25
83	29	100r. lilac	48·00	1·75
84	30	300r. blue	£200	26·00
85a	31	500r. olive	£110	12·00
86	32	700r. lilac	75·00	£125
87	33	1000r. blue	£225	£125

1890.

97a	35	20r. green	2·40	2·40
89		50r. green	4·75	2·40
110a		100r. purple	30·00	1·75
91		200r. violet	10·50	2·40
100		300r. slate	70·00	6·00
92		300r. blue	70·00	6·00
93		500r. buff	18·00	10·50
94		500r. grey	18·00	10·50
95		700r. brown	26·00	35·00
96		1000r. yellow	18·00	3·50

37 Head of Liberty

38 Head of Liberty

1891.

111d	37	100r. red and blue	35·00	1·75

1893.

114	38	100r. red	70·00	1·75

39 Sugar-loaf Mountain

41 Head of Liberty

43 Head of Mercury

1894.

124	39	10r. blue and red	1·90	60
125		20r. blue and orange	90	45
126		50r. blue	5·25	3·50
232		50r. green	9·00	3·75
127	41	100r. black and red	3·50	40
239		100r. red	18·00	35
128		200r. black and orange	90	35
234		200r. blue	10·50	35
129		300r. black and green	14·00	60
153		500r. black and blue	26·00	1·75
131a		700r. black and mauve	14·50	1·75
132	43	1000r. mauve and green	55·00	1·75
133		2000r. purple and grey	55·00	12·00

1897. As T **39** but inscr "REIS REIS" instead of "DEZ REIS".

165a		10r. blue and red	1·60	60

1898. Newspaper stamps of 1889 surch **1898** between value twice in figures.

168	N 34	100r. on 50r. orange	1·90	55·00
169		200r. on 100r. mauve	3·50	95
170		300r. on 200r. black	3·50	95
171		500r. on 300r. red	5·25	4·00
173		700r. on 500r. green	7·00	1·75
172		700r. on 500r. orange	7·00	18·00
174		1000r. on 700r. orange	35·00	35·00
175		1000r. on 700r. blue	25·00	18·00

176 2000r. on 1000r. orange 25·00 18·00
177 2000r. on 1000r. brown 19·00 7·00

1898. Newspaper stamp of 1890 surch **200** over **1898**.
180 N **37** 200r. on 100r. mauve 14·00 9·00

1898. Newspaper stamps of 1890 surch **1898** over new value.
182 N **38** 20r. on 10r. blue 1·75 3·50
183 50r. on 20r. green 9·00 10·50
184 100r. on 50r. green 18·00 21·00

1899. Postage stamps of 1890 surch **1899** over new value.
194 **35** 50r. on 20r. green 1·75 3·50
195 100r. on 50r. green 1·75 3·50
196 300r. on 200r. violet 9·00 18·00
190b 500r. on 300r. slate 55·00 12·50
190 500r. on 300r. blue 55·00 12·50
191 700r. on 500r. buff 35·00 10·50
192a 1,000r. on 700r. brown 25·00 10·50
193 2,000r. on 1,000r. yellow 35·00 5·25

50 Discovery of Brazil
52 Emancipation of Slaves

1900. 400th Anniv of Discovery of Brazil.
226 **50** 100r. red 7·00 3·50
227 – 200r. green and yellow 7·00 3·50
228 **52** 500r. blue 7·00 3·50
229 – 700r. green 7·00 3·50
DESIGNS—HORIZ: 200r. Declaration of Independence. VERT: 700r. Allegory of Republic.

56 Pan-American Congress

1906.
259a **56** 100r. red 42·00 26·00
259b 200r. blue 90·00 8·75

57 Aristides Lobo
61 Liberty

1906.
260 **57** 10r. grey 90 20
261 – 20r. violet 90 20
262 – 50r. green 90 20
264 – 100r. red 1·75 20
265 – 200r. blue 1·75 20
267 – 300r. brown 3·50 60
268 – 400r. olive 26·00 1·75
269 – 500r. violet 5·25 60
272 – 600r. olive 2·75 90
273 – 700r. brown 5·25 2·75
274 **61** 1000r. red 28·00 90
275 – 1000r. green 3·50 35
276 – 1000r. grey 19·00 60
277 **61** 2000r. green 18·00 60
278 2000r. blue 9·00 90
279 5000r. pink 7·00 1·75
280 – 5000r. brown 55·00 10·50
281 – 10000r. brown 7·00 1·75
PORTRAITS: 20r. B. Constant. 50r. A. Cabral. 100r. Wandendkolk. 200r. D. da Fonseca. 300r. F. Peixoto. 400r., 600r. P. de Moraes. 500r. C. Salles. 700r., 5000r. (No. 280) R. Alves. 1000r. (Nos. 275/6) B. do Rio Branco. 10000r. N. Pecanha.

64 King Carlos and Pres. Affonso Penna and Emblems of Portuguese-Brazilian Amity
65 Emblems of Peace, Commerce and Industry

1908. Centenary of Opening of Brazilian Ports to Foreign Commerce.
282 **64** 100r. red 14·50 1·75

1908. National Exhibition, Rio de Janeiro.
283 **65** 100r. red 45·00 2·40

66 Bonifacio, San Martin, Hidalgo, Washington, O'Higgins, Bolivar
67 Cape Frio

1909. Pan-American Congress, Rio de Janeiro.
284 **66** 200r. blue 14·50 1·25

1915. 300th Anniv of Discovery of Cape Frio.
285 **67** 100r. turquoise on yellow 7·00 5·25

69 Bay of Guajara

1916. 300th Anniv of City of Belem.
286 **69** 100r. red 12·50 5·00

70 Revolutionary Flag

1917. Centenary of Pernambuco Revolution.
287 **70** 100r. blue 18·00 9·00

71 Liberty
72 Liberty
74 Inscr "BRAZIL"

1918. Various frames.
288 **71** 10r. brown 60 35
289 20r. violet 60 35
290 25r. grey 60 35
291 50r. green 1·75 60
292 **72** 100r. red 1·75 35
293 200r. blue 7·00 45
294 300r. orange 19·00 3·50
295 500r. purple 19·00 3·50
296 600r. orange 2·75 8·75
297 **74** 1000r. blue 7·00 35
298 2000r. brown 26·00 7·00
299 5000r. lilac 7·00 7·00
300 10,000r. red 9·00 1·00

77 Steam Locomotive
78 "Industry"
79 "Agriculture"

80 "Aviation"
81 Mercury
82 "Shipping"

1920. T **74** inscr "BRASIL".
317 **77** 10r. purple 60 60
387 **80** 10r. brown 35 35
318 **77** 20r. grey 60 60
388 **80** 20r. violet 35 35
389 **78** 25r. purple 35 1·10
354 **79** 40r. brown 60 60
306 **78** 50r. green 1·25 60
355 50r. brown 60 60
390 **80** 50r. purple 35 35
391 50r. green 35 35
308 **79** 80r. green 20 3·50
309 **80** 100r. red 3·50 60
392 100r. orange 60 35
367 100r. green 1·25 60
420 100r. yellow 1·75 35
311 150r. violet 1·75 60
312 200r. blue 5·25 60
330 200r. red 1·25 60
383 200r. green 4·75 60
405 **81** 300r. grey 60 35
394 300r. green 1·50 35
333 300r. red 1·25 35
406 400r. blue 1·50 35
335 400r. orange 1·25 3·50
407 500r. brown 1·75 35
385 500r. blue 2·40 60
397 600r. brown 9·00 30
422 600r. orange 5·25 35
341 **82** 600r. orange 1·75 60
409 **81** 700r. violet 3·50 35
342 **82** 1000r. purple 3·50 35
410 **81** 1000r. blue 9·00 35
362c **74** 2000r. blue 10·50 1·25
411 2000r. violet 10·50 1·25
363a 5000r. brown 21·00 1·25
364 10000r. purple 21·00 1·75

93 King Albert and Pres. Pessoa

1920. Visit of King of the Belgians.
431 **93** 100r. red 70 50

94 Declaration of Ypiranga
97 Brazilian Army entering Bahia

1922. Centenary of Independence.
432 **94** 100r. blue 5·25 90
433 – 200r. red 10·50 60
434 – 300r. green 10·50 60
DESIGNS: 200r. Dom Pedro I and J. Bonifacio; 300r. National Exn. and Pres. Pessoa.

1923. Centenary of Capture of Bahia from the Portuguese.
435 **97** 200r. red 12·00 7·00

98 Arms of the Confederation
99 Ruy Barbosa

1924. Centenary of Confederation of the Equator.
436 **98** 200r. multicoloured 3·50 1·90

1927.
438b **99** 1000r. red 2·40 1·25

100 "Justice"

1927. Centenary of Law Courses.
439 **100** 100r. blue 1·75 60
440 – 200r. red 1·25 35
DESIGN: 200r. Map and Balances.

1928. Air. Official stamps of 1913, Type O **67**, surch **SERVICO AEREO** and new value. Centres in black.
441 50r. on 10r. grey 35 35
442 200r. on 1000r. brown 2·40 4·50
443 200r. on 2000r. brown 1·25 9·50
444 200r. on 5000r. bistre 1·50 1·25
445 300r. on 500r. yellow 1·50 1·90
446 300r. on 600r. purple 90 65
447 500r. on 50r. grey 1·50 65
448 1000r. on 20r. olive 1·25 35
449 2000r. on 100r. red 2·25 1·50
450 2000r. on 200r. blue 3·00 1·60
451 2000r. on 10,000r. black 2·25 65
452 5000r. on 20,000r. blue 8·75 3·75
453 5000r. on 50,000r. green 8·75 3·75
454 5000r. on 100,000r. red 24·00 30·00
455 10,000r. on 500,000r. brown 24·00 24·00
456 10,000r. on 1,000,000r. sepia 24·00 24·00

104 Liberty holding Coffee Leaves
106 Ruy Barbosa

1928. Bicent of Introduction of the Coffee Plant.
457 **104** 100r. green 3·50 2·40
458 200r. red 1·75 1·25
459 300r. black 10·50 60

1928. Official stamps of 1919 surch.
460 O **77** 700r. on 500r. orange 9·00 9·00
461 1000r. on 100r. red 5·25 60
462 2000r. on 200r. blue 7·00 1·25
463 5000r. on 50r. green 7·00 1·75
464 10,000r. on 10r. brown 25·00 1·75

1929.
465 **106** 5000r. blue 21·00 1·25

108 Santos Dumonts Airship "Ballon No. 6"
109 Santos Dumont

1929. Air.
469 – 50r. green 15 10
470 **108** 200r. red 1·50 15
471 – 300r. blue 2·00 15
472 – 500r. purple 2·40 15
473 – 1000r. brown 7·00 25
479 – 2000r. green 12·00 1·25
480 – 5000r. red 14·50 1·40
481 **109** 10,000r. grey 14·50 3·00
DESIGNS: 50r. De Gusmao's monument; 300r. A. Severo's airship "Pax"; 500r. Santos Dumont's biplane "14 bis"; 1000r. R. de Barros's flying boat "Jahu"; 2000r. De Gusmao; 5000r. A. Severo.

110
112

1930. Air.
486 **110** 3000r. violet 1·75 1·75

1930. 4th Pan-American Architectural Congress.
487 – 100r. turquoise 3·50 3·50
488 **112** 200r. grey 6·00 2·40
489 – 300r. red 8·25 3·50
DESIGNS: 100r. Sun rays inscr "ARCHITECTOS"; 300r. Architrave and Southern Cross.

113 G. Vargas and J. Pessoa – "Redemption of Brazil"
114 O. Aranha – "What is the matter?"

1931. Charity. Revolution of 3 October 1930.
490 **113** 10r.+10r. blue 15 12·00
491 20r.+20r. brown 15 9·00
492 **114** 50r.+50r. green, red and yellow 15 15
493 **113** 100r.+50r. orange 1·25 60
494 200r.+100r. green 60 60
495 – 300r.+150r. mult 60 60
496 **113** 400r.+200r. red 1·75 1·75
497 500r.+250r. blue 1·25 90
498 600r.+300r. purple 90 18·00
499 700r.+350r. mult 1·25 90
500 1$+500r. green, red and yellow 3·50 60
501 – 2$+1$ grey and red 12·00 1·25
502 – 5$+2$ 500r. black & red 24·00 12·00
503 – 10$+5$ green & yellow 60·00 18·00
DESIGNS: 300r., 700r. as Type **113**, but portraits in circles and frames altered. Milreis values as Type **114** with different portraits and frames.

1931. No. 333 surch **1931 200 Reis**.
507 **81** 200r. on 300r. red 60 35

1931. Zeppelin Air Stamps. Surch **ZEPPELIN** and value.
508 **108** 2$500 on 200r. red (No. 470) 35·00 35·00
511 **106** 3$500 on 5000r. blue (No. 468b) 25·00 25·00
509 – 5$000 on 300r. blue (No. 471) 45·00 45·00
512 **74** 7$000 on 10,000r. red (No. 364) 28·00 28·00

1931. Air. No. 486 surch **2.500 REIS**.
510 **110** 2500r. on 3000r. violet 26·00 26·00

121 Brazil

1932. 400th Anniv of Colonization of Sao Vicente.
513 **121** 20r. purple 35 35
514 – 100r. black 90 90
515 – 200r. violet 1·75 35
516 – 600r. brown 3·00 2·75
517 – 700r. blue 3·50 3·00

DESIGNS: 100r. Natives; 200r. M. Afonso de Souza; 600r. King John III of Portugal; 700r. Founding of Sao Vicente.

125 Soldier and Flag **130** "Justice"

1932. Sao Paulo Revolutionary Government issue.

518	–	100r. brown	1·25	3·50
519	**125**	200r. red	60	1·25
520	–	300r. green	2·40	7·00
521	–	400r. blue	5·25	9·00
522	–	500r. sepia	7·00	9·00
523	–	600r. red	7·00	9·00
524	**125**	700r. violet	3·50	9·00
525	–	1000r. orange	2·40	9·00
526	–	2000r. brown	21·00	35·00
527	–	5000r. green	26·00	60·00
528	**130**	10,000r. purple	30·00	70·00

DESIGNS—As Type **125**: 100, 500r. Map of Brazil; 300r., 600r. Symbolical of freedom, etc., 400, 1000r. Soldier in tin helmet. As Type **130**: 2000r. "LEX" and sword; 5000r. "Justice" and soldiers with bayonets.

131 Campo Bello Square and memorial. Vassouras

1933. Centenary of Vassouras.

529	**131**	200r. red	1·25	1·25

132 Flag and Dornier Wal Flying Boat

1933. Air.

532	**132**	3500r. blue, green & yell	1·75	1·75

1933. Surch **200 REIS**.

536	**81**	200r. on 300r. red	60	60

134 Flag of the Race

1933. 441st Anniv of Departure of Columbus from Polos.

537	**134**	200r. red	1·75	1·25

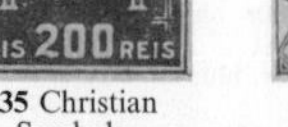
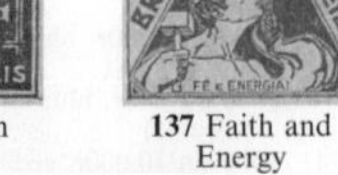

135 Christian Symbols **137** Faith and Energy

136 From Santos Dumont Statue, St. Cloud

1933. 1st Eucharistic Congress, Sao Salvador.

538	**135**	200r. red	70	40

1933. Obligatory Tax for Airport Fund.

539	**136**	100r. purple	60	10

1933.

540	**137**	200r. red	60	35
543		200r. violet	1·25	35

138 "Republic" and Flags **139** Santos Dumont Statue, St. Cloud

1933. Visit of Pres. Justo of Argentina.

545	**138**	200r. blue	65	60
546		400r. green	1·75	1·75
547		600r. red	5·25	7·00
548		1000r. violet	7·00	5·25

1934. 1st National Aviation Congress, Sao Paulo.

549	**139**	200r. blue	1·25	70

140 Exhibition Building

1934. 7th International Sample Fair, Rio de Janeiro.

550	**140**	200r. brown	65	65
551		400r. red	3·50	3·50
552		700r. blue	3·50	3·00
553		1000r. orange	7·00	1·75

141 Brazilian Stamp of 1844

1934. National Philatelic Exhibition, Rio. Imperf.

555	**141**	200r.+100r. purple	1·25	3·00
556		300r.+100r. red	1·25	3·00
557		700r.+100r. blue	6·00	24·00
558		1000r.+100r. black	6·00	24·00

142 Christ of Mt. Corcovado **143** Jose de Anchieta

1934. Visit of Cardinal Pacelli.

559	**142**	300r. red	3·00	3·00
560		700r. blue	12·00	12·00

1934. 400th Anniv of Founding of Sao Paulo by Anchieta.

561	**143**	200r. brown	1·25	1·25
562		300r. violet	1·25	60
563		700c. blue	3·00	3·50
564		1000r. green	5·25	2·40

145 "Brazil" and "Uruguay" **146** Town of Igarassu

1935. Visit of President Terra of Uruguay.

565	–	200r. orange	65	60
566	**145**	300r. yellow	1·25	1·75
567		700r. blue	8·75	15·00
568	–	1000r. violet	18·00	10·50

DESIGN—HORIZ: 200, 1000r. Female figures as in Type **145** and bridge.

1935. 400th Anniv of Founding of Pernambuco.

569	**146**	200r. brown and red	1·75	1·25
570		300r. olive and violet	1·75	90

147 Nurse and Patient

1935. 3rd Pan-American Red Cross Conference.

571	**147**	200r.+100r. violet	3·00	3·00
572		300r.+100r. brown	3·00	3·00
573		700r.+100r. blue	15·00	13·00

149 Gen. da Silva

1935. Cent of Farroupilha "Ragged Revolution".

574	–	200r. black	1·75	1·25
575	–	300r. red	1·25	65
576	**149**	700r. blue	4·00	10·50
577	–	1000r. violet	5·25	5·25

DESIGNS: 200, 300r. Mounted Gaucho; 1000r. Marshal Caxias.

151 Gavea

1935. Children's Day.

578	**151**	300r. violet and brown	2·40	1·60
579		300r. turquoise and black	2·40	1·60
580		300r. blue and green	2·40	1·60
581		300r. black and red	2·40	1·60

152 Federal District Coat of Arms

1935. 8th International Fair.

582	**152**	200r. blue	3·50	3·50

153 Coutinho's ship "Gloria", 1535

1935. 400th Anniv of Colonization of State of Espirito Santo.

583	**153**	300r. red	6·00	3·00
584	–	700r. blue	9·00	6·00

DESIGN—VERT: 700r. Arms of Coutinho.

154a Viscount Cairu **155** Cameta

1936. Death Centenary of Cairu.

585	**154a**	1200r. violet	14·00	9·00

1936. Tercentenary of Founding of Cameta.

586	**155**	200r. buff	2·40	2·40
587		500r. green	2·40	1·25

156 Coin Press **157** Scales of "Justice"

1936. Numismatic Congress, Sao Paulo.

588	**156**	300r. brown	1·75	1·75

1936. 1st National Juridical Congress, Rio.

589	**157**	300r. red	1·25	1·25

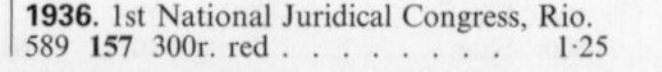

158 A. Carlos Gomes

159 "Il Guarany"

1936. Birth Centenary of C. Gomes (composer).

590	**158**	300r. red	1·25	1·25
591		300r. brown	1·25	1·25
592	**159**	700r. blue	3·50	1·75
593		700r. buff	4·75	3·00

1936. 9th International Sample Fair, Rio. As T **152** with inscription and date altered.

594	**152**	200r. red	1·75	1·25

160 Congress Seal **161** Botafogo Bay

1936. 2nd National Eucharistic Congress, Belo Horizonte.

595	**160**	300r. multicoloured	1·75	1·25

1937. Birth Centenary of Dr. Francisco Pereira Passos.

596	**161**	700r. blue	1·25	1·25
597		700r. black	1·25	1·25

162 Esperanto Star and National Flags

1937. 9th Brazilian Esperanto Congress, Rio de Janeiro.

598	**162**	300r. green	1·75	1·25

163 Bay of Rio de Janeiro

1937. 2nd S. American Radio Conference.

599	**163**	300r. black and orange	1·25	1·25
600		700r. brown and blue	3·00	1·75

164 Globe

1937. Golden Jubilee of Esperanto.

601	**164**	300r. green	1·75	1·25

166 Iguazu Falls

1937. Tourist Propaganda.
602 – 200r. blue and brown . . 1·25 1·25
603 – 300r. green and orange . . 1·25 1·25
604 **166** 1000r. brown and sepia 3·50 2·40
605 – 2000r. red and green . . . 15·00 16·00
606 **166** 5000r. green and black . . 30·00 30·00
607 – 10,000r. blue and red . . 60·00 60·00
DESIGNS—HORIZ: 200, 2000r. Monroe Palace, Rio. VERT: 300, 10,000r. Botanical Gardens, Rio.

168 J. Da Silva Paes **169** Eagle and Shield

1937. Bicent of Founding of Rio Grande do Sul.
608 **168** 300r. blue . . . . 1·25 60

1937. 150th Anniv of U.S. Constitution.
609 **169** 400r. blue . . . . 1·25 60

170 Coffee **171** "Grito" Memorial

1938. Coffee Propaganda.
610 **170** 1200r. multicoloured . . . 7·00 60

1938. Commemoration of Abortive Proclamation of Republic.
611 **171** 400r. brown . . . . . . 1·25 60

172 Arms of Olinda

1938. 4th Centenary of Olinda.
612 **172** 400r. violet . . . . 1·25 60

173 Couto de Magalhaes **174** National Archives

1938. Birth Centenary of De Magalhaes.
613 **173** 400r. green 90 60

1938. Centenary of Founding of National Archives.
614 **174** 400r. brown 90 60

175 Rio de Janeiro **176** Santos

1939.
615 **175** 1200r. purple . . . . . . 2·40 15

1939. Centenary of Santos City.
616 **176** 400r. blue 65 60

177 Chalice-vine and Cup-of-gold Blossoms **178** Seal of Congress

1939. 1st S. American Botanical Congress, Rio.
617 **177** 400r. green . . . . 1·25 60

1939. 3rd National Eucharistic Congress, Recife.
618 **178** 400r. red 65 60

179 Duke of Caxias **180** Washington

1939. Soldiers' Day.
619 **179** 400r. blue 65 60

1939. New York World's Fair. Inscr "FEIRA MUNDIAL DE NOVA YORK".
620 **180** 400r. orange 50 25
621 – 800r. green 30 15
633 – 1m. violet . . . . 3·00 3·00
622 – 1200r. red 60 15
623 – 1600r. blue 60 25
634 – 5m. red . . . . 12·00 12·00
635 – 10m. slate . . . . 12·00 6·00
DESIGNS—HORIZ: 1200r. Grover Cleveland. VERT: 800r. Dom Pedro II; 1m. Water lily; 1600r. Statue of Liberty, Rio de Janeiro; 5m. Bust of Pres. Vargas; 10m. Relief map of Brazil.

184 Benjamin Constant **188** Child and Southern Cross

1939. 50th Anniv of Constitution.
624 **184** 400r. green 90 60
625 – 800r. black 60 60
626 – 1200r. brown . . . . . . 1·50 60
DESIGNS—VERT: 800r. Marshal da Fonseca. HORIZ: 1200r. Marshal da Fonseca and Pres. Vargas.

1940. Child Welfare.
627 – 100r.+100r. violet 60 60
628 – 200r.+100r. blue . . . . 1·00 95
629 **188** 400r.+200r. olive 70 60
630 – 1200r.+400r. red . . . . 3·00 1·60
DESIGNS: 100r. Three Wise Men; 200r. Angel and Child; 1200r. Mother and Child.

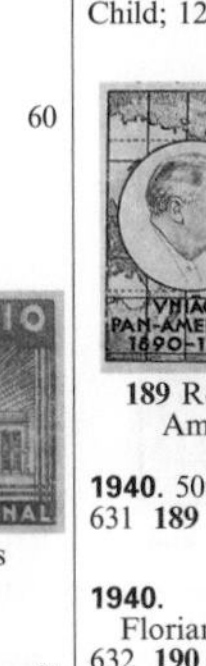

189 Roosevelt, Vargas and American Continents **190** Map of Brazil

1940. 50th Anniv of Pan-American Union.
631 **189** 400r. blue 90 65

1940. 9th National Geographical Congress, Florianopolis.
632 **190** 400r. red 60 60

1940. Birth Centenary of Machado de Assis (poet and novelist). As T **173** but portrait of de Assis, dated "1839–1939".
636 400r. black 50 50

193 Two Workers **195** Brazilian Flags and Head of Liberty

194 Acclaiming King John IV of Portugal

1940. Bicentenary of Colonization of Porto Alegre.
637 **193** 400r. green 65 60

1940. Centenaries of Portugal (1140–1640-1940) (1st issue).
638 **194** 1200r. grey . . . . 3·50 60
See also Nos. 642/5.

1940. 10th Anniv of Govt. of President Vargas.
639 **195** 400r. purple 50 50

196 Date of Fifth Census **197** Globe showing Spotlight on Brazil

1941. 5th General Census.
640 **196** 400r. blue & red (postage) 30 10
641 **197** 1200r. brown (air) . . . . 5·25 90

199 Father Antonio Vieira **202** Father Jose Anchieta

1941. Centenaries of Portugal (2nd issue).
642 – 200r. pink 15 10
643 **199** 400r. blue 15 10
644 – 800r. violet 20 10
645 – 5400r. green . . . . . . 2·40 90
DESIGNS—VERT: 200r. Alfonso Henriques; 800r. Governor-Gen. Benevides. HORIZ: 5,400r. Carmona and Vargas.

1941. 400th Anniv of Order of Jesuits.
646 **202** 1m. violet . . . . 1·25 70

205 Oil Wells **210** Count of Porto Alegre

1941. Value in reis.
647 **205** 10r. orange 10 10
648 20r. olive 10 10
649 50r. brown 10 10
650 100r. turquoise 15 10
651 – 200r. brown 60 35
652 – 300r. red 15 10
653 – 400r. blue 20 10
654 – 500r. red 15 10
655 – 600r. violet . . . . . . 1·75 35
656 – 700r. red 60 35
657 – 1000r. grey . . . . . . 3·50 35
658 – 1200r. blue . . . . . . 5·25 35
659 – 2000r. purple . . . . . 7·00 35
660 – 5000r. blue . . . . . . 9·00 60
661 **210** 10,000r. red . . . . . . 18·00 60
662 – 20,000r. brown . . . . . 16·00 60
663 – 50m. red . . . . 26·00 26·00
664 – 100m. blue . . . . . . 1·25 7·00
DESIGNS: 200r. to 500r. Wheat harvesting machinery; 600r. to 1200r. Smelting works; 2000r. "Commerce"; 5000r. Marshal F. Peixoto; 20,000r. Admiral Maurity; 50m. "Armed Forces"; 100m. Pres. Vargas.
For stamps with values in centavos and cruzeiros see Nos. 751, etc.

213 Amador Bueno **214** Brazilian Air Force Emblem

1941. 300th Anniv of Amador Bueno as King of Sao Paulo.
665 **213** 400r. black 55 35

1941. Aviation Week.
666 **214** 5400r. green . . . . . . 5·25 2·40

1941. Air. 4th Anniv of President Vargas's New Constitution. Optd **AEREO "10 Nov." 937-941**.
667 5400r. green (No. 645) . . . 5·25 1·75

215 Indo-Brazilian Cow **216** Bernardino de Campos

1942. 2nd Agriculture and Cattle Show, Uberaba.
668a **215** 200r. blue 90 60
669a 400r. brown 90 60

1942. Birth Centenaries of B. de Campos and P. de Morais (lawyers and statesmen).
670 **216** 1000r. red . . . . 3·50 95
671 – 1200r. blue . . . . 9·00 65
PORTRAIT: 1200r. Prudente de Morais.

217 Torch of Learning **218** Map of Brazil showing Goiania

1942. 8th National Education Congress, Goiania.
672 **217** 400r. brown 45 25

1942. Founding of Goiania City.
673 **218** 400r. violet 45 25

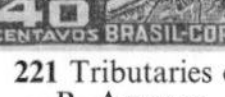

219 Congressional Seal **221** Tributaries of R. Amazon

1942. 4th National Eucharistic Congress, Sao Paulo.
674 **219** 400r. brown 60 40

1942. Air. 5th Anniv of President Vargas's New Constitution. No. 645 surch **AEREO "10 Nov." 937-942** and value.
675 5cr.40 on 5400r. green . . . 4·75 2·40

1943. 400th Anniv of Discovery of River Amazon.
676 **221** 40c. brown 90 60

222 Early Brazilian Stamp **223** Memorial Tablet

1943. Centenary of Petropolis.
677 **222** 40c. violet . . . . 1·25 60

1943. Air. Visit of Pres. Morinigo of Paraguay.
678 **223** 1cr.20 blue . . . . 4·75 1·25

224 Map of S. America showing Brazil and Bolivia

1943. Air. Visit of President Penaranda of Bolivia.
679 **224** 1cr.20 multicoloured . . . 3·50 90

225 "Bulls-eye" **226**

1943. Centenary of 1st Brazilian Postage Stamps.
(a) Postage. Imperf.
680 **225** 30c. black . . . . 1·75 90
681 60c. black . . . . 2·40 60
682 90c. black . . . . 1·25 90

(b) Air. Perf.
683 **226** 1cr. black and yellow . . 3·50 1·25
684 2cr. black and green . . . 4·75 1·25
685 5cr. black and red . . . . 6·00 1·75

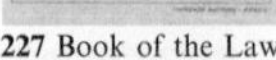

227 Book of the Law **228** Ubaldino do Amaral

1943. Air. Inter-American Advocates Conference.
686 **227** 1cr.20 red and brown . . 2·40 60

1943. Birth Centenary of Ubaldino do Amaral.
687 **228** 40c. grey 60 20

229 Indo-Brazilian Cow

1943. 9th Cattle Show, Bahia.
688 **229** 40c. brown . . . . 1·50 50

230 Justice and Seal **231** Santa Casa de Misericordia Hospital

1943. Centenary of Institute of Brazilian Lawyers.
689 **230** 2cr. red . . . . 3·50 1·75

1943. 400th Anniv of Santa Casa de Misericordia de Santos.
690 **231** 1cr. blue . . . . 1·25 60

232 Barbosa Rodrigues **233** Pedro Americo

1943. Birth Centenary of B. Rodrigues (botanist).
691 **232** 40c. green 40 15

1943. Birth Cent of Americo (artist and author).
692 **233** 40c. brown 90 20

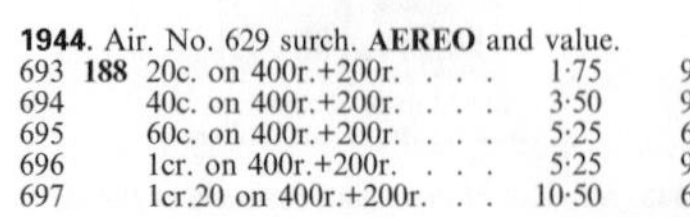

1944. Air. No. 629 surch. **AEREO** and value.
693 **188** 20c. on 400r.+200r. . . . 1·75 90
694 40c. on 400r.+200r. . . . 3·50 90
695 60c. on 400r.+200r. . . . 5·25 60
696 1cr. on 400r.+200r. . . . 5·25 90
697 1cr.20 on 400r.+200r. . . 10·50 60

235 Gen. Carneiro and Defenders of Lapa **236** Baron do Rio Branco

1944. 50th Anniv of Siege of Lapa.
698 **235** 1cr.20c. red . . . . 1·75 60

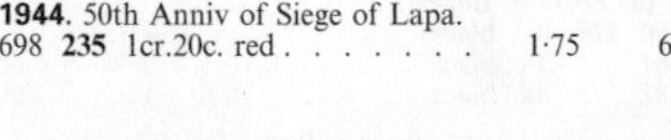

1944. Inauguration of Monument to Baron do Rio Branco.
699 **236** 1cr. blue . . . . 1·50 60

237 Duke of Caxias **238** Emblems of Y.M.C.A.

1944. Centenary of Pacification of Revolutionary Uprising of 1842.
700 **237** 1cr.20 green and yellow 1·75 60

1944. Centenary of Y.M.C.A.
701 **238** 40c. blue, red and yellow 90 20

239 Rio Grande Chamber of Commerce **240** "Bartolomeo de Gusmao and the Aerostat" (Bernardino de Souza Pereira)

1944. Centenary of Founding of Rio Grande Chamber of Commerce.
702 **239** 40c. brown 90 25

1944. Air. Air Week.
703 **240** 1cr.20 red . . . . 1·25 15

241 Ribeiro de Andrada

1945. Death Cent of M. de Andrada (statesman).
704 **241** 40c. blue 90 15

242 Meeting between Caxias and Canabarro

1945. Cent of Pacification of Rio Grande do Sul.
705 **242** 40c. blue 90 15

244 L. L. Zamenhof **247** Baron do Rio Branco (statesman)

1945. 10th Brazilian Esperanto Congress, Rio de Janeiro.
706 – 40c. green (postage) . . . 90 60
707 **244** 1cr.20 brown (air) . . . . 1·25 60
DESIGN: 40c. Woman and map.

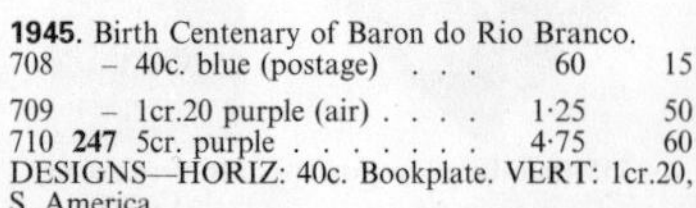

1945. Birth Centenary of Baron do Rio Branco.
708 – 40c. blue (postage) . . . 60 15
709 – 1cr.20 purple (air) . . . . 1·25 50
710 **247** 5cr. purple . . . . 4·75 60
DESIGNS—HORIZ: 40c. Bookplate. VERT: 1cr.20, S. America.

248 "Glory"

250 "Co-operation"

1945. Victory of Allied Nations in Europe. Roul.
711 – 20c. violet 50 10
712 **248** 40c. red 50 10
713 – 1cr. orange . . . . 1·75 60
714 – 2cr. blue . . . . 1·75 90
715 **250** 5cr. green . . . . 3·50 1·25
SYMBOLICAL DESIGNS—VERT: 20c. Tranquility (inscr "SAUDADE"). HORIZ: 1cr. "Victory" (inscr "VITORIA"); 2cr. "Peace" (inscr "PAZ").

251 F. M. da Silva **252** Bahia Institute

1945. 150th Birth Anniv of Francisco Manoel da Silva (composer of Brazilian National Anthem).
716 **251** 40c. red . . . . 1·25 60

1945. 50th Anniv of Founding of Bahia Institute of Geography and History.
717 **252** 40c. blue . . . . 1·75 15

253 Shoulder Flash **255** "V" Sign and Flashes

1945. Return of Brazilian Expeditionary Force.
718 **253** 20c. blue, red and green 50 15
719 – 40c. multicoloured 50 15
720 – 1cr. multicoloured . . . . 2·40 50
721 – 2cr. multicoloured . . . . 3·50 1·25
722 **255** 5cr. multicoloured . . . . 6·00 1·25
DESIGNS (embodying shoulder flashes) As Type **253**: 40c. B.E.F. flash. As Type **255**. HORIZ: 1cr. U.S.A. flag; 2cr. Brazilian flag.

256 Wireless Mast and Map **257** Admiral Saldanha da Gama

1945. 3rd Inter-American Radio Communication Conference.
723 **256** 1cr.20 black . . . . . . 1·25 15

1946. Birth Centenary of Admiral S. da Gama.
724 **257** 40c. grey . . . . 90 1·25

258 Princess Isabel d'Orleans-Braganza **261** P.O., Rio de Janeiro

260 Lockheed Super Electra over Bay of Rio de Janiero

1946. Birth Centenary of Princess Isabel d'Orleans-Braganza.
725 **258** 40c. black . . . . 90 1·75

1946. 5th Postal Union. Congress of the Americas and Spain.
726 – 40c. orange and black . . 50 15
727 **260** 1cr.30 orange and green 90 60
728 1cr.70 orange and red . . 1·25 90
729 **261** 2cr. blue and slate . . . . 1·75 50
730 **260** 2cr.20 orange and blue . . 1·25 90
731 **261** 5cr. blue and brown . . . 4·75 1·25
732 10cr. blue and violet . . . 6·00 90
DESIGN (25×37 mm): 40c. Post-horn, V and envelope.

262 Proposed Columbus Lighthouse **263** "Liberty"

1946. Construction of Columbus Lighthouse, Dominican Republic.
733 **262** 5cr. blue . . . . 9·00 2·50

1946. New Constitution.
734 **263** 40c. grey 10 10

264 Orchid

1946. 4th National Exn of Orchids, Rio de Janeiro.
735 **264** 40c. blue, red and yellow 65 10

265 Gen. A. E. Gomes Carneiro **266** Academy of Arts

1946. Birth Cent of Gen. A. E. Gomes Carneiro.
736 **265** 40c. green 35 10

1946. 50th Anniv of Brazilian Academy of Arts.
737 **266** 40c. blue 35 10

267 Antonio de Castro Alves **268** Pres. Gonzalez

1947. Birth Centenary of Castro Alves (poet).
738 **267** 40c. turquoise 35 10

1947. Visit of Chilean President.
739 **268** 40c. brown 35 10

269 "Peace and Security" **270** "Dove of Peace"

1947. Inter-American Defence Conference, Rio de Janeiro.
740 **269** 1cr.20 blue (postage) . . . 90 10
741 **270** 2cr.20 green (air) . . . . 1·25 50

271 Pres. Truman, Map of S. America and Statue of Liberty

1947. Visit of President Truman.
742 **271** 40c. blue 50 10

272 Pres. Enrico Gaspar Dutra **273** Woman and Child

1947. Commemorating Pres. Dutra.
743 **272** 20c. green 10 10
744 40c. red 15 10
745 1cr.20 blue 50 10

1947. Children's Week. 1st Brazilian Infant Welfare Convention and Paediatrics.
747 **273** 40c. blue 50 10

274 Icarus

1947. Obligatory Tax. "Week of the Wing" Aviation Fund.
748 **274** 40c.+10c. orange 50 10

275 Santos Dumont Monument, St. Cloud, France **276** Arms of Belo Horizonte

1947. Air. Homage to Santos Dumont (aviation pioneer).
749 **275** 1cr.20c. brown & green 1·25 50

1947. 50th Anniv of Founding of City of Belo Horizonte.
750 **276** 1cr.20c. red 65 10

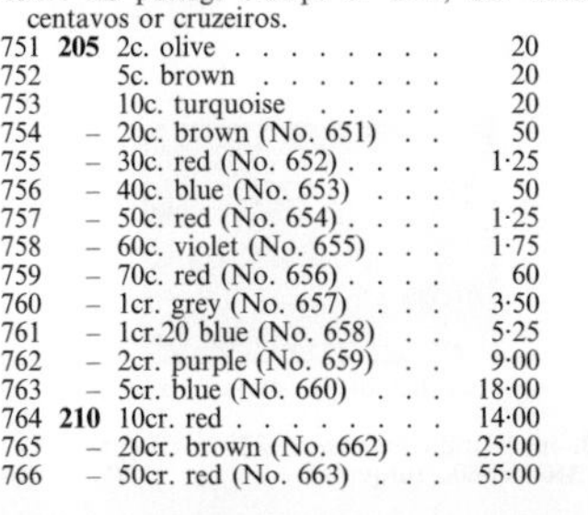
1947. As postage stamps of 1941, but values in centavos or cruzeiros.
751 **205** 2c. olive 20 10
752 5c. brown 20 10
753 10c. turquoise 20 10
754 – 20c. brown (No. 651) . . 50 10
755 – 30c. red (No. 652) . . . . 1·25 10
756 – 40c. blue (No. 653) . . . 50 10
757 – 50c. red (No. 654) . . . . 1·25 10
758 – 60c. violet (No. 655) . . . 1·75 10
759 – 70c. red (No. 656) 60 10
760 – 1cr. grey (No. 657) . . . 3·50 10
761 – 1cr.20 blue (No. 658) . . 5·25 10
762 – 2cr. purple (No. 659) . . 9·00 10
763 – 5cr. blue (No. 660) . . . 18·00 10
764 **210** 10cr. red . . . . 14·00 10
765 – 20cr. brown (No. 662) . . 25·00 10
766 – 50cr. red (No. 663) . . . 55·00 10

277 Rio de Janeiro and Rotary Emblem **278** Globe

279 Quitandinha Hotel

1948. Air. 39th Rotary Congress Rio de Janeiro.
769 **277** 1cr.20 red . . . . 1·25 50
770 3cr.80 violet . . . . . . 3·50 60

1948. International Industrial and Commercial Exhibition, Quitandinha.
771 **278** 40c. grn & mve (postage) 15 10
772 **279** 1cr.20 brown (air) 50 15
773 3cr.80 violet . . . . . . 1·75 15

280 Arms of Paranagua **281** Girl Reading

1948. Tercentenary of Founding of Paranagua.
774 **280** 5cr. brown . . . . 4·75 1·25

1948. National Children's Campaign.
775 **281** 40c. green 15 35

282 Three Muses (after Henrique Bernardelli)

1948. Air. Centenary of National School of Music.
776 **282** 1cr.20 blue . . . . 1·25 10

283 President Berres

1948. Air. Visit of Uruguayan President.
777 **283** 1cr.70 blue 50 10

284 Merino Ram

1948. Air. International Livestock Show, Bage.
778 **284** 1cr.20 orange . . . . . . 1·75 50

285 Congress Seal **286** "Tiradentes" (trans. "Tooth-puller")

1948. Air. 5th National Eucharistic Congress, Porto Alegre.
779 **285** 1cr.20 purple 50 10

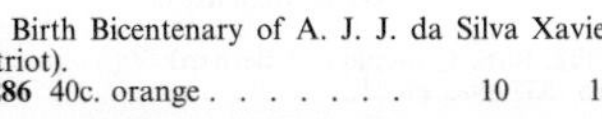
1948. Birth Bicentenary of A. J. J. da Silva Xavier (patriot).
780 **286** 40c. orange 10 10

287 Crab and Globe **288** Adult Student

1948. Anti-cancer Campaign.
781 **287** 40c. purple 50 60

1949. Campaign for Adult Education.
782 **288** 60c. purple 50 10

289 Battle of Guararapes

1949. 300th Anniv of 2nd Battle of Guararapes.
783 **289** 60c. blue (postage) . . . 2·40 50
784 – 1cr.20 pink (air) . . . . . 4·75 1·75
DESIGN: 1cr.20, View of Guararapes.

290 St. Francis of Paula Church **291** Father Nobrega

292 De Souza meeting Indians **293** Franklin D. Roosevelt

1949. Bicentenary of Ouro Fino.
785 **290** 60c. brown 50 10

1949. 4th Centenary of Founding of Bahia. (a) Postage. Imperf.
786 **291** 60c. violet 50 10

(b) Air. Perf.
787 **292** 1cr.20 blue . . . . 1·25 15

1949. Air. Homage to Franklin D. Roosevelt. Imperf.
788 **293** 3cr.80 blue . . . . 2·40 1·75

294 Douglas DC-3 and Air Force Badge

1949. Homage to Brazilian Air Force. Imperf.
789 **294** 60c. violet 50 10

295 Joaquim Nabuco **296** "Revelation"

1949. Air. Birth Centenary of J. Nabuco (lawyer and author).
790 **295** 3cr.80 purple . . . . . . 2·40 10

1949. 1st Sacerdotal Vocational Congress, Bahia.
791 **296** 60c. purple 50 10

297 Globe

1949. 75th Anniv of U.P.U.
792 **297** 1cr.50 blue 90 10

298 Ruy Barbosa **299** Cardinal Arcoverde

1949. Birth Cent of Ruy Barbosa (statesman).
793 **298** 1cr.20 red . . . . 1·25 15

1950. Birth Cent of Cardinal Joaquim Arcoverde.
794 **299** 60c. pink 50 10

300 "Agriculture and Industry" **301** Virgin of the Globe

1950. 75th Anniv of Arrival of Italian Immigrants.
795 **300** 60c. red 60 10

1950. Centenary of Establishment of Daughters of Charity of St. Vincent de Paul.
796 **301** 60c. blue and black . . . 50 10

302 Globe and Footballers **303** Stadium

1950. 4th World Football Championship, Rio de Janeiro.
797 **302** 60c. grey & bl (postage) 1·25 15
798 **303** 1cr.20 orange and blue (air) . . . . 1·60 50
799 – 5cr.80 yellow, green and blue . . . . 7·00 60
DESIGN—VERT: 5cr.80 Linesman and flag.

304 Three Heads, Map and Graph **305** Line of People and Map

1950. 6th Brazilian Census, 1950.
800 **304** 60c. red (postage) 50 10
801 **305** 1cr.20 brown (air) . . . . 1·25 10

306 Oswaldo Cruz **307** Blumenau and Itajai River

1950. 5th International Microbiological Congress. Rio de Janeiro.
802 **306** 60c. brown 50 10

1950. Centenary of Founding of Blumenau.
803 **307** 60c. pink 50 10

308 Government Offices **309** Arms

1950. Centenary of Amazon Province.
804 **308** 60c. red 60 10

1950. Centenary of Juiz de Fora City.
805 **309** 60c. red 60 10

310 P.O. Building, Recife

1951. Inauguration of Head Post Office, Pernambuco Province.
806 **310** 60c. red 50 10
807 1cr.20 red 60 10

311 Arms of Joinville **312** S. Romero

1951. Centenary of Founding of Joinville.
808 **311** 60c. brown 60 10

1951. Birth Centenary of Sylvio Romero (poet).
809 **312** 60c. brown 60 10

313 De La Salle **314** Heart and Flowers

1951. Birth Tricentenary of Jean-Baptiste de la Salle (educational reformer).
810 **313** 60c. blue 65 10

1951. Mothers' Day.
811 **314** 60c. purple 90 50

315 J. Caetano and Stage **316** O. A. Derby

1951. 1st Brazilian Theatrical Congress.
812 **315** 60c. blue 50 10

1951. Birth Centenary of Derby (geologist).
813 **316** 2cr. slate 65 35

317 Crucifix and Congregation **318** E. P. Martins and Map

1951. 4th Inter-American Catholic Education Congress, Rio de Janeiro.
814 **317** 60c. brown and buff . . . 65 10

1951. 29th Anniv of First Rio–New York Flight.
815 **318** 3cr.80 brown & lemon . . 3·25 50

319 Penha Convent **320** Santos Dumont and Boys with Model Aircraft

1951. 400th Anniv of Founding of Vitoria.
816 **319** 60c. brown and buff . . . 65 10

1951. "Week of the Wing" and 50th Anniv of Santos Dumont's Flight over Paris.
817 **320** 60c. brn & orge (postage) 65 15
818 – 3cr.80 violet (air) . . . . 1·90 20
DESIGN: 3cr.80, "Ballon No. 6" airship over Eiffel Tower.

321 Wheat Harvesters **322** Bible and Map

1951. Wheat Festival, Bage.
819 **321** 60c. green and grey . . . 50 50

1951. Bible Day.
820 **322** 1cr.20 brown . . . . . . 1·25 35

323 Isabella the Catholic **324** Henrique Oswald

1952. 500th Birth Anniv of Isabella the Catholic.
821 **323** 3cr.80 blue . . . . 1·90 50

1952. Birth Centenary of Oswald (composer).
822 **324** 60c. brown 65 10

325 Map and Symbol of Labour **326** Dr. L. Cardoso

1952. 5th Conf of American Members of I.L.O.
823 **325** 1cr.50 red 65 10

1952. Birth Centenary of Cardoso (scientist) and 4th Brazilian Homoeopathic Congress, Porto Alegre.
824 **326** 60c. blue 50 15

327 Gen. da Fonseca **328** L. de Albuquerque

1952. Centenary of Telegraphs in Brazil.
825 **327** 2cr.40 red 65 15
826 – 5cr. blue . . . . 3·50 15
827 – 10cr. turquoise . . . . . 3·50 15
PORTRAITS—VERT: 5cr. Baron de Capanema. 10cr. E. de Queiros.

1952. Bicentenary of Mato Grosso City.
828 **328** 1cr.20 violet 65 10

329 Olympic Flame and Athletes **330** Councillor J. A. Saraiva

1952. 50th Anniv of Fluminense Football Club.
829 **329** 1cr.20 blue . . . . 1·25 60

1952. 100th Anniv of Terezina City.
830 **330** 60c. mauve 65 10

331 Emperor Dom Pedro II **332** Globe, Staff and Rio de Janeiro Bay

1952. Stamp Day and 2nd Philatelic Exhibition, Sao Paulo.
831 **331** 60c. black and blue . . . 65 10

1952. 2nd American Congress of Industrial Medicine.
832 **332** 3cr.80 green and brown 1·60 60

333 Dove, Globe and Flags

1952. United Nations Day.
833 **333** 3cr.80 blue . . . . 2·40 50

334 Compasses and Modern Buildings, Sao Paulo **335** D. A. Feijo (Statesman)

1952. City Planning Day.
834 **334** 60c. yellow, green & blue 50 10

1952. Homage to D. A. Feijo.
835 **335** 60c. brown 60 10

336 Father Damien

1952. Obligatory Tax. Leprosy Research Fund.
836 **336** 10c. brown 50 15
837 10c. green 15 10

337 R. Bernardelli

1952. Birth Centenary of Bernardelli (sculptor).
838 **337** 60c. blue 65 10

338 Arms of Sao Paulo and Settler **339** "Expansion"

1953. 400th Anniv of Sao Paulo (1st issue).
839 **338** 1cr.20 black and brown 1·75 50
840 – 2cr. green and yellow . . 3·50 50
841 – 2cr.80 brown and orange 1·90 15
842 **339** 3cr.80 brown and green 1·90 15
843 5cr.80 blue and green . . 1·50 15
DESIGNS—VERT: (Inscr as Type **339**): 2cr. Coffee blossom and berries; 2cr.80, Monk planting tree.
See also Nos. 875/9.

340 **341** J. Ramalho

1953. 6th Brazilian Accountancy Congress, Port Alegre.
844 **340** 1cr.20 brown 95 10

1953. 4th Centenary of Santo Andre.
845 **341** 60c. blue 10 10

342 A. Reis and Plan of Belo Horizonte **343** "Almirante Saldanha" (cadet ship)

1953. Birth Centenary of A. Reis (engineer).
846 **342** 1cr.20 brown 15 10

1953. 4th Voyage of Circumnavigation by Training Ship "Almirante Saldanha".
847 **343** 1cr.50 blue 90 20

344 Viscount de Itaborahy **345** Lamp and Rio-Petropolis Highway

1953. Centenary of Bank of Brazil.
848 **344** 1cr.20 violet 15 10

1953. 10th Int Nursing Congress, Petropolis.
849 **345** 1cr.20 grey 15 10

346 Bay of Rio de Janeiro

1953. 4th World Conference of Young Baptists.
850 **346** 3cr.80c. turquoise 95 10

347 Ministry of Health and Education

348 Arms and Map

1953. Stamp Day and 1st National Philatelic Exhibition of Education, Rio de Janeiro.
851 **347** 1cr.20 turquoise 15 10

1953. Centenary of Jau City.
852 **348** 1cr.20 violet 15 10

349 Maria Quiteria de Jesus

350 Pres. Odria

1953. Death Centenary of Maria Quiteria de Jesus.
853 **349** 60c. blue 10 10

1953. Visit of President of Peru.
854 **350** 1cr.40 purple 15 10

351 Caxias leading Troops

352 Quill-pen and Map

1953. 150th Birth Anniv of Duke of Caxias.
855 **351** 60c. turquoise 35 15
856 – 1cr.20 purple 50 15
857 – 1cr.70 blue 50 15
858 – 3cr.80 brown . . . . . . 1·60 15
859 – 5cr.80 violet 85 15
DESIGNS: 1cr.20, Tomb; 1cr.70, 5cr.80, Portrait of Caxias; 3cr.80, Coat of arms.

1953. 5th National Congress of Journalists, Curitiba.
860 **352** 60c. blue 10 10

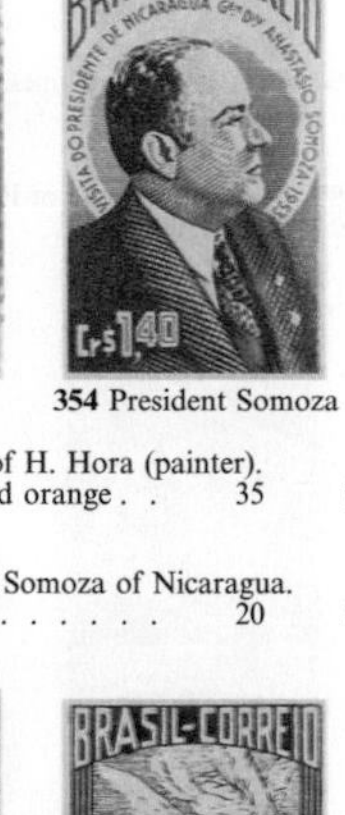

353 H. Hora

354 President Somoza

1953. Birth Centenary of H. Hora (painter).
861 **353** 60c. purple and orange . . 35 10

1953. Visit of President Somoza of Nicaragua.
862 **354** 1cr.40 purple 20 15

355 A. de Saint-Hilaire

356 J. do Patrocinio and "Spirit of Emancipation" (after R. Amoedo)

1953. Death Centenary of A. de Saint-Hilaire (explorer and botanist).
863 **355** 1cr.20 lake 20 10

1953. Death Centenary of J. do Patrocinio (slavery abolitionist).
864 **356** 60c. slate 10 10

357 Clock Tower, Crato

358 C. de Abreu

1953. Centenary of Crato City.
865 **357** 60c. green 15 10

1953. Birth Centenary of Abreu (historian).
866 **358** 60c. blue 20 10
867 5cr. violet . . . . 1·90 20

359 "Justice"

360 Harvesting

1953. 50th Anniv of Treaty of Petropolis.
868 **359** 60c. blue 15 10
869 1cr.20 purple 15 10

1953. 3rd National Wheat Festival, Erechim.
870 **360** 60c. turquoise 15 10

361 Teacher and Pupils

362 Porters with Trays of Coffee Beans

1953. 1st National Congress of Elementary Schoolteachers, Salvador.
871 **361** 60c. red 15 10

1953. Centenary of State of Parana.
872a – 2cr. brown and black . . 1·75 60
873 **362** 5cr. orange and black . . 2·40 60
DESIGN: 2cr. Portrait of Z. de Gois e Vasconcellos.

363 A. de Gusmao

364 Growth of Sao Paulo

365 Sao Paulo and Arms

1954. Death Bicent of Gusmao (statesman).
874 **363** 1cr.20 purple 50 10

1954. 400th Anniv of Sao Paulo (2nd issue).
875 **364** 1cr.20 brown . . . . . . 1·25 90
876 – 2cr. mauve . . . . 1·90 65
877 – 2cr.80 violet . . . . . . 3·00 55
878 **365** 3cr.80 green . . . . . . 3·00 55
879 5cr.80 red . . . . 3·00 55
DESIGNS—VERT: 2cr. Priest, pioneer and Indian; 2cr.80, J. de Anchieta.

366 J. F. Vieira, A. V. de Negreiros, A. F. Camarao and H. Dias

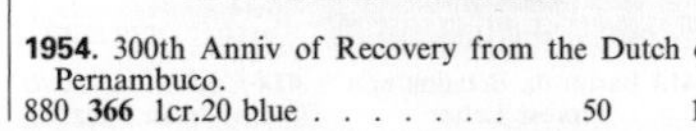

1954. 300th Anniv of Recovery from the Dutch of Pernambuco.
880 **366** 1cr.20 blue 50 10

367 Sao Paulo and Allegorical Figure

1954. 10th International Congress of Scientific Organization, Sao Paulo.
881 **367** 1cr.50 purple 15 10

368 Grapes and Winejar

369 Immigrants' Monument

1954. Grape Festival, Rio Grande do Sul.
882 **368** 40c. lake 15 10

1954. Immigrants' Monument, Caxias do Sul.
883 **369** 60c. violet 15 10

370 "Baronesa", 1852 (first locomotive used in Brazil)

371 Pres. Chamoun

1954. Centenary of Brazilian Railways.
884 **370** 40c. red . . . . 1·25 40

1954. Visit of President of Lebanon.
885 **371** 1cr.50 lake 20 10

372 Sao Jose College, Rio de Janeiro

373 Vel Marcelino Champagnat

1954. 50th Anniv of Marists in Brazil.
886 **372** 60c. violet 20 15
887 **373** 1cr.20 blue 20 15

374 Apolonia Pinto

375 Admiral Tamandare

1954. Birth Centenary of Apolonia Pinto (actress).
888 **374** 1cr.20 green 10 10

1954. Portraits.
889 **375** 2c. blue 15 15
890 5c. red 15 10
891 10c. green 15 10
892 – 20c. red 20 10
893 – 30c. slate 55 10
894 – 40c. red . . . . 1·25 10
895 – 50c. lilac . . . . 1·75 10
896 – 60c. turquoise 55 10
897 – 90c. salmon . . . . . . 1·50 15
904a – 1cr. brown . . . . . . 1·25 50
899 – 1cr.50 blue 25 10
904b – 2cr. green . . . . . . 1·75 50
904c – 5cr. purple . . . . . . 5·25 10
902 – 10cr. green . . . . . . 2·75 10
903 – 20cr. red . . . . 3·50 30
904 – 50cr. blue . . . . 10·50 10
PORTRAITS—20, 30, 40c. O. Cruz; 50c. to 90c. J. Murtinho; 1cr., 1cr.50, 2cr. Duke of Caxias; 5, 10cr., R. Barbosa; 20, 50cr. J. Bonifacio.

376 Boy Scout

377 B. Fernandes

1954. International Scout Encampment, Sao Paulo.
905 **376** 1cr.20 blue 95 15

1954. Tercentenary of Sorocaba City.
906 **377** 60c. red 10 10

378 Cardinal Piazza

379 Virgin and Map

1954. Visit of Cardinal Piazza (Papal Legate).
907 **378** 4cr.20 red 95 10

1954. Marian Year. Inscr "ANO MARIANO".
908 **379** 60c. lake 55 10
909 – 1cr.20 blue 65 10
DESIGN: 1cr.20, Virgin and globe.
No. 909 also commemorates the Centenary of the Proclamation of the Dogma of the Immaculate Conception.

380 Benjamin Constant and Braille Book

1954. Cent of Education for the Blind in Brazil.
910 **380** 60c. green 15 10

381 River Battle of Riachuelo

382 Admiral Barroso

1954. 150th Birth Anniv of Admiral Barroso.
911 **381** 40c. brown 90 15
912 **382** 60c. violet 25 10

383 S. Hahnemann (physician)

384 Nisia Floresta (suffragist)

1954. 1st World Congress of Homoeopathy.
913 **383** 2cr.70 green 95 10

1954. Removal of Ashes of Nisia Floresta (suffragist) from France to Brazil.
914 **384** 60c. mauve 10 10

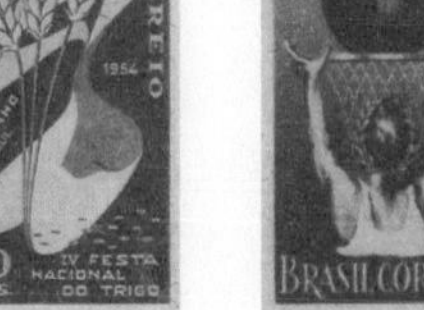

385 Ears of Wheat **386** Globe and Basketball Player

1954. 4th Wheat Festival, Carazinho.
915 **385** 60c. olive 15 10

1954. 2nd World Basketball Championship.
916 **386** 1cr.40 red 95 15

387 Girl, Torch and Spring Flowers **388** Father Bento

1954. 6th Spring Games.
917 **387** 60c. brown 50 10

1954. Obligatory Tax. Leprosy Research Fund.
918 **388** 10c. blue 15 10
919 10c. mauve 15 10
919a 10c. salmon 15 10
919b 10c. green 15 10
919c 10c. lilac 15 10
919d 10c. brown 15 10
919e 10c. slate 15 10
919f 2cr. lake 15 10
919g 2cr. lilac 15 10
919h 2cr. orange 15 10
See also Nos. 1239/40.

389 Sao Francisco Power Station

1955. Inauguration of Sao Francisco Hydro-electric Station.
920 **389** 60c. orange 15 10

390 Itutinga Power Plant

1955. Inaug of Itutinga Hydro-electric Station.
921 **390** 40c. blue 15 10

391 Rotary Symbol and Rio Bay **392** Aviation Symbols

1955. 50th Anniv of Rotary International.
922 **391** 2cr.70 green and black . . 2·40 10

1955. 3rd Aeronautical Congress, Sao Paulo.
923 **392** 60c. grey and black . . . 15 10

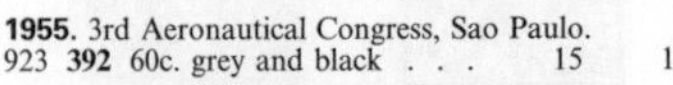

393 Fausto Cardoso Palace

1955. Centenary of Aracaju.
924 **393** 40c. brown 10 10

394 Arms of Botucatu

1955. Centenary of Botucatu.
925 **394** 60c. brown 10 10
926 1cr.20 green 15 10

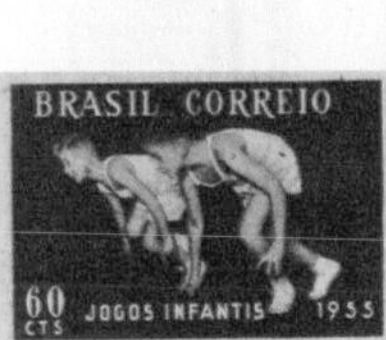

395 Young Athletes **396** Marshal da Fonseca

1955. 5th Children's Games, Rio de Janeiro.
927 **395** 60c. brown 50 10

1955. Birth Centenary of Marshal da Fonseca.
928 **396** 60c. violet 10 10

397 Congress Altar, Sail and Sugar-loaf Mountain **398** Cardinal Masella

1955. 36th International Eucharistic Congress.
929 **397** 1cr.40 green 10 10
930 – 2cr.70 lake (St. Pascoal) 90 90

1955. Visit of Cardinal Masella (Papal Legate) to Eucharistic Congress.
931 **398** 4cr.20 blue . . . . 1·75 15

399 Gymnasts

1955. 7th Spring Games.
932 **399** 60c. mauve 20 10

400 Monteiro Lobato **401** A. Lutz

1955. Honouring M. Lobato (author).
933 **400** 40c. green 10 10

1955. Birth Cent of Lutz (public health pioneer).
934 **401** 60c. green 15 10

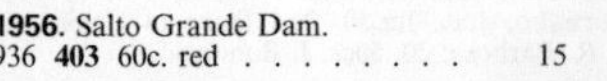

402 Lt.-Col. T. C. Vilagran Cabrita **403** Salto Grande Dam

1955. Centenary of 1st Battalion of Engineers.
935 **402** 60c. blue 15 10

1956. Salto Grande Dam.
936 **403** 60c. red 15 10

404 **405** Arms of Mococa

1956. 18th International Geographical Congress, Rio de Janeiro.
937 **404** 1cr.20 blue 50 10

1956. Centenary of Mococa, Sao Paulo.
938 **405** 60c. red 35 10

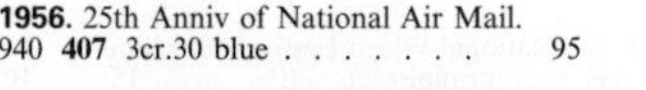

406 Girls Running **407** Douglas DC-3 and Map

1956. 6th Children's Games.
939 **406** 2cr.50 blue 65 10

1956. 25th Anniv of National Air Mail.
940 **407** 3cr.30 blue 95 10

408 Rescue Work

1956. Centenary of Firemen's Corps, Rio de Janeiro.
941 **408** 2cr.50 red 90 35

409 Franca Cathedral **410** Open book with Inscription and Map

1956. Centenary of City of Franca.
942 **409** 2cr.50 blue 60 10

1956. 50th Anniv of Arrival of Marist Brothers in N. Brazil.
943 **410** 2cr.50 blue (postage) . . . 50 10
944 – 3cr.30 purple (air) 15 10
DESIGN—VERT: 3cr.30, Father J. B. Marcelino Champagnat.

411 Hurdler **412** Forest and Map of Brazil

1956. 8th Spring Games.
945 **411** 2cr.50 red . . . . 1·25 35

1956. Afforestation Campaign.
946 **412** 2cr.50 green 50 10

413 Baron da Bocaina and Express Letter **414** Commemorative Stamp from Panama

1956. Birth Centenary of Baron da Bocaina.
947 **413** 2cr.50 brown 50 10

1956. Pan-American Congress. Panama.
948 **414** 3cr.30 black and green . . 95 15

415 Santos Dumont's Biplane "14 bis"

1956. Air. Alberto Santos Dumont (aviation pioneer) Commemoration.
949 **415** 3cr. green . . . . 1·60 40
950 3cr.30 blue 20 10
951 4cr. purple . . . . . . 1·25 10
952 6cr.50 brown 20 10
953 11cr.50 orange . . . . . 2·50 30

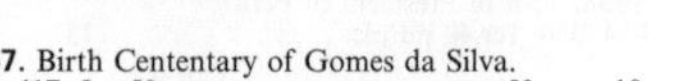

416 Volta Redonda Steel Mill, and Molten Steel **417** J. E. Gomes da Silva (civil engineer)

1957. Nat Steel Company's Expansion Campaign.
955 **416** 2cr.50 brown 40 10

1957. Birth Centenary of Gomes da Silva.
956 **417** 2cr.50 green 50 10

418 Allan Kardec, Code and Globe

1957. Centenary of Spiritualism Code.
957 **418** 2cr.50 brown 15 10

419 Young Gymnast **420** Gen. Craveiro Lopes

1957. 7th Children's Games.
958 **419** 2cr.50 lake . . . . 1·25 10

1957. Visit of President of Portugal.
959 **420** 6cr.50 blue 95 10

421 Stamp of 1932 **422** Lord Baden-Powell

1957. 25th Anniv of Sao Paulo Revolutionary Government.
960 **421** 2cr.50 red 60 10

1957. Air. Birth Centenary of Lord Baden-Powell.
961 **422** 3cr.30 lake 95 10

423 Convent of Santo Antonio

1957. 300th Anniv of Emancipation of Santo Antonio Province.
962 **423** 2cr.50 purple 15 10

424 Volleyball **425** Basketball

1957. 9th Spring Games.
963 **424** 2cr.50 brown . . . . . . 1·25 10

1957. 2nd Women's World Basketball Championships.
964 **425** 3cr.30 green and brown 1·25 10

426 U.N. Emblem, Map of Suez Canal and Soldier

1957. Air. United Nations Day.
965 **426** 5cr.30 blue 15 30

427 Count of Pinhal (founder), Arms and Locomotive **428** Auguste Comte (philosopher)

1957. Centenary of City of San Carlos.
966 **427** 2cr.50 red 90 30

1957. Death Centenary of Comte.
967 **428** 2cr.50 brown 50 10

429 Sarapui Radio Station

1957. Inauguration of Sarapui Radio Station.
968 **429** 2cr.50 myrtle 50 10

430 Admiral Tamandare (founder) and "Almirante Tamandare" (cruiser) **431** Coffee Beans and Emblem

1957. 150th Anniv of Brazilian Navy.
969 **430** 2cr.50 blue 55 15
970 – 3cr.30 green 70 15
DESIGN: 3cr.30, Aircraft-carrier "Minas Gerais".

1957. Centenary of City of Ribeirao Preto.
971 **431** 2cr.50 red 60 10

432 King John VI of Portugal and Sail Merchantman

1958. 150th Anniv of Opening of Ports to Foreign Trade.
972 **432** 2cr.50 purple 60 10

433 Bugler **434** Locomotive "Baronesa", 1852, and Dom Pedro II Station, Rio de Janeiro

1958. 150th Anniv of Corps of Brazilian Marines.
973 **433** 2cr.50 red 50 10

1958. Centenary of Central Brazil Railway.
974 **434** 2cr.50 brown 85 20

435 High Court Building **436** Brazilian Pavilion

1958. 150th Anniv of Military High Courts.
975 **435** 2cr.50 green 15 10

1958. Brussels International Exhibition.
976 **436** 2cr.50 blue 10 10

437 Marshal C. M. da Silva Ronden **438** Jumping

1958. Rondon Commem and "Day of the Indian".
977 **437** 2cr.50 purple 15 10

1958. 8th Children's Games, Rio de Janeiro.
978 **438** 2cr.50 red 50 10

439 Hydro-electric Station

1958. Inaug of Salto Grande Hydro-electric Station.
979 **439** 2cr.50 purple 15 10

440 National Printing Works **441** Marshal Osorio

1958. 150th Anniv of National Printing Works.
980 **440** 2cr.50 brown 10 10

1958. 150th Birth Anniv of Marshal Osorio.
981 **441** 2cr.50 violet 10 10

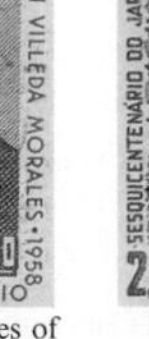
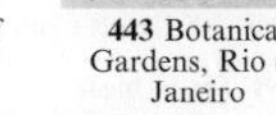

442 Pres. Morales of Honduras **443** Botanical Gardens, Rio de Janeiro

1958. Visit of President of Honduras.
982 **442** 6cr.50 green . . . . . . 3·50 90

1958. 150th Anniv of Botanical Gardens, Rio de Janeiro.
983 **443** 2cr.50 green 10 10

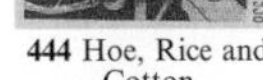

444 Hoe, Rice and Cotton **445** Prophet Joel

1958. 50th Anniv of Japanese Immigration.
984 **444** 2cr.50 red 10 10

1958. Bicentenary of Basilica of the Good Jesus, Matosinhos.
985 **445** 2cr.50 blue 35 10

446 Brazil on Globe

1958. Int Investments Conf, Belo Horizonte.
986 **446** 2cr.50 brown 10 10

447 Tiradentes Palace, Rio de Janeiro **448** J. B. Brandao (statesman)

1958. 47th Inter-Parliamentary Union Conf.
987 **447** 2cr.50 brown 10 10

1958. Centenary of Brandao.
988 **448** 2cr.50 brown 10 10

449 Dawn Palace, Brasilia

1958. Construction of Presidential Palace.
989 **449** 2cr.50 blue 10 10

450 Freighters

1958. Govt Aid for Brazilian Merchant Navy.
990 **450** 2cr.50 blue 55 10

451 J. C. da Silva **452** Pres. Gronchi

1958. Birth Centenary of Da Silva (author).
991 **451** 2cr.50 brown 10 10

1958. Visit of President of Italy.
992 **452** 7cr. blue . . . . 1·75 10

453 Archers **454** Old People within Hour-glass

1958. 10th Spring Games, Rio de Janeiro.
993 **453** 2cr.50 orange 90 10

1958. Old People's Day.
994 **454** 2cr.50 lake 15 10

455 Machado de Assis (writer) **456** Pres. Vargas with oily Hand

1958. 50th Death Anniv of Machado de Assis.
995 **455** 2cr.50 brown 10 10

1958. 5th Anniv of State Petroleum Law.
996 **456** 2cr.50 blue 10 10

457 Globe showing Brazil and the Americas **458** Gen. L. Sodre

1958. 7th Inter-American Municipalities Congress, Rio de Janeiro.
997 **457** 2cr.50 blue 50 10

1958. Birth Centenary of Sodre.
998 **458** 3cr.30 green 10 10

459 U.N. Emblem **460** Footballer

1958. 10th Anniv of Human Rights Declaration.
999 **459** 2cr.50 blue 10 10

1959. World Football Cup Victory, 1958.
1000 **460** 3cr.30 brown & green . . 95 10

461 Map and Railway Line **462** Pres. Sukarno

1959. Centenary of Opening of Patos-Campina Grande Railway.
1001 **461** 2cr.50 brown 30 15

1959. Visit of President of Indonesia.
1002 **462** 2cr.50 blue 10 10

463 Basketball Player

464 King John VI of Portugal

1959. Air. World Basketball Championships 1959.
1003 **463** 3cr.30 brown & blue . . 90 10

1959.
1004 **464** 2cr.50 red 15 10

465 Polo Players

1959. Children's Games.
1005 **465** 2cr.50 brown 20 10

466 Dockside Scene

467 Church Organ, Diamantina

1959. Rehabilitation of National Ports Law.
1006 **466** 2cr.50 green 15 10

1959. Bicent of Carmelite Order in Brazil.
1007 **467** 3cr.30 lake 10 10

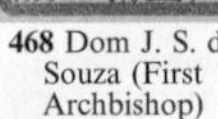
468 Dom J. S. de Souza (First Archbishop)

469 Sugar-loaf Mountain and Road

1959. Birth Cent of Archbishop of Diamantina.
1008 **468** 2cr.50 brown 10 10

1959. 11th International Roads Congress.
1009 **469** 3cr.30 blue and green . . 15 10

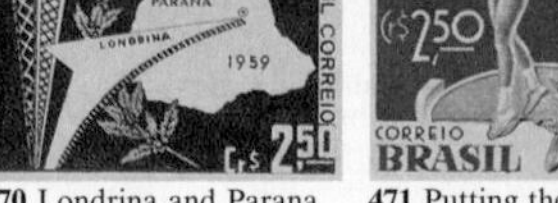
470 Londrina and Parana

471 Putting the Shot

1959. 25th Anniv of Londrina.
1010 **470** 2cr.50 green 10 10

1959. Spring Games.
1011 **471** 2cr.50 mauve 65 10

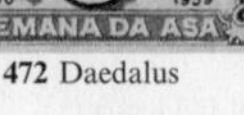
472 Daedalus

473 Globe and "Snipe" Class Yachts

1959. Air. Aviation Week.
1012 **472** 3cr.30 blue 10 10

1959. World Sailing Championships, Porto Alegre.
1013 **473** 6cr.50 green 10 10

474 Lusignan Cross and Arms of Salvador, Bahia

475 Gunpowder Factory

1959. 4th International Brazilian–Portuguese Study Conference, Bahia University.
1014 **474** 6cr.50 blue 10 10

1959. 50th Anniv of President Vargas Gunpowder Factory.
1015 **475** 3cr.30 brown 10 10

476

477 Sud Aviation Caravelle

1959. Thanksgiving Day.
1016 **476** 2cr.50 blue 50 10

1959. Air. Inauguration of "Caravelle" Airliners by Brazilian National Airlines.
1017 **477** 6cr.50 blue 15 10

478 Burning Bush

1959. Centenary of Presbyterian Work in Brazil.
1018 **478** 3cr.30 green 10 10

479 P. da Silva and "Schistosoma mansoni"

1959. 50th Anniv of Discovery and Identification of "Schistosoma mansoni" (fluke).
1019 **479** 2cr.50 purple 50 10

480 L. de Matos and Church

481 Pres. Lopez Mateos of Mexico

1960. Birth Centenary of Luiz de Matos (Christian evangelist).
1020 **480** 3cr.30 brown 10 10

1960. Air. Visit of Mexican President.
1021 **481** 6cr.50 brown 10 10

482 Pres. Eisenhower

483 Dr. L. Zamenhof

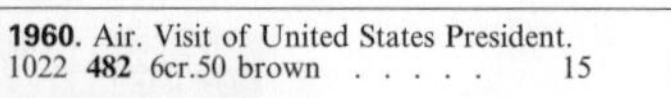

1960. Air. Visit of United States President.
1022 **482** 6cr.50 brown 15 10

1960. Birth Centenary of Zamenhof (inventor of Esperanto).
1023 **483** 6cr.50 green 35 10

484 Adel Pinto (engineer)

485 "Care of Refugees"

1960. Birth Centenary of Adel Pinto.
1024 **484** 11cr.50 red 25 10

1960. Air. World Refugee Year.
1025 **485** 6cr.50 blue 20 10

486 Plan of Brasilia

1960. Inauguration of Brasilia as Capital.
1026 – 2cr.50 green (postage) . . 15 10
1027 – 3cr.30 violet (air) 10 10
1028 – 4cr. blue . . . . 1·25 10
1029 – 6cr.50 mauve 10 10
1030 **486** 11cr.50 brown 15 10
DESIGNS—Outlines representing: HORIZ: 2cr.50, President's Palace of the Plateau; 3cr.30, Parliament Buildings; 4cr. Cathedral. VERT: 6cr.50, Tower.

487 Congress Emblem

1960. Air. 7th Nat Eucharistic Congress, Curitiba.
1032 **487** 3cr.30 mauve 10 10

488 Congress Emblem, Sugar-loaf Mountain and Cross

489 Boy Scout

1960. Air. 10th Baptist World Alliance Congress, Rio de Janeiro.
1033 **488** 6cr.50 blue 10 10

1960. Air. 50th Anniv of Scouting in Brazil.
1034 **489** 3cr.30 orange 10 10

490 "Agriculture"

491 Caravel

1960. Cent of Brazilian Ministry of Agriculture.
1035 **490** 2cr.50 brown 15 10

1960. Air. 5th Death Centenary of Prince Henry the Navigator.
1036 **491** 6cr.50 black 30 10

492 P. de Frontin

493 Locomotive Piston Gear

1960. Birth Cent of Paulo de Frontin (engineer).
1037 **492** 2cr.50 orange 10 10

1960. 10th Pan-American Railways Congress.
1038 **493** 2cr.50 blue 35 10

494 Athlete

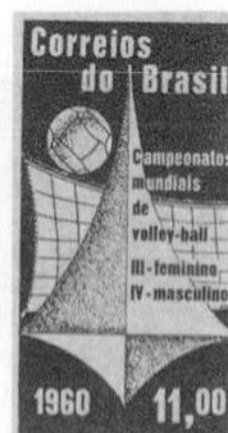
495

1960. 12th Spring Games.
1039 **494** 2cr.50 turquoise 15 10

1960. World Volleyball Championships.
1040 **495** 11cr. blue 60 10

496 Maria Bueno in play

1960. Air. Maria Bueno's Wimbledon Tennis Victories, 1959–60.
1041 **496** 6cr. brown 15 10

497 Exhibition Emblem

1960. International Industrial and Commercial Exhibition, Rio de Janeiro.
1042 **497** 2cr.50 brown & yellow 10 10

498 War Memorial, Rio de Janeiro

499 Pylon and Map

1960. Air. Return of Ashes of World War II Heroes from Italy.
1043 **498** 3cr.30 lake 15 10

1961. Air. Inauguration of Tres Marias Hydro-electric Station.
1044 **499** 3cr.30 mauve 15 10

500 Emperor Haile Selassie

501 Sacred Book and Map of Brazil

1961. Visit of Emperor of Ethiopia.
1045 **500** 2cr.50 brown 10 10

1961. 50th Anniv of Sacre-Coeur de Marie College.
1046 **501** 2cr.50 blue 15 10

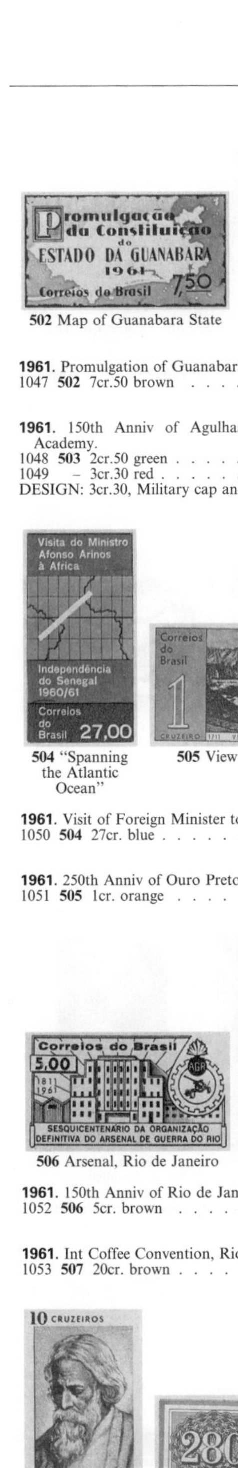

502 Map of Guanabara State

503 Arms of Academy

1961. Promulgation of Guanabara Constitution.
1047 **502** 7cr.50 brown 60 10

1961. 150th Anniv of Agulhas Negras Military Academy.
1048 **503** 2cr.50 green 20 10
1049 – 3cr.30 red 10 10
DESIGN: 3cr.30, Military cap and sabre.

504 "Spanning the Atlantic Ocean"

505 View of Ouro Preto

1961. Visit of Foreign Minister to Senegal.
1050 **504** 27cr. blue 95 10

1961. 250th Anniv of Ouro Preto.
1051 **505** 1cr. orange 35 10

506 Arsenal, Rio de Janeiro

507 Coffee Plant

1961. 150th Anniv of Rio de Janeiro Arsenal.
1052 **506** 5cr. brown 45 10

1961. Int Coffee Convention, Rio de Janeiro.
1053 **507** 20cr. brown . . . . . . 2·40 10

508 Tagore

509 280r. Stamp of 1861 and Map of France

1960. Birth Cent of Rabindranath Tagore (poet).
1054 **508** 10cr. mauve 90 10

1961. "Goat's Eyes" Stamp Centenary.
1055 **509** 10cr. red . . . . 1·25 10
1056 – 20cr. orange . . . . . . 3·75 10
DESIGN: 20cr. 430r. stamp and map of the Netherlands.

510 Cloudburst

511 Pinnacle, Rope and Haversack

1962. World Meteorological Day.
1057 **510** 10cr. brown . . . . . . 1·25 10

1962. 50th Anniv of 1st Ascent of "Finger of God" Mountain.
1058 **511** 8cr. green 10 10

512 Dr. G. Vianna and parasites

1962. 50th Anniv of Vianna's Cure for Leishman's Disease.
1059 **512** 8cr. blue 20 10

513 Campaign Emblem

514 Henrique Dias (patriot)

1962. Air. Malaria Eradication.
1060 **513** 21cr. blue 10 10

1962. 300th Death Anniv of Dias.
1061 **514** 10cr. purple 15 10

515 Metric Measure

516 "Snipe" Sailing-boats

1962. Cent of Brazil's Adoption of Metric System.
1062 **515** 100cr. red . . . . 1·25 10

1962. 13th "Snipe" Class Sailing Championships, Rio de Janeiro.
1063 **516** 8cr. turquoise 20 10

517 J. Mesquita and Newspaper "O Estado de Sao Paulo"

1962. Birth Centenary of Mesquita (journalist and founder of "O Estado de Sao Paulo").
1064 **517** 8cr. bistre . . . . 1·25 10

518 Empress Leopoldina

519 Brasilia

1962. 140th Anniv of Independence.
1065 **518** 8cr. mauve 15 10

1962. 51st Interparliamentary Conference, Brasilia.
1066 **519** 10cr. orange 40 10

520 Foundry Ladle

521 U.P.A.E. Emblem

1962. Inauguration of "Usiminas" (national iron and steel foundry).
1067 **520** 8cr. orange 10 10

1962. 50th Anniv of Postal Union of the Americas and Spain.
1068 **521** 8cr. mauve 10 10

522 Emblems of Industry

523 Q. Bocaiuva

1962. 10th Anniv of National Bank.
1069 **522** 10cr. turquoise 15 10

1962. 50th Death Anniv of Bocaiuva (journalist and patriot).
1070 **523** 8cr. brown 10 10

524 Footballer

1962. Brazil's Victory in World Football Championships, 1962.
1071 **524** 10cr. turquoise . . . . . 1·25 10

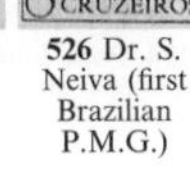

525 Carrier Pigeon

526 Dr. S. Neiva (first Brazilian P.M.G.)

1962. Tercentenary of Brazilian Posts.
1072 **525** 8cr. multicoloured . . . 10 10

1963.

1073	**526**	8cr. violet	50	10
1073a	–	30cr. turquoise (Euclides da Cunha)	4·75	10
1073b	–	50cr. brown (Prof. A. Moreira da Costa Lima)	3·50	10
1073c	–	100cr. blue (G. Dias)	1·75	10
1073d	–	200cr. red (Tiradentes)	7·00	10
1073e	–	500cr. brown (Emperor Pedro I)	35·00	20
1073f	–	1000cr. blue (Emperor Pedro II)	90·00	60

527 Rockets and "Dish" Aerial

528 Cross

1963. Int Aeronautics and Space Exn, Sao Paulo.
1074 **527** 21cr. blue 60 10

1963. Ecumenical Council, Vatican City.
1075 **528** 8cr. purple 10 10

529 "abc" Symbol

530 Basketball

1963. National Education Week.
1076 **529** 8cr. blue 10 10

1963. 4th World Basketball Championships.
1077 **530** 8cr. mauve 50 10

531 Torch Emblem

1963. 4th Pan-American Games, Sao Paulo.
1078 **531** 10cr. red 65 10

532 "OEA" and Map

533 J. B. de Andrada e Silva

1963. 15th Anniv of Organization of American States.
1079 **532** 10cr. orange 50 10

1963. Birth Bicentenary of Jose B. de Andrada e Silva ("Father of Independence")
1080 **533** 8cr. bistre 10 10

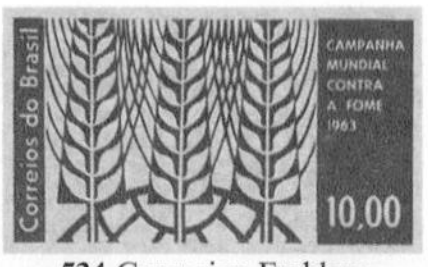

534 Campaign Emblem

1963. Freedom from Hunger.
1081 **534** 10cr. blue 50 10

535 Centenary Emblem

536 J. Caetano

1963. Red Cross Centenary.
1082 **535** 8cr. red and yellow . . . 20 10

1963. Death Centenary of Joao Caetano (actor).
1083 **536** 8cr. black 10 10

537 "Atomic" Development

538 Throwing the Hammer

1963. 1st Anniv of National Nuclear Energy Commission.
1084 **537** 10cr. mauve 50 10

1963. International Students' Games, Porto Alegre.
1085 **538** 10cr. black and grey . . 65 10

539 Pres. Tito

540 Cross and Map

1963. Visit of President Tito of Yugoslavia.
1086 **539** 80cr. drab . . . . 2·40 10

1963. 8th Int Leprology Congress, Rio de Janeiro.
1087 **540** 8cr. turquoise 10 10

541 Petroleum Installations

543 A. Borges de Medeiros

542 "Jogos da Primavera"

1963. 10th Anniv of National Petroleum Industry.
1088 **541** 8cr. green 10 10

1963. Spring Games.
1089 **542** 8cr. yellow 10 10

1963. Birth Centenary of A. Borges de Medeiros (politician).
1090 **543** 8cr. brown 10 10

544 Bridge of Sao Joao del Rey

546 Viscount de Maua

545 Dr. A. Alvim

1963. 250th Anniv of Sao Joao del Rey.
1091 **544** 8cr. blue 10 10

1963. Birth Cent of Dr. Alvaro Alvim (scientist).
1092 **545** 8cr. slate 10 10

1963. 150th Birth Anniv of Viscount de Maua (builder of Santos–Jundiai Railway).
1093 **546** 8cr. mauve 45 20

547 Cactus

548 C. Netto

1964. 10th Anniv of North-East Bank.
1094 **547** 8cr. green 10 10

1964. Birth Centenary of Coelho Netto (author).
1095 **548** 8cr. violet 10 10

549 L. Muller

550 Child with Spoon

1964. Birth Cent of Lauro Muller (patriot).
1096 **549** 8cr. red 10 10

1964. Schoolchildren's Nourishment Week.
1097 **550** 8cr. yellow and brown 10 10

551 "Chalice" (carved rock), Vila Velha, Parana

552 A. Kardec (author)

1964. Tourism.
1098 **551** 80cr. red 65 10

1964. Cent of Spiritual Code, "O Evangelho".
1099 **552** 30cr. green 95 10

553 Pres. Lubke

554 Pope John XXIII

1964. Visit of Pres. Lubke of West Germany.
1100 **553** 100cr. brown . . . . . 1·25 10

1964. Pope John Commemoration.
1101 **554** 20cr. lake 60 35

555 Pres. Senghor

1964. Visit of Pres. Senghor of Senegal.
1102 **555** 20cr. sepia 15 10

556 "Visit Rio de Janeiro"

1964. 400th Anniv (1965) of Rio de Janeiro.
1103 **556** 15cr. blue and orange . . 25 10
1104 – 30cr. red and blue . . . 65 10
1105 – 30cr. black and blue . . 1·60 40
1106 – 35cr. black and orange 15 10
1107 – 100cr. brn & grn on yell 65 10
1108 – 200cr. red and green . . 6·00 10

DESIGNS: As Type **556**—HORIZ: 30cr. (No. 1105), Tramway viaduct; 200cr. Copacabana Beach. VERT: 35cr. Estacio de Sa's statue; 100cr. Church of Our Lady of the Rock. SMALLER ($24\frac{1}{2} \times 37$ mm): 30cr. (No. 1104), Statue of St. Sebastian.

558 Pres. De Gaulle

559 Pres. Kennedy

1964. Visit of Pres. De Gaulle.
1110 **558** 100cr. brown 95 10

1964. Pres. Kennedy Commemoration.
1111 **559** 100cr. black 15 15

560 Nahum (statue)

1964. 150th Death Anniv of A. F. Lisboa (sculptor).
1112 **560** 10cr. black 30 10

561 Cross and Sword

562 V. Brazil (scientist)

1965. 1st Anniv of Democratic Revolution.
1113 **561** 120cr. grey 15 10

1965. Birth Cent of Vital Brazil.
1114 **562** 120cr. orange . . . . . 1·25 10

563 Shah of Iran

564 Marshal Rondon and Map

1965. Visit of Shah of Iran.
1115 **563** 120cr. red 65 10

1965. Birth Cent of Marshal C. M. da S. Rondon.
1116 **564** 30cr. purple 50 10

565 Lions Emblem

566 I.T.U. Emblem and Symbols

1965. Brazilian Lions Clubs National Convention, Rio de Janeiro.
1117 **565** 35cr. black and lilac . . 15 10

1965. I.T.U. Centenary.
1118 **566** 120cr. green and yellow 65 10

567 E. Pessoa

568 Barrosos Statue

1965. Birth Centenary of Epitacio Pessoa.
1119 **567** 35cr. slate 10 10

1965. Centenary of Naval Battle of Riachuelo.
1120 **568** 30cr. blue 15 10

569 Author and Heroine

570 Sir Winston Churchill

1965. Centenary of Publication of Jose de Alencar's "Iracema".
1121 **569** 30cr. purple 15 10

1965. Churchill Commemoration.
1122 **570** 200cr. slate . . . . . . 1·25 10

571 Scout Badge and Emblem of Rio's 400th Anniv

572 I.C.Y. Emblem

1965. 1st Pan-American Scout Jamboree, Rio de Janeiro.
1123 **571** 30r. multicoloured . . . 1·10 10

1965. International Co-operation Year.
1124 **572** 120cr. black and blue . . 1·25 10

573 L. Correia

574 Exhibition Emblem

1965. Birth Centenary of Leoncia Correia (poet).
1125 **573** 35cr. green 10 10

1965. Sao Paulo Biennale (Art Exn).
1126 **574** 30cr. red 10 10

575 President Saragat

576 Grand Duke and Duchess of Luxembourg

1965. Visit of President of Italy.
1127 **575** 100cr. green on pink . . 15 10

1965. Visit of Grand Duke and Duchess of Luxembourg.
1128 **576** 100cr. brown 15 10

577 Curtiss Fledgling on Map

578 O.E.A. Emblem

1965. Aviation Week and 3rd Philatelic Exn.
1129 **577** 35cr. blue 15 10

1965. Inter-American Conference, Rio de Janeiro.
1130 **578** 100cr. black and blue . . 45 10

579 King Baudouin and Queen Fabiola 580 Coffee Beans

1965. Visit of King and Queen of the Belgians.
1131 **579** 100cr. slate 50 10

1965. Brazilian Coffee.
1132 **580** 30cr. brown on cream 65 10

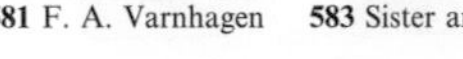

581 F. A. Varnhagen 583 Sister and Globe

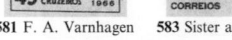

582 Emblem and Map

1965. Air. 150th Birth Anniv of Francisco Varnhagen (historian).
1133 **581** 45cr. brown 15 10

1966. Air. 5th Anniv of "Alliance for Progress".
1134 **582** 120cr. blue & turquoise 95 10

1966. Air. Centenary of Dorothean Sisters Educational Work in Brazil.
1135 **583** 35cr. violet 10 10

584 Loading Ore at Quayside 585 "Steel"

1966. Inauguration of Rio Doce Iron-ore Terminal Tubarao, Espirito Santo.
1136 **584** 110cr. black and bistre 50 10

1966. Silver Jubilee of National Steel Company.
1137 **585** 30cr. black on orange . . 35 10

586 Prof. Rocha Lima 587 Battle Scene

1966. 50th Anniv of Professor Lima's Discovery of the Characteristics of "Rickettsia prowazeki" (cause of typhus fever).
1138 **586** 30cr. turquoise 65 10

1966. Centenary of Battle of Tuiuti.
1139 **587** 30cr. green 65 10

588 "The Sacred Face" 589 Mariz e Barros

1966. Air. "Concilio Vaticano II".
1140 **588** 45cr. brown 35 35

1966. Air. Death Centenary of Commander Mariz e Barros.
1141 **589** 35cr. brown 15 10

590 Decade Symbol 591 Pres. Shazar

1966. International Hydrological Decade.
1142 **590** 100cr. blue and brown 65 10

1966. Visit of President Shazar of Israel.
1143 **591** 100cr. blue 95 10

592 "Youth" 593 Imperial Academy of Fine Arts

1966. Air. Birth Centenary of Eliseu Visconti (painter).
1144 **592** 120cr. brown . . . . . 1·90 10

1966. 150th Anniv of French Art Mission's Arrival in Brazil.
1145 **593** 100cr. brown . . . . . 1·75 10

594 Military Service Emblem 595 R. Dario

1966. New Military Service Law.
1146 **594** 30cr. blue and yellow . . 15 10

1966. 50th Death Anniv of Ruben Dario (Nicaraguan poet).
1148 **595** 100cr. purple 65 10

596 Santarem Candlestick 597 Arms of Santa Cruz do Sul

1966. Centenary of Goeldi Museum.
1149 **596** 30cr. brown on salmon 15 10

1966. 1st National Tobacco Exn, Santa Cruz.
1150 **597** 30cr. green 15 10

598 U.N.E.S.C.O. Emblem 599 Capt. A. C. Pinto and Map

1966. 20th Anniv of U.N.E.S.C.O.
1151 **598** 120cr. black . . . . . . 1·25 35

1966. Bicentenary of Arrival of Captain A. C. Pinto.
1153 **599** 30cr. red 15 10

600 Lusignan Cross and Southern Cross 601 Madonna and Child

1966. "Lubrapex 1966" Stamp Exn, Rio de Janeiro.
1154 **600** 100cr. green 95 10

1966. Christmas.
1155 **601** 30cr. green 20 10
1156 – 35cr. blue and orange . . 20 15
1157 – 150cr. pink and blue . . 3·50 3·50
DESIGN—DIAMOND(34 × 34 mm). 35cr. Madonna and child (different). VERT (46 × 103 mm). 150cr. As 35cr. inscr "Pax Hominibus" but not "Brazil Correio".

602 Arms of Laguna

1967. Centenary of Laguna Postal and Telegraphic Agency.
1158 **602** 60cr. sepia 10 10

603 Grota Funda Viaduct and 1866 Viaduct

1967. Centenary of Santos–Jundiai Railway.
1159 **603** 50cr. orange . . . . . . 1·40 30

604 Polish Cross and "Black Madonna"

1967. Polish Millennium.
1160 **604** 50cr. red, blue & yellow 50 10

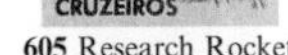

605 Research Rocket 606 Anita Garibaldi

1967. World Meteorological Day.
1161 **605** 50cr. black and blue . . 95 10

1967.
1162 – 1c. blue 10 10
1163 – 2c. red 10 10
1164 – 3c. green 15 10
1165 **606** 5c. black 15 10
1166 – 6c. brown 15 10
1167 – 10c. green . . . . 1·40 10

PORTRAITS: 1c. Mother Angelica. 2c. Marilia de Dirceu. 3c. Dr. R. Lobato. 6c. Ana Neri. 10c. Darci Vargas.

607 "VARIG 40 Years" 608 Lions Emblem and Globes

1967. 40th Anniv of Varig Airlines.
1171 **607** 6c. black and blue . . . 15 10

1967. 50th Anniv of Lions International.
1172 **608** 6c. green 25 10

609 "Madonna and Child" 610 Prince Akihito and Princess Michiko

1967. Mothers' Day.
1174 **609** 5c. violet 10 10

1967. Visit of Crown Prince and Princess of Japan.
1176 **610** 10c. black and red . . . 15 10

611 Radar Aerial and Pigeon 612 Brother Vicente do Salvador

1967. Inaug of Communications Ministry, Brasilia.
1177 **611** 10c. black and mauve . . 15 10

1967. 400th Birth Anniv of Brother Vicente do Salvador (founder of Franciscan Brotherhood, Rio de Janeiro).
1178 **612** 5c. brown 15 10

613 Emblem and Members 614 Mobius Symbol

1967. National 4-S ("4-H") Clubs Day.
1179 **613** 5c. green and black . . . 15 10

1967. 6th Brazilian Mathematical Congress. Rio de Janeiro.
1180 **614** 5c. black and blue . . . 15 10

615 Dorado (fish) and "Waves"

1967. Bicentenary of Piracicaba.
1181 **615** 5c. black and blue . . . 20 10

616 Papal Arms and "Golden Rose"

1967. Pope Paul's "Golden Rose" Offering to Our Lady of Fatima.
1182 **616** 20c. mauve and yellow 1·25 35

617 General A. de Sampaio

1967. Gen. Sampaio Commem.
1183 **617** 5c. blue 15 10

618 King Olav of Norway

619 Sun and Rio de Janeiro

1967. Visit of King Olav.
1184 **618** 10c. brown 15 10

1967. Meeting of International Monetary Fund, Rio de Janeiro.
1185 **619** 10c. black and red . . . 15 10

620 N. Pecanha (statesman)

621 Our Lady of the Apparition and Basilica

1967. Birth Centenary of Nilo Pecanha.
1186 **620** 5c. purple 10 10

1967. 250th Anniv of Discovery of Statue of Our Lady of the Apparition.
1187 **621** 5c. blue and ochre . . . 15 10

622 "Song Bird"

623 Balloon, Rocket and Airplane

1967. International Song Festival.
1189 **622** 20c. multicoloured . . . 55 35

1967. Aviation Week.
1190 **623** 10c. blue 60 10

624 Pres. Venceslau Braz

625 Rio Carnival

1967.
1192 – 10c. blue 35 10
1193 – 20c. brown . . . . . . 1·75 10
1195 **624** 50c. black . . . . . . 12·00 10
1198 – 1cr. purple . . . . . . 18·00 10
1199 – 2cr. green . . . . . . 3·75 10
Portraits of Brazilian Presidents: 10c. Arthur Bernardes. 20c. Campos Salles. 1cr. Washington Luiz. 2cr. Castello Branco.

1967. International Tourist Year.
1200 **625** 10c. multicoloured . . . 15 10

626 Sailor, Anchor and "Almirante Tamandare" (cruiser)

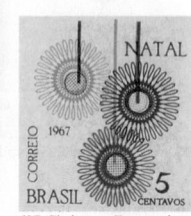

627 Christmas Decorations

1967. Navy Week.
1202 **626** 10c. blue 30 15

1967. Christmas.
1203 **627** 5c. multicoloured 15 10

628 O. Bilac (poet), Aircraft, Tank and Aircraft carrier "Minas Gerais"

629 J. Rodrigues de Carvalho

1967. Reservists Day.
1204 **628** 5c. blue and yellow . . . 60 15

1967. Birth Centenary of Jose Rodriques de Carvalho (jurist and writer).
1205 **629** 10c. green 10 10

630 O. Rangel

1968. Birth Cent of Orlando Rangel (chemist).
1206 **630** 5c. black and blue . . . 15 10

631 Madonna and Diver

632 Map of Free Zone

1968. 250th Anniv of Paranagua Underwater Exploration.
1207 **631** 10c. green and slate . . 20 10

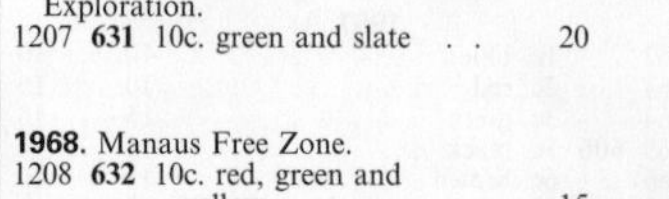

1968. Manaus Free Zone.
1208 **632** 10c. red, green and yellow 15 10

633 Human Rights Emblem

634 Paul Harris

1968. 20th Anniv of Declaration of Human Rights.
1209 **633** 10c. red and blue 10 10

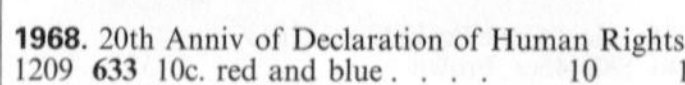

GUM. All the following issues to No. 1425 are without gum, except where otherwise stated.

1968. Birth Centenary of Paul Harris (founder of Rotary International).
1210 **634** 20c. brown and green . . 1·25 60

635 College Arms

1968. Centenary of St. Luiz College. With gum.
1211 **635** 10c. gold, blue and red 25 10

636 Cabral and his Fleet, 1500

1968. 500th Birth Anniv of Pedro Cabral (discoverer of Brazil).
1212 **636** 10c. multicoloured . . . 30 15
1213 – 20c. multicoloured . . . 90 60
DESIGN: 20c. "The First Mass" (C. Portinari).

637 "Maternity" (after H. Bernardeli)

1968. Mother's Day.
1214 **637** 5c. multicoloured 20 15

638 Harpy Eagle

1968. 150th Anniv of National Museum. With gum.
1215 **638** 20c. black and blue . . . 2·50 60

639 Women of Brazil and Japan

1968. Inaug of "VARIG" Brazil–Japan Air Service.
1216 **639** 10c. multicoloured . . . 25 15

640 Horse-racing

1968. Centenary of Brazilian Jockey Club.
1217 **640** 10c. multicoloured . . . 20 10

641 Musician Wren

1968. Birds.
1218 – 10c. multicoloured . . . 50 25
1219 **641** 20c. brown, green & bl 1·50 25
1220 – 50c. multicoloured . . . 1·90 40
DESIGNS—VERT: 10c. Red-crested cardinal; 50c. Royal flycatcher.

642 Ancient Post-box

643 Marshal E. Luiz Mallet

1968. Stamp Day. With gum.
1221 **642** 5c. black, green & yellow 10 10

1968. Mallet Commemoration. With gum.
1222 **643** 10c. lilac 10 10

644 Map of South America

645 Lyceum Badge

1968. Visit of Chilean President. With gum.
1223 **644** 10c. orange 10 10

1968. Centenary of Portuguese Literacy Lyceum (High School). With gum.
1224 **645** 5c. green and pink . . . 10 10

646 Map and Telex Tape

1968. "Telex Service for 25th City (Curitiba)". With gum.
1225 **646** 20c. green and yellow . . 55 35

647 Soldiers on Medallion

648 "Cock" shaped as Treble Clef

1968. 3rd Int Song Festival, Rio de Janeiro.
1226 **647** 6c. multicoloured 25 15

1968. 8th American Armed Forces Conference
1227 **648** 5c. black and blue . . . 15 10

649 "Petrobras" Refinery

650 Boy walking towards Rising Sun

1968. 15th Anniv of National Petroleum Industry.
1228 **649** 6c. multicoloured 50 15

1968. U.N.I.C.E.F.
1229 **650** 5c. black and blue . . . 20 15
1230 – 10c. black, red & blue 20 15
1231 – 20c. multicoloured . . . 50 15
DESIGNS—HORIZ: 10c. Hand protecting child. VERT: 20c. Young girl in plaits.

651 Children with Books

1968. Book Week.
1232 **651** 5c. multicoloured 15 10

652 W.H.O. Emblem and Flags

1968. 20th Anniv of W.H.O.
1233 **652** 20c. multicoloured . . . 30 15

653 J. B. Debret (painter)

1968. Birth Bicentenary of Jean Baptiste Debret (1st issue).
1234 **653** 10c. black and yellow . . 20 10
See Nos. 1273/4.

654 Queen Elizabeth II

1968. State Visit of Queen Elizabeth II.
1235 **654** 70c. multicoloured . . . 1·50 90

655 Brazilian Flag

656 F. Braga and part of "Hymn of National Flag"

1968. Brazilian Flag Day.
1236 **655** 10c. multicoloured . . . 20 15

1968. Birth Cent of Francisco Braga (composer).
1237 **656** 5c. purple 25 10

657 Clasped Hands

1968. Blood Donors' Day.
1238 **657** 5c. red, black and blue 15 10

1968. Obligatory Tax. Leprosy Research Fund. Revalued currency. With gum.
1239 **388** 5c. green . . . . 5·25 1·25
1240 5c. red . . . . 2·40 60

658 Steam Locomotive No. 1 "Maria Fumaca", 1868

1968. Centenary of Sao Paulo Railway.
1241 **658** 5c. multicoloured . . . . 2·50 2·50

659 Angelus Bell

660 F.A.V. Caldas Jr

1968. Christmas. Multicoloured.
1242 5c. Type **659** 15 10
1243 6c. Father Christmas giving present 15 10

1968. Birth Centenary of Francisco Caldas Junior (founder of "Correio do Povo" newspaper).
1244 **660** 10c. black, pink & red 15 10

661 Reservists Emblem and Memorial

1968. Reservists' Day. With gum.
1245 **661** 5c. green and brown . . 15 10

662 Dish Aerial

663 Viscount do Rio Branco

1969. Inaug of Satellite Communications System.
1246 **662** 30c. black and blue . . . 90 60

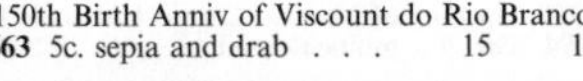

1969. 150th Birth Anniv of Viscount do Rio Branco.
1247 **663** 5c. sepia and drab . . . 15 10

664 St. Gabriel

1969. St. Gabriel's Day (Patron Saint of Telecommunications).
1248 **664** 5c. multicoloured 15 10

665 Shoemaker's Last and Globe

1969. 4th Int Shoe Fair, Novo, Hamburgo.
1249 **665** 5c. multicoloured 15 10

666 Kardec and Monument

1969. Death Centenary of "Allan Kardec" (Professor H. Rivail) (French educationalist and spiritualist).
1250 **666** 5c. brown and green . . 15 10

667 Men of Three Races and Arms of Cuiaba

1969. 250th Anniv of Cuiaba (capital of Mato Grosso state).
1251 **667** 5c. multicoloured 10 10

668 Mint and Banknote Pattern

1969. Opening of New State Mint Printing Works.
1252 **668** 5c. bistre and orange . . 20 15

669 Society Emblem and Stamps

1969. 50th Anniv of Sao Paulo Philatelic Society.
1253 **669** 5c. multicoloured 10 10

670 "Our Lady of Santana" (statue)

1969. Mothers' Day.
1254 **670** 5c. multicoloured 20 15

671 I.L.O. Emblem

1969. 50th Anniv of I.L.O. With gum.
1255 **671** 5c. gold and red 10 10

672 Diving Platform and Swimming Pool

673 "Mother and Child at Window" (after Di Cavalcanti)

1969. 40th Anniv of Cearense Water Sports Club, Fortaleza.
1256 **672** 20c. black, green & brn 40 15

1969. 10th Art Exhibition Biennale, Sao Paulo. Multicoloured.
1257 10c. Type **673** 60 15
1258 20c. Modern sculpture (F. Leirner) 90 30
1259 50c. "Sunset in Brasilia" (D. di Prete) . . . . 1·75 1·25
1260 1cr. "Angelfish" (A. Martins) . . . . . . 1·75 80
No. 1258 is square, size 33 × 33 mm and Nos. 1259/60 vertical, size 33 × 53mm.

674 Freshwater Angelfish

675 I. O. Teles de Manezes (founder)

1969. A.C.A.P.I. Fish Preservation and Development Campaign.
1261 **674** 20c. multicoloured . . . 45 15

1969. Centenary of Spiritualist Press. With gum.
1263 **675** 50c. green and orange 1·50 90

676 Postman delivering Letter

677 General Fragoso

1969. Stamp Day. With gum.
1264 **676** 30c. blue . . . . 1·25 60

1969. Birth Centenary of General Tasso Fragoso. With gum.
1265 **677** 20c. green 90 60

678 Map of Army Bases

1969. Army Week. Multicoloured.
1266 10c. Type **678** 25 15
1267 20c. Monument and railway bridge (39 × 22 mm) . . . 1·75 60

679 Jupia Dam

1969. Inauguration of Jupia Dam.
1268 **679** 20c. multicoloured . . . 55 55

680 Mahatma Gandhi and Spinning-wheel

1969. Birth Centenary of Mahatma Gandhi.
1269 **680** 20c. black and yellow . . 1·25 60

681 Alberto Santos Dumont, "Ballon No. 6", Eiffel Tower and Moon Landing

1969. 1st Man on the Moon and Santos Dumont's Flight (1906). Commemoration.
1270 **681** 50c. multicoloured . . . 1·75 1·25

682 Smelting Plant

1969. Expansion of USIMINAS Steel Consortium.
1271 **682** 20c. multicoloured . . . 55 15

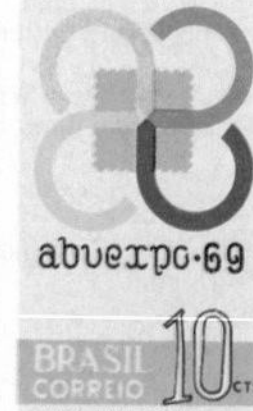

683 Steel Furnace **685** Exhibition Emblem

684 "The Water Cart" (after Debrot)

1969. 25th Anniv of ACESITA Steel Works.
1272 **683** 10c. multicoloured . . . 55 15

1969. Birth Centenary of J. B. Debret (painter) (2nd issue). Multicoloured. No. 1274 dated "1970".
1273 20c. Type **684** . . . . . . 1·25 60
1274 30c. "Street Scene" . . . . 1·00 95

1969. "Abuexpo 69" Stamp Exn.
1275 **685** 10c. multicoloured . . . 20 15

686 Embraer Bandeirante Airplane

1969. Brazilian Aeronautical Industry Expansion Year.
1276 **686** 50c. multicoloured . . . 1·75 1·25

687 Pele scoring Goal

1969. Footballer Pele's 1,000th Goal.
1277 **687** 10c. multicoloured . . . 1·25 1·75

688 "Madonna and Child" (painted panel)

1969. Christmas.
1279 **688** 10c. multicoloured . . . 55 35

689 "Pernambuco" (destroyer) and "Bahia" (submarine)

1969. Navy Day. With gum.
1281 **689** 5c. blue . . . . 1·00 15

690 Dr. H. Blumenau

1969. 150th Birth Anniv of Dr. Hermann Blumenau (German immigrant leader). With gum.
1282 **690** 20c. green 60 60

691 Carnival Dancers

1969. Carioca Carnival, Rio de Janeiro (1970). Multicoloured.
1283 5c. Type **691** 25 20
1284 10c. Samba dancers (horiz) 25 20
1285 20c. Clowns (horiz) 25 30
1286 30c. Confetti and mask . . 2·75 1·50
1287 50c. Tambourine-player . . 2·75 1·40

692 Carlos Gomes conducting

1970. Centenary of Opera "O. Guarani" by A. Carlos Gomes.
1288 **692** 20c. multicoloured . . . 60 20

693 Monastery

1970. 400th Anniv of Penha Monastery, Vilha Velha.
1289 **693** 20c. multicoloured . . . 25 15

694 National Assembly Building

1970. 10th Anniv of Brasilia. Multicoloured.
1290 20c. Type **694** 25 15
1291 50c. Reflecting Pool . . . . 1·75 1·50
1292 1cr. Presidential Palace . . . 1·75 1·50

695 Emblem on Map

1970. Rondon Project (students' practical training scheme).
1293 **695** 50c. multicoloured . . . 1·50 1·50

696 Marshal Osorio and Arms

1970. Opening of Marshal Osorio Historical Park.
1294 **696** 20c. multicoloured . . . 1·25 45

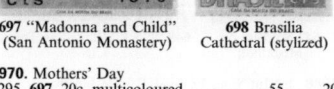

697 "Madonna and Child" (San Antonio Monastery) **698** Brasilia Cathedral (stylized)

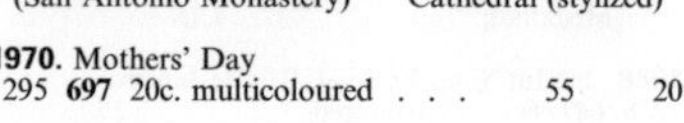

1970. Mothers' Day
1295 **697** 20c. multicoloured . . . 55 20

1970. 8th National Eucharistic Congress, Brasilia. With gum.
1296 **698** 20c. green 15 15

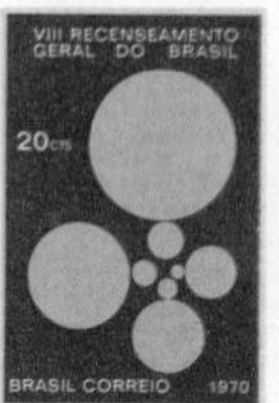

699 Census Symbol **700** Jules Rimet Cup, and Map

1970. 8th National Census.
1297 **699** 20c. yellow and green . . 55 50

1970. World Cup Football Championships Mexico.
1298 **700** 50c. black, gold & blue 50 40

701 Statue of Christ

1970. Marist Students. 6th World Congress.
1299 **701** 50c. multicoloured . . . 1·50 1·50

702 Bellini and Swedish Flag (1958)

1970. Brazil's Third Victory in World Cup Football Championships. Multicoloured.
1300 1cr. Type **702** . . . . 1·75 90
1301 2cr. Garrincha and Chilean flag (1962) . . . . 5·25 1·75
1302 3cr. Pele and Mexican flag (1970) . . . . 2·75 90

703 Pandia Calogeras **704** Brazilian Forces Badges and Map

1970. Birth Centenary of Calogeras (author and politician).
1303 **703** 20c. green . . . . 1·75 60

1970. 25th Anniv of World War II. Victory.
1304 **704** 20c. multicoloured . . . 50 15

705 "The Annunciation" (Cassio M'Boy)

1970. St. Gabriel's Day (Patron Saint of Telecommunications).
1305 **705** 20c. multicoloured . . . 90 40

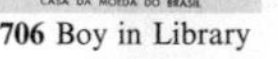
706 Boy in Library **707** U.N. Emblem

1970. Book Week.
1306 **706** 20c. multicoloured . . . 90 60

1970. 25th Anniv of United Nations.
1307 **707** 50c. blue, silver & ultram 90 75

708 "Rio de Janeiro, circa 1820"

1970. 3rd Brazilian–Portuguese Stamp Exhibition "Lubrapex 70", Rio de Janeiro.
1308 **708** 20c. multicoloured . . . 60 60
1309 – 50c. brown and black . . 2·75 1·75
1310 – 1cr. multicoloured . . . 2·75 2·75
DESIGNS: 50c. Post Office Symbol; 1cr. Rio de Janeiro (modern view).

709 "The Holy Family" (C. Portinari) **710** "Graca Aranha" (destroyer)

1970. Christmas.
1312 **709** 50c. multicoloured . . . 90 90

1970. Navy Day.
1314 **710** 20c. multicoloured . . . 1·75 80

711 Congress Emblem **712** Links and Globe

1971. 3rd Inter-American Housing Congress, Rio de Janeiro.
1315 **711** 50c. red and black . . . 80 80

1971. Racial Equality Year.
1316 **712** 20c. multicoloured . . . 60 30

713 "Morpho melacheilus"

1971. Butterflies. Multicoloured.
1317 20c. Type **713** . . . . . . 1·25 35
1318 1cr. "Papilio thoas brasiliensis" . . . . . . 6·00 2·40

714 Madonna and Child **715** Hands reaching for Ball

1971. Mothers' Day.
1319 **714** 20c. multicoloured . . . 60 15

1971. 6th Women's Basketball World Championships.
1320 **715** 70c. multicoloured . . . 1·25 95

716 Eastern Part of Highway Map

1971. Trans-Amazon Highway Project. Mult.
1321 40c. Type **716** . . . . . . 6·25 3·75
1322 1cr. Western part of Highway Map . . . . . 6·25 5·25
Nos. 1321/2 were issued together se-tenant, forming a composite design.

717 "Head of Man" (V. M. Lima)

1971. Stamp Day. Multicoloured.
1323 40c. Type **717** . . . . . . 1·25 45
1324 1cr. "Arab Violinist" (Pedro Americo) . . . . 3·00 1·25

718 General Caxias and Map **719** Anita Garibaldi

1971. Army Week.
1325 **718** 20c. red and green . . . 50 15

1971. 150th Birth Anniv of Anita Garibaldi.
1326 **719** 20c. multicoloured . . . 20 15

720 Xavante and Santos Dumont's Biplane "14 bis"

1971. 1st Flight of Embraer Xavante Jet Fighter.
1327 **720** 40c. multicoloured . . . 1·25 45

721 Flags of Central American Republics **722** Exhibition Emblem

1971. 150th Anniv of Central American Republics' Independence.
1328 **721** 40c. multicoloured . . . 80 40

1971. "Franca 71" Industrial, Technical and Scientific Exhibition, Sao Paulo.
1329 **722** 1cr.30 multicoloured . . 1·25 90

723 "The Black Mother" (L. de Albuquerque) **724** Archangel Gabriel

1971. Centenary of Slaves Emancipation Law.
1330 **723** 40c. multicoloured . . . 40 20

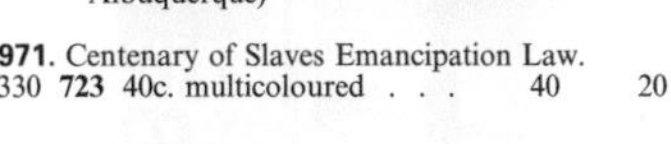

1971. St. Gabriel's Day (Patron Saint of Communications).
1331 **724** 40c. multicoloured . . . 45 50

725 "Couple on Bridge" (Marisa da Silva Chaves)

1971. Children's Day. Multicoloured.
1332 35c. Type **725** 35 30
1333 45c. "Couple on Riverbank" (Mary Rosa e Silva) . . . 90 30
1334 60c. "Girl in Hat" (Teresa A. P. Ferreira) 35 30

726 "Laelia purpurata Werkhauserii superba" **727** Eunice Weaver

1971. Brazilian Orchids.
1335 **726** 40c. multicoloured . . . 1·50 50

1971. Obligatory Tax. Leprosy Research Fund.
1336 **727** 10c. green . . . . 1·25 65
1337 10c. purple 55 15

728 "25 Senac"

1971. 25th Annivs of SENAC (apprenticeship scheme) and SESC (workers' social service).
1338 **728** 20c. blue and black . . . 90 60
1339 – 40c. orange and black 90 60
DESIGN: 40c. As Type **728**, but inscribed "25 SESC".

729 "Parati" (gunboat)

1971. Navy Day.
1340 **729** 20c. multicoloured . . . 2·00 50

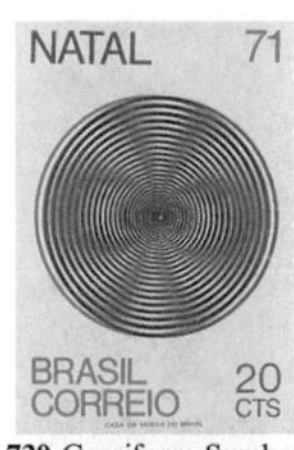

730 Cruciform Symbol **731** Washing Bomfim Church

1971. Christmas.
1341 **730** 20c. lilac, red and blue 30 15
1342 75c. black on silver . . . 55 1·75
1343 1cr.30 multicoloured . . 2·40 1·50

1972. Tourism. Multicoloured.
1344 20c. Type **731** . . . . . . 1·75 90
1345 40c. Cogwheel and grapes (Grape Festival, Rio Grande do Sul) . . . . . 1·75 20
1346 75c. Nazareth Festival procession, Belem . . . . 1·75 1·75
1347 1cr.30 Street scene (Winter Festival of Ouro Preto) 3·50 1·75

732 Pres. Lanusse

1972. Visit of President Lanusse of Argentina.
1348 **732** 40c. multicoloured . . . 90 75

733 Presidents Castello Branco, Costa e Silva and Medici **734** Post Office Symbol

1972. 8th Anniv of 1964 Revolution.
1349 **733** 20c. multicoloured . . . 40 30

1972.
1350 **734** 20c. brown . . . . . . 1·50 10

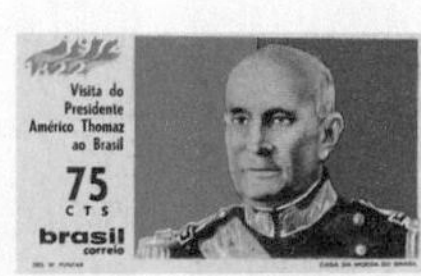

735 Pres. Tomas

1972. Visit of Pres. Tomas of Portugal.
1351 **735** 75c. multicoloured . . . . 1·25 95

736 Exploratory Borehole (C.P.R.M.)

1972. Mineral Resources. Multicoloured.
1352 20c. Type **736** 60 15
1353 40c. Oil rig (PETROBRAS) (vert) . . . . 2·75 50
1354 75c. Power station and dam (ELECTROBRAS) . . . 95 1·25
1355 1cr.30 Iron ore production (Vale do Rio Doce Co.) 3·25 1·25

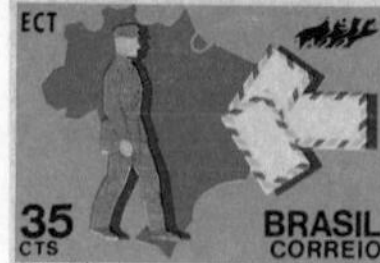
738 Postman and Map (Post Office)

1972. Communications. Multicoloured.
1357 35c. Type **738** 90 20
1358 45c. Microwave Transmitter (Telecommunications) (vert) 90 90
1359 60c. Symbol and diagram of Amazon microwave system 90 70
1360 70c. Worker and route map (Amazon Basin development) . . . . . . 1·25 70

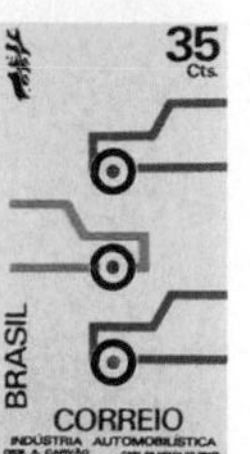
739 Motor Cars

740 Footballer (Independence Cup Championships)

1972. Major Industries.
1361 **739** 35c. orange, red & black 45 25
1362 – 45c. multicoloured . . . 45 40
1363 – 70c. multicoloured . . . 45 25
DESIGNS—HORIZ: 45c. Three hulls (Shipbuilding); 70c. Metal Blocks (Iron and Steel Industry).

1972. "Sports and Pastimes".
1364 **740** 20c. black and brown . . 40 15
1365 – 75c. black and red . . . 1·25 1·50
1366 – 1cr.30 black and blue . . 2·00 1·50
DESIGNS: 75c. Treble clef in open mouth ("Popular Music"); 1cr.30, Hand grasping plastic ("Plastic Arts").

741 Diego Homem's Map of Brazil, 1568

1972. "EXFILBRA 72" 4th International Stamp Exhibition, Rio de Janeiro. Multicoloured.
1367 70c. Type **741** 60 35
1368 1cr. Nicolau Visscher's Map of Americas, c. 1652 . . . 5·25 60
1369 2cr. Lopo Homem's World Map, 1519 . . . . 2·40 90

742 Figurehead, Sao Francisco River

743 "Institution of Brazilian Flag"

1972. Brazilian Folklore. Multicoloured.
1371 45c. Type **742** 45 15
1372 60c. Fandango, Rio Grande do Sul 75 75
1373 75c. Capoeira (game), Bahia 30 15
1374 1cr.15 Karaja statuette . . . 30 25
1375 1cr.30 "Bumba-Meu-Boi" (folk play) . . . . 2·50 1·10

1972. 150th Anniv of Independence.
1376 **743** 30c. green and yellow . . 1·75 1·00
1377 – 70c. mauve and pink . . 75 30
1378 – 1cr. red and brown . . . 4·00 85
1379 – 2cr. black and brown . . 2·40 85
1380 – 3cr.50 black and grey . . 4·00 2·40
DESIGNS—HORIZ: 70c. "Proclamation of Emperor Pedro I" (lithograph after Debret); 2cr. Commemorative gold coin of Pedro I; 3cr.50, Declaration of Ypiranga monument. VERT: 1cr. "Emperor Pedro I" (H. J. da Silva).

744 Numeral and P.T.T. Symbol

747 Writing Hand and People ("Mobral" Literacy Campaign)

745 Scroll

1972.
1383 **744** 5c. orange 30 10
1384 10c. brown 40 10
1394 15c. blue 15 10
1385 20c. blue . . . . . . 2·40 10
1396 25c. brown 15 10
1386 30c. red . . . . 1·50 10
1387 40c. green 15 10
1388 50c. green . . . . . . 1·50 10
1398 70c. purple 60 10
1389 **745** 1cr. purple 60 10
1390 2cr. blue . . . . 1·75 10
1391 4cr. orange and lilac . . 3·50 35
1392 5cr. brown, cinnamon and red . . . . 3·50 10
1393 10cr. green, brown & blk 7·00 35
Nos. 1392/3 have a background of multiple P.T.T. symbols.

1972. Social Development. Multicoloured.
1412 10c. Type **747** 20 20
1413 20c. Graph and people (National Census Cent) 50 40
1414 1cr. House in hand (Pension Fund system) . . . . . . 9·00 20
1415 2cr. Workers and factory (Gross National Product) 1·25 45

748 Legislative Building, Brasilia

1972. National Congress Building, Brasilia.
1416 **748** 1cr. black, orange & bl 9·00 4·50

749 Pottery Crib

750 Farm-worker and Pension Book (Rural Social Security Scheme)

1972. Christmas.
1417 **749** 20c. black and brown . . 40 20

1972. Government Services.
1418 **750** 10c. black, orange & bl 25 20
1419 – 10c. multicoloured . . . 90 90
1420 – 70c. black, brown & red 4·50 2·00
1421 – 2cr. multicoloured . . . 5·50 2·50
DESIGNS—VERT: 70c. Dr. Oswald Cruz, public health pioneer (birth cent.). HORIZ: 10c. (No. 1419), Children and traffic lights (Transport system development); 2cr. Bull, fish and produce (Agricultural exports).

751 Brazilian Expeditionary Force Monument

1972. Armed Forces' Day.
1422 **751** 10c. black, purple & brn 1·40 85
1423 – 30c. multicoloured . . . 2·00 85
1424 – 30c. multicoloured . . . 1·40 85
1425 – 30c. black, brn & lilac 1·40 85
DESIGNS: No. 1423, Sail-training ship (Navy); No. 1424, Trooper (Army); No. 1425, Dassault Mirage IIIC jet fighter (Air Force).

GUM. All the following issues are with gum, except where otherwise stated.

752 Emblem and Cogwheels

1973. 50th Anniv of Rotary in Brazil.
1426 **752** 1cr. blue, lt blue & yell 1·75 1·00

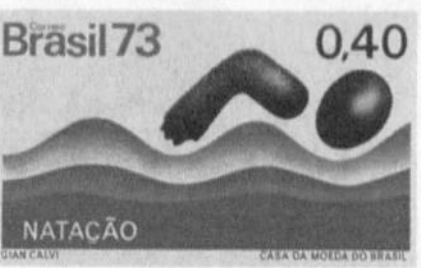
753 Swimming

1973. Sporting Events.
1427 **753** 40c. brown and blue . . 25 20
1428 – 40c. red and green . . . 2·75 55
1429 – 40c. brown and purple 90 45
DESIGNS AND EVENTS—HORIZ: No. 1427, ("Latin Cup" Swimming Championships); No. 1428, Gymnast (Olympic Festival of Gymnastics, Rio de Janeiro). VERT: No. 1429, Volleyball player (Internation Volleyball Championships, Rio de Janeiro).

754 Paraguayan Flag

1973. Visit of Pres. Stroessner of Paraguay.
1430 **754** 70c. multicoloured . . . 1·40 80

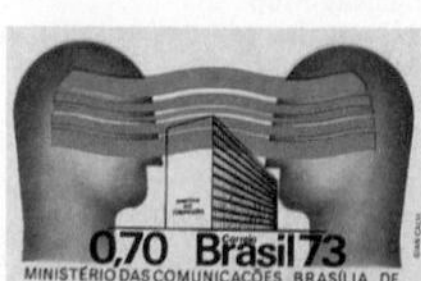
755 "Communications"

1973. Inauguration of Ministry of Communications Building, Brasilia.
1431 **755** 70c. multicoloured . . . 90 50

756 Neptune and Map

1973. Inauguration of "Bracan I" Underwater Cable, Recife to Canary Islands.
1432 **756** 1cr. multicoloured . . . 4·25 2·40

757 Congress Emblem

758 Swallow-tailed Manakin and "Acacia decurrens"

1973. 24th Int Chamber of Commerce Congress.
1433 **757** 1cr. purple and orange 4·25 2·40

1973. Tropical Birds and Plants. Mult.
1434 20c. Type **758** 65 30
1435 20c. Troupial and "Cereus peruvianus" 65 30
1436 20c. Brazilian ruby and "Tecoma umbellata" . . 65 30

759 "Tourism"

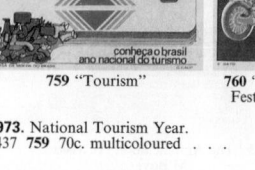

760 "Caboclo" Festival Cart

1973. National Tourism Year.
1437 **759** 70c. multicoloured . . . 60 30

1973. Anniversaries. Multicoloured.
1438 20c. Type **760** 90 30
1439 20c. Arariboia (Indian chief) 90 30
1440 20c. Convention delegates 90 30
1441 20c. "The Graciosa Road" 90 30
EVENTS: No. 1438, 150th anniv of Liberation Day; 1439, 400th anniv of Niteroi; 1440, Cent of Itu Convention; 1441, Cent of Nhundiaquara highway.

761 "Institute of Space Research"

1973. Scientific Research Institute. Mult.
1442 20c. Type **761** 50 25
1443 70c. "Federal Engineering School", Itajuba . . . . 1·50 50
1444 1cr. "Institute for Pure and Applied Mechanics" . . . 2·00 45

762 Santos Dumont and Biplane "14 bis"

1973. Birth Centenary of Alberto Santos Dumont (aviation pioneer).
1445 **762** 20c. brown, grn & lt grn 50 20
1446 – 70c. brown, red & yellow 1·25 1·25
1447 – 2cr. brown, ultram & bl 1·60 1·25
DESIGNS: 70c. Airship "Ballon No. 6"; 2cr. Monoplane No. 20 "Demoiselle".

763 Map of the World

1973. Stamp Day.
1448 **763** 40c. black and red . . . 1·90 1·25
1449 – 40c. black and red . . . 1·90 1·25
The design of No. 1449 differs from Type **763** in that the red portion is to the top and right, instead of to the top and left.

764 G. Dias

766 Festival Banner

1973. 150th Birth Anniv of Goncalves Dias (poet).
1450 **764** 40c. black and violet . . 60 30
See also Nos. 1459 and 1477.

1973. National Folklore Festival.
1452 **766** 40c. multicoloured . . . 60 20

767 Masonic Emblems

1973. 150th Anniv of Masonic Grand Orient Lodge of Brazil.
1453 **767** 1cr. blue . . . . 2·00 95

768 Fire Protection

1973. National Protection Campaign. Mult.
1454 40c. Type **768** 60 20
1455 40c. Cross and cornice (cultural protection) . . . 60 20
1456 40c. Winged emblem (protection in flight) . . . 60 20
1457 40c. Leaf (protection of nature) 60 20

1973. Birth Centenary of St. Theresa of Lisieux. As T **764**.
1459 2cr. brown and orange . . . 2·75 1·40
DESIGN: Portrait of St. Theresa.

770 M. Lobato and "Emilia"

1973. Monteiro Lobato's Children's Stories. Multicoloured.
1460 40c. Type **770** 50 50
1461 40c. "Aunt Nastasia" . . . 50 50
1462 40c. "Nazarinho", "Pedrinho" and "Quindim" 50 50
1463 40c. "Visconde de Sabugosa" 50 50
1464 40c. "Dona Benta" 50 50

771 Father J. M. Nunes Garcia

1973. "The Baroque Age". Multicoloured.
1465 40c. Wood carving, Church of St. Francia, Bahia . . 60 50
1466 40c. "Prophet Isaiah" (detail, sculpture by Aleijadinho) 60 50
1467 70c. Type **771** . . . . . . 1·75 1·75
1468 1cr. Portal, Church of Conceicao da Praia . . . 5·25 2·75
1469 2cr. "Glorification of Holy Virgin", ceiling, St. Francis Assisi Church, Ouro Preto . . . . 4·25 2·75

772 Early Telephone and Modern Instruments

1973. 50th Anniv of Brazilian Telephone Company.
1470 **772** 40c. multicoloured . . . 35 15

773 "Angel" (J. Kopke)

1973. Christmas.
1471 **773** 40c. multicoloured . . . 25 10

774 "Gailora" (river steamboat)

1973. Brazilian Boats. Multicoloured.
1472 40c. Type **774** 70 50
1473 70c. "Regatao" (river trading boat) . . . . . . 1·40 1·75
1474 1cr. "Jangada" (coastal raft) 4·75 2·40
1475 2cr. "Saveiro" (passenger boat) . . . . 4·75 2·40

775 Scales of Justice

1973. Judiciary Power.
1476 **775** 40c. violet and mauve . . 30 15

1973. Birth Centenary of Placido de Castro. As T **764**.
1477 40c. black and red 55 20
DESIGN: Portrait of Castro.

776 Scarlet Ibis and "Victoria Regia" Lilies
777 Saci Perere (goblin)

1973. Brazilian Flora and Fauna. Mult.
1478 40c. Type **776** . . . . . . 1·00 50
1479 70c. Jaguar and Indian tulip 4·75 45
1480 1cr. Scarlet macaw and palm . . . . 8·50 3·75
1481 2cr. Greater rhea and mulunga plant . . . . . 8·50 3·75

1974. Brazilian Folk Tales. Multicoloured.
1482 40c. Type **777** 35 15
1483 80c. Zumbi (warrior) . . . 90 40
1484 1cr. Chico Rei (African king) . . . . 1·25 20
1485 1cr.30 Little black boy of the pasture (32 × 33 mm) 2·40 80
1486 2cr.50 Iara, queen of the waters (32 × 33 mm) . . . 9·00 4·25

778 View of Bridge

1974. Inauguration of President Costa e Silva (Rio de Janeiro–Niteroi) Bridge.
1487 **778** 40c. multicoloured . . . 35 20

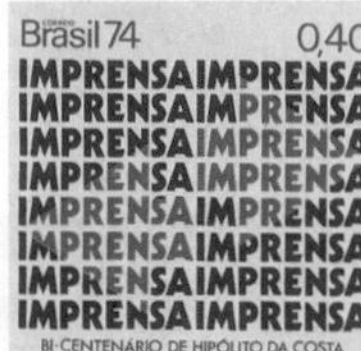

779 "Press"

1974. Brazilian Communications Pioneers.
1488 **779** 40c. red, blue & bistre 30 15
1489 – 40c. brown, blue & bistre 25 15
1490 – 40c. blue, pink & brown 30 15
DESIGNS AND EVENTS: No. 1488, Birth bicentenary of Hipolito da Costa (founder of newspaper "Correio Brasiliense", 1808); 1489, "Radio waves" (Edgar R. Pinto, founder of Radio Sociedade do Rio de Janeiro, 1923); 1490, "Television screen" (F. de Assis Chateaubriand, founder of first T.V. station, Sao Paulo, 1950).

780 "Construction"

1974. 10th Anniv of March Revolution.
1491 **780** 40c. multicoloured . . . 25 20

781 Christ of the Andes

1974. Birth Cent of G. Marconi (radio pioneer).
1492 **781** 2cr.50 multicoloured . . 7·00 3·50

782 Heads of Three Races

1974. Ethnical Origins and Immigration. Mult.
1493 40c. Type **782** 25 20
1494 40c. Heads of many races 10 20
1495 2cr.50 German immigration 3·75 1·25
1496 2cr.50 Italian immigration 9·00 1·25
1497 2cr.50 Japanese immigration 2·75 1·25

783 Artwork and Stamp-printing Press

1974. State Mint.
1498 **783** 80c. multicoloured . . . 95 20

784 Sete Cidades National Park

1974. Tourism. Multicoloured.
1499 40c. Type **784** 60 25
1500 80c. Ruins of church of St. Michael of the Missions 60 25

786 Caraca College

1974. Bicentenary of Caraca College.
1502 **786** 40c. multicoloured . . . 20 15

787 Wave Pattern

1974. 3rd Brazilian Telecommunications Congress, Brasilia.
1503 **787** 40c. black and blue . . . 15 15

788 Fernao Dias Paes

1974. 300th Anniv of Paes Expedition.
1504 **788** 20c. multicoloured . . . 15 15

1974. Visit of President Alvarez of Mexico. As T **754**. Multicoloured.
1505 80c. Mexican Flag . . . . . 1·75 1·25

789 Flags and Crowd in Stadium
791 Pederneiras (after J. Carlos)

1974. World Cup Football Championships, West Germany (2nd issue).
1506 **789** 40c. multicoloured . . . 50 50

1974. Birth Centenary of Raul Pederneiras (lawyer, author and artist).
1508 **791** 40c. black & yell on brn 20 20

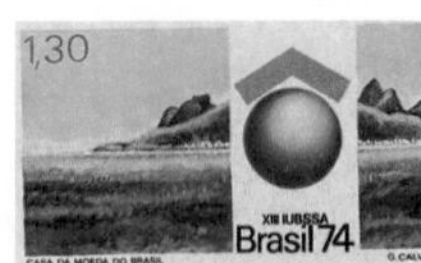

792 Emblem and Seascape

1974. 13th Int Union of Building Societies and Savings Associations Congress, Rio de Janeiro.
1509 **792** 1cr.30 multicoloured . . 75 60

794 "UPU" on World Map

1974. Centenary of U.P.U.
1511 **794** 2cr.50 black and blue . . 7·00 3·50

795 Aruak Hammock

1974. "Popular Culture".
1512 **795** 50c. purple 75 30
1513 – 50c. light blue and blue 1·25 30
1514 – 50c. brown, red & yellow 40 30
1515 – 50c. brown and yellow 50 30
DESIGNS—SQUARE: No. 1513, Bilro Lace. VERT: (24 × 37 mm), No. 1514, Guitar player (folk literature); 1515, Horseman (statuette by Vitalino).

796 Coffee Beans

1974. Bicentenary of City of Campinas.
1516 **796** 50c. multicoloured . . . 90 50

797 Hornless Tabapua

1974. Domestic Animals. Multicoloured.
1517 80c. Type **797** 95 60
1518 1cr.30 Creole horse 90 70
1519 2cr.50 Brazilian mastiff . . 9·00 1·75

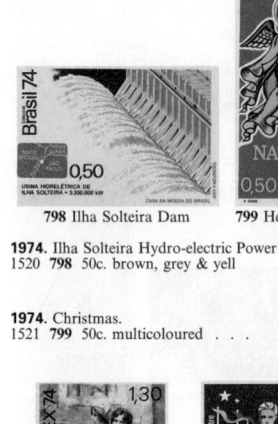

798 Ilha Solteira Dam **799** Herald Angel

1974. Ilha Solteira Hydro-electric Power Project.
1520 **798** 50c. brown, grey & yell . . . 65 20

1974. Christmas.
1521 **799** 50c. multicoloured . . . 30 15

800 "The Girls" (Carlos Reis) **802** Athlete

801 "Justice for Juveniles"

1974. "Lubrapex 74" Stamp Exhibition, Sao Paulo (2nd issue).
1522 **800** 1cr.30 multicoloured . . 40 25

1974. 50th Anniv of Brazilian Juvenile Court.
1523 **801** 90c. multicoloured . . . 20 20

1974. 50th Anniv of Sao Silvestre Long-distance Race.
1524 **802** 3cr.30 multicoloured . . 90 55

803 Mounted Newsvendor and Newspaper Masthead

1975. Cent of Newspaper "O Estado de S. Paulo".
1525 **803** 50c. multicoloured . . . 60 30

804 Industrial Complex, Sao Paulo

1975. Economic Resources.
1526 **804** 50c. yellow and blue . . 95 25
1527 – 1cr.40 yellow & brown 60 60
1528 – 4cr.50 yellow & black . . 3·00 25
DESIGNS: 1cr.40 Rubber industry, Acre; 4cr.50, Manganese industry, Amapa.

805 Santa Cruz Fortress, Rio de Janeiro

1975. Colonial Forts. Each brown on yellow.
1529 50c. Type **805** 10 15
1530 50c. Reis Magos Fort, Rio Grande do Norte 30 15
1531 50c. Monte Serrat Fort, Bahia 50 15
1532 90c. Nossa Senhora dos Remedios Fort, Fernando de Noronha 10 25

806 "Palafita" House, Amazonas

1975. Brazilian Architecture. Multicoloured.
1533 50c. Modern Architecture, Brasilia . . . . 1·50 1·50
1534 50c. Modern Architecture, Brasilia (yellow line at left) . . . . 16·00 8·00
1535 1cr. Type **806** 30 15
1536 1cr.40 Indian hut, Rondonia (yellow line at left) . . . 3·00 3·00
1537 1cr.40 As No. 1536 but yellow line at right . . . 55 60
1538 3cr.30 "Enxaimel" house, Santa Catarina (yellow line at right) 95 95
1539 3cr.30 As No. 1538 but yellow line at left . . . . 4·25 4·25

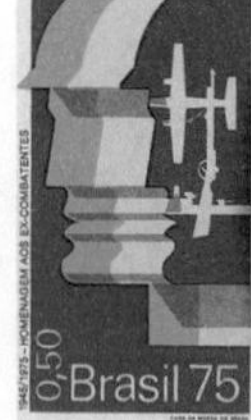

807 Oscar ("Astronotus ocellatus")

1975. Freshwater Fishes. Multicoloured.
1540 50c. Type **807** . . . . . . 1·40 25
1541 50c. South American pufferfish ("Colomesus psitacus") 55 35
1542 50c. Tail-spot livebearer ("Phallocerus caudimaculatus") 55 40
1543 50c. Red discus ("Symphysodon discus") 85 35

808 Flags forming Serviceman's Head **809** Brazilian Pines

1975. Honouring Ex-Servicemen of Second World War.
1544 **808** 50c. multicoloured . . . 25 15

1975. Fauna and Flora Preservation. Mult.
1545 70c. Type **809** . . . . . . 1·60 20
1546 1cr. Giant otter (vert) . . . 1·00 40
1547 3cr.30 Marsh cayman . . . 95 40

810 Inga Carved Stone, from Paraiba **811** Statue of the Virgin Mary

1975. Archaeology. Multicoloured.
1548 70c. Type **810** 95 20
1549 1cr. Marajoara pot from Para 25 20
1550 1cr. Fossilized garfish from Ceara (horiz) 30 20

1975. Holy Year. 300th Anniv of Franciscan Province of Our Lady of the Immaculate Conception.
1551 **811** 3cr.30 multicoloured . . 95 60

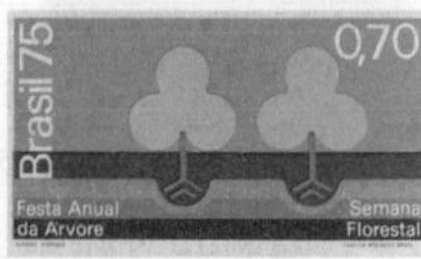

812 Ministry of Communications Building, Rio de Janeiro **813** "Congada" Sword Dance, Minas Gerais

1975. Stamp Day.
1552 **812** 70c. red 45 15

1975. Folk Dances. Multicoloured.
1553 70c. Type **813** 25 30
1554 70c. "Frevo" umbrella dance, Pernambuco . . . 25 30
1555 70c. "Warrior" dance, Alagoas 25 30

814 Stylized Trees

1975. Tree Festival.
1556 **814** 70c. multicoloured . . . 25 10

815 Dish Aerial and Globe **816** Woman holding Globe

1975. Inauguration of Tangua Satellite Telecommunications Station.
1557 **815** 3cr.30 multicoloured . . 90 60

1975. International Women's Year.
1558 **816** 3cr.30 multicoloured . . 1·25 45

817 Tile, Balcony Rail and Memorial Column, Alcantara

1975. Historic Towns. Multicoloured.
1559 70c. Type **817** 40 25
1560 70c. Belfry, weather vane and jug, Goias (26 × 38 mm) 40 25
1561 70c. Sao Francisco Convent, Sao Cristovao (40 × 22 mm) 40 25

818 Crowd welcoming Walking Book

1975. Day of the Book.
1562 **818** 70c. multicoloured . . . 20 15

819 ASTA Emblem and Arrows

1975. 45th American Society of Travel Agents Congress.
1563 **819** 70c. multicoloured . . . 20 15

820 Two Angels **821** Aerial, and Map of America

1975. Christmas.
1564 **820** 70c. brown and red . . . 15 10

1975. 2nd International Telecommunications Conference, Rio de Janeiro.
1565 **821** 5cr.20 multicoloured . . 3·50 1·75

822 Friar Nicodemus **823** People in front of Cross

1975. Obligatory Tax. Leprosy Research Fund.
1566 **822** 10c. brown 20 10

1975. Thanksgiving Day.
1567 **823** 70c. turquoise and blue 30 25

824 Emperor Pedro II in Naval Uniform (after P. P. da Silva Manuel) **825** Sal Stone Beach, Piaui

1975. 150th Birth Anniv of Emperor Pedro II.
1568 **824** 70c. brown 40 20

1975. Tourism. Multicoloured.
1569 70c. Type **825** 30 20
1570 70c. Guarapari Beach, Espirito Santo 30 20
1571 70c. Torres Cliffs Rio Grande do Sul 30 20

826 Triple Jump

1975. 7th Pan-American Games, Santo Domingo, Dominican Republic.
1572 **826** 1cr.60 turquoise & black 20 20

827 U.N. Emblem and H.Q. Building, New York

1975. 30th Anniv of United Nations.
1573 **827** 1cr.30 violet on blue . . 15 15

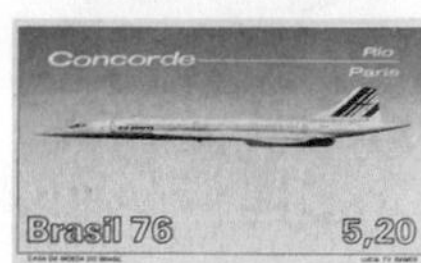

828 Light Bulbs and House

1976. "Preservation of Fuel Resources". Mult.
1574 70c. Type **828** 25 10
1575 70c. Drops of petrol and car 25 10

829 Concorde

1976. Concorde's First Commercial Flight, Paris–Rio de Janeiro.
1576 **829** 5cr.20 black and grey . . 1·10 40

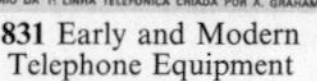

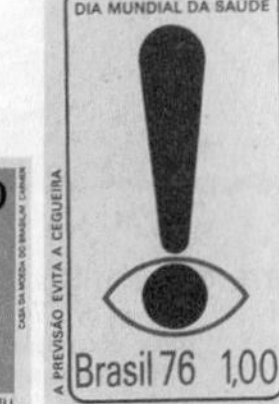

831 Early and Modern Telephone Equipment **832** "Eye"-part of Exclamation Mark

1976. Telephone Centenary.
1578 **831** 5cr.20 black & orange . . . 1·25 1·25

1976. World Health Day.
1579 **832** 1cr. red, brown & violet . . . 30 50

833 Kaiapo Body-painting

834 Itamaraty Palace, Brasilia

1976. Brazil's Indigenous Culture. Mult.
1580 1cr. Type **833** 20 10
1581 1cr. Bakairi ceremonial mask 20 10
1582 1cr. Karaja feather head-dress 20 10

1976. Diplomats' Day.
1583 **834** 1cr. multicoloured . . . 35 60

835 "The Sprinkler" (3D composition by J. Tarcisio)

836 Basketball

1976. Modern Brazilian Art. Multicoloured.
1584 1cr. Type **835** 15 10
1585 1cr. "Beribboned Fingers" (P. Checcacci) (horiz) . . 15 10

1976. Olympic Games, Montreal.
1586 **836** 1cr. black and green . . 10 10
1587 – 1cr.40 black and blue . . 25 10
1588 – 5cr.20 black and orange 1·25 1·25
DESIGNS: 1cr.40, Olympic yachts; 5cr.20, Judo.

837 Golden Lion-Tamarin

838 Cine Camera on Screen

1976. Nature Protection. Multicoloured.
1589 1cr. Type **837** 25 20
1590 1cr. Orchid ("Acacallis cyanea") 25 30

1976. Brazilian Cinematograph Industry.
1591 **838** 1cr. multicoloured . . . 20 10

839 Ox-cart Driver

1976.

1592	**839**	10c. red	10	10
1593	–	15c. brown	25	10
1594	–	20c. blue	20	10
1595	–	30c. red	20	10
1596	–	40c. orange	20	10
1597a	–	50c. brown	25	10
1598	–	70c. black	15	10
1599	–	80c. green	1·75	10
1600a	–	1cr. black	20	10
1601	–	1cr.10 purple	20	10
1602	–	1cr.30 red	20	10
1603a	–	1cr.80 violet	20	10
1604a	–	2cr. brown	1·50	10
1605	–	2cr.50 brown	25	10
1605a	–	3cr.20 blue	25	10
1606a	–	5cr. lilac	95	10
1607	–	7cr. violet	6·00	10
1608a	–	10cr. green	95	10
1609	–	15cr. green	1·75	10
1610	–	20cr. blue	1·75	10
1611	–	21cr. purple	1·25	10
1612	–	27cr. brown	1·40	10

DESIGNS—HORIZ: 20c. Pirogue fisherman; 40c. Cowboy; 3cr.20, Sao Francisco boatman; 27cr. Muleteer. VERT: 15c. Bahia woman; 30c. Rubber gatherer; 50c. Gaucho; 70c. Women breaking Babacu chestnuts; 80c. Gold-washer; 1cr. Banana gatherer; 1cr.10, Grape harvester; 1cr.30, Coffee harvester; 1cr.80, Carnauba cutter; 2cr. Potter; 2cr.50, Basket maker; 5cr. Sugar-cane cutter; 7cr. Salt worker; 10cr. Fisherman; 15cr. Coconut vendor; 20cr. Lace maker; 21cr. Ramie cutter.

840 Neon Tetra ("Paracheirodon innesi")

1976. Brazilian Freshwater Fishes. Mult.
1613 1cr. Type **840** 50 45
1614 1cr. Splash tetra ("Copeina arnold") 50 45
1615 1cr. Prochilodus ("Prochilodus insignis") 50 45
1616 1cr. Spotted pike cichlid ("Crenicichla lepidota") 50 45
1617 1cr. Bottle-nosed catfish ("Ageneiosus sp.") . . . 50 45
1618 1cr. Reticulated corydoras ("Corydoras reticulatus") 50 45

841 Santa Marta Lighthouse

842 Postage Stamps as Magic Carpet

1976. 300th Anniv of Laguna.
1619 **841** 1cr. blue 40 15

1976. Stamp Day.
1620 **842** 1cr. multicoloured . . . 15 10

843 Oil Lamp and Profile

1976. 50th Anniv of Brazilian Nursing Assn.
1621 **843** 1cr. multicoloured . . . 20 10

844 Puppet Soldier

845 Winner's Medal

1976. Mamulengo Puppet Theatre. Mult.
1622 1cr. Type **844** 20 15
1623 1cr.30 Puppet girl 20 15
1624 1cr.60 Finger puppets (horiz) 20 15

1976. 27th International Military Athletics Championships, Rio de Janeiro.
1625 **845** 5cr.20 multicoloured . . 45 20

846 Family within "House"

847 Rotten Tree

1976. SESC and SENAC National Organizations for Appenticeship and Welfare.
1626 **846** 1cr. blue 15 10

1976. Conservation of the Environment.
1627 **847** 1cr. multicoloured . . . 15 10

848 Electron Orbits and Atomic Agency Emblem

1976. 20th International Atomic Energy Conference, Rio de Janeiro.
1628 **848** 5cr.20 multicoloured . . 45 25

849 Underground Train

851 School Building

850 St. Francis

1976. Inauguration of Sao Paulo Underground Railway.
1629 **849** 1cr.60 multicoloured . . 45 25

1976. 750th Death Anniv of St. Francis of Assisi.
1630 **850** 5cr.20 multicoloured . . 45 20

1976. Centenary of Ouro Preto Mining School.
1631 **851** 1cr. violet 25 30

852 "Three Kings" (J. A. da Silva)

1976. Christmas. Multicoloured.
1632 80c. Type **852** 30 20
1633 80c. "Father Christmas" (T. Onivaldo Cogo) . . . 30 20
1634 80c. "Nativity Scene" (R. Yabe) 30 20
1635 80c. "Angels" (E. Folchini) 30 20
1636 80c. "Nativity" (A.L. Cintra) 30 20

854 "Our Lady of Monte Serrat" (Friar A. da Piedade)

1976. Brazilian Sculpture. Multicoloured.
1638 80c. Type **854** 15 10
1639 5cr. "St. Joseph" (unknown artist) (25 × 37 mm) . . . 40 20
1640 5cr.60 "The Dance" (J. Bernardelli) (square) 45 20
1641 6cr.50 "The Caravel" (B. Giorgi) (As 5cr.) . . . 35 20

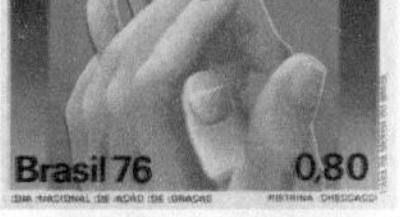

855 Hands in Prayer

856 Sailor of 1840

1976. Thanksgiving Day.
1642 **855** 80c. multicoloured . . . 15 10

1976. Brazilian Navy Commemoration. Mult.
1643 80c. Type **856** 20 10
1644 2cr. Marine of 1808 . . . . 25 15

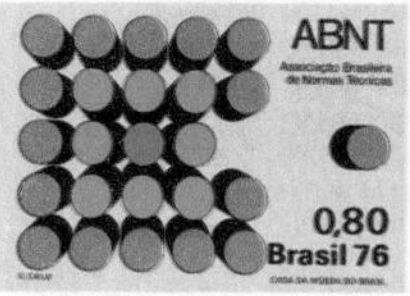

857 "Natural Resources"

858 "Wheel of Life" (wood-carving, G. T. de Oliveira)

1976. Brazilian Bureau of Standards.
1645 **857** 80c. multicoloured . . . 15 10

1977. 2nd World Black and African Festival of Arts and Culture, Lagos (Nigeria). Multicoloured.
1646 5cr. Type **858** 50 20
1647 5cr.60 "The Beggar" (wood-carving, A. dos Santos) 50 20
1648 6cr.50 Benin pectoral mask 90 20

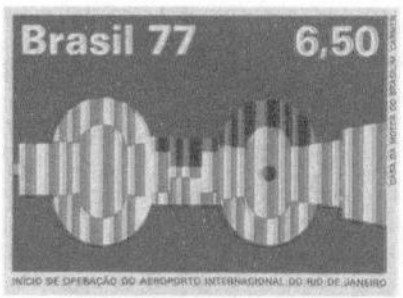

859 Airport Layout

860 Seminar Emblem

1977. Inauguration of Operation of International Airport, Rio de Janeiro.
1649 **859** 6c.50 multicoloured . . . 85 25

1977. 6th InterAmerican Budget Seminar.
1650 **860** 1cr.10 turq, bl & stone 20 10

861 Salicylic Acid Crystals

862 Emblem of Lions Clubs

1977. World Rheumatism Year.
1651 **861** 1cr.10 multicoloured . . 20 10

1977. 25th Anniv of Brazilian Lions Clubs.
1652 **862** 1cr.10 multicoloured . . 20 10

863 H. Villa-Lobos and Music

1977. Brazilian Composers. Multicoloured.
1653 1cr.10 Type **863** 25 10
1654 1cr.10 Chiquinha Gonzaga and guitar 25 10
1655 1cr.10 Noel Rosa and guitar 25 10

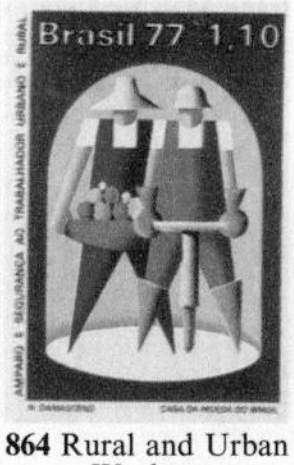

864 Rural and Urban Workers

865 Memorial, Porto Seguro

1977. Industrial Protection and Safety. Mult.
1656 1cr.10 Type **864** 15 10
1657 1cr.10 Laboratory vessels . . 15 10

1977. Centenary of U.P.U. Membership. Views of Porto Seguro. Multicoloured.
1658 1cr.10 Type **865** 15 10
1659 5cr. Beach . . . . 1·25 20
1660 5cr.60 Old houses 55 20
1661 6cr.50 Post Office 50 25

866 Newspaper Title in Linotype and Print

1977. 150th Anniv of Brazilian Newspaper "Diario de Porto Allegre".
1662 **866** 1cr.10 black & purple . . 15 10

867 Blue Whale **868** "Cell System"

1977. Fauna Preservation.
1663 **867** 1cr.30 multicoloured . . 55 15

1977. 25th Anniv of National Economic Development Bank.
1664 **868** 1cr.30 multicoloured . . 15 10

869 Locomotive leaving Tunnel **870** Goliath Conch

1977. Centenary of Rio de Janeiro–Sao Paulo Railway.
1665 **869** 1c.30 black 60 25

1977. Brazilian Molluscs, Multicoloured.
1666 1cr.30 Type **870** 30 15
1667 1cr.30 Thin-bladed murex ("Murex tenuivaricosus") 30 15
1668 1cr.30 Helmet vase ("Vasum cassiforme") 30 15

871 Caduceus **872** Masonic Symbols

1977. 3rd International Congress of Odontology.
1669 **871** 1cr.30 brown, bis & orge 20 10

1977. 50th Anniv of Brazilian Grand Masonic Lodge.
1670 **872** 1cr.30 blue, dp bl & blk 25 10

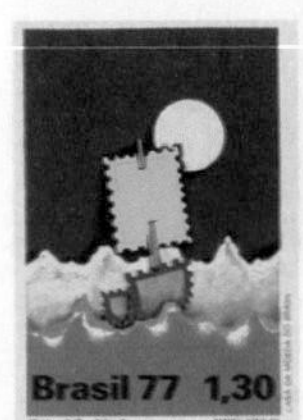

873 "Sailboat" **874** Law Proclamation

1977. Stamp Day.
1671 **873** 1cr.30 multicoloured . . 15 10

1977. 150th Anniv of Juridical Courses.
1672 **874** 1cr.30 multicoloured . . 15 10

875 "Cavalhada" (horsemen) **876** Doubloon

1977. Folklore. Multicoloured.
1673 1cr.30 Type **875** 20 10
1674 1cr.30 Horseman with flag 20 10
1675 1cr.30 Jousting (horiz) . . . 20 10

1977. Brazilian Colonial Coins. Multicoloured.
1676 1cr.30 Type **876** 20 10
1677 1cr.30 Pataca 20 10
1678 1cr.30 Vintem 20 10

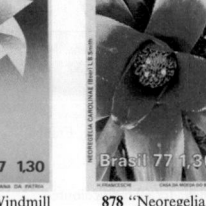

877 Toy Windmill **878** "Neoregelia carolinae"

1977. National Day.
1679 **877** 1cr.30 multicoloured . . 15 10

1977. Nature Conservation.
1680 **878** 1cr.30 multicoloured . . 20 10

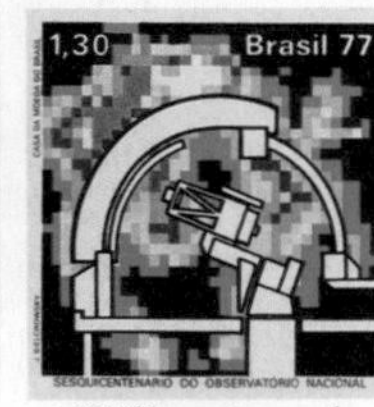

879 Pen, Pencil and Writing **880** Observatory and Electrochromograph of Supernova

1977. 150th Anniv of Official Elementary Schooling.
1681 **879** 1cr.30 multicoloured . . 15 10

1977. 150th Anniv of National Observatory.
1682 **880** 1cr.30 multicoloured . . 20 10

881 Airship "Pax" **882** Text from "O Guarani" and Ceci

1977. Aviation Anniversaries. Multicoloured.
1683 1cr.30 Type **881** 20 10
1684 1cr.30 Savoia Marchetti flying boat "Jahu" . . . 20 10
ANNIVERSARIES: No. 1683, 75th anniv of "Pax" flight; 1684, 50th anniv of "Jahu" South Atlantic crossing.

1977. Day of the Book and Jose de Alencar Commemoration.
1685 **882** 1cr.30 multicoloured . . 15 10

883 Radio Waves **884** Nativity (in carved gourd)

1977. Amateur Radio Operators' Day.
1686 **883** 1cr.30 multicoloured . . 15 10

1977. Christmas. Multicoloured.
1687 1cr.30 Type **884** 15 10
1688 2cr. The Annunciation . . . 25 10
1689 5cr. Nativity 55 15

885 Emerald **886** Angel holding Cornucopia

1977. "Portucale 77" Thematic Stamp Exhibition. Multicoloured.
1690 1cr.30 Type **885** 20 10
1691 1cr.30 Topaz 20 10
1692 1cr.30 Aquamarine 20 10

1977. Thanksgiving Day.
1693 **886** 1cr.30 multicoloured . . 15 10

887 Curtiss Fledgling Douglas DC-3 and Badge (National Airmail Service)

1977. National Integration. Multicoloured.
1694 1cr.30 Type **887** 30 10
1695 1cr.30 Amazon River naval patrol boat and badge (Amazon Fleet) 50 10
1696 1cr.30 Train crossing bridge and badges (Engineering Corps and Railway Battalion) 75 25

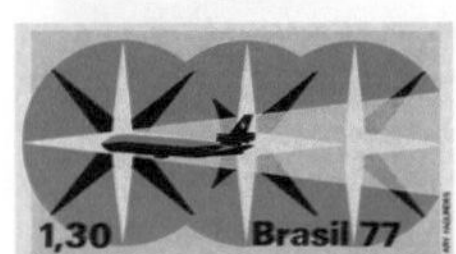

888 Douglas DC-10 and Varig Airline Emblems

1977. 50th Anniv of Varig State Airline.
1697 **888** 1cr.30 black, lt bl & bl 15 10

889 Sts. Cosmus and Damian Church, Igaracu **890** Woman with Wheat Sheaf

1977. Regional Architecture, Churches. Mult.
1698 2cr.70 Type **889** 20 10
1699 7cr.50 St. Bento Monastery Church, Rio de Janeiro 60 25
1700 8cr.50 St. Francis Assisi Church, Ouro Preto . . . 65 25
1701 9cr.50 St. Anthony Convent Church, Joao Pessoa . . 80 30

1977. Diplomats' Day.
1702 **890** 1cr.30 multicoloured . . 15 10

891 Scene from "Fosca" and Carlos Gomes (composer) **892** Foot kicking Ball

1978. Bicentenary of La Scala Opera House, Milan, and Carlos Gomes Commemoration.
1703 **891** 1cr.80 multicoloured . . 30 10

1978. World Cup Football Championship, Argentina. Multicoloured.
1704 1cr.80 Type **892** 20 10
1705 1cr.80 Ball in net 20 10
1706 1cr.80 Stylized player with cup 20 10

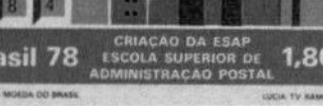

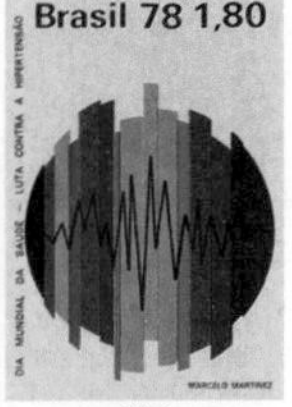

893 "Postal Efficiency" **894** Electrocardiogram

1978. Postal Staff College.
1707 **893** 1cr.80 multicoloured . . 15 10

1978. World Hypertension Month.
1708 **894** 1cr.80 multicoloured . . 20 10

895 World Map and Antenna **896** Saffron Finch

1978. World Telecommunications Day.
1709 **895** 1cr.80 multicoloured . . 15 10

1978. Birds. Multicoloured.
1710 7cr.50 Type **896** . . . . . . 1·25 50
1711 8cr.50 Banded cotinga . . . 1·60 60
1712 9cr.50 Seven-coloured tanager . . . . 1·90 85

897 "Discussing the Opening Speech" (G. Mondin)

1978. 85th Anniv of Union Court of Audit.
1713 **897** 1cr.80 multicoloured . . 15 10

898 Post and Telegraph Headquarters, Brasilia

1978. Opening of Post and Telegraph Headquarters.
1714 **898** 1cr.80 multicoloured . . 15 10

899 President Geisel **900** Savoia Marchetti S-64 and Map

1978. President Geisel Commemoration.
1716 **899** 1cr.80 olive 20 10

1978. 50th Anniv of South Atlantic Flight by del Prete and Ferrarin.
1717 **900** 1cr.80 multicoloured . . 25 10

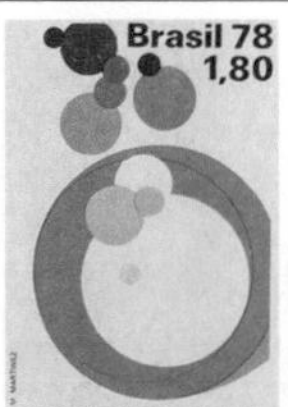

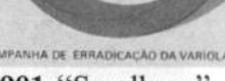

901 "Smallpox"

902 10r. Pedro II "White Beard" Stamp of 1878

1978. Global Eradication of Smallpox.
1718 **901** 1cr.80 multicoloured . . 20 10

1978. Stamp Day.
1719 **902** 1cr.80 multicoloured . . 15 10

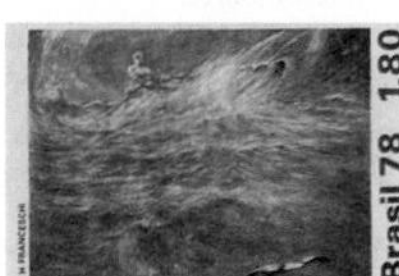

903 "Jangadeiros"

1978. Birth Centenary of Helios Seelinger (painter).
1720 **903** 1cr.80 multicoloured . . 15 10

904 Musicians with Violas

1978. Folk Musicians. Multicoloured.
1721 1cr.80 Type **904** 20 10
1722 1cr.80 Two fife players . . . 20 10
1723 1cr.80 Berimbau players . . 20 10

905 Children playing Football

1978. National Week.
1724 **905** 1cr.80 multicoloured . . 20 10

906 Patio de Colegio Church

1978. Restoration of Patio de Colegio Church, Sao Paulo.
1725 **906** 1cr.80 brown 15 10

907 "Justice" (A. Ceschiatti)

1978. 150th Anniv of Federal Supreme Court.
1726 **907** 1cr.80 black and bistre 15 10

908 Ipe (flowering tree)

1978. Environment Protection. Iguacu Falls National Park. Multicoloured.
1727 1cr.80 Type **908** 25 10
1728 1cr.80 Iguacu Falls 25 10

909 Stages of "Intelsat" Assembly

1978. 3rd Assembly. Users of "Intelsat" Telecommunications Satellite.
1729 **909** 1cr.80 multicoloured . . 15 10

910 Flag of the Order of Christ

1978. "Lubrapex 78" Stamp Exhibition. Flags. Multicoloured.
1730 1cr.80 Type **910** 60 30
1731 1cr.80 Principality of Brazil 60 30
1732 1cr.80 United Kingdom of Brazil 60 30
1733 8cr.50 Empire of Brazil . . 60 30
1734 8cr.50 National Flag of Brazil 60 30

911 Postal Tramcar

1978. 18th U.P.U. Congress, Rio de Janeiro.
1735 **911** 1cr.80 brown, blk & bl 1·10 1·00
1736 – 1cr.80 brown, blk & bl 60 60
1737 – 1cr.80 grey, blk & rose 60 60
1738 – 7cr.50 grey, blk & rose 2·00 1·10
1739 – 8cr.50 brown, blk & grn 1·00 60
1740 – 9cr.50 brown, blk & grn 1·00 60
DESIGNS: No. 1736, Post container truck; 1737, Post van, 1914; 1738, Travelling post office; 1739, Mail coach; 1740, Mule caravan.

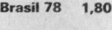

912 Gaucho

913 "Morro de Santo Antonio" (Nicolas Antoine Taunay)

1978. Day of the Book and J. Guimaraes Rosa Commemoration.
1741 **912** 1cr.80 multicoloured . . 20 10

1978. Landscape Paintings. Multicoloured.
1742 1cr.80 Type **913** 20 10
1743 1cr.80 "View of Pernambuco" (Frans Post) 20 10
1744 1cr.80 "Morro de Castelo" (Victor Meirelles) 20 10
1745 1cr.80 "Landscape at Sabara" (Alberto da Veiga Guignard) 20 10

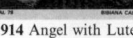

914 Angel with Lute

915 "Thanksgiving"

1978. Christmas. Multicoloured.
1746 1cr.80 Type **914** 15 10
1747 1cr.80 Angel with lyre . . . 15 10
1748 1cr.80 Angel with trumpet 15 10

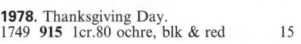

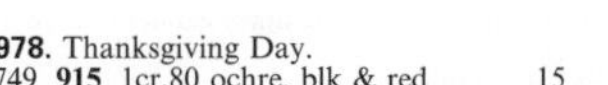
1978. Thanksgiving Day.
1749 **915** 1cr.80 ochre, blk & red 15 10

916 Red Cross Services

1978. 70th Anniv of Brazilian Red Cross.
1750 **916** 1cr.80 red and black . . 15 10

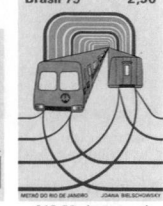

917 Peace Theatre, Belem

918 Underground Trains

1978. Brazilian Theatres. Multicoloured.
1751 10cr.50 Type **917** 50 15
1752 12cr. Jose de Alencar Theatre, Fortaleza 55 20
1753 12cr.50 Rio de Janeiro Municipal Theatre 60 20

1979. Inauguration of Rio de Janeiro Underground Railway.
1754 **918** 2cr.50 multicoloured . . 50 10

919 Old and New Post Offices

1979. 10th Anniv of Post & Telegraph Department and 18th U.P.U. Congress (2nd issue). Multicoloured.
1755 2cr.50 Type **919** 25 15
1756 2cr.50 Mail boxes 25 15
1757 2cr.50 Mail sorting 25 15
1758 2cr.50 Mail planes 25 15
1759 2cr.50 Telegraph and telex machines 25 15
1760 2cr.50 Postmen 25 15

920 "O'Day 23" Class Yacht

1979. "Brasiliana 79" 3rd World Thematic Stamp Exhibition (1st issue). Multicoloured.
1761 2cr.50 Type **920** 25 10
1762 10cr.50 "Penguin" class dinghy 55 20
1763 12cr. "Hobie Cat" class catamaran 55 20
1764 12cr.50 "Snipe" class dinghy 55 25
See Nos. 1773/6 and 1785/90.

921 Joao Bolinha (characters from children's story)

1979. Children's Book Day.
1765 **921** 2cr.50 multicoloured . . 20 10

922 "Victoria amazonica"

1979. 18th U.P.U. Congress (3rd issue). Amazon National Park. Multicoloured.
1766 10cr.50 Type **922** 60 20
1767 12cr. Amazon manatee . . . 65 25
1768 12cr.50 Tortoise 70 25

923 Bank Emblem

1979. 25th Anniv of Northeast Bank of Brazil.
1769 **923** 2cr.50 multicoloured . . 15 10

924 Physicians and Patient (15th cent woodcut)

1979. 150th Anniv of National Academy of Medicine.
1770 **924** 2cr.50 yellow and black 15 10

925 Clover with Hearts as Leaves

1979. 35th Brazilian Cardiology Congress.
1771 **925** 2cr.50 multicoloured . . 15 10

927 "Cithaerias aurora"

1979. "Brasiliana 79" (2nd issue). Butterflies. Multicoloured.
1773 2cr.50 Type **927** 30 15
1774 10cr.50 "Evenus regalis" . . 90 25
1775 12cr. "Caligo eurilochus" . . 1·00 35
1776 12cr.50 "Diaethria clymena janeira" . . . . 1·10 40

928 Embraer Xingu

929 Globe illuminating Land

1979. 10th Anniv of Brazilian Aeronautical Industry.
1777 **928** 2cr.50 dp blue and blue 15 10

1979. National Week.
1778 **929** 3cr.20 blue, green & yell 15 10

930 Our Lady Aparecida

931 Envelope and Transport

1979. 75th Anniv of Coronation of Our Lady Aparecida.
1779 **930** 2cr.50 multicoloured . . 15 10

1979. 18th U.P.U. Congress, Rio de Janeiro (4th issue). Multicoloured.
1780 2cr.50 Type **931** 75 30
1781 2cr.50 Post Office emblems 20 10
1782 10cr.50 Globe 35 20

1783 12cr. Flags of Brazil and U.P.U 40 20
1784 12cr.50 U.P.U. emblem . . 40 20

932 "Igreja da Gloria"

933 Pyramid Fountain, Rio de Janeiro

1979. "Brasiliana 79" Third World Thematic Stamp Exhibition (3rd issue). Paintings by Leandro Joaquim. Multicoloured.

1785 2cr.50 Type **932** 15 10
1786 12cr. "Fishing on Guanabara Bay" 35 20
1787 12cr.50 "Boqueirao Lake and Carioca Arches" . . 45 25

1979. "Brasiliana 79" (4th issue). 1st International Exhibition of Classical Philately. Fountains.

1788 **933** 2cr.50 black, grn & emer 10 10
1789 – 10cr.50 black, turq & bl 35 20
1790 – 12cr. black, red and pink 40 25

DESIGNS—VERT: 12cr. Boa Vista, Recife. HORIZ: 10cr.50, Marilia Fountain, Ouro Preto.

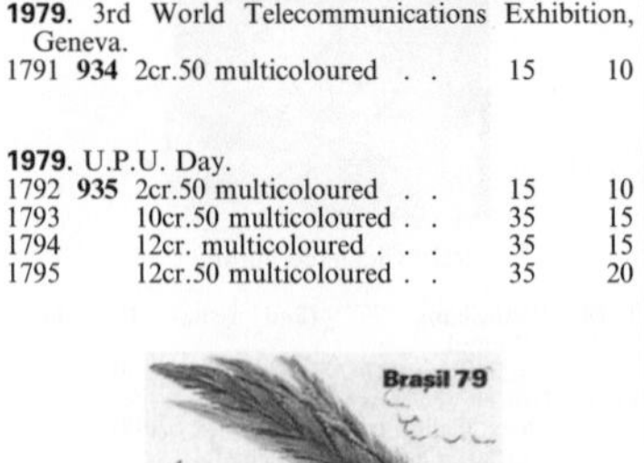

934 World Map

935 "UPU" and Emblem

1979. 3rd World Telecommunications Exhibition, Geneva.

1791 **934** 2cr.50 multicoloured . . 15 10

1979. U.P.U. Day.

1792 **935** 2cr.50 multicoloured . . 15 10
1793 10cr.50 multicoloured . . 35 15
1794 12cr. multicoloured . . . 35 15
1795 12cr.50 multicoloured . . 35 20

936 "Peteca" (shuttlecock)

1979. International Year of the Child. Mult.

1796 2cr.50 Type **936** 20 10
1797 3cr.20 Spinning top 20 10
1798 3cr.20 Jumping Jack 20 10
1799 3cr.20 Rag doll 20 10

937 "The Birth of Jesus"

1979. Christmas. Tiles from the Church of Our Lady of Health and Glory, Salvador. Multicoloured.

1800 3cr.20 Type **937** 15 10
1801 3cr.20 "Adoration of the Kings" 15 10
1802 3cr.20 "The Boy Jesus among the Doctors" . . . 15 10

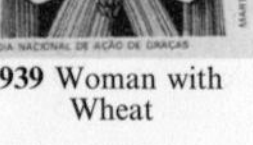

939 Woman with Wheat

940 Steel Mill

1979. Thanksgiving Day.

1804 **939** 3cr.20 multicoloured . . 15 10

1979. 25th Anniv of Cosipa Steel Works, Sao Paulo.

1805 **940** 3cr.20 multicoloured . . 15 10

941 Plant within Raindrop

942 Coal Trucks

1980. Energy Conservation. Multicoloured.

1806 3cr.20 Type **941** 25 10
1807 17cr.+7cr. Sun and lightbulb 35 10
1808 20cr.+8cr. Windmill and lightbulb 90 55
1809 21cr.+9cr. Dam and lightbulb . . . . 1·50 30

1980. Coal Industry.

1810 **942** 4cr. black, orge & red 65 30

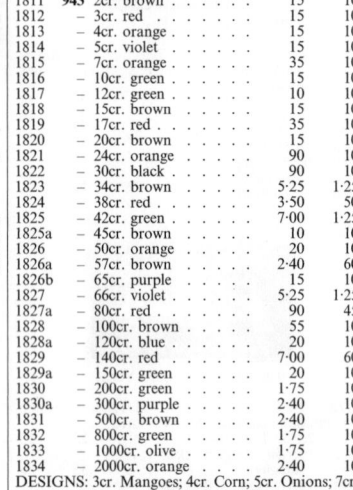

943 Coconuts

1980.

1811 **943** 2cr. brown 15 10
1812 – 3cr. red 15 10
1813 – 4cr. orange 15 10
1814 – 5cr. violet 15 10
1815 – 7cr. orange 35 10
1816 – 10cr. green 15 10
1817 – 12cr. green 10 10
1818 – 15cr. brown 15 10
1819 – 17cr. red 35 10
1820 – 20cr. brown 15 10
1821 – 24cr. orange 90 10
1822 – 30cr. black 90 10
1823 – 34cr. brown . . . . . 5·25 1·25
1824 – 38cr. red . . . . . . 3·50 50
1825 – 42cr. green . . . . . 7·00 1·25
1825a – 45cr. brown 10 10
1826 – 50cr. orange 20 10
1826a – 57cr. brown . . . . . 2·40 60
1826b – 65cr. purple 15 10
1827 – 66cr. violet . . . . . 5·25 1·25
1827a – 80cr. red 90 45
1828 – 100cr. brown 55 10
1828a – 120cr. blue 20 10
1829 – 140cr. red . . . . . 7·00 60
1829a – 150cr. green 20 10
1830 – 200cr. green . . . . . 1·75 10
1830a – 300cr. purple . . . . . 2·40 10
1831 – 500cr. brown . . . . . 2·40 10
1832 – 800cr. green . . . . . 1·75 10
1833 – 1000cr. olive . . . . . 1·75 10
1834 – 2000cr. orange . . . . . 2·40 10

DESIGNS: 3cr. Mangoes; 4cr. Corn; 5cr. Onions; 7cr. Oranges; 10cr. Passion fruit; 12cr. Pineapple; 15cr. Bananas; 17cr. Guarana; 20cr. Sugar cane; 24cr. Bee and honeycomb; 30cr. Silkworm and mulberry; 34cr. Cocoa beans; 38cr. Coffee; 42cr. Soya bean; 45cr. Manioc; 50cr. Wheat; 57cr. Peanuts; 65cr. Rubber; 66cr. Grapes; 80cr. Brazil nuts; 100cr. Cashews; 120cr. Rice; 140cr. Tomatoes; 150cr. Eucalyptus; 200cr. Castor-oil bean; 300cr. Parana pine; 500cr. Cotton; 800cr. Carnauba palm; 1000cr. Babassu palm; 2000cr. Sunflower.

944 Banknote with Development Symbols

1980. 21st Inter-American Bank of Development Directors' Annual Assembly Meeting, Rio de Janeiro.

1836 **944** 4cr. blue, brown & blk 15 10

945 Tapirape Mask

1980. Indian Art. Ritual Masks. Mult.

1837 4cr. Type **945** 20 10
1838 4cr. Tukuna mask (vert) . . 20 10
1839 4cr. Kanela mask (vert) . . 20 10

946 Geometric Head

947 Duke of Caxias (after Miranda Junior)

1980. 30th Anniv of Brazilian Television.

1840 **946** 4cr. multicoloured . . . 15 10

1980. Death Centenary of Duke de Caxias (General and statesman).

1841 **947** 4cr. multicoloured . . . 15 10

948 "The Labourer" (Candido Portinari)

1980. Art in Brazilian Museums. Mult.

1842 24cr. Type **948** 75 25
1843 28cr. "Mademoiselle Pogany" (statuette, Constantin Brancusi) . . 75 25
1844 30cr. "The Glass of Water" (A. de Figueiredo) 95 30

MUSEUMS. 24cr. Sao Paulo Museum of Art. 28cr. Rio de Janeiro Museum of Modern Art. 30cr. Rio de Janeiro Museum of Fine Art.

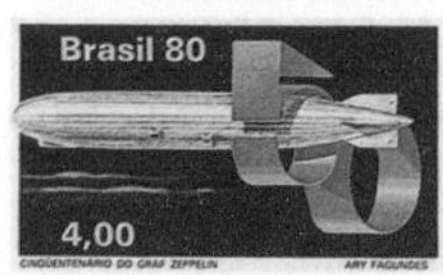

949 "Graf Zeppelin" flying through "50"

1980. 50th Annivs of "Graf Zeppelin" and First South Atlantic Air Mail Flight.

1845 **949** 4cr. black, blue & violet 20 15
1846 – 4cr. multicoloured . . . 20 15

DESIGN: No. 1846, Latecoere seaplane "Comte de la Vaulx".

951 Pope John Paul II and Fortaleza Cathedral

952 Shooting

1980. Papal Visit and 10th National Eucharistic Congress. Pope John Paul II and cathedrals. Multicoloured.

1848 4cr. Type **951** 25 15
1849 4cr. St. Peter's, Rome (horiz) 25 15
1850 24cr. Apericida (horiz) . . . 65 40
1851 28cr. Rio de Janeiro (horiz) 65 20
1852 30cr. Brasilia (horiz) . . . . 1·50 25

1980. Olympic Games, Moscow. Mult.

1853 4cr. Type **952** 20 10
1854 4cr. Cycling 20 10
1855 4cr. Rowing 20 10

953 Classroom

1980. Rondon Project (voluntary student work in rural areas).

1856 **953** 4cr. multicoloured . . . 20 10

954 Helen Keller and Anne Sullivan

956 Houses and Microscope

1980. Birth Centenary of Helen Keller, and 4th Brazilian Congress on Prevention of Blindness, Belo Horizonte.

1857 **954** 4cr. multicoloured . . . 20 10

1980. National Health Day. Campaign against Chagas Disease (barber bug fever).

1859 **956** 4cr. multicoloured . . . 20 10

957 Communications Equipment

1980. 15th Anniv of National Telecommunications System.

1860 **957** 5cr. stone, blue & green 20 10

959 "Cattleya amethystoglossa"

960 Vinaceous Amazon

1980. "Espamer 80" International Stamp Exhibition, Madrid. Orchids. Multicoloured.

1862 5cr. Type **959** 30 10
1863 5cr. "Laelia cinnabarina" 30 10
1864 24cr. "Zygopetalum crinitum" . . . . 1·75 35
1865 28cr. "Laelia tenebrosa" . . 1·75 40

1980. "Lubrapex 80" Portuguese–Brazilian Stamp Exhibition, Lisbon. Parrots. Multicoloured.

1866 5cr. Type **960** 60 40
1867 5cr. Red-tailed amazon . . 60 40
1868 28cr. Red-spectacled amazon 3·00 1·00
1869 28cr. Brown backed parrotlet . . . . 3·00 1·00

961 Captain Rodrigo (fictional character)

962 Flight into Egypt

1980. Book Day and Erico Verissimo (writer). Commemoration.

1870 **961** 5cr. multicoloured . . . 20 10

1980. Christmas.

1871 **962** 5cr. multicoloured . . . 20 10

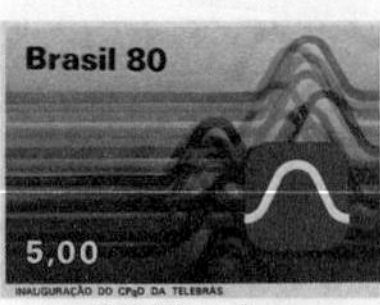

963 Wave-form

1980. Inauguration of Telecommunications Centre for Research and Development, Campanas City.

1872 **963** 5cr. multicoloured . . . 20 10

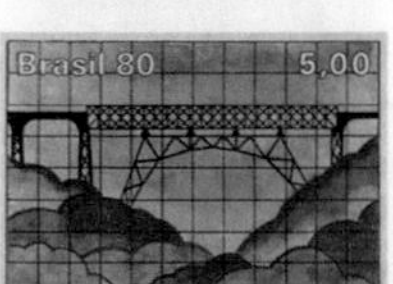

964 Carvalho Viaduct, Paranagua–Curitiba Railway Line

1980. Centenary of Engineering Club.
1873 **964** 5cr. multicoloured . . . 45 25

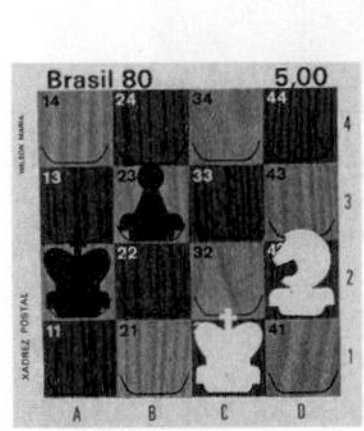

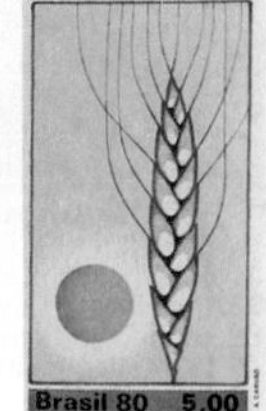

965 Postal Chessboard **966** Sun and Wheat

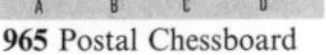

1980. Postal Chess.
1874 **965** 5cr. multicoloured . . . 55 20

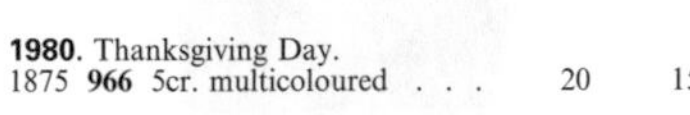

1980. Thanksgiving Day.
1875 **966** 5cr. multicoloured . . . 20 15

967 Father Anchieta writing Poem in Sand

1980. Beatification of Father Jose de Anchieta.
1876 **967** 5cr. multicoloured . . . 20 10

968 Christ on the Mount of Olives

1980. 250th Birth Anniv of Antonio Lisboa (Aleijadinho) (sculptor). Wood sculptures of Christ's head. Multicoloured.
1877 5cr. Type **968** 30 30
1878 5cr. The Arrest in the Garden 30 30
1879 5cr. Flagellation 30 30
1880 5cr. Wearing Crown of Thorns 30 30
1881 5cr. Carrying the cross . . . 30 30
1882 5cr. Crucifixion 30 30

969 Agricultural Produce

1981. Agricultural Development. Mult.
1883 30cr. Type **969** . . . . . . 1·25 25
1884 35cr. Shopping 80 30
1885 40cr. Exporting 80 30

970 Scout sitting by Camp Fire

1981. 4th Pan-American Jamboree. Multicoloured.
1886 5cr. Type **970** 25 10
1887 5cr. Troop cooking 25 10
1888 5cr. Scout with totem pole 25 10

973 Lima Barreto and Rio de Janeiro Street Scene

1981. Birth Centenary of Lima Barreto (author).
1891 **973** 7cr. multicoloured . . . 60 25

974 Tupi-Guarani Ceramic Funeral Urn

1981. Artefacts from Brazilian Museums. Mult.
1892 7cr. Type **974** (Archaeology and Popular Arts Museum, Paranagua) . . 20 15
1893 7cr. Marajoara "tanga" ceramic loincloth (Emilio Goeldi Museum, Para) . . 20 15
1894 7cr. Maraca tribe funeral urn (National Museum, Rio de Janeiro) 20 15

975 Ruby-topaz Hummingbird

1981. Hummingbirds. Multicoloured.
1895 7cr. Type **975** . . . . 1·00 25
1896 7cr. Horned sungem . . . . 1·00 25
1897 7cr. Frilled coquette . . . . 1·00 25
1898 7cr. Planalto hermit . . . . 1·00 25

976 Hands and Cogwheels

1981. 72nd Int Rotary Convention, Sao Paulo.
1899 **976** 7cr. red and black . . . 15 10
1900 – 35cr. multicoloured . . . 1·50 60
DESIGN: 35cr. Head and cogwheels.

977 "Protection of the Water"

1981. Environment Protection. Multicoloured.
1901 7cr. Type **977** 25 15
1902 7cr. "Protection of the forests" 25 15
1903 7cr. "Protection of the air" 25 15
1904 7cr. "Protection of the soil" 25 15

978 Curtiss Fledgling

1981. 50th Anniv of National Air Mail Service.
1905 **978** 7cr. multicoloured . . . 20 10

979 Locomotive "Colonel Church" and Map of Railway

1981. 50th Anniv of Madeira–Mamore Railway Nationalization.
1906 **979** 7cr. multicoloured . . . 55 30

980 Esperanto Star and Arches of Alvorada Governmental Palace, Brasilia

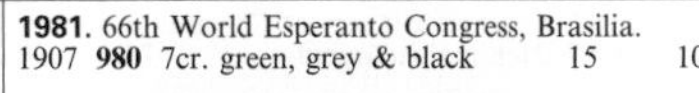

1981. 66th World Esperanto Congress, Brasilia.
1907 **980** 7cr. green, grey & black 15 10

981 Pedro II and 50r. "Small Head" Stamp

1981. Cent of Pedro II "Small Head" Stamps.
1908 **981** 50cr. brown, blk & bl . . 1·10 25
1909 – 55cr. mauve and green 1·10 25
1910 – 60cr. blue, black & orge 95 30
DESIGNS: 55cr. Pedro II and 100r. "Small Head" stamp; 60r. Pedro II and 200r. "Small Head" stamp.

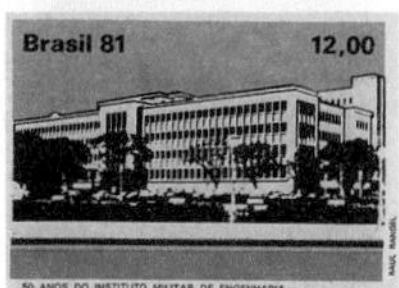

982 Military Institute of Engineering

1981. 50th Anniv of Military Institute of Engineering.
1911 **982** 12cr. multicoloured . . . 15 10

983 Caboclinhos Folkdance

1981. Festivities. Multicoloured.
1912 50cr. Type **983** 90 15
1913 55cr. Marujada folk festival 90 15
1914 60cr. Resado parade 90 20

984 Sun and Erect, Drooping, and Supported Flowers

1981. International Year of Disabled Persons.
1915 **984** 12cr. multicoloured . . . 20 10

985 "Dalechampia caperoniodes" **986** Image of Our Lady of Nazareth

1981. Flowers of the Central Plateau. Multicoloured.
1916 12cr. Type **985** 20 15
1917 12cr. "Palicourea rigida" . . 20 15
1918 12cr. "Eremanthus sphaerocephalus"(vert) . . 20 15
1919 12cr. "Cassia clausseni" (vert) 20 15

1981. Festival of Our Lady of Nazareth, Belem.
1920 **986** 12cr. multicoloured . . . 15 10

987 Christ the Redeemer Monument **988** Farmhands seeding the Land

1981. 50th Anniv of Christ the Redeemer Monument, Rio de Janeiro.
1921 **987** 12cr. multicoloured . . . 15 10

1981. World Food Day.
1922 **988** 12cr. multicoloured . . . 15 10

989 Santos Dumont and Biplane "14 bis" landing at Paris

1981. 75th Anniv of Santos Dumont's First Powered Flight.
1923 **989** 60cr. multicoloured . . . 75 20

990 Friar Santos Rita Durao, Title Page and Scene from "Caramuru"

1981. Book Day and Bicentenary of Publication of Epic Poem "Caramuru".
1924 **990** 12cr. multicoloured . . . 15 10

991 Crib, Juazeiro de Norte (Cica)

1981. Christmas. Various designs showing Cribs. Multicoloured.
1925 12cr. Type **991** 15 10
1926 50cr. Caruaru (Vitalino Filho) 75 15
1927 55cr. Sao Jose dos Campos (Eugenia) (vert) 75 15
1928 60cr. Taubate (Candida) (vert) . . . . 1·10 20

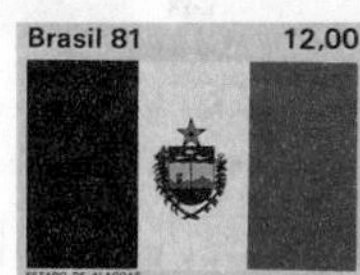

992 Alagoas

1981. State Flags (1st series). Multicoloured.
1929 12cr. Type **992** 50 50
1930 12cr. Bahia 50 50
1931 12cr. Federal District . . . 50 50
1932 12cr. Pernambuco 50 50
1933 12cr. Sergipe 50 50
See also Nos. 1988/92, 2051/5, 2113/17, 2204/7 and 3043/4.

993 Girls with Wheat **994** Heads and Symbols of Occupations

1981. Thanksgiving Day.
1934 **993** 12cr. multicoloured . . . 15 10

1981. 50th Anniv of Ministry of Labour.
1935 **994** 12cr. multicoloured . . . 15 10

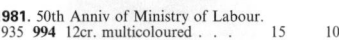

995 Federal Engineering School, Itajuba

1981. Birth Centenary of Theodomiro Carneiro Santiago (founder of Federal Engineering School).
1936 **995** 15cr. green and mauve 15 10

996 Musician of Police Military Band and Headquarters **997** Army Library "Ex Libris"

1981. 150th Anniv of Sao Paulo Military Police. Multicoloured.
1937 12cr. Type **996** 25 10
1938 12cr. Lancers of Ninth of July Regiment, Mounted Police 25 10

1981. Centenary of Army Library.
1939 **997** 12cr. multicoloured . . . 15 10

999 Brigadier Eduardo Gomes

1982. Brigadier Eduardo Gomes Commem.
1941 **999** 12cr. blue and black . . 15 10

1000 Lage, Coal Trucks, "Ita" freighter and HL-1 Airplane

1981. Birth Cent of Henrique Lage (industrialist)
1942 **1000** 17cr. multicoloured . . 1·60 45

1001 Tackle

1002 Microscope, Bacillus and Lung

1982. World Cup Football Championship, Spain. Multicoloured.
1943 75cr. Type **1001** . . . . . . 1·75 50
1944 80cr. Kicking ball . . . . . . 1·75 50
1945 85cr. Goalkeeper . . . . . . 1·75 50

1982. Centenary of Robert Koch's Discovery of Tubercle Bacillus. Multicoloured.
1947 90cr. Type **1002** . . . . . . 4·25 1·75
1948 100cr. Flasks, tablets, syringe, bacillus and lung 4·25 1·75

1004 Oil Rig Workers

1982. Birth Centenary of Monteiro Lobato (writer).
1950 **1004** 17cr. multicoloured . . 20 10

1005 St. Vincent de Paul

1982. 400th Birth Anniv of St. Vincent de Paul.
1951 **1005** 17cr. multicoloured . . 15 10

1006 Fifth Fall

1982. Guaira's Seven Falls. Multicoloured.
1952 17cr. Type **1006** 20 10
1953 21cr. Seventh fall 25 10

1007 Envelope, Telephone, Antenna and Postcode

1982. 15th Anniv of Ministry of Communications.
1954 **1007** 21cr. multicoloured . . 15 10

1008 The Old Arsenal (National Historical Museum)

1982. 50th Anniv of Museology Course.
1955 **1008** 17cr. black and pink . . 15 10

1009 Cogwheels and Ore Mountains

1982. 40th Anniv of Vale do Rio Doce Company.
1956 **1009** 17cr. multicoloured . . 15 10

1010 Martim Afonso de Souza proclaiming Sao Vicente a Town

1982. 450th Anniv of Sao Vicente.
1957 **1010** 17cr. multicoloured . . 15 10

1011 Giant Anteater

1982. Animals. Multicoloured.
1958 17cr. Type **1011** 40 10
1959 21cr. Maned wolf 90 15
1960 30cr. Pampas deer . . . . . 1·75 25

1012 Film and "Golden Palm"

1014 Church of Our Lady of O, Sabara

1982. 20th Anniv of "Golden Palm" Film Award to "The Given World".
1961 **1012** 17cr. multicoloured . . 20 10

1982. Baroque-style Architecture in Minas Gerais. Multicoloured.
1963 17cr. Type **1014** 55 10
1964 17cr. Church of Our Lady of Carmo, Mariana (horiz) 55 10
1965 17cr. Church of Our Lady of Rosary, Diamantina (horiz) 55 10

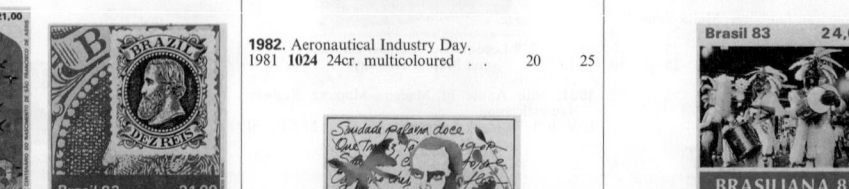

1015 St. Francis of Assisi

1016 "Large Head" Stamp of 1882

1982. 800th Birth Anniv of St. Francis of Assisi.
1966 **1015** 21cr. multicoloured . . 15 10

1982. Centenary of Pedro II "Large Head" Stamps.
1967 **1016** 21cr. yellow, brn & blk 15 10

1017 Amazon River and Hands holding Seedling, Screw and Coin

1982. Manaus Free Trade Zone.
1968 **1017** 75cr. multicoloured . . 95 20

1019 Xango

1982. Orixas Religious Costumes. Mult.
1970 20cr. Type **1019** 20 10
1971 20cr. Iemanja 20 10
1972 20cr. Oxumare 20 10

1020 XII Florin

1982. 10th Anniv of Brazilian Central Bank Values Museum. Multicoloured.
1973 25cr. Type **1020** 20 10
1974 25cr. Pedro I Coronation piece 20 10

1021 "Ipiranga Cry" (Dom Pedro proclaiming independence)

1022 St. Theresa of Jesus

1982. Independence Week.
1975 **1021** 25cr. multicoloured . . 20 10

1982. 400th Death Anniv of St. Theresa of Jesus.
1976 **1022** 85cr. multicoloured . . 2·40 50

1023 Musical Instrument Maker

1024 Embraer Tucano Trainers

1982. "Lubrapex 82" Brazilian–Portuguese Stamp Exhibition, Curitiba. The Paranaense Fandango. Multicoloured.
1977 75cr. Type **1023** . . . . . . 1·75 50
1978 80cr. Dancers . . . . 1·75 50
1979 85cr. Musicians . . . . . . 1·75 50

1982. Aeronautical Industry Day.
1981 **1024** 24cr. multicoloured . . 20 25

1025 Bastos Tigre and Verse from "Saudade"

1982. Day of the Book and Birth Centenary of Bastos Tigre (poet).
1982 **1025** 24cr. multicoloured . . 15 10

1026 Telephone Dial on Map of Brazil

1982. 10th Anniv of Telebras (Brazilian Telecommunications Corporation).
1983 **1026** 24cr. multicoloured . . 15 10

1027 "Nativity" (C.S. Miyaba)

1982. Christmas. Children's Paintings. Mult.
1984 24cr. Type **1027** . . . . . . 1·25 10
1985 24cr. "Choir of Angels" (N. N. Aleluia) . . . . . . 1·25 10
1986 30cr. "Holy Family" (F. T. Filho) . . . . 1·25 15
1987 30cr. "Nativity with Angel" (N. Arand) . . . . 1·25 15

1982. State Flags (2nd series). As T **992**. Mult.
1988 24cr. Ceara . . . . 1·75 60
1989 24cr. Espirito Santo . . . . 1·75 60
1990 24cr. Paraiba . . . . 1·75 60
1991 24cr. Rio Grande do Norte 1·75 60
1992 24cr. Rondonia . . . . . . 1·75 60

1028 "Germination"

1029 "Efeta" (S. Tempel)

1982. Thanksgiving Day.
1993 **1028** 24cr. multicoloured . . 50 10

1982. The Hard of Hearing.
1994 **1029** 24cr. multicoloured . . 15 10

1030 "Benjamin Constant" (cadet ship)

1982. Bicentenary of Naval Academy. Mult.
1995 24cr. Type **1030** 85 25
1996 24cr. "Almirante Saldanha" (cadet ship) 85 25
1997 24cr. "Brasil" (training frigate) 85 25

1032 Samba Parade Drummers

1983. "Brasiliana 83" International Stamp Exhibition, Rio de Janeiro. Carnival. Multicoloured.
1999 24cr. Type **1032** 90 35
2000 130cr. Masked clowns . . . 3·00 90
2001 140cr. Dancer . . . . 3·00 90
2002 150cr. Indian . . . . 3·00 90

1033 Support Ship "Barao de Teffe" in Antarctic

1983. 1st Brazilian Antarctic Expedition.
2003 **1033** 150cr. multicoloured . . 1·75 45

1034 Woman with Ballot Paper
1035 Itaipu Dam

1983. 50th Anniv of Women's Suffrage in Brazil.
2004 **1034** 130cr. multicoloured . . 1·75 50

1983. Itaipu Brazilian–Paraguayan Hydro-electric Project.
2005 **1035** 140cr. multicoloured . . 1·75 50

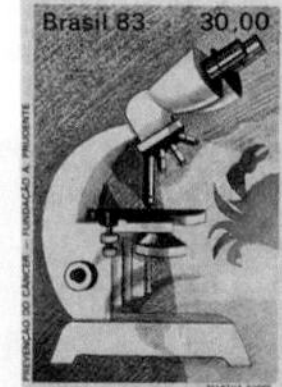

1036 Luther
1037 Microscope and Crab

1983. 500th Birth Anniv of Martin Luther (Protestant reformer).
2006 **1036** 150cr. deep green, green and black . . . . . 2·40 50

1983. Cancer Prevention. 30th Anniv of Antonio Prudente Foundation and A.C. Camargo Hospital. Multicoloured.
2007 30cr. Type **1037** 25 20
2008 38cr. Antonio Prudente, hospital and crab 25 20

1038 Tissue Culture

1983. Agricultural Research. Multicoloured.
2009 30cr. Type **1038** 20 10
2010 30cr. Brazilian wild chestnut tree 20 10
2011 38cr. Tropical soya beans 20 10

1039 Friar Rogerio Neuhaus before Altar
1040 Council Emblem and World Map

1983. Cent of Ordination of Friar Rogerio Neuhaus.
2012 **1039** 30cr. multicoloured . . 20 10

1983. 30th Anniv of Customs Co-operation Council.
2013 **1040** 30cr. multicoloured . . 20 10

1041 Satellite

1983. World Communications Year.
2014 **1041** 250cr. multicoloured . . 3·50 1·25

1042 Toco Toucan

1983. Toucans. Multicoloured.
2015 30cr. Type **1042** 90 20
2016 185cr. Red-billed toucan . . 3·00 85
2017 205cr. Red-breasted toucan 3·00 90
2018 215cr. Channel-billed toucan 3·00 1·10

1044 Baldwin Locomotive No. 1, 1881
1045 Basketball Players

1983. Locomotives. Multicoloured.
2020 30cr. Type **1044** 55 30
2021 30cr. Hohenzollern locomotive No. 980, 1875 55 30
2022 38cr. Locomotive No. 1 "Maria Fumaca", 1868 55 30

1983. 9th Women's World Basketball Championship, Sao Paulo.
2023 30cr. Type **1045** 25 10
2024 30cr. Basketball players (different) 25 10

1046 Bolivar (after Tito Salas)

1983. Birth Bicentenary of Simon Bolivar.
2025 **1046** 30cr. multicoloured . . 20 10

1047 Boy with Kite and Boy waiting for Polio Vaccination
1048 Minerva and Computer Punched Tape

1983. Polio and Measles Vaccination Campaign. Multicoloured.
2026 30cr. Type **1047** 30 10
2027 30cr. Girl on bicycle and girl receiving measles vaccination 30 10

1983. 20th Anniv of Post-graduate Master's Programmes in Engineering.
2028 **1048** 30cr. light brown, blue and brown 20 10

1049 30r. "Bulls Eye" Stamp and Rio de Janeiro Bay

1983. "Brasiliana 83" International Stamp Exhibition, Rio de Janeiro. 140th Anniv of "Bull's Eye" Stamps.
2029 **1049** 185cr. black and blue 1·50 90
2030 – 205cr. black and blue 1·50 90
2031 – 215cr. black and violet 1·50 90
DESIGNS: Nos. 2030/1, As Type **1049** but showing 60r. and 90r. "Bull's Eye" stamp respectively.

1052 Embraer EMB-120

1983. Brazilian Aeronautics Industry.
2035 **1052** 30cr. multicoloured . . 25 10

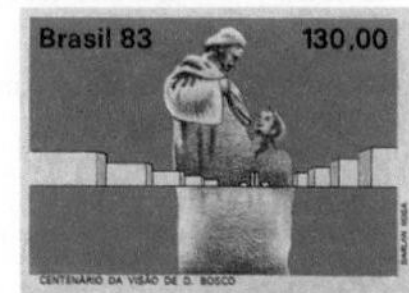

1053 Bosco and State Departments Esplanade, Brasilia

1983. Dom Bosco's Dream of Brazil.
2036 **1053** 130cr. multicoloured . . 75 10

1054 "Council of State decides on Independence" (detail, Georgina de Albuquerque)

1983. National Week.
2037 **1054** 50cr. multicoloured . . 15 10

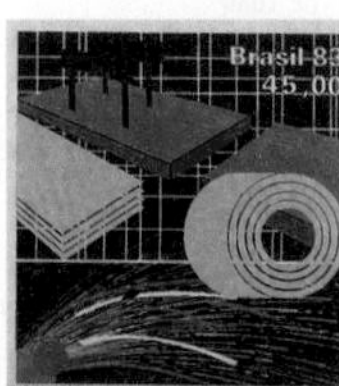

1055 Iron and Steel Production

1983. 10th Anniv of Siderbras (Brazilian Steel Corporation).
2038 **1055** 45cr. multicoloured . . 15 10

1056 "Pilosocereus gounellei"

1983. Cacti. Multicoloured.
2039 45cr. Type **1056** 95 10
2040 45cr. "Melocactus bahiensis" 95 10
2041 57cr. "Cereus jamacari" . . 95 10

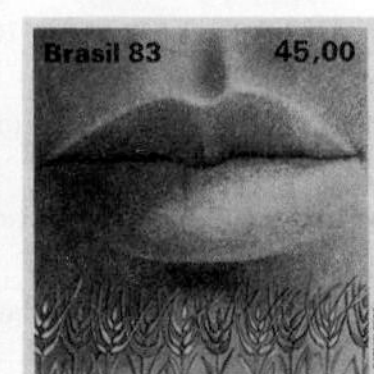

1057 Monstrance
1058 Mouth and Wheat

1983. 50th Anniv of National Eucharistic Congress.
2042 **1057** 45cr. multicoloured . . 15 10

1983. 20th Anniv of World Food Programme. Fishery Resources. Multicoloured.
2043 45cr. Type **1058** 20 15
2044 57cr. Fish and fishing pirogue 80 15

1060 "Our Lady of Angels" (wood, Franisco Xavier de Brito)

1983. Christmas. Statues of the Madonna. Multicoloured.
2046 45cr. Type **1060** 90 10
2047 315cr. "Our Lady of Birth" 2·75 90
2048 335cr. "Our Lady of Joy" (fired clay, Agostinho de Jesus) . . . . 2·75 90
2049 345cr. "Our Lady of Presentation" . . . . . . 2·75 90

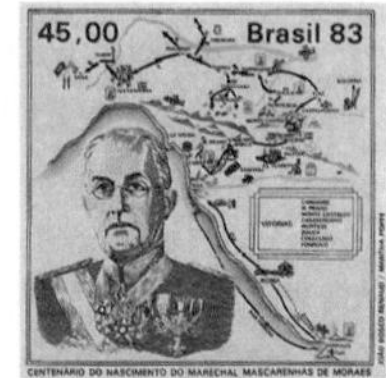

1061 Moraes and Map of Italian Campaign

1983. Birth Centenary of Marshal Mascarenhas de Moraes.
2050 **1061** 45cr. pink, green & pur 20 15

1983. State Flags (3rd series). As Type **992**. Multicoloured.
2051 45cr. Amazonas 90 55
2052 45cr. Goias 90 55
2053 45cr. Rio de Janeiro 90 55
2054 45cr. Mato Grosso do Sul 90 55
2055 45cr. Parana 90 55

1062 Praying Figure and Wheat

1983. Thanksgiving Day.
2056 **1062** 45cr. multicoloured . . 15 10

1063 Friar Vincente Borgard
1064 Montgolfier Balloon

1983. Obligatory Tax. Anti-leprosy Week.
2057 **1063** 10cr. brown . . . . . 2·75 90

1983. Bicentenary of Manned Flight.
2058 **1064** 345cr. multicoloured . . 4·25 2·40

1065 Indian, Portuguese Navigator and Negro

1984. 50th Anniv of Publication of "Masters and Slaves" by Gilberto Freyre.
2059 **1065** 45cr. multicoloured . . 60 10

1066 Crystal Palace

1984. Centenary of Crystal Palace, Petropolis.
2060 **1066** 45cr. multicoloured . . 25 10

1068 "Don Afonso" (sail/steam warship) and Figurehead

1984. Cent of Naval Oceanographic Museum.
2062 **1068** 620cr. multicoloured . . 1·25 35

1069 Manacled Hands and Beached Fishing Pirogue

1984. Centenary of Abolition of Slavery in Ceara and Amazonas. Multicoloured.

2063 585cr. Type **1069** . . . . . 1·75 90
2064 610cr. Emancipated slave . . 1·75 90

1071 Long Jumping

1984. Olympic Games, Los Angeles. Mult.

2066 65cr. Type **1071** 90 50
2067 65cr. 100 metres 90 50
2068 65cr. Relay 90 50
2069 585cr. Pole vaulting 90 75
2070 610cr. High jumping 90 75
2071 620cr. Hurdling 90 75

1072 Oil Rigs and Blast Furnace
1073 Pedro Alvares Cabral

1984. Birth Cent (1983) of Getulio Vargas (President 1930–45 and 1951–54). Multicoloured.

2072 65cr. Type **1072** 15 10
2073 65cr. Ballot boxes and symbols of professions and trades 15 10
2074 65cr. Sugar refinery and electricity pylons 15 10

1984. "Espana 84" International Stamp Exhibition, Madrid. Explorers. Multicoloured.

2075 65cr. Type **1073** 15 10
2076 610cr. Christopher Columbus . . . . 1·75 20

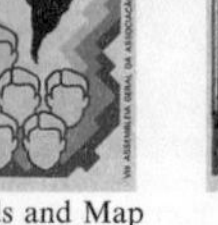

1074 Heads and Map of Americas
1075 Chinese Painting

1984. 8th Pan-American Surety Association General Assembly.

2077 **1074** 65cr. multicoloured . . 15 10

1984. "Lubrapex 84" Brazilian-Portuguese Stamp Exhibition, Lisbon.

2078 **1075** 65cr. multicoloured . . 15 10
2079 – 585cr. multicoloured . . 90 50
2080 – 610cr. multicoloured . . 90 50
2081 – 620cr. multicoloured . . 90 50

DESIGNS: 585 to 620cr. Chinese paintings from Mariana Cathedral.

1077 Marsh Deer and Great Egret

1984. Mato Grosso Flood Plain. Multicoloured.

2083 65cr. Type **1077** 80 50
2084 65cr. Jaguar, capybara and roseate spoonbill 80 50
2085 80cr. Alligator, jabiru and red-cowled cardinals . . . 85 55

1078 "The First Letter Sent from Brazil" (Guido Mondin)
1079 Route Map and Dornier Wal Flying Boat

1984. 1st Anniv of Postal Union of the Americas and Spain H.Q., Montevideo, Uruguay.

2086 **1078** 65cr. multicoloured . . 40 15

1984. 50th Anniv of First Trans-Oceanic Air Route. Multicoloured.

2087 610cr. Type **1079** . . . . . 1·60 50
2088 620cr. Support ship "Westfalen" and Dornier Wal . . . . 2·00 45

1080 Mother and Baby
1081 Murrah Buffaloes

1984. Wildlife Preservation. Woolley Spider Monkey. Multicoloured.

2089 65cr. Type **1080** 50 10
2090 80cr. Monkey in tree . . . 25 10

1984. Marajo Island Water Buffaloes. Designs showing different races. Multicoloured.

2091 65cr. Type **1081** 40 30
2092 65cr. Carabao buffaloes . . 40 30
2093 65cr. Mediterranean buffaloes 30 25

Nos. 2091/3 were issued together, se-tenant, forming a composite design.

1082 Headquarters, Salvador

1984. 150th Anniv of Economic Bank.

2094 **1082** 65cr. multicoloured . . 15 10

1083 Da Luz Station, Sao Paulo
1085 Roof protecting Couple

1984. Preservation of Historic Railway Stations. Multicoloured.

2095 65cr. Type **1083** . . . . . . 1·00 35
2096 65cr. Japeri station Rio de Janeiro . . . . 1·00 35
2097 80cr. Sao Joao del Rei station, Minas Gerais . . 1·00 35

1984. 20th Anniv of National Housing Bank.

2099 **1085** 65cr. multicoloured . . 10 10

1086 "Pedro I" (Solano Peixoto Machado)

1984. National Week. Designs showing children's paintings. Multicoloured.

2100 100cr. Type **1086** 15 10
2101 100cr. Girl painting word "BRASIL" (Juruce Maria Klein) 15 10
2102 100cr. Children of different races under rainbow (Priscela Barreto da Fonseca Bara) 15 10
2103 100cr. Caravels (Carlos Peixoto Mangueira) . . . 15 10

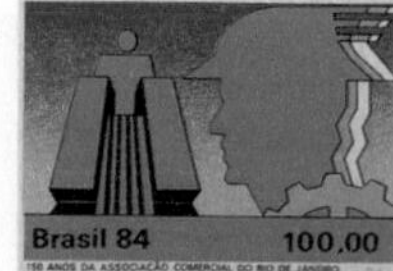

1087 Headquarters, Mercury and Cogwheel

1984. 150th Anniv of Rio de Janeiro Commercial Association.

2104 **1087** 100cr. multicoloured . . 15 10

1088 Pedro I

1984. 150th Death Anniv of Emperor Pedro I.

2105 **1088** 1000cr. multicoloured 3·50 1·75

1089 "Pycnoporus sanguineus"
1090 Child stepping from Open Book

1984. Fungi. Multicoloured.

2106 120cr. Type **1089** 40 15
2107 1050cr. "Calvatia" sp. . . . 2·75 60
2108 1080cr. "Pleurotus" sp. (horiz) . . . . 2·75 60

1984. Book Day. Children's Literature.

2109 **1090** 120cr. multicoloured . . 20 10

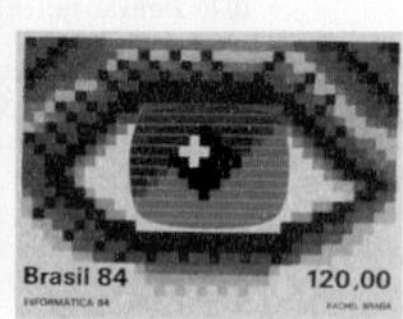

1091 New State Mint and 17th-century Minter
1092 Computer Image of Eye

1984. Inauguration of New State Mint, Santa Cruz, Rio de Janeiro.

2110 **1091** 120cr. blue & deep blue 15 10

1984. "Informatica 84" 17th National Information Congress and 4th International Informatics Fair, Rio de Janeiro.

2111 **1092** 120cr. multicoloured . . 15 10

1093 Sculpture by Bruno Giorgi and Flags
1094 Brasilia Cathedral and Wheat

1984. 14th General Assembly of Organization of American States, Brasilia.

2112 **1093** 120cr. multicoloured . . 15 10

1984. State Flags (4th series). As T **992**.

2113 120cr. red, black & buff . . 90 50
2114 120cr. multicoloured 90 50
2115 120cr. multicoloured 90 50
2116 120cr. multicoloured 90 50
2117 120cr. multicoloured 90 50

DESIGNS: No. 2113, Minas Gerais; 2114, Mato Grosso; 2115, Piaui; 2116, Maranhao; 2117, Santa Catarina.

1984. Thanksgiving Day.

2118 **1094** 120cr. multicoloured . . 15 10

1095 Father Bento Dias Pacheco
1096 "Nativity" (Djanira da Mota e Silva)

1984. Obligatory Tax. Anti-leprosy Week.

2119 **1095** 30cr. blue 50 10

See also Nos. 2208, 2263 and 2291.

1984. Christmas. Paintings from Federal Savings Bank collection. Multicoloured.

2120 120cr. Type **1096** 15 10
2121 120cr. "Virgin and Child" (Glauco Rodrigues) . . . 75 25
2122 1050cr. "Flight into Egypt" (Paul Garfunkel) . . . . 2·75 50
2123 1080cr. "Nativity" (Emiliano Augusto di Cavalcanti) . . 2·75 50

1097 Airbus Industrie A300

1984. 40th Anniv of I.C.A.O.

2124 **1097** 120cr. multicoloured . . 15 10

1098 Symbols of Agriculture and Industry on Hat

1984. 25th Anniv of North-east Development Office.

2125 **1098** 120cr. multicoloured . . 15 10

1099 "Virgin of Safe Journeys Church" (detail)

1985. 77th Death Anniv of Emilio Rouede (artist).

2126 **1099** 120cr. multicoloured . . 20 10

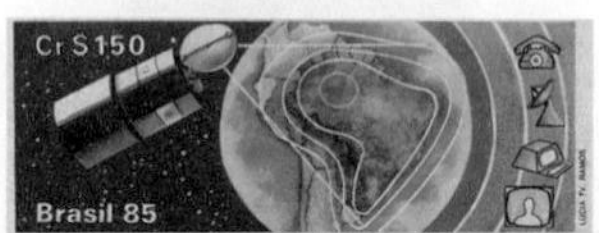

1100 "Brasilsat" over Brazil

1985. Launch of "Brasilsat" (first Brazilian telecommunications satellite).

2127 **1100** 150cr. multicoloured . . 25 10

1101 Electric Trains and Plan of Port Alegre Station

1985. Inauguration of Metropolitan Surface Railway, Recife and Porto Alegre.

2128 **1101** 200cr. multicoloured . . 60 20

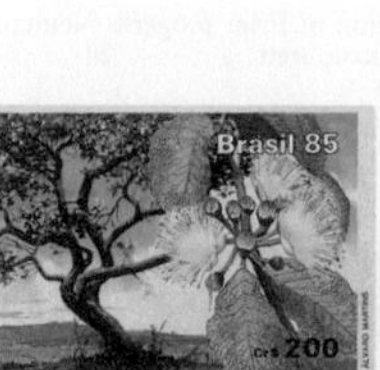

1102 Butternut Tree
1103 Parachutist

1985. Opening of Botanical Gardens, Brasilia.

2129 **1102** 200cr. multicoloured . . 20 10

1985. 40th Anniv of Military Parachuting.

2130 **1103** 200cr. multicoloured . . 20 10

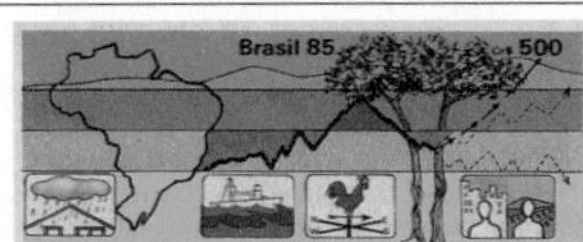
1104 Map, Temperature Graph and Weather Scenes

1985. National Climate Programme.
2131 **1104** 500cr. multicoloured . . 20 10

1105 Campolina

1107 "Polyvolume" (Mary Vieira)

1106 Ouro Preto

1985. Brazilian Horses. Multicoloured.
2132 1000cr. Type **1105** . . . . . 1·25 15
2133 1500cr. Marajoara . . . . . 1·25 15
2134 1500cr. Mangalarga pacer 1·25 15

1985. U.N.E.S.C.O. World Heritage Sites. Multicoloured.
2135 220cr. Type **1106** 15 10
2136 220cr. Sao Miguel das Missoes 15 10
2137 220cr. Olinda 15 10

1985. 40th Anniv of Rio-Branco Institute (diplomatic training academy).
2138 **1107** 220cr. multicoloured . . 10 10

1108 National Theatre

1985. 25th Anniv of Brasilia. Multicoloured.
2139 220cr. Type **1108** 10 10
2140 220cr. Catetinho (home of former President Juscelino Keubitschek) and memorial 10 15

1109 Rondon and Morse Telegraph

1110 Fontoura and Pharmaceutical Equipment

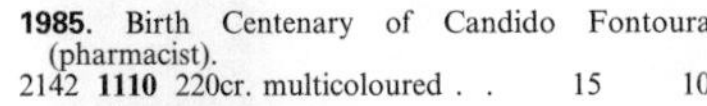

1985. 120th Birth Anniv of Marshal Candido Mariano da Silva Rondon (military engineer and explorer).
2141 **1109** 220cr. multicoloured . . 10 10

1985. Birth Centenary of Candido Fontoura (pharmacist).
2142 **1110** 220cr. multicoloured . . 15 10

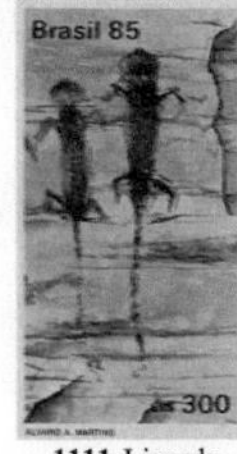
1111 Lizards

1112 Numeral

1113 Numeral

1985. Rock Paintings. Multicoloured.
2143 300cr. Type **1111** 10 10
2144 300cr. Deer 10 10
2145 2000cr. Various animals . . 75 15

1985.
2147 **1112** 50cr. red 10 10
2148 100cr. purple 10 10
2149 150cr. lilac 10 10
2150 200cr. blue 10 10
2151 220cr. green 50 10
2152 300cr. blue 10 10
2153 500cr. black 10 10
2154 **1113** 1000cr. brown 10 10
2155 2000cr. green 15 10
2156 3000cr. lilac 15 10
2157 5000cr. brown . . . . 1·75 10

1114 Common Noddies

1985. National Marine Park, Abrolhos. Mult.
2168 220cr. Type **1114** 55 35
2169 220cr. Magnificent frigate birds and blue-faced booby 55 35
2170 220cr. Blue-faced boobies and red-billed tropic bird 55 35
2171 2000cr. Grey plovers . . . . 2·75 65

1115 Breast-feeding

1116 Bell 47J Ranger Helicopter rescuing Man, "Brasil" (corvette) and Diver

1985. United Nations Children's Fund Child Survival Campaign. Multicoloured.
2172 220cr. Type **1115** 15 10
2173 220cr. Growth chart and oral rehydration 15 10

1985. International Sea Search and Rescue Convention, Rio de Janeiro.
2174 **1116** 220cr. multicoloured . . 1·00 30

1118 Children holding Hands

1119 Hands holding Host

1985. International Youth Year.
2176 **1118** 220cr. multicoloured . . 15 10

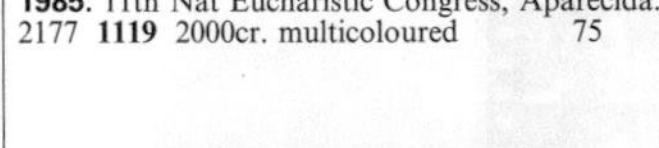

1985. 11th Nat Eucharistic Congress, Aparecida.
2177 **1119** 2000cr. multicoloured 75 50

1120 Scene from "Mineiro Blood", Camera and Mauro

1985. 60th Anniv of Humberto Mauro's Cataguases Cycle of Films.
2178 **1120** 300cr. multicoloured . . 15 10

1121 Escola e Sacro Museum

1122 Inconfidencia Museum, Ouro Preto

1985. 400th Anniv of Paraiba State.
2179 **1121** 330cr. multicoloured . . 15 10

1985. Museums. Multicoloured.
2180 300cr. Type **1122** 15 10
2181 300cr. Historical and Diplomatic Museum Itamaraty 15 10

1123 "Cabano" (Guido Mondin)

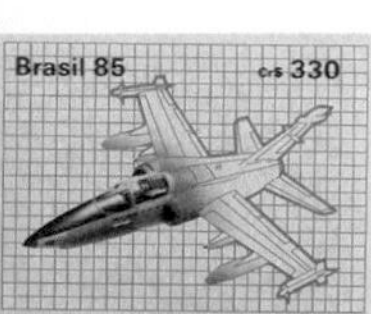

1124 Aeritalia/Aermacchi AM-X Fighter

1985. 150th Anniv of Cabanagem Insurrection, Belem City.
2182 **1123** 330cr. multicoloured . . 15 10

1985. AM-X (military airplane) Project.
2183 **1124** 330cr. multicoloured . . 15 10

1125 Captain and Crossbowman (early 16th century)

1985. Military Dress. Multicoloured.
2184 300cr. Type **1125** 15 10
2185 300cr. Arquebusier and sergeant (late 16th cent) 15 10
2186 300cr. Musketeer and pikeman (early 17th century) 15 10
2187 300cr. Mulatto fusilier and pikeman with scimitar (early 17th century) . . . 15 10

1126 "Farroupilha Rebels" (Guido Mondin)

1985. 150th Anniv of Farroupilha Revolution.
2188 **1126** 330cr. multicoloured . . 15 10

1127 Itaimbezinho Canyon

1985. Aparados da Serra National Park. Mult.
2189 3100cr. Type **1127** 95 15
2190 3320cr. Mountain range . . 95 15
2191 3480cr. Pine forest 95 15

1128 Neves and Brasilia Buildings

1985. Tancredo Neves (President-elect) Commem.
2192 **1128** 330cr. black & orange 15 10

1129 "FEB" on Envelope

1985. 40th Anniv (1984) of Brazilian Expeditionary Force Postal Service.
2193 **1129** 500cr. multicoloured . . 15 10

1130 "Especuladora", 1835

1985. 150th Anniv of Rio de Janeiro–Niteroi Ferry Service. Multicoloured.
2194 500cr. Type **1130** 70 20
2195 500cr. "Segunda", 1862 . . 70 20
2196 500cr. "Terceira", 1911 . . 70 20
2197 500cr. "Urca", 1981 . . . . 70 20

1131 Muniz M-7

1985. 50th Anniv of Muniz M-7 Biplane's Maiden Flight.
2198 **1131** 500cr. multicoloured . . 30 15

1132 Dove Emblem and Stylized Flags

1133 Front Page of First Edition

1985. 40th Anniv of U.N.O.
2199 **1132** 500cr. multicoloured . . 15 10

1985. 160th Anniv of "Pernambuco Daily News".
2200 **1133** 500cr. multicoloured . . 15 10

1134 Adoration

1135 Child holding Wheat

1985. Christmas. Multicoloured.
2201 500cr. Type **1134** 15 10
2202 500cr. Adoration of the Magi 15 10
2203 500cr. Flight into Egypt . . 15 10

1985. State Flags (5th series). As T **992**. Mult.
2204 500cr. Para 15 10
2205 500cr. Rio Grande do Sul 15 10
2206 500cr. Acre 15 10
2207 500cr. Sao Paulo 15 10

1985. Obligatory Tax. Anti-leprosy Week.
2208 **1095** 100cr. red 25 25

1985. Thanksgiving Day.
2209 **1135** 500cr. multicoloured . . 10 10

1136 Transport, Mined Ore and Trees

1985. Carajas Development Programme.
2210 **1136** 500cr. multicoloured . . 20 10

1137 Gusmao and Balloons

1985. 300th Birth Anniv of Bartolomeu Lourenco de Gusmao (inventor).
2211 **1137** 500cr. multicoloured . . 10 10

1138 "The Trees"

1985. Birth Centenary of Antonio Francisco da Costa e Silva (poet).
2212 **1138** 500cr. multicoloured . . 10 10

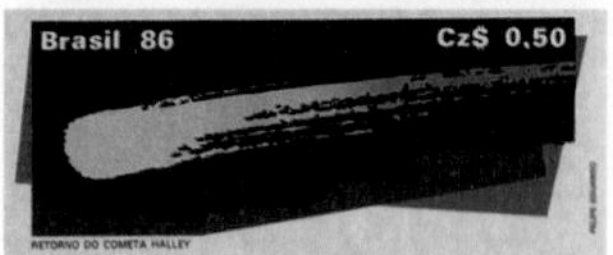

1140 Comet

1986. Appearance of Halley's Comet.
2214 **1140** 50c. multicoloured . . . 35 15

1141 Flags and Station

1142 Symbols of Industry, Agriculture and Commerce

1986. 2nd Anniv of Commander Ferraz Antarctic Station.
2215 **1141** 50c. multicoloured . . . 10 15

1986. Labour Day.
2216 **1142** 50c. multicoloured . . . 10 10

1143 "Maternity"

1144 Broken Chain Links as Birds

1986. 50th Death Anniv of Henrique Bernardelli (artist).
2217 **1143** 50c. multicoloured . . . 10 10

1986. 25th Anniv of Amnesty International.
2218 **1144** 50c. multicoloured . . . 10 10

1145 "Pyrrhopyge ruficauda"

1986. Butterflies. Multicoloured.
2219 50c. Type **1145** 85 30
2220 50c. "Pierriballia mandela molione" 85 30
2221 50c. "Prepona eugenes diluta" 85 30

1146 Gomes Peri, and Score of "O Guarani"

1147 Man in Safety Harness

1986. 150th Birth Anniv of Antonio Carlos Gomes (composer).
2222 **1146** 50c. multicoloured . . . 15 10

1986. Prevention of Industrial Accidents.
2223 **1147** 50c. multicoloured . . . 15 10

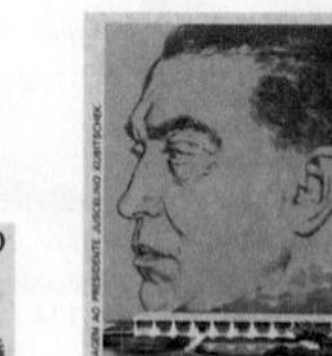

1149 Garcia D'Avilas House Chapel, Nazare de Mata

1150 Kubitschek and Alvorada Palace

1986.
2225 **1149** 10c. green 10 10
2226 – 20c. blue 10 10
2228 – 50c. orange 55 10
2230 – 1cz. brown 10 10
2231 – 2cz. red 10 10
2233 – 5cz. green 10 10
2235 – 10cz. blue 10 10
2236 – 20cz. red 10 10
2238 – 50cz. orange 15 15
2240 – 100cz. green 30 25
2241 – 200cz. blue 10 30
2242 – 500cz. brown 50 10
DESIGNS—HORIZ: 20c. Church of Our Lady of the Assumptiom, Anchieta; 50c. Reis Magos Fortress, Natal; 1cz. Pelourinho, Alcantara; 2cz. St. Francis's Monastery, Olinda; 5cz. St. Anthony's Chapel, Sao Roque; 10cz. St Lawrence of the Indians Church, Niteroi; 20cz. Principe da Beira Fortress, Costa Marques, Rondobua; 100cz. Church of Our Lady of Sorrows, Campanha; 200cz. Counting House, Ouro Preto; 500cz. Customs building, Belem. VERT: 50cz. Church of the Good Jesus, Matasinhos.

1986. 10th Death Anniv of Juscelino Kubitschek (President 1956–61).
2244 **1150** 50c. multicoloured . . . 25 10

1151 Mangabeira and Itamaraty Palace, Rio de Janeiro

1986. Birth Cent of Octavio Mangabeira (politician).
2245 **1151** 50c. multicoloured . . . 10 10

1152 Congress Emblem and Sao Paulo

1153 Microphone and Radio Waves

1986. 8th World Gastroenterology Congress, Sao Paulo.
2246 **1152** 50c. multicoloured . . . 10 10

1986. 50th Annivs. of National Radio and Education and Culture Ministry Radio.
2247 **1153** 50c. multicoloured . . . 10 10

1154 "Peace" (detail, Candido Portinari)

1155 "Urera mitis"

1986. International Peace Year.
2248 **1154** 50c. multicoloured . . . 10 10

1986. Flowers. Multicoloured.
2249 50c. Type **1155** 15 10
2250 6cz.50 "Couroupita guyanensis" 85 20
2251 6cz.90 Mountain ebony (horiz) 90 20

1156 Simoes Filho and Newspaper

1157 Title Page of Gregorio de Matto's MS

1986. Birth Centenary of Ernesto Simoes Filho (politician and founder of "A Tarde").
2252 **1156** 50c. multicoloured . . . 10 10

1986. Book Day. Poets' Birth Anniversaries.
2253 **1157** 50c. brown & lt brown 10 10
2254 – 50c. green and red . . . 10 10
DESIGNS: No. 2253, Type **1157** (350th anniv); 2254, Manuel Bandeira and last verse of "I'll Return to Pasargada" (centenary).

1158 Head Office, Brasilia

1159 Birds around Baby lying in Nest

1986. 125th Anniv of Federal Savings Bank.
2255 **1158** 50c. multicoloured . . . 10 10

1986. Christmas. Multicoloured.
2256 50c. Type **1159** 75 15
2257 6cz.50 Birds around tree with Christmas decorations . . . . 1·50 25
2258 7cz.30 Birds wearing Santa Claus caps . . . . 1·25 30

1160 Rocha on Strip of Film

1161 "History of Empress Porcina"

1986. 5th Death Anniv of Glauber Rocha (film producer).
2259 **1160** 50c. multicoloured . . . 10 10

1986. "Lubrapex 86" Brazilian–Portuguese Stamp Exhibition, Rio de Janeiro. Design showing scenes from Cordel Literature. Multicoloured.
2260 6cz.90 Type **1161** 55 40
2261 6cz.90 "Romance of the Mysterious Peacock" . . 55 40

1986. Obligatory Tax. Anti-leprosy Week.
2263 **1095** 10c. brown 10 10

1162 Lieutenant Commander, 1930

1163 "Graf Zeppelin" over Hangar

1986. Military Uniforms. Multicoloured.
2264 50c. Type **1162** 60 10
2265 50c. Military Aviation flight lieutenant, 1930 . . . . . 10 10

1986. 50th Anniv of Bartolomeu de Gusmao Airport, Santa Cruz.
2266 **1163** 1cz. multicoloured . . . 10 10

1164 Museum

1987. 50th Anniv of National Fine Arts Museum, Rio de Janeiro.
2267 **1164** 1cz. multicoloured . . . 10 10

1165 Villa-Lobos conducting and Musical Motifs

1167 Landscape on Open Envelope (Rural Post Office Network)

1166 Flag, Lockheed Hercules Aircraft and Antarctic Landscape

1987. Birth Cent of Heitor Villa-Lobos (composer).
2268 **1165** 1cz.50 multicoloured . . 30 10

1987. Air Force Participation in Brazilian Antarctic Programme.
2269 **1166** 1cz. multicoloured . . . 90 20

1987. Special Mail Services. Multicoloured.
2270 1cz. Type **1167** 10 10
2271 1cz. Satchel and globe (International Express Mail Service) 10 10

1168 "Brasilsat" Satellite, Radio Wave and Globe

1169 Modern Pentathlon

1987. "Telecom 87" World Telecommunications Exhibition, Geneva.
2272 **1168** 2cz. multicoloured . . . 10 10

1987. 10th Pan-American Games, Indianapolis, U.S.A.
2273 **1169** 18cz. multicoloured . . 1·75 50

1170 Hawksbill Turtle

1987. Endangered Animals. Multicoloured.
2274 2cz. Type **1170** 60 35
2275 2cz. Right whale 60 35

1171 Old and New Court Buildings and Symbol of Justice

1172 Arms

1987. 40th Anniv of Federal Appeal Court.
2276 **1171** 2cz. multicoloured . . . 10 10

1987. Centenary of Military Club.
2277 **1172** 3cz. multicoloured . . . 10 10

1173 Institute and Foodstuffs

1987. Centenary of Agronomic Institute, Campinas.
2278 **1173** 2cz. multicoloured . . . 10 10

1174 "Fulgora servillei"

1987. 50th Anniv of Brazilian Entomology Society. Multicoloured.
2279 3cz. Type **1174** 60 35
2280 3cz. "Zoolea lopiceps" . . . 60 35

1175 Features of Northern and North-east Regions

1176 Main Tower

1987. National Tourism Year. Multicoloured.
2281 3cz. Type **1175** 50 15
2282 3cz. Features of mid-west, south-east and south regions 10 10

1987. 150th Anniv of Royal Portuguese Reading Cabinet, Rio de Janeiro.
2283 **1176** 30cz. green and red . . 25 20

1177 International Sport Club (1975, 1976, 1979)

1987. Brazilian Football Championship Gold Cup Winners (1st series). Designs showing footballers and Club emblems.
2284 **1177** 3cz. red, black & yellow 35 10
2285 – 3cz. red, yellow & black 35 10
2286 – 3cz. multicoloured . . . 35 10
2287 – 3cz. red, black & yellow 35 10
DESIGNS: No. 2285, Sao Paulo Football Club (1977, 1986); 2286, Guarani Football Club (1978); 2287, Regatas do Flamengo Club (1980, 1982, 1983).

See also Nos. 2322/5, 2398 and 2408.

1178 St. Francis's Church and Tiled Column

1987. 400th Anniv of St. Francis's Monastery, Salvador.
2288 **1178** 4cz. multicoloured . . . 10 10

1179 Almeida and Scenes from "A Bagaceira"

1987. Birth Centenary of Jose Americo de Almeida (writer).
2289 **1179** 4cz. multicoloured . . . 10 10

1180 Barra do Picao

1987. 450th Anniv of Recife.
2290 **1180** 5cz. multicoloured . . . 30 10

1987. Obligatory Tax. Anti-leprosy Week.
2291 **1095** 30cz. green 15 15

1181 Rainbow, Dove and Open Hands

1182 Angels

1987. Thanksgiving Day.
2292 **1181** 5cz. multicoloured . . . 10 10

1987. Christmas. Multicoloured.
2293 6cz. Type **1182** 10 10
2294 6cz. Dancers on stage . . . 10 10
2295 6cz. Shepherd playing flute 10 10

1183 Bernardo Pereira de Vasconcelos (founder) and Pedro II

1987. 150th Anniv of Pedro II School, Rio de Janeiro.
2296 **1183** 6cz. yellow, blk & red 10 10

1184 "Cattleya guttata"

1987. 50th Anniv of Brazilian Orchid Growers Society. Multicoloured.
2297 6cz. Type **1184** 50 10
2298 6cz. "Laelia lobata" 50 10

1185 Statue and Fatima Basilica, Portugal

1987. Marian Year. Visit to Brazil of Statue of Our Lady of Fatima.
2299 **1185** 50cz. multicoloured . . 90 60

1186 Sousa, Indians and Fauna

1987. 400th Anniv of "Descriptive Treaties of Brazil" by Gabriel Soares de Sousa.
2300 **1186** 7cz. multicoloured . . . 40 15

1187 Page from Book of Gregorian Chants and Computer Terminal

1988. 150th Anniv of National Archives.
2301 **1187** 7cz. multicoloured . . . 10 10

1188 National Colours, Caravel and Modern Ship

1988. 180th Anniv of Opening of Brazilian Ports to Free Trade.
2302 **1188** 7cz. multicoloured . . . 10 10

1190 Petrol Droplet

1192 Bonifacio and Emblems of his Life

1988. Energy Conservation. Multicoloured.
2304 14cz. Type **1190** 10 10
2305 14cz. Flash of electricity . . 10 10

1988. 150th Death Anniv of Jose Bonifacio de Andrada e Silva (scientist, writer and "Patriarch of the Independence").
2307 **1192** 20cz. multicoloured . . 10 10

1193 Quill Pen on Page of Aurea Law

1988. Centenary of Abolition of Slavery. Mult.
2308 20cz. Type **1193** 10 10
2309 50cz. Norris map of Africa, 1773, slave ship and plan of trading routes 20 10

1194 Church of the Good Jesus of Matosinhos

1195 Concentric Circles on Map of Americas

1988. U.N.E.S.C.O. World Heritage Sites. Mult.
2310 20cz. Type **1194** 10 10
2311 50cz. Brasilia 15 15
2312 100cz. Pelourinho, Salvador 15 15

1988. "Americas Telecom 88" Telecommunications Exhibition, Rio de Janeiro.
2313 **1195** 50cz. multicoloured . . 15 15

1196 "Kasato Maru" (first immigrant ship) and Japanese Family

1197 Postal Authority Emblem

1988. 80th Anniv of Japanese Immigration into Brazil.
2314 **1196** 100cz. multicoloured . . 55 25

1988. No value expressed.
2315 **1197** (–) blue 80 10
No. 2315 was valid for use at the current first class inland letter rate. It could not be used to pay postage to foreign countries.

1198 Judo

1199 Giant Anteater

1988. Olympic Games, Seoul.
2316 **1198** 20cz. multicoloured . . 80 10

1988. Endangered Mammals. Multicoloured.
2317 20cz. Type **1199** 50 10
2318 50cz. Thin-spined porcupine 60 15
2319 100cz. Bush dog . . . . . 1·25 25

1201 Industrial Symbols

1988. 50th Anniv of National Confederation of Industry.
2321 **1201** 50cz. multicoloured . . 15 15

1988. Brazilian Football Championship Gold Cup Winners (2nd series). As T **1177**. Multicoloured.
2322 50cz. Sport Club do Recife (1987) 40 15
2323 50cz. Coritiba Football Club (1985) 40 15
2324 100cz. Gremio Football Porto Alegrense (1981) . . 55 25
2325 200cz. Fluminense Football Club (1984) 75 40

1203 Raul Pompeia and Lines from "O Ateneu"

1988. Book Day. Centenaries of Publication of "O Ateneu" and "Verses". Multicoloured.
2327 50cz. Type **1203** 15 15
2328 100cz. Olavo Bilac and lines from "Verses" 30 25

1204 Church **1205** Father Santiago Uchoa

1988. Christmas. Origami by Marcia Bloch. Multicoloured.
2329 50cz. Type **1204** 15 15
2330 100cz. Nativity 30 25
2331 200cz. Santa Claus and parcels 55 45

1988. Obligatory Tax. Anti-leprosy Week.
2332 **1205** 1cz.30 brown 50 10
See also Nos. 2614 and 2686.

1206 Mate and Rodeo Rider

1988. "Abrafex" Argentine–Brazilian Stamp Exhibition, Buenos Aires.
2333 **1206** 400cz. multicoloured . . 2·25 1·10

1207 Hatchetfish ("Gasteropelecus sp.")

1988. Freshwater Fishes. Multicoloured.
2334 55cz. Type **1207** 30 30
2335 55cz. Black arawana ("Osteoglossum ferreira") 30 30
2336 55cz. Green moenkhausia ("Moenkhausia sp.") . . 30 30
2337 55cz. Pearlfish ("Xavantei") 30 30
2338 55cz. Armoured bristlemouth catfish ("Ancistrus hoplogenys") 30 30
2339 55cz. Emerald catfish ("Brochis splendens") . . 30 30

1209 Dish Aerials **1210** "Four Arts"

1988. 10th Anniv of Ansat 10 (first Brazilian dish aerial), Macapa.
2341 **1209** 70cz. multicoloured . . 20 15

1988. Establishment of National Foundation of Scenic Arts.
2342 **1210** 70cz. multicoloured . . 20 15

1211 Court Building

1989. 380th Anniv of Bahia Court of Justice.
2343 **1211** 25c. multicoloured . . . 10 10

1212 Library Building and Detail of Main Door

1989. Public Library Year. 178th Anniv of First Public Library, Bahia.
2344 **1212** 25c. multicoloured . . . 10 10

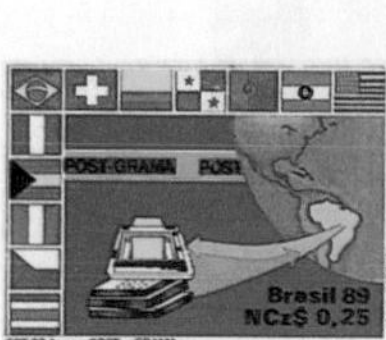

1213 Facsimile Machine **1215** Emblem

1989. 20th Anniv of Post and Telegraph Department. Postal Services. Multicoloured.
2345 25c. Type **1213** 10 10
2346 25c. Hand holding parcel (Express Mail Service) . . 10 10
2347 25c. Airbus Industrie 300 airplane on runway (SEDEX express parcel service) 10 10
2348 25c. Putting coin in savings box (CEF postal savings) 10 10

1989. "Our Nature" Programme.
2350 **1215** 25c. multicoloured . . . 10 10

1216 Hand reaching for Symbol of Freedom

1989. Bicentenary of Inconfidencia Mineira (independence movement). Multicoloured.
2351 30c. Type **1216** 10 10
2352 30c. Man's profile and colonial buildings 10 10
2353 40c. Baroque buildings in disarray 10 10

1217 School

1989. Cent of Rio de Janeiro Military School.
2354 **1217** 50c. multicoloured . . . 10 10

1218 "Pavonia alnifolia"

1989. Endangered Plants. Multicoloured.
2355 50c. Type **1218** 90 10
2356 1cz. "Worsleya rayneri" (vert) 90 10
2357 1cz.50 "Heliconia farinosa" (vert) . . . . 1·10 10

1219 Barreto and Pedro II Square, Recife Law School **1220** "Quiabentia zehntneri"

1989. 150th Birth Anniv of Tobias Barreto (writer).
2358 **1219** 50c. multicoloured . . . 10 10

1989. Flowers. Currency expressed as "NCz $". Multicoloured.
2359 10c. "Dichorisandra" sp. . . 10 10
2360 20c. Type **1220** 10 10
2361 50c. "Bougainvillea glabra" 10 10
2363 1cz. "Impatiens" sp. . . . 50 10
2364 3cz. "Chorisia crispiflora" (vert) 10 15
2366 5cz. "Hibiscus trilineatus" 10 10
See also Nos. 2413/24.

1221 Shooting of "Revistinha"

1989. 20th Anniv of TV Cultura.
2371 **1221** 50c. multicoloured . . . 10 10

1222 Postal Authority Emblem **1223** Brasilia T.V. Tower and Microlight

1989. No value expressed.
2372 **1222** (–) blue and orange . . 80 10
No. 2372 was sold at the current rate for first class internal postage.

1989. Aerosports and 80th Anniv of Santos Dumont's Flight in "Demoiselle". Mult.
2373 50c. Type **1223** 50 10
2374 1cz.50 Eiffel Tower and "Demoiselle" 60 10

1225 Tourmaline

1989. Precious Stones. Multicoloured.
2376 50c. Type **1225** 10 10
2377 1cz.50 Amethyst 15 10

1226 Rainbow and Association H.Q. Mercury

1989. 150th Anniv of Pernambuco Trade Assn.
2379 **1226** 50c. multicoloured . . . 10 10

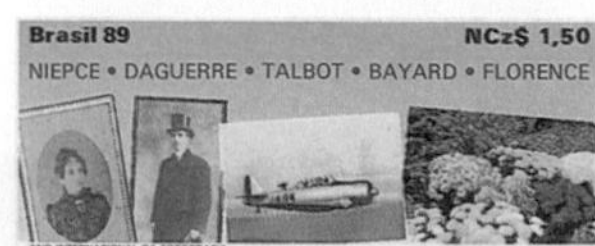

1228 Pioneers' Names and 19th-century to Modern Photographs

1989. International Photography Year.
2380 **1228** 1cz.50 multicoloured . . 15 10

1229 Power Station

1989. Centenary of Marmelos-o Power Station (first South American hydro-electric power station).
2381 **1229** 50c. multicoloured . . . 10 10

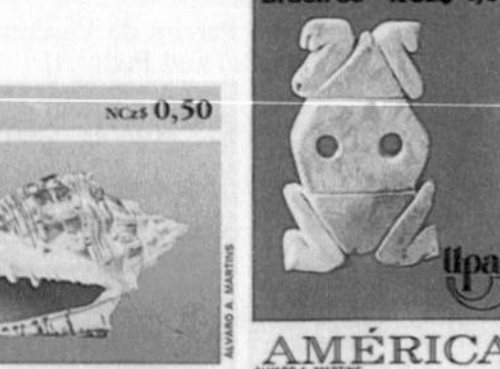

1230 Hebrew Volute **1231** Muiraquita

1989. Molluscs. Multicoloured.
2382 50c. Type **1230** 50 10
2383 1cz. Matthew's morum . . . 55 15
2384 1cz.50 Travasso's ancilla . . 60 20

1989. America. Pre-Columbian Artefacts. Mult.
2385 1cz. Type **1231** 80 10
2386 4cz. Caryatid vase (horiz) 80 10

1233 Casimiro de Abreu **1234** Postal Authority Emblem

1989. Book Day. Writers' Birth Annivs. Mult.
2388 1cz. Type **1233** (150th anniv) 10 10
2389 1cz. Machado de Assis (150th anniv) 10 10
2390 1cz. Cora Coralina (cent) . . 10 10

1989. No value expressed. Burelage in second colour.
2391 **1234** (–) red and orange . . 3·25 35
No. 2391 was sold at the current rate for first class international postage.

1235 Police Emblem

1989. 25th Anniv of Federal Police Department.
2392 **1235** 1cz. multicoloured . . . 10 10

1237 Angel **1238** Candle Flame as Dove

1989. Christmas. Multicoloured.
2394 70c. Type **1237** 10 10
2395 1cz. Nativity 10 10

1989. Thanksgiving Day.
2396 **1238** 1cz. multicoloured . . . 10 10

1239 Fr. Damien de Veuster **1240** "The Yellow Man"

1989. Obligatory Tax. Anti-leprosy Week.
2397 **1239** 2c. red 10 10
See also Nos. 2458, 2509 and 2565.

1989. Football Clubs. As T **1177**. Multicoloured.
2398 50c. Bahia Sports Club . . 10 10

1989. Birth Cent of Anita Malfatti (painter).
2399 **1240** 1cz. multicoloured . . . 10 10

1241 Archive and Proclamation by Bento Goncalves

1990. Cent of Bahia State Public Archive.
2400 **1241** 2cz. multicoloured . . . 20 15

1242 "Mimosa caesalpiniifolia"

1990. 40th Anniv of Brazilian Botanical Society. Multicoloured.
2401 2cz. Type **1242** 10 10
2402 13cz. "Caesalpinia echinata" 10 10

1243 Cathedral of St. John the Baptist, Santa Cruz do Sul

1244 Sailing Barque and Modern Container Ship

1990. Churches. Multicoloured.
2403 2cz. Type **1243** 10 10
2404 3cz. Our Lady of Victory Church, Oeiras (horiz) . . 10 10
2405 5cz. Our Lady of the Rosary Church, Ouro Preto . . . 10 10

1990. Cent of Lloyd Brasileiro Navigation Company.
2406 **1244** 3cz. multicoloured . . . 30 10

1990. Brazilian Football Clubs As T **1177**. Multicoloured.
2408 10cz. Vasco da Gama Regatas Club 15 10

1246 Collor and Newspaper Mastheads

1247 Sarney

1990. Birth Cent of Lindolfo Collor (journalist).
2409 **1246** 20cz. multicoloured . . 25 20

1990. Tribute to Jose Sarney (retiring President).
2410 **1247** 20cz. blue 25 20

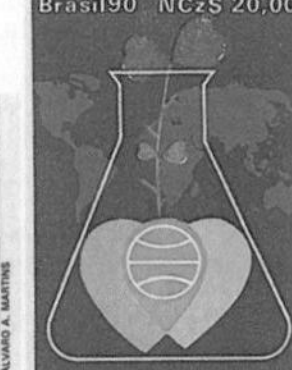

1248 Gold Coin, Anniversary Emblem and Bank Headquarters, Brasilia

1249 Hearts sprouting in Flask

1990. 25th Anniv of Brazil Central Bank.
2411 **1248** 20cr. multicoloured . . 25 20

1990. World Health Day. Anti-AIDS Campaign.
2412 **1249** 20cr. multicoloured . . 25 20

1990. Flowers. As T **1220** but with currency expressed as "Cr$".
2413 1cr. "Impatiens sp" . . . 10 10
2414 2cr. "Chorisia crispiflora" (vert) 10 10
2415 5cr. "Hibiscus trilineatus" 10 10
2417 10cr. "Tibouchina granulosa" (vert) 15 10
2418 20cr. "Cassia micranthera" (vert) 25 20
2420 50cr. "Clitoria fairchildiana" (vert) . . 30 10
2421 50cr. "Tibouchina mutabilis" (vert) 75 65
2422 100cr. "Erythrina crista-galli" (vert) 65 10
2423 200cr. "Jacaranda mimosifolia" (vert) . . . 65 10
2424 500cr. "Caesalpinia peltophoroides" (vert) 65 15
2424a 1000cr. "Pachira aquatica" (vert) 15 10
2424b 2000cr. "Hibiscus pernambucensis" (vert) 25 20
2424c 5000cr. "Triplaris surinamensis" (vert) . . 90 30
2424d 10000cr. "Tabebuia heptaphylia" (vert) . . . 65 10
2424e 20000cr. "Erythrina speciosa" (vert) 65 10

1250 Amazon Post Launch

1990. River Post Network.
2425 **1250** 20cr. multicoloured . . 55 25

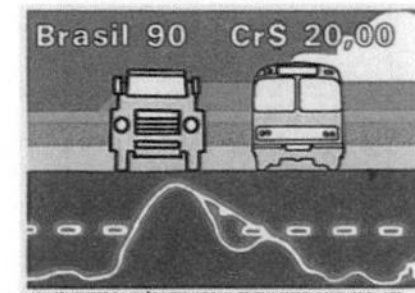

1253 Lorry and Coach

1990. 22nd World Congress of Int Road Transport Union, Rio de Janeiro. Multicoloured.
2428 20cr. Type **1253** . . . . . . 1·00 55
2429 80cr. Van and motor car . . 1·25 55
Nos. 2428/29 were printed together, se-tenant, forming a composite design.

1254 Imperial Crown (Imperial Museum, Petropolis)

1990. Museum 50th Anniversaries. Multicoloured.
2430 20cr. Type **1254** 25 20
2431 20cr. "Our Lady of the Immaculate Conception" (woodcarving) (Missionary Museum, Sao Miguel das Missoes) . . . 25 20

1990. Creation of State of Tocantins. As T **992**, showing state flag.
2432 20cr. yellow, blue and black 25 20

1255 Service Building. Hildebrand Theodolite and Map of Rio de Janeiro

1990. Centenary of Army Geographic Service.
2433 **1255** 20cr. multicoloured . . 25 20

1256 Adhemar Gonzaga (producer)

1990. Brazilian Film Industry. Each maroon and purple.
2434 25cr. Type **1256** 80 25
2435 25cr. Carmen Miranda (actress) 80 25
2436 25cr. Carmen Santos (actress) 80 25
2437 25cr. Oscarito (actor) . . . 80 25

1257 Aerial View of House

1258 Ball and Net

1990. 5th Anniv of France–Brazil House, Rio de Janeiro.
2438 **1257** 50cr. multicoloured . . 60 10

1990. 12th World Men's Volleyball Championship, Brazil.
2439 **1258** 10cr. multicoloured . . 55 10

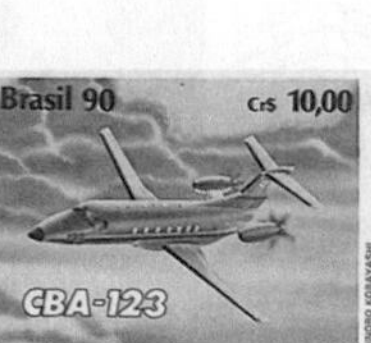

1259 Embraer/FMA Vector

1260 Globe, Pencil and Alphabet

1990. Aeronautics Industry.
2440 **1259** 10cr. multicoloured . . 15 10

1990. International Literacy Year.
2441 **1260** 10cr. multicoloured . . 15 10

1261 Institute

1990. Cent of Granbery Institute, Juiz de Fora.
2442 **1261** 13cr. multicoloured . . 15 10

1262 Map, Track and Diesel Locomotive

1990. 18th Pan-American Railways Congress, Rio de Janeiro.
2443 **1262** 95cr. multicoloured . . 1·50 1·50

1263 Satellite and Computer Communication

1990. 25th Anniv of Embratel (Telecommunications Enterprise).
2444 **1263** 13cr. multicoloured . . 15 10

1264 "Bathers" (Alfredo Ceschiatti)

1990. "Lubrapex 90" Brazilian–Portuguese Stamp Exhibition, Brasilia. Brasilia Sculptures. Mult.
2445 25cr. Type **1264** 30 25
2446 25cr. "Warriors" (Bruno Giorgi) 30 25
2447 100cr. "St. John" (Ceschiatti) . . . . 1·40 50
2448 100cr. "Justice" (Ceschiatti) 1·40 50

1265 "Bromelia antiacantha"

1990. America. 500th Anniv of Discovery of America by Columbus. Praia do Sul Nature Reserve. Multicoloured.
2450 15cr. Type **1265** 90 10
2451 105cr. Wooded shoreline of Lagoa do Sul . . . . . . 1·25 50
Nos. 2450/1 were printed together, se-tenant, forming a composite design.

1266 Oswald de Andrade (birth centenary) and Illustration from "Anthropophagic Manifesto"

1990. Book Day. Anniversaries. Mult.
2452 15cr. Type **1266** 15 10
2453 15cr. Guilherme de Almeida (birth cent) and illustration of "Greek Songs" 15 10
2454 15cr. National Library (180th anniv) and illuminated book 15 10

1267 Emblem and Tribunal Offices, Brasilia

1990. Centenary of National Accounts Tribunal.
2455 **1267** 15cr. multicoloured . . 15 10

1268 National Congress Building

1269 Fingers touching across Map of Americas

1990. Christmas. Brasilia Lights. Mult.
2456 15cr. Type **1268** 15 10
2457 15cr. Television Tower . . . 15 10

1990. Obligatory Tax. Anti-Leprosy Week. As No. 2397 but value and colour changed.
2458 **1239** 50c. blue 10 10

1990. Centenary of Organization of American States.
2459 **1269** 15cr. multicoloured . . 15 10

1270 "Nike Apache" Rocket on Launch Pad

1271 Sao Cristovao City

1990. 25th Anniv of Launch of "Nike Apache" Rocket.
2460 **1270** 15cr. multicoloured . . 15 10

1990. 400th Anniv of Colonization of Sergipe State.
2461 **1271** 15cr. multicoloured . . 15 10

1272 Gymnasts

1991. World Congress on Physical Education, Sports and Recreation, Foz do Iguacu.
2462 **1272** 17cr. multicoloured . . 20 15

1273 Cazuza

1991. "Rock in Rio" Concert. Multicoloured.
2463 25cr. Type **1273** 60 60
2464 185cr. Raul Seixas 80 80
Nos. 2463/4 were printed together, se-tenant, forming a composite design.

1274 Aeritalia/Aermacchi AM-X and Republic Thunderbolt

1991. 50th Anniv of Aeronautics Ministry.
2465 **1274** 17cr. multicoloured . . 20 15

1275 Effigies of Day Woman and Midnight Man, Olinda
1276 Antarctic Wildlife

1991. Carnival. Multicoloured.
2466 25cr. Type **1275** 10 10
2467 30cr. Electric trio on truck, Salvador 10 10
2468 280cr. Samba dancers, Rio de Janeiro 80 45

1991. Visit of President Collor to Antarctica.
2469 **1276** 300cr. multicoloured . . 3·25 2·00

1277 Hang-gliders

1991. 8th World Free Flight Championships, Governador Valadares.
2470 **1277** 36cr. multicoloured . . 15 10

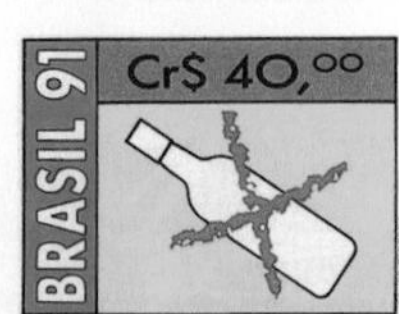
1278 Yachting

1991. 11th Pan-American Games, Cuba, and Olympic Games, Barcelona (1992). Mult.
2471 36cr. Type **1278** 30 10
2472 36cr. Rowing 10 10
2473 300cr. Swimming 85 75

1279 Cross over Bottle (alcoholism)

1991. Anti-addiction Campaign. Mult.
2474 40cr. Type **1279** 10 10
2475 40cr. Cross over cigarette (smoking) 10 10
2476 40cr. Cross over syringe (drug abuse) 10 10

1280 Old and Present Offices and Mastheads
1281 Yanomami Youth in Ceremonial Paint

1991. Cent of "Jornal do Brasil" (newspaper).
2477 **1280** 40cr. multicoloured . . 10 10

1991. Indian Culture. The Yanomami. Mult.
2478 40cr. Type **1281** 10 10
2479 400cr. Hunter (horiz) . . . 80 70

1282 Orinoco Goose

1991. United Nations Conference on Environment and Development.
2480 **1282** 45cr. multicoloured . . 55 30

1283 Jararaca
1284 National Flag

1991. 90th Anniv of Butantan Institute (2481/2) and 173rd Anniv of National Museum (others). Multicoloured.
2481 45cr. Type **1283** 35 10
2482 45cr. Green tree boa 35 10
2483 45cr. Theropoda (dinosaurs) 35 10
2484 350cr. Sauropoda (dinosaurs) . . . . 1·25 60

1991. No value expressed.
2485 **1284** (–) multicoloured . . . 80 10

1285 Early Steam Pump and Santos City 6th Fire Group's Headquarters

1991. Fire Fighting.
2486 **1285** 45cr. multicoloured . . 10 10

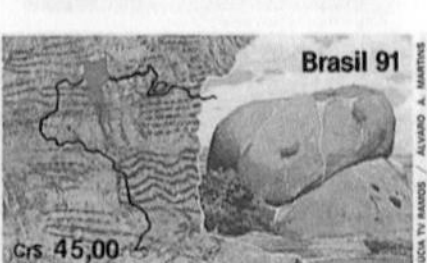
1286 Pedra Pintada, Boa Vista, Roraima

1991. Tourism. Centenaries of Boa Vista (1990) and Teresopolis. Multicoloured.
2487 45cr. Type **1286** 10 10
2488 350cr. God's Finger, Teresopolis, Rio de Janeiro 70 60

1287 Welder, "Justice" and Farmer

1991. 50th Anniv of Labour Justice Legal System.
2489 **1287** 45cr. multicoloured . . 10 10

1288 Folklore Characters, Singers and Mota

1991. 5th International Festival of Folklore and Birth Centenary of Leonardo Mota (folklorist).
2490 **1288** 45cr. red, ochre & black 10 10

1289 Jose Basilio da Gama (poet)
1290 Pope John Paul II

1991. Writers' Birth Anniversaries. Mult.
2491 45cr. Type **1289** (250th anniv) 10 10
2492 50cr. Luis Nicolau Fagundes Varela (poet, 150th anniv) 10 10
2493 50cr. Jackson de Figueiredo (essayist and philosopher, centenary) 10 10

1991. Papal Visit and 12th National Eucharistic Congress, Natal. Multicoloured.
2494 50cr. Type **1290** 60 50
2495 400cr. Congress emblem . . 90 70
Nos. 2494/5 were issued together, se-tenant, forming a composite design.

1291 "The Constitutional Commitment" (Aurelio de Figueiredo)
1292 Exhibition Emblem and dish Aerial

1991. Centenary of 1891 Constitution.
2496 **1291** 50cr. multicoloured . . 10 10

1991. "Telecom 91" International Telecommunications Exhibition, Geneva.
2497 **1292** 50cr. multicoloured . . 10 10

1293 Ferdinand Magellan
1294 White-vented Violetear and "Cattleya warneri"

1991. America. Voyages of Discovery. Mult.
2498 50cr. Type **1293** 15 10
2499 400cr. Francisco de Orellana on River Amazon . . . . 1·25 75

1991. "Brapex 91" National Stamp Exhibition, Vitoria. Humming Birds and Orchids in Mata Atlantica Forest. Multicoloured.
2500 50cr. Type **1294** 60 15
2501 65cr. Glittering-bellied emerald and "Rodriguezia venusta" 80 35
2502 65cr. Brazilian ruby and "Zygopetalum intermedium" 80 35

1295 "Self-portrait III"
1296 Agricultural Projects

1991. Birth Cent of Lasar Segall (artist).
2504 **1295** 400cr. multicoloured . . 80 30

1991. Centenary of Bureau of Agriculture and Provision, Sao Paulo.
2505 **1296** 70cr. multicoloured . . 20 10

1297 Dr. Manuel Ferraz de Campos Salles (President, 1898–1902)
1298 Madonna and Child

1991. 150th Birth Anniversaries. Mult.
2506 70cr. Type **1297** 10 10
2507 90cr. Dr. Prudente de Moraes (President, 1894–98) and Catete Palace, Rio de Janeiro (former Executive Headquarters) 10 10
Nos. 2506/7 were issued together, se-tenant, forming a composite design.

1991. Christmas.
2508 **1298** 70cr. multicoloured . . 10 10

1991. Obligatory Tax. Anti-leprosy Week.
2509 **1239** 3cr. green 35 10

1299 Hand holding Prayer Book

1991. Thanksgiving Day.
2510 **1299** 70cr. multicoloured . . 10 10

1301 Policeman in Historic Uniform and Tobias de Aguiar Battalion Building, Sao Paulo
1302 First Baptist Church, Niteroi (centenary)

1991. Military Police.
2512 **1301** 80cr. multicoloured . . 10 10

1992. Church Anniversaries. Multicoloured.
2513 250cr. Type **1302** 20 15
2514 250cr. Presbyterian Cathedral, Rio de Janeiro (130th anniv) 20 15

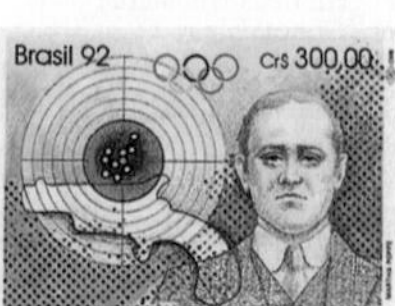
1303 Afranio Costa (silver, free pistol)

1992. Olympic Games, Barcelona (1st issue). 1920 Olympics Shooting Medal Winners. Multicoloured.
2515 300cr. Type **1303** 55 20
2516 2500cr. Guilherme Paraense (gold, 30 m revolver) . . 1·75 60
See also No. 2526.

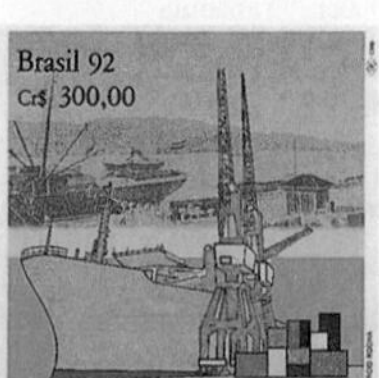
1304 Old and Modern Views of Port

1992. Centenary of Port of Santos.
2517 **1304** 300cr. multicoloured . . 50 20

1305 White-tailed Tropic Birds

1992. 2nd United Nations Conference on Environment and Development, Rio de Janeiro (1st issue). Multicoloured.
2518 400cr. Type **1305** 75 60
2519 2500cr. Spinner dolphins . . 2·00 1·90
See also Nos. 2532/5, 2536/8, 2539/42 and 2543/6.

1306 Ipe 1307 Hunting using Boleadeira

1992. No value expressed.
2520 **1306** (–) multicoloured . . . 1·25 10
No. 2520 was valid for use at the second class inland letter rate.

1992. "Abrafex '92" Argentinian–Brazilian Stamp Exhibition, Porto Alegre. Multicoloured.
2521 250cr. Type **1307** 35 35
2522 250cr. Traditional folk dancing 20 15
2523 250cr. Horse and cart . . . 20 15
2524 1000cr. Rounding-up cattle 85 75

1308 Sportsmen on Globe

1992. Olympic Games, Barcelona (2nd issue).
2526 **1308** 300cr. multicoloured . . 20 15

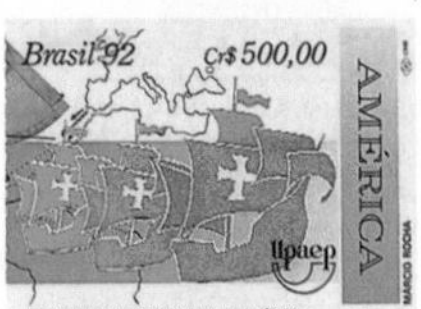
1310 Columbus's Fleet

1992. America. 500th Anniv of Discovery of America by Columbus. Multicoloured.
2528 500cr. Type **1310** 75 25
2529 3500cr. Columbus, route map and quadrant . . . 75 60
Nos. 2528/9 were issued together, se-tenant, forming a composite design.

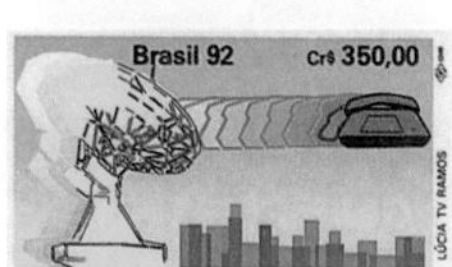
1311 Dish Aerial, Telephone and City

1992. Installation of 10,000,000th Telephone Line in Brazil.
2530 **1311** 350cr. multicoloured . . 15 10

1313 Hercule Florence (botanist)

1992. 2nd U.N. Conference on Environment and Development (2nd issue). 170th Anniv of Langsdorff Expedition. Multicoloured.
2532 500cr. Type **1313** 20 15
2533 500cr. Aime-Adrien Taunay (ethnographer) and Amerindians 20 15
2534 500cr. Johann Moritz Rugendas (zoologist) . . 20 15
2535 3000cr. Gregory Ivanovich Langsdorff and route map 60 60

1314 Urban and Rural Symbols

1992. 2nd U.N. Conference on Environment and Development (3rd issue). Multicoloured.
2536 450cr. Type **1314** 20 15
2537 450cr. Flags of Sweden (host of first conference) and Brazil around globe . . . 20 15
2538 3000cr. Globe, map, flora and fauna 60 30

1315 Monica sitting by Waterfall

1992. 2nd U.N. Conference on Environment and Development (4th issue). Ecology. Designs showing cartoon characters. Multicoloured.
2539 500cr. Type **1315** 20 15
2540 500cr. Cebolinha in canoe 20 15
2541 500cr. Cascao photographing wildlife . . 20 15
2542 500cr. Magali picking wild fruit 20 15
Nos. 2539/42 were issued together, se-tenant, forming a composite design.

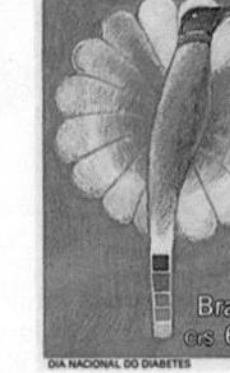
1316 "Nidularium innocentii" 1317 Humming-bird's Wings forming Flower

1992. 2nd U.N. Conference on Environment and Development (5th issue). 3rd Anniv of Margaret Mee Brazilian Botanical Foundation. Flower paintings by Margaret Mee. Multicoloured.
2543 600cr. Type **1316** 25 20
2544 600cr. "Canistrum exiguum" 25 20
2545 700cr. "Nidularium rubens" 25 20
2546 700cr. "Canistrum cyathiforme" 25 20

1992. National Diabetes Day.
2547 **1317** 600cr. multicoloured . . 20 15

1318 Training Tower and First Manual Pump 1319 Animals, Cave Paintings and Map of Piaui State

1992. Centenary of Joinville Volunteer Fire Service.
2548 **1318** 550cr. multicoloured . . 20 15

1992. 13th Anniv of Capivara Mountain National Park. Multicoloured.
2549 550cr. Type **1319** 20 15
2550 550cr. Canyons and map of Brazil 20 15
Nos. 2549/50 were issued together, se-tenant, forming a composite design.

1320 Projects within Flask 1322 Santa Cruz Fortress, Anhatomirim Island

1321 Students at Work

1992. 24th Anniv of Financing Agency for Studies and Projects.
2551 **1320** 550cr. multicoloured . . 1·25 40

1992. 50th Anniv of National Industrial Training Service.
2552 **1321** 650cr. multicoloured . . 15 10

1992. Santa Catarina Fortresses. Multicoloured.
2553 650cr. Type **1322** 15 10
2554 3000cr. Santo Antonio Fort, Ratones Grande island . . 65 60

1323 Masonic Emblem and Palace, Brasilia 1324 Profiles of Child and Man forming Hourglass

1992. 170th Anniv of Grande Oriente (Federation of Brazil's Freemasonry Lodges).
2555 **1323** 650cr. multicoloured . . 10 10

1992. 50th Anniv of Brazilian Legion of Assistance.
2556 **1324** 650cr. multicoloured . . 10 10

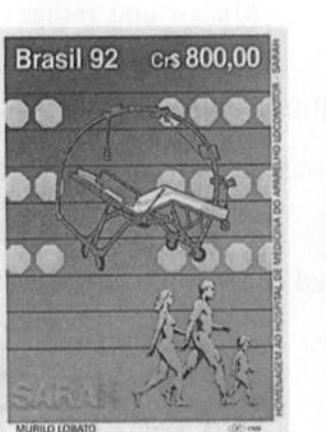

1325 Medical Equipment and Patients 1326 Menotti del Picchia

1992. Sarah Locomotor Hospital, Brasilia.
2557 **1325** 800cr. multicoloured . . 10 10

1992. Book Day. Writers' Birth Centenaries. Multicoloured.
2558 900cr. Type **1326** 10 10
2559 900cr. Graciliano Ramos . . 10 10
2560 1000cr. Assis Chateaubriand (journalist) (horiz) 15 10

1327 Meridian Circle, Map, Cruls and Tent

1992. Centenary of Luiz Cruls's Exploration of Central Plateau.
2561 **1327** 900cr. multicoloured . . 10 10

1328 Productivity Graph on Flag

1992. 2nd Anniv of Brazilian Quality and Productivity Programme.
2562 **1328** 1200cr. multicoloured 15 10

1330 Father Christmas

1992. Christmas. No value expressed.
2564 **1330** (–) multicoloured . . . 90 10

1992. Obligatory Tax. Anti-leprosy Week.
2565 **1239** 30cr. brown 35 10

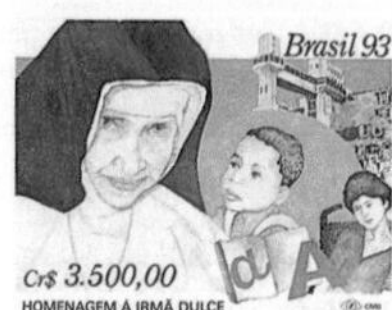
1331 Sister Dulce, Patients and Lacerda Lift, Salvador

1993. Sister Dulce (founder of Santo Antonio Hospital and Simoes Filho Educational Centre) Commemoration.
2566 **1331** 3500cr. multicoloured 20 20

1333 Tube Station, Pine Trees and Church of the Third Order of St. Francis of Assisi and Stigmata

1993. 300th Anniv of Curitiba.
2568 **1333** 4500cr. multicoloured 25 20

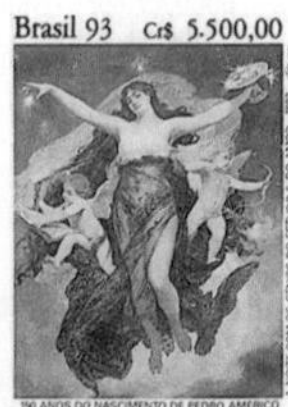
1334 Heart dripping Blood onto Flowers 1335 "Night with the Geniuses of Study and Love"

1993. Health and Preservation of Life. Mult.
2569 4500cr. Type **1334** (blood donation) 20 20
2570 4500cr. Crab attacking healthy cell (anti-cancer campaign) 20 20
2571 4500cr. Rainbow, head and encephalogram (mental health) 20 20

1993. 150th Birth Anniv of Pedro Americo (painter). Multicoloured.
2572 5500cr. Type **1335** 20 20
2573 36000cr. "David and Abizag" (horiz) 30 20
2574 36000cr. "A Carioca" . . . 30 20

1336 Flag 1337 "Dynastes hercules"

1993. No value expressed. Self-adhesive. Die-cut.
2575 **1336** (–) blue, yellow & grn 1·75 20
No. 2575 was valid for use at the current first class inland letter rate. It could not be used to pay postage to foreign countries.

1993. World Environment Day. Beetles. Mult.
2576 8000cr. Type **1337** 30 25
2577 55000cr. "Batus barbicornis" 90 25

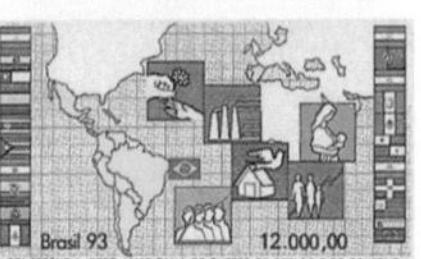
1338 Map, Flags and Discussion Themes

1993. 3rd Iberian–American Summit Conference, Salvador.
2578 **1338** 12000cr. multicoloured 25 20

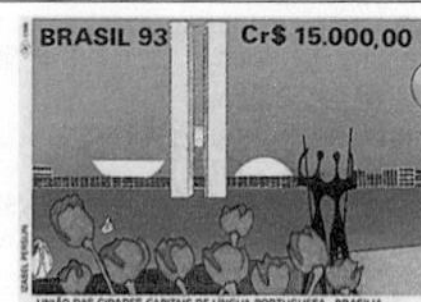

1339 Lake, Congress Building and "Os Candangos" (statue), Brasilia

1993. Union of Portuguese-speaking Capital Cities. Multicoloured.
2579 15000cr. Type **1339** 30 25
2580 71000cr. Copacabana beach and "Christ the Redeemer" (statue), Rio de Janeiro 30 25
Nos. 2579/80 were issued together, se-tenant, forming a composite design.

1340 30r. "Bulls Eye" Stamp

1993. 150th Anniv of First Brazilian Stamps (1st issue) and "Brasiliana 93" International Stamp Exhibition, Rio de Janeiro. Each black, red and yellow.
2581 30000cr. Type **1340** 90 50
2582 60000cr.60r. "Bull's Eye" stamp 90 50
2583 90000cr.90r. "Bull's Eye" stamp 90 50
See also Nos. 2585/8.

1341 Cebolinha designing Stamp

1993. 150th Anniv of First Brazilian Stamps (2nd issue). No value expressed. Cartoon characters. Multicoloured.
2585 (–) Type **1341** 90 15
2586 (–) Cascao as King and 30r. "Bull's Eye" stamp . . . 90 15
2587 (–) Monica writing letter and 60r. "Bull's Eye" stamp 90 15
2588 (–) Magali receiving letter and 90r. "Bull's Eye" stamp 90 15
Nos. 2585/8 were issued together, se-tenant, forming a composite design.
Nos. 2585/8 were valid for use at the current first class inland letter rate. They could not be used to pay postage to other countries.

1342 Imperial Palace (former postal H.Q.), Rio de Janeiro

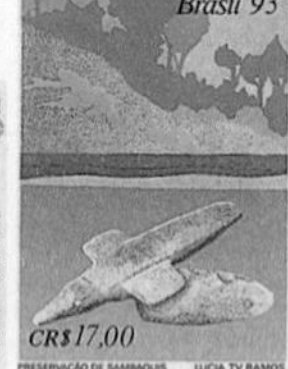

1344 Forest Mound and Tools

1343 Polytechnic School, Sao Paulo University

1993. 330th Anniv of Postal Service. Mult.
2589 20000cr. Type **1342** 40 35
2590 20000cr. Petropolis post office 40 35
2591 20000cr. Main post office, Rio de Janeiro 40 35
2592 20000cr. Niteroi post office 40 35

Currency Reform
1 (new) cruzeiro real = 1000 (old) cruzeiros.

1993. Engineering Schools. Multicoloured.
2593 17cr. Type **1343** (centenary, 1994) 30 25
2594 17cr. Old and new engineering schools, Rio de Janeiro Federal University (bicent, 1992) 30 25

1993. Preservation of Archaeological Sites. Mult.
2595 17cr. Type **1344** 20 15
2596 17cr. Coastal mound, shells and tools 20 15

1345 Guimaraes and National Congress

1993. Ulysses Guimaraes (politician).
2597 **1346** 22cr. Multicoloured. . . 25 20

1346 Hands holding Candles and Rope around Statue

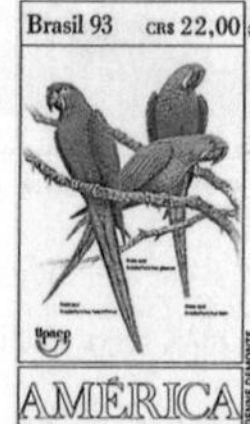

1347 Hyacinth Macaw, Glaucous Macaw and Indige Macaw

1993. Bicentenary of Procession of "Virgin of Nazareth", Belem.
2598 **1346** 22cr. multicoloured . . 25 20

1993. America. Endangered Macaws. Mult.
2599 22cr. Type **1347** 25 20
2600 130cr. Spix's macaw . . . . 1·10 90

1348 Vinicius de Moraes

1349 Liberty

1993. Composers' Anniversaries. Mult.
2601 22cr. Type **1348** (80th birth anniv) 25 20
2602 22cr. Alfredo da Rocha Vianna (pseud. Pixinguinha) and score of "Carinhoso" (20th death anniv) 25 20

1993. No value expressed.
2603 **1349** (–) blue, turq & yell . . 1·75 45
No. 2603 was sold at the current rate for first class international postage.

1350 Mario de Andrade

1351 Knot

1993. Book Day. Writers' Birth Centenaries. Multicoloured.
2604 30cr. Type **1350** 30 25
2605 30cr. Alceu Amoroso Lima (pseud. Tristao de Athayde) 30 25
2606 30cr. Gilka Machado (poet) 30 25

1993. 40th Anniv of Brazil–Portugal Consultation and Friendship Treaty.
2607 **1351** 30cr. multicoloured . . 30 25

1352 Nho-Quim

1993. 2nd International Comic Strip Biennial. No value expressed. Multicoloured.
2608 (–) Type **1352** 90 30
2609 (–) Benjamin (Louneiro) . . 60 25
2610 (–) Lamparina 60 25
2611 (–) Reco-Reco, Bolao and Azeitona (Luiz Sa) . . . 60 25
See note below Nos. 2585/8.

1353 Diagram and "Tamoio" (submarine)

1993. Launch of First Brazilian-built Submarine.
2612 **1353** 240cr. multicoloured . . 1·10 70

1354 Nativity

1993. Christmas. No value expressed.
2613 **1354** (–) multicoloured . . . 80 25
See note below Nos. 2585/8.

1993. Obligatory Tax. Anti-leprosy Week.
2614 **1205** 50c. blue 20 15

1355 Republic P-47 Thunderbolt Fighters over Tarquinia Camp, Italy

1356 Flag

1993. 50th Anniv of Formation of 1st Fighter Group, Brazilian Expeditionary Force.
2615 **1355** 42cr. multicoloured . . 60 25

1994. No value expressed. Self-adhesive. Imperf.
2616 **1356** (–) blue, yellow & green 60 30
See note below Nos. 2585/8.

1357 Foundation of Republican Memory, Convent and Cloisters

1994. 340th Anniv of Convent of Merces (now Cultural Centre), Sao Luis.
2617 **1357** 58cr. multicoloured . . 40 35

1358 "Mae Menininha"

1994. Birth Centenary of Mae Menininha do Gantois (Escolastica Maria da Conceiao Nazare).
2618 **1358** 80cr. multicoloured . . 20 20

1359 Olympic Rings and Rower

1360 Blue and White Swallow

1994. Centenaries of International Olympic Committee and Rowing Federation, Rio Grande do Sul. No value expressed.
2619 **1359** (–) multicoloured . . . 1·75 90
See note below No. 2603.

1994. Birds. Multicoloured.
2620 10cr. Type **1360** 10 10
2621 20cr. Roadside hawk . . . 10 10
2622 50cr. Rufous-bellied thrush 10 10
2623 100cr. Ruddy ground dove 15 10
2624 200cr. Southern lapwing . . 30 25
2625 500cr. Rufous-collared sparrow 80 70
See after Nos. 2649/61.

1361 Map and Prince Henry

1994. 600th Birth Anniv of Prince Henry the Navigator.
2626 **1361** 635cr. multicoloured . . 1·75 90

1362 Bicycle

1994. America. Postal Vehicles. Mult.
2627 110cr. Type **1362** 15 10
2628 635cr. Motor cycle . . . . 1·75 20

1363 Statue, Grain Store and Chapel of Help, Juazeiro do Norte

1994. 150th Anniv of Birth of Father Cicero Romao Batista. With service indicator.
2629 **1363** (–) multicoloured . . . 60 15
See note below Nos. 2585/8.

1364 Sabin and Children

1994. 1st Death Anniv of Albert Sabin (developer of oral polio vaccine).
2630 **1364** 160cr. multicoloured . . 25 20

1365 Castello Branco and Brasilia

1994. Carlos Castello Branco (journalist).
2631 **1365** 160cr. multicoloured . . 25 20

1366 "Euterpe oleracea"

1367 "Brazil"

1994. Birth Bicentenary of Karl Friedrich Phillip von Martius (botanist). With service indicator. Multicoloured. (a) Inscr "1. PORTE NACIONAL".
2632 (–) Type **1366** 85 15
2633 (–) "Jacaranda paucifoliolata" 85 15

(b) Inscr "1. PORTE INTERNACIONAL TAXE PERCUE".
2634 (–) "Barbacenia tomentosa" 1·50 30
Nos. 2632/3 were for use at the current first class inland letter rate and Nos. 2634 for first class international postage.

1994. With service indicator. (a) Size 21 × 28mm. Self-adhesive. Rouletted. (i) PRINTED MATTER. Inscr "1. PORTE IMPRESSO CATEGORIA II".
2635 **1367** (–) blue 10 10

(ii) INLAND POSTAGE. Inscr "3. PORTE NACIONAL".
2636 **1367** (3rd) red 30 20

(b) INLAND POSTAGE. Inscr "PORTE NACIONAL". Size 26 × 35mm.
2637 **1367** (4th) green 40 30
2638 (5th) red 75 30
Nos. 2635/8 were valid for internal use in the category described.

1368 Brazilian Player wearing "100"

1994. Centenary of Football in Brazil and World Cup Football Championship, U.S.A. With service indicator.
2639 **1368** (–) multicoloured . . . 2·40 90
See note below No. 2603.

1369 Emperor Tamarin ("Saguinus imperator") **1371** Pencils Crossing over Fingerprint

1994. Endangered Mammals. With service indicator. Multicoloured.
2640 (–) Type **1369** 60 15
2641 (–) Bare-faced tamarin ("Saguinus bicolor") . . . 60 15
2642 (–) Golden lion tamarin ("Leontopithecus rosalia") 60 15
See note below Nos. 2585/8.

1994. 10 Year Education Plan. With service indicator. Multicoloured.
2644 (–) Type **1371** (literacy campaign) 60 15
2645 (–) PRONAICA pencil and school (National Programme of Integral Care to Children and Teenagers) 60 15
2646 (–) Lecture scene and graph (increase in qualified teachers) 60 15
2647 (–) Pencil and "lecturers" on television (distance learning by video) 60 15
See note below Nos. 2585/8.

1994. Birds. As T **1360** but with value expressed as "R$". Multicoloured.
2649 1c. Type **1360** 10 10
2650 2c. As No. 2621 . . . . . 10 10
2652 5c. As No. 2622 . . . . . 10 10
2654 10c. As No. 2623 . . . . . 15 10
2655 15c. Saffron finch 20 15
2656 20c. As No. 2624 . . . . . 30 25
2657 22c. Fork-tailed fly-catcher 30 25
2658 50c. As No. 2625 . . . . . 75 65
2661 1r. Rufous hornero . . . . 1·50 1·25

1373 Edgard Santos (founder of Bahia University)

1374 "Petrobras X" (drilling platform), Campos Basin. Rio de Janeiro

1994. Anniversaries. With service indicator. Multicoloured.
2662 (–) Type **1373** (birth centenary) 20 15
2663 (–) Oswaldo Aranha (politician, birth centenary) 20 15
2664 (–) Otto Lara Resende (author and journalist, 2nd death anniv) 20 15
See note below Nos. 2585/8.

1994. 40th Anniv of Petrobras (state oil company).
2665 **1374** 12c. multicoloured . . . 40 15

1375 17th century Coin Production **1376** Loaf of Bread

1994. 300th Anniv of Brazilian Mint.
2666 **1375** 12c. multicoloured . . . 20 15

1994. Campaign against Famine and Misery. With service indicator.
2667 **1376** (–) multicoloured . . . 20 15
2668 – (–) black and blue . . . 20 15
DESIGN: No. 2668, Fish.
See note below Nos. 2585/8.

1377 Writing with Quill and Scales of Justice

1994. 150th Anniv of Brazilian Lawyers Institute.
2669 **1377** 12c. multicoloured . . . 20 15

1378 Family within Heart

1994. International Year of the Family.
2670 **1378** 84c. multicoloured . . . 1·25 60

1379 Hospital, White Stork and Babies forming "1000000"

1994. Centenary of Sao Paulo Maternity Hospital. Its Millionth Birth.
2671 **1379** 12c. multicoloured . . . 20 15

1380 Celestino performing and "Maternal Heart" (record sleeve)

1994. Birth Centenary of Vicente Celestino (singer).
2672 **1380** 12c. multicoloured . . . 20 15

1381 Fernando de Azevedo (educationist)

1994. Writers' Birth Anniversaries. Mult.
2673 12c. Type **1381** (cent) . . . 20 15
2674 12c. Tomas Antonio Gonzaga (poet, 250th) . . 20 15

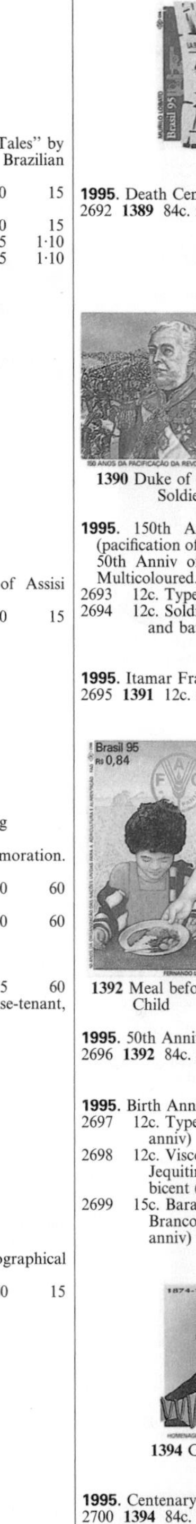

1382 "Joao and Maria" (Hansel and Gretel)

1994. Centenary of Publication of "Fairy Tales" by Alberto Figueiredo Pimentel (first Brazilian children's book). Multicoloured.
2675 12c. Type **1382** 20 15
2676 12c. "Dona Baratinha" (Little Mrs Cockroach) 20 15
2677 84c. "Puss in Boots" . . . 1·25 1·10
2678 84c. "Tom Thumb" . . . . 1·25 1·10

1383 St. Clare, St. Damian's Convent and Statue of St. Francis

1994. 800th Birth Anniv of St. Clare of Assisi (founder of order of Poor Clares).
2679 **1383** 12c. multicoloured . . . 20 15

1384 Racing Car and Brazilian Flag

1994. Ayrton Senna (racing driver) Commemoration. Multicoloured.
2680 12c. Type **1384** 90 60
2681 12c. Senna and crowd waving farewell 90 60
2682 84c. Brazilian and chequered flags, racing cars and Senna giving victory salute . . . . 1·75 60
Nos. 2680/2 were issued together, se-tenant, forming a composite design.

1385 Books and Globe

1994. Centenary of Historical and Geographical Institute, Sao Paulo.
2683 **1385** 12c. multicoloured . . . 20 15

1386 Adoniran Barbosa and "11 o'Clock Train"

1994. Composers. Multicoloured.
2684 12c. Type **1386** 20 15
2685 12c. Score of "The Sea" (Dorival Caymmi) 20 15

1994. Obligatory Tax. Anti-Leprosy Week.
2686 **1205** 1c. purple 10 10

1387 Maggot wearing Santa Claus Hat in Apple

1994. Christmas. Multicoloured.
2687 12c. Type **1387** 20 15
2688 12c. Carol singers 20 15
2689 12c. Boy smoking pipe and letter in boot 20 15
2690 84c. Boy wearing saucepan on head and Santa Claus cloak 90 60

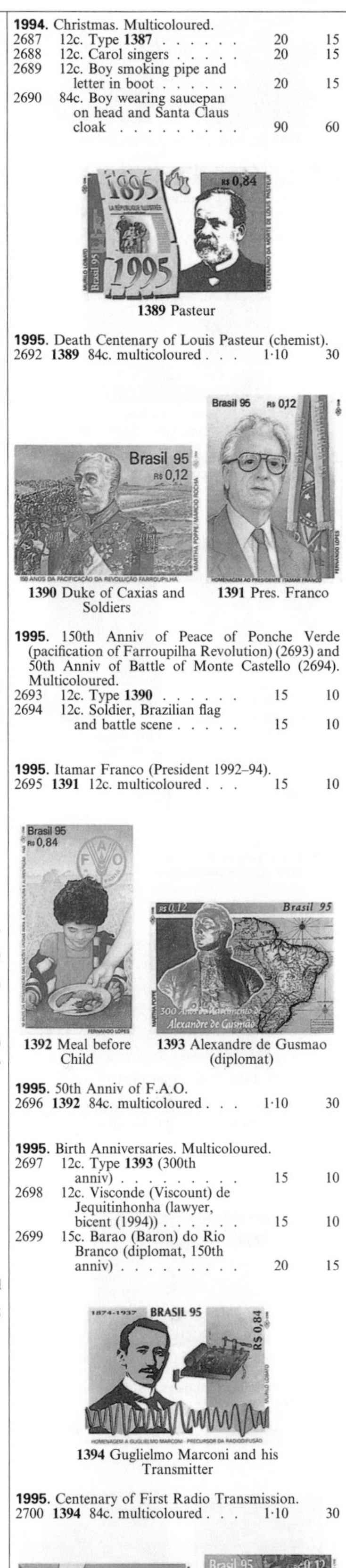

1389 Pasteur

1995. Death Centenary of Louis Pasteur (chemist).
2692 **1389** 84c. multicoloured . . . 1·10 30

1390 Duke of Caxias and Soldiers **1391** Pres. Franco

1995. 150th Anniv of Peace of Ponche Verde (pacification of Farroupilha Revolution) (2693) and 50th Anniv of Battle of Monte Castello (2694). Multicoloured.
2693 12c. Type **1390** 15 10
2694 12c. Soldier, Brazilian flag and battle scene 15 10

1995. Itamar Franco (President 1992–94).
2695 **1391** 12c. multicoloured . . . 15 10

1392 Meal before Child **1393** Alexandre de Gusmao (diplomat)

1995. 50th Anniv of F.A.O.
2696 **1392** 84c. multicoloured . . . 1·10 30

1995. Birth Anniversaries. Multicoloured.
2697 12c. Type **1393** (300th anniv) 15 10
2698 12c. Visconde (Viscount) de Jequitinhonha (lawyer, bicent (1994)) 15 10
2699 15c. Barao (Baron) do Rio Branco (diplomat, 150th anniv) 20 15

1394 Guglielmo Marconi and his Transmitter

1995. Centenary of First Radio Transmission.
2700 **1394** 84c. multicoloured . . . 1·10 30

1395 Ipe-amarelo and Cherry Blossom

1396 Solitary Tinamou ("Tinamus solitarius")

1995. Centenary of Brazil–Japan Friendship Treaty.
2701 **1395** 84c. multicoloured . . . 1·10 30

1995. Birds. Multicoloured.
2702 12c. Type **1396** 15 10
2703 12c. Razor-billed curassow ("Mitu mitu") 15 10

1397 St. John's Party, Campina Grande

1995. June Festivals. Multicoloured.

2704	12c. Type **1397**	15	10
2705	12c. Country wedding, Caruaru	15	10

1398 St. Antony holding Child Jesus (painting, Vieira Lusitano)

1995. 800th Birth Anniv of St. Antony of Padua.

2706	**1398** 84c. multicoloured	1·10	30

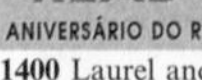

1400 Laurel and "Republic" **1401** Player, Net and Anniversary Emblem

1995. 1st Anniv of Real Currency.

2708	**1400** 12c. brown, green & blk	15	10

1995. Centenary of Volleyball.

2709	**1401** 15c. multicoloured	20	15

1402 "Angaturama limai"

1995. 14th Brazilian Palaeontology Society Congress, Uberaba. Dinosaurs. Multicoloured.

2710	15c. Type **1402**	20	10
2711	1r.50 Titanosaurus	2·00	1·75

1403 Crash Test Dummies in Car

1995. Road Safety Campaign. Multicoloured.

2712	12c. Type **1403**	15	10
2713	71c. Car crashing into glass of whisky	95	85

1404 "Calathea burle-marxii" **1405** Paratroopers

1995. "Singapore '95" International Stamp Exhibition. 10th Anniv of Donation to Nation by Roberto Burle Marx of his Botanical Collection. Multicoloured.

2714	15c. Type **1404**	20	15
2715	15c. "Vellozia burle-marxii"	20	15
2716	1r.50 "Heliconia aemygdiana"	2·00	1·75

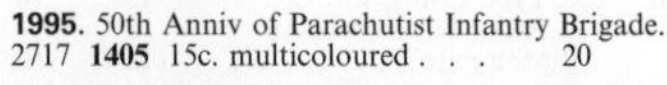

1995. 50th Anniv of Parachutist Infantry Brigade.

2717	**1405** 15c. multicoloured	20	15

1406 Paulista Museum and "Fernao Dias Paes Leme" (statue, Luigi Brizzolara)

1995. Centenary of Paulista Museum of the University of Sao Paulo.

2718	**1406** 15c. multicoloured	20	15

1407 Olinda **1408** Scarlet Ibis and Stoat catching Fish

1995. Lighthouses. Multicoloured.

2719	15c. Type **1407**	35	25
2720	15c. Sao Joao	35	25
2721	15c. Santo Antonio da Barra	35	25

1995. "Lubrapex 95" Brazilian–Portuguese Stamp Exhibition, Sao Paulo. Fauna of the Tiete River Valley. Multicoloured.

2722	15c. Type **1408**	30	15
2723	84c. Great egret flying over canoe	1·10	95

1409 X-Ray of Hand

1995. 150th Birth Anniv of Wilhelm Rontgen and Centenary of his Discovery of X-Rays.

2725	**1409** 84c. multicoloured	1·10	30

1410 Arms and Crowd

1995. Centenary of Flamengo Regatta Club.

2726	**1410** 15c. multicoloured	20	15

1411 Fungi and Alligator

1995. America. Environmental Protection. Mult.

2727	15c. Type **1411**	20	15
2728	84c. Black-necked swans on lake	1·10	95

Nos. 2727/8 were issued together, se-tenant, forming a composite design.

1412 Dove over World Map (left detail) **1413** Jose Maria Eca de Queiroz

1995. 50th Anniv of U.N.O. Multicoloured.

2729	1r.05 Type **1412**	1·40	1·25
2730	1r.05 Dove over world map (right detail)	1·40	1·25

Nos. 2729/30 were issued together, se-tenant, forming a composite design.

1995. Book Day. Writers' Anniversaries. Mult.

2731	15c. Type **1413** (150th birth)	20	15
2732	15c. Rubem Braga (5th death)	20	15
2733	23c. Carlos Drummond de Andrade (8th death)	30	25

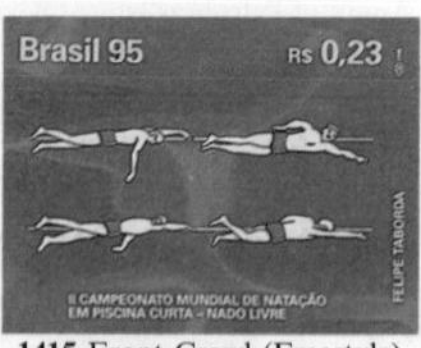

1415 Front Crawl (Freestyle)

1995. 11th World Short-course Swimming Championships, Rio de Janeiro. Multicoloured.

2735	23c. Type **1415**	30	25
2736	23c. Backstroke	30	25
2737	23c. Butterfly	30	25
2738	23c. Breaststroke	30	25

Nos. 2735/8 were issued together, se-tenant, forming a composite design of a swimming pool.

1416 Cherub

1995. Christmas. Multicoloured.

2739	15c. Type **1416**	20	15
2740	23c. Cherub (different)	30	25

Nos. 2739/40 were issued together, se-tenant, forming a composite design.

1417 Flag, Former Headquarters and "Manequinho" (statue)

1995. Centenary (1994) of Botafogo Football and Regatta Club.

2741	**1417** 15c. multicoloured	20	15

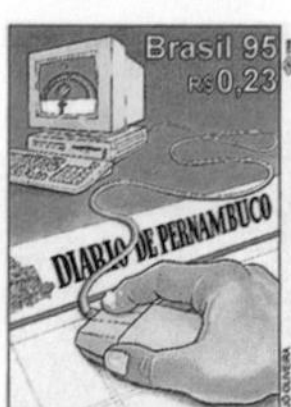

1418 Computer, Mouse and Masthead

1995. 170th Anniv of "Diario de Pernambuco" (newspaper)

2742	**1418** 23c. multicoloured	30	25

1420 Prestes Maia and Sao Paulo

1996. Birth Centenary of Francisco Prestes Maia (Mayor of Sao Paulo).

2744	**1420** 18c. multicoloured	20	15

1421 Bornhausen and Santa Catarina

1996. Birth Centenary of Irineu Bornhausen (Governor of State of Santa Catarina).

2745	**1421** 27c. multicoloured	35	30

1422 "Ouro Preto Landscape" (Alberto da Veiga Guignard) **1423** Doll

1996. Artists' Birth Centenaries. Mult.

2746	15c. Type **1422**	20	15
2747	15c. "Boat with Little Flags and Birds" (Alfredo Volpi)	20	15

1996. 50th Anniv of United Nations Children's Fund. Campaign against Sexual Abuse.

2748	**1423** 23c. multicoloured	30	25

1424 Anniversary Emblem **1426** Pantanal

1425 Pinheiro da Silva and National Congress

1996. 500th Anniv (2000) of Discovery of Brazil by the Portuguese.

2749	**1424** 1r.05 multicoloured	1·25	1·10

1996. Birth Centenary of Israel Pinheiro da Silva (politician).

2750	**1425** 18c. multicoloured	20	15

1996. Tourism. Multicoloured. Self-adhesive. Imperf (backing paper rouletted).

2751	23c. Amazon River	30	25
2752	23c. Type **1426**	30	25
2753	23c. Jangada raft	30	25
2754	23c. "The Sugarloaf", Guanabara Bay	30	25
2755	23c. Iguazu Falls	30	25

1427 Crimson Topaz

1996. "Espamer 96" Spanish and Latin-American Stamp Exhibition, Seville, Spain. Hummingbirds. Multicoloured.

2756	15c. Type **1427**	20	15
2757	1r.05 Black-breasted plover-crest	1·25	1·10
2758	1r.15 Swallow-tailed hummingbird	1·40	1·25

1428 Marathon Runners

1996. Cent of Modern Olympic Games. Mult.

2759	18c. Type **1428**	20	15
2760	23c. Gymnastics	30	25
2761	1r.05 Swimming	1·25	1·10
2762	1r.05 Beach volleyball	1·25	1·10

1430 Dish Aerial, Satellite over Earth and Sports

1996. "Americas Telecom 96" International Telecommunications Exn, Rio de Janeiro.
2764 **1430** 1r.05 multicoloured . . 1·25 25

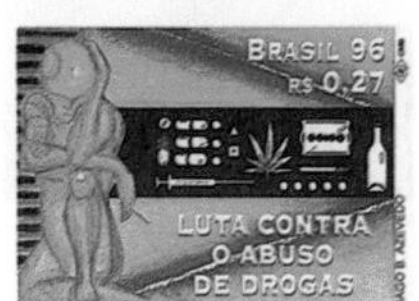

1432 Addict and Drugs

1996. Anti-drug Abuse Campaign.
2766 **1432** 27c. multicoloured . . . 35 30

1433 Coloured Pencils

1435 Gomes and Peace Theatre

1434 Princess Isabel and Aurea Law

1996. Education Year.
2767 **1433** 23c. multicoloured . . . 30 25

1996. 150th Birth Anniv of Princess Isabel the Redeemer.
2768 **1434** 18c. multicoloured . . . 20 15
The Aurea Law abolished slavery in Brazil.

1996. Death Centenary of Carlos Gomes (opera composer).
2769 **1435** 50c. multicoloured . . . 60 50

1436 "Cattleya eldorado"

1996. 15th International Orchid Conference, Rio de Janeiro. Multicoloured.
2770 15c. Type **1436** 20 15
2771 15c. "Cattleya loddigesii" 20 15
2772 15c. "Promenaea stapellioides" 20 15

1437 Melania and Maximino and Virgin Mary

1996. 150th Anniv of Apparition of Our Lady at La Salette, France.
2773 **1437** 1r. multicoloured . . . 1·25 1·10

1439 "Marilyn Monroe" (Andy Warhol)

1996. 23rd International Biennale, Sao Paulo. Paintings. Multicoloured.
2775 55c. Type **1439** 60 50
2776 55c. "The Scream" (Edvard Munch) 60 50
2777 55c. "Mirror for the red Room" (Louise Bourgeois) 60 50
2778 55c. "Lent" (Pablo Picasso) 60 50

1440 Emblem

1996. Defenders of Nature (environmental organization).
2779 **1440** 10r. multicoloured . . . 11·00 9·50

1441 Vaqueiro

1442 Poinsettia and Lighted Candle

1996. America. Traditional Costumes. Mult.
2780 50c. Type **1441** 60 50
2781 1r. Baiana (seller of beancakes) . . . . 1·25 1·10

1996. Christmas.
2782 **1442** (–) multicoloured . . . 20 15
See second note below No. 2588.

1443 "Melindrosa" (cover of 1931 "O Cruzeiro" magazine)

1444 Ipiranga Monument

1996. 46th Death Anniv of Jose Carlos (caricaturist).
2783 **1443** (–) multicoloured . . . 20 15
See second note below No. 2588.

1996. Tourism. Multicoloured. Self-adhesive. Imperf (backing paper rouletted).
2784 (–) Type **1444** 15 10
2785 (–) Hercilio Luz Bridge . . 15 10
2786 (–) National Congress building 15 10
2787 (–) Pelourinho 15 10
2788 (–) Ver-o-Peso market . . . 15 10
Nos. 2784/8 were valid for use at the current first stage inland letter rate.

1445 Campaign Emblem and Guanabara Bay

1997. Bid by Rio de Janeiro for 2004 Olympic Games.
2789 **1445** (–) multicoloured . . . 60 50
No. 2789 was valid for use at the current first stage international letter rate.

1446 Postman and Letter Recipients

1997. America. The Postman.
2790 **1446** (–) multicoloured . . . 15 10
No. 2790 was valid for use at the current first stage inland letter rate.

1447 Alves, Flogging and Salvador Harbour

1997. 150th Birth Anniv of Antonio de Castro Alves (poet).
2791 **1447** 15c. multicoloured . . . 30 10

1448 Tamandare (after Miranda Junior) and "Rescue of 'Ocean Monarch by 'Don Afonso " (Samuel Walters)

1997. Death Centenary of Marquis of Tamandare (naval reformer).
2792 **1448** 23c. multicoloured . . . 40 20

1449 "Joy. Joy"

1997. Winning Entry in "Art on Stamps" Competition.
2793 **1449** 15c. multicoloured . . . 15 10

1450 Globe in Glass of Water

1451 Embraer EMB-145

1997. World Water Day.
2794 **1450** 1r.05 multicoloured . . 1·10 95

1997. Brazilian Aircraft. Multicoloured. Self-adhesive. Imperf (backing paper rouletted).
2795 15c. Type **1451** 15 10
2796 15c. Aeritalia/Aermacchi AM-X jet fighter 15 10
2797 15c. Embraer EMB-312 H Super Tucano 15 10
2798 15c. Embraer EMB-120 Brasilia 15 10
2799 15c. Embraer EMB-312 Tucano trainer 15 10

1452 Red Ribbon inside Condom

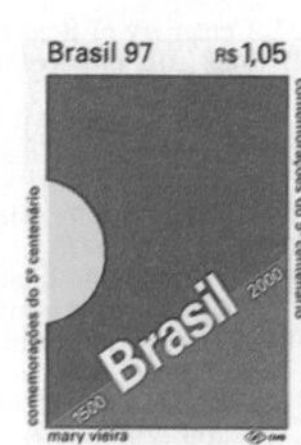

1454 Emblem

1997. Family Health Association (A.S.F.) Anti-AIDS Campaign.
2810 **1452** 23c. multicoloured . . . 25 20

1997. 500th Anniv (2000) of Discovery of Brazil by the Portuguese.
2812 **1454** 1r.05 multicoloured . . 1·10 95

1455 Pixinguinha

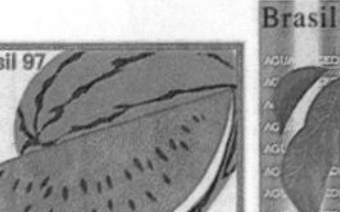

1457 Inscription

1997. Birth Centenary of Pixinguinha (musician).
2813 **1455** 15c. multicoloured . . . 15 10

1997. "Human Rights, Rights of All".
2815 **1457** 18c. black and red . . . 20 15

1459 Melon

1460 Mahogany ("Swietenia macropylla")

1997. Fruits. Self-adhesive. (a) Imperf (backing paper rouletted). (i) With service indicator.
2817 **1459** (–) red and green . . . 20 15

(ii) With face values.
2818 – 1c. yellow, orange & grn 10 10
2819 – 2c. yellow, brown & blk . . 10 10
2820 – 5c. orange, yellow & blk 10 10
2821 – 10c. yellow, brown & grn 10 10
2822 – 20c. yellow, red & green 20 15

(b) Die-cut wavy edge.
2823 – 1c. yellow, orange & grn 10 10
2826 – 10c. yellow, brown & grn 10 10
2828 – 20c. lt green, grn & blk . . 20 15
2829 – 22c. red, purple & green 20 15
2830 – 27c. orange, brown and green 55 50
2831 – 40c. multicoloured 40 35
2832 – 50c. multicoloured 30 25
2833 – 51c. green, lt grn & brn . . 50 45
2834 – 80c. red, green & yellow 80 70
2835 – 82c. lt grn, grn & dp grn 80 70
2836 – 1r. red, green & yellow . . 1·00 90

DESIGNS—HORIZ: Nos. 2818, 2823, Oranges; 2819, Bananas; 2820, Mango. VERT: Nos. 2821, 2826, Pineapple; 2822, Cashew nuts; 2828, Sugar-apple; 2829, Grapes; 2830, Cupuacu; 2831, Soursop; 2832, Suriname cherry ("Pitanga"); 2833, Coconut; 2834, Apples; 2835, Limes; 2836, Strawberries.
No. 2817 was valid for use at the current first stage inland letter rate.

1997. World Environment Day. Amazon Flora and Fauna. Multicoloured.
2836 27c. Type **1460** 30 25
2837 27c. Arapaima (55 × 22 mm) 30 25

1461 Antonio Vieira in Pulpit

1997. Death Anniversaries of Missionaries to Brazil. Multicoloured.
2838 1r.05 Type **1461** (300th) . . 1·10 95
2839 1r.05 Indian children and Jose de Auchieta (400th) 1·10 95

1462 Parnaiba Delta and Sculpture (Mestre Dezinho)

1463 Blue-black Grassquit

1997. Tourism. With service indicator. Mult.
2840 (–) Type **1462** . . . . . . 1·25 1·10
2841 (–) Lencois Maranhenses National Park and costume . . . . 1·25 1·10

Nos. 2840/1 were valid for use at the current rate for first class international postage.

1997. Birds. Multicoloured. Self-adhesive. Imperf (backing paper rouletted). (a) With service indicator.

2842	(–) Type **1463**	20	15

(b) With face value.

2843	22c. Social flycatcher ("Vermilion-crowned Flycatcher")	20	15

No. 2842 was valid for use at the current first stage inland letter rate.

1464 Academy

1998. Cent of Brazilian Literature Academy.

2850	**1464** 22c. multicoloured	20	15

1465 "Gipsies" (Di Cavalcanti)

1997. Birth Centenary of Emiliano di Cavalcanti (artist).

2851	**1465** 31c. multicoloured	30	25

1466 Pope John Paul II, "Christ the Redeemer" and Family

1997. 2nd World Meeting of Pope with Families, Rio de Janeiro.

2852	**1466** 1r.20 multicoloured	1·25	1·10

1467 Flags of Member Countries

1468 Antonio Conselheiro (religious leader)

1997. Mercosur (South American Common Market).

2853	**1467** 80c. multicoloured	80	70

1997. Centenary of End of Canudos War.

2854	**1468** 22c. multicoloured	20	15

1469 Mercosur Members starred on Map of South America

1997. 25th Anniv of Telebras.

2855	**1469** 80c. multicoloured	80	70

1470 Lorenzo Fernandez and Score of "Sonata Breve"

1997. Composers' Birth Centenaries. Each black and gold.

2856	22c. Type **1470**	20	15
2857	22c. Francisco Mignone and score of "Second Brazilian Fantasia"	20	15

1471 "Our Good Mother" and Blackboard with Marist Motto

1997. Centenary of Marist Brothers in Brazil.

2858	**1471** 22c. multicoloured	20	15

1472 Angel playing Trumpet

1473 "Equality" (Gian Calvi)

1997. Christmas.

2859	**1472** 22c. multicoloured	20	15

1997. Children and Citizenship. Multicoloured.

2860	22c.+8c. Type **1473**	30	25
2861	22c.+8c. "Love and Tenderness" (Alcy Linares)	30	25
2862	22c.+8c. "Admission to School" (Ziraldo)	30	25
2863	22c.+8c. "Healthy Pregnancy" (Claudio Martins)	30	25
2864	22c.+8c. "Being Happy" (Cica Fittipaldi)	30	25
2865	22c.+8c. "Work for Parents, School for Children" (Roger Mello)	30	25
2866	22c.+8c. "Breast-feeding" (Angela Lago)	30	25
2867	22c.+8c. "Civil Registration" (Mauricio de Sousa)	30	25
2868	22c.+8c. "Integration of the Handicapped" (Nelson Cruz)	30	25
2869	22c.+8c. "Presence of Parents during Illness" (Eliardo Franca)	30	25
2870	22c.+8c. "Quality of Teaching" (Graca Lima)	30	25
2871	22c.+8c. "Safe Delivery" (Eva Furnari)	30	25
2872	22c.+8c. "Family and Community Life" (Gerson Conforti)	30	25
2873	22c.+8c. "Music playing" (Ana Raquel)	30	25
2874	22c.+8c. "Respect and Dignity" (Helena Alexandrino)	30	25
2875	22c.+8c. "Summary of Children's Statute" (Darlan Rosa)	30	25

1474 Children and Globe

1997. Education and Citizenship.

2876	**1474** 31c. blue and yellow	30	25

1475 Belo Horizonte at Night

1476 Outline Map and Books (Education)

1997. Centenary of Belo Horizonte.

2877	**1475** 31c. multicoloured	30	25

1997. Citizens' Rights. Mult. Self-adhesive.

2878	22c. Type **1476**	20	15
2879	22c. Map and hand holding labour card (work)	20	15
2880	22c. Map and fruit (agriculture)	20	15
2881	22c. Map and stethoscope (health)	20	15
2882	22c. Clapper-board and paint brush (culture)	20	15

1477 Alexandrite

1998. Minerals. Multicoloured.

2883	22c. Type **1477**	15	10
2884	22c. Chrysoberyl cat's-eye	15	10
2885	22c. Indicolite	15	10

1478 Elis Regina (singer)

1998. America. Famous Women. Multicoloured.

2886	22c. Type **1478**	15	10
2887	22c. Clementina de Jesus (singer)	15	10
2888	22c. Dulcina de Moraes (actress)	15	10
2889	22c. Clarice Lispector (writer)	15	10

1479 Pupils

1998. Education. Multicoloured.

2890	31c. Type **1479** (universal schooling)	20	15
2891	31c. Teacher (teacher appraisal)	20	15

Nos. 2390/1 were issued together, se-tenant, forming a composite design of a classroom.

1480 Cruze Sousa

1998. Death Centenary of Joao da Cruze Sousa (poet).

2892	**1480** 36c. multicoloured	20	15

1481 Map, 1519

1998. 500th Anniv (2000) of Discovery of Brazil by the Portuguese. Multicoloured.

2893	1r.05 Type **1481**	65	55
2894	1r.05 Galleon	1·10	90

Nos. 2893/4 were issued together, se-tenant, forming a composite design.

1482 Woman Caring for Elderly Man

1998. Voluntary Work. Multicoloured.

2895	31c. Type **1482**	20	15
2896	31c. Woman caring for child	20	15
2897	31c. Fighting forest fire	20	15
2898	31c. Adult's and child's hands	20	15

Nos. 2895/8 were issued together, se-tenant, forming a composite design.

1483 Clown

1485 Ball breaking Net (Antonio Henrique Amaral)

1484 Turtle

1998. Circus. Multicoloured.

2899	31c. Type **1483**	20	15
2900	31c. Clown resting on stick	20	15
2901	31c. Clown (left half) and outside of Big Top	20	15
2902	31c. Clown (right half) and inside of Big Top	20	15

Nos. 2899/2902 were issued together, se-tenant, forming a composite design.

1998. Expo '98 World's Fair, Lisbon. International Year of the Ocean. Multicoloured.

2903	31c. Type **1484**	20	15
2904	31c. Tail of whale	20	15
2905	31c. Barracuda	20	15
2906	31c. Jellyfish and fishes	20	15
2907	31c. Diver and school of fishes	20	15
2908	31c. Two dolphins	20	15
2909	31c. Angelfish (brown spotted fish)	20	15
2910	31c. Two whales	20	15
2911	31c. Two long-nosed butterflyfishes (with black stripe across eye)	20	15
2912	31c. Sea perch (red and yellow fish)	20	15
2913	31c. Manatee	20	15
2914	31c. Seabream (blue, yellow and white fish)	20	15
2915	31c. Emperor angelfish and coral	20	15
2916	31c. School of snappers (blue and yellow striped fishes)	20	15
2917	31c. Flying gurnard	20	15
2918	31c. Manta ray	20	15
2919	31c. Two butterflyfishes (black and green fishes)	20	15
2920	31c. Pipefish	20	15
2921	31c. Moray eel	20	15
2922	31c. Angelfish (blue, yellow and black) and coral	20	15
2923	31c. Red and yellow fish, starfish and coral	20	15
2924	31c. Crab and coral	20	15
2925	31c. Snapper and coral	20	15
2926	31c. Seahorse and coral	20	15

Nos. 2903/26 were issued together, se-tenant, forming a composite design.

1998. World Cup Football Championship, France. Designs depicting football art by named artists. Multicoloured.

2927	22c. Type **1485**	15	10
2928	22c. Aldemir Martins	15	10
2929	22c. Glauco Rodrigues	15	10
2930	22c. Marcia Grostein	15	10
2931	22c. Claudio Tozzi	15	10
2932	22c. Zelio Alves Pinto	15	10
2933	22c. Guto Lacaz	15	10
2934	22c. Antonio Peticov	15	10
2935	22c. Cildo Meireles	15	10
2936	22c. Mauricio Nogueira Lima	15	10
2937	22c. Roberto Magalhaes	15	10
2938	22c. Luiz Zerbine	15	10
2939	22c. Maciej Babinski (horiz)	15	10
2940	22c. Wesley Duke Lee (horiz)	15	10
2941	22c. Joao Camara (horiz)	15	10
2942	22c. Jose Zaragoza (horiz)	15	10
2943	22c. Mario Gruber (horiz)	15	10
2944	22c. Nelson Leirner (horiz)	15	10
2945	22c. Carlos Vergara (horiz)	15	10
2946	22c. Tomoshige Kusuno (horiz)	15	10
2947	22c. Gregorio Gruber (horiz)	15	10
2948	22c. Jose Roberto Aguilar (horiz)	15	10
2949	22c. Ivald Granato (horiz)	15	10
2950	22c. Leda Catunda (horiz)	15	10

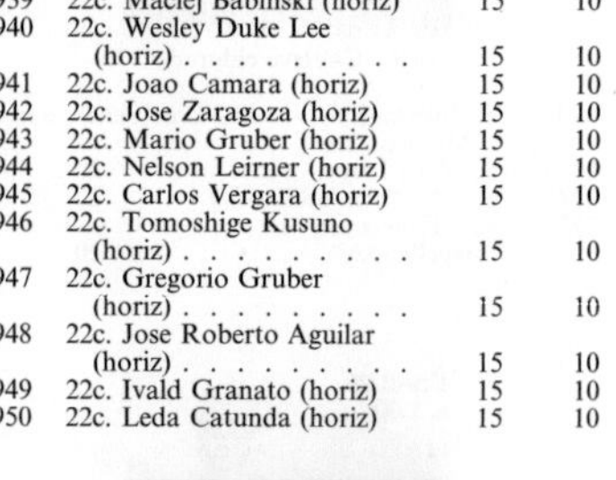

1486 Bean Casserole and Vegetables

1998. Cultural Dishes.
2951 **1486** 31c. multicoloured . . . 20 15

1487 "Araucaria angustifolia"

1998. Environmental Protection. Multicoloured.
2952 22c. Type **1487** 15 10
2953 22c. Azure jay ("Cyanocorax caeruleus") 15 10
Nos. 2952/3 were issued together, se-tenant, forming a composite design.

1488 "Tapajo"

1998. Launching of Submarine "Tapajo".
2954 **1488** 51c. multicoloured . . . 60 35

1489 Bust of Queiroz and College Building

1998. Death Centenary of Luiz de Queiroz (founder of Agricultural College, Piracicaba).
2955 **1489** 36c. multicoloured . . . 20 15

1490 Statue of St. Benedict and Monastery

1998. 400th Anniv of St. Benedict's Monastery, Sao Paulo.
2956 **1490** 22c. multicoloured . . . 15 10

1491 Santos-Dumont and his First Balloon "Brasil"

1998. Aviation. Aircraft Designs by Alberto Santos-Dumont (aviator). Multicoloured.
2957 31c. Type **1491** 20 15
2958 31c. Santos-Dumont and Dirigible "No.1" 20 15

1492 Early Film of Guanabara Bay

1998. Centenary (1997) of Brazilian Cinema. Multicoloured.
2959 31c. Type **1492** 20 15
2960 31c. Taciana Reis (actress) in "Limite" (dir. Mario Peixoto, 1912) 20 15
2961 31c. Grande Otela and Oscarito in "A Dupla do Barulho" (dir. Carlos Manga, 1953) (inscr "Chanchada") 20 15
2962 31c. Mazzaropi (actor) and film titles (Vera Cruz film company) 20 15
2963 31c. Glauber Rocha (director) ("New Cinema") 20 15
2964 31c. Titles of prize-winning films, 1962–98 . . . . . 20 15

1493 Andrade, Entrance to St. Antony's Church (Tiradentes) and Church of Our Lady of the Rosary (Ouro Preto)

1998. Birth Centenary of Rodrigo Melo Franco de Andrade (founder of Federal Institution for Preservation of the National Historic and Artistic Patrimony).
2965 **1493** 51c. multicoloured . . . 30 25

1494 Cascudo and Folk Characters

1998. Birth Centenary of Luis da Camara Cascudo (writer).
2966 **1494** 22c. multicoloured . . . 15 10

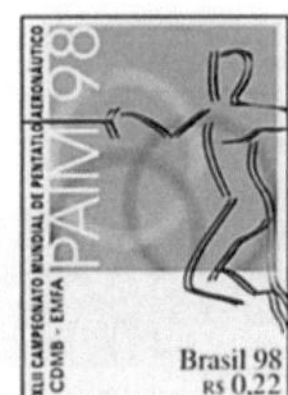
1495 Fencing

1998. 42nd World Aeronautical Pentathlon Championships, Natal. Multicoloured.
2967 22c. Type **1495** 15 10
2968 22c. Running 15 10
2969 22c. Swimming 15 10
2970 22c. Shooting 15 10
2971 22c. Basketball 15 10

1496 Missionary Cross and St. Michael of the Missions Church

1998. Mercosur. Missions.
2972 **1496** 80c. multicoloured . . . 50 45

1497 Untitled Work (Jose Leonilson) (Biennale emblem)

1998. 24th Art Biennale, Sao Paulo. Paintings. Mult.
2973 31c. Type **1497** 20 15
2974 31c. "Tapuia Dance" (Albert von Eckhout) . . 20 15
2975 31c. "The Schoolboy" (Vincent van Gogh) (vert) 20 15
2976 31c. "Portrait of Michel Leiris" (Francis Bacon) (vert) 20 15
2977 31c. "The King's Museum" (Rene Magritte) (vert) . . 20 15
2978 31c. "Urutu" (Tarsila do Amaral) 20 15
2979 31c. "Facade with Arcs, Circle and Fascia" (Alfredo Volpi) (vert) . . 20 15
2980 31c. "The Raft of the Medusa" (Asger Jorn) . . 20 15

1498 "Citizenship" (Erika Albuquerque)

1998. Child and Citizenship.
2981 **1498** 22c. multicoloured . . . 15 10

1499 Mail Coach and "Postilhao da America" (brigantine)

1998. Bicentenary of Reorganization of Maritime Mail Service between Portugal and Brazil.
2982 **1499** 1r.20 multicoloured . . 1·10 90

1500 "D. Pedro I" (Simplicio Rodrigues da Sa), Crown and Sceptre

1501 Mangoes and Glasses of Juice

1998. Birth Bicentenary of Emperor Pedro I.
2983 **1500** 22c. multicoloured . . . 15 10

1998. Frisco (fruit juice) Publicity Campaign. Self-adhesive.
2984 **1501** 36c. multicoloured . . . 20 15

1502 "Solanum lycocarpum"

1998. Cerrado Flowers. Multicoloured.
2985 31c. Type **1502** 20 15
2986 31c. "Cattleya walkeriana" 20 15
2987 31c. "Kielmeyera coriacea" 20 15

1503 Mother Teresa (founder of Missionaries of Charity)

1998. Peace and Fraternity. Multicoloured.
2988 31c. Type **1503** 20 15
2989 31c. Friar Galvao (first Brazilian to be beatified, 1998) 20 15
2990 31c. Betinho (Herbert Jose de Souza) 20 15
2991 31c. Friar Damiao 20 15
Nos. 2988/91 were issued together, se-tenant, forming a central composite design of the Earth.

1504 Sergio Motta and Headquarters, Brasilia

1998. 1st Anniv of National Telecommunications Agency.
2992 **1504** 31c. multicoloured . . . 20 15
Motta was Minister of Communications when the agency was established.

1505 Tiles and Church of Our Lady of Fatima, Brasilia

1998. Christmas.
2993 **1505** 22c. multicoloured . . . 15 10

1506 Moxoto Goat

1507 Man casting Winged Shadow

1998. Domestic Animals. Mult. Self-adhesive.
2994 22c. Type **1506** 15 10
2995 22c. North-eastern donkey 15 10
2996 22c. Junqueira ox 15 10
2997 22c. Brazilian terrier (vert) 15 10
2998 22c. Brazilian shorthair (vert) 15 10

1998. 50th Anniv of Universal Declaration of Human Rights.
2999 **1507** 1r.20 multicoloured . . 75 65

1508 Mother Luiza Lighthouse, Natal

1510 Stamp Vending Machines of 1940s and 1998

1509 Extent of Economic Zone, Satellite and Belmonte Lighthouse

1999. 400th Annivs of Natal (1999) and of Wise Men's Fortress (1998). Multicoloured.
3000 31c. Type **1508** 20 15
3001 31c. Wise Men's Fortress, Natal (horiz) 20 15

1999. Evaluation Programme of Sustainable Potential of Living Resources in the Exclusive Economic Zone (REVIZEE). Multicoloured.
3002 31c. Type **1509** (Sao Pedro and Sao Paulo Archipelago Research Programme) 20 15
3003 31c. Blue-faced booby on buoy 20 15
3004 31c. "Riobaldo" (research ship) 20 15
3005 31c. Turtle 20 15
3006 31c. Dolphin 20 15
3007 31c. Diver 20 15
Nos. 3002/7 were issued together, se-tenant, forming a composite design.
No. 3004 includes the emblem of "Australia 99" International Stamp Exhibition, Melbourne.

1999. 125th Anniv of Universal Postal Union. Multicoloured.
3008 31c. Type **1510** 20 15
3009 31c. Postal products vending machines of 1906 and 1998 . . . . 20 15
3010 31c. Postboxes of 1870 and 1973 . . . . 20 15
3011 31c. Brazilian Quality and Productivity Programme silver award to Rio Grande postal region, 1998 . . . . 20 15
Nos. 3008/11 were issued together, se-tenant, forming a composite design of the U.P.U. emblem.

1511 Lacerda Lift, Barra Lighthouse and Church of Our Lady of the Rosary

1999. 450th Anniv of Salvador.
3012 **1511** 1r.05 multicoloured . . 65 55

1512 Footprint, Iguanodon, Stegosaurus and Allosaurus

1999. "iBRA 99" International Stamp Exhibition, Nuremberg, Germany. Valley of the Dinosaurs, Sousa.
3013 **1512** 1r.05 multicoloured . . 65 55

1513 Fortress

1999. 415th Anniv of St. Amaro of Barra Grande Fortress, Guaruja.

3014 **1513** 22c. multicoloured . . . 15 10

1515 Camouflaged Airplane, Emblem, Dove and Globe

1999. 30th Anniv of 6th Air Transportation Squadron.

3016 **1515** 51c. multicoloured . . . 30 25

1516 Banner and Revellers   1519 Santos-Dumont and Ballon No.3

1518 Symbols of Computer Science, Chemistry, Engineering, Metallurgy and Geology

1999. Feast of the Holy Spirit, Planaltina.

3017 **1516** 22c. multicoloured . . . 15 10

1999. Centenary of Institute for Technological Research, Sao Paulo.

3019 **1518** 36c. multicoloured . . . 20 15

1999. Centenary of Flight of Alberto Santos-Dumont's Airship Ballon No.3.

3020 **1519** 1r.20 multicoloured . . 75 70

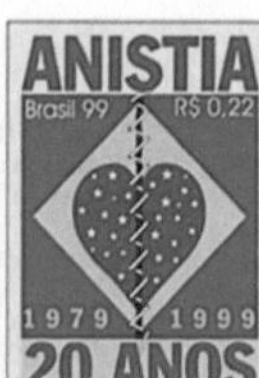

1520 Anteater and Emblem   1522 Stitched Heart

1999. National Campaign for Prevention and Combat of Forest Fires (PREVFOGO). Mult. Self-adhesive.

3021 51c. Type **1520** 35 30
3022 51c. Flower and IBAMA emblem 35 30
3023 51c. Leaf and IBAMA emblem 35 30
3024 51c. Burnt tree trunk and PREVFOGO emblem . . 35 30

Nos. 3021/4 were issued together, se-tenant, forming a composite design of a map and flames.

Nos. 3021/4 are also impregnated with the scent of burnt wood.

1999. 20th Anniv of Political Amnesty in Brazil.

3026 **1522** 22c. multicoloured . . . 15 10

1523 Joaquim Nabuco (politician)

1999. 150th Birth Anniversaries. Multicoloured.

3027 22c. Type **1523** 15 10
3028 31c. Rui Barbosa (politician) 20 15

1524 Dorado

1999. "China '99" International Stamp Exhibition, Peking. Fishes. Multicoloured.

3029 22c. Type **1524** 15 10
3030 31c. *Brycon microlepis* . . . 20 15
3031 36c. *Acestrorhynchus pantaneiro* 25 20
3032 51c. Tetra "*Hyphessobrycon eques*" 35 30
3033 80c. *Rineloricaria* sp. . . . 55 45
3034 90c. *Leporinus macrocephalus* 65 55
3035 1r.05 *Abramites* sp. 75 65
3036 1r.20 Bristle-mouthed catfish 85 75

Nos. 3029/36 were issued together, se-tenant, with the backgrounds forming a composite design.

No. 3036 also includes a hologram of the exhibition emblem.

1525 Open Book and Flags of Member Countries

1999. Mercosur. The Book.

3037 **1525** 80c. multicoloured . . . 55 45

1526 Aguas Emendadas Ecological Station

1999. Water Resources. Multicoloured.

3038 31c. Type **1526** 20 15
3039 31c. House and jetty 20 15
3040 31c. Cedro Dam 20 15
3041 31c. Oros Dam 20 15

Nos. 3038/41 were issued together, se-tenant, forming a composite design of a whirlpool.

1527 "Ex Libris" (Eliseu Visconti)

1999. National Library, Rio de Janeiro.

3042 **1527** 22c. multicoloured . . . 15 10

1999. State Flags (6th series). As T **992**.

3043 31c. Amapa 20 15
3044 36c. Roraima 25 20

1528 Piano and Woman

1999. 5th Death Anniv of Antonio Carlos Jobim (composer).

3045 **1528** 31c. multicoloured . . . 20 15

1529 The Annunciation

1999. Christmas. Birth Bimillenary of Jesus Christ. Multicoloured.

3046 22c. Type **1529** 15 10
3047 22c. Adoration of the Magi 15 10
3048 22c. Presentation of Jesus in the Temple 15 10
3049 22c. Baptism of Jesus by John the Baptist 15 10
3050 22c. Jesus and the Twelve Apostles 15 10
3051 22c. Death and resurrection of Jesus 15 10

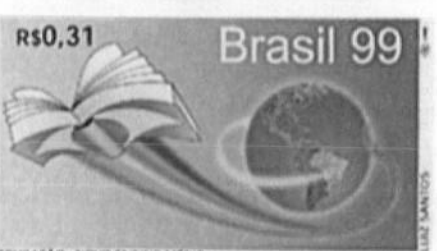

1530 Open Book and Globe

1999. New Middle School Education Programme.

3052 **1530** 31c. multicoloured . . . 20 15

1531 Itamaraty Palace, Rio de Janeiro

1999. Centenary of Installation of Ministry of Foreign Relations Headquarters in Itamaraty Palace, Rio de Janeiro.

3053 **1531** 1r.05 brown and stone 75 65

1532 Buildings and Trees (Milena Karoline Ribeiro Reis)

2000. "Stampin the Future". Winning Entries in Children's International Painting Competition. Mult.

3054 22c.+8c. Type **1532** 20 15
3055 22c.+8c. Globe, sun, trees, children and whale (Caio Ferreira Guimaraes de Oliveira) 20 15
3056 22c.+8c. Woman with globe on dress (Clarissa Cazane) 20 15
3057 22c.+8c. Children hugging globe (Jonas Sampaio de Freitas) 20 15

1533 "2000"

2000. New Millennium.

3058 **1533** 90c. multicoloured . . . 65 55

1534 Map of South America and Children holding Books

2000. National School Book Programme.

3059 **1534** 31c. multicoloured . . . 20 15

1535 Ada Rogato

2000. Women Aviators. Multicoloured.

3060 22c. Type **1535** 15 10
3061 22c. Thereza de Marzo . . . 15 10
3062 22c. Anesia Pinheiro 15 10

1536 Moqueca Capixaba

2000. Cultural Dishes. Multicoloured.

3063 1r.05 Type **1536** 75 65
3064 1r.05 Moqueca baiana . . . 75 65

1537 Freyre and Institute Facade

2000. Birth Centenary of Gilberto Freyre (writer).

3065 **1537** 36c. multicoloured . . . 25 15

1538 Painting and Emblem

2000. 500th Anniv of the Discovery of Brazil.

3066 **1538** 51c. multicoloured . . . 30 25

1539 Natives

2000. 500th Anniv of the Discovery of Brazil. Multicoloured.

3067 31c. Type **1539** 15 10
3068 31c. Natives watching ships 15 10
3069 31c. Sailors in rigging . . . 15 10
3070 31c. Ships sails and natives 15 10

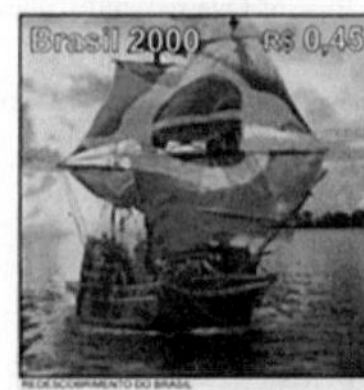

1540 Sailing Ship and Brazilian Flag

2000. 500th Anniv of the Discovery of Brazil. Multicoloured.

3071 45c. Type **1540** 25 10
3072 45c. Man dressed in red suit, pineapple and telephone dial 25 10
3073 45c. Red-spectacled amazon and silhouettes of sailing ships 25 10
3074 45c. Four babies 25 10
3075 45c. Go-kart, Formula 1 racing car and Ayrton Senna 25 10
3076 45c. Sloth, Toco toucan, crocodile, penguin and tiger 25 10
3077 45c. Outline of Brazil and compass roses 25 10
3078 45c. Peace dove 25 10
3079 45c. Child with decorated face 25 10
3080 45c. "500" emblem 25 10
3081 45c. Man wearing feather headdress 25 10
3082 45c. Man in boat, sails and town (Nataly M. N. Moriya) 25 10
3083 45c. Wristwatch, balloon, Alberto Santos-Dumont and his biplane *14 bis* . . 25 10
3084 45c. Sailing ship and document (first report of discovery) 25 10
3085 45c. Jules Rimet Cup and World Cup trophies, player, football and year dates (Brazilian victories in World Cup Football Championship) 25 10
3086 45c. Hand writing, street lights and fireworks . . . 25 10
3087 45c. Banners and Brazilian flag forming cow 25 10
3088 45c. Golden conure perched on branch 25 10
3089 45c. Bakairi masks 25 10
3090 45c. Globe, ship and emblem 25 10

1541 Globe and Map of Brazil

2000. 2nd Anniv of BrazilTradeNet (business information web site).
3091 **1541** 27c. multicoloured . . . 10 10

1542 Turtle, Scarlet Macaw and Map

2000. National Coastal Management Programme (G.E.R.C.O.).
3092 **1542** 40c. multicoloured . . . 20 10

1544 Cruz, Students and Building Facade

2000. Centenary of the Oswaldo Cruz Foundation (medical research institution).
3094 **1544** 40c. multicoloured . . . 20 10

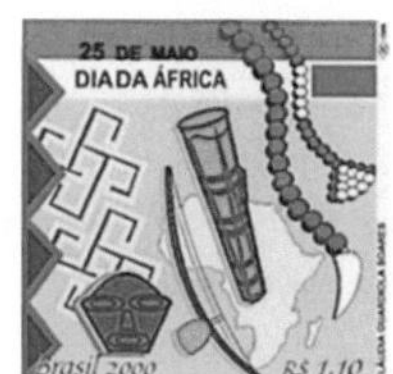

1545 Mask, Musical Instruments and Jewellery

2000. Africa Day.
3095 **1545** 1r.10 multicoloured . . 60 20

1546 Klink in Rowing Boat and Portion of Globe showing Route

2000. Voyages by Amyr Klink (navigator). Multicoloured.
3096 1r. Type **1546** (first South Atlantic crossing by rowing boat (1984)) . . . 55 30
3097 1r. *Paratii* (polar sailing boat) in Antarctica and portion of globe showing route (first single-handed circumnavigation of Antarctica (1999)) 55 30
Nos. 3096/7 were issued together, se-tenant, forming a composite design.

1547 Flag, Buildings, Map and City Arms

2000. 150th Anniv of Juiz de Fora.
3098 **1547** 60c. multicoloured . . . 35 20

1548 Hang Gliding

2000. Outdoor Pursuits. Multicoloured. Self-adhesive.
3099 27c. Type **1548** 10 10
3100 27c. Surfing 10 10
3101 40c. Rock climbing 20 10
3102 40c. Skateboarding 20 10

1549 Forest

2000. Environmental Protection. Multicoloured.
3103 40c. Type **1549** 20 10
3104 40c. Oncilla standing on branch in forest 20 10
3105 40c. Vegetation, adult oncilla and head of kitten 20 10
3106 40c. Vegetation, adult oncilla and body of kitten 20 10
Nos. 3103/6 were issued together, se-tenant, forming a composite design.

1550 *Cisne Branco* (full-rigged cadet ship)

2000. Brazilian Navy. Cadet Ships. Multicoloured.
3107 27c. Type **1550** 10 10
3108 27c. *Brasil* (cadet frigate) . . 10 10

1553 Teixeira, Carneiro Ribeiro Education Center, Salvador and Pupils

2000. Birth Centenary of Anisio Teixeira (education reformer).
3111 **1553** 45c. multicoloured . . . 25 10

1554 Child walking to School

2000. 10th Anniv of the Children and Teenagers Statute (3112) and 15th Anniv of National Movement of Street Boys and Girls (3113). Multicoloured.
3112 27c. Type **1554** 10 10
3113 40c. Rainbow with girl and boy holding star 20 10

1555 Capanema

2000. Birth Centenary of Gustavo Capanema Filho (politician).
3114 **1555** 60c. multicoloured . . . 40 20

1556 Television and Hand writing in Notebook

2000. 5th Anniv of Telecourse 2000 (educational television programme).
3115 **1556** 27c. multicoloured . . . 20 10

1557 Campos

2000. Birth Centenary of Milton Campos (politician and lawyer).
3116 **1557** 1r. multicoloured . . . 70 40

1558 Hand protecting Globe

2000. World Day for Protection of the Ozone Layer.
3117 **1558** 1r.45 multicoloured . . 1·00 60

1559 Archery

2000. Olympic Games, Sydney. Multicoloured.
3118 40c. Type **1559** 30 15
3119 40c. Beach volleyball . . . 30 15
3120 40c. Boxing 30 15
3121 40c. Football 30 15
3122 40c. Canoeing 30 15
3123 40c. Handball 30 15
3124 40c. Diving 30 15
3125 40c. Rhythmic gymnastics 30 15
3126 40c. Badminton 30 15
3127 40c. Swimming 30 15
3128 40c. Hurdling 30 15
3129 40c. Pentathlon 30 15
3130 40c. Basketball 30 15
3131 40c. Tennis 30 15
3132 40c. Marathon 30 15
3133 40c. High-jump 30 15
3134 40c. Long-distance running 30 15
3135 40c. Triple jump 30 15
3136 40c. Triathlon 30 15
3137 40c. Sailing 30 15
3138 40c. Pommel horse (gymnastics) 30 15
3139 40c. Weightlifting 30 15
3140 40c. Discus 30 15
3141 40c. Rings (gymnastics) . . 30 15
3142 40c. Athletics 30 15
3143 40c. Javelin 30 15
3144 40c. Artistic gymnastics . . 30 15
3145 40c. Hockey 30 15
3146 40c. Volleyball 30 15
3147 40c. Synchronized swimming 30 15
3148 40c. Judo 30 15
3149 40c. Wrestling 30 15
3150 40c. Cycling 30 15
3151 40c. Rowing 30 15
3152 40c. Parallel bars (gymnastics) 30 15
3153 40c. Horse riding 30 15
3154 40c. Pole vault 30 15
3155 40c. Fencing 30 15
3156 40c. Rifle shooting 30 15
3157 40c. Taekwondo 30 15

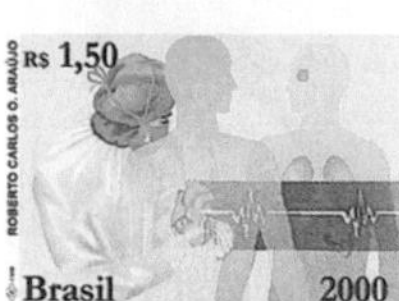

1560 Surgeon and Electrocardiogram Graph

2000. Organ Donation. Multicoloured.
3158 1r.50 Type **1560** . . . . . 1·10 65
3159 1r.50 Hands holding heart 1·10 65
Nos. 3158/9 were issued together, se-tenant, each pair forming a composite design.

1561 Brazilian Clovis Mask

2000. Brazil–China Joint Issue. 25th Anniv of Diplomatic Relations between Brazil and China. Multicoloured.
3160 27c. Type **1561** 20 10
3161 27c. Chinese Monkey King puppet 20 10

1562 Chico Landi and Ferrari 125 Formula 1 Racing Car

2000. Motor Racing Personalities. Multicoloured.
3162 1r.30 Type **1562** 90 50
3163 1r.45 Ayrton Senna and Formula 1 racing car . . 1·00 60

1563 Embraer EMB 145 AEW

1565 Conductor's Baton and Music Score

1564 Hand reaching for Star

2000. Brazilian Aircraft. Multicoloured. Self-adhesive.
3164 27c. Type **1563** 20 10
3165 27c. Super Tucano 20 10
3166 27c. Embraer AMX-T . . . 20 10
3167 27c. Embraer ERJ 135 . . . 20 10
3168 27c. Embraer ERJ 170 . . . 20 10
3169 27c. Embraer ERJ 145 . . . 20 10
3170 27c. Embraer ERJ 190 . . . 20 10
3171 27c. Embraer EMB 145 RS/MP 20 10
3172 27c. Embraer ERJ 140 . . . 20 10
3173 27c. Embraer EMB 120 . . 20 10

2000. Christmas. Multicoloured.
3174 27c. Type **1564** 20 10
3175 27c. Mary and Jesus 20 10
3176 27c. Family and fishes . . . 20 10
3177 27c. Jesus pointing to his heart 20 10
3178 27c. Trees, Globe and open hand 20 10
3179 27c. Jesus and Globe . . . 20 10
Nos. 3174/5, 3176/7 and 3178/9 respectively were issued together, se-tenant, forming a composite design.

2000. Light and Sound Shows.
3180 **1565** 1r.30 multicoloured . . 90 50

1566 Maps and Baron Rio Branco

2000. Centenary of Arbitration Ruling setting Boundary between Brazil and French Guiana.
3181 **1566** 40c. multicoloured . . . 30 15

1567 Three Wise Men, Chalice and Dove

2001. New Millennium. Multicoloured.
3182 40c. Type **1567** 30 15
3183 1r.30 Star of David, Menorah, scroll and stone tablets 90 50
3184 1r.30 Minaret, dome and Holy Kaaba 90 50
MS3185 68 × 113 mm. As Nos. 3182/4 . . . . 2·10 1·25
No. **MS**3185 also has a barcode at the bottom of the sheet, separated from the miniature sheet by a line of rouletting

1568 Map of Americas, Flags, Emblems and Waterfall

2001. 11th Pan American Scout Jamboree, Foz do Iguacu. Multicoloured.
3186 1r.10 Type **1568** 80 45
3187 1r.10 Waterfall, canoeists and emblems 80 45
Nos. 3186/7 were issued together, se-tenant, forming a composite design.

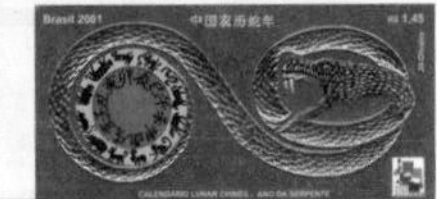
1569 Snake and Chinese Zodiac (½-size illustration)

2001. "HONG KONG 2001" Stamp Exhibition. New Year. Year of the Snake.
3188 **1569** 1r.45 multicoloured . . 1·00 60

1570 *Dirphya* sp. and Institute

2001. Centenary of Butantan Institute (vaccine research centre), Sao Paulo. Venomous Animals. Sheet 115 × 155 mm containing T **1570** and similar horiz designs showing Institute building. Multicoloured.
3189 40c. Type **1570** 30 15
3190 40c. Puss caterpillar (*Megalopyge* sp.) 30 15
3191 40c. *Phoneutria* sp. 30 15
3192 40c. Brown scorpion (*Tityus bahiensis*) 30 15
3193 40c. Brazilian rattle snake (*Crotalus durissus*) 30 15
3194 40c. Coral snake (*Micrurus corallinus*) 30 15
3195 40c. Bushmaster (*Lachesis muta*) 30 15
3196 40c. Jararaca (*Bothrops jacaraca*) 30 15

1571 Old and Modern Printing Methods

2001. Publishing.
3197 **1571** 27c. multicoloured . . . 20 10

1572 Airplane, World Map and Ship

2001. Exports.
3198 **1572** 1r.30 multicoloured . . 90 50

1573 Books and Library Facade

2001. 190th Anniv of National Library, Rio de Janeiro.
3199 **1573** 27c. multicoloured . . . 20 10

1574 Man, Microscope and Emblem

2001. Brazilian Council for Scientific and Technological Development (CNPq).
3200 **1574** 40c. blue 30 15

1575 Footballer and Emblem **1576** Children

2001. 89th Anniv of Santos Football Club.
3201 **1575** 1r. multicoloured . . . 70 40

2001. International Decade for a Culture of Peace.
3202 **1576** 1r.10 multicoloured . . 80 45

1577 Mendes and Halfeld Street

2001. Birth Centenary of Muriles Mendes (poet).
3203 **1577** 40c. multicoloured . . . 30 15

1578 Building Facade and View of Town

2001. Centenary of Minas Gerais Trade Association.
3204 **1578** 40c. multicoloured . . . 30 15

1579 Sunflower and No-Smoking Signs

2001. World No-Smoking Day.
3205 **1579** 40c. multicoloured . . . 30 15

1580 Do Rego and Illustrations from his Novels

2001. Birth Centenary of Jose Lins do Rego (writer).
3206 **1580** 60c. multicoloured . . . 40 20

1581 Hyacinth Macaw (*Anodorhynchus hyacinthinus*)

2001. Birds. Sheet 106 × 149 mm containing T **1581** and similar vert designs. Multicoloured.
MS3207 1r.30 Type **1581**; 1r.30 Sun conure (*Aratinga solititialis auricapilla*); 1r.30 Blue-throated conure (*Pyrrhura cruentata*); 1r.30 Yellow-faced amazon (*Amazona xanthops*) . . . . 2·10 2·10

1582 Sobrinho

2001. 1st Death Anniv of Alexandre Jose Barbosa Lima Sobrinho (journalist).
3208 **1582** 40c. multicoloured . . . 15 10

1583 Jericoacoara Beach, Ceara

2001. Beaches. Multicoloured.
3209 40c. Type **1583** 15 10
3210 40c. Ponta Negra beach, Rio Grande do Norte . . 15 10
3211 40c. Rosa beach, Santa Catarina 15 10

1584 Romi-Isetta, 1959 (½-size illustration)

2001. Cars. Sheet 159 × 115 mm containing T **1584** and similar horiz designs. Multicoloured.
MS3212 1r.10 Type **1584**; 1r.10 DKW-Vemag, 1965; 1r.10 Renault Gordini, 1962; 1r.10 Fusca-Volkswagen 1200, 1959; 1r.10 Simca Chambord, 1964; 1r.10 Aero Willys, 1961 . . . . . . 2·75 2·75

1585 Sayao

2001. Birth Centenary of Bernado Sayao (politician and construction pioneer).
3213 **1585** 60c. multicoloured . . . 25 15

1586 Eleazar de Carvalho, Musical Notation and Musicians

2001. Eleazar de Carvalho (composer and conductor) Commemoration.
3214 **1586** 45c. multicoloured . . . 15 10

1587 Racquet and Ball

2001. Roland Garros Tennis Championship. Sheet 70 × 112 mm.
MS3215 **1587** 1r.30 multicoloured 50 30

1588 Emblem

2001. 50th Anniv of CAPES (training fund).
3216 **1588** 40c. multicoloured . . . 15 10

1589 Buildings, Symbols of Justice and Pedro Alexio

2001. Birth Centenary of Pedro Alexio (Judge and politician).
3217 **1589** 55c. multicoloured . . . 20 10

1590 Player and Ball **1592** Player and Ball

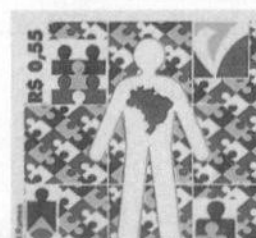

1591 Figure enclosing Map of Brazil (½-size illustration)

2001. Vasco da Gama Football Club.
3218 **1590** 70c. multicoloured . . . 25 15

2001. 5th Anniv of Solidarity Council. Multicoloured.
3219 55c. Type **1591** 20 10
3220 55c. Map enclosing figure 20 10
Nos. 3219/20 were issued together, se-tenant, forming a composite design.

2001. Palmeiras Football Club.
3221 **1592** 70c. multicoloured . . . 25 15

1593 Emblem **1594** Player and Ball

2001. World Conference on Racism, Durban, South Africa.
3222 **1593** 1r.30 multicoloured . . 50 30

2001. Gremio Football Porto Algrense (football club).
3223 **1594** 70c. multicoloured . . . 25 15

1595 Tambourine **1596** Clòvis Bevilǵqua

2001. Musical Instruments. Multicoloured. Self-adhesive.
3224 1c. Type **1595** 10 10
3225 5c. Saxophone 10 10
3226 10c. Cavaquinho (guitar) . . 10 10
3227 40c. Flute 15 10
3228 50c. Fiddle 20 10
3229 55c. Violao (guitar) 20 10
3230 60c. Zabumba (drum) . . . 20 10
3231 70c. Viola Caipira (guitar) 25 15
3232 1r. Trombone 40 20

2001. Clóvis Beviláqua (lawyer) Commemoration.
3250 **1596** 55c. multicoloured . . . 20 10

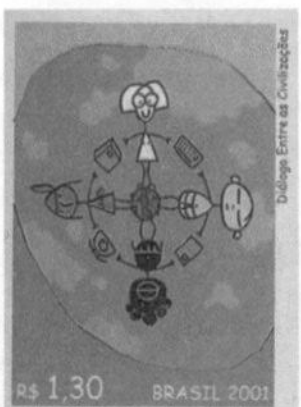

1597 Children encircling Globe

2001. United Nations Year of Dialogue among Civilizations.
3251 **1597** 1r.30 multicoloured . . 50 30

1598 Map of Brazil and Jewish and Dutch Flags

2001. 365th Anniv of First Jewish Synagogue in Recife.
3252 **1598** 1r.30 multicoloured . . 50 30

1599 Junker F13 Passenger Aircraft

2001. Commercial Aircraft. Sheet 107 × 149 mm containing T **1599** and similar horiz designs. Multicoloured.
MS3253 55c. Type **1599**; 55c. Douglas DC-3/C47; 55c. Dornier Do-J Wal flying boat; 55c. Lockheed Constellation; 55c. Convair CV 340; 55c. Caravelle VI R jet airliner . . . . 1·60 1·60

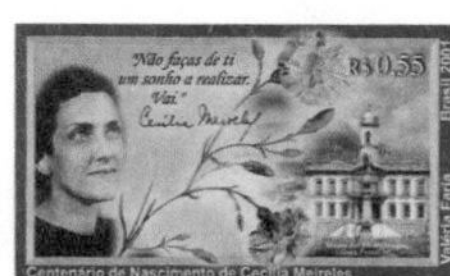

1600 Cecíla Meireles

2001. Birth Centenary of Cecíla Meireles (writer).
3254 **1600** 55c. multicoloured . . . 20 10

1601 Aleijadinho (sculptor) and Bom Jesus de Matosinhos Sanctuary

2001. America. UNESCO World Heritage Sites.
3255 **1601** 1r.30 multicoloured . . 50 30

1602 Madalena Caramuru and Page

2001. Madalena Caramuru (first literate Brazilian woman) Commemoration.
3256 **1602** 55c. multicoloured . . . 20 10

1603 Face, Gavel, Book and Dove

2001. National Black Awareness Day.
3257 **1603** 40c. multicoloured . . . 15 10

1604 Caiman (*Caiman crocodilus*) and Roseate Spoonbill (*Platalea ajaja*) (inscr "*Plataleia*")

2001. Flora and Fauna. Multicoloured. Self-adhesive.
3258 55c. Type **1604** 20 10
3259 55c. American darter (*Anhinga anhinga*) 20 10
3260 55c. Cocoi heron (*Ardea cocoi*) 20 10
3261 55c. Jabiru (*Ephippiorhynchus mycteria*) (inscr "Jabiru") 20 10
3262 55c. *Pseudoplatystoma fasciatum* (fish) 20 10
3263 55c. *Leporinus macrocephalus* (fish) . . . 20 10
3264 55c. Capybara (*Hydrochoerus hydrochaeris*) (inscr "hydrochoeris") 20 10
3265 55c. Southern coati (*Nasua nasua*) 20 10
3266 55c. Water hyacinth (*Eichornia crassipes*) . . . 20 10
3267 55c. Purple gallinule (*Porphyrula martinica*) . . 20 10

1605 Three Kings and Holy Family

2001. Christmas.
3268 **1605** 40c. multicoloured . . . 15 10

1606 Emblem, Player and Football

1607 Imperial Topaz Necklace and Earrings

2001. Libertadores da America Football Championship Winners (1st issue). Flamengo Football Club (1981).
3269 **1606** 1r. multicoloured . . . 40 20
See also No. 3275.

2001. Jewellery. Sheet 101 × 70 mm containing T **1607** and similar vert design. Multicoloured.
MS3270 1r.30 Type **1607**; 1r.30 Garnet ring . . . . 1·00 1·00
No. **MS**3270 was issued with a strip containing a barcode separated by a line of rouletting.

1608 Stylized Eye, Mouth, Hand and Ear (½-size illustration)

2001. International Day of the Disabled.
3271 **1608** 1r.45 multicoloured . . 55 30

1609 Cup of Coffee and Beans

2001. Coffee.
3272 **1609** 1r.30 multicoloured . . 50 30

1610 *Copocabana*

2001. Merchant Ships. Multicoloured.
3273 55c. Type **1610** 20 10
3274 55c. *Flamengo* 20 10
Nos. 3273/4 were issued together, se-tenant, forming a composite design.

1611 Emblem, Player and Football

2001. Libertadores da America Football Championship Winners (2nd issue). Sao Paulo Football Club (1992 and 1993).
3275 **1611** 70c. multicoloured . . . 25 15

1612 Water Hyacinth (*Eichornia crassipes*)

2001. Mercosur. Flora.
3276 **1612** 1r. multicoloured . . . 40 20

1613 Chinese Zodiac and Horse (½-size illustration)

2002. New Year. Year of the Horse.
3277 **1613** 1r.45 multicoloured . . 55 30

1614 Alpine skier

2002. Winter Olympic Games, Salt Lake City, USA. Multicoloured.
3278 1r.10 Type **1614** 40 20
3279 1r.10 Cross country skier . . 40 20
3280 1r.10 Luge 40 20
3281 1r.10 Bobsled 40 20
Nos. 3278/81 were issued together, se-tenant, forming a composite design.

1615 Brasilia and Lucio Costa

2002. Birth Centenary of Lucio Costa (architect).
3282 **1615** 55c. multicoloured . . . 20 10

1616 Women encircling Globe

2002. International Women's Day.
3283 **1616** 40c. multicoloured . . . 15 10

1617 View of City from River

2002. 150th Anniv of Sao Jose do Rio Preto.
3284 **1617** 40c. multicoloured . . . 15 10

1618 Brasilia and Juscelino Kubitschek

2002. Birth Centenary of Juscelino Kubitschek (president, 1956–61).
3285 **1618** 55c. multicoloured . . . 20 10

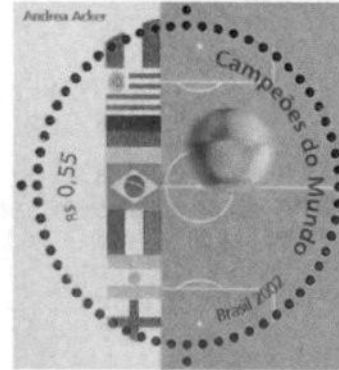

1619 Winners' Flags and Football

2002. World Cup Football Championship, Japan and South Korea. Multicoloured.
3286 46c. Type **1619** 15 10
3287 46c. Footballer 15 10

1620 School Children and Alphabet

2002. Education. Multicoloured.
3288 40c. Type **1620** 15 10
3289 40c. Computer, globe and alphabet 15 10

1621 Josemaria Escriva

2002. Birth Centenary of Josemaria Escriva de Balaguer (founder of Opus Dei (religious organization)).
3290 **1621** 55c. multicoloured . . . 20 10

1622 North American T6

2002. Smoke Air Squadron (air force display team). Sheet 105 × 150 mm containing T **1622** and similar horiz designs. Multicoloured.
MS3291 55c. × 6, Type **1622**; T-24 Fouga Magister; Neiva T-25 Universal (inscr "T-25 Universal"); Two Embraer EMB-312 Tucano (inscr "T-27 Tucano") and plateau; T-27 Tucano and heart-shape; T-27 Tucano over forest . . . . . . 1·20 1·20

1623 Boy wearing Crown, Girls carrying Banners and Boy with Sword

2002. Cavalhadinha (children's festival). Multicoloured.
3292 40c. Type **1623** 15 10
3293 40c. Boys riding hobby horses 15 10
3294 40c. Children wearing masks 15 10
3295 40c. Musicians and drinks vendor 15 10

1624 Cannonball Tree (*Couroupita guianensis*)

2002. Self-adhesive.
3296 **1624** 55c. multicoloured . . . 20 10

1625 Coral and Fish

2002. Coral Reefs. Sheet 105 × 150 mm containing T **1625** and similar square designs. Multicoloured.
MS3297 40c. × 4, Type **1625**; Seahorse; Corals and fish; Fish and starfish 60 30

1626 Building Facade

2002. 150th Anniv of Sisterhood of Charity Hospital, Curitiba.

3298	**1626**	70c. multicoloured	25	15

1627 Jules Rimet and World Cup Trophies

1629 Footballer and Emblem

1628 White-browed Guan (*Penelope jacucaca*)

2002. Brasil, Football World Cup Championship Winners (1958, 1962, 1970, 1994, 2002).

3299	**1627**	55c. multicoloured	20	10

2002. Conservation of North Eastern Caatinga Region. Sheet 70 × 111 mm.

MS3300	**1628**	1r.10 multicoloured	40	20

2002. Centenary of Santos Football Club.

3301	**1629**	55c. multicoloured	20	10

1630 House Facade

2002. "The Enchanted House" Museum (house of Alberto Santos Dumont (aviation pioneer)), Rio De Janeiro. Sheet containing T **1630** and similar square design. Multicoloured.

MS3302	1r. × 2, Type **1630**; Alberto Santos Dumont	40	20

1631 Radar, Airplane, Boy, Animals and Birds

2002. SIVAM (environmental monitoring of Amazon project).

3303	**1631**	1r.10 multicoloured	40	20

1632 Families enclosed in Wheel

2002. Crianca Esperanca (Hope of the Child) Awareness Campaign. Multicoloured.

3304	10c. Type **1632** (child development)	10	10
3305	10c. Children playing (eradication of child labour)	10	10

EXPRESS STAMP

1930. Surch **1000 REIS EXPRESSO** and bars.

E490	**66**	1000r. on 200r. blue	5·25	2·40

NEWSPAPER STAMPS

N 34

N 37

1889. Roul.

N88	**N 34**	10r. orange	3·50	3·50
N89		20r. orange	9·00	9·00
N90		50r. orange	15·00	7·00
N91		100r. orange	6·00	3·50
N92		200r. orange	3·50	1·75
N93		300r. orange	4·00	1·75
N94		500r. orange	30·00	9·00
N95		700r. orange	4·75	15·00
N96		1000r. orange	4·75	15·00

1889. Roul.

N 97	**N 34**	10r. green	1·75	60
N 98		20r. green	1·75	60
N 99		50r. buff	2·40	1·25
N100a		100r. mauve	4·75	1·75
N101		200r. black	4·00	1·75
N102		300r. red	18·00	15·00
N103		500r. green	70·00	90·00
N104		700r. blue	38·00	60·00
N105		1000r. brown	18·00	45·00

1890. Perf.

N111	**N 37**	10r. blue	18·00	15·00
N112		20r. green	55·00	21·00
N113		100r. mauve	18·00	18·00

N 38 Southern Cross and Sugar-loaf Mountain

1890. Perf.

N119	**N 38**	10r. blue	2·40	1·75
N123a		20r. green	7·00	4·00
N127		50r. green	18·00	15·00

OFFICIAL STAMPS

O 64 Pres. Affonso Penna

O 67 Pres. Hermes de Fonseca

O 77 Pres. Wenceslao Braz

1906. Various frames.

O282	**O 64**	10r. green & orange	90	10
O283		20r. green & orange	1·25	10
O284		50r. green & orange	1·75	10
O285		100r. green & orange	90	10
O286		200r. green & orange	1·25	35
O287		300r. green & orange	3·50	60
O288		400r. green & orange	7·00	3·00
O289		500r. green & orange	3·50	1·75
O290		700r. green & orange	4·75	4·00
O291		1000r. green & orange	4·75	1·25
O292		2000r. green & orange	5·25	2·40
O293		5000r. green & orange	10·50	1·75
O294		10000r. green & orange	10·50	1·40

1913. Various frames.

O295	**O 67**	10r. black and grey	20	60
O296		20r. black and olive	20	60
O297		50r. black and grey	25	60
O298		100r. black and red	90	35
O299		200r. black and blue	1·25	35
O300		500r. black & yellow	3·00	60
O301		600r. black & purple	3·50	3·00
O302		1000r. black & brown	4·00	1·75
O303		2000r. black & brown	7·00	2·40
O304		5000r. black & bistre	9·00	3·50
O305		10000r. black	15·00	7·00
O306		20000r. black & blue	27·00	27·00
O307		50000r. black & green	48·00	48·00
O308		100000r. black & red	£140	£140
O309		500000r. black & brn	£200	£200
O310		1000000r. black & brn	£225	£225

1919.

O311	**O 77**	10r. brown	25	3·50
O312		50r. green	90	1·25
O313		100r. red	1·75	60
O314		200r. blue	2·40	60
O315		500r. orange	9·00	18·00

POSTAGE DUE STAMPS

D 34

D 45

D 64

1889. Roul.

D88	**D 34**	10r. red	3·50	1·25
D89		20r. red	5·25	2·40
D90		50r. red	7·00	4·75
D91		100r. red	3·50	1·75
D92		200r. red	70·00	21·00
D93		300r. red	10·50	10·50
D94		500r. red	9·00	9·00
D95		700r. red	16·00	18·00
D96		1000r. red	16·00	14·00

1890. Roul.

D 97	**D 34**	10r. orange	60	35
D 98		20r. blue	60	35
D 99		50r. olive	1·25	35
D100		200r. red	7·00	1·25
D101		300r. green	3·50	1·75
D102		500r. grey	4·75	3·50
D103		700r. violet	5·25	10·50
D104		1000r. purple	7·00	7·00

1895. Perf.

D172	**D 45**	10r. blue	1·75	1·25
D173		20r. green	9·00	7·00
D174		50r. green	14·00	9·00
D175		100r. red	7·00	2·40
D176b		200r. lilac	7·00	1·75
D177a		300r. blue	3·00	2·40
D178		2000r. brown	18·00	18·00

1906.

D282	**D 64**	10r. slate	35	35
D283		20r. violet	35	35
D284		50r. green	40	35
D285		100r. red	1·25	60
D286		200r. blue	90	40
D287		300r. grey	60	1·25
D288		400r. green	1·25	50
D289		500r. lilac	30·00	30·00
D290		600r. purple	1·25	2·40
D291		700r. brown	26·00	26·00
D292		1000r. red	3·00	3·50
D293		2000r. green	4·75	5·25
D294		5000r. brown	1·25	38·00

D 77

1919.

D345	**D 77**	5r. brown	40	40
D403		10r. mauve	35	35
D365		20r. olive	40	40
D404		20r. black	40	35
D405		50r. green	45	45
D375		100r. red	60	60
D407		200r. blue	1·75	60
D408		400r. brown	1·25	1·25
D401		600r. violet	60	60
D350		600r. orange	1·25	1·25
D409		1000r. turquoise	60	60
D439		2000r. brown	1·25	1·25
D411		5000r. blue	85	85

BREMEN Pt. 7

A free city of the Hanseatic League, situated on the R. Weser in northern Germany. Joined the North German Confederation in 1868.

72 grote = 1 thaler (internal).
22 grote = 10 silbergroschen (overseas mail).

1 2 3

1855. Imperf.

1	**1**	3g. black on blue	£170	£250

1856. Imperf.

3	**2**	5g. black on red	£140	£250
4		7g. black on yellow	£190	£550
5	**3**	5sg. green	£100	£200

4

5

1861. Zigzag roulette or perf.

17	**4**	2g. orange	60·00	£225
19	**1**	3g. black on blue	65·00	£275
20	**2**	5g. black on red	£100	£225
21		7g. black on yellow	£120	£3250
22	**5**	10g. black	£170	£900
24	**3**	5sg. green	£150	£150

BRITISH ANTARCTIC TERRITORY Pt. 1

Constituted in 1962 comprising territories south of latitude 60°S., from the former Falkland Island Dependencies.

1963. 12 pence = 1 shilling;
20 shillings = 1 pound.
1971. 100 (new) pence = 1 pound.

1 M.V. "Kista Dan"

1963.

1	**1**	½d. blue	1·25	1·75
2	–	1d. brown	1·25	80
3	–	1½d. red and purple	1·25	1·50
4	–	2d. purple	1·25	80
5	–	2½d. myrtle	3·25	1·25
6	–	3d. turquoise	3·75	1·50
7	–	4d. sepia	2·75	1·50
8	–	6d. olive and blue	4·75	2·50
9	–	9d. green	3·50	2·00
10	–	1s. turquoise	3·75	1·50
11	–	2s. violet and brown	20·00	10·00
12	–	2s.6d. blue	20·00	12·00
13	–	5s. orange and red	21·00	16·00
14	–	10s. blue and green	45·00	26·00
15	–	£1 black and blue	48·00	48·00
15a	–	£1 red and black	£130	£120

DESIGNS: 1d. Manhauling; 1½d. Muskeg (tractor); 2d. Skiing; 2½d. De Havilland D.H.C.2 Beaver (aircraft); 3d. R.R.S. "John Biscoe II"; 4d. Camp scene; 6d. H.M.S. "Protector"; 9d. Sledging; 1s. De Havilland D.H.C.3 Otter (aircraft); 2s. Huskies; 2s.6d. Westland Whirlwind helicopter; 5s. Snocat (tractor); 10s. R.R.S. "Shackleton"; £1 (No. 15), Antarctic map; £1 (No. 15a), H.M.S. "Endurance I".

1966. Churchill Commemoration. As T **38** of Antigua.

16	½d. blue	80	3·25
17	1d. green	3·00	3·25
18	1s. brown	21·00	6·50
19	2s. violet	24·00	7·00

17 Lemaire Channel and Icebergs

1969. 25th Anniv of Continuous Scientific Work.

20	**17**	3½d. black, blue and ultram	3·50	3·00
21	–	6d. multicoloured	1·00	2·50
22	–	1s. black, blue and red	1·00	2·00
23	–	2s. black, orange and turquoise	1·00	3·00

DESIGNS: 6d. Radio Sonde balloon; 1s. Muskeg pulling tent equipment; 2s. Surveyors with theodolite.

1971. Decimal Currency. Nos. 1/14 surch.

24	½p. on ½d. blue	60	3·00
25	1p. on 1d. brown	1·00	90
26	1½p. on 1½d. red and purple	1·25	75
27	2p. on 2d. purple	1·25	40
28	2½p. on 2½d. green	3·00	2·25
29	3p. on 3d. blue	2·50	75
30	4p. on 4d. brown	2·25	75
31	5p. on 6d. green and blue	4·75	3·50
32	6p. on 9d. green	16·00	8·00
33	7½p. on 1s. blue	20·00	8·50
34	10p. on 2s. violet and brown	20·00	14·00
35	15p. on 2s.6d. blue	20·00	15·00
36	25p. on 5s. orange and red	24·00	17·00
37	50p. on 10s. blue and green	40·00	30·00

19 Setting up Camp, Graham Land

21 James Cook and H.M.S. "Resolution"

1971. 10th Anniv of Antarctic Treaty. Muticoloured.

38	1½p. Type **19**	6·00	5·50
39	4p. Snow petrels	16·00	8·00

40	5p. Weddell seals	9·50	8·00
41	10p. Adelie penguins	22·00	9·00

Nos. 38/41 each include Antarctic map and Queen Elizabeth in their design.

1972. Royal Silver Wedding. As T **52** of Ascension, but with Kerguelen fur seals and Emperor penguins in background.

42	5p. brown	3·00	3·00
43	10p. green	3·00	3·00

1973. Multicoloured.

64a	½p. Type **21**	75	2·50
65	1p. Thaddeus von Bellingshausen and "Vostok"	60	2·25
66	1½p. James Weddell and "Jane"	60	2·25
47	2p. John Biscoe and "Tula"	3·00	1·75
48	2½p. J. S. C. Dumont d'Urville and "L'Astrolabe"	1·50	1·75
49	3p. James Clark Ross and H.M.S. "Erebus"	1·00	1·75
50	4p. C. A. Larsen and "Jason"	1·00	1·75
51	5p. Adrien de Gerlache and "Belgica"	1·00	1·75
52	6p. Otto Nordenskjold and "Antarctic"	1·25	2·25
53	7½p. W. S. Bruce and "Scotia"	1·50	2·50
74a	10p. Jean-Baptiste Charcot and "Pourquoi Pas?"	50	3·00
75	15p. Ernest Shackleton and "Endurance"	1·25	2·25
76	25p. Hubert Wilkins and Lockheed Vega "San Francisco"	1·25	1·50
77b	50p. Lincoln Ellsworth and Northrop Gamma "Polar Star"	85	2·75
78	£1 John Rymill and "Penola"	2·75	2·00

The 25p. and 50p. show aircraft; the rest show ships.

1973. Royal Wedding. As T **47** of Anguilla. Background colour given. Multicoloured.

59	5p. brown	40	20
60	15p. blue	70	30

22 Churchill and Churchill Peninsula, B.A.T.

1974. Birth Centenary of Sir Winston Churchill. Multicoloured.

61	5p. Type **22**	1·50	1·75
62	15p. Churchill and "Trepassey"	1·75	2·25

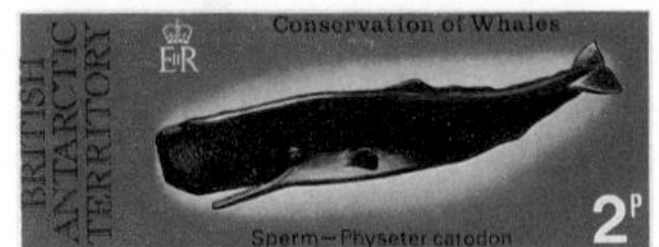

23 Sperm Whale

1977. Whale Conservation. Multicoloured.

79	2p. Type **23**	6·50	4·00
80	8p. Fin whale	7·50	4·50
81	11p. Humpback whale	8·00	4·50
82	25p. Blue whale	8·50	6·00

24 The Queen before Taking the Oath

1977. Silver Jubilee. Multicoloured.

83	6p. Prince Philip's visit, 1956/7	70	40
84	11p. The Coronation Oath	80	50
85	33p. Type **24**	1·25	65

25 Emperor Penguin

1978. 25th Anniv of Coronation.

86	–	25p. green, deep green and silver	80	1·00
87	–	25p. multicoloured	80	1·00
88	**25**	25p. green, deep green and silver	80	1·00

DESIGNS: No. 86, Black Bull of Clarence; 87, Queen Elizabeth II.

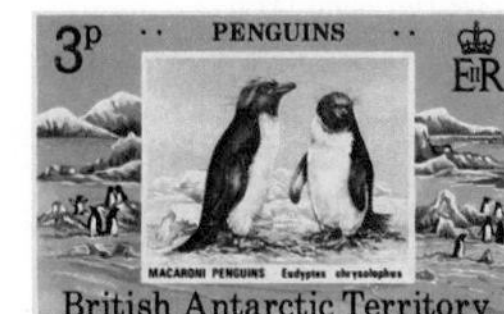

26 Macaroni Penguins

1979. Penguins. Multicoloured.

89	3p. Type **26**	11·00	11·00
90	8p. Gentoo penguins	3·00	3·00
91	11p. Adelie penguins	3·50	3·50
92	25p. Emperor penguins	4·50	4·50

27 Sir John Barrow and "Tula"

1980. 150th Anniv of Royal Geographical Society. Former Presidents. Multicoloured.

93	3p. Type **27**	15	15
94	7p. Sir Clement Markham and "Discovery"	15	25
95	11p. Lord Curzon and whaleboat "James Caird"	20	30
96	15p. Sir William Goodenough	20	35
97	22p. Sir James Wordie	25	55
98	30p. Sir Raymond Priestley	30	65

28 Map of Antarctic

1981. 20th Anniv of Antarctic Treaty.

99	**28**	10p. black, blue and light blue	40	80
100	–	13p. black, blue and green	45	90
101	–	25p. black, blue and mauve	55	1·00
102	–	26p. black, brown and red	55	1·00

DESIGNS: 13p. Conservation research ("scientific co-operation"); 25p. Satellite image mapping ("technical co-operation"); 26p. Global geophysics ("scientific co-operation").

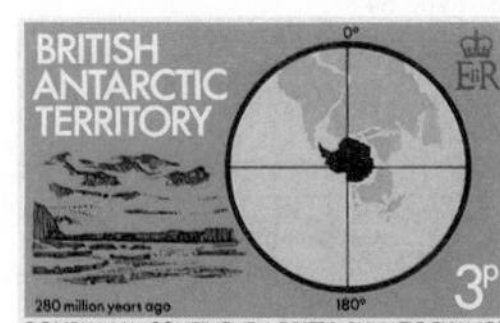

29 Map of Gondwana 280 million years ago and Contemporary Landscape Scene

1982. Gondwana – Continental Drift and Climatic Change. Maps of Gondwana showing position of continents, and contemporary landscapes. Mult.

103	3p. Type **29**	25	40
104	6p. 260 million years ago	30	50
105	10p. 230 million years ago	35	60
106	13p. 175 million years ago	45	70
107	25p. 50 million years ago	55	75
108	26p. Present day	55	75

30 British Antarctic Territory Coat of Arms

1982. 21st Birthday of Princess of Wales. Multicoloured.

109	5p. Type **30**	20	30
110	17p. Princess of Wales (detail of painting by Bryan Organ)	45	60
111	37p. Wedding ceremony	70	90
112	50p. Formal portrait	1·10	1·25

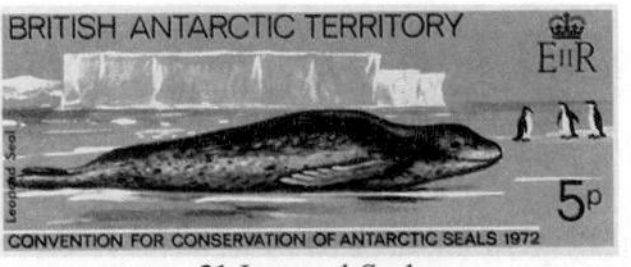

31 Leopard Seal

1983. 10th Anniv of Antarctic Seal Conservation Convention. Multicoloured.

113	5p. Type **31**	25	35
114	10p. Weddell seals	30	40
115	13p. Southern elephant seals	30	45
116	17p. Kerguelen fur seals	30	55
117	25p. Ross seals	30	65
118	34p. Crabeater seals	35	85

32 De Havilland Twin Otter 200/300

1983. Bicentenary of Manned Flight. Multicoloured.

119	5p. Type **32**	25	30
120	13p. De Havilland D.H.C.3 Otter	35	45
121	17p. Consolidated PBY-5A Canso amphibian	45	60
122	50p. Lockheed Vega "San Francisco"	70	1·25

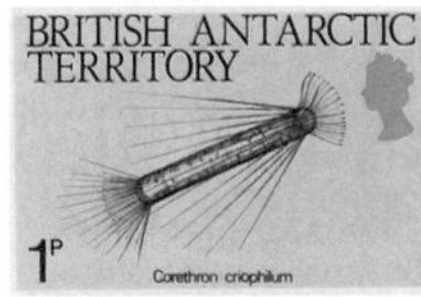

33 "Corethron criophilum"

1984. Marine Life. Multicoloured.

123	1p. Type **33**	60	1·75
124	2p. "Desmonema gaudichaudi"	65	1·75
125	3p. "Tomopteris carpenteri"	65	1·75
126	4p. "Pareuchaeta antarctica"	70	1·75
127	5p. "Antarctomysis maxima"	70	1·75
128	6p. "Antarcturus signiensis"	70	1·75
129	7p. "Serolis cornuta"	70	1·75
130	8p. "Parathemisto gaudichaudii"	70	1·75
131	9p. "Bovallia gigantea"	70	1·75
132	10p. "Euphausia superba"	70	1·75
133	15p. "Colossendeis australis"	70	1·75
134	20p. "Todarodes sagittatus"	75	1·75
135	25p. Antarctic rockcod	80	1·75
136	50p. Black-finned icefish	1·25	2·00
137	£1 Crabeater seal	1·75	2·50
138	£3 Antarctic marine food chain	5·00	6·50

34 M.Y. "Penola" in Stella Creek

1985. 50th Anniv of British Graham Land Expedition. Multicoloured.

139	7p. Type **34**	40	75
140	22p. Northern Base, Winter Island	70	1·40
141	27p. De Havilland Fox Moth at Southern Base, Barry Island	80	1·60
142	54p. Dog Team, near Ablation Point, George VI Sound	1·50	2·25

35 Robert McCormick and South Polar Skua **36** Dr. Edmond Halley

1985. Early Naturalists. Multicoloured.

143	7p. Type **35**	1·00	1·50
144	22p. Sir Joseph Dalton Hooker and "Deschampsia antarctica"	1·50	2·75
145	27p. Jean Rene C. Quoy and hourglass dolphin	1·60	2·75
146	54p. James Weddell and Weddell seal	2·25	4·00

1986. Appearance of Halley's Comet. Multicoloured.

147	7p. Type **36**	75	1·25
148	22p. Halley Station, Antarctica	1·25	2·25
149	27p. "Halley's Comet, 1531" (from Peter Apian woodcut, 1532)	1·50	2·50
150	44p. "Giotto" spacecraft	2·75	4·50

37 Snow Crystal

38 Captain Scott, 1904

1986. 50th Anniv of International Glaciological Society. Snow Crystals.

151	**37**	10p. light blue and blue	50	75
152	–	24p. green and deep green	65	1·40
153	–	29p. mauve and deep mauve	70	1·50
154	–	58p. blue and violet	1·00	2·50

1987. 75th Anniv of Captain Scott's Arrival at South Pole. Multicoloured.

155	10p. Type **38**	65	95
156	24p. Hut Point and "Discovery" Ross Island, 1902–4	1·10	2·00
157	29p. Cape Evans Hut, 1911–13	1·25	2·25
158	58p. Scott's expedition at South Pole, 1912	1·75	3·00

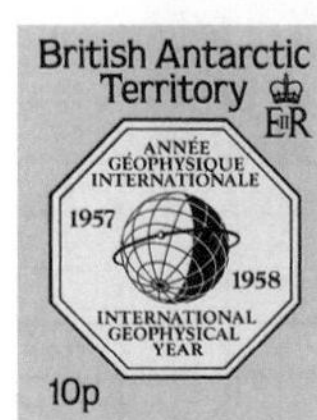

39 I.G.Y. Logo

40 Aurora over South Ice Plateau Station

1987. 30th Anniv of International Geophysical Year.

159	**39**	10p. black and green	30	75
160	–	24p. multicoloured	60	1·40
161	–	29p. multicoloured	75	1·75
162	–	58p. multicoloured	1·40	2·50

DESIGNS: 24p. Port Lockroy; 29p. Argentine Islands; 58p. Halley Bay.

1988. 30th Anniv of Commonwealth Trans-Antarctic Expedition. Multicoloured.

163	10p. Type **40**	30	75
164	24p. "Otter" aircraft at Theron Mountains	60	1·40
165	29p. Seismic ice-depth sounding	70	1·60
166	58p. "Sno-cat" over crevasse	1·25	2·50

41 "Xanthoria elegans"

1989. Lichens. Multicoloured.

167	10p. Type **41**	90	1·00
168	24p. "Usnea aurantiaco-atra"	1·60	2·00
169	29p. "Cladonia chlorophaea"	1·75	2·25
170	58p. "Umbilicaria antarctica"	2·50	3·25

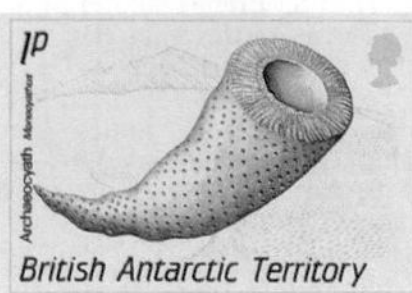

42 "Monocyathus" (archaeocyath)

1990. Fossils. Multicoloured.

171	1p. Type **42**	1·00	1·50
172	2p. "Lingulella" (brachiopod)	1·00	1·50
173	3p. "Triplagnoslus" (trilobite)	1·00	1·50
174	4p. "Lyriaspis" (trilobite)	1·25	1·50
175	5p. "Glossopteris" leaf (gymnosperm)	1·25	1·50
176	6p. "Gonatosorus" (fern)	1·25	1·60
177	7p. "Belemnopsis aucklandica" (belemnite)	1·25	1·60
178	8p. "Sanmartinoceras africanum insignicostatum" (ammonite)	1·25	1·60
179	9p. "Pinna antarctica" (mussel)	1·25	1·60
180	10p. "Aucellina andina" (mussel)	1·25	1·60
181	20p. "Pterotrigonia malagninoi" (mussel)	1·75	2·25
182	25p. "Perissoptera" (conch shell)	1·75	2·25
183	50p. "Ainoceras sp." (ammonite)	2·25	3·50

184 £1 "Gunnarites zinsmeisteri" (ammonite) . . . . 3·50 4·75
185 £4 "Hoploparia" (crayfish) 7·00 8·50

1990. 90th Birthday of Queen Elizabeth the Queen Mother. As T **134** of Ascension.
186 26p. multicoloured . . . . . 2·00 2·75
187 £1 black and brown . . . . 4·00 4·75
DESIGNS: 29 × 36 mm: 26p. Wedding of Prince Albert and Lady Elizabeth Bowes-Lyon, 1923. 29 × 37 mm: £1 The Royal Family, 1940.

43 Late Cretaceous Forest and Southern Beech Fossil

1991. Age of the Dinosaurs. Multicoloured.
188 12p. Type **43** . . . . 1·25 1·25
189 26p. Hypsilophodont dinosaurs and skull . . . . 2·00 2·25
190 31p. Frilled sharks and tooth 2·25 2·50
191 62p. Mosasaur, plesiosaur, and mosasaur vertebra . . 3·50 4·00

44 Launching Meteorological Balloon, Halley IV Station

1991. Discovery of Antarctic Ozone Hole. Mult.
192 12p. Type **44** . . . . 90 1·75
193 26p. Measuring ozone with Dobson spectrophotometer 1·60 2·75
194 31p. Satellite map showing ozone hole . . . . 1·90 3·00
195 62p. Lockheed ER-2 aircraft and graph of chlorine monoxide and ozone levels 3·25 4·50

45 Researching Dry Valley

1991. 30th Anniv of Antarctic Treaty.
196 **45** 12p. multicoloured 90 90
197 – 26p. multicoloured . . . . 1·60 1·75
198 – 31p. black and green . . . 1·75 1·90
199 – 62p. multicoloured . . . . 3·00 3·25
DESIGNS: 26p. Relief map of ice sheet; 31p. BIOMASS logo; 62p. Ross seal.

46 "H.M.S. 'Erebus' and H.M.S. 'Terror' in the Antarctic" (J. Carmichael)

1991. Maiden Voyage of "James Clark Ross" (research ship). Multicoloured.
200 12p. Type **46** . . . . 90 1·50
201 26p. Launch of "James Clark Ross" . . . . 1·60 2·50
202 31p. "James Clark Ross" in Antarctica . . . . 1·75 2·75
203 62p. Scientific research . . . 3·00 3·75

1991. Birth Bicentenary of Michael Faraday (scientist). Nos. 200/3 additionally inscr "200th Anniversary M. Faraday 1791–1867".
204 12p. Type **46** . . . . 90 1·75
205 26p. Launch of "James Clark Ross" . . . . 1·60 2·75
206 31p. "James Clark Ross" in Antarctica . . . . 1·75 3·00
207 62p. Scientific research . . . 3·00 4·50

47 Ross Seals

1992. Endangered Species. Seals and Penguins. Multicoloured.
208 4p. Type **47** . . . . 80 1·25
209 5p. Adelie penguins . . . . 80 1·25
210 7p. Weddell seal with pup . . 80 1·25
211 29p. Emperor penguins with chicks . . . . 2·00 2·25
212 34p. Crabeater seals with pup 1·75 2·25
213 68p. Bearded penguins ("Chinstrap Penguin") with young . . . . 2·25 2·75

48 Sun Pillar at Faraday

1992. Lower Atmospheric Phenomena. Mult.
214 14p. Type **48** . . . . 80 1·50
215 29p. Halo over iceberg . . . 1·40 1·90
216 34p. Lee Wave cloud . . . . 1·75 2·25
217 68p. Nacreous clouds . . . . 2·75 4·00

49 "Fitzroy" (mail and supply ship)

1993. Antarctic Ships. Multicoloured.
218 1p. Type **49** . . . . 1·00 1·50
219 2p. "William Scoresby" (research ship) . . . . . . 1·25 1·50
220 3p. "Eagle" (sealer) . . . . 1·25 1·50
221 4p. "Trepassey" (supply ship) 1·25 1·50
222 5p. "John Biscoe I" (research ship) . . . . 1·25 1·50
223 10p. "Norsel" (supply ship) 1·50 1·75
224 20p. H.M.S. "Protector" (ice patrol ship) . . . . 2·00 2·25
225 30p. "Oluf Sven" (supply ship) . . . . 2·25 2·50
226 50p. "John Biscoe II" and "Shackleton" (research ships) . . . . 2·75 3·25
227 £1 "Tottan" (supply ship) . . 3·75 4·50
228 £3 "Perla Dan" (supply ship) 7·50 8·50
229 £5 H.M.S. "Endurance I" (ice patrol ship) . . . . . 10·00 12·00

1994. "Hong Kong '94", International Stamp Exhibition. Nos. 240/5 optd **HONG KONG '94** and emblem.
230 15p. Type **51** . . . . 1·10 1·10
231 24p. De Havilland Turbo Beaver III aircraft . . . . 1·60 1·75
232 31p. De Havilland Otter aircraft and dog team . . . 1·75 1·90
233 36p. De Havilland Twin Otter 200/300 aircraft and dog team . . . . 1·90 2·00
234 62p. De Havilland Dash Seven aircraft over landing strip, Rothera Point . . . 2·75 2·75
235 72p. De Havilland Dash Seven aircraft on runway 2·75 2·75

50 Bransfield House Post Office, Port Lockroy

1994. 50th Anniv of Operation Tabarin. Multicoloured.
236 15p. Type **50** . . . . 90 1·25
237 31p. Survey team, Hope Bay 1·40 1·75
238 36p. Dog team, Hope Bay . . 2·25 1·90
239 72p. "Fitzroy" (supply ship) and H.M.S. "William Scoresby" (minesweeper) 3·00 3·75

51 Huskies and Sledge

1994. Forms of Transportation. Multicoloured.
240 15p. Type **51** 70 80
241 24p. De Havilland Turbo Beaver III aircraft . . . . 90 1·00
242 31p. De Havilland Otter aircraft and dog team . . . 1·00 1·10
243 36p. De Havilland Twin Otter 200/300 aircraft and dog team . . . . 1·10 1·40
244 62p. De Havilland Dash Seven aircraft over landing strip, Rothera Point . . . 2·00 2·50
245 72p. De Havilland Dash Seven aircraft on runway 2·00 2·75

52 Capt. James Cook and H.M.S. "Resolution"

1994. Antarctic Heritage Fund. Multicoloured.
246 17p.+3p. Type **52** . . . . . 1·75 1·90
247 35p.+15p. Sir James Clark Ross with H.M.S. "Erebus" and H.M.S. "Terror" . . . . 2·00 2·25
248 40p.+10p. Capt. Robert Falcon Scott and interior of hut . . . . 2·00 2·25
249 76p.+4p. Sir Ernest Shackleton and "Endurance" . . . . . . 2·75 3·00

53 Pair of Crabeater Seals

1994. Antarctic Food Chain. Multicoloured.
250 35p. Type **53** . . . . 1·50 1·75
251 35p. Blue whale . . . . . . 1·50 1·75
252 35p. Wandering albatross . . 1·50 1·75
253 35p. Mackerel icefish . . . . 1·50 1·75
254 35p. Krill . . . . 1·50 1·75
255 35p. Seven star flying squid 1·50 1·75

54 Hauberg Mountains

1995. Geological Structures. Multicoloured.
256 17p. Type **54** . . . . 80 1·00
257 35p. Arrowsmith Peninsula 1·60 1·75
258 40p. Colbert Mountains . . . 1·90 2·00
259 76p. Succession Cliffs . . . . 2·75 3·25

55 World Map showing Member Countries

1996. 24th Meeting of Scientific Committee on Antarctic Research. Multicoloured.
260 17p. Type **55** . . . . 1·00 1·00
261 35p. Scientist analysing ice samples . . . . 1·75 1·75
262 40p. Releasing balloon . . . 2·00 2·00
263 76p. Antarctic research ship catching marine life . . . . 2·75 2·75
MS264 100 × 90 mm. £1 S.C.A.R. logo . . . . 4·00 4·25

56 Killer Whales

1996. Whales. Multicoloured.
265 17p. Type **56** 80 75
266 35p. Sperm whales . . . . . 1·40 1·25
267 40p. Minke whales . . . . . 1·60 1·50
268 76p. Blue whale and calf . . 2·50 2·25
MS269 105 × 82 mm. £1 Humpback whale . . . . 3·50 3·75

1996. 70th Birthday of Queen Elizabeth II. As T **165** of Ascension, each incorporating a different photograph of the Queen. Mult.
270 17p. At premiere of "Chaplin", Leicester Square, 1992 . . . . . . 1·00 70
271 35p. At Buckingham Palace dinner, 1991 . . . . 1·50 1·25
272 40p. In Aberdeen, 1993 . . . 1·75 1·50
273 76p. At Royal Military School of Music, 1990 . . 2·25 2·25

1997. "HONG KONG '97" International Stamp Exhibition. Sheet 130 × 90 mm, containing design as No. 226. Multicoloured.
MS274 50p. "John Biscoe II" and "Shackleton" (research ships) 1·75 2·00

1997. Return of Hong Kong to China. Sheet 130 × 90 mm containing design as No. 227, but with "1997" imprint date.
MS275 £1 "Tottan" . . . . . . 2·75 3·25

57 Chinstrap Penguins sledging

58 Chart of South Shetland Islands (Swedish South Polar Expedition, 1902–3)

1997. Christmas. Multicoloured.
276 17p. Type **57** . . . . 1·25 75
277 35p. Emperor penguins carol singing . . . . 1·75 1·40
278 40p. Adelie penguins throwing snowballs . . . . 1·90 1·60
279 76p. Gentoo penguins ice-skating . . . . 2·50 2·75

1998. Diana, Princess of Wales Commemoration. Sheet 145 × 70 mm, containing vert designs as T **177** of Ascension. Multicoloured.
MS280 35p. Wearing sunglasses; 35p. Wearing round-necked white blouse, 1993; 35p. Wearing white blouse and jacket, 1990; 35p. Wearing green jacket, 1992 (sold at £1.40+20p. charity premium) 3·75 3·75

1998. History of Mapping in Antarctica. Multicoloured.
281 16p. Type **58** . . . . 1·25 1·00
282 30p. Map of Antarctic Peninsula (1949) . . . . . 1·75 1·50
283 35p. Map of AntarcticPeninsula (1964) 1·90 1·60
284 40p. Map of Antarctic Peninsula from Landsat (1981) . . . . 1·90 2·00
285 65p. Map of Antarctic Peninsula from satellite (1995) . . . . 2·50 2·75

59 Antarctic Explorer and H.M.S. "Erebus", 1843

1998. Antarctic Clothing. Multicoloured.
286 30p. Type **59** . . . . 1·25 1·00
287 35p. Explorer with dog, and "Discovery I", 1900 . . . 1·50 1·10
288 40p. Surveyor, and "Fitzroy", 1943 . . . . 1·50 1·50
289 65p. Scientist with Adelie penguins, and "James Clark Ross", 1998 . . . . 2·25 2·25

60 Snowy Sheathbill

1998. Antarctic Birds. Multicoloured.
290 1p. Type **60** . . . . 1·25 1·50
291 2p. Dove prion ("Antarctic Prion") . . . . 1·25 1·50
292 5p. Adelie penguin . . . . . 1·25 1·50
293 10p. Emperor penguin . . . 1·25 1·50
294 20p. Antarctic tern . . . . . 1·50 1·75
295 30p. Black-bellied storm petrel . . . . 1·50 1·75
296 35p. Southern fulmar ("Antarctic Fulmar") . . . 1·75 1·75
297 40p. Blue-eyed cormorant ("Blue-eyed Shag") . . . . 1·75 1·75
298 50p. South polar skua ("McCormick's Skua") . . 2·00 2·00
299 £1 Southern black-backed gull ("Kelp Gull") . . . . 3·25 3·50
300 £3 Wilson's storm petrel . . 7·00 8·00
301 £5 Antactic skua ("Brown Skua") . . . . 11·00 12·00

61 Mackerel Icefish

1999. Fish of the Southern Ocean. Multicoloured.
302 10p. Type **61** 75 60
303 20p. Blenny rockcod ("Toothfish") . . . . . . 1·25 80
304 25p. Borch . . . . 1·40 90
305 50p. Marbled rockcod ("Marbled notothen") . . 2·25 1·75
306 80p. Bernacchi's rockcod ("Bernach") . . . . 2·75 2·50

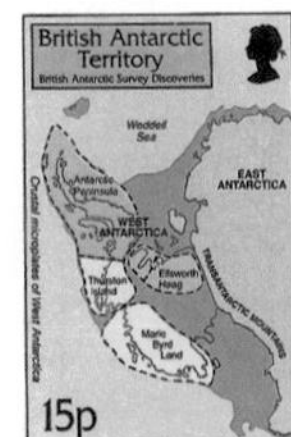

62 Map showing Crustal Microplates of West Antarctica

1999. British Antarctic Survey Discoveries. Mult.
307 15p. Type **62** . . . . 1·25 80
308 30p. Testing lead levels in ice 1·50 1·10
309 35p. Decolopodid sea spider (Gigantism in marine invertebrates) (horiz) . . . 1·60 1·25
310 40p. Scientist operating Dobson Spectrophotometer for testing ozone layer (horiz) . . . . 1·75 1·40
311 70p. Radar antenna (aurora electric field research) (horiz) . . . . 2·25 2·25

63 Wreck of "Endurance"

2000. Shackleton's Trans-Antarctic Expedition, 1914–17, Commemoration. Multicoloured.
312 35p. Type **63** . . . . 2·25 1·75
313 40p. Ocean Camp on ice . . 2·25 1·75
314 65p. Launching "James Caird" from Elephant Island . . . . 3·00 3·50

64 Iceberg and Opening Bars

2000. Composition of *Antarctic Symphony* by Sir Peter Maxwell Davies. Multicoloured.
315 37p. Type **64** . . . . 1·75 1·75
316 37p. Stern of *James Clark Ross* and pack ice . . . . 1·75 1·75
317 43p. Aircraft and camp on Jones Ice Self . . . . . . 2·00 2·00
318 43p. Frozen sea . . . . . . 2·00 2·00

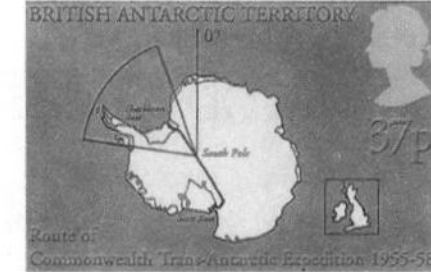

65 Route of Commonwealth Trans-Antarctic Expedition, 1955–58

2000. "Heroic Age of Antarctica" (1st series). Commonwealth Trans-Antarctic Expedition, 1955–8. Multicoloured.
319 37p. Type **65** . . . . 1·75 1·75
320 37p. Expedition at South Pole, 1958 . . . . 1·75 1·75
321 37p. *Magga Dan* (Antarctic supply ship) . . . . 1·75 1·75
322 37p. "Sno-cat" repair camp 1·75 1·75
323 37p. "Sno-cat" over crevasse 1·75 1·75
324 37p. Seismic explosion . . . 1·75 1·75
See also Nos. 333/8 and 351/6.

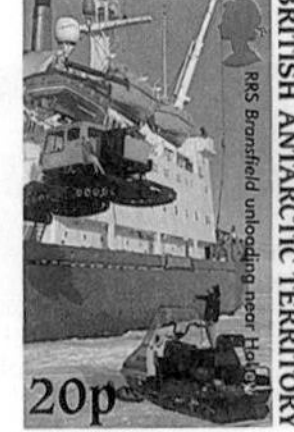

66 *Bransfield* unloading "Sno-cat", Halley

2000. Survey Ships. Multicoloured.
325 20p. Type **66** . . . . 1·25 1·00
326 33p. *Ernest Shackelton* unloading supplies into *Tula* . . . . 1·75 1·40
327 37p. *Bransfield* in the ice (horiz) . . . . 1·90 1·60
328 43p. *Ernest Shackelton* with helicopter (horiz) . . . . . 2·50 2·25

67 Tourists at Port Lockroy

2001. Restoration of Port Lockroy Base. Multicoloured.
329 33p. Type **67** . . . . 1·40 1·25
330 37p. Port Lockroy and cruise ship . . . . 1·60 1·25
331 43p. Port Lockroy huts in 1945 . . . . 1·75 1·50
332 65p. Interior of Port Lockroy laboratory in 1945 . . . . 2·50 2·50

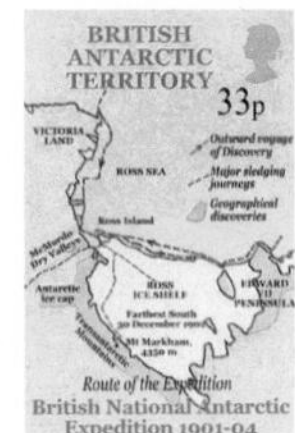

68 Map of Ross Sea Area

2001. "Heroic Age of Antarctica" (2nd series). Captain Scott's 1901–04 Expedition. Multicoloured.
333 33p. Type **68** . . . . 1·10 1·10
334 37p. Captain Robert F. Scott 1·40 1·40
335 43p. First Antarctic balloon ascent, 1902 (horiz) . . . . 1·50 1·50
336 65p. "Emperor Penguin chick" (drawing by Edward Wilson) . . . . 2·00 2·00
337 70p. Shackleton, Scott and Wilson and most southerly camp, 1902 (horiz) . . . . 2·00 2·00
338 80p. *Discovery I* trapped in ice off Hut Point (horiz) 2·25 2·25

2002. Golden Jubilee. As T **200** of Ascension.
339 20p. black, mauve and gold 80 80
340 37p. multicoloured . . . . . 1·10 1·10
341 43p. black, mauve and gold 1·40 1·40
342 50p multicoloured . . . . . 1·75 2·00
MS343 162 × 95 mm. Nos. 339/42 and 50p. multicoloured . . . . 6·00 7·00
DESIGNS—HORIZ: 20p. Princess Elizabeth and Princess Margaret making radio broadcast, 1940; 37p. Queen Elizabeth in Garter robes, 1998; 43p. Queen Elizabeth at Balmoral, 1952; 50p. Queen Elizabeth in London, 1996. VERT (38 × 51 mm)—50p. Queen Elizabeth after Annigoni.
Designs as Nos. 339/42 in No. **MS**343 omit the gold frame around each stamp and the "Golden Jubilee 1952–2002" inscription.

2002. Queen Elizabeth the Queen Mother Commemoration. As T **202** of Ascension.
344 40p. black, gold and purple 1·50 1·50
345 45p. multicoloured . . . . . 1·50 1·50
MS346 145 × 70 mm. 70p. black and gold; 95p. multicoloured . . . 4·00 4·25
DESIGNS: 40p. Lady Elizabeth Bowes-Lyon, 1913; 45p. Queen Mother on her birthday, 1996; 70p. Queen Elizabeth at niece's wedding, London, 1951; 95p. Queen Mother at Cheltenham Races, 1999.
Designs in No. **MS**346 omit the "1900–2002" inscription and the coloured frame.

69 Satellite and Antarctica

2002. 20th Anniv of Commission for Conservation of Antarctic Marine Living Resources (CCAMLR). Multicoloured.
347 37p. Type **69** . . . . 1·10 1·25
348 37p. Trawler and wandering albatross . . . . 1·10 1·25
349 37p. Icefish, toothfish and crabeater seal . . . . . . 1·10 1·25
350 37p. Krill and phytoplankton 1·10 1·25

2002. "Heroic Age of Antarctica" (3rd series). Scottish National Antarctic Expedition, 1902–04. As T **68** but horiz. Multicoloured.
351 30p. Map of Weddell Sea . . 1·40 1·40
352 40p. Piper Gilbert Kerr and emperor penguin (horiz) . . 1·60 1·60
353 45p. *Scotia* (expedition ship) 1·75 1·75
354 70p. Weather station and meteorologist (horiz) . . . 2·50 2·50
355 95p. William Speirs Bruce . . 2·75 2·75
356 £1 Omond House, Laurie Island (horiz) . . . . . . 2·75 2·75

2003. 50th Anniv of Coronation. As T **206** of Ascension. Multicoloured.
357 40p. Coronation Coach in procession . . . . 1·40 1·40
358 45p. Queen Elizabeth II with Prince Charles on Buckingham Palace balcony . . . . 1·40 1·40
MS359 95 × 115 mm. 95p. As 40p.; 95p. As 45p. . . . . 4·25 4·50
Nos. 357/8 have scarlet frame; stamps from **MS**359 have no frame and country name in mauve panel.

2003. As T **207** of Ascension.
360 £2 multicoloured . . . . . . 4·00 4·25

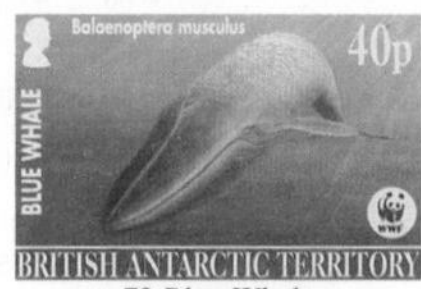

70 Blue Whale

71 Emperor Penguins

2003. Endangered Species. Blue Whale. Multicoloured.
361 40p. Type **70** . . . . 1·25 1·25
362 45p. Tail fluke . . . . 1·25 1·25
363 45p. Two blue whales . . . . 1·25 1·25
364 70p. Two blue whales at surface . . . . 1·75 1·75

2003. Penguins of the Antarctic. Multicoloured.
365 (–) Type **71** . . . . 1·00 1·00
366 (–) Head of macaroni penguin . . . . 1·00 1·00
367 (–) Gentoo penguin . . . . . 1·00 1·00
368 (–) Pair of adelie penguins . . 1·00 1·00
369 (–) Chinstrap penguin . . . . 1·00 1·00
370 (–) Gentoo penguin chick . . 1·00 1·00
371 (–) Emperor penguins (different) . . . . 1·00 1·00
372 (–) Chinstrap penguin chick 1·00 1·00
373 (–) Group of adelie penguins 1·00 1·00
374 (–) Gentoo penguin and chick 1·00 1·00
375 (–) Pair of macaroni penguins 1·00 1·00
376 (–) Emperor penguin chick 1·00 1·00
Nos. 365/76, inscribed "AIRMAIL POSTCARD", were initially sold at 40p.

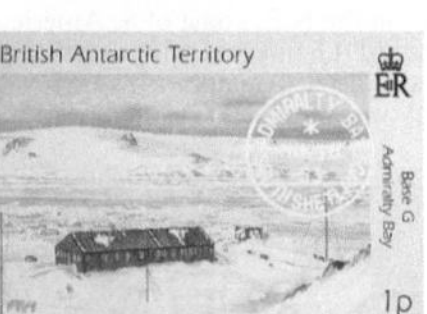

72 Base G, Admiralty Bay

2003. Research Bases and Postmarks. Multicoloured.
377 1p. Type **72** 10 10
378 2p. Base B, Deception Island 10 10
379 5p. Base D, Hope Bay . . . 10 10
380 22p. Base F, Argentine Islands 45 50
381 25p. Base E, Stonington Island 50 55
382 40p. Base A, Port Lockroy 80 85
383 45p. Base H, Signy 90 95
384 50p. Base N, Anvers Island 1·00 1·10
385 95p. Base P, Rothera . . . . 1·90 2·00
386 £1 Base T, Adelaide Island 2·00 2·10
387 £3 Base Y, Horseshoe Island 6·00 6·25
388 £5 Base Z, Halley Bay . . . 10·00 10·50

BRITISH COLUMBIA AND VANCOUVER ISLAND Pt. 1

Former British colonies, now a Western province of the Dominion of Canada, whose stamps are now used.

1860. 12 pence = 1 shilling;
20 shillings = 1 pound.
1865. 100 cents = 1 dollar.

1

1860. Imperf or perf.
2 **1** 2½d. pink £350 £180

VANCOUVER ISLAND

2

1865. Imperf or perf. Various frames.
13 **2** 5c. red £275 £150
14 – 10c. blue £225 £140

BRITISH COLUMBIA

4 Emblems of United Kingdom

1865.
21 **4** 3d. blue . . . . 85·00 65·00

1868. Surch in words or figures and words.
28 **4** 2c. brown £130 £130
29 5c. red £160 £130
24 10c. red £600 £475
31 25c. yellow £160 £130
26 50c. mauve £475 £425
27 $1 green £850 £900

BRITISH COMMONWEALTH OCCUPATION OF JAPAN Pt. 1

Stamps used by British Commonwealth Occupation Forces, 1946–49.

12 pence = 1 shilling;
20 shillings = 1 pound.

1946. Stamps of Australia optd **B.C.O.F. JAPAN 1946.**
J1 **27** ½d. orange . . . . 3·75 6·00
J2 **46** 1d. purple . . . . 3·00 3·00
J3 **31** 3d. brown . . . . 2·50 2·50
J4 – 6d. brown (No. 189a) . . . 16·00 11·00
J5 – 1s. green (No. 191) . . . . 16·00 13·00
J6 **1** 2s. red . . . . 42·00 50·00
J7 **38** 5s. red . . . . 95·00 £130

BRITISH EAST AFRICA Pt. 1

Now incorporated in Kenya and Uganda.

16 annas = 100 cents = 1 rupee.

1890. Stamps of Great Britain (1881) surch **BRITISH EAST AFRICA COMPANY** and value in annas.
1 **57** ½a. on 1d. lilac £275 £200
2 **73** 1a. on 2d. green and red . . £475 £275
3 **78** 4a. on 5d. purple and blue £500 £300

3 Arms of the Company

11

1890. Nos. 16/19 are larger (24 × 25 mm).
4b **3** ½a. brown . . . . 70 4·75
5 1a. green . . . . 4·75 6·00
6 2a. red . . . . 2·75 4·25
7c 2½a. black on yellow . . . . 4·50 5·00
8a 3a. black on red . . . . . 2·00 6·50

9		4a. brown	2·50	6·50
11a		4½a. purple	2·50	17·00
29		5a. black on blue	1·25	10·00
30		7½a. black	1·25	16·00
12		8a. blue	5·50	9·50
13		8a. grey	£275	£225
14		1r. red	6·00	9·00
15		1r. grey	£225	£225
16	–	2r. red	14·00	29·00
17	–	3r. purple	8·50	42·00
18	–	4r. blue	12·00	42·00
19	–	5r. green	30·00	70·00

1891. With handstamped or pen surcharges. Initialled in black.

20	3	½a. on 2a. red	£4750	£850
31		½a. on 3a. black on red	£425	50·00
32		1a. on 3a. black on red	£5500	£2500
26		1a. on 4a. brown	£4250	£1500

1894. Surch in words and figures.

27	3	5a. on 8a. blue	65·00	85·00
28		7½a. on 1r. red	65·00	85·00

1895. Optd **BRITISH EAST AFRICA**.

33	3	½a. brown	70·00	42·00
34		1a. green	£150	£110
35		2a. red	£180	95·00
36		2½a. black on yellow	£180	55·00
37		3a. black on red	80·00	50·00
38		4a. brown	45·00	35·00
39		4½a. purple	£200	£100
40		5a. black on blue	£225	£140
41		7½a. black	£120	80·00
42		8a. blue	95·00	75·00
43		1r. red	55·00	50·00
44	–	2r. red	£450	£250
45	–	3r. purple	£225	£120
46	–	4r. blue	£190	£160
47	–	5r. green	£425	£250

1895. Surch with large 2½.

48	3	2½a. on 4½a. purple	£160	75·00

1895. Stamps of India (Queen Victoria) optd **British East Africa**.

49	23	½a. turquoise	6·50	5·50
50	–	1a. purple	5·50	6·00
51	–	1½a. brown	4·00	4·00
52	–	2a. blue	5·50	3·00
53	–	2a.6p. green	7·00	2·50
54	–	3a. orange	10·00	11·00
55a	–	4a. green (No. 96)	28·00	24·00
56	–	6a. brown (No. 80)	35·00	50·00
57c	–	8a. mauve	28·00	50·00
58	–	12a. purple on red	22·00	32·00
59	–	1r. grey (No. 101)	90·00	65·00
60	37	1r. green and red	45·00	£120
61	38	2r. red and orange	90·00	£150
62		3r. brown and green	90·00	£150
63		5r. blue and violet	£110	£160

1895. No. 51 surch with small 2½.

64		2½ on 1½a. brown	90·00	42·00

1896.

65	11	¼a. green	2·50	80
66		1a. red	6·00	40
67		2a. brown	4·50	4·25
68		2½a. blue	8·00	1·75
69		3a. grey	3·75	7·00
70		4a. green	6·00	3·50
71		4½a. yellow	8·00	16·00
72		5a. brown	7·50	4·25
73		7½a. mauve	5·00	22·00
74		8a. grey	4·50	5·50
75		1r. blue	55·00	23·00
76		2r. orange	75·00	25·00
77		3r. violet	65·00	30·00
78		4r. red	55·00	70·00
79		5r. brown	55·00	40·00

1897. Stamps of Zanzibar, 1896, optd **British East Africa**.

80	13	½a. green and red	55·00	45·00
81		1a. blue and red	95·00	90·00
82		2a. brown and red	38·00	21·00
83		4½a. orange and red	50·00	30·00
84		5a. brown and red	55·00	35·00
85		7½a. mauve and red	50·00	35·00

1897. As last, surch 2½.

86	13	2½ on 1a. blue and red	£110	65·00
89		2½ on 3a. grey and red	£110	55·00

1897. As Type 11, but larger.

92a		1r. blue	65·00	32·00
93		2r. orange	85·00	85·00
94		3r. violet	£100	£120
95		4r. red	£325	£375
96		5r. brown	£250	£325
97		10r. brown	£325	£350
98		20r. green	£700	£1500
99		50r. mauve	£1600	

BRITISH FORCES IN EGYPT Pt. 1

SPECIAL SEALS AND STAMPS FOR THE USE OF BRITISH FORCES IN EGYPT

A. SEALS

A 1

1932. (a) Inscr "POSTAL SEAL".

A1	A 1	1p. blue and red	90·00	3·50

(b) Inscr "LETTER SEAL".

A2	A 1	1p. blue and red	28·00	85

A 2

1932. Christmas Seals.

A3	A 2	3m. black on blue	48·00	70·00
A4		3m. lake	7·50	50·00
A5		3m. blue	7·00	26·00
A6a		3m. red	7·50	20·00

A 3

1934.

A9	A 3	1p. red	2·25	3·00
A8		1p. green	4·00	4·00

1935. Silver Jubilee. Optd **JUBILEE COMMEMORATION 1935.**

A10	A 3	1p. blue	£225	£180

1935. Provisional Christmas Seal. Surch **Xmas 1935 3 Milliemes.**

A11	A 3	3m. on 1p. red	16·00	70·00

B. POSTAGE STAMPS

A 6 King Fuad I A 7 King Farouk

1936.

A12	A 6	3m. green	1·00	1·00
A13		10m. red	3·75	10

1939.

A14	A 7	3m. green	3·25	5·00
A15		10m. red	4·75	10

BRITISH GUIANA Pt. 1

Situated on the N.E. coast of S. America. A British colony granted full internal self-government in August 1951. Attained independence on 26 May 1966, when the country was renamed Guyana.

100 cents = 1 dollar.

1

1850. Imperf.

1	1	2c. black on red	—	£70000
2		4c. black on orange	£3200	£5000
4		8c. black on green	£18000	£3750
5		12c. black on blue	£6500	£2500

Prices are for used stamps cut round. Stamps cut square are worth much more.

2

3 Seal of the Colony

1852. Imperf.

9	2	1c. black on magenta	£8500	£4250
10		4c. black on blue	£11000	£6000

1853. Imperf.

12	3	1c. red	£2750	£1000
20		4c. blue	£950	£375

6

1856. Imperf.

23	6	1c. black on magenta	†	—
24		4c. black on magenta	†	£6500
25		4c. black on blue	£22000	£9000

7

9

1860. Perf.

29	7	1c. red	£1400	£200
40		1c. brown	£325	95·00
85		1c. black	11·00	4·50
87		2c. orange	27·00	3·50
89		4c. blue	90·00	13·00
92	9	6c. blue	£130	32·00
95	7	8c. red	£130	25·00
98		12c. lilac	£170	18·00
99		12c. grey	£170	16·00
64		24c. green	£190	50·00
79	9	24c. green	£160	10·00
82		48c. red	£250	55·00

The prices quoted for Nos. 29/82 are for fine copies with four margins. Medium specimens can be supplied at much lower rates.

10

16

1862. Various borders. Roul.

116	10	1c. black on red	£2750	£475
119		2c. black on yellow	£2750	£325
122		4c. black on blue	£3000	£600

The above prices are for stamps signed in the centre by the Postmaster. Unsigned stamps are worth considerably less.

1876.

126	16	1c. grey	2·75	1·40
171		2c. orange	23·00	15
172		4c. blue	90·00	5·00
173		6c. brown	5·00	6·50
174		8c. red	90·00	40
131		12c. violet	50·00	1·25
132		24c. green	60·00	3·00
133		48c. brown	£120	28·00
134		96c. olive	£475	£250

1878. Optd with thick horiz or horiz and vert bars.

(a) On postage stamps.

137	16	1c. on 6c. brown	38·00	£110
141	9	1c. on 6c. blue	£170	75·00

(b) On official stamps of 1875 and 1877.

138	7	1c. black	£225	75·00
139	16	1c. grey	£170	60·00
140		2c. orange	£325	65·00
144		4c. blue	£300	£100
145		6c. brown	£400	£100
146	7	8c. red	£1900	£275
148	16	8c. red	£375	£110

1881. Surch with figure. Old value barred out in ink.

(a) On postage stamps.

152	9	"1" on 48c. red	45·00	5·00
149	16	"1" on 96c. olive	3·50	6·00
150		"2" on 96c. olive	5·00	11·00

(b) On stamps optd **OFFICIAL**.

153	7	"1" on 12c. lilac	£120	70·00
154	16	"1" on 48c. brown	£150	95·00
155		"2" on 12c. violet	75·00	28·00
157		"2" on 24c. green	85·00	45·00

26

30

1882.

162	26	1c. black on red	45·00	28·00
165		2c. black on yellow	75·00	42·00

Each stamp is perforated with the word "SPECIMEN".

1888. T **16** without value in bottom tablet, surch **INLAND REVENUE** and value.

175	16	1c. purple	1·25	20
176		2c. purple	1·25	40
177		3c. purple	1·00	20
178		4c. purple	9·00	30
179		6c. purple	9·00	3·75
180		8c. purple	1·50	30
181		10c. purple	6·00	2·50
182		20c. purple	20·00	12·00
183		40c. purple	22·00	21·00
184		72c. purple	42·00	55·00
185		$1 green	£425	£500
186		$2 green	£200	£250
187		$3 green	£140	£180
188		$4 green	£450	£600
189		$5 green	£275	£300

1889. No. 176 surch with additional **2**.

192	16	"2" on 2c. purple	2·00	15

1889.

193	30	1c. purple and grey	3·50	1·75
213		1c. green	75	10
194		2c. purple and orange	2·25	10
234		2c. purple and red	3·25	30
241a		2c. purple & black on red	3·50	10
253a		2c. red	8·50	10
195		4c. purple and blue	4·50	2·00
254		4c. brown and purple	2·25	60
214		5c. blue	2·75	10
243a		5c. purple & blue on blue	3·50	6·50
198		6c. purple and brown	7·00	12·00
236		6c. black and blue	6·50	11·00
256		6c. grey and black	13·00	7·00
199		8c. purple and red	12·00	1·50
215		8c. purple and black	2·75	1·10
200a		12c. purple and mauve	8·50	2·25
257		12c. orange and purple	4·00	4·00
246a		24c. purple and green	3·75	4·50
202		48c. purple and red	16·00	9·00
247a		48c. grey and brown	14·00	20·00
248a		60c. green and red	14·00	85·00
203		72c. purple and brown	28·00	38·00
205		96c. purple and red	65·00	70·00
250		96c. black & red on yellow	35·00	45·00

1890. Nos. 185/8 surch **ONE CENT**.

207	16	1 cent on $1 green	1·25	35
208		1 cent on $2 green	2·00	60
209		1 cent on $3 green	2·00	1·25
210		1 cent on $4 green	2·00	7·00

32 Mount Roraima

33 Kaieteur Falls

37

1898. Jubilee.

216	32	1c. black and red	5·00	75
217	33	2c. brown and blue	25·00	2·50
219	32	5c. green and brown	48·00	3·75
220	33	10c. black and red	25·00	20·00
221	32	15c. brown and blue	30·00	16·00

1899. Nos. 219/21 surch **TWO CENTS**.

222	32	2c. on 5c. green and brown	3·25	2·00
223	33	2c. on 10c. black and red	2·25	2·25
224	32	2c. on 15c. brown and blue	1·50	1·25

1905. T **30** but inscr "REVENUE", optd **POSTAGE AND REVENUE**.

251	30	$2.40 green and violet	£160	£275

1913.

259a	37	1c. green	1·50	25
260		2c. red	1·25	10
274		2c. violet	2·50	10
261b		4c. brown and purple	3·75	25
262		5c. blue	1·75	1·00
263		6c. grey and black	2·75	1·25
276		6c. blue	3·00	30
264		12c. orange and violet	1·25	1·00
278		24c. purple and green	2·00	4·50
279		48c. grey and purple	9·50	3·50
280		60c. green and red	10·00	48·00

No.	Type	Description	Unused	Used
281		72c. purple and brown	23·00	65·00
269a		96c. black and red on yellow	19·00	48·00

1918. Optd **WAR TAX**.

No.	Type	Description	Unused	Used
271	**37**	2c. red	1·25	15

39 Ploughing a Rice Field

40 Indian shooting Fish

41 Kaieteur Falls

42 Public Buildings, Georgetown

1931. Centenary of County Union.

No.	Type	Description	Unused	Used
283	**39**	1c. green	2·50	1·25
284	**40**	2c. brown	2·00	10
285	**41**	4c. red	1·75	45
286	**42**	6c. blue	2·25	2·75
287	**41**	$1 violet	24·00	48·00

43 Ploughing a Rice Field

44 Gold Mining

53 South America

1934.

No.	Type	Description	Unused	Used
288	**43**	1c. green	60	80
289	**40**	2c. brown	1·50	70
290	**44**	3c. red	30	10
291	**41**	4c. violet	2·00	1·75
292	–	6c. blue	2·75	3·75
293	–	12c. orange	20	20
294	–	24c. purple	3·50	7·00
295	–	48c. black	7·00	8·50
296	**41**	50c. green	10·00	17·00
297	–	60c. brown	26·00	27·00
298	–	72c. purple	1·25	2·25
299	–	96c. black	20·00	30·00
300	–	$1 violet	32·00	30·00

DESIGNS—HORIZ: 6c. Shooting logs over falls; 12c. Stabroek Market; 24c. Sugar canes in punts; 48c. Forest road; 60c. Victoria Regia lilies; 72c. Mount Roraima; $1 Botanical Gardens. VERT: 96c. Sir Walter Raleigh and his son.

The 2c., 4c. and 50c. are without the dates shown in Types **40/44** and the 12, 48, 72 and 96c. have no portrait.

1935. Silver Jubilee. As T **13** of Antigua.

No.	Type	Description	Unused	Used
301		2c. blue and grey	20	10
302		6c. brown and blue	1·00	2·00
303		12c. green and blue	4·25	8·00
304		24c. grey and purple	6·00	8·00

1937. Coronation. As T **2** of Aden.

No.	Type	Description	Unused	Used
305		2c. brown	15	10
306		4c. grey	50	40
307		6c. blue	60	1·25

1938. Designs as for same values of 1934 issue (except where indicated) but with portrait of King George VI (as in T **53**) where portrait of King George V previously appeared.

No.	Type	Description	Unused	Used
308a	**43**	1c. green	30	10
309a	–	2c. violet (As 4c.)	30	10
310b	**53**	4c. red and black	50	15
311	–	6c. blue (As 2c.)	40	10
312a	–	24c. green	1·25	10
313	–	36c. violet (As 4c.)	2·00	20
314	–	48c. orange	60	50
315	–	60c. brown (As 6c.)	13·00	4·50
316	–	96c. purple	2·50	2·75
317	–	$1 violet	13·00	35
318	–	$2 purple (As 72c.)	5·50	16·00
319	–	$3 brown	27·00	25·00

DESIGN—HORIZ: $3 Victoria Regia lilies.

1946. Victory. As T **9** of Aden.

No.	Type	Description	Unused	Used
320		3c. red	10	30
321		6c. blue	30	70

1948. Silver Wedding. As T **10/11** of Aden.

No.	Type	Description	Unused	Used
322		3c. red	10	40
323		$3 brown	12·00	23·00

1949. U.P.U. As T **20/23** of Antigua.

No.	Type	Description	Unused	Used
324		4c. red	10	30
325		6c. blue	1·50	1·00
326		12c. orange	15	45
327		24c. green	15	60

1951. Inauguration of B.W.I. University College. As T **24/25** of Antigua.

No.	Type	Description	Unused	Used
328		3c. black and red	30	30
329		6c. black and blue	30	60

1953. Coronation. As T **13** of Aden.

No.	Type	Description	Unused	Used
330		4c. black and red	20	10

55 G.P.O., Georgetown

1954.

No.	Type	Description	Unused	Used
331	**55**	1c. black	10	10
332	–	2c. myrtle	10	10
333	–	3c. olive and brown	3·50	20
334	–	4c. violet	75	10
335	–	5c. red and black	30	10
336	–	6c. green	50	10
337	–	8c. blue	20	20
338a	–	12c. black and brown	20	10
360	–	24c. black and orange	4·00	10
361	–	36c. red and black	60	60
341a	–	48c. blue and brown	1·00	80
342	–	72c. red and green	12·00	2·75
364	–	$1 multicoloured	7·00	90
344	–	$2 mauve	20·00	6·00
345	–	$5 blue and black	18·00	23·00

DESIGNS—HORIZ: 2c. Botanical Gardens; 3c. Victoria Regia lilies; 5c. Map of Caribbean; 6c. Rice combine-harvester; 8c. Sugar cane entering factory; 24c. Bauxite mining; 36c. Mount Roraima; $1 Channel-billed toucan; $2 Dredging gold. VERT: 4c. Amerindian shooting fish; 12c. Felling greenheart; 48c. Kaieteur Falls; 72c. Arapaima (fish); $5 Arms of British Guiana.

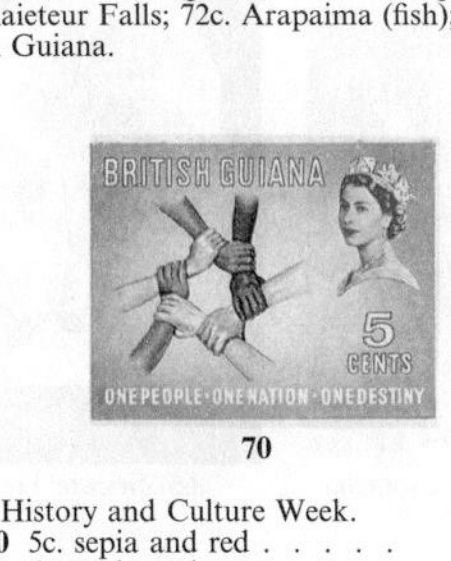

70

1961. History and Culture Week.

No.	Type	Description	Unused	Used
346	**70**	5c. sepia and red	20	10
347		6c. sepia and green	20	15
348		30c. sepia and orange	45	45

1963. Freedom from Hunger. As T **28** of Aden.

No.	Type	Description	Unused	Used
349		20c. violet	30	10

1963. Centenary of Red Cross. As T **33** of Antigua.

No.	Type	Description	Unused	Used
350		5c. red and black	20	20
351		20c. red and blue	55	35

71 Weightlifting

1964. Olympic Games, Tokyo.

No.	Type	Description	Unused	Used
367	**71**	5c. orange	10	10
368		8c. blue	15	35
369		25c. mauve	25	40

1965. Centenary of I.T.U. As T **36** of Antigua.

No.	Type	Description	Unused	Used
370		5c. green and olive	10	15
371		25c. blue and mauve	20	15

1965. I.C.Y. As T **37** of Antigua.

No.	Type	Description	Unused	Used
372		5c. purple and turquoise	15	10
373		25c. green and lavender	30	20

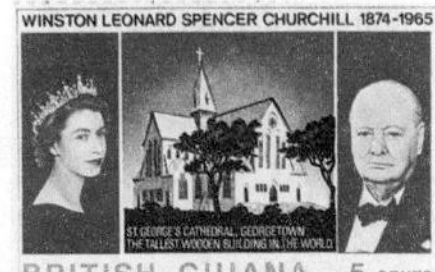

72 St George's Cathedral, Georgetown

1966. Churchill Commemoration.

No.	Type	Description	Unused	Used
374	**72**	5c. black, red and gold	50	10
375		25c. black, blue and gold	1·75	50

1966. Royal Visit. As T **39** of Antigua.

No.	Type	Description	Unused	Used
376		3c. black and blue	75	15
377		25c. black and mauve	1·50	60

OFFICIAL STAMPS

1875. Optd **OFFICIAL**.

No.	Type	Description	Unused	Used
O1	**7**	1c. black	55·00	18·00
O2		2c. orange	£180	14·00
O3		8c. red	£325	£120
O4		12c. lilac	£2250	£500
O5	**9**	24c. green	£1100	£225

1877. Optd **OFFICIAL**.

No.	Type	Description	Unused	Used
O 6	**16**	1c. grey	£250	65·00
O 7		2c. orange	£120	15·00
O 8		4c. blue	85·00	20·00
O 9		6c. brown	£5500	£600
O10		8c. red	£2000	£450

POSTAGE DUE STAMPS

1940. As Type D **1** of Barbados, but inscr "BRITISH GUIANA".

No.	Type	Description	Unused	Used
D1a		1c. green	1·50	13·00
D2a		2c. black	1·75	3·75
D3		4c. blue	30	9·50
D4		12c. red	30·00	4·50

For later issues see **GUYANA**.

BRITISH HONDURAS Pt. 1

A British colony on the East coast of Central America. Self-government was granted on 1 January 1964. The country was renamed Belize from 1 June 1973.

1866. 12 pence = 1 shilling;
20 shillings = 1 pound.
1888. 100 cents = 1 dollar.

1

8

1866.

No.	Type	Description	Unused	Used
17	**1**	1d. blue	45·00	13·00
18		1d. red	23·00	13·00
13		3d. brown	£130	17·00
20		4d. mauve	75·00	4·75
9		6d. red	£275	40·00
21		6d. yellow	£275	£100
16		1s. green	£225	11·00
22		1s. grey	£250	£160

1888. Surch as **2 CENTS**.

No.	Type	Description	Unused	Used
36	**1**	1c. on 1d. green	80	1·50
37		2c. on 1d. red	60	2·25
25		2c. on 6d. red	£140	£120
38		3c. on 3d. brown	3·25	1·40
39		6c. on 3d. blue	2·75	16·00
40		10c. on 4d. mauve	11·00	50
41		20c. on 6d. yellow	12·00	14·00
42		50c. on 1s. grey	29·00	85·00

1888. No. 42 surch **TWO**.

No.	Type	Description	Unused	Used
35	**1**	"TWO" on 50c. on 1s. grey	50·00	95·00

1891. No. 40 surch **6** and bar.

No.	Type	Description	Unused	Used
44	**1**	6c. on 10c. on 4d. mauve	1·25	1·50

1891. Nos. 38 and 39 surch.

No.	Type	Description	Unused	Used
49	**1**	"FIVE" on 3c. on 3d. brown	1·25	1·40
50		"15" on 6c. on 3d. blue	13·00	27·00

1891.

No.	Type	Description	Unused	Used
51	**8**	1c. green	2·50	1·25
52		2c. red	2·50	20
53		3c. brown	6·50	4·00
54		5c. blue	12·00	75
55		5c. black and blue on blue	16·00	2·50
56		6c. blue	6·50	2·00
57		10c. mauve and green (A)	10·00	8·50
58		10c. purple and green (B)	11·00	7·50
59a		12c. mauve and green	2·50	2·00
60		24c. yellow and blue	5·50	14·00
61		25c. brown and green	75·00	£130
62		50c. green and red	24·00	60·00
63		$1 green and red	70·00	£130
64		$2 green and blue	£100	£160
65		$5 green and black	£275	£350

NOTE: 10c. (A) inscr "POSTAGE POSTAGE"; (B) inscr "POSTAGE & REVENUE".

1899. Optd **REVENUE**.

No.	Type	Description	Unused	Used
66	**8**	5c. blue	13·00	2·50
67		10c. mauve and green	5·00	16·00
68		25c. brown and green	2·75	35·00
69	**1**	50c. on 1s. grey	£160	£300

14

16

1902.

No.	Type	Description	Unused	Used
84a	**14**	1c. green	1·00	2·25
85a		2c. purple and black on red	75	20
96		2c. red	12·00	10
86		5c. black and blue on blue	1·75	20
97		5c. blue	1·75	10
87		10c. purple and green	5·00	11·00
83		20c. purple	6·00	17·00
89		25c. purple and orange	7·00	48·00
100		25c. black on green	3·00	45·00
90		50c. green and red	15·00	70·00
91		$1 green and red	55·00	75·00
92		$2 green and blue	95·00	£150
93		$5 green and black	£250	£275

1913.

No.	Type	Description	Unused	Used
101	**16**	1c. green	3·75	1·50
102		2c. red	3·50	1·00
103		3c. orange	80	20
104		5c. blue	2·00	85
105		10c. purple and green	3·00	6·50
106		25c. black on green	1·25	12·00
107		50c. purple and blue on blue	12·00	15·00
108		$1 black and red	19·00	50·00
109		$2 purple and green	65·00	80·00
110		$5 purple and black on red	£200	£225

1915. Optd with pattern of wavy lines.

No.	Type	Description	Unused	Used
111a	**16**	1c. green	50	13·00
112		2c. red	3·50	50
113		5c. blue	30	6·00

1916. Optd **WAR**.

No.	Type	Description	Unused	Used
114	**16**	1c. green (No. 111a)	10	1·25
119		1c. green (No. 101)	10	30
120		3c. orange (No. 103)	70	1·75

21

1921. Peace.

No.	Type	Description	Unused	Used
121	**21**	2c. red	3·25	50

As last, but without word "PEACE"

No.	Type	Description	Unused	Used
123		4c. grey	7·50	50

22

24 Maya figures

1922.

No.	Type	Description	Unused	Used
126	**22**	1c. green	6·00	6·50
127		2c. brown	1·50	1·50
128		2c. red	2·50	1·50
129		3c. orange	17·00	4·00
130		4c. grey	8·00	85
131		5c. blue	1·50	55
132		10c. purple and olive	1·25	30
133		25c. black on green	1·25	8·50
134		50c. purple and blue on blue	4·75	16·00
136		$1 black and red	8·00	23·00
137		$2 green and purple	32·00	80·00
125		$5 purple and black on red	£200	£225

1932. Optd **BELIZE RELIEF FUND PLUS** and value.

No.	Type	Description	Unused	Used
138	**22**	1c.+1c. green	80	8·00
139		2c.+2c. red	85	8·00
140		3c.+3c. orange	90	19·00
141		4c.+4c. grey	11·00	22·00
142		5c.+5c. blue	6·50	14·00

1935. Silver Jubilee. As T **13** of Antigua.

No.	Type	Description	Unused	Used
143		3c. blue and black	2·00	50
144		4c. green and blue	2·00	3·50
145		5c. brown and blue	2·00	1·50
146		25c. grey and purple	4·00	4·00

1937. Coronation. As T **2** of Aden.

No.	Type	Description	Unused	Used
147		3c. orange	30	30
148		4c. grey	70	30
149		5c. blue	80	1·90

1938.

No.	Type	Description	Unused	Used
150	**24**	1c. purple and green	10	1·50
151	–	2c. black and red	20	1·00
152	–	3c. purple and brown	50	80
153	–	4c. black and green	50	70

154 – 5c. purple and blue 1·50 70
155 – 10c. green and brown 1·50 60
156 – 15c. brown and blue 3·25 70
157 – 25c. blue and green 3·00 1·25
158 – 50c. black and purple 12·00 3·50
159 – $1 red and olive 22·00 10·00
160 – $2 blue and purple 29·00 17·00
161 – $5 red and brown 32·00 25·00
DESIGNS—VERT: 2c. Chicle tapping; 3c. Cohune palm; $1 Court House, Belize; $2 Mahogany felling; $5 Arms of Colony. HORIZ: 4c. Local products; 5c. Grapefruit; 10c. Mahogany logs in river; 15c. Sergeant's Cay; 25c. Dorey; 50c. Chicle industry.

1946. Victory. As T **9** of Aden.
162 3c. brown 10 10
163 5c. blue 10 10

1948. Silver Wedding. As T **10** and **11** of Aden.
164 4c. green 15 20
165 $5 brown 17·00 45·00

36 Island of Saint George's Cay

1949. 150th Anniv of Battle of Saint George's Cay.
166 **36** 1c. blue and green 10 1·00
167 3c. blue and brown 10 1·50
168 4c. olive and violet 10 1·00
169 – 5c. brown and blue 1·00 40
170 – 10c. green and brown 1·00 30
171 – 15c. green and blue 1·00 30
DESIGNS: 5, 10 and 15c. H.M.S. "Merlin".

1949. U.P.U. As T **20/23** of Antigua.
172 4c. green 30 30
173 5c. blue 1·50 50
174 10c. brown 40 3·00
175 25c. blue 35 50

1951. Inauguration of B.W.I. University College. As T **24/25** of Antigua.
176 3c. violet and brown 45 1·50
177 10c. green and brown 45 30

1953. Coronation. As T **13** of Aden.
178 4c. black and green 40 30

39 Baird's Tapir

49 Mountain Orchid

1953.
179 – 1c. green and black 10 40
180a **39** 2c. brown and black 70 10
181a – 3c. lilac and mauve 10 10
182 – 4c. brown and green 50 30
183 – 5c. olive and red 10 10
184 – 10c. slate and blue 10 10
185 – 15c. green and violet 15 10
186 – 25c. blue and brown 6·00 2·50
187 – 50c. brown and purple 10·00 1·75
188 – $1 slate and brown 5·50 5·00
189 – $2 red and grey 6·50 4·50
190 **49** $5 purple and slate 48·00 17·00
DESIGNS—HORIZ: 1c. Arms of British Honduras; 3c. Mace and Legislative Council Chamber; 4c. Pine industry; 5c. Spiny lobster; 10c. Stanley Field Airport; 15c. Maya frieze, Xunantunich; 25c. "Morpho peleides" (butterfly); $1 Nine-banded armadillo; $2 Hawkesworth Bridge. VERT: 50c. Maya indian.

50 "Belize from Fort George, 1842" (C. J. Hullmandel)

1960. Post Office Centenary.
191 **50** 2c. green 30 1·25
192 – 10c. red 30 10
193 – 15c. blue 35 35
DESIGNS: 10c. Public seals, 1860 and 1960; 15c. Tamarind tree, Newtown Barracks.

1961. New Constitution. Stamps of 1953 optd **NEW CONSTITUTION 1960.**
194 **39** 2c. brown and black 25 20
195 – 3c. lilac and mauve 30 20
196 – 10c. slate and blue 30 10
197 – 15c. green and violet 30 20

1962. Hurricane Hattie Relief Fund. Stamps of 1953 optd **HURRICANE HATTIE**.
198 1c. green and black 10 65
199 10c. slate and blue 30 10
200 25c. blue and brown 1·40 80
201 50c. brown and purple 50 1·00

55 Great Curassow

1962. Birds in natural colours; portrait and inscr in black; background colours given.
239 **55** 1c. yellow 10 50
240 – 2c. grey 30 1·00
204 – 3c. green 2·50 3·00
241 – 4c. grey 1·75 2·00
242 – 5c. buff 40 10
243 – 10c. stone 40 10
244 – 15c. stone 40 10
209 – 25c. slate 4·50 30
210 – 50c. grey 6·00 35
211 – $1 blue 9·00 1·00
212 – $2 stone 14·00 3·00
213 $5 grey 25·00 16·00
BIRDS: 2c. Red-legged honeycreeper; 3c. Northern jacana ("American Jacana"); 4c. Great kiskadee; 5c. Scarlet-rumped tanager; 10c. Scarlet macaw; 15c. Slaty-tailed trogon ("Massena Trogon"); 25c. Red-footed booby; 50c. Keel-billed toucan; $1 Magnificent frigate bird; $2 Rufous-tailed jacamar; $5 Montezuma oropendola.

1963. Freedom from Hunger. As T **28** of Aden.
214 22c. green 30 15

1963. Centenary of Red Cross. As T **33** of Antigua.
215 4c. red and black 20 75
216 22c. red and blue 40 1·25

1964. New Constitution. Nos. 202, 204, 205, 207 and 209 optd **SELF GOVERNMENT 1964**.
217 **55** 1c. yellow 10 30
218 – 3c. green 45 30
219 – 4c. pale grey 45 30
220 – 10c. stone 45 10
221 – 25c. slate 55 30

1965. Centenary of I.T.U. As T **36** of Antigua.
222 2c. red and green 10 10
223 50c. yellow and purple 35 25

1965. I.C.Y. As T **37** of Antigua.
224 1c. purple and turquoise 10 15
225 22c. green and lavender 20 15

1966. Churchill Commemoration. As T **38** of Antigua.
226 1c. blue 10 75
227 4c. green 40 10
228 22c. brown 65 10
229 25c. violet 80 45

1966. Dedication of new Capital Site. Nos. 202, 204/5 207 and 209 optd **DEDICATION OF SITE NEW CAPITAL 9th OCTOBER 1965**.
230 **55** 1c. yellow 10 40
231 – 3c. green 45 40
232 – 4c. grey 45 40
233 – 10c. stone 45 10
234 – 25c. slate 55 35

58 Citrus Grove

1966. Stamp Centenary. Multicoloured
235 5c. Type **58** 10 10
236 10c. Half Moon Cay 10 10
237 22c. Hidden Valley Falls 10 10
238 25c. Maya ruins, Xunantunich 15 45

59 Sailfish

1967. International Tourist Year.
246 **59** 5c. blue, black and yellow 15 30
247 – 10c. brown, black and red 15 10
248 – 22c. orange, black and green 30 10
249 – 25c. blue, black and yellow 30 60
DESIGNS: 10c. Red brocket; 22c. Jaguar; 25c. Atlantic tarpon.

60 "Schomburgkia tibicinis"

61 Monument Belizean Patriots

1968. 20th Anniv of Economic Commission for Latin America. Orchids. Multicoloured.
250 5c. Type **60** 20 15
251 10c. "Maxillaria tenuifolia" 25 10
252 22c. "Bletia purpurea" 30 10
253 25c. "Sobralia macrantha" 40 20

1968. Human Rights Year. Multicoloured.
254 22c. Type **61** 15 10
255 50c. Monument at site of new capital 15 20

63 Spotted Jewfish

1968. Wildlife.
276 – ½c. multicoloured and blue 10 10
277 – ½c. multicoloured and yellow 2·50 1·00
256 **63** 1c. black, brown and yellow 20 10
257 – 2c. black, green and yellow 10 10
258 – 3c. black, brown and lilac 20 10
259 – 4c. multicoloured 15 1·25
260 – 5c. black and red 15 1·25
261 – 10c. multicoloured 15 10
262 – 15c. multicoloured 1·50 20
263 – 25c. multicoloured 30 20
264 – 50c. multicoloured 70 1·25
265 – $1 multicoloured 2·50 1·25
266 – $2 multicoloured 2·50 2·00
278 – $5 multicoloured 4·00 12·00
DESIGNS: ½c. (Nos. 276 and 277) Mozambique mouthbrooder ("Crana"); 2c. White-lipped peccary; 3c. Misty grouper; 4c. Collared anteater; 5c. Bonefish; 10c. Paca; 15c. Dolphin; 25c. Kinkajou; 50c. Mutton snapper; $1 Tayra; $2 Great barracuda; $5 Puma.

64 "Rhyncholaelia digbyana"

65 Ziricote Tree

1969. Orchids of Belize (1st series). Multicoloured.
268 5c. Type **64** 50 20
269 10c. "Cattleya bowringiana" 55 15
270 22c. "Lycaste cochleatum" 85 15
271 25c. "Coryanthes speciosum" 1·10 1·10
See also Nos. 287/90.

1969. Indigenous Hardwoods (1st series). Mult.
272 5c. Type **65** 10 20
273 10c. Rosewood 10 10
274 22c. Mayflower 20 10
275 25c. Mahogany 20 45
See also Nos. 291/4, 315/18 and 333/7.

66 "The Virgin and Child" (Bellini)

69 Santa Maria

1969. Christmas. Paintings. Multicoloured.
279 5c. Type **66** 10 10
280 15c. Type **66** 10 10
281 22c. "The Adoration of the Magi" (Veronese) 10 10
282 25c. As No. 281 10 20

1970. Population Census. Nos. 260/3 optd **POPULATION CENSUS 1970**.
283 5c. multicoloured 10 10
284 10c. multicoloured 15 10
285 15c. multicoloured 20 10
286 25c. multicoloured 20 15

1970. Orchids of Belize (2nd series). As T **64**. Mult.
287 5c. Black orchid 35 15
288 15c. White butterfly orchid 50 10
289 22c. Swan orchid 70 10
290 25c. Butterfly orchid 70 40

1970. Indigenous Hardwoods (2nd series). Mult.
291 5c. Type **69** 25 10
292 15c. Nargusta 40 10
293 22c. Cedar 45 10
294 25c. Sapodilla 45 35

70 "The Nativity" (A. Hughes)

71 Legislative Assembly House

1970. Christmas. Multicoloured.
295 ½c. Type **70** 10 10
296 5c. "The Mystic Nativity" (Botticelli) 10 10
297 10c. Type **70** 10 10
298 15c. As 5c. 20 10
299 22c. Type **70** 25 10
300 50c. As 5c. 40 85

1971. Establishment of New Capital, Belmopan. Multicoloured.
301 5c. Old capital, Belize 10 10
302 10c. Government Plaza 10 10
303 15c. Type **71** 10 10
304 22c. Magistrates' Court 15 10
305 25c. Police H.Q 15 15
306 50c. New G.P.O 25 40
The 5c. and 10c. are larger, 60 × 22 mm.

72 "Tabebuia chrysantha"

1971. Easter. Flowers. Multicoloured.
307 ½c. Type **72** 10 10
308 5c. "Hymenocallis littorallis" 10 10
309 10c. "Hippeastrum equestre" 10 10
310 15c. Type **72** 20 10
311 22c. As 5c. 20 10
312 25c. As 10c. 20 30

1971. Racial Equality Year. Nos. 261 and 264 optd **RACIAL EQUALITY YEAR–1971**.
313 10c. multicoloured 25 10
314 50c. multicoloured 55 20

74 Tubroos

76 "Petrae volubis"

75 Hawksworth and Belcan Bridges

1971. Indigenous Hardwoods (3rd series). Mult.
315 5c. Type **74** 60 10
316 15c. Yemeri 80 30
317 26c. Billywebb 1·10 35
318 50c. Logwood 1·75 4·25
MS319 96 × 171 mm. Nos. 315/18 3·50 7·50

1971. Bridges of the World. Multicoloured.
320 ½c. Type **75** 10 20
321 5c. Narrows Bridge, N.Y. and Quebec Bridge 30 15

322 26c. London Bridge (1871) and reconstructed, Arizona (1971) 80 15
323 50c. Belize Mexican Bridge and Swing Bridge . . . . 1·00 1·25

1972. Easter. Wild Flowers. Multicoloured.
324 6c. Type **76** 15 10
325 15c. Yemeri 25 30
326 26c. Mayflower 50 45
327 50c. Tiger's Claw . . . . . . 80 1·40

77 Seated Figure

78 Banak

1972. Mayan Artefacts. Multicoloured.
328 3c. Type **77** 25 10
329 6c. Priest in "dancing" pose 25 10
330 16c. Sun God's head (horiz) 50 15
331 26c. Priest and Sun God . . 70 20
332 50c. Full-front figure . . . . 1·40 3·75

1972. Indigenous Hardwoods (4th series). Mult.
333 3c. Type **78** 25 10
334 5c. Quamwood 25 10
335 16c. Waika Chewstick . . . 55 15
336 26c. Mamee-Apple 75 25
337 50c. My Lady . . . . 1·60 3·25

1972. Royal Silver Wedding. As T **52** of Ascension, but with Orchids of Belize in background.
341 26c. green 25 10
342 50c. violet 40 65

80 Baron Bliss Day

1973. Festivals of Belize. Multicoloured.
343 3c. Type **80** 15 10
344 10c. Labour Day 15 10
345 26c. Carib Settlement Day . . 30 10
346 50c. Pan American Day . . . 50 85

POSTAGE DUE STAMPS

D 1

1923.
D1 D 1 1c. black . . . . 2·25 13·00
D4 2c. black . . . . 2·75 5·50
D5 4c. black . . . . 90 6·00

For later issues see **BELIZE**.

BRITISH INDIAN OCEAN TERRITORY Pt. 1

A Crown Colony, established 8 November 1965, comprising the Chagos Archipelago (previously administered by Mauritius) and Aldabra, Farquhar and Desroches, previously administered by Seychelles to which country they were returned on 29 June 1976.

The Chagos Archipelago has no indigenous population, but stamps were provided from 1990 for use by civilian workers at the U.S. Navy base on Diego Garcia.

1968. 100 cents = 1 rupee.
1990. 100 pence = 1 pound.

1968. Nos 196/200, 202/4 and 206/12 of Seychelles optd **B.I.O.T.**
1 **24** 5c. multicoloured . . . . 1·00 1·50
2 – 10c. multicoloured 10 15
3 – 15c. multicoloured 10 15
4 – 20c. multicoloured 15 15
5 – 25c. multicoloured 15 15
6 – 40c. multicoloured 20 20
7 – 45c. multicoloured 20 30
8 – 50c. multicoloured 20 30
9 – 75c. multicoloured 60 35
10 – 1r. multicoloured 70 35
11 – 1r.50 multicoloured . . . . 1·75 1·50
12 – 2r.25 multicoloured . . . . 3·00 3·75
13 – 3r.50 multicoloured . . . . 3·00 4·50
14 – 5r. multicoloured . . . . . 10·00 7·50
15 – 10r. multicoloured . . . . . 20·00 20·00

2 Lascar

1968. Marine Life. Multicoloured.
16 5c. Type **2** . . . . 70 2·00
17 10c. Smooth hammerhead (vert) . . . . 30 1·25
18 15c. Tiger shark . . . . . . 30 1·50
19 20c. Spotted eagle ray ("Bat ray") . . . . 30 1·00
20 25c. Yellow-finned butterflyfish and ear-spot angelfish (vert) . . . . . . 80 1·00
20a 30c. Robber crab . . . . . . 3·50 2·75
21 40c. Blue-finned trevalley ("Caranx") . . . . 1·25 40
22 45c. Crocodile needlefish ("Garfish") (vert) . . . . 2·25 2·50
23 50c. Pickhandle barracuda . . 1·25 30
23a 60c. Spotted pebble crab . . 3·50 3·25
24 75c. Indian Ocean steep-headed parrotfish . . . . 2·50 2·75
24a 85c. Rainbow runner ("Dorade") . . . . 4·50 3·50
25 1r. Giant hermit crab . . . . 1·50 35
26 1r.50 Parrotfish ("Humphead") . . . . . . 2·50 3·00
27 2r.25 Yellow-edged lyre-tail andAredate grouper ("Rock cod") . . . . . . 12·00 10·00
28 3r.50 Black marlin . . . . . 4·00 3·75
29 5r. black, green and blue (Whale shark) (vert) . . . 12·00 11·00
30 10r. Lionfish . . . . 8·00 8·00

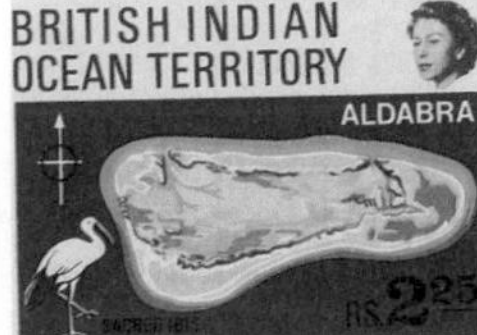

3 Sacred Ibis and Aldabra Coral Atoll

1969. Coral Atolls
31 **3** 2r.25 multicoloured . . . . . 1·75 1·00

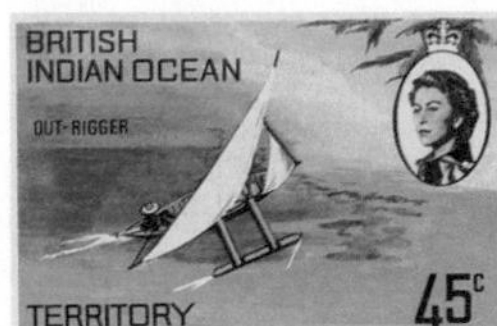

4 Outrigger Canoe

1969. Ships of the Islands. Multicoloured.
32 45c. Type **4** 55 75
33 75c. Pirogue 55 80
34 1r. M.V. "Nordvaer" 60 90
35 1r.50 "Isle of Farquhar" . . . 65 1·00

5 Giant Land Tortoise

1971. Aldabra Nature Reserve. Multicoloured.
36 45c. Type **5** . . . . 2·50 2·50
37 75c. Aldabra lily . . . . . . 3·00 2·50
38 1r. Aldabra tree snail . . . . 3·50 2·75
39 1r.50 Western reef heron ("Dimorphic Egrets") . . . 12·00 10·00

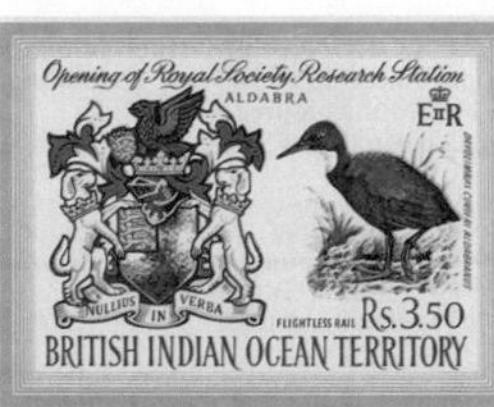

6 Arms of Royal Society and White-throated Rail

1971. Opening of Royal Society Research Station, Aldabra.
40 **6** 3r.50 multicoloured . . . . . 15·00 8·50

7 Staghorn Coral

1972. Coral. Multicoloured.
41 40c. Type **7** . . . . 3·50 4·00
42 60c. Brain coral . . . . . . 4·00 4·25
43 1r. Mushroom coral . . . . . 4·00 4·25
44 1r.75 Organ pipe coral . . . . 5·00 6·50

1972. Royal Silver Wedding. As T **52** of Ascension, but with White-throated rail and Sacred ibis in background.
45 95c. green 50 40
46 1r.50 violet 50 40

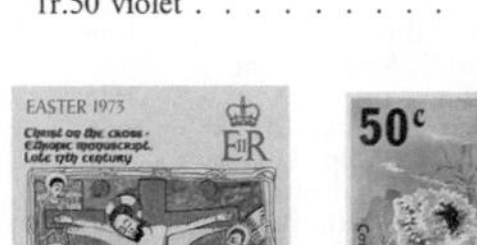

9 "Christ on the Cross"

10 Upsidedown Jellyfish

1973. Easter. Multicoloured.
47 45c. Type **9** 20 40
48 75c. "Joseph and Nicodemus burying Jesus" 30 55
49 1r. Type **9** 30 60
50 1r.50 As 75c. 30 70
MS51 126 × 110 mm. Nos. 47/50 1·00 4·00

1973. Wildlife (1st series). Multicoloured.
53 50c. Type **10** . . . . 3·50 3·00
54 1r. "Hypolimnas misippus" and "Belenois aldabrensis" (butterflies) . . . . 4·00 3·00
55 1r.50 "Nephila madagascarienis" (spider) 4·25 3·00

See also Nos. 58/61, 77/80 and 86/9.

11 M.V. "Nordvaer"

13 Aldabra Drongo

12 Red-cloud Auger and Subulat Auger

1974. 5th Anniv of "Nordvaer" Travelling Post Office. Multicoloured.
56 85c. Type **11** 85 75
57 2r.50 "Nordvaer" off shore . . 1·40 1·25

1974. Wildlife (2nd series). Shells. Multicoloured.
58 45c. Type **12** . . . . 2·25 1·25
59 75c. Great green turban . . . 2·50 1·50
60 1r. Strawberry drupe . . . . 2·75 1·75
61 1r.50 Bull-mouth helmet . . . 3·00 2·00

1975. Birds. Multicoloured.
62 5c. Type **13** . . . . 1·25 2·75
63 10c. Black coucal ("Malagasy Coucal") . . . . 1·25 2·75
64 20c. Mascarene fody ("Red-Headed Forest Foddy") . . 1·25 2·75
65 25c. White tern . . . . 1·25 2·75
66 30c. Crested tern . . . . . . 1·25 2·75
67 40c. Brown booby . . . . . . 1·25 2·75
68 50c. Common noddy ("Noddy Tern") (horiz) . . . . . . 1·25 3·00
69 60c. Grey heron . . . . 1·25 3·00
70 65c. Blue-faced booby (horiz) 1·25 3·00
71 95c. Madagascar white eye ("Malagasy White-eye") (horiz) . . . . 1·25 3·00
72 1r. Green-backed heron (horiz) 1·25 3·00
73 1r.75 Lesser frigate bird (horiz) 2·00 5·50
74 3r.50 White-tailed tropic bird (horiz) . . . . 2·75 5·50
75 5r. Souimanga sunbird (horiz) 4·00 5·00
76 10r. Madagascar turtle dove ("Malagasy Turtle Dove") (horiz) . . . . 8·00 9·00

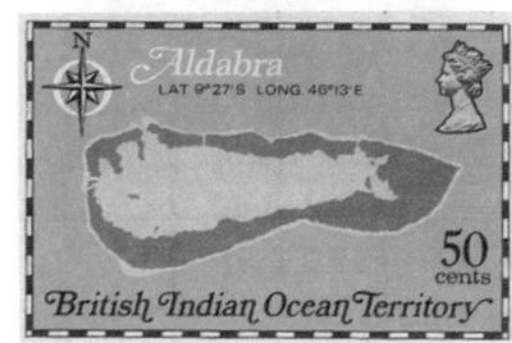

14 "Grewia salicifolia"

1975. Wildlife (3rd series). Seashore Plants. Multicoloured.
77 50c. Type **14** . . . . 50 1·40
78 65c. "Cassia aldabrensis" . . . 55 1·50
79 1r. "Hypoestes aldabrensis" 65 1·60
80 1r.60 "Euphorbia pyrifolia" 80 1·75

15 Map of Aldabra

1975. 10th Anniv of Territory. Maps. Multicoloured.
81 50c. Type **15** 80 65
82 1r. Desroches 95 85
83 1r.50 Farquhar . . . . 1·10 1·00
84 2r. Diego Garcia . . . . . . 1·25 1·25
MS85 147 × 147 mm. Nos. 81/4 7·00 14·00

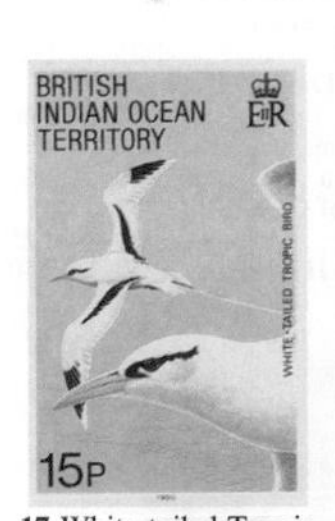

16 "Utetheisa pulchella" (moth)

1976. Wildlife (4th series). Multicoloured.
86 65c. Type **16** . . . . 60 1·10
87 1r.20 "Dysdercus fasciatus" (bug) . . . . 75 1·25
88 1r.50 "Sphex torridus" (wasp) 80 1·40
89 2r. "Oryctes rhinoceros" (beetle) . . . . 85 1·40

17 White-tailed Tropic Bird

19 Territory Flag

18 1974 Wildlife 1r.50 Stamp

1990. Birds. Multicoloured.
90 15p. Type **17** . . . . 1·10 2·00
91 20p. Madagascar turtle dove ("Turtle Dove") . . . . 1·25 2·00
92 24p. Great frigate bird ("Greater Frigate") . . . . 1·40 2·00
93 30p. Green-backed heron ("Little Green Heron") . . 1·50 2·25
94 34p. Great sand plover ("Greater Sand Plover") 1·60 2·25
95 41p. Crab plover . . . . . . 1·75 2·50
96 45p. Crested tern . . . . . . 3·00 2·50
97 54p. Lesser crested tern . . . 2·25 2·75
98 62p. White tern ("Fairy Tern") . . . . 2·25 2·75
99 71p. Red-footed booby . . . 2·25 3·00
100 80p. Common mynah ("Indian Mynah") . . . . 2·50 3·25
101 £1 Madagascar red fody ("Madagascar Fody") . . 3·25 3·50

1990. "Stamp World London 90" International Stamp Exhibition. Multicoloured.
102 15p. Type **18** . . . . 3·50 3·25
103 20p. 1976 Wildlife 2r. stamp 3·75 3·50

104 34p. 1975 Diego Garcia map 2r. stamp . . . . 6·00 5·50
105 54p. 1969 "Nordvaer" 1r. stamp . . . . 8·00 7·50

1990. 90th Birthday of Queen Elizabeth the Queen Mother. As T **34** of Ascension.
106 24p. multicoloured . . . . . 3·50 3·50
107 £1 black and ochre . . . . . 6·50 6·50
DESIGNS—21 × 36 mm: Lady Elizabeth Bowes-Lyon, 1923. 29 × 37 mm: £1 Queen Elizabeth and her daughters, 1940.

1990. 25th Anniv of British Indian Ocean Territory. Multicoloured.
108 20p. Type **19** . . . . 4·00 4·50
109 24p. Coat of arms . . . . . . 4·00 4·50
MS110 63 × 99 mm. £1 map of Chagos Archipelago . . . . . 9·50 11·00

20 Postman emptying Pillar Box

1991. British Indian Ocean Territory Administration. Multicoloured.
111 20p. Type **20** . . . . 2·00 2·50
112 24p. Commissioner inspecting guard of Royal Marines . . 2·25 2·50
113 34p. Policeman outside station . . . . 4·00 4·50
114 54p. Customs officers boarding yacht . . . . . 5·50 6·00

21 "Experiment" (E.I.C. survey brig), 1786

1991. Visiting Ships. Multicoloured.
115 20p. Type **21** . . . . 2·75 3·00
116 24p. "Pickering" (American brig), 1819 . . . . 3·00 3·25
117 34p. "Emden" (German cruiser), 1914 . . . . . . 4·00 4·25
118 54p. H.M.S. "Edinburgh" (destroyer), 1988 . . . . . 5·00 5·50

1992. 40th Anniv of Queen Elizabeth II's Accession. As T **143** of Ascension. Multicoloured.
119 15p. Catholic chapel, Diego Garcia . . . . 1·25 1·25
120 20p. Planter's house, Diego Garcia . . . . 1·40 1·40
121 24p. Railway tracks on wharf, Diego Garcia . . . 3·00 2·00
122 34p. Three portraits of Queen Elizabeth . . . . 2·50 2·25
123 54p. Queen Elizabeth II . . . 2·50 2·50

22 R.A.F. Consolidated PBY-5 Catalina (flying boat)

1992. Visiting Aircraft. Multicoloured.
124 20p. Type **22** . . . . 2·00 2·50
125 24p. R.A.F. Hawker Siddeley Nimrod M.R.2 (maritime reconnaissance aircraft) . . 2·25 2·50
126 34p. Lockheed P-3 Orion (transport aircraft) . . . . 2·75 3·25
127 54p. U.S.A.A.F. Boeing B-52 Stratofortress (heavy bomber) . . . . 3·50 4·50

23 "The Mystical Marriage of St. Catherine" (Correggio)

1992. Christmas. Religious Paintings. Mult.
128 5p. Type **23** 70 80
129 24p. "Madonna" (anon) . . 1·50 1·60
130 34p. "Madonna" (anon) (different) . . . . 1·75 2·25
131 54p. "The Birth of Jesus" (Kaspar Jele) . . . . . . 2·50 3·50

24 Coconut Crab and Rock

1993. Endangered Species. Coconut Crab. Mult.
132 10p. Type **24** . . . . . . 1·25 1·25
133 10p. Crab on beach . . . . 1·25 1·25
134 10p. Two crabs . . . . . . 1·25 1·25
135 15p. Crab climbing coconut tree . . . . 1·50 1·50

1993. 75th Anniv of Royal Air Force. As T **149** of Ascension. Multicoloured.
136 20p. Vickers Virginia Mk X 1·25 1·50
137 24p. Bristol Bulldog IIA . . 1·40 1·50
138 34p. Short S.25 Sunderland Mk III . . . . 1·75 2·00
139 54p. Bristol Blenheim Mk IV 2·75 3·25
MS140 110 × 77 mm. 20p. Douglas DC-3 Dakota; 20p. Gloster G.41 Javelin; 20p. Blackburn Beverley C1; 20p. Vickers VC-10 . . . 7·50 8·00

25 "Stachytarpheta urticifolia"

26 Forrest's Map of Diego Garcia, 1778

1993. Christmas. Flowers. Multicoloured.
141 20p. Type **25** . . . . 1·25 1·50
142 24p. "Ipomea pes-caprae" . . 1·25 1·50
143 34p. "Sida pusilla" . . . . . 1·50 2·25
144 54p. "Catharanthus roseus" 2·50 3·50

1994. "Hong Kong '94" International Stamp Exhibition. Nos. 92 and 101 optd **HONG KONG '94** and emblem.
145 24p. Great frigate bird ("Greater Frigate") . . . . 2·75 2·00
146 £1 Madagascar red fody ("Madagascar Fody") . . 3·75 6·00

1994. 18th-century Maps. Each black and blue.
147 20p. Type **26** . . . . 90 1·50
148 24p. Blair's plan of Diego Garcia harbour, 1786–87 1·00 1·60
149 34p. Blair's chart of Chagos Archipelago, 1786–87 . . . 1·10 1·75
150 44p. Plan of part of Diego Garcia, 1774 . . . . . . 1·40 1·90
151 54p. Fontaine's plan of Diego Garcia, 1770 . . . . . . 1·60 2·00

27 "Junonia villida"

1994. Butterflies. Multicoloured.
152 24p. Type **27** . . . . 1·75 1·75
153 30p. "Petrelaea dana" . . . 2·25 2·50
154 56p. "Hypolimnas misippus" 3·75 4·00

28 Short-tailed Nurse Sharks

1994. Sharks. Multicoloured.
155 15p. Type **28** . . . . 1·75 1·75
156 20p. Silver-tipped sharks . . 1·75 1·75
157 24p. Black-finned reef shark 1·75 1·75
158 30p. Oceanic white-tipped sharks . . . . 2·00 2·00
159 35p. Black-tipped shark . . 2·25 2·25
160 41p. Smooth hammerhead . . 2·25 2·25
161 46p. Sickle-finned lemon shark . . . . 2·25 2·25
162 55p. White-tipped reef shark 2·50 2·75
163 65p. Tiger sharks . . . . . 2·50 2·75
164 74p. Indian sand tiger . . . 3·00 3·50
165 80p. Great hammerhead . . . 3·00 3·50
166 £1 Great white shark . . . . 3·25 3·75

1995. 50th Anniv of End of Second World War. As T **161** of Ascension. Multicoloured.
167 20p. Military cemetery . . . 1·50 1·75
168 24p. Rusty 6-inch naval gun at Cannon Point . . . . . 1·75 1·75
169 30p. Short S.25 Sunderland flying boat . . . . 2·00 2·25
170 56p. H.M.I.S. "Clive"(sloop) 3·00 3·75
MS171 75 × 85 mm. £1 Reverse of 1939–45 War Medal (vert) . . 2·50 3·00

29 Dolphin (fish)

1995. Gamefish. Multicoloured.
172 20p. Type **29** . . . . 1·50 1·60
173 24p. Sailfish . . . . 1·60 1·60
174 30p. Wahoo . . . . 2·25 2·50
175 56p. Striped marlin . . . . . 3·25 3·75

30 "Terebra crenulata"

1996. Sea Shells. Multicoloured.
176 20p. Type **30** . . . . 1·25 1·50
177 24p. "Bursa bufonia" . . . . 1·25 1·50
178 30p. "Nassarius papillosus" 1·75 2·00
179 56p. "Lopha cristagalli" . . . 3·00 3·25

1996. 70th Birthday of Queen Elizabeth II. As T **165** of Ascension, each incorporating a different photograph of the Queen. Multicoloured.
180 20p. View of lagoon from south . . . . 75 1·00
181 24p. Manager's House, Peros Banhos . . . . 80 1·00
182 30p. Wireless hut, Peros Banhos . . . . 1·00 1·40
183 56p. Sunset . . . . 1·50 2·00
MS184 64 × 66 mm. £1 Queen Elizabeth II . . . . 2·50 3·50

31 Loggerhead Turtle

1996. Turtles. Multicoloured.
185 20p. Type **31** . . . . 1·00 1·25
186 24p. Leatherback turtle . . . 1·10 1·25
187 30p. Hawksbill turtle . . . . 1·40 1·60
188 56p. Green turtle . . . . . . 2·00 2·50

32 Commissioner's Representative (naval officer)

1996. Uniforms. Multicoloured.
189 20p. Type **32** . . . . 1·00 1·10
190 24p. Royal Marine officer . . 1·10 1·10
191 30p. Royal Marine in battle-dress . . . . 1·50 1·75
192 56p. Police officers . . . . . 2·25 2·75

1997. "HONG KONG '97" International Stamp Exhibition. Sheet 130 × 90 mm, containing design as No. 163. Multicoloured.
MS193 65p. Tiger sharks . . . . 2·00 2·50

1997. Return of Hong Kong to China. Sheet 130 × 90 mm, containing design as No. 164, but with "1997" imprint date.
MS194 74p. Indian sand tiger . . 2·75 3·50

1997. Golden Wedding of Queen Elizabeth and Prince Philip. As T **173** of Ascension. Mult.
195 20p. Queen Elizabeth at Bristol, 1994 . . . . 1·40 1·60
196 20p. Prince Philip competing in Royal Windsor Horse Show, 1996 . . . . 1·40 1·60
197 24p. Queen Elizabeth in phaeton, Trooping the Colour, 1987 . . . . . . 1·40 1·60
198 24p. Prince Philip . . . . . 1·40 1·60
199 30p. Queen Elizabeth and Prince Philip with Land Rover . . . . 1·40 1·60
200 30p. Queen Elizabeth at Balmoral . . . . 1·40 1·60
MS201 110 × 71 mm. £1.50, Queen Elizabeth and Prince Philip in landau (horiz) . . . . 6·00 6·50
Nos. 195/6, 197/8 and 199/20 respectively were printed together, se-tenant, with the backgrounds forming a compsite design.

33 H.M.S. "Richmond" (frigate) and H.M.S. "Beaver" (frigate)

1997. Exercise Ocean Wave. Multicoloured.
202 24p. Type **33** . . . . 1·10 1·40
203 24p. H.M.S. "Illustrious" (aircraft carrier) launching aircraft . . . . 1·10 1·40
204 24p. H.M.S. "Beaver" . . . 1·10 1·40
205 24p. Royal Yacht "Britannia", R.F.A. "Sir Percival" and H.M.S. "Beaver" . . . . 1·10 1·40
206 24p. Royal Yacht "Britannia" . . . . 1·10 1·40
207 24p. H.M.S. "Richmond", H.M.S. "Beaver" and H.M.S. "Gloucester" (destroyer) . . . . 1·10 1·40
208 24p. H.M.S. "Richmond" . . 1·10 1·40
209 24p. Aerial view of H.M.S. "Illustrious" . . . . 1·10 1·40
210 24p. H.M.S. "Gloucester" (wrongly inscr "Sheffield") 1·10 1·40
211 24p. H.M.S. "Trenchant" (submarine) and R.F.A. "Diligence" . . . . 1·10 1·40
212 24p. R.F.A. "Fort George" replenishing H.M.S. "Illustrious" and H.M.S. "Gloucester" . . . . . . 1·10 1·40
213 24p. Aerial view of H.M.S. "Richmond", H.M.S. "Beaver" and H.M.S. "Gloucester" . . . . . . 1·10 1·40

1998. Diana, Princess of Wales Commemoration. Sheet 145 × 70 mm, containing vert designs as T **177** of Ascension. Multicoloured.
MS214 26p. Wearing patterned jacket, 1993; 26p. Wearing heart-shaped earrings, 1988; 34p. Wearing cream jacket, 1993; 60p. Wearing blue blouse, 1982 (sold at £1.46 + 20p. charity premium) 3·25 4·00

1998. 80th Anniv of the Royal Air Force. As T **178** of Ascension. Multicoloured.
215 26p. Blackburn Iris . . . . . 1·00 1·10
216 34p. Gloster Gamecock . . . 1·25 1·40
217 60p. North American Sabre F.4 . . . . 2·25 2·50
218 80p. Avro Lincoln . . . . . 2·75 3·00
MS219 110 × 77 mm. 34p. Sopwith Baby (seaplane); 34p. Martinsyde Elephant; 34p. De Havilland Tiger Moth; 34p. North American Mustang III . . . . 5·00 6·00

34 Bryde's Whale

1998. International Year of the Ocean. Multicoloured.
220 26p. Type **34** . . . . 1·75 1·75
221 26p. Striped dolphin . . . . 1·75 1·75
222 34p. Pilot whale . . . . . . 1·75 1·75
223 34p. Spinner dolphin . . . . 1·75 1·75

35 "Westminster" (East Indiaman), 1837

1999. Ships. Multicoloured.
224 2p. Type **35** 10 10
225 15p. "Sao Cristovao" (Spanish galleon), 1589 . . 30 35
226 20p. "Sea Witch" (U.S. clipper), 1849 . . . . . . 40 45
227 26p. H.M.S. "Royal George" (ship of the line), 1778 . . 55 60

228 34p. "Cutty Sark" (clipper), 1883 . . . . 70 75
229 60p. "Mentor" (East Indiaman), 1789 . . . . . 1·25 1·40
230 80p. H.M.S. "Trinculo" (brig), 1809 . . . . 1·60 1·70
231 £1 "Enterprise" (paddle-steamer), 1825 . . . . . . 2·00 2·10
232 £1.15 "Confiance" (French privateer), 1800 . . . . . 2·25 2·40
233 £2 "Kent" (East Indiaman), 1820 . . . . 4·00 4·25

36 Cutty Sark (clipper)

1999. "Australia '99" World Stamp Exhibition, Melbourne. Sheet 150 × 75 mm, containing T **36** and similar horiz design. Multicoloured.
MS234 60p. Type **36**; 60p. "Thermopylae" (clipper) . . . 4·00 4·50

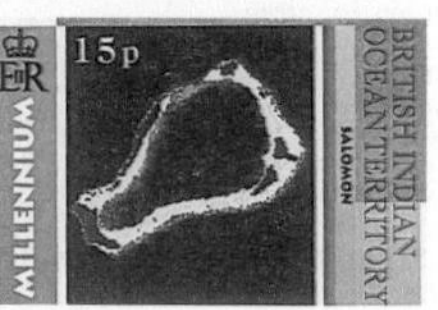

37 Field Vole (Colin Sargent)

2000. "The Stamp Show 2000", International Stamp Exhibition, London. "Shoot a Stamp" Competition Winners. Sheet 150 × 100 mm, containing T **37** and similar vert designs. Multicoloured.
MS235 26p. Type **37**; 34p. Atlantic puffin (P. J. Royal); 55p. Red fox (Jim Wilson); £1 European robin ("Robin") (Harry Smith) . . . 5·50 7·00

38 Satellite Image of Salomon Island

2000. New Millennium. Satellite Images of Islands. Multicoloured.
236 15p. Type **38** . . . . 1·00 1·10
237 20p. Egmont . . . . 1·10 1·25
238 60p. Blenheim Reef . . . . . 2·00 2·25
239 80p. Diego Garcia . . . . . 2·25 2·50

39 Queen Elizabeth the Queen Mother

40 *Delonix regia*

2000. Queen Elizabeth the Queen Mother's 100th Birthday. Multicoloured.
240 26p. Type **39** . . . . 1·10 1·10
241 34p. Wearing green hat and outfit . . . . 1·25 1·25
MS242 113 × 88 mm. 55p. In blue hat and outfit . . . . 4·00 4·50

2000. Christmas Flowers. Multicoloured.
243 26p. Type **40** . . . . 1·10 1·10
244 34p. *Barringtonia asiatica* . . 1·40 1·40
245 60p. *Zephyranthes rosea* . . . 2·25 2·50

2000. "HONG KONG 2001" Stamp Exhibition. Sheet 150 × 90 mm, containing T **41** and similar design showing butterfly. Multicoloured.
MS246 26p. Type **41**; 34p. "Junonia villida chagoensis" . . . . . . 1·75 2·00

42 H.M.S. *Turbulent*

2001. Centenary of Royal Navy Submarine Service. Multicoloured (except Nos. 248 and 250).
247 26p. Type **42** . . . . 90 1·00
248 26p. H.M.S. *Churchill* (grey and black) . . . . 90 1·00
249 34p. H.M.S. *Resolution* . . . 1·25 1·40
250 34p. H.M.S. *Vanguard* . . . 1·25 1·40
251 60p. H.M.S. *Otter* (73 × 27 mm) . . . . . . 1·90 2·25
252 60p. H.M.S. *Oberon* (73 × 27 mm) (grey and black) . . . . 1·90 2·25

43 Cushion Star

2001. Endangered Species. Seastars. Multicoloured.
253 15p. Type **43** 75 75
254 26p. Azure sea star . . . . . 1·00 1·00
255 34p. Crown-of-Thorns . . . 1·25 1·25
256 56p. Banded bubble star . . 2·00 2·25

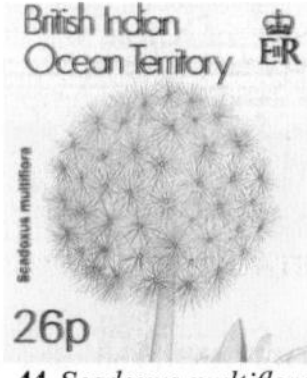

44 *Scadoxus multiflora*

2001. Plants (1st series). Flowers. Multicoloured.
257 26p. Type **44** . . . . 90 1·00
258 34p. *Striga asiatica* . . . . . 1·00 1·10
MS259 173 × 78 mm. Nos. 257/8 and 10p. "Catharanthus roseus" (horiz); 60p. "Argusia argentea" (horiz); 70p. "Euphorbia cyathophora" (horiz) . . . . . 5·50 6·00
In No. **MS**259 the 60p. is inscribed "argentia" in error.

45 Crab Plovers on Beach

2001. Birdlife World Bird Festival. Crab Plovers. Sheet 175 × 80 mm, containing T **45** and similar multicoloured designs.
MS260 50p. Type **45**; 50p. Crab plover catching crab (vert); 50p. Head of crab plover (vert); 50p. Crab plovers in flight; 50p. Crab plover standing on one leg . . 6·50 7·00

2002. Golden Jubilee. As T **200** of Ascension.
261 10p. brown, blue and gold . . 65 65
262 25p. multicoloured . . . . . 1·00 1·00
263 35p. black, blue and gold . . 1·40 1·40
264 55p. multicoloured . . . . . 2·00 2·25
MS265 162 × 95 mm. Nos. 261/4 and 75p. multicoloured . . . . . 6·50 7·00
DESIGNS—HORIZ: 10p. Princess Elizabeth in pantomime, Windsor, 1943; 25p. Queen Elizabeth in floral hat, 1967; 35p. Princess Elizabeth and Prince Philip on their engagement, 1947; 55p. Queen Elizabeth in evening dress. VERT (38 × 51 mm)—75p. Queen Elizabeth after Annigoni.
Designs as Nos. 261/4 in No. **MS**265 omit the gold frame around each stamp and the "Golden Jubilee 1952–2002" inscription.

46 Adult Red-footed Booby

2002. Birdlife International. Red-footed Booby. Sheet 175 × 80 mm, containing T **46** and similar multicoloured designs.
MS266 50p. Type **46**; 50p. Head of dark morph red-footed booby; 50p. Adult bird in flight (vert); 50p. Dark morph on nest (vert); 50p. Fledgling on nest . . . . 6·50 7·00

2002. Queen Elizabeth the Queen Mother Commemoration. As T **202** of Ascension.
267 26p. brown, gold and purple 1·00 1·00
268 £1 multicoloured . . . . . . 2·50 2·75
MS269 145 × 70 mm. £1 black and gold; £1 multicoloured . . . . 5·00 5·50
DESIGNS: 26p. Lady Elizabeth Bowes-Lyon, 1921; £1 (No. 268) Queen Mother, 1986; £1 brownish black and gold (No. **MS**269) Queen Elizabeth at garden party, 1951; £1 multicoloured (No. **MS**269) Queen Mother at Cheltenham Races, 1994.

Designs in No. **MS**269 omit the "1900–2002" inscription and the coloured frame.

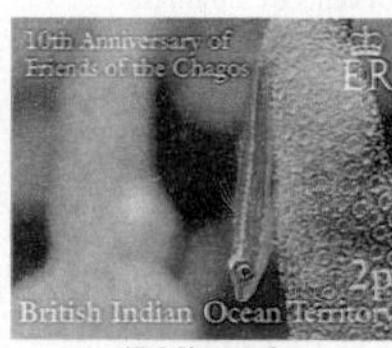

47 Microgoby

2002. 10th Anniv of Friends of Chagos (conservation association). Reef Fish. Mult.
270 2p. Type **47** 20 30
271 15p. Angel fish 60 60
272 26p. Surgeonfish 85 85
273 34p. Trunkfish . . . . 1·10 1·10
274 58p. Soldierfish . . . . . . 1·90 2·25
275 £1 Chagos anemonefish . . . 3·25 3·50

48 *Halgerda tesselata*

2003. Sea Slugs. Multicoloured.
276 2p. Type **48** 20 30
277 15p. *Notodoris minor* 60 60
278 26p. *Nembrotha lineolata* . . 85 85
279 50p. *Chromodoris quadricolor* 1·50 1·75
280 76p. *Glossodoris cincta* . . . 2·25 2·50
281 £1.10 *Chromodoris cf leopardus* . . . . 3·00 3·25

2003. 50th Anniv of Coronation. As T **206** of Ascension. Multicoloured.
282 £1 Queen Elizabeth II wearing Imperial State Crown in Coronation Coach . . . . 2·00 2·10
283 £2 Queen with members of Royal Family in Coronation robes . . . . 2·10 2·25
MS284 95 × 115 mm. £1 As No. 282; £2 As No. 283 . . . . 6·00 6·25
Nos. 282/3 have red frame; stamps from **MS**284 have no frame and country name in mauve panel.

2003. As T **207** of Ascension.
285 £2.50 black, pink and red . . 5·00 5·25

2003. 21st Birthday of Prince William of Wales. As T **208** of Ascension. Multicoloured.
286 50p. Prince William at Cirencester Polo Club . . . 1·00 1·10
287 £1 With Prince Charles on skiing holiday and at Cirencester Polo Club . . . 2·00 2·10

2003. Centenary of Powered Flight. As Type **209** of Ascension. Multicoloured.
288 34p. Avro Type 683 Lancaster 70 75
289 34p. De Havilland D.H.98 Mosquito 70 75
290 58p. Hawker Hurricane . . . 1·20 1·30
291 58p. Supermarine Spitfire . . 1·20 1·30
292 76p. Vickers-Armstrong Wellington . . . . 1·50 1·60
293 76p. Lockheed C-130 Hercules . . . . 1·50 1·60
MS294 233 × 85 mm. 26p. Boeing E-3A Sentry AWACS; 26p. Boeing B-17 Flying Fortress; 26p. Lockheed P-3 Orion; 26p. Consolidated B-24 Liberator; 26p. Lockheed C-141 StarLifter; 26p. Supermarine Walrus; 26p. Short S.25 Sunderland (flying boat); 26p. Supermarine Stranraer; 26p. PBY Catalina; 26p. Supermarine Sea Otter . . . . 2·40 2·50

49 *Pacific Marlin* (fisheries patrol ship)

2004. Fisheries Patrol. Multicoloured.
MS295 150 × 110 mm. 34p. Type **49**; 34p. Marlin; 58p. Skipjack tuna; 58p. Yellowfin tuna; 76p. Swordfish; 76p. Bigeye tuna . . 6·75 7·00

PARCEL POST STAMPS

2002. 10th Anniv of Friends of Chagos (conservation association). Reef Fish. Sheet 115 × 95 mm, containing horiz design as T **47**. Multicoloured.
PMS1 £1.90 Parrotfish . . . . . 3·75 4·00

BRITISH LEVANT Pt. 1

Stamps used at British post offices in the Turkish Empire. These offices closed in 1914. The stamps were again in use after 1918, during the British Occupation of Turkey.

Stamps of Great Britain surcharged or overprinted

A. BRITISH POST OFFICES IN TURKISH EMPIRE

I. TURKISH CURRENCY.

40 paras = 1 piastre.

1885. Queen Victoria stamps surch in **PARAS** or **PIASTRES**.
7 **71** 40pa. on ½d. red £425 £100
1 **64** 40pa. on 2½d. lilac . . . . 95·00 1·25
4 **74** 40pa. on 2½d. purple on blue . . . . 3·75 10
2 **62** 80pa. on 5d. green . . . . £180 9·50
5 **78** 80pa. on 5d. purple & blue 15·00 30
6 **81** 4pi. on 10d. purple and red 42·00 8·00
3a **58** 12pi. on 2s.6d. lilac . . . . 45·00 22·00

1902. King Edward VII stamps surch in **PARAS** or **PIASTRES**.
29 – 30pa. on 1½d. purple & grn 6·50 55
8 **83** 40pa. on 2½d. blue . . . . 14·00 10
9 – 80pa. on 5d. purple and blue . . . . 7·00 2·50
13 **83** 1pi. on 2½d. blue . . . . . 11·00 10
30 – 2pi. on 5d. purple and blue 9·50 1·50
10 – 4pi. on 10d. purple and red 11·00 4·00
21 – 5pi. on 1s. green and red . . 4·25 9·00
11 – 12pi. on 2s.6d. purple . . . 35·00 35·00
12 – 24pi. on 5s. red . . . . . . 32·00 40·00

1906. Surch **1 Piastre**.
15 – 1pi. on 2d. green and red . . £1300 £600

1909. King Edward VII stamps surch in **PIASTRE PARAS**.
17 – 1pi. 10pa. on 3d. pur on yell 12·00 35·00
18 – 1pi. 30pa. on 4d. grn & brn 5·00 17·00
19 – 1pi. 30pa. on 4d. orange . . 17·00 60·00
20 **83** 2pi. 20pa. on 6d. purple . . 19·00 60·00

1910. King Edward VII stamps surch in **PIASTRES**.
22 – 1¼pi. on 3d. purple on yellow . . . . 50 1·00
23 – 1¾pi. on 4d. orange 50 60
24 **83** 2½pi. on 6d. purple . . . . 1·40 65

1913. King George V stamps surch.
41 **105** 30pa. on ½d. green . . . 75 12·00
35 30pa. on 1½d. brown . . . 3·50 14·00
36a **104** 1pi. on 2½d. blue . . . . 5·00 15
37 **106** 1¼pi. on 3d. violet . . . . 4·75 4·25
42 **104** 1½pi. on 1d. red . . . . . 1·50 1·25
38 **106** 1¾pi. on 4d. grey-green . . 3·00 6·00
43 **104** 3¾pi. on 2½d. blue . . . . 1·25 25
39 **108** 4pi. on 10d. blue . . . . 7·50 19·00
44 **106** 4½pi. on 3d. violet . . . . 2·00 3·75
40 **108** 5pi. on 1s. brown . . . . 40·00 60·00
45 **107** 7½pi. on 5d. brown . . . 50 10
46 **108** 15pi. on 10d. blue 70 15
47 18¾pi. on 1s. brown . . . 4·25 4·25
48 **109** 45pi. on 2s.6d. brown . . 20·00 45·00
49 90pi. on 5s. red . . . . . 25·00 30·00
50 180pi. on 10s. blue . . . 45·00 40·00

II. BRITISH CURRENCY

1905. King Edward VII stamps optd **LEVANT**.
L 1 **83** ½d. green . . . . 8·50 15
L 2 1d. red . . . . 7·00 15
L 3 – 1½d. purple and green . . 5·00 1·75
L 4a – 2d. green and red . . . . 3·00 7·00
L 5 **83** 2½d. blue . . . . 8·50 20·00
L 6 – 3d. purple and yellow . . 6·00 12·00
L 7 – 4d. green and brown . . 8·50 42·00
L 8 – 5d. purple and blue . . . 16·00 29·00
L 9 **83** 6d. purple . . . . 12·00 25·00
L10 1s. green and red . . . . 35·00 50·00

1911. King George V stamps optd **LEVANT**.
L12 **98** ½d. green . . . . 1·50 1·50
L14 **101** ½d. green 75 20
L16 **105** ½d. green . . . . 30 1·00
L13 **99** 1d. red . . . . 50 5·50
L15 **102** 1d. red . . . . 50 1·60
L17 **104** 1d. red . . . . 30 4·50
L18 **106** 2d. orange . . . . . . 1·25 29·00
L19 3d. violet . . . . 7·50 10·00
L20 4d. green . . . . 5·00 14·00
L21 **107** 5d. brown . . . . . . 12·00 28·00
L22a 6d. purple . . . . . . 26·00 8·50
L23 **108** 1s. brown . . . . 13·00 8·50
L24 **109** 2s.6d. brown . . . . . 38·00 90·00

B. BRITISH FIELD OFFICE IN SALONICA

1916. King George V stamps of Great Britain optd **Levant**.
S1 **105** ½d. green . . . . 42·00 £200
S2 **104** 1d. red . . . . 42·00 £190
S3 **106** 2d. orange £140 £350
S4 3d. violet £100 £350
S5 4d. green £140 £350
S6 **107** 6d. purple . . . . 80·00 £300
S7 **108** 9d. black £300 £550
S8 1s. brown £250 £475
The above stamps were optd at Salonica during the war of 1914–18.

BRITISH OCCUPATION OF ITALIAN COLONIES Pt. 1

Issues for use in Italian colonies occupied by British Forces. Middle East Forces overprints were used in Cyrenaica, Dodecanese Islands, Eritrea, Italian Somaliland and Tripolitania.

MIDDLE EAST FORCES

12 pence = 1 shilling;
20 shillings = 1 pound.

1942. Stamps of Great Britain optd **M.E.F.**

No.	Type	Description	Unused	Used
M11	128	1d. red	1·50	10
M12		2d. orange	1·50	1·25
M13		2½d. blue	50	10
M 4		3d. violet	60	20
M 5	129	5d. brown	60	20
M16		6d. purple	40	10
M17	130	9d. olive	85	10
M18		1s. brown	50	10
M19	131	2s.6d. green	7·00	1·00
M20		5s. red	13·00	17·00
M21		10s. blue (No. 478a)	15·00	10·00

PRICES. Our prices for Nos. M1/21 in used condition are for stamps with identifiable postmarks of the territories in which they were issued. These stamps were also used in the United Kingdom with official sanction, from the summer of 1950 onwards, and with U.K. postmarks are worth about 25 per cent less.

POSTAGE DUE STAMPS

1942. Postage Due stamps of Great Britain optd **M.E.F.**

No.	Type	Description	Unused	Used
MD1	D 1	½d. green	30	12·00
MD2		1d. red	30	1·75
MD3		2d. black	1·25	1·25
MD4		3d. violet	50	4·25
MD5		1s. blue	3·75	12·00

CYRENAICA

10 milliemes = 1 piastre;
100 piastres = 1 Egyptian pound.

24 Mounted Warrior 25 Mounted Warrior

1950.

No.	Type	Description	Unused	Used
136	24	1m. brown	1·75	3·50
137		2m. red	2·00	3·50
138		3m. yellow	2·00	3·50
139		4m. green	2·00	3·50
140		5m. grey	2·00	2·50
141		8m. orange	2·00	2·00
142		10m. violet	2·00	1·50
143		12m. red	2·00	1·50
144		20m. blue	2·00	1·50
145	25	50m. blue and brown	3·25	3·50
146		100m. red and black	8·00	9·00
147		200m. violet and blue	12·00	25·00
148		500m. yellow and green	42·00	65·00

POSTAGE DUE STAMPS

D 26

1950.

No.	Type	Description	Unused	Used
D149	D 26	2m. brown	45·00	95·00
D150		4m. green	45·00	95·00
D151		8m. red	45·00	£100
D152		10m. orange	45·00	£100
D153		20m. yellow	45·00	£110
D154		40m. blue	45·00	£140
D155		100m. brown	45·00	£150

ERITREA

100 cents = 1 shilling.

BRITISH MILITARY ADMINISTRATION

1948. Stamps of Great Britain surch **B.M.A. ERITREA** and value in cents or shillings.

No.	Type	Description	Unused	Used
E 1	128	5c. on ½d. green	70	65
E 2		10c. on 1d. red	1·00	2·50
E 3		20c. on 2d. orange	50	2·25
E 4		25c. on 2½d. blue	70	60
E 5		30c. on 3d. violet	1·25	4·50
E 6	129	40c. on 5d. brown	50	4·25
E 7		50c. on 6d. purple	50	1·00
E 7a	130	65c. on 8d. red	7·00	2·00
E 8		75c. on 9d. olive	70	75
E 9		1s. on 1s. brown	70	50
E10	131	2s.50 on 2s.6d. green	8·00	10·00
E11		5s. on 5s. red	8·00	16·00
E12	–	10s. on 10s. blue (No. 478a)	22·00	22·00

BRITISH ADMINISTRATION

1950. Stamps of Great Britain surch **B.A. ERITREA** and value in cents or shillings.

No.	Type	Description	Unused	Used
E13	128	5c. on ½d. green	1·25	8·00
E26		5c. on ½d. orange	30	75
E14		10c. on 1d. red	30	3·00
E27		10c. on 1d. blue	30	75
E15		20c. on 2d. orange	30	80
E28		20c. on 2d. brown	30	30
E16		25c. on 2½d. blue	30	60
E29		25c. on 2½d. red	30	30
E17		30c. on 3d. violet	30	2·25
E18	129	40c. on 5d. brown	50	1·75
E19		50c. on 6d. purple	30	20
E20	130	65c. on 8d. red	2·25	1·50
E21		75c. on 9d. olive	30	25
E22		1s. on 1s. brown	30	15
E23	131	2s.50 on 2s.6d. green	7·00	4·75
E24		5s. on 5s. red	7·00	12·00
E25	–	10s. on 10s. blue (No. 478a)	60·00	55·00

1951. Nos. 509/11 of Great Britain surch **B.A. ERITREA** and value in cents and shillings.

No.	Type	Description	Unused	Used
E30	147	2s.50 on 2s.6d. green	10·00	23·00
E31	–	5s. on 5s. red	21·00	23·00
E32	–	10s. on 10s. blue	22·00	23·00

POSTAGE DUE STAMPS

1948. Postage Due stamps of Great Britain surch **B.M.A ERITREA** and new value in cents and shillings.

No.	Type	Description	Unused	Used
ED1	D 1	5c. on ½d. green	9·50	22·00
ED2		10c. on 1d. red	9·50	24·00
ED3		20c. on 2d. black	7·00	16·00
ED4		30c. on 3d. violet	9·50	16·00
ED5		1s. on 1s. blue	17·00	30·00

1950. Postage Due stamps of Great Britain surch **B.A. ERITREA** and new value in cents or shillings.

No.	Type	Description	Unused	Used
ED 6	D 1	5c. on ½d. green	11·00	48·00
ED 7		10c. on 1d. red	10·00	15·00
ED 8		20c. on 2d. black	11·00	14·00
ED 9		30c. on 3d. violet	13·00	22·00
ED10		1s. on 1s. blue	15·00	23·00

SOMALIA

BRITISH OCCUPATION

1943. Stamps of Great Britain optd **E.A.F.** (East African Forces).

No.	Type	Description	Unused	Used
S1	128	1d. red	60	60
S2		2d. orange	1·50	1·25
S3		2½d. blue	50	3·50
S4		3d. violet	80	15
S5	129	5d. brown	1·00	40
S6		6d. purple	50	1·25
S7	130	9d. olive	1·00	2·25
S8		1s. brown	2·25	15
S9	131	2s.6d. green	10·00	6·50

PRICES. Our prices for Nos. S1/9 in used condition are for stamps with identifiable postmarks of the territories in which they were issued. These stamps were also used in the United Kingdom with official sanction, from the summer of 1950, and with U.K. postmarks are worth about 25 per cent less.

BRITISH MILITARY ADMINISTRATION

1948. Stamps of Great Britain surch **B.M.A. SOMALIA** and new value in cents and shillings.

No.	Type	Description	Unused	Used
S10	128	5c. on ½d. green	1·25	1·75
S11		15c. on 1½d. brown	1·75	15·00
S12		20c. on 2d. orange	3·00	4·00
S13		25c. on 2½d. blue	2·25	4·50
S14		30c. on 3d. violet	2·25	9·00
S15	129	40c. on 5d. brown	1·25	20
S16		50c. on 6d. purple	50	2·00
S17	130	75c. on 9d. olive	2·00	18·00
S18		1s. on 1s. brown	1·25	20
S19	131	2s.50 on 2s.6d. green	4·25	25·00
S20		5s. on 5s. red	9·50	40·00

BRITISH ADMINISTRATION

1950. Stamps of Great Britain surch **B.A. SOMALIA** and value in cents and shillings.

No.	Type	Description	Unused	Used
S21	128	5c. on ½d. green	20	3·00
S22		15c. on 1½d. brown	75	17·00
S23		20c. on 2d. orange	75	7·50
S24		25c. on 2½d. blue	50	7·50
S25		30c. on 3d. violet	1·25	4·50
S26	129	40c. on 5d. brown	55	1·00
S27		50c. on 6d. purple	50	1·00
S28	130	75c. on 9d. olive	2·00	7·00
S29		1s. on 1s. brown	60	1·50
S30	131	2s.50 on 2s.6d. green	4·00	24·00
S31		5s. on 5s. red	11·00	95·00

TRIPOLITANIA

BRITISH MILITARY ADMINISTRATION

1948. Stamps of Great Britain surch **B.M.A. TRIPOLITANIA** and value in **M.A.L.** (Military Administration lire).

No.	Type	Description	Unused	Used
T 1	128	1l. on ½d. green	90	1·50
T 2		2l. on 1d. red	30	15
T 3		3l. on 1½d. brown	30	50
T 4		4l. on 2d. orange	30	50
T 5		5l. on 2½d. blue	30	20
T 6		6l. on 3d. violet	30	40
T 7	129	10l. on 5d. brown	30	15
T 8		12l. on 6d. purple	30	20
T 9	130	18l. on 9d. olive	80	65
T10		24l. on 1s. brown	70	1·50
T11	131	60l. on 2s.6d. green	3·50	8·50
T12		120l. on 5s. red	15·00	19·00
T13		240l. on 10s. blue (No. 478a)	22·00	95·00

BRITISH ADMINISTRATION

1950. As Nos. T1/13 but surch **B.A. TRIPOLITANIA** and value in **M.A.L.**

No.	Type	Description	Unused	Used
T14	128	1l. on ½d. green	2·75	12·00
T27		1l. on ½d. orange	20	6·00
T15		2l. on 1d. red	2·50	40
T28		2l. on 1d. blue	20	1·00
T16		3l. on 1½d. brown	1·00	12·00
T29		3l. on 1½d. green	30	8·00
T17		4l. on 2d. orange	1·00	4·50
T30		4l. on 2d. brown	20	1·25
T18		5l. on 2½d. blue	70	70
T31		5l. on 2½d. red	30	7·50
T19		6l. on 3d. violet	1·75	3·25
T20	129	10l. on 5d. brown	50	4·00
T21		12l. on 6d. purple	2·00	50
T22	130	18l. on 9d. olive	2·25	2·50
T23		24l. on 1s. brown	2·50	3·75
T24	131	60l. on 2s.6d. green	6·50	12·00
T25		120l. on 5s. red	20·00	22·00
T26	–	240l. on 10s. blue (No. 478a)	35·00	65·00

1951. Nos. 509/11 of Great Britain surch **B.A. TRIPOLITANIA** and value in **M.A.L.**

No.	Type	Description	Unused	Used
T32	147	60l. on 2s.6d. green	5·50	22·00
T33	–	120l. on 5s. red	9·00	27·00
T34	–	240l. on 10s. blue	38·00	50·00

POSTAGE DUE STAMPS

1948. Postage Due stamps of Great Britain surch **B.M.A. TRIPOLITANIA** and value in **M.A.L.**

No.	Type	Description	Unused	Used
TD1	D 1	1l. on ½d. green	5·50	50·00
TD2		2l. on 1d. red	2·50	32·00
TD3		4l. on 2d. black	7·50	32·00
TD4		6l. on 3d. violet	7·50	21·00
TD5		24l. on 1s. blue	28·00	£100

1950. As Nos. TD1/5 but surch **B.A. TRIPOLITANIA** and value in **M.A.L.**

No.	Type	Description	Unused	Used
TD 6	D 1	1l. on ½d. green	12·00	80·00
TD 7		2l. on 1d. red	2·50	27·00
TD 8		4l. on 2d. black	4·00	35·00
TD 9		6l. on 3d. violet	18·00	60·00
TD10		24l. on 1s. blue	48·00	£140

BRITISH POST OFFICES IN CHINA Pt. 1

Stamps for use in Wei Hai Wei, and the neighbouring islands, leased to Great Britain from 1898 to 1 October 1930, when they were returned to China. The stamps were also used in the Treaty Ports from 1917 until 1922.

100 cents = 1 dollar.

1917. Stamps of Hong Kong (King George V) optd **CHINA**.

No.	Type	Description	Unused	Used
1	24	1c. brown	3·50	1·50
2		2c. green	5·00	30
3		4c. red	4·25	30
4		6c. orange	4·25	60
5		8c. grey	11·00	1·25
6		10c. blue	10·00	30
7		12c. purple on yellow	8·50	3·00
8		20c. purple and olive	11·00	60
9		25c. purple	8·00	15·00
11		30c. purple and orange	27·00	5·00
12b		50c. black on green	30·00	5·50
13		$1 purple and blue on blue	65·00	2·50
14		$2 red and black	£200	50·00
15		$3 green and purple	£425	£180
16		$5 green and red on green	£350	£250
17		$10 purple and black on red	£850	£450

BRITISH POST OFFICES IN CRETE Pt. 1

40 paras = 1 piastre.

B 1

B 2

1898.

No.	Type	Description	Unused	Used
B1	B 1	20pa. violet	£425	£225

1898.

No.	Type	Description	Unused	Used
B2	B 2	10pa. blue	8·00	19·00
B4		10pa. brown	8·00	26·00
B3		20pa. green	14·00	17·00
B5		20pa. red	19·00	15·00

BRITISH POST OFFICES IN SIAM Pt. 1

Used at Bangkok.

100 cents = 1 dollar.

1882. Stamps of Straits Settlements optd **B** on issue of 1867.

No.	Type	Description	Unused	Used
1	19	32c. on 2a. yellow	£35000	

On issues of 1867 to 1883.

No.	Type	Description	Unused	Used
14	5	2c. brown	£475	£350
13	9	2c. on 32c. red (No. 60)	£3000	£3000
15	5	2c. red	55·00	45·00
16		4c. red	£550	£325
17		4c. brown	75·00	70·00
4	18	5c. brown	£300	£325
18		5c. blue	£250	£170
5	5	6c. lilac	£225	£120
20		8c. orange	£160	65·00
21	19	10c. grey	£160	85·00
8	5	12c. blue	£950	£475
22		12c. purple	£275	£150
9		24c. green	£700	£150
10	8	30c. red	£30000	£20000
11	9	96c. grey	£5000	£2750

BRITISH POSTAL AGENCIES IN EASTERN ARABIA Pt. 1

British stamps surcharged for use in parts of the Persian Gulf.

The stamps were used in Muscat from 1 April 1948 to 29 April 1966; in Dubai from 1 April 1948 to 6 January 1961; In Qatar: Doha from August 1950, Umm Said from February 1956 to 31 March 1957; and in Abu Dhabi from 30 March 1963 (Das Island from December 1960) to 29 March 1964.

Nos. 21/2 were placed on sale in Kuwait Post Offices in 1951 and from February to November 1953 due to shortages of stamps with "KUWAIT" overprint. Isolated examples of other values can be found commercially used from Bahrain and Kuwait.

1948. 12 pies = 1 anna; 16 annas = 1 rupee.
1957. 100 naya paise = 1 rupee.

Stamps of Great Britain surch in Indian currency.

1948. King George VI.

No.	Type	Description	Unused	Used
16	128	½a. on ½d. green	2·75	7·00
35		½a. on ½d. orange	70	9·00
17		1a. on 1d. red	3·00	30
36		1a. on 1d. blue	30	7·50
18		1½a. on 1½d. brown	9·00	2·75
37		1½a. on 1½d. green	9·00	24·00
19		2a. on 2d. orange	2·00	3·25
38		2a. on 2d. brown	30	8·50
20		2½a. on 2½d. blue	3·50	6·00
39		2½a. on 2½d. red	30	16·00
21		3a. on 3d. violet	3·50	10
40	129	4a. on 4d. blue	30	3·50
22		6a. on 6d. purple	4·00	10
23	130	1r. on 1s. brown	4·50	50
24	131	2r. on 2s.6d. green	10·00	38·00

1948. Royal Silver Wedding.

No.	Type	Description	Unused	Used
25	137	2½a. on 2½d. blue	2·00	2·75
26	138	15r. on £1 blue	23·00	35·00

1948. Olympic Games.

No.	Type	Description	Unused	Used
27	139	2½a. on 2½d. blue	35	2·50
28	140	3a. on 3d. violet	45	2·50
29	–	6a. on 6d. purple	45	2·75
30	–	1r. on 1s. brown	1·25	2·75

1949. 75th Anniv of U.P.U.

No.	Type	Description	Unused	Used
31	143	2½a. on 2½d. blue	50	3·00
32	144	3a. on 3d. violet	50	3·00
33	–	6a. on 6d. purple	50	2·75
34	–	1r. on 1s. brown	2·00	3·50

1951. Pictorial.

No.	Type	Description	Unused	Used
41	147	2r. on 2s.6d. green	28·00	7·00

1952. Queen Elizabeth.

No.	Type	Description	Unused	Used
42	154	½a. on ½d. orange	10	2·25
43		1a. on 1d. blue	10	2·25
44		1½a. on 1½d. green	10	2·25
45		2a. on 2d. brown	10	10
46	155	2½a. on 2½d. red	10	10
47		3a. on 3d. lilac	20	1·25
48		4a. on 4d. blue	1·00	4·00
49	157	6a. on 6d. purple	35	10
50	160	12a. on 1s.3d. green	3·00	30
51		1r. on 1s.6d. blue	2·25	10

1953. Coronation.

No.	Type	Description	Unused	Used
52	161	2½a. on 2½d. red	1·75	2·00
53	–	4a. on 4d. blue	1·75	1·00
54	163	12a. on 1s.3d. green	2·25	1·00
55	–	1r. on 1s.6d. blue	2·50	50

1955. Pictorials.

No.	Type	Description	Unused	Used
56	166	2r. on 2s.6d. brown	6·50	70
57	–	5r. on 5s. red	10·00	2·25

1957. Value in naye paise. Queen Elizabeth II stamps surch **NP** twice (once only on 75n.p.) and value.

No.	Type	Description	Unused	Used
79	157	1n.p. on 5d. brown	10	20
80	154	3n.p. on ½d. orange	55	80
81		5n.p. on 1d. blue	1·75	2·25
67		6n.p. on 1d. blue	20	2·75
68		9n.p. on 1½d. green	20	2·50
83		10n.p. on 1½d. green	1·00	2·75
69		12n.p. on 2d. brown	30	2·75
85	155	15n.p. on 2½d. red	25	10
71		20n.p. on 3d. lilac	20	10

72 25n.p. on 4d. blue 70 4·00
87 30n.p. on 4½d. brown 40 50
73 **157** 40n.p. on 6d. purple 30 10
89 **158** 50n.p. on 9d. olive 1·00 2·25
75 **160** 75n.p. on 1s.3d. green 2·00 40

1957. World Scout Jubilee Jamboree.
76 **170** 15n.p. on 2½d. red 25 85
77 **171** 25n.p. on 4d. blue 30 85
78 – 75n.p. on 3d. green 35 85

BRITISH VIRGIN ISLANDS Pt. 1

A group of the Leeward Islands, Br. W. Indies. Used general issues for Leeward Islands concurrently with Virgin Islands stamps until 1 July 1956. A Crown Colony.

1951. 100 cents = 1 West Indian dollar.
1962. 100 cents = 1 U.S. dollar.

1 St. Ursula
2
3
4

1866.
1 **1** 1d. green 45·00 60·00
16 **3** 4d. red 40·00 60·00
7 **2** 6d. red 60·00 90·00
11 **4** 1s. black and red £225 £300
No. 11 has a double-lined frame.

1867. With heavy coloured border.
18 **4** 1s. black and red 50·00 60·00

6
8

1880.
26 **6** ½d. yellow 85·00 80·00
27 ½d. green 4·50 8·50
24 1d. green 65·00 85·00
29 1d. red 25·00 28·00
25 2½d. brown 90·00 £120
31 2½d. blue 2·75 14·00

1887.
32 **1** 1d. red 2·25 7·00
35 **3** 4d. brown 35·00 65·00
39 **2** 6d. violet 13·00 42·00
41 **4** 1s. brown 45·00 70·00

1888. No. 18 surch **4D.**
42 **4** 4d. on 1s. black and red £120 £150

1899.
43 **8** ½d. green 1·50 55
44 1d. red 2·75 3·00
45 2½d. blue 12·00 3·25
46 4d. brown 4·00 18·00
47 6d. violet 4·50 3·50
48 7d. green 8·00 7·00
49 1s. yellow 22·00 35·00
50 5s. blue 70·00 85·00

9
11

1904.
54 **9** ½d. purple and green 75 40
55 1d. purple and red 2·50 35
56 2d. purple and brown 6·00 4·50
57 2½d. purple and blue 2·00 2·00
58 3d. purple and black 3·50 3·00
59 6d. purple and brown 2·75 3·00
60 1s. green and red 4·00 5·00
61 2s.6d. green and black 23·00 55·00
62 5s. green and blue 48·00 65·00

1913.
69 **11** ½d. green 1·50 3·75
70 1d. red 2·25 14·00
71 2d. grey 4·00 23·00
72 2½d. blue 5·50 9·00
73 3d. purple on yellow 2·75 6·50
74 6d. purple 5·00 11·00
75 1s. black on green 3·25 9·00
76 2s.6d. black and red on blue 48·00 50·00
77 5s. green and red on yellow 35·00 £110

1917. Optd **WAR STAMP.**
78c **11** 1d. red 30 3·75
79a 3d. purple on yellow 3·00 11·00

14
15 King George VI and Badge of Colony

1922.
86 **14** ½d. green 85 2·75
87 1d. red 60 60
88 1d. violet 1·00 3·50
91 1½d. red 1·75 2·00
92 2d. grey 1·00 6·00
95 2½d. blue 2·50 3·50
94 2½d. orange 1·25 1·50
96 3d. purple on yellow 2·25 11·00
97 5d. purple and olive 5·50 45·00
98 6d. purple 1·50 6·50
83 1s. black on green 75 14·00
84 2s.6d. black and red on blue 5·50 11·00
101 5s. green and red on yellow 19·00 70·00

1935. Silver Jubilee. As T **13** of Antigua.
103 1d. blue and red 1·25 3·75
104 1½d. blue and grey 1·25 3·50
105 2½d. brown and blue 1·50 3·50
106 1s. grey and purple 7·00 17·00

1937. Coronation. As T **2** of Aden.
107 1d. red 20 1·25
108 1½d. brown 50 2·50
109 2½d. blue 50 1·00

1938.
110a **15** ½d. green 30 1·00
111a 1d. red 30 60
112a 1½d. brown 1·00 1·00
113a 2d. grey 1·00 90
114a 2½d. blue 70 2·50
115a 3d. orange 70 80
116a 6d. mauve 2·00 80
117a 1s. brown 1·50 70
118a 2s.6d. brown 15·00 3·00
119a 5s. red 13·00 4·00
120 10s. blue 6·00 8·00
121 £1 black 8·00 20·00

1946. Victory. As T **9** of Aden.
122 1½d. brown 10 10
123 3d. orange 10 20

1949. Silver Wedding. As T **10/11** of Aden.
124 2½d. blue 10 10
125 £1 grey 13·00 16·00

1949. 75th Anniv of U.P.U. As T **20/23** of Antigua.
126 2½d. blue 30 45
127 3d. orange 1·00 2·25
128 6d. mauve 30 40
129 1s. olive 30 40

1951. Inauguration of B.W.I. University College. As T **24/25** of Antigua.
130 3c. black and red 40 1·50
131 12c. black and violet 60 1·50

16 Map

1951. Restoration of Legislative Council.
132 **16** 6c. orange 30 1·00
133 12c. purple 30 50
134 24c. olive 30 50
135 $1.20 red 1·00 1·00

18 Map of Jost Van Dyke

1952.
136 – 1c. black 80 1·50
137 **18** 2c. green 70 30
138 – 3c. black and brown 80 1·25
139 – 4c. red 70 1·25
140 – 5c. red and black 1·50 50
141 – 8c. blue 70 1·25
142 – 12c. violet 80 1·40
143 – 24c. brown 70 50
144 – 60c. green and blue 4·00 11·00
145 – $1.20 black and blue 4·75 12·00
146 – $2.40 green and brown 11·00 16·00
147 – $4.80 blue and red 12·00 16·00

DESIGNS—VERT: 1c. Sombrero lighthouse; 24c. Badge of Presidency. HORIZ—VIEWS: 3c. Sheep industry; 5c. Cattle industry; 60c. Dead Man's Chest (Is); $1.20, Sir Francis Drake Channel; $2.40, Road Town. HORIZ—MAPS: 4c. Anegada Island; 8c. Virgin Gorda Island; 12c. Tortola Island; $4.80, Virgin Islands.

1953. Coronation. As T **13** of Aden.
148 2c. black and green 30 1·25

29 Map of Tortola

30 Brown Pelican

1956.
149 **29** ½c. black and purple 60 20
150 – 1c. turquoise and slate 1·50 75
151 – 2c. red and black 30 10
152 – 3c. blue and olive 30 30
153 – 4c. brown and turquoise 70 30
154 – 5c. black 50 10
155 – 8c. orange and blue 2·00 40
156 – 12c. blue and red 4·00 75
157 – 24c. green and brown 1·00 65
158 – 60c. blue and orange 8·50 8·00
159 – $1.20 green and red 2·00 8·00
160 **30** $2.40 yellow and purple 40·00 13·00
161 – $4.80 sepia and turquoise 40·00 13·00

DESIGNS—HORIZ: As Type **13**: 1c. Virgin Islands sloop; 2c. Nelthrop Red Poll bull; 3c. Road Harbour; 4c. Mountain travel; 5c. Badge of the Presidency; 8c. Beach scene; 12c. Boat launching; 24c. White cedar tree; 60c. Skipjack tuna ("Bonito"); $1.20, Treasury Square Coronation celebrations. As Type **30**: $4.80, Magnificent frigate bird ("Man-o'-War Bird").

1962. New Currency. Nos. 149/53, 155/61 surch in U.S. Currency.
162 **29** 1c. on ½c. black and purple 30 10
163 – 2c. on 1c. turq & vio 1·75 10
164 – 3c. on 2c. red and black 70 10
165 – 4c. on 3c. blue and olive 30 10
166 – 5c. on 4c. brown & turq 30 10
167 – 8c. on 8c. orange and blue 30 10
168 – 10c. on 12c. blue and red 2·00 10
169 – 12c. on 24c. green & brn 30 10
170 – 25c. on 60c. blue and orange 2·75 45
171 – 70c. on $1.20 green and red 35 45
172 **30** $1.40 on $2.40 yellow and purple 9·50 4·00
173 – $2.80 on $4.80 sepia & turq 9·50 4·00

1963. Freedom from Hunger. As T **28** of Aden.
174 25c. violet 20 10

1963. Centenary of Red Cross. As T **33** of Antigua.
175 2c. red and black 15 20
176 25c. red and blue 50 20

1964. 400th Birth Anniv of Shakespeare. As T **34** of Antigua.
177 10c. blue 20 10

43 Skipjack Tuna
44 Map of Tortola

1964.
178 **43** 1c. blue and olive 30 1·75
179 – 2c. olive and red 15 30
180 3c. sepia and turquoise 4·00 1·25
181 – 4c. black and red 80 2·25
182 – 5c. black and green 1·00 2·25
183 – 6c. black and orange 30 85
184 – 8c. black and mauve 30 50
185 – 10c. lake and lilac 2·50 30
186 – 12c. green and blue 2·00 2·75
187 – 15c. green and black 35 2·75
188 – 25c. green and purple 11·00 1·75
189 **44** 70c. black and brown 4·25 7·00
190 – $1 green and brown 3·00 2·00
191 – $1.40 blue and red 24·00 9·00
192 – $2.80 black and purple 24·00 9·00

DESIGNS—HORIZ (As Type **43**): 2c. Soper's Hole; 3c. Brown pelican; 4c. Dead Man's Chest; 5c. Road Harbour; 6c. Fallen Jerusalem; 8c. The Baths, Virgin Gorda; 10c. Map of Virgin Islands; 12c. "Youth of Tortola" (Tortola–St Thomas ferry); 15c. The Towers, Tortola; 25c. Beef Island Airfield. VERT (As Type **44**): $1 Virgin Gorda: $1.40, Yachts at anchor. (27½ × 37½ mm): $2.80, Badge of the Colony.

1965. Centenary of I.T.U. As T **36** of Antigua.
193 4c. yellow and turquoise 20 10
194 25c. blue and buff 45 20

1965. I.C.Y. As T **37** of Antigua.
195 1c. purple and turquoise 10 15
196 25c. green and lavender 30 15

1966. Churchill Commemoration. As T **38** of Antigua.
197 1c. blue 10 30
198 2c. green 15 30
199 10c. brown 30 10
200 25c. violet 60 25

1966. Royal Visit. As T **39** of Antigua.
201 4c. black and blue 40 10
202 70c. black and mauve 1·40 45

58 "Atrato I" (paddle-steamer), 1866

1966. Stamp Centenary. Multicoloured.
203 5c. Type **58** 35 10
204 10c. 1d. and 6d. stamps of 1866 35 10
205 25c. Mail transport, Beef Island, and 6d. stamp of 1866 55 10
206 60c. Landing mail at Roadtown, 1866 and 1d. stamp of 1866 1·00 2·50

1966. Nos. 189 and 191/2 surch.
207 **44** 50c. on 70c. blk & brn 1·25 90
208 – $1.50 on $1.40 blue and red 2·25 2·00
209 – $3 on $2.80 black and purple 2·25 2·75

1966. 20th Anniv of U.N.E.S.C.O. As T **54/6** of Antigua.
210 2c. multicoloured 10 10
211 12c. yellow, violet and olive 20 10
212 60c. black, purple and orange 50 45

63 Map of Virgin Islands

1967. New Constitution.
213 **63** 2c. multicoloured 10 10
214 10c. multicoloured 15 10
215 25c. multicoloured 15 10
216 $1 multicoloured 55 40

64 "Mercury" (cable ship) and Bermuda–Tortola Link

1967. Inauguration of Bermuda–Tortola Telephone Service. Multicoloured.
217 4c. Type **64** 30 10
218 10c. Chalwell Telecommunications Station 20 10
219 50c. "Mercury" (cable ship) 60 30

67 Blue Marlin

1968. Game Fishing. Multicoloured.
220 2c. Type **67** 10 65
221 10c. Cobia 25 10

222 25c. Wahoo 55 10
223 40c. Fishing launch and map 85 75

1968. Human Rights Year. Nos. 185 and 188 optd **1968 INTERNATIONAL YEAR FOR HUMAN RIGHTS.**
224 10c. lake and lilac 20 10
225 25c. green and purple 30 40

72 Dr. Martin Luther King, Bible, Sword and Armour Gauntlet

1968. Martin Luther King Commemoration.
226 **72** 4c. multicoloured 25 20
227 25c. multicoloured 40 40

73 De Havilland Twin Otter 100

1968. Opening of Beef Island Airport Extension. Multicoloured.
228 2c. Type **73** . . . . 15 1·00
229 10c. Hawker Siddeley H.S.748 airliner 20 10
230 25c. De Havilland Heron 2 airplane 40 10
231 $1 Royal Engineers' cap badge . . . . 50 2·00

77 Long John Silver and Jim Hawkins

1969. 75th Death Anniv of Robert Louis Stevenson. Scenes from "Treasure Island".
232 **77** 4c. blue, yellow and red . . 20 15
233 – 10c. multicoloured 20 10
234 – 40c. brown, black and blue 25 30
235 – $1 multicoloured . . . . . 45 1·00
DESIGNS—HORIZ: 10c. Jim Hawkins escaping from the pirates; $1 Treasure trove. VERT: 40c. The fight with Israel Hands.

82 Yachts in Road Harbour, Tortola

1969. Tourism. Multicoloured.
236 2c. Tourist and yellow-finned grouper (fish) 15 50
237 10c. Type **82** 30 10
238 20c. Sun-bathing at Virgin Gorda National Park . . . 40 20
239 $1 Tourist and Pipe Organ cactus at Virgin Gorda . . 90 1·50
Nos. 236 and 239 are vert.

85 Carib Canoe

1970.
240 **85** ½c. buff, brown and sepia 10 1·50
241 – 1c. blue and green 15 30
242 – 2c. orange, brown and slate 40 1·00
243 – 3c. red, blue and sepia . . 30 1·25
244 – 4c. turquoise, blue & brn 30 50
245 – 5c. green, pink and black 30 10
246 – 6c. violet, mauve and green 40 2·00
247 – 8c. green, yellow and sepia 50 3·75
248 – 10c. blue and brown . . . 50 15
249 – 12c. yellow, red and brown 65 1·50
250 – 15c. green, orange and brown . . . . 6·00 85
251 – 25c. green, blue and purple 4·00 1·75
252 – 50c. mauve, green and brown . . . . 3·25 1·50
253 – $1 salmon, green and brown . . . . 4·00 3·75
254 – $2 buff, slate and grey . . 7·50 7·00
255 – $3 ochre, blue and sepia . 2·75 4·50
256 – $5 violet and grey . . . . 2·75 5·00
DESIGNS: 1c. "Santa Maria" (Columbus's flagship); 2c. "Elizabeth Bonaventure" (Drake's flagship); 3c. Dutch buccaneer, c. 1660; 4c. "Thetis", 1827 (after etching by E. W. Cooke); 5c. Henry Morgan's ship (17th-century); 6c. H.M.S. "Boreas" (Captain Nelson, 1784); 8c. H.M.S. "Eclair", 1804; 10c. H.M.S. "Formidable", 1782; 12c. H.M.S. "Nymph", 1778; 15c. "Windsor Castle" (sailing packet) engaging "Jeune Richard" (French brig), 1807; 25c. H.M.S. "Astrea", 1808; 50c. Wreck of R.M.S. "Rhone", 1867; $1 Tortola sloop; $2 H.M.S. "Frobisher"; $3 "Booker Viking" (cargo liner), 1967; $5 Hydrofoil "Sun Arrow".

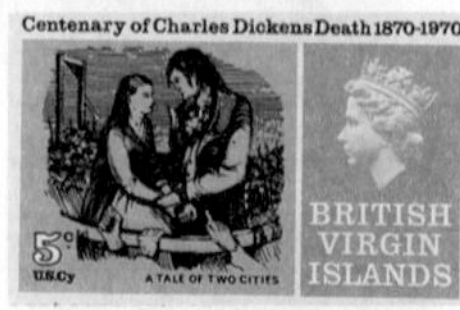

102 "A Tale of Two Cities"

1970. Death Centenary of Charles Dickens.
257 **102** 5c. black, red and grey . . 10 75
258 – 10c. black, blue and green 20 10
259 – 25c. black, green and yellow 30 25
DESIGNS: 10c. "Oliver Twist"; 25c. "Great Expectations".

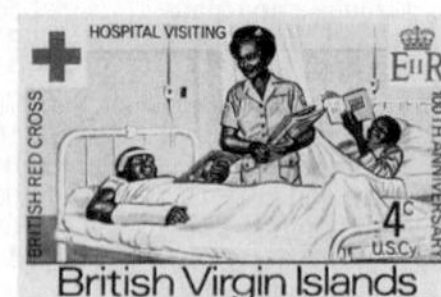

103 Hospital Visit

1970. Centenary of British Red Cross. Multicoloured.
260 4c. Type **103** 20 45
261 10c. First Aid class 20 10
262 25c. Red Cross and coat of arms 50 55

104 Mary Read

1970. Pirates. Multicoloured.
263 ½c. Type **104** 10 15
264 10c. George Lowther 30 10
265 30c. Edward Teach (Blackbeard) 60 25
266 60c. Henry Morgan . . . . 80 1·00

105 Children and "UNICEF"

1971. 25th Anniv of U.N.I.C.E.F.
267 **105** 15c. multicoloured 10 10
268 30c. multicoloured 20 25

1972. Royal Visit of Princess Margaret. Nos 244 and 251 optd **VISIT OF H.R.H. THE PRINCESS MARGARET 1972 1972.**
269 4c. blue, light blue and brown 20 15
270 25c. green, blue and plum . . 30 45

107 Seaman of 1800

110 J. C. Lettsom

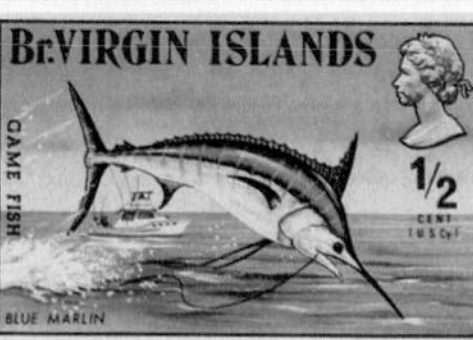

109 Blue Marlin

1972. "Interpex" Stamp Exhibition, New York. Naval Uniforms. Multicoloured.
271 ½c. Type **107** 10 40
272 10c. Boatswain, 1787–1807 35 10
273 30c. Captain, 1795–1812 . . 85 55
274 60c. Admiral, 1787–95 . . . 1·50 2·50

1972. Royal Silver Wedding. As T **52** of Ascension, but with sailfish and "Sir Winston Churchill" (cadet schooner) in background.
275 15c. blue 25 15
276 25c. blue 25 15

1972. Game Fish. Multicoloured.
277 ½c. Type **109** . . . . 15 1·10
278 ½c. Wahoo . . . . 15 1·10
279 15c. Yellow-finned tuna ("Allison tuna") 65 25
280 25c. White marlin 75 30
281 50c. Sailfish . . . . 1·25 1·50
282 $1 Dolphin . . . . 2·00 2·75
MS283 194 × 158 mm. Nos. 277/82 8·50 8·50

1973. "Interpex 1973" (Quakers). Multicoloured.
284 ½c. Type **110** 10 15
285 10c. Lettsom House (horiz) 15 10
286 15c. Dr. W. Thornton . . . 20 10
287 30c. Dr. Thornton and Capitol, Washington (horiz) 25 20
288 $1 William Penn (horiz) . . . 60 1·10

111 Green-throated Carib and Antillean Crested Hummingbird

1973. First Issue of Coinage. Coins and local scenery. Multicoloured.
289 1c. Type **111** 10 30
290 5c. "Zenaida Dove" (5c. coin) 60 10
291 10c. "Ringed Kingfisher" (10c. coin) 75 10
292 25c. "Mangrove Cuckoo" (25c. coin) 95 15
293 50c. "Brown Pelican" (50c. coin) . . . . 1·10 1·00
294 $1 "Magnificent Frigate-bird ($1 coin) . . . . 1·40 2·00

1973. Royal Wedding. As T **47** of Anguilla. Multicoloured. Background colours given.
301 5c. brown 10 10
302 50c. blue 20 20

112 "Virgin and Child" (Pintoricchio)

113 Crest of the "Canopus" (French)

1973. Christmas. Multicoloured.
303 ½c. Type **112** 10 10
304 3c. "Virgin and Child" (Lorenzo di Credi) 10 10
305 25c. "Virgin and Child" (Crivelli) 15 10
306 50c. "Virgin and Child with St. John" (Luini) 30 40

1974. "Interpex 1974". Naval Crests. Multicoloured.
307 5c. Type **113** 15 10
308 18c. U.S.S. "Saginaw" . . . 25 25
309 25c. H.M.S. "Rothesay" . . . 25 30
310 50c. H.M.C.S. "Ottawa" . . 45 60
MS311 196 × 128 mm. Nos. 307/10 1·25 4·50

114 Christopher Columbus

1974. Historical Figures.
312 **114** 5c. orange and black . . 20 10
313 – 10c. blue and black . . . 20 10
314 – 25c. violet and black . . . 25 25
315 – 40c. brown and deep brown 45 75
MS316 84 × 119 mm. Nos. 312/15 1·00 2·25
PORTRAITS: 10c. Sir Walter Raleigh; 25c. Sir Martin Frobisher; 40c. Sir Francis Drake.

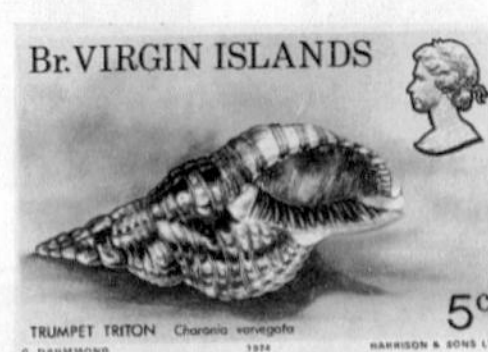

115 Atlantic Trumpet Triton

1974. Seashells. Multicoloured.
317 5c. Type **115** 30 15
318 18c. West Indian murex . . . 50 30
319 25c. Bleeding tooth 60 35
320 75c. Virgin Islands latirus . . 1·25 2·00
MS321 146 × 95 mm. Nos. 317/20 3·00 6·50

116 Churchill and St. Mary, Aldermanbury, London

1974. Birth Centenary of Sir Winston Churchill. Multicoloured.
322 10c. Type **116** 15 10
323 50c. St. Mary, Fulton, Missouri 35 50
MS324 141 × 108 mm. Nos. 322/3 80 1·40

117 H.M.S. "Boreas"

1975. "Interpex 1975" Stamp Exhibition, New York. Ships' Figure-heads. Multicoloured.
325 5c. Type **117** 20 10
326 18c. "Golden Hind" 40 15
327 40c. H.M.S. "Superb" . . . 50 25
328 85c. H.M.S. "Formidable" . . 1·00 1·50
MS329 192 × 127 mm. Nos. 325/8 1·75 8·00

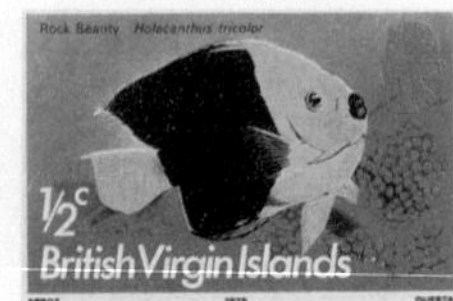

118 Rock Beauty

1975. Fishes. Multicoloured.
330 ½c. Type **118** 15 50
331 1c. Long-spined squirrelfish 40 2·75
332 3c. Queen triggerfish . . . 1·00 2·75
333 5c. Blue angelfish 30 20
334 8c. Stoplight parrotfish . . . 30 25
335 10c. Queen angelfish 30 25
336 12c. Nassau grouper 40 35
337 13c. Blue tang 40 30
338 15c. Sergeant major 40 35
339 18c. Spotted jewfish . . . . 80 1·50
340 20c. Bluehead wrasse 60 80
341 25c. Grey angelfish . . . . 1·00 60
342 60c. Glass-eyed snapper . . . 1·25 2·25
343 $1 Blue chromis . . . . . . 1·75 1·75
344 $2.50 French angelfish . . . 2·00 4·50
345 $3 Queen parrotfish . . . . 2·50 4·50
346 $5 Four-eyed butterflyfish . . 2·75 6·00

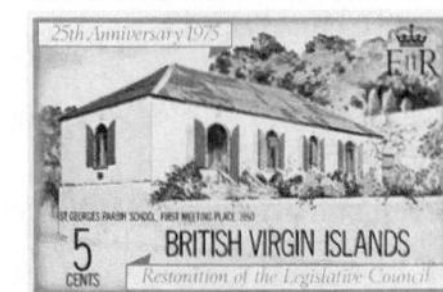

119 St. George's Parish School (first meeting-place, 1950)

1975. 25th Anniv of Restoration of Legislative Council. Multicoloured.
347 5c. Type **119** 10 10
348 25c. Legislative Council Building 20 10
349 40c. Mace and gavel 25 15
350 75c. Commemorative scroll 35 65

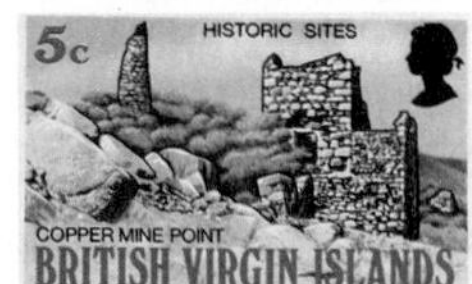

120 Copper Mine Point

1976. Historic Sites. Multicoloured.
351 5c. Type **120** 10 10
352 18c. Pleasant Valley 20 10
353 50c. Callwood Distillery . . . 40 30
354 75c. The Dungeon 60 65

121 Massachusetts Brig "Hazard"

1976. Bicentenary of American Revolution. Mult.
355 8c. Type **121** 30 15
356 22c. American privateer "Spy" 45 20
357 40c. "Raleigh" (American frigate) 55 60
358 75c. Frigate "Alliance" and H.M.S. "Trepassy" . . . . 80 1·25
MS359 114 × 89 mm. Nos. 355/8 3·50 11·00

122 Government House, Tortola

1976. 5th Anniv of Friendship Day with U.S. Virgin Islands. Multicoloured.
360 8c. Type **122** 10 10
361 15c. Government House, St. Croix (vert) 10 10
362 30c. Flags (vert) 15 10
363 75c. Government seals . . . 30 40

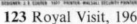

123 Royal Visit, 1966 125 Divers checking Equipment

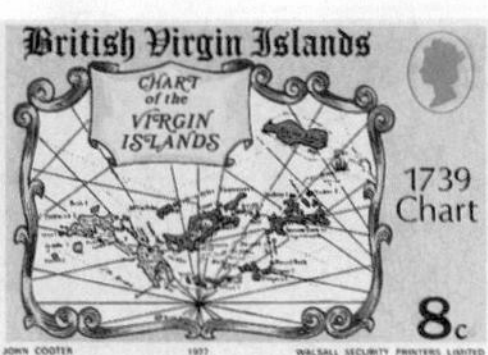

124 Chart of 1739

1977. Silver Jubilee. Multicoloured.
364 8c. Type **123** 10 10
365 30c. The Holy Bible 15 15
366 60c. Presentation of Holy Bible 25 40

1977. 18th-century Maps. Multicoloured.
367 8c. Type **124** 40 10
368 22c. French map, 1758 . . . 55 30
369 30c. Map from English and Danish surveys, 1775 . . . 65 65
370 75c. Map of 1779 . . . . . 85 1·50

1977. Royal Visit. As Nos. 364/6 inscr "SILVER JUBILEE ROYAL VISIT".
371 5c. Type **123** 10 10
372 25c. The Holy Bible 20 10
373 50c. Presentation of Holy Bible 35 25

1978. Tourism. Multicoloured.
374 ½c. Type **125** 10 10
375 5c. Cup coral on wreck of "Rhone" 20 10
376 8c. Sponge formation on wreck of "Rhone" 25 10
377 22c. Cup coral and sponges 45 15
378 30c. Sponges inside cave . . 60 20
379 75c. Marine life 90 85

126 Fire Coral 127 Iguana

1978. Corals. Multicoloured.
380 8c. Type **126** 25 15
381 15c. Staghorn coral 40 30
382 40c. Brain coral 75 85
383 75c. Elkhorn coral . . . . . 1·50 1·60

1978. 25th Anniv of Coronation.
384 – 50c. brown, green and silver 20 40
385 – 50c. multicoloured 20 40
386 **127** 50c. brown, green and silver 20 40
DESIGNS: No. 384, Plantagenet Falcon; 385, Queen Elizabeth II.

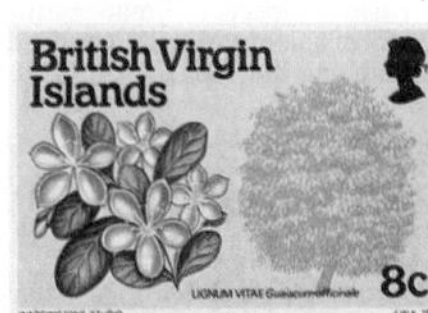

128 Lignum Vitae

1978. Flowering Trees. Multicoloured.
387 8c. Type **128** 15 10
388 22c. Ginger Thomas 20 15
389 40c. Dog almond 30 20
390 75c. White cedar 45 70
MS391 131 × 95 mm. Nos. 387/90 1·00 3·00

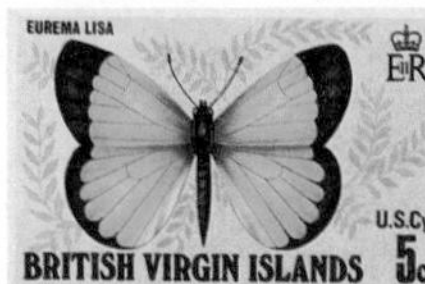

129 "Eurema lisa"

1978. Butterflies. Multicoloured.
392 5c. Type **129** 25 10
393 22c. "Agraulis vanillae" . . . 40 20
394 30c. "Heliconius charithonia" 1·10 30
395 75c. "Hemiargus hanno" . . 1·40 1·25
MS396 159 × 113 mm. No. 392 × 6 and No. 393 × 3 . . . . 2·50 5·50

130 Spiny Lobster

1978. Wildlife Conservation. Multicoloured.
397 5c. Type **130** 15 10
398 15c. Large iguana (vert) . . . 25 10
399 22c. Hawksbill turtle 40 15
400 75c. Black coral (vert) . . . 75 90
MS401 130 × 153 mm. Nos. 397/400 1·75 3·75

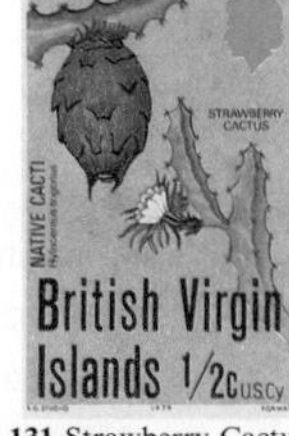

131 Strawberry Cactus 132 West Indian Girl

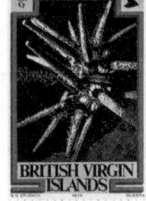

1979. Native Cacti. Multicoloured.
402 ½c. Type **131** 10 10
403 5c. Snowy cactus 15 10
404 13c. Barrel cactus 20 20
405 22c. Tree cactus 25 35
406 30c. Prickly pear 30 40
407 75c. Dildo cactus . . . . . . 40 1·00

1979. International Year of the Child. Multicoloured.
408 5c. Type **132** 10 10
409 10c. African boy 10 10
410 13c. Asian girl 10 10
411 $1 European boy 50 85
MS412 91 × 114 mm. Nos. 408/11 70 1·50

133 1956 Road Harbour 3c. Definitive Stamp 134 Pencil Urchin

1979. Death Centenary of Sir Rowland Hill.
413 **133** 5c. dp blue, blue & green 10 10
414 – 13c. blue and mauve . . . 10 10
415 – 75c. blue and purple . . . 45 50
MS416 37 × 91 mm. $1 blue and red 70 1·25
DESIGNS (39 × 27 mm)—13c. 1880 2½d. red-brown; 75c. Great Britain 1910 unissued 2d. Tyrian plum. (40 × 28 mm)—$1 1867 1s. "Missing Virgin" error.

1979. Marine Life. Multicoloured.
417 ½c. Calcified algae . . . . . 40 2·75
418 1c. Purple-tipped sea anemone . . . . 55 2·75
419 3c. Common starfish . . . . 1·25 2·75
420 5c. Type **134** . . . . 1·25 2·25
421 8c. Atlantic trumpet triton 1·25 1·75
422 10c. Christmas tree worms 30 1·00
423a 13c. Flamingo tongue snail 1·50 75
424 15c. Spider crab . . . . . . 40 1·00
425 18c. Sea squirts . . . . . . 2·00 4·00
426 20c. True tulip . . . . . . 55 1·50
427 25c. Rooster-tail conch . . . 1·25 3·75
428 30c. West Indian fighting conch . . . . 2·50 1·50
429 60c. Mangrove crab . . . . 1·50 2·50
430 $1 Coral polyps . . . . . . 1·25 4·00
431 $2.50 Peppermint shrimp . . 1·25 4·00
432 $3 West Indian murex . . . 1·25 4·50
433 $5 Carpet anemone . . . . 1·75 5·50

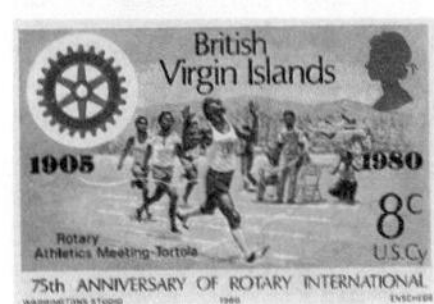

135 Rotary Athletics Meeting, Tortola

1980. 75th Anniv of Rotary International. Mult.
434 8c. Type **135** 10 10
435 22c. Paul P. Harris (founder) 15 10
436 60c. Mount Saga, Tortola ("Creation of National Park") 30 40
437 $1 Rotary anniversary emblem 55 75
MS438 149 × 148 mm. Nos. 434/7 1·00 3·75

136 Brown Booby 138 Sir Francis Drake

1980. "London 1980" International Stamp Exhibition. Birds. Multicoloured.
439 20c. Type **136** 20 20
440 25c. Magnificent frigate bird 25 25
441 50c. White-tailed tropic bird 40 40
442 75c. Brown pelican 55 55
MS443 152 × 130 mm. Nos. 439/42 1·25 2·25

1980. Caribbean Commonwealth Parliamentary Association Meeting, Tortola. Nos. 414/15 optd **CARIBBEAN COMMONWEALTH PARLIAMENTARY ASSOCIATION MEETING TORTOLA 11–19 JULY 1980**.
444 13c. blue and red 15 10
445 75c. deep blue and blue . . . 40 40

1980. Sir Francis Drake Commemoration. Mult.
446 8c. Type **138** 50 10
447 15c. Queen Elizabeth I . . . 70 15
448 30c. Drake receiving knighthood 90 30
449 75c. "Golden Hind" and coat of arms . . . . 1·75 1·25
MS450 171 × 121 mm. Nos. 446/9 3·75 6·50

139 Jost Van Dyke

1980. Island Profiles. Multicoloured
451 2c. Type **139** 10 10
452 5c. Peter Island 10 10
453 13c. Virgin Gorda 15 10
454 22c. Anegada 20 10
455 30c. Norman Island 25 15
456 $1 Tortola . . . . 70 1·00
MS457 95 × 88 mm. No. 456 . . 85 1·50

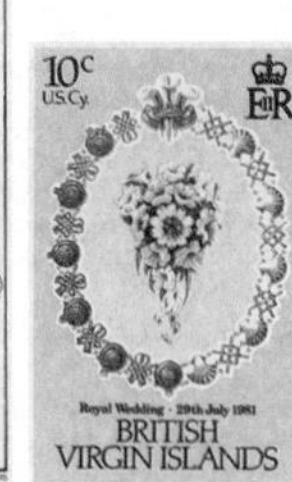

140 Dancing Lady 141 Wedding Bouquet from British Virgin Islands

1981. Flowers. Multicoloured.
458 5c. Type **140** 10 10
459 20c. Love in the mist 15 15
460 22c. "Pitcairnia angustifolia" 15 15
461 75c. Dutchman's pipe 35 65
462 $1 Maiden apple 35 80

1981. Royal Wedding. Multicoloured.
463 10c. Type **141** 10 10
464 35c. Prince Charles and Queen Elizabeth the Queen Mother in Garter robes . . 20 15
465 $1.25 Prince Charles and Lady Diana Spencer . . . 60 80

142 Stamp Collecting 144 Detail from "The Adoration of the Shepherds" (Rubens)

143 "Development through Education"

1981. 25th Anniv of Duke of Edinburgh Award Scheme. Multicoloured.
466 10c. Type **142** 10 10
467 15c. Athletics 10 10
468 50c. Camping 25 25
469 $1 Duke of Edinburgh . . . 40 45

1981. International Year for Disabled Persons. Multicoloured.
470 15c. Type **143** 15 15
471 20c. Fort Charlotte Children's Centre 15 20
472 30c. "Developing cultural awareness" 20 30
473 $1 Fort Charlotte Children's Centre (different) . . . . . 60 1·25

1981. Christmas.
474 **144** 5c. multicoloured 15 10
475 – 15c. multicoloured 25 10
476 – 30c. multicoloured 45 15
477 – $1 multicoloured . . . . 1·10 1·10
MS478 117 × 90 mm. 50c. multicoloured (horiz) . . . . . 1·75 85
DESIGNS: 15c. to $1 Further details from "The Adoration of the Shepherds" by Rubens.

145 Green-throated Caribs and Erythrina

147 Princess at Victoria and Albert Museum, November, 1981

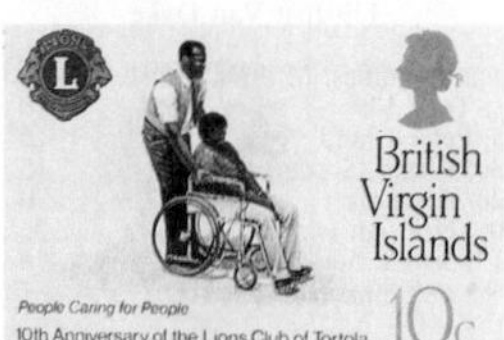

146 "People caring for People"

1982. Hummingbirds. Multicoloured.
479 15c. Type **145** 50 15
480 30c. Green-throated carib and bougainvillea 60 45
481 35c. Antillean crested hummingbirds and "granadilla passiflora" . . 70 55
482 $1.25 Antillean crested hummingbirds and hibiscus 1·75 3·00

1982. 10th Anniv of Lions Club of Tortola. Mult.
483 10c. Type **146** 15 10
484 20c. Tortola Headquarters . . 20 15
485 30c. "We Serve" 25 15
486 $1.50 "Lions" symbol . . . 60 1·00
MS487 124 × 102 mm. Nos. 483/6 1·75 4·25

1982. 21st Birthday of Princess of Wales. Mult.
488 10c. British Virgin Islands coat of arms 15 10
489 35c. Type **147** 30 15
490 50c. Bride and groom proceeding into Vestry . . 45 35
491 $1.50 Formal portrait . . . . 1·10 1·10

148 Douglas DC-3

1982. 10th Anniv of Air BVI. Multicoloured.
492 10c. Type **148** 45 15
493 15c. Britten Norman Islander 60 20
494 60c. Hawker Siddeley H.S.748 . . . . 1·10 75
495 75c. Runway scene . . . . . 1·25 90

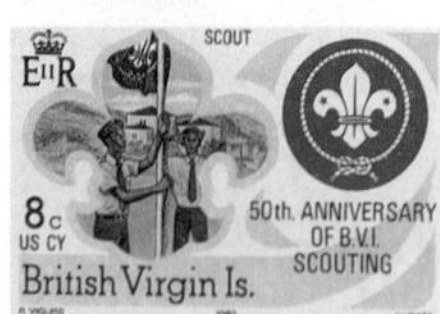

149 Scouts raising Flag

1982. 75th Anniv of Boy Scout Movement and 50th Anniv of Scouting in B.V.I. Multicoloured.
496 8c. Type **149** 20 10
497 20c. Cub Scout 30 25
498 50c. Sea Scout 40 55
499 $1 First camp, Brownsea Island, and portrait of Lord Baden-Powell . . . . 70 1·50

150 Legislature in Session

1983. Commonwealth Day. Multicoloured.
500 10c. Type **150** 10 10
501 30c. Tourism 25 20
502 35c. Satellite view of Earth showing Virgin Islands . . 25 25
503 75c. B.V.I. and Commonwealth flags . . . 70 90

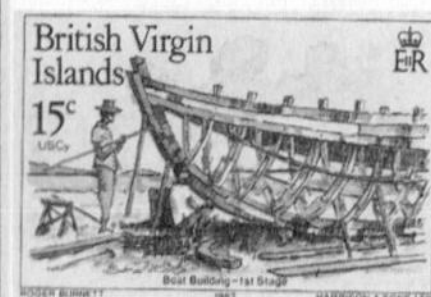

151 Florence Nightingale

152 Frame Construction

1983. Nursing Week. Multicoloured.
504 10c. Type **151** 50 15
505 30c. Staff nurse and assistant nurse 90 45
506 60c. Public Health nurses testing blood pressure (horiz) . . . . 1·75 1·25
507 75c. Peebles Hospital (horiz) 1·90 1·75

1983. Traditional Boat-building. Multicoloured.
508 15c. Type **152** 25 25
509 25c. Planking 30 45
510 50c. Launching 50 80
511 $1 Maiden voyage . . . . . 65 1·75
MS512 127 × 101 mm. Nos. 508/11 1·50 3·75

153 Grumman Goose Amphibian

1983. Bicentenary of Manned Flight. Multicoloured.
513 10c. Type **153** 20 15
514 30c. Riley Turbo Skyliner . . 45 45
515 60c. Embraer Bandeirante . . 65 85
516 $1.25 Hawker Siddeley H.S.748 . . . . 90 1·60

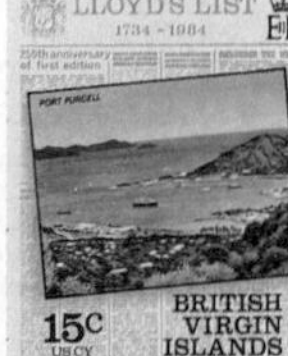

154 "Madonna and Child with the Infant Baptist"

156 Port Purcell

155 Local Tournament

1983. Christmas. 500th Birth Anniv of Raphael. Multicoloured.
517 8c. Type **154** 10 10
518 15c. "La Belle Jardiniere" . . 20 15
519 50c. "Madonna del Granduca" 50 60
520 $1 "The Terranuova Madonna" . . . . 90 1·10
MS521 108 × 101 mm. Nos. 517/20 2·75 4·00

1984. 60th Anniv of International Chess Federation. Multicoloured.
522 10c. Type **155** . . . . 1·00 40
523 35c. Staunton king, rook and pawn (vert) . . . . 2·00 1·50
524 75c. Karpov's winning position against Jakobsen in 1980 Olympiad (vert) . . 3·75 4·25
525 $1 B.V.I. Gold Medal won by Bill Hook at 1980 Chess Olympiad . . . . 4·25 5·50

1984. 250th Anniv of "Lloyd's List" (newspaper). Multicoloured.
526 15c. Type **156** 25 30
527 25c. Boeing 747-100 . . . . 45 50
528 50c. Wreck of "Rhone" (mail steamer), 1867 . . . . . . 90 95
529 $1 "Booker Viking" (cargo liner) . . . . 1·50 1·60

157 Mail Ship "Boyne", Boeing 747-100 and U.P.U. Logo

1984. Universal Postal Union Congress, Hamburg. Sheet 90 × 69 mm.
MS530 **157** $1 blue and black . . 2·25 2·50

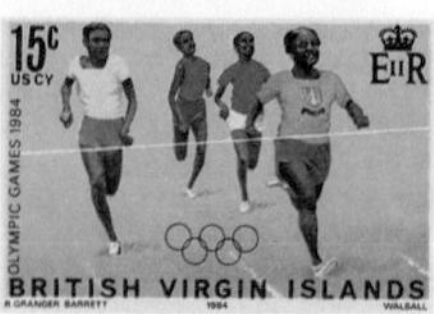

158 Running

1984. Olympic Games, Los Angeles. Multicoloured.
531 15c. Type **158** 40 40
532 15c. Runner 40 40
533 20c. Wind-surfing 45 45
534 20c. Surfer 45 45
535 30c. Sailing 65 65
536 30c. Yacht 65 65

159 Steel Band

1984. 150th Anniv of Abolition of Slavery. Mult.
538 10c. Type **159** 30 35
539 10c. Dancing girls 30 35
540 10c. Men in traditional costumes 30 35
541 10c. Girl in traditional costumes 30 35
542 10c. Festival Queen 30 35
543 30c. Green and yellow dinghies 45 50
544 30c. Blue and red dinghies . . 45 50
545 30c. White and blue dinghies 45 50
546 30c. Red and yellow dinghies 45 50
547 30c. Blue and white dinghies 45 50

DESIGNS: Various aspects of Emancipation Festival. Nos. 543/7 form a composite design, the sail colours of the dinghies being described.

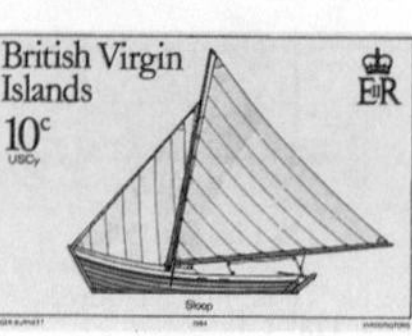

160 Sloop

1984. Boats. Multicoloured.
548 10c. Type **160** 40 20
549 35c. Fishing boat 60 65
550 60c. Schooner . . . . 75 1·25
551 75c. Cargo boat . . . . . . 75 1·60
MS552 125 × 90 mm. Nos. 548/51 1·50 4·00

161 One Cent Coin and Aerial View

1985. New Coinage. Coins and Local Scenery. Multicoloured.
553 1c. Type **161** 10 10
554 5c. Five cent coin and boulders on beach 10 10
555 10c. Ten cent coin and scuba diving 20 20
556 25c. Twenty-five cent coin and yachts 45 50
557 50c. Fifty cent coin and jetty 90 1·25
558 $1 One dollar coin and beach at night . . . . 1·75 2·25
MS559 103 × 159 mm. Nos. 553/8 3·00 7·00

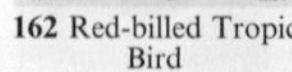

162 Red-billed Tropic Bird

163 The Queen Mother at Festival of Remembrance

1985. Birds of the British Virgin Islands. Multicoloured.
560 1c. Type **162** . . . . 70 2·25
561 2c. Yellow-crowned night heron ("Night Gaulin") . . 70 2·25
562 5c. Mangrove cuckoo ("Rain Bird") . . . . 1·00 2·00
563 8c. Northern mockingbird ("Mockingbird") . . . . . 1·00 2·75
564 10c. Grey kingbird ("Chinchary") . . . . . . 1·00 40
565 12c. Red-necked pigeon ("Wild Pigeon") . . . . . 2·00 1·25
649 15c. Least bittern ("Bittlin") 2·50 1·25
567 18c. Smooth-billed ani ("Black Witch") . . . . . 2·50 3·00
651 20c. Clapper rail ("Pond Shakey") . . . . 2·50 1·25
652 25c. American kestrel ("Killy-killy") . . . . 2·50 1·25
570 30c. Pearly-eyed thrasher ("Thrushie") . . . . 2·50 1·40
654 35c. Bridled quail dove ("Marmi Dove") . . . . . 2·50 1·25
572 40c. Green-backed heron ("Little Gaulin") . . . . . 2·75 1·75
573 50c. Scaly-breasted ground dove ("Ground Dove") . . 3·00 3·25
574 60c. Little blue heron ("Blue Gaulin") . . . . 3·50 4·50
658 $1 Audubon's shearwater ("Pimleco") . . . . 4·00 4·75
576 $2 Blue-faced booby ("White Booby") . . . . 4·75 8·00
577 $3 Cattle egret ("Cow Bird") 6·00 10·00
578 $5 Zenaida dove ("Turtle Dove") . . . . 8·00 12·00

1985. Life and Times of Queen Elizabeth the Queen Mother. Multicoloured.
579A 10c. Type **163** 10 20
580A 10c. At Victoria Palace Theatre, 1984 . . . . . 10 20
581A 25c. At the engagement of the Prince of Wales, 1981 15 40
582A 25c. Opening Celia Johnson Theatre, 1985 . . . . . 15 40
583A 50c. The Queen Mother on her 82nd birthday . . . 20 70
584A 50c. At the Tate Gallery, 1983 . . . . 20 70
585A 75c. At the Royal Smithfield Show, 1983 . . . 25 1·00
586A 75c. Unveiling Mountbatten Statue, 1983 . . . . . . 25 1·00
MS587A 85 × 114 mm. $1 At Columbia University; $1 At a Wedding, St. Margaret's, Westminster, 1983 . . . . . . 85 4·00

164 Seaside Sparrow

165 S.V. "Flying Cloud"

1985. Birth Bicentenary of John J. Audubon (ornithologist). Designs showing original paintings. Multicoloured.
588 5c. Type **164** 30 20
589 30c. Passenger pigeon 40 70
590 50c. Yellow-breasted chat . . 45 1·75
591 $1 American kestrel . . . . 50 2·75

1986. Visiting Cruise Ships. Multicoloured.
592 35c. Type **165** 80 85
593 50c. M.V. "Newport Clipper" 1·10 1·50
594 75c. M.V. "Cunard Countess" . . . . 1·10 2·50
595 $1 M.V. "Sea Goddess" . . . 1·25 3·00

1986. Inaugural Flight of Miami–Beef Island Air Service. Nos 581/2 and 585/6 optd **MIAMI B.V.I. INAUGURAL FLIGHT.**
596A 25c. At the engagement of the Prince of Wales, 1981 40 50
597A 25c. Opening Celia Johnson Theatre, 1985 . . . . . 40 50
598A 75c. At the Royal Smithfield Show, 1983 . . 1·25 1·50
599A 75c. Unveiling Mountbatten statue, 1983 . . . . . . 1·25 1·50

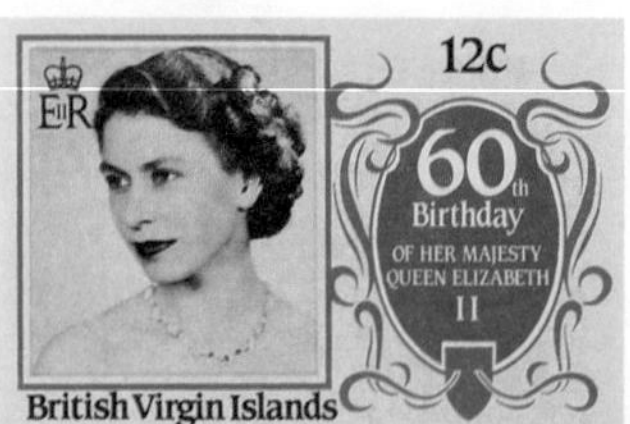

167 Queen Elizabeth II in 1958

1986. 60th Birthday of Queen Elizabeth II. Multicoloured.
600 12c. Type **167** 15 20
601 35c. At a Maundy Service . . 20 45
602 $1.50 Queen Elizabeth . . . 45 1·75
603 $2 During a visit to Canberra, 1982 (vert) . . . 60 2·25
MS604 85 × 115 mm. $3 Queen with bouquet . . . . 3·50 6·00

168 Miss Sarah Ferguson

1986. Royal Wedding. Multicoloured.
605 35c. Type **168** 30 70
606 35c. Prince Andrew and Miss Sarah Ferguson 30 70
607 $1 Prince Andrew in morning dress (horiz) . . . . 50 1·25
608 $1 Miss Sarah Ferguson (different) (horiz) . . . . . 50 1·25
MS609 115 × 85 mm. $4 Duke and Duchess of York in carriage after wedding (horiz) . . . . 2·50 6·00

169 Harvesting Sugar Cane

1986. History of Rum Making. Multicoloured.
610 12c. Type **169** 80 20
611 40c. Bringing sugar cane to mill . . . . 1·50 1·25
612 60c. Rum distillery . . . . . 2·00 3·25
613 $1 Delivering barrels of rum to ship . . . . 4·25 4·75
MS614 115 × 84 mm. $2 Royal Navy rum issue . . . . 6·50 8·50

170 "Sentinel"

1986. 20th Anniv of Cable and Wireless Caribbean Headquarters, Tortola. Cable Ships. Multicoloured.
615 35c. Type **170** 60 80
616 35c. "Retriever" (1961) . . . 60 80
617 60c. "Cable Enterprise" (1964) . . . . 75 1·50
618 60c. "Mercury" (1962) . . . 75 1·50
619 75c. "Recorder" (1955) . . . 75 1·75
620 75c. "Pacific Guardian" (1984) . . . . 75 1·75
621 $1 "Great Eastern" (1860's) 80 2·00
622 $1 "Cable Venture" (1977) 80 2·00
MS623 Four sheets, each 102 × 131 mm. (a) 40c. × 2 As 35c. (b) 50c. × 2 As 60c. (c) 80c. × 2 As 75c. (d) $1.50 × 2 As $1 Set of 4 sheets . . . . 5·00 12·00

1986. Centenary of Statue of Liberty. T **17** and similar vert views of Statue in separate miniature sheets. Multicoloured.
MS624 Nine sheets, each 85 × 115 mm. 50c.; 75c.; 90c.; $1; $1.25; $1.50; $1.75; $2; $2.50 Set of 9 sheets . . . . 6·00 13·00

172 18th-century Spanish Galleon

1987. Shipwrecks. Multicoloured
625 12c. Type **172** . . . . 2·25 55
626 35c. H.M.S. "Astrea" (frigate), 1808 . . . . . . 3·50 1·40
627 75c. "Rhone" (mail steamer), 1867 . . . . 5·00 4·50
628 $1.50 "Captain Rokos" (freighter), 1929 . . . . . 7·50 10·00
MS629 85 × 65 mm. $1.50, "Volvart", 1819 . . . . . . 15·00 15·00

173 Outline Map and Flag of Montserrat

174 Spider Lily

1987. 11th Meeting of Organization of Eastern Caribbean States. Each showing map and flag. Multicoloured.
630 10c. Type **173** 70 70
631 15c. Grenada 80 75
632 20c. Dominica 85 80
633 25c. St. Kitts-Nevis . . . . . 90 1·00
634 35c. St. Vincent and Grenadines . . . . 1·40 1·00
635 50c. British Virgin Islands . . 2·00 2·50
636 75c. Antigua and Barbuda . . 2·25 3·25
637 $1 St. Lucia . . . . 2·75 3·50

1987. Opening of Botanical Gardens. Multicoloured.
638 12c. Type **174** 80 35
639 35c. Barrel cactus . . . . . 1·75 1·00
640 $1 Wild plantain . . . . . . 2·75 3·25
641 $1.50 Little butterfly orchid 8·00 8·50
MS642 139 × 104 mm. $2.50, White cedar . . . . 3·75 6·00

175 Early Mail Packet and 1867 1s. Stamp

1987. Bicentenary of Postal Services. Multicoloured.
662 10c. Type **175** . . . . 1·75 80
663 20c. Map and 1899 1d. stamp 2·25 1·25
664 35c. Road Town Post Office and Customs House, c. 1913, and 1847 4d. stamp . . . . 2·50 1·75
665 $1.50 Piper Apache mail plane and 1964 25c. definitive . . . . 7·50 11·00
MS666 70 × 60 mm. $2.50, Mail ship, 1880's, and 1880 1d. . . . . . 6·00 10·00

1988. 500th Birth Anniv of Titian (artist). As T **238** of Antigua. Multicoloured.
667 10c. "Salome" 55 55
668 12c. "Man with the Glove" 60 60
669 20c. "Fabrizio Salvaresio" . . 80 80
670 25c. "Daughter of Roberto Strozzi" 90 90
671 40c. "Pope Julius II" . . . . 1·40 2·00
672 50c. "Bishop Ludovico Beccadelli" . . . . 1·60 2·00
673 60c. "King Philip II" . . . . 1·75 2·50
674 $1 "Empress Isabella of Portugal" . . . . 2·25 2·75
MS675 Two sheets, each 110 × 95 mm. (a) $2 "Emperor Charles V at Muhlberg" (detail). (b) $2 "Pope Paul III and his Grandsons" (detail) Set of 2 sheets 13·00 15·00

176 De Havilland D.H.C.5 over Sir Francis Drake Channel and Staunton Pawn

1988. 1st British Virgin Islands Open Chess Tournament. Multicoloured.
676 35c. Type **176** . . . . 6·00 1·75
677 $1 Jose Capablanca (former World Champion) and Staunton king . . . . . . 10·00 8·50
MS678 109 × 81 mm. $2 Chess match . . . . 10·00 11·00

177 Hurdling

1988. Olympic Games, Seoul. Multicoloured.
679 12c. Type **177** 35 25
680 20c. Windsurfing 60 45
681 75c. Basketball . . . . 3·75 3·25
682 $1 Tennis . . . . 3·75 3·75
MS683 71 × 102 mm. $2 Athletics 3·00 4·50

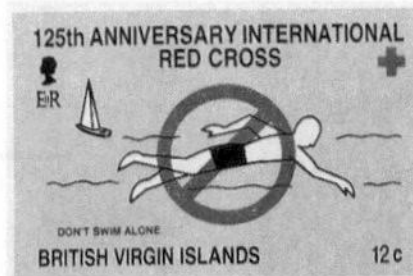

178 Swimmer ("Don't Swim Alone")

1988. 125th Anniv of International Red Cross
684 **178** 12c. black, red and blue 1·25 40
685 – 30c. black, red and blue 2·00 80
686 – 60c. black, red and blue 3·25 3·00
687 – $1 black, red and blue . . 4·00 4·00
MS688 68 × 96 mm. 50c. × 4 black and red . . . . 5·00 6·50
DESIGNS—HORIZ: 30c. Swimmers ("No swimming during electrical storms"); 60c. Beach picnic ("Don't eat before swimming"); $1 Boat and equipment ("Proper equipment for boating"). VERT: 50c. × 4 Recovery position, clearing airway, mouth-to-mouth resuscitation, cardiac massage.

179 Princess Alexandra

180 Brown Pelican in Flight

1988. Visit of Princess Alexandra. Designs showing different portraits.
689 **179** 40c. multicoloured . . . . 2·00 75
690 – $1.50 multicoloured . . . 5·00 4·75
MS691 102 × 98 mm. $2 multicoloured . . . . 5·00 6·50

1988. Wildlife (1st series). Aquatic Birds. Mult.
692 10c. Type **180** . . . . 1·60 50
693 12c. Brown pelican perched on post . . . . 1·60 55
694 15c. Brown pelican . . . . . 1·75 1·10
695 35c. Brown pelican swallowing fish . . . . . 2·75 3·00
MS696 106 × 76 mm. $2 Common shoveler (horiz) . . . . 9·50 9·00
No. **MS**696 is without the W.W.F. logo.

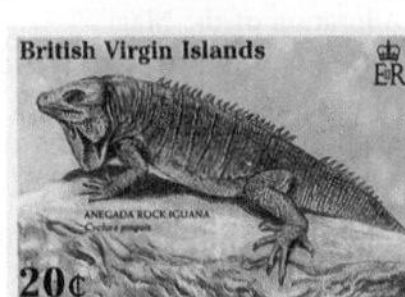

181 Anegada Rock Iguana

1988. Wildlife (2nd series). Endangered Species. Multicoloured.
697 20c. Type **181** . . . . 1·25 75
698 40c. Virgin Gorda dwarf gecko . . . . 1·50 1·40
699 60c. Hawksbill turtle . . . . 2·50 3·50
700 $1 Humpback whale . . . . 7·00 8·00
MS701 106 × 77 mm. $2 Trunk turtle (vert) . . . . 5·50 7·50

182 Yachts at Start

1989. Spring Regatta. Multicoloured.
702 12c. Type **182** 45 40
703 40c. Yacht tacking (horiz) . . 1·00 1·00
704 75c. Yachts at sunset . . . . 1·60 2·50
705 $1 Yachts rounding buoy (horiz) . . . . 2·00 2·75
MS706 83 × 69 mm. $2 Yacht under full sail . . . . 5·50 6·50

1989. 500th Anniv (1992) of Discovery of America by Columbus (1st issue). Pre-Columbian Arawak Society. As T **247** of Antigua. Multicoloured.
707 10c. Arawak in hammock . . 70 45
708 20c. Making fire . . . . . . 1·00 50
709 25c. Making implements . . 1·00 60
710 $1.50 Arawak family . . . . 4·50 7·00
MS711 85 × 70 mm. $2 Religious ceremony . . . . 8·00 10·00
See also Nos. 741/5, 793/7 and 818/26.

183 "Apollo II" Emblem

1989. 20th Anniv of First Manned Landing on the Moon. Multicoloured.
712 15c. Type **183** . . . . 1·00 60
713 30c. Edwin Aldrin deploying scientific experiments . . . 2·00 1·00
714 65c. Aldrin and U.S. flag on Moon . . . . 2·75 3·75
715 $1 "Apollo II" capsule after splashdown . . . . 3·75 4·00
MS716 102 × 77 mm. $2 Neil Armstrong (38 × 50 mm) . . . 8·00 9·50

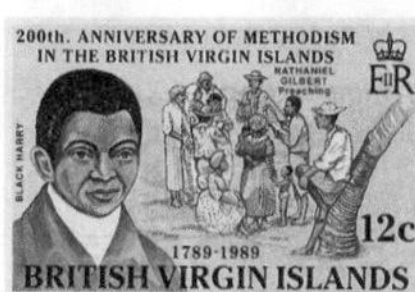

184 Black Harry and Nathaniel Gilbert preaching to Slaves

1989. Bicentenary of Methodist Church in British Virgin Islands. Multicoloured
717 12c. Type **184** . . . . 1·00 50
718 25c. Methodist school exercise book . . . . . . 1·40 75
719 35c. East End Methodist Church, 1810 . . . . . . 1·60 85
720 $1.25 Reverend John Wesley (founder of Methodism) and church youth choir . . 3·25 6·50
MS721 100 × 69 mm. $2 Dr. Thomas Cole . . . . 4·75 9·00

185 Player tackling

1989. World Cup Football Championships, Italy, 1990. Multicoloured.
722 5c. Type **185** 80 80
723 10c. Player dribbling ball . . 80 80
724 20c. Two players chasing ball 1·50 80
725 $1.75 Goalkeeper diving for ball . . . . 7·00 7·50
MS726 100 × 70 mm. $2 British Virgin Islands team captain . . 8·50 11·00

186 Princess Alexandra and Sunset House

1990. "Stamp World London 90" International Stamp Exhibition. Royal Visitors. Multicoloured.
727 50c. Type **186** . . . . 2·75 3·00
728 50c. Princess Margaret and Government House . . . . 2·75 3·00
729 50c. Hon. Angus Ogilvy and Little Dix Bay Hotel . . . 2·75 3·00
730 50c. Princess Diana with Princes William and Henry and Necker Island Resort 2·75 3·00
MS731 89 × 80 mm. $2 Royal Yacht "Britannia" . . . . 9·50 9·50

187 Audubon's Shearwater

1990. Birds. Multicoloured.
732 5c. Type **187** . . . . 1·00 1·25
733 12c. Red-necked pigeon . . . 1·50 40
734 20c. Moorhen ("Common Gallinule") . . . . 1·75 50
735 25c. Green-backed heron ("Green Heron") . . . . . 1·75 50
736 40c. Yellow warbler . . . . 2·00 1·50
737 60c. Smooth-billed ani . . . 2·25 2·75

738 $1 Antillean crested hummingbird 2·25 3·25
739 $1.25 Black-faced grassquit 2·25 4·25
MS740 Two sheets, each 98 × 70 mm. (a) $2 Royal tern egg (vert) (b) $2 Red-billed tropicbird egg (vert) Set of 2 sheets 8·50 7·00

1990. 500th Anniv (1992) of Discovery of America by Columbus (2nd issue). New World Natural History–Fishes. As T **260** of Antigua. Mult.
741 10c. Blue tang (horiz) 1·50 60
742 35c. Glass-eyed snapper (horiz) 2·50 70
743 50c. Slippery dick (horiz) 3·00 3·50
744 $1 Porkfish (horiz) 4·50 4·75
MS745 100 × 70 mm. $2 Yellow-tailed snapper 5·00 6·50

188 Queen Elizabeth the Queen Mother
189 Footballers

1990. 90th Birthday of Queen Elizabeth the Queen Mother.
746 **188** 12c. multicoloured 50 25
747 – 25c. multicoloured 90 55
748 – 60c. multicoloured 1·75 2·25
749 – $1 multicoloured 2·00 2·50
MS750 75 × 75 mm. $2 multicoloured 2·75 2·75
DESIGNS: 25, 60c., $2 Recent photographs.

1990. World Cup Football Championships, Italy.
751 **189** 12c. multicoloured 60 40
752 – 20c. multicoloured 90 50
753 – 50c. multicoloured 1·75 2·00
754 – $1.25 multicoloured 2·50 3·75
MS755 91 × 76 mm. $2 multicoloured 4·50 4·50
DESIGNS: 20, 50c., $2, Footballers.

190 Judo

1990. Olympic Games, Barcelona (1992). Mult.
756 12c. Type **190** 1·25 45
757 40c. Yachting 2·00 1·60
758 60c. Hurdling 2·50 3·50
759 $1 Show jumping 3·75 4·25
MS760 78 × 105 mm. $2 Windsurfing 4·50 4·00

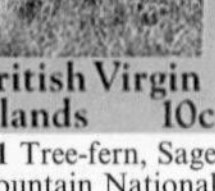
191 Tree-fern, Sage Mountain National Park

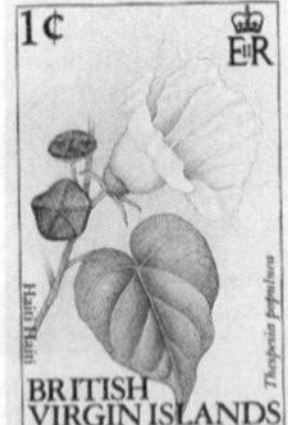
192 Haiti Haiti

1991. 30th Anniv of National Parks Trust. Multicoloured.
761 10c. Type **191** 70 80
762 25c. Coppermine ruins, Virgin Gorda (horiz) 1·25 80
763 35c. Ruined windmill, Mt. Healthy 1·25 80
764 $2 The Baths (rock formation), Virgin Gorda (horiz) 8·00 10·00

1991. Flowers. Multicoloured.
765 1c. Type **192** 20 1·25
766 2c. Lobster claw 20 1·25
767 5c. Frangipani 20 1·25
887 10c. Autograph tree 50 1·40
769 12c. Yellow allamanda 40 30
889 15c. Lantana 65 40
771 20c. Jerusalem thorn 50 30
772 25c. Turk's cap 55 40
892 30c. Swamp immortelle 70 50
893 35c. White cedar 85 55
775 40c. Mahoe tree 75 65
895 45c. Pinguin 95 80
896 50c. Christmas orchid 2·25 1·75
778 70c. Lignum vitae 1·10 2·00
779 $1 African tulip tree 1·25 2·00
899 $2 Beach morning glory 3·00 5·00
781 $3 Organ pipe cactus 4·00 7·00
901 $5 Tall ground orchid 8·50 12·00
783 $10 Ground orchid 14·00 18·00

193 "Phoebis sennae"

194 "Agaricus bisporus"

1991. Butterflies. Multicoloured.
784 5c. Type **193** 70 90
785 10c. "Dryas iulia" 80 90
786 15c. "Junonia evarete" 1·00 75
787 20c. "Dione vanillae" 1·10 80
788 25c. "Battus polydamus" 1·25 1·00
789 30c. "Eurema lisa" 1·40 1·00
790 35c. "Heliconius charitonius" 1·50 1·10
791 $1.50 "Siproeta stelenes" 3·50 5·50
MS792 Two sheets. (a) 77 × 117 mm. $2 "Danaus plexippus" (horiz). (b) 117 × 77 mm. $2 "Biblis hyperia" (horiz) Set of 2 sheets 14·00 15·00

1991. 500th Anniv (1992) of Discovery of America by Columbus (3rd issue). History of Exploration. As T **277** of Antigua. Multicoloured.
793 12c. multicoloured 1·25 50
794 50c. multicoloured 2·25 2·00
795 75c. multicoloured 3·00 2·75
796 $1 multicoloured 3·50 3·50
MS797 105 × 76 mm. $2 black and orange 6·50 7·50
DESIGNS—HORIZ: 12c. "Vitoria" in Pacific (Magellan 1519–21); 50c. La Salle on the Mississippi, 1682; 75c. John Cabot landing in Nova Scotia, 1497–98; $1 Cartier discovering the St. Lawrence, 1534. VERT: $2 "Santa Maria" (woodcut).

1991. Death Centenary (1990) of Vincent Van Gogh (artist). As T **278** of Antigua. Multicoloured.
798 15c. "Cottage with Decrepit Barn and Stooping Woman" (horiz) 1·25 50
799 30c. "Paul Gauguin's Armchair" 1·75 80
800 75c. "Breton Women" (horiz) 3·00 3·00
801 $1 "Vase with Red Gladioli" 3·50 3·50
MS802 103 × 81 mm. $2 "Dance Hall in Arles" (detail) (horiz) 9·50 11·00

1991. Christmas. Religious Paintings by Quinten Massys. As T **291** of Antigua. Multicoloured.
803 15c. "The Virgin and Child Enthroned" (detail) 1·25 25
804 30c. "The Virgin and Child Enthroned" (different detail) 2·00 50
805 60c. "Adoration of the Magi" (detail) 3·50 3·75
806 $1 "Virgin in Adoration" 3·75 4·00
MS807 Two sheets, each 102 × 127 mm. (a) $2 "The Virgin standing with Angels". (b) $2 "The Adoration of the Magi" Set of 2 sheets 13·00 15·00

1992. Fungi. Multicoloured.
808 12c. Type **194** 1·50 55
809 30c. "Lentinula edodes" (horiz) 2·25 85
810 45c. "Hygocybe acutoconica" 2·25 1·00
811 $1 "Gymnopilus chrysopellus" (horiz) 4·00 6·00
MS812 94 × 68 mm. $2 "Pleurotous ostreatus" (horiz) 9·00 11·00

1992. 40th Anniv of Queen Elizabeth II's Accession. As T **288** of Antigua. Multicoloured.
813 12c. Little Dix Bay, Virgin Gorda 85 30
814 25c. Deadchest Bay, Peter Island 1·75 90
815 60c. Pond Bay, Virgin Gorda 2·25 2·25
816 $1 Cane Garden Bay, Tortola 2·50 2·75
MS817 75 × 97 mm. $2 Long Bay, Beef Island 7·50 8·00

195 Queen Isabella of Spain

196 Basketball

1992. 500th Anniv of Discovery of America by Columbus (4th issue). Multicoloured.
818 10c. Type **195** 80 75
819 15c. Fleet of Columbus (horiz) 1·40 90
820 20c. Arms awarded to Columbus 1·40 90
821 30c. Landing Monument, Watling Island and Columbus's signature (horiz) 1·40 1·00
822 45c. Christopher Columbus 1·90 1·40
823 50c. Landing in New World and Spanish royal standard (horiz) 1·90 1·90
824 70c. Convent at La Rabida 2·25 3·25
825 $1.50 Replica of "Santa Maria" and Caribbean Pavilion, New York World's Fair (horiz) 3·50 4·75
MS826 Two sheets. (a) 116 × 86 mm. $2 Ships of second voyage at Virgin, Gorda (horiz). (b) 86 × 116 mm. $2 De la Cosa's map of New World (horiz) Set of 2 sheets 8·00 12·00

1992. Olympic Games, Barcelona. Multicoloured.
827 15c. Type **196** 2·50 75
828 30c. Tennis 2·50 90
829 60c. Volleyball 2·75 3·00
830 $1 Football 3·00 3·75
MS831 100 × 70 mm. $2 Olympic flame 9·00 11·00

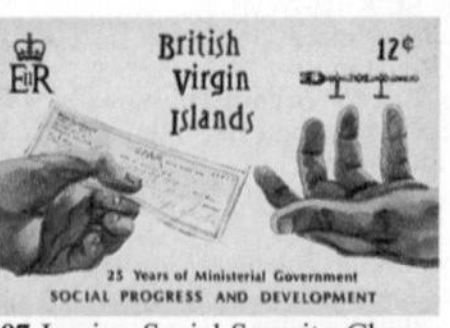
197 Issuing Social Security Cheque

1993. 25th Anniv of Ministerial Government. Multicoloured.
832 12c. Type **197** 40 40
833 15c. Map of British Virgin Islands 1·25 70
834 45c. Administration building 80 70
835 $1.30 International currency abbreviations 2·25 4·25

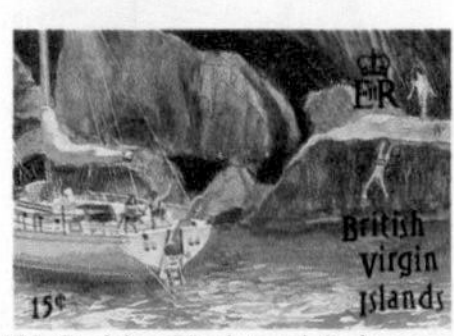
198 Cruising Yacht and Swimmers, The Baths, Virgin Gorda

1993. Tourism. Multicoloured.
836 15c. Type **198** 1·50 50
837 30c. Cruising yacht under sail (vert) 1·75 60
838 60c. Scuba diving 2·50 2·75
839 $1 Cruising yacht at anchor and snorklers (vert) 2·75 3·25
MS840 79 × 108 mm. $1 "Promenade" (trimaran) (vert); $1 Scuba diving (different) (vert) 7·50 8·50

1993. 40th Anniv of Coronation. As T **307** of Antigua.
841 12c. multicoloured 90 1·25
842 45c. multicoloured 1·25 1·50
843 60c. grey and black 1·40 1·75
844 $1 multicoloured 1·60 1·90
DESIGNS: 12c. Queen Elizabeth II at Coronation (photograph by Cecil Beaton); 45c. Orb; 60c. Queen with Prince Philip, Queen Mother and Princess Margaret, 1953; $1 Queen Elizabeth II on official visit.

200 Columbus with King Ferdinand and Queen Isabella

1993. 500th Anniv of Discovery of Virgin Islands by Columbus. Multicoloured.
846 3c. Type **200** 15 40
847 12c. Columbus's ship leaving port 40 40
848 15c. Blessing the fleet 45 45
849 25c. Arms and flag of B.V.I. 60 60
850 30c. Columbus and "Santa Maria" 70 70
851 45c. Ships of second voyage 95 95
852 60c. Columbus in ship's boat 1·50 2·25
853 $1 Landing of Columbus 2·00 2·50
MS854 Two sheets, each 120 × 80 mm. (a) $2 Amerindians sighting fleet. (b) $2 Christopher Columbus and ships Set of 2 sheets 9·00 11·00

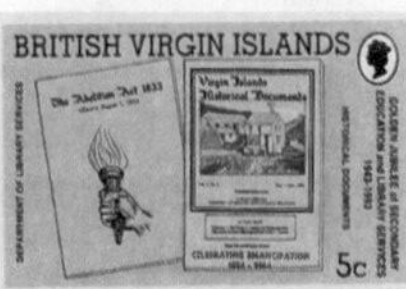
201 Library Services Publications

1993. 50th Anniv of Secondary Education and Library Services. Multicoloured.
855 5c. Type **201** 60 1·00
856 10c. Secondary school sports 1·50 1·25
857 15c. Stanley Nibbs (school teacher) (vert) 80 60
858 20c. Mobile library 1·25 70
859 30c. Dr. Norwell Harrigan (adminstrator and lecturer) (vert) 1·25 70
860 35c. Children in library 1·25 70
861 70c. Commemorative inscription on book 2·25 3·50
862 $1 B.V.I. High School 2·50 3·50

202 Anegada Ground Iguana

1994. Endangered Species. Anegada Ground Iguana.
863 **202** 5c. multicoloured 70 70
864 – 10c. multicoloured 70 70
865 – 15c. multicoloured 80 60
866 – 45c. multicoloured 1·25 1·25
MS867 106 × 77 mm. $2 multicoloured 3·00 4·00
DESIGNS: 10c. to $2 Different iguanas.
No. **MS**867 does not carry the W.W.F. Panda emblem.

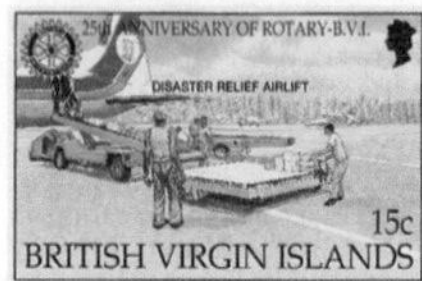
203 Loading Disaster Relief Aircraft

1994. Centenary of Rotary International in B.V.I. Multicoloured.
868 15c. Type **203** 35 35
869 45c. Training children in marine safety 85 85
870 50c. Donated operating table 90 1·00
871 90c. Paul Harris (founder) and emblem 1·60 2·50

1994. 25th Anniv of First Manned Moon Landing. As T **326** of Antigua. Multicoloured.
872 50c. Anniversary logo 2·00 2·25
873 50c. Lunar landing training vehicle 2·00 2·25
874 50c. Launch of "Apollo 11" 2·00 2·25
875 50c. Lunar module "Eagle" in flight 2·00 2·25
876 50c. Moon's surface 2·00 2·25
877 50c. Neil Armstrong (astronaut) taking first step 2·00 2·25
MS878 106 × 76 mm. $2 Signatures and mission logo 11·00 11·00

204 Argentina v. Netherlands, 1978

205 Pair of Juvenile Greater Flamingos

1994. World Cup Football Championship, U.S.A. Previous Winners. Multicoloured.
879 15c. Type **204** 1·25 50
880 35c. Italy v. West Germany, 1982 2·00 70
881 50c. Argentina v. West Germany, 1986 2·75 2·25
882 $1.30 West Germany v. Argentina, 1990 4·50 6·50
MS883 74 × 101 mm. $2 U.S. flag and World Cup trophy (horiz) 9·50 11·00

1995. 50th Anniv of United Nations. As T **213** of Bahamas. Multicoloured.
903 15c. Peugeot P4 all-purpose field cars 45 40
904 30c. Foden medium road tanker 75 60
905 45c. SISU all-terrain vehicle 1·00 90
906 $2 Westland Lynx AH7 helicopter 3·75 5·50

1995. Anegada Flamingos Restoration Project. Multicoloured.
907 15c. Type **205** 85 50
908 20c. Pair of adults 85 55
909 60c. Adult feeding 1·40 2·00
910 $1.45 Adult feeding chick 2·50 4·00
MS911 80 × 70 mm. $2 Chicks 5·50 6·00

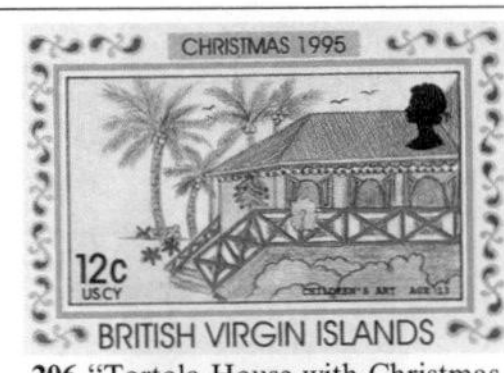

206 "Tortola House with Christmas Tree" (Maureen Walters)

1995. Christmas. Children's Paintings. Mult.
912 12c. Type **206** . . . . 1·50 30
913 50c. "Father Christmas in Rowing Boat" (Collin Collins) . . . . 2·75 1·40
914 70c. "Christmas Tree and Gifts" (Clare Wassell) . . 3·00 2·75
915 $1.30 "Peace Dove" (Nicholas Scott) . . . . . 4·00 5·50

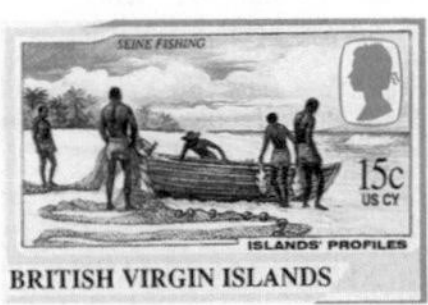

207 Seine Fishing

1996. Island Profiles (1st series). Jost Van Dyke. Multicoloured.
916 15c. Type **207** . . . . 1·25 40
917 35c. Sandy Spit . . . . . . 1·50 55
918 90c. Map . . . . 3·50 3·50
919 $1.50 Foxy's Regatta . . . . 3·75 5·00
See also Nos. 1003/6 and 1105/10.

1996. 70th Birthday of Queen Elizabeth II. As T **165** of Ascension, each incorporating a different photograph of the Queen. Multicoloured.
920 10c. Government House, Tortola 30 20
921 30c. Legislative Council Building 65 55
922 45c. Liner in Road Harbour 1·50 70
923 $1.50 Map of British Virgin Islands . . . . 3·25 5·00
MS924 63 × 65 mm. $2 Queen Elizabeth II . . . . 3·00 3·75

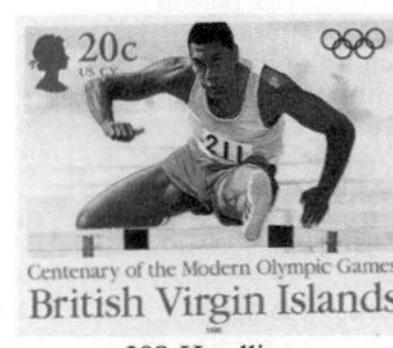

208 Hurdling

1996. Centenary of Modern Olympic Games. Multicoloured.
925 20c. Type **208** 45 30
926 35c. Volley ball 70 60
927 50c. Swimming . . . . . . 1·10 1·75
928 $1 Yachting . . . . 2·00 2·75

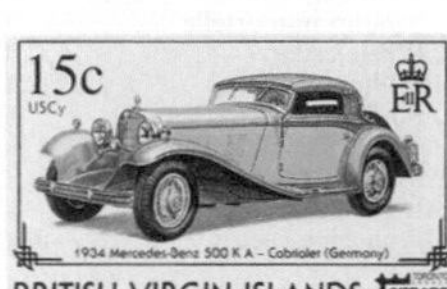

209 Mercedes-Benz "500 K A", 1934

1996. "CAPEX '96" International Stamp Exhibition, Toronto. Early Motor Cars. Multicoloured.
929 15c. Type **209** 45 30
930 40c. Citroen "12", 1934 . . . 1·00 70
931 60c. Cadillac "V-8 Sport Phaeton", 1932 . . . . . . 1·25 1·75
932 $1.35 Rolls Royce "Phantom II", 1934 . . . . 2·75 4·00
MS933 79 × 62 mm. $2 Ford "Sport Coupe", 1932 . . . . 3·25 4·25

210 Children with Computer

1996. 50th Anniv of U.N.I.C.E.F. Multicoloured.
934 10c. Type **210** 40 40
935 15c. Carnival costume . . . 50 50
936 30c. Children on Scales of Justice 80 80
937 45c. Children on beach . . . 1·25 1·25

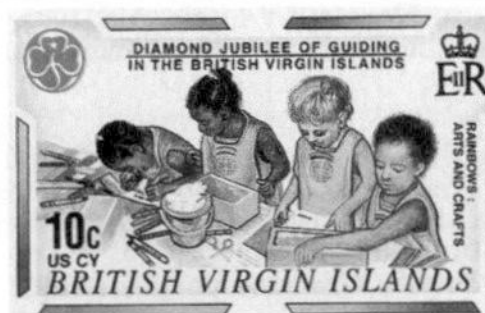

211 Young Rainbows in Art Class

1996. 75th Anniv of Guiding in the British Virgin Islands. Multicoloured.
938 10c. Type **211** 20 20
939 15c. Brownies serving meals 30 25
940 30c. Guides around campfire 50 45
941 45c. Rangers on parade . . . 65 60
942 $2 Lady Baden-Powell . . . 2·75 4·00

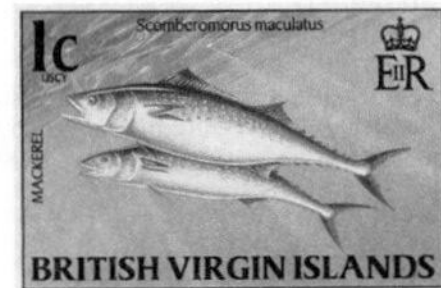

212 Spanish Mackerel

1997. Game Fishes. Multicoloured.
943 1c. Type **212** 10 10
944 10c. Wahoo 10 15
945 15c. Great barracuda 15 20
946 20c. Tarpon 20 25
947 25c. Tiger shark 25 30
948 35c. Sailfish 40 45
949 40c. Dolphin 45 50
950 50c. Black-finned tuna . . . 55 60
951 60c. Yellow-finned tuna . . . 65 70
952 75c. King mackerel ("Kingfish") 80 85
953 $1.50 White marlin . . . . . 1·60 1·70
954 $1.85 Amberjack . . . . . . 2·00 2·10
955 $2 Atlantic bonito . . . . . 2·20 2·30
956 $5 Bonefish . . . . 5·50 5·75
957 $10 Blue marlin . . . . . . 11·00 11·50

1997. "HONG KONG '97" International Stamp Exhibition. Sheet 130 × 90 mm, containing design as No. 953, but with "1997" imprint date. Mult.
MS958 $1.50, White marlin . . . 2·25 2·75

1997. Golden Wedding of Queen Elizabeth and Prince Philip. As T **173** of Ascension. Multicoloured.
959 30c. Prince Philip with horse 70 1·00
960 30c. Queen Elizabeth at Windsor, 1989 . . . . . . 70 1·00
961 45c. Queen in phaeton, Trooping the Colour . . . 90 1·25
962 45c. Prince Philip in Scots Guards uniform . . . . . 90 1·25
963 70c. Queen Elizabeth and Prince Philip at the Derby, 1993 . . . . 1·25 1·60
964 70c. Prince Charles playing polo, Mexico, 1993 . . . 1·25 1·60
MS965 110 × 70 mm. $2 Queen Elizabeth and Prince Philip in landau (horiz) . . . . 3·25 4·00

213 Fiddler Crab

1997. Crabs. Multicoloured.
966 12c. Type **213** 55 50
967 15c. Coral crab 60 50
968 35c. Blue crab 85 60
969 $1 Giant hermit crab . . . . 1·75 2·75
MS970 76 × 67 mm. $2 Arrow crab 3·50 4·50

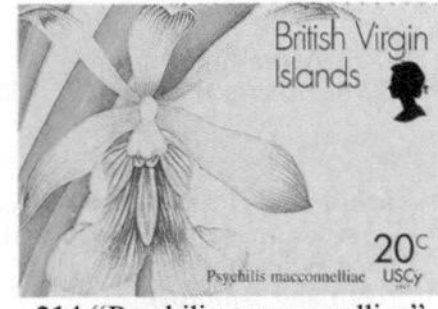

214 "Psychilis macconnelliae"

1997. Orchids of the World. Multicoloured.
971 20c. Type **214** 70 85
972 50c. "Tolumnia prionochila" 1·00 1·10
973 60c. "Tetramicra canaliculata" . . . . . . 1·00 1·40
974 75c. "Liparis elata" . . . . 1·10 1·40
MS975 59 × 79 mm. $2 "Dendrobium crumenatum" (vert) 3·25 4·25

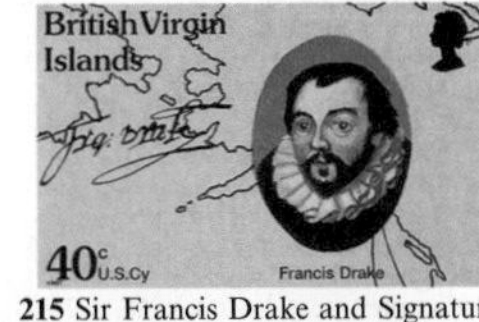

215 Sir Francis Drake and Signature

1997. 420th Anniv of Drake's Circumnavigation of the World. Multicoloured.
976 40c. Type **215** 95 95
977 40c. Drake's coat of arms . . 95 95
978 40c. Queen Elizabeth I and signature 95 95
979 40c. "Christopher" and "Marigold" 95 95
980 40c. "Golden Hind" 95 95
981 40c. "Swan" 95 95
982 40c. "Cacafuego" (Spanish galleon) 95 95
983 40c. "Elizabeth" 95 95
984 40c. "Maria" (Spanish merchant ship) 95 95
985 40c. Drake's astrolabe . . . 95 95
986 40c. "Golden Hind's" figurehead 95 95
987 40c. Compass rose 95 95
MS988 96 × 76 mm. $2 "Sir Francis Drake" (ketch) . . . . 3·50 4·25
Nos. 976/87 were printed together, se-tenant, with the backgrounds forming a composite map of Drake's route.

1998. Diana, Princess of Wales Commemoration. Sheet 145 × 70 mm, containing vert designs as T **177** of Ascension. Multicoloured.
MS989 15c. Wearing pink jacket, 1992; 45c. Holding child, 1991; 70c. Laughing, 1991; $1 Wearing high-collared blouse, 1986 (sold at $2.30 + 20c. charity premium) 3·50 4·00

1998. 80th Anniv of Royal Air Force. As T **178** of Ascension. Multicoloured.
990 20c. Fairey IIIF (seaplane) 60 40
991 35c. Supermarine Scapa (flying boat) 85 50
992 50c. Westland Sea King H.A.R.3 (helicopter) . . . 1·40 1·10
993 $1.50 BAe Harrier GR7 . . . 2·50 3·25
MS994 110 × 77 mm. 75c. Curtiss H.16 (flying boat); 75c. Curtiss JN-4A; 75c. Bell Airacobra; 75c. Boulton-Paul Defiant . . . . . 6·50 7·00

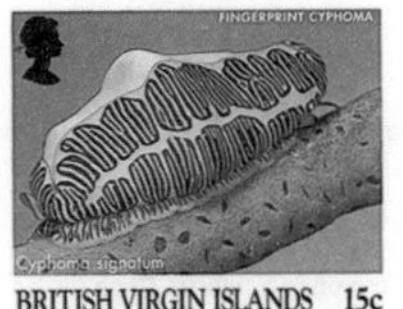

216 Fingerprint Cyphoma

1998. Marine Life. Multicoloured.
995 15c. Type **216** 80 40
996 30c. Long-spined sea urchin 1·00 55
997 45c. Split crown feather duster worm . . . . 1·40 70
998 $1 Upside down jelly . . . . 2·25 3·00
MS999 77 × 56 mm. $2 Giant anemone . . . . 4·75 5·00

217 "Carnival Reveller" (Rebecca Peck)

1998. Festival. Children's Paintings. Multicoloured.
1000 30c. Type **217** 85 50
1001 45c. "Leader of a Troupe" (Jehiah Maduro) . . . . 1·00 65
1002 $1.30 "Steel Pans" (Rebecca McKenzie) (horiz) . . . . 2·75 3·50

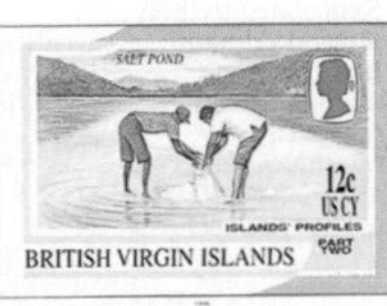

218 Salt Pond

1998. Island Profiles (2nd series). Salt Island. Multicoloured.
1003 12c. Type **218** 75 50
1004 30c. Wreck of "Rhone" (mail steamer) . . . . . 1·25 55
1005 70c. Traditional house . . . 1·25 1·75
1006 $1.45 Salt Island from the air . . . . 2·50 3·50
MS1007 118 × 78 mm. $2 Collecting salt . . . . 4·50 5·00

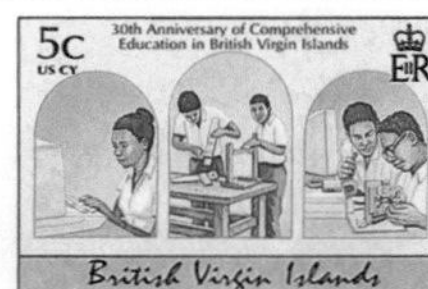

219 Business Studies, Woodwork and Technology Students

1998. Anniversaries. Multicoloured.
1008 5c. Type **219** 25 50
1009 15c. Comprehensive school band 45 30
1010 30c. Chapel, Mona Campus, Jamaica 60 40
1011 45c. Anniversary plaque and University arms 75 60
1012 50c. Dr. John Coakley Lettsom and map of Little Jost Van Dyke . . . . . 1·00 1·10
1013 $1 The Medical Society of London building and arms . . . . 1·60 2·25
EVENTS: 5, 15c. 30th anniv of Comprehensive Education in B.V.I.; 30, 45c. 50th anniv of University of West Indies; 50c., $1 250th anniv of Medical Society of London.

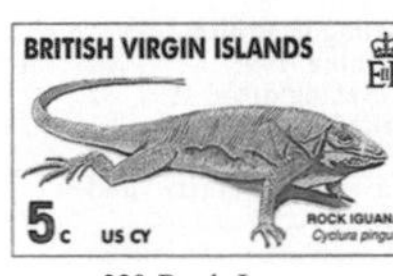

220 Rock Iguana

1999. Lizards. Multicoloured.
1014 5c. Type **220** 30 40
1015 35c. Pygmy gecko 85 45
1016 60c. Slippery back skink . . 1·50 1·25
1017 $1.50 Wood slave gecko . . 2·25 3·25
MS1018 100 × 70 mm. 75c. Doctor lizard; 75c. Yellow-bellied lizard; 75c. Man lizard; 75c. Ground lizard . . . . 5·00 6·00

1999. Royal Wedding. As T **185** of Ascension. Multicoloured.
1019 20c. Photographs of Prince Edward and Miss Sophie Rhys-Jones . . . . 1·00 40
1020 $3 Engagement photograph 4·75 6·00

1999. 30th Anniv of First Manned Landing on Moon. As T **186** of Ascension. Multicoloured.
1021 10c. "Apollo 11" on launch pad 45 35
1022 40c. Firing of second stage rockets . . . . 1·00 65
1023 50c. Lunar module on Moon . . . . 1·10 85
1024 $2 Astronauts transfer to command module . . . . 3·00 4·00
MS1025 90 × 80 mm. $2.50, Earth as seen from moon (circular, 40 mm diam) . . . . 3·75 4·50

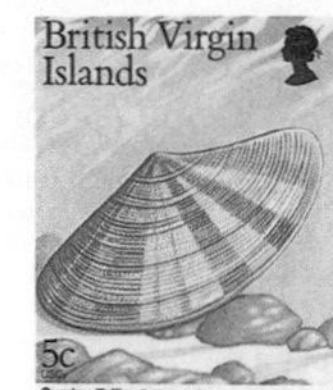

221 Sunrise Tellin

1999. Sea Shells. Multicoloured.
1026A 5c. Type **221** 45 55
1027A 10c. King helmet 45 55
1028A 25c. Measle cowrie 65 75
1029A 35c. West Indian top shell 75 85
1030A 75c. Zigzag scallop . . . . 1·00 1·25
1031A $1 West Indian fighting conch . . . . 1·25 1·50
Nos. 1026A/31A were printed together, se-tenant, with the backgrounds forming a composite design.

222 Zion Hill Methodist Church

1999. Christmas. Church Buildings. Multicoloured.
1032 20c. Type **222** 45 35
1033 35c. Seventh Day Adventist Church, Fat Hogs Bay, 1982 . . . . 60 45
1034 50c. Ruins of St. Phillip's Anglican Church, Kingstown . . . . 85 1·00
1035 $1 St. William's Catholic Church, Road Town . . . 1·60 2·25

223 King Henry VII **224** Duchess of York, 1920s

2000. "Stamp Show 2000" International Stamp Exhibition, London. Kings and Queens of England. Multicoloured.
1036 60c. Type **223** . . . . . . 1·10 1·25
1037 60c. Lady Jane Grey . . . . 1·10 1·25
1038 60c. King Charles I . . . . . 1·10 1·25
1039 60c. King William III . . . 1·10 1·25
1040 60c. King George III . . . 1·10 1·25
1041 60c. King Edward VII . . . 1·10 1·25

2000. 18th Birthday of Prince William. As T **191** of Ascension. Multicoloured.
1042 20c. Prince William as baby (horiz) 60 35
1043 40c. Prince William playing with ball, 1984 . . . . . 90 60
1044 50c. Skiing in British Columbia, 1998 . . . . . 1·25 1·00
1045 $1 In evening dress, 1997 (horiz) . . . . 2·00 2·50
MS1046 175×95 mm. 60c. Prince William in 1999 (horiz) and Nos. 1042/5 . . . . 7·00 7·00

2000. 100th Birthday of Queen Elizabeth the Queen Mother. Multicoloured.
1047 15c. Type **224** 50 25
1048 35c. As Queen Mother in 1957 . . . . 1·00 55
1049 70c. In evening dress, 1970 1·50 1·50
1050 $1.50 With family on 99th birthday . . . . 2·50 3·25

225 Red Hibiscus

2000. Flowers. Multicoloured.
1051 10c. Type **225** 30 30
1052 15c. Pink oleander 35 30
1053 35c. Yellow bell 75 55
1054 50c. Yellow and white frangipani . . . . 1·00 75
1055 75c. Flamboyant . . . . . 1·50 2·00
1056 $2 Bougainvillea . . . . . 3·25 4·50

226 Sunday Morning Well (Site of Emancipation Proclamation)

2000. New Millennium. Multicoloured.
1057 5c. Type **226** 15 25
1058 20c. Nurse Mary Louise Davies M.B.E. 45 35
1059 30c. Cheyney University, U.S.A. 60 45
1060 45c. Enid Leona Scatliffe (former chief education officer) 80 70
1061 50c. H. Lavity Stoutt Community College . . . 90 1·00
1062 $1 Sir J. Olva Georges . . . 1·60 2·00
MS1063 69×59 mm. $2 Private Samuel Hodge's Victoria Cross (vert) . . . . 3·25 3·75

227 Dr. Q. William Osborne and Arnando Scatliffe

2000. 50th Anniv of Restoration of Legislative Council. Multicoloured.
1064 10c. Type **227** 25 30
1065 15c. H. Robinson O'Neal and A. Austin Henley . . 35 30
1066 20c. Wilfred W. Smith and John C. Brudenell-Bruce 45 35
1067 35c. Howard R. Penn and I. G. Fonseca 65 55
1068 50c. Carlton L. de Castro and Theodolph H. Faulkner 90 90
1069 60c. Willard W. Wheatley (Chief Minister, 1971–79) 1·25 1·40
1070 $1 H. Lavity Stoutt (Chief Minister, 1967–71, 1979–83 and 1986–95) . . . . 1·60 2·00

2001. "HONG KONG 2001" Stamp Exhibition. Sheet 150×90 mm, containing T **228** and similar horiz design showing dove. Multicoloured.
MS1071 50c. Type **41**; 50c. Bar-tailed cuckoo dove . . . . . . 2·00 2·25

229 H.M.S. *Wistaria* (sloop), 1923–30

2001. Royal Navy Ships connected to British Virgin Islands (1st series). Multicoloured.
1072 35c. Type **229** 75 55
1073 50c. H.M.S. *Dundee* (sloop), 1934–35 . . . . 95 75
1074 60c. H.M.S. *Eurydice* (frigate), 1787 . . . . . 1·25 1·25
1075 75c. H.M.S. *Pegasus* (frigate), 1787 . . . . . 1·50 1·50
1076 $1 H.M.S. *Astrea* (frigate), 1807 . . . . 1·75 1·75
1077 $1.50 Royal Yacht *Britannia*, 1966 . . . . . 2·75 3·50
See also Nos. 1101/4.

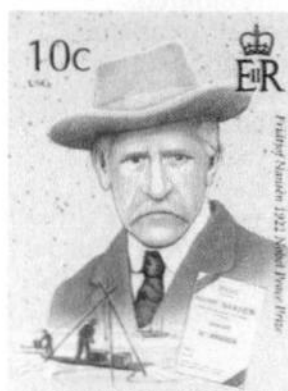

230 Fridtjof Nansen (Peace Prize, 1922)

2001. Centenary of Nobel Prize. Multicoloured.
1078 10c. Type **230** 50 50
1079 20c. Albert Einstein (Physics Prize,1921) 60 50
1080 25c. Sir Arthur Lewis (Economic Sciences Prize, 1979) 60 50
1081 40c. Saint-John Perse (Literature Prize, 1960) . . 70 70
1082 70c. Mother Teresa (Peace Prize, 1979) . . . . . . 2·50 2·50
1083 $2 Christian Lous Lange (Peace Prize, 1921) . . . 3·25 3·75

2002. Golden Jubilee. As T **200** of Ascension.
1084 15c. brown, mauve and gold 70 25
1085 50c. multicoloured . . . . . 1·25 1·00
1086 60c. multicoloured . . . . . 1·25 1·40
1087 75c. multicoloured . . . . . 1·50 1·75
MS1088 162×95 mm. Nos. 1084/7 and $1 multicoloured . . . . . 5·50 6·50
DESIGNS—HORIZ: 15c. Princess Elizabeth in A.T.S. uniform, changing wheel; 50c. Queen Elizabeth in fur hat, 1977; 60c. Queen Elizabeth carrying bouquet; 75c. Queen Elizabeth at banquet, Prague, 1996. VERT (38×51 mm)—$1 Queen Elizabeth after Annigoni.
Designs as Nos. 1084/7 in No. **MS**1088 omit the gold frame around each stamp and the "Golden Jubilee 1952–2002" inscription.

231 Estuarine Crocodile

2002. Reptiles. Multicoloured.
1089 5c. Type **231** 20 30
1090 20c. Reticulated python . . 40 30
1091 30c. Komodo dragon . . . 60 45
1092 40c. Boa constrictor 75 65
1093 $1 Dwarf caiman . . . . . 1·75 1·75
1094 $2 *Sphaerodactylus parthenopion* (gecko) . . . 3·25 4·00
MS1095 89×68 mm. $1.50, Head of *Sphaerodactylus parthenopion* on finger . . . . 2·75 3·25

2002. Queen Elizabeth the Queen Mother Commemoration. As T **202** of Ascension.
1096 20c. brown, gold and purple 45 30
1097 60c. multicoloured . . . . . 1·25 1·00
1098 $2 black, gold and purple 3·50 3·75
1099 $3 multicoloured . . . . . 4·75 5·50
MS1100 145×70 mm. Nos. 1098/9 8·50 9·50
DESIGNS—20c. Duchess of York, 1920s; 60c. Queen Mother at Somerset House, 2000; $2 Lady Elizabeth Bowes-Lyon, 1920; $3 Queen Mother inspecting guard of honour.
Designs as Nos. 1098/9 in No. **MS**1100 omit the "1900–2002" inscription and the coloured frame.

2002. Royal Navy Ships connected to British Virgin Islands (2nd series). As T **229**. Multicoloured.
1101 20c. H.M.S. Invincible (ship of the line) re-capturing H.M.S. *Argo* (frigate), 1783 . . . . 50 30
1102 35c. H.M.S. *Boreas* and H.M.S. *Solebay* (sailing frigates) 80 50
1103 50c. H.M.S. *Coventry* (frigate) . . . . 1·25 80
1104 $3 H.M.S. *Argyll* (frigate) 5·50 6·00

2002. Island Profiles (3rd series). Virgin Gorda. As T **218**. Multicoloured.
1105 5c. Spring Bay 20 30
1106 40c. Devils Bay 75 55
1107 60c. The Baths . . . . . . 1·10 1·00
1108 75c. St. Thomas Bay . . . 1·40 1·40
1109 $1 Savannah and Pond Bay 1·60 1·60
1110 $2 Trunk Bay . . . . . . 3·00 4·00

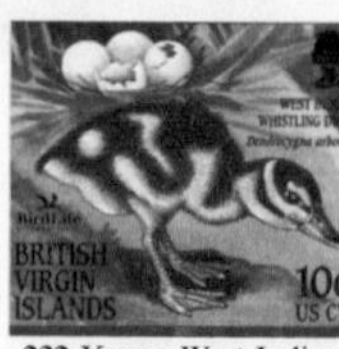

232 Young West Indian Whistling Duck and Nest

2002. Birdlife International. West Indian Whistling Duck. Multicoloured.
1111 10c. Type **232** 30 40
1112 35c. Adult bird on rock (vert) 70 55
1113 40c. Adult bird landing on water (vert) 75 70
1114 70c. Two adult birds . . . . 1·25 1·50
MS1115 175×80 mm. Nos. 1111/14 and $2 Head of duck . . . . 5·50 6·50

233 200 Metres Race

2003. Anniversaries and Events. Multicoloured.
1116 10c. Type **233** 50 70
1117 10c. Indoor cycling 50 70
1118 35c. Laser class dinghy racing 75 75
1119 35c. Women's long-jumping 75 75
1120 50c. Bareboat class yachts 1·00 1·25
1121 50c. Racing cruiser class yachts . . . . 1·00 1·25
1122 $1.35 Carlos and Esme Downing (founders) . . . 2·00 2·25
1123 $1.35 Copies of newspaper and anniversary logo . . 2·00 2·25
ANNIVERSARIES AND EVENTS: 10c. Commonwealth Games, 2002; 35c. 20th anniv of British Virgin Islands' admission to Olympic Games; 50c. 30th anniv of Spring Regatta; $1.35, 40th anniv of *The Island Sun* (newspaper).

2003. 50th Anniv of Coronation. A T **206** of Ascension. Multicoloured.
1124 15c. Queen Elizabeth II . . 15 20
1125 $5 Queen and Royal Family on Buckingham Palace balcony . . . . 5·50 5·75
MS1126 95×115 mm. As Nos. 1124/5 . . . . 5·75 6·00
Nos. 1124/5 have red frame; stamps from **MS**1126 have no frame and country name in mauve panel.

2003. As T **207** of Ascension.
1127 $5 black, bistre and brown 5·50 6·00

2003. 21st Birthday of Prince William of Wales. As T **208** of Ascension. (a) Multicoloured.
1128 50c. Prince William at Tidworth and Beaufort Polo Clubs, 2002 . . . . . 55 60
1129 $2 Playing polo, 2002 and at Holyrood House, 2001 . . 2·20 2·30

(b) As Nos. 1128/9 but with grey frame.
1130 50c. As No. 1128 . . . . . 55 60
1131 $2 As No. 1129 . . . . . . 2·20 2·30

2003. Centenary of Powered Flight. As T **209** of Ascension. Multicoloured.
1132 15c. Douglas DC-4 . . . . . 15 20
1133 20c. Boeing Stearman "Kaydet" 20 25
1134 35c. North American B-25 J Mitchell 40 45
1135 40c. McDonnell Douglas F-4B Phantom 45 50
1136 70c. Boeing-Vertol CH-47 Chinook helicopter . . . 75 80
1137 $2 Hughes AH-64 Apache helicopter . . . . 2·20 2·30

234 Townsmen under Arcades

2003. Christmas. "Stories from the Life of St. Ursula: Arrival of the English Ambassadors" by Carpaccio. Multicoloured.
1138 20c. Type **234** 20 25
1139 40c. English ambassadors 45 50
1140 $2.50 King Maurus of Brittany . . . . 3·25 3·25
MS1141 172×87 mm. $1 King Maurus receiving English ambassadors (35×35 mm) and Nos. 1138/40 . . . . 5·00 5·25
Nos. 1138/40 show details of the painting and No. **MS**1141 the complete painting.

OFFICIAL STAMPS

1985. Nos. 418/21 and 423/33 optd **OFFICIAL**.
O 1 1c. Purple-tipped sea anemone . . . . 30 1·25
O 2 3c. Common starfish . . . . 45 1·25
O 3 5c. Type **134** 45 45
O 4 8c. Triton's trumpet (shell) 55 60
O 5 13c. Flamingo tongue snail 80 75
O 6 15c. Spider crab 85 70
O 7 18c. Sea squirts . . . . . . 90 1·75
O 8 20c. True tulip (shell) . . . 90 80
O 9 25c. Rooster tail conch (shell) . . . . 1·25 2·00
O10 30c. Fighting conch (shell) 1·40 1·00
O11 60c. Mangrove crab . . . . 2·00 2·50
O12 $1 Coral polyps . . . . . . 3·00 3·75
O13 $2.50 Peppermint shrimp . . 4·50 9·00
O14 $3 West Indian murex (shell) 5·50 10·00
O15 $5 Carpet anemone . . . . 7·50 10·00

1986. Nos. 560/78 optd **OFFICIAL**.
O16 1c. Type **162** . . . . 40 1·50
O17 2c. Yellow-crowned night heron . . . . 40 1·50
O18 5c. Mangrove cuckoo . . . 55 1·50
O19 8c. Northern mockingbird 55 2·25
O20 10c. Grey kingbird . . . . . 70 1·50
O21 12c. Red-necked pigeon . . 70 40
O22 15c. Least bittern 70 40
O23 18c. Smooth-billed ani . . . 70 75
O24 20c. Clipper rail . . . . . . 1·00 1·00
O25 25c. American kestrel . . . 1·00 1·00
O26 30c. Pearly-eyed thrasher . . 1·25 1·00
O27 35c. Bridled quail dove . . . 1·25 1·00
O28 40c. Green-backed heron . . 1·25 1·00
O29 50c. Scaly-breasted ground dove . . . . 1·40 1·75
O30 60c. Little blue heron . . . 1·50 2·50
O31 $1 Audubon's shearwater . . 2·25 3·50
O32 $2 Blue-faced booby . . . . 2·50 4·00
O33 $3 Cattle egret . . . . . . 6·00 7·00
O34 $5 Zenaida dove . . . . . . 6·50 7·50

1991. Nos. 767/8, 771, 773/9 and 781 optd **OFFICIAL**.
O35 5c. Frangipani . . . . . . 45 1·25
O36 10c. Autograph tree . . . . 45 1·25
O37 20c. Jerusalem thorn 55 55
O38 30c. Swamp immortelle . . . 70 55
O39 35c. White cedar 70 55
O40 40c. Mahoe tree 80 70
O41 45c. Pinguin 80 75
O42 50c. Christmas orchid . . . 1·50 90
O43 70c. Lignum vitae . . . . . 1·50 2·25
O44 $1 African tulip tree . . . . 1·50 2·50
O45 $3 Organ pipe cactus . . . . 4·00 6·50

BRUNEI Pt. 1

A Sultanate on the North Coast of Borneo.

100 cents = 1 dollar.

1 Star and Local Scene

1895.
1 **1** ½c. brown . . . . 3·25 20·00
2 1c. brown . . . . 3·25 15·00
3 2c. black . . . . 4·00 15·00
4 3c. blue . . . . 3·75 14·00
5 5c. green . . . . 6·50 16·00
6 8c. purple . . . . 6·50 28·00
7 10c. red . . . . 8·00 28·00
8 25c. green . . . . 65·00 80·00

9 50c. green . . . . 18·00 95·00
10 $1 green . . . . 20·00 £110

1906. Stamps of Labuan optd **BRUNEI.** or surch also.
11 **18** 1c. black and purple . . . . 30·00 55·00
12 2c. on 3c. black and brown 2·75 10·00
13 2c. on 8c. black and orange 27·00 80·00
14 3c. black and brown . . . . 29·00 85·00
15 4c. on 12c. black and yellow 4·00 5·00
16 5c. on 16c. green and brown 45·00 75·00
17 8c. black and orange . . . 9·00 32·00
18 10c. on 16c. green and brown . . . . 6·50 22·00
19 25c. on 16c. green and brown £100 £120
20 30c. on 16c. green and brown £100 £120
21 50c. on 16c. green and brown £100 £120
22 $1 on 8c. black and orange £100 £120

5 View on Brunei River

1907.
23 **5** 1c. black and green . . . . . 2·25 11·00
24 2c. black and red . . . . . 2·50 4·50
25 3c. black and brown . . . . 10·00 22·00
26 4c. black and mauve . . . . 7·50 10·00
27 5c. black and blue . . . . . 50·00 90·00
28 8c. black and orange . . . . 7·50 23·00
29 10c. black and green . . . . 4·50 6·00
30 25c. blue and brown . . . . 32·00 48·00
31 30c. violet and black . . . . 23·00 22·00
32 50c. green and brown . . . . 15·00 22·00
33 $1 red and grey . . . . . . 60·00 90·00

1908.
35 **5** 1c. green . . . . 60 2·00
60 1c. black . . . . 1·00 75
79 1c. brown . . . . 50 2·00
36 2c. black and brown . . . . 3·25 1·25
61 2c. brown . . . . 90 7·00
62 2c. green . . . . 2·00 1·00
80 2c. grey . . . . 60 4·25
37 3c. red . . . . 4·00 1·25
63 3c. green . . . . 80 6·50
64 4c. purple . . . . 1·50 1·25
65 4c. orange . . . . 2·00 1·00
40 5c. black and orange . . . . 7·00 7·00
82 5c. orange . . . . 80 1·25
67 5c. grey . . . . 15·00 12·00
68 5c. brown . . . . 13·00 70
41 8c. blue and indigo . . . . . 7·00 11·00
71 8c. blue . . . . 6·00 5·00
72 8c. black . . . . 13·00 75
84 8c. red . . . . 40 1·00
42 10c. purple on yellow . . . . 2·00 1·75
85 10c. violet 70 30
86 15c. blue . . . . 1·50 70
87 25c. purple . . . . 2·25 1·00
44 30c. purple and yellow . . . 9·00 12·00
88 30c. black and orange . . . 1·75 1·00
77 50c. black on green . . . . . 8·00 15·00
89 50c. black . . . . 3·25 80
46 $1 black and red on blue . . 21·00 48·00
90 $1 black and red . . . . . . 8·00 75
47 $5 red on green £130 £200
91 $5 green and orange . . . . 16·00 17·00
92 $10 black and purple . . . . 65·00 30·00
48 $25 black on red £550 £950

1922. Optd **MALAYA- BORNEO EXHIBITION. 1922.**
51 **5** 1c. green . . . . 4·25 27·00
52 2c. black and brown . . . . 4·50 32·00
53 3c. red . . . . 6·00 42·00
54 4c. red . . . . 9·00 50·00
55 5c. orange . . . . 13·00 55·00
56 10c. purple on yellow . . . . 6·50 55·00
57 25c. lilac . . . . 14·00 80·00
58 50c. black on green . . . . . 45·00 £150
59 $1 black and red on blue . . 70·00 £190

7 Native Houses, Water Village

1924.
81 **7** 3c. green . . . . 1·00 5·00
83 6c. black . . . . 1·00 4·00
70 6c. red . . . . 3·75 11·00
74 12c. blue . . . . 4·50 9·00

8 Sultan Ahmed Tajudin and Water Village

1949. Silver Jubilee of H.H. the Sultan.
93 **8** 8c. black and red . . . . . 85 1·25
94 25c. purple and orange . . . 85 1·60
95 50c. black and blue . . . . . 85 1·60

1949. 75th Anniv of U.P.U. As T **20/23** of Antigua.
96 8c. red . . . . 1·00 1·25
97 15c. blue . . . . 3·50 1·50
98 25c. mauve . . . . 1·00 1·50
99 50c. black . . . . 1·00 1·25

9 Sultan Omar Ali Saifuddin

1952. Dollar values as T **8**, but with arms instead of portrait inset.
100 **9** 1c. black 10 50
101 2c. black and orange . . . 10 50
102 3c. black and brown 10 30
103 4c. black and green 10 20
104 6c. black and grey 30 10
123 8c. black and red . . . . . 1·00 10
106 10c. black and sepia 15 10
125 12c. black and violet . . . . 1·50 10
126 15c. black and blue 55 10
109 25c. black and purple . . . 2·50 10
110 50c. black and blue . . . . 1·75 10
111 $1 black and green (horiz) 1·50 1·40
112 $2 black and red (horiz) . . 4·50 2·50
113 $5 black and purple (horiz) 16·00 7·00

11 Brunei Mosque and Sultan Omar

1958. Opening of the Brunei Mosque.
114 **11** 8c. black and green 20 65
115 15c. black and red 25 15
116 35c. black and lilac 30 90

12 "Protein Foods"

1963. Freedom from Hunger.
117 **12** 12c. sepia . . . . 2·75 1·00

13 I.T.U. Emblem

1965. Centenary of I.T.U.
132 **13** 4c. mauve and brown . . . 35 10
133 75c. yellow and green . . . 1·00 75

14 I.C.Y. Emblem

1965. International Co-operation Year.
134 **14** 4c. purple and turquoise 20 10
135 15c. green and lavender . . 55 35

15 Sir Winston Churchill and St. Paul's Cathedral in Wartime

1966. Churchill Commemoration. Designs in black, red and gold and with backgrounds in colours given.
136 **15** 3c. blue 30 20
137 10c. green . . . . 1·50 20
138 15c. brown . . . . 1·75 35
139 75c. violet . . . . 4·25 2·25

16 Footballer's Legs, Ball and Jules Rimet Cup

1966. World Cup Football Championships.
140 **16** 4c. multicoloured 20 15
141 75c. multicoloured 80 60

17 W.H.O. Building

1966. Inauguration of W.H.O. Headquarters, Geneva.
142 **17** 12c. black, green and blue 40 65
143 25c. black, purple and ochre . . . . 60 1·25

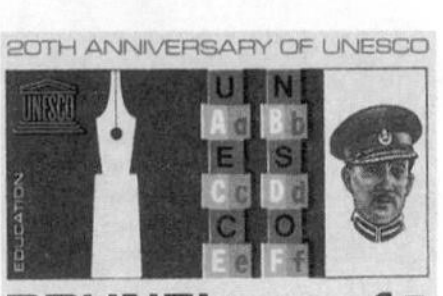

18 "Education"

1966. 20th Anniv of U.N.E.S.C.O.
144 **18** 4c. multicoloured 35 10
145 – 15c. yellow, violet and olive 75 50
146 – 75c. black, purple and orange . . . . 2·50 6·00
DESIGNS: 15c. "Science"; 75c. "Culture".

21 Religious Headquarters Building

1967. 1400th Anniv of Revelation of the Koran.
147 **21** 4c. multicoloured 10 10
148 10c. multicoloured 15 10
149 – 25c. multicoloured 20 30
150 – 50c. multicoloured . . . . 35 1·50
Nos. 149/50 have sprigs of laurel flanking the main design (which has a smaller circle) in place of flagpoles.

22 Sultan of Brunei, Mosque and Flags

1968. Installation of Y.T.M. Seri Paduka Duli Pengiran Temenggong. Multicoloured.
151 4c. Type **22** 15 60
152 12c. Sultan of Brunei, Mosque and Flags (different) (horiz) . . . . . 40 1·50
153 25c. Type **22** . . . . 55 2·00

23 Sultan of Brunei

24 Sultan of Brunei

1968. Birthday of Sultan.
154 **23** 4c. multicoloured 10 35
155 12c. multicoloured 20 75
156 25c. multicoloured . . . . 30 1·10

1968. Coronation of Sultan of Brunei.
157 4c. multicoloured 15 25
158 12c. multicoloured 25 50
159 25c. multicoloured 40 75

25 New Building and Sultan's Portrait

1968. Opening of Hall of Language and Literature Bureau. Multicoloured.
160 10c. Type **25** . . . . 20 1·75
161 15c. New Building and Sultan's portrait (48½ × 22 mm) 20 35
162 30c. As 15c. 45 90

27 Human Rights Emblem and struggling Man

1968. Human Rights Year.
163 **27** 12c. black, yellow and green 10 20
164 25c. black, yellow and blue 15 25
165 75c. black, yellow and purple . . . . 45 1·75

28 Sultan of Brunei and W.H.O. Emblem

1968. 20th Anniv of World Health Organization.
166 **28** 4c. yellow, black and blue 30 30
167 15c. yellow, black and violet 55 65
168 25c. yellow, black and olive 65 1·25

29 Deep Sea Oil-Rig, Sultan of Brunei and inset portrait of Pengiran Di-Gadong

1969. Installation (9th May, 1968) of Pengiran Shar-bandar as Y.T.M. Seri Paduka Duli Pengiran Di-Gadong Sahibol Mal.
169 **29** 12c. multicoloured 85 50
170 40c. multicoloured . . . . 1·25 2·00
171 50c. multicoloured . . . . 1·25 2·00

30 Aerial View of Parliament Buildings

1969. Opening of Royal Audience Hall and Legislative Council Chamber.
172 **30** 12c. multicoloured 20 25
173 25c. multicoloured 30 45
174 – 50c. red and violet . . . . 60 2·25
DESIGN: 50c. Elevation of new buildings.

32 Youth Centre and Sultan's Portrait

1969. Opening of New Youth Centre.
175 **32** 6c. multicoloured . . . . . 20 1·00
176 10c. multicoloured 25 10
177 30c. multicoloured . . . . 70 1·00

33 Soldier, Sultan and Badge

34 Badge, and Officer in Full-dress Uniform

1971. 10th Anniv of Royal Brunei Malay Regiment. Multicoloured.
178 10c. Type **33** 80 30
179 15c. Bell 205 Iroquois helicopter, Sultan and badge (horiz) . . . . . . 1·75 70
180 75c. "Pahlawan" (patrol boat), Sultan and badge (horiz) . . . . 3·25 7·00

1971. 50th Anniv of Royal Brunei Police Force. Multicoloured.
181 10c. Type **34** 50 30
182 15c. Badge and Patrol Constable 60 90
183 50c. Badge and Traffic Constable . . . . 1·10 6·00

35 Perdana Wazir, Sultan of Brunei and View of Water Village

1971. Installation of the Yang Teramat Mulia as the Perdana Wazir.
184 **35** 15c. multicoloured 40 50
185 – 25c. multicoloured . . . . 70 1·00
186 – 50c. multicoloured . . . . 1·40 5·00
Nos. 185/6 show various views of Brunei Town.

36 Pottery

1972. Opening of Brunei Museum. Mult.
187 10c. Type **36** 30 10
188 12c. Straw-work 40 20
189 15c. Leather-work 45 20
190 25c. Gold-work . . . . . . 1·25 1·25
191 50c. Museum Building (58 × 21 mm) . . . . . . 2·25 5·50

37 Modern Building, Queen Elizabeth and Sultan of Brunei

1972. Royal Visit. Each design with portrait of Queen and Sultan. Multicoloured.
192 10c. Type **37** 70 20
193 15c. Native houses 95 55
194 25c. Mosque . . . . 2·00 1·60
195 50c. Royal Assembly Hall . . 3·75 7·00

38 Secretariat Building

1972. Renaming of Brunei Town as Bandar Seri Begawan.
196 **38** 10c. multicoloured 20 15
197 – 15c. green, yellow and black 25 15
198 – 25c. blue, yellow and black 45 50
199 – 50c. red, blue and black . . 75 2·25
VIEWS: 15c. Darul Hana Palace; 25c. Old Brunei Town; 50c. Town and Water Village.

39 Blackburn Beverley C1 parachuting Supplies

1972. Opening of R.A.F. Museum, Hendon. Multicoloured.
200 25c. Type **39** . . . . 1·75 1·25
201 75c. Blackburn Beverley C1 landing . . . . 3·25 4·75

1972. Royal Silver Wedding. As T **52** of Ascension, but with girl with traditional flower-pot, and boy with bowl and pipe in background.
210 12c. red 10 10
211 75c. green 20 50

41 Interpol H.Q., Paris

1973. 50th Anniv of Interpol.
212 **41** 25c. green, purple and black . . . . 1·50 1·25
213 – 50c. blue, ultram & red . . 1·50 1·25
DESIGN: 50c. Different view of the H.Q.

42 Sultan, Princess Anne and Captain Phillips

1973. Royal Wedding.
214 **42** 25c. multicoloured 15 10
215 50c. multicoloured 15 25

43 Churchill Painting

44 Sultan Sir Hassanal Bolkiah Mu'izzaddin Waddaulah

1973. Opening of Churchill Memorial Building. Multicoloured.
216 12c. Type **43** 10 20
217 50c. Churchill statue . . . . 30 1·40

1975. Multicoloured. Background colours given.
218 **44** 4c. green 20 20
219 5c. blue 20 30
220 6c. green . . . . 3·25 5·50
221 10c. lilac 30 10
222 15c. brown . . . . 2·50 40
223 20c. stone 30 20
224 25c. green 40 15
225 30c. blue 40 15
226 35c. grey 40 20
227 40c. purple 40 20
228 50c. brown 40 20
229 75c. green . . . . 60 3·50
256 $1 orange . . . . 1·50 3·50
231 $2 yellow . . . . 2·25 11·00
232 $5 silver . . . . 3·00 18·00
233 $10 gold . . . . 5·00 32·00

45 Aerial View of Airport

1974. Inauguration of Brunei International Airport. Multicoloured.
234 50c. Type **45** . . . . 1·25 1·00
235 75c. Sultan in Army uniform, and airport (48 × 36 mm) 1·50 1·50

46 U.P.U. Emblem and Sultan

1974. Centenary of Universal Postal Union.
236 **46** 12c. multicoloured 20 20
237 50c. multicoloured . . . . 40 1·40
238 75c. multicoloured . . . . 50 1·75

47 Sir Winston Churchill

1974. Birth Centenary of Sir Winston Churchill.
239 **47** 12c. black, blue and gold 25 20
240 – 75c. black, green and gold 45 1·40
DESIGN: 75c. Churchill smoking cigar (profile).

48 Boeing 737 and R.B.A. Crest

1975. Inauguration of Royal Brunei Airlines. Mult.
241 12c. Type **48** . . . . 1·00 25
242 35c. Boeing 737 over Bandar Seri Begawan Mosque . . 1·75 1·50
243 75c. Boeing 737 in flight . . 2·50 3·00

1976. Surch **10 sen**.
263 **44** 10c. on 6c. brown . . . . 1·75 1·75

50 Royal Coat of Arms

51 The Moment of Crowning

1977. Silver Jubilee. Multicoloured.
264 10c. Type **50** 15 15
265 20c. Imperial State Crown . . 20 20
266 75c. Queen Elizabeth (portrait by Annigoni) . . 45 60

1978. 25th Anniv of Coronation. Multicoloured.
267 10c. Type **51** 15 10
268 20c. Queen in Coronation regalia 20 20
269 75c. Queen's departure from Abbey 55 80

52 Royal Crest

53 Human Rights Emblem and Struggling Man

1978. 10th Anniv of Coronation of Sultan.
270 **52** 10c. black, red and yellow 20 10
271 – 20c. multicoloured 40 25
272 – 75c. multicoloured . . . . 1·10 3·25
MS273 182 × 77 mm. Nos. 270/2 12·00 16·00
DESIGNS: 20c. Coronation; 75c. Sultan's Crown.

1978. Human Rights Year.
274 **53** 10c. black, yellow and red 15 10
275 20c. black, yellow and violet 20 35
276 75c. black, yellow and bistre . . . . 40 2·50

Type **53** is similar to the design used for the previous Human Rights issue in 1968.

54 Smiling Children

1979. International Year of the Child.
277 **54** 10c. multicoloured 20 10
278 – $1 black and green . . . . 80 2·50
DESIGN: $1 I.Y.C. emblem.

55 Earth Satellite Station

1979. Telisai Earth Satellite Station. Multicoloured.
279 10c. Type **55** 20 15
280 20c. Satellite and antenna . . 30 40
281 75c. Television camera, telex machine and telephone . . 60 2·75

56 Hegira Symbol

57 Installation Ceremony

1979. Moslem Year 1400 A.H. Commemoration.
282 **56** 10c. black, yellow and green 10 15
283 20c. black, yellow and blue 15 30
284 75c. black, yellow and lilac 45 2·00
MS285 178 × 200 mm. Nos. 282/4 3·00 7·00

1980. 1st Anniv of Prince Sufri Bolkiah's Installation as First Wazir. Multicoloured. Blue borders.
286 10c. Type **57** 15 10
287 75c. Prince Sufri . . . . . . 85 2·00

1980. 1st Anniv of Prince Jefri Bolkiah's Installation as Second Wazir. Designs similar to T **57**. Multicoloured. Green borders.
288 10c. Installation ceremony . . 15 10
289 75c. Prince Jefri . . . . . . 85 2·25

58 Royal Umbrella and Sash

59 I.T.U. and W.H.O. Emblems

1981. Royal Regalia (1st series). Multicoloured.
290 10c. Type **58** 20 15
291 15c. Sword and Shield . . . 35 25
292 20c. Lance and Sheath . . . 40 40
293 30c. Betel Leaf Container . . 60 1·25
294 50c. Coronation Crown (39 × 22 mm) . . . . . . 1·25 5·00
MS295 98 × 142 mm. Nos. 290/4 3·75 7·50
See Nos. 298/303, 314/19 and 320/5.

1981. World Telecommunications and Health Day.
296 **59** 10c. black and red 50 25
297 75c. black, blue and violet 2·25 5·00

60 Shield and Broadsword

61 Prince Charles as Colonel of the Welsh Guards

1981. Royal Regalia (2nd series). Multicoloured.
298 10c. Type **60** 10 10
299 15c. Blunderbuss and Pouch 20 20
300 20c. Crossed Lances and Sash 30 30
301 30c. Sword, Shield and Sash 40 75
302 50c. Forked Lance . . . . . 60 2·50
303 75c. Royal Drum (29 × 45 mm) . . . . . . 80 4·50

1981. Royal Wedding. Multicoloured.
304 10c. Wedding bouquet from Brunei 15 15
305 $1 Type **61** . . . . 35 1·50
306 $2 Prince Charles and Lady Diana Spencer . . . . . . 50 2·50

62 Fishing

63 Blind Man and Braille Alphabet

1981. World Food Day. Multicoloured.
307 10c. Type **62** 50 15
308 $1 Farm produce and machinery . . . . 4·50 7·50

1981. International Year for Disabled Persons. Multicoloured.
309 10c. Type **63** 65 20
310 20c. Deaf people and sign language . . . . 1·50 80
311 75c. Disabled person and wheelchairs . . . . 3·00 6·75

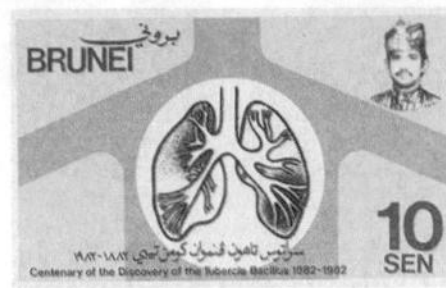

64 Drawing of Infected Lungs

1982. Centenary of Robert Koch's Discovery of Tubercle Bacillus. Multicoloured.
312 10c. Type **64** 50 25
313 75c. Magnified tubercle bacillus and microscope . . 3·00 5·50

1982. Royal Regalia (3rd series). As T **60**. Mult.
314 10c. Ceremonial Ornament 10 10
315 15c. Silver Betel Caddy . . . 20 20
316 20c. Traditional Flowerpot 25 30
317 30c. Solitary Candle 50 90
318 50c. Golden Pipe . . . . . . 70 2·50
319 75c. Royal Chin Support (28 × 45 mm) . . . . . . 90 4·00

1982. Royal Regalia (4th series). As T **60**. Mult.
320 10c. Royal Mace 25 10
321 15c. Ceremonial Shield and Spears 35 30
322 20c. Embroidered Ornament 45 40
323 30c. Golden-tasseled Cushion 75 1·50
324 50c. Ceremonial Dagger and Sheath . . . . 1·25 3·50
325 75c. Religious Mace (28 × 45 mm) . . . . 1·60 4·50

65 Brunei Flag

67 Football

66 "Postal Service"

1983. Commonwealth Day.
326 **65** 10c. multicoloured 15 70
327 – 20c. blue, black and buff 20 80
328 – 75c. blue, black and green 45 1·25
329 – $2 blue, black and yellow 1·10 1·75
DESIGNS: 20c. Brunei Mosque; 75c. Machinery; $2 Sultan of Brunei.

1983. World Communications Year.
330 **66** 10c. multicoloured 15 10
331 – 75c. yellow, brown and black 60 75
332 – $2 multicoloured . . . . . 1·75 2·25
DESIGNS: 75c. "Telephone Service"; $2 "Communications".

1983. Official Opening of the National Hassanal Bolkiah Stadium. Multicoloured.
333 10c. Type **67** 55 15
334 75c. Athletics . . . . 2·25 1·50
335 $1 View of stadium (44 × 27 mm) . . . . . . 2·75 4·00

68 Fishermen and Crustacea

1983. Fishery Resources. Multicoloured.
336 10c. Type **68** . . . . 1·00 15
337 50c. Fishermen with net . . . 3·25 1·50
338 75c. Fishing trawler . . . . 3·50 4·00
339 $1 Fishing with hook and tackle . . . . 3·75 4·50

69 Royal Assembly Hall

1984. Independence.
340 **69** 10c. brown and orange . . 20 10
341 – 20c. pink and red 30 20
342 – 35c. pink and purple . . . 60 60
343 – 50c. light blue and blue . . 1·75 1·25
344 – 75c. light green and green 1·75 2·00
345 – $1 grey and brown . . . . 2·00 2·50
346 – $3 multicoloured . . . . . 7·00 10·00
MS347 150 × 120 mm. Nos. 340/6 9·50 15·00
MS348 Two sheets, each 150 × 120 mm, containing 4 stamps (34 × 69 mm). (a) 25c. × 4 grey-black and new blue (Signing of the Brunei Constitution). (b) 25c. × 4 multicoloured (Signing of Brunei–U.K. Friendship Agreement) Set of 2 sheets . . 2·00 4·50
DESIGNS—34 × 25 mm: 20c. Government Secretariat Building; 35c. New Supreme Court; 50c. Natural gas well; 75c. Omar Ali Saifuddin Mosque; $1 Sultan's Palace. 68 × 24 mm: $3 Brunei flag and map of South-East Asia.

70 Natural Forests and Enrichment Planting

1984. Forestry Resources. Multicoloured.
349 10c. Type **70** . . . . 1·00 25
350 50c. Forests and water resources . . . . 2·50 2·25
351 75c. Recreation forests . . . 3·25 4·50
352 $1 Forests and wildlife . . . 4·75 6·00

71 Sultan Omar Saiffuddin 50c. Stamp of 1952

72 United Nations Emblem

1984. "Philakorea" International Stamp Exhibition, Seoul. Multicoloured.
353 10c. Type **71** 50 15
354 75c. Brunei River view 10c.stamp of 1907 . . . . 1·50 2·25
355 $2 Star and view ½c. stamp of 1895 . . . . 2·50 6·50
MS356 Three sheets, 117 × 100 mm, each containing one stamp as Nos. 353/5 Set of 3 sheets . . . 3·75 7·00

1985. Admission of Brunei to World Organizations (1st issue).
357 **72** 50c. black, gold and blue 50 70
358 – 50c. multicoloured 50 70
359 – 50c. multicoloured 50 70
360 – 50c. multicoloured 50 70
MS361 110 × 151 mm. Nos. 357/60 2·25 3·00
DESIGNS: No. 358, Islamic Conference Organization logo; 359, Commonwealth logo; 360, A.S.E.A.N. emblem.
See also Nos. 383/7.

73 Young People and Brunei Flag

1985. International Youth Year. Multicoloured.
362 10c. Type **73** . . . . 1·25 20
363 75c. Young people at work 5·00 7·00
364 $1 Young people serving the community . . . . 6·00 7·50

74 Palestinian Emblem

1985. International Palestinian Solidarity Day.
365 **74** 10c. multicoloured . . . . 2·00 20
366 50c. multicoloured . . . . 4·25 1·50
367 $1 multicoloured . . . . . 5·25 3·00

75 Early and Modern Scout Uniforms

76 Sultan Sir Hassanal Bolkiah Mu'izzaddin Waddaulah

1985. National Scout Jamboree. Multicoloured.
368 10c. Type **75** 60 10
369 20c. Scout on tower signalling with flag 90 40
370 $2 Jamboree emblem . . . . 2·75 3·25

1985.
371 **76** 10c. multicoloured 30 10
372 15c. multicoloured 30 10
373 20c. multicoloured 40 10
374 25c. multicoloured 40 15
375 35c. multicoloured 55 20
376 40c. multicoloured 60 25
377 50c. multicoloured 70 35
378 75c. multicoloured 90 50
379 $1 multicoloured . . . . . 1·25 70
380 $2 multicoloured . . . . . 2·75 1·75
381 $5 multicoloured . . . . . 4·25 5·00
382 $10 multicoloured . . . . 8·00 11·00
Nos. 379/82 are larger, size 32 × 39 mm.

1986. Admission of Brunei to World Organizations (2nd issue). As T **72**.
383 50c. black, gold and green . . 50 60
384 50c. black, gold and mauve 50 60
385 50c. black, gold and red . . . 50 60
386 50c. black, gold and blue . . 50 60
MS387 105 × 155 mm. Nos. 383/6 1·50 4·00
DESIGNS: No. 383, World Meteorological Organization emblem; 384, International Telecommunication Union emblem; 385, Universal Postal Union emblem; 386, International Civil Aviation Organization emblem.

78 Soldiers on Assault Course and Bell 205 Iroquois Helicopter

1986. 25th Anniv of Brunei Armed Forces. Multicoloured.
388 10c. Type **78** . . . . 3·75 3·75
389 20c. Operating computer . . 4·00 4·00
390 50c. Anti-aircraft missile, MBB-Bolkow Bo 150L helicopter and missile boat 5·00 5·00
391 75c. Army, commanders and parade . . . . 5·50 5·50
Nos. 388/91 were printed together, se-tenant, forming a composite design.

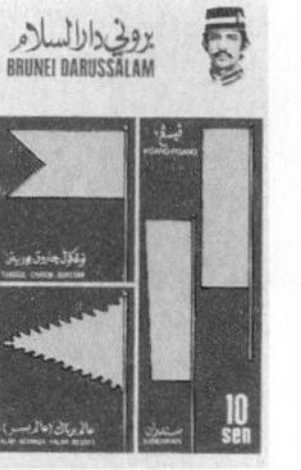

79 Tunggul Charok Buritan, Alam Bernaga (Alam Besar), Pisang-Pisang and Sandaran

80 Stylized Peace Doves

1986. Royal Ensigns (1st series).
392 **79** 10c. black, yellow and red 30 10
393 – 75c. multicoloured . . . . 1·10 1·10
394 – $2 black, yellow and green 2·25 2·75
DESIGNS: 75c. Ula-Ula Besar, Sumbu Layang and Payong Haram; $2 Panji-Panji, Chogan Istiadat (Chogan Di-Raja) and Chogan Ugama.

1986. Royal Ensigns (2nd series). As T **79**.
395 10c. multicoloured 30 10
396 75c. black, red and yellow . . 1·10 1·10
397 $2 multicoloured . . . . . . 2·25 2·75
DESIGNS: 10c. Dadap, Tunggul Kawan, Ambal, Payong Ubor-Ubor, Sapu-Sapu Ayeng and Rawai Lidah; 75c. Payong Tinggi and Payong Ubor-Ubor Tiga Ringkat; $2 Lambang Duli Yang Maha Mulia and Mahligai.

1986. International Peace Year. Multicoloured.
398 50c. Type **80** 75 75
399 75c. Stylized hands and "1986" . . . . 1·00 1·10
400 $1 International Peace Year emblem and arms of Brunei . . . . 1·25 1·50

81 Drug Addict in Cage and Syringe (poster by Othman bin Ramboh)

82 Cannon ("badil")

1987. National Anti-drug Campaign. Children's Posters. Multicoloured.
401 10c. Type **81** . . . . 1·25 35
402 75c. Drug addict and noose (Arman bin Mohd. Zaman) 2·75 4·00
403 $1 Blindfolded drug addict and noose (Abidin bin Hj. Rashid) . . . . 3·25 5·00

1987. Brassware (1st series). Multicoloured.
404 50c. Type **82** 50 50
405 50c. Lamp ("pelita") 50 50
406 50c. Betel container ("langguai") 50 50
407 50c. Water jug ("kiri") . . . 50 50
See also Nos. 434/7.

83 Map showing Member Countries

1987. 20th Anniv of Association of South East Asian Nations. Multicoloured.
408 20c. Type **83** 35 20
409 50c. Dates and figures "20" 60 50
410 $1 Flags of member states . . 1·25 1·25

84 Brunei Citizens

1987. 25th Anniv (1986) of Language and Literature Bureau. Multicoloured.

411 10c. Type **84** 30 30

412 50c. Flame emblem and hands holding open book 60 60

413 $2 Scenes of village life . . . 1·50 1·50

Nos. 411/13 were printed together, se-tenant, forming a composite design taken from a mural.

85 "Artocarpus odoratissima"

1987. Local Fruits (1st series). Multicoloured.

414 50c. Type **85** 45 55

415 50c. "Canarium odontophyllum mig" . . . 45 55

416 50c. "Litsea garciae" 45 55

417 50c. "Mangifera foetida lour" 45 55

See also Nos. 421/4, 459/62, 480/2 and 525/8.

86 Modern House

1987. International Year of Shelter for the Homeless.

418 **86** 50c. multicoloured 40 50

419 – 75c. multicoloured 55 65

420 – $1 multicoloured 80 90

DESIGNS: 75c., $1 Modern Brunei housing projects.

1988. Local Fruits (2nd series). As T **85**. Mult.

421 50c. "Durio spp" . . . . . 95 1·25

422 50c. "Durio oxleyanus" . . . 95 1·25

423 50c. "Durio graveolens" (blue background) . . . . 95 1·25

424 50c. "Durio graveolens" (white background) . . . . 95 1·25

87 Wooden Lathe

89 Sultan reading Proclamation

88 Patterned Cloth

1988. Opening of Malay Technology Museum. Multicoloured.

425 10c. Type **87** 15 10

426 75c. Crushing sugar cane . . 55 70

427 $1 Bird scarer 70 85

1988. Handwoven Material (1st series). Mult.

428 10c. Type **88** 10 10

429 20c. Jong Sarat cloth 15 15

430 25c. Si Pugut cloth 20 25

431 40c. Si Pugut Bunga Berlapis cloth 30 35

432 75c. Si Lobang Bangsi Bunga Belitang Kipas cloth . . . 55 80

MS433 105 × 204 mm. Nos. 428/32 2·25 4·25

See also Nos. 442/7.

1988. Brassware (2nd series). As T **82**. Multicoloured.

434 50c. Lidded two-handled pot ("periok") 40 50

435 50c. Candlestick ("lampong") 40 50

436 50c. Shallow circular dish with stand ("gangsa") . . . 40 50

437 50c. Repousse box with lid ("celapa") 40 50

1988. 20th Anniv of Sultan's Coronation. Mult.

438 20c. Type **89** 25 15

439 75c. Sultan reading from Koran 80 60

440 $2 In Coronation robes (26 × 63 mm) . . . . . . 2·00 1·60

MS441 164 × 125 mm. Nos. 438/40 2·40 2·50

1988. Handwoven Material (2nd series). As T **88**. Multicoloured.

442 10c. Beragi cloth 15 10

443 20c. Bertabur cloth 20 20

444 25c. Sukma Indra cloth . . . 25 35

445 40c. Si Pugut Bunga cloth . . 40 75

446 75c. Beragi Si Lobang Bangsi Bunga Cendera Kesuma cloth . . . . 75 1·40

MS447 150 × 204 mm. Nos. 442/6 3·00 4·25

90 Malaria-carrying Mosquito

1988. 40th Anniv of W.H.O. Multicoloured.

448 25c. Type **90** . . . . 1·10 30

449 35c. Man with insecticide spray and sample on slide 1·25 45

450 $2 Microscope and magnified malaria cells . . . . 3·00 2·00

91 Sultan and Council of Ministers

1989. 5th Anniv of National Day. Mult.

451 20c. Type **91** 15 10

452 30c. Guard of honour . . . 20 15

453 60c. Firework display (27 × 55 mm) 45 40

454 $2 Congregation in mosque 1·50 1·75

MS455 164 × 124 mm. Nos. 451/4 2·25 2·75

92 Dove escaping from Cage

1989. "Freedom of Palestine". Multicoloured.

456 20c. Type **92** 40 20

457 75c. Map and Palestinian flag 1·50 1·00

458 $1 Dome of the Rock, Jerusalem . . . . 2·25 1·40

1989. Local Fruits (3rd series). As T **85**. Mult.

459 60c. "Daemonorops fissa" . . 2·00 2·50

460 60c. "Eleiodoxa conferta" . . 2·00 2·50

461 60c. "Salacca zalacca" . . . 2·00 2·50

462 60c. "Calamus ornatus" . . . 2·00 2·50

93 Oil Pump

1989. 60th Anniv of Brunei Oil and Gas Industry. Multicoloured.

463 20c. Type **93** . . . . 2·00 30

464 60c. Loading tanker . . . . 3·50 2·25

465 90c. Oil well at sunset . . . 3·75 3·00

466 $1 Pipe laying . . . . 3·75 3·00

467 $2 Oil terminal . . . . . . 7·00 8·00

94 Museum Building and Exhibits

1990. 25th Anniv of Brunei Museum. Multicoloured.

468 30c. Type **94** . . . . 1·50 70

469 60c. Official opening, 1965 2·25 2·25

470 $1 Brunei Museum . . . . . 3·00 3·75

95 Letters from Malay Alphabet

1990. International Literacy Year. Multicoloured.

471 15c. Type **95** 80 40

472 90c. English alphabet . . . . 3·50 4·25

473 $1 Literacy Year emblem and letters . . . . 3·50 4·25

96 Tarsier in Tree

97 Symbolic Family

1990. Endangered Species. Western Tarsier. Multicoloured.

474 20c. Western Tarsier on branch . . . . 1·25 45

475 60c. Western Tarsier feeding 2·50 3·00

476 90c. Type **96** . . . . 3·50 4·50

1990. Worldwide Campaign against AIDS. Multicoloured.

477 20c. Type **97** . . . . 2·25 60

478 30c. Sources of infection . . 3·00 2·00

479 90c. "AIDS" headstone surrounded by skulls . . . 7·50 8·00

1990. Local Fruits (4th series). As T **85**. Mult.

480 60c. "Willoughbea sp." (brown fruit) . . . . . . 2·75 3·75

481 60c. Ripe "Willoughbea sp." (yellow fruit) . . . . . . 2·75 3·75

482 60c. "Willoughbea angustifolia" . . . . . . 2·75 3·75

98 Proboscis Monkey on Ground

1991. Endangered Species. Proboscis Monkey. Multicoloured.

483 15c. Type **98** . . . . 1·50 60

484 20c. Head of monkey . . . . 1·60 70

485 50c. Monkey sitting on branch . . . . 3·00 3·25

486 60c. Female monkey with baby climbing tree . . . . 3·25 3·75

99 Junior School Classes

1991. Teachers' Day. Multicoloured.

487 60c. Type **99** . . . . 2·25 2·50

488 90c. Secondary school class 2·75 3·50

100 Young Brunei Beauty

1991. Fishes. Brunei Beauty. Multicoloured

489 30c. Type **100** . . . . 1·50 85

490 60c. Female fish . . . . . . 2·50 4·00

491 $1 Male fish . . . . 3·00 4·75

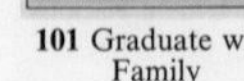

101 Graduate with Family

102 Symbolic Heart and Trace

1991. Happy Family Campaign. Multicoloured.

492 20c. Type **101** 70 50

493 60c. Mothers with children 1·75 2·00

494 90c. Family . . . . 2·00 3·25

1992. World Health Day.

495 **102** 20c. multicoloured . . . . 1·75 50

496 – 50c. multicoloured . . . . 3·25 2·50

497 – 75c. multicoloured . . . . 4·50 6·00

DESIGNS: 50c., 70c. (48 × 27 mm) Heart and heartbeat trace.

103 Map of Cable System

1992. Launching of Singapore–Borneo–Philippines Fibre Optic Submarine Cable System. Mult.

498 20c. Type **103** . . . . 2·25 50

499 30c. Diagram of Brunei connection . . . . 2·25 1·50

500 90c. Submarine cable . . . . 4·75 6·00

104 Modern Sculptures

1992. Visit A.S.E.A.N. Year. Multicoloured.

501 20c. Type **104** . . . . 2·00 2·25

502 60c. Traditional martial arts 2·25 2·75

503 $1 Modern sculptures (different) . . . . 2·50 3·00

Nos. 501/3 were printed together, se-tenant, the backgrounds forming a composite design.

105 "A.S.E.A.N. 25" and Logo

106 Sultan in Procession

1992. 25th Anniv of A.S.E.A.N (Association of South East Asian Nations). Multicoloured.

504 20c. Type **105** . . . . 1·25 65

505 60c. Headquarters building 2·75 2·75

506 90c. National landmarks . . 3·50 4·50

1992. 25th Anniv of Sultan's Accession. Mult.

507 25c. Type **106** . . . . 1·50 1·75

508 25c. Brunei International Airport . . . . 1·50 1·75

509 25c. Sultan's Palace . . . . 1·50 1·75

510 25c. Docks and Brunei University . . . . 1·50 1·75

511 25c. Mosque . . . . 1·50 1·75

Nos. 507/11 were printed together, se-tenant, forming a composite design.

107 Crested Wood Partridge

108 National Flag and "10"

1992. Birds (1st series). Multicoloured.
512 30c. Type **107** . . . . 1·00 50
513 60c. Asiatic paradise flycatcher ("Asian Paradise Flycatcher") . . . . 2·00 2·25
514 $1 Great argus pheasant . . 2·25 3·00
See also Nos. 515/17, 518/20, 575/7 and 602/5.

1993. Birds (2nd series). As T **107**. Multicoloured.
515 30c. Long-tailed parakeet . . 1·00 50
516 60c. Magpie robin . . . . . 2·00 2·25
517 $1 Blue-crowned hanging parrot ("Malay Lorikeet") 2·50 3·00

1993. Birds (3rd series). As T **107**. Multicoloured.
518 30c. Chesnut-breasted malkoha . . . . 1·25 50
519 60c. White-rumped shama . . 2·25 2·50
520 $1 Black and red broadbill (vert) . . . . 3·00 3·50

1994. 10th Anniv of National Day. Multicoloured.
521 10c. Type **108** . . . . 80 1·00
522 20c. Symbolic hands 85 85
523 30c. Previous National Day symbols 95 95
524 60c. Coat of arms . . . . . 1·25 1·50

1994. Local Fruits (5th issue). As T **85**, but each 36 × 26 mm. Multicoloured.
525 60c. "Nephelium mutabile" 85 1·40
526 60c. "Nephelium xerospermoides" . . . . . 85 1·40
527 60c. "Nephelium spp" . . . 85 1·40
528 60c. "Nephelium macrophyllum" . . . . . 85 1·40

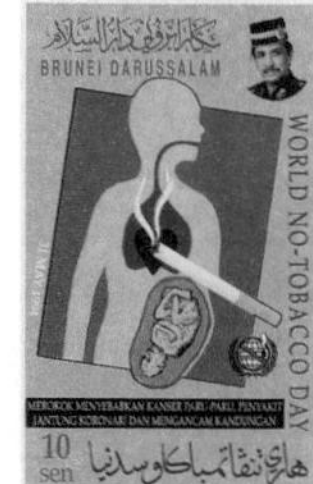
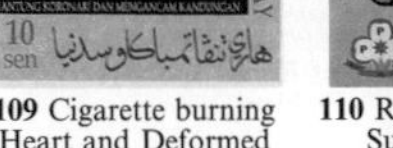

109 Cigarette burning Heart and Deformed Baby in Womb

110 Raja Isteri (wife of Sultan in Guide uniform)

1994. World No Tobacco Day. Multicoloured.
529 10c. Type **109** 25 20
530 15c. Symbols of smoking over crowd of people . . . 25 20
531 $2 Globe crushing cigarettes 2·75 4·50

1994. 40th Anniv of Brunei Girl Guides' Association. Multicoloured.
532 40c. Type **110** . . . . 1·40 1·50
533 40c. Guide receiving award 1·40 1·50
534 40c. Guide reading . . . . . 1·40 1·50
535 40c. Group of guides . . . . 1·40 1·50
536 40c. Guides erecting tent . . 1·40 1·50

111 Turbo-prop Airliner on Runway

1994. 20th Anniv of Royal Brunei Airlines. Multicoloured.
537 10c. Type **111** 55 30
538 20c. Jet airliner on runway 85 35
539 $1 Jet airliner in the air . . . 2·00 3·50

112 Malay Family

1994. International Day against Drug Abuse and Trafficking. Multicoloured.
540 20c. Type **112** . . . . 80 1·40
541 60c. Chinese family . . . . . 1·25 1·75
542 $1 Doctor, police officers and members of youth organizations . . . . . . 1·60 2·25
Nos. 540/2 were printed together, se-tenant, forming a composite design.

113 Aerial View of City, 1970

1995. 25th Anniv of Bandar Seri Begawan. Mult.
543 30c. Type **113** . . . . 1·00 45
544 50c. City in 1980 . . . . . . 1·50 1·50
545 $1 City in 1990 . . . . . . 2·25 3·00

114 United Nations General Assembly

115 Students in Laboratory

1995. 50th Anniv of United Nations. Multicoloured.
546 20c. Type **114** 40 25
547 60c. Security Council in session 75 80
548 90c. United Nations Building, New York (27 × 44 mm) 1·25 2·25

1995. 10th Anniv of University of Brunei. Mult.
549 30c. Type **115** 45 35
550 50c. University building . . . 70 70
551 90c. Sultan visiting University 1·25 2·25

116 Police Officers

117 Telephones

1996. 75th Anniv of Royal Brunei Police Force. Multicoloured.
552 25c. Type **116** 85 40
553 50c. Aspects of police work 1·25 1·25
554 75c. Sultan inspecting parade 2·00 3·00

1996. World Telecommunications Day. Children's Paintings. Multicoloured.
555 20c. Type **117** 50 30
556 35c. Telephone dial and aspects of telecommunications 65 45
557 $1 Globe and aspects of telecommunications . . . . 2·25 3·25

118 Sultan and Crowd

119 Sultan Hassanal Bolkiah Mu'izzaddin Waddaulah

1996. 50th Birthday of Sultan Hassanal Bolkiah Mu'izzaddin Waddaulah. Multicoloured.
558 50c. Type **118** . . . . 85 1·25
559 50c. Sultan in ceremonial dress . . . . 85 1·25
560 50c. Sultan receiving dignitaries at mosque . . . 85 1·25
561 50c. Sultan with subjects . . 85 1·25
MS562 152 × 100 mm. $1 Sultan in ceremonial dress (different) . . 1·75 2·50

1996.
563 **119** 10c. multicoloured 10 10
564 15c. multicoloured 10 15
565 20c. multicoloured 15 20
566 30c. multicoloured 20 25
567 50c. multicoloured 30 35
568 60c. multicoloured 40 45
569 75c. multicoloured 45 50
570 90c. multicoloured 55 60
571 – $1 multicoloured 65 70
572 – $2 multicoloured . . . . 1·25 1·40
573 – $5 multicoloured . . . . 3·25 3·50
574 – $10 multicoloured . . . . 6·25 6·50
DESIGN—27 × 39 mm: $1 to $10 Sultan in ceremonial robes.

121 Black-naped Tern

1996. Birds (4th series). Sea Birds. Multicoloured.
575 20c. Type **121** 75 50
576 30c. Roseate tern 75 50
577 $1 Bridled tern . . . . . . 1·75 2·75
No. 576 is inscr "ROSLATE TERN" in error.

122 "Acanthus ebracteatus"

1997. Mangrove Flowers. Multicoloured.
578 20c. Type **122** 45 25
579 30c. "Lumnitzera littorea" . . 50 35
580 $1 "Nypa fruticans" . . . . 1·40 2·50

123 "Heterocentrotus mammillatus"

1997. Marine Life. Multicoloured.
581 60c. Type **123** 60 85
582 60c. "Linckia laevigata" (starfish) 60 85
583 60c. "Oxycomanthus bennetti" (plant) 60 85
584 60c. "Bohadschia argus" (sea slug) 60 85

124 Children and Sign Language

1998. Asian and Pacific Decade of Disabled Persons, 1993–2002. Multicoloured.
585 20c. Type **124** 30 25
586 50c. Woman typing and firework display 60 75
587 $1 Disabled athletes . . . . 1·00 1·75

125 Sultan performing Ceremonial Duties

1998. 30th Anniv of Coronation of Sultan Hassanal Bolkiah Mu'izzaddin Waddaulah. Multicoloured.
588 60c. Type **125** 70 50
589 90c. Sultan on Coronation throne . . . . 1·10 1·40
590 $1 Coronation parade . . . 1·25 1·40
MS591 150 × 180 mm. Nos. 588/90 2·75 3·50

126 A.S.E.A.N. Architecture and Transport

127 Crown Prince at Desk

1998. 30th Anniv of Association of South-east Asian Nations. Multicoloured.
592 30c. Type **126** 90 90
593 30c. Map of Brunei and city scenes 90 90
594 30c. Flags of member nations 90 90

1998. Proclamation of Prince Al-Muhtadee Billah as Crown Prince. Multicoloured.
595 $1 Type **127** . . . . 1·00 1·00
596 $2 Crown Prince in military uniform . . . . 1·75 2·75
597 $3 Crown Prince's emblem 2·25 3·75
MS598 175 × 153 mm. Nos. 595/7. 5·50 7·00

128 Koran, Civil Servants and Handshake

129 Blue-eared Kingfisher

1998. 5th Anniv of Civil Service Day. Multicoloured.
599 30c. Type **128** 40 30
600 60c. Symbols of progress . . 65 65
601 90c. Civil servants at work 95 1·25

1998. Birds (5th series). Kingfishers. Multicoloured.
602 20c. Type **129** 70 50
603 30c. River kingfisher ("Common Kingfisher") . . 80 50
604 60c. White-collared kingfisher 1·25 95
605 $1 Stork-billed kingfisher . . 1·50 2·00

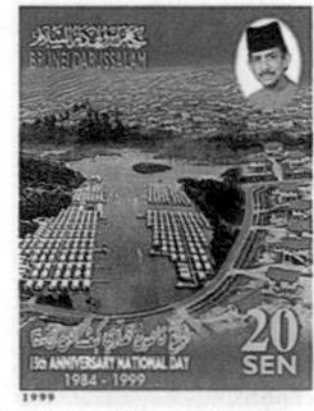

130 Water Village, Bandar Seri Begawan

1999. 15th Anniv of National Day. Multicoloured.
606 20c. Type **130** 30 20
607 60c. Modern telecommunications and air travel 80 80
608 90c. Aspects of modern Brunei . . . . 1·25 1·50
MS609 118 × 85 mm. Nos. 606/8 2·00 2·75

131 Rifle-shooting

132 Clasped Hands and Globe

1999. 20th South-east Asia Games, Brunei. Mult.
610 20c. Type **131** 45 50
611 20c. Golf and tennis 45 50
612 20c. Boxing and judo 45 50
613 20c. Squash and table tennis 45 50
614 20c. Swimming and canoe racing 45 50
615 20c. Hockey and cycling . . 45 50
616 20c. Basketball and football 45 50
617 20c. High jumping, shot putting and running . . . 45 50
618 20c. Snooker 45 50
619 20c. Bowling 45 50
MS620 110 × 73 mm. $1 Various sports . . . . 1·60 2·40

1999. 125th Anniv of Universal Postal Union. Multicoloured.
621 20c. Type **132** 40 20
622 30c. "125" and logos 50 25
623 75c. Aspects of postal service 1·10 1·50

133 Modern Building and Children using Computer

134 Sultan Mohamed Jemal-ul-Alam and Traditional Buildings, 1901–20

2000. New Millennium. Multicoloured.
624 20c. Type **133** 45 50
625 20c. Royal Palace, tree and people using computer . . 45 50
626 20c. Aerial view of mosque and factory 45 50
627 20c. Plan of Parterre Gardens 45 50
628 20c. Container ships and airliner 45 50
629 20c. Satellite dish aerials . . 45 50
MS630 221 × 121 mm. Nos. 624/9 1·75 2·25
Nos. 624/9 were printed together, se-tenant, with the backgrounds forming a composite design.

2000. Brunei in the 20th Century. Multicoloured.
631 30c. Type **134** 55 55
632 30c. Sultan Ahmed Tajudin, oil well and Brunei police, 1921–40 . . . . 55 55
633 30c. Signing of the Constitution and Brunei Mosque, 1941–60 . . . . 55 55
634 30c. Oil installation, satellite dish, Royal Brunei Airlines and bank note, 1961–80 . . 55 55
635 30c. Sultan on throne, international organisation emblems and crowd with trophy, 1981–99 . . . . . 55 55

135 Sultan Hashim Jalil-ul-Alam, 1885–1906

2000. The Sultans of Brunei. Multicoloured.
636 60c. Type **135** 90 95
637 60c. Sultan Mohamed Jemal-ul-Alam, 1906–24 . . . . 90 95
638 60c. Sultan Ahmed Tajudin, 1924–50 . . . . 90 95
639 60c. Sultan Omar Ali Saifuddin, 1950–67 . . . . 90 95
640 60c. Sultan Hassanal Bolkiah, 1967 . . . . 90 95
MS641 190 × 99 mm. Nos. 636/40 3·50 5·00

136 *Rafflesia pricei*

2000. Local Flowers. Multicoloured.
642 30c. Type **136** 45 30
643 50c. *Rhizanthes lowi* 70 70
644 60c. *Nepenthes rafflesiana* . . 80 80

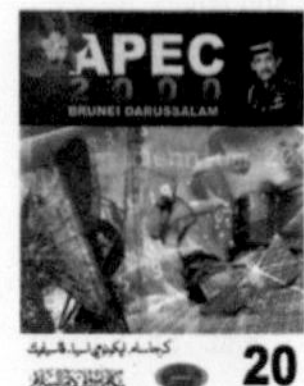

137 Information Technology

2000. Asia–Pacific Economic Cooperation. Heads of Government Meeting. Multicoloured.
645 20c. Type **137** 45 30
646 30c. Small and medium businesses 55 35
647 60c. Tourism . . . . 1·00 1·10
MS648 150 × 108 mm. Nos. 645/7 1·75 2·25

138 Green Turtle

2000. Turtles. Multicoloured.
649 30c. Type **138** 60 65
650 30c. Hawksbill turtle 60 65
651 30c. Olive Ridley turtle . . . 60 65

139 Tourist Canoe on River

2001. "Visit Brunei Year" (1st series). Multicoloured.
652 20c. Type **139** 60 45
653 30c. Traditional water village 70 45
654 60c. Carved building facade 1·50 1·50
See also Nos. 669/72.

140 Sultan in Army Uniform

141 First Aid Demonstration

2001. 55th Birthday of Sultan Hassanal Bolkiah Muizzaddin Waddaulah. Multicoloured.
655 55c. Type **140** 80 85
656 55c. Sultan in Air Force uniform 80 85
657 55c. Sultan in traditional dress 80 85
658 55c. Sultan in Army camouflage jacket 80 85
659 55c. Sultan in Navy uniform 80 85
MS660 100 × 75 mm. 55c. Sultan and Bandar Seri Begawan (40 × 71 mm) . . . . 1·25 1·50

2001. International Youth Camp. Multicoloured.
661 30c. Type **141** 60 65
662 30c. Brunei guides and tent demonstration 60 65
663 30c. Scouts with cooking pot 60 65
MS664 110 × 77 mm. Nos. 661/3 1·60 2·00
Nos. 661/3 were printed together, se-tenant, forming a composite design.

142 Islamic Regalia

2001. 1st Islamic International Exhibition, Brunei. Multicoloured.
665 20c. Type **142** 45 50
666 20c. Exhibition centre 45 50
667 20c. Computer communications 45 50
668 20c. Opening ceremony . . . 45 50

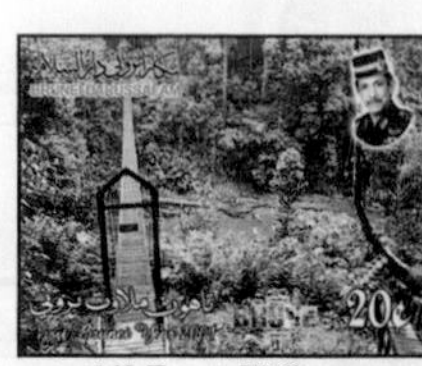

143 Forest Walkway

2001. Visit Brunei (2nd series). Multicoloured.
669 20c. Type **143** 45 50
670 20c. Waterfall 45 50
671 20c. Jerudong Theme Park 45 50
672 20c. Footbridges across lake 45 50

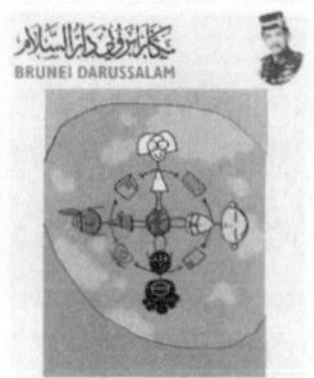

144 "Children encircling Globe" (Urska Golob)

2001. U.N. Year of Dialogue among Civilisations. Multicoloured.
673 30c. Type **144** 50 55
674 30c. Quotation marks illustrated with faces . . . 50 55
675 30c. Cubist portrait and Japanese girl 50 55
676 30c. Coloured leaves 50 55

145 Male and Female Bulwer's Pheasants

2001. Endangered Species. Bulwer's Pheasant. Mult.
677 30c. Type **145** 50 55
678 30c. Male pheasant 50 55
679 30c. Female pheasant with chicks 50 55
680 30c. Female pheasant 50 55

146 Early and Modern Telephone Systems

147 50th Anniversary Logo

2002. 50th Anniv of Department of Telecommunications (JTB). Multicoloured.
681 50c. Type **146** 50 60
682 50c. JTB Golden Jubilee emblem 50 60
683 50c. Computer networks . . 50 60

2002. 50th Anniv of Survey Department. Mult.
684 50c. Type **147** 50 60
685 50c. Survey Department Offices 50 60
686 50c. Theodolite and thermal map 50 60

148 Modern Housing, Water Village

2002. 10th Anniv of Yayasan Sultan Haji Hassanal Bolkiah Foundation. Multicoloured.
687 10c. Type **148** 30 30
688 10c. Mosque and interior . . 30 30
689 10c. School and computer class 30 30
690 10c. University of Brunei . . 30 30

149 Anti-Corruption Bureau Headquarters

2002. 20th Anniv of Anti-Corruption Bureau. Multicoloured.
691 20c. Type **149** 45 50
692 20c. Skyscrapers and mosque 45 50
693 20c. Anti-Corruption Bureau posters 45 50

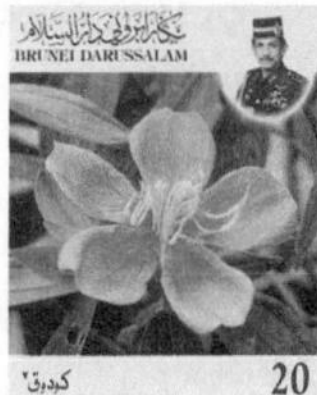

150 *Melastoma malabathricum*

2003. Flowering Medicinal Plants. Multicoloured.
694 20c. Type **150** 15 20
695 20c. *Etlingera solaris* 15 20
696 20c. *Dillenia suffruticosa* . . . 15 20
697 20c. *Costus speciosus* 15 20

151 Drums and Musicians

2003. ASEAN—Japan Exchange Year. Multicoloured.
698 20c. Type **151** 15 20
699 20c. Woodworker and handicrafts 15 20
700 20c. Exchange Year logo . . 15 20

152 Sultan of Brunei and UN Emblem

2004. 20th Anniv of National Day. Multicoloured.
701 20c. Type **152** 15 20
702 20c. In military uniform . . . 15 20
703 20c. Reading speech at National Day celebration 15 20
704 20c. Emblem 15 20
MS705 185 × 140 mm. Nos. 701/4 60 80

153 Brunei 1895 ½c. Stamp

2004. Brunei Darussalam National Philatelic Society. Multicoloured.
706 25c. Type **153** 15 20
707 25c. Magnifying glass, perforation gauge, tweezers and stamps 15 20
708 25c. Postmarks, stamp catalogue and first day covers 15 20

JAPANESE OCCUPATION OF BRUNEI

These stamps were valid throughout British Borneo (i.e. in Brunei, Labuan, North Borneo and Sarawak).

100 cents = 1 dollar.

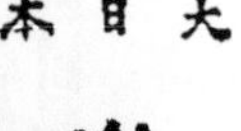

(1) ("Imperial Japanese Government")

(2) ("Imperial Japanese Postal Service $3")

1942. Stamps of Brunei optd with T **1**.
J 1 **5** 1c. black . . . . 7·00 23·00
J 2 2c. green . . . . 50·00 £110
J 3 2c. orange . . . . 4·00 9·00
J 4 3c. green . . . . 28·00 75·00
J 5 4c. orange . . . . 3·00 13·00
J 6 5c. brown . . . . 3·00 13·00

J 7	7	6c. grey	40·00	£225
J 8		6c. red	£550	£550
J 9	5	8c. black	£650	£850
J10	7	8c. red	4·50	12·00
J11	5	10c. purple on yellow	8·50	26·00
J12	7	12c. blue	26·00	26·00
J13		15c. blue	15·00	26·00
J14	5	25c. lilac	25·00	50·00
J15		30c. purple and orange	95·00	£180
J16		50c. black on green	38·00	60·00
J17		$1 black and red on blue	55·00	70·00
J18		$5 red on green	£850	£1900
J19		$25 black on red	£900	£1900

1944. No. J1 surch with T **2**.

J20	5	$3 on 1c. black	£6000	£5500

BRUNSWICK Pt. 7

Formerly a duchy of N. Germany. Joined North German Confederation in 1868.

30 silbergroschen = 1 thaler.

1

1852. Imperf.

1	1	1sg. red	£4500	£250
2		2sg. blue	£2750	£200
3		3sg. red	£2750	£200

1853. Imperf.

4	1	¼gg. black on brown	£650	£225
5		⅓gg. black	£120	£300
15		½sg. black on green	20·00	£200
7		1sg. black on buff	£325	55·00
8		2sg. black on blue	£325	55·00
11		3sg. black on red	£375	70·00

3

4

1857. Imperf

12	3	4/4gg. black on brown	35·00	85·00

1864. Rouletted

22	1	⅓gg. black	£400	£1800
23		½sg. black on green	£180	£2500
24		1sg. black on yellow	£2500	£1300
25		1sg. yellow	£325	£120
26		2sg. black on blue	£325	£300
27		3sg. pink	£650	£425

1865. Roul.

28	4	⅓g. black	24·00	£325
29		1g. red	2·00	40·00
32		2g. blue	6·75	£100
34		3g. brown	5·75	£130

BUENOS AIRES Pt. 20

A province of the Argentine Republic. Issued its own stamps from 1858 to 1862.

8 reales = 1 peso.

1 Paddle Steamer

2 Head of Liberty

1858. Imperf.

P13	1	4r. brown	£100	80·00
P17		1 (IN) p. brown	£125	80·00
P20		1 (IN) p. blue	65·00	50·00
P25		1 (TO) p. blue	£150	£100
P 1		2p. blue	90·00	50·00
P 4		3p. green	£450	£250
P 7		4p. red	£1500	£900
P10		5p. yellow	£1500	£900

1859. Imperf.

P37	2	4r. green on blue	90·00	50·00
P38		1p. blue	12·00	7·50
P45		1p. red	60·00	30·00
P43		2p. red	£120	80·00
P48		2p. blue	£120	45·00

BULGARIA Pt. 3

Formerly a Turkish province; a principality under Turkish suzerainty from 1878 to 1908, when an independent kingdom was proclaimed. A People's Republic since 1946.

1879. 100 centimes = 1 franc.
1881. 100 stotinki = 1 lev.

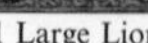
1 Large Lion

2 Large Lion

1879. Value in centimes and franc.
1 **1** 5c. black and yellow . . . . . 85·00 25·00
3 10c. black and green . . . . . £375 75·00
5 25c. black and purple . . . . £200 20·00
7 50c. black and blue . . . . . £350 80·00
8 1f. black and red . . . . . . 50·00 22·00

1881. Value in stotinki.
10 **2** 3s. red and grey . . . . . . 17·00 3·50
11 5s. black and yellow . . . . 17·00 3·50
14 10s. black and green . . . . 85·00 10·00
15 15s. red and green . . . . . 85·00 10·00
18 25s. black and purple . . . . £400 50·00
19 30s. blue and brown . . . . 17·00 10·00
See also No. 275/9.

A

B

C

D

1882.
46 **2** 1s. violet (Type A) . . . . . 12·50 5·00
48 1s. violet (Type C) 85 20
47 2s. green (Type B) . . . . . 11·50 3·75
49 2s. green (Type D) 85 20
21 3s. orange and yellow 85 35
23 5s. green . . . . 6·75 75
26 10s. red . . . . 8·50 75
28 15s. purple and mauve . . . . 6·75 50
31 25s. blue . . . . 6·75 90
33 30s. lilac and green . . . . . 7·00 85
34 50s. blue and red . . . . . . 7·00 1·00
50 1l. black and red . . . . . . 30·00 4·00

1884. Surch with large figure of value.
38 **2** 3 on 10s. red . . . . 45·00 35·00
43 5 on 30s. blue and brown . . 45·00 40·00
45 15 on 25s. blue . . . . 65·00 50·00
40 50 on 1f. black and red . . . £300 £190

7

11 Arms of Bulgaria

13 Cherry wood Cannon used against the Turks

1889.
85 **7** 1s. mauve 10 10
88 2s. grey 45 20
89 3s. brown 15 10
90 5s. green 15 10
94 10s. red 50 10
96 15s. orange 35 10
100 25s. blue 50 10
58 30s. brown . . . . 4·00 10
59 50s. green 50 10
60 1l. red 45 40
83 2l. red and pink . . . . . . 1·60 1·40
84 3l. black and buff . . . . . 3·25 2·75

1892. Surch **15**.
61 **7** 15 on 30s. brown . . . . . 8·50 70

1895. Surch **01**.
74 **2a** 01 on 2s. green (No. 49) . . 65 15

1896. Baptism of Prince Boris.
78 **11** 1s. green 35 15
79 5s. blue 35 15
81 15s. violet 45 15
82 25s. red . . . . 4·00 30

1901. Surch in figures.
101 **7** 5 on 3s. brown . . . . . . 1·60 70
103 10 on 50s. green . . . . . . 1·60 90

1901. 25th Anniv of Uprising against Turkey.
104 **13** 5s. red . . . . 1·00 85
105 15s. green . . . . 1·00 85

14 Prince Ferdinand

16 Fighting at Shipka Pass

1901.
106 **14** 1s. black and purple . . . 10 10
107 2s. blue and green 20 10
108 3s. black and orange . . . 20 10
109 5s. brown and green . . . 1·00 10
110 10s. brown and red . . . . 1·25 10
113 15s. black and lake 65 10
114 25s. black and blue 65 10
116 30s. black and brown . . . 18·00 50
117 50s. brown and blue . . . 1·00 15
118 1l. green and red . . . . . 2·00 15
120 2l. black and red . . . . . 3·75 50
123 3l. red and grey . . . . . 4·50 85

1902. 25th Anniv of Battle of Shipka Pass.
124 **16** 5s. red . . . . 1·25 50
125 10s. green . . . . 1·25 50
126 15s. blue . . . . 4·50 1·75

1903. Surch.
140 **15** 5 on 15s. black and red . . 1·25 75
141 10 on 15s. black and red 2·50 40
143 25 on 30s. black & brown 7·50 90

18 Ferdinand I in 1887 and 1907

1907. 20th Anniv of Prince Ferdinand's Accession.
132 **18** 5s. green . . . . 7·00 90
134 10s. brown . . . . 12·50 90
137 25s. blue . . . . 24·00 1·90

1909. Optd **1909**.
146 **7** 1s. mauve . . . . 1·00 45
149 5s. green . . . . 1·00 45

1909. Surch **1909** and new value.
151 **7** 5 on 30s. brown . . . . . 1·50 35
153 10 on 15s. orange . . . . . 11·50 50
156 10 on 50s. green . . . . . 1·50 55

1910. Surch **1910** and new value.
157 **14** 1 on 3s. black and orange 3·50 75
158 5 on 15s. black and lake 1·00 60

23 King Asen Tower

24 Tsar in General's Uniform

25 Veliko Turnovo

1911.
159 **23** 1s. green 10 10
182a 1s. slate 10 10
160 **24** 2s. black and red 10 10
161 **25** 3s. black and lake . . . . 1·50 25
162 – 5s. black and green . . . 60 10
181 – 5s. purple and green . . . 1·25 10
163 – 10s. black and red 55 10
181a – 10s. sepia and brown . . 10 10
164 – 15s. bistre . . . . 7·50 30
183 – 15s. olive . . . . 1·00 30
165 – 25s. black and blue . . . 30 10
166 – 30s. black and blue . . . 2·75 15
182 – 30s. brown and olive . . . 1·00 30
167 – 50s. black and yellow . . 16·00 15
168 – 1l. brown . . . . 4·25 15
169 – 2l. black and purple . . . 1·00 60
170 – 3l. black and violet . . . 9·00 2·75
DESIGNS—VERT: 5, 10, 25s., 1l. Portraits of Tsar Ferdinand. HORIZ: 15s. R. Isker; 30s. Rila Monastery; 50s. Tsars and Princes (after Ya. Veshin); 2l. Monastery of the Holy Trinity, Veliko Turnovo; 3l. Varna.
See also Nos. 229/30 and 236/7.

35 Tsar Ferdinand

1912. Tsar's Silver Jubilee
171 **35** 5s. grey . . . . 2·25 65
172 10s. red . . . . 3·50 1·25
173 25s. blue . . . . 4·50 1·90

ОСВОБ. ВОЙНА
1912-1913
(36) "War of Liberation" 1912–13

3
СТОТИНКИ
(37a)

1913. Victory over Turks. Stamps of 1911 optd as T **36**.
174 **23** 1s. green 25 10
175 **24** 2s. black and red 25 10
176 **25** 3s. black and lake 90 40
177 – 5s. black and green 25 10
178 – 10s. black and red 30 10
179 – 15s. bistre . . . . 2·75 75
180 – 25s. black and blue . . . . 1·75 40

1915. No. 165 surch **10 CT.** and bar.
180a – 10s. on 25s. blk & blue . . 45 10

1916. Red Cross Fund. Surch with T **37a**.
185 **7** 3s. on 1s. mauve . . . . . 5·00 5·75

45 Veles

46 Bulgarian Ploughman

38

39 Bulgarian Peasant

1917. Liberation of Macedonia.
193 **45** 1s. grey 10 10
194 **46** 1s. green 10 10
195 – 5s. green 10 10
186 **38** 5s. green 45 20
187 **39** 15s. grey 15 15
188 – 25s. blue 15 15
189 – 30s. orange 15 20
190 – 50s. violet 45 30
191 – 2l. brown 50 30
192 – 3l. red 75 45
DESIGNS—As Type **45**: 5s. Monastery of St. John, Ohrid. As Type **38**: 25s. Soldier and Mt. Sonichka; 50s. Ohrid and Lake. As Type **39**: 30s. Nish. 2l. Demir Kapija; 3l. Gevgeli.

48 Tsar Ferdinand

1918. 30th Anniv of Tsar's Accession.
196 **48** 1s. slate 10 10
197 2s. brown 10 10
198 3s. blue 25 20
199 10s. red 25 20

49 Parliament Building

50 King Boris III

1919.
201 **49** 1s. black 10 10
202 2s. olive 10 10

1919. 1st Anniv of Enthronement of King Boris III.
203 **50** 3s. red 10 10
204 5s. green 10 10
205 10s. red 10 10
206 15s. violet 10 10
207 25s. blue 10 10
208 30s. brown 10 10
209 50s. brown 10 10

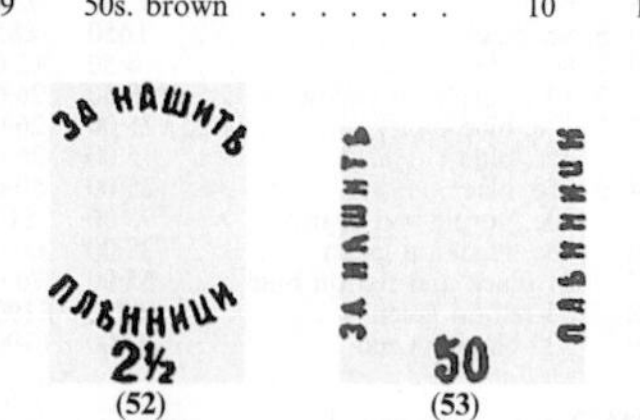

(52) (53)

1920. Prisoners of War Fund. Surch as T **52/53**.
210 **49** 1 on 2s. olive 10 10
211 **50** 2½ on 5s. green 10 10
212 5 on 10s. red 10 10
213 7½ on 15s. violet 10 10
214 12½ on 25s. blue 10 10
215 15 on 30s. brown 10 10
216 25 on 50s. brown 10 10
217 – 50 on 1l. brown (No. 168) 10 10
218 – 1 on 2l. brown (No. 191) 15 15
219 – 1½ on 3l. red (No. 192) . . 30 35

54 Vazov's Birthplace at Sopot and Cherry-wood Cannon

55 "The Bear-fighter", character from "Under the Yoke"

1920. 70th Birth Anniv of Ivan Vazov (writer).
220 **54** 30s. red 10 10
221 **55** 50s. green 10 10
222 – 1l. sepia 20 15
223 – 2l. brown 60 40
224 – 3l. violet 75 60
225 – 5l. blue 95 75
DESIGNS—HORIZ: 1l. Ivan Vazov in 1870 and 1920; 3l. Vazov's Houses in Plovdiv and Sofia. VERT: 2l. Vazov; 5l. Father Paisii Khilendarski (historian).

59 Aleksandr Nevski Cathedral, Sofia

62 King Boris III

1921.
226 **59** 10s. violet 10 10
227 – 20s. green 10 10
228 **62** 25s. blue 10 10
229 **25** 50s. orange 75 20
230 50s. blue . . . . 8·50 2·50
231 – 75s. violet 10 10
232 – 75s. blue 20 10
233 **62** 1l. red 15 10
234 1l. blue 10 10
235 – 2l. brown 25 10
236 – 3l. purple 45 10
237 – 5l. blue . . . . 2·00 30
238 **62** 10l. red . . . . 6·75 2·25
DESIGNS—HORIZ: 20s. Alexander II "The Liberator" Monument, Sofia; 75s. Shipka Pass Monastery; 5l. Rila Monastery. VERT: 2l. Harvester; 3l. King Asen Tower.

66 Tsar Ferdinand and Map

68 Mt. Shar

1921.
239 **66** 10s. red 10 10
240 – 10s. red 10 10
241 **68** 10s. red 10 10
242 – 10s. mauve 15 10
243 – 20s. blue 45 10
DESIGNS—VERT: No. 240, Tsar Ferdinand. HORIZ: No. 242, Bridge over Vardar, at Skopje; 243, St. Clement's Monastery, Ohrid.

71 Bourchier in Bulgarian Costume

72 J. D. Bourchier

73 Rila Monastery, Bourchier's Resting-place

1921. James Bourchier ("Times" Correspondent) Commemoration.
244 **71** 10s. red 10 10
245 20s. orange 10 10
246 **72** 30s. grey 10 10
247 50s. lilac 10 10
248 1l. purple 20 10
249 **73** 1½l. green 20 20
250 2l. green 20 10
251 3l. blue 45 20
252 5l. red 75 30

1924. Surch.
253 **49** 10s. on 1s. black 10 10
254 **D 37** 10s. on 20s. orange . . 10 10
255 20s. on 5s. green . . . 5·00 5·00
256 20s. on 10s. violet . . . 1·40 1·40
257 20s. on 30s. orange . . 10 10
258 **50** 1l. on 5s. green 15 10
259 **25** 3l. on 50s. blue . . . . 1·10 40
260 **62** 6l. on 1l. red 50 30

77

78

79 King Boris III

81 Aleksandr Nevski Cathedral, Sofia

82 Harvesters

83 Proposed Rest-home, Verona

1925.
261 **77** 10s. blue & red on rose 10 10
262 15s. orange & red on blue 10 10
263 30s. buff and black . . . 10 10
264 **78** 50s. brown on green . . . 15 10
265 **79** 1l. olive 35 10
266 1l. green 50 10
267 **81** 2l. green and buff 85 10
267a **79** 2l. brown 40 10
268 **82** 4l. red and yellow 75 10

1925. Sunday Delivery Stamps.
268b **83** 1l. black on green . . . . 2·75 15
268c 1l. brown . . . . 2·50 15
268d 1l. orange . . . . 3·50 15
268e 1l. pink . . . . 3·50 15
268f 1l. violet on red . . . . . 3·50 15
268g – 2l. green 40 15
268h – 2l. violet 40 20
268i – 5l. blue . . . . 3·75 45
268j – 5l. red . . . . 4·00 45
DESIGN: 2, 5l., Proposed Sanatorium, Bankya.

85 St. Nedelya's Cathedral, Sofia after Bomb Outrage

86 C. Botev (poet)

1926.
269 **85** 50s. black 10 10

1926. Botev Commemoration.
270 **86** 1l. green 30 15
271 2l. blue 65 15
272 4l. red 65 50

87

89 King Boris III

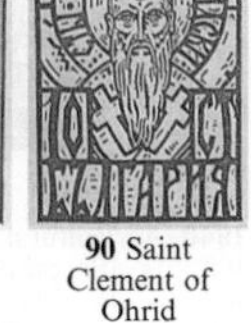
90 Saint Clement of Ohrid

1926.
273 **87** 6l. olive and blue 75 20
274 10l. brown and sepia . . . 3·00 75

1927. As T **2** in new colours.
275 10s. red and green 10 10
276 15s. black and yellow 15 10
277 30s. slate and buff 10 10
278 30s. blue and buff 15 10
279 50s. black and red 15 10

1927. Air. Various stamps optd with Albatros biplane and No. 281 surch **1l** also.
281 **87** 1l. on 6l. green and blue 1·60 1·60
282 **79** 2l. brown . . . . 1·60 1·60
283 **82** 4l. red and yellow . . . . 2·75 2·00
284 **87** 10l. orange and brown . . 50·00 30·00

1928.
285 **89** 1l. green 75 10
286 2l. brown . . . . 1·25 10

1929. 50th Anniv of Liberation of Bulgaria and Millenary of Tsar Simeon.
287 **90** 10s. violet 15 10
288 – 15s. purple 15 10
289 – 30s. red 15 10
290 – 50s. green 25 10
291 – 1l. red 70 10
292 – 2l. blue 95 15
293 – 3l. green . . . . 2·10 50
294 – 4l. brown . . . . 3·00 25
295 – 5l. brown 95 55
296 – 6l. blue . . . . 2·75 1·25
PORTRAITS—23½ × 33½ mm: 15s. Konstantin Miladinov (poet and folklorist); 1l. Father Paisii Khilendarski (historian); 2l. Tsar Simeon; 4l. Vasil Levski (revolutionary); 5l. Georgi Benkovski (revolutionary); 6l. Tsar Alexander II of Russia, "The Liberator". 19 × 28½ mm: 30s. Georgi Rakovski (writer). 19 × 26 mm: 3l. Lyuben Karavelov (journalist).

98 Convalescent Home, Varna

1930. Sunday Delivery stamps.
297 **98** 1l. green and purple . . . 5·00 15
298 1l. yellow and green . . . 50 15
299 1l. brown and red 50 15

99

101 King Boris III

1930. Wedding of King Boris and Princess Giovanna of Italy.
300 **99** 1l. green 20 20
301 – 2l. purple 35 20
302 **99** 4l. red 35 30
303 – 6l. blue 45 35
DESIGN: 2, 6l. Portraits in separate ovals.

1931.
304a **101** 1l. green (A) 15 10
305 2l. red (A) 50 10
306 4l. orange (A) 30 10
308a 4l. orange (B) 70 10
307 6l. blue (A) 35 10
308b 6l. blue (B) 70 10
308c 7l. blue (B) 25 20
308d 10l. slate (B) . . . . . . 10·00 55
308 12l. brown (A) 45 10
308e 14l. brown (B) 35 20
308f – 20l. brown & pur (B) . . 85 60
(A) Without coloured frame-lines at top and bottom; (B) with frame-lines.
The 20l. is 24½ × 33½ mm.

103 Gymnastics

1831. Balkan Olympic Games.
309 **103** 1l. green 60 60
326 1l. turquoise . . . . . . 2·25 1·75
310 – 2l. red . . . . 1·10 60
327 – 2l. blue . . . . 3·00 1·75
311 – 4l. red . . . . 1·75 75
328 – 4l. purple . . . . 4·00 1·75
312 – 6l. green . . . . 4·75 1·50
329 – 6l. red . . . . 8·00 3·50
313 – 10l. red . . . . 10·00 5·00
330 – 10l. brown . . . . 45·00 20·00
314 – 12l. blue . . . . 45·00 10·50
331 – 12l. red . . . . 75·00 40·00
315 – 50l. brown . . . . 35·00 30·00
332 – 50l. red £225 £200
DESIGNS—VERT (23 × 28 mm): 2l. Footballer; 4l. Horse-riding. As Type **103**—HORIZ: 6l. Fencing; 10l. Cycling. VERT: 12l. Diving; 50l. Spirit of Victory.

108

109 Rila Monastery

1931. Air.
316 **108** 1l. green 25 10
316a 1l. purple 10 10
317 2l. purple 25 10
317a 2l. green 15 10
318 6l. blue 35 20
318a 6l. red 40 20
319 12l. red 60 25
319a 12l. blue 50 30
320 20l. violet 60 40
321 30l. orange . . . . 1·25 75
322 50l. brown . . . . 1·50 95

1932. Air.
323 **109** 18l. green . . . . 55·00 40·00
324 24l. red . . . . 50·00 35·00
325 28l. blue . . . . 35·00 24·00

1934. Surch **2**.
333 **101** 2 on 3l. olive . . . . . . 3·75 35

111 Defending the Pass

113 Convalescent Home, Troyan

1934. Unveiling of Shipka Pass Memorial.
334 **111** 1l. green 45 50
340 1l. green 45 50
335 – 2l. red 45 20
341 – 2l. orange 45 20
336 – 3l. brown . . . . 1·50 1·50
342 – 3l. yellow . . . . 1·50 1·50
337 – 4l. red . . . . 1·25 40
343 – 4l. red . . . . 1·25 40
338 – 7l. blue . . . . 2·25 1·75
344 – 7l. light blue . . . . . . 2·25 1·75
339 – 14l. purple . . . . 7·50 7·50
345 – 14l. bistre . . . . 7·50 7·50
DESIGNS—VERT: 2l. Shipka Memorial; 3, 7l. Veteran standard-bearer; 14l. Widow showing memorial to orphans. HORIZ: 4l. Bulgarian veteran.

1935. Sunday Delivery stamps.
346 **113** 1l. red and brown 45 10
347 1l. blue and green 45 10
348 – 5l. blue and red . . . . 1·75 60
DESIGN: 5l. Convalescent Home, Bakya.

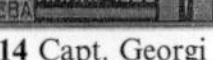
114 Capt. Georgi Mamarchef

115 Aleksandr Nevski Cathedral, Sofia

1935. Centenary of Turnovo Insurrection.
349 – 1l. blue 85 35
350 **114** 2l. purple 85 60
DESIGN: 1l. Velcho Atanasov Dzhamdzhiyata.

1935. 5th Balkan Football Tournament.
351 – 1l. green . . . . 1·60 1·50
352 **115** 2l. grey . . . . 3·00 2·50
353 – 4l. red . . . . 5·50 4·00
354 – 7l. blue . . . . 12·50 9·00
355 – 14l. orange . . . . 10·00 8·00
356 – 50l. brown £140 £150
DESIGNS—HORIZ: 1l. Match in progress at Yunak Stadium, Sofia; 4l. Footballers. VERT: 7l. Herald and Balkan map; 14l. Footballer and trophy; 50l. Trophy.

116 Girl Gymnast

117 Janos Hunyadi

1935. 8th Bulgarian Gymnastic Tournament. Dated "12–14. VII. 1935".
357 – 1l. green . . . . 1·75 2·00
358 – 2l. blue . . . . 2·50 2·00
359 **116** 4l. red . . . . 6·00 5·00
360 – 7l. blue . . . . 6·50 6·50
361 – 14l. brown . . . . 6·50 7·00
362 – 50l. orange . . . . 90·00 £100
DESIGNS—VERT: 1l. Parallel bars; 2l. Male gymnast in uniform; 7l. Pole vault; 50l. Athlete and lion. HORIZ: 14l. Yunak Stadium, Sofia.

1935. Unveiling of Monument to Ladislas III of Poland at Varna. Inscr "WARNEN CZYK(A)", etc.
363 **117** 1l. orange 75 45
364 – 2l. red . . . . 2·25 60
365 – 4l. red . . . . 9·00 4·50
366 – 7l. blue . . . . 1·75 1·40
367 – 14l. green . . . . 1·75 1·10
DESIGNS—VERT: 2l. King Ladislas of Hungary enthroned (22 × 32 mm); 7l. King Ladislas in armour (20 × 31 mm). HORIZ: 4l. Varna Memorial (33 × 24 mm); 14l. Battle scene (30 × 25 mm).

118 Dimitur

119

120

1935. 67th Death Anniv of Khadzhi Dimitur (revolutionary).
368 – 1l. green . . . . 1·75 55
369 **118** 2l. brown . . . . 2·25 1·10
370 – 4l. red . . . . 5·00 3·25
371 – 7l. blue . . . . 6·50 5·00
372 – 14l. orange . . . . 6·50 6·00
DESIGNS—VERT: 1l. Dimitur's monument at Sliven; 7l. Revolutionary group (dated 1868). HORIZ: 4l. Dimitur and Stefan Karadzha (revolutionary); 14l. Dimitur's birthplace at Sliven.

1936.
373 **119** 10s. red 10 10
373a 15s. green 10 10
374 **120** 30s. red 10 10
374a 30s. brown 10 10
374b 30s. blue 10 10
375 50s. blue 10 10
375a 50s. red 10 10
375b 50s. green 10 10

121 Nesebur

122 St. Cyril and St. Methodius

1936. Slav Geographical and Ethnographical Congress, Sofia.
376 – 1l. violet . . . . 1·00 1·50
377 – 2l. blue . . . . 1·00 1·25
378 **121** 7l. blue . . . . 3·25 2·50
DESIGNS—25 × 34 mm: 1l. Meteorological Bureau, Mt. Musala; 23 × 34 mm: 2l. Peasant girl.

1937. Millenary of Introduction of Cyrillic Alphabet and Slavonic Liturgy.
379 **122** 1l. green 35 15
380 2l. purple 35 15
381 – 4l. red 45 15
382 **122** 7l. blue . . . . 1·50 1·10
383 – 14l. red . . . . 1·50 1·25
DESIGN: 4., 14l. The Saints Preaching.

124 Princess Marie Louise

125 King Boris III

1937.
384 **124** 1l. green 35 10
385 2l. red 40 15
386 4l. red 40 20

1937. 19th Anniv of Accession.
387 **125** 2l. red 30 30

126 Harvesting **129** Prince Simeon

1938. Agricultural Products.
388 **126** 10s. orange 10 10
389 10s. red 10 10
390 – 15s. red 30 10
391 – 15s. purple 30 10
392 – 30s. brown 15 10
393 – 30s. brown 15 10
394 – 50s. blue 55 10
395 – 50s. black 55 10
396 – 1l. green 60 10
397 – 1l. green 60 10
398 – 2l. red 55 10
399 – 2l. brown 55 10
400 – 3l. purple . . . . . . 1·10 35
401 – 3l. purple . . . . . . 1·10 35
402 – 4l. brown 70 20
403 – 4l. purple 70 20
404 – 7l. violet . . . . . . 1·40 55
405 – 7l. blue . . . . 1·40 55
406 – 14l. brown . . . . . . 2·25 1·40
407 – 14l. brown . . . . . . 2·25 1·40
DESIGNS—VERT: 15s. Sunflower; 30s. Wheat; 50s. Chickens and eggs; 1l. Grapes; 3l. Strawberries; 4l. Girl carrying grapes; 7l. Roses; 14l. Tobacco leaves. HORIZ: 2l. "Attar of Roses".

1938. 1st Birthday of Heir Apparent.
408 **129** 1l. green 10 10
409 2l. red 15 10
410 – 4l. red 20 10
411 **129** 7l. blue 80 35
412 – 14l. brown 80 35
DESIGN: 4, 14l. Another portrait.

131 King Boris III

132 First Locomotive in Bulgaria, 1866

1938. 20th Anniv of King's Accession. Portraits of King in various uniforms.
413 **131** 1l. green 10 10
414 – 2l. red 75 10
415 – 4l. brown 10 10
416 – 7l. blue 30 30
417 – 14l. mauve 30 30

1939. 50th Anniv of Bulgarian State Railways. Locomotive types dated "1888–1938".
418 **132** 1l. green 55 50
419 – 2l. brown 70 50
420 – 4l. orange . . . . . . 2·00 80
421 – 7l. blue . . . . 7·25 6·50
DESIGNS: 2l. Class 01 steam locomotive; 4l. Train crossing viaduct; 7l. King Boris as engine-driver.

133 P.O. Emblem

135 Gymnast

1939. 60th Anniv of Bulgarian P.O. Inscr "1879 1939".
422 **133** 1l. green 15 10
423 – 2l. red (G.P.O., Sofia) . . 20 10

1939. Yunak Gymnastic Society's Rally, Sofia.
424 **135** 1l. green 25 15
425 – 2l. red 25 15
426 – 4l. brown 40 15
427 – 7l. blue . . . . 1·40 60
428 – 14l. mauve . . . . . . 6·00 4·50
DESIGNS: 2l. Yunak badge; 4l. "The Discus-thrower" (statue by Miron); 7l. Rhythmic dancer; 14l. Athlete holding weight aloft.

Наводнението
1939
1+1
лева
(**136**) ("Inundation 1939")

1939. Sevlievo and Turnovo Floods Relief Fund. Surch as T **136** and value.
429 **39** 1l.+1l. on 15s. grey 15 15
430 **73** 2l.+1l. on 1½l. olive 15 15
431 4l.+2l. on 2l. green 20 20
432 7l.+4l. on 3l. blue 55 55
433 14l.+7l. on 5l. red . . . . 1·10 1·10

137 Mail Plane

138 King Boris III

1940. Air.
434 **137** 1l. green 15 10
435 – 2l. red . . . . 2·10 10
436 – 4l. orange 20 10
437 – 6l. blue 25 15
438 – 10l. brown . . . . 3·75 1·25
439 – 12l. brown . . . . 1·00 35
440 16l. violet . . . . . . 1·10 55
441 – 19l. blue . . . . 1·25 75
442 – 30l. mauve . . . . . . 1·90 1·10
443 – 45l. violet . . . . . . 4·75 2·25
444 – 70l. red . . . . 5·00 2·75
445 – 100l. blue . . . . . . 12·00 8·00
DESIGNS—VERT: Aircraft over: King Asen's Tower (2l.), Bachovo Monastery (4l.), Aleksandr Nevski Cathedral, Sofia (45l.), Shipka Pass Memorial (70l.); 10l. Airplane, mail train and express motor cycle; 30l. Airplane and swallow; 100l. Airplane and Royal cypher. HORIZ: 6l. Loading mails at aerodrome. Aircraft over: Sofia Palace (12l.), Mt. El Tepe (16l.), Rila Lakes and mountains (19l.).

1940.
445a **138** 1l. green 15 10
446 2l. red 30 10

139 First Bulgarian Postage Stamp

1940. Cent of 1st Adhesive Postage Stamp.
447 **139** 10l. olive . . . . 1·50 1·25
448 – 20l. blue . . . . 1·50 1·25
DESIGN: 20l. has scroll dated "1840–1940".

140 Grapes

142 King Boris III

141 Ploughing

1940.
449 **140** 10s. orange 10 10
450 – 15s. blue 10 10
451 **141** 30s. brown 10 10
452 – 50s. violet 10 10
452a – 50s. green 10 10
453 **142** 1l. green 10 10
454 2l. red 10 10
455 4l. orange 10 10
456 6l. violet 20 10
457 7l. blue 25 10
458 10l. green 25 10
DESIGNS—VERT: 15s. Beehive. HORIZ: 50s. Shepherd and flock.

143 Peasant Couple and King Boris

144 King Boris and Map of Dobrudja

1940. Recovery of Dobrudja from Rumania. Designs incorporating miniature portrait of King Boris.
464 **143** 1l. green 15 10
465 – 2l. red 15 10
466 **144** 4l. brown 15 10
467 7l. blue 55 30
DESIGN—VERT: 2l. Bulgarian flags and wheat-field.

145 Bee-keeping

1940. Agricultural Scenes.
468 – 10s. purple 10 10
469 – 10s. blue 10 10
470 – 15s. green 10 10
471 – 15s. olive 10 10
472 **145** 30s. orange 10 10
473 30s. green 10 10
474 – 50s. violet 10 10
475 – 50s. purple 10 10
476 – 3l. brown 55 10
477 – 3l. black 60 40
478 – 5l. brown . . . . . . 1·25 50
479 – 5l. blue 75 40
DESIGNS: 10s. Threshing; 15s. Ploughing with oxen; 50s. Picking apples; 3l. Shepherd; 5l. Cattle.

146 Pencko Slaveikov (poet)

147 St. Ivan Rilski

1940. National Relief.
480 **146** 1l. green 10 10
481 – 2l. red 15 10
482 **147** 3l. brown 15 10
483 – 4l. orange 15 10
484 – 7l. blue . . . . 1·00 75
485 – 10l. brown . . . . . . 2·00 75
DESIGNS: 2l. Bishop Sofronii of Vratsa; 4l. Marin Drinov (historian); 7l. Chernorisets Khratur (monk); 10l. Kolo Ficheto (writer).

148 Johannes Gutenberg

149 Nikola Karastoyanov

1940. 500th Anniv of Invention of Printing and Centenary of Bulgarian Printing.
486 **148** 1l. green 15 10
487 **149** 2l. brown 15 10

150 Botev

151 Arrival in Koslodui

1941. 65th Death Anniv of Khristo Botev (poet and revolutionary).
488 **150** 1l. green 10 10
489 **151** 2l. red 15 10
490 – 3l. brown 55 35
DESIGN—VERT: 3l. Botev Memorial Cross.

152 National History Museum

1941. Buildings in Sofia.
491 **152** 14l. brown 95 60
492 – 20l. green 35 15
493 – 50l. blue . . . . 1·75 1·25
DESIGNS: 20l. Tsarita Icanna Workers' Hospital; 50l. National Bank.

153 Thasos Island **154** Ohrid

1941. Reacquisition of Macedonia.
494 – 1l. green 10 10
495 **153** 2l. orange 10 10
496 – 2l. red 10 10
497 – 4l. brown 15 10
498 **154** 7l. blue 45 30
DESIGNS—VERT: 1l. Macedonian girl. HORIZ: 2l. (No. 496) King Boris and map dated "1941"; 4l. Poganovski Monastery.

155 Children on Beach

1942. Sunday Delivery. Inscr as in T **155**.
499 – 1l. green 10 10
500 **155** 2l. orange 10 10
501 – 5l. blue 30 25
DESIGNS: 1l. St. Konstantin Sanatorium, Varna; 5l. Sun-bathing terrace, Bankya.

156 Bugler at Camp

157 Folk Dancers

1942. "Work and Joy". Inscr as at foot of T **157**.
502 – 1l. green 10 10
503 – 2l. red 15 10
504 – 4l. black 15 10
505 **156** 7l. blue 20 10
506 **157** 14l. brown 35 20
DESIGNS—VERT: 1l. Guitarist and accordion player; 2l. Camp orchestra; 4l. Hoisting the flag.

158 Wounded Soldier

159 Queen visiting Wounded

1942. War Invalids. Inscr as T **158/9**.
507 **158** 1l. green 10 10
508 – 2l. red 10 10
509 – 4l. orange 10 10
510 – 7l. blue 10 10
511 – 14l. brown 10 10
512 **159** 20l. black 30 10
DESIGNS—HORIZ: 2l. Soldier and family; 4l. First aid on battlefield; 7l. Widow and orphans at grave; 14l. Unknown Soldiers Memorial.

160 Khan Kubrat (ruled 595–642)

161 King Boris III

1942. Historical series.
513 **160** 10s. black 10 10
514 – 15s. blue 10 10
515 – 30s. mauve 10 10
516 – 50s. blue 10 10
517 – 1l. green 10 10
518 – 2l. red 10 10
519 – 3l. brown 10 10
520 – 4l. orange 10 10
521 – 5l. green 15 10
522 – 7l. blue 15 10
523 – 10l. black 15 10
524 – 14l. olive 15 10
525 – 20l. brown 50 20
526 – 30l. black 90 30
DESIGNS: 15s. Cavalry charge (Khan as parukh, 680–701); 30s. Equestrian statue of Khan Krum (803–814); 50s. Baptism of King Boris I; 1l. St. Naum's School; 2l. King Boris crowns his son, Tsar Simeon; 3l. Golden Era of Bulgarian literature; 4l. Trial of Bogomil Vasilii; 5l. Proclamation of Second Bulgarian Empire; 7l. Ivan Asen II (1214–81) at Tebizond; 10l. Expulsion of Eutimil Patriarch of Turnovo; 14l. Wandering minstrels; 20l. Father Paisii Khilendarski (historian); 30l. Shipka Pass Memorial.

1944. King Boris Mourning Issue. Portraits dated "1894–1943". Perf or imperf.
527 **161** 1l. olive 10 10
528 – 2l. brown 15 15
529 – 4l. brown 15 15
530 – 5l. violet 35 35
531 – 7l. blue 35 35

163 King Simeon II

ВСИЧКО
ЗА
ФРОНТА
(164)

1944.
532 **163** 3l. orange 10 10

1945. "All for the Front". Parcel Post stamps optd as T **164** or surch also.
533 P **163** 1l. red 10 10
534 4l. on 1l. red 10 10
535 7l. purple 10 10
536 20l. brown 15 10
537 30l. purple 15 10
538 50l. orange 40 20
539 100l. blue 70 45

1945. Air. Optd with airplane or surch also.
540 **142** 1l. green 10 10
541 4l. orange 15 10
542 P **163** 10l. on 100l. yellow . . 30 15
543 45l. on 100l. yellow . . 35 15
544 75l. on 100l. yellow . . 55 30
545 100l. yellow 85 40
Nos. 540/1 are perf; the rest imperf.

167

1945. Slav Congress. Perf or imperf.
546 **167** 4l. red 10 10
547 10l. blue 10 10
548 50l. red 30 30

СЪБИРАЙТЕ
ВСЪКАКВИ
ПАРЦАЛИ
(**168**) "Collect All Rags"

СЪБИРАЙТЕ
СТАРО
ЖЕЛЬЗО
(**169**) "Collect Old Iron"

СЪБИРАЙТЕ
ХАРТИЕНИ
ОТПАДЪЦИ
(**170**) "Collect Wastepaper"

1945. Salvage Campaign. Nos. 457/9 optd with T **168/70**.
549 **142** 1l. green 15 10
550 2l. red 50 10
551 4l. orange 30 10
Prices are the same for these stamps with any one of the overprints illustrated.

171 Lion Rampant

172

1945. Lion Rampant, in various frames.
552 – 30s. green 10 10
553 – 50s. blue 10 10
554 **171** 1l. green 10 10
555 – 2l. brown 10 10
556 – 4l. blue 10 10
557 – 5l. violet 10 10
558 **172** 9l. grey 10 10
559 – 10l. blue 10 10
560 – 15l. brown 20 10
561 – 20l. black 20 10
562 – 20l. red 20 10

173 Chain-breaker

174 "VE Day"

1945. Liberty Loan. Imperf.
563 **173** 50l. orange 15 10
564 50l. lake 15 10
565 – 100l. blue 20 10
566 – 100l. brown 20 10
567 – 150l. red 45 20
568 – 150l. green 45 20
569 – 200l. olive 75 60
570 – 200l. blue 75 60
MS570a Two blocks 88 × 123 mm, with the four values imperf (a) in brown-red and (b) in violet. Pair 6·00 6·00
DESIGNS: 100l. Hand holding coin; 150l. Water-mill; 200l. Coin and symbols of industry and agriculture.

1945. "Victory in Europe".
571 **174** 10l. green and brown . . 10 10
572 50l. green and red 30 10

175

176

1945. 1st Anniv of Fatherland Front Coalition.
573 **175** 1l. olive 10 10
574 4l. blue 10 10
575 5l. mauve 10 10
576 **176** 10l. blue 10 10
577 20l. red 15 10
578 **175** 50l. green 30 20
579 100l. brown 50 30

177 Refugee Children

178 Red Cross Train

1946. Red Cross. Cross in red.
580 **177** 2l. olive 10 10
645d 2l. brown 10 10
581 – 4l. violet 10 10
645e – 4l. black 10 10
582 **177** 10l. purple 10 10
645f 10l. green 15 10
583 – 20l. dark blue 15 10
645g – 20l. light blue 25 15
584 – 30l. brown 15 15
645h – 30l. green 35 25
585 **178** 35l. black . . . . 2·25 1·50
645i 35l. green . . . . 1·75 1·10
586 – 50l. purple 35 25
645j – 50l. lake 70 45
587 **178** 100l. brown . . . . . . 4·25 2·75
645k 100l. blue . . . . 3·50 2·00
DESIGNS—HORIZ: 4l., 20l. Soldier on stretcher. VERT: 30l., 50l. Nurse and wounded soldier.

179 Postal Savings Emblem

180 Savings Bank-Note

1946. 50th Anniv of Savings Bank.
588 **179** 4l. red 40 25
589 **180** 10l. olive 15 10
590 – 20l. blue 15 10
591 – 50l. black 60 55
DESIGNS—VERT: 20l. Child filling money-box; 50l. Postal Savings Bank.

181 Arms of Russia and Bulgaria and Spray of Oak

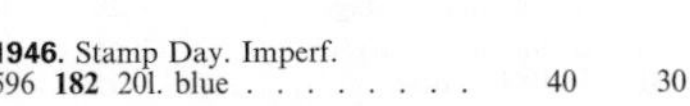

182 Lion Rampant

1946. Bulgo-Russian Congress.
592 **181** 4l. red . . . . 7·00 7·00
593 4l. orange 10 10
594 20l. blue . . . . 7·00 7·00
595 20l. green 20 20

1946. Stamp Day. Imperf.
596 **182** 20l. blue 40 30

183

190

1946. Air. Inscr "PAR AVION".
597 **183** 1l. purple 15 10
598 2l. grey 15 10
599 – 4l. black 30 15
600 – 6l. blue 40 30
601 – 10l. green 10 10
602 – 12l. brown 10 10
603 – 16l. purple 10 10
604 – 19l. red 10 10
605 – 30l. orange 15 10
606 – 45l. green 45 15
607 – 75l. brown 55 15
608 **190** 100l. red . . . . 1·10 25
609 – 100l. grey . . . . 1·10 25
DESIGNS—23 × 18 mm: 4l. Bird carrying envelope; 100l. (No. 609), Airplane. 18 × 23 mm: 6l. Airplane and envelope; 10, 12, 19l. Wings and posthorn; 16l. Wings and envelope; 30l. Airplane; 45, 75l. Dove and posthorn.

192 Stamboliiski

193 Flags of Albania, Bulgaria, Yugoslavia and Rumania

1946. 25th Death Anniv of Aleksandur Stamboliiski (Prime Minister 1919–23).
610 **192** 100l. orange . . . . . . 7·00 7·00

1946. Balkan Games.
611 **193** 100l. brown . . . . . . 1·40 1·40

196 Artillery

195 Junkers Ju87B "Stuka" Dive Bombers

1946. Military and Air Services.
612 – 2l. red 10 10
613 – 4l. grey 10 10
614 **196** 5l. red 10 10
615 **195** 6l. brown 10 10
616 – 9l. mauve 10 10
617 – 10l. violet 10 10
618 – 20l. blue 35 15
619 – 30l. orange 35 15
620 – 40l. olive 40 20
621 – 50l. green 50 50
622 – 60l. brown 75 50
DESIGNS—HORIZ: 2, 20l. Grenade thrower and machine-gunner; 9l. Building pontoon-bridge; 10, 30l. Cavalry charge; 40l. Supply column; 50l. Motor convoy; 60l. Tanks. VERT: 4l. Grenade thrower.

203 St. Ivan Rilski

208 "New Republic"

1946. Death Millenary of St. Ivan Rilski.
623 **203** 1l. brown 10 10
624 – 4l. sepia 10 10
625 – 10l. green 25 10
626 – 20l. blue 30 10
627 – 50l. red . . . . 1·25 55
DESIGNS—HORIZ: 4l. Rila Monastery; 10l. Monastery entrance; 50l. Cloistered courtyard. VERT: 20l. Aerial view of Monastery.

1946. Referendum.
628 **208** 4l. red 10 10
629 20l. blue 10 10
630 50l. brown 25 15

209 Assault

210 Ambuscade

1946. Partisan Activities.
631 **209** 1l. purple 10 10
632 **210** 4l. green 10 10
633 – 5l. brown 10 10
634 **210** 10l. red 10 10
635 **209** 20l. blue 30 10
636 – 30l. brown 30 15
637 – 50l. black 40 25
DESIGNS—VERT: 5l., 50l. Partisan riflemen; 30l. Partisan leader.

211 Nurse and Children

212a Partisans

1947. Winter Relief.
638 **211** 1l. violet 10 10
639 – 4l. red 10 10
640 – 9l. olive 10 10
641 **211** 10l. grey 10 10
642 – 20l. blue 15 10
643 – 30l. brown 15 10
644 – 40l. red 30 25
645 **211** 50l. green 50 35
DESIGNS: 4l., 9l. Child carrying gifts; 20l., 40l. Hungry child; 30l. Destitute mother and child.

1947. Anti-fascists of 1923, 1941 and 1944 Commem.
645a – 10l. brown and orange 40 40
645b **212a** 20l. dp blue & lt blue 40 40
645c – 70l. brown and red . . 35·00 35·00
DESIGNS—HORIZ: 10l. Group of fighters; 70l. Soldier addressing crowd.

213 Olive Branch

214 Dove of Peace

1947. Peace.
646 **213** 4l. olive 10 10
647 **214** 10l. brown 10 10
648 20l. blue 20 15
"BULGARIA" is in Roman characters on the 20l.

215 "U.S.A." and "Bulgaria"

1947. Air. Stamp Day and New York International Philatelic Exhibition.
649 **215** 70l.+30l. brown . . . . . 1·75 2·00

216 Esperanto Emblem and Map of Bulgaria

1947. 30th Esperanto Jubilee Congress, Sofia.
650 **216** 20l.+10l. purple & green 75 50

217 G.P.O., Sofia

218 National Theatre, Sofia

219 Parliament Building
220 President's Palace

221 G.P.O., Sofia

1947. Government Buildings. (a) T **217**.
651 1l. green 10 10

(b) T **218**.
652 50s. green 10 10
653 2l. red 10 10
654 4l. blue 10 10
655 9l. red 25 10

(c) T **219**.
656 50s. green 10 10
657 2l. blue 10 10
658 4l. blue 10 10
659 20l. blue 85 30

(d) T **220**.
660 1l. green 10 10

(e) T **221**.
661 1l. green 10 10
662 2l. red 10 10
663 4l. blue 10 10

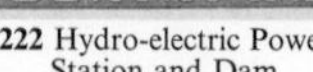

222 Hydro-electric Power Station and Dam
223 Emblem of Industry

1947. Reconstruction.
664 **222** 4l. green 15 15
665 – 9l. brown (Miner) 15 15
666 **223** 20l. blue 25 25
667 – 40l. green (Motor plough) 85 85

224 Exhibition Building
225 Former Residence of the French Poet Lamartine

226 Rose and Grapes
227 Airplane over City

1947. Plovdiv Fair. (a) Postage.
668 **224** 4l. red 10 10
669 **225** 9l. red 10 10
670 **226** 20l. blue 25 15

(b) Air. Imperf.
671 **227** 40l. green . . . . 1·10 1·00

228 Cycle Racing

229 Basketball
231 V. E. Aprilov

1947. Balkan Games.
672 **228** 2l. lilac 40 20
673 **229** 4l. green 40 20
674 – 9l. brown . . . . 1·10 40
675 – 20l. blue . . . . 1·25 50
676 – 60l. red . . . . 3·00 2·00
DESIGNS—VERT: 9l. Chess; 20l. Football; 60l. Balkan flags.

1947. Death Cent of Vasil Aprilov (educationist).
678 – 4l. red 15 10
677 **231** 40l. blue 35 25
DESIGN: 4l. Another portrait of Aprilov.

233 Postman
235 Geno Kirov

1947. Postal Employees' Relief Fund.
679 **233** 4l.+2l. olive 10 10
680 – 10l.+5l. red 20 20
681 – 20l.+10l. blue 25 25
682 – 40l.+20l. brown . . . . 1·00 1·00
DESIGNS: 10l. Linesman; 20l. Telephonists; 40l. Wireless masts.

1947. Theatrical Artists' Benevolent Fund.
683 **235** 50s. brown 10 10
684 – 1l. green 10 10
685 – 2l. green 10 10
686 – 3l. blue 10 10
687 – 4l. red 10 10
688 – 5l. purple 10 10
689 – 9l.+5l. blue 15 15
690 – 10l.+6l. red 20 20
691 – 15l.+7l. violet 25 25
692 – 20l.+15l. blue 50 25
693 – 30l.+20l. purple . . . . 1·00 85
PORTRAITS: 1l. Zlotina Nedeva; 2l. Ivan Popov; 3l. Atanas Kirchev; 4l. Elena Snezhina; 5l. Stoyan Buchvarov; 9l. Khristo Ganchev; 10l. Adriana Budevska; 15l. Vasil Kirkov; 20l. Save Orgnyanov; 30l. Krustyn Sarafov.

236 "Rodina" (freighter)

1947. National Shipping Revival.
694 **236** 50l. blue . . . . 1·25 35

237 Worker and Flag
238 Worker and Globe

1948. 2nd General Workers' Union Congress.
695 **237** 4l. blue (postage) 15 10
696 **238** 60l. brown (air) 65 50

239
240

1948. Leisure and Culture.
697 **239** 4l. red 15 10
698 **240** 20l. blue 25 15
699 – 40l. green 40 20
700 – 60l. brown 65 40
DESIGNS—VERT: 40l. Workers' musical interlude; 60l. Sports girl.

241 Kikola Vaptsarov
242 Petlyakov Pe-2 Bomber over Baldwin's Tower

1948. Poets.
701 **241** 4l. red on cream 10 10
702 – 9l. brown on cream . . . 15 10
703 – 15l. purple on cream . . . 15 15
704 – 20l. blue on cream . . . 20 15
705 – 45l. green on cream . . . 65 75
PORTRAITS: 9l. Peya Yavorov; 15l. Khristo Smirnenski; 20l. Ivan Vazov; 45l. Petko Slaveikov.

1948. Air. Stamp Day.
706 **242** 50l. brown on cream . . . 1·40 1·10

243 Soldier
244 Peasants and Soldiers

1948. Soviet Army Monument.
707 **243** 4l. red on cream 10 10
708 **244** 10l. green on cream . . . 15 10
709 – 20l. blue on cream . . . 25 15
710 – 60l. olive on cream . . . 75 45
DESIGNS—HORIZ: 20l. Soldiers of 1878 and 1944. VERT: 60l. Stalin and Spassky Tower, Kremlin.

245 Bath, Gorna Banya
246 Lion Emblem

1948. Bulgarian Health Resorts.
711 **245** 2l. red 10 10
712 – 3l. orange 10 10
713 – 4l. blue 15 10
717 – 5l. brown 15 10
714 – 10l. purple 25 10
718 – 15l. olive 35 10
715 **245** 20l. blue . . . . 1·00 15
716 – 20l. blue . . . . 1·50 15
DESIGNS: 3, 10l. Bath, Bankya; 4, 20l. (No. 716), Mineral bath, Sofia; 5, 15l. Malyovitsa Peak.

1948.
719 **246** 50s. orange 10 10
719a 50s. brown 10 10
720 1l. green 10 10
721 9l. black 15 10

247 Dimitur Blagoev
248 Youths marching

1948. 25th Anniv of September Uprising.
722 **247** 4l. brown 10 10
723 – 9l. orange 10 10
724 – 20l. blue 40 25
725 **248** 60l. brown . . . . . . 1·00 75
DESIGNS—VERT: 9l. Gabrit Genov. HORIZ: 20l. Bishop Andrei Monument.

249 Khristo Smirnenski
250 Miner

1948. 500th Birth Anniv of Smirnenski (poet and revolutionary).
726 **249** 4l. blue 10 10
727 16l. brown 15 10

1948.
728 **250** 4l. blue 75 25

251 Battle of Grivitsa

1948. Treaty of Friendship with Rumania.
729 **251** 20l. blue (postage) 20 10
730 – 40l. black (air) 25 15
731 – 100l. mauve 95 85
DESIGNS: 40l. Parliament Buildings in Sofia and Bucharest; 100l. Projected Danube Bridge.

252 Botev's House, Kalofer
253 Botev

1948. Birth Centenary of Khristo Botev (poet and revolutionary).
732 **252** 1l. green 10 10
733 **253** 4l. brown 15 10
734 4l. purple 15 10
735 – 9l. violet 40 10
736 – 15l. brown 20 10
737a – 20l. blue 20 10
738 – 40l. brown 45 20
739 – 50l. black 65 30
DESIGNS—HORIZ: 9l. River paddle-steamer "Radetski"; 15l. Village of Kalofer; 40l. Botev's mother and verse of poem. VERT: 20l. Botev in uniform; 50l. Quill, pistol and laurel wreath.

254 Lenin
255 Road Construction

1949. 25th Death Anniv of Lenin. Inscr "1924–1949".
740 **254** 4l. brown 15 10
741 – 20l. red 40 25
DESIGN—(27 × 37 mm): 20l. Lenin as an orator.

1949. National Youth Movement.
742 **255** 4l. red 20 10
743 – 5l. brown . . . . 1·10 40
744 – 9l. green . . . . 2·25 30
745 – 10l. violet 50 20
746 – 20l. blue 85 45
747 – 40l. brown . . . . . . 1·75 1·00
DESIGNS—HORIZ: 5l. Tunnel construction; 9l. Class 10 steam locomotive; 10l. Textile workers; 20l. Girl driving tractor; 40l. Workers in lorry.

256 Lisunov Li-2 over Pleven Mausoleum

1949. Air. 7th Philatelic Congress, Pleven.
748 **256** 50l. bistre . . . . 4·50 3·75

257 G. Dimitrov
258 G. Dimitrov

1949. Death of Georgi Dimitrov (Prime Minister 1946–49).
749 **257** 4l. red 15 10
750 **258** 20l. blue . . . . 1·00 25

259 Hydro-electric Power Station
260 Symbols of Agriculture and Industry

1949. Five Year Industrial and Agricultural Plan.
751 **259** 4l. olive (postage) 15 10
752 – 9l. red 25 15
753 – 15l. violet 40 20
754 – 20l. blue . . . . 1·25 40
755 **260** 50l. brown (air) . . . . . 2·75 1·50
DESIGNS—VERT: 9l. Cement works; 15l. Tractors in garage. HORIZ: 20l. Tractors in field.

261 Javelin and Grenade Throwing
262 Motor-cyclist and Tractor

1949. Physical Culture Campaign.
756 **261** 4l. red 30 15
757 – 9l. olive . . . . 1·40 50
758 **262** 20l. blue . . . . 2·00 1·00
759 – 50l. red . . . . 5·00 2·75
DESIGNS—HORIZ: 9l. Hurdling and leaping barbed-wire. VERT: 50l. Two athletes marching.

263 Globe
265 Guardsman with Dog

264 Guardsman and Peasant

1949. Air. 75th Anniv of Universal Postal Union.
760 **263** 50l. blue . . . . 2·40 1·10

1949. Frontier Guards.
761 **264** 4l. brown (postage) . . . 15 15
762 – 20l. blue . . . . 1·00 75
763 **265** 60l. green (air) . . . . . 2·75 2·75
DESIGN—VERT: 20l. Guardsman on coast.

266 Georgi Dimitrov (Prime Minister 1946–49)
267 "Unanimity"
268 Zosif Stalin

1949. Fatherland Front.
764 **266** 4l. brown 15 10
765 **267** 9l. violet 20 10
766 – 20l. blue 30 20
767 – 50l. red . . . . 1·00 1·00
DESIGNS: 20l. Man and woman with wheelbarrow and spade; 50l. Young people marching with banners.

1949. 70th Birthday of Stalin.
768 **268** 4l. orange 25 10
769 – 40l. red 90 70
DESIGN—VERT: (25 × 37 mm): 40l. Stalin as an orator.

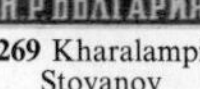

269 Kharalampi Stoyanov
270 Strikers and Train

1950. 30th Anniv of Railway Strike.
770 **269** 4l. brown 15 10
771 **270** 20l. blue . . . . 1·10 40
772 – 60l. olive . . . . 2·25 1·25
DESIGN—VERT: 60l. Two workers and flag.

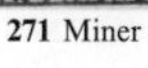

271 Miner
272 Class 48 Steam Shunting Locomotive

1950.
773 **271** 1l. olive 10 10
773a 1l. violet 15 10
774 **272** 2l. black . . . . 3·00 40
774a 2l. brown . . . . 2·50 25
775 – 3l. blue 45 10
776a – 4l. green 40 10
777 – 5l. red 40 10
778 – 9l. grey 20 10
779 – 10l. purple 25 10
780 – 15l. red 45 15
781 – 20l. blue 80 45
DESIGNS—VERT: 3l. Ship under construction; 10l. Power station; 15l., 20l. Woman in factory. HORIZ: 4l. Tractor; 5l., 9l. Threshing machines.

273 Kolarov

1950. Death of Vasil Kolarov (Prime Minister 1949–50). Inscr "1877–1950".
782 **273** 4l. brown 10 10
783 – 20l. blue 40 35
DESIGN—(27½ × 39½ mm): 20l. Portrait as Type **273**, but different frame.

274 Starislas Dospevski (self-portrait)
274a "In the Field" (Khristo Storclev)

1950. Painters and paintings.
784 **274** 1l. green 30 15
785 – 4l. orange . . . . 1·60 25
786 – 9l. brown . . . . 2·10 25
787 **274a** 15l. brown . . . . . . 2·90 70
788 20l. blue . . . . 4·75 2·00
789 – 40l. brown . . . . . . 5·50 2·75
790 – 60l. orange . . . . . . 6·25 4·00
DESIGNS—VERT: 4l. King Kaloyan and Desislava; 9l. Nikolai Pavlovich; 40l. Statue of Debeyanov (Ivan Lazarov); 60l. "Peasant" (Vladimir Dimitrov the Master).

275 Ivan Vazov and Birthplace, Sopot
276a G. Dimitrov (statesman)

1950. Birth Centenary of Ivan Vazov (poet).
791 **275** 4l. olive 15 10

1950. 1st Death Anniv of Georgi Dimitrov.
792 – 50s. brown (postage) . . 15 10
793 – 50s. green 15 10
794 **276a** 1l. brown 20 10
795 – 2l. slate 20 10
796 – 4l. purple 75 20
797 – 9l. red . . . . 1·25 40
798 – 10l. red . . . . 1·90 85
799 – 15l. grey . . . . 1·90 85
800 – 20l. blue . . . . 3·00 1·75
801 – 40l. brown (air) . . . . 5·50 3·25
DESIGNS—HORIZ: 50s. green, Dimitrov and birthplace, Kovachevtsi; 2l. Dimitrov's house, Sofia; 15l. Dimitrov signing new constitution; 20l. Dimitrov; 40l. Mausoleum. VERT: 50s. brown, 4, 9, 10l. Dimitrov in various poses.

277 Runners
278 Workers and Tractor

1950.
802 **277** 4l. green 65 25
803 – 9l. brown (Cycling) . . . 85 40
804 – 20l. blue (Putting the shot) . . . . 1·10 85
805 – 40l. purple (Volleyball) . . 2·40 2·10

1950. 2nd National Peace Congress.
806 **278** 4l. red 10 10
807 – 20l. blue 40 25
DESIGN—VERT: 20l. Stalin on flag and three heads.

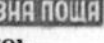

278b
279 Children on Beach

1950. Arms designs.
807a – 2l. brown 10 10
807b – 3l. red 10 10
807c **278b** 5l. red 10 10
807d – 9l. blue 20 10
Although inscribed "OFFICIAL MAIL", the above were issued as regular postage stamps.

1950. Sunday Delivery.
808 – 1l. green (Sanatorium) . . 15 10
809 **279** 2l. red 20 10
810 – 5l. orange (Sunbathing) 40 15
811 **279** 10l. blue 80 35

280 Molotov, Kolarov, Stalin and Dimitrov
281 Russian and Bulgarian Girls

1950. 2nd Anniv of Soviet–Bulgarian Treaty of Friendship.
812 **280** 4l. brown 10 10
813 – 9l. red 15 10
814 **281** 20l. blue 30 25
815 – 50l. green . . . . 2·00 75
DESIGNS—VERT: 9l. Spassky Tower and flags; 50l. Freighter and tractor.

282 Marshal Tolbukhin
284 A. S. Popov
286 Georgi Kirkov

1950. Honouring Marshal Tolbukhin.
816 **282** 4l. mauve 15 10
817 – 20l. blue . . . . 1·00 30
DESIGN—HORIZ: 20l. Bulgarians greeting Tolbukhin.

1951. 45th Death Anniv of Aleksandr Popov (radio pioneer).
818 **284** 4l. brown 25 15
819 20l. blue 85 30

1951. Anti-fascist Heroes.
823 – 1l. mauve 15 10
824 – 2l. plum 20 10
825 **286** 4l. red 20 10
826 – 9l. brown 60 40
827 – 15l. olive . . . . 1·75 70
828 – 20l. blue . . . . 1·75 1·00
829 – 50l. grey . . . . 4·25 1·50
PORTRAITS: 1l. Chankova, Adalbert Antonov-Malchika, Sasho Dimitrov and Lilyana Dimitrova; 2l. Stanke Dimitrov; 9l. Anton Ivanov; 15l. Mikhailov; 20l. Georgi Dimitrov at Leipzig; 50l. Nocho Ivanov and Acram Stoyahov.

285 First Bulgarian Truck
289 Embroidery

1951. National Occupations. (a) As T **285**.
820 – 1l. violet (Tractor) 15 10
821 – 2l. green (Steam-roller) . . 20 10
822 **285** 4l. brown 25 10

(b) As T **289**.
830 – 1l. brown (Tractor) . . . 15 10
831 – 2l. violet (Steam-roller) . . 20 10
832 – 4l. brown (Truck) 45 40
833 **289** 9l. violet 85 30
834 – 15l. purple (Carpets) . . . 1·50 1·00
835 – 20l. blue (Roses and Tobacco) . . . . . . 3·25 1·50
836 – 40l. green (Fruit) . . . . 5·00 2·10
The 9l. and 20l. are vert, the remainder horiz.

290 Turkish Attack

1951. 75th Anniv of April Uprising.
837 **290** 1l. brown 50 15
838 – 4l. green 50 15
839 – 9l. purple 85 45
840 – 20l. blue . . . . 1·25 80
841 – 40l. lake . . . . 1·90 1·50
DESIGNS—HORIZ: 4l. Proclamation of Uprising; 9l. Cannon and cavalry; 20l. Patriots in 1876 and 1944; 40l. Georgi Benkovsky and Georgi Dimitrov.

291 Dimitur Blagoev as Orator

1951. 60th Anniv of First Bulgarian Social Democratic Party Congress, Buzludzha.
842 **291** 1l. violet 20 10
843 4l. green 40 15
844 9l. purple . . . . 1·10 80

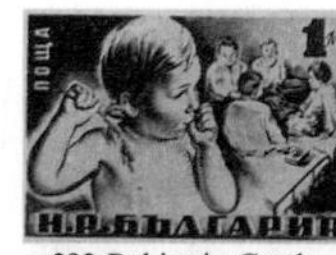

292 Babies in Creche

1951. Children's Day.
845 **292** 1l. brown 20 10
846 – 4l. purple 50 15
847 – 9l. green . . . . 1·00 35
848 – 20l. blue . . . . 2·00 1·25
DESIGNS: 4l. Children building models; 9l. Girl and children's play ground; 20l. Boy bugler and children marching.

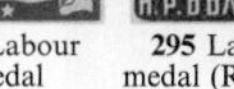

293 Workers
294 Labour medal (Obverse)
295 Labour medal (Reverse)

1951. 3rd General Workers' Union Congress.
849 **293** 1l. black 10 10
850 – 4l. brown 15 10
DESIGN inscr "16 XII 1951"; 4l. Georgi Dimitrov and Valdo Chervenkov (Prime minister).

1952. Order of Labour.
851 **294** 1l. red 10 10
852 **295** 1l. brown 10 10
853 **294** 4l. green 10 10
854 **295** 4l. green 10 10
855 **294** 9l. violet 35 15
856 **295** 9l. blue 35 15

296 Vasil Kolarov Dam
297 G. Dimitrov and Chemical Works

1952.
857 **296** 4s. green 15 10
858 12s. violet 20 10
859 16s. brown 25 10
860 44s. red 60 10
861 80s. blue . . . . 3·00 25

1952. 70th Birth Anniv of Georgi Dimitrov (statesman). Dated "1882–1952".
862 **297** 16s. brown 40 20
863 – 44s. brown . . . . 1·00 35
864 – 80s. blue . . . . 1·75 1·00
DESIGNS—HORIZ: 44s. Georgi Dimitrov (Prime minister 1946–49) and Prime minister Vulko Chervenkov. VERT: 80s. Full-face portrait of Georgi Dimitrov.

298 Republika Power Station

299 N. Vaptsarov (revolutionary)

1952.

866 **298** 16s. sepia 40 10
867 44s. purple . . . . 1·25 15

1952. 10th Death Anniv of Nikola Vaptsarov (poet and revolutionary).
869 **299** 16s. lake 30 25
870 – 44s. brown . . . . 1·10 90
871 – 80s. sepia . . . . 2·10 90
PORTRAITS: 44s. Facing bayonets; 80s. Full-face.

300 Congress Delegates

1952. 40th Anniv of First Workers' Social Democratic Youth League Congress.
872 **300** 2s. lake 15 10
873 – 16s. violet 25 10
874 – 44s. green . . . . 1·50 65
875 – 80s. sepia . . . . 1·90 1·40
DESIGNS: 16s. Young partisans; 44s. Factory and guards; 80s. Dimitrov addressing young workers.

301 Attack on Winter Palace, St. Petersburg

1952. 35th Anniv of Russian Revolution. Dated "1917 1952".
876 **301** 4s. lake 10 10
877 – 8s. green 15 10
878 – 16s. blue 15 10
879 – 44s. sepia 50 20
880 – 80s. olive . . . . 1·25 40
DESIGNS: 8s. Volga–Don canal; 16s. Dove and globe; 44s. Lenin and Stalin; 80s. Lenin, Stalin and Himlay hydro-electric station.

302

303 Vintagers and Grapes

1952. Wood Carvings depicting National Products.
881 – 2s. brown 10 10
882 – 8s. green 10 10
883 – 12s. brown 20 10
884 – 16s. purple 45 10
885 **302** 28s. green 85 15
886 – 44s. brown 90 15
887 **303** 80s. blue . . . . 1·50 15
888 1l. violet . . . . 3·25 30
889 4l. red . . . . 4·25 1·90
DESIGNS—VERT: 2s. Numeral in carved frame. HORIZ: 8s. Gift-offering to idol; 12s. Birds and grapes; 16s. Rose-gathering; 44s. "Attar of Roses".

304 V. Levski

1953. 80th Anniv of Execution of Vasil Levski (revolutionary).
890 **304** 16s. brown on cream . . 15 10
891 – 44s. brown on cream . . 30 15
DESIGN: 44s. Levski addressing crowd.

305 Russian Army Crossing R. Danube

306 Mother and Children

1953. 75th Anniv of Liberation from Turkey.
892 **305** 8s. blue 30 10
893 – 16s. brown 25 10
894 – 44s. green 55 20
895 – 80s. lake . . . . 1·60 1·00
896 – 1l. black . . . . 2·00 1·60
DESIGNS—VERT: 16s. Battle of Shipka Pass. HORIZ: 44s. Peasants welcoming Russian soldiers; 80s. Bulgarians and Russians embracing; 1l. Shipka Pass memorial and Dimitrovgrad.

1953. International Women's Day.
897 **306** 16s. blue 15 10
898 16s. green 15 10

307 Karl Marx

308 May Day Parade

1953. 70th Death Anniv of Karl Marx.
899 **307** 16s. blue 15 15
900 – 44s. brown 40 25
DESIGN—VERT: 44s. Book "Das Kapital".

1953. Labour Day.
901 **308** 16s. red 20 10

309 Stalin

310 Goce Delcev (Macedonian revolutionary)

1953. Death of Stalin.
902 **309** 16s. brown 25 10
903 16s. black 25 15

1953. 50th Anniv of Ilinden–Preobrazhenie Rising.
904 **310** 16s. brown 10 10
905 – 44s. violet 40 25
906 – 1l. purple 55 30
DESIGNS. 44s. Insurgents and flag facing left. HORIZ: 1l. Insurgents and flag facing right.

311 Soldier and Insurgents

312 Dimitur Blagoev

1953. Army Day.
907 **311** 16s. red 25 10
908 – 44s. blue 65 15
DESIGN: 44s. Soldier, factories and combine-harvester.

1953. 50th Anniv of Bulgarian Workers' Social Democratic Party.
909 **312** 16s. brown 30 15
910 – 44s. red 65 20
DESIGN: 44s. Dimitrov and Blagoev.

313 Georgi Dimitrov and Vasil Kolarov

314 Railway Viaduct

1953. 30th Anniv of September Uprising.
911 **313** 8s. black 25 10
912 – 16s. brown 25 10
913 – 44s. red 80 30
DESIGNS: 16s. Insurgent and flag; 44s. Crowd of Insurgents.

1953. Bulgarian–Russian Friendship.
914 **314** 8s. blue 50 35
915 – 16s. slate 10 10
916 – 44s. brown 30 15
917 – 80s. orange 90 30
DESIGNS—HORIZ: 16s. Welder and industrial plant; 80s. Combine-harvester. VERT: 44s. Iron foundry.

315 Dog Rose

316 Vasil Kolarov Library

1953. Medicinal Flowers.
918 – 2s. blue 10 10
919 – 4s. orange 10 10
920 – 8s. turquoise 15 10
921 **315** 12s. green 15 10
922 – 12s. red 15 10
923 – 16s. blue 25 10
924 – 16s. brown 25 10
925 – 20s. red 50 10
926 – 28s. green 50 15
927 – 40s. blue 55 25
928 – 44s. brown 75 25
929 – 80s. brown . . . . 1·50 55
930 – 1l. brown . . . . 4·00 1·00
931 – 2l. purple . . . . 6·75 2·50
MS931a 161 × 172 mm. Twelve values as above in green (sold at 6l.) . . . . 70·00 70·00
FLOWERS: 2s. Deadly nightshade; 4s. Thorn-apple; 8s. Sage; 16s. Great yellow gentian; 20s. Opium poppy; 28s. Peppermint; 40s. Bear-berry; 44s. Coltsfoot; 80s. Primula; 1l. Dandelion; 2l. Foxglove.

1953. 75th Anniv of Kolarov Library, Sofia.
932 **316** 44s. brown 30 15

317 Singer and Musician

318 Airplane over Mountains

1953. Amateur Theatricals.
933 **317** 16s. brown 15 10
934 – 44s. green 40 20
DESIGN: 44s. Folk-dancers.

1954. Air.
935 **318** 8s. green 10 10
936 – 12s. lake 10 10
937 – 16s. brown 15 10
938 – 20s. salmon 15 10
939 – 28s. blue 20 10
940 – 44s. purple 25 10
941 – 60s. brown 45 10
942 – 80s. green 75 25
943 – 1l. green . . . . 2·25 50
944 – 4l. blue . . . . 4·50 1·75
DESIGNS—VERT: 12s. Exhibition buildings, Plovdiv; 80s. Tirnovo; 4l. Partisans' Monument. HORIZ: 16s. Seaside promenade, Varna; 20s. Combine-harvester in cornfield; 28s. Rila Monastery; 44s. Studena hydro-electric barrage; 60s. Dimitrovgrad; 1l. Sofia University and equestrian statue.

319 Lenin and Stalin

320 Dimitur Blagoev and Crowd

1954. 30th Death Anniv of Lenin.
945 **319** 16s. brown 15 10
946 – 44s. lake 30 10
947 – 80s. blue 70 20
948 – 1l. green 95 75
DESIGNS—VERT: 44s. Lenin statue; 80s. Lenin–Stalin Mausoleum and Kremlin; 1l. Lenin.

1954. 30th Death Anniv of Blagoev.
949 **320** 16s. brown 15 10
950 – 44s. sepia 40 15
DESIGN: 44s. Blagoev writing at desk.

321 Dimitrov Speaking

322 Class 10 Steam Locomotive

1954. 5th Death Anniv of Dimitrov.
951 **321** 44s. lake 20 15
952 – 80s. brown 75 20
DESIGN—HORIZ: 80s. Dimitrov and blast-furnace.

1954. Railway Workers' Day.
953 **322** 44s. turquoise . . . . . . 1·90 20
954 44s. black . . . . 1·90 20

323 Miner Operating Machinery

324 Marching Soldiers

1954. Miners' Day.
955 **323** 44s. green 25 15

1954. 10th Anniv of Fatherland Front Government.
956 **324** 12s. lake 10 10
957 – 16s. red 10 10
958 – 28s. slate 20 10
959 – 44s. brown 25 10
960 – 80s. blue 70 30
961 – 1l. green . . . . 1·00 30
DESIGNS—VERT: 16s. Soldier and parents; 80s. Girl and boy pioneers; 1l. Dimitrov. HORIZ: 28s. Industrial plant; 44s. Dimitrov and workers.

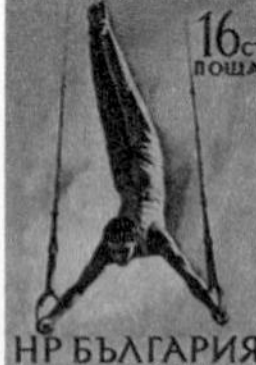

325 Academy Building

326 Gymnast

1954. 85th Anniv of Academy of Sciences.
962 **325** 80s. black . . . . 1·00 50

1954. Sports. Cream paper.
963 **326** 16s. green . . . . 1·50 20
964 – 44s. red . . . . 1·50 65
965 – 80s. brown . . . . 2·50 1·00
966 – 2l. blue . . . . 4·75 3·25
DESIGNS—VERT: 44s. Wrestlers; 2l. Ski-jumper. HORIZ: 80s. Horse-jumper.

327 Velingrad Rest Home

1954. 50th Anniv of Trade Union Movement.
967 **327** 16s. green 15 10
968 – 44s. red 15 15
969 – 80s. blue 85 30
DESIGNS—VERT: 44s. Foundryman. HORIZ: 80s. Georgi Dimitrov, Dimitur Blagoev and Georgi Kirkov.

328 Geese

329 Communist Party Building

1955.

970 **328** 2s. green 10 10
971 – 4s. olive 20 10
972 – 12s. brown 35 10
973 – 16s. brown 60 10
974 – 28s. blue 30 10
975 **329** 44s. red . . . . 10·50 20
976 – 80s. brown 70 20
977 – 1l. green . . . . 1·75 30
DESIGNS: 4s. Rooster and hens; 12s. Sow and piglets; 16s. Ewe and lambs; 28s. Telephone exchange; 80s. Flats; 1l. Cellulose factory.

330 Mill Girl

332 Rejoicing Crowds

1955. International Women's Day.
978 **330** 12s. brown 10 10
979 – 16s. green 20 10
980 – 44s. blue 75 10
981 – 44s. red 75 10
DESIGNS—HORIZ: 16s. Girl feeding cattle. VERT: 44s. Mother and baby.

1955. As Nos. 820 and 822 surch **16 CT.**
981a – 16s. on 1l. violet 20 10
982 **285** 16s. on 4l. brown 75 10

1955. Labour Day.
983 **332** 16s. red 15 10
984 – 44s. blue 50 10
DESIGN: 44s. Three workers and globe.

333 St. Cyril and St. Methodius **334** Sergei Rumyantsev

1955. 1100th Anniv of 1st Bulgarian Literature. On cream paper.
985 **333** 4s. blue 10 10
986 – 8s. olive 10 10
987 – 16s. black 15 10
988 – 28s. red 25 15
989 – 44s. brown 45 20
990 – 80s. red . . . . 1·00 80
991 – 2l. black . . . . 2·50 1·60
DESIGNS: 8s. Monk writing; 16s. Early printing press; 28s. Khristo Botev (poet); 44s. Ivan Vazov (poet and novelist); 80s. Dimitur Blagoev (writer and editor) and books; 2l. Dimitur Blagoev Polygraphic Complex, Sofia.

1955. 30th Death Annivs of Bulgarian Poets. On cream paper.
992 **334** 12s. brown 30 10
993 – 16s. brown 40 10
994 – 44s. green 60 25
DESIGNS: 16s. Khristo Yusenov; 44s. Geo Milev.

335 F. Engels and Book **336** Mother and Children

1955. 60th Death Anniv of Engels.
995 **335** 44s. brown on cream . . 55 20

1955. World Mothers' Congress, Lausanne.
996 **336** 44s. lake on cream . . . 35 10

337 "Youth of the World" **338** Main Entrance in 1892

1955. 5th World Youth Festival, Warsaw.
997 **337** 44s. blue on cream . . . 30 15

1955. 16th International Fair, Plovdiv.
998 **338** 4s. brown on cream . . 10 10
999 – 16s. red on cream . . . 10 10
1000 – 44s. green on cream . . 20 15
1001 – 80s. cream 85 20
DESIGNS—VERT: 16s. Sculptured group; 80s. Fair poster. HORIZ: 44s. Fruit.

339 Friedrich Schiller (dramatist) (150th death anniv) **340** Industrial Plant

1955. Cultural Annivs. Writers. On cream paper.
1002 **339** 16s. brown 30 15
1003 – 44s. red 75 15
1004 – 60s. blue 85 15
1005 – 80s. black . . . . . . 1·25 15
1006 – 1l. purple . . . . 2·50 1·00
1007 – 2l. olive . . . . 3·25 2·00
PORTRAITS: 44s. Adam Mickiewicz (poet, death centenary); 60s. Hans Christian Andersen (150th birth anniv); 80s. Baron de Montesquieu (philosopher, death bicentenary); 1l. Miguel de Cervantes (350th anniv of publication of "Don Quixote"); 2l. Walt Whitman (poet) (centenary of publication of "Leaves of Grass").

1955. Bulgarian–Russian Friendship. On cream paper.
1008 **340** 2s. slate 10 10
1009 – 4s. blue 10 10
1010 – 16s. green 55 25
1011 – 44s. brown 35 10
1012 – 80s. green 70 15
1013 – 1l. black 90 30
DESIGNS—HORIZ: 4s. Dam; 16s. Friendship railway bridge over River Danube between Ruse and Giurgiu (Rumania). VERT: 44s. Monument; 80s. Ivan-Michurin (botanist); 1l. Vladimir Mayakovsky (writer).

341 Emblem **342** Quinces

1956. Centenary of Library Reading Rooms. On cream paper.
1014 **341** 12s. red 10 10
1015 – 16s. brown 10 10
1016 – 44s. myrtle 50 20
DESIGNS: 16s. K. Pshourka writing; 44s. B. Kiro reading.

1956. Fruits.
1017 **342** 4s. red . . . . 1·40 10
1017a 4s. green 15 10
1018 – 8s. green (Pears) . . . 60 15
1018a – 8s. brown (Pears) . . . 15 10
1019 – 16s. dark red (Apples) 1·25 15
1019a – 16s. red (Apples) . . . 35 10
1020 – 44s. violet (Grapes) . . 1·40 30
1020a – 44s. ochre (Grapes) . . 70 20

343 Artillerymen

1956. 80th Anniv of April Uprising.
1021 **343** 16s. brown 25 20
1022 – 44s. green (Cavalry charge) 30 25

344 Blagoev and Birthplace at Zagovichane

1956. Birth Centenary of Dimitur Blagoev (socialist writer).
1023 **344** 44s. turquoise 30 15

345 Cherries **346** Football

1956. Fruits.
1024 **345** 2s. lake 15 10
1025 – 12s. blue (Plums) 20 10
1026 – 28s. buff (Greengages) 35 10
1027 – 80s. red (Strawberries) 1·00 35

1956. Olympic Games.
1028 – 4s. blue 40 15
1029 – 12s. red 55 10
1030 – 16s. brown 60 10
1031 **346** 44s. green . . . . 1·10 30
1032 – 80s. brown . . . . . . 1·60 1·00
1033 – 1l. lake . . . . 2·40 1·40
DESIGNS—VERT: 4s. Gymnastics; 12s. Throwing the discus; 80s. Basketball. HORIZ: 16s. Pole vaulting; 1l. Boxing.

347 Tobacco and Rose **348** Gliders

1956. 17th International Fair, Plovdiv.
1034 **347** 44s. red 60 35
1035 44s. green 60 35

1956. Air. 30th Anniv of Gliding Club.
1036 – 44s. blue 30 15
1037 – 60s. violet 55 20
1038 **348** 80s. green 80 25
DESIGNS: 44s. Launching glider; 60s. Glider over hangar.

349 National Theatre **350** Wolfgang Mozart (composer, birth bicent)

1956. Centenary of National Theatre.
1039 **349** 16s. brown 15 10
1040 – 44s. turquoise 40 15
DESIGN: 44s. Dobri Voinikov and Sava Dobroplodni (dramatist).

1956. Cultural Anniversaries.
1041 – 16s. olive 20 10
1042 – 20s. brown 25 10
1043 **350** 40s. red 50 10
1044 – 44s. brown 40 15
1045 – 60s. slate 65 15
1046 – 80s. brown 75 15
1047 – 1l. green . . . . 1·25 60
1048 – 2l. green . . . . 2·40 1·25
PORTRAITS: 16s. Benjamin Franklin (journalist and statesman, 150th birth anniv); 20s. Rembrandt (artist, 350th birth anniv); 44s. Heinrich Heine (poet, death centenary); 60s. George Bernard Shaw (dramatist, birth centenary); 80s. Fyodor Dostoevsky (novelist, 75th death anniv); 1l. Henrik Ibsen (dramatist, 50th death anniv); 2l. Pierre Curie (physicist, 50th death anniv).

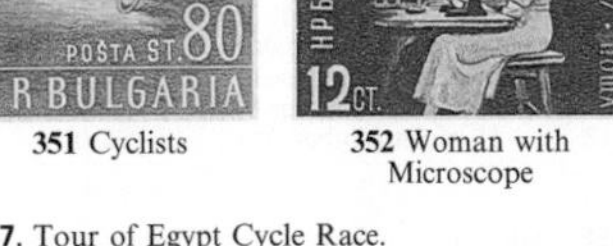
351 Cyclists **352** Woman with Microscope

1957. Tour of Egypt Cycle Race.
1049 **351** 80s. brown 90 30
1050 80s. turquoise 90 30

1957. International Women's Day. Inscr as in T **352**.
1051 **352** 12s. blue 10 10
1052 – 16s. brown 15 10
1053 – 44s. green 35 15
DESIGNS: 16s. Woman and children; 44s. Woman feeding poultry.

353 "New Times"

1957. 60th Anniv of "New Times" (book).
1054 **353** 16s. red 20 10

354 Lisunov Li-2 Airliner

1957. Air. 10th Anniv of Bulgarian Airways.
1055 **354** 80s. blue . . . . 1·00 30

355 St. Cyril and St. Methodius **356** Basketball

1957. Centenary of Canonization of Saints Cyril and Methodius (founders of Cyrillic alphabet).
1056 **355** 44s. olive and buff . . . 85 20

1957. 10th European Basketball Championships.
1057 **356** 44s. green . . . . 1·60 30

357 Girl in National Costume **358** G. Dimitrov

1957. 6th World Youth Festival, Moscow.
1058 **357** 44s. blue 50 15

1957. 75th Birth Anniv of Georgi Dimitrov (statesman).
1059 **358** 44s. red . . . . 1·00 15

359 V. Levski

1957. 120th Birth Anniv of Vasil Levski (revolutionary).
1060 **359** 44s. green 85 15

360 View of Turnovo and Ludwig Zamenhof (inventor)

1957. 70th Anniv of Esperanto (invented language) and 50th Anniv of Bulgarian Esperanto Association.
1061 **360** 44s. green . . . . 1·00 20

361 Soldiers in Battle **362** Woman Planting Tree

1957. 80th Anniv of Liberation from Turkey.
1062 – 16s. green 20 10
1063 **361** 44s. brown 55 15
DESIGN: 16s. Old and young soldiers.

1957. Reafforestation Campaign.
1064 **362** 2s. green 10 10
1065 – 12s. brown 10 10
1066 – 16s. blue 10 10
1067 – 44s. turquoise 40 10
1068 – 80s. green 85 25
DESIGNS—HORIZ: 12s. Red deer in forest; 16s. Dam and trees; 44s. Polikarpov Po-2 biplane over forest; 80s. Trees and cornfield.

363 Two Hemispheres

1957. 4th World T.U.C., Leipzig.
1069 **363** 44s. blue 45 15

364 Lenin

1957. 40th Anniv of Russian Revolution. Inscr "1917–1957".
1070 **364** 12s. brown 30 10
1071 – 16s. turquoise . . . . . 1·10 10
1072 – 44s. blue . . . . 1·10 30
1073 – 60s. red . . . . 1·75 25
1074 – 80s. green . . . . 2·75 50
DESIGNS: 16s. Cruiser "Aurora"; 44s. Dove of Peace over Europe; 60s. Revolutionaries; 80s. Oil refinery.

365 Youth and Girl 366 Partisans

1957. 10th Anniv of Dimitrov National Youth Movement.
1075 **365** 16s. red 15 10

1957. 15th Anniv of Fatherland Front.
1076 **366** 16s. brown 15 10

367 Mikhail Glinka (composer, death centenary) 368 Hotel Vasil, Kolarov

1957. Cultural Celebrities.
1077 **367** 12s. brown 30 10
1078 – 16s. green 30 10
1079 – 40s. blue . . . . 1·00 25
1080 – 44s. brown . . . . . . 1·10 25
1081 – 60s. brown . . . . . . 1·25 50
1082 – 80s. purple . . . . . . 3·25 2·10
DESIGNS: 16s. Ion Comenius (educationist) (300th anniv of publication of "Didoetica Opera Omria"); 40s. Carl Linnaeus (botanist, 250th birth anniv); 44s. William Blake (writer, birth bicent); 60s. Carlo Goldoni (dramatist, 250th birth anniv); 80s. Auguste Comte (philosopher, death centenary).

1958. Holiday Resorts.
1083 – 4s. blue 10 10
1084 – 8s. brown 10 10
1085 – 12s. green 10 10
1086 **368** 16s. green 15 10
1087 – 44s. turquoise 30 15
1088 – 60s. blue 40 15
1089 – 80s. brown 50 25
1090 – 1l. brown 60 25
DESIGNS—HORIZ: 4s. Skis and Pirin Mts; 8s. Old house in Koprivshtita; 12s. Hostel at Yelingrad; 44s. Hotel at Momin-Prokhod; 60s. Seaside hotel and peninsula, Nesebur; 80s. Beach scene, Varna; 1l. Modern hotels, Varna.

369 Brown Hare 371 Wrestlers

370 Marx and Lenin

1958. Forest Animals.
1091 **369** 2s. deep green & green 15 10
1092 – 12s. brown and green . . 40 10
1093 – 16s. brown and green . . 50 15
1094 – 44s. brown and blue . . 75 15
1095 – 80s. brown and ochre . . 1·00 40
1096 – 1l. brown and blue . . . 2·25 70
DESIGNS—VERT: 12s. Roe doe. HORIZ: 16s. Red deer; 44s. Chamois; 80s. Brown bear; 1l. Wild boar.

1958. 7th Bulgarian Communist Party Congress. Inscr as in T **370**.
1097 **370** 12s. brown 30 10
1098 – 16s. red 60 15
1099 – 44s. blue . . . . 1·25 15
DESIGNS: 16s. Workers marching with banners; 44s. Lenin blast furnaces.

1958. Wrestling Championships.
1100 **371** 60s. lake . . . . 1·75 1·00
1101 80s. sepia . . . . 2·00 1·25

372 Chessmen and "Oval Chessboard"

1958. 5th World Students' Team Chess Championship, Varna.
1102 **372** 80s. green . . . . 7·50 7·50

373 Russian Pavilion

1958. 18th International Fair, Plovdiv.
1103 **373** 44s. red 45 25

374 Swimmer

1958. Bulgarian Students' Games.
1104 **374** 16s. blue 15 10
1105 – 28s. brown 30 15
1106 – 44s. green 50 15
DESIGNS: 28s. Dancer; 44s. Volleyball players at net.

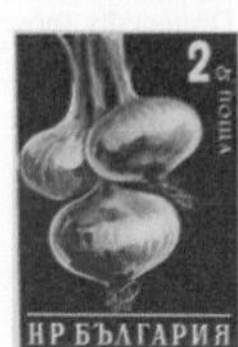

375 Onions 376 Insurgent with Rifle

1958. "Agricultural Propaganda".
1107 **375** 2s. brown 10 10
1108 – 12s. lake (Garlic) . . . 10 10
1109 – 16s. myrtle (Peppers) . . 15 10
1110 – 44s. red (Tomatoes) . . 20 10
1111 – 80s. green (Cucumbers) 55 20
1112 – 1l. violet (Aubergines) 1·10 20

1958. 35th Anniv of September Uprising.
1113 **376** 16s. orange 15 10
1114 – 44s. lake 40 20
DESIGN—HORIZ: 44s. Insurgent helping wounded comrade.

377 Conference Emblem

1958. 1st World Trade Union's Young Workers' Conference, Prague.
1115 **377** 44s. blue 65 45

378 Exhibition Emblem

1958. Brussels International Exhibition.
1116 **378** 1l. blue and black . . . 10·50 8·50

379 Sputnik over Globe 380 Running

1958. Air. I.G.Y.
1117 **379** 80s. turquoise . . . . . 6·00 3·25

1958. Balkan Games. Inscr "1958".
1118 **380** 16s. brown 60 15
1119 – 44s. olive 70 20
1120 – 60s. blue . . . . 1·10 25
1121 – 80s. green . . . . 1·75 65
1122 – 4l. lake . . . . 9·25 6·75
DESIGNS—HORIZ: 44s. Throwing the javelin; 60s. High-jumping; 80s. Hurdling. VERT: 4l. Putting the shot.

381 Young Gardeners 382 Smirnenski

1958. 4th Dimitrov National Youth Movement Congress. Inscr as in T **381**.
1123 **381** 8s. green 10 10
1124 – 12s. brown 10 10
1125 – 16s. purple 15 10
1126 – 40s. blue 30 15
1127 – 44s. red 75 25
DESIGNS—HORIZ: 12s. Farm girl with cattle; 40s. Youth with wheel-barrow. VERT: 16s. Youth with pickaxe and girl with spade; 44s. Communist Party Building.

1958. 60th Birth Anniv of Khristo Smirnenski (poet and revolutionary).
1128 **382** 16s. red 15 15

383 First Cosmic Rockets 384 Footballers

1959. Air. Launching of First Cosmic Rocket.
1129 **383** 2l. brown and blue . . . 8·50 8·50

1959. Youth Football Games, Sofia.
1130 **384** 2l. brown on cream . . . 2·40 1·75

385 U.N.E.S.C.O. Headquarters, Paris

1959. Inauguration of U.N.E.S.C.O. Headquarters Building.
1131 **385** 2l. purple on cream . . . 2·40 1·90

386 Skier 388 Military Telegraph Linesman

1959. 40 Years of Skiing in Bulgaria.
1132 **386** 1l. blue on cream . . . 1·50 85

1959. No. 1110 surch **45 CT.**
1133 45s. on 44s. red . . . . . . 1·00 15

1959. 80th Anniv of 1st Bulgarian Postage Stamps.
1134 **388** 12s. yellow and green . . 15 10
1135 – 16s. mauve and purple 35 10
1136 – 60s. yellow and brown 85 25
1137 – 80s. salmon and red . . 95 25
1138 – 1l. blue . . . . 1·10 50
1139 – 2l. brown . . . . 3·50 1·90
MS1139a 91 × 121 mm. 60s. (+41.40) yellow and black (as 1136). Imperf 65·00 65·00
MS1139b 125 × 125 mm. Remaining values in different colours (sold at 5l.)Imperf . . . . 65·00 65·00
DESIGNS—HORIZ: 16s. 19th-century mail-coach; 80s. Early postal car; 2l. Striking railway workers. VERT: 60s. Bulgarian 1879 stamp; 1l. Radio tower.

389 Great Tits 390 Cotton-picking

1959. Birds.
1140 **389** 2s. slate and yellow . . . 15 10
1141 – 8s. green and brown . . 20 15
1142 – 16s. sepia and brown . . 70 35
1143 – 45s. myrtle and brown 1·10 50
1144 – 60s. grey and blue . . . 2·75 75
1145 – 80s. drab and turquoise 4·25 70
DESIGNS—HORIZ: 8s. Hoopoe; 60s. Rock partridge; 80s. European cuckoo. VERT: 16s. Great spotted woodpecker; 45s. Grey partridge.

1959. Five Year Plan.
1146 – 2s. brown 10 10
1147 – 4s. bistre 20 10
1148 **390** 5s. green 20 10
1149 – 10s. brown 20 10
1150 – 12s. brown 15 10
1151 – 15s. mauve 20 10
1152 – 16s. violet 20 10
1153 – 20s. orange 30 10
1154 – 25s. blue 25 10
1155 – 28s. green 35 10
1156 – 40s. blue 45 10
1157 – 45s. brown 35 15
1158 – 60s. red 60 20
1159 – 80s. olive . . . . 1·25 20
1160 – 1l. lake 90 20
1161 – 1l.25 blue . . . . 2·25 75
1162 – 2l. red . . . . 1·25 35
DESIGNS—HORIZ: 2s. Children at play; 10s. Dairymaid milking cow; 16s. Industrial plant; 20s. Combine-harvester; 40s. Hydro-electric barrage; 60s. Furnaceman; 1l.25, Machinist. VERT: 4s. Woman doctor examining child; 12s. Tobacco harvesting; 15s. Machinist; 25s. Power linesman; 28s. Tending sunflowers; 45s. Miner; 80s. Fruit-picker; 1l. Workers with symbols of agriculture and industry; 2l. Worker with banner.

391 Patriots 392 Piper

1959. 300th Anniv of Batak.
1163 **391** 16s. brown 25 10

1959. Spartacist Games. Inscr "1958–1959".
1164 **392** 4s. olive on cream . . . 20 10
1165 – 12s. red on yellow . . . 20 10
1166 – 16s. lake on salmon . . 20 15
1167 – 20s. blue on blue . . . 30 15
1168 – 80s. green on green . . . 90 35
1169 – 1l. brown on orange . . 1·25 60
DESIGNS—VERT: 12s. Gymnastics; 1l. Urn. HORIZ: 16s. Girls exercising with hoops; 20s. Dancers leaping; 80s. Ballet dancers.

393 Soldiers in Lorry

1959. 15th Anniv of Fatherland Front Government.
1170 **393** 12s. blue and red . . . 10 10
1171 – 16s. black and red . . . 10 10
1172 – 45s. blue and red . . . 20 10
1173 – 60s. green and red . . . 25 20
1174 – 80s. brown and red . . . 45 25
1175 – 1l.25 brown and red . . 95 45
DESIGNS—HORIZ: 16s. Partisans meeting Red Army soldiers; 45s. Blast furnaces; 60s. Tanks; 80s. Combine-harvester in cornfield. VERT: 1l.25, Pioneers with banner.

394 Footballer

1959. 50th Anniv of Football in Bulgaria.
1176 **394** 1l.25 green on yellow . . 6·75 5·00

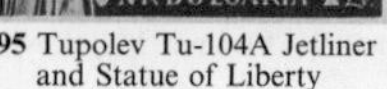

395 Tupolev Tu-104A Jetliner and Statue of Liberty 396 Globe and Letter

1959. Air. Visit of Nikita Khrushchev (Russian Prime Minister) to U.S.A.
1177 **395** 1l. pink and blue . . . . 3·00 2·75

1959. International Correspondence Week.
1178 **396** 45s. black and green . . 60 15
1179 – 1l.25 red, black & blue 85 25
DESIGN: 1l.25, Pigeon and letter.

397 Parachutist

398 N. Vaptsarov

1960. 3rd Voluntary Defence Congress.
1180 **397** 1l.25 cream & turquoise 2·40 1·10

1960. 50th Birth Anniv of Nikola Vaptsarov (poet and revolutionary).
1181 **398** 80s. brown and green . . 45 15

399 Dr. L. Zamenhof

400

1960. Birth Centenary of Dr. Ludwig Zamenhof (inventor of Esperanto).
1182 **399** 1l.25 green & lt green . . 1·40 85

1960. 50th Anniv of State Opera.
1183 **400** 80s. black and green . . 85 25
1184 – 1l.25 black and red . . . 1·25 30
DESIGN: 1l.25, Lyre.

401 Track of Trajectory of "Lunik 3" around the Moon

1960. Flight of "Lunik 3".
1185 **401** 1l.25 green, yellow & bl 7·00 5·00

402 Skier

1960. Winter Olympic Games.
1186 **402** 2l. brown, blue & black 1·60 1·00

403 Vela Blagoeva

404 Lenin

1960. 50th Anniv of International Women's Day. Inscr "1910–1960".
1187 **403** 16s. brown and pink . . 10 10
1188 – 28s. olive and yellow . . 15 10
1189 – 45s. green and olive . . 20 10
1190 – 60s. blue and light blue 30 15
1191 – 80s. brown and red . . . 35 15
1192 – 1l.25 olive and ochre . . 70 30
PORTRAITS: 28s. Anna Maimunkowa; 45s. Vela Piskova; 60s. Rosa Luxemburg; 80s. Clara Zetkin; 1l.25, Nadezhda Krupskaya.

1960. 90th Birth Anniv of Lenin.
1193 **404** 16s. flesh and brown . . 1·25 25
1194 – 45s. black and pink . . . 2·00 30
DESIGN: 45s. "Lenin at Smolny" (writing in chair).

406 Basketball Players

407 Moon Rocket

1960. 7th European Women's Basketball Championships.
1195 **406** 1l.25 black and yellow 1·50 45

1960. Air. Landing of Russian Rocket on Moon.
1196 **407** 1l.25 black, yellow & bl 8·25 5·00

408 Parachutist

409 "Gentiana lutea"

1960. World Parachuting Championships, 1960.
1197 **408** 16s. blue and lilac . . . 60 55
1198 – 1l.25 red and blue . . . 2·75 85
DESIGN: 1l.25, Parachutes descending.

1960. Flowers.
1199 **409** 2s. orange, grn & drab 15 10
1200 – 5s. red, green and yellow 20 10
1201 – 25s. orge, grn & salmon 60 10
1202 – 45s. mauve, grn & lilac 75 15
1203 – 60s. red, green and buff 1·25 15
1204 – 80s. blue, green & drab 1·50 65
FLOWERS: 5s. "Tulipa rhodopea"; 25s. "Lilium jankae"; 45s. "Rhododendron ponticum"; 60s. "Cypripedium calceolus"; 80s. "Haberlea rhodopensis".

410 Football

1960. Olympic Games.
1205 **410** 8s. pink and brown . . . 10 10
1206 – 12s. pink and violet . . 15 10
1207 – 16s. pink & turquoise . . 25 15
1208 – 45s. pink and purple . . 50 15
1209 – 80s. pink and blue . . . 75 30
1210 – 2l. pink and green . . . 1·60 55
DESIGNS: 12s. Wrestling; 16s. Weightlifting; 45s. Gymnastics; 80s. Canoeing; 2l. Running.

411 Racing Cyclists

1960. Tour of Bulgaria Cycle Race.
1211 **411** 1l. black, yellow & red 1·75 1·10

412 Globes

1960. 15th Anniv of W.F.T.U.
1212 **412** 1l.25 cobalt and blue . . 60 30

413 Popov

414 Y. Veshin

1960. Birth Centenary of Alexsandr Popov (Russian radio pioneer).
1213 **413** 90s. black and blue . . . 1·10 30

1960. Birth Centenary of Yavoslav Veshin (painter).
1214 **414** 1l. olive and yellow . . . 5·00 2·40

415 U.N. Headquarters, New York

416 Boyana Church

1961. 15th Anniv of U.N.O.
1215 **415** 1l. cream and brown . . 2·00 1·50
MS1215a 74 × 57 mm. **415** 1l. (+1l.) pink and green. Imperf . . . . 12·50 12·50

1961. 700th Anniv of Boyana Murals (1959).
1216 **416** 60s. black, emer & grn 1·00 15
1217 – 80s. grn, cream & orange 1·25 25
1218 – 1l.25 red, cream & green 2·00 65
DESIGNS (Frescoes of): 80s. Theodor Tiron; 1l.25, Desislava.

417 Cosmic Rocket and Dogs Belda and Strelka

1961. Russian Cosmic Rocket Flight of August, 1960.
1219 **417** 1l.25 blue and red . . . 8·50 6·00

419 Pleven Costume

420 Clock Tower, Vratsa

1961. Provincial Costumes.
1220 – 12s. yellow, green & orge 15 10
1221 **419** 16s. brown, buff & lilac 15 10
1222 – 28s. red, black, & green 25 10
1223 – 45s. blue and red 40 15
1224 – 60s. yellow, blue & turq 70 20
1225 – 80s. red, green & yellow 90 30
COSTUMES: 12s. Kyustendil; 28s. Sliven; 45s. Sofia; 60s. Rhodope; 80c. Karnobat.

1961. Museums and Monuments. Values and star in red.
1226 **420** 8s. green 10 10
1227 – 12s. violet 10 10
1228 – 16s. brown 15 10
1229 – 20s. blue 20 10
1230 – 28s. turquoise 25 15
1231 – 40s. brown 30 10
1232 – 45s. olive 35 15
1233 – 60s. slate 65 15
1234 – 80s. brown 85 20
1235 – 1l. turquoise . . . . . 1·25 45
DESIGNS—As Type **420**. VERT: 12s. Clock Tower, Bansko; 20s. "Agushev" building, Mogilitsa (Smolensk). HORIZ: 28s. Oslekoff House, Koprivshtitsa; 40s. Pasha's House, Melnik. SQUARE (27 × 27 mm): 16s. Wine jug; 45s. Lion (bas-relief); 60s. "Horseman of Madara"; 80s. Fresco, Bachkovo Monastery; 1l. Coin of Tsar Konstantin-Asen (13th cent).

421 Dalmatian Pelican

422 "Communications and Transport"

1961. Birds.
1236 – 2s. turquoise, blk & red 10 10
1237 **421** 4s. orange, blk & grn . . 15 10
1238 – 16s. orange, brn & grn 15 10
1239 – 80s. yellow, brn & turq 1·75 30
1240 – 1l. yellow, sepia and blue 1·75 75
1241 – 2l. yellow, brown & blue 2·75 80
DESIGNS: 2s. White capercaillie; 16s. Common pheasant; 80s. Great bustard; 1l. Lammergeier; 2l. Hazel grouse.

1961. 50th Anniv of Transport Workers' Union.
1242 **422** 80s. green and black . . 85 20

423 Gagarin and Rocket

1961. World's First Manned Space Flight.
1243 **423** 4l. turquoise, blk & red 5·00 3·25

424 Shevchenko (Ukrainian poet)

1961. Death Centenary of Taras Shevchenko.
1244 **424** 1l. brown and green . . 4·75 2·40

425 Throwing the Discus

1961. World Students' Games. Values and inscr in black.
1245 – 4s. blue 10 10
1246 – 5s. red 20 10
1247 – 16s. olive 30 10
1248 **425** 45s. blue 45 20
1249 – 1l.25 brown . . . . . . 1·00 35
1250 – 2l. mauve . . . . 1·25 80
MS1250a 66 × 66 mm. 5l. blue, yellow and green (Sports Palace and inscriptions). Imperf . . . 17·00 17·00
DESIGNS—VERT: 4s. Water polo; 2l. Basketball. HORIZ: 5s. Tennis; 16s. Fencing; 1l.25, Sports Palace, Sofia.

426 Short-snouted Seahorse

427 "Space" Dogs

1961. Black Sea Fauna.
1251 – 2s. sepia and green . . . 10 10
1252 – 12s. pink and blue . . . 25 10
1253 – 16s. violet and blue . . . 40 10
1254 **426** 45s. brown and blue . . 1·40 50
1255 – 1l. blue and green . . . 2·75 1·00
1256 – 1l.25 brown and blue . . 4·00 1·50
DESIGNS—HORIZ: 2s. Mediterranean monk seal; 12s. Lung jellyfish; 16s. Common dolphins; 1l. Stellate sturgeons; 1l.25, Thorn-backed ray.

1961. Air. Space Exploration.
1257 **427** 2l. slate and purple . . . 4·00 3·00
1258 – 2l. blue, yellow & orange 8·25 5·00
DESIGN: No. 1258, "Venus" rocket in flight (24 × 41½ mm).

428 Dimitur Blagoev as Orator

1961. 70th Anniv of First Bulgarian Social Democratic Party Congress, Buzludzha.
1259 **428** 45s. red and cream . . . 25 15
1260 80s. blue and pink . . . 40 15
1261 2l. sepia and green . . . 1·40 45

429 Hotel

1961. Tourist issue. Inscr in black; designs green. Background colours given.
1262 **429** 4s. green 10 10
1263 – 12s. blue (Hikers) . . . 10 10

1264 – 16s. green (Tents) . . . 10 10
1265 – 1l.25 bistre (Climber) . . 85 15
Nos. 1263/5 are vert.

430 "The Golden Girl"

1961. Bulgarian Fables.
1266 **430** 2s. multicoloured 15 10
1267 – 8s. grey, black & purple 20 10
1268 – 12s. pink, black & green 25 10
1269 – 16s. multicoloured . . . 85 20
1270 – 45s. multicoloured . . . 1·50 30
1271 – 80s. multicoloured . . . 2·00 45
DESIGNS: 8s. Man and woman ("The Living Water"); 12s. Archer and dragon ("The Golden Apple"); 16s. Horseman ("Krali Marko", national hero); 45s. Female archer on stag ("Samovila-Vila", fairy); 80s. "Tom Thumb" and cockerel.

431 Major Titov in Space-suit

432 "Amanita caesarea"

1961. Air. 2nd Russian Manned Space Flight.
1272 **431** 75s. flesh, blue & olive 3·50 2·50
1273 – 1l.25 pink, bl & violet 4·50 3·75
DESIGN: 1l.25, "Vostok-2" in flight.

1961. Mushrooms.
1274 **432** 2s. red, bistre & black 10 10
1275 – 4s. brown, grn & blk . . 15 10
1276 – 12s. brown, bistre & blk 20 10
1277 – 16s. brown, mve & blk 20 10
1278 – 45s. multicoloured . . . 40 15
1279 – 80s. orange, sepia & blk 75 25
1280 – 1l.25 lav, brn & blk . . 90 45
1281 – 2l. brown, bistre & black 1·75 80
MUSHROOMS: 4s. "Psalliota silvatica"; 12s. "Boletus elegans"; 16s. "Boletus edulis"; 45s. "Lactarius deliciosus"; 80s. "Lepiota procera"; 1l.25, "Pleurotus ostreatus"; 2l. "Armillariella mellea".

433 Dimitur and Konstantin Miladinov (authors)

436 Isker River

1961. Publication Centenary of "Bulgarian Popular Songs".
1282 **433** 1l.25 black and olive . . 1·00 30

(Currency revaluation)

1962. Surch. (A) Surch in one line; (B) in two lines.
1283 1s. on 10s. brown (1149) . . 10 10
1284 1s. on 12s. brown (1150) . . 10 10
1285 2s. on 15s. mauve (1151) . . 10 10
1286 2s. on 16s. violet (1152) . . 10 10
1287 2s. on 20s. orange (1153) (A) 10 10
1288 2s. on 20s. orange (1153) (B) 25 10
1289 3s. on 25s. blue (1154) . . . 20 10
1290 3s. on 28s. green (1155) . . 20 10
1291 5s. on 44s. green (1087) . . 25 10
1292 5s. on 44s. red (1110) . . . 25 10
1293 5s. on 45s. brown (1157) . . 25 10
1294 10s. on 1l. red (1160) . . . 45 15
1295 20s. on 2l. red (1162) . . . 75 40
1296 40s. on 4l. red (889) . . . . 2·00 75

1962. Air.
1297 **436** 1s. blue and violet . . . 10 10
1298 – 2s. blue and pink 30 10
1299 – 3s. brown and chestnut 20 10
1300 – 10s. black and bistre . . 60 15
1301 – 40s. black and green . . 2·00 45
DESIGNS: 2s. Yacht at Varna; 3s. Melnik; 10s. Turnovo; 40s. Pirin Mountains.

437 Freighter "Varna"

1962. Bulgarian Merchant Navy.
1302 **437** 1s. green and blue . . . 10 10
1303 – 5s. light blue and green 60 10
1304 – 20s. violet and blue . . . 1·75 35
SHIPS: 5s. Tanker "Komsomols"; 20s. Liner "Georgi Dimitrov".

438 Rila Mountains

1962. Views.
1305 **438** 1s. turquoise 10 10
1306 – 2s. blue 10 10
1307 – 6s. turquoise 60 10
1308 – 8s. purple 80 20
1309 – 13s. green 65 15
1310 – 1l. deep green . . . . . 5·25 40
VIEWS: 2s. Pirin Mts; 6s. Fishing boats, Nesebur; 8s. Danube shipping; 13s. Viden Castle; 1l. Rhodope Mts.

439 Georgi Dimitrov as Typesetter

440 Pink Roses

1962. 80th Anniv of State Printing Office.
1311 **439** 2s. red, black & yellow 10 10
1312 – 13s. black, orange & yell 75 15
DESIGN: 13s. Emblem of Printing Office.

1962. Bulgarian Roses. T **440** and similar designs.
1313 1s. pink, green and violet . . 10 10
1314 2s. red, green and buff . . . 10 10
1315 3s. red, green and blue . . . 25 10
1316 4s. yellow, turquoise & grn 35 10
1317 5s. pink, green and blue . . 65 20
1318 6s. red, green and turquoise 80 40
1319 8s. red, green and yellow . . 2·75 65
1320 13s. yellow, green and blue 4·75 1·10

441 "The World United against Malaria"

1962. Malaria Eradication.
1321 **441** 5s. yellow, black & brn 60 15
1322 – 20s. yellow, green & blk 1·40 60
DESIGN: 20s. Campaign emblem.

442 Lenin and Front Page of "Pravda"

1962. 50th Anniv of "Pravda" Newspaper.
1323 **442** 5s. blue, red and black 90 25

443 Text-book and Blackboard

444 Footballer

1962. Bulgarian Teachers' Congress.
1324 **443** 5s. black, yellow & blue 15 10

1962. World Football Championship, Chile.
1325 **444** 13s. brown, green & blk 1·10 35

445 Dimitrov

1962. 80th Birth Anniv of Georgi Dimitrov (Prime Minister 1946–49).
1326 **445** 2s. green 15 10
1327 5s. blue 75 35

446 Bishop

448 Festival Emblem

1962. 15th Chess Olympiad, Varna. Inscr "1962". Inscr in black.
1328 **446** 1s. green and grey . . . 15 10
1329 – 2s. bistre and grey . . . 15 10
1330 – 3s. purple and grey . . . 15 10
1331 – 13s. orange and grey . . 1·50 40
1332 – 20s. blue and grey . . . 2·00 70
MS1332a 76×66 mm. 20s. (+30s.) red and green (Chess pieces). Imperf . . . . 17·00 17·00
CHESS PIECES: 2s. Rook; 3s. Queen; 13s. Knight; 20s. Pawn.

XXXV КОНГРЕС
1962
13 =
(447)

1962. 35th Esperanto Congress, Burgas. Surch as T **447**.
1333 **360** 13s. on 44s. green . . . 4·75 3·00

1962. World Youth Festival, Helsinki. Inscr "1962".
1334 **448** 5s. blue, pink and green 20 10
1335 – 13s. blue, purple & grey 50 20
DESIGN: 13s. Girl and emblem.

449 Ilyushin Il-18 Airliner

1962. Air. 13th Anniv of TABSO Airline.
1336 **449** 13s. blue, ultram & blk 1·25 20

450 Apollo

1962. Butterflies and Moths. Multicoloured.
1337 1s. Type **450** 10 10
1338 2s. Eastern festoon 15 10
1339 3s. Meleager's blue 20 10
1340 4s. Camberwell beauty . . . 25 10
1341 5s. Crimson underwing . . . 30 10
1342 6s. Hebe tiger moth 85 15
1343 10s. Danube clouded . . . 3·00 60
1344 13s. Cardinal . . . . 2·75 90

451 K. E. Tsiolkovsky (scientist)

1962. Air. 13th International Astronautics Congress. Inscr "1962".
1345 **451** 5s. drab and green . . . 4·00 1·50
1346 – 13s. blue and yellow . . 2·00 75
DESIGN: 13s. Moon rocket.

452 Combine Harvester

1962. 8th Bulgarian Communist Party Congress.
1347 **452** 1s. olive and turquoise 10 10
1348 – 2s. turquoise and blue 15 30
1349 – 3s. brown and red . . . 20 10
1350 – 13s. sepia, red & purple 1·00 30
DESIGNS: 2s. Electric train; 3s. Steel furnace; 13s. Blagoev and Dimitrov.

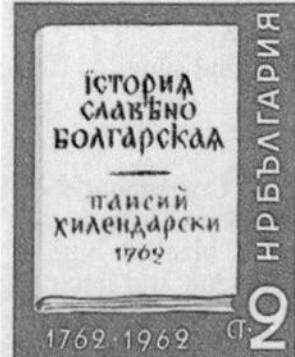
453 Cover of "History of Bulgaria"

1962. Bicentenary of Paisii Khilendarski's "History of Bulgaria".
1351 **453** 2s. black and olive . . . 10 10
1352 – 5s. sepia and brown . . . 25 10
DESIGN—HORIZ: 5s. Father Paisii at work on book.

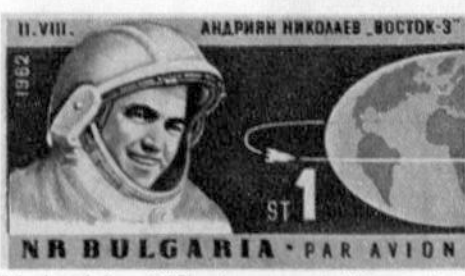
454 Andrian Nikolaev and "Vostok 3"

1962. Air. 1st "Team" Manned Space Flight.
1353 **454** 1s. olive, blue and black 15 10
1354 – 2s. olive, green & black 30 15
1355 – 40s. pink, turquoise & blk . . . . 3·25 2·10
DESIGNS: 2s. Pavel Ropovich and "Vostok 4"; 40s. "Vostoks 3" and "4" in flight.

455 Parachutist

456 Aleko Konstantinov

1963.
1356 – 1s. lake 10 10
1357 – 1s. brown 10 10
1358 – 1s. turquoise 10 10
1359 – 1s. green 10 10
1360 **455** 1s. blue 10 10
DESIGNS—VERT: No. 1356, State crest. HORIZ: No. 1357, Sofia University; 1358, "Vasil Levski" Stadium, Sofia; 1359, "The Camels" (archway), Hisar.

1963. Birth Cent of Konstantinov (author).
1361 **456** 5s. green and red 20 10

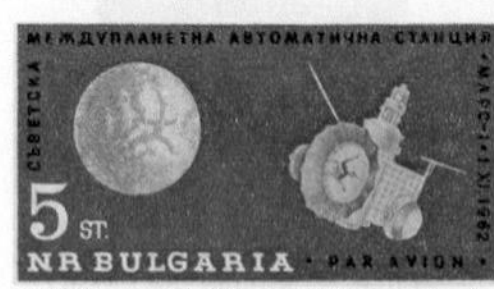
457 Mars and "Mars 1" Space Probe

1963. Air. Launching of Soviet Space Station "Mars 1".
1362 **457** 5s. multicoloured 70 30
1363 – 13s. turquoise, red & blk 1·40 75
DESIGN: 13s. Release of probe from rocket.

458 Orpheus Restaurant, "Sunny Beach"

459 V. Levski

1963. Black Sea Coast Resorts.
1364 **458** 1s. blue 10 10
1365a – 2s. red 80 15
1366 – 3s. bistre 25 10
1367 – 5s. purple 45 10
1368 – 13s. turquoise . . . . . 1·25 15
1369 – 20s. green . . . . 1·75 30
VIEWS "Sunny Beach": 5s. The Dunes Restaurant; 20s. Hotel. "Golden Sands"; 2s., 3s., 13s. Various hotels.

1963. 90th Anniv of Execution of Vasil Levski (revolutionary).
1370 **459** 13s. blue and yellow . . 75 30

460 Dimitrov, Boy and Girl

461 Eurasian Red Squirrel

1963. 10th Dimitrov Communist Youth League Congress, Sofia.
1371 **460** 2s. brown, red & black 15 10
1372 – 13s. brown, turq & blk 45 20
DESIGN: 13s. Girl and youth holding book and hammer aloft.

1963. Woodland Animals.
1373 **461** 1s. brown, red and green on turquoise 10 10
1374 – 2s. blk, red & grn on yell 15 10
1375 – 3s. sep, red & ol on drab 10 10
1376 – 5s. brown, red and blue on violet 60 10
1377 – 13s. black, red and brown on pink . . . . 2·25 25
1378 – 20s. sepia, red and blue on blue . . . . 3·50 40
ANIMALS—HORIZ: 2s. East European hedgehog; 3s. Marbled polecat; 5s. Beech marten; 13s. Eurasian badger. VERT: 20s. European otter.

462 Wrestling

1963. 15th International Open Wrestling Championships, Sofia.
1379 **462** 5s. bistre and black . . . 20 15
1380 – 20s. brown and black . . 1·25 30
DESIGN—HORIZ: 20s. As Type **462** but different hold.

463 Congress Emblem and Allegory

1963. World Women's Congress, Moscow.
1381 **463** 20s. blue and black . . . 1·00 25

464 Esperanto Star and Sofia Arms
465 Rocket, Globe and Moon

1963. 48th World Esperanto Congress, Sofia.
1382 **464** 13s. multicoloured . . . 1·00 25

1963. Launching of Soviet Moon Rocket "Luna 4". Inscr "2.IV.1963".
1383 **465** 1s. blue 10 10
1384 – 2s. purple 10 10
1385 – 3s. turquoise 15 10
DESIGNS: 2s. Tracking equipment; 3s. Sputniks.

466 Valery Bykovsky in Spacesuit

1963. Air. 2nd "Team" Manned Space Flights. Inscr "14.VI.1963".
1386 **466** 1s. turquoise and lilac 10 10
1387 – 2s. brown and yellow . . 15 10
1388 – 5s. red and light red . . 25 10
1389 – 20s.+10s. grn & lt bl . . 2·10 80
MS1389a 79 × 68 mm. 50s. purple and brown (Spassk Tower and Globe). Imperf . . . . 5·00 4·25
DESIGNS: 2s. Valentina Tereshkova in spacesuit; 5s. Globe; 20s. Bykovsky and Tereshkova.

1963. Europa Fair, Riccione. Nos. 1314/5 and 1318 (Roses) optd **MOSTRA EUROPEISTICA.1963 RICCIONE** and sailing boat motif or additionally surch.
1390 2s. red, green and buff . . . 30 15
1391 5s. on 3s. red, green and blue 40 15
1392 13s. on 6s. red, green & turq 1·40 40

468 Relay-racing

1963. Balkan Games. Flags in red, yellow, blue, green and black.
1393 **468** 1s. green 10 10
1394 – 2s. violet 15 10
1395 – 3s. turquoise 20 10
1396 – 5s. red 50 20
1397 – 13s. brown . . . . . . 3·00 2·25
MS1397a 74 × 69 mm. 50s. black and green (as T **468**). Imperf . . . 8·50 8·00
DESIGNS: 2s. Throwing the hammer; 3s. Long jumping; 5s. High jumping; 13s. Throwing the discus. Each design includes the flags of the competing countries.

469 Slavonic Scroll
470 Insurgents

1963. 5th International Slav Congress, Sofia.
1398 **469** 5s. red, yellow & dp grn 20 10

1963. 40th Anniv of September Uprising.
1399 **470** 2s. black and red 15 10

471 "Aquilegia aurea"

472 Khristo Smirnenski

1963. Nature Protection. Flowers in natural colours; background colours given.
1400 **471** 1s. turquoise 10 10
1401 – 2s. olive 10 10
1402 – 3s. yellow 20 10
1403 – 5s. blue 40 10
1404 – 6s. purple 45 15
1405 – 8s. light grey 65 15
1406 – 10s. mauve . . . . . . 1·75 25
1407 – 13s. olive . . . . 2·75 45
FLOWERS: 2s. Edelweiss; 3s. "Primula deorum"; 5s. White water-lily; 6s. Tulip; 8s. "Viola delphinantha"; 10s. Alpine clematis; 13s. "Anemone narcissiflora".

1963. 65th Birth Anniv of Smirnenski (poet and revolutionary).
1408 **472** 13s. black and lilac . . . 75 15

473 Chariot Horses (wall-painting)

474 Hemispheres and Centenary Emblem

1963. Thracian Tombs, Kazanilk.
1409 **473** 1s. red, yellow and grey 10 10
1410 – 2s. violet, yellow & grey 15 10
1411 – 3s. turquiose, yell & grey 20 10
1412 – 5s. brown, yellow & grn 25 10
1413 – 13s. black, yellow & grn 60 15
1414 – 20s. red, yellow & green 1·40 55
DESIGNS (wall paintings on tombs): 2s. Chariot race; 3s. Flautists; 5s. Tray-bearer; 13s. Funeral feast; 20s. Seated woman.

1964. Centenary of Red Cross.
1415 **474** 1s. yellow, red & black 10 10
1416 – 2s. blue, red and black 10 10
1417 – 3s. multicoloured 10 10
1418 – 5s. turq, red & black . . 25 10
1419 – 13s. black, red & orange 85 25
DESIGNS: 2s. Blood donation; 3s. Bandaging wrist; 5s. Nurse; 13s. Henri Dunant.

475 Speed-skating

1964. Winter Olympic Games, Innsbruck.
1420 **475** 1s. indigo, brown & blue 10 10
1421 – 2s. olive, mauve & black 10 10
1422 – 3s. green, brown & blk 15 10
1423 – 5s. multicoloured 25 15
1424 – 10s. orange, blk & grey 85 20
1425 – 13s. mauve, violet & blk 1·00 25
MS1425a 64 × 67 mm. 50s. red, blue and grey (Girl skater). Imperf 7·50 7·50
DESIGNS: 2s. Figure skating; 3s. Cross-country skiing; 5s. Ski jumping. Ice hockey—10s. Goalkeeper; 13s. Players.

476 Head (2nd cent)

1964. 2500 Years of Bulgarian Art. Borders in grey.
1426 **476** 1s. turquoise and red . . 10 10
1427 – 2s. sepia and red 10 10
1428 – 3s. bistre and red . . . 10 10
1429 – 5s. blue and red 25 10
1430 – 6s. brown and red . . . 35 10
1431 – 8s. brown and red . . . 50 15
1432 – 10s. olive and red . . . 60 15
1433 – 13s. olive and red . . . 1·10 25
DESIGNS: 2s. Horseman (1st to 4th cent); 3s. Jug (19th cent); 5s. Buckle (19th cent); 6s. Pot (19th cent); 8s. Angel (17th cent); 10s. Animals (8th to 10th cent); 13s. Peasant woman (20th cent).

477 "The Unborn Maid"

1964. Folk Tales. Multicoloured.
1434 1s. Type **477** 10 10
1435 2s. "Grandfather's Glove" 10 10
1436 3s. "The Big Turnip" . . . 10 10
1437 5s. "The Wolf and the Seven Kids" 25 10
1438 8s. "Cunning Peter" 40 15
1439 13s. "The Loaf of Corn" . . 1·25 30

478 Turkish Lacewing ("Ascalaphus ottomanus")

1964. Insects.
1440 **478** 1s. black, yellow & brn 10 10
1441 – 2s. black, ochre & turq 15 10
1442 – 3s. green, black & drab 20 10
1443 – 5s. violet, black & green 65 10
1444 – 13s. brown, black & vio 1·40 25
1445 – 20s. yellow, black & bl 2·50 40
DESIGNS—VERT: 2s. Thread lacewing fly ("Nemoptera coa"); 5s. Alpine longhorn beetle ("Rosalia alpina"); 13s. Cockchafer ("Anisoplia austriaca"). HORIZ: 3s. Cricket ("Saga natalia"); 20s. Hunting wasp ("Scolia flavitrons").

479 Football

1964. 50th Anniv of Levski Physical Culture Association.
1446 2s. Type **479** 15 10
1447 13s. Handball 95 30
MS1447a 60 × 60 mm. 60s. green and yellow (Cup and Map of Europe). Imperf . . . . 4·50 3·50

480 Title Page and Petar Beron (author)

1964. 40th Anniv of First Bulgarian Primer.
1448 **480** 20s. black and brown . . 2·00 2·00

481 Stephenson's "Rocket", 1829

1964. Railway Transport. Multicoloured.
1449 1s. Type **481** 10 10
1450 2s. Class 05 steam locomotive 15 10
1451 3s. German V.320.001 diesel locomotive 25 10
1452 5s. Electric locomotive . . . 45 10
1453 8s. Class 05 steam locomotive and train on bridge 70 15
1454 13s. Class E41 electric train emerging from tunnel . . 1·10 25

482 Alsatian
(483)

1964. Dogs. Multicoloured.
1455 1s. Type **482** 10 10
1456 2s. Setter 20 10
1457 3s. Poodle 25 10
1458 4s. Pomeranian 30 10
1459 5s. St. Bernard 40 15
1460 6s. Fox terrier 85 15
1461 10s. Pointer . . . . 3·00 55
1462 13s. Dachshund . . . . . . 3·50 1·40

1964. Air. International Cosmic Exhibition, Riccione. No. 1386 surch with T **483** and No. 1387 surch as T **483**, but in Italian.
1463 **466** 10s. on 1s. turquoise and lilac 50 20
1464 – 20s. on 2s. brown & yell 1·00 30

484 Partisans and Flag

1964. 20th Anniv of Fatherland. Front Government. Flag in red.
1465 **484** 1s. blue and light blue 10 10
1466 – 2s. olive and bistre . . . 10 10
1467 – 3s. lake and mauve . . . 10 10
1468 – 4s. violet and lavender 15 10
1469 – 5s. brown and orange . . 20 10
1470 – 6s. blue and light blue 30 10
1471 – 8s. green and light green 70 10
1472 – 13s. brown and salmon 1·00 50
DESIGNS: 2s. Greeting Soviet troops; 3s. Soviet aid—arrival of goods; 4s. Industrial plant, Kremikovtsi; 5s. Combine-harvester; 6s. "Peace" campaigners; 8s. Soldier of National Guard; 3s. Blagoev and Dimitrov. All with flag as Type **484**.

(485)
486 Transport

1964. 21st Int Fair, Plovdiv. Surch with T **485**.
1473 20s. on 44s. ochre (No. 1020a) . . . . . . 1·90 35

1964. 1st National Stamp Exn, Sofia.
1474 **486** 20s. blue . . . . 2·75 1·00

487 Gymnastics

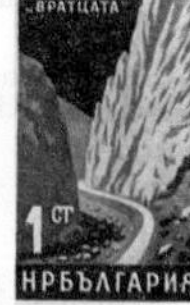

488 Vratsata

1964. Olympic Games, Tokyo. Rings and values in red.
1475 **487** 1s. green and light green 10 10
1476 – 2s. blue and lavender . . 10 10
1477 – 3s. blue and turquoise 15 10
1478 – 5s. violet and red 15 10
1479 – 13s. blue and light blue 1·00 15
1480 – 20s. green and buff . . . 1·40 25
MS1480a 61 × 67 mm. 40s.+20s. ochre, red and blue (Rings, tracks etc.). Imperf . . . . 4·00 3·00

DESIGNS: 2s. Long-jump; 3s. Swimmer on starting block; 5s. Football; 13s. Volleyball; 20s. Wrestling.

1964. Landscapes.

1481	**488**	1s. green	10	10
1482	–	2s. brown	10	10
1483	–	3s. blue	15	10
1484	–	4s. brown	20	10
1485	–	5s. green	30	10
1486	–	6s. violet	40	10

DESIGNS: 2s. The Ritli; 3s. Maliovitsa; 4s. Broken Rocks; 5s. Erkyupria; 6s. Rhodope mountain pass.

489 Paper and Cellulose Factory, Bukovtsi

1964. Air. Industrial Buildings.

1487	**489**	8s. turquoise	25	10
1488	–	10s. purple	35	10
1489	–	13s. violet	40	10
1490	–	20s. blue	1·00	15
1491	–	40s. green	1·90	60

DESIGNS: 10s. Metal works, Plovdiv; 13s. Metallurgical works, Kremikovtzi; 20s. Petrol refinery, Burgas; 40s. Fertiliser factory, Stara-Zagora.

490 Rila Monastery

1964. Philatelic Exn for Franco–Bulgarian Amity.

1492	**490**	5s. black and drab	30	15
1493	–	13s. black and blue	1·10	30

DESIGN: 13s. Notre-Dame, Paris (inscr in French).

491 500-year-old Walnut **492**

1964. Ancient Trees. Values and inscr in black.

1494	**491**	1s. brown	10	10
1495	–	2s. purple	10	10
1496	–	3s. sepia	15	10
1497	–	4s. blue	15	10
1498	–	10s. green	45	20
1499	–	13s. olive	80	25

TREES: 2s. Plane (1000 yrs.); 3s. Plane (600 yrs.); 4s. Poplar (800 yrs.); 10s. Oak (800 yrs.); 13s. Fir (1200 yrs.).

1964. 8th Congress of Int Union of Students, Sofia.

1500	**492**	13s. black and blue	80	15

493 Bulgarian Veteran and Soviet Soldier (Sculpture by T. Zlatarev) **494** "Gold Medal"

1965. 30 Years of Bulgarian–Russian Friendship.

1501	**493**	2s. red and black	20	10

1965. Olympic Games, Tokyo (1964).

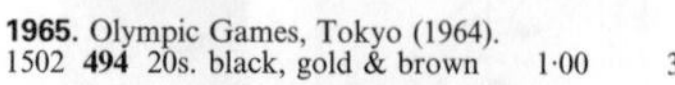

1502	**494**	20s. black, gold & brown	1·00	30

495 Vladimir Komarov

1965. Flight of "Voskhod 1". Multicoloured.

1503	1s. Type **495**	10	10
1504	2s. Konstantin Feoktistov	10	10
1505	5s. Boris Yegorov	15	10
1506	13s. The three astronauts	85	15
1507	20s. "Voskhod l"	1·40	25

496 Corn-cob **497** "Victory against Fascism"

1965. Agricultural Products.

1508	**496**	1s. yellow	10	10
1509	–	2s. green	10	10
1510	–	3s. orange	15	10
1511	–	4s. olive	20	10
1512	–	5s. red	30	10
1513	–	10s. blue	55	20
1514	–	13s. bistre	1·25	25

DESIGNS: 2s. Ears of Wheat; 3s. Sunflowers; 4s. Sugar beet; 5s. Clover; 10s. Cotton; 13s. Tobacco.

1965. 20th Anniv of "Victory of 9 May, 1945".

1515	**497**	5s. black, bistre & grey	15	10
1516	–	13s. blue, black & grey	40	20

DESIGN: 13s. Globes on dove ("Peace").

498 Northern Bullfinch **499** Transport, Globe and Whale

1965. Song Birds. Multicoloured.

1517	1s. Type **498**	10	10
1518	2s. Golden oriole	15	10
1519	3s. Rock thrush	20	10
1520	5s. Barn swallows	60	10
1521	8s. European roller	95	15
1522	10s. Eurasian goldfinch	3·75	25
1523	13s. Rose-coloured starling	3·75	55
1524	20s. Nightingale	4·00	1·25

1965. 4th International Transport Conf, Sofia.

1525	**499**	13s. multicoloured	1·10	30

500 I.C.Y. Emblem **501** I.T.U. Emblem and Symbols

1965. International Co-operation Year.

1526	**500**	20s. orange, olive & blk	90	25

1965. Centenary of I.T.U.

1527	**501**	20s. yellow, green & bl	1·25	30

502 Pavel Belyaev and Aleksei Leonov

1965. "Voskhod 2" Space Flight.

1528	**502**	2s. purple, grn & drab	30	10
1529	–	20s. multicoloured	3·00	1·10

DESIGN: 20s. Leonov on space.

503 Common Stingray **504** Marx and Lenin

1965. Fishes. Borders in grey.

1530	**503**	1s. gold, black & orange	10	10
1531	–	2s. silver, indigo & blue	10	10
1532	–	3s. gold, black & green	20	10
1533	–	5s. gold, black and red	25	10
1534	–	10s. silver, blue & turq	1·50	25
1535	–	13s. gold, black & brown	1·75	45

FISHES: 2s. Atlantic bonito; 3s. Brown scorpionfish; 5s. Tub gurnard; 10s. Mediterranean horse-mackerel; 13s. Black Sea turbot.

1965. Organization of Socialist Countries' Postal Ministers' Conference, Peking.

1536	**504**	13s. brown and red	1·10	20

505 Film and Screen **506** Quinces

1965. Balkan Film Festival. Varna.

1537	**505**	13s. black, silver & blue	85	20

1965. Fruits.

1538	**506**	1s. orange	10	10
1539	–	2s. olive (Grapes)	10	10
1540	–	3s. bistre (Pears)	10	10
1541	–	4s. orange (Plums)	15	10
1542	–	5s. red (Strawberries)	30	10
1543	–	6s. brown (Walnuts)	50	15

507 Ballerina **508** Dove, Emblem and Map

1965. Ballet Competitions, Varna.

1544	**507**	5s. black and mauve	85	30

1965. "Balkanphila" Stamp Exhibition, Varna.

1545	**508**	1s. silver, blue & yellow	10	10
1546	–	2s. silver, violet & yellow	10	10
1547	–	3s. gold, green & yellow	15	10
1548	–	13s. gold, red & yellow	1·00	85
1549	–	20s. brown, blue & silver	1·40	1·00
MS1550		71 × 62 mm. 40s. gold and blue (T **508**). Imperf	4·00	3·00

DESIGNS: 2s. Yacht emblem; 3s. Stylised fish and flowers; 13s. Stylised sun, planet and rocket. LARGER (45 × 25½ mm): 20s. Cosmonauts Pavel Belyaev and Aleksei Leonov.

509 Escapers in Boat **511** Gymnast

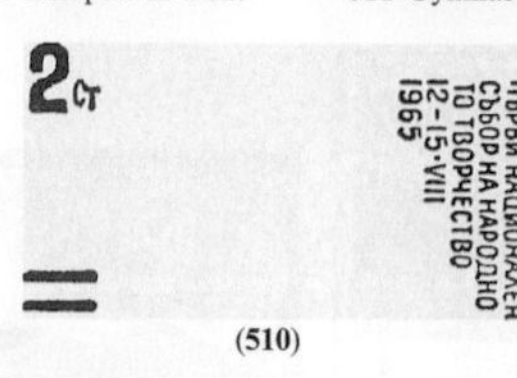

(**510**)

1965. 40th Anniv of Political Prisoners' Escape from "Bolshevik Island".

1551	**509**	2s. black and slate	20	15

1965. National Folklore Competition. No. 1084 surch with T **510**.

1552	2s. on 8s. brown	1·75	1·40

1965. Balkan Games.

1553	**511**	1s. black and red	10	10
1554	–	2s. purple and black	10	10
1555	–	3s. purple, black & red	10	10
1556	–	5s. brown, black & red	25	10
1557	–	10s. purple, black & mve	1·25	20
1558	–	13s. purple and black	1·00	25

DESIGNS: 2s. Gymnastics on bars; 3s. Weight-lifting; 5s. Rally car and building; 10s. Basketball; 13s. Rally car and map.

512 Dressage

1965. Horsemanship.

1559	**512**	1s. plum, black & blue	10	10
1560	–	2s. brown, black & ochre	10	10
1561	–	3s. red, black and purple	15	10
1562	–	5s. brown and green	55	10
1563	–	10s. brown, blk & grey	2·00	25
1564	–	13s. brown, grn & buff	2·10	35
MS1565		80 × 80 mm. 40s.+20s. plum and grey (as 13s.). Imperf	5·50	3·50

DESIGNS: 5s. Horse-racing. Others, Horse-jumping (various).

513 Young Pioneers

1965. Dimitrov Septembrist Pioneers Organization.

1566	**513**	1s. green and turquoise	10	10
1567	–	2s. mauve and violet	10	10
1568	–	3s. bistre and olive	10	10
1569	–	5s. ochre and blue	15	10
1570	–	8s. orange and brown	50	15
1571	–	13s. violet and red	95	30

DESIGNS: 2s. Admitting recruit; 3s. Camp bugler; 5s. Flying model airplane; 8s. Girls singing; 13s. Young athlete.

514 Junkers Ju 52/3m over Turnovo **515** Women of N. and S. Bulgaria

1965. Bulgarian Civil Aviation. Multicoloured.

1572	1s. Type **514**	10	10
1573	2s. Ilyushin Il-14M over Plovdiv	10	10
1574	3s. Mil Mi-4 helicopter over Dimitrovgrad	15	10
1575	5s. Tupolev Tu-104A over Ruse	35	10
1576	13s. Ilyushin Il-18 over Varna	1·40	20
1577	20s. Tupolev Tu-114 over Sofia	1·75	50

1965. 80th Anniv of Union of North and South Bulgaria.

1578	**515**	13s. black and green	85	30

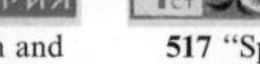

516 I.Q.S.Y. Emblem and Earth's Radiation Zones **517** "Spring Greetings"

1965. International Quiet Sun Year.

1579	**516**	1s. yellow, green & blue	10	10
1580	–	2s. multicoloured	10	10
1581	–	13s. multicoloured	90	20

DESIGNS (I.Q.S.Y. emblem and): 2s. Sun and solar flares; 13s. Total eclipse of the Sun.

1966. "Spring". National Folklore.

1582	**517**	1s. mauve, blue & drab	10	10
1583	–	2s. red, black and drab	10	10
1584	–	3s. violet, red and grey	10	10
1585	–	5s. red, violet and black	15	10
1586	–	8s. purple, brown & mve	35	15
1587	–	13s. mauve, black & bl	70	20

DESIGNS: 2s. Drummer; 3s. "Birds" (stylised); 5s. Folk dancer; 8s. Vase of flowers; 13s. Bagpiper.

518 Byala Bridge

1966. Ancient Monuments.

1588	**518**	1s. turquoise	10	10
1589	–	1s. green	10	10
1590	–	2s. green	10	10
1591	–	2s. purple	10	10
1592	–	8s. brown	40	15
1593	–	13s. blue	65	25

DESIGNS: No. 1589, Svilengrand Bridge; 1590, Fountain, Samokov; 1591, Ruins of Matochina Castle, Khaskovo; 1592, Cherven Castle, Ruse; 1593, Cafe, Bozhentsi, Gabrovo.

519 "Christ" (from fresco Boyana Church)

1966. "2,500 Years of Culture". Multicoloured.
1594 1s. Type **519** . . . . 5·50 4·25
1595 2s. "Destruction of the Idols" (from fresco, Boyana Church) (horiz) 30 15
1596 3s. Bachkovo Monastery . . 50 20
1597 4s. Zemen Monastery (horiz) 50 20
1598 5s. John the Baptist Church, Nesebur 60 30
1599 13s. "Nativity" (icon, Aleksandr Nevski Cathedral, Sofia) . . . . 1·10 85
1600 20s. "Virgin and Child" (icon, Archaeological Museum, Sofia) . . . . . 1·75 1·00

520 "The First Gunshot" at Koprivshtitsa

1966. 90th Anniv of April Uprising.
1601 **520** 1s. black, brown & gold 10 10
1602 – 2s. black, red and gold 10 10
1603 – 3s. black, green & gold 10 10
1604 – 5s. black, blue & gold 15 10
1605 – 10s. black, purple & gold 60 15
1606 – 13s. black, violet & gold 60 20
DESIGNS: 2s. Georgi Benkovski and Todor Kableskov; 3s. "Showing the Flag" at Panagyurishte; 5s. Vasil Petleshkov and Tsanko Dyustabanov; 10s. Landing of Khristo Botev's detachment at Kozlodui; 13s. Panyot Volov and Zlarion Dragostinov.

521 Luna reaching for the Moon

1966. Moon Landing of "Luna 9". Sheet 70 × 50 mm.
MS1607 **521** 60s. silver, black and red . . . . 4·75 4·75

522 W.H.O. Building

1966. Inaug of W.H.O. Headquarters, Geneva.
1608 **522** 13s. blue and silver . . . 1·00 20

523 Worker

1966. 6th Trades Union Congress, Sofia
1609 **523** 20s. black and pink . . . 1·10 20

524 Indian Elephant **525** Boy and Girl holding Banners

1966. Sofia Zoo Animals. Multicoloured.
1610 1s. Type **524** 10 10
1611 2s. Tiger 10 10
1612 3s. Chimpanzee 15 10
1613 4s. Ibex 20 10
1614 5s. Polar bear 50 15
1615 8s. Lion 65 25
1616 13s. American bison . . . . 2·50 45
1617 20s. Eastern grey kangaroo 3·00 70

1966. 3rd Congress of Bulgarian Sports Federation.
1618 **525** 13s. blue, orge & cobalt 45 20

526 "Radetski" and Pioneer

1966. 90th Anniv of Khristo Botev's Seizure of River Paddle-steamer "Radetski".
1619 **526** 2s. multicoloured 20 10

527 Standard-bearer Simov-Kuruto **529** U.N.E.S.C.O. Emblem

528 Federation Emblem

1966. 90th Death Anniv of Nikola Simov-Kuruto (hero of the Uprising against Turkey).
1620 **527** 5s. multicoloured 30 10

1966. 7th Int Youth Federation Assembly, Sofia.
1621 **528** 13s. blue and black . . . 65 15

1966. 20th Anniv of U.N.E.S.C.O.
1622 **529** 20s. ochre, red & black 85 30

530 Footballer with Ball

531 Jules Rimet Cup

1966. World Cup Football Championships, London.
(a) Showing players in action. Borders in grey.
1623 **530** 1s. black and brown . . 10 10
1624 – 2s. black and red 10 10
1625 – 5s. black and bistre . . . 20 10
1626 – 13s. black and blue . . . 65 15
1627 – 20s. black and blue . . . 1·00 30
(b) Sheet 60 × 65½ mm. T **531**.
MS1628 50s. gold, cerise and grey 4·00 2·75

532 Wrestling

1966. 3rd Int Wrestling Championships, Sofia.
1629 **532** 13s. sepia, green & brn 45 20

533 Throwing the Javelin

1966. 3rd Republican Spartakiade.
1630 **533** 2s. green, red & yellow 10 10
1631 – 13s. green, red & yellow 65 25
DESIGN: 13s. Running.

534 Map of Balkans, Globe and U.N.E.S.C.O. Emblem

1966. Int Balkan Studies Congress, Sofia.
1632 **534** 13s. green, pink & blue 65 15

535 Children with Construction Toy

1966. Children's Day.
1633 **535** 1s. black, yellow & red 10 10
1634 – 2s. black, brown & grn 10 10
1635 – 3s. black, yellow & blue 15 10
1636 – 13s. black, mauve & bl 1·00 25
DESIGNS: 2s. Rabbit and Teddy Bear; 3s. Children as astronauts; 13s. Children with gardening equipment.

536 Yuri Gagarin and "Vostok 1"

1966. Russian Space Exploration.
1637 **536** 1s. slate and grey . . . 10 10
1638 – 2s. purple and grey . . . 10 10
1639 – 3s. brown and grey . . . 10 10
1640 – 5s. lake and grey 20 10
1641 – 8s. blue and grey 25 15
1642 – 13s. turquoise and grey 80 25
1643 – 20s.+10s. vio & grey . . 1·75 55
MS1644 70 × 62½ mm. 30s.+10s. black, red and grey. Imperf . . 3·50 2·50
DESIGNS: 2s. German Titov and "Vostok 2"; 3s. Andrian Nikolaev, Povel Popovich and "Vostok 3" and "4"; 5s. Valentina Tereshkova, Vallery Bykovsky and "Vostok 5" and "6"; 8s. Vladimir Komarov, Boris Yegorov, Konstantin Feoktistov and "Voskhod 1"; 13s. Povel Belyaev, Aleksei Leonov and "Voskhod 2"; 20s. Gagarin, Leonov and Tereshkova; 30s. Rocket and globe.

537 St. Clement (14th-cent wood-carving) **538** Metodi Shatorov

1966. 1050th Death Anniv of St. Clement of Ohrid.
1645 **537** 5s. brown, red & drab 65 15

1966. Anti-fascist Fighters. Frames in gold; value in black.
1646 **538** 2s. violet and red 10 10
1647 – 3s. brown and mauve . . 10 10
1648 – 5s. blue and red 15 10
1649 – 10s. brown and orange 35 15
1650 – 13s. brown and red . . . 70 15
PORTRAITS: 3s. Vladno Trichkov; 5s. Vulcho Ivanov; 10s. Rasko Daskalov; 13s. Gen. Vladimir Zaimov.

539 Georgi Dimitrov (statesman) **541** Bansko Hotel

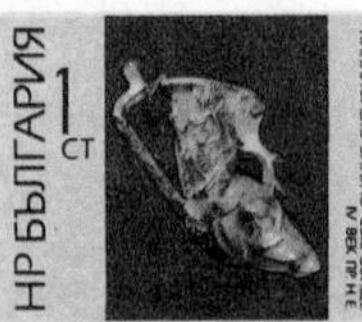

540 Deer's Head Vessel

1966. 9th Bulgarian Communist Party Congress, Sofia.
1651 **539** 2s. black and red 20 10
1652 – 20s. black, red and grey 1·10 20
DESIGN: 20s. Furnaceman and steelworks.

1966. The Gold Treasures of Panagyurishte. Multicoloured.
1653 1s. Type **540** 10 10
1654 2s. Amazon 20 10
1655 3s. Ram 25 10
1656 5s. Plate 30 10
1657 6s. Venus 35 10
1658 8s. Roe-buck . . . . 1·10 15
1659 10s. Amazon (different) . . 1·25 15
1660 13s. Amphora . . . . . . 1·40 30
1661 20s. Goat . . . . 2·00 65
Except for the 5s. and 13s. the designs show vessels with animal heads.

1966. Tourist Resorts.
1662 **541** 1s. blue 10 10
1663 – 2s. green (Belogradchik) 10 10
1664 – 2s. lake (Tryavna) . . . 10 10
1665 – 20s. pur (Malovitsa, Rila) 70 15

542 Christmas Tree

1966. New Year. Multicoloured.
1666 2s. Type **542** 10 10
1667 13s. Money-box 45 15

543 Percho Slaveikov (poet) **544** Dahlias

1966. Cultural Celebrities.
1668 **543** 1s. bistre, blue & orange 10 10
1669 – 2s. brown, orge & grey 10 10
1670 – 3s. blue, bistre & orange 10 10
1671 – 5s. purple, drab & orge 10 10
1672 – 8s. grey, purple & blue 50 15
1673 – 13s. violet, blue & purple 65 25
CELEBRITIES. Writers (with pen emblem): 2s. Dimcho Debelyanov (poet); 3s. Petko Todorov. Painters (with brush emblem): 5s. Dimitur Dobrovich; 8s. Ivan Murkvichka; 13s. Iliya Beshkov.

1966. Flowers. Multicoloured.
1674 1s. Type **544** 10 10
1675 1s. Clematis 10 10
1676 2s. Poet's narcissus 15 10
1677 2s. Foxgloves 15 10
1678 3s. Snowdrops 25 10
1679 5s. Petunias 25 10
1680 13s. Tiger lilies . . . . . 1·00 25
1681 20s. Canterbury bells . . . 1·40 35

545 Common Pheasant

1967. Hunting. Multicoloured.
1682 1s. Type **545** 40 10
1683 2s. Chukar partridge 40 10
1684 3s. Grey partridge 30 10
1685 5s. Brown hare 75 10
1686 8s. Roe deer 2·00 20
1687 13s. Red deer 2·25 40

546 "Philately" 547 6th-cent B.C. Coin of Thrace

1967. 10th Bulgarian Philatelic Federation Congress, Sofia.
1688 **546** 10s. yellow, black & grn 1·60 1·00

1967. Ancient Bulgarian Coins. Coins in silver on black background except 13s. (gold on black). Frame colours given.
1689 **547** 1s. brown 10 10
1690 – 2s. purple 10 10
1691 – 3s. green 15 10
1692 – 5s. brown 25 10
1693 – 13s. turquoise 1·40 40
1694 – 20s. violet 1·90 75
COINS—SQUARE: 2s. 2nd-cent B.C. Macedonian tetradrachm; 3s. 2nd-cent B.C. Odessos (Varna) tetradrachm; 5s. 4th-cent B.C. Macedonian coin of Philip II. HORIZ: (38 × 25 mm): 13s. Obverse and reverse of 4th cent B.C. coin of King Sevt (Thrace); 20s. Obverse and reverse of 5th-cent B.C. coin of Apollonia (Sozopol).

548 Partisans listening to radio

1967. 25th Anniv of Fatherland Front. Mult.
1695 1s. Type **548** 10 10
1696 20s. Dimitrov speaking at rally 75 25

549 Nikola Kofardzhiev 550 "Cultural Development"

1967. Anti-fascist Fighters.
1697 **549** 1s. red, black & blue 10 10
1698 – 2s. green, black & blue 10 10
1699 – 5s. brown, black & blue 15 10
1700 – 10s. blue, black & lilac 30 10
1701 – 13s. purple, black & grey 55 15
PORTRAITS: 2s. Petko Napetov; 5s. Petko Petkov; 10s. Emil Markov; 13s. Traicho Kostov.

1967. 1st Cultural Conference, Sofia.
1702 **550** 13s. yellow, grn & gold 80 15

551 Angora Kitten

1967. Cats. Multicoloured.
1703 1s. Type **551** 10 10
1704 2s. Siamese (horiz) 20 10
1705 3s. Abyssinian 25 10
1706 5s. European black and white 1·25 10
1707 13s. Persian (horiz) 1·50 25
1708 20s. European tabby 2·25 90

552 "Golden Sands" Resort

1967. International Tourist Year. Multicoloured.
1709 13s. Type **552** 35 15
1710 20s. Pamporovo 80 20
1711 40s. Old Church, Nesebur 1·60 50

553 Scene from Iliev's Opera "The Master of Boyana"

1967. 3rd International Young Opera Singers' Competition, Sofia.
1712 **553** 5s. red, blue and grey 20 10
1713 – 13s. red, blue and grey 60 15
DESIGN—VERT: 13s. "Vocal Art" (song-bird on piano-keys).

554 G. Kirkov

1967. Birth Cent of Georgi Kirkov (patriot).
1714 **554** 2s. bistre and red 15 10

555 Roses and Distillery

1967. Economic Achievements. Multicoloured.
1715 1s. Type **555** 10 10
1716 1s. Chick and incubator 10 10
1717 2s. Cucumber and glass-houses 10 10
1718 2s. Lamb and farm building 10 10
1719 3s. Sunflower and oil-extraction plant 10 10
1720 4s. Pigs and piggery 15 10
1721 5s. Hops and vines 15 10
1722 6s. Grain and irrigation canals 20 10
1723 8s. Grapes and "Bulgar" tractor 20 10
1724 10s. Apples and tree 35 10
1725 13s. Honey bees and honey 60 15
1726 20s. Honey bee on flower, and hives 1·10 25

556 D.K.M.S. Emblem 557 Map and Spassky Tower, Moscow Kremlin

1967. 11th Anniv of Dimitrov Communist Youth League.
1727 **556** 13s. black, red and blue 70 15

1967. 50th Anniv of October Revolution.
1728 **557** 1s. multicoloured 10 10
1729 – 2s. olive and purple 10 10
1730 – 3s. violet and purple 10 10
1731 – 5s. red and purple 15 10
1732 – 13s. blue and purple 30 15
1733 – 20s. blue and purple 1·00 20
DESIGNS: 2s. Lenin directing revolutionaries; 3s. Revolutionaries; 5s. Marx, Engels and Lenin; 13s. Soviet oil refinery; 20s. "Molniya" satellite and Moon (Soviet space research).

558 Scenic "Fish" and Rod 560 Bogdan Peak, Sredna Mts

559 Cross-country Skiing

1967. 7th World Angling Championships, Varna.
1734 **558** 10s. multicoloured 40 15

1967. Winter Olympic Games, Grenoble (1968).
1735 **559** 1s. black, red & turq 10 10
1736 – 2s. black, bistre & blue 10 10
1737 – 3s. black, blue & purple 10 10
1738 – 5s. black, yellow & grn 15 10
1739 – 13s. black, buff & blue 1·00 15
1740 – 20s.+10s. mult 1·90 50
MS1741 98 × 98 mm. (diamond) 40s.+10s. black, ochre and blue. Imperf 3·50 2·50
DESIGNS: 2s. Ski jumping; 3s. Biathlon; 5s. Ice hockey; 13, 40s. Ice skating (pairs); 20s. Men's slalom.

1967. Tourism. Mountain Peaks.
1742 **560** 1s. green and yellow 10 10
1743 – 2s. sepia and blue 10 10
1744 – 3s. indigo and blue 10 10
1745 – 5s. green and blue 15 10
1746 – 10s. brown and blue 30 10
1747 – 13s. black and blue 40 15
1748 – 20s. blue and purple 70 25
DESIGNS—HORIZ: 2s. Cherni Vruh, Vitosha; 5s. Persenk, Rhodopes; 10s. Botev, Stara-Planina; 20s. Vikhren, Pirin. VERT: 3s. Ruen, Osogovska Planina; 13s. Musala, Rila.

561 G. Rakovski

1967. Death Cent of G. Rakovski (revolutionary).
1749 **561** 13s. black and green 45 15

562 Yuri Gagarin, Valentina Tereshkova and Aleksei Leonov

1967. Space Exploration. Multicoloured.
1750 1s. Type **562** 10 10
1751 2s. John Glenn and Edward White 15 10
1752 5s. "Molniya 1" 25 10
1753 10s. "Gemini 6" and "7" 65 15
1754 13s. "Luna 13" 85 15
1755 20s. "Gemini 10" docking with "Agena" 1·10 35

563 Railway Bridge over Yantra River

1967. Views of Turnovo (ancient capital).
1756 **563** 1s. black, drab and blue 15 10
1757 – 2s. multicoloured 10 10
1758 – 3s. multicoloured 10 10
1759 – 5s. black, slate and red 65 20
1760 – 13s. multicoloured 65 15
1761 – 20s. black, orange & lav 1·00 25
DESIGNS: 2s. Hadji Nikola's Inn; 3s. Houses on hillside; 5s. Town and river; 13s. "House of the Monkeys"; 20s. Gurko street.

564 "The Ruchenitsa" (folk dance, from painting by Murkvichka)

1967. Belgian–Bulgarian "Painting and Philately" Exhibition, Brussels.
1762 **564** 20s. green and gold 1·90 1·50

565 "The Shepherd" (Zlatko Boyadzhiev)

1967. Paintings in the National Gallery, Sofia. Multicoloured.
1763 1s. Type **565** 10 10
1764 2s. "The Wedding" (Vladimir Dimitrov) (vert) 10 10
1765 3s. "The Partisans" Ilya Petrov (55 × 35 mm) 20 10
1766 5s. "Anastasia Penchovich" (Nikolai Pavlovich) (vert) 85 15
1767 13s. "Self-portrait" (Zakharii Zograf) (vert) 1·50 50
1768 20s. "Old Town of Plovdiv" (Tsanko Lavrenov) 2·00 1·00
MS1769 65 × 85 mm. 60s. "St. Clement of Ohrid" (Anton Mitov) 6·50 5·00

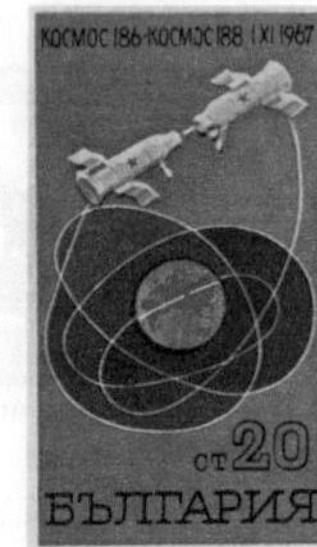

566 Linked Satellites "Cosmos 186" and "188"

1968. "Cosmic Activities". Multicoloured.
1770 20s. Type **566** 1·00 25
1771 40s. "Venus 4" and orbital diagram (horiz) 1·90 50

567 "Crossing the Danube" (Orenburgski)

1968. 90th Anniv of Liberation from Turkey. Paintings. Inscr and frames in black and gold; centre colours below.
1772 **567** 1s. green 25 10
1773 – 2s. blue 10 10
1774 – 3s. brown 15 10
1775 – 13s. blue 60 25
1776 – 20s. turquoise 1·00 40
DESIGNS—VERT: 2s. "Flag of Samara" (Veschin); 13s. "Battle of Orlovo Gnezdo" (Popov). HORIZ: 3s. "Battle of Pleven" (Orenburgski); 20s. "Greeting Russian Soldiers" (Goudienov).

568 Karl Marx 569 Gorky

1968. 150th Birth Anniv of Karl Marx.
1777 **568** 13s. grey, red & black 65 15

1968. Birth Cent of Maksim Gorky (writer).
1778 **569** 13s. green, orange & blk 65 15

570 Dancers

1968. 9th World Youth and Students' Festival. Sofia. Multicoloured.
1779 2s. Type **570** 10 10
1780 5s. Running 10 10

1781 13s. "Doves" 75 10
1782 20s. "Youth" (symbolic design) 85 25
1783 40s. Bulgarian 5c. stamp of 1879 under magnifier and Globe . . . . 1·50 55

571 "Campanula alpina" **572** "The Unknown Hero" (Ran Bosilek)

1968. Wild Flowers. Multicoloured.
1784 1s. Type **571** 10 10
1785 2s. Trumpet gentian 10 10
1786 3s. "Crocus veluchensis" . . 15 10
1787 5s. Siberian iris 20 10
1788 10s. Dog's-tooth violet . . . 30 10
1789 13s. House leek . . . . . . 1·00 15
1790 20s. Burning bush . . . . . 1·40 30

1968. Bulgarian–Danish Stamp Exhibition. Fairy Tales. Multicoloured.
1791 13s. Type **572** 45 20
1792 20s. "The Witch and the Young Men" (Hans Andersen) 55 35

573 Memorial Temple, Shipka **574** Copper Rolling-mill, Medet

1968. Bulgarian–West Berlin Stamp Exn.
1793 **573** 13s. multicoloured . . . 1·00 35

1968. Air.
1794 **574** 1l. red . . . . 2·75 35

575 Lake Smolyan **576** Gymnastics

1968.
1795 **575** 1s. green 10 10
1796 – 2s. myrtle 10 10
1797 – 3s. sepia 10 10
1798 – 8s. green 25 10
1799 – 10s. brown 65 10
1800 – 13s. olive 45 15
1801 – 40s. blue . . . . 1·25 35
1802 – 2l. brown . . . . 6·00 1·40
DESIGNS: 2s. River Ropotamo; 3s. Lomnitza Gorge, Erma River; 8s. River Isker; 10s. Cruise ship "Die Fregatte"; 13s. Cape Kaliakra; 40s. Sozopol; 2l. Mountain road, Kamchia River.

1968. Olympic Games, Mexico.
1803 **576** 1s. black and red 10 10
1804 – 2s. black, brown & grey 10 10
1805 – 3s. black and mauve . . 15 10
1806 – 10s. black, yell & turq 50 10
1807 – 13s. black, pink & blue 1·00 20
1808 – 20s.+10s. grey, pk & bl 1·75 40
MS1809 74 × 76 mm. 50s.+10s. black, grey and blue. Imperf 3·50 3·00
DESIGNS: 2s. Horse-jumping; 3s. Fencing; 10s. Boxing; 13s. Throwing the discus; 20s. Rowing; 50s. Stadium and communications satellite.

577 Dimitur on Mt. Buzludzha, 1868

1968. Centenary of Exploits of Khadzhi Dimitur and Stefan Karadzha (revolutionaries).
1810 **577** 2s. brown and silver . . 15 10
1811 – 13s. green and gold . . . 35 15
DESIGN: 13s. Dimitur and Karadzha.

578 Human Rights Emblem **579** Cinereous Black Vulture

1968. Human Rights Year.
1812 **578** 20s. gold and blue . . . 1·00 15

1968. 80th Anniv of Sofia Zoo.
1813 **579** 1s. black, brown & blue 50 10
1814 – 2s. black, yellow & brn 50 10
1815 – 3s. black and green . . . 30 10
1816 – 5s. black, yellow & red 50 10
1817 – 13s. black, bistre & grn 1·60 15
1818 – 20s. black, green & blue 2·50 55
DESIGNS: 2s. South African crowned crane; 3s. Common zebra; 5s. Leopard; 13s. Python; 20s. Crocodile.

580 Battle Scene

1968. 280th Anniv of Chiprovtsi Rising.
1819 **580** 13s. multicoloured . . . 80 15

581 Caterpillar-hunter **582** Flying Swans

1968. Insects.
1820 **581** 1s. green 15 10
1821 – 1s. brown 15 10
1822 – 1s. blue 15 10
1823 – 1s. brown 15 10
1824 – 1s. purple 35 10
DESIGNS—VERT: No. 1821, Stag beetle ("Lucanus cervus"); 1822, "Procerus scabrosus" (ground beetle). HORIZ: No. 1823, European rhinoceros beetle ("Oryctes nasicornis"); 1824, "Perisomena caecigena" (moth).

1968. "Co-operation with Scandinavia".
1825 – 2s. ochre and green . . . 1·25 1·25
1826 **582** 5s. blue, grey & black . . 1·25 1·25
1827 – 13s. purple and maroon 1·25 1·25
1828 – 20s. grey and violet . . . 1·25 1·25
DESIGNS: 2s. Wooden flask; 13s. Rose; 20s. "Viking ship".

583 Congress Building and Emblem

1968. International Dental Congress, Varna.
1829 **583** 20s. gold, green and red 85 15

584 Smirnenski and Verse from "Red Squadrons"

1968. 70th Birth Anniv of Khristo Smirnenski (poet).
1830 **584** 13s. black, orange & gold 45 15

585 Dove with Letter

1968. National Stamp Exhibition, Sofia and 75th Anniv of "National Philately".
1831 **585** 20s. green . . . . 1·10 85

586 Dalmatian Pelican

1968. Srebirna Wildlife Reservation. Birds. Mult.
1832 1s. Type **586** 10 10
1833 2s. Little egret 15 10
1834 3s. Great crested grebe . . . 20 10
1835 5s. Common tern 50 15
1836 13s. White spoonbill . . . . 1·50 50
1837 20s. Glossy ibis . . . . . . 2·75 85

587 Silistra Costume

1968. Provincial Costumes. Multicoloured.
1838 1s. Type **587** 10 10
1839 2s. Lovech 10 10
1840 3s. Yamboi 15 10
1841 13s. Chirpan 45 10
1842 20s. Razgrad . . . . 1·00 25
1843 40s. Ikhtiman . . . . 2·00 50

588 "St. Arsenius" (icon)

1968. Rila Monastery. Icons and murals. Mult.
1844 1s. Type **588** 10 10
1845 2s. "Carrying St. Ivan Rilski's Relics" (horiz) . . 10 10
1846 3s. "St. Michael torments the Rich Man's Soul" . . 15 10
1847 13s. "St. Ivan Rilski" . . . 1·00 15
1848 20s. "Prophet Joel" . . . . 1·40 30
1849 40s. "St. George" . . . . . 2·40 1·00
MS1850 100 × 74 mm. 1l. "Arrival of Relics at Rila Monastery". Imperf 7·00 6·00

589 "Matricaria chamomilla"

1968. Medicinal Plants. Multicoloured.
1851 1s. Type **589** 10 10
1852 1s. "Mespilus oxyacantha" 10 10
1853 2s. Lily of the valley . . . 10 10
1854 3s. Deadly nightshade . . . 10 10
1855 5s. Common mallow 15 10
1856 10s. Yellow peasant's eye . . 25 10
1857 13s. Common poppy 50 15
1858 20s. Wild thyme . . . . . 1·00 25

590 Silkworms and Spindles

1969. Silk Industry. Multicoloured.
1859 1s. Type **590** 10 10
1860 2s. Worm, cocoons and pattern 10 10
1861 3s. Cocoons and spinning wheel 10 10
1862 5s. Cocoons and pattern . . 15 10
1863 13s. Moth, cocoon and spindles 40 15
1864 20s. Moth, eggs and shuttle 85 25

591 "Death of Ivan Asen" **592** "Saints Cyril and Methodius" (mural, Troyan Monastery)

1969. Manasses Chronicle (1st series). Mult.
1865 1s. Type **591** 10 10
1866 2s. "Emperor Nicephorus invading Bulgaria" . . . 10 10
1867 3s. "Khan Krum's Feast" 15 10
1868 13s. "Prince Sviatoslav invading Bulgaria" . . . 85 15
1869 20s. "The Russian invasion" 1·10 25
1870 40s. "Jesus Christ, Tsar Ivan Alexander and Constantine Manasses" 2·10 75
See also Nos. 1911/16.

1969. Saints Cyril and Methodius Commem.
1871 **592** 28s. multicoloured . . . 1·40 45

593 Galleon **594** Posthorn Emblem

1969. Air. "SOFIA 1969" International Stamp Exhibition. Transport. Multicoloured.
1872 1s. Type **593** 10 10
1873 2s. Mail coach 10 10
1874 3s. Steam locomotive . . . 20 10
1875 5s. Early motor-car 15 10
1876 10s. Montgolfier's balloon and Henri Giffard's steam-powered dirigible airship 20 10
1877 13s. Early flying machines 30 15
1878 20s. Modern aircraft 85 25
1879 40s. Rocket and planets . . 1·50 50
MS1880 57 × 55 mm. 1l. gold and orange. Imperf . . . . 5·00 5·00
DESIGN: 1l. Postal courier.

1969. 90th Anniv of Bulgarian Postal Services.
1881 **594** 2s. yellow and green . . 10 10
1882 – 13s. multicoloured . . . 65 10
1883 – 20s. blue 85 25
DESIGNS: 13s. Bulgarian Stamps of 1879 and 1946; 20s. Post Office workers' strike, 1919.

595 I.L.O. Emblem **596** "Fox" and "Rabbit"

1969. 50th Anniv of I.L.O.
1884 **595** 13s. black and green . . 35 15

1969. Children's Book Week.
1885 **596** 1s. black, orange & grn 10 10
1886 – 2s. black, blue and red 10 10
1887 – 13s. black, olive & blue 65 15
DESIGNS: 2s. Boy with "hedgehog" and "squirrel"; 13s. "The Singing Lesson".

597 Hand with Seedling

1969. "10,000,000 Hectares of New Forests".
1888 **597** 2s. black, green & purple 15 10

598 "St. George" (14th Century)

1969. Religious Art. Multicoloured.
1889 1s. Type **598** 10 10
1890 2s. "The Virgin and St. John Bogoslov" (14th century) 10 10
1891 3s. "Archangel Michael" (17th century) 15 10
1892 5s. "Three Saints" (17th century) 25 10
1893 8s. "Jesus Christ" (17th century) 30 10
1894 13s. "St. George and St. Dimitr" (19th century) 75 15
1895 20s. "Christ the Universal" (19th century) . . . . . 1·10 15
1896 60s. "The Forty Martyrs" (19th century) . . . . . 3·25 90
1897 80s. "The Transfiguration" (19th century) . . . . . 4·00 1·60
MS1898 103 × 165 mm. 40s. × 4, "St. Dimitur" (17th-century) 10·00 10·00

599 Roman Coin 600 St. George and the Dragon

1969. "SOFIA 1969" International Stamp Exhibition. "Sofia Through the Ages".
1899 **599** 1s. silver, blue and gold 10 10
1900 – 2s. silver, green & gold 10 10
1901 – 3s. silver, lake and gold 10 10
1902 – 4s. silver, violet & gold 15 10
1903 – 5s. silver, purple & gold 15 10
1904 – 13s. silver, green & gold 50 15
1905 – 20s. silver, blue & gold 1·00 15
1906 – 40s. silver, red & gold 2·00 35
MS1907 78 × 72 mm. 1l. multicoloured. Imperf . . . 4·50 4·00
DESIGNS: 2s. Roman coin showing Temple of Aesculapius; 3s. Church of St. Sophia; 4s. Boyana Church; 5s. Parliament Building; 13s. National Theatre; 20s. Aleksandr Nevski Cathedral; 40s. Sofia University. 44 × 44 mm. 1l. Arms.

1969. Int Philatelic Federation Congress, Sofia.
1908 **600** 40s. black, orange & sil 2·00 75

601 St. Cyril

1969. 1,100th Death Anniv of St. Cyril.
1909 **601** 2s. green & red on silver 15 10
1910 – 28s. blue & red on silver 1·40 35
DESIGN: 28s. St. Cyril and procession.

1969. Manasses Chronicle (2nd series). Designs as T **591**, but all horiz. Multicoloured.
1911 1s. "Nebuchadnezzar II and Balthasar of Babylon, Cyrus and Darius of Persia" 10 10
1912 2s. "Cambyses, Gyges and Darius of Persia" 10 10
1913 5s. "Prophet David and Tsar Ivan Alexander" . . 15 10
1914 13s. "Rout of the Byzantine Army, 811" 85 15
1915 20s. "Christening of Khan Boris" . . . . 1·60 20
1916 60s. "Tsar Simeon's attack on Constantinople" . . . 3·25 1·10

602 Partisans

1969. 25th Anniv of Fatherland Front Government.
1917 **602** 1s. lilac, red and black 10 10
1918 – 2s. brown, red & black 10 10
1919 – 3s. green, red and black 10 10
1920 – 5s. brown, red & black 20 10
1921 – 13s. blue, red & black 30 10
1922 – 20s. multicoloured . . . 75 20
DESIGNS: 2s. Combine-harvester; 3s. Dam; 5s. Folk singers; 13s. Petroleum refinery; 20s. Lenin, Dimitrov and flags.

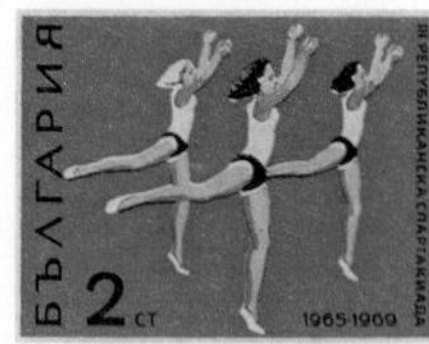
603 Gymnastics

1969. 3rd Republican Spartakiad. Multicoloured.
1923 2s. Type **603** 10 10
1924 20s. Wrestling 85 25

604 "Construction" and soldier 605 T. Tserkovski

1969. 25th Anniv of Army Engineers.
1925 **604** 6s. black and blue . . . 15 10

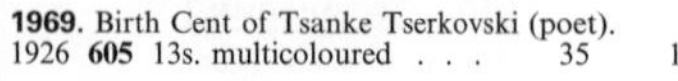

1969. Birth Cent of Tsanke Tserkovski (poet).
1926 **605** 13s. multicoloured . . . 35 15

606 "Woman" (Roman Statue) 607 Skipping-rope Exercise

1969. 1,800th Anniv of Silistra.
1927 **606** 2s. grey, blue and silver 15 10
1928 – 13s. brown, grn & silver 75 15
DESIGN—HORIZ: 13s. "Wolf" (bronze statue).

1969. World Gymnastics Competition, Varna.
1929 **607** 1s. grey, blue and green 10 10
1930 – 2s. grey and blue 10 10
1931 – 3s. grey, green and emerald 10 10
1932 – 5s. grey, purple and red 10 10
1933 – 13s.+5s. grey, bl & red 85 25
1934 – 20s.+10s. grey, green and yellow . . . . 1·40 40
DESIGNS: 2s. Hoop exercise (pair); 3s. Hoop exercise (solo); 5s. Ball exercise (pair); 13s. Ball exercise (solo); 20s. Solo gymnast.

608 Marin Drinov (founder)

1969. Cent of Bulgarian Academy of Sciences.
1935 **608** 20s. black and red . . . 45 15

609 "Neophit Rilski" (Zakharii Zograf)

1969. Paintings in National Gallery, Sofia. Mult.
1936 1s. Type **609** 10 10
1937 2s. "German's Mother" (Vasil Stoilov) 10 10
1938 3s. "Workers' Family" (Neuko Balkanski) (horiz) 20 10
1939 4s. "Woman Dressing" (Ivan Nenov) 30 10
1940 5s. "Portrait of a Woman" (Nikolai Pavlovich) . . . 30 10
1941 13s. "Krustyn Sarafov as Falstaff" (Dechko Uzunov) 85 15
1942 20s. "Artist's Wife" (N. Mikhailov) (horiz) . . 1·00 25
1943 20s. "Worker's Lunch" (Stoyan Sotirov) (horiz) 1·10 30
1944 40s. "Self-portrait" (Tseno Todorov) (horiz) . . . . 1·60 80

610 Pavel Banya

1969. Sanatoria.
1945 **610** 2s. blue 10 10
1946 – 5s. blue 10 10
1947 – 6s. green 20 10
1948 – 20s. green 55 15
SANATORIA: 5s. Khisar; 6s. Kotel; 20s. Narechen Polyclinic.

611 Deep-sea Trawler

1969. Ocean Fisheries.
1949 **611** 1s. grey and blue 30 10
1950 – 1s. green and black . . . 10 10
1951 – 2s. violet and black . . . 10 10
1952 – 3s. blue and black . . . 10 10
1953 – 5s. mauve and black . . 20 10
1954 – 10s. grey and black . . . 1·00 15
1955 – 13s. flesh, orange & blk 1·50 25
1956 – 20s. brown, ochre & blk 2·00 35
DESIGNS: 1s. (No. 1950), Cape hake; 2s. Atlantic horse-mackerel; 3s. South African pilchard; 5s. Large-eyed dentex; 10s. Chub mackerel; 13s. Senegal croaker; 20s. Vadigo.

612 Trapeze Act 613 V. Kubasov, Georgi Shonin and "Soyuz 6"

1969. Circus. Multicoloured.
1957 1s. Type **612** 10 10
1958 2s. Acrobats 10 10
1959 3s. Balancing act with hoops 10 10
1960 5s. Juggler, and bear on cycle 10 10
1961 13s. Equestrian act 40 15
1962 20s. Clowns . . . . 1·00 35

1970. Space Flights of "Soyuz 6, 7 and 8".
1963 **613** 1s. multicoloured 10 10
1964 – 2s. multicoloured 10 10
1965 – 3s. multicoloured 15 10
1966 – 28s. pink and blue . . . 1·40 30
DESIGNS: 2s. Viktor Gorbacko, Vladislav Volkov, Anatoly Filipchenko and "Soyuz 7"; 3s. Aleksei Elseev, Vladimir Shatalov and "Soyuz 8"; 28s. Three "Soyuz" spacecraft in orbit.

614 Khan Asparerch and "Old-Bulgars" crossing the Danube, 679

1970. History of Bulgaria. Multicoloured.
1967 1s. Type **614** 10 10
1968 2s. Khan Krum and defeat of Emperor Nicephorus, 811 . . . . 10 10
1969 3s. Conversion of Khan Boris I to Christianity, 865 . . . . 15 10
1970 5s. Tsar Simeon and Battle of Akhelo, 917 . . . . . 20 10
1971 8s. Tsar Samuel and defeat of Byzantines, 976 . . . . 20 10
1972 10s. Tsar Kaloyan and victory over Emperor Baldwin, 1205 . . . . . . 30 15
1973 13s. Tsar Ivan Assen II and defeat of Komnine of Epirus, 1230 . . . . . . 85 15
1974 20s. Coronation of Tsar Ivailo, 1277 . . . . . . 1·40 25

615 Bulgarian Pavilion

1970. "Expo 70" World's Fair, Osaka, Japan (1st issue).
1975 **615** 20s. silver, yellow & brn 1·40 85
See Nos. 2009/12.

616 Footballers

1970. World Football Cup, Mexico.
1976 **616** 1s. multicoloured 10 10
1977 – 2s. multicoloured 10 10
1978 – 3s. multicoloured 15 10
1979 – 5s. multicoloured 20 10
1980 – 20s. multicoloured . . . 1·25 35
1981 – 40s. multicoloured . . . 2·40 60
MS1982 55 × 99 mm. 80s.+20s. multicoloured. Imperf . . . . 4·50 4·00
DESIGNS—HORIZ: 2s. to 40s. Various football scenes. VERT (45 × 69 mm.) 80s. Football and inscription.

617 Lenin 618 "Tephrocactus Alexanderi v. bruchi"

1970. Birth Cent of Lenin. Multicoloured.
1983 2s. Type **617** 10 10
1984 13s. Full-face portrait . . . 40 15
1985 20s. Lenin writing 75 25

1970. Flowering Cacti. Multicoloured.
1986 1s. Type **618** 10 10
1987 2s. "Opuntia drummondii" 15 10
1988 3s. "Hatiora cilindrica" . . 20 10
1989 5s. "Gymnocalycium vatteri" 25 10
1990 8s. "Helianthо cereus grandiflorus" 40 20
1991 10s. "Neochilenia andreaeana" . . . . . . 1·75 25
1992 13s. "Peireskia vargasii v. longispina" . . . . . . 1·90 30
1993 20s. "Neobesseya rosiflora" 2·50 45

619 Rose

620 Union Badge

1970. Bulgarian Roses.

No.	Type	Description		
1994	619	1s. multicoloured	10	10
1995	–	2s. multicoloured	15	10
1996	–	3s. multicoloured	25	10
1997	–	4s. multicoloured	30	10
1998	–	5s. multicoloured	35	10
1999	–	13s. multicoloured . . .	55	10
2000	–	20s. multicoloured . . .	1·60	45
2001	–	28s. multicoloured . . .	2·75	85

DESIGNS: 2s. to 28s. Various roses.

1970. 70th Anniv of Agricultural Union.

No.	Type	Description		
2002	620	20s. black, gold and red	1·00	25

621 Gold Bowl

1970. Gold Treasures of Thrace.

No.	Type	Description		
2003	621	1s. black, blue and gold	10	10
2004	–	2s. black, lilac and gold	10	10
2005	–	3s. black, red and gold	15	10
2006	–	5s. black, green & gold	20	10
2007	–	13s. black, orge & gold	1·00	15
2008	–	20s. black, violet & gold	1·50	30

DESIGNS: 2s. Three small bowls; 3s. Plain lid; 5s. Pear shaped ornaments; 13s. Large lid with pattern; 20s. Vase.

622 Rose and Woman with Baskets of Produce

1970. "Expo 70" World's Fair, Osaka, Japan (2nd issue). Multicoloured.

2009	1s. Type 622	10	10
2010	2s. Three Dancers	10	10
2011	3s. Girl in National costume	10	10
2012	28s. Dancing couples . . .	1·25	35
MS2013	75 × 90 mm. 40s. Bulgarian pavilion	1·75	1·50

623 U.N. Emblem

1970. 25th Anniv of United Nations.

No.	Type	Description		
2014	623	20s. gold and blue . . .	85	15

624 I. Vasov

1970. 120th Birth Anniv of Ivan Vasov (poet).

No.	Type	Description		
2015	624	13s. blue	45	15

625 Edelweiss Sanatorium, Borovets

1970. Health Resorts.

No.	Type	Description		
2016	625	1s. green	10	10
2017	–	2s. olive	10	10
2018	–	4s. blue	20	10
2019	–	8s. blue	30	10
2020	–	10s. blue	35	10

DESIGNS: 2s. Panorama Hotel, Pamporovo; 4s. Yachts, Albena; 8s. Harbour scene, Rousalka; 10s. Shtastlivetsa Hotel, Mt. Vitosha.

626 Hungarian Retriever

1970. Dogs. Multicoloured.

2021	1s. Type 626	15	10
2022	2s. Retriever (vert)	20	10
2023	3s. Great Dane (vert) . . .	30	10
2024	4s. Boxer (vert)	40	10
2025	5s. Cocker spaniel (vert) . .	50	10
2026	13s. Dobermann pinscher (vert)	1·25	25
2027	20s. Scottish terrier (vert) . .	2·25	50
2028	28s. Russian hound	2·75	75

627 Fireman with Hose

628 Congress Emblem

1970. Fire Protection.

No.	Type	Description		
2029	627	1s. grey, yellow & black	10	10
2030	–	3s. red, grey and black	15	10

DESIGN. 3s. Fire-engine.

1970. 7th World Sociological Congress, Varna.

No.	Type	Description		
2031	628	13s. multicoloured . . .	50	15

629 Two Male Players

630 Cyclists

1970. World Volleyball Championships.

No.	Type	Description		
2032	629	2s. black and brown . .	10	10
2033	–	2s. orange, black & blue	15	10
2034	–	20s. yellow, black & grn	1·00	20
2035	–	20s. multicoloured . . .	1·00	20

DESIGNS: No. 2033, Two female players; 2034, Male player; 2035, Female player.

1970. 20th Round-Bulgaria Cycle Race.

No.	Type	Description		
2036	630	20s. mauve, yellow & grn	75	20

631 Enrico Caruso and Scene from "II Pagliacci"

1970. Opera Singers. Multicoloured.

2037	1s. Type 631	10	10
2038	2s. Khristina Morfova and "The Bartered Bride" . .	10	10
2039	3s. Petur Raichev and "Tosca"	10	10
2040	10s. Tsvetana Tabakova and "The Flying Dutchman"	40	20
2041	13s. Katya Popova and "The Masters of Nuremberg"	45	10
2042	20s. Fyodor Chaliapin and "Boris Godunov"	1·75	40

632 Beethoven

1970. Birth Bicentenary of Ludwig von Beethoven (composer).

No.	Type	Description		
2043	632	28s. blue and purple . .	3·00	50

633 Ivan Asen II Coin

1970. Bulgarian Coins of the 14th century. Multicoloured.

2044	1s. Type 633	10	10
2045	2s. Theodor Svetoslav . . .	10	10
2046	3s. Mikhail Shishman . . .	10	10
2047	13s. Ivan Alexander and Mikhail Asen	45	10
2048	20s. Ivan Sratsimir	1·00	15
2049	28s. Ivan Shishman (initials)	1·25	20

634 "Luna 16"

1970. Moon Mission of "Luna 16". Sheet 51 × 70 mm.

No.	Type	Description		
MS2050	634	1l. red, silver and blue	9·00	7·50

635 Engels

636 Snow Crystal

1970. 150th Birth Anniv of Friedrich Engels.

No.	Type	Description		
2051	635	13s. brown and red . . .	60	15

1970. New Year.

No.	Type	Description		
2052	636	2s. multicoloured	15	10

637 "Lunokhod 1" on Moon

1970. Moon Mission of "Lunokhod 1". Sheet 60 × 72 mm.

No.	Type	Description		
MS2053	637	80s. silver, purple and blue	6·50	5·00

638 "Girl's Head" (Zheko Spiridonov)

1971. Modern Bulgarian Sculpture.

No.	Type	Description		
2054	638	1s. violet and gold . . .	10	10
2055	–	2s. green and gold . . .	35	10
2056	–	3s. brown and gold . . .	10	10
2057	–	13s. green and gold . . .	45	15
2058	–	20s. red and gold . . .	1·10	20
2059	–	28s. brown and gold . . .	1·50	45
MS2060		61 × 72 mm. 1l. chestnut and gold	4·00	3·50

SCULPTURES: 2s. "Third Class Carriage" (Ivan Funev); 3s. "Elin Pelin" (Marko Markov); 13s. "Nina" (Andrei Nikolov); 20s. "Kneeling Woman" (Yavorov monument, Ivan Lazarov); 28s. "Engineer" (Ivan Funev). 36½ × 41 mm. 1l. "Refugees" (Sekul Knimov).

639 Birds and Flowers

1971. Spring.

No.	Type	Description		
2061	639	1s. multicoloured	10	10
2062	–	2s. multicoloured	10	10
2063	–	3s. multicoloured	10	10
2064	–	5s. multicoloured	10	10
2065	–	13s. multicoloured . . .	25	10
2066	–	20s. multicoloured . . .	1·00	20

DESIGNS: 2s. to 20s. Various designs of birds and flowers similar to Type 639.

640 "Khan Asparuch crossing Danube" (Boris Angelushev)

1971. Bulgarian History. Paintings. Mult.

2067	2s. Type 640	10	10
2068	3s. "Ivajlo in Turnovo" (Ilya Petrov)	15	10
2069	5s. "Cavalry Charge, Benkovski" (P. Morosov)	50	10
2070	8s. "Gen. Gzrko entering Sofia, 1878" (D. Gyudzhenov)	85	10
2071	28s. "Greeting Red Army" (Stefan Venev)	4·25	1·50
MS2072	137 × 131 mm. Nos. 2067/70	1·75	1·50

641 Running

1971. 2nd European Indoor Track and Field Championships. Multicoloured.

2073	2s. Type 641	15	10
2074	20s. Putting the shot	1·60	25

642 School Building

1971. Foundation of First Bulgarian Secondary School, Bolgrad.

No.	Type	Description		
2075	642	2s. green, brown & sil	10	10
2076	–	20s. violet, brown & sil	95	20

DESIGN: 20s. Dimitur Mutev, Prince Bogoridi and Sava Radulov (founders).

643 Communards

1971. Centenary of Paris Commune.

No.	Type	Description		
2077	643	20s. black and red . . .	65	25

644 Georgi Dimitrov challenging Hermann Goering

1971. 20th Anniv of "Federation Internationale des Resistants".

No.	Type	Description		
2078	644	2s. multicoloured	15	10
2079		13s. multicoloured . . .	1·10	20

645 Gagarin and Space Scenes (⅔-size illustration)

1971. 10th Anniv of First Manned Space Flight. Sheet 80 × 53 mm.
MS2080 **645** 40s.+20s. multicoloured 4·00 4·00

646 G. Rakovski **647** Worker and Banner ("People's Progress")

1971. 150th Birth Anniv of Georgi Rakovski (politician and Revolutionary).
2081 **646** 13s. brown, cream & grn 35 15

1971. 10th Bulgarian Communist Party Congress. Multicoloured.
2082 1s. Type **647** 10 10
2083 2s. Symbols of "Technical Progress" (horiz) 10 10
2084 12s. Men clasping hands ("Bulgarian-Soviet Friendship") 75 10

648 Pipkov and Music

1971. Birth Centenary of Panaiot Pipokov.
2085 **648** 13s. black, green & silver 60 20

649 "Three Races" **650** Mammoth

1971. Racial Equality Year.
2086 **649** 13s. multicoloured 45 15

1971. Prehistoric Animals. Multicoloured.
2087 1s. Type **650** 10 10
2088 2s. Bear (vert) 10 10
2089 3s. Hipparion 15 10
2090 13s. Mastodon 90 15
2091 20s. Dinotherium (vert) 1·40 25
2092 28s. Sabre-toothed tiger 1·90 35

651 Facade of Ancient Building **652** Weights Emblem on Map of Europe

1971. Ancient Buildings of Koprivshitsa.
2093 **651** 1s. green, brown & grn 10 10
2094 – 2s. brown, green & buff 10 10
2095 – 6s. violet, brown & blue 20 10
2096 – 13s. red, blue & orange 65 25
DESIGNS: 1s. to 13s. Different facades.

1971. 30th European Weightlifting Championships, Sofia. Multicoloured.
2097 2s. Type **652** 10 10
2098 13s. Figures supporting weights 1·25 20

653 Frontier Guard and Dog **654** Tweezers, Magnifying Glass and "Stamp"

1971. 25th Anniv of Frontier Guards.
2099 **653** 2s. olive, green & turq 10 10

1971. 9th Congress of Bulgarian Philatelic Federation.
2100 **654** 20s.+10s. brown, black and red 1·50 50

655 Congress Meeting (sculpture)

1971. 80th Anniv of Bulgarian Social Democratic Party Congress, Buzludzha.
2101 **655** 2s. green, cream and red 15 10

656 "Mother" (Ivan Nenov) **657** Factory Botevgrad

1971. Paintings from the National Art Gallery (1st series). Multicoloured.
2102 1s. Type **656** 10 10
2103 2s. "Lazorova" (Stefan Ivanov) 10 10
2104 3s. "Portrait of Yu. Kh." (Kiril Tsonev) 15 10
2105 13s. "Portrait of a Lady" (Dechko Uzunov) 75 15
2106 30s. "Young Woman from Kalotina" (Vladimir Dimitrov) 1·10 35
2107 40s. "Goryanin" (Stryan Venev) 2·00 60
See also Nos. 2145/50.

1971. Industrial Buildings.
2108 **657** 1s. violet 10 10
2109 – 2s. red 10 10
2110 – 10s. violet 20 10
2111 – 13s. red 25 10
2112 – 40s. brown 1·10 10
DESIGNS—VERT: 2s. Petro-chemical plant, Pleven. HORIZ: 10s. Chemical works, Vratsa; 13s. "Maritsa-Istok" plant, Dimitrovgrad; 40s. Electronics factory, Sofia.

658 Free Style Wrestling

1971. European Wrestling Championships, Sofia.
2113 **658** 2s. green, black and blue 10 10
2114 – 13s. black, red and blue 75 20
DESIGN: 13s. Greco-Roman wrestling.

659 Posthorn Emblem

1971. Organization of Socialist Countries' Postal Administrations Congress.
2115 **659** 20s. gold and green 65 25

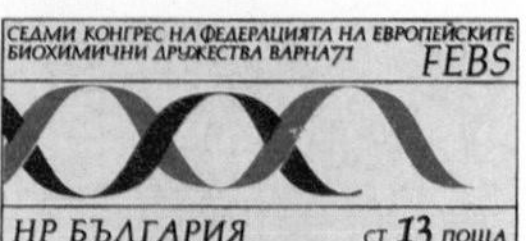

660 Entwined Ribbons

1971. 7th European Biochemical Congress, Varna.
2116 **660** 13s. red, brown & black 65 25

661 "New Republic" Statue

1971. 25th Anniv of People's Republic.
2117 **661** 2s. red, yellow and gold 10 10
2118 – 13s. green, red and gold 50 20
DESIGN: 13s. Bulgarian flag.

662 Cross-country Skiing

1971. Winter Olympic Games, Sapporo, Japan. Multicoloured.
2119 1s. Type **662** 10 10
2120 2s. Downhill skiing 10 10
2121 3s. Ski jumping 15 10
2122 4s. Figure skating 15 10
2123 13s. Ice hockey 85 75
2124 28s. Slalom skiing 1·50 40
MS2125 60 × 70 mm. 1l. Olympic flame and stadium 7·00 4·50

663 Brigade Members **664** U.N.E.S.C.O. Emblem and Wreath

1971. 25th Anniv of Youth Brigades Movement.
2126 **663** 2s. blue 15 10

1971. 25th Anniv of U.N.E.S.C.O.
2127 **664** 20s. multicoloured 75 25

665 "The Footballer"

1971. Paintings by Kiril Tsonev. Multicoloured.
2128 1s. Type **665** 10 10
2129 2s. "Landscape" (horiz) 10 10
2130 3s. Self-portrait 15 10
2131 13s. "Lilies" 75 10
2132 20s. "Woodland Scene" (horiz) 1·10 30
2133 40s. "Portrait of a Young Woman" 2·00 40

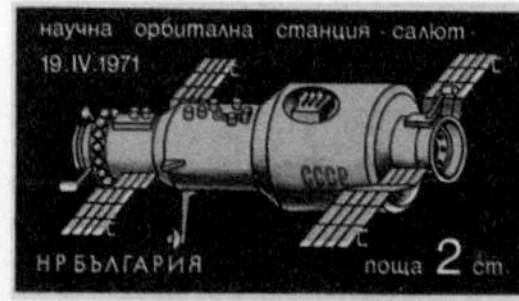

666 "Salyut" Space-station

1971. Space Flights of "Salyut" and "Soyuz 11". Multicoloured.
2134 2s. Type **666** 10 10
2135 13s. "Soyuz 11" 40 15
2136 40s. "Salyut" and "Soyuz 11" joined together 1·90 45
MS2137 70 × 74 mm. 80s. Cosmonauts G. Dobrovolsky, Vladislav Volkov and V. Patsaev (victims of "Soyuz 11" disaster). Imperf 3·50 2·75

667 "Vikhren" (ore carrier)

1972. "One Million Tons of Bulgarian Shipping".
2138 **667** 18s. lilac, red and black 1·25 20

668 Goce Delcev

1972. Birth Centenaries of Macedonian Revolutionaries.
2139 **668** 2s. black and red 10 10
2140 – 5s. black and green 10 10
2141 – 13s. black and yellow 45 15
PATRIOTS: 5s. Jan Sandanski (1972); 13s. Dume Gruev (1971).

669 Gymnast with Ball

1972. World Gymnastics Championships, Havana (Cuba). Multicoloured.
2142 13s. Type **669** 85 15
2143 18s. Gymnast with hoop 1·00 25
MS2144 61 × 74 mm. 70s. Team with hoops. Imperf 5·00 5·00

1972. Paintings in Bulgarian National Gallery (2nd series). As T **656** but horiz. Multicoloured.
2145 1s. "Melnik" (Petur Mladenov) 10 10
2146 2s. "Ploughman" (Pencho Georgiev) 10 10
2147 3s. "By the Death-bed" (Aleksandur Zhendov) 15 10
2148 13s. "Family" (Vladimir Dimitrov) 75 15
2149 20s. "Family" (Neuko Balkanski) 1·25 25
2150 40s. "Father Paisii" (Koyu Denchev) 2·00 40

670 Bulgarian Worker **671** "Singing Harvesters"

1972. 7th Bulgarian Trade Unions Congress.
2151 **670** 13s. multicoloured 35 15

1972. 90th Birth Anniv of Vladimir Dimitrov, the Master (painter). Multicoloured.
2152 1s. Type **671** 10 10
2153 2s. "Farm Worker" 10 10
2154 3s. "Women Cultivators" (horiz) 10 10
2155 13s. "Peasant Girl" (horiz) 75 10
2156 20s. "My Mother" 1·10 30
2157 40s. Self-portrait 2·00 40

672 Heart and Tree Emblem **673** St. Mark's Cathedral

1972. World Heart Month.

2158	**672**	13s. multicoloured	1·10	50

1972. U.N.E.S.C.O. "Save Venice" Campaign.

2159	**673**	2s. green, turquoise & bl	10	10
2160	–	13s. brown, violet & grn	70	20

DESIGN: 13s. Doge's Palace.

674 Dimitrov at Typesetting Desk

1972. 90th Birth Anniv of Georgi Dimitrov (statesman). Multicoloured.

2161	1s. Type **674**	10	10
2162	2s. Dimitrov leading uprising of 1923	10	10
2163	3s. Dimitrov at Leipzig Trial	10	10
2164	5s. Dimitrov addressing workers	15	10
2165	13s. Dimitrov with Bulgarian crowd	40	15
2166	18s. Addressing young people	1·00	15
2167	28s. Dimitrov with children	1·40	20
2168	40s. Dimitrov's mausoleum	2·00	25
2169	80s. Portrait head (green and gold)	5·75	60
2173	80s. As No. 2169	10·00	10·00
MS2170	87×84 mm. As No. 2169, but centre in red and gold. Imperf	8·00	8·00

No. 2173 has the centre in red and gold, and is imperforate.

675 "Lamp of Learning" and Quotation

1972. 250th Birth Anniv of Father Paisii Khilendurski (historian).

2171	**675**	2s. brown, green & gold	15	10
2172	–	13s. brown, grn & gold	75	20

DESIGN: 13s. Paisii writing.

676 Canoeing

1972. Olympic Games, Munich. Multicoloured.

2174	1s. Type **676**	10	10
2175	2s. Gymnastics	10	10
2176	3s. Swimming	10	10
2177	13s. Volleyball	35	10
2178	18s. Hurdling	85	25
2179	40s. Wrestling	1·50	45
MS2180	64×60 mm. 80s. Running track and sports. Imperf	3·00	2·75

677 Angel Kunchev

1972. Death Cent of Angel Kunchev (patriot).

2181	**677**	2s. mauve, gold & purple	10	10

678 "Golden Sands"

1972. Black Sea Resorts. Hotels. Multicoloured.

2182	1s. Type **678**	10	10
2183	2s. Druzhba	10	10
2184	3s. "Sunny Beach"	10	10
2185	13s. Primorsko	25	10
2186	28s. Rusalka	80	25
2187	40s. Albena	1·25	30

679 Canoeing (Bronze Medal)

1972. Bulgarian Medal Winners, Olympic Games, Munich. Multicoloured.

2188	1s. Type **679**	10	10
2189	2s. Long jumping (Silver Medal)	15	10
2190	3s. Boxing (Gold Medal)	15	10
2191	18s. Wrestling (Gold Medal)	1·00	30
2192	40s. Weightlifting (Gold Medal)	1·60	40

680 Subi Dimitrov

682 "Lilium rhodopaeum"

681 Commemorative Text

1972. Resistance Heroes. Multicoloured.

2193	1s. Type **680**	10	10
2194	2s. Tsvyatko Radoinov	10	10
2195	3s. Iordan Lyutibrodski	10	10
2196	5s. Mito Ganev	10	10
2197	13s. Nedelcho Nikolov	35	10

1972. 50th Anniv of U.S.S.R.

2198	**681**	13s. red, yellow & gold	50	15

1972. Protected Flowers. Multicoloured.

2199	1s. Type **682**	10	10
2200	2s. Marsh gentian	10	10
2201	3s. Sea lily	15	10
2202	4s. Globe flower	20	10
2203	18s. "Primula frondosa"	70	20
2204	23s. Pale pasque flower	1·00	30
2205	40s. "Fritillaria stribrnyi"	2·00	50

СВЕТОВЕН ПЪРВЕНЕЦ
(683)

684 Dobri Chintulov

1972. "Bulgaria, World Weightlifting Champions". No. 2192 optd with T **683**.

2206	40s. multicoloured	1·75	50

1972. 150th Birth Anniv of Dobri Chintulov (poet).

2207	**684**	2s. multicoloured	10	10

685 Forehead Ornament (19th-century)

686 Divers with Cameras

1972. Antique Ornaments.

2208	**685**	1s. black and brown	10	10
2209	–	2s. black and green	10	10
2210	–	3s. black and blue	10	10
2211	–	8s. black and red	20	10
2212	–	23s. black and brown	60	10
2213	–	40s. black and violet	1·25	20

DESIGNS: 2s. Belt-buckle (19th-century); 3s. Amulet (18th-century); 8s. Pendant (18th-century); 23s. Earrings (14th-century); 40s. Necklace (18th-century).

1973. Underwater Research in the Black Sea.

2214	**686**	1s. black, yellow & blue	10	10
2215	–	2s. black, yellow & blue	20	10
2216	–	18s. black, yellow & blue	90	25
2217	–	40s. black, yellow & blue	1·10	20
MS2218		118×98 mm. 20s. ×4. Designs as Nos. 2214/17, but background colours changed (sold at 1l.)	6·50	5·50

DESIGNS—HORIZ: 2s. Divers with underwater research vessel "Shelf 1". VERT: 18s. Diver and "NIV 100" diving bell; 40s. Lifting balloon.

687 "The Hanging of Vasil Levski" (Boris Angelushev)

688 Elhovo Mask

1973. Death Cent of Vasil Levski (patriot).

2219	**687**	2s. green and red	10	10
2220	–	20s. brown, cream & grn	1·50	40

DESIGN: 20s. "Vasil Levski" (Georgi Danchov).

1973. Kukeris' Festival Masks. Mult.

2221	1a. Type **688**	10	10
2222	2s. Breznik	10	10
2223	3s. Khisar	10	10
2224	13s. Radomir	40	15
2225	20s. Karnobat	50	25
2226	40s. Pernik	4·50	2·75

689 Copernicus

690 Vietnamese "Girl"

1973. 500th Birth Anniv of Copernicus.

2227	**689**	28s. purple, black & brn	1·50	50

1973. "Visit Bulgaria by Air". No. **MS**2072 surch with various airline emblems and new sheet value.

MS2228	137×131 mm. Nos. 2067/70 surch with new sheet value 1l.	23·00	23·00

1973. Vietnam Peace Treaty.

2229	**690**	18s. multicoloured	20	10

1973. "IBRA 73" Stamp Exhibition, Munich. No. **MS**1907 optd with "IBRA" and Olympic symbols in green.

MS2230	78×72 mm. 1l. multicoloured	£110	£110

691 Common Poppy

692 C. Botev (after T. Todorov)

1973. Wild Flowers. Multicoloured.

2231	1s. Type **691**	10	10
2232	2s. Ox-eye daisy	10	10
2233	3s. Peony	15	10
2234	13s. Cornflower	40	15
2235	18s. Corn cockle	4·75	2·25
2236	28s. Meadow buttercup	1·25	65

1973. 125th Birth Anniv of Khristo Botev (poet and revolutionary).

2237	**692**	2s. yellow, brown & grn	10	10
2238		18s. grn, lt grn & bronze	80	65

693 Asen Khalachev and Insurgents

1973. 50th Anniv of June Uprising.

2239	**693**	1s. black, red and gold	10	10
2240	–	2s. black, orange & gold	10	10

DESIGN: 2s. "Wounded Worker" (illustration by Boris Angelushev to the poem "September" by Geo Milev).

694 Stamboliiski (from sculpture by A. Nikolov)

1973. 50th Death Anniv of Aleksandur Stamboliiski (Prime Minister 1919–23).

2241	**694**	18s. lt brn, brn & orge	40	20
2242		18s. orange	4·50	3·25

695 Muskrat

1973. Bulgarian Fauna. Multicoloured.

2243	1s. Type **695**	10	10
2244	2s. Racoon-dog	10	10
2245	3s. Mouflon (vert)	20	10
2246	12s. Fallow deer (vert)	50	25
2247	18s. European bison	3·25	1·50
2248	40s. Elk	2·00	55

696 Turnovo

698 Congress Emblem

697 Insurgents on the March (Boris Angelushev)

1973. Air. Tourism. Views of Bulgarian Towns and Cities. Multicoloured.

2249	2s. Type **696**	10	10
2250	13s. Rusalka	30	10
2251	20s. Plovdiv	2·10	1·75
2252	28s. Sofia	80	50

1973. 50th Anniv of September Uprising.

2253	**697**	2s. multicoloured	10	10
2254	–	5s. violet, pink & red	75	35
2255	–	13s. multicoloured	15	10
2256	–	18s. olive, cream & red	45	25

DESIGNS—HORIZ: 5s. "Armed Train" (Boris Angelushev). VERT: 13s. Patriotic poster by N. Mirchev. HORIZ: 18s. Georgi Dimitrov and Vasil Kolarov.

1973. 8th World Trade Union Congress, Varna.

2257	**698**	2s. multicoloured	10	10

699 "Sun" Emblem and Olympic Rings

700 "Prince Kaloyan"

1973. Olympic Congress, Varna. Multicoloured.

2258	13s. Type **699**	40	20
2259	28s. Lion Emblem of Bulgarian Olympic Committee (vert)	70	40
MS2260	61×77 mm. 80s. Footballers (40×25 mm)	4·50	4·00

1973. Fresco Portraits, Boyana Church. Mult.

2261	1s. Type **700**	10	10
2262	2s. "Desislava"	30	10
2263	3s. "Saint"	20	10
2264	5s. "St. Eustratius"	25	10
2265	10s. "Tsar Constantine-Asen"	60	10

2266 13s. "Deacon Laurentius" 80 10
2267 18s. "Virgin Mary" . . . . 1·25 30
2268 20s. "St. Ephraim" . . . . 1·50 40
2269 28s. "Jesus Christ" . . . . 5·00 1·00
MS2270 56 × 76 mm. 80s. "Scribes". Imperf . . . . 8·00 8·00

701 Smirnenski and Cavalry Charge

1973. 75th Birth Anniv of Khristo Smirnenski (poet and revolutionary).
2271 **701** 1s. blue, red and gold . . 10 10
2272 2s. blue, red and gold . . 10 10

702 Human Rights Emblem **704** "Finn" One-man Dinghy

703 Tsar Todor Svetoslav meeting the Byzantine Embassy, 1307

1973. 25th Anniv of Declaration of Human Rights.
2273 **702** 13s. gold, red and blue 15 10

1973. Bulgarian History. Multicoloured.
2274 1s. Type **703** 10 10
2275 2s. Tsar Mikhail Shishman in battle against Byzantines, 1328 . . . . 10 10
2276 3s. Battle of Rosokastro, 1332 and Tsar Ivan Aleksandur 10 10
2277 4s. Defence of Turnovo, 1393 and Patriarch Evtimii 10 10
2278 5s. Tsar Ivan Shisman's attack on the Turks . . 10 10
2279 13s. Momchil attacks Turkish ships at Umur, 1344 . . . . 15 10
2280 18s. Meeting of Tsar Ivan Sratsimir and Crusaders, 1396 . . . . 25 10
2281 28s. Embassy of Empress Anne of Savoy meets Boyars Balik, Teodor and Dobrotitsa 75 30

1973. Sailing. Various Yachts. Multicoloured.
2282 1s. Type **704** 10 10
2283 2s. "Flying Dutchman" two-man dinghy 10 10
2284 3s. "Soling" yacht 15 10
2285 13s. "Tempest" dinghy . . . 60 35
2286 20s. "470" two-man dinghy 80 65
2287 40s. "Tornado" catamaran 3·25 1·50

705 "Balchik" (Bercho Obreshkov)

1973. 25th Anniv of National Art Gallery, Sofia and 150th Birth Anniv of Stanislav Dospevski (painter). Multicoloured.
2288 1s. Type **705** 10 10
2289 2s. "Mother and Child" (Stryan Venev) 10 10
2290 3s. "Rest" (Tsenko Boyadzhiev) 10 10
2291 13s. "Vase with Flowers" (Siruk Skitnik) (vert) . . . 20 10
2292 18s. "Mary Kuneva" (Iliya Petrov) (vert) 30 10
2293 40s. "Winter in Plovdiv" (Zlatyn Boyadzhiev) (vert) 1·10 50
MS2294 100 × 95 mm. 50s. "Domnika Lambreva" (S. Dospevski) (vert); 50s. "Self-portrait" (S. Dospevski) (vert) 5·00 5·00

706 Footballers and Emblem

1973. World Cup Football Championship, Munich (1974). Sheet 62 × 94 mm.
MS2295 **706** 28s. multicoloured (sold at 1l.) . . . . 5·00 5·00

707 Old Testament Scene (Wood-carving)

1974. Wood-Carvings from Rozhen Monastery.
2296 **707** 1s. dk brn, cream & brn 10 10
2297 – 2s. dk brn, cream & brn 10 10
2298 – 3s. dk brn, cream & brn 10 10
2299 – 5s. olive, cream & green 10 10
2300 – 8s. olive, cream & green 10 10
2301 – 13s. brown, cream and chestnut 25 15
2302 – 28s. brown, cream and chestnut 40 15
DESIGNS: Nos. 2296/8, "Passover Table"; 2299/2300, "Abraham and the Angel"; 2301/2, "The Expulsion from Eden".
Nos. 2296/8, 2299/300 and 2301/2 form three composite designs.

708 "Lenin" (N. Mirchev)

1974. 50th Death Anniv of Lenin. Mult.
2303 2s. Type **708** 10 10
2304 18s. "Lenin with Workers" (W. A. Serov) 20 10

709 "Blagoev addressing Meeting" (G. Kovachev)

1974. 50th Death Anniv of D. Blagoev (founder of Bulgarian Social Democratic Party).
2305 **709** 2s. multicoloured 10 10

710 Sheep

1974. Domestic Animals.
2306 **710** 1s. brown, buff & green 10 10
2307 – 2s. purple, violet & red 10 10
2308 – 3s. brown, pink & green 10 10
2309 – 5s. brown, buff & blue 10 10
2310 – 13s. black, blue and brown 15 10
2311 – 20s. brown, pink & blue 1·10 25
DESIGNS: 2s. Goat; 3s. Pig; 5s. Cow; 13s. Buffalo; 20s. Horse.

711 Social Economic Integration Emblem

1974. 25th Anniv of Council for Mutual Economic Aid.
2312 **711** 13s. multicoloured . . . 20 10

712 Footballers

1974. World Cup Football Championship.
2313 **712** 1s. multicoloured 10 10
2314 – 2s. multicoloured 10 10
2315 – 3s. multicoloured 10 10
2316 – 13s. multicoloured . . . 25 10
2317 – 28s. multicoloured . . . 50 10
2318 – 40s. multicoloured . . . 2·00 75
MS2319 66 × 78 mm. 1l. multicoloured (55 × 30 mm) . . 5·00 4·50
DESIGNS: Nos. 2314/19, Various designs similar to Type **712**.

713 Folk-singers **714** "Cosmic Research" (Penko Barnbov)

1974. Amateur Arts and Sports Festival. Multicoloured.
2320 1s. Type **713** 10 10
2321 2s. Folk-dancers 10 10
2322 3s. Piper and drummer . . . 10 10
2323 5s. Wrestling 10 10
2324 13s. Athletics . . . . 1·00 50
2325 18s. Gymnastics . . . . . . 1·60 20

1974. "Mladost '74" Youth Stamp Exhibition, Sofia. Multicoloured.
2326 1s. Type **714** 10 10
2327 2s. "Salt Production" (Mariana Bliznakaa) . . . 20 10
2328 3s. "Fire-dancer" (Detelina Lalova) 10 10
2329 28s. "Friendship Train" (Vanya Boyanova) . . . 3·00 1·75
MS2330 70 × 70 mm. 60s. "Spring" (Vladimir Kunchev) (40 × 40 mm) 3·50 3·50

715 Motor-cars

1974. World Automobile Federation's Spring Congress, Sofia.
2331 **715** 13s. multicoloured . . . 20 10

716 Period Architecture

1974. U.N.E.S.C.O. Executive Council's 94th Session, Varna.
2332 **716** 18s. multicoloured . . . 15 10

717 Chinese Aster

1974. Bulgarian Flowers. Multicoloured.
2333 1s. Type **717** 10 10
2334 2s. Mallow 10 10
2335 3s. Columbine 10 10
2336 18s. Tulip 40 10
2337 20s. Marigold 50 20
2338 28s. Pansy . . . . 1·60 50
MS2339 80 × 60 mm. 80s. Gaillarde (44 × 33 mm) . . . . 3·50 3·50

718 19th Century Post-boy

1974. Centenary of U.P.U.
2340 **718** 2s. violet & blk on orge 10 10
2341 – 18s. green & blk on orge 25 10
MS2342 80 × 58 mm. 28s. blue and orange (sold at 80st.) . . . . . 4·00 3·50
DESIGN: 18s. First Bulgarian mail-coach; 20s. U.P.U. emblem.

719 Young Pioneer and Komsomol Girl **720** Communist Soldiers with Flag

1974. 30th Anniv of Dimitrov's Septembrist Pioneers Organization. Multicoloured.
2343 1s. Type **719** 10 10
2344 2s. Pioneer with doves . . . 10 10
MS2345 60 × 84 mm. 60s. Emblem with portrait of Dimitrov (34 × 44 mm) . . . . 2·00 2·00

1974. 30th Anniv of Fatherland Front Government. Multicoloured.
2346 1s. Type **720** 10 10
2347 2s. "Soviet Liberators" . . . 10 10
2348 5s. "Industrialisation" . . . 10 10
2349 13s. "Modern Agriculture" 10 10
2350 18s. "Science and Technology" 25 15

721 Stockholm and Emblems

1974. "Stockholm '74" International Stamp Exhibition. Sheet 65 × 72 mm.
MS2351 **721** 40s. blue, green and yellow . . . . 7·50 7·50

722 Gymnast on Beam **723** Doves on Script

1974. 18th World Gymnastic Championships, Varna. Multicoloured.
2352 2s. Type **722** 10 10
2353 13s. Gymnast on horse . . . 40 15

1974. European Security and Co-operation Conference. Sheet 97 × 117 mm containing T **723** and similar vert designs.
MS2354 13s. yellow, blue and chestnut (T **723**); 13s. blue, mauve and chestnut (Map of Europe and script); 13s. green, blue and chestnut (Leaves on script); 13s. multicoloured (Commemorative text) (sold at 60s.) . . . . . . 3·00 2·50

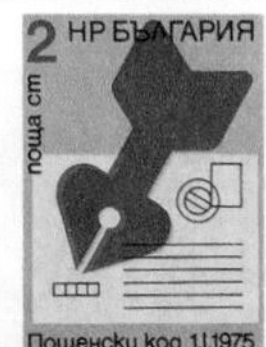

724 Envelope with Arrow pointing to Postal Code

1974. Introduction of Postal Coding System (1 January 1975).
2355 **724** 2s. green, orange & blk . . . 10 10

725 "Sourovachka" (twig decorated with coloured ribbons)

1974. New Year.
2356 **725** 2s. multicoloured 10 10

726 Icon of St. Theodor Stratilar

727 Apricot

1974. Bulgarian History.
2357 **726** 1s. multicoloured 10 10
2358 – 2s. grey, mauve & black 10 10
2359 – 3s. grey, blue and black 10 10
2360 – 5s. grey, lilac and black 10 10
2361 – 8s. black, buff and brown 10 10
2362 – 13s. grey, green & black 15 10
2363 – 18s. black, gold & red 20 10
2364 – 28s. grey, blue & black 75 50
DESIGNS: 2s. Bronze medallion; 3s. Carved capital; 5s. Silver bowl of Sivin Jupan; 8s. Clay goblet; 13s. Lioness (torso); 18s. Gold tray; 28s. Double-headed eagle.

1975. Fruit-tree Blossoms. Multicoloured.
2365 1s. Type **727** 10 10
2366 2s. Apple 10 10
2367 3s. Cherry 10 10
2368 19s. Pear 25 10
2369 28s. Peach 50 15

728 Peasant with Flag

1975. 75th Anniv of Bulgarian People's Agrarian Union. Sheet 104 × 95 mm containing T **728** and similar vert designs.
MS2370 2s. brown, orange and green; 5s. brown, orange and green; 13s. sepia, orange and green; 18s. chestnut, orange and green . . . . 1·00 1·00
DESIGNS: 5s. Rebels keeping watch during 1923 September uprising; 13s. Dancing; 18s. Woman harvesting fruit.

729 Spanish 6c. Stamp of 1850 and "Espana" Emblem

1975. "Espana 1975" International Stamp Exhibition, Madrid. Sheet 68 × 100 mm.
MS2371 **729** 40s. multicoloured 6·50 4·50

730 Star and Arrow

731 "Weights and Measures"

1975. 30th Anniv of "Victory in Europe" Day.
2372 **730** 2s. red, black & brown 10 10
2373 – 13s. black, brown & bl 20 10
DESIGNS: 13s. Peace dove and broken sword.

1975. Centenary of Metre Convention.
2374 **731** 13s. violet, black & silver 10 10

732 Tree and open Book

1975. 50th Anniv of Forestry School.
2375 **732** 2s. multicoloured 10 10

733 Michelangelo

734 Festival Emblem

1975. 500th Birth Anniv of Michelangelo.
2376 **733** 2s. purple and blue . . . 10 10
2377 – 13s. violet and purple . . 15 10
2378 – 18s. brown and green . . 20 10
MS2379 70 × 84 mm. **733** 2s. green and red (sold at 60s.) . . . . . 1·50 1·50
DESIGNS—HORIZ: Sculptures from Giuliano de Medici's tomb: 13s. "Night"; 18s. "Day".

1975. Festival of Humour and Satire, Gabrovo.
2380 **734** 2s. multicoloured 10 10

735 Women's Head and Emblem

1975. International Women's Year.
2381 **735** 13s. multicoloured . . . 10 10

736 Vasil and Sava Kokareshkov

1975. "Young Martyrs to Fascism".
2382 **736** 1s. black, green & gold 10 10
2383 – 2s. black, mauve & gold 10 10
2384 – 5s. black, red and gold 10 10
2385 – 13s. black, blue & gold 20 10
DESIGNS—HORIZ: 2s. Mitko Palauzov and Ivan Vasilev; 5s. Nikola Nakev and Stefcho Kraichev; 13s. Ivanka Pashkolouva and Detelina Mincheva.

737 "Mother feeding Child" (Jean Millet)

738 Gabrovo Costume

1975. World Graphics Exhibition, Sofia. Celebrated Drawings and Engravings. Multicoloured.
2386 1s. Type **737** 10 10
2387 2s. "Mourning a Dead Daughter" (Goya) 10 10
2388 3s. "The Reunion" (Iliya Beshkov) 10 10
2389 13s. "Seated Nude" (Auguste Renoir) 10 10
2390 20s. "Man in a Fur Hat" (Rembrandt) 10 10
2391 40s. "The Dream" (Horore Daumier) (horiz) 70 20
MS2392 80 × 95 mm. 1l. "Temptation" (Albrecht Durer) (37 × 53 mm) . . . . 2·50 2·50

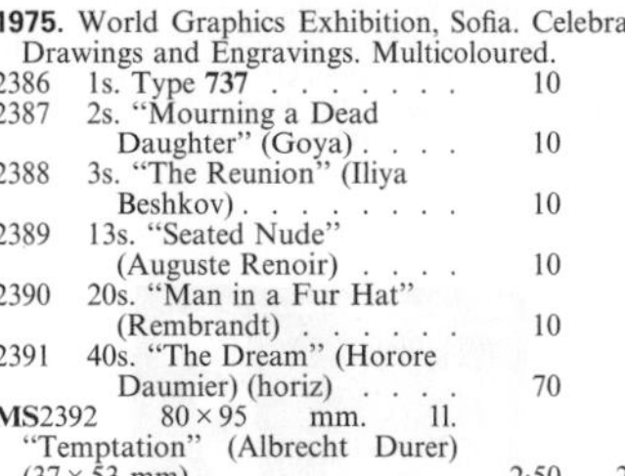

1975. Women's Regional Costumes. Mult.
2393 2s. Type **738** 10 10
2394 3s. Trun costume 10 10
2395 5s. Vidin costume 10 10
2396 13s. Goce Delcev costume 15 10
2397 18s. Ruse costume 40 15

739 "Bird" (manuscript illumination)

740 Ivan Vasov

1975. Original Bulgarian Manuscripts. Mult.
2398 1s. Type **739** 10 10
2399 2s. "Head" 10 10
2400 3s. Abstract design 10 10
2401 8s. "Pointing finger" 10 10
2402 13s. "Imaginary creature" 10 10
2403 18s. Abstract design 40 15

1975. 125th Anniv of Ivan Vasov (writer). Multicoloured.
2404 2s. Type **740** 10 10
2405 13s. Vasov seated 10 10

741 "Soyuz" and Aleksei Leonov

1975. "Apollo"–"Soyuz" Space Link.
2406 **741** 13s. multicoloured . . . 30 10
2407 – 18s. multicoloured . . . 50 10
2408 – 28s. multicoloured . . . 1·50 20
MS2409 76 × 84 mm. 1l. blue, grey and red . . . . 3·00 3·50
DESIGNS: 18s. "Apollo" and Thomas Stafford; 28s. The Link-up; 1l. "Apollo" and "Soyuz" after docking.

742 Ryukyu Sailing Boat, Map and Emblems

1975. International Exposition, Okinawa.
2410 **742** 13s. multicoloured . . . 30 10

743 St. Cyril and St. Methodius

744 Footballer

1975. "Balkanphila V" Stamp Exhibition, Sofia.
2411 **743** 2s. brown, lt brn & red 10 10
2412 – 13s. brown, lt brn & grn 10 10
MS2413 90 × 86 mm. 50s. sepia, brown and orange . . . . . . 1·50 1·50
DESIGNS—VERT: 13s. St. Constantine and St. Helene. HORIZ: 50s. Sophia Church, Sofia (53 × 43 mm.).

1975. 8th Inter-Toto (Football Pools) Congress, Varna.
2414 **744** 2s. multicoloured 10 10

745 Deaths-head Hawk Moth

1975. Hawk Moths. Multicoloured.
2415 1s. Type **745** 10 10
2416 2s. Oleander hawk moth . . 10 10
2417 3s. Eyed hawk moth 15 10
2418 10s. Mediterranean hawk moth 25 20
2419 13s. Elephant hawk moth 50 25
2420 18s. Broad-bordered bee hawk moth . . . . 1·10 40

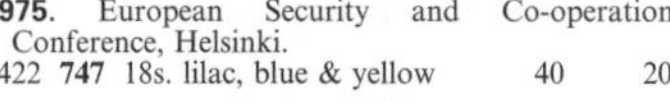
746 U.N. Emblem

747 Map of Europe on Peace Dove

1975. 30th Anniv of U.N.O.
2421 **746** 13s. red, brown & black 10 10

1975. European Security and Co-operation Conference, Helsinki.
2422 **747** 18s. lilac, blue & yellow 40 20

748 D. Khristov

1975. Birth Cent of Dobri Khristov (composer).
2423 **748** 5s. brown, yellow & grn 10 10

749 Constantine's Rebellion against the Turks

1975. Bulgarian History. Multicoloured.
2424 1s. Type **749** 10 10
2425 2s. Vladislav III's campaign 10 10
2426 3s. Battle of Turnovo . . . 10 10
2427 10s. Battle of Chiprovtsi . . 10 10
2428 13s. 17 th-century partisans 25 10
2429 18s. Return of banished peasants 40 25

750 "First Aid"

1975. 90th Anniv of Bulgarian Red Cross.
2430 **750** 2s. brown, black and red . . . 10 10
2431 – 13s. green, black and red . . . 25 10
DESIGN: 13s. "Peace and international Co-operation".

751 Ethnographical Museum, Plovdiv

1975. European Architectural Heritage Year.
2432 **751** 80s. brown, yellow & grn . . . 1·75 1·75

752 Christmas Lanterns

1975. Christmas and New Year. Multicoloured.
2433 2s. Type **752** 10 10
2434 13s. Stylized peace dove . . . 10 10

753 Egyptian Galley

1975. Historic Ships (1st series). Multicoloured.
2435 1s. Type **753** 10 10
2436 2s. Phoenician galley . . . 10 10
2437 3s. Greek trireme 10 10
2438 5s. Roman galley 10 10
2439 13s. "Mora" (Norman ship) . . 50 25
2440 18s. Venetian galley 90 35
See also Nos. 2597/2602, 2864/9, 3286/91 and 3372/7.

754 Modern Articulated Tramcar

1976. 75th Anniv of Sofia Tramways. Mult.
2441 2s. Type **754** 30 15
2442 13s. Early 20th-century tramcar . . . . 1·10 50

755 Skiing

1976. Winter Olympic Games, Innsbruck. Mult.
2443 1s. Type **755** 10 10
2444 2s. Cross-country skiing (vert) 10 10
2445 2s. Ski jumping 10 10
2446 13s. Biathlon (vert) 20 15
2447 18s. Ice hockey (vert) . . . 40 25
2448 18s. Speed skating (vert) . . 1·00 30
MS2449 70 × 80 mm. 80s. Ice skating (pairs) (30 × 55 mm) . . . . . 2·50 2·50

756 Stylized Bird

1976. 11th Bulgarian Communists Party Congress. Multicoloured.
2450 2s. Type **756** 10 10
2451 5s. "1956–1976, Fulfilment of the Five Year Plans" . . 10 10
2452 13s. Hammer and Sickle . . 10 10
MS2453 55 × 65 mm. 50s. Georgi Dimitrov (Prime Minister and Party secretary-general, 1945–49) (33 × 43 mm) . . . . 1·00 1·00

757 Alexander Graham Bell and early Telephone

1976. Telephone Centenary.
2454 **757** 18s. lt brown, brn & pur . . 20 10

758 Mute Swan

1976. Waterfowl. Multicoloured.
2455 1s. Type **758** 20 10
2456 2s. Ruddy shelduck 25 10
2457 3s. Common shelduck . . . 40 15
2458 5s. Garganey 60 20
2459 13s. Mallard . . . . 1·25 30
2460 18s. Red-crested pochard . . 1·75 80

759 Guerillas' Briefing

1976. Cent of April Uprising (1st issue). Mult.
2461 1s. Type **759** 10 10
2462 2s. Peasants' briefing . . . 10 10
2463 5s. Krishina, horse and guard 10 10
2464 13s. Rebels with cannon . . 20 10
See also Nos. 2529/33.

760 Kozlodui Atomic Energy Centre

1976. Modern Industrial Installations.
2465 **760** 5s. green 10 10
2466 – 8s. red 10 10
2467 – 10s. green 10 10
2468 – 13s. violet 10 10
2469 – 20s. green 15 10
DESIGNS: 8s. Bobaudol plant; 10s. Sviloza chemical works; 13s. Devaya chemical works; 20s. Sestvitro dam.

761 Guard with Patrol-dog

1976. 30th Anniv of Frontier Guards. Mult.
2470 2s. Type **761** 10 10
2471 13s. Mounted guards . . . 10 10

762 Worker with Spade

1976. 30th Anniv of Youth Brigades Movement.
2472 **762** 2s. multicoloured 10 10

764 "Martyrs of First Congress" (relief)

765 Dimitur Blagoev

1976. Death Cent of Khristo Botev (poet).
2473 **763** 13s. green and brown . . 10 10

1976. 85th Anniv of 1st Bulgarian Social Democratic Party Congress, Buzludzha. Multicoloured.
2474 2s. Type **764** 10 10
2475 5s. Modern memorial, Buzludzha Peak 10 10

1976. 120th Birth Anniv of Dimitur Blagoev (founder of Bulgarian Social Democratic Party).
2476 **765** 13s. black, red and gold . . 10 10

766 "Thematic Stamps"

1976. 12th Bulgarian Philatelic Federation Congress. Sheet 73 × 103 mm.
MS2477 **766** 50s. multicoloured . . . 2·50 2·50

767 Children Playing

1976. Child Welfare.
2478 **767** 1s. multicoloured 10 10
2479 – 2s. multicoloured 10 10
2480 – 5s. multicoloured 10 10
2481 – 23s. multicoloured . . . 25 20
DESIGNS: 2s. Girls with pram and boy on rocking horse; 5s. Playing ball; 23s. Dancing.

768 Wrestling

1976. Olympic Games, Montreal. Multicoloured.
2482 1s. Type **768** 10 10
2483 2s. Boxing (vert) 10 10
2484 3s. Weight-lifting (vert) . . 10 10
2485 13s. Canoeing (vert) 20 10
2486 18s. Gymnastics (vert) . . . 30 15
2487 28s. Diving (vert) 45 20
2488 40s. Athletics (vert) 65 30
MS2489 70 × 80 mm. 1l. Weightlifting (vert) . . . . . . 2·50 2·50

769 Belt Buckle, Vidin

771 Weightlifting

770 "Partisans at Night" (Petrov)

1976. Thracian Art (8th–4th Centuries B.C.). Mult.
2490 1s. Type **769** 10 10
2491 2s. Brooch, Durzhanitsa . . 10 10
2492 3s. Mirror handle, Chukarka . 10 10
2493 5s. Helmet cheek guard, Gurlo 10 10
2494 13s. Gold decoration, Orizovo 10 10
2495 18s. Decorated horse-harness, Brezovo 15 15
2496 20s. Greave, Mogilanska Mogila 20 15
2497 28s. Pendant, Bukovtsi . . . 25 25

1976. Paintings by Iliya Petrov and Tsanko Lavrenov from the National Gallery. Multicoloured.
2498 2s. Type **770** 10 10
2499 5s. "Kurshum-Khan" (Lavrenov) 10 10
2500 13s. "Seated Woman" (Petrov) 15 10
2501 18s. "Boy seated in chair" (Petrov) (vert) 25 10
2502 28s. "Old Plovdiv" (Lavrenov) (vert) 40 15
MS2503 60 × 82 mm. 80s. "Self-portrait" (Petrov) (vert) . . . . 1·75 1·75

1976. Gold Medal Winners, Montreal Olympic Games. Sheet 98 × 116 mm containing vert designs as T **771**, each with medal in red and gold.
MS2504 25s. yellow (T **771**); 25s. blue (rowing); 25s. green (running); 25s. red (wrestling) . . . 2·00 2·00

772 Fish on line

1976. World Sports Fishing Congress, Varna.
2505 **772** 5s. multicoloured 10 10

773 "The Pianist" 774 St. Theodor

1976. 75th Birth Anniv of Alex Jhendov (caricaturist).
2506 **773** 2s. dp grn, cream & grn . . 10 10
2507 – 5s. dp violet, vio & lilac . 10 10
2508 – 13s. black, pink & red . . 20 10
DESIGNS: 5s. "Trick or Treat"; 13s. "The Leader".

1976. Zemen Monastery. Frescoes. Multicoloured.
2509 2s. Type **774** 10 10
2510 3s. St. Paul and Apostle . . 10 10
2511 5s. St. Joachim 10 10
2512 13s. Prophet Melchisadek . . 10 10
2513 19s. St. Porphyrus 15 10
2514 28s. Queen Doya 25 15
MS2515 60 × 76 mm. 1l. Holy Communion . . . . 1·50 1·50

775 Legal Document **776** Horse Chestnut

1976. 25th Anniv of State Archives.

2516 **775** 5s. multicoloured 10 10

1976. Plants. Multicoloured.

2517 1s. Type **776** 10 10
2518 2s. Shrubby cinquefoil . . . 10 10
2519 5s. Holly 15 10
2520 8s. Yew 15 10
2521 13s. "Daphne pontica" . . . 30 15
2522 23s. Judas tree 75 30

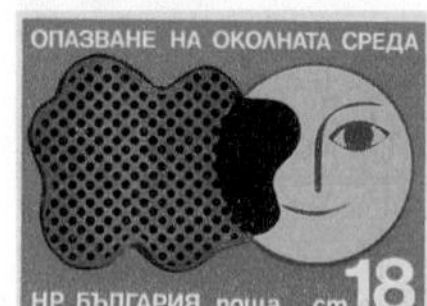

777 Cloud over Sun

1976. Protection of the Environment. Mult.

2523 2s. Cloud over tree 10 10
2524 18s. Type **777** 20 10

778 Dimitur Polyanov

1976. Birth Cent of Dimitur Polyanov (poet).

2525 **778** 2s. lilac and orange . . . 10 10

779 Congress Emblem

1976. 33rd Bulgarian People's Agrarian Union Congress. Multicoloured.

2526 2s. Type **779** 10 10
2527 13s. Flags 10 10

780 Warrior with Horses (vase painting)

1976. 30th Anniv of United Nations Educational Scientific and Cultural Organization. Sheet 71 × 81 mm.

MS2528 **780** 50s. multicoloured 1·50 1·50

781 "Khristo Botev" (Zlatyu Boyadzhiev)

1976. Centenary of April Uprising (2nd issue). Multicoloured.

2529 1s. Type **781** 10 10
2530 2s. "Partisan carrying Cherrywood Cannon" (Iliya Petrov) 10 10
2531 3s. "Necklace of Immortality" (Dechko Uzunov) 10 10
2532 13s. "April 1876" (Georgi Popov) 10 15
2533 18s. "Partisans" (Stoyan Venev) 25 20
MS2534 45 × 82 mm. 60s. "The Oath" (Svetlin Rusev) . . . . 1·25 1·25

782 Tobacco Workers

1976. 70th Birth Anniv of Veselin Staikov (artist). Multicoloured.

2535 1s. Type **782** 10 10
2536 2s. "Melnik" 10 10
2537 13s. "Boat Builders" 20 10

783 "Snowflake"

1976. New Year.

2538 **783** 2s. multicoloured 10 10

784 Zakhari Stojanov

1976. 125th Birth Anniv of Zakhari Stojanov (writer).

2539 **784** 2s. brown, red and gold 10 10

785 Bronze Coin of Septimus Severus

1977. Roman Coins struck in Serdica. Mult.

2540 1s. Type **785** 10 10
2541 2s. Bronze coin of Caracalla 10 10
2542 13s. Bronze coin of Caracalla (diff.) 10 10
2543 18s. Bronze coin of Caracalla (diff.) 15 15
2544 23s. Copper coin of Diocletian 25 20

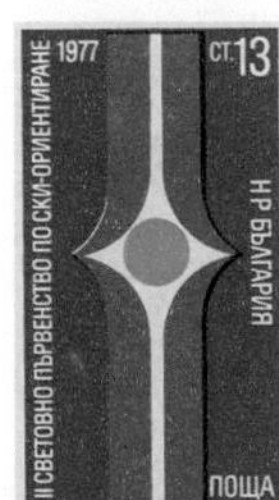

786 Championships Emblem **787** Congress Emblem

1977. World Ski-orienteering Championships.

2545 **786** 13s. blue, red & ultram 20 10

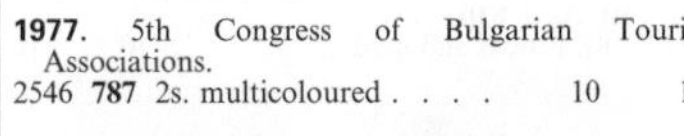

1977. 5th Congress of Bulgarian Tourist Associations.

2546 **787** 2s. multicoloured 10 10

788 "Symphyandra wanneri" **789** V. Kolarov

1977. Mountain Flowers. Multicoloured.

2547 1s. Type **788** 10 10
2548 2s. "Petcovia orphanidea" 10 10
2549 3s. "Campanula lanatre" . . 10 10
2550 13s. "Campanula scutellata" 15 10
2551 43s. Nettle-leaved bellflower 60 40

1977. Birth Centenary of Vasil Kolarov (Prime Minister 1949–50).

2552 **789** 2s. grey, black & blue . . 10 10

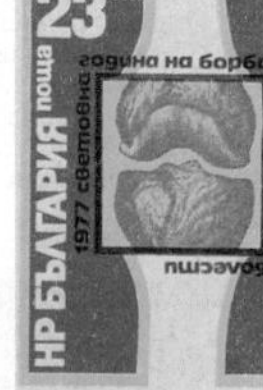

790 Congress Emblem **791** Joint

1977. 8th Bulgarian Trade Unions Congress.

2553 **790** 2s. multicoloured 10 10

1977. World Rheumatism Year.

2554 **791** 23s. multicoloured . . . 20 10

792 Wrestling

1977. World University Games, Sofia. Mult.

2555 2s. Type **792** 10 10
2556 13s. Running 20 10
2557 23s. Handball 40 15
2558 43s. Gymnastics 70 25

793 Ivan Vazov National Theatre **794** Congress Emblem

1977. Buildings in Sofia. Pale brown backgrounds.

2559 **793** 12s. red 10 10
2560 – 13s. brown 10 10
2561 – 23s. blue 15 10
2562 – 30s. green 20 10
2563 – 80s. violet 60 25
2564 – 1l. brown 80 80

DESIGNS: 13s. Party Building; 23s. People's Army Building; 30s. Clement of Ohrid University; 80s. National Art Gallery; 1l. National Assembly Building.

1977. 13th Dimitrov Communist Youth League Congress.

2565 **794** 2s. red, green and gold 10 10

795 "St. Nicholas" Nesebur

1977. Bulgarian Icons. Multicoloured.

2566 1s. Type **795** 10 10
2567 2s. "Old Testament Trinity", Sofia 10 10
2568 3s. "The Royal Gates", Veliko Turnovo 10 10
2569 5s. "Deisis", Nesebur . . . 10 10
2570 13s. "St. Nicholas", Elena 10 10
2571 23s. "The Presentation of the Blessed Virgin", Rila Monastery 30 10
2572 35s. "The Virgin Mary with Infant", Varna 40 15
2573 40s. "St. Demetrius on Horseback", Provadya . . 50 20
MS2574 100 × 99 mm. 1l. "The Twelve Festival Days", Rila Monastery. Imperf . . . . . . 1·50 1·50

796 Wolf

1977. Wild Animals. Multicoloured.

2575 1s. Type **796** 10 10
2576 2s. Red fox 10 10
2577 10s. Weasel 20 10
2578 13s. Wild cat 35 15
2579 23s. Golden jackal 60 25

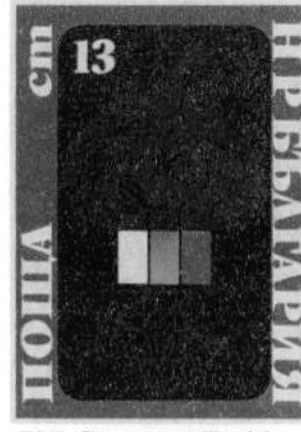

797 Congress Emblem **798** "Crafty Peter riding a Donkey" (drawing by Iliya Beshkov)

1977. 3rd Bulgarian Culture Congress.

2580 **797** 13s. multicoloured . . . 10 10

1977. 11th Festival of Humour and Satire, Gabrovo.

2581 **798** 2s. multicoloured 10 10

799 Congress Emblem

1977. 8th Congress of the Popular Front, Sofia.

2582 **799** 2s. multicoloured 10 10

800 Newspaper Masthead

1977. Centenary of Bulgarian Daily Press.

2583 **800** 2s. multicoloured 10 10

801 St. Cyril

1977. 1150th Birth Anniv of St. Cyril. Sheet 106 × 87 mm.

MS2584 **801** 1l. multicoloured . . 1·50 1·50

802 Conference Emblem

1977. International Writers Conference, Sofia.

2585 **802** 23s. blue, lt blue & grn 75 40

803 Map of Europe

1977. 21st Congress of European Organization for Quality Control, Varna.
2586 **803** 23s. multicoloured . . . 25 10

804 Basketball **805** Weightlifter

1977. Women's European Basketball Championships.
2587 **804** 23s. multicoloured . . . 40 10

1977. World Junior Weightlifting Championships.
2588 **805** 13s. multicoloured . . . 30 10

806 Georgi Dimitrov

1977. 95th Birth Anniv of Georgi Dimitrov (statesman).
2589 **806** 13s. brown and red . . . 15 10

807 Tail Section of Tupolev Tu-154

1977. Air. 30th Anniv of Bulgarian Airline "Balkanair".
2590 **807** 35s. multicoloured . . . 75 25

808 Games Emblem

1977. World University Games, Sofia (2nd issue). Sheet 84 × 76 mm.
MS2591 **808** 1l. multicoloured . . 1·50 1·50

809 T.V. Towers, Berlin and Sofia **810** Elin Pelin alias Dimitur Stoyanov (writer)

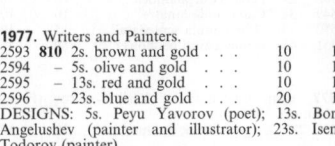

1977. "Sozphilex 77" Stamp Exhibition, East Berlin.
2592 **809** 25s. blue and deep blue 40 10

1977. Writers and Painters.
2593 **810** 2s. brown and gold . . . 10 10
2594 – 5s. olive and gold . . . 10 10
2595 – 13s. red and gold . . . 10 10
2596 – 23s. blue and gold . . . 20 15
DESIGNS: 5s. Peyu Yavorov (poet); 13s. Boris Angelushev (painter and illustrator); 23s. Iseno Todorov (painter).

1977. Historic Ships (2nd series). As T **753**. Multicoloured.
2597 1s. Hansa Kogge 10 10
2598 2s. "Santa Maria" 10 10
2599 3s. Drake's "Golden Hind" 10 10
2600 12s. Carrack "Santa Catherina" 30 10
2601 13s. "La Couronne" (French galleon) 35 15
2602 43s. Mediterranean galley 1·10 40

811 Women Canoeists

1977. World Canoe Championships.
2603 **811** 2s. blue and yellow . . . 10 10
2604 – 23s. blue and turquoise 30 10
DESIGN: 23s. Men canoeists.

812 Balloon over Plovdiv **813** Presidents Zhivkov and Brezhnev

1977. Air. 85th Anniv "Panair". International Aviation Exhibition, Plovdiv.
2605 **812** 25s. orange, yell & brn 85 20

1977. Soviet–Bulgarian Friendship.
2606 **813** 18s. brown, red & gold 10 10

814 Conference Building

1977. 64th International Parliamentary Conference, Sofia.
2607 **814** 23s. green, pink and red 15 10

815 Newspaper Mastheads **816** "The Union of Earth and Water"

1977. 50th Anniv of Official Newspaper "Rabotnichesko Delo" (Workers' Press).
2608 **815** 2s. red, green and grey 10 10

1977. 400th Birth Anniv of Rubens. Mult.
2609 13s. Type **816** 25 10
2610 23s. "Venus and Adonis" (detail) 45 20
2611 40s. "Amorous Shepherd" (detail) 90 30
MS2612 71 × 87 mm. 1l. "Portrait of a Chambermaid" . . . . . . 2·50 2·50

817 Cossack with Bulgarian Child (Angelushev) **818** Albena, Black Sea

1977. Centenary of Liberation from Turkey. (1978). Posters.
2613 **817** 2s. multicoloured 10 10
2614 – 13s. green, blue & red 10 10
2615 – 23s. blue, red & green 20 15
2616 – 25s. multicoloured . . . 20 15
DESIGNS: 13s. Bugler (Cheklarov); 23s. Mars (god of war) and Russian soldiers (Petrov); 25s. Flag of Russian Imperial Army.

1977. Tourism.
2617 **818** 35s. blue, turq & brn . . 75 20
2618 – 43s. yellow, grn & blue 75 20
DESIGN: 43s. Rila Monastery.

819 Dr. Nikolai Pirogov (Russian surgeon) **821** Soviet Emblems and Decree

820 Space walking

1977. Cent of Dr. Pirogov's Visit to Bulgaria.
2619 **819** 13s. brown, buff & grn 10 10

1977. Air. 20th Anniv of First Artificial Satellite. Multicoloured.
2620 12s. Type **820** 20 10
2621 25s. Space probe over Mars 40 10
2622 35s. Space probe "Venus-4" over Venus 55 10

1977. 60th Anniv of Russian Revolution.
2623 **821** 2s. red, black & stone . . 10 10
2624 – 13s. red and purple . . . 10 10
2625 – 23s. red and violet . . . 15 10
DESIGNS: 13s. Lenin; 23s. "1977" as flame.

822 Diesel Train on Bridge

1977. 50th Anniv of Transport, Bridges and Highways Organization.
2626 **822** 13s. yellow, green & olive 65 15

1977. 150th Birth Anniv of Petko Ratshev Slaveikov (poet). As T **810**.
2627 8s. brown and gold 10 10

824 Decorative Initials of New Year Greeting

1977. New Year. Multicoloured.
2628 2s. Type **824** 10 10
2629 13s. "Fireworks" 10 10

825 Footballer

1978. World Cup Football Championship, Argentina. Multicoloured.
2630 13s. Type **825** 20 10
2631 23s. Shooting the ball . . . 35 10
MS2632 77 × 61 mm. 50s. Tackle for ball . . . . 1·50 1·50

826 Baba Vida Fortress, Vidin

1977. Air. "The Danube – European River". Mult.
2633 25s. Type **826** 45 20
2634 35s. Friendship Bridge . . . 1·25 1·25

827 Television Mast, Moscow **828** Shipka Monument

1978. 20th Anniv of Organization of Socialist Postal Administrations (O.S.S.).
2635 **827** 13s. multicoloured . . . 10 10

1978. Centenary of Liberation from Turkey (2nd issue). Sheet 55 × 73 mm.
MS2636 **828** 50s. multicoloured 1·00 1·00

829 Red Cross in Laurel Wreath

1978. Centenary of Bulgarian Red Cross.
2637 **829** 25s. red, brown & blue 50 10

830 "XXX" formed from Bulgarian and Russian National Colours

1978. 30th Anniv of Bulgarian–Soviet Friendship.
2638 **830** 2s. multicoloured 10 10

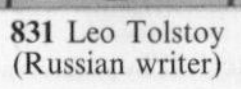

831 Leo Tolstoy (Russian writer) **832** Nikolai Roerich (artist)

1978. Famous Personalities.
2639 **831** 2s. green and yellow . . 10 10
2640 – 5s. brown and bistre . . 10 10
2641 – 13s. green and mauve . . 10 10
2642 – 23s. brown and grey . . 15 15
2643 – 25s. brown and green . . 15 15
2644 – 35s. violet and blue . . . 25 20

DESIGNS: 5s. Fyodor Dostoevsky (Russian writer); 13s. Ivan Turgenev (Russian writer); 23s. Vassily Vereshchagin (Russian artist); 25s. Giuseppe Garibaldi (Italian patriot); 35s. Victor Hugo (French writer).

1978. Nikolai Roerich Exhibition, Sofia.
2645 **832** 8s. brown, green & red . . . 10 10

833 Bulgarian Flag and Red Star

1978. Communist Party National Conference, Sofia.
2646 **833** 2s. multicoloured 10 10

834 Goddess **835** "Spirit of Nature"

1978. "Philaserdica 79" International Stamp Exhibition (1st issue). Ancient Ceramics. Mult.
2647 2s. Type **834** 10 10
2648 5s. Mask with beard 10 10
2649 13s. Decorated vase 25 10
2650 23s. Vase with scallop design 45 15
2651 35s. Head of Silenus 60 20
2652 53s. Cockerel . . . . 1·25 30
See also Nos. 2674/9, 2714/18, 2721/5 and 2753/4.

1978. Birth Cent of Andrei Nikolov (sculptor).
2653 **835** 13s. blue, mauve & vio . . 10 10

836 Heart and Arrows

1978. World Hypertension Month.
2654 **836** 23s. red, orange & grey . . 20 10

837 "Kor Karoli" and Map of Route

1978. Georgi Georgiev's World Voyage.
2655 **837** 23s. blue, mauve & grn . . 55 25

838 Doves

1978. 11th World Youth and Students' Festival, Havana.
2656 **838** 13s. multicoloured . . . 10 10

839 "Portrait of a Young Man" (Durer) **840** "Fritillaria stribrnyi"

1978. Paintings. Multicoloured.
2657 13s. Type **839** 10 10
2658 23s. "Bathsheba at the Fountain" (Rubens) . . . 20 10
2659 25s. "Signor de Moret" (Hans Holbein the Younger) 20 10
2660 35s. "Self portrait with Saskia" (Rembrandt) . . 30 10
2661 43s. "Lady in Mourning" (Tintoretto) 40 15
2662 60s. "Old Man with a Beard" (Rembrandt) . . . 45 20
2663 80s. "Man in Armour" (Van Dyck) 60 25

1978. Flowers. Multicoloured.
2664 1s. Type **840** 10 10
2665 2s. "Fritillaria drenovskyi" 10 10
2666 3s. "Lilium rhodopaeum" 10 10
2667 13s. "Tulipa urumoffii" . . 25 10
2668 23s. "Lilium jankae" . . . 40 15
2669 43s. "Tulipa rhodopaea" . . 70 30

841 Varna

1978. 63rd Esperanto Congress, Varna.
2670 **841** 13s. orange, red & green . . 10 10

842 Delcev

1978. 75th Death Anniv of Goce Delcev (Macedonian revolutionary).
2671 **842** 13s. multicoloured . . . 10 10

843 Freedom Fighters

1978. 75th Anniv of Ilinden-Preobrazhenie Rising.
2672 **843** 5s. black and red 10 10

844 "The Sleeping Venus"

1978. World Masters of Art. Sheet 71 × 71 mm. Imperf.
MS2673 **844** 1l. multicoloured . . 2·00 2·00

845 "Market" (Noiden Petkov)

1978. "Philaserdica 79" International Stamp Exhibition (2nd issue). Paintings of Sofia. Multicoloured.
2674 2s. Type **845** 10 10
2675 5s. "View of Sofia" (Euril Stoichev) 10 10
2676 13s. "View of Sofia" (Boris Ivanov) . . . . 1·10 20
2677 23s. "Tolbukhin Boulevard" (Nikola Tanev) 20 10
2678 35s. "National Theatre" (Nikola Petrov) 25 10
2679 53s. "Market" (Anton Mitov) 35 15
MS2679a 186 × 106 mm. Nos. 2674/9 5·00 5·00

846 Black Woodpecker **848** "Elka 55" Computer

847 Ivan Vazov National Theatre, Sofia

1978. Woodpeckers. Multicoloured.
2680 1s. Type **846** 15 10
2681 2s. Syrian woodpecker . . . 15 10
2682 3s. Three-toed woodpecker 20 10
2683 13s. Middle-spotted woodpecker 70 30
2684 23s. Lesser spotted woodpecker . . . . . . 1·25 50
2685 43s. Green woodpecker . . 2·25 1·00

1978. "Praga 78" and "Philaserdica 79" International Stamp Exhibitions. Sheet 153 × 110 mm containing T **847** and similar horiz designs. Multicoloured.
MS2686 (a) 40s. Type **847**; (b) 40s. Festival Hall, Sofia; (c) 40s. Charles Bridge, Prague; (d) 40s. Belvedere Palace, Prague . . . 3·00 3·00

1978. Plovdiv International Fair.
2687 **848** 2s. multicoloured 10 10

849 "September 1923" (Boris Angelushev)

1978. 55th Anniv of September Uprising.
2688 **849** 2s. red and brown . . . 10 10

850 Khristo Danov

1978. 150th Birth Anniv of Khristo Danov (first Bulgarian publisher).
2689 **850** 2s. orange and lake . . . 10 10

851 "The People of Vladaya" (Todor Panayotov)

1978. 60th Anniv of Vladaya Mutiny.
2690 **851** 2s. lilac, brown and red . . 10 10

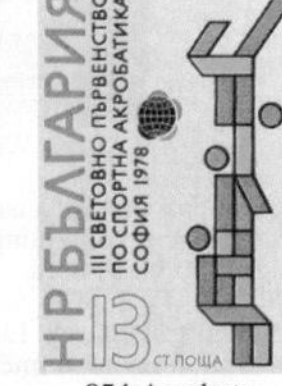

852 Hands supporting Rainbow **854** Acrobats

853 Pipeline and Flags

1978. International Anti-apartheid Year.
2691 **852** 13s. multicoloured . . . 10 10

1978. Inauguration of Orenburg–U.S.S.R. Natural Gas Pipeline.
2692 **853** 13s. multicoloured . . . 10 10

1978. 3rd World Sports Acrobatics Championships, Sofia.
2693 **854** 13s. multicoloured . . . 25 10

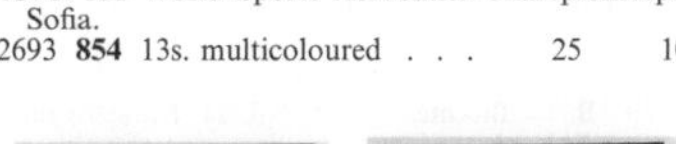

855 Salvador Allende **856** Human Rights Emblem

1978. 70th Birth Anniv of Salvador Allende (Chilean politician).
2694 **855** 13s. brown and red . . . 10 10

1978. 30th Anniv of Declaration of Human Rights.
2695 **856** 23s. yellow, red & blue . . 40 10

857 "Levski and Matei Mitkaloto" (Kalina Taseva) **858** Tourist Home, Plovdiv

1978. History of Bulgaria. Paintings. Multicoloured.
2696 1s. Type **857** 10 10
2697 2s. "Give Strength to my Arm" (Zlatyu Boyadzhiev) 10 10
2698 3s. "Rumena Voevoda" (Nikola Mirchev) (horiz) 10 10
2699 13s. "Kolya Ficheto" (Elza Goeva) 20 15
2700 23s. "A Family of the National Revival Period" (Naiden Petkov) 35 25

1978. European Architectural Heritage. Mult.
2701 43s. Type **858** 30 15
2702 43s. Tower of the Prince, Rila Monastery 30 15

859 "Geroi Plevny" and Route Map

1978. Opening of the Varna–Ilichovsk Ferry Service.
2703 **859** 13s. blue, red & green . . 70 10

860 Mosaic Bird (Santa Sofia Church)

1978. "Bulgaria 78" National Stamp Exhibition, Sofia.
2704 **860** 5s. multicoloured 15 10

861 Monument to St. Clement of Ohrid (university patron) (Lyubemir Dalcher)

862 Nikola Karastoyanov

1978. 90th Anniv of Sofia University.
2705 **861** 2s. lilac, black & green . . . 10 10

1978. Birth Bicentenary of Nikola Karastoyanov (first Bulgarian printer).
2706 **862** 2s. brn, yell & chestnut . . . 10 10

863 Initial from 13th Century Bible Manuscript

1978. Centenary of Cyril and Methodius People's Library. Multicoloured.
2707 2s. Type **863** 10 10
2708 13s. Monk writing (from a 1567 manuscript) 10 10
2709 23s. Decorated page from 16th-century manuscript Bible 15 10
MS2710 63 × 94 mm. 80s. Seated saint with attendant (from 13th century manuscript Bible) . . . 1·50 1·50

864 Ballet Dancers

1978. 50th Anniv of Bulgarian Ballet.
2711 **864** 13s. green, mauve & lav . . . 15 10

865 Tree of Birds

1978. New Year. Multicoloured.
2712 2s. Type **865** 10 10
2713 13s. Posthorn 10 10

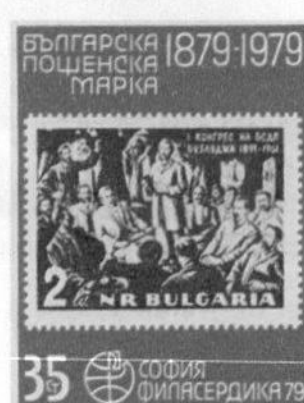

866 1961 Communist Congress Stamp

1978. "Philaserdica 79" International Stamp Exhibition (3rd issue) and Bulgarian Stamp Centenary (1st issue).
2714 – 2s. red and green 10 10
2715 – 13s. claret and blue . . . 20 10
2716 – 23s. green and mauve . . 35 15
2717 **866** 35s. grey and blue . . . 50 20
2718 – 53s. green and red . . . 75 30
MS2719 62 × 87 mm. 1l. black, yellow and green . . . . . . 2·00 2·00
DESIGNS—HORIZ: 2s. 1901 "Cherrywood Cannon" stamp; 13s. 1946 "New Republic" stamp; 23s. 1957 Canonisation of St. Cyril and St. Methodius stamp; 1l. First Bulgarian stamp. VERT: 53s. 1962 Dimitrov stamp.
See also Nos. 2721/5 and **MS**2755.

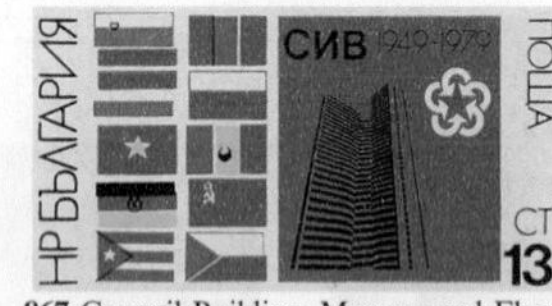

867 Council Building, Moscow and Flags

1979. 30th Anniv of Council of Mutual Economic Aid.
2720 **867** 13s. multicoloured . . . 10 10

1979. "Philaserdica 79" Int Stamp Exn (4th issue) and Bulgarian Stamp Cent (2nd issue). As Nos. 2714/18 but inscr "1979" and colours changed.
2721 – 2s. red and blue 10 10
2722 – 13s. claret and green . . 20 10
2723 – 23s. green, yellow & red 35 15
2724 **866** 35s. grey and red 50 20
2725 – 53s. brown and violet . . 75 30

868 National Bank

868a

1979. Centenary of Bulgarian National Bank.
2726 **868** 2s. grey and yellow . . . 10 10

1979. Coil stamps.
2726a **868a** 2s. blue 10 10
2726b 5s. red 10 10
The 5s. is as T **868a** but different pattern.

869 Stamboliiski

870 Child's Head as Flower

1979. Birth Centenary of Alexandur Stamboliiski (Prime Minister 1919–23).
2727 **869** 2s. brown and yellow . . 10 10

1979. International Year of the Child.
2728 **870** 23s. multicoloured . . . 20 10

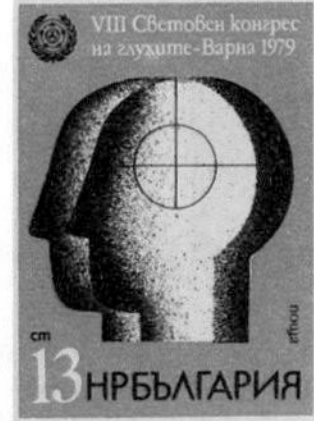

871 Profiles

872 "75" and Emblem

1979. 8th World Congress for the Deaf, Varna.
2729 **871** 13s. green and blue . . . 10 10

1979. 75th Anniv of Bulgarian Trade Unions.
2730 **872** 2s. green and orange . . 10 10

873 Soviet War Memorial

1979. Centenary of Sofia as Capital of Bulgaria. Sheet 106 × 105 mm containing T **873** and similar vert designs. Multicoloured.
MS2731 2s. Type **873**, 5s. Mother and child (sculpture); 13, 23, 25s. Bas-relief from monument to the Liberators of 1876 . . . . . . 2·50 2·25
The 13, 23 and 25s. values form a composite design.

874 Rocket

876 Running

875 Carrier Pigeon and Tupolev Tu-154 Jet

1979. Soviet–Bulgarian Space Flight. Multicoloured.
2732 2s. Georgi Ivanov (horiz) . . 10 10
2733 12s. Type **874** 10 10
2734 13s. Nikolai Rukavishnikov and Ivanov (horiz) . . . 10 10
2735 25s. Link-up with "Salyut" space station (horiz) . . . 20 15
2736 35s. Capsule descending by parachute 30 20
MS2737 67 × 86 mm. 1l. Globe and orbiting space craft (horiz) . . 1·50 1·50

1979. Centenary of Bulgarian Post and Telegraph Services. Multicoloured.
2738 2s. Type **875** 10 10
2739 5s. Old and new telephones 10 10
2740 13s. Morse key and teleprinter 10 10
2741 23s. Old radio transmitter and aerials 20 15
2742 35s. T.V. tower and satellite 30 20
MS2743 64 × 69 mm. 50s. Ground receiving station (38 × 28 mm) 1·50 1·50

1979. Olympic Games. Moscow (1980) (1st issue). Athletics. Multicoloured.
2744 2s. Type **876** 10 10
2745 13s. Pole vault (horiz) . . . 15 10
2746 25s. Discus 30 10
2747 35s. Hurdles (horiz) 40 15
2748 43s. High jump (horiz) . . . 50 20
2749 1l. Long jump . . . . . . 1·10 45
MS2750 90 × 65 mm. 2l. Shot put 6·00 6·00
See also Nos. 2773/**MS**2779, 2803/**MS**2809, 2816/**MS**2822, 2834/**MS**2840 and 2851/**MS**2857.

877 Thracian Gold Leaf Collar

1979. 48th International Philatelic Federation Congress, Sofia. Sheet 77 × 86 mm.
MS2751 **877** 1l. multicoloured . . 5·00 5·00

878 First Bulgarian Stamp and 1975 European Security Conference Stamp

879 Hotel Vitosha-New Otani

1979. "Philaserdica 79" International Exhibition, Sofia (5th issue). Sheet 63 × 61 mm.
MS2752 **878** 1l. multicoloured . . 5·00 5·00

1979. "Philaserdica 79" International Stamp Exhibition, Sofia (5th issue) and Bulgaria Day.
2753 **879** 2s. pink and blue 10 10

880 "Good Morning, Little Brother" (illus by Kukuliev of folktale)

1979. "Philaserdica 79" International Stamp Exhibition, Sofia (6th issue) and Bulgarian–Russian Friendship Day.
2754 **880** 2s. multicoloured 10 10

881 First Bulgarian Stamp

882 "Man on Donkey" (Boris Angelushev)

1979. Centenary of First Bulgarian Stamp (3rd issue). Sheet 91 × 121 mm.
MS2755 **881** 5s. multicoloured . . 30·00 30·00

1979. 12th Festival of Humour and Satire, Grabovo.
2756 **882** 2s. multicoloured 10 10

883 "Four Women"

1979. 450th Death Anniv of Albrecht Durer (artist). Multicoloured.
2757 13s. Type **883** 20 10
2758 23s. "Three Peasants Talking" 55 20
2759 25s. "The Cook and his Wife" 40 20
2760 35s. "Portrait of Eobanus Hessus" 55 15
MS2761 80 × 81 mm. 80s. "Rhinoceros" (horiz). Imperf 1·50 1·50

884 Clocktower, Byala Cherkva

885 Petko Todorov (birth centenary)

1979. Air. Clocktowers (1st series). Mult.
2762 13s. Type **884** 10 10
2763 23s. Botevgrad 20 10
2764 25s. Pazardzhik 25 10
2765 35s. Gabrovo 35 15
2766 53s. Tryavna 50 20
See also Nos. 2891/5.

1979. Bulgarian Writers.
2767 **885** 2s. black, brown & yell 10 10
2768 – 2s. green and yellow . . 10 10
2769 – 2s. red and yellow . . . 10 10
DESIGNS: No. 2768, Dimitur Dimov (70th birth anniv); 2769, Stefan Kostov (birth cent).

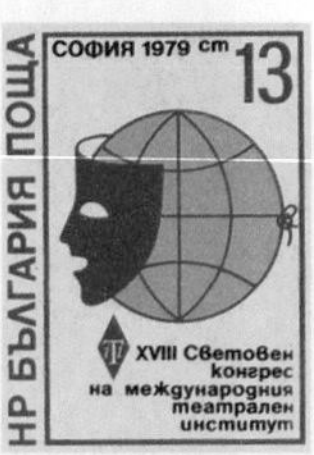

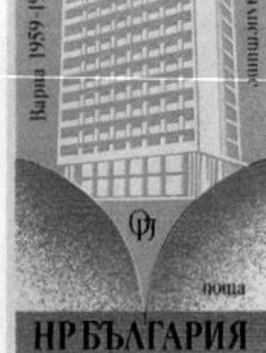

886 Congress Emblem

887 House of Journalists, Varna

1979. 18th Congress of International Theatrical Institute, Sofia.
2770 **886** 13s. cobalt, blue & black 10 10

1979. 20th Anniv of House of Journalists (holiday home), Varna.
2771 **887** 8s. orange, black & blue 10 10

888 Children of Different Races

889 Parallel Bars

1979. "Banners for Peace" Children's Meeting, Sofia.
2772 **888** 2s. multicoloured 10 10

1979. Olympic Games, Moscow (1980) (2nd issue). Gymnastics. Multicoloured.
2773 2s. Type **889** 10 10
2774 13s. Horse exercise (horiz) 15 10
2775 25s. Rings exercise 30 10
2776 35s. Beam exercise 40 15
2777 43s. Uneven bars 50 20
2778 1l. Floor exercise . . . . . 1·10 45
MS2779 65 × 88 mm. 2l. Horizontal bars . . . . 6·00 6·00

890 "Virgin and Child" (Nesebur)

1979. Icons of the Virgin and Child. Mult.
2780 13s. Type **890** 10 10
2781 23s. Nesebur (diff) 25 10
2782 35s. Sozopol 40 10
2783 43s. Sozopol (diff) 50 15
2784 53s. Samokov 70 20

891 Anton Bezenshek

892 Mountaineer

1979. Centenary of Bulgarian Stenography.
2785 **891** 2s. yellow and grey . . . 10 10

1979. 50th Anniv of Bulgarian Alpine Club.
2786 **892** 2s. multicoloured 10 10

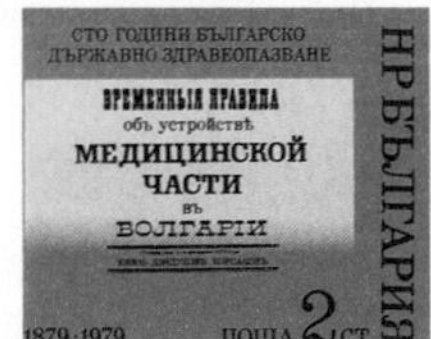
893 Commemorative Inscription

1979. Centenary of Bulgarian Public Health Services.
2787 **893** 2s. black, silver & green 10 10

894 Rocket and Flowers

896 Games Emblem

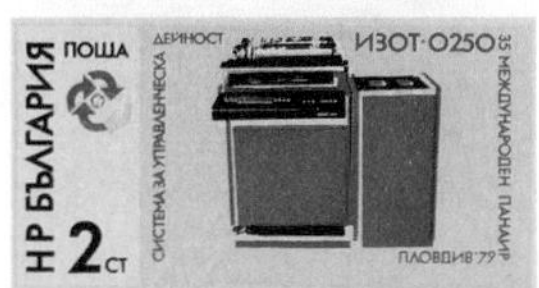
895 "IZOT–0250" Computer

1979. 35th Anniv of Fatherland Front Government. Multicoloured.
2788 2s. Type **894** 10 10
2789 5s. Russian and Bulgarian flags 10 10
2790 13s. "35" in national colours 10 10

1979. 35th Plovdiv Fair.
2791 **895** 2s. multicoloured 10 10

1979. World University Games, Mexico.
2792 **896** 5s. red, yellow and blue 10 10

897 Footballer

1979. 50th Anniv of DFS Lokomotiv Football Team.
2793 **897** 2s. red and black 40 10

898 Lyuben Karavelov

899 Cross-country Skiing

1979. Death Centenary of Lyuben Karavelov (newspaper editor and President of Bulgarian Revolutionary Committee).
2794 **898** 2s. green and blue . . . 10 10

1979. Winter Olympic Games, Lake Placid (1980).
2795 **899** 2s. red, purple and black 10 10
2796 – 13s. orange, blue & blk 10 10
2797 – 23s. turquoise, blue and black 20 10
2798 – 43s. purple, turq & blk 40 20
MS2799 68 × 77 mm. 1l. green, blue and black. Imperf . . . . . . 2·00 2·00
DESIGNS: 13s. Speed skating; 23s. Skiing; 43s. Luge; 1l. Skiing (different).

900 "Woman from Thrace"

901 Canoeing (Canadian pairs)

1979. 80th Birth Anniv of Dechko Uzunov (artist). Multicoloured.
2800 12s. "Figure in Red" . . . 10 10
2801 13s. Type **900** 10 10
2802 23s. "Composition II" . . . 20 10

1979. Olympic Games, Moscow (1980) (3rd issue). Water Sports. Multicoloured.
2803 2s. Type **901** 10 10
2804 13s. Swimming (freestyle) . . 15 10
2805 25s. Swimming (backstroke) (horiz) 30 10
2806 35s. Kayak (horiz) 40 15
2807 43s. Diving 50 20
2808 1l. Springboard diving . . . 1·10 45
MS2809 64 × 88 mm. 2l. Water polo 6·00 6·00

902 Nikola Vaptsarov

1979. 70th Birth Anniv of Nikola Vaptsarov (writer).
2810 **902** 2s. pink and red 10 10

903 "Dawn in Plovdiv" (Ioan Leviev)

1979. History of Bulgaria. Paintings. Mult.
2811 2s. "The First Socialists" (Boyan Petrov) (horiz) . . 10 10
2812 13s. "Dimitur Blagoev as Editor of "Rabotnik" (Dimitur Gyvdzhenov) (horiz) 10 10
2813 25s. "Workers' Party March" (Stoyan Sotirov) (horiz) 20 15
2814 35s. Type **903** 30 20

904 Doves in a Girl's Hair

1979. New Year.
2815 **904** 13s. multicoloured . . . 10 10

905 Shooting

906 Procession with Relics of Saints

1979. Olympic Games, Moscow (1980) (4th issue). Multicoloured.
2816 2s. Type **905** 10 10
2817 13s. Judo (horiz) 15 10
2818 25s. Wrestling (horiz) . . . 30 10
2819 35s. Archery 40 15
2820 43s. Fencing (horiz) 50 20
2821 1l. Fencing (different) . . . 1·10 45
MS2822 65 × 89 mm. 2l. Boxing 6·00 6·00

1979. Frescoes of Saints Cyril and Methodius in St. Clement's Basilica, Rome. Multicoloured.
2823 2s. Type **906** 10 10
2824 13s. Cyril and Methodius received by Pope Adrian II 10 10
2825 23s. Burial of Cyril the Philosopher 15 15
2826 25s. St. Cyril 20 15
2827 35s. St. Methodius 25 20

907 Television Screen showing Emblem

908 Puppet of Krali Marko (national hero)

1979. 25th Anniv of Bulgarian Television.
2828 **907** 5s. blue and deep blue 10 10

1980. 50th Anniv of International Puppet Theatre Organization (U.N.I.M.A.).
2829 **908** 2s. multicoloured 10 10

909 Thracian Rider (3rd-cent votive tablet)

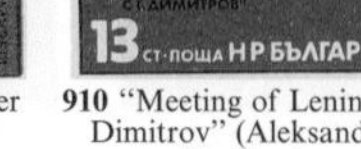
910 "Meeting of Lenin and Dimitrov" (Aleksandur Poplilov)

1980. Centenary of National Archaeological Museum, Sofia.
2830 **909** 2s. brown, gold & purple 10 10
2831 – 13s. brown, gold & grn 10 10
DESIGN: 13s. Grave stele of Deines (5th–6th cent).

1980. 110th Birth Anniv of Lenin.
2832 **910** 13s. multicoloured . . . 10 10

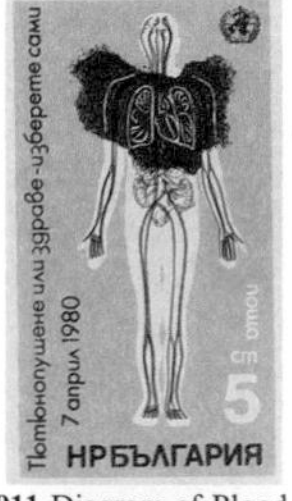
911 Diagram of Blood Circulation and Lungs obscured by Smoke

912 Basketball

1980. World Health Day. Anti-smoking Campaign.
2833 **911** 5s. multicoloured 10 10

1980. Olympic Games, Moscow (5th issue). Multicoloured.
2834 2s. Type **912** 10 10
2835 13s. Football 15 10
2836 25s. Hockey 30 10
2837 35s. Cycling 40 15
2838 43s. Handball 50 20
2839 1l. Volleyball . . . . 1·10 45
MS2840 66 × 90 mm. 2s. Weightlifting . . . . 6·00 6·00

913 Emblem, Cosmonauts and Space Station

1980. "Intercosmos" Space Programme. Sheet 111 × 102 mm.
MS2841 **913** 50s. multicoloured 1·00 1·00

914 Penyo Penev

915 Penny Black

1980. 50th Birth Anniv of Penyo Penev (poet).
2842 **914** 5s. brown, red & turq . . 10 10

1980. "London 1980" International Stamp Exhibition.
2843 **915** 25s. black and red . . . 75 25

916 Dimitur Khv. Chorbadzhuski-Chudomir (self-portrait)

1980. 90th Birth Anniv of Dimitur Khv. Chorbadzhusk-Chudomir (artist).
2844 **916** 5s. pink, brown & turq 10 10
2845 – 13s. black, blue & turq 10 10
DESIGN: 13s. "Our People".

917 Nikolai Gyaurov

918 Soviet Soldiers raising Flag on Berlin Reichstag

1980. 50th Birth Anniv of Nikolai Gyaurov (opera singer).
2846 **917** 5s. yellow, brown & grn . . . 10 10

1980. 35th Anniv of "Victory in Europe" Day.
2847 **918** 5s. gold, brown & black . . . 10 10
2848 – 13s. gold, brown & black . . . 10 10
DESIGN: 13s. Soviet Army memorial, Berlin–Treptow.

919 Open Book and Sun

920 Stars representing Member Countries

1980. 75th Anniv Bulgarian Teachers' Union.
2849 **919** 5s. purple and yellow . . 10 10

1980. 25th Anniv of Warsaw Pact.
2850 **920** 13s. multicoloured . . . 10 10

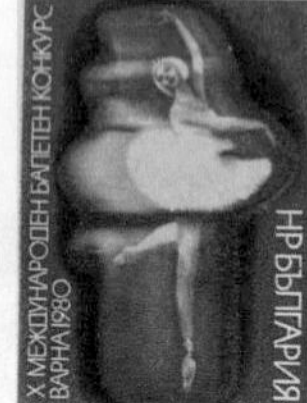

921 Greek Girl with Olympic Flame

922 Ballerina

1980. Olympic Games, Moscow (6th issue). Multicoloured.
2851 2s. Type **921** 10 10
2852 13s. Spartacus monument, Sandanski 15 10
2853 25s. Liberation monument, Sofia (detail) 30 10
2854 35s. Liberation monument, Plovdiv 40 15
2855 43s. Liberation monument, Shipka Pass 50 20
2856 1l. Liberation monument, Ruse . . . . 1·10 45
MS2857 66 × 92 mm. 2l. Athlete with Olympic flame, Moscow . . . 6·00 6·00

1980. 10th International Ballet Competition, Varna.
2858 **922** 13s. multicoloured . . . 10 10

923 Europa Hotel, Sofia

1980. Hotels. Multicoloured.
2859 23s. Type **923** 20 10
2860 23s. Bulgaria Hotel, Burgas (vert) 20 10
2861 23s. Plovdiv Hotel, Plovdiv 20 10
2862 23s. Riga Hotel, Ruse (vert) 20 10
2863 23s. Varna Hotel, Prazhba 20 10

1980. Historic Ships (3rd series). As T **753**. Multicoloured.
2864 5s. Hansa kogge "Jesus of Lubeck" 10 10
2865 8s. Roman galley 20 10
2866 13s. Galleon "Eagle" . . . 25 10
2867 23s. "Mayflower" 40 15
2868 35s. Maltese galleon 55 25
2869 53s. Galleon "Royal Louis" 1·10 40

924 Parachute Descent

1980. 15th World Parachute Championships, Kazanluk. Multicoloured.
2870 13s. Type **924** 10 10
2871 25s. Parachutist in free fall 20 10

925 Clown and Children

1980. 1st Anniv of "Banners for Peace" Children's Meeting. Multicoloured.
2872 3s. Type **925** 10 10
2873 5s. "Cosmonauts in Spaceship" (vert) 10 10
2874 8s. "Picnic" 10 10
2875 13s. "Children with Ices" . . 10 10
2876 25s. "Children with Cat" (vert) 20 10
2877 35s. "Crowd" . . . . 1·10 40
2878 43s. "Banners for Peace" monument (vert) 40 20

926 Assembly Emblem

927 Iordan Iovkov

1980. Assembly of Peoples' Parliament for Peace, Sofia.
2879 **926** 25s. multicoloured . . . 15 10

1980. Birth Centenary of Iordan Iovkov (writer).
2880 **927** 5s. multicoloured 10 10

928 Yakovlev Yak-24 Helicopter, Missile Launcher and Tank

1980. Bulgarian Armed Forces. Multicoloured.
2881 3s. Type **928** 15 10
2882 5s. Mikoyan Gurevich MiG-21 bomber, radar antennae and missile transporter 25 10
2883 8s. Mil Mi-24 helicopter, missile boat and landing ship "Ropucha" 60 15

929 Computer

1980. 36th Plovdiv Fair.
2884 **929** 5s. multicoloured 10 10

930 "Virgin and Child with St. Anne"

1980. Paintings by Leonardo da Vinci. Mult.
2885 5s. Type **930** 10 10
2886 8s. Angel (detail, "The Annunciation") 10 10
2887 13s. Virgin (detail, "The Annunciation") 10 10
2888 25s. "Adoration of the Kings" (detail) 20 15
2889 35s. "Woman with Ermine" 30 20
MS2890 57 × 80 mm. 50s. "Mona Lisa". Imperf 75 75

1980. Air. Clocktowers (2nd series). As T **884**. Multicoloured.
2891 13s. Byala 10 10
2892 23s. Razgrad 20 10
2893 25s. Karnobat 25 10
2894 35s. Sevlievo 35 15
2895 53s. Berkovitsa 50 20

931 "Parodia saint-pieana"

1980. Cacti. Multicoloured.
2896 5s. Type **931** 10 10
2897 13s. "Echinopsis bridgesii" 25 10
2898 25s. "Echinocereus purpureus" 50 10
2899 35s. "Opuntia bispinosa" . . 65 15
2900 53s. "Mamillopsis senilis" 90 20

932 U.N. Building and Bulgarian Arms

1980. 25th Anniv of United Nations Membership. Sheet 64 × 86 mm.
MS2901 **932** 60s. multicoloured 2·00 2·00

933 Wild Horse

1980. Horses. Multicoloured.
2902 3s. Type **933** 20 10
2903 5s. Tarpan 25 10
2904 13s. Arabian 40 10
2905 23s. Anglo-Arabian 60 15
2906 35s. Draught horse . . . . 1·00 20

934 Vasil Stoin

1980. Birth Centenary of Vasil Stoin (collector of folk songs).
2907 **934** 5s. violet, yellow & gold 10 10

935 Armorial Lion

936 Red Star

1980. New Year. 1300th Anniv of Bulgarian State. Multicoloured.
2908 5s. Type **935** 10 10
2909 13s. Dish and dates "681–1981" 10 10

1980. 12th Bulgarian Communist Party Congress (1st issue).
2910 **936** 5s. yellow and red . . . 10 10
See also Nos. 2920/2.

937 Cross-country Skier

1981. World Ski-racing Championship, Velingrad.
2911 **937** 43s. orange, blue & blk 40 10

938 Midland Hawthorn ("Crataegus oxpacantha")

939 Skier

1981. Useful Plants. Multicoloured.
2912 3s. Type **938** 10 10
2913 5s. Perforate St. John's wort ("Hypericum perforatum") 10 10
2914 13s. Elder ("Sambucus nigra") 20 10
2915 25s. Dewberry ("Rubus caesius") 40 15
2916 35s. Lime ("Tilia argentea") 50 20
2917 43s. Dog rose ("Rosa canina") 75 25

1981. Alpine Skiing World Championships, Borovets.
2918 **939** 43s. yellow, black & blue 40 10

940 Nuclear Traces

1981. 25th Anniv of Nuclear Research Institute, Dubna, U.S.S.R.
2919 **940** 13s. black and silver . . 10 10

941 "XII" formed from Flag

1981. 12th Bulgarian Communist Party Congress (2nd issue).
2920 **941** 5s. multicoloured 10 10
2921 – 13s. red, black and blue 10 10
2922 – 23s. red, black and blue 10 10
MS2923 68 × 86 mm. 50s. multicoloured 75 75
DESIGNS: 13s. Stars; 23s. Computer tape; 50s. Georgi Dimitrov and Dimitur Blagoev.

942 Palace of Culture

1981. Opening of Palace of Culture, Sofia.
2924 **942** 5s. dp green, grn & red 10 10

943 "Self-portrait"

1981. 170th Birth Anniv (1980) of Zakharu Zograf (artist). Multicoloured.

2925 5s. Type **943** 10 10
2926 13s. "Portrait of Khristionia Zografska" 10 10
2927 23s. "The Transfiguration" (icon from Preobrazhenie Monastery) 20 10
2928 25s. "Doomsday" (detail) (horiz) 25 15
2929 35s. "Doomsday" (detail – different) (horiz) 40 20

944 Squacco Heron

1981. Birds. Multicoloured.

2930 5s. Type **944** 20 10
2931 8s. Eurasian bittern 40 15
2932 13s. Cattle egret 70 20
2933 25s. Great egret . . . . . . 1·25 50
2934 53s. Black stork . . . . . . 2·50 1·00

945 Liner "Georgi Dimitrov"

1981. Centenary of Bulgarian Shipbuilding. Mult.

2935 35s. Type **945** . . . . . . 1·00 30
2936 43s. Freighter "Petimata of RMS" . . . . 1·40 40
2937 53s. Tanker "Khan Asparuch" . . . . 2·00 70

946 Hofburg Palace, Vienna

1981. "WIPA 1981" International Stamp Exhibition, Vienna.

2938 **946** 35s. crimson, red & green 20 10

947 "XXXIV"

1981. 34th Bulgarian People's Agrarian Union Congress.

2939 **947** 5s. multicoloured 10 10
2940 – 8s. orange, black & blue 10 10
2941 – 13s. multicoloured . . . 10 10

DESIGNS: 8s. Flags; 13s. Bulgarian Communist Party and Agrarian Union flags.

948 Wild Cat

1981. International Hunting Exhibition, Plovdiv.

2942 **948** 5s. stone, black & brown 15 10
2943 – 13s. black, brn & stone 40 15
2944 – 23s. brown, blk & orge 60 20
2945 – 25s. black, brown & mve 70 40
2946 – 35s. lt brown, blk & brn 95 35
2947 – 53s. brown, blk & grn 1·50 50
MS2948 78 × 103 mm. 1l. brown, black and green (52 × 42 mm) 3·00 3·00

DESIGNS: 13s. Wild boar; 23s. Mouflon; 25s. Chamois; 35s. Roebuck; 53s. Fallow deer; 1l. Red deer.

949 "Crafty Peter" (sculpture, Georgi Chapkanov)

950 Bulgarian Arms and U.N.E.S.C.O. Emblem

1981. Festival of Humour and Satire, Gabrovo.

2949 **949** 5s. multicoloured 10 10

1981. 25th Anniv of U.N.E.S.C.O. Membership.

2950 **950** 13s. multicoloured . . . 10 10

951 Deutsche Flugzeugwerke D.F.W. C.V. Biplane

1981. Air. Aircraft. Multicoloured.

2951 5s. Type **951** 10 10
2952 12s. LAS-7 monoplane . . . 35 15
2953 25s. LAS-8 monoplane . . . 70 30
2954 35s. DAR-1 biplane 85 45
2955 45s. DAR-3 biplane . . . . 1·25 55
2956 55s. DAR-9 biplane . . . . 1·75 70

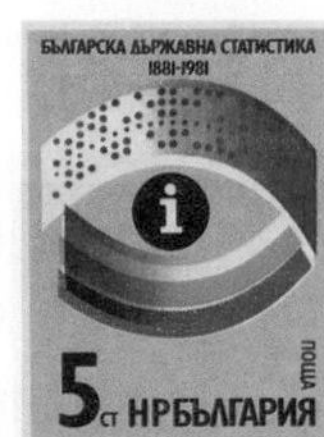

952 "Eye"

1981. Centenary of State Statistical Office.

2957 **952** 5s. multicoloured 10 10

953 Veliko Tirnovo Hotel

1981. Hotels.

2958 **953** 23s. multicoloured . . . 15 10

954 "Flying Figure"

1981. 90th Anniv of First Bulgarian Social Democratic Party Congress, Buzludzha. Sculptures by Velichko Minekov.

2959 **954** 5s. blue, black and green 10 10
2960 – 13s. brown, blk & orge 10 10

DESIGN: 13s. "Advancing Female".

955 Animal-shaped Dish

1981. Golden Treasure of Old St. Nicholas. Multicoloured.

2961 5s. Type **955** 10 10
2962 13s. Jug with decorated neck 10 10
2963 23s. Jug with loop pattern 20 10
2964 25s. Jug with bird pattern 25 10
2965 35s. Decorated vase 35 15
2966 53s. Decorated dish 50 25

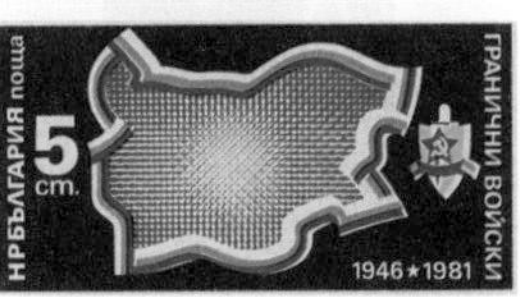

956 Badge and Map of Bulgaria

1981. 35th Anniv of Frontier Guards.

2967 **956** 5s. multicoloured 10 10

957 Saints Cyril and Methodius (9th century)

1981. 1300th Anniv of Bulgarian State.

2968 – 5s. green and grey . . . 10 10
2969 **957** 5s. brown and yellow . . 10 10
2970 – 8s. violet and lilac . . . 10 10
2971 – 12s. mauve and purple 10 10
2972 – 13s. purple and brown 10 10
2973 – 13s. green and black . . 10 10
2974 – 16s. green & deep green 15 10
2975 – 23s. black and blue . . . 20 10
2976 – 25s. green and light green 20 10
2977 – 35s. brown and light brown 30 15
2978 – 41s. red and pink . . . 35 20
2979 – 43s. red and pink . . . 35 20
2980 – 53s. dp brown and brown 40 25
2981 – 55s. dp green and green 40 25
MS2982 Two sheets, each 83 × 74 mm. (a) 50s. grey and green; (b) 1l. brown, black and brown . . . . 2·50 2·50

DESIGNS: No. 2968, Madara horsemen (8th century); 2970, Plan of Round Church at Veliki Preslav (10th century); 2971, Four Evangelists of King Ivan, 1356; 2972, Column of Ivan Asen II (13th century); 2973, Manasiev Chronicle (14th century); 2974, Rising of April 1876; 2975, Arrival of Russian liberation troops; 2976, Foundation ceremony of Bulgarian Social Democratic Party, 1891; 2977, Rising of September 1923; 2978, Formation of Fatherland Front Government, 9 September 1944; 2979, Bulgarian Communist Party Congress, 1948; 50s. Bas-relief of lion at Stara Zagora (10th century); 2980, 10th Communist Party Congress, 1971; 2981, Kremikovski metallurgical combine; 1l. Leonid Brezhnev and Todor Yovkov.

958 Volleyball Players

959 "Pegasus" (bronze sculpture)

1981. European Volleyball Championships.

2983 **958** 13s. red, blue and black 10 10

1981. Day of the Word.

2984 **959** 5s. green 10 10

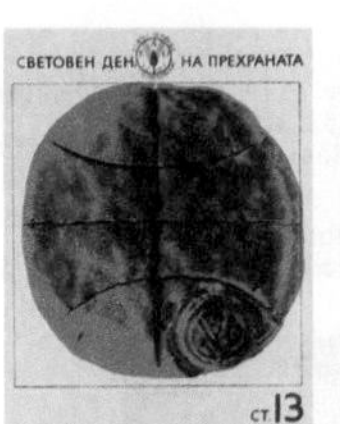

960 Loaf of Bread

961 Mask

1981. World Food Day.

2985 **960** 13s. brown, black & grn 10 10

1981. Cent of Bulgarian Professional Theatre.

2986 **961** 5s. multicoloured 10 10

962 Examples of Bulgarian Art

1981. Cultural Heritage Day.

2987 **962** 13s. green and brown . . 10 10

963 Footballer

1981. World Cup Football Championship, Spain (1982). Multicoloured.

2988 5s. Type **963** 10 10
2989 13s. Heading ball 25 10
2990 43s. Saving a goal 70 25
2991 53s. Running with ball . . . 90 35

964 Dove encircled by Barbed Wire

1981. Anti-apartheid Campaign.

2992 **964** 5s. red, black and yellow 10 10

1981. 13th Bulgarian Philatelic Federation Congress. Sheet 51 × 72 mm containing design as T **962** but inscr "XIII KONGRES NA SBF SOFIYA" at foot.

MS2993 60s. blue and red . . . 2·50 2·50

965 "Mother" (Lilyann Ruseva)

1981. 35th Anniv of U.N.I.C.E.F. Various designs showing mother and child paintings by named artists. Multicoloured.

2994 53s. Type **965** 50 20
2995 53s. "Bulgarian Madonna" (Vasil Stoilov) 50 20
2996 53s. "Village Madonna" (Ivan Milev) 50 20
2997 53s. "Mother" (Vladimir Dimitrov) 50 20

966 8th century Ceramic from Pliska

1981. New Year. Multicoloured.

2998 5s. Armorial lion 10 10
2999 13s. Type **966** 10 10

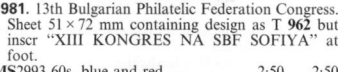

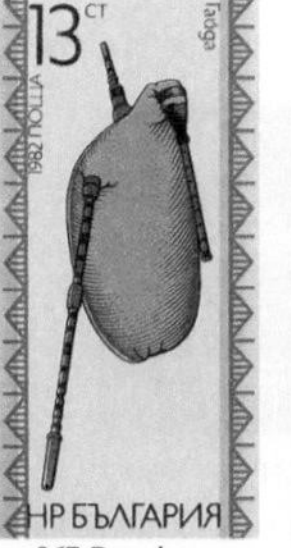

967 Bagpipes

968 Open Book

1982. Musical Instruments. Multicoloured.

3000	13s. Type **967**	10	10
3001	25s. Single and double flutes	20	10
3002	30s. Rebec	25	10
3003	35s. Flute and pipe	30	15
3004	44s. Mandolin	40	15

1982. 125th Anniv of Public Libraries.

3005	**968** 5s. green	10	10

969 "Sofia Plains"

1982. Birth Centenary of Nikola Petrov (artist).

3006	5s. Type **969**	10	10
3007	13s. "Girl Embroidering"	10	10
3008	30s. "Fields of Peshtera"	25	10

971 "Peasant Woman"

1982. Birth Centenary of Valadimir Dimitrov (artist). Multicoloured.

3010	5s. Figures in a landscape (horiz)	10	10
3011	8s. Town and harbour (horiz)	10	10
3012	13s. Town scene (horiz)	10	10
3013	25s. "Reapers"	20	10
3014	30s. Woman and child	20	15
3015	35s. Type **971**	25	15
MS3016	65 × 58 mm. 50s. "Self-portrait" (horiz)	75	75

972 Georgi Dimitrov

1982. 9th Bulgarian Trade Unions Congress, Sofia.

3017	**972** 5s. lt brn, dp brn & brn	10	10
3018	– 5s. brown and blue	10	10

DESIGN: No. 3018, Palace of Culture, Sofia.

973 Summer Snowflake

1982. Medicinal Plants. Multicoloured.

3019	3s. Type **973**	10	10
3020	5s. Chicory	10	10
3021	8s. Rosebay willowherb	20	10
3022	13s. Solomon's seal	25	10
3023	25s. Sweet violet	50	15
3024	35s. "Ficaria verna"	50	25

974 Russian Space Station

1982. 25th Anniv of First Soviet Artificial Satellite.

3025	**974** 13s. multicoloured	10	10

975 Georgi Dimitrov

1982. "Sozphilex '82" Stamp Exhibition, Veliko, Tirnovo. Sheet 61 × 82 mm.

MS3026	**975** 50s. red and black	2·00	2·00

976 Dimitrov and Congress Emblem

1982. 14th Dimitrov Communist Youth League Congress, Sofia.

3027	**976** 5s. blue, red & yellow	10	10

977 First French and Bulgarian Stamps

1982. "Philexfrance 82" International Stamp Exhibition, Paris.

3028	**977** 42s. multicoloured	75	25

978 Abstract with Birds **980** Georgi Dimitrov

979 Georgi Dimitrov

1982. Alafrangi Frescoes from 19th-century Houses.

3029	**978** 5s. multicoloured	10	10
3030	– 13s. multicoloured	10	10
3031	– 25s. multicoloured	20	10
3032	– 30s. multicoloured	20	10
3033	– 42s. multicoloured	30	15
3034	– 60s. multicoloured	45	25

DESIGNS: 13s. to 60s. Various flower and bird patterns.

During 1982 sets were issued for World Cup Football Championship, Spain (5, 13, 30s.), Tenth Anniv of First European Security and Co-operation Conference (5, 13, 25, 30s.), World Cup Results (5, 13, 30s.) and 10th Anniv (1983) of European Security and Co-operation Conference, Helsinki (5, 13, 25, 30s.). Supplies and distribution of these stamps were restricted and it is understood they were not available at face value.

1982. Birth Centenary of Georgi Dimitrov (statesman). Sheet 76 × 52 mm.

MS3035	**979** 50s. multicoloured	75	75

1982. 9th Fatherland Front Congress, Sofia.

3036	**980** 5s. multicoloured	10	10

981 Airplane

1982. 35th Anniv of Balkanair (state airline).

3037	**981** 42s. blue, green & red	65	30

982 Atomic Bomb Mushroom-cloud **983** Lyudmila Zhivkova

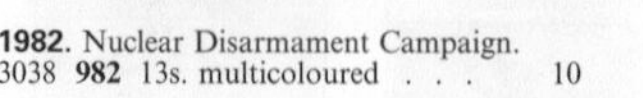

1982. Nuclear Disarmament Campaign.

3038	**982** 13s. multicoloured	10	10

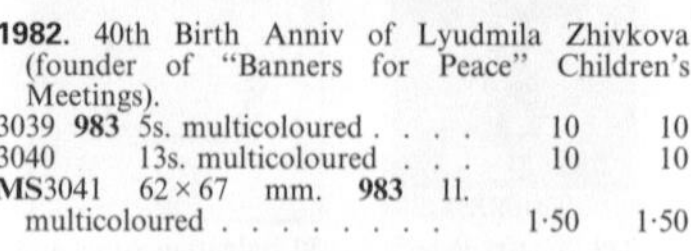

1982. 40th Birth Anniv of Lyudmila Zhivkova (founder of "Banners for Peace" Children's Meetings).

3039	**983** 5s. multicoloured	10	10
3040	13s. multicoloured	10	10
MS3041	62 × 67 mm. **983** 1l. multicoloured	1·50	1·50

984 Emblem

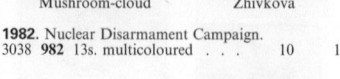

1982. 10th Anniv of U.N. Environment Programme.

3042	**984** 13s. green and blue	10	10

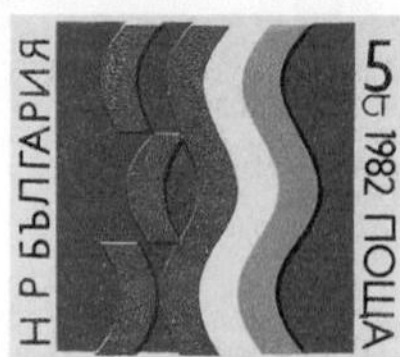

985 Wave Pattern

1982. 5th Bulgarian Painters' Association Congress.

3043	**985** 5s. multicoloured	10	10

986 Child Musicians

1982. 2nd "Banners for Peace" Children's Meeting (1st issue). Children's Paintings. Multicoloured.

3044	3s. Type **986**	10	10
3045	5s. Children skating	10	10
3046	8s. Adults, children and flowers	10	10
3047	13s. Children with flags	20	15
MS3048	70 × 110 mm. 50s. Children in "Sun" balloon (vert)	1·25	1·25

See also Nos. 3057/**MS**3063.

987 Moscow Park Hotel, Sofia **988** Cruiser "Aurora" and Satellite

1982. Hotels. Multicoloured.

3049	32s. Type **987**	20	10
3050	32s. Black Sea Hotel, Varna	20	10

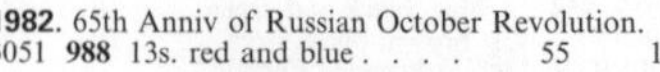

1982. 65th Anniv of Russian October Revolution.

3051	**988** 13s. red and blue	55	10

989 Hammer and Sickle

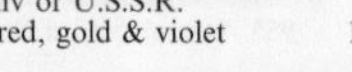

1982. 60th Anniv of U.S.S.R.

3052	**989** 13s. red, gold & violet	10	10

990 "The Piano"

1982. Birth Cent of Pablo Picasso (artist). Mult.

3053	13s. Type **990**	20	10
3054	30s. "Portrait of Jacqueline"	55	10
3055	42s. "Maternity"	75	10
MS3056	61 × 79 mm. 1l. "Self-portrait"	2·00	2·00

991 Boy and Girl

1982. 2nd "Banners for Peace" Children's Meeting (2nd issue). Multicoloured.

3057	3s. Type **991**	10	10
3058	5s. Market place	10	10
3059	8s. Children in fancy dress (vert)	10	10
3060	13s. Chickens (vert)	15	10
3061	25s. Interlocking heads	25	15
3062	30s. Lion	30	20
MS3063	70 × 109 mm. 50s. Boy and girl in garden (vert). Perf or imperf	1·25	1·25

992 Lions

1982. New Year. Multicoloured.

3064	5s. Type **992**	10	10
3065	13s. Decorated letters	10	10

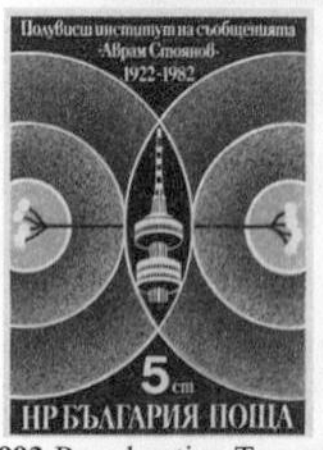

993 Broadcasting Tower **994** Dr. Robert Koch

1982. 60th Anniv of Avram Stoyanov Broadcasting Institute.

3066	**993** 5s. blue	10	10

1982. Cent of Discovery of Tubercle Bacillus.

3067	**994** 25s. brown and green	15	10

995 Simon Bolivar **996** Vasil Levski

1982. Birth Anniversaries.

3068	**995** 30s. green and grey	20	10
3069	– 30s. yellow and brown	20	10

DESIGN: No. 3068, Type **995** (bicent); 3069, Rabindranath Tagore (philosopher, 120th anniv).

1983. 110th Death Anniv of Vasil Levski (revolutionary).

3070	**996** 5s. brown & green	10	10

997 Skier

1983. "Universiade 83" University Games, Sofia.
3071 **997** 30s. multicoloured . . . 20 10

998 Northern Pike

1983. Freshwater Fishes. Multicoloured.

3072	3s. Type **998**	10	10
3073	5s. Beluga sturgeon	10	10
3074	13s. Chub	10	10
3075	25s. Zander	20	10
3076	30s. Wels	25	15
3077	42s. Brown trout	35	20

999 Karl Marx

1983. Death Centenary of Karl Marx.
3078 **999** 13s. red, purple & yellow 10 10

1000 Hasek and Illustrations from "The Good Soldier Schweik"

1983. Birth Centenary of Jaroslav Hasek (Czech writer).
3079 **1000** 13s. brown, grey & grn 10 10

1001 Martin Luther

1983. 500th Birth Anniv of Martin Luther (Protestant reformer).
3080 **1001** 13s. grey, black & brn 10 10

1002 Figures forming Initials

1983. 55th Anniv of Young Workers' Union.
3081 **1002** 5s. red, black & orange 10 10

1003 Khaskovo Costume **1004** Old Man feeding a Chicken

1983. Folk Costumes. Multicoloured.

3082	5s. Type **1003**	10	10
3083	8s. Pernik	10	10
3084	13s. Burgas	10	10
3085	25s. Tolbukhin	15	15
3086	30s. Blagoevgrad	20	15
3087	42s. Topolovgrad	30	25

1983. 6th International Festival of Humour and Satire, Gabrovo.
3088 **1004** 5s. multicoloured . . . 10 10

During 1983 sets were issued for European Security and Co-operation Conference, Budapest (5, 13, 25, 30s.), Olympic Games, Los Angeles (5, 13, 30, 42s.), Winter Olympic Games, Sarajevo (horiz designs, 5, 13, 30, 42s.) and European Security and Co-operation Conference, Madrid (5, 13, 30, 42s.). Supplies and distribution of these stamps were restricted, and it is understood they were not available at face value.

1005 Smirnenski

1983. 85th Birth Anniv of Khristo Smirnenski (poet).
3089 **1005** 5s. red, brown & yellow 10 10

1006 Emblem **1008** Staunton Chessmen on Map of Europe

1007 Stylized Houses

1983. 17th Int Geodesy Federation Congress.
3090 **1006** 30s. green, blue & yell 15 10

1983. "Interarch 83" World Architecture Biennale, Sofia.
3091 **1007** 30s. multicoloured . . . 15 10

1983. 8th European Chess Team Championship, Plovdiv.
3092 **1008** 13s. multicoloured . . . 20 10

1009 Brazilian and Bulgarian Football Stamps

1983. "Brasiliana 83" International Stamp Exhibition, Rio de Janeiro. Sheet 73 × 103 mm.
MS3093 **1009** 1l. green, brown and gold . . . 1·50 1·50

1010 Valentina Tereshkova

1983. Air. 20th Anniv of First Woman in Space. Sheet 121 × 75 mm containing T **1010** and similar vert design, each blue and brown.
MS3094 50s. Type **1010**; 50s. Svetlana Savitskaya, 1982, cosmonaut . . . 1·50 1·50

1011 Television Mast, Tolbukhin

1983. Air. World Communications Year.

3095	**1011**	5s. blue and red	10	10
3096	–	13s. mauve and red	15	10
3097	–	30s. yellow and red	20	10

DESIGNS: 13s. Postwoman; 30s. Radio tower, Mount Botev.

1012 Lenin addressing Congress

1983. 80th Anniv of 2nd Russian Social Democratic Workers' Party Congress.
3098 **1012** 5s. pur, dp pur & yell 10 10

1013 Pistol and Dagger on Book

1983. 80th Anniv of Ilinden-Preobrazhenie Rising.
3099 **1013** 5s. yellow and green . . 10 10

1014 Crystals and Hammers within Gearwheels

1983. 30th Anniv of Mining and Geology Institute, Sofia.
3100 **1014** 5s. grey, purple & blue 10 10

1015 Georgi Dimitrov and Revolution Scenes

1983. 60th Anniv of September Uprising. Mult.

3101	5s. Type **1015**	10	10
3102	13s. Wreath and revolution scenes	10	10

1016 Animated Drawings **1017** Angora

1983. 3rd Animated Film Festival, Varna.
3103 **1016** 5s. multicoloured . . . 10 10

1983. Cats. Multicoloured.

3104	5s. Type **1017**	15	10
3105	13s. Siamese	35	10
3106	20s. Abyssinian (vert)	50	10
3107	25s. European	60	15
3108	30s. Persian (vert)	75	15
3109	42s. Khmer	1·00	20

1018 Richard Trevithick's Locomotive, 1803

1983. Locomotives (1st series). Multicoloured.

3110	5s. Type **1018**	20	10
3111	13s. John Blenkinsop's rack locomotive "Prince Royal", 1810	30	10
3112	42s. William Hedley's "Puffing Billy", 1813–14	2·25	50
3113	60s. Stephenson locomotive "Adler", 1835, Germany	3·75	75

See also Nos. 3159/63.

1019 Liberation Monument, Plovdiv

1983. 90th Anniv of Bulgarian Philatelic Federation and Fourth National Stamp Exhibition, Plovdiv. Sheet 65 × 79 mm.
MS3114 **1019** 50s. grey, blue and red 75 75

1020 Mask and Laurel as Lyre **1021** Ioan Kukuzel

1983. 75th Anniv of National Opera, Sofia.
3115 **1020** 5s. red, black & gold 10 10

1983. Bulgarian Composers.

3116	**1021**	5s. yellow, brown & grn	10	10
3117	–	8s. yellow, brown & red	10	10
3118	–	13s. yellow, brown and green	10	10
3119	–	20s. yellow, brown & bl	15	10
3120	–	25s. yellow, brn & grey	20	15
3121	–	30s. yell, dp brn & brn	25	20

DESIGNS: 8s. Georgi Atanasov; 13s. Petko Stainov; 20s. Veselin Stoyanov; 25s. Lyubomir Pipkov; 30s. Pancho Vladigerov.

1022 Snowflake

1983. New Year.
3122 **1022** 5s. green, blue & gold 10 10

1023 "Angelo Donni"

1983. 500th Birth Anniv of Raphael (artist). Multicoloured.

3123	5s. Type **1023**	10	10
3124	13s. "Portrait of a Cardinal"	10	10
3125	30s. "Baldassare Castiglioni"	25	15
3126	42s. "Woman with a Veil"	35	25
MS3127	59 × 98 mm. 1l. "Sistine Madonna"	1·50	1·50

1024 Eurasian Common Shrew

1983. Protected Mammals. Multicoloured.

3128	12s. Type **1024**	45	20
3129	13s. Greater horseshoe bat	55	20
3130	20s. Common long-eared bat	85	30
3131	30s. Forest dormouse . . .	1·00	40
3132	42s. Fat dormouse	1·50	60

1025 Karavelov

1984. 150th Birth Anniv of Lyuben Karavelov (poet).
3133 **1025** 5s. blue, bistre & brn 10 10

During 1984 sets were issued for European Confidence- and Security-building Measures and Disarmament Conference, Stockholm (5, 13, 30, 42s.) and Winter Olympic Games, Sarajevo (vert designs, 5, 13, 30, 42s.). Supplies and distribution of these stamps were restricted and it is understood that they were not available at face value.

1026 Mendeleev and Formulae

1984. 150th Birth Anniv of Dmitry Mendeleev (chemist).
3134 **1026** 13s. multicoloured . . . 10 10

1027 Bulk Carrier "Gen. Vl. Zaimov"

1984. Ships. Multicoloured.

3135	5s. Type **1027**	20	10
3136	13s. Tanker "Mesta" . . .	45	10
3137	25s. Tanker "Veleka" . . .	85	20
3138	32s. Train ferry "Geroite na Odesa"	95	45
3139	42s. Bulk carrier "Rozhen"	1·40	55

1028 World Cup Stamps

1984. "Espana 84" International Stamp Exhibition, Madrid. Sheet 89 × 110 mm.
MS3140 **1028** 2l. multicoloured 6·00 6·00

1029 Pigeon with Letter over Globe **1030** Wild Cherries

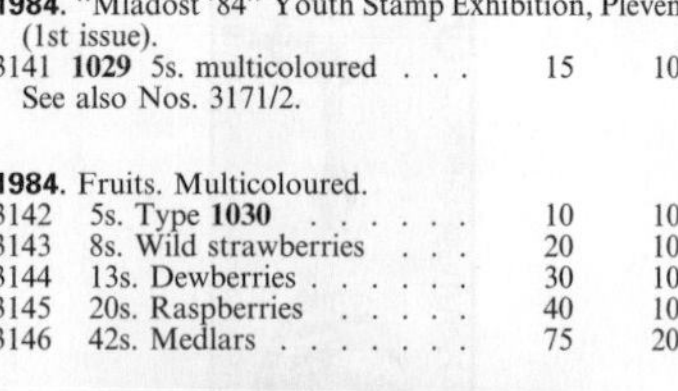

1984. "Mladost '84" Youth Stamp Exhibition, Pleven (1st issue).
3141 **1029** 5s. multicoloured . . . 15 10
See also Nos. 3171/2.

1984. Fruits. Multicoloured.

3142	5s. Type **1030**	10	10
3143	8s. Wild strawberries . . .	20	10
3144	13s. Dewberries	30	10
3145	20s. Raspberries	40	10
3146	42s. Medlars	75	20

1031 "Vitosha Conference" (K. Buyukliiski and P. Petrov)

1984. 60th Anniv of Bulgarian Communist Party Conference, Vitosha.
3147 **1031** 5s. purple, brn & red 10 10

1032 Security Conference 1980 13s. Stamp

1984. 5th International Stamp Fair, Essen. Sheet 94 × 147 mm containing T **1032** and similar horiz design. Multicoloured.
MS3148 1l.50, Type **1032**; 1l.50, Security Conference 35s. stamp 7·50 7·50

1033 Athletes and Doves **1034** Mt. Everest

1984. 6th Republican Spartakiad.
3149 **1033** 13s. multicoloured . . . 10 10

1984. Bulgarian Expedition to Mt. Everest.
3150 **1034** 5s. multicoloured . . . 10 10

1035 Kogge

1984. Universal Postal Union Congress Philatelic Salon, Hamburg. Sheet 100 × 107 mm.
MS3151 **1035** 3l. multicoloured 7·50 7·50

1036 Drummer

1984. 6th Amateur Performers Festival.
3152 **1036** 5s. multicoloured . . . 10 10

1037 Seal

1984. 50 Years of Bulgarian–U.S.S.R. Diplomatic Relations.
3153 **1037** 13s. multicoloured . . . 10 10

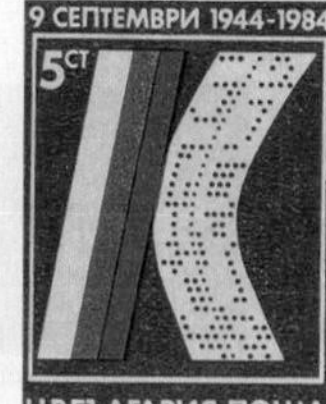

1038 Feral Rock Pigeon **1039** Production Quality Emblem

1984. Pigeons and Doves. Multicoloured.

3154	5s. Type **1038**	20	10
3155	13s. Stock pigeon	55	15
3156	20s. Wood pigeon	80	25
3157	30s. Turtle dove	1·25	45
3158	42s. Domestic pigeon . . .	1·60	60

1984. Locomotives (2nd series). As T **1018**. Multicoloured.

3159	13s. "Best Friend of Charleston", 1830, U.S.A.	30	10
3160	25s. "Saxonia", 1836, Saxony	55	10
3161	30s. "Lafayette", 1837, U.S.A.	65	15
3162	42s. "Borsig", 1841, Germany	1·25	20
3163	60s. "Philadelphia", 1843, U.S.A.	1·90	30

1984. 40th Anniv of Fatherland Front Government.

3164	**1039** 5s. red, lt green & green	10	10
3165	– 20s. red and violet . . .	10	10
3166	– 30s. red and blue . . .	15	10

DESIGNS: 20s. Monument to Soviet Army, Sofia; 30s. Figure nine and star.

1040 "Boy with Harmonica" **1041** Mausoleum of Russian Soldiers

1984. Paintings by Nenko Balkanski. Multicoloured.

3167	5s. Type **1040**	10	10
3168	30s. "Window in Paris" . .	15	10
3169	42s. "Portrait of Two Women" (horiz)	20	10
MS3170	65 × 110 mm. 1l. "Self-portrait"	2·00	2·00

1984. "Mladost '84" Youth Stamp Exhibition, Pleven (2nd issue).

3171	**1041** 5s. multicoloured . . .	10	10
3172	– 13s. black, grn & red	10	10

DESIGN: 13s. Panorama building.

1042 Pioneers saluting

1984. 40th Anniv of Dimitrov Septembrist Pioneers Organization.
3173 **1042** 5s. multicoloured . . . 10 10

1043 Vaptsarov (after D. Nikolov)

1984. 75th Birth Anniv of Nikola I. Vaptsarov (poet).
3174 **1043** 5s. yellow and red . . . 10 10

1044 Goalkeeper saving Goal

1984. 75th Anniv of Bulgarian Football.
3175 **1044** 42s. multicoloured . . . 50 15

1045 Profiles

1984. "Miadost '84" Youth Stamp Exhibition, Pleven (3rd issue). Sheet 50 × 76 mm.
MS3176 **1045** 50s. multicoloured 1·00 1·00

1046 Devil's Bridge, R. Arda

1984. Bridges. Multicoloured.

3177	5s. Type **1046**	10	10
3178	13s. Kolo Ficheto Bridge, Byala	25	10
3179	30s. Asparukhov Bridge, Varna	50	20
3180	42s. Bebresh Bridge, Botevgrad	70	30

1047 Olympic Emblem

1984. 90th Anniv of International Olympic Committee.
3181 **1047** 13s. multicoloured . . . 10 10

1048 Moon and "Luna I", "II" and "III"

1984. 25th Anniv of First Moon Rocket. Sheet 79 × 57 mm.
MS3182 **1048** 1l. multicoloured 2·00 2·00

1049 Dalmatian Pelican with Chicks **1050** Anton Ivanov

1984. Wildlife Protection. Dalmatian Pelican.

3183	**1049** 5s. multicoloured . . .	40	15
3184	– 13s. lav, blk & brn . .	90	25
3185	– 20s. multicoloured . . .	1·75	40
3186	– 32s. multicoloured . . .	2·50	75

DESIGNS: 13s. Two pelicans; 20s. Pelican on water; 32s. Pelican in flight.

1984. Birth Cent of Anton Ivanov (revolutionary).
3187 **1050** 5s. yell, brn & red . . . 10 10

1051 Girl's Profile with Text as Hair

1984. 70th Anniv of Bulgarian Women's Socialist Movement.
3188 **1051** 5s. multicoloured . . . 10 10

1052 Snezhanka Television Tower

1984. Television Towers.
3189 **1052** 5s. blue, green & mve 10 10
3190 – 1l. brown, mauve & bis 75 20
DESIGN: 1l. Orelek television tower.

1053 Birds and Posthorns

1984. New Year. Multicoloured.
3191 5s. Type **1053** 10 10
3192 13s. Decorative pattern . . 10 10

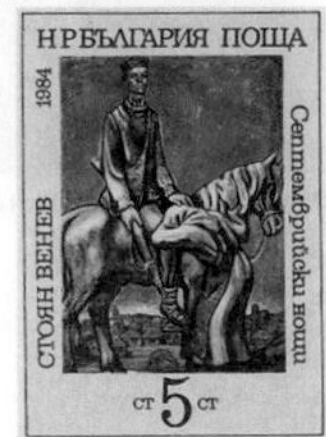

1054 "September Nights"

1984. 80th Birth Anniv of Stoyan Venev (artist). Multicoloured.
3193 5s. Type **1054** 10 10
3194 30s. "Man with Three Orders" 10 10
3195 42s. "The Hero" 15 10

1055 Peacock (butterfly)

1056 Augusto Sandino

1984. Butterflies. Multicoloured.
3196 13s. Type **1055** 30 10
3197 25s. Swallowtail 50 20
3198 30s. Great banded grayling 60 25
3199 42s. Orange-tip 90 40
3200 60s. Red admiral . . . . . 1·25 60
MS3201 75 × 60 mm. 1l. Poplar admiral (*Limenitis populi*) . . . 2·50 2·50

1984. 50th Death Anniv of Augusto Sandino (Nicaraguan revolutionary).
3202 **1056** 13s. black, red & yell 10 10

1057 Tupolev Tu-154 Jetliner

1984. 40th Anniv of I.C.A.O.
3203 **1057** 42s. multicoloured . . . 90 35

1058 "The Three Graces" (detail)

1984. 500th Birth Anniv (1983) of Raphael (artist) (2nd issue). Multicoloured.
3204 5s. Type **1058** 10 10
3205 13s. "Cupid and the Three Graces" (detail) 15 10
3206 30s. "Original Sin" (detail) 35 15
3207 42s. "La Fornarina" 50 20
MS3208 106 × 95 mm. 1l. "Galatea" (detail) . . . . 2·00 2·00

1059 "Sofia"

1984. Maiden Voyage of Danube Cruise Ship "Sofia".
3209 **1059** 13s. dp blue, blue & yell 90 10

1060 Eastern Hog-nosed Skunk

1985. Mammals.
3210 **1060** 13s. black, blue & orge 25 10
3211 – 25s. black, brown & grn 45 20
3212 – 30s. black, brown & yell 65 20
3213 – 42s. multicoloured . . . 1·00 25
3214 – 60s. multicoloured . . . 1·25 40
DESIGNS: 25s. Banded linsang; 30s. Zorilla; 42s. Banded palm civet; 60s. Broad-striped galidia.

1061 Nikolai Liliev

1985. Birth Centenary of Nikolai Liliev (poet).
3215 **1061** 30s. lt brn, brn & gold 15 10

1062 Tsvyatko Radoinov

1985. 90th Birth Anniv of Tsvyatko Radoinov (resistance fighter).
3216 **1062** 5s. brown and red . . . 10 10

1063 Asen Zlatarov

1065 Lenin Monument, Sofia

1064 Research Ship "Akademik"

1985. Birth Cent. of Asen Zlatarov (biochemist).
3217 **1063** 5s. purple, yellow & grn 10 10

1985. 13th General Assembley and 125th Anniv of Intergovernmental Oceanographic Commission. Sheet 90 × 60 mm.
MS3218 **1064** 80s. multicoloured 1·75 1·75

1985. 115th Birth Anniv of Lenin. Sheet 55 × 87 mm.
MS3219 **1065** 50s. multicoloured 75 75

1066 Olive Branch and Sword Blade

1985. 30th Anniv of Warsaw Pact.
3220 **1066** 13s. multicoloured . . . 20 10

1067 Bach

1069 St. Methodius

1068 Girl with Birds

1985. Composers.
3221 **1067** 42s. blue and red . . . 1·00 25
3222 – 42s. violet and green . . 1·00 25
3223 – 42s. yellow, brn & orge 1·00 25
3224 – 42s. yellow, brn & red 1·00 25
3225 – 42s. yellow, grn & blue 1·00 25
3226 – 42s. yellow, red & grn 1·00 25
DESIGNS: No. 3222, Mozart; 3223, Tchaikovsky; 3224, Modest Petrovich Musorgsky; 3225, Giuseppe Verdi; 3226, Filip Kutev.

1985. 3rd "Banners for Peace" Children's Meeting, Sofia. Multicoloured.
3227 5s. Type **1068** 10 10
3228 8s. Children painting . . . 10 10
3229 13s. Girl among flowers . . 10 10
3230 20s. Children at market stall 15 10
3231 25s. Circle of children . . . 20 15
3232 30s. Nurse 20 15
MS3233 70 × 110 mm. 50st. Children dancing (vert). Perf or imperf 75 75

1985. 1100th Death Anniv of St. Methodius.
3234 **1069** 13s. multicoloured . . . 10 10

1070 Soldiers and Nazi Flags

1985. 40th Anniv of V.E. ("Victory in Europe") Day. Multicoloured.
3235 5s. Type **1070** 10 10
3236 13s. 11th Infantry parade, Sofia 15 10
3237 30s. Soviet soldier with orphan 40 10
MS3238 90 × 123 mm. 50s. Soldier raising Soviet flag . . . . . . 1·00 1·00

1071 Woman carrying Child and Man on Donkey

1985. 7th International Festival of Humour and Satire, Gabrovo.
3239 **1071** 13s. black, yell & red 10 10

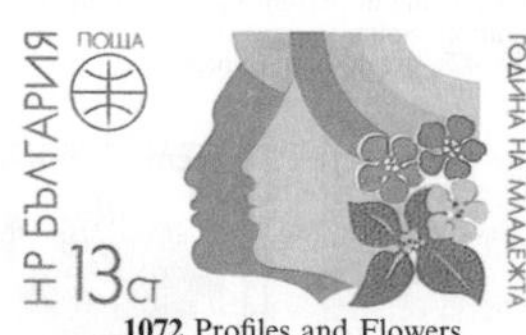

1072 Profiles and Flowers

1985. International Youth Year.
3240 **1072** 13s. multicoloured . . . 20 10

1073 Ivan Vazov

1985. 135th Birth Anniv of Ivan Vazov (poet).
3241 **1073** 5s. brown and stone . . 10 10

1074 Monument to Unknown Soldiers and City Arms

1985. Millenary of Khaskovo.
3242 **1074** 5s. multicoloured . . . 10 10

1075 Festival Emblem

1077 Vasil E. Aprilov (founder)

1076 Indira Gandhi

1985. 12th World Youth and Students' Festival, Moscow.
3243 **1075** 13s. multicoloured . . . 10 10

1985. Indira Gandhi (Indian Prime Minister) Commemoration.
3244 **1076** 30s. brown, orge & yell 20 10

1985. 150th Anniv of New Bulgarian School, Gabrovo.
3245 **1077** 5s. blue, purple & grn 10 10

1078 Congress Emblem

1985. 36th International Shorthand and Typing Federation Congress ("Intersteno"), Sofia.
3246 **1078** 13s. multicoloured . . . 10 10

1079 Alexandr Nevski Cathedral, Sofia

1985. Sixth General Assembly of World Tourism Organization, Sofia.
3247 **1079** 42s. green, blue & orge 30 15

1080 State Arms and U.N. Flag **1081** Rosa "Trakijka"

1985. 40th Anniv of U.N.O. (3248) and 30th Anniv of Bulgaria's Membership (3249). Multicoloured.
3248 13s. Dove around U.N. emblem 10 10
3249 13s. Type **1080** 10 10

1985. Roses. Multicoloured.
3250 5s. "Rosa damascena" . . . 10 10
3251 13s. Type **1081** 20 10
3252 20s. "Radiman" 30 10
3253 30s. "Marista" 45 15
3254 42s. "Valentina" 60 25
3255 60s. "Maria" 85 40

1082 Peace Dove

1985. 10th Anniv of European Security and Co-operation Conference, Helsinki.
3256 **1082** 13s. multicoloured . . . 10 10

1083 Water Polo

1985. European Swimming Championships, Sofia. Multicoloured.
3257 5s. Butterfly stroke (horiz) 10 10
3258 13s. Type **1083** 20 10
3259 42s. Diving 60 15
3260 60s. Synchronized swimming (horiz) 85 20

1084 Edelweiss

1985. 90th Anniv of Bulgarian Tourist Organization.
3261 **1084** 5s. multicoloured . . . 10 10

1085 State Arms **1086** Footballers

1985. Cent of Union of E. Roumelia and Bulgaria.
3262 **1085** 5s. black, orge & green 10 10

1985. World Cup Football Championship, Mexico (1986) (1st issue).
3263 **1086** 5s. multicoloured . . . 10 10
3264 – 13s. multicoloured . . . 20 10
3265 – 30s. multicoloured . . . 45 15
3266 – 42s. multicoloured . . . 60 20
MS3267 54 × 76 mm. 1l. multicoloured (horiz) . . . . . 2·00 2·00
DESIGNS: 13s. to 1l. Various footballers.
See also Nos. 3346/**MS**3352.

1087 Computer Picture of Boy

1985. International Young Inventors' Exhibition, Plovdiv. Multicoloured.
3268 5s. Type **1087** 10 10
3269 13s. Computer picture of youth 10 10
3270 30s. Computer picture of cosmonaut 20 10

1088 St. John's Church, Nesebur

1985. 40th Anniv of U.N.E.S.C.O. Mult.
3271 5s. Type **1088** 10 10
3272 13s. Rila Monastery 10 10
3273 35s. Soldier (fresco, Ivanovo Rock Church) 25 10
3274 42s. Archangel Gabriel (fresco, Boyana Church) 30 15
3275 60s. Thracian woman (fresco, Kazanlak tomb) 50 20
MS3276 100 × 83 mm. 1l. Madara horseman (horiz). Imperf . . . 2·00 2·00

1089 Lyudmila Zhivkova Palace of Culture

1985. 23rd United Nations Educational, Scientific and Cultural Organization General Session, Sofia. Sheet 62 × 95 mm.
MS3277 **1089** 1l. multicoloured 2·00 2·00

1090 Colosseum, Rome **1091** "Gladiolus"

1985. "Italia '85" International Stamp Exhibition, Rome.
3278 **1090** 42s. multicoloured . . . 25 10

1985. Flowers.
3279 **1091** 5s. pink and red . . . 10 10
3280 – 5s. blue and light blue 10 10
3281 – 5s. lt violet & violet . . 10 10
3282 – 8s. light blue and blue 15 10
3283 – 8s. orange and red . . 15 10
3284 – 32s. orange and brown 50 30
DESIGNS: No. 3280, Garden iris; 3281, Dwarf morning glory; 3282, Morning glory; 3283, "Anemone coronaria"; 3284, Golden-rayed lily.

1092 St. Methodius **1093** Cologne Cathedral

1985. Cultural Congress of European Security and Co-operation Conference, Budapest. Sheet 105 × 93 mm containing T **1092** and similar vert designs. Multicoloured.
MS3285 50s. St. Cyril; 50s. Map of Europe; 50s. Type **1092** . . . 3·00 3·00

1985. Historic Ships (4th series). As T **753**. Multicoloured.
3286 5s. 17th-century Dutch fly 15 10
3287 12s. "Sovereign of the Seas" (English galleon) 30 10
3288 20s. Mediterranean polacca 55 20
3289 25s. "Prince Royal" (English warship) 60 25
3290 42s. Xebec 80 40
3291 60s. 17th-century English warship . . . . 1·25 60

1985. "Philatelia '85" International Stamp Exhibition, Cologne. Sheet 109 × 56 mm containing T **1093** and similar vert design, each black, blue and red.
MS3292 30s. Type **1093**; 30s. Alexandr Nevski Cathedral, Sofia 1·25 1·25

1094 Bacho Kiro **1095** Hands, Sword and Bible

1985. Revolutionaries.
3293 **1094** 5s. light brown, brown and blue 10 10
3294 – 5s. green, purple & brown 10 10
DESIGN: No. 3294, Georgi S. Rakovski

1985. 150th Anniv of Turnovo Uprising.
3295 **1095** 13s. brown, blue & pur 10 10

1096 "1185 Revolution" (G. Bogdanov)

1985. 800th Anniv of Liberation from Byzantine Empire. Multicoloured.
3296 5s. Type **1096** 10 10
3297 13s. "1185 Revolution" (Al. Terziev) 10 10
3298 30s. "Battle of Klakotnitsa, 1230" (B. Grigorov and M. Ganovski) 20 15
3299 42s. "Veliko Turnovo" (Ts. Lavrenov) 30 20
MS3300 74 × 80 mm. 1l. Church of St. Dimitrius, Veliko Turnovo (38 × 28 mm). Imperf . . . . . 1·40 1·40

1097 Emblem

1985. "Bralkanfila '85" Stamp Exhibition, Vratsa. Sheet 55 × 80 mm.
MS3301 **1097** 40s. blue, black and deep blue 85 85

1098 Emblem and Globe

1985. International Development Programme for Posts and Telecommunications.
3302 **1098** 13s. multicoloured . . . 10 10

1099 Popov

1985. 70th Birth Anniv of Anton Popov (revolutionary).
3303 **1099** 5s. red 10 10

1100 Doves around Snowflake

1985. New Year. Multicoloured.
3304 5s. Type **1100** 10 10
3305 13s. Circle of stylized doves 10 10

1101 Pointer and Chukar Partridge

1985. Hunting Dogs. Multicoloured.
3306 5s. Type **1101** 50 20
3307 8s. Irish setter and common pochard 65 20
3308 13s. English setter and mallard 85 20
3309 20s. Cocker spaniel and Eurasian woodcock . . . 1·25 30
3310 25s. German pointer and rabbit 25 20
3311 30s. Bulgarian bloodhound and boar 30 20
3312 42s. Dachshund and fox . . 4·25 1·10

1102 Person in Wheelchair and Runners

1985. International Year of Disabled Persons (1984).
3313 **1102** 5s. multicoloured . . . 10 10

1103 Georgi Dimitrov (statesman)

1985. 50th Anniv of 7th Communist International Congress, Moscow.
3314 **1103** 13s. red 10 10

1104 Emblem within "40"

1986. 40th Anniv of U.N.I.C.E.F.
3315 **1104** 13s. blue, gold & black 10 10

1105 Blagoev **1106** Hands and Dove within Laurel Wreath

1986. 130th Birth Anniv of Dimitur Blagoev (founder of Bulgarian Social Democratic Party).
3316 **1105** 5s. purple and orange . . . 10 10

1986. International Peace Year.
3317 **1106** 5s. multicoloured . . . 10 10

1107 "Dactylorhiza romana"

1986. Orchids. Multicoloured.
3318 5s. Type **1107** 10 10
3319 13s. "Epipactis palustris" . . 20 10
3320 30s. "Ophrys cornuta" . . . 40 10
3321 32s. "Limodorum abrotivum" 40 15
3322 42s. "Cypripedium calceolus" 55 20
3323 60s. "Orchis papilionacea" 1·40 25

1108 Angora Rabbit

1986. Rabbits.
3324 – 5s. grey, black & brown 10 10
3325 **1108** 25s. red and black . . . 35 10
3326 – 30s. brown, yell & blk 40 10
3327 – 32s. orange and black 40 15
3328 – 42s. red and black . . . 55 15
3329 – 60s. blue and black . . 1·50 25
DESIGNS: 5s. French grey; 30s. English lop-eared; 32s. Belgian; 42s. English spotted; 60s. Dutch black and white rabbit.

1109 Front Page and Ivan Bogorov

1986. 140th Anniv of "Bulgarian Eagle".
3330 **1109** 5s. multicoloured . . . 10 10

1110 Neptune and Comet Position, 1980

1986. Appearance of Halley's Comet. Sheet 120 × 114 mm containing T **1110** and similar horiz designs, each violet, blue and yellow.
MS3331 25s. Type **1110**; 25s. Sun, Earth, Mars, Saturn and comet postitions, 1985 and 1910/86; 25s. Uranus and comet positions, 1960, 1926, 1948 and 1970; 25s. Jupiter and comet position, 1911 . . . 2·00 2·00

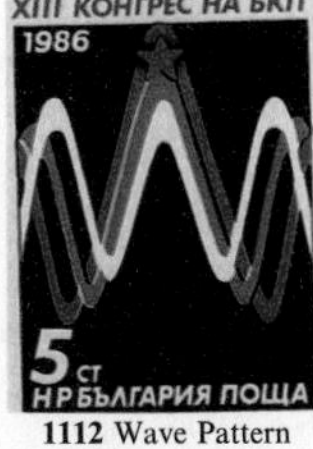

1111 Bashev **1112** Wave Pattern

1986. 50th Birth Anniv (1985) of Vladimir Bashev (poet).
3332 **1111** 5s. blue & light blue . . 10 10

1986. 13th Bulgarian Communist Party Congress.
3333 **1112** 5s. blue, green and red 10 10
3334 – 8s. blue and red 10 10
3335 – 13s. blue, red & lt blue 10 10
MS3336 60 × 77 mm. 50s. multicoloured 75 75
DESIGNS: 8s. Printed circuit as tail of shooting star; 13s. Computer picture of man; 50s. Steel construction tower.

1113 "Vostok 1"

1986. 25th Anniv of First Man in Space. Sheet 105 × 100 mm containing T **1113** and similar horiz design, each deep blue and blue.
MS3337 50s. Type **1113**; 50s. Yuri Gagarin . . . . 1·75 1·75

1114 Monument, Panagyurishte **1116** Stylized Ear of Wheat

1115 Gymnast

1986. 110th Anniv of April Uprising.
3338 **1114** 5s. black, stone and green 10 10
3339 – 13s. black, stone & red 10 10
DESIGN: 13s. Statue of Khristo Botev, Vratsa.

1986. 75th Anniv of Levski-Spartak Sports Club. Sheet 81 × 65 mm. Imperf.
MS3340 **1115** 50s. multicoloured 75 75

1986. 35th Bulgarian People's Agrarian Union Congress.
3341 **1116** 5s. gold, orange & blk 10 10
3342 – 8s. gold, blue and black 10 10
3343 – 13s. multicoloured . . . 10 10
DESIGNS: 8s. Stylized ear of wheat on globe; 13s. Flags.

1117 Transport Systems **1118** Emblem

1986. Socialist Countries' Transport Ministers Conference.
3344 **1117** 13s. multicoloured . . . 30 10

1986. 17th International Book Fair, Sofia.
3345 **1118** 13s. grey, red and black 10 10

1119 Player with Ball

1986. World Cup Football Championship, Mexico (2nd issue). Multicoloured.
3346 5s. Type **1119** 20 10
3347 13s. Player tackling (horiz) 30 10
3348 20s. Player heading ball (horiz) 50 15
3349 30s. Player kicking ball (horiz) 75 20
3350 42s. Goalkeeper (horiz) . . 90 40
3351 60s. Player with trophy . . 1·25 40
MS3352 95 × 75 mm. 1l. Azteca Stadium (42 × 31 mm) . . . . 2·50 2·50

1120 Square Brooch

1986. Treasures of Preslav. Multicoloured.
3353 5s. Type **1120** 10 10
3354 13s. Pendant (vert) 10 10
3355 20s. Wheel-shaped pendant 15 10
3356 30s. Breast plate decorated with birds and chalice . . 20 10
3357 42s. Pear-shaped pendant (vert) 25 15
3358 60s. Enamelled cockerel on gold base 40 25

1121 Fencers with Sabres

1986. World Fencing Championships, Sofia. Mult.
3359 5s. Type **1121** 10 10
3360 13s. Fencers 10 10
3361 25s. Fencers with rapiers . . 20 10

1122 Stockholm Town Hall **1123** White Stork (*Ciconia ciconia*)

1986. "Stockholmia 86" International Stamp Exn.
3362 **1122** 42s. brn, red & dp red 60 25

1986. Nature Protection. Sheet 138 × 90 mm containing T **1123** and similar vert designs. Multicoloured.
MS3363 30s. Type **1132**; 30s. Yellow water-lily (*Nuphar lutea*); 30s. Fire salamander (*Salamandra salamandra*); 30s. White water-lily (*Nymphaea alba*) . . . . 3·75 3·00

1124 Arms and Parliament Building, Sofia

1986. 40th Anniv of People's Republic.
3364 **1124** 5s. green, red & lt grn 10 10

1125 Posthorn

1986. 15th Organization of Socialist Countries' Postal Administrations Session, Sofia.
3365 **1125** 13s. multicoloured . . . 10 10

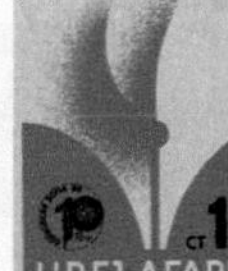

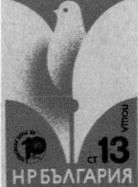

1126 "All Pull Together" **1127** Dove and Book as Pen Nib

1986. 40th Anniv of Voluntary Brigades.
3366 **1126** 5s. multicoloured . . . 10 10

1986. 10th International Journalists Association Congress, Sofia.
3367 **1127** 13s. blue & deep blue 10 10

1128 Wrestlers

1986. 75th Anniv of Levski-Spartak Sports Club.
3368 **1128** 5s. multicoloured . . . 10 10

1129 Saints Cyril and Methodius with Disciples (fresco)

1986. 1100th Anniv of Arrival in Bulgaria of Pupils of Saints Cyril and Methodius.
3369 **1129** 13s. brown and buff . . 15 10

1130 Old and Modern Telephones

1986. Centenary of Telephone in Bulgaria.
3370 **1130** 5s. multicoloured . . . 10 10

1131 Weightlifter

1986. World Weightlifting Championships, Sofia.
3371 **1131** 13s. multicoloured . . . 15 10

1986. Historic Ships (5th series). 18th-century ships. As T **753**. Multicoloured.
3372 5s. "King of Prussia" . . . 15 10
3373 13s. Indiaman 30 10
3374 25s. Xebec 55 25
3375 30s. "Sv. Paul" 70 30
3376 32s. Topsail schooner . . . 70 30
3377 42s. "Victory" 90 35

1132 (½-size illustration)

1986. European Security and Co-operation Conference Review Meeting, Vienna. Sheet 109 × 86 mm containing T **1132** and similar vert designs.
MS3378 50s. olive, orange and green; 50s. green, orange and blue (Vienna Town Hall); 50s. multicoloured (United Nations Centre, Vienna) . . . . 4·00 4·00

1133 Silver Jug decorated with Seated Woman

1986. 14th Congress of Bulgarian Philatelic Federation and 60th Anniv of International Philatelic Federation. Repousse work found at Rogozen.

3379 **1133** 10s. grey, black & bl . . . 15 15
3380 – 10s. green, blk & red . . . 15 15
DESIGN: No. 3380, Silver jug decorated with sphinx.

1134 Doves between Pine Branches

1986. New Year.

3381 **1134** 5s. red, green and blue . . . 10 10
3382 – 13s. mauve, blue & vio . . . 15 10
DESIGN: 13s. Fireworks and snowflakes.

1135 Earphones as "60" on Globe

1986. 60th Anniv of Bulgarian Amateur Radio.

3383 **1135** 13s. multicoloured . . . 10 10

1136 "The Walnut Tree" (Danail Dechev)

1986. 90th Anniv of Sofia Art Academy. Modern Paintings. Sheet 146 × 102 mm containing T **1136** and similar horiz designs. Multicoloured.

MS3384 25s. Type **1136**; 25s. "Resistance Fighters and Soldiers" (Iliya Beshkov); 30s. "Melnik" (Veselin Staikov); 30s. "The Olive Grove" (Kiril Tsonev) . . . . 2·50 2·50

1137 Gen. Augusto Sandino and Flag

1988. 25th Anniv of Sandinista National Liberation Front of Nicaragua.

3385 **1137** 13s. multicoloured . . . 15 10

1138 Dimitur and Konstantin Miladinov (authors)

1139 Pencho Slaveikov (poet)

1986. 125th Anniv of "Bulgarian Popular Songs".

3386 **1138** 10s. blue, brn & red . . . 15 10

1986. Writers' Birth Annivs. Multicoloured.

3387 5s. Type **1139** (125th anniv) . . . 10 10
3388 5s. Stoyan Mikhailovski (130th anniv) 10 10
3389 8s. Nikola Atanasov (dramatist) (centenary) . . 10 10
3390 8s. Ran Bosilek (children's author) (centenary) . . . 10 10

1140 Raiko Daskalov

1141 "Girl with Fruit"

1986. Birth Cent of Raiko Daskalov (politician).

3391 **1140** 5s. brown 10 10

1986. 500th Birth Anniv of Titian (painter). Multicoloured.

3392 5s. Type **1141** 10 10
3393 13s. "Flora" 20 10
3394 20s. "Lucretia and Tarquin" . . 30 10
3395 30s. Caiphas and Mary Magdalene 50 15
3396 32s. "Toilette of Venus" (detail) 50 15
3397 42s. "Self-portrait" . . . . 1·10 20
MS3398 105 × 75 mm. 1l. "Danae" (32 × 54 mm) . . . . 2·50 1·50

1142 Fiat, 1905

1986. Racing Cars.

3399 **1142** 5s. brown, red & black . . . 10 10
3400 – 10s. red, orange & blk . . . 20 10
3401 – 25s. green, red & black . . . 45 20
3402 – 32s. brown, red & blk . . . 60 20
3403 – 40s. violet, red & black . . . 70 25
3404 – 42s. grey, black and red . . 1·25 25
DESIGNS: 10s. Bugatti, 1928; 25s. Mercedes, 1936; 32s. Ferrari, 1952; 40s. Lotus, 1985; 42s. Maclaren, 1986.

1143 Steam Locomotive

1987. 120th Anniv of Ruse–Varna Railway.

3405 **1143** 5s. multicoloured . . . 20 10

1144 Debelyanov

1987. Birth Cent of Dimcho Debelyanov (poet).

3406 **1144** 5s. dp blue, yellow & bl . . 10 10

1145 Lazarus Ludwig Zamenhof (inventor)

1987. Centenary of Esperanto (invented language).

3407 **1145** 13s. blue, yellow & grn . . 15 10

1146 The Blusher

1147 Worker

1987. Edible Fungi. Multicoloured.

3408 5s. Type **1146** 10 10
3409 20s. Royal boletus 35 15
3410 30s. Red-capped scaber stalk . . 60 30
3411 32s. Shaggy ink cap 70 30
3412 40s. Bare-toothed russula . . 90 35
3413 60s. Chanterelle . . . . . . 1·25 75

1987. 10th Trade Unions Congress, Sofia.

3414 **1147** 5s. violet and red . . . 10 10

1148 Silver-gilt Plate with Design of Hercules and Auge

1987. Treasure of Rogozen. Multicoloured.

3415 5s. Type **1148** 10 10
3416 8s. Silver-gilt jug with design of lioness attacking stag . . 10 10
3417 20s. Silver-gilt plate with quatrefoil design 15 10
3418 30s. Silver-gilt jug with design of horse rider . . . 25 15
3419 32s. Silver-gilt pot with palm design 30 15
3420 42s. Silver jug with chariot and horses design 50 20

1149 Ludmila Zhivkova Feastival Complex, Varna

1987. Modern Architecture. Sheet 107 × 100 mm containing T **1149** and similar horiz designs. Multicoloured.

MS3421 30s. Type **1149**; 30s. Ministry of Foreign Affairs building, Sofia; 30s. Interpred building, Sofia; 30s. Hotel, Sandanski . . . . 2·50 2·50

1150 Wrestlers

1152 "X" and Flags

1151 Totem Pole

1987. 30th European Freestyle Wrestling Championships, Turnovo.

3422 **1150** 5s. lilac, red and violet . . 10 10
3423 – 13s. dp blue, red & blue . . 15 10
DESIGNS: 13st. Wrestlers (different).

1987. "Capex '87" International Stamp Exhibition, Toronto.

3424 **1151** 42s. multicoloured . . . 60 20

1987. 10th Fatherland Front Congress.

3425 **1152** 5s. green, orange & bl . . 10 10

1153 Georgi Dimitrov and Profiles

1987. 15th Dimitrov Communist Youth League Congress.

3426 **1153** 5s. purple, green & red . . 10 10

1154 Mask

1156 Mariya Gigova

1155 Mastheads

1987. 8th International Festival of Humour and Satire, Gabrovo.

3427 **1154** 13s. multicoloured . . . 15 10

1987. 60th Anniv of "Rabotnichesko Delo" (newspaper).

3428 **1155** 5s. red and black . . . 10 10

1987. 13th World Rhythmic Gymnastics Championships, Varna.

3429 **1156** 5s. blue and yellow . . 10 10
3430 – 8s. red and yellow . . . 10 10
3431 – 13s. blue and stone . . . 15 10
3432 – 25s. red and yellow . . 30 10
3433 – 30s. black and yellow . . 30 10
3434 – 42s. mauve and yellow . . 45 20
MS3435 78 × 87 mm. 1l. violet and ochre . . . . 1·40 1·40
DESIGNS: 8s. Iliana Raeva; 13s. Aneliya Ralenkova; 25s. Dilyana Georgieva; 30s. Liliya Ignatova; 42s. Bianka Panova; 1l. Neshka Robeva.

1157 Man breaking Chains around Globe and Kolarov

1987. 110th Birth Anniv of Vasil Kolarov (Prime Minister 1949–50).

3436 **1157** 5s. multicoloured . . . 10 10

1158 Stela Blagoeva

1160 Roe Deer

1159 Levski

1987. Birth Centenary of Stela Blagoeva.

3437 **1158** 5s. brown and pink . . 10 10

1987. 150th Birth Anniv of Vasil Levski (revolutionary).

3438 **1159** 5s. brown and green . . 10 10
3439 – 13s. green and brown . . 15 10
DESIGN: 13s. Levski and Bulgarian Revolutionary Central Committee emblem.

1987. Stags. Multicoloured.

3440 5s. Type **1160** 10 10
3441 10s. Elk (horiz) 15 10
3442 32s. Fallow deer 50 20
3443 40s. Sika deer 60 20
3444 42s. Red deer (horiz) . . . 60 20
3445 60s. Reindeer 90 30
MS3445a 145 × 131 mm. Nos. 3340/5. Imperf . . . . . 2·75 2·75

1161 Barbed Wire as Dove

1987. International Namibia Day.
3446 **1161** 13s. black, red & orge 15 10

1162 Kirkov **1163** "Phacelia tanacetifolia"

1987. 120th Birth Anniv of Georgi Kirkov (pseudonym Maistora) (politician).
3447 **1162** 5s. red and pink . . . 10 10

1987. Flowers. Multicoloured.
3448 5s. Type **1163** 10 10
3449 10s. Sunflower 15 10
3450 30s. False acacia 45 20
3451 32s. Dutch lavender 50 20
3452 42s. Small-leaved lime . . . 60 20
3453 60s. "Onobrychis sativa" . . 90 30

1164 Mil Mi-8 Helicopter, Tupolev Tu-154 and Antonov An-12 Aircraft

1987. 40th Anniv of Balkanair.
3454 **1164** 25s. multicoloured . . . 70 30

1165 1879 5c. Stamp

1987. "Bulgaria '89" International Stamp Exhibition, Sofia (1st issue).
3455 **1165** 13s. multicoloured . . . 20 10
See also Nos. 3569, 3579/82 and 3602/5.

1166 Copenhagen Town Hall **1167** "Portrait of Girl" (Stefan Ivanov)

1987. "Hafnia '87" International Stamp Exhibition, Copenhagen.
3456 **1166** 42s. multicoloured . . . 50 20

1987. Paintings in Sofia National Gallery. Mult.
3457 5s. Type **1167** 10 10
3458 8s. "Woman carrying Grapes" (Bencho Obreshkov) 10 10
3459 20s. "Portrait of a Woman wearing a Straw Hat" (David Perez) 30 10
3460 25s. "Women listening to Marimba" (Kiril Tsonev) 40 15
3461 32s. "Boy with Harmonica" (Nenko Balkanski) . . . 50 15
3462 60s. "Rumyana" (Vasil Stoilov) 90 20

1168 Battle Scene

1987. 75th Anniv of Balkan War.
3463 **1168** 5s. black, stone and red 10 10

1169 Emblem

1987. 30th Anniv of International Atomic Energy Agency.
3464 **1169** 13s. blue, green and red 15 10

1170 Mastheads

1987. 95th Anniv of "Rabotnik", 90th Anniv of "Rabotnicheski Vestnik" and 60th Anniv of "Rabotnichesko Delo" (newspapers).
3465 **1170** 5s. red, blue and gold 10 10

1171 Winter Wren

1987. Birds. Multicoloured.
3466 5s. Type **1171** 10 10
3467 13s. Yellowhammer 30 15
3468 20s. Eurasian nuthatch . . . 40 20
3469 30s. Blackbird 60 35
3470 42s. Hawfinch 90 40
3471 60s. White-throated dipper 1·25 60

1172 "Vega" Automatic Space Station

1987. 30th Anniv of Soviet Space Exploration. Sheet 98 × 98 mm containing T **1172** and similar horiz design.
MS3472 50s. blue, orange and purple (Type **1172**); 50s. deep blue, blue and purple ("Soyuz" spacecraft docking with "Mir" space station) 3·50 3·50

1173 Lenin and Revolutionary

1987. 70th Anniv of Russian Revolution.
3473 **1173** 5s. purple and red . . . 10 10
3474 – 13s. blue and red . . . 15 10
DESIGN: 13s. Lenin and cosmonaut.

1174 Biathlon

1987. Winter Olympic Games, Calgary. Mult.
3475 5s. Type **1174** 10 10
3476 13s. Slalom 20 10
3477 30s. Figure skating (women's) 45 10
3478 42s. Four-man bobsleigh . . 65 15
MS3479 65 × 87 mm. 1l. Ice hockey 1·75 1·75

1175 "Socfilex" Emblem within Folk-design Ornament

1987. New Year. Multicoloured.
3480 5s. Type **1175** 10 10
3481 13s. Emblem within flower ornament 15 10

1176 Helsinki Conference Centre

1987. European Security and Co-operation Conference Review Meeting, Vienna. Sheet 140 × 100 mm containing T **1176** and similar vert designs.
MS3482 50s. lavender, brown and red; 50s. multicoloured (Map of Europe); 50s. multicoloured (Vienna Conference Centre) . . 3·50 3·50

1177 Kabakchiev **1178** "Scilla bythynica"

1988. 110th Birth Anniv of Khristo Kabakchiev (Communist Party official).
3483 **1177** 5s. multicoloured . . . 10 10

1988. Marsh Flowers. Multicoloured.
3484 5s. Type **1178** 10 10
3485 10s. "Geum rhodopaeum" 15 10
3486 13s. "Caltha polypetala" . . 20 10
3487 25s. Fringed water-lily . . . 35 15
3488 30s. "Cortusa matthioli" . . 40 20
3489 42s. Water soldier 60 25

1179 Commander on Horseback

1988. 110th Anniv of Liberation from Turkey. Multicoloured.
3490 5s. Type **1179** 10 10
3491 13s. Soldiers 15 10

1180 Emblem

1988. Public Sector Workers' 8th International Congress, Sofia.
3492 **1180** 13s. multicoloured . . . 15 10

1181 "Yantra", 1888

1988. Centenary of State Railways. Locomotives. Multicoloured.
3493 5s. Type **1181** 20 10
3494 13s. "Khristo Botev", 1905 30 10
3495 25s. Steam locomotive No. 807, 1918 . . . . . 40 15
3496 32s. Class 46 steam locomotive, 1943 . . . . 55 20
3497 42s. Diesel locomotive, 1964 90 25
3498 60s. Electric locomotive, 1979 . . . . 1·25 40

1182 Ivan Nedyalkov (Shablin) **1183** Traikov

1988. Post Office Anti-fascist Heroes.
3499 **1182** 5s. light brown and brown 10 10
3500 – 8s. grey and blue . . . 10 10
3501 – 10s. green and olive . . 10 10
3502 – 13s. pink and red . . . 15 10
DESIGNS: 8s. Delcho Spasov; 10s. Nikola Ganchev (Gudzho); 13s. Ganka Rasheva (Boika).

1988. 90th Birth Anniv of Georgi Traikov (politician).
3503 **1183** 5s. orange and brown 10 10

1184 Red Cross, Red Crescent and Globe **1185** Girl

1988. 125th Anniv of International Red Cross.
3504 **1184** 13s. multicoloured . . . 20 10

1988. 4th "Banners for Peace" Children's Meeting, Sofia. Children's paintings. Multicoloured.
3505 5s. Type **1185** 10 10
3506 8s. Artist at work 10 10
3507 13s. Circus (horiz) 20 10
3508 20s. Kite flying (horiz) . . . 30 15
3509 32s. Accordion player . . . 45 20
3510 42s. Cosmonaut 60 25
MS3511 86 × 90 mm. 50s. Emblem with film frame (Youth Film Festival) (horiz) . . . . 1·25 1·25

1186 Marx

1988. 170th Birth Anniv of Karl Marx.
3512 **1186** 13s. red, black & yellow 15 10

1187 Herring Gull **1189** "Soyuz TM" Spacecraft, Flags and Globe

1188 African Elephant

1988. Birds. Multicoloured.
3513 5s. Type **1187** 25 10
3514 5s. White stork 25 10
3515 8s. Grey heron 45 15

3516 8s. Carrion crow 45 15
3517 10s. Northern goshawk . . 60 20
3518 42s. Eagle owl . . . . . . 1·25 30

1988. Centenary of Sofia Zoo. Multicoloured.
3519 5s. Type **1188** 10 10
3520 13s. White rhinoceros . . . 20 10
3521 25s. Hunting dog 35 15
3522 30s. Eastern white pelican 70 30
3523 32s. Abyssinian ground hornbill 75 35
3524 42s. Snowy owl . . . . . . 1·75 55

1988. 2nd Soviet–Bulgarian Space Flight. Mult.
3525 5s. Type **1189** 10 10
3526 13s. Rocket on globe . . . 20 10

1190 Young Inventor

1988. International Young Inventors' Exhibition, Plovdiv.
3527 **1190** 13s. multicoloured . . . 20 10

1191 1856 Handstamp of Russian Duchy of Finland

1988. "Finlandia '88" International Stamp Exhibition, Helsinki.
3528 **1191** 30s. blue and red . . . 40 20

1192 Player taking Corner Kick **1193** "Portrait of Child"

1988. 8th European Football Championship, West Germany. Multicoloured.
3529 5s. Type **1192** 10 10
3530 13s. Goalkeeper and player 20 10
3531 30s. Referee and player . . 40 20
3532 42s. Player with trophy . . 60 25
MS3533 90 × 69 mm. 1l. Stadium (horiz) . . . . 1·75 1·75

1988. 2nd Death Anniv of Dechko Uzunov (painter). Multicoloured.
3534 5s. Type **1193** 10 10
3535 13s. "Portrait of Mariya Vasileva" 20 10
3536 30s. "Self-portrait" 40 20

1194 Valentina Tereshkova

1988. 25th Anniv of First Woman in Space. Sheet 87 × 56 mm.
MS3537 **1194** 1l. pink and blue 2·00 2·00

1195 "St. John" **1196** High Jumping

1988. Icons from Kurdzhali. Multicoloured.
3538 5s. Type **1195** 10 10
3539 8s. "St. George and Dragon" 10 10

1988. Olympic Games, Seoul. Multicoloured.
3540 5s. Type **1196** 10 10
3541 13s. Weightlifting 20 10
3542 30s. Wrestling 40 20
3543 42s. Gymnastics 60 25
MS3544 115 × 75 mm. 1l. Volleyball 1·75 1·75

1197 Dimitur and Karadzha

1988. 120th Death Anniv of Khadzhi Dimitur and Stefan Karadzha (revolutionaries).
3545 **1197** 5s. green, black & brn 10 10

1198 Magazines

1988. 30th Anniv of "Problems of Peace and Socialism" (magazine).
3546 **1198** 13s. multicoloured . . . 15 10

1199 "The Dead Tree" (Roland Udo)

1988. Paintings in Lyudmila Zhivkova Art Gallery. Multicoloured.
3547 30s. Type **1199** 45 15
3548 30s. "Algiers Harbour" (Albert Marque) 45 15
3549 30s. "Portrait of Hermine David" (Jule Pasquin) . . 45 15
3550 30s. "Madonna and Child with two Saints" (Giovanni Rosso) 45 15

1200 University Building

1988. Centenary of St. Clement of Ohrid University, Sofia.
3551 **1200** 5s. black, yellow & grn 10 10

1201 Czechoslovakia 1918 Stamp Design

1988. "Praga '88" International Stamp Exhibition, Prague.
3552 **1201** 25s. red and blue . . . 35 15

1202 Korea 1884 5m. Stamp

1988. "Olymphilex '88" Olympic Stamps Exhibition, Seoul.
3553 **1202** 62s. red and green . . . 90 40

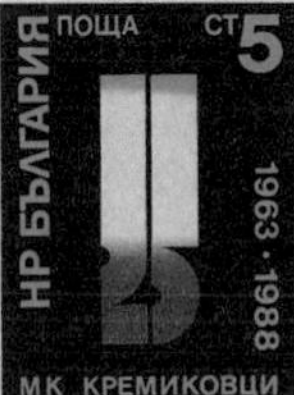

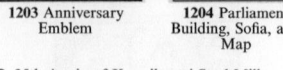

1203 Anniversary Emblem **1204** Parliament Building, Sofia, and Map

1988. 25th Anniv of Kremikovtsi Steel Mills.
3554 **1203** 5s. violet, red and blue 10 10

1988. 80th Interparliamentary Conference, Sofia.
3555 **1204** 13s. blue and red . . . 15 10

1205 Chalice, Glinena

1988. Kurdzhali Culture. Multicoloured.
3556 5s. Type **1205** 10 10
3557 8s. Part of ruined fortifications, Perperikon (vert) 10 10

1206 Soldiers

1988. 300th Anniv of Chiprovtsi Rising.
3558 **1206** 5s. multicoloured . . . 10 10

1207 Brown Bear

1988. Bears. Multicoloured.
3559 5s. Type **1207** 10 10
3560 8s. Polar bear 10 10
3561 13s. Sloth bear 25 10
3562 20s. Sun bear 35 15
3563 32s. Asiatic black bear . . . 50 20
3564 42s. Spectacled bear 65 25

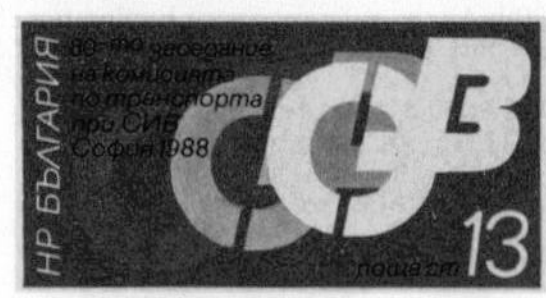

1208 Emblem

1988. 80th Council of Mutual Economic Aid Transport Commission Meeting, Sofia.
3565 **1208** 13s. red and black . . . 15 10

1209 Emblem

1988. World Ecoforum.
3566 **1209** 20s. multicoloured . . . 25 10

1210 Amphitheatre, Plovdiv

1988. "Plovdiv '88" National Stamp Exhibition.
3567 **1210** 5s. multicoloured . . . 10 10

1211 Transmission Towers

1988. 25th Anniv of Radio and Television.
3568 **1211** 5s. green, blue & brown 10 10

1212 1879 5c. Stamp

1988. "Bulgaria '89" International Stamp Exhibition (2nd issue).
3569 **1212** 42s. orange, blk & mve 60 25

1213 "Ruse" (river boat)

1988. 40th Anniv of Danube Commission. Sheet 104 × 124 mm containing T **1213** and similar horiz design. Multicoloured.
MS3570 1l. Type **1213**; 1l. *Al. Stamboliiski* (river cruiser) . . 4·00 2·50

1214 Children and Cars

1988. Road Safety Campaign.
3571 **1214** 5s. multicoloured . . . 10 10

1215 Rila Hotel, Borovets

1988. Hotels. Multicoloured.
3572 5s. Type **1215** 10 10
3573 8s. Pirin Hotel, Bansko . . 10 10
3574 13s. Shtastlivetsa Hotel, Vitosha 15 10
3575 30s. Perelik Hotel, Pamporovo 40 15

1216 Tree Decoration

1988. New Year. Multicoloured.
3576 5s. Type **1216** 10 10
3577 13s. "Bulgaria '89" emblem, tree and decorations . . . 15 10

1217 Space Shuttle "Buran"

1988. Energiya--Buran Space Flight. Sheet 102 × 67 mm.
MS3578 **1217** 1l. blue . . . . . 1·75 1·50

1218 Mail Coach

1988. "Bulgaria '89" International Stamp Exhibition, Sofia (3rd issue). Mail Transport. Multicoloured.

3579	25s. Type **1218**	35	15
3580	25s. Paddle-steamer	35	15
3581	25s. Lorry	35	15
3582	25s. Biplane	45	15

1219 India 1947 1½a. Independence Stamp

1989. "India 89" International Stamp Exhibition, New Delhi.

3583	**1219** 62s. green and orange	1·40	60

1220 France 1850 10c. Ceres Stamp

1989. "Philexfrance '89" International Stamp Exhibition, Paris.

3584	**1220** 42s. brown and blue	90	40

1221 Slalom

1989. "Sofia '89" University Winter Games, Sofia. Sheet 84 × 142 mm containing T **1221** and similar vert designs. Multicoloured. Imperf.

MS3585	25s. Type **1221**; 25s. Ice hockey; 25s. Biathlon; 25s. Speed skating	1·75	1·50

1222 Don Quixote (sculpture, House of Humour and Satire)

1223 "Ramonda serbica"

1989. International Festival of Humour and Satire, Gabrovo.

3586	**1222** 13s. multicoloured	20	10

1989. Flowers. Multicoloured.

3587	5s. Type **1223**	10	10
3588	10s. "Paeonia maskula"	15	10
3589	25s. "Viola perinensis"	35	30
3590	30s. "Dracunculus vulgaris"	45	40
3591	42s. "Tulipa splendens"	60	55
3592	60s. "Rindera umbellata"	90	80

1224 Common Noctule Bat

1989. Bats. Multicoloured.

3593	5s. Type **1224**	10	10
3594	13s. Greater horseshoe bat	25	10
3595	30s. Large mouse-eared bat	65	20
3596	42s. Particoloured frosted bat	95	25

1225 Stamboliiski

1989. 110th Birth Anniv of Aleksandur Stamboliiski (Prime Minister 1919–23).

3597	**1225** 5s. black and orange	10	10

1226 Launch of "Soyuz 33"

1989. 10th Anniv of Soviet–Bulgarian Space Flight. Sheet 130 × 90 mm containing T **1226** and similar vert design. Multicoloured.

MS3598	50s. Type **1226**; 50s. Cosmonauts Nicolai Rukavishnikov and Georgi Ivanov	2·50	2·00

1227 Young Inventor

1989. International Young Inventors' Exhibition, Plovdiv.

3599	**1227** 5s. multicoloured	10	10

1228 Stanke Dimitrov-Marek (Party activist)

1229 "John the Baptist" (Toma Vishanov)

1989. Birth Centenaries.

3600	**1228** 5s. red and black	10	10
3601	– 5s. red and black	10	10

DESIGN: No. 3601, Petko Yenev (revolutionary).

1989. "Bulgaria '89" International Stamp Exhibition, Sofia (4th issue). Icons. Multicoloured.

3602	30s. Type **1229**	45	15
3603	30s. "St. Dimitur" (Ivan Terziev)	45	15
3604	30s. "Archangel Michael" (Dimitur Molerov)	45	15
3605	30s. "Madonna and Child" (Toma Vishanov)	45	15

1230 Fax Machine and Woman reading letter

1989. 110th Anniv of Bulgarian Post and Telegraph Services. Multicoloured.

3606	5s. Type **1230**	10	10
3607	8s. Telex machine and old telegraph machine	10	10
3608	35s. Modern and old telephones	40	15
3609	42s. Dish aerial and old radio	50	20

1231 "Nike in Quadriga" (relief)

1989. 58th International Philatelic Federation Congress, Sofia. Sheet 87 × 120 mm.

MS3610	**1231** 1l. multicoloured	1·75	1·50

1232 A. P. Aleksandrov, A. Ya. Solovov and V. P. Savinikh

1989. Air. "Soyuz TM5" Soviet-Bulgarian Space Flight.

3611	**1232** 13s. multicoloured	20	10

1233 Party Programme

1234 Sofronii Vrachanski (250th anniv)

1989. 70th Anniv of First Bulgarian Communist Party Congress, Sofia.

3612	**1233** 5s. blk, red & dp red	10	10

1989. Writers' Birth Anniversaries.

3613	**1234** 5s. green, brown & blk	10	10
3614	– 5s. green, brown & blk	10	10

DESIGN: No. 3614, Iliya Bluskov (150th anniv).

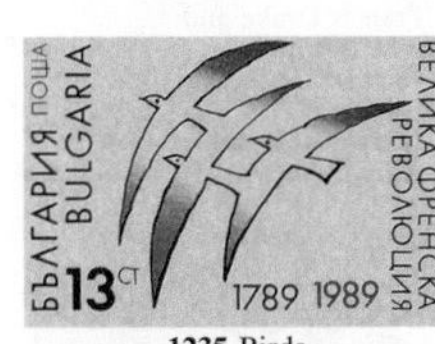

1235 Birds

1989. Bicentenary of French Revolution. Each black, red and blue.

3615	13s. Type **1235**	20	10
3616	30s. Jean-Paul Marat	40	15
3617	42s. Robespierre	50	20

1236 Gymnastics

1989. 7th Friendly Armies Summer Spartakiad. Multicoloured.

3618	5s. Type **1236**	10	10
3619	13s. Show jumping	20	10
3620	30s. Long jumping	40	15
3621	42s. Shooting	50	20

1237 Aprilov

1238 Zagorchinov

1989. Birth Bicent of Vasil Aprilov (educationist).

3622	**1237** 8s. lt blue, blue & blk	10	10

1989. Birth Centenary of Stoyan Zagorchinov (writer).

3623	**1238** 10s. turq, brown & blk	15	10

1239 Woman in Kayak

1989. Canoeing and Kayak Championships, Plovdiv. Multicoloured.

3624	13s. Type **1239**	20	10
3625	30s. Man in kayak	45	15

1240 Felix Nadar taking Photograph from his Balloon "Le Geant" (1863) and Airship "Graf Zeppelin" over Alexsandr Nevski Cathedral, Sofia

1989. 150th Anniv of Photography.

3626	**1240** 42s. black, stone & yell	80	30

1241 Lammergeier and Lynx

1989. Centenary of Natural History Museum.

3627	**1241** 13s. multicoloured	1·00	20

1242 Soldiers

1243 Lyubomir Dardzhikov

1989. 45th Anniv of Fatherland Front Government. Multicoloured.

3628	5s. Type **1242**	10	10
3629	8s. Welcoming officers	10	10
3630	13s. Crowd of youths	15	10

1989. 48th Death Anniversaries of Post Office War Heroes. Multicoloured.

3631	5s. Type **1243**	10	10
3632	8s. Ivan Bankov Dobrev	10	10
3633	13s. Nestor Antonov	10	10

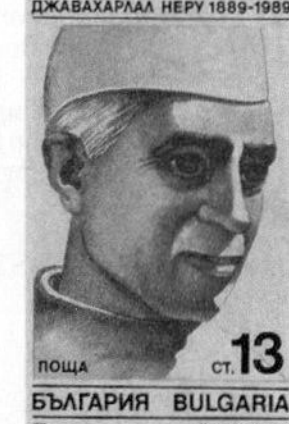

1244 Yasenov

1246 Nehru

1245 Lorry leaving Weighbridge

1989. Birth Cent of Khisto Yasenov (writer).
3634 **1244** 8s. grey, brown & blk 10 10

1989. 21st Transport Congress, Sofia.
3635 **1245** 42s. blue & deep blue 50 20

1989. Birth Centenary of Jawaharlal Nehru (Indian statesman).
3636 **1246** 13s. yellow, brn & blk 15 10

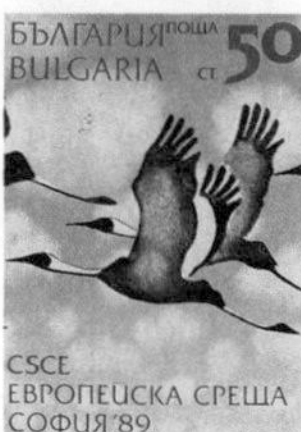

1247 Cranes flying

1989. Ecology Congress of European Security and Co-operation Conference, Sofia. Sheet 130 × 85 mm containing T **1247** and similar vert design. Multicoloured.
MS3637 50s. Type **1247**; 1l. Cranes flying (different) . . . . 3·50 3·50

1248 Javelin Sand Boa

1989. Snakes. Multicoloured.
3638 5s. Type **1248** 10 10
3639 10s. Aesculapian snake . . . 10 10
3640 25s. Leopard snake 35 10
3641 30s. Four-lined rat snake . . 45 15
3642 42s. Cat snake 60 25
3643 60s. Whip snake 90 40

1249 Tiger and Balloon of Flags
1250 Boy on Skateboard

1989. Young Inventors' Exhibition, Plovdiv.
3644 **1249** 13s. multicoloured . . . 15 10

1989. Children's Games. Sheet 100 × 120 mm containing T **1250** and similar vert designs. Multicoloured.
MS3645 30s.+15s. Type **1250**; 30s.+15s. Girl with ball and doll; 30s.+15s. Girl jumping over ropes; 30s.+15s. Boy with toy train 4·00 4·00

1251 Goalkeeper saving Ball

1989. World Cup Football Championship, Italy (1990) (1st issue). Multicoloured.
3646 5s. Type **1251** 15 10
3647 13s. Player tackling 25 15
3648 30s. Player heading ball . . 65 30
3649 42s. Player kicking ball . . 90 40
MS3650 109 × 54 mm. 50s. Player tackling; 50s. Players . . . . 2·00 1·50
See also Nos. 3675/**MS**3679.

1252 Gliders

1989. 82nd International Airsports Federation General Conference, Varna. Aerial Sports. Mult.
3651 5s. Type **1252** 10 10
3652 13s. Hang gliding 20 15
3653 30s. Parachutist landing . . 40 20
3654 42s. Free falling parachutist 60 30

1253 Children on Road Crossing

1989. Road Safety.
3655 **1253** 5s. multicoloured . . . 10 10

1254 Santa Claus's Sleigh
1255 European Shorthair

1989. New Year. Multicoloured.
3656 5s. Type **1254** 10 10
3657 13s. Snowman 15 10

1989. Cats.
3658 **1255** 5s. black and yellow . . 15 10
3659 – 5s. black and grey . . 15 10
3660 – 8s. black and yellow . . 20 10
3661 – 10s. black & brown . . 25 15
3662 – 10s. black and blue . . 25 15
3663 – 13s. black and red . . 40 20
DESIGNS—HORIZ: No. 3659, Persian; 3660, European shorthair (different); 3662, Persian (different). VERT: No. 3661, Persian (different); 3663, Siamese.

1256 Christopher Columbus and "Santa Maria"

1990. Navigators and their Ships. Multicoloured.
3664 5s. Type **1256** 20 10
3665 8s. Vasco da Gama and "Sao Gabriel" 20 10
3666 13s. Ferdinand Magellan and "Vitoria" 35 10
3667 32s. Francis Drake and "Golden Hind" 45 20
3668 42s. Henry Hudson and "Discoverie" 65 25
3669 60s. James Cook and H.M.S. "Endeavour" . . 90 25

1257 Banner

1990. Centenary of Esperanto (invented language) in Bulgaria.
3670 **1257** 10s. stone, green & blk 10 10

1258 "Portrait of Madeleine Rono" (Maurice Brianchon)

1990. Paintings. Multicoloured.
3671 30s. Type **1258** 45 20
3672 30s. "Still Life" (Suzanne Valadon) 45 20
3673 30s. "Portrait of a Woman" (Moise Kisling) 45 20
3674 30s. "Portrait of a Woman" (Giovanni Boltraffio) . . 45 20

1259 Players

1990. World Cup Football Championship, Italy.
3675 **1259** 5s. multicoloured . . . 10 10
3676 – 13s. multicoloured . . . 15 10
3677 – 30s. multicoloured . . . 45 20
3678 – 42s. multicoloured . . . 70 30
MS3679 80 × 125 mm. 2 × 50s. multicoloured . . . . 2·50 2·50
DESIGNS: 13 to 50s. Various match scenes.

1260 Bavaria 1849 1k. Stamp

1990. "Essen 90" International Stamp Fair.
3680 **1260** 42s. black and red . . . 70 40

1261 Penny Black

1990. "Stamp World London 90" International Stamp Exhibition. Sheet 90 × 140 mm containing T **1261** and similar horiz design.
MS3681 50s. black and blue (Type **1261**); 50s. black and red (Sir Rowland Hill (instigator of postage stamps)) . . . . . . 2·50 2·50

1262 "100" and Rainbow

1990. Centenary of Co-operative Farming.
3682 **1262** 5s. multicoloured . . . 10 10

1263 "Elderly Couple at Rest"

1990. Birth Centenary of Dimitur Chorbadzhiiski-Chudomir (artist).
3683 **1263** 5s. multicoloured . . . 10 10

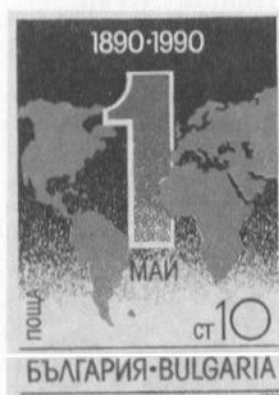

1264 Map

1990. Centenary of Labour Day.
3684 **1264** 10s. multicoloured . . . 15 10

1265 Emblem

1990. 125th Anniv of I.T.U.
3685 **1265** 20s. blue, red & black 25 15

1266 Belgium 1849 10c. "Epaulettes" Stamp

1990. "Belgica 90" International Stamp Exhibition, Brussels.
3686 **1266** 30s. brown and green 50 35

1267 Lamartine and his House

1990. Birth Bicentenary of Alphonse de Lamartine (poet).
3687 **1267** 20s. multicoloured . . . 25 15

1268 Brontosaurus

1990. Prehistoric Animals. Multicoloured.
3688 5s. Type **1268** 10 10
3689 8s. Stegosaurus 15 10
3690 13s. Edaphosaurus 20 10
3691 25s. Rhamphorhynchus . . 50 20
3692 32s. Protoceratops 65 30
3693 42s. Triceratops 90 40

1269 Swimming

1990. Olympic Games, Barcelona (1992) (1st issue). Multicoloured.
3694 5s. Type **1269** 10 10
3695 13s. Handball 20 10
3696 30s. Hurdling 50 25
3697 42s. Cycling 75 35
MS3698 77 × 117 mm. 50s. Tennis player serving; 50s. Tennis player waiting to receive ball . . . . 1·75 1·50
See also Nos. 3840/**MS**3844.

1270 Southern Festoon

1990. Butterflies and Moths. Multicoloured.
3699 5s. Type **1270** 10 10
3700 10s. Jersey tiger moth . . . 15 10
3701 20s. Willow-herb hawk moth 20 10
3702 30s. Striped hawk moth . . 50 20
3703 42s. "Thecla betulae" . . . 70 30
3704 60s. Cynthia's fritillary . . . 1·00 60

1271 Airbus Industrie A310 Jetliner

1990. Aircraft. Multicoloured.
3705 5s. Type **1271** 10 10
3706 10s. Tupolev Tu-204 . . . . 15 10
3707 25s. Concorde 40 20
3708 30s. Douglas DC-9 . . . . 45 25
3709 42s. Ilyushin Il-86 . . . . . 60 35
3710 60s. Boeing 747-300/400 . . 90 55
No. 3705 is wrongly inscribed Airbus "A300".

1272 Iosif I

1274 Putting the Shot

1273 Road and U.N. Emblem within Triangles

1990. 150th Birth Anniv of Exarch Iosif I.
3711 **1272** 5s. mauve, black & grn 10 10

1990. International Road Safety Year.
3712 **1273** 5s. multicoloured . . . 10 10

1990. "Olymphilex '90" Olympic Stamps Exhibition, Varna. Multicoloured.
3713 5s. Type **1274** 10 10
3714 13s. Throwing the discus . . 20 10
3715 42s. Throwing the hammer 70 35
3716 60s. Throwing the javelin . . 95 55

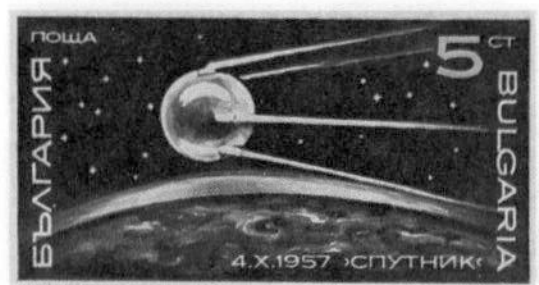

1275 "Sputnik" (first artificial satellite, 1957)

1990. Space Research. Multicoloured.
3717 5s. Type **1275** 10 10
3718 8s. "Vostok" and Yuri Gagarin (first manned flight, 1961) 10 10
3719 10s. Aleksei Leonov spacewalking from "Voskhod 2" (first spacewalk, 1965) 15 10
3720 20s. "Soyuz"–"Apollo" link, 1975 . . . . 30 15
3721 42s. Space shuttle "Columbia", 1981 . . . . 65 30
3722 60s. Space probe "Galileo" 90 45
MS3723 90 × 71 mm. 1l. Neil Armstrong from "Apollo 11" on lunar surface (first manned moon landing, 1969) (28 × 53 mm) . . 1·75 1·50

1276 St. Clement of Ohrid

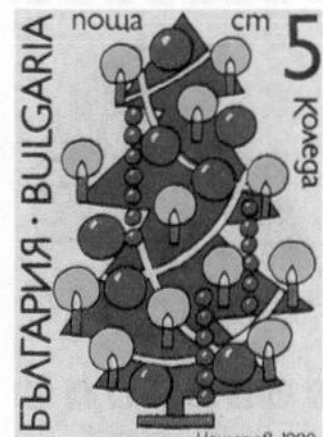

1277 Tree

1990. 1150th Birth Anniv of St. Clement of Ohrid.
3724 **1276** 5s. brown, black & grn 10 10

1990. Christmas. Multicoloured.
3725 5s. Type **1277** 10 10
3726 20s. Father Christmas . . . 15 10

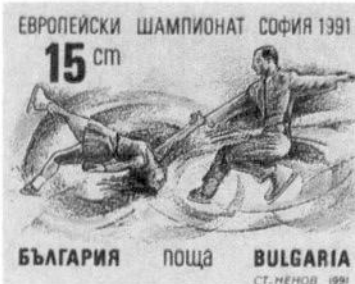

1278 Skaters

1991. European Figure Skating Championships, Sofia.
3727 **1278** 15s. multicoloured . . . 20 10

1279 Chicken

1281 "Good Day" (Paul Gauguin)

1280 Death Cap

1991. Farm Animals.
3728 – 20s. brown and black 10 10
3729 – 25s. blue and black . . 10 10
3730 **1279** 30s. brown and black 10 10
3731 – 40s. brown and black 15 10
3732 – 62s. green and black . . 25 10
3733 – 86s. red and black . . . 30 10
3734 – 95s. mauve and black 35 10
3735 – 1l. brown and black . . 40 15
3736 – 2l. green and black . . 60 25
3737 – 5l. violet and black . . 1·50 75
3738 – 10l. blue and black . . 1·75 75
DESIGNS: 20s. Sheep; 25s. Goose; 40s. Horse; 62, 95s. Billy goat; 86s. Sow; 1l. Donkey; 2l. Bull; 5l. Common turkey; 10l. Cow.

1991. Fungi. Multicoloured.
3746 5s. Type **1280** 10 10
3747 10s. "Amanita verna" . . . 25 10
3748 20s. Panther cap 60 15
3749 32s. Fly agaric 90 15
3750 42s. Beefsteak morel . . . . 1·25 35
3751 60s. Satan's mushroom . . 1·90 60

1991. Paintings. Multicoloured.
3752 20s. Type **1281** 10 10
3753 43s. "Madame Dobini" (Edgar Degas) 10 10
3754 62s. "Peasant Woman" (Camille Pissarro) 30 15
3755 67s. "Woman with Black hair" (Edouard Manet) 40 15
3756 80s. "Blue Vase" (Paul Cezanne) 50 20
3757 2l. "Madame Samari" (Pierre Auguste Renoir) 1·10 50
MS3758 65 × 90 mm. 3l. "Self-portrait" (Vincent van Gogh) 2·50 2·00

1282 Map

1991. 700th Anniv of Swiss Confederation.
3759 **1282** 62s. red and violet . . . 40 10

1283 Postman on Bicycle, Envelopes and Paper

1991. 100 Years of Philatelic Publications in Bulgaria.
3760 **1283** 30s. multicoloured . . . 10 10

1284 "Meteosat" Weather Satellite

1991. Europa. Europe in Space. Multicoloured.
3761 43s. Type **1284** 10 10
3762 62s. "Ariane" rocket 40 10

1285 Przewalski's Horse

1991. Horses. Multicoloured.
3763 5s. Type **1285** 10 10
3764 10s. Tarpan 10 10
3765 25s. Black arab 15 10
3766 35s. White arab 20 15
3767 42s. Shetland pony 40 15
3768 60s. Draught horse 70 20

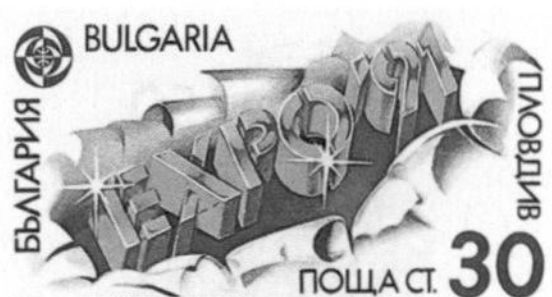

1286 "Expo '91"

1991. "Expo '91" Exhibition, Plovdiv.
3769 **1286** 30s. multicoloured . . . 10 10

1287 Mozart

1991. Death Bicentenary of Wolfgang Amadeus Mozart (composer).
3770 **1287** 62s. multicoloured . . . 40 10

1288 Astronaut and Rear of Space Shuttle "Columbia"

1991. Space Shuttles. Multicoloured.
3771 12s. Type **1288** 10 10
3772 32s. Satellite and "Challenger" 10 10
3773 50s. "Discovery" and satellite 30 10
3774 86s. Satellite and "Atlantis" (vert) 40 20
3775 1l.50 Launch of "Buran" (vert) 75 30
3776 2l. Satellite and "Atlantis" (vert) . . . . 1·10 40
MS3777 86 × 74 mm. 3l. Earth, "Atlantis" and Moon . . . . 1·50 1·25

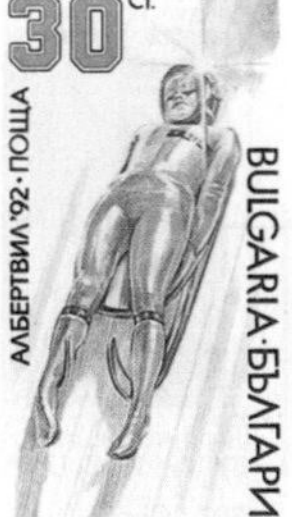

1289 Luge

1291 Japanese Chin

1290 Sheraton Hotel Balkan, Sofia

1991. Winter Olympic Games, Albertville (1992). Multicoloured.
3778 30s. Type **1289** 10 10
3779 43s. Skiing 20 10
3780 67s. Ski jumping 30 10
3781 2l. Biathlon 80 30
MS3782 128 × 86 mm. 3l. Two-man bobsleigh . . . . 1·50 1·25

1991.
3783 **1290** 62s. multicoloured . . . 20 10

1991. Dogs. Multicoloured.
3784 30s. Type **1291** 10 10
3785 43s. Chihuahua 10 10
3786 62s. Miniature pinscher . . 20 10
3787 80s. Yorkshire terrier . . . 40 10
3788 1l. Mexican hairless 50 15
3789 3l. Pug . . . . 1·50 45

1292 Arms

1991. "Philatelia '91" Stamp Fair, Cologne.
3790 **1292** 86s. multicoloured . . . 50 10

1293 Brandenburg Gate

1991. Bicentenary of Brandenburg Gate, Berlin. Sheet 90 × 70 mm.
MS3791 **1293** 4l. green and blue 3·00 2·50

1294 Japan 1871 48mon "Dragon" Stamp

1991. "Phila Nippon '91" International Stamp Exhibition, Tokyo.
3792 **1294** 62s. black, brown & bl 20 10

1295 Early Steam Locomotive and Tender

1991. 125th Anniv of the Railway in Bulgaria. Multicoloured.
3793 30s. Type **1295** 30 10
3794 30s. Early six-wheeled carriage 30 10

1296 Ball ascending to Basket

1297 "Christ carrying the Cross"

1991. Centenary of Basketball. Multicoloured.

3795	43s. Type **1296**	10	10
3796	62s. Ball level with basket mouth	10	10
3797	90s. Ball entering basket	40	10
3798	1l. Ball in basket	40	15

1991. 450th Birth Anniv of El Greco (painter). Multicoloured.

3799	43s. Type **1297**	10	10
3800	50s. "Holy Family with St. Anna"	10	10
3801	60s. "St. John of the Cross and St. John the Evangelist"	15	10
3802	62s. "St. Andrew and St. Francis"	15	10
3803	1l. "Holy Family with Magdalene"	35	15
3804	2l. "Cardinal Fernando Nino de Guevara"	85	30
MS3805	68 × 86 mm. 3l. Detail of "Holy Family with St. Anna" (different) (39 × 50 mm)	1·25	1·00

1298 Snowman, Moon, Candle, Bell and Heart

1991. Christmas. Multicoloured.

3806	30s. Type **1298**	10	10
3807	62s. Star, clover, angel, house and Christmas tree	10	10

1299 Small Pasque Flower

1991. Medicinal Plants. Multicoloured.

3808	30s.(+15s.) Pale pasque flower	10	10
3809	40s. Type **1299**	10	10
3810	55s. "Pulsatilla halleri"	15	10
3811	60s. "Aquilegia nigricans"	15	10
3812	1l. Sea buckthorn	35	15
3813	2l. Blackcurrant	85	30

No. 3808 includes a se-tenant premium-carrying label for 15s. inscribed "ACTION 2000. For Environment Protection".

1300 Greenland Seals

1991. Marine Mammals. Multicoloured.

3814	30s. Type **1300**	10	10
3815	43s. Killer whales	10	10
3816	62s. Walruses	15	10
3817	68s. Bottle-nosed dolphins	15	10
3818	1l. Mediterranean monk seals	35	15
3819	2l. Common porpoises	85	30

1301 Synagogue

1992. 500th Anniv of Jewish Settlement in Bulgaria.

3820	**1301** 1l. multicoloured	30	10

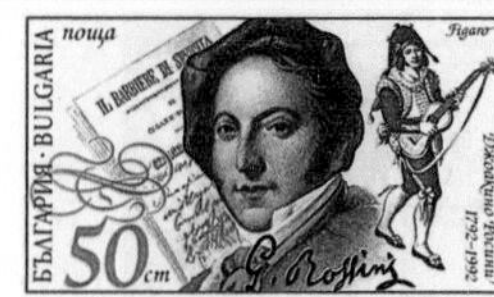

1302 Rossini, "The Barber of Seville" and Figaro

1992. Birth Bicentenary of Gioacchino Rossini (composer).

3821	**1302** 50s. multicoloured	10	10

1303 Plan of Fair

1992. Centenary of Plovdiv Fair.

3822	**1303** 1l. black and stone	20	10

1304 Volvo "740"

1992. Motor Cars. Multicoloured.

3823	30s. Type **1304**	10	10
3824	45s. Ford "Escort"	10	10
3825	50s. Fiat "Croma"	15	10
3826	50s. Mercedes Benz "600"	15	10
3827	1l. Peugeot "605"	35	15
3828	2l. B.M.W. "316"	85	30

1305 Amerigo Vespucci

1992. Explorers. Multicoloured.

3829	50s. Type **1305**	20	10
3830	50s. Francisco de Orellana	20	10
3831	1l. Ferdinand Magellan	40	10
3832	1l. Jimenez de Quesada	40	10
3833	2l. Sir Francis Drake	85	35
3834	3l. Pedro de Valdivia	1·25	50
MS3835	121 × 83 mm. 4l. Christopher Columbus	1·75	1·50

1306 Granada

1992. "Granada '92" Int Stamp Exhibition.

3836	**1306** 62s. multicoloured	25	10

1307 "Santa Maria"

1992. Europa. 500th Anniv of Discovery of America by Columbus. Multicoloured.

3837	1l. Type **1307**	50	20
3838	2l. Christopher Columbus	1·00	40

Nos. 3837/8 were issued together, se-tenant, forming a composite design.

1308 House

1992. S.O.S. Children's Village.

3839	**1308** 1l. multicoloured	40	10

1309 Long Jumping

1992. Olympic Games, Barcelona (2nd issue). Multicoloured.

3840	50s. Type **1309**	15	10
3841	50s. Swimming	15	10
3842	1l. High jumping	40	15
3843	3l. Gymnastics	1·25	50
MS3844	52 × 75 mm. 4l. Olympic Torch (vert)	1·75	1·50

1310 1902 Laurin and Klement Motor Cycle

1992. Motor Cycles. Multicoloured.

3845	30s. Type **1310**	10	10
3846	50s. 1928 Puch "200 Luxus"	10	10
3847	50s. 1931 Norton "CS 1"	10	10
3848	70s. 1950 Harley Davidson	15	10
3849	1l. 1986 Gilera "SP 01"	35	15
3850	2l. 1990 BMW "K 1"	85	30

1311 Genoa

1992. "Genova '92" International Thematic Stamp Exhibition.

3851	**1311** 1l. multicoloured	40	10

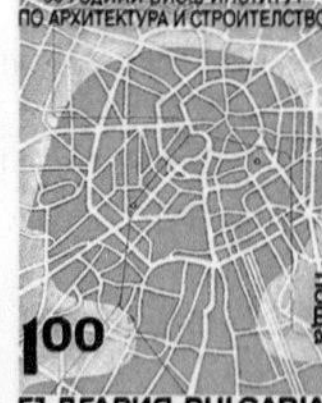

1312 Grasshopper

1313 Silhouette of Head on Town Plan

1992. Insects. Multicoloured.

3852	1l. Four-spotted libellula	10	10
3853	2l. "Raphidia notata"	20	10
3854	3l. Type **1312**	40	10
3855	4l. Stag beetle	50	10
3856	5l. Fire bug	75	10
3857	7l. Ant	1·40	25
3858	20l. Wasp	3·00	1·25
3859	50l. Praying mantis	7·50	3·00

1992. 50th Anniv of Institute of Architecture and Building.

3862	**1313** 1l. red and black	35	10

1314 Oak

1992. Trees. Multicoloured.

3863	50s. Type **1314**	10	10
3864	50s. Horse chestnut	10	10
3865	1l. Oak	40	10
3866	1l. Macedonian pine	40	10
3867	2l. Maple	80	20
3868	3l. Pear	1·25	35

1315 Embroidered Flower

1992. Centenary of Folk Museum, Sofia.

3869	**1315** 1l. multicoloured	35	10

1316 "Bulgaria" (freighter)

1992. Centenary of National Shipping Fleet. Multicoloured.

3870	30s. Type **1316**	10	10
3871	50s. "Kastor" (tanker)	20	10
3872	1l. "Geroite na Sevastopol" (train ferry)	65	25
3873	2l. "Aleko Konstantinov" (tanker)	65	25
3874	2l. "Bulgaria" (tanker)	85	40
3875	3l. "Varna" (container ship)	1·40	55

1317 Council Emblem

1992. Admission to Council of Europe.

3876	**1317** 7l. multicoloured	2·75	1·00

1319 "Santa Claus" (Ani Bacheva)

1992. Christmas. Children's Drawings. Mult.

3878	1l. Type **1319**	35	10
3879	7l. "Madonna and Child" (Georgi Petkov)	2·25	75

1320 Leopard

1322 Tengmalm's Owl

1321 Cricket

1992. Big Cats. Multicoloured.

3880	50s. Type **1320**	15	10
3881	50s. Cheetah	15	10
3882	1l. Jaguar	40	40
3883	2l. Puma	80	30
3884	2l. Tiger	80	30
3885	3l. Lion	1·25	45

1992. Sport. Multicoloured.

3886	50s. Type **1321**	10	10
3887	50s. Baseball	10	10
3888	1l. Pony and trap racing	40	10
3889	1l. Polo	40	10

3890 2l. Hockey 80 15
3891 3l. American football . . . 1·25 40

1992. Owls. Multicoloured.
3892 30s. Type **1322** 15 10
3893 50s. Tawny owl (horiz) . . . 15 10
3894 1l. Long-eared owl 40 20
3895 2l. Short-eared owl 80 35
3896 2l. Eurasian scops owl (horiz) 80 35
3897 3l. Barn owl . . . . 1·25 55

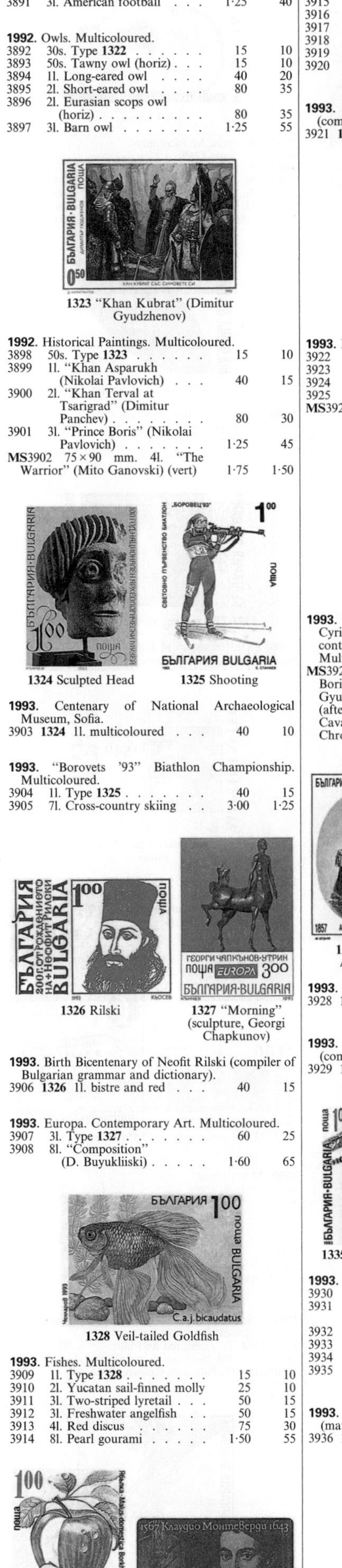

1323 "Khan Kubrat" (Dimitur Gyudzhenov)

1992. Historical Paintings. Multicoloured.
3898 50s. Type **1323** 15 10
3899 1l. "Khan Asparukh (Nikolai Pavlovich) . . . 40 15
3900 2l. "Khan Terval at Tsarigrad" (Dimitur Panchev) 80 30
3901 3l. "Prince Boris" (Nikolai Pavlovich) . . . . 1·25 45
MS3902 75 × 90 mm. 4l. "The Warrior" (Mito Ganovski) (vert) 1·75 1·50

1324 Sculpted Head **1325** Shooting

1993. Centenary of National Archaeological Museum, Sofia.
3903 **1324** 1l. multicoloured . . . 40 10

1993. "Borovets '93" Biathlon Championship. Multicoloured.
3904 1l. Type **1325** 40 15
3905 7l. Cross-country skiing . . 3·00 1·25

1326 Rilski **1327** "Morning" (sculpture, Georgi Chapkunov)

1993. Birth Bicentenary of Neofit Rilski (compiler of Bulgarian grammar and dictionary).
3906 **1326** 1l. bistre and red . . . 40 15

1993. Europa. Contemporary Art. Multicoloured.
3907 3l. Type **1327** 60 25
3908 8l. "Composition" (D. Buyukliiski) . . . . . 1·60 65

1328 Veil-tailed Goldfish

1993. Fishes. Multicoloured.
3909 1l. Type **1328** 15 10
3910 2l. Yucatan sail-finned molly 25 10
3911 3l. Two-striped lyretail . . 50 15
3912 3l. Freshwater angelfish . . 50 15
3913 4l. Red discus 75 30
3914 8l. Pearl gourami . . . . . 1·50 55

1329 Apple **1330** Monteverdi

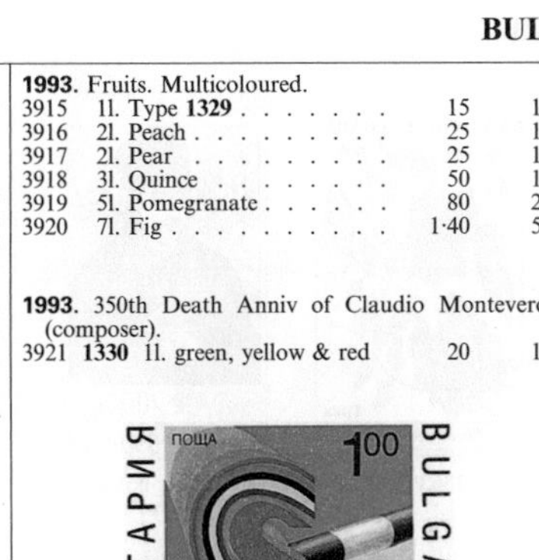

1993. Fruits. Multicoloured.
3915 1l. Type **1329** 15 10
3916 2l. Peach 25 10
3917 2l. Pear 25 10
3918 3l. Quince 50 15
3919 5l. Pomegranate 80 25
3920 7l. Fig . . . . 1·40 50

1993. 350th Death Anniv of Claudio Monteverdi (composer).
3921 **1330** 1l. green, yellow & red 20 10

1331 High Jumping

1993. Int Games for the Deaf, Sofia. Mult.
3922 1l. Type **1331** 20 10
3923 2l. Swimming 40 10
3924 3l. Cycling 50 20
3925 4l. Tennis 70 25
MS3926 86 × 75 mm. 5l. Football 80 80

1332 Baptism (from Manasses Chronicle)

1993. 1100th Anniv of Preslav and Introduction of Cyrillic Script. Sheet 113 × 110 mm containing T **1332** and similar horiz designs. Multicoloured.
MS3927 5l. Type **1332**; 5l. Prince Boris I (after Dimitur Gyudzhenov); 5l. Tsar Simeon I (after Dimitur Gyudzhenov); 5l. Cavalry charge (after Manasses Chronicle) . . . . 2·50 2·00

1333 Prince Alexander **1334** Tchaikovsky

1993. Death Centenary of Prince Alexander I.
3928 **1333** 3l. multicoloured . . . 50 20

1993. Death Centenary of Pyotr Tchaikovsky (composer).
3929 **1334** 3l. multicoloured . . . 50 20

1335 Crossbow

1336 Newton

1993. Weapons. Multicoloured.
3930 1l. Type **1335** 15 10
3931 2l. 18th-century flintlock pistol 25 10
3932 3l. Revolver 50 15
3933 3l. Luger pistol 50 15
3934 5l. Mauser rifle 80 30
3935 7l. Kalashnikov assault rifle 1·40 55

1993. 350th Birth Anniv of Sir Isaac Newton (mathematician).
3936 **1336** 1l. multicoloured . . . 15 10

1337 "100" on Stamps and Globe

1993. Centenary of Bulgarian Philately.
3937 **1337** 1l. multicoloured . . . 25 10

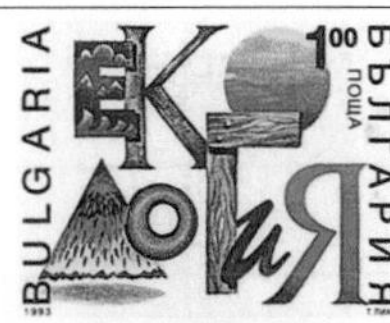

1338 "Ecology" in Cyrillic Script

1993. Ecology. Multicoloured.
3938 1l. Type **1338** 15 10
3939 7l. "Ecology" in English . . 1·00 40

1339 Mallard

1993. Hunting. Multicoloured.
3940 1l. Type **1339** 20 10
3941 1l. Common pheasant . . . 20 10
3942 2l. Red fox 25 15
3943 3l. Roe deer 50 20
3944 6l. European brown hare . . 1·00 40
3945 8l. Wild boar . . . . 1·50 55

1340 "Taurus", "Gemini" and "Cancer"

1341 Sofia Costume

1993. Christmas. Signs of the Zodiac. Mult.
3946 1l. Type **1340** 15 10
3947 1l. "Leo", "Virgo" and "Libra" 15 10
3948 7l. "Aquarius", "Pisces" and "Aries" . . . . 1·00 40
3949 7l. "Scorpio", "Sagittarius" and "Capricorn" . . . . 1·00 40

Nos. 3946/7 and 3948/9 were each issued together, se-tenant; when placed together the four stamps form a composite design.

1993. Costumes. Multicoloured.
3950 1l. Type **1341** 15 10
3951 1l. Plovdiv 15 10
3952 2l. Belograd 25 15
3953 3l. Oryakhovo 35 20
3954 3l. Shumen 35 20
3955 8l. Kurdzhali . . . . 1·25 55

1342 Freestyle Skiing

1343 "Self-portrait" and "Tsar Simeon"

1994. Winter Olympic Games, Lillehammer, Norway. Multicoloured.
3956 1l. Type **1342** 15 10
3957 2l. Speed skating 25 10
3958 3l. Two-man luge 50 15
3959 4l. Ice hockey 75 30
MS3960 59 × 90 mm. 3l. multicoloured . . . . 1·00 75

1994. Death Centenary of Nikolai Pavlovich (artist).
3961 **1343** 3l. multicoloured . . . 20 10

1344 Plesiosaurus

1994. Prehistoric Animals. Multicoloured.
3962 2l. Type **1344** 35 10
3963 3l. Archaeopteryx 50 20
3964 3l. Iguanodon 50 15
3965 4l. Edmontonia 70 25
3966 5l. Styracosaurus 85 35
3967 7l. Tyrannosaurus . . . . . 1·00 40

1345 Players (Chile, 1962)

1994. World Cup Football Championship, U.S.A. Multicoloured.
3968 3l. Type **1345** 45 10
3969 6l. Players (England, 1966) 90 30
3970 7l. Goalkeeper making save (Mexico, 1970) . . . . . 1·00 40
3971 9l. Player kicking (West Germany, 1974) . . . . . 1·25 50
MS3972 90 × 123 mm. 5l. Player punching air (Mexico, 1986) (vert); 5l. Player tackling (U.S.A., 1994) 1·50 1·25

1346 Photoelectric Analysis (Georgi Nadzhakov)

1994. Europa. Discoveries. Multicoloured.
3973 3l. Type **1346** 40 10
3974 15l. Cardiogram and heart (Prof. Ivan Mitev) . . . . 2·00 75

1347 Khristov

1994. 80th Birth Anniv of Boris Khristov (actor).
3975 **1347** 3l. multicoloured . . . 25 10

1348 Sleeping Hamster

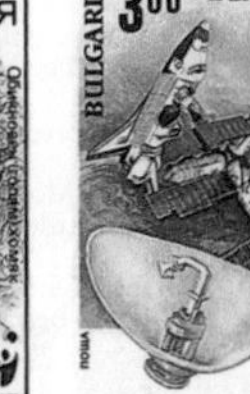

1349 Space Shuttle, Satellite and Dish Aerial

1994. The Common Hamster. Multicoloured.
3976 3l. Type **1348** 45 10
3977 7l. Hamster looking out of burrow . . . . 1·00 40
3978 10l. Hamster sitting up in grass . . . . 1·25 50
3979 15l. Hamster approaching berry . . . . 2·00 75

1994. North Atlantic Co-operation Council (North Atlantic Treaty Organization and Warsaw Pact members).
3980 **1349** 3l. multicoloured . . . 25 10

1350 Baron Pierre de Coubertin (founder of modern games)

1351 "Christ Pantocrator"

1994. Cent of International Olympic Committee.
3981 **1350** 3l. multicoloured . . . 50 20

1994. Icons. Multicoloured.
3982 2l. Type **1351** 30 10
3983 3l. "Raising of Lazarus" . . 45 10
3984 5l. "Passion of Christ" . . . 75 25
3985 7l. "Archangel Michael" . . 1·00 40
3986 8l. "Sts. Cyril and Methodius" . . . . . . 1·10 50
3987 15l. "Madonna Enthroned" 2·00 75

1352 Vechernik

1994. Christmas. Breads. Multicoloured.

3988	3l. Type **1352**	40	10
3989	15l. Bogovitsa	2·00	75

1353 "Golden Showers"

(1354)

БЪЛГАРИЯ - С БРОНЗОВИ МЕДАЛИ

1994. Roses. Multicoloured.

3990	2l. Type **1353**	30	10
3991	3l. "Caen Peace Monument"	45	10
3992	5l. "Theresa of Lisieux"	75	25
3993	7l. "Zambra 93"	1·00	40
3994	10l. "Gustave Courbet"	1·60	50
3995	15l. "Honore de Balzac	2·25	75

1994. Bulgaria's Fourth Place in World Cup Football Championship. No. **MS**3972 overprinted with T **1354** in margin.

MS3996 90 × 123 mm. 5l. multicoloured; 5l. multicoloured 5·00 5·00

1355 "AM/ASES", 1912

1994. Trams. Multicoloured.

3997	1l. Type **1355**	15	10
3998	2l. "AM/ASES", 1928	35	15
3999	3l. "M.A.N./AEG", 1931	50	20
4000	5l. "D.T.O.", 1942	80	35
4001	8l. Republika, 1951	1·75	65
4002	10l. Kosmonavt articulated tramcar set, 1961	1·90	80

1356 Petleshkov and Flag

1995. 150th Birth Anniv of Vasil Petleshkov (leader of 1876 April uprising).

4003	**1356** 3l. multicoloured	40	15

1357 Daisy growing through Cracked Helmet

1995. Europa. Peace and Freedom. Mult.

4004	3l. Type **1357**	40	15
4005	15l. Dove with olive branch on rifle barrel	1·90	75

1358 Player

1995. Centenary of Volleyball. Sheet 92 × 75 mm containing T **1358** and similar multicoloured design.

MS4006 10l. Type **1358**; 15l. Player hitting ball (vert) 3·25 3·25

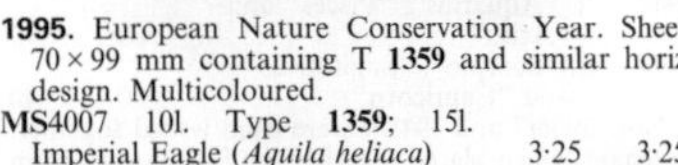

1359 Sea Lily (*Pancratium martimum*)

1995. European Nature Conservation Year. Sheet 70 × 99 mm containing T **1359** and similar horiz design. Multicoloured.

MS4007 10l. Type **1359**; 15l. Imperial Eagle (*Aquila heliaca*) 3·25 3·25

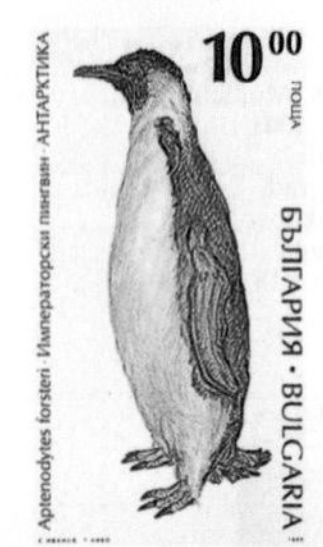

1360 Emperor Penguin

1995. Antarctic Animals. Multicoloured.

4008	1l. Shrimp (horiz)	15	10
4009	2l. Ice fish (horiz)	30	10
4010	3l. Sperm whale (horiz)	45	20
4011	5l. Weddell's seal (horiz)	70	30
4012	8l. South polar skua (horiz)	1·10	45
4013	10l. Type **1360**	1·40	55

1361 Stambolov

1995. Death Cent of Stefan Stambolov (politician).

4014	**1361** 3l. multicoloured	40	15

1362 Pole Vaulting

1995. Olympic Games, Atlanta (1996) (1st issue). Multicoloured.

4015	3l. Type **1362**	45	10
4016	7l. High jumping	1·00	40
4017	10l. Long jumping	1·40	55
4018	15l. Triple jumping	2·10	85

See also Nos. 4083/6.

1363 Pea

1365 "Ivan Nikolov-Zograf"

1995. Food Plants. Multicoloured.

4019	2l. Type **1363**	30	10
4020	3l. Chickpea	40	15
4021	3l. Soya bean	40	15
4022	4l. Spinach	55	20
4023	5l. Peanut	70	30
4024	15l. Lentil	2·10	85

1364 "100"

1995. Centenary of Organized Tourism.

4025	**1364** 1l. multicoloured	40	15

1995. Birth Centenary of Vasil Zakhariev (painter).

4026	**1365** 2l. multicoloured	30	10
4027	– 3l. multicoloured	40	15
4028	– 5l. black, brown & grn	70	30
4029	– 10l. multicoloured	1·40	55

DESIGNS: 3l. "Rila Monastery"; 5l. "Self-portrait"; 10l. "Raspberry Collectors".

1366 "Dove-Hands" holding Globe

1995. 50th Anniv of U.N.O.

4030	**1366** 3l. multicoloured	40	15

1367 Polikarpov Po-2 Biplane

1995. Aircraft. Multicoloured.

4031	3l. Type **1367**	45	20
4032	5l. Lisunov Li-2 airliner	70	30
4033	7l. Junkers Ju 52	1·00	40
4034	10l. Focke Wulf Fw 58	1·40	55

1368 Charlie Chaplin and Mickey Mouse

1995. Centenary of Motion Pictures. Mult.

4035	2l. Type **1368**	30	10
4036	3l. Marilyn Monroe and Marlene Dietrich	45	20
4037	5l. Nikolai Cherkasov and Humphrey Bogart	70	30
4038	8l. Sophia Loren and Liza Minelli	1·10	45
4039	10l. Gerard Philipe and Toshiro Mifune	1·40	55
4040	15l. Katya Paskaleva and Nevena Kokanova	2·10	85

1369 Agate

1995. Minerals. Multicoloured.

4041	1l. Type **1369**	15	10
4042	2l. Sphalerite	30	10
4043	5l. Calcite	70	30
4044	7l. Quartz	1·00	40
4045	8l. Pyromorphite	1·10	45
4046	10l. Almandine	1·40	55

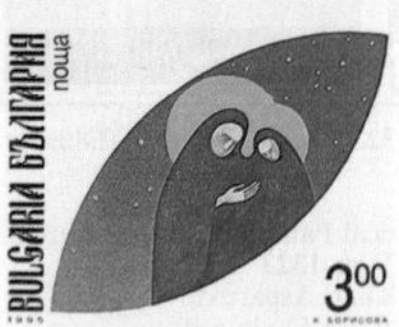

1370 Mary and Joseph

1995. Christmas. Multicoloured.

4047	3l. Type **1370**	40	15
4048	15l. Three wise men approaching stable	1·90	75

1371 "Polynesian Woman with Fruit"

1996. Birth Centenary of Kiril Tsonev (painter).

4049	**1371** 3l. multicoloured	30	10

1372 Luther (after Lucas Cranach the elder)

1996. 450th Death Anniv of Martin Luther (Protestant reformer).

4050	**1372** 3l. multicoloured	30	10

1373 Preobrazhenie

1374 Bulgarian National Bank

1996. Monasteries.

4051	**1373** 3l. green	20	10
4052	– 5l. red	35	15
4053	– 10l. blue	70	30
4054	– 20l. orange	1·40	55
4055	– 25l. brown	1·75	70
4056	– 40l. purple	2·75	1·10

DESIGNS: 5l. Arapov; 10l. Dryanovo; 20l. Bachkov; 25l. Troyan; 40l. Zograf.

1996. 5th Anniv of European Reconstruction and Development Bank.

4063	**1374** 7l. green, red and blue	45	20
4064	– 30l. blue, red & purple	1·90	75

DESIGN: 30l. Palace of Culture, Sofia.

1375 Yew

1996. Conifers. Multicoloured.

4065	5l. Type **1375**	35	15
4066	8l. Silver fir	60	25
4067	10l. Norway spruce	70	30
4068	20l. Scots pine	1·40	55
4069	25l. "Pinus heldreichii"	1·75	70
4070	40l. Juniper	3·00	1·25

1376 Battle Scene and Mourning Women

1377 Modern Officer's Parade Uniform

1996. 120th Anniversaries. Multicoloured.
4071 10l. Type **1376** (April uprising) 65 25
4072 40l. Khristo Botev and script (poet, death anniv) (horiz) . . . . 2·50 1·00

1996. Military Uniforms. Multicoloured.
4073 5l. Type **1377** 35 15
4074 8l. Second World War combat uniform 60 25
4075 10l. Balkan War uniform . . 70 30
4076 20l. Guard officer's ceremonial uniform . . . 1·40 55
4077 25l. Serbo-Bulgarian War officer's uniform . . . . 1·75 70
4078 40l. Russo-Turkish War soldier's uniform . . . . 3·00 1·75

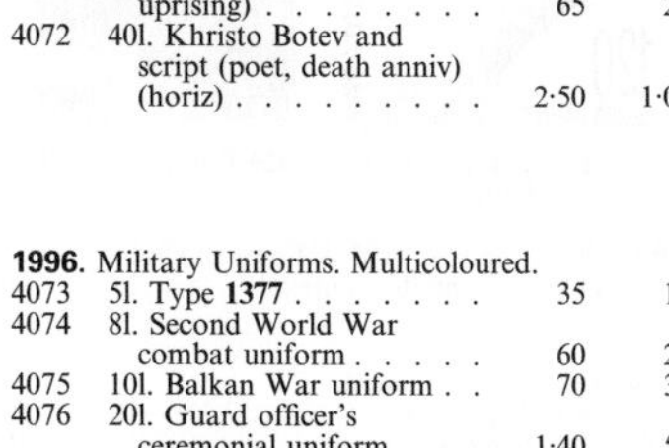
1378 Monument

1996. 50th Anniv of the Republic.
4079 **1378** 10l. multicoloured . . . 70 30

1379 Elisaveta Bagryana (poet)

1996. Europa. Famous Women. Multicoloured.
4080 10l. Type **1379** 65 25
4081 40l. Katya Popova (opera singer) . . . . 2·50 1·00

1380 Player

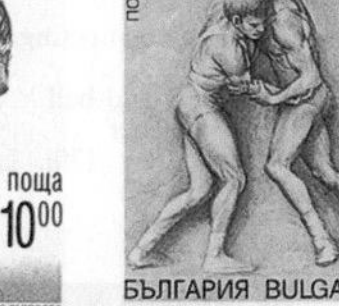
1381 Nikola Stanchev (wrestling, Melbourne 1956)

1996. European Football Championship, England. Sheet 71 × 86 mm containing T **1380** and similar vert design. Multicoloured.
MS4082 10l. Type **1380**; 15l. Player (different) . . . . 1·00 1·00

1996. Olympic Games, Atlanta (2nd issue). Bulgarian Medal Winners. Multicoloured.
4083 5l. Type **1381** 20 10
4084 8l. Boris Georgiev (boxing, Helsinki 1952) 35 10
4085 10l. Ivanka Khristova (putting the shot, Montreal 1976) 40 15
4086 25l. Z. Iordanova and S. Otsetova (double sculls, Montreal 1976) . . . . . . 1·00 40
MS4087 89 × 68 mm. 15l. Olympic Stadium, Athens, 1896 . . . . 60 60

1382 "The Letter" (detail)

1384 St. Ivan

1383 Water Flea

1996. 250th Birth Anniv of Francisco Goya (painter). Multicoloured.
4088 5l. Detail of fresco 20 10
4089 8l. Type **1382** 35 10
4090 26l. "3rd of May 1808 in Madrid" (detail) . . . . 1·10 45
4091 40l. "Neighbours on a Balcony" (detail) . . . . 1·75 70
MS4092 99 × 73 mm. 10l. "Clothed Maja" (50 × 26 mm); 15l. "Naked Maja" (50 × 26 mm) . . . . . 1·00 1·00

1996. Aquatic Life. Multicoloured.
4093 5l. Type **1383** 20 10
4094 10l. Common water louse 45 15
4095 12l. European river crayfish 50 20
4096 25l. Prawn . . . . 1·10 45
4097 30l. "Cumella limicola" . . 1·25 50
4098 40l. Mediterranean shore crab . . . . 1·75 70

1996. 1050th Death Anniv of Ivan Rilski (founder of Rila Monastery). Sheet 56 × 87 mm.
MS4099 **1384** 10l. multicoloured 40 15

1385 Tryavna

1996. Houses.
4100 **1385** 10l. brown and stone 30 10
4101 – 15l. red and yellow . . 45 15
4102 – 30l. green and yellow 90 35
4103 – 50l. violet and mauve 1·50 60
4104 – 60l. green and lt green 1·75 70
4105 – 100l. ultramarine & bl 3·00 1·25
DESIGNS: 15l. Nesebur; 30l. Tryavna (different); 50l. Koprivshtitsa; 60l. Plovdiv; 100l. Koprivshtitsa (different).

1386 "Philadelphia", 1836

1996. Steam Locomotives. Multicoloured.
4106 5l. Type **1386** 15 10
4107 10l. "Jenny Lind", 1847 . . 30 10
4108 12l. "Liverpool", 1848 . . . 35 15
4109 26l. "Anglet", 1876 . . . . 80 30

1387 Anniversary Emblem and Academy

1996. Centenary of National Arts Academy.
4110 **1387** 15l. black and yellow 40 15

1388 Sword and Miniature from "Chronicle of Ivan Skilitsa"

1996. 1100th Anniv of Tsar Simeon's Victory over the Turks. Multicoloured.
4111 10l. Type **1388** 25 10
4112 40l. Dagger and right-hand detail of miniature . . . . 1·00 40
Nos. 4111/12 were issued together, se-tenant, forming a composite design.

1389 Fishes and Diver (Dilyana Lokmadzhieva)

1996. 50th Anniv of U.N.I.C.E.F. Children's Paintings. Multicoloured.
4113 7l. Type **1389** 20 10
4114 15l. Circus (Velislava Dimitrova) 40 15
4115 20l. Man and artist's pallet (Miglena Nikolova) . . . 55 20
4116 60l. Family meal (Darena Dencheva) . . . . 1·60 65

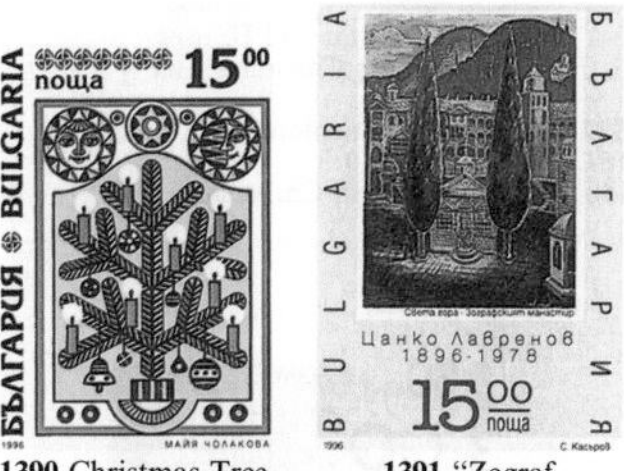
1390 Christmas Tree

1391 "Zograf Monastery"

1996. Christmas. Multicoloured.
4117 15l. Type **1390** 40 15
4118 60l. Star over basilica and Christmas tree . . . . . 1·50 60

1996. Birth Centenary of Tsanko Lavrenov (painter).
4119 **1391** 15l. multicoloured . . . 40 15

1392 Pointer

1997. Puppies. Multicoloured.
4120 5l. Type **1392** 15 10
4121 7l. Chow chow 20 10
4122 25l. Carakachan dog 70 30
4123 50l. Basset hound . . . . . 1·40 55

1393 Bell

1997. 150th Birth Anniv of Alexander Graham Bell (telephone pioneer).
4124 **1393** 30l. multicoloured . . . 50 20

1394 Man drinking

1395 Lady March (symbol of spring)

1997. Birth Centenary of Ivan Milev (painter). Murals from Kazaluk. Multicoloured.
4125 5l. Type **1394** 10 10
4126 15l. Woman praying 25 10
4127 30l. Reaper 45 20
4128 60l. Mother and child . . . 90 35

1997. Europa. Tales and Legends. Mult.
4129 120l. Type **1395** 25 10
4130 600l. St. George (national symbol) 85 35

1396 Kisimov in Character

1997. Birth Cent of Konstantin Kisimov (actor).
4131 **1396** 120l. multicoloured . . 20 10

1397 Von Stephan

1398 Old Town, Nesebur

1997. Death Centenary of Heinrich von Stephan (founder of U.P.U.).
4132 **1397** 60l. multicoloured . . . 10 10

1997. Historic Sights.
4133 **1398** 80l. brown and black 10 10
4134 – 200l. violet and black 15 10
4135 – 300l. yellow and black 20 10
4136 – 500l. green and black 25 10
4137 – 600l. yellow and black 35 15
4138 – 1000l. orange and black 55 20
DESIGNS: 200l. Sculpture, Ivanovski Church; 300l. Christ (detail of icon), Boyana Church; 500l. Horseman (stone relief), Madara; 600l. Figure of woman (carving from sarcophagus), Sveshary; 1000l. Tomb decoration, Kazanlak.

1399 Gaetano Donizetti

1997. Composers' Anniversaries. Multicoloured.
4139 120l. Type **1399** (birth bicentenary) 20 10
4140 120l. Franz Schubert (birth bicentenary) 20 10
4141 120l. Felix Mendelssohn-Bartholdy (150th death anniv) 20 10
4142 120l. Johannes Brahms (death centenary) 20 10

1400 "Trifolium rubens"

1997. Flowers in the Red Book. Multicoloured.
4143 80l. Type **1400** 15 10
4144 100l. "Tulipa hageri" . . . 25 10
4145 120l. "Inula spiraeifolia" . . 45 20
4146 200l. Thin-leafed peony . . 60 25

1401 Anniversary Emblem

1402 Georgiev

1997. 50th Anniv of Civil Aviation.
4147 **1401** 120l. multicoloured . . 20 10

1997. Death Centenary of Evlogii Georgiev.
4148 **1402** 120l. multicoloured . . 20 10

1403 Show Jumping and Running

1997. World Modern Pentathlon Championship, Sofia. Multicoloured.
4149 60l. Type **1403** 10 10
4150 80l. Fencing and swimming 15 10
4151 100l. Running and fencing 25 10
4152 120l. Shooting and swimming 40 15
4153 200l. Show jumping and shooting 60 25

1404 St. Basil's Cathedral

1997. 850th Anniv of Moscow and "Moskva 97" International Stamp Exhibition. Sheet 87 × 96 mm.
MS4154 **1404** 120l. multicoloured 55 25

1405 D 2500 M Boat Engine

1997. Centenary of Diesel Engine. Multicoloured.
4155 80l. Type **1405** 10 10
4156 100l. D 2900 T tractor engine 15 10
4157 120l. D 3900 A truck engine 25 10
4158 200l. D 2500 K fork-lift truck engine 35 15

1406 Goddess with Mural Crown

1997. 43rd General Assembly of Atlantic Club, Sofia.
4159 **1406** 120l. mve, bl & ultram 25 10
4160 – 120l. grn, bl & ultram 25 10
4161 – 120l. brn, bl & ultram 25 10
4162 – 120l. vio, bl & ultram 25 10
DESIGNS: No. 4160, Eagle on globe; 4161, Venue; 4162, Venue (different).

1407 Cervantes and Don Quixote with Sancho

1997. 450th Birth Anniv of Miguel de Cervantes (writer).
4163 **1407** 120l. multicoloured . . 30 10

1408 Raztsvetnikov

1997. Birth Centenary of Asen Raztsvetnikov (writer and translator).
4164 **1408** 120l. multicoloured . . 30 10

1409 Fragment of Tombstone

1997. Millenary of Coronation of Tsar Samuel. Multicoloured.
4165 120l. Type **1409** 20 10
4166 600l. Tsar Samuel and knights in battle . . . . 1·10 45

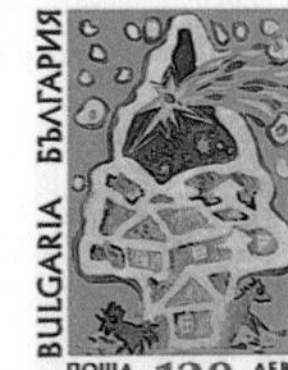
1410 Star and Houses forming Christmas Tree

1997. Christmas. Multicoloured.
4167 120l. Type **1410** 15 10
4168 600l. Stable with Christmas tree roof . . . . 1·00 40

1411 Speed Skating

1997. Winter Olympic Games, Nagano, Japan (1998). Multicoloured.
4169 60l. Type **1411** 10 10
4170 80l. Skiing 15 10
4171 120l. Shooting (biathlon) . . 25 10
4172 600l. Ice skating . . . . . . 1·25 50

1412 Radiometric System R-400

1997. 25th Anniv of Bulgarian Space Experiments. Sheet 87 × 68 mm.
MS4173 **1412** 120l. multicoloured 75 40

1413 State Arms

1997.
4174 **1413** 120l. multicoloured . . 20 10

1414 Botev (after B. Petrov) 1415 Brecht

1998. 150th Birth and 120th Death (1996) Anniv of Khristo Botev (poet and revolutionary).
4175 **1414** 120l. multicoloured . . 20 10

1998. Birth Cent of Bertolt Brecht (playwright).
4176 **1415** 120l. multicoloured . . 20 10

1416 Arrows

1998. Cent of Bulgarian Telegraph Agency.
4177 **1416** 120l. multicoloured . . 20 10

1417 Barn Swallow at Window

1998. 120th Birth Anniv of Aleksandur Bozhinov (children's illustrator). Multicoloured.
4178 120l. Type **1417** 25 10
4179 120l. Blackbird with backpack on branch . . . 25 10
4180 120l. Father Frost and children 25 10
4181 120l. Maiden Rositsa in field holding hands up to rain 25 10

1418 Tsar Alexander II 1419 Christ ascending and Hare pulling Cart of Eggs

1998. 120th Anniv of Liberation from Turkey. Multicoloured.
4182 120l. Type **1418** 15 10
4183 600l. Independence monument, Ruse . . . . 1·00 40

1998. Easter.
4184 **1419** 120l. multicoloured . . 20 10

1420 Torch Bearer

1998. 75th Anniv of Bulgarian Olympic Committee.
4185 **1420** 120l. multicoloured . . 20 10

1421 Map of Participating Countries

1998. Phare International Programme for Telecommunications and Post.
4186 **1421** 120l. multicoloured . . 20 10

1422 Girls in Folk Costumes

1998. Europa. National Festivals. Multicoloured.
4187 120l. Type **1422** 20 10
4188 600l. Boys wearing dance masks . . . . 1·00 40

ПЪРВИ ЗЛАТЕН МЕДАЛ ЗА БЪЛГАРИЯ Е. ДАФОВСКА
(1423)

1424 "Dante and Virgil in Hell"

1998. Winning of Gold Medal in 15km Biathlon by Ekaterina Dafovska at Winter Olympic Games, Nagano. No. 4171 optd with T **1423**.
4189 120l. multicoloured 15 10

1998. Birth Bicentenary of Eugene Delacroix (artist).
4190 **1424** 120l. multicoloured . . 15 10

1425 Footballer and Club Badge 1426 European Tabby

1998. 50th Anniv of TsSKA Football Club.
4191 **1425** 120l. multicoloured . . 15 10

1998. Cats. Multicoloured.
4192 60l. Type **1426** 10 10
4193 80l. Siamese 15 10
4194 120l. Exotic shorthair . . . 25 10
4195 600l. Birman . . . . 1·10 45

1427 "Oh, You are Jealous!"

1998. 150th Birth Anniv of Paul Gauguin (artist).
4196 **1427** 120l. multicoloured . . 15 10

1428 Khilendarski-Bozveli

1998. 150th Death Anniv of Neofit Khilendarski-Bozveli (priest and writer).
4197 **1428** 120l. multicoloured . . 15 10

1429 Tackling

1998. World Cup Football Championship, France. Multicoloured.
4198 60l. Type **1429** 10 10
4199 180l. Players competing for ball 15 10
4200 120l. Players and ball . . . 25 10
4201 600l. Goalkeeper . . . . . 1·10 40
MS4202 68 × 91 mm. 120l. Lion, ball and Eiffel Tower 75 40

1430 A. Aleksandrov

1998. 10th Anniv of Second Soviet–Bulgarian Space Flight.
4203 **1430** 120l. multicoloured . . 15 10

1431 Vasco da Gama

1998. "Expo '98" World's Fair, Lisbon. 500th Anniv of Vasco da Gama's Voyage to India. Multicoloured.
4204 600l. Type **1431** 80 30
4205 600l. "Sao Gabriel" (Vasco da Gama's ship) . . . . 1·00 40
Nos. 4204/5 were issued together, se-tenant, forming a composite design.

1432 Focke Wolf FW 61, 1937

1998. Helicopters. Multicoloured.
4206 80l. Type **1432** 10 10
4207 100l. Sikorsky R-4, 1943 . . 10 10
4208 120l. Mil Mi-V12, 1970 . . 15 10
4209 200l. McDonnell-Douglas MD-900, 1995 . . . . . 35 10

1433 Mediterranean Monk Seal (*Monachus monachus*)

1998. International Year of the Ocean. Sheet 67 × 88 mm.
MS4210 **1433** 120l. multicoloured 75 40

1434 Talev

1998. Birth Centenary of Dimitur Talev (writer).
4211 **1434** 180l. multicoloured . . 20 10

1435 Aleksandur Malinov (Prime Minister, 1931)

1436 "Limenitis redukta" and "Ligularia sibirica"

1998. 90th Anniv of Independence.
4212 **1435** 180l. black, blue & yell 25 10

1998. Butterflies and Flowers. Multicoloured.
4213 60l. Type **1436** 10 10
4214 180l. Painted lady and "Anthemis macrantha" 25 10
4215 200l. Red admiral and "Trachelium jacquinii" . . 25 10
4216 600l. "Anthocharis gruneri" and "Geranium tuberosum" 95 40

1437 Smirnenski

1998. Birth Cent of Khristo Smirnenski (writer).
4217 **1437** 180l. multicoloured . . 25 10

1438 Silhouette of Man

1998. 50th Anniv of Universal Declaration of Human Rights.
4218 **1438** 180l. multicoloured . . 25 10

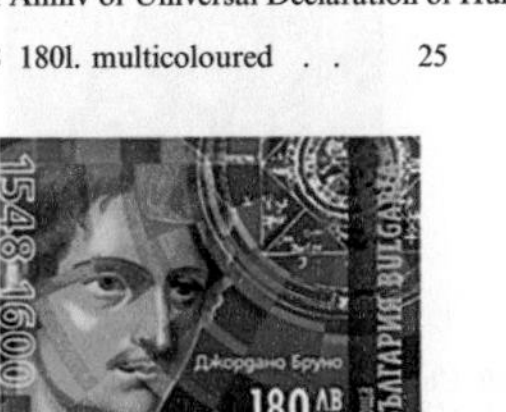

1439 Bruno

1998. 450th Birth Anniv of Giordano Bruno (scholar).
4219 **1439** 180l. multicoloured . . 25 10

1440 Man diving through Heart ("I Love You")

1998. Greetings Stamps. Multicoloured.
4220 180l. Type **1440** 25 10
4221 180l. Making wine (holiday) (vert) 25 10
4222 180l. Man in chalice (birthday) (vert) 25 10
4223 180l. Waiter serving wine (name day) (vert) 25 10

1441 Madonna and Child

1998. Christmas.
4224 **1441** 180l. multicoloured . . 25 10

1442 Geshov

1999. 150th Birth Anniv of Ivan Evstratiev Geshov (politician).
4225 **1442** 180l. multicoloured . . 25 10

1443 National Assembly Building, Sofia

1999. 120th Anniv of Third Bulgarian State. Mult.
4226 180l. Type **1443** 25 10
4227 180l. Council of Ministers 25 10
4228 180l. Statue of Justice (Supreme Court of Appeal) 25 10
4229 180l. Coins (National Bank) 25 10
4230 180l. Army 25 10
4231 180l. Lion emblem of Sofia and lamp post 25 10

1444 Georgi Karakashev (stage designer) and Set of "Kismet"

1999. Birth Centenaries. Multicoloured.
4232 180l. Type **1444** 25 10
4233 200l. Bencho Obreshkov (artist) and "Lodki" . . . 25 10
4234 300l. Score and Asen Naidenov (conductor of Sofia Opera) 35 15
4235 600l. Pancho Vladigerov (composer) and score of "Vardar" 75 30

1445 Rainbow Lory (*Trichoglossus haematodus*)

1999. "Bulgaria '99" European Stamp Exhibition. Parrots. Sheet 100 × 110 mm containing T **1445** and similar vert designs. Multicoloured.
MS4236 600l. Type **1445**; 600l. Eastern rosella; 600l. Budgerigar; 600l. Green-winged macaw . . 4·25 3·50

1446 Sun and Emblem

1999. 50th Anniv of North Atlantic Treaty Organization.
4237 **1446** 180l. multicoloured . . 25 10

1447 Decorated Eggs

1999. Easter.
4238 **1447** 180l. multicoloured . . 25 10

1448 Red-crested Pochard and Ropotamo Reserve

1999. Europa. Parks and Gardens. Multicoloured.
4239 180l. Type **1448** 25 10
4240 600l. Central Balkan National Park 75 30

1449 Albrecht Durer (self-portrait) and Nuremberg

1999. "iBRA '99" International Stamp Exhibition, Nuremberg, Germany.
4241 **1449** 600l. multicoloured . . 75 30

1450 Anniversary Emblem

1999. 50th Anniv of Council of Europe.
4242 **1450** 180l. multicoloured . . 25 10

1451 Honore de Balzac (novelist)

1999. Birth Anniversaries. Multicoloured.
4243 180l. Type **1451** (bicentenary) 25 10
4244 200l. Johann Wolfgang von Goethe (poet and playwright) (250th anniv) 25 10
4245 300l. Aleksandr Pushkin (poet) (bicentenary) . . . 35 15
4246 600l. Diego de Silva Velazquez (painter) (400th anniv) 75 30

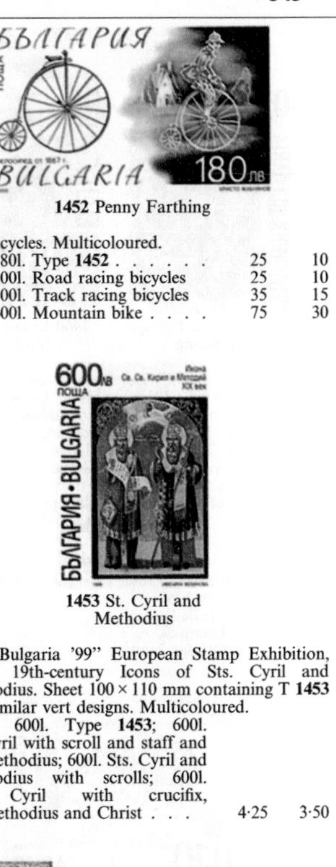

1452 Penny Farthing

1999. Bicycles. Multicoloured.
4247 180l. Type **1452** 25 10
4248 200l. Road racing bicycles 25 10
4249 300l. Track racing bicycles 35 15
4250 600l. Mountain bike 75 30

1453 St. Cyril and Methodius

1999. "Bulgaria '99" European Stamp Exhibition, Sofia. 19th-century Icons of Sts. Cyril and Methodius. Sheet 100 × 110 mm containing T **1453** and similar vert designs. Multicoloured.
MS4251 600l. Type **1453**; 600l. St. Cyril with scroll and staff and St. Methodius; 600l. Sts. Cyril and Methodius with scrolls; 600l. St. Cyril with crucifix, St. Methodius and Christ . . . 4·25 3·50

1454 Sopot Monastery Fountain

1456 Cracked Green Russula

1455 *Oxytropis urumovii*

1999. Fountains.
4252 **1454** 1st. light brown 10 10
4254 – 8st. green and black . . 10 10
4255 – 10st. deep brown . . . 10 10
4257 – 18st. light blue 10 10
4258 – 20st. bright blue . . . 10 10
4260 – 60st. brown and black 85 60
DESIGNS: 8st. Peacock Fountain, Karlovo; 10st. Peev Fountain, Kopivshtitsa; 18st. Sandanski Fountain; 20st. Eagle Owl Fountain, Karlovo; 60st. Fountain, Sokolski Monastery.

1999. "Bulgaria '99" European Stamp Exhibition, Sofia (2nd issue). Flowers in Pirin National Park. Sheet 109 × 100 mm containing T **1455** and similar horiz designs. Multicoloured.
MS4265 60st. Type **1455**; 60st. Bellflower; 60st. Iris; 60st. Spotted gentian . . . . 4·25 3·50

1999. Fungi. Multicoloured.
4266 10st. Type **1456** 10 10
4267 18st. Field mushroom . . . 25 20
4268 20st. "Hygrophorus russula" 30 20
4269 60st. Wood blewit 85 60

1457 Diagram of path of Eclipse

1458 Four-leaved Clover

1999. Solar Eclipse (11 Aug 1999). Sheet 90 × 90 mm.
MS4270 **1457** 20st. multicoloured 1·20 80

1999. Centenary of Organized Peasant Movement.
4271 **1458** 18st. multicoloured . . 25 20

1459 1884 25st. Postage Due Stamp
1460 Lesser Grey Shrike

1999. "Bulgaria '99" European Stamp Exhibition, Sofia (3rd issue). 125th Anniv of Universal Postal Union. Sheet 110 × 102 mm containing T **1459** and similar vert deisgns. Multicoloured.

MS4272 60st. Type **1459**; 60st. Dove and hand with letter; 60st. Globe and left half of messenger; 60st. Right half of messenger with letter and globe . . . . 3·50 2·75

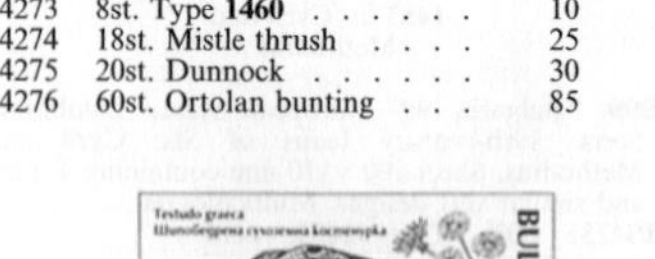

1999. Song Birds and their Eggs. Multicoloured.

4273 8st. Type **1460** 10 10
4274 18st. Mistle thrush 25 20
4275 20st. Dunnock 30 20
4276 60st. Ortolan bunting . . . 85 60

1461 Greek Tortoise

1999. Reptiles. Multicoloured.

4277 10st. Type **1461** 10 10
4278 18st. Swamp turtle 30 20
4279 30st. Hermann's tortoise . . 35 25
4280 60st. Caspian turtle 85 60

1462 Boxing (16 medals)

1999. Bulgarian Olympic Medal Winning Sports. Multicoloured.

4281 10st. Type **1462** 10 10
4282 20st. High jumping (17 medals) 30 20
4283 30st. Weightlifting (31 medals) 35 25
4284 60st. Wrestling (60 medals) 85 60

1463 Police Light and Emblem

1999. 10th European Police Conference.

4285 **1463** 18st. multicoloured . . 20 10

1464 Jug
1465 Virgin and Child

1999. Gold Artefacts from Panagyurishte.

4286 **1464** 2st. brown and green 10 10
4287 – 3st. brown and green 10 10
4288 – 5st. brown and blue . 10 10
4289 – 30st. brown and violet 20 10
4290 – 1l. brown and red . . . 90 35

DESIGNS: 3st. Human figures around top of drinking horn; 5st. Bottom of chamois-shaped drinking horn; 30st. Decorated handle and spout; 1l. Head-shaped jug.

1999. Christmas. Religious Icons. Multicoloured.

4291 18st. Type **1465** 15 10
4292 60st. Jesus Christ 85 30

1466 Scout beside Fire

1999. Scouts. Multicoloured.

4293 10st. Type **1466** 10 10
4294 18st. Scout helping child . . 15 10
4295 30st. Scout saluting 30 10
4296 60st. Girl and boy scouts . . 85 30

1467 Emblem
1469 White Stork (*Ciconia ciconia*)

1468 Emblem and Flag

1999. "Expo 2005" World's Fair, Aichi, Japan.

4297 **1467** 18st. multicoloured . . 20 10

2000. Bulgarian Membership of European Union.

4298 **1468** 18st. multicoloured . . 10 10

2000. Endangered Species. Sheet 80 × 60 mm.

MS4299 **1469** 60st. multicoloured 1·50 1·10

1470 Peter Beron and Scientific Instruments

2000. Birth Anniversaries. Multicoloured.

4300 10st. Type **1470** (scientist, bicentenary) 10 10
4301 20st. Zakhari Stoyanov (writer, 150th anniv) . . . 15 10
4302 50st. Kolyo Ficheto (architect, bicentenary) . . 30 10

1471 Madonna and Child with Circuit Board

2000. Europa. Multicoloured.

4303 18st. Type **1471** 10 10
4304 60st. Madonna and Child (Leonardo da Vinci) with circuit board 40 10

1472 Judo

2000. Olympic Games, Sydney. Multicoloured.

4305 10st. Type **1472** 10 10
4306 18st. Tennis 10 10
4307 20st. Pistol shooting 15 10
4308 60st. Long jump 40 10

1473 *Puss in Boots* (Charles Perrault)

2000. Children's Fairytales. Multicoloured.

4309 18st. Type **1473** 10 10
4310 18st. *Little Red Riding Hood* (Brothers Grimm) 10 10
4311 18st. *Thumbelina* (Hans Christian Andersen) . . . 10 10

1474 "Friends" (detail) (Assen Vasiliev)

2000. Artists Birth Centenaries. Art. Multicoloured.

4312 18st. Type **1474** 10 10
4313 18st. "All Soul's Day" (detail) (Pencho Georgiev) 10 10
4314 18st. "Veliko Tunovo" (detail) (Ivan Khristov) 10 10
4315 18st. "At the Fountain" (sculpture) (detail) (Ivan Funev) 10 10

1475 Roman Mosaic (detail), Stara Zagora

2000. "EXPO 2000" World's Fair, Hanover, Germany.

4316 **1475** 60st. multicoloured . . 40 10

1476 Johannes Gutenberg (inventor of printing) and Printed Characters

2000. Anniversaries. Multicoloured.

4317 10st. Type **1476** (600th birth anniv) 10 10
4318 18st. Johann Sebastian Bach (composer, 250th death anniv) 10 10
4319 20st. Guy de Maupassant (writer, 150th birth anniv) 15 10
4320 60st. Antoine de Saint-Exupery (writer and aviator, birth centenary) 40 10

1477 *La Jeune* (Lebardy-Juillot airship) and Eiffel Tower, 1903

2000. Centenary of First Zeppelin Flight. Airship Development. Multicoloured.

4321 10st. Type **1477** 10 10
4322 18st. LZ-13 *Hansa* (Zeppelin airship) over Cologne . . 10 10
4323 20st. N-1 *Norge* over Rome 15 10
4324 60st. *Graf Zeppelin* over Sofia 40 10

1478 Vazov and Text

2000. 150th Birth Anniv of Ivan Vazov (writer).

4325 **1478** 18st. multicoloured . . 10 10

1479 Letter "e" with Hands

2000. 25th Anniv of Organization for Security and Co-operation in Europe. Helsinki Final Act (establishing governing principles). Sheet 68 × 72 mm containing T **1479** and similar horiz design. Multicoloured.

MS4326 20st. Type **1479**; 20st. Three "e's" . . . . 1·50 1·10

1480 St. Atanasii Church, Startsevo

2000. Churches.

4327 **1480** 22st. black and blue . . 15 10
4328 – 24st. black and mauve 15 10
4329 – 50st. black and yellow 30 10
4330 – 65st. black and green 40 10
4331 – 3l. black and orange 2·00 40
4332 – 5l. black and rose . . 3·00 80

DESIGNS: 24st. St. Clement of Orhid, Sofia; 50st. Mary of the Ascension, Sofia; 65st. St. Nedelya, Nedelino; 3l. Mary of the Ascension, Sofia (different), Sofia; 5l. Mary of the Ascension, Pamporovo.

1481 Ibex (*Capra ibex*)

2000. Animals. Multicoloured.

4333 10st. Type **1481** 10 10
4334 22st. Argali (*Ovis ammon*) 15 10
4335 30st. European bison (*Bison bonasus*) 20 10
4336 65st. Yak (*Bos grunniens*) . . 40 10

1482 Field Gladiolus (*Gladiolus segetum*)
1484 Order of Gallantry, 1880

1483 Crowd and Emblem

2000. Spring Flowers. Multicoloured.

4337 10st. Type **1482** 10 10
4338 22st. Liverwort (*Hepatica nobilis*) 15 10
4339 30st. Pheasant's eye (*Adonis vernalis*) 20 10
4340 65st. Peacock anemone (*Anemone pavonina*) . . . 40 10

2000. 50th Anniv of European Convention on Human Rights.

4341 **1483** 65st. multicoloured . . 40 10

2000. Medals. Multicoloured.

4342 12st. Type **1484** 10 10
4343 22st. Order of St. Aleksandu, 1882 . . . 15 10
4344 30st. Order of Merit, 1891 20 10
4345 65st. Order of Cyril and Methodius, 1909 . . . . 40 10

1485 Prince Boris-Mihail

2000. Bimillenary of Christianity. Multicoloured.
4346 22st. Type **1485** 15 10
4347 22st. St. Sofroni Vrachanski 15 10
4348 65st. Mary and Child (detail) 40 10
4349 65st. Antim I 40 10

1486 Seal

2000. 120th Anniv of Supreme Audit Office.
4350 **1486** 22st. multicoloured . . 15 10

1487 Microchip, Planets and "The Proportions of Man" (Leonardo DaVinci)

2001. New Millennium.
4351 **1487** 22st. multicoloured . . 15 10

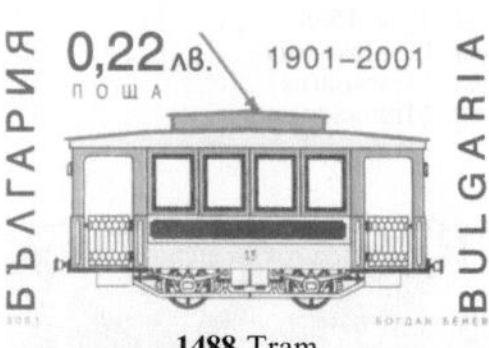

1488 Tram

2001. Centenary of the Electrification of Bulgarian Transport. Multicoloured.
4352 22st. Type **1488** 15 10
4353 65st. Train carriages 45 10

1489 Muscat Grapes and Evsinograd Palace

2001. Viticulture. Multicoloured.
4354 12st. Type **1489** 10 10
4355 22st. Gumza grapes and Baba Vida Fortress . . . 15 10
4356 30st. Shiroka Melnishka Loza grapes and Melnik Winery 20 10
4357 65st. Mavrud grapes and Asenova Krepost Fortress 45 10

1490 “ ” and Microcircuits

2001. Information Technology. Sheet 82 x 95 mm containing T **1490** and similar horiz design. Multicoloured.
MS4358 Type **1490**; 65st. John Atanasoff (computer pioneer) and ABC 45 45

1491 Southern Europe and Emblem

2001. 10th Anniv of the Atlantic Club of Bulgaria. Sheet 87 × 67 mm.
MS4359 **1491** 65st. multicoloured 45 45

1492 Eagle and Lakes, Rila

2001. Europa. Water Resources. Multicoloured.
4360 22st. Type **1492** 15 10
4361 65st. Cave and waterfall, Rhodope 45 10

1493 Building, Bridge and Kableschkov

2001. 125th Anniv of the April Uprising and 150th Birth Anniv of Todor Kableschkov (revolutionary leader).
4362 **1493** 22st. multicoloured . . 15 10

1494 Juvenile Egyptian Vulture in Flight

2001. Endangered Species. Egyptian Vulture (*Neophron percopterus*). Multicoloured.
4363 12st. Type **1494** 10 10
4364 22st. Juvenile landing . . . 15 10
4365 30st. Adult and chick . . . 20 10
4366 65st. Adult and eggs 45 10

1495 Georgi (Gundy) Asparuchov (footballer)

2001. Sportsmen. Multicoloured.
4367 22st. Type **1495** 15 10
4368 30st. Dancho (Dan) Kolev (wrestler) 20 10
4369 65st. Gen. Krum Lekarski (equestrian) 45 10

1496 Rainbow and People

2001. 50th Anniv United Nations High Commissioner for Refugees.
4370 **1496** 65st. multicoloured . . 45 10

1497 Alexander Zhendov

2001. Artists Birth Centenaries. Multicoloured.
4371 22st. Type **1497** 15 10
4372 65st. Ilya Beshkov 45 10

1498 Court Seal

2001. 10th Anniv of Constitutional Court.
4373 **1498** 25st. multicoloured . . 15 10

1499 Flags

2001. North Atlantic Treaty Organization Summit, Sofia. Sheet 116 × 111 mm containing T **1499** and similar horiz designs.
MS4374 12st. Type **1499**; 24st. Streamer of flags; 25st. Flags in upper right semi-circle; 65st. Flags in upper left semi-circle 85 85

1500 Children encircling Globe

2001. United Nations Year of Dialogue among Civilizations.
4375 **1500** 65st. multicoloured . . 45 10

1501 Black Sea Turbot (*Scopthalmus maeoticus*)

2001. International Day for the Protection of the Black Sea. Sheet 73 × 91 mm.
MS4376 **1501** 65st. multicoloured 45 10

1502 The Nativity

1503 Cape Shabla Lighthouse

2001. Christmas.
4377 **1502** 25st. multicoloured . . 15 10

2001. Lighthouses.
4378 **1503** 25st. red and green . . 15 10
4379 – 32st. blue and yellow 20 10
DESIGN: 32st. Kaliakra Cape lighthouse.

1504 Monastery Buildings

2001. Zographu Monastery Mount Athos. Sheet 85 × 105 mm containing T **1504** and similar horiz design. Multicoloured.
MS4380 25st. Type **1504**; 65st. Icon 60 60

1505 Father Christmas (from film by Al. Zahariev)

2001. Bulgarian Animation.
4381 **1505** 25c. multicoloured . . . 15 10

1506 Vincenzo Bellini

2001. Birth Bicentenary of Vincenzo Bellini (composer).
4382 **1506** 25st. multicoloured . . 15 10

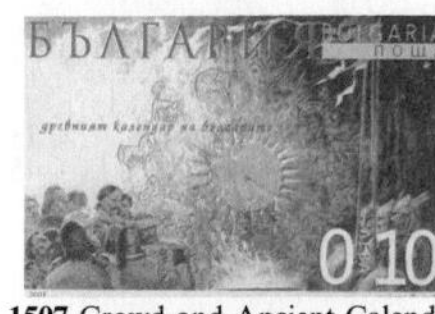

1507 Crowd and Ancient Calendar

2001. Founders of Bulgarian State (1st series). Multicoloured.
4383 10st. Type **1507** 10 10
4384 25st. Khans, Kubrat and Asparuh 15 10
4385 30st. Khans, Krum and Omurtag 20 10
4386 65st. King Boris and Tsar Simeon 45 10
See also Nos. 4427/7 and 4456/9.

1508 “€” Symbol and Stars

2002. The Euro (European currency).
4387 **1508** 65st. multicoloured . . 45 10

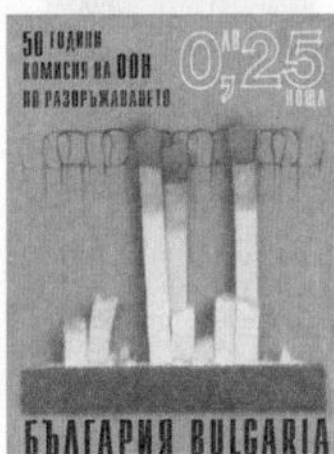

1509 Matches

2002. 50th Anniv of United Nations Disarmament Commission.
4388 **1509** 25st. multicoloured . . 15 10

1510 Limestone Arch

2002. “BALKANMAX '02” International Stamp Exhibition. Sheet 95 × 87 mm containing T **1510** and similar vert design. Multicoloured.
MS4389 25st. Type **1510**; 65st. Long-legged buzzard (*Buteo rufinus*) 60 60

1511 Figure Skater

2002. Winter Olympic Games, Salt Lake City. Multicoloured.

4390	25st. Type **1511**	15	10
4391	65st. Speed skater	45	10

1512 Station Building and Bearded Penguins

2002. 10th National Antarctic Expedition.

4392	**1512** 25st. multicoloured	15	10

1513 Performing Elephant

2002. Europa. Circus. Multicoloured.

4393	25st. Type **1513**	15	10
4394	65st. Clown	45	10

1514 Veselin Stojano

2002. Birth Centenaries. Multicoloured.

4395	25st. Type **514** (composer)	15	10
4396	65st. Angel Karaliechev (writer)	45	10

1515 "Illustrated Landscape" (Vasil Barakov)

2002. Art. Multicoloured.

4397	10st. Type **1515**	10	10
4398	25st. Book illustration from "Under the Yoke" (novel by Ivan Vazov) (Boris Angulshev) (horiz)	15	10
4399	65st. "The Balcony and Canary" (Ivan Nenov)	45	10

1516 Stefan Kanchev

2002. 1st Death Annivs of Stamp Designers. Multicoloured.

4400	25st. Type **1516**	15	10
4401	65st. Alex Popilov	45	10

1517 Melon (*Cucumis melo*)

2002. Fruits. Multicoloured.

4402	10st. Type **1517**	10	10
4403	25st. Watermelon (*Citrullus lanatus*)	15	10
4404	27st. Pumpkin (*Cucurbita pepo*)	20	10
4405	65st. Calabash (*Lagenaria siceraria*)	45	10

1518 Cock Bird

1520 Chess Pieces

1519 Pope John Paul II and Monument to Cyril & Methodius

2002. Poultry. Multicoloured.

4406	10st. Type **1518**	10	10
4407	20st. Leghorn pair (horiz)	15	10
4408	25st. Two cocks fighting (horiz)	15	10
4409	65st. Plymouth rock pair (inscr "Plimouth Rock")	65	15

2002. Pope John Paul II's Visit to Bulgaria.

4410	**1519** 65st. multicoloured	65	15

2002. Sheet 91 × 71 mm containing T **1520** and similar vert design.

MS4411	25st. brown, cinnamon and black (Type **1520**); 65st. multicoloured (Hand holding pawn)	60	60

1521 Flag and Stars

2002. 10th Anniv of Bulgaria's Admission to Council of Europe.

4412	**1521** 25st. multicoloured	15	10

1522 Rabbit

2002. Woodcarvings by Peter Kuschlev.

4413	**1522** 6st. brown and black	10	10
4414	– 12st. orange and black	10	10
4415	– 36st. green and black	25	10
4416	– 44st. pink and black	30	10

DESIGNS: 12st. Deer; 36st. Bird; 44st. Boar.

1523 *Marie-Luisa* (1st ocean-going liner)

2002. Merchant Ships. Multicoloured.

4417	12st. Type **1523**	10	10
4418	36st. *Persenk* (cargo ship)	25	10
4419	49st. *Kaliakra* (sail training ship)	35	10
4420	65st. *Sofia* (container ship)	45	10

1524 Father Christmas and Sun

2002. Christmas.

4421	**1524** 36st. multicoloured	25	10

1525 Flag and NATO Emblem

2002. Bulgaria's Participation in NATO Conference, Prague. Sheet 85 × 65 mm.

MS4422	**1525** 65st. multicoloured	45	45

1526 Paper Bird

2002. 30th Anniv of Security and Co-operation in Europe Conference. Sheet 85 × 60 mm.

MS4423	**1526** 65st. multicoloured	45	45

1527 Tsar Samuil

2002. Founders of Bulgarian State (2nd series). Multicoloured.

4424	18st. Type **1527**	10	10
4425	36st. Tsars Peter II and Assen	25	10
4426	49st. Tsar Kaloyan	35	10
4427	65st. Tsar Ivan Assen II	45	10

1528 Exhibition Emblem

2003. Europalia Cultural Exhibition, Belgium.

4428	**1528** 65st. multicoloured	45	10

1529 "Rose Pickers" (Stoyan Sotirov)

2003. Artists' Birth Centenaries. Multicoloured.

4429	18st. Type **1529**	10	10
4430	36st. "The Blind Fiddler" (Illya Petrov)	25	10
4431	65st. "Swineherd" (Zlatyo Boyadjiev)	45	10

1530 Space Construction surrounding Earth

1531 Statue of Russian and Bulgarian Soldiers

2003. Space Exploration. Sheet 104 × 85 mm.

MS4432	**1530** 65st. multicoloured	45	45

2003. 125th Anniv of Bulgarian State.

4433	**1531** 36st. multicoloured	25	10

1532 Exarch Stefan I, Menorah Candlestick and Dimitar Peshev

2003. 60th Anniv of Rescue of Bulgarian Jews.

4434	**1532** 36st. multicoloured	25	10

1533 Silhouettes of Birds and Woman

2003. Europa. Poster Art. Multicoloured.

4435	36st. Type **1533**	25	10
4436	65st. Chicken, legs and farm animals	45	10

1534 "Vase with Fifteen Sunflowers"

2003. 150th Birth Anniv of Vincent van Gogh (artist). Sheet 70 × 90 mm.

MS4437	**1534** 65st. multicoloured	45	45

1535 Pterodactylus

2003. Dinosaurs. Multicoloured.

4438	30st. Type **1535**	20	10
4439	36st. Gorgosaurus	25	10
4440	49st. Mesosaurus	35	10
4441	65st. Monoclonius	45	10

1536 *Nymphoides Peltata*

2003. Water Plants (1st issue). Multicoloured.

4442	**1536** 36st. multicoloured	25	10

See also Nos. 4447/50.

1537 Honey Bee (*Apis mellifera*)

2003. Bees. Multicoloured.

4443	20st. Type **1537**	15	10
4444	30st. *Anthidium manicatum*	20	10
4445	36st. Bumble bee (*Bombus subterraneus*)	25	10
4446	65st. Blue carpenter bee (*Xylocopa violacea*)	45	10

1538 *Butomus umbellatus*

2003. Water Plants (2nd issue). Multicoloured.

4447	20st. Type **1538**	15	10
4448	36st. *Sagirraria sagittifolia*	15	10
4449	50st. *Menyanthes trifoliate*	35	10
4450	65st. *Iris pseudoacorus*	45	10

1539 Gotze Delchev

2003. Death Centenary of Gotze Delchev (revolutionary). Centenary of Macedonian Uprising.
4451 **1539** 36st. multicoloured . . 15 10

1540 Mountains

2003. International Year of Mountains.
4452 **1540** 65st. multicoloured . . 45 10

1541 Bulgarian and USA Flags as Bowtie

2003. Centenary of Bulgaria—USA Diplomatic Relations. .
4453 **1541** 65st. multicoloured . . 45 10

1542 John Atanasoff **1543** Pawn and Buildings

2003. Birth Centenary of John Atanasoff (computer pioneer).
4454 **1542** 65st. multicoloured . . 45 10

2003. European Chess Championship, Plovdiv.
4455 **1543** 65st. multicoloured . . 45 10

1544 Tsar Ivan Alexander

2003. Founders of Bulgarian State (3rd series). Multicoloured.
4456 30st. Type **1544** 20 10
4457 45st. Despot Dobrotitsa . . 30 10
4458 65st. Tsar Ivan Shishman 45 10
4459 89st. Tsar Ivan Sratsimir . . 60 10

1545 Taekwondo **1546** Father Christmas

2003. 80th Anniv of National Olympic Committee. Multicoloured.
4460 20st. Type **1545** 15 10
4461 36st. Mountain biking . . . 25 10
4462 50st. Softball 35 10
4463 65st. Canoe slalom 45 10

2003. Christmas.
4464 **1546** 65st. multicoloured . . 45 10

1547 Carriage and Man wearing Top Hat

2003. Carriages. Multicoloured.
4465 30st. Type **1547** 20 10
4466 36st. Closed carriage with woman passenger 25 10
4467 50st. State coach, woman and dog 35 10
4468 65st. Couple and large carriage 45 10

1548 FIFA Centenary Emblem

2003. Centenary of FIFA (Federation Internationale de Football Association). Multicoloured.
4469 20st. Type **1548** 15 10
4470 25st. Early players 15 10
4471 36st. Early players and rules 25 10
4472 50st. FIFA fair play trophy (vert) 35 10
4473 65st. FIFA world player trophy (vert) 45 10

1549 Eye, Square, Compass and Statue **1550** *Noctua tertia*

2003. 10th Anniv of Re-establishment of Masonic Activity in Bulgaria.
4474 **1549** 80st. multicoloured . . 55 10

2004. Moths. Multicoloured.
4475 40st. Type **1550** 25 10
4476 45st. *Rethera komarovi* . . . 30 10
4477 55st. *Symtomis marjana* . . 35 10
4478 80st. *Arctia caja* 55 10

1551 Mask

2004. SERVA, International Masquerade Festival, Pernik.
4479 **1551** 80st. multicoloured . . 55 10

1552 OSCE Emblem and Bridge

2004. Bulgaria, Chair of Organization for Security and Co-operation in Europe.
4480 **1552** 80st. multicoloured . . 55 10

1553 Theatre Facade

2004. Centenary of Ivan Vazov National Theatre, Sofia.
4481 **1553** 45st. multicoloured . . 30 10

1554 Atanas Dalchev

2004. Birth Centenaries. Multicoloured.
4482 45st. Type **1554** (poet) . . . 30 10
4483 80st. Lubomir Pipkov (composer) 55 10

1555 NATO Emblem and National Colours

2004. Accession to Full Membership of NATO.
4484 **1555** 80st. multicoloured . . 55 10

1556 Georgi Ivanov

2004. 25th Anniv of First Bulgarian in Space. Sheet 84 × 68 mm.
MS4485 **1556** 80st. multicoloured 55 55

1557 Cover of Document **1558** Globe surmounted by Mortar Board

2004. 125th Anniv of Turnovska Constitution and Restoration of Bulgarian State. Sheet 86 × 67 mm.
MS4486 **1557** 45st. multicoloured 30 30

2004. "Bulgarian Dream" (graduate assistance) Programme.
4487 **1558** 45st. multicoloured . . 30 15

EXPRESS STAMPS

E **137** Express Delivery Van

1939.
E429 – 5l. blue 50 25
E430 E **137** 6l. brown 30 25
E431 – 7l. brown 40 30
E432 E **137** 8l. red 65 30
E433 – 20l. red . . . . 1·25 65
DESIGNS—VERT: 5l., 20l. Bicycle messenger; 7l. Motor-cyclist and sidecar.

OFFICIAL STAMPS

O **158** O **177**

1942.
O507 O **158** 10s. green 10 10
O508 30s. orange 10 10
O509 50s. brown 10 10
O510 – 1l. blue 10 10
O511 – 2l. green 10 10
O534 – 2l. red 20 10
O512 – 3l. mauve 10 10
O513 – 4l. pink 10 10
O514 – 5l. red 10 10
The 1l. to 5l. are larger (19 × 23 mm).

1945. Arms designs. Imperf or perf.
O580 – 1l. mauve 10 10
O581 O **177** 2l. green 10 10
O582 – 3l. brown 10 10
O583 – 4l. blue 10 10
O584 – 5l. red 10 10

PARCEL POST STAMPS

P **153** Weighing Machine P **154** Loading Motor Lorry

1941.
P494 P **153** 1l. green 10 10
P495 A 2l. red 30 10
P496 P **154** 3l. brown 10 10
P497 B 4l. orange 10 10
P498 P **153** 5l. blue 10 10
P506 5l. green 10 10
P499 B 6l. purple 10 10
P507 6l. brown 10 10
P500 P **153** 7l. blue 10 10
P508 7l. sepia 10 10
P501 P **154** 8l. turquoise 10 10
P509 8l. green 10 10
P502 A 9l. olive 50 15
P503 B 10l. orange 15 10
P504 P **154** 20l. violet 35 10
P505 A 30l. black . . . . . . 1·60 15
DESIGNS—HORIZ: A, Loading mall coach; B, Motor-cycle combination.

P **163**

1944. Imperf.
P532 P **163** 1l. red 10 10
P533 3l. green 10 10
P534 5l. green 10 10
P535 7l. mauve 10 10
P536 10l. blue 10 10
P537 20l. brown 10 10
P538 30l. purple 10 10
P539 50l. orange 35 10
P540 100l. blue 60 25

POSTAGE DUE STAMPS

D **7** D **12** D **16**

1884. Perf.
D75 D **7** 5s. orange . . . . 17·00 2·50
D54 25s. lake . . . . 7·50 2·50
D55 50s. blue . . . . 3·50 2·50

1886. Imperf.
D50 D **7** 5s. orange . . . . . . £150 8·50
D51 25s. lake . . . . £250 7·50
D52a 50s. blue . . . . 8·00 6·50

1893. Surch with bar and **30**.
D78d D **7** 30s. on 50s. blue (perf) 13·50 5·00
D79 30s. on 50s. blue (imperf) . . . . . . 10·00 4·00

1896. Perf.
D83 D **12** 5s. orange . . . . . . 6·75 1·25
D84 10s. violet . . . . . . 4·25 1·60
D85 30s. green . . . . . . 3·15 1·00

1901.
D124 D **16** 5s. red 35 20
D125 10s. green 70 25
D126 20s. blue . . . . 5·00 25
D127 30s. red 50 30
D128 50s. orange . . . . . 7·50 4·50

D **37** D **110**

1915.

D200 D 37 5s. green 15 10
D240 10s. violet 10 10
D202 20s. red 15 10
D241 20s. orange 10 10
D203a 30s. red 15 10
D242 50s. blue 10 10
D243 1l. green 10 10
D244 2l. red 10 10
D245 3l. brown 20 10

1932.

D326 D 110 1l. bistre 50 40
D327 2l. red 50 40
D328 6l. purple . . . . . 1·50 60

D 111

D 112

D 293

1933.

D333 D 111 20s. sepia 10 10
D334 40s. blue 10 10
D335 80s. red 10 10
D336 D 112 1l. brown 40 40
D337 2l. olive 50 50
D338 6l. violet 30 30
D339 14l. blue 40 40

1947. As Type D 112, but larger (18 × 24 mm).
D646 1l. brown 10 10
D647 2l. red 10 10
D648 8l. orange 15 10
D649 20l. blue 35 15

1951.

D849 D 293 1l. brown 10 10
D850 2l. purple 10 10
D851 8l. orange 40 30
D852 20l. blue . . . . . . 1·10 90

BULGARIAN OCCUPATION OF RUMANIA Pt. 3

(DOBRUJA DISTRICT)

100 stotinki = 1 leva.

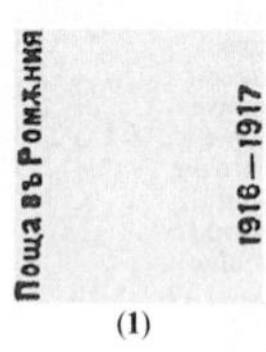

(1)

1916. Bulgarian stamps of 1911 optd with T 1.
1 23 1s. grey 10 10
2 – 5s. brown and green . . . . 1·50 1·25
3 – 10s. sepia and brown 15 10
4 – 25s. black and blue 15 10

BUNDI Pt. 1

A state of Rajasthan, India. Now uses Indian stamps.

12 pies = 1 anna; 16 annas = 1 rupee.

3 Native Dagger

11 Raja protecting Sacred Cows

1894. Imperf.
12 3 ½a. grey . . . . 3·75 3·75
13 1a. red . . . . 2·75 2·75
14 2a. green . . . . 8·00 12·00
8 4a. green . . . . 50·00 75·00
15 8a. red . . . . 9·50 13·00
16a 1r. yellow on blue . . . . . 12·00 21·00

1898. As T 3, but with dagger point to left.
17a 3 4a. green . . . . 12·00 17·00

1914. Roul or perf.
26 11 ⅛a. blue . . . . 1·90 4·25
38 ¼a. black . . . . 1·50 4·50
28 1a. red . . . . 3·25 10·00
20a 2a. green . . . . 3·50 9·00
30 2½a. yellow . . . . 6·00 23·00
31 3a. brown . . . . 6·00 35·00
32 4a. green . . . . 3·50 38·00
33 6a. blue . . . . 13·00 85·00
42 8a. orange . . . . 9·00 55·00
43 10a. olive . . . . 16·00 85·00
44 12a. green . . . . 13·00 85·00
25 1r. lilac . . . . 23·00 95·00
46 2r. brown and black . . . 70·00 £225
47 3r. blue and brown £100 £275
48 4r. green and red £200 £350
49 5r. red and green £225 £375

20

21 Maharao Rajah Bahadur Singh

1941. Perf.
79 20 3p. blue . . . . 2·00 3·50
80 6p. blue . . . . 3·50 6·00
81 1a. red . . . . 4·50 7·50
82 2a. brown . . . . 6·50 15·00
83 4a. green . . . . 12·00 42·00
84 8a. green . . . . 15·00 £150
85 1r. blue . . . . 38·00 £225

1947.

86 21 ¼a. green . . . . 1·90 30·00
87 ½a. violet . . . . 1·90 28·00
88 1a. green . . . . 1·90 27·00
89 – 2a. red . . . . 1·90 55·00
90 – 4a. orange . . . . 1·90 80·00
91 – 8a. blue . . . . 2·50
92 – 1r. brown . . . . 15·00
DESIGNS: 2, 4a. Rajah in Indian dress; 8a., 1r. View of Bundi.

OFFICIAL STAMPS

सरविस
(O 1)

1915. Optd as Type O 1.
O 6A ¼a. blue . . . . 1·60
O16A ¼a. black . . . . 8·00
O 8A 1a. red . . . . 4·00
O18A 2a. green . . . . 5·00
O 2A 2½a. yellow . . . . 3·00
O 3A 3a. brown . . . . 3·00
O19A 4a. green . . . . 9·50
O11A 6a. blue . . . . 13·00
O20A 8a. orange . . . . 15·00
O21A 10a. olive . . . . 50·00
O22A 12a. green . . . . 42·00
O 5A 1r. lilac . . . . 48·00
O24A 2r. brown and black . . . £375
O25A 3r. blue and brown . . . £350
O26A 4r green and red £300
O27A 5r. red and green £325

1915. Optd **BUNDI SERVICE**.
O 6B 11 ¼a. blue . . . . 1·75
O16B ¼a. black . . . . 3·00
O 8bB 1a. red . . . . 12·00
O18 B 2a. green . . . . 16·00
O 2 B 2½a. yellow . . . . . . 16·00
O 3 B 3a. brown . . . . 21·00
O19 B 4a. green . . . . 70·00
O11 B 6a. blue £225
O20 B 8a. orange . . . . . . 26·00
O21 B 10a. olive . . . . 80·00
O22 B 12a. green . . . . 95·00
O 5 B 1r. lilac . . . . 42·00
O24 B 2r. brown and black . . £180
O25 B 3r. blue and brown . . £200
O26 B 4r. green and red . . . £300
O27 B 5r. red and green . . . £325

Prices for Nos. O2/27 are for unused examples. Used examples are generally worth a small premium over the prices quoted.

1941. Optd **SERVICE**.
O53 20 3p. blue . . . . 5·50 12·00
O54 6p. blue . . . . 13·00 12·00
O55 1a. red . . . . 13·00 8·50
O56 2a. brown . . . . 12·00 9·50
O57 4a. green . . . . 35·00 80·00
O58 20 8a. green £140 £425
O59 1r. blue £160 £450

For later issues see **RAJASTHAN**.

BURKINA FASO Pt. 12

A country in W. Africa, formerly known as Upper Volta. The name was changed in August 1984.

100 centimes = 1 franc.

249 "Graphium pylades"

1984. Air. Butterflies. Multicoloured.
738 10f. Type **249** 10 10
739 120f. "Hyploimnas misippus" 65 40
740 400f. "Danaus chrysippus" 2·10 1·50
741 450f. "Papilio demodocus" 2·40 1·60

250 Soldier with Gun

253 Footballers and Statue

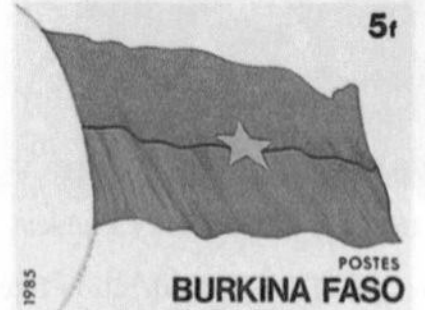

252 National Flag

1984. 1st Anniv of Captain Thomas Sankara's Presidency. Multicoloured.
742 90f. Type **250** 40 25
743 120f. Capt. Sankara and crowd 50 35

1984. Aid for the Sahel. No. 682 of Upper Volta optd **BURKINA FASO Aide au Sahel 84**.
743a 100f. multicoloured 20 15

1985. Nos. 716/21 of Upper Volta optd **BURKINA FASO**.
744 25f. Type **246** (postage) . . . 15 10
745 185f. "Pterocarpus lucens" 80 65
746 200f. "Phlebopus colossus sudanicus" . . . . 1·50 85
747 250f. "Cosmos sulphureus" 1·10 90
748 300f. "Trametes versicolor" (air) . . . . 1·75 1·25
749 400f. "Ganoderma lucidum" 2·25 1·75

1985. National Symbols. Multicoloured.
750 5f. Type **252** (postage) . . . 10 10
751 15f. National arms (vert) . . 10 10
752 90f. Maps of Africa and Burkina Faso 40 25
753 120f. Type **252** (air) 50 35
754 150f. As No. 751 . . . . . . 65 50
755 185f. As No. 752 . . . . . . 80 65

1985. World Cup Football Championship, Mexico.
756 253 25f. mult. (postage) . . . 15 10
757 – 45f. multicoloured 20 15
758 – 90f. multicoloured 40 25
759 – 100f. multicoloured (air) 45 30
760 – 150f. multicoloured . . . 65 50
761 – 200f. mult (horiz) . . . 90 75
762 – 250f. mult (horiz) . . . 1·10 90
DESIGNS: 45f. to 250f. Mexican statues and various footballing scenes.

254 Children playing and Boy

1985. Air "Philexafrique" International Stamp Exhibition, Lome, Togo (1st issue). Multicoloured.
764 200f. Type **254** 90 75
765 200f. Solar panels, transmission mast, windmill, dish aerial and tree 90 75
See also Nos. 839/40.

255 G. A. Long's Steam Tricycle

1985. Centenary of Motor Cycle. Multicoloured.
766 50f. Type **255** (postage) . . . 20 15
767 75f. Pope 30 20
768 80f. Manet 35 25
769 100f. Ducati (air) 45 30
770 150f. Jawa 65 50
771 200f. Honda 90 75
772 250f. B.M.W. . . . . 1·10 90

256 "Chamaeleon dilepis"

1985. Reptiles and Amphibians. Multicoloured.
773 5f. Type **256** (postage) . . . 10 10
774 15f. "Agama stellio" 10 10
775 33f. "Lacerta lepida" (horiz) 15 10
776 85f. "Hiperolius marmoratus" (horiz) 35 25
777 100f. "Echis leucogaster" (horiz) (air) 45 30
778 150f. "Kinixys erosa" (horiz) 65 50
779 250f. "Python regius" (horiz) 1·10 90

257 Benz "Victoria", 1893

1985. Motor Cars and Aircraft. Multicoloured.
780 5f. Type **257** (postage) . . . 10 10
781 25f. Peugeot "174", 1927 . . 15 10
782 45f. Bleriot XI airplane . . 40 15
783 50f. Breguet 14T biplane . . 40 15
784 500f. Bugatti "Napoleon T41 Royale" (air) . . . . . . 2·75 2·25
785 500f. Airbus Industrie A300 2·75 2·25
786 600f. Mercedes-Benz "540 K", 1938 . . . . 3·00 2·50
787 600f. Airbus Industrie A300 3·00 2·50

258 Wood Duck

1985. Birth Bicentenary of John J. Audubon (ornithologist). Multicoloured.
789 60f. Type **258** (postage) . . . 40 25
790 100f. Northern mockingbird 80 40
791 300f. Northern oriole . . . . 2·25 75
792 400f. White-breasted nuthatch 2·50 1·75
793 500f. Common flicker (air) 3·50 2·40
794 600f. Rough-legged buzzard 3·75 2·75

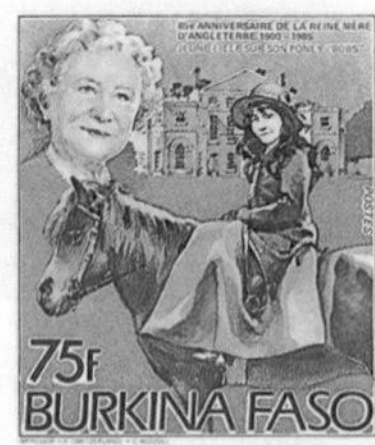

259 Young Lady Elizabeth Bowes-Lyon on Pony

1985. 85th Birthday of Queen Elizabeth the Queen Mother. Multicoloured.
796 75f. Type **259** (postage) . . . 30 20
797 85f. Marriage of Lady Elizabeth Bowes-Lyon and Albert, Duke of York . . 35 25
798 500f. Duke and Duchess of York with Princess Elizabeth (air) . . . . . . 2·25 1·90
799 600f. Royal family in Coronation robes . . . . 2·50 2·25

260 Gaucho on Piebald Horse

1985. "Argentina '85" International Stamp Exhibition, Buenos Aires. Horses. Multicoloured.
801 25f. Type **260** (postage) . . . 15 10
802 45f. Gaucho on horse 20 15
803 90f. Rodeo rider 45 30

804 100f. Rider hunting gazelle (air) . . . 45 30
805 150f. Horses and gauchos at camp fire . . . 65 50
806 200f. Horse and man sitting on steps . . . 90 75
807 250f. Riding contest . . . 1·10 90

261 Electric Locomotive No. 105-30 and Tank Wagon

1985. Trains. Multicoloured.
809 50f. Type **261** (postage) . . . 50 10
810 75f. Diesel shunting locomotive . . . 65 15
811 80f. Diesel passenger locomotive . . . 70 20
812 100f. Diesel railcar (air) . . . 90 20
813 150f. Diesel locomotive No. 6093 . . . 1·25 35
814 200f. Diesel railcar No. 105 . . . 1·60 50
815 250f. Diesel locomotive pulling passenger train . . . 2·40 70

262 Pot (Tikare) **263** "Pholiota mutabilis"

1985. Handicrafts. Multicoloured.
816 10f. Type **262** (postage) . . . 10 10
817 40f. Pot with lid decorated with birds (P. Bazega) . . . 20 15
818 90f. Bronze statuette of mother with child (Ouagadougou) . . . 40 25
819 120f. Bronze statuette of drummer (Ouagadougou) (air) . . . 50 35

1985. Fungi. Multicoloured.
820 15f. Type **263** (postage) . . . 15 10
821 20f. "Hypholoma (nematoloma) fasciculare" 20 10
822 30f. "Ixocomus granulatus" 25 10
823 60f. "Agaricus campestris" 50 20
824 80f. "Trachypus scaber" . . . 70 40
825 250f. "Marasmius scorodonius" . . . 2·25 1·40
826 150f. "Armillaria mellea" (air) . . . 1·10 60

264 "Virgin and Child"

1985. "Italia '85" International Stamp Exhibition, Rome. Paintings by Botticelli.
827 25f. Type **264** (postage) . . . 15 10
828 45f. "Portrait of an Unknown Man" . . . 20 15
829 90f. "Mars and Venus" . . . 50 30
830 100f. "Birth of Venus" (air) 55 40
831 150f. "Allegory of Calumny" 75 60
832 200f. "Pallas and the Centaur" . . . 90 75
833 250f. "Allegory of Spring" 1·10 90

265 Sikorsky S-55 Helicopter

1985. Red Cross. Multicoloured.
835 40f. Type **265** (postage) . . . 30 15
836 85f. Ambulance . . . 35 25
837 150f. Henri Dunant (founder) (vert) (air) . . . 65 50
838 250f. Nurse attending patient (vert) . . . 1·10 90

266 Transport and Communications (development)

1985. Air. "Philexafrique" International Stamp Exhibition, Lome, Togo (2nd issue). Mult.
839 250f. Type **266** . . . 3·75 1·50
840 250f. Youth activities (youth) 1·10 90

267 Girls drumming and clapping

1986. Dodo Carnival. Multicoloured.
841 20f. Type **267** . . . 10 10
842 25f. Masked lion dancers . . . 15 10
843 40f. Masked stick dancers and drummers . . . 20 15
844 45f. Stick dancers with elaborate headdresses . . . 20 15
845 90f. Masked elephant dancer 40 25
846 90f. Animal dancers . . . 40 25

268 Mother breast-feeding Baby

1986. Child Survival Campaign.
847 **268** 90f. multicoloured . . . 40 25

269 Couple carrying Rail

1986. Railway Construction. Multicoloured.
848 90f. Type **269** (postage) . . . 70 15
849 120f. Laying tracks . . . 85 25
850 185f. Workers waving to passing train . . . 1·60 60
851 500f. "Inauguration of First German Railway" (Heim) (air) . . . 4·00 1·75
No. 851 commemorates the 150th anniv of German railways.

270 Columbus before King of Portugal, and "Nina" **271** Village and First Aid Post

1986. 480th Death Anniv of Christopher Columbus (explorer). Multicoloured.
853 250f. Type **270** (postage) . . 1·60 90
854 300f. "Santa Maria" and Columbus with astrolabe 2·00 1·00
855 400f. Columbus imprisoned and "Santa Maria" . . . 2·60 1·50
856 450f. Landing at San Salvador and "Pinta" (air) 3·25 1·60

1986. "Health For All by Year 2000". Mult.
858 90f. Type **271** . . . 40 25
859 100f. Man receiving first aid (26 × 36 mm) . . . 40 25
860 120f. People queuing for vaccinations (26 × 36 mm) 50 35

272 "Phryneta aurocinta" **273** Woman feeding Child and Fresh Foods

1986. Insects. Multicoloured.
861 15f. Type **272** . . . 10 10
862 20f. "Sternocera interrupta" 10 10
863 40f. "Prosoprocera lactator" 35 15
864 45f. "Gonimbrasia hecate" 40 15
865 85f. "Charaxes epijasius" . . 70 50

1986. Gobi Health Strategy. Multicoloured.
866 30f. Type **273** . . . 15 10
867 60f. Ingredients of oral rehydration therapy . . . 25 15
868 90f. Mother holding child for vaccination . . . 40 25
869 120f. Doctor weighing child 50 35

274 U.P.U. Emblem on Dove **275** Emblem

1986. World Post Day.
870 **274** 120f. multicoloured . . . 50 35

1986. International Peace Year.
871 **275** 90f. blue . . . 40 25

276 Namende Dancers **277** Warthog

1986. National Bobo Culture Week. Mult.
872 10f. Type **276** . . . 10 10
873 25f. Mouhoun dancers . . . 10 10
874 90f. Houet dancer . . . 40 25
875 105f. Seno musicians . . . 40 25
876 120f. Ganzourgou dancers . . 50 35

1986. Wildlife. Multicoloured.
877 50f. Type **277** . . . 20 15
878 65f. Spotted hyena . . . 25 15
879 90f. Antelope . . . 40 25
880 100f. Red-fronted gazelle . . 40 25
881 120f. Harnessed antelope . . 50 35
882 145f. Hartebeest . . . 60 45
883 500f. Kob . . . 2·00 1·50

278 Peul **279** Charlie Chaplin within Film Frame (10th death anniv)

1986. Traditional Hairstyles. Multicoloured.
884 35f. Type **278** . . . 25 15
885 75f. Dafing . . . 30 20
886 90f. Peul (different) . . . 55 30
887 120f. Mossi . . . 60 35
888 185f. Peul (different) . . . 1·00 80

1987. 10th Fespaco Film Festival.
889 – 90f. mauve, black & brn 40 25
890 – 120f. multicoloured . . . 50 35
891 **279** 185f. multicoloured . . . 75 60
DESIGNS: 90f. Camera on map in film frame; 120f. Cameraman and soundman (60th anniv of first talking film "The Jazz Singer").

280 Woman trimming Rug **281** "Calotripis procera"

1987. International Women's Day.
892 **280** 90f. multicoloured . . . 40 25

1987. Flowers. Multicoloured.
893 70f. Type **281** . . . 30 20
894 75f. "Acacia seyal" . . . 30 20
895 85f. "Parkia biglobosa" . . . 35 25
896 90f. "Sterospernum kunthianum" . . . 40 25
897 100f. "Dichrostachys cinerea" 40 25
898 300f. "Combretum paniculatum" . . . 1·25 1·00

282 High Jumping

1987. Olympic Games, Seoul (1988). 50th Death Anniv of Pierre de Coubertin (founder of modern Olympic Games). Multicoloured.
899 75f. Type **282** . . . 30 20
900 85f. Tennis (vert) . . . 35 25
901 90f. Ski jumping . . . 40 25
902 100f. Football . . . 40 25
903 145f. Running . . . 60 45
904 350f. Pierre de Coubertin and tennis game (vert) . . . 1·50 1·25

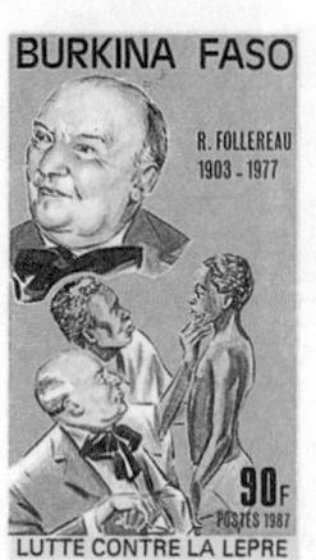

283 Follereau and Doctor treating Patient **285** Globe in Envelope

284 Woman sweeping

1987. Anti-leprosy Campaign. 10th Death Anniv of Raoul Follereau (pioneer). Multicoloured.
905 90f. Type **283** . . . 40 25
906 100f. Laboratory technicians 40 25
907 120f. Gerhard Hansen (discoverer of bacillus) . . 50 35
908 300f. Follereau kissing patient 1·25 1·00

1987. World Environment Day. Multicoloured.
909 90f. Type **284** . . . 40 25
910 145f. Emblem . . . 60 45

1987. World Post Day.
911 **285** 90f. multicoloured . . . 35 25

286 Luthuli and Open Book

1987. Anti-Apartheid Campaign. 20th Death Anniv of Albert John Luthuli (anti-apartheid campaigner). Multicoloured.
912 90f. Barbed wire and apartheid victims . . . 35 25
913 100f. Type **286** . . . 40 25

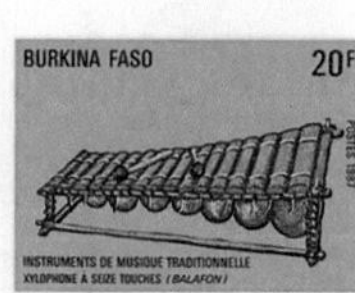

287 Dagari **288** Balafon (16 key xylophone)

1987. Traditional Costumes. Multicoloured.
914 10f. Type **287** 10 10
915 30f. Peul 15 10
916 90f. Mossi (female) 35 25
917 200f. Senoufo 80 60
918 500f. Mossi (male) 1·90 1·40

1987. Traditional Music Instruments. Multicoloured.
919 20f. Type **288** 10 10
920 25f. Kunde en more (3 stringed lute) (vert) 10 10
921 35f. Tiahoun en bwaba (zither) 15 10
922 90f. Jembe en dioula (conical drum) 35 25
923 1000f. Bendre en more (calabash drum) (vert) 3·75 2·40

289 Dwellings

1987. International Year of Shelter for the Homeless.
924 **289** 90f. multicoloured 35 25

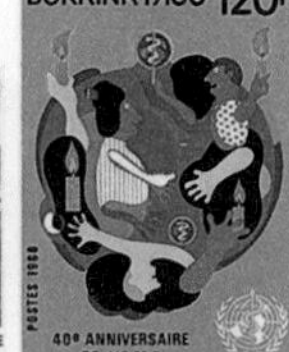

290 Small Industrial Units **291** People with Candles

1987. Five Year Plan for Popular Development. Multicoloured.
925 40f. Type **290** 15 10
926 55f. Management of dams 20 15
927 60f. Village community building primary school 25 15
928 90f. Bus (Transport and communications) 35 25
929 100f. National education: literacy campaign 40 25
930 120f. Intensive cattle farming 45 30

1988. 40th Anniv of W.H.O.
931 **291** 120f. multicoloured 45 30

292 Exhibition Emblem and Games Mascot **293** Houet "Sparrow Hawk" Mask

1988. Olympic Games, Seoul, and "Olymphilex '88" Olympic Stamps Exhibition, Rome (932). Multicoloured.
932 30f. Type **292** 15 10
933 160f. Olympic flame (vert) 60 45
934 175f. Football 65 45
935 235f. Volleyball (vert) 90 65
936 450f. Basketball (vert) 1·75 1·25

1988. Masks. Multicoloured.
938 10f. Type **293** 10 10
939 20f. Ouillo "Young Girls" mask 10 10
940 30f. Houet "Hartebeest" mask 15 10
941 40f. Mouhoun "Blacksmith" mask 15 10
942 120f. Ouri "Nanny" mask 45 30
943 175f. Ouri "Bat" mask (horiz) 65 45

294 Kieriba Jug **295** Envelopes forming Map

1988. Handicrafts. Multicoloured.
944 5f. Type **294** 10 10
945 15f. Mossi basket (horiz) 10 10
946 25f. Gurunsi chair (horiz) 10 10
947 30f. Bissa basket (horiz) 15 10
948 45f. Ouagadougou hide box (horiz) 15 10
949 85f. Ouagadougou bronze statuette 35 20
950 120f. Ouagadougou hide travelling bag (horiz) 45 30

1988. World Post Day.
951 **295** 120f. blue, black & yellow 45 30

296 White-collared Kingfisher

1988. Aquatic Wildlife. Multicoloured.
952 70f. Type **296** 1·25 40
953 100f. Elephantfish 1·00 35
954 120f. Frog 55 30
955 160f. White-faced whistling duck 2·50 1·00

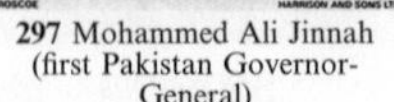

297 Mohammed Ali Jinnah (first Pakistan Governor-General) **298** Shepherds adoring Child

1988. Death Anniversaries. Multicoloured.
956 80f. Type **297** (40th anniv) (postage) 30 20
957 120f. Mahatma Gandhi (Indian human rights activist, 40th anniv) 45 30
958 160f. John Fitzgerald Kennedy (U.S. President, 25th anniv) 60 45
959 235f. Martin Luther King (human rights activist, 20th anniv) (air) 90 65

1988. Christmas. Stained Glass Windows. Mult.
960 120f. Type **298** 45 30
961 160f. Wise men presenting gifts to Child 60 45
962 450f. Virgin and Child 1·75 1·25
963 1000f. Flight into Egypt 3·75 2·75

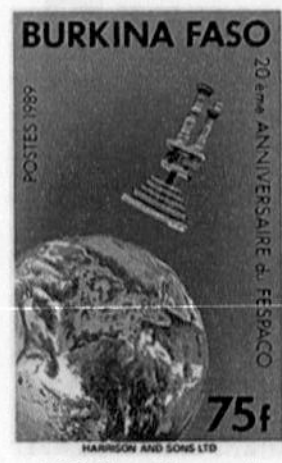

299 Satellite and Globe **300** W.H.O. and Aids Emblems

1989. 20th Anniv of FESPACO Film Festival. Multicoloured.
964 75f. Type **299** (postage) 30 20
965 500f. Ababacar Samb Makharam (air) 1·90 1·40
966 500f. Jean Michel Tchissoukou 1·90 1·40
967 500f. Paulin Soumanou Vieyra 1·90 1·40

1989. Campaign against AIDS.
969 **300** 120f. multicoloured 45 30

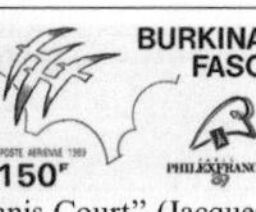

301 "Oath of the Tennis Court" (Jacques Louis David) (½-size illustration)

1989. Air. "Philexfrance 89" International Stamp Exhibition, Paris, and Bicentenary of French Revolution. Multicoloured.
970 150f. Type **301** 60 45
971 200f. "Storming of the Bastille" (Thevenin) 75 50
972 600f. "Rouget de Lisle singing La Marseillaise" (Pils) 2·25 1·60

302 Map and Tractor

1989. 30th Anniv of Council of Unity.
973 **302** 75f. multicoloured 30 20

303 "Striga generioides" **304** Sahel Dog

1989. Parasitic Plants. Multicoloured.
974 20f. Type **303** 10 10
975 50f. "Striga hermonthica" 20 15
976 235f. "Striga aspera" 90 65
977 450f. "Alectra vogelii" 1·75 1·25

1989. Dogs. Multicoloured.
978 35f. Type **304** 10 10
979 50f. Young dog 20 15
980 60f. Hunting dog 20 15
981 350f. Guard dog 1·50 1·00

305 Statue **307** Pilgrims at Shrine of Our Lady of Yagma

1989. Solidarity with Palestinian People.
982 **305** 120f. multicoloured 45 30

1989. Nos. 647/9 of Upper Volta optd **BURKINA FASO**.
983 **229** 90f. multicoloured 35 20
984 120f. multicoloured 50 35
985 170f. multicoloured 70 50

1990. Visit of Pope John Paul II. Multicoloured.
986 120f. Type **307** 50 35
987 160f. Pope and crowd 65 45

308 Mail Steamer, Globe and Penny Black **309** Goalkeeper catching Ball

1990. 150th Anniv of Penny Black and "Stamp World London 90" International Stamp Exhibition.
988 **308** 120f. multicoloured 90 45

1990. World Cup Football Championship, Italy. Multicoloured.
990 30f. Type **309** 15 10
991 150f. Footballers 60 45

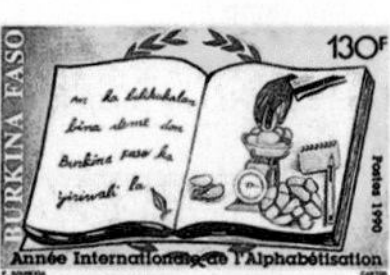

310 "Cantharellus cibarius" **311** Open Book

1990. Fungi. Multicoloured.
993 10f. Type **310** 10 10
994 15f. "Psalliota bispora" 15 10
995 60f. "Amanita caesarea" 75 35
996 190f. "Boletus badius" 2·40 1·25

1990. International Literacy Year.
998 **311** 40f. multicoloured 15 10
999 130f. multicoloured 50 35

312 Maps, Emblem and Native Artefacts **313** De Gaulle

1990. 2nd International Salon of Arts and Crafts, Ouagadougou. Multicoloured.
1000 35f. Type **312** 15 10
1001 45f. Pottery (horiz) 20 15
1002 270f. Cane chair 1·10 75

1990. Birth Centenary of Charles de Gaulle (French statesman).
1003 **313** 200f. multicoloured 80 55

314 Quartz **315** Hand Holding Cigarette, Syringe and Tablets

1991. Rocks. Multicoloured.
1004 20f. Type **314** 10 10
1005 50f. Granite 20 15
1006 280f. Amphibolite 1·10 75

1991. Anti-drugs Campaign.
1007 **315** 130f. multicoloured 50 35

316 Film and Landscape **318** Traditional Hairstyle

317 Morse and Key

1991. 12th "Fespaco 91" Pan-African Cinema and Television Festival. Multicoloured.
1008 **316** 150f. multicoloured 60 40

1991. Birth Bicentenary of Samuel Morse (inventor of signalling system).
1010 **317** 200f. multicoloured 80 55

1991.
1011 **318** 5f. multicoloured 10 10
1012 10f. multicoloured 10 10
1013 25f. multicoloured 10 10
1014 50f. multicoloured 10 10
1018 130f. multicoloured 30 20
1019 150f. multicoloured 60 40
1020 200f. multicoloured 80 55
1021 330f. multicoloured 80 55

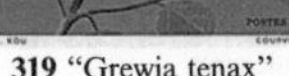

319 "Grewia tenax" **320** Warba

1991. Flowers. Multicoloured.

1025	5f. Type **319**	10	10
1026	15f. "Hymenocardia acide"	10	10
1027	60f. "Cassia sieberiana" (vert)	25	20
1028	100f. "Adenium obesum"	40	30
1029	300f. "Mitragyna inermis"	1·25	85

1991. Dance Costumes. Multicoloured.

1030	75f. Type **320**	40	25
1031	130f. Wiskamba	65	40
1032	280f. Pa-Zenin	1·40	85

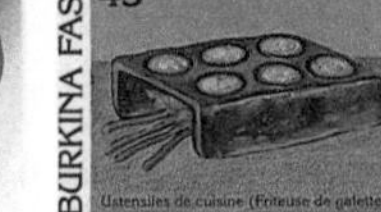

321 Pillar Box and Globe **322** Cake Tin

1991. World Post Day.

1033	**321** 130f. multicoloured	50	35

1992. Cooking Utensils.

1034	45f. Type **322**	40	20
1035	130f. Cooking pot (vert)	1·00	70
1036	310f. Pestle and mortar (vert)	1·50	1·00
1037	500f. Ladle and bowl	2·40	1·60

323 Yousouf Fofana **325** Child and Cardiograph

324 Disabled Man at Potter's Wheel

1992. African Nations Cup Football Championship, Senegal. Multicoloured.

1038	50f. Type **323**	25	20
1039	100f. Francois-Jules Bocande	50	35

1992. U.N. Decade of the Handicapped.

1041	**324** 100f. multicoloured	50	35

1992. World Health Day. "Health in Rhythm with the Heart".

1042	**325** 330f. multicoloured	1·60	1·10

326 Columbus and "Santa Maria"

1992. "Genova '92" International Thematic Stamp Exhibition and 500th Anniv of Discovery of America by Columbus. Multicoloured.

1043	50f. Type **326**	25	20
1044	150f. Amerindians watching Columbus's fleet off San Salvador	75	55

327 "Dysdercus voelkeri" (fire bug) on Cotton Boll **328** Crib

1992. Insects. Multicoloured.

1046	20f. Type **327**	10	10
1047	40f. "Rhizopertha dominica" (beetle) on leaf	20	15
1048	85f. "Orthetrum microstigma" (dragonfly) on stem	40	30
1049	500f. Honey bee on flower	2·40	1·60

1992. Christmas. Multicoloured.

1050	10f. Type **328**	10	10
1051	130f. Children decorating crib	60	40
1052	1000f. Boy with Christmas card	4·50	3·00

329 Film Makers' Monument **330** Yellow-billed Stork

1993. 13th "Fespaco" Pan-African Film Festival, Ouagadougou. Multicoloured.

1053	250f. Type **329**	1·10	75
1054	750f. Douta Seck (comedian) (horiz)	3·50	2·40

1993. Birds. Multicoloured.

1055	100f. Type **330**	95	60
1056	200f. Marabou stork	1·75	1·40
1057	500f. Saddle-bill stork	4·50	2·75

331 Statue of Liberty, Globe and Ball

1993. World Cup Football Championship, U.S.A. (1994). Multicoloured.

1059	500f. Type **331**	2·25	1·50
1060	1000f. Players, map of world and U.S. flag	4·50	3·00

332 Peterbilt Canadian Hauler and Diesel Locomotive Type BB 852, France **333** "Saba senegalensis"

1993. Centenary of Invention of Diesel Engine.

1061	**332** 1000f. multicoloured	5·75	3·00

1993. Wild Fruits. Multicoloured.

1062	150f. Type **333**	70	50
1063	300f. Karite (horiz)	1·40	95
1064	600f. Baobab	2·75	1·90

334 Flowers, "Stamps" and Sights of Paris

1993. 1st European Stamp Salon, Flower Gardens, Paris (1994). Multicoloured.

1065	400f. Type **334**	95	65
1066	650f. "Stamps", sights of Paris, daffodils and irises	1·50	1·00

335 Peulh Copper Hair Ornament

1993. Jewellery. Multicoloured.

1067	200f. Type **335**	50	35
1068	250f. Mossi agate necklace (vert)	60	40
1069	500f. Gourounsi copper bracelet	1·25	85

336 Gazelle

1993. The Red-fronted Gazelle. Multicoloured.

1070	30f. Type **336**	10	10
1071	40f. Two gazelle	10	10
1072	60f. Two gazelle (different)	15	10
1073	100f. Gazelle	25	20

337 Woodland Kingfisher

1994. Kingfishers.

1075	600f. Type **337**	1·50	1·00
1076	1200f. Striped kingfisher	3·00	2·00

338 Players

1994. World Cup Football Championship, United States. Multicoloured.

1078	1000f. Type **338**	2·40	1·60
1079	1800f. Goalkeeper saving ball	4·25	3·00

339 Dog with Puppy

1994. 1st European Stamp Salon, Flower Gardens, Paris, France.

1081	**339** 1500f. multicoloured	3·75	2·50

340 Astronaut planting Flag on Moon **341** Guinea Sorrel

1994. 25th Anniv of First Manned Moon Landing. Multicoloured.

1083	750f. Type **340**	1·75	1·25
1084	750f. Landing module on Moon	1·75	1·25

Nos. 1083/4 were issued together, se-tenant, forming a composite design.

1994. Vegetables. Multicoloured.

1085	40f. Type **341**	10	10
1086	45f. Aubergine	10	10
1087	75f. Aubergine	20	15
1088	100f. Okra	25	20

342 Pig **343** Pierre de Coubertin (founder) and Anniversary Emblem

1994. Domestic Animals. Multicoloured.

1089	150f. Type **342**	35	25
1090	1000f. Goat (vert)	2·40	1·60
1091	1500f. Sheep	3·75	2·50

1994. Centenary of Int Olympic Committee.

1092	**343** 320f. multicoloured	80	55

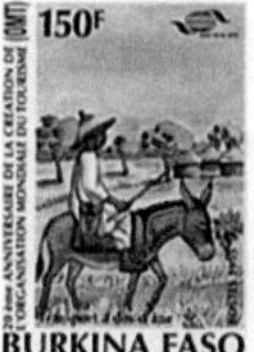

344 Donkey Rider **345** Crocodile

1995. 20th Anniv of World Tourism Organization. Multicoloured.

1093	150f. Type **344**	40	30
1094	350f. Bobo-Dioulasso railway station (horiz)	90	60
1095	450f. Great Mosque, Bani (horiz)	1·10	75
1096	650f. Roan antelope and map (horiz)	1·60	1·10

1995. Multicoloured, colour of frame given.

1097	**345** 10f. brown	10	10
1098	20f. mauve	10	10
1099	25f. brown	10	10
1100	30f. green	10	10
1101	40f. purple	10	10
1102	50f. grey	15	10
1103	75f. purple	20	15
1104	100f. brown	20	15
1105	150f. green	40	30
1106	175f. blue	45	30
1107	250f. brown	65	45
1108	400f. green	1·00	70

346 "Rabi" (dir. Gaston Kabore)

1995. "Fespaco 95" Pan-African Film Festival and Centenary of Motion Pictures. Multicoloured.

1109	150f. Type **346**	40	30
1110	250f. "Tila" (Idrissa Ouedraogo)	65	45

347 Elvis Presley in "Loving You"

1995. Entertainers. Multicoloured.

1111	300f. Type **347**	75	50
1112	400f. Marilyn Monroe	1·00	70
1113	500f. Elvis Presley in "Jailhouse Rock"	1·25	85
1114	650f. Marilyn Monroe in "Asphalt Jungle"	1·60	1·10
1115	750f. Marilyn Monroe in "Niagara"	1·90	1·40
1116	1000f. Elvis Presley in "Blue Hawaii"	2·50	1·75

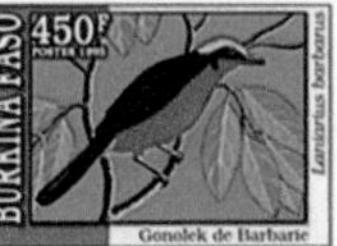

348 Common Gonolek

1995. Birds. Multicoloured.

1118	450f. Type **348**	1·10	75
1119	600f. Red-cheeked cordon-bleu	1·50	1·10
1120	750f. Golden bishop	1·90	1·40

349 Hissing Sand Snake

1995. Reptiles. Multicoloured.

1122	450f. Type **349**	1·10	75
1123	500f. Sand python	1·25	85
1124	1500f. Tortoise	4·00	2·75

350 Basketball

1995. Olympic Games, Atlanta (1996). Mult.

1125	150f. Type **350**	40	30
1126	250f. Baseball	65	45
1127	650f. Tennis	1·60	1·10
1128	750f. Table tennis	1·90	1·40

351 Juan Manuel Fangio (racing driver)

1995. Sportsmen. Multicoloured.

1130	300f. Type **351**	75	50
1131	400f. Andre Agassi (tennis player)	1·00	70
1132	500f. Ayrton Senna (racing driver)	1·25	85
1133	1000f. Michael Schumacher (racing driver)	2·50	1·75

352 Children and Christmas Tree

1995. Christmas. Multicoloured.

1135	150f. Type **352**	40	30
1136	450f. Grotto, Yagma	1·10	75
1137	500f. Flight into Egypt	1·25	85
1138	1000f. Adoration of the Wise Men	2·50	1·75

353 Headquarters Building, New York

1995. 50th Anniv of United Nations. Multicoloured.

1139	500f. Type **353**	1·25	85
1140	1000f. Village council under tree with superimposed U.N. emblem (vert)	2·50	1·75

354 Mossi Type

1995. Traditional Houses. Multicoloured.

1141	70f. Type **354**	20	15
1142	100f. Kassena type	25	15
1143	200f. Roro type	50	35
1144	250f. Peulh type	65	45

APPENDIX

The following stamps have either been issued in excess of postal needs or have not been available to the public in reasonable quantities at face value. Such stamps may later be given full listing if there is evidence of regular postal use.

1985.

85th Birthday of Queen Elizabeth the Queen Mother. 1500f.

BURMA Pt. 1, Pt. 21

A territory in the east of India, which was granted independence by the British in 1948. From May 1990 it was known as Myanmar.

1937. 12 pies = 1 anna; 16 annas = 1 rupee.
1953. 100 pyas = 1 kyat.

1937. Stamps of India (King George V) optd **BURMA**.

1	**55**	3p. grey	60	10
2	**79**	½a. green	1·00	10
3	**80**	9p. green	1·00	10
4	**81**	1a. brown	1·00	10
5	**59**	2a. red	75	10
6	**61**	2½a. orange	60	10
7	**62**	3a. red	1·00	30
8	**83**	3½a. blue	2·00	10
9	**63**	4a. olive	1·00	10
10	**64**	6a. bistre	75	35
11	**65**	8a. mauve	1·50	10
12	**66**	12a. red	4·25	1·25
13	**67**	1r. brown and green	24·00	3·00
14		2r. red and orange	28·00	11·00
15		5r. blue and violet	38·00	18·00
16		10r. green and red	90·00	60·00
17		15r. blue and olive	£325	£125
18		25r. orange and blue	£650	£300

2 King George VI and "Chinthes" **3** King George VI and "Nagas"

4 "Karaweik" (royal barge)

8 King George VI and Peacock

1938. King George VI.

18a	**2**	1p. orange	3·00	1·00
19		3p. violet	20	1·00
20		6p. blue	20	10
21		9p. green	1·00	1·00
22	**3**	1a. brown	20	10
23		1½a. green	20	1·25
24		2a. red	45	10
25	**4**	2a.6p. red	14·00	1·50
26	–	3a. mauve	14·00	2·25
27	–	3a.6p. blue	1·25	4·50
28	**3**	4a. blue	60	10
29	–	8a. green	5·00	30
30	**8**	1r. purple and blue	5·00	20
31		2r. brown and purple	16·00	1·75
32	–	5r. violet and red	48·00	25·00
33	–	10r. brown and green	55·00	50·00

DESIGNS—HORIZ: As Type **4**: 3a. Burma teak; 3a.6p. Burma rice; 8a. River Irrawaddy. VERT: As Type **3**: 5, 10r. King George VI and "Nats".

1940. Cent of First Adhesive Postage Stamp. Surch **COMMEMORATION POSTAGE STAMP 6th MAY 1840 ONE ANNA 1A** and value in native characters.

34	**4**	1a. on 2a.6p. red	4·00	2·00

For Japanese issues see "Japanese Occupation of Burma".

1945. British Military Administration. Stamps of 1938 optd **MILY ADMN**.

35	**2**	1p. orange	10	10
36		3p. violet	10	75
37		6p. blue	10	30
38		9p. green	30	75
39	**3**	1a. brown	10	10
40		1½a. green	10	15
41		2a. red	10	15
42	**4**	2a.6p. red	2·00	1·00
43	–	3a. mauve	1·50	20
44	–	3a.6p. blue	10	70
45	**3**	4a. blue	10	60
46	–	8a. green	10	70
47	**8**	1r. purple and blue	40	50
48		2r. brown and purple	40	1·25
49	–	5r. violet and red	40	1·25
50	–	10r. brown and green	40	1·25

1946. British Civil Administration. As 1938, but colours changed.

51	**2**	3p. brown	10	2·00
52		6p. violet	10	30
53		9p. green	15	2·50
54	**3**	1a. blue	15	20
55		1½a. orange	15	10
56		2a. red	15	40
57	**4**	2a.6p. blue	2·75	4·00
57a	–	3a. blue	6·50	4·00
57b	–	3a. 6p. black and blue	50	2·00
58	**3**	4a. purple	50	30
59	–	8a. mauve	1·75	3·00
60	**8**	1r. violet and mauve	1·25	1·00
61		2r. brown and orange	6·00	3·75
62	–	5r. green and brown	6·00	17·00
63	–	10r. red and violet	8·50	21·00

14 Burman

(**18** Trans. "Interim Government")

1946. Victory.

64	**14**	9p. green	20	20
65	–	1½a. violet (Burmese woman)	20	10
66	–	2a. red (Chinthe)	20	10
67	–	3a.6p. (Elephant)	50	20

1947. Stamps of 1946 opt with T **18** or with larger opt on large stamps.

68	**2**	3p. brown	70	70
69		6p. violet	10	30
70		9p. green	10	30
71	**3**	1a. blue	10	30
72		1½a. orange	1·00	10
73		2a. red	30	15
74	**4**	2a.6p. blue	1·75	1·00
75	–	3a. blue	2·50	1·75
76	–	3a.6p. black and blue	50	2·00
77	**3**	4a. purple	1·75	30
78	–	8a. mauve	1·75	1·75
79	**8**	1r. violet and mauve	4·50	1·00
80		2r. brown and orange	4·50	4·00
81	–	5r. green and brown	4·50	4·50
82	–	10r. red and violet	3·25	4·50

20 Gen. Aung San, Chinthe and Map of Burma

21 Martyrs' Memorial

1948. Independence Day.

83	**20**	½a. green	10	10
84		1a. pink	10	10
85		2a. red	15	15
86		3½a. blue	20	15
87		8a. brown	25	25

1948. 1st Anniv of Murder of Aung San and his Ministers.

88	**21**	3p. blue	10	10
89		6p. green	10	10
90		9p. red	10	10
91		1a. violet	10	10
92		2a. mauve	10	10
93		3½a. green	15	15
94		4a. brown	15	15
95		8a. red	20	15
96		12a. purple	25	20
97		1r. green	35	20
98		2r. blue	60	40
99		5r. brown	1·90	1·10

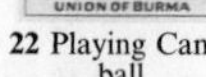

22 Playing Cane-ball

25 Bell, Mingun Pagoda

27 Transplanting Rice

28 Lion Throne

1949. 1st Anniv of Independence.

100	**22**	3p. blue	95	25
120		3p. orange	65	25
101	–	6p. green	10	10
121	–	6p. purple	10	10
102	–	9p. red	10	10
122	–	9p. blue	10	10
103	**25**	1a. red	15	10
123		1a. blue	10	10
104	–	2a. orange	45	10
124	–	2a. green	40	20
105	**27**	2a.6p. mauve	20	15
125		2a.6p. green	20	15
106	–	3a. violet	20	15
126	–	3a. red	20	15
107	–	3a.6p. green	25	15
127	–	3a.6p. orange	25	15
108	–	4a. brown	25	15
128	–	4a. red	25	15
109	–	8a. red	35	15
129	–	8a. blue	25	20
110	**28**	1r. green	50	15
130		1r. violet	50	35
111		2r. blue	1·25	40
131		2r. green	85	75
112		5r. brown	2·50	1·25
132		5r. blue	2·25	2·25
113		10r. orange	4·25	1·90
133		10r. blue	5·50	4·25

DESIGNS—As Type **22**: 6p. Dancer; 9p. Girl playing saunggaut (string instrument); 2a. Hintha (legendary bird). As Type **25**: 4a. Elephant hauling log. As Type **27**: 3a. Girl weaving; 3a.6p. Royal Palace; 8a. Ploughing paddy field with oxen.

See also Nos. 137/50.

29 U.P.U. Monument, Berne

30 Independence Monument, Rangoon, and Map

1949. 75th Anniv of U.P.U.

114	**29**	2a. orange	15	15
115		3½a. green	20	15
116		6a. violet	25	25
117		8a. red	40	25
118		12½a. blue	70	40
119		1r. green	90	50

1953. 5th Anniv of Independence.

134	**30**	14p. green (22 × 18 mm)	20	10
135		20p. red (36½ × 26½ mm)	25	15
136		25p. blue (36½ × 26½ mm)	35	20

1954. New Currency. As 1949 issue but values in pyas and kyats.

137	**22**	1p. orange	65	10
138	–	2p. purple (as 6p.)	10	10
139	–	3p. blue (as 9p.)	10	10
140	**25**	5p. blue	10	10
141	**27**	10p. green	10	10
142	–	15p. green (as 2a.)	25	10
143	–	20p. red (as 3a.)	15	10
144	–	25p. orange (as 3a.6p.)	15	10
145	–	30p. red (as 4a.)	25	15
146	–	50p. blue (as 8a.)	25	15
147	**28**	1k. violet	75	25
148		2k. green	1·25	35
149		5k. blue	3·75	70
150		10k. blue	6·50	1·25

31 Sangiti Mahapasana Rock Cave in Grounds of Kaba-Aye Pagoda

1954. 6th Buddhist Council, Rangoon.

151	–	10p. blue	10	10
152	–	15p. purple	15	15
153	**31**	35p. brown	25	20
154	–	50p. green	40	25
155	–	1k. red	90	50
156	–	2k. violet	1·40	1·00

DESIGNS: 10p. Rock caves and Songha of Cambodia; 15p. Buddhist priests and Kuthodaw Pagoda, Mandalay; 50p. Rock cave and Songha of Thailand; 1k. Rock cave and Songha of Ceylon; 2k. Rock cave and Songha of Laos.

32 Fifth Buddhist Council Monuments

1956. Buddha Jayanti.
157 **32** 20p. green and blue . . . 20 15
158 – 40p. green and blue . . . 25 20
159 – 60p. yellow and green . . . 45 35
160 – 1k.25 blue and yellow . . . 85 70
DESIGNS: 40p. Thatbyinnyu Pagoda, Pagan; 60p. Shwedagan Pagoda, Rangoon; 1k.25, Sangiti Mahapasana Rock Cave and Kaba-Aye Pagoda, Rangoon (venue of 6th Buddhist Council).

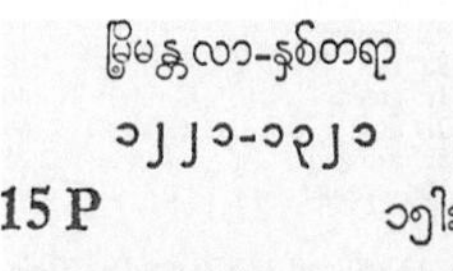

(**33**) ("Mandalay Town—100 Years/ 1221–1321")

1959. Centenary of Mandalay. No. 144 surch with T **33** and Nos. 147/8 with two-line opt only.
161 – 15p. on 25p. orange . . . 15 20
162 **28** 1k. violet 70 60
163 2k. green . . . . 1·50 1·25

1961. No. 134 surch as right-hand characters in third line of T **33**.
164 **30** 15p. on 14p. green 60 25

35 Torch-bearer in Rangoon

1961. 2nd South-East Asia Peninsula Games, Rangoon.
165 **35** 15p. blue and red 20 10
166 – 25p. green and brown . . . 25 15
167 – 50p. mauve and blue . . . 50 25
168 – 1k. yellow and green . . . 95 75
DESIGNS—VERT: 25p. Contestants; 50p. Women sprinting in Aung San Stadium, Rangoon. HORIZ: 1k. Contestants.

36 Children at Play

1961. 15th Anniv of U.N.I.C.E.F.
169 **36** 15p. red and pink 30 10

37 Flag and Map

အလုပ်သမားနေ့
၁၉၆၃

(**39**)

1963. 1st Anniv of Military Coup by General Ne Win.
170 **37** 15p. red 30 20

1963. Freedom from Hunger. Nos. 141 and 146 optd **FREEDOM FROM HUNGER**.
171 **27** 10p. green 40 35
172 – 50p. blue 75 65

1963. Labour Day. No. 143 optd with T **39**.
173 20p. red 35 20

40 White-browed Fantail

41 I.T.U. Emblem and Symbols

1964. Burmese Birds (1st series).
174 **40** 1p. black 15 15
175 2p. red 20 15
176 3p. green 20 15
177 – 5p. blue 25 20
178 – 10p. brown 25 20
179 – 15p. green 25 20
180 – 20p. brown and red . . . 45 25
181 – 25p. brown and yellow . . 45 25
182 – 50p. blue and red 85 30
183 – 1k. blue, yellow & grey . . 2·40 70
184 – 2k. blue, green and red . . 4·75 1·75
185 – 5k. multicoloured . . . . 9·75 4·50
BIRDS—22 × 26 mm: 5 to 15p. Indian roller. 27 × 37 mm: 25p. Crested serpent eagle. 50p. Sarus crane. 1k. Indian pied hornbill. 5k. Green peafowl. 35½ × 25 mm: 20p. Red-whiskered bulbul. 37 × 27 mm: 2k. Kalij pheasant.
See also Nos. 195/206.

1965. Centenary of I.T.U.
186 **41** 20p. mauve 15 15
187 50p. green (34 × 24½ mm) 40 40

42 I.C.Y. Emblem **43** Harvesting

1965. International Co-operation Year.
188 **42** 5p. blue 10 10
189 10p. brown 20 10
190 15p. olive 25 10

1966. Peasants' Day
191 **43** 15p. multicoloured 25 15

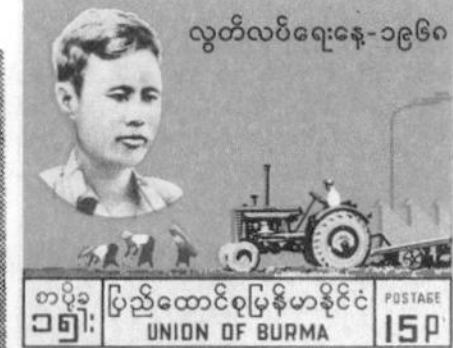

44 Cogwheel and Hammer **45** Aung San and Agricultural Cultivation

1967. May Day.
192 **44** 15p. yellow, black & blue 25 20

1968. 20th Anniv of Independence.
193 **45** 15p. multicoloured 25 20

46 Burma Pearls **47** Spike of Paddy

1968. Burmese Gems, Jades and Pearls Emporium, Rangoon.
194 **46** 15p. ultram, blue & yell . . 40 15

1968. Burmese Birds (2nd series). Designs and colours as Nos. 174/85 but formats and sizes changed.
195 **40** 1p. black 15 15
196 2p. red 15 15
197 3p. green 20 15
198 – 5p. blue 20 15
199 – 10p. brown 20 15
200 – 15p. yellow 25 20
201 – 20p. brown and red . . . 25 20
202 – 25p. brown and yellow . . 30 25
203 – 50p. blue and red 55 45
204 – 1k. blue, yellow & grey . . 1·60 45
205 – 2k. blue, green and red . . 4·50 1·10
206 – 5k. multicoloured . . . . 9·50 4·50
NEW SIZES—21 × 17 mm: 1, 2, 3p. 39 × 21 mm: 20p., 2k. 23 × 28 mm: 5, 10, 15p. 21 × 39 mm: 25, 50p., 1, 5k.

1969. Peasants' Day.
218 **47** 15p. yellow, blue & green 25 10

48 I.L.O. Emblem **49** Football

1969. 50th Anniv of I.L.O.
219 **48** 15p. gold and green . . . 15 10
220 50p. gold and red 40 25

1969. 5th South-East Asian Peninsula Games, Rangoon.
221 **49** 15p. multicoloured 20 10
222 – 25p. multicoloured 25 15
223 – 50p. multicoloured 50 20
224 – 1k. black, green & blue . . 95 50
DESIGNS—HORIZ: 25p. Running. VERT: 50p. Weightlifting; 1k. Volleyball.

50 Marchers with Independence, Resistance and Union Flags

1970. 25th Anniv of Burmese Armed Forces.
225 **50** 15p. multicoloured 20 15

51 "Peace and Progress"

1970. 25th Anniv of United Nations.
226 **51** 15p. multicoloured 25 20

52 Boycott Declaration and Marchers

1970. National Day and 50th Anniv of University Boycott. Multicoloured.
227 15p. Type **52** 10 10
228 25p. Students on boycott march 20 10
229 50p. Banner and demonstrators 40 20

53 Burmese Workers

1971. 1st Burmese Socialist Programme Party Congress. Multicoloured.
230 5p. Type **53** 10 10
231 15p. Burmese races and flags 15 10
232 25p. Hands holding scroll . . 25 15
233 50p. Party flag 50 30

54 Child drinking Milk

1971. 25th Anniv of U.N.I.C.E.F. Multicoloured.
235 15p. Type **54** 25 15
236 50p. Marionettes 55 40

55 Aung San and Independence Monument, Panglong

1972. 25th Anniv of Independence. Multicoloured.
237 15p. Type **55** 10 10
238 50p. Aung San and Burmese in national costumes . . . 25 20
239 1k. Flag and map (vert) . . . 60 40

56 Burmese and Stars

1972. 10th Anniv of Revolutionary Council.
240 **56** 15p. multicoloured 20 10

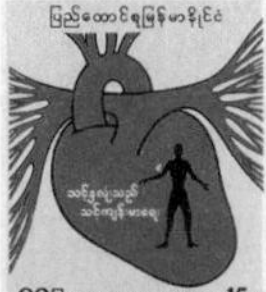

57 Human Heart **59** Casting Vote

58 Ethnic Groups

1972. World Health Day.
241 **57** 15p. red, black & yellow 20 15

1973. National Census.
242 **58** 15p. multicoloured 20 10

1973. National Constitutional Referendum.
243 **59** 5p. red and black 15 10
244 – 10p. multicoloured 15 10
245 – 15p. multicoloured 15 10
DESIGNS—HORIZ: 10p. Voter supporting map. VERT: 15p. Burmese with ballot papers.

60 Open-air Meeting

1974. Opening of 1st Pyithu Hluttaw (People's Assembly). Multicoloured.
246 15p. Burmese flags, 1752–1974 (80 × 26 mm) 20 15
247 50p. Type **60** 40 25
248 1k. Burmese badge 80 55

61 U.P.U. Emblem and Carrier Pigeon

1974. Centenary of Universal Postal Union. Mult.
249 15p. Type **61** 15 10
250 20p. Woman reading letter (vert) 20 10
251 50p. U.P.U. emblem on "stamps" (vert) 45 20
252 1k. Stylized doll (vert) . . . 75 35
253 2k. Postman delivering letter to family . . . . 1·75 75

62 Kachin Couple **63** Bamar Couple

1974. Burmese Costumes. Inscr "SOCIALIST REPUBLIC OF THE UNION OF BURMA".
254 **62** 1p. mauve 10 10
255 3p. brown and mauve . . . 10 10
256 5p. violet and mauve . . . 10 10
257 10p. blue 10 10
258 15p. green and light green 10 10
259 **63** 20p. black, brown & blue 15 10
260 – 50p. violet, brown & ochre 40 15
261 – 1k. violet, mauve & black 1·10 60
262 – 5k. multicoloured . . . . 4·00 2·25
DESIGNS—As Type **62**: 3p. Kayah girl; 5p. Kayin couple and bronze drum; 15p. Chin couple. As Type **63**: 50p. Mon woman; 1k. Rakhine woman; 5k. Musician.
For 15, 50p. and 1k. stamps in these designs, but inscr "UNION OF BURMA", see Nos. 309/11.

64 Woman on Globe and I.W.Y. Emblem

1975. International Women's Year
263 **64** 50p. black and green . . . 30 20
264 – 2k. black and blue . . . . 1·25 95
DESIGN—VERT: 2k. Globe on flower and I.W.Y. emblem.

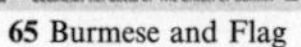

65 Burmese and Flag

66 Emblem and Burmese Learning Alphabet

1976. Constitution Day.
265 **65** 20p. black and blue . . . 15 10
266 – 50p. brown and blue . . . 35 30
267 – 1k. multicoloured . . . . 1·00 60
DESIGNS—As Type **65**: 50p. Burmese with banners and flag. 57×21 mm: 1k. Map of Burma, Burmese and flag.

1976. International Literacy Year.
268 **66** 10p. brown and red . . . 10 10
269 – 15p. turquoise, grn & blk 10 10
270 – 50p. blue, orange & black 40 20
271 – 1k. multicoloured 75 50
DESIGNS—HORIZ: 15p. Abacus and open books. 50p. Emblem. VERT: 1k. Emblem, open book and globe.

67 Early Train and Ox-cart

1977. Centenary of Railway.
272 – 15p. green, black & mauve 5·25 1·10
273 **67** 20p. multicoloured . . . . 1·75 40
274 – 25p. multicoloured . . . . 2·75 60
275 – 50p. multicoloured . . . . 3·50 1·00
276 – 1k. multicoloured . . . . 7·75 1·90
DESIGNS—26×17 mm: 15p. Early steam locomotive. As Type **67**—HORIZ: 25p. Diesel locomotive DD1517, steam train and railway station; 50p. Ava railway bridge over River Irrawaddy. VERT: Diesel train emerging from tunnel.

68 Karaweik Hall

1978.
277 **68** 50p. brown 35 25
278 – 1k. multicoloured 95 60
DESIGN—79½×25 mm: 1k. Side view of Karaweik Hall.

69 Jade Naga and Gem

1979. 16th Gem Emporium.
279 **69** 15p. green and turquoise 15 10
280 – 20p. blue, yellow & mauve 35 15
281 – 50p. blue, brown & green 65 40
282 – 1k. multicoloured . . . . 1·25 70
DESIGNS—As T **69**: 20p. Hintha (legendary bird) holding pearl in beak; 50p. Hand holding pearl and amethyst pendant. 55×20 mm: 1k. Gold jewel-studded dragon.

70 "Intelsat IV" Satellite over Burma

1979. Introduction of Satellite Communications System.
283 **70** 25p. multicoloured 25 15

71 I.Y.C. Emblem on Map of Burma

72 Weather Balloon

1979. International Year of the Child.
284 **71** 25p. orange and blue . . . 35 25
285 50p. red and violet 65 40

1980. World Meteorological Day.
286 **72** 25p. blue, yellow & black 25 15
287 – 50p. green, black and red 50 35
DESIGN: 50p. Meteorological satellite and W.M.O. emblem.

73 Weightlifting

1980. Olympic Games, Moscow.
288 **73** 20p. green, orange & blk 20 10
289 – 50p. black, orange and red 45 25
290 – 1k. black, orange and blue 90 50
DESIGNS: 50p. Boxing; 1k. Football.

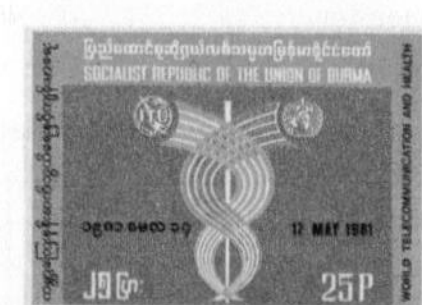

74 I.T.U. and W.H.O. Emblems with Ribbons forming Caduceus

1981. World Telecommunications Day.
291 **74** 25p. orange and black . . 20 10

75 Livestock and Vegetables

1981. World Food Day. Multicoloured.
292 25p. Type **75** 35 10
293 50p. Farm produce and farmer holding wheat . . . 55 20
294 1k. Globe and stylized bird 75 45

76 Athletes and Person in Wheelchair

1981. International Year of Disabled Persons.
295 **76** 25p. multicoloured 25 15

77 Telephone, Satellite and Antenna

1983. World Communications Year.
296 **77** 15p. blue and black . . . 10 10
297 25p. mauve and black . . 30 15
298 50p. green, black and red 50 35
299 1k. brown, black & green 1·25 70

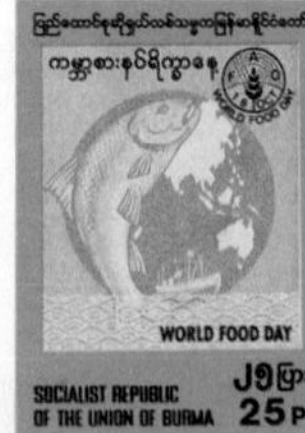

78 Fish and Globe

1983. World Food Day.
300 **78** 15p. yellow, blue & black 15 10
301 25p. orange, green & black 25 15
302 50p. green, yellow & black 60 60
303 1k. blue, yellow and black 1·75 1·40

79 Globe and Log

1984. World Food Day.
304 **79** 15p. blue, yellow & black 10 10
305 25p. violet, yellow & black 15 10
306 50p. green, pink and black 50 40
307 1k. mauve, yellow & black 1·00 90

80 Potted Plant

1985. International Youth Year.
308 **80** 15p. multicoloured 25 20

1989. As Nos. 258/9 and 260/1 but inscr "UNION OF BURMA".
309 **62** 15p. dp green & green . . 25 20
309a – 20p. black, brown & blue 5·00
310 – 50p. violet and brown . . 50 30
311 – 1k. violet, mauve & black 85 65

OFFICIAL STAMPS

1937. Stamps of India (King George V) optd **BURMA SERVICE.**
O 1 **55** 3p. grey . . . . 2·00 10
O 2 **79** ½a. green . . . . 9·00 10
O 3 **80** 9p. green . . . . 5·00 30
O 4 **81** 1a. brown . . . . 5·00 10
O 5 **59** 2a. red . . . . 9·50 35
O 6 **61** 2½a. orange . . . . . . 5·00 2·00
O 7 **63** 4a. olive . . . . 5·00 10
O 8 **64** 6a. bistre . . . . 4·25 8·00
O 9 **65** 8a. mauve . . . . 4·00 1·00
O10 **66** 12a. red . . . . 4·00 6·00
O11 **67** 1r. brown and green . . . 15·00 4·25
O12 2r. red and orange . . . . 35·00 40·00
O13 5r. blue and violet . . . . 95·00 50·00
O14 10r. green and red £275 £130

1939. Stamps of 1938 optd **SERVICE.**
O15 **2** 3p. violet 15 20
O16 6p. blue 15 20
O17 9p. green . . . . 4·00 3·75
O18 **3** 1a. brown 15 15
O19 1½a. green . . . . 3·50 1·75
O20 2a. red . . . . 1·25 20
O21 **4** 2a.6p. red . . . . 16·00 14·00
O22 **3** 4a. blue . . . . 4·50 45
O23 – 8a. green (No. 29) . . . 15·00 4·00
O24 **8** 1r. purple and blue . . . 15·00 5·50
O25 2r. brown and purple . . . 30·00 15·00
O26 – 5r. violet and red (No. 32) 25·00 29·00
O27 – 10r. brown and green (No. 33) . . . . £130 38·00

1946. Stamps of 1946 optd **SERVICE.**
O28 **2** 3p. brown . . . . 2·00 3·50
O29 6p. violet . . . . 2·00 2·25
O30 9p. green . . . . 50 3·25
O31 **3** 1a. blue . . . . 20 2·00
O32 1½a. orange 20 20
O33 2a. red . . . . 20 2·00
O34 **4** 2a.6p. blue . . . . . . 1·75 6·50
O35 **3** 4a. purple 20 70
O36 – 8a. mauve (No. 59) . . . 3·25 3·50
O37 **8** 1r. violet and mauve . . . 60 4·25
O38 2r. brown and orange . . . 7·50 45·00
O39 – 5r. green and brown (No. 62) . . . . 9·00 50·00
O40 – 10r. red and violet (No. 63) 17·00 60·00

1947. Interim Government. Nos. O28 etc., optd with T **18** or with large overprint on larger stamps.
O41 **2** 3p. brown 30 40
O42 6p. violet . . . . 2·00 10
O43 9p. green . . . . 3·00 90
O44 **3** 1a. blue . . . . 3·00 80
O45 1½a. orange . . . . . . 6·00 30
O46 2a. red . . . . 3·25 15
O47 **4** 2a.6p. blue . . . . . . 27·00 12·00
O48 **3** 4a. purple . . . . 13·00 40
O49 – 8a. mauve . . . . 12·00 4·00
O50 **8** 1r. violet and mauve . . . 14·00 2·25
O51 2r. brown and orange . . . 14·00 20·00
O52 – 5r. green and brown . . . 14·00 20·00
O53 – 10r. red and violet . . . . 14·00 30·00

အစိုးရကိစ္စ

(O **29**) (size of opt varies)

1949. 1st Anniv of Independence. Nos. 100/4 and 107/113 optd as Type O **29**.
O114 **22** 3p. blue 40 10
O115 – 6p. green 10 15
O116 – 9p. red 10 15
O117 **25** 1a. red 10 15
O118 – 2a. orange 15 15
O119 – 3a.6p. green 15 15
O120 – 4a. brown 15 15
O121 – 8a. red 15 15
O122 **28** 1r. green 40 25
O123 2r. blue 65 45
O124 5r. brown . . . . 2·25 1·50
O125 10r. orange . . . . 5·00 3·75

1954. Nos. 137/40 and 142/50 optd as Type O **29**.
O151 **22** 1p. orange 10 10
O152 – 2p. purple 10 10
O153 – 3p. blue 10 10
O154 **25** 5p. blue 10 10
O155 – 15p. green 10 10
O156 – 20p. red 15 10
O157 – 25p. orange 15 10
O158 – 30p. red 15 10
O159 – 50p. blue 25 20
O160 **28** 1k. violet 45 20
O161 2k. green . . . . 1·25 35
O162 5k. blue . . . . 2·50 90
O163 10k. blue . . . . 6·00 2·50

1964. No. 139 optd **Service.**
O174 – 3p. blue . . . . 9·50 6·50

1965. Nos. 174/7 and 179/85 optd as Type O **29**.
O196 **40** 1p. black 20 15
O197 2p. red 30 25
O198 3p. green 30 25
O199 – 5p. blue 35 30
O200 – 15p. green 35 30
O201 – 20p. brown and red . . . 65 60
O202 – 25p. brown and yellow . . 70 65
O203 – 50p. blue and red . . . . 1·25 80
O204 – 1k. blue, yellow & grey . 3·50 1·90
O205 – 2k. blue, green & red . . 4·75 1·75
O206 – 5k. multicoloured . . . . 14·00 12·00

1968. Nos. 195/8 and 200/6 optd as Type O **29**.
O207 1p. black 20 15
O208 2p. red 25 20
O209 3p. green 30 25
O210 5p. blue 30 25
O211 15p. green 30 25
O212 20p. brown and red 40 30
O213 25p. brown and yellow . . 30 25
O214 50p. blue and red 30 25
O215 1k. blue, yellow and grey 1·75 45
O216 2k. blue, green and red . . 3·50 1·10
O217 5k. multicoloured . . . . 5·00 4·50

For later issues see **MYANMAR**.

JAPANESE OCCUPATION OF BURMA

1942. 12 pies = 1 anna; 16 annas = 1 rupee.
1942. 100 cents = 1 rupee.

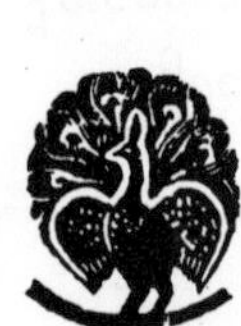

(1)

(3)

Note.—There are various types of the Peacock overprint. Our prices, as usual in this Catalogue, are for the cheapest type.

1942. Postage stamps of Burma of 1937 (India types) optd as T **1**.
J22 **55** 3p. grey . . . . 3·50 20·00
J23 **80** 9p. green . . . . 24·00 65·00
J24 **59** 2a. red £100 £180
J 2 **83** 3½a. blue . . . . 55·00

1942. Official stamp of Burma of 1937 (India type) optd as T **1**.
J3 **64** 6a. bistre . . . . 75·00

1942. Postage stamps of Burma, 1938, optd as T **1** or with T **3** (rupee values).
J25 **1** 1p. orange £200 £300
J12 3p. violet . . . . 18·00 70·00
J27 6p. blue . . . . 25·00 50·00
J14 9p. green . . . . 21·00 65·00
J29 **3** 1a. brown . . . . 9·00 40·00
J30 1½a. green . . . . 21·00 65·00
J16 2a. red . . . . 21·00 80·00
J17 4a. blue . . . . 40·00 £100
J18 **8** 1r. purple and blue . . . £275
J19 2r. brown and purple . . . £160

1942. Official stamps of Burma of 1939 optd with T **1**.
J 7 **1** 3p. violet . . . . 26·00 85·00
J 8 6p. blue . . . . 18·00 16·00
J 9 **3** 1a. brown . . . . 18·00 15·00

J35 1½a. green	£170	£300
J10 2a. red	24·00	95·00
J11 4a. blue	24·00	75·00

(6a) ("Yon Thon" = "Office Use")

1942. Official stamp of Burma of 1939 optd with T **6a**.

J44 8a. green (No. O23)	90·00	

7

8 Farmer

1942. Yano Seal.

J45 **7** (1a.) red	38·00	65·00

1942.

J46 **8** 1a. red	17·00	17·00

1942. Stamps of Japan surch in annas or rupees.

J47 – ¼a. on 1s. brown (No. 314)	25·00	35·00
J48 **83** ½a. on 2s. red	35·00	38·00
J49 – ¾ a on 3s. green (No. 316)	60·00	65·00
J50 – 1a. on 5s. purple (No. 396)	50·00	48·00
J51 – 3a. on 7s. green (No. 320)	90·00	£100
J52 – 4a. on 4s. green (No. 317)	48·00	50·00
J53 – 8a. on 8s. violet (No. 321)	£150	£150
J54 – 1r. on 10s. red (No. 322)	19·00	25·00
J55 – 2r. on 20s. blue (No. 325)	50·00	50·00
J56 – 5r. on 30s. blue (No. 327)	12·00	27·00

1942. No. 386 of Japan commemorating the fall of Singapore, surch in figures.

J56g – 4a. on 4s.+2s. green and red	£150	£160

1942. Handstamped **5 C.**

J57 **5** 5c. on 1a. red (No. J46)	14·00	18·00

1942. Nos. J47/53 with anna surcharges obliterated, and handstamped with new values in figures.

J58 – 1c. on ¼a. on 1s. brown	50·00	50·00
J59 **84** 2c. on ½a. on 2s. red	48·00	50·00
J60 – 3c. on ¾a. on 3s. green	50·00	50·00
J61 – 5c. on 1a. on 5s. red	65·00	65·00
J62 – 10c. on 3a. on 7s. green	£110	£100
J63 – 15c. on 4a. on 4s. green	38·00	40·00
J64 – 20c. on 8a. on 8s. violet	£475	£425

1942. Stamps of Japan surch in cents.

J65 – 1c. on 1s. brown (No. 314)	24·00	20·00
J66 **83** 2c. on 2s. red	48·00	32·00
J67 – 3c. on 3s. green (No. 316)	60·00	50·00
J68 – 5c. on 5s. purple (No. 396)	65·00	48·00
J69 – 10c. on 7s. green (No. 320)	75·00	60·00
J70 – 15c. on 4s. green (No. 317)	18·00	21·00
J71 – 20c. on 8s. violet (No. 321)	£160	85·00

14 Burma State Crest

15 Farmer

1943. Perf or imperf.

J72 **14** 5c. red	19·00	23·00

1943.

J73a **15** 1c. orange	2·25	4·75
J74 2c. green	60	1·00
J75 3c. blue	3·00	1·00
J77 5c. red	3·00	4·00
J78 10c. brown	6·00	4·50
J79 15c. mauve	30	2·00
J80 20c. lilac	30	1·00
J81 30c. green	30	1·25

16 Soldier carving word "Independence"

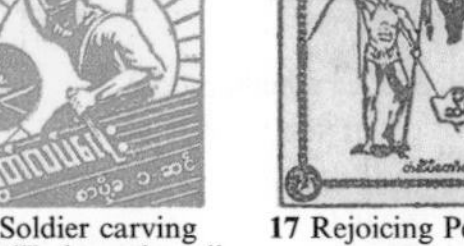
17 Rejoicing Peasant

18 Boy with National Flag

1943. Independence Day. Perf or roul.

J85 **16** 1c. orange	1·25	1·75
J86 **17** 3c. blue	2·50	2·50
J87 **18** 5c. red	2·00	2·50

19 Burmese Woman

20 Elephant carrying Log

21 Watch Tower Mandalay

1943.

J88 **19** 1c. orange	20·00	15·00
J89 2c. green	50	2·00
J90 3c. violet	50	2·25
J91 **20** 5c. red	55	60
J92 10c. blue	1·75	1·10
J93 15c. orange	1·00	3·00
J94 20c. green	1·00	1·75
J95 30c. brown	1·00	2·00
J96 **21** 1r. orange	30	2·00
J97 2r. violet	30	2·25

22 Bullock Cart

23 Shan Woman

1943. Shan States issue.

J 98 **22** 1c. brown	28·00	35·00
J 99 2c. green	28·00	35·00
J100 3c. violet	4·00	10·00
J101 5c. blue	2·00	5·50
J102 **23** 10c. blue	14·00	17·00
J103 20c. red	30·00	17·00
J104 30c. brown	19·00	48·00

ဗမာနိုင်ငံတော်

၂၀ ဆင့်။

(24 "Burma State" and value)

1944. Optd with T **24**.

J105 **22** 1c. brown	3·50	6·00
J106 2c. green	50	2·75
J107 3c. violet	2·25	7·00
J108 5c. blue	1·00	1·50
J109 **23** 10c. blue	3·25	2·00
J110 20c. red	50	1·50
J111 30c. brown	50	1·75

BURUNDI Pt. 12

Once part of the Belgian territory, Ruanda-Urundi. Independent on 1 July 1962, when a monarchy was established. After a revolution in 1967 Burundi became a republic.

100 centimes = 1 franc.

1962. Stamps of Ruanda-Urundi optd **Royaume du Burundi** and bar or surch also. (a) Flowers. (Nos. 178, etc.).

1 25c. multicoloured	25	20
2 40c. multicoloured	25	20
3 60c. multicoloured	35	35
4 1f.25 multicoloured	16·00	16·00
5 1f.50 multicoloured	60	60
6 5f. multicoloured	1·10	90
7 7f. multicoloured	1·75	1·40
8 10f. multicoloured	2·50	2·25

(b) Animals (Nos. 203/14).

9 10c. black, red and brown	10	10
10 20c. black and green	10	10
11 40c. black, olive and mauve	10	10
12 50c. brown, yellow & green	10	10
13 1f. black, blue and brown	10	10
14 1f.50 black and orange	10	10
15 2f. black, brown and turq	10	10
16 3f. black, red and brown	10	10
17 3f.50 on 3f. black, red & brn	10	10
18a 4f. on 10f. multicoloured	20	20
19 5f. multicoloured	20	20
20 6f.50 brown, yellow and red	20	20
21 8f. black, mauve and blue	35	25
23 10f. multicoloured	50	30

(c) Animals (Nos. 229/30).

24 **25** 20f. multicoloured	1·60	60
25 – 50f. multicoloured	1·90	1·10

10 King Mwambutsa IV and Royal Drummers

1962. Independence. Inscr "1.7.1962".

26 **10** 50c. sepia and lake	10	10
27 A 1f. green, red & deep green	10	10
28 B 2f. sepia and olive	10	10
29 **10** 3f. sepia and red	10	10
30 A 4f. green, red and blue	15	10
31 B 8f. sepia and violet	30	15
32 **10** 10f. sepia and green	40	15
33 A 20f. green, red and sepia	45	20
34 B 50f. sepia and mauve	1·25	45

DESIGNS—VERT: A, Burundi flag and arms. HORIZ: B, King and outline map of Burundi.

1962. Dag Hammarskjold Commem. No. 222 of Ruanda-Urundi surch **HOMMAGE A DAG HAMMARSKJOLD ROYAUME DU BURUNDI** and new value. U.N. emblem and wavy pattern at foot. Inscr in French or Flemish.

35 3f.50 on 3f. salmon and blue	35	35
36 6f.50 on 3f. salmon and blue	65	45
37 10f. on 3f. salmon and blue	1·25	1·10

1962. Malaria Eradication. As Nos. 31 and 34 but colours changed and with campaign emblem superimposed on map.

38 B 8f. sepia, turquoise & bistre	55	35
39 50f. sepia, turquoise & olive	1·40	35

12 Prince Louis Rwagasore

13 "Sowing"

1963. Prince Rwagasore Memorial and Stadium Fund.

40 **12** 50c.+25c. violet	10	10
41 – 1f.+50c. blue and orange	10	10
42 – 1f.50+75c. vio & bistre	10	10
43 **12** 3f.50+1f.50 mauve	20	10
44 – 5f.+2f. blue and pink	20	10
45 – 6f.50+3f. violet & olive	25	10

DESIGNS—HORIZ: 1f., 5f. Prince and stadium; 1f.50, 6f.50 Prince and memorial.

1963. Freedom from Hunger.

46 **13** 4f. purple and olive	15	15
47 8f. purple and olive	20	15
48 15f. purple and green	35	15

1963. "Peaceful Uses of Outer Space" Nos. 28 and 34 optd **UTILISATIONS PACIFIQUES DE L'ESPACE** around globe encircled by rocket.

49 B 2f. sepia and olive	2·25	2·25
50 50f. sepia and mauve	3·50	3·50

1963. 1st Anniv of Independence. Nos. 30/3 but with colours changed and optd **Premier Anniversaire**.

51 A 4f. green, red and olive	20	10
52 B 8f. sepia and orange	30	10
53 **10** 10f. sepia and mauve	40	20
54 A 20f. green, red and grey	90	30

1963. Nos. 27 and 33 surch.

55 A 6f.50 on 1f. green, red and deep green	55	10
56 15f. on 20f. grn, red & sepia	85	35

17 Globe and Red Cross Flag

1963. Centenary of Red Cross.

57 **17** 4f. green, red and grey	20	10
58 8f. brown, red and grey	40	20
59 10f. blue, red and grey	50	20
60 20f. violet, red and grey	1·10	40

IMPERF STAMPS. Many Burundi stamps from No. 61 onwards exist imperf from limited printings and/or miniature sheets.

18 "1962" and U.N.E.S.C.O. Emblem

1963. 1st Anniv of Admission to U.N.O. Emblems and values in black.

61 **18** 4f. olive and yellow	15	10
62 – 8f. blue and lilac	25	10
63 – 10f. violet and blue	40	10
64 – 20f. green and yellow	65	20
65 – 50f. brown and ochre	1·75	35

EMBLEMS: 8f. I.T.U.; 10f. W.M.O.; 20f. U.P.U.; 50f. F.A.O.

19 U.N.E.S.C.O. Emblem and Scales of Justice

1963. 15th Anniv of Declaration of Human Rights.

66 **19** 50c. blk, blue and pink	10	10
67 – 1f.50 black, blue & orange	10	10
68 – 3f.50 black, green & brown	15	10
69 – 6f.50 black, green and lilac	25	10
70 – 10f. black, bistre and blue	40	15
71 – 20f. multicoloured	70	25

DESIGNS: 3f.50, 6f.50, Scroll; 10f., 20f. Lincoln.

20 Ice-hockey

22 Burundi Dancer

21 Hippopotamus

1964. Winter Olympic Games, Innsbruck.
72 **20** 50c. black, gold and olive 15 10
73 – 3f.50 black, gold & brown 20 10
74 – 6f.50 black, gold and grey 45 20
75 – 10f. black, gold and grey . . 90 35
76 – 20f. black, gold and bistre 2·10 65
DESIGNS: 3f.50, Figure-skating; 6f.50, Olympic flame; 10f. Speed-skating; 20f. Skiing (slalom).

1964. Burundi Animals. Multicoloured. (i) Postage. (a) Size as T **21**.
77 50c. Impala 10 10
78 1f. Type **21** 10 10
79 1f.50 Giraffe 10 10
80 2f. African buffalo 20 10
81 3f. Common zebra 20 10
82 3f.50 Waterbuck 20 10

(b) Size 16 × 42½ mm or 42½ × 26 mm.
83 4f. Impala 25 10
84 5f. Hippopotamus 30 10
85 6f.50 Common zebra 30 10
86 8f. African buffalo 55 20
87 10f. Giraffe 60 20
88 15f. Waterbuck 85 30

(c) Size 53½ × 33½ mm.
89 20f. Cheetah . . . . 1·50 40
90 50f. African elephant . . . . 4·00 65
91 100f. Lion . . . . 6·50 1·10

(ii) Air. Inscr "POSTE AERIENNE" and optd with gold border. (a) Size 26 × 42½ mm or 42½ × 26 mm.
92 6f. Common zebra 35 10
93 8f. African buffalo 60 10
94 10f. Impala 70 10
95 14f. Hippopotamus 85 15
96 15f. Waterbuck . . . . 1·40 35

(b) Size 53½ × 33½ mm.
97 20f. Cheetah . . . . 1·75 40
98 50f. African elephant . . . . 4·00 90
The impala, giraffe and waterbuck stamps are all vert. designs, and the remainder are horiz.

1964. World's Fair, New York (1st series). Gold backgrounds.
99 **22** 50c. multicoloured 10 10
100 – 1f. multicoloured 10 10
101 – 4f. multicoloured 15 10
102 – 6f.50 multicoloured 20 10
103 – 10f. multicoloured 40 15
104 – 15f. multicoloured 70 20
105 – 20f. multicoloured 90 30
DESIGNS: 1f. to 20f. Various dancers and drummers as Type **22**.
See also Nos. 175/81.

23 Pope Paul and King Mwambutsa IV

1964. Canonization of 22 African Martyrs. Inscriptions in gold.
106 **23** 50c. lake and blue 15 10
107 – 1f. blue and purple 15 10
108 – 4f. sepia and mauve 25 10
109 – 8f. brown and red 40 15
110 – 14f. brown and turquoise 40 20
111 **23** 20f. green and red 65 40
DESIGNS—VERT: 1f., 8f. Group of martyrs. HORIZ: 4f., 14f., Pope John XXIII and King Mwambutsa IV.

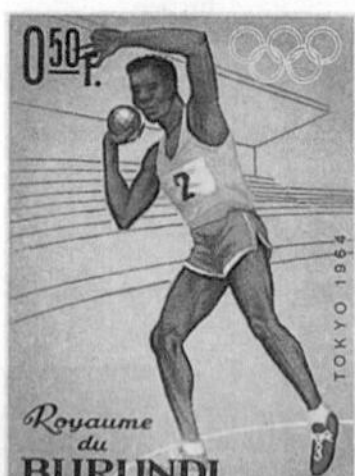

24 Putting the Shot

1964. Olympic Games, Tokyo. Inscr "TOKYO 1964". Multicoloured.
112 50c. Type **24** 10 10
113 1f. Throwing the discus . . . 10 10
114 3f. Swimming (horiz) 10 10
115 4f. Relay-racing 10 10
116 6f.50 Throwing the javelin . . 30 20
117 8f. Hurdling (horiz) 35 20
118 10f. Long-jumping (horiz) . . 40 20
119 14f. High-diving 55 20
120 18f. High-jumping (horiz) . . 65 35
121 20f. Gymnastics (horiz) . . . 85 35

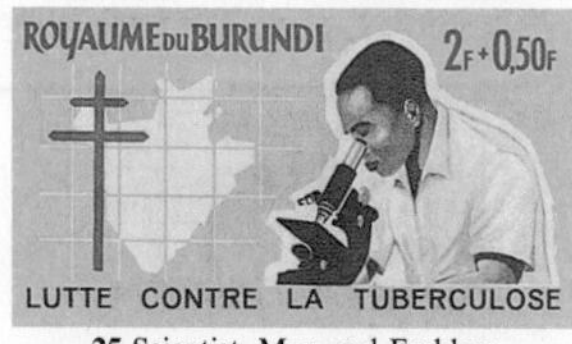

25 Scientist, Map and Emblem

1965. Anti-T.B. Campaign. Country name, values and Lorraine Cross in red.
122 **25** 2f.+50c. sepia and drab . . 10 10
123 4f.+1f.50 green & pink . . 25 10
124 5f.+2f.50 violet & buff . . 30 15
125 8f.+3f. blue and grey . . . 40 20
126 10f.+5f. red and green . . 55 30

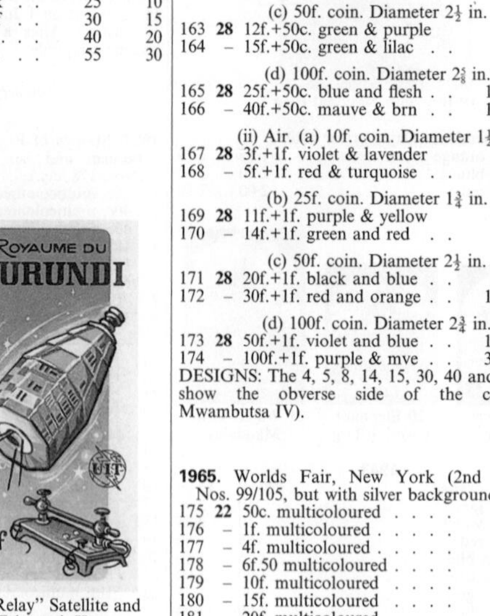

26 Purple Swamphen
27 "Relay" Satellite and Telegraph Key

1965. Birds. Multicoloured. (i) Postage. (a) Size as T **26**.
127 50c. Type **26** 10 10
128 1f. Little bee eater 10 10
129 1f.50 Secretary bird 10 10
130 2f. Painted stork 20 10
131 3f. Congo peafowl 25 10
132 3f.50 African darter 30 10

(b) Size 26 × 42½ mm.
133 4f. Type **26** 40 10
134 5f. Little bee eater 50 15
135 6f.50 Secretary bird 60 15
136 8f. Painted stork 60 15
137 10f. Congo peafowl 70 15
138 15f. African darter 85 25

(c) Size 33½ × 53 mm.
139 20f. Saddle-bill stork . . . . 1·25 25
140 50f. Abyssinian ground hornbill . . . . 2·40 50
141 100f. South African crowned crane . . . . 4·00 90

(ii) Air. Inscr "POSTE AERIENNE". Optd with gold border. (a) Size 26 × 42½ mm.
142 6f. Secretary bird 50 10
143 8f. African darter 60 15
144 10f. Congo peafowl 70 15
145 14f. Little bee eater 75 20
146 15f. Painted stork 85 20

(b) Size 33½ × 53 mm.
147 20f. Saddle-bill stork . . . . 1·25 30
148 50f. Abyssinian ground hornbill . . . . 2·25 80
149 75f. Martial eagle . . . . . 2·50 1·00
150 130f. Lesser flamingo . . . . 4·75 1·60

1965. Centenary of I.T.U. Multicoloured.
151 1f. Type **27** 10 10
152 3f. "Telstar 1" and hand telephone 10 10
153 4f. "Lunik 3" and wall telephone 10 10
154 6f.50 Weather satellite and tracking station 15 10
155 8f. "Telstar 2" and headphones 15 15
156 10f. "Sputnik" and radar scanner 20 15
157 14f. "Syncom" and aerial . . 30 20
158 20f. "Pioneer 5" space probe and radio aerial 35 30

28 Arms (reverse of 10f. coin)

1965. 1st Independence Anniv Gold Coinage Commem. Circular designs on gold foil, backed with multicoloured patterned paper. Imperf. (i) Postage. (a) 10f. coin. Diameter 1½ in.
159 **28** 2f.+50c. red & yellow . . . 15 15
160 – 4f.+50c. blue & red 20 20

(b) 25f. coin. Diameter 1¾ in.
161 **28** 6f.+50c. orange & grey . . 50 30
162 – 8f.+50c. blue & purple . . 60 60

(c) 50f. coin. Diameter 2½ in.
163 **28** 12f.+50c. green & purple 60 60
164 – 15f.+50c. green & lilac . . 65 65

(d) 100f. coin. Diameter 2⅝ in.
165 **28** 25f.+50c. blue and flesh . . 1·25 1·25
166 – 40f.+50c. mauve & brn . . 1·75 1·75

(ii) Air. (a) 10f. coin. Diameter 1½ in.
167 **28** 3f.+1f. violet & lavender 30 30
168 – 5f.+1f. red & turquoise . . 40 40

(b) 25f. coin. Diameter 1¾ in.
169 **28** 11f.+1f. purple & yellow 60 60
170 – 14f.+1f. green and red . . 60 60

(c) 50f. coin. Diameter 2½ in.
171 **28** 20f.+1f. black and blue . . 85 85
172 – 30f.+1f. red and orange . . 1·10 1·10

(d) 100f. coin. Diameter 2¾ in.
173 **28** 50f.+1f. violet and blue . . 1·25 1·25
174 – 100f.+1f. purple & mve . . 3·00 3·00
DESIGNS: The 4, 5, 8, 14, 15, 30, 40 and 100f. each show the obverse side of the coin (King Mwambutsa IV).

1965. Worlds Fair, New York (2nd series). As Nos. 99/105, but with silver backgrounds.
175 **22** 50c. multicoloured 10 10
176 – 1f. multicoloured 10 10
177 – 4f. multicoloured 15 10
178 – 6f.50 multicoloured 25 10
179 – 10f. multicoloured 45 20
180 – 15f. multicoloured 55 30
181 – 20f. multicoloured 70 35

29 Globe and I.C.Y. Emblem

1965. International Co-operation Year. Mult.
182 1f. Type **29** 10 10
183 4f. Map of Africa and cogwheel emblem of U.N. Science and Technology Conference 15 10
184 8f. Map of South-East Asia and Colombo Plan emblem 20 10
185 10f. Globe and U.N. emblem 25 10
186 18f. Map of Americas and "Alliance for Progress" emblem 40 10
187 25f. Map of Europe and C.E.P.T. emblems 60 30
188 40f. Space map and satellite (U.N.—"Peaceful Uses of Outer Space") . . . . . . 1·00 50

30 Prince Rwagasore and Memorial

1966. Prince Rwagasore and Pres. Kennedy Commemoration.
189 **30** 4f.+1f. brown and blue . . 20 10
190 – 10f.+1f. blue, brn & grn . . 30 10
191 – 20f.+2f. green and lilac . . 65 15
192 – 40f.+2f. brown & green . . 75 30
DESIGNS—HORIZ: 10f. Prince Rwagasore and Pres. Kennedy; 20f. Pres. Kennedy and memorial library. VERT: 40f. King Mwambutsa at Pres. Kennedy's grave.

31 Protea

1966. Flowers. Multicoloured. (i) Postage. (a) Size as T **31**.
194 50c. Type **31** 15 10
195 1f. Crossandra 15 10
196 1f.50 Ansellia 15 10
197 2f. Thunbergia 15 10
198 3f. Schizoglossum 25 10
199 3f.50 Dissotis 25 10

(b) Size 41 × 41 mm.
200 4f. Type **31** 25 10
201 5f. Crossandra 35 10
202 6f.50 Ansellia 45 10
203 8f. Thunbergia 65 10
204 10f. Schizoglossum 70 10
205 15f. Dissotis 85 10

(c) Size 50 × 50 mm.
206 20f. Type **31** . . . . 1·10 15
207 50f. Gazania . . . . 2·50 35
208 100f. Hibiscus . . . . 4·00 55
209 150f. Markhamia . . . . . . 6·25 75

(ii) Air. (a) Size 41 × 41 mm.
210 6f. Dissotis 25 15
211 8f. Crossandra 35 15
212 10f. Ansellia 35 15
213 14f. Thunbergia 40 15
214 15f. Schizoglossum 40 15

(b) Size 50 × 50 mm.
215 20f. Gazania 65 20
216 50f. Type **31** . . . . 1·75 40
217 75f. Hibiscus . . . . 2·50 1·00
218 130f. Markhamia . . . . . . 3·75 1·40

1967. Various stamps optd. (i) Nos. 127, etc. (Birds) optd **REPUBLIQUE DU BURUNDI** and bar. (a) Postage.
221 50c. multicoloured . . . . . 1·60 25
222 1f.50 multicoloured 35 25
223 3f.50 multicoloured 45 35
224 5f. multicoloured 60 45
225 6f.50 multicoloured 60 65
226 8f. multicoloured 70 80
227 10f. multicoloured 80 80
228 15f. multicoloured . . . . . . 1·10 1·25
229 20f. multicoloured . . . . . . 2·75 1·75
230 50f. multicoloured . . . . . . 5·25 3·75
231 100f. multicoloured . . . . . 8·50 7·00

(b) Air.
232 6f. multicoloured 55 25
233 8f. multicoloured 70 40
234 10f. multicoloured 85 65
235 14f. multicoloured . . . . . 1·10 65
236 15f. multicoloured . . . . . 1·25 80
237 20f. multicoloured . . . . . 1·75 95
238 50f. multicoloured . . . . . 6·25 2·75
239 75f. multicoloured . . . . . 8·50 3·50
240 130f. multicoloured . . . . . 12·00 5·75

(ii) Nos. 194, etc. (Flowers) optd as Nos. 221, etc., but with two bars. (a) Postage.
241 50c. multicoloured 15 15
242 1f. multicoloured 15 15
243 1f.50 multicoloured 15 15
244 2f. multicoloured 15 15
245 3f. multicoloured 20 15
246 3f.50 multicoloured 30 15
247 4f. multicoloured . . . . . . 1·90 15
248 5f. multicoloured 50 20
249 6f.50 multicoloured 45 30
250 8f. multicoloured 45 30
251 10f. multicoloured 60 40
252 15f. multicoloured 75 45
253 50f. multicoloured . . . . . 3·75 65
254 100f. multicoloured . . . . . 9·00 2·50
255 150f. multicoloured . . . . . 8·50 9·25

(b) Air.
256 6f. multicoloured 20 15
257 8f. multicoloured 30 15
258 10f. multicoloured 35 15
259 14f. multicoloured 45 30
260 15f. multicoloured 55 30
261 20f. multicoloured . . . . . 1·75 40
262 50f. multicoloured . . . . . 3·75 65
263 75f. multicoloured . . . . . 5·75 90
264 130f. multicoloured . . . . . 5·75 1·50

35 Sir Winston Churchill and St. Paul's Cathedral

1967. Churchill Commemoration.
265 **35** 4f.+1f. multicoloured . . . 30 10
266 – 15f.+2f. multicoloured . . 50 25
267 – 20f.+3f. multicoloured . . 60 35
DESIGNS (Churchill and): 15f. Tower of London; 20f. Big Ben and Boadicea statue, Westminster.

36 Egyptian Mouthbrooder

1967. Fishes. Multicoloured. (a) Postage. (i) Size as T **36**.
269 50c. Type **36** 15 20
270 1f. Spotted climbing-perch . . 15 20
271 1f.50 Six-banded lyretail . . 15 20
272 2f. Congo tetra 15 20
273 3f. Jewel cichlid 15 20
274 3f.50 Spotted mouthbrooder 15 20

(ii) Size 53½ × 27 mm.
275 4f. Type **36** 50 20
276 5f. As 1f. 50 20
277 6f.50. As 1f.50 . . . . 65 20
278 8f. As 2f. 65 20

279	10f. As 3f.	1·00	20
280	15f. As 3f.50	1·10	20
	(iii) Size 63½ × 31½ mm.		
281	20f. Type **36**	1·90	30
282	50f. Dusky snakehead	3·50	50
283	100f. Red-tailed notho	7·50	75
284	150f. African tetra	7·50	1·10
	(b) Air. (i) Size 50 × 23 mm.		
285	6f. Type **36**	30	20
286	8f. As 1f.	45	20
287	10f. As 1f.50	55	20
288	14f. As 2f.	65	20
289	15f. As 3f.	80	20
	(ii) Size 59 × 27 mm.		
290	20f. As 3f.50	95	20
291	50f. As 50f. (No. 282)	4·75	30
292	75f. As 100f.	6·00	50
293	130f. As 150f.	11·00	1·00

37 Baule Ancestral Figures

1967. "African Art". Multicoloured.

294	50c. Type **37** (postage)	10	10
295	1f. "Master of Buli's" carved seat	10	10
296	1f.50 Karumba antelope's head	10	10
297	2f. Bobo buffalo's head	10	10
298	4f. Guma-Goffa funeral figures	15	10
299	10f. Bakoutou "spirit" (carving) (air)	30	20
300	14f. Bamum sultan's throne	40	20
301	17f. Bebin bronze head	45	20
302	24f. Statue of 109th Bakouba king	55	30
303	26f. Burundi basketwork and lances	60	35

1967. 50th Anniv of Lions International. Nos. 265/7 optd **1917 1967** and emblem.

304	4f.+1f. multicoloured	50	20
305	15f.+2f. multicoloured	80	35
306	20f.+3f. multicoloured	95	35

39 Lord Baden-Powell (founder)

1967. 60th Anniv of Scout Movement and World Scout Jamboree, Idaho.

308	50c. Scouts climbing (postage)	20	10
309	1f. Scouts preparing meal	20	10
310	1f.50 Type **39**	20	10
311	2f. Two scouts	20	10
312	4f. Giving first aid	30	10
313	10f. As 50c. (air)	60	15
314	14f. As 1f.	70	15
315	17f. Type **39**	85	15
316	24f. As 2f.	1·10	35
317	26f. As 4f.	1·25	40

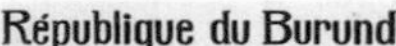

40 "The Gleaners" (Millet)

1967. World Fair, Montreal. Multicoloured.

318	4f. Type **40**	15	10
319	8f. "The Water-carrier of Seville" (Velasquez)	15	10
320	14f. "The Triumph of Neptune and Amphitrite" (Poussin)	35	15
321	18f. "Acrobat with a ball" (Picasso)	35	15
322	25f. "Margaret van Eyck" (Van Eyck)	95	25
323	40f. "St. Peter denying Christ" (Rembrandt)	1·10	50

41 Boeing 707

1967. Air. Opening of Bujumbura Airport. Aircraft and inscr in black and silver.

325 **41**	10f. green	40	10
326 –	14f. yellow	65	20
327 –	17f. blue	95	20
328 –	26f. purple	1·60	30

AIRCRAFT: 14f. Boeing 727 over lakes. 17f. Vickers Super VC-10 over lake. 26f. Boeing 727 over Bujumbura Airport.

42 Pres. Micombero and Flag

1967. 1st Anniv of Republic. Multicoloured.

329	5f. Type **42**	25	10
330	14f. Memorial and Arms	35	15
331	20f. View of Bujumbura and Arms	50	20
332	30f. "Place de la Revolution" and President Micombero	90	30

43 "The Adoration of the Shepherds" (J. B. Mayno)

1967. Christmas. Religious Paintings. Mult.

333	1f. Type **43**	10	10
334	4f. "The Holy Family" (A. van Dyck)	15	10
335	14f. "The Nativity" (Maitre de Moulins)	40	20
336	26f. "Madonna and Child" (C. Crivelli)	75	30

45 Downhill Skiing

1968. Winter Olympic Games, Grenoble. Mult.

339	5f. Type **45**	20	10
340	10f. Ice-hockey	25	10
341	14f. Figure-skating	40	10
342	17f. Bobsleighing	50	10
343	26f. Ski-jumping	65	10
344	40f. Speed-skating	1·10	25
345	60f. Olympic torch	1·75	30

46 "Portrait of a Young Man" (Botticelli)

1968. Famous Paintings. Multicoloured.

347	1f.50 Type **46** (postage)	10	10
348	2f. "La Maja Vestida" (Goya) (horiz)	10	10
349	4f. "The Lacemaker" (Vermeer)	15	10
350	17f. "Woman and Cat" (Renoir) (air)	40	20
351	24f. "The Jewish Bride" (Rembrandt) (horiz)	55	30
352	26f. "Pope Innocent X" (Velasquez)	80	40

47 Module landing on Moon

1968. Space Exploration. Multicoloured.

353	4f. Type **47** (postage)	20	10
354	6f. Russian cosmonaut in Space	30	10
355	8f. Weather satellite	30	10
356	10f. American astronaut in Space	45	15
357	14f. Type **47** (air)	40	15
358	18f. As 6f.	50	15
359	25f. As 8f.	80	25
360	40f. As 10f.	1·10	40

48 "Salamis aethiops"

1968. Butterflies. Multicoloured. (a) Postage. (i) Size 30½ × 34 mm.

362	50c. Type **48**	15	15
363	1f. "Graphium ridleyanus"	20	15
364	1f.50 "Cymothoe"	25	15
365	2f. "Charaxes eupale"	35	15
366	3f. "Papilio bromius"	40	15
367	3f.50 "Teracolus annae"	50	15
	(ii) Size 34 × 38 mm.		
368	4f. Type **48**	50	15
369	5f. As 1f.	50	15
370	6f.50 As 1f.50	60	15
371	8f. As 2f.	90	20
372	10f. As 3f.	1·10	20
373	15f. As 3f.50	1·40	25
	(iii) Size 41 × 46 mm.		
374	20f. Type **48**	2·50	30
375	50f. "Papilio zenobia"	4·50	75
376	100f. "Danais chrysippus"	8·25	1·25
377	150f. "Salamis temora"	14·00	2·10
	(b) Air. With gold frames. (i) Size 33 × 37 mm.		
378	6f. As 3f.50	50	15
379	8f. As 1f.	55	15
380	10f. As 1f.50	60	15
381	14f. As 2f.	70	20
382	15f. As 3f.	1·00	20
	(ii) Size 39 × 44 mm.		
383	20f. As 50f. (No. 375)	2·40	25
384	50f. Type **48**	5·50	50
385	75f. As 100f.	6·75	90
386	130f. As 150f.	12·50	1·10

49 "Woman by the Manzanares" (Goya)

1968. International Letter-writing Week. Mult.

387	4f. Type **49** (postage)	25	10
388	7f. "Reading a Letter" (De Hooch)	35	10
389	11f. "Woman reading a Letter" (Terborch)	40	10
390	14f. "Man writing a Letter" (Metsu)	45	10
391	17f. "The Letter" (Fragonard) (air)	60	10
392	26f. "Young Woman reading Letter" (Vermeer)	80	20
393	40f. "Folding a Letter" (Vigee-Lebrun)	90	25
394	50f. "Mademoiselle Lavergne" (Liotard)	95	35

50 Football

1968. Olympic Games, Mexico. Multicoloured.

396	4f. Type **50** (postage)	25	10
397	7f. Basketball	30	10
398	13f. High jumping	35	10
399	24f. Relay racing	55	20
400	40f. Throwing the javelin	1·25	40
401	10f. Putting the shot (air)	25	15
402	17f. Running	45	15
403	26f. Throwing the hammer	70	25
404	50f. Hurdling	1·40	45
405	75f. Long jumping	2·25	60

51 "Virgin and Child" (Lippi)

1968. Christmas. Paintings. Multicoloured.

407	3f. Type **51** (postage)	20	10
408	5f. "The Magnificat" (Botticelli)	25	10
409	6f. "Virgin and Child" (Durer)	40	10
410	11f. "Virgin and Child" (Raphael)	40	10
411	10f. "Madonna" (Correggio) (air)	25	10
412	14f. "The Nativity" (Baroccio)	35	15
413	17f. "The Holy Family" (El Greco)	55	20
414	26f. "Adoration of the Magi" (Maino)	75	35

52 W.H.O. Emblem and Map

1969. 20th Anniv of World Health Organization Operation in Africa.

416 **52**	5f. multicoloured	15	10
417	6f. multicoloured	20	10
418	11f. multicoloured	25	15

53 Hand holding Flame

1969. Air. Human Rights Year.
419 **53** 10f. multicoloured 35 10
420 14f. multicoloured 45 10
421 26f. multicoloured 65 25

1969. Space Flight of "Apollo 8". Nos. 407/14 optd ***VOL DE NOEL APOLLO 8*** and space module.
422 3f. multicoloured (postage) 15 10
423 5f. multicoloured 25 10
424 6f. multicoloured 40 10
425 11f. multicoloured 50 20
426 10f. multicoloured (air) . . . 30 15
427 14f. multicoloured 35 20
428 17f. multicoloured 55 25
429 26f. multicoloured 70 35

55 Map showing African Members

1969. 5th Anniv of Yaounde Agreement between Common Market Countries and African-Malagasy Economic Community. Multicoloured.
430 5f. Type **55** 20 10
431 14f. Ploughing with tractor 40 15
432 17f. Teacher and pupil . . . 55 20
433 26f. Maps of Africa and Europe (horiz) 75 25

56 "Resurrection" (Isenmann)

1969. Easter. Multicoloured.
434 11f. Type **56** 30 10
435 14f. "Resurrection" (Caron) 40 15
436 17f. "Noli me Tangere" (Schongauer) 45 20
437 26f. "Resurrection" (El Greco) 75 30

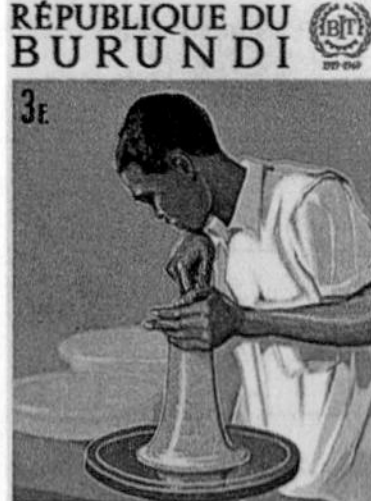

57 Potter

1969. 50th Anniv of I.L.O. Multicoloured.
439 3f. Type **57** 10 10
440 5f. Farm workers 10 10
441 7f. Foundry worker 25 10
442 10f. Harvester 25 15

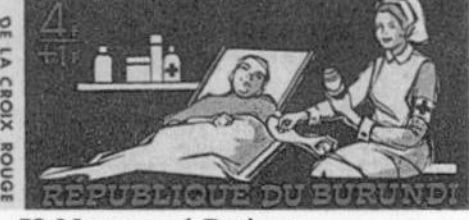

58 Nurse and Patient

1969. 50th Anniv of League of Red Cross Societies. Multicoloured.
443 4f.+1f. Type **58** (postage) . . 15 10
444 7f.+1f. Stretcher bearers . . . 35 10
445 11f.+1f. Operating theatre . . 50 15
446 17f.+1f. Blood bank 60 25
447 26f.+3f. Laboratory (air) . . 75 25
448 40f.+3f. Red Cross truck in African village . . . . . . 1·10 45
449 50f.+3f. Nurse and woman patient . . . . 1·60 50

59 Steel Works

1969. 5th Anniv of African Development Bank. Multicoloured.
451 10f. Type **59** 30 30
452 17f. Broadcaster 50 50
453 30f. Language laboratory . . 70 70
454 50f. Tractor and harrow . . 1·25 1·25

60 Pope Paul VI

1969. 1st Papal Visit to Africa. Multicoloured.
456 3f.+2f. Type **60** 15 10
457 5f.+2f. Pope Paul and map of Africa (horiz) 30 10
458 10f.+2f. Pope Paul and African flags (horiz) . . . 30 10
459 14f.+2f. Pope Paul and the Vatican (horiz) 55 10
460 17f.+2f. Type **60** 60 10
461 40f.+2f. Pope Paul and Uganda Martyrs (horiz) . . 1·25 30
462 50f.+2f. Pope Paul enthroned (horiz) . . . . 1·60 35

61 "Girl reading Letter" (Vermeer)

1969. International Letter-writing Week. Mult.
464 4f. Type **61** 15 10
465 7f. "Graziella" (Renoir) . . . 20 10
466 14f. "Woman writing a Letter" (Terborch) 30 10
467 26f. "Galileo" (unknown painter) 55 15
468 40f. "Beethoven" (unknown painter) . . . . 1·10 35

62 Blast-off

63 "Adoration of the Magi" (detail, Rubens)

1969. 1st Man on the Moon. Multicoloured.
470 4f. Type **62** (postage) 30 10
471 6f.50 Rocket in Space 40 10
472 7f. Separation of lunar module 50 10
473 14f. Module landing on Moon 80 15
474 17f. Command module in orbit . . . . 1·10 25
475 26f. Astronaut descending ladder (air) . . . . 1·25 20
476 40f. Astronaut on Moon's surface . . . . 2·00 25
477 50f. Module in sea . . . . . 3·00 45

1969. Christmas. Multicoloured.
479 5f. Type **63** (postage) 15 10
480 6f. "Virgin and Child with St. John" (Romano) . . . 15 10
481 10f. "Madonna of the Magnificat" (Botticelli) . . 40 15
482 17f. "Virgin and Child" (Garofalo) (horiz) (air) . . 60 15
483 26f. "Madonna and Child" (Negretti) (horiz) 80 20
484 50f. "Virgin and Child" (Barbarelli) (horiz) . . . . 1·60 35

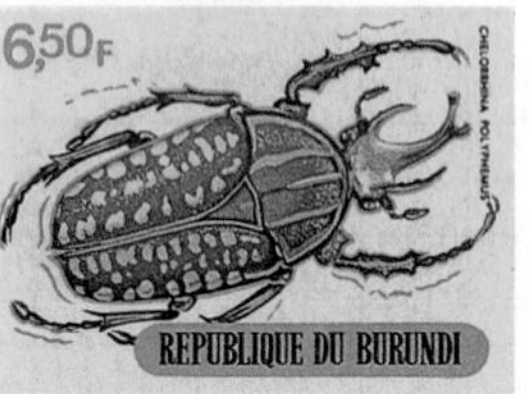

64 "Chelorrhina polyphemus"

1970. Beetles. Multicoloured. (a) Postage. (i) Size 39 × 28 mm.
486 50c. "Sternotomis bohemani" 20 10
487 1f. "Tetralobus flabellicornis" 20 10
488 1f.50 Type **64** 20 10
489 2f. "Brachytritus hieroglyphicus" 20 10
490 3f. "Goliathus goliathus" . . 20 10
491 3f.50 "Homoderus mellyi" . . 30 10

(ii) Size 46 × 32 mm.
492 4f. As 50c. 45 10
493 5f. As 1f. 65 10
494 6f. Type **64** 65 10
495 8f. As 2f. 65 10
496 10f. As 3f. 70 10
497 15f. As 3f.50 . . . . 1·10 15

(iii) Size 62 × 36 mm.
498 20f. As 50c. . . . . 1·50 30
499 50f. "Stephanorrhina guttata" 4·00 40
500 100f. "Phyllocnema viridocostata" . . . . . . 6·75 85
501 150f. "Mecynorrhina oberthueri" . . . . 8·25 1·60

(b) Air. (i) Size 46 × 32 mm.
502 6f. As 3f.50 . . . . 35 10
503 8f. As 1f. 45 10
504 10f. Type **64** 60 15
505 14f. As 2f. 70 15
506 15f. As 3f. 75 20

(ii) Size 52 × 36 mm.
507 20f. As 50f. (No. 499) . . . . 1·25 25
508 50f. As 50c. . . . . 4·00 35
509 75f. As 100f. . . . . 5·00 55
510 130f. As 150f. . . . . 8·00 80

65 "Jesus Condemned to Death"

1970. Easter. "The Stations of the Cross" (Carredano). Multicoloured.
511 1f. Type **65** (postage) . . . 10 10
512 1f.50 "Carrying the Cross" 10 10
513 2f. "Jesus falls for the First Time" 10 10
514 3f. "Jesus meets His Mother" 10 10
515 3f.50 "Simon of Cyrene takes the Cross" 15 10
516 4f. "Veronica wipes the face of Christ" 15 10
517 5f. "Jesus falls for the Second Time" 15 10
518 8f. "The Women of Jerusalem" (air) 20 10
519 10f. "Jesus falls for the Third Time" 25 15
520 14f. "Christ stripped" 30 25
521 15f. "Jesus nailed to the Cross" 40 25
522 18f. "The Crucifixion" . . . 40 30
523 20f. "Descent from the Cross" 50 30
524 50f. "Christ laid in the Tomb" . . . . 1·25 45

66 Japanese Parade

1970. World Fair, Osaka, Japan (EXPO '70). Multicoloured.
526 4f. Type **66** 15 10
527 6f.50 Exhibition site from the air 75 15
528 7f. African pavilions 20 10
529 14f. Pagoda (vert) 30 10
530 26f. Recording pavilion and pool 60 15
531 40f. Tower of the Sun (vert) 1·00 30
532 50f. National flags (vert) . . 1·25 35

67 Burundi Cow

1970. Source of the Nile. Multicoloured.
534 7f. Any design (postage) . . 95 30
535 14f. Any design (air) . . . . 1·25 30

Nos. 534 and 535 were each issued in se-tenant sheets of 18 stamps as Type **67**, showing map sections, animals and birds, forming a map of the Nile from Cairo to Burundi.

68 Common Redstart

1970. Birds. Multicoloured. (a) Postage. Size 44 × 33 mm or 33 × 44 mm.
536 2f. Great grey shrike (vert) 25 10
537 2f. Common starling (vert) 25 10
538 2f. Yellow wagtail (vert) . . . 25 10
539 2f. Sand martin (vert) 25 10
540 3f. Winter wren 60 10
541 3f. Firecrest 60 10
542 3f. Eurasian sky lark 60 10
543 3f. Crested lark 60 10
544 3f.50 Woodchat shrike (vert) 65 10
545 3f.50 Rock thrush (vert) . . . 65 10
546 3f.50 Black redstarts (vert) . . 65 10
547 3f.50 Ring ousel (vert) . . . 65 10
548 4f. Type **68** 95 10
549 4f. Dunnock 95 10
550 4f. Grey wagtail 95 10
551 4f. Meadow pipit 95 10
552 5f. Hoopoe (vert) . . . . . 1·25 15
553 5f. Pied flycatcher (vert) . . 1·25 15
554 5f. Great reed warbler (vert) 1·25 15
555 5f. River kingfisher (vert) . . 1·25 15
556 6f.50 House martin . . . . . 1·40 20
557 6f.50 Sedge warbler . . . . . 1·40 20
558 6f.50 Fieldfare . . . . 1·40 20
559 6f.50 Golden oriole . . . . . 1·40 20

(b) Air. Size 52 × 44 mm or 44 × 52 mm.
560 8f. As No. 536 . . . . 1·50 20
561 8f. As No. 537 . . . . 1·50 20
562 8f. As No. 538 . . . . 1·50 20
563 8f. As No. 539 . . . . 1·50 20
564 10f. As No. 540 . . . . . . 1·75 25
565 10f. As No. 541 . . . . . . 1·75 25
566 10f. As No. 542 . . . . . . 1·75 25
567 10f. As No. 543 . . . . . . 1·75 25
568 14f. As No. 544 . . . . . . 1·75 25
569 14f. As No. 545 . . . . . . 1·75 25
570 14f. As No. 546 . . . . . . 1·75 25
571 14f. As No. 547 . . . . . . 1·75 25
572 20f. Type **68** . . . . 2·10 30
573 20f. As No. 549 . . . . . . 2·10 30
574 20f. As No. 550 . . . . . . 2·10 30
575 20f. As No. 551 . . . . . . 2·10 30
576 30f. As No. 552 . . . . . . 2·25 30
577 30f. As No. 553 . . . . . . 2·25 30
578 30f. As No. 554 . . . . . . 2·25 30
579 30f. As No. 555 . . . . . . 2·25 30
580 50f. As No. 556 . . . . . . 3·75 30
581 50f. As No. 557 . . . . . . 3·75 30
582 50f. As No. 558 . . . . . . 3·75 30
583 50f. As No. 559 . . . . . . 3·75 30

69 Library

1970. International Educational Year. Mult.

584	3f. Type **69**	10	10
585	5f. Examination	15	10
586	7f. Experiments in the laboratory	25	10
587	10f. Students with electron microscope	30	10

70 United Nations Building, New York

1970. Air. 25th Anniv of United Nations. Mult.

588	7f. Type **70**	25	10
589	11f. Security Council in session	30	10
590	26f. Paul VI and U Thant	70	20
591	40f. U.N. and National flags	1·00	30

71 Pres. Micombero and Wife

1970. 4th Anniv of Republic.

593	4f. Type **71**	10	10
594	7f. Pres. Micombero and flag	25	10
595	11f. Revolution Memorial	35	15

72 King Baudouin and Queen Fabiola

1970. Air. Visit of King and Queen of the Belgians. Each brown, purple and gold.

597	6f. Type **72**	65	15
598	20f. Pres. Micombero and King Baudouin	1·50	40
599	40f. Pres. Micombero in evening dress	3·00	70

73 "Adoration of the Magi" (Durer)

1970. Christmas. Multicoloured.

601	6f.50+1f. Type **73** (postage)	50	15
602	11f.+1f. "The Virgin of the Eucharist" (Botticelli)	60	25
603	20f.+1f. "The Holy Family" (El Greco)	90	30
604	14f.+3f. "The Adoration of the Magi" (Velasquez) (air)	50	25
605	26f.+3f. "The Holy Family" (Van Cleve)	85	40
606	40f.+3f. "Virgin and Child" (Van der Weyden)	1·40	60

74 Lenin in Discussion

76 "The Resurrection" (Il Sodoma)

75 Lion

1970. Birth Cent of Lenin. Each brown and gold.

608	3f.50 Type **74**	20	15
609	5f. Lenin addressing Soviet	30	15
610	6f.50 Lenin with soldier and sailor	40	15
611	15f. Lenin speaking to crowd	60	25
612	50f. Lenin	2·00	55

1971. African Animals (1st series). Multicoloured. (a) Postage. Size 38 × 38 mm.

613	1f. Type **75**	35	10
614	1f. African buffalo	35	10
615	1f. Hippopotamus	35	10
616	1f. Giraffe	35	10
617	2f. Topi	50	15
618	2f. Black rhinoceros	50	15
619	2f. Common zebra	50	15
620	2f. Leopard	50	15
621	3f. Grant's gazelle	85	25
622	3f. Cheetah	85	25
623	3f. African white-backed vultures	85	25
624	3f. Okapi	85	25
625	5f. Chimpanzee	1·00	25
626	5f. African elephant	1·00	25
627	5f. Spotted hyena	1·00	25
628	5f. Gemsbok	1·00	25
629	6f. Gorilla	1·40	25
630	6f. Blue wildebeest	1·40	25
631	6f. Warthog	1·40	25
632	6f. Hunting dog	1·40	25
633	11f. Sable antelope	2·25	30
634	11f. Caracal	2·25	30
635	11f. Ostriches	2·25	30
636	11f. Bongo	2·25	30

(b) Air. Size 44 × 44 mm.

637	10f. Type **75**	70	35
638	10f. As No. 614	70	35
639	10f. As No. 615	70	35
640	10f. As No. 616	70	35
641	14f. As No. 617	80	40
642	14f. As No. 618	80	40
643	14f. As No. 619	80	40
644	14f. As No. 620	80	40
645	17f. As No. 621	90	40
646	17f. As No. 622	90	40
647	17f. As No. 623	90	40
648	17f. As No. 624	90	40
649	24f. As No. 625	1·50	55
650	24f. As No. 626	1·50	55
651	24f. As No. 627	1·50	55
652	24f. As No. 628	1·50	55
653	26f. As No. 629	1·50	55
654	26f. As No. 630	1·50	55
655	26f. As No. 631	1·50	55
656	26f. As No. 632	1·50	55
657	31f. As No. 633	1·60	70
658	31f. As No. 634	1·60	70
659	31f. As No. 635	1·60	70
660	31f. As No. 636	1·60	70

See also Nos. 1028/75, 1178/1225 and 1385/97.

1971. Easter. Multicoloured.

661	3f. Type **76** (postage)	15	10
662	6f. "The Resurrection" (Del Castagno)	30	10
663	11f. "Noli Me Tangere" (Correggio)	45	15
664	14f. "The Resurrection" (Borrassa) (air)	50	20
665	17f. "The Resurrection" (Della Francesca)	65	20
666	26f. "The Resurrection" (Pleydenwyurff)	85	30

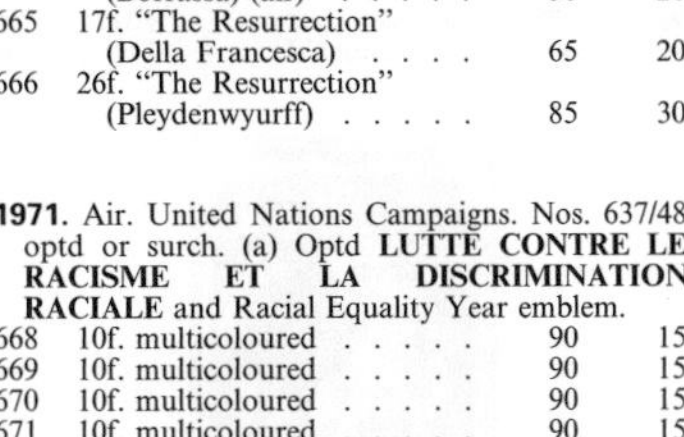

1971. Air. United Nations Campaigns. Nos. 637/48 optd or surch. (a) Optd **LUTTE CONTRE LE RACISME ET LA DISCRIMINATION RACIALE** and Racial Equality Year emblem.

668	10f. multicoloured	90	15
669	10f. multicoloured	90	15
670	10f. multicoloured	90	15
671	10f. multicoloured	90	15

(b) Surch **LUTTE CONTRE L'ANALPHABETISME**, U.N.E.S.C.O. emblem and premium (Campaign against Illiteracy).

672	14f.+2f. multicoloured	1·40	25
673	14f.+2f. multicoloured	1·40	25
674	14f.+2f. multicoloured	1·40	25
675	14f.+2f. multicoloured	1·40	25

(c) Surch **AIDE INTERNATIONALE AUX REFUGIES**, emblem and premium (Int Help for Refugees).

676	17f.+1f. multicoloured	2·25	40
677	17f.+1f. multicoloured	2·25	40
678	17f.+1f. multicoloured	2·25	40
679	17f.+1f. multicoloured	2·25	40

1971. Air. Olympic Commems. Nos. 653/56 surch. (a) Surch **75eme ANNIVERSAIRE DES JEUX OLYMPIQUES MODERNES (1896–1971)**, Olympic rings and premium.

680	26f.+1f. multicoloured	1·25	35
681	26f.+1f. multicoloured	1·25	35
682	26f.+1f. multicoloured	1·25	35
683	26f.+1f. multicoloured	1·25	35

(b) Surch **JEUX PRE-OLYMPIQUES MUNICH 1972**, rings and premium (Olympic Games, Munich (1972)).

684	31f.+1f. multicoloured	2·25	1·10
685	31f.+1f. multicoloured	2·25	1·10
686	31f.+1f. multicoloured	2·25	1·10
687	31f.+1f. multicoloured	2·25	1·10

79 "Venetian Girl"

81 "The Virgin and Child" (Il Perugino)

1971. International Letter-writing Week. Paintings by Durer. Multicoloured.

688	6f. Type **79**	30	30
689	11f. "Jerome Holzschuhers"	35	35
690	14f. "Emperor Maximilian"	40	40
691	17f. Altar painting, Paumgartner	65	65
692	26f. "The Halle Madonna"	80	80
693	31f. Self-portrait	1·00	1·00

1971. 6th Congress of International Institute of French Law, Bujumbura. Nos. 668/693 optd **VIeme CONGRES DE L'INSTITUT INTERNATIONAL DE DROIT D'EXPRESSION FRANCAISE**.

695	6f. multicoloured	30	10
696	11f. multicoloured	35	10
697	14f. multicoloured	45	20
698	17f. multicoloured	65	20
699	26f. multicoloured	75	25
700	31f. multicoloured	1·00	25

1971. Christmas. Paintings of "Virgin and Child" by following artists. Multicoloured.

702	3f. Type **81** (postage)	15	10
703	5f. Del Sarto	25	10
704	6f. Morales	50	10
705	14f. Da Conegliano (air)	55	15
706	17f. Lippi	60	20
707	31f. Leonardo da Vinci	1·10	45

1971. 25th Anniv of U.N.I.C.E.F. Nos. 702/7 surch **UNICEF XXVe ANNIVERSAIRE 1946–1971**, emblem and premium.

709	3f.+1f. mult (postage)	30	10
710	5f.+1f. multicoloured	50	20
711	6f.+1f. multicoloured	60	30
712	14f.+1f. mult (air)	40	20
713	17f.+1f. multicoloured	95	25
714	31f.+1f. multicoloured	1·50	45

83 "Archangel Michael" (icon, St. Mark's)

1971. U.N.E.S.C.O. "Save Venice" Campaign. Multicoloured.

716	3f.+1f. Type **83** (postage)	25	10
717	5f.+1f. "La Polenta" (Longhi)	35	15
718	6f.+1f. "Gossip" (Longhi)	35	15
719	11f.+1f. "Diana's Bath" (Pittoni)	45	25
720	10f.+1f. Casa d'Oro (air)	45	10
721	17f.+1f. Doge's Palace	65	15
722	24f.+1f. St. John and St. Paul Church	90	25
723	31f.+1f. "Doge's Palace and Piazzetta" (Canaletto)	2·00	40

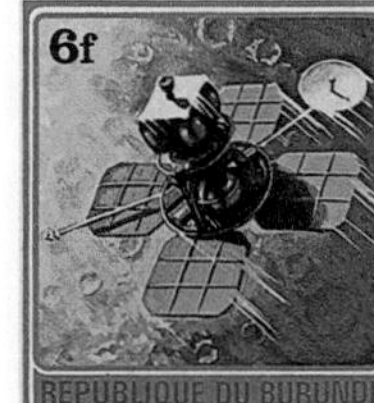

84 "Lunar Orbiter"

1972. Conquest of Space. Multicoloured.

725	6f. Type **84**	15	15
726	11f. "Vostok" spaceship	40	15
727	14f. "Luna 1"	45	30
728	17f. First Man on Moon	65	30
729	26f. "Soyuz 11" space flight	80	40
730	40f. "Lunar Rover"	1·60	95

85 Slalom skiing

1972. Winter Olympic Games, Sapporo, Japan. Multicoloured.

732	5f. Type **85**	15	10
733	6f. Pair skating	20	10
734	11f. Figure-skating	35	10
735	14f. Ski-jumping	35	20
736	17f. Ice-hockey	50	20
737	24f. Speed skating	60	25
738	26f. Ski-bobbing	60	25
739	31f. Downhill skiing	75	25
740	50f. Bobsleighing	1·50	35

86 "Ecce Homo" (Metzys)

1972. Easter. Paintings. Multicoloured.

742	3f.50 Type **86**	20	10
743	6f.50 "The Crucifixion" (Rubens)	30	10
744	10f. "The Descent from the Cross" (Portormo)	40	10
745	18f. "Pieta" (Gallegos)	70	15
746	27f. "The Trinity" (El Greco)	1·40	30

87 Gymnastics

1972. Olympic Games. Munich. Multicoloured.

748	5f. Type **87** (postage)	20	10
749	6f. Throwing the javelin	20	10
750	11f. Fencing	35	15
751	14f. Cycling	50	20
752	17f. Pole-vaulting	75	20
753	24f. Weightlifting (air)	65	25
754	26f. Hurdling	90	25
755	31f. Throwing the discus	1·40	40
756	40f. Football	1·50	50

88 Prince Rwagasore, Pres. Micombero and Drummers

1972. 10th Anniv of Independence. Multicoloured.

758	5f. Type **88** (postage)	15	10
759	7f. Rwagasore, Micombero and map	25	10
760	13f. Pres. Micombero and Burundi flag	40	15
761	15f. Type **65** (air)	30	15
762	18f. As 7f.	35	15
763	27f. As 13f.	60	30

89 "Madonna and Child" (A. Solario)

1972. Christmas. "Madonna and Child" paintings by artists given below. Multicoloured.

765	5f. Type **89** (postage)	30	10
766	10f. Raphael	50	10
767	15f. Botticelli	75	15
768	18f. S. Mainardi (air)	50	15
769	27f. H. Memling	1·00	25
770	40f. Lotto	1·50	40

90 "Platycoryne crocea"

1972. Orchids. Multicoloured.

772	50c. Type **90** (postage)	30	15
773	1f. "Cattleya trianaei"	30	15
774	2f. "Eulophia cucullata"	30	15
775	3f. "Cymbidium hamsey"	30	15
776	4f. "Thelymitra pauciflora"	30	15
777	5f. "Miltassia"	30	15
778	6f. "Miltonia"	1·25	15
779	7f. Type **90**	1·25	15
780	8f. As 1f.	1·40	15
781	9f. As 2f.	1·40	20
782	10f. As 3f.	1·90	20
783	13f. As 4f. (air)	1·25	15
784	14f. As 5f.	1·25	15
785	15f. As 6f.	1·60	20
786	18f. Type **90**	1·60	20
787	20f. As 1f.	1·60	25
788	27f. As 2f.	2·75	30
789	36f. As 3f.	4·50	40

Nos. 779/89 are size 53 × 53 mm.

1972. Christmas Charity. Nos. 765/770 surch.

790	5f.+1f. mult (postage)	35	15
791	10f.+1f. multicoloured	65	20
792	15f.+1f. multicoloured	75	25
793	18f.+1f. multicoloured (air)	60	20
794	27f.+1f. multicoloured	90	25
795	40f.+1f. multicoloured	1·50	45

92 H. M. Stanley

1973. Centenary of Stanley/Livingstone African Exploration. Multicoloured.

797	5f. Type **92** (postage)	20	10
798	7f. Expedition bearers	25	10
799	13f. Stanley directing foray	45	15
800	15f. Dr. Livingstone (air)	35	20
801	18f. Stanley meets Livingstone	55	20
802	27f. Stanley conferring with Livingstone	1·00	30

93 "The Scourging" (Caravaggio)

1973. Easter. Multicoloured.

804	5f. Type **93** (postage)	15	10
805	7f. "Crucifixion" (Van der Weyden)	25	10
806	13f. "The Deposition" (Raphael)	50	15
807	15f. "Christ bound to the Pillar" (Guido Reni) (air)	45	25
808	18f. "Crucifixion" (M. Grunewald)	70	25
809	27f. "The Descent from the Cross" (Caravaggio)	1·10	30

94 Interpol Emblem

1973. 50th Anniv of Interpol. Multicoloured.

811	5f. Type **94** (postage)	25	10
812	10f. Burundi flag	40	10
813	18f. Interpol H.Q., Paris	60	15
814	27f. As 5f. (air)	75	25
815	40f. As 10f.	1·25	35

95 Capricorn, Aquarius and Pisces

1973. 500th Birth Anniv of Copernicus.

816 **95**	3f. gold, red and black (postage)	20	10
817 –	3f. gold, red and black	20	10
818 –	3f. gold, red and black	20	10
819 –	3f. gold, red and black	20	10
820 –	5f. multicoloured	30	10
821 –	5f. multicoloured	30	10
822 –	5f. multicoloured	30	10
823 –	5f. multicoloured	30	10
824 –	7f. multicoloured	40	10
825 –	7f. multicoloured	40	10
826 –	7f. multicoloured	40	10
827 –	7f. multicoloured	40	10
828 –	13f. multicoloured	60	10
829 –	13f. multicoloured	60	10
830 –	13f. multicoloured	60	10
831 –	13f. multicoloured	60	10
832 –	15f. multicoloured (air)	40	15
833 –	15f. multicoloured	40	15
834 –	15f. multicoloured	40	15
835 –	15f. multicoloured	40	15
836 –	18f. multicoloured	55	15
837 –	18f. multicoloured	55	15
838 –	18f. multicoloured	55	15
839 –	18f. multicoloured	55	15
840 –	27f. multicoloured	95	25
841 –	27f. multicoloured	95	25
842 –	27f. multicoloured	95	25
843 –	27f. multicoloured	95	25
844 –	36f. multicoloured	2·10	40
845 –	36f. multicoloured	2·10	40
846 –	36f. multicoloured	2·10	40
847 –	36f. multicoloured	2·10	40

DESIGNS: No. 816, Type **95**; 817, Aries, Taurus and Gemini; 818, Cancer, Leo and Virgo; 819, Libra, Scorpio and Sagittarius; 820/23, Greek and Roman Gods; 824/7, Ptolemy and Ptolemaic System; 828/31, Copernicus and Solar System; 823/5, Copernicus, Earth, Pluto and Jupiter; 836/39, Copernicus, Venus, Saturn and Mars; 840/43, Copernicus, Uranus, Neptune and Mercury; 844/7, Earth and spacecraft.

The four designs of each value were issued se-tenant in blocks of four within the sheet, forming composite designs.

96 "Protea cynaroides"

1973. Flora and Butterflies. Multicoloured.

849	1f. Type **96** (postage)	70	15
850	1f. "Precis octavia"	70	15
851	1f. "Epiphora bauhiniae"	70	15
852	1f. "Gazania longiscapa"	70	15
853	2f. "Kniphofia" – "Royal Standard"	70	15
854	2f. "Cymothoe coccinata hew"	1·00	20
855	2f. "Nudaurelia zambesina"	1·00	20
856	2f. "Freesia refracta"	1·00	15
857	3f. "Calotis eupompe"	1·00	20
858	3f. Narcissus	1·00	15
859	3f. "Cineraria hybrida"	1·00	15
860	3f. "Cyrestis camillus"	1·00	20
861	5f. "Iris tingitana"	1·40	15
862	5f. "Papilio demodocus"	2·10	20
863	5f. "Catopsilia avelaneda"	2·10	20
864	5f. "Nerine sarniensis"	1·40	15
865	6f. "Hypolimnas dexithea"	2·10	20
866	6f. "Zantedeschia tropicalis"	1·40	15
867	6f. "Sandersonia aurantiaca"	1·40	15
868	6f. "Drurya antimachus"	2·10	20
869	11f. "Nymphaea capensis"	1·75	20
870	11f. "Pandoriana pandora"	2·75	25
871	11f. "Precis orythia"	2·75	25
872	11f. "Pelargonium domesticum"–"Aztec"	1·75	20
873	10f. Type **96** (air)	50	10
874	10f. As No. 850	90	10
875	10f. As No. 851	90	10
876	10f. As No. 852	50	10
877	14f. As No. 853	60	10
878	14f. As No. 854	1·00	20
879	14f. As No. 855	1·00	20
880	14f. As No. 856	40	15
881	17f. As No. 857	1·25	25
882	17f. As No. 858	90	20
883	17f. As No. 859	90	20
884	17f. As No. 860	1·25	25
885	24f. As No. 861	1·40	25
886	24f. As No. 862	1·75	30
887	24f. As No. 863	1·75	30
888	24f. As No. 864	1·10	25
889	26f. As No. 865	1·75	30
890	26f. As No. 866	1·10	30
891	26f. As No. 867	1·10	30
892	26f. As No. 868	1·75	30
893	31f. As No. 869	1·25	35
894	31f. As No. 870	1·90	45
895	31f. As No. 871	1·90	45
896	31f. As No. 872	1·25	35

Nos. 849, 852/3, 856, 858/9, 861, 864, 866/7, 869, 872, 876/7, 880, 882/3, 885, 888, 890/1, 893 and 896 depict flora and the remainder butterflies.

The four designs of each value were issued se-tenant in blocks of four within the sheet, forming composite designs.

97 "Virgin and Child" (G. Bellini)

1973. Christmas. Various paintings of "The Virgin and Child" by artists listed below. Multicoloured.

897	5f. Type **97** (postage)	45	10
898	10f. Van Eyck	55	15
899	15f. G. A. Boltraffio	75	20
900	18f. Raphael (air)	35	10
901	27f. P. Perugino	1·10	30
902	40f. Titian	1·60	40

1973. Christmas Charity. Nos. 897/902 surch.

904 **97**	5f.+1f. mult (postage)	50	15
905 –	10f.+1f. multicoloured	80	20
906 –	15f.+1f. multicoloured	95	25
907 –	18f.+1f. mult (air)	70	15
908 –	27f.+1f. multicoloured	1·10	35
909 –	40f.+1f. multicoloured	1·60	50

98 "The Pieta" (Veronese)

1974. Easter. Religious Paintings. Multicoloured.

911	5f. Type **98**	15	10
912	10f. "The Virgin and St. John" (Van der Weyden)	30	15
913	18f. "The Crucifixion" (Van der Weyden)	60	20
914	27f. "The Entombment" (Titian)	85	30
915	40f. "The Pieta" (El Greco)	2·10	50

99 Egyptian Mouthbrooder ("Haplochromis multicolor")

1974. Fishes. Multicoloured.

917	1f. Type **99** (postage)	55	10
918	1f. Spotted mouthbrooder ("Tropheus duboisi")	55	10
919	1f. Freshwater butterfly-fish ("Pantodon buchholzi")	55	10
920	1f. Six-banded distichodus ("Distichodus sexfasciatus")	55	10
921	2f. Rainbow krib ("Pelmatochromis kribensis")	55	10
922	2f. African leaf-fish ("Polycentropsis abbreviata")	55	10
923	2f. Three-lined tetra ("Nannaethiops tritaeniatus")	55	10
924	2f. Jewel cichlid ("Hemichromis bimaculatus")	55	10
925	3f. Spotted climbing-perch ("Ctenopoma acutirostre")	55	10
926	3f. African mouthbrooder ("Tilapia melanopleura")	55	10
927	3f. Angel squeaker ("Synodontis angelicus")	55	10
928	3f. Two-striped lyretail ("Aphyosemion bivittatum")	55	10
929	5f. Diamond fingerfish ("Monodactylus argenteus")	90	10
930	5f. Regal angelfish ("Pygoplites diacanthus")	90	10
931	5f. Moorish idol ("Zanclus canescens")	90	10
932	5f. Peacock hind ("Cephalopholis argus") and surgeonfish	90	10
933	6f. Bigeye ("Priacanthus arenatus")	2·75	10
934	6f. Rainbow parrotfish ("Scarus guacamaia") and French angelfish	2·75	10
935	6f. French angelfish ("Pomacanthus arcuatus")	2·75	10
936	6f. John dory ("Zeus faber")	2·75	10
937	11f. Scribbled cowfish ("Lactophrys quadricornis")	3·00	20
938	11f. Ocean surgeonfish ("Acanthurus bahianus")	3·00	20
939	11f. Queen triggerfish ("Balistes vetula")	3·00	20
940	11f. Queen angelfish ("Holocanthus ciliaris")	3·00	20
941	10f. Type **99** (air)	45	10
942	10f. As No. 918	45	10
943	10f. As No. 919	45	10
944	10f. As No. 920	45	10
945	14f. As No. 921	95	10
946	14f. As No. 922	95	10
947	14f. As No. 923	95	10
948	14f. As No. 924	95	10
949	17f. As No. 925	95	10
950	17f. As No. 926	95	10
951	17f. As No. 927	95	10
952	17f. As No. 928	95	10
953	24f. As No. 929	2·10	10
954	24f. As No. 930	2·10	10
955	24f. As No. 931	2·10	10
956	24f. As No. 932	2·10	10
957	26f. As No. 933	3·00	20
958	26f. As No. 934	3·00	20
959	26f. As No. 935	3·00	20
960	26f. As No. 936	3·00	20
961	31f. As No. 937	3·75	30
962	31f. As No. 938	3·75	30
963	31f. As No. 939	3·75	30
964	31f. As No. 940	3·75	30

The four designs of each value are arranged together in se-tenant blocks of four within the sheet, forming composite designs.

100 Footballers and World Cup Trophy

1974. World Cup Football Championships.
965 **100** 5f. mult (postage) 25 10
966 – 6f. multicoloured 30 10
967 – 11f. multicoloured 40 20
968 – 14f. multicoloured 50 25
969 – 17f. multicoloured 55 25
970 – 20f. multicoloured (air) 70 35
971 – 26f. multicoloured 90 45
972 – 40f. multicoloured . . . . 1·40 60
DESIGNS: Nos. 966/72, Football scenes as Type **100**.

101 Burundi Flag

1974. Centenary of U.P.U. Multicoloured.
974 6f. Type **101** (postage) . . . 20 10
975 6f. Burundi P.T.T. Building 20 10
976 11f. Postmen carrying letters 30 10
977 11f. Postmen carrying letters 30 10
978 14f. U.P.U. Monument . . . 1·25 70
979 14f. Mail transport . . . . . 1·25 70
980 17f. Burundi on map 55 10
981 17f. Dove and letter 55 10
982 24f. Type **101** (air) 80 20
983 24f. As No. 975 . . . . . . 80 20
984 26f. As No. 976 . . . . . . 1·10 30
985 26f. As No. 977 . . . . . . 1·10 30
986 31f. As No. 978 . . . . . . 2·75 1·10
987 31f. As No. 979 . . . . . . 2·75 1·10
988 40f. As No. 980 . . . . . . 3·50 45
989 40f. As No. 981 . . . . . . 3·50 45
The two designs in each denomination were arranged together in se-tenant pairs within the sheet, each pair forming a composite design.

102 "St. Ildefonse writing a letter" (El Greco)

1974. International Letter-writing Week. Mult.
991 6f. Type **102** 30 15
992 11f. "Lady sealing a letter" (Chardin) 50 20
993 14f. "Titus at desk" (Rembrandt) 55 30
994 17f. "The Love-letter" (Vermeer) 60 30
995 26f. "The Merchant G. Gisze" (Holbein) . . . 65 50
996 31f. "A. Lenoir" (David) . . 90 55

103 "Virgin and Child". (Van Orley)

1974. Christmas. Showing "Virgin and Child" paintings by artists named. Multicoloured.
998 5f. Type **103** (postage) . . . 25 10
999 10f. Hans Memling 45 15
1000 15f. Botticelli . . . . 1·00 20
1001 18f. Hans Memling (different) (air) 35 20
1002 27f. F. Lippi . . . . 1·10 35
1003 40f. L. di Gredi . . . . . . 1·50 45

1974. Christmas Charity. Nos. 998/1003 surch.
1005 **103** 5f.+1f. mult (postage) . . 30 10
1006 – 10f.+1f. multicoloured 40 25
1007 – 15f.+1f. multicoloured 1·10 30
1008 – 18f.+1f. mult (air) . . . 55 20
1009 – 27f.+1f. multicoloured 85 35
1010 – 40f.+1f. multicoloured 1·60 45

104 "Apollo" Spacecraft with Docking Tunnel

1975. "Apollo–Soyuz" Space Project.
1012 26f. Type **104** (postage) . . 45 30
1013 26f. Leonov and Kubasov 45 30
1014 26f. "Soyuz" Spacecraft . . 45 30
1015 26f. Slayton, Brand and Stafford 45 30
1016 31f. "Soyuz" launch 55 40
1017 31f. "Apollo" and "Soyuz" spacecraft 55 40
1018 31f. "Apollo" third stage separation 55 40
1019 31f. Slayton, Brand, Stafford, Leonov and Kubasov 55 40
1020 27f. Type **104** (air) 60 45
1021 27f. As No. 1012 . . . . . 60 45
1022 27f. As No. 1013 . . . . . 60 45
1023 27f. As No. 1014 . . . . . 60 45
1024 40f. As No. 1015 . . . . . 80 60
1025 40f. As No. 1016 . . . . . 80 60
1026 40f. As No. 1017 . . . . . 80 60
1027 40f. As No. 1018 . . . . . 80 60
The four designs in each value were issued together in se-tenant blocks of four within the sheet.

105 Addax

1975. African Animals (2nd series). Multicoloured.
1028 1f. Type **105** (postage) . . . 40 15
1029 1f. Roan antelope 40 15
1030 1f. Nyala 40 15
1031 1f. White rhinoceros 40 15
1032 2f. Mandrill 40 15
1033 2f. Eland 40 15
1034 2f. Salt's dik-dik 40 15
1035 2f. Thomson's gazelles . . . 40 15
1036 3f. African claw-less otter 55 15
1037 3f. Bohar reedbuck 55 15
1038 3f. African civet 55 15
1039 3f. African buffalo 55 15
1040 5f. Black wildebeest 55 15
1041 5f. African asses 55 15
1042 5f. Angolan black and white colobus 55 15
1043 5f. Gerenuk 55 15
1044 6f. Addra gazelle 95 20
1045 6f. Black-backed jackal . . 95 20
1046 6f. Sitatungas 95 20
1047 6f. Banded duiker 95 20
1048 11f. Fennec fox . . . . . . 1·40 20
1049 11f. Lesser kudus . . . . . 1·40 20
1050 11f. Blesbok . . . . 1·40 20
1051 11f. Serval . . . . 1·40 20
1052 10f. Type **105** (air) 60 10
1053 10f. As No. 1029 . . . . . 60 10
1054 10f. As No. 1030 . . . . . 60 10
1055 10f. As No. 1031 . . . . . 60 10
1056 14f. As No. 1032 . . . . . 70 15
1057 14f. As No. 1033 . . . . . 70 15
1058 14f. As No. 1034 . . . . . 70 15
1059 14f. As No. 1035 . . . . . 70 15
1060 17f. As No. 1036 . . . . . 1·10 15
1061 17f. As No. 1037 . . . . . 1·10 15
1062 17f. As No. 1038 . . . . . 1·10 15
1063 17f. As No. 1039 . . . . . 1·10 15
1064 24f. As No. 1040 . . . . . 1·75 20
1065 24f. As No. 1041 . . . . . 1·75 20
1066 24f. As No. 1042 . . . . . 1·75 20
1067 24f. As No. 1043 . . . . . 1·75 20
1068 26f. As No. 1044 . . . . . 1·90 20
1069 26f. As No. 1045 . . . . . 1·90 20
1070 26f. As No. 1046 . . . . . 1·90 20
1071 26f. As No. 1047 . . . . . 1·90 20
1072 31f. As No. 1048 . . . . . 2·25 25
1073 31f. As No. 1049 . . . . . 2·25 25
1074 31f. As No. 1050 . . . . . 2·25 25
1075 31f. As No. 1051 . . . . . 2·25 25
The four designs in each value were issued together in horiz. se-tenant strips within the sheet, forming composite designs.

1975. Air. International Women's Year. Nos. 1052/9 optd **ANNEE INTERNATIONALE DE LA FEMME**.
1076 **105** 10f. multicoloured . . . 80 50
1077 – 10f. multicoloured . . . 80 50
1078 – 10f. multicoloured . . . 80 50
1079 – 10f. multicoloured . . . 80 50
1080 – 14f. multicoloured . . . 1·40 60
1081 – 14f. multicoloured . . . 1·40 60
1082 – 14f. multicoloured . . . 1·40 60
1083 – 14f. multicoloured . . . 1·40 60

1975. Air. 30th Anniv of United Nations. Nos. 1068/75 optd **30eme ANNIVERSAIRE DES NATIONS UNIES**.
1084 26f. multicoloured . . . . . 1·40 1·25
1085 26f. multicoloured . . . . . 1·40 1·25
1086 26f. multicoloured . . . . . 1·40 1·25
1087 26f. multicoloured . . . . . 1·40 1·25
1088 31f. multicoloured . . . . . 2·25 2·00
1089 31f. multicoloured . . . . . 2·25 2·00
1090 31f. multicoloured . . . . . 2·25 2·00
1091 31f. multicoloured . . . . . 2·25 2·00

108 "Jonah"

1975. Christmas. 500th Birth Anniv of Michaelangelo. Multicoloured.
1092 5f. Type **108** (postage) . . . 25 10
1093 5f. "Libyan Sibyl" 25 10
1094 13f. "Daniel" 90 10
1095 13f. "Cumaean Sybil" . . . 90 10
1096 27f. "Isaiah" . . . . 1·25 15
1097 27f. "Delphic Sybil" (different) . . . . 1·25 15
1098 18f. "Zachariah" (air) . . . 90 10
1099 18f. "Joel" 90 10
1100 31f. "Erythraean Sybil" . . 1·60 30
1101 31f. "Ezekiel" . . . . . . 1·60 30
1102 40f. "Persian Sybil" . . . . 2·00 35
1103 40f. "Jeremiah" . . . . . . 2·00 35

1975. Christmas Charity. Nos. 1092/1103 surch **+1F**.
1105 **108** 5f.+1f. mult (postage) . . 45 10
1106 – 5f.+1f. multicoloured . . 45 10
1107 – 13f.+1f. multicoloured 75 10
1108 – 13f.+1f. multicoloured 75 10
1109 – 27f.+1f. multicoloured 1·25 15
1110 – 27f.+1f. multicoloured 1·25 15
1111 – 18f.+1f. mult (air) . . . 1·00 10
1112 – 18f.+1f. multicoloured 1·00 10
1113 – 31f.+1f. multicoloured 1·60 30
1114 – 31f.+1f. multicoloured 1·60 30
1115 – 40f.+1f. multicoloured 1·90 35
1116 – 40f.+1f. multicoloured 1·90 35

110 Speed Skating

111 Basketball

1976. Winter Olympic Games, Innsbruck. Mult.
1118 17f. Type **110** (postage) . . 45 20
1119 24f. Figure-skating 50 20
1120 26f. Two-man bobsleigh . . 60 20
1121 31f. Cross-country skiing . . 70 30
1122 18f. Ski-jumping (air) . . . 40 25
1123 36f. Skiing (slalom) . . . . 1·50 40
1124 50f. Ice-hockey . . . . . . 1·60 60

1976. Olympic Games, Montreal. Multicoloured.
1126 14f. Type **111** (postage) . . 40 30
1127 14f. Pole-vaulting 40 30
1128 17f. Running 60 45
1129 17f. Football 60 45
1130 28f. As No. 1127 . . . . . 90 65
1131 28f. As No. 1128 . . . . . 90 65
1132 40f. As No. 1129 . . . . . 1·50 1·10
1133 40f. Type **111** . . . . 1·50 1·10
1134 27f. Hurdling (air) 90 65
1135 27f. High-jumping (horiz) 90 65
1136 31f. Gymnastics (horiz) . . 1·25 90
1137 31f. As No. 1134 (horiz) . . 1·25 90
1138 50f. As No. 1135 (horiz) . . 1·90 1·40
1139 50f. As No. 1136 (horiz) . . 1·90 1·40

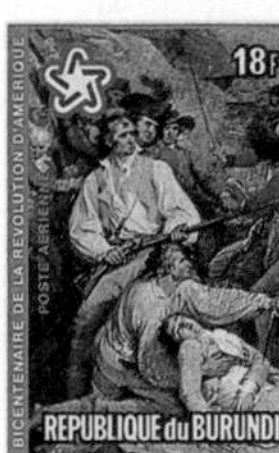
112 "Battle of Bunker Hill" (detail, John Trumbull)

113 "Virgin and Child" (Dirk Bouts)

1976. Air. Bicent of American Revolution. Mult.
1141 18f. Type **112** 55 15
1142 18f. As Type **112** 55 15
1143 26f. Franklin, Jefferson and John Adams 75 25
1144 26f. As No. 1143 . . . . . 75 25
1145 36f. "Signing of Declaration of Independence" (Trumbull) . . . . 1·25 35
1146 36f. As No. 1145 . . . . . 1·25 35
The two designs of each value form composite pictures. Type **112** is the left-hand portion of the painting.

1976. Christmas. Multicoloured.
1148 5f. Type **113** (postage) . . . 35 10
1149 13f. "Virgin of the Trees" (Bellini) 65 10
1150 27f. "Virgin and Child" (C. Crivelli) . . . . . . 1·00 25
1151 18f. "Virgin and Child" with St. Anne" (Leonardo) (air) 80 30
1152 31f. "Holy Family with Lamb" (Raphael) . . . . 1·10 60
1153 40f. "Virgin with Basket" (Correggio) . . . . 1·60 70

1976. Christmas Charity. Nos. 1148/53 surch **+1F**.
1155 **113** 5f.+1f. mult (postage) . . 25 10
1156 – 13f.+1f. multicoloured 70 30
1157 – 27f.+1f. multicoloured 1·10 50
1158 – 18f.+1f. mult (air) . . . 60 30
1159 – 31f.+1f. multicoloured 1·00 45
1160 – 40f.+1f. multicoloured 1·90 65

115 "The Ascent of Calvary" (Rubens)

1977. Easter. 400th Birth Anniv of Peter Paul Rubens. Multicoloured.
1162 10f. Type **115** 35 25
1163 21f. "Christ Crucified" . . . 95 70
1164 27f. "The Descent from the Cross" . . . . 1·10 80
1165 35f. "The Deposition" . . . 1·50 1·10

116 Alexander Graham Bell

117 Kobs

1977. Telephone Centenary and World Telecommunications Day. Multicoloured.
1167 10f. Type **116** (postage) . . 25 15
1168 10f. Satellite, Globe and telephones 25 15
1169 17f. Switchboard operator and wall telephone . . . 45 30
1170 17f. Satellite transmitting to Earth 45 30
1171 26f. A. G. Bell and first telephone 80 60
1172 26f. Satellites circling Globe, and videophone 80 60
1173 18f. Type **116** (air) 40 30
1174 18f. As No. 1172 . . . . . 40 30
1175 36f. As No. 1169 . . . . . 1·10 80
1176 36f. As No. 1168 . . . . . 1·10 80

1977. African Animals (3rd series). Multicoloured.
1178 2f. Type **117** (postage) . . . 75 20
1179 2f. Marabou storks 75 20
1180 2f. Blue wildebeest 75 20
1181 2f. Bush pig 75 20
1182 5f. Grevy's zebras 85 20
1183 5f. Whale-headed stork . . 85 20
1184 5f. Striped hyenas 85 20
1185 5f. Pygmy chimpanzee . . . 85 20
1186 8f. Greater flamingoes . . . 95 20
1187 8f. Nile crocodiles 95 20
1188 8f. Green tree snake 95 20
1189 8f. Greater kudus 95 20
1190 11f. Large-toothed rock hyrax . . . . 1·00 20
1191 11f. Cobra . . . . 1·00 20
1192 11f. Golden jackals . . . . 1·00 20
1193 11f. Verreaux eagles . . . . 1·00 20
1194 21f. Ratel . . . . 1·25 30
1195 21f. Bushbuck . . . . 1·25 30
1196 21f. Secretary bird . . . . . 1·25 30
1197 21f. Klipspringer . . . . . 1·25 30
1198 27f. Bat-eared fox . . . . . 1·60 30
1199 27f. African elephants . . . 1·60 30
1200 27f. Vulturine guineafowl . . 1·60 30
1201 27f. Impalas . . . . 1·60 30
1202 9f. Type **117** (air) 60 25
1203 9f. As No. 1179 . . . . . . 60 25
1204 9f. As No. 1180 . . . . . . 60 25
1205 9f. As No. 1181 . . . . . . 60 25

1206 13f. As No. 1182 85 30
1207 13f. As No. 1183 85 30
1208 13f. As No. 1184 85 30
1209 13f. As No. 1185 85 30
1210 30f. As No. 1186 1·25 50
1211 30f. As No. 1187 1·25 50
1212 30f. As No. 1188 1·25 50
1213 30f. As No. 1189 1·25 50
1214 35f. As No. 1190 1·40 60
1215 35f. As No. 1191 1·40 60
1216 35f. As No. 1192 1·40 60
1217 35f. As No. 1193 1·40 60
1218 54f. As No. 1194 2·40 70
1219 54f. As No. 1195 2·40 70
1220 54f. As No. 1196 2·40 70
1221 54f. As No. 1197 2·40 70
1222 70f. As No. 1198 3·25 85
1223 70f. As No. 1199 3·25 85
1224 70f. As No. 1200 3·25 85
1225 70f. As No. 1201 3·25 85

The four designs in each value were issued together se-tenant in horizontal strips within the sheet, forming composite designs.

118 "The Man of Iron" (Grimm)

119 U.N. General Assembly and U.N. 3c. Stamp, 1954

1977. Fairy Tales. Multicoloured.
1226 5f. Type **118** 20 10
1227 5f. "Snow White and Rose Red" (Grimm) 20 10
1228 5f. "The Goose Girl" (Grimm) 20 10
1229 5f. "The Two Wanderers" (Grimm) 20 10
1230 11f. "The Hermit and the Bear" (Aesop) 60 10
1231 11f. "The Fox and the Stork" (Aesop) 60 10
1232 11f. "The Litigious Cats" (Aesop) 60 10
1233 11f. "The Blind and the Lame" (Aesop) 60 10
1234 14f. "The Ice Maiden" (Andersen) 70 10
1235 14f. "The Old House" (Andersen) 70 10
1236 14f. "The Princess and the Pea" (Andersen) 70 10
1237 14f. "The Elder Tree Mother" (Andersen) 70 10
1238 17f. "Hen with the Golden Eggs" (La Fontaine) 80 15
1239 17f. "The Wolf Turned Shepherd" (La Fontaine) 80 15
1240 17f. "The Oyster and Litigants" (La Fontaine) 80 15
1241 17f. "The Wolf and the Lamb" (La Fontaine) 80 15
1242 26f. "Jack and the Beanstalk" (traditional) 1·60 25
1243 26f. "Alice in Wonderland" (Lewis Carroll) 1·60 25
1244 26f. "Three Heads in the Well" (traditional) 1·60 25
1245 26f. "Tales of Mother Goose" (traditional) 1·60 25

1977. 25th Anniv of United Nations Postal Administration. Multicoloured.
1246 8f. Type **119** (postage) 40 30
1247 8f. U.N. 4c. stamp, 1957 40 30
1248 8f. U.N. 3c. stamp, 1954 (FAO) 40 30
1249 8f. U.N. 1½c. stamp, 1951 40 30
1250 10f. Security Council and U.N. 8c. red, 1954 50 35
1251 10f. U.N. 8c. green, 1956 50 35
1252 10f. U.N. 8c. black, 1955 50 35
1253 10f. U.N. 7c. stamp, 1959 50 35
1254 21f. Meeting hall and U.N. 3c. grey, 1956 80 60
1255 21f. U.N. 8c. stamp, 1956 80 60
1256 21f. U.N. 3c. brown, 1953 80 60
1257 21f. U.N. 3c. green, 1952 80 60
1258 24f. Building by night and U.N. 4c. red, 1957 (air) 80 60
1259 24f. U.N. 8c. brn & grn, 1960 80 60
1260 24f. U.N. 8c. green, 1955 80 60
1261 24f. U.N. 8c. red, 1955 80 60
1262 27f. Aerial view of U.N. 8c. red, 1957 90 65
1263 27f. U.N. 3c. stamp, 1953 90 65
1264 27f. U.N. 8c. green, 1954 90 65
1265 27f. U.N. 8c. brown, 1956 90 65
1266 35f. U.N. Building by day and U.N. 5c. stamp, 1959 1·40 1·00
1267 35f. U.N. 3c. stamp, 1962 1·40 1·00
1268 35f. U.N. 3c. bl & pur, 1951 1·40 1·00
1269 35f. U.N. 1c. stamp, 1951 1·40 1·00

The four designs in each value were issued together in se-tenant blocks of four, each design in the block having the same background.

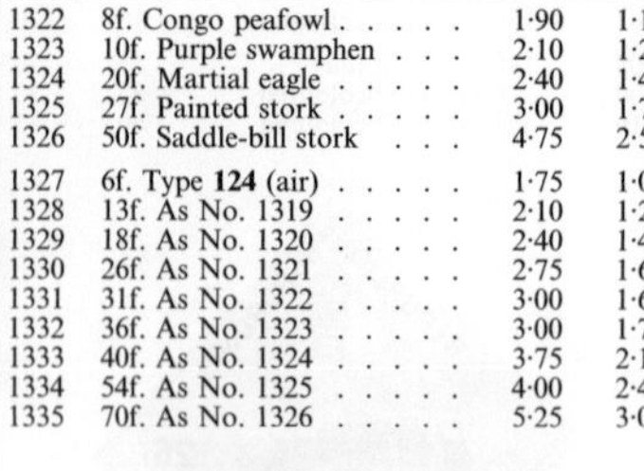

120 "Virgin and Child" (Jean Lambardos)

121 Cruiser "Aurora" and Russian 5r. Stamp, 1922

1977. Christmas. Paintings of Virgin and Child by artists named. Multicoloured.
1271 5f. Type **120** (postage) 15 10
1272 13f. Melides Toscano 65 50
1273 27f. Emmanuel Tzanes 95 70
1274 18f. Master of Moulins (air) 50 35
1275 31f. Lorenzo di Credi 1·00 75
1276 40f. Palma the Elder 1·25 90

1977. 60th Anniv of Russian Revolution. Mult.
1278 5f. Type **121** 40 10
1279 5f. Russia S.G. 455 40 10
1280 5f. Russia S.G. 1392 40 10
1281 5f. Russia S.G. 199 40 10
1282 8f. Decemberists' Square, Leningrad and Russia S.G. 983 25 10
1283 8f. Russia S.G. 2122 25 10
1284 8f. Russia S.G. 1041 25 10
1285 8f. Russia S.G. 2653 25 10
1286 11f. Pokrovski Cathedral, Moscow and Russia S.G. 3929 45 10
1287 11f. Russia S.G. 3540 45 10
1288 11f. Russia S.G. 3468 45 10
1289 11f. Russia S.G. 3921 45 10
1290 13f. May Day celebrations, Moscow and Russia S.G. 4518 60 15
1291 13f. Russia S.G. 3585 60 15
1292 13f. Russia S.G. 3024 60 15
1293 13f. Russia S.G. 2471 60 15

The four designs in each value were issued in se-tenant blocks of four, each design in the block having the same background.

122 Tanker Unloading (Commerce)

1977. 15th Anniv of Independence. Mult.
1294 1f. Type **122** 20 15
1295 5f. Assembling electric armatures (Economy) 20 15
1296 11f. Native dancers (Tourism) 30 20
1297 14f. Picking coffee (Agriculture) 45 30
1298 17f. National Palace, Bujumbura 55 40

1977. Christmas Charity. Nos. 1271/6 surch **+1F.**
1299 **120** 5f.+1f. mult (postage) 30 15
1300 – 13f.+1f. multicoloured 65 20
1301 – 27f.+1f. multicoloured 95 45
1302 – 18f.+1f. mult (air) 65 25
1303 – 31f.+1f. multicoloured 1·00 45
1304 – 40f.+1f. multicoloured 1·60 60

123 "Madonna and Child" (Solario)

124 Abyssinian Ground Hornbill

1979. Christmas (1978). Paintings of Virgin and Child by named artists. Multicoloured.
1306 13f. Rubens 85 85
1307 17f. Type **123** 90 90
1308 27f. Tiepolo 1·40 1·40
1309 31f. Gerard David 1·60 1·60
1310 40f. Bellini 2·00 2·00

1979. Christmas Charity. Nos. 1306/10 surch **+1F.**
1312 – 13f.+1f. multicoloured 85 85
1313 **123** 17f.+1f. multicoloured 90 90
1314 – 27f.+1f. multicoloured 1·40 1·40
1315 – 31f.+1f. multicoloured 1·60 1·60
1316 – 40f.+1f. multicoloured 2·00 2·00

1979. Birds. Multicoloured.
1318 1f. Type **124** (postage) 1·10 60
1319 2f. African darter 1·10 60
1320 3f. Little bee eater 1·10 60
1321 5f. Lesser flamingo 1·50 80
1322 8f. Congo peafowl 1·90 1·10
1323 10f. Purple swamphen 2·10 1·25
1324 20f. Martial eagle 2·40 1·40
1325 27f. Painted stork 3·00 1·75
1326 50f. Saddle-bill stork 4·75 2·50
1327 6f. Type **124** (air) 1·75 1·00
1328 13f. As No. 1319 2·10 1·25
1329 18f. As No. 1320 2·40 1·40
1330 26f. As No. 1321 2·75 1·60
1331 31f. As No. 1322 3·00 1·60
1332 36f. As No. 1323 3·00 1·75
1333 40f. As No. 1324 3·75 2·10
1334 54f. As No. 1325 4·00 2·40
1335 70f. As No. 1326 5·25 3·00

125 Mother and Child

1979. International Year of the Child. Mult.
1336 10f. Type **125** 90 90
1337 20f. Baby 1·40 1·40
1338 27f. Child with doll 1·50 1·50
1339 50f. S.O.S. village, Gitega 2·00 2·00

126 "Virgin and Child" (Raffaellino Del Garbo)

127 Sir Rowland Hill and Penny Black

1979. Christmas. "Virgin and Child" paintings by named artists. Multicoloured.
1341 20f. Type **126** 90 90
1342 27f. Giovanni Penni 1·10 1·10
1343 31f. Giulio Romano 1·25 1·25
1344 50f. Detail of "Adoration of the Shepherds" (Jacopo Bassano) 1·75 1·75

1979. Death Centenary of Sir Rowland Hill. Mult.
1346 20f. Type **127** 80 80
1347 27f. German East Africa 25p. stamp and Ruanda-Urundi 5c. stamp 95 95
1348 31f. Burundi 1f.25 and 50f. stamps of 1962 1·10 1·10
1349 40f. 4f. (1962) and 14f. (1969) stamps of Burundi 1·25 1·25
1350 60f. Heinrich von Stephan (founder of U.P.U.) and Burundi 14f. U.P.U. stamps of 1974 6·75 3·00

1979. Christmas Charity. Nos. 1341/4 additionally inscr with premium.
1352 20f.+1f. multicoloured 65 65
1353 27f.+1f. multicoloured 1·40 1·40
1354 31f.+1f. multicoloured 1·60 1·60
1355 50f.+1f. multicoloured 2·10 2·10

1980. As Nos. 1318/19 and 1321/3 but new values. (a) With copper frames.
1356a 5f. Abyssinian ground hornbill
1356b 10f. African darter
1356c 40f. Lesser flamingo
1356d 45f. Congo peafowl
1356e 50f. Purple swamphen

(b) With grey-green frames.
1356f 5f. As No. 1356a
1356g 10f. As No. 1356b
1356h 40f. As No. 1356c
1356i 45f. As No. 1356d
1356j 50f. As No. 1356e

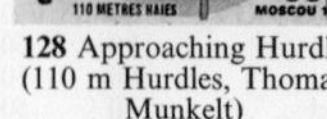

128 Approaching Hurdle (110 m Hurdles, Thomas Munkelt)

130 Congress Emblem

129 "The Virgin and Child" (Sebastiano Mainardi)

1980. Olympic Medal Winners. Multicoloured.
1357 20f. Type **128** 95 95
1358 20f. Jumping hurdle 95 95
1359 20f. Completing jump 95 95
1360 30f. Discus—beginning to throw 1·40 1·40
1361 30f. Continuing throw 1·40 1·40
1362 30f. Releasing discus 1·40 1·40
1363 40f. Football—running for goal (Czechoslovakia) 1·50 1·50
1364 40f. Kicking ball 1·50 1·50
1365 40f. Saving ball 1·50 1·50

1980. Christmas. Multicoloured.
1367 10f. Type **129** 90 90
1368 30f. "Doni Tondo" (Michelangelo) 1·50 1·50
1369 40f. "The Virgin and Child" (Piero di Cosimo) 2·10 2·10
1370 45f. "The Holy Family" (Fra Bartolomeo) 2·25 2·25

1980. 1st National Party Congress, Uprona.
1372 **130** 10f. multicoloured 30 30
1373 40f. multicoloured 1·50 1·50
1374 45f. multicoloured 1·60 1·60

1981. Christmas Charity. Nos. 1367/70 additionally inscr with premium.
1376 10f.+1f. multicoloured 75 75
1377 30f.+1f. multicoloured 1·75 1·75
1378 40f.+1f. multicoloured 2·25 2·25
1379 50f.+1f. multicoloured 2·50 2·50

131 Kepler and Dish Aerial

1981. 350th Death Anniv of Johannes Kepler (astronomer). First Earth Satellite Station in Burundi. Multicoloured.
1381 10f. Type **131** 60 60
1382 40f. Satellite and antenna 1·50 1·50
1383 45f. Satellite (different) and antenna 1·90 1·90

132 Giraffes

1982. African Animals (4th series). Multicoloured.
1385 2f. Lion 4·75 2·10
1386 3f. Type **132** 4·75 2·10
1387 5f. Black rhinoceros 4·75 2·10
1388 10f. African buffalo 15·00 6·75
1389 20f. African elephant 23·00 11·50
1390 25f. Hippopotamus 26·00 12·50
1391 30f. Common zebra 30·00 14·50
1392 50f. Warthog 55·00 26·00
1393 60f. Eland 70·00 32·00
1394 65f. Black-backed jackal 85·00 40·00
1395 70f. Cheetah 95·00 45·00
1396 75f. Blue Wildebeest £100 48·00
1397 85f. Spotted hyena £120 60·00

1983. Animal Protection Year. Nos. 1385/97 optd with World Wildlife Fund Emblem.
1398 2f. Type **131** 5·00 4·25
1399 3f. Giraffe 5·00 4·25
1400 5f. Black rhinoceros 5·00 4·25
1401 10f. African buffalo 14·00 13·00
1402 20f. African elephant 23·00 20·00
1403 25f. Hippopotamus 26·00 24·00
1404 30f. Common zebra 28·00 25·00
1405 50f. Warthog 55·00 48·00
1406 60f. Eland 70·00 60·00
1407 65f. Jackal ("Canis mesomelas") 80·00 75·00
1408 70f. Cheetah 95·00 80·00
1409 75f. Blue wildebeest £100 90·00
1410 85f. Spotted Hyena £120 £110

133 Flag and National Party Emblem

1983. 20th Anniv (1982) of Independence. Multicoloured.

1411	10f. Type **133**	65	65
1412	25f. Flag and arms	1·00	1·00
1413	30f. Flag and map of Africa	1·10	1·10
1414	50f. Flag and emblem	1·50	1·50
1415	65f. Flag and President Bagaza	2·00	2·00

134 "Virgin and Child" (Lucas Signorelli)

1983. Christmas. Multicoloured.

1416	10f. Type **134**	1·10	1·10
1417	25f. E. Murillo	1·50	1·50
1418	30f. Carlo Crivelli	1·75	1·75
1419	50f. Nicolas Poussin	2·40	2·40

DESIGNS: Virgin and Child paintings by named artists.

1983. Christmas Charity. Nos. 1416/19 additionally inscr with premium.

1421	10f.+1f. multicoloured	1·10	1·10
1422	25f.+1f. multicoloured	1·50	1·50
1423	30f.+1f. multicoloured	1·75	1·75
1424	50f.+1f. multicoloured	2·40	2·40

135 "Papilio zalmoxis"

1984. Butterflies. Multicoloured.

1426	5f. Type **135**	2·00	85
1427	5f. "Cymothoe coccinata"	2·00	85
1428	10f. "Papilio antimachus"	4·75	2·10
1429	10f. "Asterope pechueli"	4·75	2·10
1430	30f. "Bebearia mardania"	9·25	4·00
1431	30f. "Papilio hesperus"	9·25	4·00
1432	35f. "Euphaedra perseis"	12·00	5·25
1433	35f. "Euphaedra neophron"	12·00	5·25
1434	65f. "Pseudacraea striata"	22·00	9·75
1435	65f. "Euphaedra imperialis"	22·00	9·75

136 Stamps of German East Africa and Belgian Occupation

1984. 19th U.P.U. Congress, Hamburg. Mult.

1436	10f. Type **136**	65	65
1437	30f. 1962 Burundi overprinted stamps	1·10	1·10
1438	35f. 1969 14f. Letter-writing Week and 1982 30f. Zebra stamps	1·25	1·25
1439	65f. Heinrich von Stephan (founder of U.P.U.) and 1974 14f. U.P.U. Centenary stamps	18·00	11·50

137 Jesse Owens (runner)

1984. Olympic Games, Los Angeles. Mult.

1441	10f. Type **137**	1·10	1·10
1442	30f. Rafer Johnson (discus thrower)	1·60	1·60
1443	35f. Bob Beamon (long jumper)	1·75	1·75
1444	65f. K. Keino (sprinter)	2·25	2·25

138 "Virgin and Child" (Botticelli)

1984. Christmas. Multicoloured.

1446	10f. "Rest on the Flight into Egypt" (Murillo)	30	30
1447	25f. "Virgin and Child" (R. del Garbo)	1·10	1·10
1448	30f. Type **138**	1·60	1·60
1449	50f. "Adoration of the Shepherds" (J. Bassano)	2·00	2·00

1984. Christmas Charity. As Nos. 1446/49 but with additional premium.

1451	10f.+1f. multicoloured	30	30
1452	25f.+1f. multicoloured	1·10	1·10
1453	30f.+1f. multicoloured	1·60	1·60
1454	50f.+1f. multicoloured	2·00	2·00

139 Thunbergia

140 Bombs as Flats

1986. Flowers. Multicoloured.

1456	2f. Type **139** (postage)	1·40	80
1457	3f. African violets	1·40	80
1458	5f. "Clivia"	1·40	80
1459	10f. "Cassia"	1·40	80
1460	20f. Bird of Paradise flower	2·50	1·60
1461	35f. "Gloriosa"	4·50	3·00
1462	70f. Type **139** (air)	2·50	2·10
1463	75f. As No. 1457	2·75	2·25
1464	80f. As No. 1458	2·75	2·40
1465	85f. As No. 1459	3·25	2·75
1466	100f. As No. 1460	3·50	2·75
1467	150f. As No. 1461	6·00	5·00

1987. International Peace Year (1986). Mult.

1468	10f. Type **140**	20	20
1469	20f. Molecular diagrams as flower	40	40
1470	30f. Clasped hands across globe	1·10	1·10
1471	40f. Chicks in split globe	1·25	1·25

141 Map, Airplane and Emblem

1987. 10th Anniv of Great Lakes Countries Economic Community. Multicoloured.

1473	5f. Type **141**	55	55
1474	10f. Map, ear of wheat, cogwheel and emblem	65	65
1475	15f. Map, factory and emblem	75	75
1476	25f. Map, electricity pylons and emblem	1·60	1·60
1477	35f. Map, flags and emblem	2·25	2·25

142 Leaves and Sticks Shelter

1988. International Year of Shelter for the Homeless (1987). Multicoloured.

1479	10f. Type **142**	55	55
1480	20f. People living in concrete pipes	70	70
1481	80f. Boys mixing mortar	1·50	1·50
1482	150f. Boys with model house	3·00	3·00

143 Skull between Cigarettes

144 Pope John Paul II

1989. Anti-smoking Campaign. Multicoloured.

1484	5f. Type **143**	70	70
1485	20f. Cigarettes, lungs and skull	1·40	1·40
1486	80f. Cigarettes piercing skull	2·25	2·25

1989. Various stamps surch.

1487b	20f. on 3f. mult (No. 1457)	70	70
1487c	80f. on 30f. mult (No. 1430)	2·00	2·00
1487d	80f. on 30f. mult (No. 1431)	2·00	2·00
1487e	80f. on 35f. mult (No. 1432)	2·00	2·00
1487f	80f. on 35f. mult (No. 1433)	2·00	2·00
1487g	85f. on 65f. mult (No. 1435)		

1990. Papal Visit.

1488 **144**	5f. multicoloured	45	45
1489	10f. multicoloured	45	45
1490	20f. multicoloured	70	70
1491	30f. multicoloured	70	70
1492	50f. multicoloured	1·40	1·40
1493	80f. multicoloured	2·00	2·00

145 Hippopotamus

1991. Animals. Multicoloured.

1495	5f. Type **145**	1·10	75
1496	10f. Hen and cockerel	1·10	75
1497	20f. Lion	1·10	75
1498	30f. Elephant	1·10	1·10
1499	50f. Helmet guineafowl ("Pintade")	3·00	2·25
1500	80f. Crocodile	4·50	3·25

146 Drummer

147 "Impatiens petersiana"

1992. Traditional Dancing. Multicoloured.

1502	15f. Type **146**	25	25
1503	30f. Men dancing	40	40
1504	115f. Group of drummers (horiz)	1·90	1·90
1505	200f. Men dancing in fields (horiz)	3·25	3·25

1992. Flowers. Multicoloured.

1507	15f. Type **147**	90	65
1508	20f. "Lachenalia aloides" "Nelsonii"	90	65
1509	30f. Egyptian lotus	1·40	1·00
1510	50f. Kaffir lily	3·00	2·25

148 Pigtail Macaque

1992. Air. Animals. Multicoloured.

1512	100f. Type **148**	2·40	1·75
1513	115f. Grevy's zebra	2·75	2·10
1514	200f. Ox	4·00	3·00
1515	220f. Eastern white pelican	5·00	3·75

149 People holding Hands and Flag

1992. 30th Anniv of Independence. Multicoloured.

1517	30f. Type **149**	20	20
1518	85f. State flag	80	80
1519	110f. Independence monument (vert)	1·10	1·10
1520	115f. As No. 1518	1·10	1·10
1521	120f. Map (vert)	1·40	1·40
1522	140f. Type **149**	1·50	1·50
1523	200f. As No. 1519	2·10	2·10
1524	250f. As No. 1521	2·75	2·75

150 "Russula ingens"

1992. Fungi. Multicoloured.

1525	10f. Type **150**	15	15
1526	15f. "Russula brunneorigida"	20	20
1527	20f. "Amanita zambiana"	25	30
1528	30f. "Russula subfistulosa"	40	45
1529	75f. "Russula meleagris"	90	95
1530	85f. As No. 1529	1·00	1·10
1531	100f. "Russula immaculata"	1·25	1·25
1532	110f. Type **150**	1·40	1·40
1533	115f. As No. 1526	1·40	1·40
1534	120f. "Russula sejuncta"	1·40	1·60
1535	130f. As No. 1534	1·50	1·60
1536	250f. "Afroboletus luteolus"	3·00	3·25

151 Columbus's Fleet, Treasure and Globes

1992. 500th Anniv of Discovery of America by Columbus. Multicoloured.

1541	200f. Type **151**	2·00	2·00
1542	400f. American produce, globes and Columbus's fleet	4·25	4·25

152 Serval

1992. The Serval. Multicoloured.

1543	30f. Type **152**	60	50
1544	130f. Pair sitting and crouching	2·40	2·00
1545	200f. Pair, one standing over the other	3·75	3·00
1546	220f. Heads of pair	4·00	3·50

153 Running

154 Emblems

1992. Olympic Games, Barcelona. Multicoloured.

1547	130f. Type **153**	1·50	1·50
1548	500f. Hurdling	5·25	5·25

1992. International Nutrition Conference, Rome. Multicoloured.

1549	200f. Type **154**	2·00	2·00
1550	220f. Woman's face made from vegetables (G. Arcimboldo)	2·40	2·40

155 Horsemen

156 Flags of Member Countries and European Community Emblem

1992. Christmas. Details of "Adoration of the Magi" by Gentile da Fabriano. Multicoloured.
1551 100f. Type **155** 90 90
1552 130f. Three Kings . . . . . 1·10 1·10
1553 250f. Holy family . . . . . 2·50 2·50

1993. European Single Market. Multicoloured.
1555 130f. Type **156** . . . . . . 1·25 1·25
1556 500f. Europe shaking hands with Africa . . . . 5·00 5·00

157 Indonongo

1993. Musical Instruments. Multicoloured.
1557 200f. Type **157** . . . . . . 2·00 2·00
1558 220f. Ingoma (drum) . . . 2·25 2·25
1559 250f. Ikembe (xylophone) 2·50 2·50
1560 300f. Umuduri (musical bow) . . . . 3·25 3·25

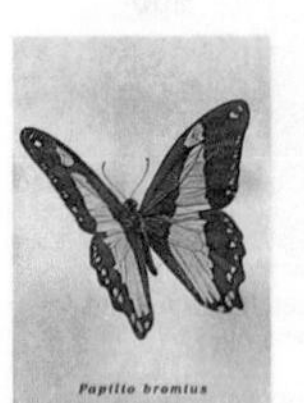

158 Broad Blue-banded Swallowtail

159 Players, Stadium, United States Flag and Statue of Liberty

1993. Butterflies. Multicoloured.
1561 130f. Type **158** . . . . . . 1·50 1·25
1562 200f. Green charaxes . . . 2·40 2·10
1563 250f. Migratory glider . . . 3·00 2·50
1564 300f. Red swallowtail . . . 3·75 3·50

1993. World Cup Football Championship, U.S.A. (1994). Multicoloured.
1566 130f. Type **159** . . . . . . 1·25 1·25
1567 200f. Players, stadium, United States flag and Golden Gate Bridge . . . 2·50 2·50

160 Cattle

161 Woman with Baby and Two Men

1993. Domestic Animals. Multicoloured.
1568 100f. Type **160** . . . . . . 1·00 1·00
1569 120f. Sheep . . . . 1·10 1·10
1570 130f. Pigs . . . . 1·25 1·25
1571 250f. Goats . . . . 2·50 2·50

1993. Christmas. Each orange and black.
1572 100f. Type **161** . . . . . . 1·25 1·25
1573 130f. Nativity . . . . 1·50 1·50
1574 250f. Woman with baby and three men . . . . 3·00 3·00

162 Elvis Presley

163 "The Discus Thrower" (statue)

1994. Entertainers. Multicoloured.
1576 60f. Type **162** 30 30
1577 115f. Mick Jagger 55 55
1578 120f. John Lennon 60 60
1579 200f. Michael Jackson . . . 1·00 1·00

1994. Cent of International Olympic Committee.
1581 **163** 150f. multicoloured . . . 75 75

164 Pres. Buyoya handing over Baton of Power to Pres. Ndadaye

165 Madonna, China

1994. 1st Anniv of First Multi-party Elections in Burundi. Multicoloured.
1582 30f.+10f. Type **164** 20 20
1583 110f.+10f. Pres. Ndadaye (first elected President) giving inauguration speech 60 60
1584 115f.+10f. Arms on map . . 60 60
1585 120f.+10f. Warrior on map 65 65

1994. Christmas. Multicoloured.
1586 115f. Type **165** 55 55
1587 120f. Madonna, Japan . . . 60 60
1588 250f. Black Virgin, Poland 1·25 1·25

166 Emblem and Earth

167 "Cassia didymobotrya"

1995. 50th Anniversaries. Multicoloured.
1590 115f. Type **166** (F.A.O.) . . 55 55
1591 120f. U.N.O. emblems and dove 60 60

1995. Flowers. Multicoloured.
1592 15f. Type **167** 15 15
1593 20f. "Mitragyna rubrostipulosa" 15 15
1594 30f. "Phytolacca dodecandra" 25 20
1595 85f. "Acanthus pubescens" 65 60
1596 100f. "Bulbophyllum comatum" 80 75
1597 110f. "Angraecum evrardianum" 90 80
1598 115f. "Eulophia burundiensis" 90 80
1599 120f. "Habenaria adolphii" 1·00 90

168 Otraca Bus

169 Boy with Panga

1995. Transport. Multicoloured.
1600 30f. Type **168** 15 15
1601 115f. Transintra lorry . . . 65 65
1602 120f. Lake ferry 90 70
1603 250f. Air Burundi airplane 1·40 1·40

1995. Christmas. Multicoloured.
1604 100f. Type **169** 55 55
1605 130f. Boy with sheaf of wheat 75 75
1606 250f. Mother and children 1·40 1·40

170 Venuste Niyongabo

1996. Olympic Games, Atlanta. Runners. Mult.
1608 130f. Type **170** (5000 m gold medal winner) 40 40
1609 500f. Arthemon Hatungimana . . . . . . 1·50 1·50

171 Hadada Ibis

1996. Birds. Multicoloured.
1610 15f. Type **171** 25 25
1611 20f. Egyptian goose 25 25
1612 30f. African fish eagle . . . 25 25
1613 120f. Goliath heron 75 75
1614 165f. South African crowned crane . . . . 1·00 1·00
1615 220f. African jacana . . . . . 1·40 1·40

172 Marlier's Julie

1996. Fishes of Lake Tanganyika. Multicoloured.
1616 30f. Type **172** 25 20
1617 115f. "Cyphotilapia frontosa" 75 60
1618 120f. "Lamprologus brichardi" 75 60
1619 250f. Stone squeaker . . . . 1·50 1·25

173 Children

1998. 50th Anniv of S.O.S Children's Villages. Multicoloured.
1621 100f. Type **173** 25 25
1622 250f. Flags, "50" and children waving 65 65
1623 270f. Children dancing around flag 70 70

174 Madonna and Child

175 Diana, Princess of Wales

1999. Christmas (1996–98). Multicoloured.
1624 100f. Type **174** (1996) . . . 25 25
1625 130f. Madonna and Child (different) (1997) 30 30
1626 250f. Madonna and Child (different) (1998) 65 65

1999. 2nd Death Anniv of Diana, Princess of Wales.
1628 **175** 100f. multicoloured . . . 20 20
1629 250f. multicoloured . . . 20 20
1630 300f. multicoloured . . . 50 50

176 Danny Kaye (entertainer) holding African Baby

2000. New Millennium. "A World Free from Hunger".
1631 **176** 350f. multicoloured . . . 60 60

BUSHIRE Pt. 1

An Iranian seaport. Stamps issued during the British occupation in the 1914–18 War.

20 chahis = 1 kran, 10 krans = 1 toman.

1915. Portrait stamps of Iran (1911) optd **BUSHIRE Under British Occupation**.
1 **57** 1ch. orange and green . . . 42·00 45·00
2 2ch. brown and red . . . . 42·00 40·00
3 3ch. green and grey . . . . 50·00 60·00
4 5ch. red and brown £300 £300
5 6ch. lake and green . . . . 40·00 28·00
6 9ch. lilac and brown . . . . 40·00 45·00
7 10ch. brown and red . . . . 42·00 45·00
8 12ch. blue and green . . . . 55·00 55·00
9 24ch. green and purple . . . 90·00 60·00
10 1kr. red and blue . . . . . 85·00 32·00
11 2kr. red and green £225 £170
12 3kr. black and lilac £180 £190
13 5kr. blue and red £130 £110
14 10kr. red and brown £110 £100

1915. Coronation issue of Iran optd **BUSHIRE Under British Occupation**.
15 **66** 1ch. blue and red £375 £350
16 2ch. red and blue £6500 £7000
17 3ch. green £450 £425
18 5ch. red £5500 £5500
19 6ch. red and green £4500 £4500
20 9ch. violet and brown . . . £650 £650
21 10ch. brown and green . . . £950 £950
22 12ch. blue £1200 £1200
23 24ch. black and brown . . . £450 £425
24 **67** 1kr. black, brown and silver £450 £475
25 2kr. red, blue and silver . . £425 £450
26 3kr. black, lilac and silver £550 £550
27 5kr. slate, brown and silver £500 £550
28 – 1t. black, violet and gold . . £450 £500
29 – 3t. red, lake and gold . . . £3250 £3250

BUSSAHIR (BASHAHR) Pt. 1

A state in the Punjab, India. Now uses Indian stamps.

12 pies = 1 anna; 16 annas = 1 rupee.

1

1895. Various frames. Imperf, perf or roul.
9 **1** ¼a. pink . . . . 50·00 85·00
10 ½a. grey . . . . 20·00 £100
11 1a. red . . . . 21·00 80·00
12 2a. yellow . . . . 30·00 85·00
13 4a. violet . . . . 21·00 85·00
14 8a. brown . . . . 22·00 95·00
15 12a. green . . . . 65·00 £110
16 1r. blue . . . . 38·00 £100

1896. Similar types, but inscriptions on white ground and inscr "POSTAGE" instead of "STAMP".
27 **1** ¼a. violet . . . . 17·00 15·00
37 ½a. red . . . . 3·50 8·50
25 ½a. blue . . . . 7·00 15·00
26 1a. olive . . . . 14·00 32·00
32 1a. red . . . . 4·00 12·00
41 2a. yellow . . . . 38·00 65·00
36 4a. red . . . . 42·00 95·00

CAICOS ISLANDS Pt. 1

Separate issues for these islands, part of the Turks and Caicos Islands group, appeared from 1981 to 1985.

100 cents = 1 dollar.

1981. Nos. 514, 518, 520, 523 and 525/7 of Turks and Caicos Islands optd **CAICOS ISLANDS**.
1 1c. Indigo hamlet 15 15
2 5c. Spanish grunt 20 20
3 8c. Four-eyed butterflyfish . . . 20 20
4 20c. Queen angelfish 35 30
5 50c. Royal gramma ("Fairy Basslet") . . . . 40 1·00

6 $1 Fin-spot wrasse 60 1·75
7 $2 Stoplight parrotfish 1·10 3·25

1981. Royal Wedding. Nos. 653/6 of Turks and Caicos Islands optd. (A) **Caicos Islands**.
8A 35c. Prince Charles and Lady Diana Spencer 20 25
9A 65c. Kensington Palace 30 40
10A 90c. Prince Charles as Colonel of the Welsh Guards 40 50

(B) **CAICOS ISLANDS**.
8B 35c. Prince Charles and Lady Diana Spencer 30 70
9B 65c. Kensington Palace 40 1·00
10B 90c. Prince Charles as Colonel of the Welsh Guards 50 1·50

1981. Royal Wedding. As Nos. 657/9 of Turks and Caicos Islands, but each inscr "Caicos Islands". Mult. Self-adhesive.
12 20c. Lady Diana Spencer 30 40
13 $1 Prince Charles 80 1·25
14 $2 Prince Charles and Lady Diana Spencer 4·00 5·50

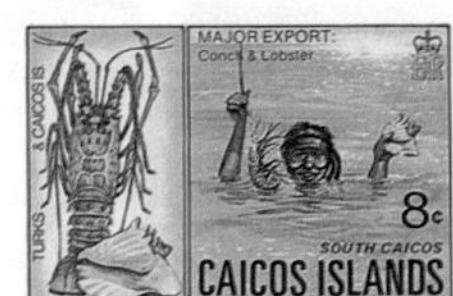

4 Queen or Pink Conch and Lobster Fishing, South Caicos

1983. Multicoloured.
15 8c. Type **4** 1·50 85
16 10c. Hawksbill turtle, East Caicos 1·75 1·00
17 20c. Arawak Indians and idol, Middle Caicos 1·75 1·00
18 35c. Boat-building, North Caicos 2·00 1·50
19 50c. Marine biologist at work, Pine Cay 3·00 2·25
20 95c. Boeing 707 airliner at new airport, Providenciales 5·50 3·00
21 $1.10 Columbus's "Pinta", West Caicos 5·50 3·00
22 $2 Fort George Cay 3·75 4·75
23 $3 Pirates Anne Bonny and Calico Jack at Parrot Cay 6·00 4·75

5 Goofy and Patch

1983. Christmas. Multicoloured.
30 1c. Type **5** 10 30
31 1c. Chip and Dale 10 30
32 2c. Morty 10 30
33 2c. Morty and Ferdie 10 30
34 3c. Goofy and Louie 10 30
35 3c. Donald Duck, Huey, Dewey and Louie 10 30
36 50c. Uncle Scrooge 3·75 3·00
37 70c. Mickey Mouse and Ferdie 4·00 3·50
38 $1.10 Pinocchio, Jiminy Cricket and Figaro 4·75 4·25
MS39 126 × 101 mm. $2 Morty and Ferdie 3·75 3·50

6 "Leda and the Swan"

7 High Jumping

1984. 500th Birth Anniv of Raphael. Mult.
40 35c. Type **6** 75 50
41 50c. "Study of Apollo for Parnassus" 1·00 70
42 95c. "Study of two figures for the battle of Ostia" 2·00 1·25
43 $1.10 "Study for the Madonna of the Goldfinch" 2·00 1·50
MS44 71 × 100 mm. $2.50, "The Garvagh Madonna" 3·00 3·25

1984. Olympic Games, Los Angeles.
45 **7** 4c. multicoloured 15 10
46 – 25c. multicoloured 30 20
47 – 65c. black, deep blue and blue 1·75 50
48 – $1.10 multicoloured 1·25 85
MS49 105 × 75 mm. $2 multicoloured 2·25 3·00
DESIGNS—VERT: 25c. Archery; 65c. Cycling; $1.10, Football. HORIZ: $2.50, Show jumping.

8 Horace Horsecollar and Clarabelle Cow

1984. Easter. Walt Disney Cartoon Characters. Multicoloured.
50 35c. Type **8** 1·40 60
51 45c. Mickey and Minnie Mouse, and Chip 1·50 75
52 75c. Gyro Gearloose, Chip 'n Dale 1·90 1·25
53 85c. Mickey Mouse, Chip 'n Dale 1·90 1·40
MS54 127 × 101 mm. $2.20, Donald Duck 5·50 3·75

1984. Universal Postal Union Congress Hamburg. Nos. 20/1 optd **UNIVERSAL POSTAL UNION 1874–1984** and emblem.
55 95c. Boeing 707 airliner at new airport, Providenciales 1·00 1·25
56 $1.10 Columbus's "Pinta", West Caicos 1·25 1·50

1984. "Ausipex" International Stamp Exhibition, Melbourne. No. 22 optd **AUSIPEX 1984**.
57 $2 Fort George Cay 2·40 2·50

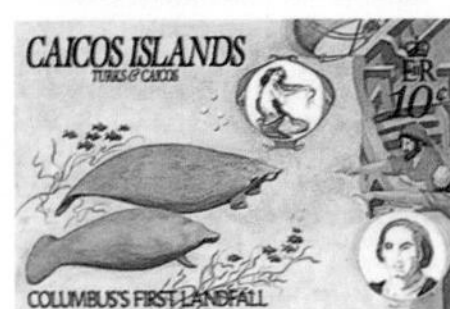

11 Seamen sighting American Manatees

1984. 492nd Anniv of Columbus's First Landfall. Multicoloured.
58 10c. Type **11** 1·00 80
59 70c. Columbus's fleet 3·75 3·25
60 $1 First landing in the West Indies 4·25 3·75
MS61 99 × 69 mm. $2 Fleet of Columbus (different) 2·75 3·00

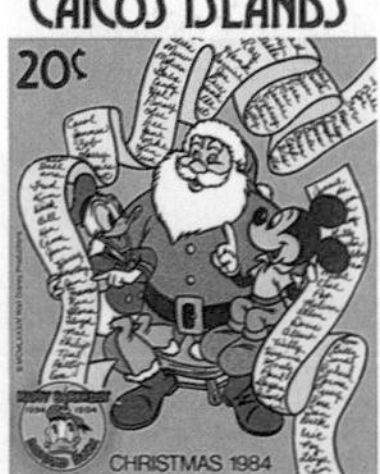

12 Donald Duck and Mickey Mouse with Father Christmas

1984. Christmas. Walt Disney Cartoon Characters. Multicoloured.
62 20c. Type **12** 1·50 85
63 35c. Donald Duck opening refrigerator 1·75 1·00
64 50c. Mickey Mouse, Donald Duck and toy train 2·50 2·25
65 75c. Donald Duck and parcels 3·00 3·00
66 $1.10 Donald Duck and carol singers 3·25 3·25
MS67 127 × 102 mm. $2 Donald Duck as Christmas tree 3·75 4·00

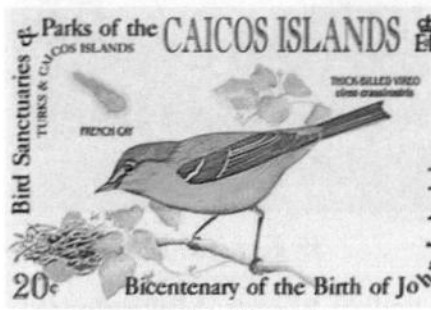

13 Thick-billed Vireo

1985. Birth Bicentenary of John J. Audubon (ornithologist). Multicoloured.
68 20c. Type **13** 1·75 70
69 35c. Black-faced grassquit 2·00 95
70 50c. Pearly-eyed thrasher 2·25 1·50
71 $1 Greater Antillean bullfinch 2·75 2·50
MS72 100 × 70 mm. $2 Striped-headed tanager 3·50 3·50

14 Two Children learning to Read and Write (Education)

16 The Queen Mother visiting Foundation for the Disabled, Leatherhead

15 Douglas DC-3 on Ground

1985. International Youth Year. 40th Anniv of United Nations. Multicoloured.
73 16c. Type **14** 20 25
74 35c. Two children on playground swings (Health) 50 55
75 70c. Boy and girl (Love) 1·00 1·10
76 90c. Three children (Peace) 1·25 1·40
MS77 101 × 71 mm. $2 Child, dove carrying ears of wheat and map of the Americas 2·75 3·25

1985. 40th Anniv of International Civil Aviation Organization. Multicoloured.
78 35c. Type **15** 3·00 55
79 75c. Convair CV 440 Metropolitan 4·00 1·40
80 90c. Britten Norman Islander 4·00 1·60
MS81 100 × 70 mm. $2.20, Hand-gliding over the Caicos Islands 3·00 3·25

1985. Life and Times of Queen Elizabeth the Queen Mother. Multicoloured.
82 35c. Type **16** 1·25 55
83 65c. With Princess Anne (horiz) 1·75 95
84 95c. At Epsom, 1961 2·25 1·60
MS85 56 × 85 mm. $2 Visiting Royal Hospital, Chelsea 4·75 3·00

1985. 150th Birth Anniv of Mark Twain (author). Designs as T **118** of Anguilla, showing Walt Disney cartoon characters in scenes from "Tom Sawyer, Detective". Multicoloured.
86 8c. Huckleberry Finn (Goofy) and Tom Sawyer (Mickey Mouse) reading reward notice 60 20
87 35c. Huck and Tom meeting Jake Dunlap 1·75 65
88 95c. Huck and Tom spying on Jubiter Dunlap 3·25 2·00
89 $1.10 Huck and Tom with hound (Pluto) 3·25 2·25
MS90 127 × 101 mm. Tom unmasking Jubiter Dunlap 4·75 4·25

1985. Birth Bicentenaries of Grimm Brothers (folklorists). Designs as T **119** of Anguilla, showing Walt Disney cartoon characters in scenes from "Six Soldiers of Fortune". Multicoloured.
91 16c. The Soldier (Donald Duck) with his meagre pay 1·75 30
92 25c. The Soldier meeting the Strong Man (Horace Horsecollar) 2·00 45
93 65c. The Soldier meeting the Marksman (Mickey Mouse) 3·50 1·25
94 $1.35 The Fast Runner (Goofy) winning the race against the Princess (Daisy Duck) 4·25 2·25
MS95 126 × 101 mm. $2 The Soldier and the Strong Man with sack of gold 4·75 4·00

CAMBODIA Pt. 21

A kingdom in south-east Asia.

From 1887 Cambodia was part of the Union of Indo-China. In 1949 it became an Associated State of the French Union, in 1953 it attained sovereign independence and in 1955 it left the Union.

Following the introduction of a republican constitution in 1970 the name of the country was changed to Khmer Republic and in 1975 to Kampuchea.

In 1989 it reverted to the name of Cambodia. Under a new constitution in 1993 it became a parliamentary monarchy.

1951. 100 cents = 1 piastre.
1955. 100 cents = 1 riel.

1 "Apsara" or Dancing Nymph

2 Throne Room, Phnom-Penh

3 King Norodom Sihanouk

5 "Kinnari"

1951.
1 **1** 10c. green and deep green 50 3·50
2 20c. brown and red 45 1·50
3 30c. blue and violet 55 60
4 40c. blue and ultramarine 1·10 90
5 **2** 50c. green and deep green 95 85
6 **3** 80c. green and blue 1·70 4·25
7 **2** 1p. violet and blue 1·30 45
8 **3** 1p.10 red and lake 2·10 4·25
9 **1** 1p.50 red and lake 2·00 1·40
10 **2** 1p.50 blue and indigo 2·10 2·30
11 **3** 1p.50 brown and chocolate 2·10 1·80
12 1p.90 blue and indigo 3·75 6·00
13 **2** 2p. brown and red 2·75 75
14 **3** 3p. brown and red 4·25 2·30
15 **1** 5p. violet and blue 12·50 5·75
16 **2** 10p. blue and violet 13·50 10·50
17 **3** 15p. violet and deep violet 28·00 45·00

1952. Students' Aid Fund. Surch **AIDE A L'ETUDIANT** and premium.
18 **3** 1p.10+40c. red and lake 3·50 13·00
19 1p.90+60c. blue & indigo 3·50 13·00
20 3p.+1p. brown and red 3·50 13·00
21 **1** 5p.+2p. violet and blue 3·75 13·00

1953. Air.
22 **5** 50c. green 1·10 2·10
23 3p. red 2·00 1·80
24 3p.30 violet 2·50 5·25
25 4p. blue and brown 2·75 1·20
26 5p.10 ochre, red and brown 4·00 6·75
27 6p.50 purple and brown 3·75 8·75
28 9p. green and mauve 5·00 13·00
29 11p.50 multicoloured 9·75 18·00
30 30p. ochre, brown and green 16·00 26·00

6 Arms of Cambodia

7 "Postal Transport"

1954.
31 – 10c. red 1·20 1·80
32 – 20c. green 1·40 50
33 – 30c. blue 1·40 2·10
34 – 40c. violet 1·40 85
35 – 50c. purple 1·40 25
36 – 70c. brown 1·60 3·25
37 – 1p. violet 1·70 1·80
38 – 1p.50 red 1·70 60
39 **6** 2p. red 1·30 45
40 2p.50 green 1·60 60
41 **7** 2p.50 green 2·50 2·10
42 **6** 3p. blue 2·10 1·70
43 **7** 4p. sepia 3·25 2·75
44 **6** 4p.50 violet 2·75 1·80
45 **7** 5p. red 3·50 2·50
46 **6** 6p. brown 3·00 2·50
47 **7** 10p. violet 4·00 2·75
48 15p. blue 5·00 5·00
49 – 20p. blue 11·50 5·75
50 – 30p. green 18·00 9·75
DESIGNS—VERT: 10c. to 50c. View of Phnom Daun Penah. HORIZ: 70c. 1, 1p.50, 20, 30p. East Gate, Temple of Angkor.

8 King Norodom Suramarit

9 King and Queen of Cambodia

1955.
51 – 50c. blue 25 20
52 8 50c. violet 35 30
53 1r. red 40 30
54 2r. blue 70 45
55 – 2r.50 brown . . . . 1·00 35
56 – 4r. green . . . . 1·40 45
57 – 6r. lake . . . . 1·90 1·20
58 8 7r. brown . . . . 2·30 1·40
59 – 15r. lilac . . . . 3·25 1·20
60 8 20r. green . . . . 4·75 4·25
PORTRAIT: Nos. 51, 55/7 and 59, Queen Kossamak.
For stamps as Nos. 58 and 60, but with black border, see Nos. 101/2.

1955. Coronation (1st issue).
61 9 1r.50 sepia and brown . . . 75 45
62 2r. black and blue 75 55
63 3r. red and orange 95 30
64 5r. black and green . . . . . 1·50 55
65 10r. purple and violet . . . . 2·50 55
See Nos. 66/71.

10 King Norodom Suramarit
11 Prince Sihanouk, Flags and Globe

1956. Coronation (2nd issue).
66 10 2r. red . . . . 1·10 2·30
67 – 3r. blue . . . . 1·60 3·25
68 – 5r. green . . . . 2·40 4·50
69 10 10r. green . . . . 6·25 9·25
70 30r. violet . . . . 13·00 22·00
71 – 50r. purple . . . . 25·00 25·00
PORTRAIT—VERT: 3, 5, 50r. Queen of Cambodia.

1957. 1st Anniv of Admission of Cambodia to U.N.O.
72 11 2r. red, blue and green . . . 1·20 90
73 4r.50 blue . . . . 1·20 90
74 8r.50 red . . . . 1·20 90

12
13 Mythological Bird

1957. 2,500th Anniv of Buddhism. (a) With premiums.
75 12 1r.50+50c. bis, red & bl . . 1·40 1·80
76 6r.50+1r.50 bis, red & pur 2·10 2·75
77 8r.+2r. bistre, red & blue . . 3·50 4·50
(b) Colours changed and premiums omitted.
78 12 1r.50 red . . . . 1·30 1·00
79 6r.50 violet . . . . 1·50 1·20
80 8r. green . . . . 1·50 1·50

1957. Air.
81 13 50c. lake 35 10
82 1r. green 60 10
83 4r. blue . . . . 1·80 45
84 50r. red . . . . 7·50 2·75
85 100r. red, green and blue . . 13·00 5·00

14 King Ang Duong
15 King Norodom I

1958. King Ang Duong Commemoration.
86 14 1r.50 brown and violet . . . 55 45
87 5r. bistre and black 70 65
88 10r. sepia and purple . . . 1·40 90

1958. King Norodom I Commemoration.
89 15 2r. brown and blue 60 35
90 6r. green and orange 85 55
91 15r. brown and green . . . 1·70 1·10

16 Children

1959. Children's World Friendship.
92 16 20c. purple 25 35
93 50c. blue 45 45
94 80c. red 90 85

1959. Red Cross Fund. Nos. 92/4 surch with red cross and premium.
95 16 20c.+20c. purple 30 45
96 50c.+30c. blue 65 65
97 80c.+50c. red . . . . 1·30 1·20

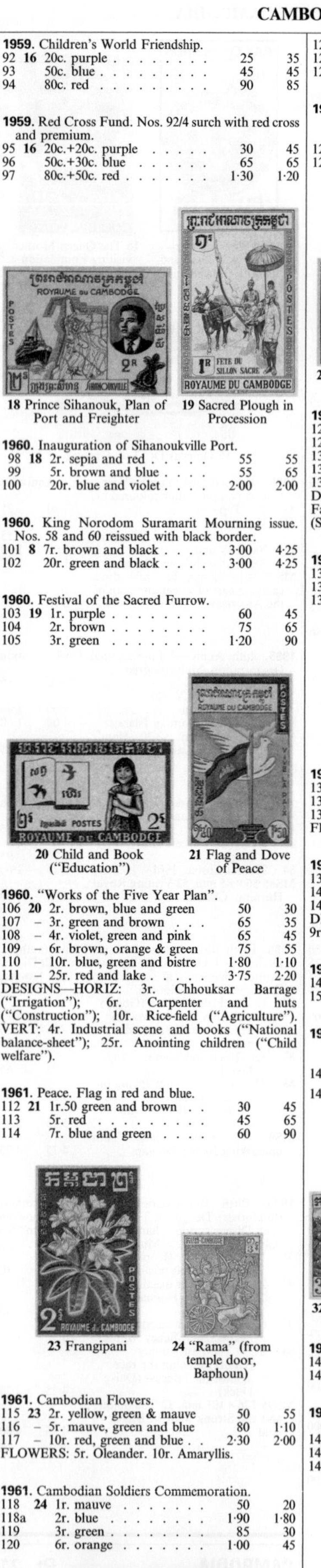

18 Prince Sihanouk, Plan of Port and Freighter
19 Sacred Plough in Procession

1960. Inauguration of Sihanoukville Port.
98 18 2r. sepia and red 55 55
99 5r. brown and blue 55 65
100 20r. blue and violet . . . . 2·00 2·00

1960. King Norodom Suramarit Mourning issue. Nos. 58 and 60 reissued with black border.
101 8 7r. brown and black . . . . 3·00 4·25
102 20r. green and black . . . . 3·00 4·25

1960. Festival of the Sacred Furrow.
103 19 1r. purple 60 45
104 2r. brown 75 65
105 3r. green . . . . 1·20 90

20 Child and Book ("Education")
21 Flag and Dove of Peace

1960. "Works of the Five Year Plan".
106 20 2r. brown, blue and green 50 30
107 – 3r. green and brown . . . 65 35
108 – 4r. violet, green and pink 65 45
109 – 6r. brown, orange & green 75 55
110 – 10r. blue, green and bistre 1·80 1·10
111 – 25r. red and lake . . . . 3·75 2·20
DESIGNS—HORIZ: 3r. Chhouksar Barrage ("Irrigation"); 6r. Carpenter and huts ("Construction"); 10r. Rice-field ("Agriculture"). VERT: 4r. Industrial scene and books ("National balance-sheet"); 25r. Anointing children ("Child welfare").

1961. Peace. Flag in red and blue.
112 21 1r.50 green and brown . . 30 45
113 5r. red 45 65
114 7r. blue and green 60 90

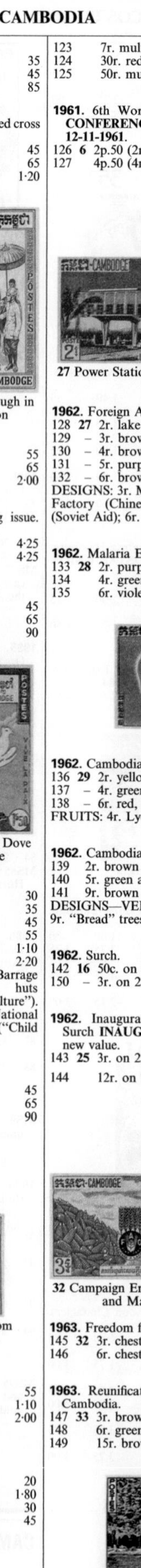

23 Frangipani
24 "Rama" (from temple door, Baphoun)

1961. Cambodian Flowers.
115 23 2r. yellow, green & mauve 50 55
116 – 5r. mauve, green and blue 80 1·10
117 – 10r. red, green and blue . . 2·30 2·00
FLOWERS: 5r. Oleander. 10r. Amaryllis.

1961. Cambodian Soldiers Commemoration.
118 24 1r. mauve 50 20
118a 2r. blue . . . . 1·90 1·80
119 3r. green 85 30
120 6r. orange . . . . 1·00 45

25 Prince Norodom Sihanouk and Independence Monument

1961. Independence Monument.
121 25 2r. green (postage) 80 35
122 4r. sepia 80 45
123 7r. multicoloured (air) . . 75 75
124 30r. red, blue and green . . 2·30 2·30
125 50r. multicoloured . . . . 3·50 3·75

1961. 6th World Buddhist Conference. Optd **VIe CONFERENCE MONDIALE BOUDDHIQUE 12-11-1961.**
126 6 2p.50 (2r.50) green 90 55
127 4p.50 (4r.50) violet . . . . 1·40 85

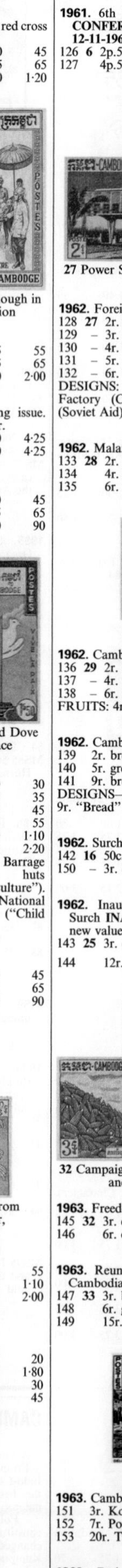

27 Power Station (Czech Aid)
28 Campaign Emblem

1962. Foreign Aid Programme.
128 27 2r. lake and red 30 20
129 – 3r. brown, green and blue 35 20
130 – 4r. brown, red and blue . . 35 30
131 – 5r. purple and green . . . 55 35
132 – 6r. brown and blue . . . . 1·00 35
DESIGNS: 3r. Motorway (American Aid); 4r. Textile Factory (Chinese Aid); 5r. Friendship Hospital (Soviet Aid); 6r. Airport (French Aid).

1962. Malaria Eradication.
133 28 2r. purple and brown . . . 35 30
134 4r. green and brown . . . 40 35
135 6r. violet and bistre 35 45

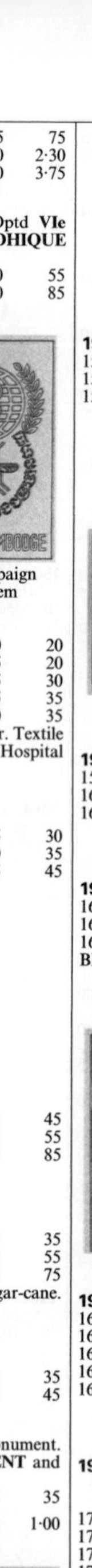

29 Curucmas

1962. Cambodian Fruits (1st issue).
136 29 2r. yellow and brown . . . 45 45
137 – 4r. green and turquoise . . 65 55
138 – 6r. red, green and blue . . 75 85
FRUITS: 4r. Lychees. 6r. Mangosteens.

1962. Cambodian Fruits (2nd issue).
139 2r. brown and green 75 35
140 5r. green and brown . . . . 1·10 55
141 9r. brown and green . . . . 1·30 75
DESIGNS—VERT: 2r. Pineapples. 5r. Sugar-cane. 9r. "Bread" trees.

1962. Surch.
142 16 50c. on 80c. red 55 35
150 – 3r. on 2r.50 brn (No. 55) 75 45

1962. Inauguration of Independence Monument. Surch **INAUGURATION DU MONUMENT** and new value.
143 25 3r. on 2r. green (postage) 55 35
144 12r. on 7r. mult (air) . . . 1·50 1·00

32 Campaign Emblem, Corn and Maize
33 Temple Preah Vihear

1963. Freedom from Hunger.
145 32 3r. chestnut, brown & blue 50 45
146 6r. chestnut, brown & blue 50 45

1963. Reunification of Preah Vihear Temple with Cambodia.
147 33 3r. brown, purple & green 40 35
148 6r. green, orange and blue 70 55
149 15r. brown, blue & green 1·10 90

35 Kep sur Mer

1963. Cambodian Resorts. Multicoloured.
151 3r. Koh Tonsay (vert) . . . 40 30
152 7r. Popokvil (waterfall) (vert) 65 35
153 20r. Type 35 . . . . 2·10 90

1963. Red Cross Centenary. Surch **1863 1963 CENTENAIRE DE LA CROIX-ROUGE** and premium.
154 28 4r.+40c. green & brown . . 65 75
155 6r.+60c. violet & bistre . . 1·00 1·10

37 Scales of Justice

1963. 15th Anniv of Declaration of Human Rights.
156 37 1r. green, red and blue . . 40 45
157 3r. red, blue and green . . 70 55
158 12r. blue, green and red . . 1·30 1·30

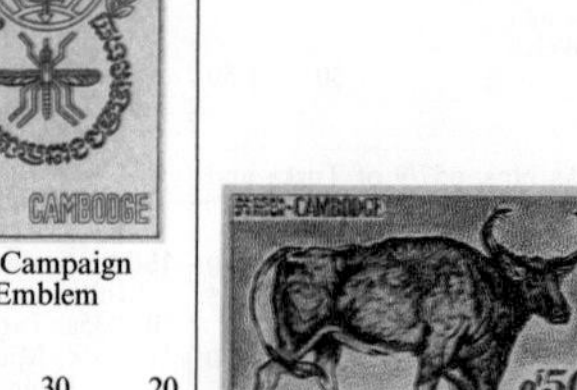

38 Kouprey
39 Black-billed Magpie

1964. Wild Animal Protection.
159 38 50c. brown, green & chest 85 35
160 3r. brown, chestnut & grn 1·20 55
161 6r. brown, blue and green 1·80 1·10

1964. Birds.
162 39 3r. blue, green and indigo 1·10 65
163 – 6r. orange, purple & blue 1·80 1·00
164 – 12r. green and purple . . . 3·25 2·00
BIRDS: 6r. River kingfisher. 12r. Grey heron.

40 "Hanuman"
42 Airline Emblem

1964. Air.
165 40 5r. mauve, brown & blue 65 45
166 10r. bistre, mauve & green 1·00 55
167 20r. bistre, violet and blue 1·70 1·10
168 40r. bistre, blue and red . . 3·75 2·00
169 80r. orange, green & purple 6·00 5·00

1964. Air Olympic Games, Tokyo. Surch **JEUX OLYMPIQUES TOKYO-1964**, Olympic rings and value.
170 40 3r. on 5r. mve, brn and bl 60 35
171 6r. on 10r. bis, mve & grn 1·00 55
172 9r. on 20r. bistre, vio & bl 1·10 90
173 12r. on 40r. bis, bl & red 2·30 1·40

1964. 8th Anniv of Royal Air Cambodia.
174 42 1r.50 red and violet 25 20
175 3r. red and blue 45 30
176 7r.50 red and blue 90 45

43 Prince Norodom Sihanouk
44 Weaving

1964. 10th Anniv of Foundation of Sangkum (Popular Socialist Community).
177 43 2r. violet 45 30
178 3r. brown 60 35
179 10r. blue . . . . 1·20 75

1965. Native Handicrafts.
180 44 1r. violet, brown & bistre 30 30
181 – 3r. brown, green & purple 55 35
182 – 5r. red, purple and green 85 75
DESIGNS: 3r. Engraving. 5r. Basket-making.

1965. Indo-Chinese People's Conference. Nos. 178/9 optd **CONFERENCE DES PEUPLES INDOCHINOIS.**
183 43 3r. brown 45 45
184 10r. blue 70 65

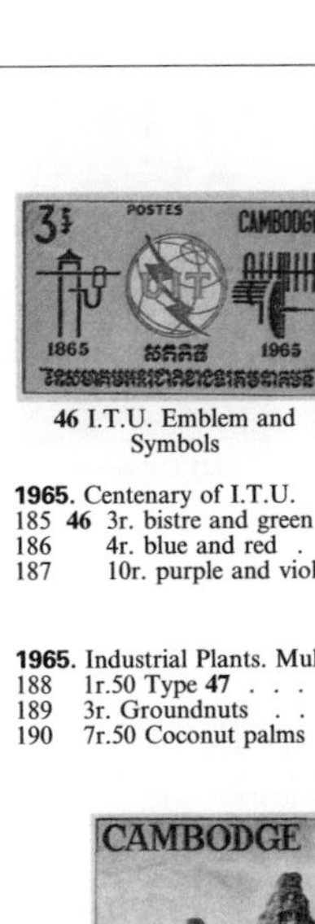

46 I.T.U. Emblem and Symbols 47 Cotton

1965. Centenary of I.T.U.
185 **46** 3r. bistre and green 35 35
186 4r. blue and red 45 55
187 10r. purple and violet . . . 75 75

1965. Industrial Plants. Multicoloured.
188 1r.50 Type **47** 45 30
189 3r. Groundnuts 70 35
190 7r.50 Coconut palms . . . . 1·10 75

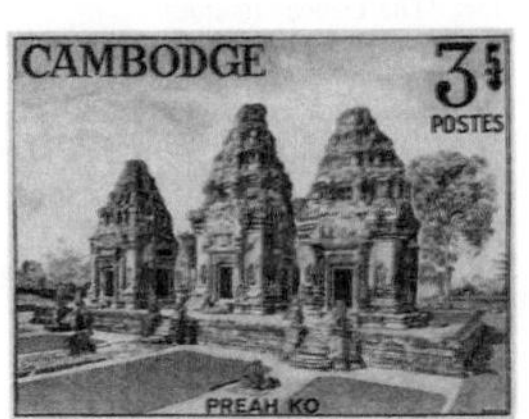

48 Preah Ko

1966. Cambodian Temples.
191 **48** 3r. green, turquoise & brn 75 45
192 – 5r. brown, green & purple 95 55
193 – 7r. brown, green & ochre 1·30 65
194 – 9r. purple, green and blue 2·20 90
195 – 12r. red, green & verm . . 2·75 1·60
TEMPLES: 5r. Baksei Chamkrong, 7r. Banteay Srei, 9r. Angkor Vat. 12r. Bayon.

49 W.H.O. Building 50 Tree-planting

1966. Inaug of W.H.O. Headquarters, Geneva.
196 **49** 2r. multicoloured 30 20
197 3r. multicoloured 35 30
198 5r. multicoloured 60 45

1966. Tree Day.
199 **50** 1r. brown, green & dp brn 25 30
200 3r. brown, green & orange 40 35
201 7r. brown, green and grey 70 45

51 U.N.E.S.C.O. Emblem 52 Stadium

1966. 20th Anniv of U.N.E.S.C.O.
202 **51** 3r. multicoloured 35 30
203 7r. multicoloured 45 55

1966. "Ganefo" Games, Phnom Penh.
204 **52** 3r. blue 15 20
205 – 4r. green 20 35
206 – 7r. red 30 55
207 – 10r. brown 40 75
DESIGNS: 4r., 7r., 10r. Various bas-reliefs of ancient sports from Angkor Vat.

53 Wild Boar

56 Ballet Dancer

1967. Fauna.
208 **53** 3r. black, green and blue 70 45
209 – 5r. multicoloured 80 75
210 – 7r. multicoloured . . . . . 1·30 1·10
FAUNA—VERT: 5r. Hog-deer. HORIZ: 7r. Indian elephant.

1967. International Tourist Year. Nos. 191/2, 194/5 and 149 optd **ANNEE INTERNATIONALE DU TOURISME 1967**.
211 **48** 3r. green, turquoise & brn 65 45
212 5r. brown, green & purple 75 45
213 – 9r. purple, green and blue 1·10 75
214 – 12r. red, green & verm . . 1·30 90
215 **33** 15r. brown, blue & green 1·60 1·10

1967. Millenary of Banteay Srei Temple. No. 193 optd **MILLENAIRE DE BANTEAY SREI 967–1967**.
216 7r. brown, green and ochre 1·10 45

1967. Cambodian Royal Ballet. Designs showing ballet dancers.
217 **56** 1r. orange 30 35
218 – 3r. blue 65 35
219 – 5r. blue 85 45
220 – 7r. red . . . . 1·30 65
221 – 10r. multicoloured . . . . 1·70 90

1967. Int Literacy Day. Surch **Journee Internationale de l'Alphabetisation 8-9-67** and new value.
222 **37** 6r. on 12r. blue, grn & red 70 35
223 **15** 7r. on 15r. brown & green 85 55

58 Decade Emblem 59 Royal University of Kompong-Cham

1967. International Hydrological Decade.
224 **58** 1r. orange, blue and black 20 20
225 6r. orange, blue and violet 40 35
226 10r. orange, lt green & grn 60 55

1968. Cambodian Universities and Institutes.
227 **59** 4r. purple, blue & brown 40 30
228 – 6r. brown, green and blue 55 35
229 – 9r. brown, green and blue 75 45
DESIGNS: 6r. "Khmero-Soviet Friendship" Higher Technical Institute; 9r. Sangkum Reaster Niyum University Centre.

60 Doctor tending child

1968. 20th Anniv of W.H.O.
230 **60** 3r. blue 45 30
231 – 7r. blue 65 45
DESIGN: 7r. Man using insecticide.

61 Stadium

1968. Olympic Games, Mexico.
232 **61** 1r. brown, green and red 40 30
233 – 2r. brown, red and blue . . 45 35
234 – 3r. brown, blue and purple 55 35
235 – 5r. violet 60 35
236 – 7r.50 brown, green & red 85 45
DESIGNS—HORIZ: 2r. Wrestling; 3r. Cycling. VERT: 5r. Boxing; 7r.50, Runner with torch.

62 Stretcher-party

1968. Cambodian Red Cross Fortnight.
237 **62** 3r. red, green and blue . . 70 30

63 Prince Norodom Sihanouk

1968. 15th Anniv of Independence.
238 **63** 7r. violet, green and blue 45 45
239 – 8r. brown, green and blue 45 65
DESIGN: 8r. Soldiers wading through stream.

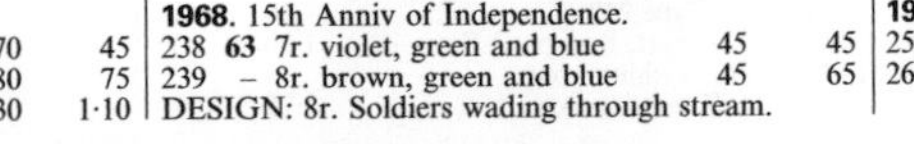

64 Human Rights Emblem and Prince Norodom Sihanouk

1968. Human Rights Year.
240 **64** 3r. blue 30 20
241 5r. purple 65 30
242 7r. black, orange & green 95 45

65 I.L.O. Emblem

1969. 50th Anniv of I.L.O.
243 **65** 3r. blue 25 20
244 6r. red 40 30
245 9r. green 65 45

66 Red Cross Emblems around Globe

1969. 50th Anniv of League of Red Cross Societies.
246 **66** 1r. multicoloured 30 20
247 3r. multicoloured 40 30
248 10r. multicoloured 85 45

67 Golden Birdwing

1969. Butterflies.
249 **67** 3r. black, yellow & violet 1·40 55
250 – 4r. black, green & verm . . 1·40 85
251 – 8r. black, orange & green 1·80 1·40
DESIGNS: 4r. Tailed jay. 8r. Orange tiger.

68 Diesel Train and Route Map

1969. Opening of Phnom Penh–Sihanoukville Railway.
252 **68** 3r. multicoloured 30 30
253 – 6r. brown, black & green 45 30
254 – 8r. black 75 35
255 – 9r. blue, turquoise & grn 85 45
DESIGNS: 6r. Phnom Penh Station; 8r. Diesel locomotive and Kampor Station; 9r. Steam locomotive at Sihanoukville Station.

69 Siamese Tigerfish

1970. Fishes. Multicoloured.
256 3r. Type **69** 75 65
257 7r. Marbled sleeper . . . . . 1·50 1·10
258 9r. Chevron snakehead . . . 2·40 1·50

70 Vat Tepthidaram 71 Dish Aerial and Open Book

1970. Buddhist Monasteries in Cambodia. Mult.
259 2r. Type **70** 40 30
260 3r. Vat Maniratanaram (horiz) 45 30
261 6r. Vat Patumavati (horiz) . . 85 35
262 8r. Vat Unnalom (horiz) . . 1·60 45

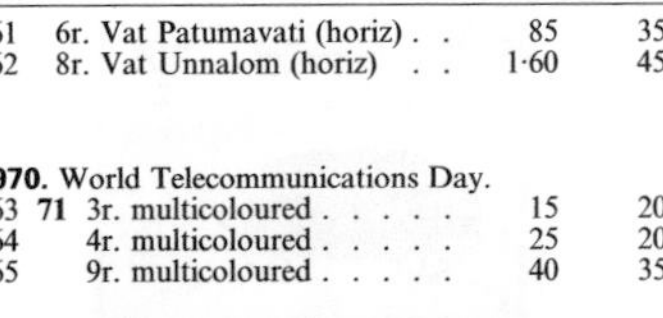

1970. World Telecommunications Day.
263 **71** 3r. multicoloured 15 20
264 4r. multicoloured 25 20
265 9r. multicoloured 40 35

72 New Headquarters Building

1970. Opening of New U.P.U. Headquarters Building, Berne.
266 **72** 1r. multicoloured 20 10
267 3r. multicoloured 30 10
268 4r. multicoloured 55 10
269 10r. multicoloured . . . . 1·10 35

73 "Nelumbium speciosum"

1970. Aquatic Plants. Multicoloured.
270 3r. Type **73** 40 55
271 4r. "Eichhornia crassipes" . . 60 55
272 13r. "Nymphea lotus" . . . 1·10 85

74 "Banteay-srei" (bas-relief)

1970. World Meteorological Day.
273 **74** 3r. red and green 30 10
274 4r. red, green and blue . . 45 30
275 7r. green, blue and black 60 55

75 Rocket, Dove and Globe

1970. 25th Anniv of United Nations.
276 **75** 3r. multicoloured 25 20
277 5r. multicoloured 45 35
278 10r. multicoloured 65 55

76 I.E.Y. Emblem

1970. International Education Year.
279 **76** 1r. blue 15 10
280 3r. purple 20 10
281 8r. green 50 35

77 Samdech Chuon Nath

1971. 2nd Death Anniv of Samdech Chuon-Nath (Khmer language scholar).
282 **77** 3r. multicoloured 25 10
283 8r. multicoloured 60 30
284 9r. multicoloured 75 45

For issues between 1971 and 1989 see under KHMER REPUBLIC and KAMPUCHEA in volume 3.

203 17th-century Coach

1989. Coaches. Multicoloured.

No.	Description	Mint	Used
1020	2r. Type **203**	10	10
1021	3r. Paris–Lyon coach, 1720	15	10
1022	5r. Mail coach, 1793	25	10
1023	10r. Light mail coach, 1805	55	20
1024	15r. Royal mail coach	80	30
1025	20r. Russian mail coach	95	35
1026	35r. Paris–Lille coupe, 1837 (vert)	1·90	55

204 "Papilio zagreus"

1989. "Brasiliana 89" International Stamp Exhibition, Rio de Janeiro. Butterflies. Multicoloured.

No.	Description	Mint	Used
1028	2r. Type **204**	10	10
1029	3r. "Morpho catenarius"	15	10
1030	5r. "Morpho aega"	25	10
1031	10r. "Callithea sapphira" ("wrongly inscr "saphhira")	50	10
1032	15r. "Catagramma sorana"	75	20
1033	20r. "Pierella nereis"	95	20
1034	35r. "Papilio brasiliensis"	1·90	20

205 Pirogue

1989. Khmer Culture. Multicoloured.

No.	Description	Mint	Used
1036	3r. Type **205**	20	10
1037	12r. Pirogue (two sets of oars)	80	35
1038	30r. Pirogue with cabin	2·10	90

206 Youth **207** Goalkeeper

1989. National Development. Multicoloured.

No.	Description	Mint	Used
1039	3r. Type **206**	20	10
1040	12r. Trade unions emblem (horiz)	60	20
1041	30r. National Front emblem (horiz)	1·70	75

1990. World Cup Football Championship, Italy. Multicoloured.

No.	Description	Mint	Used
1042	2r. Type **207**	10	10
1043	3r. Dribbling ball	15	10
1044	5r. Controlling ball with thigh	25	10
1045	10r. Running with ball	55	10
1046	15r. Shooting	80	20
1047	20r. Tackling	95	20
1048	35r. Tackling (different)	1·90	20

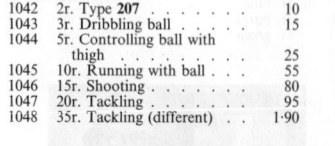

208 Two-horse Postal Van

1990. "Stamp World London 90" International Stamp Exhibition. Royal Mail Horse-drawn Transport. Multicoloured.

No.	Description	Mint	Used
1050	2r. Type **208**	10	10
1051	3r. One-horse cart	10	10
1052	5r. Rural post office cart	15	10
1053	10r. Rural post office van	25	10
1054	15r. Local post office van	40	20
1055	20r. Parcel-post cart	55	20
1056	35r. Two-horse wagon	1·10	20

209 Rice Grains **210** Shooting

1990. Cultivation of Rice. Multicoloured.

No.	Description	Mint	Used
1058	3r. Type **209**	20	10
1059	12r. Transporting rice (horiz)	80	35
1060	30r. Threshing rice	2·10	90

1990. Olympic Games, Barcelona (1992) (1st issue). Multicoloured.

No.	Description	Mint	Used
1061	2r. Type **210**	10	10
1062	3r. Putting the shot	15	10
1063	5r. Weightlifting	25	10
1064	10r. Boxing	55	10
1065	15r. Pole vaulting	80	20
1066	20r. Basketball	1·10	20
1067	35r. Fencing	1·90	20

See also Nos. 1163/9, 1208/12 and 1241/5.

211 Four-man Bobsleighing

1990. Winter Olympic Games, Albertville (1992) (1st issue). Multicoloured.

No.	Description	Mint	Used
1069	2r. Type **211**	10	10
1070	3r. Speed skating	15	10
1071	5r. Figure skating	20	10
1072	10r. Ice hockey	45	10
1073	15r. Biathlon	70	20
1074	20r. Lugeing	90	20
1075	35r. Ski jumping	1·70	20

See also Nos. 1152/8.

212 Facade of Banteay Srei

1990. Khmer Culture. Multicoloured.

No.	Description	Mint	Used
1077	3r. Type **212**	20	10
1078	12r. Ox-carts (12th-century relief)	80	35
1079	30r. Banon ruins (36 × 21 mm)	2·10	90

213 "Zizina oxleyi"

1990. "New Zealand 1990" International Stamp Exhibition, Auckland. Butterflies. Multicoloured.

No.	Description	Mint	Used
1080	2r. Type **213**	10	10
1081	3r. "Cupha prosope"	10	10
1082	5r. "Heteronympha merope"	15	10
1083	10r. "Dodonidia helmsi"	30	20
1084	15r. "Argirophenga antipodum"	55	20
1085	20r. "Tysonotis danis"	80	20
1086	35r. "Pyrameis gonnarilla"	1·20	30

214 "Vostok"

1990. Spacecraft. Multicoloured.

No.	Description	Mint	Used
1088	2r. Type **214**	10	10
1089	3r. "Soyuz"	10	10
1090	5r. Satellite	15	10
1091	10r. "Luna 10"	35	20
1092	15r. "Mars 1"	55	30
1093	20r. "Venus 3"	70	35
1094	35r. "Mir" space station	1·10	75

215 Poodle

1990. Dogs. Multicoloured.

No.	Description	Mint	Used
1096	20c. Type **215**	20	10
1097	80c. Shetland sheepdog	20	10
1098	3r. Samoyede	45	10
1099	6r. Springer spaniel	85	10
1100	10r. Wire-haired fox terrier	1·10	20
1101	15r. Afghan hound	1·70	20
1102	25r. Dalmatian	2·30	20

216 "Cereus hexagonus" **217** Learning to Write

1990. Cacti. Multicoloured.

No.	Description	Mint	Used
1104	20c. Type **216**	10	10
1105	80c. "Arthrocereus rondonianus"	10	10
1106	3r. "Matucana multicolor"	15	10
1107	6r. "Hildewintera aureispina"	25	10
1108	10r. "Opuntia retrosa"	50	20
1109	15r. "Erdisia tenuicula"	75	20
1110	25r. "Mamillaria yaquensis"	1·10	20

1990. International Literacy Year.

No.	Type	Description	Mint	Used
1111	**217**	3r. black and blue	15	10
1112		12r. black and yellow	1·10	35
1113		30r. black and pink	3·50	90

218 English Nef, 1200

1990. Ships. Multicoloured.

No.	Description	Mint	Used
1114	20c. Type **218**	20	10
1115	80c. 16th-century Spanish galleon	30	10
1116	3r. Dutch jacht, 1627	45	10
1117	6r. "La Couronne" (French galleon), 1638	85	10
1118	10r. Dumont d'Urville's ship "L'Astrolabe", 1826	1·10	20
1119	15r. "Louisiane" (steamer), 1864	1·90	20
1120	25r. Clipper, 1900 (vert)	2·30	20

No. 1118 is wrongly inscribed "d'Uville".

219 Phnom-Penh–Kampong Som Railway

1990. National Development. Multicoloured.

No.	Description	Mint	Used
1122	3r. Type **219**	30	10
1123	12r. Port, Kampong Som	1·30	35
1124	30r. Fishing boats, Kampong Som	3·75	90

220 Sacre-Coeur de Montmartre and White Bishop **221** Columbus

1990. "Paris '90" World Chess Championship, Paris. Multicoloured.

No.	Description	Mint	Used
1125	2r. Type **220**	20	10
1126	3r. "The Horse Trainer" (statue) and white knight	30	10
1127	5r. "Victory of Samothrace" (statue) and white queen	45	10
1128	10r. Azay-le-Rideau Chateau and white rook	95	20
1129	15r. "The Dance" (statue) and white pawn	1·40	30
1130	20r. Eiffel Tower and white king	1·90	35
1131	35r. Arc de Triomphe and black chessmen	3·25	55

1990. 500th Anniv (1992) of Discovery of America by Columbus (1st issue). Multicoloured.

No.	Description	Mint	Used
1133	2r. Type **221**	30	10
1134	3r. Queen Isabella's jewel-chest	45	10
1135	5r. Queen Isabella the Catholic	55	10
1136	10r. "Santa Maria" (flagship)	95	10
1137	15r. Juan de la Cosa	1·40	10
1138	20r. Monument to Columbus	1·90	20
1139	35r. Devin Pyramid, Yucatan	3·50	20

See also Nos. 1186/92.

222 Tyre Factory **223** Tackle

1991. National Festival. Multicoloured.

No.	Description	Mint	Used
1141	100r. Type **222**	55	20
1142	300r. Rural hospital	2·10	90
1143	500r. Freshwater fishing (27 × 40 mm)	3·25	1·20

1991. World Cup Football Championship, U.S.A. (1994) (1st issue).

No.	Type	Description	Mint	Used
1144	**223**	5r. multicoloured	15	10
1145	–	25r. multicoloured	15	10
1146	–	70r. multicoloured	35	10
1147	–	100r. multicoloured	40	10
1148	–	200r. multicoloured	75	20
1149	–	400r. multicoloured	1·50	20
1150	–	1000r. multicoloured	3·50	20

DESIGNS: 25r. to 1000r. Different footballing scenes.

See also Nos. 1220/4, 1317/21 and 1381/5.

224 Speed Skating

1991. Winter Olympic Games, Albertville (1992) (2nd issue). Multicoloured.

No.	Description	Mint	Used
1152	5r. Type **224**	20	10
1153	25r. Slalom skiing	30	10
1154	70r. Ice hockey	55	10
1155	100r. Bobsleighing	65	10
1156	200r. Freestyle skiing	1·30	20
1157	400r. Ice skating	2·50	20
1158	1000r. Downhill skiing	3·75	20

225 "Torso of Vishnu Reclining" (11th cent)

1991. Sculpture. Multicoloured.
1160 100r. "Garuda" (Koh Ker, 10th century) 35 20
1161 300r. Type **225** 1·10 90
1162 500r. "Reclining Nandin" (7th century) 1·90 1·10

226 Pole Vaulting

1991. Olympic Games, Barcelona (1992) (2nd issue). Multicoloured.
1163 5r. Type **226** 20 10
1164 25r. Table tennis 30 10
1165 70r. Running 45 10
1166 100r. Wrestling 55 10
1167 200r. Gymnastics (bars) 95 20
1168 400r. Tennis 1·80 20
1169 1000r. Boxing 4·25 20

227 Douglas DC-10-30

1991. Airplanes. Multicoloured.
1171 5r. Type **227** 15 10
1172 25r. McDonnell Douglas MD-11 20 10
1173 70r. Ilyushin Il-96-300 30 10
1174 100r. Airbus Industrie A310 40 10
1175 200r. Yakovlev Yak-42 80 20
1176 400r. Tupolev Tu-154 1·50 20
1177 1000r. Douglas DC-9 3·75 20

228 Diaguita Funerary Urn, Catamarca

1991. "Espamer '91" Iberia–Latin America Stamp Exhibition, Buenos Aires. Multicoloured.
1178 5r. Bareales glass pot, Catamarca (horiz) 15 10
1179 25r. Type **228** 20 10
1180 70r. Quiroga urn, Tucuman 30 10
1181 100r. Round glass pot, Santiago del Estero (horiz) 45 10
1182 200r. Pitcher, Santiago del Estero (horiz) 85 20
1183 400r. Diaguita funerary urn, Tucuman 1·60 20
1184 1000r. Bareales funerary urn, Catamarca (horiz) 4·00 20

229 "Pinta"

1991. 500th Anniv (1992) of Discovery of America by Columbus (2nd issue). Each brown, stone and black.
1186 5r. Type **229** 20 10
1187 25r. "Nina" 30 10
1188 70r. "Santa Maria" 55 10
1189 100r. Landing at Guanahani, 1492 (horiz) 65 10
1190 200r. Meeting of two cultures (horiz) 1·30 20
1191 400r. La Navidad (first European settlement in America) (horiz) 2·50 20
1192 1000r. Amerindian village (horiz) 5·75 20

230 "Neptis pryeri"

1991. "Phila Nippon '91" International Stamp Exhibition, Tokyo. Butterflies. Multicoloured.
1194 5r. Type **230** 15 10
1195 25r. "Papilio xuthus" 15 10
1196 70r. Common map butterfly 10 10
1197 100r. "Argynnis anadiomene" 40 10
1198 200r. "Lethe marginalis" 75 20
1199 400r. "Artopoetes pryeri" 95 20
1200 1000r. African monarch 3·50 20

231 Coastal Fishing Port

1991. National Development. Food Industry. Multicoloured.
1202 100r. Type **231** 50 45
1203 300r. Preparing palm sugar (29 × 40 mm) 1·40 90
1204 500r. Picking peppers 2·40 1·20

232 Chakdomuk Costumes

233 Wrestling

1992. National Festival. Traditional Costumes. Multicoloured.
1205 150r. Type **232** 50 20
1206 350r. Longvek 1·40 30
1207 1000r. Angkor 2·50 45

1992. Olympic Games, Barcelona (3rd issue). Multicoloured.
1208 5r. Type **233** 15 10
1209 15r. Football 15 10
1210 80r. Weightlifting 20 10
1211 400r. Archery 1·00 30
1212 1500r. Gymnastics 3·50 35

234 Neon Tetra

1992. Fishes. Multicoloured.
1214 5r. Type **234** 15 10
1215 15r. Siamese fighting fish 15 10
1216 80r. Kaiser tetra 20 10
1217 400r. Dwarf gourami 1·00 30
1218 1500r. Port hoplo 3·50 35

235 Germany v. Columbia

236 Monument

1992. World Cup Football Championship, U.S.A. (1994) (2nd issue). Multicoloured.
1220 5r. Type **235** 15 10
1221 15r. Netherlands player (horiz) 15 10
1222 80r. Uruguay v. C.I.S. (ex-Soviet states) 20 10
1223 400r. Cameroun v. Yugoslavia 1·00 30
1224 1500r. Italy v. Sweden 3·50 35

1992. Khmer Culture. 19th-century Architecture. Multicoloured.
1226 150r. Type **236** 55 35
1227 350r. Stupa 1·30 85
1228 1000r. Mandapa library 3·50 2·00

237 Motor Car

1992. 540th Birth Anniv (1992) of Leonardo da Vinci (artist and inventor). Multicoloured.
1229 5r. Type **237** 20 10
1230 15r. Container ship 20 10
1231 80r. Helicopter 30 10
1232 400r. Scuba diver 1·50 30
1233 1500r. Parachutists (vert) 4·75 35

238 Juan de la Cierva and Autogyro

1992. "Expo '92" World's Fair, Seville. Inventors. Multicoloured.
1235 5r. Type **238** 20 10
1236 15r. Thomas Edison and electric light bulb 20 10
1237 80r. Samuel Morse and Morse telegraph 30 10
1238 400r. Narciso Monturiol and "Ictineo" (early submarine) 1·40 30
1239 1500r. Alexander Graham Bell and early telephone 2·75 35

239 Weightlifting

1992. Olympic Games, Barcelona (4th issue). Multicoloured.
1241 5r. Type **239** 20 10
1242 15r. Boxing 20 10
1243 80r. Basketball 30 10
1244 400r. Running 1·40 30
1245 1500r. Water polo 4·75 35

240 Palm Trees

1992. Environmental Protection. Multicoloured.
1247 5r. Couple on riverside 20 10
1248 15r. Pagoda 20 10
1249 80r. Type **240** 30 10
1250 400r. Boy riding water buffalo 1·40 30
1251 1500r. Swimming in river 4·75 35

241 Louis de Bougainville and "La Boudeuse"

242 "Albatrellus confluens"

1992. "Genova '92" International Thematic Stamp Exhibition, Genoa. Multicoloured.
1253 5r. Type **241** 20 10
1254 15r. James Cook and H.M.S. "Endeavour" 30 10
1255 80r. Charles Darwin and H.M.S. "Beagle" 45 10
1256 400r. Jacques Cousteau and "Calypso" 1·50 30
1257 1500r. "Kon Tiki" (replica of balsa raft) 5·25 35

1992. Fungi. Multicoloured.
1259 5r. Type **242** 15 10
1260 15r. Scarlet-stemmed boletus 20 10
1261 80r. Verdigris agaric 25 10
1262 400r. "Telamonia armillata" 1·00 30
1263 1500r. Goaty smell cortinarius 3·75 35

243 Bellanca Pacemaker Seaplane, 1930

1992. Aircraft. Multicoloured.
1264 5r. Type **243** 20 10
1265 15r. Canadair CL-215 fire-fighting amphibian, 1965 20 10
1266 80r. Grumman G-21 Goose amphibian, 1937 30 10
1267 400r. Grumman SA-6 Sealand flying boat, 1947 1·30 30
1268 1500r. Short S.23 Empire "C" Class flying boat, 1936 4·50 35

244 Dish Aerial

1992. National Development. Multicoloured.
1270 150r. Type **244** 55 20
1271 350r. Dish aerial, flags and satellite 1·30 30
1272 1000r. Hotel Cambodiana 4·00 45

245 Sociological Institute

1993. National Festival. Multicoloured.
1273 50r. Type **245** 45 20
1274 450r. Motel Cambodiana 1·40 30
1275 1000r. Theatre, Bassac 4·00 45

246 Bottle-nosed Dolphin and Submarine

1993. Wildlife and Technology. Multicoloured.
1276 150r. Type **246** 55 10
1277 200r. Supersonic jet airplane and peregrine falcon 65 20
1278 250r. Eurasian beaver and dam 75 20
1279 500r. Satellite and natterer's bat 2·00 20
1280 900r. Rufous humming-bird and helicopter 3·00 30

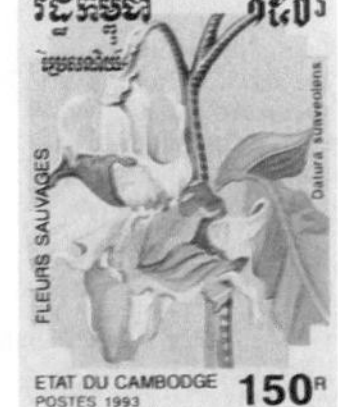

247 "Datura suaveolens"

1993. Wild Flowers. Multicoloured.
1281 150r. Type **247** 55 10
1282 200r. "Convolvulus tricolor" 65 20
1283 250r. "Hippeastrum" hybrid 75 20
1284 500r. "Camellia" hybrid 1·90 20
1285 900r. "Lilium speciosum" 3·00 30

248 Vihear Temple

1993. Khmer Culture. Multicoloured.
1287 50r. Sculpture of ox 45 20
1288 450r. Type **248** . . . . . . 1·30 75
1289 1000r. Offering to Buddha 3·75 1·70

249 Philippine Flying Lemur

1993. Animals. Multicoloured.
1290 150r. Type **249** 55 20
1291 200r. Red giant flying squirrel 65 20
1292 250r. Fringed gecko 75 30
1293 500r. Wallace's flying frog 2·00 35
1294 900r. Flying lizard . . . . . 3·00 65

250 "Symbrenthia hypselis"

1993. "Brasiliana '93" International Stamp Exhibition, Rio de Janeiro. Butterflies. Mult.
1295 250r. Type **250** 75 20
1296 350r. "Sithon nedymond" 1·30 20
1297 600r. "Geitoneura minyas" 1·90 30
1298 800r. "Argyreus hyperbius" 2·40 35
1299 1000r. "Argyrophenga antipodum" . . . . . . 3·25 65

251 Armed Cambodians reporting to U.N. Base
253 Santos-Dumont, Eiffel Tower and "Ballon No. 6", 1901

252 Venetian Felucca

1993. United Nations Transitional Authority in Cambodia Pacification Programme. Each black and blue.
1301 150r. Type **251** 55 10
1302 200r. Military camp 65 20
1303 250r. Surrender of arms . . 75 20
1304 500r. Vocational training . . 1·70 20
1305 900r. Liberation . . . . . . 2·75 30

1993. Sailing Ships. Multicoloured.
1307 150r. Type **252** 40 10
1308 200r. Phoenician galley . . 50 20
1309 250r. Egyptian merchantman 65 20
1310 500r. Genoese merchantman 1·50 20
1311 900r. English merchantman 2·40 30

1993. 120th Birth Anniv of Alberto Santos-Dumont (aviator). Multicoloured.
1312 150r. Type **253** 55 10
1313 200r. "14 bis" (biplane), 1906 (horiz) 65 20
1314 250r. "Demoiselle" (monoplane), 1909 (horiz) 75 20
1315 500r. Embraer EMB-201 A (horiz) . . . . 2·00 20
1316 900r. Embraer EMB-111 (horiz) . . . . 3·00 30

254 Footballer

1993. World Cup Football Championship, U.S.A. (1994) (3rd issue).
1317 **254** 250r. multicoloured . . . 75 10
1318 – 350r. multicoloured . . . 1·30 20
1319 – 600r. multicoloured . . . 1·90 20
1320 – 800r. multicoloured . . . 2·40 20
1321 – 1000r. mult (vert) . . . 3·25 30
DESIGNS: 350r. to 1000r. Various footballing scenes.

255 European Wigeon

1993. "Bangkok 1993" International Stamp Exhibition, Thailand. Ducks. Multicoloured.
1323 250r. Type **255** 75 20
1324 350r. Baikal teal . . . . . 1·30 30
1325 600r. Mandarin . . . . . . 1·90 35
1326 800r. Wood duck . . . . . 2·40 65
1327 1000r. Harlequin duck . . . 3·25 85

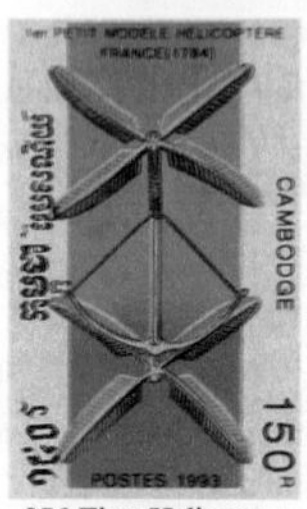

256 First Helicopter Model, France, 1784
257 "Cnaphalocrosis medinalis"

1993. Vertical Take-off Aircraft. Multicoloured.
1329 150r. Type **256** 55 10
1330 200r. Model of steam helicopter, 1863 . . . . 65 20
1331 250r. New York–Atlanta–Miami autogyro flight, 1927 (horiz) 75 20
1332 500r. Sikorsky helicopter, 1943 (horiz) . . . . . 1·70 20
1333 900r. French vertical take-off jet . . . . 3·00 30

1993. National Development. Harmful Insects. Multicoloured.
1335 50r. Type **257** 30 20
1336 450r. Brown leaf-hopper . . 1·50 20
1337 500r. "Scirpophaga incertulas" . . . . 1·70 30
1338 1000r. Stalk-eyed fly . . . . 3·50 30

258 Ministry of Posts and Telecommunications

1993. 40th Anniv of Independence.
1340 **258** 300r. multicoloured . . . 1·10 30
1341 – 500r. multicoloured . . . 1·70 65
1342 – 700r. blue, red & black 2·50 90
DESIGNS—VERT: 500r. Independence monument. HORIZ: 700r. National flag.

259 Boy with Pony
260 Figure Skating

1993. Figurines by M. J. Hummel. Multicoloured.
1343 50r. Type **259** 20 10
1344 100r. Girl and pram 55 10
1345 150r. Girl bathing doll . . . 75 10
1346 200r. Girl holding doll . . . 95 20
1347 250r. Boys playing . . . . . 1·20 20
1348 300r. Girls pulling boy in cart . . . . 1·50 30
1349 350r. Girls playing ring-o-roses . . . . 1·70 35
1350 600r. Boys with stick and drum . . . . 2·75 55

1994. Winter Olympic Games, Lillehammer, Norway. Multicoloured.
1351 150r. Type **260** 45 10
1352 250r. Two-man luge (horiz) 75 20
1353 400r. Skiing (horiz) . . . . 1·30 20
1354 700r. Biathlon (horiz) . . . 2·30 20
1355 1000r. Speed skating . . . . 3·25 30

261 Opel, 1924

1994. Motor Cars. Multicoloured.
1357 150r. Type **261** 55 10
1358 200r. Mercedes, 1901 . . . 65 20
1359 250r. Ford Model "T", 1927 75 20
1360 500r. Rolls Royce, 1907 . . 1·70 20
1361 900r. Hutton, 1908 . . . . 2·75 30

262 Gymnastics
263 Siva and Uma (10th century, Banteay Srei)

1994. Olympic Games, Atlanta (1996) (1st issue). Multicoloured.
1363 150r. Type **262** 45 10
1364 200r. Football 65 10
1365 250r. Throwing the javelin 75 20
1366 300r. Canoeing 85 20
1367 600r. Running . . . . . . 1·90 20
1368 1000r. Diving (horiz) . . . 3·50 20
See also Nos. 1437/41 and 1495/1500.

1994. Khmer Culture. Statues. Multicoloured.
1370 300r. Type **263** . . . . . . 1·10 55
1371 500r. Vishnu (6th cent, Tvol Dai-Buon) . . . . 1·90 90
1372 700r. King Jayavarman VII (12th–13th century, Krol Romeas Angkor) . . . . 2·75 1·30

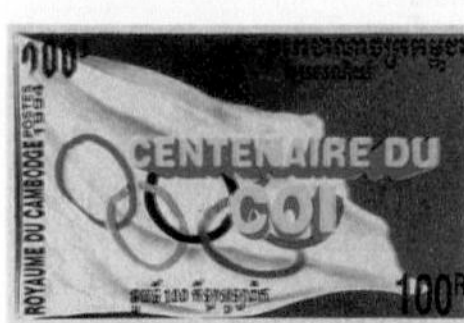

264 Olympic Flag

1994. Centenary of International Olympic Committee. Multicoloured.
1373 100r. Type **264** 30 10
1374 300r. Flag and torch . . . . 1·10 45
1375 600r. Flag and Pierre de Coubertin (reviver of modern Olympic Games) 2·30 85

265 Mesonyx

1994. Prehistoric Animals. Multicoloured.
1376 150r. Type **265** 55 20
1377 250r. Doedicurus 85 30
1378 400r. Mylodon . . . . . . 1·50 45
1379 700r. Uintatherium . . . . 2·50 55
1380 1000r. Hyrachyus . . . . . 3·50 85

266 Players
267 "Soldiers in Combat"

1994. World Cup Football Championship, U.S.A. (4th issue).
1381 **266** 150r. multicoloured . . . 45 10
1382 – 250r. multicoloured . . . 75 20
1383 – 400r. multicoloured . . . 1·30 20
1384 – 700r. multicoloured . . . 2·30 20
1385 – 1000r. multicoloured . . 3·25 30
DESIGNS: 250r. to 1000r. Different footballing scenes.

1994. Tourism. Statues in Public Gardens. Mult.
1387 300r. "Stag and Hind" . . . 1·30 45
1388 500r. Type **267** . . . . . . 1·90 90
1389 700r. "Lions" . . . . 2·75 1·40

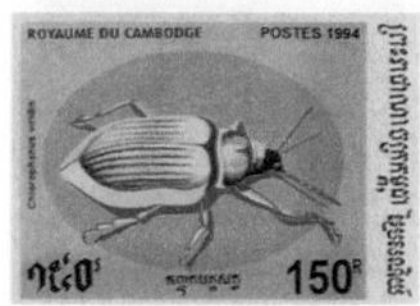

268 "Chlorophanus viridis"

1994. Beetles. Multicoloured.
1390 150r. Type **268** 55 10
1391 200r. "Chrysochroa fulgidissima" 65 20
1392 250r. "Lytta vesicatoria" . . 75 20
1393 500r. "Purpuricenus kaehleri" . . . . 2·00 45
1394 900r. Herculese beetle . . . 3·00 75

269 Halley's Diving-bell, 1690

1994. Submarines. Multicoloured.
1396 150r. Type **269** 55 10
1397 200r. "Gimnote", 1886 (horiz) 65 20
1398 250r. "Peral" (Spain), 1888 (horiz) 75 20
1399 500r. "Nautilus" (first nuclear-powered submarine), 1954 (horiz) 2·00 20
1400 900r. "Trieste" (bathyscaphe), 1953 (horiz) . . . . 3·00 30

270 Francois-Andre Philidor, 1795

1994. Chess Champions. Multicoloured.
1402 150r. Type **270** 55 10
1403 200r. Mahe de la Bourdonnais, 1821 . . . 65 20
1404 250r. Karl Anderssen, 1851 75 20
1405 500r. Paul Morphy, 1858 . . 2·00 45
1406 900r. Wilhelm Steinitz, 1866 3·00 75

271 Sikorsky S-42 Flying Boat

1994. Aircraft. Multicoloured.
1408 150r. Type **271** 55 10
1409 200r. Vought-Sikorsky VS-300A helicopter prototype 65 20
1410 250r. Sikorsky S-37 biplane 75 20
1411 500r. Sikorsky S-35 biplane 2·00 20
1412 900r. Sikorsky S-43 amphibian . . . . 3·00 30

272 Penduline Tit

1994. Birds. Multicoloured.
1414 150r. Type **272** 45 10
1415 250r. Bearded reedling . . . 75 20
1416 400r. Little bunting . . . . 1·40 20
1417 700r. Cirl bunting . . . . . 2·40 45
1418 1000r. Goldcrest . . . . . 3·50 75

273 Postal Service Float

1994. National Independence Festival. Mult.
1420 300r. Type **273** . . . . . . 1·10 45
1421 500r. Soldiers marching . . 1·60 90
1422 700r. Women's army units
on parade . . . . 2·50 1·40

274 Chruoi Changwar Bridge

1994. National Development. Multicoloured.
1423 300r. Type **274** 85 30
1424 500r. Olympique
Commercial Centre . . . 1·50 45
1425 700r. Sakyamony Chedei
Temple . . . . 1·90 65

275 Psittacosaurus

1995. Prehistoric Animals. Multicoloured.
1426 100r. Type **275** 20 10
1427 200r. Protoceratops 45 20
1428 300r. Montanoceraptors . . 65 20
1429 400r. Centrosaurus . . . . 1·40 30
1430 700r. Styracosaurus . . . . 2·30 35
1431 800r. Triceratops . . . . . 3·00 55

276 Orange-tip **278** Death Cap

277 Swimming

1995. Butterflies. Multicoloured.
1432 100r. Type **276** 20 10
1433 200r. Scarce swallowtail . . 65 20
1434 300r. Dark green fritillary 95 20
1435 600r. Red admiral . . . . . 1·40 20
1436 800r. Peacock . . . . 2·10 30

1995. Olympic Games, Atlanta (1996) (2nd issue). Multicoloured.
1437 100r. Type **277** 30 10
1438 200r. Callisthenics (vert) . . 65 20
1439 400r. Basketball (vert) . . . 1·20 20
1440 800r. Football (vert) . . . . 2·75 20
1441 1000r. Cycling (vert) . . . . 3·25 30

1995. Fungi. Multicoloured.
1443 100r. Type **278** 30 10
1444 200r. Chanterelle 75 20
1445 300r. Honey fungus . . . . 1·10 20
1446 600r. Field mushroom . . . 1·80 20
1447 800r. Fly agaric . . . . . . 2·40 30

279 Kneeling Ascetic **281** Black-capped Lory

280 Gaur

1995. Khmer Culture. Statues. Multicoloured.
1448 300r. Type **279** 85 30
1449 500r. Parasurama . . . . . 1·50 45
1450 700r. Shiva . . . . 1·90 65

1995. Protected Animals. Multicoloured.
1451 300r. Type **280** 85 20
1452 500r. Kouprey (vert) . . . . 1·50 30
1453 700r. Saurus crane (vert) . . 1·90 45

1995. Parrot Family. Multicoloured.
1454 100r. Type **281** 30 10
1455 200r. Princess parrot 65 20
1456 400r. Eclectus parrot . . . 1·20 20
1457 800r. Scarlet macaw . . . . 2·75 20
1458 1000r. Budgerigar . . . . . 3·25 30

282 Bird (sculpture)

1995. Tourism. Public Gardens. Multicoloured.
1460 300r. Type **282** 85 30
1461 500r. Water feature . . . . 1·50 45
1462 700r. Mythical figures
(sculpture) . . . . 1·60 65

283 Richard Trevithick's Locomotive, 1804

1995. Steam Locomotives. Multicoloured.
1463 100r. Type **283** 20 10
1464 200r. G. and
R. Stephenson's
"Rocket", 1829 . . . . . 75 20
1465 300r. George Stephenson's
"Locomotion", 1825 . . . 1·10 20
1466 600r. "Lafayette", 1837 . . 1·70 45
1467 800r. "Best Friend of
Charleston", 1830 . . . . 2·10 75

284 Bristol Type 142 Blenheim Mk II Bomber

1995. Second World War Planes. Multicoloured.
1469 100r. Type **284** 20 10
1470 200r. North American
B-25B Mitchell bomber
(horiz) 75 20
1471 300r. Avro Type 652 Anson
Mk I general purpose
plane (horiz) . . . . . . 1·10 20
1472 600r. Avro Manchester
bomber (horiz) . . . . . 1·70 20
1473 800r. Consolidated B-24
Liberator bomber (horiz) 2·10 30

285 Gathering Crops

1995. 50th Anniv of F.A.O. Multicoloured.
1475 300r. Type **285** 55 30
1476 500r. Transplanting crops 1·10 45
1477 700r. Paddy field . . . . . 1·60 65

286 Bridge

1995. 50th Anniv of U.N.O. Preah Kunlorng Bridge. Multicoloured.
1478 300r. Type **286** 55 30
1479 500r. People on bridge . . . 1·10 45
1480 700r. Closer view of bridge 1·60 65

287 Queen Monineath

1995. National Independence. Multicoloured.
1481 700r. Type **287** . . . . . . 2·10 65
1482 800r. King Norodom
Sihanouk . . . . 2·75 75

288 Pennant Coralfish

1995. Fishes. Multicoloured.
1483 100r. Type **288** 30 10
1484 200r. Copper-banded
butterflyfish 65 20
1485 400r. Crown anemonefish 1·20 20
1486 800r. Palette surgeonfish . . 2·75 20
1487 1000r. Queen angelfish . . . 2·10 30

289 Post Office Building

1995. Cent of Head Post Office, Phnom Penh.
1489 **289** 300r. multicoloured . . . 85 30
1490 500r. multicoloured . . . 1·60 45
1491 700r. multicoloured . . . 2·30 65

290 Independence Monument

1995. 40th Anniv of Admission of Cambodia to United Nations Organization. Multicoloured.
1492 300r. Type **290** 55 30
1493 400r. Angkor Wat . . . . . 1·10 45
1494 800r. U.N. emblem and
national flag (vert) . . . 1·60 65

291 Tennis **292** Kep State Chalet

1996. Olympic Games, Atlanta (3rd issue). Mult.
1495 100r. Type **291** 10 10
1496 200r. Volleyball 25 10
1497 300r. Football 45 20
1498 500r. Running 60 20
1499 900r. Baseball . . . . . . 1·10 20
1500 1000r. Basketball . . . . . 1·10 20

1996.
1502 **292** 50r. blue and black . . . 20 10
1503 – 100r. red and black . . . 20 10
1504 – 200r. yellow and black 20 10
1505 – 500r. blue and black . . 55 20
1506 – 800r. mauve and black 95 30
1507 – 1000r. yellow and black 1·30 45
1508 – 1500r. green and black 1·90 65
DESIGNS—HORIZ: 100r. Power station; 200r. Wheelchair; 500r. Handicapped basketball team; 1000r. Kep beach; 1500r. Serpent Island. VERT: 800r. Man making crutches.

293 European Wild Cat

1996. Wild Cats. Multicoloured.
1509 100r. "Felis libyca" (vert) 20 10
1510 200r. Type **293** 35 10
1511 300r. Caracal 50 20
1512 500r. Geoffroy's cat 80 20
1513 900r. Black-footed cat . . . 1·20 20
1514 1000r. Flat-headed cat . . . 1·40 20

294 Player dribbling Ball **295** Tusmukh

1996. World Cup Football Championship, France (1998) (1st issue). Multicoloured.
1515 **294** 100r. multicoloured . . . 30 10
1516 – 200r. multicoloured . . . 45 10
1517 – 300r. multicoloured . . . 75 20
1518 – 500r. multicoloured . . . 1·30 20
1519 – 900r. multicoloured . . . 2·30 20
1520 – 1000r. mult (horiz) . . . 2·75 20
DESIGNS: 200r. to 1000r. Different players.
See also Nos. 1613/18 and 1726/31.

1996. Khmer Culture. Multicoloured.
1522 100r. Type **295** 20 10
1523 300r. Ream Iso . . . . . . 1·30 45
1524 900r. Isei . . . . 2·20 85

296 Pacific Steam Locomotive No. 620, Finland

1996. Railway Locomotives. Multicoloured.
1525 100r. Type **296** 10 10
1526 200r. GNR steam
locomotive No. 261,
Great Britain 10 10
1527 300r. Steam tank
locomotive, 1930 . . . . 30 20
1528 500r. Steam tank locomotive
No. 1362, 1914 . . . . . 40 20
1529 900r. LMS Turbomotive
No. 6202, 1930, Great
Britain 55 20
1530 1000r. Locomotive "Snake",
1884, New Zealand . . . 75 20

297 White-rumped Shama

1996. Birds. Multicoloured.
1532 100r. Type **297** 30 10
1533 200r. Pekin robin 45 10
1534 300r. Varied tit 75 20
1535 500r. Black-naped oriole . . 1·30 20
1536 900r. Japanese bush warbler 2·30 20
1537 1000r. Blue and white flycatcher . . . . 2·75 20

298 Rhythmic Gymnastics

1996. "Olymphilex '96" Olympic Stamps Exhibition, Atlanta, U.S.A. Multicoloured.
1538 100r. Type **298** 20 10
1539 200r. Judo 30 10
1540 300r. High jumping 55 20
1541 500r. Wrestling . . . . . . 1·10 20
1542 900r. Weightlifting . . . . 1·90 20
1543 1000r. Football . . . . . . 2·30 20

299 Douglas M-2, 1926

1996. Biplanes. Multicoloured.
1545 100r. Type **299** 30 10
1546 200r. Pitcairn PS-5 Mailwing, 1926 . . . . . 45 10
1547 300r. Boeing 40-B, 1928 . . 75 20
1548 500r. Potez 25. 1925 . . . . 1·30 20
1549 900r. Stearman C-3MB, 1927 . . . . 2·30 20
1550 1000r. De Havilland D.H.4. 1918 . . . . 2·75 20

300 Aspara

302 Jose Raul Capablanca (1921–27)

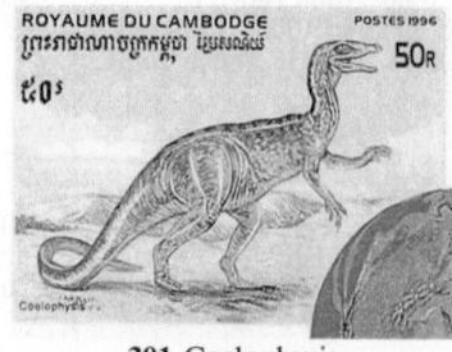

301 Coelophysis

1996. Tonle Bati Temple Ruins.
1552 **300** 50r. black and yellow . . 20 10
1553 – 100r. black and blue . . 20 10
1554 – 200r. black and brown 45 10
1555 – 500r. black and blue . . 75 20
1556 – 800r. black and green . . 1·10 30
1557 – 1000r. black and green 1·40 45
1558 – 1500r. black and bistre 2·30 65
DESIGNS—VERT: 100r. Aspara (different); 200r. Aspara (different); 800r. Taprum Temple; 1000r. Grandmother Peou Temple. HORIZ: 500r. Reliefs on wall; 1500r. Overall view of Tonle Bati.

1996. Prehistoric Animals. Multicoloured.
1559 50r. Type **301** 10 10
1560 100r. Euparkeria 10 10
1561 150r. Plateosaurus 30 10
1562 200r. Herrerasaurus 50 10
1563 250r. Dilophosaurus 55 10
1564 300r. Tuojiangosaurus . . . 70 10
1565 350r. Camarasaurus . . . . 1·10 20
1566 400r. Ceratosaurus . . . . 1·30 20
1567 500r. Espinosaurio . . . . 1·50 30
1568 700r. Ouranosaurus . . . . 2·00 35
1569 800r. Avimimus . . . . . . 2·50 55
1570 1200r. Deinonychus . . . . 3·50 65

Nos. 1559/62, 1563/6 and 1567/70 respectively were issued together, se-tenant, each sheetlet containing a composite design of a globe.

1996. World Chess Champions. Multicoloured.
1571 100r. Type **302** 30 10
1572 200r. Aleksandr Alekhine (1927–35, 1937–46) . . . 45 10
1573 300r. Vasily Vasilevich Smyslov (1957–58) . . . 75 20
1574 500r. Mikhail Nekhemyevich Tal (1960–61) . . . . . . 1·30 20
1575 900r. Robert Fischer (1972–75) . . . . 2·30 20
1576 1000r. Anatoly Karpov (1975–85) . . . . 2·75 20

303 Brown Bear

1996. Mammals and their Young. Multicoloured.
1578 100r. Type **303** 30 10
1579 200r. Lion 45 10
1580 300r. Malayan tapir 65 20
1581 500r. Bactrian camel . . . . 1·30 20
1582 900r. Ibex (vert) . . . . . 2·10 20
1583 1000r. Californian sealion (vert) . . . . 2·75 20

304 Rough Collie

1996. Dogs. Multicoloured.
1584 200r. Type **304** 45 10
1585 300r. Labrador retriever . . 65 20
1586 500r. Dobermann pinscher 1·30 20
1587 900r. German shepherd . . 2·10 20
1588 1000r. Boxer . . . . 2·40 30

305 Chinese Junk

1996. Ships. Multicoloured.
1589 200r. Type **305** 45 10
1590 300r. Phoenician warship, 1500–1000 B.C. 65 20
1591 500r. Roman war galley, 264–241 B.C. . . . . . . 1·30 20
1592 900r. 19th-century full-rigged ship . . . . 2·10 20
1593 1000r. "Sirius" (paddle-steamer), 1838 . . . . . 2·40 30

306 Silver Pagoda, Phnom Penh

1996. 45th Anniv of Cambodian Membership of Universal Postal Union.
1595 **306** 200r. multicoloured . . . 55 20
1596 400r. multicoloured . . . 1·10 35
1597 900r. multicoloured . . . 2·10 85

307 Environmental Vessel and Helicopter

1996. 25th Anniv of Greenpeace (environmental organization). Multicoloured.
1598 200r. Type **307** 75 10
1599 300r. Float-helicopter hovering over motor launch . . . . 1·40 20
1600 500r. Helicopter on deck and motor launches . . . 2·10 30
1601 900r. Helicopter with two barrels suspended beneath 3·75 35

308 Ox

1996. New Year. Year of the Ox. Details of painting by Han Huang. Multicoloured.
1603 500r. Type **308** 65 20
1604 500r. Ox with head turned to right (upright horns) 65 20
1605 500r. Brown and white ox with head up ("handlebar" horns) . . . 65 20
1606 500r. Ox with head in bush ("ram's" horns) . . . 65 20

309 Dam, Phnom Kaun Sat

1996. 10th International United Nations Volunteers Day. Multicoloured.
1607 100r. Type **309** 30 10
1608 500r. Canal, O Angkrung 1·40 45
1609 900r. Canal, Chrey Krem 2·50 85

310 Architect's Model of Reservoir

1996. 43rd Anniv of Independence. Water Management. Multicoloured.
1610 100r. Type **310** 30 10
1611 500r. Reservoir . . . . . . 1·40 45
1612 900r. Reservoir (different) 2·50 85

311 Players

1997. World Cup Football Championship, France (1998) (2nd issue).
1613 **311** 100r. multicoloured . . . 30 10
1614 – 200r. multicoloured . . . 45 10
1615 – 300r. multicoloured . . . 75 20
1616 – 500r. multicoloured . . . 1·30 20
1617 – 900r. multicoloured . . . 2·30 20
1618 – 1000r. multicoloured . . . 2·75 20
DESIGNS: 200r. to 1000r. Different footballing scenes.

312 Two Elephants

1997. The Indian Elephant. Multicoloured.
1620 300r. Type **312** 30 10
1621 500r. Group of three . . . 55 20
1622 900r. Elephants fighting . . 1·10 30
1623 1000r. Adult and calf . . . 1·30 35

314 Horse-drawn Water Pump, 1731

315 Statue on Plinth

1997. Fire Engines. Multicoloured.
1630 200r. Type **314** 30 10
1631 500r. Putnam horse-drawn water pump, 1863 . . . . 45 10
1632 900r. Merryweather horse-drawn engine, 1894 . . . 65 20
1633 1000r. Shand Mason Co horse-drawn water pump, 1901 . . . . 85 20
1634 1500r. Maxin Motor Co automatic pump, 1949 . . 1·30 20
1635 4000r. Merryweather exhaust pump, 1950 . . . 3·50 20

1997. Angkor Wat.
1637 **315** 300r. black and red . . . 30 10
1638 – 300r. black and blue . . 30 10
1639 – 800r. black and green . . 65 10
1640 – 1500r. black & brown . . 1·30 10
1641 – 1700r. black & orange 1·50 20
1642 – 2500r. black and blue . . 1·90 20
1643 – 3000r. black & green . . 2·50 20
DESIGNS—VERT: No. 1638, Statue in wall recess; 1639, Walled courtyard; 1640, Decorative panel with two figures. HORIZ: No. 1641, Rectangular gateway; 1642, Statues and arched gateway; 1643, Stupa and ruins.

316 Steller's Eider

1997. Aquatic Birds. Multicoloured.
1644 200r. Type **316** 10 10
1645 500r. Egyptian goose . . . 25 10
1646 900r. American wigeon . . 40 20
1647 1000r. Falcated teal 45 20
1648 1500r. Surf scoter 65 20
1649 4000r. Blue-winged teal . . 1·90 20

317 Von Stephan

318 Main Entrance

1997. Death Centenary of Heinrich von Stephan (founder of U.P.U.).
1651 **317** 500r. blue & dp blue . . 45 20
1652 1500r. green and olive 1·30 30
1653 2000r. yellow & green . . 1·80 45

1997. Khmer Culture. Banteay Srei Temple. Multicoloured.
1654 500r. Type **318** 45 20
1655 1500r. Main and side entrances . . . . 1·30 30
1656 2000r. Courtyard . . . . . 1·80 45

319 Birman

1997. Cats. Multicoloured.
1657 200r. Type **319** 30 10
1658 500r. Exotic shorthair . . . 45 10
1659 900r. Persian 65 20
1660 1000r. Turkish van 85 20
1661 1500r. American shorthair 1·30 20
1662 4000r. Scottish fold . . . . 3·50 20

320 No. 488

1997. Steam Railway Locomotives. Multicoloured.

No.	Description	Mint	Used
1664	200r. Type **320**	30	10
1665	500r. "Frederick Smith"	45	10
1666	900r. No. 3131	65	20
1667	1000r. London Transport No. L44, Great Britain	85	20
1668	1500r. LNER No. 1711, Great Britain	1·30	20
1669	4000r. No. 60523 "Chateau du Soleil"	3·50	20

321 Shar-pei

1997. Dogs. Multicoloured.

No.	Description	Mint	Used
1671	200r. Type **321**	30	10
1672	500r. Chin-chin	45	10
1673	900r. Pekingese	55	20
1674	1000r. Chow-chow (vert)	65	20
1675	1500r. Pug (vert)	1·30	20
1676	4000r. Akita (vert)	3·50	20

322 Qunalom Temple

1997. 30th Anniv of Association of South East Asian Nations. Multicoloured.

No.	Description	Mint	Used
1678	500r. Type **322**	45	20
1679	1500r. Royal Palace	1·30	30
1680	2000r. National Museum	1·80	45

323 15th-century Caravelle

1997. Sailing Ships. Multicoloured.

No.	Description	Mint	Used
1681	200r. Type **323**	30	10
1682	500r. Spanish galleon	45	10
1683	900r. "Great Harry" (British galleon)	65	20
1684	1000r. "La Couronne" (French galleon)	85	20
1685	1500r. 18th-century East Indiaman	1·30	20
1686	4000r. 19th-century clipper	3·50	20

324 Public Garden 325 Satan's Mushroom

1997. Public Gardens (Nos. 1688/91) and Tuk Chha Canal (others).

No.	Description	Mint	Used
1688 **324**	300r. green and black	30	10
1689 –	300r. red and black	30	10
1690 –	800r. yellow and black	65	10
1691 –	1500r. orange and black	1·30	10
1692 –	1700r. pink and black	1·50	20
1693 –	2500r. blue and black	1·90	20
1694 –	3000r. blue and black	2·50	20

DESIGNS—HORIZ: 300r. Statue at intersection of paths; 300r. Hedging in triangular bed; 1500r. Tree and statue of lion; 1700r. View along canal; 2500r. View across canal; 3000r. Closed lock gates. VERT: 800r. Mounted bowl.

1997. Fungi. Multicoloured.

No.	Description	Mint	Used
1695	200r. Type **325**	30	10
1696	500r. "Amanita regalis"	45	10
1697	900r. "Morchella semilibera"	65	20
1698	1000r. "Gomphus clavatus"	85	20
1699	1500r. "Hygrophorus hypothejus"	1·30	20
1700	4000r. "Albatrellus confluens"	3·50	20

326 Peaceful Fightingfish ("Betta imbellis") and Siamese Fightingfish ("Betta splendens")

1997. Fishes. Multicoloured.

No.	Description	Mint	Used
1702	200r. Type **326**	20	10
1703	500r. Banded gourami	25	10
1704	900r. Rosy barbs	40	20
1705	1000r. Paradise fish	55	20
1706	1500r. "Epalzeorhynchos frenatus"	1·00	20
1707	4000r. "Capoeta tetrazona"	2·10	20

327 Kampot Post Office

1997. 44th Anniv of Independence. Multicoloured.

No.	Description	Mint	Used
1709	1000r. Type **327**	85	30
1710	3000r. Prey Veng Post Office	2·75	65

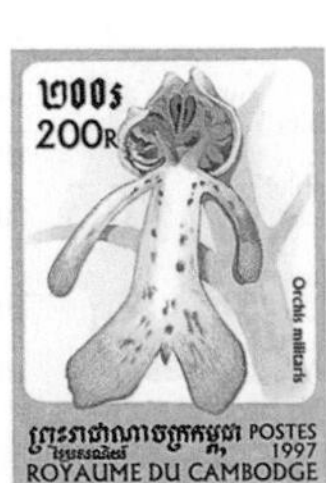

328 "Orchis militaris" 329 In black Jacket

1997. Orchids. Multicoloured.

No.	Description	Mint	Used
1711	200r. Type **328**	20	10
1712	500r. "Orchiaceras bivonae"	30	10
1713	900r. "Orchiaceras spuria"	50	20
1714	1000r. "Gymnadenia conopsea"	60	20
1715	1500r. "Serapias neglecta"	1·30	20
1716	4000r. "Pseudorhiza bruniana"	2·75	20

1997. Diana, Princess of Wales Commemoration. Multicoloured.

No.	Description	Mint	Used
1718	100r. Type **329**	15	10
1719	200r. In black dress	15	10
1720	300r. In blue jacket	15	10
1721	500r. Close-up of Princess in visor	30	10
1722	1000r. In mine-protection clothing	50	10
1723	1500r. With Elizabeth Dole	85	10
1724	2000r. Holding landmine	1·20	20
1725	2500r. With Mother Teresa and Sisters of Charity	1·40	20

330 Player with Ball 331 Suorprat Gateway

1998. World Cup Football Championship, France (3rd issue).

No.	Description	Mint	Used
1726 **330**	200r. multicoloured	15	10
1727 –	500r. multicoloured	25	10
1728 –	900r. multicoloured	45	20
1729 –	1000r. multicoloured	55	20
1730 –	1500r. multicoloured	80	20
1731 –	4000r. multicoloured	2·30	20

DESIGNS: 500r. to 4000r. Different footballing scenes.

1998. Temple Ruins.

No.	Description	Mint	Used
1733 **331**	300r. orange and black	20	10
1734 –	500r. pink and black	30	10
1735 –	1200r. orange and black	45	10
1736 –	1500r. orange and black	65	10
1737 –	1700r. blue and black	75	20
1738 –	2000r. green and black	95	20
1739 –	3000r. lilac and black	1·50	20

DESIGNS—HORIZ: No. 1734, Kumlung wall; 1735, Bapuon entrance; 1737, Prerup; 1738, Preah Khan. VERT: No. 1736, Palilai; 1739, Bayon.

332 Tiger Cub 334 Rottweiler

333 Oakland, Antioch and Eastern Electric Locomotive No. 105

1998. New Year. Year of the Tiger. Multicoloured.

No.	Description	Mint	Used
1740	200r. Type **332**	20	10
1741	500r. Tiger and cubs	30	10
1742	990r. Tiger on alert	45	20
1743	1000r. Tiger washing itself (horiz)	55	20
1744	1500r. Tiger lying in grass (horiz)	80	20
1745	4000r. Tiger snarling (horiz)	2·30	20

1998. Railway Locomotives. Multicoloured.

No.	Description	Mint	Used
1747	200r. Type **333**	20	10
1748	500r. New York, Westchester and electric locomotive No. 1	45	10
1749	900r. Spokane and Inland electric locomotive No. MII	55	20
1750	1000r. International Railway electric locomotive	75	20
1751	1500r. British Columbia Electric Railway locomotive No. 823	1·10	20
1752	4000r. Southern Pacific electric locomotive No. 200	3·00	20

1998. Dogs. Multicoloured.

No.	Description	Mint	Used
1754	200r. Type **334**	15	10
1755	500r. Beauceron	35	10
1756	900r. Boxer	50	20
1757	1000r. Siberian husky	60	20
1758	1500r. Welsh Pembroke corgi	85	20
1759	4000r. Basset hound	2·30	20

335 Stag Beetle

1998. Beetles. Multicoloured.

No.	Description	Mint	Used
1761	200r. Type **335**	20	10
1762	500r. "Carabus auronitens" (ground beetle)	45	10
1763	900r. Alpine longhorn beetle	65	20
1764	1000r. "Geotrupes" (dor beetle)	75	20
1765	1500r. "Megasoma elephas"	1·10	20
1766	4000r. "Chalcosoma"	2·75	20

336 Prerup Temple

1998. Khmer Culture. Multicoloured.

No.	Description	Mint	Used
1768	500r. Type **336**	30	20
1769	1500r. Bayon Temple	75	30
1770	2000r. Angkor Vat	1·10	45

337 Cutter

1998. Ships. Multicoloured.

No.	Description	Mint	Used
1771	200r. Type **337**	20	10
1772	500r. "Britannia" (mail paddle-steamer, 1840)	45	10
1773	900r. Viking longship, Gokstad	65	20
1774	1000r. "Great Britain" (steam/sail)	75	20
1775	1500r. Medieval coasting nau	1·10	20
1776	4000r. Full-rigged ship (inscr "Fregate")	2·75	20

338 Scottish Fold

1998. Domestic Cats. Multicoloured.

No.	Description	Mint	Used
1778	200r. Type **338**	15	10
1779	500r. Ragdoll	35	10
1780	900r. Cymric	50	20
1781	1000r. Devon rex	60	20
1782	1500r. American curl	85	20
1783	4000r. Sphinx	2·30	20

339 "Petasites japonica"

1998. Flowers. Multicoloured.

No.	Description	Mint	Used
1785	200r. Type **339**	15	10
1786	500r. "Gentiana triflora"	30	10
1787	900r. "Doronicum cordatum"	50	20
1788	1000r. "Scabiosa japonica"	55	20
1789	1500r. "Magnolia sieboldii"	75	20
1790	4000r. "Erythronium japonica"	2·30	20

340 "Baptism of Christ" (Gerard David)

1998. "Italia 98" International Stamp Exhibition, Milan. Paintings. Multicoloured.

No.	Description	Mint	Used
1792	200r. Type **340**	20	10
1793	500r. "Madonna of Martin van Niuwenhoven" (Hans Memling)	30	10
1794	900r. "Baptism of Christ" (Hendrich Holtzius)	55	20
1795	1000r. "Christ with the Cross" (Luis de Morales)	65	20
1796	1500r. "Elias in the Desert" (Dirk Bouts)	95	20
1797	4000r. "The Virgin" (Petrus Christus)	2·75	20

There are errors of spelling in some of the inscriptions.

341 "Phyciodes tharos"

1998. Butterflies. Multicoloured.

No.	Description	Mint	Used
1799	200r. Type **341**	20	10
1800	500r. "Pararge megera"	30	10
1801	900r. Monarch	55	20
1802	1000r. Apollo	65	20
1803	1500r. Swallowtail	95	20
1804	4000r. "Eumenis semele"	2·75	20

342 Post Box, 1997

1998. World Post Day. Multicoloured.

1806 1000r. Type **342** 55 30
1807 3000r. Wall-mounted post box, 1951 . . . . 1·40 65

343 Big-Headed Turtle

1998. Tortoise and Turtles. Multicoloured.

1808 200r. Type **343** 15 10
1809 500r. Green turtle 25 10
1810 900r. American soft-shelled turtle 40 20
1811 1000r. Hawksbill turtle . . . 50 20
1812 1500r. Aldabra tortoise . . 70 20
1813 4000r. Leatherback sea turtle . . . . 2·00 20

344 Bayon Dance

1998. 45th Anniv of Independence. Multicoloured.

1815 500r. Type **344** 35 20
1816 1500r. Bayon dance (different) 85 30
1817 2000r. Bayon dance (different) . . . . 1·20 45

345 Cheetah

1998. Big Cats. Multicoloured.

1818 200r. Type **345** 15 10
1819 500r. Snow leopard 25 10
1820 900r. Ocelot 40 20
1821 1000r. Leopard 50 20
1822 1500r. Serval 70 20
1823 4000r. Jaguar . . . . 2·00 20

346 Rabbit

1999. New Year. Year of the Rabbit. Multicoloured. Showing rabbits.

1825 200r. Type **346** 30 10
1826 500r. Facing left 45 10
1827 900r. Sitting in bush 75 20
1828 1000r. Sitting on rock . . . 85 20
1829 1500r. Sitting upright . . . 1·40 20
1830 4000r. Head looking out from grass (vert) . . . . 3·75 20

347 Foster and Rastik's "Stourbridge Lion", 1829, U.S.A.

1999. Steam Railway Locomotives. Multicoloured.

1832 200r. Type **347** 20 10
1833 500r. "Atlantic", 1832 . . . 30 10
1834 900r. No. O35, 1934 . . . . 45 20
1835 1000r. Daniel Gooch's "Iron Duke", 1847, Great Britain 60 20
1836 1500r. "4-6-0" 95 20
1837 4000r. "4-4-2" . . . . . . 2·50 20

348 Aquamarine **349** Alsatian

1999. Minerals. Multicoloured.

1839 200r. Type **348** 10 10
1840 500r. Cat's eye 20 10
1841 900r. Malachite 35 20
1842 1000r. Emerald 45 20
1843 1500r. Turquoise 65 20
1844 4000r. Ruby . . . . 1·80 20

1999. Dogs. Multicoloured.

1846 200r. Type **349** 20 10
1847 500r. Shih tzu (horiz) . . . 30 10
1848 900r. Tibetan spaniel (horiz) 50 20
1849 1000r. Ainu-ken 55 20
1850 1500r. Lhassa apso (horiz) 90 20
1851 4000r. Tibetan terrier (horiz) 2·50 20

350 La Rapide, 1881

1999. Cars. Multicoloured.

1853 200r. Type **350** 15 10
1854 500r. Car designed by Frank Duryea, 1895 . . . . . . 25 10
1855 900r. Car designed by Marius Barbarou, 1898 40 20
1856 1000r. Panhard, 1898 . . . 50 20
1857 1500r. Mercedes-Benz "Tonneau", 1901 . . . . 70 20
1858 4000r. Ford, 1915 . . . . . 2·00 20

351 Ragdoll **353** *Araschnia levana*

352 Dragon Bridge

1999. Cats. Multicoloured.

1860 200r. Type **351** 20 10
1861 500r. Russian blue 25 10
1862 900r. Bombay 50 20
1863 1000r. Siamese 55 20
1864 1500r. Oriental shorthair . . 95 20
1865 4000r. Somali . . . . 2·50 20

1999. Khmer Culture. Multicoloured.

1867 500r. Type **352** 25 20
1868 1500r. Temple of 100 Columns, Kratie 80 30
1869 2000r. Krapum Chhouk, Kratie . . . . 1·20 45

1999. Butterflies. Multicoloured.

1870 200r. Type **353** 20 10
1871 500r. Painted lady (horiz) 25 10
1872 900r. *Clossiana euphrosyne* 50 20
1873 1000r. *Coenonympha hero* 55 20
1874 1500r. Apollo (horiz) . . . 90 20
1875 4000r. *Plebejus argus* . . . 2·50 20

354 Saurornitholestes

1999. Prehistoric Animals. Multicoloured.

1877 200r. Type **354** 15 10
1878 500r. Prenocephale 20 10
1879 900r. Wuerhosaurus 40 20
1880 1000r. Muttaburrasaurus . . 45 20
1881 1500r. Shantungosaurus . . 70 20
1882 4000r. Microceratops . . . 2·10 20

355 *Flabellina affinis* **357** Prasat Neak Poan

356 "Flowers in a Vase" (Henri Fantin-Latour)

1999. Molluscs. Multicoloured.

1884 200r. Type **355** 20 10
1885 500r. *Octopus macropus* . . 30 10
1886 900r. *Helix hortensis* . . . 55 20
1887 1000r. *Lima hians* 65 20
1888 1500r. *Arion empiricorum* 95 20
1889 4000r. Swan mussel . . . . 2·75 20

1999. "Philexfrance 99" International Stamp Exhibition, Paris. Paintings. Multicoloured.

1891 200r. Type **356** 30 10
1892 500r. "Fruit" (Paul Cezanne) 45 10
1893 900r. "Table and Chairs" (Andre Derain) 75 20
1894 1000r. "Vase on a Table" (Henri Matisse) 85 20
1895 1500r. "Tulips and Marquerites" (Othon Friesz) . . . . 1·40 20
1896 4000r. "Still Life with Tapestry" (Matisse) . . . 3·75 20

1999. Temples.

1898 **357** 100r. blue and black . . 20 10
1899 – 300r. red and black . . . 20 10
1900 – 500r. grn & blk (vert) . . 30 10
1901 – 1400r. green and black 85 10
1902 – 1600r. mauve and black 95 20
1903 – 1800r. vio & blk (vert) 1·10 20
1904 – 1900r. brown and black 1·20 20

DESIGNS: 300r. Statue, Neak Poan; 500r. Banteay Srey; 1400r. Banteay Samre; 1600r. Banteay Srey; 1800r. Bas-relief, Angkor Vat; 1900r. Brasat Takeo.

358 Pagoda, Tongzhou **359** *Cymbidium insigne*

1999. "China 1999" International Stamp Exhibition, Peking. Multicoloured.

1905 200r. Type **358** 20 10
1906 500r. Pagoda, Tianning Temple 30 10
1907 900r. Pagoda, Summer Palace 75 10
1908 900r. Pagoda, Blue Cloud Temple 75 10
1909 1000r. White pagoda, Bei Hai 75 10
1910 1000r. Pagoda, Scented Hill 75 10
1911 1500r. Pagoda, Yunju Temple . . . . 1·30 20
1912 4000r. White pagoda, Miaoying Temple . . . . 3·25 20

1999. Orchids. Multicoloured.

1913 200r. Type **359** 20 10
1914 500r. *Papilionanthe teres* . . 30 10
1915 900r. *Panisea uniflora* . . . 55 20
1916 1000r. *Euanthe sanderiana* 65 20
1917 1500r. *Dendrobium trigonopus* 95 20
1918 4000r. *Vanda coerulea* . . . 2·75 20

360 Northern Bullfinch

1999. Birds. Multicoloured.

1920 200r. Type **360** 30 10
1921 500r. Hawfinch 45 10
1922 900r. Western greenfinch . . 75 20
1923 1000r. Yellow warbler . . . 85 20
1924 1500r. Great grey shrike . . 1·40 20
1925 4000r. Blue tit . . . . . . 3·75 20

361 Emblem

1999. 46th Anniv of Independence. Multicoloured.

1927 500r. Type **361** 30 20
1928 1500r. People with symbols of transport and industry 75 30
1929 2000r. People queueing to vote . . . . 1·10 45

362 Tiger Barbs

1999. Fishes. Multicoloured.

1930 200r. Type **362** 30 10
1931 500r. Rainbow shark minnow 45 10
1932 900r. Clown rasbora 75 20
1933 1000r. Orange-spotted cichlid 85 20
1934 1500r. Crescent betta . . . 1·40 20
1935 4000r. Honey gourami . . . 3·75 20

363 Harpy Eagle

1999. Birds of Prey. Multicoloured.

1937 200r. Type **363** 30 10
1938 500r. Bateleur (vert) 45 10
1939 900r. Egyptian vulture (vert) 75 20
1940 1000r. Peregrine falcon (vert) 85 20
1941 1500r. Red-tailed hawk (vert) . . . . 1·40 20
1942 4000r. American bald eagle 3·75 20

364 Mail Carriage and Globe

1999. 125th Anniv of Universal Postal Union.

1944 **364** 1600r. multicoloured . . 1·60 90

365 Giant Panda

1999. Mammals. Multicoloured.

1945 200r. Type **365** 20 10
1946 500r. Yak 30 10
1947 900r. Chinese water deer . . 55 20
1948 1000r. Eurasian water shrew (horiz) 65 20
1949 1500r. European otter (horiz) 95 20
1950 4000r. Tiger (horiz) . . . . 2·75 20

366 Coral Snake

1999. Snakes. Multicoloured.
1952 200r. Type **366** 30 10
1953 500r. Rainbow boa 45 10
1954 900r. Yellow anaconda . . . 75 20
1955 1000r. Southern ring-necked snake 85 20
1956 1500r. Harlequin snake . . 1·40 20
1957 4000r. Eastern tiger snake 3·75 20

367 Dragon

2000. New Year. Year of the Dragon.
1959 **367** 200r. multicoloured . . . 30 10
1960 – 500r. red, buff and black 45 10
1961 – 900r. multicoloured . . . 75 20
1962 – 1000r. multicoloured . . 85 20
1963 – 1500r. multicoloured . . 1·40 20
1964 – 4000r. multicoloured . . 3·75 20
MS1965 86 × 110 mm. 4500r. multicoloured . . . . 3·25 90
DESIGNS: 500r. Dragon enclosed in circle; 900r. Green dragon with red flames; 1000r. Heraldic dragon; 1500r. Red dragon with blue extremities; 4000r. Blue dragon with yellow flames; 4500r. Dragon's head (32 × 40 mm).

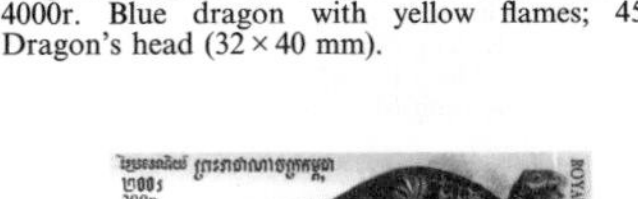

368 Iguanodon (½-size illustration)

2000. Dinosaurs. Multicoloured.
1966 200r. Type **368** 20 10
1967 500r. Euoplocepalus 30 10
1968 900r. Diplosaurus 55 20
1969 1000r. Diplodocus 65 20
1970 1500r. Stegoceras 95 20
1971 4000r. Stegosaurus . . . . 2·75 20
MS1972 110 × 85 mm. 4500r. Brachiosaurus (32 × 40 mm) . . 3·75 90

369 Ground Beetle (*Calosoma sycophanta*)

2000. Insects. Multicoloured.
1973 200r. Type **369** 30 10
1974 500r. European rhinoceros beetle (*Oryctes nasicornis*) 45 10
1975 900r. *Diochrysa fastuosa* . . 75 20
1976 1000r. *Blaps gigas* 85 20
1977 1500r. Green tiger beetle (*Cincindela campestris*) . . 1·40 20
1978 4000r. *Cissistes cephalotes* 3·75 20
MS1979 107 × 85 mm. 4500r. Scarab beetle (*Scarabaeus aegyptiorum*) (40 × 32 mm) . . . . 3·25 90

370 Box Turtle (*Cuora amboinensis*)

2000. "Bangkok 2000" International Stamp Exhibition. Turtles and Tortoise. Multicoloured.
1980 200r. Type **370** 30 10
1981 500r. Yellow box turtle (*Cuora flavomarginata*) . . 45 10
1982 900r. Black-breasted leaf turtle (*Geoemyda spengleri*) (horiz) 75 20
1983 1000r. Impressed tortoise (*Manouria (Geochelone) impressa*) (horiz) 85 20
1984 1500r. Reeves' turtle (*Chinemys reevesi*) (horiz) 1·40 20
1985 4000r. Spiny turtle (*Heosemys spinosa*) (horiz) 3·75 20
MS1986 111 × 86 mm. 4500r. Annadal's turtle (*Hieremys annandalei*) (horiz) (40 × 32 mm) 3·25 90

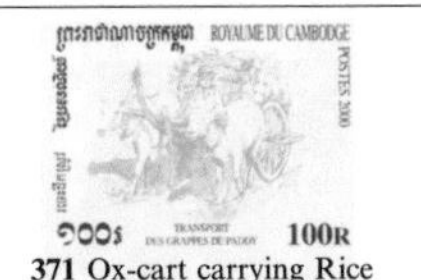

371 Ox-cart carrying Rice

2000. Rice Cultivation.
1987 **371** 100r. green and black . . 20 10
1988 – 300r. blue and black . . 30 10
1989 – 500r. mauve and black 45 10
1990 – 1400r. blue and black . . 1·10 10
1991 – 1600r. brown and black 1·50 20
1992 – 1900r. brown and black 1·80 20
1993 – 2200r. red and black . . 2·10 20
DESIGNS: 300r. Harrowing; 500r. Threshing; 1400r. Winnowing; 1600r. Planting; 1900r. Ploughing; 2200r. Binding sheaves.

372 *Jules Petiet* Steam Locomotive

2000. Locomotives. "WIPA 2000" International Stamp Exhibition, Vienna (**MS**2000). Multicoloured.
1994 200r. Type **372** 30 10
1995 500r. *Longue Chaudiere* steam locomotive, 1891 45 10
1996 900r. *Glehn du Busquet* steam locomotive, 1891 65 20
1997 1000r. *Le Grand Chocolats* steam locomotive 85 20
1998 1500r. *Le Pendule Francais* diesel locomotive . . . . 1·30 20
1999 4000r. TGV 001 locomotive, 1976 . . . . 3·50 20
MS2000 110 × 86 mm. 4500r. "Le Shuttle" in tunnel (80 × 32 mm) 3·25 90

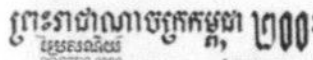

373 Fly Agaric (*Amanita muscaria*)

2000. Fungi. Multicoloured.
2001 200r. Type **373** 20 10
2002 500r. Panther cap (*Amanita pantherina*) 30 10
2003 900r. *Clitocybe olearia* . . . 55 20
2004 1000r. *Lactarius scrobiculatus* 65 20
2005 1500r. *Scleroderma vulgare* 95 20
2006 4000r. *Amanita verna* . . . 2·75 20
MS2007 110 × 86 mm. 4500r. Death cap (*Amanita phalloides*) (32 × 40 mm) . . . . 3·75 90

374 *Betta unimaculata* and *Betta pugnax* (½-size illustration)

2000. Fighting Fish. Multicoloured.
2008 200r. Type **374** 10 10
2009 500r. *Betta macrostoma* and *Betta taeniata* 30 10
2010 900r. *Betta foerschi* and *Betta imbellis* 65 20
2011 1000r. *Betta tessyae* and *Betta picta* 65 20
2012 1500r. *Betta edithae* and *Betta bellica* 95 20
2013 4000r. *Betta smaragdina* . . 2·75 20
MS2014 110 × 85 mm. 4500r. Siamese fighting fish (*Betta splendens*) (40 × 32 mm) . . . . 3·25 90

375 Woman in Arched Alcove (stone carving)

2000. Khmer Cultural Heritage. Each brown and black.
2015 500r. Type **375** 30 20
2016 1000r. Woman in flowered head-dress in rectangula bas-relief 75 30
2017 2000r. Woman with right arm raised in arche bas-relief . . . . 1·10 45

376 Galapagos Albatross (*Diomedea irrorata*)

2000. Sea Birds. Multicoloured.
2018 200r. Type **376** 30 10
2019 500r. Kentish plover (*Charadrius alexandrinus*) (*vert*) 45 10
2020 900r. Blue-footed booby (*Sula nebouxii*) 65 20
2021 1000r. Common tern (*Sterna hirundo*) 85 20
2022 1500r. Herring gull (*Larus argentatus*) (*vert*) . . . . 1·30 20
2023 4000r. Whiskered tern (*Chlidonias hybrida*) . . . 3·50 20
MS2024 108 × 83 mm. 4500r. Gannet (*Sula (Morus) bassana*) 3·25 90

377 *Cypripedium macranthum*

2000. Orchids. Multicoloured.
2025 200r. Type **377** 30 10
2026 500r. *Vandopsis gigantean* 45 10
2027 900r. *Calypso bulbosa* . . . 65 20
2028 1000r. *Vanda luzonica* . . . 85 20
2029 1500r. *Paphiopedilum villosum* . . . . 1·30 20
2030 4000r. *Vanda merrillii* . . . 3·50 20
MS2031 81 × 107 mm. 4500r. *Paphiopedilum Victoria* . . . . 3·25 90

378 Rowers in Large Canoe

2000. Tourism. Multicoloured.
2032 500r. Type **378** 30 20
2033 1500r. Front of decorated canoe 75 30
2034 2000r. Temple, elephant and dancer . . . . 1·10 45

379 Weightlifting

2000. Sports. Multicoloured.
2035 200r. Type **379** 20 10
2036 500r. Gymnastics 45 10
2037 900r. Baseball 55 20
2038 1000r. Tennis 65 20
2039 1500r. Basketball . . . . . 1·10 20
2040 4000r. High jump . . . . 2·75 20
MS2041 110 × 85 mm. 4500r. Running . . . . 3·00 90

380 Metz DLK 23-6

2000. Fire Engines. Multicoloured.
2042 200r. Type **380** 20 20
2043 500r. Iveco-Magirus SLF 24/100 . . . . 45 35
2044 900r. Metz SLF 7000 WS 55 45
2045 1000r. Iveco-Magirus TLF 24/50 . . . . 65 55
2046 1500r. Saval-Konenburg RFF-11.000 . . . . . . 1·10 90
2047 4000r. Metz TLF 24/50 . . 2·75 2·30
MS2048 110 × 85 mm. 4500r. Metz TLF 16/25 . . . . 6·50 5·50

381 Smooth Haired Dachshund

2000. Dachshunds. Multicoloured.
2049 200r. Type **381** 20 10
2050 500r. Wire haired 45 10
2051 900r. Long haired 55 20
2052 1000r. Two smooth haired 65 20
2053 1500r. Mother and pups . . 1·10 20
2054 4000r. Two puppies . . . . 2·75 20
MS2055 117 × 86 mm. 4500r. Head of wire haired (32 × 40 mm) . . 3·00 90

382 Rover 12 C (1912)

2000. Cars. Espana 2000 International Stamp Exhibition, Madrid. Multicoloured.
2056 200r. Type **382** 20 10
2057 500r. Austin 30 CV (1907) 45 10
2058 900r. Rolls-Royce Silver Ghost (1909) 55 20
2059 1000r. Graham Paige (1929) 65 20
2060 1500r. Austin 12 (1937) . . 1·10 20
2061 4000r. Mercedes-Benz 300SL (1957) . . . . 2·75 20
MS2062 110 × 86 mm. 4500r. MG (1936) (40 × 32 mm) . . . . . 3·00 90

383 18th-century Korean Painting and Two Kittens

2000. Cats. Multicoloured.
2063 200r. Type **383** 20 10
2064 500r. 18th-century Portuguese tiles and tabby cat 45 10
2065 900r. Satsuma ceramic cat and two cats 55 20
2066 1000r. Goddess Basset (Egyptian) and mother cat and kittens 65 20
2067 1500r. Goddess Freya (engraving) and tortoiseshell cat . . . . . 1·10 20
2068 4000r. Japanese painting and Manx cat . . . . . . 2·75 20
MS2069 110 × 86 mm. 4500r. Leaping cat (40 × 32 mm) . . . 3·00 90

384 Flowers, Monument and Flag

2000. 47th Anniv of Independence. Multicoloured.
2070 500r. Type **384** 30 20
2071 1500r. Dove, monument and flag 75 30
2072 2000r. Flag, monument and crowd . . . . 1·10 45

385 The Courageous Little Tailor

2000. Children's Stories. Multicoloured.

2073 200r. Type **385** 20 10
2074 500r. Tom Thumb 45 10
2075 900r. Thumbelina 50 20
2076 1000r. Pinocchio (*horiz*) . . 65 20
2077 1500r. The Crayfish (*horiz*) 1·10 20
2078 4000r. Peter Pan (*horiz*) . . 2·75 20
MS2079 110 × 85 mm. 4500r. Pied Piper of Hamelin (32 × 40 mm) 3·00 90

386 Wattled Starling (*Creatophora cinera*)

2000. Birds. Multicoloured.

2080 200r. Type **386** 20 10
2081 500r. Common starling (*Sturnus vulgaris*) 45 10
2082 900r. Pekin robin (*Leiothrix lutea*) 55 20
2083 1000r. Guianian cock of the rock (*Rupicola rupicola*) 85 20
2084 1500r. Alpine accentor (*Prunella collaris*) . . . . 1·10 20
2085 4000r. Bearded reedling (*Panurus biarmicus*) (inscr "biarnicus") . . . . . . 2·75 20
MS2086 85 × 110 mm. 4500r. Inscr "Muscicapula pallipes" (32 × 40 mm) . . . . 3·00 90

387 Johannes Gutenberg (invention of printing press)

2001. Millennium. Multicoloured.

2087 200r. Type **387** 20 10
2088 500r. Michael Faraday (discovery of electricity) 45 10
2089 900r. Samuel Morse (invention of Morse code) 55 20
2090 1000r. Alexander Bell (invention of telephone) 65 20
2091 1500r. Enrico Fermi (discovery of nuclear fission) . . . . 1·10 20
2092 4000r. Edward Roberts (invention of personal computer) . . . . 2·75 20
MS2093 86 × 112 mm. 5400r. Christopher Columbus (discovery of America) (40 × 32 mm); 5400r. Neil Armstrong (first moon walk) (40 × 32 mm) . . . . 7·50 90

388 Snake Head

2001. Year of the Snake. Multicoloured.

2094 200r. Type **388** 20 10
2095 500r. Two snakes entwined 45 10
2096 900r. Snake entwined with moon 55 20
2097 1000r. Entwined snakes (*different*) 65 20
2098 1500r. Snake encircling moon . . . . 1·10 20
2099 4000r. Three snakes' heads 2·75 20
MS2100 110 × 86 mm. 5400r. Snake head (*different*) (40 × 32 mm) 3·75 90

389 Sandou Ladder Transport (1910)

2001. Fire Engines. Multicoloured.

2101 200r. Type **389** 20 10
2102 500r. Gallo ladder transport (1899) 45 10
2103 900r. Merry Weather appliance (1950) 55 20
2104 1000r. Merry Weather ambulance (1940) 65 20
2105 1500r. Man-Metz appliance (1972) . . . . 1·10 20
2106 4000r. Roman diesel appliance (1970) . . . . 2·75 20
MS2107 111 × 87 mm. 5400r. Metropolitan steam engine (1898) (40 × 32 mm). . . . . 3·75 90

390 Puff Ball (*Lycoperdon perlatum*)

2001. Fungi. Multicoloured.

2108 200r. Type **390** 20 10
2109 500r. *Trametes versicolor* . . 45 10
2110 900r. *Hypholoma sublaterium* (inscr "Hipholoma") . . . 55 20
2111 1000r. Fly agaric (*Amanita muscaria*) 65 20
2112 1500r. *Lycoperdon umbrinum* 1·10 20
2113 4000r. *Cortinarius orellanus* 2·75 20
MS2114 111 × 84 mm. 5400r. Death cap (*Amanita phalloides*) (32 × 40 mm) . . . . 3·75 90

391 Preah Vihear

2001. Temples.

2115 **391** 200r. blue and black . . 20 10
2116 – 300r. red and black . . . 30 10
2117 – 600r. green and black . . 45 10
2118 – 1000r. orange and black 65 10
2119 – 1500r. green and black 95 20
2120 – 1700r. violet and black 1·20 20
2121 – 2200r. brown and black 1·40 20

DESIGNS: 300r. Thonmanom; 600r. Tasom; 1000r. Kravan; 1500r. Takeo; 1700r. Mebon; 2200r. Banteay Kdei.

392 Angkor Wat

2001. 3rd Anniv of Day of Khmer Culture. Showing bas-reliefs. Multicoloured.

2122 500r. Type **392** 30 20
2123 1500r. Bayon Temple . . . 1·10 30
2124 2000r. Bayon Temple (*different*) . . . . 1·40 45

393 Large Tortoiseshell (*Nymphalis polychloros*)

2001. Butterflies. Belgica 2001 International Stamp Exhibition, Brussels. Multicoloured.

2125 200r. Type **393** 20 10
2126 500r. *Cethosia hypsea* . . . 45 10
2127 900r. *Papilio palinurus* . . . 55 20
2128 1000r. Lesser purple emperor (*Apatua ilia*) . . 65 20
2129 1500r. Clipper (*Parthenos Sylvia*) . . . . 1·10 20
2130 4000r. *Morpho grandensis* 2·75 20
MS2131 111 × 85 mm. 5400r. *Heliconius melpomene* (40 × 32 mm) . . . . 3·75 90

394 Gary Cooper

2001. Cinema Actors. Multicoloured.

2132 200r. Type **394** 20 10
2133 500r. Marlene Dietrich . . . 45 10
2134 900r. Walt Disney 55 20
2135 1000r. Clark Gable 65 20
2136 1500r. Jeanette Macdonald 1·10 20
2137 4000r. Melvyn Souglas . . . 2·75 20
MS2138 86 × 111 mm. 5400r. Rudolf Valentino (32 × 40 mm); 5400r. Marilyn Monroe (32 × 40 mm) 7·50 90

395 TVR M series (1972)

2001. Cars. Multicoloured.

2139 200r. Type **395** 20 10
2140 500r. Ferrari 410 (1956) . . 45 10
2141 900r. Peugeot 405 (1995) . . 55 20
2142 1000r. Fiat 8VZ (1953) . . . 65 20
2143 1500r. Citroen Xsara (1997) 1·10 20
2144 4000r. Renault Espace (1997) . . . . 2·75 20
MS2145 111 × 85 mm. 5400r. Ferrari 250 GT (1963) (40 × 32 mm) 3·75 90

396 Bayon Temple

2001. Tourism. Bayon Temple. Multicoloured.

2146 500r. Type **396** 30 30
2147 1500r. Faces and monument 1·10 90
2148 2000r. Face and trees . . . 1·40 1·20

397 Steam Locomotive 4-6-0

2001. Trains. Philanippon '01 International Stamp Exhibition, Tokyo. Multicoloured.

2149 200r. Type **397** 20 20
2150 500r. Steam locomotive 4-6-4 . . . . 45 35
2151 900r. Steam locomotive 4-4-0 . . . . 55 45
2152 1000r. Steam locomotive 4-6-4 . . . . 65 55
2153 1500r. Locomotive 4-6-2 . . 1·10 90
2154 4000r. Locomotive 4-8-2 . . 2·75 2·30
MS2155 110 × 84 mm. 5400r. Steam locomotive 2-8-2 (40 × 32 mm). 3·75 3·25

398 Emperor Penguin (*Aptenodytes forsteri*)

2001. Penguins. Multicoloured.

2156 200r. Type **398** 20 20
2157 500r. Jackass penguin (*Spheniscus demersus*) . . 45 35
2158 900r. Humboldt penguin (*Spheniscus humboldti*) . . 55 45
2159 1000r. Rockhopper penguin (*Eudypes crestatus*) (inscr "cristatus") 65 55
2160 1500r. King penguin (*Aptenodytes patagonica*) 1·10 90
2161 4000r. Bearded penguin (*Pygocelis Antarctica*) . . 2·75 2·30
MS2162 108 × 83 mm. 5400r. Gentoo penguin (*Pygoscelis papua*) (40 × 32 mm) . . . . . 3·75 3·25

399 Singapura

2001. Cats. Multicoloured.

2163 200r. Type **399** 10 10
2164 500r. Cymric 30 30
2165 900r. Exotic short haired (inscr "shirthair") 65 55
2166 1000r. Ragdoll 65 55
2167 1500r. Manx . . . . 1·10 90
2168 4000r. Somali . . . . 2·75 2·40
MS2169 110 × 85 mm. 5400r. Egyptian mau (40 × 32 mm) . . 3·75 3·25

400 Khleng Chak

2001. Traditional Kites. Multicoloured.

2170 300r. Type **400** 20 20
2171 500r. Khleng Kanton . . . 30 30
2172 1000r. Khleng Phnong . . . 55 45
2173 1500r. Khleng KaunMorn 1·10 90
2174 3000r. Khleng Me Ambao 2·10 1·80

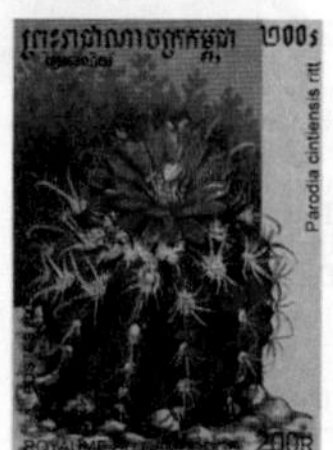

401 *Parodia cintiensis*

2001. Cacti. Multicoloured.

2175 200r. Type **401** 10 10
2176 500r. *Astrophytum asterias* 30 30
2177 900r. *Parodia faustiana* . . . 65 55
2178 1000r. *Coryphantha sulcolanata* 65 55
2179 1500r. *Neochilenia hankena* 1·10 90
2180 4000r. *Mammillaria boolii* (inscr "Mamillaria") . . . 2·75 2·40
MS2181 110 × 85 mm. 5400r. *Mammillaria* inscr "Mamilleria swinglei" (32 × 40 mm) . . . . 3·75 3·25

402 Fishing Dance

2001. Dances. Multicoloured.

2182 500r. Type **402** 30 30
2183 1500r. Red fish dance . . . 1·10 90
2184 2000r. Dance of Apsara . . 1·50 1·30

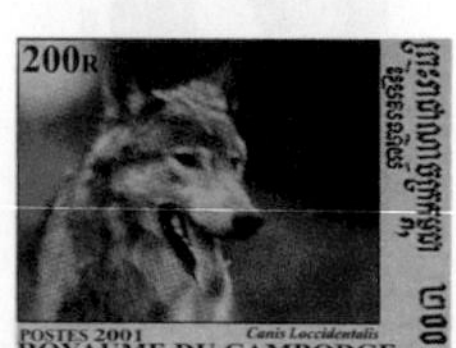

403 Timber Wolf (*Canis occidentalis*)

2001. Wolves and Foxes. Multicoloured.

2185 200r. Type **403** 20 20
2186 500r. Alaska tundra wolf (*Canis tundrorum*) 45 30
2187 900r. Fox (inscr "Vulpes fulvas") 55 45
2188 1000r. Coyote (*Canis latrans*) 65 55
2189 1500r. Fennec fox (*Vulpes zerda*) . . . . 1·10 90
2190 4000r. Arctic fox (*Alopex lagopus*) . . . . 2·75 2·30
MS2191 112 × 87 mm. 5400r. Iberian wolf (*Canis signatus*) (40 × 32 mm) 3·75 3·25

404 *Australopithecus anamensis*

2001. Prehistoric Man. Multicoloured.

2192		100r. Type **404**	10	10
2193		200r. *Australopithecus afarensis*	20	20
2194		300r. *Australopithecus africanus*	20	20
2195		500r. *Australopithecus rudolfensis*	30	30
2196		500r. *Australopithecus boisei*	30	30
2197		1000r. *Homo habilis*	65	55
2198		1500r. *Homo erectus*	1·10	90
2199		4000r. *Homo sapiens neanderthalensis* (inscr "nesnderthalensis")	2·75	2·40
MS2200		110 × 85 mm. 5400r. *Homo sapiens sapiens* (40 × 32 mm)	3·75	3·25

EXPRESS MAIL STAMPS

E **313** Bohemian Waxwing

1997. Birds. Multicoloured.

E1624		600r. Type E **313**	1·10	45
E1625		900r. Great grey shrike	1·30	65
E1626		1000r. Eurasian tree sparrow	1·80	75
E1627		2000r. Black redstart	3·50	1·70
E1628		2500r. Reed bunting	4·75	2·00
E1629		3000r. Ortolan bunting	5·25	2·50

POSTAGE DUE STAMPS

D **13**

1957.

D81	D **13**	10c. red, blue & black	20	20
D82		50c. red, blue & black	55	45
D83		1r. red, blue & black	85	75
D84		3r. red, blue & black	1·10	90
D85		5r. red, blue & black	1·80	1·60

CAMEROON Pt. 1

12 pence = 1 shilling;
20 shillings = 1 pound.

Former German colony occupied by British and French troops during 1914–16. The territory was divided between them and the two areas were administered under League of Nations mandates from 1922, converted into United Nations trusteeships in 1946.

The British section was administered as part of Nigeria until 1960, when a plebiscite was held. The northern area voted to join Nigeria and the southern part joined the newly-independent Cameroun Republic (formerly the French trust territory). In November 1995 this republic joined the Commonwealth.

I. CAMEROONS EXPEDITIONARY FORCE

1915. "Yacht" key-types of German Kamerun surch **C.E.F.** and value in English currency.

B 1	N	½d. on 3pf. brown	13·00	32·00
B 2		½d. on 5pf. green	3·25	9·50
B 3		1d. on 10pf. red	1·25	9·50
B 4		2d. on 20pf. blue	3·50	21·00
B 5		2½d. on 25pf. black and red on yellow	12·00	48·00
B 6		3d. on 30pf. black and orange on buff	12·00	48·00
B 7		4d. on 40pf. black and red	12·00	48·00
B 8		6d. on 50pf. black and purple on buff	12·00	48·00
B 9		8d. on 80pf. black and red on rose	12·00	48·00
B10	O	1s. on 1m. red	£160	£700
B11		2s. on 2m. blue	£160	£700
B12		3s. on 3m. black	£160	£700
B13		5s. on 5m. red and black	£190	£750

II. CAMEROONS TRUST TERRITORY

Issue used in the British trusteeship from October 1960 until June 1961 in the northern area and until September 1961 in the southern area, when they joined with Nigeria and the Cameroun Republic respectively.

1960. Stamps of Nigeria of 1953 optd **CAMEROONS U.K.T.T.**

T1	**18**	½d. black and orange	10	1·25
T2	–	1d. black and green	10	70
T3	–	1½d. green	10	20
T4c	–	2d. grey	10	40
T5	–	3d. black and lilac	15	10
T6	–	4d. black and blue	10	1·25
T7	–	6d. brown and black	30	20
T8	–	1s. black and purple	15	10
T9	**26**	2s.6d. black and green	1·10	80
T10	–	5s. black and orange	1·60	3·50
T11	–	10s. black and brown	2·50	6·50
T12	**29**	£1 black and violet	8·50	20·00

III. REPUBLIC OF CAMEROON

The Republic of Cameroon joined the Commonwealth on 1 November 1995 and issues from that date will be listed below, when examples and information have been received.

CAMEROUN Pt. 7; Pt. 6; Pt. 12

Territory in western Africa which became a German Protectorate in 1884. During 1914–16 it was occupied by Allied troops and in 1922 Britain and France were granted separate United Nations mandates.

In 1960 the French trust territory became an independent republic and, following a plebiscite, in September 1961 the southern part of the area under British control joined the Cameroun Republic. In November 1995 the republic joined the Commonwealth.

A. GERMAN COLONY OF KAMERUN

100 pfennig = 1 mark.

1897. Stamps of Germany optd **Kamerun**.

K1a	**8**	3pf. brown	7·00	13·00
K2		5pf. green	4·00	5·00
K3	**9**	10pf. red	4·00	5·00
K4		20pf. blue	3·50	6·25
K5		25pf. orange	18·00	29·00
K6a		50pf. brown	13·00	22·00

1900. "Yacht" key-types inscr "KAMERUN".

K 7	N	3pf. brown	95	1·25
K21		5pf. green	55	95
K22		10pf. red	45	45
K10		20pf. blue	20·00	1·60
K11		25pf. black & red on yell	1·25	4·25
K12		30pf. black & orge on buff	1·40	3·25
K13		40pf. black and red	1·40	3·25
K14		50pf. black & pur on buff	1·75	4·00
K15		80pf. black & red on rose	2·25	8·25
K16	O	1m. red	48·00	48·00
K17		2m. blue	5·50	42·00
K18		3m. black	5·00	80·00
K19		5m. red and black	£100	£400

B. FRENCH ADMINISTRATION OF CAMEROUN

100 centimes = 1 franc.

1915. Stamps of Gabon with inscription "AFRIQUE EQUATORIALE-GABON" optd **Corps Expeditionnaire Franco-Anglais CAMEROUN**.

1	**7**	1c. brown and orange	60·00	32·00
2		2c. black and brown	£120	£120
3		4c. violet and blue	£120	£120
4		5c. olive and green	27·00	23·00
5		10c. red and lake (on No. 37 of Gabon)	25·00	16·00
6		20c. brown and violet	£120	£130
7	**8**	25c. brown and blue	48·00	32·00
8		30c. red and grey	£120	£120
9		35c. green and violet	50·00	32·00
10		40c. blue and brown	£120	£120
11		45c. violet and red	£120	£120
12		50c. grey and green	£120	£120
13		75c. brown and orange	£180	£130
14	**9**	1f. yellow and brown	£180	£130
15		2f. brown and red	£200	£170

1916. Optd **Occupation Francaise du Cameroun**.

(a) On stamps of Middle Congo.

16	**1**	1c. olive and brown	65·00	65·00
17		2c. violet and brown	75·00	65·00
18		4c. blue and brown	75·00	65·00
19		5c. green and blue	32·00	25·00
20	**2**	35c. brown and blue	85·00	65·00
21		45c. violet and orange	70·00	60·00

(b) On stamps of French Congo

22	**6**	15c. violet and green	75·00	70·00
23	**8**	20c. green and red	£110	75·00
24		30c. red and yellow	70·00	60·00
25		40c. brown and green	70·00	60·00
26		50c. violet and lilac	75·00	55·00
27		75c. purple and orange	80·00	55·00
28	–	1f. drab and grey (48)	£100	80·00
29	–	2f. red and brown (49)	£120	80·00

1916. Stamps of Middle Congo optd **CAMEROUN Occupation Francaise.**

30	**1**	1c. olive and brown	10	2·40
31		2c. violet and brown	10	2·40
32		4c. blue and brown	10	2·40
33		5c. green and blue	60	1·90
34		10c. red and blue	50	2·40
34a		15c. purple and red	2·50	2·75
35		20c. brown and blue	1·25	2·75
36	**2**	25c. blue and green	1·00	1·25
37		30c. pink and green	2·00	2·40
38		35c. brown and blue	1·75	2·75
39		40c. green and brown	1·40	3·25
40		45c. violet and orange	2·25	3·25
41		50c. green and orange	2·50	3·25
42		75c. brown and blue	2·50	3·25
43	**3**	1f. green and violet	1·75	3·00
44		2f. violet and green	6·50	9·50
45		5f. blue and pink	8·25	14·00

1921. Stamps of Middle Congo (colours changed) optd **CAMEROUN**.

46	**1**	1c. orange and green	10	2·75
47		2c. red and brown	10	2·75
48		4c. green and grey	20	2·75
49		5c. orange and red	20	2·50
50		10c. light green and green	30	2·75
51		15c. orange and blue	80	3·00
52		20c. grey and purple	1·40	3·00
53	**2**	25c. orange and grey	1·40	1·90
54		30c. red and carmine	1·75	3·00
55		35c. blue and grey	1·50	3·00
56		40c. orange and green	1·75	3·00
57		45c. red and brown	1·75	3·00
58		50c. ultramarine and blue	1·00	2·75
59		75c. green and purple	1·00	3·00
60	**3**	1f. orange and grey	3·75	4·00
61		2f. red and green	7·00	9·00
62		5f. grey and red	6·50	14·00

1924. Stamps of 1921 surch.

63	**1**	25c. on 15c. orange & blue	55	3·00
64	**3**	25c. on 2f. red and green	1·50	3·00
65		25c. on 5f. grey and red	1·25	3·50
66	**2**	"65" on 45c. red and brown	1·10	4·00
67		"85" on 75c. green & red	2·25	4·25

5 Cattle fording River

1925.

68	**5**	1c. mauve and olive	10	1·75
69		2c. green & red on green	10	1·75
70		4c. black and blue	30	2·00
71		5c. mauve and yellow	35	40
72		10c. orange & pur on yell	90	50
73		15c. green	1·90	2·75
88		15c. red and lilac	55	2·50
74	A	20c. brown and olive	1·60	3·00
89		20c. green	80	2·50
90		20c. brown and red	20	25
75		25c. black and green	55	25
76		30c. red and green	45	1·00
91		30c. green and olive	50	1·40
77		35c. black and brown	1·25	3·00
91a		35c. green	2·50	3·00
78		40c. violet and orange	2·75	3·25
79		45c. red	40	3·00
92		45c. brown and mauve	3·25	3·50
80		50c. red and green	2·25	40
93		55c. red and blue	2·75	3·75
81		60c. black and mauve	2·50	2·75
94		60c. red	1·50	2·75
82		65c. brown and blue	2·25	40
83		75c. blue	60	2·75
95		75c. mauve and brown	50	1·25
95a		80c. brown and red	90	3·50
84		85c. blue and red	80	2·50
96		90c. red	2·50	3·00
85	B	1f. brown and blue	55	3·00
97		1f. blue	75	1·40
98		1f. mauve and brown	1·00	2·25
99		1f. brown and green	2·50	1·75
100		1f.10 brown and red	2·75	6·00
100a		1f.25 blue and brown	7·75	6·00
101		1f.50 blue	2·50	75
101a		1f.75 red and brown	95	1·90
101b		1f.75 blue	7·00	7·00
86		2f. orange and olive	3·00	60
102		3f. mauve and brown	4·75	3·75
87		5f. black & brown on bl	3·75	60
103		10f. mauve and orange	9·50	9·00
104		20f. green and red	20·00	16·00

DESIGNS—VERT: A, Tapping rubber-trees. HORIZ: B, Liana suspension bridge.

1926. Surch with new value.

105	B	1f.25 on 1f. blue	60	2·75

1931. "Colonial Exhibition" key-types inscribed "CAMEROUN".

106	E	40c. green	4·25	4·50
107	F	50c. mauve	4·75	5·00
108	G	90c. orange	4·75	5·25
109	H	1f.50 blue	6·25	5·25

14 Sailing Ships

1937. Paris International Exhibition. Inscr "EXPOSITION INTERNATIONALE PARIS 1937".

110	–	20c. violet	2·25	4·00
111	**14**	30c. green	2·25	3·50
112	–	40c. red	1·10	3·75
113	–	50c. brown & deep brown	1·90	3·25
114	–	90c. red	1·25	4·00
115	–	1f.50 blue	1·50	3·75

DESIGNS—VERT: 20c. Allegory of Commerce; 50c. Allegory of Agriculture. HORIZ: 40c. Berber, Negress and Annamite; 90c. France extends torch of Civilization; 1f.50, Diane de Poitiers.

19 Pierre and Marie Curie

1938. International Anti-cancer Fund.

116	**19**	1f.75+50c. blue	6·00	14·00

20

21 Lamido Woman

1939. New York World's Fair.

117	**20**	1f.25 red	2·00	3·25
118		2f.25 blue	2·00	3·50

1939.

119	**21**	2c. black	20	2·50
120		3c. mauve	15	2·00
121		4c. blue	65	2·50
122		5c. brown	45	2·50
123		10c. green	45	2·25
124		15c. red	70	2·75
125		20c. purple	55	2·75
126	A	25c. black	1·10	2·75
127		30c. orange	35	3·00
128		40c. blue	50	3·00
129		45c. green	1·40	4·50
130		50c. brown	70	3·00
131		60c. blue	1·10	3·25
132		70c. purple	2·25	4·25
133	B	80c. blue	1·25	4·50
134		90c. blue	2·75	2·00
135		1f. red	2·50	3·00
135a		1f. brown	1·75	2·25
136		1f.25 red	3·75	7·00
137		1f.40 orange	1·90	3·25
138		1f.50 brown	90	1·60
139		1f.60 brown	2·25	4·25
140		1f.75 blue	1·40	2·75
141		2f. green	1·50	1·25
142		2f.25 blue	1·90	2·75
143		2f.50 purple	2·00	2·75
144		3f. violet	1·25	2·25
145	C	5f. brown	1·75	3·00
146		10f. purple	1·50	3·75
147		20f. green	3·50	5·00

DESIGNS—VERT: A, Banyo Waterfall; C, African boatman. HORIZ: B, African elephants.

25 Storming the Bastille

1939. 150th Anniv of Revolution.

148	**25**	45c.+25c. green	6·25	11·50
149		70c.+30c. brown	4·75	11·50
150		90c.+35c. orange	5·50	13·00
151		1f.25+1f. red	5·50	16·00
152		2f.25+2f. blue	8·75	20·00

1940. Adherence to General de Gaulle. Optd **CAMEROUN FRANCAIS 27-8-40**.

153	**21**	2c. black	1·10	60
154		3c. mauve	85	1·00
155		4c. blue	65	45
156		5c. brown	3·75	4·00
157		10c. green	80	25
158		15c. red	1·25	2·75
159		20c. purple	12·00	10·50
160	A	25c. black	1·00	70
161		30c. orange	9·75	10·50
162		40c. blue	3·25	1·40
163		45c. green	2·00	1·10
164	–	50c. red & green (No. 80)	80	45
165	A	60c. blue	3·75	4·50
166		70c. purple	1·75	75
167	B	80c. blue	4·75	1·75
168		90c. blue	75	30
169	**20**	1f.25 red	3·75	1·40
170	B	1f.25 red	80	85
171		1f.40 orange	1·50	1·10
172		1f.50 brown	75	50
173		1f.60 brown	1·50	85
174		1f.75 blue	1·50	1·10
175	**20**	2f.25 blue	3·75	1·50
176	B	2f.25 blue	70	60
177		2f.50 purple	55	40
178	–	5f. black and brown on blue (No. 87)	17·00	6·25
179	C	5f. brown	16·00	6·00
180	–	10f. mve & orge (No. 103)	30·00	6·50
181	C	10f. purple	55·00	45·00

182 – 20f. green & red (No. 104) 50·00 13·00
183 C 20f. green £140 £180

1940. War Relief Fund. Nos. 100a, 101a and 86 surch **OEUVRES DE GUERRE** and premium.
184 1f.25+2f. blue and brown 19·00 22·00
185 1f.75+3f. red and brown 19·00 22·00
186 2f.+5f. orange and olive 16·00 16·00

1940. Spitfire Fund. Nos. 126, 129, 131/2 surch **+5 Frs. SPITFIRE.**
187 A 25c.+5f. black 95·00 £100
188 45c.+5f. green £110 £100
189 60c.+5f. blue £110 £110
190 70c.+5f. purple £100 £110

1941. Spitfire Fund. Surch **SPITFIRE +10 fr. General de GAULLE.**
190a **20** 1f.25+10f. red £100 £100
190b 2f.25+10f. blue £100 £100

29b Sikorsky S-43 over Map

29c Sikorsky S-43 Amphibian

1941. Air.
190c **29b** 25c. red 90 3·00
190d 50c. green 50 3·00
190e 1f. purple 1·75 3·00
190f **29c** 2f. olive 65 2·75
190g 3f. brown 90 2·75
190h 4f. blue 55 1·75
190i 6f. myrtle 70 2·75
190j 7f. purple 55 2·75
190k 12f. orange 5·50 6·75
190l 20f. red 3·00 3·50
190m – 50f. blue 3·25 3·75
DESIGN: 50f. Latecoere 631 flying boat over harbour.

1941. Laquintinie Hospital Fund. Surch **+10 Frs. AMBULANCE LAQUINTINIE.**
191 **20** 1f.25+10f. red 32·00 28·00
192 2f.25+10f. blue 32·00 28·00

31 Cross of Lorraine, Sword and Shield

32 Fairey FC-1

1942. Free French Issue.
193 **31** 5c. brown (postage) 10 1·25
194 10c. blue 10 15
195 25c. green 10 40
196 30c. red 10 40
197 40c. green 10 30
198 80c. purple 10 35
199 1f. mauve 35 15
200 1f.50 red 40 15
201 2f. black 45 15
202 2f.50 blue 45 30
203 4f. violet 20 30
204 5f. yellow 40 25
205 10f. brown 30 45
206 20f. green 55 65

207 **32** 1f. orange (air) 1·50 2·75
208 1f.50 red 1·90 2·75
209 5f. purple 80 2·75
210 10f. black 45 3·00
211 25f. blue 1·75 3·00
212 50f. green 2·25 3·00
213 100f. red 2·00 2·75

1943. Surch **Valmy +100 frs.**
213a – 1f.25+100f. blue and brown (No. 100a) 16·00 32·00
213b **20** 1f.25+100f. red 10·00 32·00
213c – 1f.25+100f. red (No. 136) 21·00 32·00
213d – 1f.50+100f. brown (No. 138) 19·00 32·00
213e **20** 2f.25+100f. blue 12·00 32·00

33

34 Felix Eboue

1944. Mutual Aid and Red Cross Funds.
214 **33** 5f.+20f. red 80 4·50

1945. Surch.
215 **31** 50c. on 5c. brown 1·40 2·75
216 60c. on 5c. brown 60 3·00
217 70c. on 5c. brown 75 30
218 1f.20 on 5c. brown 1·10 30
219 2f.40 on 25c. green 1·25 1·00
220 3f. on 25c. green 1·00 1·25
221 4f.50 on 25c. green 1·60 3·50
222 15f. on 2f.50 blue 1·75 3·50

1945.
223 **34** 2f. black 20 1·75
224 25f. green 1·25 3·00

35 "Victory"

1946. Air. Victory.
225 **35** 8f. purple 25 2·00

36 Chad

1946. Air. From Chad to the Rhine. Inscr "DU TCHAD AU RHIN".
226 **36** 5f. blue 2·00 3·50
227 – 10f. purple 1·40 3·50
228 – 15f. red 1·75 3·25
229 – 20f. blue 1·75 3·50
230 – 25f. brown 2·25 3·50
231 – 50f. black 1·25 3·75
DESIGNS: 10f. Koufra; 15f. Mareth; 20f. Normandy; 25f. Paris; 50f. Strasbourg.

37 Zebu and Herdsman

45 Aeroplane, African and Mask

1946.
232 **37** 10c. green (postage) 15 60
233 30c. orange 15 2·00
234 40c. blue 15 2·75
235 – 50c. sepia 55 1·40
236 – 60c. purple 15 2·25
237 – 80c. brown 30 2·75
238 – 1f. orange 40 15
239 – 1f.20 green 35 3·00
240 – 1f.50 red 1·10 1·10
241 – 2f. black 35 10
242 – 3f. red 1·50 10
243 – 3f.60 red 1·25 3·00
244 – 4f. blue 85 15
245 – 5f. red 1·75 15
246 – 6f. blue 1·50 15
247 – 10f. green 1·25 15
248 – 15f. blue 1·25 15
249 – 20f. green 1·50 25
250 – 25f. black 1·50 60

251 – 50f. green (air) 1·75 75
252 – 100f. brown 2·25 2·25
253 **45** 200f. olive 4·25 4·75
DESIGNS—VERT: 50c. to 80c. Tikar women; 1f. to 1f.50, Africans carrying bananas; 2f. to 4f. Bowman; 5f. to 10f. Lamido horsemen; 15f. to 25f. Native head. HORIZ: 50f. Birds over mountains; 100f. African horsemen and Dewoitine D-333 trimotor airplane.

46 People of Five Races, Lockheed Constellation Airplane and Globe

1949. Air. 75th Anniv of U.P.U.
254 **46** 25f. multicoloured 2·50 6·00

47 Doctor and Patient

1950. Colonial Welfare Fund.
255 **47** 10f.+2f. green & turq 4·50 7·75

48 Military Medal

49 Porters Carrying Bananas

50 Transporting Logs

1952. Military Medal Centenary.
256 **48** 15f. red, yellow and green 4·50 5·00

1953.
257 **49** 8f. violet, orange and purple (postage) 35 10
258 15f. brown, yellow & red 1·50 35
259 – 40f. brown, pink & choc 1·25 30

260 **50** 50f. ol, brn & sep (air) 2·50 65
261 – 100f. sepia, brown & turq 5·75 1·10
262 – 200f. brown, blue & grn 8·25 7·25
262a – 500f. indigo, blue and lilac 16·00 14·50
DESIGNS—As Type **49**: 40f. Woman gathering coffee. As Type **50**: HORIZ: 100f. Airplane over giraffes; 200f. Freighters, Douala Port. VERT: 500f. Sud Ouest Corse II over Piton d'Humsiki.

51 Edea Barrage

1953. Air. Opening of Edea Barrage.
263 **51** 15f. blue, lake and brown 2·75 1·50

52 "D-Day"

1954. Air. 10th Anniv of Liberation.
264 **52** 15f. green and turquoise 4·00 4·00

53 Dr. Jamot and Students

1954. Air. 75th Birthday of Dr. Jamot (physician).
265 **53** 15f. brown, blue & green 4·50 4·00

54 Native Cattle

1956. Economic and Social Development Fund. Inscr "F.I.D.E.S.".
266 **54** 5f. brown and sepia 30 25
267 – 15f. turq, blue & black 1·25 25
268 – 20f. turquoise and blue 1·10 30
269 – 25f. blue 1·50 35
DESIGNS: 15f. R. Wouri bridge; 20f. Technical education; 25f. Mobile medical unit.

55 Coffee

1956.
270 **55** 15f. vermilion and red 40 15

56 Woman, Child and Flag

57 "Human Rights"

1958. 1st Anniv of First Cameroun Govt.
271 **56** 20f. multicoloured 35 25

1958. 30th Anniv of Declaration of Human Rights.
272 **57** 20f. brown and red 75 2·75

58 "Randia malleifera"

1958. Tropical Flora.
273 **58** 20f. multicoloured 1·50 45

59 Loading Bananas on Ship at Douala

60 Prime Minister A. Ahidjo

1959.
274 **59** 20f. multicoloured 65 45
275 – 25f. green, brn & pur 60 40
DESIGN—VERT: 25f. Bunch of bananas and native bearers in jungle path.

C. INDEPENDENT REPUBLIC

1960. Proclamation of Independence. Inscr "1 ER JANVIER 1960".
276 – 20f. multicoloured 55 15
277 **60** 25f. green, bistre & black 55 15
DESIGN: 20f. Cameroun flag and map.

61 "Uprooted Tree"

62 C.C.T.A. Emblem

1960. World Refugee Year.
278 **61** 30f. green, blue and brown 1·00 50

1960. 10th Anniv of African Technical Co-operation Commission.
279 **62** 50f. black and purple 1·10 60

63 Map and Flag

64 U.N. Headquarters, Emblem and Cameroun Flag

1961. Red Cross Fund. Flag in green, red and yellow; cross in red; background colours given.
280 **63** 20f.+5f. green and red . . 70 70
281 25f.+10f. red and green . . 95 95
282 30f.+15f. red and green . . 1·75 1·75

1961. Admission to U.N.O. Flag in green, red and yellow; emblem in blue, buildings and inscr in colours given.
283 **64** 15f. brown and green . . . 45 30
284 25f. green and blue 55 30
285 85f. purple, blue and red 2·10 1·10

1961. Surch **REPUBLIQUE FEDERALE** and value in Sterling currency.
286 – ½d. on 1f. orange (238) (postage) 35 25
287 – 1d. on 2f. black (241) . . 45 30
288 **54** 1½d. on 5f. brown & sepia 50 40
289 – 2d. on 10f. green (247) . . 95 50
290 – 3d. on 15f. turquoise, indigo and black (267) 1·25 35
291 – 4d. on 15f. vermilion and red (270) . . . . 1·10 85
292 – 6d. on 20f. mult (274) . . 2·25 1·25
293 **60** 1s. on 25f. grn, bis & blk 2·75 2·00
294a **61** 2s.6d. on 30f. green, blue and brown . . . . . . 4·75 4·75
295a – 5s. on 100r. sepia, brown and turquoise (264) (air) . . . . 9·00 9·00
296a – 10s. on 200f. brown, blue and green (265) . . . . 18·00 18·00
297a – £1 on 500f. indigo, blue and lilac (253a) . . . . 30·00 30·00
The above were for use in the former British Cameroon Trust Territory pending the introduction of the Cameroun franc.

66 Pres. Ahidjo and Prime Minister Foncha

1962. Reunification. (a) T **66**.
298 20f. brown and violet . . . . 16·00 14·00
299 25f. brown and green . . . . 16·00 14·00
300 60f. green and red . . . . . 16·00 14·00
(b) T **66** surch in Sterling currency.
301 3d. on 20f. brown & violet
302 6d. on 25f. brown and green
303 2s.6d. on 60f. green and red
Set of 3 . . . . £375 £375

68 Lions International Badge, Doctor and Leper

1962. World Leprosy Day. Lions International Relief Fund.
304 **68** 20f.+5f. purple & brown 60 60
305 25f.+10f. purple & blue . . 70 70
306 50f.+15f. purple & green 1·40 1·40

69 European, African and Boeing 707 Airliners

1962. Air. Foundation of "Air Afrique" Airline.
307 **69** 25f. purple, violet & grn 65 40

70 Campaign Emblem **71** Giraffes and Waza Camp

1962. Malaria Eradication.
308 **70** 25f.+5f. mauve 65 60

1962. (a) Postage. Animals.
309 A 50c. sepia, blue & turquoise 10 10
310 B 1f. black, turquoise & orge 10 10
311 C 1f.50 brown, sage & blk . . 10 10
312 D 2f. black, blue and green 15 10
313 C 3f. brown, orange & purple 15 10
314 B 4f. sepia, green & turq . . 20 10
315 D 5f. purple, green & brown 20 10
316 A 6f. sepia, blue and lemon 30 15
317 E 8f. blue, red and green . . 65 45
318 F 10f. black, orange & blue 50 15
319 A 15f. brown, blue & turq . . 65 35
320 **71** 20f. brown and grey . . . 85 35
321 F 25f. brown, yellow & grn 2·10 85
322 E 30f. black, blue & brown 2·50 90
323 **71** 40f. lake and green . . . . 4·75 1·40
(b) Air.
324 – 50f. brown, myrtle & blue 90 40
325 – 100f. multicoloured . . . . 2·75 85
326 – 200f. black, brn & turq . . 8·50 2·10
327 – 500f. buff, purple and blue 9·50 3·00
DESIGNS—HORIZ: As Type **71**: A, Moustached monkey; B, African elephant and Ntem Falls; C, Kob, Dschang; D, Hippopotamus, Hippo Camp; E, African manatee, Lake Ossa; F, Buffalo, Batoun Region. (48 × 27 mm): 50f. Cocotiers Hotel, Douala; 100f. "Cymothoe sangaris" (butterfly); 200f. Ostriches; 500f. Kapsikis, Mokolo (landscape).

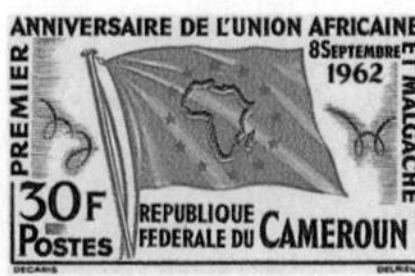

72 Union Flag

1962. 1st Anniv of Union of African and Malagasy States. Flag in green, red and gold.
328 **72** 30f. brown . . . . 1·40 65

73 Map and View **74** "The School Under the Tree"

1962. 1st Anniv of Reunification.
329 **73** 9f. bistre, violet & brown 30 20
330 18f. red, green and blue . . 40 30
331 – 20f. bistre, blue and purple 45 30
332 – 25f. orange, sepia & blue 45 35
333 – 50f. blue, sepia and red . . 1·25 80
DESIGNS: 20f., 25f. Sunrise over Cameroun; 50f. Commemorative scroll.

1962. Literacy and Popular Education Plan.
334 **74** 20f. red, yellow and green 65 35

75 Globe and "Telstar"

1963. 1st Trans-Atlantic Television Satellite Link.
335 **75** 1f. ol, vio & blue (postage) 10 10
336 2f. lake, green and blue . . 15 15
337 3f. olive, purple and green 20 20
338 25f. blue and green 85 85
339 100f. brown and green (air) (48 × 27 mm) . . . . . 1·90 1·10

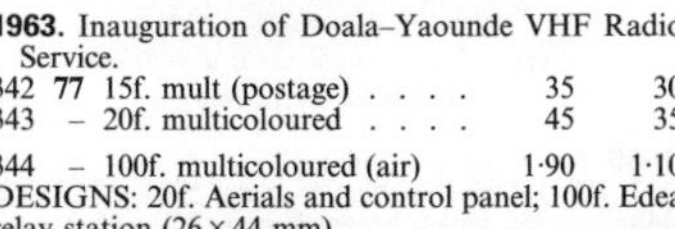

76 Globe and Emblem **77** VHF Station, Mt. Bankolo, Yaounde

1963. Freedom from Hunger.
340 **76** 18f.+5f. blue, brn & grn . . 70 40
341 25f.+5f. green & brown . . 85 45

1963. Inauguration of Doala–Yaounde VHF Radio Service.
342 **77** 15f. mult (postage) 35 30
343 – 20f. multicoloured 45 35
344 – 100f. multicoloured (air) 1·90 1·10
DESIGNS: 20f. Aerials and control panel; 100f. Edea relay station (26 × 44 mm).

78 "Centre regional ..." **80** Pres. Ahidjo

1963. Inauguration of U.N.E.S.C.O. Regional Schoolbooks Production Centre, Yaounde.
345 **78** 20f. red, black and green 35 20
346 25f. red, black and orange 40 20
347 100f. red, black and gold 1·50 85

1963. Air. African and Malagasian Posts and Telecommunications Union. As T **18** of Central African Republic.
348 85f. multicoloured . . . . . 1·60 1·10

1963. 2nd Anniv of Reunification. Multicoloured.
349 9f. Type **80** 30 20
350 18f. Map and flag 40 20
351 20f. Type **80** 45 30

1963. Air. Inauguration of "DC-8" Service. As T **11** of Congo Republic.
352 50f. multicoloured 90 45

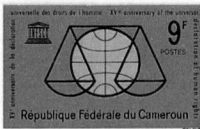

82 Globe and Scales of Justice

1963. 15th Anniv of Declaration of Human Rights.
353 **82** 9f. brown, black and blue 35 15
354 18f. red, black and green 40 20
355 25f. green, black & red . . 50 30
356 75f. blue, black & yellow 1·60 65

83 Lion

1964. Waza National Park.
357 **83** 10f. bistre green & brown 1·25 35
358 25f. bistre and green . . . 2·40 80

84 Football Stadium, Yaounde

1964. Tropics Cup. Inscr as in T **84**.
359 **84** 10f. brown, turquoise & grn 35 20
360 – 18f. green, red and violet 40 30
361 – 30f. blue, brown and black 70 40
DESIGNS: 18f. Sports Equipment; 30f. Stadium Entrance, Yaounde.

85 Palace of Justice, Yaounde

1964. 1st Anniv of European–African Economic Convention. Multicoloured.
362 15f. Type **85** . . . . 1·25 55
363 40f. Sun, moon and economic emblems (vert) . . . . . . 2·10 1·10

86 Olympic Flame and Hurdling

1964. Olympic Games, Toyko.
364 **86** 9f. red, blk & grn (postage) 1·75 1·40
365 – 10f. brown, violet and red 1·90 1·40
366 – 300f. turquoise, brown and red (air) . . . . 7·75 4·25
DESIGNS—VERT: 10f. Running. HORIZ: 300f. Wrestling.

87 Ntem Falls **88** Co-operation

1964. Folklore and Tourism.
367 – 9f. red, blue & grn (postage) 45 20
368 – 18f. blue, brown and red 55 35
369 **87** 20f. drab, green and red . . 65 35
370 – 25f. red, brown & orange 1·40 55
371 – 50f. brown, grn & bl (air) 90 55
372 – 250f. sepia, grn & brn . . 9·75 3·25
DESIGNS—As Type **87**. VERT: 9f. Bamileke dance costume; 18f. Bamenda dance mask. HORIZ: 25f. Fulani horseman. LARGER (43 × 27½ mm): 50f. View of Kribi and Longji; 250f. Black rhinoceros.

1964. French, African and Malagasy Co-operation.
373 **88** 18f. brown, green and blue 1·25 75
374 30f. brown, turq & brn . . 2·50 1·00

89 Pres. Kennedy

1964. Air. Pres. Kennedy Commem.
375 **89** 100f. sepia, grn & apple . . 2·00 2·00

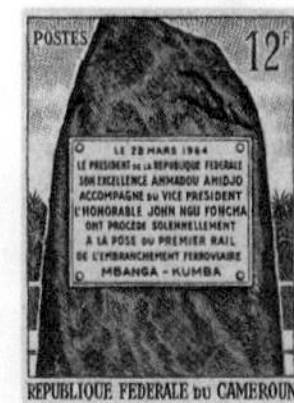

90 Inscription recording laying of First Rail

1965. Opening of Mbanga–Kumba Railway.
376 **90** 12f. indigo, green and blue 1·00 60
377 – 20f. yellow, green and red 2·75 1·25
DESIGN—HORIZ: (36 × 22 mm): 20f. Series BB500 diesel locomotive.

91 Abraham Lincoln

1965. Air. Death Centenary of Abraham Lincoln.
378 **91** 100f. multicoloured . . . . 2·00 1·40

92 Ambulance and First Aid Post

1965. Cameroun Red Cross.
379 **92** 25f. yellow, green and red 50 30
380 – 50f. brown, red and grey 1·25 45
DESIGN—VERT: 50f. Nurse and child.

93 "Syncom" and I.T.U. Emblem

1965. Air. Centenary of I.T.U.
381 **93** 70f. black, blue and red . . 1·40 70

94 Churchill giving "V" Sign

95 "Map" Savings Bank

1965. Air. Churchill Commem. Multicoloured.
382 12f. Type **94** . . . . 1·00 55
383 18f. Churchill, oak spray and cruiser "De Grasse" . . . 1·40 60

1965. Federal Postal Savings Bank.
384 **95** 9f. yellow, red and green 30 15
385 – 15f. brown, green & blue 40 20
386 – 20f. brown, chest & turq 45 30
DESIGNS—HORIZ: (48 × 27 mm): 15f. Savings Bank building. VERT: (27 × 48 mm): 20f. "Cocoa-bean" savings bank.

96 Africa Cup and Players

1965. Winning of Africa Cup by Oryx Football Club.
387 **96** 9f. brown, yellow and red 55 35
388 20f. blue, yellow and red 1·40 45

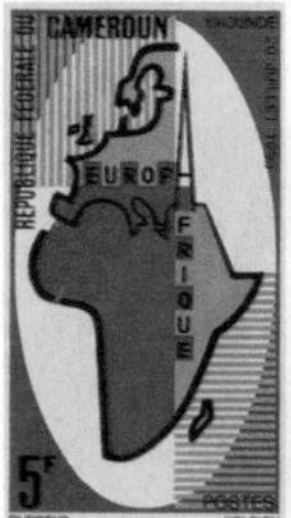

97 Map of Europe and Africa

98 U.P.U. Monument, Berne and Doves

1965. "Europafrique".
389 **97** 5f. red, lilac and black . . 20 15
390 – 40f. multicoloured 90 60
DESIGN: 40f. Yaounde Conference.

1965. 5th Anniv of Admission to U.P.U.
391 **98** 30f. purple and red 60 45

99 I.C.Y. Emblem

1965. International Co-operation Year.
392 **99** 10f. red & blue (postage) 35 30
393 100f. blue and red (air) . . 1·60 90

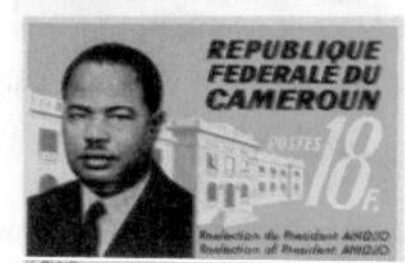

100 Pres. Ahidjo and Government House

1965. Re-election of Pres. Ahidjo. Multicoloured.
394 9f. Pres. Ahidjo wearing hat, and Government House (vert) 20 10
395 18f. Type **100** 35 15
396 20f. As 9f. 45 20
397 25f. Type **100** 55 30

101 Musgum Huts, Pouss

1965. Folklore and Tourism.
398 **101** 9f. green, brown and red (postage) 35 15
399 – 18f. brown, green & blue 50 30
400 – 20f. brown and blue . . . 70 30
401 – 25f. grey, lake and green 95 30
402 – 50f. brown, blue and green (48 × 27 mm) (air) 2·00 80
DESIGNS—HORIZ: 18f. Great Calao's dance (N. Cameroons); 25f. National Tourist office, Yaounde; 50f. Racing pirogue on Sanaga River, Edea. VERT: 20f. Sultan's palace gate Foumban.

102 "Vostok 6"

1966. Air. Spacecraft.
403 **102** 50f. green and red 80 45
404 – 100f. blue and purple . . 2·00 85
405 – 200f. violet and blue . . . 3·50 2·10
406 – 500f. blue and indigo . . 8·50 4·25
DESIGNS: 100f. "Gemini 4", and White in space; 200f. "Gemini 5"; 500f. "Gemini 6" and "Gemini 7" making rendezvous.

103 Mountain's Hotel, Buea

1966. Cameroun Hotels.
407 **103** 9f. bistre, green and red (postage) 30 15
408 – 20f. black, green & blue 35 20
409 – 35f. red, brown & green 60 40
410 **103** 18f. black, grn & bl (air) 35 20
411 – 25f. indigo, red and blue 55 20
412 – 50f. brown, orange & grn 5·25 3·00
413 – 60f. brown, green & blue 1·40 55
414 – 85f. blue, red and green 1·75 65
415 – 100f. purple, blue & grn 2·40 95
416 – 150f. orange, brn & blue 3·25 1·60
HOTELS—HORIZ: 20f. Deputies, Yaounde. 25f. Akwa Palace, Douala. 35f. Dschang. 50f. Terminus, Yaounde. 60f. Imperial, Yaounde. 85f. Independence, Yaounde. 150f. Huts, Waza Camp. VERT: 100f. Hunting Lodge, Mora.

104 Foumban Bas-relief

1966. World Festival of Negro Arts, Dakar
417 **104** 9f. black and red 55 15
418 – 18f. purple, brn and grn 55 30
419 – 20f. brown, blue & violet 80 30
420 – 25f. brown and plum . . 90 30
DESIGNS—VERT: 18f. Ekoi mask; 20f. Bamileke statue. HORIZ: 25f. Bamoun stool.

105 W.H.O. Headquarters, Geneva

106 "Phaeomeria magnifica"

1966. U.N. Agency Buildings.
421 **105** 50f. lake, blue and yellow 90 50
422 – 50f. yellow, blue & green 90 50
DESIGN: No. 422, I.T.U. Headquarters, Geneva.

1966. Flowers. Multicoloured. (a) Postage. Size as T **106**.
423 9f. Type **106** 45 15
424 15f. "Strelitzia reginae" . . . 65 15
425 18f. "Hibiscus schizopetalus x rosa-sinensis" 55 20
426 20f. "Antigonon leptopus" 55 15

(b) Air. Size 26 × 45½ mm.
427 25f. "Hibiscus mutabilis" ("Caprice des dames") . . 80 20
428 50f. "Delonix regia" . . . . 1·40 30
429 100f. "Bougainvillea glabra" 2·50 50
430 200f. "Thevetia peruviana" 3·75 1·50
431 250f. "Hippeastrum equestre" 4·50 1·90
For stamps as Type **106** but showing fruits, see Nos. 463/71.

107 Mobile Gendarmerie

1966. Air. Cameroun Armed Forces.
432 **107** 20f. blue, brown & plum 45 20
433 – 25f. green, violet & brown 45 20
434 – 60f. indigo, green & blue 1·60 80
435 – 100f. blue, red & purple 2·40 95
DESIGNS: 25f. Paratrooper; 60f. Gunboat "Vigilant"; 100f. Dassault MD-315 Flamant airplane.

108 Wembley Stadium

1966. Air. World Cup Football Championships.
436 **108** 50f. green, blue and red 1·40 45
437 – 200f. red, blue and green 3·75 2·10
DESIGN: 200f. Footballers.

109 Douglas DC-8F Jet Trader and "Air Afrique" Emblem

1966. Air. Inaugeration of DC-8 Air Service.
438 **109** 25f. grey, black & purple 60 35

110 U.N. General Assembly

1966. 6th Anniv of Admission to U.N.
439 **110** 50f. purple, green & blue 65 20
440 – 100f. blue, brown & green 1·40 65
DESIGN—VERT: 100f. Africans encircling U.N. emblem within figure "6".

111 1st Minister's Residency, Buea (side view)

1966. 5th Anniv of Cameroun's Reunification. Multicoloured.
441 9f. Type **111** 30 15
442 18f. Prime Minister's Residency, Yaounde (front view) 40 20
443 20f. As 18f. but side view . . 45 30
444 25f. As Type **111** but front view 55 30

112 Learning to Write

1966. 20th Anniv of U.N.E.S.C.O. and U.N.I.C.E.F.
445 **112** 50f. brown, purple & blue 90 45
446 – 50f. black, blue & purple 90 45
DESIGN: No. 446. Cameroun children.

113 Buea Cathedral

1966. Air. Religious Buildings.
447 **113** 18f. purple, blue & green 35 20
448 – 25f. violet, brown & green 45 20
449 – 30f. lake, green & purple 55 30
450 – 60f. green, red & turquoise . . . . 1·10 50
BUILDINGS: 25f. Yaounde Cathedral. 30f. Orthodox Church, Yaounde. 60f. Garoua Mosque.

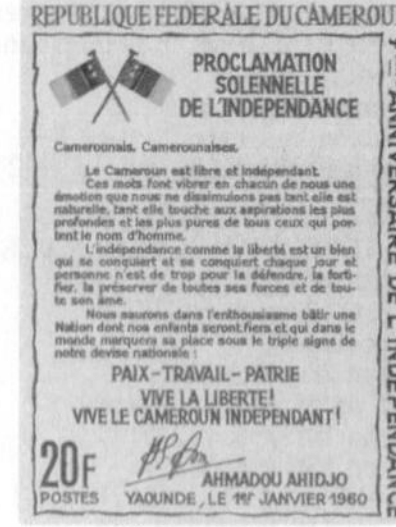

114 Proclamation

1967. 7th Anniv of Independence.
451 **114** 20f. red, green & yellow 1·90 1·10

115 Map of Africa, Railway Lines and Signals

116 Lions Emblem and Jungle

117 Aircraft and I.C.A.O. Emblem

1967. 5th African and Malagasy Railway Technicians Conference, Yaounde. Multicoloured.
452 20f. Type **115** . . . . 2·00 1·00
453 20f. Map of Africa and diesel train . . . . 3·25 1·25

1967. 50th Anniv of Lions International. Mult.
454 50f. Type **116** 80 45
455 100f. Lions emblem and palms . . . . 1·75 95

1967. International Civil Aviation Organization.
456 **117** 50f. multicoloured 90 45

118 Dove and I.A.E.A. Emblem

1967. International Atomic Energy Agency.
457 **118** 50f. blue and green . . . 90 45

119 Rotary Banner and Emblem

1967. 10th Anniv of Cameroun Branch, Rotary Int.
458 **119** 25f. red, gold and blue . . 80 45

120 "Pioneer A"

1967. Air. "Conquest of the Moon".
459 **120** 25f. green, brown & blue 40 20
460 – 50f. violet, purple & grn 85 35
461 – 100f. purple, brown & bl 2·00 85
462 – 250f. purple, grey and brown . . . . 4·50 2·50
DESIGNS: 50f. "Ranger 6"; 100f. "Luna 9"; 250f. "Luna 10".

121 Grapefruit

122 Sanaga Waterfalls

1967. Fruits. Multicoloured.
463 1f. Type **121** 10 10
464 2f. Papaw 10 10
465 3f. Custard-apple 15 15
466 4f. Breadfruit 15 15
467 5f. Coconut 30 15
468 6f. Mango 35 15
469 8f. Avocado 65 30
470 10f. Pineapple . . . . 1·10 40
471 30f. Bananas . . . . 3·00 1·25

1967. International Tourist Year.
472 **122** 30f. multicoloured 55 30

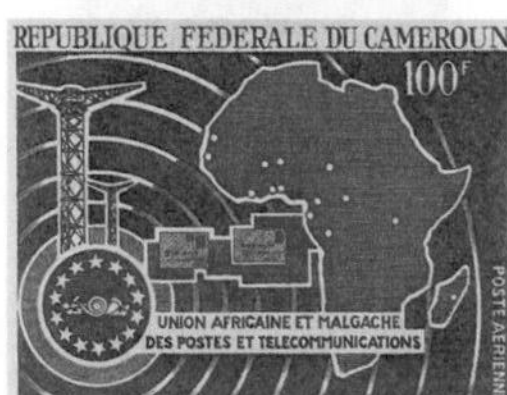

123 Map, Letters and Pylons

1967. Air. 5th Anniv of African and Malagasy Posts and Telecommunications Union (U.A.M.P.T.).
473 **123** 100f. pur, lake & turq . . 2·00 85

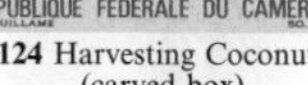
124 Harvesting Coconuts (carved box)

125 Crossed Skis

1967. Cameroun Art.
474 **124** 10f. brown, red and blue 30 15
475 – 20f. brown, green & yell 45 30
476 – 30f. brown, red & green 65 30
477 – 100f. brown, red & grn 2·00 70
DESIGNS (Carved boxes): 20f. Lion-hunting; 30f. Harvesting coconuts (different); 100f. Carved chest.

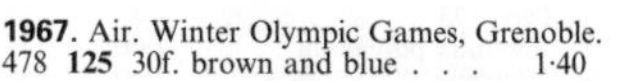

1967. Air. Winter Olympic Games, Grenoble.
478 **125** 30f. brown and blue . . . 1·40 65

126 Cameroun Exhibit

1967. Air. World Fair, Montreal.
479 **126** 50f. brown, chest & pur 90 35
480 – 100f. brown, purple & grn 2·75 95
481 – 200f. green, purple & brn 3·75 1·90
DESIGNS: 100f. Totem poles; 200f. African pavilion.
For No. 481 optd **PREMIER HOMME SUR LA LUNE 20 JUILLET 1969/FIRST MAN LANDING ON MOON 20 JULY 1969** see note below Nos. 512/17.

127 Chancellor Adenauer and Cologne Cathedral

128 Arms of the Republic

1967. Air. Adenauer Commem. Multicoloured.
482 30f. Type **127** 80 30
483 70f. Adenauer and Chancellor's residence, Bonn . . . . 1·75 55

1968. 8th Anniv of Independence.
484 **128** 30f. multicoloured 65 35

129 Pres. Ahidjo and King Faisal of Saudi Arabia

1968. Air. Pres. Ahidjo's Pilgrimage to Mecca and Visit to the Vatican. Multicoloured.
485 30f. Type **129** 65 35
486 60f. Pope Paul VI greeting Pres. Ahidjo . . . . 1·60 55

130 "Explorer VI" (televised picture of Earth)

1968. Air. Telecommunications Satellites.
487 **130** 20f. grey, red and blue . . 40 20
488 – 30f. blue, indigo and red 55 30
489 – 40f. green, red & plum . . 80 40
DESIGNS: 30f. "Molnya"; 40f. "Molnya" (televised picture of Earth).

131 Douala Port

1968. Air. Five-year Development Plan.
490 – 20f. blue, red and green 35 20
491 – 30f. blue, green & brown 4·25 1·75
492 – 30f. blue, brown & green 65 30
493 – 40f. brown, green & turq 65 30
494 **131** 60f. purple, indigo & blue 1·75 70
DESIGNS—VERT: 20f. Steel forge; 30f. (No. 491), "Transcamerounais" express train leaving tunnel; 30f. (No. 492), Tea-harvesting; 40f. Rubber-tapping.

132 Spiny Lobster

1968. Fishes and Crustaceans.
495 **132** 5f. green, brown & violet 15 15
496 – 10f. slate, brown & blue 20 15
497 – 15f. brown, chest & pur 60 15
498 – 20f. brown and blue . . . 70 15
499 – 25f. blue, brown and green 80 45
500 – 30f. brown, blue and red 1·00 45
501 – 40f. blue, brown & orge 1·40 55
502 – 50f. red, slate and green 2·00 65
503 – 55f. purple, brown & blue 2·75 1·10
504 – 60f. blue, purple & green 4·25 1·40
DESIGNS—HORIZ: 10f. Freshwater crayfish; 15f. Nile mouthbrooder; 20f. Sole. 25f. Northern pike; 30f. Swimming crab; 55f. Dusky snakehead; 60f. Capitaine threadfin. VERT: 40f. African spadefish; 50f. Prawn.

133 Refinery and Tanker

1968. Inauguration of Petroleum Refinery, Port Gentil, Gabon.
505 **133** 30f. multicoloured . . . . 1·00 40

134 Boxing

1968. Air. Olympic Games, Mexico.
506 **134** 30f. brown, green & emer 60 30
507 – 50f. brown, red & green 1·25 50
508 – 60f. brown, blue & green 1·50 55
DESIGNS: 50f. Long-jumping; 60f. Gymnastics.

135 Human Rights Emblem

1968. Human Rights Year.
510 **135** 15f. blue & orge (postage) 45 20
511 30f. green & purple (air) 55 35

136 Mahatma Gandhi and Map of India

137 "The Letter" (A. Cambon)

1968. Air. "Apostles of Peace".
512 **136** 30f. black, yellow & blue 45 30
513 – 30f. black and blue . . . 45 30
514 – 40f. black and pink . . . 65 55
515 – 60f. black and lilac . . . 90 65
516 – 70f. black, blue & buff . . 1·25 80
517 – 70f. black and green . . . 1·25 80
PORTRAITS: No. 513, Martin Luther King. No. 514, J. F. Kennedy. No. 515, R. F. Kennedy. No. 516, Gandhi (full-face). No. 517, Martin Luther King (half-length).

During 1969, Nos. 481 and 512/17 were issued optd **PREMIER HOMME SUR LA LUNE 20 JUILLET 1969/FIRST MAN LANDING ON MOON 20 JULY 1969** in very limited quantities.

1968. Air. "Philexafrique" Stamp Exhibition, Abidjan (in 1969). (1st issue).
519 **137** 100f. multicoloured . . . 3·00 2·40

138 Wouri Bridge and 1f. stamp of 1925

1969. Air. "Philexafrique" Stamp Exhibition, Abidjan, Ivory Coast (2nd issue).
520 **138** 50f. blue, olive and green 1·50 1·10

139 President Ahidjo

1969. 9th Anniv of Independence.
521 **139** 30f. multicoloured 65 25

140 Vat of Chocolate

1969. Chocolate Industry Development.
522 **140** 15f. blue, brown and red 30 20
523 – 30f. brown, choc & grn 55 30
524 – 50f. red, green & bistre 80 35
DESIGNS—HORIZ: 30f. Chocolate factory. VERT: 50f. Making confectionery.

141 "Caladium bicolor"

142 Reproduction Symbol

1969. Air. 3rd Int Flower Show, Paris. Mult.
525 30f. Type **141** 65 45
526 50f. "Aristolochia elegans" 1·40 65
527 100f. "Gloriosa simplex" . . 3·00 1·40

1969. Abbia Arts and Folklore.
528 **142** 5f. purple, turq & blue . . 20 15
529 – 10f. orange, olive & blue 30 15
530 – 15f. indigo, red & blue . . 40 20
531 – 30f. green, brown & blue 60 30
532 – 70f. red, green and blue 1·50 70
DESIGNS—HORIZ: 10f. "Two Toucans"; 30f. "Vulture attacking Monkey". VERT: 15f. Forest Symbol; 70f. Oliphant-player.

143 Post Office, Douala

1969. Air. New Post Office Buildings.
533 **143** 30f. brown, blue & green 40 20
534 – 50f. red, slate & turquoise 65 35
535 – 100f. brown and turquoise 1·40 65
DESIGNS: 50f. G.P.O., Buea; 100f. G.P.O., Bafoussam.

144 "Coronation of Napoleon" (David)

1969. Air. Birth Bicent of Napoleon Bonaparte.
536 **144** 30f. multicoloured 90 55
537 – 1,000f. gold . . . . . . 35·00
DESIGN: 1,000f. "Napoleon crossing the Alps". No. 537 is embossed on gold foil.

145 Kumba Station

146 Bank Emblem

1969. Opening of Mbanga–Kumba Railway. Mult.
538 30f. Type **145** . . . . 1·00 75
539 50f. Diesel train on bridge over River Mungo (vert) 3·25 1·50

1969. 5th Anniv of African Development Bank.
540 **146** 30f. brown, green & vio 60 30

1969. Air. Negro Writers. Portrait designs as T **136**.
541 15f. brown and blue 40 20
542 30f. brown and purple . . . 50 20
543 30f. brown and yellow . . . 50 20
544 50f. brown and green 70 40
545 50f. brown and agate 70 40
546 100f. brown and yellow . . . 1·75 1·10
DESIGNS—VERT: No. 541, Dr. P. Mars (Haiti); No. 542, W. Dubois (U.S.A.); No. 543, A. Cesaire (Martinique); No. 544, M. Garvey (Jamaica); No. 545, L. Hughes (U.S.A.); No. 546, R. Maran (Martinique).

148 I.L.O. Emblem

1969. Air. 50th Anniv of I.L.O.
548 **148** 30f. black and turquoise 55 30
549 50f. black and mauve . . 90 40

149 Astronauts and "Apollo 11" in Sea

1969. Air. 1st Man on the Moon. Multicoloured.
550 200f. Type **149** . . . . 3·25 1·75
551 500f. Astronaut and module on Moon . . . . 7·75 3·50

150 Airplane, Map and Airport

1969. 10th Anniv of Aerial Navigation Security Agency for Africa and Madagascar (ASECNA).
552 **150** 100f. green . . . . 1·50 70

151 President Ahidjo, Arms and Map

1970. Air. 10th Anniv of Independence.
553 **151** 1,000f. gold & mult . . . 21·00
No. 553 is embossed on gold foil.

152 Mont Febe Hotel, Yaounde

1970. Air. Tourism.
554 **152** 30f. grey, green & brn . . 60 30

153 Lenin

154 "Lantana camara"

1970. Air. Birth Centenary of Lenin.
555 **153** 50f. brown and yellow . . 1·40 35

1970. African Climbing Plants. Multicoloured.
556 15f. Type **154** (postage) . . . 35 15
557 30f. "Passiflora quadrangularis" 80 20
558 50f. "Cleome speciosa" (air) 1·40 55
559 100f. "Mussaenda erythrophylla" . . . . . . 2·50 1·40

155 Lions' Emblem and Map of Africa

1970. Air. 13th Congress of Lions International District 403, Yaounde.
560 **155** 100f. multicoloured . . . 1·90 80

156 New U.P.U. H.Q.

1970. New U.P.U. Headquarters Building, Berne.
561 **156** 30f. green, violet & blue 55 20
562 50f. blue, red and grey . . 80 30

157 U.N. Emblem and Stylized Doves

1970. Air. 25th Anniv of United Nations.
563 **157** 30f. brown and orange . . 65 30
564 – 50f. indigo and blue . . . 90 40
DESIGN—VERT: 50f. U.N. emblem and stylized dove.

158 Fermenting Vats

1970. Brewing Industry.
565 **158** 15f. brown, green & grey 35 20
566 – 30f. red, brown and blue 65 30
DESIGN: 30f. Storage tanks.

159 Japanese Pavilion

1970. Air. Expo 70.
567 **159** 50f. blue, red and green 90 45
568 – 100f. red, blue and green 1·90 80
569 – 150f. brown, slate & blue 3·00 1·50
DESIGNS—VERT: 100f. Expo Emblem and Map of Japan. HORIZ: 150f. Australian Pavilion.

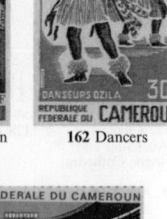

160 Gen. De Gaulle in Tropical Kit

162 Dancers

161 Aztec Stadium, Mexico City

1970. Air. "Homage to General De Gaulle".
570 **160** 100f. brown, blue & grn 2·50 1·60
571 – 200f. blue, green & brn 4·50 2·25
DESIGN: 200f. Gen. De Gaulle in military uniform.
Nos. 570/1 were issued together as a triptych, separated by a stamp-size label showing maps of France and Cameroun.

1970. Air. World Cup Football Championships, Mexico. Multicoloured.
572 50f. Type **161** 80 40
573 100f. Mexican team . . . . 1·75 1·00
574 200f. Pele and Brazilian team with World Cup (vert) . . 3·00 1·40

1970. Ozila Dancers.
575 **162** 30f. red, orange & grn . . 70 35
576 50f. red, brown & scar . . 1·90 80

163 Doll in National Costume

164 Beethoven (after Stieler)

1970. Cameroun Dolls.
577 **163** 10f. green, black & red . . 45 35
578 15f. red, green & yellow 55 45
579 30f. brown, green & blk 1·50 55

1970. Air. Birth Bicent of Beethoven.
580 **164** 250f. multicoloured . . . 3·75 1·90

1970. Air. Rembrandt Paintings. As T **144**. Mult.
581 70f. "Christ at Emmaus" . . 1·40 45
582 150f. "The Anatomy Lesson" 2·50 95

166 "Industry and Agriculture"

167 Bust of Dickens

1970. "Europafrique" Economic Community.
583 **166** 30f. multicoloured 60 30

1970. Air. Death Centenary of Charles Dickens.
584 **167** 40f. brown and red . . . 65 30
585 – 50f. multicoloured 80 35
586 – 100f. multicoloured . . . 1·40 90
DESIGNS: 50f. Characters from David Copperfield; 100f. Dickens writing.

1971. Air. De Gaulle Memorial Issue. Nos. 570/1 optd **IN MEMORIAM 1890-1970**.
587 **160** 100f. brown, blue & grn 2·50 1·40
588 – 200f. blue, green & brn 4·50 2·00

169 University Buildings

1971. Inauguration of Federal University, Yaounde.
589 **169** 50f. green, blue & brown 65 30

170 Presidents Ahidjo and Pompidou

1971. Visit of Pres. Pompidou of France.
590 **170** 30f. multicoloured 90 55

171 "Cameroun Youth"

1971. 5th National Youth Festival.
591 **171** 30f. multicoloured 55 30

172 Timber Yard, Douala

1971. Air. Industrial Expansion.
592 **172** 40f. brown, green & red 40 20
593 – 70f. brown, green and blue 90 40
594 – 100f. red, blue & green . . 1·50 50
DESIGNS—VERT: 70f. "Alucam" aluminium plant, Edea. HORIZ: 100f. Mbakaou Dam.

173 "Gerbera hybrida"

174 "World Races"

1971. Flowers. Multicoloured.
595 20f. Type **173** 45 35
596 40f. "Opuntia polyantha" . . 1·00 45
597 50f. "Hemerocallis hybrida" 1·40 55
For similar designs inscr "United Republic of Cameroon" etc., see Nos. 648/52.

1971. Racial Equality Year. Multicoloured.
598 20f. Type **174** 35 15
599 30f. Hands of four races clasping globe 50 20

175 Crowned Cranes, Camp de Waza

1971. Landscapes.
600 **175** 10f. blue, red and green 1·00 30
601 – 20f. red, brown & green 40 25
602 – 30f. green, blue & brown 55 25
DESIGNS: 20f. African pirogue; 30f. Sanaga River.

176 Relay-racing

1971. Air. 75th Anniv of Modern Olympic Games.
603 **176** 30f. blue, red and brown 45 30
604 – 50f. purple and blue . . . 65 30
605 – 100f. black, green & red 1·40 55
DESIGNS—VERT: 50f. Olympic runner with torch. HORIZ: 100f. Throwing the discus.

177 "Villalba" (deep-sea trawler)

1971. Air. Fishing Industry.
606 **177** 30f. brown, green & blue 65 45
607 – 40f. purple, blue & green 80 45
608 – 70f. brown, red and blue 1·75 65
609 – 150f. multicoloured . . . 3·75 1·75
DESIGNS: 40f. Traditional fishing method, Northern Cameroun; 70f. Fish quay, Douala; 150f. Shrimp-boats, Douala.

178 Peace Palace, The Hague

1971. 25th Anniv of International Court of Justice, The Hague.
610 **178** 50f. brown, blue & green 65 30

179 1916 French Occupation 20c. and 1914–18 War Memorial, Yaounde

1971. Air. "Philatecam 71" Stamp Exhibition, Yaounde (1st issue).
611 **179** 20f. brown, ochre & grn 35 20
612 – 25f. brown, green & blue 40 20
613 – 40f. green, grey & brown 65 20
614 – 50f. multicoloured 85 35
615 – 100f. green, brown & orge 2·00 65
DESIGNS: 25f. 1954 15f. Jamot stamp and memorial; 40f. 1965 25f. Tourist Office stamp and public buildings, Yaounde; 50f. German stamp and Imperial German postal emblem; 100f. 1915 Expeditionary Force optd, error, and Expeditionary Force memorial.
See also No. 620.

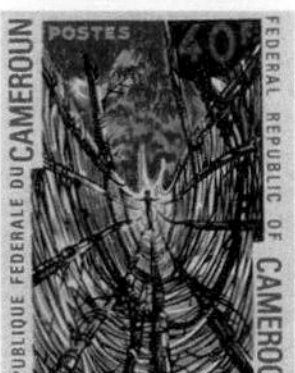

180 Rope Bridge **181** Bamoun Horseman (carving)

1971. "Rural Life". Multicoloured.
616 40f. Type **180** 70 20
617 45f. Local market (horiz) . . 85 30

1971. Cameroun Carving.
618 **181** 10f. brown and yellow . . 35 15
619 – 15f. brown and yellow . . 35 20
DESIGN: 15f. Fetish statuette.

182 Pres. Ahidjo, Flag and "Reunification" Road

1971. Air. "Philatecam 71" Stamp Exhibition, Yaounde (2nd issue).
620 **182** 250f. multicoloured . . . 5·25 3·75

183 Satellite and Globe

1971. Pan-African Telecommunications Network.
621 **183** 40f. multicoloured 55 35

184 U.A.M.P.T. Headquarters, Brazzaville and Carved Stool

1971. Air. 10th Anniv of African and Malagasy Posts and Telecommunications Union.
622 **184** 100f. multicoloured . . . 1·40 65

185 Children acclaiming Emblem

1971. 25th Anniv of U.N.I.C.E.F.
623 **185** 40f. purple, blue & slate 60 20
624 – 50f. red, green and blue 70 35
DESIGN—VERT: 50f. Ear of Wheat and Emblem.

186 "The Annunciation" (Fra Angelico)

1971. Air. Christmas. Paintings. Multicoloured.
625 40f. Type **186** 45 15
626 45f. "Virgin and Child" (Del Sarto) 55 30
627 150f. "The Holy Family with the Lamb" (detail Raphael) (vert) . . . . 2·75 95

187 Cabin, South-Central Region

1972. Traditional Cameroun Houses. Mult.
628 10f. Type **187** 20 15
629 15f. Adamaoua round house 35 20

188 Airline Emblem

1972. Air. Cameroun Airlines' Inaugural Flight.
630 **188** 50f. multicoloured 55 20

189 Giraffe and Palm Tree **190** Africa Cup

1972. Festival of Youth. Multicoloured.
631 2f. Type **189** 15 10
632 5f. Domestic scene 15 10
633 10f. Blacksmith (horiz) . . . 20 15
634 15f. Women 20 15

1972. African Football Cup Championships. Mult.
635 20f. Type **190** 45 20
636 40f. Players with ball (horiz) 65 35
637 45f. Team captains . . . . . 1·10 35

191 "St. Mark's Square and Doge's Palace" (detail-Caffi)

1972. Air. U.N.E.S.C.O. "Save Venice" Campaign, Multicoloured.
638 40f. Type **191** 55 30
639 100f. "Regatta on the Grand Canal" (detail – Canaletto) 1·75 55
640 200f. "Regatta on the Grand Canal" (detail – Canaletto) (different) . . . . 3·50 1·40

192 Assembly Building, Yaounde

1972. 110th Session of Inter-Parliamentary Council, Yaounde.
641 **192** 40f. multicoloured 55 30

193 Horseman, North Cameroun

1972. Traditional Life and Folklore. Mult.
642 15f. Type **193** 30 15
643 20f. Bororo woman (vert) . . 35 15
644 40f. Wouri River and Mt. Cameroun . . . . 1·40 45

194 Pataiev, Dobrovolsky and Volkov

1972. Air. "Soyuz 11" Cosmonauts. Memorial Issue.
645 **194** 50f. multicoloured 65 35

195 U.N. Building, New York, Gate of Heavenly Peace, Peking and Chinese Flag

1972. Air. Admission of Chinese People's Republic to U.N.
646 **195** 50f. multicoloured 55 20

196 Chemistry Laboratory, Federal University

1972. Pres. Ahidjo Prize.
647 **196** 40f. red, green & purple 55 35

1972. Flowers. As T **173**, but inscr "UNITED REPUBLIC OF CAMEROON", etc. Mult.
648 40f. "Solanum macranthum" 55 20
649 40f. "Kaempferia aethiopica" 65 20
650 45f. "Hoya carnosa" 65 35
651 45f. "Cassia alata" 65 20
652 50f. "Crinum sanderianum" 90 35

197 Swimming

1972. Air. Olympic Games, Munich.
653 **197** 50f. green, brown & lake 80 35
654 – 50f. brown, blue and sepia 80 35
655 – 200f. lake, grey & purple 3·25 1·40
DESIGNS—HORIZ: No. 655, Horse-jumping. VERT: No. 654, Boxing.

198 "Charaxes ameliae" **201** Great Blue Turacos

1972. Butterflies. Multicoloured.
657 40f. Type **198** . . . . 2·00 55
658 45f. "Papiliotynderaeus" . . 2·50 1·10

1972. No. 471 surch.
659 40f. on 30f. multicoloured . . 60 40

1972. Air. Olympic Gold Medal Winners. Nos. 653/5 optd as listed below.
660 50f. green, brown and red . . 80 35
661 50f. brown, blue and sepia 80 35
662 200f. lake, grey and purple 3·25 1·40
OVERPRINTS: No. 660, **NATATION MARK SPITZ 7 MEDAILLES D'OR**. No. 661, **SUPER-WELTER KOTTYSCH MEDAILLE D'OR**. No. 662, **CONCOURS COMPLET MEADE MEDAILLE D'OR**.

1972. Birds. Multicoloured.
663 10f. Type **201** . . . . 1·00 50
664 45f. Red-faced lovebirds (horiz) . . . . 2·25 1·00

202 "The Virgin with Angels" (Cimabue) **203** St. Theresa

1972. Air. Christmas. Multicoloured.
665 45f. Type **202** 80 35
666 140f. "The Madonna of the Rose Arbour" (S. Lochner) 2·25 1·25

1973. Air. Birth Centenary of St. Theresa of Lisieux.
667 **203** 45f. blue, brown & violet 55 20
668 – 100f. mauve, brown, & bl 1·40 55
DESIGN: 100f. Lisieux Basilica.

204 Emperor Haile Selassie and "Africa Hall", Addis Ababa

1973. Air. 80th Birthday of Emperor Haile Selassie of Ethiopia.
669 **204** 45f. multicoloured 60 35

205 Cotton Cultivation, North Cameroun
207 Human Hearts

206 "Food for All"

1973. 3rd Five Year Plan. Multicoloured.
670 5f. Type **205** 10 10
671 10f. Cacao pods, South-central region . . . 10 10
672 15f. Forestry, South-eastern area 20 10
673 20f. Coffee plant, West Cameroun 45 15
674 45f. Tea-picking, West Cameroun 95 30

1973. Air. 10th Anniv of World Food Programme.
675 **206** 45f. multicoloured 60 35

1973. Air. 25th Anniv of W.H.O.
676 **207** 50f. red and blue 60 30

208 Pres. Ahidjo, Map, Flag and Cameroun Stamp

1973. 1st Anniv of United Republic. Mult.
677 10f. Type **208** (postage) . . . 45 20
678 20f. Pres. Ahidjo, proclamation and stamp 65 35
679 45f. Pres. Ahidjo, map of Cameroun rivers and stamp (air) 55 20
680 70f. Significant dates on Cameroun flag 80 50

209 Mask

210 Dr. G. A. Hansen

1973. Bamoun Masks.
681 **209** 5f. black, brown & green 10 10
682 – 10f. brown, black & purple 20 10
683 – 45f. brown, black & red 55 30
684 – 100f. brown, black & blue 1·40 55
DESIGNS: 10f., 45f., 100f., as Type **209**, but different masks.

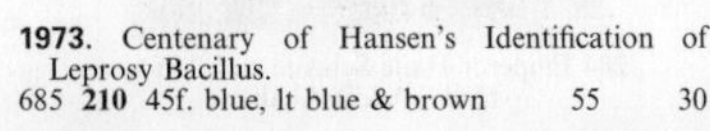

1973. Centenary of Hansen's Identification of Leprosy Bacillus.
685 **210** 45f. blue, lt blue & brown 55 30

211 Scout Emblem and Flags

213 Folk-dancers

1973. Air. Admission of Cameroun to 24th World Scout Conference.
686 **211** 40f. multicoloured 50 30
687 45f. multicoloured 60 35
688 100f. multicoloured . . . 1·40 60

1973. African Solidarity "Drought Relief". No. 670 surch **100F. SECHERESSE SOLIDARITE AFRICAINE.**
689 **205** 100f. on 5f. multicoloured 1·25 90

1973. Folklore Dances of South-west Cameroun. Multicoloured.
690 10f. Type **213** 15 10
691 25f. Dancer in plumed hat . . 45 15
692 45f. Dancers with "totem" 80 30

214 W.M.O. Emblem

1973. Centenary of W.M.O.
693 **214** 45f. blue and green . . . 55 30

215 Garoua Party H.Q. Building

1973. 7th Anniv of Cameroun National Union.
694 **215** 40f. multicoloured 55 30

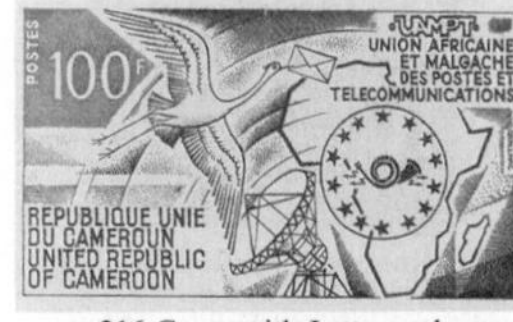

216 Crane with Letter and Telecommunications Emblem

1973. 12th Anniv of U.A.M.P.T.
695 **216** 100f. blue, lt blue & green 1·40 55

217 African Mask and Old Town Hall, Brussels

218 Avocado

1973. Air. African Fortnight, Brussels.
696 **217** 40f. brown and purple . . 55 30

1973. Cameroun Fruits. Multicoloured.
697 10f. Type **218** 30 15
698 20f. Mango 35 15
699 45f. Plum 85 20
700 50f. Custard-apple . . . . . 1·25 35

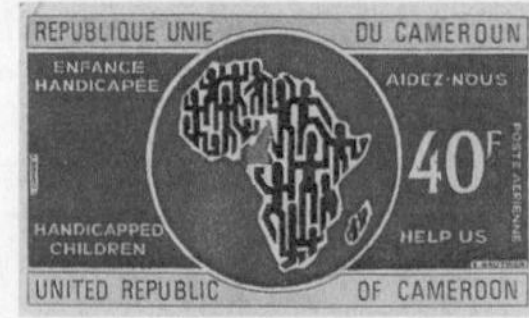

219 Map of Africa

1973. Air. Aid for Handicapped Children.
701 **219** 40f. red, brown & green 55 35

220 Kirdi Village

1973. Cameroun Villages.
702 **220** 15f. black, green & brown 20 15
703 – 45f. brown, red & orange 50 30
704 – 50f. black, green & orange 70 35
DESIGNS: 45f. Mabas village. 50f. Fishing village.

221 Earth Station

1973. Air. Inauguration of Satellite Earth Station, Zamengoe.
705 **221** 100f. brown, blue & grn 1·10 55

222 "The Madonna with Chancellor Rolin" (Van Eyck)

223 Handclasp on Map of Africa

1973. Air. Christmas. Multicoloured.
706 45f. Type **222** 80 40
707 140f. "The Nativity" (Federico Fiori–Il Barocci) 2·25 1·50

1974. 10th Anniv of Organization of African Unity.
708 **223** 40f. blue, red and green 40 20
709 45f. green, blue and red 50 20

224 Mill-worker

1974. C.I.C.A.M. Industrial Complex.
710 **224** 45f. brown, green & red 55 20

225 Bilinga Carved Panel (detail)

1974. Cameroun Art.
711 **225** 10f. brown and green . . 20 15
712 – 40f. brown and red . . . 50 20
713 – 45f. red and blue 70 30
DESIGNS: 40f. Tubinga carving (detail); 45f. Acajou Ngollon carved panel (detail).

1974. No. 469 surch.
714 40f. on 8f. multicoloured . . 60 30

227 Cameroun Cow

228 Route-map and Track

1974. Cattle-raising in North Cameroun. Mult.
715 40f. Type **227** (postage) . . . 65 30
716 45f. Cattle in pen (air) . . . 65 35

1974. Trans-Cameroun Railway. Inauguration of Yaounde–Ngaoundere Line.
717 **228** 5f. brown, blue & green 70 55
718 – 20f. brown, blue & violet 1·25 75
719 – 40f. red, blue & green . . 2·00 1·25
720 – 100f. green, blue & brown 3·75 2·10
DESIGNS—HORIZ: 20f. Laying track; 100f. Railway bridge over Djerem River. VERT: 40f. Welding rails.

229 Sir Winston Churchill

1974. Air. Birth Cent of Sir Winston Churchill.
721 **229** 100f. black, red & blue . . 1·10 55

230 Footballer and City Crests

1974. Air. World Cup Football Championships.
722 **230** 45f. orange, slate & grey 55 20
723 – 100f. orange, slate & grey 1·00 50
724 – 200f. blue, orange & blk 2·00 1·25
DESIGNS: 100f. Goalkeeper and city crests; 200f. World Cup.

1974. Air. West Germany's Victory in World Cup Football Championships. Nos. 722/4 optd **7th JULY 1974 R.F.A. 2 HOLLANDE 1 7 JUILLET 1974.**
725 **230** 45f. orange, slate & grey 55 20
726 – 100f. orange, slate & grey 1·25 50
727 – 200f. blue, orange & blk 2·40 1·50

232 U.P.U. Emblem and Hands with Letters

1974. Centenary of Universal Postal Union.
728 **232** 40f. red, blue and green (postage) 65 35
729 – 100f. green, vio & bl (air) 1·40 65
730 – 200f. green, red and blue 2·25 1·40
DESIGNS: 100f. Cameroun U.P.U. headquarters stamps of 1970; 200f. Cameroun U.P.U. 75th anniv stamps of 1949.

233 Copernicus and Solar System

1974. Air. 500th Birth Anniv (1973) of Copernicus.
731 **233** 250f. blue, red & brown 3·50 2·25

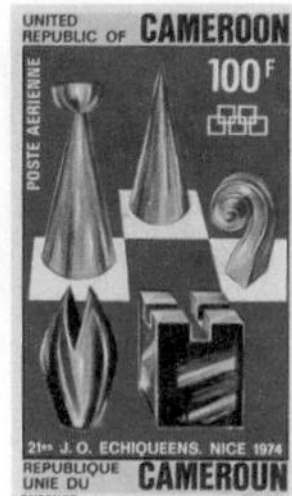

234 Modern Chess Pieces

1974. Air. Chess Olympics, Nice.
732 **234** 100f. multicoloured . . . 2·75 1·10

235 African Mask and "Arphila" Emblem

1974. Air. "Arphila 75" Stamp Exhibition, Paris.
733 **235** 50f. brown and red . . . 45 30

236 African Leaders, U.D.E.A.C. H.Q. and Flags

1974. 10th Anniv of Central African Customs and Economics Union.
734 **236** 40f. mult (postage) . . . 55 30
735 – 100f. multicoloured (air) 1·40 50
DESIGN: 100f. Similar to Type **236**.

1974. No. 717 surch **100F 10 DECEMBRE 1974**.
736 **228** 100f. on 5f. brn, bl & grn 2·00 1·50

238 "Apollo" Emblem, Astronaut, Module and Astronaut's Boots

1974. Air. 5th Anniv of 1st Landing on Moon.
737 **238** 200f. brown, red & blue 2·75 1·40

1974. Christmas. As T **222**. Multicoloured.
738 40f. "Virgin of Autumn" (15th-century sculpture) . . 60 35
739 45f. "Virgin and Child" (Luis de Morales) 80 45

239 De Gaulle and Eboue

1975. Air. 30th Anniv of Felix Eboue ("Free French" leader).
740 **239** 45f. multicoloured . . . . 1·40 55
741 200f. multicoloured . . . 4·50 2·50

240 "Celosia cristata"

242 Afo Akom Statue

241 Fish and Fishing-boat

1975. Flowers of North Cameroun. Mult.
742 5f. Type **240** 15 10
743 40f. "Costus spectabilis" . . 60 20
744 45f. "Mussaenda erythrophylla" 80 30

1975. Offshore Fishing.
745 **241** 40f. brown, blue & choc 95 30
746 – 45f. brown, bistre & blue 1·25 45
DESIGN: 45f. Fishing-boat and fish in net.

1975.
747 **242** 40f. multicoloured 45 20
748 45f. multicoloured 55 35
749 200f. multicoloured . . . 2·10 1·50

243 "Polypore" (fungus)

244 View of Building

1975. Natural History. Multicoloured.
750 15f. Type **243** . . . . 3·25 1·25
751 40f. "Nymphalis Chrysalis" 2·00 55

1975. Inaug of New Ministry of Posts Building.
752 **244** 40f. blue, green & brown 45 15
753 45f. brown, green & blue 65 35

245 Presbyterian Church, Elat

1975. Churches and Mosque.
754 **245** 40f. brown, blue & black 35 15
755 – 40f. brown, blue & slate 35 15
756 – 45f. brown, green & blk 45 20
DESIGNS: No. 755, Foumban Mosque; No. 756, Catholic Church, Ngaoundere.

246 Marquis de Lafayette (after Chappel) and Naval Battle

247 Harvesting Maize

1975. Air. Bicent (1976) of American Revolution.
757 **246** 100f. blue, turq & brn . . 1·75 85
758 – 140f. blue, brown & green 1·90 90
759 – 500f. green, brown & blue 6·00 1·25
DESIGNS: 140f. George Washington (after Stuart) and Continental Infantry (after Ogden); 500f. Benjamin Franklin (after Peale and Nee) and Boston.

1975. "Green Revolution". Multicoloured.
760 40f. Type **247** 45 15
761 40f. Ploughing with oxen (horiz) 40 20

248 "The Burning Bush" (N. Froment)

1975. Air. Christmas. Multicoloured.
762 50f. Type **248** 55 45
763 500f. "Adoration of the Magi" (Gentile da Fabriano) (horiz) . . . . . 6·50 4·75

249 Tracking Aerial

1976. Inauguration of Satellite Monitoring Station, Zamengoe. Multicoloured.
764 40f. Type **249** 35 15
765 100f. Close-up of tracking aerial (vert) 65 40

250 Porcelain Rose

252 Masked Dancer

251 Concorde

1976. Flowers. Multicoloured.
766 40f. Type **250** 55 15
767 50f. Flower of North Cameroun 85 20

1976. Air. Concorde's First Commercial Flight, Paris to Rio de Janeiro.
768 **251** 500f. multicoloured . . . 4·50 2·40

1976. Cameroun Dances. Multicoloured.
770 40f. Type **252** (postage) . . . 55 35
771 50f. Drummers and two dancers (air) 45 20
772 100f. Female dancer 90 35

253 Telephone Exchange

255 Dr. Adenauer and Cologne Cathedral

254 Young Men Building House

1976. Air. Telephone Centenary.
773 **253** 50f. multicoloured 40 30

1976. 10th Anniv of National Youth Day. Multicoloured.
774 40f. Type **254** 30 15
775 45f. Gathering palm leaves 40 15

1976. Birth Centenary of Dr. Konrad Adenauer (Statesman).
776 **255** 100f. multicoloured . . . 65 35

256 "Adoration of the Shepherds" (Charles Le Brun)

1976. Air. Christmas.
777 30f. Type **256** 45 15
778 60f. "Adoration of the Magi" (Rubens) 55 30
779 70f. "Virgin and Child" (Bellini) 80 40
780 500f. "The New-born" (G. de la Tour) . . . . 5·75 3·50

257 Pres. Ahidjo and Douala Party H.Q.

1976. 10th Anniv of Cameroun National Union. Multicoloured.
782 50f. Type **257** 35 15
783 50f. Pres. Ahidjo and Yaounde Party H.Q. . . . 35 15

258 Bamoun Copper Pipe

259 Crowned Cranes ("Crown-Cranes")

1977. 2nd World Festival of Negro Arts, Nigeria. Multicoloured.
784 50f. Type **258** (postage) . . . 55 30
785 60f. Traditional chief on throne (sculpture) (air) . . 85 35

1977. Cameroun Birds. Multicoloured.
786 30f. Ostrich . . . . 2·75 65
787 50f. Type **259** . . . . 2·75 95

260 "Christ on the Cross" (Issenheim Altarpiece, Mathias Grunewald)

1977. Air. Easter. Multicoloured.
788 50f. Type **260** 65 30
789 125f. "Christ on the Cross" (Veslasquez) (vert) . . . . 1·40 55
790 150f. "The Entombment" (Titian) . . . . 2·25 85

261 Lions Club Emblem

262 Rotary Club Emblem, Mountain and Road

1977. Air. 19th Congress of Douala Lions Club.
792 **261** 250f. multicoloured . . . 3·25 2·00

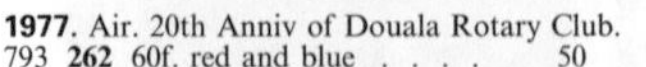

1977. Air. 20th Anniv of Douala Rotary Club.
793 **262** 60f. red and blue 50 30

263 Jean Mermoz and Seaplane "Comte de la Vaulx"

1977. Air. History of Aviation.
794 **263** 50f. blue, orange & brown 65 35
795 – 60f. purple and orange . . 70 45
796 – 80f. lake and blue 85 45
797 – 100f. green and yellow . . 1·40 65
798 – 300f. blue, red & purple 4·50 2·40
799 – 500f. purple, grn & plum 6·50 3·75
DESIGNS—VERT: 60f. Antoine de Saint-Exupery and Latecoere 2b. HORIZ: 80f. Maryse Bastie and Caudron C-635 Simoun; 100f. Sikorski S-43 amphibian (1st airmail, Marignane–Douala, 1937); 300f. Concorde; 500f. Charles Lindbergh and "Spirit of St. Louis".

1977. Air. 10th Anniv of International French Language Council. As T **204** of Benin.
801 70f. multicoloured 55 30

264 Cameroun 40f. and Basle 2½r. Stamps

1977. "Jufilex" Stamp Exhibition, Berne.
802 **264** 50f. multicoloured 65 35
803 – 70f. green, black & brown 90 45
804 – 100f. multicoloured . . . 1·90 65
DESIGNS: 70f. Zurich 4r. and Kamerun 1m. stamps; 100f. Geneva 5+5c. and Cameroun 20f. stamps.

265 Stafford and "Apollo" Rocket

1977. U.S.A.–U.S.S.R. Space Co-operation. Mult.
805 40f. Type **265** (postage) . . . 35 15
806 60f. Leonov and "Soyuz" rocket 45 20
807 100f. Brand and "Apollo" space vehicle (air) 65 35
808 250f. "Apollo–Soyuz" link-up 2·00 1·10
809 350f. Kubasov and "Soyuz" vehicle . . . . 2·75 1·40

266 Luge Sledging

1977. Winter Olympics. Innsbruck. Multicoloured.
811 40f. Type **266** (postage) . . . 30 15
812 50f. Ski-jumping 40 15
813 140f. Ski-marathon (air) . . . 90 45
814 200f. Ice-hockey . . . . . . 1·40 65
815 350f. Figure-skating . . . . 2·75 1·10

1977. Palestinian Welfare. No. 765 optd **Au bien-etre des familles des martyrs et des combattants pour la liberte de la Palestine. To the Welfare of the families of martyrs and freedom fighters of Palestine.**
817 100f. multicoloured 65 45

268 Mao Tse-tung and Great Wall of China

1977. 1st Death Anniv of Mao Tse-tung.
818 **268** 100f. brown and green . . 1·50 65

269 Knee Joint

1977. Air. World Rheumatism Year.
819 **269** 70f. brown, red & blue . . 55 20

1977. Air. 1st Paris–New York Commercial Flight of Concorde. Nos. 798 and 768 optd **PREMIER VOL PARIS-NEW YORK FIRST FLIGHT PARIS-NEW YORK 22 nov. 1977 — 22nd Nov. 1977.**
820 – 300f. blue, red & purple 2·75 1·40
821 **251** 500f. multicoloured . . . 4·25 2·25

271 "The Nativity" (Albrecht Altdorfer)

1977. Christmas. Multicoloured.
822 30f. Type **271** (postage) . . . 40 15
823 50f. "Madonna of the Grand Duke" (Raphael) 70 30
824 60f. "Virgin and Child with Four Saints" (Bellini) (horiz) (air) 80 30
825 400f. "Adoration of the Shepherds" (G. de la Tour) (horiz) . . . . 4·50 2·25

272 Club Flag and Rotary Emblem

273 Pres. Ahidjo, Flag and Map

1978. 20th Anniv of Yaounde Rotary Club.
826 **272** 50f. multicoloured 60 30

1978. New Cameroun Flag. Multicoloured.
827 50f. Type **273** (postage) . . . 55 20
828 60f. President, Flag and arms (air) 30 20

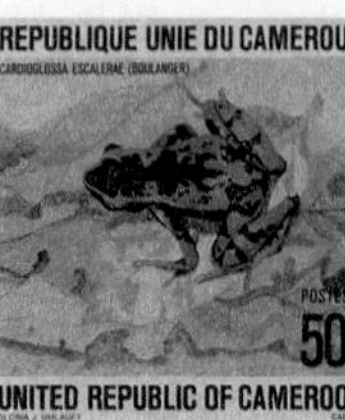

274 "Cardioglossa escalerae"

1978. Cameroun Frogs. Multicoloured.
829 50f. Type **274** (postage) . . . 50 35
830 60f. "Cardioglossa elegans" 1·00 45
831 100f. "Cardioglossa trifasciata" (air) . . . . . 1·25 35

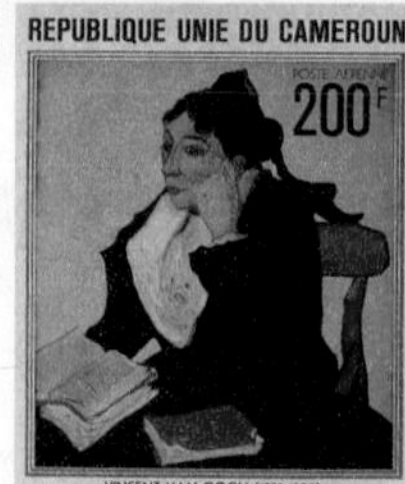

275 "L'Arlesienne" (Van Gogh)

1978. Air. Paintings. Multicoloured.
832 200f. Type **275** . . . . 3·00 1·40
833 200f. "Deposition of Christ" (Durer) . . . . 2·25 65

276 Raoul Follereau and Leprosy Distribution Map

1978. Air. World Leprosy Day.
834 **276** 100f. multicoloured . . . 80 45

277 Capt. Cook and the Siege of Quebec

1978. Air. 250th Birth Anniv of Capt. James Cook.
835 **277** 100f. green, blue & lilac 1·40 55
836 – 250f. brown, red and lilac 3·25 1·40
DESIGN: 250f. Capt. Cook, H.M.S. "Adventure" and H.M.S. "Resolution".

278 Footballers

1978. Air. World Cup Football Championship, Argentina. Multicoloured.
837 100f. Argentinian Team (horiz) 70 35
838 200f. Type **278** . . . . 1·50 65
839 1000f. Football illuminating globe . . . . 9·00 4·50

279 Jules Verne and scene from "From the Earth to the Moon"

1978. 150th Birth Anniv of Jules Verne (novelist). Multicoloured.
840 250f. Type **279** (postage) . . 1·90 55
841 400f. Portrait and "20,000 Leagues under the Sea" (horiz) (air) . . . . 3·25 1·40

280 "Hypolimnas salmacis"

1978. Butterflies. Multicoloured.
842 20f. Type **280** 35 20
843 25f. "Euxanthe trajanus" . . 35 20
844 30f. "Euphaedra cyparissa" 45 20

281 Planting Trees

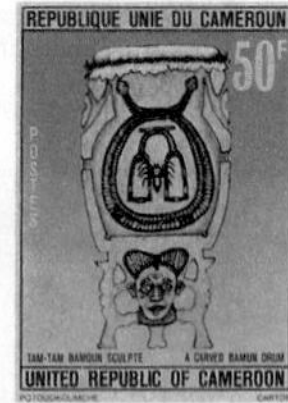

282 Carved Bamoun Drum

1978. Protection against Saharan Encroachment.
845 **281** 10f. multicoloured 15 10
846 15f. multicoloured 20 10

1978. Musical Instruments. Multicoloured.
847 50f. Type **282** (postage) . . . 35 20
848 60f. Gueguerou (horiz) . . . 50 30
849 100f. Mvet Zither (air) . . . 80 35

283 Presidents of Cameroun and France with Independence Monument, Douala

1978. Visit of President Giscard d'Estaing.
850 **283** 60f. multicoloured 85 40

284 African, Human Rights Charter and Emblem

1979. 30th Anniv of Declaration of Human Rights.
851 **284** 5f. mult (postage) 15 10
852 500f. multicoloured (air) 5·25 2·50
See also No. 1070.

285 Lions Emblem and Map of Cameroun

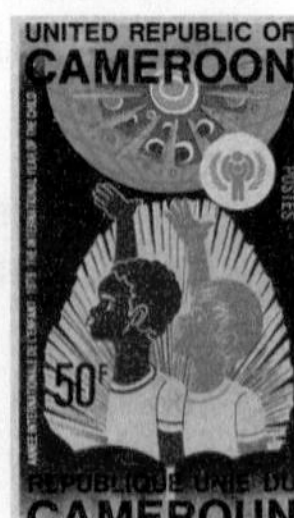

286 Globe, Emblem and Waving Children

1979. Air. Lions International Congress.
853 **285** 60f. multicoloured 60 30

1979. International Year of the Child.
854 **286** 50f. multicoloured 55 20

287 Penny Black, Rowland Hill and German Cameroun 10pf. Stamp

1979. Air. Death Cent of Sir Rowland Hill.
855 **287** 100f. black, red & turq . . 1·10 45

288 Black Rhinoceros **289** "Telecom 79"

1979. Endangered Animals (1st series). Mult.
856 50f. Type **288** 65 30
857 60f. Giraffe (vert) 80 45
858 60f. Gorilla 80 35
859 100f. African elephant (vert) 2·75 1·00
860 100f. Leopard . . . . 1·75 75
See also Nos. 891/2, 904/6, 975/7, 939/40 and 1007/8.

1979. Air. 3rd World Telecommunications Exhibition, Geneva.
861 **289** 100f. orange, blue & grey 90 45

290 Pope John Paul II **291** Dr. Jamot, Map and "Glossina palpalis"

1979. Air. Popes.
862 **290** 100f. blue, violet & grn 1·90 55
863 – 100f. brown, red & green 1·90 55
864 – 100f. chestnut, olive & grn 1·90 55
DESIGNS: No. 863, Pope John Paul I. No. 864, Pope Paul VI.

1979. Birth Centenary of Dr. Eugene Jamot (discoverer of sleeping sickness cure).
865 **291** 50f. brown, blue and red 60 30

292 "The Annunciation" (Fra Filippo Lippi)

1979. Christmas. Multicoloured.
866 10f. Type **292** 10 10
867 50f. "Rest during the Flight into Egypt" (Antwerp Master) 35 10
868 60f. "The Nativity" (Kalkar) 50 15
869 60f. "The Flight into Egypt" (Kalkar) 50 15
870 100f. "The Nativity" (Boticelli) . . . . 1·25 35

293 "Double Eagle II" and Balloonists

1979. Air. 1st Atlantic Crossing by Balloon. Multicoloured.
871 500f. Type **293** . . . . 4·50 1·40
872 500f. "Double Eagle II" over Atlantic and balloonists in basket . . . . 4·50 1·40

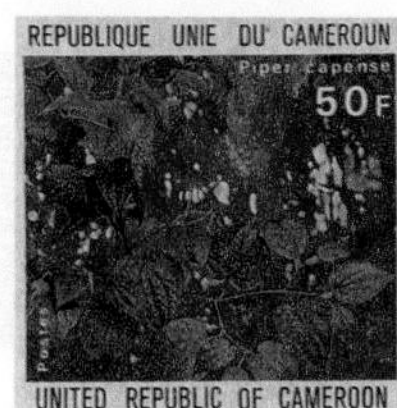

294 "Piper capense"

1979. Medicinal Plants. Multicoloured.
873 50f. Type **294** 65 15
874 60f. "Pteridium aquilinum" 70 20

295 Pres. Ahidjo, Map, Independence Stamp and Arms

1980. 20th Anniv of Independence.
875 **295** 50f. multicoloured 45 20

296 Congress Building

1980. 3rd Ordinary Congress of Cameroun National Union, Bafoussam.
876 **296** 50f. multicoloured 45 20

297 Globe

1980. 75th Anniv of Rotary International. Mult.
877 200f. Type **297** . . . . 2·00 65
878 200f. Map of Cameroun . . 2·00 65

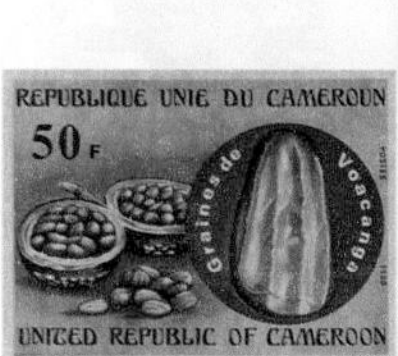

298 Voacanga Fruit and Seeds **299** "Dissotis perkinsiae"

1980. Medicinal Plants. Multicoloured.
880 50f. Type **298** 45 10
881 60f. Voacanga tree 45 15
882 100f. Voacanga flowers . . . 80 20

1980. Flowers. Multicoloured.
883 50f. Type **299** 45 10
884 60f. "Brillantaisia" sp. . . . 65 15
885 100f. "Clerodendron splendens" . . . . 1·40 20

300 Ka'aba, Mecca

1980. 1350th Anniv of Mohammed's Occupation of Mecca.
886 **300** 50f. multicoloured 65 35

301 Ice Skating

1980. Air. Olympic Games, Moscow and Lake Placid.
887 – 100f. brown and ochre . . 65 30
888 **301** 150f. brown and blue . . 1·00 45
889 – 200f. brown and green . . 1·75 55
890 – 300f. brown and red . . . 2·25 95
DESIGNS: 100f. Running; 200f. Throwing the Javelin; 300f. Wrestling.

302 Crocodile

1980. Endangered Animals (2nd series). Mult.
891 200f. Type **302** . . . . 2·50 55
892 300f. Kob . . . . 3·25 90

303 Bororo Girls and Roumsiki Peak

1980. Tourism. Multicoloured.
893 50f. Type **303** 40 15
894 60f. Dschang tourist centre 45 20

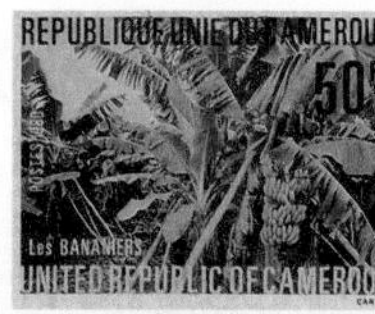

304 Banana Trees

1981. Bertona Agricultural Research Station. Multicoloured.
895 50f. Type **304** 45 10
896 60f. Cattle in watering hole 55 15

305 Girl on Crutches

1981. Int Year of Disabled People. Multicoloured.
897 60f. Type **305** 40 20
898 150f. Boy in wheelchair . . . 1·00 50

306 Camair Headquarters, Douala

1981. 10th Anniv of Cameroun Airlines. Mult.
899 100f. Type **306** 65 20
900 200f. Boeing 747 "Mount Cameroun" . . . . 1·60 45
901 300f. Douala International Airport . . . . 2·50 65

307 Presentation African Club Champions Cup **308** African Buffalo

1981. Football Victories of Cameroun Clubs. Multicoloured.
902 60f. Type **307** 65 35
903 60f. Cup presentation (African Cup Winner's Cup) 65 35

1981. Endangered Animals (3rd series). Mult.
904 50f. Type **308** 65 20
905 50f. Cameroun tortoise . . . 65 20
906 100f. Long-tailed pangolin . . 1·40 35

309 Prince Charles, Lady Diana Spencer and St. Paul's Cathedral **310** Bafoussam–Bamenda Road

1981. Wedding of Prince of Wales. Multicoloured.
907 500f. Type **309** . . . . 3·75 1·75
908 500f. Prince Charles, Lady Diana and Royal Coach 3·75 1·75

1981. Tourism.
910 **310** 50f. multicoloured 45 15

311 Yuri Gagarin and "Vostok 1"

1981. 20th Anniv of 1st Men in Space. Mult.
911 500f. Type **311** . . . . 4·50 1·40
912 500f. Alan Shepard and "Freedom 7" . . . . . . 4·50 1·40

312 "Cam Iroko" (freighter) in Harbour

1981. Cameroun Shipping Lines.
913 **312** 60f. multicoloured 65 30

313 Scout Salute and Badge within Knotted Rope, and National Flag

1981. Air. 4th African Scouting Conference, Abidjan. Multicoloured.
914 100f. Type **313** 55 30
915 500f. Saluting Girl Guide . . 3·75 1·40

314 Unity Monument

1981. 20th Anniv of Reunification.
916 **314** 50f. multicoloured 45 20

315 "L'Estaque" (Cezanne)

1981. Air. Paintings. Multicoloured.
917 500f. Type **315** . . . . 5·25 1·50
918 500f. "Guernica" (detail) (Picasso) . . . . 5·25 1·50

316 "Virgin and Child" (detail of San Zeno altarpiece, Mantegna)

1981. Air. Christmas. Paintings. Multicoloured.
919 50f. "Virgin and Child" (detail, "The Burning Bush") (Nicholas Froment) 30 10
920 60f. Type **316** 45 15
921 400f. "The Flight into Egypt" (Giotto) (horiz) . . . . . 3·00 1·25

317 "Voacanga thouarsii"

1981. Medicinal Plants. Multicoloured.
923 60f. Type **317** 55 15
924 70f. "Cassia alata" 65 20

318 "Descent from the Cross" (detail, Giotto)

1982. Easter. Paintings. Multicoloured.
925 100f. "Christ in the Garden of Olives" (Eugene Delacroix) 65 20
926 200f. Type **318** . . . . 1·40 45
927 250f. "Pieta in the Countryside" (Bellini) . . . 2·00 55

319 Carving, Giraffes and Map

1982. "Philexfrance 82" International Stamp Exhibition, Paris.
928 **319** 90f. multicoloured 80 20

320 Clay Water Jug

1982. Local Handicrafts. Multicoloured.
929 60f. Python-skin handbag . . 45 15
930 70f. Type **320** 55 20

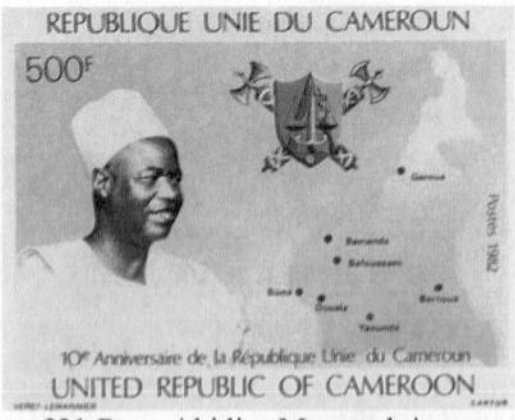

321 Pres. Ahidjo, Map and Arms

1982. 10th Anniv of United Republic.
931 **321** 500f. multicoloured . . . 4·50 1·40

322 Douala Town Hall

1982. Town Halls. Multicoloured.
932 40f. Type **322** 35 10
933 60f. Yaounde town hall . . . 45 15
See also No. 1139.

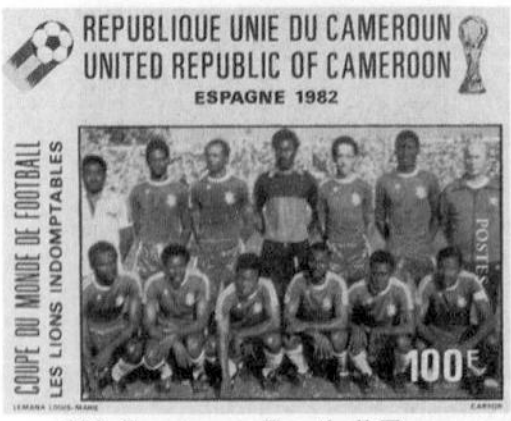

323 Cameroun Football Team

1982. World Cup Football Championship, Spain. Multicoloured.
934 100f. Type **323** . . . . 1·40 35
935 200f. Cameroun and Algerian teams . . . . 2·50 55
936 300f. Nkono Thomas, Cameroun goalkeeper . . . 3·75 80
937 400f. Cameroun team (different) . . . . 5·25 1·40

324 Bongo

325 Cameroun Mountain Francolin ("Perdrix")

1982. Endangered Animals (4th series). Mult.
939 200f. Type **324** . . . . 2·40 85
940 300f. Black colobus . . . . . 3·50 1·40

1982. Birds. Multicoloured.
941 10f. Type **325** 60 35
942 15f. Red-eyed dove ("Tourterelle") 70 50
943 20f. Barn swallow ("Hirondelle") . . . . . . 1·00 90
See also No. 1071.

326 Scouts round Campfire

1982. 75th Anniv of Boy Scout Movement. Multicoloured.
944 200f. Type **326** . . . . . . 2·00 55
945 400f. Lord Baden-Powell . . 3·50 1·40

327 I.T.U. Emblem

328 Nyasoso Chapel

1982. I.T.U. Delegates' Conference, Nairobi.
946 **327** 70f. multicoloured 55 20

1982. 25th Anniv of Presbyterian Church. Multicoloured.
947 45f. Buea Chapel 40 15
948 60f. Type **328** 50 20

329 World Cup, Footballers and Globe

1982. World Cup Football Championship Result.
949 **329** 500f. multicoloured . . . 4·50 1·90
950 1000f. multicoloured . . . 8·50 3·25

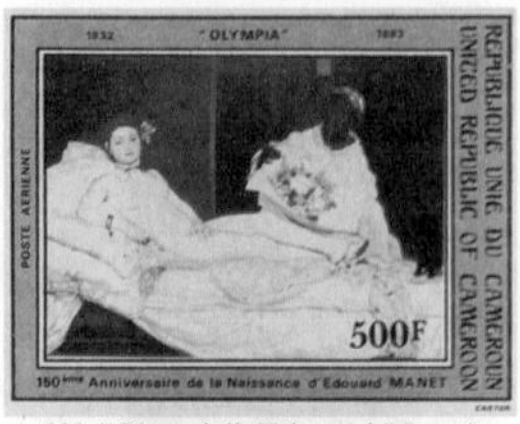

330 "Olympia" (Edouard Manet)

1982. Air. Artists' Anniversaries. Multicoloured.
951 500f. Type **330** (150th birth anniv) . . . . 4·50 1·75
952 500f. "Still-life" (Georges Braque, birth centenary) 4·50 1·75

331 Council Headquarters, Brussels

333 Pres. Kennedy

332 Yaounde University Hospital

1983. 30th Anniv of Customs Co-operation Council. Multicoloured.
953 250f. Type **331** . . . . . . 1·90 1·10
954 250f. Council emblem . . . . 1·90 1·10

1983. Second Yaounde Medical Days.
955 **332** 60f. multicoloured 55 15
956 70f. multicoloured 65 20

1983. Air. 20th Death Anniv of John F. Kennedy (U.S. President).
957 **333** 500f. multicoloured . . . 4·50 2·00

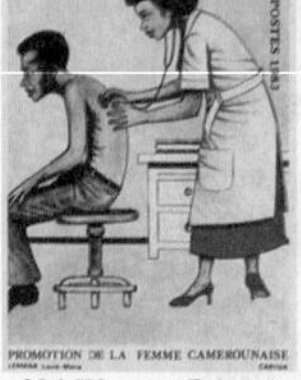

334 Woman Doctor

335 Lions Emblem and Map

1983. Cameroun Women. Multicoloured.
958 60f. Type **334** 55 20
959 70f. Woman lawyer 55 20

1983. Air. District 403 of Lions International Convention, Douala.
960 **335** 70f. multicoloured 45 20
961 150f. multicoloured . . . 1·25 55

336 Bafoussam Town Hall

1983. Town Halls. Multicoloured.
962 60f. Type **336** 45 15
963 70f. Garoua town hall . . . 55 20

337 President Biya and National Flag

1983. 11th Anniv of United Republic. Mult.
964 60f. Type **337** 45 15
965 70f. Pres. Biya and national arms 55 20

338 Container Ship and Buoy

1983. 25th Anniv of I.M.O.
966 **338** 500f. multicoloured . . . 5·00 2·00

339 Martial Eagle ("L'Aigle Martial")

340 Bread Mask ("Wery-Nwen-Nto")

1983. Birds. Multicoloured.
967 25f. Type **339** . . . . 1·60 40
968 30f. Rufous-breasted sparrow hawk ("L'Epervier") . . . 2·25 90
969 50f. Purple heron ("Le Heron Pourpre") . . . . 4·50 1·25
See also Nos. 1157 and 1169.

1983. Cameroun Artists. Multicoloured.
970 60f. Type **340** 55 15
971 70f. Basket with lid ("Chechia Bamoun") . . . 65 20

341 Mobile Rural Post Office

1983. World Communications Year. Multicoloured.
972 90f. Type **341** 65 20
973 150f. Radio operator with morse key . . . . 1·40 35
974 250f. Tom-tom drums . . . 2·40 55

342 African Civet

1983. Endangered Animals (5th series). Mult.
975 200f. Type **342** . . . . 2·40 65
976 200f. Gorilla . . . . 2·40 65
977 350f. Guinea-pig (vert) . . . 3·75 1·25
See also No. 1170.

343 "Jeanne d'Aragon" (Raphael)

1983. Air. Paintings. Multicoloured.
978 500f. Type **343** . . . . 4·50 1·75
979 500f. "Massacre of Scio" (Delacroix) . . . . 4·50 1·75

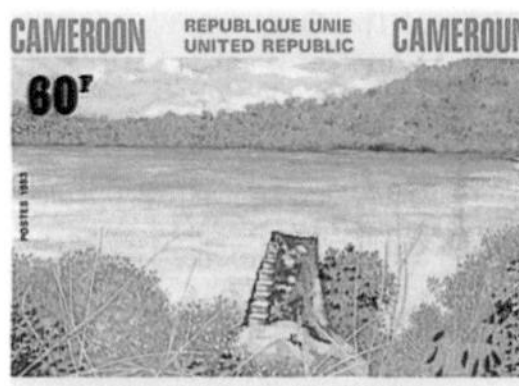

344 Lake Tizon

1983. Landscapes. Multicoloured.
980 60f. Type **344** 45 15
981 70f. Mount Cameroun in eruption 55 15

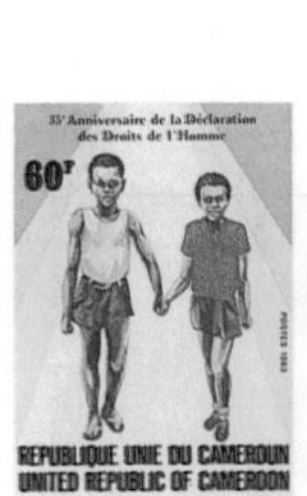

345 Boy and Girl holding Hands

346 Christmas Tree

1983. 35th Anniv of Declaration of Human Rights.
982 **345** 60f. multicoloured 45 15
983 70f. multicoloured 55 15

1983. Christmas. Multicoloured.
984 60f. Type **346** 35 15
985 200f. Stained-glass window, Yaounde Cathedral . . . . 1·40 55
986 500f. Statue of angel, Reims Cathedral . . . . 3·75 1·40
987 500f. "The Rest on the Flight into Egypt" (Philipp Otto Runge) (horiz) . . . . . . 3·75 1·40

348 "Pieta" (G. Hernandez)

1984. Air. Easter. Multicoloured.
992 200f. Type **348** . . . . 1·75 55
993 500f. "Martyrdom of St. John the Evangelist" (C. le Brun) . . . . 4·00 2·00

349 Urban Council Building, Bamenda

1984. Town Halls. Multicoloured.
995 60f. Type **349** 45 15
996 70f. Mbalmayo 55 20

350 High Jump **351** Running with Ball

1984. Air. Olympic Games, Los Angeles. Mult.
997 100f. Type **350** 65 30
998 150f. Volleyball . . . . . . 1·25 45
999 250f. Basketball . . . . . . 2·00 65
1000 500f. Cycling . . . . 3·75 1·40

1984. Air. European Football Championship. Multicoloured.
1001 250f. Type **351** . . . . . . 2·00 65
1002 250f. Heading ball . . . . . 2·00 65
1003 500f. Tackle . . . . 3·75 1·40

352 Catholic Church, Zoetele

1984. Churches. Multicoloured.
1005 60f. Type **352** 45 15
1006 70f. Marie Gocker Protestant Church, Yaounde 55 20

353 Antelope

1984. Endangered Animals (6th series). Mult.
1007 250f. Type **353** . . . . . . 2·50 1·10
1008 250f. Wild boar . . . . . . 2·50 1·10

354 Pres. Biya and Arms

1984. Air. President's Oath-taking Ceremony.
(a) Inscr in French.
1009 **354** 60f. multicoloured . . . 40 15
1010 70f. multicoloured . . . 45 15
1011 200f. multicoloured . . . 1·40 40

(b) Inscr in English.
1012 **354** 60f. multicoloured . . . 40 15
1013 70f. multicoloured . . . 45 15
1014 200f. multicoloured . . . 1·40 40

355 "Diana Bathing" (Watteau)

1984. Air. Anniversaries. Multicoloured.
1015 500f. Type **355** (300th birth anniv) (wrongly inscr "1624") . . . . 4·75 1·40
1016 500f. Diderot (encyclopaedist, death bicentenary) . . . . . . 4·75 1·40

1984. Air. Olympic Games Medal Winners. Nos. 997/1000 optd.
1017 100f. **MOEGENBURG (R.F.A.) 11-08-84** . . . 65 35
1018 150f. **U.S.A. 11-08-84** . . . 1·25 50
1019 250f. **YOUGOSLAVIE 9-08-84** . . . . 2·00 1·10
1020 500f. **GORSKI (U.S.A.) 3-08-84** . . . . 3·75 1·90

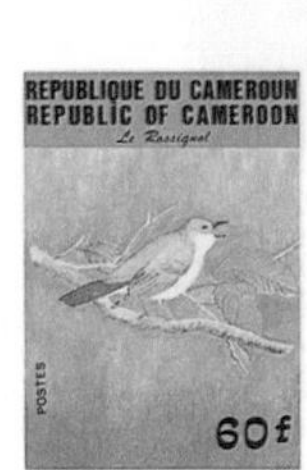

357 Nightingale ("Le Rossignol") **358** Neil Armstrong

1984. Birds. Multicoloured.
1021 60f. Type **357** . . . . 2·00 70
1022 60f. Ruppell's griffon ("Le Vautour") . . . . 2·00 70
See also No. 1158.

1984. Air. 15th Anniv of 1st Man on the Moon. Multicoloured.
1023 500f. Type **358** . . . . . . 4·50 1·75
1024 500f. Launching of "Apollo 12" . . . . . . 4·50 1·75

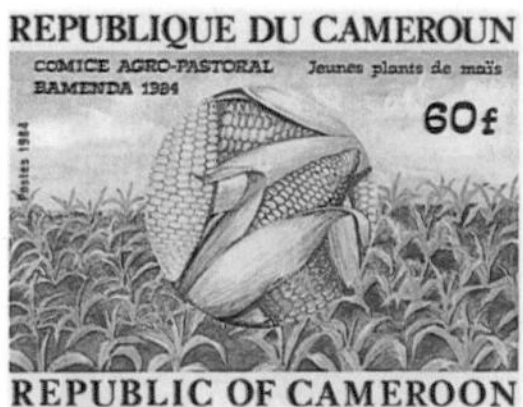

359 Maize and Young Plants

1984. Agro-pastoral Fair. Bamenda. Mult.
1025 60f. Type **359** 45 15
1026 70f. Zebus 55 20
1027 300f. Potatoes . . . . . . 2·50 85

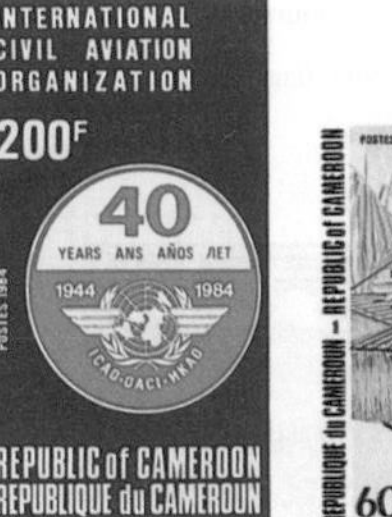

360 Anniversary Emblem **362** Balafons (xylophone)

361 Wrestling

1984. 40th Anniv of I.C.A.O.
1028 – 200f. multicoloured . . . 1·40 55
1029 **360** 200f. blue & deep blue . . . 1·40 55
1030 – 300f. multicoloured . . . 2·40 85
1031 – 300f. multicoloured . . . 3·00 1·40
DESIGNS: No. 1028, "Icarus" (Hans Herni); 1030, Cameroon Airlines Boeing 737; 1031, "Solar Princess" (Sadiou Diouf).

1985. "Olymphilex '85" International Thematic Stamps Exhibition, Lausanne.
1032 **361** 150f. multicoloured . . . 1·40 55

1985. Musical Instruments. Multicoloured.
1033 60f. Type **362** 45 10
1034 70f. Mvet (stringed instrument) 55 15
1035 100f. Flute . . . . 1·10 20

363 Intelcam Headquarters, Yaounde

1985. 20th Anniv of Int Telecommunications Satellite Consortium.
1036 – 125f. black, orange & bl 1·40 45
1037 **363** 200f. multicoloured . . . 1·75 50
DESIGN: 125f. "Intelsat V" satellite.

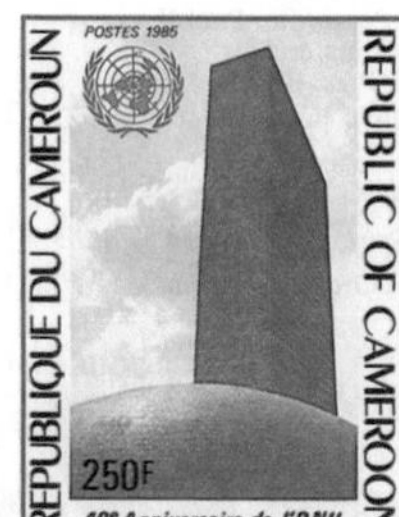

365 U.N. Emblem and Headquarters

1985. 40th Anniv of U.N.O.
1038 **365** 250f. multicoloured . . . 2·40 65
1039 500f. multicoloured . . . 4·50 1·40

366 French and Cameroun Flags and Presidents

1985. President Mitterrand of France's Visit to Cameroun. (a) Inscr "Mitterand" in error.
1040 **366** 60f. multicoloured . . .
1041 70f. multicoloured . . .

(b) Inscr corrected to "Mitterrand".
1041a **366** 60f. multicoloured . . . 55 30
1041b 70f. multicoloured . . . 65 30

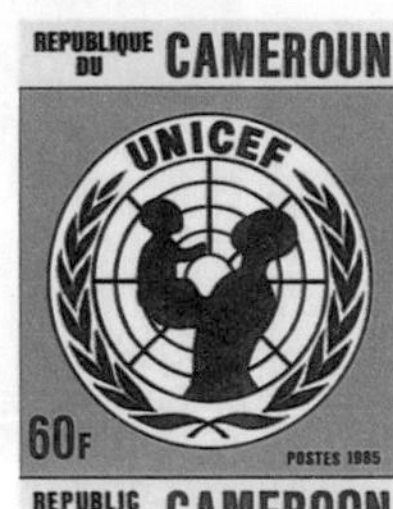

367 U.N.I.C.E.F. Emblem

1985. Child Survival Campaign.
1042 **367** 60f. black, blue & yell 45 15
1043 – 300f. multicoloured . . . 2·40 80
DESIGN: Doctor inoculating babies.

368 Lake Barumbi, Kumba

1985. Landscapes. Multicoloured.
1044 60f. Type **368** 55 10
1045 70f. Pygmy village, Bonando 55 15
1046 150f. River Cameroun . . . 1·40 35

369 Ebolowa Town Hall

1985. Town Halls. Multicoloured.

1047 60f. Type **369** 45 15
1048 60f. Ngaoundere town hall 45 15

370 Pope John Paul II **371** Porcupine

1985. Papal Visit to Cameroun. Multicoloured.

1049 60f. Type **370** 60 30
1050 70f. Pope John Paul II holding crucifix 80 30
1051 200f. Pres. Biya and Pope John Paul II . . . . . . 2·25 1·25

1985. Animals. Multicoloured.

1053 125f. Type **371** . . . . . . 1·25 35
1054 200f. Squirrel . . . . 1·75 55
1055 350f. Greater cane rat . . . 2·75 90

372 Wooden Mask **373** "Tomb of Henri Claude d'Harcourt" (detail)

1985. Cameroun Art (1st series). Multicoloured.

1056 60f. Type **372** 45 15
1057 70f. Wooden mask (different) 55 20
1058 100f. Men using pestle and mortar (wooden bas-relief) 80 30

See also Nos. 1081/3.

1985. Air. Death Anniversaries. Multicoloured.

1059 500f. Type **373** (bicentenary Jean Baptiste Pigalle (sculptor)) . . . . 4·75 1·40
1060 500f. Louis Pasteur (bacteriologist, 90th anniv) (after Edelfelt) . . 4·75 1·40

374 Yellow-casqued Hornbill ("Le Toucan") **375** Child's Toys

1985. Birds. Multicoloured.

1061 140f. Type **374** . . . . . . 2·10 70
1062 150f. Cock . . . . 1·75 60
1063 200f. European robins ("Le Rouge-gorge") . . . . . 3·25 1·10

See also No. 1156.

1985. Air. Christmas. Multicoloured.

1064 250f. Type **375** . . . . . . 1·90 65
1065 300f. Akono church . . . . 2·25 80
1066 400f. Christmas crib . . . . 2·75 1·10
1067 500f. "The Virgin of the Blue Diadem" (Raphael) 4·50 1·40

376 Emblem, Flag and Volunteers

1986. 25th Anniv of American Peace Corps in Cameroun.

1068 **376** 70f. multicoloured . . . 55 20
1069 100f. multicoloured . . . 80 35

1986. As Nos. 851 and 941 but inscr "Republique du Cameroun/Republic of Cameroon".

1070 **284** 5f. multicoloured 10 10
1071 **325** 10f. multicoloured 80 40

377 "Virgin Mary" (Pierre Prud'hon)

1986. Easter. Multicoloured.

1072 210f. Type **377** . . . . . . 1·40 65
1073 350f. "Stoning of St. Stephen" (Van Scorel) 2·50 1·25

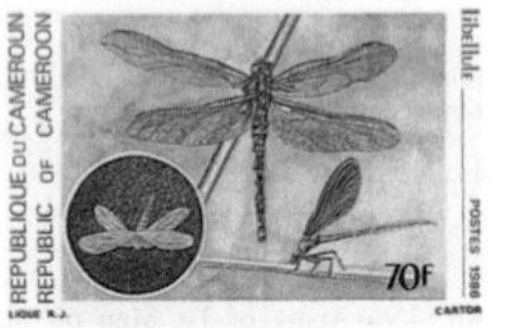

378 "Anax sp."

1986. Insects. Multicoloured.

1074 70f. Type **378** 60 40
1075 70f. Bee on flower (vert) . . 60 40
1076 100f. Grasshopper 90 55

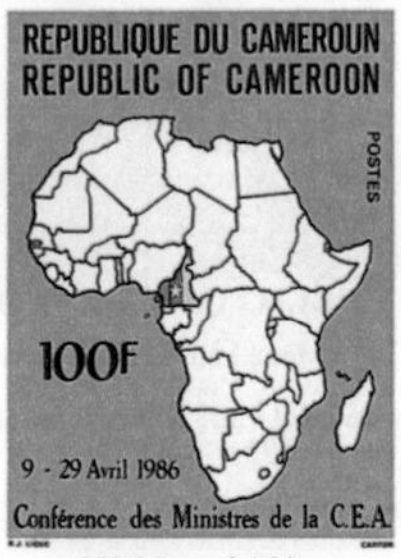

379 Map of Africa

1986. Economic Commission for Africa Ministers' Conference. Multicoloured.

1077 100f. Type **379** 80 45
1078 175f. Members' flags . . . . 1·40 65

380 Azteca Stadium

1986. Air. World Cup Football Championship, Mexico. Multicoloured.

1079 300f. Type **380** . . . . . . 2·25 1·10
1080 400f. Mexico team . . . . 3·00 1·40

1986. Cameroun Art (2nd series). As T **372**. Multicoloured.

1081 70f. Copper Statuette . . . 45 15
1082 100f. Wooden ash-tray . . . 70 20
1083 130f. Wooden horseman . . 1·40 35

381 Queen Elizabeth

1986. 60th Birthday of Queen Elizabeth II. Multicoloured.

1084 100f. Type **381** 80 35
1085 175f. Queen and President Biya . . . . 1·40 55
1086 210f. Queen Elizabeth (different) . . . . 1·75 80

382 President Biya

1986. 1st Anniv of Cameroun Republic Democratic Party. Multicoloured.

1087 70f. Type **382** 50 20
1088 70f. Bamenda Party headquarters (horiz) . . . 50 20
1089 100f. President Biya making speech 65 30

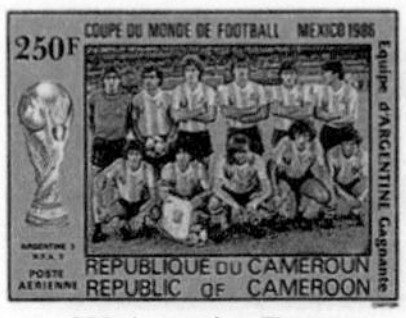

383 Argentine Team **384** Mask Dancer with Sword

1986. Air. World Cup Football Championship Winners.

1090 **383** 250f. multicoloured . . . 2·50 1·10

1986. Traditional Dances of North-west Kwem. Multicoloured.

1091 100f. Type **384** 70 45
1092 130f. Mask dancer with rattle . . . . 1·25 55

385 Cheetah **386** Bishop Desmond Tutu (Nobel Peace Prize Winner)

1986. Endangered Animals (7th series). Mult.

1093 300f. Type **385** . . . . . . 2·50 1·40
1094 300f. Varan . . . . 2·50 1·40

1986. International Peace Year. Multicoloured.

1095 175f. Type **386** . . . . . . 1·40 55
1096 200f. Type **386** . . . . . . 1·75 65
1097 250f. I.P.Y. and U.N. emblems . . . . 2·00 1·10

387 Pierre Curie (physicist)

1986. Air. Death Anniversaries. Multicoloured.

1098 500f. Type **387** (80th anniv) 5·25 2·25
1099 500f. Jean Mermoz and "Arc en Ciel" (aviation pioneer, 50th anniv) . . . 5·25 2·25

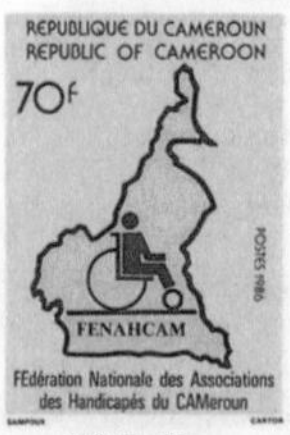

388 Emblem **389** Man holding Syringe and National Flag "Umbrella" over Woman and Child

1986. National Federation of Cameroun Handicapped Associations.

1100 **388** 70f. yellow and red . . . 50 20

1986. African Vaccination Year.

1101 70f. Type **389** 50 15
1102 100f. Flag behind woman holding child being immunised 65 30

390 Trees on Map **391** Loading Palm Nuts onto Trailer at Dibombari

1986. National Tree Day.

1103 70f. Type **390** 50 15
1104 100f. Hands holding clump of earth and seedling . . 65 30

1986. Agricultural Development. Multicoloured.

1105 70f. Type **391** 50 20
1106 70f. Payment for produce harvested 50 20
1107 200f. Pineapple plantation 1·40 65

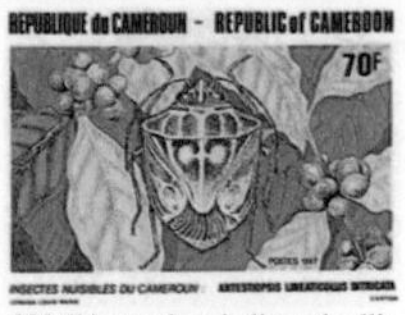

392 "Antestiopsis lineaticollis intricata"

1987. Harmful Insects. Multicoloured.

1108 70f. Type **392** 70 45
1109 100f. "Distantiella theobroma" 85 55

393 Millet

1987. Agricultural Show, Maroua. Multicoloured.

1110 70f. Type **393** 50 30
1111 100f. Cotton 65 40
1112 150f. Cattle . . . . 1·25 55

394 Shot-putting

1987. 4th All-Africa Games, Kenya. Mult.

1113 100f. Type **394** 65 35
1114 140f. Pole-vaulting . . . . 1·25 45

395 Drill Baboon

1988. Endangered Mammals. Drill Baboon. Multicoloured.

1115 30f. Type **395** 30 15
1116 40f. Adult baboons 35 15
1117 70f. Young baboon 60 35
1118 100f. Mother with baby . . 1·10 55

396 National Assembly Building

1989. Centenary of Interparliamentary Union.

1119 **396** 50f. multicoloured . . . 35 15

397 Cameroun and Argentine Players

1990. World Cup Football Championship, Italy. Multicoloured.
1120 200f. Type **397** 1·50 55
1121 250f. Cameroun player and match scene 2·00 1·10
1122 250f. Cameroun winning goal 2·00 1·10
1123 300f. Cameroun first eleven 2·25 1·40

1990. Nos. 1062 and 1093 surch.
1125 – 20f. on 150f. mult 15 10
1126 **385** 70f. on 300f. mult 45 20

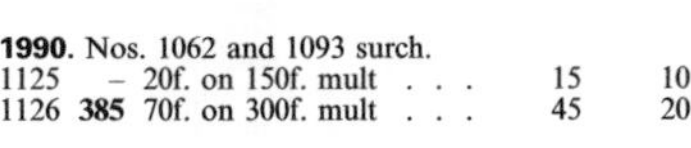

399 Milla and Match Scene

1990. Roger Milla, 4th Best Player in World Cup.
1127 **399** 500f. multicoloured 3·75 2·50

400 Anniversary Emblem

1990. 40th Anniv of United Nations Development Programme.
1129 **400** 50f. multicoloured 35 20

401 U.N.E.S.C.O. and I.L.Y. Emblems

1990. International Literacy Year.
1130 **401** 200f. black, lt blue & bl 1·40 55

402 Arms and Pres. Paul Biya

1991. 30th Anniv (1990) of Independence. Multicoloured.
1131 150f. Type **402** 1·40 55
1132 1000f. Flag, city and 1960 20f. Independence stamp 7·75 3·75

403 Treating Cacao Plantation

1991. Unissued stamps (for Ebolowa Agricultural Show) with bars over inscr and surch **125F**. Multicoloured.
1134 125f. on 70f. Type **403**
1135 125f. on 100f. Sheep
The stamps without surcharge were sold only by the Paris agency.

405 Snake on National Colours and Map

1991. Anti-AIDS Campaign. Multicoloured.
1137 15f. Type **405** 10 10
1138 25f. Youth pushing back "AIDS" in French and English (horiz) 15 10
See also Nos. 1171/2.

1991. As No. 932 but inscr "Republic du Cameroun / Republic of Cameroon".
1139 **322** 40f. multicoloured 30 15

406 Oribi

1991. Sovereign Military Order of Malta Child Survival Project. Antelopes. Multicoloured.
1140 125f.+10f. Type **406** 1·25 95
1141 250f.+20f. Waterbucks 2·25 2·25

407 Serle's Bush Shrike ("La Pie Grieche du Mont-kupe")

408 African Elephant

1991. Birds. Multicoloured.
1143 70f. Type **407** 60 45
1144 70f. Grey-necked bald crow ("Le Picathartes Chauve") (horiz) 60 45
1145 300f. As No. 1144 2·50 1·50
1146 350f. Type **407** 3·00 1·75

1991. Animals. Multicoloured.
1148 125f. Type **408** 1·10 55
1149 250f. Buffalo 2·00 1·40

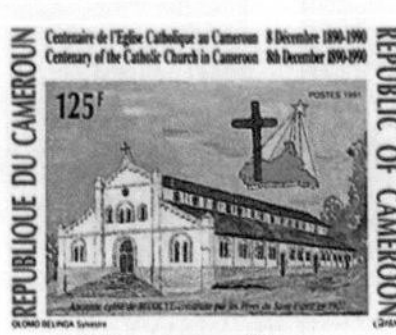

409 Mvolye Church

1991. Centenary (1990) of Catholic Church in Cameroun. Multicoloured.
1151 125f. Type **409** 1·10 55
1152 250f. Akono church 2·00 1·40

410 Emblems

1991. 7th African Group Meeting of Int Savings Banks Institute, Yaounde.
1154 **410** 250f. multicoloured 2·00 1·10

1992. Birds. As previous designs but with values changed. Multicoloured.
1156 125f. As No. 1063 1·40 50
1157 200f. As No. 968 1·60 60
1158 350f. Type **357** 2·75 1·50

411 Columbus's Fleet

412 Mbappe Lepe (footballer)

1992. 500th Anniv of Discovery of America by Columbus. Multicoloured.
1159 125f. Type **411** 1·40 50
1160 250f. Columbus kneeling on beach 2·10 1·40
1161 400f. Meeting Amerindians 3·00 1·90
1162 500f. Fleet crossing the Atlantic 4·75 3·00

1992. Cameroun Football. Multicoloured.
1163 125f. Type **412** 1·10 40
1164 250f. League emblem 2·10 1·40
1165 400f. National Football Federation emblem (horiz) 3·00 1·90
1166 500f. Ahmadou Ahidjo Stadium, Yaounde (horiz) 4·25 4·75
See also Nos. 1173/5.

413 Crocodile

1993. Endangered Animals. Mult. Self-adhesive.
1167 125f. Type **413** 1·00 65
1168 250f. Kob (vert) 2·00 1·40

1993. As Nos. 967 and 975 but inscr "REPUBLIQUE DU CAMEROUN REPUBLIC OF CAMEROON" and with values changed.
1169 **339** 370f. multicoloured 2·50 1·60
1170 **342** 410f. multicoloured 3·25 2·00

1993. Anti-AIDS Campaign. As Nos. 1137/8 but values changed. Multicoloured.
1171 100f. Type **405** 80 55
1172 175f. As No. 1138 1·40 80

1993. As Nos. 1163/5 but values changed.
1173 10f. As No. 1165 10 10
1174 25f. As No. 1164 10 10
1175 50f. Type **412** 15 10

414 President Biya holding Football and Lion (national team mascot)

1994. World Cup Football Championship, United States. Multicoloured.
1176 125f. Type **414** 50 40
1177 250f. Emblem, lion, player and map of Cameroun 90 65
1178 450f. Players, ball showing world map, national flag and trophy 1·75 1·25
1179 500f. Eagle and lion supporting ball 1·90 1·50

415 Grey Parrot

417 Anniversary Emblem and Dove carrying Branch

416 Chi-rho, Cross and Pope John Paul II

1995.
1181 **415** 125f. multicoloured 50 35

1995. 2nd Papal Visit.
1182 **416** 55f. black, pink & yell 25 20
1183 – 125f. multicoloured 50 35
DESIGN: 125f. Pope and open book.

1995. 50th Anniv of U.N.O. Multicoloured.
1184 200f. Type **417** 55 40
1185 250f. Anniversary emblem and figures joining hands 65 45

Cameroun joined the Commonwealth on 1 November 1995.

MILITARY FRANK STAMP

M **78** Arms and Crossed Swords

1963. No value indicated.
M1 M **78** (–) lake 3·25 3·25

POSTAGE DUE STAMPS

D **8** Felling Mahogany Tree

D **25** African Idols

1925.
D 88 D **8** 2c. black and blue 10 2·00
D 89 4c. purple and olive 10 1·60
D 90 5c. black and lilac 20 1·90
D 91 10c. black and red 45 2·75
D 92 15c. black and grey 85 2·50
D 93 20c. black and olive 1·75 2·75
D 94 25c. black and yellow 80 3·25
D 95 30c. orange and blue 1·60 3·50
D 96 50c. black and brown 1·25 3·50
D 97 60c. red and green 1·40 4·00
D 98 1f. green & red on grn 1·25 95
D 99 2f. mauve and red 1·90 5·75
D100 3f. blue and brown 4·25 7·75

1939.
D148 D **25** 5c. purple 10 2·50
D149 10c. blue 20 3·00
D150 15c. red 10 8·50
D151 20c. brown 20 2·50
D152 30c. blue 20 1·90
D153 50c. green 25 2·75
D154 60c. purple 25 2·75
D155 1f. violet 45 1·75
D156 2f. orange 40 3·00
D157 3f. blue 50 3·50

D **46**

1947.
D254 D **46** 10c. red 10 2·75
D255 30c. orange 10 2·75
D256 50c. black 10 2·75
D257 1f. red 15 2·75
D258 2f. green 1·75 3·00
D259 3f. mauve 2·00 3·25
D260 4f. blue 2·00 2·75
D261 5f. brown 1·75 3·00
D262 10f. blue 1·75 1·60
D263 20f. sepia 1·90 4·00

D **77** "Hibiscus rosa sinensis"

1963. Flowers. Multicoloured.
D342 50c. Type D **77** 10 10
D343 50c. "Erythrine" 10 10
D344 1f. "Plumeria lutea" 10 10
D345 1f. "Ipomoea sp." 10 10
D346 1f.50 "Grinum sp." 10 10
D347 1f.50 "Hoodia gordonii" 10 10
D348 2f. "Ochna" 10 10
D349 2f. "Gloriosa" 10 10
D350 5f. "Costus spectabilis" 15 15
D351 5f. "Bougainvillea spectabilis" 15 15
D352 10f. "Delonix regia" 40 40

D353 10f. "Haemanthus" 40 40
D354 20f. "Titanopsis" 1·25 1·25
D355 20f. "Ophthalmophyllum" 1·25 1·25
D356 40f. "Zingiberacee" 1·75 1·75
D357 40f. "Amorphophalus" 1·75 1·75

CANADA Pt. 1

A British dominion consisting of the former province of Canada with British Columbia, New Brunswick, Newfoundland, Nova Scotia and Prince Edward Island.

1851. 12 pence = 1 shilling (Canadian).
1859. 100 cents = 1 dollar.

COLONY OF CANADA

1 Beaver 2 Prince Albert

3 4

5 6 Jacques Cartier

1851. Imperf.
17 **4** ½d. red £800 £450
5 **1** 3d. red £1200 £160
2 **2** 6d. purple £17000 £950
12 **5** 7½d. green £7000 £1500
14 **6** 10d. blue £6500 £1100
4 **3** 12d. black £75000 £40000

1858. Perf.
25 **4** ½d. red £1900 £600
26 **1** 3d. red £2500 £300
27a **2** 6d. purple £7500 £2250

1859. Values in cents. Perf.
29 **4** 1c. red £225 28·00
44 2c. red £425 £150
31 **1** 5c. red £250 11·00
38 **2** 10c. purple £800 45·00
36 10c. brown £750 45·00
40 **5** 12½c. green £650 42·00
42 **6** 17c. blue £850 60·00

DOMINION OF CANADA

13 14

1868. Various frames.
54 **13** ½c. black 60·00 50·00
55 **14** 1c. brown £300 40·00
56a 1c. yellow £650 60·00
57 2c. green £350 30·00
49 3c. red £700 25·00
63 5c. green £700 65·00
59b 6c. brown £700 38·00
60 12½c. blue £500 40·00
70 15c. purple 65·00 17·00
69 15c. blue £150 29·00

27 21 28

1870. Various frames.
101 **27** ½c. black 11·00 7·00
75 **21** 1c. yellow 26·00 1·00
104 2c. green 38·00 1·75
105 3c. red 32·00 80
106 5c. grey 65·00 1·75
107 6c. brown 32·00 8·50
117 – 8c. grey 90·00 4·50
120 – 8c. purple 80·00 4·50
111 **21** 10c. pink £170 24·00
On 8c. head is to left.

1893.
115 **28** 20c. red £160 42·00
116 50c. blue £225 24·00

30 31

1897. Jubilee.
121 **30** ½c. black 48·00 48·00
122 1c. orange 10·00 4·50
124 2c. green 16·00 9·00
126 3c. red 12·00 2·25
128 5c. blue 40·00 14·00
129 6c. brown 85·00 85·00
130 8c. violet 32·00 29·00
131 10c. purple 50·00 42·00
132 15c. slate 85·00 85·00
133 20c. red 85·00 85·00
134 50c. blue £130 95·00
136 $1 red £425 £425
137 $2 violet £700 £350
138 $3 bistre £850 £700
139 $4 violet £800 £600
140 $5 green £800 £600

1897. Maple-leaves in four corners.
141 **31** ½c. black 6·00 4·75
143 1c. green 18·00 90
144 2c. violet 18·00 1·50
145 3c. red 25·00 50
146 5c. blue 60·00 2·75
147 6c. brown 60·00 30·00
148 8c. orange 75·00 7·00
149 10c. purple £130 55·00

1898. As T **31** but figures in lower corners.
150 ½c. black 3·25 1·10
151 1c. green 23·00 40
154 2c. purple 22·00 30
155 2c. red 30·00 30
156 3c. red 48·00 1·00
157 5c. blue 95·00 2·00
159 6c. brown 85·00 50·00
160 7c. yellow 55·00 14·00
162 8c. orange £100 27·00
163 10c. purple £160 14·00
165 20c. green £300 48·00

33 35 King Edward VII

1898. Imperial Penny Postage.
168 **33** 2c. black, red and blue 25·00 4·75

1899. Surch **2 CENTS.**
171 2c. on 3c. red (No. 145) 13·00 8·00
172 2c. on 3c. red (No. 156) 17·00 4·25

1903.
175 **35** 1c. green 21·00 50
176 2c. red 20·00 50
178 5c. blue 70·00 2·50
180 7c. olive 55·00 2·75
182 10c. purple £110 12·00
185 20c. olive £200 23·00
187 50c. violet £350 85·00

36 King George V and Queen Mary, when Prince and Princess of Wales 44

1908. Tercentenary of Quebec. Dated "1608 1908".
188 **36** ½c. brown 3·50 3·50
189 – 1c. green 13·00 2·75
190 – 2c. red 18·00 1·00
191 – 5c. blue 45·00 20·00
192 – 7c. olive 50·00 40·00
193 – 10c. violet 55·00 45·00
194 – 15c. orange 80·00 70·00
195 – 20c. brown £110 90·00
DESIGNS: 1c. Cartier and Champlain; 2c. King Edward VII and Queen Alexandra; 5c. Champlain's House in Quebec; 7c. Generals Montcalm and Wolfe; 10c. Quebec in 1700; 15c. Champlain's departure for the West; 20c. Cartier's arrival before Quebec.

1912.
196 **44** 1c. green 5·50 50
200 2c. red 5·00 50
205 3c. brown 5·00 50
205b 5c. blue 60·00 75
209 7c. yellow 20·00 3·00
210 10c. purple 90·00 2·75
212 20c. olive 29·00 1·50
215 50c. brown 48·00 3·75
See also Nos. 246/55.

1915. Optd **WAR TAX** diagonally.
225 **44** 5c. blue £110 £200
226 20c. olive 55·00 £100
227 50c. brown £110 £160

46 47

1915.
228 **46** 1c. green 8·00 50
229 2c. red 13·00 70

1916.
233 **47** 2c.+1c. red 22·00 1·25
239 2c.+1c. brown 4·00 50

48 Quebec Conference, 1864, from painting "The Fathers of the Confederation" by Robert Harris

1917. 50th Anniv of Confederation.
244 **48** 3c. brown 18·00 1·75

1922.
246 **44** 1c. yellow 2·50 60
247 2c. green 2·25 10
248 3c. red 3·75 10
249 4c. yellow 8·00 3·50
250 5c. violet 5·00 1·75
251 7c. brown 12·00 7·00
252 8c. blue 19·00 10·00
253 10c. blue 20·00 3·25
254 10c. brown 18·00 3·00
255 $1 orange 50·00 8·00

1926. Surch **2 CENTS** in one line.
264 **44** 2c. on 3c. red 42·00 50·00

1926. Surch **2 CENTS** in two lines.
265 **44** 2c. on 3c. red 16·00 21·00

51 Sir J. A. Macdonald 52 "The Fathers of the Confederation"

1927. 60th Anniv of Confederation. I. Commemoration Issue. Dated "1867–1927".
266 **51** 1c. orange 2·50 1·50
267 **52** 2c. green 2·25 30
268 – 3c. red 7·00 5·00
269 – 5c. violet 3·50 3·50
270 – 12c. blue 24·00 5·00
DESIGNS—HORIZ: As Type **52**: 3c. Parliament Buildings, Ottawa; 12c. Map of Canada, 1867–1927. VERT: As Type **51**: 5c. Sir W. Laurier.

56 Darcy McGee 57 Sir W. Laurier and Sir J. A. Macdonald

II. Historical Issue.
271 **56** 5c. violet 3·00 2·50
272 **57** 12c. green 16·00 4·50
273 – 20c. red 17·00 12·00
DESIGN—As Type **57**: 20c. R. Baldwin and L. H. Lafontaine.

59

1928. Air.
274 **59** 5c. brown 6·00 3·50

60 King George V 61 Mount Hurd and Indian Totem Poles

1928.
275 **60** 1c. orange 2·75 60
276 2c. green 1·25 20
277 3c. red 17·00 15·00
278 4c. yellow 13·00 6·50
279 5c. violet 6·50 3·50
280 8c. blue 7·50 4·75
281 **61** 10c. green 8·50 1·25
282 – 12c. black 22·00 10·00
283 – 20c. red 27·00 12·00
284 – 50c. blue £100 38·00
285 – $1 olive £110 65·00
DESIGNS—HORIZ: 12c. Quebec Bridge; 20c. Harvesting with horses; 50c. "Bluenose" (fishing schooner); $1 Parliament Buildings, Ottawa.

66 67 Parliamentary Library, Ottawa

68 The Old Citadel, Quebec

1930.
288 **66** 1c. orange 1·75 1·00
289 1c. green 1·50 10
290 2c. green 1·75 10
291 2c. red 70 1·25
292b 2c. brown 1·25 10
293 3c. red 90 10
294 4c. yellow 6·50 4·50
295 5c. violet 2·75 4·50
296 5c. blue 5·50 20
297 8c. blue 11·00 16·00
298 8c. red 7·50 5·50
299 **67** 10c. olive 15·00 1·00
300 **68** 12c. black 14·00 5·50
325 13c. violet 32·00 2·25
301 – 20c. red 22·00 1·00
302 – 50c. blue 80·00 17·00
303 – $1 olive 95·00 23·00
DESIGNS—HORIZ: 20c. Harvesting with tractor; 50c. Acadian Memorial Church, Grand Pre, Nova Scotia; $1 Mount Edith Cavell.

72 Mercury and Western Hemisphere 73 Sir Georges Etienne Cartier

1930. Air.
310 **72** 5c. brown 19·00 18·00

1931.
312 **73** 10c. green 6·00 20

1932. Air. Surch **6** and bars.
313 **59** 6c. on 5c. brown 3·00 2·50

1932. Surch **3** between bars.
314a **66** 3c. on 2c. red 1·00 60

76 King George V 77 Duke of Windsor when Prince of Wales

78 Allegory of British Empire 80 King George V

1932. Ottawa Conference. (a) Postage.
315 **76** 3c. red 70 80
316 **77** 5c. blue 9·00 5·00
317 **78** 13c. green 9·50 6·00

(b) Air. Surch **6 6 OTTAWA CONFERENCE 1932.**
318 **72** 6c. on 5c. brown 10·00 12·00

1932.
319 **80** 1c. green 60 10
320 2c. brown 70 10
321b 3c. red 85 10
322 4c. brown 35·00 9·00
323 5c. blue 10·00 10
324 8c. orange 23·00 4·25

81 Parliament Buildings, Ottawa

1933. U.P.U. Congress (Preliminary Meeting).

No.	Type	Description	Unused	Used
329	**81**	5c. blue	6·00	3·00

1933. Optd **WORLD'S GRAIN EXHIBITION & CONFERENCE REGINA 1933**.

No.	Type	Description	Unused	Used
330	–	20c. red (No. 295)	16·00	7·00

83 S.S. "Royal William" (after S. Skillett)

1933. Cent of 1st Transatlantic Steamboat Crossing.

No.	Type	Description	Unused	Used
331	**83**	5c. blue	9·50	3·00

84 Jacques Cartier approaching Land

1934. 4th-century of Discovery of Canada.

No.	Type	Description	Unused	Used
332	**84**	3c. blue	2·50	1·50

85 U.E.L. Statue, Hamilton

1934. 150th Anniv of Arrival of United Empire Loyalists.

No.	Type	Description	Unused	Used
333	**85**	10c. olive	8·50	5·00

86 Seal of New Brunswick

1934. 150th Anniv of New Brunswick.

No.	Type	Description	Unused	Used
334	**86**	2c. brown	1·50	2·25

87 Queen Elizabeth II when Princess

88 King George VI when Duke of York

89 King George V and Queen Mary

1935. Silver Jubilee. Dated "1910–1935".

No.	Type	Description	Unused	Used
335	**87**	1c. green	55	70
336	**88**	2c. brown	60	70
337	**89**	3c. red	1·75	70
338	–	5c. blue	5·50	6·50
339	–	10c. green	3·25	4·25
340	–	13c. blue	6·50	6·50

DESIGNS—VERT: 5c. Duke of Windsor when Prince of Wales. HORIZ: 10c. Windsor Castle; 13c. Royal Yacht "Britannia".

93 King George V

94 Royal Canadian Mounted Policeman

1935.

No.	Type	Description	Unused	Used
341	**93**	1c. green	1·50	10
342		2c. brown	1·50	10
343		3c. red	1·50	10
344		4c. yellow	3·25	1·75
345		5c. blue	3·00	10
346		8c. orange	3·75	3·50
347	**94**	10c. red	6·50	50
348	–	13c. violet	7·00	65
349	–	20c. green	17·00	70
350	–	50c. violet	25·00	4·75
351	–	$1 blue	40·00	11·00

DESIGNS—HORIZ: 13c. Confederation, Charlottetown, 1864; 20c. Niagara Falls; 50c. Parliament Buildings, Victoria, B.C.; $1 Champlain Monument, Quebec.

99 Daedalus

1935. Air.

No.	Type	Description	Unused	Used
355	**99**	6c. brown	3·00	1·00

100 King George VI and Queen Elizabeth

1937. Coronation.

No.	Type	Description	Unused	Used
356	**100**	3c. red	1·25	65

101 King George VI

102 Memorial Chamber Parliament Buildings, Ottawa

104 Fort Garry Gate, Winnipeg

1937.

No.	Type	Description	Unused	Used
357	**101**	1c. green	1·50	10
358		2c. brown	1·75	10
359		3c. red	1·75	10
360		4c. yellow	4·00	1·75
361		5c. blue	4·00	10
362		8c. orange	3·75	1·75
363	**102**	10c. red	5·00	10
364	–	13c. blue	16·00	1·25
365	**104**	20c. brown	22·00	1·00
366	–	50c. green	45·00	9·00
367	–	$1 violet	60·00	9·50

DESIGNS—HORIZ: 13c. Halifax Harbour; 50c. Vancouver Harbour; $1 Chateau de Ramezay, Montreal.

107 Fairchild 45-80 Sekani Seaplane over "Distributor" on Mackenzie River

1938. Air.

No.	Type	Description	Unused	Used
371	**107**	6c. blue	11·00	80

108 Queen Elizabeth II when Princess and Princess Margaret

1939. Royal Visit.

No.	Type	Description	Unused	Used
372	**108**	1c. black and green	1·75	10
373	–	2c. black and brown	80	60
374	–	3c. black and red	80	10

DESIGNS—HORIZ: 3c. King George VI and Queen Elizabeth. VERT: 2c. National War Memorial, Ottawa.

111 King George VI in Naval Uniform

112 King George VI in Military Uniform

114 Grain Elevator

115 Farm Scene

121 Air Training Camp

1942. War Effort.

No.	Type	Description	Unused	Used
375	**111**	1c. green (postage)	1·50	10
376	**112**	2c. brown	1·75	10
377	–	3c. red	1·25	60
378	–	3c. purple	90	10
379	**114**	4c. grey	5·50	1·00
380	**112**	4c. red	70	10
381	**111**	5c. blue	3·00	10
382	**115**	8c. sepia	5·50	75
383	–	10c. brown	6·50	10
384	–	13c. green	7·00	7·00
385	–	14c. green	18·00	1·00
386	–	20c. brown	14·00	35
387	–	50c. violet	26·00	3·50
388	–	$1 blue	42·00	6·00
399	**121**	6c. blue (air)	21·00	6·00
400		7c. blue	3·25	10

DESIGNS—As Type **112**: 3c. King George VI. As Type **121**. VERT: 10c. Parliament Buildings. HORIZ: 13, 14c. Ram tank; 20c. Corvette; 50c. Munitions factory; $1 H.M.S. "Cossack" (destroyer).

122 Ontario Farm Scene

1946. Re-conversion to Peace.

No.	Type	Description	Unused	Used
401	**122**	8c. brown (postage)	1·25	2·00
402	–	10c. green	1·75	10
403	–	14c. brown	4·00	1·25
404	–	20c. grey	3·00	10
405	–	50c. green	16·00	3·25
406	–	$1 purple	25·00	3·25
407	–	7c. blue (air)	4·50	10

DESIGNS: 10c. Great Bear Lake; 14c. St. Maurice River power station; 20c. Combine harvester; 50c. Lumbering in British Columbia; $1 "Abegweit" (train ferry); 7c. Canada geese in flight.

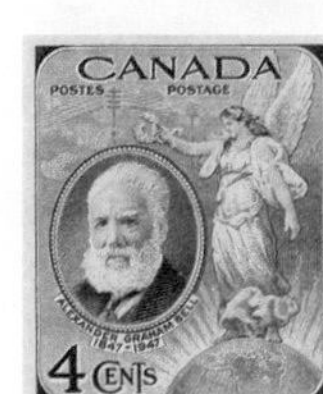
129 Alexander Graham Bell and "Fame"

130 "Canadian Citizenship"

1947. Birth Centenary of Graham Bell (inventor of the telephone).

No.	Type	Description	Unused	Used
408	**129**	4c. blue	15	10

1947. Advent of Canadian Citizenship and 80th Anniv of Confederation.

No.	Type	Description	Unused	Used
409	**130**	4c. blue	10	10

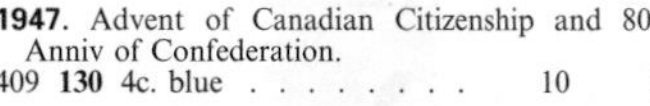

131 Queen Elizabeth II when Princess

132 Queen Victoria. Parliament Building, Ottawa, and King George VI

1948. Princess Elizabeth's Wedding.

No.	Type	Description	Unused	Used
410	**131**	4c. blue	10	10

1948. Centenary of Responsible Government.

No.	Type	Description	Unused	Used
411	**132**	4c. grey	10	10

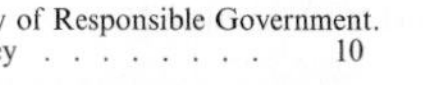

133 Cabot's Ship "Matthew"

1949. Entry of Newfoundland into Canadian Confederation.

No.	Type	Description	Unused	Used
412	**133**	4c. green	30	10

134 "Founding of Halifax, 1749" (after C. W. Jeffries)

135 King George VI

1949. Halifax Bicentenary.

No.	Type	Description	Unused	Used
413	**134**	4c. violet	30	10

1949. Portraits of King George VI.

No.	Type	Description	Unused	Used
414	**135**	1c. green	10	10
415	–	2c. brown	1·00	35
415a	–	2c. green	75	10
416	–	3c. purple	30	10
417	–	4c. red	20	10
418	–	5c. blue	2·00	10

1950. As Nos. 414 and 416/18 but without "POSTES POSTAGE".

No.	Type	Description	Unused	Used
424		1c. green	10	50
425		2c. brown	10	1·75
426		3c. purple	10	65
427		4c. red	10	20
428		5c. blue	30	1·25

142 Drying Furs

141 Oil Wells in Alberta

145 Mackenzie King

1950.

No.	Type	Description	Unused	Used
432	**142**	10c. purple	2·00	10
441	–	20c. grey	1·50	10
431	**141**	50c. green	6·00	1·00
433	–	$1 blue	38·00	5·00

DESIGNS: 20c. Forestry products; $1 Fisherman.

1951. Canadian Prime Ministers.

No.	Type	Description	Unused	Used
434	–	3c. green (Borden)	10	50
444	–	3c. purple (Abbott)	15	20
435	**145**	4c. red	10	10
445	–	4c. red (A. Mackenzie)	20	10
475	–	4c. violet (Thompson)	15	20
483	–	4c. violet (Bennett)	10	20
476	–	5c. blue (Bowell)	15	10
484	–	5c. blue (Tupper)	10	10

146 Mail Trains, 1851 and 1951

149 Reproduction of 3d., 1851

1951. Centenary of First Canadian Postage Stamp. Dated "1851 1951".

No.	Type	Description	Unused	Used
436	**146**	4c. black	35	10
437	–	5c. violet	65	1·75
438	–	7c. blue	35	1·00
439	**149**	15c. red	1·40	10

DESIGNS—As Type **146**: 5c. "City of Toronto" and S.S. "Prince George"; 7c. Mail coach and Canadair DC-4M North Star airplane.

150 Queen Elizabeth II when Princess and Duke of Edinburgh

1951. Royal Visit.

No.	Type	Description	Unused	Used
440	**150**	4c. violet	10	10

152 Red Cross Emblem

1952. 18th Int Red Cross Conf, Toronto.
442 **152** 4c. red and blue 15 10

153 Canada Goose

1952.
443 **153** 7c. blue 75 10

165 Eskimo Hunter

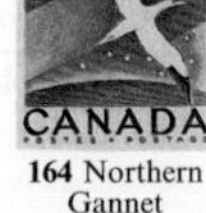
164 Northern Gannet

160 Textile Industry

154 Pacific Coast Indian House and Totem Pole

1953.
477 **165** 10c. brown 30 10
474 **164** 15c. black . . . . 1·00 10
488 – 20c. green 55 10
489 – 25c. red 55 10
462 **160** 50c. green . . . . 1·25 10
446 **154** $1 black . . . . 3·75 20
DESIGNS (As Type **160**)—HORIZ: 20c. Pulp and paper industry. VERT: 25c. Chemical industry.

155 Polar Bear

158 Queen Elizabeth II

1953. National Wild Life Week.
447 **155** 2c. blue 10 10
448 – 3c. sepia (Elk) 10 40
449 – 4c. slate (American bighorn) 15 10

1953.
450 **158** 1c. brown 10 10
451 2c. green 15 10
452 3c. red 15 15
453 4c. violet 20 10
454 5c. blue 20 10

159 Queen Elizabeth II

161

1953. Coronation.
461 **159** 4c. violet 10 10

1954.
463 **161** 1c. brown 10 10
464 2c. green 20 10
465 3c. red 70 10
466 4c. violet 30 10
467 5c. blue 30 10
468 6c. orange . . . . 1·00 45

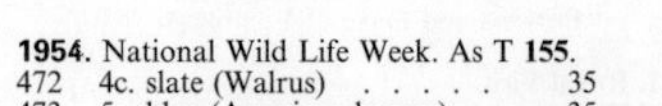
1954. National Wild Life Week. As T **155**.
472 4c. slate (Walrus) 35 10
473 5c. blue (American beaver) 35 10

166 Musk-ox

168 Dove and Torch

167 Whooping Cranes

1955. National Wild Life Week.
478 **166** 4c. violet 30 10
479 **167** 5c. blue . . . . 1·00 20

1955. 10th Anniv of I.C.A.O.
480 **168** 5c. blue 20 20

169 Pioneer Settlers

1955. 50th Anniv of Alberta and Saskatchewan Provinces.
481 **169** 5c. blue 15 20

170 Scout Badge and Globe

1955. 8th World Scout Jamboree.
482 **170** 5c. brown and green . . . 20 10

173 Ice-hockey Players

1956. Ice-hockey Commemoration.
485 **173** 5c. blue 20 20

1956. National Wild Life Week. As T **155**.
486 4c. violet (Reindeer) 20 15
487 5c. blue (Mountain goat) . . 20 10

178

179 Fishing

1956. Fire Prevention Week.
490 **178** 5c. red and black 30 10

1957. Outdoor Recreation.
491 **179** 5c. blue 25 10
492 – 5c. blue 25 10
493 – 5c. blue 25 10
494 – 5c. blue 25 10
DESIGNS: No. 492, Swimming; 493, Hunting; 494, Skiing.

183 White-billed Diver

1957. National Wild Life Week.
495 **183** 5c. black 50 20

184 Thompson with Sextant, and North American Map

185 Parliament Buildings, Ottawa

1957. Death Cent of David Thompson (explorer).
496 **184** 5c. blue 15 30

1957. 14th U.P.U. Congress, Ottawa.
497 **185** 5c. slate 15 10
498 – 15c. slate . . . . 55 1·75
DESIGNS—HORIZ ($33\frac{1}{2} \times 22$ mm): 15c. Globe within posthorn.

187 Miner

188 Queen Elizabeth II and Duke of Edinburgh

1957. Mining Industry.
499 **187** 5c. black 35 10

1957. Royal Visit.
500 **188** 5c. black 30 10

189 "A Free Press"

190 Microscope

1958. The Canadian Press.
501 **189** 5c. black 15 50

1958. International Geophysical Year.
502 **190** 5c. blue 20 10

191 Miner panning for Gold

1958. Centenary of British Columbia.
503 **191** 5c. turquoise 20 10

192 La Verendrye statue

1958. La Verendrye (explorer) Commemoration.
504 **192** 5c. blue 15 10

193 Samuel de Champlain and Heights of Quebec

194 Nurse

1958. 350th Anniv of Founding of Quebec by Samuel de Champlain.
505 **193** 5c. brown and green . . . 30 10

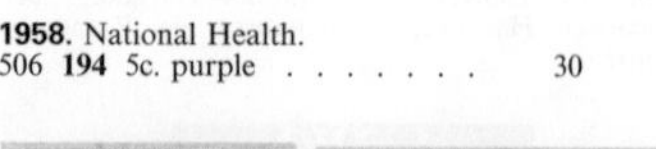
1958. National Health.
506 **194** 5c. purple 30 10

195 "Petroleum 1858–1958"

196 Speaker's Chair and Mace

1958. Centenary of Canadian Oil Industry.
507 **195** 5c. red and olive 30 10

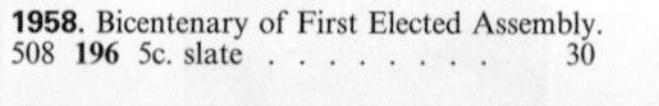
1958. Bicentenary of First Elected Assembly.
508 **196** 5c. slate 30 10

197 John McCurdy's Biplane "Silver Dart"

198 Globe showing N.A.T.O. Countries

1959. 50th Anniv of First Flight of the "Silver Dart" in Canada.
509 **197** 5c. black and blue 30 10

1959. 10th Anniv of N.A.T.O.
510 **198** 5c. blue 40 10

199

200 Queen Elizabeth II

1959. "Associated Country Women of the World" Commemoration.
511 **199** 5c. black and olive . . . 15 10

1959. Royal Visit.
512 **200** 5c. red 30 10

201 Maple Leaf linked with American Eagle

1959. Opening of St. Lawrence Seaway.
513 **201** 5c. blue and red 20 10

202 Maple Leaves

203 Girl Guides Badge

1959. Bicentenary of Battle of Quebec.
514 **202** 5c. green and red 30 10

1960. Golden Jubilee of Canadian Girl Guides Movement.
515 **203** 5c. blue and brown . . . 20 10

204 Dollard des Ormeaux

205 Surveyor, Bulldozer and Compass Rose

1960. Tercent of Battle of Long Sault.
516 **204** 5c. blue and brown . . . 20 10

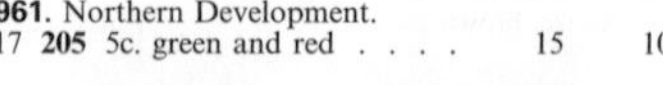
1961. Northern Development.
517 **205** 5c. green and red 15 10

206 E. Pauline Johnson

207 Arthur Meighen (statesman)

1961. Birth Centenary of E. Pauline Johnson (Mohawk poetess).
518 **206** 5c. green and red 15 10

1961. Arthur Meighen Commemoration.
519 **207** 5c. blue 15 10

208 Engineers and Dam

1961. Colombo Plan.
520 **208** 5c. brown and blue . . . 30 10

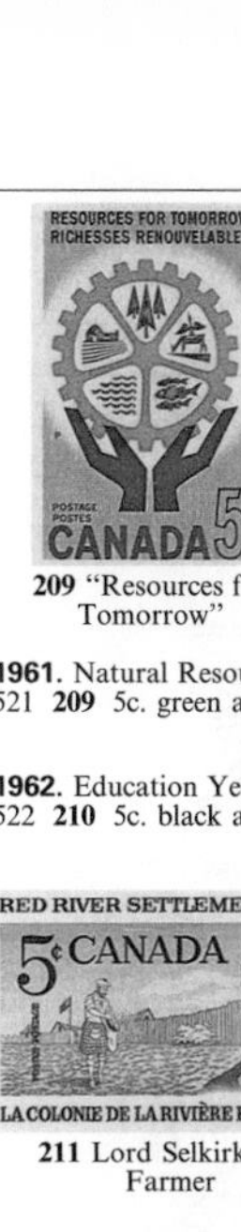

209 "Resources for Tomorrow" 210 "Education"

1961. Natural Resources.
521 **209** 5c. green and brown . . . 15 10

1962. Education Year.
522 **210** 5c. black and brown . . . 15 10

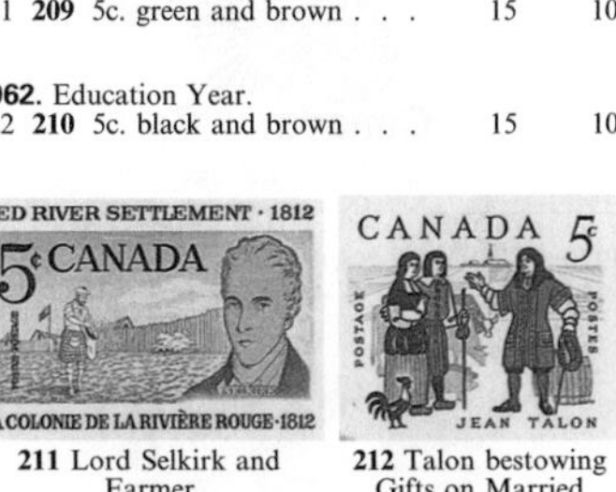

211 Lord Selkirk and Farmer 212 Talon bestowing Gifts on Married Couple

1962. 150th Anniv of Red River Settlement.
523 **211** 5c. brown and green . . . 20 10

1962. Jean Talon Commemoration.
524 **212** 5c. blue 20 10

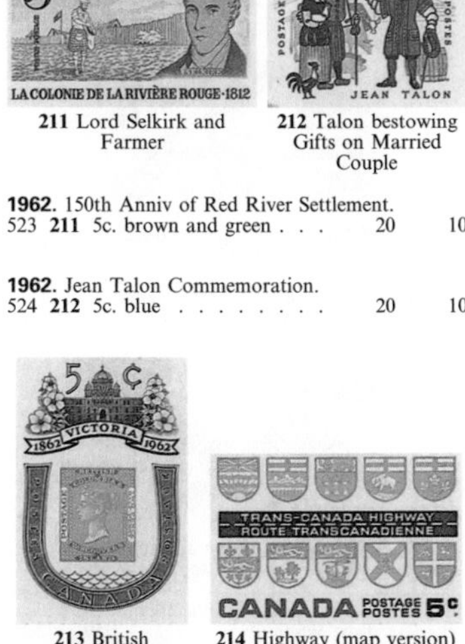

213 British Columbia and Vancouver Island 2½d. Stamp of 1860, and Parliament Buildings, B.C. 214 Highway (map version) and Provincial Arms

1962. Centenary of Victoria, B.C.
525 **213** 5c. red and black 30 10

1962. Opening of Trans-Canada Highway.
526 **214** 5c. black and brown . . . 15 10

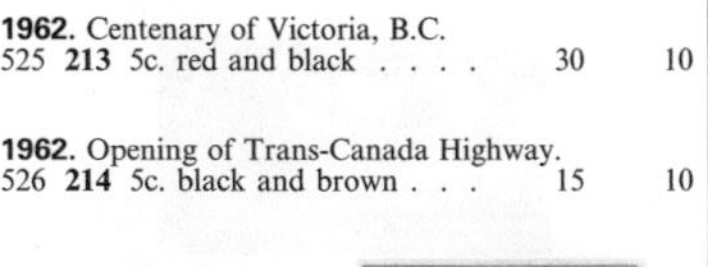

215 Queen Elizabeth II and Wheat (agriculture) Symbol 216 Sir Casimir Gzowski

1962. Different symbols in top left corner.
527 **215** 1c. brown 10 10
528 – 2c. green 15 10
529 – 3c. violet 15 10
530 – 4c. red 15 10
531 – 5c. blue 15 10
SYMBOLS: 1c. Crystals (Mining); 2c. Tree (Forestry); 3c. Fish (Fisheries); 4c. Electricity pylon (Industrial power); 5c. Wheat (Agriculture).

1963. 150th Birth Anniv of Sir Casimir Gzowski (engineer).
535 **216** 5c. purple 10 10

217 "Export Trade" 218 Frobisher and barque "Gabriel"

1963.
536 **217** $1 red . . . . 4·75 2·00

1963. Sir Martin Frobisher Commemoration.
537 **218** 5c. blue 20 10

219 Horseman and Map

1963. Bicent of Quebec–Trois-Rivieres–Montreal Postal Service.
538 **219** 5c. brown and green . . . 15 10

220 Canada Geese 221 Douglas DC-9 Airliner and Uplands Airport, Ottawa

1963.
540 **221** 7c. blue 35 70
540a 8c. blue 50 50
539 **220** 15c. blue . . . . 1·00 10

222 "Peace on Earth" 223 Maple Leaves

1964. "Peace".
541 **222** 5c. ochre, blue & turq . . 15 10

1964. "Canadian Unity".
542 **223** 5c. lake and blue 10 10

224 White Trillium and Arms of Ontario

1964. Provincial Badges.
543 **224** 5c. green, brown and orange 40 20
544 – 5c. green, brown and yellow 40 20
545 – 5c. red, green and violet 30 20
546 – 5c. blue, red and green . . 30 20
547 – 5c. purple, green and brown 30 20
548 – 5c. brown, green and mauve 30 20
549 – 5c. lilac, green and purple 50 20
550 – 5c. green, yellow and red 30 20
551 – 5c. sepia, orange and green 30 20
552 – 5c. black, red and green 30 20
553 – 5c. drab, green and yellow 30 20
554 – 5c. blue, green and red . . 30 20
555 – 5c. red and blue 30 20
FLOWERS AND ARMS OF: No. 544, Madonna Lily, Quebec; 545, Purple Violet, New Brunswick; 546, Mayflower, Nova Scotia; 547, Dogwood, British Columbia; 548, Prairie Crocus, Manitoba; 549, Lady's Slipper, Prince Edward Island; 550, Wild Rose, Alberta; 551, Prairie Lily, Saskatchewan; 552, Pitcher Plant, Newfoundland; 553, Mountain Avens, Northwest Territories; 554, Fireweed, Yukon Territory; 555, Maple Leaf, Canada.

1964. Surch **8**.
556 **221** 8c. on 7c. blue 15 15

238 Fathers of the Confederation Memorial, Charlottetown

1964. Centenary of Charlottetown Conference.
557 **238** 5c. black 10 10

239 Maple Leaf and Hand with Quill Pen

1964. Centenary of Quebec Conference.
558 **239** 5c. red and brown 15 10

240 Queen Elizabeth II 241 "Canadian Family"

1964. Royal Visit.
559 **240** 5c. purple 15 10

1964. Christmas.
560 **241** 3c. red 10 10
561 5c. blue 10 10

242 "Co-operation"

1965. International Co-operation Year.
562 **242** 5c. green 35 10

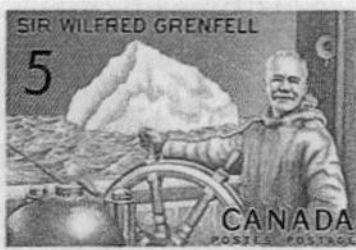

243 Sir W. Grenfell

1965. Birth Centenary of Sir Wilfred Grenfell (missionary).
563 **243** 5c. green 20 10

244 National Flag

1965. Inauguration of National Flag.
564 **244** 5c. red and blue 15 10

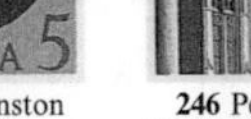

245 Sir Winston Churchill 246 Peace Tower, Parliament Buildings, Ottawa

1965. Churchill Commemoration.
565 **245** 5c. brown 15 10

1965. Inter-Parliamentary Union Conference, Ottawa.
566 **246** 5c. green 10 10

247 Parliament Buildings, Ottawa, 1865 248 "Gold, Frankincense and Myrrh"

1965. Centenary of Proclamation of Ottawa as Capital.
567 **247** 5c. brown 10 10

1965. Christmas.
568 **248** 3c. green 10 10
569 5c. blue 10 10

249 "Alouette 2" over Canada 250 La Salle

1966. Launching of Canadian Satellite, "Alouette 2".
570 **249** 5c. blue 15 10

1966. 300th Anniv of La Salle's Arrival in Canada.
571 **250** 5c. green 15 10

251 Road Signs 252 Canadian Delegation and Houses of Parliament

1966. Highway Safety.
572 **251** 5c. yellow, blue and black 15 10

1966. Centenary of London Conference.
573 **252** 5c. brown 10 10

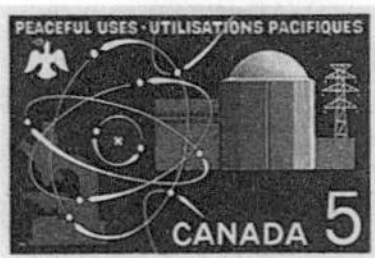

253 Douglas Point Nuclear Power Station 254 Parliamentary Library, Ottawa

1966. Peaceful Uses of Atomic Energy.
574 **253** 5c. blue 10 10

1966. Commonwealth Parliamentary Association Conference, Ottawa.
575 **254** 5c. purple 10 10

255 "Praying Hands", after Durer 256 Flags and Canada on Globe

1966. Christmas.
576 **255** 3c. red 10 10
577 5c. orange 10 10

1967. Canadian Centennial.
578 **256** 5c. red and blue 10 10

257 Queen Elizabeth, Northern Lights and Dog-team 262 "Alaska Highway" (A. Y. Jackson)

1967.
579 **257** 1c. brown 10 10
580 – 2c. green 10 10
581 – 3c. purple 30 10
582 – 4c. red 20 10
583 – 5c. blue 20 10
601 – 6c. red 45 10
607 – 6c. black 30 10
609 – 7c. green 30 10
584 **262** 8c. purple 25 50
610 – 8c. black 30 10
585 – 10c. olive 25 10
586 – 15c. purple 30 10
587 – 20c. blue . . . . 1·25 10
588 – 25c. green 75 10
589 – 50c. brown . . . . . . 1·25 10
590 – $1 red . . . . 1·50 65
DESIGNS—As Type **257**: 2c. Totem pole; 3c. Combine-harvester and oil derrick; 4c. Ship in lock; 5c., Harbour scene; 6c., 7c. "Transport"; 8c. (No. 610), Library of Parliament. As Type **262**: 10c. "The Jack Pine" (T. Thomson); 15c. "Bylot Island" (L. Harris); 20c. "Quebec Ferry" (J. W. Morrice); 25c. "The Solemn Land" (J. E. H. MacDonald); 50c. "Summer's Stores" (Grain elevators, J. Ensor); $1 "Oilfield" (near Edmonton, H. G. Glyde).

269 Canadian Pavilion 270 Allegory of "Womanhood" on Ballot-box

1967. World Fair, Montreal.
611 **269** 5c. blue and red 10 10

1967. 50th Anniv of Women's Franchise.
612 **270** 5c. purple and black . . . 10 10

271 Queen Elizabeth II and Centennial Emblem

272 Athlete

1967. Royal Visit.
613 **271** 5c. plum and brown . . . 15 10

1967. Pan-American Games, Winnipeg.
614 **272** 5c. red 10 10

273 "World News"

1967. 50th Anniv of Canadian Press.
615 **273** 5c. blue 10 10

274 Governor-General Vanier

1967. Vanier Commemoration.
616 **274** 5c. black 10 10

275 People of 1867, and Toronto, 1967

276 Carol Singers

1967. Cent of Toronto as Capital City of Ontario.
617 **275** 5c. green and red 10 10

1967. Christmas.
618 **276** 3c. red 10 10
619 5c. green 10 10

277 Grey Jays

278 Weather Map and Instruments

1968. Wild Life.
620 **277** 5c. multicoloured 30 10
See also Nos. 638/40.

1968. 20th Anniv of First Meteorological Readings.
621 **278** 5c. multicoloured 15 10

279 Narwhal

1968. Wild Life.
622 **279** 5c. multicoloured 15 10

280 Globe, Maple Leaf and Rain Gauge

1968. International Hydrological Decade.
623 **280** 5c. multicoloured 15 10

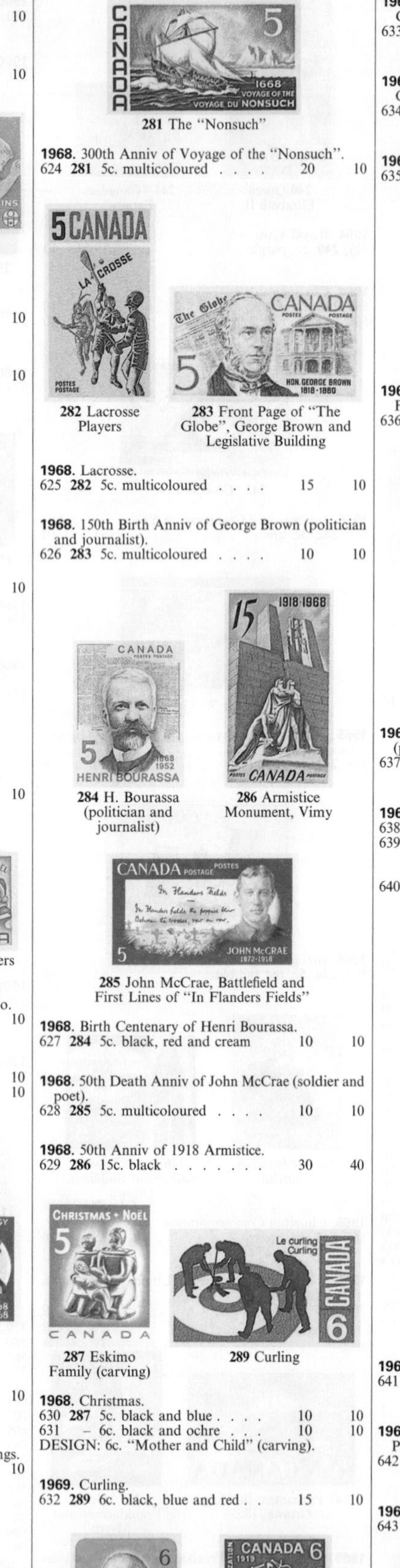

281 The "Nonsuch"

1968. 300th Anniv of Voyage of the "Nonsuch".
624 **281** 5c. multicoloured 20 10

282 Lacrosse Players

283 Front Page of "The Globe", George Brown and Legislative Building

1968. Lacrosse.
625 **282** 5c. multicoloured 15 10

1968. 150th Birth Anniv of George Brown (politician and journalist).
626 **283** 5c. multicoloured 10 10

284 H. Bourassa (politician and journalist)

286 Armistice Monument, Vimy

285 John McCrae, Battlefield and First Lines of "In Flanders Fields"

1968. Birth Centenary of Henri Bourassa.
627 **284** 5c. black, red and cream 10 10

1968. 50th Death Anniv of John McCrae (soldier and poet).
628 **285** 5c. multicoloured 10 10

1968. 50th Anniv of 1918 Armistice.
629 **286** 15c. black 30 40

287 Eskimo Family (carving)

289 Curling

1968. Christmas.
630 **287** 5c. black and blue 10 10
631 – 6c. black and ochre 10 10
DESIGN: 6c. "Mother and Child" (carving).

1969. Curling.
632 **289** 6c. black, blue and red . . 15 10

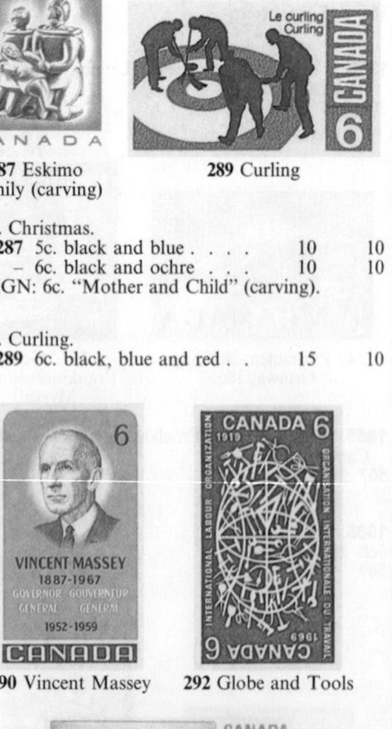

290 Vincent Massey

292 Globe and Tools

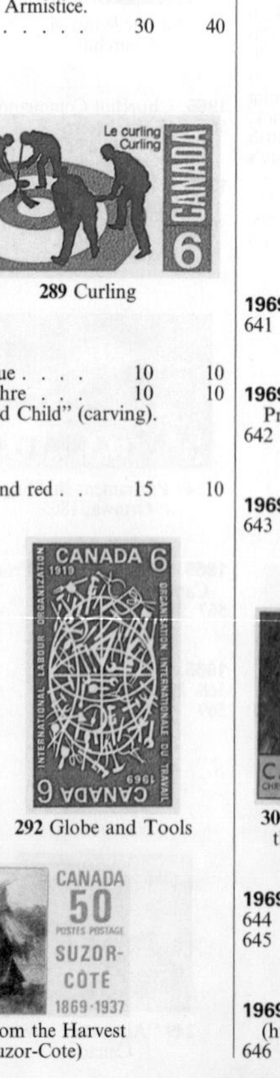

291 "Return from the Harvest Field" (Suzor-Cote)

1969. Vincent Massey, First Canadian-born Governor-General.
633 **290** 6c. sepia and ochre . . . 10 10

1969. Birth Centenary of Marc Aurele de Foy Suzor-Cote (painter).
634 **291** 50c. multicoloured . . . . 70 2·00

1969. 50th Anniv of I.L.O.
635 **292** 6c. green 10 10

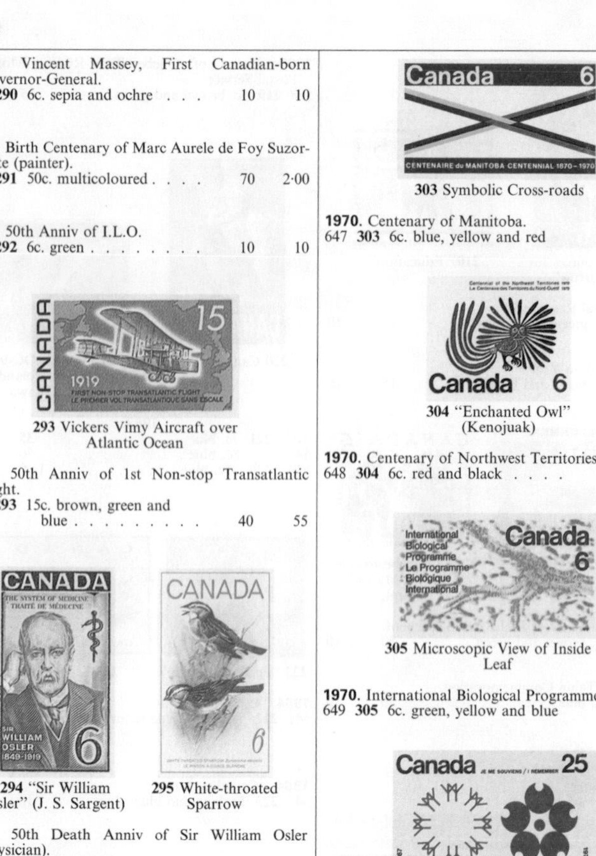

293 Vickers Vimy Aircraft over Atlantic Ocean

1969. 50th Anniv of 1st Non-stop Transatlantic Flight.
636 **293** 15c. brown, green and blue 40 55

294 "Sir William Osler" (J. S. Sargent)

295 White-throated Sparrow

1969. 50th Death Anniv of Sir William Osler (physician).
637 **294** 6c. blue and brown . . . 20 10

1969. Birds. Multicoloured.
638 6c. Type **295** 25 10
639 10c. Savannah sparrow ("Ipswich Sparrow") (horiz) . . . . 35 1·10
640 25c. Hermit thrush (horiz) . . 1·10 3·50

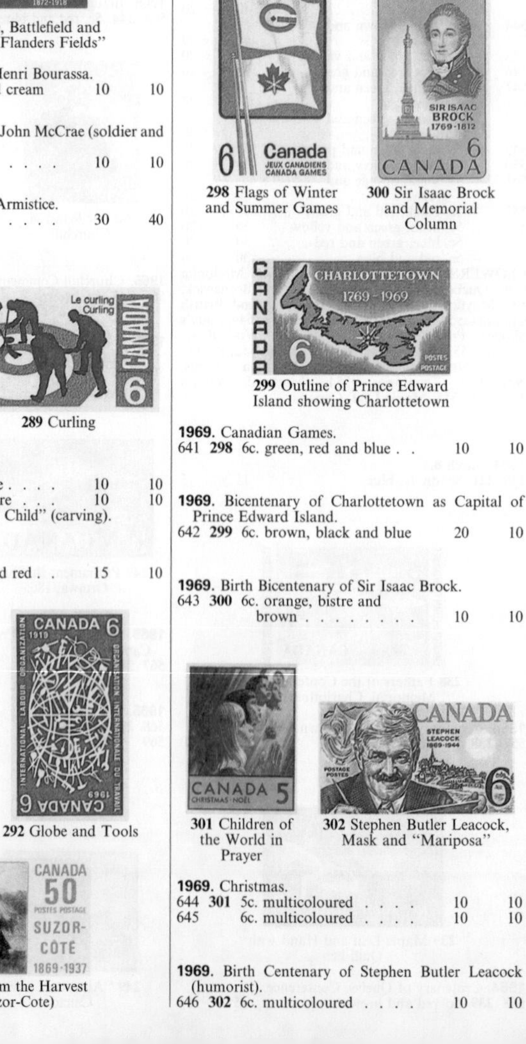

298 Flags of Winter and Summer Games

300 Sir Isaac Brock and Memorial Column

299 Outline of Prince Edward Island showing Charlottetown

1969. Canadian Games.
641 **298** 6c. green, red and blue . . 10 10

1969. Bicentenary of Charlottetown as Capital of Prince Edward Island.
642 **299** 6c. brown, black and blue 20 10

1969. Birth Bicentenary of Sir Isaac Brock.
643 **300** 6c. orange, bistre and brown 10 10

301 Children of the World in Prayer

302 Stephen Butler Leacock, Mask and "Mariposa"

1969. Christmas.
644 **301** 5c. multicoloured 10 10
645 6c. multicoloured 10 10

1969. Birth Centenary of Stephen Butler Leacock (humorist).
646 **302** 6c. multicoloured 10 10

303 Symbolic Cross-roads

1970. Centenary of Manitoba.
647 **303** 6c. blue, yellow and red 15 10

304 "Enchanted Owl" (Kenojuak)

1970. Centenary of Northwest Territories.
648 **304** 6c. red and black 10 10

305 Microscopic View of Inside of Leaf

1970. International Biological Programme.
649 **305** 6c. green, yellow and blue 15 10

306 Expo 67 Emblem and stylized Cherry Blossom

1970. World Fair, Osaka. Multicoloured.
650 25c. Type **306** (red) . . . . . 1·50 2·25
651 25c. Dogwood (violet) . . . 1·50 2·25
652 25c. White trillium (green) . . 1·50 2·25
653 25c. White garden lily (blue) 1·50 2·25
NOTE: Each stamp shows a stylized cherry blossom, in a different colour, given above in brackets.

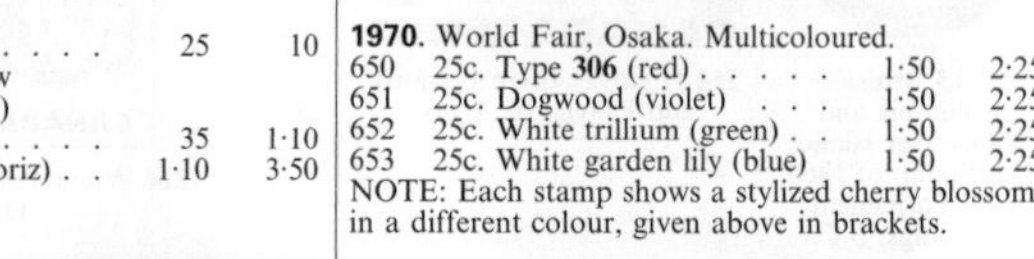

310 Henry Kelsey

1970. 300th Birth Anniv of Henry Kelsey (explorer).
654 **310** 6c. multicoloured 10 10

311 "Towards Unification"

1970. 25th Anniv of U.N.O.
655 **311** 10c. blue 50 50
656 15c. mauve and lilac . . . 50 50

312 Louis Riel (Metis leader)

313 Mackenzie's Inscription, Dean Channel

1970. Louis Riel Commemoration.
657 **312** 6c. blue and red 10 10

1970. Sir Alexander Mackenzie (explorer).
658 **313** 6c. brown 15 10

314 Sir Oliver Mowat (statesman)

1970. Sir Oliver Mowat Commemoration.
659 **314** 6c. red and black 10 10

315 "Isles of Spruce" (A. Lismer)

1970. 50th Anniv of "Group of Seven" (artists).
660 **315** 6c. multicoloured 10 10

316 "Horse-drawn Sleigh" (D. Niskala) **328** Sir Donald A. Smith

1970. Christmas. Children's Drawings. Mult.
661 5c. Type **316** 50 20
662 5c. "Stable and Star of Bethlehem" (L. Wilson) . . 50 20
663 5c. "Snowmen" (M. Lecompte) 50 20
664 5c. "Skiing" (D. Durham) . . 50 20
665 5c. "Santa Claus" (A. Martin) 50 20
666 6c. "Santa Claus" (E. Bhattacharya) 50 20
667 6c. "Christ in Manger" (J. McKinney) 50 20
668 6c. "Toy Shop" (N. Whateley) 50 20
669 6c. "Christmas Tree" (J. Pomperleau) 50 20
670 6c. "Church" (J. McMillan) 50 20
671 10c. "Christ in Manger" (C. Fortier) (37 × 20 mm) 30 30
672 15c. "Trees and Sledge" (J. Dojcak) (37 × 20 mm) 45 60

1970. 150th Birth Anniv of Sir Donald Alexander Smith.
673 **328** 6c. yellow, brown and green 15 10

329 "Big Raven" (E. Carr)

1971. Birth Centenary of Emily Carr (painter).
674 **329** 6c. multicoloured 20 30

330 Laboratory Equipment **332** Maple "Keys"

331 "The Atom"

1971. 50th Anniv of Discovery of Insulin.
675 **330** 6c. multicoloured 30 30

1971. Birth Centenary of Lord Rutherford (scientist).
676 **331** 6c. yellow, red and brown 20 20

1971. "The Maple Leaf in Four Seasons". Mult.
677 6c. Type **332** (spring) 20 20
678 6c. Green leaves (summer) . . 20 20
679 7c. Autumn leaves 20 20
680 7c. Withered leaves and snow (winter) 20 20

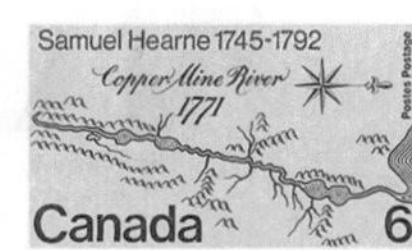

333 Louis Papineau **334** Chart of Coppermine River

1971. Death Centenary of Louis-Joseph Papineau (politician).
681 **333** 6c. multicoloured 15 20

1971. Bicentenary of Samuel Hearne's Expedition to the Coppermine River.
682 **334** 6c. red, brown and buff 40 40

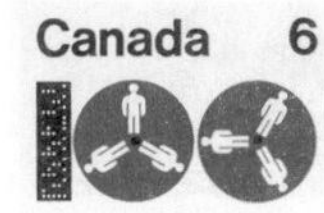

335 "People" and Computer Tapes

1971. Centenary of 1st Canadian Census.
683 **335** 6c. blue, red and black . . 30 20

336 Maple Leaves

1971. Radio Canada International.
684 **336** 15c. red, yellow and black 50 1·50

337 "B. C."

1971. Centenary of British Columbia's Entry into the Confederation.
685 **337** 7c. multicoloured 15 10

338 "Indian Encampment on Lake Huron" (Kane) **339** "Snowflake"

1971. Death Centenary of Paul Kane (painter).
686 **338** 7c. multicoloured 20 10

1971. Christmas.
687 **339** 6c. blue 10 10
688 7c. green 15 10
689 – 10c. silver and red . . . . 50 1·25
690 – 15c. silver, purple and lavender . . . . 65 2·00
DESIGN: 10c., 15c. "Snowflake" design similar to Type **339** but square (26 × 26 mm).

340 Pierre Laporte (Quebec Cabinet Minister) **341** Skaters

1971. 1st Anniv of Assassination of Pierre Laporte.
691 **340** 7c. black on buff 15 10

1972. World Figure Skating Championships, Calgary.
692 **341** 8c. purple 15 10

342 J. A. MacDonald **343** Forest, Central Canada

344 Vancouver

1972.
693 **342** 1c. orange 10 30
694 – 2c. green 10 10
695 – 3c. brown 10 50
696 – 4c. black 10 50
697 – 5c. mauve 10 10
698 – 6c. red 10 50
699 – 7c. brown 40 50
700 – 8c. blue 15 10
701 – 10c. red 75 10
702a **343** 10c. green, turquoise and orange 40 15
703b – 15c. blue and brown . . 1·00 10
704a – 20c. orange, violet and blue . . . . 1·00 10
705b – 25c. ultram and blue . . 1·00 10
706 – 50c. green, blue and brown 80 30
709a **344** $1 multicoloured 85 70
708 – $2 multicoloured . . . . 1·50 2·00
DESIGNS—As Type **342** (1 to 7c. show Canadian Prime Ministers): 2c. W. Laurier; 3c. R. Borden; 4c. W. L. Mackenzie King; 5c. R. B. Bennett; 6c. L. B. Pearson; 7c. Louis St. Laurent; 8, 10c. Queen Elizabeth II. As Type **343**: 15c. American bighorn; 20c. Prairie landscape from the air; 25c. Polar bears; 50c. Seashore, Eastern Canada. As Type **344**: $2 Quebec.

345 Heart

1972. World Health Day.
719 **345** 8c. red 30 10

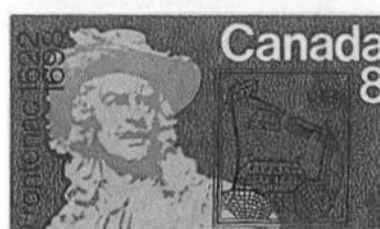

346 Frontenac and Fort Saint-Louis, Quebec

1972. 300th Anniv of Governor Frontenac's Appointment to New France.
720 **346** 8c. red, brown and blue 15 15

347 Plains Indians' Artefacts

347a Buffalo Chase

348 Thunderbird and Tribal Pattern **348a** Dancer in Ceremonial Costume

1972. Canadian Indians. (a) Horiz designs showing Artefacts as T **347** or Scenes from Indian Life as T **347a**.
721 **347** 8c. multicoloured 40 10
722 **347a** 8c. brown, yellow & blk 40 10
723 – 8c. multicoloured 40 10
724 – 8c. multicoloured 40 10
725 – 8c. multicoloured 40 10
726 – 8c. brown, yellow & blk 40 10
727 – 8c. multicoloured 40 10
728 – 8c. multicoloured 40 10
729 – 10c. multicoloured . . . 40 20
730 – 10c. red, brown and black 40 20
TRIBES: Nos. 721/2, Plains Indians; Nos. 723/4, Algonkians; Nos. 725/6, Pacific Coast Indians; Nos. 727/8, Subarctic Indians; Nos. 729/30, Iroquoians.

(b) Vert designs showing Thunderbird and pattern as T **348** or Costumes as T **348a**.
731 **348** 8c. orange, red and black 40 15
732 **348a** 8c. multicoloured 40 15
733 – 8c. red, violet and black 40 10
734 – 8c. green, brown and black 40 10
735 – 8c. red and black 40 10
736 – 8c. multicoloured 40 10
737 – 8c. green, brown and black 40 10
738 – 8c. multicoloured 40 10
739 – 10c. brown, orange & blk 40 20
740 – 10c. multicoloured . . . 40 20
TRIBES: Nos. 731/2, Plains Indians; Nos. 733/4, Algonkians; Nos. 735/6, Pacific Coast Indians; Nos. 737/8, Subarctic Indians; Nos. 739/40, Iroquoians.

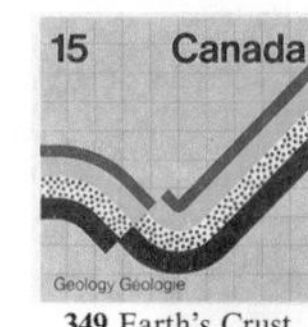

349 Earth's Crust **350** Candles

1972. Earth Sciences.
741 – 15c. multicoloured . . . . 1·10 1·90
742 – 15c. grey, blue and black 1·10 1·90
743 **349** 15c. multicoloured . . . . 1·10 1·90
744 – 15c. green, orange and black . . . . 1·10 1·90
DESIGNS AND EVENTS: No. 741 Photogrammetric surveying (12th Congress of International Society of Photogrammetry); No. 742 "Siegfried" lines (6th Conference of Int Cartographic Association); No. 743 (24th International Geological Congress); No. 744 Diagram of village at road-intersection (22nd Int Geographical Congress).

1972. Christmas. Multicoloured.
745 6c. Type **350** 15 10
746 8c. Type **350** 15 10
747 10c. Candles with fruits and pine boughs (horiz) . . . . 50 1·10
748 15c. Candles with prayer-book, caskets and vase (horiz) . . . . 60 1·50
Nos. 747/8 are size 36 × 20 mm.

351 "The Blacksmith's Shop" (Krieghoff) **352** F. de Montmorency-Laval

1972. Death Centenary of Cornelius Krieghoff (painter).
749 **351** 8c. multicoloured 30 15

1973. 350th Birth Anniv of Monsignor de Laval (1st Bishop of Quebec).
750 **352** 8c. blue, gold and silver 20 40

353 Commissioner French and Route of the March West

1973. Centenary of Royal Canadian Mounted Police.
751 **353** 8c. brown, orange and red 35 20
752 – 10c. multicoloured . . . . 1·00 1·25
753 – 15c. multicoloured . . . . 2·00 2·00
DESIGNS: 10c. Spectrograph; 15c. Mounted policeman.

354 Jeanne Mance

1973. 300th Death Anniv of Jeanne Mance (nurse).
754 **354** 8c. multicoloured 20 40

355 Joseph Howe

356 "Mist Fantasy" (MacDonald)

1973. Death Centenary of Joseph Howe (Nova Scotian politician).
755 **355** 8c. gold and black 20 40

1973. Birth Cent of J. E. H. MacDonald (artist).
756 **356** 15c. multicoloured 30 55

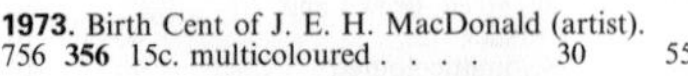

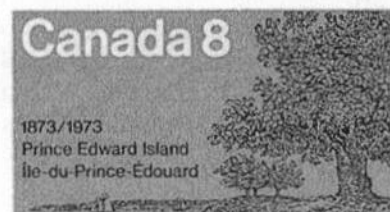

357 Oaks and Harbour

1973. Centenary of Prince Edward Island's Entry into the Confederation.
757 **357** 8c. orange and red . . . 20 30

358 Scottish Settlers

1973. Bicentenary of Arrival of Scottish Settlers at Pictou, Nova Scotia.
758 **358** 8c. multicoloured 25 20

359 Queen Elizabeth II

1973. Royal Visit and Commonwealth Heads of Government Meeting, Ottawa.
759 **359** 8c. multicoloured 25 20
760 15c. multicoloured . . . . 80 1·50

360 Nellie McClung

361 Emblem of 1976 Olympics

1973. Birth Centenary of Nellie McClung (feminist).
761 **360** 8c. multicoloured 20 50

1973. 1976 Olympic Games, Montreal (1st issue).
762 **361** 8c. multicoloured 25 15
763 15c. multicoloured . . . . 45 1·25
See also Nos. 768/71, 772/4, 786/9, 798/802, 809/11, 814/16, 829/32, 833/7 and 842/4.

362 Ice-skate

363 Diving

1973. Christmas. Multicoloured.
764 6c. Type **362** 15 10
765 8c. Bird decoration 20 10
766 10c. Santa Claus (20 × 36 mm) . . . . . . 70 1·40
767 15c. Shepherd (20 × 36 mm) 80 1·75

1974. 1976 Olympic Games, Montreal. (2nd issue). "Summer Activities". Each blue.
768 8c. Type **363** 30 50
769 8c. "Jogging" 30 50
770 8c. Cycling 30 50
771 8c. Hiking 30 50

1974. 1976 Olympic Games, Montreal. (3rd issue). As T **361** but smaller (20 × 36½ mm).
772 **361** 8c.+2c. multicoloured . . 25 45
773 10c.+5c. multicoloured . . 40 1·00
774 15c.+5c. multicoloured . . 45 1·40

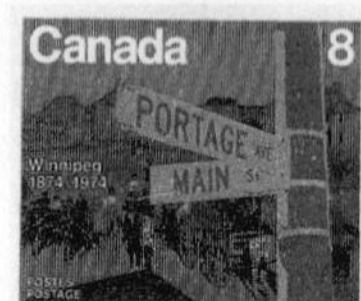

364 Winnipeg Signpost, 1872

1974. Winnipeg Centennial.
775 **364** 8c. multicoloured 20 15

365 Postmaster and Customer

366 "Canada's Contribution to Agriculture"

1974. Centenary of Canadian Letter Carrier Delivery Service. Multicoloured.
776 8c. Type **365** 50 80
777 8c. Postman collecting mail 50 80
778 8c. Mail handler 50 80
779 8c. Mail sorters 50 80
780 8c. Postman making delivery 50 80
781 8c. Rural delivery by car . . 50 80

1974. Centenary of "Agricultural Education". Ontario Agricultural College.
782 **366** 8c. multicoloured 20 20

367 Telephone Development

1974. Centenary of Invention of Telephone by Alexander Graham Bell.
783 **367** 8c. multicoloured 20 20

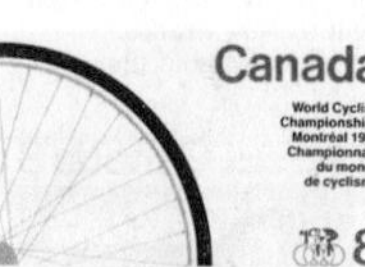

368 Bicycle Wheel

1974. World Cycling Championships, Montreal.
784 **368** 8c. black, red and silver 20 30

369 Mennonite Settlers

1974. Centenary of Arrival of Mennonites in Manitoba.
785 **369** 8c. multicoloured 20 20

1974. 1976 Olympic Games, Montreal (4th issue). "Winter Activities". As T **363**. Each red.
786 8c. Snow-shoeing 55 60
787 8c. Skiing 55 60
788 8c. Skating 55 60
789 8c. Curling 55 60

370 Mercury, Winged Horses and U.P.U. Emblem

1974. Centenary of U.P.U.
790 **370** 8c. violet, red and blue . . 15 15
791 15c. red, violet and blue 50 1·50

371 "The Nativity" (J. P. Lemieux)

1974. Christmas. Multicoloured.
792 6c. Type **371** 10 10
793 8c. "Skaters in Hull" (H. Masson) (34 × 31 mm) 10 10
794 10c. "The Ice Cone, Montmorency Falls" (R. C. Todd) 30 75
795 15c. "Village in the Laurentian Mountains" (C. A. Gagnon) . . . . . 35 1·10

372 Marconi and St. John's Harbour, Newfoundland

1974. Birth Centenary of Guglielmo Marconi (radio pioneer).
796 **372** 8c. multicoloured 20 20

373 Merritt and Welland Canal

1974. William Merritt Commemoration.
797 **373** 8c. multicoloured 20 30

374 Swimming

376 "Anne of Green Gables" (Lucy Maud Montgomery)

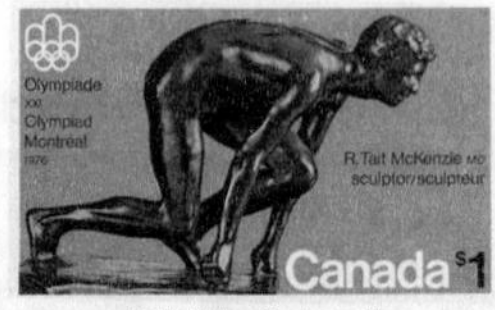

375 "The Sprinter"

1975. 1976 Olympic Games, Montreal (5th issue). Multicoloured.
798 8c.+2c. Type **374** 45 65
799 10c.+5c. Rowing . . . . . . 60 1·25
800 15c.+5c. Sailing . . . . . . 70 1·40

1975. 1976 Olympic Games, Montreal (6th issue). Multicoloured.
801 $1 Type **375** . . . . 1·50 2·25
802 $2 "The Diver" (vert) . . . . 2·25 4·25

1975. Canadian Writers (1st series). Multicoloured.
803 8c. Type **376** 30 10
804 8c. "Maria Chapdelaine" (Louis Hemon) 30 10
See also Nos. 846/7, 940/1 and 1085/6.

377 Marguerite Bourgeoys (founder of the Order of Notre Dame)

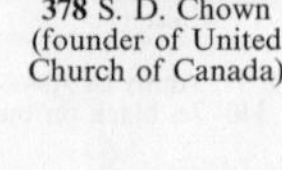

378 S. D. Chown (founder of United Church of Canada)

1975. Canadian Celebrities.
805 **377** 8c. multicoloured 60 40
806 – 8c. multicoloured 60 40
807 **378** 8c. multicoloured 30 75
808 – 8c. multicoloured 30 75

DESIGNS—As Type **377**: No. 806, Alphonse Desjardins (leader of Credit Union movement). As Type **378**: No. 808, Dr. J. Cook (first moderator of Presbyterian Church in Canada).

379 Pole-vaulting

380 "Untamed" (photo by Walt Petrigo)

1975. 1976 Olympics (7th issue). Multicoloured.
809 20c. Type **379** 40 50
810 25c. Marathon-running . . . 55 80
811 50c. Hurdling . . . . 70 1·25

1975. Centenary of Calgary.
812 **380** 8c. multicoloured 30 30

381 I. W. Y. Symbol

382 Fencing

1975. International Women's Year.
813 **381** 8c. grey, brown and black 30 30

1975. Olympic Games, Montreal (1976) (8th issue). Multicoloured.
814 8c.+2c. Type **382** 35 65
815 10c.+5c. Boxing . . . . . . 45 1·40
816 15c.+5c. Judo . . . . 55 1·60

383 "Justice-Justitia" (statue by W. S. Allward)

385 "Santa Claus" (G. Kelly)

384 "William D. Lawrence" (full-rigged ship)

1975. Centenary of Canadian Supreme Court.
817 **383** 8c. multicoloured 20 30

1975. Canadian Ships (1st series). Coastal Vessels.
818 **384** 8c. brown and black . . . 70 75
819 – 8c. green and black . . . 70 75
820 – 8c. green and black . . . 70 75
821 – 8c. brown and black . . . 70 75
DESIGNS: No. 819, "Neptune" (steamer); 820, "Beaver" (paddle-steamer); 821, "Quadra" (steamer).
See also Nos. 851/4, 902/5 and 931/4.

1975. Christmas. Multicoloured.
822 6c. Type **385** 15 10
823 6c. "Skater" (B. Cawsey) . . 15 10
824 8c. "Child" (D. Hebert) . . . 15 10
825 8c. "Family" (L. Caldwell) 15 10
826 10c. "Gift" (D. Lovely) . . . 30 50
827 15c. "Trees" (R. Kowalski) (horiz) 40 75

386 Text, Badge and Bugle

387 Basketball

1975. 50th Anniv of Royal Canadian Legion.

828	**386**	8c. multicoloured	20	20

1976. Olympic Games, Montreal (9th issue). Mult.

829	8c.+2c. Type **387**	1·50	1·00
830	10c.+5c. Gymnastics	60	1·40
831	20c.+5c. Soccer	70	1·60

388 Games Symbol and Snow Crystal

389 "Communications Arts"

1976. 12th Winter Olympic Games, Innsbruck.

832	**388**	20c. multicoloured	20	40

1976. Olympic Games, Montreal (10th issue). Multicoloured.

833	20c. Type **389**	40	25
834	25c. Handicrafts	65	75
835	50c. Performing Arts	95	1·60

390 Place Ville Marie and Notre-Dame Church

1976. Olympic Games, Montreal (11th issue). Multicoloured.

836	$1 Type **390**	2·25	4·50
837	$2 Olympic stadium and flags	2·75	5·50

391 Flower and Urban Sprawl

1976. HABITAT. U.N. Conference on Human Settlements, Vancouver.

838	**391**	20c. multicoloured	20	30

392 Benjamin Franklin and Map

1976. Bicentenary of American Revolution.

839	**392**	10c. multicoloured	20	35

393 Wing Parade before Mackenzie Building

394 Transfer of Olympic Flame by Satellite

1976. Centenary of Royal Military College. Mult.

840	8c. Colour party and Memorial Arch	15	20
841	8c. Type **393**	15	20

1976. Olympic Games, Montreal (12th issue). Multicoloured.

842	8c. Type **394**	20	10
843	20c. Carrying the Olympic flag	45	60
844	25c. Athletes with medals . .	45	85

395 Archer

1976. Disabled Olympics.

845	**395**	20c. multicoloured	20	30

396 "Sam McGee" (Robert W. Service)

397 "Nativity" (F. Mayer)

1976. Canadian Writers (2nd series). Mult.

846	8c. Type **396**	15	40
847	8c. "Le Survenant" (Germaine Guevremont)	15	40

1976. Christmas. Stained-glass Windows. Multi.

848	8c. Type **397**	10	10
849	10c. "Nativity" (G. Maile & Son)	10	10
850	20c. "Nativity" (Yvonne Williams)	20	60

398 "Northcote" (paddle-steamer)

1976. Canadian Ships (2nd series). Inland Vessels.

851	**398**	10c. lt brown, brn & blk	45	60
852	–	10c. blue and black . . .	45	60
853	–	10c. blue and black . . .	45	60
854	–	10c. lt green, green & blk	45	60

DESIGNS: No. 852, "Passport" (paddle-steamer); 853, "Chicora" (paddle-steamer); 854, "Athabasca" (steamer).

399 Queen Elizabeth II

1977. Silver Jubilee.

855	**399**	25c. multicoloured	30	50

400 Bottle Gentian

401 Queen Elizabeth II (bas-relief by J. Huta)

402 Houses of Parliament

403 Trembling Aspen

404 Prairie Town Main Street

405 Fundy National Park

1977.

856	**400**	1c. multicoloured . . .	10	20
870	**402**	1c. blue	1·25	2·75
857	–	2c. multicoloured . . .	10	10
858	–	3c. multicoloured . . .	10	10
859	–	4c. multicoloured . . .	10	10
860	–	5c. multicoloured . . .	10	10
871	**402**	5c. lilac	65	1·00
861	–	10c. multicoloured . . .	15	10
867	**401**	12c. blue, grey and black	15	10
872	**402**	12c. blue	70	30
866	–	12c. multicoloured . . .	15	60
868	**401**	14c. red, grey and black	20	10
873	**402**	14c. red	20	10
875	**403**	15c. multicoloured . . .	15	10
866a	–	15c. multicoloured . . .	15	15
869	**401**	17c. black, grey and green	50	10
874	**402**	17c. green	30	10
876	–	20c. multicoloured . . .	20	10
877	–	25c. multicoloured . . .	15	10
878	–	30c. multicoloured . . .	20	10
869b	**401**	30c. dp pur, grey & pur	70	80
869c		32c. black, grey and blue	50	70
879	–	35c. multicoloured . . .	25	10
883	**404**	50c. multicoloured . . .	85	80
883a	–	60c. multicoloured . . .	65	70
881	–	75c. multicoloured . . .	85	1·25
882	–	80c. multicoloured . . .	85	1·00
884	**405**	$1 multicoloured . . .	70	50
884b	–	$1 multicoloured	85	45
884c	–	$1.50 multicoloured . .	2·00	2·75
885	–	$2 multicoloured	1·00	45
885c	–	$2 multicoloured	3·75	1·50
885d	–	$5 multicoloured	3·00	2·50
885e	–	$5 multicoloured	7·00	4·00

DESIGN—As Type **400**: 2c. Red columbine; 3c. Canada lily; 4c. Hepatica; 5c. Shooting star; 10c. Franklin's lady's slipper orchid. 12c. Jewel-weed; 15c. (No. 866a) Canada violet. As Type **403**: 20c. Douglas fir; 25c. Sugar maple; 30c. Red oak; 35c. White pine. As Type **404**: 60c. Ontario City street; 75c. Eastern City street; 80c. Maritimes street. As Type **405**: $1 Glacier; $1.50, Waterton Lakes; $2 (No. 885) Kluane; $2 (No. 885c) Banff; $5 (No. 885d) Point Pelee; $5 (No. 885e) La Maurice.

406 Puma

407 "April in Algonquin Park"

1977. Endangered Wildlife (1st series).

886	**406**	12c. multicoloured	20	20

See also Nos. 906, 936/7, 976/7 and 1006/7.

1977. Birth Centenary of Tom Thomson (painter). Multicoloured.

887	12c. Type **407**	15	20
888	12c. "Autumn Birches" . . .	15	20

408 Crown and Lion

1977. Anniversaries. Multicoloured.

889	12c. Type **408**	15	20
890	12c. Order of Canada	15	20

EVENTS: No. 889, 25th anniv of First Canadian-born Governor-General; No. 890, 10th anniv of Order of Canada.

409 Peace Bridge, Niagara River

1977. 50th Anniv of Opening of Peace Bridge.

891	**409**	12c. multicoloured	15	15

410 Sir Sandford Fleming (engineer)

1977. Famous Canadians.

892	**410**	12c. blue	30	30
893	–	12c. brown	30	30

DESIGN: No. 893, Joseph E. Bernier (explorer) and "Arctic" (survey ship).

411 Peace Tower, Parliament Buildings, Ottawa

1977. 23rd Commonwealth Parliamentary Conference

894	**411**	25c. multicoloured	20	30

412 Hunter Braves following Star

1977. Christmas. Canada's first carol "Jesous Ahatonhia". Multicoloured.

895	10c. Type **412**	10	10
896	12c. Angelic choir	10	10
897	25c. Christ Child and "Chiefs from afar"	20	45

413 Seal Hunter (soapstone sculpture)

1977. Canadian Eskimos ("Inuits") (1st series). Hunting. Multicoloured.

898	12c. Type **413**	35	35
899	12c. Fishing with spear . . .	35	35
900	12c. Disguised archer	35	35
901	12c. Walrus hunting	35	35

See also Nos. 924/7, 958/61 and 989/92.

414 Pinky (fishing boat)

1977. Canadian Ships (3rd series). Sailing Craft. Multicoloured.

902	12c. Type **414**	20	35
903	12c. "Malahat" (schooner)	20	35
904	12c. Tern schooner	20	35
905	12c. Mackinaw boat	20	35

415 Peregrine Falcon

1978. Endangered Wildlife (2nd series).

906	**415**	12c. multicoloured	30	20

416 Pair of 1851 12d. Black Stamps

1978. "CAPEX '78" International Philatelic Exhibition, Toronto.

907	**416**	12c. black and sepia . . .	10	10
914	–	14c. blue, lt grey & grey	15	10
915	–	30c. red, lt grey and grey	25	40
916	–	$1.25 violet, lt grey & grey	70	1·50
MS917		101 × 96 mm. Nos. 914/16	1·25	2·50

DESIGNS: 14c. Pair of 1855 10d. Cartier stamps; 30c. Pair of 1857 ½d. red stamps; $1.25, Pair of 1851 6d. Prince Albert stamps.

417 Games Emblem

1978. 11th Commonwealth Games, Edmonton (1st issue). Multicoloured.

908	14c. Type **417**	10	10
909	30c. Badminton	20	60

See also Nos. 918/21.

418 "Captain Cook" (Nathaniel Dance)

419 Hardrock Silver Mine, Cobalt, Ontario

1978. Bicentenary of Cook's 3rd Voyage. Mult.

910	14c. Type **418**	20	20
911	14c. "Nootka Sound" (J. Webber)	20	20

1978. Resources Development. Multicoloured.

912	14c. Type **419**	15	20
913	14c. Giant excavators, Athabasca Tar Sands . . .	15	20

1978. 11th Commonwealth Games, Edmonton (2nd issue). As T **417**. Multicoloured.

918	14c. Games stadium	20	20
919	14c. Running	20	20
920	30c. Alberta legislature building	50	50
921	30c. Bowls	50	50

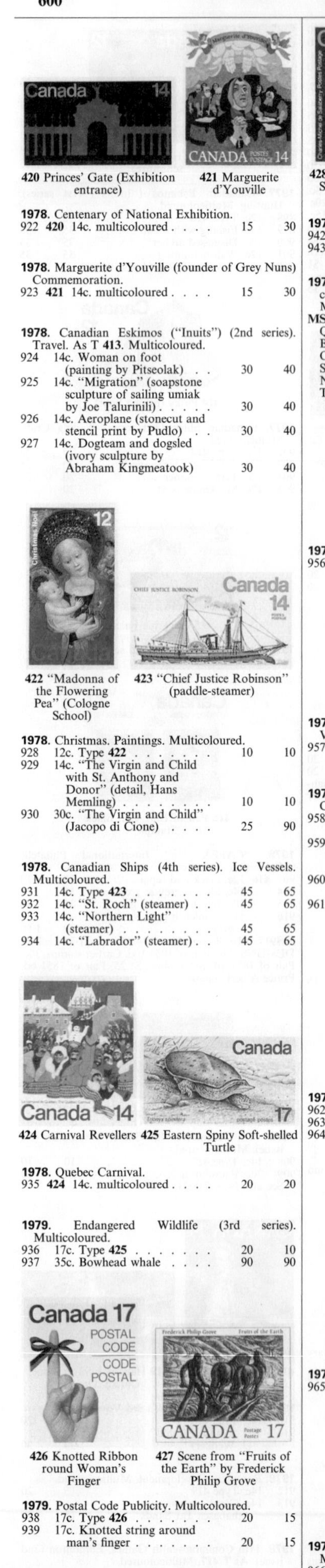

420 Princes' Gate (Exhibition entrance)
421 Marguerite d'Youville

1978. Centenary of National Exhibition.
922 **420** 14c. multicoloured 15 30

1978. Marguerite d'Youville (founder of Grey Nuns) Commemoration.
923 **421** 14c. multicoloured 15 30

1978. Canadian Eskimos ("Inuits") (2nd series). Travel. As T **413**. Multicoloured.
924 14c. Woman on foot (painting by Pitseolak) . . 30 40
925 14c. "Migration" (soapstone sculpture of sailing umiak by Joe Talurinili) 30 40
926 14c. Aeroplane (stonecut and stencil print by Pudlo) . . 30 40
927 14c. Dogteam and dogsled (ivory sculpture by Abraham Kingmeatook) 30 40

422 "Madonna of the Flowering Pea" (Cologne School)
423 "Chief Justice Robinson" (paddle-steamer)

1978. Christmas. Paintings. Multicoloured.
928 12c. Type **422** 10 10
929 14c. "The Virgin and Child with St. Anthony and Donor" (detail, Hans Memling) 10 10
930 30c. "The Virgin and Child" (Jacopo di Cione) 25 90

1978. Canadian Ships (4th series). Ice Vessels. Multicoloured.
931 14c. Type **423** 45 65
932 14c. "St. Roch" (steamer) . . 45 65
933 14c. "Northern Light" (steamer) 45 65
934 14c. "Labrador" (steamer) . . 45 65

424 Carnival Revellers
425 Eastern Spiny Soft-shelled Turtle

1978. Quebec Carnival.
935 **424** 14c. multicoloured 20 20

1979. Endangered Wildlife (3rd series). Multicoloured.
936 17c. Type **425** 20 10
937 35c. Bowhead whale 90 90

426 Knotted Ribbon round Woman's Finger
427 Scene from "Fruits of the Earth" by Frederick Philip Grove

1979. Postal Code Publicity. Multicoloured.
938 17c. Type **426** 20 15
939 17c. Knotted string around man's finger 20 15

1979. Canadian Writers (3rd series). Multicoloured.
940 17c. Type **427** 15 15
941 17c. Scene from "Le Vaisseau d'Or" by Emile Nelligan 15 15

428 Charles-Michel de Salaberry (military hero)
429 Ontario

1979. Famous Canadians. Multicoloured.
942 17c. Type **428** 25 15
943 17c. John By (engineer) . . . 25 15

1979. Canada Day. Flags. Sheet 128 × 140 mm containing T **429** and similar horiz designs. Multicoloured.
MS944 17c. × 12; Type **429**; Quebec; Nova Scotia; New Brunswick; Manitoba; British Columbia; Prince Edward Island; Saskatchewan; Alberta; Newfoundland; Northwest Territories; Yukon Territory 2·75 4·50

430 Paddling Kayak

1979. Canoe-Kayak Championships.
956 **430** 17c. multicoloured 15 30

431 Hockey Players

1979. Women's Field Hockey Championships, Vancouver.
957 **431** 17c. black, yellow and green 15 30

1979. Canadian Eskimos (3rd series). Shelter and the Community. As T **413**. Multicoloured.
958 17c. "Summer Tent" (print by Kiakshuk" 15 40
959 17c. "Five Eskimos building an Igloo" (soapstone sculpture by Abraham) . . 15 40
960 17c. "The Dance" (print by Kalvak) 15 40
961 17c. "Inuit drum dance" (soapstone sculptures by Madeleine Isserkut and Jean Mapsalak) 15 40

432 Toy Train

1979. Christmas. Multicoloured.
962 15c. Type **432** 10 10
963 17c. Hobby-horse 10 10
964 35c. Rag doll (vert) . . . . . 25 1·00

433 Child watering Tree of Life (painting by Marie-Annick Viatour)

1979. International Year of the Child.
965 **433** 17c. multicoloured 15 30

434 Canadair CL-215

1979. Canadian Aircraft (1st series). Flying Boats. Multicoloured.
966 17c. Type **434** 25 20
967 17c. Curtiss HS-2L 25 20
968 35c. Vickers Vedette 65 65
969 35c. Consolidated Canso . . . 65 65
See also Nos. 996/9, 1026/9 and 1050/3.

435 Map of Arctic Islands

1980. Centenary of Arctic Islands Acquisition.
970 **435** 17c. multicoloured 15 30

436 Skier

1980. Winter Olympic Games, Lake Placid.
971 **436** 35c. multicoloured 55 85

437 "A Meeting of the School Trustees" (Robert Harris)

1980. Centenary of Royal Canadian Academy of Arts. Multicoloured.
972 17c. Type **437** 25 20
973 17c. "Inspiration" (Philippe Hebert) 25 20
974 35c. "Sunrise on the Saguenay" (Lucius O'Brien) 50 55
975 35c. Thomas Fuller's design sketch for the original Parliament Buildings . . . 50 55

438 Canadian Whitefish
439 Garden Flowers

1980. Endangered Wildlife (4th series). Multicoloured.
976 17c. Type **438** 30 15
977 17c. Prairie chicken 30 15

1980. International Flower Show, Montreal.
978 **439** 17c. multicoloured 15 20

440 "Helping Hand"
441 Opening Bars of "O Canada"

1980. Rehabilitation.
979 **440** 17c. gold and blue 15 20

1980. Centenary of "O Canada" (national song). Multicoloured.
980 17c. Type **441** 15 15
981 17c. Calixa Lavallee (composer), Adolphe-Basile Routhier (original writer) and Robert Stanley Weir (writer of English version) 15 15

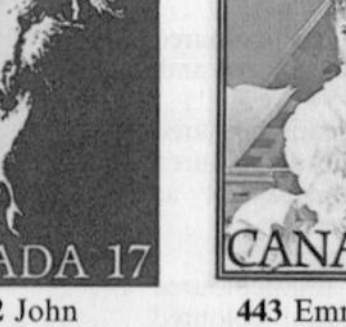

442 John G. Diefenbaker (statesman)
443 Emma Albani (singer)

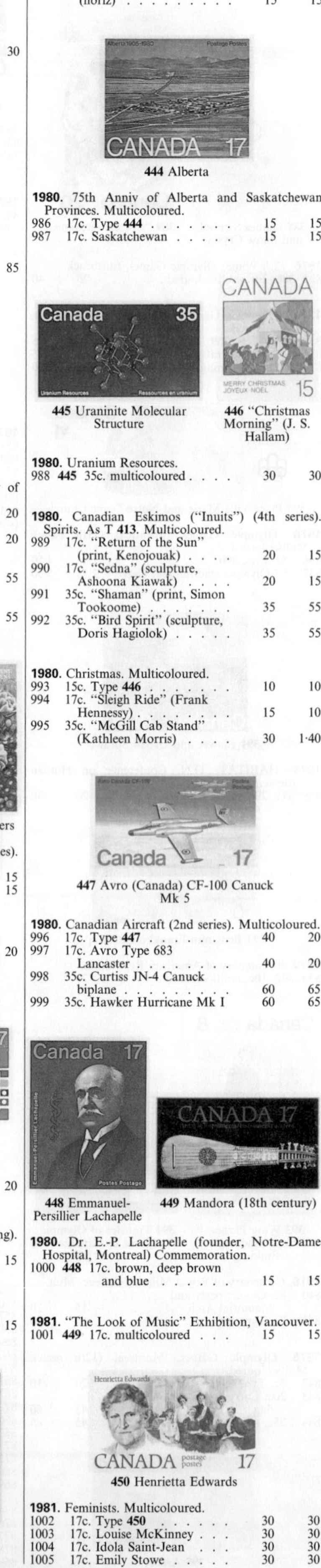

1980. John G. Diefenbaker Commemoration.
982 **442** 17c. blue 15 20

1980. Famous Canadians. Multicoloured.
983 17c. Type **443** 15 25
984 17c. Healey Willan (composer) 15 25
985 17c. Ned Hanlan (oarsman) (horiz) 15 15

444 Alberta

1980. 75th Anniv of Alberta and Saskatchewan Provinces. Multicoloured.
986 17c. Type **444** 15 15
987 17c. Saskatchewan 15 15

445 Uraninite Molecular Structure
446 "Christmas Morning" (J. S. Hallam)

1980. Uranium Resources.
988 **445** 35c. multicoloured 30 30

1980. Canadian Eskimos ("Inuits") (4th series). Spirits. As T **413**. Multicoloured.
989 17c. "Return of the Sun" (print, Kenojouak) 20 15
990 17c. "Sedna" (sculpture, Ashoona Kiawak) 20 15
991 35c. "Shaman" (print, Simon Tookoome) 35 55
992 35c. "Bird Spirit" (sculpture, Doris Hagiolok) 35 55

1980. Christmas. Multicoloured.
993 15c. Type **446** 10 10
994 17c. "Sleigh Ride" (Frank Hennessy) 15 10
995 35c. "McGill Cab Stand" (Kathleen Morris) . . . . 30 1·40

447 Avro (Canada) CF-100 Canuck Mk 5

1980. Canadian Aircraft (2nd series). Multicoloured.
996 17c. Type **447** 40 20
997 17c. Avro Type 683 Lancaster 40 20
998 35c. Curtiss JN-4 Canuck biplane 60 65
999 35c. Hawker Hurricane Mk I 60 65

448 Emmanuel-Persillier Lachapelle
449 Mandora (18th century)

1980. Dr. E.-P. Lachapelle (founder, Notre-Dame Hospital, Montreal) Commemoration.
1000 **448** 17c. brown, deep brown and blue 15 15

1981. "The Look of Music" Exhibition, Vancouver.
1001 **449** 17c. multicoloured 15 15

450 Henrietta Edwards

1981. Feminists. Multicoloured.
1002 17c. Type **450** 30 30
1003 17c. Louise McKinney . . . 30 30
1004 17c. Idola Saint-Jean 30 30
1005 17c. Emily Stowe 30 30

451 Vancouver Marmot

1981. Endangered Wildlife (5th series). Multicoloured.

1006	17c. Type **451**	15	10
1007	35c. American bison	35	30

452 Kateri Tekakwitha **453** "Self Portrait" (Frederick H. Varley)

1981. 17th-century Canadian Women. Statues by Emile Brunet.

1008 **452**	17c. brown and green	15	20
1009 –	17c. deep blue and blue	15	20

DESIGN: No. 1009, Marie de l'Incarnation

1981. Canadian Paintings. Multicoloured.

1010	17c. Type **453**	20	10
1011	17c. "At Baie Saint-Paul" (Marc-Aurele Fortin) (horiz)	20	10
1012	35c. "Untitled No 6" (Paul-Emile Borduas)	40	45

454 Canada in 1867

1981. Canada Day. Maps showing evolution of Canada from Confederation to present day. Multicoloured.

1013	17c. Type **454**	15	20
1014	17c. Canada in 1873	15	20
1015	17c. Canada in 1905	15	20
1016	17c. Canada since 1949	15	20

455 Frere Marie-Victorin **456** The Montreal Rose

1981. Canadian Botanists. Multicoloured.

1017	17c. Type **455**	20	30
1018	17c. John Macoun	20	30

1981. Montreal Flower Show.

1019 **456**	17c. multicoloured	15	20

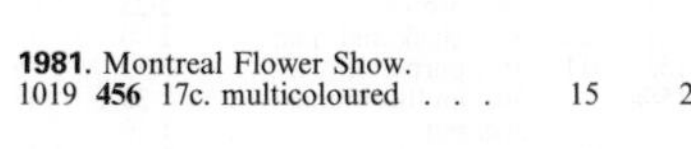

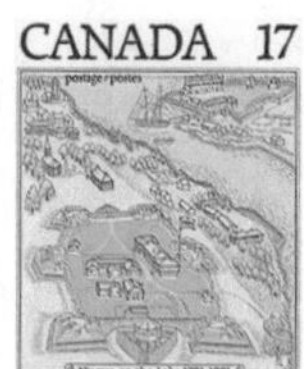
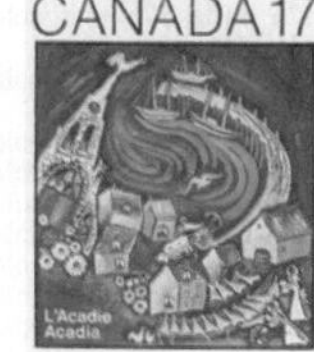

457 Drawing of Niagara-on-the-Lake **458** Acadian Community

1981. Bicentenary of Niagara-on-the-Lake (town).

1020 **457**	17c. multicoloured	15	20

1981. Centenary of First Acadia (community) Convention.

1021 **458**	17c. multicoloured	15	20

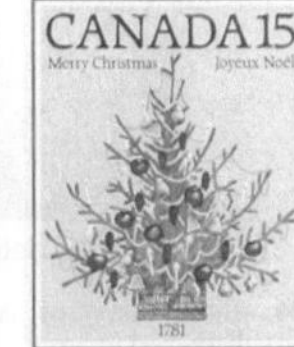

459 Aaron R. Mosher **460** Christmas Tree, 1781

1981. Birth Centenary of Aaron R. Mosher (founder of Canadian Labour Congress).

1022 **459**	17c. multicoloured	15	20

1981. Christmas. Bicentenary of First Illuminated Christmas Tree in Canada.

1023	15c. Type **460**	20	15
1024	15c. Christmas Tree, 1881	20	15
1025	15c. Christmas Tree, 1981	20	15

461 De Havilland Tiger Moth **462** Canadian Maple Leaf Emblem

1981. Canadian Aircraft (3rd series). Multicoloured.

1026	17c. Type **461**	20	15
1027	17c. Canadair CL-41 Tutor jet trainer	20	15
1028	35c. Avro (Canada) CF-102 jet airliner	35	40
1029	35c. De Havilland D.H.C.7 Dash 7	35	40

1981.

1030a **462**	A (30c.) red	20	25

No. 1030a was printed before a new first class domestic letter rate had been agreed, "A" representing the face value of the stamp, later decided to be 30c.

1982. As T **462** but including face values.

1033 **462**	5c. purple	10	20
1033d	8c. blue	1·75	2·50
1034	10c. green	1·50	2·25
1036	30c. red	35	30
1032	30c. red, grey and blue	30	45
1036b	32c. red	1·75	2·25
1032b	32c. red, brown and stone	45	45

463 1851 3d. Stamp

1982. "Canada 82" International Philatelic Youth Exhibition, Toronto. Stamps on Stamps. Mult.

1037	30c. Type **463**	30	30
1038	30c. 1908 Centenary of Quebec 15c. commemorative	30	30
1039	35c. 1935 10c. R.C.M.P	30	50
1040	35c. 1928 10c.	30	50
1041	60c. 1929 50c.	60	1·00
MS1042	159 × 108 mm. Nos. 1037/41	2·25	3·75

464 Jules Leger **465** Stylized drawing of Terry Fox

1982. Jules Leger (politician) Commemoration.

1043 **464**	30c. multicoloured	20	20

1982. Cancer victim Terry Fox's "Marathon of Hope" (Trans-Canada fund-raising run) Commemoration.

1044 **465**	30c. multicoloured	20	20

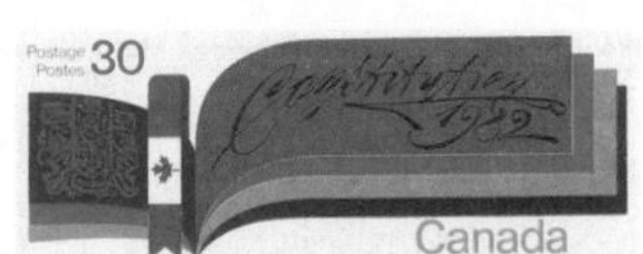

466 Stylized Open Book

1982. Patriation of Constitution.

1045 **466**	30c. multicoloured	20	20

467 Male and Female Salvationists with Street Scene

1982. Centenary of Salvation Army in Canada.

1046 **467**	30c. multicoloured	20	20

468 "The Highway near Kluane Lake" (Yukon Territory) (Jackson)

1982. Canada Day. Paintings of Canadian Landscapes. Sheet 139 × 139 mm, containing T **468** and similar horiz designs. Multicoloured.

MS1047	30c. × 12, Type **468**; "Street Scene, Montreal" (Quebec) (Hébert); "Breakwater" (Newfoundland) (Pratt); "Along Great Slave Lake" (Northwest Territories) (Richard); "Till Hill" (Prince Edward Island) (Lamb); "Family and Rainstorm" (Nova Scotia) (Colville); "Brown Shadows" (Saskatchewan) (Knowles); "The Red Brick House" (Ontario) (Milne); "Campus Gates" (New Brunswick) (Bobak); "Prairie Town—Early Morning" (Alberta) (Kerr); "Totems at Ninstints" (British Columbia) (Plaskett); "Doc Snider's House" (Manitoba) (FitzGerald)	4·75	6·50

469 Regina Legislative Building

1982. Centenary of Regina.

1048 **469**	30c. multicoloured	20	20

470 Finish of Race

1982. Centenary of Royal Canadian Henley Regatta.

1049 **470**	30c. multicoloured	20	25

471 Fairchild FC-2W1

1982. Canadian Aircraft (4th series). Bush Aircraft. Multicoloured.

1050	30c. Type **471**	35	20
1051	30c. De Havilland D.H.C.2 Beaver	35	20
1052	60c. Fokker Super Universal	65	85
1053	60c. Noorduyn Norseman	65	85

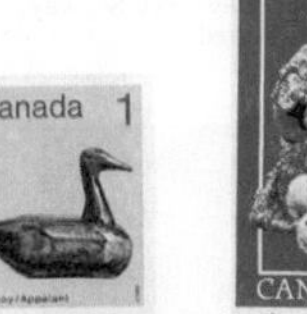

472 Decoy **475** Mary, Joseph and Baby Jesus

1982. Heritage Artefacts.

1054 **472**	1c. black, lt brn and brn	10	10
1055 –	2c. black, blue and green	10	10
1056 –	3c. black and deep blue	10	10
1057 –	5c. black, pink and brown	10	10
1058 –	10c. black, blue & turq	10	10
1059 –	20c. black, lt brn & brn	20	10
1060 –	25c. multicoloured	60	10
1061 –	37c. black, grn & dp grn	60	50
1062 –	39c. black, grey and violet	1·75	1·50
1063 –	42c. multicoloured	1·50	15
1064 –	48c. dp brn, brn & pink	70	40
1065 –	50c. black, lt blue & blue	1·75	20
1066 –	55c. multicoloured	1·25	30
1067 –	64c. dp grey, blk & grey	80	35
1068 –	68c. black, lt brn & brn	1·75	50
1069 –	72c. multicoloured	1·25	35

DESIGNS—VERT: 2c. Fishing spear; 3c. Stable lantern; 5c. Bucket; 10c. Weathercock; 20c. Skates; 25c. Butter stamp. HORIZ: 37c. Plough; 39c. Settle-bed; 42c. Linen chest; 48c. Cradle; 50c. Sleigh; 55c. Iron kettle; 64c. Kitchen stove; 68c. Spinning wheel; 72c. Hand-drawn cart.

1982. Christmas. Nativity Scenes.

1080	30c. Type **475**	20	10
1081	35c. The Shepherds	25	60
1082	60c. The Three Wise Men	45	1·50

476 Globes forming Symbolic Designs **478** Scene from Novel "Angeline de Montbrun" by "Laure Conan" (Felicite Angers)

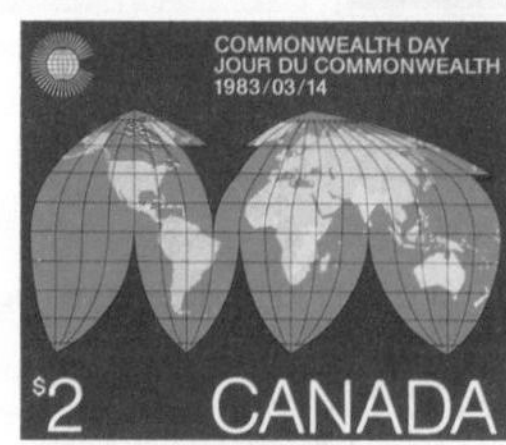

477 Map of World showing Canada

1983. World Communications Year.

1083 **476**	32c. multicoloured	30	30

1983. Commonwealth Day.

1084 **477**	$2 multicoloured	2·00	3·25

1983. Canadian Writers (4th series).

1085	32c. Type **478**	40	90
1086	32c. Woodcut illustrating "Sea-gulls" (poem by E. J. Pratt)	40	90

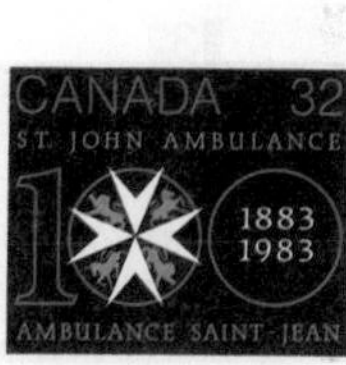

479 St. John Ambulance Badge and "100" **480** Victory Pictogram

1983. Centenary of St. John Ambulance in Canada.

1087 **479**	32c. red, yellow and brown	30	30

1983. "Universiade 83" World University Games, Edmonton.

1088 **480**	32c. multicoloured	25	15
1089	64c. multicoloured	50	70

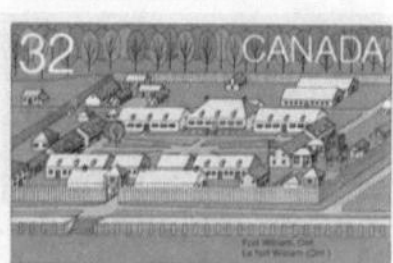

481 Fort William, Ontario

1983. Canada Day. Forts (1st series). Multicoloured.

1090	32c. Fort Henry, Ontario (44 × 22 mm)	65	80
1091	32c. Type **481**	65	80
1092	32c. Fort Rodd Hill, British Columbia	55	75
1093	32c. Fort Wellington, Ontario (28 × 22 mm)	55	75
1094	32c. Fort Prince of Wales, Manitoba (28 × 22 mm)	55	75
1095	32c. Halifax Citadel, Nova Scotia (44 × 22 mm)	55	75
1096	32c. Fort Chambly, Quebec	55	75
1097	32c. Fort No. 1, Point Levis, Quebec	55	75
1098	32c. Coteau-du-Lac Fort, Quebec (28 × 22 mm)	55	75
1099	32c. Fort Beausejour, New Brunswick (28 × 22 mm)	65	80

See also Nos. 1163/72.

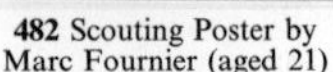

482 Scouting Poster by Marc Fournier (aged 21)

483 Cross Symbol

1983. Scouting in Canada (75th Anniv) and 15th World Scout Jamboree, Alberta.
1100 **482** 32c. multicoloured . . . 30 30

1983. 6th Assembly of the World Council of Churches, Vancouver.
1101 **483** 32c. green and lilac . . . 30 20

484 Sir Humphrey Gilbert (founder)

485 "NICKEL" Deposits

1983. 400th Anniv of Newfoundland.
1102 **484** 32c. multicoloured . . . 30 30

1983. Cent of Discovery of Sudbury Nickel Deposits.
1103 **485** 32c. multicoloured . . . 30 30

486 Josiah Henson and Escaping Slaves

1983. 19th-century Social Reformers. Multicoloured.
1104 32c. Type **486** 35 50
1105 32c. Father Antoine Labelle and rural village (32 × 26 mm) 35 50

487 Robert Stephenson's Locomotive "Dorchester", 1836

1983. Railway Locomotives (1st series). Mult.
1106 32c. Type **487** . . . . . . 90 1·00
1107 32c. Locomotive "Toronto", 1853 . . . . 90 1·00
1108 37c. Timothy Hackworth's locomotive "Samson", 1838 . . . . 90 1·00
1109 64c. Western Canadian Railway locomotive "Adam Brown", 1855 . . 1·40 2·25
See also Nos. 1132/5, 1185/8 and 1223/6.

488 School Coat of Arms

1983. Centenary of Dalhousie Law School.
1110 **488** 32c. multicoloured . . . 30 40

489 City Church

1983. Christmas. Churches. Multicoloured.
1111 32c. Type **489** 30 10
1112 37c. Family walking to church 40 90
1113 64c. Country chapel . . . . 1·00 2·00

490 Royal Canadian Regiment and British Columbia Regiment

491 Gold Mine in Prospecting Pan

1983. Canadian Army Regiments. Multicoloured.
1114 32c. Type **490** . . . . . . 75 1·25
1115 32c. Royal Winnipeg Rifles and Royal Canadian Dragoons . . . . 75 1·25

1984. 50th Anniv of Yellowknife.
1116 **491** 32c. multicoloured . . . 30 30

492 Montreal Symphony Orchestra

1983. 50th Anniv of Montreal Symphony Orchestra.
1117 **492** 32c. multicoloured . . . 35 30

493 Jacques Cartier

494 U.S.C.S. "Eagle"

1984. 450th Anniv of Jacques Cartier's Voyage to Canada.
1118 **493** 32c. multicoloured . . . 40 30

1984. Tall Ships Visit.
1119 **494** 32c. multicoloured . . . 35 30

495 Service Medal

496 Oared Galleys

1984. 75th Anniv of Canadian Red Cross Society.
1120 **495** 32c. multicoloured . . . 35 40

1984. Bicentenary of New Brunswick.
1121 **496** 32c. multicoloured . . . 35 30

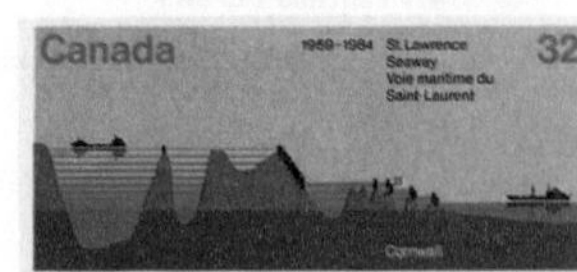

497 St. Lawrence Seaway

1984. 25th Anniv of St. Lawrence Seaway.
1122 **497** 32c. multicoloured . . . 45 30

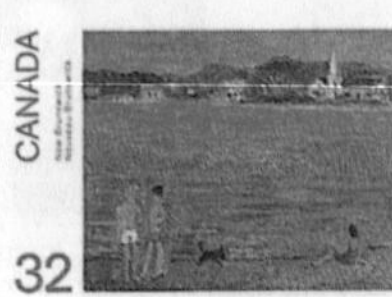

498 New Brunswick

1984. Canada Day. Paintings by Jean Paul Lemieux. Sheet 138 × 122 mm, containing T **498** and similar multicoloured designs.
MS1123 32c. × 12, Type **498**; British Columbia; Northwest Territories; Quebec; Manitoba; Alberta; Prince Edward Island; Saskatchewan; Nova Scotia (vert); Yukon Territory, Newfoundland; Ontario (vert) . . . . 6·50 7·50
The captions on the Northwest Territories and Yukon Territory paintings were transposed at the design stage.

499 Loyalists of 1784

1984. Bicentenary of Arrival of United Empire Loyalists.
1124 **499** 32c. multicoloured . . . 30 30

500 St. John's Basilica

501 Coat of Arms of Pope John Paul II

1984. Bicentenary of Roman Catholic Church in Newfoundland.
1125 **500** 32c. multicoloured . . . 30 25

1984. Papal Visit.
1126 **501** 32c. multicoloured . . . 40 20
1127 64c. multicoloured . . . 85 1·10

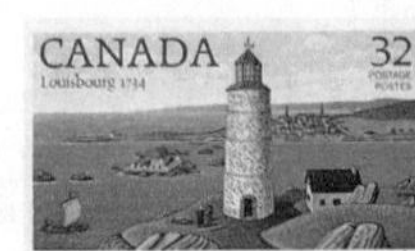

502 Louisbourg Lighthouse, 1734

1984. Canadian Lighthouse (1st series). Mult.
1128 32c. Type **502** . . . . . . 1·75 1·75
1129 32c. Fisgard Lighthouse, 1860 . . . . 1·75 1·75
1130 32c. Ile Verte Lighthouse, 1809 . . . . 1·75 1·75
1131 32c. Gibraltar Point Lighthouse, 1808 . . . . 1·75 1·75
See also Nos. 1176/9.

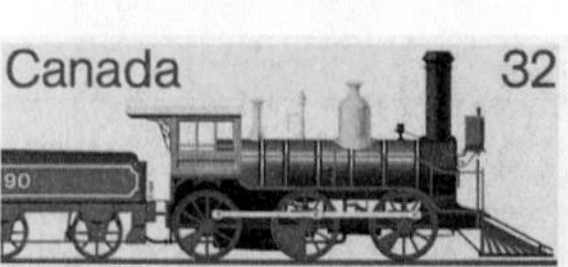

503 Great Western Railway Locomotive "Scotia", 1860

1984. Railway Locomotives (2nd series). Mult.
1132 32c. Type **503** . . . . . . 1·40 1·40
1133 32c. Northern Pacific Railroad locomotive "Countess of Dufferin", 1872 . . . . 1·40 1·40
1134 37c. Grand Trunk Railway Class E3 locomotive, 1886 1·40 1·60
1135 64c. Canadian Pacific Class D10a steam locomotive 2·00 2·75
MS1136 153 × 104 mm. As Nos. 1132/5, but with background colour changed from green to blue 5·50 7·00
No. **MS**1136 commemorates "CANADA '84" National Stamp Exhibition, Montreal.
See also Nos. 1185/8 and 1223/6.

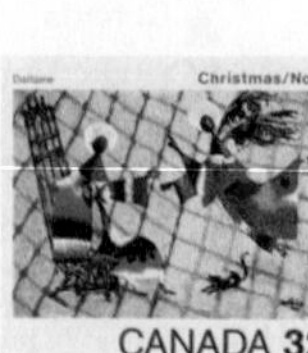

504 "The Annunciation" (Jean Dallaire)

505 Pilots of 1914–18, 1939–45 and 1984

1984. Christmas. Religious Paintings. Multicoloured.
1137 32c. Type **504** 40 10
1138 37c. "The Three Kings" (Simone Bouchard) . . . 70 1·00
1139 64c. "Snow in Bethlehem" (David Milne) . . . . . 90 1·75

1984. 60th Anniv of Royal Canadian Air Force.
1140 **505** 32c. multicoloured . . . 35 30

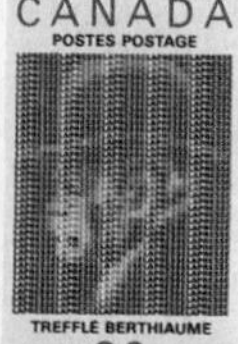

506 Treffle Berthiaume (editor)

508 Astronaut in Space, and Planet Earth

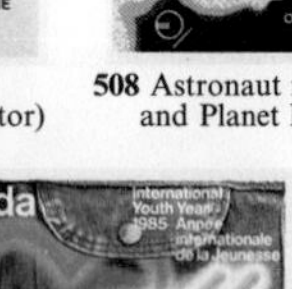

507 Heart and Arrow

1984. Centenary of "La Presse" (newspaper).
1141 **506** 32c. brown, red & lt brn 35 30

1985. International Youth Year.
1142 **507** 32c. multicoloured . . . 30 30

1985. Canadian Space Programme.
1143 **508** 32c. multicoloured . . . 40 30

509 Emily Murphy

1985. Women's Rights Activists. Multicoloured.
1144 32c. Type **509** 40 90
1145 32c. Therese Casgrain . . . 40 90

510 Gabriel Dumont (Metis leader) and Battle of Batoche, 1885

1985. Centenary of the North-West Rebellion.
1146 **510** 32c. blue, red and grey 30 30

511 Rear View, Parliament Building, Ottawa

512 Queen Elizabeth II

512a Queen Elizabeth II in 1984 (from photo by Karsh)

1985.

1147b	–	1c. green	70	80
1148	–	2c. green	20	1·00
1149	–	5c. brown	40	1·10
1150a	–	6c. brown	50	30
1150b	–	6c. purple	1·75	1·00
1151	**511**	34c. black	1·75	2·00
1155		34c. multicoloured . .	60	10
1158		34c. brown	2·25	3·00
1161	**512**	34c. black and blue . .	1·00	30
1152	**511**	36c. purple	3·75	3·75
1156a		36c. multicoloured . .	30	45
1159		36c. red	1·50	55
1162	**512**	36c. purple	2·75	1·10
1153	**511**	37c. blue	1·25	30
1157	–	37c. multicoloured . .	85	10
1162a	**512a**	37c. multicoloured . .	2·75	10
1154	**511**	38c. blue	2·25	1·25
1157c	–	38c. multicoloured . .	50	10
1160b	**511**	38c. green	50	30
1162b	**512a**	38c. multicoloured . .	55	20
1162c		39c. multicoloured . .	1·00	20
1162d		40c. multicoloured . .	1·00	20
1162e		42c. multicoloured . .	1·00	40
1162f		43c. multicoloured . .	1·25	65
1162g		45c. multicoloured . .	1·50	80
1162h		46c. multicoloured . .	50	45
1162i		47c. multicoloured . .	50	45

DESIGNS: 1, 5, 6c. (1150b) East Block, Parliament Building; 2, 6c. (1150a) West Block, Parliament Building; 37c. (1157) Front view, Parliament Building; 38c. (1157c) Side view, Parliament Building.

1985. Canada Day. Forts (2nd series). As T **481**. Multicoloured.
1163 34c. Lower Fort Garry, Manitoba 50 60
1164 34c. Fort Anne, Nova Scotia 50 60

1165 34c. Fort York, Ontario . . 50 60
1166 34c. Castle Hill, Newfoundland 50 60
1167 34c. Fort Whoop Up, Alberta 50 60
1168 34c. Fort Erie, Ontario . . 50 60
1169 34c. Fort Walsh, Saskatchewan 50 60
1170 34c. Fort Lennox, Quebec 50 60
1171 34c. York Redoubt, Nova Scotia 50 60
1172 34c. Fort Frederick, Ontario 50 60

Nos. 1163 and 1168 measure 44 × 22 mm and Nos. 1166/7 and 1171/2 28 × 22 mm.

513 Louis Hebert (apothecary)

514 Parliament Buildings and Map of World

1985. 45th International Pharmaceutical Sciences Congress of Pharmaceutical Federation, Montreal.
1173 **513** 34c. multicoloured . . . 45 35

1985. 74th Conference of Inter-Parliamentary Union, Ottawa.
1174 **514** 34c. multicoloured . . . 45 35

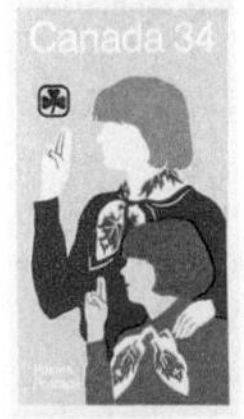

515 Guide and Brownie Saluting

516 Sisters Islets Lighthouse

1985. 75th Anniv of Girl Guide Movement.
1175 **515** 34c. multicoloured . . . 45 35

1985. Canadian Lighthouses (2nd series). Multicoloured.
1176 34c. Type **516** . . . . . . 2·00 2·00
1177 34c. Pelee Passage Lighthouse . . . . 2·00 2·00
1178 34c. Haut-fond Prince Lighthouse . . . . 2·00 2·00
1179 34c. Rose Blanche Lighthouse, Cains Island 2·00 2·00
MS1180 190 × 90 mm. Nos. 1176/9 7·50 8·00

No. **MS**1180 publicises "Capex 87" International Stamp Exhibition, Toronto.

517 Santa Claus in Reindeer-drawn Sleigh

518 Naval Personnel of 1910, 1939–45 and 1985

1985. Christmas. Santa Claus Parade. Multicoloured.
1181 32c. Canada Post's parade float . . . . 80 1·10
1182 34c. Type **517** 70 20
1183 39c. Acrobats and horse-drawn carriage . . . . . 80 1·25
1184 68c. Christmas tree, pudding and goose on float . . . 1·75 2·25

1985. Steam Railway Locomotives (3rd series). As T **503**. Multicoloured.
1185 34c. Grand Trunk Railway Class K2 . . . . 1·00 1·40
1186 34c. Canadian Pacific Class P2a . . . . 1·00 1·40
1187 39c. Canadian Northern Class O10a . . . . 1·25 1·50
1188 68c. Canadian Govt Railway Class H4D . . . 2·00 2·50

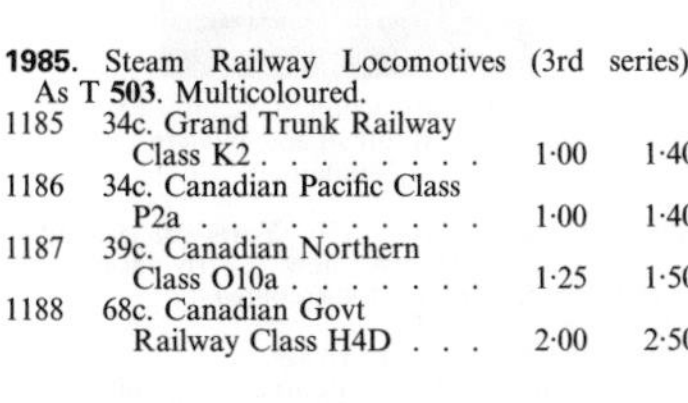

1985. 75th Anniv of Royal Canadian Navy.
1189 **518** 34c. multicoloured . . . 65 65

519 "The Old Holton House, Montreal" (James Wilson Morrice)

1985. 125th Anniv of Montreal Museum of Fine Arts.
1190 **519** 34c. multicoloured . . . 40 50

520 Map of Alberta showing Olympic Sites

1986. Winter Olympic Games, Calgary (1988) (1st issue).
1191 **520** 34c. multicoloured . . . 40 50

See also Nos. 1216/17, 1236/7, 1258/9 and 1281/4.

521 Canada Pavilion

1986. "Expo '86" World Fair, Vancouver (1st issue). Multicoloured.
1192 34p. Type **521** . . . . . . 1·25 50
1193 39p. Early telephone, dish aerial and satellite . . . . 2·00 2·75

See also Nos. 1196/7.

522 Molly Brant

523 Aubert de Gaspe and Scene from "Les Anciens Canadiens"

1986. 250th Birth Anniv of Molly Brant (Iroquois leader)
1194 **522** 34c. multicoloured . . . 40 50

1986. Birth Bicentenary of Philippe Aubert de Gaspe (author).
1195 **523** 34c. multicoloured . . . 40 50

1986. "Expo '86" World Fair, Vancouver (2nd issue). As T **521**. Multicoloured.
1196 34c. Expo Centre, Vancouver (vert) 70 50
1197 68c. Early and modern trains . . . . 1·40 2·75

524 Canadian Field Post Office and Cancellation, 1944

1986. 75th Anniv of Canadian Forces Postal Service.
1198 **524** 34c. multicoloured . . . 85 60

525 Great Blue Heron

526 Railway Rotary Snowplough

1986. Birds of Canada. Multicoloured.
1199 34c. Type **525** . . . . . . 1·50 1·75
1200 34c. Snow goose . . . . . 1·50 1·75
1201 34c. Great horned owl . . . 1·50 1·75
1202 34c. Spruce grouse . . . . 1·50 1·75

1986. Canada Day. Science and Technology. Canadian Inventions (1st series). Multicoloured.
1203 34c. Type **526** . . . . . . 1·10 1·75
1204 34c. Space shuttle "Challenger" launching satellite with Canadarm 1·10 1·75
1205 34c. Pilot wearing anti-gravity flight suit and Supermarine Spitfire . . . 1·10 1·75
1206 34c. Variable-pitch propeller and Avro 504 airplane . . 1·10 1·75

See also Nos. 1241/4 and 1292/5.

527 C.B.C. Logos over Map of Canada

1986. 50th Anniv of Canadian Broadcasting Corporation.
1207 **527** 34c. multicoloured . . . 40 50

528 Ice Age Artefacts, Tools and Settlement

1986. Exploration of Canada (1st series). Discoverers. Multicoloured.
1208 34c. Type **528** . . . . . . 1·25 1·75
1209 34c. Viking ships . . . . . 1·25 1·75
1210 34c. John Cabot's "Matthew", 1497, compass and Arctic char (fish) . . . . 1·25 1·75
1211 34c. Henry Hudson cast adrift, 1611 . . . . 1·25 1·75
MS1212 119 × 84 mm. Nos. 1208/11 5·50 6·50

No. **MS**1212 publicises "Capex '87" International Stamp Exhibition, Toronto.

See also Nos. 1232/5, 1285/8 and 1319/22.

529 Crowfoot (Blackfoot Chief) and Indian Village

1986. Founders of the Canadian West. Multicoloured.
1213 34c. Type **529** 70 90
1214 34c. James Macleod of the North West Mounted Police and Fort Macleod 70 90

530 Peace Dove and Globe

1986. International Peace Year.
1215 **530** 34c. multicoloured . . . 60 60

531 Ice Hockey

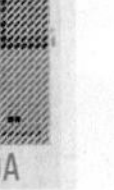

532 Angel with Crown

1986. Winter Olympic Games, Calgary (1988) (2nd issue). Multicoloured.
1216 34c. Type **531** . . . . . . 1·50 1·50
1217 34c. Biathlon . . . . 1·50 1·50

1986. Christmas. Multicoloured.
1218 29c. Angel singing carol (36 × 22 mm) 65 35
1219 34c. Type **532** 60 25
1220 39c. Angel playing lute . . . 1·00 1·60
1221 68c. Angel with ribbon . . . 1·50 2·75

533 John Molson with Theatre Royal, Montreal, "Accomodation" (paddle-steamer) and Railway Train

1986. 150th Death Anniv of John Molson (businessman).
1222 **533** 34c. multicoloured . . . 1·00 50

1986. Railway Locomotives (4th series). As T **503** but size 60 × 22 mm. Multicoloured.
1223 34c. Canadian National Class V-1-a diesel locomotive No. 9000 . . 1·75 1·75
1224 34c. Canadian Pacific Class T1a steam locomotive No. 9000 . . . . 1·75 1·75
1225 39c. Canadian National Class U-2-a steam locomotive . . . . 1·75 1·00
1226 68c. Canadian Pacific Class H1c steam locomotive No. 2850 . . . . 2·50 3·25

534 Toronto's First Post Office

1987. "Capex '87" International Stamp Exhibition, Toronto. Post Offices.
1227 34c. Type **534** 60 20
1228 36c. Nelson-Miramichi, New Brunswick 65 45
1229 42c. Saint-Ours, Quebec . . 70 65
1230 72c. Battleford, Saskatchewan . . . . . . 1·00 1·25
MS1231 155 × 92 mm. 36c. As No. 1227 and Nos. 1228/30, but main inscr in green . . . . . 3·25 2·75

535 Etienne Brule exploring Lake Superior

1987. Exploration of Canada (2nd series). Pioneers of New France. Multicoloured.
1232 34c. Type **535** . . . . . . 1·10 1·40
1233 34c. Radisson and Des Groseilliers with British and French flags . . . . 1·10 1·40
1234 34c. Jolliet and Father Marquette on the Mississippi . . . . 1·10 1·40
1235 34c. Jesuit missionary preaching to Indians . . . 1·10 1·40

1987. Winter Olympic Games, Calgary (1988) (3rd issue). As T **531**. Multicoloured.
1236 36c. Speed skating 50 40
1237 42c. Bobsleighing 75 60

536 Volunteer Activities

1987. National Volunteer Week.
1238 **536** 36c. multicoloured . . . 30 35

537 Canadian Coat of Arms

539 R. A. Fessenden (AM Radio)

538 Steel Girder, Gear Wheel and Microchip

1987. 5th Anniv of Canadian Charter of Rights and Freedoms.
1239 **537** 36c. multicoloured . . . 65 35

1987. Centenary of Engineering Institute of Canada.
1240 **538** 36c. multicoloured . . . 65 40

1987. Canada Day. Science and Technology. Canadian Inventors (2nd series). Multicoloured.
1241 36c. Type **539** . . . . . . 1·10 1·40
1242 36c. C. Fenerty (newsprint pulp) . . . . 1·10 1·40
1243 36c. G.-E. Desbarats and W. Leggo (half-tone engraving) . . . . 1·10 1·40
1244 36c. F. N. Gisborne (first North American undersea telegraph) . . . . 1·10 1·40

540 "Segwun"

1987. Canadian Steamships. Multicoloured.
1245 36c. Type **540** . . . . . . 1·75 2·50
1246 36c. "Princess Marguerite" (52 × 22 mm) . . . . . . 1·75 2·50

541 Figurehead from "Hamilton", 1813

1987. Historic Shipwrecks. Multicoloured.
1247 36c. Type **541** . . . . . . 1·00 1·40
1248 36c. Hull of "San Juan", 1565 . . . . 1·00 1·40
1249 36c. Wheel from "Breadalbane", 1853 . . . 1·00 1·40
1250 36c. Bell from "Ericsson", 1892 . . . . 1·00 1·40

542 Air Canada Boeing 767-200 and Globe

543 Summit Symbol

1987. 50th Anniv of Air Canada.
1251 **542** 36c. multicoloured . . . 1·00 35

1987. 2nd Int Francophone Summit, Quebec.
1252 **543** 36c. multicoloured . . . 30 35

544 Commonwealth Symbol

545 Poinsettia

1987. Commonwealth Heads of Government Meeting, Vancouver.
1253 **544** 36c. multicoloured . . . 35 40

1987. Christmas. Christmas Plants. Multicoloured.
1254 31c. Decorated Christmas tree and presents (36 × 20 mm) 60 35
1255 36c. Type **545** 40 40
1256 42c. Holly wreath 85 50
1257 72c. Mistletoe and decorated tree . . . . 1·10 80

1987. Winter Olympic Games, Calgary (1988) (4th issue). As T **531**. Multicoloured.
1258 36c. Cross-country skiing . . 75 75
1259 36c. Ski-jumping 75 75

546 Football, Grey Cup and Spectators

547 Flying Squirrel

548a Runnymede Library, Toronto

1987. 75th Grey Cup Final (Canadian football championship), Vancouver.
1260 **546** 36c. multicoloured . . . 35 40

1988. Canadian Mammals and Architecture. Multicoloured. (a) As T **547**.
1261 1c. Type **547** 10 10
1262 2c. Porcupine 10 10
1263 3c. Muskrat 10 10
1264 5c. Varying hare 10 10
1265 6c. Red fox 10 10
1266 10c. Striped skunk 10 10
1267 25c. American beaver . . . 30 15
1268 43c. Lynx (26 × 20 mm) . . 1·40 30
1269 44c. Walrus (27 × 21 mm) 1·40 20
1270 45c. Pronghorn (27 × 21 mm) 40 40
1270c 46c. Wolverine (27 × 21 mm) . . . . . 1·25 75
1271 57c. Killer whale (26 × 20 mm) . . . . . 2·00 55
1272 59c. Musk ox (27 × 21 mm) 2·75 1·50
1273 61c. Wolf (27 × 21 mm) . . 60 1·00
1273b 63c. Harbour porpoise (27 × 21 mm) . . . . . 1·50 1·75
1274 74c. Wapiti (26 × 20 mm) 1·60 50
1275 76c. Brown bear (27 × 21 mm) . . . . . 1·00 50
1276 78c. White whale (27 × 21 mm) . . . . . 1·00 55
1276c 80c. Peary caribou (27 × 21 mm) . . . . . 1·00 60

(b) As T **548a**.
1277 $1 Type **548a** . . . . 1·25 30
1278 $2 McAdam Railway Station, New Brunswick 2·00 50
1279 $5 Bonsecours Market, Montreal . . . . 4·75 4·00

1988. Winter Olympic Games, Calgary (5th issue). As T **531**. Multicoloured.
1281 37c. Slalom skiing 85 50
1282 37c. Curling 85 50
1283 43c. Figure skating 85 45
1284 74c. Luge . . . . 1·40 80

549 Trade Goods, Blackfoot Encampment and Page from Anthony Henday's Journal

1988. Exploration of Canada (3rd series). Explorers of the West. Multicoloured.
1285 37c. Type **549** . . . . . . 1·00 70
1286 37c. Discovery and map of George Vancouver's voyage . . . . 1·00 70
1287 37c. Simon Fraser's expedition portaging canoes . . . . 1·00 70
1288 37c. John Palliser's surveying equipment and view of prairie . . . . . 1·00 70

550 "The Young Reader" (Ozias Leduc)

1988. Canadian Art (1st series).
1289 **550** 50c. multicoloured . . . 70 70
See also Nos. 1327, 1384, 1421, 1504, 1539, 1589, 1629, 1681, 1721, 1825, 1912, 2011, 2097 and 2133.

551 Mallard landing on Marsh

552 Kerosene Lamp and Diagram of Distillation Plant

1988. Wildlife and Habitat Conservation. Mult.
1290 37c. Type **551** . . . . . . 1·00 50
1291 37c. Moose feeding in marsh 1·00 50

1988. Canada Day. Science and Technology. Canadian Inventions (3rd series). Multicoloured.
1292 37c. Type **552** . . . . . . 75 1·00
1293 37c. Ears of Marquis wheat 75 1·00
1294 37c. Electron microscope and magnified image . . . 75 1·00
1295 37c. Patient under "Cobalt 60" cancer therapy . . . 75 1·00

553 "Papilio brevicauda"

1988. Canadian Butterflies. Multicoloured.
1296 37c. Type **553** 80 90
1297 37c. "Lycaeides idas" . . . 80 90
1298 37c. "Oeneis macounii" . . 80 90
1299 37c. "Papilio glaucus" . . . 80 90

554 St. John's Harbour Entrance and Skyline

1988. Centenary of Incorporation of St. John's, Newfoundland.
1300 **554** 37c. multicoloured . . . 35 40

555 Club Members working on Forestry Project and Rural Scene

1988. 75th Anniv of 4-H Clubs.
1301 **555** 37c. multicoloured . . . 35 40

556 Saint-Maurice Ironworks

557 Tahltan Bear Dog

1988. 250th Anniv of Saint-Maurice Ironworks, Quebec.
1302 **556** 37c. black, orange & brn 40 40

1988. Canadian Dogs. Multicoloured.
1303 37c. Type **557** . . . . . . 1·00 1·25
1304 37c. Nova Scotia duck tolling retriever . . . . . 1·00 1·25
1305 37c. Canadian eskimo dog 1·00 1·25
1306 37c. Newfoundland . . . . 1·00 1·25

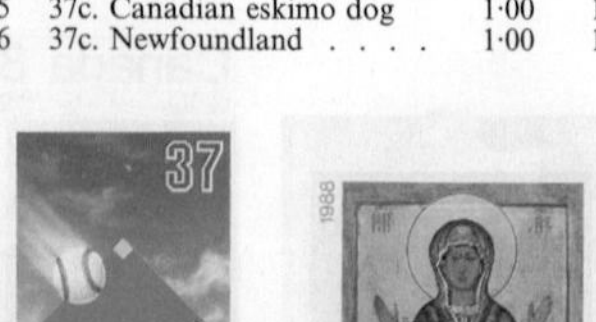

558 Baseball, Glove and Pitch

559 Virgin with Inset of Holy Child

1988. 150th Anniv of Baseball in Canada. Multicoloured.
1307 **558** 37c. multicoloured . . . 35 40

1988. Christmas. Icons. Multicoloured.
1308 32c. Holy Family (36 × 21 mm) 45 35
1309 37c. Type **559** 45 40
1310 43c. Virgin and Child . . . 50 45
1311 74c. Virgin and Child (different) 90 75

On No. 1308 the left-hand third of the design area is taken up by the bar code.
No. 1309 also commemorates the millennium of Ukrainian Christianity.

560 Bishop Inglis and Nova Scotia Church

1988. Bicentenary of Consecration of Charles Inglis (first Canadian Anglican bishop) (1987).
1312 **560** 37c. multicoloured . . . 35 40

561 Frances Ann Hopkins and "Canoe manned by Voyageurs"

1988. 150th Birth Anniv of Frances Anne Hopkins (artist).
1313 **561** 37c. multicoloured . . . 35 40

562 Angus Walters and "Bluenose" (yacht)

563 Chipewyan Canoe

1988. 20th Death Anniv of Angus Walters (yachtsman).
1314 **562** 37c. multicoloured . . . 40 40

1989. Small Craft of Canada (1st series). Native Canoes. Multicoloured.
1315 38c. Type **563** 85 70
1316 38c. Haida canoe 85 70
1317 38c. Inuit kayak 85 70
1318 38c. Micmac canoe 85 70
See also Nos. 1377/80 and 1428/31.

564 Matonabbee and Hearne's Expedition

1989. Exploration of Canada (4th issue). Explorers of the North. Multicoloured.
1319 38c. Type **564** . . . . . . 1·10 75
1320 38c. Relics of Franklin's expedition and White Ensign . . . . 1·10 75
1321 38c. Joseph Tyrell's compass, hammer and fossil . . . . 1·10 75
1322 38c. Vilhjalmur Stefansson, camera on tripod and sledge dog team . . . . . 1·10 75

565 Construction of Victoria Bridge, Montreal and William Notman

1989. Canada Day. "150 Years of Canadian Photography". Designs showing early photographs and photographers. Multicoloured.
1323 38c. Type **565** 60 60
1324 38c. Plains Indian village and W. Hanson Boorne 60 60
1325 38c. Horse-drawn sleigh and Alexander Henderson . . 60 60
1326 38c. Quebec street scene and Jules-Ernest Livernois . . 60 60

566 Tsimshian Ceremonial Frontlet, c. 1900

1989. Canadian Art (2nd series).
1327 **566** 50c. multicoloured . . . 80 60

567 Canadian Flag and Forest

1989. Self-adhesive. Multicoloured.

1328	38c. Type **567**	1·50	2·00
1328b	39c. Canadian flag and prairie	1·50	2·25
1328c	40c. Canadian flag and sea	1·25	1·25
1328d	42c. Canadian flag over mountains	2·00	2·50
1328e	43c. Canadian flag over lake	1·40	1·75

568 Archibald Lampman **569** "Clavulinopsis fusiformis"

1989. Canadian Poets. Multicoloured.

1329	38c. Type **568**	50	50
1330	38c. Louis-Honore Frechette	50	50

1989. Mushrooms. Multicoloured.

1331	38c. Type **569**	70	90
1332	38c. "Boletus mirabilis" . .	70	90
1333	38c. "Cantharellus cinnabarinus"	70	90
1334	38c. "Morchella esculenta"	70	90

570 Night Patrol, Korea

1989. 75th Anniv of Canadian Regiments. Mult.

1335	38c. Type **570** (Princess Patricia's Canadian Light Infantry)	1·40	1·50
1336	38c. Trench raid, France, 1914–18 (Royal 22e Regiment)	1·40	1·50

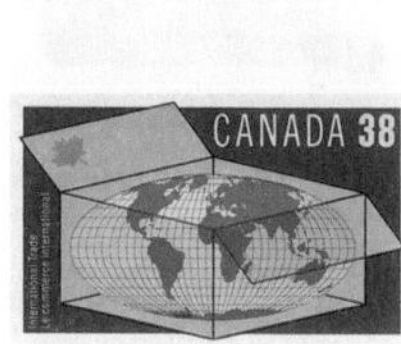

571 Globe in Box **572** Film Director

1989. Canada Export Trade Month.
1337 **571** 38c. multicoloured . . . 40 45

1989. Arts and Entertainment.

1338	**572**	38c. brown, dp brn & vio	75	75
1339	–	38c. brown, dp brn & grn	75	75
1340	–	38c. brown, dp brn & mve	75	75
1341	–	38c. brown, dp brn & bl	75	75

DESIGNS: No. 1339, Actors; No. 1340, Dancers; No. 1341, Musicians.

573 "Snow II" (Lawren S. Harris)

1989. Christmas. Paintings of Winter Landscapes. Multicoloured.

1342	33c. "Champ-de-Mars, Winter" (William Brymner) (35 × 21 mm)	1·00	55
1343	38c. "Bend in the Gosselin River" (Marc-Aurele Suzor-Cote) (21 × 35 mm)	40	35
1344	44c. Type **573**	65	50
1345	76c. "Ste. Agnes" (A. H. Robinson)	1·40	85

On No. 1342 the left-hand third of the design area is taken up by a bar code.

574 Canadians listening to Declaration of War, 1939

1989. 50th Anniv of Outbreak of Second World War (1st issue).

1346	**574**	38c. black, silver & pur	1·10	1·00
1347	–	38c. black, silver and grey	1·10	1·00
1348	–	38c. black, silver and green	1·10	1·00
1349	–	38c. black, silver and blue	1·10	1·00

DESIGNS: No. 1347, Army mobilization; No. 1348, British Commonwealth air crew training; No. 1349, North Atlantic convoy.

See also Nos. 1409/12, 1456/9, 1521/4, 1576/9, 1621/4, and 1625/8.

575 Canadian Flag **576**

1989.

1350	**575**	1c. multicoloured . . .	20	1·00
1351	–	5c. multicoloured . . .	40	30
1352	–	39c. multicoloured . .	2·25	2·25
1354	**576**	39c. multicoloured . .	70	10
1360	–	39c. purple	60	75
1353	–	40c. multicoloured . .	2·00	2·50
1355	–	40c. multicoloured . .	80	10
1361	–	40c. blue	40	50
1356	–	42c. multicoloured . .	90	15
1362	–	42c. red	40	50
1357	–	43c. multicoloured . .	80	80
1363	–	43c. green	1·50	2·00
1358d	–	45c. multicoloured . .	50	65
1364	–	45c. green	65	65
1359	–	46c. multicoloured . .	70	45
1365	–	46c. red	50	50
1367	–	47c. multicoloured . .	50	55
1368	–	48c. multicoloured . .	50	45
1369	–	49c. multicoloured . .	55	50

DESIGNS: Nos. 1351/3, 1360/5, As T **575** but different folds in flag. As T **576**: No. 1355, Flag over forest; 1356, Flag over mountains; 1357, Flag over prairie; 1358d, Flag and skyscraper; 1359, Flag and iceberg; 1367, Flag and inukshuk (Inuit cairn); 1368, Flag in front of Canada Post Headquarters, Ottawa, 1369, Flag and Edmonton.

No. 1359 comes with ordinary or self-adhesive gum and 1367/9 are self-adhesive.

577 Norman Bethune in 1937 and performing Operation, Montreal

1990. Birth Centenary of Dr. Norman Bethune (surgeon). Multicoloured.

1375	39c. Type **577**	1·25	1·40
1376	39c. Bethune in 1939, and treating wounded Chinese soldiers	1·25	1·40

1990. Small Craft of Canada (2nd series). Early Work Boats. As T **563**. Multicoloured.

1377	39c. Fishing dory	1·10	1·40
1378	39c. Logging pointer	1·10	1·40
1379	39c. York boat	1·10	1·40
1380	39c. North canoe	1·10	1·40

578 Maple Leaf Mosaic

1990. Multiculturalism.
1381 **578** 39c. multicoloured . . . 35 40

579 Mail Van (facing left) **580** Amerindian and Inuit Dolls

1990. "Moving the Mail". Multicoloured.

1382	39c. Type **579**	75	75
1383	39c. Mail van (facing right)	75	75

1990. Canadian Art (3rd series). As T **550**. Multicoloured.

1384	50c. "The West Wind" (Tom Thomson)	55	65

1990. Dolls. Multicoloured.

1385	39c. Type **580**	1·00	1·00
1386	39c. 19th-century settlers' dolls	1·00	1·00
1387	39c. Commerical dolls, 1917–36	1·00	1·00
1388	39c. Commercial dolls, 1940–60	1·00	1·00

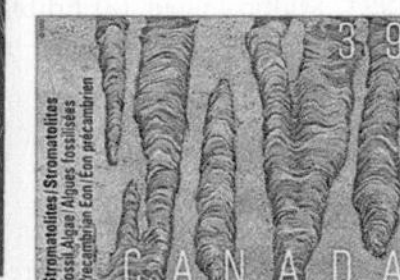
581 Canadian Flag and Fireworks **582** "Stromatolites" (fossil algae)

1990. Canada Day.
1389 **581** 39c. multicoloured . . . 50 50

1990. Prehistoric Canada (1st series). Primitive Life. Multicoloured.

1390	39c. Type **582**	1·00	1·10
1391	39c. "Opabinia regalis" (soft invertebrate)	1·00	1·10
1392	39c. "Paradoxides davidis" (trilobite)	1·00	1·10
1393	39c. "Eurypterus remipes" (sea scorpion)	1·00	1·10

See also Nos. 1417/20, 1568/71 and 1613/16.

583 Acadian Forest

1990. Canadian Forests. Multicoloured.

1394	39c. Type **583**	70	70
1395	39c. Great Lakes– St. Lawrence forest . . .	70	70
1396	39c. Pacific Coast forest . .	70	70
1397	39c. Boreal forest	70	70

584 Clouds and Rainbow

1990. 150th Anniv of Weather Observing in Canada.
1398 **584** 39c. multicoloured . . . 40 50

585 "Alphabet" Bird

1990. International Literacy Year.
1399 **585** 39c. multicoloured . . . 40 50

586 Sasquatch

1990. Legendary Creatures. Multicoloured.

1400	39c. Type **586**	1·10	1·40
1401	39c. Kraken	1·10	1·40
1402	39c. Werewolf	1·10	1·40
1403	39c. Ogopogo	1·10	1·40

587 Agnes Macphail **588** "Virgin Mary with Christ Child and St. John the Baptist" (Norval Morrisseau)

1990. Birth Centenary of Agnes Macphail (first woman elected to Parliament).
1404 **587** 39c. multicoloured . . . 40 50

1990. Christmas. Native Art.

1405	–	34c. multicoloured . . .	50	35
1406	**588**	39c. multicoloured . . .	40	40
1407	–	45c. multicoloured . . .	40	45
1408	–	78c. black, red and grey	70	75

DESIGNS—35 × 21 mm: 34c. "Rebirth" (Jackson Beardy). As T **588**: 45c. "Mother and Child" (Inuit sculpture, Cape Dorset); 78c. "Children of the Raven" (Bill Reid).

No. 1405 includes a bar code in the design.

1990. 50th Anniv of Second World War (2nd issue). As T **574**.

1409	39c. black, silver and green	1·60	1·60
1410	39c. black, silver and brown	1·60	1·60
1411	39c. black, silver and brown	1·60	1·60
1412	39c. black, silver and mauve	1·60	1·60

DESIGNS: No. 1409, Canadian family at home, 1940; 1410, Packing parcels for the troops; 1411, Harvesting; 1412, Testing anti-gravity flying suit.

589 Jennie Trout (first woman physician) and Women's Medical College, Kingston **590** Blue Poppies and Butchart Gardens, Victoria

1991. Medical Pioneers. Multicoloured.

1413	40c. Type **589**	1·00	90
1414	40c. Wilder Penfield (neurosurgeon) and Montreal Neurological Institute	1·00	90
1415	40c. Frederick Banting (discoverer of insulin) and University of Toronto medical faculty	1·00	90
1416	40c. Harold Griffith (anesthesiologist) and Queen Elizabeth Hospital, Montreal	1·00	90

1991. Prehistoric Canada (2nd series). Primitive Vertebrates. As T **582**. Multicoloured.

1417	40c. Foord's crossopt ("Eusthenopteron foordi") (fish fossil)	1·50	1·40
1418	40c. "Hylonomus lyelli" (land reptile)	1·50	1·40
1419	40c. Fossil conodonts (fossil teeth)	1·50	1·40
1420	40c. "Archaeopteris halliana" (early tree) . . .	1·50	1·40

1991. Canadian Art (4th series). As T **550**. Multicoloured.

1421	50c. "Forest, British Columbia" (Emily Carr)	1·25	1·50

1991. Public Gardens. Multicoloured.

1422	40c. Type **590**	55	55
1423	40c. Marigolds and International Peace Garden, Boissevain . . .	55	55
1424	40c. Lilac and Royal Botanical Gardens, Hamilton	55	55

1425 40c. Roses and Montreal Botanical Gardens . . . 55 55
1426 40c. Rhododendrons and Halifax Public Gardens 55 55

591 Maple Leaf

592 South Nahanni River

1991. Canada Day.
1427 **591** 40c. multicoloured . . . 50 60

1991. Small Craft of Canada (3rd series). As T **563**. Multicoloured.
1428 40c. Verchere rowboat . . . 1·40 1·40
1429 40c. Touring kayak . . . . 1·40 1·40
1430 40c. Sailing dinghy . . . . 1·40 1·40
1431 40c. Cedar strip canoe . . . 1·40 1·40

1991. Canadian Rivers (1st series). Multicoloured.
1432 40c. Type **592** . . . . . 1·00 1·40
1433 40c. Athabasca River . . . 1·00 1·40
1434 40c. Boundary Waters, Voyageur Waterway . . . 1·00 1·40
1435 40c. Jacques-Cartier River 1·00 1·40
1436 40c. Main River . . . . . 1·00 1·40
See also Nos. 1492/6, 1558/62 and 1584/8.

593 "Leaving Europe"

594 Ski Patrol rescuing Climber

1991. Centenary of Ukrainian Immigration. Panels from "The Ukrainian Pioneer" by William Kurelek. Multicoloured.
1437 40c. Type **593** 80 85
1438 40c. "Canadian Winter" . . 80 85
1439 40c. "Clearing the Land" . . 80 85
1440 40c. "Harvest" 80 85

1991. Emergency Services. Multicoloured.
1441 40c. Type **594** . . . . . . 1·75 1·75
1442 40c. Police at road traffic accident . . . . 1·75 1·75
1443 40c. Firemen on extending ladder . . . . 1·75 1·75
1444 40c. Boeing-Vertol Chinook rescue helicopter and "Spindrift" (lifeboat) . . 1·75 1·75

595 "The Witched Canoe"

596 Grant Hall Tower

1991. Canadian Folktales. Multicoloured.
1445 40c. Type **595** . . . . . . 1·10 95
1446 40c. "The Orphan Boy" . . 1·10 95
1447 40c. "Chinook" . . . . . . 1·10 95
1448 40c. "Buried Treasure" . . 1·10 95

1991. 150th Anniv of Queen's University, Kingston.
1449 **596** 40c. multicoloured . . . 1·10 1·00

597 North American Santa Claus

598 Players jumping for Ball

1991. Christmas. Multicoloured.
1450 35c. British Father Christmas (35 × 21 mm) . . . 90 55
1451 40c. Type **597** 90 20
1452 46c. French Bonhomme Noel . . . . 1·00 1·40
1453 80c. Dutch Sinterklaas . . . 1·90 3·00

1991. Basketball Centenary. Multicoloured.
1454 40c. Type **598** . . . . . . 1·50 75
MS1455 155 × 90 mm. 40c. Type **598**, but with shorter inscr below face value; 46c. Player taking shot; 80c. Player challenging opponent . . . . . 6·50 6·00

1991. 50th Anniv of Second World War (3rd issue). As T **574**.
1456 40c. black, silver and blue 1·50 1·25
1457 40c. black, silver and brown 1·50 1·25
1458 40c. black, silver and lilac 1·50 1·25
1459 40c. black, silver and brown 1·50 1·25
DESIGNS: No. 1456, Women's services, 1941; 1457, Armament factory; 1458, Cadets and veterans, 1459, Defence of Hong Kong.

599 Blueberry

600 McIntosh Apple

600a Court House, Yorktown

1991. Multicoloured. (a) Edible Berries. As T **599**.
1460 1c. Type **599** 10 10
1461 2c. Wild strawberry 10 10
1462 3c. Black crowberry 50 10
1463 5c. Rose hip 10 10
1464 6c. Black raspberry 10 10
1465 10c. Kinnikinnick 10 10
1466 25c. Saskatoon berry . . . 25 25

(b) Fruit and Nut Trees. As T **600**
1467 48c. Type **600** 50 35
1468 49c. Delicious apple . . . . 1·75 1·00
1469 50c. Snow apple . . . . . 1·50 1·00
1470 52c. Grauenstein apple . . 1·10 50
1471 65c. Black walnut . . . . . 1·25 50
1472 67c. Beaked hazelnut . . . 1·00 1·25
1473 69c. Shagbark hickory . . . 1·75 1·25
1474 71c. American chestnut . . 2·00 1·00
1475 84c. Stanley plum . . . . . 1·00 75
1476 86c. Bartlett pear . . . . . 1·00 1·00
1477 88c. Westcot apricot . . . . 1·75 1·60
1478 90c. Elberta peach . . . . . 1·00 1·00

(c) Architecture. As T **600a**
1479 $1 Type **600a** . . . . . . 2·25 1·00
1480a $2 Provincial Normal School, Truro . . . . . 3·00 1·60
1481 $5 Public Library, Victoria 4·50 4·75

601 Ski Jumping

1992. Winter Olympic Games, Albertville. Mult.
1482 42c. Type **601** . . . . . . 1·00 90
1483 42c. Figure skating . . . . 1·00 90
1484 42c. Ice hockey . . . . . . 1·00 90
1485 42c. Bobsleighing . . . . . 1·00 90
1486 42c. Alpine skiing . . . . . 1·00 90

602 Ville-Marie in 17th Century

1992. "CANADA 92" International Youth Stamp Exhibition, Montreal. Multicoloured.
1487 42c. Type **602** . . . . . . 1·00 1·25
1488 42c. Modern Montreal . . . 1·00 1·25
1489 48c. Compass rose, snow shoe and crow's nest of Cartier's ship "Grande Hermine" . . . . 1·75 1·00
1490 84c. Atlantic map, Aztec "calendar stone" and navigational instrument 2·50 2·50
MS1491 181 × 120 mm. Nos. 1487/90 7·00 7·00

1992. Canadian Rivers (2nd series). As T **592** but horiz. Multicoloured.
1492 42c. Margaree River . . . . 1·25 1·25
1493 42c. West (Eliot) River . . . 1·25 1·25
1494 42c. Ottawa River . . . . . 1·25 1·25
1495 42c. Niagara River . . . . 1·25 1·25
1496 42c. South Saskatchewan River . . . . 1·25 1·25

603 Road Bed Construction and Route Map

605 Jerry Potts (scout)

604 "Quebec, Patrimoine Mondial" (A. Dumas)

1992. 50th Anniv of Alaska Highway.
1497 **603** 42c. multicoloured . . . 1·10 70

1992. Olympic Games, Barcelona. As T **601**. Multicoloured.
1498 42c. Gymnastics . . . . . 1·10 1·25
1499 42c. Athletics . . . . 1·10 1·25
1500 42c. Diving . . . . 1·10 1·25
1501 42c. Cycling . . . . 1·10 1·25
1502 42c. Swimming . . . . . . 1·10 1·25

1992. Canada Day. Paintings. Sheet 190 × 256 mm, containing T **604** and similar diamond-shaped designs. Multicoloured.
MS1503 42c. Type **604**; 42c. "Christie Passage, Hurst Island, British Columbia" (E. J. Hughes); 42c. "Toronto, Landmarks of Time" (Ontario) (V. Mcindoe); 42c. "Near the Forks" (Manitoba) (S. Gouthro); 42c. "Off Cape St. Francis" (Newfoundland) (R. Shepherd); 42c. "Crowd at City Hall" (New Brunswick) (Molly Bobak); 42c. "Across the Tracks to Shop" (Alberta) (Janet Mitchell); 42c. "Cove Scene" (Nova Scotia) (J. Norris); 42c. "Untitled" (Saskatchewan) (D. Thauberger); 42c. "Town Life" (Yukon) (T. Harrison); 42c. "Country Scene" (Prince Edward Island) (Erica Rutherford); 42c. "Playing on an Igloo" (Northwest Territories) (Agnes Nanogak) 14·00 15·00

1992. Canadian Art (5th series). As T **550**. Multicoloured.
1504 50c. "Red Nasturtiums" (David Milne) . . . . . 1·60 1·10

1992. Folk Heroes. Multicoloured.
1505 42c. Type **605** . . . . . . 1·10 1·25
1506 42c. Capt. William Jackman and wreck of "Sea Clipper", 1867 . . . . . 1·10 1·25
1507 42c. Laura Secord (messenger) . . . . 1·10 1·25
1508 42c. Jos Montferrand (lumberjack) . . . . . . 1·10 1·25

606 Copper

1992. 150th Anniv of Geological Survey of Canada. Minerals. Multicoloured.
1509 42c. Type **606** . . . . . . 1·40 1·60
1510 42c. Sodalite . . . . 1·40 1·60
1511 42c. Gold . . . . 1·40 1·60
1512 42c. Galena . . . . 1·40 1·60
1513 42c. Grossular . . . . . . 1·40 1·60

607 Satellite and Photographs from Space

1992. Canadian Space Programme. Multicoloured.
1514 42c. Type **607** . . . . . . 1·25 1·75
1515 42c. Space shuttle over Canada (hologram) (32 × 26 mm) . . . . . . 1·25 1·75

608 Babe Siebert, Skates and Stick

609 Companion of the Order of Canada Insignia

1992. 75th Anniv of National Ice Hockey League. Multicoloured.
1516 42c. Type **608** . . . . . . 1·40 1·60
1517 42c. Claude Provost, Terry Sawchuck and team badges . . . . 1·40 1·60
1518 42c. Hockey mask, gloves and modern player . . . 1·40 1·60

1992. 25th Anniv of the Order of Canada and Daniel Roland Michener (former Governor-General) Commemoration. Multicoloured.
1519 42c. Type **609** . . . . . . 1·40 1·60
1520 42c. Daniel Roland Michener . . . . 1·40 1·60

1992. 50th Anniv of Second World War (4th issue). As T **574**.
1521 42c. black, silver & brown 1·50 1·75
1522 42c. black, silver & green . . 1·50 1·75
1523 42c. black, silver & brown 1·50 1·75
1524 42c. black, silver and blue 1·50 1·75
DESIGNS: No. 1521, Reporters and soldier, 1942; 1522, Consolidated Liberator bombers over Newfoundland; 1523 Dieppe raid; 1524, U-boat sinking merchant ship.

610 Estonian Jouluvana

611 Adelaide Hoodless (women's movement pioneer)

1992. Christmas. Multicoloured.
1525 37c. North American Santa Claus (35 × 21 mm) . . . 85 80
1526 42c. Type **610** 40 20
1527 48c. Italian La Befana . . . 1·40 1·60
1528 84c. German Weihnachtsmann . . . . 1·90 2·75

1993. Prominent Canadian Women. Multicoloured.
1529 43c. Type **611** . . . . . . 85 1·10
1530 43c. Marie-Josephine Gerin-Lajoie (social reformer) 85 1·10
1531 43c. Pitseolak Ashoona (Inuit artist) . . . . . . 85 1·10
1532 43c. Helen Kinnear (lawyer) 85 1·10

612 Ice Hockey Players with Cup

613 Coverlet, New Brunswick

1993. Centenary of Stanley Cup.
1533 **612** 43c. multicoloured . . . 75 60

1993. Hand-crafted Textiles. Multicoloured.
1534 43c. Type **613** . . . . . . 1·10 1·40
1535 43c. Pieced quilt, Ontario 1·10 1·40
1536 43c. Doukhobor bedcover, Saskatchewan . . . . . . 1·10 1·40
1537 43c. Ceremonial robe, Kwakwaka'wakw . . . . 1·10 1·40
1538 43c. Boutonne coverlet, Quebec . . . . 1·10 1·40

1993. Canadian Art (6th series). As T **550**. Multicoloured.
1539 86c. "The Owl" (Kenojuak Ashevak) . . . . 2·25 2·75

614 Empress Hotel, Victoria

1993. Historic Hotels. Multicoloured.
1540 43c. Type **614** . . . . . . 70 1·10
1541 43c. Banff Springs Hotel . . 70 1·10
1542 43c. Royal York Hotel, Toronto . . . . 70 1·10
1543 43c. Le Chateau Frontenac, Quebec . . . . 70 1·10
1544 43c. Algonquin Hotel, St. Andrews . . . . . . 70 1·10

615 Algonquin Park, Ontario

616 Toronto Skyscrapers

1993. Canada Day. Provincial and Territorial Parks. Multicoloured.
1545 43c. Type **615** 70 80
1546 43c. De La Gaspesie Park, Quebec 70 80
1547 43c. Cedar Dunes Park, Prince Edward Island . . 70 80
1548 43c. Cape St. Mary's Seabird Reserve, Newfoundland 70 80
1549 43c. Mount Robson Park, British Columbia 70 80
1550 43c. Writing-on-Stone Park, Alberta 70 80
1551 43c. Spruce Woods Park, Manitoba 70 80
1552 43c. Herschel Island Park, Yukon 70 80
1553 43c. Cypress Hills Park, Saskatchewan 70 80
1554 43c. The Rocks Park, New Brunswick 70 80
1555 43c. Blomidon Park, Nova Scotia 70 80
1556 43c. Katannilik Park, Northwest Territories . . 70 80

1993. Bicentenary of Toronto.
1557 **616** 43c. multicoloured . . . 1·00 70

1993. Canadian Rivers (3rd series). As T **592**. Multicoloured.
1558 43c. Fraser River . . . . . 1·00 1·10
1559 43c. Yukon River . . . . . 1·00 1·10
1560 43c. Red River . . . . . . 1·00 1·10
1561 43c. St. Lawrence River . . 1·00 1·10
1562 43c. St. John River . . . . 1·00 1·10

617 Taylor's Steam Buggy, 1867

1993. Historic Automobiles (1st issue). Sheet 177 × 125 mm, containing T **617** and similar horiz designs. Multicoloured.
MS1563 43c. Type **617**; 43c. Russel "Model L" touring car, 1908; 49c. Ford "Model T" touring car, 1914 (43 × 22 mm); 49c. Studebaker "Champion Deluxe Starlight" coupe, 1950 (43 × 22 mm); 86c. McLaughlin-Buick "28–496 special", 1928 (43 × 22 mm); 86c. Gray-Dort "25 SM" luxury sedan, 1923 (43 × 22 mm) . . . . . . 7·50 8·00
See also Nos. **MS**1611, **MS**1636 and **MS**1683/4.

618 "The Alberta Homesteader"

1993. Folk Songs. Multicoloured.
1564 43c. Type **618** . . . . . . 70 1·00
1565 43c. "Les Raftmans" (Quebec) . . . . 70 1·00
1566 43c. "I'se the B'y that Builds the Boat" (Newfoundland) . . . . . 70 1·00
1567 43c. "Onkwa:ri Tenhanonniahkwe" (Mohawk Indian) . . . . 70 1·00

1993. Prehistoric Canada (3rd series). Dinosaurs. As T **582** but 40 × 28 mm. Multicoloured.
1568 43c. Massospondylus . . . 80 80
1569 43c. Stryacosaurus 80 80
1570 43c. Albertosaurus 80 80
1571 43c. Platecarpus 80 80

619 Polish Swiety Mikolaj

1993. Christmas. Multicoloured.
1572 38c. North American Santa Claus (35 × 22 mm) . . . 90 90
1573 43c. Type **619** 55 20
1574 49c. Russian Ded Moroz . . 1·10 1·40
1575 86c. Australian Father Christmas . . . . 1·90 2·75

1993. 50th Anniv of Second World War (5th issue). As T **574**.
1576 43c. black, silver and green 1·50 1·75
1577 43c. black, silver and blue 1·50 1·75
1578 43c. black, silver and blue 1·50 1·75
1579 43c. black, silver and brown 1·50 1·75
DESIGNS: No. 1576, Loading munitions for Russia, 1943; No. 1577, Loading bombs on Avro Lancaster; No. 1578, Escorts attacking U-boat; No. 1579, Infantry advancing, Italy.

620 (face value at right)

1994. Self-adhesive Greetings stamps. Mult.
1580 43c. Type **620** . . . . . . 80 1·00
1581 43c. As Type **620** but face value at left . . . . . . 80 1·00
It was intended that the sender should insert an appropriate greetings label into the circular space on each stamp before use.
For 45c. values in this design see Nos. 1654/5.

621 Jeanne Sauve

1994. Jeanne Sauve (former Governor-General) Commemoration.
1582 **621** 43c. multicoloured . . . 60 60

622 Timothy Eaton, Toronto Store of 1869 and Merchandise

1994. 125th Anniv of T. Eaton Company Ltd (department store group).
1583 **622** 43c. multicoloured . . . 55 75

1994. Canadian Rivers (4th series). As T **592**, but horiz. Multicoloured.
1584 43c. Saguenay River 80 90
1585 43c. French River 80 90
1586 43c. Mackenzie River . . . 80 90
1587 43c. Churchill River 80 90
1588 43c. Columbia River 80 90

1994. Canadian Art (7th series). As T **550**. Multicoloured.
1589 88c. "Vera" (detail) (Frederick Varley) . . . . 1·50 2·00

623 Lawn Bowls

1994. 15th Commonwealth Games, Victoria. Multicoloured.
1590 43c. Type **623** 40 55
1591 43c. Lacrosse 40 55
1592 43c. Wheelchair race 40 55
1593 43c. High jumping 40 55
1594 50c. Diving 45 70
1595 88c. Cycling . . . . 1·10 1·60

624 Mother and Baby

1994. International Year of the Family. Sheet 178 × 134 mm, containing T **624** and similar vert designs. Multicoloured.
MS1596 43c. Type **624**; 43c. Family outing; 43c. Grandmother and granddaughter; 43c. Computer class; 43c. Play group, nurse with patient and female lawyer . . . 3·00 3·50

625 Big Leaf Maple Tree

1994. Canada Day. Maple Trees. Multicoloured.
1597 43c. Type **625** 70 80
1598 43c. Sugar maple 70 80
1599 43c. Silver maple 70 80
1600 43c. Striped maple 70 80
1601 43c. Norway maple 70 80
1602 43c. Manitoba maple . . . 70 80
1603 43c. Black maple 70 80
1604 43c. Douglas maple 70 80
1605 43c. Mountain maple . . . 70 80
1606 43c. Vine maple 70 80
1607 43c. Hedge maple 70 80
1608 43c. Red maple 70 80

626 Billy Bishop (fighter ace) and Nieuport 17

627 Symbolic Aircraft, Radar Screen and Clouds

1994. Birth Centenaries. Multicoloured.
1609 43c. Type **626** . . . . . . 1·00 1·25
1610 43c. Mary Travers ("La Bolduc") (singer) and musicians . . . . 1·00 1·25

1994. Historic Automobiles (2nd issue). Sheet 177 × 125 mm, containing horiz designs as T **617**. Multicoloured.
MS1611 43c. Ford "Model F60L-AMB" military ambulance, 1942–43; 43c. Winnipeg police wagon, 1925; 50c. Sicard snowblower, 1927 (43 × 22 mm); 50c. Bickle "Chieftain" fire engine, 1936 (43 × 22 mm); 88c. St. John Railway Company tramcar No. 40, 1894 (51 × 22 mm), 88c. Motor Coach Industries "Courier 50 Skyview" coach, 1950 (51 × 22 mm) . . . . 9·00 9·50
No. **MS**1611 was sold in a protective pack.

1994. 50th Anniv of I.C.A.O.
1612 **627** 43c. multicoloured . . . 1·00 70

1994. Prehistoric Canada (4th series). Mammals. As T **582**, but 40 × 28 mm. Multicoloured.
1613 43c. Coryphodon . . . . . 1·75 1·75
1614 43c. Megacerops . . . . . 1·75 1·75
1615 43c. Arctodus simus (bear) 1·75 1·75
1616 43c. Mammuthus primigenius (mammoth) 1·75 1·75

628 Carol Singing around Christmas Tree

629 Flag and Lake

1994. Christmas. Multicoloured.
1617 (–)c. Carol singer (35 × 21 mm) 80 90
1618 43c. Type **628** 50 20
1619 50c. Choir (vert) . . . . . 1·00 1·40
1620 88c. Couple carol singing in snow (vert) . . . . . . 2·25 3·00
No. 1617 is without face value, but was intended for use as a 38c. on internal greetings cards posted before 31 January 1995. The design shows a barcode at left.

1994. 50th Anniv of Second World War (6th issue). As T **574**.
1621 43c. black, silver and green 1·75 1·75
1622 43c. black, silver and red . . 1·75 1·75
1623 43c. black, silver and blue 1·75 1·75
1624 43c. black, silver and grey 1·75 1·75
DESIGNS: No. 1621, D-Day landings, Normandy; No. 1622, Canadian artillery, Normandy; No. 1623, Hawker Typhoons on patrol; No. 1624, Canadian infantry and disabled German self-propelled gun, Walcheren.

1995. 50th Anniv of Second World War (7th issue). As T **574**.
1625 43c. black, silver and purple 1·75 1·75
1626 43c. black, silver and brown 1·75 1·75
1627 43c. black, silver and green 1·75 1·75
1628 43c. black, silver and blue 1·75 1·75
DESIGNS: No. 1625, Returning troop ship; 1626, Canadian P.O.W.s celebrating freedom; 1627, Canadian tank liberating Dutch town; 1628, Parachute drop in support of Rhine Crossing.

1995. Canadian Art (8th series). As T **550**. Multicoloured
1629 88c. "Floraison" (Alfred Pellan) . . . . 1·50 2·00

1995. 30th Anniv of National Flag. No face value.
1630 **629** (43c.) multicoloured . . 75 50

630 Louisbourg Harbour

1995. 275th Anniv of Fortress of Louisbourg. Multicoloured.
1631 (43c.) Type **630** 70 80
1632 (43c.) Barracks (32 × 29 mm) 70 80
1633 (43c.) King's Bastion (40 × 29 mm) 70 80
1634 (43c.) Site of King's Garden, convent and hospital (56 × 29 mm) 70 80
1635 (43c.) Site of coastal fortifications 70 80

1995. Historic Automobiles (3rd issue). Sheet 177 × 125 mm, containing horiz designs as T **617**. Multicoloured.
MS1636 43c. Cockshutt "30" farm tractor, 1950; 43c. Bombadier "Ski-Doo Olympique 335" snowmobile, 1970; 50c. Bombadier "B-12 CS" multi-passenger snowmobile, 1948 (43 × 22 mm); 50c. Gotfredson "Model 20" farm truck, 1924 (43 × 22 mm); 88c. Robin-Nodwell "RN 110" tracked carrier, 1962 (43 × 22 mm); 88c. Massey-Harris "No. 21" self-propelled combine-harvester, 1942 (43 × 22 mm) . . . . 7·00 7·50
No. **MS**1636 was sold in a protective pack.

631 Banff Springs Golf Club, Alberta

1995. Centenaries of Canadian Amateur Golf Championship and of the Royal Canadian Golf Association. Multicoloured.
1637 43c. Type **631** 80 80
1638 43c. Riverside Country Club, New Brunswick . . 80 80
1639 43c. Glen Abbey Golf Club, Ontario 80 80
1640 43c. Victoria Golf Club, British Columbia 80 80
1641 43c. Royal Montreal Golf Club, Quebec 80 80

632 "October Gold" (Franklin Carmichael)

1995. Canada Day. 75th Anniv of "Group of Seven" (artists). Three sheets, each 180 × 80 mm, containing T **632** and similar square designs. Multicoloured.

MS1642 (a) 43c. Type **632**; 43c. "From the North Shore, Lake Superior" (Lawren Harris); 43c. "Evening, Les Eboulements, Quebec" (A. Jackson). (b) 43c. "Serenity, Lake of the Woods" (Frank Johnston); 43c. "A September Gale, Georgian Bay" (Arthur Lismer); 43c. "Falls, Montreal River" (J. E. H. MacDonald); 43c. "Open Window" (Frederick Varley). (c) 43c. "Mill Houses" (Alfred Casson); 43c. "Pembina Valley" (Lionel FitzGerald); 43c. "The Lumberjack" (Edwin Holgate)
Set of 3 sheets . . . . 9·00 10·00

The three sheets of No. **MS**1642 were sold together in an envelope which also includes a small descriptive booklet.

633 Academy Building and Ship Plan

634 Aspects of Manitoba

1995. Centenary of Lunenburg Academy.
1643 **633** 43c. multicoloured . . . 50 45

1995. 125th Anniv of Manitoba as Canadian Province.
1644 **634** 43c. multicoloured . . . 50 45

635 Monarch Butterfly

1995. Migratory Wildlife. Multicoloured.
1645 45c. Type **635** . . . . 1·10 1·40
1646 45c. Belted kingfisher* . . . 1·10 1·40
1647 45c. Belted kingfisher* . . . 1·10 1·40
1648 45c. Pintail . . . . 1·10 1·40
1649 45c. Hoary bat . . . . 1·10 1·40

*No. 1646: Inscr "aune migratrice" in error. No. 1647: Inscr corrected to "faune migratrice".

636 Quebec Railway Bridge

1995. 20th World Road Congress, Montreal. Bridges. Multicoloured.
1650 45c. Type **636** . . . . 1·50 1·75
1651 45c. 401-403-410 Interchange, Mississauga . . . 1·50 1·75
1652 45c. Hartland Bridge, New Brunswick . . . . 1·50 1·75
1653 45c. Alex Fraser Bridge, British Columbia . . . . 1·50 1·75

1995. Self-adhesive Greetings stamps. As T **620**. Multicoloured. Imperf.
1654 45c. Face value at right . . 60 75
1655 45c. Face value at left . . . 60 75

It is intended the sender should insert an appropriate greetings label into the circular space on each stamp before use.

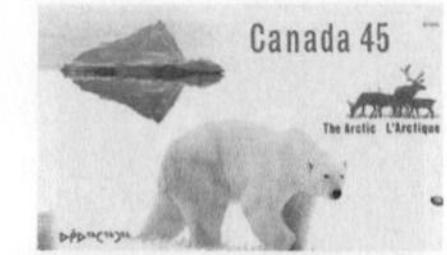

637 Mountain, Baffin Island, Polar Bear and Caribou

1995. 50th Anniv of Arctic Institute of North America. Multicoloured.
1656 45c. Type **637** . . . . . . 1·00 1·25
1657 45c. Arctic poppy, Auyuittuq National Park and cargo canoe . . . . 1·00 1·25
1658 45c. Inuk man and igloo . . 1·00 1·25
1659 45c. Ogilvie Mountains, dog team and ski-equipped airplane . . . . 1·00 1·25
1660 45c. Inuit children . . . . . 1·00 1·25

638 Superman 640 "The Nativity"

639 Prime Minister MacKenzie King signing U.N. Charter, 1945

1995. Comic Book Superheroes. Multicoloured.
1661 45c. Type **638** 75 85
1662 45c. Johnny Canuck 75 85
1663 45c. Nelvana 75 85
1664 45c. Captain Canuck . . . 75 85
1665 45c. Fleur de Lys 75 85

1995. 50th Anniv of United Nations.
1666 **639** 45c. multicoloured . . . 75 50

1995. Christmas. Sculptured Capitals from Ste.-Anne-de-Beaupre Basilica designed by Emile Brunet (Nos. 1668/70). Multicoloured.
1667 40c. Sprig of holly (35 × 22 mm) 65 65
1668 45c. Type **640** 50 20
1669 52c. "The Annunciation" . . 1·00 1·25
1670 90c. "The Flight to Egypt" 1·75 2·50

641 World Map and Emblem

1995. 25th Anniv of La Francophonie and The Agency for Cultural and Technical Co-operation.
1671 **641** 45c. multicoloured . . . 50 50

642 Concentration Camp Victims, Uniform and Identity Card

1995. 50th Anniv of the End of The Holocaust.
1672 **642** 45c. multicoloured . . . 50 50

643 American Kestrel

1996. Birds (1st series). Multicoloured.
1673 45c. Type **643** . . . . . . 1·40 1·40
1674 45c. Atlantic puffin . . . . 1·40 1·40
1675 45c. Pileated woodpecker . . 1·40 1·40
1676 45c. Ruby-throated hummingbird . . . . . . 1·40 1·40

See also Nos. 1717/20, 1779/82, 1865/8, 1974/7 and 2058/61.

644 "Louis R. Desmarais" (tanker), Three-dimensional Map and Radar Screen

1996. High Technology Industries. Multicoloured.
1677 45c. Type **644** . . . . . . 75 1·00
1678 45c. Canadair Challenger 601-3R, jet engine and navigational aid . . . . . 75 1·00
1679 45c. Map of North America and eye . . . . 75 1·00
1680 45c. Genetic engineering experiment and Canola (plant) . . . . 75 1·00

1996. Canadian Art (9th series). As T **550**. Multicoloured.
1681 90c. "The Spirit of Haida Gwaii" (sculpture) (Bill Reid) . . . . 1·40 2·00

645 "One World, One Hope" (Joe Average)

1996. 11th International Conference on AIDS, Vancouver.
1682 **645** 45c. multicoloured . . . 70 70

1996. Historic Automobies (4th issue). Sheet 177 × 125 mm, containing horiz designs as T **617**. Multicoloured.

MS1683 45c. Still Motor Co electric van, 1899; 45c. Waterous Engine Works steam roller, 1914; 52c. International "D.35" delivery truck, 1938; 52c. Champion road grader, 1936; 90c. White "Model WA 122" articulated lorry, 1947 (51 × 22 mm); 90c. Hayes "HDX 45-115" logging truck, 1975 (51 × 22 mm) . . . . 7·50 8·00

No. **MS**1683 also includes the "CAPEX '96" International Stamp Exhibition logo on the sheet margin and was sold in a protective pack.

1996. "CAPEX '96" International Stamp Exhibitiion, Toronto. Sheet 368 × 182 mm, containing horiz designs as Nos. **MS**1563, **MS**1611, **MS**1636 and **MS**1683, but with different face values, and one new design (45c.).

MS1684 5c. Bombadier "Ski–Doo Olympique 335" snowmobile, 1970; 5c. Cockshutt "30" farm tractor, 1950; 5c. Type **617**; 5c. Ford "Model F160L-AMB" military ambulance, 1942; 5c. Still Motor Co electric van, 1895; 5c. International "D.35" delivery truck, 1936; 5c. Russel "Model L" touring car, 1908; 5c. Winnipeg police wagon, 1925; 5c. Waterous Engine Works steam roller, 1914; 5c. Champion road grader, 1936; 10c. White "Model WA 122" articulated lorry, 1947 (51 × 22 mm); 10c. St. John Railway Company tramcar, 1894 (51 × 22 mm); 10c. Hayes "HDX 45-115" logging truck, 1975 (51 × 22 mm); 10c. Motor Couch Industries "Courier 50 Skyview" coach, 1950 (51 × 22 mm); 20c. Ford "Model T" touring car, 1914 (43 × 22 mm); 20c. McLaughlin-Buick "28-496 special", 1928 (43 × 22 mm); 20c. Bombadier "B-12 CS" multi-passenger snowmobile, 1948 (43 × 22 mm); 20c. Robin-Nodwell "RN 110" tracked carrier, 1962 (43 × 22 mm); 20c. Studebaker "Champion Deluxe Starlight" coupe, 1950 (43 × 22 mm); 20c. Gray-Dort "25 SM" luxury sedan, 1923 (43 × 22 mm); 20c. Gotfredson "Model 20" farm truck, 1924 (43 × 22 mm); 20c. Massey-Harris "No. 21" self-propelled combine-harvester, 1942 (43 × 22 mm); 20c. Bickle "Chieftain" fire engine, 1936 (43 × 22 mm); 20c. Sicard snowblower, 1927 (43 × 22 mm); 45c. Bricklin "SV-1" sports car, 1975 (51 × 22 mm) . . . . . . 8·00 9·00

The price quoted for No. **MS**1684 is for a folded example.

646 Skookum Jim Mason and Bonanza Creek

1996. Centenary of Yukon Gold Rush. Multicoloured.
1685 45c. Type **646** . . . . . . 80 1·00
1686 45c. Prospector and boats on Lake Laberge . . . . 80 1·00
1687 45c. Superintendent Sam Steele (N.W.M.P.) and U.S.A.–Canada border . . 80 1·00
1688 45c. Dawson saloon . . . . 80 1·00
1689 45c. Miner with rocker box and sluice . . . . 80 1·00

647 Patchwork Quilt Maple Leaf 648 Ethel Catherwood (high jump), 1928

1996. Canada Day. Self-adhesive. Imperf.
1690 **647** 45c. multicoloured . . . 50 50

1996. Canadian Olympic Gold Medal Winners. Multicoloured.
1691 45c. Type **648** 85 85
1692 45c. Etienne Desmarteau (56lb weight throw), 1904 85 85
1693 45c. Fanny Rosenfeld (400 m relay), 1928 . . . 85 85
1694 45c. Gerald Ouellette (small bore rifle, prone), 1956 . . 85 85
1695 45c. Percy Williams (100 and 200 m), 1928 . . . . 85 85

649 Indian Totems, City Skyline, Forest and Mountains

650 Canadian Heraldic Symbols

1996. 125th Anniv of British Columbia.
1696 **649** 45c. multicoloured . . . 50 50

1996. 22nd International Congress of Genealogical and Heraldic Sciences, Ottawa.
1697 **650** 45c. multicoloured . . . 50 50

651 "L'Arivee d'un Train en Gare" (1896)

1996. Centenary of Cinema. Two sheets, each 180 × 100 mm, containing T **651** and similar vert designs. Multicoloured. Self-adhesive.

MS1698 (a) 45c. Type **651**; 45c. "Back to God's Country" (1919); 45c. "Hen Hop!" (1942); "Pour la Suite du Monde" (1963); 45c. "Goin' Down the Road" (1970). (b) 45c. "Mon Oncle Antione" (1971); 45c. "The Apprenticeship of Duddy Kravitz" (1974); 45c. "Les Ordres" (1974); 45c. "Les Bons Debarras" (1980); 45c. "The Grey Fox" (1982) . . . . . . 8·50 9·50

The two sheets of No. **MS**1698 were sold together in an envelope with a descriptive booklet.

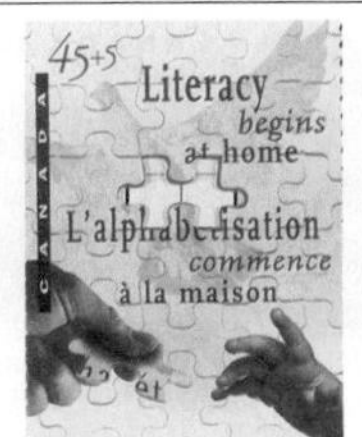

652 Interlocking Jigsaw Pieces and Hands

1996. Literacy Campaign.
1699 **652** 45c.+5c. mult . . . . . 85 1·00

653 Edouard Montpetit and Montreal University

1996. Edouard Montpetit (academic) Commem.
1700 **653** 45c. multicoloured . . . 50 50

654 Winnie and Lt. Colebourn, 1914

1996. Stamp Collecting Month. Winnie the Pooh. Multicoloured.
1701 45c. Type **654** . . . . . . 1·25 1·25
1702 45c. Christopher Robin Milne and teddy bear, 1925 . . . . 1·25 1·25
1703 45c. Illustration from "Winnie the Pooh", 1926 1·25 1·25
1704 45c. Winnie the Pooh at Walt Disney World, 1996 1·25 1·25
MS1705 152 × 112 mm. Nos 1701/4 4·50 4·75

655 Margaret Laurence   656 Children tobogganing

1996. Canadian Authors.
1706 **655** 45c. multicoloured . . . 1·10 1·40
1707 – 45c. black, grey and red 1·10 1·40
1708 – 45c. multicoloured . . . 1·10 1·40
1709 – 45c. multicoloured . . . 1·10 1·40
1710 – 45c. multicoloured . . . 1·10 1·40
DESIGNS: No. 1707, Donald G. Creighton; 1708, Gabrielle Roy; 1709, Felix-Antoine Savard; 1710, Thomas C. Haliburton.

1996. Christmas. 50th Anniv of U.N.I.C.E.F. Multicoloured.
1711 45c. Type **656** 50 20
1712 52c. Father Christmas skiing . . . . 80 1·00
1713a 90c. Couple ice-skating . . 1·25 2·00

657 Head of Ox   659 Abbe Charles-Emile Gadbois

658 Man and Boy with Bike, and A. J. and J. W. Billes (company founders)

1997. Chinese New Year ("Year of the Ox").
1714 **657** 45c. multicoloured . . . 85 90
MS1715 155 × 75 mm. Nos. 1714 × 2 2·00 2·50
No. **MS**1715 is an extended fan shape with overall measurements as quoted.

1997. "HONG KONG '97" International Stamp Exhibition. As No. **MS**1715, but with exhibition logo added to the sheet margin in gold.
MS1716 155 × 75 mm. No. 1714 × 2 6·00 6·50

1997. Birds (2nd series). As T **643**. Multicoloured.
1717 45c. Mountain bluebird . . 1·00 1·10
1718 45c. Western grebe . . . . 1·00 1·10
1719 45c. Northern gannet . . . 1·00 1·10
1720 45c. Scarlet tanager . . . . 1·00 1·10

1997. Canadian Art (10th series). As T **550**. Multicoloured.
1721 90c. "York Boat on Lake Winnipeg, 1930" (Walter Phillips) . . . . 1·50 2·00

1997. 75th Anniv of the Canadian Tire Corporation.
1722 **658** 45c. multicoloured . . . 80 50

1997. Abbe Charles-Emile Gadbois (musicologist) Commemoration.
1723 **659** 45c. multicoloured . . . 50 50

660 Blue Poppy   662 Osgoode Hall and Seal of Law School

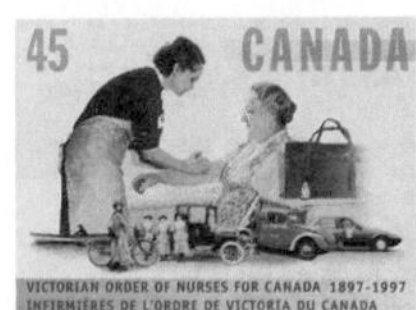

661 Nurse attending Patient

1997. "Quebec in Bloom" International Floral Festival.
1724 **660** 45c. multicoloured . . . 60 55

1997. Centenary of Victorian Order of Nurses.
1725 **661** 45c. multicoloured . . . 1·00 50

1997. Bicentenary of Law Society of Upper Canada.
1726 **662** 45c. multicoloured . . . 75 50

663 Great White Shark

1997. Ocean Fishes. Multicoloured.
1727 45c. Type **663** . . . . . . 1·00 1·25
1728 45c. Pacific halibut . . . . 1·00 1·25
1729 45c. Common sturgeon . . 1·00 1·25
1730 45c. Blue-finned tuna . . . 1·00 1·25

664 Lighthouse and Confederation Bridge

1997. Opening of Confederation Bridge, Northumberland Strait. Multicoloured.
1731 45c. Type **664** . . . . . . 1·00 90
1732 45c. Confederation Bridge and great blue heron . . 1·00 90

665 Gilles Villeneuve in Ferrari T-3

1997. 15th Death Anniv of Gilles Villeneuve (racing car driver). Multicoloured.
1733 45c. Type **665** . . . . . . 1·00 60
1734 90c. Villeneuve in Ferrari T-4 . . . . 2·00 2·25
MS1735 203 × 115 mm. Nos. 1733/4 each × 4 . . . . 8·00 8·00

666 Globe and the "Matthew"

1997. 500th Anniv of John Cabot's Discovery of North America.
1736 **666** 45c. multicoloured . . . 1·00 55

667 Sea to Sky Highway, British Columbia, and Skier

1997. Scenic Highways (1st series). Multicoloured.
1737 45c. Type **667** . . . . . . 1·00 1·10
1738 45c. Cabot Trail, Nova Scotia, and rug-making 1·00 1·10
1739 45c. Wine route, Ontario, and glasses of wine . . . 1·00 1·10
1740 45c. Highway 34, Saskatchewan, and cowboy . . . . 1·00 1·10
See also Nos. 1810/13 and 1876/9.

668 Kettle, Ski-bike, Lounger and Plastic Cases

1997. 20th Congress of International Council of Societies for Industrial Design.
1741 **668** 45c. multicoloured . . . 60 50

669 Caber Thrower, Bagpiper, Drummer and Highland Dancer

1997. 50th Anniv of Glengarry Highland Games, Ontario.
1742 **669** 45c. multicoloured . . . 1·00 50

670 Knights of Columbus Emblem

1997. Centenary of Knights of Columbus (welfare charity) in Canada.
1743 **670** 45c. multicoloured . . . 50 50

671 Postal and Telephone Workers with P.T.T.I. Emblem

1997. 28th World Congress of Postal, Telegraph and Telephone International Staff Federation, Montreal.
1744 **671** 45c. multicoloured . . . 50 50

672 C.Y.A.P. Logo

1997. Canada's Year of Asia Pacific.
1745 **672** 45c. multicoloured . . . 1·00 50

673 Paul Henderson celebrating Goal

1997. 25th Anniv of Canada–U.S.S.R. Ice Hockey Series. Multicoloured.
1746 45c. Type **673** . . . . . . 1·00 1·00
1747 45c. Canadian team celebrating . . . . 1·00 1·00

674 Martha Black

1997. Federal Politicians. Multicoloured.
1748 45c. Type **674** 70 90
1749 45c. Lionel Chevrier 70 90
1750 45c. Judy LaMarsh 70 90
1751 45c. Real Caouette 70 90

675 Vampire and Bat

1997. The Supernatural. Centenary of Publication of Bram Stoker's "Dracula". Multicoloured.
1752 45c. Type **675** 65 80
1753 45c. Werewolf 65 80
1754 45c. Ghost 65 80
1755 45c. Goblin 65 80

676 Grizzly Bear

1997. Mammals. Multicoloured.
1756 $1 Great northern diver ("Loon") (47 × 39 mm) . . 90 95
1757 $2 Polar bear (47 × 39 mm) 1·75 1·90
1758 $5 Moose . . . . 4·50 4·75
1759 $8 Type **676** . . . . 6·25 6·50

677 "Our Lady of the Rosary" (detail, Holy Rosary Cathedral, Vancouver)

1997. Christmas. Stained Glass Windows. Multicoloured.
1763a 45c. Type **677** 45 20
1764 52c. "Nativity" (detail, Leith United Church, Ontario) 65 65
1765 90c. "Life of the Blessed Virgin" (detail, St. Stephen's Ukrainian Catholic Church, Calgary) . . . . 1·10 1·50

678 Livestock and Produce

1997. 75th Anniv of Royal Agricultural Winter Fair, Toronto.
1766 **678** 45c. multicoloured . . . 1·00 55

679 Tiger

1998. Chinese New Year ("Year of the Tiger").
1767 **679** 45c. multicoloured . . . 60 50
MS1768 130 × 110 mm. As No. 1767 × 2 . . . . 1·25 1·50
No. **MS**1768 is diamond-shaped with overall measurements as quoted.

680 John Robarts (Ontario, 1961–71) **681** Maple Leaf

1998. Canadian Provincial Premiers. Multicoloured.
1769 45c. Type **680** 60 75
1770 45c. Jean Lesage (Quebec, 1960–66) 60 75
1771 45c. John McNair (New Brunswick, 1940–52) . . . 60 75
1772 45c. Tommy Douglas (Saskatchewan, 1944–61) 60 75
1773 45c. Joseph Smallwood (Newfoundland, 1949–72) 60 75
1774 45c. Angus MacDonald (Nova Scotia, 1933–40, 1945–54) 60 75
1775 45c. W. A. C. Bennett (British Columbia, 1960–66) 60 75
1776 45c. Ernest Manning (Alberta, 1943–68) 60 75
1777 45c. John Bracken (Manitoba, 1922–43) 60 75
1778 45c. J. Walter Jones (Prince Edward Island, 1943–53) 60 75

1998. Birds (3rd series). As T **643**. Multicoloured.
1779 45c. Hairy woodpecker . . 90 90
1780 45c. Great crested flycatcher 90 90
1781 45c. Eastern screech owl . . 90 90
1782 45c. Rosy finch ("Gray-crowned Rosy-finch") . . 90 90

1998. Self-adhesive Automatic Cash Machine Stamps. Imperf.
1783 **681** 45c. multicoloured . . . 45 40
For stamps in this design, but without "POSTAGE POSTES" at top left see Nos. 1836/40.

682 Coquihalla Orange Fly

1998. Fishing Flies. Multicoloured.
1784 45c. Type **682** 90 90
1785 45c. Steelhead Bee 90 90
1786 45c. Dark Montreal 90 90
1787 45c. Lady Amherst 90 90
1788 45c. Coho Blue 90 90
1789 45c. Cosseboom Special . . 90 90

683 Mineral Excavation, Oil Rig and Pickaxe **684** 1898 2c. Imperial Penny Postage Stamp and Postmaster General Sir William Mulock

1998. Centenary of Canadian Institute of Mining, Metallurgy and Petroleum.
1790 **683** 45c. multicoloured . . . 60 50

1998. Centenary of Imperial Penny Postage.
1791 **684** 45c. multicoloured . . . 1·00 55

685 Two Sumo Wrestlers

1998. 1st Canadian Sumo Basho (tournament), Vancouver. Multicoloured.
1792 45c. Type **685** 65 75
1793 45c. Sumo wrestler in ceremonial ritual 65 75
MS1794 84 × 152 mm. Nos. 1792/3 1·25 1·50

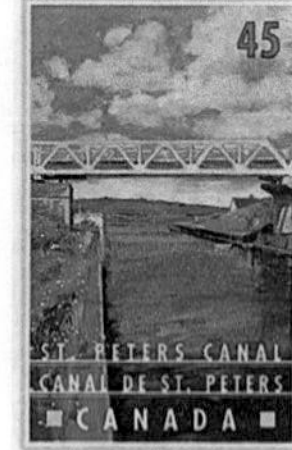

686 St. Peters Canal, Nova Scotia **687** Staff of Aesculapius and Cross

1998. Canadian Canals. Multicoloured.
1795 45c. Type **686** . . . . . . 1·25 1·25
1796 45c. St. Ours Canal, Quebec 1·25 1·25
1797 45c. Port Carling Lock, Ontario . . . . 1·25 1·25
1798 45c. Lock on Rideau Canal, Ontario . . . . 1·25 1·25
1799 45c. Towers and platform of Peterborough Lift Lock, Trent–Severn Waterway, Ontario . . . . 1·25 1·25
1800 45c. Chambly Canal, Quebec . . . . 1·25 1·25
1801 45c. Lachine Canal, Quebec 1·25 1·25
1802 45c. Rideau Canal in winter, Ontario . . . . 1·25 1·25
1803 45c. Boat on Big Chute incline railway, Trent–Severn Waterway, Ontario 1·25 1·25
1804 45c. Sault Ste. Marie Canal, Ontario . . . . 1·25 1·25

1998. Canadian Health Professionals.
1805 **687** 45c. multicoloured . . . 1·00 55

688 Policeman of 1873 and Visit to Indian Village

1998. 125th Anniv of Royal Canadian Mounted Police. Multicoloured.
1806 45c. Type **688** 75 75
1807 45c. Policewoman of 1998 and aspects of modern law enforcement 75 75
MS1808 160 × 102 mm. Nos. 1806/7 1·40 1·60

689 William J. Roue (designer) and "Bluenose" (schooner)

1998. William James Roue (naval architect) Commemoration.
1809 **689** 45c. multicoloured . . . 60 50

1998. Scenic Highways (2nd series). As T **667**. Multicoloured.
1810 45c. Dempster Highway, Yukon, and caribou . . . 65 75
1811 45c. Dinosaur Trail, Alberta, and skeleton . . 65 75
1812 45c. River Valley Drive, New Brunswick, and fern 65 75
1813 45c. Blue Heron Route, Prince Edward Island, and lobster 65 75

690 "Painting" (Jean-Paul Riopelle)

1998. 50th Anniv of "Refus Global" (manifesto of The Automatistes group of artists). Multicoloured. Self-adhesive. Imperf.
1814 45c. Type **690** . . . . . . 1·10 1·10
1815 45c. "La derniere campagne de Napoleon" (Fernand Leduc) (37 × 31½ mm) . . 1·10 1·10
1816 45c. "Jet fuligineux sur noir torture" (Jean-Paul Mousseau) . . . . 1·10 1·10
1817 45c. "Le fond du garde-robe" (Pierre Gauvreau) (29½ × 42 mm) . . . . . 1·10 1·10
1818 45c. "Joie lacustre" (Paul-Emile Borduas) . . . . . 1·10 1·10
1819 45c. "Seafarers Union" (Marcelle Ferron) (36 × 34 mm) . . . . . . 1·10 1·10
1820 45c. "Le tumulte a la machoire crispee" (Marcel Barbeau) (36 × 34 mm) . . 1·10 1·10

691 Napoleon-Alexandre Comeau (naturalist)

1998. Legendary Canadians. Multicoloured.
1821 45c. Type **691** 55 65
1822 45c. Phyllis Munday (mountaineer) 55 65
1823 45c. Bill Mason (film-maker) 55 65
1824 45c. Harry Red Foster (sports commentator) . . 55 65

1998. Canadian Art (11th series). As T **550**. Multicoloured.
1825 90c. "The Farmer's Family" (Bruno Bobak) . . . . . 1·00 1·40

692 Indian Wigwam

1998. Canadian Houses. Multicoloured.
1826 45c. Type **692** 50 60
1827 45c. Settler sod hut 50 60
1828 45c. Maison Saint-Gabriel (17th-century farmhouse), Quebec 50 60
1829 45c. Queen Anne style brick house, Ontario 50 60
1830 45c. Terrace of town houses 50 60
1831 45c. Prefabricated house . . 50 60
1832 45c. Veterans' houses . . . 50 60
1833 45c. Modern bungalow . . 50 60
1834 45c. Healthy House, Toronto 50 60

693 University of Ottawa

1998. 150th Anniv of University of Ottawa.
1835 **693** 45c. multicoloured . . . 50 50

1998. As T **681**, but without "POSTAGE POSTES" at top left. Self-adhesive gum, imperf (46c.) or ordinary gum, perf (others).
1839 **681** 45c. multicoloured . . . 65 75
1840 46c. multicoloured . . . 70 80
1836 55c. multicoloured . . . 80 80
1837 73c. multicoloured . . . 65 70
1838 95c. multicoloured . . . 1·25 1·40

694 Performing Animals

1998. Canadian Circus. Multicoloured.
1851 45c. Type **694** . . . . . . 1·10 1·10
1852 45c. Flying trapeze and acrobat on horseback . . 1·10 1·10
1853 45c. Lion tamer . . . . . . 1·10 1·10
1854 45c. Acrobats and trapeze artists . . . . 1·10 1·10
MS1855 133 × 133 mm. Nos. 1851/4 3·50 4·00

695 John Peters Humphrey (author of original Declaration draft)

1998. 50th Anniv of Universal Declaration of Human Rights.
1856 **695** 45c. multicoloured . . . 50 50

696 H.M.C.S. "Sackville" (corvette)

1998. 75th Anniv of Canadian Naval Reserve. Multicoloured.
1857 45c. Type **696** 65 75
1858 45c. H.M.C.S. "Shawinigan" (coastal defence vessel) . . 65 75

697 Angel blowing Trumpet **698** Rabbit

1998. Christmas. Statues of Angels. Multicoloured.
1859 45c. Type **697** 60 20
1860b 52c. Adoring Angel . . . 70 55
1861b 90c. Angel at prayer . . . 1·40 1·75

1999. Chinese New Year ("Year of the Rabbit").
1862 **698** 46c. multicoloured . . . 50 50
MS1863 Circular 100 mm diam. **698** 95c. mult (40 × 40 mm) . . . . 1·75 1·50
No. **MS**1863 also exists with the "CHINA '99" World Stamp Exhibition, Beijing, logo overprinted in gold on the top of the margin.

699 Stylized Mask and Curtain **701** "Marco Polo" (full-rigged ship)

700 "The Raven and the First Men" (B. Reid) and The Great Hall

1999. 50th Anniv of Le Theatre du Rideau Vert.
1864 **699** 46c. multicoloured . . . 50 50

1999. Birds (4th series). As T **643**. Multicoloured. Ordinary or self-adhesive gum.
1865 46c. Northern goshawk . . 85 85
1866 46c. Red-winged blackbird 85 85
1867 46c. American goldfinch . . 85 85
1868 46c. Sandhill crane 85 85

1999. 50th Anniv of University of British Columbia Museum of Anthropology.
1873 **700** 46c. multicoloured . . . 50 50

1999. Canada–Australia Joint Issue. "Marco Polo" (emigrant ship).
1874 **701** 46c. multicoloured . . . 50 50
MS1875 160 × 95 mm. 85c. As No. 1728 of Australia. 46c. Type **701**. (No. **MS**1875 was sold at $1.25 in Canada) . . . . 1·75 1·75
No. **MS**1875 includes the "Australia '99" emblem on the sheet margin and was postally valid in Canada to the value of 46c.

The same miniature sheet was also available in Australia.

1999. Scenic Highways (3rd series). As T **667**. Multicoloured.

1876	46c. Route 132, Quebec, and hang-glider	75	80
1877	46c. Yellowhead Highway, Manitoba, and bison	75	80
1878	46c. Dempster Highway, Northwest Territories, and Indian village elder	75	80
1879	46c. The Discovery Trail, Newfoundland, and whale's tailfin	75	80

702 Inuit Children and Landscape

1999. Creation of Nunavut Territory.

1880	**702** 46c. multicoloured	50	50

703 Elderly Couple on Country Path

1999. International Year of Older Persons.

1881	**703** 46c. multicoloured	50	50

704 Khanda (Sikh symbol)

705 "Arethusa bulbosa" (orchid)

1999. Centenary of Sikhs in Canada.

1882	**704** 46c. multicoloured	50	50

1999. 16th World Orchid Conference, Vancouver. Multicoloured.

1883	46c. Type **705**	60	60
1884	46c. "Amerorchis rotundifolia"	60	60
1885	46c. "Cypripedium pubescens"	60	60
1886	46c. "Platanthera psycodes"	60	60

706 Bookbinding

707 "Northern Dancer" (racehorse)

1999. Traditional Trades. Multicoloured.

(a) Ordinary gum.

1887	1c. Type **706**	10	10
1888	2c. Decorative ironwork	10	10
1889	3c. Glass-blowing	10	10
1890	4c. Oyster farming	10	10
1891	5c. Weaving	10	10
1892	9c. Quilting	10	10
1893	10c. Wood carving	10	15
1894	25c. Leatherworking	20	25

(b) Self-adhesive.

1895	65c. Jewellery making (horiz)	50	55
1896	77c. Basket weaving (horiz)	60	65
1897	$1.25 Wood-carving (horiz)	1·00	1·10

1999. Canadian Horses. Multicoloured. Ordinary or self-adhesive gum.

1903	46c. Type **707**	70	75
1904	46c. "Kingsway Skoal" (rodeo horse)	70	75
1905	46c. "Big Ben" (show jumper)	70	75
1906	46c. "Armbro Flight" (trotter)	70	75

708 Logo engraved on Limestone

709 Athletics

1999. 150th Anniv of Barreau du Quebec (Quebec lawyers' association).

1911	**708** 46c. multicoloured	50	50

1999. Canadian Art (12th series). As T **550**. Mult.

1912	95c. "Coq licorne" (Jean Dallaire)	1·25	1·50

1999. 13th Pan-American Games, Winnipeg. Mult.

1913	46c. Type **709**	70	70
1914	46c. Cycling	70	70
1915	46c. Swimming	70	70
1916	46c. Football	70	70

1999. "China '99" International Stamp Exhibition, Beijing. Sheet 78 × 133 mm, containing Nos. 1883/6. Multicoloured.

MS1917	46c. Type **705**; 46c. Amerorchis rotundifolia; 46c. Cypripedium pubescens; 46c. Platanthera psycodes	2·25	2·75

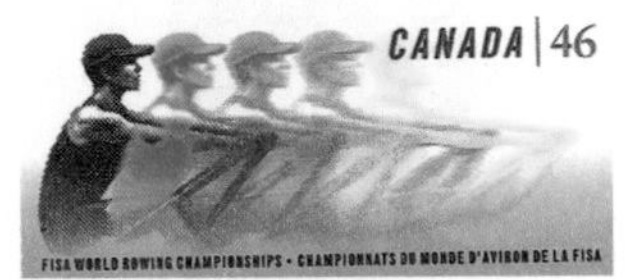

710 Female Rower

1999. 23rd World Rowing Championships, St. Catharines.

1918	**710** 46c. multicoloured	50	50

711 U.P.U. Emblem and World Map

1999. 125th Anniv of Universal Postal Union.

1919	**711** 46c. multicoloured	50	50

712 De Havilland Mosquito F.B. VI

1999. 75th Anniv of Canadian Air Force. Mult.

1920	46c. Type **712**	55	60
1921	46c. Sopwith F.1 Camel	55	60
1922	46c. De Havilland Canada DHC-3 Otter	55	60
1923	46c. De Havilland Canada CC-108 Caribou	55	60
1924	46c. Canadair CL-28 Argus Mk 2	55	60
1925	46c. Canadair (North American) F-86 Sabre 6	55	60
1926	46c. McDonnell Douglas CF-18	55	60
1927	46c. Sopwith 5.F.1 Dolphin	55	60
1928	46c. Armstrong Whitworth Siskin IIIA	55	60
1929	46c. Canadian Vickers (Northrop) Delta II	55	60
1930	46c. Sikorsky CH-124A Sea King helicopter	55	60
1931	46c. Vickers-Armstrong Wellington Mk II	55	60
1932	46c. Avro Anson Mk I	55	60
1933	46c. Canadair (Lockheed) CF-104G Starfighter	55	60
1934	46c. Burgess-Dunne	55	60
1935	46c. Avro 504K	55	60

713 Fokker DR-1

1999. 50th Anniv of Canadian International Air Show. Multicoloured.

1936	46c. Type **713**	70	70
1937	46c. H101 Salto glider	70	70
1938	46c. De Havilland DH100 Vampire Mk III	70	70
1939	46c. Wing walker on Stearman A-75	70	70

Nos. 1936/9 were printed together, se-tenant, forming a composite design which includes a nine-plane Snowbird formation of Canadair CT114 Tutor in the background.

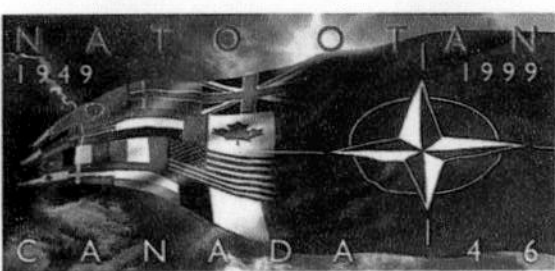

714 N.A.T.O. Emblem and National Flags

1999. 50th Anniv of North Atlantic Treaty Organization.

1940	**714** 46c. multicoloured	60	50

715 Man ploughing on Book

1999. Centenary of Frontier College (workers' education organization).

1941	**715** 46c. multicoloured	50	50

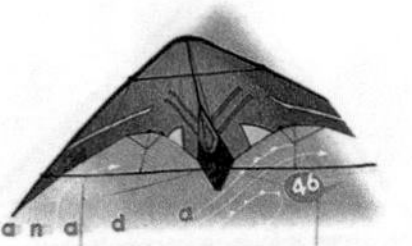

716 Master Control Sports Kite

1999. Stamp Collecting Month. Kites. Mult.

1942	46c. Type **716**	55	60
1943	46c. Indian Garden Flying Carpet (irregular rectangle, 35½ × 32 mm)	55	60
1944	46c. Gibson Girl box kite (horiz, 38½ × 25 mm)	55	60
1945	46c. Dragon Centipede (oval, 39 × 29 mm)	55	60

717 Boy holding Dove

1999. New Millennium. Three sheets, each 108 × 108 mm, containing T **717** and similar square designs in blocks of 4. Self-adhesive.

MS1946	– 46c. × 4 multicoloured	2·00	2·50
MS1947	**717** 55c. × 4 multicoloured	4·50	4·75
MS1948	– 95c. × 4 brown	3·75	4·50

DESIGNS: 46c. Holographic image of dove in flight; 95c. Dove with olive branch.

718 Angel playing Drum

1999. Christmas. Victorian Angels. Multicoloured.

1949	46c. Type **718**	60	20
1950	55c. Angel with toys	70	50
1951	95c. Angel with star	1·40	2·00

719 Portia White (singer)

1999. Millennium Collection (1st series). Entertainment and Arts. Miniature sheets, each 108 × 112 mm, containing T **719** and similar vert designs. Multicoloured.

MS1952	46c. Type **719**; 46c. Glenn Gould (pianist); 46c. Guy Lombardo (conductor of "Royal Canadians"); 46c. Félix Leclerc (musician, playwright and actor)	2·00	2·50
MS1953	46c. Artists looking at painting (Royal Canadian Academy of Arts); 46c. Cloud, stave and pencil marks (The Canada Council); 46c. Man with video camera (National Film Board of Canada); 46c. Newsreader (Canadian Broadcasting Corporation)	2·00	2·50
MS1954	46c. Calgary Stampede; 46c. Circus performers; 46c. Ice hockey (Hockey Night); 46c. Goalkeeper (Ice hockey live from The Forum)	2·00	2·50
MS1955	46c. IMAX cinema; 46c. Computer image (Softimage); 46c. Ted Rogers Sr ("Plugging in the Radio"); 46c. Sir William Stephenson (inventor of radio facsimile system)	2·00	2·50
MS1952/5	Set of 4 sheets	7·25	9·00

See also Nos. **MS**1959/62, **MS**1969/73 and **MS**1982/5.

720 Millennium Partnership Programme Logo

2000. Canada Millennium Partnership Programme.

1956	**720** 46c. red, green and blue	50	50

721 Chinese Dragon

2000. Chinese New Year ("Year of the Dragon").

1957	**721** 46c. multicoloured	50	50
MS1958	150 × 85 mm. **721** 90c. multicoloured	1·25	1·50

2000. Millennium Collection (2nd series). Charities, Medical Pioneers, Peacekeepers and Social Reforms. Miniature sheets, each 108 × 112 mm, containing vert designs as T **719**. Multicoloured.

MS1959	46c. Providing equipment (Canadian International Development Agency); 46c. Dr. Lucille Teasdale (medical missionary); 46c. Terry Fox (Marathon of Hope); 46c. Delivering meal (Meals on Wheels)	1·90	2·25
MS1960	46c. Sir Frederick Banting (discovery of insulin); 46c. Armand Frappier (developer of BCG vaccine); 46c. Dr. Hans Selye (research into stress); 46c. "Dr. Maude Abbott" (pathologist) (M. Bell Eastlake)	1·90	2·25
MS1961	46c. Senator Raoul Dandurand (diplomat); 46c. Pauline Vanier and Elizabeth Smellie (nursing pioneers); 46c. Lester B. Pearson (diplomat); 46c. One-legged man (Ottawa Convention on Banning Landmines)	1·90	2·25
MS1962	46c. Nun and surgeon (medical care); 46c. "Women are persons" (sculpture by Barbara Paterson) (Appointment of women senators); 46c. Alphonse and Dorimène Desjardins (People's bank movement); 46c. Father Moses Coady (Adult education pioneer)	1·90	2·25
MS1959/62	Set of 4 sheets	7·00	8·00

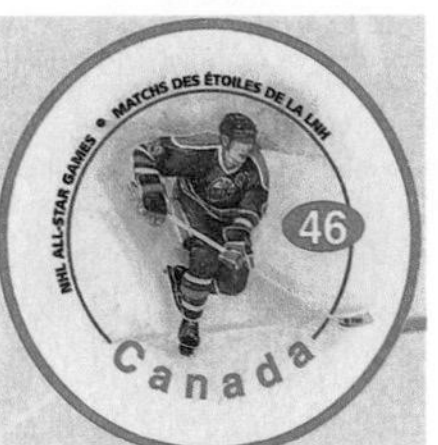

722 Wayne Gretzky (ice-hockey player)

2000. 50th National Hockey League All-Star Game. Multicoloured.

1963	46c. Type **722**	65	70
1964	46c. Gordie Howe (No. 9 in white jersey)	65	70

1965 46c. Maurice Richard (No. 9 in blue and red jersey) . . 65 70
1966 46c. Doug Harvey (No. 2) 65 70
1967 46c. Bobby Orr (No. 4) . . 65 70
1968 46c. Jacques Plante (No. 1) 65 70
See also Nos. 2052/7, 2118/23 and 2178/3.

2000. Millennium Collection (3rd series). First Inhabitants, Great Thinkers, Culture and Literary Legends, and Charitable Foundations. Miniature sheets, each 108 × 112 mm, containing vert designs as T **719**. Multicoloured.

MS1969 46c. Pontiac (Ottawa chief); 46c. Tom Longboat (long-distance runner); 46c. "Inuit Shaman" (sculpture by Paul Toolooktook); 46c. Shaman and patient (Indian medicine) . . . . 1·90 2·25
MS1970 46c. Prof. Marshall McLuhan (media philosopher); 46c. Northrop Frye (literary critic); 46c. Roger Lemelin (novelist); 46c. Prof. Hilda Marion Neatby (educator) . . . . . . 1·90 2·25
MS1971 46c. Bow of Viking longship (L'Anse aux Meadows World Heritage Site); 46c. Immigrant family (Pier 21 monument); 46c. Neptune mask (Neptune Theatre, Halifax); 46c. Auditorium and actor (The Stratford Festival) . . . . . . 1·90 2·25
MS1972 46c. W. O. Mitchell (writer); 46c. Gratien Gélinas (actor, producer and playwright); 46c. Text and fountain pen (Cercle du Livre de France); 46c. Harlequin and roses (Harlequin Books) 1·90 2·25
MS1973 46c. Hart Massey (Massey Foundation); 46c. Izaak Walton Killam and Dorothy Killam; 46f. Eric Lafferty Harvie (Glenbow Foundation); 46c. Macdonald Stewart Foundation . . . . . 1·90 2·25
MS1969/73 Set of 5 sheets . . . 8·50 10·00

2000. Birds (5th series). As T **643**. Multicoloured. Ordinary or self-adhesive gum.
1974 46c. Canadian warbler . . . 70 70
1975 46c. Osprey 70 70
1976 46c. Pacific diver ("Pacific Loon") 70 70
1977 46c. Blue jay 70 70

2000. Millennium Collection (4th series). Canadian Agriculture, Commerce and Technology. Miniature sheets, each 108 × 112 mm, containing vert designs as T **719**. Multicoloured.

MS1982 46c. Sir Charles Saunders (developer of Marquis wheat); 46c. Baby (Pablum baby food); 46c. Dr. Archibald Gowanlock Huntsman (frozen fish pioneer); 46c. Oven chips and field of potatoes (McCain Frozen Foods) 1·90 2·25
MS1983 46c. Early trader and Indian (Hudson's Bay Company); 46c. Satellite over earth (Bell Canada Enterprises); 46c. Jos. Louis biscuits and Vachon family (Vachon Family Bakery); 46c. Bread and eggs (George Weston Limited) . . . . 1·90 2·25
MS1984 46c. George Klein and cog wheels (inventor of electric wheelchair and micro-surgical staple gun); 46c. Abraham Gesner (developer of kerosene); 46c. Alexander Graham Bell (inventor of telephone); 46c. Joseph-Armand Bombadier (inventor of snowmobile) . . . . 1·90 2·25
MS1985 46c. Workers and steam locomotive (Rogers Pass rail tunnel); 46c. Manic 5 dam (Manicouagan River hydro-electric project); 46c. Mobile Servicing System for International Space Station (Canadian Space Program); 46c. CN Tower (World's tallest building) . . . . 1·90 2·25
MS1982/5 Set of 4 sheets . . . . 7·00 8·00

723 Judges and Supreme Court Building

2000. 125th Anniv of Supreme Court of Canada.
1986 **723** 46c. multicoloured . . . 50 50

724 Lethbridge Bridge, Synthetic Rubber Plant, X-ray of Heart Pacemaker and Microwave Radio System

2000. 75th Anniv of Ceremony for Calling of an Engineer.
1987 **724** 46c. multicoloured . . . 50 50
Each vertical pair completes the engineer's ring as shown on Type **274**.

725

2000. "Picture Postage" Greetings Stamps. Self-adhesive.
1988 **725** 46c. multicoloured . . . 50 50
No. 1988 was issued to include appropriate greetings labels which could be inserted into the rectangular space on each stamp.
See also Nos. 2045 and 2099.

726 Coastal-style Mailboxes in Autumn

2000. Traditional Rural Mailboxes. Multicoloured.
1989 46c. Type **726** 60 65
1990 46c. House and cow-shaped mailboxes in springtime 60 65
1991 46c. Tractor-shaped mailbox in summertime 60 65
1992 46c. Barn and duck-shaped mailboxes in winter . . . 60 65

727 Gorge and Fir Tree

2000. Canadian Rivers and Lakes. Multicoloured. Self-adhesive.
1993 55c. Type **727** 60 65
1994 55c. Lake and water lilies 60 65
1995 55c. Glacier and reflected mountains 60 65
1996 55c. Estuary and aerial view 60 65
1997 55c. Waterfall and forest edge 60 65
1998 95c. Iceberg and mountain river . . . . 95 1·10
1999 95c. Rapids and waterfall 95 1·10
2000 95c. Moraine and river . . . 95 1·10
2001 95c. Shallows and waves on lake . . . . 95 1·10
2002 95c. Forest sloping to waters edge and tree . . . . . . 95 1·10

728 Queen Elizabeth the Queen Mother with Roses

729 Teenager with Two Children

2000. Queen Elizabeth the Queen Mother's 100th Birthday.
2003 **728** 95c. multicoloured . . . 1·10 1·25

2000. Centenary of Boys and Girls Clubs of Canada.
2004 **729** 46c. multicoloured . . . 50 50

730 Clouds over Rockies and Symbol

2000. 57th General Conference Session of Seventh-day Adventist Church, Toronto.
2005 **730** 46c. multicoloured . . . 50 50

731 "Space Travellers and Canadian Flag" (Rosalie Anne Nardelli)

2000. "Stampin' the Future" (children's stamp design competition). Multicoloured.
2006 46c. Type **731** 60 60
2007 46c. "Travelling to the Moon" (Sarah Lutgen) . . 60 60
2008 46c. "Astronauts in shuttle" (Andrew Wright) 60 60
2009 46c. "Children completing Canada as jigsaw" (Christine Weera) 60 60
MS2010 114 × 90 mm. Nos. 2006/9 1·90 2·25

2000. Canadian Art (13th series). As T **550**. Mult.
2011 95c. "The Artist at Niagara, 1858" (Cornelius Krieghoff) . . . . 1·25 1·40

732 Tall Ships, Halifax Harbour

2000. Tall Ships Race. Multicoloured. Self-adhesive.
2012 46c. Type **732** 65 75
2013 46c. Tall ships, Halifax Harbour (face value top right) 65 75
Nos. 2012/13 are arranged as five se-tenant pairs on a background photograph of Halifax Harbour.

733 Workers, Factory and Transport

2000. Centenary of Department of Labour.
2014 **733** 46c. multicoloured . . . 50 50

734 Petro-Canada Sign, Oil Rig and Consumers

2000. 25th Anniv of Petro-Canada (oil company). Self-adhesive.
2015 **734** 46c. multicoloured . . . 60 50

735 Narwhal

2000. Whales. Multicoloured.
2016 46c. Type **735** 70 70
2017 46c. Blue whale (*Balaenoptera musculus*) 70 70
2018 46c. Bowhead whale (*Balaena mysticetus*) . . . 70 70
2019 46c. White whales (*Delphinapterus leucas*) . . 70 70
Nos. 2016/19 were printed together, se-tenant, with the backgrounds forming an overall composite design.

736

2000. "Picture Postage" Christmas Greetings. Self-adhesive.
2020 **736** 46c. multicoloured . . . 50 50
See also Nos. 2045/9 and 2099/103.

737 "The Nativity" (Susie Matthias)

738 Lieut.-Col. Sam Steele, Lord Strathcona's Horse

2000. Christmas. Religious Paintings by Mouth and Foot Artists. Multicoloured.
2021 46c. Type **737** 50 20
2022 55c. "The Nativity and Christmas Star" (Michael Guillemette) 65 60
2023 95c. "Mary and Joseph journeying to Bethlehem" (David Allan Carter) . . 1·25 1·75

2000. Canadian Regiments. Multicoloured.
2024 46c. Type **738** 65 65
2025 46c. Drummer, Voltigeurs de Quebec 65 65

739 Red Fox

740 Maple Leaves

740a Maple Leaves and Key

740b Red Maple Leaf and Stem

2000. Wildlife. Multicoloured.
2026 60c. Type **739** 65 70
2027 75c. Grey wolf 80 95
2028 $1.05 White-tailed deer . . . 1·10 1·25

2000. Self-adhesive coil stamp.
2029 **740** 47c. multicoloured . . . 75 75
2030 48c. multicoloured . . . 50 50
2031 **740a** 49c. multicoloured . . . 50 50
2032 **740b** 80c. multicoloured . . . 90 95
2033 $1.40 multicoloured (green leaf) . . . . . 1·75 2·00

2000. "Picture Postage" Greetings Stamps. As T **725** and **736**. Multicoloured. Self-adhesive.
2045 47c. Type **725** 50 55
2046 47c. Type **736** 50 55
2047 47c. Roses frame 50 55
2048 47c. Mahogany frame . . . 50 55
2049 47c. Silver frame 50 55

741 Green Jade Snake

2001. Chinese New Year. ("Year of the Snake").
2050 **741** 47c. multicoloured . . . 50 50
MS2051 112 × 75 mm. $1.05, Brown jade snake . . . . 1·25 1·60

2001. National Hockey League. All-Star Game Players (1st series). As T **722**. Multicoloured.
2052 47c. Jean Beliveau (wearing No. 4) 65 65
2053 47c. Terry Sawchuk (on one knee) 65 65
2054 47c. Eddie Shore (wearing No. 2) 65 65
2055 47c. Denis Potvin (wearing No. 5) 65 65
2056 47c. Bobby Hull (wearing No. 9) 65 65
2057 47c. Syl Apps (in Toronto jersey) 65 65
See also Nos. 2118/23 and 2178/83.

2001. Birds (6th series). As T **643**. Multicoloured. Ordinary or self-adhesive gum.
2058 47c. Golden eagle 65 65
2059 47c. Arctic tern 65 65
2060 47c. Rock ptarmigan . . . 65 65
2061 47c. Lapland bunting ("Lapland Longspur") . . 65 65

742 Highjumping

2001. 4th Francophonie Games. Multicoloured.
2066 47c. Type **742** 70 70
2067 47c. Folk dancing 70 70

743 Ice Dancing

2001. World Figure Skating Championships, Vancouver. Multicoloured.
2068 47c. Type **743** 65 65
2069 47c. Pairs 65 65
2070 47c. Men's singles 65 65
2071 47c. Women's singles . . . 65 65

744 3d. Beaver Stamp of 1851

2001. 150th Anniv of the Canadian Postal Service.
2072 **744** 47c. multicoloured . . . 60 50

745 Toronto Blue Jay Emblem, Maple Leaf and Baseball

2001. 25th Season of the Toronto Blue Jays (baseball team). Self-adhesive.
2073 **745** 47c. multicoloured . . . 60 50

746 North and South America on Globe

748 Christ on Palm Sunday and Khachkar (stone cross)

747 Butchart Gardens, British Columbia

2001. Summit of the Americas, Quebec.
2074 **746** 47c. multicoloured . . . 60 50

2001. Tourist Attractions (1st series). Multicoloured. Self-adhesive.
2075 60c. Type **747** 70 75
2076 60c. Apple Blossom Festival, Nova Scotia 70 75
2077 60c. White Pass and Yukon Route 70 75
2078 60c. Sugar Bushes, Quebec 70 75
2079 60c. Court House, Niagra-on-the-Lake, Ontario . . 70 75
2080 $1.05 The Forks, Winnipeg, Manitoba . . . . 1·25 1·40
2081 $1.05 Barkerville, British Colombia . . . . 1·25 1·40
2082 $1.05 Canadian Tulip Festival, Ontario . . . . 1·25 1·40
2083 $1.05 Auyuittuq National Park, Nunavut . . . . . 1·25 1·40
2084 $1.05 Signal Hill, St. John's, Newfoundland . . . . . 1·25 1·40
See also Nos. 2143/52.

2001. 1700th Anniv of Armenian Church.
2085 **748** 47c. multicoloured . . . 60 45

749 Cadets, Mackenzie Building and Military Equipment

2001. 125th Anniv of Royal Military College of Canada.
2086 **749** 47c. multicoloured . . . 60 45

750 Pole-vaulting

751 "Pierre Trudeau" (Myfanwy Pavelic)

2001. 8th International Amateur Athletic Federation World Championships, Edmonton. Multicoloured.
2087 47c. Type **750** 65 65
2088 47c. Sprinting 65 65

2001. Pierre Trudeau (former Prime Minister) Commemoration.
2089 **751** 47c. multicoloured . . . 60 45
MS2090 128 × 155 mm. No. 2090 × 4 . . . . 2·00 2·25

752 "Morden Centennial" Rose (⅔-size illustration)

2001. Canadian Roses. Multicoloured. Self-adhesive.
2091 47c. Type **752** 60 65
2092 47c. "Agnes" 60 65
2093 47c. "Champlain" 60 65
2094 47c. "Canadian White Star" 60 65
MS2095 145 × 90 mm. Nos. 2091/4 2·25 2·50

753 Ottawa Chief Hassaki addressing Peace Delegates

2001. 300th Anniv of Great Peace Treaty of Montreal between American Indians and New France.
2096 **753** 47c. multicoloured . . . 60 45

2001. Canadian Art (14th series). As T **550**. Multicoloured.
2097 $1.05 "The Space Between Columns 21 (Italian)" (Jack Shadbolt) . . . . . 1·40 1·60

754 Clown juggling with Crutches and Handicapped Boy

2001. The Shriners (charitable organization) Commemoration.
2098 **754** 47c. multicoloured . . . 60 45

755 Toys and Flowers

2001. "Picture Postage" Greetings Stamps. Frames as Nos. 2045/7 and 2049, but each inscr "Domestic Lettermail Postes-lettres du regime interieur". Multicoloured. Self-adhesive.
2099 – As Type **725** 40 45
2100 – As Type **736** 40 45
2101 – Type **755** 40 45
2102 – Roses frame 40 45
2103 – Silver frame 40 45

756 Jean Gascon and Jean-Louis Roux (founders of Theatre du Nouveau Monde, Montreal)

2001. Theatre Anniversaries. Multicoloured.
2104 47c. Type **756** (50th anniv) 65 65
2105 47c. Ambrose Small (founder of Grand Theatre, London, Ontario) (centenary) . . . 65 65

757 Hot Air Balloons

2001. Stamp Collecting Month. Hot Air Balloons. Multicoloured, background colours given below. Self-adhesive.
2106 47c. Type **757** (green background) 65 65
2107 47c. Balloons with lavender background 65 65
2108 47c. Balloons with mauve background 65 65
2109 47c. Balloons with bistre background 65 65

758 Horse-drawn Sleigh and Christmas Lights

2001. Christmas. Festive Lights. Multicoloured.
2110 47c. Type **758** 50 20
2111 60c. Ice skaters and Christmas lights 70 70
2112 $1.05 Children with snowman and Christmas lights . . . . 1·25 1·40

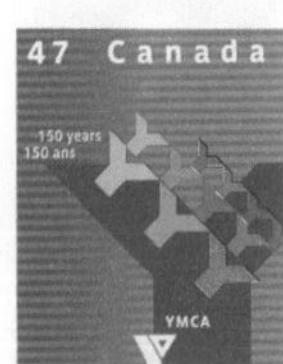
759 Pattern of Ys Logo

2001. 150th Anniv of Y.M.C.A. in Canada.
2113 **759** 47c. multicoloured . . . 60 45

760 Statues from Canadian War Memorial, Ottawa and Badge

2001. 75th Anniv of Royal Canadian Legion.
2114 **760** 47c. multicoloured . . . 60 45

761 Queen Elizabeth II and Maple Leaf

2002. Golden Jubilee.
2115 **761** 48c. multicoloured . . . 60 45

762 Horse and Bamboo Leaves

763 Speed Skating

2002. Chinese New Year ("Year of the Horse"). Multicoloured.
2116 **762** 48c. multicoloured . . . 60 45
MS2117 102 × 102 mm. $1.25, Horse and peach blossom . . . . . 1·40 1·60

2002. National Hockey League. All-Star Game Players (2nd series). As T **722**. Multicoloured.
2118 48c. Tim Horton (wearing Maple Leaf No. 7 jersey) 65 65
2119 48c. Guy Lafleur (wearing Canadiens No. 10 jersey) 65 65
2120 48c. Howie Morenz (wearing Canadiens jersey and brown gloves) 65 65
2121 48c. Glenn Hall (wearing Chicago Blackhawks jersey) 65 65
2122 48c. Red Kelly (wearing Maple Leaf No. 4 jersey) 65 65
2123 48c. Phil Esposito (wearing Boston Bruins No. 7 jersey) 65 65

2002. Winter Olympic Games, Salt Lake City. Multicoloured.
2124 48c. Type **763** 65 65
2125 48c. Curling 65 65
2126 48c. Aerial skiing 65 65
2127 48c. Women's ice hockey . . 65 65

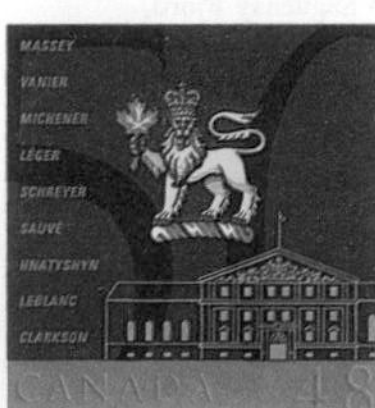
764 Lion Symbol of Governor General and Rideau Hall, Ottawa

2002. 50th Anniv of First Canadian Governor-General.
2128 **764** 48c. multicoloured . . . 60 45

765 University of Manitoba (125th Anniv)

2002. Canadian Universities' Anniversaries. Mult.
2129 48c. Type **765** 60 60
2130 48c. Universite Laval, Quebec (150th anniv of charter) 60 60
2131 48c. Trinity College, Toronto (150th anniv of foundation) 60 60
2132 48c. Saint Mary's University, Halifax (bicent) 60 60
See also Nos. 2190/1.

2002. Canadian Art (15th series). As T **550**. Multicoloured.
2133 $1.25 "Church and Horse" (Alex Colville) . . . . . 1·40 1·60

766 "City of Vancouver" Tulip and Vancouver Skyline

2002. 50th Canadian Tulip Festival, Ottawa. Tulips. Multicoloured. Self-adhesive.
2134 48c. Type **766** 60 65
2135 48c. "Monte Carlo" and Dows Lake tulip beds . . 60 65

2136 48c. "Ottawa" and National War Memorial 60 65
2137 48c. "The Bishop" and Ottawa Hospital 60 65

767 *Dendronepthea gigantea* and *Dendronepthea* (coral)

2002. Canada–Hong Kong Joint Issue. Corals. Multicoloured.
2138 48c. Type **767** 60 65
2139 48c. *Tubastrea*, *Echinogorgia* and island 60 65
2140 48c. North Atlantic pink tree coral, Pacific orange cup and North Pacific horn coral 60 65
2141 48c. North Atlantic giant orange tree coral and black coral 60 65
MS2142 161 × 87 mm. Nos. 2138/41 2·25 2·50

2002. Tourist Attractions (2nd series). As T **747**. Multicoloured. Self-adhesive.
2143 65c. Yukon Quest Sled Dog Race 75 80
2144 65c. Icefields Parkway, Alberta 75 80
2145 65c. Train in Agawa Canyon, Northern Ontario 75 80
2146 65c. Old Port, Montreal . . 75 80
2147 65c. Saw mill, Kings Landing, New Brunswick 75 80
2148 $1.25 Northern Lights, Northwest Territories . . 1·25 1·40
2149 $1.25 Stanley Park, British Columbia . . . . 1·25 1·40
2150 $1.25 Head-Smashed-In Buffalo Jump, Alberta . . 1·25 1·40
2151 $1.25 Saguenay Fjord, Quebec . . . . 1·25 1·40
2152 $1.25 Lighthouse, Peggy's Cove, Nova Scotia . . . 1·25 1·40

768 "Embacle" (Charles Daudelin)

2002. Sculptures. Multicoloured.
2153 48c. Type **768** 60 65
2154 48c. "Lumberjacks" (Leo Mol) 60 65

769 1899 Queen Victoria 2c. Stamp, Stonewall Post Office and Postmark

2002. Centenary of Canadian Postmasters and Assistants Association.
2155 **769** 48c. multicoloured . . . 60 45

770 World Youth Day Logo

2002. 17th World Youth Day, Toronto. Self-adhesive.
2156 **770** 48c. multicoloured . . . 60 45

2002. "Amphilex 2002" International Stamp Exhibition, Amsterdam. Ordinary gum.
MS2157 160 × 97 mm. As Nos. 2134/7 . . . . 2·25 2·50

771 Hands gripping Rope and P.S.I. Logo

2002. Public Services International World Congress, Ottawa.
2158 **771** 48c. multicoloured . . . 60 45

772 Tree in Four Seasons

2002. 75th Anniv of Public Pensions.
2159 **772** 48c. multicoloured . . . 60 45

773 Mount Elbrus, Russia

2002. International Year of Mountains. Multicoloured. Self-adhesive.
2160 48c. Type **773** 60 60
2161 48c. Puncak Jaya, Indonesia 60 60
2162 48c. Mount Everest, Nepal 60 60
2163 48c. Mount Kilimanjaro, Tanzania 60 60
2164 48c. Vinson Massif, Antarctica 60 60
2165 48c. Mount Aconcagua, Argentina 60 60
2166 48c. Mount McKinley, U.S.A. 60 60
2167 48c. Mount Logan, Canada 60 60

774 Teacher writing on Board

2002. World Teachers' Day.
2168 **774** 48c. multicoloured . . . 60 45

775 Frieze from Toronto Stock Exchange and Globe

2002. 150th Anniv of Toronto Stock Exchange.
2169 **775** 48c. multicoloured . . . 60 45

776 Sir Sandford Fleming, Map of Canada and *Iris* (cable ship)

2002. Communications Centenaries. Multicoloured.
2170 48c. Type **776** (opening of Pacific Cable) 65 65
2171 48c. Guglielmo Marconi, Map of Canada and wireless equipment (first Transatlantic radio message) 65 65

777 "Genesis" (painting by Daphne Odjig)

2002. Christmas. Aboriginal Art. Multicoloured.
2172 48c. Type **777** 55 20
2173 65c. "Winter Travel" (painting by Cecil Youngfox) 70 70
2174 $1.25 "Mary and Child" (sculpture by Irene Katak Angutitaq) . . . . 1·25 1·50

778 Conductor's Hands and Original Orchestra

2002. Centenary of Quebec Symphony Orchestra.
2175 **778** 48c. multicoloured . . . 75 45

779 Sculpture of Ram's Head

2003. Chinese New Year ("Year of the Ram"). Multicoloured.
2176 48c. Type **779** 60 45
MS2177 125 × 103 mm. $1.25 Sculpture of goat's head (33 × 57 mm) . . . . 1·25 1·50

2003. National Hockey League. All-Star Game Players (3rd series). As T **722**. Multicoloured. Ordinary or self-adhesive.
2178 48c. Frank Mahovlich (wearing Maple Leaf No. 27 jersey) 60 65
2179 48c. Raymond Bourque (wearing Boston Bruins No. 77 jersey) 60 65
2180 48c. Serge Savard (wearing Canadiens No. 18 jersey) 60 65
2181 48c. Stan Mikita (wearing Chicago Blackhawks No. 21 jersey) 60 65
2182 48c. Mike Bossy (wearing New York Islanders No. 22 jersey) 60 65
2183 48c. Bill Durnan (wearing Canadiens jersey and brown gloves) 60 65

2003. Canadian Universities' Anniversaries. As T **765** but vert. Multicoloured.
2190 48c. Bishop's University, Quebec (150th anniv of university status) 65 65
2191 48c. University of Western Ontario, London (125th anniv) 65 65
2192 48c. St. Francis Xavier University, Nova Scotia (150th Anniv) 65 65
2193 48c. Macdonald Institute, University of Guelph, Ontana (centenary) . . . 65 65
2194 48c. Universite de Montreal (125th anniv) 65 65

780 Leach's Storm Petrel

2003. Bird Paintings by John Audubon. Multicoloured. Ordinary gum.
2195 48c. Type **780** 60 60
2196 48c. Brent goose ("Brant") 60 60
2197 48c. Great cormorant . . . 60 60
2198 48c. Common murre 60 60

(b) Self-adhesive.
2199 65c. Gyrfalcon (vert) . . . . 1·00 1·10

781 Ranger looking through Binoculars

2003. 60th Anniv of Canadian Rangers.
2200 **781** 48c. multicoloured . . . 60 45

782 Greek Figure with Dove

2003. 75th Anniv of American Hellenic Educational Progressive Association in Canada.
2201 **782** 48c. multicoloured . . . 60 45

783 Firefighter carrying Boy and Burning Buildings

2003. Volunteer Firefighters.
2202 **783** 48c. multicoloured . . . 50 55

784 Queen Elizabeth II

2003. 50th Anniv of Coronation.
2203 **784** 48c. multicoloured . . . 50 55

785 Quebec City (c. 1703) Seal and Excerpt from Letter

2003. Pedro da Silva (first official courier of New France).
2204 **785** 48c. multicoloured . . . 50 55

2003. Tourist Attractions (3rd series). As T **747**. Multicoloured. Self-adhesive.
2205 65c. Wilberforce Falls, Nunavut 80 85
2206 65c. Inside Passage, British Columbia 80 85
2207 65c. Royal Canadian Mounted Police Depot Division, Regina, Saskatchewan 80 85
2208 65c. Casa Loma, Toronto 80 85
2209 65c. Gatineau Park, Quebec 80 85
2210 $1.25 Dragon boat race, Vancouver . . . . 1·60 1·75
2211 $1.25 Polar bear, Churchill, Manitoba . . . . 1·60 1·75
2212 $1.25 Niagara Falls, Ontario 1·60 1·75
2213 $1.25 Magdalen Islands, Quebec . . . . 1·60 1·75
2214 $1.25 Province House, Charlottetown, Prince Edward Island . . . . . 1·75 1·75

786 Assembly Logo

2003. 10th Lutheran World Federation Assembly, Winnipeg.
2215 **786** 48c. multicoloured . . . 50 55

2003. Vancouver's Successful Bid for Winter Olympic Games, 2010. No. 1368 (Canadian flag definitive) optd **VANCOUVER 2010**.
2216 48c. multicoloured 50 55

788 Mountains and Sea

2003. Canada--Alaska Cruise "Picture Postage". Multicoloured. Self-adhesive.

2217	(–)	Type **788**	3·00	3·25
2218	(–)	Tail fin of whale, mountains and sea	3·00	3·25

789 Canadian F-86 Sabre Fighter Plane, Sailors and Infantrymen

2003. 50th Anniv of Signing of Korea Armistice.

2219	**789**	48c. multicoloured	50	55

790 Anne Hebert

2003. 50th Anniv of National Library of Canada. Showing authors and portions of their handwritten text. Multicoloured.

2220	48c. Type **790**	50	55
2221	48c. Hector de Saint-Denys Garneau	50	55
2222	48c. Morley Callaghan	50	55
2223	48c. Susanna Moodie and Catharine Parr Traill	50	55

791 Cyclists in Road Race

2003. World Road Cycling Championships, Hamilton, Ontario.

2224	**791**	48c. multicoloured	50	55

792 Marc Garneau

2003. Stamp Collecting Month. Canadian Astronauts. Multicoloured. Self-adhesive.

2225	48c. Type **792**	50	55
2226	48c. Roberta Bondar	50	55
2227	48c. Steve MacLean	50	55
2228	48c. Chris Hadfield	50	55
2229	48c. Robert Thirsk	50	55
2230	48c. Bjarni Tryggvason	50	55
2231	48c. Dave Williams	50	55
2232	48c. Julie Payette	50	55

793 Maple Leaves, Canada

795 Ice Skates and Wrapped Presents

794 White Birds

2003. National Emblems. Multicoloured.

2233	48c. Type **793**	50	55
2234	48c. Cassis fistula flowers, Thailand	50	55
MS2235	120 × 96 mm. Nos. 2233/4	1·00	1·10

No. **MS**2235 commemorates Bangkok 2003 International Stamp Exhibition, Thailand.

Stamps of the same designs were issued by Thailand.

2003. 80th Birth Anniv of Jean-Paul Riopelle (painter and sculptor). T **794** and similar horiz designs showing details from fresco "L'Hommage a Rosa Luxemburg". Multicoloured.

MS2236	178 × 244 mm. 48c. Type **794**; 48c. Two white herons and white birds; 48c. Flying bird, flower and three white birds in cameo; 48c. Grouse on moor, white bird and sun; 48c. Two flying white birds in cameo and silhouette of falcon; 48c. Two white birds and cameo of flying duck	3·00	3·25
MS2237	159 × 95 mm. $1.25 Eggs and bird silhouette	1·60	1·75

2003. Christmas. Multicoloured.

2238	48c. Type **795**	50	55
2239	65c. Teddy bear and wrapped presents	80	85
2240	$1.25 Toy duck on wheels and wrapped presents	1·60	1·75

796 Queen Elizabeth II, 2002

797 Monkey King on Cloud

2003. Self-adhesive.

2241	**796**	49c. black, mauve and scarlet	50	55

2004. Chinese New Year ("Year of the Monkey"). Showing scenes from "Journey to the West" by Wu Ch'eng-en. Multicoloured

2247	49c. Type **797**	50	55
MS2248	115 × 82 mm. $1.40 Monkey on road to India	1·75	2·00

2004. Hong Kong 2004 International Stamp Exhibition. No. **MS**2248 optd **Hong Kong Stamp Expo 2004** and exhibition emblem in gold on sheet margin.

MS2249	115 × 82 mm. $1.40 Monkey on road to India	1·75	2·00

OFFICIAL STAMPS

1949. Optd **O.H.M.S.**

O162	**111**	1c. green (postage)	2·00	2·50
O163	**112**	2c. brown	12·00	12·00
O164	–	3c. purple (No. 378)	1·25	2·00
O165	**112**	4c. red	2·25	2·00
O166	–	10c. green (No. 402)	4·00	15
O167	–	14c. brown (No. 403)	4·50	3·00
O168	–	20c. grey (No. 404)	12·00	60
O169	–	50c. green (No. 405)	£160	£120
O170	–	$1 purple (No. 406)	45·00	48·00
O171	–	7c. blue (No. 407) (air)	24·00	7·00

1949. Optd **O.H.M.S.**

O172	**135**	1c. green	1·75	1·00
O173	–	2c. brown (No. 415)	3·00	1·50
O174	–	3c. purple (No. 416)	2·25	1·00
O175	–	4c. red (No. 417)	2·25	15
O176	–	5c. blue (No. 418)	4·00	2·00
O177	**141**	50c. green	32·00	28·00

1950. Optd **G.**

O178	**135**	1c. green (postage)	1·25	10
O179	–	2c. brown (No. 415)	2·50	2·75
O180	–	2c. green (No. 415a)	1·75	10
O181	–	3c. purple (No. 416)	2·00	10
O183	–	4c. red (No. 417)	2·25	30
O184	–	5c. blue (No. 418)	3·00	1·00
O193	**153**	7c. blue	2·00	2·00
O185	–	10c. green (No. 402)	3·00	10
O191	**142**	10c. purple	3·75	10
O186	–	14c. brown (No. 403)	14·00	5·00
O187	–	20c. grey (No. 404)	25·00	30
O194	–	20c. grey (No. 441)	2·00	10
O188	**141**	50c. green	13·00	13·00
O189	–	$1 purple (No. 406)	70·00	70·00
O192	–	$1 blue (No. 433)	60·00	70·00
O190	–	7c. blue (No. 407) (air)	24·00	14·00

1953. First Queen Elizabeth II stamps optd **G.**

O196	**158**	1c. brown	15	10
O197		2c. green	20	10
O198		3c. red	20	10
O199		4c. violet	30	10
O200		5c. blue	30	10

1953. Pictorial stamps optd **G.**

O206	**165**	10c. brown	60	10
O207	–	20c. green (No. 488)	2·50	10
O201	**160**	50c. green	3·00	2·25
O195	**154**	$1 black	10·00	12·00

1955. Second Queen Elizabeth II stamps optd **G.**

O202	**161**	1c. brown	55	20
O203		2c. green	15	10
O204		4c. violet	40	10
O205		5c. blue	15	10

1963. Third Queen Elizabeth II stamps optd **G.**

O208	**215**	1c. brown	40	3·75
O209		2c. green	40	3·50
O210		4c. red	40	2·25
O211		5c. blue	40	1·25

OFFICIAL SPECIAL DELIVERY STAMPS

1950. Optd **O.H.M.S.**

OS20	10c. green (No. S15)	17·00	24·00

1950. Optd **G.**

OS21	10c. green (No. S15)	26·00	29·00

POSTAGE DUE STAMPS

D 1　D 2

1906.

D1	**D 1**	1c. violet	9·00	2·75
D3		2c. violet	20·00	1·00
D5		4c. violet	45·00	50·00
D7		5c. violet	26·00	3·50
D8		10c. violet	32·00	19·00

1930.

D 9	**D 2**	1c. violet	8·50	11·00
D10		2c. violet	7·50	1·90
D11		4c. violet	15·00	6·50
D12		5c. violet	16·00	28·00
D13		10c. violet	65·00	65·00

D 3　D 4

1933.

D14	**D 3**	1c. violet	9·50	14·00
D15		2c. violet	7·50	4·50
D16		4c. violet	12·00	15·00
D17		10c. violet	24·00	32·00

1935.

D18	**D 4**	1c. violet	80	10
D19		2c. violet	2·00	10
D20		3c. violet	5·00	5·00
D21		4c. violet	1·50	10
D22		5c. violet	3·75	2·00
D23		6c. violet	2·25	3·00
D24		10c. violet	70	10

D 5

1967. (a) Size 21 × 17½ mm.

D25	**D 5**	1c. red	1·75	4·00
D26		2c. red	1·00	1·00
D27		3c. red	1·00	4·25
D28		4c. red	2·75	1·25
D29		5c. red	4·25	4·50
D30		6c. red	1·60	3·75
D31		10c. red	2·00	2·50

(b) Size 19½ × 16 mm.

D32	**D 5**	1c. red	30	30
D33		2c. red	1·00	3·00
D34		3c. red	2·50	3·50
D35		4c. red	30	60
D36a		5c. red	30	2·00
D37		6c. red	2·75	3·75
D38		8c. red	30	45
D39		10c. red	30	45
D40		12c. red	30	50
D41		16c. red	2·25	3·50
D42		20c. red	30	1·25
D43		24c. red	30	1·75
D44		50c. red	40	2·25

REGISTRATION STAMPS

R 1

1875.

R1	**R 1**	2c. orange	60·00	1·00
R6		5c. green	80·00	1·25
R8		8c. blue	£325	£225

SPECIAL DELIVERY STAMPS

S 1

1898.

S2	**S 1**	10c. green	48·00	7·00

S 2

1922.

S4	**S 2**	20c. red	35·00	6·50

S 3 Mail-carrying, 1867 and 1927

1927. 60th Anniv of Confederation.

S5	**S 3**	20c. orange	11·00	10·00

S 4

1930.

S6	**S 4**	20c. red	42·00	7·00

1932. As Type **S 4**, but inscr "CENTS" instead of "TWENTY CENTS".

S7		20c. red	45·00	15·00

S 5 Allegory of Progress

1935.

S8	**S 5**	20c. red	3·50	2·75

S 6 Canadian Coat of Arms

1938.

S 9	**S 6**	10c. green	20·00	3·50
S10		20c. red	40·00	26·00

1939. Surch **10 10** and bars.

S11	**S 6**	10c. on 20c. red	10·00	10·00

S 8 Coat of Arms and Flags

S 9 Lockheed L.18 Lodestar

1942.
S12 **S 8** 10c. green (postage) 7·00 30
S13 **S 9** 16c. blue (air) 6·00 45
S14 17c. blue 4·50 55

1946.
S15 10c. green (postage) 3·50 30
S16 17c. blue (air) 4·50 5·00
DESIGNS: 10c. As Type S **8** but with wreath of leaves; 17c. As Type S **9** but with Canadair DC-4M North Star airplane.

CANAL ZONE Pt. 22

Territory adjacent to the Panama Canal leased by the U.S.A. from the Republic of Panama. The U.S. Canal Zone postal service closed on 30 September 1979.

1904. 100 centavos = 1 peso.
1906. 100 centesimos = 1 balboa.
1924. 100 cents = 1 dollar (U.S.).

1904. Stamps of Panama (with **PANAMA** optd twice) optd **CANAL ZONE** horiz in one line.
1 **5** 2c. red (No. 54) £375 £300
2 5c. blue (No. 55) £160 £120
3 10c. orange (No. 56) £275 £160

1904. Stamps of the United States of 1902 optd **CANAL ZONE PANAMA.**
4 **103** 1c. green 22·00 16·00
5 **117** 2c. red 20·00 17·00
6 **107** 5c. blue 70·00 45·00
7 **109** 8c. violet £120 60·00
8 **110** 10c. brown £100 65·00

Stamps of Panama overprinted.

1904. 1905 stamps optd **CANAL ZONE** in two lines.
9 **38** 1c. green 1·90 1·60
10 2c. red 3·25 1·75

1904. Stamps with **PANAMA** optd twice, optd **CANAL ZONE** in two lines or surch also.
11 **5** 2c. red (No. 54) 5·00 3·50
12 5c. blue (No. 55) 5·50 2·50
14 8c. on 50c. brown (No. 65) 22·00 16·00
13 10c. orange (No. 56) 15·00 8·50

1906. 1892 stamps surch **PANAMA** on both sides and **CANAL ZONE** and new value in centre between bars.
21 **5** 1c. on 20c. violet (No. 64) 1·25 1·10
22 2c. on 1p. red (No. 66) 1·90 1·90

1906. 1906 stamps optd **CANAL ZONE** vert.
26 **42** 1c. black and green 1·60 85
27 **43** 2c. black and red 2·25 95
28 **45** 5c. black and blue 4·50 1·50
29 **46** 8c. black and purple 15·00 5·50
30 **47** 10c. black and violet 14·00 5·50

1909. 1909 stamps optd **CANAL ZONE** vert.
35 **48** 1c. black and green 3·00 1·25
36 **49** 2c. black and red 3·00 1·25
37 **51** 5c. black and blue 11·50 3·00
38 **52** 8c. black and purple 8·50 4·00
43 **53** 10c. black and purple 38·00 6·75

1911. Surch **CANAL ZONE 10 cts.**
53 **38** 10c. on 13c. grey 4·50 1·75

1914. Optd **CANAL ZONE** vert.
54 **38** 10c. grey 42·00 9·75

1915. 1915 and 1918 stamps optd **CANAL ZONE** vert.
55 1c. black and green (No. 162) 6·75 5·00
56 2c. black and red (No. 163) 7·75 3·25
57 5c. black and blue (No. 166) 9·00 5·00
58 10c. black & orange (No. 167) 18·00 11·00
59 12c. black & violet (No. 178) 13·50 4·75
60 15c. black & blue (No. 179) 42·00 18·00
61 24c. black & brown (No. 180) 60·00 16·00
62 50c. black & orange (No. 181) £375 £190
63 1b. black & violet (No. 182) £160 65·00

1921. 1921 stamps optd **CANAL ZONE** vert.
64 **65** 1c. green 3·00 1·00
65 – 2c. red (No. 186) 2·25 1·10
66 **68** 5c. blue 8·50 3·50
67 – 10c. violet (No. 191) 14·00 5·75
68 – 15c. blue (No. 192) 38·00 13·50
69 – 24c. sepia (No. 194) 55·00 17·00
70 – 50c. black (No. 195) £120 80·00

1924. 1924 stamps optd **CANAL ZONE** vert.
72 **72** 1c. green 8·50 3·50
73 2c. red 6·50 2·25

1924. Stamps of the United States of 1922 optd **CANAL ZONE** horiz.
74 ½c. sepia (No. 559) 95 60
75 1c. green (No. 602) 1·10 45
76 1½c. brown (No. 603) 1·50 1·00
103 2c. red (No. 604) 2·00 75
87 3c. violet (No. 638a) 3·00 2·25
88 5c. blue (No. 640) 3·00 1·75
106 10c. orange (No. 645) 14·00 5·00
90 12c. purple (No. 693) 18·00 11·50
141 14c. blue (No. 695) 3·75 2·25
92 15c. grey (No. 696) 5·50 3·50
93 17c. black (No. 697) 3·00 2·40
94 20c. red (No. 698) 6·00 2·50
95 30c. sepia (No. 700) 4·00 3·00
84 50c. mauve (No. 701) 60·00 35·00
97 $1 brown (No. 579) £100 45·00

1926. Liberty Bell stamp of United States optd **CANAL ZONE.**
101 **177** 2c. red 3·50 3·00

22 Gen. Gorgas
24 Panama Canal under Construction

1928.
107 **22** 1c. green 10 10
108 – 2c. red 20 15
109 **24** 5c. blue 1·90 35
110 – 10c. orange 30 20
111 – 12c. purple 60 50
112 – 14c. blue 80 80
113 – 15c. grey 60 40
114 – 20c. brown 50 20
115 – 30c. black 80 80
116 – 50c. mauve 1·25 55
PORTRAITS: 2c. Gen. Goethals. 10c. H. F. Hodges. 12c. Col. Gaillard. 14c. Gen. Sibert. 15c. Jackson Smith. 20c. Admiral Rousseau. 30c. Col. S. B. Williamson. 50c. Governor Blackburn.

1929. Air. Stamps of 1928 surch **AIR MAIL** and value.
124 – 10c. on 50c. mauve 7·50 5·50
117 **22** 15c. on 1c. green 7·50 4·50
125 – 20c. on 2c. red 4·50 1·50
119 – 25c. on 2c. red 3·00 1·75

36 Steamer, Panama Canal

1931. Air.
126 **36** 4c. purple 55 65
127 5c. green 45 30
128 6c. brown 60 35
129 10c. orange 70 30
130 15c. blue 1·00 25
131 20c. violet 2·00 25
132 30c. red 2·75 1·00
133 40c. yellow 2·50 1·00
134 $1 black 8·50 1·75

1933. No. 720 of United States optd **CANAL ZONE.**
140 3c. violet 2·25 25

38 Gen. Goethals
45 Balboa (before construction)

1934. 20th Anniv of Opening of Panama Canal.
142 **38** 3c. violet 15 10

1939. 25th Anniv of Opening of Panama Canal and 10th Anniv of Canal Zone Airmail Service. (a) Postage. As T **45**. Inscr "25TH ANNIVERSARY 1939 OPENING PANAMA CANAL 1914".
149 **45** 1c. green 1·25 75
150 – 2c. red 50 40
151 – 3c. violet 1·25 50
152 – 5c. blue 1·40 95
153 – 6c. orange 4·25 2·75
154 – 7c. black 2·75 1·40
155 – 8c. green 5·00 3·00
156 – 10c. blue 5·00 2·25
157 – 11c. green 14·00 10·00
158 – 12c. purple 7·00 5·50
159 – 14c. violet 16·00 10·00
160 – 15c. olive 22·00 11·00
161 – 18c. red 16·00 16·00
162 – 20c. brown 20·00 9·50
163 – 25c. orange 14·00 14·00
164 – 50c. purple 18·00 3·75
DESIGNS: 2c. Balboa (after construction); 3c., 5c. Gaillard Cut; 6c., 7c. Bas Obispo; 8c., 10c. Gatun Locks; 11c., 12c. Canal Channel; 14c., 15c. Gamboa; 18c., 20c. Pedro Miguel Locks; 25c.50c. Gatun Spillway.

(b) Air. Inscr "TENTH ANNIVERSARY AIR MAIL" and "25TH ANNIVERSARY OPENING PANAMA CANAL".
143 5c. black 3·25 3·00
144 10c. violet 3·25 2·25
145 15c. brown 3·25 1·10
146 25c. blue 16·00 11·00
147 30c. red 12·00 8·00
148 $1 green 30·00 30·00

DESIGNS—HORIZ: As Type **45**: 5c. Douglas DC-3 airplane over Sosa Hill; 10c. Douglas DC-3 airplane, Sikorsky S-42A flying boat and map of Central America; 15c. Sikorsky S-42A and Fort Amador; 25c. Sikorsky S-42A at Cristobal Harbour, Manzanillo Island; 30c. Sikorsky S-42A over Culebra Cut. $1 Sikorsky S-42A and palm trees.

1939. Stamps of United States (1938) optd **CANAL ZONE.**
165 **276** ½c. orange 15 10
166 – 1½c. brown (No. 801) 15 10

67 John F. Stevens
69 Northern Coati and Barro Colorado Island

1946. Portraits.
188 – ½c. red (Davis) 30 15
189 – 1½c. brown (Magoon) 30 15
190 – 2c. red (Theodore Roosevelt) 15 10
191 **67** 5c. blue 30 10
192 – 25c. green (Wallace) 1·10 60

1948. 25th Anniv of Establishment of Canal Zone Biological Area.
194 **69** 10c. black 1·40 80

70 "Arriving at Chagres on the Atlantic Side."
74 Western Hemisphere

1949. Centenary of the Gold Rush.
195 **70** 3c. blue 60 30
196 – 6c. violet 80 50
197 – 12c. green 1·40 1·00
198 – 18c. mauve 2·75 2·00
DESIGNS: 6c. "Up the Chagres River to Las Cruces"; 12c. "Las Cruces Trail to Panama"; 18c. "Leaving Panama for San Francisco".

1951. Air.
199 **74** 4c. purple 75 25
200 5c. green 1·00 60
201 6c. brown 50 15
202 7c. olive 1·00 35
210 8c. red 40 20
203 10c. orange 1·00 35
204 15c. purple 3·50 1·75
205 21c. blue 7·00 2·75
206 25c. yellow 9·50 2·25
207 31c. red 7·25 3·25
208 35c. blue 6·00 2·50
209 80c. black 4·50 90

75 Labourers in Gaillard Cut
76 Locomotive "Nueva Granada", 1852

1951. West Indian Panama Canal Labourers.
211 **75** 10c. red 6·75 2·75

1955. Centenary of Panama Railway.
212 **76** 3c. violet 2·75 90

77 Gorgas Hospital

1957. 75th Anniv of Gorgas Hospital.
213 **77** 3c. black on green 40 30

78 "Ancon II" (liner)

80 "First Class" Scout Badge

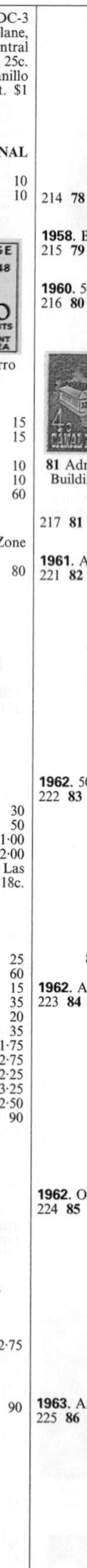

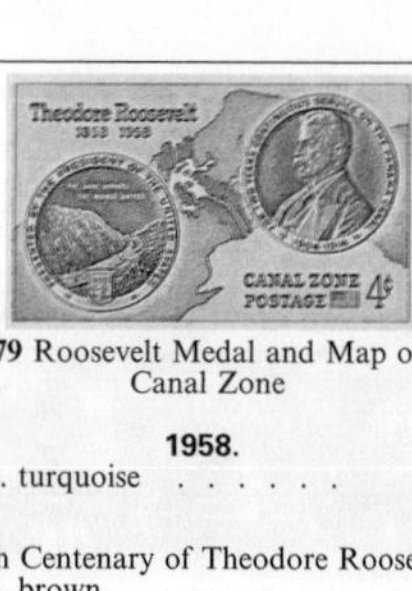

79 Roosevelt Medal and Map of Canal Zone

1958.
214 **78** 4c. turquoise 45 20

1958. Birth Centenary of Theodore Roosevelt.
215 **79** 4c. brown 40 25

1960. 50th Anniv of American Boy Scout Movement.
216 **80** 4c. ochre, red and blue 50 30

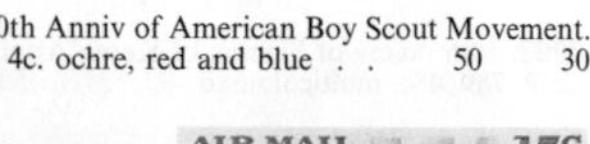

81 Administration Building, Balboa
82 U.S. Army Caribbean School Crest

1960.
217 **81** 4c. purple 20 15

1961. Air.
221 **82** 15c. blue and red 1·40 60

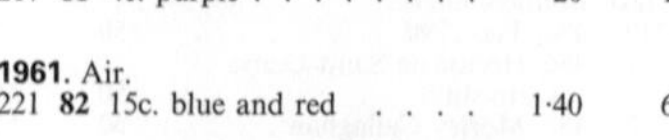

83 Girl Scout Badge and Camp on Lake Gatun

1962. 50th Anniv of U.S. Girl Scout Movement.
222 **83** 4c. ochre, green and blue 40 25

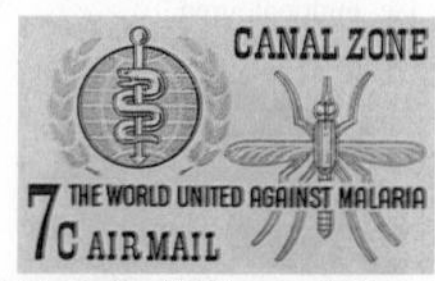

84 Campaign Emblem and Mosquito

1962. Air. Malaria Eradication.
223 **84** 7c. black on yellow 45 40

85 Thatcher Ferry Bridge

1962. Opening of Thatcher Ferry Bridge.
224 **85** 4c. black and silver 30 20

86 Torch of Progress

1963. Air. "Alliance for Progress".
225 **86** 15c. blue, green and black 1·10 75

87 Cristobal

1964. Air. 50th Anniv of Panama Canal.
226 **87** 6c. black and green 45 30
227 – 8c. black and red 1·75 75
228 – 15c. black and blue 1·25 45
229 – 20c. black and purple 2·00 85
230 – 30c. black and brown 5·75 2·25
231 – 80c. black and bistre 5·00 2·50
DESIGNS: 8c. Gatun Locks; 15c. Madden Dam; 20c. Gaillard Cut; 30c. Miraflores Locks; 80c. Balboa.

93 Seal and Jetliner

1965. Air.
232 **93** 6c. black and green 35 20
233 8c. black and red 30 10
234 10c. black and orange 30 10
235 11c. black and green 40 15
236 13c. black and green 95 20
237 15c. black and blue 50 15
238 20c. black and violet 55 25
239 22c. black and violet 75 55
240 25c. black and green 60 40
241 30c. black and brown 80 30
242 35c. black and red 90 65
243 80c. black and ochre 2·00 85

94 Goethal's Memorial, Balboa

96 Dredger "Cascadas"

1968.
244 **94** 6c. blue and green 20 20
245 – 8c. multicoloured 35 15
DESIGN: 8c. Fort San Lorenzo.

1976.
249 **96** 13c. black, green & blue 60 20

97 Electric Towing Locomotive

1978.
251 **97** 15c. green and deep green 3·00 75

OFFICIAL STAMPS

1941. Air. Optd **OFFICIAL PANAMA CANAL.**
O167 **36** 5c. green 4·25 1·25
O168 6c. brown 9·75 3·75
O169 10c. orange 8·00 1·75
O170 15c. blue 12·00 3·00
O171 20c. violet 13·00 4·00
O172 30c. red 15·00 4·00
O173 40c. yellow 17·00 7·50
O174 $1 black 20·00 10·00

1941. Optd **OFFICIAL PANAMA CANAL.**
O180 **22** 1c. green 1·50 40
O181 **38** 3c. violet 3·25 70
O182 **24** 5c. blue – 38·00
O183 – 10c. orange 4·25 1·75
O184 – 15c. grey (No. 113) 9·00 2·00
O185 – 20c. brown (No. 114) 12·00 2·75
O186 – 50c. mauve (No. 116) 30·00 4·50

1947. No. 192 optd **OFFICIAL PANAMA CANAL.**
O193 **67** 5c. blue 7·50 3·00

POSTAGE DUE STAMPS

1914. Postage Due stamps of United States of 1894 optd **CANAL ZONE** diag.
D55 D **87** 1c. red 55·00 13·00
D56 2c. red £180 38·00
D57 10c. red £475 38·00

1915. Postage Due stamps of Panama of 1915 optd **CANAL ZONE** vert.
D59 D **58** 1c. brown 9·75 3·75
D60 – 2c. brown £150 13·50
D61 – 10c. brown 38·00 8·00

1915. Postage Due stamps of Panama of 1915 surch **CANAL ZONE** vert and value in figures.
D62 D **58** 1c. on 1c. brown 80·00 11·00
D63 – 2c. on 2c. brown 20·00 5·75
D66 – 4c. on 4c. brown 27·00 11·50
D64 – 10c. on 10c. brown 17·00 3·75

1925. Postage Due stamps of United States of 1894 optd **CANAL ZONE** horiz in two lines.
D92 D **87** 1c. red 6·25 2·50
D93 2c. red 12·00 3·25
D94 10c. red £110 17·00

1925. Stamps of Canal Zone of 1924 optd **POSTAGE DUE.**
D89 1c. green (No. 75) 70·00 11·00
D90 2c. red (No. 103) 18·00 5·50
D91 10c. orange (No. 106) 40·00 8·75

1929. No. 109 surch **POSTAGE DUE** and value and bars.
D120 **24** 1c. on 5c. blue 5·75 3·75
D121 2c. on 5c. blue 11·00 5·00
D122 5c. on 5c. blue 11·00 5·75
D123 10c. on 5c. blue 11·00 5·50

D 37 Canal Zone Shield

1932.
D135 D **37** 1c. red 15 20
D136 2c. red 15 20
D137 5c. red 40 25
D138 10c. red 1·60 1·50
D139 15c. red 1·25 1·10

CANTON Pt. 17

A treaty port in S. China. Stamps issued at the French Indo-Chinese P.O., which was closed in 1922.

1901. 100 centimes = 1 franc.
1919. 100 cents = 1 piastre.
Stamps of Indo-China overprinted or surcharged.

CANTON
州 廣
(1)

1901. "Tablet" key-type, optd with T **1**. The Chinese characters represent "Canton" and are therefore the same on every value.
1 D 1c. black and blue 65 1·00
2 2c. brown on yellow 1·25 2·25
3 4c. brown on grey 2·50 2·50
4 5c. green 95 1·40
6 10c. black on lilac 3·25 7·00
7 15c. blue 3·00 3·50
8 15c. grey 5·25 4·50
9 20c. red on green 10·00 12·00
10 25c. black on pink 10·00 10·00
11 30c. brown on drab 19·00 29·00
12 40c. red on yellow 30·00 35·00
13 50c. red on rose 26·00 35·00
14 75c. brown on orange 35·00 50·00
15 1f. green 42·00 45·00
16 5f. mauve on lilac £190 £200

1903. "Tablet" key-type, surch. as T **1**. The Chinese characters indicate the value and therefore differ for each value.
17 D 1c. black on blue 2·50 2·40
18 2c. brown on yellow 3·25 3·75
19 4c. brown on grey 2·25 3·75
20 5c. green 2·25 3·75
21 10c. red 2·50 3·75
22 15c. grey 2·75 4·25
23 20c. red on green 12·00 19·00
24 25c. blue 7·00 6·75
25 25c. black on pink 8·50 6·75
26 30c. brown on drab 22·00 24·00
27 40c. red on yellow 60·00 50·00
28 50c. red on rose £275 £250
29 50c. brown on blue 65·00 60·00
30 75c. brown on orange 70·00 60·00
31 1f. green 55·00 55·00
32 5f. mauve on lilac 50·00 60·00

1906. Surch **CANTON** (letters without serifs) and value in Chinese.
33 **8** 1c. green 1·10 3·00
34 2c. purple on yellow 1·25 2·75
35 4c. mauve on blue 95 2·25
36 5c. green 2·25 3·00
37 10c. red 2·75 3·25
38 15c. brown on blue 3·00 4·50
39 20c. red on green 3·00 4·00
40 25c. blue 2·75 3·00
41 30c. brown on cream 4·25 4·50
42 35c. black on yellow 2·50 3·50
43 40c. black on grey 4·50 6·50
44 50c. brown on cream 6·75 7·25
45 D 75c. brown on orange 55·00 60·00
46 **8** 1f. green 13·00 15·00
47 2f. brown on yellow 35·00 40·00
48 D 5f. mauve on lilac 65·00 85·00
49 **8** 10f. red on green 75·00 85·00

1908. 1907 stamps surch **CANTON** and value in Chinese.
50 **10** 1c. black and brown 70 50
51 2c. black and brown 55 85
52 4c. black and blue 75 1·75
53 5c. black and green 1·25 1·40
54 10c. black and red 2·50 75
55 15c. black and violet 2·75 2·50
56 **11** 20c. black and violet 3·50 3·25
57 25c. black and blue 4·00 50
58 30c. black and brown 6·75 6·75
59 35c. black and green 8·25 6·25
60 40c. black and brown 12·00 6·50
61 50c. black and red 12·50 5·50
62 **12** 75c. black and orange 11·50 8·50
63 – 1f. black and red 17·00 13·00
64 – 2f. black and green 45·00 38·00
65 – 5f. black and blue 55·00 45·00
66 – 10f. black and violet 90·00 70·00

1919. As last, but additionally surch.
67 **10** ⅖c. on 1c. black and brown 75 2·50
68 ⅘c. on 2c. black and brown 60 1·75
69 1⅗c. on 4c. black and blue 1·25 1·25
70 2c. on 5c. black and green 1·60 1·10
71 4c. on 10c. black and red 2·50 1·90
72 6c. on 15c. black & violet 1·90 1·90
73 **11** 8c. on 20c. black & violet 2·75 2·50
74 10c. on 25c. black & blue 3·00 50
75 12c. on 30c. black & brown 3·50 2·25
76 14c. on 35c. black & green 1·75 1·50
77 16c. on 40c. black & brown 2·75 1·60
78 20c. on 50c. black and red 3·25 65
79 **12** 30c. on 75c. black & orange 3·50 1·25
80 – 40c. on 1f. black and red 1·50 8·00
81 – 80c. on 2f. black and green 13·50 12·50
82 – 2p. on 5f. black and blue 14·00 16·00
83 – 4p. on 10f. black & violet 15·00 19·00

CAPE JUBY Pt. 9

Former Spanish possession on the N.W. coast of Africa, ceded to Morocco in 1958.

100 centimos = 1 peseta.

1916. Stamps of Rio de Oro surch **CABO JUBI** and value.
1a **12** 5c. on 4p. red 90·00 26·00
2 10c. on 10p. violet 33·00 16·00
3 15c. on 50c. brown 33·00 16·00
4 40c. on 1p. lilac 55·00 22·00

1919. Stamps of Spain optd **CABO JUBY.**
5 **38a** ¼c. green 15 15
18 **66** 1c. green (imperf) 18·00 11·50
6 **64** 2c. brown 15 15
7 5c. green 40 25
8 10c. red 50 30
9 15c. yellow 2·20 1·70
10 20c. green 14·00 11·00
19 20c. violet 80·00 30·00
11 25c. blue 2·10 70
12 30c. green 2·10 80
13 40c. orange 2·10 40
14 50c. blue 2·50 2·20
15 1p. red 7·25 6·00
16 4p. purple 29·00 25·00
17 10p. orange 42·00 39·00

1925. Stamps of Spain optd **CABO JUBY.**
19a **68** 2c. green £225 55·00
20 5c. purple 3·50 2·75
21 10c. green 9·75 2·75
22 20c. violet 20·00 9·00

1926. As Red Cross stamps of Spain of 1926 optd **CABO-JUBY.**
23 **70** 1c. orange 10·00 10·00
24 – 2c. red 10·00 10·00
25 – 5c. brown 2·50 2·50
26 – 10c. green 1·30 1·30
27 **70** 15c. violet 90 90
28 – 20c. purple 90 90
29 **71** 25c. red 90 90
30 **70** 30c. green 90 90
31 – 40c. blue 30 30
32 – 50c. red 30 30
33 – 1p. red 30 30
34 – 4p. bistre 1·20 1·20
35 **71** 10p. violet 2·75 2·75

1929. Seville and Barcelona Exhibition stamps of Spain (Nos. 504/14) optd **CABO JUBY.**
36 – 5c. red 30 45
37 – 10c. green 30 45
38 **83** 15c. blue 30 45
39 **84** 20c. violet 30 45
40 **83** 25c. red 30 45
41 – 30c. brown 30 45
42 – 40c. blue 30 45
43 **84** 50c. orange 35 55
44 – 1p. grey 15·00 22·00
45 – 4p. red 22·00 33·00
46 – 10p. brown 22·00 33·00

1934. Stamps of Spanish Morocco optd **Cabo Juby.**
(a) Stamps of 1928
47 **11** 1c. red 1·50 1·30
48 2c. violet 3·25 1·60
49 5c. blue 3·25 1·60
50 10c. green 7·50 4·50
51 15c. brown 17·00 11·00
52 **12** 25c. red 3·25 3·25
53 – 1p. green 30·00 24·00
54 – 2p.50 purple 70·00 48·00
55 – 4p. blue 90·00 65·00

(b) Stamps of 1933.
56 **14** 1c. red 35 35
57 – 10c. green 2·20 2·30
58 **14** 20c. black 6·50 6·00
59 – 30c. red 6·50 6·00
60 **15** 40c. blue 23·00 21·00
61 50c. orange 44·00 36·00

1935. Stamps of Spanish Morocco of 1933 optd **CABO JUBY.**
62 **14** 1c. red 15 15
63 – 2c. green 50 40
64 – 5c. mauve 1·90 60
65 – 10c. green 11·50 6·00
66 – 15c. yellow 4·50 3·00
67 **14** 20c. black 4·25 3·50
68 – 25c. red 48·00 35·00
73 – 25c. violet 3·00 3·00
74 – 30c. red 3·00 3·00
75 – 40c. orange 4·25 4·25
76 – 50c. blue 8·25 8·25
77 – 60c. green 10·50 10·50
69 – 1p. grey 7·00 6·50
78 – 2p. brown 55·00 55·00
70 – 2p.50 brown 28·00 20·00
71 – 4p. green 45·00 30·00
72 – 5p. black 37·00 32·00

1937. 1st Anniv of Civil War. Nos. 184/99 of Spanish Morocco optd **CABO JUBY.**
79 1c. blue 30 30
80 2c. brown 30 30
81 5c. mauve 30 30
82 10c. green 30 30
83 15c. blue 30 30
84 20c. purple 30 30
85 25c. mauve 30 30
86 30c. red 30 30
87 40c. orange 90 90
88 50c. blue 90 90
89 60c. green 90 90
90 1p. violet 90 90
91 2p. blue 60·00 60·00
92 2p.50 black 60·00 60·00
93 4p. brown 60·00 60·00
94 10p. black 60·00 60·00

1938. Air. Nos. 203/12 of Spanish Morocco optd **CABO JUBY.**
95 5c. brown 10 10
96 10c. green 10 30
97 25c. red 10 10
98 40c. blue 1·50 1·50
99 50c. mauve 10 10
100 75c. blue 10 15
101 1p. brown 10 15
102 1p.50 violet 3·00 90
103 2p. red 2·10 2·10
104 3p. black 5·50 5·50

1939. As Nos. 213/16 of Spanish Morocco optd **CABO JUBY.**
105 5c. red 35 35
106 10c. green 35 35
107 15c. purple 35 35
108 20c. blue 35 35

1940. Nos. 217/32 of Spanish Morocco, but without "ZONA" on back, optd **CABO JUBY.**
109 1c. brown 10 10
110 2c. green 10 10
111 5c. blue 10 10
112 10c. mauve 10 10
113 15c. green 10 10
114 20c. violet 10 10
115 25c. brown 10 10
116 30c. green 10 10
117 40c. green 45 45
118 45c. red 45 45
119 50c. brown 45 45
120 75c. blue 1·40 1·00
121 1p. brown and blue 2·75 1·90
122 2p.50 green and brown 7·75 5·25
123 5p. brown and purple 7·75 5·25
124 10p. brown & deep brown 23·00 19·00

1942. Air. Nos. 258/62 of Spanish Morocco, but without "Z" opt and inscr "CABO JUBY".
125 5c. blue 10 10
126 10c. brown 10 10
127 15c. green 10 10
128 90c. pink 35 35
129 5p. black 1·30 1·30

1944. Nos. 269/82 (agricultural scenes) of Spanish Morocco optd **CABO JUBY.**
130 – 1c. blue and brown 10 10
131 – 2c. light green & green 10 10
132 **26** 5c. green and brown 10 10
133 – 10c. orange and blue 10 10
134 – 15c. light green & green 10 10
135 – 20c. black and purple 10 10
136 – 25c. brown and blue 10 10
137 – 30c. blue and green 10 10
138 – 40c. purple and brown 10 10
139 **26** 50c. brown and blue 10 10
140 – 75c. blue and green 95 95
141 – 1p. brown and blue 95 95
142 – 2p.50 blue and black 2·75 2·75
143 – 10p. black and orange 19·00 17·00

1946. Nos. 285/94 (craftsmen) of Spanish Morocco optd **CABO JUBY.**
144 – 1c. brown and purple 10 10
145 **27** 2c. violet and green 10 10
146 – 10c. blue and orange 10 10
147 **27** 15c. green and blue 10 10
148 – 25c. blue and green 10 10
149 – 40c. brown and blue 10 10
150 **27** 45c. red and black 20 20
151 – 1p. blue and green 1·20 1·20
152 – 2p.50 green and orange 3·50 3·50
153 – 10p. grey and blue 10·00 10·00

1948. Nos. 307/17 (transport and commerce) of Spanish Morocco, but without "Z" on back, optd **CABO JUBY.**
154 **30** 2c. brown and violet 25 80
155 – 5c. violet and purple 10 10
156 – 15c. green and blue 10 10
157 – 25c. green and black 10 10
158 – 35c. black and blue 10 10
159 – 50c. violet and red 10 10
160 – 70c. blue and green 10 10
161 – 90c. green and mauve 10 10
162 – 1p. violet and blue 25 20
163 **30** 2p.50 green and purple 7·75 8·25
164 – 10p. blue and black 3·25 3·25

EXPRESS LETTER STAMPS

1919. Express letter stamp of Spain optd **CABO JUBY.**
E18 E **53** 20c. red 2·75 2·75

1926. Red Cross stamp. As Express letter stamp of Spain optd **CABO-JUBY.**
E36 E **77** 20c. black and blue 2·75 2·75

1934. Stamp of Spanish Morocco optd **Cabo Juby.**
E62 E **12** 20c. black 2·00 2·00

1935. Stamp of Spanish Morocco optd **CABO JUBY.**
E79 E **16** 20c. red 3·00 3·00

1937. No. E200 of Spanish Morocco optd **CABO JUBY.**
E95 E **19** 20c. red 90 90

1940. No. E233 of Spanish Morocco optd **CABO JUBY.**
E125 E **21** 25c. red 35 35

CAPE OF GOOD HOPE Pt. 1

Formerly a British Colony, later the southern-most province of the Union of South Africa.

12 pence = 1 shilling;
20 shillings = 1 pound.

1 "Hope"

1853. Imperf.

18	1	1d. red	£140	£225
19		4d. blue	£140	50·00
20		6d. lilac	£180	£450
8b		1s. green	£250	£500

3

1861. Imperf.

13	3	1d. red	£14000	£2250
14		4d. blue	£10000	£1600

4 "Hope" seated, with vine and ram (with outer frame-line)

6 (No outer frame-line)

1864. With outer frame line. Perf.

23a	4	1d. red	80·00	22·00
24		4d. blue	£100	2·75
52a		6d. purple	8·50	20
53a		1s. green	80·00	40

1868. Surch.

32	4	1d. on 6d. violet	£475	90·00
33		1d. on 1s. green	70·00	45·00
34	6	3d. on 4d. blue	£100	1·75
27	4	4d. on 6d. violet	£225	16·00

1880. No outer frame line.

48	6	½d. black	4·00	10
49		1d. red	4·00	10
36		3d. pink	£190	23·00
43		3d. purple	6·50	1·00
51		4d. blue	9·50	50
54		5s. orange	85·00	4·75

1880. Surch **THREEPENCE**.

35	6	3d. on 4d. pink	70·00	1·75

1880. Surch **3**.

37	6	"3" on 3d. pink	75·00	1·50

1882. Surch **One Half-penny**.

47	6	½d. on 3d. purple	25·00	3·25

1882.

61	6	½d. green	1·50	50
62		2d. brown	2·00	40
56		2½d. olive	8·00	10
63a		2½d. blue	4·00	10
64		3d. mauve	7·00	85
65		4d. olive	4·00	1·75
66		1s. green	60·00	3·75
67		1s. yellow	8·00	1·00

On the 2½d. stamps the value is in a white square at upper right-hand corner as well as at foot.

1891. Surch **2½d.**

55a	6	2½d. on 3d. mauve	3·25	20

1893. Surch **ONE PENNY**.

57a	6	1d. on 2d. brown	2·50	50

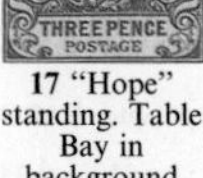

17 "Hope" standing. Table Bay in background

18 Table Mountain and Bay and Arms of the Colony

19

1893.

58	17	½d. green	2·00	10
59a		1d. red	1·25	10
60		3d. mauve	4·00	1·50

1900.

69	18	1d. red	2·50	10

1902. Various frames.

70	19	½d. green	2·25	10
71		1d. red	2·00	10
72		2d. brown	9·50	80
73		2½d. blue	2·75	6·50
74		3d. purple	7·00	75
75		4d. green	8·00	65
76		6d. mauve	15·00	30
77		1s. yellow	12·00	80
78		5s. orange	75·00	13·00

CAPE VERDE ISLANDS Pt. 9; Pt. 12

Islands in the Atlantic. Formerly Portuguese; became independent on 5 July 1975.

1877. 1000 reis = 1 milreis.
1913. 100 centavos = 1 escudo.

1877. "Crown" key-type inscr "CABO VERDE".

1	P	5r. black	2·50	1·70
2a		10r. yellow	15·00	10·50
18		10r. green	2·20	1·70
3		20r. bistre	1·50	1·20
19		20r. red	4·50	3·00
4		25r. pink	1·90	80
20		25r. lilac	3·25	2·40
5		40r. blue	75·00	45·00
21		40r. yellow	1·90	1·40
15		50r. green	£120	65·00
22		50r. blue	5·50	3·50
7b		100r. lilac	6·75	2·75
8		200r. orange	4·00	3·00
9b		300r. brown	4·75	4·25

1886. "Embossed" key-type inscr "PROVINCIA DE CABO-VERDE".

33	Q	5r. black	3·75	2·50
34		10r. green	5·50	2·40
35		20r. red	6·75	4·25
26		25r. mauve	6·75	4·50
27		40r. brown	6·75	2·75
28		50r. blue	6·75	2·75
29		100r. brown	6·75	3·75
30		200r. lilac	15·00	8·50
31		300r. orange	17·00	3·50

1894. "Figures" key-type inscr "CABO-VERDE".

37	R	5r. orange	1·30	1·00
38		10r. mauve	1·30	1·00
39		15r. brown	3·25	2·10
40		20r. lilac	3·25	2·10
41		25r. green	2·75	1·70
42		50r. blue	2·75	1·70
51		75r. red	9·25	4·75
43		80r. green	10·00	5·25
44		100r. brown on buff	7·50	4·25
58		150r. red on rose	26·00	22·00
59		200r. blue on blue	26·00	22·00
46		300r. blue on buff	30·00	14·00

1898. "King Carlos" key-type inscr "CABO VERDE".

60	S	2½r. grey	30	25
61		5r. orange	40	25
62		10r. green	40	25
63		15r. brown	4·50	1·60
111		15r. green	1·50	1·00
64		20r. lilac	1·30	75
65		25r. green	2·75	1·00
112		25r. red	80	30
66		50r. blue	2·75	1·20
113		50r. brown	3·00	1·90
114		65r. blue	19·00	12·00
67		75r. red	7·00	2·75
115		75r. purple	2·75	1·70
68		80r. mauve	7·00	2·75
69		100r. blue on blue	2·75	1·50
116		115r. brown on pink	12·00	8·00
117		130r. brown on yellow	12·50	8·00
70		150r. brown on yellow	2·20	1·20
71		200r. purple on pink	3·25	2·40
72		300r. blue on pink	8·25	4·00
118		400r. blue on yellow	13·00	8·50
73		500r. black on blue	8·25	4·00
74		700r. mauve on yellow	23·00	14·50

1902. Key-types of Cape Verde Is. surch.

119	S	50r. on 65r. blue	3·25	2·40
75	Q	65r. on 5r. black	4·50	3·00
78	R	65r. on 10r. mauve	5·50	3·00
79		65r. on 20r. lilac	5·50	3·00
80		65r. on 100r. brn on buff	7·00	4·25
76	Q	65r. on 200r. lilac	4·50	3·00
77		65r. on 300r. orange	4·50	3·00
85	R	115r. on 5r. orange	3·25	2·40
82	Q	115r. on 10r. green	4·50	3·00
83		115r. on 20r. red	4·50	3·00
87	R	115r. on 25r. green	2·30	1·70
88		115r. on 150r. red on rose	6·75	5·25
90	Q	130r. on 50r. blue	4·50	3·00
93	R	130r. on 75r. red	3·25	2·40
96		130r. on 80r. green	2·75	1·60
92	Q	130r. on 100r. brown	4·50	3·00
97	R	130r. on 200r. blue on blue	3·00	2·10
106	V	400r. on 2½r. brown	1·30	1·20
98	Q	400r. on 25r. mauve	2·20	2·10
99		400r. on 40r. brown	4·50	3·00
101	R	400r. on 50r. blue	4·50	2·40
103		400r. on 300r. blue on buff	2·00	1·40

1902. "King Carlos" key-type of Cape Verde Is. optd **PROVISORIO**.

107	S	15r. brown	1·50	1·00
108		25r. green	1·50	1·00
109		50r. blue	1·50	1·00
110		75r. red	3·00	2·10

1911. "King Carlos" key-type of Cape Verde Is. optd **REPUBLICA**.

120	S	2½r. grey	20	20
121		5r. orange	20	20
122		10r. green	80	65
123		15r. green	70	35
124		20r. lilac	1·20	65
125		25r. red	70	35
126		50r. brown	7·00	4·75
127		75r. purple	1·10	65
128		100r. blue on blue	1·10	65
129		115r. brown on pink	1·10	65
130		130r. brown on yellow	1·10	65
131		200r. purple on pink	5·25	3·25
132		400r. blue on yellow	2·75	95
133		500r. black on blue	2·75	95
134		700r. mauve on yellow	2·75	1·10

1912. "King Manoel" key-type inscr "CABO VERDE" and optd **REPUBLICA**.

135	T	2½r. lilac	15	15
136		5r. black	15	15
137		10r. green	35	30
138		20r. red	1·90	1·10
139		25r. brown	35	15
140		50r. blue	3·75	2·75
141		75r. brown	90	80
142		100r. brown on green	90	80
143		200r. green on pink	1·40	80
144		300r. black on blue	1·40	80
145		400r. blue and black	3·00	2·40
146		500r. brown and olive	3·00	2·40

1913. Surch. **REPUBLICA CABO VERDE** and new value on "Vasco da Gama" issues of (a) Portuguese Colonies.

147		¼c. on 2½r. green	1·10	50
148		½c. on 5r. red	1·10	50
149		1c. on 10r. purple	1·10	50
150		2½c. on 25r. green	1·10	50
151		5c. on 50r. blue	1·50	1·20
152		7½c. on 75r. brown	3·00	2·30
153		10c. on 100r. brown	1·50	1·50
154		15c. on 150r. bistre	2·00	2·00

(b) Macao.

155		¼c. on ½a. green	1·10	70
156		½c. on 1a. red	1·10	70
157		1c. on 2a. purple	1·10	70
158		2½c. on 4a. green	1·10	70
159		5c. on 8a. blue	5·75	5·00
160		7½c. on 12a. brown	4·75	2·00
161		10c. on 16a. brown	1·70	1·30
162		15c. on 24a. bistre	4·75	2·75

(c) Timor.

163		¼c. on ½a. green	1·10	70
164		½c. on 1a. red	1·10	70
165		1c. on 2a. purple	1·10	70
166		2½c. on 4a. green	1·00	70
167		5c. on 8a. blue	5·75	4·50
168		7½c. on 12a. brown	4·50	2·50
169		10c. on 16a. brown	1·80	1·50
170		15c. on 24a. bistre	3·75	1·90

1913. Stamps of 1902 optd **REPUBLICA**.

171	S	75r. red (No. 110)	4·50	3·00
192	R	115r. on 5r. (No. 85)	1·10	60
193	Q	115r. on 10r. (No. 82)	2·00	1·20
195		115r. on 20r. (No. 83)	2·20	1·40
198	R	115r. on 25r. (No. 87)	2·00	1·40
200		115r. on 150r. (No. 88)	65	60
201	Q	130r. on 50r. (No. 90)	2·00	1·00
202	R	130r. on 75r. (No. 93)	2·00	80
204		130r. on 80r. (No. 96)	2·00	80
206	Q	130r. on 100r. (No. 92)	1·30	80
208	R	130r. on 200r. (No. 97)	1·30	80

1914. "Ceres" key-type inscr "CABO VERDE". Name and value in black.

219	U	¼c. green	60	45
220		½c. black	60	45
221		1c. green	60	45
222		1½c. brown	60	45
223		2c. red	1·00	55
224		2c. grey	25	20
180		2½c. violet	50	45
214		2½c. mauve	20	20
215		3c. orange	2·10	1·90
216		4c. red	20	15
228		4½c. grey	30	30
229		5c. blue	75	65
230		6c. mauve	30	30
231		7c. blue	30	30
232		7½c. brown	30	25
233		8c. grey	50	40
234		10c. red	30	30
235		12c. green	50	45
236		15c. pink	30	25
237		20c. green	30	25
238		24c. blue	90	70
239		25c. brown	90	70
188		30c. brown on green	3·75	2·50
240		30c. green	40	40
189		40c. brown on pink	2·20	1·90
241		40c. turquoise	40	40
190		50c. orange on orange	2·75	1·90
242		50c. mauve	75	60
243		60c. blue	1·00	70
244		60c. red	1·10	70
245		80c. red	3·50	1·00
191		1e. green on blue	2·75	2·10
246		1e. pink	4·25	2·20
247		1e. blue	4·50	2·75
248		2e. purple	4·25	2·20
249		5e. brown	7·50	5·25
250		10e. pink	17·00	10·50
251		20e. green	48·00	35·00

1921. Nos. 153/4 surch.

252		2c. on 15c. on 150r. brown	1·80	1·20
253		4c. on 10c. on 100r. brown	2·20	2·10

1921. No. 69 surch **6 c. REPUBLICA**.

254	S	6c. on 100r. blue on blue	2·20	1·70

1921. Charity Tax stamp of Portuguese Colonies (General issues) optd **CABO VERDE CORREIOS** or surch also.

255		¼ on 1c. green	45	30
256		½c. on 1c. green	55	40
257		1c. green	50	40

1922. Provisionals of 1913 surch **$04**.

260	R	4c. on 130r. on 75r. red (No. 202)	80	60
262		4c. on 130r. on 80r. green (No. 204)	80	60
265		4c. on 130r. on 200r. blue (No. 208)	80	65

1925. Provisional stamps of 1902 surch **Republica 40 C.**

267	V	40c. on 400r. on 2½r. brown (No. 106)	80	65

268 R 40c. on 400r. on 300r. blue on buff (No. 103) 80 60

1931. No. 245 surch **70 C.**
269 U 70c. on 80c. red 21·00 8·25

1934. As T **17** of Angola (new "Ceres" type).
270 **17** 1c. brown 15 10
271 5c. sepia 15 10
272 10c. mauve 15 10
273 15c. black 20 20
274 20c. grey 20 20
275 30c. green 20 20
276 40c. red 20 20
277 45c. blue 1·60 70
278 50c. brown 75 45
279 60c. olive 75 45
280 70c. brown 75 45
281 80c. green 75 45
282 85c. red 3·25 2·10
283 1e. red 2·20 40
284 1e.40 blue 3·00 2·50
285 2e. mauve 3·75 2·10
286 5e. green 17·00 4·00
287 10e. brown 26·00 15·00
288 20e. orange 50·00 20·00

1938. As Nos. 383/409 of Angola.
289 1c. olive (postage) 15 10
290 5c. brown 15 10
291 10c. red 15 10
292 15c. purple 80 70
293 20c. slate 40 20
294 30c. purple 40 20
295 35c. green 40 20
296 40c. brown 40 20
297 50c. mauve 40 20
298 60c. black 40 20
299 70c. violet 40 20
300 80c. orange 35 20
301 1e. red 55 20
302 1e.75 blue 1·50 55
303 2e. green 2·75 1·60
304 5e. olive 6·50 1·60
305 10e. blue 10·50 2·10
306 20e. brown 35·00 4·25
307 10c. red (air) 65 50
308 20c. violet 65 50
309 50c. orange 65 50
310 1e. blue 65 50
311 2e. red 1·50 80
312 3e. green 2·00 1·40
313 5e. brown 5·75 2·00
314 9e. red 9·50 3·50
315 10e. mauve 10·50 4·50

14 Route of President's Tour

16 Machado Point, Sao Vicente

17 Ribeira Brava, Sao Nicolau

1939. Pres. Carmona's 2nd Colonial Tour.
316 **14** 80c. violet on mauve 4·50 3·00
317 1e.75 blue on blue 37·00 27·00
318 20e. brown on cream 75·00 25·00

1948. Nos. 276 and 294 surch.
319 10c. on 30c. purple 1·80 1·00
320 25c. on 40c. red 1·90 1·00

1948.
321 **16** 5c. purple and bistre 40 30
322 – 10c. green and light green 40 30
323 **17** 50c. purple and lilac 75 30
324 – 1e. purple 2·75 1·10
325 – 1e.75 blue and green 3·25 1·70
326 – 2e. brown and ochre 7·50 2·10
327 – 5e. green and yellow 15·00 4·00
328 – 10e. red and orange 24·00 14·00
329 – 20e. violet and buff 60·00 26·00
DESIGNS—VERT: 10c. Ribeira Grande. HORIZ: 1e. Porto Grande, Sao Vicente; 1e.75, 5e. Mindelo, Sao Vicente; 2e. Joao de Evora beach, Sao Vicente; 10e. Volcano, Fogo; 20e. Paul.

1948. Honouring the Statue of Our Lady of Fatima. As T **33** of Angola.
330 50c. blue 8·75 3·75

1949. 75th Anniv of U.P.U. As T **39** of Angola.
331 1e. mauve 7·00 3·50

1950. Holy Year. As T **41/2** of Angola.
332 1e. brown 85 45
333 2e. blue 3·50 1·70

1951. Surch with figures and bars over old value.
334 10c. on 35c. (No. 295) 45 40
335 20c. on 70c. (No. 299) 60 45
336 40c. on 70c. (No. 299) 70 45
337 50c. on 80c. (No. 300) 70 45
338 1e. on 1e.75 (No. 302) 75 45
339 2e. on 10e. (No. 305) 1·40 1·50

1951. Termination of Holy Year. As T **44** of Angola.
340 2e. violet and mauve 1·00 80

1952. No. 302 surch with figures and cross over old values.
341 10c. on 1e.75 blue 1·10 95
342 20c. on 1e.75 blue 1·10 95
343 50c. on 1e.75 blue 4·75 4·25
344 1e. on 1e.75 blue 60 15
345 1e.50 on 1e.75 blue 60 15

20 Map, c. 1471

21 V. Dias and G. de Cintra

1952. Portuguese Navigators as T **20/21**. Mult.
346 5c. Type **20** 10 10
347 10c. Type **21** 10 10
348 30c. D. Afonso and A. Fernandes 15 10
349 50c. Lancarote and S. da Costa 15 10
350 1e. D. Gomes and A. da Nola 15 10
351 2e. Princes Fernando and Henry the Navigator 1·10 10
352 3e. A. Goncalves and D. Dias 9·50 1·30
353 5e. A. Goncalves Baldaia and J. Fernandes 3·25 65
354 10e. D. Fanes da Gra and A. de Freitas 6·25 1·60
355 20e. Map, 1502 11·50 2·10

22 Doctor giving Injection

23 Facade of Monastery

1952. 1st Tropical Medicine Congress, Lisbon.
356 **22** 20c. black and green 55 40

1953. Missionary Art Exhibition.
357 **23** 10c. brown and olive 10 10
358 50c. violet and salmon 70 35
359 1e. green and orange 1·70 1·00

1953. Portuguese Stamp Centenary. As T **48** of Angola.
360 50c. multicoloured 1·40 90

1954. 4th Cent of Sao Paulo. As T **49** of Angola.
361 1e. black, green and buff 55 45

24 Arms of Cape Verde Is. and Portuguese Guinea

26 Prince Henry the Navigator

25 Arms of Praia

1955. Presidential Visit.
362 **24** 1e. multicoloured 40 20
363 1e.60c. multicoloured 60 55

1958. Centenary of City of Praia. Multicoloured.
364 **25** 1e. on yellow 50 40
365 2e.50 on salmon 1·00 80

1958. Brussels International Exn. As T **55** of Angola.
366 2e. multicoloured 65 30

1958. 6th International Congress of Tropical Medicine. As T **56** of Angola. Multicoloured.
367 3c. "Aloe vera" (plant) 1·70 1·90

1960. 500th Death Anniv of Prince Henry the Navigator.
368 **26** 2e. multicoloured 40 20

27 Antonio da Nola

28 "Education"

1960. 500th Anniv of Colonization of Cape Verde Islands. Multicoloured.
369 1e. Type **27** 60 40
370 2e.50 Diogo Gomes 1·70 90

1960. 10th Anniv of African Technical Co-operation Commission.
371 **28** 2e.50 multicoloured 1·10 60

29 Arms of Praia

30 Militia Regiment Drummer, 1806

1961. Urban Arms. As T **29**. Arms multicoloured; inscriptions in red and green; background colours given.
372 5c. buff 20 15
373 15c. blue 20 15
374 20c. yellow 20 15
375 30c. lilac 20 15
376 1e. green 65 15
377 2e. lemon 65 15
378 2e.50 pink 95 15
379 3e. brown 1·50 45
380 5e. blue 1·50 45
381 7e.50 olive 1·60 80
382 15e. mauve 2·30 80
383 30e. yellow 6·00 2·30
ARMS: 15c. Nova Sintra. 20c. Ribeira Brava. 30c. Assomada. 1e. Maio. 2e. Mindelo. 2e.50 Santa Maria. 3e. Pombas. 5e. Sal-Rei. 7e.50, Tarrafal. 15e. Maria Pia. 30e. San Felipe.

1962. Sports. As T **62** of Angola. Multicoloured.
384 50c. Throwing the javelin 25 20
385 1e. Discus thrower 85 20
386 1e.50 Batsman (cricket) 60 30
387 2e.50 Boxing 85 35
388 4e.50 Hurdler 1·40 95
389 12e.50 Golfers 2·75 1·90

1962. Malaria Eradication. Mosquito design as T **63** of Angola. Multicoloured.
390 2e.50 "Anopheles pretoriensis" 1·20 85

1963. 10th Anniv of T.A.P. Airline. As T **69** of Angola.
391 2e.50 multicoloured 90 60

1964. Centenary of National Overseas Bank. As T **71** of Angola but portrait of J. da S. M. Leal.
392 1e.50 multicoloured 85 65

1965. Centenary of I.T.U. As T **73** of Angola.
393 2e.50 multicoloured 1·70 1·20

1965. Portuguese Military Uniforms. Mult.
394 50c. Type **30** 25 20
395 1e. Militiaman, 1806 45 20
396 1e.50 Infantry Grenadiers officers, 1833 60 35
397 2e.50 Infantry grenadier, 1833 1·10 30
398 3e. Cavalry officer, 1834 2·30 45
399 4e. Infantry grenadier, 1835 1·10 45
400 5e. Artillery officer, 1848 1·20 45
401 10e. Infantry drum-major, 1856 2·50 1·50

1966. 40th Anniv of National Revolution. As T **77** of Angola, but showing different building. Multicoloured.
402 1e. Dr A. Moreira's Academy and Public Assistance Building 50 40

1967. Centenary of Military Naval Association. As T **79** of Angola. Multicoloured.
403 1e. F. da Costa and gunboat "Mandovy" 60 45
404 1e. 50 C. Araujo and minesweeper "Augusto Castilho" 1·00 75

1967. 50th Anniv of Fatima Apparitions. As T **80** of Angola. Multicoloured.
405 1e. Image of Virgin Mary 25 20

33 President Tomas

34 Port of Sao Vicente

1968. Visit of President Tomas of Portugal.
406 **33** 1e. multicoloured 25 20

1968. 500th Birth Anniv of Pedro Cabral (explorer). As T **84** of Angola. Multicoloured.
407 1e. Cantino's map, 1502 65 60
408 1e.50 Pedro Alvares Cabral (vert) 1·10 65

1968. "Produce of Cape Verde Islands". Mult.
409 50c. Type **34** 20 15
410 1e. "Purgueira" (Jatrophus curcus) (vert) 35 20
411 1e.50 Groundnuts (vert) 35 20
412 2e.50 Castor-oil plant (vert) 35 20
413 3e.50 "Inhame" (Dioscorea alata) (vert) 40 20
414 4e. Date palm (vert) 40 20
415 4e.50 "Goiabeira" (Psidium guajava) (vert) 65 20
416 5e. Tamarind (vert) 95 25
417 10e. Manioc (vert) 1·20 50
418 30e. Girl of Cape Verde (vert) 3·00 2·10

1969. Birth Centenary of Admiral Gago Coutinho. As T **86** of Angola. Multicoloured.
419 30c. Fairey IIID seaplane "Lusitania" and map of Lisbon-Rio flight (vert) 15 15

1969. 500th Birth Anniv of Vasco da Gama (explorer). Multicoloured. As T **87** of Angola.
420 1e.50 Vasco da Gama (vert) 30 25

1969. Centenary of Overseas Administrative Reforms. As T **88** of Angola.
421 2e. multicoloured 30 20

1969. 500th Birth Anniv of King Manoel I. As T **89** of Angola. Multicoloured.
422 3e. Manoel I 40 30

1970. Birth Centenary of Marshal Carmona. As T **91** of Angola. Multicoloured.
423 2e.50 Half-length portrait 40 30

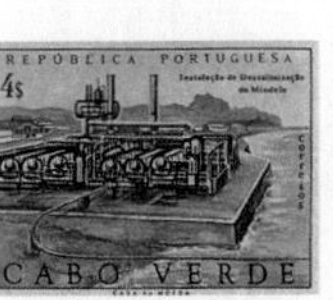

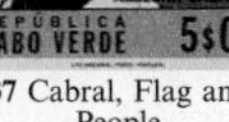

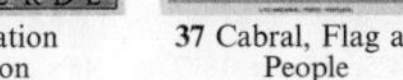

35 Desalination Installation

37 Cabral, Flag and People

1971. Inauguration of Desalination Plant, Mindelo.
424 **35** 4e. multicoloured . . . . . 1·00 70

1972. 400th Anniv of Camoens' "Lusiad" (epic poem). As T **96** of Angola. Multicoloured.
425 5e. Galleons at Cape Verde 50 25

1972. Olympic Games, Munich. As T **97** of Angola. Multicoloured.
426 4e. Basketball and boxing . . 50 25

1972. 50th Anniv of 1st Flight Lisbon–Rio de Janeiro. As T **98** of Angola. Multicoloured.
427 3e.50 Fairey IIID seaplane "Lusitania" near Sao Vicente 50 25

1973. Centenary of I.M.O./W.M.O. As Type **99** of Angola.
428 2e.50 multicoloured 50 25

1975. Independence. No. 407 optd **INDEPENDÊNCIA 5-Julho-75.**
430 1e. multicoloured 15 10

1975. 3rd Anniv of Amilcar Cabral's Assassination.
431 **37** 5e. multicoloured 20 15

38 Islanders with Broken Shackles

1976. 1st Anniv of Independence.
432 **38** 50c. multicoloured 10 10
433 3e. multicoloured 15 10
434 15e. multicoloured 40 20
435 50e. multicoloured . . . . 1·25 65

1976. Nos. 428, 424 and 415 optd **REPUBLICA DE.**
437 2e.50 multicoloured (No. 428) 15 10
438 4e. multicoloured (No. 424) 11·00 1·75
439 4e.50 multicoloured (No. 415) 11·00 1·00

40 Cabral and Map **41** Map of Islands

1976. 20th Anniv of PAIGC (Revolutionary Party).
440 **40** 1e. multicoloured 10 10

1977. Red Cross.
441 **41** 50c. multicoloured 10 10

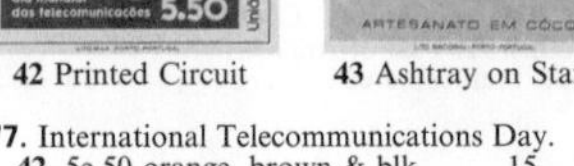

42 Printed Circuit **43** Ashtray on Stand

1977. International Telecommunications Day.
442 **42** 5e.50 orange, brown & blk 15 10

1977. Craftsmanship in Coconut. Multicoloured.
443 20c. Type **43** 10 10
444 30c. Ornamental bell 10 10
445 50c. Lamp 10 10
446 1e. Nativity 10 10
447 1e.50 Desk lamp 10 10
448 5e. Storage jar 15 10
449 10e. Container with hinged lid 35 15
450 20e. Tobacco jar 65 20
451 30e. Stringed instrument . . 1·10 35

44 5r. Stamp, 1877

45 Congress Emblem

1977. Centenary of First Cape Verde Stamps.
452 **44** 4e. multicoloured 15 10
453 8e. multicoloured 25 10

1977. 3rd PAIGC Congress, Bissau.
454 **45** 3e.50 multicoloured 15 10

1978. No. 419 surch **3$00.**
455 3e. on 30c. multicoloured . . 15 10

47 Microwave Antenna

1978. 10th World Telecommunications Day.
456 **47** 3e.50 multicoloured 15 10

48 Textile Pattern

1978. Handicrafts. Multicoloured.
457 50c. Type **48** 10 10
458 1e.50 Carpet runner and map of Islands 10 10
459 2e. Woven ribbon and map of Islands 10 10
460 3e. Shoulder bag and map of Islands 10 10
461 10e. Woven Cushions (vert) 30 20

49 Map of Africa **51** Human Rights Emblem

50 Freighter "Cabo Verde"

1978. International Anti-Apartheid Year.
462 **49** 4e.50 multicoloured 15 10

1978. 1st Cape Verde Merchant Ship.
463 **50** 1e. multicoloured 50 10

1978. 30th Anniv of Declaration of Human Rights.
464 **51** 1e.50 multicoloured 10 10
465 2e. multicoloured 10 10

52 Children with Flowers

1979. International Year of the Child. Mult.
466 1e.50 Children with balloons and flags 10 10
467 3e.50 Type **52** 10 10

53 Monument

54 Poster

1979. 20th Anniv of Pindjiguiti Massacre.
468 **53** 4e.50 multicoloured 15 10

1979. 1st National Youth Week.
469 **54** 3e.50 multicoloured 15 10

55 Mindelo

1980. Centenary of Mindelo City.
470 **55** 4e. multicoloured 55 15

56 Family, Graph and Map

57 National Flag

1980. 1st Population and Housing Census.
471 **56** 3e.50 multicoloured 10 10
472 4e.50 multicoloured 15 10

1980. 5th Anniv of Independence (1st issue).
473 **57** 4e. multicoloured 10 10
See also Nos. 481/3.

58 Running

59 Stylized Bird

1980. Olympic Games, Moscow. Multicoloured.
474 1e. Type **58** 10 10
475 2e.50 Boxing 10 10
476 3e. Basketball 10 10
477 4e. Volleyball 10 10
478 20e. Swimming 55 25
479 50e. Tennis . . . . 1·25 50

1980. 5th Anniv of Independence (2nd issue).
481 **59** 4e. multicoloured 10 10
482 7e. multicoloured 15 10
483 11e. multicoloured 25 15

60 Cigarette, Cigar, Pipe and Diseased Heart

1980. World Health Day. Anti-smoking Campaign. Multicoloured.
484 4e. Type **60** 10 10
485 7e. Healthy lungs plus smoking equals diseased lungs 20 10

61 Albacore

1980. Marine Life. Multicoloured.
486 50c. Type **61** 10 10
487 4e.50 Atlantic horse-mackerel 15 10
488 8e. Mediterranean moray . . 40 15
489 10e. Brown meagre 40 15
490 12e. Skipjack tuna 50 20
491 50e. Blue shark . . . . . . 1·50 70

62 "Area Verdel"

1980. Freighters. Multicoloured.
492 3e. Type **62** 25 15
493 5e.50 "Ilha do Maio" 30 20
494 7e.50 "Ilha de Komo" . . . 65 25
495 9e. "Boa Vista" 65 25
496 12e. "Santo Antao" 75 35
497 30e. "Santiago" . . . . . . 1·75 75

63 "Lochnera rosea"

1980. Flowers. Multicoloured.
498 50c. Type **63** 10 10
499 4e.50 "Poinciana regia Bojer" 10 10
500 8e. "Mirabilis jalapa" 25 10
501 10e. "Nerium oleander" . . . 25 10
502 12e. "Bougainvillea litoralis" 30 10
503 30e. "Hibiscus rosa sinenis" 70 30

64 Desert Scene and Hands holding plant

1981. Desert Erosion Prevention. Multicoloured.
504 4e.50 Type **64** 15 10
505 10e.50 Hands caring for plant and river scene 25 15

65 Map, Flag, and "Official Bulletin" announcing Constitution

67 Antenna

1981. 6th Anniv of Constitution.
506 **65** 4e.50 multicoloured 15 10

1981. Telecommunications. Multicoloured.
508 4e.50 Type **67** 10 10
509 8e. Dish antenna 25 10
510 20e. Dish antenna and satellite 50 30

68 Disabled Person in Wheelchair and I.Y.D.P. Emblem

1981. International Year of Disabled Persons.
511 **68** 4e.50 multicoloured 15 10

69 Moorhens

1981. Birds. Multicoloured.
512 1e. Little egret (vert) 25 10
513 4e.50 Barn owl (vert) 40 20

514 8e. Grey-headed kingfisher (vert) 90 30
515 10e. Type **69** . . . . 1·90 40
516 12e. Helmet guineafowls . . 2·60 40

70 Map showing Member States

1982. CILSS Congress, Praia.
518 **70** 11e.50 multicoloured . . . 30 10

71 Tackle

1982. "Amilcar Cabral" Football Cup Competition. Multicoloured.
519 4e.50 Type **71** 15 10
520 7e.50 Running with ball . . . 20 10
521 11e.50 Goalmouth scene . . 30 10

72 Militiawomen

1982. 1st Anniv of Cape Verde Women's Organization. Multicoloured.
522 4e.50 Type **72** 15 10
523 8e. Women farmers 20 10
524 12e. Nursery teacher 30 10

73 Footballers

1982. World Cup Football Championship, Spain.
525 **73** 1e.50 multicoloured 10 10
526 – 4e.50 multicoloured 15 10
527 – 8e. multicoloured 20 10
528 – 10e.50 multicoloured . . . 25 10
529 – 12e. multicoloured 30 10
530 – 20e. multicoloured 50 30
DESIGNS: 4e.50 to 20e. Various football scenes.

74 "Morrissey-Ernestina"

1982. Return of Schooner "Morrissey-Ernestina".
532 **74** 12e. multicoloured . . . . 1·50 45

75 San Vicente Shipyard

1982. 7th Anniv of Independence.
533 **75** 10e.50 multicoloured . . . 1·25 45

76 "Hypolimnas misippus"

1982. Butterflies. Multicoloured.
534 2e. Type **76** 15 10
535 4e.50 "Melanitis lede" . . . 25 15
536 8e. "Catopsilia florella" . . . 40 20
537 10e.50 "Colias electo" . . . 55 20
538 11e.50 "Danaus chrysippus" 65 20
539 12e. "Papilio demodecus" . . 65 20

77 Amilcar Cabral

1983. Amilcar Cabral Symposium.
540 **77** 7e. multicoloured 15 10
541 10e.50 multicoloured . . . 20 10

78 Francisco Xavier de Cruz (composer)

1983. Composers and Poets. Multicoloured.
543 7e. Type **78** 15 10
544 14e. Eugenio Tavares (poet) 30 10

79 "World Communications Network" **80** Cape Verde Cone

1983. World Communications Year.
545 **79** 13e. multicoloured 20 10

1983. Shells. Multicoloured.
546 50c. Type **80** 10 10
547 1e. "Conus decoratus" . . . 10 10
548 3e. "Conus salreiensis" . . . 15 10
549 10e. "Conus verdensis" . . . 30 20
550 50e. "Conus cuneolus" . . . 1·40 90

81 Arch and Cross **82** Auster D5/160 Husky

1983. 450th Anniv of Christianity in Cape Verde Islands.
551 **81** 7e. multicoloured 15 10

1984. 40th Anniv of I.C.A.O. Multicoloured.
552 50c. Type **82** 10 10
553 2e. De Havilland Dove . . . 10 10
554 10e. Hawker Siddeley HS748 25 15
555 13e. De Havilland Dragon Rapide 25 15
556 20e. De Havilland Twin Otter 50 30
557 50e. Britten-Norman Islander 1·10 65

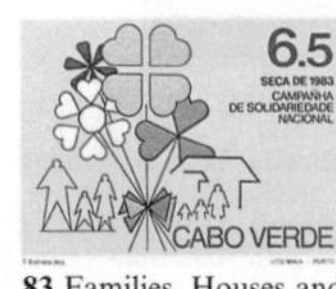

83 Families, Houses and Emblems as Balloons **84** Figure rising from Nautilus Shell

1984. National Solidarity Campaign.
558 **83** 6e.50 multicoloured 10 10
559 13e.50 multicoloured . . . 20 10

1985. 2nd Cape Verde Womens' Organization Conference.
560 **84** 8e. multicoloured 25 15

85 Emblem **87** "Steamer"

1985. 10th Anniv of Independence.
561 **85** 8e. multicoloured 15 10
562 12e. multicoloured 20 10

1985.
564 **87** 30e. on 10c. multicoloured 40 40

88 "Mabuya vaillanti" **89** Food in Pot over Fire

1986. Endangered Reptiles. Multicoloured.
566 8e. Type **88** 30 10
567 10e. "Tarentola gigas brancoensis" 35 10
568 15e. "Tarentola gigas gigas" 45 10
569 30e. "Hemidactylus bouvieri" 90 20

1986. World Food Day. Multicoloured.
571 8e. Type **89** 15 10
572 12e. Women pounding food in mortar 15 10
573 15e. Woman rolling flat bread with stone 20 10

90 Dove and Olive Branch

1986. International Peace Year.
574 **90** 12e. multicoloured 15 10
575 30e. multicoloured 40 20

91 Family Planning and Child Health Centre, Praia, and Woman breast-feeding Baby

1987. Child Survival Campaign. Multicoloured.
576 8e. Type **91** 15 10
577 10e. Assomada SOS children's village 15 10
578 12e. Family planning clinic, Mindelo, and nurse with child 15 10
579 16e. Children's home, Mindelo, and nurse with baby 25 10
580 100e. Calouste Gulbenkian kindergarten, Praia, and child writing . . . . 1·40 1·25

92 Mindelo City

1987. Tourism. Multicoloured.
581 1e. Type **92** 10 10
582 2e.50 Santo Antao island . . 10 10
583 5e. Fogo island 10 10
584 8e. Pillory, Velha City . . . 15 10
585 10e. Boa Entrada valley, Santiago island 15 10
586 12e. Fishing boats, Santiago 50 15
587 100e. Furna harbour, Brava island . . . . 1·40 65

93 "Carvalho" (schooner)

1987. Sailing Ships. Multicoloured.
588 **93** 12e. black, mauve & blue 45 20
589 – 16e. black, blue & mauve 45 20
590 – 50e. black, blue & dp blue 1·90 70
DESIGNS: 16e. "Nauta" (cutter); 50e. "Maria Sony" (schooner).

94 Emblem

1987. 2nd National Development Plan.
592 **94** 8e. multicoloured 15 10

95 Moths on Stem

1988. Crop Protection. Multicoloured.
593 50c. Type **95** 10 10
594 2e. Caterpillars on plant treated with bio-insecticides 10 10
595 9e. Use of imported predators 20 10
596 13e. Use of imported predatorial insects 30 15
597 16e. Locust on stem 35 15
598 19e. Damaged wood 45 20

96 17th-century Dutch Map

1988. Antique Maps of Cape Verde Islands. Multicoloured.
600 1e.50 Type **96** 10 10
601 2e.50 18th-cent Belgian map 10 10
602 4e.50 18th-cent French map 10 10
603 9e.50 18th-cent English map 15 10
604 19e.50 19th-cent English map 30 15
605 20e. 18th-cent French map (vert) 30 15

97 Church of the Abbot of the Holy Shelter, Tarrafal, Santiago

1988. Churches. Multicoloured.
606 5e. Type **97** 10 10
607 8e. Church of Our Lady of Light, Maio 15 10
608 10e. Church of the Nazarene, Praia, Santiago 15 10
609 12e. Church of Our Lady of the Rosary, Sao Nicolau 20 10
610 15e. Church of the Nazarene, Mindelo, Sao Vicente . . . 25 15
611 20e. Church of Our Lady of Grace, Praia, Santiago . . 30 15

98 Boy filling Tin with Water

1988. Water Economy Campaign.
612 **98** 12e. multicoloured 20 10

99 Red Cross Workers

1988. 125th Anniv of Red Cross Movement.
613 **99** 7e. multicoloured 10 10

100 Group of Youths and Pres. Pereira

1988. 3rd Congress of African Party for the Independence of Cape Verde. Multicoloured.
614 7e. Type **100** 10 10
615 10e.50 Pres. Pereira and Perez de Cuellar (U.N. Secretary-General) 15 10
616 30e. Emblem and Pres. Pereira 50 25

101 Handball

1988. Olympic Games, Seoul. Multicoloured.
618 12e. Type **101** 20 10
619 15e. Tennis 25 15
620 20e. Football 30 15
621 30e. Boxing 50 25

102 Hot-air Balloon "Pro Juventute"

1989. 2nd Pro Juventute Congress.
623 **102** 30e. multicoloured 45 25

103 Silva

1989. Death Centenary of Roberto Duarte Silva (chemist).
624 **103** 12e.50 multicoloured 20 10

104 "Liberty guiding the People" (Eugene Delacroix)

1989. Bicentenary of French Revolution.
625 **104** 20e. multicoloured 30 15
626 24e. multicoloured 35 20
627 25e. multicoloured 40 20

105 Anniversary Emblem

1989. Centenary of Interparliamentary Union. Mult.
629 2e. Type **105** 10 10
630 4e. Dove 10 10
631 13e. National Assembly building 20 10

106 Fonte Lima Women firing Pots

1989. Traditional Pottery. Multicoloured.
632 13e. Type **106** 20 10
633 20e. Terra di Monti women and children arranging pots to bake in sun (vert) 30 15
634 24e. Terra di Monti woman shaping pot 35 20
635 25e. Fonte Lima women kneading clay (vert) 40 20

107 Boy and Truck

108 Pope John Paul II

1989. Christmas. Home-made Toys. Mult.
636 1e. Type **107** 10 10
637 6e. Boy with car on waste ground 10 10
638 8e. Boy with truck on pavement 15 10
639 11e.50 Boys with various vehicles 15 10
640 18e. Boys and sit-on scooter 30 15
641 100e. Boy with boat 1·50 75

1990. Papal Visit.
642 **108** 13e. multicoloured 20 10
643 20e. multicoloured 30 15

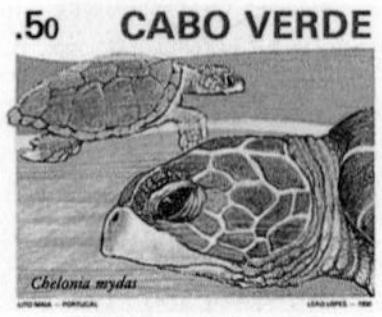

109 Green Turtles

1990. Turtles. Multicoloured.
645 50c. Type **109** 10 10
646 1e. Leatherback turtles 10 10
647 5e. Olive ridley turtles 10 10
648 10e. Loggerhead turtles 15 10
649 42e. Hawksbill turtles 65 35

110 Footballers

1990. World Cup Football Championship, Italy.
650 **110** 4e. multicoloured 10 10
651 – 7e.50 multicoloured 15 10
652 – 8e. multicoloured 15 10
653 – 100e. multicoloured 1·60 80
DESIGNS: 7e.50 to 100e. Different footballing scenes.

111 Face

1990. 1st Congress of Cape Verde Women's Movement.
655 **111** 9e. multicoloured 15 10

112 Teacher helping Boy to Read

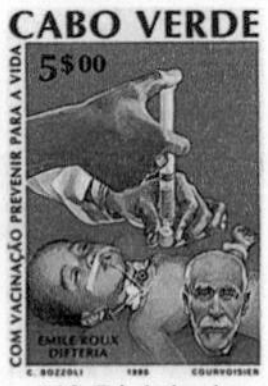

113 Diphtheria Treatment and Emile Roux (pioneer of antitoxic method)

1990. International Literacy Year. Multicoloured.
656 2e. Type **112** 10 10
657 3e. Teacher with adult class 10 10
658 15e. Teacher with flash-card 25 15
659 19e. Adult student pointing to letters on blackboard 30 15

1990. Vaccination Campaign. Multicoloured.
660 5e. Type **113** 10 10
661 13e. Tuberculosis vaccination and Robert Koch (discoverer of tubercle bacillus) 20 10
662 20e. Tetanus vaccination and Gaston Ramon 30 15
663 24e. Poliomyelitis oral vaccination and Jonas Edward Salk (discoverer of vaccine) 40 20

114 Musician on Bull's Back

1990. Traditional Stories. Multicoloured.
664 50c. Type **114** 10 10
665 2e.50 Fisherman and mermaid ("Joao Piquinote") 10 10
666 12e. Girl and snake 20 10
667 25e. Couple and eggs ("Ti Lobo, Ti Lobo") 40 20

115 World Map and Beam destroying AIDS Virus

1991. Anti-AIDS Campaign. Multicoloured.
668 13e. Type **115** 20 10
669 24e. Beam, AIDS virus and "SIDA" 40 20

116 Fishing Boat at Sea and Fishermen on Shore

1991. Fishing Industry. Multicoloured.
670 10e. Type **116** 20 15
671 24e. Fisherman removing hook from fish 70 30
672 25e. Fishing boats 55 30
673 50e. Fishermen taking in lines 1·10 65

117 Our Lady of the Rosary Church

1991. Tourism. Ruins of Ribeira Grande, Santiago Island. Multicoloured.
674 12e.50 Type **117** 20 10
675 15e. Se Cathedral 25 15
676 20e. Sao Filipe fortress 30 15
677 30e. St. Francis's Convent 45 20

118 "Lavandula rotundifolia"

119 Guitar

1991. Medicinal Plants. Multicoloured.
679 10e. Type **118** 15 10
680 15e. "Micromeria forbesii" 25 15
681 21e. "Sarcostemma daltonii" 30 15
682 24e. "Periploca chevalieri" 40 20
683 30e. "Echium hypertropicum" 45 20
684 35e. "Erysimum caboverdeanum" 55 25

1991. Musical Instruments. Multicoloured.
685 10e. Type **119** 25 15
686 20e. Violin 50 35
687 29e. Guitar with five double strings 80 40
688 47e. Cimboa 1·25 75

120 Crib (Tito Livio Goncalves)

1991. Christmas. Multicoloured.
690 31e. Type **120** 50 25
691 50e. Fonte-Lima crib 80 40

121 Rose Apples

1992. Tropical Fruits. Multicoloured.
692 16e. Type **121** 35 15
693 25e. Mangoes 50 25
694 31e. Cashews 65 30
695 32e. Avocados 70 35

122 Ships anchored in Bay

1992. 500th Anniv of Discovery of America by Columbus. Columbus's Landings in Cape Verde Islands. Multicoloured.
696 40e. Type **122** 1·10 70
697 40e. Caravel 1·10 70

124 Throwing the Javelin

1992. Olympic Games, Barcelona. Multicoloured.
700 16e. Type **124** 35 15
701 20e. Weightlifting 40 20
702 32e. Pole vaulting 70 35
703 40e. Putting the shot 85 40

125 Oxen and Sugar Cane

1992. Production of Molasses. Multicoloured.
705 19e. Type **125** 35 15
706 20e. Crushing cane 35 15
707 37e. Feeding cane into mill 70 35
708 38e. Cooking molasses 70 35

126 Cat

1992. Domestic Animals. Multicoloured.
709 16e. Type **126** 30 15
710 31e. Chickens 55 25
711 32e. Dog (vert) 60 30
712 50e. Horse 90 45

127 "Tubastrea aurea"

1993. Corals. Multicoloured.
713 5e. Type **127** 10 10
714 31e. "Corallium rubrum" . . 55 25
715 37e. "Porites porites" 65 30
716 50e. "Millepora alcicornis" 90 45

129 King Ferdinand and Queen Isabella of Spain and Pope Alexander VI
130 "Palinurus charlestoni"

1993. 500th Annivs of Pope Alexander VI's Bulls (on Portuguese and Spanish spheres of influence) and of Treaty of Tordesillas. Multicoloured.
718 37e. Type **129** 65 30
719 37e. King Joao II of Portugal and Pope Julius II 65 30
720 38e. Astrolabe, quill and left-half of globe 70 35
721 38e. Map of Iberian Peninsula and right-half of globe with Cape Verde Islands highlighted 70 35
Stamps of the same value were issued together in se-tenant pairs, each pair forming a composite design.

1993. Lobsters. Multicoloured.
722 2e. Type **130** 10 10
723 10e. Brown lobster 20 10
724 17e. Royal lobster 30 15
725 38e. Stone lobster 70 35

131 Cory's Shearwater

1993. Nature Reserves. Multicoloured.
727 10e. Type **131** (Branco and Raso Islets) 25 15
728 30e. Brown booby (De Cima and Raso Islets) 80 25
729 40e. Magnificent frigate bird (Curral Velho and Baluarte Islets) . . . . 1·50 35
730 41e. Red-billed tropic bird (Raso and De Cima Islets) 1·90 40

132 Rose

1993. Flowers. Multicoloured.
731 5e. Type **132** 10 10
732 30e. Bird of Paradise flower 55 25
733 37e. Sweet William 65 30
734 50e. Cactus dahlia 90 45

133 Map and Prince Henry (½-size illustration)

1994. 600th Birth Anniv of Prince Henry the Navigator.
736 **133** 37e. multicoloured 55 25

134 Players and Giants Stadium, New York

1994. World Cup Football Championship, U.S.A. Multicoloured.
737 1e. Type **134** 10 10
738 20e. Referee showing red card and Rose Bowl, Los Angeles 30 15
739 37e. Scoring goal and Foxboro Stadium, Boston 55 25
740 38e. Linesman raising flag and Silverdome, Detroit . . 55 25

135 Sand Tiger
136 "Prata" Bananas

1994. Sharks. Multicoloured.
742 21e. Type **135** 45 15
743 27e. Black-tipped shark . . . 60 25
744 37e. Whale shark . . . . . 1·00 50
745 38e. Velvet belly . . . . . . 1·00 50

1994. Bananas. Multicoloured.
746 12e. Type **136** 20 10
747 16e. "Pao" bananas (horiz) 25 10
748 30e. "Ana roberta" bananas 45 20
749 40e. "Roxa" bananas 60 30

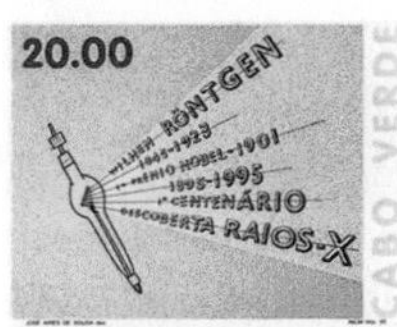

137 Fontes Pereira de Melo

1994. Lighthouses. Multicoloured.
751 2e. Type **137** 10 10
752 37e. Morro Negro 60 30
753 38e. D. Amelia (vert) 60 30
754 50e. D. Maria Pia (vert) . . . 80 40

138 X-Ray Tube and Dates

1995. Centenary of Discovery of X-Rays by Wilhelm Rontgen.
755 **138** 20e. multicoloured 30 15
756 37e. multicoloured 60 30

139 Child with Tuna
141 Communications

140 Wire-haired Fox Terrier and "Two Foxhounds and Fox Terrier" (John Emms)

1995. 50th Anniv of F.A.O. Multicoloured.
758 37e. Type **139** 70 30
759 38e. Globe and wheat ear . . 60 30

1995. Dogs. Heads of dogs and paintings. Mult.
760 1e. Type **140** 10 10
761 10e. Cavalier King Charles and "Shooting Over Dogs" (Richard Ansdell) 15 10
762 40e. German shepherd and rough collies 65 30
763 50e. Bearded collie and "Hounds at Full Cry" (Thomas Blinks) 80 40

1995. 20th Anniv of Independence.
764 **141** 37e. multicoloured . . . . 1·00 40

143 Horse Race

1995. St. Philip's Flag Festival, Fogo. Mult.
766 2e. Type **143** 10 10
767 10e. Preparing for horse race 15 10
768 37e. Preparing food and clapping to music 55 25
769 40e. Crowd watching final horse race 60 30

144 Grasshopper playing Guitar
145 "Sonchus daltonii"

1995. Childrens' Stories. 300th Death Anniv of Jean de La Fontaine (writer). Scenes from "The Ant and the Grasshopper". Multicoloured.
770 10e. Type **144** 15 10
771 25e. Grasshopper in snowstorm looking through ants' window 40 20
772 38e. Ant laying-in supplies for winter 55 25
773 45e. Ants welcoming grasshopper into their home 70 35

1996. Endangered Flowers. Multicoloured.
774 20e. Type **145** 30 15
775 37e. "Echium vulcanorum" 55 25
776 38e. "Nauplius smithii" . . . 55 25
777 50e. "Campanula jacobaea" 75 35

146 Table Tennis

1996. Olympic Games, Atlanta. Multicoloured.
778 1e. Type **146** 10 10
779 37e. Gymnastics 55 25
780 100e. Athletics . . . . 1·50 75

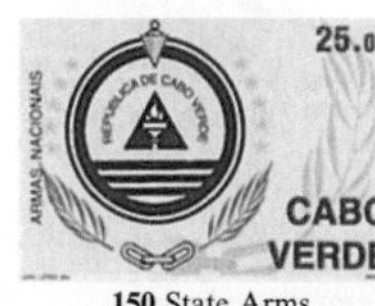

147 Student (Education of Girls)
148 Deep Sea Fishing

1996. 50th Anniv of U.N.I.C.E.F. Multicoloured.
781 20e. Type **147** 25 10
782 40e. Mother kissing child (Right to Love) 50 25

1996. Water Sports. Multicoloured.
783 2e.50 Type **148** 10 10
784 10e. Sailboard 20 10
785 22e.50 Jet skiing 30 15
786 100e. Surfing (horiz) . . . . 1·25 60

1997. Nos. 582 and 650/1 surch.
788 3e. on 2e.50 multicoloured . . 10 10
789 37e. on 4e. multicoloured . . 50 25
790 38e. on 7e.50 multicoloured 55 25

150 State Arms

1997. National Symbols. Multicoloured.
791 25e. Type **150** 30 15
792 37e. National anthem 40 20
793 50e. State flag 60 30

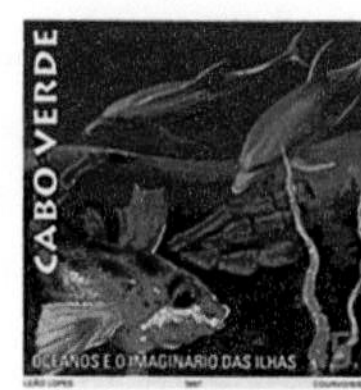

151 Small-toothed Sawfish

1997. The Small-toothed Sawfish. Multicoloured.
794 15e. Type **151** 20 10
795 15e. Underside of sawfish . . 20 10
796 15e. Sawfish and school of fishes 20 10
797 15e. Two sawfishes 20 10

152 Fish and Dolphins

1997. Oceans. Multicoloured.
798 45e. Type **152** 55 25
799 45e. Mermaid and merman 55 25
800 45e. Fishes, eel, coral and sunken gate 55 25
Nos. 798/800 were issued together, se-tenant, forming a composite design.

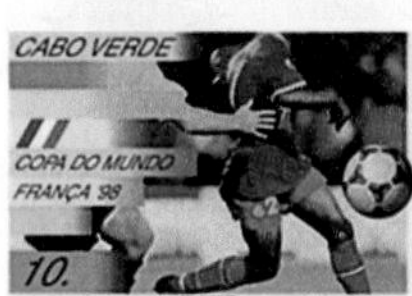

153 Yellow-finned Tuna

1997. Tuna. Multicoloured.
801 13e. Type **153** 15 10
802 21e. Big-eyed tuna 25 10
803 41e. Little tuna 50 25
804 45e. Skipjack tuna 55 25

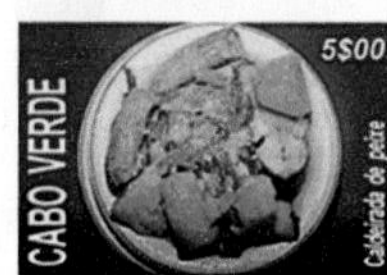

154 Players chasing Ball

1998. World Cup Football Championship, France. Multicoloured.
805 10e. Type **154** 10 10
806 30e. Ball in net (vert) 45 20
807 45e. Player with ball (vert) 55 25
808 50e. Globe, football and trophy 60 30

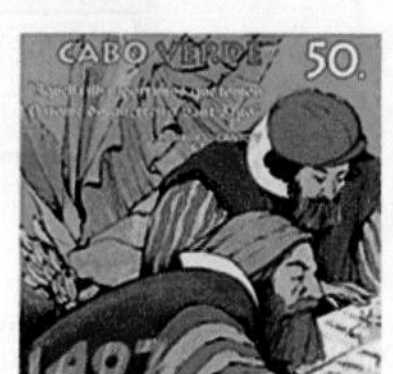

155 Fish Dish

1998. Local Cuisine.
809 **155** 5e. multicoloured 10 10
810 – 25e. multicoloured 30 15
811 – 35e. multicoloured 40 20
812 – 40e. multicoloured 45 20
DESIGNS: 25e. to 40e. Different food dishes.

156 Navigators reading Books and Banana Tree

1998. 500th Anniv (1997) of Vasco da Gama's Expedition to India. Multicoloured.
813 50e. Type **156** 60 30
814 50e. Seaman with sword and couple 60 30
815 50e. Compass rose and Portuguese galleon in harbour . . . . 1·00 40
Nos. 813/15 were issued together, se-tenant, forming a composite design.

157 Brava Island Costume **158** "Byblia ilithyia"

1998. Local Women's Costumes. Multicoloured.

816	10e. Type **157**	10	10
817	18e. Fogo Island	20	10
818	30e. Boa Vista Island	35	15
819	50e. Santiago Island	60	30

1999. Butterflies and Moths. Multicoloured.

820	5e. Type **158**	10	10
821	10e. "Aganais speciosa"	10	10
822	20e. Crimson-speckled moth	25	10
823	30e. Painted lady	35	15
824	50e. Cabbage looper	60	30
825	100e. "Grammodes congenita"	1·25	60

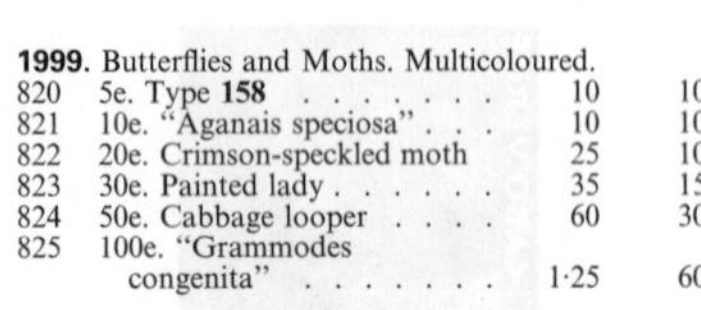

159 Concorde in Flight

1999. 30th Anniv of Concorde (supersonic airplane). Multicoloured.

827	30e. Type **159**	35	15
828	50e. Concorde on airport apron	60	30

160 Alain Gerbault (solo yachtsman) and Mindelo Harbour

1999. "Philexfrance 99" International Stamp Exhibition, Paris, France. Multicoloured.

829	30e. Type **160**	40	20
830	50e. Roberto Duarte Silva (chemist) and Eiffel Tower, Paris	60	30

161 Globe in Envelope and U.P.U. Emblem

1999. 125th Anniv of Universal Postal Union. Mult.

832	30e. Type **161**	40	20
833	50e. Paper airplanes	60	30

Nos. 832/3 are not inscribed with the country name.

162 Cola Sanjon Dance **163** Globe, Open Book and Hourglass

1999. Local Dances. Multicoloured.

834	10e. Type **162**	10	10
835	30e. Contradanca	30	15
836	50e. Desfile de Tabanca (horiz)	50	25
837	100e. Batuque (horiz)	1·00	50

2000. New Millennium. Multicoloured.

838	40e. Type **163**	40	20
839	50e. "2000" (horiz)	50	25

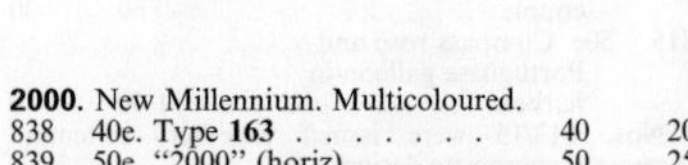

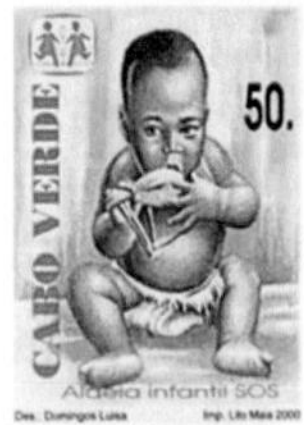

164 Baby

2000. 50th Anniv (1999) of S.O.S. Children's Villages. Multicoloured.

840	50e. Type **164**	50	25
841	100e. Child and emblem (horiz)	1·00	50

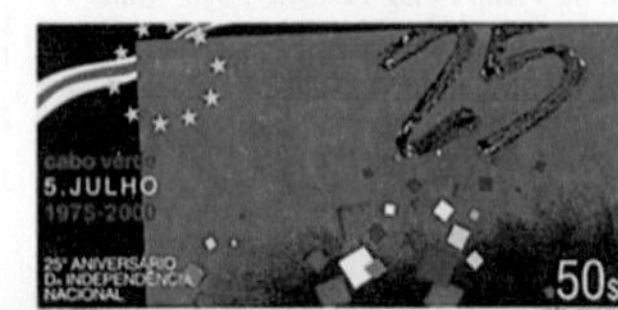

165 "25" and Emblem

2000. 25th Anniv of Independence.

842	**165** 50e. multicoloured	50	25

166 Gymnastics

2000. Olympic Games, Sydney. Multicoloured.

843	10e. Type **166**	10	10
844	40e. Taekwondo	40	20
845	50e. Athletics	50	25

167 Dragon Tree **168** Students (left-hand detail)

2000. Dragon Tree.

847 **167**	5e. green	10	10
848	40e. red	50	25
849	60e. brown	70	35

2000. 134th Anniv of the Liceu de Sao Nicolau Seminary. Multicoloured.

850	60e. Type **168**	70	35
851	60e. Students (right-hand detail)	70	35
852	60e. Jose Alves Feio, Jose Julio Dias (co-founders) and Antonio Jose de Oliveira Boucas (Principal) (56 × 26 mm)	70	35

Nos. 850/2 were issued together, se-tenant, forming a composite design.

169 White Sea Bream (*Diplodus sargus*)

2001. Fish. Multicoloured.

853	10e. Type **169**	10	10
854	22e. *Diplodus prayensis*	20	10
855	28e. Marmora sea bream (*Lithognathus mormyrus*)	25	15
856	48e. *Diplodus fasciatus*	45	20
857	60e. *Diplodus puntazzo*	55	25

170 *Thomisus onustus*

2001. Spiders. Multicoloured.

858	13e. Type **170**	10	10
859	16e. *Scytodes velutina*	15	10
860	40e. *Hersiliola simony*	35	15
861	100e. *Loxosceles rufescens*	95	45

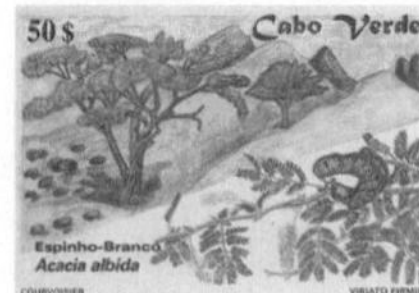

171 *Acacia albida*

2001. Trees. Multicoloured.

862	50e. Type **171**	45	20
863	60e. *Ficus sycomorus*	55	25

172 Grand Place, Brussels and Fountain

2001. "Belgica 2001" International Stamp Exhibition, Brussels. Sheet 116 × 86 mm.

MS864	**172** 100e. multicoloured	95	45

173 Artemisia gorgonum (inscr "Artimisia") **174** Children encircling Globe

2001. Plants (1st series). Multicoloured.

865	20e. Type **173**	20	10
866	27e. *Globularia amygdalifolia*	25	15
867	47e.50 *Sidereoxylon marginata* (*horiz*)	45	25
868	50e. *Umbilicus schmidtii* (*horiz*)	45	20
869	60e. *Verbascum cystolithicum*	55	25
870	100e. *Limonium lobinii*	95	45

See also Nos. 873/6.

2001. United Nations Year of Dialogue among Civilizations.

871	**174** 60e. multicoloured	55	25

175 Antonio Goncalves

2001. Birth Centenary of Antonio Aurelio Goncalves (writer).

872	**175** 100e. multicoloured	95	45

2002. Plants (2nd series). As T **173**. Multicoloured.

873	10e. *Euphorbia tuckeyana* (inscr "tuckeyna") (*horiz*)	10	10
874	50e. *Limonium*	45	20
875	60e. *Aeonium gorgoneum*	55	25
876	100e. *Polycarpaea gayi*	95	45

176 Player heading Ball into Goal

2002. World Cup Football Championship, Japan and South Korea. Multicoloured.

877	60e. Type **176**	55	25
878	100e. Player kicking ball towards goal	95	45

177 Two Adult Turtles

2002. Marine Turtles (*Caretta caretta*). Multicoloured.

879	10e. Type **177**	10	10
880	20e. Laying eggs	20	10
881	30e. Young emerging from sand	30	15
882	60e. Young crawling towards sea	55	25
883	100e. Adult swimming	95	45
MS884	150 × 110 mm. 100e. Adult on beach (80 × 61 mm)	95	45

178 Basket from St. Nicholas Island

2002. Traditional Baskets. Multicoloured.

885	20e. Type **178**	20	10
886	33e. From St. Anthony Island	30	15
887	60e. From Santiago Island	55	25
888	100e. From Boa Vista Island	95	45

179 Carlos Alberto Silva Martins (Katchass) (musician)

2003. Poets and Musicians. Multicoloured.

889	12e. Type **179**	10	10
890	20e. Jorge Monteiro (Jotamonte) (composer)	20	10
891	32e. Luís Rendall (composer)	30	15
892	47e.50 Jorge Barbosa (poet)	45	20
893	60e. Januario Leite (poet)	55	25
894	100e. Jose Lopes (poet)	95	45

180 Cesaria Evora

2003. Cesaria Evora (singer) Commemoration. Multicoloured.

895	60e. Type **180**	55	25
896	100e. Cesaria Evora (different)	95	45
MS897	85 × 115 mm. 200e. Cesaria Evora's legs (51 × 38 mm)	1·90	1·90

MS897 forms a composite design of Cesaria Evora singing.

181 Purple Heron (*Ardea purpurea bournei*)

2003. Herons and Egrets. Multicoloured.

898	10e. Type **181**	10	10
899	27e. Grey heron (*Ardea cinerea*)	25	10
900	42e. Cattle egret (*Bubulcus ibis*)	40	20
901	60e. Little egret (*Egretta garzeta*)	55	25

CHARITY TAX STAMPS

Used on certain days of the year as an additional postal tax on internal letters. Other values in some of the types were for use on telegrams only. The proceeds were devoted to public charities. If one was not affixed in addition to the ordinary postage, postage due stamps were used to collect the deficiency and the fine.

1925. As Marquis de Pombal issue of Portugal but inscr "CABO VERDE".

C266	C **73** 15c. violet	25	25
C267	– 15c. violet	25	25
C268	C **75** 15c. violet	25	25

C 16 St. Isabel **C 31** **C 32**

1948.
C321 C **16** 50c. green 1·25 85
C322 1e. red 2·50 1·00

1959. Surch.
C368 C **16** 50c. on 1e. red 50 30

1959. Colours changed.
C369 C **16** 50c. mauve 1·10 65
C370 1e. blue 1·10 65

1967.
C406 C **31** 30c. multicoloured 15 15
C407 50c. mult (purple panel) 30 30
C408 50c. mult (red panel) 15 15
C409 1e. mult (brown panel) 45 45
C410 1e. mult (purple panel) 45 45

1968. Pharmaceutical Tax stamps surch as in Type C **32**.
C411a C **32** 50c. on 1c. black, orange and green 80 60
C412c 50c. on 2c. black, orange and green 40 25
C413 50c. on 3c. black, orange and green 55 40
C414 50c. on 5c. black, orange and green 55 40
C415 50c. on 10c. black, orange and green 65 55
C416 1e. on 1c. black, orange and green 1·50 1·00
C417a 1e. on 2c. black, orange and green 1·00 85

NEWSPAPER STAMP

1893. "Newspaper" key-type inscr "CABO VERDE".
N37 V 2½r. brown 55 35

POSTAGE DUE STAMPS

1904. "Due" key-type inscr "CABO VERDE".
D119 W 5r. green 15 15
D120 10r. grey 15 15
D121 20r. brown 15 15
D122 30r. orange 40 20
D123 50r. brown 20 15
D124 60r. brown 3·00 1·75
D125 100r. mauve 80 50
D126 130r. blue 80 50
D127 200r. red 85 75
D128 500r. lilac 2·10 1·50

1911. Nos. D119/28 optd **REPUBLICA**.
D135 W 5r. green 10 10
D136 10r. grey 10 10
D137 20r. brown 15 10
D138 30r. orange 15 10
D139 50r. brown 15 10
D140 60r. brown 30 20
D141 100r. mauve 30 20
D142 130r. blue 35 25
D143 200r. red 75 60
D144 500r. lilac 90 75

1921. "Due" key-type inscr "CABO VERDE" with currency in centavos.
D252 W ½c. green 10 10
D253 1c. slate 10 10
D254 2c. brown 10 10
D255 3c. orange 10 10
D256 5c. brown 10 10
D257 6c. brown 10 10
D258 10c. mauve 15 15
D259 13c. blue 30 25
D260 20c. red 30 25
D261 50c. grey 60 45

1925. As Nos. C266/8, optd **MULTA**.
D266 C **73** 30c. violet 25 25
D267 – 30c. violet 25 25
D268 C **75** 30c. violet 25 25

1952. As Type D **45** of Angola, but inscr "CABO VERDE". Numerals in red; name in black.
D356 10c. brown and grey 10 10
D357 30c. black, blue & mauve 10 10
D358 50c. blue, green & yellow 10 10
D359 1e. blue and pale blue 10 10
D360 2e. brown and orange 20 20
D361 5e. green and grey 45 45

CAROLINE ISLANDS Pt. 7

A group of islands in the Pacific Ocean, formerly a German protectorate; under Japanese mandate after 1918. Now under United States trusteeship.

100 pfennig = 1 mark.

1899. Stamps of Germany optd **Karolinen**.
7 **8** 3pf. brown 9·50 10·50
8 5pf. green 10·50 11·00
9 **9** 10pf. red 17·00 13·00
10 20pf. blue 17·00 19·00
11 25pf. orange 38·00 48·00
12 50pf. brown 42·00 42·00

1901. "Yacht" key-types inscr "KAROLINEN".
13 N 3pf. brown 65 1·40
14 5pf. green 65 1·40
15 10pf. red 80 3·50
16 20pf. blue 95 5·00
17 25f. black & red on yellow 1·25 10·00
18 30pf. black & orge on buff 1·25 10·00
19 40pf. black and red 1·10 11·00
20 50pf. black & pur on buff 1·40 14·00
21 80pf. black & red on rose 2·10 17·00
22 O 1m. red 3·50 42·00
23 2m. blue 6·00 60·00
24 3m. black 10·00 £110
25 5m. red and black £140 £425

1910. No. 13 surch **5 Pf.**
26 N 5pf. on 3pf. brown — £4250

CASTELROSSO Pt. 3

One of the Aegean Is. Occupied by the French Navy on 27 December 1915. The French withdrew in August 1921 and, after a period of Italian Naval administration, the island was included in the Dodecanese territory.

A. FRENCH OCCUPATION

100 centimes = 1 franc = 4 piastres.

1920. Stamps of 1902–20 of French Post Offices in Turkish Empire optd **B. N. F. CASTELLORIZO**.
F 1 A 1c. grey 30·00 30·00
F 2 2c. purple 30·00 30·00
F 3 3c. red 30·00 30·00
F 4 5c. green 38·00 38·00
F 5 B 10c. red 38·00 38·00
F 6 15c. red 55·00 55·00
F 7 20c. brown 60·00 60·00
F 8 1pi. on 20c. blue 60·00 60·00
F 9 30c. lilac 65·00 65·00
F10 C 40c. red and blue £120 £120
F11 2pi. on 50c. brown & lilac £130 £130
F12 4pi. on 1f. red & green £170 £170
F13 20pi. on 5f. blue & brown £450 £450

1920. Optd **O. N. F. Castellorizo**. (a) On stamps of 1902–20 of French Post Offices in Turkish Empire.
F14 A 1c. grey 19·00 19·00
F15 2c. purple 19·00 19·00
F16 3c. red 19·00 19·00
F17 5c. green 19·00 19·00
F18 B 10c. red 21·00 21·00
F19 15c. red 26·00 26·00
F20 20c. brown 45·00 45·00
F21 1pi. on 25c. blue 45·00 45·00
F22 30c. lilac 40·00 40·00
F23 C 40c. red and blue 40·00 40·00
F24 2pi. on 50c. brown & lilac 40·00 40·00
F25 4pi. on 1f. red and green 55·00 55·00
F26 20pi. on 5f. blue & brown £250 £250

(b) On Nos. 334 and 341 of France.
F27 **18** 10c. red 26·00 16·00
F28 25c. blue 26·00 16·00

1920. Stamps of France optd **O F CASTELLORISO**.
F29 **18** 5c. green £120 £120
F30 10c. red £120 £120
F31 20c. red £120 £120
F32 25c. blue £120 £120
F33 **13** 50c. brown and lilac £700 £700
F34 1f. red and green £700 £700

B. ITALIAN OCCUPATION

100 centesimi = 1 lira.

1922. Stamps of Italy optd **CASTELROSSO**.
15 **37** 5c. green 90 15·00
16 10c. red 90 15·00
17 15c. grey 90 18·00
18 **41** 20c. orange 90 18·00
19 **39** 25c. blue 90 15·00
20 40c. brown 90 15·00
21 50c. violet 90 17·00
22 60c. red 90 21·00
23 85c. brown 90 26·00
24 **34** 1l. brown and green 90 26·00

2

1923.
10 **2** 5c. green 1·90 11·00
11 10c. red 1·90 11·00
12 25c. blue 1·90 11·00
13 50c. purple 1·90 11·00
14 1l. brown 1·90 11·00

1930. Ferrucci stamps of Italy optd **CASTELROSSO**.
25 **114** 20c. violet 4·25 3·25
26 – 25c. green (No. 283) 4·25 6·00
27 – 50c. black (as No. 284) 4·25 3·25
28 – 1l.25 blue (No. 285) 4·25 8·00
29 – 5l.+2l. red (as No. 286) 15·00 35·00

1932. Garibaldi stamps of Italy optd **CASTELROSSO**.
30 – 10c. brown 15·00 25·00
31 **128** 20c. brown 15·00 25·00
32 – 25c. green 15·00 25·00
33 **128** 30c. blue 15·00 25·00
34 – 50c. purple 15·00 25·00
35 – 75c. red 15·00 25·00
36 – 1l.25 blue 15·00 25·00
37 – 1l.75+25c. brown 15·00 25·00
38 – 2l.55+50c. red 15·00 25·00
39 – 5l.+1l. violet 15·00 25·00

CAUCA Pt. 20

A State of Colombia, reduced to a Department in 1886, now uses Colombian stamps.

100 centavos = 1 peso.

2

1902. Imperf.
2 **2** 10c. black on red 1·00 1·00
3 20c. black on orange 85 85

CAVALLA (KAVALLA) Pt. 16

French P.O. in a former Turkish port, now closed.

100 centimes = 1 franc.
40 paras = 1 piastre.

1893. Stamps of France optd **Cavalle** or surch also in figures and words.
41 **10** 5c. green 10·50 8·25
43 10c. black on lilac 14·50 10·50
45 15c. blue 22·00 13·00
46 1pi. on 25c. black on pink 17·00 12·50
47 2pi. on 50c. red 55·00 38·00
48a 4pi. on 1f. green 55·00 48·00
49 8pi. on 2f. brown on blue 70·00 65·00

1902. "Blanc", "Mouchon" and "Merson" key-types inscr "CAVALLE". The four higher values surch also.
50 A 5c. green 1·10 90
51 B 10c. red 1·10 95
52 15c. red 6·00 6·00
53 15c. orange 1·50 1·10
54 1pi. on 25c. blue 2·25 1·50
55 C 2pi. on 50c. brown & lilac 6·00 4·00
56 4pi. on 1f. red and green 8·00 6·00
57 8pi. on 2f. lilac and brown 10·00 9·00

CAYES OF BELIZE Pt. 1

A chain of several hundred islands, coral atolls, reefs and sandbanks stretching along the eastern seaboard of Belize.

The following issues for the Cayes of Belize fall outside the criteria for full listing as detailed on page viii.

100 cents = 1 dollar.

APPENDIX

1984.

Marine Life, Map and Views, 1, 2, 5, 10, 15, 25, 75c., $3, $5.

250th Anniv of "Lloyd's List" (newspaper). 25, 75c., $1, $2.

Olympic Games, Los Angeles. 10, 15, 75c., $2.

90th Anniv of "Caye Service" Local Stamps. 10, 15, 75c., $2.

1985.

Birth Bicent of John J. Audubon (ornithologist). 25, 75c., $1, $3.

Shipwrecks. $1 × 4.

CAYMAN ISLANDS Pt. 1

A group of islands in the British West Indies. A dependency of Jamaica until August 1962, when it became a Crown Colony.

1900. 12 pence = 1 shilling;
20 shillings = 1 pound.
1969. 100 cents = 1 Jamaican dollar.

1

2

1900.
1a **1** ¼d. green 4·50 15·00
2 1d. red 4·50 2·25

1902.
8 **2** ½d. green 7·00 8·00
4 1d. red 10·00 9·00
10 2½d. blue 6·50 3·25
13 4d. brown and blue 32·00 60·00
11 6d. brown 16·00 38·00
14 6d. olive and red 32·00 70·00
12 1s. orange 32·00 48·00
15 1s. violet and green 55·00 80·00
16 5s. orange and green £180 £300

1907. Surch **One Halfpenny.**
17 **2** ½d. on 1d. red 42·00 70·00

1907. Surch.
18 **2** ½d. on 5s. orange and green £250 £375
19 1d. on 5s. orange and green £250 £350
35 2½d. on 4d. brown and blue £1500 £2500

11

8

1907.
38 **11** ¼d. brown 2·00 50
25 **8** ½d. green 2·50 4·00
26 1d. red 1·50 75
27 2½d. blue 3·50 3·50
28 3d. purple on yellow 3·25 6·50
29 4d. black and red on yellow 50·00 70·00
30 6d. purple 9·50 35·00
31 1s. black on green 7·50 22·00
32 5s. green and red on yellow 38·00 60·00
34 10s. green and red on green £160 £225

12

19

1912.
40 **12** ¼d. brown 1·00 40
41 ½d. green 2·75 5·00
42 1d. red 3·25 2·50
43 2d. grey 1·00 10·00
44 2½d. blue 7·00 11·00
45a 3d. purple on yellow 3·50 8·00
46 4d. black and red on yellow 1·00 10·00
47 6d. purple 3·75 7·50
48b 1s. black on green 3·50 3·50
49 2s. purple and blue on blue 12·00 48·00
50 3s. green and violet 19·00 65·00
51 5s. green and red on yellow 75·00 £160
52b 10s. green and red on green 85·00 £150

1917. Surch **1½d** with **WAR STAMP.** in two lines.
54 **12** 1½d. on 2½d. blue 1·75 6·00

1917. Optd or surch as last, but with **WAR STAMP** in one line and without full point.
57 **12** ½d. green 60 2·50
58 1½d. on 2d. grey 1·50 7·00
56 1½d. on 2½d. blue 30 60
59 1½d. on 2½d. orange 80 1·25

1921.
69 **19** ¼d. brown 50 1·50
70 ½d. green 50 30
71 1d. red 1·40 85
72 1½d. brown 1·75 30
73 2d. grey 1·75 4·00
74 2½d. blue 50 50
75 3d. purple on yellow 1·00 4·00
62 4d. red on yellow 1·00 4·00
76 4½d. green 2·25 3·00
77 6d. red 5·50 32·00
63 1s. black on green 1·25 9·50
80 2s. violet on blue 14·00 24·00
81 3s. violet 23·00 16·00
82 5s. green on yellow 24·00 45·00
83 10s. red on green 60·00 85·00

20 Kings William IV and George V

1932. Centenary of "Assembly of Justices and Vestry".
84 **20** ¼d. brown 1·50 1·00
85 ½d. green 2·75 8·00
86 1d. red 2·75 8·00
87 1½d. orange 2·75 2·75
88 2d. grey 2·75 3·50
89 2½d. blue 2·75 1·50
90 3d. green 3·25 5·00
91 6d. purple 9·50 23·00
92 1s. black and brown 17·00 32·00
93 2s. black and blue 45·00 75·00
94 5s. black and green 85·00 £120
95 10s. black and red £250 £350

21 Cayman Islands

1935.
96 **21** ¼d. black and brown . . . 50 1·00
97 – ½d. blue and green . . . . 1·00 1·00
98 – 1d. blue and red . . . . . 4·00 2·25
99 – 1½d. black and orange . . 1·50 1·75
100 – 2d. blue and purple . . . . 3·75 1·10
101 – 2½d. blue and black . . . 3·25 1·25
102 **21** 3d. black and green . . . 2·50 3·00
103 – 6d. purple and black . . . 8·50 4·00
104 – 1s. blue and orange . . . . 6·00 6·50
105 – 2s. blue and black . . . . 45·00 35·00
106 – 5s. green and black . . . . 50·00 50·00
107 – 10s. black and red . . . . 70·00 90·00
DESIGNS—HORIZ: ¼, 2d., 1s. Cat boat; 1d., 2s. Red-footed boobys ("Booby-birds"); 2½, 6d., 5s. Hawksbill turtles. VERT: 1½d., 10s. Queen or pink conch shells and coconut palms.

1935. Silver Jubilee. As T **13** of Antigua.
108 ½d. black and green . . . . 15 1·00
109 2½d. brown and blue . . . . 1·00 1·00
110 6d. blue and olive . . . . . 1·00 4·00
111 1s. grey and purple . . . . . 7·00 7·00

1937. Coronation. As T **2** of Aden.
112 ½d. green . . . . 30 1·60
113 1d. red 50 20
114 2½d. blue 95 40

26 Beach View

30 Hawksbill Turtles

1938.
115a **26** ¼d. orange 10 65
116 – ½d. green 90 55
117 – 1d. red 30 75
118 **26** 1½d. black 30 10
119a **30** 2d. violet 60 30
120 – 2½d. blue 40 20
120a – 2½d. orange . . . . . . 3·00 50
121 – 3d. orange 40 15
121a – 3d. blue . . . . 2·50 30
122a **30** 6d. olive . . . . 2·50 1·25
123a – 1s. brown . . . . 4·50 2·00
124a **26** 2s. green . . . . 25·00 9·00
125 – 5s. red . . . . 32·00 15·00
126a **30** 10s. brown . . . . . . 23·00 9·00
DESIGNS—HORIZ: ½d., 1s. Caribbean dolphin; 1d., 3d. Map of Islands; 2½d., 5s. "Rembro" (schooner).

1946. Victory. As T **9** of Aden.
127 1½d. black 20 10
128 3d. yellow 20 10

1948. Silver Wedding. As T **10/11** of Aden.
129 ½d. green 10 20
130 10s. blue . . . . 14·00 16·00

1949. U.P.U. As T **20/25** of Antigua.
131 2½d. orange . . . . 30 1·00
132 3d. blue . . . . 1·50 2·25
133 6d. olive . . . . 60 2·25
134 1s. brown 60 50

31 Cat Boat

44 South Sound Lighthouse, Grand Cayman

1950.
135 **31** ¼d. blue and red 15 60
136 – ½d. violet and green . . . 15 1·25
137 – 1d. olive and blue 60 75
138 – 1½d. green and brown . . . 30 75
139 – 2d. violet and red . . . . 1·25 1·50
140 – 2½d. blue and black . . . 1·25 60
141 – 3d. green and blue . . . . 1·40 1·50
142 – 6d. brown and blue . . . . 2·00 1·25
143 – 9d. red and green . . . . 7·00 2·00
144 – 1s. brown and orange . . . 3·25 2·75
145 – 2s. violet and purple . . . 8·50 9·50
146 – 5s. olive and violet . . . 13·00 7·00
147 – 10s. black and red . . . . 18·00 15·00
DESIGNS: ½d. Coconut grove, Cayman Brac; 1d. Green turtle; 1½d. Making thatch rope; 2d. Cayman seamen; 2½d. Map; 3d. Parrotfish; 6d. Bluff, Cayman Brac; 9d. Georgetown Harbour. 1s. Turtle in "crawl"; 2s. "Ziroma" (schooner); 5s. Boat-building; 10s. Government offices, Grand Cayman.

1953. As 1950 issue but with portrait of Queen Elizabeth II as in T **44**.
148 ¼d. blue and red . . . . . 1·00 50
149 ½d. violet and green 75 50
150 1d. olive and blue 70 40
151 1½d. green and brown 50 20
152 2d. violet and red . . . . . 3·00 85
153 2½d. blue and black . . . . 3·50 80
154 3d. green and blue . . . . . 4·00 60
155 4d. black and blue . . . . . 2·00 40
156 6d. brown and blue . . . . . 1·75 30
157 9d. red and green . . . . . 7·00 30
158 1s. brown and orange . . . . 3·50 20
159 2s. violet and purple . . . . 13·00 8·00
160 5s. olive and violet . . . . 15·00 7·00
161 10s. black and red . . . . . 15·00 7·50
161a £1 blue . . . . 32·00 10·00
Portrait faces right on ½d., 2d., 2½d., 4d., 1s. and 10s. values and left on others. The £1 shows a larger portrait of the Queen (vert).

1953. Coronation. As T **13** of Aden.
162 1d. black and green . . . . 30 2·00

46 Arms of the Cayman Islands

1959. New Constitution.
163 **46** 2½d. black and blue . . . 45 2·50
164 1s. black and orange . . . 55 50

48 Cat Boat

1962. Portraits as in T **48**.
165 – ¼d. green and red . . . . 55 1·00
166 **48** 1d. black and olive 80 20
167 – 1½d. yellow and purple . . 2·75 80
168 – 2d. blue and brown . . . . 1·00 30
169 – 2½d. violet and turquoise 85 1·00
170 – 3d. blue and red 30 10
171 – 4d. green and purple . . . 1·75 60
172 – 6d. turquoise and sepia . . 3·25 30
173 **48** 9d. blue and purple . . . . 3·00 40
174 – 1s. sepia and red . . . . . 1·25 10
175 – 1s.3d. turquoise and brown 3·75 2·25
176 – 1s.9d. turquoise and violet 16·00 1·25
177 – 5s. plum and green . . . . 9·50 7·00
178 – 10s. olive and blue . . . . 19·00 8·00
179 – £1 red and black . . . . . 19·00 17·00
DESIGNS—VERT: ¼d. Cuban amazon ("Cayman Parrot"); 9d. Angler with king mackerel; 10s. Arms; £1 Queen Elizabeth II. HORIZ: 1½d. "Schomburgkia thomsoniana" (orchid); 2d. Cayman Islands map; 2½d. Fisherman casting net; 3d. West Bay Beach; 4d. Green turtle; 6d. "Lydia E. Wilson" (schooner), 1s Iguana; 1s.3d. Swimming pool, Cayman Brac; 1s.9d. Water sports; 5s. Fort George.

1963. Freedom from Hunger. As T **28** of Aden.
180 1s.9d. red 30 15

1963. Centenary of Red Cross. As T **33** of Antigua.
181 1d. red and black 30 75
182 1s.9d. red and blue . . . . 70 1·75

1964. 400th Birth Anniv of Shakespeare. As T **34** of Antigua.
183 6d. purple 20 10

1965. Centenary of I.T.U. As T **36** of Antigua.
184 1d. blue and purple 15 10
185 1s.3d. purple and green . . . 55 45

1965. I.C.Y. As T **37** of Antigua.
186 1d. purple and turquoise . . 15 10
187 1s. green and lavender . . . 50 25

1966. Churchill Commemoration. As T **38** of Antigua.
188 ¼d. blue . . . . 10 1·50
189 1d. green 50 10
190 1s. brown . . . . 1·25 10
191 1s.9d. violet . . . . 1·40 75

1966. Royal Visit. As T **39** of Antigua.
192 1d. black and blue 60 30
193 1s.9d. black and mauve . . . 2·25 1·25

1966. World Cup Football Championship. As T **40** of Antigua.
194 1½d. multicoloured 15 10
195 1s.9d. multicoloured 50 25

1966. Inauguration of W.H.O. Headquarters, Geneva. As T **41** of Antigua.
196 2d. black, green and blue . . 60 15
197 1s.3d. black, purple and ochre . . . . 1·40 60

62 Telephone and Map

1966. International Telephone Links.
198 **62** 4d. multicoloured 20 20
199 9d. multicoloured 20 30

1966. 20th Anniv of U.N.E.S.C.O. As T **54/6** of Antigua.
200 1d. multicoloured 15 10
201 1s.9d. yellow, violet and olive 60 10
202 5s. black, purple and orange 1·50 70

63 B.A.C One Eleven 200/400 Airliner over "Ziroma" (Cayman schooner)

1966. Opening of Cayman Jet Service.
203 **63** 1s. black, blue and green 35 30
204 1s.9d. purple, blue and green 40 35

64 Water-skiing

1967. International Tourist Year. Multicoloured.
205 4d. Type **64** 35 10
206 6d. Skin diving 35 30
207 1s. Sport fishing 35 30
208 1s.9d. Sailing 40 75

68 Former Slaves and Emblem

1968. Human Rights Year.
209 **68** 3d. green, black and gold 10 10
210 9d. brown, gold and green 10 10
211 5s. ultram, gold and green 30 90

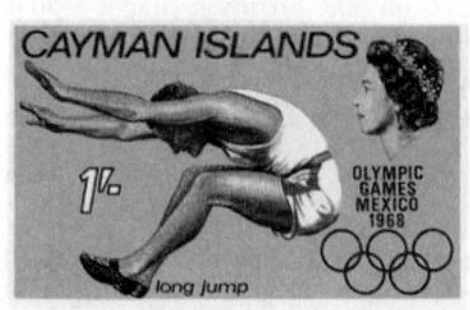

69 Long-jumping

1968. Olympic Games, Mexico. Multicoloured.
212 1s. Type **69** 15 10
213 1s.3d. High-jumping 20 25
214 2s. Pole-vaulting 20 75

72 "The Adoration of the Shepherds" (Fabritius)

1968. Christmas. Multicoloured.
215 ¼d. Type **72*** 10 20
221 ¼d. Type **72*** 10 20
216 1d. "The Adoration of the Shepherds" (Rembrandt) 10 10
217 6d. Type **72** 15 10
218 8d. As 1d. 15 15
219 1s.3d. Type **72** 20 25
220 2s. As 1d. 25 35
*No. 215 has a brown background and No. 221 a bright purple one.

74 Grand Cayman Thrush ("Cayman Thrush")

1969. Multicoloured.
222 ¼d. Type **74** 10 75
223 1d. Brahmin cattle 10 10
224 2d. Blowholes on the coast . 10 10
225 2½d. Map of Grand Cayman . 15 10
226 3d. Georgetown scene . . . 10 10
227 4d. Royal "Poinciana" . . . 15 10
228 6d. Cayman Brac and Little Cayman on chart 20 10
229 8d. Motor vessels at berth . 25 10
230 1s. Basket-making 15 10
231 1s.3d. Beach scene . . . . 35 1·00
232 1s.6d. Straw-rope making . . 35 1·00
233 2s. Great barracuda . . . . 1·25 80
234 4s. Government House . . . 35 80
235 10s. Arms of the Cayman Islands (vert) . . . . . . 1·00 1·50
236 £1 black, ochre and red (Queen Elizabeth II) (vert) 1·25 2·00

1969. Decimal Currency. Nos. 222/36 surch **C-DAY 8th September 1969**. Multicoloured.
238 **74** ¼c. on ¼d. 10 75
239 – 1c. on 1d. 10 10
240 – 2c. on 2d. 10 10
241 – 3c. on 4d. 10 10
242 – 4c. on 2½d. 10 10
243 – 5c. on 6d. 10 10
244 – 7c. on 8d. 10 10
245 – 8c. on 3d. 15 10
246 – 10c. on 1s. 25 10
247 – 12c. on 1s.3d. . . . . . . 35 1·75
248 – 15c. on 1s.6d. . . . . . . 45 1·50
249 – 20c. on 2s. . . . . 1·25 1·75
250 – 40c. on 4s. 45 85
251 – $1 on 10s. . . . . 1·00 2·50
252 – $2 on £1 . . . . 1·50 3·25

90 "Madonna and Child" (Vivarini)

92 "Noli me tangere" (Titian)

1969. Christmas. Multicoloured. Background colours given.
253 **90** ¼c. red 10 10
254 ¼c. mauve 10 10
255 ¼c. green 10 10
256 ¼c. blue 10 10
257 – 1c. blue 10 10
258 **90** 5c. red 10 10
259 – 7c. green 10 10
260 **90** 12c. green 15 15
261 – 20c. purple 20 25
DESIGNS: 1c., 7c., 20c. "The Adoration of the Kings" (Gossaert).

1970. Easter. Multicoloured; frame colours given.
262 **92** ¼c. red 10 10
263 ¼c. green 10 10
264 ¼c. brown 10 10
265 ¼c. violet 10 10
266 10c. blue 35 10
267 12c. brown 40 10
268 40c. plum 55 60

93 Barnaby ("Barnaby Rudge")

1970. Death Centenary of Charles Dickens.
269 **93** 1c. black, green and yellow 10 10
270 – 12c. black, brown and red 35 10
271 – 20c. black, brown and gold 40 10
272 – 40c. black, ultram & blue 45 25
DESIGNS: 12c. Sairey Gamp ("Martin Chuzzlewit"); 20c. Mr. Micawber and David ("David Copperfield"); 40c. The "Marchioness" ("The Old Curiosity Shop").

97 Grand Cayman Thrush ("Cayman Thrush")

1970. Decimal Currency. Designs as Nos. 222/36, but with values inscribed in decimal currency as in T **97**.
273 ¼c. multicoloured 65 30
274 1c. multicoloured 10 10
275 2c. multicoloured 10 10
276 3c. multicoloured 20 10
277 4c. multicoloured 20 10
278 5c. multicoloured 35 10
279 7c. multicoloured 30 10
280 8c. multicoloured 30 10
281 10c. multicoloured 30 10
282 12c. multicoloured . . . . . 90 1·00
283 15c. multicoloured . . . . . 1·25 4·00
284 20c. multicoloured . . . . . 3·25 1·25
285 40c. multicoloured 85 75
286 $1 multicoloured . . . . . . 1·25 4·75
287 $2 black, ochre and red . . . 2·00 4·75

98 The Three Wise Men

1970. Christmas.
288 **98** ¼c. green, grey and emerald 10 10
289 – 1c. black, yellow and green 10 10
290 **98** 5c. grey, orange and red 10 10
291 – 10c. black, yellow and red 10 10
292 **98** 12c. grey, green and blue 15 10
293 – 20c. black, yellow and green 20 15
DESIGN: 1, 10, 20c. Nativity scene and Globe.

100 Grand Cayman Terrapin

1971. Turtles. Multicoloured.
294 5c. Type **100** 30 25
295 7c. Green turtle 35 25
296 12c. Hawksbill turtle 55 30
297 20c. Turtle farm 1·00 1·40

101 "Dendrophylax fawcettii"

102 "Adoration of the Kings" (French 15th century)

1971. Orchids. Multicoloured.
298 ¼c. Type **101** 10 1·25
299 2c. "Schomburgkia thomsoniana" 60 90
300 10c. "Vanilla claviculata" 2·00 50
301 40c. "Oncidium variegatum" 4·00 3·50

1971. Christmas. Multicoloured.
302 ¼c. Type **102** 10 10
303 1c. "The Nativity" (Parisian, 14th century) 10 10
304 5c. "Adoration of the Magi" (Burgundian, 15th century) 10 10
305 12c. Type **102** 20 15
306 15c. As 1c. 20 25
307 20c. As 5c. 25 35
MS308 113 × 115 mm. Nos. 302/7 1·25 2·25

103 Turtle and Telephone Cable

1972. Co-axial Telephone Cable.
309 **103** 2c. multicoloured 10 10
310 10c. multicoloured 15 10
311 40c. multicoloured 30 40

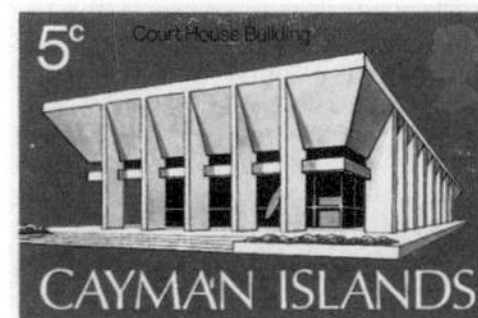
104 Court House Building

1972. New Government Buildings. Multicoloured.
312 5c. Type **104** 10 10
313 15c. Legislative Assembly Building 10 10
314 25c. Type **104** 15 15
315 40c. As 15c. 20 30
MS316 121 × 108 mm. Nos. 312/15 50 2·00

1972. Royal Silver Wedding. As T **52** of Ascension but with Hawksbill Turtle and Queen or Pink Conch in background.
317 12c. violet 15 10
318 30c. green 15 20

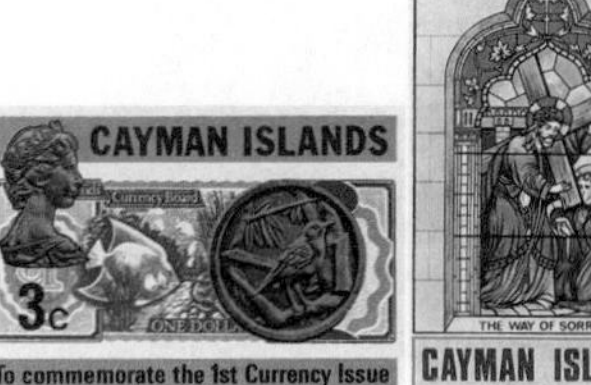
106 $1 Coin and Note

107 "The Way of Sorrow"

1972. First Issue of Currency. Multicoloured.
319 3c. Type **106** 20 10
320 6c. $5 Coin and note 20 70
321 15c. $10 Coin and note 60 30
322 25c. $25 Coin and note 80 45
MS323 128 × 107 mm. Nos. 319/22 3·50 3·25

1973. Easter. Stained-glass Windows. Multicoloured.
324 10c. Type **107** 15 10
325 12c. "Christ Resurrected" 20 10
326 20c. "The Last Supper" (horiz) 25 15
327 30c. "Christ on the Cross" (horiz) 30 25
MS328 122 × 105 mm. Nos. 324/7 (imperf) 1·00 1·60

108 "The Nativity" (Sforza Book of Hours)

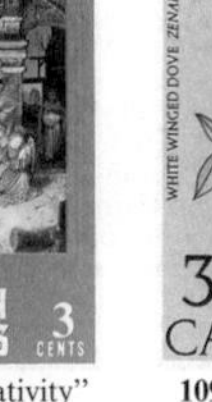
109 White-winged Dove

1973. Christmas.
329 **108** 3c. multicoloured 10 10
330 – 5c. multicoloured 10 10
331 **108** 9c. multicoloured 15 10
332 – 12c. multicoloured 15 10
333 **108** 15c. multicoloured 15 15
334 – 25c. multicoloured 20 25
DESIGN: 5, 12, 25c. "The Adoration of the Magi" (Breviary of Queen Isabella).

1973. Royal Wedding. As T **47** of Anguilla. Background colour given. Multicoloured.
335 10c. green 10 10
336 30c. mauve 15 10

1974. Birds (1st series). Multicoloured.
337 3c. Type **109** 2·00 30
338 10c. Vitelline warbler 2·75 30
339 12c. Antillean grackle ("Greater Antillean Grackle") 2·75 30
340 20c. Great red-bellied woodpecker ("West Indian Red-bellied Woodpecker") 4·25 80
341 30c. Stripe-headed tanager 5·50 1·50
342 50c. Yucatan vireo 7·00 5·50
See also Nos. 383/8.

110 Old School Building

1974. 25th Anniv of University of West Indies. Multicoloured.
343 12c. Type **110** 10 15
344 20c. New Comprehensive School 15 20
345 30c. Creative Arts Centre, Mona 15 60

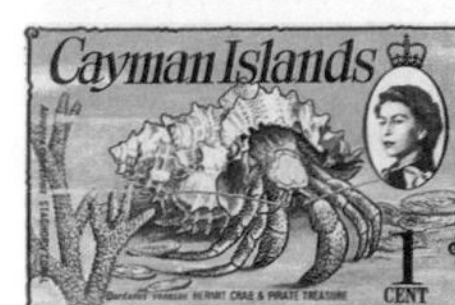
111 Hermit Crab and Staghorn Coral

1974. Size 41½ × 27 mm or 27 × 41½ mm. Mult.
346 1c. Type **111** 3·50 1·25
347 3c. Treasure-chest and lion's paw 3·50 75
348 4c. Treasure and spotted scorpionfish 50 70
349 5c. Flintlock pistol and brain coral 3·00 75
350 6c. Blackbeard and green turtle 35 2·25
366 8c. As 9c. 2·50 8·50
351 9c. Jewelled pomander and porkfish 4·00 11·00
352 10c. Spiny lobster and treasure 4·50 80
353 12c. Jewelled sword and dagger and sea-fan 35 2·00
354 15c. Cabrit's murex and treasure 45 1·25
417 20c. Queen or pink conch and treasure 3·50 3·00
356 25c. Hogfish and treasure 45 70
357 40c. Gold chalice and seawhip 4·00 1·25
358 $1 Coat of arms (vert) 2·75 3·25
419 $2 Queen Elizabeth II (vert) 7·50 6·50
For smaller designs see Nos. 445/52.

112 Sea Captain and Ship (Shipbuilding)

1974. Local Industries. Multicoloured.
360 8c. Type **112** 30 10
361 12c. Thatcher and cottage 25 10
362 20c. Farmer and plantation 25 20
MS363 92 × 132 mm. Nos. 360/2 1·50 3·25

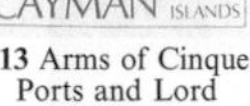
113 Arms of Cinque Ports and Lord Warden's Flag

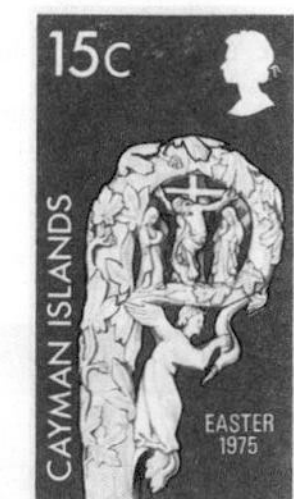
114 "The Crucifixion"

1974. Birth Centenary of Sir Winston Churchill. Multicoloured.
380 12c. Type **113** 15 10
381 50c. Churchill's coat of arms 45 70
MS382 98 × 86 mm. Nos. 380/1 60 1·60

1975. Birds (2nd series). As T **109**. Multicoloured.
383 3c. Common flicker ("Yellow-shafted Flicker") 70 50
384 10c. Black-billed whistling duck ("West Indian Tree Duck") 1·25 50
385 12c. Yellow warbler 1·40 65
386 20c. White-bellied dove 2·00 2·00
387 30c. Magnificent frigate bird 3·25 4·25
388 50c. Cuban amazon ("Cayman Amazon") 3·75 12·00

1975. Easter. French Pastoral Staffs.
389 **114** 15c. multicoloured 10 20
390 – 35c. multicoloured 20 45
MS391 128 × 98 mm. Nos, 389/90 65 2·75
DESIGN: 35c. Pastoral staff similar to Type **114**.

115 Israel Hands

1975. Pirates. Multicoloured.
392 10c. Type **115** 30 15
393 12c. John Fenn 30 30
394 20c. Thomas Anstis 50 50
395 30c. Edward Low 60 1·50

1975. Christmas. "Virgin and Child with Angels". As T **114**.
396 12c. multicoloured 10 10
397 50c. multicoloured 30 30
MS398 113 × 85 mm. Nos. 396/7 1·00 3·00

116 Registered Cover, Government House and Sub-Post Office

1975. 75th Anniv of First Cayman Islands Postage Stamp. Multicoloured.
399 10c. Type **116** 15 10
400 20c. ½d. stamp and 1890–94 postmark 20 15
401 30c. 1d. stamp and 1908 surcharge 30 25
402 50c. ½d. and 1d. stamps 45 65
MS403 117 × 147 mm. Nos. 399/402 2·50 3·00

117 Seals of Georgia, Delaware and New Hampshire

1976. Bicentenary of American Revolution. Mult.
404 10c. Type **117** 40 15
405 15c. Carolina, New Jersey and Maryland seals 55 20
406 20c. Virginia, Rhode Island and Massachusetts seals 65 25
407 25c. New York, Connecticut and North Carolina seals 65 35
408 30c. Pennsylvania seal, Liberty Bell and U.S. Great Seal 70 40
MS409 166 × 124 mm. Nos. 404/8 4·00 8·00

118 "470" Dinghies

119 Queen Elizabeth II and Westminster Abbey

1976. Olympic Games, Montreal. Multicoloured.
410 20c. Type **118** 40 10
411 50c. Racing dinghy 70 50

1977. Silver Jubilee. Multicoloured.
427 8c. The Prince of Wales' visit, 1973 10 20
428 30c. Type **119** 15 40
429 50c. Preparation for the Anointing (horiz) 30 75

120 Scuba Diving

1977. Tourism. Multicoloured.
430 5c. Type **120** 10 10
431 10c. Exploring a wreck 15 10
432 20c. Royal gramma ("Fairy basslet") (fish) 45 20
433 25c. Sergeant major (fish) 55 35
MS434 146 × 89 mm. Nos. 430/3 2·00 4·25

121 "Composia fidelissima" (moth)

1977. Butterflies and Moth. Multicoloured.
435 5c. Type **121** 75 20
436 8c. "Heliconius charithonia" 85 20
437 10c. "Danaus gilippus" 85 20
438 15c. "Agraulis vanillae" 1·25 45
439 20c. "Junonia evarete" 1·25 45
440 30c. "Anartia jatrophae" 1·50 70

122 Cruise Liner "Southward"

123 "The Crucifixion" (Durer)

1978. New Harbour and Cruise Ships. Multicoloured.
441 3c. Type **122** 40 10
442 5c. Cruise liner "Renaissance" 40 10
443 30c. New harbour (vert) 90 25
444 50c. Cruise liner "Daphne" (vert) 1·25 65

1978. As Nos. 346/7, 349, 352, 417, 357/8 and 419, but designs smaller, 40 × 26 mm or 26 × 40 mm.
445 1c. Type **111** 1·00 1·25
446 3c. Treasure chest and lion's paw 80 50

447 5c. Flintlock pistol and brain coral . . . . 1·50 2·00
448 10c. Spiny lobster and treasure . . . . 1·25 60
449 20c. Queen or pink conch and treasure . . . . 2·25 1·00
450 40c. Gold chalice and seawhip . . . . 13·00 17·00
451 $1 Coat of arms (vert) . . . 19·00 5·50
452 $2 Queen Elizabeth II (vert) 4·00 18·00

1978. Easter and 450th Death Anniv of Durer.
459 **123** 10c. mauve and black . . 30 10
460 – 15c. yellow and black . . 40 15
461 – 20c. turquoise and black 50 20
462 – 30c. lilac and black . . . 60 35
MS463 120 × 108 mm. Nos. 459/62 4·00 5·50
DESIGNS: 15c. "Christ at Emmaus"; 20c. "The Entry into Jerusalem"; 30c. "Christ washing Peter's Feet".

124 "Explorers" Singing Game

125 Yale of Beaufort

1978. 3rd International Council Meeting of Girls' Brigade. Multicoloured.
464 3c. Type **124** 20 10
465 10c. Colour party 25 10
466 20c. Girls and Duke of Edinburgh Award interests 40 20
467 50c. Girls using domestic skills 70 80

1978. 25th Anniv of Coronation.
468 **125** 30c. green, mauve and silver 20 25
469 – 30c. multicoloured 20 25
470 – 30c. green, mauve and silver 20 25
DESIGNS: No. 469, Queen Elizabeth II; 470, Barn owl.

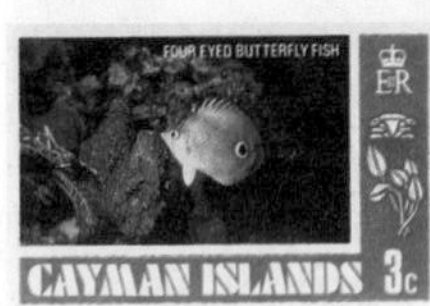

126 Four-eyed Butterflyfish

1978. Fish (1st series). Multicoloured.
471 3c. Type **126** 25 10
472 5c. Grey angelfish 30 10
473 10c. Squirrelfish 45 10
474 15c. Queen parrotfish 60 30
475 20c. Spanish hogfish 70 35
476 30c. Queen angelfish 80 50

127 Lockheed L.18 Lodestar

1979. 25th Anniv of Owen Roberts Airfield. Mult.
477 3c. Type **127** 30 15
478 5c. Consolidated PBY-5A Catalina amphibian . . . 30 15
479 10c. Vickers Viking 1B . . . 35 15
480 15c. B.A.C. One Eleven 455 on tarmac 65 25
481 20c. Piper PA-31 Cheyenne II, Bell 47G Trooper helicopter and Hawker Siddeley H.S.125 . . . . . 75 35
482 30c. B.A.C. One Eleven 475 over airfield . . . . 1·00 50

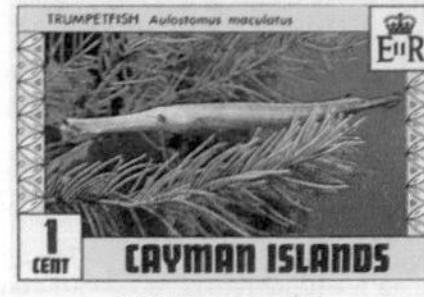

128 Trumpetfish

1979. Fishes (2nd series). Multicoloured.
483 1c. Type **128** 10 10
484 3c. Nassau grouper 25 10
485 5c. French angelfish 25 10
486 10c. Schoolmaster snapper . . 35 10
487 20c. Banded butterflyfish . . 55 25
488 50c. Black-barred soldierfish 1·00 70

129 1900 1d. Stamp

1979. Death Centenary of Sir Rowland Hill.
489 **129** 5c. black, carmine and blue 10 10
490 – 10c. multicoloured 15 10
491 – 20c. multicoloured 20 25
MS492 138 × 90 mm. 50c. mult 55 65
DESIGNS: 10c. Great Britain 1902 3d. purple on lemon; 20c. 1955 £1 blue.

130 The Holy Family and Angels

1979. Christmas. Multicoloured.
493 10c. Type **130** 15 10
494 20c. Angels appearing to Shepherds 25 10
495 30c. Nativity 30 20
496 40c. The Magi 40 30

131 Local Rotary Project

1980. 75th Anniv of Rotary International.
497 **131** 20c. blue, black and yellow 20 15
498 – 30c. blue, black and yellow 25 20
499 – 50c. blue, yellow and black 35 30
DESIGNS—VERT: 30c. Paul P. Harris (founder); 50c. Rotary anniversary emblem.

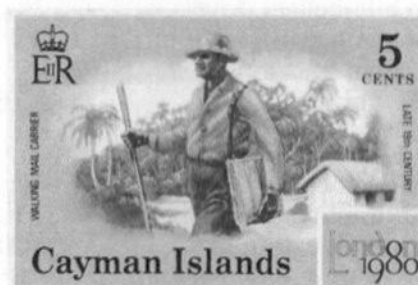

132 Walking Mail Carrier

1980. "London 1980" International Stamp Exhibition. Multicoloured.
500 5c. Type **132** 10 10
501 10c. Delivering mail by cat boat 15 10
502 15c. Mounted mail carrier . . 20 10
503 30c. Horse-drawn wagonette 25 15
504 40c. Postman on bicycle . . . 35 15
505 $1 Motor transport 45 55

133 Queen Elizabeth the Queen Mother at the Derby, 1976

1980. 80th Birthday of the Queen Mother.
506 **133** 20c. multicoloured 20 25

134 American Thorny Oyster

1980. Shells (1st series). Multicoloured.
507 5c. Type **134** 40 10
508 10c. West Indian murex . . . 40 10
509 30c. Angular triton 80 40
510 50c. Caribbean vase 90 80
See also Nos. 565/8 and 582/5.

135 Lantana

1980. Flowers (1st series). Multicoloured.
511 5c. Type **135** 15 10
512 15c. "Bauhinia" 20 10
513 30c. "Hibiscus Rosa" 30 10
514 $1 "Milk and Wine Lily" . . 70 90
See also Nos. 541/4.

136 Juvenile Tarpon and Fire Sponge

137 Eucharist

1980. Multicoloured.
515A 3c. Type **136** . . . . 1·00 2·00
516B 5c. Flat tree or mangrove-root oyster . . . . . . 1·25 80
517A 10c. Mangrove crab . . . . 50 1·50
518A 15c. Lizard and "Phyciodes phaon" (butterfly) . . . 1·00 1·75
519A 20c. Louisiana heron ("Tricoloured Heron") 1·50 2·25
520A 30c. Red mangrove flower 70 1·00
521A 40c. Red mangrove seeds 75 1·50
522A 50c. Waterhouse's leaf-nosed bat . . . . 1·25 1·50
523A $1 Black-crowned night heron . . . . 5·50 5·00
524A $2 Coat of arms . . . . . 1·50 3·75
525A $4 Queen Elizabeth II . . . 2·25 4·75

1981. Easter. Multicoloured.
526 3c. Type **137** 10 10
527 10c. Crown of thorns 10 10
528 20c. Crucifix 15 10
529 $1 Lord Jesus Christ 50 60

138 Wood Slave

1981. Reptiles and Amphibians. Multicoloured.
530 20c. Type **138** 25 20
531 30c. Cayman iguana 30 35
532 40c. Lion lizard 40 45
533 50c. Terrapin ("Hickatee") 45 55

139 Prince Charles

1981. Royal Wedding. Multicoloured.
534 20c. Wedding bouquet from Cayman Islands 15 10
535 30c. Type **139** 20 10
536 $1 Prince Charles and Lady Diana Spencer 50 75

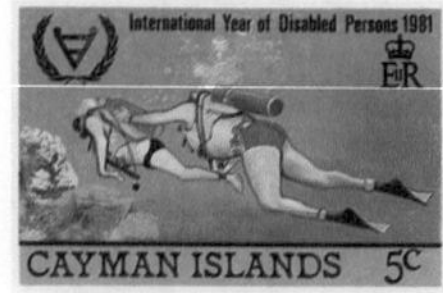

140 Disabled Scuba Divers

1981. Int Year for Disabled Persons. Mult.
537 5c. Type **140** 10 10
538 15c. Old school for the handicapped 25 20
539 20c. New school for the handicapped 30 25
540 $1 Disabled people in wheelchairs by the sea . . 1·25 85

1981. Flowers (2nd series). As T **135**. Multicoloured.
541 3c. Bougainvillea 10 10
542 10c. Morning Glory 15 10
543 20c. Wild amaryllis 25 25
544 $1 Cordia . . . . 70 1·75

141 Dr. Robert Koch and Microscope

1982. Centenary of Robert Koch's Discovery of Tubercle Bacillus. Multicoloured.
545 15c. Type **141** 25 25
546 30c. Koch looking through microscope (vert) 45 45
547 40c. Microscope (vert) . . . 70 70
548 50c. Dr. Robert Koch (vert) 80 80

142 Bride and Groom walking down Aisle

144 "Madonna and Child with the Infant Baptist"

143 Pitching Tent

1982. 21st Birthday of Princess of Wales. Mult.
549 20c. Cayman Islands coat of arms 30 35
550 30c. Lady Diana Spencer in London, June, 1981 . . . 70 45
551 40c. Type **142** 70 65
552 50c. Formal portrait . . . . 2·50 90

1982. 75th Anniv of Boy Scout Movement. Mult.
553 3c. Type **143** 15 10
554 20c. Scouts camping 40 40
555 30c. Cub Scouts and Leaders 60 55
556 50c. Boating skills 80 85

1982. Christmas. Raphael Paintings. Multicoloured.
557 3c. Type **144** 10 10
558 10c. "Madonna of the Tower" 20 20
559 20c. "Ansidei Madonna" . . 35 35
560 30c. "Madonna and Child" 50 50

145 Mace

1982. 150th Anniv of Representative Government. Multicoloured.
561 3c. Type **145** 10 30
562 10c. Old Courthouse 20 30
563 20c. Commonwealth Parliamentary Association coat of arms 35 50
564 30c. Legislative Assembly building 50 90

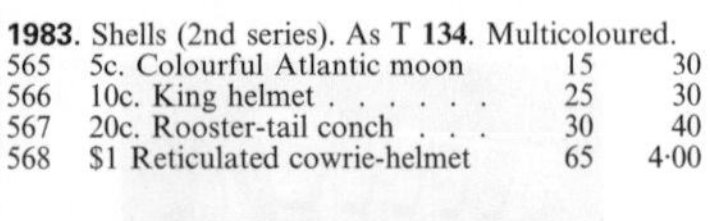

1983. Shells (2nd series). As T **134**. Multicoloured.
565 5c. Colourful Atlantic moon 15 30
566 10c. King helmet 25 30
567 20c. Rooster-tail conch . . . 30 40
568 $1 Reticulated cowrie-helmet 65 4·00

146 Legislative Building, Cayman Brac

1983. Royal Visit. Multicoloured.
569 20c. Type **146** 45 35
570 30c. Legislative Building, Grand Cayman 60 50
571 50c. Duke of Edinburgh (vert) . . . . 1·25 90
572 $1 Queen Elizabeth II (vert) 2·00 2·00
MS573 113 × 94 mm. Nos. 569/72 5·50 4·25

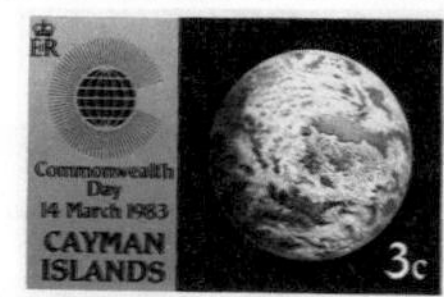

147 Satellite View of Earth

1983. Commonwealth Day. Multicoloured.
574 3c. Type **147** 15 10
575 15c. Cayman Islands and Commonwealth flags . . . 35 30
576 20c. Fishing 40 35
577 40c. Portrait of Queen Elizabeth II 65 65

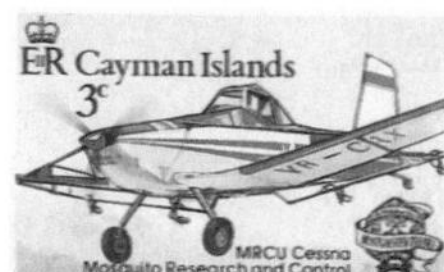

148 MRCU Cessna Ag Wagon

1983. Bicentenary of Manned Flight. Multicoloured.
578 3c. Type **148** 60 50
579 10c. Consolidated PBY-5A Catalina amphibian . . . 65 50
580 20c. Boeing 727-200 . . . . 1·25 1·50
581 40c. Hawker Siddeley H.S.748 . . . . 1·75 3·75

1984. Shells (3rd series). As T **134**. Multicoloured.
582 3c. Florida moon 70 40
583 10c. Austin's cone 80 40
584 30c. Leaning dwarf triton . . 2·25 2·75
585 50c. Filose or threaded turban . . . . 2·50 4·75

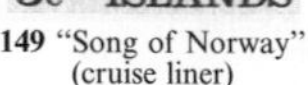

149 "Song of Norway" (cruise liner)
152 Couple on Beach at Sunset

151 Snowy Egret

1984. 250th Anniv of "Lloyd's List" (newspaper). Multicoloured.
586 5c. Type **149** 45 20
587 10c. View of old harbour . . 50 25
588 25c. Wreck of "Ridgefield" (freighter) . . . . 1·00 1·00
589 50c. "Goldfield" (schooner) 2·00 2·25
MS590 105×75 mm. $1 "Goldfield" (schooner) (different) . . . . . 2·10 2·25

1984. Universal Postal Union Congress, Hamburg. No. 589 optd **U.P.U. CONGRESS HAMBURG 1984**.
591 50c. Schooner "Goldfield" . . 1·00 1·75

1984. Birds of the Cayman Islands (1st series). Multicoloured.
592 5c. Type **151** . . . . 1·00 75
593 10c. Bananaquit . . . . . . 1·00 75
594 35c. Belted kingfisher ("Kingfisher") . . . . . . 3·25 2·50
595 $1 Brown booby . . . . . . 6·00 11·00
See also Nos. 627/30.

1984. Christmas. Local Festivities. Multicoloured.
596 5c. Type **152** . . . . 80 1·40
597 5c. Family and schooner . . 80 1·40
598 5c. Carol singers . . . . . . 80 1·40
599 5c. East End bonfire . . . . 80 1·40
600 25c. Yachts . . . . 1·10 1·40
601 25c. Father Christmas in power-boat . . . . 1·10 1·40
602 25c. Children on beach . . . 1·10 1·40
603 25c. Beach party . . . . . . 1·10 1·40
MS604 59×79 mm. $1 As No. 599, but larger 27×41 mm . . . . . 3·50 3·00
Nos. 596/9 and 600/3 were each printed together, se-tenant, the four designs of each value forming a composite picture of a beach scene at night (5c.) or in the daytime (25c.).

153 "Schomburgkia thomsoniana" (var. minor)
154 Freighter Aground

1985. Orchids. Multicoloured.
605 5c. Type **153** . . . . 1·00 30
606 10c. "Schomburgkia thomsoniana" . . . . . . 1·00 30
607 25c. "Encyclia plicata" . . . 2·50 1·00
608 50c. "Dendrophylax fawcettii" . . . . 3·75 3·00

1985. Shipwrecks. Multicoloured.
609 5c. Type **154** 90 50
610 25c. Submerged sailing ship 2·75 1·25
611 35c. Wrecked trawler . . . . 3·00 2·50
612 40c. Submerged wreck on its side . . . . 3·25 3·50

155 Athletics
156 Morse Key (1935)

1985. International Youth Year. Multicoloured.
613 5c. Type **155** 20 20
614 15c. Students in library . . . 35 30
615 25c. Football (vert) 65 55
616 50c. Netball (vert) . . . . . 1·25 2·00

1985. 50th Anniv of Telecommunications System. Multicoloured.
617 5c. Type **156** 40 60
618 10c. Hand cranked telephone 45 60
619 25c. Tropospheric scatter dish (1966) . . . . 1·25 80
620 50c. Earth station dish aerial (1979) . . . . 2·00 4·50

1986. 60th Birthday of Queen Elizabeth II. As T **110** of Ascension. Multicoloured.
621 5c. Princess Elizabeth at wedding of Lady May Cambridge, 1931 . . . . . 10 30
622 10c. In Norway, 1955 . . . . 15 30
623 25c. Queen inspecting Royal Cayman Islands Police, 1983 . . . . 1·50 75
624 50c. During Gulf tour, 1979 75 2·00
625 $1 At Crown Agents Head Office, London, 1983 . . . 1·10 2·75

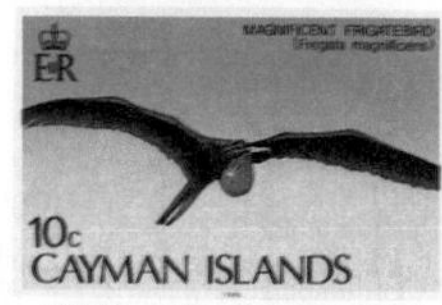

157 Magnificent Frigate Bird

1986. Birds of the Cayman Islands (2nd series). Multicoloured.
627 10c. Type **157** . . . . 1·50 75
628 25c. Black-billed whistling duck ("West Indian Whistling Duck") (vert) . . 2·00 1·40
629 35c. La Sagra's flycatcher (vert) . . . . 2·25 2·50
630 40c. Yellow-faced grassquit 2·50 5·00

1986. Royal Wedding. As T **112** of Ascension. Multicoloured.
633 5c. Prince Andrew and Miss Sarah Ferguson 25 15
634 50c. Prince Andrew aboard H.M.S. "Brazen" . . . . 1·25 1·75

158 Red Coral Shrimp
159 Golf

1986. Marine Life. Multicoloured.
635 5c. Type **158** . . . . 40 1·00
636 10c. Yellow crinoid 40 50
637 15c. Hermit crab 35 60
638 20c. Tube dwelling anemone 35 1·75
639 25c. Christmas tree worm . . 45 2·50
640 35c. Porcupinefish . . . . . 70 2·75
641 50c. Orangeball anemone . . 80 4·50
642 60c. Basket starfish . . . . . 3·50 9·00
643 75c. Flamingo tongue . . . . 10·00 11·00
644 $1 Sea anenome . . . . . . 1·10 2·50
645 $2 Diamond blenny . . . . . 1·25 4·50
646 $4 Rough file shell . . . . . 2·00 6·50

1987. Tourism. Multicoloured.
647 10c. Type **159** . . . . 2·25 1·25
648 15c. Sailing . . . . 2·25 1·25
649 25c. Snorkelling . . . . . . 2·25 1·50
650 35c. Paragliding . . . . . . 2·50 2·00
651 $1 Game fishing . . . . . . 5·00 10·00

160 Ackee
162 Poinsettia

161 Lion Lizard

1987. Cayman Islands Fruits. Multicoloured.
652 5c. Type **160** . . . . 75 1·00
653 25c. Breadfruit . . . . 1·75 55
654 35c. Pawpaw . . . . 1·75 70
655 $1 Soursop . . . . 4·00 7·50

1987. Lizards. Multicoloured.
656 10c. Type **161** . . . . 1·75 65
657 50c. Iguana . . . . 3·50 3·00
658 $1 Anole . . . . 4·75 5·25

1987. Flowers. Multicoloured.
659 5c. Type **162** 90 70
660 25c. Periwinkle . . . . . . 2·25 75
661 35c. Yellow allamanda . . . 2·25 1·10
662 75c. Blood lily . . . . 4·00 6·50

163 "Hemiargus ammon" and "Strymon martialis"
164 Green-backed Heron

1988. Butterflies. Multicoloured.
663 5c. Type **163** . . . . 1·25 65
664 25c. "Phocides pigmalion" . . 2·50 85
665 50c. "Anaea troglodyta" . . 4·00 3·75
666 $1 "Papilio andraemon" . . 5·00 5·00

1988. Herons. Multicoloured.
667 5c. Type **164** . . . . 1·25 65
668 25c. Louisiana heron . . . . 2·25 85
669 50c. Yellow-crowned night heron . . . . 3·00 3·00
670 $1 Little blue heron . . . . 3·50 4·25

165 Cycling
166 Princess Alexandra

1988. Olympic Games, Seoul. Multicoloured.
671 10c. Type **165** . . . . 2·25 85
672 50c. Cayman Airways Boeing 727 airliner and national team . . . . 3·50 3·00
673 $1 "470" dinghy . . . . . . 3·75 4·00
MS674 53×60 mm. $1 Tennis . . 4·00 3·00

1988. Visit of Princess Alexandra. Multicoloured.
675 5c. Type **166** . . . . 1·75 1·00
676 $1 Princess Alexandra in evening dress . . . . . . 6·50 5·50

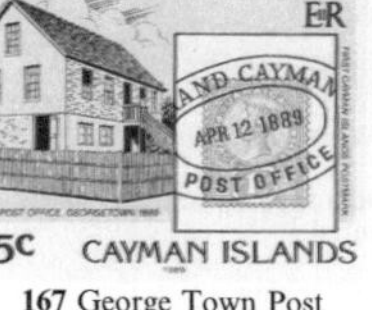

167 George Town Post Office, and Cayman Postmark on Jamaica 1d., 1889
168 Captain Bligh ashore in West Indies

1989. Centenary of Cayman Islands Postal Service. Multicoloured.
677 **167** 5c. multicoloured . . . . 85 1·00
678 – 25c. green, black and blue 2·00 1·00
679 – 35c. multicoloured . . . . 2·00 1·25
680 – $1 multicoloured . . . . 8·00 9·50
DESIGNS: 25c. "Orinoco" (mail steamer) and 1900 ½d. stamp; 35c. G.P.O., Grand Cayman and "London 1980" $1 stamp; $1 Cayman Airways B.A.C. One Eleven 200/400 airplane and 1966 1s. Jet Service stamp.

1989. Captain Bligh's Second Breadfruit Voyage, 1791–93. Multicoloured.
681 50c. Type **168** . . . . 4·00 4·25
682 50c. H.M.S. "Providence" (sloop) at anchor . . . . . 4·00 4·25
683 50c. Breadfruit in tubs and H.M.S. "Assistant" (transport) . . . . 4·00 4·25
684 50c. Sailors moving tubs of breadfruit . . . . 4·00 4·25
685 50c. Midshipman and stores 4·00 4·25
Nos. 681/5 were printed together, se-tenant, forming a composite design.

169 Panton House
170 Map of Grand Cayman, 1773, and Surveying Instruments

1989. Architecture. Designs showing George Town buildings. Multicoloured.
686 5c. Type **169** 75 75
687 10c. Town hall and clock tower 75 75
688 25c. Old Court House . . . 1·40 55
689 35c. Elmslie Memorial Church . . . . 1·60 75
690 $1 Post Office . . . . 3·50 6·00

1989. Island Maps and Survey Ships. Multicoloured.
691 5c. Type **170** . . . . 1·75 1·50
692 25c. Map of Cayman Islands, 1956, and surveying instruments . . . . 3·50 1·25
693 50c. H.M.S. "Mutine", 1914 5·00 4·50
694 $1 H.M.S. "Vidal", 1956 . . 8·00 9·50

171 French Angelfish

1990. Angelfishes. Multicoloured.
707 10c. Type **171** . . . . 1·25 70
708 25c. Grey angelfish . . . . . 2·25 90
709 50c. Queen angelfish . . . . 3·50 4·25
710 $1 Rock beauty . . . . . . 5·50 8·00

1990. 90th Birthday of Queen Elizabeth the Queen Mother. As T **134** of Ascension.
711 50c. multicoloured . . . . . 1·25 2·25
712 $1 black and blue . . . . . 2·75 4·00
DESIGNS—21×36 mm: 50c. Silver Wedding photograph, 1948. 29×37 mm: $1 King George VI and Queen Elizabeth with Winston Churchill, 1940.

172 "Danaus eresimus"

1990. "Expo 90" International Garden and Greenery Exhibition, Osaka. Butterflies. Multicoloured.
713 5c. Type **172** 65 60
714 25c. "Brephidium exilis" . . 1·50 1·10
715 35c. "Phyciodes phaon" . . 1·75 1·25
716 $1 "Agraulis vanillae" . . . 4·00 6·50

173 Goes Weather Satellite

1991. International Decade for Natural Disaster Reduction. Multicoloured.
717 5c. Type **173** 80 75
718 30c. Meteorologist tracking hurricane 2·00 1·10
719 40c. Damaged buildings 2·25 1·25
720 $1 U.S. Dept of Commerce weather reconnaisance Lockheed WP-3D Orion 5·00 8·00

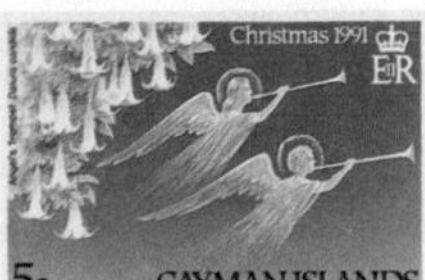

174 Angels and "Datura candida"

1991. Christmas. Multicoloured.
721 5c. Type **174** 60 70
722 30c. Mary and Joseph going to Bethlehem and "Allamanda cathartica" 1·60 60
723 40c. Adoration of the Kings and "Euphorbia pulcherrima" 1·75 1·10
724 60c. Holy Family and "Guaiacum officinale" 2·50 4·50

175 Coconut Palm

177 Woman and Donkey with Panniers

176 Single Cyclist

1991. Island Scenes. Multicoloured.
725 5c. Type **175** 50 30
726 15c. Beach scene (horiz) 1·75 30
727 20c. Poincianas in bloom (horiz) 70 35
728 30c. Blowholes (horiz) 1·75 50
729 40c. Police band (horiz) 2·50 1·40
730 50c. "Song of Norway" (liner) at George Town 2·00 1·40
731 60c. The Bluff, Cayman Brac (horiz) 1·75 2·00
732 80c. Coat of arms 1·50 2·25
733 90c. View of Hell (horiz) 1·60 2·25
734 $1 Game fishing (horiz) 3·25 2·25
735 $2 "Nieuw Amsterdam" (1983) and "Holiday" (liners) in harbour 8·00 6·00
736 $8 Queen Elizabeth II 16·00 17·00

1992. 40th Anniv of Queen Elizabeth II's Accession. As T **143** of Ascension. Multicoloured.
737 5c. Caymans' house 30 30
738 20c. Sunset over islands 1·00 50
739 30c. Beach 1·10 65
740 40c. Three portraits of Queen Elizabeth 1·10 1·00
741 $1 Queen Elizabeth II 2·00 3·50

1992. Olympic Games, Barcelona. Cycling. Mult.
742 15c. Type **176** 1·75 65
743 40c. Two cyclists 2·50 1·50
744 60c. Cyclist's legs 3·00 3·25
745 $1 Two pursuit cyclists 3·75 4·50

1992. Island Heritage. Multicoloured.
746 5c. Type **177** 50 50
747 30c. Fisherman weaving net 1·25 85
748 40c. Maypole dancing 1·50 1·10
749 60c. Basket making 2·50 3·50
750 $1 Cooking on caboose 3·00 4·50

178 Yellow Stingray

1993. Rays. Multicoloured.
751 5c. Type **178** 70 60
752 30c. Southern stingray 1·75 1·25
753 40c. Spotted eagle-ray 2·00 1·50
754 $1 Manta 4·25 5·50

179 Turtle and Sailing Dinghies

180 Cuban Amazon with Wings spread

1993. Tourism. Multicoloured.
755 15c. Type **179** 1·40 1·60
756 15c. Tourist boat, fishing launch and scuba diver 1·40 1·60
757 15c. Golf 1·40 1·60
758 15c. Tennis 1·40 1·60
759 15c. Pirates and ship 1·40 1·60
760 30c. Liner, tourist launch and yacht 1·50 1·75
761 30c. George Town street 1·50 1·75
762 30c. Tourist submarine 1·50 1·75
763 30c. Motor scooter riders and cyclist 1·50 1·75
764 30c. Cayman Airways Boeing 737 airliners 1·50 1·75

1993. Endangered Species. Cuban Amazon ("Grand Cayman Parrot"). Multicoloured.
765 5c. Type **180** 85 1·50
766 5c. On branch with wings folded 85 1·50
767 30c. Head of parrot 2·25 2·50
768 30c. Pair of parrots 2·25 2·50

181 "Ionopsis utricularioides" and Manger

1993. Christmas. Orchids. Multicoloured.
769 5c. Type **181** 1·00 75
770 40c. "Encyclia cochleata" and shepherd 2·50 85
771 60c. "Vanilla pompona" and wise men 3·50 3·75
772 $1 "Oncidium caymanense" and Virgin Mary 4·50 6·50

182 Queen Angelfish

1994. "Hong Kong '94" International Stamp Exhibition. Reef Life. Sheet 121 × 85 mm, containing T **182** and similar vert designs. Multicoloured.
MS773 60c. Type **182**; 60c. Diver with porkfish and short-finned hogfish; 60c. Rock beauty and Royal gramma; 60c. French angelfish and Banded butterflyfish 9·50 12·00

183 Flags of Great Britain and Cayman Islands

184 Black-billed Whistling Duck

1994. Royal Visit. Multicoloured.
774 5c. Type **183** 1·25 75
775 15c. Royal Yacht "Britannia" 2·25 1·00
776 30c. Queen Elizabeth II 2·25 1·10
777 $2 Queen Elizabeth and Prince Philip disembarking 6·50 9·00

1994. Black-billed Whistling Duck ("West Indian Whistling Duck"). Multicoloured.
778 5c. Type **184** 1·00 80
779 15c. Duck landing on water (horiz) 1·75 75
780 20c. Duck preening (horiz) 1·75 80
781 80c. Duck flapping wings 4·00 4·75
782 $1 Adult and duckling 4·50 5·50
MS783 71 × 45 mm. $1 As No. 782, but including Cayman Islands National Trust symbol 7·00 8·00

185 "Electrostrymon angelia"

186 H.M.S. "Convert" (frigate)

1994. Butterflies. Multicoloured.
784 10c. Type **185** 1·00 1·50
785 10c. "Eumaeus atala" 1·00 1·50
786 $1 "Eurema daira" 4·75 5·00
787 $1 "Urbanus dorantes" 4·75 5·00

1994. Bicentenary of Wreck of Ten Sail off Grand Cayman. Multicoloured.
788 10c. Type **186** 55 55
789 10c. Merchant brig and full-rigged ship 55 55
790 15c. Full-rigged ship near rock 75 50
791 20c. Long boat leaving full-rigged ship 85 55
792 $2 Merchant brig 4·50 7·50

187 Young Green Turtles

1995. Sea Turtles. Multicoloured.
793 10c. Type **187** 55 45
794 20c. Kemp's ridley turtle 80 55
795 25c. Hawksbill turtle 90 60
796 30c. Leatherback turtle 95 70
797 $1.30 Loggerhead turtle 3·50 4·75
798 $2 Pacific ridley turtles 4·50 6·00
MS799 167 × 94 mm. Nos. 793/8 10·00 12·00

188 Running

1995. C.A.R.I.F.T.A. and I.A.A.F. Games, George Town. Multicoloured.
800 10c. Type **188** 60 40
801 20c. High jumping 90 70
802 30c. Javelin throwing 1·25 80
803 $1.30 Yachting 4·25 6·00
MS804 100 × 70 mm. $2 Athletes with medals 6·50 7·50

1995. 50th Anniv of End of Second World War. As T **161** of Ascension. Multicoloured.
805 10c. Members of Cayman Home Guard 70 55
806 25c. "Comayagua" (freighter) 1·75 85
807 40c. U-boat "U125" 2·00 1·50
808 $1 U.S. Navy L-3 airship 3·75 6·00
MS809 75 × 85 mm. $1.30, Reverse of 1939–45 War Medal (vert) 2·50 3·00

189 Queen Elizabeth the Queen Mother

1995. 95th Birthday of Queen Elizabeth the Queen Mother. Sheet 70 × 90 mm.
MS810 **189** $4 multicoloured 8·50 9·50

190 Ox and Christ Child

191 Sea Grape

1995. Christmas. Nativity Animals. Multicoloured.
811 10c. Type **190** 70 30
812 20c. Sheep and lamb 1·25 45
813 30c. Donkey 1·75 60
814 $2 Camels 7·00 9·50
MS815 160 × 75 mm. Nos. 811/14 8·75 9·00

1996. Wild Fruit. Multicoloured.
816 10c. Type **191** 50 40
817 25c. Guava 1·00 50
818 40c. West Indian cherry 1·50 80
819 $1 Tamarind 2·75 4·50

192 "Laser" Dinghy

193 Guitar and Score of National Song

1996. Centenary of Modern Olympic Games. Multicoloured.
820 10c. Type **192** 55 40
821 20c. Sailboarding 85 60
822 30c. "Finn" dinghy 1·00 80
823 $2 Running 4·25 7·00

1996. National Identity. Multicoloured.
824 10c. Type **193** 35 30
825 20c. Cayman Airways Boeing 737-200 1·00 55
826 25c. Queen Elizabeth opening Legislative Assembly 75 50
827 30c. Seven Mile Beach 75 55
828 40c. Scuba diver and stingrays 1·00 75
829 60c. Children at turtle farm 1·75 1·10
830 80c. Cuban amazon ("Cayman Parrot") (national bird) 2·75 2·00
831 90c. Silver thatch palm (national tree) 1·75 2·00
832 $1 Cayman Islands flag 3·25 2·25
833 $2 Wild Banana Orchid (national flower) 5·00 5·50
834 $4 Cayman Islands coat of arms 9·00 12·00
835 $6 Cayman Islands currency 11·00 14·00

194 "Christmas Time on North Church Street" (Joanne Sibley)

1996. Christmas. Paintings. Multicoloured.
836 10c. Type **194** 40 30
837 25c. "Gone Fishing" (Lois Brezinsky) 70 50
838 30c. "Claus Encounters" (John Doak) 80 70
839 $2 "A Caymanian Christmas" (Debbie van der Bol) 4·00 6·50

1997. "HONG KONG '97" International Stamp Exhibition. Sheet 130 × 90 mm, containing design as No. 830 with "1997" imprint date. Multicoloured.
MS840 80c. Cuban amazon ("Cayman Parrot") 1·75 2·50

1997. Golden Wedding of Queen Elizabeth and Prince Philip. As T **173** of Ascension. Multicoloured.
841 10c. Queen Elizabeth 1·00 1·25
842 10c. Prince Philip and Prince Charles at Trooping the Colour 1·00 1·25
843 30c. Prince William horse riding, 1989 1·60 1·75
844 30c. Queen Elizabeth and Prince Philip at Royal Ascot 1·60 1·75

845 40c. Prince Philip at the Brighton Driving Trials . . 1·75 1·90
846 40c. Queen Elizabeth at Windsor Horse Show, 1993 1·75 1·90
MS847 110×70 mm. $1 Queen Elizabeth and Prince Philip in landau (horiz) . . . . 4·50 4·75

195 Children accessing Internet
196 Santa in Hammock

1997. Telecommunications. Multicoloured.
848 10c. Type **195** 35 25
849 25c. Cable & Wireless cable ship 70 45
850 30c. New area code "345" on children's T-shirts 75 60
851 60c. Satellite dish . . . . . 1·50 2·25

1997. Christmas. Multicoloured.
852 10c. Type **196** 35 25
853 30c. Santa with children on the Bluff 65 45
854 40c. Santa playing golf . . . 1·50 80
855 $1 Santa scuba diving . . . 2·00 3·50

1998. Diana, Princess of Wales Commemoration. As T **91** of Kiribati. Multicoloured.
856 10c. Wearing gold earrings, 1997 . . . . 40 40
857 20c. Wearing black hat . . . 70 70
MS858 145×70 mm. 10c. As No. 856; 20c. As No. 857; 40c. With bouquet, 1995; $1 Wearing black and white blouse, 1983 (sold at $1.70 + 30c. charity premium) 3·50 4·00

1998. 80th Anniv of the Royal Air Force. As T **178** of Ascension. Multicoloured.
859 10c. Hawker Horsley 60 70
860 20c. Fairey Hendon 75 80
861 25c. Hawker Siddeley Gnat 85 90
862 30c. Hawker Siddeley Dominie . . . . 95 1·00
MS863 110×77 mm. 40c. Airco D.H.9; 60c. Spad 13 Scout; 80c. Airspeed Oxford; $1 Martin Baltimore . . . . 5·50 6·50

197 Black-billed Whistling Duck ("West Indian Whistling Duck")
198 Santa at the Blowholes

1998. Birds. Multicoloured.
864 10c. Type **197** 80 60
865 20c. Magnificent frigate bird ("Magnificant Frigatbird") 1·25 60
866 60c. Red-footed booby . . . 2·25 2·50
867 $1 Cuban amazon ("Grand Cayman Parrot") . . . . 2·75 3·50

1998. Christmas. Multicoloured.
868 10c. Type **198** 30 30
869 30c. Santa diving on wreck of "Capt. Keith Tibbetts" . . 75 60
870 40c. Santa at Pedro Castle . . 90 75
871 60c. Santa arriving on Little Cayman . . . . 1·75 2·25

199 "They Rolled the Stone Away" (Miss Lassie)

1999. Easter. Paintings by Miss Lassie (Gladwyn Bush). Multicoloured.
884 10c. Type **199** 30 30
885 20c. "Ascension" (vert) . . . 60 60
886 30c. "The World Praying for Peace" 75 75
887 40c. "Calvary" (vert) 95 95

200 "Cayman House" (Jessica Cranston)

1999. Vision 2008 Project. Children's Paintings. Multicoloured.
888 10c. Type **200** 40 20
889 30c. "Coral Reef" (Sarah Hetley) . . . . 1·00 55
890 40c. "Fisherman on North Sound" (Sarah Cuff) . . . 1·10 70
891 $2 "Three Fish and a Turtle" (Ryan Martinez) . . . . . 4·25 6·00

1999. Royal Wedding. As T **185** of Ascension. Multicoloured.
892 10c. Photographs of Prince Edward and Miss Sophie Rhys-Jones 50 30
893 $2 Engagement photograph 3·75 4·75

1999. 30th Anniv of First Manned Landing on Moon. As T **186** of Ascension. Multicoloured.
894 10c. Coastguard cutter on patrol during launch . . . 45 35
895 25c. Firing of third stage rockets 80 60
896 30c. Buzz Aldrin descending to Moon's surface 85 65
897 60c. Jettisoning of lunar module . . . . 1·40 2·25
MS898 90×80 mm. $1.50, Earth as seen from Moon (circular, 40 mm diam) . . . . 3·00 4·00

1999. "Queen Elizabeth the Queen Mother's Century". As T **187** of Ascension. Multicoloured.
899 10c. Visiting anti-aircraft battery, London, 1940 . . 45 30
900 20c. With children on her 94th birthday, 1994 . . . 65 55
901 30c. With Prince Charles and Prince William, 1997 . . . 80 80
902 40c. Reviewing Chelsea Pensioners, 1986 . . . . . 90 90
MS903 145×70 mm. $1.50, Duchess of York with Princess Elizabeth, 1926, and Royal Wedding, 1923 2·75 3·25

201 1969 Christmas ¼c. Stamp

1999. Christmas. Designs showing previous Christmas stamps. Multicoloured.
904 10c. Type **201** 40 25
905 30c. 1984 Christmas 5c. . . . 70 50
906 40c. 1997 Christmas 10c. . . 85 65
907 $1 1979 Christmas 20c. (horiz) . . . . 1·90 2·75
MS908 111×100 mm. Nos. 904/7 2·75 4·00

2000. "Stamp Show 2000" International Stamp Exhibition, London. Kings and Queens of England. As T **223** of British Virgin Islands. Multicoloured.
909 10c. King Henry VII 35 50
910 40c. King Henry VIII . . . . 90 1·25
911 40c. Queen Mary I . . . . . 90 1·25
912 40c. King Charles II . . . . 90 1·25
913 40c. Queen Anne . . . . . . 90 1·25
914 40c. King George IV . . . . 90 1·25
915 40c. King George V . . . . 90 1·25

202 Ernie fishing from Rubber Ring

2000. "Sesame Street" (children's T.V. programme). Multicoloured.
916 10c. Type **202** 25 25
917 20c. Grover flying 40 50
918 20c. Zoe in airplane 40 50
919 20c. Oscar the Grouch in balloon 40 50
920 20c. The Count on motorbike 40 50
921 20c. Big Bird rollerskating . . 40 50
922 20c. Cookie Monster heading for Cookie Factory 40 50
923 20c. Type **202** 40 50
924 20c. Bert in rowing boat . . 40 50
925 20c. Elmo snorkeling 40 50
926 30c. As No. 920 . . . . . . 55 55
MS927 139×86 mm. 20c. Elmo with stamps 60 80
Nos. 917/25 were printed together, se-tenant, with the backgrounds forming a composite design.

2000. 18th Birthday of Prince William. As T **191** of Ascension. Multicoloured.
928 10c. Prince William in 1999 (horiz) 40 35
929 20c. In evening dress, 1997 (horiz) 65 55
930 30c. At Muick Falls, 1997 . . 80 70
931 40c. In uniform of Parachute Regiment, 1986 . . . . . 1·00 1·00
MS932 175×95 mm. $1 As baby with toy mouse (horiz) and Nos. 928/31 . . . . 6·50 6·50

203 Green Turtle

2000. Marine Life. Multicoloured.
933 10c. Type **203** 40 35
934 20c. Queen angel fish 65 45
935 30c. Sleeping parrotfish . . . 85 65
936 $1 Green moray eel . . . . 3·00 3·75

204 Boy thinking about Drugs and Fitness

2000. National Drugs Council. Multicoloured.
937 10c. Type **204** 55 35
938 15c. Rainbow, sun, clouds and "ez2B Drug Free" . . 75 35
939 30c. Musicians dancing . . . 1·25 65
940 $2 Hammock between two palm trees . . . . 4·75 7·00

205 Children on Beach ("Backing Sand")
206 Woman on Beach

2000. Christmas. Traditional Customs. Mult.
941 10c. Type **205** 65 45
942 30c. Christmas dinner . . . . 1·50 70
943 40c. Yard dance . . . . . . 1·60 85
944 60c. Conch shell borders . . 2·25 2·50

2001. United Nations Women's Human Rights Campaign.
945 **206** 10c. multicoloured 50 50

207 Red Mangrove Cay

2001. Cayman Brac Tourism Project. Mult.
946 15c. Type **207** 60 50
947 20c. Peter's Cave (vert) . . . 70 60
948 25c. Bight Road steps (vert) 80 70
949 30c. Westerly Ponds 90 85
950 40c. Aerial view of Spot Bay 1·10 1·10
951 60c. The Marshes . . . . . 1·75 2·25

208 Work of National Council of Voluntary Organizations

2001. Non-Profit Organizations. Multicoloured.
952 15c. Type **208** 45 45
953 20c. Pet welfare (Cayman Humane Society) 75 75
954 25c. Stick figures (Red Cross and Red Crescent) 80 80
955 30c. Pink flowers (Cayman Islands Cancer Society) (vert) 80 80
956 40c. Women's silhouettes and insignia (Lions Club Breast Cancer Awareness Campaign) (vert) 95 95
MS957 145×95 mm. Nos. 952/6 (sold at $1.80) . . . . 3·25 4·25
No. **MS**957 was sold at $1.80 which included a 50c. donation to the featured organisations.

209 Children walking Home

2001. Transportation. Multicoloured.
958 15c. Type **209** 20 25
959 15c. Boy on donkey 20 25
960 20c. Bananas by canoe . . . 25 30
961 25c. Horse and buggy 30 35
962 30c. Catboats fishing 40 45
963 40c. Schooner 50 55
964 60c. Police cyclist (vert) . . 80 85
965 80c. Lady drivers . . . . . 1·00 1·10
966 90c. Launching *Cimboco* (motor coaster) (vert) . . 1·20 1·30
967 $1 Amphibian aircraft . . . 1·30 1·40
968 $4 Container ship . . . . . 5·25 5·50
969 $10 Boeing 767 airliner . . . 13·00 13·50

210 Father Christmas on Scooter with Children, Cayman Brac

2001. Christmas. Multicoloured.
970 15c. Type **210** 55 40
971 30c. Father Christmas on eagle ray, Little Cayman 85 55
972 40c. Father Christmas in catboat, Grand Cayman 1·00 80
973 60c. Father Christmas parasailing over Grand Cayman . . . . 1·50 2·00

211 Statue of Liberty, U.S. and Cayman Flags

2002. In Remembrance. Victims of Terrorist Attacks on U.S.A. (11 September 2001).
974 **211** $1 multicoloured . . . . 2·25 3·00

2002. Golden Jubilee. As T **200** of Ascension.
975 15c. grey, blue and gold . . . 40 30
976 20c. multicoloured 55 40
977 30c. black, blue and gold . . 70 60
978 80c. multicoloured . . . . . 1·75 2·00
MS979 162×95 mm. Nos. 975/8 and $1 multicoloured . . . . . . 7·00 7·00
DESIGNS—HORIZ: 15c. Princess Elizabeth as young child; 20c. Queen Elizabeth in evening dress, 1976; 30c. Princess Elizabeth and Princess Margaret as Girl Guides, 1942; 80c. Queen Elizabeth at Newbury, 1996. VERT (38×51 mm)—$1 Queen Elizabeth after Annigoni.
Designs as Nos. 975/8 in No. **MS**979 omit the gold frame around each stamp and the "Golden Jubilee 1952–2002" inscription.

212 Snoopy painting Woodstock at Cayman Brac Bluff

2002. "A Cayman Vacation". Peanuts (cartoon characters by Charles Schulz). Multicoloured.
980 15c. Type **212** 50 40
981 20c. Charlie Brown and Sally at Hell Post Office, Grand Cayman 55 40
982 25c. Peppermint Patty and Marcie on beach, Little Cayman 65 50
983 30c. Snoopy as Red Baron and Boeing 737-200 over Grand Cayman 80 65

984 40c. Linus and Snoopy at Point of Sand, Little Cayman . . . . 1·10 85
985 60c. Charlie Brown playing golf at The Links, Grand Cayman . . . . 1·50 2·00
MS986 230 × 160 mm. Nos. 980/5 4·75 5·50
No. **MS**986 is die-cut in the shape of a suitcase.

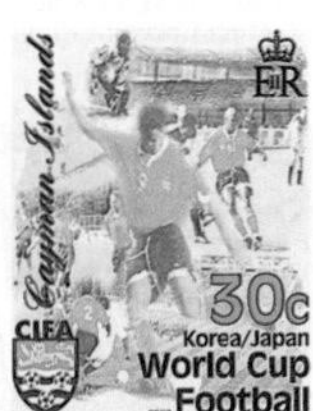

213 Cayman Islands Footballers

2002. World Cup Football Championship, Japan and Korea and 35th Anniv of Cayman Islands Football Association.
987 **213** 30c. multicoloured . . . . 1·25 1·00
988 40c. multicoloured . . . . 1·25 1·00

2002. Queen Elizabeth the Queen Mother Commemoration. As T **202** of Ascension.
989 15c. black, gold and purple 70 30
990 30c. multicoloured 1·00 60
991 40c. black, gold and purple 1·50 1·00
992 $1 multicoloured . . . . . . 2·50 2·75
MS993 145 × 70 mm. Nos. 991/2 4·00 4·50
DESIGNS: 15c. Queen Elizabeth at Red Corss and St. John's summer fair, London, 1943; 30c. Queen Mother at Royal Caledonian School, Bushey; 40c. Duchess of York in 1936; $1 Queen Mother at film premiere in 1989.
Designs in No. **MS**993 omit the "1900–2002" inscription and the coloured frame.

214 Angel Gabriel appearing to Virgin Mary

2002. Christmas. Multicoloured.
994 15c. Type **214** 40 35
995 20c. Mary and Joseph travelling to Bethlehem . . 50 40
996 30c. The Holy Family . . . 65 50
997 40c. Angel appearing to shepherds 80 65
998 60c. Three Wise Men . . . . 1·25 1·50
MS999 234 × 195 mm. Nos. 994/8 3·25 3·75

215 Catalina Flying Boat, North Sound, Grand Cayman

2002. 50th Anniv of Cayman Islands. Aviation. Multicoloured.
1000 15c. Type **215** 60 45
1001 20c. Grand Cayman Airport, 1952 . . . . . . 70 50
1002 25c. Cayman Brac Airways AC 50 . . . . 75 55
1003 30c. Cayman Airways Boeing 737 . . . . 80 60
1004 40c. British Airways Concorde at Grand Cayman, 1984 . . . . . 1·25 90
1005 $1.30 Island Air DHC 6 Twin Otter on Little Cayman . . . . 3·00 3·50

216 Skipping

2003. Children's Games. Multicoloured.
1006 15c. Type **216** 20 25
1007 20c. Maypole dancing . . . 25 30
1008 25c. Gig 30 35
1009 30c. Hopscotch 40 45
1010 $1 Marbles . . . . 1·30 1·40

2003. 50th Anniv of Coronation. As T **206** of Ascension. Multicoloured.
1011 15c. Queen Elizabeth II wearing Imperial State Crown 20 25
1012 $2 Newly crowned Queen flanked by Bishops of Durham and Bath & Wells . . . . 2·60 2·75
MS1013 95 × 115 mm. 20c. As 15c.; $4 As $2 . . . . 5·50 5·75
Nos. 1011/12 have red frames; stamps from **MS**1013 have no frame and country name in mauve panel.

2003. As T **207** of Ascension.
1014 $4 black, red and violet . . 5·25 5·50

2003. 21st Birthday of Prince William of Wales. As T **208** of Ascension. Multicoloured.
1015 15c. Prince William at Tidworth Polo Club, 2002 and on Raleigh International Expedition, 2000 . . . . 20 15
1016 40c. At Golden Jubilee church service, 2002 and Queen Mother's 101st birthday, 2001 . . . . . 50 55
1017 80c. At Queen Mother's 101st birthday and at Holyrood House, 2001 . . 1·00 1·10
1018 $1 At Eton College and at Christmas Day church service in 2000 . . . . . 1·30 1·40

217 Turtles hatching

2003. 500th Anniv of Discovery of Cayman Islands. Multicoloured.
1019 15c. Type **217** 20 25
1020 20c. Old waterfront, George Town, 1975 . . . . . . 25 30
1021 20c. *Santa Maria* (Columbus) and turtle . . 25 30
1022 25c. Nassau grouper (fish) and corals 30 35
1023 30c. *Kirk-B* (Cayman Brac schooner) 40 45
1024 40c. George Town harbour 50 55
1025 60c. Musical instruments . . 60 85
1026 80c. Smokewood tree and ghost orchids . . . . . . 1·00 1·10
1027 90c. Little Cayman Baptist Church . . . . 1·20 1·30
1028 $1 Loading thatch rope onto *Caymania* . . . . 1·30 1·40
1029 $1.30 Children's dance troupe . . . . 1·60 1·75
1030 $2 Cayman Parliament in session . . . . 2·60 2·75
MS1031 216 × 151 mm. Nos. 1019/30 10·00 2·25

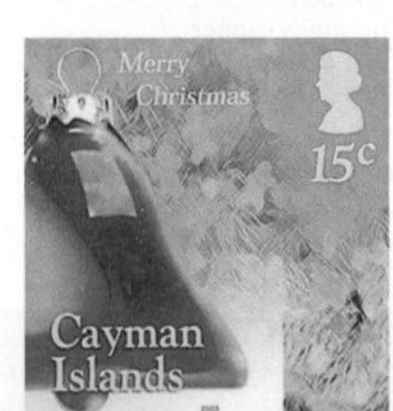

218 Bell and "Merry Christmas"

2003. Christmas. Multicoloured.
1032 15c. Type **218** 20 25
1033 20c. Christmas wreath and "Celebrate with Family" 25 30
1034 30c. Gold star, angel and "Happy New Year" . . . 40 45
1035 40c. Christmas lights and "Happy Holidays" . . . 50 55
1036 60c. Poinsettias and "Seasons Greetings" . . . 80 85

219 Female and Calf

2003. Endangered Species. Short-finned Pilot Whale. Multicoloured.
1037 15c. Type **219** 20 25
1038 20c. Four pilot whales . . . 25 30
1039 30c. Two pilot whales at surface 40 45
1040 40c. Short-finned pilot whale 50 55

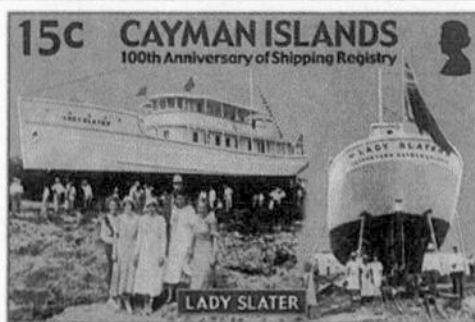

220 *Lady Slater*

2004. Centenary of Shipping Registry. Multicoloured.
1041 15c. Type **220** 20 25
1042 20c. *Seanostrum* 25 20
1043 30c. *Kirk Pride* 40 45
1044 $1 *Boadicea* . . . . 1·30 1·40

221 "Jesus carrying His Cross" (Carole Mayer)

2004. Easter. Multicoloured.
1045 15c. Type **221** 20 25
1046 30c. "The Ascension" (Natasha Claire Kozaily) 40 45

CENTRAL AFRICAN EMPIRE

Pt. 12

Central African Republic was renamed Central African Empire on 4 December 1976, when Pres. Bokassa became Emperor.
The country reverted to Central African Republic on his overthrow in 1979.

100 centimes = 1 franc.

1977. Various stamps of Central African Republic optd **EMPIRE CENTRAFRICAIN**.
439 **150** 3f. mult (postage) 40 35
444 **167** 10f. multicoloured 25 25
457 – 10f. red and blue (386) . . 25 25
459 **172** 10f. multicoloured 35 35
460 – 15f. multicoloured (391) 45 45
465 – 15f. brown, grn & bl (397) 25 25
445 – 20f. multicoloured (366) 25 25
461 – 20f. multicoloured (392) 40 40
446 – 25f. multicoloured (367) 25 25
451 – 25f. multicoloured (376) 25 25
449 **168** 30f. multicoloured 40 40
452 – 30f. multicoloured (377) 40 40
462 – 30f. multicoloured (393) 45 45
447 – 40f. multicoloured (370) 40 40
450 – 40f. multicoloured (373) 45 45
453 – 40f. multicoloured (378) 40 40
454 – 40f. multicoloured (380) 45 45
455 **170** 40f. multicoloured 40 40
456 – 40f. multicoloured (384) 40 40
458 – 40f. multicoloured (389) 40 35
482 – 40f. multicoloured (423) 65 55
466 – 50f. blue, brn & grn (398) 55 55
440 **163** 100f. multicoloured . . . 13·00 13·00
441 **164** 100f. grn, red & brn . . . 1·25 1·25
442 **165** 100f. brn, grn & blue . . 1·60 1·60
468 **179** 100f. black and yellow . . 1·25 1·25
469 **180** 100f. purple, blue & grn 1·25 1·25
491 **185** 100f. multicoloured . . . 1·25 1·25
483 – 50f. mult (424) (air) . . . 45 30
448 – 100f. multicoloured (371) 85 85
463 **173** 100f. red and blue 90 90
467 **178** 100f. multicoloured . . . 85 85
484 – 100f. multicoloured (425) 85 85
464 **174** 200f. multicoloured . . . 1·90 1·90
443 **166** 500f. red, green & brown 6·25 6·25

1977. "Apollo–Soyuz" Space Link. Nos. 410/14 of Central African Republic optd **EMPIRE CENTRAFRICAIN**.
470 **181** 40f. mult (postage) . . . 50 50
471 – 50f. multicoloured 60 60
472 – 100f. multicoloured (air) 85 85
473 – 200f. multicoloured . . . 1·90 1·90
474 – 300f. multicoloured . . . 2·50 2·50

1977. Air. Bicentenary of American Revolution. Nos. 416/20 of Central African Republic optd **EMPIRE CENTRAFRICAIN**.
476 **182** 100f. multicoloured . . . 75 45
477 – 125f. multicoloured . . . 95 60
478 – 150f. multicoloured . . . 1·25 70
479 – 200f. multicoloured . . . 1·60 95
480 – 250f. multicoloured . . . 1·90 1·25

1977. Winners of Winter Olympic Games, Innsbruck. Nos. 426/30 of Central African Republic optd **EMPIRE CENTRAFRICAIN**.
485 – 40f. mult (postage) . . . 40 35
486 – 60f. multicoloured 50 35
487 **184** 100f. multicoloured (air) 65 45
488 – 200f. multicoloured . . . 1·50 85
489 – 300f. multicoloured . . . 2·25 1·25

1977. "Viking" Space Mission. Nos. 433/7 of Central African Republic optd **EMPIRE CENTRAFRICAIN**.
492 **186** 40f. mult (postage) . . . 40 30
493 – 60f. multicoloured 50 35
494 – 100f. multicoloured (air) 65 45
495 – 200f. multicoloured . . . 1·50 85
496 – 300f. multicoloured . . . 2·25 1·25

189 Pierre and Marie Curie (Physics, 1903)

1977. Nobel Prize-winners. Multicoloured.
503 40f. Type **189** (postage) . . . 60 25
504 60f. W. C. Rontgen (Physics, 1901) 60 35
505 100f. Rudyard Kipling (Literature, 1907) (air) . . 75 35
506 200f. Ernest Hemingway (Literature, 1954) . . . . 1·50 65
507 300f. L. Pirandello (Literature, 1934) . . . . 2·25 75

190 Roman Temple and Italy 1933 3l. stamp

1977. "Graf Zeppelin" Flights. Multicoloured.
509 40f. Type **190** (postage) . . . 60 25
510 60f. St. Basil's Cathedral, Moscow, and Russia 1930 40k. stamp 70 40
511 100f. North Pole and Germany 1931 "Polarfahrt" stamp (air) 1·10 45
512 200f. Museum of Science and Industry, Chicago, and Germany 1933 "Chicagofahrt" stamp . . 2·10 65
513 300f. Brandenburg Gate, Berlin, and German 1931 stamp . . . . 3·25 95

191 Charles Lindbergh and "Spirit of St. Louis"

1977. History of Aviation. Multicoloured.
515 50f. Type **191** 45 20
516 60f. Alberto Santos-Dumont and "14 bis" biplane . . . 55 25
517 100f. Louis Bleriot and Bleriot XI 95 40
518 200f. Roald Amundsen and Dornier Wal flying boat . . 1·60 60
519 300f. Concorde . . . . . . 3·00 1·25

192 Lily

193 Group of Africans and Rotary Emblem

1977. Flowers. Multicoloured.
521 5f. Type **192** 50 35
522 10f. Hibiscus . . . . 1·00 60

1977. 20th Anniv of Bangui Rotary Club.
523 **193** 60f. multicoloured . . . . 1·90 1·25

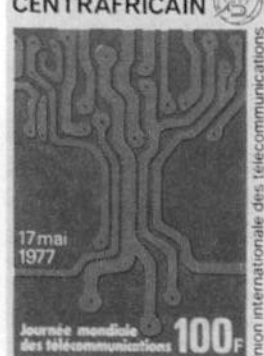

194 Africans queueing beside Bible

195 Printed Circuit

1977. Bible Week.
524 **194** 40f. multicoloured . . . . 1·50 95

1977. World Telecommunications Day.
525 **195** 100f. orange, brown & blk 2·25 1·90

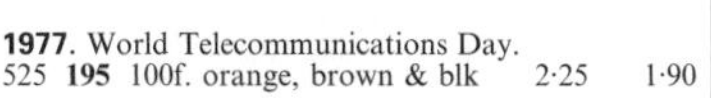

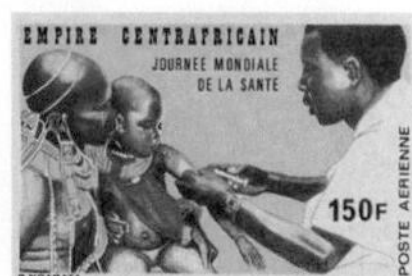

196 Doctor inoculating Child

1977. Air. World Health Day.
526 **196** 150f. multicoloured . . . 1·00 70

197 Goalkeeper

1977. World Cup Football Championship (1978). Multicoloured.
527 50f. Type **197** 40 20
528 60f. Goalmouth melee . . . 45 25
529 100f. Mid-field play 75 30
530 200f. World Cup poster . . . 1·60 50
531 300f. Mario Jorge Lobo Zagalo (Argentine trainer) and Buenos Aires stadium 2·50 90

198 Emperor Bokassa I

1977. Coronation of Emperor Bokassa.
533 **198** 40f. mult (postage) . . . 25 20
534 60f. multicoloured 40 25
535 100f. multicoloured . . . 75 45
536 150f. multicoloured . . . 1·25 70
537 200f. mult (air) . . . . . 1·50 75
538 300f. multicoloured . . . 2·25 1·25

199 Bangui Telephone Exchange

1978. Opening of Automatic Telephone Exchange, Bangui. Multicoloured.
541 40f. Type **199** 40 25
542 60f. Bangui Telephone Exchange (different) . . . 50 35

200 Bokassa Sports Palace

1978. Bokassa Sports Palace. Multicoloured.
543 40f. Type **200** 40 25
544 60f. Sports Palace (different) 50 35

201 "The Holy Family"

1978. 400th Birth Anniv of Rubens. Mult.
545 60f. Type **201** 50 20
546 150f. "Marie de Medici" . . 1·10 40
547 200f. "The Artist's Sons" . . 1·60 60
548 300f. "Neptune" (horiz) . . . 2·50 75

202 Black Rhinoceros

1978. Endangered Animals. Multicoloured.
550 40f. Type **202** 50 15
551 50f. Crocodile 65 20
552 60f. Leopard (vert) 75 25
553 100f. Giraffe (vert) . . . . . 1·25 40
554 200f. African elephant . . . 3·25 60
555 300f. Gorilla (vert) . . . . . 3·75 1·00

203 Mail Coach and Satellite

1978. 100 Years of Progress in Posts and Telecommunications. Multicoloured.
556 40f. Type **203** (postage) . . . 35 20
557 50f. Steam locomotive and space communications . . 5·50 2·75
558 60f. Paddle-steamer and ship-to-shore communications 45 25
559 80f. Renault car and "Pioneer" satellite 65 25
560 100f. Mail balloon and "Apollo"–"Soyuz" link-up (air) 75 40
561 200f. Seaplane "Comte da la Vaulx" and Concorde . . 1·50 65

205 H.M.S. "Endeavour" under Repair (after W. Byrne)

1978. 250th Birth Anniv of Captain Cook. Mult.
578 60f. Type **205** . . . . 1·00 35
579 80f. Cook on board "Endeavour" (vert) 75 25
580 200f. Landing party in New Hebrides . . . . 1·90 65
581 350f. Masked paddlers in canoe (after Webber) . . . 3·75 1·25

206 Ife Bronze Head

1978. 2nd World Festival of Negro Arts, Lagos.
582 **206** 20f. black and yellow . . 25 20
583 – 30f. black and blue . . . 25 20
584 – 60f. multicoloured 65 40
585 – 100f. multicoloured . . . 1·10 65

DESIGNS—VERT: 30f. Carved mask. HORIZ: 60f. Dancers; 100f. Dancers with musical instruments.

207 Clement Ader and "Avion III"

1978. Air. Aviation Pioneers. Multicoloured.
586 40f. Type **207** 40 20
587 50f. Wright Brothers and glider No. III 40 20
588 60f. Alcock, Brown and Vickers Vimy 45 30
589 100f. Sir Alan Cobham and De Havilland D.H.50 . . . 90 45
590 150f. Dr. Claude Dornier and Dornier Gs1 flying boat . . 1·40 65

208 "Self-portrait"

1978. 450th Death Anniv of Albrecht Durer (artist). Multicoloured.
592 60f. Type **208** 50 20
593 80f. "The Four Apostles" . . 75 25
594 200f. "The Virgin and Child" 1·90 80
595 350f. "The Emperor Maxillian I" . . . . 3·25 1·25

1978. Air. "Philexafrique" Stamp Exhibition, Gabon (1st issue) and International Stamp Fair, Essen. As T **237** of Benin. Multicoloured.
596 100f. Red crossbills and Mecklenberg-Schwerin 1856 $\frac{1}{4}$s. stamp . . . . . . 1·50 1·25
597 100f. Crocodile and Central African Republic 1960 500f. stamp . . . . 1·50 1·25

See also Nos. 647/8.

209 Third Mummiform Coffin

1978. Treasures of Tutankhamun. Mult.
598 40f. Type **209** 35 20
599 60f. Tutankhamun and Ankhesenamun (back of gilt throne) 45 25
600 80f. Ecclesiastical throne . . 65 35
601 100f. Head of Tutankhamun (wooden statuette) 75 35
602 120f. Lion's head (funerary bedhead) 95 40
603 150f. Life-size statue of Tutankhamun . . . . . . 1·25 45
604 180f. Gilt throne . . . . . . 1·50 55
605 250f. Canopic coffin . . . . 1·90 75

210 Lenin speaking at the Smolny Institute

211 Catherine Bokassa

1978. 60th Anniv of Russian Revolution.
606 **210** 40f. multicoloured 40 25
607 – 60f. multicoloured 50 35
608 – 100f. black, grey and gold 90 40
609 – 150f. red, black and gold 1·40 65
610 – 200f. multicoloured . . . 1·90 95
611 – 300f. multicoloured . . . 2·50 1·25

DESIGNS—VERT: 60f. Lenin addressing crowd in Red Square; 200f. Lenin at Smolny Institute; 300f. Lenin and banner. HORIZ: 100f. Lenin, Krupskaya and family; 150f. Lenin, Cruiser "Aurora" and revolutionaries.

1978. 1st Anniv of Emperor Bokassa's Coronation. Multicoloured.
613 40f. Type **211** (postage) . . . 40 20
614 60f. Emperor Bokassa . . . 50 35
615 150f. The Emperor and Empress (horiz) (air) . . . 1·25 70

212 Rowland Hill, Letter-weighing Scale and Penny Black

1978. Death Centenary of Sir Rowland Hill (1st issue). Multicoloured.
617 40f. Type **212** (postage) . . . 35 20
618 50f. Postman on bicycle and U.S. 5c. stamp, 1847 . . . 40 25
619 60f. Danish postman and Austrian newspaper stamp, 1856 . . . . 45 30
620 80f. Postilion, mail coach and Geneva 5+5c. stamp, 1843 65 25
621 100f. Postman, mail train and Tuscan 3l. stamp, 1860 (air) . . . . 3·25 1·60
622 200f. Mail balloon and French 10c. stamp, 1850 1·50 65

See also Nos. 671/4.

1978. Argentina's Victory in World Cup Football Championship. Nos. 527/31 optd **VAINQUEUR ARGENTINE**.
625 50f. Type **197** 40 25
626 60f. Goalmouth melee . . . 45 35
627 100f. Mid-field play 75 45
628 200f. World Cup poster . . . 1·50 95
629 300f. Mario Jorge Lobo Zagalo and Buenos Aires Stadium . . . . 2·25 1·25

214 Children painting and Dutch Master

1979. International Year of the Child (1st issue). Multicoloured.
631 40f. Type **214** (postage) . . . 40 15
632 50f. Eskimo children and skier 50 20
633 60f. Benz automobile and children with toy car . . . 65 20
634 80f. Satellite and children launching rocket 90 25
635 100f. Dornier Do-X flying boat and Chinese child flying kite (air) 95 40
636 200f. Hurdler and children playing leap-frog . . . . . 1·90 45

See also Nos. 666/70.

215 High Jump

1979. Pre-Olympic Year (1st issue). Mult.
639 40f. Type **215** (postage) . . . 35 15
640 50f. Cycling 40 20
641 60f. Weightlifting 45 20
642 80f. Judo 65 30
643 100f. Hurdles (air) 75 35
644 200f. Long jump . . . . . . 1·50 50

See also Nos. 676/70 and 705.

216 Co-operation Monument, "Aurivillius arata" and Hibiscus

1979. "Philexafrique" Exhibition (2nd issue). Mult.
647 60f. Type **216** . . . . 1·60 1·10
648 150f. Envelopes, van, canoeist and U.P.U. emblem . . . 3·25 2·10

217 School Teacher

1979. 50th Anniv of International Bureau of Education.
649 **217** 70f. multicoloured 65 40

219 Chicken

1979. National Association of Farmers. Mult.
651 10f. Type **219** (postage) . . . 1·25 90
652 20f. Bullock . . . . 1·25 90
653 40f. Sheep . . . . 2·50 1·75
654 60f. Horse (air) . . . . . . 3·50 1·60

OFFICIAL STAMPS

1977. Official stamps of Central African Republic optd **EMPIRE CENTRAFRICAIN**.
O498 O **109** 5f. multicoloured . . 25 20
O499 40f. multicoloured . . 40 20
O500 100f. multicoloured 1·00 45
O501 140f. multicoloured 1·25 70
O502 200f. multicoloured 2·25 1·00

O **204** Coat of Arms

1978.
O564 O **204** 1f. multicoloured . . 20 15
O565 2f. multicoloured . . 15 15
O566 5f. multicoloured . . 15 15
O567 10f. multicoloured . . 20 15
O568 15f. multicoloured . . 20 15
O569 20f. multicoloured . . 25 20
O570 30f. multicoloured . . 35 25
O571 40f. multicoloured . . 40 30
O572 50f. multicoloured . . 50 35
O673 60f. multicoloured . . 65 45
O574 100f. multicoloured 75 60
O575 130f. multicoloured 1·25 90
O576 140f. multicoloured 1·25 90
O577 200f. multicoloured 2·50 1·25

CENTRAL AFRICAN REPUBLIC
Pt. 12

Formerly Ubangi-Shari. An independent republic within the french Community.

100 centimes = 1 franc.

1 President Boganda

3 "Dactyloceras widenmanni"

4 Abyssinian Roller

1959. Republic. 1st Anniv. Centres multicoloured. Frame colours given.
1 **1** 15f. blue 35 25
2 – 25f. red 45 25
DESIGN—HORIZ: 25f. As Type **1** but flag behind portrait.

1960. 10th Anniv of African Technical Co-operation Commission. As T **62** of Cameroun.
3 50f. blue and green . . . . . . 1·25 75

1960.
4 – 50c. brn, red & turq (postage) 10 10
5 – 1f. myrtle, brown & violet . . 10 10
6 – 2f. myrtle, brown and green 15 15
7 – 3f. brown, red and olive . . . 25 20
8 **3** 5f. brown and green 35 25
9 – 10f. blue, black and green . . 70 45
10 – 20f. red, black and green . . 1·50 65
11 – 85f. red, black and green . . 5·75 1·60
12 – 50f. turq, red & green (air) 4·25 1·40
13 **4** 100f. violet, brown & green 7·00 2·00
14 – 200f. multicoloured . . . . . 12·00 4·75
15 – 250f. multicoloured . . . . . 12·50 5·00
16 – 500f. brown, blue and green 42·00 8·50
BUTTERFLIES—As Type **3**: 50c., 3f. "Cymothoe sangaris"; 1f., 2f. "Charaxe mobilis"; 10f. "Charaxes ameliae"; 20f. "Charaxes zingha"; 85f. "Drurya antimachus". BIRDS—As Type **4**: 50f. Great blue turaco; 200f. Green turaco; 250f. Red-faced lovebirds; 500f. African fish eagle.
See also Nos. 42/5.

1960. National Festival. No. 2 optd **FETE NATIONALE 1-12-1960.**
17 25f. multicoloured . . . . . . 1·25 1·25

1960. Air. Olympic Games. No. 276 of French Equatorial Africa optd with Olympic rings, **XVIIe OLYMPIADE 1960 REPUBLIQUE CENTRAFRICAINE** and surch **250F** and bars.
18 250f. on 500f. blue, blk & grn 7·75 7·50

7 Pasteur Institute, Bangui

1961. Opening of Pasteur Institute, Bangui.
19 **7** 20f. multicoloured 75 65

8 U.N. Emblem, Map and Flag

1961. Admission into U.N.O.
20 **8** 15f. multicoloured 40 35
21 25f. multicoloured 45 35
22 85f. multicoloured . . . . . 1·40 95

1961. National Festival. Optd with star and **FETE NATIONALE 1-12-01.**
23 **8** 25f. multicoloured . . . . . 1·75 1·75

1962. Air. "Air Afrique" Airline. As T **69** of Cameroun.
24 50f. violet, brown and green 95 60

1962. Union of African States and Madagascar Conference, Bangui. Surch **U.A.M. CONFERENCE DE BANGUI 25-27 MARS 1962 50F.**
25 **8** 50f. on 85f. multicoloured . . 1·25 1·25

1962. Malaria Eradication. As T **70** of Cameroun.
26 25f.+5f. slate 85 85

12 Hurdling

13 Pres. Dacko

1962. Sports.
27 **12** 20f. sep, yell & grn (postage) 45 35
28 – 50f. sepia, yellow and green 1·10 65
29 – 100f. sep, yell & grn (air) . . 2·10 1·40
DESIGNS—As Type **12**: 50f. Cycling. VERT: (26 × 47 mm): 100f. Pole-vaulting.

1962.
30 **13** 20f. multicoloured 35 20
31 25f. multicoloured 45 20

1962. 1st Anniv of Union of African and Malagasy States. As T **72** of Cameroun.
32 30f. green 65 45

15 Athlete

18 "Posts and Telecommunications"

17 "National Army"

19 "Telecommunications"

1962. Air. "Coupe des Tropiques" Games, Bangui.
33 **15** 100f. brown, turquoise & red . . . . 2·25 1·40

1963. Freedom from Hunger. As T **76** of Cameroun.
34 25f.+5f. turquoise, brn & bis 75 75

1963. 3rd Anniv of Proclamation of Republic.
35 **17** 20f. multicoloured 60 40

1963. Air. African and Malagasy Posts and Telecommunications Union.
36 **18** 85f. multicoloured . . . . . 1·60 80

1963. Space Telecommunications.
37 **19** 25f. green and purple . . . 65 50
38 – 100f. green, orange & blue 1·60 1·40
DESIGN: 100f. Radio waves and globe.

20 "Young Pioneers"

21 Boali Falls

1963. Young Pioneers.
39 **20** 30f. brown, blue & turquoise 65 45

1963.
40 **21** 30f. purple, green and blue 65 40

22 Map of Africa and Sun

1963. Air. "African Unity".
41 **22** 25f. ultramarine, yellow & bl 55 35

23 "Colotis evippe"

24 "Europafrique"

1963. Butterflies. Multicoloured.
42 1f. Type **23** 20 15
43 3f. "Papilio dardanus" 30 25
44 4f. "Papilio lormieri" 50 30
45 60f. "Papilio zalmoxis" . . . 3·50 2·25

1963. Air. European–African Economic Convention.
46 **24** 50f. multicoloured . . . . . 2·25 1·75

25 ABJ-6 Diesel Railcar

26 U.N.E.S.C.O. Emblem, Scales of Justice and Tree

1963. Air. Bangui–Douala Railway Project.
47 – 20f. green, purple & brown 75 80
48 **25** 25f. chocolate, blue & brn 90 1·00
49 – 50f. violet, purple & brown 3·00 3·25
50 – 100f. purple, turquoise and brown . . . . 3·75 3·75
DESIGNS: (Diesel rolling stock)—HORIZ: 20f. ABJ-6 railcar; 100f. Diesel locomotive. VERT: 50f. Series BB500 diesel shunter.

1963. 15th Anniv of Declaration of Human Rights.
51 **26** 25f. bistre, green and brown 70 50

27 Bangui Cathedral

1964. Air.
52 **27** 100f. brown, green & blue 1·50 85

28 Cleopatra, Temple of Kalabsha
30 "Tree" and Sun Emblem

29 Radar Scanner

1964. Air. Nubian Monuments Preservation.
53 **28** 25f.+10f. mauve, bl & grn 1·10 1·10
54 50f.+10f. brn, grn & turq . . 1·90 1·90
55 100f.+10f. pur, vio & grn 3·00 3·00

1964. Air. World Meteorological Day.
56 **29** 50f. violet, brown and blue 95 95

1964. International Quiet Sun Years.
57 **30** 25f. orange, ochre & turq 1·00 75

31 Map and African Heads of State
33 Pres. Kennedy

32 Throwing the Javelin

1964. Air. 5th Anniv of Equatorial African Heads of State Conference.
58 **31** 100f. multicoloured . . . . 1·60 85

1964. Air. Olympic Games, Tokyo.
59 **32** 25f. brown, green and blue 40 30
60 – 50f. red, black and green . . 85 40
61 – 100f. brown, blue and green 1·90 85
62 – 250f. black, green and red 5·00 2·50
DESIGNS: 50f. Basketball; 100f. Running; 250f. Diving and swimming.

1964. Air. Pres. Kennedy Memorial Issue.
63 **33** 100f. brown, black & violet 1·90 1·40

34 African Child
35 Silhouettes of European and African

1964. Child Welfare. Different portraits of children. As T **34**.
64 **34** 20f. brown, green & purple 35 25
65 – 25f. brown, blue and red . . 40 35
66 – 40f. brown, purple & green 60 45
67 – 50f. brown, green and red 70 50

1964. French, African and Malagasy Co-operation. As T **88** of Cameroun.
68 25f. brown, red and green . . 60 40

1964. National Unity.
69 **35** 25f. multicoloured 65 40

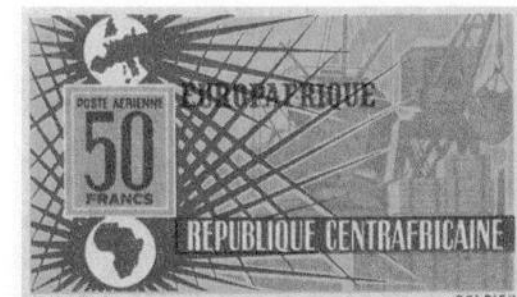

36 "Economic Co-operation"

1964. Air. "Europafrique".
70 **36** 50f. green, red and yellow 95 65

37 Handclasp

1965. Air. International Co-operation Year.
71 **37** 100f. multicoloured . . . . 1·60 85

38 Weather Satellite

1965. Air. World Meteorological Day.
72 **38** 100f. blue and brown . . . 1·60 85

39 Abraham Lincoln

1965. Air. Death Centenary of Abraham Lincoln.
73 **39** 100f. flesh, blue & green . . 1·60 85

40 Team of Oxen

1965. Harnessed Animals in Agriculture.
74 **40** 25f. red, brown and green 50 35
75 – 50f. purple, green and blue 85 45
76 – 85f. brown, green and blue 1·25 70
77 – 100f. multicoloured . . . . 1·60 90
DESIGNS: 50f. Ploughing with bullock; 85f. Ploughing with oxen; 100f. Oxen with hay cart.

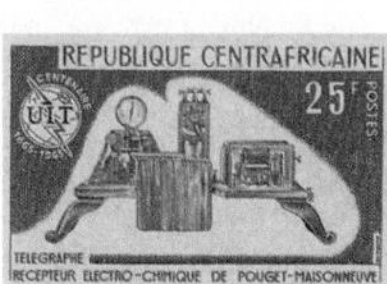

41 Pouget-Maisonneuve Telegraph Instrument

1965. Centenary of I.T.U.
78 **41** 25f. blue, red & grn (post) 50 40
79 – 30f. lake and green 60 45
80 – 50f. red and violet 90 65
81 – 85f. blue and purple . . . . 1·60 95
82 – 100f. brown, blue & green (48½ × 27 mm) (air) . . . 1·90 1·10
DESIGNS—VERT: 30f. Chappe's telegraph instrument; 50f. Doignon regulator for Hughes telegraph. HORIZ: 85f. Pouillet's telegraph apparatus; 100f. "Relay" satellite and I.T.U. emblem.

42 Women and Loom ("To Clothe")
43 Coffee Plant, Hammer Grubs and "Epicampoptera strandi"

1965. "M.E.S.A.N." Welfare Campaign. Designs depicting "Five Aims".
83 **42** 25f. green, brown and blue (postage) 45 35
84 – 50f. brown, blue and green 75 45
85 – 60f. brown, blue and green 85 60
86 – 85f. multicoloured . . . . . 1·25 65
87 – 100f. blue, brown and green (48 × 27 mm) (air) . . . . 1·25 70
DESIGNS: 50f. Doctor examining child, and hospital ("To care for"); 60f. Student and school ("To instruct"); 85f. Women and child, and harvesting scene ("To nourish"); 100f. Village houses ("To house"). "M.E.S.A.N.—Mouvement Evolution Social Afrique Noire".

1965. Plant Protection.
88 **43** 2f. purple, red and green . . 10 10
89 – 3f. red, green and black . . 25 15
90 – 30f. purple, green and red 1·50 65
DESIGNS—HORIZ: 3f. Coffee plant, caterpillar and hawk-moth. VERT: 30f. Cotton plant caterpillar and rose-moth.

1965. Surch.
91 – 2f. on 3f. (No. 43) . . . . . 2·50 2·50
92 **1** 5f. on 15f. . . . . 2·50 2·50
93 – 5f. on 85f. (No. 76) 35 35
94 **13** 10f. on 20f. . . . . 3·25 3·25
95 – 10f. on 100f. (No. 77) . . . 45 45

45 Camp Fire
47 "Industry and Agriculture"

46 U.N. and Campaign Emblems

1965. Scouting.
96 **45** 25f. red, purple and blue . . 75 25
97 – 50f. brown and blue (Boy Scout) . . . . 1·00 60

1965. Freedom from Hunger.
98 **46** 50f. brown, blue and green 90 65

1965. Air. "Europafrique".
99 **47** 50f. multicoloured 80 50

48 Mercury (statue after Coysevox)
49 Father and Child

1965. Air. 5th Anniv of Admission to U.P.U..
100 **48** 100f. black, blue & red . . 1·90 1·10

1965. Air. Red Cross.
101 **49** 50f. black, blue and red . . 1·00 50
102 – 100f. brown, green and red (Mother and Child) . . 2·10 1·00

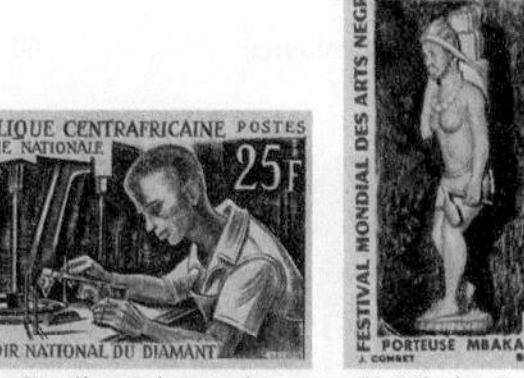

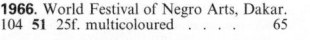

50 Grading Diamonds
51 Mbaka Porter

1966. National Diamond Industry.
103 **50** 25f. brown, violet and red 75 40

1966. World Festival of Negro Arts, Dakar.
104 **51** 25f. multicoloured 65 40

52 W.H.O. Building
53 "Eulophia cucullata"

1966. W.H.O. Headquarters, Geneva. Inaug.
105 **52** 25f. violet, blue & yellow 65 40

1966. Flowers. Multicoloured.
106 2f. Type **53** 10 10
107 5f. "Lissochilus horsfalii" . . 20 10
108 10f. "Tridactyle bicaudata" 25 20
109 15f. "Polystachya" 50 25
110 20f. "Eulophia alta" 75 40
111 25f. "Microcelia macrorrhynchium" . . . . 1·00 50

54 Douglas DC-8F Aircraft and "Air Afrique" Emblem

1966. Air. Inaug of "DC-8" Air Services.
112 **54** 25f. multicoloured 60 30

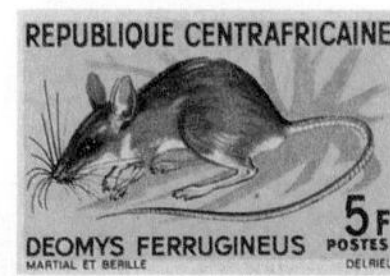

55 Congo Forest Mouse

1966. Rodents. Multicoloured.
113 5f. Type **55** 50 25
114 10f. Black-striped mouse . . 85 40
115 20f. Dollman's tree mouse . . 1·75 70

56 "Luna 9"

1966. Air. "Conquest of the Moon". Mult.
116 130f. Type **56** . . . . 1·60 95
117 130f. "Surveyor" . . . . . . 1·60 95
118 200f. "From the Earth to the Moon" (Jules Verne) . . . 2·75 1·60

57 Cernan
59 U.N.E.S.C.O. Emblem

58 Satellite "D 1" and Rocket "Diamant"

1966. Air. Astronauts. Multicoloured.
120 50f. Type **57** 85 50
121 50f. Popovich 85 50

1966. Air. Launching of Satellite "D 1".
122 **58** 100f. purple and brown . . 1·60 80

1966. 20th Anniv of U.N.E.S.C.O.
123 **59** 30f. multicoloured 65 40

60 Symbols of Industry and Agriculture

61 Pres. Bokassa

1966. Air. Europafrique.
124 **60** 50f. multicoloured . . . . 1·10 75

1967.
125 **61** 30f. black, ochre & green 60 35

1967. Provisional Stamps. (a) Postage. No. 111 surch **XX** and value.
126 10f. on 25f. multicoloured . . 45 20

(b) Air. No. 112 with face value altered by obliteration of figure "2" in "25".
127 **54** 5f. multicoloured 25 20

63 Douglas DC-8 over Bangui M'Poko Airport

1967. Air.
128 **63** 100f. blue, green & brown 2·10 1·00

64 Aerial View of Fair

1967. Air. World Fair, Montreal.
129 **64** 100f. brown, ultram & bl 2·75 1·25

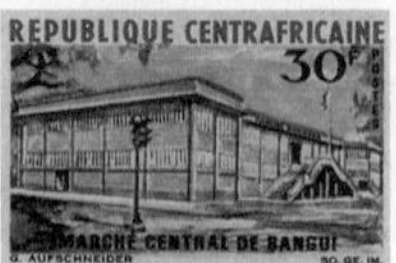

65 Central Market, Bangui

1967. Multicoloured.
130 30f. Type **65** 65 35
131 30f. Safari Hotel, Bangui . . 65 35

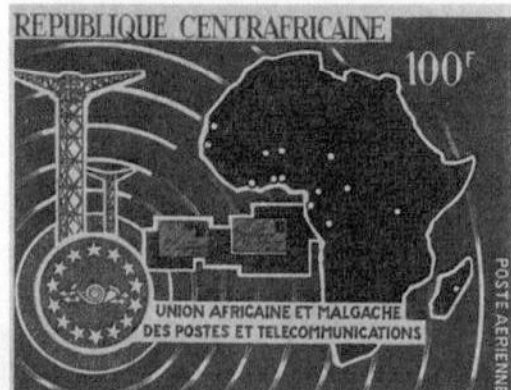

66 Map, Letters and Pylons

1967. Air. 5th Anniv of African and Malagasy Posts and Telecommunications Union (U.A.M.P.T.).
132 **66** 100f. purple, grn & red . . 1·50 70

67 "Leucocoprinus africanus"

68 Projector, Africans and Map

1967. Mushrooms. Multicoloured.
133 5f. Type **67** 95 30
134 10f. "Synpodia arborescens" 1·25 60
135 15f. "Phlebopus sudanicus" 1·40 90
136 30f. "Termitomyces schimperi" . . . . 4·75 1·50
137 50f. "Psalliota sebedulis" . . 7·25 2·75

1967. "Radiovision" Service.
138 **68** 30f. blue, green and brown 65 40

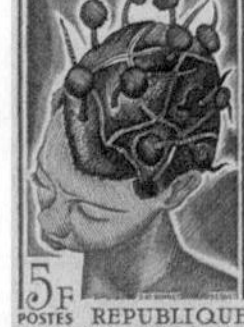

69 Coiffure

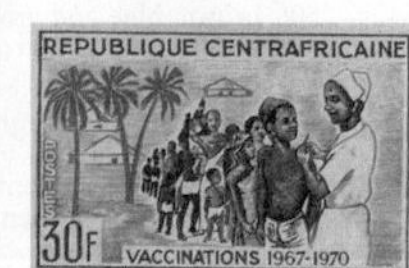

70 Inoculation Session

1967. Female Coiffures. Showing different hairstyles.
139 **69** 5f. brown and blue 25 20
140 – 10f. brown, choc & red . . 40 25
141 – 15f. brown, choc & grn . . 65 45
142 – 20f. brown, choc & orge 75 45
143 – 30f. brown, choc & purple 1·25 60

1967. Vaccination Programme, 1967–70.
144 **70** 30f. brown, green & red . . 65 45

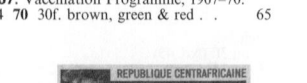

71 Douglas DC-3

1967. Aircraft.
145 **71** 1f. grey, grn & brn (post) 20 10
146 – 2f. black, blue and purple 20 10
147 – 5f. black, green and blue 25 15
148 – 100f. brown, grn & bl (air) 1·75 80
149 – 200f. blue, brown and green . . . . 3·75 1·75
150 – 500f. slate, red and blue . . 11·00 4·50
DESIGNS—As T **71**: 2f. Beechcraft Baron; 5f. Douglas DC-4. 48 × 27 mm: 100f. Potez 25-TOE; 200f. Junkers 52/3m; 500f. Sud Aviation Caravelle.

72 Presidents Boganda and Bokassa

1967. Air. 9th Anniv of Republic.
151 **72** 130f. multicoloured . . . . 1·60 1·10

73 Primitive Shelter, Toulou

1967. 6th Pan-African Prehistory Congress, Dakar.
152 **73** 30f. blue, purple and red 65 25
153 – 50f. bistre, ochre & green 1·25 65
154 – 100f. purple, brown & blue 2·50 95
155 – 130f. red, green & brown 2·50 95
DESIGNS—VERT: 50f. Kwe perforated stone; 100f. Megaliths, Bouar. HORIZ: 130f. Rock drawings, Toulou.

74 Pres. Bokassa

1968. Air.
156 **74** 30f. multicoloured 60 35

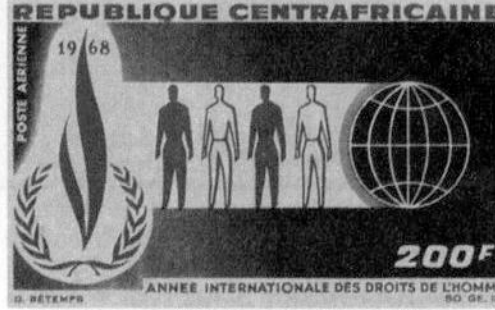

75 Human Rights Emblem, Human Figures and Globe

1968. Air. Human Rights Year.
157 **75** 200f. red, green and violet 3·25 1·50

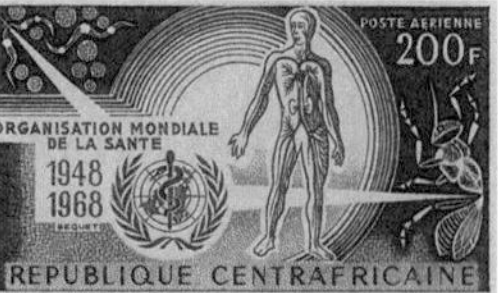

76 Human Figure and W.H.O. Emblem

1968. Air. 20th Anniv of W.H.O.
158 **76** 200f. red, blue & brown . . 3·50 1·90

77 Alpine Skiing

78 Parachute-landing on Venus

1968. Air. Olympic Games, Grenoble and Mexico.
159 **77** 200f. brown, blue and red 4·25 2·50
160 – 200f. brown, blue and red 4·25 2·50
DESIGN: No. 160, Throwing the javelin.

1968. Air. "Venus 4". Exploration of planet Venus.
161 **78** 100f. blue, turquoise & grn 1·60 80

79 Marie Curie and impaled Crab (of Cancer)

1968. Air. Marie Curie Commem.
162 **79** 100f. brown, violet & blue 1·90 1·00

80 Refinery and Tanker

1968. Inauguration of Petroleum Refinery, Port Gentil, Gabon.
163 **80** 30f. multicoloured 90 30

1968. Air. Surch. Nos. 165/6 are obliterated with digit.
164 **56** 5f. on 130f. (No. 116) . . . 15 10
165 – 10f. (100f. No. 148) . . . 20 15
166 – 20f. (200f. No. 149) . . . 35 25
167 – 50f. on 130f. (No. 117) . . 75 50

82 "CD-8" Bulldozer

1968. Bokassa Project.
168 **82** 5f. brown, black & green 25 15
169 – 10f. black, brown & green 40 25
170 – 20f. green, yellow & brown 65 25
171 – 30f. blue, drab and brown 95 45
172 – 30f. red, blue and green . . 95 50
DESIGNS: 10f. Baoule cattle; 20f. Spinning-machine; 30f. (No. 171), Automatic looms; 30f. (No. 172), "D4-C" bulldozer.

83 Bangui Mosque

1968. 2nd Anniv of Bangui Mosque.
173 **83** 30f. flesh, green and blue 70 40

84 Za Throwing-knife

1968. Hunting Weapons.
174 **84** 10f. blue and bistre 45 25
175 – 20f. green, brown & blue 60 35
176 – 30f. green, orange & blue 65 45
DESIGNS: 20f. Kpinga-Gbengue throwing-knife; 30f. Mbano cross-bow.

85 "Ville de Bangui" (1958)

1968. River Craft.
177 **85** 10f. blue, green and purple (postage) 50 40
178 – 30f. brown, blue & green 90 50
179 – 50f. black, brown & grn . . 1·40 65
180 – 100f. brown, grn & bl (air) 2·10 95
181 – 130f. blue, green & purple 2·10 1·25
DESIGNS: 30f. "J. B. Gouandjia" (1968); 50f. "Lamblin" (1944). LARGER (48 × 27 mm): 100f. "Pie X" (Bangui, 1894); 130f. "Ballay" (Bangui, 1891).

86 "Madame de Sevigne" (French School, 17th century)

1968. Air. "Philexafrique" Stamp Exhibition, Abidjan, Ivory Coast (1969) (1st issue).
182 **86** 100f. multicoloured . . . . 2·25 2·00

87 President Bokassa, Cotton Plantation, and Ubangui Chari stamp of 1930

1969. Air. "Philexafrique" Stamp Exhibition, Abidjan, Ivory Coast (2nd issue).
183 **87** 50f. black, green & brown 1·75 1·75

88 "Holocerina angulata"

1969. Air. Butterflies. Multicoloured.
184 10f. Type **88** 50 25
185 20f. "Nudaurelia dione" . . 75 35
186 30f. "Eustera troglophylla" (vert) . . . . 1·90 60
187 50f. "Aurivillius aratus" . . . 3·00 1·60
188 100f. "Epiphora albida" . . . 5·00 2·50

89 Throwing the Javelin

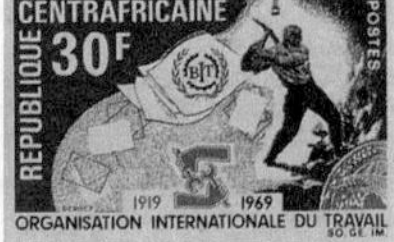

90 Miner and Emblems

1969. Sports. Multicoloured.
189 5f. Type **89** (postage) 20 10
190 10f. Start of race 25 15
191 15f. Football 40 20

192 50f. Boxing (air) 80 30
193 100f. Basketball . . . . . . 1·75 65
Nos. 192/3 are 48 × 28 mm.

1969. 50th Anniv of I.L.O.
194 **90** 30f. multicoloured 50 25
195 50f. multicoloured 75 40

91 "Apollo 8" over Moon's Surface

1969. Air. Flight of "Apollo 8" Around Moon.
196 **91** 200f. multicoloured . . . . 3·00 1·60

92 Nuremberg Spire and Toys

1969. Air. International Toy Fair, Nuremberg.
197 **92** 100f. black, purple & grn 3·25 1·75

1969. Air. Birth Bicentenary of Napoleon Bonaparte. As T **144** of Cameroun. Multicoloured.
198 100f. "Napoleon as First Consul" (Girodet-Trioson) (vert) . . . . 1·90 1·25
199 130f. "Meeting of Napoleon and Francis II of Austria" (Gros) . . . . 2·50 1·40
200 200f. "Marriage of Napoleon and Marie-Louise" (Rouget) . . . . 3·75 2·50

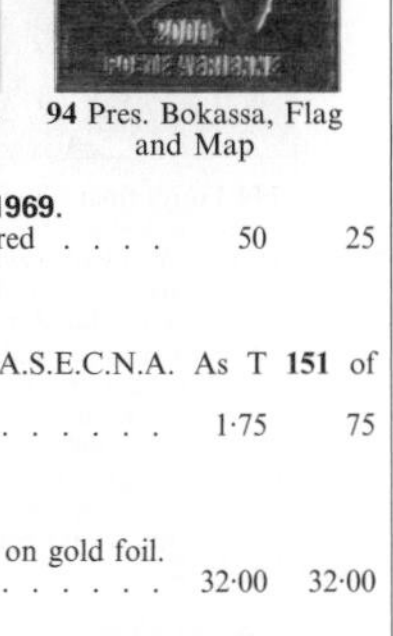

93 President Bokassa in Military Uniform
94 Pres. Bokassa, Flag and Map

1969.
201 **93** 30f. multicoloured 50 25

1969. 10th Anniv of A.S.E.C.N.A. As T **151** of Cameroun.
202 100f. blue . . . . 1·75 75

1970. Air. Die-stamped on gold foil.
203 **94** 2000f. gold . . . . 32·00 32·00

95 Garayah
97 F. D. Roosevelt (25th Death Anniv)

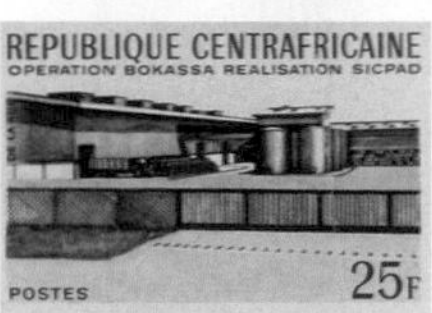

96 Flour Storage Depot

1970. Musical Instruments.
204 **95** 10f. brown, sepia & green 40 15
205 – 15f. brown and green . . . 45 20
206 – 30f. brown, lake & yellow 70 35
207 – 50f. blue and red . . . . . 1·00 40
208 – 130f. brown, olive & blue 3·25 1·00

DESIGNS—VERT: 130f. Gatta and Babylon. HORIZ: 15f. Ngombi; 30f. Xylophone; 50f. Nadla.

1970. Societie Industrielle Centrafricaine des Produits Alimentaires et Derives (S.I.C.P.A.D.) Project. Multicoloured.
209 25f. Type **96** 45 25
210 50f. Mill machinery 90 70
211 100f. View of flour mill . . . 1·40 1·00

1970. Air. World Leaders. Multicoloured.
212 100f. Lenin (birth centenary) 2·50 1·10
213 100f. Type **97** . . . . 1·50 85

1970. New U.P.U. Headquarters Building, Berne. As T **156** of Cameroun.
214 100f. vermilion, red and blue 1·40 65

1970. Air. Moon Landing of "Apollo 12". No. 196 optd **ATTERRISSAGE d'APOLLO 12 19 novembre 1969**.
215 **91** 200f. multicoloured . . . . 12·50 9·25

99 Pres. Bokassa
101 Silkworm

100 Cheese Factory, Sarki

1970.
216 **99** 30f. multicoloured . . . . 5·00 3·75
217 40f. multicoloured . . . . 6·25 4·50

1970. "Operation Bokassa" Development Projects. Multicoloured.
218 5f. Type **100** (postage) . . . 35 20
219 10f. M'Bali Ranch . . . . . 4·75 3·75
220 20f. Zebu bull and herdsman (vert) 65 45
221 40f. Type **101** . . . . 1·90 65
222 140f. Type **101** (air) . . . . 3·00 1·25

102 African Dancer

1970. Air. "Knokphila 70" Stamp Exhibition, Knokke, Belgium. Multicoloured.
223 100f. Type **102** . . . . 1·50 50
224 100f. African produce . . . . 1·50 50

103 Footballer

1970. Air. World Cup Football Championship, Mexico.
225 **103** 200f. multicoloured . . . 3·00 1·60

104 Central African Republic's Pavilion

1970. Air. "EXPO 70", Osaka, Japan.
226 **104** 200f. multicoloured . . . 3·50 1·75

105 Dove and Cogwheel

1970. Air. 25th Anniv of U.N.O.
227 **105** 200f. black, yellow & bl 3·00 1·50

106 Presidents Mobutu, Bokassa and Tombalbaye

1970. Air. Reconciliation with Chad and Zaire.
228 **106** 140f. multicoloured . . . 1·90 80

107 Scaly Francolin and Helmeted Guineafowl

1971. Wildlife. Multicoloured.
229 5f.+5f. Type **107** . . . . . . 4·00 2·25
230 10f.+5f. Common duiker and true achatina (snail) . . . 4·75 2·75
231 20f.+5f. Hippopotamus, African elephant and tortoise in tug-of-war . . . 5·75 3·00
232 30f.+10f. Tortoise and Senegal coucal . . . . . . 8·50 7·50
233 50f.+20f. Monkey and leopard . . . . 12·50 10·50

108 Lengue Dancer

1971. Traditional Dances. Multicoloured.
234 20f.+5f. Type **108** 50 25
235 40f.+10f. Lengue (diff) . . . 75 40
236 100f.+40f. Teke . . . . . . 2·25 1·25
237 140f.+40f. Englabolo . . . . 3·00 1·40

110 Monteir's Mormyrid

1971. Fishes. Multicoloured.
244 10f. Type **110** 40 30
245 20f. Trunk-nosed mormyrid 75 40
246 30f. Wilverth's mormyrid . . 1·10 70
247 40f. Elephant-nosed mormyrid . . . . 2·25 80
248 50f. Curve-nosed mormyrid 2·75 1·40

111 Satellite and Globe

1971. Air. World Telecommunications Day.
249 **111** 100f. multicoloured . . . 1·50 75

112 Berberati Cathedral
113 Gen. De Gaulle

1971. Consecration of Roman Catholic Cathedral, Berberati.
250 **112** 5f. multicoloured 25 15

1971. 1st Death Anniv of De Gaulle.
251 **113** 100f. multicoloured . . . 3·25 1·90

114 Lesser Bushbaby

1971. Animals: Primates. Multicoloured.
252 30f. Type **114** 65 60
253 40f. Western needle-clawed bushbaby 95 65
254 100f. Angwantibo (horiz) . . 2·25 1·40
255 150f. Potto (horiz) . . . . . 3·75 2·40
256 200f. Red colobus (horiz) . . 5·00 3·25

1971. Air. 10th Anniv of African and Malagasy Posts and Telecommunications Union. Similar to T **184** of Cameroun. Multicoloured.
257 100f. Headquarters and carved head . . . . 1·50 75

115 Shepard in Capsule

1971. Space Achievements. Multicoloured.
258 40f. Type **115** 45 30
259 40f. Gagarin in helmet . . . 45 30
260 100f. Aldrin in Space . . . . 1·10 45
261 100f. Leonov in Space . . . 1·10 45
262 200f. Armstrong on Moon 2·25 1·00
263 200f. "Lunokhod 1" on Moon . . . . 2·25 1·00

116 Crab Emblem **117** "Operation Bokassa"

1971. Air. Anti-cancer Campaign.
264 **116** 100f. multicoloured . . . 1·90 95

1971. 12th Year of Independence.
265 **117** 40f. multicoloured 65 40

118 Racial Equality Year Emblem

1971. Racial Equality Year.
266 **118** 50f. multicoloured 65 40

119 I.E.Y. Emblem and Child with Toy Bricks

1971. Air. 25th Anniv of U.N.E.S.C.O.
267 **119** 140f. multicoloured . . . 1·50 70

120 African Children

1971. Air. 25th Anniv of U.N.I.C.E.F.
268 **120** 140f.+50f. mult . . . . . 2·50 1·60

121 Arms and Parade **122** Pres. G. Nasser

1972. Bokassa Military School.
269 **121** 30f. multicoloured 65 45

1972. Air. Nasser Commemoration.
270 **122** 100f. ochre, brown & red 1·60 80

123 Book Year Emblem **124** Heart Emblem

1972. International Book Year.
271 **123** 100f. gold, yellow & brn 1·60 95

1972. World Heart Month.
272 **124** 100f. red, black & yellow 1·40 80

125 First-Aid Post **126** Global Emblem

1972. Red Cross Day.
273 **125** 150f. multicoloured . . . 2·25 1·25

1972. World Telecommunications Day.
274 **126** 50f. black, yellow & red 75 50

127 Boxing

1972. Air. Olympic Games, Munich.
275 **127** 100f. bistre and brown . . 1·60 95
276 – 100f. violet and green . . 1·60 1·10
DESIGN—VERT: No. 276, Long-jumping.

128 Pres. Bokassa and Family

1972. Mothers' Day.
278 **128** 30f. multicoloured 75 40

129 Pres. Bokassa planting Cotton Bush **130** Savings Bank Building

1972. "Operation Bokassa" Cotton Development.
279 **129** 40f. multicoloured 55 35

1972. Opening of New Postal Cheques and Savings Bank Building.
280 **130** 30f. multicoloured 50 35

131 "Le Pacifique" Hotel

1972. "Operation Bokassa" Completion of "Le Pacifique" Hotel.
281 **131** 30f. blue, red and green 35 25

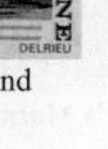

132 Giraffe and Monkeys **133** Postal Runner

134 Tiling's Postal Rocket, 1931

1972. Clock-faces from Central African HORCEN Factory. Multicoloured.
282 5f. Rhinoceros chasing African 20 20
283 10f. Camp fire and Native warriors 25 20
284 20f. Fishermen 60 30
285 30f. Type **132** 65 45
286 40f. Warriors fighting 90 65

1972. "CENTRAPHILEX" Stamp Exhibition, Bangui.
287 **133** 10f. mult (postage) . . . 25 20
288 – 20f. multicoloured 40 30
289 **134** 40f. orange, blue and slate (air) 55 45
290 – 50f. blue, slate & orange 70 50
291 – 150f. grey, orange & brn 1·90 1·25
292 – 200f. blue, orange & brn 2·75 1·90
DESIGNS—AS Type **133**: HORIZ: Protestant Youth Centre. As Type **134**: VERT: 50f. Douglas DC-3 and camel postman; 150f. "Sirio" satellite and rocket. HORIZ: 200f. "Intelsat 4" satellite and rocket.

135 University Buildings

1972. Inauguration of Bokassa University.
294 **135** 40f. grey, blue and red . . 55 35

136 Mail Van

1972. World U.P.U. Day.
295 **136** 100f. multicoloured . . . 1·75 85

137 Paddy Field

1972. Bokassa Plan. State Farms. Multicoloured.
296 5f. Type **137** 20 15
297 25f. Rice cultivation 35 20

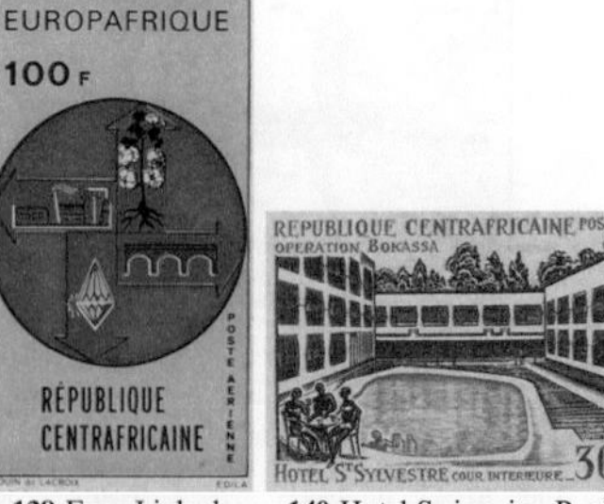

138 Four Linked Arrows **140** Hotel Swimming Pool

1972. Air. "Europafrique".
298 **138** 100f. multicoloured . . . 1·25 75

1972. Air. Munich Olympic Gold Medal Winners. Nos. 275/6 optd as listed below.
299 **127** 100f. bistre and brown . . 1·25 80
300 – 100f. violet and green . . 1·25 80
OVERPRINTS: No. 299, **POIDS-MOYEN LEMECHEV MEDAILLE D'OR**. No. 300, **LONGUEUR WILLIAMS MEDAILLE D'OR**.

1972. Opening of Hotel St. Sylvestre.
302 **140** 30f. brown, turq & grn 40 30
303 – 40f. purple, green & blue 40 30
DESIGN: 40f. Facade of Hotel.

141 Landing Module and Lunar Rover on Moon

1972. Air. Moon Flight of "Apollo 16".
304 **141** 100f. green, blue & grey 1·25 60

142 "Virgin and Child" (F. Pesellino)

1972. Air. Christmas. Multicoloured.
305 100f. Type **142** . . . . 1·60 95
306 150f. "Adoration of the Child" (F. Lippi) . . . . . 2·25 1·25

143 Learning to Write

1972. "Central African Mothers". Multicoloured.
307 5f. Type **143** 15 10
308 10f. Baby-care 25 20
309 15f. Dressing hair 25 20
310 20f. Learning to read 40 25
311 180f. Suckling baby . . . . 2·40 1·25
312 190f. Learning to walk . . . 2·40 1·25

144 Louys (marathon), Athens, 1896

1972. Air. 75th Anniv of Revival of Olympic Games.
313 **144** 30f. purple, brown & grn 30 25
314 – 40f. green, blue & brown 35 25
315 – 50f. violet, blue and red 50 40
316 – 100f. purple, brn & grey 1·00 50
317 – 150f. black, blue & purple 1·60 1·10
DESIGNS: 40f. Barrelet (sculling), Paris, 1900; 50f. Prinstein (triple-jump), St. Louis, U.S.A., 1904; 100f. Taylor (400 m freestyle swimming), London, 1908; 150f. Johansson (Greco-Roman wrestling), Stockholm, 1912.

145 W.H.O. Emblem, Doctor and Nurse

1973. Air. 25th Anniv of W.H.O.
318 **145** 100f. multicoloured . . . 1·25 70

146 "Telecommunications"

1973. World Telecommunications Day.
319 **146** 200f. orange, blue & black 1·90 1·00

147 Harvesting

1973. 10th Anniv of World Food Programme.
320 **147** 50f. multicoloured 65 40

148 "Garcinia punctata"

1973. "Flora". Multicoloured.
321 10f. Type **148** 25 15
322 20f. "Bertiera racemosa" . . 35 20
323 30f. "Coryanthe pachyceras" 50 30
324 40f. "Combretodendron africanum" 70 30
325 50f. "Xylopia villosa" 85 45

149 Pygmy Chameleon

1973.
326 **149** 15f. multicoloured 60 25

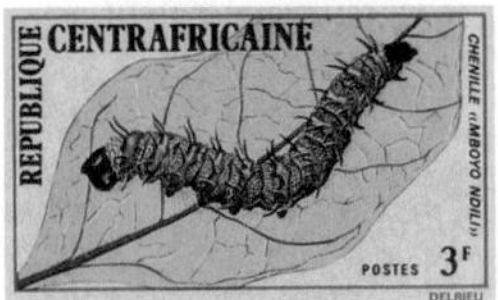

150 "Mboyo Ndili"

1973. Caterpillars. Multicoloured.
327 3f. Type **150** 25 20
328 5f. "Piwili" 40 25
329 25f. "Loulia Konga" 90 40

1973. African Solidarity "Drought Relief". No. 321 surch **SECHERESSE SOLIDARITE AFRICAINE** and value.
330 **148** 100f. on 10f. mult . . . . 1·25 95

1973. U.A.M.P.T. As Type **216** of Cameroun.
331 100f. red, brown and olive . . 1·10 70

1973. Air. African Fortnight, Brussels. As T **217** of Cameroun.
332 100f. brown and violet . . . 1·00 60

152 African and Symbolic Map

1973. Air. Europafrique.
333 **152** 100f. red, green & brown 1·25 75

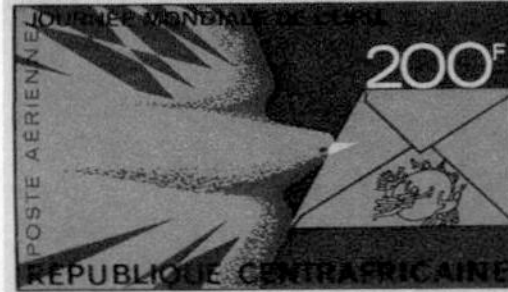

153 Bird with Letter

1973. Air. World U.P.U. Day.
334 **153** 200f. multicoloured . . . 2·25 1·40

154 Weather Map

1973. Air. Centenary of I.M.O./W.M.O.
335 **154** 150f. multicoloured . . . 1·90 85

155 Copernicus

1973. Air. 500th Birth Anniv of Copernicus.
336 **155** 100f. multicoloured . . . 2·25 1·50

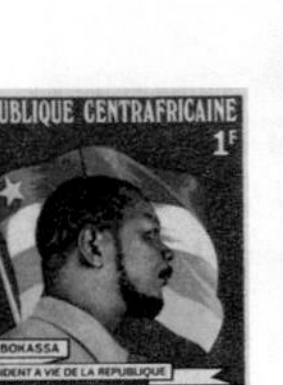

156 Pres. Bokassa

158 Launch

1973.
337 **156** 1f. mult (postage) 10 10
338 2f. multicoloured 10 10
339 3f. multicoloured 15 10
340 5f. multicoloured 15 10
341 10f. multicoloured 25 15
342 15f. multicoloured 25 20
343 20f. multicoloured 35 20
344 30f. multicoloured 35 25
345 40f. multicoloured 45 35
346 – 50f. multicoloured (air) 50 35
347 – 100f. multicoloured . . . 1·00 50
DESIGNS—SQUARE (35 × 35 mm): 50f. Pres. Bokassa facing left. VERT (26 × 47 mm): 100f. Pres. Bokassa in military uniform.

1973. Air. Moon Flight of "Apollo 17".
348 **158** 50f. red, green & brown 50 30
349 – 65f. green, red & purple 60 35
350 – 100f. blue, brown & red 1·00 50
351 – 150f. green, brown & red 1·50 70
352 – 200f. green, red and blue 2·00 1·10
DESIGNS—HORIZ: 65f. Surveying lunar surfaces; 100f. Descent on Moon. VERT: 150f. Astronauts on Moon's surface; 200f. Splashdown.

159 Interpol Emblem within "Eye"

1973. 50th Anniv of Interpol.
353 **159** 50f. multicoloured 70 50

160 St. Theresa

1973. Air. Birth Centenary of St. Theresa of Lisieux.
354 **160** 500f. blue and light blue 5·00 3·50

161 Main Entrance

1974. Opening of "Catherine Bokassa" Mother-and-Child Centre.
355 **161** 30f. brown, red and blue 35 25
356 – 40f. brown, blue and red 45 35
DESIGN: 40f. General view of Centre.

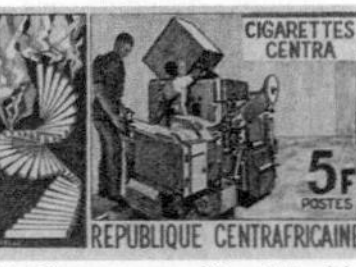

162 Cigarette-packing Machine

1974. "Centra" Cigarette Factory.
357 **162** 5f. purple, green & red . . 10 10
358 – 10f. blue, green & brown 25 15
359 – 30f. blue, green and red 30 20
DESIGNS: 10f. Administration block and factory building; 30f. Tobacco warehouse.

163 "Telecommunications"

165 Mother and Baby

164 "Peoples of the World"

1974. World Telecommunications Day.
360 **163** 100f. multicoloured . . . 6·50 4·00

1974. World Population Year.
361 **164** 100f. green, red & brown 1·10 65

1974. 26th Anniv of W.H.O.
362 **165** 100f. brown, blue & grn 1·25 65

166 Letter and U.P.U. Emblem

168 Modern Building

167 Battle Scene

1974. Centenary of U.P.U.
363 **166** 500f. red, green & brown 4·00 3·00

1974. "Activities of Forces' Veterans". Mult.
364 10f. Type **167** 15 10
365 15f. "Today" (Peace-time activities) 20 15
366 20f. Planting rice 20 15
367 25f. Cattle-shed 25 20
368 30f. Workers hoeing 25 20
369 40f. Veterans' houses 40 20

1974. 10th Anniv of Central African Customs and Economics Union. As Nos. 734/5 of Cameroun.
370 40f. multicoloured (postage) 50 35
371 100f. multicoloured (air) . . 1·00 65

1975. "OCAM City" Project.
372 **168** 30f. multicoloured 25 20
373 – 40f. multicoloured 35 25
374 – 50f. multicoloured 40 30
375 – 100f. multicoloured . . . 75 50
DESIGNS: Nos. 373/5, Various views similar to Type **150**.

1975. "J. B. Bokassa Pilot Village Project". As T **168**, but inscr "VILLAGE PILOTE J. B. BOKASSA".
376 25f. multicoloured 20 15
377 30f. multicoloured 30 20
378 40f. multicoloured 35 25
DESIGNS: Nos. 376/8, Various views similar to Type **168**.

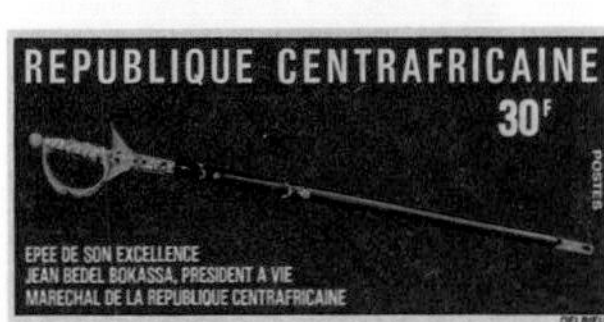

169 President Bokassa's Sword

1975. "Homage to President Bokassa". Mult.
379 30f. Type **169** (postage) . . . 45 25
380 40f. President Bokassa's baton 45 30
381 50f. Pres. Bokassa in uniform (vert, 36 × 49 mm) (air) . . 50 35
382 100f. Pres. Bokassa in cap and cape (vert, 36 × 49 mm) . . . . 1·00 45

170 Foreign Minister and Ministry

1975. Government Buildings. Multicoloured.
383 40f. Type **170** 50 35
384 40f. Television Centre (36 × 23 mm) 50 35

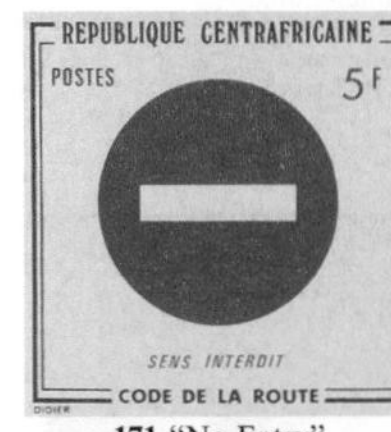

171 "No Entry"

1975. Road Signs.
385 **171** 5f. red and blue 10 10
386 – 10f. red and blue 15 10
387 – 20f. red and blue 20 15
388 – 30f. multicoloured 35 20
389 – 40f. multicoloured 50 25
SIGNS: 10f. "Stop"; 20f. "No stopping"; 30f. "School"; 40f. "Crossroads".

172 Kob

173 Carved Wooden Mask

1975. Wild Animals. Multicoloured.
390 10f. Type **172** 25 20
391 15f. Warthog 50 20
392 20f. Waterbuck 75 25
393 30f. Lion 75 35

1975. Air. "Arphila" International Stamp Exhibition. Paris.
394 **173** 100f. red, rose and blue 1·00 60

174 Dr. Schweitzer and Dug-out Canoe

175 Forest Scene

1975. Air. Birth Centenary of Dr. Albert Schweitzer.
395 **174** 200f. black, blue & brown 2·50 1·60

1975. Central African Woods.
396 **175** 10f. brown, green & red 20 15
397 – 15f. brown, green & blue 25 15
398 – 50f. blue, brown & green 45 20
399 – 100f. brown, blue & grn 95 55
400 – 150f. blue, brown & grn 1·25 95
401 – 200f. brown, red & green 1·75 1·25
DESIGNS—VERT: 15f. Cutting sapeles. HORIZ: 50f. Mobile crane; 100f. Log stack; 150f. Floating logs; 200f. Timber-sorting yard.

176 Women's Heads and Women Working

1975. International Women's Year.

No.	Type	Description	Mint	Used
402	176	40f. multicoloured	45	25
403		100f. multicoloured	1·25	65

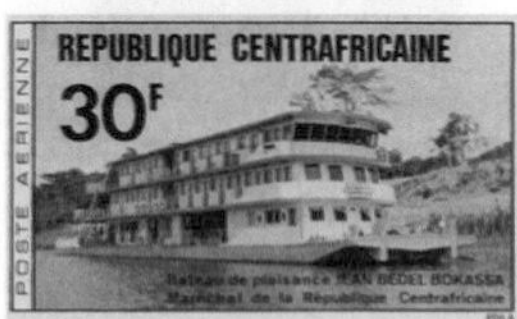

177 River Vessel "Jean Bedel Bokassa"

1976. Air. Multicoloured.

No.	Type	Description	Mint	Used
404		30f. Type **177**	50	25
405		40f. Frontal view of "Jean Bedel Bokassa"	60	40

178 Co-operation Monument

1976. Air. Central African–French Co-operation and Visit of President Giscard d'Estaing. Mult.

No.	Type	Description	Mint	Used
406		100f. Type **178**	1·00	75
407		200f. Flags and Presidents Giscard d'Estaing and Bokassa	2·10	1·25

179 Alexander Graham Bell

1976. Telephone Centenary.

No.	Type	Description	Mint	Used
408	179	100f. black and yellow	1·25	75

180 Telecommunications Satellite

1976. World Telecommunications Day.

No.	Type	Description	Mint	Used
409	180	100f. purple, blue & grn	1·40	95

181 Rocket on Launch-pad

1976. Apollo–Soyuz Space Link. Multicoloured.

No.	Type	Description	Mint	Used
410		40f. Type **181** (postage)	45	25
411		50f. Blast-off	55	25
412		100f. "Soyuz" in flight (air)	75	25
413		200f. "Apollo" in flight	1·50	50
414		300f. Crew meeting in space	2·25	85

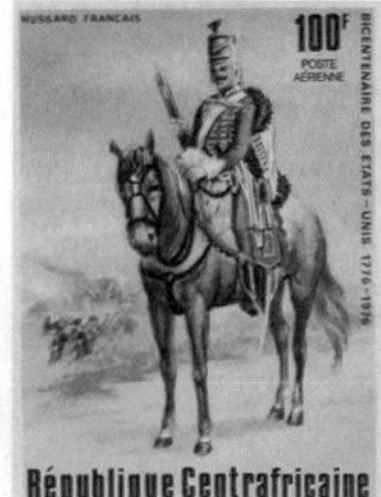

182 French Hussar

1976. Air. American Revolution Bicent. Mult.

No.	Type	Description	Mint	Used
416		100f. Type **182**	75	30
417		125f. Black Watch soldier	95	45
418		150f. German Dragoons' officer	1·10	50
419		200f. British Grenadiers' officer	1·90	55
420		250f. American Ranger	2·25	75

183 "Drurya antimachus"

1976. Butterflies. Multicoloured.

No.	Type	Description	Mint	Used
422		30f. Type **183** (postage)	1·25	75
423		40f. "Argema mittrei" (vert)	1·90	75
424		50f. "Acherontia atropos" and "Saturnia pyri" (air)	1·25	75
425		100f. "Papilio nireus" and "Heniocha marnois"	2·50	1·10

184 Dorothy Hamill of U.S.A. (figure skating)

1976. Medal Winners, Winter Olympic Games, Innsbruck. Multicoloured.

No.	Type	Description	Mint	Used
426		40f. Piero Gros of Italy (slalom) (horiz) (postage)	45	25
427		60f. Karl Schnabl and Toni Innauer of Austria (ski-jumping) (horiz)	55	35
428		100f. Type **184** (air)	70	35
429		200f. Alexandre Gorshkov and Ludmilla Pakhomova (figure-skating, pairs) (horiz)	1·25	60
430		300f. John Curry of Great Britain (figure-skating)	2·25	95

185 U.P.U. Emblem, Letters, and Types of Mail Transport

1976. World U.P.U. Day.

No.	Type	Description	Mint	Used
432	185	100f. multicoloured	1·60	95

186 Assembly of "Viking"

1976. "Viking" Space Mission to Mars. Multicoloured.

No.	Type	Description	Mint	Used
433		40f. Type **186** (postage)	45	25
434		60f. Launch of "Viking"	55	35
435		100f. Parachute descent on Mars (air)	70	35
436		200f. "Viking" on Mars (horiz)	1·25	60
437		300f. "Viking" operating gravel scoop	2·25	75

Issues between 1977 and 1979 are listed under **CENTRAL AFRICAN EMPIRE**.

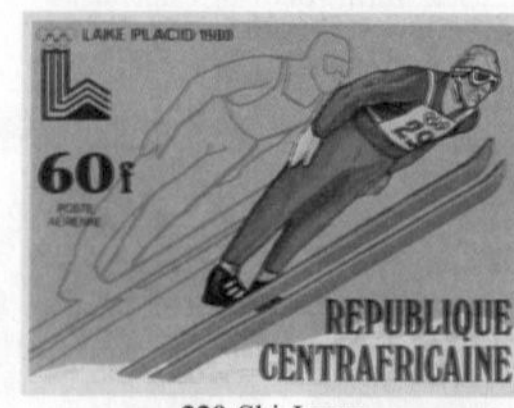

220 Ski Jump

1979. Air. Winter Olympic Games, Lake Placid (1980). Multicoloured.

No.	Type	Description	Mint	Used
655		60f. Type **220**	45	20
656		100f. Downhill skiing	75	35
657		200f. Ice hockey	1·60	80
658		300f. Skiing (slalom)	2·25	1·10

1979. "Apollo 11" Moon Landing. 10th Anniv. Nos. 433/7 optd **ALUNISSAGE APOLLO XI JUILLET 1969** and lunar module.

No.	Type	Description	Mint	Used
660	186	40f. mult (postage)	40	35
661	–	60f. multicoloured	45	40
662	–	100f. multicoloured (air)	75	50
663	–	200f. multicoloured	1·25	85
664	–	300f. multicoloured	2·25	1·10

222 Thumbellina (Andersen) **224** Basketball

223 Steam Locomotive, U.S.A. Stamp and Hill

1979. International Year of the Child (2nd issue). Multicoloured.

No.	Type	Description	Mint	Used
666		30f. Type **222**	25	15
667		40f. Sleeping Beauty (horiz)	35	20
668		60f. Hansel and Gretel	50	25
669		200f. The Match Girl (horiz)	1·25	60
670		250f. The Little Mermaid	1·90	70

1979. Death Centenary of Sir Rowland Hill (2nd issue). Multicoloured.

No.	Type	Description	Mint	Used
671		60f. Type **223**	90	20
672		100f. Locomotive "Champion" (1882, U.S.A.), French stamp and Hill	1·25	35
673		150f. Steam locomotive, German stamp and Hill	1·75	45
674		250f. Steam locomotive, British stamp and Hill	3·25	95

1979. Olympic Games, Moscow (2nd issue). Basketball.

No.	Type	Description	Mint	Used
676	224	50f. multicoloured	40	20
677	–	125f. multicoloured	90	35
678	–	200f. multicoloured	1·50	60
679	–	300f. multicoloured	2·25	85
680	–	500f. multicoloured	3·75	1·25

DESIGNS: 125f. to 500f. Views of different basketball matches.

1980. Various stamps, including one unissued, of Central African Empire optd **REPUBLIQUE CENTRAFRICAINE**.

No.	Type	Description	Mint	Used
681	192	5f. multicoloured	10	10
682	–	10f. mult (No. 522)	10	10
683	–	20f. multicoloured (Balambo (stand))	15	10
684	206	20f. black and yellow	15	10
685	–	30f. black and blue (No. 583)	25	15

226 "Viking"

1980. Space Exploration. Multicoloured.

No.	Type	Description	Mint	Used
686		40f. Type **226** (postage)	35	15
687		50f. "Apollo"–"Soyuz" link	40	20
688		60f. "Voyager"	45	20
689		100f. European Space Agency	75	25
690		150f. Early satellites (air)	1·25	30
691		200f. Space shuttle	1·60	45

1980. Air. Winter Olympic Medal Winners. Nos. 655/8 optd as listed below.

No.	Type	Description	Mint	Used
693	220	60f. multicoloured	45	20
694	–	100f. multicoloured	75	35
695	–	200f. multicoloured	1·60	80
696	–	300f. multicoloured	2·25	1·10

OVERPRINTS: 60f. **VAINQUEUR INNAVER AUTRICHE**; 100f. **VAINQUEUR MOSER-PROELL AUTRICHE**; 200f. **VAINQUEUR ETATS-UNIS**; 300f. **VAINQUEUR STENMARK SUEDE**.

228 Telephone and Sun

1980. World Telecommunications Day. Mult.

No.	Type	Description	Mint	Used
698		100f. Type **228**	90	50
699		150f. Telephone and sun (different)	1·25	65

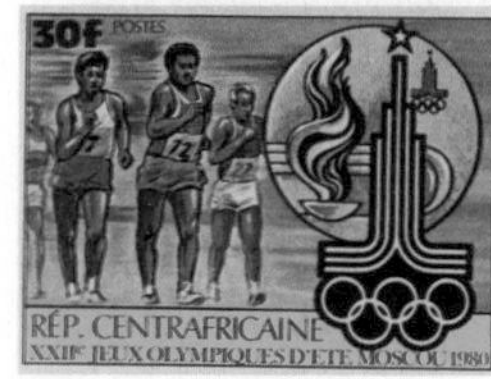

229 Walking

1980. Olympic Games, Moscow (3rd issue). Mult.

No.	Type	Description	Mint	Used
700		30f. Type **229** (postage)	35	15
701		40f. Women's relay	40	20
702		70f. Running	60	20
703		80f. Women's high jump	65	30
704		100f. Boxing (air)	75	25
705		150f. Hurdles	1·10	30

229a Fruit

1980.

No.	Type	Description	Mint	Used
706a	229a	40f. multicoloured		

230 Agriculture **232** "Foligne Madonna" (detail)

1980. European-African Co-operation. Mult.

No.	Type	Description	Mint	Used
707		30f. Type **230** (postage)	25	15
708		40f. Industry	40	15
709		70f. Communications	65	20
710		100f. Building construction and rocket	95	45
711		150f. Meteorological satellite (air)	1·25	30
712		200f. Space shuttle	1·50	45

1980. Olympic Medal Winners. Nos. 676/80 optd.

No.	Type	Description	Mint	Used
717		50f. **MEDAILLE OR YOUGOSLAVIE**	40	20
718		125f. **MEDAILLE OR URSS**	90	45

719 200f. **MEDAILLE OR URSS** 1·50 65
720 300f. **MEDAILLE ARGEN TITALIE** 2·25 1·00
721 500f. **MEDAILLE BRONZE URSS** 3·75 1·50

1980. Christmas. Multicoloured.
722 60f. Type **232** 50 20
723 150f. "Virgin and Saints" 1·25 50
724 250f. "Conestabile Madonna" 2·00 85

1980. 5th Anniv of African Posts and Telecommunications Union. As T **269** of Benin.
725 70f. multicoloured 65 40

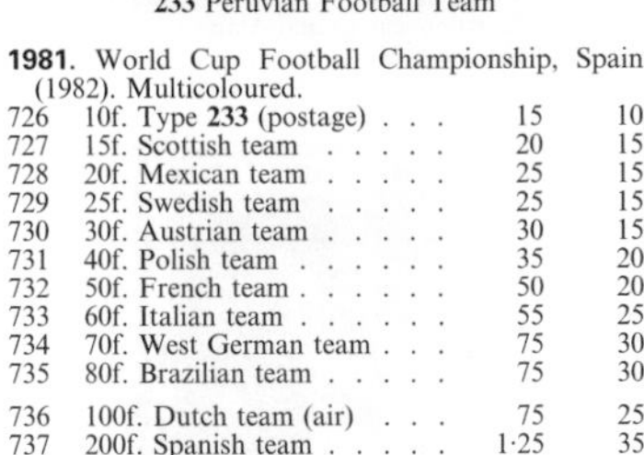

233 Peruvian Football Team

1981. World Cup Football Championship, Spain (1982). Multicoloured.
726 10f. Type **233** (postage) 15 10
727 15f. Scottish team 20 15
728 20f. Mexican team 25 15
729 25f. Swedish team 25 15
730 30f. Austrian team 30 15
731 40f. Polish team 35 20
732 50f. French team 50 20
733 60f. Italian team 55 25
734 70f. West German team 75 30
735 80f. Brazilian team 75 30
736 100f. Dutch team (air) 75 25
737 200f. Spanish team 1·25 35

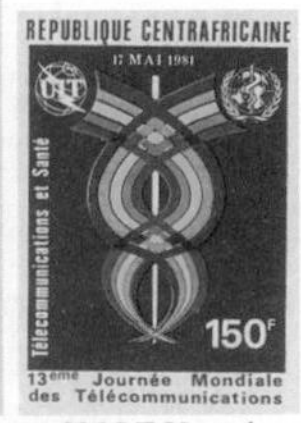

234 "Fight between Jacob and the Angel"

236 I.T.U. and W.H.O. Emblems and Ribbons forming Caduceus

1981. Air. 375th Birth Anniv of Rembrandt. Multicoloured.
739 60f. Type **234** 50 20
740 90f. "Christ in the Tempest" 75 25
741 150f. "Jeremiah mourning the Destruction of Jerusalem" 1·25 50
742 250f. "Anna accused by Tobit of Theft of a Goat" 2·25 60

1981. Olympic Games Winners. Nos. 701/5 optd with events and names of winners.
744 30f. Type **229** (postage) 25 15
745 40f. Women's relay 30 20
746 70f. Running 50 30
747 80f. Women's high jump 55 35
748 100f. Boxing (air) 45 30
749 150f. Hurdles 70 45

OPTS—30f. **50 KM. MARCHE HARTWIG GAUDER – G.D.R.**; 40f. **4 × 400 M. DAMES – U.R.S.S.**; 70f. **100 M. COURSE HOMMES ALAN WELLS – G.B.R.**; 80f. **SAUT EN HAUTEUR DAMES SARA SIMEONI – ITALIE**; 100f. **BOXE 71 KG ARMANDO MARTINEZ – CUBA**; 150f. **110 M. HAIES HOMMES THOMAS MUNKELT – G.D.R.**

1981. World Telecommunications Day.
751 **236** 150f. multicoloured 1·10 65

237 Boeing 747 carrying Space Shuttle "Enterprise"

1981. Conquest of Space. Multicoloured.
752 100f. "Apollo 15" and jeep on the Moon 75 30
753 150f. Type **237** 1·10 50
754 200f. Space Shuttle launch 1·60 55
755 300f. Space Shuttle performing experiment in space 2·50 90

238 "Family of Acrobats with a Monkey"

1981. Birth Bicentenary of Pablo Picasso. Mult.
757 40f. Type **238** (postage) 35 15
758 50f. "The Balcony" 50 20
759 80f. "The Artist's Son as Pierrot" 90 25
760 100f. "The Three Dancers" 1·10 35
761 150f. "Woman and Mirror with Self-portrait" (air) 1·75 40
762 200f. "Sleeping Woman, the Dream" 1·90 45

239 Tractor and Plough breaking Chain

1981. 1st Anniv of Zimbabwe's Independence.
764 **239** 100f. multicoloured 75 45
765 150f. multicoloured 1·10 50
766 200f. multicoloured 1·60 65

240 Prince Charles

1981. Royal Wedding (1st issue). Multicoloured.
767 75f. Type **240** 55 20
768 100f. Lady Diana Spencer 70 30
769 150f. St. Paul's Cathedral 1·10 45
770 175f. Couple and Prince's personal Standard 1·40 55

See also Nos. 772/7.

241 Lady Diana Spencer with Children

1981. Royal Wedding (2nd issue). Multicoloured.
772 40f. Type **241** (postage) 30 15
773 50f. Investiture of the Prince of Wales 35 20
774 80f. Lady Diana Spencer at Althorp House 60 25
775 100f. Prince Charles in naval uniform 75 30
776 150f. Prince of Wales's feathers (air) 1·10 35
777 200f. Highgrove House 1·40 45

242 C. V. Rietschoten

1981. Navigators. Multicoloured.
779 40f. Type **242** (postage) 35 25
780 50f. M. Pajot 45 40
781 60f. L. Jaworski 55 50
782 80f. M. Birch 75 55
783 100f. O. Kersauson (air) 80 65
784 200f. Sir Francis Chichester 1·75 1·25

243 Renault, 1906

1981. 75th Anniv of French Grand Prix Motor Race. Multicoloured.
786 20f. Type **243** 25 10
787 40f. Mercedes-Benz, 1937 45 15
788 50f. Matra-Ford, 1969 50 25
789 110f. Tazio Nuvolari 1·10 45
790 150f. Jackie Stewart 1·25 65

244 Emperor's Crown pierced by Bayonet

1981. Overthrow of the Empire. Multicoloured.
792 5f. Type **244** 10 10
793 10f. Type **244** 15 10
794 25f. Axe splitting crown, and angel holding map 20 15
795 60f. As 25f. 45 25
796 90f. Emperor Bokassa's statue being toppled and map of Republic 70 30
797 500f. As 90f. 3·75 1·60

245 F.A.O. Emblem

1981. World Food Day.
798 **245** 90f. green, brown & yell 75 25
799 110f. green, brown & bl 90 30

246 Lizard

247 Plumed Guineafowl ("Komba")

1981. Air. Reptiles. Multicoloured.
800 30f. Type **246** 50 15
801 60f. Snake 55 20
802 110f. Crocodile 1·10 30

1981. Birds. Multicoloured.
803 50f. Type **247** 90 50
804 90f. Schlegel's francolin ("Dodoro") 1·40 60
805 140f. Black-headed bunting and ortolan bunting ("Kaya") 2·40 1·10

248 Bank Building

1981. Central African States' Bank.
806 **248** 90f. multicoloured 75 25
807 110f. multicoloured 90 30

249 "Madonna and Child" (Fra Angelico)

1981. Christmas. Various paintings showing Virgin and Child by named artists. Multicoloured.
808 50f. Type **249** (postage) 35 20
809 60f. Cosme-Tura 45 25
810 90f. Bramantino 65 30
811 110f. Memling 80 45
812 140f. Correge (air) 95 30
813 200f. Gentileschi 1·60 45

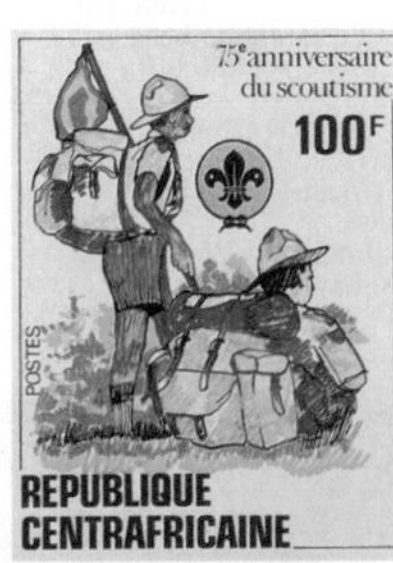

250 Scouts with Packs

1982. 75th Anniv of Boy Scout Movement. Mult.
815 100f. Type **250** 75 35
816 150f. Three scouts (horiz) 1·10 55
817 200f. Scouts admiring mountain view (horiz) 1·25 75
818 300f. Scouts taking oath 2·25 1·10

251 African Elephant

1982. Animals. Multicoloured.
820 60f. Type **251** (postage) 50 35
821 90f. Giraffe 70 40
822 100f. Addax 75 45
823 110f. Okapi 85 50
824 300f. Mandrill (air) 2·25 1·25
825 500f. Lion 3·75 2·10

252 "Grandfather Snowman"

1982. Norman Rockwell Illustrations. Mult.
827 30f. Type **252** 25 15
828 60f. "Croquet Players" 55 25
829 110f. "Women talking" 1·00 35
830 150f. "Searching" 1·25 50

253 Vickers Valentia biplane, 1928

1982. Transport. Multicoloured.
831 5f. Astra Torres AT-16 airship, 1919 (postage) 15 15
832 10f. Beyer-Garratt 1 locomotive 2·50 1·60

No.	Description	Unused	Used
833	20f. Bugatti "Royale" car, 1926	20	15
834	110f. Type **253**	80	40
835	300f. Nuclear-powered freighter "Savannah" (air)	3·50	1·75
836	500f. Space shuttle	4·25	1·25

254 George Washington

1982. Anniversaries. Multicoloured.

No.	Description	Unused	Used
838	200f. "Le Jardin de Bellevue" (E. Manet) (150th birth anniv) (horiz)	2·25	60
839	300f. Type **254** (250th birth anniv)	2·25	85
840	400f. Goethe (150th death anniv)	3·00	1·25
841	500f. Princess of Wales (21st Birthday)	3·75	1·90

255 Edward VII and Lady Diana Spencer with her Brother

1982. 21st Birthday of Princess of Wales. Mult.

No.	Description	Unused	Used
843	5f. George II and portrait of Lady Diana as child (postage)	10	10
844	10f. Type **255**	15	10
845	20f. Charles I and Lady Diana with guinea pig	20	15
846	110f. George V and Lady Diana as student in Switzerland	80	25
847	300f. Charles II and Lady Diana in skiing clothes (air)	2·25	65
848	500f. George IV and Lady Diana as nursery teacher	3·75	1·25

256 Football

1982. Olympic Games, Los Angeles. (1984). Multicoloured.

No.	Description	Unused	Used
850	5f. Type **256** (postage)	10	10
851	10f. Boxing	15	10
852	20f. Running	20	15
853	110f. Hurdling	80	25
854	300f. Diving (air)	2·25	65
855	500f. Show jumping	3·75	1·25

257 Weather Satellite

259 Pestle and Mortar, Chopping Board and Dish

1982. Space Resources. Multicoloured.

No.	Description	Unused	Used
857	5f. Space shuttle and scientist (Food resources) (postage)	10	10
858	10f. Type **257**	15	10
859	20f. Space laboratory (Industrial use)	20	15
860	110f. Astronaut on Moon (Lunar resources)	80	25
861	300f. Satellite and energy map (Planetary energy) (air)	2·25	65
862	500f. Satellite and solar panels (Solar energy)	3·75	1·25

1982. Birth of Prince William of Wales. Nos. 767/70 optd **NAISSANCE ROYALE 1982**.

No.	Description	Unused	Used
864	**240** 75f. multicoloured	50	25
865	– 100f. multicoloured	60	35
866	– 150f. multicoloured	1·10	50
867	– 175f. multicoloured	1·50	75

1982. Utensils. Multicoloured.

No.	Description	Unused	Used
869	5f. Basket of vegetables (horiz)	10	10
870	10f. As. No. 869	15	10
871	25f. Flagon made from decorated gourd	20	15
872	60f. As No. 871	40	20
873	120f. Clay jars (horiz)	1·00	35
874	175f. Decorated bowls (horiz)	1·25	50
875	300f. Type **259**	2·50	1·10

260 Footballers

1982. World Cup Football Championship Results. Unissued stamps optd as T **260**. Multicoloured.

No.	Description	Unused	Used
876	60f. **ITALIE 1er ALLEMAGNE 2e (R.F.A.)**	50	25
877	150f. **POLOGNE 3e**	1·10	50
878	300f. **FRANCE 4e**	2·50	1·10

261 Jean Tubind

262 Globe and U.P.U. Emblem

1982. Painters. Multicoloured.

No.	Description	Unused	Used
880	40f. Type **261**	35	15
881	70f. Pierre Ndarata and 10f. stamp	55	25
882	90f. As No. 881	75	30
883	140f. Type **261**	1·10	45

1982. U.P.U. Day.

No.	Description	Unused	Used
884	**262** 60f. violet, blue and red	50	25
885	120f. violet, yellow & red	1·00	45

263 Hairpins and Comb

1983. Hair Accessories.

No.	Description	Unused	Used
886	**263** 20f. multicoloured	10	10
887	30f. multicoloured	25	15
888	70f. multicoloured	50	25
889	80f. multicoloured	70	30
890	120f. multicoloured	95	35

264 Koch and Microscope

1982. Centenary of Discovery of Tubercle Bacillus by Dr. Robert Koch.

No.	Description	Unused	Used
891	**264** 100f. mauve and black	85	30
892	120f. red and black	1·00	45
893	175f. blue and black	1·60	60

265 Emblem

1982. 10th Anniv of United Nations Environment Programme.

No.	Description	Unused	Used
894	**265** 120f. blue, orange & blk	1·00	35
895	150f. blue, yellow & blk	1·10	50
896	300f. blue, green & black	2·25	1·00

266 Granary

1982.

No.	Description	Unused	Used
897	**266** 60f. multicoloured	50	25
898	80f. multicoloured	75	35
899	120f. multicoloured	1·00	50
900	200f. multicoloured	1·75	85

267 "The Beautiful Gardener"

268 Stylized Transmitter

1982. Air. Christmas. Paintings by Raphael. Multicoloured.

No.	Description	Unused	Used
901	150f. Type **267**	1·60	35
902	500f. "The Holy Family"	4·00	1·25

1983. I.T.U. Delegates' Conference, Nairobi (1982).

No.	Description	Unused	Used
903	**268** 100f. multicoloured	75	30
904	120f. multicoloured	1·00	45

269 Steinitz

1983. Chess Masters. Multicoloured.

No.	Description	Unused	Used
905	5f. Type **269** (postage)	10	10
906	10f. Aaron Niemsovich	10	10
907	20f. Aleksandr Alekhine	15	10
908	110f. Botvinnik	1·10	30
909	300f. Boris Spassky (air)	2·50	75
910	500f. Bobby Fischer	4·00	1·40

270 George Washington

271 Telephone, Satellite and Globe

1983. Celebrities. Multicoloured.

No.	Description	Unused	Used
912	20f. Type **270** (postage)	15	10
913	110f. Pres. Tito of Yugoslavia	90	25
914	500f. Princess of Wales with Prince William (air)	3·75	1·00

1983. U.N. Decade for African Transport and Communications. Multicoloured.

No.	Description	Unused	Used
916	5f. Type **271**	15	15
917	60f. Type **271**	50	20
918	120f. Radar screen and map of Africa	95	40
919	175f. As No. 918	1·25	60

272 Billy Hamilton and Bruno Pezzey

1983. World Cup Football Championship, Spain. Multicoloured.

No.	Description	Unused	Used
920	5f. Type **272** (postage)	10	10
921	10f. Sergeij Borovski and Zbigniew Boniek	10	10
922	20f. Pierre Littbarski and Jesus Maria Zamora	15	10
923	110f. Zico and Alberto Pajsarella	85	25
924	300f. Paolo Rossi and Smolarek (air)	2·25	60
925	500f. Rummenigge and Alain Giresse	3·75	95

273 "Entombment"

1983. Easter. Paintings by Rembrandt. Mult.

No.	Description	Unused	Used
927	100f. Type **273**	75	35
928	300f. "Christ on the Cross"	2·25	1·10
929	400f. "Descent from the Cross"	3·00	1·50

274 J. and L. Robert and Colin Hullin's Balloon, 1784

1983. Air. Bicentenary of Manned Flight. Mult.

No.	Description	Unused	Used
930	65f. Type **274**	60	30
931	130f. John Wise and "Atlantic", 1859	1·10	55
932	350f. "Ville d'Orleans", Paris, 1870	3·00	1·50
933	400f. Modern advertising balloon	3·50	1·60

275 Emile Levassor, Rene Panhard and Panhard-Levassor Car, 1895

276 I.M.O. Emblem

1983. Car Manufacturers. Multicoloured.

No.	Description	Unused	Used
935	10f. Type **275** (postage)	10	10
936	20f. Henry Ford and first Ford car, 1896	15	10
937	30f. Louis Renault and first Renault car, 1899	20	15
938	80f. Ettore Bugatti and Bugatti "Type 37", 1925	70	25
939	400f. Enzo Ferrari and Ferrari "815 Sport", 1940 (air)	3·25	85
940	500f. Ferdinand Porsche and Porsche "356 Coupe", 1951	3·75	1·00

1983. 25th Anniv of Int Maritime Organization.

No.	Description	Unused	Used
942	**276** 40f. blue, lt blue & turq	35	15
943	100f. multicoloured	85	35

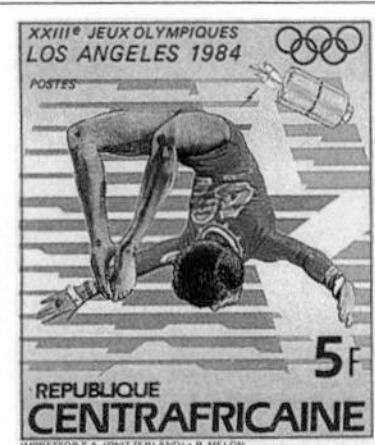

277 Gymnastics

1983. Olympic Games, Los Angeles. Mult.
944 5f. Type **277** (postage) . . . 15 15
945 40f. Javelin 25 15
946 60f. High jump 45 20
947 120f. Fencing 95 25
948 200f. Cycling (air) . . . . . 1·50 35
949 300f. Sailing . . . . 2·25 60

278 W.C.Y. Emblem and Satellite

1983. World Communications Year. Mult.
951 50f. Type **278** 40 20
952 130f. W.C.Y. emblem and satellite (different) . . . . 1·00 45

279 Horse Jumping

1983. Air. Pre-Olympic Year. Multicoloured.
953 100f. Type **279** 80 40
954 200f. Dressage 80 65
955 300f. Jumping double jump . . 2·50 75
956 400f. Trotting . . . . 3·00 1·00

280 Andre Kolingba

281 Antenna, Bangui M'Poko Earth Station

1983. 2nd Anniv of Military Committee for National Recovery.
958 **280** 65f. multicoloured 55 20
959 130f. multicoloured . . . 1·10 40

1983. Bangui M'Poko Earth Station.
960 **281** 130f. multicoloured . . . 1·10 50

282 Flower and Broken Chain on Map of Africa

1983. Namibia Day.
961 **282** 100f. green, lt grn & red 75 35
962 200f. multicoloured . . . 1·50 75

283 J. Montgolfier and Balloon

1983. Bicentenary of Manned Flight. Mult.
963 50f. Type **283** (postage) . . . 35 15
964 100f. J. Blanchard and Channel crossing, 1785 . . 75 35
965 200f. Joseph Gay-Lussac and ascent to 4000 m, 1804 . . 1·60 65
966 300f. Henri Giffard and steam-powered dirigible airship, 1852 . . . . . . 2·25 1·00
967 400f. Santos-Dumont and airship "Ballon No. 6", Paris, 1901 (air) . . . . . 3·00 1·25
968 500f. A. Laquot and captive observation balloon, 1914 3·75 1·50

284 "Global Communications"

1983. World Communications Year. U.P.U. Day.
970 **284** 205f. multicoloured . . . 1·75 90

285 Black Rhinoceros

1983. Endangered Animals. Multicoloured.
971 10f. Type **285** (postage) . . . 10 10
972 40f. Two rhinoceros 65 20
973 70f. Black rhinoceros (different) 75 20
974 180f. Black rhinoceros and young . . . . 3·50 1·25
975 400f. Rangers attending sick rhinoceros (air) . . . . . 6·50 3·25
976 500f. Wild animals and flag 7·50 3·75

286 Handicapped Person and Old Man

1983. National Day of the Handicapped and Old.
978 **286** 65f. orange and mauve . . 50 25
979 130f. orange and blue . . 1·00 50
980 250f. orange and green . . 1·50 75

287 Fish Pond

1983. Fishery Resources. Multicoloured.
981 25f. Type **287** 15 10
982 65f. Net fishing 70 25
983 100f. Traditional fishing . . . 80 35
984 130f. Butter catfish, eel and cichlids on plate . . . . . 1·60 70
985 205f. Weir basket . . . . . 1·60 70

288 "The Annunciation" (Leonardo da Vinci)

1984. Air. Christmas. Multicoloured.
986 130f. Type **288** 95 25
987 205f. "The Virgin of the Rocks" (Leonardo da Vinci) . . . . 1·60 45
988 350f. "Adoration of the Shepherds" (Rubens) . . . 2·50 80
989 500f. "A. Goubeau before the Virgin" (Rubens) . . . . . 3·75 1·00

289 Bush Fire

1984. Nature Protection. Multicoloured.
990 30f. Type **289** 75 25
991 130f. Soldiers protecting wildlife from hunters . . . 1·10 70

290 Goethe and Scene from "Faust"

1984. Celebrities. Multicoloured.
992 50f. Type **290** (postage) . . . 40 15
993 100f. Henri Dunant and battle scene 75 35
994 200f. Alfred Nobel . . . . . 1·60 55
995 300f. Lord Baden-Powell and scout camp . . . . 2·25 90
996 400f. President Kennedy and first foot-print on Moon (air) . . . . 3·00 90
997 500f. Prince and Princess of Wales . . . . 3·75 1·00

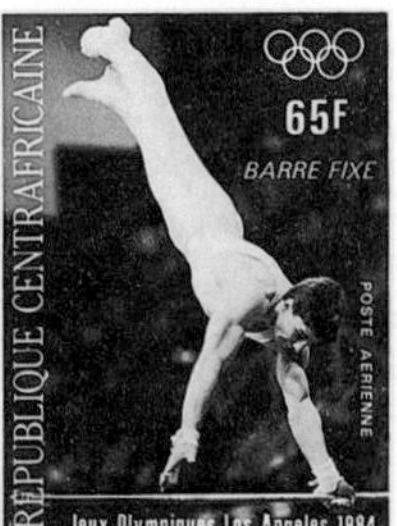

291 Fixed Bar

1984. Air. Olympic Games, Los Angeles. Gymnastics. Multicoloured.
999 65f. Type **291** 50 20
1000 100f. Parallel bars 85 25
1001 130f. Ribbon (horiz) . . . . 1·10 30
1002 205f. Cord . . . . 1·90 45
1003 350f. Hoop . . . . 3·00 85

292 "Madonna and Child" (Raphael)

1984. Paintings. Multicoloured.
1005 50f. Type **292** (postage) . . 35 15
1006 100f. "The Madonna of the Pear" (Durer) 75 20
1007 200f. "Aldobrandini Madonna" (Raphael) . . 1·60 35
1008 300f. "Madonna of the Pink" (Durer) . . . . . 2·25 70
1009 400f. "Virgin and Child" (Correggio) (air) . . . . 3·00 1·50
1010 500f. "The Bohemian" (Modigliani) . . . . . . 3·75 2·10

293 "Le Pericles" (mail ship)

1984. Transport. Multicoloured. (a) Ships.
1012 65f. Type **293** 50 25
1013 120f. "Pereire" (steamer) . . 90 50
1014 250f. "Admella" (passenger steamer) . . . . 1·75 85
1015 400f. "Royal William" (paddle-steamer) . . . . 3·00 1·50
1016 500f. "Great Britain" (steam/sail) . . . . 3·75 2·10

(b) Locomotives.
1017 110f. CC-1500 ch 85 20
1018 240f. Series 210, 1968 . . . . 1·90 40
1019 350f. 231-726, 1937 . . . . 2·75 60
1020 440f. Pacific Series S3/6, 1908 . . . . 3·50 75
1021 500f. Henschel 151 Series 45, 1937 . . . . 4·00 85

Nos. 1017/21 each include an inset portrait of George Stephenson in the design.

294 Forest

295 Weighing Baby and Emblem

1984. Forest Resources. Multicoloured.
1022 70f. Type **294** 65 25
1023 130f. Log cabin and timber 1·25 50

1984. Infant Survival Campaign. Multicoloured.
1024 10f. Type **295** 15 10
1025 30f. Vaccinating baby . . . 30 25
1026 65f. Feeding dehydrated baby 50 30
1027 100f. Mother, healthy baby and foodstuffs 95 50

296 Bangui-Kette Conical Trap

1984. Fish Traps. Multicoloured.
1028 50f. Type **296** 60 30
1029 80f. Mbres fish trap 85 50
1030 150f. Bangui-Kette round fish trap . . . . 1·60 50

297 Galileo and "Ariane" Rocket

298 "Leptoporus lignosus"

1984. Space Technology. Multicoloured.
1031 20f. Type **297** (postage) . . 15 10
1032 70f. Auguste Piccard and stratosphere balloon "F.N.R.S." 50 20
1033 150f. Hermann Oberth and satellite . . . . 1·10 45
1034 205f. Albert Einstein and "Giotto" satellite . . . . 1·50 55
1035 300f. Marie Curie and "Viking I" and "II" (air) 2·50 65
1036 500f. Dr. U. Merbold and "Navette" space laboratory . . . . 3·75 95

1984. Fungi. Multicoloured.
1038 5f. Type **298** (postage) . . . 10 10
1039 10f. "Phlebopus sudanicus" 20 10
1040 40f. "Termitomyces letestui" 45 20
1041 130f. "Lepiota esculenta" 1·25 60
1042 300f. "Termitomyces aurantiacus" (air) . . . . 3·25 1·40
1043 500f. "Termitomyces robustus" . . . . 5·75 2·25

299 Hibiscus

300 G. Boucher (speed skating)

1984. Flowers. Multicoloured.

1045	65f. Type **299**	60	35
1046	130f. Canna	1·10	50
1047	205f. Water Hyacinth	1·75	85

1984. Winter Olympic Gold Medallists. Mult.

1048	30f. Type **300** (postage)	20	15
1049	90f. W. Hoppe, R. Wetzig, D. Schauerhammer and A. Kirchner (bobsleigh)	70	25
1050	140f. P. Magoni (ladies' slalom)	1·10	35
1051	200f. J. Torvill and C. Dean (ice skating)	1·50	50
1052	400f. M. Nykanen (90 m ski jump) (air)	3·00	90
1053	400f. Russia (ice hockey)	3·75	1·00

301 Workers sowing Cotton Seeds

1984. Economic Campaign. Multicoloured.

1055	25f. Type **301**	25	20
1056	40f. Selling cotton	45	30
1057	130f. Cotton market	1·25	50

302 Woman picking corn

1984. World Food Day.

1058 **302**	205f. multicoloured	1·75	85

303 Abraham Lincoln

1984. Celebrities. Multicoloured.

1059	50f. Type **303** (postage)	45	15
1060	90f. Auguste Piccard (undersea explorer)	80	30
1061	120f. Gottlieb Daimler (automobile designer)	1·25	35
1062	200f. Louis Bleriot (pilot)	1·90	55
1063	350f. A. Karpov (chess champion) (air)	3·00	75
1064	400f. Henri Dunant (founder of Red Cross)	3·00	85

304 Profile, Water and Emblem

1984. Bangui Rotary Club and Water.

1066 **304**	130f. multicoloured	1·25	35
1067	205f. multicoloured	1·90	60

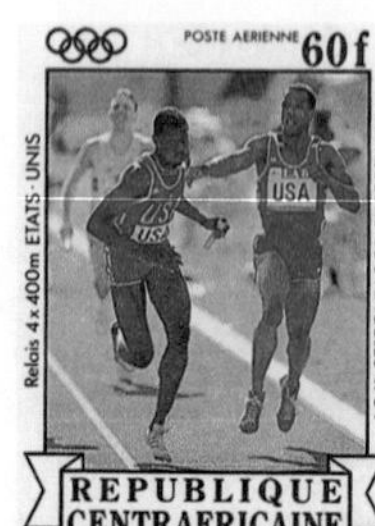

305 United States (4 × 400 m relay)

1985. Air. Olympic Games Gold Medallists. Multicoloured.

1068	60f. Type **305**	45	20
1069	140f. E. Moses (400 m hurdles)	1·10	30
1070	300f. S. Aouita (5000 m)	2·50	75
1071	440f. D. Thompson (decathlon)	3·50	1·00

306 "Virgin and Infant Jesus" (Titian)

1985. Air. Christmas (1984). Multicoloured.

1073	130f. Type **306**	95	45
1074	350f. "Virgin with Rabbit" (Titian)	2·50	1·10
1075	400f. "Virgin and Child" (Titian)	3·00	1·25

307 Eastern Screech Owls

1985. Air. Birth Bicentenary of John J. Audubon (ornithologist) (1st issue). Multicoloured.

1076	60f. Type **307**	1·25	70
1077	110f. Mangrove cuckoo (vert)	1·90	1·10
1078	200f. Mourning doves (vert)	3·25	1·75
1079	500f. Wood ducks	8·00	4·50

See also Nos. 1099/1104.

1985. International Exhibitions. Nos. 1014/15 and 1019/20 overprinted as listed below.

1083	250f. multicoloured	1·90	95
1084	350f. multicoloured	2·50	1·10
1085	400f. multicoloured	3·75	1·90
1086	440f. multicoloured	3·00	1·40

OVERPRINTS: 250f. **ARGENTINA '85 BUENOS AIRES** and emblem; 350f. **TSUKUBA EXPO '85**; 400f. **Italia '85 ROME** and emblem; 440f. **MOPHILA '85 HAMBOURG**.

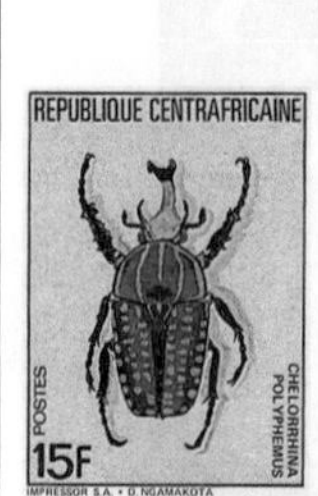

310 "Chelorrhina polyphemus"

312 Blue Jay

311 Olympic Games Poster and Stockholm

1985. Beetles. Multicoloured.

1088	15f. Type **310**	20	15
1089	20f. "Fornasinius russus"	25	15
1090	25f. "Goliathus giganteus"	30	15
1091	65f. "Goliathus meleagris"	80	50

1985. "Olymphilex '85" Olympic Stamps Exhibition, Lausanne. Multicoloured.

1092	5f. Type **311** (postage)	15	10
1093	10f. Olympic Games poster and Paris	20	15
1094	20f. Olympic Games poster and London	20	15
1095	100f. Olympic Games poster and Tokyo	7·50	1·75
1096	400f. Olympic Games poster and Mexico (air)	3·25	85
1097	500f. Olympic Games poster and Munich	3·75	1·00

1985. Birth Bicentenary of John J. Audubon (ornithologist) (2nd issue). Multicoloured.

1099	40f. Type **312** (postage)	45	25
1100	80f. Chuck Will's widow	85	55
1101	130f. Ivory-billed woodpecker	1·10	80
1102	250f. Collie's magpie-jay	2·50	1·75
1103	300f. Mangrove cuckoo (horiz) (air)	2·75	1·90
1104	500f. Barn swallow (horiz)	5·50	3·75

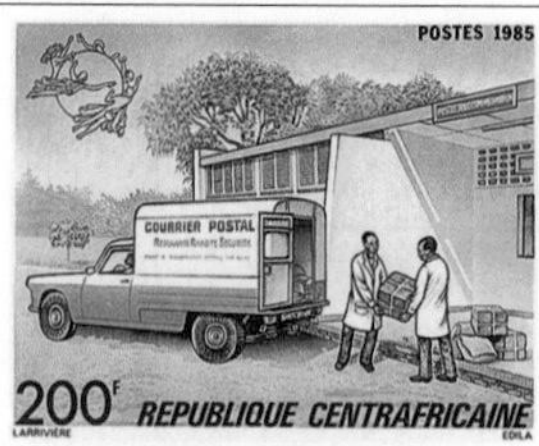

313 Delivering Post by Van

1985. "Philexafrique" Stamp Exhibition, Lome, Togo (1st issue). Multicoloured.

1106	200f. Type **313**	1·90	1·00
1107	200f. Scouts and flag	1·90	1·00

See also Nos. 1154/5.

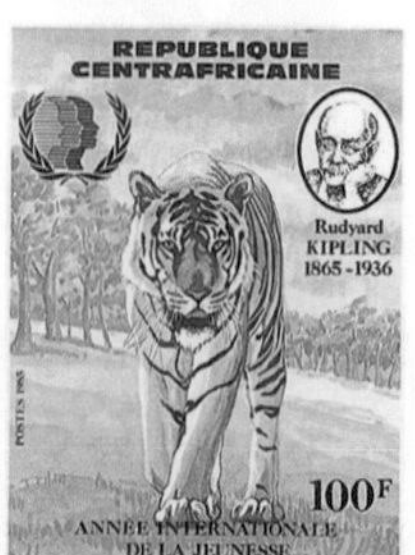

314 Tiger and Rudyard Kipling

1985. Int Youth Year (1st issue). Multicoloured.

1108	100f. Type **314**	1·00	30
1109	200f. Men on horseback and Joseph Kessel	1·90	55
1110	300f. Submarine gripped by octopus and Jules Verne	2·25	1·10
1111	400f. Mississippi stern-wheeler, Huckleberry Finn and Mark Twain	3·00	1·75

See also Nos. 1163/68.

315 Louis Pasteur

1985. Anniversaries. Multicoloured.

1112	150f. Type **315** (centenary of discovery of anti-rabies vaccine) (postage)	1·75	40
1113	200f. Henri Dunant (founder of Red Cross) and 125th anniv of Battle of Solferino (horiz)	1·90	50
1114	300f. Girl guides (75th anniv of Girl Guide Movement) (air)	1·90	75
1115	450f. Queen Elizabeth the Queen Mother (85th birthday)	3·25	1·25
1116	500f. Statue of Liberty (cent)	3·75	1·50

316 Pele and Footballers

1985. World Cup Football Championship, Mexico. Multicoloured.

1117	5f. Type **316** (postage)	10	10
1118	10f. Harald "Tony" Schumacher	15	10
1119	20f. Paolo Rossi	15	15
1120	350f. Kevin Keegan (wrongly inscr "Kervin")	2·75	90
1121	400f. Michel Platini (air)	3·00	90
1122	500f. Karl Heinz Rummenigge	3·75	1·00

317 La Kotto Waterfalls

318 Pope with Hand raised in Blessing

1985.

1124 **317**	65f. multicoloured	60	25
1125	90f. multicoloured	75	30
1126	130f. multicoloured	1·10	50

1985. Papal Visit. Multicoloured.

1127	65f. Type **318**	55	25
1128	130f. Pope John Paul II in Communion robes	1·10	50

319 Soldier using Ox-drawn Plough

1985. Economic Campaign. Multicoloured.

1129	5f. Type **319**	15	10
1130	60f. Soldier sowing cotton	35	20
1131	130f. Soldier sowing cotton (different)	1·00	35

320 As Young Girl with her Brother

1985. 85th Birthday of Queen Elizabeth the Queen Mother. Multicoloured.

1132	100f. Type **320** (postage)	60	20
1133	200f. Queen Mary with Duke and Duchess of York	1·50	35
1134	300f. Duchess of York inspecting Irish Guards	2·25	70
1135	350f. Duke and Duchess of York with the young Princesses	2·50	80
1136	400f. In the Golden State Coach at Coronation of King George VI (air)	3·00	90
1137	500f. At the service for her Silver Wedding	3·75	1·00

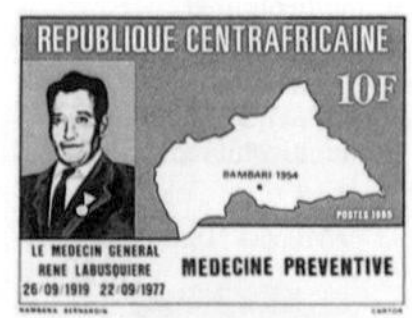

321 Dr. Labusquiere and Map of Republic

1985. 8th Death Anniv of General Doctor Labusquiere. Multicoloured.

1139 **321**	10f. multicoloured	15	10
1140	45f. multicoloured	35	20
1141	110f. multicoloured	1·00	35

322 Mail Van delivering Parcels to Local Post Office

1985. Postal Service. Multicoloured.

1142	15f. Type **322**	15	10
1143	60f. Van collecting mail from local post office	45	20
1144	150f. Vans at main post office	1·10	50

323 Gagarin, Korolev and Space Station Complex

1985. Space Research. Multicoloured.
1145 40f. Type **323** (postage) . . 20 10
1146 110f. Copernicus and "Cassini" space probe . . 75 25
1147 240f. Galileo and "Viking" orbiter . . . . 1·75 50
1148 300f. T. von Karman and astronaut recovering satellite . . . . 2·25 70
1149 450f. Percival Lowell and "Viking" space probe (air) 3·50 90
1150 500f. Dr. U. Merbold and "Columbus" space station 3·75 1·00

324 Damara Solar Energy Plant

1985.
1152 **324** 65f. multicoloured . . . 55 25
1153 130f. multicoloured . . . 1·10 50

325 Ouaka Sugar Refinery

1985. "Philexafrique" Stamp Exhibition, Lome, Togo (2nd issue). Multicoloured.
1154 250f. Nature studies . . . . 3·25 1·60
1155 250f. Type **325** . . . . . . 2·10 1·40

326 Pres. Mitterrand, Gen. Kolingba and Flags

1985. Visit of President Mitterrand of France.
1156 **326** 65f. multicoloured . . . 50 20
1157 130f. multicoloured . . . 1·00 45
1158 160f. multicoloured . . . 1·40 60

327 Map and U.N. Emblem **328** "Virgin and Angels" (Master of Burgo de Osma)

1985. 40th Anniv of U.N.O. and 25th Anniv of Central African Republic Membership.
1159 **327** 140f. multicoloured . . . 1·10 50

1985. Air. Christmas. Multicoloured.
1160 100f. Type **328** 80 25
1161 200f. "Nativity" (Louis Le Nain) . . . . 1·75 1·00
1162 400f. "Virgin and Child with Dove" (Piero di Cosimo) 3·25 1·00

329 Leonardo da Vinci and "Madonna of the Eyelet"

1985. Int Youth Year (2nd issue). Multicoloured.
1163 40f. Type **329** (postage) . . 30 15
1164 80f. Johann Sebastian Bach 75 20
1165 100f. Diego Velasquez and "St. John of Patmos" . . 1·00 20
1166 250f. Franz Schubert and illustration of "King of Aulnes" . . . . 2·00 50
1167 400f. Francisco Goya and "Vicente Osario de Moscoso" (air) . . . . . 3·50 90
1168 500f. Wolfang Amadeus Mozart . . . . 4·00 1·00

330 Halley and "Comet"

1985. Appearance of Halley's Comet (1st issue). Multicoloured.
1170 100f. Type **330** (postage) . . 60 20
1171 200f. Newton's telescope . . 1·50 35
1172 300f. Halley and Newton observing comet . . . . 2·25 45
1173 350f. American space probe and comet . . . . 2·50 80
1174 400f. Sun, Russian space probe and diagram of comet trajectory (air) . . 3·00 90
1175 500f. Infra-red picture of comet . . . . 3·75 1·00
See also Nos. 1184/8.

331 Columbus with Globe

1986. 480th Death Anniv of Christopher Columbus (explorer). Multicoloured.
1177 90f. Type **331** (postage) . . 70 20
1178 110f. Receiving blessing . . 85 25
1179 240f. Crew going ashore in rowing boat . . . . . . 2·00 1·25
1180 300f. Columbus with American Indians . . . . 2·50 60
1181 400f. Ships at sea in storm (air) . . . . 3·50 2·00
1182 500f. Sun breaking through clouds over fleet . . . . 4·00 2·25

332 Halley and Comet

1986. Air. Appearance of Halley's Comet (2nd issue). Multicoloured.
1184 110f. Type **332** 80 25
1185 130f. "Giotto" space probe 1·00 25
1186 200f. Comet and globe . . . 1·50 45
1187 300f. "Vega" space probe 2·25 60
1188 400f. Space shuttle . . . . 3·25 95

1986. Nos. 874/5 surch.
1188a – 30f. on 175f. mult . . .
1188b **259** 65f. on 300f. mult . . .

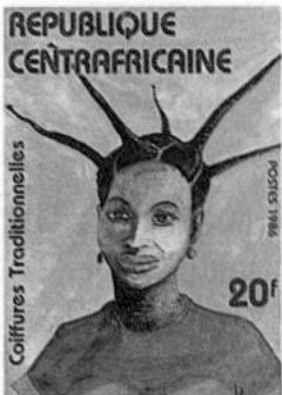

333 Spiky Hair Style **334** Communications

1986. Traditional Hair Styles. Multicoloured.
1189 20f. Type **333** 20 10
1190 30f. Braids around head . . 25 15
1191 65f. Plaits 30 25
1192 160f. Braids from front to back of head . . . . . . 1·50 50

1986. Franco-Central African Week. Mult.
1193 40f. Type **334** 30 15
1194 60f. Youth 50 20
1195 100f. Basket weaver (craft) 75 30
1196 130f. Cyclists (sport) . . . . 1·25 50

335 "Allamanda neriifolia"

1986. Flora and Fauna. Multicoloured.
1197 25f. Type **335** (postage) . . 20 15
1198 65f. Bongo (horiz) 50 20
1199 160f. "Plumieria acuminata" 1·10 40
1200 300f. Cheetah (horiz) . . . 2·25 1·00
1201 400f. "Eulophia erthoplata" (air) . . . . 2·75 90
1202 500f. Leopard (horiz) . . . 3·75 1·75

336 Palm Tree and Bossongo Oil Refinery

1986. Centrapalm. Multicoloured.
1204 25f. Type **336** 20 15
1205 65f. Type **336** 50 30
1206 120f. Palm tree and Bossongo agro-industrial complex 85 60
1207 160f. As No. 1206 . . . . . 1·25 50

337 Pointer

1986. Dogs and Cats. Multicoloured.
1208 10f. Type **337** (postage) . . 15 10
1209 20f. Egyptian mau 25 15
1210 200f. Newfoundland . . . . 1·75 50
1211 300f. Borzoi (air) . . . . . 2·50 60
1212 400f. Persian red . . . . . 3·50 80

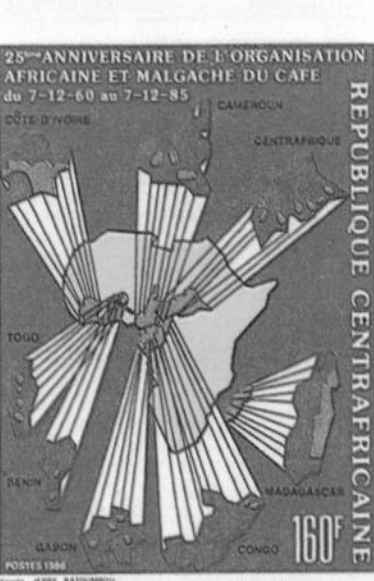

338 Map of Africa showing Member Countries

1986. 25th Anniv of African and Malagasy Coffee Producers Organization.
1214 **338** 160f. multicoloured . . . 1·40 60

339 Trophy, Brazilian flag, L.-A. Muller and Socrates

1986. World Cup Football Championship, Mexico. Multicoloured.
1215 30f. Type **339** (postage) . . 20 15
1216 110f. Trophy, Belgian flag, V. Scifo and F. Ceulemans 70 20
1217 160f. Trophy, French flag, Y. Stopyra and M. Platini 1·00 25
1218 350f. Trophy, West German flag, A. Brehme and H. Schumacher . . . . . 2·50 70
1219 450f. Trophy, Argentinian flag and Diego Maradona (air) . . . . 3·00 1·00

340 Judith Resnik and Astronaut **341** People around Globe within Emblem

1986. Anniversaries and "Challenger" Astronauts Commemoration. Multicoloured.
1221 15f. Type **340** (postage) . . 15 10
1222 25f. Frederic Bartholdi and torch (centenary of Statue of Liberty) 25 15
1223 70f. Elvis Presley (9th death anniv) 95 20
1224 300f. Ronald MacNair and man watching astronaut on screen . . . . 2·10 65
1225 485f. on 70f. No. 1223 . . . 5·25 1·00
1226 450f. Christa McAulife and Shuttle lifting off (air) . . 3·25 1·10

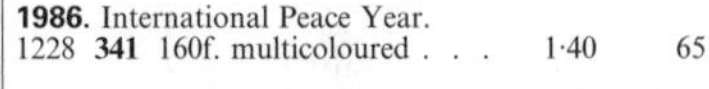
1986. International Peace Year.
1228 **341** 160f. multicoloured . . . 1·40 65

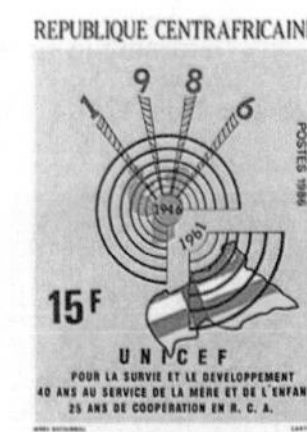

342 Globe, Douglas DC-10 and "25" **343** Emblem and Flag as Map

1986. 25th Anniv of Air Afrique.
1229 **342** 200f. multicoloured . . . 1·50 85

1986. U.N.I.C.E.F. Child Survival Campaign. Multicoloured.
1230 15f. Type **343** 15 10
1231 130f. Doctor vaccinating child . . . . 1·10 50
1232 160f. Basket of fruit and boy holding fish on map 2·25 1·00

344 "Nativity" (detail, Giotto)

1986. Air. Christmas. Multicoloured.
1233 250f. Type **344** . . . . . . 1·90 60
1234 440f. "Adoration of the Magi" (detail, Sandro Botticelli) (vert) . . . . . 3·25 1·10
1235 500f. "Nativity" (detail, Giotto) (different) . . . . 4·00 1·10

345 Transmission Mast, People with Radios and Baskets of Produce

1986. African Telecommunications Day. Telecommunications and Agriculture. Mult.
1236 170f. Type **345** (Rural Radio Agriculture Project) . . . 1·40 75
1237 265f. Lorry, satellite, men using telephones and sacks of produce . . . . 2·10 1·10

346 Steam Locomotive Class "DH 2 Green Elephant" and Alfred de Glehn

1986. 150th Anniv of German Railways. Mult.
1238 40f. Type **346** (postage) . . 50 10
1239 70f. Rudolf Diesel (engineer) and steam locomotive No. 1829 Rheingold . . . 80 15
1240 160f. Electric locomotive Type 103 Rapide and Carl Golsdorf . . . . . 2·00 40
1241 300f. Wilhelm Schmidt and Beyer-Garratt type steam locomotive . . . . 3·50 95
1242 400f. De Bousquet and compound locomotive Class 3500 (air) . . . . . 4·75 1·10

347 Player returning Ball

1986. Air. Olympic Games, Seoul (1988) (1st issue). Tennis. Multicoloured.
1244 150f. Type **347** . . . . . . 1·25 45
1245 250f. Player serving (vert) 2·25 60
1246 440f. Right-handed player returning to left-handed player (vert) . . . . . . 3·00 1·10
1247 600f. Left-handed player returning to right-handed player . . . . 4·50 1·25
See also Nos. 1261/4, 1310/13 and 1315/18.

348 "Miranda" Satellite, Uranus, "Mariner II" and William Herschel (astronomer)
349 Footballer and "Woman with Umbrella" Fountain

1987. Space Research. Multicoloured.
1248 25f. Type **348** (postage) . . 20 15
1249 65f. Mars Rover vehicle and Werner von Braun (rocket pioneer) 45 20
1250 160f. "Mariner II", Titan and Rudolf Hanel . . . . 1·25 35
1251 300f. Space ship "Hermes", space platform "Eureka" and Patrick Baudry . . . 2·25 70
1252 400f. Halley's Comet, "Giotto" space probe and Dr. U. Keller (air) . . . . 2·75 85
1253 500f. European space station "Columbus", Wubbo Ockels and Ulf Merbold 3·25 1·00

1987. Olympic Games, Barcelona (1992). Mult.
1255 30f. Type **349** (postage) . . 25 15
1256 150f. Judo competitors and Barcelona Cathedral . . . 1·00 40
1257 265f. Cyclist and Church of the Holy Family . . . . 1·90 65
1258 350f. Diver and Christopher Columbus's tomb (air) . . 2·50 85
1259 495f. Runner and human tower . . . . 3·75 1·10

350 Triple Jumping

1987. Air. Olympic Games, Seoul (1988) (2nd issue). Multicoloured.
1261 100f. Type **350** 75 25
1262 200f. High jumping (horiz) 1·50 50
1263 300f. Long jumping (horiz) 2·25 75
1264 400f. Pole vaulting . . . . 3·00 1·00

351 Two-man Luge
352 Peace Medal

1987. Winter Olympic Games, Calgary (1988) (1st issue). Multicoloured.
1266 20f. Type **351** (postage) . . 20 15
1267 140f. Cross-country skiing 1·10 40
1268 250f. Figure skating . . . . 1·90 65
1269 300f. Ice hockey (air) . . . 2·25 75
1270 400f. Slalom . . . . 2·75 1·00
See also Nos. 1320/3.

1987. International Peace Year (1986).
1272 **352** 50f. brown, blue & blk 35 25
1273 160f. brown, grn & blk 1·25 65

1987. 10th Death Anniv of Elvis Presley (singer). Nos. 1223 and 1225 optd **Elvis Presley 1977–1987**.
1274 70f. multicoloured 75 50
1275 485f. on 70f. multicoloured 5·00 1·75

354 Woman at Village Pump

1987. International Decade of Drinkable Water. Multicoloured.
1276 5f. Type **354** . . . .
1277 10f. Woman at village pump (different) . . . .
1278 200f. Three women at village pump . . . . . .

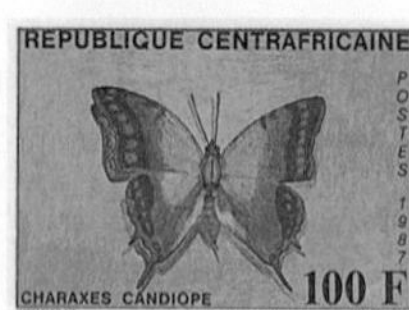

355 "Charaxes candiope"

1987. Butterflies. Multicoloured.
1279 100f. Type **355** 75 55
1280 120f. "Graphium leonidas" 95 60
1281 130f. "Charaxes brutus" . . 1·10 60
1282 160f. "Salamis aetiops" . . 1·25 70

356 Nola Football Team

1987. Campaign for Integration of Pygmies.
1283 **356** 90f. multicoloured . . . 1·10 75
1284 160f. multicoloured . . . 1·75 1·10

357 James Madison (U.S. President, 1809–17)

1987. Anniversaries and Celebrities. Mult.
1285 40f. Type **357** (bicent of U.S. constitution) (postage) 30 15
1286 160f. Queen Elizabeth II and Prince Philip (40th wedding anniv) . . . . . 1·25 25
1287 200f. Steffi Graf (tennis player) . . . . 1·60 45
1288 300f. Gary Kasparov (chess champion) and "The Chess Players" (after Honore Daumier) (air) . . 2·50 75
1289 400f. Boris Becker (tennis player) . . . . 3·00 1·00

358 Brontosaurus

1988. Prehistoric Animals. Multicoloured.
1291 50f. Type **358** 35 15
1292 65f. Triceratops 50 15
1293 100f. Ankylosaurus 75 25
1294 160f. Stegosaurus . . . . . 1·25 45
1295 200f. Tyrannosaurus rex (vert) . . . . 1·50 50
1296 240f. Corythosaurus (vert) 1·90 65
1297 300f. Allosaurus (vert) . . . 2·25 75
1298 350f. Brachiosaurus (vert) 2·75 95

359 Pres. Kolingba vaccinating Baby
360 Carmine Bee Eater

1988. 40th Anniv of W.H.O.
1299 **359** 70f. multicoloured . . . 60 40
1300 120f. multicoloured . . . 1·60 45

1988. Scouts and Birds. Multicoloured.
1301 25f. Type **360** (postage) . . 15 10
1302 170f. Red-crowned bishop 1·10 80
1303 300f. Lesser pied kingfisher 3·25 2·25
1304 400f. Red-cheeked cordon-bleu (air) . . . . 2·75 2·40
1305 450f. Lizard buzzard . . . . 3·50 2·75

361 Schools replanting Campaign

1988. National Tree Day. Multicoloured.
1307 50f. Type **361** 35 25
1308 100f. Type **361** 75 50
1309 130f. Felling tree and planting saplings . . . . 1·10 60

362 1972 100f. Stamp and Beam Exercise

1988. Air. Olympic Games, Seoul (3rd issue). Gymnastics. Multicoloured.
1310 90f. Type **362** 75 25
1311 200f. 1964 50f. stamp and beam exercise (horiz) . . 1·50 35
1312 300f. 1964 100f. stamp and vault exercise (horiz) . . . 2·25 75
1313 400f. 1964 250f. stamp and parallel bars exercise (horiz) . . . . 3·00 1·10

363 Running
364 Cross-country Skiing

1988. Olympic Games, Seoul (4th issue). Mult.
1315 150f. Type **363** (postage) . . 1·10 25
1316 300f. Judo . . . . 2·25 60
1317 400f. Football (air) . . . . 2·75 85
1318 450f. Tennis . . . . 3·00 1·00

1988. Winter Olympic Games, Calgary (2nd issue). Multicoloured.
1320 170f. Type **364** (postage) . . 1·25 30
1321 350f. Ice hockey . . . . . 2·25 60
1322 400f. Downhill skiing (air) 2·75 85
1323 450f. Slalom . . . . 3·00 1·00

1988. Nos. 1302/5 surch.
1325 30f. on 170f. mult (postage) 40 20
1326 70f. on 300f. mult . . . . . 1·50 85
1327 160f. on 400f. mult (air) . . 2·50 1·40
1328 200f. on 450f. mult . . . . 3·00 1·90

366 Hospital and Grounds

1988. 1st Anniv of L'Amitie Hospital. Mult.
1329 5f. Type **366** 15 10
1330 60f. Aerial view of hospital complex 50 35
1331 160f. Hospital entrance . . 1·25 75

367 Buildings Complex

1988. 30th Anniv of Republic. Multicoloured.
1332 65f. Family on map, flags and dove . . . .
1334 240f. Type **367** . . . . . .

368 Kristine Otto (East Germany)
369 Hebmuller and Volkswagen Cabriolet, 1953

1989. Olympic Games, Seoul, Gold Medal Winners. Multicoloured.

1335 150f. Type **368** (100 m butterfly and 100 m backstroke) (postage) . . . . 1·00 35
1336 240f. Matt Biondi (100 m freestyle) . . . . 1·50 50
1337 300f. Florence Griffith-Joyner (U.S.A.) (100 and 200 m sprints) . . . . . 1·90 75
1338 450f. Pierre Durand (France) (show jumping) (air) . . . . 3·00 1·10

1989. Transport. Multicoloured.

1340 20f. Type **369** (postage) . . 20 15
1341 205f. Werner von Siemens and his first electric locomotive, 1879 . . . . 2·25 75
1342 300f. Dennis Conner and "Stars and Stripes" (winner of Americas Cup yacht races) . . . . . . 2·25 65
1343 400f. Andre Citroen and "16 Six" car, 1955 . . . . . 3·00 1·00
1344 450f. Mare Seguin and Decauville Mallet locomotive, 1895 (air) . . 3·75 75

370 Allegory in Honour of Liberty

1989. Bicentenary of French Revolution and "Philexfrance 89" International Stamp Exhibition, Paris (1st issue). Multicoloured.

1346 200f. Type **370** . . . . . . 1·75 60
1347 300f. Declaration of Rights of Man . . . . 2·50 1·25

See also Nos. 1366/9.

371 Statue of Liberty at Night

1989. Centenary of Statue of Liberty. Mult.

1349 150f. Type **371** . . . . . . 1·10 60
1350 150f. Maintenance worker 1·10 60
1351 150f. Close-up of face . . . 1·10 60
1352 200f. Maintenance worker (different) . . . . 1·40 95
1353 200f. Colour party in front of statue . . . . 1·40 95
1354 200f. Close-up of head at night . . . . 1·40 95

373 "Apollo 11" Astronaut on Moon

1989. Air. 20th Anniv of First Manned Landing on Moon. Multicoloured.

1355 40f. Type **373** 30 20
1356 80f. "Apollo 15" astronaut and moon buggy 55 25
1357 130f. "Apollo 16" module landing in sea . . . . . 1·00 50
1358 1000f. "Apollo 17" astronaut on Moon . . . 7·50 2·25

374 Champagnat, Map and "Madonna and Child"

1989. Birth Bicentenary of Marcelino Champagnat (founder of Marist Brothers). Multicoloured.

1359 15f. Type **374** 15 15
1360 50f. Champagnat, cross, globe and emblem 35 25
1361 160f. Champagnat and flags (horiz) . . . . 1·40 1·00

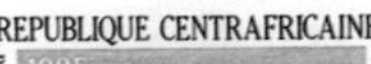

375 Food Products

1989. Bambari Harvest Festival. Multicoloured.

1362 100f. Type **375** . . . . . . 1·25 65
1363 160f. Ploughing with oxen 1·25 60

376 Raising of Livestock

1989. World Food Day. Multicoloured.

1364 60f. Type **376** 50 35
1365 240f. Soldiers catching poachers . . . . 2·00 1·10

377 Gen. Kellermann and Battle of Valmy

1989. Bicentenary of French Revolution and "Philexfrance 89" International Stamp Exhibition, Paris (2nd issue). Multicoloured.

1366 160f. Type **377** (postage) . . 1·25 35
1367 200f. Gen. Dumouriez and Battle of Jemappes (wrongly inscr "JEMMAPES") . . . . 1·60 50
1368 500f. Gen. Pichegru and capture of Dutch fleet (air) . . . . 4·50 1·25
1369 600f. Gen. Hoche and Royalist landing at Quiberon . . . . 4·25 1·00

378 Players and Trophy

1989. Victory in 1987 African Basketball Championships, Tunis (1st issue). Multicoloured.

1371 160f. Type **378** . . . . . . 1·25 60
1372 240f. National team with medals and trophy (horiz) 1·60 80
1373 500f. Type **378** . . . . . . 4·00 1·75

See also Nos. 1383/4.

379 Governor's Palace, 1906

1989. Centenary of Bangui. Multicoloured.

1374 100f. Type **379** 75 35
1375 160f. Bangui post office . . 1·10 90
1376 200f. A. Dosilie (founder of Bangui post office) (vert) 1·50 85
1377 1000f. Michel Dolisie and Chief Gbembo agreeing peace pact (vert) . . . . 7·25 3·75

380 Footballer and Palermo Cathedral Belltower

381 Trophy and Map of Africa

1989. World Cup Football Championship, Italy (1990) (1st issue). Multicoloured.

1378 20f. Type **380** (postage) . . 20 15
1379 160f. Footballer and St. Francis's church, Bologna . . . . 1·10 35
1380 200f. Footballer and Old Palace, Florence . . . . 1·50 50
1381 120f. Footballer and Church of Trinita dei Monti, Rome (air) 90 35

See also Nos. 1405/8.

1990. Victory in 1987 African Basketball Championships, Tunis (2nd issue).

1383 **381** 100f. multicoloured . . . 80 35
1384 130f. multicoloured . . . 1·10 60

382 Tree with Map as Foliage

383 Speed Skating

1990. Inauguration (1989) of Forest Conservation Organization.

1385 **382** 160f. multicoloured . . . 1·40 65

1990. Winter Olympic Games, Albertville (1992). Multicoloured.

1386 10f. Type **383** (postage) . . 15 15
1387 60f. Cross-country skiing . . 45 25
1388 500f. Slalom skiing (air) . . 3·75 95
1389 750f. Ice dancing . . . . . 5·50 1·25

384 "Euphaera eusemoides"

1990. Scouts and Butterflies. Multicoloured.

1391 25f. Type **384** 20 15
1392 65f. Becker's glider 45 15
1393 160f. "Pseudacraea clarki" 1·10 25
1394 250f. Giant charaxes . . . . 1·75 50
1395 300f. "Euphaedra gausape" 2·25 60
1396 500f. Red swallowtail . . . 3·75 85

385 Throwing the Javelin

1990. Olympic Games, Barcelona (1992). Mult.

1398 10f. Type **385** (postage) . . 15 15
1399 40f. Running 35 15
1400 130f. Tennis 95 25
1401 240f. Hurdling (horiz) . . . 1·75 50
1402 400f. Yachting (horiz) (air) 3·00 85
1403 500f. Football (horiz) . . . 3·75 1·00

386 Footballers and Globe

1990. Air. World Cup Football Championship, Italy (2nd issue).

1405 **386** 5f. multicoloured 10 10
1406 – 30f. multicoloured . . . 20 15
1407 – 500f. multicoloured . . . 3·25 1·00
1408 – 1000f. multicoloured . . 7·50 1·60

DESIGNS: 30 to 1000f. Various footballing scenes.

387 Pres. Gorbachev of U.S.S.R., Map of Malta and Pres. Bush of U.S.A.

1990. Anniversaries and Events. Multicoloured.

1409 120f. Type **387** (summit conference, Malta) (postage) 85 20
1410 130f. Sir Rowland Hill and Penny Black (150th anniv of first postage stamps) 85 20
1411 160f. Galileo space probe and planet Jupiter . . . . 1·10 25
1412 200f. Pres. Gorbachev meeting Pope John Paul II, statue of Saturn and dove . . . . 1·50 35
1413 240f. Neil Armstrong and eagle (21st anniv of first manned landing on Moon) . . . . 1·90 45
1414 250f. Concorde, German experimental Maglev train and Rotary International emblem . . . . 3·75 50
1415 300f. Don Mattingly (baseball player) and New York Yankees club badge (air) . . . . 2·25 60
1416 500f. Charles de Gaulle (French statesman, birth centenary) . . . . 3·75 85

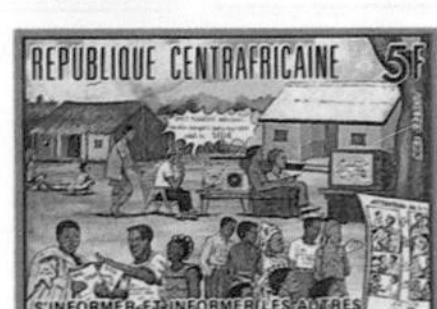

388 AIDS Information on Radio, Television and Leaflets

1991. Anti-AIDS Campaign. Multicoloured.

1418 5f. Type **388** 15 10
1419 70f. Type **388** 55 35
1420 120f. Lecture on AIDS (vert) 85 50

389 Demonstrators

1991. Protection of Animals. Multicoloured.
1421 15f. Type **389** 15 10
1422 60f. Type **389** 50 25
1423 100f. Decrease in elephant population, 1945–2045 (vert) 75 35

390 Butter Catfish

1991. Fishes. Multicoloured.
1424 50f. Type **390** 50 35
1425 160f. Type **390** . . . . . . 2·10 1·00
1426 240f. Distichodus . . . . . 3·50 1·90

391 President Kolingba

1992. 10th Anniv (1991) of Assumption of Power by Military Committee under Andre Kolingba.
1427 **391** 160f. multicoloured . . . 1·25 50

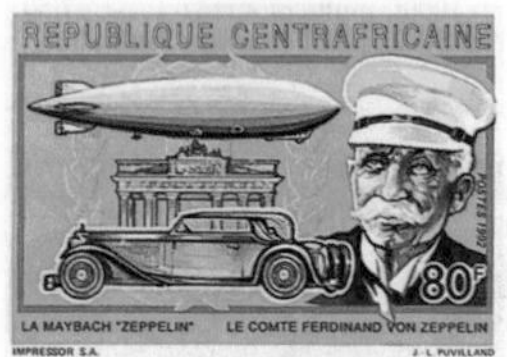

392 Count Ferdinand von Zeppelin (airship pioneer)

1992. Celebrities, Anniversaries and Events. Multicoloured.
1428 80f. Type **392** (75th death anniv) (postage) 40 10
1429 140f. Henri Dunant (founder of Red Cross) 95 15
1430 160f. Michael Schumacher (racing driver) . . . . . 1·10 25
1431 350f. Brandenburg Gate (bicent) and Konrad Adenauer (German Federal Republic Chancellor) signing 1949 constitution . . . . . . 2·50 75
1432 500f. Pope John Paul II (tour of West Africa) (air) 3·50 90
1433 600f. Wolfgang Amadeus Mozart (composer, death bicent (1991)) . . . . . . 4·50 1·00

393 Dam **395** Breastfeeding

394 Compass Rose and Organization Emblem

1993. River M'Bali Dam. Multicoloured.
1435 160f. Type **393** 80 15
1436 200f. People fishing near dam (self-sufficiency in food) . . . . 1·00 25

1993. International Customs Day and 40th Anniv of Customs Co-operation Council.
1437 **394** 240f. multicoloured . . . 1·10 25

1993. International Nutrition Conference, Rome (1992). Multicoloured.
1438 90f. Type **395** 40 10
1439 140f. Foodstuffs 70 15

396 Bangui University

1993.
1440 **396** 100f. multicoloured . . . 50 15

397 Masako Owada as Baby

1993. Wedding of Crown Prince Naruhito of Japan and Masako Owada. Multicoloured.
1441 50f. Type **397** (postage) . . 10 10
1442 65f. Prince Naruhito as child with parents 25 10
1443 160f. Masako Owada at Harvard University, U.S.A. 70 15
1444 450f. Prince Naruhito at Oxford University (air) . . 1·75 50

398 Presley singing "Heartbreak Hotel" (1956)

1993. 16th Death Anniv of Elvis Presley (entertainer). Multicoloured.
1446 200f. Type **398** . . . . . . 1·00 15
1447 300f. "Love Me Tender", 1957 . . . . 1·50 25
1448 400f. "Jailhouse Rock", 1957 . . . . 1·75 30
1449 600f. "Harum Scarum", 1965 (air) . . . . 2·50 50

399 First World Cup Final, 1928, and Uruguay v. Argentina, 1930

1993. World Cup Football Championship, U.S.A. (1994). History of the World Cup. Multicoloured.
1451 40f. Type **399** 10 10
1452 50f. Italy v. Czechoslovakia, 1934, and Italy v. Hungary, 1938 . . . . . 10 10
1453 60f. Uruguay v. Brazil, 1950, and Germany v. Hungary, 1954 . . . . . 15 10
1454 80f. Brazil v. Sweden, 1958, and Brazil v. Czechoslovakia, 1962 . . 20 10
1455 160f. England v. West Germany, 1966, and Brazil v. Italy, 1970 . . . 40 15
1456 200f. West Germany v. The Netherlands, 1974, and Argentina v. The Netherlands, 1978 . . . . 55 20
1457 400f. Italy v. West Germany, 1982, and Argentina v. West Germany, 1986 . . . . . 1·00 35
1458 500f. West Germany v. Argentina, 1990, and 1994 Championship emblem and player . . . . 1·40 45

400 Baron Pierre de Coubertin (founder of modern games)

1993. Centenary (1996) of Modern Olympic Games. Multicoloured.
1460 90f. Ancient Greek athlete 25 10
1461 90f. Type **400** 25 10
1462 90f. Charles Bennett (running), Paris, 1900 . . 25 10
1463 90f. Etienne Desmarteau (stone throwing), St. Louis, 1904 . . . . . 25 10
1464 90f. Harry Porter (high jump), London, 1908 . . 25 10
1465 90f. Patrick MacDonald (putting the shot), Stockholm, 1912 . . . . 25 10
1466 90f. Coloured and black Olympic rings (1916) . . 25 10
1467 90f. Frank Loomis (400 m hurdles), Antwerp, 1920 . . . . 25 10
1468 90f. Albert White (diving), Paris, 1924 . . . . . . 25 10
1469 100f. El Ouafi (marathon), Amsterdam, 1928 . . . . 25 10
1470 100f. Eddie Tolan (100 m), Los Angeles, 1932 . . . . 25 10
1471 100f. Jesse Owens (100 m, long jump and 200 m hurdles), Berlin, 1936 . . . . 25 10
1472 100f. Coloured and black Olympic rings (1940) . . 25 10
1473 100f. Coloured and black Olympic rings (1944) . . 25 10
1474 100f. Tapio Rautavaara (throwing the javelin), London, 1948 . . . . . 25 10
1475 100f. Jean Boiteux (400 m freestyle swimming), Helsinki, 1952 25 10
1476 100f. Petrus Kasterman (three-day equestrian event), Melbourne, 1956 25 10
1477 100f. Sante Gaiardoni (cycling), Rome, 1960 . . 25 10
1478 160f. Anton Geesink (judo), Tokyo, 1964 . . . . . . 40 15
1479 160f. Bob Beamon (long jump), Mexico, 1968 . . . 40 15
1480 160f. Mark Spitz (swimming), Munich, 1972 40 15
1481 160f. Nadia Comaneci (gymnastics (beam)), Montreal, 1976 . . . . . . 40 15
1482 160f. Aleksandre Ditjatin (gymnastics (rings) and dressage), Moscow, 1980 40 15
1483 160f. J. F. Lamour (sabre), Los Angeles, 1984 . . . . 40 15
1484 160f. Pierre Durand (show jumping), Seoul, 1988 . . 40 15
1485 160f. Michael Jordan (basketball), Barcelona, 1992 . . . . 40 15
1486 160f. Footballer and Games emblem, Atlanta, 1996 . . 40 15

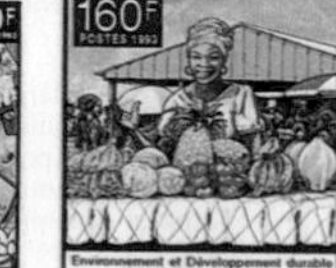

401 Man planting Sapling, and Animals **402** Woman selling Foodstuffs

1993. Biodiversity. Multicoloured.
1487 100f. Type **401** 25 10
1488 130f. Man amongst flora and fauna (vert) 35 15

1993. The Environment and Sustainable Development. Multicoloured.
1489 160f. Type **402** 40 15
1490 240f. Woman tending cooking pot 60 20

403 Saltoposuchus

1993. Prehistoric Animals. Multicoloured.
1491 25f. Type **403** 10 10
1492 25f. Rhamphorhynchus . . 10 10
1493 25f. Dimorphodon 10 10
1494 25f. Archaeopteryx 10 10
1495 30f. "Compsognathos longipes" 10 10
1496 30f. "Cryptocleidus oxoniensis" 10 10
1497 30f. Stegosaurus 10 10
1498 30f. Cetiosaurus 10 10
1499 50f. Brontosaurus 10 10
1500 50f. "Corythosaurus casuarius" 10 10
1501 50f. Styracosaurus 10 10
1502 50f. Gorgosaurus 10 10
1503 500f. Scolosaurus . . . . . 1·40 45
1504 500f. Trachodon . . . . . 1·40 45
1505 500f. Struthiomimus . . . . 1·40 45
1506 500f. "Tarbosaurus bataar" 1·40 45

Nos. 1491/1506 were issued together, se-tenant, forming a composite design of a volcanic landscape.

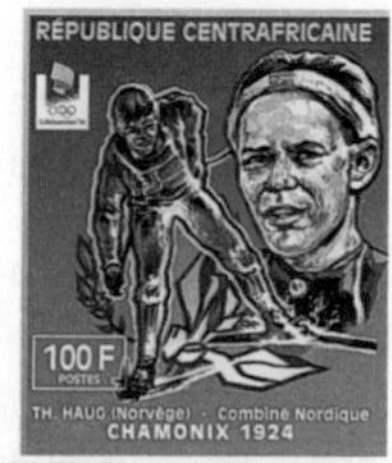

404 Th. Haug (combined skiing, Chamonix, 1924)

1994. Winter Olympic Games, Lillehammer, Norway. Previous Medal Winners. Multicoloured.
1508 100f. Type **404** 25 10
1509 100f. J. Heaton (luge, St. Moritz, 1928) 25 10
1510 100f. B. Ruud (ski jumping, Lake Placid, 1932) . . . 25 10
1511 100f. I. Ballangrud (speed skating, Garmisch-Partenkirchen, 1936) . . . 25 10
1512 100f. G. Fraser (slalom, St. Moritz, 1948) 25 10
1513 100f. West German 4-man bobsleigh team (Oslo, 1952) 25 10
1514 100f. U.S.S.R. ice hockey team (Cortina d'Ampezzo, 1956) 25 10
1515 100f. J. Vuarnet (downhill skiing, Squaw Valley, 1960) 25 10
1516 200f. M. Goitschel (giant slalom, Innsbruck, 1964) 50 15
1517 200f. Jean-Claud Killy (special slalom, Grenoble, 1968) 50 15
1518 200f. U. Wehling (cross-country skiing, Sapporo, 1972) 50 15
1519 200f. Irina Rodnina and Aleksandr Zaitsev (figure skating, Innsbruck, 1976) 50 15
1520 200f. E. Heiden (speed skating, Lake Placid, 1980) 50 15
1521 200f. Katarina Witt (figure skating, Sarajevo, 1984) 50 15
1522 200f. J. Mueller (single luge, Calgary, 1988) 50 15
1523 200f. E. Grospiron (acrobatic skiing, Albertville, 1992) 50 15
1524 200f. Speed skiing, Lillehammer, 1994 . . . . 50 15

405 "Ansellia africa"

1994. Flowers, Vegetables, Fruit and Fungi. Multicoloured.
1525 25f. Type **405** 10 10
1526 30f. Yams 10 10
1527 40f. Oranges 10 10
1528 50f. Termite mushroom . . 10 10
1529 60f. "Polystachia bella" (flower) 15 10
1530 65f. Manioc 15 10
1531 70f. Banana 15 10
1532 80f. "Synpodia arborescens" (wrongly inscr "Sympodia") (fungi) . . . 20 10
1533 90f. "Aerangis rhodosticta" (flower) 20 10
1534 100f. Maize 25 10
1535 160f. Mango 40 15
1536 200f. "Phlebopus sudanicus" (fungi) 50 15
1537 300f. Coffee beans 75 25
1538 400f. Sweet potato 95 30
1539 500f. "Angraecum eburneum" (flower) . . . 1·25 40
1540 600f. "Leucocoprinus africanus" (fungi) . . . . 1·50 50

Nos. 1525/40 were issued together, se-tenant, the backgrounds forming a composite design.

MILITARY FRANK STAMPS

1963. Optd **FM**. No. M1 also has the value obliterated with two bars. Centre multicoloured; frame colour given.

M35	**1**	(–) on 15f. blue	4·50	
M36		15f. blue	3·00	

OFFICIAL STAMPS

O 41 Arms

O 109 Arms

1965.

O78	**O 41**	1f. multicoloured	15	10
O79		2f. multicoloured	10	10
O80		5f. multicoloured	10	10
O81		10f. multicoloured	25	10
O82		20f. multicoloured	35	30
O83		30f. multicoloured	70	50
O84		50f. multicoloured	80	70
O85		100f. multicoloured	2·10	1·00
O86		130f. multicoloured	3·00	1·90
O87		200f. multicoloured	4·75	2·25

1971.

O238	**O 109**	5f. multicoloured	10	10
O239		30f. multicoloured	30	20
O240		40f. multicoloured	50	25
O241		100f. multicoloured	1·25	55
O242		140f. multicoloured	2·25	75
O243		200f. multicoloured	2·75	1·25

POSTAGE DUE STAMPS

D 15 "Sternotomis gama" (Beetle)

1962. Beetles.

D33		50c. brown and turquoise	10	10
D34		50c. turquoise and brown	10	10
D35		1f. brown and green	10	10
D36		1f. green and brown	10	10
D37		2f. pink and black	10	10
D38		2f. green, black and pink	10	10
D39		5f. green and brown	25	25
D40		5f. green and brown	25	25
D41		10f. green, black and drab	50	50
D42		10f. drab, black and green	50	50
D43		25f. brown, black and green	1·40	1·40
D44		25f. brown, green and black	1·40	1·40

DESIGNS: No. D33, Type D **15**; D34, "Sternotomis virescens"; D35, "Augosoma centaurus"; D36, "Phosphorus virescens" and "Ceroplesis carabarica"; D37, "Ceroplesis S.P."; D38, "Cetoine scaraboidae"; D39, "Cetoine scaraboidae"; D40, "Macrorhina S.P."; D41, "Taurina longiceps"; D42, "Phryneta leprosa"; D43, "Monohamus griseoplagiatus"; D44, "Jambonus trifasciatus".

D 308 Giant Pangolin ("Manis gigantea")

1985.

D1080	**D 308**	5f. multicoloured	10	10
D1081		20f. multicoloured	20	20
D1082		30f. multicoloured	25	25

APPENDIX

The following stamps have either been issued in excess of postal needs or have not been availble to the public in reasonable quantities at face value. Such stamps may later be given full listing if there is evidence of regular postal use.

All the stamps listed below are embossed on gold foil.

1977.

Coronation of Emperor Bokassa. Air 2500f.

1978.

100 Years of Progress in Posts and Telecommunications. Air 1500f.

Death Centenary of Sir Rowland Hill. Air 1500f.

1979.

International Year of the Child. Air 1500f.

Olympic Games, Moscow. Air 1500f. ("The Discus-thrower")

Space Exploration. Air 1500f.

1980.

Olympic Games, Moscow. Air 1500f. (Relay)

European-African Co-operation. Air 1500f.

World Cup Football Championship, Spain. Air 1500f.

1981.

Olympic Games Medal Winners. 1980 Olympic Games issue optd. Air 1500f.

Birth Centenary of Pablo Picasso. Air 1500f.

Wedding of Prince of Wales. Air 1500f.

Navigators. Air 1500f.

Christmas. Air 1500f.

1982.

Animals and Rotary International. Air 1500f.

Transport. Air 1500f.

21st Birthday of Princess of Wales. Air 1500f.

Olympic Games, Los Angeles.Air 1500f. (horiz)

Space Resources. Air 1500f.

1983.

Chess Masters. Air 1500f.

World Cup Football Championship, Spain. Air 1500f.

Car Manufacturers. Air 1500f.

Olympic Games, Los Angeles. Air 1500f. (vert)

Bicentenary of manned flight. Air 1500f.

1984.

Winter Olympic Gold Medalists. Air 1500f.

Celebrities. Air 1500f.

1985.

85th Birthday of Queen Elizabeth the Queen Mother. Air 1500f.

Appearence of Halley's Comet. Air 1500f.

480th Death Anniv of Christopher Columbus. Air 1500f.

1988.

Olympic Games, Seoul. Air 1500f.

Scouts and Birds. Air 1500f.

1989.

Olympic Games, Seoul, Gold Medal Winner. Air 1500f.

Bicentenary of French Revolution. Air 1500f.

World Cup Football Championship, Italy. Air 1500f.

1990.

Winter Olympic Games, Albertville (1992). Air 1500f.

Scouts and Butterflies. Air 1500f.

Birth Centenary of Charles de Gaulle. Air 1500f.

1993.

Wedding of Crown Prince Naruhito of Japan and Masako Owada. Air 1500f.

16th Death Anniv of Elvis Presley. Air 1500f.

World Cup Football Championship, U.S.A. (1994). Air 1500f.

Visit of Pope John Paul II to Africa. Air 1500f.

1994.

Winter Olympic Games, Lillehammer. Air 1500f.

CENTRAL LITHUANIA Pt. 10

Became temporarily independent in 1918 and was subsequently absorbed by Poland.

100 fenigi = 1 mark.

1

3 Girl

1920. Imperf or perf.

1	**1**	25f. red	10	10
20		25f. green	20	30
2		1m. blue	10	10
21		1m. brown	20	30
3		2m. violet	15	15
22		2m. yellow	20	30

1920. Stamps of Lithuania of 1919 surch **SRODKOWA LITWA POCZTA**, new value and Arms of Poland and Lithuania. Perf.

4	**5**	2m. on 15s. violet	6·50	8·00
5		4m. on 10s. red	4·00	5·00
6		4m. on 20s. blue	6·00	8·00
7		4m. on 30s. orange	5·00	6·00
8	**6**	6m. on 50s. green	6·00	7·00
9		6m. on 60s. red and violet	6·00	7·00
10		6m. on 75s. red & yellow	6·00	8·00
11	**7**	10m. on 1a. red & grey	12·00	14·00
12		10m. on 3a. red & brown	£450	£550
13		10m. on 5a. red and green	£450	£550

1920. Imperf or perf. Inscr "LITWA SRODKOWA".

14	**3**	25f. grey	15	15
15	–	1m. orange	20	15
16	–	2m. red	40	50
17	–	4m. olive and yellow	60	75
18	–	6m. grey and red	1·00	1·25
19	–	10m. yellow and brown	1·50	2·00

DESIGNS: 1m. Warrior; 2m. Ostrabrama Gate, Vilnius; 4m. St. Stanislaus Cathedral and Tower, Vilnius; 6m. Rector's insignia; 10m. Gen. Zeligowski.

1921. Fund for Polish Participation in Plebiscite for Upper Silesia. Surch **NA SLASK** and new value. Imperf or perf.

23	**1**	25f.+2m. red	50	60
24		25f.+2m. green	50	60
25		1m.+2m. blue	60	80
26		1m.+2m. brown	60	80
27		2m.+2m. violet	70	1·10
28		2m.+2m. yellow	70	1·10

1921. Red Cross Fund. Nos. 16/17 surch with cross and value. Imperf or perf.

29		2m.+1m. red	50	65
30		4m.+1m. green and yellow	50	65

1921. White Cross Fund. As Nos. 16, 17 and 19, but with cross and value in white added. Imperf or perf.

31		2m.+1m. purple	30	30
32		4m.+1m. green and buff	30	30
33		10m.+2m. yellow and brown	30	30

13 St. Nicholas Cathedral

14 St. Stanislaus Cathedral

1921. Imperf or perf.

34	**13**	1m. yellow and slate	30	40
35	**14**	2m. green and red	30	40
36	–	3m. green	40	50
37	–	4m. brown	40	60
38	–	5m. brown	40	60
39	–	6m. buff and green	40	60
40	–	10m. buff and purple	60	80
41	–	20m. buff and brown	60	90

DESIGNS—HORIZ: 4m. Queen Jadwiga and King Wladislaw Jagiello; 6m. Poczobut Observatory, Vilnius University; 10m. Union of Lithuania and Poland, 1569; 20m. Kosciuszko and Mickiewicz. VERT: 3m. Arms (Eagle); 5m. Arms (Shield).

21 Entry into Vilnius

22 General Zeligowski

1921. Ist Anniv of Entry of Gen. Zeligowski into Vilnius. Imperf or perf.

42	**21**	100m. blue and bistre	1·75	1·75
43	**22**	150m. green and brown	2·25	2·25

24 Arms

1922. Opening of National Parliament. Inscr "SEJM—WILNIE". Imperf or perf.

44	–	10m. brown	1·50	1·75
45	**24**	25m. red and buff	1·75	1·90
46	–	50m. blue	2·75	3·00
47	–	75m. lilac	4·00	4·50

DESIGNS—HORIZ: 50m. National Assembly, Vilnius. VERT: 10m. Agriculture; 75m. Industry.

POSTAGE DUE STAMPS

D 9 Government Offices

1921. Inscr "DOPLATA". Imperf or perf.

D23	**D 9**	50f. red	50	60
D24	–	1m. green	50	60
D25	–	2m. purple	50	60
D26	–	3m. purple	75	90
D27	–	5m. purple	75	90
D28	–	20m. red	1·00	1·25

DESIGNS—HORIZ: 2m. Castle on Troki Island. VERT: 1m. Castle Hill, Vilnius; 3m. Ostrabrama Gate, Vilnius; 5m. St. Stanislaus Cathedral; 20m. (larger) St. Nicholas Cathedral.

CEYLON Pt. 1

An island to the south of India formerly under British administration, then a self-governing Dominion. The island became a Republic within the Commonwealth on 22 May 1972 and was renamed Sri Lanka (q.v.).

1857. 12 pence = 1 shilling;
20 shillings = 1 pound.
1872. 100 cents = 1 rupee.

1

2

4

8

1857. Imperf.

17	**4**	½d. lilac	£170	£180
2	**1**	1d. blue	£650	28·00
3		2d. green	£150	55·00
4	**2**	4d. red	£50000	£4500
5	**1**	5d. brown	£1500	£150
6		6d. brown	£1800	£140
7	**2**	8d. brown	£22000	£1500
8		9d. brown	£32000	£900
9	**1**	10d. orange	£800	£300
10		1s. violet	£4500	£200
11	**2**	1s.9d. green	£750	£800
12		2s. blue	£5500	£1200

The prices of these imperf stamps vary greatly according to condition. The above prices are for fine copies with four margins. Poor to medium specimens are worth much less.

1861. Perf.

48c	**4**	½d. lilac	30·00	30·00
49	**1**	1d. blue	£110	5·00
50		2d. green	70·00	10·00
64b		2d. yellow	50·00	7·00
65b	**2**	4d. red	55·00	15·00
22	**1**	5d. brown	80·00	8·00
66c		5d. green	32·00	45·00
67b		6d. brown	32·00	35·00
56	**2**	8d. brown	90·00	45·00
69b		9d. brown	45·00	6·00
70b	**1**	10d. orange	48·00	12·00
71b		1s. violet	90·00	7·00
72b	**2**	2s. blue	£120	12·00

1866. The 3d. has portrait in circle.

61	**8**	1d. blue	20·00	8·00
62	–	3d. red	70·00	40·00

9

10

30

1872. Various frames.

256	**9**	2c. brown	2·50	30
147		2c. green	2·50	15
122	**10**	4c. grey	32·00	1·50
148		4c. purple	3·00	30
149		4c. red	3·75	11·00
258		4c. yellow	3·00	2·75
150a	–	8c. yellow	3·50	7·00
126	–	16c. violet	85·00	2·75
127	–	24c. green	55·00	2·00
128	–	32c. grey	£150	15·00
129	–	36c. blue	£150	18·00
130	–	48c. red	75·00	5·50
131	–	64c. brown	£275	65·00
132	–	90c. grey	£200	26·00
201	**30**	1r.12 red	22·00	20·00

138 2r.50 red £475 £300
249 2r.50 purple on red . . . 28·00 48·00

1882. Nos. 127 and 131 surch in words and figures.
142 16c. on 24c. green . . . . . 24·00 6·50
143 20c. on 64c. brown . . . . . 9·50 5·00

1885. As Nos. 148/132 surch **Postage & Revenue** and value in words.
178 5c. on 4c. red . . . . 20·00 3·50
179 5c. on 8c. yellow . . . . . . 70·00 7·00
180 5c. on 16c. violet . . . . . 95·00 11·00
154 5c. on 24c. green £2750 £100
182 5c. on 24c. purple . . . . . — £500
155 5c. on 32c. grey . . . . . . 55·00 15·00
156 5c. on 36c. blue . . . . . . £250 10·00
157 5c. on 48c. red . . . . . . £1100 55·00
158 5c. on 64c. brown . . . . . 95·00 6·00
159 5c. on 96c. grey . . . . . . £450 65·00

1885. As Nos. 126/249 surch with new value in words.
184 10c. on 16c. violet £5000 £1100
162 10c. on 24c. green £450 £110
185 10c. on 24c. purple . . . . 13·00 6·00
163 10c. on 36c. blue £375 £170
174 10c. on 64c. brown . . . . 60·00 95·00
186 15c. on 16c. violet . . . . 11·00 7·50
165 20c. on 24c. green . . . . . 55·00 18·00
166a 20c. on 32c. grey . . . . . 60·00 45·00
167 25c. on 32c. grey . . . . . 15·00 4·50
168 28c. on 48c. red . . . . . . 38·00 6·00
169x 30c. on 36c. blue . . . . . 11·00 8·50
170 56c. on 96c. grey . . . . . 24·00 18·00
176 1r.12 on 2r.50 red . . . . . 95·00 42·00

1885. Surch **REVENUE AND POSTAGE 5 CENTS**.
187 5c. on 8c. lilac (as No. 150a) 16·00 1·40

1885. As Nos. 126/32 surch in words and figures.
188 10c. on 24c. purple . . . . . 9·50 6·50
189 15c. on 16c. yellow . . . . . 55·00 9·00
190 28c. on 32c. grey . . . . . . 23·00 2·50
191 30c. on 36c. olive . . . . . 28·00 14·00
192 56c. on 96c. grey . . . . . . 50·00 14·00

1885. Surch **1 R. 12 C.**
193 **30** 1r.12 on 2r.50 red . . . . 38·00 85·00

39 28

43

1886.
245 **39** 3c. brown and green . . . 3·25 45
257 3c. green . . . . 2·50 55
195 **28** 5c. purple . . . . 2·25 10
259 **39** 6c. red and black . . . . 1·50 45
260 12c. olive and red . . . . 4·00 7·00
196 15c. olive . . . . 5·00 1·25
261 15c. blue . . . . 5·50 1·25
198 25c. brown . . . . 3·75 1·00
199 28c. grey . . . . 18·00 1·40
247 30c. mauve and brown . . 4·25 2·00
262 75c. black and brown . . . 4·75 6·00
263 **43** 1r.50 red . . . . 19·00 35·00
264 2r.25 blue . . . . 30·00 35·00

1887. Nos. 148/9 surch. A. Surch **TWO CENTS**.
202 **10** 2c. on 4c. purple . . . . . 1·40 80
203 2c. on 4c. red . . . . . . 2·25 30

B. Surch **TWO**.
204 **10** 2c. on 4c. purple 75 30
205 2c. on 4c. red . . . . . . 5·00 20

C. Surch **2 Cents** and bar.
206 **10** 2c. on 4c. purple . . . . . 65·00 28·00
207 2c. on 4c. red . . . . . . 2·25 75

D. Surch **Two Cents** and bar.
208 **10** 2c. on 4c. purple . . . . . 45·00 19·00
209 2c. on 4c. red . . . . . . 2·50 1·10

E. Surch **2 Cents** without bar.
210 **10** 2c. on 4c. purple . . . . . 45·00 27·00
211 2c. on 4c. red . . . . . . 10·00 1·00

1890. Surch **POSTAGE Five Cents REVENUE**.
233 **39** 5c. on 15c. olive . . . . . 2·50 2·00

1891. Surch **FIFTEEN CENTS**.
239 **39** 15c. on 25c. brown . . . . 11·00 12·00
240 15c. on 28c. grey . . . . . 14·00 8·50

1892. Surch **3 Cents** and bar.
241 **10** 3c. on 4c. purple . . . . . 1·00 3·25
242 3c. on 4c. red . . . . . . 3·75 7·00
243 **39** 3c. on 28c. grey . . . . . 4·00 3·50

1898. Surch **Six Cents**.
250 **39** 6c. on 15c. green 70 75

1898. Surch with new value.
254 **30** 1r.50 on 2r.50 grey . . . . 20·00 45·00
255 2r.25 on 2r.50 yellow . . . 35·00 80·00

44 45

1903. Various frames.
277 **44** 2c. brown . . . . 1·50 10
278 **45** 3c. green (A) . . . . . . 1·50 15
293 3c. green (B) . . . . . . 1·00 75
279 4c. orange and blue . . . 2·00 1·50
268 – 5c. purple . . . . 1·50 60
289 – 5c. purple . . . . 2·50 10
281 – 6c. red . . . . 1·50 15
291 – 6c. red . . . . 1·25 10
294 **45** 10c. olive and red . . . . 2·00 2·25
282 12c. olive and red . . . . 1·50 1·75
283 15c. blue . . . . 2·00 60
284 25c. brown . . . . 6·00 3·75
295 25c. grey . . . . 2·50 1·50
285 30c. violet and green . . . 2·50 3·00
296 50c. brown . . . . 4·00 7·50
286 75c. blue and orange . . . 5·25 8·00
297 1r. purple on yellow . . . 7·50 10·00
287 1r.50 grey . . . . 24·00 10·00
298 2r. red on yellow . . . . . 15·00 27·00
288 2r.25 brown and green . . 22·00 29·00
299 5r. black on green . . . . 38·00 65·00
300 10r. black on red . . . . . 85·00 £170
(A) has value in shaded tablet; (B) in white tablet as in Type **45**.
Nos. 268 and 281 have the value in words; Nos. 289 and 291 in figures.

52 57

1912.
301 **52** 1c. brown . . . . 1·00 10
307a 2c. orange 30 20
339 3c. green . . . . 2·75 75
340 3c. grey 75 20
341 5c. purple 50 15
342 6c. red . . . . 2·00 75
343 6c. violet . . . . 1·00 15
345 9c. red on yellow 80 30
346 10c. olive . . . . 1·40 40
347a 12c. red . . . . 1·00 2·25
311a 15c. blue . . . . 1·75 1·25
349a 15c. green on yellow . . . 1·50 1·00
350b 20c. blue . . . . 3·50 45
351 25c. yellow and blue . . . 1·60 1·90
352a 30c. green and violet . . . 3·00 1·25
353 50c. black and red . . . 1·60 80
315 1r. purple on yellow . . . 3·25 3·50
355 2r. black and red on yellow . . . . 7·00 7·50
317 5r. black on green . . . . 17·00 28·00
318 10r. purple & blk on red 60·00 80·00
319 20r. black and red on blue £120 £130

Large type, As Bermuda T **15**.
358 50r. purple £140 £180
359 100r. black £1500
360 100r. purple and blue £1300

1918. Optd **WAR STAMP**, No. 335 surch **ONE CENT** and bar also.
335 **52** 1c. on 5c. purple 50 40
330 2c. orange 20 40
332 3c. green 20 50
333 5c. purple 50 30

1918. Surch **ONE CENT** and bar.
337 **52** 1c. on 5c. purple 15 25

1926. Surch with new value and bar.
361 **52** 2c. on 3c. grey . . . . . . 80 1·00
362 5c. on 6c. violet 50 40

1927.
363 **57** 1r. purple . . . . 2·50 1·25
364 2r. green and red . . . . . 3·75 2·75
365 5r. green and purple . . . 14·00 20·00
366 10r. green and orange . . . 35·00 80·00
367 20r. purple and blue . . . £100 £180

60 Adam's Peak

1935. King George V.
368 – 2c. black and red 30 40
369 **60** 3c. black and green 35 40
370 – 6c. black and blue 30 30
371 – 9c. green and orange . . . 1·00 65
372 – 10c. black and purple . . 1·25 2·25
373 – 15c. brown and green . . . 1·00 50
374 – 20c. black and blue . . . . 1·75 2·50
375 – 25c. blue and brown . . . 1·40 1·25
376 – 30c. red and green . . . . 3·00 2·75
377 – 50c. black and violet . . . 8·50 1·75
378 – 1r. violet and brown . . . 18·00 16·00
DESIGNS—VERT: 2c. Tapping rubber; 6c. Colombo Harbour; 9c. Plucking tea; 20c. Coconut palms. HORIZ: 10c. Hill paddy (rice); 15c. River scene; 25c. Temple of the Tooth, Kandy; 30c. Ancient irrigation tank; 50c. Indian elephants; 1r. Trincomalee.

1935. Silver Jubilee. As T **13** of Antigua.
379 6c. blue and grey 65 30
380 9c. green and blue . . . . . 70 1·25
381 20c. brown and blue . . . . 4·25 2·75
382 50c. grey and purple . . . . 5·25 9·00

1937. Coronation. As T **2** of Aden.
383 6c. red 65 15
384 9c. green . . . . 2·50 3·50
385 20c. blue . . . . 3·50 3·00

70 Sigiriya (Lion Rock)

1938. As 1935 issue but with portrait of King George VI, and "POSTAGE & REVENUE" omitted.
386b – 2c. black and red . . . . 2·00 10
387d **60** 3c. black and green . . . 80 10
387f – 5c. green and orange . . 30 10
388 – 6c. black and blue . . . 30 10
389 **70** 10c. black and blue . . . 2·25 10
390 – 15c. green and brown . . 2·00 10
391 – 20c. black and blue . . . 3·25 10
392a – 25c. blue and brown . . . 4·25 10
393 – 30c. red and green . . . 11·00 2·00
394e – 50c. black and violet . . 4·00 20
395 – 1r. blue and brown . . . 16·00 1·25
396 – 2r. black and red . . . . 13·00 2·50
396b – 2r. black and violet . . . 2·00 1·60
DESIGNS—VERT: 5c. Coconut palms; 20c. Plucking tea; 2r. Ancient guard-stone, Anuradhapura. Others, same as for corresponding values of 1935 issue.

1938. As T **57**, but head of King George VI to right.
397a 5r. green and purple . . . . 14·00 3·50

1940. Surch with new value and bars.
398 3c. on 6c. blk & bl (No. 388) 25 10
399 3c. on 20c. blk & bl (No. 391) . . . . 2·50 1·50

1946. Victory. As T **9** of Aden.
400 6c. blue 10 20
401 15c. brown 10 80

75 Parliament Building

1947. New Constitution.
402 **75** 6c. black and blue 10 15
403 – 10c. black, orange and red 15 20
404 – 15c. green and purple . . . 15 80
405 – 25c. yellow and green . . . 15 50
DESIGNS—VERT: 10c. Adam's Peak; 25c. Anuradhapura. HORIZ: 15c. Temple of the Tooth.

79 Lion Flag of Dominion 80 D. S. Senanayake

1949. 1st Anniv of Independence.
406 **79** 4c. red, yellow and brown 15 20
407 **80** 5c. brown and green . . . 10 10
408 **79** 15c. red, yellow and orange 30 15
409 **80** 25c. brown and blue . . . 15 65
No. 408 is larger, 28 × 22 mm.

82 Globe and Forms of Transport

1949. 75th Anniv of U.P.U. Inscr as in T **82**. Designs showing globe.
410 **82** 5c. brown and green . . . 75 10
411 – 15c. black and red (horiz) 1·10 2·25
412 – 25c. black and blue (vert) 1·10 1·10

85 Kandyan Dancer 88 Sigiriya (Lion Rock)

90 Ruins at Madirigiriya

1950.
413 **85** 4c. purple and red 10 10
414 – 5c. green 10 10
415 – 15c. green and violet . . . 1·50 30
416 **88** 30c. red and yellow 30 40
417 – 75c. blue and orange . . . 4·75 10
418 **90** 1r. blue and brown . . . . 1·75 30
DESIGNS—VERT (As Types **85** and **88**): 5c. Kiri Vehera, Polonnaruwa; 15c. Vesak orchid. (As Type **90**): 75c. Octagon Library, Temple of the Tooth.

94 Coconut Trees 99 Tea Plantation

1951.
419 – 2c. brown and turquoise 10 1·25
420 – 3c. black and violet . . . 10 1·00
421 – 6c. sepia and green 10 30
422 **94** 10c. green and grey . . . . 1·00 65
423 – 25c. orange and blue . . . 10 20
424 – 35c. red and green . . . . 1·50 1·50
425 – 40c. brown . . . . 5·00 1·00
426 – 50c. slate 30 10
427 **99** 85c. black and turquoise 60 20
428 – 2r. blue and brown . . . . 6·50 1·25
429 – 5r. brown and orange . . . 4·75 1·40
430 – 10r. brown and buff . . . 38·00 11·00
DESIGNS—VERT (As Type **94**): 2c. Sambars, Ruhuna National Park; 3c. Ancient guardstone, Anuradhapura; 6c. Harvesting rice; 25c. Sigiriya fresco; 35c. Star orchid. (As Type **99**): 5r. Bas-relief, Anuradhapura; 10r. Harvesting rice. HORIZ (As Type **94**): 40c. Rubber plantation; 50c. Outrigger canoe. (As Type **99**): 2r. River Gal Dam.

103 Ceylon, Mace and Symbols of Progress 104 Queen Elizabeth II

1952. Colombo Plan Exhibition.
431 **103** 5c. green 10 10
432 15c. blue 30 60

1953. Coronation.
433 **104** 5c. green . . . . 1·25 10

105 Ceremonial Procession 106 King Coconuts

1954. Royal Visit.
434 **105** 10c. blue 75 10

1954.
435 **106** 10c. orange, brown and buff 10 10

107 Farm Produce

1955. Royal Agricultural and Food Exhibition.
436 **107** 10c. brown and orange . . 10 10

108 Sir John Kotelawala and House of Representatives

1956. Prime Minister's 25 Years of Public Service.
437 **108** 10c. green 10 10

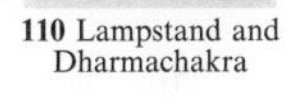
109 Arrival of Vijaya in Ceylon   **110** Lampstand and Dharmachakra

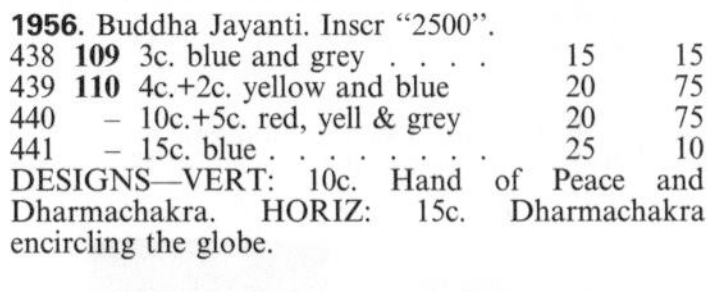

1956. Buddha Jayanti. Inscr "2500".
438 **109** 3c. blue and grey 15 15
439 **110** 4c.+2c. yellow and blue 20 75
440 – 10c.+5c. red, yell & grey 20 75
441 – 15c. blue 25 10
DESIGNS—VERT: 10c. Hand of Peace and Dharmachakra. HORIZ: 15c. Dharmachakra encircling the globe.

113 Mail Transport   **114** Stamp of 1857

1957. Stamp Centenary.
442 **113** 4c. red and turquoise . . 75 40
443 10c. red and blue 75 10
444 **114** 35c. brown, yellow and blue 30 50
445 85c. brown, yellow & grn 80 1·60

1958. Nos. 439/40 with premium obliterated with bars.
446 **110** 4c. yellow and blue . . . 10 10
447 – 10c. red, yellow and grey 10 10

117 Kandyan Dancwer   **118** "Human Rights"

1958. As Nos. 413 and 419 etc, and 435, but with inscriptions changed as in T **117**.
448 2c. brown and turquoise . . 10 50
449 3c. black and violet 10 70
450 4c. purple and red 10 10
451 5c. green . . . . 10 1·60
452 6c. sepia and green 10 65
453 10c. orange, brown and buff 10 10
454 15c. green and violet . . . . 3·50 80
455 25c. orange and blue . . . 10 10
456 30c. red and yellow . . . . 15 1·40
457 35c. red and green . . . . 6·50 30
459 50c. slate 30 10
460a 75c. blue and orange . . . 9·00 2·25
461 85c. black and turquoise . . 3·75 5·00
462 1r. blue and brown 60 10
463 2r. blue and brown . . . . 1·00 30
464 5r. brown and orange . . . 4·50 30
465 10r. brown and buff . . . . 10·00 1·00

1958. 10th Anniv of Declaration of Human Rights.
466 **118** 10c. red, brown and purple 10 10
467 85c. red, turq & grn . . . 30 55

119 Portraits of Founders and University Buildings

1959. Institution of Pirivena Universities.
468 **119** 10c. orange and blue . . 10 10

120 "Uprooted Tree"   **121** S. W. R. D. Bandaranaike

1960. World Refugee Year.
469 **120** 4c. brown and gold . . . 10 85
470 25c. violet and gold . . . 10 15

1961. Prime Minister Bandaranaike Commemoration.
471 **121** 10c. blue and turquoise 10 10
See also Nos. 479 and 481.

122 Ceylon Scout Badge   **123** Campaign Emblem

1962. Golden Jubilee of Ceylon Boy Scouts Association
472 **122** 35.c buff and blue 15 10

1962. Malaria Eradication.
473 **123** 25c. red and drab 10 10

124 De Havilland Leopard Moth and Hawker Siddeley Comet 4

1963. 25th Anniv of Airmail Services.
474 **124** 50c. black and blue . . . 50 50

125 "Produce" and Campaign Emblem

ශත
2
சதம்
(126)

1963. Freedom from Hunger.
475 **125** 5c. red and blue . . . . 50 2·00
476 25c. brown and olive . . 2·00 30

1963. No. 450 surch with T **126**.
477 2c. on 4c. purple and red . . 10 10

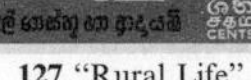

127 "Rural Life"   **131** Anagarika Dharmapala (Buddhist missionary)

129 Terrain, Indian Elephant and Tree

1963. Golden Jubilee of Ceylon Co-operative Movement (1962).
478 **127** 60c. red and black . . . . 1·25 60

1963. Design as T **121**, but smaller (21 × 26 mm) and with inscription rearranged at top.
479 10c. blue 10 10
481 10c. violet and grey 10 10

No. 481 has a decorative pattern at foot instead of the inscription.

1963. National Conservation Week.
480 **129** 5c. sepia and blue 60 40

1964. Birth Centenary of A. Dharmapala (founder of Maha Bodhi Society)
482 **131** 25c. sepia and yellow . . 10 10

135 D. S. Senanayake   **143** Ceylon Jungle Fowl

138 Ruins at Madirigiriya

1964.
485 – 5c. multicoloured . . . . 2·00 1·50
486 **135** 10c. green 80 10
487 – 10c. green 10 10
488 – 15c. multicoloured . . . . 3·00 30
489 **138** 20c. purple and buff . . . 20 25
494 **143** 60c. multicoloured . . . . 4·00 1·25
495 – 75c. multicoloured . . . . 2·75 70
497 – 1r. brown and green . . . 1·00 30
499 – 5r. multicoloured . . . . 5·00 5·00
500 – 10r. multicoloured . . . . 19·00 3·50
MS500a 148 × 174 mm. As Nos. 485, 488, 494 and 495 (imperf) . . . 7·00 13·00
DESIGNS—HORIZ (As Type **143**): 5c. Southern grackle ("Grackle"); 15c. Common peafowl ("Peacock"); 75c. Asian black-headed oriole ("Oriole"). (As Type **138**): 5r. Girls transplanting rice. VERT (As Type **135**): 10c. (No. 487) Similar portrait, but large head and smaller inscriptions. (21 × 35 mm): 1r. Tea plantation. (23 × 36 mm): 10r. Map of Ceylon.

150 Exhibition Buildings and Cogwheels

1964. Industrial Exhibition.
501 – 5c. multicoloured 10 75
502 **150** 5c. multicoloured 10 75
No. 501 is inscribed "INDUSTRIAL EXHIBITION" in Sinhala and Tamil, No. 502 in Sinhala and English.

151 Trains of 1864 and 1964

1964. Centenary of Ceylon Railways.
503 – 60c. blue, purple and green . . . . 2·75 40
504 **151** 60c. blue, purple and green . . . . 2·75 40
No. 503 is inscribed "RAILWAY CENTENARY" in Sinhala and Tamil, No. 504 in Sinhala and English.

152 I.T.U. Emblem and Symbols

1965. Centenary of I.T.U.
505 **152** 2c. blue and red . . . . 1·00 1·10
506 30c. brown and red . . . 3·00 45

153 I.C.Y. Emblem

1965. International Co-operation Year.
507 **153** 3c. blue and red . . . . 1·25 1·00
508 50c. black, red and gold 3·25 50

154 Town Hall, Colombo

1965. Centenary of Colombo Municipal Council.
509 **154** 25c. green and sepia . . . 20 20

1965. No. 481 surch **5**.
510 5c. on 10c. violet and grey . . 10 40

157 Kandy and Council Crest

1966. Centenary of Kandy Municipal Council.
512 **157** 25c. multicoloured 20 20

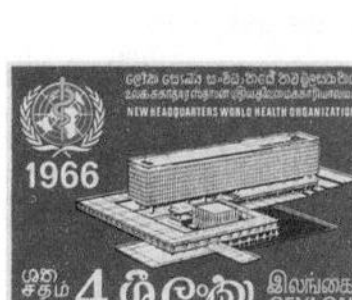
158 W.H.O. Building   **159** Rice Paddy and Map of Ceylon

1966. Inauguration of W.H.O. Headquarters, Geneva.
513 **158** 4c. multicoloured . . . . 1·75 3·00
514 1r. multicoloured . . . . 6·75 1·50

1966. International Rice Year. Multicoloured.
515 6c. Type **159** 20 75
516 30c. Rice paddy and globe 30 15

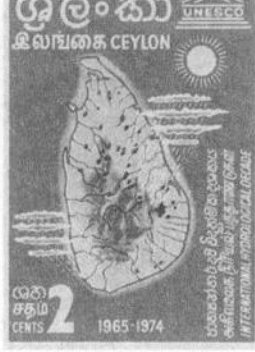
161 U.N.E.S.C.O. Emblem   **162** Water-resources Map

1966. 20th Anniv of U.N.E.S.C.O.
517 **161** 3c. multicoloured . . . . 2·00 3·25
518 50c. multicoloured . . . . 5·50 30

1966. International Hydrological Decade.
519 **162** 2c. brown, yellow and blue 30 85
520 2r. multicoloured . . . . 1·50 2·25

163 Devotees at Buddhist Temple

1967. Poya Holiday System. Multicoloured.
521 5c. Type **163** 15 60
522 20c. Mihintale 15 10
523 35c. Sacred Bo-tree, Anuradhapura 15 15
524 60c. Adam's Peak 15 10

167 Galle Fort and Clock Tower

1967. Centenary of Galle Municipal Council.
525 **167** 25c. multicoloured 70 20

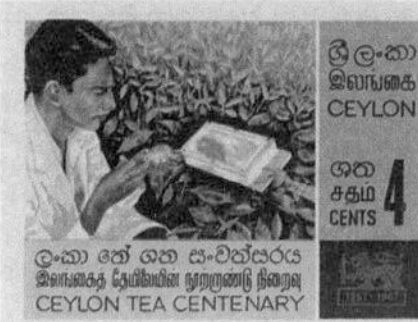
168 Field Research

1967. Centenary of Ceylon Tea Industry. Mult.
526 4c. Type **168** 60 80
527 40c. Tea-tasting equipment 1·75 1·50
528 50c. Leaves and bud . . . . 1·75 20
529 1r. Shipping tea . . . . . . 1·75 10

172 Elephant Ride

1967. International Tourist Year.
530 **172** 45c. multicoloured . . . . 2·25 80

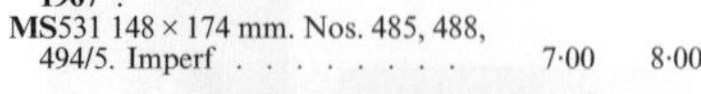
1967. 1st National Stamp Exhibition. No. **MS**500a optd "**FIRST NATIONAL STAMP EXHIBITION 1967**".
MS531 148 × 174 mm. Nos. 485, 488, 494/5. Imperf . . . . 7·00 8·00

173 Ranger, Jubilee Emblem and Flag

1967. Golden Jubilee of Ceylon Girl Guides' Association.
532 **173** 3c. multicoloured 50 20
533 25c. multicoloured 75 10

174 Colonel Olcott and Buddhist Flag

1967. 60th Death Anniv of Colonel Olcott (theosophist).
534 **174** 15c. multicoloured 30 20

175 Independence Hall

177 Sir D. B. Jayatilleke

1968. 20th Anniv of Independence. Multicoloured.
535 5c. Type **175** 10 55
536 1r. Lion flag and sceptre . . 50 10

1968. Birth Centenary of Sir Baron Jayatilleke (scholar and statesman).
537 **177** 25c. brown 10 10

178 Institute of Hygiene

1968. 20th Anniv of World Health Organization.
538 **178** 50c. multicoloured 10 10

179 Vickers Super VC-10 over Terminal Building

1968. Opening of Colombo Airport.
539 **179** 60c. multicoloured 60 10

181 Open Koran and "1400"

1968. 1400th Anniv of Koran.
541 **181** 25c. multicoloured 10 10

182 Human Rights Emblem

1968. Human Rights Year.
542 **182** 2c. multicoloured 10 15
543 20c. multicoloured 10 10
544 40c. multicoloured 10 10
545 2r. multicoloured . . . . 70 3·50

183 All-Ceylon Buddhist Congress Headquarters

1968. Golden Jubilee of All-Ceylon Buddhist Congress.
546 **183** 5c. multicoloured 10 50

184 E. W. Perera (patriot)

185 Symbols of Strength in Savings

1969. Perera Commemoration.
547 **184** 60c. brown 10 30

1969. Silver Jubilee of National Savings Movement.
548 **185** 3c. multicoloured 10 10

186 Seat of Enlightenment under Sacred Bodhi Tree

188 A. E. Goonesinghe

1969. Vesak Day. Inscr "Wesak".
549 **186** 4c. multicoloured 10 50
550 – 6c. multicoloured 10 50
551 **186** 35c. multicoloured 10 10
DESIGN: 6c. Buduresmala (six-fold Buddha-rays).

1969. Goonesinghe Commemoration.
552 **188** 15c. multicoloured 10 10

189 I.L.O. Emblem

1969. 50th Anniv of I.L.O.
553 **189** 5c. black and blue 10 10
554 25c. black and red 10 10

190 Convocation Hall, University of Ceylon

194 Ath Pana (Elephant Lamp)

1969. Educational Centenary. Multicoloured.
555 4c. Type **190** 10 80
556 35c. Lamp of learning, globe and flags (horiz) 20 10
557 50c. Uranium atom 20 10
558 60c. Symbols of scientific education 30 10

1969. Archaeological Centenary. Multicoloured.
559 6c. Type **194** . . . . 25 1·50
560 1r. Rock fortress of Sigiriya 25 10

196 Leopard

1970. Wild Life Conservation. Multicoloured.
561 5c. Water buffalo . . . . . 60 1·25
562 15c. Slender loris . . . . . . 1·25 30
563 50c. Spotted deer . . . . . . 1·25 1·25
564 1r. Type **196** . . . . 1·25 1·75

197 Emblem and Symbols

1970. Asian Productivity Year.
565 **197** 60c. multicoloured 10 10

198 New U.P.U. H.Q. Building

199 Oil Lamp and Caduceus

1970. New U.P.U. Headquarters Building.
566 **198** 50c. orange, black and blue 20 10
567 1r.10 red, black and blue 3·25 30

1970. Centenary of Colombo Medical School.
568 **199** 5c. multicoloured 65 80
569 45c. multicoloured 65 60

200 Victory March and S. W. R. D. Bandaranaike

1970. Establishment of United Front Government.
570 **200** 10c. multicoloured 10 10

201 U.N. Emblem and Dove of Peace

202 Keppetipola Dissawa

1970. 25th Anniv of United Nations.
571 **201** 2r. multicoloured . . . . 2·00 3·50

1970. 152nd Death Anniv of Keppetipola Dissawa (Kandyan patriot).
572 **202** 25c. multicoloured 10 10

203 Ola Leaf Manuscript

1970. International Education Year.
573 **203** 15c. multicoloured . . . . 2·25 1·25

204 C. H. de Soysa

205 D. E. H. Pedris (patriot)

1971. 135th Birth Anniv of C. H. de Soysa (philanthropist)
574 **204** 20c. multicoloured 15 50

1971. D. E. H. Pedris Commemoration.
575 **205** 25c. multicoloured 15 50

206 Lenin

207 Ananda Rajakaruna

1971. Lenin Commemoration.
576 **206** 40c. multicoloured 15 50

1971. Poets and Philosophers.
577 **207** 5c. blue 10 15
578 – 5c. brown 10 15
579 – 5c. orange 10 15
580 – 5c. blue 10 15
581 – 5c. brown 10 15
PORTRAITS: No. 578, Arumuga Navalar; 579, Rev. S. Mahinda; 580, Ananda Coomaraswamy; 581, Cumaratunga Munidasa.

1971. Surch in figures.
582 **186** 5c. on 4c. multicoloured 6·50 1·75
583 **190** 5c. on 4c. multicoloured 10 1·25
584 **200** 15c. on 10c. multicoloured 10 30
585 – 25c. on 6c. mult (No. 550) 30 60
586 **194** 25c. on 6c. multicoloured 30 2·25

209 Colombo Plan Emblem and Ceylon

1971. 20th Anniv of Colombo Plan.
587 **209** 20c. multicoloured 15 30

210 Globe and C.A.R.E. Package

1971. 20th Anniv of Co-operative for American Relief Everywhere.
588 **210** 50c. blue, violet and lilac 35 30

211 W.H.O. Emblem and Heart

1972. World Health Day.
589 **211** 25c. multicoloured . . . . 2·50 60

212 Map of Asia and U.N. Emblem

1972. 25th Anniv of E.C.A.F.E.
590 **212** 85c. multicoloured 4·75 2·75

OFFICIAL STAMPS

1895. Stamps of Queen Victoria optd **On Service**.
O 1 **9** 2c. green 8·50 45
O 8 2c. brown 7·00 60
O 2 **39** 3c. brown and green 10·00 80
O 9 3c. green 8·00 2·25
O 3 **28** 5c. purple 3·50 30
O 4 **39** 15c. olive 12·00 50
O10 15c. blue 16·00 60
O 5 25c. brown 10·00 1·75
O 6 30c. mauve and brown 13·00 60
O11 75c. black and brown 5·50 6·50
O 7 **30** 1r.12 red 75·00 55·00

1903. Stamps of King Edward VII optd **On Service**.
O12 **44** 2c. brown 13·00 1·00
O13 **45** 3c. green 7·50 2·00
O14 – 5c. purple (No. 268) 19·00 1·50
O15 **45** 15c. blue 28·00 2·50
O16 25c. brown 22·00 18·00
O17 30c. violet and green 12·00 1·50

For later issues see **SRI LANKA**.

CHAD Pt. 6; Pt. 12

Formerly a dependency of Ubangi-Shari. Became one of the separate colonies of Fr. Equatorial Africa in 1937. In 1958 became a republic within the French Community.

100 centimes = 1 franc.

1922. Stamps of Middle Congo, colours changed, optd **TCHAD**.
1 **1** 1c. pink and violet 50 2·75
2 2c. brown and pink 90 2·75
3 4c. blue and violet 1·75 3·00
4 5c. brown and green 1·90 3·25
5 10c. green and turquoise 3·25 3·75
6 15c. violet and pink 3·25 4·00
7 20c. green and violet 5·75 7·50
8 **2** 25c. brown and chocolate 10·00 13·50
9 30c. red 2·50 3·25
10 35c. blue and pink 3·25 4·25
11 40c. brown and green 3·50 4·50
12 45c. violet and green 3·75 4·50
13 50c. blue and light blue 2·50 4·50
14 60 on 75c. violet on pink 4·75 6·50
15 75c. pink and violet 3·75 4·25
16 **3** 1f. blue and pink 13·50 16·00
17 2f. blue and violet 19·00 24·00
18 5f. blue and brown 16·00 22·00

1924. Stamps of 1922 and similar stamps further optd **AFRIQUE EQUATORIALE FRANCAISE**.
19 **1** 1c. pink and violet 25 2·50
20 2c. brown and pink 15 2·25
21 4c. blue and violet 15 2·25
22 5c. brown and green 50 2·50
23 10c. green and turquoise 2·00 2·75
24 10c. red and grey 80 2·50
25 15c. violet and red 60 2·25
26 20c. green and violet 1·75 2·50
27 **2** 25c. brown and chocolate 1·60 2·50
28 30c. red 85 2·50
29 30c. grey and blue 65 2·25
30 30c. olive and green 2·00 3·00
31 35c. blue and pink 75 2·50
32 40c. brown and green 2·00 2·50
33 45c. violet and green 1·60 2·75
34 50c. blue and light blue 85 2·75
35 50c. green and purple 2·50 1·75
36 60 on 75c. violet on pink 40 2·75
37 65c. brown and blue 3·50 4·25
38 75c. pink and violet 1·00 2·75
39 75c. blue and light blue 2·00 2·50
40 75c. purple and brown 3·25 4·00
41 90c. carmine and red 5·00 10·00
42 **3** 1f. blue and pink 2·50 2·50
43 1f.10 green and blue 3·00 4·25
44 1f.25 brown and blue 7·75 11·50
45 1f.50 ultramarine and blue 4·75 11·50
46 1f.75 brown and mauve 50·00 60·00
47 2f. blue and violet 3·25 3·75
48 3f. mauve on pink 7·50 15·00
49 5f. blue and brown 3·75 4·25

1925. Stamps of Middle Congo optd **TCHAD** and **AFRIQUE EQUATORIALE FRANCAISE** and surch also.
50 **3** 65 on 1f. brown and green 2·25 3·50
51 85 on 1f. brown and green 2·50 3·50
52 **2** 90 on 75c. red and pink 2·75 3·50
53 **3** 1f.25 on 1f. blue & ultram 1·50 3·00
54 1f.50 on 1f. blue & ultram 2·75 3·50
55 3f. on 5f. brown and red 5·75 6·00
56 10f. on 5f. green and red 12·00 14·50
57a 20f. on 5f. violet & orange 19·00 19·00

1931. "Colonial Exhibition" key-types inscr "TCHAD".
58 E 40c. green 4·00 7·00
59 F 50c. mauve 4·50 7·00
60 G 90c. red 3·50 5·50
61 H 1f.50 blue 4·50 6·50

2 "Birth of the Republic"

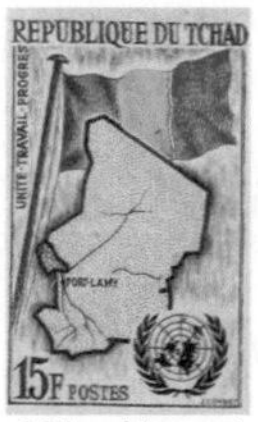

3 Flag, Map and U.N. Emblem

1959. 1st Anniv of Republic.
62 **2** 15f. multicoloured 3·00 1·10
63 – 25f. lake and myrtle 80 75
DESIGN: 25f. Map and birds.

1960. 10th African Technical Co-operation Commission. As T **62** of Cameroun.
64 50f. violet and purple 1·60 1·75

1960. Air. Olympic Games. No. 276 of French Equatorial Africa surch with Olympic rings and **XVIIe OLYMPIADE 1960 REPUBLIQUE DU TCHAD 250F**.
65 250f. on 500f. blue, black & grn 9·50 9·50

1961. Admission into U.N.
66 **3** 15f. multicoloured 45 20
67 25f. multicoloured 50 25
68 85f. multicoloured 1·60 80

4 Shari Bridge and Hippopotamus

1961.
69 – 50c. green and black 10 10
70 – 1f. green and black 10 10
71 – 2f. brown and black 10 10
72 – 3f. orange and green 10 10
73 – 4f. red and black 10 10
74 **4** 5f. lemon and black 20 15
75 – 10f. pink and black 20 20
76 – 15f. violet and black 45 20
77 – 20f. red and black 55 30
78 – 25f. blue and black 60 30
79 – 30f. blue and black 70 45
80 – 60f. yellow and black 1·40 65
81 – 85f. orange and black 1·60 95
DESIGNS (with animal silhouettes)—VERT: 50c. Biltine and Dorcas gazelle; 1f. Logone and elephant; 2f. Batha and lion; 3f. Salamat and buffalo; 4f. Ouaddai and greater kudu; 10f. Abtouyour and bullock; 15f. Bessada and Derby's eland; 20f. Tibesti and moufflon; 25f. Tikem Rocks and hartebeest; 30f. Kanem and cheetah; 60f. Borkou and oryx; 85f. Guelta D'Archei and addax.

5 Red Bishops

1961. Air.
82 **5** 50f. black, red and green 3·00 1·10
83 – 100f. multicoloured 6·75 2·00
84 – 200f. multicoloured 12·00 3·75
85 – 250f. blue, orange and green 15·00 5·25
86 – 500f. multicoloured 30·00 11·00
BIRDS: 100f. Scarlet-chested sunbird; 200f. African paradise flycatcher; 250f. Malachite kingfisher; 500f. Carmine bee eater.

1962. Air. "Air Afrique" Airline. As T **69** of Cameroun.
87 25f. blue, brown and black 60 25

1962. Malaria Eradication. As T **70** of Cameroun.
88 25f.+5f. orange 75 75

1962. Sports. As T **12** of Central African Republic. Multicoloured.
89 20f. Relay-racing (horiz) (postage) 45 30
90 50f. High-jumping (horiz) 1·10 55
91 100f. Throwing the discus (air) 2·50 1·25
The 100f. is 26 × 47 mm.

1962. 1st Anniv of Union of African and Malagasy States. As No. 328 of Cameroun.
92 **72** 30f. blue 70 40

1963. Freedom from Hunger. As T **76** of Cameroun.
93 25f.+5f. blue, brown & green 80 80

6 Pres. Tombalbaye

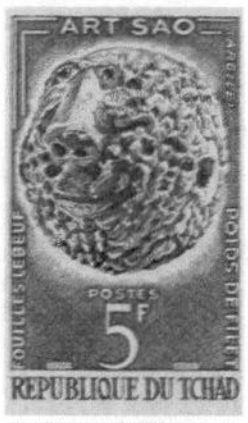

7 Carved Thread-weight

1963.
94 **6** 20f. multicoloured 45 20
95 85f. multicoloured 1·10 55

1963. Air. African and Malagasy Posts and Telecommunications Union. As T **11** of Central African Republic.
96 85f. multicoloured 1·25 55

1963. Space Telecommunications, As Nos. 37/8 of Central African Republic.
97 25f. violet, emerald and green 50 35
98 100f. blue and pink 2·00 1·25

1963. Air. 1st Anniv of "Air Afrique" and Inauguration of "DC-8" Service. As T **11** of Congo Republic.
99 50f. multicoloured 1·50 75

1963. Air. European–African Economic Convention. As T **24** of Central African Republic.
100 50f. multicoloured 1·00 60

1963. Sao Art.
101 **7** 5f. orange and turquoise 10 10
102 – 15f. purple, slate and red 30 25
103 – 25f. brown and blue 60 35
104 – 60f. bronze and brown 1·40 60
105 – 80f. bronze and brown 1·60 80
DESIGNS: 15f. Ancestral mask; 25f. Ancestral statuette; 60f. Gazelle's-head pendant; 80f. Pectoral.

1963. 15th Anniv of Declaration of Human Rights. As Central African Republic T **26**.
106 25f. purple and green 65 35

8 Broussard Monoplane

1963. Air.
107 **8** 100f. blue, green & brown 2·25 1·25

9 Pottery

1964. Sao Handicrafts.
108 **9** 10f. black, orange & blue 30 20
109 – 30f. red, black and yellow 55 30
110 – 50f. black, red and green 1·00 45
111 – 85f. black, yellow & purple 1·25 65
DESIGNS: 30f. Canoe-building; 50f. Carpet-weaving; 85f. Blacksmith working iron.

10 Rameses II in War Chariot, Abu Simbel

1964. Air. Nubian Monuments Preservation Fund.
112 **10** 10f.+5f. violet, grn & red 60 35
113 25f.+5f. purple, grn & red 95 50
114 50f.+5f. turq, grn & red 1·90 1·40

1964. World Meteorological Day. As T **14** of Congo Republic.
115 50f. violet, blue and purple 1·00 50

11 Cotton

1964. Multicoloured.
116 20f. Type **11** 95 50
117 25f. Flamboyant tree 1·10 55

1964. Air. 5th Anniv of Equatorial African Heads of State Conf. As T **31** of Central African Republic.
118 100f. multicoloured 1·50 75

12 Globe, Chimneys and Ears of Wheat

1964. Air. Europafrique.
119 **12** 50f. orange, purple & brn 1·00 55

13 Football

1964. Air. Olympic Games. Tokyo.
120 **13** 25f. green, lt green & brn 75 45
121 – 50f. brown, indigo & blue 1·00 55
122 – 100f. black, green and red 2·00 1·10
123 – 200f. black, bistre and red 4·25 2·10
DESIGNS—VERT: 50f. Throwing the javelin; 100f. High-jumping. HORIZ: 200f. Running.

1964. Air. Pan-African and Malagasy Post and Telecommunications Congress, Cairo. As T **23** of Congo Republic.
124 25f. sepia, red and mauve 60 25

1964. French, African and Malagasy Co-operation. As T **88** of Cameroun.
125 25f. brown, blue and red 60 30

14 Pres. Kennedy

15 National Guard

1964. Air. Pres. Kennedy Commem.
126 **14** 100f. multicoloured 1·75 1·10

1964. Chad Army. Multicoloured.
127 20f. Type **15** 50 20
128 25f. Standard-bearer and troops of Land Forces 55 25

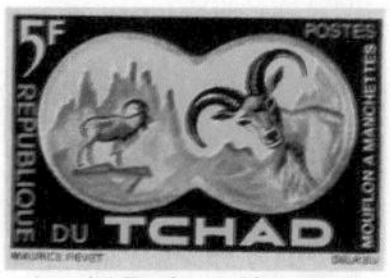

16 Barbary Sheep

1964. Fauna. Protection. Multicoloured.
129 5f. Type **16** 25 15
130 10f. Addax 35 20
131 20f. Scimitar oryx 65 30
132 25f. Giant eland (vert) 95 35
133 30f. Giraffe, African buffalo and lion (Zakouma Park)(vert) 1·25 50
134 85f. Greater kudu (vert) 3·00 1·10

17 Perforator of Olsen's Telegraph Apparatus

1965. I.T.U. Centenary.
135 **17** 30f. brown, red and green 55 25
136 – 60f. green, red and brown 1·00 45
137 – 100f. green, brown & red 1·90 80
DESIGNS—VERT: 60f. Milde's telephone. HORIZ: 100f. Distributor of Baudot's telegraph apparatus.

18 Badge and Mobile Gendarmes

1965. National Gendarmerie.
138 **18** 25f. multicoloured 60 35

19 I.C.Y. Emblem

1965. Air. International Co-operation Year.
139 **19** 100f. multicoloured . . . . 1·25 70

20 Abraham Lincoln

1965. Air. Death Centenary of Abraham Lincoln.
140 **20** 100f. multicoloured . . . . 1·75 75

21 Guitar

1965. Native Musical Instruments.
141 – 1f. brown & grn (postage) 10 10
142 **21** 2f. brown, purple and red 10 10
143 – 3f. lake, black and brown 20 15
144 – 15f. green, orange and red 50 25
145 – 60f. green and lake . . . . 1·60 80
146 – 100f. ultram, brn & bl (48½ × 27 mm) (air) . . . 1·90 1·25
DESIGNS—VERT: 1f. Drum and seat; 3f. Shoulder drum; 60f. Harp. HORIZ: 15f. Viol; 100f. Xylophone.

22 Sir Winston Churchill

1965. Air. Churchill Commemoration.
147 **22** 50f. black and green . . . 1·00 50

23 Dr. Albert Schweitzer (philosopher and missionary) and "Appealing Hands"

1966. Air. Schweitzer Commemoration.
148 **23** 100f. multicoloured . . . . 1·90 95

24 Mask in Mortar

26 W.H.O. Building

1966. World Festival of Negro Arts, Dakar.
149 **24** 15f. purple, bistre & blue 35 20
150 – 20f. brown, red and green 50 25
151 – 60f. purple, blue and red 1·40 55
152 – 80f. green, brown & violet 2·10 85

DESIGNS—Sao Art: 20f. Mask; 60f. Mask (different) (All from J. Courtin's excavations at Bouta Kebira); 80f. Armband (from I.N.T.S.H. excavations, Gawi).

1966. No. 94 surch.
153 **6** 25f. on 20f. multicoloured 60 30

1966. Inaug of W.H.O. Headquarters, Geneva.
154 **26** 25f. blue, yellow and red 45 20
155 32f. blue, yellow & green 50 25

27 Caduceus and Map of Africa

28 Footballer

1966. Central African Customs and Economic Union.
156 **27** 30f. multicoloured 60 30

1966. World Cup Football Championship.
157 **28** 30f. red, green and emerald 50 25
158 – 60f. red, black and blue . . 1·25 50
DESIGN—VERT: 60f. Footballer (different).

29 Youths, Flag and Arms

1966. Youth Movement.
159 **29** 25f. multicoloured 60 30

30 Columns

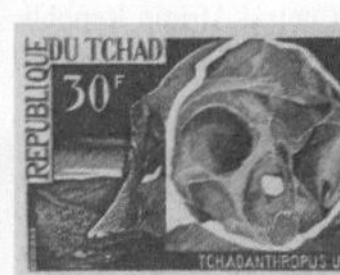
31 Skull of Lake Chad Man ("Tchadanthropus uxoris")

1966. 20th Anniv of U.N.E.S.C.O.
160 **30** 32f. blue, violet and red . . 65 50

1966. Air. Inauguration of "DC-8" Air Services. As T **54** of Central African Republic.
161 30f. grey, black and green . . 60 25

1966. Archaeological Excavation.
162 **31** 30f. slate, yellow and red 1·60 75

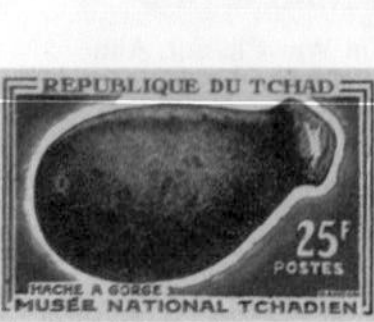
32 White-throated Bee Eater

1966. Air. Birds. Multicoloured.
163 50f. Greater blue-eared glossy starling . . . . 3·50 1·40
164 100f. Type **32** . . . . 4·50 2·40
165 200f. African pigmy kingfisher . . . . 8·50 2·50
166 250f. Red-throated bee eater 12·50 3·25
167 500f. Little green bee eater 18·00 7·00

33 Battle-axe

35 Sportsmen and Dais on Map

34 Congress Palace

1966. Prehistoric Implements.
168 **33** 25f. brown, blue and red 35 25
169 – 30f. black, brown & blue 45 25
170 – 85f. brown, red and blue 1·50 60
171 – 100f. brown, turq & sepia 1·75 85
DESIGNS: 30f. Arrowhead; 85f. Harpoon; 100f. Sandstone grindstone and pounder. From Tchad National Museum.

1967. Air.
173 **34** 25f. multicoloured 55 25

1967. Sports Day.
174 **35** 25f. multicoloured 60 35

36 "Colotis protomedia klug"

1967. Butterflies. Multicoloured.
175 5f. Type **36** 20 15
176 10f. "Charaxes jasius epijasius L" 35 20
177 20f. "Junonia cebrene trim" 1·00 50
178 130f. "Danaida petiverana H.D." . . . . 3·25 1·40

37 Lions Emblem

39 H.Q. Building

38 Dagnaux's Breguet "19" Aircraft

1967. Air. 50th Anniv of Lions International.
179 **37** 50f.+10f. multicoloured . . 1·25 65

1967. Air. 1st Anniv of Air Chad Airline.
180 **38** 25f. green, blue & brown 55 40
181 – 30f. indigo, green and blue 75 40
182 – 50f. brown, green & blue 1·25 75
183 – 100f. red, blue and green 2·50 1·10
DESIGNS: 30f. Latecoere "631" flying-boat; 50f. Douglas "DC-3"; 100f. Piper Cherokee "6".

1967. Air. 5th Anniv of U.A.M.P.T. As T **66** of Central African Republic.
184 100f. brown, bistre & mve . . 1·25 75

1967. Opening of W.H.O. Regional Headquarters, Brazzaville.
185 **39** 30f. multicoloured 60 30

40 Scouts and Jamboree Emblem

1967. World Scout Jamboree, Idaho. Multicoloured.
186 25f. Type **40** 45 20
187 32f. Scout and Jamboree emblem 65 25

41 Flour Mills

1967. Economic Development.
188 **41** 25f. slate, brown and blue 45 20
189 – 30f. blue, brown & green 55 30
DESIGN: 30f. Land reclamation, Lake Bol.

42 Woman and Harpist

43 Emblem of Rotary International

1967. Bailloud Mission in the Ennedi. Rock paintings.
190 – 2f. choc, brn & red (post) 20 15
191 – 10f. red, brown and violet 45 25
192 **42** 15f. lake, brown and blue 55 25
193 – 20f. red, brown and green 1·25 50
194 – 25f. red, brown and blue 1·60 60
195 – 30f. lake, brown and blue 1·00 50
196 – 50f. lake, brown and green 1·90 80
197 – 100f. red, brn & grn (air) 3·00 1·40
198 – 125f. lake, brown & blue 4·25 2·10
DESIGNS: 2f. Archers; 10f. Male and female costumes; 20f. Funeral vigil; 25f. "Dispute"; 30f. Giraffes; 50f. Cameleer pursuing ostrich. (48 × 27 mm): 100f. Masked dancers; 125f. Hunters and hare.

1968. 10th Anniv of Rotary Club, Fort Lamy.
199 **43** 50f. multicoloured 95 45

44 Downhill Skiing

1968. Air. Winter Olympic Games, Grenoble.
200 **44** 30f. brown, green & purple 95 35
201 – 100f. blue, green & turq . . 2·50 1·10
DESIGN—VERT: 100f. Ski-jumping.

45 Chancellor Adenauer

46 "Health Services"

1968. Air. Adenauer Commemoration.
202 **45** 52f. brown, lilac and green 1·00 50

1968. Air. Anniv of W.H.O.
204 **46** 25f. multicoloured 45 20
205 32f. multicoloured 55 25

47 Allegory of Irrigation

1968. International Hydrological Decade.
206 **47** 50f. blue, brown & green 75 30

48 "The Snake-charmer"

1968. Air. Paintings by Henri Rousseau. Mult.
207 100f. Type **48** . . . . 2·50 1·60
208 130f. "The War" (49 × 35 mm) . . . . . . 3·75 2·25

49 College Building, Student and Emblem

1968. National College of Administration.
209 **49** 25f. purple, blue and red . . . 45 25

50 Child writing and Blackboard

52 "Utetheisa pulchella"

51 Harvesting Cotton

1968. Literacy Day.
210 **50** 60f. black, blue & brown . . . 80 35

1968. Cotton Industry.
211 **51** 25f. purple, green & blue . . . 50 20
212 – 30f. brown, blue & green . . . 50 20
DESIGN—VERT: 30f. Loom, Fort Archambault Mill.

1968. Butterflies and Moths. Multicoloured.
213 25f. Type **52** . . . . 1·10 35
214 30f. "Ophideres materna" . . 1·40 35
215 50f. "Gynanisa maja" . . . 2·75 70
216 100f. "Epiphora bauhiniae" . . . 3·75 1·25

53 Hurdling

1968. Air. Olympic Games, Mexico.
217 **53** 32f. chocolate, grn & brn . . . 80 50
218 – 80f. purple, blue and red . . . 1·75 75
DESIGN: 80f. Relay-racing.

54 Human Rights Emblem within Man

1968. Human Rights Year.
219 **54** 32f. red, green and blue . . . 60 25

1969. Air. "Philexafrique" Stamp Exn, Abidjan, Ivory Coast (1st issue). As T **137** of Cameroun. Multicoloured.
220 100f. "The actor Wolf, called Bernard" (J. L. David) . . . 2·75 2·75

1969. Air. "Philexafrique" Stamp Exn, Abidjan, Ivory Coast (2nd issue). As T **138** of Cameroun. Multicoloured.
221 50f. Moundangs dancers and Chad postage due stamp of 1930 . . . . 1·90 1·90

55 G. Nachtigal and Tibesti landscape, 1869

1969. Air. Chad Explorers.
222 – 100f. violet, green & blue . . . 1·75 75
223 **55** 100f. purple, blue & brown . . . 1·75 75
DESIGN: No. 222, H. Barth (portrait) and aboard canoe, Lake Region, 1851.

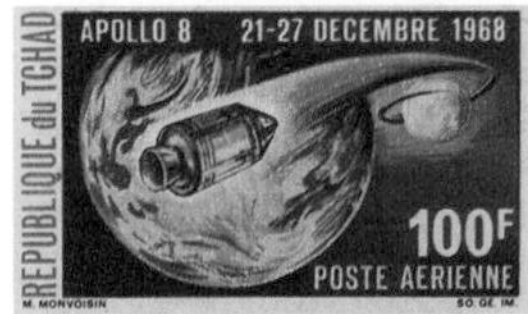

56 "Apollo 8" circling Moon

1969. Air. Flight of "Apollo 8" around the Moon.
224 **56** 100f. black, blue & orange . . . 1·75 75

57 St. Bartholomew

1969. Jubilee Year of Catholic Church. Mult.
225 50c. St. Paul 10 10
226 1f. St. Peter 10 10
227 2f. St. Thomas 10 10
228 5f. St. John the Evangelist . . 10 10
229 10f. Type **57** 10 10
230 20f. St. Matthew 25 15
231 25f. St. James the Less . . . 25 15
232 30f. St. Andrew 30 20
233 40f. St. Jude 35 20
234 50f. St. James the Greater . . 45 25
235 85f. St. Philip 70 45
236 100f. St. Simon 80 55

58 Mahatma Gandhi

59 Motor Vehicles and I.L.O. Emblem

1969. Air. "Apostles of Peace".
237 **58** 50f. brown and green . . . 95 45
238 – 50f. sepia and agate . . . 95 45
239 – 50f. brown and pink . . . 95 45
240 – 50f. brown and blue . . . 95 45
DESIGNS: No. 238, President Kennedy; No. 239, Martin Luther King; No. 240, Robert F. Kennedy.

1969. 50th Anniv of I.L.O.
242 **59** 32f. blue, purple & green . . . 60 30

60 Cipolla, Baran and Sambo (pair with cox)

61 "African Woman" (Bezombes)

1969. "World Solidarity". Multicoloured. (a) Gold Medal Winners, Mexico Olympics.
243 1f. Type **60** 25 25
244 1f. R. Beamon (long-jump) . . 25 25
245 1f. I. Becker (women's pentathlon) 25 25
246 1f. C. Besson (women's 400 m) 25 25
247 1f. W. Davenport (110 m hurdles) 25 25
248 1f. K. Dibiasi (diving) . . . 25 25
249 1f. R. Fosbury (high-jump) . . 25 25
250 1f. M. Gamoudi (5000 m) . . 25 25
251 1f. Great Britain (sailing) . . 25 25
252 1f. J. Guyon (cross-country riding) 25 25
253 1f. D. Hemery (200 m hurdles) 25 25
254 1f. S. Kato (gymnastics) . . . 25 25
255 1f. B. Klinger (small bore rifle shooting) 25 25
256 1f. R. Matson (shot put) . . 25 25
257 1f. R. Matthes (100 m backstroke) 25 25
258 1f. D. Meyer (women's 200 m freestyle) 25 25
259 1f. Morelon and Trentin (tandem cycle) 25 25
260 1f. D. Rebillard (4000 m cycle pursuit) . . 25 25
261 1f. T. Smith (200 m) 25 25
262 1f. P. Trentin (1000 m cycle) 25 25
263 1f. F. Vianelli (196 km cycle race) 25 25
264 1f. West Germany (dressage) 25 25
265 1f. M. Wolke (welterweight boxing) 25 25
266 1f. Zimmermann and Esser (women's kayak pair) . . . 25 25

(b) Paintings.
267 1f. Type **61** 25 25
268 1f. "Mother and Child" (Gauguin) 25 25
269 1f. "Holy Family" (Murillo) (horiz) 25 25
270 1f. "Adoration of the Kings" (Rubens) 25 25
271 1f. "Three Negroes" (Rubens) 25 25
272 1f. "Woman with Flowers" (Veneto) 25 25

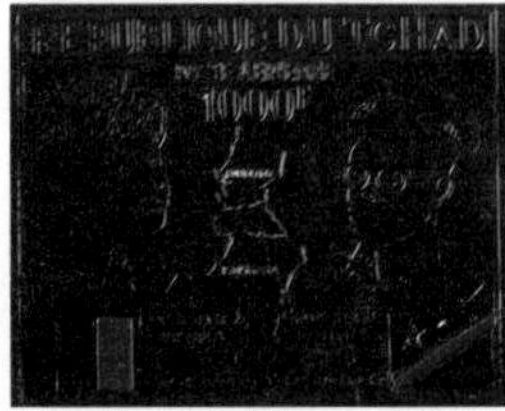
62 Presidents Tombalbaye and Mobutu

1969. Air. 1st Anniv of Central African States Union.
273 **62** 1000f. gold, red and blue . . . 20·00 20·00
This stamp is embossed in gold foil; colours of flags enamelled.

63 "Cochlospermum tinctorium"

1969. Flowers. Multicoloured.
274 1f. Type **63** 10 10
275 4f. "Parkia biglobosa" . . . 20 15
276 10f. "Pancratium trianthum" . . 30 20
277 15f. "Ipomoea aquatica" . . . 45 20

1969. Air. Birth Bicentenary of Napoleon Bonaparte. Multicoloured. As T **144** of Cameroun.
278 30f. "Napoleon visiting the Hotel des Invalides" (Veron-Bellecourt) 95 50
279 85f. "The Battle of Wagram" (H. Vernet) . . . . 1·90 1·00
280 130f. "The Battle of Austerlitz" (Gerard) . . . 3·50 1·90

64 Frozen Carcases

1969. Frozen Meat Industry.
281 **64** 25f. red, green and orange . . . 35 20
282 – 30f. brown, slate & green . . . 50 25
DESIGN: 30f. Cattle and refrigerated abattoir, Farcha.

1969. 5th Anniv of African Development Bank. As T **146** of Cameroun.
283 30f. brown, green and red . . . 45 25

66 Astronaut and Lunar Module

1969. Air. 1st Man on the Moon. Embossed on gold foil.
289 **66** 1000f. gold . . . . 22·00 22·00

67 Nile Mouthbrooder

68 President Tombalbaye

1969. Fishes.
290 **67** 2f. purple, grey and green . . . 20 10
291 – 3f. grey, red and blue . . . 30 25
292 – 5f. blue, yellow and ochre . . . 55 25
293 – 20f. blue, green and red . . . 1·75 60
FISHES: 3f. Deep-sided citharinid; 5f. Nile pufferfish; 20f. Lesser tigerfish.

1969. 10th Anniv of A.S.E.C.N.A. As T **150** of Cameroun.
294 30f. orange 55 30

1970. President Tombalbaye.
295 **68** 25f. multicoloured 45 20

69 "Village Life" (G. Narcisse)

1970. Air. African Paintings. Multicoloured.
296 100f. Type **69** . . . . 2·10 1·00
297 250f. "Market Woman" (I. N'Diaye) . . . . 4·00 1·60
298 250f. "Flower-seller" (I. N'Diaye) (vert) . . . . 4·00 1·60

70 Lenin

72 Osaka Print

71 Class and Torchbearers

1970. Birth Centenary of Lenin.
299 **70** 150f. black, cream & gold . . . 2·50 1·25

1970. New U.P.U. Headquarters Building, Berne, As T **156** of Cameroun.
300 30f. brown, violet and red . . . 55 30

1970. International Education Year.
301 **71** 100f. multicoloured . . . . 1·50 80

1970. Air. World Fair "EXPO 70", Osaka, Japan.
302 **72** 50f. green, blue and red . . . 45 30
303 – 100f. blue, green and red . . . 75 45
304 – 125f. slate, brown & red . . . 1·00 55
DESIGNS: 100f. Tower of the Sun; 125f. Osaka print (different).

1970. Air. "Apollo" Moon Flights. Nos. 164/6 surch with new value, and optd with various inscriptions and diagrams concerning space flights.
305 **32** 50f. on 100f. mult ("Apollo 11") . . . . . 1·50 1·00
306 – 100f. on 200f. mult ("Apollo 12") . . . . . 2·75 1·40
307 – 125f. on 250f. mult ("Apollo 13") . . . . . 4·25 2·25

74 Meteorological Equipment and "Agriculture"

76 Ahmed Mangue (Minister of Education)

75 "DC-8-63" over Airport

1970. World Meteorological Day.
308 **74** 50f. grey, green & orange 75 30

1970. Air. "Air Afrique" DC-8 "Fort Lamy".
309 **75** 30f. multicoloured 75 35

1970. Ahmed Mangue (air crash victim) Commem.
310 **76** 100f. black, red and gold 1·10 50

77 Tanning

1970. Trades and Handicrafts.
311 **77** 1f. bistre, brown and blue 10 10
312 – 2f. brown, blue and green 15 10
313 – 3f. violet, brown & mauve 20 15
314 – 4f. brown, bistre & green 25 15
315 – 5f. brown, green and red 35 35
DESIGNS—VERT: 2f. Dyeing; 4f. Water-carrying. HORIZ: 3f. Milling palm-nuts for oil; 5f. Copper-founding.

78 U.N. Emblem and Dove **79** "The Visitation" (Venetian School, 15th cent)

1970. 25th Anniv of United Nations.
316 **78** 32f. multicoloured 60 35

1970. Air. Christmas. Multicoloured.
317 20f. Type **79** 50 30
318 25f. "The Nativity" (Venetian School, 15th cent) 75 35
319 30f. "Virgin and Child" (Veneziano) 95 45

80 Map and O.C.A.M. Building

1971. O.C.A.M. (Organization Commune Africane et Malgache) Conference, Fort Lamy.
320 **80** 30f. multicoloured 60 30

81 Maritius "Post Office" 2d. of 1847

1971. Air. "PHILEXOCAM" Stamp Exhibition, Fort-Lamy.
321 **81** 10f. slate, brown & turq . . 30 20
322 – 20f. brown, black & turq 45 20
323 – 30f. brown, black and red 55 30
324 – 60f. black, brown & purple 80 50
325 – 80f. slate, brown and blue 1·25 70
326 – 100f. brown, slate & blue 1·60 95
DESIGNS—20f. Tuscany 3 lire of 1860; 30f. France 1f. of 1849; 30f., 60f. U.S.A. 10c. of 1847; 80f. Japan 5 sen of 1872; 100f. Saxony 3pf. of 1850.

82 Pres. Nasser **83** "Racial Harmony" Tree

1971. Air. 1st Death Anniv of Gamal Abdel Nasser (Egypt).
328 **82** 75f. multicoloured 80 35

1971. Racial Equality Year.
329 **83** 40f. red, green and blue . . 75 30

1971. Air. Reconciliation with Central African Republic and Zaire. As T **106** of Central African Republic.
330 100f. multicoloured . . . . . 1·50 75

84 Map and Dish Aerial

1971. World Telecommunications Day.
331 **84** 5f. orge, red & bl (postage) 20 15
332 – 40f. green, brown & pur 55 25
333 – 50f. black, brown & red . . 75 30
334 – 125f. red, green & blue (air) . . . . 1·90 85
DESIGNS: 40f. Map and communications tower; 50f. Map and satellite. (48 × 27 mm): 125f. Map and telecommunications symbols.

85 Scouts by Camp-fire

1971. Air. World Scout Jamboree, Asagiri, Japan.
335 **85** 250f. multicoloured . . . . 3·75 1·90

86 Great Egret

1971. Air.
336 **86** 1000f. multicoloured . . . 29·00 16·00

87 Ancient Marathon Race

1971. Air. 75th Anniv of Modern Olympic Games. Multicoloured.
337 40f. Type **87** 55 30
338 45f. Ancient stadium, Olympia 80 35
339 75f. Ancient wrestling . . . . 1·00 50
340 130f. Athens Stadium, 1896 Games . . . . 1·75 85

88 Sidney Bechet

89 Gen. de Gaulle

1971. Air. Famous American Black Musicians. Multicoloured.
341 50f. Type **88** . . . . 1·25 50
342 75f. Duke Ellington . . . . 1·60 75
343 100f. Louis Armstrong . . . 2·50 1·25

1971. Air. 1st Death Anniv of De Gaulle.
344 – 200f. gold, blue and light blue . . . . 6·25 6·25
345 **89** 200f. gold, green & yellow 6·25 6·25
DESIGN: No. 344, Governor-General Felix Eboue.

1971. Air. 10th Anniv of African and Malagasy Posts and Telecommunications Union. As T **184** of Cameroun. Multicoloured.
347 100f. Headquarters building and Sao carved animal head . . . . 1·25 60

90 Children's Heads

1971. 25th Anniv of U.N.I.C.E.F.
348 **90** 50f. blue, green & purple 85 35
On the above stamp, "24e" has been obliterated and "25e" inserted in the commemorative inscription.

91 Gorane Nangara Dancers

1971. Chad Dancers. Multicoloured.
349 10f. Type **91** 30 20
350 15f. Yondo initiates 45 25
351 30f. M'Boum (vert) 80 35
352 40f. Sara Kaba (vert) . . . . 1·25 55

93 Presidents Pompidou and Tombalbaye

1972. Visit of French President.
354 **93** 40f. multicoloured . . . . 1·25 60

94 Bobsleighing

1972. Air. Winter Olympic Games, Sapporo, Japan.
355 **94** 50f. red and blue 70 40
356 – 100f. green and purple . . 1·50 60
DESIGN: 100f. Slalom.

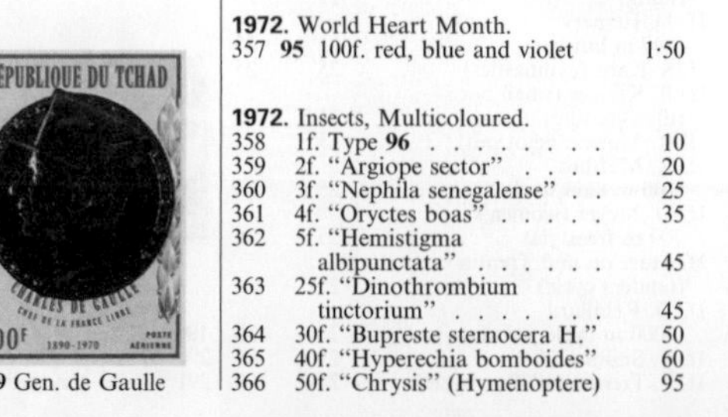
95 Human Heart

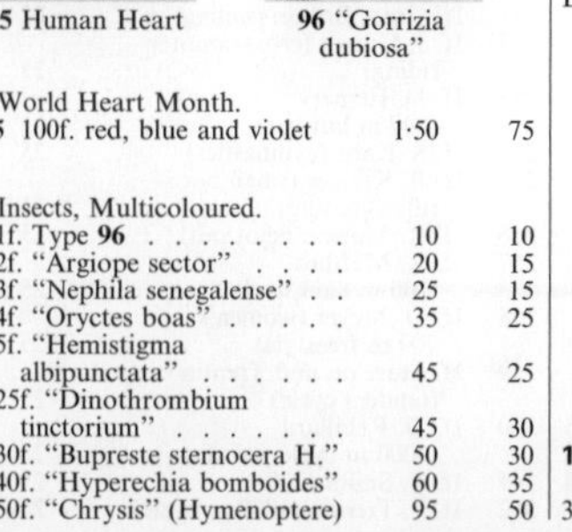
96 "Gorrizia dubiosa"

1972. World Heart Month.
357 **95** 100f. red, blue and violet 1·50 75

1972. Insects, Multicoloured.
358 1f. Type **96** 10 10
359 2f. "Argiope sector" 20 15
360 3f. "Nephila senegalense" . . . 25 15
361 4f. "Oryctes boas" 35 25
362 5f. "Hemistigma albipunctata" 45 25
363 25f. "Dinothrombium tinctorium" 45 30
364 30f. "Bupreste sternocera H." 50 30
365 40f. "Hyperechia bomboides" 60 35
366 50f. "Chrysis" (Hymenoptere) 95 50
367 100f. "Tithoes confinis" (Longicore) . . . . 2·50 85
368 130f. "Galeodes araba" (Solifuge) . . . . 3·75 1·40

1972. Air. U.N.E.S.C.O. "Save Venice" Campaign. As T **191** of Cameroun. Multicoloured.
369 40f. "Harbour Panorama" (detail, Caffi) 95 50
370 45f. "Venice Panorama" (detail, Caffi) (horiz) . . . 1·25 60
371 140f. "Grand Canal" (detail, Caffi) . . . . 3·00 1·40

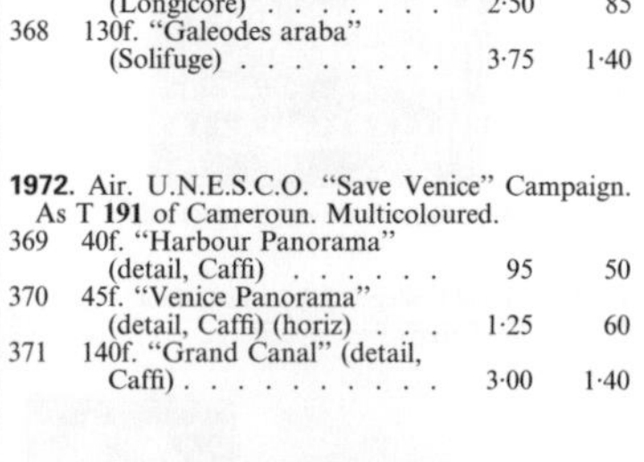
97 Hurdling

1972. Olympic Games, Munich. Multicoloured.
372 50f. Type **97** 75 35
373 130f. Gymnastics . . . . . . 1·50 75
374 150f. Swimming . . . . . . 1·90 85

98 Alphonse Daudet and Scene from "Tartarin de Tarascon"

1972. Air. International Book Year.
376 **98** 100f. brown, red & purple 1·50 75

99 Dromedary

1972. Domestic Animals.
377 **99** 25f. brown and violet . . . 45 20
378 – 30f. blue and mauve . . . 50 25
379 – 40f. brown and green . . . 70 30
380 – 45f. brown and blue . . . 85 35
DESIGNS: 30f. Horse; 40f. Saluki hound; 45f. Goat.

100 "Luna 16" and Moon Probe **101** Tobacco Production

1972. Air. Russian Moon Exploration.
381 **100** 100f. violet, brown & blue 1·40 70
382 – 150f. brown, blue & purple . . . . 2·10 80
DESIGN—HORIZ: 150f. "Lunokhod 1" Moon vehicle.

1972. Economic Development.
383 **101** 40f. green, red & brown 50 25
384 – 50f. brown, green & blue 75 35
DESIGN: 50f. Ploughing with oxen.

102 Microscope, Cattle and Laboratory

1972. Air. 20th Anniv of Farcha Veterinary Laboratory.
385 **102** 75f. multicoloured 80 35

103 Massa Warrior

1972. Chad Warriors. Multicoloured.
386 15f. Type **103** 55 25
387 20f. Moudang archer 70 35

104 King Faisal and Pres. Tombalbaye

1972. Visit of King Faisal of Saudi Arabia. Multicoloured.
388 100f. Type **104** (postage) . . 1·90 95
389 75f. King Faisal and Ka'aba, Mecca (air) . . . . 1·00 50

105 Gen. Gowon, Pres. Tombalbaye and Map

1972. Visit of Gen. Gowon, Nigerian Head-of-State.
390 **105** 70f. multicoloured 75 30

106 "Madonna and Child" (G. Bellini)

1972. Air. Christmas. Paintings. Multicoloured.
391 40f. Type **106** 45 25
392 75f. "Virgin and Child" (bas-relief, Da Santivo, Dall' Occhio) 80 45
393 80f. "Nativity" (B. Angelico) (horiz) . . . . 1·25 65
394 90f. "Adoration of the Magi" (P. Perugino) . . . . . . 1·60 80

107 Commemorative Scroll

1972. 50th Anniv of U.S.S.R.
395 **107** 150f. multicoloured . . . 1·50 55

108 High-jumping

1973. 2nd African Games, Lagos. Multicoloured.
396 50f. Type **108** 75 35
397 125f. Running . . . . 1·40 60
398 200f. Putting the shot . . . . 2·00 1·00

109 Copernicus and Planetary System Diagram

1973. Air. 500th Birth Anniv of Nicholas Copernicus.
400 **109** 250f. grey, brown & mve 4·00 1·90

1973. African Solidarity. "Drought Relief". No. 377 surch **SECHERESSE SOLIDARITE AFRICAINE 100F**.
401 **99** 100f. on 25f. brown & vio 1·60 90

1973. U.A.M.P.T. As Type **216** of Cameroun.
402 100f. green, red & brown . . 1·50 75

111 "Skylab" over Globe

1974. Air. "Skylab" Exploits.
403 **111** 100f. brown, red & blue 1·25 55
404 – 150f. turquoise, blue & brn . . . . 1·90 80
DESIGN: 150f. Close-up of "Skylab".

112 Chad Mother and Children

1974. 1st Anniv of Chad Red Cross.
405 **112** 30f.+10f. multicoloured 60 60

113 Football Players

1974. Air. World Cup Football Championship, West Germany.
406 **113** 50f. brown and red . . . 50 30
407 – 125f. green and red (vert) 1·40 60
408 – 150f. red and green . . . 1·90 95
DESIGNS: Nos. 407/8, Footballers in action similar to Type **113**.

114 Chad Family

116 Rotary Emblem

115 U.P.C. Emblem and Mail Canoe

1974. Air. World Population Year.
409 **114** 250f. brown, green & bl 3·00 1·60

1974. Air. Centenary of U.P.U.
410 **115** 30f. brown, red & green 50 25
411 – 40f. black and blue . . . 2·75 1·50
412 – 100f. blue, brown & blk 1·60 70
413 – 150f. violet, green & turq 2·25 75
DESIGNS—U.P.U. Emblem and: 40f. Electric train; 100f. Jet airliner; 150f. Satellite.

1975. 70th Anniv of Rotary International.
414 **116** 50f. multicoloured 75 35

117 Heads of Women of Four Races

1975. Air. International Women's Year.
415 **117** 250f. multicoloured . . . 3·75 1·90

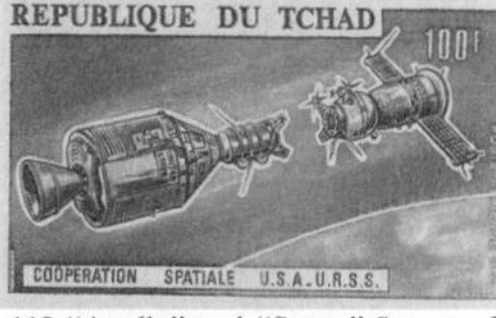

118 "Apollo" and "Soyuz" Spacecraft about to dock

1975. Air. "Apollo–Soyuz" Test Project.
416 **118** 100f. brown, blue & green 1·10 50
417 – 130f. brown, blue & green 1·40 75
DESIGN: 130f. "Apollo" and "Soyuz" spacecraft docked.

119 "Craterostigma plantagineum"

1975. Flowers. Multicoloured.
418 5f. Type **119** 10 10
419 10f. "Tapinanthus globiferus" 20 15
420 15f. "Commelina forsalaei" (vert) 30 15
421 20f. "Adenium obasum" . . 35 15
422 25f. "Hibiscus esulenus" . . 60 20
423 30f. "Hibiscus sabdariffa" . . 75 25
424 40f. "Kigelia africana" . . . 1·10 30

120 Football

1975. Air. Olympic Games, Montreal (1976).
425 **120** 75f. green and red 80 30
426 – 100f. brown, blue & red 1·25 55
427 – 125f. blue and brown . . 1·40 80
DESIGNS: 100f. Throwing the discus; 125f. Running.

1975. Air. Successful Rendezvous of "Apollo–Soyuz" Mission. Optd **JONCTION 17 JUILLET 1975**.
428 **118** 100f. brown, blue & grn 1·10 70
429 – 130f. brown, blue & grn 1·40 90

122 Stylized British and American Flags

1975. Air. Bicentenary of American Revolution.
430 **122** 150f. blue, red & brown 1·90 95

123 "Adoration of the Shepherds" (Murillo)

1975. Air. Christmas. Religious Paintings. Mult.
431 40f. Type **123** 55 35
432 75f. "Adoration of the Shepherds" (G. de la Tour) 1·00 55
433 80f. "Virgin of the Bible" (R. van der Weyden) (vert) . . 1·25 60
434 100f. "Holy Family with the Lamb" (attrib. Raphael) (vert) . . . . 1·90 95

124 Alexander Graham Bell and Satellite

1976. Telephone Centenary.
435 **124** 100f. multicoloured . . . 1·00 50
436 125f. multicoloured . . . 1·50 75

125 U.S.S.R. (ice hockey)

1976. Winter Olympics. Medal-winners, Innsbruck. Multicoloured.
437 60f. Type **125** (postage) . . . 75 35
438 90f. Ski-jumping (K. Schnabl, Austria) 95 40
439 250f. Bobsleighing (West Germany) (air) . . . . . . 2·25 75
440 300f. Speed-skating (J. E. Storholt, Norway) . . . . 2·75 1·10
These stamps were not issued without overprints.

126 Paul Revere (after Copley) and his Night Ride

1976. Air. Bicentenary of American Revolution.
442 100f. Type **126** 80 25
443 125f. Washington (after Stuart) and "Washington crossing the Delaware" (detail, Leutze) 95 35
444 150f. Lafayette offering his services to America . . . . 1·25 45
445 200f. Rochambeau and detail "Siege of Yorktown" (Couder) . . . . 1·60 70
446 250f. Franklin (after Duplessis) and "Declaration of Independence" (detail, Trumball) . . . . 2·25 80

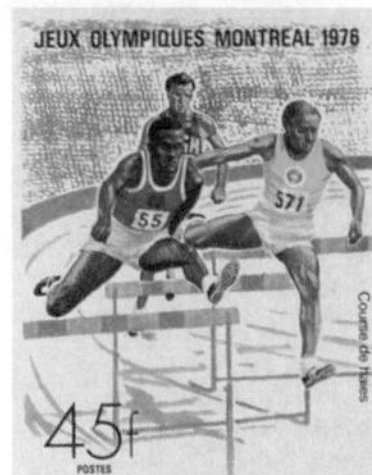

127 Hurdles

1976. Olympic Games, Montreal. Multicoloured.
448 45f. Type **127** (postage) . . . 60 25
449 100f. Boxing (air) 95 35
450 200f. Pole vaulting . . . . . 1·90 55
451 300f. Putting the shot . . . . 2·75 95

128 Launch of "Viking"

1976. "Viking" landing on Mars. Mult.
453 45f. Type **128** (postage) . . . 45 20
454 90f. Trajectory of flight . . . 80 30
455 100f. Descent to Mars (air) 85 35
456 200f. "Viking" in flight . . . 1·60 50
457 250f. "Viking" on landing approach . . . . 1·90 75

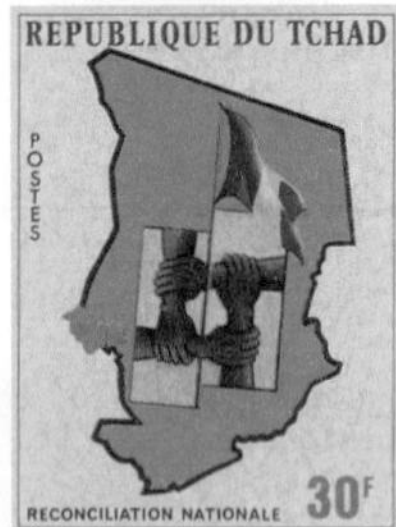

129 Flag and Clasped Hands on Map of Chad

1976. National Reconciliation. Mult.
459 30f. Type **129** 35 25
460 60f. Type **129** 85 30
461 120f. Map, people and various occupations . . . 1·60 70

130 Release of Political Prisoners

1976. 1st Anniv of April 1st Revolution. Mult.
462 30f. Type **130** 25 20
463 60f. Officer-cadets on parade 50 30
464 120f. Type **130** . . . . 1·10 55

131 Concorde

1976. Air. Concorde's First Commercial Flight.
465 **131** 250f. blue, red & black . . 4·25 2·75

132 Gourd and Ladle

1976. Pyrograved Gourds.
466 **132** 30f. multicoloured 30 20
467 – 60f. multicoloured 60 25
468 – 120f. multicoloured . . . 1·25 60
DESIGNS: 60f., 120f. Gourds with different decorations.

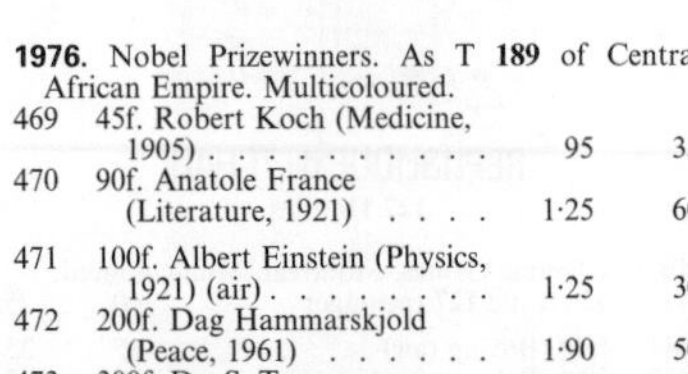

1976. Nobel Prizewinners. As T **189** of Central African Empire. Multicoloured.
469 45f. Robert Koch (Medicine, 1905) 95 35
470 90f. Anatole France (Literature, 1921) . . . . 1·25 60
471 100f. Albert Einstein (Physics, 1921) (air) . . . . 1·25 30
472 200f. Dag Hammarskjold (Peace, 1961) . . . . . . 1·90 50
473 300f. Dr. S. Tomonaga (Physics, 1965) . . . . . . 2·75 75

133 "The Nativity" (Hans Holbein)

1976. Air. Christmas. Multicoloured.
475 30f. "The Nativity" (Altdorfer) 30 20
476 60f. Type **133** 55 30
477 120f. "Adoration of the Shepherds" (Honthorst) (horiz) . . . . 1·00 60
478 150f. "Adoration of the Magi" (David) (horiz) . . 1·60 95

134 "Lesdiguieres Bridge"

1976. Air. Centenary of Impressionism. Paintings by Johan Bathold Jongkind. Multicoloured.
479 100f. Type **134** . . . . 1·40 70
480 120f. "Warship" . . . . . . 3·00 1·10

1977. Zeppelin Flights. As T **190** of Central African Empire. Multicoloured.
481 100f. Friedrichshafen and German 50pf. stamp, 1936 (postage) . . . . 1·25 50
482 125f. Polar scene and German 1m. stamp, 1931 (air) . . . . 1·10 30
483 150f. Chicago store and German 4m. stamp, 1933 2·00 45
484 175f. New York, London and German 2m. stamp, 1928 4·00 75
485 200f. New York and U.S. $2.60 stamp, 1930 . . . . 2·75 85

1977. Air. 10th Anniv of International French Language Council. As T **204** of Benin.
487 100f. multicoloured 85 50

135 Simon Bolivar

1977. Great Personalities. Multicoloured.
488 150f. Type **135** . . . . 1·25 50
489 175f. Joseph J. Roberts . . . 1·50 50
490 200f. Queen Wilhelmina . . . 1·75 60
491 200f. General de Gaulle . . . 2·50 85
493 250f. Coronation of Queen Elizabeth II (horiz) . . . . 2·50 90
492 325f. King Baudouin and Queen Fabiola . . . . 2·75 95

137 Lafayette and Arrival in America

1977. Air. Bicentenary of American Independence. Multicoloured.
495 100f. Type **137** . . . . 1·10 50
496 120f. Abraham Lincoln . . . 1·25 60
497 150f. F. J. Madison . . . . 1·75 75

138 Radio Aerial, Sound Waves and Map

1977. Posts and Telecommunications Emblems.
498 – 30f. black and yellow . . 35 20
499 **138** 60f. multicoloured 70 25
500 – 120f. multicoloured . . . 1·25 60
DESIGNS—HORIZ (47 × 26 mm): 30f. Posthorn and initials "ONPT". VERT (26 × 36 mm): 120f. Telecommunications skyline and initials "TIT".

139 Concorde

1977. Air. "North Atlantic"—Concorde and Lindbergh Commemorations.
501 **139** 100f. blue, red & lt blue 75 45
502 – 120f. brown, blue & grn 85 50
503 – 150f. violet, red & green 1·10 65
504 – 200f. orange, pur & brn 1·60 85
505 – 300f. blue, purple & blk 2·50 1·25
DESIGNS: 120f. to 300f. Various portraits of Lindbergh with "Spirit of St. Louis" against different backgrounds.

140 "Mariner 10"

1977. Air. Space Research.
506 **140** 100f. blue, olive & green 80 50
507 – 200f. brown, green & red 1·75 1·00
508 – 300f. brown, grn & bistre 2·50 1·25
DESIGNS: 200f. "Luna 21"; 300f. "Viking".

141 Running

142 "Back Pain"

1977. Air. Sports.
509 **141** 30f. brown, red & blue . . 30 20
510 – 60f. brown, blue & orge 55 30
511 – 120f. multicoloured . . . 1·00 50
512 – 125f. mauve, violet & grn 1·25 60
DESIGNS: 60f. Volleyball; 120f. Football; 125f. Basketball.

1977. World Rheumatism Year.
513 **142** 30f. red, green and violet 35 20
514 – 60f. red, violet and green 55 25
515 – 120f. blue, red & lt blue 1·25 60
DESIGNS—HORIZ: 60f. "Neck pain". VERT: 120f. "Knee pain".

1977. Air. 1st Commercial Paris–New York Flight of Concorde. Optd **PARIS NEW-YORK 22.11.77**.
516 **139** 100f. blue, red & lt blue 2·25 1·25

144 Saving a Goal

1977. World Football Cup Championship. Mult.
517 40f. Type **144** 35 15
518 60f. Heading the ball 55 20
519 100f. Referee 95 30
520 200f. Foot kicking ball . . . 1·90 60
521 300f. Pele (Brazilian player) 3·00 95

145 "Christ in the Manger" (detail)

1977. Air. Christmas. Paintings by Rubens. Mult.
523 30f. Type **145** 45 25
524 60f. "Virgin and Child with Two Donors" 75 35
525 100f. "The Adoration of the Shepherds" . . . . 1·25 60
526 125f. "The Adoration of the Magi" (detail) . . . . . . 1·60 80

1978. Coronation of Queen Elizabeth II. No. 493 optd **ANNIVERSAIRE DU COURONNEMENT 1953–1978**.
527 250f. multicoloured . . . . . 2·50 1·50

147 Antoine de Saint-Exupery

1978. Air. History of Aviation. Multicoloured.
529 40f. Type **147** 50 20
530 50f. Wright Brothers and aircraft in flight 60 25
531 80f. Hugo Junkers 85 45
532 100f. Italo Balbo . . . . . . 1·10 55
533 120f. "Concorde" . . . . . 1·25 75

1978. Air. "Philexafrique" Stamp Exhibition, Gabon (1st issue), and International Stamp Fair, Essen. As T **237** of Benin. Multicoloured.
535 100f. Grey heron and Mecklenburg-Strelitz, ⅛sgr. stamp, 1864 . . . . 2·75 1·90
536 100f. Black rhinoceros and Chad 500f. stamp, 1961 . . 2·75 1·90

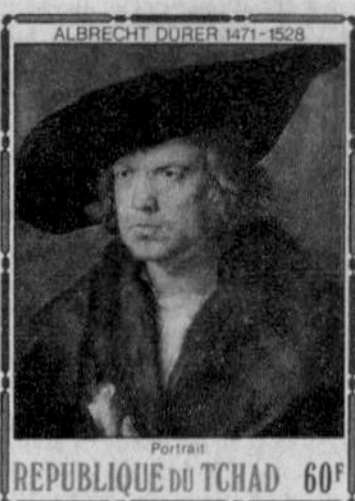

148 "Portrait"

150 Head and Unhealthy and Healthy Villages

149 "Helene Fourment"

1978. 450th Death Anniv of Albrecht Durer (artist). Multicoloured.
537 60f. Type **148** 50 15
538 150f. "Jacob Muffel" . . . . 1·40 30
539 250f. "Young Girl" . . . . 2·25 60
540 350f. "Oswolt Krel" . . . . 3·50 80

1978. 400th Birth Anniv of Peter Paul Rubens (artist). Multicoloured.
541 60f. "Abraham and Melchisedek" (horiz) . . . 60 15
542 120f. Type **149** . . . . 1·10 25

543 200f. "David and the Elders of Israel" (horiz) . . . . . 1·90 60
544 300f. "Anne of Austria" . . 3·25 85

1978. National Health Day.
546 **150** 60f. multicoloured 60 35

1978. World Cup Football Championship Finalists. Nos. 517/21 optd with teams and scores of past finals.
547 **144** 40f. multicoloured 35 20
548 – 60f. multicoloured 50 30
549 – 100f. multicoloured . . . 85 50
550 – 200f. multicoloured . . . 1·90 95
551 – 300f. multicoloured . . . 3·00 1·50

OPTS: 40f. **1962 BRESIL-TCHECOSLOVAQUIE 3-1**; 60f. **1966 GRAND BRETAGNE-ALLEMAGNE (RFA) 4-2**; 100f. **1970 BRESIL-ITALIE 4-1**; 200f. **1974 ALLEMAGNE (RFA)-PAYS BAS 2-1**; 300f. **1978 ARGENTINE-PAYS BAS 3-1**.

152 Camel Riders, Satellites and U.P.U. Emblem

1978. "Philexafrique 2" Exhibition, Libreville, Gabon (2nd issue).
553 **152** 60f. red, mauve & blue . . 1·60 95
554 – 150f. multicoloured . . . 3·00 2·25

DESIGN: 150f. Mother and child, native village and hibiscus.

153 Sand Gazelle

1979. Endangered Animals. Multicoloured.
555 40f. Type **153** 45 15
556 50f. Addax 50 15
557 60f. Scimitar oryx 60 20
558 100f. Cheetah . . . . 1·00 40
559 150f. African ass . . . . . . 1·60 50
560 300f. Black rhinoceros . . . 3·25 90

154 African Boy and Wall Painting

1979. International Year of the Child. Mult.
561 65f. Type **154** 50 20
562 75f. Asian girl 55 25
563 100f. European child and doves 80 30
564 150f. African boys and drawing of boats . . . . . 1·25 50

1979. 10th Anniv of "Apollo 11" Moon Landing. Nos. 453/7 optd with lunar module and **ALUNISSAGE APOLLO XI JUILLET 1969**.
567 45f. Type **128** (postage) . . . 35 25
568 90f. Trajectory of flight . . . 80 35
569 100f. Descent on Mars (air) 75 50
570 200f. "Viking" in flight . . . 1·50 85
571 250f. "Viking" on landing approach . . . . 1·90 1·10

157 Hurdles

1979. Air. Olympic Games, Moscow 1980. Mult.
573 15f. Type **157** 20 15
574 30f. Hockey 30 20
575 250f. Swimming . . . . . . 1·90 70
576 350f. Running . . . . 2·50 90

158 Reed Canoe and Austrian 10k. stamp, 1910

1979. Air. Death Centenary of Sir Rowland Hill. Multicoloured.
578 65f. Type **158** 50 15
579 100f. Sailing canoe and U.S. $1 stamp of 1894 . . . . . 85 30
580 200f. "Curacao" (paddle-steamer) and French 1f. stamp of 1853 . . . . . . 1·75 60
581 300f. "Calypso" (liner) and Holstein 1¼s. stamp of 1864 . . . . 2·25 1·10

159 Slalom

160 "Concorde" and Map of Africa

1979. Winter Olympic Games, Lake Placid (1980). Multicoloured.
583 20f. Type **159** 20 15
584 40f. Biathlon 35 15
585 60f. Ski jump (horiz) 40 15
586 150f. Women's giant slalom 1·10 35
587 350f. Cross-country skiing (horiz) . . . . 2·50 80
588 500f. Downhill skiing (horiz) 3·75 1·25

1980. 20th Anniv of African Air Safety Organization (ASECNA).
589 **160** 15f. multicoloured 30 10
590 30f. multicoloured 45 25
591 60f. multicoloured 90 50

1981. Various stamps optd **POSTES 1981** or surch also.
592 **157** 30f. on 15f. multicoloured 75 60
593 – 30f. mult (No. 574) . . . 75 60
594 **158** 60f. on 65f. multicoloured 1·50 1·00
595 – 60f. on 100f. mult (No. 579) . . . . . . 1·50 1·00

162 Footballer

1982. World Cup Football Championship, Spain. Multicoloured.
596 30f. Hungary (postage) . . . 25 15
597 40f. Type **162** 30 15
598 50f. Algeria 35 20
599 60f. Argentina 45 20
600 80f. Brazil (air) 55 20
601 300f. West Germany . . . . 2·25 70

DESIGNS: As T **162** but each value showing different team's footballer.

163 Lady Diana and her Brother (1967)

1982. 21st Birthday of Princess of Wales. Mult.
603 30f. Lady Diana in christening robe (1961) (postage) 30 15
604 40f. Portrait of Lady Diana (1965) 35 15
605 50f. Type **163** 45 20
606 60f. Lady Diana and her pony (1975) 55 20
607 80f. Lady Diana in Switzerland (1977) (air) . . 60 20
608 300f. Lady Diana as nursery teacher (1980) . . . . . . 2·50 70

164 West German Scouts

1982. 75th Anniv of Scout Movement. Mult.
610 30f. Type **164** (postage) . . . 35 15
611 40f. Upper Volta scouts . . . 35 15
612 50f. Mali scouts and African dancers 50 20
613 60f. Scottish scout, piper and dancer 60 20
614 80f. Kuwait scouts (air) . . . 55 20
615 300f. Chad cub scout . . . . 2·25 70

165 Judo

1982. Olympic Games, Los Angeles (1984) (1st issue). Multicoloured.
617 30f. Gymnastics (horse exercise) (postage) 30 15
618 40f. Show jumping 30 15
619 50f. Type **165** 35 20
620 60f. High jumping 60 20
621 80f. Hurdling (air) 55 20
622 300f. Gymnastics (floor exercise) . . . . 2·25 70

See also Nos. 678/83 and 735/8.

1982. Birth of Prince William of Wales. Nos. 603/8 optd **21 JUIN 1982 WILLIAM ARTHUR PHILIP LOUIS PRINCE DE GALLES**.
624 30f. Type **163** (postage) . . . 30 15
625 40f. Portrait of Lady Diana as a young girl 35 15
626 50f. Lady Diana and her brother 45 20
627 60f. Lady Diana with her pony 50 20
628 80f. Lady Diana in Switzerland (air) 60 20
629 300f. Lady Diana with children . . . . 2·50 70

167 Marco Tardelli (Italy) and Passarella (Argentine)

1983. World Cup Football Championship Results. Multicoloured.
631 30f. Type **167** (postage) . . . 25 10
632 40f. Paolo Rossi (Italy) and Zico (Brazil) 30 15
633 50f. Pierre Littbarski (West Germany) and Platini (France) 35 20
634 60f. Gabriele Oriali (Italy) and Smolarek (Poland) . . 45 20
635 70f. Boniek (Poland) and Alain Giresse (France) (air) 55 20
636 300f. Bruno Conti (Italy) and Paul Breitner (West Germany) . . . . 2·25 70

168 Philidor and 19th-century European Rook

1982. Chess Grand Masters. Multicoloured.
638 30f. Type **168** (postage) . . . 35 15
639 40f. Paul Morphy and 19th-century Chinese knight 50 15
640 50f. Howard Staunton and Lewis knight 60 25
641 60f. Jean-Paul Capablanca and African knight 75 25
642 80f. Boris Spassky and Staunton knight (air) . . . 1·25 25
643 300f. Anatoly Karpov and 19th-century Chinese knight . . . . 3·00 1·00

169 K. E. Tsiolkovski and "Soyuz"

1983. Exploitation of Space. Multicoloured.
645 30f. Type **169** (postage) . . . 25 10
646 40f. R. H. Goddard and space telescope 30 15
647 50f. Korolev and ultra-violet telescope 35 20
648 60f. Von Braun and Space Shuttle 45 20
649 80f. Esnault Pelterie and "Ariane" rocket and "Symphonie" satellite (air) 55 25
650 300f. H. Oberth and construction of orbiting space station . . . . . . 2·25 70

170 Charles and Robert Balloon, 1783

1983. Air. Balloons. Multicoloured.
652 100f. Type **170** 95 50
653 200f. Blanchard balloon, Berlin, 1788 . . . . 1·90 95
654 300f. Charles Green balloon, London, 1837 (horiz) . . . 2·50 1·75
655 400f. Modern advertising airship (horiz) . . . . . . 3·25 1·75

171 Bobsleigh

1983. Winter Olympic Games, Sarajevo. Mult.
657 30f. Type **171** (postage) . . . 25 10
658 40f. Speed skating 30 15
659 50f. Cross-country skiing . . 30 20
660 60f. Ice hockey 35 20
661 80f. Ski jump (air) 55 20
662 300f. Downhill skiing . . . . 2·25 70

172 Montgolfier Brothers and "Le Martial" Balloon, 1783

1983. Bicentenary of Manned Flight. Multicoloured.
664 25f. Type **172** (postage) . . . 20 15
665 45f. Pilatre de Rozier and first manned flight, 1783 35 20
666 50f. Jacques Garnerin and balloon (first parachute descent, 1797) 35 20
667 60f. J. P. Blanchard and balloon at Chelsea, 1784 45 30
668 80f. H. Giffard and steam-powered dirigible, 1852 (air) 75 40
669 250f. Zeppelin and airship "L 21", 1900 . . . . 2·10 1·25

173 Gottlieb Daimler, Karl Benz and Mercedes "Type S," 1927

1983. Car Manufacturers. Multicoloured.

671 25f. Type **173** (postage) . . . 30 10
672 35f. Friedrich von Martini and Torpedo, Martini "Type GC 32", 1913 . . . 45 15
673 50f. Walter P. Chrysler and Chrysler "70", 1926 . . . 70 20
674 60f. Nicola Romeo and Alfa Romeo "6 C 1750 Grand Sport", 1929 . . . . . . 75 20
675 80f. Stewart Rolls, Henry Royce and "Phantom II Continental", 1934 (air) . . 95 20
676 250f. Lord Shrewsbury and Talbot-Lago "Record", 1948 . . . . 2·50 70

174 Kayak

1983. Olympic Games, Los Angeles (2nd issue). Multicoloured.

678 25f. Type **174** (postage) . . . 20 10
679 45f. Long jumping 30 15
680 50f. Boxing 35 15
681 60f. Discus-throwing 45 20
682 80f. Relay race (air) 60 20
683 350f. Horse jumping . . . . 2·50 70

175 Dove on Map

1983. Peace and Reconciliation. Multicoloured.

685 50f. Type **175** (postage) . . . 35 15
686 50f. Foodstuffs on map . . . 45 20
687 50f. President Habre 35 15
688 60f. As No. 687 . . . . . . 45 15
689 80f. Type **175** 65 25
690 80f. As No. 686 . . . . . . 80 30
691 80f. As No. 687 . . . . . . 65 25
692 100f. As No. 687 . . . . . . 75 25
693 150f. Type **175** (air) . . . . 1·00 30
694 150f. As No. 686 . . . . . . 1·40 50
695 200f. Type **175** . . . . . . 1·25 45
696 200f. As No. 686 . . . . . . 1·75 65

1983. 15th World Scout Jamboree, Canada. Nos. 610/15 optd **XV WORLD JAMBOREE MONDIAL ALBERTA CANADA 1983**.

697 30f. multicoloured (postage) 25 15
698 40f. multicoloured 30 15
699 50f. multicoloured 35 20
700 60f. multicoloured 45 20
701 80f. multicoloured (air) . . . 55 20
702 300f. multicoloured . . . . . 2·25 70

1983. 60th Anniv of Int Chess Federation. Nos. 638/43 optd **60e ANNIVERSAIRE FEDERATION MONDIAL D'ECHECS 1924–1984**.

704 30f. multicoloured (postage) 50 20
705 40f. multicoloured 60 20
706 50f. multicoloured 60 25
707 60f. multicoloured 75 25
708 80f. multicoloured (air) . . . 1·25 45
709 300f. multicoloured . . . . . 3·75 1·25

178 Chad Martyrs

1984. Celebrities. Multicoloured.

711 50f. Type **178**(postage) . . . 35 15
712 200f. P. Harris and Rotary Headquarters, U.S.A. . . . 1·50 35
713 300f. Alfred Nobel and will 2·50 60
714 350f. Raphael and "Virgin with the Infant and St. John the Baptist" . . . 3·75 75
715 400f. Rembrandt and "The Holy Family" (air) . . . . 3·75 85
716 500f. Goethe and Scenes from "Faust" . . . . 4·25 1·00

179 Martyrs Memorial

1984. Martyrs Memorial.

718 **179** 50f. mult (postage) . . . 35 15
719 80f. multicoloured 60 25
720 120f. multicoloured . . . 85 25
721 200f. multicoloured (air) 1·60 50
722 250f. multicoloured . . . 2·25 75

180 Durer and Painting

1984. Celebrities and Events. Multicoloured.

723 50f. Type **180** (postage) . . . 75 15
724 200f. Henri Dunant and battle scene . . . . 1·75 35
725 300f. Early telephone and satellite receiving station, Goonhilly Downs . . . . 2·25 60
726 350f. President Kennedy and first foot-print on Moon 2·75 75
727 400f. Infra-red satellite picture (Europe–Africa co-operation) (air) . . . . . 2·50 75
728 500f. Prince and Princess of Wales . . . . 3·75 1·00

181 "Communications"

1984. World Communications Year.

730 **181** 50f. mult (postage) . . . 45 15
731 60f. multicoloured 50 35
732 70f. multicoloured 50 35
733 125f. multicoloured (air) 1·00 55
734 250f. multicoloured . . . 1·90 1·10

182 Two-man Kayak

1984. Air. Olympic Games, Los Angeles (3rd issue). Multicoloured.

735 100f. Type **182** 75 25
736 200f. Kayaks (close-up) . . . 1·50 50
737 300f. One-man kayak . . . . 2·25 75
738 400f. Coxed fours . . . . . 3·00 1·00

183 Class 13 Kitson Steam Locomotive

1984. Historic Transport. Multicoloured.

740 50f. Type **183** (postage) . . . 1·50 1·00
741 200f. Sailing boat on Lake Chad . . . . 1·75 65
742 300f. Graf Zeppelin (airship) 3·00 1·25
743 350f. Six-wheel Renault automobile, 1930 . . . . . 2·75 1·25
744 400f. Bloch "120" airplane (air) . . . . 2·50 1·50
745 500f. Douglas "DC-8" airplane . . . . 3·75 2·00

184 African with broken Manacles

185 Pres. Hissein Habre

1984. 2nd Anniv of Entrance of Government Forces in N'Djamena.

747 **184** 50f. multicoloured 50 25

1984.

748 **185** 125f. black, blue & yellow 1·25 50

186 British East Indiaman

1984. Transport. Multicoloured. (a) Ships.

749 90f. Type **186** 95 45
750 125f. "Vera Cruz" (steamer) 1·25 55
751 200f. "Carlisle Castle" (sail merchantman) . . . . . 2·25 75
752 300f. "Britannia" (steamer) 2·75 1·25

(b) Locomotives.

753 100f. Series 701, 1885, France 1·25 15
754 150f. "Columbia", 1888, Belgium . . . . 1·90 25
755 250f. Mediterranean locomotive, 1900, Italy . . 3·00 40
756 350f. MAV 114 . . . . . . 4·50 55

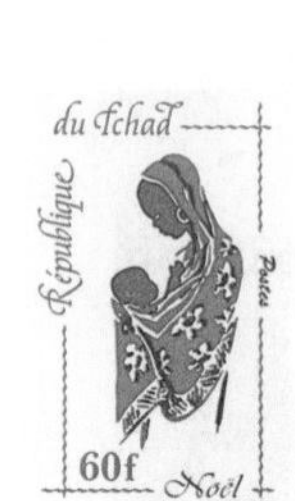

187 Virgin and Child

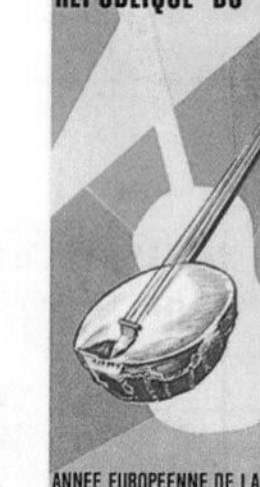

188 Guitars

1984. Christmas.

757 **187** 50f. brown and blue . . . 45 15
758 60f. brown and orange . . 50 20
759 80f. brown and green . . 65 25
760 85f. brown and purple . . 70 25
761 100f. brown and orange 85 30
762 135f. brown and blue . . 1·25 45

1985. European Music Year. Multicoloured.

763 20f. Type **188** 20 10
764 25f. Harps 25 15
765 30f. Xylophones 30 15
766 50f. Drums 45 20
767 70f. As No. 766 . . . . . . 55 20
768 80f. As No. 764 . . . . . . 75 30
769 100f. Type **188** 90 45
770 250f. As No. 765 . . . . . 2·25 85

189 "Chlorophyllum molybdites"

1985. Fungi. Multicoloured.

771 25f. Type **189** 55 30
772 30f. "Tulostoma volvulatum" 70 35
773 50f. "Lentinus tuberregium" 1·00 45
774 70f. As No. 773 . . . . . . 1·40 60
775 80f. "Podaxis pistillaris" . . 1·75 65
776 100f. Type **189** . . . . . . 2·50 1·00

190 Stylized Tree and Scout

1985. Air. "Philexafrique" Stamp Exhibition, Lome, Togo (1st issue). Multicoloured.

777 200f. Type **190** . . . . 1·90 1·50
778 200f. Fokker "27" airplane 1·90 1·50

See also Nos. 808/9.

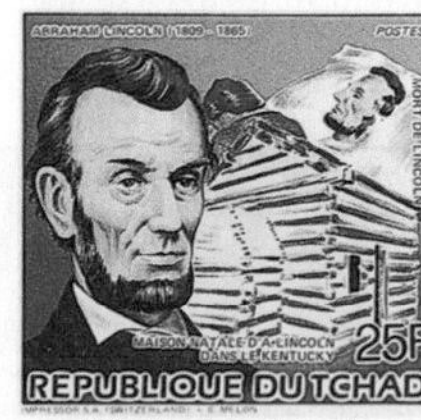

191 Abraham Lincoln

1985. Celebrities. Multicoloured.

779 25f. Type **191** (postage) . . . 20 10
780 45f. Henri Dunant (founder of Red Cross) 45 15
781 50f. Gottlieb Daimler (automobile designer) . . . 60 15
782 60f. Louis Bleriot (pilot) (air) 55 30
783 80f. Paul Harris (founder of Rotary International) . . . 55 20
784 350f. Auguste Piccard (undersea explorer) . . . . 3·75 1·60

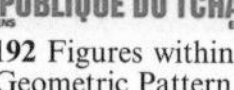

192 Figures within Geometric Pattern

193 Sun and Hands breaking through Darkness

1985. International Youth Year. Multicoloured.

786 70f. Type **192** 50 25
787 200f. Figures on ribbon around globe . . . . . . 1·50 75

1985. 3rd Anniv of Entrance of Government Forces in N'DJamena. Multicoloured.

788 70f. Type **193** 55 25
789 70f. Claw attacking hand . . 55 25
790 70f. Pres. Hissein Habre (36×48 mm) 25 20
791 110f. Type **193** 80 35
792 110f. As No. 789 . . . . . . 80 35
793 110f. As No. 790 . . . . . . 1·10 35

194 Saddle-bill Stork ("Jabiru")

196 Sitatunga

195 Fokker Friendship, Farman M.F.11 and Emblem

1985. Birth Bicentenary of John J. Audubon (ornithologist).

794 **194** 70f. black, blue & brown 1·40 85
795 – 110f. olive, green & brown . . . . 2·00 1·25
796 – 150f. blue, red and olive 3·00 1·90
797 – 200f. dp blue, mauve & bl 3·50 2·10

DESIGNS: 110f. Ostrich ("Autruche"); 150f. Marabou stork ("Marabout"); 200f. Secretary bird ("Messager Serpentaire").

1985. Air. 25th Anniv of ASECNA (navigation agency). Multicoloured.
799 70f. Type **195** 50 30
800 110f. Fokker "F.27" "Friendship" and "Spirit of St. Louis" 75 50
801 250f. Fokker "F.27" "Friendship" and Vickers Vimy . . . . 1·90 1·25

1985. Mammals.
802 **196** 50f. brown, bl & dp brn 55 35
803 – 70f. brown, green and red 70 50
804 – 250f. multicoloured . . . 2·50 1·60
DESIGNS—HORIZ: 70f. Greater kudus. VERT: 250f. Bearded mouflons.

197 U.N. Emblem on Peace Dove and Girl with Flowers

1985. 40th Anniv of U.N.O. and 25th Anniv of U.N. Membership.
806 **197** 200f. blue, red & brown 1·50 1·00
807 – 300f. blue, red & yellow 2·25 1·50
DESIGN: 300f. U.N. emblem as flower with peace doves forming stalk.

198 Girl with Posy, Youth Ceremony and I.Y.Y. Emblem

1985. Air. "Philexafrique" Stamp Exhibition, Lome, Togo (2nd issue). Multicoloured.
808 250f. Type **198** (International Youth Year) . . . . 2·25 1·90
809 250f. Computer terminal, liner, airplane, diesel freight train, rocket and U.P.U. emblem . . . . 4·25 1·00

199 Hugo

1985. Air. Death Centenary of Victor Hugo (writer).
810 **199** 70f. blue, sepia and brown 50 35
811 110f. brown, green & red 75 50
812 250f. black, red & orange 1·90 1·00
813 300f. purple, blue and red 2·25 1·25

200 Nativity **201** Pictures of Visit on Map

1985. Air. Christmas.
814 **200** 250f. multicoloured . . . 1·90 75

1986. Visit of President to Interior.
815 **201** 100f. yellow, black & grn 95 50
816 170f. yellow, black & pink 1·90 75
817 200f. yellow, black & grn 2·25 1·25

1987. Various stamps surch.
818 – 170f. on 300f. mult (725) (postage) 70 60
819 – 230f. on 300f. blue, red and yellow (807) . . . 1·00 85
820 – 240f. on 300f. mult (742) 1·00 85
822 **175** 100f. on 200f. mult (air) 70 55
823 – 100f. on 200f. mult (696) 60 60
824 – 100f. on 250f. mult (669) 70 55
825 – 100f. on 300f. mult (643) 40 30
826 – 100f. on 300f. mult (662) 40 30
827 **179** 170f. on 200f. mult . . . 70 60
828 **181** 170f. on 250f. mult . . . 1·10 90
829 – 170f. on 300f. mult (601) 70 60
830 – 170f. on 300f. mult (622) 70 60
831 – 240f. on 300f. mult (636) 1·00 90

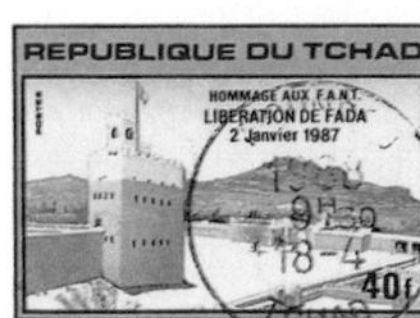

203 Fada

1987. Liberation of Fada.
832 **203** 40f. multicoloured . . . .

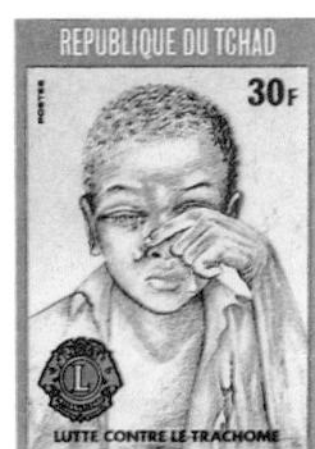

204 Boy suffering from Trachoma

1987. Lions Club Anti-trachoma Campaign. Mult.
835 30f. Type **204** . . . .
837 100f. Type **204** . . . .
838 120f. Healthy boy and afflicted boys (horiz) . . .
840 200f. Doctor examining boy (horiz) . . . .

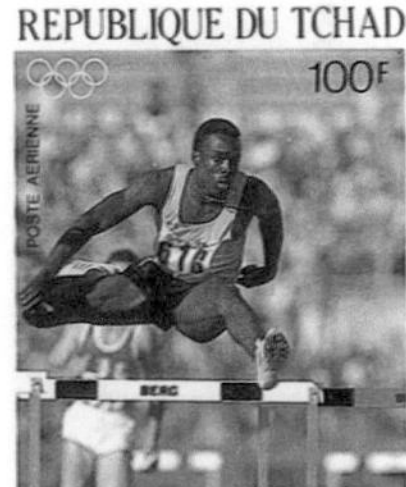

205 400 m Hurdles

1988. Air. Olympic Games, Seoul. Multicoloured.
841 100f. Type **205** 75 25
842 170f. 5000 m (horiz) . . . . 1·25 35
843 200f. Long jump (horiz) . . . 1·50 50
844 600f. Triple jump . . . . . 4·50 1·40

206 Barbary Sheep

1988. Endangered Animals. Barbary Sheep. Mult.
846 25f. Type **206** 25 20
847 45f. Mother and lamb . . . 50 25
848 70f. Two sheep 75 30
849 100f. Two adults with lamb 1·00 50

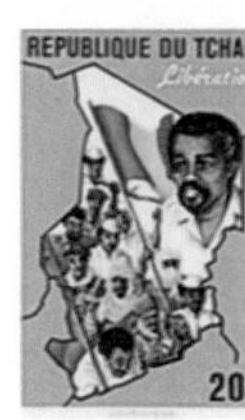

207 President and Crowd on Map **208** Boy posting Letter

1989. "Liberation".
850 **207** 20f. multicoloured 25 15
851 25f. multicoloured 25 15
852 40f. multicoloured 35 20
853 100f. multicoloured . . . 1·00 30
854 170f. multicoloured . . . 1·60 50

1989. World Post Day.
855 **208** 100f. multicoloured . . .
856 120f. multicoloured . . .
857 170f. multicoloured . . .
858 250f. multicoloured . . .

209 N'Djamena Cathedral and Pope with Crucifix

1990. Visit of Pope John Paul II. Multicoloured.
859 20f. Type **209** 25 10
860 80f. Cathedral and Pope (different) 70 35
861 100f. Type **209** 95 60
862 170f. As No. 860 . . . . . . 1·60 1·10

210 Traditional Hairstyle

1990.
863 **210** 100f. multicoloured . . . 45 25
864 120f. multicoloured . . . 55 30
865 170f. multicoloured . . . 80 45
866 250f. multicoloured . . . 1·10 65

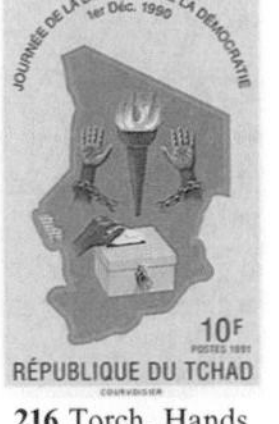

215 Queues and Nurse vaccinating Child **216** Torch, Hands with Broken Manacles and Ballot Box

1991. "Child Vaccination—Assured Future".
880 **215** 30f. multicoloured 25 20
881 100f. multicoloured . . . 75 45
882 170f. multicoloured . . . 1·25 75
883 180f. multicoloured . . . 1·25 75
884 200f. multicoloured . . . 1·50 1·00

1991. Day of Freedom and Democracy.
885 **216** 10f. multicoloured 10 10
886 20f. multicoloured 20 15
887 40f. multicoloured 30 20
888 70f. multicoloured 50 30
889 130f. multicoloured . . . 95 60
890 200f. multicoloured . . . 1·50 80

217 Mother and Child **219** Mother and Child, Globe and Cereals

218 Class

1992. 20th Anniv of Medecins sans Frontieres (medical relief organization).
891 **217** 20f. multicoloured 20 10
892 45f. multicoloured 30 20
893 85f. multicoloured 70 35
894 170f. multicoloured . . . 1·25 70
895 300f. multicoloured . . . 2·25 1·10

1992. Literacy Campaign.
896 **218** 25f. multicoloured 20 10
897 40f. multicoloured 30 20
898 70f. multicoloured 50 25
899 100f. multicoloured . . . 75 35
900 180f. multicoloured . . . 1·25 60
901 200f. multicoloured . . . 1·50 95

1992. International Nutrition Conference, Rome.
902 **219** 10f. multicoloured 15 10
903 60f. multicoloured 45 25
904 120f. multicoloured . . . 95 55
905 500f. multicoloured . . . 3·50 1·60

MILITARY FRANK STAMPS

1965. No. 77 optd **F.M.**
M148 20f. red and black £250 £250

M 24 Soldier with Standard **M 92** Shoulder Flash of 1st Regiment

1966. No value indicated.
M149 **M 24** (–) multicoloured . . 1·50 1·00

1972. No value indicated.
M353 **M 92** (–) multicoloured . . 75 35

OFFICIAL STAMPS

O 23 Flag and Map

1966. Flag in blue, yellow and red.
O148 **O 23** 1f. blue 10 10
O149 2f. grey 10 10
O150 5f. black 15 10
O151 10f. blue 25 10
O152 25f. orange 25 15
O153 30f. turquoise 40 20
O154 40f. red 45 20
O155 50f. purple 55 25
O156 85f. green 85 45
O157 100f. brown . . . . . 1·40 50
O158 200f. red . . . . . . 2·50 95

POSTAGE DUE STAMPS

1928. Postage Due type of France optd **TCHAD A. E. F.**
D58 **D 11** 5c. blue . . . . 10 2·50
D59 10c. brown . . . . . . 35 2·50
D60 20c. olive . . . . . . 35 2·50
D61 25c. red . . . . 40 2·75
D62 30c. red . . . . 50 2·75
D63 45c. green . . . . . . 55 3·00
D64 50c. purple . . . . . . 40 3·25
D65 60c. brown on cream 90 4·00
D66 1f. red on cream . . . 90 4·00
D67 2f. red . . . . 1·60 7·00
D68 3f. violet . . . . 90 4·25

D 3 Village of Straw Huts **D 4** Pirogue on Lake Chad

1930.
D69 **D 3** 5c. olive and blue . . . 25 2·75
D70 10c. brown and red . . . 50 3·00
D71 20c. brown and green . . 1·75 3·00
D72 25c. brown and blue . . 1·90 3·25
D73 30c. green and brown . . 1·75 3·25
D74 45c. olive and green . . 2·25 3·50
D75 50c. brown & mauve . . 2·50 4·00
D76 60c. black and lilac . . 3·25 5·00
D77 **D 4** 1f. black and brown . . 4·00 5·25
D78 2f. brown and mauve . . 4·00 8·50
D79 3f. brown and red . . . 20·00 55·00

D 6 Gonoa Hippopotamus

1962.
D 89 50c. bistre 10 10
D 90 50c. brown 10 10
D 91 1f. blue 10 10
D 92 1f. green 10 10
D 93 2f. red 15 15
D 94 2f. red 15 15
D 95 5f. myrtle 30 30
D 96 5f. violet 30 30
D 97 10f. brown 75 75
D 98 10f. brown 75 75

D 99 25f. purple . . . . 1·75 1·75
D100 25f. violet . . . . 1·75 1·75
DESIGNS (rock-paintings): No. D89, Type D **6**; D90, Gonoa kudu; D91, Two Gonoa antelopes; D92, Three Gonoa antelopes; D93, Gonoa antelope; D94, Tibestiram; D95, Tibestiox; D96, Oudingueur boar; D97, Gonoa elephant; D98, Gira-Gira rhinoceros; D99, Bardai warrior; D100, Gonoa masked archer. The two designs in each value are arranged in tete-beche pairs throughout the sheet.

D **65** Kanem Puppet

1969. Native Puppets.

D284	D **65**	1f. brown, red & grn	10	10
D285	–	2f. brown, grn & red	10	10
D286	–	5f. green and brown	10	10
D287	–	10f. brown, pur & grn	20	20
D288	–	25f. brown, pur & grn	45	25

DESIGNS: 2f. Kotoko doll; 5f. Copper doll; 10f. Kotoko (diff); 25f. Guera doll.

APPENDIX

The following stamps have either been issued in excess of postal needs or have not been available to the public in reasonable quantities at face value. Such stamps may later be given full listing if there is evidence of regular postal use.

1970.

"Apollo programme". Postage 40f.; Air 15, 25f.

Birth Bicent of Napoleon. Air. 10, 25, 32f.

World Cup Football Championship, Mexico. Air 5f.

World Cup. Previous Winners. 1, 4f., 5f. × 2.

"Expo 70" World Fair, Osaka, Japan. Japanese Paintings. 50c., 1, 2f.

Christmas. Paintings. Postage 3, 25f.; Air 32f.

Past Olympic Venues. Postage 3, 8, 20f.; Air 10, 35f.

1971.

Space Exploration. 8, 10, 35f.

Winter Olympic Games, Sapporo, Japan. Japanese Paintings. 50c., 1, 2f.

Kings and Queens of France. Postage 25f. × 2, 30, 32, 35f., 40f. × 2, 50f. × 4, 60f.; Air 40, 50, 60, 70, 75, 80f., 100f. × 5, 150f., 200f. × 4.

150th Death Anniv of Napoleon. Air. 10f.

Famous Paintings. 1, 4, 5f.

Past Olympic Venues. Postage 15, 20f.; Air 25, 50f.

Winter Olympic Games, Sapporo, Japan. Optd on 1970 "Expo 70" issue 50c., 1, 2f.

Olympic Games Munich. World Cup Previous Winners issue (1970) optd **1f.**

1972.

Moon Flight of "Apollo 15". Air 40, 80, 150, 250, 300, 500f.

"Soyuz 11" Disaster. Air 30, 50, 100, 200, 300, 400f.

Pres. Tombalbaye. Postage 30, 40f.; Air 70, 80f.

Winter Olympic Games, Sapporo, Japan. Postage 25, 75, 150f.; Air 130, 200f.

13th World Scout Jamboree, Asagiri, Japan (1971). Postage 30, 70, 80f.; Air 100, 200f.

Medal Winners, Sapporo Winter Olympics. Postage 25, 75, 100, 130f.; Air 150, 200f.

Olympic Games, Munich. Postage 20, 40, 60f.; Air 100, 120, 150f.

African Animals. Air 20, 30, 100, 130, 150f.

Medal Winners, Munich Olympics (1st series). Postage 10, 20, 40, 60f.; Air 150, 250f.

Medal Winners, Munich Olympics (2nd series). Gold frames, Postage 20, 30, 50f.; Air 150, 250f.

1973.

Locomotives. 10, 40, 50, 150, 200f.

Domestic Animals (2nd issue). Postage 20, 30f.; Air 100, 130, 150f.

Horses. 20, 60, 100, 120f.

Airplanes. Air 5, 25, 70, 150, 200f.

Christmas. Postage 30, 40, 55f.; Air 60, 250f.

Other issues exist which were prepared by various agencies, but it is uncertain whether these were placed on sale in Chad. They include further values in the "Kings and Queens of France" series.

All the stamps below are on gold foil.

1982.

World Cup Football Championship, Spain. Air 1500f.

21st Birthday of Princess of Wales. Air 1500f.

75th Anniv of Scout Movement. Air 1500f.

Olympic Games, Los Angeles. Air 1500f.

Birth of Prince William of Wales. 21st Birthday of Princess of Wales stamp optd. Air 1500f.

1983.

World Cup Football Championship Results. Air 1500f.

Chess Grand Masters. Air 1500f.

Exploitation of Space. Air 1500f.

Winter Olympic Games, Sarajevo. Air 1500f.

Bicentary of Manned Flight. Air 1500f.

Olympic Games, Los Angeles. Air 1500f.

CHAMBA Pt. 1

An Indian "convention" state of the Punjab.

Stamps of India overprinted.

12 pies = 1 anna; 16 annas = 1 rupee.

1886. Queen Victoria. Optd **CHAMBA STATE** in two lines.
1 **23** ½a. turquoise 40 50
2 – 1a. purple 1·25 1·50
4 – 1a.6p. brown 1·50 10·00
6 – 2a. blue 1·10 1·40
7 – 2a.6p. green 29·00 80·00
9 – 3a. orange 1·50 4·25
11 – 4a. green (No. 96) 4·25 5·50
12 – 6a. brown (No. 80) 3·50 15·00
14 – 8a. mauve 6·50 8·00
16 – 12a. purple on red 5·50 12·00
17 – 1r. grey (No. 101) 38·00 £110
18 **37** 1r. green and red 7·00 13·00
19 **38** 2r. red and brown 85·00 £300
20 3r. brown and green 90·00 £250
21 5r. blue and violet £100 £425

1900. Queen Victoria. Optd **CHAMBA STATE** in two lines.
22 **40** 3p. red 30 50
23 3p. grey 30 1·60
25 **23** ½a. green 40 1·00
26 – 1a. red 30 30
27 – 2a. lilac 7·50 24·00

1903. King Edward VII. Optd **CHAMBA STATE** in two lines.
28 **41** 3p. grey 15 1·00
30 – ½a. green (No. 122) 30 25
31 – 1a. red (No. 123) 1·25 40
33 – 2a. lilac 1·25 2·50
34 – 3a. orange 3·00 4·00
35 – 4a. olive 4·25 15·00
36 – 6a. bistre 3·50 18·00
37 – 8a. mauve 4·25 17·00
39 – 12a. purple on red 6·00 23·00
40 – 1r. green and red 6·50 20·00

1907. King Edward VII. Optd **CHAMBA STATE** in two lines.
41 – ½a. green (No. 149) 1·25 3·00
42 – 1a. red (No. 150) 1·40 3·00

1913. King George V. Optd **CHAMBA STATE** in two lines.
43 **55** 3p. grey 20 60
44 **56** ½a. green 35 65
45a **57** 1a. red 1·00 2·75
55 1a. brown 2·00 3·75
56 **58** 1½a. brown (No. 163) 22·00 £100
57 1½a. brown (No. 165) 1·40 4·75
58 1½a. red 75 17·00
47 **59** 2a. purple 2·50 8·00
59 **61** 2a.6p. blue 60 3·00
60 2a.6p. orange 1·60 15·00
48 **62** 3a. orange 2·75 6·50
61 3a. blue 2·75 18·00
49 **63** 4a. olive 2·50 3·75
50 **64** 6a. bistre 2·75 4·50
51a **65** 8a. mauve 4·25 10·00
52 **66** 12a. red 3·50 10·00
53 **67** 1r. brown and green 13·00 23·00

1921. No. 192 of India optd **CHAMBA**.
54 **57** 9p. on 1a. red 1·00 17·00

1927. Stamps of India (King George V) optd **CHAMBA STATE** in one line.
62 **55** 3p. grey 10 1·10
63 **56** ½a. green 20 1·60
76 **79** ½a. green 1·10 8·00
64 **80** 9p. green 2·50 13·00
65 **57** 1a. brown 1·60 70
77 **81** 1a. brown 1·50 70
66 **82** 1a.3p. mauve 1·10 4·75
67w **58** 1½a. red 5·00 5·50
68 **70** 2a. lilac 1·40 2·25
78 **59** 2a. red 1·00 21·00
69 **61** 2a.6p. orange 1·75 14·00
70 **62** 3a. blue 1·00 16·00
80 3a. red 2·00 9·00
71 **71** 4a. green 1·00 4·50
81 **63** 4a. olive 3·25 13·00
72 **64** 6a. bistre 26·00 £150
73 **65** 8a. mauve 1·40 9·00
74 **66** 12a. red 1·40 11·00
75 **67** 1r. brown and green 6·00 22·00

1938. Stamps of India (King George VI Nos. 247/64) optd **CHAMBA STATE**.
82 **91** 3p. slate 7·00 12·00
83 ½a. brown 1·00 7·00
84 9p. green 7·50 27·00
85 1a. red 1·00 2·50
86 **92** 2a. red 5·00 9·50
87 – 2a.6p. violet 5·50 22·00
88 – 3a. green 6·00 22·00
89 – 3a.6p. blue 6·00 23·00
90 – 4a. brown 18·00 18·00
91 – 6a. green 18·00 50·00
92 – 8a. violet 18·00 48·00
93 – 12a. red 12·00 48·00
94 **93** 1r. slate and brown 27·00 55·00
95 2r. purple and brown 48·00 £250
96 5r. green and blue 80·00 £375
97 10r. purple and red £130 £500
98 15r. brown and green £160 £800
99 25r. slate and purple £225 £850

1942. Stamps of India (King George VI) optd **CHAMBA**. (a) On issue of 1938
100 **91** ½a. brown 35·00 25·00
101 1a. red 45·00 32·00
102 **93** 1r. slate and brown 20·00 50·00
103 2r. purple and brown 24·00 £200
104 5r. green and blue 45·00 £225
105 10r. purple and red 65·00 £425
106 15r. brown and green £150 £650
107 25r. slate and purple £140 £650

(b) On issue of 1940.
108 **100a** 3p. slate 70 4·00
109 ½a. mauve 70 4·00
110 9p. green 1·00 13·00
111 1a. red 1·00 3·50
112 **101** 1½a. violet 1·00 8·50
113 2a. red 5·00 9·50
114 3a. violet 15·00 32·00
115 3½a. blue 8·00 32·00
116 **102** 4a. brown 10·00 10·00
117 6a. green 13·00 35·00
118 8a. violet 13·00 42·00
119 12a. purple 19·00 55·00
120 – 14a. purple (No. 277) 11·00 3·00

OFFICIAL STAMPS

Stamps of India overprinted.

1886. Queen Victoria. Optd **SERVICE CHAMBA STATE**.
O 1 **23** ½a. turquoise 30 10
O 3 – 1a. purple 1·25 10
O 5 – 2a. blue 1·50 1·50
O 7 – 3a. orange 2·00 9·50
O 8 – 4a. green (No. 96) 2·50 4·50
O10 – 6a. brown (No. 80) 4·25 10·00
O13 – 8a. mauve 2·00 1·75
O14 – 12a. purple on red 7·50 38·00
O15 – 1r. grey (No. 101) 13·00 £110
O16 **37** 1r. green and red 6·00 32·00

1902. Queen Victoria. Optd **SERVICE CHAMBA STATE**.
O17 **40** 3p. grey 40 50
O18 **23** ½a. green 45 3·00
O20 – 1a. red 70 40
O21 – 2a. lilac 9·00 27·00

1903. King Edward VII. Optd **SERVICE CHAMBA STATE**.
O22 **41** 3p. grey 30 15
O24 ½a. green (No. 122) 25 10
O25 1a. red (No. 123) 75 30
O27 – 2a. lilac 1·25 70
O28 – 4a. olive 3·50 16·00
O29 – 8a. mauve 5·00 15·00
O31 – 1r. green and red 1·75 10·00

1907. King Edward VII. Optd **SERVICE CHAMBA STATE**.
O32 – ½a. green (No. 149) 40 75
O33 – 1a. red (No. 150) 2·25 1·50

1913. King George V Official stamps optd **CHAMBA STATE**.
O34 **55** 3p. grey 20 40
O36 **56** ½a. green 10 15
O38 **57** 1a. red 10 10
O47 1a. brown 2·50 50
O40 **59** 2a. lilac (No. O83) 1·10 12·00
O41 **63** 4a. olive (No. O86) 1·10 15·00
O42 **65** 8a. mauve 1·75 16·00
O43 **67** 1r. brown and green 4·25 25·00

1914. King George V Postage stamps optd **SERVICE CHAMBA STATE**.
O44 **59** 2a. lilac (No. 166) 15·00
O45 **63** 4a. olive (No. 210) 12·00

1921. No O97 of India optd **CHAMBA**.
O46 **57** 9p. on 1a. red 15 6·00

1927. King George V Postage stamps optd **CHAMBA STATE SERVICE**.
O48 **55** 3p. grey 50 30
O49 **56** ½a. green 35 15
O61 **79** ½a. green 3·50 50
O50 **80** 9p. green 2·50 8·50
O51 **57** 1a. brown 20 10
O62 **81** 1a. brown 2·50 45
O52 **82** 1¼a. mauve 5·00 60
O53 **70** 2a. lilac 1·40 60
O63 **59** 2a. red 3·75 1·00
O54 **71** 4a. olive 1·10 1·75
O65 **63** 4a. green 6·00 5·00
O55 **65** 8a. mauve 4·50 8·00
O56 **66** 12a. red 2·75 20·00
O57 **67** 1r. brown and green 12·00 35·00
O58 2r. red and orange 21·00 £180
O59 5r. blue and violet 42·00 £250
O60 1r. green and red 60·00 £250

1938. King George VI Postage stamps of India optd **CHAMBA STATE SERVICE**.
O66 **91** 9p. green 13·00 48·00
O67 1a. red 12·00 3·00
O68 **93** 1r. slate and brown £250 £700
O69 2r. purple and brown 40·00 £325
O70 5r. green and blue 60·00 £400
O71 10r. purple and red 90·00 £700

1940. Official stamps of India optd **CHAMBA**.
O72 **O 20** 3p. grey 70 80
O73 ½a. brown 15·00 2·25
O74 ½a. purple 70 2·50
O75 9p. green 5·00 8·00
O76 1a. red 70 2·00
O77 1a.3p. brown 55·00 16·00
O78 1½a. violet 5·50 6·50
O79 2a. orange 5·50 6·00
O80 2½a. violet 2·50 19·00
O81 4a. brown 5·50 10·00
O82w 8a. violet 12·00 50·00

1942. King George VI Postage stamps of India optd **CHAMBA SERVICE**.
O83 **93** 1r. slate and brown 20·00 £170
O84 2r. purple and brown 35·00 £225
O85 5r. green and blue 65·00 £350
O86 10r. purple and red 80·00 £600

CHARKHARI Pt. 1

A state of Central India. Now uses Indian stamps.

12 pies = 1 anna; 16 annas = 1 rupee.

1 2

1894. Imperf. No gum.
10 **1** ¼a. purple 1·75 2·50
6a ¼a. purple 2·50 3·00
7a 1a. green 4·00 4·75
8a 2a. green 7·00 8·00
9a 4a. green 6·00 10·00

1909. Perf or imperf.
15a **2** 1p. brown 3·75 38·00
16 1p. blue 60 45
33 1p. violet 17·00 £120
32 1p. green 55·00 £170
25 ½a. red 1·60 1·60
34 ½a. olive 1·50 14·00
35 ½a. brown 5·50 22·00
36 ½a. black 60·00 £150
18a 1a. green 1·90 1·60
40 1a. brown 8·50 22·00
41 1a. red 95·00 55·00
19 2a. blue 3·00 3·25
43 2a. grey 48·00 60·00
20 4a. green 3·75 4·75
44 4a. red 3·00 19·00
21 8a. red 7·50 17·00
22 1r. brown 13·00 35·00

4 7 Imlia Palace

5

1912. Imperf.
28 **4** 1p. violet 7·00 5·00

1922. Imperf.
29 **5** 1a. violet 70·00 80·00

1931. Perf.
45 – ½a. green 1·40 10
46 **7** 1a. sepia 1·40 10
47 – 2a. violet 1·10 10
48 – 4a. olive 1·10 15
49 – 8a. mauve 1·40 10
50 – 1r. green and red 2·00 20
51 – 2r. red and brown 3·50 25
52 – 3r. brown and green 11·00 40
53 – 5r. blue and lilac 8·50 50
DESIGNS—HORIZ: ½a. The Lake; 2a. Industrial school; 4a. Bird's-eye view of city; 8a. Fort; 1r. Guest House; 2r. Palace Gate; 3r. Temples at Rainpur; 5r. Goverdhan Temple.

1940. Nos. 21/2 surch.
54 **2** ½a. on 8a. red 28·00 £120
55 1a. on 1r. brown 90·00 £350
56 "1 ANNA" on 1r. brown £650 £650

CHILE Pt. 20

A republic on the W. coast of S. America.

1853. 100 centavos = 1 peso.
1960. 10 milesimos = 1 centesimo; 100 centesimos = 1 escudo.
1975. 100 centavos = 1 peso.

1 Columbus 9 10

1853. Imperf.
29 **1** 1c. yellow 18·00 20·00
17 5c. brown £100 11·00
37 5c. red 23·00 6·50
32 10c. blue 32·00 5·00
33 20c. green 35·00 28·00

1867. Perf.
41 **9** 1c. orange 12·50 1·25
43 2c. black 17·00 2·75
45 5c. red 13·00 90
46 10c. blue 13·00 1·10
48 20c. green 22·00 2·00

1877. Roul.
49 **10** 1c. slate 2·00 75
50 2c. orange 9·00 1·50
51 5c. lake 11·50 50
52 10c. blue 10·00 1·60
53 20c. green 13·00 2·50

12 15

1878. Roul.
55 **12** 1c. green 1·00 15
57 2c. red 1·00 15
58 5c. red 5·00 25
59a 5c. blue 1·50 50
60a 10c. orange 2·25 10
61 15c. green 2·50 15
62 20c. grey 2·50 35
63 25c. brown 2·50 15
64 30c. red 5·00 2·00
65a 50c. violet 2·50 1·00
66 **15** 1p. black and brown 13·50 2·00

16 18

1900. Roul.
82 **16** 1c. green 75 10
83 2c. red 75 10
84a 5c. blue 3·50 25
85 10c. lilac 4·00 35
79 20c. grey 4·00 1·25
80 30c. brown 4·50 1·25
81 50c. brown 5·50 1·50

1900. Surch **5**.
86 **12** 5c. on 30c. red 1·00 20

1901. Perf.
87 **18** 1c. green 25 15
88 2c. red 35 15
89 5c. blue 1·10 15
90 10c. black and red 2·10 25
91 30c. black and violet 6·75 65
92 50c. black and red 6·50 1·75

1903. Surch **Diez CENTAVOS**.
93 **16** 10c. on 30c. brown 1·60 95

20 Huemul (mountain deer) 24 Pedro Valdivia

1904. Animal supporting shield at left without mane and tail. Optd **CORREOS** in frame.
94 **20** 2c. brown 25 15
95 5c. red 40 15
96 10c. olive 1·40 40

1904. As T **20**, but animal with mane and tail optd **CORREOS** in frame and the 1p. also surch **CENTAVOS 3 3**.
97 **20** 2c. brown 5·00
98 3c. on 1p. brown 35 20
99 5c. red 6·00
100 10c. green 12·00

1904. Surch **CORREOS** in frame and new value.
101 **24** 1c. on 20c. blue 25 15
102 3c. on 5c. red 40·00 40·00
103 12c. on 5c. red 85 35

26 Christopher Columbus 28 Christopher Columbus

27 Christopher Columbus

1905.
104 **26** 1c. green 25 15
105 2c. red 25 15
106 3c. brown 60 25
107 5c. blue 60 15
108 **27** 10c. black and grey . . . . 1·25 15
109 12c. black and lake . . . . 5·25 2·00
110 15c. black and lilac . . . . 1·25 15
111 20c. black and brown . . . 2·50 15
112 30c. black and green . . . 3·50 25
113 50c. black and blue . . . 3·50 25
114 **28** 1p. grey and green . . . . 12·50 8·50

1910. Optd **ISLAS DE JUAN FERNANDEZ** or surch also.
115 **27** 5c. on 12c. black & red . . 40 30
116 **28** 10c. on 1p. grey & green 1·10 65
117 20c. on 1p. grey & green 1·75 1·00
118 1p. grey and green . . . . 3·50 2·40

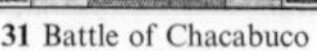

31 Battle of Chacabuco **33** San Martin Monument

1910. Centenary of Independence. Centres in black.
119 – 1c. green 25 15
120 **31** 2c. lake 25 15
121 – 3c. brown . . . . 1·00 65
122 – 5c. blue 35 10
123 – 10c. brown . . . . 1·50 25
124 – 12c. red . . . . 3·00 90
125 – 15c. slate . . . . 1·60 65
126 – 20c. orange . . . . 2·50 1·00
127 – 25c. blue . . . . 3·50 2·40
128 – 30c. mauve . . . . 3·25 1·40
129 – 50c. olive . . . . 6·75 1·50
130 **33** 1p. yellow . . . . 13·50 4·50
131 – 2p. red . . . . 13·50 3·75
132 – 5p. green . . . . 35·00 17·00
133 – 10p. purple . . . . 30·00 13·50
DESIGNS—HORIZ: 1c. Oath of Independence; 3c. Battle of Roble; 5c. Battle of Maipu; 10c. Fight between frigates "Lautaro" and "Esmeralda"; 12c. Capture of the "Maria Isabella"; 15c. First sortie of the liberating forces; 20c. Abdication of O'Higgins; 25c. First Chilean Congress. VERT: 30c. O'Higgins Monument; 50c. Carrera Monument; 2p. General Blanco; 5p. General Zenteno; 10p. Admiral Cochrane.

46 Columbus **47** Valdivia **49** O'Higgins

64 Admiral Cochrane **50** Freire **52** Prieto

65 M. Rengifo **57** A. Pinto

1911. Inscr "CHILE CORREOS".
135 **46** 1c. green 15 10
136 **47** 2c. red 15 10
150 **46** 2c. red 15 10
137 – 3c. sepia 50 35
151 – 4c. sepia 20 10
138 **49** 5c. blue 15 10
161 **64** 5c. blue 35 15
152 – 8c. grey 70 30
139 **50** 10c. black and grey . . . 50 30
153 **49** 10c. black and blue . . . 70 10
140 – 12c. black and red . . . 85 30
154 – 14c. black and red . . . 70 10
141 **52** 15c. black and purple . . 70 30
142 – 20c. black and orange . . 1·40 15
167 – 25c. black and blue . . . 50 15
168 – 30c. black and brown . . 1·50 15
155 **52** 40c. black and purple . . 4·50 65
186 **65** 40c. black and violet . . . 40 15
170 – 50c. black and green . . 1·50 15
156 – 60c. black and blue . . . 8·50 1·60
171 – 80c. black and sepia . . . 1·90 55
188 **57** 1p. black and green . . . 70 10
189 – 2p. black and red . . . 3·25 30
190 – 5p. black and olive . . . 8·00 70
190a – 10p. black and orange . . 8·00 1·00
PORTRAITS: 3c., 4c. Toro Z. 8c. Freire. 12, 14c. F. A. Pinto. 20c. Bulnes. 25c., 60c. Montt. 30c. Perez. 50c. Errazuriz Z. 80c. Admiral Latorre. 2p. Santa Maria. 5p. Balmaceda. 10p. Errazuriz E.

61 Columbus **62** Valdivia **63** Columbus

1915. Larger Stars.
157 **61** 1c. green 20 10
158 **62** 2c. red 20 10
160 **61** 4c. brown (small head) . . 30 10
159 **63** 4c. brown (large head) . . 25 10

67 Chilean Congress Building **67a** O'Higgins

1923. Pan-American Conference.
176 **67** 2c. red 15 10
177 4c. brown 15 10
178 10c. black and blue 15 10
179 20c. black and orange . . 40 15
180 40c. black and mauve . . . 70 20
181 1p. black and green . . . 85 35
182 2p. black and red . . . 3·00 40
183 5p. black and green . . . 10·00 2·25

1927. Air. Unissued stamp surch **Correo Aereo** and value.
184 **67a** 40c. on 10c. blue & brn £200 30·00
184a 80c. on 10c. blue & brn £200 42·00
184b 1p.20 on 10c. bl & brn £200 50·00
184c 1p.60 on 10c. bl & brn £200 50·00
184d 2p. on 10c. blue & brn £200 50·00

1928. Air. Optd **CORREO AEREO** and bird or surch also.
191 – 20c. blk & orge (No. 141) 35 15
199 **65** 40c. black and violet . . . 40 20
200 **57** 1p. black and green . . . 1·10 35
194 – 2p. black & red (No. 189) 1·60 25
201 **64** 3p. on 5c. blue . . . . . . 40·00 30·00
195 – 5p. black & ol (No. 190) 2·75 70
196 **49** 6p. on 10c. black & blue 50·00 30·00
198 – 10p. blk & orge (No. 190a) 9·00 2·75

1928. As Types of 1911, but inscr "CORREOS DE CHILE".
205 **64** 5c. blue 50 10
206 5c. green 50 10
204 **49** 10c. black and blue . . . 75 25
208 **52** 15c. black and purple . . 1·75 10
209 – 20c. black and orange (As No. 142) . . . . 4·00 15
210 – 25c. black and blue (As No. 167) 75 10
211 – 30c. black and brown (As No. 168) 55 20
212 – 50c. black and green (As No. 170) 50 10

1929. Air. Nos. 209/12 optd **CORREO AEREO** and bird.
213a 20c. black and orange . . . 25 15
214 25c. black and blue 40 15
215 30c. black and brown . . . 25 15
216 50c. black and green . . . 35 15

71 Winged Wheel **72** Sower

1930. Centenary of Nitrate Industry.
217 **71** 5c. green 35 15
218 10c. brown 35 15
219 15c. violet 35 15
220 – 25c. slate (Girl harvester) 1·40 15
221 **72** 70c. blue . . . . 3·25 1·00
222 1p. green (24½ × 30 mm) . . 2·50 50

73 Andean Condor and Fokker Super Universal Airplane **75** Ford 4AT Trimotor over Los Cerrillos Airport

1931. Air. Inscr "LINEA AEREA NACIONAL".
223 **73** 5c. green 40 25
224 10c. brown 40 25
225 20c. red 40 10
226a – 50c. sepia 40 25
227 **75** 50c. blue . . . . 1·75 85
228 – 1p. violet 55 30
229 – 2p. slate . . . . 1·50 25
230 **75** 5p. red . . . . 3·50 60
DESIGN: 50c. (No. 226a), 1p., 2p. Fokker Super Universal airplane.

76 O'Higgins **79** Mariano Egana

1931.
231 **76** 10c. blue . . . . 1·00 10
232 – 20c. brown (Bulnes) . . . 85 10
233 – 30c. mauve (Perez) . . . . 1·40 10

1934. Centenary of Constitution of 1833.
234 **79** 30c. mauve 50 25
235 – 1p.20 blue 90 25
PORTRAIT: 1p.20, Joaquin Tocornal (24½ × 29 mm).

83 Fokker Super Universal Aircraft over Globe **87** Diego de Almagro

1934. Air. As T **83**.
236 10c. green 15 10
237 15c. green 25 20
238 20c. blue 20 15
239 30c. black 20 15
239a 40c. blue 20 15
240 50c. brown 20 15
241 60c. black 20 15
356a 70c. blue 30 20
243 80c. green 20 15
244 1p. grey 20 15
245 2p. blue 20 15
360 3p. brown 25 15
361 4p. brown 25 15
248 5p. red 20 10
249 6p. brown 35 15
250 8p. green 30 10
251 10p. purple 35 15
252 20p. olive 35 15
253 30p. grey 35 10
254 40p. violet 70 40
255a 50p. purple 85 40
DESIGNS—21 × 25 mm: 10, 15, 20c. Fokker Super Universal over Santiago; 30, 40, 50c. Junkers G.24 over landscape; 60c. Condor in flight; 70c. Airplane and star; 80c. Condor and statue of Caupolican; 25 × 29 mm: 1, 2p. Type **83**; 3, 4, 5p. Stinson Faucett F.19 seaplane in flight; 6, 8, 10p. Northrop Alpha monoplane and rainbow; 20, 30p. Stylized Dornier Wal flying boat and compass; 40, 50p. Airplane riding a storm.

1936. 400th Anniv of Discovery of Chile.
256 – 5c. red 35 15
257 – 10c. violet 15 10
258 – 20c. mauve 20 10
259 – 25c. blue . . . . 2·00 55
260 – 30c. green 20 10
261 – 40c. black . . . . 2·00 50
262 – 50c. blue . . . . 1·10 20
263 – 1p. green . . . . 1·50 35
264 – 1p.20 blue . . . . 1·25 45
265 **87** 2p. brown . . . . 1·25 55
266 – 5p. red . . . . 3·50 1·40
267 – 10p. purple . . . . 9·00 7·00
DESIGNS: 5c. Atacama desert; 10c. Fishing boats; 20c. Coquito palms; 25c. Sheep. 30c. Coal mines; 40c. Lonquimay forests; 50c. Lota coal port; 1p. "Orduna" (liner), Valparaiso; 1p.20. Mt. Puntiaguda; 5p. Cattle; 10p. Shovelling nitrate.

88 Laja Waterfall **90** "Calbuco" (fishing boat)

1938.
268 **88** 5c. purple 15 10
269 – 10c. red 15 10
269a – 15c. red 15 10
270 – 20c. blue 45 10
271 – 30c. pink 15 10
272 – 40c. green 15 10
273 – 50c. violet 15 10
274 **90** 1p. orange 15 10
275 – 1p.80 blue 85 20
338h – 2p. red 50 10
278 – 5p. green 35 10
338j – 10p. purple . . . . 1·10 10
DESIGNS—As Type **88**: 10c. Rural landscape; 15c. Boldo tree; 20c. Nitrate works; 30c. Mineral spas; 40c. Copper mine; 50c. Petroleum tanks. As Type **90**: 1p.80, Osorno Volcano; 2p. "Conte de Biancamano" (freighter) and "Ponderoso" (tug); 5p. Lake Villarrica; 10p. Steam locomotive No. 908.

92 "Abtao" (armed steamer) and Policarpo Toro

1940. 50th Anniv of Occupation of Easter Island and Local Hospital Fund.
279 **92** 80c.+2p.20 red & green . . 2·00 1·40
280 – 3p.60+6p.40 green and red 2·00 1·40
DESIGN: 3p.60, "Abtao" and E. Eyraud.

93 Western Hemisphere

1940. 50th Anniv of Pan-American Union.
281 **93** 40c. green 20 10

1940. Air. Surch with winged device above new values.
282 **73** 80c. on 20c. red 45 25
283 **75** 1p.60 on 5p. red . . . . . 3·25 85
284 – 5p.10 on 2p. slate (No. 229) . . . . 2·50 1·00

96 Fray Camilo Henriquez **97** Founding of Santiago

1941. 400th Anniv of Santiago.
285 **96** 10c. red 30 15
286 – 40c. green 40 10
287 – 1p.10 red . . . . 1·00 85
288 **97** 1p.80 blue . . . . 1·00 50
289 – 3p.60 blue . . . . 3·25 1·60
PORTRAITS—As Type **96**: 40c. P. Valdivia. 1p.10, B. V. MacKenna. 3p.60, D. B. Arana.

98 Potez 56 and Globe **99** Sikorsky S-43 Amphibian and Galleon

1941. Air. No. 304 is dated "1541–1941" and commemorates the 4th Centenary of Santiago.
290 – 10c. olive 30 10
291 – 10c. mauve 30 10
316 – 10c. blue 20 10
292 **98** 20c. red 30 10
318 20c. green 20 10
294 20c. brown 20 10
295 – 30c. violet 30 10
295a – 30c. olive 20 10
296 – 40c. brown 30 10
297 – 40c. blue 20 10
324 – 50c. red 30 10
325 – 50c. orange 30 10
299a – 60c. green 20 15
326 – 60c. orange 30 10
300 – 70c. red 60 20
301 – 80c. blue . . . . 3·00 35
302 – 80c. olive 20 15
303a – 90c. brown 30 10
304 **99** 1p. blue 60 20
304a 1p. green and blue . . . 30 10
305 – 1p.60 violet 30 15
306 – 1p.80 violet 30 10
307 – 2p. lake 85 25
308 – 2p. brown 60 10
309 – 3p. green . . . . 1·25 45
310a – 3p. violet and yellow . . 2·50 25
334 – 3p. violet and orange . . 85 15
311 – 4p. violet and brown . . 2·00 55
335 – 4p. green 85 30
336a – 5p. brown 35 20
336 – 5p. red 35 25
314 – 10p. green and blue . . . 9·50 4·00
337 – 10p. blue 85 25
DESIGNS: (each incorporating a different type of airplane): 10c. Steeple; 30c. Flag; 40c. Stars; 50c. Mountains; 60c. Tree; 70c. Estuary; 80c. Shore; 90c.

Sun rays; 1p.60, 1p.80, Wireless mast; 2p. Compass; 3p. Telegraph wires; 4p. Rainbow; 5p. Factory; 10p. Snow-capped mountain.

See also Nos. 395 etc.

101 V. Letelier — 102 University of Chile

103 Coat of arms and Aeroplane

1942. Centenary of Santiago de Chile University.

339 **101** 30c. red (postage) 20 10
340 – 40c. green 20 10
341 – 90c. violet . . . . 1·50 70
342 **102** 1p. brown . . . . 1·00 40
343 – 1p.80 blue . . . . 2·50 1·40

344 **103** 100p. red (air) . . . . . 30·00 20·00

DESIGNS—As Type **101**: 40c. A. Bello; 90c. M. Bulnes; 1p.80, M. Montt.

104 Manuel Bulnes — 105 Straits of Magellan

1944. Centenary of Occupation of Magellan Straits.

345 **104** 15c. black 15 10
346 – 30c. red 15 10
347 – 40c. green 15 10
348 – 1p. brown 85 25
349 **105** 1p.80 blue . . . . 1·25 70

PORTRAITS: 30c. J. W. Wilson. 40c. D. D. Almeida. 1p. Jose de los Santos Mardones.

106 "Lamp of Life"

1944. International Red Cross.

350 **106** 40c. black, red and green 50 10
351 – 1p.80 red and blue . . . 1·00 50

DESIGN: 1p.80, Serpent and chalice symbol of Hygiene.

107 O'Higgins (after J. G. de Castro) — 108 Battle of Rancagua (after Subercaseaux)

1944. Death Centenary of Bernardo O'Higgins.

367 **107** 15c. black and red 15 10
368 – 30c. black and brown . . 25 10
369 – 40c. black and green . . . 25 10
370 **108** 1p.80 black and blue . . 1·25 80

DESIGNS—As Type **108**: 30c. Battle of the Maipu; 40c. Abdication of O'Higgins.

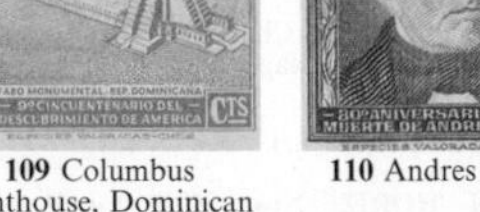

109 Columbus Lighthouse, Dominican Republic — 110 Andres Bello

1945. 450th Anniv of Discovery of America by Columbus.

371 **109** 40c. green 30 15

1946. 80th Death Anniv of Andres Bello (educationist).

372 **110** 40c. green 15 10
373 1p.80 blue 15 10

111 Antarctic Territory — 113 Miguel de Cervantes

112 Eusebio Lillo and Ramon Carnicer

1947.

374 **111** 40c. red 40 15
375 2p.50 blue . . . . 1·25 30

1947. Centenary of National Anthem.

376 **112** 40c. green 15 10

1947. 400th Birth Anniv of Cervantes.

377 **113** 40c. red 15 10

114 Arturo Prat and "Esmeralda" (sail corvette)

1948. Birth Centenary of Arturo Prat.

378 **114** 40c. blue 35 10

115 O'Higgins — 119 "Chiasognathus granti"

1948.

379 **115** 60c. black 10 10

1948. No. 272 surch **VEINTE CTS.** and bar.

380 20c. on 40c. green 10 10

1948. Centenary of Publication on Chilean Flora and Fauna. Botanical and zoological designs, as T **119** inscr "CENTENARIO DEL LIBRO DE GAY 1844–1944".

381a/y 60c. blue (postage) 80 35
382a/y 2p.60 green . . . . 1·50 90

383a/y 3p. red (air) . . . . 1·60 1·10

Each value in 25 different designs. Prices are for individual stamps.

120 Airline Badge — 121 B. V. Mackenna

1949. Air. 20th Anniv of National Airline.

384 **120** 2p. blue 15 25

1949. Vicuna Mackenna Museum.

385 **121** 60c. blue (postage) . . . 10 10

386 3p. red (air) 15 10

122 Wheel and Lamp

1949. Cent of School of Arts and Crafts, Santiago.

387 **122** 60c. mauve (postage) . . 15 10
388 – 2p.60 blue 30 20

389 – 5p. green (air) 45 30
390 – 10p. brown 75 40

DESIGNS: 2p.60, Shield and book; 5p. Shield, book and factory; 10p. Wheel and column.

123 Heinrich von Stephan — 124 Douglas DC-6B and Globe

1950. 75th Anniv of U.P.U.

391 **123** 60c. red (postage) 10 10
392 2p.50 blue 45 20

393 **124** 5p. green (air) 30 20
394 10p. brown 60 35

1950. Air. As T **98/99**.

395 20c. brown 15 10
396 40c. violet 15 10
404c 60c. blue 25 10
398 1p. green 15 10
399 2p. brown 15 10
404f 3p. blue 15 10
401 4p. orange 30 10
402 5p. violet 15 10
403 10p. green 20 10
480 20p. brown 30 10
481 50p. green 35 10
482 100p. red 75 10
483 200p. blue 80 10

DESIGNS (each including an aeroplane): 20c. Mountains; 40c. Coastline; 60c. Fishing vessel; 1p. Araucanian pine tree; 2p. Chilean flag; 3p. Dock crane; 4p. River; 5p. Industrial plant; 10p. Landscape; 20p. Aerial railway; 50p. Mountainous coastline; 100p. Antarctic map; 200p. Rock "bridge" in sea.

126 Crossing the Andes (after Y. Prades)

1951. Death Centenary of Gen. San Martin.

405 – 60c. blue (postage) . . . 10 10

406 **126** 5p. purple (air) 50 15

PORTRAIT (25 × 29 mm): 60c. San Martin.

1951. Air. No. 303a surch **UN PESO**.

407 1p. on 90c. brown 15 10

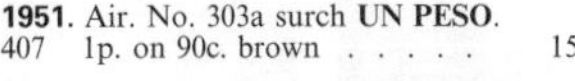

128 Issabella the Catholic

1952. 500th Birth Anniv of Issabella the Catholic.

408 **128** 60c. blue (postage) . . . 10 10

409 10p. red (air) 40 20

1952. Surch **40 Ctvs.**

410 **115** 40c. on 60c. black 10 10

1952. Air. No. 302 surch **40 Centavos**.

411 40c. on 80c. olive 15 10

116 M. de Toro y Zambrano — 131 Arms of Valdivia

132 Old Spanish Watch-tower

1952.

379b **116** 80c. green 15 10
379c – 1p. turquoise (O'Higgins) 10 10
446 – 2p. lilac (Carrera) . . . 10 10
447 – 3p. blue (R. Freire) . . . 10 10
448 – 5p. sepia (M. Bulnes) . . 10 10
449 – 10p. violet (F. A. Pinto) 10 10
450 – 50p. red (M. Montt) . . 35 10

1953. 400th Anniv of Valdivia.

414 **131** 1p. blue (postage) 15 10
415 – 2p. violet 15 10
416 – 3p. green 35 10
417 – 5p. brown 45 10

418 **132** 10p. red (air) . . . . . . 1·25 20

DESIGNS—As Type **132**: 2p. Ancient cannons, Corral Fort; 3p. Valdivia from the river; 5p. Street scene (after old engraving).

133 J. Toribio Medina — 134 Stamp of 1853

1953. Birth Centenary of Toribio Medina.

419 **133** 1p. brown 15 10
420 2p.50 blue 25 10

1953. Chilean Stamp Centenary.

421 **134** 1p. brown (postage) . . . 15 10

422 100p. turquoise (air) . . . 3·00 1·75

135 Map and Graph — 136 Aircraft of 1929 and 1954

1953. 12th National Census.

423 **135** 1p. green 10 10
424 2p.50 blue 15 10
425 3p. brown 25 15
426 4p. red 35 15

1954. Air. 25th Anniv of National Air Line.

427 **136** 3p. blue 10 10

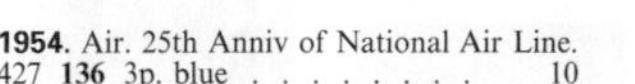

137 Arms of Angol — 138 I. Domeyko

1954. 400th Anniv of Angol City.

428 **137** 2p. red 10 15

1954. 150th Birth Anniv of Domeyko (educationist and mineralogist).

429 **138** 1p. blue (postage) 15 10

430 5p. brown (air) 15 10

139 Locomotive "Tiger", 1856

1954. Centenary of Chilean Railways.

431 **139** 1p. red (postage) 20 25

432 10p. purple (air) . . . . 90 1·25

140 Arturo Prat **141** Arms of Vina del Mar

1954. 75th Anniv of Naval Battle of Iquique.
433 **140** 2p. violet 15 10

1955. Int Philatelic Exhibition, Valparaiso.
434 **141** 1p. blue 15 10
435 – 2p. red 15 10
DESIGN: 2p. Arms of Valparaiso.

142 Dr. A. del Rio **143** Christ of the Andes

1955. 14th Pan-American Sanitary Conference.
436 **142** 2p. blue 10 10

1955. Exchange of Visits between Argentine and Chilean Presidents.
437 **143** 1p. blue (postage) 15 10
438 100p. red (air) . . . . . 1·90 75

144 De Havilland Comet 1 **145** M. Rengifo

1955. Air.
441a **144** 100p. green 75 15
441b – 200p. blue . . . . . . 4·50 75
441c – 500p. red . . . . . . 6·00 75
AIRCRAFT: 200p. Morane Saulnier Paris I. 500p. Douglas DC-6B.

1955. Death Centenary of Joaquin Prieto (President, 1833–41).
442 **145** 3p. blue 10 10
443 – 5p. red (Egana) 10 10
444 – 50p. purple (Portales) . . 1·40 25
For 15p. in similar design see under Compulsory Tax Stamps.

147 Bell Trooper Helicopter and Bridge **148** F. Santa Maria

149 Atomic Symbol and Cogwheels

1956. Air.
451 – 1p. red 20 10
452 **147** 2p. sepia 20 10
455 – 5p. violet 20 10
456 – 10p. green 15 10
456a – 20p. blue 15 10
456b – 50p. red 20 10
DESIGNS: 1p. De Havilland Venom FB.4; 5p. Diesel locomotive and Douglas DC-6B; 10p. Oil derricks and Douglas DC-6B; 20p. De Havilland Venom FB.4 and Easter Island monolith; 50p. Douglas DC-2 and control tower.
See also Nos. 524/7.

1956. 25th Anniv of Santa Maria Technical University, Valparaiso.
457 **148** 5p. brown (postage) . . . 15 10
458 **149** 20p. green (air) 25 15
459 – 100p. violet 70 40
DESIGN—As Type **149**: 100p. Aerial view of University.

150 Gabriela Mistral **151** Arms of Osorno

1958. Gabriela Mistral (poetess, Nobel Prize Winner).
460 **150** 10p. brown (postage) . . 15 10
461 100p. green (air) 30 10

1958. 400th Anniv of Osorno.
462 **151** 10p. red (postage) 15 10
463 – 50p. green 35 10
464 – 100p. blue (air) 65 25
PORTRAITS: 50p. G. H. de Mendoza. 100p. O'Higgins.

152 "La Araucana" (poem) and Antarctic Map **153** Arms of Santiago de Chile

1958. Antarctic issue.
465 **152** 10p. blue (postage) . . . 20 10
466 – 200p. purple . . . . . . 3·25 1·25
467 **152** 20p. violet (air) 45 10
468 – 500p. blue . . . . 5·50 1·75
DESIGN: 200p., 500p. Chilean map of 1588.

1958. National Philatelic Exhibition, Santiago.
469 **153** 10p. purple (postage) . . 15 10
470 50p. green (air) 25 10

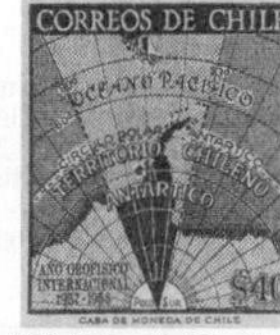

154 **155** Antarctic Territory

1958. Cent of Chilean Civil Servants' Savings Bank.
471 **154** 10p. blue (postage) . . . 10 10
472 50p. brown (air) 25 10

1958. I.G.Y.
473 **155** 40p. red (postage) 40 10
474 50p. green (air) 50 15

156 Religious Emblems **157** Bridge, Valdivia

1959. Air. Human Rights Day.
475 **156** 50p. red . . . . 65 1·00

1959. Centenary of German School, Valdivia and Philatelic Exhibition.
476 **157** 40p. green (postage) . . . 20 10
477 – 20p. red (air) 15 15
DESIGN—VERT: 20p. A. C. Anwandter (founder).

158 Expedition Map **159** D. Barros-Arana

1959. 400th Anniv of Juan Ladrillero's Expedition of 1557.
484 **158** 10p. violet (postage) . . . 25 10
485 50p. green (air) 35 10

1959. 50th Death Anniv of D. Barros-Arana (historian).
486 **159** 40p. blue (postage) . . . 15 10
487 100p. lilac (air) 40 20

160 J. H. Dunant (founder)

1959. Red Cross Commemoration.
488 **160** 20p. lake & red (postage) 20 10
489 50p. black & red (air) . . 25 10

161 F. A. Pinto **162** Choshuenco Volcano

1960. (a) Portraits as T **161**.
490 – 5m. turquoise 10 10
491 **161** 1c. red 10 10
493 – 5c. blue 10 10

(b) Views as T **162**.
492 **162** 2c. blue 10 10
492a 2c. blue (23½ × 18 mm) 10 10
494 – 10c. green 20 10
495 – 20c. blue 35 10
496 – 1E. turquoise 40 15
DESIGNS—As Type **161**: 5m. M. Bulnes; 5c. M. Montt. As Type **162**: 10c. R. Maule Valley; 20c., 1E. Inca Lake.

163 Martin 4-0-4 Airplane and Dock Crane **164** Refugee Family

1960. Air (Inland).
497 – 1m. orange 10 10
498 – 2m. green 10 10
499 **163** 3m. violet 10 10
500 – 4m. olive 10 10
501 – 5m. turquoise 10 10
502 – 1c. blue 10 10
503 – 2c. brown 25 10
504 – 5c. green . . . . 1·90 15
505 – 10c. red 45 10
506 – 20c. blue 60 10
DESIGNS: Airplane over—1m. Araucanian pine; 2m. Chilean flag; 4m. River; 5m. Industrial plant; 1c. Landscape; 2c. Aerial railway; 5c. Mountainous coastline; 10c. Antarctic map; 20c. Rock "bridge" in sea.

1960. World Refugee Year.
507 **164** 1c. green (postage) . . . 35 10
508 10c. violet (air) 60 10

165 Arms of Chile

1960. 150th Anniv of 1st National Government (1st issue).
509 **165** 1c. brn & red (postage) 15 10
510 10c. chestnut & brn (air) 20 10
See also Nos. 512/23.

166 Rotary Emblem and Map

1960. Air. Rotary International S. American Regional Conference, Santiago.
511 **166** 10c. blue 25 10

167 J. M. Carrera **168** "Population"

1960. 150th Anniv of 1st National Government (2nd issue). (a) Postage.
512 – 1c. red and brown 15 10
513 – 5c. turquoise & green . . 15 10
514 – 10c. purple and brown . . 15 10
515 – 20c. green and blue . . . 15 10
516 – 50c. red and brown . . . 50 10
517 **167** 1E. brown and green . . 1·40 40
DESIGNS—HORIZ: 1c. Palace of Justice; 10c. M. de Toro y Zambrano and M. de Rozas; 20c. M. de Salas and Juan Egana; 50c. M. Rodriguez and J. Mackenna. VERT: 5c. Temple of the National Vow.

(b) Air.
518 – 2c. violet and red 10 10
519 – 5c. purple and blue . . . 15 10
520 – 10c. bistre and brown . . 15 10
521 – 20c. violet and blue . . . 25 10
522 – 50c. blue and green . . . 45 20
523 – 1E. brown and red . . . 1·40 40
DESIGNS—HORIZ: 2c. Palace of Justice; 10c. J. G. Martin and J. G. Argomedo; 20c. J. A. Eyzaguirre and J. M. Infante; 50c. Bishop J. I. Cienfuegos and Fray C. Henriquez. VERT: 5c. Temple of the National Vow. 1E. O'Higgins.

1961. Air (Foreign). As T **147** or **144** (10c. and 50c.), but values in new currency.
524 5m. brown 15 10
525 1c. blue 10 10
526 2c. blue 10 10
527 5c. red 10 10
528 10c. blue 10 10
529 20c. red 10 10
530 50c. turquoise 10 10
DESIGNS: 5m. Diesel locomotive and Douglas DC-6B; 1c. Oil derricks and Douglas DC-6B; 2c. De Havilland Venom FB.4 and monolith; 5c. Douglas DC-2 and control tower; 10c. De Havilland Comet 1; 20c. Morane Saulnier Paris I; 50c. Douglas DC-6B.

1961. National Census. 13th Population Census (5c.); 2nd Housing Census (10c.).
531 **168** 5c. green 40 10
532 – 10c. violet (buildings) . . 40 10

169 Pedro de Valdivia **170** Congress Building

1961. Earthquake Relief Fund. Inscr "ESPANA A CHILE".
533 **169** 5c.+5c. green and pink (postage) . . . . . . 1·00 15
534 – 10c.+10c. violet & buff . . 1·00 15
535 – 10c.+10c. brown and orange (air) . . . . . 1·00 20
536 – 20c.+20c. red and blue . . 1·00 20
PORTRAITS: No. 534, J. T. Medina. No. 535, A. de Ercilla. No. 536, Gabriela Mistral.

1961. 150th Anniv of 1st National Congress.
537 **170** 2c. brown (postage) . . . 40 10
538 10c. green (air) . . . . . 1·10 70

171 Footballers and Globe

1962. World Football Championships, Chile.
539 **171** 2c. blue (postage) 10 10
540 – 5c. green 15 10
541 – 5c. purple (air) 15 10
542 **171** 10c. lake 25 10
DESIGN—HORIZ: Nos. 540/1, Goalkeeper and stadium.

172 Mother and Child

1963. Freedom from Hunger.
543 **172** 3c. purple (postage) . . . 10 10
544 – 20c. green (air) 15 10
DESIGN—HORIZ: 20c. Mother holding out food bowl.

173 Centenary Emblem **174** Fire Brigade Monument

1963. Red Cross Centenary.
545 **173** 3c. red & grey (postage) 10 10
546 – 20c. red and grey (air) . . 15 10
DESIGN—HORIZ: 20c. Centenary emblem and silhouette of aircraft.

1963. Centenary of Santiago Fire Brigade.
547 **174** 3c. violet (postage) . . . 10 10
548 – 30c. red (air) 30 15
DESIGN—HORIZ: (39 × 30 mm): 30c. Fire engine of 1863.

175 Band encircling Globe **176** Enrique Molina

1964. Air. "Alliance for Progress" and Pres. Kennedy Commemoration
549 **175** 4c. blue 10 10

1964. Molina Commemoration (founder of Concepcion University).
550 **176** 4c. bistre (postage) . . . 10 10
551 60c. violet (air) 10 10

1965. Casanueva Commemoration. As T **176** but portrait of Mons. Carlos Casanueva, Rector of Catholic University.
552 4c. purple (postage) 10 10
553 60c. green (air) 10 10

177 Battle Scene (after Subercaseaux)

1965. Air. 150th Anniv of Battle of Rancagua.
554 **177** 5c. brown and green . . . 10 10

178 Monolith **179** I.T.U. Emblem and Symbols

1965. Easter Island Discoveries.
555 **178** 6c. purple 10 10
556 10c. mauve 15 10

1965. Air. Centenary of I.T.U.
557 **179** 40c. purple and red . . . 15 10

180 Crusoe on Juan Fernandez **181** Skier descending slope

1965. Robinson Crusoe Commemoration.
558 **180** 30c. red 15 10

1965. World Skiing Championships.
559 **181** 4c. green (postage) . . . 15 10
560 – 20c. blue (air) 10 10
DESIGN—HORIZ: 20c. Skier crossing slope.

182 Angelmo Harbour **183** Aviators, Monument

1965. Air.
561 **182** 40c. brown 30 10
562 **183** 1E. red 20 10

184 Copihue (National Flower) **185** A. Bello

1965.
563 **184** 15c. red and green . . . 15 10
563a 20c. red and green . . . 15 10

1965. Air. Death Centenary of Andres Bello (poet).
564 **185** 10c. red 10 10

186 Dr. L. Sazie **187** Skiers

1966. Death Centenary of Dr. L. Sazie.
565 **186** 1E. green . . . . 1·25 10

1966. Air. World Skiing Championships.
566 – 75c. red and lilac 20 10
567 – 3E. ultramarine and blue 40 10
568 **187** 4E. brown and blue . . . 85 25
DESIGN—HORIZ: (38 × 25 mm): 75c., 3E. Skier in slalom race.

188 Ball and Basket **189** J. Montt

1966. Air. World Basketball Championships.
569 **188** 13c. red 15 10

1966.
570 **189** 30c. violet 10 10
571 – 50c. brown (G. Riesco) 10 10

190 W. Wheelwright and Paddle-steamers "Chile" and "Peru"

1966. 125th Anniv (1965) of Arrival of Paddle-steamers "Chile" and "Peru".
572 **190** 10c. ultram & bl (postage) 40 10
573 70c. blue and green (air) 60 10

191 "Learning" **193** Chilean Flag and Ships

192 I.C.Y. Emblem

1966. Education Campaign.
574 **191** 10c. purple 10 10

1966. International Co-operation Year (1965).
575 **192** 1E. brn & green (postage) 1·75 10
576 3E. red and blue (air) . . 60 20

1966. Air. Antofagasta Centenary.
577 **193** 13c. purple 10 10

194 Capt. Pardo and "Yelcho" (coastguard vessel)

1967. 50th Anniv of Pardo's Rescue of Shackleton Expedition.
578 **194** 20c. turquoise (postage) 1·40 10
579 – 40c. blue (air) 30 15
DESIGN: 40c. Capt. Pardo and Antarctic sectoral map.

195 Chilean Family **197** Pine Forest

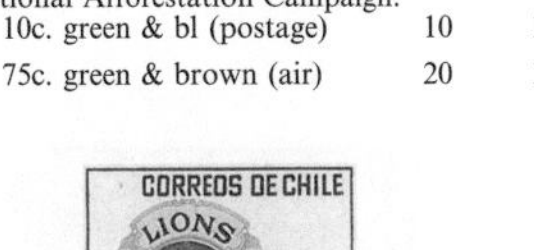

196 R. Dario (poet)

1967. 8th International Family Planning Congress.
580 **195** 10c. black and purple (postage) 10 10
581 80c. black and blue (air) 20 10

1967. Air. Birth Centenary of Ruben Dario (Nicaraguan poet).
582 **196** 10c. blue 15 10

1967. National Afforestation Campaign.
583 **197** 10c. green & bl (postage) 10 10
584 75c. green & brown (air) 20 10

198 Lions Emblem

1967. 50th Anniv of Lions International.
585 **198** 20c. blue & brn (postage) 15 10
586 1E. violet & yellow (air) 15 10
587 5E. blue and yellow . . . 1·40 50

199 Chilean Flag

1967. 150th Anniv of National Flag.
588 **199** 80c. red & blue (post) . . 20 10
589 50c. red and blue (air) . . 15 10

200 I.T.Y. Emblem

1967. Air. International Tourist Year.
590 **200** 30c. black and blue . . . 10 10

201 Cardinal Caro **203** Farmer and Wife

202 San Martin and O'Higgins

1967. Birth Centenary of Cardinal Caro.
591 **201** 20c. lake (postage) . . . 35 20
592 40c. violet (air) 75 15

1968. 150th Anniv of Battles of Chacabuco and Maipu.
593 **202** 3E. blue (postage) 10 10
594 2E. violet (air) 10 10

1968. Agrarian Reform.
595 **203** 20c. black, green and orange (postage) . . . 15 10
596 50c. black, green and orange (air) 15 10

204 Juan I. Molina (scientist) and "Lamp of Learning" **205** Hand supporting Cogwheel

1968. Molina Commemoration.
597 **204** 2E. purple (postage) . . . 10 10
598 – 1E. green (air) 10 10
DESIGN: 1E. Molina and books.

1968. 4th Manufacturing Census.
599 **205** 30c. red 15 10

206 Map, "San Sebastian" (galleon) and "Alonso de Erckla" (ferry)

1968. "Five Towns" Centenaries.
600 **206** 30c. blue (postage) . . . 50 10
601 – 1E. purple (air) 15 10
DESIGN—VERT: 1E. Map of Chiloe Province.

207 Club Emblem

1968. 40th Anniv of Chilean Automobile Club.
602 **207** 1E. red (postage) 20 10
603 5E. blue (air) 15 15

208 Chilean Arms

1968. Air. State Visit of Queen Elizabeth II.
604 **208** 50c. brown and green . . 15 10
605 – 3E. brown and blue . . . 15 10
606 – 5E. purple and plum . . . 25 15
DESIGN—HORIZ: 3E. Royal arms of Great Britain. VERT: 5E. St. Edward's Crown on map of South America.

209 Don Francisco Garcia Huidobro (founder)

1968. 225th Anniv of Chilean Mint.
608 **209** 2E. blue & red (postage) 10 10
609 – 5E. brown and green . . 20 10
610 – 50c. purple & yell (air) . . 10 10
611 – 1E. red and blue 15 15
DESIGNS: 50c. First Chilean coin and press; 1E. First Chilean stamp printed by the mint (1915); 5E. Philip V of Spain.

210 Satellite and Dish Aerial

1969. Inauguration of "ENTEL-CHILE" Satellite Communications Ground Station, Longovilo (1st issue).
613 **210** 30c. blue (postage) . . . 10 10
614 2E. purple (air) 20 10
See also Nos. 668/9.

211 Red Cross Symbols

1969. 50th Anniv of League of Red Cross Societies.
615 **211** 2E. red & violet (postage) 15 10
616 5E. red and black (air) . . 15 10

212 Rapel Dam

1969. Rapel Hydro-electric Project.
617 **212** 40c. green (postage) . . . 10 10
618 3E. blue (air) 15 10

213 Rodriguez Memorial

1969. 150th Death Anniv of Col. Manuel Rodriguez.
619 **213** 2E. red (postage) 10 10
620 30c. brown (air) 10 10

214 Open Bible

1969. 400th Anniv of Spanish Translation of Bible.
621 **214** 40c. brown (postage) . . 10 10
622 1E. green (air) 15 10

215 Hemispheres and I.L.O. Emblem

1969. 50th Anniv of I.L.O.
623 **215** 1E. grn & blk (postage) 10 10
624 2E. purple & black (air) 10 10

216 Human Rights Emblem

217 "EXPO" Emblem

1969. Human Rights Year (1968).
625 **216** 4E. red and blue (postage) 35 25
626 4E. red and brown (air) 45 25

1969. World Fair "EXPO 70", Osaka, Japan.
628 **217** 3E. blue (postage) 10 10
629 5E. red (air) 15 10

218 Mint, Santiago (18th cent)

1970. Spanish Colonization of Chile.
630 **218** 2E. purple 20 10
631 – 3E. red 15 10
632 – 4E. blue 15 10
633 – 5E. brown 15 10
634 – 10E. green 15 10
DESIGNS—HORIZ: 5E. Cal y Canto Bridge. VERT: 3E. Pedro de Valdivia; 4E. Santo Domingo Church, Santiago; 10E. Ambrosio O'Higgins.

219 Policarpo Toro and Map

1970. 80th Anniv of Seizure of Easter Island.
636 **219** 5E. violet (postage) . . . 25 10
637 50c. turquoise (air) . . . 35 10

221 Chilean Schooner and Arms

1970. 150th Anniv of Capture of Valdivia by Lord Cochrane.
640 **221** 40c. lake (postage) . . . 45 10
641 2E. blue (air) 90 10

222 Paul Harris **223** Mahatma Gandhi

1970. Birth Centenary of Paul Harris (founder of Rotary International).
642 **222** 10E. blue (postage) . . . 90 20
643 1E. red (air) 30 15

1970. Birth Centenary of Gandhi.
644 **223** 40c. green (postage) . . . 2·50 20
645 1E. brown (air) 30 15

225 Education Year Emblem

226 "Virgin and Child"

1970. International Education Year.
648 **225** 2E. red (postage) 10 10
649 4E. brown (air) 15 10

1970. O'Higgins National Shrine, Maipu.
650 **226** 40c. green (postage) . . . 10 10
651 1E. blue (air) 15 15

227 Snake and Torch Emblem **228** Chilean Arms and Copper Symbol

1970. 10th Int Cancer Congress, Houston, U.S.A.
652 **227** 40c. purple & bl (postage) 80 10
653 2E. brown and green (air) 50 10

1970. Copper Mines Nationalization.
654 **228** 40c. red & brn (postage) 15 10
655 3E. green & brown (air) 25 10

229 Globe, Dove and Cogwheel

1970. 25th Anniv of United Nations.
656 **229** 3E. vio & red (postage) 10 10
657 5E. green and red (air) . . 20 10

1970. Nos. 613/14 surch.
658 **210** 52c. on 30c. blue (postage) 30 10
659 52c. on 2E. purple (air) 50 15

231 Freighter "Lago Maihue" and Ship's Wheel

233 Scout Badge

232 Bernardo O'Higgins and Fleet

1971. State Maritime Corporation.
660 **231** 52c. red (postage) 30 10
661 5E. brown (air) 50 10

1971. 150th Anniv of Peruvian Liberation Expedition.
662 **232** 5E. grn & blue (postage) 35 10
663 1E. purple & blue (air) . . 50 10

1971. 60th Anniv of Chilean Scouting Association.
664 **233** 1E. brn & grn (postage) 20 10
665 5c. green & lake (air) . . 20 10

234 Young People and U.N. Emblem

1971. 1st Latin-American Meeting of U.N.I.C.E.F. Executive Council, Santiago (1969).
666 **234** 52c. brn & blue (postage) 10 10
667 2E. green & blue (air) . . 15 10

1971. Longovilo Satellite Communications Ground Station (2nd issue). As T **210**, but with "LONGOVILO" added to centre inscr and wording at foot of design changed to "PRIMERA ESTACION LATINOAMERICANA".
668 40c. green (postage) 30 10
669 2E. brown (air) 50 15

235 Diver with Harpoon Gun

1971. 10th World Underwater Fishing Championships, Iquique.
670 **235** 1E.15 myrtle and green 65 10
671 2E.35 ultramarine & blue 15 10

239 Magellan and Caravel

1971. 450th Anniv of Discovery of Magellan Straits.
676 **239** 35c. plum and blue . . . 30 10

240 Dagoberto Godoy and Bristol Monoplane over Andes

1971. 1st Trans-Andes Flight (1918) Commem.
677 **240** 1E.15 green and blue . . 20 10

241 Statue of the Virgin, San Cristobal

1971. 10th Postal Union of the Americas and Spain Congress, Santiago.
678 **241** 1E.15 blue 75 10
679 – 2E.35 blue and red . . . 45 10
680 – 4E.35 red 45 10
681 – 9E.35 lilac 45 10
682 – 18E.35 mauve 60 10

DESIGNS—VERT: 4E.35, St. Francis's Church, Santiago. HORIZ: 2E.35, U.P.A.E. emblem; 9E.35, Central Post Office, Santiago; 18E.35, Corregidor Inn.

242 Cerro el Tololo Observatory

1972. Inauguration of Astronomical Observatory, Cerro el Tololo.
683 **242** 1E.95 blue & dp blue . . 20 10

243 Boeing 707 over Tahiti

1972. 1st Air Service Santiago–Easter Island–Tahiti.
684 **243** 2E.35 purple and ochre 30 10

244 Alonso de Ercilla y Zuniga

246 Human Heart

245 Antarctic Map and Dog-sledge

1972. 400th Anniv (1969) of "La Araucana" (epic poem by de Ercilla y Zungia).
685 **244** 1E. brown (postage) . . . 15 10
686 2E. blue (air) 20 15

1972. 10th Anniv of Antarctic Treaty.
687 **245** 1E.15 black and blue . . 80 15
688 3E.50 blue and green . . 55 10

1972. World Heart Month.
689 **246** 1E.15 red and black . . . 20 10

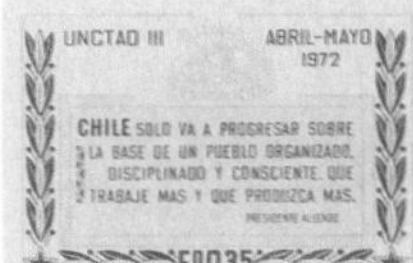

247 Text of Speech by Pres. Allende

1972. 3rd United Nations Conference on Trade and Development, Santiago.
690 **247** 35c. green and brown . . 25 15
691 – 1E.15 violet and blue . . 10 10
692 **247** 4E. violet and pink . . . 50 25
693 – 6E. blue and orange . . . 20 10
DESIGNS: 1E.15, 6E. Conference Hall Santiago.
Nos. 690 and 692 each include a se-tenant label showing Chilean workers and inscr "CORREOS DE CHILE". The stamp was only valid for postage with the label attached.

248 Soldier and Crest

1972. 150th Anniv of O'Higgins Military Academy.
694 **248** 1E.15 yellow and blue . . 15 10

249 Copper Miner

250 Barquentine "Esmeralda"

1972. Copper Mines Nationalization Law (1971).
695 **249** 1E.15 blue and red . . . 15 10
696 5E. black, blue and red 30 10

1972. 150th Anniv of Arturo Prat Naval College.
697 **250** 1E.15 purple . . . . . . 1·00 20

251 Observatory and Telescope

1972. Inauguration of Cerro Calan Observatory.
698 **251** 50c. blue 20 10

252 Dove with Letter

1972. International Correspondence Week.
699 **252** 1E.15 violet & mauve . . 15 10

253 Gen. Schneider, Flag and Quotation

1972. 2nd Death Anniv of General Rene Schneider.
700 **253** 2E.30 multicoloured . . . 30 20

254 Book and Students

1972. International Book Year.
701 **254** 50c. black and red 15 10

255 Folklore and Handicrafts

1972. Tourist Year of the Americas.
702 **255** 1E.15 black and red . . . 15 10
703 – 2E.65 purple and blue . . 40 10
704 – 3E.50 brown and red . . 15 10
DESIGNS—HORIZ: 2E.65, Natural produce. VERT: 3E.50, Stove and rug.

256 Carrera in Prison

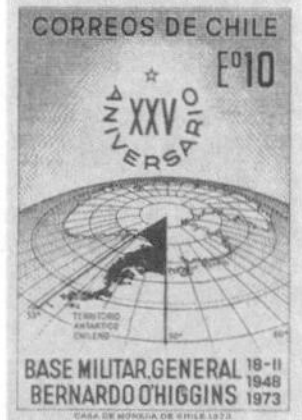

257 Antarctic Map

1973. 150th Death Anniv of General J. M. Carrera.
705 **256** 2E.30 blue 20 10

1973. 25th Anniv of General Bernardo O'Higgins Antarctic Base.
706 **257** 10E. red and blue 35 15

258 "Latorre" (cruiser) and Emblem

259 Telescope

1973. 50 Years of Chilean Naval Aviation.
707 **258** 20E. blue and brown . . 55 10

1973. Inaug of La Silla Astronomical Observatory.
708 **259** 2E.30 black and blue . . 20 10

260 Interpol Emblem

261 Bunch of Grapes

1973. 50th Anniv of Interpol.
709 **260** 30E. blue, black & brown 1·40 20
710 – 50E. black and red . . . 1·40 25
DESIGN: 50E. Fingerprint superimposed on globe.

1973. Chilean Wine Exports. Multicoloured.
711 20E. Type **261** 50 10
712 100E. Inscribed globe . . . . 1·00 20

1974. Centenary of World Meteorological Organization. No. 668 surch **"Centenario de la Organizacion Meteorologica Mundial IMO-W-MO 1973"** and value.
713 27E.+3E. on 40c. green . . . 15 10

263 U.P.U. Headquarters Building, Berne

1974. Centenary of U.P.U. Unissued stamp surch.
714 **263** 500E. on 45c. green . . . 85 20

264 Bernardo O'Higgins and Emblems

1974. Chilean Armed Forces.
715 **264** 30E. yellow and red . . . 20 10
716 – 30E. lake and red 20 10
717 – 30E. blue and light blue 20 10
718 – 30E. blue and lilac . . . 20 10
719 – 30E. emerald and green 20 10

DESIGNS: No. 716, Soldiers with mortar; No. 717, Naval gunners; No. 718, Air Force pilot; No. 719, Mounted policeman.

1974. 500th Birth Anniv (1973) of Copernicus. No. 683 surch **"V Centenario del Nacimiento de Copernico 1473 - 1973"** and value.
720 **242** 27E.+3E. on 1E.95 blue and deep blue 30 10

1974. Centenary of Vina del Mar. No. 496 surch **"Centenario de la ciudad de Vina del Mar 1874 - 1974"** and value.
721 27E.+3E. on 1E. turquoise 15 10

267 Football and Globe

269 Police and Gloved Hand

1974. World Cup Football Championships, West Germany.
722 **267** 500E. orange and red . . 20 10
723 – 1000E. blue & dp blue . . 1·00 15
DESIGN—HORIZ: 1000E. Football on stylized stadium.

1974. Various stamps surch.
724 **212** 47E.+3E. on 40c. green 15 10
725 **228** 67E.+3E. on 40c. red and brown 15 10
726 **214** 97E.+3E. on 40c. brown 15 10
727 **223** 100E. on 40c. green . . . 20 10
728 – 300E. on 50c. brown (No. 571) 20 10

1974. Campaign for Prevention of Traffic Accidents.
729 **269** 30E. brown and green . . 25 10

270 Manutara and Part of Globe

271 Core of Globe

1974. Inaugural LAN Flight to Tahiti, Fiji and Australia. Each green and brown.
730 200E. Type **270** 40 15
731 200E. Tahitian dancer and part of Globe 40 15
732 200E. Map of Fiji and part of Globe 40 15
733 200E. Eastern grey kangaroo and part of Globe 40 15

1974. International Symposium of Volcanology, Santiago de Chile.
734 **271** 500E. orange & brown . . 60 10

1974. Inauguration of Votive Temple. No. 650 surch **24 OCTUBRE 1974 INAUGURACION TEMPLO VOTIVO** and value.
735 **226** 100E. on 40c. green . . . 15 10

273 Map of Robinson Crusoe Island

275 F. Vidal Gormaz and Seal

274 O'Higgins and Bolivar

1974. 400th Anniv of Discovery of Juan Fernandez Archipelago. Each brown and blue.
736 200E. Type **273** 85 20
737 200E. Chontas (hardwood palm-trees) 40 20

738 200E. Mountain goat 40 20
739 200E. Spiny lobster 40 20

1974. 150th Anniv of Battles of Junin and Ayacucho.
740 **274** 100E. brown and buff . . 20 10

1975. Centenary of Naval Hydrographic Institute.
741 **275** 100E. blue and mauve . . 20 10

1975. Surch **Revalorizada 1975** and value.
742 **228** 70c. on 40c. red & brown 15 10

277 Dr. Schweitzer **278** Lighthouse

1975. Birth Centenary of Dr. Albert Schweitzer (missionary).
743 **277** 500E. brown and yellow 35 10

1975. 50th Anniv of Valparaiso Lifeboat Service. Each blue and green.
744 150E. Type **278** 55 20
745 150E. Wreck of "Teotopoulis" 75 25
746 150E. "Cap Christiansen" (lifeboat) 75 25
747 150E. Survivor in water . . . 55 20

279 Sail/steam Corvette "Baquedano"

1975. 30th Anniv of Shipwreck of Sail Frigate "Lautaro".
749 **279** 500E. black and green . . 75 20
750 – 500E. black and green . . 75 20
751 – 500E. black and green . . 75 20
752 – 500E. black and green . . 75 20
753 **279** 800E. black and brown 1·00 25
754 – 800E. black and brown 1·00 25
755 – 800E. black and brown 1·00 25
756 – 800E. black and brown 1·00 25
757 **279** 1000E. black and blue . . 1·25 25
758 – 1000E. black and blue . . 1·25 25
759 – 1000E. black and blue . . 1·25 25
760 – 1000E. black and blue . . 1·25 25
DESIGNS: Nos. 750, 754, 758, Sail frigate "Lautaro"; Nos. 751, 755, 759, Cruiser "Chacabuco"; Nos. 752, 756, 760, Cadet barquentine "Esmeralda".

280 "The Happy Mother" (A. Valenzuela) **281** Diego Portales (politician)

1975. International Women's Year. Chilean Paintings. Multicoloured.
761 50c. Type **280** 65 15
762 50c. "Girl" (F. J. Mandiola) 65 15
763 50c. "Lucia Guzman" (P. L. Rencoret) 65 15
764 50c. "Unknown Woman" (Magdalena M. Mena) . . 65 15

1975. Inscr "D. PORTALES".
765 **281** 10c. green 20 10
765a 20c. lilac 10 10
765b 30c. orange 10 10
766 50c. brown 15 10
767 1p. blue 15 10
767a 1p.50 brown 15 10
767b 2p. black 15 10
767c 2p.50 brown 15 10
767d 3p.50 red 15 10
768 5p. mauve 15 15
For this design inscr "DIEGO PORTALES", see Nos. 901 etc.

282 Lord Cochrane and Fleet, 1820

1975. Birth Bicentenary of Lord Thomas Cochrane. Multicoloured.
769 1p. Type **282** 80 25
770 1p. Cochrane's capture of Valdivia, 1820 . . . . . . 80 25
771 1p. Capture of "Esmeralda", 1820 . . . . 80 25
772 1p. Cruiser "Cochrane", 1874 80 25
773 1p. Destroyer "Cochrane", 1962 . . . . 80 25

283 Flags of Chile and Bolivia

1976. 150th Anniv of Bolivia's Independence.
774 **283** 1p.50 multicoloured . . . 1·75 10

284 Lake of the Incas

1976. 6th General Assembly of Organization of American States.
775 **284** 1p.50 multicoloured . . . 1·40 10

285 George Washington

1976. Bicentenary of American Revolution.
776 **285** 5p. multicoloured . . . . 1·50 15

286 Minerva and Academy Emblem

1976. 50th Anniv of Polytechnic Military Academy.
777 **286** 2p.50 multicoloured . . . 1·00 10

287 Indian Warrior

1976. 3rd Anniv of Military Junta. Multicoloured.
778 1p. Type **287** 25 15
779 2p. Andean condor with broken chain . . . . . . 2·50 1·00
780 3p. Winged woman ("Rebirth of the Country") 25 15

288 Chilean Base, Antarctica

1977. Presidential Visit to Antarctica.
781 **288** 2p. multicoloured . . . . 5·25 25

289 College Emblem and Cultivated Field **290** Statue of Justice

1977. Cent of Advanced Agricultural Education.
782 **289** 2p. multicoloured . . . . 1·40 15

1977. 150th Anniv of Supreme Court.
783 **290** 2p. brown and grey . . . 1·40 10

291 Globe within "Eye"

1977. 11th Pan-American Ophthalmological Congress.
784 **291** 2p. multicoloured . . . . 2·00 10

292 Police Emblem and Activities

1977. 50th Anniv of Chilean Police Force. Multicoloured.
785 2p. Type **292** 60 10
786 2p. Mounted carabinero (vert) 25 10
787 2p. Policewoman with children (vert) 25 10
788 2p. Torres del Paine and Osorno Volcano (vert) . . 25 10

293 "Intelsat" Satellite and Globe

1977. World Telecommunications Day.
789 **293** 2p. multicoloured 25 10

294 Front Page, Press and Schooner

1977. 150th Anniv of Newspaper "El Mercurio de Valparaiso".
790 **294** 2p. multicoloured 20 15

295 St. Francis of Assisi **296** "Science and Technology"

1977. 750th Death Anniv of St. Francis of Assisi.
791 **295** 5p. multicoloured . . . . 1·00 15

1977. Council for Science and Technology.
792 **296** 4p. multicoloured 40 15

297 Weaving (Mothers' Centres) **298** Diego de Almagro (discoverer of Chile)

1977. 4th Anniv of Government Junta. Welfare Facilities. Multicoloured.
793 5p. Type **297** 55 10
794 5p. Nurse with cripple (Care of the Disabled) 55 10
795 10p. Children dancing (Protection of Minors) (horiz) . . . . 1·00 15
796 10p. Elderly man (Care for the Aged) (horiz) . . . . . 1·00 15

1977. Columbus Day.
797 **298** 5p. brown 45 10

299 Boy, Christmas Bell and Post Box

1977. Christmas.
798 **299** 2p.50 multicoloured . . . 15 15

300 Freighter loading Timber

1978. Timber Export. Multicoloured.
799 10p. Type **300** . . . . 1·00 25
800 20p. As T **300** but inscr "CORREOS" and with ship flying Chilean flag . . 1·50 35

301 Papal Arms and Globe

1978. World Peace Day.
801 **301** 10p. multicoloured . . . 80 15

302 University

1978. 50th Anniv of Catholic University, Valparaiso.
802 **302** 25p. multicoloured . . . 2·50 60

303 "Bernardo O'Higgins" (Gil de Castro)

1978. Birth Bicentenary of Bernardo O'Higgins (1st issue).
803 **303** 10p. multicoloured . . . 1·00 15
See also Nos. 804, 806/8 and 816.

304 Chacabuco Victory Monument

1978. Birth Bicentenary of Bernardo O'Higgins (2nd issue), and 5th Anniv of Military Junta.
804 **304** 10p. multicoloured . . . 1·00 15

305 Teacher writing on Blackboard

1978. 10th Anniv and 9th Meeting of Inter-American Council for Education, Science and Culture.
805 **305** 15p. multicoloured . . . 60 15

306 "The Last Moments at Rancagua" (Pedro Subercaseaux)

1978. Birth Bicentenary of Bernardo O'Higgins (3rd issue).
806 **306** 30p. multicoloured . . . 2·00 65

307 "First National Naval Squadron" (Thomas Somerscales)

1978. Birth Bicentenary of Bernardo O'Higgins (4th issue).
807 **307** 20p. multicoloured . . . 1·75 80

308 Medallion

1978. Birth Bicentenaries of O'Higgins (5th issue) and San Martin.
808 **308** 7p. multicoloured 30 10

309 Council Emblem

310 Three Kings

1978. 30th Anniv of International Council of Military Sports.
809 **309** 50p. multicoloured . . . 3·50 1·00

1978. Christmas. Multicoloured.
810 3p. Type **310** 65 15
811 11p. Virgin and Child . . . . 1·25 20

311 Bernardo and Rodulfo Philippi

1978. The Philippi Brothers (scientists and travellers).
812 **311** 3p.50 multicoloured . . . 20 10

1979. No. 765 surch **$ 3.50.**
813 **281** 3p.50 on 10c. green . . . 15 10

313 Flowers and Flags of Chile and Salvation Army

1979. 70th Anniv of Salvation Army in Chile.
814 **313** 10p. multicoloured . . . 55 25

314 Pope Paul VI

1979. Pope Paul VI Commemoration.
815 **314** 11p. multicoloured . . . 80 25

315 Battle of Maipu Monument

1979. Birth Bicentenary of Bernardo O'Higgins (6th issue).
816 **315** 8p.50 multicoloured . . . 55 20

316 "Battle of Iquique" (Thomas Somerscales)

1979. Naval Battle Centenaries. Multicoloured.
817 3p.50 Type **316** 75 25
818 3p.50 "Battle of Punta Gruesa" (Alvaro Casanova Zenteno) 75 25
819 3p.50 "Battle of Angamos" (Alvaro Casanova Zenteno) 75 25

317 Diego Portales

319 Monument at Puntas Arenas (Miodrag Zivkovic)

318 Horse-drawn Ambulance

1979.
820 **317** 1p.50 brown 15 10
821 2p. grey 10 10
822 3p.50 red 10 10
823 4p.50 blue 20 10
824 5p. red 20 10
825 6p. green 20 10
826 7p. yellow 20 10
827 10p. blue 25 10
828 12p. orange 10 10

The 1p.50, 3p.50, 5p. and 6p. are inscribed "D. PORTALES" and have the imprint "CAMONEDA CHILE". The 2p., 4p.50, 7p. and 10p. are inscribed "DIEGO PORTALES" and have the imprint "CASA DE MONEDA DE CHILE".

1979. 75th Anniv of Chilean Red Cross.
831 **318** 25p. multicoloured . . . 2·75 60

1979. Centenary of Yugoslav Immigration.
832 **319** 10p. multicoloured . . . 45 15

320 Children in Playground (Kiochi Kayano Gomez)

1979. International Year of the Child. Mult.
833 9p.50 Type **320** 45 30
834 11p. Running girl (Carmed Pizarro Toto) (vert) . . . 55 35
835 12p. Children dancing in circle (Ana Pizarro Munizaga) . . . . 1·00 50

321 Laveredo and Arms of Coyhaique

1979. 50th Anniv of Coyhaique.
836 **321** 20p. multicoloured . . . 80 40

322 Exhibition Emblem and Posthorn

1979. 3rd World Telecommunications Exhibition, Geneva.
837 **322** 15p. grey, blue & orange 70 30

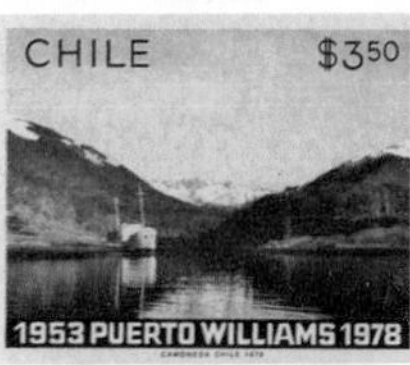

323 Canal

1979. 25th Anniv of Puerto Williams, Navirino Island.
838 **323** 3p.50 multicoloured . . . 70 15

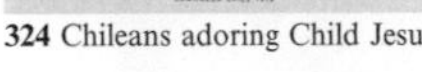

324 Chileans adoring Child Jesus

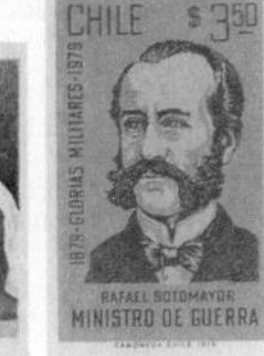

325 Rafael Sotomayor (Minister of War)

1979. Christmas.
839 **324** 3p.50 multicoloured . . . 1·10 20

1979. Military Heroes. Each ochre and brown.
840 3p.50 Type **325** 50 10
841 3p.50 General Erasmo Escala (Commander in Chief of Army) 50 10
842 3p.50 Colonel (later General) Emilio Sotomayor (Commander of troops at Battle of Dolores) 50 10
843 3p.50 Colonel Eleuterio Ramirez (Commander of 2nd Line Regiment) . . . 50 10

326 Bell Model 205 Iroquois Rescue Helicopter at Tinguiririca Volcano

1980. 50th Anniv of Chilean Air Force. Mult.
844 3p.50 Type **326** 40 15
845 3p.50 Consolidated Catalina Skua amphibian in Antarctic 40 15
846 3p.50 Northrop Tiger II jet fighter in Andes 40 15

327 Rotary Emblem and Globe

1980. 75th Anniv of Rotary International.
847 **327** 10p. multicoloured . . . 80 25

328 "The Death of Bueras" (Pedro Leon Carmona)

329 "Gen. Manuel Gaquedano" (after Pedro Subercaseaux)

1980. Cavalry Charge led by Colonel Santiago Bueras at Battle of Maipu, 1818.
848 **328** 12p. multicoloured . . . 65 30

1980. Centenary of Battle of Arica Head. Mult.
849 3p.50 Type **329** 25 10
850 3p.50 Gen. Pedro Largos (43 × 26 mm) 25 10
851 3p.50 Col. Juan Jose San Martin (43 × 26 mm) . . . 25 10

330 Freire and Bars of "Ay, Ay, Ay!"

1980. Birth Centenary of Osman Perez Freire (composer).
852 **330** 6p. multicoloured 35 15

331 Mt. Gasherbrum II, Chilean flag and Ice-pick

1980. Chilean Himalayan Expedition (1979).
853 **331** 15p. multicoloured . . . 1·00 35

332 "St Vincent de Paul" (stained glass window, former Mother House)

334 Mummy of Inca Child

333 Andean Condor

1980. 125th Anniv of Sisters of Charity in Chile.
854 **332** 10p. multicoloured . . . 50 25

1980. 7th Anniv of Military Government.
855 **333** 3p.50 multicoloured . . . 40 20

1980. 150th Anniv of National History Museum. Multicoloured.
856 5p. Type **334** 55 15
857 5p. Claudio Gay (founder) (after Alejandro Laemlein) 55 15

335 "Pablo Burchard" (Pedro Lira)

336 Emblem and Buildings

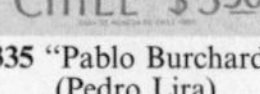

1980. Centenary of National Museum of Fine Arts.
858 **335** 3p.50 multicoloured . . . 20 10

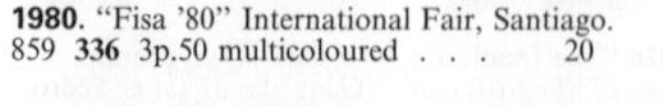

1980. "Fisa '80" International Fair, Santiago.
859 **336** 3p.50 multicoloured . . . 20 10

337 "Family and Angels" (Sara Hinojosa Orellana)

338 Infantryman

1980. Christmas. Multicoloured.
860 3p.50 Type **337** 85 10
861 10p.50 "The Holy Family" (Catalina Imboden Fernandez) . . . . 1·10 20

1980. Army Uniforms of 1879 (1st series). Multicoloured.
862 3p.50 Type **338** 55 15
863 3p.50 Cavalry officer (parade uniform) 55 15
864 3p.50 Artillery officer 55 15
865 3p.50 Colonel of Engineers (parade uniform) 55 15
See also Nos. 887/90.

339 Congress Emblem

340 Cattle

1980. 23rd International Congress of Military Medicine and Pharmacy, Santiago.
866 **339** 11p.50 multicoloured . . 55 30

1981. Eradication of Foot and Mouth Disease from Chile.
867 **340** 9p.50 multicoloured . . . 45 20

341 Robinson Crusoe Island

1981. Tourism. Multicoloured.
868 3p.50 Type **341** 25 15
869 3p.50 Easter Island monoliths 60 15
870 10p.50 Gentoo penguins, Antarctica . . . . 1·75 50

342 "Javiera Carrera" (after D. M. Pizarro) and Flag

1981. Birth Bicentenary of Javiera Carrera (creator of first national flag).
871 **342** 3p.50 multicoloured . . . 20 10

343 U.P.U. Emblem

1981. Centenary of U.P.U. Membership.
872 **343** 3p. multicoloured 25 15

344 Unloading Cargo from Lockheed Hercules

1981. 1st Anniv of Lieutenant Marsh Antarctic Air Force Base.
873 **344** 3p.50 multicoloured . . . 50 15

345 I.T.U. and W.H.O. Emblems and Ribbons forming Caduceus

1981. World Telecommunications Day.
874 **345** 3p.50 multicoloured . . . 20 15

346 Arturo Prat Antarctic Naval Base

1981. 20th Anniv of Antarctic Treaty.
875 **346** 3p.50 multicoloured . . . 1·00 20

347 Capt. Jose Luis Araneda

1981. Centenary of Battle of Sangrar.
876 **347** 3p.50 multicoloured . . . 25 15

348 Philatelic Society Yearbook and Medal

1981. 92nd Anniv of Philatelic Society of Chile.
877 **348** 4p.50 multicoloured . . . 25 15

349 "Exchange of Speeches between Minister Recabarren and Indian Chief Conuepan at the Nielol Hill" (Hector Robles Acuna)

1981. Centenary of Temuco City.
878 **349** 4p.50 multicoloured . . . 25 15

350 Exports (embroidery by J.L. Gutierrez)

1981. Exports.
879 **350** 14p. multicoloured . . . 65 20

351 Moneda Palace (seat of Government)

1981. 8th Anniv of Military Government.
880 **351** 4p.50 multicoloured . . . 25 15

352 St. Vincent de Paul

1981. 400th Birth Anniv of St. Vincent de Paul (founder of Sisters of Charity).
881 **352** 4p.50 multicoloured . . . 25 15

353 Medallion by Rene Thenot, Quill and Law Code

1981. Birth Bicentenary of Andres Bello (statesman, lawyer, and founder of Chile University). Multicoloured.
882 4p.50 Type **353** 25 15
883 9p.50 Profile of Bello and three of his books 40 20
884 11p.50 University of Chile arms and Nicanor Plaza's statue of Bello 45 20

354 Flag on Map of South America and Police Badge

1981. 2nd South American Uniformed Police Congress, Santiago.
885 **354** 4p.50 multicoloured . . . 30 15

355 F.A.O. and U.N. Emblems

1981. World Food Day.
886 **355** 5p.50 multicoloured . . . 30 15

1981. Army Uniforms of 1879 (2nd series). As T **338**. Multicoloured.
887 5p.50 Infantryman 55 20
888 5p.50 Military School cadet 55 20
889 5p.50 Cavalryman 55 20
890 5p.50 Artilleryman 55 20

356 Mother and Child

1981. International Year of Disabled Persons.
891 **356** 5p.50 multicoloured . . . 30 15

357 "Nativity" (Ruth Tatiana Aguero Eguiliz)

1981. Christmas. Multicoloured.
892 5p.50 Type **357** 75 10
893 11p.50 "The Three Kings" (Ignacio Jorge Manriquez Gonzalez) 95 20

358 Dario Salas

1981. Birth Cent of Dario Salas (educationist).
894 **358** 5p.50 multicoloured . . . 25 15

359 Main Buildings of University

1981. 50th Anniv of Federico Santa Maria Technical University, Valparaiso.
895 **359** 5p.50 multicoloured . . . 25 15

360 Fair Emblem

1982. "Fida '82" International Air Fair.
896 **360** 4p.50 multicoloured . . . 30 15

361 Cardinal Caro and Chilean Family

1982. 1st Anniv of New Constitution. Mult.
897 4p.50 Type **361** 25 15
898 11p. Diego Portales and national arms 45 20
899 30p. Bernardo O'Higgins and national arms 65 40

362 Globe on Chilean Flag

363 Pedro Montt (President, 1906–10)

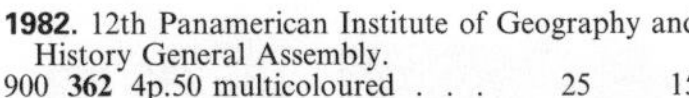

1982. 12th Panamerican Institute of Geography and History General Assembly.
900 **362** 4p.50 multicoloured . . . 25 15

1982. As T **281** but inscr "DIEGO PORTALES" and designs as T **363**.
901 **281** 1p. blue 60 10
902 – 1p. blue 10 10
903 **281** 1p.50 orange 10 10
904 2p. grey 10 10
905 – 2p. lilac 10 10
906 **281** 2p.50 yellow 10 10
907 **363** 4p.50 mauve 30 10
908 – 5p. red 10 10
909 **281** 5p. mauve 60 10
910 – 7p. blue 25 10
911 – 10p. black 15 10
DESIGNS: Nos. 902, 905, 908, 910, 911, Ramon Barros Luco (President, 1911–15).

364 Dassault Mirage IIIC Airplane and Chilean Air Force and American Air Forces Co-operation System Badges

1982. American Air Forces Co-operation System.
916 **364** 4p.50 multicoloured . . . 50 15

365 Trawler and Map

367 Capt. Ignacio Carrera Pinto

366 Scout Emblems and Brownsea Island

1982. Fisheries Exports.
917 **365** 20p. multicoloured . . . 2·00 80

1982. 75th Anniv of Boy Scout Movement and 125th Birth Anniv of Lord Baden-Powell (founder). Multicoloured.
918 4p.50 Type **366** 75 15
919 4p.50 Lord Baden-Powell and Brownsea Island 75 15
Nos. 918/19 were printed together, se-tenant, forming a composite design.

1982. Centenary of Battle of Concepcion. Mult.
920 4p.50 Type **367** 25 20
921 4p.50 Sub-lieutenant Arturo Perez Canto 25 20
922 4p.50 Sub-lieutenant Julio Montt Salamanca 25 20
923 4p.50 Sub-lieutenant Luis Cruz Martinez 25 20

368 Old Man at Window

1982. World Assembly on Ageing, Vienna.
924 **368** 4p.50 multicoloured . . . 25 15

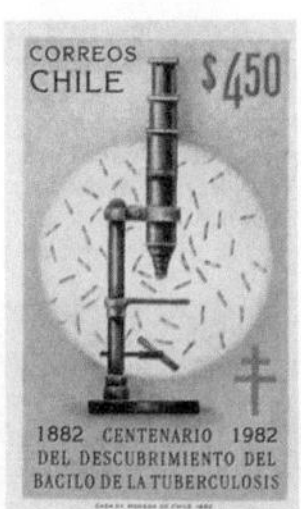

369 Microscope and Bacillus

1982. Centenary of Discovery of Tubercle Bacillus.
925 **369** 4p.50 multicoloured . . . 30 15

370 National Flag and Flame of Freedom

1982. 9th Anniv of Military Government.
926 **370** 4p.50 multicoloured . . . 25 15

1982. Nos. 688/9 surch.
927 **245** 1p. on 3E.50 blue & grn 30 10
928 **246** 2p. on 1E.15 red & black 35 10

372 "Nativity" (Mariela Espinoza Fuetes)

1982. Christmas. Multicoloured.
929 10p. Type **372** 25 10
930 25p. "Adoration of the Shepherds" (Jared Jeria Abarca) (vert) . . . . . . 1·25 40

373 "Virgin Mary and Marcellus" (stained-glass window, Sacred Heart of Jesus Church, Barcelona)

374 "El Sur", Quill and Printing Press

1982. 9th World Union of Former Marist Alumni Congress.
931 **373** 7p. multicoloured . . . . 1·60 40

1982. Cent of Concepcion's Newspaper "El Sur".
932 **374** 7p. multicoloured 25 15

375 "Steamship Copiapo" (W. Yorke)

1982. 110th Anniv of South American Steamship Company.
933 **375** 7p. multicoloured . . . . 1·50 30

376 Club Badge, Radio Aerial, Dove and Globe

1982. 60th Anniv of Radio Club of Chile.
934 **376** 7p. multicoloured 25 10

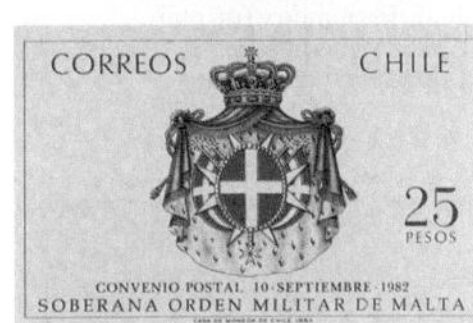

377 Arms of Sovereign Military Order

1983. Postal Agreement with Sovereign Military Order of Malta. Multicoloured.
935 25p. Type **377** 65 40
936 50p. Arms of Chile . . . . . 1·00 55

378 Badge

380 Child watching Railway

379 Cardinal Samore

1983. 50th Anniv of Criminal Investigation Bureau.
937 **378** 20p. multicoloured . . . 65 20

1983. Cardinal Antonio Samore Commem.
938 **379** 30p. multicoloured . . . 80 25

1983. Centenary of Valparaiso Incline Railway.
939 **380** 40p. multicoloured . . . 1·25 65

381 Puoko Tangata (carved head from Easter Island)

383 General Francisco Morazan

382 Winged Girl with Broken Chains

1983. Tourism. Multicoloured.
940 7p. Type **381** 25 15
941 7p. Ruins of Pucar de Quitor, San Pedro de Atacama . . 25 15
942 7p. Rock painting, Rio Ibanez, Aisen 25 15
943 7p. Diaguita pot 25 15

1983. 10th Anniv of Military Government. Mult.
944 7p. Type **382** 50 15
945 7p. Young couple with flag 50 15
946 10p. Family with torch . . . 55 15
947 40p. National arms . . . . . 1·10 40

1983. Famous Hondurans. Multicoloured.
948 7p. Type **383** 20 10
949 7p. Sabio Jose Cecilio del Valle 20 10

384 Central Post Office, Santiago

385 "Holy Family" (Lucrecia Cardenas Gomez)

1983. World Communications Year. Mult.
950 7p. Type **384** 55 10
951 7p. Space Shuttle "Challenger" 55 10
Nos. 950/1 were printed together in se-tenant pairs within the sheet forming a composite design.

1983. Christmas. Children's Paintings. Mult.
952 10p. "Nativity" (Hanny Chacon Scheel) 25 10
953 30p. Type **385** 90 25

386 Presidential Coach, 1911

1984. Railway Centenary. Multicoloured.
954 9p. Type **386** . . . . 1·40 60
955 9p. Service car and tender . . 1·40 60
956 9p. Class 80 steam locomotive, 1929 . . . . . 1·40 60
Nos. 954/6 were printed together, se-tenant, forming a composite design.

387 Juan Luis Sanfuentes

1984. (a) Inscr "CORREOS CHILE".
989 **387** 5p. red 10 10
958 9p. green 15 10
959 10p. grey 15 10
960 15p. blue 15 10

(b) Inscr "D.S. No. 20 CHILE".
961 **387** 9p. brown 15 10
962 15p. blue 15 10
963 20p. yellow 20 10

388 Piper Pillan Trainer and Flags

1984. 3rd International Aeronautical Fair.
966 **388** 9p. multicoloured 85 10

389 Agriculture, Industry and Science

1984. 20th Anniv of Chilean Nuclear Energy Commission.
967 **389** 9p. multicoloured 25 10

1984. Nos. 944/5 surch.
968 9p. on 7p. Type **382** 65 10
969 9p. on 7p. Young couple with flag 65 10

391 Chilean Women's Antarctic Expedition

1984. Chile's Antarctic Territories. Mult.
970 15p. Type **391** 90 50
971 15p. Villa Las Estrellas Antarctic settlement 75 30
972 15p. Scouts visiting Antarctic, 1983 . . . . 75 30

392 Parinacota Church (Tarapaca Region)

1984. 10th Anniv of Regionalization. Mult.
973 9p. Type **392** 50 20
974 9p. El Tatio geyser (Antofagasta Region) . . . 50 20
975 9p. Copper miners (Atacama Region) 50 20
976 9p. El Tololo observatory (Coquimbo Region) . . . 50 20
977 9p. Valparaiso harbour (Valparaiso Region) . . . 75 20
978 9p. Stone images (Easter Island Province) 50 20
979 9p. St. Francis's Church (Santiago Metropolitan Region) 50 20
980 9p. El Huique Hacienda (Libertador General Bernardo O'Higgins Region) 50 20
981 9p. Hydro-electric dam and reservoir, Machicura (Maule Region) 50 20
982 9p. Sta. Juana de Gaudalcazar Fort (Bio Bio Region) 50 20
983 9p. Araucana woman (Araucania Region) 50 20
984 9p. Church, Guar Island (Los Lagos Region) 50 20
985 9p. South Highway (Aisen del General Carlos Ibanez del Campo Region) 50 20
986 9p. Shepherd (Magallanes Region) 50 20
987 9p. Villa Las Estrellas (Chile Antarctic Territories) . . . 75 30

393 Pedro Sarmiento de Gamboa and Map

1984. 400th Anniv of Spanish Settlements on Straits of Magellan.
988 **393** 100p. multicoloured . . . 2·25 80

394 Antonio Varas de la Barra (founder) and Coin

1984. Centenary of State Savings Bank.
990 **394** 35p. multicoloured . . . 50 20

395 Flame and Bernardo O'Higgins Monument

1984. 11th Anniv of Military Government.
991 **395** 20p. multicoloured . . . 30 15

396 Clown

1984. Centenary of Circus in Chile.
992 **396** 45p. multicoloured . . . 80 25

397 Blue Whale

1984. Endangered Animals. Multicoloured.
993 9p. Type **397** 70 20
994 9p. Juan Fernandez fur seal 70 20
995 9p. Chilean guemal 70 20
996 9p. Long-tailed chinchilla . . 70 20

398 "Shepherds following Star" (Ruth M. Flores Rival)

1984. Christmas. Multicoloured.
997 9p. Type **398** 15 10
998 40p. "Bethlehem" (Vianka Pastrian Navea) 95 30

399 Satellite and Planetarium

1984. Inaug of Santiago University Planetarium.
999 **399** 10p. multicoloured . . . 30 15

400 Andean Hog-nosed Skunk

401 Flags and Emblem

1985. Flora and Fauna. Multicoloured.
1000 10p. Type **400** 60 25
1001 10p. "Leucocoryne purpurea" 60 25
1002 10p. Black-winged stilt . . . 90 30
1003 10p. Marine otter 60 25
1004 10p. "Balbisia peduncularis" 60 25
1005 10p. Patagonian conure . . 90 30
1006 10p. Southern pudu 60 25
1007 10p. "Fuchsia magellanica" 60 25
1008 10p. Common diuca finch 90 30
1009 10p. Argentine grey fox . . 60 25
1010 10p. "Alstroemeria sierrae" 60 25
1011 10p. Austral pygmy owl . . 90 30

1985. 25th Anniv (1986) of American Air forces Co-operation System.
1012 **401** 45p. multicoloured . . . 1·50 1·00

402 Chile and Argentina Flags and Papal Arms

1985. Chilean–Argentinian Peace Treaty.
1013 **402** 20p. multicoloured . . . 45 25

403 Kentenich and Schoenstatt Sanctuary, La Florida

1985. Birth Centenary of Father Jose Kentenich (founder of Schoenstatt Movement).
1014 **403** 40p. multicoloured . . . 75 40

404 Landscape and Shrimp

1985. Antarctic Territories and 25th Anniv of Antarctic Treaty. Multicoloured.
1015 15p. Type **404** 50 30
1016 20p. Seismological Station, O'Higgins Base 65 40
1017 35p. Earth receiving station, Anvers Island . . . . . . 1·10 70

405 "Canis fulvipes"

1985. Endangered Animals. Multicoloured.
1018 20p. Type **405** 70 30
1019 20p. James's flamingo . . . 1·90 40
1020 20p. Giant coot . . . . . . 1·90 40
1021 20p. Huidobria otter 70 30

406 Doves and "J"

1985. International Youth Year (1022) and 40th Anniv of U.N.O. (1023). Multicoloured.
1022 15p. Type **406** 20 15
1023 15p. U.N. emblem 20 15

407 Farmer with Haycart

1985. Occupations. Each in brown.
1024 10p. Type **407** 10 15
1025 10p. Photographer with plate camera 10 15
1026 10p. Street entertainer 10 15
1027 10p. Basket maker 10 15

408 Carrera and Statue

1985. Birth Bicentenary of Gen. Jose Miguel Carrera (Independence leader and first President).
1028 **408** 40p. multicoloured . . . 75 30

409 "Holy Family" **411** Escort of Light Infantry, 1818

410 "Nativity" (Jennifer Gomez)

1985. Chilean Art.
1029 **409** 10p. brown and ochre 10 15

1985. Christmas. Multicoloured.
1030 15p. Type **410** 20 10
1031 100p. Man with donkey (Esteban Morales Medina) (vert) . . . . 2·00 90

1985. 16th American Armies Conference. Mult.
1032 20p. Type **411** 35 20
1033 35p. Officer of the Hussars of the Grand Guard, 1813 75 30

412 Moon, Earth and Comet

1985. Appearance of Halley's Comet.
1034 **412** 45p. multicoloured . . . 35 20

413 Living Trees and Flame **414** Saltpetre

1985. Forest Fires Prevention. Multicoloured.
1036 40p. Type **413** 65 20
1037 40p. Burnt trees and flame 70 20

1986. Exports. Each brown and blue.
1038 12p. Type **414** 15 10
1039 12p. Iron 15 10
1040 12p. Copper 15 10
1041 12p. Molybdenum 15 10

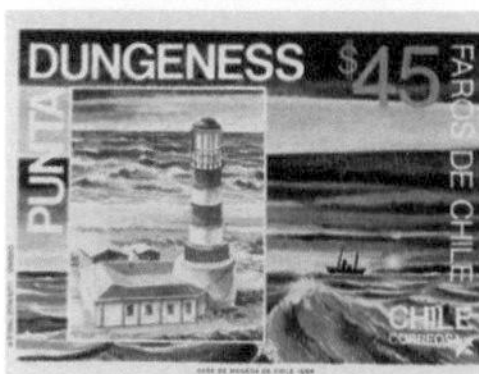

415 Dungeness Point Lighthouse

1986. Chilean Lighthouses. Multicoloured.

1042	45p. Type **415**	45	25
1043	45p. Evangelistas lighthouse in storm	45	25

416 St. Lucia Hill, Santiago

1986. Death Centenary of Benjamin Vicuna Mackenna (Municipal Superintendent).

1044	**416** 30p. multicoloured . . .	30	20

417 Diego Portales

1986. Unissued stamp surch.

1045	**417** 12p. on 3p.50 mult . . .	70	10

418 National Stadium, Chile, 1962

1986. World Cup Football Championship, Mexico. Multicoloured.

1046	15p. Type **418**	15	10
1047	20p. Azteca Stadium, Mexico, 1970	20	15
1048	35p. Maracana Stadium, Brazil, 1950	35	25
1049	50p. Wembley Stadium, England, 1966	50	40

419 Birds flying above City

1986. Environmental Protection. Mult.

1050	20p. Type **419**	20	10
1051	20p. Fish	30	10
1052	20p. Full litter bin in forest	20	10

420 "Santiaguillo" (caravel) and flags **421** Emblem

1986. 450th Anniv of Valparaiso.

1053	**420** 40p. multicoloured . . .	85	30

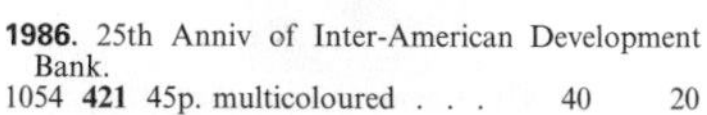

1986. 25th Anniv of Inter-American Development Bank.

1054	**421** 45p. multicoloured . . .	40	20

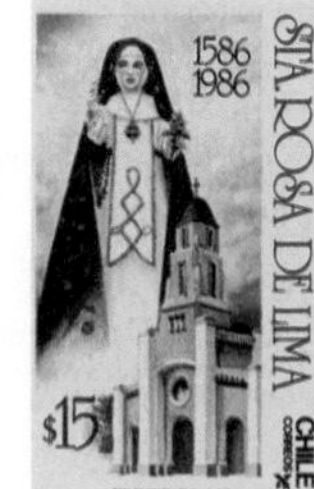

422 St. Rosa and Pelequen Sanctuary

1986. 400th Birth Anniv of St. Rosa of Lima.

1055	**422** 15p. multicoloured . . .	15	10

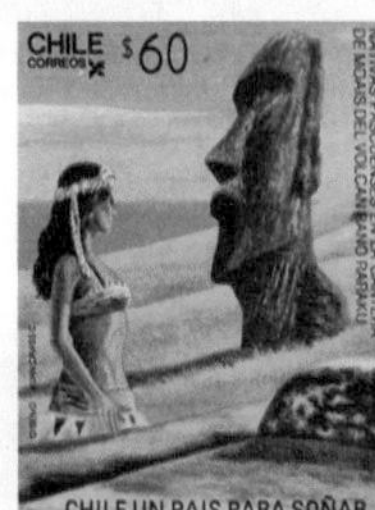

423 Stone Head on Raraku Volcano

1986. Easter Island. Multicoloured.

1056	60p. Type **423**	1·00	25
1057	100p. Tongariki ruins . . .	1·60	45

424 Flags, Stamps in Album, Magnifying Glass and Tweezers

1986. "Ameripex '86" International Stamp Exhibition, Chicago.

1059	**424** 100p. multicoloured . .	1·40	50

425 Schooner "Ancud"

1986. Naval Traditions. Multicoloured.

1060	35p. Type **425**	80	45
1061	35p. Brigantine "Aguila" . .	80	45
1062	35p. Sail corvette "Esmeralda"	80	45
1063	35p. Sail frigate "O'Higgins"	80	45

426 "Gate of Serenity"

1986. Paintings by Juan F. Gonzalez. Mult.

1064	30p. "Rushes and Chrysanthemums"	25	15
1065	30p. Type **426**	25	15

427 Antarctic Terns

1986. Antarctic Fauna. Sea Birds. Mult.

1066	40p. Type **427**	1·40	55
1067	40p. Blue-eyed cormorants	1·40	55
1068	40p. Emperor penguins . .	1·40	55
1069	40p. Antarctic skuas	1·40	55

428 Pedro de Ona (poet)

1986. Chilean Literature. Multicoloured.

1070	20p. Type **428**	15	15
1071	20p. Vicente Huidobro . . .	15	15

429 Major-General, 1878

1986. Centenary of Military Academy. Mult.

1072	45p. Type **429**	65	20
1073	45p. Major, 1950	65	20

430 Diaguita Art

1986. Indian Art. Multicoloured.

1074	30p. Type **430**	20	15
1075	30p. Mapuche art	20	15

431 "Nativity" (Begona Andrea Orrego Castro)

1986. Christmas. Multicoloured.

1076	15p. Type **431**	15	10
1077	105p. "Shrine and Mountains" (Andrea Maribel Riquelme Labarde)	1·60	80

432 Shepherds looking at Hill Town **433** Emblem and Globe

1986. Christmas.

1078	**432** 12p. multicoloured . . .	20	10

1986. International Peace Year.

1079	**433** 85p. multicoloured . . .	1·00	50

1986. No. 1029 surch.

1080	**409** 12p. on 10p. brown and ochre	15	10

1986. Nos. 1024/7 surch.

1081	12p. on 10p. Farmer with haycart	25	10
1082	12p. on 10p. Photographer with plate camera	25	10
1083	12p. on 10p. Street entertainer	25	10
1084	12p. on 10p. Basket maker	25	10
1085	15p. on 10p. Farmer with haycart	25	10
1086	15p. on 10p. Photographer with plate camera	25	10
1087	15p. on 10p. Street entertainer	25	10
1088	15p. on 10p. Basket maker	25	10

436 Profiles and Flag

1986. Women's Voluntary Organization.

1089	**436** 15p. multicoloured . . .	15	10

437 Virgin of Carmelites **439** "The Guitarist of Quinchamali"

438 Kitson Meyer Steam Locomotive No. 59

1986. 60th Anniv of Coronation of Virgin of the Carmelites.

1090	**437** 25p. multicoloured . . .	40	15

1987. Railways.

1091	**438** 95p. multicoloured . . .	1·75	80

1987. Folk Tales. (a) As T **439**.

1092	**439** 15p. green	20	10
1093	– 15p. blue	40	10
1094	– 15p. brown	20	10
1095	– 15p. mauve	20	10

(b) Discount stamps. Inscr "D/S No 20" in colour of stamp in right-hand margin and dated "1992".

1092C	15p. As Type **439**	10	10
1093C	15p. As No. 1093	10	10
1094C	15p. As No. 1094	10	10
1095C	15p. As No. 1095	10	10

DESIGNS: No. 1093, "El Caleuche"; 1094, "El Pihuychen"; 1095, "La Lola".

440 Rowing Boat and Storage Tanks

1987. 40th Anniv of Capt. Arturo Prat Antarctic Naval Base. Multicoloured.

1096	100p. Type **440**	2·50	1·10
1097	100p. Buildings and rowing boat at jetty	2·50	1·10

Nos. 1096/7 were printed together, se-tenant, forming a composite design.

441 Pope and "Christ the Redeemer" Statue

1987. Visit of Pope John Paul II. Mult.

1098	20p. Type **441**	10	10
1099	25p. Votive Temple, Maipu	35	10
1100	90p. "Cross of the Seas", Magellan Straits	1·10	50
1101	115p. "Virgin of the Hill" statue, Santiago	1·60	80

442 Horse-riding Display **443** Players and Ball

1987. 60th Anniv of Carabineers. Mult.
1103 50p. Type **442** 65 15
1104 50p. Sea rescue by Air Police 65 15

1987. World Youth Football Cup. Mult.
1105 45p. Type **443** 50 15
1106 45p. Player and Concepcion stadium 50 15
1107 45p. Player and Antofagasta stadium 50 15
1108 45p. Player and Valparaiso stadium 50 15

444 Battleship "Almirante Latorre"

1987. Naval Tradition. Multicoloured.
1110 60p. Type **444** 95 45
1111 60p. Cruiser "O'Higgins" . . 95 45

445 Portales and "El Vigia" Newspaper

1987. 150th Death Anniv of Diego Portales (statesman).
1112 **445** 30p. multicoloured . . . 40 10

446 Works Projects

1987. Centenary of Ministry of Public Works.
1113 **446** 25p. multicoloured . . . 1·00 30

447 School Entrance

1987. Centenary of Infantry School. Mult.
1114 50p. Type **447** 25 10
1115 100p. Soldiers and national flag 80 40

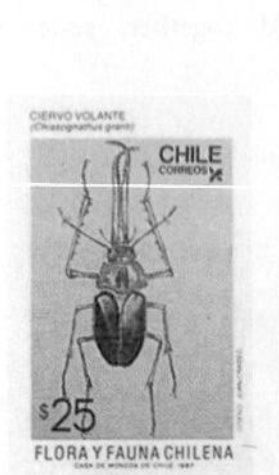

448 "Chiasognathus granti" **449** Family

1987. Flora and Fauna. Multicoloured.
1116 25p. Type **448** 40 25
1117 25p. Sanderling 50 30
1118 25p. Peruvian guemal . . . 40 25
1119 25p. Chilean palm 40 25
1120 25p. "Colias vauthieri" (butterfly) 50 25
1121 25p. Osprey 50 30
1122 25p. Commerson's dolphin 50 25
1123 25p. Mountain cypress . . . 40 25
1124 25p. San Fernandez Island spiny lobster 40 25
1125 25p. Fernandez firecrown 50 30
1126 25p. Vicuna 50 25
1127 25p. Arboreal fern 40 25
1128 25p. Spider-crab 45 25
1129 25p. Lesser rhea 50 30
1130 25p. Mountain viscacha . . 50 25
1131 25p. Giant cactus 40 25

1987. International Year of Shelter for the Homeless.
1132 **449** 40p. multicoloured . . . 45 10

450 Emblem **452** "Holy Family" (Ximena Soledad Rosales Opazo)

451 Condell, Battle of Iquique and Statue

1987. "fisa'87", 25th International Santiago Fair.
1133 **450** 20p. multicoloured . . . 10 15

1987. Death Centenary of Admiral Carlos Condell.
1134 **451** 50p. multicoloured . . . 1·00 60

1987. Christmas. Multicoloured.
1135 30p. Type **452** 35 10
1136 100p. "Star over Bethlehem" (Marcelo Bordones Meneses) . . . . 1·00 60

453 Casting **454** "Nativity"

1987. "Cobre '87" International Copper Conference, Vina del Mar.
1137 **453** 40p. multicoloured . . . 20 10

1987. Christmas. (a) Non-discount.
1139 **454** 15p. blue and orange . . 20 10

(b) Discount stamps. Additionally inscr "D.S. No. 20".
1140 **454** 15p. blue and orange . . 20 10

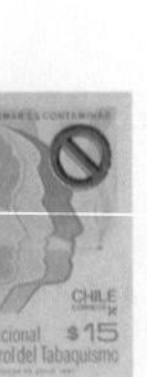

455 Non-smokers inhaling Smoke **457** Freire

456 "Capitan Luis Alcazar" (supply ship) and Antarctic Landscape

1987. Anti-smoking Campaign.
1141 **455** 15p. blue and orange . . 20 10

1987. 25th Anniv of National Antarctic Research Commission.
1142 **456** 45p. multicoloured . . . 1·25 40

1987. Birth Bicentenary of General Ramon Freire Serrano (Director, 1823–27).
1143 **457** 20p. red and purple . . 25 20

458 Violin and Frutillar Church and Lake

1988. 20th Music Weeks, Frutillar.
1144 **458** 30p. multicoloured . . . 15 10

459 St. John with Boy (after C. Di Girolamo) **460** Bird, Da Vinci's Glider, Wright's Flyer 1, Junkers Ju 52/3m, De Havilland Vampire and Grumman Tomcat

1988. Death Centenary of St. John Bosco (founder of Salesian Brothers).
1145 **459** 40p. multicoloured . . . 45 10

1988. "Fida'88" 5th International Air Fair.
1146 **460** 60p. blue and deep blue 75 25

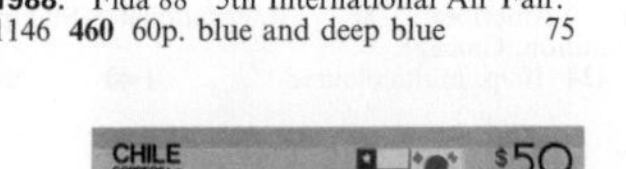

461 Shot Putting, Pole Vaulting and Javelin Throwing

1988. Olympic Games, Seoul. Multicoloured.
1147 50p. Type **461** 60 45
1148 100p. Swimming, cycling and running . . . . . . 1·25 1·00

1988. Discount stamp. No. 958 surch **$20 D.S.No 20.**
1150 **387** 20p. on 9p. green . . . 10 20

463 Kava-Kava Head

1988. Easter Island. (a) Inscr "CORREOS" only.
1151 **463** 20p. black and pink . . 25 15
1152 – 20p. black and pink . . 25 15

(b) Discount stamps. As T **463** but additionally inscr "D.S.No 20".
1153 **463** 20p. black and yellow . . 25 15
1154 – 20p. black and yellow . . 25 15

DESIGN: Nos. 1152, 1154, Tangata Manu bird-man (petroglyph).

464 Medal, Scientist, Bull and Farm Workers

1988. 150th Anniv of National Agricultural Society.
1155 **464** 45p. multicoloured . . . 25 15

465 Tending Accident Victim

1988. 125th Anniv of Red Cross.
1156 **465** 150p. multicoloured . . 2·25 2·00

466 Gipsy Moth, Boeing 767, Mirage 50 and Merino

1988. Birth Centenary of Commodore Arturo Merino Benitez (air pioneer).
1157 **466** 35p. multicoloured . . . 45 10

467 Cadet Barquentine "Esmeralda"

1988. Naval Tradition. Multicoloured.
1158 50p. Type **467** 75 45
1159 50p. "Capt. Arturo Prat" (stained glass window, Valparaiso Naval Museum) 75 45

468 Vatican City and University Arms

1988. Centenary of Pontifical Catholic University of Chile.
1160 **468** 40p. multicoloured . . . 45 10

469 Esslingen Locomotive No. 3331

1988. Railway Anniversaries. Multicoloured.
1161 60p. Type **469** (75th anniv of Arica–La Paz railway) 2·40 1·25
1162 60p. North British locomotive No. 45 (cent of Antofagasta–Bolivia railway) 35 25

470 Chemistry Student

1988. 175th Anniv of Jose Miguel Carrera National Institute.
1164 **470** 45p. multicoloured . . . 25 15

471 "Chloraea chrysantha"

1988. Flowers. Multicoloured.
1165 30p. Type **471** 45 10
1166 30p. "Lapogeria rosea" 45 10
1167 30p. "Nolana paradoxa" 45 10
1168 30p. "Rhodophiala advena" 45 10
1169 30p. "Schizanthus hookeri" 45 10
1170 30p. "Acacia caven" 45 10
1171 30p. "Cordia decanda" 45 10
1172 30p. "Leontochir ovallei" 45 10
1173 30p. "Alstroemeria pelegrina" 45 10
1174 30p. "Copiapoa cinerea" 45 10
1175 30p. "Salpiglossis sinuata" 45 10
1176 30p. "Leucocoryne coquimbensis" 45 10
1177 30p. "Eucryphia glutinosa" 45 10
1178 30p. "Calandrinia longiscapa" 45 10
1179 30p. "Desfontainia spinosa" 45 10
1180 30p. "Sophora macrocarpa" 45 10

472 Commander Policarpo Toro and "Angamos"

1988. Centenary of Incorporation of Easter Island into Chile. Multicoloured.
1181 50p. Type **472** 75 20
1182 50p. Map of Easter Island and globe 55 20
1183 100p. Dancers 90 50
1184 100p. Petroglyphs of bird-men 90 50

473 Bleriot XI over Town

1988. 70th Anniv of First National Airmail Service.
1186 **473** 150p. multicoloured 90 60

474 Pottery

1988. 15th Anniv of Centre for Education of Women. Traditional Crafts. Multicoloured.
1187 25p. Type **474** 10 10
1188 25p. Embroidery 10 10

475 Policeman and Brigade Members

1988. Schools' Security Brigade.
1189 **475** 45p. multicoloured 20 10

476 "Nativity" (Paulette Thiers)

477 Cancelled 1881 2c. Stamp

1988. Christmas. Multicoloured.
1190 35p. Type **476** 15 10
1191 100p. "Family going to church" (Jose M. Lamas) 70 35

1988. Centenary of Chile Philatelic Society.
1192 **477** 40p. multicoloured 45 10

478 Child in Manger

479 Manuel Bulnes and Battle of Yungay, 1839

1988. Christmas. (a) Non-discount.
1193 **478** 20p. purple and yellow 10 10

(b) Discount stamps. As T **478** but additionally inscr "D.S. No. 20".
1194 **478** 20p. purple and yellow 10 10

1989. Historic Heroes. Multicoloured.
1195 50p. Type **479** 20 10
1196 50p. Soldier and battle scene 20 10
1197 100p. Roberto Simpson and Battle of Casma, 1839 1·25 55
1198 100p. Sailor and battle scene 1·25 55

480 St. Ambrose's Church, Vallenar (bicentenary)

483 Sister Teresa of the Andes

1989. Town Anniversaries. Multicoloured.
1199 30p. Type **480** 10 10
1200 35p. Craftsman, Combarbala (bicent) 15 10
1201 45p. Laja Falls, Los Angeles (250th anniv) 20 10
See also No. 1306.

1989. Various stamps surch. (a) Surch **$25** only.
1202 25p. on 15p. green (1092) 10 10
1203 25p. on 15p. blue (1093) 30 10
1204 25p. on 15p. brown (1094) 10 10
1205 25p. on 15p. mauve (1095) 10 10
1206 25p. on 20p. black and pink (1151) 10 10
1207 25p. on 20p. black and pink (1152) 10 10
1208 25p. on 20p. black and yellow (1153) 10 10
1209 25p. on 20p. black and yellow (1154) 10 10

(b) Surch **D.S. No 20 $25**.
1210 25p. on 20p. black and pink (1151) 10 10
1211 25p. on 20p. black and pink (1152) 10 10

1989. Beatifications. Multicoloured.
1212 40p. Type **483** 20 10
1213 40p. Laura Vicuna 20 10

484 Christopher Columbus

1989. "Exfina '89" Stamp Exhibition, Santiago. Multicoloured.
1214 100p. Type **484** 70 35
1215 100p. "Nina", "Santa Maria" and "Pinta" 95 40

485 Container Ship and Trawler

1989. 50th Anniv of Energy Production Corporation. Multicoloured.
1217 60p. Type **485** 90 20
1218 60p. Tree trunks on trailer and factory 25 15
1219 60p. Telephone tower and pylon 25 15
1220 60p. Coal wagons and colliery 25 15

486 Town and Sketch

1989. Birth Centenary of Gabriela Mistral (writer). Multicoloured.
1221 30p. Type **486** 15 10
1222 30p. Mistral with children 15 10
1223 30p. Mistral writing 15 10
1224 30p. Mistral receiving Nobel Prize 15 10

487 Grapes

1989. Exports. (a) Inscr as T **487**.
1225 **487** 5p. blue 15 10
1226 – 5p. red and blue 15 10
1227 **487** 10p. deep blue & blue 15 10
1228 – 10p. red and blue 15 10
1229 **487** 25p. blue and green 10 10
1230 – 25p. red and green 10 10
1350 **487** 45p. blue and mauve 15 10
1351 – 45p. red and mauve 15 10

(b) Discount stamps. As T **487** but additionally inscr "D.S. No. 20".
1231 **487** 25p. blue and yellow 10 10
1232 – 25p. red and yellow 10 10
1352 **487** 45p. blue and yellow 15 15
1353 – 45p. red and yellow 15 15
DESIGNS: Nos. 1226, 1228, 1230, 1232, 1351, 1353, Apple.

488 Battle Scene, Soldiers and "Justice"

1989. 150th Anniv of Army Court of Justice.
1233 **488** 50p. multicoloured 20 10

489 Monument

490 Victoria, Vina del Mar

1989. Frontier Guards' Martyrs' Monument.
1234 **489** 35p. multicoloured 15 10

1989. Transport.
1235 **490** 30p. black and orange 15 10
1236 – 35p. black and blue 35 10
1237 – 40p. black and green 20 10
1238 – 45p. black and green 55 10
1239 – 50p. black and red 55 10
1240 – 60p. black and bistre 45 15
1241 – 100p. black and green 65 35
DESIGNS—VERT: 35p. Scow, Chiloe Archipelago. HORIZ: 40p. Ox-cart, Cautin; 45p. Raft ferry, Rio Palena; 50p. Lighters, Gen. Carrera Lake; 60p. Valparaiso incline railway; 100p. Santiago funicular.
See also Nos. 1346 and 1458.

491 Scientist and Bearded Penguins

1989. 25th Anniv of Chilean Antarctic Institute.
1245 **491** 150p. multicoloured 2·10 1·00

492 Present Naval Engineers School and "Chacabuco" (first school)

1989. Centenary of Naval Engineering. Mult.
1246 45p. Type **492** 40 10
1247 45p. Sailors in engine room 40 10
1248 45p. Destroyer, Aerospatiale Dauphin 2 helicopter and submarine 40 10
1249 45p. Launch of "Aquiles" (patrol boat) 40 10

493 Globes, Polar Bear and Gentoo Penguins

494 Atacamena Culture

1989. "World Stamp Expo '89" International Stamp Exhibition, Washington D.C.
1250 **493** 250p. multicoloured 3·00 1·75

1989. America. Pre-Columbian Cultures. Mult.
1252 30p. Type **494** 40 10
1253 150p. Selk'nam and Onas cultures 1·25 60

495 Balls

497 Vicuna, Lauca

496 "Rowing to Church" (Cristina Lopez)

1989. Christmas. (a) As T **495**.
1254 **495** 25p. yellow and green 10 10
1255 – 25p. yellow and green 10 10

(b) Discount stamps. Additionally inscr "D.S. No 20".
1256 **495** 25p. red and green 10 10
1257 – 25p. red and green 10 10
DESIGN: Nos. 1255, 1257, Bells.

1989. Christmas.
1258 **496** 100p. multicoloured 80 40

1990. National Parks. Multicoloured.
1259 35p. Type **497** 30 10
1260 35p. Chilian flamingo, Salar de Surire 50 20
1261 35p. Cactus, La Chimba 30 10
1262 35p. Guanaco, Pan de Azucar 30 10
1263 35p. Long-tailed meadowlark, Fray Jorge 50 20
1264 35p. Sooty tern, Rapa Nui 50 20
1265 35p. Lesser grison, La Campana 30 10
1266 35p. Torrent duck, Rio Clarillo 50 20
1267 35p. Mountain cypress, Rio de los Cipreses 30 10
1268 35p. Black-necked swan, Laguna de Torca 50 20
1269 35p. Puma, Laguna del Laja 40 20
1270 35p. Araucaria, Villarrica 30 10
1271 35p. "Philesia magellanica", Vicente Perez Rosales 30 10
1272 35p. "Nothofagus pumilio", Dos Lagunas 30 10
1273 35p. Leopard seal, Laguna San Rafael 40 20
1274 35p. Lesser rhea, Torres del Paine 50 20

498 Boot

1990. World Cup Football Championship, Italy. Multicoloured.
1275 50p. Type **498** 20 10
1276 50p. Hand 20 10
1277 50p. Ball in net 20 10
1278 50p. Player 20 10

499 Vickers Wibault I Biplane, 1927–37

1990. Chilean Airforce Airplanes. Multicoloured.
1279 40p. Type **499** 25 10
1280 40p. Curtiss O1E Falcon, 1928–40 . . . . 25 10
1281 40p. Pitts S-2A (Falcons aerobatic team, 1981–90) 25 10
1282 40p. Extra 33 (Falcons aerobatic team, 1990) . . 25 10
No. 1282 is inscribed "EXTRA 300".

500 Inca

1990. 500th Anniv of Discovery of America by Columbus. Multicoloured.
1284 60p. Type **500** 20 10
1285 60p. Spanish officer 20 10

501 Valparaiso

1990. Ports. Multicoloured.
1286 40p. Type **501** 15 10
1287 40p. San Vicente 15 10

502 "Piloto Pardo" (Antarctic supply ship)

1990. Naval Tradition. Multicoloured.
1288 50p. Type **502** 70 30
1289 50p. "Yelcho" (survey ship) 70 30

503 "Sunrise in Chile"

1990. "Democracy in Chile". Multicoloured.
1290 20p. Type **503** 10 10
1291 30p. Dove ("Peace in Chile") 10 10
1292 60p. "ChiLe" ("Rejoicing in Chile") 45 10
1293 100p. Star ("Thus Chile pleases me") 70 25

504 Child and Slogan

1990. "One Chile for All Chileans".
1295 **504** 45p. multicoloured . . . 15 10

505 Sir Rowland Hill

506 Flags

1990. 150th Anniv of the Penny Black.
1297 **505** 250p. multicoloured . . 1·50 75

1990. Centenary of Organization of American States.
1299 **506** 150p. multicoloured . . 95 40

507 Purplish Scallop and Diver with Net

1990. Fishing. Multicoloured.
1300 40p. Type **507** 25 15
1301 40p. Giant wedge clam and man with net 25 15
1302 40p. Swordfish ("Albacora") and harpooner on "San Antonio" (fishing boat) 40 15
1303 40p. Marine spider crab and fishing boat raising catch 40 15
1304 40p. Chilean hake ("Merluza") and trawler 40 15
1305 40p. Women baiting hooks 40 15

1990. Town Anniversaries. 250th Anniv of San Felipe. As T **480**. Multicoloured.
1306 50p. Curimon Convent . . . 20 10

508 Aerosol

509 Salvador Allende

1990. Environmental Protection. Each red and black.
(a) As T **508**.
1307 35p. Type **508** 15 10
1308 35p. Tree and tree stumps 15 10
1309 35p. Factory chimneys emitting smoke 15 10
1310 35p. Oil tanker polluting wildlife and sea 40 10
1311 35p. Deer escaping from burning forest 15 10

(b) Discount stamps. Additionally inscr "D.S. No 20".
1312 35p. Type **508** 15 10
1313 35p. As No. 1308 . . . . . 15 10
1314 35p. As No. 1309 . . . . . 15 10
1315 35p. As No. 1310 . . . . . 40 10
1316 35p. As No. 1311 . . . . . 15 10
See also Nos. 1421/30.

1990. Presidents.
1317 **509** 35p. black and blue . . 15 10
1318 – 35p. black and blue . . 15 10
1319 – 40p. black and green . . 15 10
1320 – 45p. black and green . . 15 10
1321 – 50p. black and red . . . 20 10
1322 – 60p. black and red . . . 20 10
1323 – 70p. black and blue . . 25 15
1324 – 80p. black and blue . . 30 20
1325 – 90p. black and brown . . 30 20
1326 – 100p. black & brown . . 35 25
DESIGNS: No. 1318, Eduardo Frei; 1319, Jorge Alessandri; 1320, Gabriel Gonzalez; 1321, Juan Antonio Rios; 1322, Pedro Aguirre Cerda; 1323, Juan E. Montero; 1324, Carlos Ibanez; 1325, Emiliano Figueroa; 1326, Arturo Alessandri.

510 Opening Ceremony

1990. Rodeo. Multicoloured.
1327 45p. Type **510** 15 10
1328 45p. Riders saluting crowd 15 10
1329 45p. Rider reining in . . . 15 10
1330 45p. Two riders cornering steer 15 10

511 Chilean Flamingoes

1990. America. The Natural World. Mult.
1331 30p. Type **511** 85 20
1332 150p. South American fur seals . . . . 1·40 40

512 Chilean State Arms and Spanish Royal Arms

1990. State Visit by King Juan Carlos and Queen Sofia of Spain. Multicoloured.
1333 100p. Type **512** 70 25
1334 100p. Spanish and Chilean (at right) State Arms . . 70 25

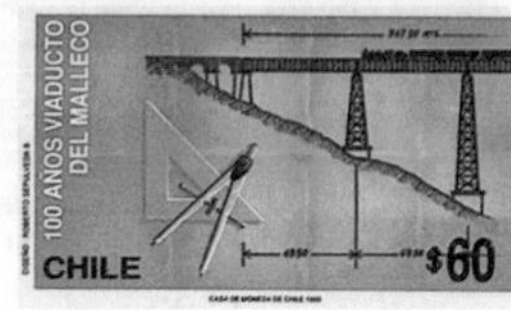

513 Construction Diagram of Viaduct

1990. Centenary of Malleco Viaduct. Mult.
1335 60p. Type **513** 55 20
1336 60p. Boy waving to steam train on completed viaduct 55 20
Nos. 1335/6 were printed together, se-tenant, forming a composite design.

514 Antarctic Skua, Whale and Supply Ship

1990. 50th Anniv of Chilean Antarctic Territory. Multicoloured.
1337 250p. Type **514** . . . . . . 1·25 85
1338 250p. Adelie penguins, Bell Model 206 jet helicopters and tents . . . . 2·00 80

515 Children decorating Tree

1990. Christmas. (a) As T **515**.
1340 **515** 35p. green & emerald . . 10 10

(b) Discount stamps. Additionally inscr "D.S. No 20".
1341 **515** 35p. green and orange 10 10

516 Santa Claus in Space (Carla Levill)

1990. Christmas. Children's drawings. Mult.
1342 35p. Type **516** 10 10
1343 150p. Television on sea bed (Jose M. Lamas) 70 35

517 Assembly Hall

1990. National Congress. Multicoloured.
1344 100p. Type **517** 75 25
1345 100p. Painting above dais 75 25

1991. Discount stamp. As No. 1238 but colour changed and additionally inscr "D.S. No 20".
1346 45p. black and yellow . . . 40 10

518 Casa Colorada

1991. 450th Anniv of Santiago. Multicoloured.
1347 100p. Type **518** 75 25
1348 100p. City landmarks . . . 75 25

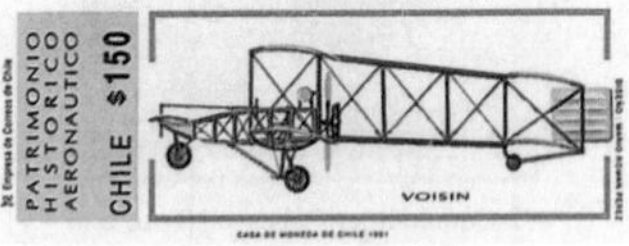

519 Voisin "Boxkite"

1991. Aviation History. Multicoloured.
1354 150p. Type **519** 90 45
1355 150p. Royal Aircraft Factory S.E.5A 90 45
1356 150p. Morane Saulnier MS 35 . . . . 90 45
1357 150p. Consolidated PBY-5A/ OA-10 Catalina amphibian 90 45

520 Map, Player and Left Half of Ball

1991. America Cup Football Championship. Mult.
1358 100p. Type **520** 75 25
1359 100p. Right half of ball and goalkeeper 75 25
Nos. 1358/9 were printed together, se-tenant, forming a composite design.

521 Drill and Miner

1991. Coal Mining. Multicoloured.
1360 200p. Type **521** . . . . . . 1·60 45
1361 200p. Miners emptying truck 1·90 45

522 Youths and Emblem
525 Santiago Cathedral

523 Dish and Hanging Ornaments

1991. Centenary of Scientific Society.
1362 **522** 45p. black and green . . 15 10

1991. Traditional Crafts. Multicoloured.
1363 90p. Type **523** 55 25
1364 90p. Carvings and ceramics 55 25

1991. Various stamps surch.
1365 **463** 45p. on 20p. black and yellow 15 10
1366 – 45p. on 20p. black and yellow (1154) 15 10

1367 **487** 45p. on 25p. blue & yell 15 10
1368 – 45p. on 25p. red and yellow (1232) 15 10

1991. National Monuments.
1369 **525** 300p. black, pink & brn 1·90 70

526 Dish Aerial and Transmission Masts

1991. World Telecommunications Day.
1370 **526** 90p. multicoloured . . . 65 25

527 Pope Leo XIII and Factory Line

528 Capt. L. Pardo and Sir Ernest Shackleton

1991. Centenary of "Rerum Novarum" (papal encyclical on workers' rights).
1371 **527** 100p. multicoloured . . 65 25

1991. Naval Tradition. 75th Anniv of Pardo's Rescue of Shackleton Expedition. Multicoloured.
1372 50p. Type **528** 40 10
1373 50p. "Yelcho" (coast-guard vessel) 75 25
1374 50p. Chilean sailor sighting stranded men on Elephant Island 40 10
1375 50p. "Endurance" 75 25

529 Flags and Globe

531 "Maipo" (container ship)

530 Building and Police Officers

1991. 21st General Assembly of Organization of American States, Santiago.
1377 **529** 70p. multicoloured . . . 80 15

1991. Opening of New Police School.
1378 **530** 50p. Multicoloured . . . 15 10

1991. National Merchant Navy Day.
1379 **531** 45p. black and red . . . 45 10

532 Opening Ceremony

1991. 11th Pan-American Games, Havana. Mult.
1380 100p. Type **532** 60 25
1381 100p. Cycling, running and basketball competitors . . 60 25

533 Carriage and Building

1991. Bicentenary of Los Andes.
1382 **533** 100p. multicoloured . . 60 25

534 Common Octopus

536 "Woman in Red" (Pedro Reszka)

535 Nitrate Processing and Jose Balmaceda (President, 1886–91)

1991. Marine Life. Multicoloured.
1383 50p. Type **534** 30 15
1384 50p. "Durvillaea antarctica" 30 15
1385 50p. Lenguado 45 15
1386 50p. "Austromegabalanus psittacus" 30 15
1387 50p. Barnacle rock shell ("Concholepas concholepas") 30 15
1388 50p. Crab ("Cancer setosus") 30 15
1389 50p. "Lessonia nigrescens" 30 15
1390 50p. Sea-urchin 30 15
1391 50p. Crab ("Homalaspis plana") 30 15
1392 50p. "Porphyra columbina" 30 15
1393 50p. Loro knife-jaw 45 15
1394 50p. "Chorus giganteus" . . 30 15
1395 50p. Rock shrimp 30 15
1396 50p. Peruvian anchovy . . . 45 15
1397 50p. "Gracilaria sp." . . . 30 15
1398 50p. "Pyura chilensis" . . . 30 15

1991. Centenary of 1891 Revolution. Pre-Revolution Events. Multicoloured.
1399 100p. Type **535** 90 25
1400 100p. Education and Balmaceda 60 25

1991. Paintings. Multicoloured.
1401 50p. Type **536** 40 10
1402 70p. "The Traveller" (Camilo Mori) . . . . . 1·25 30
1403 200p. "Head of Child" (Benito Rebolledo) . . . 90 45
1404 300p. "Child in Fez" (A. Valenzuela Puelma) 2·00 70

537 Map of South American Interests in Antartica

1991. 30th Anniv of Antarctica Treaty. Mult.
1405 80p. Type **537** 70 20
1406 80p. Wildlife 90 45

538 Glove in Envelope (Guillermo Suarez)

1991. International Letter Writing Week. Children's drawings. Multicoloured.
1407 45p. Type **538** 45 10
1408 70p. Human figures in envelope (Jorge Vargas) 60 15

539 Amerindians watching Columbus's Fleet

1991. America. Voyages of Discovery. Mult.
1409 50p. Type **539** 30 15
1410 150p. Columbus's fleet and navigator . . . . 1·40 65

540 Line Drawing of Neruda

541 Boy and Stars

1991. 20th Anniv of Award of Nobel Prize for Literature to Pablo Neruda. Multicoloured, colour of cap given.
1411 **540** 45p. blue 15 10
1412 45p. red 15 10

Nos. 1411/12 were issued together, se-tenant, the backgrounds of the stamps forming a composite design of one of Neruda's manuscripts.

1991. Christmas. Multicoloured.
1414 45p. Type **541** 15 10
1415 100p. Girl and stars 30 25

542 Postman making Delivery

544 Houses and Figures

1991. Christmas. (a) As T **542**.
1416 **542** 45p. mauve and violet 15 10
1417 – 45p. mauve and violet 30 10

(b) Discount stamps. Additionally inscr "D.S. No 20" in left-hand margin.
1418 **542** 45p. mauve and violet 15 10
1419 – 45p. mauve and violet 30 20

DESIGN: Nos. 1417, 1419, Starlit town.

1992. No. 1238 surch **$60**.
1420 60p. on 45p. black & green 40 15

1992. Environmental Protection. As Nos. 1307/16 but values and colours changed. (a) As T **508**, each yellow and green.
1421 60p. Type **508** 20 15
1422 60p. As No. 1308 . . . . . 20 15
1423 60p. As No. 1309 . . . . . 20 15
1424 60p. As No. 1310 . . . . . 40 15
1425 60p. As No. 1311 . . . . . 20 15

(b) Discount stamps. Additionally inscr "D.S. No 20". Each orange and green.
1426 60p. Type **508** 20 15
1427 60p. As No. 1308 . . . . . 20 15
1428 60p. As No. 1309 . . . . . 20 15
1429 60p. As No. 1310 . . . . . 40 15
1430 60p. As No. 1311 . . . . . 20 15

1992. 16th Population and Housing Census.
1431 **544** 60p. blue, orange & blk 20 15

545 Score and Mozart

1992. Death Bicentenary of Wolfgang Amadeus Mozart (composer). Multicoloured.
1432 60p. Type **545** 50 15
1433 200p. Mozart playing harpsichord . . . . . . 1·10 50

546 Stylized Jet Fighter

1992. "Fidae '92" International Air and Space Fair.
1435 **546** 60p. multicoloured . . . 20 15

547 Arms and Church, San Jose de Maipo

1992. 200th (80p.) or 250th (others) Anniversaries of Cities. Multicoloured.
1436 80p. Type **547** 50 20
1437 90p. Pottery (Melipilla) . . 55 25
1438 100p. Lircunlauta House (San Fernando) 60 25
1439 150p. Fruits and woodsman (Cauquenes) 75 35
1440 250p. Huilquilemu Cultural Villa (Talca) . . . . . . 1·25 60

548 Chilean Pavilion

1992. "Expo '92" World's Fair, Seville. Mult.
1441 150p. Type **548** 90 35
1442 200p. Iceberg . . . . 1·10 50

549 "Morula praecipua", Maculated Conch and Dragon's-head Cowrie

1992. Marine Flora and Fauna of Easter Island. Multicoloured.
1444 60p. Type **549** 35 20
1445 60p. "Codium pocockiae" 35 20
1446 60p. Easter Island swordfish ("Myripristis tiki") . . . 50 20
1447 60p. Seaweed 35 20
1448 60p. Fuentes' wrasse ("Pseudolabrus fuentesi") 50 20
1449 60p. Coral 35 20
1450 60p. Spiny lobster 35 20
1451 60p. Sea urchin 35 20

550 Statues, Liner and Launch

1992. Easter Island Tourism. Multicoloured.
1452 200p. Type **550** 85 50
1453 200p. Airplane, dancers and hill-carving 85 50

Nos. 1452/3 were issued together, se-tenant, forming a composite design.

551 Sun shining through Doorway and Handicapped People

552 Flags and Emblem

1992. National Council for the Handicapped.
1454 **551** 60p. multicoloured . . . 20 15

1992. 50th Anniv of National Defence Staff.
1455 **552** 60p. multicoloured . . . 45 15

553 "Simpson" (submarine)

1992. 75th Anniv of Chilean Submarine Fleet. Multicoloured.
1456 150p. Type **553** 90 35
1457 250p. Officer using periscope 1·40 60

1992. Discount stamp. As No. 1240 but additionally inscr "D/S No 20".
1458 60p. black and bistre . . . 1·10 30

1992. Nos. 1350/3 surch **$60.**
1459 **487** 60p. on 45p. blue & mve 20 15
1460 – 60p. on 45p. red & mve 20 15
1461 **487** 60p. on 45p. blue & yell 20 15
1462 – 60p. on 45p. red & yell 20 15

1992. Nos. 1416/19 surch **$60.**
1463 **542** 60p. on 45p. mauve and violet (1416) 20 15
1464 – 60p. on 45p. mauve and violet (1417) 35 15
1465 **542** 60p. on 45p. mauve and violet (1418) 20 15
1466 – 60p. on 45p. mauve and violet (1419) 35 15

556 Emperor Penguin

1992. The Emperor Penguin. Multicoloured.
1467 200p. Type **556** . . . . . . 1·40 50
1468 250p. Adult and chick . . . 1·75 60

557 Santiago Central Post Office

1992. National Monuments.
1470 **557** 200p. multicoloured . . 1·25 50

558 Columbus and Navigation Instruments

1992. America. 500th Anniv of Discovery of America by Columbus. Multicoloured.
1471 200p. Type **558** . . . . . . 1·25 50
1472 250p. Church, map of Americas and "Santa Maria" . . . . 1·10 70

559 Presenter at Microphone

560 O'Higgins, Flag and Monument

1992. 70th Anniv of Chilean Radio.
1473 **559** 250p. multicoloured . . 1·40 60

1992. 150th Death Anniv of Bernardo O'Higgins.
1474 **560** 60p. multicoloured . . . 20 15

561 Arrau as a Child

1992. Claudio Arrau (pianist). Multicoloured
1475 150p. Type **561** 80 35
1476 200p. Arrau playing piano 1·10 50

562 Statue

563 Nativity

1992. 150th Anniv of University of Chile. Mult.
1478 200p. Type **562** . . . . . . 1·00 50
1479 200p. Coat of arms, statues and clock . . . . 1·00 50
Nos. 1478/9 were issued together, se-tenant, forming a composite design.

1992. Christmas. (a) As T **563**.
1480 **563** 60p. brown and stone . . 20 15
1481 – 60p. brown and stone . . 20 15

(b) Discount stamps. Additionally inscr "DS/20" in right-hand margin.
1482 **563** 60p. red and stone . . . 20 15
1483 – 60p. red and stone . . . 20 15
DESIGN: Nos. 1481, 1483, Nativity (different).

564 Dam

1992. 23rd Ministerial Meeting of Latin-American Energy Organization.
1484 **564** 70p. black and yellow . . 25 20

565 Hands and Stars

1992. National Human Rights Day.
1485 **565** 100p. multicoloured . . 55 25

566 Achao Church

567 St. Ignatius de Loyola (founder)

1993. Churches. (a) As T **566**.
1487 **566** 70p. black and pink . . 25 20
1488 – 70p. black and pink . . 25 20

(b) Discount stamps. Additionally inscr "DS/20" in left-hand margin.
1489 **566** 70p. black and yellow . . 25 20
1490 – 70p. black and yellow . . 25 20
DESIGN: Nos. 1488, 1490, Castro church.
See also Nos. 1507/15.

1993. 400th Anniv of Jesuits' Arrival in Chile.
1491 **567** 200p. multicoloured . . 1·25 75

568 St. Teresa

569 Finger-Puppets

1993. Canonization of St. Teresa of the Andes.
1493 **568** 300p. multicoloured . . 1·50 70

1993. International Theatre Festival.
1494 **569** 250p. multicoloured . . 1·10 60

570 Satellite in Orbit

1993. 2nd Pan-American Space Conference.
1495 **570** 150p. multicoloured . . 80 35

571 Clotario Blest (Trade Union leader)

572 Drawing of Huidobro by Picasso

1993. Labour Day.
1497 **571** 70p. multicoloured . . . 50 20

1993. Birth Centenary of Vicente Huidobro (poet). Each black, stone and red.
1498 100p. Type **572** 30 25
1499 100p. Drawing of Huidobro by Juan Gris 30 25

573 Watterous, 1902

1993. Fire Engines (1st series). Multicoloured.
1500 100p. Type **573** 60 25
1501 100p. Merryweather, 1872 60 25
See also Nos. 1568/71.

574 Douglas B-26 Invader

1993. Aviation and Space. Multicoloured.
1503 100p. Type **574** 60 25
1504 100p. Mirage M 50 Pantera 60 25
1505 100p. Sanchez Besa biplane 60 25
1506 100p. Bell-47 Dl helicopter 60 25

1993. Churches. (a) As T **566**.
1507 10p. black and green . . . 10 10
1508 20p. black and brown . . . 10 10
1509 30p. black and orange . . . 10 10
1510 40p. black and blue 10 10
1511 50p. black and green . . . 15 10
1512 80p. black and buff . . . 25 20
1513 90p. black and green . . . 25 20
1514 100p. black and grey . . . 30 25

(b) Discount stamp. Additionally inscr "DS/20" at left.
1515 80p. black and lilac 25 20
1516 90p. black and red 25 20
1517 100p. black and yellow . . . 30 25
CHURCHES: 10p. Chonchi; 20p. Vilupulli; 30p. Llau-Llao; 40p. Dalcahue; 50p. Tenaun; 80p. Quinchao; 90p. Quehui; 100p. Nercon.

575 Nortina

577 Early Coin Production

576 "Late Dawn" (Mario Carreno)

1993. Regional Variations of La Cueca (national dance). Multicoloured.
1525 70p. Type **575** 45 15
1526 70p. Central 45 15
1527 70p. Chilota 45 15

1993. Santiago, Iberian-American City of Culture 1993. Paintings. Multicoloured.
1528 80p. Type **576** 50 20
1529 90p. "Summer" (Gracia Barrios) 50 20
1530 150p. "Protection" (Roser Bru) (vert) 70 35
1531 200p. "Tango, Valparaiso" (Nemesio Antunez) . . . 1·00 45

1993. 250th Anniv of Chilean Mint.
1532 **577** 250p. multicoloured . . 1·25 55

578 Patagonian Conure

579 Underground Train

1993. America. Endangered Animals. Mult.
1534 150p. Type **578** 90 35
1535 200p. Chilean guemal . . . 1·40 45

1993. 25th Anniv of Chilean Metro.
1536 **579** 80p. multicoloured . . . 45 20

580 "Ancud" (schooner) off Santa Ana Point

1993. 150th Anniv of Chilean Possession of Strait of Magellan.
1537 **580** 100p. multicoloured . . 40 25

581 Marines in Inflatable Assault Boats

1993. Naval Tradition. Multicoloured.
1538 80p. Type **581** (175th anniv of Marines) 25 20
1539 80p. Sailors making fast patrol boat (125th anniv of Alejandro Navarette Training School) 25 20
1540 80p. "Esmeralda" (cadet barquentine) and cadets in traditional "unloading the cannon" exercise (175th anniv of Arturo Prat Naval College) 25 20
1541 80p. "Sailing of First Squadron" (175th anniv) (painting, Alvaro Casanova Zenteno) . . . 25 20

582 Carved Figures

1993. International Year of Indigenous Peoples.
1542 **582** 100p. multicoloured . . 60 25

583 Holy Family **584** Adelie Penguins

1993. Christmas. (a) Sold at face value.
1543 **583** 70p. lilac and stone . . . 20 15

(b) Discount stamp. Additionally inscribed "DS/20" in right-hand margin.
1544 **583** 70p. blue and green . . 20 15

1993. Chilean Antarctic Territory. Mult.
1545 200p. Type **584** . . . . . . 1·40 45
1546 250p. Adelie penguin with young . . . . 1·60 55

585 Plaza de Armas, Ancud

1993. City Anniversaries. Multicoloured.
1548 80p. Type **585** (225th) . . . 35 20
1549 80p. Matriz church, Curico (250th) 35 20
1550 80p. Corner Pillar House, Rancagua (250th) 35 20

586 Hands

1994. International Year of the Family.
1551 **586** 100p. multicoloured . . 55 25

587 Violin

1994. 26th Music Weeks, Frutillar. Mult.
1552 150p. Type **587** 90 35
1553 150p. Cello 90 35
Nos. 1552/3 were issued together, se-tenant, forming a composite design.

588 Sukhoi Su-30 Flanker

1994. "Fidae '94" International Air and Space Fair. Multicoloured.
1554 300p. Type **588** . . . . . . 1·60 65
1555 300p. Vought Sikorsky OS2U3 Kingfisher seaplane . . . . 1·60 65
1556 300p. Lockheed F-117A Stealth . . . . 1·60 65
1557 300p. Northrop F-5E Tiger III . . . . 1·60 65

589 Ears of Grain

1994. 50th Anniv of Chile Agronomical Engineers' College.
1558 **589** 220p. multicoloured . . 1·50 45

1994. Nos. 1092/5 surch **$80**.
1559 80p. on 15p. green 25 20
1560 80p. on 15p. blue 35 20
1561 80p. on 15p. brown 25 20
1562 80p. on 15p. mauve 25 20

591 Skeletons buried under Cactus

1994. 75th Anniv of Concepcion University. Details of "Latin American Presence" (mural by Jorge Gonzalez Camarena). Multicoloured.
1563 250p. Type **591** . . . . . . 1·50 55
1564 250p. Faces . . . . 1·50 55
1565 250p. Building pyramid from spare parts . . . . 1·50 55
1566 250p. Cablework in building 1·50 55
Nos. 1563/6 were issued together, se-tenant, forming a composite design.

592 Gentoo Penguins and Harbour

1994. 30th Anniv of Chilean Antarctic Institute. Multicoloured.
1567 300p. Type **592** . . . . . . 1·90 65
1568 300p. Antarctic base . . . . 1·90 65
Nos. 1567/8 were issued together, se-tenant, forming a composite design.

593 "Vanessa terpsichore"

1994. Butterflies. Multicoloured.
1569 100p. Type **593** 60 25
1570 100p. "Hypsochila wagenknechti" 60 25
1571 100p. Polydamas swallowtail ("Battus polydamas") . . 60 25
1572 100p. "Polythysana apollina" 60 25
1573 100p. "Satyridae" 60 25
1574 100p. "Tetraphloebia stellygera" 60 25
1575 100p. "Eroessa chilensis" . . 60 25
1576 100p. Cloudless sulphur ("Phoebis sennae") . . . 60 25

594 Merryweather Steam Fire Engine, 1869

1994. Fire Engines (2nd series). Mult.
1577 150p. Type **594** 80 35
1578 150p. Poniente steam fire engine, 1863 . . . . . . 80 35
1579 150p. Mieusset steam fire engine, 1905 . . . . . . 80 35
1580 150p. Merryweather motor fire engine, 1903 . . . . 80 35

595 Bust and Banner

1994. Centenary of Javiera Carrera School for Girls, Santiago.
1581 **595** 200p. multicoloured . . 85 45

596 Door Panels, Porvenir (centenary)

1994. Town Anniversaries. Multicoloured.
1582 90p. Type **596** 50 20
1583 100p. Railway station, Villa Alemana (cent) . . . . . 1·00 25
1584 150p. Church, Constitucion (bicentenary) 70 35
1585 200p. Fountain and church, Linares (bicent) 90 45
1586 250p. Steam locomotive and statue, Copiapo (250th) 2·25 55
1587 300p. La Serena (450th) . . 1·60 65

597 Painting by Carlos Maturana **600** Fr. Hurtado

599 First Chilean Mail Van

1994. 20th International Very Large Data Bases Conference, Santiago.
1588 **597** 100p. multicoloured . . 30 25

1994. Nos. 1487/8 and 1544 surch **$80**.
1589 **566** 80p. on 70p. blk & pink 25 20
1590 – 80p. on 70p. blk & pink 25 20
1591 **583** 80p. on 70p. blue & grn 25 20

1994. America. Postal Transport. Mult.
1592 80p. Type **599** 50 20
1593 220p. De Havilland D.H.60G Gipsy Moth (first Chilean mail plane) 1·10 50

1994. Beatification of Fr. Alberto Hurtado.
1594 **600** 300p. blue, green & blk 1·40 70

601 Madonna and Child **603** "Almirante Williams" (destroyer)

602 Star

1994. Christmas. (a) Sold at face value.
1595 **601** 80p. multicoloured . . . 25 20

(b) Discount stamp. Additionally inscribed "DS/20" at foot.
1596 **601** 80p. multicoloured . . . 25 20

1995. International Women's Day. Mult.
1597 90p. Type **602** 55 25
1598 90p. Moon and sun 55 25
1599 90p. Dove 55 25
1600 90p. Earth 55 25

1995. Naval Tradition.
1601 **603** 100p. multicoloured . . 30 25

604 Emblem **605** Arms

1995. United Nations World Summit for Social Development, Copenhagen.
1602 **604** 150p. multicoloured . . 75 35

1995. 150th Anniv of Conciliar Seminary of Ancud.
1603 **605** 200p. multicoloured . . 90 45

606 Stained Glass Window, Santiago Cathedral

1995. 400th Anniv of Augustinian Order in Chile.
1604 **606** 250p. multicoloured . . 1·10 60

607 Religious Mask, Limari

1995. Rock Paintings. Multicoloured.
1605 150p. Type **607** 75 35
1606 150p. Herdsmen and llamas, Taira 75 35
1607 150p. Whale, Tal-tal 75 35
1608 150p. Masks, Encanto Valley 75 35

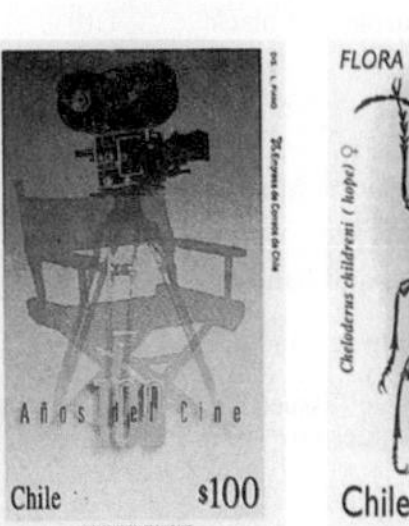

608 Camera and Director's Chair **610** "Cheloderus childreni"

609 Arms and Express Steam Train

1995. Centenary of Motion Pictures. Mult.
1609 100p. Type **608** 55 25
1610 100p. Advertising poster for "The Kid" 55 25
1611 100p. Early cinema advertising poster 55 25
1612 100p. Advertising poster for "Valparaiso Mi Amor" 55 25

1995. Bicentenary of Parral.
1613 **609** 200p. multicoloured . . 1·00 50

1995. Flora and Fauna. Multicoloured.
1614 100p. Type **610** 55 25
1615 100p. "Eulychnia acida" (cactus) 55 25

1616 100p. "Chiasognathus grantii" (stag beetle) . . . 55 25
1617 100p. "Browningia candelaris" (cactus) . . . 55 25
1618 100p. "Capiapoa dealbata" (cactus) 55 25
1619 100p. "Acanthinodera cummingi" (beetle) . . . 55 25
1620 100p. "Neoporteria subgibbosa" (cactus) . . . 55 25
1621 100p. "Semiotus luteipennis" (beetle) 55 25

611 Congress Emblem

1995. 2nd World Police Congress, Santiago.
1622 **611** 200p. multicoloured . . 90 45

612 "Tower of Babel V" (Mario Toral)

1995. 30th Anniv of Ministry of Housing and Town-planning.
1623 **612** 200p. multicoloured . . 90 45

613 Bello

614 Open Book and Emblem

1995. 25th Anniv of Andres Bello Agreement (South American co-operation in education. science and culture).
1624 **613** 250p. purple and black 1·10 60

1995. 50th Anniversaries. Multicoloured.
1625 100p. Type **614** (U.N.E.S.C.O.) 30 25
1626 100p. Globes and handshake (U.N.O.) 30 25
1627 100p. Seedling in hand (F.A.O.) 30 25
Nos. 1625/7 were issued together, se-tenant, forming a composite design.

615 Farming (M. Cruces)

616 Sailing Ship and Cape Horn

1995. America. Environmental Protection. Children's Paintings. Multicoloured.
1628 100p. Type **615** 55 25
1629 250p. Forestry (E. Munoz) (horiz) . . . . 1·00 55

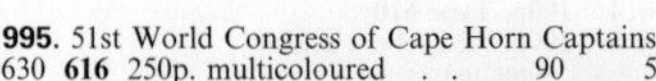
1995. 51st World Congress of Cape Horn Captains.
1630 **616** 250p. multicoloured . . 90 55

617 Crib and Inhabitants of North Chile

618 Carlos Dittborn (trainer) and Arica Stadium

1995. Christmas. (a) Sold at face value.
1631 **617** 90p. blue and violet . . 25 20
1632 – 90p. blue and violet . . 25 20

(b) Discount stamps. Additionally inscr "DS/20".
1633 **617** 90p. green and purple . . 25 20
1634 – 90p. green and purple . . 25 20
DESIGNS: Nos. 1632, 1634, Crib and people of South Chile.

1995. Centenary of Chile Football Federation. Mult.
1635 100p. Type **618** 55 25
1636 100p. Hugo Lepe (player) 55 25
1637 100p. Eladio Rojas (player) 55 25
1638 100p. Honorino Landa (player) 55 25

619 Mistral

1995. 50th Anniv of Award of Nobel Prize for Literature to Gabriela Mistral.
1639 **619** 300p. blue and black . . 1·25 65

620 Penguins

1995. Chilean Antarctic Territory. The Macaroni Penguin. Multicoloured.
1640 100p. Type **620** 60 25
1641 250p. Penguins (different) 1·50 55

621 Kiwi Fruit and Container Ship

1995. 60th Anniv of Chilean Exports Association. Fruit. Multicoloured.
1643 100p. Type **621** 40 25
1644 100p. Grapes and container ship 40 25
1645 100p. Peaches and container ship 40 25
1646 100p. Apples and container ship 40 25
1647 100p. Soft fruit and airplane 40 25

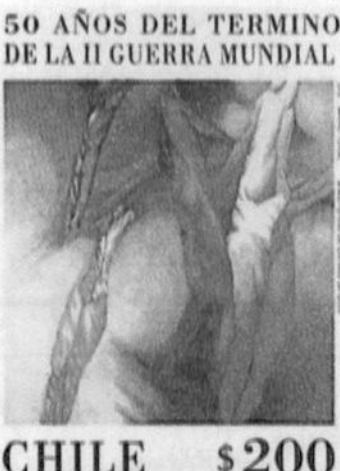

622 "Reunion" (Mario Toral)

623 Oil Rig

1995. 50th Anniv of End of Second World War.
1648 **622** 200p. multicoloured . . 90 45

1995. 50th Anniv of Discovery of Oil in Chile. Multicoloured.
1649 100p. Type **623** 40 25
1650 100p. Concon Refinery (grass in foreground) . . 40 25
1651 100p. Concepcion Refinery 40 25
1652 100p. Rig (different) 40 25

624 Embraer EMB-145

1996. "FIDAE '96" International Air and Space Fair, Santiago. Aircraft. Multicoloured.
1653 400p. Type **624** . . . . . 2·50 90
1654 400p. Mirage M5M Elkan 2·50 90
1655 400p. De Havilland D.H.C. 6 Twin Otter . . . . . 2·50 90
1656 400p. Saab JAS-39 Gripen 2·50 90

625 School

1996. 175th Anniv of Serena Boys' School.
1657 **625** 100p. multicoloured . . 75 25

626 Old Cordoba Rail Station, Seville

1996. "Espamer" and "Aviation and Space" Spanish and Latin American Stamp Exhibitions, Seville, Spain. Multicoloured.
1658 200p. Type **626** . . . . . 1·10 25
1659 200p. Lope de Vega Theatre, Seville 85 45

627 Extinguish Matches Properly

629 "Weather Rose" (Ricardo Mesa)

628 "Esmeralda" (cadet barquentine) in Dry-dock

1996. Safety Precautions. Multicoloured.
(a) Accidents in the Home.
1660 50p. Type **627** 15 10
1661 50p. Do not leave boiling water unattended 15 10
1662 50p. Keep sharp objects away from children . . . 15 10
1663 50p. Protect electrical sockets 15 10
1664 50p. Do not improvise electrical connections . . 15 10
1665 50p. Do not play the television or radio too loud 15 10
1666 50p. Check gas connections regularly 15 10
1667 50p. Do not overload electrical circuits 15 10
1668 50p. Keep inflammable materials away from fire 15 10
1669 50p. Do not leave toys lying around on the floor . . . 15 10

(b) Road Safety.
1670 50p. Use crossings 15 10
1671 50p. Obey the instructions of the traffic police . . . 15 10
1672 50p. Only cross on the green light 15 10
1673 50p. Wait on the pavement for buses 15 10
1674 50p. Do not cross the road between vehicles 15 10
1675 50p. Do not travel on the step of buses 15 10
1676 50p. Walk on the side of the road facing on-coming traffic 15 10
1677 50p. Look out for drains . . 15 10
1678 50p. Do not play ball in the road 15 10
1679 50p. Bicyclists should obey the Highway Code . . . 15 10

(c) Safety at School.
1680 50p. Do not panic in emergencies 15 10
1681 50p. Do not run around corners 15 10
1682 50p. Do not play practical jokes 15 10
1683 50p. Do not sit on banisters or railings 15 10
1684 50p. Do not run on the stairs 15 10
1685 50p. Do not drink while walking 15 10
1686 50p. Do not swing on your chair 15 10
1687 50p. Do not play with pointed or sharp objects 15 10
1688 50p. Do not open doors sharply 15 10
1689 50p. Go straight home after school and do not stop to talk to strangers 15 10

(d) Safety in the Workplace.
1690 50p. Wear protective clothing 15 10
1691 50p. Do not work with tools in bad condition 15 10
1692 50p. Keep your attention on your work (man at lathe) 15 10
1693 50p. Always use the proper tools 15 10
1694 50p. Work carefully (man at filing cabinet) 15 10
1695 50p. Do not leave objects on the stairs 15 10
1696 50p. Do not carry so much that you cannot see where you are going 15 10
1697 50p. Check ladders are safe 15 10
1698 50p. Always keep the workplace clean and tidy 15 10
1699 50p. Remove old nails first 15 10

(e) Enjoy Leisure Safely.
1700 50p. Only swim in the permitted areas 15 10
1701 50p. Do not put any part of the body out of the window of a moving vehicle 15 10
1702 50p. Avoid excessive exposure to the sun . . . 15 10
1703 50p. Do not contaminate swimming water with detergents 15 10
1704 50p. Do not throw litter . . 15 10
1705 50p. Always put out fires before leaving them . . . 15 10
1706 50p. Do not play pranks in water 15 10
1707 50p. Check safety precautions 15 10
1708 50p. Do not fly kites near overhead electrical lines 15 10
1709 50p. Do not run by the side of swimming pools . . . 15 10

(f) Alcohol and Drugs Awareness.
1710 50p. Do not drink and drive 15 10
1711 50p. Do not drink if you are pregnant 15 10
1712 50p. Do not give in to peer pressure 15 10
1713 50p. Being under the influence of alcohol is irresponsible in the workplace 15 10
1714 50p. Do not destroy your family through alcohol . . 15 10
1715 50p. You do not need drugs to have a good time . . . 15 10
1716 50p. You do not need drugs to succeed 15 10
1717 50p. You do not need drugs to entertain 15 10
1718 50p. Do not abandon your friends and family for drugs 15 10
1719 50p. Without drugs you are free and safe 15 10

1996. Centenary of Dry-dock No. 1, Talcahuano.
1720 **628** 200p. multicoloured . . 70 45

1996. Modern Sculpture. Multicoloured.
1721 150p. Type **629** 70 35
1722 150p. "Friendship" (Francisca Cerda) 70 35
1723 200p. "Memory" (Fernando Undurraga) (horiz) . . . 70 35
1724 200p. "Andean Airs" (Benito Rojo) (horiz) . . 70 35

630 Addict and Syringe full of Pills

1996. International Day against Drug Abuse.
1725 **630** 250p. multicoloured . . 75 55

631 Boxing Glove

1996. Centenary of National Olympic Committee and Modern Olympic Games. Olympic Games, Atlanta. Multicoloured.
1726 450p. Type **631** . . . . . . 2·25 1·00
1727 450p. Running shoe . . . . 2·25 1·00
1728 450p. Rollerblade . . . . . 2·25 1·00
1729 450p. Ball . . . . 2·25 1·00

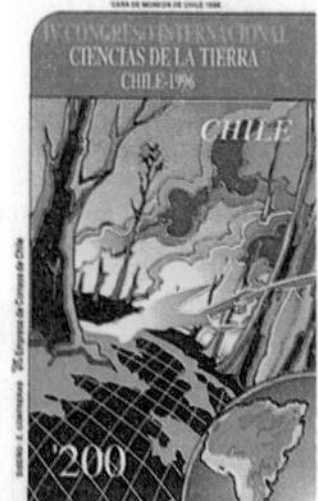

632 School

1996. 150th Anniv of San Fernando School.
1730 **632** 200p. multicoloured . . 85 45

633 Polluted Forest

1996. 4th International Congress on Earth Sciences. Multicoloured.
1731 200p. Type **633** 95 45
1732 200p. Industrial pollution 95 45
1733 200p. Deforestation 95 45
1734 200p. Map, camera and cracked earth 95 45
Nos. 1731/4 were issued together, se-tenant, forming a composite design.

634 Crookesite and Open-cast Mine

1996. Mining. Multicoloured.
1735 150p. Type **634** 70 35
1736 150p. Lapis lazuli and pendant 70 35
1737 150p. Bornite and calcium and crates 70 35
1738 150p. Azurite and atacamite 70 35

635 St. John Leonardi (founder)

1996. 50th Anniv of Order of Mother of God in Chile.
1739 **635** 200p. multicoloured . . 90 45

636 German-style Wooden house and Mt. Osorno

1996. 150th Anniv of German Immigration. Multicoloured.
1740 250p. Type **636** . . . . . . 1·00 50
1741 300p. "German Fountain" (monument) . . . . . . 1·10 60

637 King Penguins

1996. Chilean Antarctic Territory. Mult.
1742 250p. Type **637** . . . . . . 1·40 50
1743 300p. Adult and young king penguins . . . . 1·75 60

638 Lancia Fire Engine, 1937

1996. Centenary of Castro Fire Service. Mult.
1745 200p. Type **638** 90 40
1746 200p. Ford V8 fire engine, 1940 . . . . 90 40
1747 200p. Gorlitz G. A. Fischer 4-speed motor pump, 1930s 90 40
1748 200p. Lever-action pump, 1907 . . . . 90 40

639 Rafting, Vicente Perez Rosales National Park

1996. National Parks. Multicoloured.
1749 100p. Type **639** 55 25
1750 100p. Horse riding, Torres del Paine National Park 55 25
1751 100p. Cross-country skiing, Puyehue National Park 55 25
1752 100p. Walking, Pan de Azucar National Park . . 55 25

640 Latorre and "Almirante Latorre" (destroyer) **641** Women with Child

1996. 150th Birth Anniv of Admiral Juan Jose Latorre.
1753 **640** 200p. multicoloured . . 70 40

1996. America. Costumes. Multicoloured.
1754 100p. Type **641** 55 25
1755 100p. Men with horse . . . 55 25
1756 250p. Men on horseback . . 95 50

642 "Visual History of a Nation" (Mario Toral) (left-hand detail) **644** The Three Kings

643 Beach, Arms and Cathedral, Arica

1996. 6th Ibero-Latin American Heads of State Summit, Santiago. Multicoloured.
1757 110p. Type **642** 55 25
1758 110p. Right-hand detail of painting 55 25
Nos. 1757/8 were issued together, se-tenant, forming a composite design.

1996. Cities. 1st Anniv of Arica Law. Multicoloured.
1759 100p. Type **643** 55 25
1760 150p. Llamas and Chilean flamingoes, Parinacota Province 65 30

1996. Christmas. (a) Face value in black.
1761 **644** 100p. multicoloured . . 30 25

(b) Discount stamp. Additionally inscribed "DS/20" at foot and with face value in orange.
1762 **644** 100p. multicoloured . . 30 25

645 Pablo Neruda (poet), Gabriela Mistral (writer) and Nobel Prize Medal

1996. Visit of King and Queen of Sweden.
1763 **645** 300p. multicoloured . . 1·40 60

646 Children, Star and Globe

1996. 50th Anniv of U.N.I.C.E.F.
1764 **646** 200p. multicoloured . . 80 40

647 Church

1997. Centenary of Frontera Region. Mult.
1765 110p. Type **647** (centenary of Christian and Missionary Church Alliance) 60 25
1766 110p. Mountain valley (cent of Lonquimay Municipality) 60 25

648 Base Camp **649** La Pincoya

1997. 50th Anniv of Arturo Prat Antarctic Naval Base.
1767 250p. Type **648** . . . . . . 1·00 50
1768 300p. Monument and flags (horiz) . . . . 1·25 60

1997. Mythology. (a) As T **649**.
1769 40p. black and blue 10 10
1770 110p. black and orange . . 30 25

(b) Discount stamp. Additionally inscr "DS/20".
1778 110p. black and green . . . 30 25
DESIGN: Nos. 1770, 1778, La Fiura.

650 "Justice" and National Flag

1997. 70th Anniv of Controller General.
1781 **650** 110p. multicoloured . . 55 25

651 Underground Train in Station

1997. Inauguration of Metro Line No. 5.
1782 **651** 200p. multicoloured . . 1·25 60

652 Masonic Symbols and Flags

1997. 50th Anniv of Interamerican Masonic Confederation and 17th Grand General Assembly, Santiago.
1783 **652** 250p. multicoloured . . 1·00 50

653 Von Stephan

1997. Death Centenary of Heinrich von Stephan (founder of Universal Postal Union).
1785 **653** 250p. multicoloured . . 1·00 50

654 Books

1997. World Books and Copyright Day.
1786 **654** 110p. multicoloured . . 55 25

655 "Death to the Invader, Chile"

1997. Birth Centenary of David Alfaro Siqueiros (painter). Designs showing details of his murals in the Mexican School, Chillan, Chile. Multicoloured.
1787 150p. Type **655** 70 30
1788 200p. "Death to the Invader, Mexico" 95 40

656 Arms and Town Hall

1997. Centenary of Providencia.
1790 **656** 250p. multicoloured . . 1·10 50

657 Pacific Ocean and Mt. Osorno (after Hokusai Katsushika)

658 Award, National Flag and "Thumbs-up" Sign

1997. Centenary of Chile–Japan Relations.
1791 **657** 300p. multicoloured . . 1·10 60

1997. National Centre for Productivity and Quality.
1792 **658** 110p. multicoloured . . 75 25

659 Transmission from University of Chile to "El Mercurio" (newspaper) Offices

1997. 75th Anniv of First Radio Broadcast in Chile.
1793 **659** 110p. multicoloured . . 80 25

660 Postman on Bicycle, 1997

1997. America. The Postman. Multicoloured.
1794 110p. Type **660** 55 25
1795 250p. Late 19th-century mounted postman 95 50

661 Carlo Morelli in "Rigoletto"

662 Jack-in-a-Box and Baubles on Tree

1997. Opera Singers. Multicoloured.
1796 120p. Type **661** 35 25
1797 200p. Pedro Navia in "La Boheme" 55 40
1798 250p. Renato Zanelli in "Faust" 70 50
1799 300p. Rayen Quitral in "The Magic Flute" . . . . . . 1·10 60
1800 500p. Ramon Vinay in "Othello" . . . . 1·60 70

1997. Christmas. (a) "NAVIDAD '97" in blue.
1801 **662** 110p. multicoloured . . 30 25

(b) Discount stamp. "NAVIDAD '97" in orange and additionally inscr "D/S 20" below face value.
1802 **662** 110p. multicoloured . . 30 25

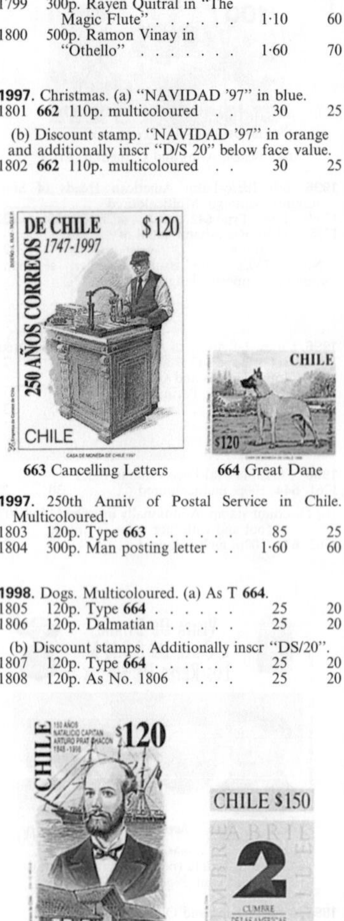

663 Cancelling Letters

664 Great Dane

1997. 250th Anniv of Postal Service in Chile. Multicoloured.
1803 120p. Type **663** 85 25
1804 300p. Man posting letter . . 1·60 60

1998. Dogs. Multicoloured. (a) As T **664**.
1805 120p. Type **664** 25 20
1806 120p. Dalmatian 25 20

(b) Discount stamps. Additionally inscr "DS/20".
1807 120p. Type **664** 25 20
1808 120p. As No. 1806 . . . . 25 20

665 Prat and "Esmeralda" (sail corvette)

666 Summit Emblem

1998. 150th Birth Anniv of Captain Arturo Prat Chacon.
1809 **665** 120p. multicoloured . . 40 25

1998. 2nd Summit of the Americas, Santiago.
1810 **666** 150p. multicoloured . . 35 25

667 Vets treating Horse

1998. Centenary of Army Veterinary Service. Mult.
1812 250p. Type **667** 55 40
1813 350p. Vet using stethoscope on horse 80 55

668 "Los Zambos de Calama" (Mauricio Moran)

1998. Paintings. Multicoloured.
1814 350p. Type **668** 80 55
1815 400p. "Soaking Watermelon" (Roser Bru) 90 65

669 Monk writing in Book

1998. 150th Anniv of Capuchin Order in Chile. Multicoloured.
1816 150p. Type **669** 35 25
1817 250p. Monk treating man's leg 55 40

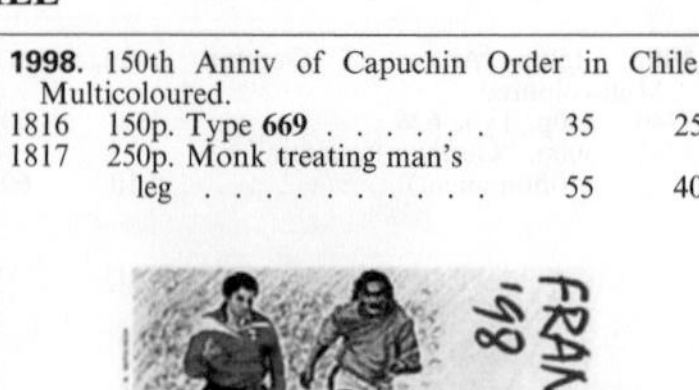

670 Players

1998. World Cup Football Championship, France. Multicoloured.
1818 250p. Type **670** 55 40
1819 350p. Players and trophy . . 80 55
1820 500p. Players and map of France . . . . 1·10 75
1821 700p. Attacker and goalkeeper . . . . 1·50 1·10

671 Bearded Penguin and Emblem

1998. 25th Meeting of Scientific Committee on Antarctic Research (1823) and 10th Meeting of Council of Managers of National Antarctic Programmes (1824), Concepcion. Multicoloured.
1823 250p. Type **671** 55 40
1824 350p. Two gentoo penguins on map of Antarctica and emblem 80 55

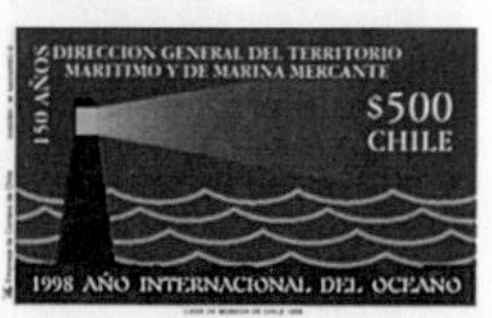

672 Lighthouse

1998. International Year of the Ocean (1st issue). 150th Anniv of General Office for Territorial Waters and the Merchant Navy.
1825 **672** 500p. multicoloured . . 1·10 85

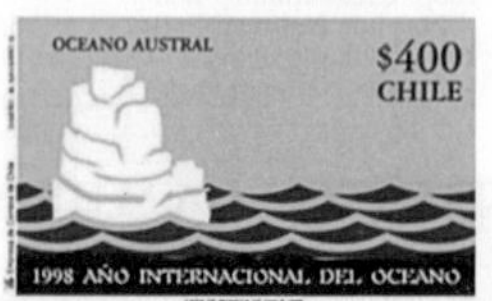

673 Iceberg and Ocean

1998. International Year of the Ocean (2nd issue).
1826 **673** 400p. blue, violet and black 90 60
1827 – 400p. blue, violet and black 90 60
1828 – 500p. multicoloured . . 1·10 75
DESIGNS: No. 1827, Compass rose, map of South Chile and ocean; 1828, Easter Island monolith and ocean.

674 Clara Solovera

1998. Composers and Folk Singers. Multicoloured.
1829 200p. Type **674** 45 30
1830 250p. Francisco Flores del Campo 55 40
1831 300p. Victor Jara 65 45
1832 350p. Violeta Parra 80 55

675 Delivery to Letter Box and Dog

1998. World Stamp Day.
1833 **675** 250p. multicoloured . . 55 40

676 Bilbao

1998. 175th Birth Anniv of Francisco Bilbao (writer).
1834 **676** 250p. purple, blue and orange 55 40

677 Amanda Labarca (educationist)

1998. America. Famous Women.
1835 **677** 120p. mauve, blue and black 25 20
1836 – 250p. yellow, mauve and black 55 40
DESIGN: 250 p, Marta Brunet (writer).

678 "Self-portrait" (Augusto Eguiluz)

1998. Paintings. Multicoloured.
1837 300p. Type **678** 65 45
1838 450p. "Solitary Tree" (Agustin Abarca) (horiz) 1·00 70

679 Arms and University

680 Rufous-collared Sparrow

1998. 70th Anniv of Valparaiso Catholic University.
1840 **679** 130p. multicoloured . . 30 20

1998. Birds. Multicoloured.
1841 10p. Type **680** 10 10
1842 20p. Austral blackbird . . . 10 10
1845 50p Magellanic woodpecker (vert) 10 10
1849 100p Peregrine falcon (vert) 25 20

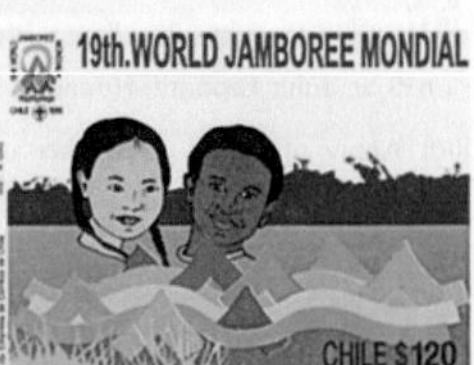

681 Children and Tents

1998. 19th World Scout Jamboree, Picarquin. Mult.
1856 120p. Type **681** 25 20
1857 200p. Lord Baden-Powell (founder of Scout movement) 40 30
1858 250p. Tents and doves . . . 55 40
1859 300p. Scout, tents and globe 65 45
1860 1000p. Emblem and singsong (vert) . . . . . 2·25 1·50

682 Capt. Alberto Larraguibel and Horse

1999. 50th Anniv of World Equestrian High Jump Record.
1862 **682** 200p. multicoloured . . 45 35

683 Fire Engine, 1990

1999. Centenary of Temuco Fire Department. Mult.
1863 140p. Type **683** 35 25
1864 200p. Ford fire engine, 1929 45 35
1865 300p. Ford K 1800 fire engine, 1955 . . . . . . 70 50
1866 350p. Mercedes Benz fire engine, 1967 . . . . . . 75 55

684 Chamber

1999. 1000th Session of Chilean Chamber of Deputies.
1868 **684** 140p. multicoloured . . 35 25

685 Facade

1999. 150th Anniv of Sagrados College.
1869 **685** 250p. multicoloured . . 60 45

686 Pedro Aguirre Cerda (Chilean President, 1938–41)

689 Weddell Seal and Blue-eyed Cormorants

687 Man with Sphere on Shoulder

1999. 60th Anniv of Economic Development Corporation.
1870 **686** 140p. multicoloured . . 35 25

1999. Centenary of Chilean Insurance Association.
1871 **687** 140p. multicoloured . . 35 25

1999. Antarctica. Multicoloured.
1873 360p. Type **689** 85 60
1874 450p. Bearded penguin . . . 1·10 80

690 Easter Island, Dancers, Ship and Figures

1999. Easter Island.
1876 **690** 360p. multicoloured . . 85 60

691 Business and Arts School

1999. 150th Anniv of Santiago University. Mult.
1877 140p. Type **691** 35 25
1878 250p. State Technical University 60 45
1879 300p. Woman using microscope, computer and building 70 50

692 J. L. Molina (naturalist), Statue of Humboldt, Mountains and Llamas

1999. Bicentenary of Alexander von Humboldt's Exploration of South America. Multicoloured.
1880 300p. Type **692** 70 50
1881 360p. Rodulfo A. Philippi (medical doctor and naturalist), statue of Humboldt and humboldt penguins 85 60

693 Cardinal Silva and Crucifix

1999. Cardinal Raul Silva Henrique Commemoration. Multicoloured.
1882 140p. Type **693** 35 25
1883 200p. Silva and image of Christ 45 35

694 Chinese and Chilean Flags with Pagoda

1999. "China 1999" International Stamp Exhibition, Peking. Multicoloured.
1884 140p. Type **694** 35 25
1885 450p. Chinese and Chilean Flags with junk . . . . . 1·10 80

695 Our Lady of the Rosary Church Tower, Train and Arms

696 Nurse and Donor

1999. Centenary of Quilpue City.
1887 **695** 250p. multicoloured . . 60 45

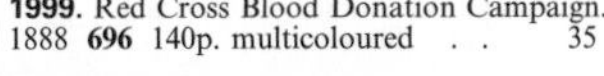

1999. Red Cross Blood Donation Campaign.
1888 **696** 140p. multicoloured . . 35 25

697 People in Glass Ball

1999. 75th Anniv of Employment Legislation.
1889 **697** 320p. multicoloured . . 75 55

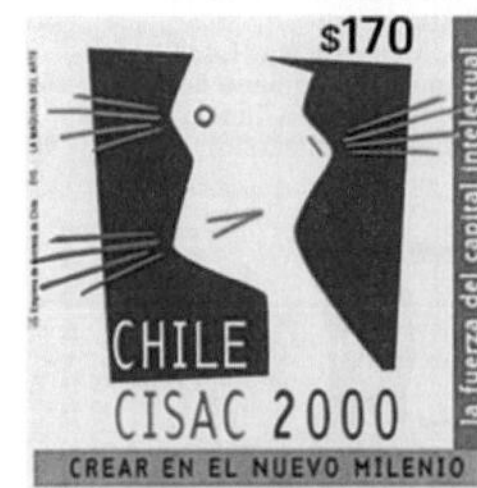

698 Emblem

1999. 42nd International Congress of Confederation of Authors' and Composers' Societies, Santiago.
1890 **698** 170p. multicoloured . . 40 30

699 Elderly Couple watching Children

1999. International Year of Elderly Persons.
1891 **699** 250p. multicoloured . . 60 45

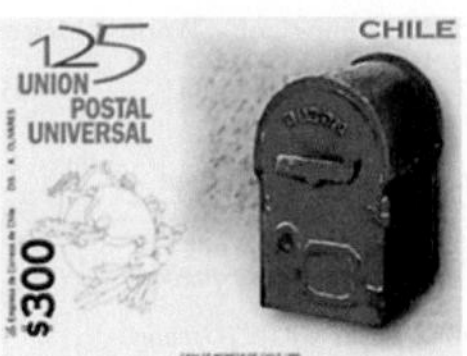

700 Post Box, 1854

1999. 125th Anniv of Universal Postal Union. Multicoloured.
1892 300p. Type **700** 70 50
1893 360p. Gold coloured post box, 1900 . . . . 85 60

701 Bomb releasing Doves

1999. America. A New Millennium without Arms. Multicoloured.
1894 140p. Type **701** 35 25
1895 320p. Broken bomb 75 55

702 Felipe Herrera Lane (first President, 1960–71) and Projects

1999. 40th Anniv of Inter-American Development Bank.
1896 **702** 360p. multicoloured . . 85 60

703 Globe and Chilean Flag

1999. Holy Year 2000.
1897 **703** 450p. multicoloured . . 1·10 80

704 Clock Face, "2000" and Fireworks (½-size illustration)

1999. New Millennium. Multicoloured. (a) As T **704**.
1898 170p. Type **704** 40 30

(b) Discount stamps. Additionally inscr "D.S. 20".
1899 170p. Type **704** 40 30

Nos. 1898/9 each include the prize draw coupons shown in T **704**.

705 Recabarren and Blest

1999. Trade Union Leaders. Multicoloured.
1900 200p. Type **705** 45 35
1901 200p. Jimenez and Bustos 45 35

Nos. 1900/1 were issued together, se-tenant, forming a composite design.

706 Mountains and Map of Islands

2000. Discovery of Juan Fernandez Archipelago. Multicoloured.
1902 360p. Type **706** 85 60
1903 360p. Mountains and map of islands (different) . . . 85 60
1904 360p. Fernandez firecrown and mountains 85 60
1905 360p. *Rhaphythamnus venustus* (plant) 85 60
1906 360p. Lobster 85 60
1907 360p. Antennae of lobster and anchored boat . . . 85 60
1908 360p. Plant and boat . . . 85 60
1909 360p. *Gavilea insularis* (orchid) 85 60

Nos. 1902/9 were issued together, se-tenant, forming a composite design.

707 Condorito celebrating

2000. 50th Anniv (1999) of Condorito (cartoon character) by Rene Rios. Multicoloured.
1910 150p. Type **707** 35 25
1911 260p. Playing football . . . 60 45
1912 480p. As a fireman . . . . 1·10 80
1913 980p. On horseback . . . . 2·40 1·75

708 Dancer and Local Crafts

2000. Easter Island. Multicoloured.
1915 200p. Type **708** 50 45
1916 260p. Statue and rock carving 60 45
1917 340p. Statue and man wearing headdress 80 60
1918 480p. Dancer and text . . . 1·10 80

709 Steam Locomotive and Pot

2000. Centenary of Carahue. Multicoloured.
1919 220p. Type **709** 55 40
1920 220p. Potato tubers and plant 55 40
Nos. 1919/20 were issued together, se-tenant, forming a composite design.

710 Iguanodon

2000. Discount stamps. Prehistoric Animals. Mult.
1921 150p. Type **710** 35 25
1922 150p. Plesiosaur 35 25
1923 150p. Titanosaurus 35 25
1924 150p. Milodon 35 25

711 Emblem, Printing Press and Office

2000. Centenary of *El Mercurio* (newspaper).
1925 **711** 370p. multicoloured . . 90 65

712 Emblems

2000. 4th National Masonic Lodge Congress.
1926 **712** 460p. multicoloured . . 1·10 80

713 *Quillaja saponaria*

2000. Medicinal Plants. Multicoloured.
1927 200p. Type **713** 40 25
1928 360p. *Fabiana imbricata* . . 70 45

714 Map and Butterfly

2000. 500th Anniv of Discovery of Brazil.
1929 **714** 260p. multicoloured . . 50 30

715 Man wearing Costume (Bailarin de Diablada Festival, La Tirana)

2000. Religious Festivals. Multicoloured.
1931 150p. Type **715** 30 20
1932 200p. Girl wearing costume (San Pedro de Atacama fiesta) 40 25
1933 370p. Men dancing (La Candelaria Copiapo fiesta) 75 45
1934 460p. Drummer (Chinese Dance of Andacollo) . . 90 55

716 San Martin

2000. 150th Death Anniv of General Jose de San Martin.
1935 **716** 320p. multicoloured . . 65 40

717 Emblem, Globe and Weather Symbols

718 Magellanic Penguin (*Spheniscus magellanicus*)

2000. 50th Anniv of World Meteorological Organization.
1936 **717** 320p. multicoloured . . 65 40

2000. Antarctica. Multicoloured.
1937 450p. Type **718** 90 55
1938 650p. Humpback whales (*Megaptera novaeangliae*) (horiz) . . . . 1·25 1·40
1939 940p. Killer whale (*Orcinus orca*) (horiz) . . . . . 1·90 2·00
No. 1937 is inscribed "Sphenis" in error.

719 Tennis, Football, Athletics and Sydney Opera House

2000. Olympic Games, Sydney. Multicoloured.
1941 290p. Type **719** 60 40
1942 290p. Archery, high jumping, cycling and Australian flag 60 40
Nos. 1941/2 were issued together, se-tenant, forming a composite design.

720 Native Chileans with Axe and Bow

2000. 450th Anniv of City of Concepcion. Depicting paintings by G. de la Fuente Riojas. Multicoloured.
1943 250p. Type **720** 50 30
1944 250p. Chileans and Spanish Conquistadors 50 30
1945 250p. Hand and scenes of destruction 50 30
1946 250p. Seated woman with shield 50 30
1947 250p. Horse, locomotive and coal truck 50 30
1948 250p. Modern Chileans and child 50 30
Nos. 1943/8 were issued together, se-tenant, forming a composite design.

721 Child's Hand holding Adult's Hand

2000. America. A.I.D.S. Awareness Campaign. Multicoloured.
1949 150p. Type **721** 30 20
1950 220p. Joined hands showing bones 45 30

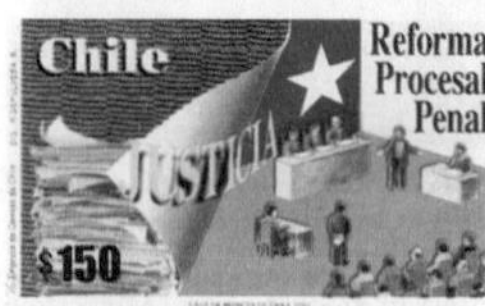

722 Documents and Courtroom

2000. Penal Reform.
1951 **722** 150p. multicoloured . . 30 20

723 Star

2000. Christmas. Multicoloured. (a) As T **723**.
1953 150p. Type **723** 30 20
1954 150p. Silhouette of sleigh and reindeer above church 30 20
1955 150p. The Three Wise Men 30 20
1956 150p. Star on Christmas tree 30 20
1957 150p. Boy posting letter . . 30 20
1958 150p. Boy asleep 30 20
1959 150p. Man with bowl of fish and hindquarters of oxen 30 20
1960 150p. Jesus in manger . . . 30 20
1961 150p. Mary and Joseph . . 30 20
1962 150p. Girl decorating tree 30 20

(b) Discount stamps. As Nos. 1953/62 additionally inscr "D S/20" above (Nos. 1963/7) or below (Nos. 1968/72) face value.
1963 150p. As No. 1953 . . . . 30 20
1964 150p. As No. 1954 . . . . 30 20
1965 150p. As No. 1955 . . . . 30 20
1966 150p. As No. 1956 . . . . 30 20
1967 150p. As No. 1957 . . . . 30 20
1968 150p. As No. 1958 . . . . 30 20
1969 150p. As No. 1959 . . . . 30 20
1970 150p. As No. 1960 . . . . 30 20
1971 150p. As No. 1961 . . . . 30 20
1972 150p. As No. 1962 . . . . 30 20
Nos. 1953/62 and Nos. 1963/72 respectively were issued together, se-tenant, forming a composite design.

724 Wild Cat, Gibbon and Ostrich

2001. 75th Anniv of Santiago National Zoo. Multicoloured.
1973 160p. Type **724** 30 20
1974 160p. Lion, elephant and bird 30 20
1975 160p. Polar bears 30 20
1976 160p. Hippopotamus, chameleon and fox . . . 30 20
Nos. 1973/6 were issued together, se-tenant, forming a composite design.

725 Antiguo de Yumbel Church and Statue

2001. San Sebastian de Yumbel Festival.
1977 **725** 210p. multicoloured . . 35 20

726 Hurtado sweeping and Car

727 Slender-billed Conure (*Enicognathus leptorhynchus*)

2001. Birth Centenary of Fr. Alberto Hurtado. Multicoloured.
1978 160p. Type **726** 30 20
1979 340p. Hurtado and children 30 20

2001. Discount Stamps. Birds. Multicoloured. Inscr "D/S No. 20".
1980 160p. Type **727** 30 20
1981 160p. Moustached turaka (*Pteroptochos megapodius*) 30 20
1982 160p. Chilean mockingbird (*Mimus thenca*) 30 20
1983 160p. Fernandez firecrown (*Sephanoides fernandensis*) 30 20

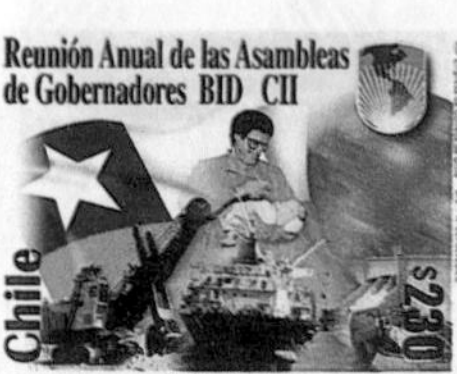

728 Flag, Globe and Industries

2001. 42nd Annual Reunion of the Governors of Inter-American Development Bank and Inter-American Investments Corporation.
1984 **728** 230p. multicoloured . . 80 50

729 Lockheed C-130 Hercules (transport)

2001. Chilean Airforce Anniversaries. Mult.
1985 260p. Type **729** (50th anniv of Chilean Air Force in Antarctica) 45 30
1986 260p. Flugzeugbau Extra-300 (20th anniv of High Acrobactics Squadron) 45 30
1987 260p. North American AT-6 Texan (75th anniv of No. 1 Aviation Group) 45 30
1988 260p. Consolidated PBY-5A/ OA-10 Catalina (amphibian) (50th Anniv of first flight to Easter Island) 45 30

730 Mine, Products and Molten Copper

2001. 30th Anniv of Nationalization of Copper Industry. Multicoloured.
1989 **730** 400p. multicoloured . . 70 40
MS1990 118 × 97 mm. 2000p. Miner and digger . . . . 3·50 3·50

731 Ambulance, Organs and Medical Staff

2001. Organ Donation Campaign.
1991 **731** 160p. multicoloured . . 30 20

732 Pampas Cat (*Lynchailurus colocolo*)

2001. Endangered Species.
1992 **732** 100p. multicoloured . . 10 10
See also Nos. 2046/7.

733 Carved Rocks, Head and Island

2001. Easter Island. Multicoloured.
1993 260p. Type **733** 50 30
1994 260p. Island, seagull, aboriginal and statue . . 50 30
MS1995 90 × 100 mm. 2000p. Carved figure and island . . . 2·60 1·50
Nos. 1993/4 were issued together, *se-tenant*, forming a composite design.

734 Manuel Blanco Encalada (first president), Elderly Firemen and Traditional Appliance

2001. 150th Anniv of Valpariso Fire Brigade. Multicoloured.
1996 160p. Type **734** 30 15
1997 260p. Traditional appliance, burning building, fireman and modern appliance . . 50 30
1998 350p. 1887 firemen 65 35
1999 490p. Helicopter, modern fire-fighters and tanker lorry 90 50
MS2000 90 × 106 mm. 2000p. Fireman, appliance and helicopter 2·60 1·50

735 *Laccata ohiensis*

2001. Fungi. Multicoloured.
2001 300p. Type **735** 55 30
2002 400p. *Macrolepiota rhacodes* 75 45

736 Flags, Badge and Soldiers

2001. 24th American Armies Conference.
2003 **736** 350p. multicoloured . . 65 35

737 Bernardo O'Higgins and First National Congress

2001. Bernardo O'Higgins Commemoration. 190th Anniv of First National Congress.
2004 **737** 260p. multicoloured . . 50 30

738 Scientist and Weddell seal

2001. Antarctica. Multicoloured.
2005 350p. Type **738** 65 35
2006 700p. Scientists holding Giant petrel . . . . . . 1·30 75
MS2007 105 × 90 mm. 2000p. Snowy sheathbill . . . . 2·60 1·50

739 Quinchao Church

2001. America. Cultural Heritage. Multicoloured.
2008 160p. Type **739** 30 15
2009 230p. Tenuan Church . . . 40 20

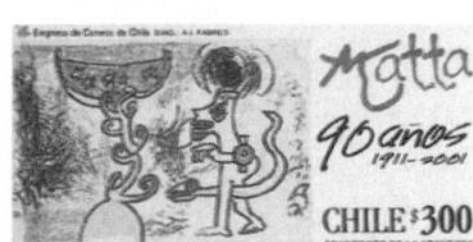

740 "La Araucana" (detail)

2001. 90th Birth Anniv of Roberto Matta (artist).
2010 **740** 300p. multicoloured . . 55 30

741 Caldera Station Buildings

2001. 150th Anniv of Chilean Railways. Multicoloured.
2011 200p. Type **741** 35 20
2012 200p. Steam locomotive and Copiapo station 35 20
2013 220p. Electric locomotive (45 × 33 mm) 35 20
Nos. 2011/12 were issued together, *se-tenant*, forming a composite design.

742 Schooner

2001. Cape Horn.
2014 **742** 220p. multicoloured . . 40 20

743 Three Shepherds

2001. Christmas. Multicoloured. (a) As T **743**.
2015 160p. Type **743** 30 15
2016 160p. Shepherd and cow . . 30 15
2017 160p. Mary and Joseph . . 30 15
2018 160p. Donkey and King . . 30 15
2019 160p. Cow and two Kings 30 15
2020 160p. Shepherd with raised hands 30 15
2021 160p. Sheep 30 15
2022 160p. Jesus in manger . . . 30 15
2023 160p. Bearded man with staff 30 15
2024 160p. Sheep facing left . . . 30 15

(b) Discount stamps. As Nos. 2015/24 additionally inscr "D S/20".
2025 160p. As No. 2015 . . . . 30 15
2026 160p. As No. 2016 . . . . 30 15
2027 160p. As No. 2017 . . . . 30 15
2028 160p. As No. 2018 . . . . 30 15
2029 160p. As No. 2019 . . . . 30 15
2030 160p. As No. 2020 . . . . 30 15
2031 160p. As No. 2021 . . . . 30 15
2032 160p. As No. 2022 . . . . 30 15
2033 160p. As No. 2023 . . . . 30 15
2034 160p. As No. 2024 . . . . 30 15
Nos. 2015/24 and 2025/34 respectively were issued together, se-tenant, forming a composite design.

744 Globe, Map of Chile and Monument

2001. Tropic of Capricorn. 75th Anniv of Rotary Club (charitable organization).
2035 **744** 240p. multicoloured . . 45 25

745 Austral Thrush (*Turdus falcklandii*)

2002. Discount Stamps. Birds. Multicoloured. Inscr "D/S No. 20".
2036 10p. Type **745** 10 10
2037 20p. Long-tailed meadow lark (*Sturnella loyca*) . . 10 10

746 Department Emblem

2002. Centenary of Internal Revenue Services.
2038 **746** 180p. multicoloured . . 30 15

747 Scull, Black-necked Swans and Spanish Turret

2002. 450th Anniv of Valdivia.
2039 **747** 260p. multicoloured . . 45 25

748 Police Officers and Vehicles

2002. 75th Anniv of Police Force.
2040 **748** 250p. multicoloured . . 40 20

749 Domeyko and Santiago University, Chile

2002. Birth Bicentenary of Ignacego Domeyko (scientist).
2041 **749** 290p. multicoloured . . 50 25
A stamp of the same design was issued by Poland.

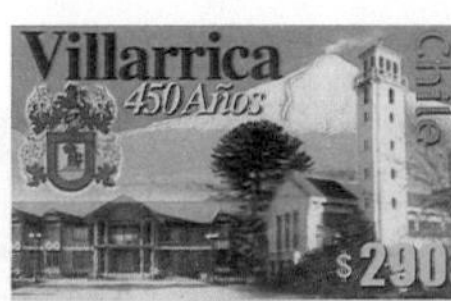

750 Town Hall, Arms and Cathedral

2002. 450th Anniv of Villarrica.
2042 **750** 290p. multicoloured . . 50 25

751 Town Arms, Road, Peninsula and Church

2002. 400th Anniv of Calbuco.
2043 **751** 230p. multicoloured . . 40 20

752 Arms, School Building and Diego Barros Arana (founder)

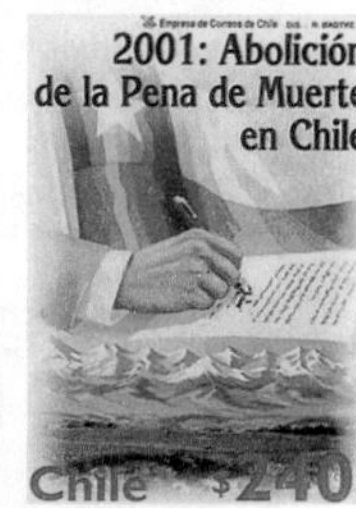

753 Flag and Hand signing Document

2002. Centenary of Barros Arana National Boarding School, Santiago.
2044 **752** 250p. multicoloured . . 40 20

2002. 1st Anniv of Abolition of the Death Penalty.
2045 **753** 240p. multicoloured . . 40 20

2002. Endangered Species. As T **732**. Multicoloured.
2046 10p. Andean mountain cat (*Oreailurus jacobita*) . . . 10 10
2047 20p. Geoffroy's cat (*Oncifelis geoffroyi* (inscr "geoffrovi")) 10 10

754 Moai, Island and Sophora toromiro (extinct tree)

2002. Easter Island. Multicoloured.
2048 250p. Type **754** 40 20
2049 450p. Common dicua finch, island and man wearing native dress 35 15
MS2050 89 × 104 mm. 2000p. *Sophora toromiro*, island and common dicua finch (48 × 48 mm) 3·25 3·25

755 Achao Church, Chiloe

2002. UNESCO World Heritage Sites. Churches. Multicoloured.
2051 230p. Type **755** 40 20
2052 290p. Dalcahue, Chiloe . . 50 25

756 Adults and Teacher

2002. America. Education and Literacy Campaign. Multicoloured.
2053 230p. Type **756** 40 20
2054 450p. Child reading, teacher, computer and boy 75 35

757 Toy Windmills

2002. Traditional Games. Multicoloured.
2055 290p. Type **757** 50 25
2056 380p. Kite flying (vert) . . . 65 30

758 Cerro Tololo Observatory

2002. Observatories. Multicoloured.
2057 450p. Type **758** 75 35
2058 550p. Paranal 95 45
MS2059 90 × 104 mm. 2000p. Cerro Tololo (different) (48 × 48 mm) 3·25 3·25

759 Hospital Building, Baby, MRI Scanner, Theatre and Doctor

2002. 50th Anniv of University of Chile Clinical Hospital.
2060 **759** 250p. multicoloured . . 40 20

760 Trees and Students

2002. 50th Anniv of Forestry Education.
2061 **760** 250p. multicoloured . . 40 20

761 Flamingo (*Phoenicoparru andinus*)

2002. 12th Convention on International Trade in Endangered Species (CITIES) Conference, Santiago, Chile. Multicoloured.
2062 300p. Type **761** 50 25
2063 450p. Vicuna (*Vicugna vicugna*) 75 35
MS2064 90 × 104 mm. 2000p. Chinchilla (*Chinchilla lanigera*) (48 × 48 mm) . . . . 3·25 3·25

762 Southern Right Whale (*Eubalaena australis*)

2002. Whales. Multicoloured.
2065 250p. Type **762** 40 20
2066 500p. Minke whale (*Balaenoptera acutorostrata*) 85 40
MS2067 90 × 104 mm. 2000p. Sperm whale (Physeter macrocephalus) (48 × 48 mm) . . . . 3·25 3·25

763 Justice

2002. Campaign to end Violence Against Women.
2068 **763** 230p. multicoloured . . 40 20

764 Church, Rose, Chilean and German Flags and Town Emblem

2002. 150th Anniv of Puerto Varas.
2069 **764** 190p. multicoloured . . 30 15

ACKNOWLEDGEMENT OF RECEIPT STAMP

1894. Portrait of Columbus. Inscr "A.R.". Perf or Imperf.
AR77 5c. brown . . . . 1·40 1·40

COMPULSORY TAX STAMPS

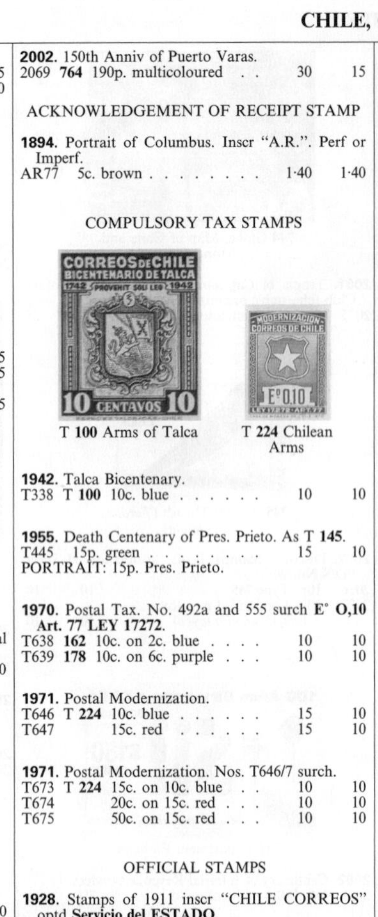

T **100** Arms of Talca T **224** Chilean Arms

1942. Talca Bicentenary.
T338 T **100** 10c. blue 10 10

1955. Death Centenary of Pres. Prieto. As T **145**.
T445 15p. green 15 10
PORTRAIT: 15p. Pres. Prieto.

1970. Postal Tax. No. 492a and 555 surch **E° O,10 Art. 77 LEY 17272.**
T638 **162** 10c. on 2c. blue 10 10
T639 **178** 10c. on 6c. purple . . . 10 10

1971. Postal Modernization.
T646 T **224** 10c. blue 15 10
T647 15c. red 15 10

1971. Postal Modernization. Nos. T646/7 surch.
T673 T **224** 15c. on 10c. blue . . . 10 10
T674 20c. on 15c. red . . . 10 10
T675 50c. on 15c. red . . . 10 10

OFFICIAL STAMPS

1928. Stamps of 1911 inscr "CHILE CORREOS" optd **Servicio del ESTADO**.
O190 **49** 10c. black and blue . . . 3·75 1·00
O191 – 20c. (No. 142) . . . . . 1·60 50
O192 – 25c. (No. 167) . . . . . 4·25 50
O193 – 50c. (No. 170) . . . . . 1·75 50
O194 **57** 1p. black and green . . . 2·75 70

1930. Stamps inscr "CORREOS DE CHILE" optd **Servicio del ESTADO**.
O217 **49** 10c. (No. 204) . . . . . 2·00 70
O234 **76** 10c. blue . . . . 1·60 35
O219 – 20c. (No. 209) 90 25
O235 – 20c. brown (No. 232) . . 1·10 25
O220 – 25c. (No. 210) 90 25
O221 – 50c. (No. 212) . . . . . 1·10 35

1934. Stamps inscr "CORREOS DE CHILE" optd **OFICIAL**.
O236 **64** 5c. green (No. 206) . . . 70 35
O237 **76** 10c. blue 70 35
O238 – 20c. brown (No. 232) . . 4·50 35

1939. Optd **Servicio del ESTADO**.
O279 – 50c. violet (No. 273) . . 4·50 2·00
O280 **90** 1p. orange . . . . 3·75 2·50

1941. Nos. 269/338j optd **OFICIAL**.
O281 – 10c. red . . . . 1·75 1·00
O282 – 15c. red 95 25
O283 – 20c. blue . . . . 4·50 2·75
O284 – 30c. red 45 25
O285 – 40c. green 45 25
O286 – 50c. violet . . . . . . 3·00 50
O339 **90** 1p. orange . . . . 2·00 80
O288 – 1p.80 blue . . . . 8·00 4·75
O442 – 2p. red . . . . 1·60 1·00
O383 – 5p. green . . . . 3·00 1·25
O443 – 10p. purple . . . . . . 10·00 5·00

1953. No. 379c optd **OFICIAL**.
O386 1p. turquoise 85 35

1956. Nos. 446/450 optd **OFICIAL**.
O451 2p. lilac . . . . 2·40 50
O452 3p. blue . . . . 8·00 4·00
O453 5p. sepia . . . . 1·50 40
O454a 10p. violet . . . . 1·25 40
O455 50p. red . . . . 5·00 1·40

1958. Optd **OFICIAL**.
O469 **152** 10p. blue . . . . £140 35·00

1960. No. 493 optd **OFICIAL**.
O507 5c. blue . . . . 3·75 1·25

POSTAGE DUE STAMPS

D **18**

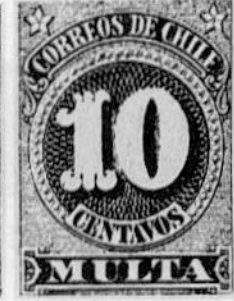

D **19**

D **68**

1895.
D 98 D **18** 1c. red on yellow . . . 1·25 40
D 99 2c. red on yellow . . . 1·25 40
D100 4c. red on yellow . . . 1·25 40
D101 6c. red on yellow . . . 1·25 40
D102 8c. red on yellow . . . 1·25 40
D103 10c. red on yellow . . 1·25 40
D104 20c. red on yellow . . 1·25 40
D 93 40c. red on yellow . . 3·00 90
D 94 50c. red on yellow . . 4·00 1·00
D 95 60c. red on yellow . . 6·00 1·50
D 96 80c. red on yellow . . 7·00 3·00
D109 100c. red on yellow . . 20·00 11·50
D 97 1p. red on yellow . . 12·00 6·00

1898.
D110 D **19** 1c. red 60 50
D111 2c. red 75 60
D112 4c. red . . . . 1·75 1·25
D113 10c. red 60 60
D114 20c. red 60 60

1924.
D184 D **68** 2c. red and blue . . . 1·25 1·00
D185 4c. red and blue . . . 1·25 1·00
D186 8c. red and blue . . . 1·25 1·00
D187 10c. red and blue . . . 1·25 1·00
D188 20c. red and blue . . . 1·25 1·00
D189 40c. red and blue . . . 1·25 1·00
D190 60c. red and blue . . . 1·25 1·00
D191 80c. red and blue . . . 1·25 1·00
D192 1p. red and blue . . . 1·40 2·50
D193 2p. red and blue . . . 2·00 4·00
D194 5p. red and blue . . . 2·50 4·00

CHINA Pt. 17

People's Republic in Eastern Asia, formerly an Empire.

CHINESE CHARACTERS

Simple	Formal	
半	半	= ½
一	壹	= 1
二	貳	= 2
三	叄	= 3
四	肆	= 4
五	伍	= 5
六	陸	= 6
七	柒	= 7
八	捌	= 8
九	玖	= 9
十	拾	= 10
百	佰	= 100
千	仟	= 1,000
萬	萬	= 10,000
	分	= cent
	圓	= dollar

Examples:

十五	= 15
五十	= 50
叄佰圓	= 300 dollars
伍仟圓	= 5,000 dollars

CHINESE EMPIRE

1878. 100 candarins = 1 tael.
1897. 100 cents = 1 dollar.

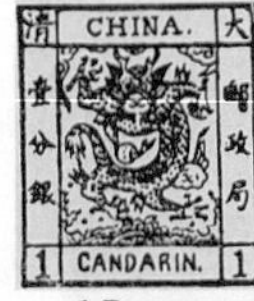

1 Dragon

2

1878.
7 **1** 1ca. green . . . . £160 85·00
2 3ca. red . . . . £225 60·00
3 5ca. orange . . . . £375 70·00

1885.
13 **2** 1ca. green . . . . 16·00 13·00
14 3ca. mauve . . . . 65·00 9·00
15 5ca. yellow . . . . 70·00 12·00

4

10

1894. Dowager Empress's 60th Birthday.
16 4 1ca. orange . . . . 10·50 8·75
17 – 2ca. green . . . . 12·00 9·50
18 – 3ca. yellow . . . . 10·00 3·75
19 – 4ca. pink . . . . 38·00 26·00
20 4 5ca. orange . . . . 70·00 55·00
21 – 6ca. brown . . . . 16·00 7·25
22 10 9ca. green . . . . 46·00 12·50
23 12ca. orange . . . . £100 55·00
24 – 24ca. red . . . . £160 44·00
DESIGNS—VERT: (as Type 4): 2ca. to 4ca. and 6ca. Dragon. HORIZ: (as Type 10): 24ca. Junks.

1897. Surch in English and Chinese characters.
78 – ½c. on 3ca. yellow (No. 18) 6·75 5·50
34 2 1c. on 1ca. green . . . . . 20·00 15·00
79 4 1c. on 1ca. orange . . . . . 6·25 5·75
80 – 2c. on 2ca. green (No. 17) 6·50 4·00
35 2 2c. on 3ca. mauve . . . . . £110 55·00
40 – 4c. on 4ca. pink (No. 19) . . 8·75 5·25
36 2 5c. on 5ca. yellow . . . . . 65·00 35·00
41 – 5c. on 5ca. orange (No. 20) 11·50 5·25
42 – 8c. on 6ca. brown (No. 21) 10·50 5·00
43 – 10c. on 6ca. brown (No. 21) 55·00 50·00
63 10 10c. on 9ca. green . . . . . 75·00 37·00
64 10c. on 12ca. orange . . . . 95·00 55·00
46 – 30c. on 24ca. red (No. 24) £110 60·00

17

24

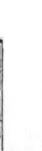

30 Carp 31 Bean Goose

1897. Surch in English and Chinese characters.
88 17 1c. on 3c. red . . . . 65·00 37·00
89 2c. on 3c. red . . . . 80·00 60·00
90 4c. on 3c. red . . . . £200 95·00
91 $1 on 3c. red £1100 £600
92 $5 on 3c. red £5500 £4250

1897. Inscr "IMPERIAL CHINESE POST".
96 24 ½c. purple . . . . 1·90 2·50
97 1c. yellow . . . . 2·20 1·30
98 2c. orange . . . . 2·30 80
99 4c. brown . . . . 4·00 1·20
100 5c. red . . . . 4·75 1·60
101 10c. green . . . . 10·50 1·30
102 30 20c. lake . . . . 26·00 6·25
103 30c. red . . . . 43·00 15·00
104 50c. green . . . . 38·00 20·00
105 31 $1 red £160 £110
106 $2 orange and yellow . . . £850 £850
107 $5 green and red £400 £600

32 Dragon

33 Carp

34 Bean Goose

1898. Inscr "CHINESE IMPERIAL POST".
121 32 ½c. brown . . . . 1·20 65
122 1c. buff . . . . 1·40 55
123 2c. red . . . . 2·30 55
151 2c. green . . . . 1·90 50
152 3c. green . . . . 1·70 50
124 4c. brown . . . . 2·50 50
153a 4c. red . . . . 3·50 75
112 5c. pink . . . . 7·00 80
126 5c. orange . . . . 14·00 4·25
154 5c. mauve . . . . 4·75 90
155 7c. red . . . . 6·00 3·75
127 10c. green . . . . 5·25 50
156 10c. blue . . . . 7·25 40
157 33 16c. green . . . . 19·00 6·00
128 20c. purple . . . . 12·00 2·10
115 30c. red . . . . 10·00 5·00
130 50c. green . . . . 24·00 4·25
131 34 $1 red and orange . . . . £140 13·50
132 $2 purple and yellow . . . £240 34·00
119 $5 green and orange . . . £450 £130

36 Temple of Heaven

1909. 1st Year of Reign of Emperor Hsuan T'ung.
165 36 2c. green and orange . . . 2·40 2·25
166 3c. blue and orange . . . 2·10 2·40
167 7c. purple and orange . . . 3·00 2·10

POSTAGE DUE STAMPS

1904. Stamps of 1898 optd **POSTAGE DUE** in English and Chinese characters.
D137 32 ½c. brown . . . . . . 4·25 3·25
D138 1c. buff . . . . 5·25 2·75
D139a 2c. red . . . . 7·75 3·75
D140 4c. brown . . . . . . 8·25 4·25
D141 5c. red . . . . 17·00 7·50
D142 10c. green . . . . . . 27·00 11·50

D 37

1904.
D143 D 37 ½c. blue . . . . 2·40 60
D144 1c. blue . . . . 4·50 50
D168 1c. brown . . . . . . 6·50 2·10
D145 2c. blue . . . . 3·50 50
D169 2c. brown . . . . . . 13·50 13·50
D146 4c. blue . . . . 5·75 60
D147 5c. blue . . . . 7·50 80
D148 10c. blue . . . . . . 7·50 1·60
D149 20c. blue . . . . . . 20·00 3·25
D150 30c. blue . . . . . . 26·00 7·50

CHINESE REPUBLIC

1912. 100 cents = 1 dollar.
1948. 100 cents = 1 gold yuan.
1949. 100 cents = 1 silver yuan.

1912. Optd vert with four Chinese characters signifying "Republic of China".
192 32 ½c. brown 55 25
193 1c. buff 85 25
194 2c. green . . . . 1·10 25
221 3c. green . . . . 1·20 25
196 4c. red . . . . 2·20 30
197 5c. mauve . . . . 3·75 30
198 7c. lake . . . . 4·50 2·25
225 10c. blue . . . . 4·00 45
200 33 16c. olive . . . . 9·25 4·00
227 20c. red . . . . 9·50 2·20
202 30c. red . . . . 10·00 2·40
203 50c. green . . . . 18·50 2·40
204 34 $1 red and salmon . . . . £150 11·00
205 $2 red and yellow . . . . £120 32·00
232 $5 green and salmon . . . £325 £275

41 Dr. Sun Yat-sen

1912. Revolution Commemoration.
242 41 1c. orange . . . . 1·50 1·80
243 2c. green . . . . 1·50 1·80
244 3c. blue . . . . 1·50 1·80
245 5c. mauve . . . . 1·75 1·50
246 8c. sepia . . . . 2·50 2·10
247 10c. blue . . . . 2·50 2·10
248 16c. olive . . . . 7·00 7·50
249 20c. lake . . . . 8·50 5·00
250 50c. green . . . . 29·00 16·00
251 $1 red . . . . 90·00 25·00
252 $2 brown £225 £160
253 $5 slate . . . . 75·00 95·00

1912. As T 41 but portrait of Pres. Yuan Shih-kai, inscr "Commemoration of the Republic".
254 1c. orange . . . . 1·10 75
255 2c. green . . . . 1·10 75
256 3c. blue . . . . 1·10 75
257 5c. mauve . . . . 1·10 85
258 8c. sepia . . . . 3·25 3·25
259 10c. blue . . . . 2·75 1·10
260 16c. olive . . . . 5·75 4·75
261 20c. lake . . . . 5·50 2·50
262 50c. green . . . . 16·00 9·75
263 $1 red . . . . 50·00 25·00
264 $2 brown . . . . 55·00 25·00
265 $5 slate £160 £160

43 Junk

44 Reaper

45 Entrance Hall of Classics, Peking

1913.
287 43 ½c. sepia 35 15
269 1c. orange 35 15
289a 1½c. purple . . . . 1·30 65
270 2c. green 90 15
271 3c. green . . . . 1·90 15
292 4c. red . . . . 2·75 35
314 4c. grey . . . . 10·50 45
315 4c. olive . . . . 1·90 15
293 5c. mauve . . . . 2·25 20
294 6c. grey . . . . 3·00 35
317 6c. red . . . . 2·50 25
318 6c. brown . . . . 24·00 3·25
295 7c. violet . . . . 8·75 3·50
296 8c. orange . . . . 4·75 20
297 10c. blue . . . . 5·25 25
298 44 13c. brown . . . . 3·50 60
278 15c. brown . . . . 11·50 3·75
323 15c. blue . . . . 4·75 35
324 16c. olive . . . . 5·00 35
325 20c. lake . . . . 5·00 30
326 30c. purple . . . . 6·00 35
282 50c. green . . . . 14·50 35
304 45 $1 black and yellow . . . 49·00 45
328 $1 sepia and brown . . . . 18·00 65
305 $2 black and blue . . . . 65·00 1·80
329 $2 brown and blue . . . . 29·00 1·10
306 $5 black and red . . . . . 1·70 60·00
330 $5 green and red . . . . . 65·00 6·25
307 $10 black and green . . . £475 £150
331 $10 mauve and green . . . £225 25·00
308 $20 black and orange . . £1900 £1700
332 $20 blue and purple . . . £375 75·00

1920. Flood Relief Fund. Surch with new value in English and Chinese characters.
349 43 1c. on 2c. green . . . . . 5·00 1·90
361 2c. on 3c. green . . . . . 3·50 40
350 3c. on 4c. red . . . . . . 7·50 2·40
351 5c. on 6c. grey . . . . . . 11·00 5·00

47 Curtiss JN-4 "Jenny" over Great Wall of China

I

II

1921. Air. Tail fin of aeroplane as Type I.
352 47 15c. black and green . . . 21·00 24·00
353 30c. black and red . . . . 20·00 24·00
354 45c. black and purple . . . 25·00 24·00
355 60c. black and blue . . . . 26·00 26·00
356 90c. black and olive . . . 36·00 26·00
For similar stamps in this type but with tail fin as Type II, see Nos. 384a/8.

48 Yen Kung-cho, Pres. Hsu Shih-chang and Chin Yung-peng

53 Temple of Heaven

1921. 25th Anniv of Chinese National Postal Service.
357 48 1c. orange . . . . 3·50 95
358 3c. turquoise . . . . . . 3·50 80
359 6c. grey . . . . 4·75 2·75
360 10c. blue . . . . 5·50 2·25

1923. Adoption of the Constitution.
362 53 1c. orange . . . . 2·75 65
363 3c. turquoise . . . . . . 2·75 1·10
364 4c. red . . . . 6·00 1·50
365 10c. blue . . . . 8·75 1·70

1925. Surch in English and Chinese characters.
366 43 1c. on 2c. green . . . . . 1·80 15
367 1c. on 3c. green 65 25
369 1c. on 4c. olive . . . . . 1·20 20
370 3c. on 4c. grey . . . . . . 2·75 15
The figures in this surcharge are at the top and are smaller than for the 1920 provisionals.

55 Marshal Chang Tso-lin

56 General Chiang Kai-shek

1928. Assumption of Title of Marshal of the Army and Navy by Chang Tso-lin.
372 55 1c. orange 90 95
373 4c. olive . . . . 1·80 1·60
374 10c. blue . . . . 5·75 3·25
375 $1 red . . . . 37·00 43·00

1929. Unification of China under Gen. Chiang Kai-shek.
376 56 1c. orange . . . . 2·75 30
377 4c. olive . . . . 4·00 50
378 10c. blue . . . . 9·75 1·40
379 $1 red . . . . 90·00 36·00

57 Mausoleum at Nanking

58 Dr. Sun Yat-sen

1929. State Burial of Dr. Sun Yat-sen.
380 57 1c. orange 95 50
381 4c. olive 90 70
382 10c. blue . . . . 4·75 1·50
383 $1 red . . . . 43·00 20·00

1929. Air. As T 47, but tail fin of airplane as Type II.
384a 47 15c. black and green . . . 3·75 60
385 30c. black and red . . . . 6·75 95
386 45c. black and purple . . . 8·50 6·75
387 60c. black and blue . . . . 10·50 8·00
388 90c. black and olive . . . 13·50 14·50

1931.
389 58 1c. orange 50 25
396 2c. olive 60 35
391 4c. green 85 15
398 5c. green 35 15
399 15c. green . . . . 1·30 85
400 15c. red 55 15
401 20c. blue 85 15
402 25c. blue 95 60
403a $1 sepia and brown . . . . 5·50 35
735 $1 violet . . . . 35 2·50
404a $2 brown and blue . . . . 10·50 2·40
736 $2 olive . . . . 35 5·00
405a $5 black and red . . . . . 18·00 3·50
737 $20 green . . . . 1·90 95
738 $30 brown 35 85
739 $50 orange 75 85

59 "Nomads of the Desert"

60 General Teng K'eng

1932. North-West China Scientific Expedition.
406 59 1c. orange . . . . 24·00 29·00
407 4c. olive . . . . 24·00 29·00
408 5c. red . . . . 24·00 29·00
409 10c. blue . . . . 24·00 29·00

1932. Martyrs of the Revolution.
410 60 ½c. brown 25 25
508 – 1c. orange 25 25
509 – 2c. blue 25 25
412 60 2½c. purple 25 25
511 – 3c. brown 25 25
512 60 4c. lilac 25 25
513 – 5c. orange 10 40
514 – 8c. orange 35 25
515 – 10c. purple 40 25
516 – 13c. green 50 25
517 – 15c. purple 40 60
417 – 17c. green 55 25
418 – 20c. red 85 25
519 – 20c. blue 35 25
520 – 21c. brown 50 35
521 – 25c. purple 35 50
541 – 28c. green 75 60
542 – 30c. purple 90 25
543 – 40c. orange . . . . 1·00 35
544 – 50c. green 90 35
DESIGNS: 1, 25, 50c. Ch'en Ying-shih; 2, 10, 17, 28c. Shung Chiao-jen; 3, 5, 15, 30c. Liao Chung-k'ai; 8, 13, 21c. Chu Chih-hsin; 20, 40c. Gen. Huang Hsing.

61 Junkers F-13 over Great Wall

1932. Air.
422 61 15c. green 35 40
556 25c. orange . . . . 90 1·00
557 30c. red 60 40
558 45c. purple 70 80
559 50c. brown 60 70
560 60c. blue 90 70
561 90c. green 90 70
562 $1 green . . . . 1·10 50
563 $2 brown . . . . 60 2·75
564 $5 red . . . . 2·10 3·75

62 Tan Yen-kai

63

1933. Tan Yen-kai Memorial.
440 62 2c. olive . . . . 1·60 50
441 5c. green . . . . 2·40 25

442 25c. blue . . . . 5·75 80
443 $1 red . . . . 43·00 18·00

1936. "New Life" Movement. Symbolic designs as T **63**.
444 **63** 2c. olive . . . . 1·70 35
445 5c. green . . . . 1·90 15
446 – 20c. blue (various emblems) 5·00 50
447 – $1 red (Lighthouse) . . . . 30·00 9·25

66 "Postal Communications."

72 Dr. Sun Yat-sen

1936. 40th Anniv of Chinese National Postal Service.
448 **66** 2c. orange . . . . 2·20 35
449 – 5c. green . . . . 1·90 15
450 – 25c. blue . . . . 5·00 50
451 – 100c. red . . . . 30·00 9·25
DESIGNS: 5c. The Bund, Shanghai; 25c. G.P.O., Shanghai; 100c. Ministry of Communications, Nanking.

1936. Surch in figures and Chinese characters.
452 **44** 5c. on 15c. blue . . . . 1·40 30
453 5c. on 16c. olive . . . . 2·40 60

1937. Surch in figures and Chinese characters.
454 **58** 1 on 4c. green 80 20
455 – 8 on 40c. orange (No. 543) 1·20 40
456 **58** 10 on 25c. blue 80 15

1938.
462 **72** 2c. green 25 25
464 3c. red 25 25
489 5c. green 25 25
492 8c. green 25 25
469 10c. green 25 25
470 15c. red . . . . 1·20 2·20
471 16c. brown . . . . 1·10 40
472 25c. blue 70 70
494 30c. red 40 25
495 50c. blue 70 25
496 $1 sepia and brown . . . 2·75 25
497 $2 brown and blue . . . 3·25 50
498 $5 green and red . . . . 2·80 50
499 $10 violet and green . . . 8·50 1·90
500 $20 blue and purple . . . 13·50 3·50
For dollar values in single colours, see Nos. 666 etc.
For 15c. brown see Japanese Occupation of China: IV Shanghai and Nanking No. 12.

74 Chinese and U.S. Flags and Map of China

1939. 150th Anniv of U.S. Constitution. Flags in red and blue.
501 **74** 5c. green . . . . 1·00 35
502 25c. blue 90 65
503 50c. brown . . . . 2·50 1·10
504 $1 red . . . . 4·00 2·00

(76)

1940. Surch as T **76**.
577 **72** 3c. on 5c. green . . . . . 1·40 2·50
582 4c. on 5c. green 85 60
619 7c. on 8c. green . . . . . 1·90 1·90

77 Dr. Sun Yat-sen

78 Industry

1941.
583 **77** ½c. brown 15 25
584 1c. orange 15 20
585 2c. blue 15 20
586 5c. green 15 20
587 8c. orange 50 40
588 8c. green 35 20
589 10c. green 15 20
590 17c. green . . . . 3·75 8·00
591 25c. purple 20 30
592 30c. red 20 20
593 50c. blue 30 20
594 $1 black and brown . . . 45 20
595 $2 black and blue 55 20
596 $5 black and red 90 25
597 $10 black and green . . . 2·75 1·40
598 $20 black and purple . . . 2·75 2·40

1941. Thrift Movement.
599 **78** 8c. green 30 35
600 21c. brown 45 75
601 28c. olive 50 70
602 33c. red . . . . 80 1·20
603 50c. blue . . . . 1·00 1·00
604 $1 purple . . . . 1·20 1·30

(79)

(81)

82 Dr. Sun Yat-sen

1941. 30th Anniv of Republic. Optd with T **79**.
606 – 1c. orange (No. 508) . . . 1·70 1·90
607 **72** 2c. green . . . . 1·70 1·90
608 **60** 4c. lilac . . . . 1·70 1·90
609 **72** 8c. green . . . . 1·70 1·90
610 10c. green . . . . 1·70 1·90
611 16c. brown . . . . 1·70 1·90
612 – 21c. brown (No. 520) . . . 1·70 1·90
613 – 28c. green (No. 541) . . . 1·70 1·90
614 **72** 30c. red . . . . 1·70 1·90
615 $1 sepia and brown . . . 1·70 1·90

1942. Provincial surcharges. Surch as T **81**.
622 **60** 1c. on ½c. brown . . . . 95 3·25
624 **77** 1c. on ½c. brown . . . . 95 2·50
690g – 20c. on 13c. green (516) 2·00 8·50
691i **72** 20c. on 16c. brown . . . 1·30 6·25
693e – 20c. on 17c. green (417) 2·00 7·25
694f – 20c. on 21c. brown (520) 1·10 8·50
695e – 20c. on 28c. green (541) 1·40 11·00
625 **72** 40c. on 50c. blue . . . . 2·25 12·00
627 **77** 40c. on 50c. blue . . . . 5·00 8·00
626 – 40c. on 50c. green (544) 6·75 8·50
689a 50c. on 16c. brown . . . 3·00 1·90

1942.
628 **82** 10c. green . . . . 25 1·70
629 16c. olive . . . . 20·00 36·00
630 20c. olive . . . . 25 1·70
631 25c. purple . . . . 25 2·40
632 30c. red . . . . 25 1·30
642 30c. brown . . . . 35 8·00
633 40c. brown . . . . 35 1·70
634 50c. green 25 25
635 $1 red . . . . 1·00 25
636 $1 olive 45 35
637 $1.50 blue 35 35
638 $2 green 35 50
645 $2 blue . . . . 6·25 10·00
646 $2 purple 25 25
639 $3 yellow 60 70
640 $4 brown 40 40
641 $5 red 35 35
650 $6 violet 85 85
651 $10 brown 25 25
652 $20 blue 25 25
653 $50 green . . . . 5·25 25
654 $70 violet . . . . 6·75 50
655 $100 brown 75 60

1942. As T **72** but emblem at top redrawn with solid background. Perf, imperf or roul.
666 **72** $4 blue . . . . 85 1·40
667 $5 grey . . . . 1·90 1·70
656 $10 brown . . . . 1·90 1·20
657 $20 green . . . . 1·90 1·00
658 $20 red . . . . 17·00 9·25
659 $30 purple . . . . 1·40 1·00
660 $40 red . . . . 1·40 1·00
661 $50 blue . . . . 2·00 1·40
662 $100 brown . . . . 8·00 5·00

(83)

(83a)

(T **83** Trans. "Surcharge for Domestic Postage Paid")

1942. Surch as T **83**.
688e **82** 16c. olive . . . . 39·00 39·00

1943. No 688e surch as T **83a**.
701e **82** 50c. on 16c. olive . . . . 3·50 3·50

89 Dr. Sun Yat-sen

91 Savings Bank and Money Box

90 War Refugees

1944.
702 **89** 40c. red . . . . 35 7·25
703 $2 brown 35 15
704 $3 red 15 15
705 $3 brown 95 60
706 $6 grey 15 35
707 $10 red 15 15
708 $20 pink 15 15
709 $50 brown . . . . 5·50 35
710 $70 violet 40 35

1944. War Refugees' Relief Fund. Various frames.
724 **90** $2+$2 on 50c.+50c. blue 1·30 4·00
725 $4+$4 on 8c.+8c. green . . 1·30 4·00
726 $5+$5 on 21c.+21c. brn . . 1·90 4·00
727 $6+$6 on 28c.+28c. olive 3·00 4·00
728 $10+$10 on 33c.+33c. red 3·75 4·00
729 $20+$20 on $1+$1 violet 5·00 5·00

1944.
731 **91** $40 slate 25 60
732 $50 green 25 25
733 $100 brown 25 25
734 $200 green 25 25

92 Dr. Sun Yat-sen

93 Dr. Sun Yat-sen

1944. 50th Anniv of Kuomintang.
740 **92** $2 green . . . . 1·40 2·10
741 $5 brown . . . . 1·70 2·40
742 $6 purple . . . . 2·40 4·75
743 $10 blue . . . . 3·00 4·75
744 $20 red . . . . 4·00 6·75

1945. 20th Death Anniv of Dr. Sun Yat-sen.
746 **93** $2 green . . . . 65 1·20
747 $5 brown . . . . 65 1·20
748 $6 blue . . . . 90 1·70
749 $10 blue . . . . 1·30 1·30
750 $20 red . . . . 1·90 2·75
751 $30 buff . . . . 2·40 3·75

94 Dr. Sun Yat-sen

96 Pres. Lin Sen

95 Gen. Chiang Kai-shek

1945.
758 **94** $2 green 25 35
759 $5 green 25 35
760 $10 blue 25 35
761 $20 red 25 35

1945. Equal Treaties with Great Britain and U.S.A., abolishing Foreign Concessions. Flags in national colours.
762 **95** $1 blue . . . . 65 1·00
763 $2 green . . . . 65 1·10
764 $5 olive . . . . 1·20 1·10
765 $6 brown . . . . 85 1·20
766 $10 red . . . . 3·75 5·75
767 $20 red . . . . 4·00 6·25

1945. In Memory of President Lin Sen.
768 **96** $1 black and blue . . . . 90 1·50
769 $2 black and green . . . . 90 1·50
770 $5 black and red . . . . . 90 1·50
771 $6 black and violet . . . 1·20 1·70
772 $10 black and brown . . . 2·75 3·25
773 $20 black and olive . . . 3·75 5·00

(97)

(98)

(99)

1945. Chinese National Currency (C.N.C.). Various issues surch as T **97** (for Japanese controlled Government at Shanghai and Nanking) and further surch as T **98**.
774 **72** 10c. on $20 on 3c. red . . 20 1·00
775 – 15c. on $30 on 2c. blue (509) . . . . 20 1·10
776 **77** 25c. on $50 on 1c. orange 20 85
777 **72** 50c. on $100 on 3c. red . . 20 35
778 **60** $1 on $200 on 1c. orange (508) 20 20
779 **72** $2 on $400 on 3c. red . . . 20 30
780 **77** $5 on $1000 on 1c. orange 20 20

1945. Kaifeng provisionals. C.N.C. surcharges. Stamps of Japanese Occupation of North China surch as T **99**.
781 **60** $10 on 20c. lake (No. 166) 9·50 9·50
782 $20 on 40c. orge (No. 168) 16·00 23·00
783 $50 on 30c. red (No. 167) 13·50 17·00

100 Pres. Chiang Kai-shek

101 Pres. Chiang Kai-shek

1945. Inauguration of Pres. Chiang Kai-shek. Flag in blue and red.
784 **100** $2 green 45 80
785 $4 blue 70 80
786 $5 olive 70 95
787 $6 brown . . . . 1·40 2·00
788 $10 grey . . . . 3·75 5·00
789 $20 red . . . . 4·25 5·25

1945. Victory. Flag in red.
790 **101** $20 green and blue . . . 25 20
791 $50 brown and blue . . . 55 45
792 $100 blue 40 35
793 $300 red and blue 40 35

(102)

103 Dr. Sun Yat-sen

1945. C.N.C. surcharges. Nos. 410, 412, 514, 516/17, 519/20 and 541 surch as T **102** (value tablet at top).
794 $3 on 2½c. purple . . . . 17·00 20·00
795 $10 on 15c. purple 25 25
796 $20 on 8c. orange 25 25
797 $20 on 20c. blue 40 40
798 $30 on ½c. brown . . . . 25 1·30
799 $50 on 21c. brown 40 50
806 $70 on 13c. green 40 95
802 $100 on 28c. green 40 40

1945. No gum.
808 **103** $20 red 15 15
809 $30 blue 15 15
810 $40 orange 55 70
811 $50 green 70 25
812 $100 brown 15 15
813 $200 brown 15 15

(104)

(108)

1946. Air. C.N.C. surcharges. Surch as T **104**.
820 **61** $23 on 30c. red . . . . . 25 1·40
821 $53 on 15c. green . . . . 25 1·40
822 $73 on 25c. orange . . . . 25 1·60
823 $100 on $2 brown 25 40
824 $200 on $5 red 25 25

1946. C.N.C. surcharges. Surch as T **108** (octagonal value tablet at bottom).
898 – $10 on 1c. orange (508) . . 25 85
903 **77** $10 on 1c. orange . . . . 35 1·90
896 **72** $20 on 2c. green . . . . . 25 1·50
904 **77** $20 on 2c. blue . . . . . 25 1·30
899 – $20 on 3c. brown (511) . . 25 1·30
897 **72** $20 on 3c. red . . . . . . 25 1·30
879 – $20 on 8c. orange (514) . . 25 1·70
869 **72** $20 on 8c. green . . . . . 1·25 25
882 **77** $20 on 8c. orange . . . . 1·00 5·00
883 **77** $20 on 8c. green . . . . . 25 1·00
900 **60** $30 on 4c. lilac 25 60
880 – $50 on 5c. orange (513) . . 25 25
876 **72** $50 on 5c. green 35 25
884 **77** $50 on 5c. green . . . . . 1·00 25

(105)

107 Dr. Sun Yat-sen

1946. C.N.C. surcharges. Surch as T **105** (rectangular value tablet at bottom). (a) Box with chequered pattern.

831	**72**	$20 on 3c. red	25	1·70
846	–	$20 on 8c. orange (514)	25	1·30
832	**72**	$50 on 3c. red	25	60
833		$50 on 5c. green	25	75
847	–	$50 on 5c. orange (513)	25	35
851	**77**	$50 on 5c. green	85	1·10
854	**82**	$50 on $1 green	25	25
848	–	$100 on 1c. orange (508)	25	25
834	**72**	$100 on 3c. red	25	25
842		$100 on 8c. green	40	40
852	**77**	$100 on 8c. green	60	35
860	**58**	$100 on $1 purple	60	25
868	**107**	$100 on $20 red	60	40
837	**72**	$200 on 10c. green	35	35
861	**58**	$200 on $4 blue	35	25
855	**82**	$250 on $1.50 blue	60	2·50
862	**58**	$250 on $2 green	35	35
863		$250 on $5 red	50	25
838	**72**	$300 on 10c. green	25	25
853	**77**	$300 on 10c. green	25	1·20
839	**72**	$500 on 3c. red	25	25
864	**58**	$500 on $20 green	25	25
865		$800 on $30 brown	25	3·75
830		$1000 on 2c. green	1·30	40
856	**82**	$1000 on $2 green	60	35
857		$1000 on $2 blue	35	2·50
858		$1000 on $2 brown	40	35
866	**94**	$1000 on $2 green	25	3·00
859	**82**	$2000 on $5 red	60	75
867	**94**	$2000 on $5 green	25	60

(b) Box with diamond pattern.

978	**58**	$500 on $20 green	25	25
979	**107**	$1250 on $70 orange	25	6·00
980	**118**	$1800 on $350 buff	25	6·25
974	**82**	$2000 on $3 yellow	60	50
976	**89**	$2000 on $3 red	25	25
975	**82**	$3000 on $3 yellow	25	25
977	**89**	$3000 on $3 brown	25	1·20

1946.

885	**107**	$20 red	9·25	25
886		$30 blue	35	25
887		$50 violet	25	15
888		$70 orange	15·00	2·50
889		$100 red	15	15
890		$200 green	15	15
891		$500 green	35	15
892		$700 brown	15	1·90
893		$10000 purple	25	15
894		$3000 blue	85	15
895		$5000 red and green	85	15

109 Douglas DC-4 over Mausoleum of Dr. Sun Yat-sen

110 Pres. Chiang Kai-shek

1946. Air. No gum.

905	**109**	$27 blue	25	95

1946. President's 60th Birthday.

906	**110**	$20 red	35	50
907		$30 green	35	65
908		$50 orange	35	55
909		$100 green	50	85
910		$200 yellow	60	70
911		$300 red	60	50

For stamps of this type, but additionally inscribed with four characters around head, see Taiwan Nos. 30/5, or North Eastern Provinces, Nos. 48/53.

111 National Assembly House, Nanking

112 Entrance to Dr. Sun Yat-sen Mausoleum

1946. Opening of National Assembly, Nanking. No gum.

912	**111**	$20 green	60	30
913		$30 blue	60	35
914		$50 brown	60	30
915		$100 red	60	30

1947. 1st Anniv of Return of Government to Nanking.

942	**112**	$100 green	25	50
943		$200 blue	35	50
944		$250 red	35	95
945		$350 brown	35	95
946		$400 purple	60	70

For stamps of this type but additionally inscribed with four characters above numeral of value, see Taiwan, Nos. 36/40, or North Eastern Provinces, Nos. 65/70.

113 Dr. Sun Yat-sen

114 Confucius

115 Confucius's Lecture School

116 Tomb of Confucius

118 Dr. Sun Yat-sen and Plum Blossoms

1947.

947	**113**	$500 olive	35	25
948		$1,000 red and green	50	25
949		$2,000 lake and blue	60	25
950		$5,000 black and orange	60	25

1947. Confucius Commem. No gum.

951	**114**	$500 red	60	75
952	**115**	$800 brown	50	1·00
953	**116**	$1,250 green	50	1·40
954		$1,800 blue	50	1·90

DESIGN—HORIZ: $1,800, Confucian Temple.

1947. (a) With noughts for cents. No gum.

955	**118**	$150 blue	25	19·00
956		$250 violet	50	6·00
957		$500 green	25	10
958		$1,000 red	25	10
959		$2,000 orange	25	10
960		$3,000 blue	25	10
961		$4,000 grey	25	25
962		$5,000 brown	25	10
963		$6,000 purple	25	25
964		$7,000 brown	25	25
965		$10,000 red and blue	50	10
966		$20,000 green and red	1·30	10
967		$50,000 blue and green	1·40	10
968		$100,000 green & orange	5·00	15
969		$200,000 blue and purple	5·00	25
970		$300,000 orange & brown	6·25	50
971		$500,000 brown & green	7·25	50

(b) Without noughts for cents.

1032	**118**	$20,000 red	50	35
1033		$30,000 brown	25	25
1034		$40,000 green	25	25
1035		$50,000 blue	25	25
1036		$100,000 olive	25	25
1037		$200,000 purple	75	25
1038		$300,000 green	3·00	1·10
1039		$500,000 mauve	1·30	25
1040		$1,000,000 red	75	25
1041		$2,000,000 orange	1·60	25
1042		$3,000,000 bistre	1·25	60
1043		$5,000,000 blue	6·25	95

119 Map of Taiwan and Chinese Flag

122 Postal Kiosk

1947. Restoration of Taiwan (Formosa) (1st issue).

972	**119**	$500 red	35	1·30
973		$1,250 green	35	1·30

See also Nos. 1003/4.

1947. Progress of the Postal Service.

981	–	$500 red	35	60
982	**122**	$1,000 violet	35	60
983		$1,250 green	35	95
984	–	$1,800 blue	35	1·30

DESIGN: $500, $1,800, Mobile Post Office.

123 Air, Sea and Rail Transport

124 Postboy and Motor Van

1947. 50th Anniv of Directorate General of Posts.

985	**123**	$100 violet	35	1·10
986	**124**	$200 green	35	1·10
987		$300 lake	35	1·10
988	–	$400 red	35	1·10
989	–	$500 blue	35	1·10

DESIGN—As T **123**: $400, $500, Junk and airplane.

126 Book of the Constitution and National Assembly Building

1947. Adoption of the Constitution.

990	**126**	$2,000 red	60	75
991		$3,000 blue	60	75
992		$5,000 green	60	75

127 Reproductions of 1947 and 1912 Stamps

1948. Perf or imperf. (a) Nanking Philatelic Exn.

1001	**127**	$5,000 red	95	3·75

(b) Shanghai Philatelic Exhibition.

1002	**127**	$5,000 green	95	3·75

128 Sun Yat-sen Memorial Hall

1948. Restoration of Taiwan (Formosa) to Chinese Rule (2nd issue).

1003	**128**	$5,000 lilac	60	1·30
1004		$10,000 red	60	1·30

(130) (129)

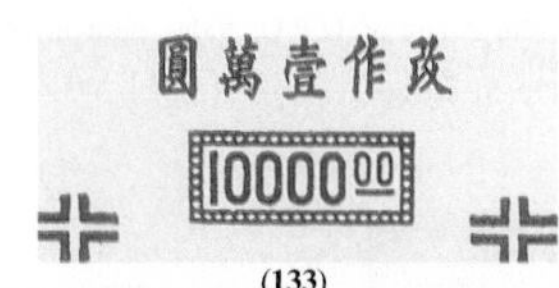
(133)

1948. "Re-valuation" surcharges. (a) Surch as T **130**.

1012	**118**	$4,000 on $100 red	25	25·00
1013		$5,000 on $100 red	25	25
1014		$8,000 on $700 brown	35	1·30

(b) Surch as T **129**.

1005	**82**	$5,000 on $1 green	25	25
1007		$5,000 on $2 green	25	25
1008	**103**	$10,000 on $20 red	25	25
1018	**82**	$15,000 on 10c. green	25	60
1015		$15,000 on 50c. green	25	95
1019		$15,000 on $4 purple	25	95
1020		$15,000 on $6 blue	40	60
1009		$20,000 on 10c. green	25	25
1010		$20,000 on 50c. green	25	40
1011		$30,000 on 30c. red	25	50
1016		$40,000 on 20c. olive	25	95
1017		$60,000 on $4 brown	35	40

(c) Air. Surch as T **133**.

1022	**61**	$10,000 on 30c. red	25	95
1028	**109**	$10,000 on $27 blue	50	1·90
1023	**61**	$20,000 on 25c. orange	25	95
1024		$30,000 on 90c. olive	25	1·30
1025		$50,000 on 60c. blue	25	1·30
1026		$50,000 on $1 green	25	1·10

On No. 1028 the Chinese characters read vertically.

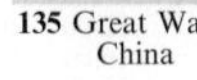
135 Great Wall of China

137 "Hai Tien" (freighter) and "Eton" (steamer) of 1872

138 "Kiang Ya" (freighter)

(138a)

1948. Tuberculosis Relief Fund. Cross in red. Perf or imperf. No gum.

1029	**135**	$5,000+$2,000 violet	25	3·25
1030		$10,000+$2,000 brown	25	3·25
1031		$15,000+$2,000 grey	25	3·25

1948. 75th Anniv of China Merchants' Steam Navigation Company. No gum.

1044	**137**	$20,000 blue	45	1·75
1045		$30,000 mauve	45	1·75
1046	**138**	$40,000 brown	45	2·75
1047		$60,000 red	45	1·20

1948. C.N.C. surcharge. Surch with T **138a**.

1048	**107**	$5,000 on $100 claret	11·00	50·00

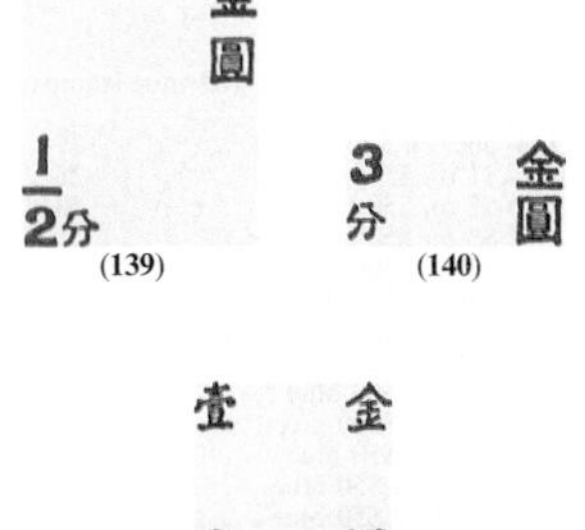
(139) (140)

(141)

1948. Gold Yuan surcharges. (a) Surch as T **139** or **140**.

1049	**82**	½c. on 30c. brown	25	5·00
1050	**118**	½c. on $500 green	25	25
1051	**107**	1c. on $20 red	25	2·50
1052	**82**	2c. on $1.50 blue	25	3·50
1053		3c. on $5 red	25	3·50
1054		4c. on $1 red	25	3·50
1055		5c. on 50c. green	25	50

(b) Surch as T **141**.

1056	**89**	5c. on $20 red	25	1·20
1057	**103**	5c. on $30 blue	25	1·50
1058	**72**	10c. on 2c. green	25	1·90
1059	**60**	10c. on 2½c. purple	25	1·20
1061	**82**	10c. on 25c. brown	25	1·40
1062	**89**	10c. on 40c. red	25	1·50
1063	**82**	10c. on $1 green	25	25
1065	**89**	10c. on $2 brown	25	25
1066	**82**	10c. on $20 blue	25	25
1067	**89**	10c. on $20 red	£300	£200
1068	**94**	10c. on $20 red	25	70
1069	**107**	10c. on $20 red	95	3·50
1070	**103**	10c. on $30 blue	25	1·90
1071	**89**	10c. on $70 violet	25	70
1072	**118**	10c. on $7,000 brown	2·50	95
1073		10c. on $20,000 red	25	5·00
1074	**89**	20c. on $6 purple	25	40
1075	**58**	20c. on $30 brown	50	5·00
1076	**107**	20c. on $30 blue	70	4·00
1077		20c. on $100 red	25	4·00
1079	**60**	50c. on ½c. brown	25	70
1081	**82**	50c. on 20c. green	25	60
1082		50c. on 30c. red	25	1·50
1083		50c. on 40c. brown	25	95
1084	**89**	50c. on 40c. red	25	1·20
1085a	**82**	50c. on $4 purple	25	2·20
1086		50c. on $20 blue	25	25
1087	**94**	50c. on $20 red	60	1·90
1088	**107**	50c. on $20 red	25	1·50
1089	**82**	50c. on $70 lilac	35	35
1090a	**118**	50c. on $6,000 purple	25	1·50
1091	**82**	$1 on 30c. brown	25	25
1092		$1 on 40c. brown	25	25
1093		$1 on $1 red	60	2·10
1094		$1 on $5 red	70	40
1095	**89**	$2 on $2 brown	25	25
1096	**102**	$2 on $20 red	25	25
1097	**107**	$2 on $100 red	25	25
1098	–	$5 on 17c. green (417)	95	95
1099	**89**	$5 on $2 brown	25	25
1100	**118**	$5 on $30,000 blue	25	1·50
1101	–	$8 on 20c. blue (519)	60	60
1102	**118**	$8 on $30,000 brown	25	2·50
1103	–	$10 on 40c. orange (543)	1·50	1·20
1104	**89**	$10 on $2 brown	25	35
1105		$20 on $2 brown	25	15
1106	**107**	$20 on $20 red	6·00	3·50
1107	**82**	$50 on 30c. red	25	35
1108	**89**	$50 on $2 brown	35	25
1109	**107**	$80 on $20 red	25	1·20
1110	**82**	$100 on $1 green	25	1·20
1111	**89**	$100 on $2 brown	40	35
1112	**118**	$20,000 on $40,000 green	11·00	14·00
1113		$50,000 on $20,000 red	1·50	50
1114		$50,000 on $30,000 brown	16·00	9·00
1115		$100,000 on $20,000 red	13·00	8·50
1116		$100,000 on $30,000 brown	2·75	45
1117		$200,000 on $40,000 green	13·00	9·00
1118		$200,000 on $50,000 blue	12·00	9·00

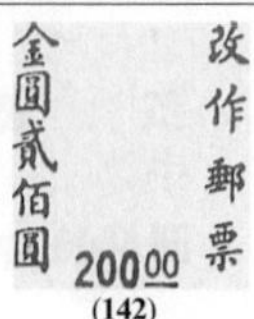
(142)

143 Liner, Train and Airplane

(144)

145 Dr. Sun Yat-sen

1949. Gold Yuan surcharges. Parcels Post stamps surch as T **142**.

No.	Type	Description	Unused	Used
1119	P **104**	$200 on $3,000 orange	1·20	70
1120		$500 on $5,000 blue	1·50	50
1121		$1,000 on $10,000 vio	2·50	70

1949. Gold Yuan surcharges. Revenue stamps surch. (a) As T **144**.

No.	Type	Description	Unused	Used
1136	**143**	50c. on $20 brown	25	70
1137		$1 on $15 orange	25	9·25
1127		$2 on $50 blue	50	1·90
1144		$3 on $50 blue	25	1·20
1138		$5 on $500 brown	25	50
1129		$10 on $30 mauve	75	1·90
1140		$15 on $20 brown	25	50
1141		$25 on $20 brown	25	50
1145		$50 on $50 blue	25	50
1147		$50 on $300 green	25	95
1130		$80 on $50 blue	25	1·50
1146		$100 on $50 blue	40	60
1124		$200 on $50 blue	95	1·20
1142		$200 on $500 brown	60	75
1125		$300 on $50 blue	1·40	1·50
1143		$500 on $15 orange	1·70	5·00
1134		$500 on $30 mauve	75	3·50
1135		$1,000 on $50 blue	9·25	9·25
1148		$1,000 on $100 olive	3·50	6·75
1126		$1,500 on $50 blue	2·50	3·75
1151		$2,000 on $300 green	50	75

(b) As T **144** but with key pattern inverted at top and bottom.

No.	Type	Description	Unused	Used
1183	**143**	$50 on $10 green	11·00	16·00
1184		$100 on $10 green	12·50	13·00
1185		$500 on $10 green	9·25	12·00
1186		$1,000 on $10 green	7·50	11·00
1187		$5,000 on $20 brown	38·00	18·00
1188		$10,000 on $20 brown	19·00	8·90
1189		$50,000 on $20 brown	20·00	9·50
1190		$100,000 on $20 brown	27·00	9·50
1191		$500,000 on $20 brown	£375	£190
1192		$2,000,000 on $20 brn	£950	£400
1193		$5,000,000 on $20 brn	£1300	£550

1949.

No.	Type	Description	Unused	Used
1152	**145**	$1 orange	40	55
1153		$10 green	40	55
1154		$20 purple	40	55
1155		$50 green	40	55
1156		$100 brown	40	55
1157		$200 red	40	55
1158		$500 mauve	40	55
1159		$800 red	40	2·50
1160		$1,000 blue	40	55
1168		$2,000 violet	35	1·90
1169		$5,000 blue	35	50
1177		$5,000 red	70	60
1170		$10,000 brown	35	50
1171		$20,000 green	35	1·90
1179		$20,000 orange	1·50	1·40
1172		$50,000 pink	35	50
1180		$50,000 blue	1·90	2·75
1173		$80,000 brown	75	5·00
1174		$100,000 green	50	50
1181		$200,000 blue	3·75	3·50
1182		$500,000 purple	3·25	2·10

For stamps of Type **145** in Silver Yuan currency see Nos. 1348/56.

146 Steam Locomotive

147 Douglas DC-4

148 Postman on Motor Cycle

149 Mountains

1949. No value indicated. Perf or roul.

No.	Type	Description	Unused	Used
1211	**146**	Orange (Ord. postage)	5·00	2·75
1212	**147**	Green (Air Mail)	7·50	10·00
1213	**148**	Mauve (Express)	8·00	10·50
1214	**149**	Red (Registration)	9·25	11·00

Owing to the collapse of the Gold Yuan the above were sold at the rate for the day for the service indicated.

(154) (159)

1949. Gold Yuan currency. Revenue stamps optd as T **154**. No gum.

No.	Type	Description	Unused	Used
1232	**143**	$10 green (B)	30·00	38·00
1233		$30 mauve (A)	£120	65·00
1234		$50 blue (C)	30·00	32·00
1235		$100 olive (D)	55·00	60·00
1236		$200 purple (A)	15·00	13·50
1237		$500 green (A)	18·00	16·00

Opt. translation: (A) Domestic Letter Fee. (B) Express Letter Fee. (C) Registered Letter Fee. (D) Air Mail Fee.

1949. Silver Yuan surcharges. Revenue stamps surch as T **159**. No gum.

No.	Type	Description	Unused	Used
1312	**143**	1c. on $20 brown	46·00	50·00
1284		1c. on $5,000 brown	8·50	6·00
1285		4c. on $100 olive	6·00	4·00
1286		4c. on $3,000 orange	6·00	1·40
1313		10c. on $20 brown	46·00	50·00
1287		10c. on $50 blue	8·50	3·00
1288		10c. on $1,000 red	8·50	3·50
1289		20c. on $1,000 red	8·50	5·50
1290		50c. on $30 mauve	10·50	6·00
1291		50c. on $50 blue	21·00	2·75
1292		$1 on $50 blue	25·00	12·50

On Nos. 1312 and 1313 the key pattern is inverted at top and bottom.

169 Tundra Swans over Globe

170 Globe and Doves

1949. No gum.

No.	Type	Description	Unused	Used
1344	**169**	$1 orange	9·50	10·00
1345		$2 blue	31·00	14·00
1346		$5 red	41·00	19·00
1347		$10 green	47·00	29·00

1949. Silver Yuan currency.

No.	Type	Description	Unused	Used
1348	**145**	1c. green	19·00	14·00
1349		2c. orange	5·75	14·00
1350		4c. green	25	45
1351		10c. lilac	25	30
1352		16c. red	55	14·00
1353		20c. blue	30	4·75
1354		50c. brown	1·70	26·00
1355		100c. blue	£250	£275
1356		500c. red	£300	£300

1949. 75th Anniv of U.P.U. Value optd in black. Imperf. No gum.

No.	Type	Description	Unused	Used
1357	**170**	$1 orange	7·75	12·00

171 Buddha's Tower, Peking

172 Bronze Bull

1949. Value optd. Roul.

No.	Type	Description	Unused	Used
1358	**171**	15c. green and brown	6·25	7·25
1359	**172**	40c. red and green	5·75	7·50

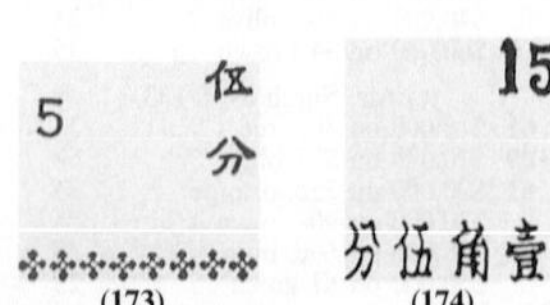
(173) (174)

1949. Silver Yuan surcharges. (a) Chungking issue. Surch as T **173**.

No.	Type	Description	Unused	Used
1360	**145**	2½c. on $50 green	2·75	4·00
1361		2½c. on $50,000 blue	6·50	4·00
1362		5c. on $1,000 blue	6·00	4·00
1363		5c. on $20,000 orange	2·20	3·50
1364		5c. on $200,000 blue	5·50	3·50
1365		5c. on $500,000 purple	5·50	3·50
1366		10c. on $5,000 red	7·00	6·25
1367		10c. on $10,000 brown	7·00	6·25
1368		15c. on $200 red	6·50	15·00
1369		25c. on $100 brown	15·50	28·00

(b) Canton issue. Surch as T **174**.

No.	Type	Description	Unused	Used
1371	**145**	1c. on $100 brown	12·00	10·00
1372		2½c. on $500 mauve	16·00	11·00
1374		15c. on $10 green	19·00	17·00
1375		15c. on $20 purple	22·00	18·00

EXPRESS DELIVERY STAMP

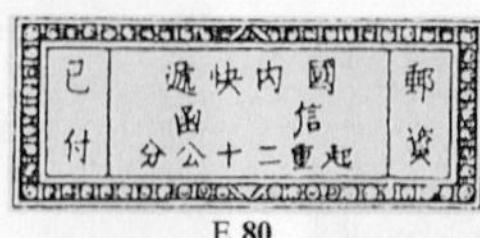
E 80

1941. Perf. No gum.

No.	Type	Description	Unused	Used
E617	E **80**	(No value) red & yellow	36·00	25·00

This stamp was sold at $2, which included ordinary postage.

MILITARY POST STAMPS

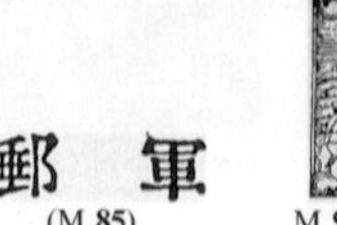
(M 85)

M **93** Entrenched Soldiers

1942. Optd variously as Type M **85**.

No.	Type	Description	Unused	Used
M682	**72**	8c. olive	4·75	12·50
M684	**77**	8c. green	10·00	14·50
M676		8c. orange	£550	
M683	**72**	16c. olive	21·00	22·00
M677	**82**	16c. olive	10·00	15·00
M678		50c. green	8·50	12·50
M679		$1 red	6·75	11·00
M680		$1 olive	7·25	11·00
M681		$2 green	8·50	14·50
M687		$2 purple	60·00	85·00

1945.

No.	Type	Description	Unused	Used
M745	M **93**	(No value) red	1·30	10·00

PARCELS POST STAMPS

P 90

P 104

P 112

1944.

No.	Type	Description	Unused	Used
P711	P **90**	$500 green	—	60
P712		$1,000 blue	—	75
P713		$3,000 red	—	85
P714		$5,000 brown	—	20·00
P715		$10,000 purple	—	38·00

1946.

No.	Type	Description	Unused	Used
P814	P **104**	$3,000 orange	—	60
P815		$5,000 blue	—	60
P816		$10,000 violet	—	3·00
P817		$20,000 red	—	5·50

1947. Type P **112** and similar design.

No.	Description	Unused	Used
P925	$1,000 yellow	—	1·50
P926	$3,000 green	—	1·50
P927	$5,000 red	—	1·50
P928	$7,000 blue	—	1·50
P929	$10,000 red	—	1·50
P930	$30,000 olive	—	1·90
P931	$50,000 black	—	1·90
P932	$70,000 brown	—	2·20
P933	$100,000 purple	—	2·20
P934	$200,000 green	—	2·75
P935	$300,000 pink	—	2·75
P936	$500,000 plum	—	3·50
P937	$3,000,000 blue	—	5·00
P938	$5,000,000 lilac	—	5·00
P939	$6,000,000 grey	—	6·25
P940	$8,000,000 red	—	6·75
P941	$10,000,000 olive	—	8·00

圓拾伍圓金
50
圓拾伍圓金
(P 146)

1949. Gold Yuan surcharges. 1947 issue surch as Type P **146**.

No.	Description	Unused	Used
P1194	$10 on $3,000 green	—	2·50
P1195	$20 on $5,000 red	—	2·50
P1196	$50 on $10,000 red	—	2·50
P1197	$100 on $3,000,000 blue	—	3·00
P1198	$200 on $5,000,000 lilac	—	3·00
P1199	$500 on $1,000 yellow	—	3·75
P1200	$1,000 on $7,000 blue	—	3·75

Parcels post stamps were not on sale in unused condition; those now on the market were probably stocks seized by the Communists.

POSTAGE DUE STAMPS

1912. Chinese Empire Postage Due Stamps optd with vertical row of Chinese characters.

No.	Type	Description	Unused	Used
D207	D **37**	½c. blue	1·30	70
D208		1c. brown	1·60	60
D209		2c. brown	2·50	85
D210		4c. blue	5·00	2·20
D211		5c. blue	£140	£140
D212		5c. brown	7·50	3·00
D213		10c. blue	11·00	4·75
D214		20c. blue	11·00	11·00
D215		30c. blue	20·00	20·00

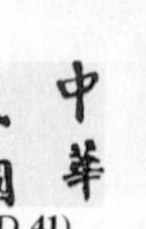
(D 41)

D 46

D 62

1912. Optd with Type D **41**.

No.	Type	Description	Unused	Used
D233	D **37**	½c. blue	10·00	6·25
D234		½c. brown	2·20	85
D235		1c. brown	2·20	1·00
D236		2c. brown	4·50	3·50
D237		4c. blue	9·25	6·25
D238		5c. brown	17·00	9·50
D239		10c. blue	20·00	14·50
D240		20c. brown	26·00	42·00
D241		30c. blue	32·00	49·00

1913.

No.	Type	Description	Unused	Used
D341	D **46**	½c. blue	1·10	40
D342		1c. blue	1·60	50
D343		2c. blue	1·75	35
D344		4c. blue	2·20	50
D345		5c. blue	4·75	95
D346		10c. blue	5·50	1·30
D347		20c. blue	14·50	3·50
D340		30c. blue	21·00	12·00

1932.

No.	Type	Description	Unused	Used
D432	D **62**	½c. orange	35	35
D433		1c. orange	35	35
D434		2c. orange	35	35
D435		4c. orange	70	35
D569		5c. orange	70	35
D570		10c. orange	80	85
D571		20c. orange	1·75	1·10
D572		30c. orange	1·90	1·60
D573		50c. orange	60	70
D574		$1 orange	60	80
D575		$2 orange	1·10	1·10

欠 暫
資 作
(D 75) ("Temporary-use Postage Due")

1940. Optd with Type D **75**.

No.	Type	Description	Unused	Used
D545	**72**	$1 brown and red	5·00	12·50
D546		$2 brown and blue	6·25	12·50

D 90 D 94 D 112

1944. No gum.

No.	Type	Description	Unused	Used
D717	D **90**	10c. green	35	2·50
D718		20c. blue	35	2·50
D719		40c. red	35	2·50
D720		50c. green	35	2·50
D721		60c. blue	35	5·00
D722		$1 red	35	2·50
D723		$2 purple	35	2·50

1945.

No.	Type	Description	Unused	Used
D752	D **94**	$2 red	35	1·60
D753		$6 red	35	1·60
D754		$8 red	35	2·00
D755		$10 red	35	2·00
D756		$20 red	35	2·00
D757		$30 red	70	1·20

1947.

No.	Type	Description	Unused	Used
D916	D **112**	$50 purple	35	2·50
D917		$80 purple	35	2·50
D918		$100 purple	35	2·50
D919		$160 purple	35	2·50
D920		$200 purple	35	2·50
D921		$400 purple	35	2·50
D922		$500 purple	35	2·50
D923		$800 purple	35	2·50
D924		$2,000 purple	35	2·50

圓仟壹作改
1000.00
(D 127)

資欠作改
壹 金
分 圓
1
(D 146)

1948. Surch as Type D **127**.

No.	Type	Description	Unused	Used
D 993	D **94**	$1,000 on $20 purple	35	3·75
D 994		$2,000 on $30 purple	35	2·50
D 995		$3,000 on $50 purple	35	2·50
D 996		$4,000 on $100 pur	35	3·75
D 997		$5,000 on $200 pur	35	2·20
D 998		$10,000 on $300 pur	35	1·00
D 999		$20,000 on $500 pur	35	1·00
D1000		$30,000 on $1,000 pur	35	60

1949. Gold Yuan surcharges. Surch as Type D **146**.

No.	Type	Description	Unused	Used
D1201	**102**	1c. on $40 orange	35	12·50
D1202		2c. on $40 orange	35	12·50
D1203		5c. on $40 orange	35	12·50
D1204		10c. on $40 orange	35	12·50
D1205		20c. on $40 orange	35	12·50
D1206		50c. on $40 orange	35	12·50

D1207 $1 on $40 orange 35 10·00
D1208 $2 on $40 orange 35 10·00
D1209 $5 on $40 orange 50 10·00
D1210 $10 on $40 orange 60 6·25

REGISTRATION STAMP

1941. Roul. No gum.
R617 E **80** (No value) grn & buff 34·00 24·00
This stamp was sold at $1.50 which included ordinary postage.

CHINESE PROVINCES

Manchuria

A. KIRIN AND HEILUNGKIANG

(1) (2)

Stamps of China optd

1927. Stamps of 1913 optd with T **1**.
1 **43** ½c. sepia 45 25
2 1c. orange 60 10
3 1½c. purple 1·75 1·50
4 2c. green 1·75 45
5 3c. green 1·50 75
6 4c. olive 1·50 10
7 5c. mauve 2·00 30
8 6c. red 1·75 90
9 7c. violet 3·00 2·25
10 8c. orange 3·50 1·75
11 10c. blue 3·00 10
12 **44** 13c. brown 4·25 3·50
13 15c. blue 4·00 1·50
14 16c. olive 4·75 3·25
15 20c. lake 5·00 2·25
16 30c. purple 7·00 2·75
17 50c. green 12·00 3·25
18 **45** $1 sepia and brown 30·00 5·00
19 $2 brown and blue 50·00 10·00
20 $5 green and red £160 £140

1928. Chang Tso-lin stamps optd with T **2**.
21 **55** 1c. orange 1·25 1·50
22 4c. olive 1·75 1·75
23 10c. blue 4·00 4·50
24 $1 red 32·00 32·00

1929. Unification stamps optd as T **2**.
25 **56** 1c. orange 1·25 1·40
26 4c. olive 2·00 2·00
27 10c. blue 11·00 5·00
28 $1 red 60·00 65·00

1929. Sun Yat-sen Memorial stamps optd as T **2**.
29 **57** 1c. orange 1·00 1·00
30 4c. olive 1·00 1·00
31 10c. blue 7·00 3·00
32 $1 red 38·00 38·00

B. NORTH-EASTERN PROVINCES

Issues made by the Chinese Nationalist Government of Chiang Kai-shek.

1 Dr. Sun Yat-sen (2)

1946. Surch as T **2**.
1 **1** 50c. on $5 red 20 3·00
2 50c. on $10 green 20 3·00
3 $1 on $10 green 20 2·00
4 $2 on $20 purple 20 1·50
5 $4 on $50 brown 20 1·25

(3) (4)

1946. Stamps of China optd with T **3** (= "Limited for use in North East").
6 – 1c. orange (508) 10 4·00
7 – 3c. brown (511) 25 3·50
8 – 5c. orange (513) 10 2·50
9 **72** 10c. green 25 3·25
11 20c. blue 20 3·50

1946. Stamps of China surch as T **4** but larger.
14 – $5 on $50 on 21c. brown (No. 799) 50·00 55·00
15 – $10 on $100 on 28c. green (No. 802) 60·00 70·00
16 **91** $20 on $200 green 50·00 55·00

5 Dr. Sun Yat-sen (6)

1946.
17 **5** 5c. lake 10 2·50
18 10c. orange 10 2·50
19 20c. green 15 2·50
20 25c. brown 10 2·75
21 50c. orange 10 2·25
22 $1 blue 15 1·75
23 $2 purple 15 2·00
24 $2.50 blue 10 2·75
25 $3 brown 15 2·25
26 $4 brown 15 2·75
27 $5 green 15 2·25
28 $10 red 10 1·25
29 $20 olive 10 1·00
34 $22 black 60·00 65·00
35 $44 red 12·00 20·00
36 $50 violet 10 50
37 $65 green 60·00 75·00
38 $100 green 10 50
39 $109 green 65·00 75·00
40 $200 brown 10 1·00
41 $300 green 10 2·00
42 $500 red 10 50
43 $1,000 orange 10 20

1946. Nanking National Assembly stamps of China surch as T **6**.
44 **111** $2 on $20 green 40 2·50
45 $3 on $30 blue 40 2·50
46 $5 on $50 brown 40 2·50
47 $10 on $100 red 40 2·50

7 Pres. Chiang Kai-shek (note characters to right of head) (8)

1947. President's 60th Birthday.
54 **7** $2 red 50 3·00
55 $3 green 80 3·00
56 $5 red 80 3·00
57 $10 green 80 3·00
58 $20 orange 1·00 3·00
59 $30 red 1·00 3·00
For other stamps as Types **7** and **9** but with different Chinese characters, see China–Taiwan Types **4** and **5**.

1947. Stamps of China surch as T **8**.
60 **107** $100 on $1,000 purple 80 3·25
61 $300 on $3,000 blue 80 3·25
62 **58** $500 on $30 brown 45 3·75
63 **107** $500 on $5,000 red & green 75 3·25

9 Entrance to Dr. Sun Yat-sen Mausoleum (note characters above face value) (10)

1947. 1st Anniv of Return of Govt. to Nanking.
64 **9** $2 green 50 1·50
65 $4 blue 50 1·50
66 $6 red 50 1·50
67 $10 brown 50 1·50
68 $20 purple 50 1·50

1948. Surch as T **10**.
70 **5** $1,500 on 20c. green 15 3·50
71 $3,000 on $1 blue 15 3·75
72 $4,000 on 25c. brown 15 3·00
73 $8,000 on 50c. orange 10 2·50
74 $10,000 on 10c. orange 10 2·50
75 $50,000 on $109 green 25 2·75
76 $100,000 on $65 green 35 2·50
77 $500,000 on $22 black 50 2·75
No. 70 has five characters on the left side of the surcharge and No. 77 four characters.

MILITARY POST STAMPS

1946. Military Post stamp of China optd as T **3** but larger.
M13 M **93** (No value) red 2·00 14·00

(M 10)

1947. Surch with Type M **10**.
M69 **5** $44 on 50c. orange 8·00 32·00

PARCELS POST STAMPS

P 11 (P 12)

1948.
P78 P **11** $500 red 30·00
P79 $1,000 red 60·00
P80 $3,000 olive 75·00
P81 $5,000 blue £120
P82 $10,000 green £150
P83 $20,000 blue £150

1948. Parcels Post stamp of China surch with Type P **12**.
P84 $500,000 on $5,000,000 lilac (No. P938) – £140
Parcels Post stamps were not on sale unused.

POSTAGE DUE STAMPS

D 7 (D 13)

1947.
D48 D **7** 10c. blue 40 6·00
D49 20c. blue 40 6·00
D50 50c. blue 40 4·50
D51 $1 blue 10 3·25
D52 $2 blue 10 4·25
D53 $5 blue 10 4·25

1948. Surch as Type D **13**.
D85 D **7** $10 on 10c. blue 10 7·00
D86 $20 on 20c. blue 10 7·00
D87 $50 on 50c. blue 10 7·00

Sinkiang

(Chinese Turkestan)

A province between Tibet and Mongolia. Issued distinguishing stamps because of its debased currency.
The following are all optd on stamps of China.

(1) (3)

1915. 1913 issue optd with T **1**.
17 **43** ½c. sepia 30 25
2 1c. orange 75 10
49 1½c. purple 1·50 2·00
3 2c. green 1·25 50
4 3c. green 1·25 10
5 4c. red 1·40 60
52 4c. grey 7·50 3·50
53 4c. olive 4·50 1·50
6 5c. mauve 1·25 40
7 6c. grey 1·40 70
55 6c. red 3·50 1·00
56 6c. brown 15·00 14·00
8 7c. violet 2·00 2·00
9 8c. orange 2·75 1·40
10 10c. blue 3·00 25
60 **44** 13c. brown 5·50 4·50
11 15c. brown 3·50 2·50
61 15c. blue 6·00 2·50
12 16c. olive 4·00 2·75
63 20c. lake 6·00 1·50
14 30c. purple 6·50 2·50
65 50c. green 10·00 3·50
34 **45** $1 black and yellow 20·00 3·75
66 $1 sepia and brown 22·00 3·50
35 $2 black and blue 35·00 12·00
67 $2 brown and blue 26·00 8·50
36 $5 black and red 75·00 22·00
68 $5 green and red 50·00 17·00
37 $10 black and green £225 £150
69 $10 mauve and green £140 £120
38 $20 black and yellow £550 £425
70 $20 blue and purple £160 £140

1921. 25th Anniv of Chinese National Postal Service stamps optd with T **3**.
39 **48** 1c. orange 1·25 1·50
40 3c. turquoise 1·25 1·50
41 6c. grey 2·75 2·50
42 10c. blue 32·00 32·00

(4)

1923. Adoption of the Constitution stamps optd with T **4**.
43 **53** 1c. orange 3·25 3·25
44 3c. turquoise 3·25 3·25
45 4c. red 3·25 3·25
46 10c. blue 4·75 4·25

(5) (6)

1928. Assumption of Title of Marshal of the Army and Navy by Chang Tso-lin. Optd with T **5**.
71 **55** 1c. orange 1·40 1·25
72 4c. olive 2·25 2·25
73 10c. blue 5·50 5·00
74 $1 red 35·00 38·00

1929. Unification of China. Optd as T **5**.
75 **56** 1c. orange 3·00 2·50
76 4c. olive 3·00 2·75
77 10c. blue 8·50 3·50
78 $1 red 60·00 50·00

1929. Sun Yat-sen State Burial. Optd as T **5**.
79 **57** 1c. orange 1·50 1·25
80 4c. olive 2·50 2·25
81 10c. blue 6·00 3·25
82 $1 red 35·00 28·00

1932. Air. Handstamped on Sinkiang issues as T **6** ("By Air Mail").
83 **43** 5c. mauve (No. 6) £300 £225
84 10c. blue (No. 10) £300 £170
85 **44** 15c. blue (No. 61) £2000 £600
86 30c. purple (No. 14) £900 £750

1932. Dr. Sun Yat-sen stamps optd as T **3**.
87 **58** 1c. orange 1·25 2·25
95 2c. olive 1·25 1·25
103 4c. green 1·00 2·25
104 5c. green 1·25 1·50
105 15c. green 1·75 3·50
114 15c. red 2·50 2·50
115 20c. blue 2·00 75
107 25c. blue 2·00 75
108 $1 sepia and brown 6·50 5·50
100 $2 brown and blue 18·00 13·00
101 $5 black and red 24·00 25·00

1933. Tan Yen-kai Memorial. Optd as T **5**.
117 **62** 2c. olive 2·25 2·25
118 5c. green 2·75 1·25
119 25c. blue 7·00 3·50
120 $1 red 45·00 42·00

1933. Martyrs' issue optd as T **3**.
121 **60** ½c. sepia 10 1·00
122 – 1c. orange 10 85
167 – 2c. blue 30 2·25
123 **60** 2½c. mauve 20 1·75
124 – 3c. brown 20 2·00
169 **60** 4c. lilac 40 2·50
125 – 8c. orange 20 2·00
126 – 10c. purple 20 2·00
171 – 13c. green 60 3·25
172 – 15c. purple 60 3·25
173 – 17c. olive 75 3·25
137 – 20c. lake 20 4·25
174 – 20c. blue 75 3·00
175 – 21c. sepia 60 3·50
185 – 25c. purple 1·00 5·00
176 – 28c. olive 75 3·25
130 – 30c. red 25 3·25
131 – 40c. orange 25 3·50
132 – 50c. green 25 3·25

1940. Dr. Sun Yat-sen stamps optd as T **3**.
139 **72** 2c. olive 30 1·50
140 3c. red 30 2·25
141 5c. green 30 1·25
143 8c. olive 40 1·10
144 10c. green 40 1·25
145 15c. red 1·00 3·25
146 16c. olive 1·00 3·50
147 25c. blue 1·40 3·25
156 30c. red 1·00 2·75
158 50c. blue 1·50 3·00
160 $1 brown and red 1·75 5·00
161 $2 brown and blue 1·75 6·00
162 $5 green and red 1·75 7·50
163 $10 violet and green 2·00 7·50
164 $20 blue and red 3·00 11·00

(8) (9)

1942. Air. Air stamps optd with T **8** or larger.
187 **61** 15c. green 4·00 7·00
197 25c. orange 5·00 10·00
198 30c. red 5·00 10·00
190 45c. purple 6·00 10·00
199 50c. brown 6·00 12·00
192 60c. blue 6·00 12·00
193 90c. olive 25·00 27·00
194 $1 green 7·50 13·00
200 $2 brown 25·00 24·00
201 $5 red 32·00 24·00

1942. Thrift stamps optd as T **8**.
221 **78** 8c. green 5·00 10·00
215 21c. brown 5·00 10·00
216 28c. olive 5·00 10·00
223 33c. red 6·50 10·00
218 50c. blue 7·50 10·00
225 $1 purple 10·00 15·00

1943. Dr. Sun Yat-sen stamps optd as T **3**.
227 **82** 10c. green 15 6·00
228 20c. olive 15 5·50
229 25c. purple 30 10·00
230 30c. red 15 6·50
231 40c. brown 15 6·00
232 50c. green 15 6·00
233 $1 red 35 5·50
234 $1 olive 25 5·00
235 $1.50 blue 25 8·00
236 $2 green 75 6·50

237 $3 yellow 35 6·50
238 $5 red 45 6·50

1943. Stamps optd with T **9**.
239 **72** 10c. green 7·50 15·00
240 – 20c. blue (No. 519) 7·50 14·00
241 **72** 50c. blue 7·50 12·00

1944. Dr. Sun Yat-sen stamps optd as T **3**.
248 **77** $4 blue 1·50 10·00
249 $5 grey 2·75 10·00
250 $10 brown 2·75 10·00
251 $20 green 1·40 11·00
243 $20 red 5·00 13·00
253 $30 purple 3·00 13·00
245 $40 red 3·75 13·00
255 $50 blue 3·50 14·00
247 $100 brown 11·00 17·00

(**10**)

1944. Nos. 227 and 229 of Sinkiang surch as T **10**.
257 **82** 12c. on 10c. green 7·00 20·00
258 24c. on 25c. purple 7·00 20·00

1945. Stamps optd as T **3**.
259 **89** 40c. red 35 16·00
260 $3 red 35 14·00

(**11**)

1949. Silver Yuan surcharges. Sun Yat-sen issues of China surch as T **11**.
261 **107** 1c. on $100 red (No. 889) 6·00 11·00
262 3c. on $200 green (No. 890) 6·00 14·00
263 5c. on $500 green (No. 891) 6·00 10·00
264 **136** 10c. on $20,000 red (No. 1032) 9·00 10·00
265 50c. on $4,000 grey (No. 961) 26·00 20·00
266 $1 on $6,000 purple (No. 963) 30·00 25·00

Szechwan

A province of China. Issued distinguishing stamps because of its debased currency.

(**1**)

Stamps of China optd with T **1**.

1933. Issue of 1913.
1 **43** 1c. orange 3·00 75
2 5c. mauve 6·00 20
3 **44** 50c. green 20·00 50

1933. Dr. Sun Yat-sen issue.
4 **58** 2c. olive 1·50 50
5 5c. green 1·50 10
6 15c. green 3·50 2·75
7 15c. red 7·00 7·50
8 25c. blue 6·00 40
9 $1 sepia and brown 18·00 2·75
10 $2 brown and blue 40·00 3·75
11 $5 black and red 80·00 12·00

1933. Martyrs issue (Nos. 410 etc).
12 **60** ½c. sepia 30 20
13 – 1c. orange 40 10
14 **60** 2½c. mauve 95 50
15 – 3c. brown 1·25 55
16 – 8c. orange 1·40 75
17 – 10c. purple 1·90 15
18 – 13c. green 2·75 60
19 – 17c. olive 2·25 1·10
20 – 20c. lake 3·00 50
21 – 30c. red 3·50 45
22 – 40c. orange 14·00 85
23 – 50c. green 16·00 1·10

Yunnan

A province of China which issued distinguishing stamps because of its debased currency.

(**1**) (**2**) (**3**)

Stamps of China optd.

1926. Issue of 1913, optd with T **1**.
1 **43** ½c. sepia 30 45
2 1c. orange 1·25 10
3 1½c. purple 1·25 1·25
4 2c. green 2·00 55
5 3c. green 1·75 40
6 4c. olive 1·75 10
7 5c. mauve 3·00 35
8 6c. red 3·75 1·25
9 7c. violet 4·75 2·50
10 8c. orange 5·50 2·00
11 10c. blue 3·75 20
12 **44** 13c. brown 5·50 4·25
13 15c. blue 5·00 1·50
14 16c. olive 6·00 3·25
15 20c. lake 5·50 1·75
16 30c. purple 16·00 11·00
17 50c. green 8·50 5·00
18 **45** $1 sepia and brown 22·00 8·50
19 $2 brown and blue 45·00 14·00
20 $5 green and red £140 £150

1929. Unification of China. Optd with T **2**.
21 **56** 1c. orange 1·75 1·50
22 4c. olive 2·50 1·25
23 10c. blue 9·00 2·00
24 $1 red 70·00 55·00

1929. Sun Yat-sen State Burial. Optd as T **2**.
25 **57** 1c. orange 1·75 1·50
26 4c. olive 1·75 1·00
27 10c. blue 7·00 1·50
28 $1 red 45·00 40·00

1932. Dr. Sun Yat-sen stamps optd with T **3**.
29 **58** 1c. orange 80 75
30 2c. olive 95 1·10
44 4c. green 1·75 1·50
45 5c. green 2·00 75
46 15c. green 4·50 4·75
47 15c. red 5·00 7·00
32 20c. blue 3·00 85
48 25c. blue 7·50 3·50
33 $1 sepia and brown 20·00 16·00
34 $2 brown and blue 45·00 30·00
35 $5 black and red £100 85·00

1933. Tan Yen-kai Memorial. Optd with T **2**.
52 **62** 2c. olive 1·75 2·25
53 5c. green 2·00 1·00
54 25c. blue 5·75 2·25
55 $1 red 48·00 48·00

1933. Martyrs issue optd as T **3**.
56 **60** ½c. sepia 65 1·00
57 – 1c. orange 1·25 20
58 **60** 2½c. mauve 1·50 2·50
59 – 3c. brown 3·25 3·25
60 – 8c. orange 8·50 8·00
61 – 10c. purple 3·75 3·50
62 – 13c. green 3·75 3·75
63 – 17c. olive 3·75 3·75
64 – 20c. lake 4·00 2·00
65 – 30c. red 8·50 7·00
66 – 40c. orange 14·00 15·00
67 – 50c. green 16·00 7·50

COMMUNIST CHINA

Issues were made by various Communist administrations from 1930 onwards. These had limited local availability and are outside the scope of this catalogue. For details of such issues see Part 17.

In 1946 (North East China) and 1949 these local issues were consolidated into Regional People's Post stamps for those local administrations listed below.

A. East China People's Post

EC **105** Methods of Transport

1949. 7th Anniv of Shandong Communist Postal Administration.
EC322 EC **105** $1 green 60 1·25
EC323 $2 green 20 85
EC324 $3 red 20 45
EC325 $5 brown 20 35
EC326 $10 blue 35 1·00
EC327 $13 violet 20 80
EC328 $18 blue 20 80
EC329 $21 red 30 1·00
EC330 $30 green 20 65
EC331 $50 red 70 80
EC332 $100 green 12·00 11·00

The $5 has an overprinted character obliterating a Japanese flag on the tower.

EC **106** Steam Train and Postal Runner
EC **107** Victorious Troops and Map of Battle

1949. Dated "1949.2.7".
EC333 EC **106** $1 green 20 85
EC334 $2 green 30 65
EC335 $3 red 20 65
EC336 $5 brown 20 55
EC337 $10 blue 75 1·10
EC338 $13 violet 25 90
EC339 $18 blue 20 1·10
EC340 $21 red 20 1·75
EC341 $30 green 2·50 1·90
EC342 $50 red 35 2·75
EC343 $100 green 1·00 55

For stamps as Type EC **106**, but dated "1949", see Nos. EC364/71.

1949. Victory in Huaihai Campaign.
EC344 EC **107** $1 green 20 80
EC345 $2 green 35 70
EC346 $3 red 20 70
EC347 $5 brown 20 40
EC348 $10 blue 60 60
EC349 $13 violet 20 80
EC350 $18 blue 20 80
EC351 $21 red 20 90
EC352 $30 green 1·00 75
EC353 $50 red 50 1·00
EC354 $100 green 4·00 2·00

EC **108** Maps of Shanghai and Nanjing

1949. Liberation of Nanjing and Shanghai.
EC355 EC **108** $1 red 20 1·25
EC356 $2 green 20 1·00
EC357 $3 violet 20 75
EC358 $5 brown 20 50
EC359 $10 blue 20 75
EC360 $30 green 40 1·00
EC361 $50 red 85 75
EC362 $100 green 1·25 15
EC363 $500 orange 3·50 75

1949. As Type EC **106** but dated "1949".
EC364 $10 blue 20 25
EC365a $15 red 20 25
EC366 $30 green 20 10
EC367 $50 red 20 10
EC368 $60 green 20 1·60
EC369 $100 green 6·00 80
EC370 $1,600 violet 2·00 4·25
EC371 $2,000 purple 2·00 3·75

EC **111** Zhu De, Mao Tse-tung and Troops

EC **112** Mao Tse-tung

1949. 22nd Anniv of Chinese People's Liberation Army.
EC378 EC **111** $70 orange 20 10
EC379 $270 red 20 15
EC380 $370 green 20 40
EC381 $470 purple 35 60
EC382 $570 blue 30 45

For other values in this design with only three characters in bottom panel, see South West China Nos. SW9/19.

1949.
EC383 EC **112** $10 blue 3·00 3·25
EC384 $15 red 3·00 3·50
EC385 $70 brown 20 35
EC386 $100 purple 20 20
EC387 $150 orange 20 30
EC388 $200 green 20 10
EC389 $500 blue 20 10
EC390 $1,000 red 20 15
EC391 $2,000 green 20 3·50

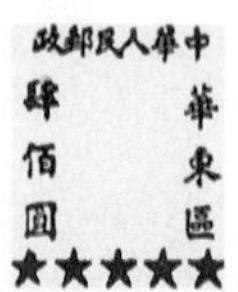

(EC **113**) ("Chinese People's Postal Service East China Region")

1949. Stamps of Nationalist China surch as Type EC **113**.
EC392 **145** $400 on $200 red 18·00 30
EC393 $1,000 on $50 green 60 25
EC394 $1,200 on $100 brown 25 1·75
EC395 $1,600 on $20,000 grn 25 2·25
EC396 $2,000 on $1,000 blue 25 15

PARCELS POST STAMPS

Stamps of Nationalist China surch.

(ECP **110**)

1949. No. 1347 surch as Type ECP **110**.
ECP372 **169** $200 on $10 green 16·00 8·00
ECP373 $500 on $10 green 16·00 3·75
ECP374 $1,000 on $10 green 18·00 7·00
ECP375 $2,000 on $10 green 26·00 13·00
ECP376 $5,000 on $10 green 40·00 21·00
ECP377 $10,000 on $10 green 75·00 29·00

(ECP **114**)

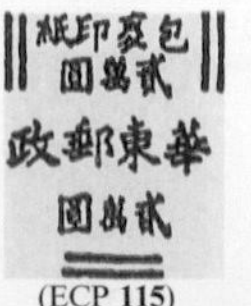

(ECP **115**)

1949. Nos. 1344/6 and unissued 10c. surch as Type ECP **114**.
ECP397 **169** $5,000 on 10c. blue 30·00 19·00
ECP398 $10,000 on $1 orange 48·00 30·00
ECP399 $20,000 on $2 blue 90·00 65·00
ECP400 $50,000 on $5 red £300 85·00

1949. Nos. P711/2 and P926/7 surch as Type ECP **115**.
ECP401 P **90** $5,000 on $500 green 20 10·00
ECP402 $10,000 on $1 blue 80·00 40·00
ECP403 P **112** $20,000 on $3 green £120 75·00
ECP404 $50,000 on $5 red 2·00 50·00

B. North China People's Post

(NC **68**) (NC **69**)

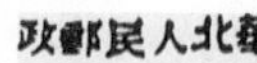

(NC **70**)

1949. Surch "North China People's Postal Administration". (a) Surch as Type NC **68**.
NC258 $5 on $500 orange 20·00 15·00
NC259 $6 on $500 orange 24·00 20·00
NC260 $12 on $200 red 4·00 5·00

(b) Surch as Type NC **69**.
NC261 $3 on 2 (20c.) brown £200 £120
NC262 $3 on 5 (50c.) blue 15·00 10·00
NC263 $5 on 2 (20c.) brown 15·00 10·00
NC264 $5 on 5 (50c.) blue £250 £150

(c) Surch as Type NC **70**.
NC265 $1 on $60 red 18·00 16·00
NC266 $5 on $80 purple 14·00 12·00
NC267 $6 on $2 brown 65·00 15·00
NC268 $6 on $40 brown 15·00 10·00
NC269 $6 on $80 purple £325 £250

NC **71** Infantry

NC **72** Industry

1948. Imperf.
NC270 NC **71** 50c. purple 60 80
NC271 $1 blue 7·50 7·00
NC272 $2 green 1·00 1·50
NC273 $3 violet 30 1·10
NC274 $5 brown 90 1·25
NC275 NC **72** $6 purple 50 1·00
NC276 NC **71** $10 green 1·00 1·75
NC277 $12 red 2·00 1·50

The 50c. and $6 have value in Chinese characters only.

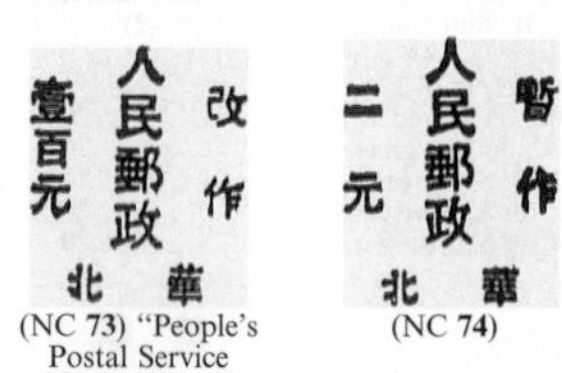

(NC **73**) "People's Postal Service North China"
(NC **74**)

1949. Surch as Type NC **73**. (a) On stamp of Nationalist China.
NC278 $100* on $100 red 14·00 50

(b) On stamps of North Eastern Provinces.
NC279 **5** 50c. on 5c. red 60 3·50
NC280 $1 on 10c. orange 75 1·00
NC281 $2 on 20c. green 30·00 2·50
NC282 $3 on 50c. orange 30 3·00
NC283 $4 on $5 green 4·00 2·75
NC284 $6 on $10 red 60 1·00
NC285 $10 on $300 green 2·75 2·50
NC286 $12 on $1 blue 1·40 1·50
NC287 $18 on $3 brown 1·75 1·00
NC288 $20* on 50c. orange 1·25 75
NC290 $20 on $20 green 1·50 80
NC291 $30 on $2.50 blue 1·75 1·50
NC292 $40 on 25c. brown 2·00 1·50
NC293 $50 on $109 green 4·00 1·50
NC294 $80* on $1 blue 7·00 1·00
NC295 $100 on $65 green 8·00 1·75

1949. Surch as Type NC **74**. (a) On stamps of Nationalist China.
NC296 **107** $100* on $100 red 25·00 7·50
NC297 $300* on $700 brown 8·00 2·50
NC298 **118** $500* on $500 green 7·50 1·00
NC299 $3,000* on $3,000 blue 8·50 2·00

(b) On stamps of North Eastern Provinces.
NC300a **5** $1* on 25c. brown 25 1·00
NC301 $2 on 20c. green 1·75 1·25
NC302 $3 on 50c. orange 25 1·00

NC303 $4 on $5 green . . . . 1·90 1·75
NC305 $6 on $10 red . . . . 2·00 1·00
NC306 $10* on $300 green . . 9·00 2·25
NC307 $12 on $1 blue 95 70
NC308 $20* on 50c. orange . . 10·00 1·90
NC309 $20* on $20 green . . 5·00 60
NC310 $40* on 25c. brown . . 6·75 90
NC311 $50* on $109 green . . 10·00 1·00
NC312 $80* on $1 blue . . . . 7·50 1·00

*On these stamps the bottom character in the left-hand column of overprints is square in shape.

NC 75

1949. Labour Day. Perf or imperf.
NC313 NC **75** $20 red . . . . . 2·00 1·75
NC314 $40 blue . . . . . 2·00 1·75
NC315 $60 brown . . . . 2·00 2·25
NC316 $80 green . . . . 2·75 2·25
NC317 $100 violet . . . . 3·50 2·25

NC **79** Mao Tse-tung

NC **80**

1949. 28th Anniv of Chinese Communist Party. Perf or imperf.
NC327A NC **79** $10 red . . . . . 1·00 1·00
NC328A NC **80** $20 blue 50 75
NC329A NC **79** $50 orange . . . 2·00 1·50
NC330A NC **80** $80 green 50 75
NC331A NC **79** $100 violet . . . 2·50 1·50
NC332A NC **80** $120 green . . . 50 1·00
NC333A NC **79** $140 purple . . . 3·50 1·75

(NC **81**) ("People's Postal Service North China")

1949. Surch as Type NC **81**. (a) On stamp of Nationalist China.
NC334 **118** $10 on $7,000 brown 15·00 7·50

(b) On stamps of North Eastern Provinces.
NC336 **5** $10 on $10 red . . . . 5·00 1·25
NC337 $30 on 20c. green . . . 4·00 1·50
NC338 $50 on $44 red . . . . 3·75 25
NC339 $100 on $3 brown . . . 8·00 1·50
NC341 $200 on $4 brown . . . 20·00 7·00

NC **83** Gate of Heavenly Peace, Peking

NC **84** Field Workers and Factory

1949.
NC349 NC **83** $50 orange . . . . 2·50 6·50
NC350 $100 red 20 30
NC351 $200 green . . . . 1·00 35
NC352 $300 purple . . . . 5·00 70
NC353 $400 blue . . . . 5·00 70
NC354 $500 brown . . . . 7·00 60
NC355 $700 violet . . . . 3·00 2·50

1949.
NC356 NC **84** $1,000 orange . . . 4·00 60
NC357 $3,000 blue 20 90
NC358 $5,000 red 20 10
NC359 $10,000 brown . . . 30 1·75

PARCELS POST STAMPS
Stamps of Nationalist China surch.

(NCP **76**)

1949. Surch as Type NCP **76**.
NCP318 P **112** $300 on $6,000,000 grey . . . . . . – 32·00
NCP319 $400 on $8,000,000 red . . . . . . – 32·00
NCP320 $500 on $10,000,000 green . . . . . . – 35·00
NCP321 $800 on $5,000,000 lilac . . . . . . – 35·00
NCP322 $1 on $3,000,000 blue . . . . . . – 40·00

NC **77** Pagoda (NCP **78**)

1949. Money Order stamps. Type NC **77** surch as Type NCP **78**. No gum.
NCP323 $6 on $5 red . . . . . 6·00 2·25
NCP324 $6 on $50 grey . . . . 6·00 2·25
NCP325 $50 on $20 purple . . . 7·00 2·00
NCP326 $100 on $10 green . . . 10·00 4·25

NCP **82** Steam Train

1949.
NCP342 NCP **82** $500 red . . . . 2·00 4·50
NCP343 $1,000 blue . . 48·00 23·00
NCP344 $2,000 green . . 48·00 23·00
NCP345 $5,000 green . . 70·00 45·00
NCP346 $10,000 orange £150 90·00
NCP347 $20,000 red . . £250 £180
NCP348 $50,000 purple £300 £350

C. Port Arthur and Dairen

The Soviet Union obtained facilities in these two ports by treaty in 1945. The Chinese Communists retained the civil administration, but a separate postal authority was established.

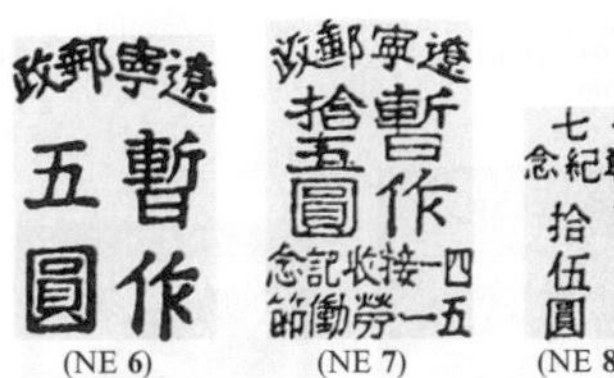

(NE **6**) (NE **7**) (NE **8**)

1946. Stamps of Japan handstamped "Liaoning Posts" and new value at Type NE **6**.
NE 8 20c. on 3s. green (No. 316) 6·00 8·00
NE 9 $1 on 17s. violet (No. 402) 6·00 7·00
NE11 $5 on 6s. red (No. 242) . . 7·00 12·00
NE12 $5 on 6s. orange (No. 319) 6·50 7·00
NE13 $15 on 40s. purple (No. 406) . . . . 32·00 30·00

1946. Transfer of Administration on 1 April and Labour Day. Stamps of Manchukuo handstamped as Type NE **7**.
NE14 **19** $1 on 1f. red . . . . . 5·00 5·00
NE15 – $5 on 4f. green (No. 84) 7·00 9·00
NE16 **20** $15 on 30f. brown . . . 16·00 20·00

1946. 9th Anniv of Outbreak of War with Japan. Stamps of Manchukuo surch as Type NE **8**.
NE17 $1 on 6f. red (No. 86) . . 4·50 7·50
NE18 $5 on 2f. green (No. 82) . . 15·00 20·00
NE19 $15 on 12f. orange (No. 90) . . . . 25·00 30·00

(NE **9**) (NE **10**)

1946. 1st Anniv of Japanese Surrender. Stamps of Manchukuo surch as Type NE **9**.
NE20 – $1 on 12f. orange (No. 90) . . . . 8·00 9·00
NE21 **19** $5 on 1f. red . . . . . 16·00 18·00
NE22 **13** $15 on 5f. black . . . . 32·00 30·00

1946. 35th Anniv of Chinese Revolution. Stamps of Manchukuo surch as Type NE **10**.
NE23 $1 on 6f. red (No. 86) . . 7·00 8·00
NE24 $5 on 12f. orange (No. 90) 16·00 16·00
NE25 $15 on 2f. green (No. 82) 32·00 32·00

(NE **11**) (NE **12**)

1946. 10th Death Anniv of Lu Xun (author). Stamps of Manchukuo surch as Type NE **11**.
NE26 **19** $1 on 1f. red . . . . . 18·00 15·00
NE27 – $5 on 6f. red (No. 86) 25·00 30·00
NE28 – $15 on 12f. orange (No. 90) . . . . . . 40·00 45·00

1947. 29th Anniv of Red Army. Stamps of Manchukuo surch as Type NE **12**.
NE29 – $1 on 2f. green (No. 82) 20·00 20·00
NE30 – $5 on 6f. red (No. 86) 35·00 35·00
NE31 **13** $15 on 13f. brown . . . £110 £130

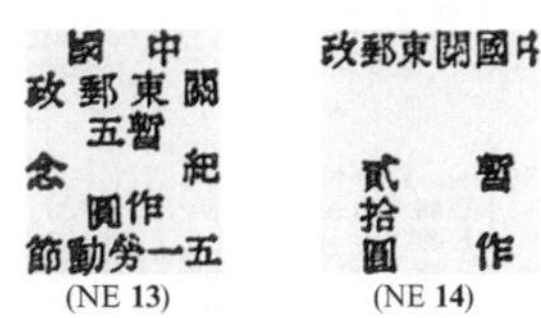

(NE **13**) (NE **14**)

1947. Labour Day. Stamps of Manchukuo surch as Type NE **13**.
NE32 – $1 on 2f. green (No. 82) 8·00 8·00
NE33 – $5 on 6f. red (No. 86) 20·00 20·00
NE34 **20** $15 on 30f. brown . . . 40·00 45·00

1947. Stamps of Manchukuo surch. "Guangdong Postal Service, China" and new value as Type NE **14**.
NE35 – $5 on 2f. green (No. 82) 20·00 20·00
NE36 – $15 on 4f. green (No. 84) 30·00 20·00
NE37 **20** $20 on 30f. brown . . . 38·00 38·00

NE **15** (NE **16**)

1948. 30th Anniv of Red Army. Surch as on Type NE **15**. (a) On stamps of Manchukuo.
NE39 $10 on 2f. green (No. 82) 70·00 50·00
NE40 $20 on 6f. red (No. 86) . . 90·00 75·00

(b) On label (Type NE **15**) commemorating 2,600th Anniv of Japanese Empire.
NE41 $100 on (no value) blue and brown £400 £350

1948. Stamps of Manchukuo surch "Guangdong Postal Administration" and new value as Type NE **16**.
NE42 $20 on 2f. green (No. 82) £100 £100
NE43 $50 on 4f. green (No. 84) £200 £180
NE44 $100 on 20f. brown (No. 152) £275 £225

(NE **17**) (NE **18**)

1948. 31st Anniv of Russian October Revolution. Stamps of Manchukuo surch as Type NE **17**.
NE45 **19** $10 on 1f. red £120 £120
NE46 – $50 on 2f. green (No. 82) £225 £225
NE47 – $100 on 4f. green (No. 84) £325 £325

1948. Guangdong Agricultural and Industrial Exhibition Stamps of Manchukuo surch as Type NE **18**.
NE48 $10 on 2f. green (No. 82) £180 £150
NE49 $50 on 20f. brown (No. 95) £750 £550

(NE **19**) (NE **20**)

1948. Stamps of Japan and Manchukuo surch "Chinese Postal Administration: Guangdong Posts and Telegraphs" and new values. (a) No. 316 of Japan surch with Type NE **19**.
NE50 $5 on 3s. green . . . . 32·00 20·00

(b) Stamps of Manchukuo surch as Type NE **19**.
NE51 $10 on 1f. red (No. 80) . . 75·00 50·00
NE52 $50 on 2f. green (No. 82) £200 £130
NE53 $100 on 4f. green (No. 84) £300 £225

(c) Stamps of Manchukuo surch as Type NE **20**.
NE54 $10 on 2f. green (No. 82) 85·00 50·00
NE55 $50 on 1f. red (No. 80) . . £100 70·00

NE **21** Peasant and Artisan

NE **23** Dalian Port

1949.
NE56 NE **21** $5 green . . . . . . 2·00 8·00
NE57 – $10 orange . . . . 25·00 25·00
NE58 NE **23** $50 red . . . . . 14·00 12·00

DESIGN—VERT: $10, "Transport".

For designs as Type NE **23** but with different character in bottom panel, see No. NE62.

NE **24** "Labour"

NE **25** Mao Tse-tung

1949. Labour Day.
NE59 NE **24** $10 red . . . . . . 15·00 18·00

1949. 28th Anniv of Chinese Communist Party.
NE61 NE **25** $50 red . . . . . . 25·00 22·00

1949. Bottom panel inscr "Lushuan and Dalian Post and Telegraphic Administration".
NE62 NE **23** $50 red . . . . . . 24·00 18·00

NE **27** Heroes' Monument, Dalian

1949. 4th Anniv of Victory over Japan and Opening of Dalian Industrial Fair.
NE63 NE **27** $10 red, blue & lt bl 32·00 35·00
NE64 $10 red, blue & green . . . . . . 10·00 12·00

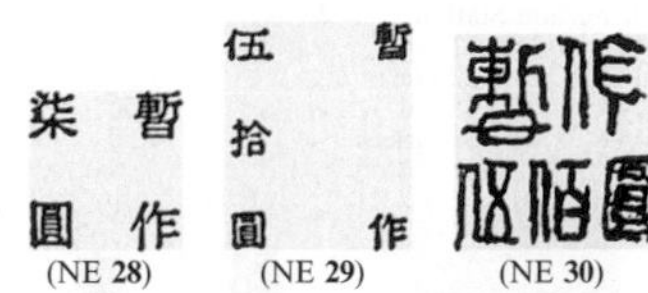

(NE **28**) (NE **29**) (NE **30**)

1949. Nos. NE56/7 surch as Types NE **28/30**.
NE65 NE **28** $7 on $5 green . . . 13·00 10·00
NE66 NE **29** $50 on $5 green . . . 38·00 35·00
NE67 $100 on $10 orange £250 £250
NE68 NE **30** $500 on $5 green . . £500
NE69 NE **29** $500 on $10 orge . . £1000 £1100
NE70 NE **30** $500 on $10 orge . . £450 £425

NE **31** Acclamation of Mao Tse-tung

1949. Founding of Chinese People's Republic.
NE71 NE **31** $35 red, yellow & bl 14·00 14·00

NE **32** Stalin and Lenin

1949. 32nd Anniv of Russian October Revolution.
NE72 NE **32** $10 green . . . . . 9·00 9·00

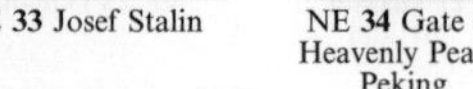

NE 33 Josef Stalin — NE 34 Gate of Heavenly Peace, Peking

1949. Stalin's 70th Birthday.
NE73 NE 33 $20 purple . . . . . 16·00 18·00
NE74 $35 red . . . . . . 16·00 18·00

1950.
NE75 NE 34 $10 blue . . . . . . 6·50 4·50
NE76 $20 green . . . . . 30·00 14·00
NE77 $35 red . . . . . . 1·25 3·50
NE78 $50 lilac . . . . . . 2·00 3·50
NE79 $100 mauve . . . . . 1·25 9·50

All Soviet forces were withdrawn by 26 May 1955 and the stamps of the Chinese People's Republic are now in use.

D. North-East China People's Post

NE 48 Mao Tse-tung — NE 49 Mao Tse-tung

1946.
NE133 NE 48 $1 violet . . . . . 5·00 6·00
NE134 NE 49 $2 red . . . . . . 1·75 2·75
NE135 $5 orange . . . . 2·25 2·75
NE136 $10 blue . . . . . 1·75 2·75

NE 50 Map of China with Communist Lion, Japanese Wolf and Chiang Kai-shek — NE 51 Railwaymen

1946. 10th Anniv of Seizure of Chiang Kai-shek at Xi'an.
NE137 NE 50 $1 violet . . . . . 50 3·50
NE138 $2 orange . . . . . 50 3·50
NE139 $5 brown . . . . . 3·50 5·50
NE140 $10 green . . . . . 10·00 8·00

1947. 24th Anniv of Massacre of Strikers at Zhengzhou Station.
NE141 NE 51 $1 red . . . . . . 1·25 3·25
NE142 $2 green . . . . . 1·50 3·25
NE143 $5 red . . . . . . 1·50 3·25
NE144 $10 green . . . . . 4·50 6·75

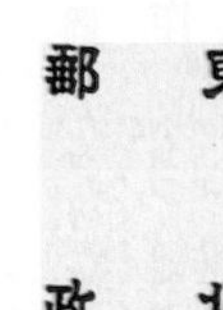

NE 52 Women Cheering — (NE 53)

1947. International Women's Day.
NE145 NE 52 $5 red . . . . . . 50 3·50
NE146 $10 brown . . . . 50 3·50

1947. Optd with Type NE 53 ("North East Postal Service").
NE147 NE 53 $5 red . . . . . . 5·00 4·50
NE148 $10 brown . . . . 5·00 4·50

NE 54 Children's Troop-comforts Unit — NE 55 Peasant and Workman

1947. Children's Day.
NE149 NE 54 $5 red . . . . . . 3·00 3·50
NE150 $10 green . . . . . 3·00 3·75
NE151 $30 orange . . . . 4·00 4·75

1947. Labour Day.
NE152 NE 55 $10 red . . . . . 1·00 2·50
NE153 $30 blue . . . . . 2·00 2·50
NE154 $50 green . . . . . 2·75 2·50

NE 56 "Freedom" — (NE 57)

1947. 28th Anniv of Students' Rebellion, Peking University.
NE155 NE 56 $10 green . . . . . 3·00 3·25
NE156 $30 brown . . . . 3·00 3·25
NE157 $50 violet . . . . 3·00 3·25

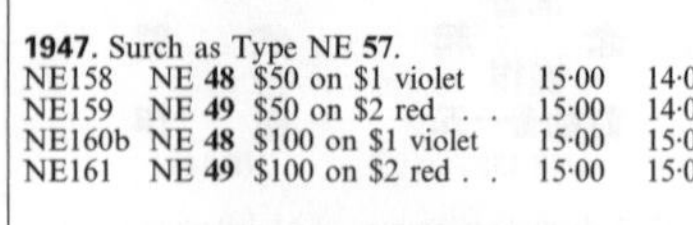

1947. Surch as Type NE 57.
NE158 NE 48 $50 on $1 violet 15·00 14·00
NE159 NE 49 $50 on $2 red . . 15·00 14·00
NE160b NE 48 $100 on $1 violet 15·00 15·00
NE161 NE 49 $100 on $2 red . . 15·00 15·00

NE 58 Youths with Banner

1947. 22nd Anniv of Nanjing Road Incident, Shanghai.
NE162 NE 58 $2 red and mauve 1·50 2·50
NE163 $5 red and green 1·50 2·50
NE164 $10 red & yellow 2·00 2·50
NE165 $20 red & violet . . 2·00 2·50
NE166 $30 red & brown 3·00 3·00
NE167 $50 red and blue 5·00 3·50
NE168 $100 red & brown 7·50 5·00

NE 59 Mao Tse-tung

1947. 26th Anniv of Chinese Communist Party.
NE170 NE 59 $10 red . . . . . 5·00 6·50
NE171 $30 mauve . . . . 5·00 6·75
NE172 $50 purple . . . . 8·00 7·00
NE173 $100 red . . . . . 12·00 9·00

NE 60 Hand grasping rifle — NE 61 Mountains and River

1947. 10th Anniv of Outbreak of War with Japan.
NE174 NE 60 $10 orange . . . . 5·00 5·50
NE175 $30 green . . . . . 5·00 5·50
NE176 $50 blue . . . . . 6·00 5·50
NE177 $100 brown . . . . 7·50 5·50

1947. 2nd Anniv of Japanese Surrender.
NE179 NE 61 $10 brown . . . . 7·50 8·00
NE180 $30 green . . . . . 7·50 8·00
NE181 $50 green . . . . . 5·00 8·00
NE182 $100 brown . . . . 12·00 8·00

(NE 62) — NE 63 Map of Manchuria

1947. Surch as Type NE 62.
NE183 NE 48 $5 on $1 violet . 20·00 20·00
NE184 NE 49 $10 on $2 red . . 20·00 20·00

1947. 16th Anniv of Japanese Attack on Manchuria.
NE185 NE 63 $10 green . . . . . 6·00 7·50
NE186 $20 mauve . . . . 4·00 7·50
NE187 $30 brown . . . . 2·00 7·50
NE188 $50 red . . . . . . 10·00 7·50

NE 64 Mao Tse-tung — NE 65 Offices of N.E. Political Council

1947.
NE189 NE 64 $1 purple . . . . . 2·50 6·00
NE190 $5 green . . . . . 3·00 6·00
NE191 $10 green . . . . . 10·00 12·00
NE192 $15 violet . . . . 5·00 10·00
NE193 $20 red . . . . . . 40 3·50
NE194 $30 green . . . . . 20 3·50
NE195 $50 brown . . . . 15·00 13·00
NE213 $50 green . . . . . 1·00 3·00
NE196 $90 blue . . . . . 75 10·00
NE197 $100 red . . . . . 30 5·00
NE215 $150 red . . . . . 2·00 4·50
NE214 $250 lilac . . . . . 75 4·25
NE228 $300 green . . . . 32·00 32·00
NE198 $500 orange . . . 10·00 6·50
NE229 $1,000 yellow . . . 60 2·50

For stamps as Type NE 64 but with "YUAN" in top right tablet, see Nos. NE236/40.

1947. 35th Anniv of Chinese Republic.
NE199 NE 65 $10 yellow . . . . 15·00 22·00
NE200 $20 red . . . . . . 15·00 22·00
NE201 $100 brown . . . . 50·00 35·00

NE 66 — NE 67 Tomb of Gen. Li Zhaolin

1947. 11th Anniv of Seizure of Chiang Kai-shek at Xi'an.
NE202 NE 66 $30 red . . . . . 5·00 10·00
NE203 $90 blue . . . . . 6·50 12·00
NE204 $150 green . . . . 8·50 12·00

1948. 2nd Death Anniv of Gen. Li Zhaolin.
NE205 NE 67 $30 green . . . . . 10·00 12·00
NE206 $150 lilac . . . . . 10·00 12·00

NE 68 Flag and Globe — NE 69 Youth with Torch

1948. Labour Day.
NE207 NE 68 $50 red . . . . . 4·00 10·00
NE208 $150 green . . . . 2·00 12·00
NE209 $250 violet . . . . 1·00 20·00

1948. Youth Day.
NE210 NE 69 $50 green . . . . . 10·00 10·00
NE211 $150 brown . . . . 10·00 10·00
NE212 $250 red . . . . . 15·00 13·00

(NE 70) — NE 71 Crane Operator

1948. Surch as Type NE 70.
NE217a NE 64 $100 on $1 purple 18·00 18·00
NE218 $100 on $15 violet 15·00 15·00
NE219 $300 on $5 green 20·00 20·00
NE220 $300 on $30 green 7·50 12·00
NE221 $300 on $90 blue 7·50 12·00
NE230 NE 49 $500 on $2 red . . 6·00 7·50
NE222 NE 64 $500 on $50 green 8·50 13·00
NE231 NE 49 $1,500 on $5 orge 6·00 7·50
NE223 NE 64 $1,500 on $150 red . . . . . . 7·50 15·00
NE232 NE 49 $2,500 on $10 blue 6·00 7·50
NE224 NE 64 $2,500 on $300 grn . . . . . . 7·50 15·00

1948. All-China Labour Conference.
NE225 NE 71 $100 red & pink . . 50 2·50
NE226 $300 brown & yell 3·00 4·50
NE227 $500 blue & green 1·25 2·50

NE 72 Workman, Soldier and Peasant — NE 74 "Production in Field and Industry"

1948. Liberation of the North East.
NE233 NE 72 $500 red . . . . . 5·00 5·50
NE234 $1,500 green . . . 7·00 7·50
NE235 $2,500 brown . . . 11·00 10·00

1949. As Type NE 64 but "YUAN" at top right.
NE236 $300 green . . . . . . 1·50 3·50
NE237 $500 orange . . . . . 2·00 2·50
NE238 $1,500 green . . . . . 20 2·50
NE239 $4,500 brown . . . . . 20 2·75
NE240 $6,500 blue . . . . . . 20 3·25

1949.
NE241 NE 74 $5,000 blue . . . . 3·75 5·50
NE242 $10,000 orange . . 20 4·25
NE243 $50,000 green . . . 20 5·00
NE244 $100,000 violet . . 20 11·00

NE 75 Workers and Banners — NE 76 Workers' Procession

1949. Labour Day.
NE245 NE 75 $1,000 red and blue 30 1·50
NE246 $1,500 red and blue 30 1·50
NE247 $4,500 red & brown 30 1·50
NE248 $6,500 brown & grn . . . . . . 30 1·50
NE249 $10,000 purple & bl 1·00 1·50

1949. 28th Anniv of Chinese Communist Party.
NE250 NE 76 $1,500 red, vio & bl 30 1·50
NE251 $4,500 red, brn & bl . . . . . . 40 1·50
NE252 $6,500 red, pink & bl . . . . . . 1·25 1·50

NE 77 North-East Heroes, Monument — NE 78 Factory

1949. 4th Anniv of Japanese Surrender.
NE253 NE 77 $1,500 red . . . . 20 1·50
NE254 $4,500 green . . . 75 1·50
NE255 $6,500 blue . . . . 85 1·50

REPRINTS. The note above No. 1401 of China also refers here to Nos. NE257/60, 261/3, 271/4, 286/89 and 312/4.

1949.
NE256 NE 78 $1,500 red . . . . 35 1·75

1949. 1st Session of Chinese People's Political Conference. As T **181** of People's Republic but with additional inscr.
NE257 $1,000 blue . . . . 5·00 7·50
NE258 $1,500 red . . . . 5·00 7·50
NE259 $3,000 green . . . . . . 5·00 7·50
NE260 $4,500 purple . . . . . . 5·00 8·50

1949. World Federation of Trade Unions, Asiatic and Australasian Conference, Peking. As T **182** of People's Republic but with additional inscr.
NE261 $5,000 red . . . . 60·00 40·00
NE262 $20,000 green . . . . . 60·00 40·00
NE263 $35,000 blue . . . . . . £100 50·00

(NE 79)

1949. Surch as T NE 79.
NE264 NE 64 $2,000 on $300 green . . . . . 5·00 6·50
NE265 $2,000 on $4,500 brown . . . . . 32·00 28·00
NE266 $2,500 on $1,500 green . . . . . 30 5·00
NE267 $2,500 on $6,500 blue . . . . . 16·00 15·00
NE268 NE 78 $5,000 on $1,500 red . . . . . 75 2·50
NE269 NE 64 $20,000 on $4,500 brown . . . . . 20 3·50
NE270 $35,000 on $300 green . . . . . 20 3·50

1950. Chinese People's Political Conference. As T **183/4** of People's Republic but with additional inscr.
NE271 $1,000 red . . . . 7·50 8·00
NE272 $1,500 blue . . . . 7·50 8·00
NE273 $5,000 purple . . . . . . 8·50 8·00
NE274 $20,000 green . . . . . . 10·00 8·00

1950. As T **185** of People's Republic but with additional four-character inscr.
NE303 **185** $250 brown . . . . . 10 5·00
NE275 $500 green . . . . . . 10 2·00

NE276		$1,000 orange	10	1·25
NE277		$1,000 mauve	10	2·00
NE306		$2,000 green	10	2·00
NE307		$2,500 yellow	20	2·00
NE300		$5,000 orange	1·50	1·25
NE309		$10,000 brown	30	2·00
NE310		$12,500 purple	50	6·00
NE283		$20,000 purple	40	2·00
NE301		$30,000 red	2·50	4·50
NE284		$35,000 blue	60	4·50
NE285		$50,000 green	2·50	4·50
NE302		$100,000 violet	1·00	4·50

1950. Foundation of People's Republic. Additional inscr at left.

NE286	**188**	$5,000 red, yell & grn	40·00	40·00
NE287		$10,000 red, yell & brn	40·00	40·00
NE288		$20,000 red, yell & pur	50·00	40·00
NE289		$30,000 red, yell & bl	60·00	55·00

1950. Peace Campaign. Additional characters below olive branch.

NE290	**191**	$2,500 brown	10·00	10·00
NE291		$5,000 green	10·00	10·00
NE292		$20,000 blue	12·00	12·00

1950. 1st Anniv of People's Republic. Additional characters at left. Flag in red, yellow and brown.

NE293	**193**	$1,000 violet	26·00	30·00
NE294		$2,500 brown	28·00	30·00
NE295		$5,000 green (44 × 53 mm)	40·00	30·00
NE296		$10,000 green	50·00	35·00
NE297		$20,000 blue	60·00	40·00

1950. 1st All-China Postal Conference. Additional characters at left.

NE298	**194**	$2,500 brown & green	5·00	5·00
NE299		$5,000 green and red	5·00	5·00

1950. Sino-Soviet Treaty. Additional characters in top right-hand coner.

NE312	**195**	$2,500 red	8·00	8·00
NE313		$5,000 green	8·00	8·00
NE314		$20,000 blue	12·00	12·00

PARCELS POST STAMPS

NEP 82

1951.

NEP315	NEP **82**	$1,000,000 violet	40·00
NEP316		$300,000 purple	£100
NEP317		$500,000 green	£170
NEP318		$1,000,000 red	£300

E. North-West China People's Post

NW **25** Mao Tse-tung

NW **26** Great Wall

1949. Imperf.

NW 97	NW **25**	$50 pink	2·50	3·25
NW 98	NW **26**	$100 blue	20	50
NW 99	NW **25**	$200 orange	4·00	3·75
NW100	NW **26**	$400 brown	3·00	2·00

F. South-West China People's Post

SW **3** Zhu De, Mao Tse-tung and Troops

SW **4** Map of China with Flag in S.W.

1949.

SW 9	SW **3**	$10 blue	5·00	3·50
SW10		$20 purple	20	2·25
SW11		$30 orange	20	1·00
SW12		$50 green	50	75
SW13		$100 red	25	60
SW14		$200 blue	1·75	75
SW15		$300 violet	5·00	1·25
SW16		$500 grey	7·50	3·25
SW17		$1,000 purple	10·00	6·00
SW18		$2,000 green	18·00	15·00
SW19		$5,000 orange	20·00	20·00

For other values in this design see East China, Nos. EC378/82.

1950. Liberation of the South West.

SW20	SW **4**	$20 blue	25	1·00
SW21		$30 green	1·60	2·25
SW22		$50 red	35	1·25
SW23		$100 brown	75	1·25

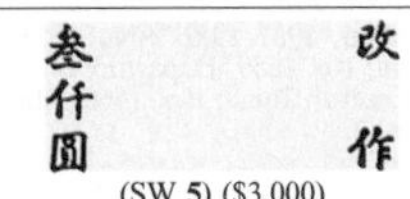

(SW 5) ($3,000)

伍仟圓 壹萬圓 貳萬圓 伍萬圓

($5,000) ($10,000) ($20,000) ($50,000)

1950. Surch as Type SW **5** (characters in left-hand column of surcharge differ as indicated in illustrations and footnote).

SW24	SW **4**	$60 on $30 green	15·00	12·00
SW25		$150 on $30 green	14·00	10·00
SW26		$300 on $20 blue	1·25	2·25
SW27		$300 on $100 brown	15·00	6·00
SW28		$1,500 on $100 brown	15·00	10·00
SW29		$3,000 on $50 red	8·50	7·00
SW30		$5,000 on $50 red	4·00	5·50
SW31		$10,000 on $50 red	40·00	20·00
SW32		$20,000 on $50 red	5·00	20·00
SW33		$50,000 on $50 red	4·00	40·00

Nos. SW24 and SW26/7 have three characters in left-hand column; Nos. SW25 and SW28 have five.

G. Chinese People's Republic

1949. Yuans.
1955. 100 fen = 1 yuan.

GUM or NO GUM. Nos. 1401/1891 were issued without gum (except Nos. 1843/5 and 1850/7). From No. 1892 onwards all postage stamps were issued with gum, unless otherwise stated. From 1965 some issues seem to have no gum, though in fact they bear an adhesive substance.

SERIAL MARKINGS. Issues other than definitive issues are divided into two categories: "commemorative" and "special". Figures below the design of each stamp of such issues indicate: (a) serial number of the issue; (b) number of stamps in the issue; (c) number of stamps within the issue; and (d) year of issue (from No. 1557 on). Neither chronological order of issue nor sequence of value is always strictly followed. From No. 2343 these serial markings were omitted until No. 2433.

REPRINTS were later made in replacement of exhausted stocks by the Chinese Postal Administration for sale to stamp collectors and were not available for postal purposes. Nos. 1401/11, 1432/5, 1456/8, 1464/73, 1507/9, 1524/37 and 1543/52. Our prices are for originals. For notes describing the distinguishing features of the reprints, see Stanley Gibbons Part 17 (China) Catalogue.

For other values in the following types see North East China.

181 Celebrations at Gate of Heavenly Peace, Peking

182 Globe, Fist and Banner

1949. Celebration of First Session of Chinese People's Political Conference.

1401	**181**	$30 blue	1·75	1·50
1402		$50 red	1·90	1·50
1403		$100 green	1·90	1·50
1404		$200 purple	2·00	1·50

1949. World Federation of Trade Unions. Asiatic and Australasian Congress, Peking.

1405	**182**	$100 red	4·50	3·50
1406		$300 green	4·50	2·50
1407		$500 blue	4·50	3·50

183 Conference Hall

184 Mao Tse-tung

1950. Chinese People's Political Conference.

1408	**183**	$50 red	3·50	2·50
1409		$100 blue	3·50	2·50
1410	**184**	$300 purple	3·50	2·50
1411		$500 green	3·50	2·50

185 Gate of Heavenly Peace, Peking

1950.

1412	**185**	$200 green	8·00	50
1413		$300 lake	20	80
1414		$500 red	20	20
1415		$800 orange	60·00	30
1420a		$1,000 lilac	1·00	20
1417		$2,000 olive	7·00	15
1420b		$3,000 brown	1·00	40
1418		$5,000 pink	10	60
1419		$8,000 blue	10	12·00
1420c		$10,000 brown	1·00	30

See also Nos. 1481a/7 and 1493/8.

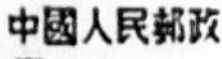

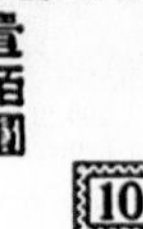

(**186**)

187 Harvesters and Ox

1950. Surch as T **186**. Perf or roul.

1427	**148**	$100 on (–) mauve	40	1·25
1428	**149**	$200 on (–) red	1·75	1·00
1429	**147**	$300 on (–) green	15	1·50
1424	**146**	$500 on (–) orange	30	15
1430		$800 on (–) orange	3·25	30
1426		$1,000 on (–) orange	20	20

1950. Unissued stamp of East China surch.

1431	**187**	$20,000 on $10,000 red	£400	32·00

188 Mao Tse-tung, Flag and Parade

1950. Foundation of People's Republic on 1 October 1949.

1432	**188**	$800 red, yellow & green	25·00	7·75
1433		$1,000 red, yellow & brn	25·00	7·75
1434		$2,000 red, yellow & pur	30·00	7·25
1435		$3,000 red, yellow & blue	30·00	9·25

中國人民郵政 伍拾圓 ☆ 50

(**189**)

中國人民郵政 壹佰圓 ★★ 100

(**190**)

1950. Stamps of North Eastern Provinces surch as T **189**.

1436	**5**	$50 on 20c. green	4·00	5·00
1437		$50 on 25c. brown	2·25	3·00
1438		$50 on 50c. orange	50	50
1439		$100 on $2.50 blue	50	50
1440		$100 on $3 brown	3·25	3·00
1441		$100 on $4 brown	3·25	5·00
1442		$100 on $5 green	3·25	2·75
1443		$100 on $10 red	11·50	7·50
1444		$400 on $20 green	70·00	32·00
1445		$400 on $44 red	2·00	3·00
1446		$400 on $65 green	£110	60·00
1447		$400 on $100 green	30·00	7·50
1448		$400 on $200 brown	60·00	14·00
1449		$400 on $300 green	60·00	15·00

1950. Nos. 1344/7 and unissued values of Nationalist China (Whistling Swans) surch as T **190**.

1450	**169**	$50 on 10c. blue	10	50
1451		$100 on 16c. green	10	35
1452		$100 on 50c. green	20	20
1453		$200 on $1 orange	20	20
1453a		$200 on $2 blue	6·00	50
1454		$400 on $5 red	20	30
1455		$400 on $10 green	40	65
1455a		$400 on $20 purple	50	95

Nos. 1451/2 are imperf.

191 "Peace" (after Picasso)

192 Gate of Heavenly Peace, Peking

1950. Peace Campaign (1st issue).

1456	**191**	$400 brown	12·00	4·50
1457		$800 green	12·00	4·50
1458		$2,000 blue	12·00	5·00

See also Nos. 1510/12 and 1590/2.

1950. Clouds redrawn.

1481a	**192**	$100 blue	20	20
1482		$200 green	7·50	1·25
1483		$300 lake	20	80
1483a		$400 green	7·50	20
1484		$500 red	30	20
1462		$800 orange	12·00	10
1485a		$1,000 violet	30	25
1463		$2,000 olive	4·00	30
1486a		$3,000 brown	40	1·00
1487		$5,000 pink	40	1·25

193 Flag of People's Republic

194 "Communications"

1950. 1st Anniv of People's Republic. Flag in red, yellow and brown.

1464	**193**	$100 violet	15·00	4·00
1465		$400 brown	15·00	4·00
1466		$800 green (44 × 53 mm)	15·00	4·00
1467		$1,000 olive	20·00	8·00
1468		$2,000 blue	35·00	10·00

1950. 1st All-China Postal Conference.

1469	**194**	$400 brown and green	7·25	3·50
1470		$800 green and red	7·25	1·75

195 Stalin greets Mao Tse-tung

1950. Sino-Soviet Treaty.

1471	**195**	$400 red	8·00	6·00
1472		$800 green	10·00	2·75
1473		$2,000 blue	14·00	5·00

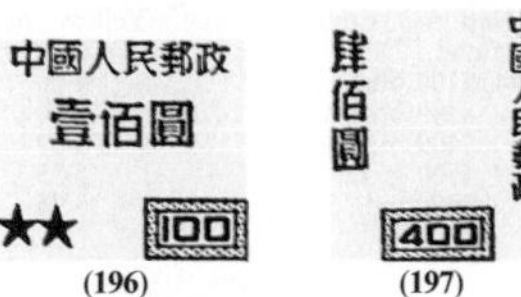

(**196**) (**197**)

1950. Nos. EC364/5a, EC367 and EC370/1 of East China People's Post surch as T **196**.

1474		$50 on $10 blue	15	40
1475		$100 on $15 red	10	25
1476		$300 on $50 red	10	25
1477		$400 on $1,600 purple	2·75	1·25
1478		$400 on $2,000 lilac	1·00	70

1950. Stamps of East China surch as T **197**.

1479	EC **112**	$50 on $10 blue	10	45
1480		$400 on $15 red	10	35
1481		$400 on $2,000 green	2·50	50

198 Temple of Heaven and Ilyushin Il-18

1951. Air.

1488	**198**	$1,000 red	35	1·00
1489		$3,000 green	40	75
1490		$5,000 orange	80	75
1491		$10,000 green and purple	1·60	1·40
1492		$30,000 brn and blue	3·50	3·50

1951. Pink network background.

1493	**185**	$10,000 brown	75	5·00
1494		$20,000 olive	1·40	2·25
1495		$30,000 green	60·00	35·00

1496		$50,000 violet	60·00	22·00
1497		$100,000 red	£3000	£120
1498		$200,000 blue	£2500	£200

中國人民郵政 貳拾伍圓 25

(200)

201 Mao Tse-tung

1951. Surch as T **200**. Perf or roul.

1503	**148**	$5 on (–) mauve	3·25	1·00
1500	**147**	$10 on (–) green	25	75
1501	**149**	$15 on (–) red	20	75
1506	**146**	$25 on (–) orange	70	75

1951. 30th Anniv of Chinese Communist Party.

1507	**201**	$400 brown	3·75	2·50
1508		$500 green	4·25	2·50
1509		$800 red	5·00	1·50

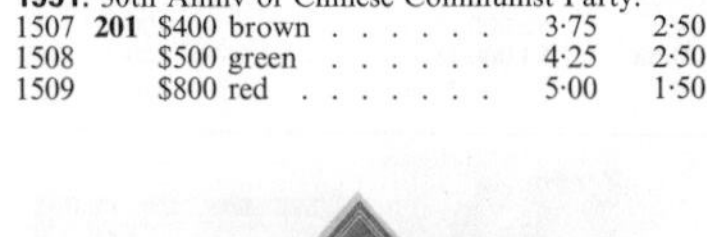

202 Dove of Peace, after Picasso

1951. Peace Campaign (2nd issue).

1510	**202**	$400 brown	10·00	4·00
1511		$800 green	10·00	2·50
1512		$1,000 violet	10·00	2·75

伍拾圓 中國人民郵政 50

(203)

204 National Emblem

1951. Money Order stamps as North China, Type NC **77**, surch with T **203**. Perf or roul.

1513		$50 on $2 green	75	2·00
1515		$50 on $5 orange	30	70
1517		$50 on $50 grey	20	15

1951. National Emblem Issue. Yellow network background.

1519	**204**	$100 blue	4·00	2·25
1520		$200 brown	4·00	2·40
1521		$400 orange	5·00	1·60
1522		$500 green	5·25	1·60
1523		$800 red	5·25	1·60

205 Lu Hsun

1951. 15th Death Anniv of Lu Hsun (author).

1524	**205**	$400 violet	3·50	2·00
1525		$800 green	5·50	1·00

206 Rebels at Chintien

1951. Centenary of Taiping Rebellion.

1526	**206**	$400 green	5·50	3·25
1527		$800 red	5·50	2·50
1528	–	$800 orange	5·50	2·50
1529	–	$1,000 blue	5·50	2·75

DESIGN: Nos. 1528/9, Coin and Documents of Taiping "Heavenly Kingdom of Great Peace".

207 Peasants and Tractor

1952. Agrarian Reform.

1530	**207**	$100 red	4·00	2·25
1531		$200 blue	4·00	2·25
1532		$400 brown	4·50	2·00
1533		$800 green	4·50	1·25

208 The Potala, Lhasa

209 "Child Protection"

1952. Liberation of Tibet.

1534	**208**	$400 red	5·50	1·60
1535	–	$800 green	5·50	1·60
1536	**208**	$800 red	5·50	1·60
1537	–	$1,000 violet	5·50	1·60

DESIGN: Nos. 1535, 1537 Tibetan ploughing with yaks.

1952. Int Child Protection Conference, Vienna.

1538	**209**	$400 green	60	10
1539		$800 blue	60	10

210 Hammer and Sickle

211 Gymnast

1952. Labour Day. Dated "1952".

1540	**210**	$800 red	20	10
1541	–	$800 green	20	10
1542	–	$800 brown	20	10

DESIGNS: No. 1541, Hand and dove; No. 1542, Hammer, dove and ear of corn.

1952. Gymnastics by Radio. As T **211**.

1543	$400 red (14–17)	3·00	1·00
1544	$400 deep blue (18–21)	3·00	1·00
1545	$400 purple (22–25)	3·00	1·00
1546	$400 green (26–29)	3·00	1·00
1547	$400 red (30–33)	3·00	1·00
1548	$400 blue (34–37)	3·00	1·00
1549	$400 orange (38–41)	3·00	1·00
1550	$400 violet (42–45)	3·00	1·00
1551	$400 bistre (46–49)	3·00	1·00
1552	$400 pale blue (50–53)	3·00	1·00

DESIGNS: Various gymnastic exercises, the stamps in each colour being arranged in blocks of four throughout the sheet, each block showing four stages of the exercise depicted. Where two stages are the same, the stamps differ only in the serial number in brackets, in the right-hand corner of the bottom margin of the stamp. The serial numbers are shown above after the colours of the stamps.

Prices are for single stamps.

212 "A Winter Hunt" (A.D. 386–580)

1952. "Glorious Mother Country" (1st issue). Tun Huang Mural Paintings.

1553	**212**	$800 sepia	50	30
1554	–	$800 brown	50	30
1555	–	$800 slate	50	30
1556	–	$800 purple	50	30

PAINTINGS: No. 1554, "Benefactor" (A.D. 581–617). No. 1555, "Celestial Flight" (A.D. 618–906). No. 1556, "Tiger" (A.D. 618–906).

See also Nos. 1565/8, 1593/96, 1601/4 and 1628/31.

213 Marco Polo Bridge, Lukouchiao

1952. 15th Anniv of War with Japan.

1557	**213**	$800 blue	75	30
1558	–	$800 green	75	30
1559	–	$800 plum	75	30
1560	–	$800 red	75	30

DESIGNS (dated "1937–1952"): No. 1558, Victory at Pinghsingkwan; No. 1559, Departure of New Fourth Army from Central China; No. 1560, Mao Tse-tung and Chu The.

214 Airman, Sailor and Soldier

217 Dove of Peace over Pacific Ocean

216 Huai River Barrage

1952. 25th Anniv of People's Liberation Army.

1561	**214**	$800 red	30	25
1562	–	$800 green	30	25
1563	–	$800 violet	50	30
1564	–	$800 brown	50	30

DESIGNS—HORIZ: No. 1562, Soldier, tanks and guns; 1563, Sailor and destroyers; 1564, Pilot, Ilyushin Il-4 DB-3 bomber and Mikoyan Gurevich MiG-15 jet fighters.

1952. "Glorious Mother Country" (2nd issue).

1565	**216**	$800 violet	25	10
1566	–	$800 red	25	10
1567	–	$800 purple	30	10
1568	–	$800 green	30	10

DESIGNS: No. 1566, Chungking–Chengtu railway viaduct; 1567, Oil refinery; 1568, Tractor, disc harrows and combine drill.

1952. Asia and Pacific Ocean Peace Conference.

1569	**217**	$400 purple	50	25
1570	–	$800 orange	50	25
1571	**217**	$800 red	60	30
1572	–	$2,500 green	60	30

DESIGNS—HORIZ: Nos. 1570 and 1572, Doves and globe.

218 Peasants collecting food for the Front

1952. 2nd Anniv of Chinese Volunteer Force in Korea.

1573	–	$800 blue	50	25
1574	**218**	$800 red	50	25
1575	–	$800 violet	50	30
1576	–	$800 brown	60	30

DESIGNS (dated "1950–1952"): HORIZ: No. 1573, Marching troops. No. 1575, Infantry attack. No. 1576, Meeting of Chinese and North Korean soldiers.

220 Textile Worker

1953. International Women's Day.

1578	**220**	$800 red	30	25
1579	–	$800 green	30	25

DESIGN: No. 1579, Woman harvesting grain.

221 Shepherdess

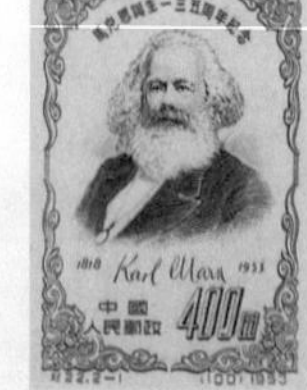

222 Karl Marx

1953.

1580	–	$50 purple	70	15
1581	**221**	$200 green	1·40	35
1582	–	$250 blue	5·00	2·00
1583	–	$800 turquoise	75	10
1584	–	$1,600 grey	70	25
1585	–	$2,000 orange	2·25	10

DESIGNS: $50, Mill girl; $250, Carved lion; $800, Lathe-operator; $1,600, Miners; $2, Old Palace, Peking.

1953. 135th Birth Anniv of Karl Marx.

1586	**222**	$400 brown	70	25
1587		$800 green	70	25

223 Workers and Flags

224 Dove of Peace

1953. 7th National Labour Union Conference.

1588	**223**	$400 blue	25	20
1589		$800 red	25	20

1953. Peace Campaign (3rd issue).

1590	**224**	$250 green	50	30
1591		$400 brown	50	30
1592		$800 violet	60	30

225 Horseman and Steed (A.D. 386–580)

1953. "Glorious Mother Country" (3rd issue).

1593	**225**	$800 green	50	10
1594	–	$800 orange	50	10
1595	–	$800 blue	50	10
1596	–	$800 red	50	10

PAINTINGS: No. 1594, Court players (A.D. 386–580). No. 1595, Battle scene (A.D. 581–617). No. 1596, Ox-drawn palanquin (A.D. 618–906).

226 Mao Tse-tung and Stalin at Kremlin

1953. 35th Anniv of Russian Revolution.

1597	**226**	$800 green	25	10
1598	–	$800 red	25	10
1599	–	$800 blue	75	10
1600	–	$800 brown	75	10

DESIGNS—HORIZ: No. 1598, Lenin addressing revolutionaries. VERT: No. 1599, Statue of Stalin; No. 1600, Stalin making speech.

227 Compass (300 B.C.)

228 Rabelais (writer)

1953. "Glorious Mother Country" (4th issue). Scientific instruments.

1601	**227**	$800 black	25	10
1602	–	$800 green	25	10
1603	–	$800 slate	30	10
1604	–	$800 brown	30	10

DESIGNS: No. 1602, Seismoscope (A.D. 132); 1603, Drum cart for measuring distances (A.D. 300); 1604, Armillary sphere (A.D. 1437).

1953. Famous Men.

1605	**228**	$250 green	40	25
1606	–	$400 purple	40	25
1607	–	$800 blue	40	30
1608	–	$2,200 brown	40	30

PORTRAITS: $400, Jose Marti (Cuban revolutionary). $800, Chu Yuan (poet). $2,200, Copernicus (astronomer).

229 Flax Mill, Harbin

1954. Industrial Development.

1609	229	$100 brown	25	15
1610	–	$200 green	30	15
1611	–	$250 violet	25	15
1612	–	$400 sepia	25	15
1613	–	$800 purple	25	15
1614	–	$800 blue	25	15
1615	–	$2,000 red	25	15
1616	–	$3,200 brown	25	15

DESIGNS: No. 1610, Tangku Harbour; 1611, Tienshui–Lanchow Railway; 1612, Heavy machine works; 1613, Blast furnace; 1614, Open-cast mines, Fuhsin; 1615, North-East Electric power station; 1616, Geological survey team.

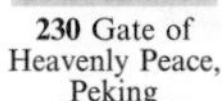

230 Gate of Heavenly Peace, Peking

231 Statue of Lenin and Stalin at Gorki

232 Lenin Speaking

233 Painted Pottery (c. 2000 B.C.)

1954.

1617	230	$50 red	10	10
1618		$100 blue	10	10
1619		$200 green	10	10
1620		$250 blue	2·25	50
1621		$400 green	45	10
1622		$800 orange	10	10
1623		$1,600 grey	10	10
1624		$2,000 olive	10	10

1954. 30th Death Anniv of Lenin.

1625	231	$400 green	90	45
1626	–	$800 brown	1·75	40
1627	232	$2,000 red	90	30

DESIGN: (25 × 37 mm) $800, Lenin (full-face portrait).

1954. "Glorious Mother Country" (5th issue).

1628	233	$800 brown	25	20
1629	–	$800 black	25	20
1630	–	$800 turquoise	30	20
1631	–	$800 lake	30	20

DESIGNS—As Type **233**: No. 1629, Musical stone (1200 B.C.); 1630, Bronze basin (816 B.C.); 1631, Lacquered wine cup and cosmetic tray (403–221 B.C.).

234 Heavy Rolling Mill

235 Statue of Stalin

1954. Anshan Steel Works.

1632	–	$400 turquoise	55	25
1633	234	$800 purple	55	25

DESIGN: $400, Seamless steel-tubing mill.

1954. 1st Death Anniv of Stalin.

1634	235	$400 black	1·60	30
1635	–	$800 sepia	75	30
1636	–	$2,000 red	1·10	45

DESIGNS—VERT: $800, Full-face portrait of Stalin (26 × 37 mm). HORIZ: $2, Stalin and hydro-electric station ($42\frac{1}{2}$ × 25 mm).

236 Exhibition Building

1954. Russian Economic and Cultural Exn, Peking.

1637	236	$800 brown on yellow	8·50	2·00

237 The Universal Fixture

238 Woman Worker

239 Rejoicing Crowds

1954. Workers' Inventions.

1638	237	$400 green	50	40
1639	–	$800 red	50	30

DESIGN: $800, The reverse repeater.

1954. 1st Session of National Congress.

1640	238	$400 purple	30	20
1641	239	$800 red	30	20

240 "New Constitution"

1954. Constitution Commemoration.

1642	240	$400 brown on buff	20	15
1643		$800 red on yellow	20	15

241 Pylons

242 Nurse and Red Cross Worker

1955. Development of Overhead Transmission of Electricity.

1644	241	$800 blue	1·50	50

1955. 50th Anniv of Chinese Red Cross.

1645	242	8f. red and green	8·50	1·40

243 Miner

244 Gate of Heavenly Peace, Peking

1955.

1646	243	½f. brown	85	10
1647	–	1f. purple	85	10
1648	–	2f. green	3·00	10
1648a	–	2½f. blue	1·75	10
1649	–	4f. green	2·40	10
1650	–	8f. red	6·00	10
1650b	–	10f. red	11·00	35
1651	–	20f. blue	11·00	40
1652	–	50f. grey	9·75	55
1653	244	1y. red	1·25	10
1654		2y. brown	1·40	10
1655		5y. grey	2·75	35
1656		10y. red	4·75	1·50
1657		20y. violet	10·00	4·50

DESIGNS—As Type **243**: 1f. Lathe operator; 2f. Airman; 2½f. Nurse; 4f. Soldier; 8f. Foundry worker; 10f. Chemist; 20f. Farm girl; 50f. Sailor.

246 Workmen and Industrial Plant

247 Chang-Heng (A.D. 78–139, astronomer)

1955. 5th Anniv of Sino–Russian Treaty.

1658	–	8f. brown	5·00	1·00
1659	246	20f. olive	7·00	1·00

DESIGN—HORIZ: (37 × 32 mm): 8f. Stalin and Mao Tse-tung.

1955. Scientists of Ancient China.

1660	247	8f. sepia on buff	2·25	25
1661	–	8f. blue on buff	2·25	25
1662	–	8f. black on buff	2·25	25
1663	–	8f. purple on buff	2·25	25

PORTRAITS: No. 1661, Tsu Chung-chi (429–500, mathematician). No. 1662, Chang-Sui (683–727, astronomer). No. 1663, Li-Shih-chen (1518–1593, pharmacologist).

248 Foundry

1955. Five Year Plan. Frames in black.

1664	248	8f. red and orange	40	10
1665	–	8f. brown and yellow	40	10
1666	–	8f. yellow and black	40	10
1667	–	8f. violet and blue	40	10
1668	–	8f. yellow and brown	40	10
1669	–	8f. yellow and red	40	10
1670	–	8f. grey and blue	40	10
1671	–	8f. orange and black	40	10
1672	–	8f. yellow and brown	40	10
1673	–	8f. red and orange	40	10
1674	–	8f. yellow and green	40	10
1675	–	8f. red and yellow	40	10
1676	–	8f. yellow and grey	40	15
1677	–	8f. yellow and blue	40	10
1678	–	8f. orange and blue	40	10
1679	–	8f. yellow and brown	40	10
1680	–	8f. red and brown	40	10
1681	–	8f. yellow and brown	40	10

DESIGNS—No. 1665, Electricity pylons; No. 1666, Mining machinery; No. 1667, Oil tankers and derricks; No. 1668, Heavy machinery workshop; No. 1669, Factory guard and industrial plant; No. 1670, Textile machinery; No. 1671, Factory workers; No. 1672, Combine-harvester; No. 1673, Dairy herd and farm girl; No. 1674, Dam; No. 1675, Artists decorating pottery; No. 1676, Lorry; No. 1677, Freighter and wharf; No. 1678, Surveyors; No. 1679, Students; No. 1680, Man, woman and child; No. 1681, Workers' rest home.

249 Lenin

1955. 85th Birth Anniv of Lenin.

1682	249	8f. blue	7·50	25
1683		20f. lake	7·50	1·40

250 Engels

1955. 60th Death Anniv of Engels.

1684	250	8f. red	7·00	25
1685		20f. sepia	7·00	1·25

251 Capture of Lu Ting Bridge

1955. 20th Anniv of Long March by Communist Army.

1686	251	8f. red	5·00	60
1687	–	8f. blue	8·00	1·25

DESIGN—VERT: (28 × 46 mm): No. 1687, Crossing the Ta Hsueh Mountains.

252 Convoy of Lorries

1956. Opening of Sikang–Tibet and Tsinghai–Tibet Highways.

1688	252	4f. blue	50	35
1689	–	8f. brown	50	20
1690	–	8f. red	50	20

DESIGNS—VERT: (21 × 42 mm): No. 1689, Suspension bridge: Tatu River. HORIZ: As T **252**: No. 1690, Opening ceremony, Lhasa.

254 Gate of Heavenly Peace

1956. Views of Peking.

1691	–	4f. red	3·00	10
1692	–	4f. green	3·00	10
1693	254	8f. red	3·00	10
1694	–	8f. blue	3·00	10
1695	–	8f. brown	3·00	10

VIEWS: No. 1691, Summer Palace; 1692, Peihai Park; 1694, Temple of Heaven; 1695, Great Throne Hall, Tai Ho Palace.

255 Salt Production

1956. Archaeological Discoveries at Chengtu.

1696	255	4f. green	40	10
1697	–	4f. black	40	10
1698	–	8f. sepia	50	10
1699	–	8f. sepia	40	10

DESIGNS—HORIZ: (Brick carvings of Tung Han Dynasty, A.D. 25–200): No. 1697, Residence; No. 1698, Hunting and farming; No. 1699, Carriage crossing bridge.

256

257 Gate of Heavenly Peace, Peking

1956. National Savings.

1700	256	4f. buff	4·50	30
1701		8f. red	5·50	25

1956. 8th National Communist Party Congress.

1702	257	4f. green	3·00	30
1703		8f. red	4·50	30
1704		16f. red	5·50	65

258 Dr. Sun Yat-sen

259 Putting the Shot

1956. 90th Birth Anniv of Dr. Sun Yat-sen.

1705	258	4f. brown	7·00	25
1706		8f. blue	6·00	1·40

1955. 1st Chinese Workers' Athletic Meeting, 1955. Inscr "1955". Flower in red and green; inscr in brown.

1707	259	4f. lake	1·10	10
1708	–	4f. purple (Weightlifting)	1·10	35
1709	–	8f. green (Sprinting)	1·50	10
1710	–	8f. blue (Football)	2·00	40
1711	–	8f. brown (Cycling)	1·50	10

260 Assembly Line

1957. Lorry Production.
1712 – 4f. brown 25 10
1713 **260** 8f. blue 40 10
DESIGN: 4f. Changchun motor plant.

261 Nanchang Revolutionaries

1957. 30th Anniv of People's Liberation Army.
1714 **261** 4f. violet 7·75 60
1715 – 4f. green 7·75 60
1716 – 8f. brown 7·75 50
1717 – 8f. blue 7·75 50
DESIGNS: No. 1715, Meeting of Red Armies at Chinkangshan; No. 1716, Liberation Army crossing the Yellow River; No. 1717, Liberation of Nanking.

262 Congress Emblem

263 Yangtse River Bridge

1957. 4th W.F.T.U. Congress, Leipzig.
1718 **262** 8f. brown 4·00 50
1719 22f. blue 3·00 50

1957. Opening of Yangtse River Bridge, Wuhan.
1720 **263** 8f. red 50 10
1721 – 20f. blue 1·00 15
DESIGN: 20f. Aerial view of bridge.

264 Fireworks over Kremlin

265 Airport Scene

1957. 40th Anniv of Russian Revolution.
1722 **264** 4f. red 4·25 20
1723 – 8f. sepia 4·25 20
1724 – 20f. green 5·50 30
1725 – 22f. brown 5·50 50
1726 – 32f. blue 9·25 1·25
DESIGNS: 8f. Soviet emblem, globe and broken chains; 20f. Dove of Peace and plant; 22f. Hands supporting book bearing portraits of Marx and Lenin; 32f. Electricity power pylon.

1957. Air.
1727 **265** 16f. blue 4·50 30
1728 – 28f. olive 10·00 2·00
1729 – 35f. black 13·00 1·75
1730 – 52f. blue 15·00 75
DESIGNS—Lisunov Li-2 over: 28f. mountain highway; 35f. railway tracks; 52f. collier at station.

266 Yellow River Dam and Power Station

1957. Harnessing of the Yellow River.
1731 – 4f. orange 7·75 30
1732 **266** 4f. blue 7·75 1·00
1733 – 8f. lake 7·75 70
1734 – 8f. green 7·75 30
DESIGNS: No. 1731, Map of Yellow River; No. 1733, Yellow River ferry; No. 1734, Aerial view of irrigation on Yellow River.

267 Ploughing

1957. Co-operative Agriculture. Multicoloured.
1735 8f. Farmer enrolling for farm 50 10
1736 8f. Type **267** 50 10
1737 8f. Tree-planting 50 10
1738 8f. Harvesting 50 10

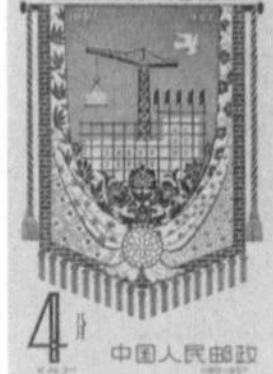
268 "Peaceful Construction"

269 High Peak Pagoda, Tenfeng

1958. Completion of First Five Year Plan.
1739 **268** 4f. green and cream 50 10
1740 – 8f. red and cream 50 10
1741 – 16f. blue and cream 50 10
DESIGNS: 8f. "Industry and Agriculture" (grapple and wheat-sheaves); 16f. "Communications and Transport" (steam train on viaduct and ship).

1958. Ancient Chinese Pagodas.
1742 **269** 8f. brown 1·40 25
1743 – 8f. blue 1·40 10
1744 – 8f. brown 1·40 15
1745 – 8f. green 1·40 10
DESIGNS: No. 1743, One Thousand League Pagoda, Tali; No. 1744, Buddha Pagoda, Yinghsien; No. 1745, Flying Rainbow Pagoda, Hungchao.

270 Trilobite of Hao Li Shan

271

1958. Chinese Fossils.
1746 **270** 4f. blue 85 10
1747 – 8f. sepia 85 10
1748 – 16f. green 85 35
DESIGNS: 8f. Dinosaur of Lufeng; 16f. "Sinomegaceros pachyospeus" (deer).

1958. Unveiling of People's Heroes Monument, Peking.
1749 **271** 8f. red 12·00 1·40

272 Karl Marx (after Zhukov)

273 Cogwheels of Industry

1958. 140th Birth Anniv of Karl Marx.
1750 **272** 8f. brown 7·50 1·40
1751 – 22f. myrtle 7·50 1·00
DESIGN: 22f. Marx addressing German workers' Educational Association, London.

1958. 8th All-China Trade Union Congress, Peking.
1752 **273** 4f. blue 6·50 1·75
1753 8f. purple 6·50 50

274 Federation Emblem

275 Mother and Child

1958. 4th International Democratic Women's Federation Congress, Vienna.
1754 **274** 8f. blue 8·50 40
1755 20f. green 8·50 2·00

1958. Chinese Children. Multicoloured.
1756 8f. Type **275** 9·75 1·10
1757 8f. Watering sunflowers 9·75 1·10
1758 8f. "Hide and seek" 9·75 1·10
1759 8f. Children sailing boat 9·75 1·10

276 Kuan Han-ching (playwright)

277 Peking Planetarium

1958. 700th Anniv of Works of Kuan Han-ching.
1760 – 4f. green on cream 6·00 2·50
1761 **276** 8f. purple on cream 8·00 1·00
1762 – 20f. black on cream 12·00 1·25
DESIGNS: Scenes from Han-ching's comedies: 4f. "The Butterfly Dream"; 20f. "The Riverside Pavilion".

1958. Peking Planetarium.
1763 **277** 8f. green 3·50 80
1764 – 20f. blue 5·00 40
DESIGN: 20f. Planetarium in operation.

278 Marx and Engels

279 Tundra Swan and Radio Pylon

1958. 110th Anniv of "Communist Manifesto".
1765 **278** 4f. purple 6·00 1·75
1766 – 8f. blue 6·00 40
DESIGN: 8f. Front cover of first German "Communist Manifesto".

1958. Organization of Socialist Countries' Postal Administrations Conference, Moscow.
1767 **279** 4f. blue 7·50 1·00
1768 8f. green 7·50 75

280 Peony and Doves

281 Chang Heng's Weather-cock

1958. International Disarmament Conf, Stockholm.
1769 **280** 4f. red 10·00 2·00
1770 – 8f. green 10·00 2·00
1771 – 22f. brown 7·50 1·75
DESIGNS: 8f. Olive branch; 22f. Atomic symbol and factory plant.

1958. Chinese Meteorology.
1772 **281** 8f. black on yellow 80 10
1773 – 8f. black on blue 80 10
1774 – 8f. black on green 80 10
DESIGNS: No. 1773, Meteorological balloon; No. 1774, Typhoon signal-tower.

282 Union Emblem within figure "5"
283 Chrysanthemum

1958. 5th International Students' Union Congress, Peking.
1775 **282** 8f. purple 7·50 50
1776 22f. green 5·50 1·00

1958. Flowers.
1777 – 1½f. mauve (Peony) 4·00 35
1778 – 3f. green (Lotus) 14·00 1·40
1779 **283** 5f. orange 2·00 35

284 Telegraph Building, Peking

1958. Opening of Peking Telegraph Building.
1780 **284** 4f. olive 1·50 30
1781 8f. red 2·75 20

285 Exhibition Emblem and Symbols

1958. National Exhibition of Industry and Communications.
1782 **285** 8f. green 6·75 80
1783 – 8f. red 6·75 80
1784 – 8f. brown 6·75 80
DESIGNS: No. 1783, Chinese dragon riding the waves; No. 1784, Horses in the sky.

286 Labourer on Reservoir Site

287 Sputnik and ancient Theodolite

1958. Inauguration of Ming Tombs Reservoir.
1785 **286** 4f. brown 50 10
1786 – 8f. blue 50 10
DESIGN: 8f. Ming Tombs Reservoir.

1958. Russian Sputnik Commemoration.
1787 **287** 4f. red 3·25 20
1788 – 8f. violet 3·25 20
1789 – 10f. green 3·50 1·10
DESIGNS: 8f. Third Russian sputnik encircling globe; 10f. Three Russian sputniks encircling globe.

288 Chinese and Korean Soldiers

1958. Return of Chinese People's Volunteers from Korea.
1790 **288** 8f. purple 1·10 10
1791 – 8f. brown 1·10 10
1792 – 8f. red 1·10 10
DESIGNS: No. 1791, Chinese soldier embracing Korean woman; No. 1792, Girl presenting bouquet to Chinese soldier.

289 Forest Landscape

1958. Afforestation Campaign.
1793 **289** 8f. green 3·00 75
1794 – 8f. slate 3·00 20
1795 – 8f. violet 3·00 20
1796 – 8f. blue 3·00 20
DESIGNS—VERT: No. 1794, Forest patrol. HORIZ: No. 1795, Tree-felling by power-saw. No. 1796, Tree planting.

290 Atomic Reactor

1958. Inauguration of China's First Atomic Reactor.
1797 **290** 8f. blue 4·50 40
1798 – 20f. brown 7·50 2·00
DESIGN: 20f. Cyclotron in action.

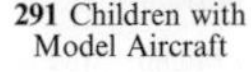

291 Children with Model Aircraft
292 Rooster

1958. Aviation Sports.
1799 **291** 4f. red 60 10
1800 – 8f. myrtle 60 10
1801 – 10f. sepia 60 10
1802 – 20f. slate . . . . 1·75 15
DESIGNS: 8f. Gliders. 10f. Parachutists; 20f. Yakovlev Yak-18U trainers.

1959. Chinese Folk Paper-cuts.
1803 – 8f. black on violet . . . 7·00 50
1804 – 8f. black on green . . . 7·00 50
1805 **292** 8f. black on red . . . 7·00 50
1806 – 8f. black on blue . . . . 7·00 50
DESIGNS: No. 1803, Camel. 1804, Pomegranate; 1806, Actress on stage.

293 Mao Tse-tung and Steel Workers
294 Chinese Women

1959. Steel Production Progress. Inscr "1958".
1807 **293** 4f. red . . . . 3·50 1·00
1808 – 8f. purple . . . . 4·50 80
1809 – 10f. red . . . . 6·00 1·00
DESIGNS: 8f. Battery of steel furnaces; 10f. Steel "blowers" and workers.

1959. International Women's Day.
1810 **294** 8f. green on cream . . . 1·00 35
1811 – 22f. mauve on cream . . 1·50 10
DESIGN: 22f. Russian and Chinese women.

295 Natural History Museum, Peking
296 Barley

1959. Opening of Natural History Museum, Peking.
1812 **295** 4f. turquoise 80 10
1813 8f. sepia 80 10

1959. Successful Harvest, 1958.
1814 8f. red (Type **296**) . . . . . 1·90 10
1815 8f. red (Rice) . . . . 1·90 10
1816 8f. red (Cotton) . . . . . . 1·90 10
1817 8f. red (Soya beans, groundnuts and rape) . . 1·90 10

297 Workers with Marx–Lenin Banner
298 Airport Building

1959. Labour Day. Inscr "1889–1959".
1818 **297** 4f. blue . . . . 4·00 80
1819 – 8f. red . . . . 6·00 70
1820 – 22f. green . . . . 5·00 30
DESIGNS: 8f. Hands clasping Red Flag; 22f. "5.1" and workers.

1959. Inauguration of Peking Airport.
1821 **298** 8f. black on lilac . . . . 6·50 95
1822 – 10f. black on green . . . 9·00 30
DESIGN: 10f. Ilyushin Il-14P at airport.

299 Students with Banners
300 F. Joliot-Curie (first President)

1959. 40th Anniv of "May 4th" Students' Rising.
1823 **299** 4f. red, brown and olive 12·00 7·00
1824 – 8f. red, brown & bistre 22·00 2·25
DESIGN: 8f. Workers with banners.

1959. 10th Anniv of World Peace Council.
1825 **300** 8f. purple . . . . 4·50 2·00
1826 – 22f. violet . . . . 7·50 50
DESIGN: 22f. Silhouettes of European, Chinese and Negro.

301 Stamp Printing Works, Peking

1959. Sino-Czech Co-operation in Postage Stamp Production.
1827 **301** 8f. myrtle . . . . 8·50 1·50

302

1959. World Table Tennis Championships, Dortmund.
1828 **302** 4f. blue and black . . . 2·50 30
1829 8f. red and black . . . . 4·00 70

303 Moon Rocket
304 "Prologue"

1959. Launching of First Lunar Rocket.
1830 **303** 8f. red, blue & black . . 13·00 1·75

1959. 1st Anniv of People's Communes.
1831 **304** 8f. red 70 20
1832 – 8f. dull purple 70 20
1833 – 8f. orange 70 20
1834 – 8f. green 70 20
1835 – 8f. blue 70 20
1836 – 8f. olive 70 20
1837 – 8f. blue 70 20
1838 – 8f. mauve 70 20
1839 – 8f. black 70 20
1840 – 8f. green 70 20
1841 – 8f. violet 70 20
1842 – 8f. red 70 20
DESIGNS: No. 1832, Steel worker ("Rural Industries"); No. 1833, Farm girl ("Agriculture"); No. 1834, Salesgirl ("Trade"); No. 1835, Peasant ("Study"); No. 1836, Militiaman ("Militia"); No. 1837, Cook with tray of food ("Community Meals"); No. 1838, Child watering flowers ("Nursery"); No. 1839, Old man with pipe ("Old People's Homes"); No. 1840, Health worker ("Public Health"); No. 1841, Young flautist ("Recreation and Entertainment"); No. 1842, Star-shaped flower ("Epilogue").

305 Mao Tse-tung and Gate of Heavenly Peace, Peking
306 Republican Emblem

1959. 10th Anniv of People's Republic. (a) 1st issue. Inscr "1949–1959". With gum.
1843 **305** 8f. red and brown . . . 10·00 1·75
1844 – 8f. red and blue . . . . 7·00 1·75
1845 – 22f. red and green . . . 7·00 1·50
DESIGNS: No. 1844, Marx, Lenin and Kremlin; No. 1845, Dove of peace and globe.

(b) 2nd issue. Emblem in red and yellow; inscriptions in yellow; background colours given.
1846 **306** 4f. turquoise . . . . . . 4·50 2·75
1847 8f. lilac . . . . 4·50 40
1848 10f. blue . . . . 5·50 50
1849 20f. buff . . . . 8·00 1·75

307 Steel Plant

(c) 3rd issue. Inscr "1949–1959". Frames in purple; centre colours given. With gum.
1850 **307** 8f. red . . . . 1·25 20
1851 – 8f. drab . . . . 1·25 50
1852 – 8f. bistre . . . . 1·25 30
1853 – 8f. blue . . . . 1·25 30
1854 – 8f. salmon . . . . . . 1·25 30
1855 – 8f. green . . . . 1·25 40
1856 – 8f. turquoise . . . . . . 1·25 30
1857 – 8f. lilac . . . . 1·25 30
DESIGNS: No. 1851, Coal-mine. No. 1852, Steelmill; No. 1853, Double-decked bridge; No. 1854, Combine-harvester; No. 1855, Dam construction; No. 1856, Textile mill; No. 1857, Chemical works.

308 Rejoicing Populace

(d) 4th Issue. Multicoloured.
1858 8f. Type **308** . . . . 2·50 1·00
1859 10f. Rejoicing people and industrial plant (vert) . . 5·00 40
1860 20f. Tree, banners and people carrying wheat and flowers (vert) . . . . . . 5·00 1·00

309 Mao Tse-tung proclaiming Republic

(e) 5th issue.
1861 **309** 20f. lake . . . . 22·00 7·25

310 Boy Bugler ("Summer Camps")
311 Exhibition Emblem and Symbols of Communication

1959. 10th Anniv of Chinese Youth Pioneers.
1862 – 4f. yellow, red & black 3·50 10
1863 **310** 4f. red and blue . . . . 3·50 10
1864 – 8f. red and brown . . . 3·50 10
1865 – 8f. red and blue . . . . 3·50 10
1866 – 8f. red and green . . . . 4·50 10
1867 – 8f. red and purple . . . 4·50 75
DESIGNS: No. 1862, Pioneers' emblem; No. 1864, Schoolgirl with flowers and satchel ("Study"); No. 1865, Girl with rain gauge ("Science"); No. 1866, Boy with sapling ("Forestry"); No. 1867, Girl skater ("Athletic Sports").

1959. National Exhibition of Industry and Communications, Peking. Inscr "1949–1959".
1868 **311** 4f. blue 45 15
1869 – 8f. red 30 15
DESIGN: 8f. Exn emblem and symbols of industry.

312 Cultural Palace of the Nationalities
313 "Statue of Sport"

1959. Inauguration of Cultural Palace of the Nationalities. Peking.
1870 **312** 4f. black and red . . . . 4·25 50
1871 8f. black and green . . . 4·25 50

1959. 1st National Games, Peking. Multicoloured.
1872 8f. Type **313** . . . . 1·40 30
1873 8f. Parachuting . . . . . . 1·40 30
1874 8f. Pistol-shooting . . . . . 1·40 30
1875 8f. Diving . . . . 1·40 30
1876 8f. Table tennis . . . . . . 1·40 30
1877 8f. Weightlifting . . . . . . 1·40 30
1878 8f. High jumping . . . . . 1·40 30
1879 8f. Rowing . . . . 1·40 30
1880 8f. Running . . . . 1·40 30
1881 8f. Basketball . . . . 1·40 30
1882 8f. Fencing . . . . 1·40 30
1883 8f. Motor cycling . . . . . 1·40 30
1884 8f. Gymnastics . . . . . . 1·40 30
1885 8f. Cycling . . . . 1·40 30
1886 8f. Horse-racing . . . . . . 1·40 30
1887 8f. Football . . . . 3·50 1·40

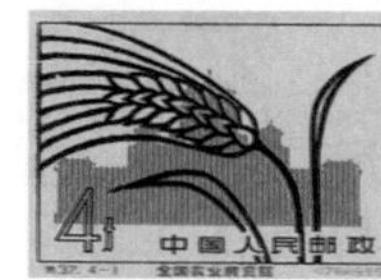

314 Wheat (Main Pavilion)

1960. Opening of National Agricultural Exhibition Hall, Peking.
1888 **314** 4f. black, red & orange 40 20
1889 – 8f. black and blue . . . 40 20
1890 – 10f. black and brown . . 50 30
1891 – 20f. black and turquoise 1·50 30
DESIGNS: 8f. Meteorological symbols (Meteorological Pavilion); 10f. Cattle (Animal Husbandry Pavilion); 20f. Fishes (Aquatic Products Pavilion).

315 Crossing the Chinsha River

1960. 25th Anniv of Conference during the Long March, Tsunyi, Kweichow.
1892 – 4f. blue . . . . 9·00 1·50
1893 – 8f. turquoise . . . . . . 9·00 3·50
1894 **315** 10f. green . . . . 18·00 1·50
DESIGNS: 4f. Conference Hall, Tsunyi; 8f. Mao Tse-tung and flags.

316 Clara Zetkin (founder)
317 Chinese and Soviet Workers

1960. 50th Anniv of International Women's Day. Frame and inscriptions black. Centre colours given.
1895 **316** 4f. blue, black & flesh 1·50 40
1896 – 8f. multicoloured . . . . 1·50 10
1897 – 10f. multicoloured . . . 1·50 20
1898 – 22f. multicoloured . . . 5·00 40
DESIGNS: 8f. Mother, child and dove; 10f. Woman tractor-driver; 22f. Women of three races.

1960. 10th Anniv of Sino-Soviet Treaty.
1899 **317** 4f. brown . . . . 7·00 1·00
1900 – 8f. black, yellow & red 7·00 1·00
1901 – 10f. blue . . . . 8·00 3·00
DESIGNS: 8f. Flowers and Sino-Soviet emblems; 10f. Chinese and Soviet soldiers.

318 Flags of Hungary and China
319 Lenin Speaking

1960. 15th Anniv of Hungarian Liberation.
1902 **318** 8f. multicoloured . . . . 9·50 1·75
1903 – 8f. red, black and blue 9·50 3·25
DESIGN: No. 1903, Parliament Building, Budapest.

1960. 90th Birth Anniv of Lenin.
1904 **319** 4f. lilac . . . . 4·50 75
1905 – 8f. black and red . . . . 5·50 2·25
1906 – 20f. brown . . . . 11·00 2·00
DESIGNS: 8f. Lenin (portrait); 20f. Lenin talking with Red Guards (after Vasilyev).

320 "Lunik 2"

321 View of Prague

1960. Lunar Rocket Flights.
1907 **320** 8f. red . . . . 4·25 75
1908 – 10f. green ("Lunik 3") 4·25 75

1960. 15th Anniv of Liberation of Czechoslovakia.
1909 – 8f. multicoloured . . . . 8·50 1·50
1910 **321** 8f. green . . . . 8·50 2·50
DESIGN—VERT: No. 1909, Child pioneers and flags of China and Czechoslovakia.

SERIAL NUMBERS. In this and many later multicoloured sets containing several stamps of the same denomination, the serial number is quoted in brackets to assist identification. This is the last figure in the bottom left corner of the stamp.

322 Narial Bouquet Goldfish

1960. Chinese Goldfish. Multicoloured.
1911 4f. (1) Type **322** . . . . . . 23·00 4·00
1912 4f. (2) Black-backed telescopic-eyed goldfish 27·00 4·00
1913 4f. (3) Bubble-eyed goldfish 27·00 5·00
1914 4f. (4) Ranchu goldfish . . . 8·00 3·00
1915 8f. (5) Pearl-scaled goldfish 40·00 6·00
1916 8f. (6) Black moor goldfish 40·00 6·00
1917 8f. (7) Celestial goldfish . . 8·00 2·50
1918 8f. (8) Oranda goldfish . . . 8·00 2·50
1919 8f. (9) Purple oranda goldfish . . . . 8·00 2·50
1920 8f. (10) Red-capped goldfish 8·00 2·50
1921 8f. (11) Red-capped oranda goldfish . . . . 27·00 6·00
1922 8f. (12) Red veil-tailed goldfish . . . . 27·00 6·00

323 Sow with Litter

1960. Pig-breeding.
1923 **323** 8f. black and red . . . . 15·00 1·50
1924 – 8f. black and green . . . 15·00 1·50
1925 – 8f. black and mauve . . . 15·00 5·00
1926 – 8f. black and olive . . . 19·00 1·50
1927 – 8f. black and orange . . 19·00 5·00
DESIGNS: No. 1924, Pig being inoculated; No. 1925, Group of pigs; No. 1926, Pig and feeding pens; No. 1927, Pig and crop-bales.

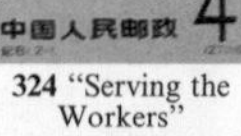

324 "Serving the Workers"

325 N. Korean and Chinese Flags, and Flowers

1960. 3rd National Literary and Art Workers' Congress, Peking. Inscr "1960".
1928 **324** 4f. red, sepia and green 7·00 1·50
1929 – 8f. red, bistre & turq . . 10·00 2·00
DESIGN: 8f. Inscribed stone seal.

1960. 15th Anniv of Liberation of Korea.
1930 **325** 8f. red, yellow and green 13·00 3·00
1931 – 8f. red, indigo and blue 13·00 3·00
DESIGN: No. 1931, "Flying Horse" of Korea.

326 Peking Railway Station

1960. Opening of New Peking Railway Station.
1932 **326** 8f. multicoloured . . . . 11·00 3·50
1933 – 10f. blue, cream & turq 16·00 4·25
DESIGN: 10f. Steam train arriving at station.

327 Chinese and N. Vietnamese Flags, and Children

328 Worker and Spray Fan

1960. 15th Anniv of N. Vietnam Republic.
1934 **327** 8f. red, yellow & black 5·50 1·00
1935 – 8f. multicoloured . . . . 5·50 2·00
DESIGN—VERT: No. 1935, "Lake of the Returning Sword", Hanoi.

1960. Public Health Campaign.
1936 **328** 8f. black and orange . . 2·10 10
1937 – 8f. green and blue . . . 2·10 10
1938 – 8f. brown and blue . . . 2·10 20
1939 – 8f. lake and brown . . . 2·10 20
1940 – 8f. blue and turquoise 2·10 65
DESIGNS: No. 1937, Spraying insecticide; No. 1938, Cleaning windows; No. 1939, Medical examination of child; No. 1940, "Tai Chi Chuan" (Chinese physical drill).

329 Facade of Great Hall

1960. Completion of "Great Hall of the People". Multicoloured.
1941 8f. Type **329** . . . . 10·00 2·50
1942 10f. Interior of Great Hall 16·00 4·00

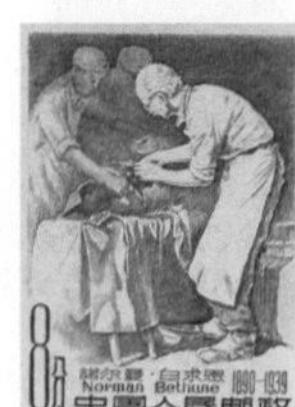

330 Dr. N. Bethune operating on Soldier

331 Friedrich Engels

1960. 70th Birth Anniv of Dr. Norman Bethune (Canadian surgeon with 8th Route Army).
1943 **330** 8f. grey, black and red 4·25 1·00
1944 – 8f. brown . . . . 4·25 30
PORTRAIT. No. 1943 Dr. N. Bethune.

1960. 140th Birth Anniv of Engels.
1945 – 8f. brown . . . . 7·00 1·75
1946 **331** 10f. orange and blue . . 10·00 2·25
DESIGN: 8f. Engels addressing congress at The Hague.

332 Big "Ju-I"

333 "Yue Jin"

1960. Chrysanthemums. Background colours given. Multicoloured.
1947 – 4f. blue . . . . 10·50 1·10
1948 – 4f. pink . . . . 21·00 1·10
1949 – 8f. grey . . . . 10·50 1·10
1950 **332** 8f. blue . . . . 10·50 1·10
1951 – 8f. green . . . . 10·50 1·10
1952 – 8f. violet . . . . 10·50 1·10
1953 – 8f. olive . . . . 10·50 1·10
1954 – 8f. turquoise . . . . . . 35·00 1·10
1955 – 10f. grey . . . . 10·50 1·10
1956 – 10f. brown . . . . 10·50 1·10
1957 – 20f. blue . . . . 10·50 1·10
1958 – 20f. red . . . . 28·00 3·50
1959 – 22f. brown . . . . 17·00 7·75
1960 – 22f. red . . . . 35·00 12·00
1961 – 30f. green . . . . 10·50 5·50
1962 – 30f. mauve . . . . 10·50 5·50
1963 – 35f. green . . . . 13·00 5·50
1964 – 52f. purple . . . . 13·00 9·25
CHRYSANTHEMUMS: No. 1947, "Hwang Shih Pa". No. 1948, "Green Peony". No. 1949, "Er Chiao". No. 1951, "Ju-I" with Golden Hooks. No. 1952, "Golden Peony". No. 1953, "Generalissimo's Banner". No. 1954, "Willow Thread". No. 1955, "Cassia on Salver of Hibiscus". No. 1956, "Pearls on Jade Salver". No. 1957, "Red Gold Lion". No. 1958, "Milky White Jade". No. 1959, "Purple Jade with Fragrant Beads". No. 1960, "Cassia on Ice Salver". No. 1961, "Inky Black Lotus". No. 1962, "Jade Bamboo Shoot of Superior Class". No. 1963, "Smiling Face". No. 1964, "Swan Ballet".

1960. 1st Chinese-built Freighter. Launching. No gum.
1965 **333** 8f. blue . . . . 3·75 1·00

334 Pantheon, Paris

336 Chan Tien-yu

335 Table Tennis Match

1961. 90th Anniv of Paris Commune.
1966 **334** 8f. black and red . . . . 9·50 1·25
1967 – 8f. sepia and red . . . . 9·50 1·25
DESIGN: No. 1967, Proclamation of Commune.

1961. 26th World Table Tennis Championships, Peking. Multicoloured.
1968 8f. Championship emblem and jasmine . . . . . . 2·25 20
1969 10f. Table tennis bat and ball and Temple of Heaven . . . . 2·50 55
1970 20f. Type **335** . . . . 2·75 55
1971 22f. Peking Workers Gymnasium . . . . . . 3·00 30

1961. Birth Centenary of Chan Tien-yu (railway construction engineer).
1972 **336** 8f. black and sage . . . 3·50 30
1973 – 10f. brown and sepia . . 6·50 1·10
DESIGN: 10f. Steam train on Peking-Changchow Railway.

337 Congress Building, Shanghai

1961. 40th Anniv of Chinese Communist Party. Flags, red; frames, gold.
1974 **337** 4f. purple . . . . 11·00 55
1975 – 8f. green . . . . 11·00 1·50
1976 – 10f. brown . . . . 11·00 5·25
1977 – 20f. blue . . . . 16·00 1·25
1978 – 30f. red . . . . 22·00 2·00
DESIGNS: 8f. "August 1" Building, Nanchang; 10f. Provisional Central Govt. Building, Juichin; 20f. Pagoda Hill, Yenan; 30f. Gate of Heavenly Peace, Peking.

338 Flags of China and Mongolia

339 "August l" Building, Nanchang

1961. 40th Anniv of Mongolian People's Revolution.
1979 **338** 8f. red, blue & yellow . . 10·00 1·40
1980 – 10f. orange, yellow & grn . . . . 17·00 6·50
DESIGN: 10f. Mongolian Government Building.

1961. Size 24 × 16½ mm. No gum.
1981 **339** 1f. blue . . . . 8·25 35
1982 1½f. red . . . . 14·00 35
1983 2f. green . . . . 8·75 1·40
1984 A 3f. violet . . . . 28·00 1·75
1985 4f. green . . . . 2·25 10
1986 5f. green . . . . 1·75 10
1987 B 8f. green . . . . 1·50 10
1988 10f. purple . . . . 3·50 10
1989 20f. blue . . . . 1·00 10
1990 C 22f. brown . . . . 1·00 10
1991 30f. blue . . . . 1·00 10
1992 50f. red . . . . 1·40 10
DESIGNS: A, Tree and Sha Chow Pa Building, Juichin; B, Yenan Pagoda; C, Gate of Heavenly Peace, Peking.
For redrawn, smaller, designs see Nos. 2010/21.

340 Military Museum

1961. People's Revolutionary Military Museum.
1993 **340** 8f. brown, green & blue 17·00 1·50
1994 10f. black, green & brn 17·00 1·50

341 Uprising at Wuhan

1961. 50th Anniv of Revolution of 1911.
1995 **341** 8f. black and grey . . . 10·00 2·25
1996 – 10f. black and brown . . 15·00 1·00
DESIGN—VERT: 10f. Dr. Sun Yat-sen.

342 Donkey

343 Tibetans Rejoicing

1961. Tang Dynasty Pottery (618–907 A.D.). Centres multicoloured. Background colours given.
1997 **342** 4f. blue . . . . 8·25 50
1998 – 8f. green . . . . 8·50 50
1999 – 8f. purple . . . . 8·50 50
2000 – 10f. blue . . . . 10·00 75
2001 – 20f. olive . . . . 10·50 2·50
2002 – 22f. turquoise . . . . . 11·50 4·00
2003 – 30f. red . . . . 13·00 10·00
2004 – 50f. slate . . . . 13·00 5·00
DESIGNS: No. 1998, Donkey; Nos. 1999/2002, Various horses; Nos. 2003/4, Various camels.

1961. "Rebirth of the Tibetan People".
2005 **343** 4f. brown and buff . . . 5·50 55
2006 – 8f. brown and turquoise 6·50 75
2007 – 10f. brown and yellow 9·50 1·25
2008 – 20f. brown and pink . . 19·00 2·25
2009 – 30f. brown and blue . . 32·00 3·50
DESIGNS: 8f. Sower; 10f. Tibetan celebrating "bumper crop"; 20f. "Responsible Citizens"; 30f. Tibetan children.

343a "August l" Building, Nanchang

344 Lu Hsun (after Hsieh Chia-seng)

1962. Size 20½ × 16½ mm. No gum.
2010 **343a** 1f. blue 50 10
2011 2f. green 50 10
2013 A 3f. violet 50 10
2014 **343a** 3f. brown . . . . 1·75 75
2015 A 4f. green 50 10
2016 B 4f. red . . . . 2·00 75
2017 C 8f. green 80 10
2018 10f. purple . . . . 1·00 10
2019 20f. blue . . . . 1·00 10
2020 B 30f. blue . . . . 1·75 10
2021 52f. red . . . . 1·90 1·00
DESIGNS: A, Tree and Sha Chow Pa Building, Juichin; B, Gate of Heavenly Peace, Peking; C, Yenan Pagoda.

1962. 80th Birth Anniv of Lu Hsun (writer).
2022 **344** 8f. black and red . . . . 1·75 50

345 Anchi Bridge, Chaohsien

1962. Ancient Chinese Bridges.
2023 **345** 4f. violet and lavender 1·75 30
2024 – 8f. slate and green . . . 1·75 30
2025 – 10f. sepia and bistre . . 2·50 65
2026 – 20f. blue and turquoise 3·50 1·25
BRIDGES: 8f. Paotai, Soochow. 10f. Chupu, Kuanhsien. 20f. Chenyang, Sankiang.

346 Tu Fu

347 Manchurian Cranes and Trees

1962. 1250th Birth Anniv of Tu Fu (poet).
2027 – 4f. black and bistre . . . 11·00 70
2028 **346** 8f. black and turquoise 11·00 1·50
DESIGN: 4f. Tu Fu's Memorial, Chengtu.

1962. "The Sacred Crane". Paintings by Chen Chi-fo. Multicoloured.
2029 8f. Type **347** . . . . 20·00 3·25
2030 10f. Two cranes in flight . . 20·00 3·75
2031 20f. Crane on rock . . . . 20·00 4·75

348 Cuban Soldier

349 Torch and Map

1962. "Support for Cuba".
2032 **348** 8f. black and lake . . . 23·00 7·00
2033 – 10f. black and green . . 23·00 2·50
2034 – 22f. black and blue . . . 50·00 17·00
DESIGNS: 10f. Sugar-cane planter; 22f. Militiaman and woman.

1961. "Support for Algeria".
2035 **349** 8f. orange and brown . . 75 15
2036 – 22f. brown and ochre . . 75 20
DESIGN: 22f. Algerian patriots.

350 Mei Lan-fang (actor)

351 Han "Flower Drum" Dance

1962. "Stage Art of Mei Lan-fang". Multicoloured. Each showing Lan-fang in stage costume with items given below.
2037 4f. Type **350** . . . . 70·00 10·00
2038 8f. Drum . . . . 20·00 3·00
2039 8f. Fan . . . . 20·00 2·50
2040 10f. Swords . . . . 20·00 3·00
2041 20f. Bag . . . . 20·00 4·00
2042 22f. Ribbons (horiz) . . . . 40·00 8·00
2043 30f. Loom (horiz) . . . . . 80·00 25·00
2044 50f. Long sleeves (horiz) . . 65·00 20·00

1962. Chinese Folk Dances (1st issue). Multicoloured. No gum.
2045 4f. Type **351** 85 35
2046 8f. Mongolian "Ordos" . . 85 35
2047 10f. Chuang "Catching shrimp" . . . . 1·00 35
2048 20f. Tibetan "Fiddle" . . . 1·25 35
2049 30f. Yi "Friend" . . . . . 2·00 75
2050 50f. Uighur "Tambourine" 5·25 1·40
See also Nos. 2104/15.

352 Soldiers storming the Winter Palace, Petrograd

1962. 45th Anniv of Russian Revolution.
2051 – 8f. brown and red . . . 18·00 1·00
2052 **352** 20f. bronze and red . . . 25·00 2·00
DESIGN—VERT: 8f. Lenin leading soldiers.

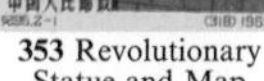
353 Revolutionary Statue and Map

354 Tsai Lun (A.D. ?–121, inventor of paper making process)

1962. 50th Anniv of Albanian Independence.
2053 **353** 8f. sepia and blue . . . 1·75 40
2054 – 10f. multicoloured . . . 2·50 60
DESIGN: 10f. Albanian flag and girl pioneer.

1962. Scientists of Ancient China. Multicoloured.
2055 4f. Type **354** . . . . . . 6·25 30
2056 4f. Paper-making . . . . . 3·25 30
2057 8f. Sun Szu-miao (581–682, physician) . . . . 3·25 30
2058 8f. Preparing medical treatise . . . . 3·25 30
2059 10f. Shen Ko (1031–1095, geologist) . . . . 3·25 40
2060 10f. Making field notes . . 4·00 50
2061 20f. Ku Shou-chin (1231–1316, astronomer) . . . . 7·75 2·75
2062 20f. Astronomical equipment 7·75 2·75

355 Tank Monument, Havana

1963. 4th Anniv of Cuban Revolution.
2063 **355** 4f. sepia and red . . . . 24·00 1·50
2064 – 4f. black and green . . . 17·00 1·50
2065 – 8f. lake and brown . . . 17·00 1·50
2066 – 8f. lake and brown . . . 55·00 4·50
2067 – 10f. black and buff . . . 55·00 6·00
2068 – 10f. sepia, red and blue 55·00 16·00
DESIGNS—As Type **355**: No. 2064, Cuban revolutionaries; No. 2067, Cuban soldier; No. 2068, Castro and Cuban flag. LARGER (48½ × 27 mm) No. 2065, Crowd in Havana (value on left); No. 2066, Crowd in Peking (value on right).

356 Tibetan Clouded Yellow

357 Marx and Engels

1963. Butterflies. Multicoloured. No gum.
2069 4f. (1) Type **356** . . . . . . 6·25 50
2070 4f. (2) Tritailed glory . . . 6·25 50
2071 4f. (3) Neumogeni jungle queen . . . . 6·25 50
2072 4f. (4) Washan swordtail . . 6·25 50
2073 4f. (5) Striped ringlet . . . 6·25 50
2074 8f. (6) Green dragontail . . 12·50 50
2075 8f. (7) Dilunuleted peacock 12·50 50
2076 8f. (8) Yamfly . . . . . . 12·50 50
2077 8f. (9) Golden kaiser-i-hind 12·50 50
2078 8f. (10) Mushaell hair-streak 12·50 50
2079 10f. (11) Yellow orange-tip 12·50 75
2080 10f. (12) Great jay . . . . 12·50 75
2081 10f. (13) Striped punch . . 12·50 75
2082 10f. (14) Beck butterfly . . . 12·50 75
2083 10f. (15) Omei skipper . . . 12·50 75
2084 20f. (16) Philippine birdwing 7·50 1·50
2085 20f. (17) Keeled apollo . . . 7·50 1·50
2086 22f. (18) Blue-banded king crow . . . . 7·50 4·00
2087 30f. (19) Solskyi copper . . 7·50 7·50
2088 50f. (20) Clipper . . . . . 15·00 15·00

1983. 145th Birth Anniv of Karl Marx. No. gum.
2089 – 8f. black, pink & gold 5·50 1·50
2090 – 8f. red and gold . . . . 5·50 1·50
2091 **357** 8f. brown and gold . . . 5·50 1·50
DESIGNS: No. 2089, Marx; No. 2090, Slogan "Workers of the World Unite" over cover of 1st edition of "Communist Manifesto".

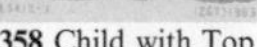
358 Child with Top

359 Giant Panda eating Apples

1963. Children. Multicoloured, background colours given. No gum.
2092 **358** 4f. turquoise 70 10
2093 – 4f. brown 70 10
2094 – 8f. grey 70 10
2095 – 8f. blue 70 10
2096 – 8f. beige 70 10
2097 – 8f. slate 70 10
2098 – 8f. green 70 10
2099 – 8f. grey 70 10
2100 – 10f. green . . . . 1·60 80
2101 – 10f. violet . . . . 1·60 80
2102 – 20f. drab . . . . 5·00 1·50
2103 – 20f. green . . . . 5·00 1·50
DESIGNS (each shows a child): No. 2093, Eating candied hawberries; No. 2094, As "traffic policeman"; No. 2095, With toy windmill; No. 2096, Listening to caged cricket; No. 2097, With toy sword; No 2098, Embroidering; No. 2099, With umbrella; No. 2100, Playing with sand; No. 2101, Playing table tennis; No. 2102, Doing sums; No. 2103, Flying kite.

1963. Chinese Folk Dances (2nd issue). As T **351** but inscr "(261) 1962" to "(266) 1962" in bottom right corner. Multicoloured. No gum.
2104 4f. Puyi "Weaving Cloth" 1·00 10
2105 8f. Kazakh . . . . 1·00 10
2106 10f. Olunchun . . . . . . 1·00 10
2107 20f. Kaochan "Labour" . . 1·00 35
2108 30f. Miao "Reed-pipe" . . . 1·75 60
2109 50f. Korean "Fan" . . . . 5·25 85

1963. Chinese Folk Dances (3rd issue). As T **351** but inscr "(279) 1963" to "(284) 1963" in bottom right corner. Multicoloured. No gum.
2110 4f. Yu "Wedding Ceremony" . . . . 1·40 20
2111 8f. Pai "Encircling Mountain Forest" . . . . 1·40 20
2112 10f. Yao "Long Drum" . . 1·60 20
2113 20f. Li "Third Day of Third Month" . . . . 1·60 40
2114 30f. Kava "Knife" . . . . 2·75 50
2115 50f. Tai "Peacock" . . . . 4·25 85

1963. Giant Panda. Perf or imperf.
2116 **359** 8f. black and blue . . . 25·00 2·00
2117 – 8f. black and green . . . 25·00 5·00
2118 – 10f. black and drab . . 25·00 3·00
DESIGNS—As Type **278**. No. 2117, Giant panda eating bamboo shoots. HORIZ: (52 × 31 mm): No. 2118, Two giant pandas.

360 Table Tennis Player

361 Snub-nosed Monkey

1963. 27th World Table-Tennis Championships.
2119 **360** 8f. grey . . . . 11·00 1·00
2120 – 8f. brown . . . . 11·00 1·50
DESIGN: No. 2120, Trophies won by Chinese team.

1963. Snub-nosed Monkeys. Multicoloured.
2121 8f. Type **361** . . . . 8·00 1·50
2122 10f. Two monkeys . . . . . 8·00 1·50
2123 22f. Two monkeys on branch of tree . . . . . 12·00 5·00

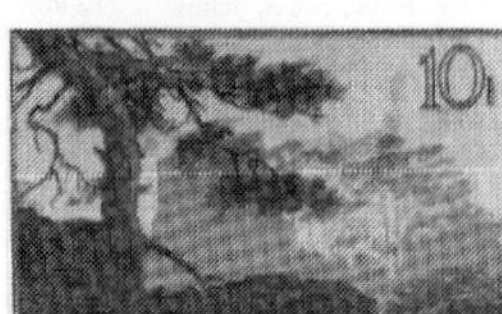
362 Old Pines of Hwangshan

1963. Hwangshan Landscapes. Multicoloured.
2124 4f. (1) Mount of The Green Jade Screen (vert) . . . . 11·50 1·00
2125 4f. (2) The Guest-welcoming Pines (vert) . . . . 11·50 1·00
2126 4f. (3) Pines and rocks behind the lake (vert) . . 11·50 1·00
2127 4f. (4) Terrace of Keeping Cool (vert) . . . . 11·50 1·00
2128 8f. (5) Mount of the Heavenly Capital (vert) 16·00 1·00
2129 8f. (6) Mount of Scissors (vert) . . . . 16·00 1·00
2130 8f. (7) Forest of Ten Thousand Pines (vert) . . 16·00 1·00
2131 8f. (8) The Flowering Bush in a Dream (vert) . . . . 16·00 1·00
2132 10f. (9) Mount of the Lotus Flower . . . . 21·00 1·00
2133 10f. (10) Cumulus Flood Wave of the Eastern Lake 21·00 1·00
2134 10f. (11) Type **362** . . . . 21·00 1·00
2135 10f. (12) Cumulus on the Eastern Lake . . . . . . 21·00 1·00
2136 20f. (13) The Stalagmite Mountain Range . . . . 28·00 7·50
2137 22f. (14) The Apes of the Stone watch the lake below . . . . 38·00 10·00
2138 30f. (15) The Forest of Lions . . . . £100 40·00
2139 50f. (16) The Fairy Isles of Peng Lai . . . . 85·00 20·00

363 Football

364 Clay Rooster and Goat

1963. "GANEFO" Athletic Games, Jakarta, Indonesia.
2140 **363** 8f. red & black on lav 11·00 75
2141 – 8f. blue & black on buff 11·00 75
2142 – 8f. brown & blk on blue 11·00 75
2143 – 8f. purple & blk on mve 11·00 75
2144 – 10f. multicoloured . . . 16·00 2·50
DESIGNS—As Type **282**: No. 2141, Throwing the discus; No. 2142, Diving; No. 2143, Gymnastics. HORIZ: (48½ × 27½ mm). No. 2144, Athletes on parade.

1963. Chinese Folk Toys. Multicoloured. No gum.
2145 4f. (1) Type **364** 85 20
2146 4f. (4) Cloth camel 85 20
2147 4f. (7) Cloth tigers 85 20
2148 8f. (2) Clay ox and rider . . 85 20
2149 8f. (5) Cloth rabbit, wooden figure and clay cock . . . 85 20
2150 8f. (8) Straw cock 85 20
2151 10f. (3) Cloth donkey and clay bird 85 20
2152 10f. (6) Clay lion 85 20
2153 10f. (9) Clay-paper tumbler and cloth tiger 85 20

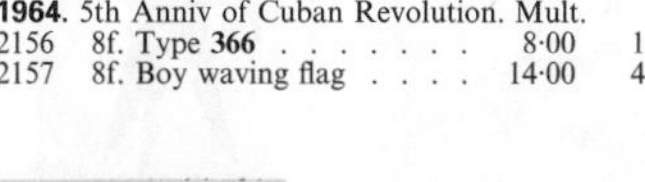
365 Vietnamese Family

366 Cuban and Chinese Flags

1963. "Liberation of South Vietnam". Mult.
2154 8f. Type **365** . . . . 4·50 1·00
2155 8f. Vietnamese with flag . . 4·50 1·00

1964. 5th Anniv of Cuban Revolution. Mult.
2156 8f. Type **366** . . . . 8·00 1·00
2157 8f. Boy waving flag . . . . 14·00 4·00

367 Woman driving Tractor

368 "Sino-African Friendship"

1964. "Women of the People's Commune". Multicoloured.
2158 8f. (1) Type **367** . . . . . . 1·10 20
2159 8f. (2) Harvesting . . . . . 1·10 20
2160 8f. (3) Picking cotton . . . 1·10 20
2161 8f. (4) Picking fruit . . . . 1·10 20
2162 8f. (5) Reading book . . . . 1·10 30
2163 8f. (6) Holding rifle . . . . 1·10 40

1964. African Freedom Day.
2164 **368** 8f. multicoloured 75 25
2165 – 8f. brown and black . . 75 25
DESIGN: No. 2165, African beating drum.

369 Marx, Engels, Lenin and Stalin

1964. Labour Day.
2166 **369** 8f. black, red & gold . . 16·00 3·50
2167 – 8f. black, red & gold . . 9·00 2·00
DESIGN: No. 2167, Workers and banners.

370 History Museum

1964. No gum.
2168 **370** 1f. brown 10 10
2169 A 1½f. purple 10 10
2170 B 2f. green 10 10
2171 C 3f. green 15 10
2172 **370** 4f. blue 15 10
2172a A 5f. purple 50 10
2173 B 8f. red 50 10
2174 C 10f. drab 75 10
2175 **370** 20f. violet 75 10
2176 A 22f. orange . . . . . . 1·40 10
2177 B 30f. green . . . . . . 2·10 40
2177a C 50f. blue . . . . . . 5·00 2·00
DESIGNS: A, Gate of Heavenly Peace; B, Great Hall of the People; C, Military Museum.

371 Date Orchard, Yenan **372** Map of Vietnam and Flag

1964. "Yenan-Shrine of the Chinese Revolution". Yenan buildings. Multicoloured.
2178 8f. (1) Type **371** . . . . . . 15·00 45
2179 8f. (2) Central Auditorium, Yang Chia Ling . . . . 3·75 25
2180 8f. (3) Mao Tse-tung's Office and Residence at Date Orchard, Yenan . . . . . 3·75 25
2181 8f. (4) Auditorium, Wang Chia Ping . . . . 3·75 30
2182 8f. (5) Border Region Assembly Hall . . . . . 22·00 75
2183 52f. (6) Pagoda Hill . . . . 12·50 5·00

1964. South Vietnam Victory Campaign.
2184 **372** 8f. multicoloured . . . . 12·50 2·50

373 "The Alchemist's Glowing Crucible" (peony) **374** "Chueh" (wine cup)

1964. Chinese Peonies. Multicoloured.
2185 4f. (1) Type **373** . . . . . . 5·75 1·00
2186 4f. (2) Night-shining Jade . . . 5·75 1·00
2187 8f. (3) Purple Kuo's Cap . . 9·50 1·00
2188 8f. (4) Chao Pinks . . . . . 9·50 1·00
2189 8f. (5) Yao Yellows . . . . 9·50 1·00
2190 8f. (6) Twin Beauties . . . 9·50 1·00
2191 8f. (7) Ice-veiled Rubies . . 9·50 1·00
2192 10f. (8) Gold-sprinkled Chinese Ink . . . . . . 12·00 1·00
2193 10f. (9) Cinnabar Jar . . . 12·00 1·00
2194 10f. (10) Lantien Jade . . . 13·50 1·00
2195 10f. (11) Imperial Robe Yellow . . . . 14·50 2·00
2196 10f. (12) Hu Reds . . . . 14·50 2·00
2197 20f. (13) Pea Green . . . . 29·00 5·00
2198 43f. (14) Wei Purples . . . 35·00 20·00
2199 52f. (15) Intoxicated Celestial Peach . . . . . 60·00 15·00

1964. Bronze Vessels of the Yin Dynasty (before 1050 B.C.).
2200 **374** 4f. (1) black, grn & yell 6·00 20
2201 – 4f. (2) black, grn & yell 6·00 20
2202 – 8f. (3) black, grn & yell 7·50 30
2203 – 8f. (4) black, blue & grn 7·50 30
2204 – 10f. (5) black and drab 9·00 40
2205 – 10f. (6) black, grn & yell 9·00 40
2206 – 20f. (7) black and grey 11·00 3·50
2207 – 20f. (8) black, bl & yell 11·00 3·50
DESIGNS: No. 2201, "Ku" (beaker); 2202, "Kuang" (wine urn); 2203, "Chia" (wine cup); 2204, "Tsun" (wine vessel); 2205, "Yu" (wine urn); 2206, "Tsun" (wine vessel); 2207, "Ting" (ceremonial cauldron).

375 "Harvesting" **376** Marx, Engels and Trafalgar Square, London (vicinity of old St. Martin's Hall)

1964. Agricultural Students. Multicoloured.
2208 8f. (1) Type **375** . . . . . . 1·60 30
2209 8f. (2) "Sapling planting" 1·60 30
2210 8f. (3) "Study" . . . . . . 1·60 30
2211 8f. (4) "Scientific experiment" . . . . . . 1·60 30

1964. Centenary of "First International".
2212 **376** 8f. red, brown and gold 35·00 7·50

377 Rejoicing People **378** Oil Derrick

1964. 15th Anniv of People's Republic. Mult.
2213 8f. (1) Type **377** . . . . . 14·00 1·75
2214 8f. (2) Chinese flag . . . . 14·00 1·75
2215 8f. (3) As T **377** in reverse 14·00 1·75
Nos. 2213/5 were issued in the form of a triptych, in sheets.

1964. Petroleum Industry. Multicoloured.
2216 4f. Geological surveyors and van (horiz) . . . . 48·00 3·00
2217 8f. Type **378** . . . . 22·00 1·00
2218 8f. Oil-extraction equipment 22·00 1·00
2219 10f. Refinery . . . . 38·00 1·00
2220 20f. Railway petroleum trucks (horiz) . . . . . 90·00 8·00

379 Albanian and Chinese Flags and Plants **380** Dam under Construction

1964. 20th Anniv of Liberation of Albania.
2221 **379** 8f. multicoloured . . . . 10·00 1·25
2222 – 10f. black, red & yellow 12·00 5·75
DESIGN: 10f. Enver Hoxha and Albanian arms.

1964. Hsinankiang Hydro-electric Power Station. Multicoloured.
2223 4f. Type **380** . . . . 60·00 2·25
2224 8f. Installation of turbo-generator rotor . . . . . 14·50 1·00
2225 8f. Main dam . . . . 45·00 1·40
2226 20f. Pylon . . . . 70·00 7·50

381 Fertilisers

1964. Chemical Industry. Main design and inscr in black; background colours given.
2227 **381** 8f. (1) red . . . . 2·00 20
2228 – 8f. (2) green . . . . . . 2·00 20
2229 – 8f. (3) brown . . . . . . 2·00 20
2230 – 8f. (4) mauve . . . . . . 2·00 20
2231 – 8f. (5) blue . . . . . . 2·00 20
2232 – 8f. (6) orange . . . . . . 2·00 20
2233 – 8f. (7) violet . . . . . . 2·00 20
2234 – 8f. (8) turquoise . . . . 2·00 20
DESIGNS: (2), Plastics; (3), Medicinal drugs; (4), Rubber; (5), Insecticides; (6), Acids; (7), Alkalis; (8), Synthetic fibres.

382 Mao Tse-tung standing in Room

1965. 30th Anniv of Tsunyi Conference. Mult.
2235 8f. (1) Type **382** . . . . . . 30·00 7·50
2236 8f. (2) Mao Tse-tung (vert) (26½ × 36 mm) . . . . . 15·00 10·00
2237 8f. (3) "Victory at Loushan Pass" . . . . 25·00 14·00

383 Conference Hall **384** Lenin

1965. 10th Anniv of Bandung Conference. Mult.
2238 8f. Type **383** . . . . 1·00 30
2239 8f. Rejoicing Africans and Asians . . . . 1·00 30

1965. 95th Birth Anniv of Lenin.
2240 **384** 8f. multicoloured . . . . 10·50 4·00

385 Table Tennis Player **386** All China T.U. Federation Team scaling Mt. Minya Konka

1965. World Table Tennis Championships, Peking.
2241 **385** 8f. (1) multicoloured . . 20 10
2242 – 8f. (2) multicoloured . . 20 10
2243 – 8f. (3) multicoloured . . 20 10
2244 – 8f. (4) multicoloured . . 20 10
DESIGNS: Nos. 2242/4 each show different views of table tennis players.

1965. Chinese Mountaineering Achievements. Each black, yellow and blue.
2245 8f. (1) Type **386** . . . . . . 4·00 50
2246 8f. (2) Men and women's mixed team on slopes of Muztagh Ata . . . . . . 5·00 50
2247 8f. (3) Climbers on Mt. Jolmo Lungma . . . . . . 5·00 50
2248 8f. (4) Women's team camping on Kongur Tiubie Tagh . . . . . . 5·00 50
2249 8f. (5) Climbers on Shishma Pangma . . . . 6·00 2·00

387 Marx and Lenin **388** Tseping

1965. Organization of Socialist Countries' Postal Administrations Conference, Peking.
2250 **387** 8f. multicoloured . . . . 12·00 4·00

1965. "Chingkang Mountains – Cradle of the Chinese Revolution". Multicoloured.
2251 4f. (1) Type **388** . . . . . . 7·00 40
2252 8f. (2) Sanwantsun . . . . 7·00 40
2253 8f. (3) Octagonal Building, Maoping . . . . 28·00 40
2254 8f. (4) River and bridge at Lungshih . . . . 21·00 75
2255 8f. (5) Tachingtsun . . . . 14·00 75
2256 10f. (6) Bridge at Lungyuankou . . . . . 14·00 40
2257 10f. (7) Hwangyangchieh . . 10·00 75
2258 52f. (8) Chingkang peaks . . 10·00 6·00

389 Soldiers with Texts

1965. People's Liberation Army. Mult.
2259 8f. (1) Type **389** . . . . . . 18·00 3·25
2260 8f. (2) Soldiers reading book 18·00 3·25
2261 8f. (3) Soldier with grenade-thrower . . . . 18·00 1·50
2262 8f. (4) Giving tuition in firing rifle . . . . 18·00 1·50
2263 8f. (5) Soldiers at rest (vert) 9·50 1·50
2264 8f. (6) Bayonet charge (vert) 9·50 1·50
2265 8f. (7) Soldier with banners (vert) . . . . 9·50 4·00
2266 8f. (8) Military band (vert) . . 9·50 2·25

390 "Welcome to Peking" **391** Soldier firing Weapon

1965. Chinese–Japanese. Youth Meeting, Peking. Multicoloured.
2267 4f. (1) Type **390** 60 30
2268 8f. (2) Chinese and Japanese youths with linked arms 60 30
2269 8f. (3) Chinese and Japanese girls 60 30
2270 10f. (4) Musical entertainment . . . . . . 1·00 30
2271 22f. (5) Emblem of Meeting 3·00 1·00

1965. "Vietnamese People's Struggle".
2272 **391** 8f. (1) brown and red . . 1·90 50
2273 – 8f. (2) olive and red . . 1·90 50
2274 – 8f. (3) purple and red . . 1·90 50
2275 – 8f. (4) black and red . . 1·90 50
DESIGNS—VERT: (2) Soldier with captured weapons; (3) Soldier giving victory salute. HORIZ: (48½ × 26 mm): (4) "Peoples of the world".

392 "Victory" **393** Football

1965. 20th Anniv of Victory over Japanese.
2276 – 8f. (1) multicoloured . . 15·00 5·00
2277 – 8f. (2) green and red . . 8·00 80
2278 **392** 8f. (3) sepia and red . . 8·00 80
2279 – 8f. (4) green and red . . 8·00 80
DESIGNS—HORIZ: (50½ × 36 mm): (1) Mao Tse-tung writing. As Type **392**—HORIZ: (2) Soldiers crossing Yellow River. (4) Recruits in cart.

1965. 2nd National Games. Multicoloured.
2280 4f. (1) Type **393** . . . . . . 6·00 30
2281 4f. (2) Archery . . . . . . 6·00 30
2282 8f. (3) Throwing the javelin 6·00 30
2283 8f. (4) Gymnastics . . . . . 6·00 30
2284 8f. (5) Volleyball . . . . . 6·00 30
2285 10f. (6) Opening ceremony (horiz) (56 × 35½ mm) . . 29·00 30
2286 10f. (7) Cycling . . . . . . 60·00 30
2287 20f. (8) Diving . . . . . . 26·00 2·50
2288 22f. (9) Hurdling . . . . . 10·00 2·75
2289 30f. (10) Weightlifting . . . 10·00 6·00
2290 43f. (11) Basketball . . . . 13·00 10·00

394 Textile Workers

1965. Women in Industry. Multicoloured.
2291 8f. (1) Type **394** . . . . . . 6·50 40
2292 8f. (2) Machine building . . 6·50 40
2293 8f. (3) Building construction 6·50 40
2294 8f. (4) Studying . . . . . . 6·50 60
2295 8f. (5) Militia guard . . . . 6·50 3·00

395 Children playing with Ball

1966. Children's Games. Multicoloured.
2296 4f. (1) Type **395** 50 30
2297 4f. (2) Racing 50 30
2298 8f. (3) Tobogganing 50 30
2299 8f. (4) Exercising 50 30
2300 8f. (5) Swimming 50 30
2301 8f. (6) Shooting 50 30
2302 10f. (7) Jumping with rope 80 30
2303 52f. (8) Playing table tennis 1·25 50

396 Mobile Transformer

1966. New Industrial Machines.
2304 **396** 4f. (1) black and yellow 6·25 50
2305 – 8f. (2) black and blue . . 9·50 30
2306 – 8f. (3) black and pink . . 9·50 30
2307 – 8f. (4) black and olive 9·50 30
2308 – 8f. (5) black and purple 9·50 30
2309 – 10f. (6) black and grey 12·50 30
2310 – 10f. (7) black & turq . . 12·50 2·00
2311 – 22f. (8) black and lilac 25·00 5·00
DESIGNS—VERT: (2), Electron microscope; (4), Vertical boring and turning machine; (6), Hydraulic press; (8), Electron accelerator. HORIZ: (3), Lathe; (5), Gear-grinding machine; (7), Milling machine.

397 Women of Military and Other Services

1966. Women in Public Service. Mult.
2312 8f. (1) Type **397** 70 25
2313 8f. (2) Train conductress . . . 70 25
2314 8f. (3) Red Cross worker . . 70 25
2315 8f. (4) Kindergarten teacher 70 25
2316 8f. (5) Roadsweeper 70 25
2317 8f. (6) Hairdresser 70 25
2318 8f. (7) Bus conductress . . . 70 25
2319 8f. (8) Travelling saleswoman 70 25
2320 8f. (9) Canteen worker . . . 70 25
2321 8f. (10) Rural postwoman 70 25

398 "Thunderstorm" (sculpture) **399** Dr. Sun Yat-sen

1966. Afro-Asian Writers' Meeting.
2322 **398** 8f. black and red . . . . 2·00 50
2323 – 22f. gold, yellow & red 4·00 1·60
DESIGN: 22f. Meeting emblem.

1966. Birth Centenary of Dr. Sun Yat-sen.
2324 **399** 8f. sepia and buff . . . 25·00 7·00

400 Athletes with Mao Tse-tung's Portrait

1966. "Cultural Revolution" Games. Multicoloured.
2325 8f. (1) Type **400** . . . . . . 21·00 6·00
2326 8f. (2) Athletes with linked arms hold Mao texts . . 21·00 6·00
2327 8f. (3) Two women athletes with Mao texts . . . . . 21·00 5·00
2328 8f. (4) Athletes reading Mao texts . . . . 21·00 5·00
SIZES: No. 2326, As Type **400**, but vert; Nos. 2327/8, 36½ × 25 mm.

401 Mao's Appreciation of Lu Hsun (patriot and writer) **402** "Be Resolute ..." (Mao Tse-tung)

1966. 30th Death Anniv of Lu Hsun.
2329 **401** 8f. (1) black & orange 40·00 15·00
2330 – 8f. (2) black, flesh & red 40·00 15·00
2331 – 8f. (3) black & orange 40·00 15·00
DESIGNS: (2) Lu Hsun; (3) Lu Hsun's manuscript.

1967. Heroic Oilwell Firefighters.
2332 **402** 8f. (1) gold, red & black 22·00 12·00
2333 – 8f. (2) black and red . . 25·00 9·00
2334 – 8f. (3) black and red . . 25·00 9·00
DESIGNS—HORIZ: (48 × 27 mm): (2) Drilling Team No. 32111 fighting flames. VERT: (3) Smothering flames with tarpaulins.

403 Liu Ying-chun (military hero)

1967. Liu Ying-chun Commem. Multicoloured.
2335 8f. (1) Type **403** . . . . . . 22·00 6·50
2336 8f. (2) Liu Ying-chun holding book of Mao texts . . . . 22·00 6·50
2337 8f. (3) Liu Ying-chun holding horse's bridle . . 22·00 6·50
2338 8f. (4) Liu Ying-chun looking at film slide . . . 22·00 6·50
2339 8f. (5) Liu Ying-chun lecturing . . . . 22·00 6·50
2340 8f. (6) Liu Ying-chun making fatal attempt to stop bolting horse . . . . 22·00 6·50

404 Soldier, Nurse, Workers and Banners

1967. 3rd Five-Year Plan. Multicoloured.
2341 8f. (1) Type **404** . . . . . . 30·00 7·50
2342 8f. (2) Armed woman, peasants and banners . . 30·00 7·50

405 Mao Tse-tung **406** Mao Text (39 characters)

1967. "Thoughts of Mao Tse-tung" (1st issue). Similar designs showing Mao texts each gold and red. To assist identification of Nos. 2344/53 the total number of Chinese characters within the frames are given. (a) Type **405**.
2343 8f. multicoloured . . . . . 85·00 15·00

(b) As Type **406**. Red outer frames.
2344 8f. Type **406** . . . . 75·00 12·00
2345 8f. (50 characters) . . . . . 75·00 12·00
2346 8f. (39–in six lines) . . . . 75·00 12·00
2347 8f. (53) . . . . 75·00 12·00
2348 8f. (46) . . . . 75·00 12·00

(c) As Type **406**. Gold outer frames.
2349 8f. (41) . . . . 75·00 12·00
2350 8f. (49) . . . . 75·00 12·00
2351 8f. (35) . . . . 75·00 12·00
2352 8f. (22) . . . . 75·00 12·00
2353 8f. (29) . . . . 75·00 12·00
See also No. 2405.

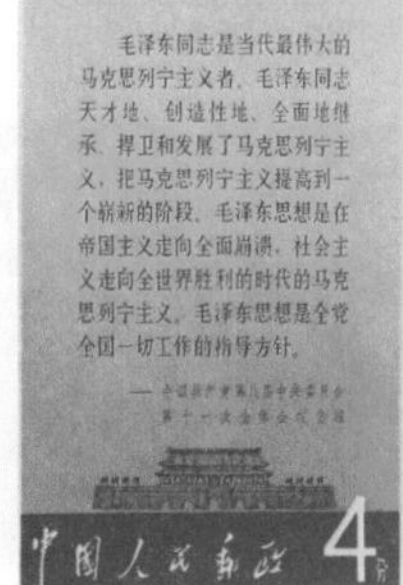

407 Text praising Mao

1967. Labour Day.
2354 **407** 4f. multicoloured . . . . 50·00 14·00
2355 – 8f. multicoloured . . . . 40·00 14·00
2356 – 8f. multicoloured . . . . 50·00 14·00
2357 – 8f. multicoloured . . . . 40·00 14·00
2358 – 8f. multicoloured . . . . 40·00 14·00
DESIGNS (Mao Tse-tung and): No. 2355, Poem; No. 2356, Multi-racial crowd with texts; No. 2357, Red Guards. (36 × 50½ mm): Mao with hand raised in greeting.
For stamps similar to No. 2358, see Nos. 2367/9.

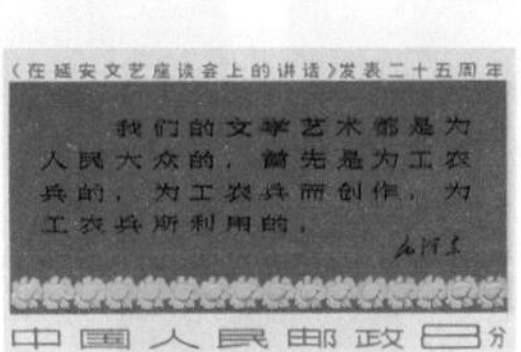

408 Mao Text

1967. 25th Anniv of Mao Tse-tung's "Talks on Literature and Art".
2359 **408** 8f. black, red & yellow £130 25·00
2360 – 8f. black, red & yellow £150 30·00
2361 – 8f. multicoloured . . . . £150 30·00
DESIGNS: No. 2360, As Type **408** but different text. (50 × 36½ mm): No. 2361, Mao supporters in procession.

409 Mao Tse-tung **410** Mao Tse-tung and Lin Piao

1967. 46th Anniv of Chinese Communist Party.
2362 **409** 4f. red . . . . 12·00 7·50
2363 8f. red . . . . 50·00 7·50
2364 35f. brown . . . . . . 35·00 25·00

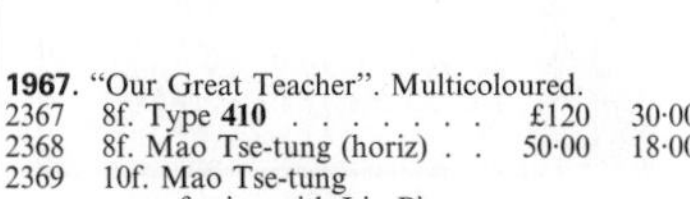

2365 43f. red . . . . 40·00 25·00
2366 52f. red . . . . 75·00 20·00

1967. "Our Great Teacher". Multicoloured.
2367 8f. Type **410** . . . . £120 30·00
2368 8f. Mao Tse-tung (horiz) . . 50·00 18·00
2369 10f. Mao Tse-tung conferring with Lin Piao (horiz) . . . . £150 30·00
For 8f. stamp showing Mao with hand raised in greeting, see No. 2358.

411 Mao Tse-tung as "Sun"

1967. 18th Anniv of People's Republic. Mult.
2370 8f. Type **411** . . . . 48·00 8·50
2371 8f. Mao Tse-tung with representatives of Communist countries . . 29·00 8·50

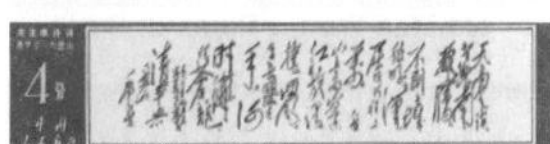

412 "Mount Liupan" (½-size illustration)

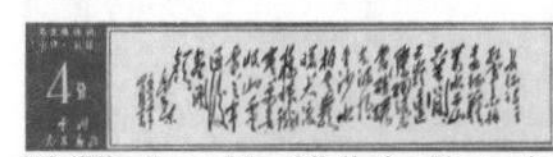

413 "The Long March" (½-size illustration)

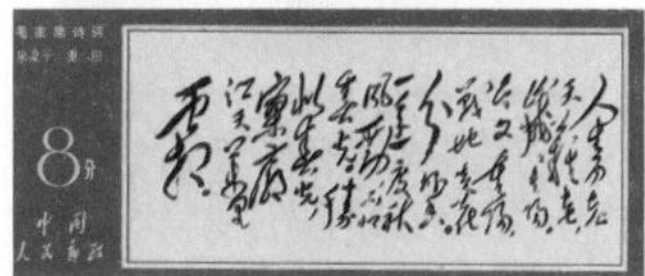

414 "Double Ninth"

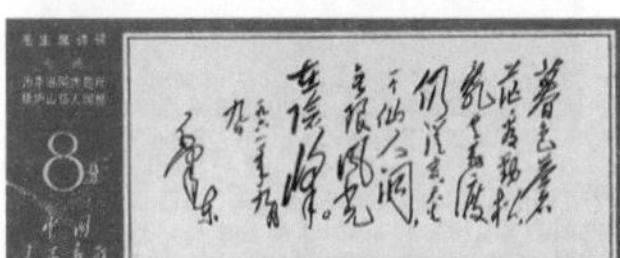

415 "Fairy Cave"

416 "Huichang" **417** "Yellow Crane Pavilion"

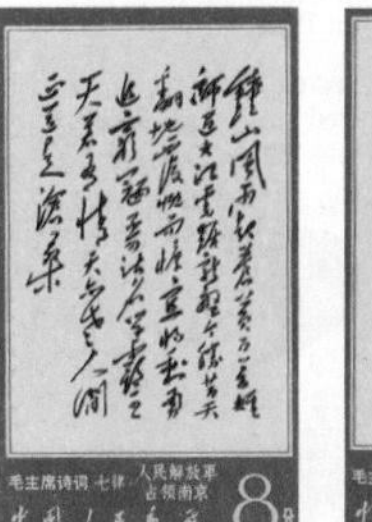

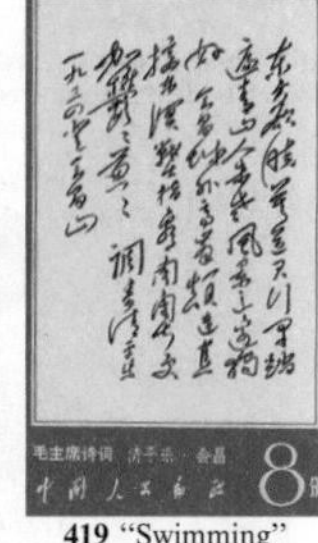

418 "Beidahe" **419** "Swimming"

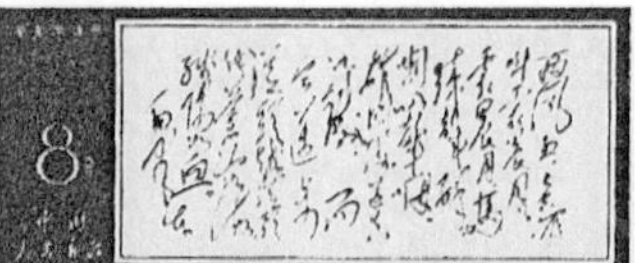

420 "Loushanguan Pass"

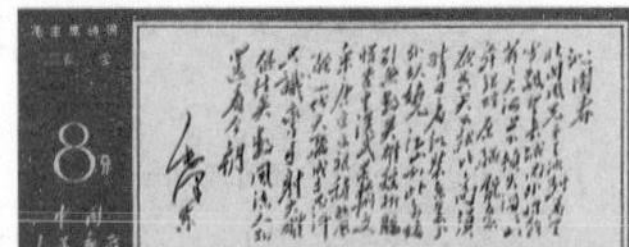
421 "Snow"

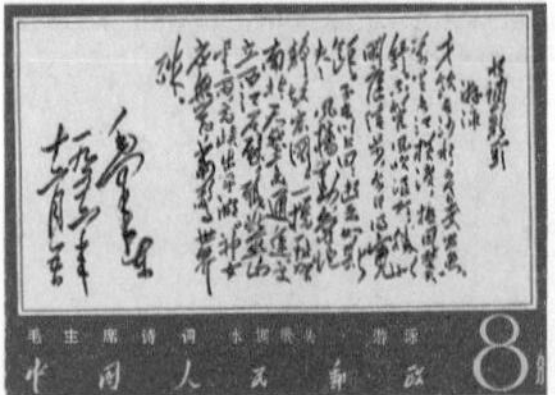
422 "Capture of Nanjing"

423 Mao Writing Poems at Desk

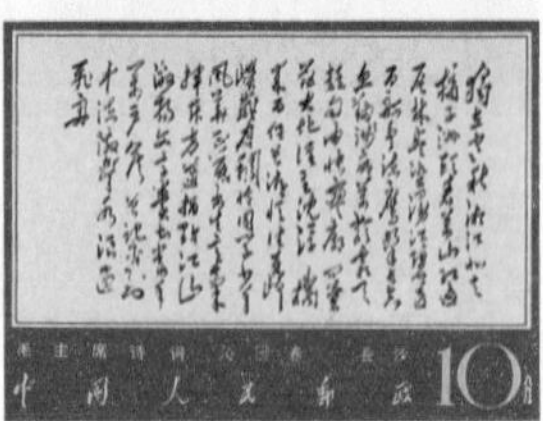
424 "Changsha"

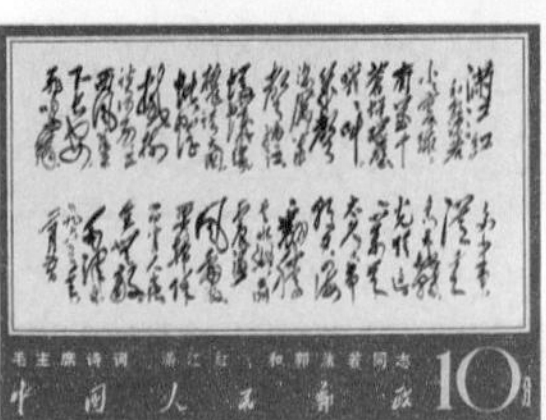
425 "Reply to Guo Moro"

1967. Poems of Mao Tse-tung.

No.	Type	Description	Unused	Used
2372	**412**	4f. black, yellow & red	50·00	14·00
2373	**413**	4f. black, yellow & red	65·00	14·00
2374	**414**	8f. black, yellow & red	65·00	12·00
2375	**415**	8f. black, yellow & red	70·00	12·00
2376	**416**	8f. black, yellow & red	£190	12·00
2377	**417**	8f. black, yellow & red	£120	20·00
2378	**418**	8f. black, yellow & red	£225	20·00
2379	**419**	8f. black, yellow & red	80·00	20·00
2380	**420**	8f. black, yellow & red	80·00	20·00
2381	**421**	8f. black, yellow & red	80·00	20·00
2382	**422**	8f. black, yellow & red	80·00	12·00
2383	**423**	10f. multicoloured	32·00	12·00
2384	**424**	10f. black, yellow & red	32·00	12·00
2385	**425**	10f. black, yellow & red	32·00	12·00

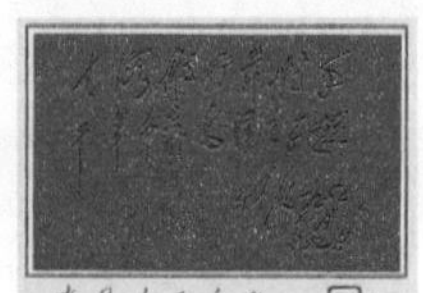
426 Epigram on Chairman Mao by Lin Piao

1967. Fleet Expansionists' Congress.

No.	Type	Description	Unused	Used
2386	**426**	8f. gold and red	26·00	8·50

427 Mao Tse-tung and Procession

1968. "Revolutionary Literature and Art" (1st issue). Multicoloured designs showing scenes from People's Operas.

No.	Description	Unused	Used
2387	8f. Type **427**	50·00	9·00
2388	8f. "Raid on the White Tiger Regiment"	40·00	9·00
2389	8f. "Taking Tiger Mountain"	50·00	8·00
2390	8f. "On the Docks"	35·00	8·00
2391	8f. "Shachiapang"	40·00	8·00
2392	8f. "The Red Lantern" (vert)	35·00	8·00

428 "Red Detachment of Women" (ballet)

1968. "Revolutionary Literature and Art" (2nd issue). Multicoloured.

No.	Description	Unused	Used
2393	8f. Type **428**	40·00	9·00
2394	8f. "The White-haired Girl" (ballet)	40·00	9·00
2395	8f. Mao Tse-tung, Symphony Orchestra and Chorus (50 × 36 mm)	80·00	11·00

429 Mao Tse-tung ("Unite still more closely")

1968. Mao's Anti-American Declaration.

No.	Type	Description	Unused	Used
2396	**429**	8f. brown, gold and red	45·00	12·00

430

431

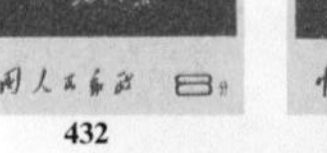
432

433

434

1968. "Directives of Mao Tse-tung".

No.	Type	Description	Unused	Used
2397	**430**	8f. brown, red & yellow	£190	40·00
2398	**431**	8f. brown, red & yellow	£190	40·00
2399	**432**	8f. brown, red & yellow	£190	40·00
2400	**433**	8f. brown, red & yellow	£190	40·00
2401	**434**	8f. brown, red & yellow	£190	40·00

435 Inscription by Lin Piao. 26 July, 1965

1968. 41st Anniv of People's Liberation Army.

No.	Type	Description	Unused	Used
2402	**435**	8f. black, gold and red	12·00	5·00

436 "Chairman Mao goes to Anyuan" (Liu Chunhua)

1968. Mao's Youth.

No.	Type	Description	Unused	Used
2403	**436**	8f. multicoloured	26·00	8·00

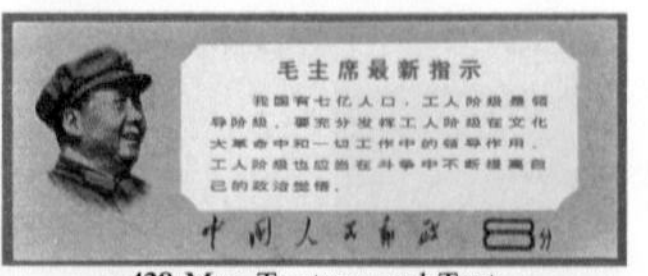

438 Mao Tse-tung and Text

1968. "Thoughts of Mao Tse-tung" (2nd issue).

No.	Type	Description	Unused	Used
2405	**438**	8f. brown and red	48·00	14·00

439 Displaying "The Words of Mao Tse-tung"

1968. "The Words of Mao Tse-tung". No gum.

No.	Type	Description	Unused	Used
2406	**439**	8f. multicoloured	15·00	3·00

440 Yangtse Bridge

1968. Completion of Yangtse Bridge, Nanking. Multicoloured. No gum.

No.	Description	Unused	Used
2407	4f. Type **440**	3·75	90
2408	8f. Buses on bridge	9·75	4·00
2409	8f. View of end portals	7·25	2·50
2410	10f. Aerial view	2·50	1·25

Nos. 2408/9 are larger, size 49 × 27 mm.

441 Li Yu-ho singing "I am filled with Courage and Strength"

1969. Songs from "The Red Lantern" Opera. Multicoloured. No gum.

No.	Description	Unused	Used
2411	8f. Type **441**	15·00	7·50
2412	8f. Li Ti-mei singing "Hatred in my Heart"	30·00	7·50

442 Communist Party Building, Shanghai

1969. No gum.

No.	Type	Description	Unused	Used
2413	**442**	1½f. red, brown & lilac	60	50
2414	–	8f. brown, grn & cream	2·00	75
2415	–	8f. red and purple	60	15
2416	–	8f. brown and blue	1·50	40
2417	–	20f. blue, purple & red	2·10	1·00
2418	–	50f. brown and green	1·75	40

DESIGNS: "Historic Sites of the Revolution"; Size 27 × 22 mm—No. 2414, Pagoda Hill, Yenan; No. 2415, Gate of Heavenly Peace, Peking; No. 2418. Mao Tse-tung's house, Yenan. Size as T **442**—No. 2416, People's Heroes Monument, Peking; No. 2417, Conference Hall, Tsunyi.

See also Nos. 2455/65.

443 Rice Harvesters

1969. Agricultural Workers. Mult. No gum.

No.	Description	Unused	Used
2419	4f. Type **443**	4·00	2·00
2420	8f. Grain harvest	9·00	1·75
2421	8f. Study Group with "Thoughts of Mao"	55·00	7·50
2422	10f. Red Cross worker with mother and child	4·00	1·50

444 Snow Patrol

445 Farm Worker

1969. Defence of Chen Pao Tao in the Ussur River. Multicoloured. No gum.

No.	Description	Unused	Used
2423	8f. Type **444**	6·00	2·50
2424	8f. Guards by river (horiz)	5·00	2·50
2425	8f. Servicemen and Militia (horiz)	20·00	3·00
2426	35f. As No. 2424	5·00	2·75
2427	43f. Type **444**	6·00	2·75

1969. "The Chinese People" (woodcuts). No gum.

No.	Type	Description	Unused	Used
2428	**445**	4f. purple and orange	20	20
2429	–	8f. purple and orange	60	25
2430	–	10f. green and orange	90	60

DESIGNS: 8f. Foundryman. 10f. Soldier.

446 Chin Hsun-hua in Water

447 Tractor-driver

1970. Heroic Death of Chin Hsun-hua in Kirin Border Floods. No gum.

No.	Type	Description	Unused	Used
2431	**446**	8f. black and red	17·00	5·00

1970. No gum.

No.	Type	Description	Unused	Used
2432	**447**	5f. black, red & orange	60	40
2433	–	1y. black and red	4·00	1·10

DESIGN—HORIZ: 1y. Foundryman.

448 Cavalry Patrol

449 "Yang Tse-jung, Army Scout"

1970. 43rd Anniv of People's Liberation Army. No gum.

No.	Type	Description	Unused	Used
2434	**448**	8f. multicoloured	6·75	3·25

1970. "Taking Tiger Mountain" (Revolutionary opera). Multicoloured. No gum.

No.	Description	Unused	Used
2435	8f. (1) Type **449**	15·00	2·50
2436	8f. (2) "The patrol sets out" (horiz)	15·00	2·50
2437	8f. (3) "Leaping through the forest"	15·00	2·50
2438	8f. (4) "Li Yung-chi's farewell" (27 × 48 mm)	15·00	2·50
2439	8f. (5) "Yang Tse-jung in disguise" (27 × 48 mm)	15·00	2·50
2440	8f. (6) "Congratulating Yang Tse-jung" (horiz)	40·00	2·50

450 Soldiers in Snow

1970. 2nd Anniv of Defence of Chen Pao Tao. No gum.
2441 **450** 4f. multicoloured . . . . 1·75 1·00

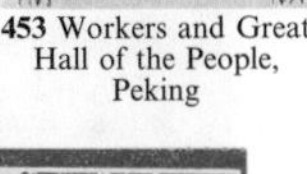

451 Communard Standard

453 Workers and Great Hall of the People, Peking

452 Communist Party Building, Shanghai

1971. Cent of Paris Commune. Mult. No gum.
2442 **451** 4f. multicoloured . . . . 40·00 10·00
2443 – 8f. brown, pink and red 80·00 20·00
2444 – 10f. red, brn and pink 40·00 10·00
2445 – 22f. brown, red & pink 40·00 10·00
DESIGNS—HORIZ: 8f. Fighting in Paris, March 1871; 22f. Communards in Place Vendome. VERT: 10f. Commune proclaimed at the Hotel de Ville.

1971. 50th Anniv of Chinese Communist Party. Multicoloured. No gum.
2446 4f. (12) Type **452** . . . . . 9·00 1·25
2447 4f. (13) National Peasant Movement Inst., Canton 9·00 1·25
2448 8f. (14) Chingkang Mountains . . . . 7·50 1·25
2449 8f. (15) Conference Building, Tsunyi . . . . 7·50 1·25
2450 8f. (16) Pagoda Hill, Yenan 7·50 1·25
2452 8f. (18) Workers and Industry . . . . 16·00 3·00
2453 8f. (19) Type **453** . . . . . 16·00 3·00
2454 8f. (20) Workers and Agriculture . . . . 16·00 3·00
2451 22f. (17) Gate of Heavenly Peace, Peking . . . . . . 6·00 1·25
SIZES: As Type **452**. Nos. 2447/2450 and 2451. As Type **453**. Nos. 2452/4.

454 National Peasant Movement Institute, Canton

455 Welcoming Bouquets

1971. Revolutionary Sites. Multicoloured. No gum.
2455 1f. Communist Party Building, Shanghai (vert) 10 10
2456 2f. Type **454** 10 10
2457 3f. Site of 1929 Congress, Kutien 10 10
2458 4f. Mao Tse-tung's house, Yenan 15 10
2459 8f. Gate of Heavenly Peace, Peking 15 10
2460 10f. Monument, Chingkang Mountains 25 10
2461 20f. River bridge, Yenan . . 40 15
2462 22f. Mao's birthplace, Shaoshan 70 20
2463 35f. Conference Building, Tsunyi . . . . 1·00 20
2464 43f. Start of the Long March, Chingkang Mountains . . . . 1·40 35
2465 52f. People's Palace, Peking 1·75 55

1971. "Afro-Asian Friendship" Table Tennis Tournament, Peking. Multicoloured. No gum.
2466 8f. (22) Type **455** . . . . . 4·00 1·00
2467 8f. (23) Group of players . . 4·00 1·00
2468 8f. (24) Asian and African players . . . . 4·00 1·00
2469 43f. (21) Tournament badge 14·50 2·50

456 Enver Hoxha making speech

457 Conference Hall, Yenan

1971. 30th Anniv of Albanian Worker's Party. Multicoloured. No gum.
2470 8f. (25) Type **456** . . . . . 7·25 4·00
2471 8f. (26) Party Headquarters 6·00 1·50
2472 8f. (27) Albanian flag, rifle and pick . . . . 6·00 1·50
2473 52f. (28) Soldier and Worker's Militia (horiz) 6·50 4·00

1972. 30th Anniv of Publication of "Yenan Forum's Discussions on Literature and Art". Multicoloured. No gum.
2474 8f. (33) Type **457** . . . . . 5·50 1·60
2475 8f. (34) Army choir . . . . 5·50 1·60
2476 8f. (35) "Brother and Sister" 7·00 1·60
2477 8f. (36) "Open-air Theatre" 7·00 1·60
2478 8f. (37) "The Red Lantern" (opera) . . . . 7·00 1·60
2479 8f. (38) "Red Detachment of Women" (ballet) . . . . 7·00 1·60

458 Ball Games

1972. 10th Anniv of Mao Tse-tungs's Edict on Physical Culture. Multicoloured. No gum.
2480 8f. (39) Type **458** . . . . . 7·00 1·50
2481 8f. (40) Gymnastics . . . . 7·00 1·50
2482 8f. (41) Tug-of-War . . . . 7·00 1·50
2483 8f. (42) Rock-climbing . . . 7·00 1·50
2484 8f. (43) High-diving . . . . 7·00 1·50
Nos. 2481/4 are size 26 × 36 mm.

460 Freighter "Fenglei"

1972. Chinese Merchant Shipping. Multicoloured. No gum.
2485 8f. (29) Type **460** . . . . . 8·00 1·75
2486 8f. (30) Tanker "Taching No. 30" . . . . 8·00 1·75
2487 8f. (31) Cargo-liner "Chang Seng" . . . . 8·00 1·75
2488 8f. (32) Dredger "Hsienfeng" . . . . . . 8·00 1·75

461 Championship Badge

462 Wang Chin-hsi, the "Iron Man"

1972. 1st Asian Table Tennis Championships, Peking. Multicoloured. No gum.
2489 8f. (45) Type **461** . . . . . 4·00 75
2490 8f. (46) Welcoming crowd (horiz) . . . . 4·00 75
2491 8f. (47) Game in progress (horiz) . . . . 4·00 75
2492 22f. (48) Players from three countries . . . . 2·50 1·50

1972. Wang Chin-hsi (workers' hero) Commem. No gum.
2493 **462** 8f. multicoloured . . . . 4·25 1·50

463 Cliff-edge Construction

464 Giant Panda eating Bamboo Shoots

1972. Construction of Red Flag Canal. Mult.
2494 8f. (49) Type **463** . . . . . 2·10 80
2495 8f. (50) "Youth" tunnel . . 2·10 80
2496 8f. (51) "Taoguan bridge" 2·10 80
2497 8f. (52) Cliff-edge canal . . 2·10 80

1973. China's Giant Pandas.
2498 **464** 4f. (61) multicoloured . . 2·00 3·50
2499 – 8f. (59) mult (horiz) . . 2·00 3·50
2500 – 8f. (60) mult (horiz) . . 2·00 3·50
2501 – 10f. (58) multicoloured £100 15·00
2502 – 20f. (57) multicoloured 85·00 15·00
2503 – 43f. (62) multicoloured 9·00 6·00
DESIGNS: 8f. to 43f. Different brush and ink drawings of pandas.

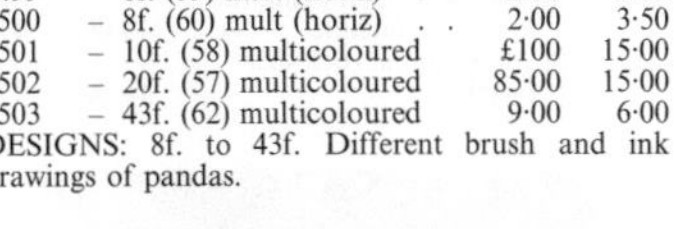

465 "New Power in the Mines" (Yang Shi-guang)

466 Girl dancing

1973. International Working Women's Day. Mult.
2504 8f. (63) Type **465** . . . . . 3·00 1·50
2505 8f. (64) "Woman Committee Member" (Tang Hsiaoming) . . . . 3·00 1·50
2506 8f. (65) "I am a Sea-gull" (Army telegraph line woman) (Pan Jiajun) . . 3·00 1·50

1973. Children's Day. Multicoloured.
2507 8f. (86) Type **466** . . . . . 1·90 50
2508 8f. (87) Boy musician . . . 1·90 50
2509 8f. (88) Boy with scarf . . . 1·90 50
2510 8f. (89) Boy with tambourine . . . . 1·90 50
2511 8f. (90) Girl with drum . . 1·90 50

467 Badge of Championships

468 "Hsi-erh"

1973. Asian, African and Latin-American Table Tennis Invitation Championships. Multicoloured.
2512 8f. (91) Type **467** . . . . . 2·50 50
2513 8f. (92) Visitors . . . . . . 2·50 50
2514 8f. (93) Player . . . . . . 2·50 50
2515 22f. (94) Guest players . . . 1·50 50

1973. Revolutionary Ballet "Hsi-erh" ("The White-haired Girl"). Multicoloured.
2516 8f. (53) Type **468** . . . . . 4·75 1·10
2517 8f. (54) Hsi-erh escapes from Huang (horiz) . . . . . 4·75 1·10
2518 8f. (55) Hsi-erh meets Tachun (horiz) . . . . . 4·75 1·10
2519 8f. (56) Hsi-erh becomes a soldier . . . . 4·75 1·10

469 Fair Building

1973. Chinese Exports Fair, Canton.
2520 **469** 8f. multicoloured . . . . 3·50 1·25

470 Mao's Birthplace, Shaoshan

471 Steam and Diesel Trains

1973. No gum.
2521 **470** 1f. green & light green 35 10
2522 – 1½f. red and yellow . . . 35 20
2523 – 2f. blue and green . . . 35 10
2524 – 3f. green and yellow . . 35 10
2525 – 4f. red and yellow . . . 35 10
2526 – 5f. brown and yellow . . 35 10
2527 – 8f. purple and flesh . . . 35 10
2528 – 10f. blue and flesh . . . 35 10
2529 – 20f. red and buff 65 10
2530 – 22f. violet and yellow . . 90 10
2531 – 35f. purple and yellow 1·25 15
2532 – 43f. brown and buff . . 1·60 25
2533 – 50f. blue and mauve . . 2·10 70
2534 – 52f. brown and yellow 2·75 90
2535 **471** 1y. multicoloured . . . 2·00 25
2536 – 2y. multicoloured . . . 1·60 40
DESIGNS—As Type **470**: 1½f. National Peasant Movement Institute, Shanghai. 2f. National Institute, Kwangchow. 3f. Headquarters Building, Nanching uprising. 4f. Great Hall of the People, Peking, 5f. Wen Chia Shih. 8f. Gate of Heavenly Peace, Peking. 10f. Chingkang Mountains. 20f. Kutien Congress building. 22f. Tsunyi Congress building. 35f. Bridge, Yenan. 43f. Hsi Pai Po. 50f. "Fairy Gate", Lushan. 52f. People's Heroes Monument, Peking. As Type **471**: 2y. Trucks on mountain road.

472 "Phoenix" Pot

473 Dance Routine

1973. Archaeological Treasures. Multicoloured.
2537 4f. (66) Type **472** . . . . . 1·75 20
2538 4f. (67) Silver pot . . . . . 1·75 20
2539 8f. (68) Porcelain horse and groom . . . . 1·40 10
2540 8f. (69) Figure of woman . . 1·40 10
2541 8f. (70) Carved pedestals . . 90 10
2542 8f. (71) Bronze horse . . . 90 10
2543 8f. (72) Gilded "frog" . . . 90 10
2544 8f. (73) Lamp-holder figurine 90 10
2545 10f. (74) Tripod jar 45 50
2546 10f. (75) Bronze vessel . . . 45 50
2547 20f. (76) Bronze wine vessel 2·00 75
2548 52f. (77) Tray with tripod 2·00 1·50

1974. Popular Gymnastics. Multicoloured.
2549 8f. (1) Type **473** . . . . . . 7·00 2·75
2550 8f. (2) Rings exercise . . . 7·00 2·75
2551 8f. (3) Dancing on beam . . 7·00 2·75
2552 8f. (4) Handstand on parallel bars . . . . . . 7·00 2·75
2553 8f. (5) Trapeze exercise . . . 8·00 2·75
2554 8f. (6) Vaulting over horse 8·00 2·75

474 Lion Dance

475 Man reading Book

1974. Acrobatics. Multicoloured.
2555 8f. (1) Type **474** . . . . . . 6·00 2·25
2556 8f. (2) Handstand on chairs 6·00 2·25
2557 8f. (3) Diabolo team (horiz) 6·00 2·25
2558 8f. Revolving jar (horiz) . . 7·00 2·25
2559 8f. (5) Spinning plates . . . 7·00 2·25
2560 8f. (6) Foot-juggling with parasol . . . . 7·00 2·25

1974. Huhsien Paintings. Multicoloured.
2561 8f. (1) Type **475** . . . . . . 2·25 1·00
2562 8f. (2) Mineshaft (23 × 57 mm) . . . . . . 2·25 1·00
2563 8f. (3) Workers hoeing field (horiz) . . . . 2·25 1·00
2564 8f. (4) Workers eating (horiz) . . . . 2·25 1·00
2565 8f. (5) Wheatfield landscape (57 × 23 mm) . . . . . . 2·25 1·00
2566 8f. (6) Harvesting (horiz) . . 2·25 1·00

476 Postman

1974. Centenary of U.P.U. Multicoloured.
2567 8f. (1) Type **476** . . . . . . 6·00 2·50
2568 8f. (2) People of five races 6·00 2·50
2569 8f. (3) Great Wall of China 6·00 2·50

477 Inoculating Children

1974. Country Doctors. Multicoloured.
2570 8f. (1) Type **477** . . . . . . 1·75 90
2571 8f. (2) On country visit (vert) . . . . 1·75 90
2572 8f. (3) Gathering herbs (vert) 1·75 90
2573 8f. (4) Giving acupuncture 1·75 90

478 Wang Chin-hsi, "The Iron Man"

1974. Chairman Mao's Directives on Industrial and Agricultural Teaching. Multicoloured. (a) "Learning Industry from Taching".
2574 8f. (1) Type **478** . . . . . . 2·00 90
2575 8f. (2) Pupils studying Mao's works . . . . 2·00 90
2576 8f. (3) Oil-workers sinking well . . . . 2·00 90
2577 8f. (4) Consultation with management . . . . . . 2·00 90
2578 8f. (5) Taching oilfield as development site . . . . 2·00 90

(b) "Learning Agriculture from Tachai".
2579 8f. (1) Tachai workers looking to future . . . . 2·25 90
2580 8f. (2) Construction workers 1·40 90
2581 8f. (3) Agricultural workers making field tests . . . . 2·25 90
2582 8f. (4) Trucks delivering grain to State granaries 1·40 90
2583 8f. (5) Workers going to fields . . . . 1·40 90

479 National Day Celebrations

480 Steel Worker, Taching

1974. 25th Anniv of Chinese People's Republic. Multicoloured. (a) National Day.
2584 8f. Type **479** . . . . 5·50 2·50

(b) Chairman Mao's Directives.
2585 8f. (1) Type **480** . . . . . . 1·50 80
2586 8f. (2) Agricultural worker, Tachai . . . . 1·50 80
2587 8f. (3) Coastal guard . . . . 1·50 80

481 Fair Building

1974. Chinese Exports Fair, Canton.
2588 **481** 8f. multicoloured . . . . 3·25 1·25

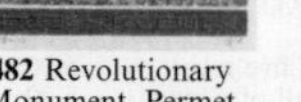

482 Revolutionary Monument, Permet

483 Capital Stadium

1974. 30th Anniv of Albania's Liberation. Mult.
2589 8f. Type **482** . . . . 2·75 1·25
2590 8f. Albanian patriots . . . 2·75 1·25

1974. Peking Buildings. No gum.
2591 **483** 4f. black and green . . . 15 15
2592 – 8f. black and blue . . . 15 10
DESIGN: 8f. Hotel Peking.

484 Water-cooled Turbine Generator

1974. Industrial Production. Multicoloured.
2593 8f. (78) Type **484** . . . . . 19·00 4·00
2594 8f. (79) Mechanical rice sprouts transplanter . . . 20·00 4·00
2595 8f. (80) Universal cylindrical grinding machine . . . . 19·00 4·00
2596 8f. (81) Mobile rock drill (vert) . . . . 19·00 4·00

485 Congress Delegates

1975. 4th National People's Congress, Peking. Multicoloured.
2597 8f. (1) Type **485** . . . . . . 4·00 1·50
2598 8f. (2) Flower-decked rostrum . . . . 4·00 1·50
2599 8f. (3) Farmer, worker, soldier and steel mill . . . 4·00 1·50

486 Teacher Studying

1975. Country Women Teachers. Multicoloured.
2600 8f. (1) Type **486** . . . . . . 9·75 2·00
2601 8f. (2) Teacher on rounds 9·75 2·00
2602 8f. (3) Open-air class . . . 9·75 2·00
2603 8f. (4) Primary class aboard boat . . . . 9·75 2·00

487 Broadsword

1975. "Wushu" (popular sport). Multicoloured.
2604 8f. (1) Type **487** . . . . . . 4·25 1·75
2605 8f. (2) Sword exercises . . . 4·25 1·75
2606 8f. (3) "Boxing" . . . . . 4·25 1·75
2607 8f. (4) Leaping with spear 4·25 1·75
2608 8f. (5) Cudgel exercise . . . 4·25 1·75
2609 43f. (6) Cudgel versus spears (60 × 30 mm) . . . . . . 5·00 3·50

488 "Mass Revolutionary Criticism"

489 Parade of Athletes

1975. Criticism of Confucius and Liu Piao. Multicoloured.
2610 8f. (1) Type **488** . . . . . . 6·00 1·50
2611 8f. (2) "Leaders of the production brigade" . . . 6·00 1·50
2612 8f. (3) "The battle continues" (horiz) . . . . 6·00 1·50
2613 8f. (4) "Liberated slave – pioneer critic" (horiz) . . 6·00 1·50

1975. 3rd National Games, Peking. Mult.
2614 8f. (1) Type **489** . . . . . 1·50 30
2615 8f. (2) Athletes studying (horiz) . . . . 1·50 30
2616 8f. (3) Volleyball players (horiz) . . . . 1·50 30
2617 8f. (4) Athlete, soldier, farmer and worker . . . 1·50 30
2618 8f. (5) Various sports (horiz) 1·50 30
2619 8f. (6) Ethnic types and horse racing (horiz) . . . 1·50 30
2620 35f. (7) Children and divers 4·00 2·00

490 Members of Expedition

492 Children sticking Posters

491 "Studying Together"

1975. Chinese Ascent of Mount Everest. Mult.
2621 8f. (2) Type **490** 80 25
2622 8f. (3) Mountaineers with flag (horiz) 80 25
2623 43f. (1) View of Mount Everest (horiz) . . . . . 1·50 50

1975. National Conference "Learning Agriculture from Tachai". Multicoloured.
2624 8f. (1) Type **491** . . . . . . 3·00 1·00
2625 8f. (2) "Promote Hard Work" . . . . 3·00 1·00
2626 8f. (3) Chinese combine-harvester . . . . 3·00 1·00

1975. "Children's Progress". Multicoloured.
2627 8f. (1) Girl and young boy 1·25 50
2628 8f. (2) Type **492** . . . . . . 1·25 50
2629 8f. (3) Studying . . . . . . 1·25 50
2630 8f. (4) Harvesting . . . . 1·25 50
2631 52f. (5) Tug-of-war . . . . 6·75 2·25

493 Ploughing Paddy Field

1975. Mechanised Farming. Multicoloured.
2632 8f. (1) Type **493** . . . . . . 2·40 90
2633 8f. (2) Mechanical rice seedlings transplanter . . 2·40 90
2634 8f. (3) Irrigation pump . . . 2·40 90
2635 8f. (4) Spraying cotton field 2·40 90
2636 8f. (5) Combine harvester 2·40 90

494 Bridge over Canal

1976. Completion of 4th Five-year Plan. Mult.
2637 8f. (1) Harvest scene . . . . 3·00 80
2638 8f. (2) Type **494** . . . . . . 3·00 80
2639 8f. (3) Fertilizer plant . . . 3·00 80
2640 8f. (4) Textile factory . . . 3·00 80
2641 8f. (5) Iron foundry . . . . 3·00 80
2642 8f. (6) Steam coal train . . . 3·00 1·00
2643 8f. (7) Hydro-electric power station . . . . 3·00 80
2644 8f. (8) Shipbuilding . . . . 3·00 80
2645 8f. (9) Oil industry . . . . 3·00 80
2646 8f. (10) Pipe-line and harbour . . . . 3·00 80
2647 8f. (11) Diesel train on viaduct . . . . 5·00 1·00
2648 8f. (12) Crystal formation (scientific research) . . . 5·00 80
2649 8f. (13) Classroom (rural education) . . . . 5·00 80
2650 8f. (14) Workers' health centre . . . . 5·00 80
2651 8f. (15) Workers' flats . . . 5·00 80
2652 8f. (16) Department store . . 5·00 80

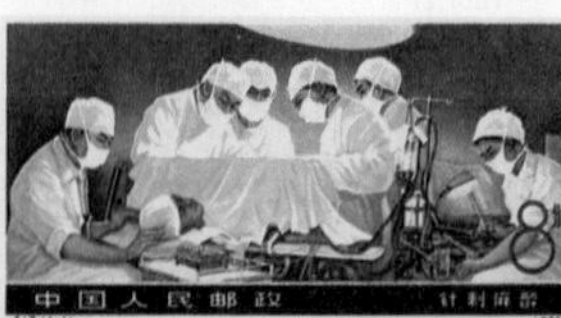

495 Heart Surgery

1976. Medical Services' Achievements. Mult.
2653 8f. (1) Type **495** . . . . . . 3·00 80
2654 8f. (2) Restoration of tractor-driver's severed arm . . . . 3·00 80
2655 8f. (3) Exercise of fractured arm . . . . 3·00 80
2656 8f. (4) Cataract operation – patient threading needle 3·00 80

496 Students studying at "May 7" School

1976. 10th Anniv of Mao's "May 7 Directive". Multicoloured.
2657 8f. (1) Type **496** . . . . . . 2·50 80
2658 8f. (2) Students in agriculture . . . . 2·50 80
2659 8f. (3) Students in production team . . . . 2·50 80

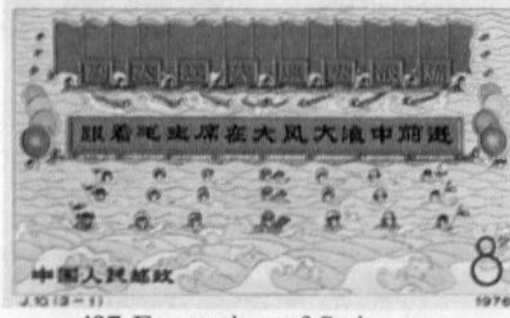

497 Formation of Swimmers

1976. 10th Anniv of Chairman Mao's Swim in Yangtse River. Multicoloured.
2660 8f. (1) Type **497** . . . . . . 2·50 80
2661 8f. (2) Swimmers crossing Yangtse . . . . 2·50 90
2662 8f. (3) Swimmers in surf . . 2·50 80
Nos. 2661/2 are smaller, 35 × 27 mm.

498 Students with Rosettes

1976. "Going to College". Multicoloured.
2663 8f. (1) Type **498** . . . . . 2·40 70
2664 8f. (2) Study group . . . . 2·40 70
2665 8f. (3) On-site instructions 2·40 70
2666 8f. (4) Students operating computer . . . . 2·40 70
2667 8f. (5) Return of graduates from college . . . . . . 2·40 70

499 Electricity Lineswoman

501 Peasant arranging Student's Headband

500 Lu Hsun

1976. Maintenance of Electric Power Lines. Multicoloured.
2668 8f. (1) Type **499** . . . . . . 2·50 70
2669 8f. (2) Linesman replacing insulator . . . . 2·50 70
2670 8f. (3) Linesman using hydraulic lift . . . . . . 2·50 70
2671 8f. (4) Technician inspecting transformer . . . . . . 2·50 70

1976. 95th Birth Anniv of Lu Hsun (revolutionary leader). Multicoloured.
2672 8f. (1) Type **500** . . . . . . 4·25 1·40
2673 8f. (2) Lu Hsun sick, writing in bed . . . . 4·25 1·40
2674 8f. (3) Lu Hsun, workers and soldiers . . . . . . 4·25 1·40

1976. Students and Country Life. Multicoloured.
2675 4f. (1) Type **501** . . . . . . 1·25 30
2676 8f. (2) Student teaching farm woman (horiz) . . . . . 1·25 30
2677 8f. (3) Irrigation survey . . 1·25 30
2678 8f. (4) Agricultural student testing wheat (horiz) . . . 1·25 30

2679 10f. (5) Student feeding lamb . . . . 2·00 1·00
2680 20f. (6) Frontier guards (horiz) . . . . 4·00 1·50

502 Mao Tse-tung's Birthplace

1976. Shaoshan Revolutionary Sites. Mult.
2681 4f. (1) Type **502** . . . . . . 1·40 60
2682 8f. (2) School building . . . 1·40 50
2683 8f. (3) Peasants' Association building . . . . 1·40 50
2684 10f. (4) Railway station . . 1·40 60

503 Chou En-lai

504 Statue of Lui Hu-lan

1977. 1st Death Anniv of Chou En-lai. Mult.
2685 8f. (1) Type **503** . . . . . . 2·00 80
2686 8f. (2) Chou En-lai making report . . . . 2·00 80
2687 8f. (3) Chou meeting "Iron Man" Wang Chin-hsi (horiz) . . . . 2·00 80
2688 8f. (4) Chou with provincial representatives (horiz) . . 2·00 80

1977. 30th Death Anniv of Lin Hu-lan (heroine and martyr). Multicoloured.
2689 8f. (1) Type **504** . . . . . . 6·00 1·25
2690 8f. (2) Text by Mao Tse-tung . . . . 2·50 1·25
2691 8f. (3) Lin Hu-lan and people . . . . 2·50 1·25

505 Revolutionaries and Text

1977. 30th Anniv of 1947 Taiwan Rising. Mult.
2692 8f. Type **505** . . . . 1·50 75
2693 10f. Three Taiwanese with banner . . . . 2·50 1·00

506 Weapon Maintenance

1977. Chinese Militiawomen. Multicoloured.
2694 8f. (1) Type **506** . . . . . . 4·00 1·25
2695 8f. (2) On horseback . . . . 4·00 1·25
2696 8f. (3) Directing traffic in tunnel . . . . 4·00 1·25

507 Sheep Rearing

508 Cadre Members

1977. Multicoloured.
2697 1f. Coal mining 20 10
2698 1½f. Type **507** 10 20
2699 2f. Exports 20 10
2700 3f. Forest and diesel-train 20 10
2701 4f. Hydro-electric power . . 10 10
2702 5f. Fishing 50 10
2703 8f. Agriculture 10 10
2704 10f. Radio tower and mail-vans 15 10
2705 20f. Steel production 20 10
2706 30f. Road transport 20 10
2707 40f. Textile manufacture . . 25 15
2708 50f. Tractor assembly . . . 40 10
2709 60f. Oil-rigs and setting sun 45 15
2710 70f. Railway viaduct, Yangtse Gorge 85 35

1977. Promoting Tachai-type Developments. Mult.
2711 8f. (1) Type **508** . . . . . . 1·25 75
2712 8f. (2) Modern cultivation 1·25 75
2713 8f. (3) Reading wall newspaper . . . . 1·25 75
2714 8f. (4) Reclaiming land for agriculture . . . . 1·25 75

509 Party Leader addressing Workers

1977. "Taching-type" Industrial Conference. Mult.
2715 8f. (1) Type **509** . . . . . . 1·75 85
2716 8f. (2) Drilling for oil in snowstorm . . . . 1·75 85
2717 8f. (3) Man with banner over mass formation of workers . . . . 1·75 85
2718 8f. (4) Smiling workers and industrial scene . . . . . 1·75 85

510 Mongolians Rejoicing

511 Rumanian Flag

1977. 30th Anniv of Inner Mongolian Autonomous Region. Multicoloured.
2719 8f. Type **510** 50 30
2720 10f. Mongolian industrial scene and iron ore train 85 40
2721 20f. Mongolian pasture . . 1·50 75

1977. Centenary of Rumanian Independence. Mult.
2722 8f. Type **511** . . . . 1·00 25
2723 10f. "The Battle of Smirdan" (Grigorescu) . . 1·50 75
2724 20f. Mihai Viteazu Memorial . . . . 2·00 75

512 Yenan and Floral Border

1977. 35th Anniv of Yenan Forum on Literature and Art. Multicoloured.
2725 8f. (1) Type **512** 75 35
2726 8f. (2) Hammer, sickle and gun 75 35

513 Chu Teh, National People's Congress Chairman

514 Soldier, Sailor and Airman under Banner of Mao Tse-tung

1977. 1st Death Anniv of Chu Teh.
2727 **513** 8f. (1) multicoloured . . 75 30
2728 – 8f. (2) multicoloured . . 75 30
2729 – 8f. (3) black, bl & gold 75 30
2730 – 8f. (4) black, bl & gold 75 30
DESIGNS—VERT: No. 2728, Chu Teh during his last session of Congress. HORIZ: No. 2729, Chu Teh at his desk. No. 2730, Chu Teh on horseback as Commander of People's Liberation Army.

1977. People's Liberation Army Day. Mult.
2731 8f. (1) Type **514** . . . . . 1·60 60
2732 8f. (2) Soldiers in Ching-kang Mountains . . . . 1·60 60
2733 8f. (3) Guerrilla fighters returning to base . . . . 1·60 60
2734 8f. (4) Chinese forces crossing Yangtse River . . 1·60 60
2735 8f. (5) "The Steel Wall" (National Defence Forces) 1·60 60

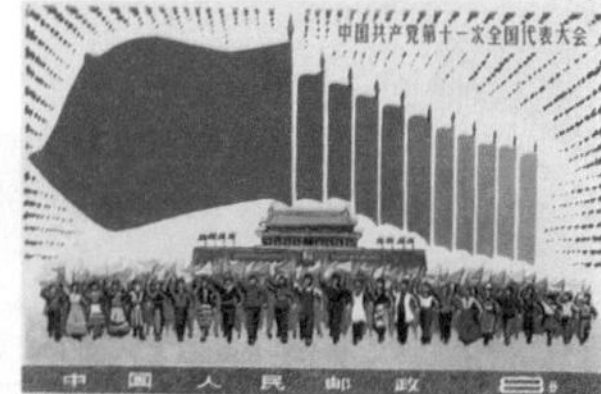

515 Red Flags and Crowd

1977. 11th National Communist Party Congress. Multicoloured.
2736 8f. (1) Type **515** . . . . . . 4·00 1·00
2737 8f. (2) Mao banner and procession . . . . 4·00 1·00
2738 8f. (3) Hammer and sickle banner and procession . . 4·00 1·00

516 Mao Tse-tung

1977. 1st Death Anniv of Mao Tse-tung. Mult.
2739 8f. (1) Type **516** . . . . . . 1·00 45
2740 8f. (2) Mao as young man 1·00 45
2741 8f. (3) Making speech . . . 1·00 45
2742 8f. (4) Mao broadcasting . . 1·00 45
2743 8f. (5) Mao with Chou En-lai and Chu Teh (horiz) 1·25 45
2744 8f. (6) Reviewing the army 1·25 45

517 Mao Memorial Hall

1977. Completion of Mao Memorial Hall, Peking. Multicoloured.
2745 8f. (1) Type **517** . . . . . . 2·50 1·10
2746 8f. (2) Commemoration text 2·50 1·10

518 Tractors transporting Oil-rig

1978. Development of Petroleum Industry. Mult.
2747 8f. (1) Type **518** 50 10
2748 8f. (2) Clearing wax from oil well 50 10
2749 8f. (3) Laying pipe-line . . . 50 10
2750 8f. (4) Tung Fang Hung oil refinery, Peking 65 20
2751 8f. (5) Loading a tanker, Taching 75 20
2752 20f. (6) Oil-rig and drilling ship "Exploration" . . . 2·75 80

519 Rifle Shooting from Sampan

1978. "Army and People are One Family". Multicoloured.
2753 8f. (1) Type **519** . . . . . . 1·25 75
2754 8f. (2) Helping with rice harvest . . . . 1·25 75

520 Great Banner of Chairman Mao

521 "Learn from Comrade Lei Feng" (Inscription by Mao Tse-tung)

1978. 5th National People's Congress. Mult.
2755 8f. (1) Type **520** 80 40
2756 8f. (2) Constitution 80 40
2757 8f. (3) Emblems of modernization 80 40

1978. Lei Feng (Communist fighter) Commem.
2758 **521** 8f. (1) gold and red . . . 1·50 50
2759 – 8f. (2) gold and red . . . 1·50 50
2760 – 8f. (3) multicoloured . . 1·50 50
DESIGNS: No. 2759, Inscription by Chairman Hua; No. 2760, Lei Feng reading Mao's works.

522 Hsiang Ching-yu (Women's Movement Pioneer)

523 Conference Emblem and Tien on Men Gate, Peking

1978. International Working Women's Day.
2761 **522** 8f. (1) black, red & gold 75 35
2762 – 8f. (2) black, red & gold 75 35
DESIGN: No. 2762, Yang Kai-hui (communist fighter).

1978. National Science Conference. Mult.
2763 8f. (1) Type **523** 75 40
2764 8f. (2) Flags 75 40
2765 8f. (3) Emblem, flag and globe 75 40

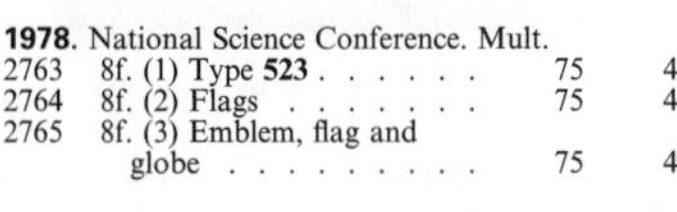

524 Launching a Radio-sonde

525 Galloping Horse

1978. Meteorological Services. Multicoloured.
2766 8f. (1) Type **524** 60 20
2767 8f. (2) Radar station 60 20
2768 8f. (3) Weather forecasting with computers 60 20
2769 8f. (4) Commune group observing sky 60 20
2770 8f. (5) Cloud-dispersing rockets 60 20

1978. Galloping Horses.
2771 **525** 4f. (1) multicoloured . . 1·00 50
2772 – 8f. (2) multicoloured . . 1·00 50
2773 – 8f. (3) multicoloured . . 1·00 55
2774 – 10f. (4) multicoloured . . 1·00 55
2775 – 20f. (5) multicoloured . . 4·00 65
2776 – 30f. (6) multicoloured . . 3·00 75
2777 – 40f. (7) mult (horiz) . . 3·00 1·00
2778 – 50f. (8) mult (horiz) . . 4·00 1·00
2779 – 60f. (9) mult (horiz) . . 3·00 2·00
2780 – 70f. (10) mult (horiz) . . 4·00 3·00
DESIGNS: No. 2772/80, various paintings of horses by Hsu Pei-hung.

526 Football

527 Material Feeder

1978. "Building up Strength for the Revolution". Multicoloured.
2782 8f. (2) Type **526** 40 10
2783 8f. (3) Swimming 40 10
2784 8f. (4) Gymnastics 40 10
2785 8f. (5) Running 40 10
2786 20f. (1) Group exercises . . 1·10 20
The 20f. is larger, 48 × 27 mm.

1978. Chemical Industry Development. Fabric Production. Multicoloured.
2787 8f. (1) Type **527** 80 20
2788 8f. (2) Drawing-out threads 80 20
2789 8f. (3) Weaving 80 20
2790 8f. (4) Dyeing and printing 80 20
2791 8f. (5) Finished products . . 80 20

528 Conference Emblem

529 Grassland Improvement, Mongolia

1978. National Finance and Trade Conference. Multicoloured.

2792 8f. (1) Type **528** 75 20
2793 8f. (2) Inscription by Mao Tse-tung 75 20

1978. Progress in Animal Husbandry. Mult.

2794 8f. (1) Type **529** . . . . . . 1·00 25
2795 8f. (2) Sheep rearing by the Kazakhs . . . . 1·00 25
2796 8f. (3) Shearing sheep, Tibet 1·00 25

530 Automated loading of Burning Coke

1978. Iron and Steel Industry. Mult.

2797 8f. (1) Type **530** . . . . . . 1·00 25
2798 8f. (2) Checking molten iron 50 25
2799 8f. (3) Pouring molten steel 50 25
2800 8f. (4) Steel-rolling mill . . 50 25
2801 8f. (5) Loading steel train 1·00 25

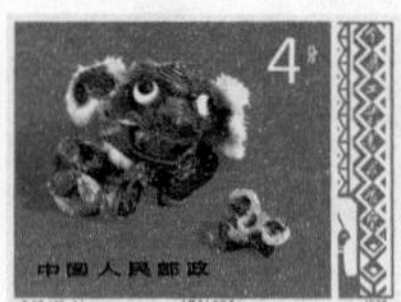

531 Soldier

532 Cloth Toy Lion

1978. Army Modernization. Multicoloured.

2802 8f. (1) Type **531** 85 30
2803 8f. (2) Soldier firing missile 85 30
2804 8f. (3) Amphibious landing 85 30

1978. Arts and Crafts. Multicoloured.

2805 4f. (1) Type **532** 45 15
2806 8f. (2) Three-legged pot (vert) 45 10
2807 8f. (3) Lacquerware rhinoceros 55 10
2808 10f. (4) Embroidered kitten (vert) 55 15
2809 20f. (5) Basketware 65 20
2810 30f. (6) Cloissone pot (vert) 70 30
2811 40f. (7) Lacquerware plate and swan 85 40
2812 50f. (8) Boxwood carving (vert) . . . . 1·00 50
2813 60f. (9) Jade carving . . . . 1·25 40
2814 70f. (10) Ivory carving (vert) 1·40 70

533 Worker, Peasant and Intellectual

534 "Panax ginseng"

1978. 4th National Women's Congress.

2816 **533** 8f. multicoloured . . . . 1·50 50

1978. Medicinal Plants. Multicoloured.

2817 8f. (1) Type **534** 60 15
2818 8f. (2) "Datura metel" . . . 60 15
2819 8f. (3) "Belamcanda chinensis" 60 15
2820 8f. (4) "Platycodon grandiflorum" 60 15
2821 55f. (5) "Rhododendron dauricum" . . . . 2·40 75

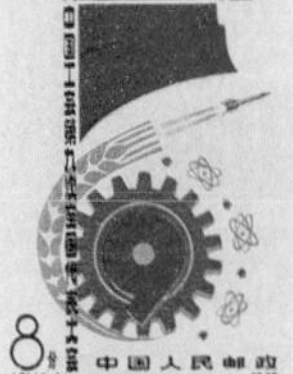

535 Cogwheel, Grain, Rocket and Flag

536 Emblem, Open Book and Flowers

1978. 9th National Trades Union Congress.

2822 **535** 8f. multicoloured . . . . 2·10 75

1978. 10th National Congress of Communist Youth League.

2823 **536** 8f. multicoloured . . . . 2·10 75

537 Chinese and Japanese Children exchanging Gifts

538 Hui, Han and Mongolian

1978. Signing of Chinese–Japanese Treaty of Peace and Friendship. Multicoloured.

2824 8f. Type **537** 30 15
2825 55f. Great Wall of China and Mt. Fuji . . . . . . 1·75 65

1978. 20th Anniv of Ningsia Hui Autonomous Region. Multicoloured.

2826 8f. (1) Type **538** 85 30
2827 8f. (2) Coal loading machine, Holan colliery 85 30
2828 10f. (3) Irrigation and Chingtunghsia power station 85 30

539 Chinsha River Bridge, West Szechuan

540 Transplanting Rice Seedlings by Machine

1978. Highway Bridges. Multicoloured.

2829 8f. (1) Type **539** 70 30
2830 8f. (2) Hsinghong Bridge, Wuhsi 70 30
2831 8f. (3) Chiuhsikou Bridge, Fengdu 70 30
2832 8f. (4) Chinsha Bridge . . . 70 30
2833 60f. (5) Shangyeh Bridge, Sanmen . . . . 1·90 90

1978. Water Country Modernization. Mult.

2835 8f. (1) Type **540** . . . . . . 2·25 1·00
2836 8f. (2) Crop spraying . . . 2·25 1·00
2837 8f. (3) Selecting seeds . . . 2·25 1·00
2838 8f. (4) Canal-side village . . 2·25 1·00
2839 8f. (5) Delivering and storing grain . . . . . . 2·25 1·00

Nos. 2835/9 were issued together, se-tenant, forming a composite design.

541 Festivities

1978. 20th Anniv of Kwangsi Chuang Autonomous Region. Multicoloured.

2840 8f. (1) Type **541** . . . . . . 2·25 40
2841 8f. (2) Industrial complexes (vert) . . . . 2·25 40
2842 10f. (3) River scene (vert) 1·50 1·00

542 Tibetan Peasant reporting Mineralogical Discovery

543 Pair of Golden Pheasants on Rock

1978. Mining Development. Multicoloured.

2843 4f. Type **542** 50 25
2844 8f. Miners with pneumatic drill 50 15
2845 10f. Open-cast mining . . . 1·25 25
2846 20f. Electric mine train . . . 1·50 40

1979. Golden Pheasants. Multicoloured.

2847 4f. Type **543** . . . . 1·25 70
2848 8f. Pheasant in flight . . . . 3·75 1·25
2849 45f. Pheasant looking for food . . . . 3·00 3·00

544 Einstein

545 Woman, Monster and Phoenix

1979. Birth Centenary of Albert Einstein (physicist).

2850 **544** 8f. brown, gold & slate 1·40 40

1979. Silk Paintings from a Tomb of the Warring States Period (475–221 B.C.). Multicoloured.

2851 8f. Type **545** . . . . 2·10 20
2852 60f. Man riding dragon . . 1·40 1·25

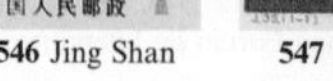

546 Jing Shan

547 Hammer and Sickle

1979. Peking Scenes. Multicoloured.

2853 1y. Type **546** 75 10
2854 2y. Summer Palace . . . . 1·50 40
2855 5y. Beihai Park . . . . . . 4·00 85

1979. 90th Anniv of International Labour Day.

2856 **547** 8f. multicoloured . . . . 1·25 50

548 Memorial Frieze

1979. 60th Anniv of May 4th Movement. Mult.

2857 8f. (1) Type **548** 70 20
2858 8f. (2) Girl and symbols of progress 70 20

549 Children of Different Races

1979. International Year of the Child. Mult.

2859 8f. I.Y.C. emblem and children with balloons . . 1·50 50
2860 60f. Type **549** . . . . 8·75 3·00

550 Spring over Great Wall

1979. The Great Wall. Multicoloured.

2861 8f. (1) Type **550** . . . . . . 1·50 75
2862 8f. (2) Summer over Great Wall . . . . 1·50 75
2863 8f. (3) Autumn over Great Wall . . . . 1·50 75
2864 60f. (4) Winter over Great Wall . . . . 11·00 5·00

551 Roaring Tiger

1979. Manchurian Tiger. Paintings by Liu Jiyou. Multicoloured.

2866 4f. Type **551** . . . . 1·00 50
2867 8f. Two young tigers . . . . 1·00 50
2868 60f. Tiger at rest . . . . . 3·25 1·10

552 Mechanical Harvester

1979. Trades of the People's Communes. Mult.

2869 4f. (1) Type **552** (Agriculture) 75 30
2870 8f. (2) Planting a sapling (Forestry) . . . . 1·00 30
2871 8f. (3) Herding ducks (Stock raising) . . . . 1·00 30
2872 8f. (4) Basket weaving . . . 1·00 30
2873 10f. (5) Fishermen with handcarts of fish (Fishing) 2·00 50

554 Games' Emblem, Running, Volleyball and Weightlifting

1979. 4th National Games.

2875 **554** 8f. (1) multicoloured . . 30 30
2876 – 8f. (2) multicoloured . . 30 30
2877 – 8f. (3) black, grn & red 30 30
2878 – 8f. (4) black, red & grn 30 30

DESIGNS: No. 2876, Football, badminton, high jumping and ice skating. No. 2877, Fencing, skiing, gymnastics and diving. No. 2878, Motor cycling, table tennis, basketball and archery.

555 National Flag and Mountains

556 National Emblem

557 National Anthem

558 Dancers and Drummer

559 Tractor and Crop-spraying Antonov An-2

1979. 30th Anniv of People's Republic of China. Multicoloured.
2880 8f. (1) National flag and rainbow . . . . 1·90 70
2881 8f. (2) Type **555** . . . . . . 1·90 70
2882 8f. Type **556** . . . . 1·25 25
2884 8f. Type **557** . . . . 3·00 1·00
2885 8f. (1) Type **558** 75 15
2886 8f. (2) Dancers and tambourine player 75 15
2887 8f. (3) Dancers and banjo player 75 15
2888 8f. (4) Dancers and drummer 75 15
2889 8f. (1) Type **559** 85 15
2890 8f. (2) Computer and cogwheels 85 15
2891 8f. (3) Rocket, jet fighter and submarine 85 15
2892 8f. (4) Atomic symbols . . . 85 15

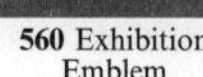

560 Exhibition Emblem

561 Children with Model Aircraft

1979. National Exhibition of Juniors' Scientific and Technological Works.
2893 **560** 8f. multicoloured . . . . 1·25 50

1979. Study of Science from Childhood. Mult.
2894 8f. (1) Type **561** 65 20
2895 8f. (2) Girls with microscope and test tube 65 20
2896 8f. (3) Children with telescope 65 20
2897 8f. (4) Boy catching butterflies 65 20
2898 8f. (5) Girl noting weather readings 65 20
2899 60f. (6) Boys with model boat . . . . 2·50 75

562 Yu Shan

1979. Taiwan Views. Multicoloured.
2901 8f. (1) Type **562** 85 45
2902 8f. (2) Sun Moon Lake . . 85 45
2903 8f. (3) Chikan Tower . . . 85 45
2904 8f. (4) Suao-Hualien highway 85 45
2905 55f. (5) Tian Xiang Falls . . 2·50 1·00
2906 60f. (6) Moonlight over Banping Mountain . . . 3·50 1·60

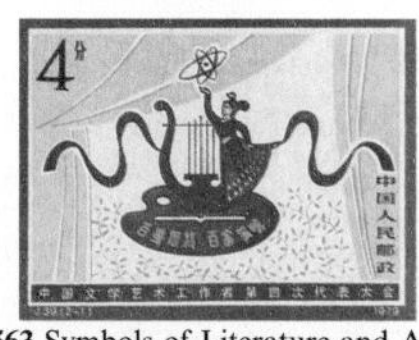

563 Symbols of Literature and Art

1979. 4th National Congress of Literary and Art Workers. Multicoloured.
2907 4f. Type **563** 50 30
2908 8f. Seals, hammer, sickle, rifle, atomic symbol and flowers . . . . 1·10 30

564 "Shaoshan" Type Electric Locomotive

1979. Railway Construction. Multicoloured.
2909 8f. (1) Type **564** . . . . . . 1·50 40
2910 8f. (2) Modern railway viaduct . . . . 1·50 40
2911 8f. (3) Goods train crossing bridge . . . . 1·50 40

565 "Chrysanthemum Petal"

1979. Camellias of Yunnan. Multicoloured.
2912 4f. (1) Type **565** 70 30
2913 8f. (2) "Lion Head" 70 30
2914 8f. (3) Camellia "Chrysantha (Hu) Tuyama" 70 30
2915 10f. (4) "Small Osmanthus Leaf" 70 30
2916 20f. (5) "Baby Face" . . . 1·75 55
2917 30f. (6) "Cornelian" . . . . 3·25 65
2918 40f. (7) Peony Camellia . . 2·50 65
2919 50f. (8) "Purple Gown" . . 2·50 75
2920 60f. (9) "Dwarf Rose" . . . 1·90 75
2921 70f. (10) "Willow Leaf Spinel Pink" . . . . . . 1·90 75

567 Dr. Bethune attending Wounded Soldier

568 Central Archives Hall

1979. 40th Death Anniv of Dr. Norman Bethune. Multicoloured.
2924 8f. Type **567** 55 10
2925 70f. Bethune Memorial, Mausoleum of Martyrs, Shijiazhuang . . . . . . 2·75 75

1979. International Archives Weeks. Mult.
2926 8f. (1) Type **568** 85 20
2927 8f. (2) Gold cabinet containing documents of Ming and Ching dynasties (vert) 85 20
2928 60f. (3) Imperial Archives Main Hall . . . . 7·75 1·75

569 Waterfall Cave, Home of Monkey King

570 Stalin

1979. Scenes from "Pilgrimage to the West" (Chinese classical novel). Multicoloured.
2929 8f. (1) Type **569** . . . . . . 1·50 75
2930 8f. (2) Necha, son of Li, fighting Monkey . . . . 1·50 75
2931 8f. (3) Monkey in Mother Queen's peach orchard . . 1·50 75
2932 8f. (4) Monkey in alchemy furnace . . . . 1·50 75
2933 10f. (5) Monkey fighting White Bone Demon . . . 4·25 75
2934 20f. (6) Monkey extinguishing fire with palm-leaf fan . . . . . . 4·25 75
2935 60f. (7) Monkey fighting Spider Demon in Cobweb Cave . . . . 3·25 3·00
2936 70f. (8) Monkey on scripture-seeking route to India . . . . 7·25 3·00

1979. Birth Centenary of Stalin.
2937 **570** 8f. (1) brown . . . . . 1·25 40
2938 – 8f. (2) black . . . . . . 1·25 40
DESIGN: No. 2038, Stalin appealing for unity against Germany.

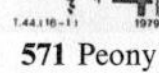

571 Peony

572 Meng Liang, "Hongyang Cave"

1980. Paintings of Qi Baishi.
2939 **571** 4f. (1) multicoloured . . 75 15
2940 – 4f. (2) multicoloured . . 75 15
2941 – 8f. (3) multicoloured . . 75 10
2942 – 8f. (4) black, blue & red 75 10
2943 – 8f. (5) multicoloured . . 75 10
2944 – 8f. (6) black, grey & red 75 10
2945 – 8f. (7) multicoloured . . 75 10
2946 – 8f. (8) multicoloured . . 75 50
2947 – 10f. (9) blk, yell and red 1·50 15
2948 – 20f. (10) grey, brn & blk 1·50 20
2949 – 30f. (11) multicoloured 1·50 30
2950 – 40f. (12) multicoloured 1·50 50
2951 – 50f. (13) blk, grey & red 3·00 75
2952 – 55f. (14) multicoloured 3·75 75
2953 – 60f. (15) blk, grey & red 5·00 1·50
2954 – 70f. (16) multicoloured 6·25 2·25
DESIGNS: No. 2940, Squirrels and grapes; 2941, Crabs and wine; 2942, Tadpoles in mountain spring; 2943, Chicks; 2944, Lotus; 2945, Red plum; 2946, River kingfisher; 2947, Bottle gourds; 2948, "The Voice of Autumn"; 2949, Wisteria; 2950, Chrysanthemums; 2951, Shrimps; 2952, Litchi; 2953, Cabbages and mushrooms; 2954, Peaches.

1980. Facial Make-up in Peking Operas. Mult.
2956 4f. (1) Type **572** . . . . . . 1·25 40
2957 4f. (2) Li Kui, "Black Whirlwind" . . . . . . 1·25 40
2958 8f. (3) Huang Gai, "Meeting of Heroes" . . . . . . 1·75 60
2959 8f. (4) Monkey King, "Havoc in Heaven" . . . 1·75 60
2960 10f. (5) Lu Zhishen, "Wild Boar Forest" . . . . . . 2·25 80
2961 20f. (6) Lian Po, "Reconciliation between the General and the Minister" . . . . 4·50 1·50
2962 60f. (7) Zhang Fei, "Reed Marsh" . . . . 8·25 3·00
2963 70f. (8) Dou Erdun, "Stealing the Emperor's Horse" . . . . 9·00 3·25

573 Chinese Olympic Committee Emblem

574 Bear Macaque

1980. Winter Olympic Games, Lake Placid. Multicoloured.
2964 8f. (1) Type **573** 50 35
2965 8f. (2) Speed skating 50 35
2966 8f. (3) Figure skating . . . 50 35
2967 60f. (4) Skiing . . . . 3·50 1·25

1980. New Year. Year of the Monkey.
2968 **574** 8f. red, black and gold £170 50·00

575 Klara Zetkin (journalist and politician)

1980. 70th Anniv of International Working Women's Day.
2969 **575** 8f. black, yellow & brn 1·25 65

576 Orchard

1980. Afforestation. Multicoloured.
2970 4f. Type **576** 70 15
2971 8f. Highway lined with trees 70 20
2972 10f. Aerial sowing by Antonov An-2 biplane . . 1·40 25
2973 20f. Factory amongst trees 1·40 60

577 Apsaras (celestial beings)

1980. 2nd National Conference of Chinese Scientific and Technical Association.
2974 **577** 8f. multicoloured . . . . 1·25 55

578 Freighter

1980. Mail Transport. Multicoloured.
2975 2f. Type **578** . . . . 1·00 75
2976 4f. Mail bus . . . . 1·25 75
2977 8f. Travelling post office coach . . . . 2·50 1·00
2978 10f. Tupolev Tu-154 airplane . . . . 3·00 1·40

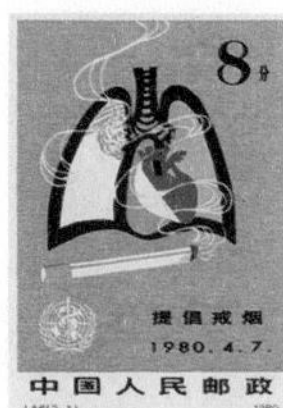

579 Cigarette damaging Heart and Lungs

1980. Anti-smoking Campaign. Multicoloured.
2979 8f. Type **579** . . . . 1·75 40
2980 60f. Face smoking and face holding flower in mouth, symbolising choice of smoking or health . . . . 5·00 2·25

580 Jian Zhen Memorial Hall, Yangzhou

1980. Return of High Monk Jian Zhen's Statue. Multicoloured.
2981 8f. (1) Type **580** . . . . . . 2·50 50
2982 8f. (2) Statue of Jian Zhen (vert) . . . . 2·50 50
2983 60f. (3) Junk in which Jian Zhen travelled to Japan 16·00 5·75

581 Lenin

582 "Swallow Chick" Kite

1980. 110th Birth Anniv of Lenin.
2984 **581** 8f. brown, pink & green 1·60 65

1980. Kites. Multicoloured.
2985 8f. (1) Type **582** . . . . . . 1·50 45
2986 8f. (2) "Slender swallow" kite . . . . 1·50 45

2987	8f. (3) "Semi-slender swallow" kite	1·50	45
2988	70f. (4) "Dual swallows" kite	12·00	4·50

583 Hare running in Fright

1980. Scenes from "Gu Dong" (Chinese fairy tale). Multicoloured.

2989	8f. (1) Type **583**	1·00	55
2990	8f. (2) Hare tells other animals "Gu Dong is coming"	1·00	55
2991	8f. (3) Lion asks "What is Gu Dong?"	1·00	55
2992	8f. (4) Animals discover sound of "Gu Dong" is made by falling papaya	1·00	55

584 Silhouette of Ilyushin Il-86 Jetliner and Plan of Terminal Building

585 Stag

1980. Peking International Airport. Multicoloured.

2993	8f. Type **584**	1·00	30
2994	10f. Airplane and runway lights	1·50	50

1980. Sika Deer. Multicoloured.

2995	4f. Type **585**	80	65
2996	8f. Doe and fawn	80	65
2997	60f. Herd	5·25	2·10

586 "White Lotus"

1980. Lotus Paintings by Yu Zhizhen. Mult.

2998	8f. (1) Type **586**	2·00	90
2999	8f. (2) "Rose-tipped Snow"	2·00	90
3000	8f. (3) "Buddha's Seat"	2·00	90
3001	70f. (4) "Variable Charming Face"	17·00	6·00

587 Returned Pearl Cave and Sword-cut Stone

1980. Guilin Landscapes. Multicoloured.

3003	8f. (1) Type **587**	1·50	45
3004	8f. (2) Distant view of three mountains	1·50	45
3005	8f. (3) Nine-horse Fresco Hill	1·50	45
3006	8f. (4) Egrets around the aged banyan	1·50	45
3007	8f. (5) Western Hills at sunset (vert)	1·50	45
3008	8f. (6) Moonlight on the Lijiang River (vert)	1·50	45
3009	60f. (7) Springhead and ferry (vert)	9·50	3·00
3010	70f. (8) Scenic path at Yangshuo (vert)	10·50	3·00

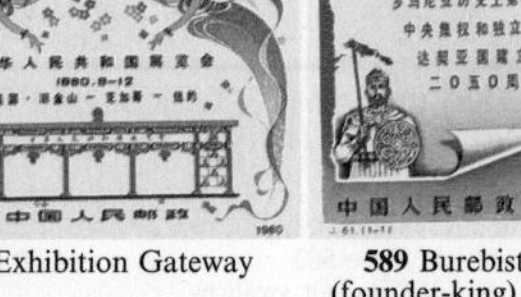

588 Exhibition Gateway

589 Burebista (founder-king) and Rumanian Flag

1980. China Exhibition in United States. Mult.

3011	8f. Type **588**	75	40
3012	70f. Great Wall and emblems of San Francisco, Chicago and New York	4·25	2·25

1980. 2050th Anniv of Dacian State.

3013 **589**	8f. multicoloured	1·60	65

590 "Sea of Clouds" (Liu Haisu)

1980. U.N.E.S.C.O. Exhibition of Chinese Paintings and Drawings. Multicoloured.

3014	8f. (1) Type **590**	1·10	40
3015	8f. (2) "Black-naped Oriole and Magnolia" (Yu Feian) (vert)	1·50	70
3016	8f. (3) "Tending Bactrian Camels" (Wu Zuoren)	1·10	40

591 Quzi Tower in Spring

1980. Liu Yuan (Tarrying Garden), Suzhou. Mult.

3017	8f. (1) Type **591**	5·75	2·10
3018	8f. (2) Yuancui Pavilion in Summer	5·75	2·10
3019	10f. (3) Hanbi Shanfang in Autumn	5·75	2·40
3020	60f. (4) Guanyun Peak in Winter	32·00	10·00

592 Xu Guangqi

593 Pistol-shooting

1980. Scientists of Ancient China. Multicoloured.

3021	8f. (1) Type **592** (agriculturalist and astronomer)	2·25	65
3022	8f. (2) Li Bing (hydraulic engineer)	2·25	65
3023	8f. (3) Jia Sixie (agronomist)	2·25	65
3024	60f. (4) Huang Daopo (textile expert)	10·00	3·00

1980. 1st Anniv of Return to International Olympic Committee. Multicoloured.

3025 **593**	4f. (1) brown, yell & mve	50	10
3026 –	8f. (2) brown, yell & grn	75	15
3027 –	8f. (3) brown, yell & blue	75	15
3028 –	10f. (4) brown, yell & orge	1·10	35
3029 –	60f. (5) multicoloured	3·75	1·00

DESIGNS: No. 3026, Gymnastics; No. 3027, Diving; No. 3028, Volleyball; No. 3029, Archery.

594 White Flag Dolphin

595 Cock

1980. White Flag Dolphin. Multicoloured.

3030	8f. Type **594**	1·25	25
3031	60f. Two dolphins	6·00	1·00

1981. New Year. Year of the Cock.

3032 **595**	8f. multicoloured	8·50	2·00

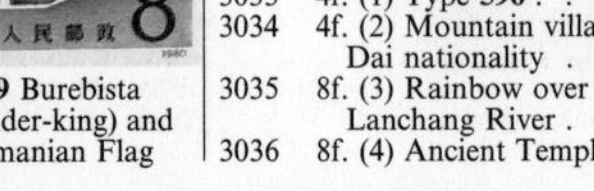

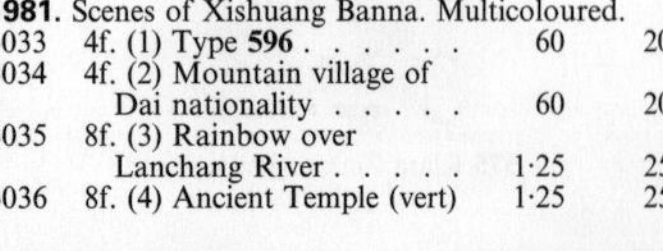

596 Early Morning

1981. Scenes of Xishuang Banna. Multicoloured.

3033	4f. (1) Type **596**	60	20
3034	4f. (2) Mountain village of Dai nationality	60	20
3035	8f. (3) Rainbow over Lanchang River	1·25	25
3036	8f. (4) Ancient Temple (vert)	1·25	25
3037	8f. (5) Moonlit night (vert)	1·25	25
3038	60f. (6) Phoenix tree in bloom (vert)	7·00	2·50

597 Flower Basket Lantern

1981. Palace Lanterns. Multicoloured.

3039	4f. (1) Type **597**	95	45
3040	8f. (2) Dragons playing with a pearl	1·50	40
3041	8f. (3) Dragon and phoenix	1·50	40
3042	8f. (4) Treasure bowl	1·50	40
3043	20f. (5) Flower and birds	4·25	1·00
3044	60f. (6) Peony lantern painted with fishes	11·50	4·00

598 Crossing the River

1981. Marking the Gunwale (Chinese fable). Multicoloured.

3045	8f. (1) Chinese text of story	70	35
3046	8f. (2) Type **598**	70	35
3047	8f. (3) The sword drops in the water	70	35
3048	8f. (4) Making mark on gunwale	70	35
3049	8f. (5) Diving into river to recover sword	70	35

599 Chinese Elm

600 Vase with Two Tigers (Song Dynasty)

1981. Miniature Landscapes (dwarf trees). Mult.

3050	4f. (1) Type **599**	45	35
3051	8f. (2) Juniper	70	30
3052	8f. (3) Maidenhair tree	70	30
3053	10f. (4) Chinese Juniper (horiz)	1·10	30
3054	20f. (5) Wild Kaki persimmon (horiz)	2·00	1·00
3055	60f. (6) Single-seed juniper (horiz)	6·25	1·40

1981. Ceramics from Cizhou Kilns. Multicoloured.

3056	4f. (1) Type **600**	35	30
3057	8f. (2) Carved black glazed vase (Jin dynasty) (horiz)	55	25
3058	8f. (3) Amphora with apricot blossoms (modern)	55	25
3059	8f. (4) Jar with two phoenixes (Yuan dynasty) (horiz)	55	25
3060	10f. (5) Flat flask with dragon and phoenix (Yuan dynasty) (horiz)	1·25	30
3061	60f. (6) Vessel with tiger-shaped handles (modern) (horiz)	4·00	1·40

601 Giant Panda "Stamp"

1981. People's Republic of China Stamp Exhibition, Japan. Multicoloured.

3062	8f. Type **601**	75	15
3063	60f. Cockerel and junk "stamps"	1·90	85

602 Qinchuan Bull

603 Inscription by Chou En-lai

1981. Cattle. Multicoloured.

3064	4f. (1) Type **602**	50	15
3065	8f. (2) Binhu buffalo	50	10
3066	8f. (3) Yak	50	10
3067	8f. (4) Black and white dairy cattle	50	10
3068	10f. (5) Red pasture bull	75	25
3069	55f. (6) Simmental crossbreed bull	5·00	1·25

1981. "To Deliver Mail for Ten Thousand Li, Has Bearing on Arteries and Veins of the Country".

3070 **603**	8f. multicoloured	50	15

604 I.T.U. and W.H.O. Emblems and Ribbons forming Caduceus

605 Safety in Building Construction

1981. World Telecommunications Day.

3071 **604**	8f. multicoloured	50	15

1981. National Safety Month. Multicoloured.

3072	8f. (1) Type **605**	40	15
3073	8f. (2) Mining safety	40	15
3074	8f. (3) Road safety	40	15
3075	8f. (4) Farming and forestry safety	40	15

606 Trunk Call Building

607 St. Bride Vase (Men's singles)

1981.

3076 **606**	8f. brown	1·60	40

1981. Chinese Team's Victories at World Table Tennis Championships. Multicoloured.

3077	8f. (3) Type **607**	25	15
3078	8f. (4) Iran Cup (Men's doubles)	25	15
3079	8f. (5) G. Geist Prize (Women's singles)	25	15
3080	8f. (6) W. J. Pope Trophy (Women's doubles)	25	15
3081	8f. (7) Heydusek Prize (Mixed doubles)	25	15
3082	20f. (1) Swathling Cup (Men's team)	80	15
3083	20f. (2) Marcel Corbillon Cup (Women's team)	80	15

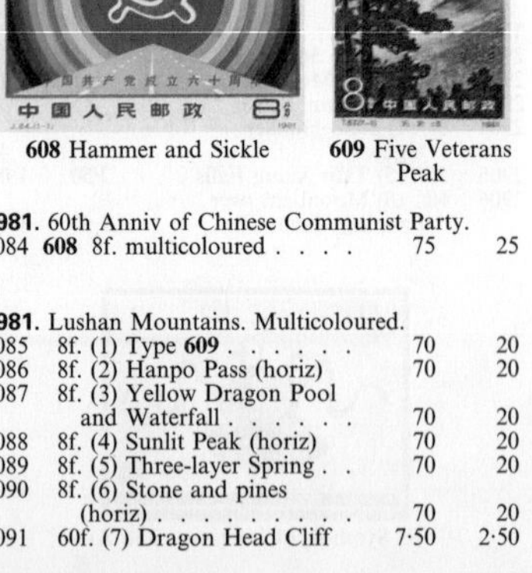

608 Hammer and Sickle

609 Five Veterans Peak

1981. 60th Anniv of Chinese Communist Party.

3084 **608**	8f. multicoloured	75	25

1981. Lushan Mountains. Multicoloured.

3085	8f. (1) Type **609**	70	20
3086	8f. (2) Hanpo Pass (horiz)	70	20
3087	8f. (3) Yellow Dragon Pool and Waterfall	70	20
3088	8f. (4) Sunlit Peak (horiz)	70	20
3089	8f. (5) Three-layer Spring	70	20
3090	8f. (6) Stone and pines (horiz)	70	20
3091	60f. (7) Dragon Head Cliff	7·50	2·50

610 Silver Ear ("Tremella fuciformis")

1981. Edible Mushrooms. Multicoloured.
3092 4f. (1) Type **610** 60 15
3093 8f. (2) Veiled stinkhorn ("Dictyophora indusiata") 80 15
3094 8f. (3) "Hericium erinaceus" 80 15
3095 8f. (4) "Russula rubra" 80 15
3096 10f. (5) Shii-take mushroom ("Lentinus edodes") 1·25 20
3097 70f. (6) White button mushroom ("Agaricus bisporus") 3·00 75

611 Medal **612** Huangguoshu Waterfall

1981. Quality Month.
3098 **611** 8f. (1) silver, black and red 75 20
3099 8f. (2) gold, brown and red 75 20

1981.
3100 – 1f. green 10 10
3101 – 1½f. red 10 10
3102 – 2f. green 10 10
3103 **612** 3f. brown 10 10
3118 – 3f. dp brn, brn & lt brn 10 10
3104 – 4f. violet 10 10
3119 – 4f. mauve and lilac 10 10
3105 – 5f. brown 10 10
3106 – 8f. blue 10 10
3107 – 10f. purple 10 10
3121 – 10f. brown 20 10
3108 – 20f. green 55 10
3122 – 20f. blue 25 10
3109 – 30f. brown 25 10
3110 – 40f. black 35 10
3111 – 50f. mauve 35 10
3112 – 70f. black 55 10
3113 – 80f. red 55 10
3114 – 1y. lilac 65 10
3115 – 2y. green 85 15
3116 – 5y. blue 1·75 25

DESIGNS—VERT: 1f. Xishuang Banna. 1½f. Huashan Mountain. 2f. Taishan Mountain. 4f. Palm trees, Hainan. 5f. Pagoda, Huqiu Hill, Suzhou. 8f. Great Wall. 10f. North-east Forest. HORIZ: 20f. Herding sheep on Tianshan Mountain. 30f. Sheep on grassland, Inner Mongolia. 40f. Stone Forest. 50f. Pagodas, Ban Pingshan Mountain, Taiwan. 70f. Mt. Zhumulangma. 80f. Seven Star Grotto, Guangdong. 1y. Gorge, Yangtze River. 2y. Guilin. 5y. Mt. Huangshan.

613 Stone Forest in Autumn

1981. Stone Forest. Multicoloured.
3125 8f. (1) Stone Forest in a mist 45 15
3126 8f. (2) Type **613** 45 15
3127 8f. (3) Pool in Stone Forest 45 15
3128 10f. (4) Dawn over Stone Forest (vert) 60 15
3129 70f. (5) Stone Forest by starlight (vert) 5·50 1·50

614 Lu Xun as Youth

1981. Birth Centenary of Lu Xun (writer).
3130 **614** 8f. black, green & yell 50 15
3131 – 20f. blk, brn & dp brn 1·00 50
DESIGN: 20f. Lu Xun in later life.

615 Dr. Sun Yat-sen **616** "Tree" symbolizing Co-ordination

1981. 70th Anniv of 1911 Revolution.
3132 **615** 8f. (1) multicoloured 40 15
3133 – 8f. (2) black, grn & yell 40 15
3134 – 8f. (3) black, pk & yell 40 15
DESIGNS: No. 3133, Grave of 72 Martyrs, Huang Hua Gate; No. 3134, Headquarters of Military Government of Hubei Province.

1981. Asian Conference of Parliamentarians on Population and Development. Multicoloured.
3135 8f. Type **616** 15 10
3136 70f. Design symbolizing Enlightenment 90 35

617 Money Cowrie and Cowrie-shaped Bronze Coin **618** Hands and Globe with I.Y.D.P. Emblem

1981. Ancient Chinese Coins (1st series). Minted before 221 B.C. Multicoloured.
3137 4f. (1) Type **617** 40 15
3138 4f. (2) Shovel coin 40 15
3139 8f. (3) Shovel coin inscribed "Li" 50 10
3140 8f. (4) Shovel coin inscribed "An Yi Er Jin" 50 10
3141 8f. (5) Knife coin inscribed "Qi Fa Ha" 50 10
3142 8f. (6) Knife coin inscribed "Jie Mo Zhi Fa Hua" 50 10
3143 60f. (7) Knife coin inscribed "Cheng Bai" 3·00 70
3144 70f. (8) Circular coin with hole inscribed "Gong" 4·25 1·40
See also Nos. 3162/69.

1981. International Year of Disabled Persons.
3145 **618** 8f. multicoloured 25 15

619 Daiyu **620** Volleyball Player

1981. The Twelve Beauties of Jinling from "A Dream of Red Mansions" by Cao Xueqin. Multicoloured. Designs showing paintings by Liu Danzhai.
3146 4f. (1) Type **619** 80 15
3147 4f. (2) Baochai chases butterfly 80 15
3148 8f. (3) Yuanchun visits parents 95 20
3149 8f. (4) Yingchun reading Buddhist sutras 95 20
3150 8f. (5) Tanchun forms poetry society 95 20
3151 8f. (6) Xichun painting 95 20
3152 8f. (7) Xiangyun picking up necklace 95 20
3153 10f. (8) Liwan lectures her son 1·40 25
3154 20f. (9) Xifeng hatches plot 1·60 65
3155 30f. (10) Sister Qiao escapes 1·90 80
3156 40f. (11) Keqing relaxing 2·10 2·25
3157 80f. (12) Miaoyu serves tea 8·00 2·50

1981. Victory of Chinese Women's Team in World Cup Volleyball Championships. Multicoloured.
3159 8f. Type **620** 15 10
3160 20f. Player holding Cup 65 30

621 Dog **622** Nie Er and Score of "March of the Volunteers"

1982. New Year. Year of the Dog.
3161 **621** 8f. multicoloured 3·00 75

1982. Ancient Chinese Coins (2nd series). As T **617**. Multicoloured.
3162 4f. (1) Guilian ("Monster Mask") 15 15
3163 4f. (2) Shu shovel coin 15 15
3164 8f. (3) Xia Zhuan shovel coin 20 10
3165 8f. (4) Han Dan shovel coin 20 10
3166 8f. (5) Pointed-head knife coin 20 10
3167 8f. (6) Ming knife coin 20 10
3168 70f. (7) Jin Hua knife coin 2·00 50
3169 80f. (8) Yi Liu Hua circular coin 2·40 70

1982. 70th Anniv of Nie Er (composer).
3170 **622** 8f. multicoloured 30 15

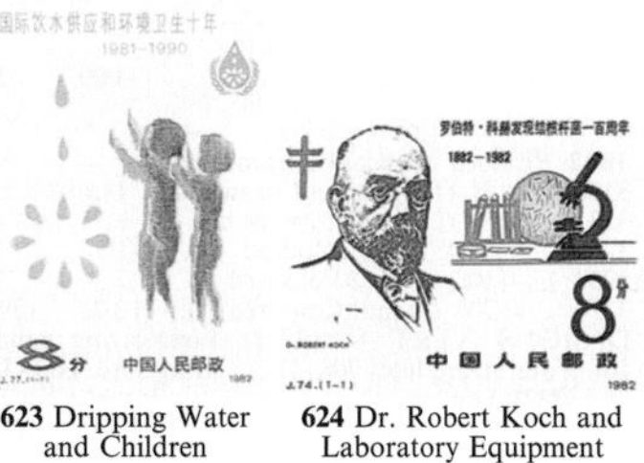

623 Dripping Water and Children **624** Dr. Robert Koch and Laboratory Equipment

1982. Int Drinking Water and Sanitation Decade.
3171 **623** 8f. grey, orange & blue 30 15

1982. Centenary of Discovery of Tubercle Bacillus.
3172 **624** 8f. multicoloured 30 15

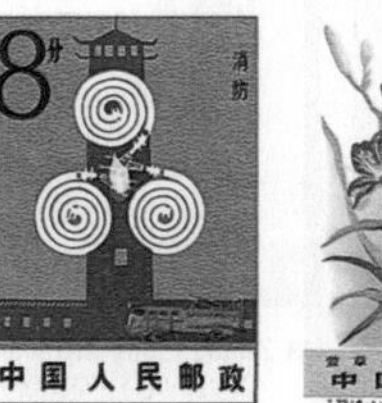

625 Building on Fire, Hoses and Fire Engine **627** "Hemerocallis flava" and "H. fulva"

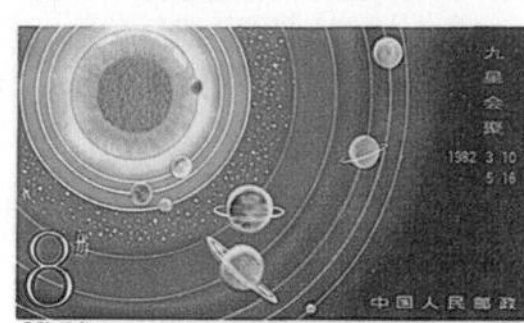

626 Solar System

1982. Fire Control. Multicoloured.
3173 8f. (1) Type **625** 60 15
3174 8f. (2) Chemical fire extinguisher 60 15

1982. "Cluster of Nine Planets" (planetary conjunction).
3175 **626** 8f. multicoloured 45 20

1982. Medicinal Plants. Multicoloured.
3176 4f. (1) Type **627** 20 10
3177 8f. (2) "Fritillaria unibracteata" 40 10
3178 8f. (3) "Aconitum carmichaeli" 40 10
3179 10f. (4) "Lilium brownii" 45 20
3180 20f. (5) "Arisaema consanguineum" 1·10 25
3181 70f. (6) "Paeonia lactiflora" 1·60 80

628 Soong Ching Ling addressing First Plenary Session

1982. 1st Death Anniv of Soong Ching Ling (former Head of State). Multicoloured.
3183 8f. Type **628** 30 15
3184 20f. Portrait of Soong Ching Ling 65 30

629 Sable

1982. The Sable. Multicoloured.
3185 8f. Type **629** 70 20
3186 80f. Sable running 3·50 1·75

630 Census Emblem **631** Text, Emblem and Globe

1982. National Census.
3187 **630** 8f. multicoloured 25 10

1982. Second U.N. Conference on the Exploration and Peaceful Uses of Outer Space, Vienna.
3188 **631** 8f. multicoloured 25 10

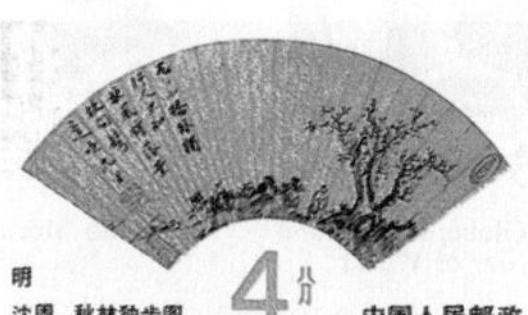

632 "Strolling Alone in Autumn Woods" (Shen Zhou)

1982. Fan Paintings of the Ming and Qing Dynasties. Multicoloured.
3189 4f. (1) Type **632** 35 10
3190 8f. (2) "Jackdaw on withered Tree" (Tang Yin) 75 30
3191 8f. (3) "Bamboos and Sparrows" (Zhou Zhimian) 75 30
3192 10f. (4) "Writing Poem under Pine" (Chen Hongshou and Bai Han) 1·00 15
3193 20f. (5) "Chrysanthemums" (Yun Shouping) 1·25 30
3194 70f. (6) "Masked Hawfinch, Grape Myrtle and Chinese Parasol" (Wang Wu) 4·25 2·25

634 Society Emblem **635** Orpiment

1982. 60th Anniv of Chinese Geological Society.
3196 **634** 8f. gold, stone & black 25 10

1982. Minerals. Multicoloured.
3197 4f. Type **635** 15 10
3198 8f. Stibnite 20 10
3199 10f. Cinnabar 25 10
3200 20f. Wolframite 40 20

636 "12", Hammer and Sickle and Great Hall of the People **637** Hoopoe

1982. 12th National Communist Party Congress.
3201 **636** 8f. multicoloured 60 10

1982. Birds. Multicoloured.
3202 8f. (1) Type **637** 75 60
3203 8f. (2) Barn swallow 75 60
3204 8f. (3) Black-naped oriole 75 60

3205 20f. (4) Great tit . . . . . 1·75 1·25
3206 70f. (5) Great spotted woodpecker . . . . . . 3·50 3·00

638 "Plum Blossom" (Guan Shanyue)

1982. 10th Anniv of Normalization of Diplomatic Relations with Japan. Multicoloured.
3208 8f. Type **638** 25 10
3209 70f. "Hibiscus" (Xiao Shufang) . . . . 1·50 35

639 Globe, Profiles and Ear of Wheat

640 Guo Moruo

1982. World Food Day.
3210 **639** 8f. multicoloured 45 10

1982. 90th Birth Anniv of Guo Moruo (writer). Multicoloured.
3211 8f. Type **640** 15 10
3212 20f. Guo Moruo writing . . 30 10

641 Head of Bodhisattva

642 Dr. D. S. Kotnis

1982. Sculptures of Liao Dynasty. Mult.
3213 8f. (1) Type **641** 60 10
3214 8f. (2) Bust of Bodhisattva 60 10
3215 8f. (3) Boy on lotus flower 60 10
3216 70f. (4) Bodhisattva . . . . 3·00 1·10

1982. 40th Death Anniv of Dr. D. S. Kotnis.
3218 **642** 8f. green and black . . . 40 10
3219 – 70f. lilac and black . . . 1·60 70
DESIGN: Dr. Kotnis in army uniform.

643 Couple holding Flaming Torch

644 Wine Container

1982. 11th National Communist Youth League Congress.
3220 **643** 8f. multicoloured 25 10

1982. Bronzes of Western Zhou Dynasty. Mult.
3221 4f. (1) Type **644** 50 20
3222 4f. (2) Cooking vessel . . 50 20
3223 8f. (3) Food container . . . 60 20
3224 8f. (4) Cooking vessel with ox head and dragon design 60 20
3225 8f. (5) Ram-shaped wine container 60 20
3226 10f. (6) Wine jar . . . . . 1·00 25
3227 20f. (7) Food bowl . . . . 2·50 35
3228 70f. (8) Wine container . . . 7·25 1·75

645 "Pig" (Han Meilin)

646 Harp

1983. New Year. Year of the Pig.
3229 **645** 8f. multicoloured . . . . 3·00 80

1983. Stringed Musical Instruments.
3230 **646** 4f. (1) green and brown 1·00 20
3231 – 8f. (2) purple, grn & brn 1·75 40
3232 – 8f. (3) multicoloured . . 1·75 40
3233 – 10f. (4) multicoloured . . 2·50 70
3234 – 70f. (5) multicoloured . . 12·00 3·00
DESIGNS—VERT: 8f. (3231), Four string guitar; 10f. Four string lute; 70f. Three string lute. HORIZ: 8f. (3232), Qin.

647 "February 7" Monument, Jiangan

648 Zhang Gong attracted by Yingying's Beauty

1983. 60th Anniv of Peking–Hankow Railway Workers' Strike.
3235 **647** 8f. (1) yellow, blk & grey 50 15
3236 – 8f. (2) stone, brown and lilac 50 15
DESIGN: No. 3236, "February 7" Memorial tower, Zhengzhou.

1983. Scenes from "The Western Chamber" (musical drama by Wang Shifu). Multicoloured.
3237 8f. (1) Type **648** . . . . 1·75 50
3238 8f. (2) Zhang Gong and Yingying listening to music . . . . 1·75 50
3239 10f. (3) Zhang Gong and Yingying's wedding . . . 2·75 1·40
3240 80f. (4) Zhang Gong and Yingying parting at Chanting Pavilion . . . . 12·50 4·00

649 Karl Marx

650 Tomb, Mt. Qiaoshan, Huangling

1983. Death Centenary of Karl Marx.
3242 **649** 8f. grey and black . . . 15 10
3243 – 20f. lilac and black . . . 70 15
DESIGN: 20f. "Marx making Speech" (Wen Guozhang).

1983. Tomb of the Yellow Emperor. Mult.
3244 8f. Type **650** 50 30
3245 10f. Hall of Founder of Chinese Culture (horiz) 1·25 30
3246 20f. Xuanyuan cypress . . . 2·25 80

651 Messengers and Globe

1983. World Communications Year.
3247 **651** 8f. multicoloured 30 15

652 Chinese Alligator

1983. Chinese Alligator. Multicoloured.
3248 8f. Type **652** 50 10
3249 20f. Alligator and hatching eggs . . . . 2·10 30

653 "Scratching" (Wang Yani)

1983. Children's Paintings. Multicoloured.
3250 8f. (1) Type **653** 25 10
3251 8f. (2) "I Love the Great Wall" (Liu Zhong) . . . 25 10
3252 8f. (3) "Kitten" (Tang Axi) 25 10
3253 8f. (4) "The Sun, Birds, Flowers and Me" (Bu Hua) 25 10

654 Congress Hall

1983. 6th National People's Congress. Mult.
3254 8f. Type **654** 25 10
3255 20f. Score of National Anthem 40 15

655 Terracotta Soldiers

656 Sun Yujiao

1983. Terracotta Figures from Qin Shi Huang's Tomb. Multicoloured.
3256 8f. (1) Type **655** 40 20
3257 8f. (2) Heads figures 40 20
3258 10f. (3) Soldiers and horses 75 30
3259 70f. (4) Aerial view of excavation . . . . 4·25 1·25

1983. Female Roles in Peking Opera. Mult.
3261 4f. (1) Type **656** 40 10
3262 8f. (2) Chen Miaochang . . 60 15
3263 8f. (3) Bai Suzhen 60 15
3264 8f. (4) Sister Thirteen . . . 60 15
3265 10f. (5) Qin Xianglian . . . 80 20
3266 20f. (6) Yang Yuhuan . . . 1·50 25
3267 50f. (7) Cui Yingying . . . 4·50 55
3268 80f. (8) Mu Guiying . . . . 8·75 95

657 Li Bai (poet)

659 Games Emblem

658 Woman and Women working

1983. Poets and Philosophers of Ancient China. Paintings by Liu Lingcang. Multicoloured.
3269 8f. (1) Type **657** 55 20
3270 8f. (2) Du Fu (poet) 55 20
3271 8f. (3) Han Yu (philosopher) 55 20
3272 70f. (4) Liu Zongyuan (philosopher) . . . . . . 6·00 2·00

1983. 5th National Women's Congress.
3273 **658** 8f. multicoloured 20 10

1983. 5th National Games. Multicoloured.
3274 4f. (1) Type **659** 35 10
3275 8f. (2) Gymnastics 40 20
3276 8f. (3) Badminton 40 20
3277 8f. (4) Diving 40 20
3278 20f. (5) High jump 80 40
3279 70f. (6) Windsurfing . . . . 2·10 1·00

660 "One Child per Couple"

1983. Family Planning. Multicoloured.
3280 8f. (1) Type **660** 15 10
3281 8f. (2) "Population, cultivated fields and grain" 15 10

661 Hammer and Cogwheel as "10"

1983. 10th National Trade Union Congress.
3282 **661** 8f. multicoloured 30 10

662 Mute Swan

1983. Swans. Multicoloured.
3283 8f. (1) Type **662** 30 30
3284 8f. (2) Mute swans 30 30
3285 10f. Tundra swans . . . . 75 1·00
3286 80f. (4) Whooper swans in flight . . . . 2·25 2·00

663 Liu Shaoqi

1983. 85th Birth Anniv of Liu Shaoqi (former Head of State).
3287 **663** 8f. (1) multicoloured . . 55 10
3288 – 8f. (2) multicoloured . . 55 10
3289 – 8f. (3) brown, bl & gold 55 10
3290 – 8f. (4) brown, bl & gold 55 10
DESIGNS: No. 3288, Liu reading a speech; 3289, Liu making a speech; 3290, Liu meeting model worker Shi Chuanxiang.

664 $100 National Emblem Stamp, 1951 **665** Mao Tse-tung in 1925

1983. National Stamp Exhibition, Peking. Mult.
3291 8f. Type **664** 20 10
3292 20f. North West China $1 Yanan Pagoda stamp, 1946 . . . . 80 40

1983. 90th Birth Anniv of Mao Tse-tung.
3293 **665** 8f. (1) multicoloured . . 20 10
3294 – 8f. (2) stone, brn & gold 20 10
3295 – 10f. (3) grey, brn & gold 50 15
3296 – 20f. (4) multicoloured . . 1·25 20
DESIGNS: No. 3294, Mao Tse-tung in Yanan, 1945. 3295, Mao Tse-tung inspecting Yellow River, 1952. 3296, Mao Tse-tung in library, 1961.

666 "Rat" (Zhan Tong) **667** Young Girl with Ball

1984. New Year. Year of the Rat.
3297 **666** 8f. black, yellow & red 2·50 70

1984. Child Welfare. Multicoloured.
3298 8f.+2f. Type **667** 20 15
3299 8f.+2f. Young boy with toy panda 20 15

668 Women with Dog

1984. Tang Dynasty Painting "Beauties wearing Flowers" by Zhou Fang. Details of scroll. Mult.
3300 8f. Type **668** . . . . 1·00 20
3301 10f. Women and Manchurian crane . . . . 1·00 50
3302 70f. Women, dog and Manchurian crane . . . . 6·25 3·00

669 "The Spring of Shanghai" **670** Ren Bishi

1984. Chinese Roses. Multicoloured.
3304 4f. (1) Type **669** 25 10
3305 8f. (2) "Rosy Dawn of the Pujiang River" 30 10
3306 8f. (3) "Pearl" 30 10
3307 10f. (4) "Black Whirlwind" 65 10
3308 20f. (5) "Yellow Flower in the Battlefield" 90 20
3309 70f. (6) "Blue Phoenix" . . 2·25 50

1984. 80th Birth Anniv of Ren Bishi (member of Communist Party Secretariat) (1st issue).
3310 **670** 8f. brown, black & pur 20 10
See also Nos. 3361/3.

671 Japanese Crested Ibis

1984. Japanese Crested Ibis. Multicoloured.
3311 8f. (1) Type **671** 35 25
3312 8f. (2) Ibis wading 35 25
3313 80f. (3) Ibis perching . . . 2·40 1·75

672 Red Cross Activities

1984. 80th Anniv of Chinese Red Cross Society.
3314 **672** 8f. multicoloured 35 15

673 Building Dam

1984. Gezhou Dam Project. Multicoloured.
3315 8f. Type **673** 10 10
3316 10f. View of dam and lock gates (vert) 40 10
3317 20f. Freighter in lock . . . 70 15

674 Inverted Image Tower and Yilang Pavilion

1984. Zhuo Zheng Garden, Suzhou. Mult.
3318 8f. (1) Type **674** 20 10
3319 8f. (2) Loquat Garden . . . 20 10
3320 10f. (3) Water court of Xiao Cang Lang 25 15
3321 70f. (4) Yuanxiang Hall and Yiyu Study . . . . 2·10 60

675 Pistol Shooting

1984. Olympic Games, Los Angeles. Multicoloured.
3322 4f. Type **675** 10 10
3323 8f. High jumping 10 10
3324 8f. Weightlifting 10 10
3325 10f. Gymnastics 10 10
3326 20f. Volley ball 25 15
3327 80f. Diving 85 50

676 Calligraphy **677** Tianjin

1984. Art Works by Wu Changshuo. Mult.
3329 4f. (1) Type **676** 10 10
3330 4f. (2) "Pair of Peaches" . . 10 10
3331 8f. (3) "Lotus" 45 15
3332 8f. (4) "Wisteria" 45 15
3333 8f. (5) "Peony" 45 15
3334 10f. (6) "Autumn Chrysanthemum" 55 15
3335 20f. (7) "Plum Blossom" . . 1·25 25
3336 70f. (8) Seal and impression 3·25 65

1984. Luanhe River–Tianjin Water Diversion Project. Multicoloured.
3337 8f. Type **677** 10 10
3338 10f. Locks and canal (horiz) 10 10
3339 20f. Tunnel and sculpture 50 15

678 Chinese and Japanese Pagodas

1984. Chinese–Japanese Youth Friendship Festival. Multicoloured.
3340 8f. Type **678** 10 10
3341 20f. Girls watering shrub . . 25 15
3342 80f. Young people dancing 85 80

679 Factory Worker

1984. 35th Anniv of People's Republic. Mult.
3343 8f. (1) Type **679** 10 10
3344 8f. (2) Girl and rainbow . . 10 10
3345 8f. (4) Girl and symbols of science 10 10
3346 8f. (5) Soldier 10 10
3347 20f. (3) Flag and Manchurian cranes (36 × 50 mm) 40 25

680 Chen Jiageng

1984. 110th Birth Anniv of Chen Jiageng (educationist and patriot). Multicoloured.
3348 8f. Type **680** 15 10
3349 80f. Jimei School 65 30

681 The Maiden's Study

1984. Scenes from "Peony Pavilion" (drama) by Tang Xianzu. Paintings by Dai Dunbang. Multicoloured.
3350 8f. (1) Type **681** 50 15
3351 8f. (2) Du Liniang dreaming 50 15
3352 20f. (3) Du Liniang drawing self-portrait . . . . . . 1·10 25
3353 70f. (4) Du Liniang and Liu Mengmei married . . . . 3·50 1·10

682 Baoguo Temple

1984. Landscapes of Mt. Emei Shan. Mult.
3355 4f. (1) Type **682** 45 10
3356 8f. (2) Leiyin Temple . . . 55 10
3357 8f. (3) Hongchun Lawn . . . 55 10
3358 10f. (4) Elephant Bath Pool 70 15
3359 20f. (5) Woyun Temple . . 1·25 25
3360 80f. (6) Shining Cloud Sea, Jinding . . . . 3·25 1·10

683 Ren Bishi **684** Flowers in Chinese Vase

1984. 80th Birth Anniv of Ren Bishi (2nd issue).
3361 **683** 8f. brown and purple . . 10 10
3362 – 10f. black and lilac . . . 15 10
3363 – 20f. black and brown . . 40 20
DESIGNS: 10f. Ren Bishi reading speech at Communist Party Congress; 20f. Ren Bishi saluting.

1984. Chinese Insurance Industry.
3364 **684** 8f. multicoloured 15 10

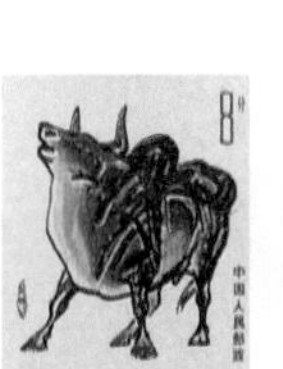

685 "Ox" (Yao Zhonghua) **687** Lotus of Good Luck

686 "Zunyi Meeting" (Liu Xiangping)

1985. New Year. Year of the Ox.
3365 **685** 8f. multicoloured 30 15

1985. 50th Anniv of Zunyi Meeting. Mult.
3366 8f. Type **686** 10 10
3367 20f. "Arrival of the Red Army in Northern Shaanxi" (Zhao Yu) . . . 60 15

1985. Festival Lanterns. Multicoloured.
3368 8f. (1) Type **687** 50 15
3369 8f. (2) Auspicious dragon and phoenix 50 15
3370 8f. (3) A hundred flowers blossoming 50 15
3371 70f. (4) Prosperity and affluence . . . . 1·75 60

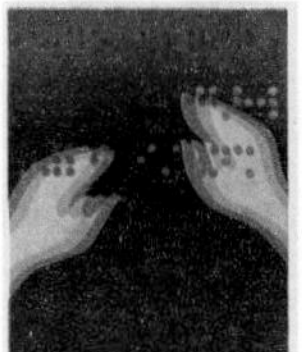

688 Stylized Dove and Women's Open Hands **689** Hands reading Braille

1985. United Nations Decade for Women.
3372 **688** 20f. multicoloured . . . 25 10

1985. Welfare Fund for the Handicapped. Multicoloured.
3373 8f.+2f. (1) Type **689** 40 15
3374 8f.+2f. (2) Lips and sign language 40 15
3375 8f.+2f. (3) Learning to use artificial limb 40 15
3376 8f.+2f. (4) Stylized figure in wheelchair 40 15

690 "Green Calyx" Mei **691** Headquarters

1985. Mei Flowers. Multicoloured.
3377 8f. (1) Type **690** 15 10
3378 8f. (2) "Pendant" mei . . . 15 10
3379 8f. (3) "Contorted dragon" mei 15 10
3380 10f. (4) "Cinnabar" mei . . 20 10
3381 20f. (5) "Versicolor" mei . . 75 15
3382 80f. (6) "Apricot" mei . . . 2·50 65

1985. 60th Anniv of All-China Trade Unions Federation.
3384 **691** 8f. multicoloured 20 10

692 Bird and Children

1985. International Youth Year.
3385 **692** 20f. multicoloured . . . 30 15

693 Giant Panda **694** Xian Xinghai (bust, Cao Chongen)

1985. Giant Panda. Multicoloured.
3386 8f. Type **693** 10 10
3387 20f. Giant panda (different) (horiz) 40 15
3388 50f. Giant panda (different) 60 30
3389 80f. Two giant pandas (horiz) 85 40

1985. 80th Birth Anniv of Xian Xianghai (composer).
3391 **694** 8f. multicoloured 25 10

695 Agnes Smedley **696** Zheng He (navigator)

1985. American Journalists in China.
3392 **695** 8f. brown, stone and ochre 10 10
3393 – 20f. olive, grey and stone 15 10
3394 – 80f. purple, lilac and cream 50 20
DESIGNS: 20f. Anna Louise Strong; 80f. Edgar Snow.

1985. 580th Anniv of Zheng He's First Voyage to Western Seas. Multicoloured.
3395 8f. (1) Type **696** 10 10
3396 8f. (2) Zheng He on elephant 10 10
3397 20f. (3) Exchanging goods 20 10
3398 80f. (4) Bidding farewell . . 75 45

697 "Self-portrait"

1985. 90th Birth Anniv of Xu Beihong (artist). Multicoloured.
3399 8f. Type **697** 10 10
3400 20f. Xu Beihong at work . . 20 15

698 Lin Zexu **699** "Prosperity"

1985. Birth Bicentenary of Lin Zexu (statesman).
3401 **698** 8f. multicoloured 15 10
3402 – 80f. brown and black . . 55 25
DESIGN—55 × 23 mm. 80f. "Burning opium at Humen" (relief).

1985. 20th Anniv of Tibet Autonomous Region. Multicoloured.
3403 8f. Type **699** 10 10
3404 10f. "Celebration" 15 10
3405 20f. "Harvest 35 10

700 Chinese Army at Lugouqiao

1985. 40th Anniv of Victory over Japan.
3406 **700** 8f. black, brown & red 10 10
3407 – 80f. black, brown & red 75 40
DESIGN: 80f. Defending the Great Wall.

701 Cycling

1985. 2nd National Workers' Games, Peking. Multicoloured.
3408 8f. Type **701** 10 10
3409 20f. Hurdling 25 15

702 Gobi Oasis **703** Athletes and Silhouette of Woman

1985. 30th Anniv of Xinjiang Uygur Autonomous Region. Multicoloured.
3410 8f. Type **702** 10 10
3411 10f. Oilfield and Lake Tianchi (54 × 26 mm) . . 15 10
3412 20f. Tianshan pasture . . . 35 15

1985. 1st National Youth Games, Zhengzhou.
3413 **703** 8f. multicoloured 10 10
3414 – 20f. red, blue and black 25 10
DESIGN: 20f. Basketball players and silhouette of man.

704 Forbidden City (½-size illustration)

1985. 60th Anniv of Imperial Palace Museum.
3415 **704** 8f. (1) multicoloured . . 10 10
3416 – 8f. (2) multicoloured . . 10 10
3417 – 20f. (3) multicoloured . . 20 10
3418 – 80f. (4) multicoloured . . 70 30
DESIGNS: Nos. 3416/18, Different parts of Forbidden City.

705 Zou Taofen **706** Memorial Pavilion

1985. 90th Anniv of Zou Taofen (journalist).
3419 **705** 8f. black, brown & silver 10 10
3420 – 20f. black, green & silver 30 10
DESIGN: 20f. Premier Chou En-lai's inscription in memory of Zou Taofen.

1985. 50th Anniv of December 9th Movement.
3421 **706** 8f. multicoloured 15 10

707 "Tiger" **708** First Experimental Satellite

1986. New Year. Year of the Tiger.
3422 **707** 8f. multicoloured 45 15

1986. Space Research. Multicoloured.
3423 4f. (1) Type **708** 10 10
3424 8f. (2) Mil-Mi8 helicopters recovering satellites . . . 10 10
3425 8f. (3) Underwater launched rocket 10 10
3426 10f. (4) Rocket launched from land 15 10
3427 20f. (5) Dish aerial 30 15
3428 70f. (6) Satellite and diagram of orbit 60 45

709 Dong Biwu **710** Lin Boqu

1986. Birth Centenary of Dong Biwu (founder of Chinese Communist Party).
3429 **709** 8f. black and brown . . 10 10
3430 – 20f. black and brown . . 20 10
DESIGN: 20f. At meeting for ratification of U.N. Charter, Los Angeles, 1945.

1986. Birth Centenary of Lin Boqu (politician).
3431 **710** 8f. brown and black . . 10 10
3432 – 20f. brown and black . . 20 10
DESIGN: 20f. At Yanan.

711 He Long

1986. 90th Birth Anniv of He Long (politician).
3433 **711** 8f. black and brown . . 10 10
3434 – 20f. black and brown . . 20 10
DESIGN: 20f. On horse.

712 Skin Tents, Inner Mongolia **713** Comet and Earth

1986. Traditional Houses.
3435 **712** 1f. green, brown & grey 10 10
3436 – 1½f. brown, red & blue 10 10
3437 – 2f. black and bistre . . 10 10
3438 – 3f. black and brown . . 10 10
3439 – 4f. red and black . . . 10 10
3439a – 5f. black, grey & green 10 10
3440 – 8f. grey, red and black 10 10
3441 – 10f. black and orange 15 10
3441b – 15f. black, grey & grn 15 10
3442 – 20f. grey, green & blk 65 10
3442b – 25f. black, grey & pink 25 15
3443 – 30f. lilac, blue & brown 15 10
3444 – 40f. brn, pur & stone 30 15
3445 – 50f. blue, mve & dp bl 15 15
3445b – 80f. black, grey & blue 70 25
3446 – 90f. black and red . . . 70 25
3447 – 1y. brown and grey . . 35 20
3448 – 1y.10 blue, blk & brn 40 25
3448a – 1y.30 blk, grey & red 40 20
3448b – 1y.60 blue & black . . 40 25
3448c – 2y. black, grey & brown 60 25
DESIGNS: 1½f. Tibet. 2f. North-East China. 3f. Hunan. 4f. Jiangsu. 5f. Shandong. 8f. Peking. 10f. Yunnan. 15f. Guangxi. 20f. Shanghai. 25f. Ningxia. 30f. Anhui. 40f. North Shaanxi. 50f. Sichuan. 80f. Shanxi. 90f. Taiwan. 1y. Fujian. 1y.10, Zhejiang, 1y.30, Qinghai. 1y.60, Guizhou. 2y. Jiangxi.

1988. Appearance of Halley's Comet.
3449 **713** 20f. grey and blue . . . 20 10

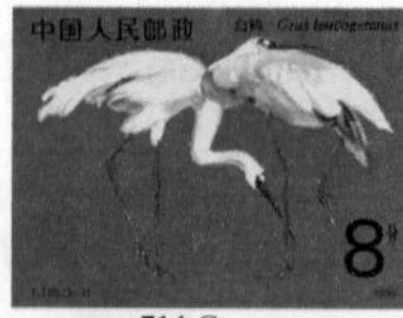

714 Cranes

1986. Great White Crane. Multicoloured.
3450 8f. Type **714** 10 10
3451 10f. Crane flying (vert) . . . 25 20
3452 70f. Four cranes (vert) . . . 75 45

715 Li Weihan

1986. 90th Birth Anniv of Li Weihan (politician). Each green and black.
3454 8f. Type **715** 10 10
3455 20f. Li Weihan at work . . 20 10

716 Stylized People on Dove

1986. International Peace Year.
3456 **716** 8f. multicoloured 20 10

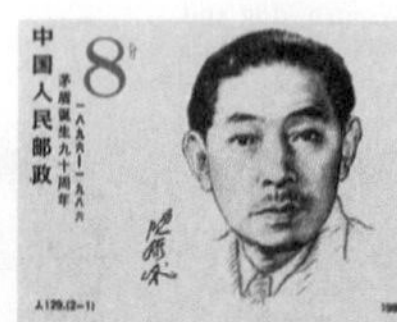

717 Mao Dun

1986. 90th Birth Anniv of Mao Dun (writer). Each grey, black and brown.
3457 8f. Type **717** 10 10
3458 20f. Mao Dun and manuscript 20 10

718 Wang Jiaxiang

1986. 80th Birth Anniv of Wang Jiaxiang (first People's Republic ambassador to U.S.S.R.). Multicoloured.
3459 8f. Type **718** 10 10
3460 20f. Wang Jiaxiang at Yan'an 20 10

719 Flowers on Desk

1986. Teachers' Day.
3461 **719** 8f. multicoloured 15 10

720 "Magnolia sinensis"

1986. Magnolias. Multicoloured.
3462 8f. (1) Type **720** 40 10
3463 8f. (2) "Manglietia patungensis" 40 10
3464 70f. (3) "Alcimandra cathcartii" . . . . 2·50 70

721 Sun Yat-sen (120th birth anniv) **724** Zhu De

1986. 75th Anniv of 1911 Revolution. Leaders. Multicoloured.
3466 8f. Type **721** 10 10
3467 10f. Huang Xing (70th death anniv) 40 10
3468 40f. Zhang Taiyan (50th death anniv) 90 15

1986. Birth Centenary of Marshal Zhu De.
3471 **724** 8f. brown 35 10
3472 – 20f. green 65 10
DESIGN: 20f. Making speech, 1950.

725 Archery **726** "Rabbit"

1986. Sport in Ancient China. Each grey, black and red.
3473 8f. (1) Type **725** 90 10
3474 8f. (2) Weiqi (horiz) 90 10
3475 10f. (3) Golf (horiz) . . . . 1·25 40
3476 50f. (4) Football . . . . . 3·50 85

1987. New Year. Year of the Rabbit.
3477 **726** 8f. multicoloured 50 15

727 Xu Xiake **728** Steller's Sea Eagle

1987. 400th Birth Anniv of Xu Xiake (explorer). Multicoloured.
3478 8f. Type **727** . . . . 1·00 20
3479 20f. Recording observations in cave . . . . 2·25 60
3480 40f. Climbing mountain . . 4·50 1·25

1987. Birds of Prey. Multicoloured.
3481 8f. (1) Black kite (horiz) . . 70 25
3482 8f. (2) Type **728** 70 30
3483 10f. (3) Himalayan griffon 1·40 30
3484 90f. (4) Upland buzzard (horiz) . . . . 5·00 1·75

729 Hawk Kite

1987. Kites. Multicoloured.
3485 8f. (1) Type **729** 20 10
3486 8f. (2) Centipede 20 10
3487 30f. (3) The Eight Diagrams 1·00 15
3488 30f. (4) Phoenix . . . . . . 1·00 15

730 Liao Zhongkai **731** "Eventful Years"

1987. 110th Birth Anniv of Liao Zhongkai (politician). Multicoloured.
3489 8f. Type **730** 10 10
3490 20f. Liao Zhongkai with wife 15 10

1987. 90th Birth Anniv of Ye Jianying (revolutionary and co-founder of People's Army). Portraits. Multicoloured.
3491 8f. Type **731** 45 10
3492 10f. "Founder of the State" 55 10
3493 30f. "Everywhere Green Hills" . . . . 1·50 15

732 Worshipping Bodhisattvas (Northern Liang Dynasty)

1987. Dunhuang Cave Murals (1st series). Mult.
3494 8f. Type **732** 50 10
3495 10f. Deer King Jataka (Northern Wei dynasty) 60 15
3496 20f. Heavenly musicians (Northern Wei dynasty) 2·00 50
3497 40f. Flying Devata (Northern Wei dynasty) 3·00 1·25
See also Nos. 3553/6, 3682/5, 3811/14, 3910/13 and 4131/4.

733 "Happy Holiday" (Yan Qinghu) **734** Town

1987. Children's Day. Childrens' drawings. Mult.
3499 8f. (1) Type **733** 10 10
3500 8f. (2) Children with doves and balloons (Liu Yuan) 10 10

1987. Improvements in Rural Areas. Multicoloured.
3501 8f. (1) Type **734** 40 10
3502 8f. (2) Fresh foods (horiz) 40 10
3503 10f. (3) Feeding cattle (horiz) 60 10
3504 20f. (4) Outdoor cinema . . 90 20

735 Emblem **736** Globe

1987. Postal Savings.
3505 **735** 8f. turquoise, yell & red 15 10

1987. Centenary of Esperanto (invented language).
3506 **736** 8f. blue, black & green 15 10

737 Flag over Great Wall

1987. 60th Anniv of People's Liberation Army. Multicoloured.
3507 8f. (1) Type **737** 35 10
3508 8f. (2) Soldier and rocket launcher 35 10
3509 10f. (3) Sailor and submarine . . . . 1·00 15
3510 30f. (4) Pilot and jet fighters 1·00 15

738 Dove above Houses

1987. Int Year of Shelter for the Homeless.
3511 **738** 8f. multicoloured 15 10

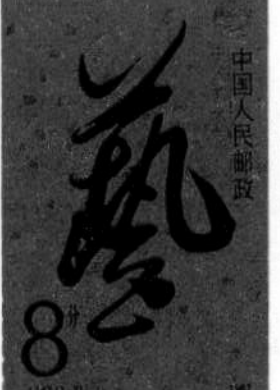

739 Chinese Character **740** Pan Gu inventing the Universe

1987. China Art Festival, Peking.
3512 **739** 8f. black, red and gold 15 10

1987. Folk Tales. Multicoloured.
3513 4f. (1) Type **740** 35 10
3514 8f. (2) Nu Wa creating human being 50 10
3515 8f. (3) Yi shooting nine suns 50 10
3516 10f. (4) Chang'e flying to the moon 60 10
3517 20f. (5) Kua Fu chasing the sun 90 15
3518 90f. (6) Jing Wei filling the sea . . . . 2·75 95

741 Sun rising behind Party Flag

1987. 13th National Communist Party Congress.
3519 **741** 8f. multicoloured 10 10

742 Yellow Crane Tower, Wuhan

1987. Ancient Buildings. Multicoloured.
3520 8f. (1) Type **742** 40 10
3521 8f. (2) Yue Yang Tower . . 40 10
3522 10f. (3) Teng Wang Pavilion 70 10
3523 90f. (4) Peng Lai Pavilion 3·25 1·40

743 Pole Vaulting

1987. 6th National Games, Guangdong Province. Multicoloured.
3525 8f. (1) Type **743** 40 10
3526 8f. (2) Women's softball . . 40 10
3527 30f. (3) Weightlifting 70 15
3528 50f. (4) Diving . . . . . . 1·25 20

745 Shi Jin practising Martial Arts

1987. Literature. "Outlaws of the Marsh" (1st series). Multicoloured.
3530 8f. Type **745** 30 10
3531 10f. Sagacious Lu uprooting willow tree 50 10
3532 30f. Lin Chon sheltering in temple of mountain spirit 1·50 50
3533 50f. Song Jian helping Chao Gai to escape . . . . . . 3·25 1·10
See also Nos. 3614/17, 3778/81, 3854/7 and 4248/51.

746 Dragon **747** Cai Yuanpri

1988. New Year. Year of the Dragon.
3535 **746** 8f. multicoloured 25 15

1988. 120th Birth Anniv of Cai Yuanpei (educationist). Multicoloured.
3536 8f. Type **747** 10 10
3537 20f. Cai Yuanpei seated in chair 15 10

748 Tao Zhu

1988. 80th Birth Anniv of Tao Zhu (Communist Party official). Multicoloured.
3538 8f. Type **748** 10 10
3539 20f. Tao Zhu (half-length portrait) 15 10

749 Harvest Festival

1988. Flourishing Rural Areas of China. Mult.
3540 8f. Type **749** 45 10
3541 10f. Couple with fish, flowers and chickens . . . 55 10
3542 20f. Couple making scientific study 75 40
3543 30f. Happy family . . . . . 1·00 65

750 Flag and Rainbow **751** Wuzhi Mountain

1988. 7th National People's Congress.
3544 **750** 8f. multicoloured 15 10

1988. Establishment of Hainan Province. Mult.
3545 8f. Type **751** 10 10
3546 10f. Wanquan River 10 10
3547 30f. Beach 20 10
3548 1y.10 Bay and deer 60 30

752 Li Siguang (geologist)

1988. Scientists (1st series). Multicoloured.
3549 8f. Type **752** 10 10
3550 10f. Zhu Kezhen (meteorologist) 10 10
3551 20f. Wu Youxun (physicist) 15 10
3552 30f. Hua Luogeng (mathematician) 20 10
See also Nos. 3702/5 and 3821/4.

1988. Dunhuang Cave Murals (2nd series). As T **732**. Multicoloured.
3553 8f. (1) Hunting (Western Wei dynasty) 35 10
3554 8f. (2) Fighting (Western Wei dynasty) 35 10

3555 10f. (3) Farming (Northern Zhou dynasty) 50 35
3556 90f. (4) Building pagoda (Northern Zhou dynasty) 1·60 80

753 Healthy Trees and Hand holding back polluted Soil

1988. Environmental Protection. Multicoloured.
3557 8f. (1) Type **753** 10 10
3558 8f. (2) Doves in clean air and hand holding back polluted air 10 10
3559 8f. (3) Fishes in clean water and hand holding back polluted water 25 10
3560 8f. (4) Peaceful landscape and hand holding back noise waves 10 10

755 Games Emblem

1988. 11th Asian Games, Peking (1990) (1st issue). Multicoloured.
3562 8f. Type **755** 10 10
3563 30f. Games mascot 15 10
See also Nos. 3653/6 and 3695/3700.

756 Warrior, Longmen Grotto, Henan
757 Peony

1988. Art of Chinese Grottoes.
3564 – 2y. brown & light brown 40 10
3565 **756** 5y. black and brown 75 15
3566 – 10y. brown and stone 1·50 35
3567 – 20y. black and brown 3·00 1·50
DESIGNS: 2y. Buddha, Yungang Grotto, Shanxi. 10y. Bodhisattva, Maijishan Grotto, Gansu. 20y. Woman with chickens, Dazu Grotto, Sichuan.

1988. 10th Anniv of Chinese–Japanese Treaty of Peace and Friendship. Multicoloured.
3568 8f. Type **757** 10 10
3569 1y.60 Cherry blossom 60 30

758 Coal Wharf, Quinghuangdao

1988. Achievements of Socialist Construction (1st series). Multicoloured.
3570 8f. Type **758** 30 15
3571 10f. Ethylene works, Shangdong 10 10
3572 20f. Baoshan steel works, Shanghai 10 10
3573 30f. Television centre, Peking 15 10
See also Nos. 3691/22, 3678/81 and 3759/62.

759 Taishan Temple

1988. Mount Taishan Views. Multicoloured.
3574 8f. Type **759** 40 10
3575 10f. Ladder to Heaven 45 10
3576 20f. Daguang Park 60 10
3577 90f. Sun Watching Peak 2·75 1·25

760 Liao Chengzhi
761 Cycling

1988. 80th Birth Anniv of Liao Chengzhi (Communist Party leader). Multicoloured.
3578 8f. Type **760** 10 10
3579 20f. Liao Chengzhi at work 15 10

1988. 1st National Peasant Games. Multicoloured.
3580 8f. Type **761** 10 10
3581 20f. Wushu 15 10

762 Peng Dehuai

1988. 90th Birth Anniv of General Peng Dehuai. Multicoloured.
3582 8f. Type **762** 10 10
3583 20f. In uniform 15 10

763 Battle against Lu Bu

1988. Literature. "Romance of the Three Kingdoms" by Luo Guanzhong (1st series). Multicoloured.
3584 8f. (1) Heroes become sworn brothers (horiz) 45 10
3585 8f. (2) Type **763** 45 10
3586 30f. (3) Fengyi Pavilion (horiz) 1·25 55
3587 50f. (4) Discussing heroes over wine 2·00 95
See also Nos. 3711/14, 3807/10, 3944/7 and 4315/18.

764 People in Heart
765 Stag's Head

1988. International Volunteers' Day.
3589 **764** 20f. multicoloured 15 10

1988. Pere David's Deer. Multicoloured.
3590 8f. Type **765** 45 10
3591 40f. Herd 85 15

766 Da Yi Pin

1988. Orchids. Multicoloured.
3592 8f. Type **766** 50 10
3593 10f. Dragon 50 10
3594 20f. Large phoenix tail 1·10 45
3595 50f. Silver-edged black orchid 2·10 70

767 Snake
768 Qu Quibai

1989. New Year. Year of the Snake.
3597 **767** 8f. multicoloured 25 15

1989. 90th Birth Anniv of Qu Qiubai (writer). Multicoloured.
3598 8f. Type **768** 10 10
3599 20f. Qu Qiubai (half-length portrait) 15 10

769 Pheasant

1989. Brown Eared-pheasant. Multicoloured.
3600 8f. Type **769** 10 10
3601 50f. Two pheasants 30 20

770 "Heaven" (top section)

1989. Silk Painting from Han Tomb, Mawangdui, Changsha. Multicoloured.
3602 8f. Type **770** 25 10
3603 20f. "Earth" (central section) 25 10
3604 30f. "Underworld" (bottom section) 25 10

771 Diagnosis by Thermography
773 Children

772 Memorial Frieze

1989. Anti-cancer Campaign.
3606 **771** 8f. grey, red & black 10 10
3607 – 20f. multicoloured 10 10
DESIGN: 8f. Crab and red crosses.

1989. 70th Anniv of May 4th Movement.
3608 **772** 8f. multicoloured 15 10

1989. 40th International Children's Day. Children's paintings. Multicoloured.
3609 8f.+4f. (1) Type **773** 10 10
3610 8f.+4f. (2) Child and penguins 10 10
3611 8f.+4f. (3) Child flying on bird 10 10
3612 8f.+4f. (4) Boy and girl playing ball 10 10

774 Globe, Doves and Lectern

1989. Cent of Interparliamentary Union.
3613 **774** 20f. multicoloured 15 10

1989. Literature. "Outlaws of the Marsh" (2nd series). As T **745**. Multicoloured.
3614 8f. Wu Song killing tiger on Jingyang Ridge 10 10
3615 10f. Qin Ming riding through hail of arrows 15 10
3616 20f. Hua Rong shooting wild goose 50 10
3617 1y.30 Li Kui fighting Zhang Shun on sampan 1·60 60

775 Anniversary Emblem

1989. 10th Anniv of Asia–Pacific Telecommunity.
3618 **775** 8f. multicoloured 10 10

1989. Achievements of Socialist Construction (2nd series). As T **758**. Multicoloured.
3619 8f. International telecommunications building, Peking (vert) 10 10
3620 10f. Xi Qu coal mine, Gu Jiao 10 10
3621 20f. Long Yang Gorge hydro-electric power station, Qinghai 15 10
3622 30f. Da Yao Shan tunnel on Guangzhou–Heng Yang railway 35 20

776 Five Peaks of Mt. Huashan

1989. Mount Huashan. Multicoloured.
3623 8f. Type **776** 10 10
3624 10f. View from top of Mt. Huashan 15 10
3625 20f. Thousand Foot Precipice 20 15
3626 90f. Blue Dragon Ridge 65 35

777 "Fable of the White Snake" (stage design, Ye Qianyu)

1989. Contemporary Art. Multicoloured.
3627 8f. Type **777** 10 10
3628 20f. "Lijiang River in Fine Rain" (Li Keran) 20 10
3629 50f. "Marching Together" (oxen) (Wu Zuoren) 90 40

778 Doves and 1949 $50 Stamp
780 Ribbons and Gate of Heavenly Peace, Peking

779 Lecturing in Temple of Apricot, Qufu

1989. 40th Anniv of Chinese People's Political Conference.
3630 **778** 8f. red, blue and black 15 10

1989. 2540th Birth Anniv of Confucius (philosopher). Multicoloured.
3631 8f. Type **779** 10 10
3632 1y.60 Confucius in ox-drawn cart 50 25

1989. 40th Anniv of People's Republic. Mult.
3634 8f. Type **780** 10 10
3635 10f. Flowers and ribbons 10 10
3636 20f. Stars and ribbons 10 10
3637 40f. Buildings and ribbons 25 15

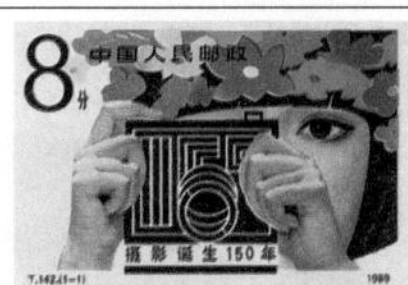

781 Woman using Camera

1989. 150th Anniv of Photography.
3640 **781** 8f. multicoloured 15 10

782 Li Dazhao

1989. Birth Centenary of Li Dazhao (co-founder of Chinese Communist Party). Multicoloured.
3641 8f. Type **782** 10 10
3642 20f. Li Dazhao and script 15 10

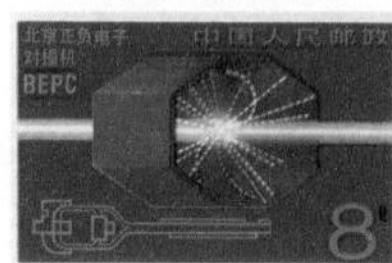

783 Diagram of Collider in Action

1989. Peking Electron-Positron Collider.
3643 **783** 8f. multicoloured 10 10

784 Rockets

1989. National Defence. Multicoloured.
3644 4f. Type **784** 10 10
3645 8f. Rocket on transporter 10 10
3646 10f. Rocket launch (vert) . . 15 10
3647 20f. Jettison of fuel tank . . 25 10

785 Spring Morning, Su Causeway

1989. West Lake, Hangzhou. Multicoloured.
3648 8f. Type **785** 10 10
3649 10f. Crooked Courtyard . . 10 10
3650 30f. Moon over Three Pools 45 20
3651 40f. Snow on Broken Bridge 90 25

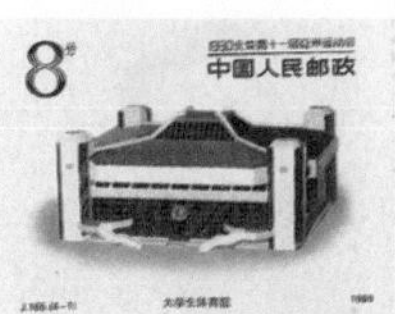

786 Peking College Gymnasium **787** Horse

1989. 11th Asian Games, Peking (1990) (2nd issue). Multicoloured.
3653 8f. Type **786** 10 10
3654 10f. Northern Suburbs swimming pool 10 10
3655 30f. Workers' Stadium . . . 10 10
3656 1y.60 Chaoyang Gymnasium 50 25

1990. New Year. Year of the Horse.
3657 **787** 8f. multicoloured 25 15

788 Narcissi **789** Bethune and Medical Team in Canada

1990. Narcissi. Multicoloured.
3658 8f. Type **788** 10 10
3659 20f. Natural group of narcissi 10 10
3660 30f. Arrangement of narcissi 20 10
3661 1y.60 Arrangement (different) 75 35

1990. Birth Centenary of Norman Bethune (surgeon). Multicoloured.
3662 8f. Type **789** 10 10
3663 1y.60 Bethune and medical team in China 50 20

790 Emblem **791** Birds flying above Trees

1990. 80th International Women's Day.
3664 **790** 20f. red, green and black 15 10

1990. Tree Planting Day. Multicoloured.
3665 8f. Type **791** 10 10
3666 10f. Trees in city 10 10
3667 20f. Great Wall and trees 15 10
3668 30f. Forest and field of wheat 25 15

792 Ban Po Plate **793** Li Fuchun

1990. Pottery. Multicoloured.
3669 8f. Type **792** 10 10
3670 20f. Miao Di Gou dish . . 10 10
3671 30f. Ma Jia Yao jar 20 10
3672 50f. Ma Chang jar 30 20

1990. 90th Birth Anniv of Li Fuchun (politician). Multicoloured.
3673 8f. Type **793** 10 10
3674 20f. Li Fuchun (different) 40 10

794 Charioteer **795** Snow Leopard

1990. 10th Anniv of Discovery of Bronze Chariots in Emperor Qin Shi Huang's Tomb. Multicoloured.
3675 8f. Type **794** 15 10
3676 50f. Horse's head 35 15

1990. Achievements of Socialist Construction (3rd series). As T **758**. Multicoloured.
3678 8f. Second automobile factory 10 10
3679 10f. Yizheng chemical and fibre company 10 10
3680 20f. Shengli oil field 15 10
3681 30f. Qinshan nuclear power station 20 15

1990. Dunhuang Cave Murals (3rd series). Sui Dynasty. As T **732**. Multicoloured.
3682 8f. Flying Devatas 10 10
3683 10f. Worshipping Bodhisattva (vert) 10 10
3684 30f. Saviour Avalokitesvara (vert) 50 15
3685 50f. Indra 70 20

1990. The Snow Leopard. Multicoloured.
3686 8f. Type **795** 10 10
3687 50f. Leopard stalking . . . 25 10

796 West Fujian Communications Bureau (Red Posts) 4p. Stamp

1990. 60th Anniv of Communist China Stamp Issues. Multicoloured.
3688 8f. Type **796** 10 10
3689 20f. Chinese Soviet Republic 1c. stamp 15 10

797 Zhang Wentian **798** Emblem

1990. 90th Birth Anniv of Zhang Wentian (revolutionary).
3690 8f. Type **797** 10 10
3691 20f. Zhang Wentian and Zunyi Meeting venue . . 15 10

1990. International Literacy Year.
3692 **798** 20f. multicoloured . . . 10 10

799 Great Wall, Film and Screen **801** Athletics

1990. 85th Anniv of Chinese Films.
3693 **799** 20f. multicoloured . . . 10 10

1990. 11th Asian Games, Peking (3rd issue). Multicoloured.
3695 4f. Type **801** 10 10
3696 8f. Gymnastics 10 10
3697 10f. Martial arts 10 10
3698 20f. Volleyball 10 10
3699 30f. Swimming 45 10
3700 1y.60 Shooting . . . . . . 1·00 50

802 Zhang Yuzhe (astronomer)

1990. Scientists (2nd series). Multicoloured.
3702 8f. Lin Qiaozhi (gynaecologist) 10 10
3703 10f. Type **802** 10 10
3704 20f. Hou Debang (chemist) 15 10
3705 30f. Ding Ying (agronomist) 20 15

803 Towering Temple

1990. Mount Hengshan, Hunan Province. Mult.
3706 8f. Type **803** 10 10
3707 10f. Aerial view of mountain 15 10
3708 20f. Trees and buildings on slopes 30 20
3709 50f. Zhurong Peak 85 20

1990. Literature. "Romance of the Three Kingdoms" by Luo Guanzhong (2nd series). As T **763**. Multicoloured.
3711 20f. (1) Cao Cao leading night attack on Wuchao (horiz) 15 10
3712 20f. (2) Liu Bei calling at Zhuge Liang's thatched cottage 15 10
3713 30f. (3) General Zhao rescuing A Dou single-handedly (horiz) 60 15
3714 50f. (4) Zhang Fei repulsing attackers at Changban Bridge 75 25

805 Revellers listening to Music

1990. Painting "Han Xizai's Night Revels" by Gu Hongzhong. Multicoloured.
3715 50f. (1) Type **805** 60 20
3716 50f. (2) Drummer and dancers 60 20
3717 50f. (3) Women attending man with fan and man and women in alcove . . 60 20
3718 50f. (4) Women playing flutes and couple by painted screen 60 20
3719 50f. (5) Young couple and women attending seated man 60 20

Nos. 3715/19 were printed together, se-tenant, forming a composite design.

806 Sheep **808** Wreath on Wall and Last Verse of the "Internationale"

807 Yuzui (dam at Dujiang)

1991. New Year. Year of the Sheep.
3720 **806** 20f. multicoloured . . . 25 15

1991. Dujiangyan Irrigation Project. Mult.
3721 20f. Type **807** 10 10
3722 50f. Feishayan (weir) . . . 15 10
3723 80f. Baopingkou (diversion of part of River Minjiang through new opening in Yulei Mountain) 70 20

1991. 120th Anniv of Paris Commune.
3724 **808** 20f. multicoloured . . . 10 10

809 Apple **810** Saiga

1991. Family Planning. Multicoloured.
3725 20f. Type **809** 10 10
3726 50f. Child's and adult's hands within heart . . . 25 10

1991. Horned Ruminants. Multicoloured.
3727 20f. Type **810** 15 20
3728 20f. Takin 15 10
3729 50f. Argali 25 10
3730 2y. Ibex 70 35

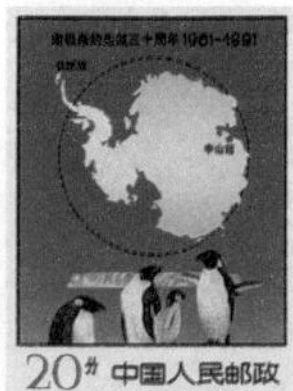

811 Dancers **812** Map and Emperor Penguins

1991. 40th Anniv of Chinese Administration of Tibet. Multicoloured.
3731 25f. Type **811** 10 10
3732 50f. Rainbows over mountain road 15 10

1991. 30th Anniv of Implementation of Antarctic Treaty.
3734 **812** 20f. multicoloured . . . 20 10

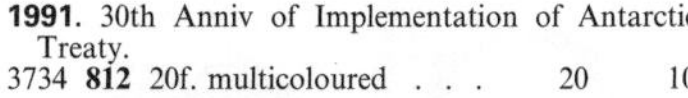

813 "Rhododendron delavayi"

1991. Rhododendrons. Multicoloured.

No.	Description	Unused	Used
3735	10f. Type **813**	10	10
3736	15f. "Rhododendron molle"	10	10
3737	20f. "Rhododendron simsii"	35	10
3738	20f. "Rhododendron fictolacteum"	35	10
3739	50f. "Rhododendron agglutinatum" (vert)	50	10
3740	80f. "Rhododendron fortunei" (vert)	65	15
3741	90f. "Rhododendron giganteum" (vert)	70	20
3742	1y.60 "Rhododendron rex" (vert)	1·10	40

814 Pleasure Boat on Lake Nanhu (venue of first Party congress)

1991. 70th Anniv of Chinese Communist Party. Multicoloured.

No.	Description	Unused	Used
3744	20f. Type **814**	30	15
3745	50f. Party emblem	15	10

815 Statue, Xuxian

1991. 2200th Anniv of Peasant Uprising led by Chen Sheng and Wu Guang.

No.	Description	Unused	Used
3746	**815** 20f. black, brown and deep brown	15	10

816 Hanging Temple

1991. Mount Hengshan, Shanxi Province. Mult.

No.	Description	Unused	Used
3747	20f. Type **816**	15	10
3748	20f. Snow-covered peak	15	10
3749	55f. "Shrine of Hengshan" carved in rock face	35	20
3750	80f. Temples in Flying Stone Grotto	75	30

817 Mammoths and Man

1991. 13th International Union for Quaternary Research Conference, Peking.

No.	Description	Unused	Used
3751	**817** 20f. multicoloured	15	10

818 Pine Valley

1991. Chengde Royal Summer Resort. Mult.

No.	Description	Unused	Used
3752	15f. Type **818**	10	10
3753	20f. Pavilions around lake	15	10
3754	90f. Maples and pavilions on islet	75	20

819 Chen Yi

820 Clasped Hands forming Heart

1991. 90th Birth Anniv of Chen Yi (co-founder of People's Army).

No.	Description	Unused	Used
3756	20f. Type **819**	10	10
3757	50f. Verse "The Green Pine" written by Chen Yi	15	10

1991. Flood Disaster Relief.

No.	Description	Unused	Used
3758	**820** 80f. multicoloured	25	10

The proceeds from the sale of No. 3758 were donated to the International Decade for Natural Disaster Reduction National Committee.

1991. Achievements of Socialist Construction (4th series). As T **758**. Multicoloured.

No.	Description	Unused	Used
3759	20f. Luoyang glassworks	10	10
3760	25f. Urumchi chemical fertilizer works	10	10
3761	55f. Shenyang–Dalian expressway	20	10
3762	80f. Xichang satellite launching centre	50	15

821 Xu Xilin

822 Wine Pot and Warming Bowl, Song Dynasty

1991. 80th Anniv of 1911 Revolution. Mult.

No.	Description	Unused	Used
3763	20f. (1) Type **821**	15	10
3764	20f. (2) Qiu Jin	15	10
3765	20f. (3) Song Jiaoren	15	10

1991. Jingdezhen China. Multicoloured.

No.	Description	Unused	Used
3766	15f. (1) Type **822**	10	10
3767	20f. (2) Blue and white porcelain vase, Yuan dynasty	10	10
3768	20f. (3) Covered jar with dragon design, Ming dynasty (horiz)	10	10
3769	25f. (4) Vase with flower design, Qing dynasty	10	10
3770	50f. (5) Modern plate with fish design	20	10
3771	2y. (6) Modern octagonal bowl (horiz)	85	45

823 Tao Xingzhi

824 Xu Xiangqian

1991. Birth Centenary of Tao Xingzhi (educationist). Each blue, grey and red.

No.	Description	Unused	Used
3772	20f. Type **823**	10	10
3773	50f. Tao Xingzhi in traditional robes	15	10

1991. 90th Birth Anniv of Xu Xiangqian (revolutionary). Multicoloured.

No.	Description	Unused	Used
3774	20f. Type **824**	10	10
3775	50f. In uniform	15	10

825 Emblem

826 Monkey

1991. 1st Women's World Football Championship, Guangdong Province. Multicoloured.

No.	Description	Unused	Used
3776	20f. Type **825**	10	10
3777	50f. Player	15	10

1991. Literature. "Outlaws of the Marsh" (3rd series). As T **745**. Multicoloured.

No.	Description	Unused	Used
3778	20f. (1) Dai Zong delivers forged letter from Liangshan Marsh	10	10
3779	25f. (2) Yi Zhangqing captures Stumpy Tiger Wang	40	10
3780	25f. (3) Mistress Gu rescues Xie brothers from Dengzhou jail	40	10
3781	90f. (4) Sun Li gains entrance to Zhu family manor in guise of military magistrate	70	30

1992. New Year. Year of the Monkey. Paper-cut designs.

No.	Description	Unused	Used
3783	**826** 20f. multicoloured	10	10
3784	– 50f. black and red	20	20

DESIGN: 50f. Magpies and plum blossom around Chinese character for monkey.

827 Black Stork

828 "Metasequoia glyptostroboides"

1992. Storks. Multicoloured.

No.	Description	Unused	Used
3785	20f. Type **827**	10	10
3786	1y.60 White stork	85	20

1992. Conifers. Multicoloured.

No.	Description	Unused	Used
3787	20f. Type **828**	10	10
3788	30f. "Cathaya argyrophylla"	10	10
3789	50f. "Taiwania flousiana"	15	10
3790	80f. "Abies beshanzuensis"	45	15

829 Madai Seabream

830 River Crossing at Yanan

1992. Offshore Breeding Projects. Multicoloured.

No.	Description	Unused	Used
3791	20f. Type **829**	30	10
3792	25f. Prawn	10	10
3793	50f. Farrer's scallops	20	15
3794	80f. "Laminaria japonica" (seaweed)	40	20

1992. 50th Anniv of Publication of Mao Tse-tung's Talks at the Yanan Forum on Literature and Art.

No.	Description	Unused	Used
3795	**830** 20f. black, orange & red	10	10

831 Flower and Landscape on Globe

1992. World Environment Day. 20th Anniv of U. N. Environment Conference, Stockholm.

No.	Description	Unused	Used
3796	**831** 20f. multicoloured	10	10

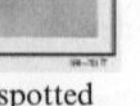

832 Seven-spotted Ladybird

833 Basketball

1992. 19th International Entomology Congress, Peking. Insects. Multicoloured.

No.	Description	Unused	Used
3797	20f. Type **832**	10	10
3798	30f. "Sympetrum croceolum" (dragonfly)	10	10
3799	50f. "Chrysopa septempunctata" (lacewing)	15	10
3800	2y. Praying mantis	90	40

1992. Olympic Games, Barcelona. Mult.

No.	Description	Unused	Used
3801	20f. Type **833**	10	10
3802	25f. Gymnastics (horiz)	10	10
3803	50f. Diving (horiz)	15	10
3804	80f. Weightlifting	30	15

834 Emblem

835 Manchurian Cranes over Great Wall

1992. International Space Year.

No.	Description	Unused	Used
3806	**834** 20f. multicoloured	10	10

1992. Literature. "Romance of the Three Kingdoms" by Luo Guanzhong (3rd series). As T **763**. Multicoloured.

No.	Description	Unused	Used
3807	20f. Zhuge Liang urging Zhang Zhao to join fight against Cao Cao (horiz)	10	10
3808	30f. Zhuge Liang's sarcastic goading of Sun Quan	10	10
3809	50f. Jiang Gan stealing forged letter from Zhou Yu (horiz)	35	10
3810	1y.60 Zhuge Liang and Lu Su in straw-covered boat under arrow attack	85	30

1992. Dunhuang Cave Murals (4th series). Tang Dynasty. As T **732**. Multicoloured.

No.	Description	Unused	Used
3811	20f. Bodhisattva (vert)	10	10
3812	25f. Musical performance (vert)	10	10
3813	55f. Flight on a dragon	20	10
3814	80f. Emperor Wudi dispatching his envoy Zhang Qian to the western regions	55	15

1992. 20th Anniv of Normalization of Diplomatic Relations with Japan. Multicoloured.

No.	Description	Unused	Used
3816	20f. Type **835**	20	20
3817	2y. Japanese and Chinese girls and dove	45	25

836 Statue of Mazu, Meizhou Islet

837 Party Emblem

1992. Mazu, Sea Goddess.

No.	Description	Unused	Used
3818	**836** 20f. brown and blue	10	10

1992. 14th National Communist Party Congress.

No.	Description	Unused	Used
3819	**837** 20f. multicoloured	10	10

838 Jiao Yulu

839 Xiong Qinglai (mathematician) and Formula

1992. 70th Birth Anniv of Jiao Yulu (Party worker).

No.	Description	Unused	Used
3820	**838** 20f. multicoloured	10	10

1992. Scientists (3rd series). Multicoloured.

No.	Description	Unused	Used
3821	20f. Type **839**	10	10
3822	30f. Tang Feifan (microbiologist) and medal	10	10
3823	50f. Zhang Xiaoqian (doctor) and hospital scene	15	10
3824	1y. Liang Sicheng (architect) and plan	25	30

840 Luo Ronghuan in Officer's Uniform

841 State Arms

1992. 90th Birth Anniv of Luo Ronghuan (army leader). Multicoloured.
3825 20f. Type **840** 10 10
3826 50f. Luo Ronghuan as young man 10 10

1992. 10th Anniv of Constitution.
3827 **841** 20f. multicoloured . . . 10 10

842 Liu Bocheng in Officer's Uniform

843 "Spring" (Zhou Baiqi)

1992. Birth Centenary of Liu Bocheng (army leader).
3828 **842** 20f. multicoloured . . . 10 10
3829 – 50f. deep green & green 10 10
DESIGN—VERT: 50f. Liu Bocheng as young man.

1992. Qingtian Stone Carvings. Multicoloured.
3830 10f. Type **843** 10 10
3831 20f. "Chinese Sorghum" (Lin Rukui) 10 10
3832 40f. "Harvest" (Zhang Aiting) 15 10
3833 2y. "Blooming Flowers and Full Moon" (Ni Dongfang) 65 40

844 Cock

845 Song Qing-ling

1993. New Year. Year of the Cock. Paper-cut designs by Cai Lanying.
3834 **844** 20f. red and black . . . 15 10
3835 – 50f. white, red & black 50 10
DESIGN: 50f. Flowers around Chinese character for rooster.

1993. Birth Centenary of Song Qing-ling (Sun Yat-sen's wife). Multicoloured.
3836 20f. Type **845** 10 10
3837 1y. Song Qing-ling with children 20 10

846 Bactrian Camel

1993. Bactrian Camel. Multicoloured.
3838 20f. Type **846** 15 10
3839 1y.60 Adult with young . . 40 15

847 Flag, Basket of Flowers and Streamers

1993. 8th National People's Congress, Peking.
3840 **847** 20f. multicoloured . . . 10 10

848 Players

849 Sportswomen

1993. Go.
3841 **848** 20f. multicoloured . . . 10 10
3842 – 1y.60 red, black & gold 30 15
DESIGN: 1y.60, "China Vogue" (black) and "linked stars" (white) formations on board.

1993. 1st East Asian Games, Shanghai. Mult.
3843 50f. Type **849** 10 10
3844 50f. Dong dong (mascot) . . 10 10
Nos. 3843/4 were printed together, se-tenant, forming a composite design of Shanghai Stadium.

850 Li Jishen

1993. Revolutionaries (1st series). Each brown and black.
3845 20f. Type **850** 10 10
3846 30f. Zhang Lan (vert) . . . 10 10
3847 50f. Shan Junru (vert) . . . 15 10
3848 1y. Huang Yanpei 35 20
See also Nos. 3888/91.

851 "Phyllostachys nigra"

1993. Bamboo. Multicoloured.
3849 20f. Type **851** 10 10
3850 30f. "Phyllostachys aureosulcata spectabilis" 10 10
3851 40f. "Bambusa ventricosa" 15 10
3852 1y. "Pseudosasa amabilis" 35 25

1993. Literature. "Outlaws of the Marsh" (4th series). As T **745**. Multicoloured.
3854 20f. Yin Tianxi and gang capturing Chai Jin . . . 10 10
3855 30f. Shi Qian stealing Xu Ning's armour 10 10
3856 50f. Xu Ning teaching use of barbed lance 40 10
3857 2y. Shi Xiu saving Lu Junyi from execution 95 35

852 Crater Lake in Winter

1993. Changbai Mountains. Multicoloured.
3858 20f. Type **852** 10 10
3859 30f. Mountain tundra in autumn 10 10
3860 50f. Waterfall in summer . . 20 10
3861 1y. Forest in spring 40 20

853 Games Emblem and Temple of Heaven

854 "Losana", Temple of Ancestors

1993. 7th National Games, Peking.
3862 **853** 20f. multicoloured . . . 10 10

1993. 1500th Anniv of Longmen Grottoes, Luoyang. Multicoloured.
3863 20f. Type **854** 10 10
3864 30f. "Sakyamuni", Middle Binyang Cave 10 10
3865 50f. "King of Northern Heavens" standing on Yaksha 20 10
3866 1y. "Bodhisattva", Guyang Cave 35 20

855 Queen Bee and Workers on Comb

1993. The Honey Bee. Multicoloured.
3868 10f. Type **855** 10 10
3869 15f. Bee extracting nectar . . 10 10
3870 20f. Two bees on blossom 10 10
3871 2y. Two bees among flowers 85 35

856 Bowl, New Stone Age

1993. Lacquer Work. Multicoloured.
3872 20f. Type **856** 10 10
3873 30f. Duck-shaped container (from Marquis Yi's tomb), Warring States Period 10 10
3874 50f. Plate decorated with foliage (Zhang Cheng), Yuan Dynasty 15 10
3875 1y. Chrysanthemum-shaped container, Qing Dynasty 35 20

857 Mao Tse-tung in North Shaanxi

1993. Birth Centenary of Mao Tse-tung. Mult.
3876 20f. Type **857** 10 10
3877 1y. Mao in library 20 10

858 Fan Painting of Bamboo and Rock

1993. 300th Birth Anniv of Zheng Banqiao (artist). Multicoloured.
3879 10f. Type **858** 10 10
3880 20f. Orchids 10 10
3881 20f. Orchids, bamboo and rock (scroll) (vert) 10 10
3882 30f. Bamboo (scroll) (vert) 35 10
3883 50f. Chrysanthemum in vase 45 10
3884 1y.60 Calligraphy on fan . . 1·25 25

859 Yang Hucheng

860 Dog (folk toy, Hebei)

1993. Birth Centenary of General Yang Hucheng.
3885 **859** 20f. multicoloured . . . 10 10

1994. New Year. Year of The Dog.
3886 **860** 20f. multicoloured . . . 15 10
3887 – 50f. black, red & yellow 50 10
DESIGN: 50f. Dogs and flowers around Chinese character for dog.

861 Ma Xulun

1994. Revolutionaries (2nd series). Each brown and black.
3888 20f. Chen Qiyou (horiz) . . 10 10
3889 20f. Chen Shutong 10 10
3890 50f. Type **861** 20 10
3891 50f. Xu Deheng (horiz) . . 20 10

862 Great Siberian Sturgeon

1994. Sturgeons. Multicoloured.
3892 20f. Type **862** 10 10
3893 40f. Chinese sturgeon . . . 20 10
3894 50f. Chinese paddlefish . . . 25 10
3895 1y. Yangtze sturgeon . . . 55 25

863 Tree in Dunes

864 Ming Dynasty Three-legged Round Teapot

1994. "Making the Desert Green". Multicoloured.
3896 15f. Type **863** 10 10
3897 20f. Flower-covered dune . . 10 10
3898 40f. Forest of poplars . . . 40 10
3899 50f. Oasis 50 10

1994. Yixing Unglazed Teapots. Multicoloured.
3900 20f. Type **864** 10 10
3901 30f. Qing dynasty four-legged square teapot . . . 10 10
3902 50f. Qing dynasty patterned teapot 15 10
3903 1y. Modern teapot 55 20

865 Entrance Gate

1994. 70th Anniv of Huang-pu Military Academy.
3904 **865** 20f. multicoloured . . . 10 10

866 "100" and Olympic Rings

1994. Centenary of Int Olympic Committee.
3905 **866** 20f. multicoloured . . . 10 10

867 Tao Yuanming (poet)

1994. Writers. Each black, brown and red.
3906 20f. Type **867** 10 10
3907 30f. Cao Zhi (poet) 10 10
3908 50f. Sima Qian (historian) 20 15
3909 1y. Qu Yuan (poet) 35 25

1994. Dunhuang Cave Murals (5th series). Tang Dynasty Frescoes in Mogao Caves. As T **732**. Multicoloured.
3910 10f. Flying Devata 10 10
3911 20f. Vimalakirti on dais . . 10 10
3912 50f. Zhang Yichao's forces 40 10
3913 1y.60 Sorceresses 75 35

868 Zhaojun

1994. Marriage of Zhaojun (from Han court) and Monarch of Xiongnu. Multicoloured.
3914 20f. Type **868** 10 10
3915 50f. Journey to Xiongnu . . 40 10

869 Emblem

870 Heaven's South Gate

1994. 6th Far East and South Pacific Games for the Disabled, Peking.
3917 **869** 20f. multicoloured . . . 10 10

1994. U.N.E.S.C.O. World Heritage Site. Wulingyuan. Multicoloured.
3918 20f. Type **870** . . . .
3919 30f. Shentangwan 10 10
3920 50f. No. One Bridge (horiz) 15 15
3921 1y. Writing Brush Peak (horiz) 55 25

871 Jade Maiden Peak

1994. Mt. Wuyi. Multicoloured.
3923 50f. (1) Type **871** 35 10
3924 50f. (2) Nine Turns Brook 35 10
3925 50f. (3) Hanging Block . . . 35 10
3926 50f. (4) Elevated Meadow 35 10
Nos. 3923/6 were issued together, se-tenant, forming a composite design.

872 Examining Scroll

873 Whooping Crane

1994. Paintings by Fu Baoshi. Multicoloured.
3927 10f. Waterfall and river . . 10 10
3928 20f. Type **872** 10 10
3929 20f. Tree 10 10
3930 40f. Musicians 20 15
3931 50f. Wooded landscape . . 25 15
3932 1y. Scholars 45 30

1994. Cranes. Multicoloured.
3933 20f. Type **873** 20 10
3934 2y. Black-necked crane . . . 65 30

875 White Emperor's City

1994. Gorges of Yangtse River. Mult.
3936 10f. (1) Type **875** 10 10
3937 20f. (2) River steamer in Qutang Gorge 10 10
3938 20f. (3) Small boat in Wuxia Gorge 10 10
3939 30f. (4) Goddess Peak . . . 10 10
3940 50f. (5) Boats in Xiling Gorge 25 15
3941 1y. (6) Qu Yuan Memorial Hall 40 30

1994. Literature. "Romance of the Three Kingdoms" by Luo Guanzhong (4th series). As T **763**. Multicoloured.
3944 20f. Cao Cao composing poem with lance in hand (horiz) 10 10
3945 30f. Liu Bei's wedding to sister of Sun Quan . . . 10 10
3946 50f. Ambush at Xiaoyaojin (horiz) 20 10
3947 1y. Lu Xun's forces destroying Liu Bei's camps 35 20

877 Shenzhen

1994. Special Economic Zones. Multicoloured.
3949 50f. (1) Type **877** 15 10
3950 50f. (2) Zhuhai 15 10
3951 50f. (3) Shantou 15 10
3952 50f. (4) Xiamen 15 10
3953 50f. (5) Hainan 15 10

878 Dayan Pagoda, Cien Temple, Xian

879 Pig

1994. Pagodas. Each black, light brown and brown.
3954 20f. (1) Type **878** 10 10
3955 20f. (2) Zhenguo Pagoda, Kaiyuan Temple, Quanzhou 10 10
3956 50f. (3) Liuhe Pagoda, Kaihua Temple, Hangzhou 15 10
3957 2y. (4) Youguo Temple, Kaifeng 60 30

1995. New Year. Year of the Pig.
3959 **879** 20f. multicoloured . . . 15 10
3960 – 50f. black and red . . . 15 10
DESIGN: 50f. Chinese character ("pig") and pigs.

880 Willows beside River Songhua

1995. Winter in Jilin. Multicoloured.
3961 20f. Type **880** 15 10
3962 50f. Jade tree on hillside (vert) 15 10

881 Relief Map and Tropic of Cancer

1995. Mt. Dinghu. Multicoloured.
3963 15f. (1) Type **881** 10 10
3964 20f. (2) Ravine 10 10
3965 20f. (3) Monastery on hillside and forest-covered slopes 10 10
3966 2y.30 (4) Pair of silver pheasants in forest . . . 65 35

882 Summit Emblem

1995. United Nations World Summit for Social Development, Copenhagen.
3967 **882** 20f. multicoloured . . . 10 10

883 Snowy Owl

1995. Owls. Multicoloured.
3968 10f. Eagle owl 15 10
3969 20f. Long-eared owl 20 10
3970 50f. Type **883** 30 10
3971 1y. Eastern grass owls . . . 60 20

884 "Osmanthus fragrans thunbergii"

1995. Sweet Osmanthus. Multicoloured.
3972 20f. (1) Type **884** 10 10
3973 20f. (2) "Osmanthus fragrans latifolius" . . . 10 10
3974 50f. (3) "Osmanthus fragrans aurantiacus" . . 25 10
3975 1y. (4) "Osmanthus fragrans semperflorens" 45 20

885 Player

1995. World Table Tennis Championships, Tianjin. Multicoloured.
3976 20f. Type **885** 10 10
3977 50f. Stadium 10 10

886 Ladies and Courtiers

1995. "Spring Outing" by Zhang Xuan. Details of the painting. Multicoloured.
3979 50f. (1) Type **886** 50 10
3980 50f. (2) Courtiers on horseback 50 10
Nos. 3979/80 were issued together, se-tenant, forming a composite design.

887 Donglu Play, Shanxi

1995. Shadow Play. Regional characters. Mult.
3981 20f. (1) Type **887** 10 10
3982 40f. (2) Luanxain play, Hebei 10 10
3983 50f. (3) Xiaoyi play, Shanxi 15 10
3984 50f. (4) Dayi play, Sichuan 15 10

888 Siyuan

1995. Motorway Interchanges, Peking. Mult.
3985 20f. Type **888** 10 10
3986 30f. Tianningsi 10 10
3987 50f. Yuting 10 10
3988 1y. Anhui 25 15

890 Asian Elephants at River

1995. 20th Anniv of China–Thailand Diplomatic Relations. Multicoloured.
3990 1y. (1) Type **890** 25 10
3991 1y. (2) Asian elephants at river (face value at left) 25 10
Nos. 3990/1 were issued together, se-tenant, forming a composite design.

891 East and West Dongting Hills

1995. Lake Taihu. Multicoloured.
3992 20f. (1) Type **891** 10 10
3993 20f. (2) Tortoise Islet in spring 10 10
3994 50f. (3) Li Garden in summer 15 10
3995 50f. (4) Jichang Garden in autumn 15 10
3996 230f. (5) Plum Garden in winter 90 35

893 Yucheng Post, Jiangsu

1995. "China'96" International Stamp Exhibition, Peking. Ancient Chinese Post Offices. Mult.
3999 20f. Type **893** 10 10
4000 50f. Jimingshan Post, Hebei 15 10

894 Hill Gate

1995. 1500th Anniv of Shaolin Temple, Henan. Multicoloured.
4001 20f. Type **894** 10 10
4002 20f. Pagoda Forest 10 10
4003 50f. Martial arts practice (detail of fresco, White Robe Hall) 15 10
4004 100f. Thirteen monks rescue the Prince of Qin (detail of fresco) 30 15

895 New Stone Age Jar

1995. Tibetan Culture. Multicoloured.
4005 20f. Type **895** 10 10
4006 30f. Helmet (7th century) . . 10 10
4007 50f. Celestial chart 15 10
4008 100f. Pearl and coral mandala 30 15

896 Koalas in Eucalyptus Tree

1995. Endangered Animals. Multicoloured.
4009 20f. Type **896** 10 10
4010 2y.90 Giant pandas amongst bamboo 90 25

897 Japanese Attack in North China, 7 July 1937

1995. 50th Anniv of End of Second World War and of War against Japan. Multicoloured.
4011 10f. (1) Type **897** 10 10
4012 20f. (2) Battle of Taier Village 10 10
4013 20f. (3) Battle at Great Wall 10 10
4014 50f. (4) Guerrillas 15 10
4015 50f. (5) Forces at Mangyo, Burma 15 10
4016 60f. (6) Airplane donated by overseas Chinese 15 10

4017	100f. (7) Liberation of Taiwan, October 1945 . .	25	15
4018	100f. (8) Crew on deck of battleship	25	15

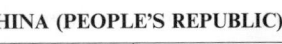

898 Woman's Profile and Flags (equality)

899 Great Wall at Jinshanling Hill

1995. 4th World Conference on Women, Peking. Multicoloured.

4019	15f. Type **898**	10	10
4020	20f. Woman's profile and wheel of colours (development)	10	10
4021	50f. Woman's profile and dove (peace)	15	10
4022	60f. Dove and flower (friendship)	20	15

1995. The Great Wall of China.

4024	–	5f. turquoise, bl & blk	10	10
4024a	–	10f. black and green . .	10	10
4024b	–	20f. black and lavender	10	10
4025	–	30f. black and yellow	10	10
4025a	–	40f. black and pink . .	10	10
4026	–	50f. black, brn & yell	10	10
4027	**899**	60f. black and brown	15	10
4027a	–	60f. black and yellow	15	10
4027b	–	80f. multicoloured . . .	15	10
4028	–	100f. black and red . .	15	10
4029	–	150f. black and green	20	10
4031	–	200f. black and pink . .	30	15
4032	–	230f. black and green	45	30
4032a	–	270f. mauve, blk & grn	50	35
4035	–	290f. black and blue . .	50	35
4036	–	300f. black and green	40	25
4036a	–	320f. mve, blk & lav . .	45	25
4037	–	420f. black and orange	60	35
4037a	–	440f. light brown, black and brown	60	35
4038	–	500f. black, brn & bl	70	40
4038a	–	540f. black and blue . .	80	45
4038b	–	10y. multicoloured . .	1·75	80
4038c	–	20y. multicoloured . .	3·25	1·60
4038d	–	50y. grey, blk & grn . .	8·75	4·25

DESIGNS: 5f. Hushan section of wall; 10f. Wall at Jiumenkou Pass; 20f. Wall at Shanhaiguan; 30f. Wall at Huangya Pass; 40f. Jinshanling section of wall; 50f. Wall seen from Gubeikou; 60f. (4027a), Huanghua Tower and wall; 80f. Mutianyu section of wall; 100f. Wall seen from Badaling; 150f. Wall at Jurong Pass; 200f. Wall at Zijing Pass; 230f. Wall at Shanhaiguan Pass; 270f. Wall at Pingxingguan Pass; 290f. Laolongtou (end of wall); 300f. Wall at Niangziguan Pass; 320f. Wall at Desheng Pass; 420f. Wall at Pianguan Pass; 440f. Wall at Yanmen Pass; 500f. Bianjing Tower; 540f. Zhenbei Tower; 10y. Huama section; 20y. Wall at Sanguankou Pass; 50y. Wall at Jiayuguan Pass.

900 Dawn on Heavenly Terrace Peak

1995. The Jiuhua Mountains, Anhui. Mult.

4039	10f. (1) Type **900**	10	10
4040	20f. (2) Hall of Meditation (vert)	10	10
4041	20f. (3) Hall of the Mortal Body	10	10
4042	50f. (4) Sunset at Zhiyuan Temple	20	10
4043	50f. (5) Roc listening to Scriptures (rock formation) (vert)	20	10
4044	290f. (6) Phoenix pine . . .	70	40

901 Black and White Film

1995. Centenary of Motion Pictures. Mult.

4045	20f. Type **901**	10	10
4046	50f. Colour film	10	10

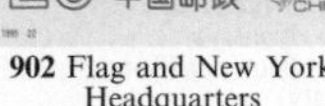

902 Flag and New York Headquarters

1995. 50th Anniv of U.N.O. Multicoloured.

4047	20f. Type **902**	10	10
4048	50f. Anniversary emblem and "flags"	10	10

903 Blessing Spot

1995. Sanqing Mountain. Multicoloured.

4049	20f. Type **903**	10	10
4050	20f. Spring Goddess	10	10
4051	50f. Music charm (vert) . .	15	10
4052	100f. Supernatural python (rock formation) (vert) . .	60	20

904 Central Mountain Temple and Huang Gai Peak

1995. Mount Song. Multicoloured.

4053	20f. Type **904**	10	10
4054	50f. Moonrise over Fawang Temple	15	10
4055	60f. Shaolin Temple in snow	15	10
4056	1y. Mountain ridge	55	20

905 Victoria Harbour

1995. Hong Kong. Multicoloured.

4057	20f. Type **905**	10	10
4058	50f. Central Plaza	15	10
4059	60f. Hong Kong Cultural Centre	15	10
4060	290f. Repulse Bay	1·10	35

906 Sun Zi

907 Rat

1995. "Art of War" (book) by Sun Zi. Mult.

4061	20f. Type **906**	10	10
4062	20f. Elaborating strategies	10	10
4063	30f. Capturing Ying	10	10
4064	50f. Battle at Ailing	15	10
4065	100f. Conference at Huangchi	55	20

1996. New Year. Year of the Rat. Mult.

4066	20f. Type **907**	40	10
4067	50f. Pattern and Chinese character	40	10

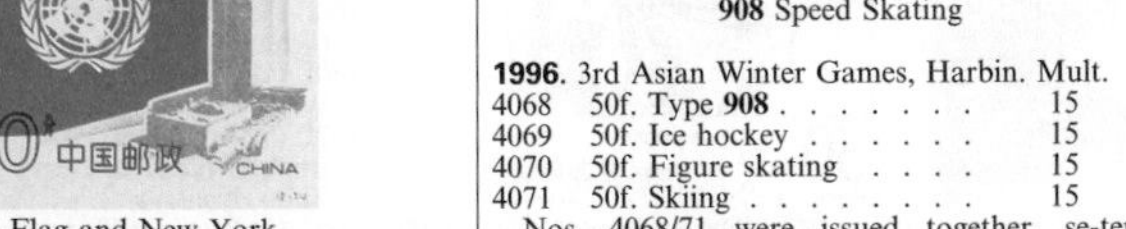

908 Speed Skating

1996. 3rd Asian Winter Games, Harbin. Mult.

4068	50f. Type **908**	15	10
4069	50f. Ice hockey	15	10
4070	50f. Figure skating	15	10
4071	50f. Skiing	15	10

Nos. 4068/71 were issued together, se-tenant, forming a composite design.

909 Cable Route

1996. Inaug of Korea–China Submarine Cable.

4072	**909**	20f. multicoloured . . .	10	10

910 Palace Complex

1996. Shenyang Imperial Palace. Multicoloured.

4073	50f. Type **910**	45	10
4074	50f. Pagoda and buildings	45	10

Nos. 4073/4 were issued together, se-tenant, forming a composite design.

911 Tianjin Posts Bureau

1996. Cent of Chinese State Postal Service. Mult.

4075	10f. Type **911**	10	10
4076	20f. Former Directorate General of North China Posts building, Peking . .	10	10
4077	50f. Postal headquarters of Chinese Soviet Republic, Zhongshi, Jiangxi	20	10
4078	100f. Present Peking postal complex	35	20

912 Calligraphy

1996. Paintings by Huang Binhong. Mult.

4080	20f. (1) Type **912**	10	10
4081	20f. (2) Mountain landscape	10	10
4082	40f. (3) Mount Qingcheng in rain	40	10
4083	50f. (4) View from Xiling . .	50	10
4084	50f. (5) Landscape	50	10
4085	230f. (6) Flowers	1·10	45

913 Shenyang F-8 Jet Fighter

1996. Chinese Aircraft. Multicoloured.

4086	20f. (1) Type **913**	10	10
4087	50f. (2) Nanchang A-5 jet fighter	15	10
4088	50f. (3) Xian Y-7 transport	15	10
4089	100f. (4) Harbin Y-12 utility plane	60	15

914 Green Scenery of Lijing River

1996. Bonsai Landscapes. Multicoloured.

4090	20f. (1) Type **914**	10	10
4091	20f. (2) Glistening Divine Peak	10	10
4092	50f. (3) Melting snow fills the river	15	10
4093	50f. (4) Eagle Beak Rock . .	15	10
4094	100f. (5) Memorable Years	60	15
4095	100f. (6) Peaks rising in Rosy Clouds	60	15

915 Sago Cycad ("Cycas revoluta")

1996. Cycads. Multicoloured.

4096	20f. Type **915**	10	10
4097	20f. Panzhihua cycad ("Cycas panzhihuaensis")	10	10
4098	50f. Nepal cycad	15	10
4099	230f. Polytomous cycad . .	55	30

916 Great Wall of China at Jinshan Ridge

1996. 25th Anniv of China–San Marino Diplomatic Relations. Multicoloured.

4100	100f. Type **916**	40	10
4101	100f. Walled rampart, San Marino	40	10

Nos. 4100/1 were issued together, se-tenant, forming a composite design.

919 Paddy Agricultural Tool

1996. Hemudu Archaeological Site, Yuyao, Zhejiang. Multicoloured.

4104	20f. Type **919**	10	10
4105	50f. Building supports . . .	10	10
4106	100f. Paddles	45	10
4107	230f. Dish engraved with two birds and sun	70	25

921 Children rejoicing

922 "The Discus Thrower" (Miron)

1996. Children. Multicoloured.

4109	20f. Type **921**	10	10
4110	30f. Girls pushing child in wheelchair in rain . . .	10	10
4111	50f. Expedition to Antarctica	10	10
4112	100f. Planting sapling . . .	50	10

1996. Centenary of Modern Olympic Games.

4113	**922**	20f. multicoloured . . .	10	10

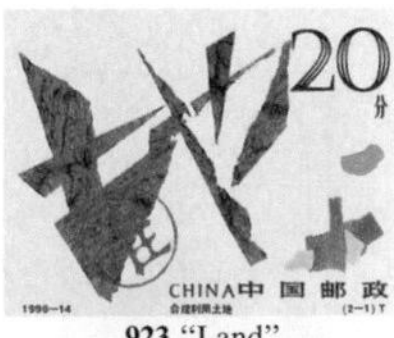

923 "Land"

1996. Preserve Land. Designs showing Chinese characters. Multicoloured.

4114	20f. Type **923**	10	10
4115	50f. "Cultivation"	10	10

924 Jinglue Terrace

1996. Jinglue Terrace, Guangxi Zhuang. Mult.
4116 20f. Type **924** 10 10
4117 50f. Structure of Zhenwu Pavilion 10 10

925 Red Flag Car

1996. Motor Vehicles. Multicoloured.
4118 20f. Type **925** 10 10
4119 20f. Dongfeng two-door truck 10 10
4120 50f. Jiefang four-door truck 10 10
4121 100f. Peking four-wheel drive 50 15

926 Banbidian Village, Kaiping District

1996. 20th Anniv of Tangshan Earthquake. Development of New City. Multicoloured.
4122 20f. (1) Type **926** 10 10
4123 50f. (2) East Hebei Cement Works 20 10
4124 50f. (3) Earthquake memorials, Xinhua Road 10 10
4125 100f. (4) Bulk carrier in Jingtang Harbour 45 15

927 Emblem, Globe and "30"

1996. 30th Int Geological Conference, Peking.
4126 **927** 20f. multicoloured . . . 10 10

928 Tianchi Lake

1996. Tianshan Mountains, Xinjiang.
4127 **928** 20f. (1) multicoloured . . 10 10
4128 – 50f. (2) multicoloured . . 10 10
4129 – 50f. (3) blue, mve & blk 10 10
4130 – 100f. (4) multicoloured 50 15
DESIGNS—VERT: No. 4128, Waterfalls; 4129, Snow-capped mountain peaks. HORIZ: No. 4130. Mountains and landscape.

1996. Dunhuang Cave Murals (6th series). As T **732**. Multicoloured.
4131 10f. Mount Wutai (Five Dynasties) (vert) 10 10
4132 20f. Li Shengtian, King of Khotan (Five Dynasties) (vert) 10 10
4133 50f. Guanyin, Goddess of Mercy, saves boat (Northern Song period) 10 10
4134 100f. Worshipping Bodhisattvas (Western Xia) 50 15

929 Tombs

1996. Emperors' Tombs of Western Xia Dynasty, Yinchuan, Ningxia Hui. Multicoloured.
4136 20f. Type **929** 10 10
4137 20f. Divine Gate ornament 10 10
4138 50f. Stone base from Stele Pavilion 10 10
4139 100f. Piece of stele from Shouling Tomb 50 10

930 Datong–Qinhuangdao Line

1996. Railways. Multicoloured.
4140 15f. Type **930** 10 10
4141 20f. Lanzhou–Xinjiang line 10 10
4142 50f. Peking–Kowloon line 25 20
4143 100f. Peking West railway station 45 35

931 Shang Dynasty Tortoise Shell **932** Ye Ting

1996. Ancient Archives. Multicoloured.
4144 20f. Type **931** 10 10
4145 20f. Han Dynasty wood slip inscribed with divinations on a marriage 10 10
4146 50f. Ming dynasty iron scroll conferring merit on General Li Wen 10 10
4147 100f. Qing dynasty diplomatic credentials (1905) 25 15

1996. Birth Cent of Ye Ting (revolutionary). Mult.
4148 20f. Type **932** 10 10
4149 50f. Ye Ting in uniform . . 10 10

933 Emblem

1996. 96th Interparliamentary Union Conference, Peking.
4150 **933** 20f. multicoloured . . . 10 10

934 Transport and Telecommunications

1996. Pudong Area of Shanghai. Mult.
4151 10f. (1) Type **934** 10 10
4152 20f. (2) People's Bank of China branch, Lujiazui finance and business area 10 10
4153 20f. (3) Jinqiao export centre 10 10
4154 50f. (4) Garden of Advance Science and Technology, Zhangjiang 40 10
4155 60f. (5) Customs House, Waigaoqiao bonded area 40 10
4156 100f. (6) Apartment blocks 50 15

935 Chinese Rocket "Long March"

1996. 47th Congress of International Astronautical Federation. Multicoloured.
4158 20f. Type **935** 10 10
4159 100f. Communications satellite 20 10

936 Singapore

1996. City Scenes. Multicoloured.
4160 20f. Type **936** 10 10
4161 290f. Panmen Gate, Suzhou 90 15

937 Red Army in Marshland

1996. 60th Anniv of Long March by Communist Army. Multicoloured.
4162 20f. Type **937** 35 10
4163 50f. Reunion of three armies 50 10

938 Two Gods

1996. Tianjin Clay Statuettes. Multicoloured.
4164 20f. (1) Type **938** 10 10
4165 50f. (2) Seated man blowing sugar figure 10 10
4166 50f. (3) Woman and child returning from fishing . . 10 10
4167 100f. (4) Women painting at table 50 15

939 Bank of China

1996. Economic Growth in Hong Kong. Mult.
4168 20f. Type **939** 10 10
4169 40f. Container terminal . . 10 10
4170 60f. Airplane taking off from Kai Tak Airport . . 40 10
4171 290f. Stock exchange . . . 95 25

940 Emblem over Farmland **941** "Horse treading on Flying Swallow" (bronze) and Great Wall of China

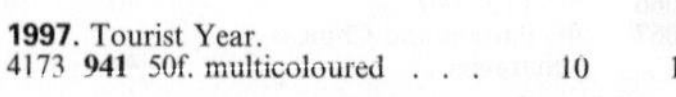

1997. 1st National Agricultural Census.
4172 **940** 50f. multicoloured . . . 10 10

1997. Tourist Year.
4173 **941** 50f. multicoloured . . . 10 10

942 Chinese Lantern **943** "Pine on Mount Huangshan"

1997. New Year. Year of the Ox. Mult.
4174 50f. Type **942** 35 10
4175 150f. Ox 65 15

1997. Birth Centenary of Pan Tianshou (artist). Multicoloured.
4176 50f. (1) Type **943** 40 10
4177 50f. (2) "Rosy Clouds of Dawn" 40 10
4178 100f. (3) "Clearing Up after Mould Rains" 80 35
4179 100f. (4) "Chrysanthemum and Bamboo" 80 35
4180 150f. (5) "Sleeping Cat" . . 1·60 70
4181 150f. (6) "Corner of Lingyan Brook" . . . . 1·60 70

944 Tea Tree at Lancang, Yunnan **945** Celebration

1997. Tea. Multicoloured.
4182 50f. (1) Type **944** 10 10
4183 50f. (2) Statue of Lu Yu (author of "Classic of Tea") 10 10
4184 150f. (3) Tea grinder (Tang dynasty) (horiz) 60 15
4185 150f. (4) "Tea Party at Huishan" (Wen Zhenming) (horiz) 60 15

1997. 50th Anniv of Autonomous Region of Inner Mongolia. Multicoloured.
4186 50f. (1) Type **945** 10 10
4187 50f. (2) People of different cultures ("Unity") (horiz) 10 10
4188 200f. (3) Galloping horses ("Advance") (horiz) . . . 80 15

946 Lady Amherst's Pheasant

1997. Rare Pheasants. Multicoloured.
4189 50f. Type **946** 10 10
4190 540f. Common pheasant . . 1·25 40

947 Zengchong Drum Tower **948** Buddha and Attendant Bodhisattva (Northern Wei dynasty)

1997. Dong Architecture. Multicoloured.
4191 50f. (1) Type **947** 10 10
4192 50f. (2) Baier drum tower 10 10
4193 150f. (3) Wind and rain bridge over River Nanjiang (horiz) 60 10
4194 150f. (4) Wind and rain shelter in field (horiz) . . 60 10

1997. Maiji Grottoes, Gansu Province. Mult.
4195 50f. (1) Type **948** 10 10
4196 50f. (2) Attendant Bodhisattva and disciple (Northern Wei dynasty) 10 10
4197 100f. (3) Maid servant (Western Wei dynasty) . . 15 10
4198 150f. (4) Buddha (Western Wei dynasty) 50 10
4199 150f. (5) Attendant Bodhisattva (Northern Zhou dynasty) 50 10
4200 200f. (6) Provider (Song dynasty) 55 15

949 Sino-British Joint Declaration and Red Roses

1997. Return of Hong Kong to China. Mult.
4201 50f. Type **949** 35 10
4202 150f. Basic Law and mixed roses 50 10

950 Taihuai Temple

1997. Ancient Temples, Wutai Mountain. Mult.
4205 40f. (1) Type **950** 10 10
4206 50f. (2) Great Hall, Nanchan Temple 10 10
4207 50f. (3) Eastern Hall, Foguang ("Buddhist Light") Temple 10 10
4208 150f. (4) Bronze Hall, Xiantong ("Revelation") Temple 60 10
4209 150f. (5) Bodhisattva Summit 60 10
4210 200f. (6) Zhenhai Temple . . 85 15

951 Tanks

1997. 70th Anniv of People's Liberation Army. Multicoloured.
4211 50f. (1) Type **951** 10 10
4212 50f. (2) Frigate flotilla . . . 10 10
4213 50f. (3) Jet fighter 10 10
4214 50f. (4) Ballistic missile . . . 10 10
4215 200f. (5) Tank, destroyer and jet fighters 90 15

952 Scene from "A Dream of Red Mansions" (carved by Jiang Yilin)

954 "Rosa rugosa"

953 Emblem

1997. Shoushan Stone Carvings. Mult.
4216 50f. (1) Type **952** 10 10
4217 50f. (2) "Rhinoceros basking in Sunshine" (Zhou Jinting) 10 10
4218 150f. (3) "Fragrance and Jade" 60 10
4219 150f. (4) "Li the Cripple, Han Zhongli and Lu Dongbin in drunken Joy" (Lin Fada) 60 10

1997. 15th National Communist Party Congress.
4221 **953** 50f. multicoloured . . . 10 10

1997. Roses. Multicoloured.
4222 150f. Type **954** 50 10
4223 150f. "Aotearoa" of New Zealand 50 10
Nos. 4222/3 were issued together, se-tenant, forming a composite design.

955 Putting the Shot and Athletes

1997. 8th National Games, Shanghai. Mult.
4224 50f. Type **955** 35 10
4225 150f. Mascot and stadium 45 10

956 Hall of Prayer for Good Harvests

1997. Temple of Heaven, Peking. Mult.
4227 50f. (1) Type **956** 10 10
4228 50f. (2) Imperial Vault of Heaven 10 10
4229 150f. (3) Circular mound altar 60 10
4230 150f. (4) Hall of Abstinence 60 10

958 Archers' Tower, Jar and Gate Tower

1997. Xi'an City Walls. Multicoloured.
4232 50f. (1) Type **958** 10 10
4233 50f. (2) Archers' Tower . . 10 10
4234 150f. (3) Watchtower . . . 45 10
4235 150f. (4) South-west corner tower 45 10

959 Diversion Canal

1997. Three Gorges Project (damming of Yangtse River). Multicoloured.
4236 50f. Type **959** 10 10
4237 50f. Dam under construction 10 10
Nos. 4236/7 were issued together, se-tenant, forming a composite design.

960 Temple of the Heavenly Queen

1997. Macao. Multicoloured.
4238 50f. Type **960** 10 10
4239 100f. Lianfeng (Lotus Peak) Temple 35 10
4240 150f. Great Sanba Archway (former facade of St. Paul's Church) 55 10
4241 200f. Songshan (Pine Hill) Lighthouse 70 10

961 Metallurgy in Ancient China

1997. Achievement in 1996 of Production of over 100,000,000 Tons of Steel a Year. Multicoloured.
4242 50f. Type **961** 10 10
4243 150f. Modern steel works 55 10

962 Digital Transmission

963 Cloth Tiger (Guo Qiuying)

1997. Telecommunications. Multicoloured.
4244 50f. (1) Type **962** 10 10
4245 50f. (2) Program-controlled switch and computer . . . 10 10
4246 150f. (3) Digital communication 60 10
4247 150f. (4) Mobile communication 60 10

1997. Literature. "Outlaws of the Marsh" (5th series). As T **745**. Multicoloured.
4248 40f. (1) Hu Yanzhuo tricks Guan Sheng 10 10
4249 50f. (2) Lu Junyi captures Shi Wengong 10 10
4250 50f. (3) Yan Qing wrestles with Qing Tianzhu . . . 10 10
4251 150f. (4) Hong Tianlei defeats government troops 80 10

1998. New Year. Year of the Tiger. Mult.
4253 50f. Type **963** 10 10
4254 150f. Chinese character . . 60 10

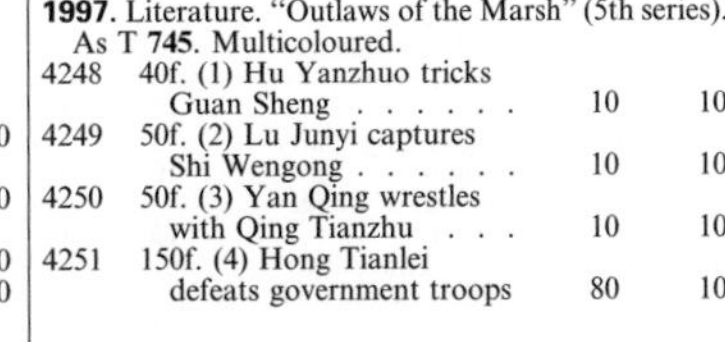

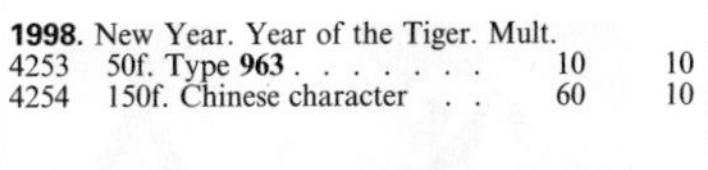

964 Keyuan Garden

1998. Villas and Gardens in Guangdong. Mult.
4255 50f. Type **964** 10 10
4256 50f. Liangyuan Garden . . 10 10
4257 100f. Qinghiu Garden . . . 40 10
4258 200f. Yuyin Villa 45 10

965 Deng Xiaoping

1998. 1st Death Anniv of Deng Xiaoping. Mult.
4259 50f. (1) Type **965** 10 10
4260 50f. (2) During Liberation War 10 10
4261 50f. (3) With Mao Tse-tung 10 10
4262 100f. (4) As Chairman of Military Commission . . 15 10
4263 150f. (5) Making speech . . 45 10
4264 200f. (6) In south China . . 55 20

966 Officers and Badge

1998. People's Police. Multicoloured.
4265 40f. (1) Type **966** 10 10
4266 50f. (2) Officers using computer and patrol officers using radio . . . 10 10
4267 50f. (3) Officer and elderly woman 10 10
4268 100f. (4) Officer on traffic control duty 15 10
4269 150f. (5) Officers on fire duty 45 10
4270 200f. (6) Border guards . . 55 15

967 State Arms

968 Chou En-lai on Horseback

1998. 9th National People's Congress, Peking.
4271 **967** 50f. multicoloured . . . 10 10

1998. Birth Centenary of Chou En-lai.
4272 **968** 50f. black, cream & red 10 10
4273 – 50f. black, cream & red 10 10
4274 – 150f. black, cream & red 45 10
4275 – 150f. multicoloured . . . 45 10
DESIGNS: No. 4273, Walking; 4274, Wearing floral decoration; 4275, Clapping.

969 Fangcao Lake

1997. World Heritage Site. Jiuzhaigou (nine-village valley). Multicoloured.
4276 50f. (1) Type **969** 10 10
4277 50f. (2) Wuhua Lake . . . 10 10
4278 150f. (3) Shuzheng Falls . . 45 10
4279 150f. (4) Nuorilang Falls . . 45 10

970 House on Stilts

1998. Dai Architecture, Xishuangbanna. Mult.
4281 50f. (1) Type **970** 10 10
4282 50f. (2) Ornamental well . . 10 10
4283 150f. (3) Pavilion and streamers 60 10
4284 150f. (4) Pagoda 60 10

971 Haikou

1998. Hainan Special Economic Zone. Mult.
4285 50f. (1) Type **971** 10 10
4286 50f. (2) Yangpu 10 10
4287 150f. (3) Sanya Phoenix International Airport . . 60 10
4288 150f. (4) Monument, Yalongwan 60 10

972 Yingtian Academy

1998. Ancient Academies. Multicoloured.
4289 50f. (1) Type **972** 10 10
4290 50f. (2) Songyang Academy 10 10
4291 150f. (3) Yuelu Academy . . 60 10
4292 150f. (4) Bailu Academy . . 60 10

973 University Buildings

1998. Centenary of Peking University.
4293 **973** 50f. multicoloured . . . 10 10

974 Congress Emblem

1998. 22nd U.P.U. Congress, Peking (1999). Mult.
4294 50f. Type **974** 10 10
4295 540f. Emblem (vert) . . . . 1·10 45

975 Mountain Peaks

1998. Shennongjia (primitive forest). Mult.
4296 50f. (1) Type **975** 10 10
4297 50f. (2) River gorge 10 10
4298 150f. (3) Forest 45 10
4299 150f. (4) Grasslands 45 10

976 Great Hall of the People of Chongqing

1998. Chongqing. Multicoloured.
4300 50f. Type **976** 10 10
4301 150f. Chongqing port . . . 20 10

977 "Tiger"

1998. Paintings by He Xiangning. Mult.
4302 50f. Type **977** 10 10
4303 100f. "Lion" (vert) 15 10
4304 150f. "Plum Blossom" (vert) 45 15

978 Grasslands

1998. Xilingguole Grasslands, Inner Mongolia. Multicoloured.
4305 50f. (1) Type **978** 10 10
4306 50f. (2) Meadow steppe . . 10 10
4307 150f. (3) Forest of poplars and birches 60 10

979 Baishilazi

1998. Jingpo Lake, Heilonjiang. Multicoloured.
4309 50f. (1) Type **979** 10 10
4310 50f. (2) Pearl Gate 10 10
4311 50f. (3) Mt. Xiaogushan . . 10 10
4312 50f. (4) Diaoshuilou waterfall 10 10

Nos. 4309/12 were issued together, se-tenant, forming a composite design.

980 Wurzburg Palace, Germany

1998. World Heritage Sites. Multicoloured.
4313 50f. Type **980** 35 10
4314 540f. Puning Temple, Chengde . . . . 1·25 45

1998. Literature. "The Romance of the Three Kingdoms" by Luo Guanzhong (5th series). As T **763**. Multicoloured.
4315 50f. (1) Liu Bei appoints a Guardian for his Heir at Baidi City (horiz) 10 10
4316 50f. (2) Zhuge Liang leads his army home 10 10
4317 100f. (3) Funeral of Zhuge Liang (horiz) 15 10
4318 150f. (4) Three Kingdoms united under the reign of Jin 45 10

981 Wave and Houses

1998. Flood Relief Fund.
4320 **981** 50f. (+50f.) mult 15 10

No. 4320 includes the se-tenant premium-carrying tab shown in Type **981**. The premium was used to help the victims of floods in the Yangtse and Songhuajiang River areas.

982 Louvre Palace, Paris

1998. Ancient Palaces. Multicoloured.
4321 50f. Type **982** 10 10
4322 200f. Imperial Palace, Peking 55 15

983 Face

1998. Rock Paintings, Helan Mountains. Mult.
4323 50f. Type **983** 10 10
4324 100f. Hunting 15 10
4325 150f. Ox 55 10

984 Vase with Five Spouts (Northern Song Dynasty)

1998. Longquan Pottery. Multicoloured.
4326 50f. (1) Type **984** 10 10
4327 50f. (2) Vase with phoenix ears (Southern Song dynasty) 10 10
4328 50f. (3) Double gourd vase (Yuan dynasty) 10 10
4329 150f. (4) Ewer decorated with three fruits (Ming dynasty) 50 10

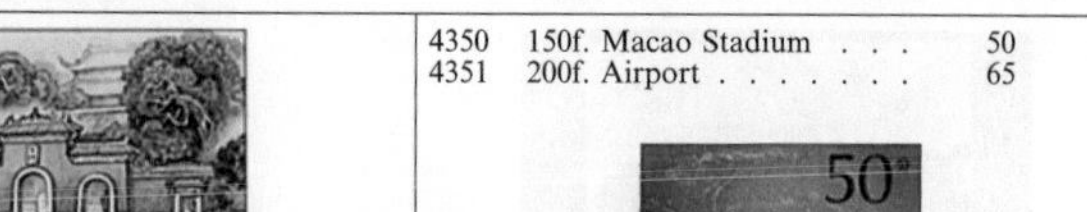

985 Meridian Gate

1998. Mausoleum of King Yandi, Yanling County, Hunan. Multicoloured.
4330 50f. Type **985** 10 10
4331 100f. Saluting Pavilion . . . 15 10
4332 150f. Tomb 55 10

986 Men discussing Campaign (Yi Rongsheng)

1998. 50th Anniv of Liberation War. Multicoloured.
4334 50f. (1) Type **986** 10 10
4335 50f. (2) Conquering Jinzhou (Ren Mengzhang, Zhang Hongzan, Li Shuji and Guang Tingbo) 10 10
4336 50f. (3) Battle of Huaihai (Chen Qi, Zhao Guangtao, Chen Jian and Wei Chuyu) 10 10
4337 50f. (4) Liberating Peking (Zhang Ruwei, Deng Jiaju, Wu Changjiang and Shen Yaoyi) 10 10
4338 150f. (5) Supporting the Front (Cui Kaixi) 60 10

987 Liu Shaoqi

1998. Birth Centenary of Liu Shaoqi (Chairman of the Republic, 1959–68).
4339 **987** 50f. (1) multicoloured . . 10 10
4340 – 50f. (2) black, buff and red 10 10
4341 – 50f. (3) multicoloured . . 10 10
4342 – 150f. (4) multicoloured 50 10

DESIGNS—VERT: No. 4340, Shaoqi at Seventh National Communist Party Congress. HORIZ: No. 4341, Presented with necklace of flowers while on diplomatic mission; 4342, Working at desk.

988 Chillon Castle, Lake Geneva, Switzerland

1998. Lakes. Multicoloured.
4343 50f. Type **988** 35 10
4344 540f. Bridge 24, Slender West Lake, Yangzhou . . 1·25 45

989 Canal Fork

1998. Lingqu Canal. Multicoloured.
4345 50f. Type **989** 10 10
4346 50f. Bridge over canal (vert) 10 10
4347 150f. Lock (vert) 45 10

990 Road into Macao

1998. Macao. Multicoloured.
4348 50f. Type **990** 10 10
4349 100f. Bridge and buildings 15 10
4350 150f. Macao Stadium . . . 50 10
4351 200f. Airport 65 15

991 Deng Xiaoping at Third Plenary Session

1998. 20th Anniv of Third Plenary Session of 11th Central Committee of Chinese Communist Party. Multicoloured.
4352 50f. Type **991** 10 10
4353 150f. Deng Xiaoping Theory and buildings 45 10

993 Ceramic Rabbit (Zhang Chang)

1999. New Year. Year of the Rabbit. Multicoloured.
4355 50f. Type **993** 10 10
4356 150f. Chinese character ("Good Luck") 45 10

994 Ploughing

1999. Stone Carvings of Han Dynasty.
4357 **994** 50f. (1) green, cream and black 10 10
4358 – 50f. (2) brown, cream and black 10 10
4359 – 50f. (3) blue, cream and black 10 10
4360 – 50f. (4) brown, cream and black 10 10
4361 – 150f. (5) green, cream and black 50 10
4362 – 150f. (6) lilac, cream and black 50 10

DESIGNS: No. 4358, Weaving; 4359, Dancing; 4360, Carriage and outriders; 4361, Jing Ke's attempted assassination of Emperor Qinshihuang; 4362, Goddess Chang'e flying to moon.

995 Wine Vessel, Northern Song Dynasty

996 Peony and Globe

1999. Ceramics from the Jun Kiln, Henan. Multicoloured.
4363 80f. Type **995** 10 10
4364 100f. Wine vessel, Northern Song Dynasty (different) 15 10
4365 150f. Double-handled stove, Yuan Dynasty 55 10
4366 200f. Double-handled vase, Yuan Dynasty 65 15

1999. World Horticulture Fair, Kunming. Mult.
4367 80f. Type **996** 10 10
4368 200f. Exhibition halls and tree 30 15

997 Stag

1999. Red Deer. Multicoloured.
4369 80f. (1) Type **997** 10 10
4370 80f. (2) Doe and fawns 10 10

998 Puji Temple

1999. Putuo Mountain, Lianhuayang. Mult.

No.	Description	Mint	Used
4371	30f. Type **998**	10	10
4372	60f. Nantian Gate (vert)	10	10
4373	60f. Step beach	10	10
4374	80f. Pantuo Rock	10	10
4375	80f. Fanyin Cave (vert)	10	10
4376	280f. Fayu Temple	40	20

1000 Fang Zhimin (sculpture)

1999. Birth Centenary of Fang Zhimin (revolutionary). Multicoloured.

No.	Description	Mint	Used
4378	80y. Type **1000**	10	10
4379	80y. Full-length portrait of Fang Zhimin	10	10

1001 First Congress Building, Berne, Switzerland (1874)

1999. 22nd Universal Postal Union Congress, Peking. Multicoloured.

No.	Description	Mint	Used
4380	80f. Type **1001**	10	10
4381	540f. 22nd Congress building, Peking	1·10	45

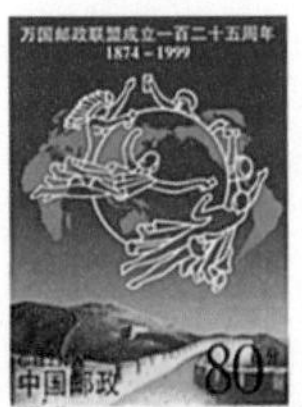

1002 U.P.U. Emblem and Great Wall　**1003** Emblem

1999. 125th Anniv of Universal Postal Union.

No.	Description	Mint	Used
4383	**1002** 80f. multicoloured	10	10

1999. International Year of the Elderly.

No.	Description	Mint	Used
4384	**1003** 80f. multicoloured	10	10

1004 Conference Hall

1999. 50th Anniv of Chinese People's Political Conference. Multicoloured.

No.	Description	Mint	Used
4385	60f. Type **1004**	10	10
4386	80f. Mao Tse-tung and emblem (vert)	10	10

1005 Han Couple

1999. 50th Anniv of People's Republic. Ethnic Groups. Couples from different ethnic groups. Multicoloured.

No.	Description	Mint	Used
4387	80f. (1) Type **1005**	10	10
4388	80f. (2) Mongolian	10	10
4389	80f. (3) Hui	10	10
4390	80f. (4) Tibetan	10	10
4391	80f. (5) Uygur	10	10
4392	80f. (6) Miao	10	10
4393	80f. (7) Yi	10	10
4394	80f. (8) Zhuang	10	10
4395	80f. (9) Bouyei	10	10
4396	80f. (10) Korean	10	10
4397	80f. (11) Manchu	10	10
4398	80f. (12) Dong	10	10
4399	80f. (13) Yao	10	10
4400	80f. (14) Bai	10	10
4401	80f. (15) Tujia	10	10
4402	80f. (16) Hani	10	10
4403	80f. (17) Kazak	10	10
4404	80f. (18) Dai	10	10
4405	80f. (19) Li	10	10
4406	80f. (20) Lisu	10	10
4407	80f. (21) Va	10	10
4408	80f. (22) She	10	10
4409	80f. (23) Gaoshan	10	10
4410	80f. (24) Lahu	10	10
4411	80f. (25) Sui	10	10
4412	80f. (26) Dongxiang	10	10
4413	80f. (27) Naxi	10	10
4414	80f. (28) Jingpo	10	10
4415	80f. (29) Kirgiz	10	10
4416	80f. (30) Tu	10	10
4417	80f. (31) Daur	10	10
4418	80f. (32) Mulam	10	10
4419	80f. (33) Qiang	10	10
4420	80f. (34) Blang	10	10
4421	80f. (35) Salar	10	10
4422	80f. (36) Maonan	10	10
4423	80f. (37) Gelao	10	10
4424	80f. (38) Xibe	10	10
4425	80f. (39) Achang	10	10
4426	80f. (40) Primi	10	10
4427	80f. (41) Tajik	10	10
4428	80f. (42) Nu	10	10
4429	80f. (43) Uzbek	10	10
4430	80f. (44) Russian	10	10
4431	80f. (45) Ewenki	10	10
4432	80f. (46) De'ang	10	10
4433	80f. (47) Bonan	10	10
4434	80f. (48) Yugur	10	10
4435	80f. (49) Gin	10	10
4436	80f. (50) Tatar	10	10
4437	80f. (51) Derung	10	10
4438	80f. (52) Oroqen	10	10
4439	80f. (53) Hezhen	10	10
4440	80f. (54) Monba	10	10
4441	80f. (55) Lhoba	10	10
4442	80f. (56) Jino	10	10

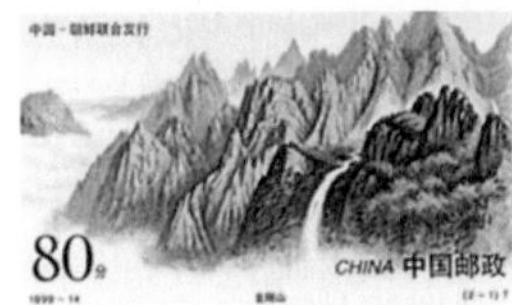

1006 Mt. Kumgang, North Korea

1999. 50th Anniv of China–North Korea Diplomatic Relations. Multicoloured.

No.	Description	Mint	Used
4443	80f. (1) Type **1006**	10	10
4444	80f. (2) Mt. Lushan, China	10	10

1007 Children reading　**1008** Early Cambrian Chengjiang Biota Fossil

1999. 10th Anniv of Project Hope (promotion of rural education).

No.	Description	Mint	Used
4445	**1007** 80f. multicoloured	10	10

1999. 50th Anniv of Chinese Academy of Sciences. Multicoloured.

No.	Description	Mint	Used
4446	80f. (1) Type **1008**	10	10
4447	80f. (2) Underwater robot	10	10
4448	80f. (3) Head and mathematical equation (vert)	10	10
4449	80f. (4) Astronomical telescope (vert)	10	10

1009 Li Lisan　**1011** Rongzhen in Uniform

1010 Sino-Portuguese Joint Declaration

1999. Birth Centenary of Li Lisan (trade unionist). Multicoloured.

No.	Description	Mint	Used
4450	80f. Type **1009**	10	10
4451	80f. Li Lisan (different)	10	10

1999. Return of Macao to China. Multicoloured.

No.	Description	Mint	Used
4452	80f. Type **1010**	10	10
4453	150f. Basic Law of Macao Special Region and Great Wall of China	20	10

1999. Birth Centenary of Nie Rongzhen (revolutionary). Multicoloured.

No.	Description	Mint	Used
4456	80f. Type **1011**	10	10
4457	80f. Rongzhen in chair	10	10

1012 1961 8f. 1911 Revolution Stamp and Dr. Sun Yat-sen

1999. The Twentieth Century. Multicoloured.

No.	Description	Mint	Used
4458	60f. (1) Type **1012**	10	10
4459	60f. (2) 1989 8f. May 4th Movement stamp	10	10
4460	80f. (3) 1991 20f. Chinese Communist Party stamp	10	10
4461	80f. (4) 1995 20f. (No. 4013) End of Second World War and of War against Japan stamp	10	10
4462	80f. (5) 1959 20f. People's Republic anniversary stamp and Mao Tse-tung	10	10
4463	200f. (6) 1989 20f. National Defence stamp	35	15
4464	260f. (7) 1996 500f. Pudong Area of Shanghai stamp	35	20
4465	280f. (8) Deng Xiaoping and fireworks (based on 1997 800f. Return of Hong Kong to China stamp)	40	25

1013 Chinese Dragon　**1014** Welcoming the Spring Festival

2000. New Year. Year of the Dragon. Each black, gold and red.

No.	Description	Mint	Used
4466	80f. Type **1013**	10	10
4467	2y.80 "The Sun Rising in the Eastern Sky" and Chinese character for dragon	40	25

2000. Spring Festival. Multicoloured.

No.	Description	Mint	Used
4468	80f. Type **1014**	10	10
4469	80f. Bidding farewell to the outgoing year	10	10
4470	2y.80 Offering sacrifices to the God of Land	40	25

1016 Neolithic Jade Dragon

2000. Chinese Dragon Artefacts. Multicoloured.

No.	Description	Mint	Used
4473	60f. (1) Type **1016**	10	10
4474	80f. (2) Dragon-shaped brooch, Warring States	15	10
4475	80f. (3) Eaves tile with carved dragon, Han Dynasty	15	10
4476	80f. (4) Coiled dragon on copper mirror, Tang Dynasty	15	10
4477	80f. (5) Bronze dragon, Jin Dynasty	15	10
4478	2y.80 (6) Dragon decoration from Qing Dynasty Red Sandalwood Throne	45	25

1017 Wanxian Bridge

2000. Road Bridges over the Yangtze River. Mult.

No.	Description	Mint	Used
4479	80f. (1) Type **1017**	15	10
4480	80f. (2) Huangshi	15	10
4481	80f. (3) Tongling	15	10
4482	2y.80 (4) Jiangyin	45	25

1018 Cangshan Mountain and Erhai Lake

2000. Landscapes of Dali, Yunnan Province. Mult.

No.	Description	Mint	Used
4483	80f. (1) Type **1018**	15	10
4484	80f. (2) Three Pagodas, Chongsheng Temple	15	10
4485	80f. (3) Jizu Mountain	15	10
4486	2y.80 (4) Shibao Mountain	45	25

1019 Mulan weaving Cloth

2000. Literature. *Mulan* (folk tale). Multicoloured.

No.	Description	Mint	Used
4487	80f. (1) Type **1019**	15	10
4488	80f. (2) Mulan dressed as male soldier	15	10
4489	80f. (3) Mulan on horseback	15	10
4490	80f. (4) Mulan resuming her female identity	15	10

1020 Good Luck Treasure Pagoda

2000. Taer Lamasery, Qinghai Province. Mult.

No.	Description	Mint	Used
4491	80f. (1) Type **1020**	15	10
4492	80f. (2) Big Golden Tile Palace	15	10
4493	80f. (3) Big Scripture Hall	15	10
4494	2y.80 (4) Banqen Residence	45	25

1021 Li Fuchan and Cai Chang

2000. Birth Centenaries of Li Fuchan and Cai Chang (revolutionary couple).

No.	Description	Mint	Used
4495	**1021** 80f. black, buff and brown	15	10

1022 "Entering a New Century" (Ling Lifei)

2000. New Millennium. Winning Entries in National Children's "Prospects in the New Century" Stamp Design Competition. Mult.

No.	Description	Mint	Used
4496	30f. (1) Type **1022**	10	10
4497	60f. (2) "I Build a Bridge to Connect the Mainland with Taiwan" (Wang Yumeng)	10	10
4498	60f. (3) "Palace in a Tree" (Li Zhao)	10	10
4499	80f. (4) "Protecting the Earth" (Chen Zhuo)	15	10
4500	80f. (5) "Communications in the New Century" (Qin Tian)	15	10
4501	80f. (6) "Space Travel" (Wang Yiru)	15	10
4502	2y.60 (7) "The Earth gets Younger" (Tian Yuan)	40	15
4503	2y.80 (8) "World Peace" (Song Zhili)	45	25

1023 Chen Yun

2000. 95th Birth Anniv of Chen Yun (revolutionary). Multicoloured.
4504 80f. (1) Type **1023** 15 10
4505 80f. (2) Chen Yun wearing white jacket and hat (vert) 15 10
4506 80f. (3) Chen Yun wearing black jacket (vert) 15 10
4507 2y.80 (4) Chen Yun 45 25

1024 He-Pot (Chinese wine vessel)

2000. Pots. Multicoloured.
4508 80f. (1) Type **1024** 15 10
4509 80f. (2) Horse milk pot, Kazakhstan 15 10

1025 Great Peak

2000. Laoshan Mountain. Multicoloured.
4510 80f. (1) Type **1025** 15 10
4511 80f. (2) Yangkou Bay . . . 15 10
4512 80f. (3) Beijiu Lake 15 10
4513 2y.80 (4) Taiqing Palace . . 45 25

1027 Grandma Carp telling a Story

2000. *Small Carp Leap Through Dragon Gate* (children's story). Multicoloured.
4516 80f. (1) Type **1027** 15 10
4517 80f. (2) Searching for Dragon Gate 15 10
4518 80f. (3) Uncle Crab helping Carp 15 10
4519 80f. (4) Carp leaping through Dragon Gate . . 15 10
4520 80f. (5) Aunt Swallow delivering a letter 15 10

1028 Financial Central District

2000. Shenzhen Special Economic Zone. Mult.
4526 80f. (1) Type **1028** 15 10
4527 80f. (2) China International New and Hi-Tech Achievement Fair Exhibition Centre 15 10
4528 80f. (3) Yantian Harbour . . 15 10
4529 80f. (4) Shenzhen Bay . . . 15 10
4530 2y.80 (5) Shekou Industrial District 15 10

1030 Coconut Forest Bay, Hainan

2000. Beaches. Multicoloured.
4532 80f. (1) Type **1030** 15 10
4533 80f. (2) Paradero seashore, Matanzas, Cuba 15 10

1031 Puppets

2000. Masks and Puppets. Multicoloured.
4534 80f. (1) Type **1031** 15 10
4535 80f. (2) Carnival masks . . . 15 10

1032 "Eternal Fidelity" Palace Lamp

1033 Confucius

2000. Relics from Tomb of Liu Sheng. Multicoloured.
4536 80f. (1) Type **1032** 15 10
4537 80f. (2) Bronze pot with dragon design 15 10
4538 80f. (3) Boshan incense burner with gold inlay . . 15 10
4539 2y.80 (4) Rosefinch-shaped cup 15 10

2000. Ancient Thinkers. Each black, red and brown.
4540 60f. (1) Type **1033** 15 10
4541 80f. (2) Mencius 15 10
4542 80f. (3) Lao Zi 15 10
4543 80f. (4) Zhuang Zi 15 10
4544 80f. (5) Mo Zi 15 10
4545 2y.80 (6) Xun Zi 15 10

1034 Launch of *Shenzhou*

2000. Test Flight of *Shenzhou* (spacecraft). Mult.
4546 80f. Type **1034** 15 10
4547 80f. Orbiting Earth 15 10

1035 Meteorological Satellite

2000. 50th Anniv of World Meteorological Organization. Multicoloured.
4548 80f. (1) Type **1035** 15 10
4549 80f. (2) Meteorological equipment and Qinghai–Tibet plateau 15 10
4550 80f. (3) Computers and numbers 15 10
4551 2y.80 (4) Airplane and wind flow diagram 15 10

1036 Scarlet Kaffir Lily

1037 Jingshu Bell, Western Zhou Dynasty

2000. Flowers. Multicoloured.
4552 80f. (1) Type **1036** 15 10
4553 80f. (2) Noble clivia 15 10
4554 80f. (3) Golden striat kaffir lily 15 10
4555 2y.80 (4) White kaffir lily . . 15 10

2000. Ancient Bells. Multicoloured.
4557 80f. (1) Type **1037** 15 10
4558 80f. (2) Su chime bell, Spring and Autumn Period 15 10
4559 80f. (3) Jingyun bell, Tang Dynasty 15 10
4560 2y.80 (4) Qianlong bell, Qing Dynasty 15 10

1038 Sun, Moon and Observatory

1039 Snake

2001. New Millennium. Multicoloured.
4561 60f. (1) Type **1038** 10 10
4562 80f. (2) Globe and white dove 15 10
4563 80f. (3) Child's hands, leaf and World map (horiz) 15 10
4564 80f. (4) Silhouette of head and circuit board (horiz) 15 10
4565 2y.80 (5) Sun, stars and sundial 50 30

2001. New Year. Year of the Snake. Multicoloured.
4566 80f. Type **1039** 15 10
4567 2y.80 "Fortune Illuminates all Things" and Chinese character for snake . . . 50 30

1040 Tang Qin

2001. Chou (Clown) Roles in Peking Opera. Multicoloured.
4568 80f. (1) Type **1040** 15 10
4569 80f. (2) Liu Lihua 15 10
4570 80f. (3) Gao Lishi 15 10
4571 80f. (4) Jiang Gan 15 10
4572 80f. (5) Yang Xiangwu . . . 15 10
4573 2y.80 (6) Shi Qian 50 30

1042 Zhouzhuang, Kunshan

2001. Ancient Towns, Taihu Lake Valley. Multicoloured.
4575 80f. (1) Type **1042** 15 10
4576 80f. (2) Tongli, Wujiang . . 15 10
4577 80f. (3) Wuzhen, Tongziang 15 10
4578 80f. (4) Nanxun, Huzhou . . 15 10
4579 80f. (5) Luzhi, Wuxian . . . 15 10
4580 2y.80 (6) Xitang, Jiashan . . 50 30

1043 "Ying Ning"

2001. Classical Literature. *Strange Stories from a Chinese Studio* by Pu Songling. Multicoloured.
4581 60f. (1) Type **1043** 15 10
4582 80f. (2) "A Bao" 15 10
4583 80f. (3) "Mask of Evildoer" 15 10
4584 2y.80 (4) "Stealing Peach" 50 30

1044 Queen Mother (detail)

2001. Yongle Temple Murals, Shanxi. "Portrait of Paying Homage to Xianyuan Emperor". Multicoloured.
4586 60f. (1) Type **1044** 15 10
4587 80f. (2) Jade Lady presenting treasure . . . 15 10
4588 80. (3) Celestial Worthy of the East 15 10
4589 2y.80 (4) Venus and Mercury 50 30

1045 Nanyan Hall in Autumn

1046 Pottery Vase

2001. Mount Wudang, Hubei Province. Multicoloured.
4590 60f. (1) Type **1045** 10 10
4591 80f. (2) Zixiao Temple in winter 15 10
4592 80f. (3) Taizi slope in summer 15 10

2001. Chinese Pottery. Multicoloured.
4594 80f. (1) Type **1046** 15 10
4595 80f. (2) Teapot 15 10

1047 Dragon Boat Race

2001. Duanwu Dragon Boat Festival. Multicoloured.
4596 80f. (1) Type **1047** 15 10
4597 80f. (2) Vase, mobile and flowers 15 10
4598 2y.80 (3) Dragon's head and expulsion of five poisons 50 30

1048 Wang Jinmei

2001. Leaders of the Chinese Communist Party. Multicoloured.
4599 80f. (1) Type **1048** 15 10
4600 80f. (2) Zhao Shiyan 15 10
4601 80f. (3) Deng Enming . . . 15 10
4602 80f. (4) Cai Hesen 15 10
4603 80f. (5) He Shuheng 15 10

1049 Party Flag

2001. 80th Anniv of Chinese Communist Party.
4604 **1049** 80f. red, yellow and black 15 10

1050 Emblem

2001. Choice of Beijing as 2008 Olympic Host City.
4605 **1050** 80f. multicoloured . . . 15 10

1051 Yinlianzhuitan Waterfall

2001. Waterfalls. Multicoloured.
4606 80f. (1) Type **1051** 15 10
4607 80f. (2) Doupotang Waterfall (horiz) 15 10
4608 80f. (3) Dishuitan Waterfall 15 10

1052 Pigeon Nest

2001. Beidaihe Summer Resort. Multicoloured.
4610 60f. (1) Type **1052** 10 10
4611 80f. (2) Umbrellas, Zhonghai Beach 15 10
4612 80f. (3) Sailing dinghies, Lianfeng Hill 15 10
4613 2y.80 Windsurfers, Tiger Stone 50 30

1053 "2001" and Emblem

2001. 21st World University Games, Beijing. Multicoloured.
4614 60f. Type **1053** 10 10
4615 80f. "2001" and sports pictograms 15 10
4616 2y.80 "2001" and globes . . 50 30

1054 Water Diversion Canal

2001. Datong River Diversion Project. Mult.
4617 80f. (1) Type **1054** 15 10
4618 80f. (2) Overland pipes, Xianming Gorge 15 10
4619 80f. (3) Canal tunnel 15 10
4620 2y.80 (4) Aqueduct, Zhuanglang River 50 30

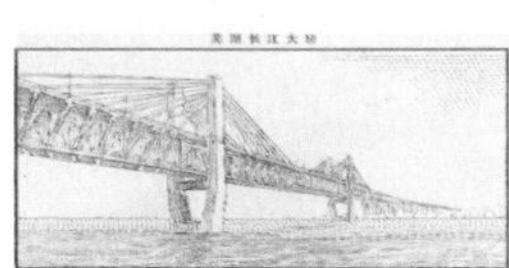

1055 Wuhu Bridge over Yangtze River

2001. Wuhu Bridge. Multicoloured.
4621 80f. Type **1055** 15 10
4622 2y.80 Road section of Wuhu Bridge 50 30

1056 *Paphiopedilum malipoense*

2001. Orchids. Multicoloured.
4623 80f. (1) Type **1056** 15 10
4624 80f. (2) *Paphiopedilum dianthum* 15 10
4625 80f. (3) *Paphiopedilum markianum* 15 10
4626 2y.80 (4) *Paphiopedilum appletonianum* 50 30

1057 Mask of San Xing Dui

2001. Golden Masks. Multicoloured.
4628 80f. Type **1057** 15 10
4629 80f. Mask of Tutankhamun 15 10
Stamps in similar designs were also issued by Egypt.

1058 Emblem

2001. 9th Asia Pacific Economic Co-operation Conference, Shanghai.
4630 **1058** 80f. multicoloured . . . 15 10

1059 Ertan Hydroelectric Power Station (½-size illustration)

2001. Sheet 150 × 85 mm.
MS4631 **1059** 8y. multicoloured 1·25 1·25

1060 Horse galloping

2001. Six Steeds (relief sculptures), Zhaoling Mausoleum. Multicoloured.
4632 60f. (1) Type **1060** 10 10
4633 80f. (2) Galloping 15 10
4634 80f. (3) Trotting 10 10
4635 80f. (4) With rider 15 10
4636 80f. (5) Trotting 15 10
4637 2y.80 (6) Galloping 40 20

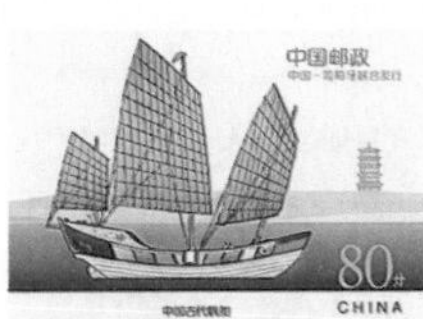

1061 Chinese Junk

2001. Ancient Sailing Craft. Multicoloured.
4638 80f. Type **1061** 15 10
4639 80f. Portuguese caravel . . . 15 10
Stamps in the same design were issued by Portugal.

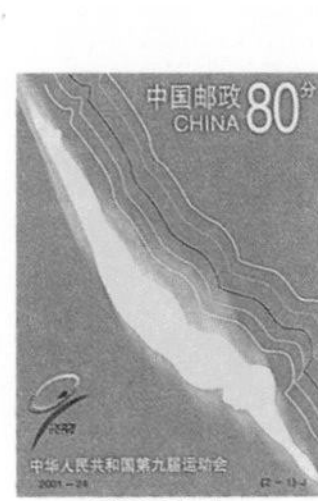

1062 Diving

1063 Liupanshan Mountains

2001. 9th National Games, Guangzhou. Mult.
4640 80f. Type **1062** 15 10
4641 2y.80 Volleyball 40 20
MS4642 140 × 90 mm. Nos. 4640/1 55 55

2001. Liupanshan Mountains. Multicoloured.
4643 80f. (1) Type **1063** 15 10
4644 80f. (2) Forest, Liangdianxia Gorge 15 10
4645 80f. (3) Old Dragon Pool, Jinghe River 15 10
4646 2y.80 (4) Wild Lotus Valley, West Gorge 40 20

1064 Lending an Umbrella by the Lake

1065 Emblem

2001. Tale of Xu Xian and the White Snake. Multicoloured.
4647 80f. (1) Type **1064** 15 10
4648 80f. (2) Stealing the Immortal Grass 15 10
4649 80f. (3) Flooding the Jinshan Hill 15 10
4650 2y.80 (4) Meeting at the Broken Bridge 40 20

2001. China's Membership of World Trade Organization.
4651 **1065** 80f. multicoloured . . . 15 10

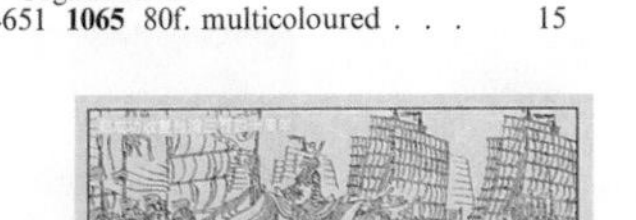

1066 Zheng's advancing Fleet

2001. 340th Anniv of Zheng Chenggong's Seizure of Formosa (Taiwan) from Dutch Colonists. Each drab, black and red.
4652 80f. (1) Type **1066** 15 10
4653 80f. (2) Populace offering troops food and water . . 15 10
4654 2y.80 Zheng viewing island 40 20

1067 Engineers and Route of Railway (½-size illustration)

2001. Construction of the Qinghai--Tibet Railway. Sheet 135 × 114 mm.
MS4655 **1067** 8y. multicoloured 1·25 1·25

1068 Horse

1069 "A Couple of Eagles"

2002. New Year. Year of the Horse. Multicoloured.
4656 80f. Type **1068** 15 10
4657 2y.80 Chinese character for horse 40 20

2002. Paintings by Badashanren. Multicoloured.
4658 60f. (1) Type **1069** 10 10
4659 80f. (2) "A Single Pine Tree" 15 10
4660 80f. (3) "Lotus Flowers" . . 15 10
4661 80f. (4) "Chrysanthemum in a Vase" 15 10
4662 2y.60 (5) "A Couple of Magpies on a Rock" . . 40 20
4663 2y.80 (6) "Landscape after Dong Yuan's Style" . . . 40 20

1070 Forest Protection

1071 Yellow-bellied Tragopan

2002. Environmental Protection. Multicoloured.
4664 5f. Maintaining low birth rate 10 10
4665 10f. Type **1070** 10 10
4666 30f. Mineral resources protection 10 10
4668 60f. Air pollution prevention 10 10
4670 80f. Water resources protection 15 10
4673 1y.50 Ocean protection . . . 20 10

2002. Birds. Multicoloured.
4675 80f. Type **1071** 15 10
4676 1y. Biddulph's ground jay 15 10
4677 2y. Taiwan blue magpie . . 30 15
4680 4y.20 Przewalski's redstart 60 30
4683 5y.40 Koslow's bunting . . 70 35

1072 Golden Camellia (*Camellia nitidissima*)

1073 Yaqin

2002. Flowers. Multicoloured.
4690 80f. Type **1072** 15 10
4691 80f. Cannonball tree flower (*Couroupita guianensis*) . . 15 10
Stamps showing similar subjects were issued by Malaysia.

2002. Stringed Musical Instruments. Multicoloured.
4692 60f. (1) Type **1073** 10 10
4693 80f. (2) Erhu 15 10
4694 80f. (3) Banhu 15 10
4695 80f. (4) Satar 15 10
4696 2y.80 (5) Matouqin 40 20

1074 "The Royal Carriage" (Yan Liben) (¼ size-illustration)

2002. Sheet 160 × 82 mm.
MS4697 **1074** 8y. multicoloured 1·25 1·25

1075 Wine Vessel

2002. Northern Song Dynasty Ceramics. Mult.
4698 60f. (1) Type **1075** 10 10
4699 80f. (2) Three-legged basin 15 10
4700 80f. (3) Bowl 15 10
4701 2y.80 (4) Dish 40 20

2001. Classical Literature. Strange Stories from a Chinese Studio by Pu Songling (2nd series). Vert designs as T **1043**. Multicoloured.
4702 60f. (1) "Xi Fangping" . . . 10 10
4703 80f. (2) "Pianpian" 15 10
4704 80f. (3) "Tian Qilang" . . . 15 10
4705 2y.80 (4) "Bai Qiulian" . . 40 20

1076 Wuliang Taoist Temple

1078 Ruyi (good luck symbol)

1077 Sifang Street

2002. Qianshan Mountain. Views of the mountain. Multicoloured.
4706 80f. (1) Type **1076** 15 10
4707 80f. (2) Maitreya peak . . . 15 10
4708 80f. (3) Longquan temple 15 10
4709 2y.80 (4) "Terrace of the Immortals" (peak) 40 20
Nos. 4706/9 were issued together, se-tenant, forming a composite design.

2002. Lijiang City.
4710 **1077** 80f. red 15 10
4711 – 80f. green (vert) 15 10
4712 – 2y.80 blue 40 20
MS4713 145 × 101 mm Nos. 4710/12 70 70

DESIGNS: 80f. Bridges over city river; 2y.80, Traditional Naxi house.

2002. Greetings Stamp.
4714 **1078** 80f. multicoloured . . . 15 10

1079 Footballer

2002. World Cup Football Championship, Japan and South Korea. Multicoloured.
4715 80f. Type **1079** 15 10
4716 2y. Players tackling 30 15

1080 Maota Pagoda Lighthouse

1082 "Avalokitesvara of the Sun and Moon"

1081 Lijia Gorge Hydro-electric Power Station

2002. Lighthouses.
4717 **1080** 80f. (1) black and green 15 10
4718 – 80f. (2) black and ochre 15 10
4719 – 80f. (3) black and grey 15 10
4720 – 80f. (4) black, brown and orange 15 10
4721 – 80f. (5) black and red 15 10
DESIGNS: 80f. (2) Jianxin pagoda lighthouse; 80f. (3) Huaniaoshan; 80f. (4) Laotieshan; 80f. (5) Lin'gao.

2002. Hydro-electric Power Generation and Water Control on the Yellow River. Multicoloured.
4722 80f. (1) Type **1081** 15 10
4723 80f. (2) Liujia Gorge Hydro-electric Power Station . . 15 10
4724 80f. (3) Qingtong Gorge dam 15 10
4725 80f. (4) Sanmen Gorge dam 15 10
MS4726 115 × 96 mm 8y. Xiaolangdi dam (39 × 59 mm) . . . . . . 1·25 1·25

2002. Stone Carvings, Dazu County, Sichuan Province. Multicoloured.
4727 80f. (1) Type **1082** 15 10
4728 80f. (2) Samantabhadra riding elephant, North Mountain 15 10
4729 80f. (3) Three Avatamasaka Sages, Holy Summit Mountain 15 10
4730 80f. (4) Man wearing headdress (statue), Cave of the Three Emperors, Stone Gate Mountain . . 15 10
MS4731 130 × 96 mm 8y. "Avalokitesvara of a Thousand Hands" (39 × 59 mm) . . . . 1·25 1·25

1083 *Ammopiptanthus mongolicus*

2002. Desert Plants. Multicoloured.
4732 80f. (1) Type **1083** 15 10
4733 80f. (2) *Calligonum rubicundum* 15 10
4734 80f. (3) *Hedysarum scoparium* 15 10
4735 2y. (4) *Tamarix leptostachys* 30 15

1084 Emperor Penguins

2002. Antarctica. Multicoloured.
4736 80f. Type **1084** 10 10
4737 80f. Aurora Australis . . . 10 10
4738 2y. Grove mountain, scientists and snowy sheathbill 25 15

1085 Shepherd on Horse-back, Sheep and Lakeside

2002. Qinghai Lake. Multicoloured.
4739 80f. Type **1085** 10 10
4740 80f. Bird island 10 10
4741 2y.80 Lake and mountain 35 20

1086 Huang Gonglue

1087 Bian Que

2002. Early 20th-century Generals. Multicoloured.
4742 80f. (1) Type **1086** 10 10
4743 80f. (2) Xu Jishen 10 10
4744 80f. (3) Cai Shengxi 10 10
4745 80f. (4) Wei Baqun 10 10
4746 80f. (5) Liu Zhidan 10 10

2002. Early Chinese Scientists.
4747 **1087** 80f. (1) grey and black 10 10
4748 – 80f. (2) grey and black 10 10
4749 – 80f. (3) grey and black 10 10
4750 – 80f. (4) stone and black 10 10
DESIGNS: 80f. (1) Type **1087**; 80f. (2) Lui Hui; 80f. (3) Su Song; 80f. (4) Song Yingxing.

1088 Xianshengmen Gate

1089 Large Family Gathering

2002. Yandang Mountain. Multicoloured.
4751 80f. (1) Type **1088** 10 10
4752 80f. (2) Dalongqiu waterfall and pond 10 10
4753 80f. (3) Beidou cave (horiz) 10 10
4754 80f. (4) Guanyin peak (horiz) 10 10

2002. Mid-autumn Festival. Multicoloured.
4755 80f. (1) Type **1089** 10 10
4756 80f. (2) Food and couple with daughter 10 10
4757 2y. (3) Courting couple with birds perched on knees . . 25 15

1090 Peng Zhen

1091 Bojnice Castle

2002. Birth Centenary of Peng Zhen (revolutionary leader).
4758 **1090** 80f. brown, cinnamon and black 10 10
4759 – 80f. sepia, cinnamon and black 10 10
DESIGNS: 80f. Type **1090**; 80f. In army uniform.

2002. Castles. Multicoloured.
4760 80f. Type **1091** 10 10
4761 80f. Congtai Pavilion, Handan 10 10
Nos. 4760/1 were issued together, *se-tenant*, forming a composite design.
Stamps of a similar design were issued by Slovakia.

1092 Immortal Maiden moved by Dong's Filial Love

1093 Flowers

2002. Tale of Dong Yong and the Seventh Immortal Maiden. Multicoloured.
4762 80f. (1) Type **1092** 10 10
4763 80f. (2) Seventh immortal maiden marrying Dong Yong 10 10
4764 80f. (3) Maiden weaving brocade to buy Dong Yong's freedom 10 10
4765 80f. (4) Everlasting love . . 10 10
4766 2y. (5) Maiden returned to Heaven leaving Dong Yong behind 25 15

2002. Greetings Stamp. Paper with fluorescent fibres
4767 **1093** 80f. multicoloured . . . 10 10

1094 Waterfalls on the Yellow River

2002. Hukou Waterfalls. Sheet 131 × 90 mm.
MS4768 **1094** 8y. multicoloured 1·10 65

1095 Shanxi History Museum

2002. Museums. Multicoloured.
4769 80f. (1) Type **1095** 10 10
4770 80f. (2) Shanghai 10 10
4771 80f. (3) Henan 10 10
4772 80f. (4) Tibet 10 10
4773 80f. (5) Tianjin Natural History museum 10 10

1096 Kung Fu

2002. Martial Arts. Multicoloured.
4774 80f. (1) Type **1096** 10 10
4775 80f. (2) Tae Kwon Do . . . 10 10

1097 White-handed Gibbon (*Hylobates lar*)

1098 Goat

2002. Gibbons. Multicoloured.
4776 80f. (1) Type **1097** 10 10
4777 80f. (2) White-cheeked gibbon (*Hylobates leucogenys*) 10 10
4778 80f. (3) Black gibbon (*Hylobates concolor*) . . . 10 10
4779 2y. (4) Hoolock gibbon (*Hylobates hoolock*) . . . 10 10

2003. New Year. Year of the Goat. Multicoloured.
4780 80f. Type **1098** 10 10
4781 2y.80 Chinese character for goat 35 20

1099 "Five Boys wrestling for a Lotus"

2003. Yangliuqing New Year Pictures (woodcut prints). Multicoloured.
4782 80f. (1) Type **1099** 10 10
4783 80f. (2) "Zhong Kui" (vert) 10 10
4784 80f. (3) "Stealing the Herb of Immortality" 10 10
4785 2y. (4) "Wealth in a Jade Hall" (vert) 10 10

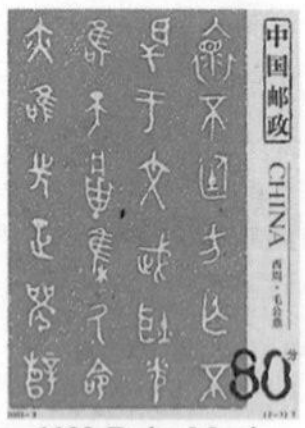

1100 Duke Mao's Tripod (Western Zhou dynasty)

1101 Knot

2003. Calligraphy. Seal Characters. Multicoloured.
4786 80f. Type **1100** 10 10
4787 80f. Carvings of Mount Tai (Qin dynasty) 10 10

2003. Greetings Stamp. Chinese Decorative Knot.
4788 **1101** 80f. multicoloured . . . 10 10

1102 Lily (*Lilium taliense*)

2003. Greetings Stamps. Lilies. Multicoloured.
4789 60f. (1) Type **1102** 10 10
4790 80f. (2) *Lilium lanongense* 10 10
4791 80f. (3) *Lilium distichum* . . 10 10
4792 2y. (4) *Lilium lophophorum* 25 10
MS4793 140 × 95 mm. 8y. *Lilium leucanthum* (76 × 54 mm) . . . 1·00 1·00

1103 Maple Bridge, Suzhou, Jiangsu Province

2003. Ancient Bridges. Multicoloured.
4794 80f. (1) Type **1103** 10 10
4795 80f. (2) Xiaoshang bridge, Linying, Henan province 10 10
4796 80f. (3) Lugouqiao bridge, Beijing 10 10
4797 80f. (4) Double Dragon bridge, Jianshui, Yunnan province 10 10

1104 Bell Tower, Xi'an

2003. Buildings. Multicoloured.
4798 80f. Type **1104** 10 10
4799 80f. Mosque, Isfahan . . . 10 10
Stamps of the same design were issued by Iran.

1105 Giant Buddha (statue, Lingyun mountain, Leshan province)

2003. UNESCO World Heritage Sites. Sheet 145 × 90 mm.
MS4800 **1105** 8y. multicoloured 1·00 1·00

1106 Eight Diagram Buildings, Gulangyu Island

2003. Gulangyu Island, Fujian Province. Multicoloured.
4801 80f. Type **1106** 10 10
4802 80f. Sunlight rock 10 10
4803 2y. Shuzhuang park 25 10
MS4804 180 × 80 mm. Nos. 4801/3 45 45
Nos. 4801/3 were issued together, *se-tenant*, forming a composite design of the island.

2003. Classical Literature. Strange Stories from a Chinese Studio by Pu Songling (3rd series). As T **1043**. Multicoloured.
4805 10f. (1) "Xiang Yu" 10 10
4806 30f. (2) "Tiger of Zhaocheng" 10 10
4807 60f. (3) "Tian Qilang" 10 10
4808 80f. (4) "Ah Xiu" 10 10
4809 1y.50 (5) "Wang Gui'an" 20 10
4810 2y. (6) "Goddess" 25 10
MS4811 144 × 85 mm. 8y. "Princess of the Dongting Lake" (90 × 60 mm) 1·00 1·00

1107 "SARS" overprinted with Stop Sign

1109 Late Spring Cottage

1108 Meteorites descending

2003. Campaign to Control Severe Acute Respiratory Syndrome (SARS).
4812 **1107** 80f. multicoloured 10 10

2003. Meteorite Shower over Jilin Province, (8 March 1976). Multicoloured.
4813 80f. Type **1108** 10 10
4814 80f. Dispersal 10 10
4815 2y. Meteorite No. 1 (largest ever found) 25 10

2003. Master-of-Nets Garden, Suzhou. Multicoloured.
4816 80f. (1) Type **1109** 10 10
4817 80f. (2) Pavilion Greeting the Moon and Breeze 10 10
4818 80f. (3) Veranda of Bamboo 10 10
4819 2y. (4) Hall of Ten Thousand Volumes 25 10
Nos. 4816/19 were issued together, *se-tenant*, forming a composite design.

1110 Antelopes

2003. Endangered Species. Tibetan Antelope (Pantholops hodgsoni). Multicoloured.
4820 80f. Type **1110** 10 10
4821 2y. Female and fawn 25 10

1111 Huangcheng (town)

2003. Kongtong Mountain, Gansu Province. Multicoloured.
4822 80f. (1) Type **1111** 10 10
4823 80f. (2) Playing the Zither Gorge 10 10
4824 80f. (3) Pagoda Courtyard 10 10
4825 2y. (4) Thunder Peak 25 10
Nos. 4822/5 were issued together, *se-tenant*, forming a composite design.

1112 Junk (sailing ship)

1114 Ruyi Maid

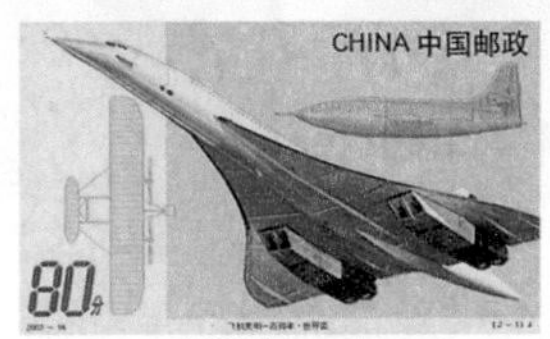

1113 Concorde

2003. Greetings Stamp. "Plain Sailing".
4826 **1112** 80f. multicoloured 10 10

2003. Centenary of Powered Flight.
4827 80f. Type **1113** 10 10
4828 2y. Chinese aircraft 25 10

2003. Painted Statues, Jinci Temple, Shanxi Province. Multicoloured.
4829 80f. (1) Type **1114** 10 10
4830 80f. (2) Maid holding towel 10 10
4831 80f. (3) Maid carrying seal 10 10
4832 2y. (4) Maid smiling 25 10

1115 Dam and Reservoir

2003. Three Gorges Hydroelectric Project on Yangtze River. Multicoloured.
4833 80f. (1) Type **1115** 10 10
4834 80f. (2) Navigation locks 10 10
4835 2y. (3) Electricity pylons 25 10

MILITARY POST STAMPS

M **225**

M **892** Armed Forces

1953.
M1593 M **225** $800 yellow, red and orange 85·00 40·00
M1594 $800 yellow, red and purple £500
M1595 $800 yellow, red and blue £28000

Nos. M1593/5 were issued for the use of the Army, Air Force and Navy respectively.

1995. No gum.
M3998 M **892** 20f. multicoloured 10 10

POSTAGE DUE STAMPS

D **192**

D **233**

1950.
D1459 D **192** $100 blue 10 85
D1460 $200 blue 10 85
D1461 $500 blue 10 1·00
D4462 $800 blue 11·00 30
D1463 $1,000 blue 10 50
D1464 $2,000 blue 10 75
D1465 $5,000 blue 10 80
D1466 $8,000 blue 15 1·50
D1467 $10,000 blue 15 2·50

1954.
D1628 D **233** $100 red 80 25
D1629 $200 red 50 25
D1630 $500 red 40 25
D1631 $800 red 25 25
D1632 $1,600 red 25 25

CHINA—TAIWAN (FORMOSA)

A. CHINESE PROVINCE

The island of Taiwan was ceded by China to Japan in 1895 and was returned to China in 1945 after the defeat of Japan. From 1949 Taiwan was controlled by the remnants of the Nationalist Government under Chiang Kai-shek.

1945. 100 sen = 1 yen.
1947. 100 cents = 1 yuan (C.N.C.).

中華民國 臺灣省

(1) "Taiwan Province, Chinese Republic"

1945. Optd as Type **1**. (a) On stamps as Nos. J1/3 of Japanese Taiwan. Imperf.
1 J **1** 3s. red 1·00 4·50
2 5s. green 1·00 75
3 10s. blue 1·00 75
4 30s. blue 5·00 4·50
5 40s. purple 5·00 3·25
6 50s. grey 4·00 2·25
7 1y. green 5·00 2·25
(b) On stamps of Japan. Imperf.
8 **87** 5y. olive (No. 424) 9·00 7·50
9 **88** 10y. purple (No. 334) 15·00 12·00

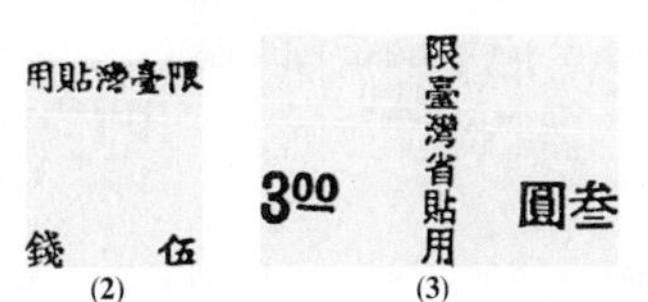

(2) (3)

1946. Stamps of China surch as T **2** with two to four characters in lower line denoting value.
10 – 2s. on 2c. blue (No. 509) 10 1·25
11 – 5s. on 5c. orange (No. 513) 10 50
12 **60** 10s. on 4c. lilac 10 60
13 – 30s. on 15c. pur (No. 517) 10 75
19 **107** 50s. on $20 red 10 1·00
16 **58** 65s. on $20 green 30 1·00
15 – $1 on 20c. blue (No. 519) 15 1·00
17 **58** $1 on $30 brown 30 85
65 **60** $2 on 2½c. red 40 75
18 **58** $2 on $50 orange 50 80
20 **107** $3 on $100 red 10 75
77 **103** $5 on $40 orange 30 90
78 **107** $5 on $50 violet 40 45
79 $5 on $70 orange 10 1·00
80 $5 on $100 red 40 25
21 $5 on $200 green 10 60
67 **82** $10 on $3 yellow 2·00 1·50
82 **118** $10 on $150 blue 50 65
22 **107** $10 on $500 green 10 40
66 **72** $20 on 2c. green 40 75
71 **89** $20 on $3 red 1·50 1·00
83 **118** $20 on $250 violet 25 50
23 **107** $20 on $700 brown 20 50
68 **82** $50 on 50c. green 1·25 85
24 **107** $50 on $1,000 red 85 60
72 **89** $100 on $20 pink 40 25
73 **94** $100 on $20 red £500
25 **107** $100 on $3,000 blue 1·00 70
74 **94** $200 on $10 blue 2·10 75
70 **72** $500 on $30 purple 8·00 2·25
81 **107** $600 on $100 red 7·50 1·25
69 **82** $800 on $4 brown 6·00 2·50
85 **118** $1,000 on $20,000 red 3·25 1·50
75 **94** $5,000 on $10 blue 5·25 2·25
76 $10,000 on $20 red 5·25 1·75
84 **118** $200,000 on $3,000 blue £425 14·00

1946. Opening of National Assembly, Nanking. Issue of China surch as Type **3**.
26 **111** 70s. on $20 green 1·50 2·25
27 $1 on $30 blue 1·50 2·25
28 $2 on $50 brown 1·50 2·25
29 $3 on $100 red 1·50 2·25

4 President Chiang Kai-shek (note characters to right of head)

5 Entrance to Dr. Sun Yat-sen Mausoleum (note characters above face value)

1947. President's 60th Birthday.
30 **4** 70s. red 1·50 2·00
31 $1 green 1·50 2·00
32 $2 red 1·50 2·00
33 $3 green 1·50 2·00
34 $7 orange 1·50 2·00
35 $10 red 1·50 2·00

1947. 1st Anniv of Return of Government to Nanking.
36 **5** 50s. green 2·00 2·75
37 $3 blue 2·00 2·75
38 $7.50 red 2·00 2·75
39 $10 brown 2·00 2·75
40 $20 purple 2·00 2·75
For other stamps as Types **4** and **5**, but with different Chinese characters, see N.E. Provinces Types **7** and **9**.

1947. No gum.
41 **169** $1 brown 30 1·50
42 $2 brown 40 1·25
43 $3 green 40 75
44 $5 orange 40 60
45 $9 blue 1·50 2·50
46 $10 red 30 75
47 $20 green 30 50
59 $25 green 50 35
48 $50 purple 40 35
49 $100 blue 40 35
50 $200 brown 40 35
60 $5,000 orange 5·50 85
61 $10,000 green 5·50 2·25
62 $20,000 brown 5·50 2·25
63 $30,000 blue 5·50 1·00
64 $40,000 brown 4·50 80

6 Sun Yat-sen and Palms

改作伍佰圓 500^{00}

(7)

1948. "Re-valuation" surcharges. Surch as T **7**.
51 **6** $25 on $100 blue 1·00 1·75
52 $300 on $3 green 75 45
53 $500 on $7.50 orange 2·75 1·50
54 $1,000 on 30c. grey 7·00 3·75
55 $1,000 on $3 green 1·25 35
56 $2,000 on $3 green 90 45
57 $3,000 on $3 green 7·00 1·75
58 $3,000 on $7.50 orange 65·00 3·00

1949. No value indicated. Stamps of China optd with five Chinese characters, similar to top line of T **2**.
86 **146** (–) Orange (Ord. postage) 3·50 75
87 **147** (–) Green (Air Mail) 4·00 95
88 **148** (–) Mauve (Express) 4·00 1·10
89 **149** (–) Red (Registration) 4·00 1·10

PARCELS POST STAMPS

1948. As Type P **112** of China, with six Chinese characters in the sky above the lorry.
P65 $100 green – 50
P66 $300 red – 50
P67 $500 olive – 50
P68 $1,000 black – 50
P69 $3,000 purple – 50
Parcels Post stamps were not on sale in unused condition.

POSTAGE DUE STAMPS

D **7**

(D **8**)

(D **9**)

1948.
D51 D **7** $1 blue 2·10 3·00
D52 $3 blue 2·10 3·25
D53 $5 blue 2·10 3·00

D54 $10 blue . . . . 2·10 3·25
D55 $20 blue . . . . 2·10 3·00

1949. "Re-valuation" surcharges. Surch as Type D **8**.
D65 D **7** $50 on $1 blue . . . . . 5·00 3·50
D66 $100 on $3 blue . . . . 5·00 2·50
D67 $300 on $5 blue . . . . 5·00 2·00
D68 $500 on $10 blue . . . . 5·00 2·00

1949. Handstamped with Type D **9**.
D86 **6** $1,000 on $3 green (No. 55) 42·00 8·00
D87 $3,000 on $3 green (No. 57) 27·00 17·00
D88 $5,000 orange (No. 60) . . 45·00 22·00

B. CHINESE NATIONALIST REPUBLIC

1949. 100 cents = 1 silver yuan (or New Taiwan Yuan).

Silver Yuan Surcharges.

(8) Small figures **(9)** Large figures

1949. Stamps of Taiwan Province surch. (a) With T **8**.
90 **6** 10c. on $50 purple . . . . . 32·00 4·50

(b) As T **9** (figures at right).
91 **6** 2c. on $30,000 blue . . . . . 32·00 11·00
92 10c. on $40,000 brown . . . 70·00 11·00

(10) **(11)**

1949. Stamps of North Eastern Provinces (Manchuria), surch as T **10**.
93 **5** 2c. on $44 red . . . . £100 9·00
95 5c. on $44 red . . . . £100 3·00
96 10c. on $44 red . . . . £120 1·90
97 20c. on $44 red £160 20
98 30c. on $44 red . . . . £200 7·50
99 50c. on $44 red . . . . £240 5·00

1950. Surch as T **11** on stamp of China but with no indication of value.
100 **169** $1 on (–) green . . . . . £160 14·00
101 $2 on (–) green . . . . . £160 13·00
102 $5 on (–) green . . . . . £1200 55·00
103 $10 on (–) green . . . . . £1500 50·00
104 $20 on (–) green £3250 £400

1950. Stamps of China surch. (a) As T **8** (figure "5" at left).
105 **118** 5c. on $200,000 purple . . 4·50 2·25

(b) As T **9** (figures at left).
106 **118** 3c. on $30,000 brown . . 3·75 4·00
107 3c. on $40,000 green . . 3·75 3·75
108 3c. on $50,000 blue . . . 4·50 4·50
108a 10c. on $4,000 grey . . . 8·00 6·00
109 10c. on $6,000 purple . . 13·50 6·75
110 10c. on $20,000 red . . 13·50 6·75
110a 10c. on $2,000,000 orge 13·50 6·75
110b 20c. on $500,000 mauve 32·00 10·00
110c 20c. on $1,000,000 red 42·00 7·00
110d 30c. on $3,000,000 bistre 50·00 10·00
110e 50c. on $5,000,000 blue 95·00 10·50

> **GUM.** All the following stamps to No. 616 were issued without gum except where otherwise stated.

12 Koxinga

1950. Rouletted. (a) Postage.
111 **12** 3c. grey . . . . 2·00 1·00
112 10c. brown . . . . 2·00 10
113 15c. yellow . . . . 18·00 2·50
114 20c. green . . . . 2·00 10
115 30c. red . . . . 40·00 9·00
116 40c. orange . . . . 4·75 10
117 50c. brown . . . . 9·50 10
118 80c. red . . . . 4·75 3·00
119 $1 violet . . . . 16·00 20
120 $1.50 green . . . . 65·00 8·00
121 $1.60 blue . . . . 80·00 75
122 $2 mauve . . . . 19·00 75
123 $5 turquoise . . . . . . 95·00 4·00

(b) Air. With character at each side of head.
124 **12** 60c. blue . . . . 12·00 7·50

13 Peasant and Ballot Box **15** Peasant and Scroll

1951. Division of Country into Self-governing Districts. Perf or imperf.
125 **13** 40c. red . . . . 22·00 10
126 $1 blue . . . . 38·00 90
127 $1.60 purple . . . . . . 50·00 75
128 $2 brown . . . . £100 8·50

1951. Silver Yuan surcharges. As T **169** of China but without value, surch as T **14**.
129 $5 on (–) green . . . . . 42·00 7·00
130 $10 on (–) green . . . . . £180 5·00
131 $20 on (–) green . . . . . £400 25·00
132 $50 on (–) green . . . . . £500 75·00

1952. Land Tax Reduction. Perf or imperf.
133 **15** 20c. orange . . . . 35·00 50
134 40c. green . . . . 48·00 30
135 $1 brown . . . . 75·00 4·00
136 $1.40 blue . . . . £150 2·00
137 $2 grey . . . . £225 38·00
138 $5 red . . . . £375 5·00

16 President and Rejoicing crowds **(17)**

1952. 2nd Anniv of Re-election of Pres. Chiang Kai-shek. Flag in red and blue. Eight characters in scroll. Perf or imperf.
139 **16** 40c. red . . . . 9·50 30
140 $1 green . . . . 29·00 2·00
141 $1.60 orange . . . . . . 50·00 1·50
142 $2 blue . . . . £110 38·00
143 $5 purple . . . . £140 2·00
See also Nos. 151/6.

1952. Stamps of China surch. with T **17**.
144 **145** 3c. on 4c. grn (No. 1350) 4·00 2·50
145 3c. on 10c. lilac (No. 1351) . . . . . . 7·50 3·75
146 3c. on 20c. bl (No. 1353) 4·00 2·00
147 3c. on 50c. brown (No. 1354) . . . . . . 12·00 7·50

(18) **(19)**

1953. T **169** of China, but without value, surch as T **18**.
148 $10 on (–) green . . . . . . £140 12·00
149 $20 on (–) green . . . . . . £425 24·00
150 $50 on (–) green £1400 £600

1953. 3rd Anniv of Re-election of Pres. Chiang Kai-shek. As T **16** but eleven characters in scroll. Flag in red and blue. Perf or imperf.
151 10c. orange . . . . 22·00 2·00
152 20c. green . . . . 22·00 2·00
153 40c. red . . . . 22·00 1·00
154 $1.40 blue . . . . 45·00 4·00
155 $2 sepia . . . . £100 6·00
156 $5 purple . . . . £170 15·00

1953. Surch as T **19**.
157 **12** 3c. on $1 violet . . . . . 85 1·00
158 10c. on 15c. yellow . . . . 10·00 1·00
159 10c. on 30c. red . . . . . 2·75 50
160 20c. on $1.60 blue . . . . 2·75 30

20 Doctor, Nurses and Patients **21** Pres. Chiang Kai-shek

1953. Establishment of Anti-tuberculosis Assn. Cross of Lorraine in red. On paper with coloured network.
161 **20** 40c. brown on stone . . . 4·25 20
162 $1.60 blue on turquoise . . 20·00 1·00
163 $2 green on yellow . . . . 32·00 85
164 $5 red on flesh . . . . . . 80·00 13·50

1953.
165 **21** 10c. brown . . . . 1·60 10
166 20c. purple . . . . 1·50 10
167 40c. green . . . . 1·50 10
168 50c. purple . . . . 4·00 10
169 80c. brown . . . . 11·00 4·00
170 $1 green . . . . 6·00 10
171 $1.40 blue . . . . 8·00 60
172 $1.60 red . . . . 8·00 10
173 $1.70 green . . . . 14·00 7·50
174 $2 brown . . . . 8·00 10
175 $3 blue . . . . £140 14·00
176 $4 turquoise . . . . . . 12·00 1·50
177 $5 red . . . . 8·00 50
178 $10 green . . . . 14·00 4·00
179 $20 purple . . . . 48·00 6·00

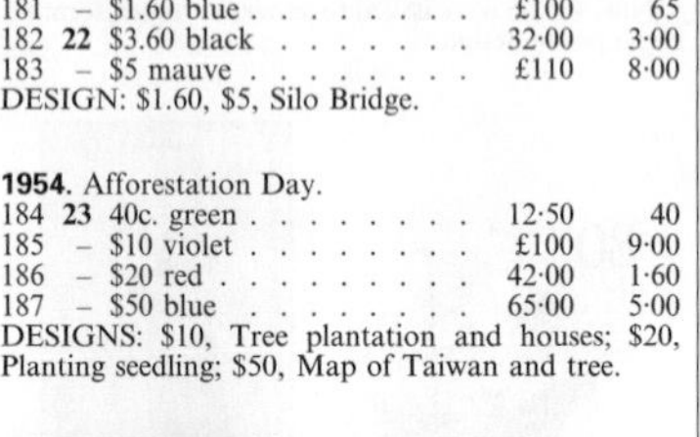
22 Silo Bridge over River Cho-Shui-Chi **23** Sapling, Tree and Plantation

1954. Completion of Silo Bridge. Various frames.
180 **22** 40c. red . . . . 7·00 30
181 – $1.60 blue £100 65
182 **22** $3.60 black . . . . 32·00 3·00
183 – $5 mauve . . . . £110 8·00
DESIGN: $1.60, $5, Silo Bridge.

1954. Afforestation Day.
184 **23** 40c. green . . . . 12·50 40
185 – $10 violet . . . . £100 9·00
186 – $20 red . . . . 42·00 1·60
187 – $50 blue . . . . 65·00 5·00
DESIGNS: $10, Tree plantation and houses; $20, Planting seedling; $50, Map of Taiwan and tree.

24 Runner

25 Douglas DC-6 over City Gate, Taipeh

1954. Youth Day.
188 **24** 40c. blue . . . . 14·00 60
189 $5 red . . . . 50·00 7·50

1954. Air. 15th Anniv of Air Force Day.
190 **25** $1 brown . . . . 20·00 60
191 – $1.60 black . . . . 10·00 10
192 – $5 blue . . . . 20·00 60
DESIGNS: $1.60, Republic F-84G Thunderjets over Chung Shang Bridge, Taipeh. $5, Doves over Chi Kan Lee (Fort Zeelandia) in Tainan City.

26 Refugees crossing Pontoon Bridge

27 Junk and Bridge

1954. Relief Fund for Chinese Refugees from North Vietnam.
193 **26** 40c.+10c. blue . . . . . . 14·50 1·50
194 $1.60+40c. purple . . . . 45·00 20·00
195 $5+$1 red £100 £100

1954. 2nd Anniv of Overseas Chinese League.
196 **27** 40c. orange . . . . 20·00 10
197 $5 blue . . . . 10·00 1·75

28 "Chainbreaker"

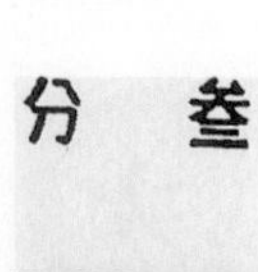
(29)

1955. Freedom Day.
198 **28** 40c. green . . . . 4·00 10
199 – $1 olive . . . . 15·00 3·00
200 – $1.60 red . . . . 11·00 1·50
DESIGNS: $1, Soldier with torch and flag; $1.60, Torch and figures "1.23".

1955. Surch. as T **29**.
201 **12** 3c. on $1 violet . . . . . . 4·50 1·25
202 20c. on 40c. orange . . . . 4·50 15

31 Pres. Chiang Kai-shek and Sun Yat-sen Memorial Building

1955. 1st Anniv of President Chiang Kai-shek's Second Re-election.
203 **31** 20c. olive . . . . 3·25 10
204 40c. green . . . . 3·25 10
205 $2 red . . . . 8·50 40
206 $7 blue . . . . 14·50 65

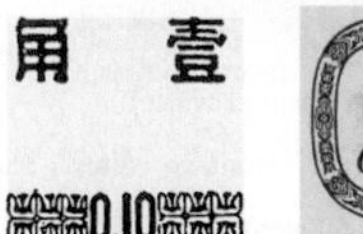
(32) **33** Air Force Badge

1955. Nos. 116/18, 120 and 124 surch as T **32**. Nos. 212/14 have additional floral ornament below two characters at top.
207 **12** 10c. on 80c. red . . . . . 4·50 40
208 10c. on $1.50 green . . . . 4·50 75
212 20c. on 40c. orange . . . . 5·00 10
213 20c. on 50c. brown . . . . 5·50 10
214 20c. on 60c. blue . . . . . 7·50 1·75

1955. Armed Forces' Day.
209 **33** 40c. blue . . . . 5·00 10
210 $2 red . . . . 19·00 1·00
211 $7 green . . . . 16·00 70

35 Flags of U.N. and Taiwan

36 Pres. Chiang Kai-shek

1955. 10th Anniv of U.N.O.
215 **35** 40c. blue . . . . 3·00 10
216 $2 red . . . . 7·50 75
217 $7 green . . . . 7·50 1·75

1955. President's 69th Birthday. With gum.
218 **36** 40c. brown, blue and red 6·00 30
219 $2 blue, green and red . . 11·00 1·25
220 $7 green, brown and red 22·00 3·25

37 Sun Yat-sen's Birthplace

(38)

1955. 90th Birth Anniv (1956) of Dr. Sun Yat-sen.
221 **37** 40c. blue . . . . 4·00 30
222 $2 brown . . . . 8·00 1·00
223 $7 red . . . . 10·50 1·75

1956. Nos. 1213 and 1211 of China surch as T **38**.
232 **148** 3c. on (–) mauve 75 40
224 **146** 20c. on (–) orange I . . . 2·25 10
304 20c. on (–) orange II . . 1·75 10
On No. 232 the characters are smaller and there are leaves on either side of the "3".
(I) Surch with Type **38**. (II) The characters are below the figures.

39 Old and Modern Postal Transport

40 Children at Play

1956. 60th Anniv of Postal Service.
225 **39** 40c. red . . . . 2·00 15
226 $1 blue . . . . 4·00 1·60
227 $1.60 brown . . . . 6·00 1·10
228 $2 green . . . . 10·00 2·00

1956. Children's Day.
229 **40** 40c. green . . . . 1·25 20
230 $1.60 blue . . . . 2·75 40
231 $2 red . . . . 6·00 1·00

42 Earliest and Latest Steam Locomotives

43 Pres. Chiang Kai-shek

1956. 75th Anniv of Chinese Railways.
233 **42** 40c. red 5·00 25
234 $2 blue 6·50 55
235 $8 green 10·00 2·00

1956. 70th Birthday of President Chiang Kai-shek. Various portraits of President. With gum.
236 **43** 20c. orange 3·00 10
237 – 40c. red 3·00 10
238 – $1 blue 8·00 20
239 – $1.60 purple 10·00 10
240 – $2 brown 18·00 20
241 – $8 turquoise 42·00 50
SIZES—21½ × 30 mm: 20c., 40c.; 26½ × 26½ mm: $1, $1.60; 30 × 21½ mm: $2, $8.

(44) **(45)** **46** Telecommunications Symbols

1956. No. 1212 of China surch with T **44**.
242 **147** 3c. on (–) green 75 15

1956. No. 1214 of China surch with T **45**.
243 **149** 10c. on (–) red 75 15

1956. 75th Anniv of Chinese Telegraph Service.
244 **46** 40c. blue 1·00 10
245 $1.40 red 2·00 10
246 $1.60 green 3·00 10
247 $2 brown 7·00 20

47 Map of China

48 Mencius with his Mother

1957. (a) Printed in one colour.
248 **47** 3c. blue 20 10
249 10c. violet 1·50 15
250 20c. orange 1·50 10
251 40c. red 1·50 10
252 $1 brown 3·00 10
253 $1.60 green 6·00 15

(b) With frames in blue.
268 **47** 3c. blue 10 10
269 10c. violet 50 10
270 20c. orange 60 10
271 40c. red 2·00 10
272 $1 brown 3·75 20
273 $1.60 green 4·50 10

1957. Mothers' Teaching.
254 **48** 40c. green 3·00 10
255 – $3 brown 4·00 50
DESIGN: $3, Marshal Yueh Fei with his mother.

49 Chinese Scout Badges and Rosettes

1957. 50th Anniv of Boy Scout Movement, Jubilee Jamboree and Birth Centenary of Lord Baden-Powell (Founder).
256 **49** 40c. violet 50 10
257 $1 green 1·75 15
258 $1.60 blue 2·00 10

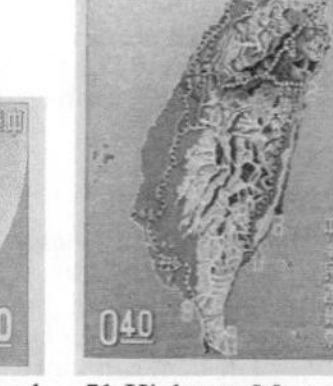

50 Globe, Radio Mast and Microphone

51 Highway Map of Taiwan

1957. 30th Anniv of Chinese Broadcasting Service.
259 **50** 40c. salmon 30 10
260 50c. mauve 75 15
261 $3.50 blue 1·75 30

1957. 1st Anniv of Taiwan Cross-Island Highway Project.
262 **51** 40c. green 2·50 10
263 $1.40 blue 6·25 50
264 $2 sepia 7·25 50

52 Freighter "Hai Min" and River Vessel "Kiang Foo"

53 "Batocera lineolata" (longhorn beetle)

1957. 85th Anniv of China Merchants' Steam Navigation Co.
265 **52** 40c. blue 80 10
266 80c. purple 2·00 25
267 $2.80 red 3·00 40

1958. Insects. Multicoloured. With gum.
274 10c. Type **53** 80 25
275 40c. "Papilio maraho" (butterfly) 1·00 10
276 $1 Atlas moth 1·75 20
277 $1.40 "Erasmia pulchella" (moth) 4·00 40
278 $1.60 "Cheirotonus macleayi" (beetle) 5·00 20
279 $2 Great mormon (butterfly) 6·00 60

54 "Phalaenopsis amabilis"

1958. Taiwan Orchids. Orchids in natural colours; backgrounds in colours given. With gum.
280 **54** 20c. brown 1·75 10
281 – 40c. violet 1·75 10
282 – $1.40 purple 3·75 20
283 – $3 blue 6·00 35
ORCHIDS—VERT: 40c. "Laeliacattleya"; $1.40, "Cycnoches chlorochilon klotzsch". HORIZ: $3, "Dendrobium phalaenopsis".

55 W.H.O. Emblem

56 Presidential Mansion, Taipeh

1958. 10th Anniv of W.H.O.
284 **55** 40c. blue 20 10
285 $1.60 red 70 15
286 $2 purple 1·10 20

1958.
290a **56** $5 green 8·00 10
290b $5.60 violet 8·00 30
290c $6 orange 8·00 10
290d $10 green 7·50 10
290e $20 red 13·50 10
289 $50 brown 60·00 8·00
290 $100 blue £120 10·00

58 Ploughman

1958. 10th Anniv of Joint Commission on Chinese Rural Reconstruction.
291 **58** 20c. green 60 10
292 40c. black 75 10
293 $1.40 purple 2·25 10
294 $3 blue 3·75 30

59 President Chiang Kai-shek Reviewing Troops

1958. 72nd Birthday of President Chiang Kai-shek and National Day Review. With gum.
295 **59** 40c. multicoloured 1·25 10

60 U.N.E.S.C.O. Headquarters, Paris

61 Flame of Freedom encircling Globe

1958. Inaug of U.N.E.S.C.O. Headquarters.
296 **60** 20c. blue 30 10
297 40c. green 80 10
298 $1.40 red 80 10
299 $3 purple 1·25 25

1958. 10th Anniv of Declaration of Human Rights.
300 **61** 40c. green 35 10
301 60c. sepia 35 10
302 $1 red 80 10
303 $3 blue 1·10 25

1958. No. 192 surch **350**.
305 $3.50 on $5 blue 7·00 2·00

64 The Constitution

65 Chu Kwang Tower, Quemoy

1958. 10th Anniv of Constitution.
306 **64** 40c. green 1·10 10
307 50c. purple 1·25 10
308 $1.40 red 4·00 10
309 $3.50 blue 4·00 30

1959.
310 **65** 3c. orange 10 10
311 5c. olive 50 10
312 10c. lilac 10 10
313 20c. blue 10 10
314 40c. brown 10 10
315 50c. turquoise 80 10
316 $1 red 80 10
317 $1.40 green 3·00 10
318 $2 myrtle 3·00 10
319 $2.80 mauve 9·00 60
320 $3 slate 5·00 10
See also Nos. 367/82f.

66 Slaty-backed Gull

67 I.L.O. Emblem and Headquarters, Geneva

1959. Air. With gum.
321 **66** $8 black, blue and green 5·50 50

1959. 40th Anniv of I.L.O.
322 **67** 40c. blue 60 10
323 $1.60 brown 65 10
324 $3 green 75 10
325 $5 red 80 25

68 Scout Bugler

1959. 10th World Scout Jamboree, Manila.
326 **68** 40c. red 65 10
327 50c. blue 1·50 30
328 $5 green 3·00 75

69 Inscribed Rock on Mt. Tai-wu, Quemoy

1959. Defence of Quemoy (Kinmen) and Matsu Islands, 1958.
329 **69** 40c. brown 40 10
330 – $1.40 blue 1·00 15
331 – $2 green 2·00 50
332 **69** $3 blue 3·00 50
DESIGN—(41 × 23½ mm): $1.40, $2, Map of Taiwan, Quemoy and Matsu Islands.

70

1959. International Correspondence Week.
333 **70** 40c. blue 85 10
334 $1 red 85 15
335 $2 sepia 85 10
336 $3.50 red 1·25 30

71 National Science Hall

72 Confederation Emblem

1959. Inauguration of Taiwan National Science Hall. With gum.
337 **71** 40c. multicoloured 1·50 10
338 – $3 mult (different view) 2·75 35

1959. 10th Anniv of International Confederation of Free Trade Unions.
339 **72** 40c. green 1·10 10
340 $1.60 purple 1·25 10
341 $3 orange 1·50 20

73 Sun Yat-sen and Abraham Lincoln

74 "Bomb Burst" by Thunder Tiger Aerobatic Squadron

1959. 150th Birth Anniv of Lincoln. With gum.
342 **73** 40c. multicoloured 30 10
343 $3 multicoloured 50 25

1960. Air. Chinese Air Force Commem. With gum.
344 **74** $1 multicoloured 7·00 75
345 – $2 multicoloured 6·00 30
346 – $5 multicoloured 8·00 1·10
DESIGNS—HORIZ: (Various aerobatics): $2, Loop; $5, Diamond formation flying over jet fighter.

75 Night Delivery

76 "Uprooted Tree"

1960. Introduction of "Prompt Delivery" and "Postal Launch" Services.
347 **75** $1.40 purple . . . . 1·75 30
348 $1.60 blue "Yu-Khi" (postal launch) . . . . . 1·75 50

1960. World Refugee Year. With gum.
349 **76** 40c. green, brown & black 30 10
350 $3 green, orange & black 40 25

77 Cross-Island Highway

79 Winged Tape-reel

1960. Inaug of Taiwan Cross-Island Highway.
351 **77** 40c. green 60 10
352 – $1 blue . . . . 3·00 20
353 – $2 purple . . . . 1·75 15
354 **77** $3 brown . . . . 3·00 25
DESIGN—VERT: $1, $2, Tunnels on the Highway.

1960. Visit of Pres. Eisenhower. Nos. 331/2 optd **WELCOME U.S. PRESIDENT DWIGHT D. EISENHOWER 1960** in English and Chinese.
355 – $2 green . . . . 1·75 1·00
356 **69** $3 blue . . . . 2·00 1·00

1960. Phonopost (tape-recordings) Service.
357 **79** $2 red . . . . 1·75 20

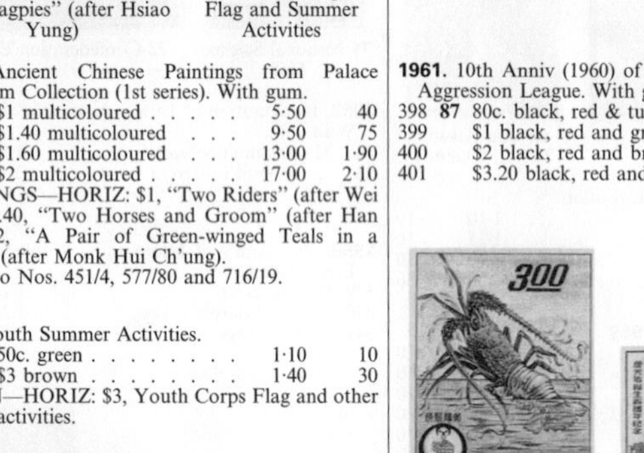

80 "Flowers and Red-billed Blue Magpies" (after Hsiao Yung)

81 Youth Corps Flag and Summer Activities

1960. Ancient Chinese Paintings from Palace Museum Collection (1st series). With gum.
358 – $1 multicoloured . . . . 5·50 40
359 – $1.40 multicoloured . . . 9·50 75
360 **80** $1.60 multicoloured . . . 13·00 1·90
361 – $2 multicoloured . . . . 17·00 2·10
PAINTINGS—HORIZ: $1, "Two Riders" (after Wei Yen). $1.40, "Two Horses and Groom" (after Han Kan). $2, "A Pair of Green-winged Teals in a Rivulet" (after Monk Hui Ch'ung).
See also Nos. 451/4, 577/80 and 716/19.

1960. Youth Summer Activities.
362 **81** 50c. green . . . . 1·10 10
363 – $3 brown . . . . 1·40 30
DESIGN—HORIZ: $3, Youth Corps Flag and other summer activities.

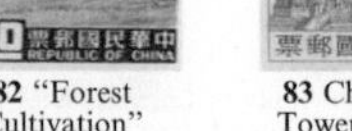

82 "Forest Cultivation"

83 Chu Kwang Tower, Quemoy

1960. 5th World Forestry Congress, Seattle. Multicoloured. With gum.
364 $1 Type **82** . . . . 2·50 10
365 $2 "Forest Protection" (trees and sika deer) . . . . . . 3·75 65
366 $3 "Lumber Production" (cable railway) . . . . . . 4·50 30

1960. As T **65** but redrawn.
367 **83** 3c. brown 10 10
382 10c. green . . . . 1·25 15
368 40c. violet 10 10
369 50c. orange 25 10
370 60c. purple 15 10
371 80c. green 10 10
372 $1 green . . . . 2·00 10
373 $1.20 green . . . . 1·00 10
374 $1.50 blue . . . . 1·25 10
375 $2 red 90 10
376 $2.50 blue 90 15
377 $3 green . . . . 1·50 10
378 $3.20 brown . . . . 5·00 10
379 $3.60 blue . . . . 4·00 20
382f $4 green . . . . 6·00 15
380 $4.50 red . . . . 5·00 30

84 Diving

85 Bronze Wine Vase (Shang Dynasty)

1960. Sports. With gum.
383 **84** 50c. brown, yellow & blue 60 10
384 – 80c. violet, yellow & purple 60 10
385 – $2 multicoloured . . . . . 1·40 10
386 – $2.50 black and orange . . 1·60 25
387 – $3 multicoloured . . . . . 2·50 35
388 – $3.20 multicoloured . . . 3·75 40
DESIGNS: 80c. Discus-throwing; $2, Basketball; $2.50, Football; $3, Hurdling; $3.20, Sprinting.

1961. Ancient Chinese Art Treasures (1st series). With gum.
389 **85** 80c. multicoloured . . . . 1·75 10
390 – $1 indigo, blue and red . . 3·50 20
391 – $1.20 blue, brown & yellow 3·50 25
392 – $1.50 brown, blue & mauve 4·00 70
393 – $2 brown, violet and green 4·00 40
394 – $2.50 black, lilac and blue 5·00 60
DESIGNS: $1, Bronze cauldron (Chou); $1.20, Porcelain vase (Sung); $1.50, Jade perforated tube (Chou); $2, Porcelain jug (Ming); $2.50, Jade flower vase (Ming).
See also Nos. 408/13 and 429/34.

86 Farmer and Mechanical Plough

87 Mme. Chiang Kai-shek

1961. Agricultural Census.
395 **86** 80c. purple 60 10
396 $2 green . . . . 3·00 75
397 $3.20 red . . . . 4·50 50

1961. 10th Anniv (1960) of Chinese Women's Anti-Aggression League. With gum.
398 **87** 80c. black, red & turquoise 1·00 10
399 $1 black, red and green . . 2·75 15
400 $2 black, red and brown 2·75 15
401 $3.20 black, red and purple 4·50 1·10

88 Taiwan Lobster

89 Jeme Tien-yao and Locomotive

1961. Mail Order Service.
402 **88** $3 myrtle . . . . 5·50 75

1961. Birth Centenary of Jeme Tien-yao (railway engineer).
403 – 80c. violet . . . . 2·00 15
404 **89** $2 black . . . . 5·00 60
DESIGN: 80c. As Type **89** but locomotive heading right.

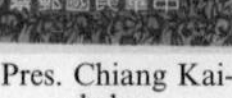

90 Pres. Chiang Kai-shek

91 Convair 880 Jetliner ("The Mandarin Jet"), Biplane and Flag

1961. 1st Anniv of Chiang Kai-shek's Third Term Inauguration. With gum.
405 – 80c. multicoloured . . . . 1·25 10
406 **90** $2 multicoloured . . . . . 5·75 1·00
DESIGN—HORIZ: 80c. Map of China inscr (in Chinese) "Recovery of the Mainland".

1961. 40th Anniv of Chinese Civil Air Service. With gum.
407 **91** $10 multicoloured . . . . 5·50 30

1961. Ancient Chinese Art Treasures (2nd issue). As T **85**. With gum.
408 80c. multicoloured . . . . . 2·00 10
409 $1 blue, brown and bistre . . 4·00 20
410 $1.50 blue and salmon . . . 6·25 75
411 $2 red, black and blue . . . 9·25 25
412 $4 blue, sepia and red . . . 11·00 45
413 $4.50 brown, sepia and blue 11·00 1·75
DESIGNS—VERT: 80c. Palace perfumer (Ching); $1, Corn vase (Warring States); $2, Jade tankard (Sung). HORIZ: $1.50, Bronze bowl (Chou); $4, Porcelain bowl (Southern Sung); $4.50, Jade chimera (Han).

92 Sun Yat-sen and Chiang Kai-shek

93 Lotus Lake

1961. 50th National Day. With gum.
414 **92** 80c. brown, blue and grey 1·50 10
415 – $5 multicoloured . . . . . 4·50 1·00
DESIGN—HORIZ: $5, Map and flag.

1961. Taiwan Scenery. Multicoloured. With gum.
416 80c. Pitan (Green Lake) (vert) 6·75 10
417 $1 Type **93** . . . . 11·00 50
418 $2 Sun-Moon Lake . . . . . 13·00 30
419 $3.20 Wulai Waterfall (vert) 17·00 75

94 Steel Furnace

95 Atomic Reactor, National Tsing Hwa University

1961. Taiwan Industries. With gum.
420 – 80c. indigo, brown & blue 1·75 10
421 **94** $1.50 multicoloured . . . 3·00 60
422 – $2.50 multicoloured . . . 4·75 55
423 – $3.20 indigo, brown & blue 7·00 50
DESIGNS—VERT: 80c. Oil refinery. $2.50, Aluminium manufacture. HORIZ: $3.20, Fertilizer plant.

1961. 1st Taiwan Atomic Reactor Inauguration. Multicoloured. With gum.
424 80c. Type **95** . . . . 1·10 10
425 $2 Interior of reactor . . . . 4·00 1·00
426 $3.20 Reactor building (horiz) 4·50 75

96 Telegraph Wires and Microwave Reflector Pylons

97 Postal Segregating, Facing and Cancelling Machine

1961. 80th Anniv of Chinese Telecommunications. Multicoloured. With gum.
427 80c. Type **96** . . . . 1·00 10
428 $3.20 Microwave parabolic antenna (horiz) . . . . . 2·75 70

1962. Ancient Chinese Art Treasures (3rd issue). As T **85**. With gum.
429 80c. brown, violet and red . . 7·00 10
430 $1 purple, brown and blue 9·50 15
431 $2.40 blue, brown and red . . 24·00 40
432 $3 multicoloured . . . . . 60·00 1·50
433 $3.20 red, green and blue . . 65·00 15
434 $3.60 multicoloured . . . . 60·00 1·50
DESIGNS—VERT: 80c. Jade topaz twin wine vessel (Chiang). $1, Bronze pouring vase (Warring States). $2.40, Porcelain vase (Ming). $3, Tsun bronze wine vase (Shang). $3.20, Porcelain jar (Ching). $3.60, Jade perforated disc (Han).

1962.
435 **97** 80c. purple . . . . 1·60 10

98 Mt. Yu Weather Station

99 Distribution of Milk and U.N. Emblem

1962. World Meteorological Day.
436 **98** 80c. brown 75 10
437 – $1 blue . . . . 1·50 40
438 – $2 green . . . . 1·75 75
DESIGNS—HORIZ: $1, Route-map of Typhoon Pamela. VERT: $2, Weather balloon passing globe.

1962. 15th Anniv of U.N.I.C.E.F.
439 **99** 80c. red 40 10
440 $3.20 green . . . . 1·75 60

100 Campaign Emblem

101 Yu Yu-jen (journalist)

1962. Malaria Eradication. With gum.
441 **100** 80c. red, green and blue 1·10 10
442 $3.60 brown, grn & dp brn . . . . 1·60 25

1962. "Elder Reporter" Yu Yu-jen Commemoration. With gum.
443 **101** 80c. sepia and pink . . . 1·60 25

102 Koxinga

103 Co-operative Emblem

1962. Tercentenary of Koxinga's Recovery of Taiwan. With gum.
444 **102** 80c. purple . . . . 3·25 10
445 $2 green . . . . 6·00 35

1962. 40th International Co-operative Day.
446 **103** 80c. brown 75 10
447 – $2 lilac . . . . 2·00 35
DESIGN: $2, Global handclasp.

104 U.N.E.S.C.O. Symbols

105 Emperor T'ai Tsu (Ming Dynasty)

1962. U.N.E.S.C.O. Activities Commem.
448 **104** 80c. mauve 50 10
449 – $2 lake . . . . 1·50 35
450 – $3.20 green . . . . . . 1·50 25
DESIGNS—HORIZ: $2, U.N.E.S.C.O. emblem on open book. $3.20, Emblem linking hemispheres.

1962. Ancient Chinese Paintings from Palace Museum Collection (2nd series). Emperors. Multicoloured. With gum.
451 80c. T'ai Tsung (Tang) . . . 12·50 10
452 $2 T'ai Tsu (Sung) . . . . . 42·00 4·75
453 $3.20 Genghis Khan (Yuan) 55·00 5·00
454 $4 Type **105** . . . . 60·00 9·25

106 "Lions" Emblem and Activities
107 Pole Vaulting

1962. 45th Anniv of Lions International With gum.
455 **106** 80c. multicoloured . . . . 1·50 10
456 $3.60 multicoloured . . . 2·50 60

1962. Sports. With gum.
457 **107** 80c. brown, black & blue 1·25 10
458 $3.20 multicoloured . . . . 3·00 40
DESIGN—HORIZ: $3.20, Rifle shooting.

108 Young Farmers

109 Liner

1962. 10th Anniv of Chinese 4-H Clubs.
459 **108** 80c. red . . . . 1·00 10
460 – $3.20 green . . . . 1·75 30
DESIGN: $3.20, 4-H Clubs emblem.

1962. 90th Anniv of China Merchants' Steam Navigation Co. Multicoloured. With gum.
461 80c. Type **109** . . . . 1·75 10
462 $3.60 Freighter "Hai Min" and Pacific route-map (horiz) . . . . 4·50 70

110 Harvesting

111 Youth, Girl, Torch and Martyrs Monument, Huang Hua Kang

1963. Freedom from Hunger. With gum.
463 **110** $10 multicoloured . . . . 4·50 1·00

1963. 20th Youth Day.
464 **111** 80c. purple 75 10
465 $3.20 green . . . . 2·00 60

112 Barn Swallows and Pagoda

113 Refugee in Tears

1963. 1st Anniv of Asian-Oceanic Postal Union. With gum. Multicoloured.
466 80c. Type **112** . . . . 5·00 30
467 $2 Northern gannet . . . . 6·00 1·00
468 $6 Manchurian crane and pine tree (vert) . . . . . . 14·00 3·75

1963. Refugees' Flight from Mainland.
469 **113** 80c. black . . . . 1·50 10
470 – $3.20 red . . . . 3·00 40
DESIGN—HORIZ: $3.20, Refugees on march.

114 Convair 880 over Tropic of Cancer Monument, Kiai

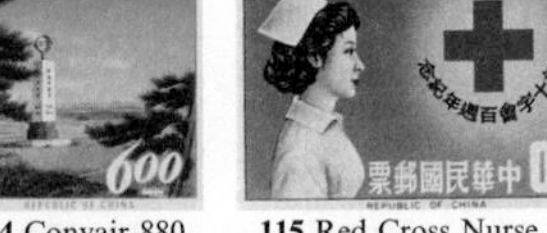

115 Red Cross Nurse and Emblem

1963. Air. Multicoloured. With gum.
471 $2.50 Suspension Bridge, Pitan (horiz) . . . . 6·00 30
472 $6 Type **114** . . . . 10·00 1·00
473 $10 Lion-head Mountain, Sinchu . . . . 14·00 2·00

1963. Red Cross Centenary. With gum.
474 **115** 80c. red and black . . . . 3·50 30
475 – $10 red, green and blue 12·00 2·50
DESIGN: $10, Globe and scroll.

116 Basketball

117 Freedom Torch

1963. 2nd Asian Basketball Championships, Taipeh.
476 **116** 80c. mauve . . . . 1·00 10
477 – $2 violet . . . . 2·00 60
DESIGN: $2, Hands reaching for inscribed ball.

1963. 15th Anniv of Declaration of Human Rights.
478 **117** 80c. green 60 10
479 – $3.20 red . . . . 1·25 20
DESIGN—HORIZ: $3.20, Human figures and scales of justice.

118 Country Scene

119 Dr. Sun Yat-sen and his Book "Three Principles of the People"

1963. "Good-People, Good-Deeds" Campaign. Multicoloured. With gum.
480 40c. Type **118** . . . . 3·00 10
481 $4.50 Lighting candle . . . . 7·00 1·00

1983. 10th Anniv of Land-to-Tillers Programme. With gum.
482 **119** $5 multicoloured . . . . 12·00 1·00

120 Torch of Liberty

121 Broadleaf Cactus

1964. 10th Anniv of Liberty Day.
483 **120** 80c. orange 50 10
484 – $3.20 blue . . . . 2·00 50
DESIGN—VERT: $3.20, Hands with broken manacles.

1964. Taiwan Cacti. Multicoloured. With gum.
485 80c. Type **121** . . . . 1·25 10
486 $1 Crab cactus . . . . 7·00 60
487 $3.20 Nopalxochia . . . . . 5·00 30
488 $5 Grizzly-Bear cactus . . . 12·00 1·00

122 Wu Chih-hwei (politician)

123 Chu Kwang Tower, Quemoy

1964. 99th Birth Anniv of Wu Chih-hwei (politician).
489 **122** 80c. brown . . . . 1·75 10

1964.

490	**123**	3c. purple	10	10
491		5c. green	10	10
492		10c. green	40	10
493		20c. green	15	10
494		40c. red	15	10
495		50c. purple	40	10
496		80c. orange	60	10
497		$1 violet	30	10
498		$1.50 purple	10·00	50
499		$2 purple	1·25	10
500		$2.50 blue	1·40	10
501		$3 grey	2·00	10
502		$3.20 blue	2·00	10
504		$4 green	3·00	10

124 Nurse and Florence Nightingale

125 Weir

1964. Nurses Day.
506 – 80c. violet . . . . 1·60 10
507 **124** $4 red . . . . 4·25 40
DESIGN—HORIZ: 80c. Nurses holding candlelight ceremony.

1964. Inaug of Shihmen Reservoir. With gum. Mult.
508 80c. Type **125** . . . . 3·00 10
509 $1 Irrigation channel . . . . 4·00 10
510 $3.20 Dam and powerhouse 8·50 10
511 $5 Main spillway . . . . . . 12·50 3·00

126 Ancient Ship and Modern Freighter

127 Bananas

1964. Navigation Day.
512 **126** $2 orange . . . . 1·00 10
513 $3.60 green . . . . 3·00 50

1964. Taiwan Fruits. Multicoloured. With gum.
514 80c. Type **127** . . . . 7·00 20
515 $1 Oranges . . . . 14·00 1·50
516 $3.20 Pineapples . . . . . . 23·00 70
517 $4 Water-melons . . . . . . 35·00 2·00

128 Lockheed Starfighters, "Tai Ho", "Tai Choa" and "Tai Tsung" (destroyers) and Artillery

129 Globe and Flags of Formosa and U.S.A.

1964. Armed Forces Day.
518 **128** 80c. blue . . . . 1·00 10
519 $6 purple . . . . 3·50 75

1964. New York World's Fair (1st issue). With gum.
520 **129** 80c. multicoloured . . . . 5·00 30
521 – $5 multicoloured . . . . 7·00 75
DESIGN—HORIZ: $5, Taiwan Pavilion at Fair.
See also Nos. 550/1.

130 Cowman holding Calf

131 Cycling

1964. Animal Protection.
522 **130** $2 purple . . . . 1·00 60
523 $4 blue . . . . 5·25 1·25

1964. Olympic Games, Tokyo.
524 **131** 80c. blue 75 10
525 – $1 red . . . . 1·75 10
526 – $3.20 green . . . . 2·50 10
527 – $10 violet . . . . 3·75 1·25
DESIGNS: $1, Runner breasting tape; $3.20, Gymnastics; $10, High jumping.

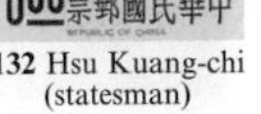

132 Hsu Kuang-chi (statesman)

133 Factory-bench ("Pharmaceutics")

1964. Famous Chinese.
528 **132** 80c. blue . . . . 2·50 10

See also Nos. 558/9, 586/7, 599, 606/9, 610, 738/40, 960 and 1072/7.

1964. Taiwan Industries. Multicoloured. With gum.
529 40c. Type **133** . . . . . . 2·50 20
530 $1.50 Loom ("Textiles") (horiz) . . . . 4·50 1·75
531 $2 Refinery ("Chemicals") . . 7·00 20
532 $3.60 Cement-mixer ("Cement") (horiz) . . . . 9·50 1·25

134 Dr. Sun Yat-sen (founder)

135 Mrs. Eleanor Roosevelt and "Human Rights" Emblem

1964. 70th Anniv of Kuomintang.
533 **134** 80c. green . . . . 2·50 10
534 $3.60 purple . . . . . . 5·50 60

1964. 16th Anniv of Declaration of Human Rights.
535 **135** $10 brown and violet . . 2·25 45

136 Law Code and Scales of Justice

137 Rotary Emblem and Mainspring

1965. 20th Judicial Day.
536 **136** 80c. red . . . . 1·00 10
537 $3.20 green . . . . 2·00 20

1965. 60th Anniv of Rotary International.
538 **137** $1.50 red 60 10
539 $2 green 60 10
540 $2.50 blue . . . . 2·00 25

138 "Double Carp"

139 Mme. Chiang Kai-shek

1965.

541	**138**	$5 violet	4·00	10
542		$5.60 blue	5·50	70
543		$6 brown	5·50	10
544		$10 mauve	27·00	10
545		$20 red	38·00	1·50
546		$50 green	38·00	1·50
547		$100 red	55·00	2·40

See also Nos. 695/698ab.

1965. 15th Anniv of Chinese Women's Anti-Aggression League. With gum.
548 **139** $2 multicoloured . . . . 15·00 70
549 $6 multicoloured . . . . 26·00 6·00

140 Unisphere and Taiwan Pavilion, N.Y. Fair

1965. New York World's Fair (2nd issue). Multicoloured. With gum.
550 $2 Type **140** . . . . 8·00 40
551 $10 Peacock and various birds ("100 birds paying tribute to Queen Phoenix") 32·00 3·00

141 I.T.U. Emblem and Symbols

1965. Centenary of I.T.U. Multicoloured. With gum.
552 80c. Type **141** . . . . 1·10 10
553 $5 I.T.U. emblem and symbols (vert) . . . . . . 2·75 50

142 Madai Seabream **143** I.C.Y. Emblem

1965. Taiwan Fishes. Mult. With gum.
554 40c. Type **142** . . . . 3·00 30
555 80c. Silver pomfret . . . . 5·00 30
556 $2 Skipjack tuna (vert) . . . 7·50 75
557 $4 Moonfish . . . . 12·50 1·00

1965. Famous Chinese. Portraits as T **132**.
558 $1 red (Confucius) . . . . . 4·75 10
559 $3.60 blue (Mencius) . . . . 6·00 50

1965. Int Co-operation Year. Mult. With gum.
560 $2 Type **143** . . . . 3·00 10
561 $6 I.C.Y. emblem (horiz) . . 3·00 80

144 Road Crossing **145** Dr. Sun Yat-sen

1965. Road Safety.
562 **144** $1 purple . . . . 1·40 10
563 $4 red . . . . 2·50 50

1965. Birth Centenary of Dr. Sun Yat-sen. Multicoloured. With gum.
564 $1 Type **145** . . . . 4·00 15
565 $4 As T **145** but with portrait, etc., on right . . . . 8·00 40
566 $5 Dr. Sun Yat-sen and flags (horiz) . . . . 14·00 1·00

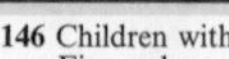
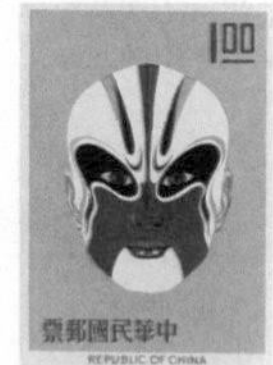

146 Children with Firework **147** Lien Po, "Marshal and Prime Minister Reconciled"

1965. Chinese Folklore (1st Series). Multicoloured. With gum.
567 $1 Type **146** . . . . 7·50 70
568 $4.50 Dragon dance . . . . 7·50 2·40
See also Nos. 581/3 and 617.

1966. Painted Faces of Chinese Opera. Multicoloured. With gum.
569 $1 Type **147** . . . . 16·00 40
570 $3 Kuan Yu, "Reunion at Ku City" . . . . 16·00 75
571 $4 Chang Fei, "Long Board Slope" . . . . 16·00 90
572 $6 Buddha, "The Flower-scattering Angel" . . . . . 32·00 3·00

148 Pigeon holding Postal Emblem **149** "Fishing on a Snowy Day" (After artist of the "Five Dynasties")

1966. 70th Anniv of Chinese Postal Services. Multicoloured. With gum.
573 $1 Type **148** . . . . 2·50 10
574 $2 Postman by Chu memorial stone (horiz) . . . . . 3·50 10
575 $3 Postal Museum (horiz) . . 3·50 45
576 $4 "Postman climbing" . . . 7·00 1·50

1966. Ancient Chinese Paintings from Palace Museum Collection (3rd series). With gum. Multicoloured.
577 $2.50 Type **149** . . . . . . 7·00 70
578 $3.50 "Calves on the Plain" 10·50 70
579 $4.50 "Snowscape" . . . . . 16·00 1·75
580 $5 "Magpies" (after Lin Ch'un) . . . . 20·00 1·75
Nos. 578/9 both after Sung artists.

1966. Chinese Folklore (2nd series). As T **146**. With gum. Multicoloured.
581 $2.50 Dragon boat racing (horiz) . . . . 17·00 70
582 $4 "Lady Chang O Flying to the Moon" (horiz) . . . . 8·00 10
583 $6 Lion Dance . . . . 3·00 15

150 Flags of Argentine and Chinese Republics **151** Lin Sen

1966. 150th Anniv of Argentine Republic's Independence. With gum.
584 **150** $10 multicoloured . . . . 3·00 50

1966. Birth Centenary of Lin Sen (statesman).
585 **151** $1 sepia . . . . 2·10 10

1966. Famous Chinese. Portraits as T **132**.
586 $2.50 sepia . . . . 4·50 10
587 $3.50 red . . . . 5·50 15
PORTRAITS: $2.50, General Yueh Fei. $3.50, Wen Tien-hsiang (statesman).

153 Bean Geese **154** Pres. Chiang Kai-shek

1966.
588 **153** $3.50 brown . . . . . . 1·25 25
589 $4 red 75 10
590 $4.50 green . . . . 2·00 15
591 $5 purple 75 10
592 $5.50 green . . . . 1·25 20
593 $6 blue . . . . 6·00 1·75
594 $6.50 violet . . . . 1·75 30
595 $7 black . . . . 1·25 10
596 $8 red . . . . 1·75 10

1966. President Chiang Kai-shek's re-election for 4th Term. With gum. Multicoloured.
597 $1 Type **154** . . . . 2·10 10
598 $5 President in Uniform . . . 4·50 50

1966. Famous Chinese. Portrait as T **132**.
599 $1 blue (Tsai Yuan-Pei, scholar) . . . . 2·50 10

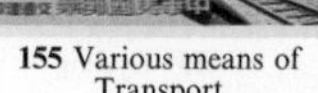

155 Various means of Transport **156** Boeing 727-100 over Chilin Pavilion, Grand Hotel, Taipeh

1967. Development of Taiwan Communications. Multicoloured. With gum.
600 $1 Mobile postman and microwave station (vert) . . 1·25 10
601 $5 Type **155** . . . . 2·50 30

1967. Air. Multicoloured. With gum.
602 $5 Type **156** . . . . 5·00 10
603 $8 Boeing 727-100 over Palace Museum, Taipeh . . 5·00 50

157 Pres. Chiang Kai-shek **158** "God of Happiness" (wood carving)

1967. Chiang Kai-shek's 4th Presidential Term. With gum.
604 **157** $1 multicoloured . . . . 2·00 10
605 $4 multicoloured . . . . 2·00 50

1967. Famous Chinese. Poets. Portraits. As T **132**.
606 $1 black (Chu Yuan) . . . . 2·75 20
607 $2 brown (Li Po) . . . . . 4·25 50
608 $2.50 brown (Tu Fu) . . . . 5·50 50
609 $3 green (Po Chu-i) . . . . 6·00 50

1967. Famous Chinese. Portrait as T **132**.
610 $1 black (Chiu Ching, female revolutionary) . . . . . . 4·00 10

1967. Chinese Handicrafts. Multicoloured. With gum.
611 $1 Type **158** . . . . 3·25 10
612 $2.50 Vase and dish . . . . 4·25 15
613 $3 Chinese dolls . . . . . 5·50 30
614 $5 Palace lanterns . . . . . 9·00 75

159 "WACL" on World Map **160** Muller's Barbet

1967. 1st World Anti-Communist League Conference, Taipei.
615 **159** $1 red 40 10
616 $5 blue 75 15

GUM. From No. 617 all stamps were issued with gum unless otherwise stated.

1967. Chinese Folklore (3rd series). Stilts Pastime. As T **146**.
617 $4.50 multicoloured . . . . 1·75 15
DESIGN: "The Fisherman and the Wood-cutter" (Chinese play on stilts).

1967. Taiwan Birds. Multicoloured.
618 $1 Type **160** . . . . 3·50 15
619 $2 Maroon oriole (horiz) . . 8·50 35
620 $2.50 Japanese green pigeon (horiz) . . . . 11·00 60
621 $3 Formosan blue magpie (horiz) . . . . 11·00 60
622 $5 Crested serpent eagle . . . 13·00 1·00
623 $8 Mikado pheasant (horiz) 13·00 1·00

161 Chung Hsing Pagoda **162** Flags and China Park, Manila

1967. International Tourist Year. Multicoloured.
624 $1 Type **161** . . . . 1·75 10
625 $2.50 Yeh Liu National Park (coastal scene) (horiz) . . . 5·00 40
626 $4 Statue of Buddha (horiz) 5·50 40
627 $5 National Palace Museum, Taipei (horiz) . . . . . . 7·00 50

1967. China–Philippines Friendship.
628 **162** $1 multicoloured 50 10
629 $5 multicoloured . . . . 1·50 40

163 Chungshan Building, Yangmingshan **164** Taroko Gorge

1968.
630 **163** 5c. brown 10 10
631 10c. green 15 15
632 50c. purple 10 10
633 $1 red 15 10
634 $1.50 green . . . . . . 4·50 20
635 $2 purple . . . . 1·40 10
636 $2.50 blue . . . . 1·40 10
637 $3 blue . . . . 1·50 10
For redrawn design see Nos. 791/8.

1968. 17th Pacific Area Travel Association Conference, Taipei. Multicoloured.
638 $5 Type **164** . . . . 3·50 60
689 $8 Chungshan Building, Yangmingshan . . . . . . 2·75 60

165 Harvesting Sugar-cane **166** Vice-Pres. Cheng

1968. Sugar-cane Technologists Congress, Taiwan.
640 **165** $1 multicoloured . . . . 1·60 10
641 $4 multicoloured . . . . 3·25 50

1968. 3rd Death Anniv of Vice-Pres. Chen Cheng.
642 **166** $1 multicoloured . . . . 1·00 10

167 Bean Geese **168** Jade Cabbage (Ching Dynasty)

1968. 90th Anniv of Chinese Postage Stamps.
643 **167** $1 red . . . . 1·00 25

1968. Chinese Art Treasures, National Palace Museum (1st series). Multicoloured.
645 $1 Type **168** . . . . 1·50 10
646 $1.50 Jade battle-axe (Warring States period) . . 3·50 35
647 $2 Lung-ch'uan porcelain flower bowl (Sung dynasty) (horiz) . . . . 3·50 10
648 $2.50 Yung Cheng enamelled vase (Ching dynasty) . . . 4·00 50
649 $4 Agate "fingered" flower-holder (Ching dynasty) (horiz) . . . . 4·50 50
650 $5 Sacrificial vessel (Western Chou) . . . . 5·00 75
See also Nos. 682/7 and 732/7.

169 W.H.O. Emblem on "20" **170** Sun, Planets and "Rainfall"

1968. 20th Anniv of W.H.O.
651 **169** $1 green 30 10
652 $5 red 85 30

1968. International Hydrological Decade.
653 **170** $1 green and orange . . . 30 10
654 $4 blue and orange . . . 85 10

171 "A City of Cathay" (Section of hand-scroll painting)

1968. "A City of Cathay" (Scroll, Palace Museum) (1st series).
655 **171** $1 (1) multicoloured . . . 2·00 10
656 – $1 (2) multicoloured . . . 2·00 10
657 – $1 (3) multicoloured . . . 2·00 10
658 – $1 (4) multicoloured . . . 2·00 10
659 – $1 (5) multicoloured . . . 2·00 10
660 – $5 multicoloured . . . . 15·00 2·50
661 – $8 multicoloured . . . . 17·00 2·50
DESIGNS—As Type **171**: Nos. 655/9 together show panorama of the city ending with the palace. LARGER (61 × 32 mm). $5, City wall and gate; $8, Great bridge.

The five $1 stamps were issued together se-tenant in horiz strips, representing the last 11 feet of the 37 foot scroll, which is viewed from right to left as it is unrolled.

The stamps may be identified by the numbers given in brackets, which correspond to the numbers in the bottom right-hand corners of the stamps.

See also Nos. 699/703.

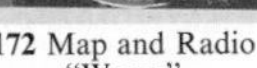

172 Map and Radio "Waves" **173** Human Rights Emblem

1968. 40th Anniv of Chinese Broadcasting Service.
662 **172** $1 grey, ultram & blue . . 40 10
663 – $4 red and blue . . . . . 1·00 10
DESIGN—VERT: $4, Stereo broadcast "waves".

1968. Human Rights Year.
664 **173** $1 multicoloured 40 10
665 $5 multicoloured . . . . 1·00 10

174 Harvesting Rice **175** Throwing the Javelin

1968. Rural Reconstruction.
666 **174** $1 brown, ochre & yellow 40 10
667 $5 bronze, green & yellow 1·00 30

1968. Olympic Games, Mexico. Multicoloured.
668 $1 Type **175** 50 10
669 $2.50 Weightlifting 75 10
670 $5 Pole-vaulting (horiz) . . . 1·00 20
671 $8 Hurdling (horiz) . . . . . 1·50 40

176 President Chiang Kai-shek and Main Gate, Whampoa Military Academy

1968. "President Chiang Kai-shek's Meritorious Services". Multicoloured.
672 $1 Type **176** 50 10
673 $2 Reviewing Northern Expedition Forces . . . . 1·25 20
674 $2.50 Suppression of bandits 4·00 60
675 $3.50 Marco Polo Bridge and Victory Parade, Nanking, 1945 . . . . 1·50 25
676 $4 Chinese Constitution . . . 1·75 25
677 $5 National flag . . . . . . 2·25 30
Each stamp bears the portrait of President Chiang Kai-shek as in Type **176**.

177 Cockerel **178** National Flag

1968. New Year Greetings. "Year of the Cock".
678 **177** $1 multicoloured . . . . 20·00 10
679 $4.50 multicoloured . . . 26·00 5·00

1968. 20th Anniv of Chinese Constitution.
680 **178** $1 multicoloured 75 10
681 $5 multicoloured . . . . 1·00 15

1969. Chinese Art Treasures, National Palace Museum (2nd series). Multicoloured as T **168**.
682 $1 Jade buckle (Ching dynasty) (horiz) 75 10
683 $1.50 Jade vase (Sung dynasty) . . . . 1·75 25
684 $2 Cloisonne enamel teapot (Ching dynasty) (horiz) . . 1·00 10
685 $2.50 Bronze sacrificial vessel (Kuei) (horiz) . . . . . . 1·75 40
686 $4 Hsuan-te "heavenly ball" vase (Ming dynasty) . . . 2·75 60
687 $5 "Gourd" vase (Ching dynasty) . . . . 4·00 60

179 Servicemen and Savings Emblem **180** Ti (flute)

1969. 10th Anniv of Forces' Savings Services.
688 **179** $1 brown 40 10
689 $4 blue . . . . 1·00 15

1969. Chinese Musical Instruments. Mult.
690 $1 Type **180** . . . . 1·00 10
691 $2.50 Sheng (pipes) . . . . . 1·50 15
692 $4 P'i-p'a (lute) . . . . . . 2·00 30
693 $5 Cheng (zither) . . . . . . 2·00 15

181 Chungshan Building, Yangmingshan **182** "Double Carp"

1969. 10th Kuomintang Congress.
694 **181** $1 multicoloured 55 10

1969.
695ab **182** $10 blue . . . . 2·50 10
695c $14 red . . . . 2·50 10
696ab $20 brown . . . . . . 2·50 10
697ab $50 green . . . . . . 5·00 15
698ab $100 red . . . . 6·50 35
Type **182** is a redrawn version of Type **138**.

1969. "A City of Cathay" (scroll) (2nd series). As T **171**. Multicoloured.
699 $1 "Musicians" . . . . . . 1·00 10
700 $1 "Bridal chair" . . . . . 1·00 10
701 $2.50 Emigrants with ox-cart 1·00 60
702 $5 "Scroll gallery" . . . . . 5·25 45
703 $8 "Roadside cafe" . . . . . 8·50 60
Nos. 699/70 form a composite picture of a bridal procession.

184 I.L.O. Emblem **185** "Food and Clothing"

1969. 50th Anniv of I.L.O.
704 **184** $1 blue 50 10
705 $8 red . . . . 1·00 20

1969. "Model Citizen's Life" Movement.
706 **185** $1 red 20 10
707 – $2.50 blue 70 15
708 – $4 green 70 15
DESIGNS: $2.50, "Housekeeping and Road Safety"; $4, "Schooling and Recreation".

186 Bean Geese over Mountains **187** Children and Symbols of Learning

1969. Air. Multicoloured.
709 $2.50 Type **186** . . . . . 4·25 75
710 $5 Bean geese over sea . . . 4·25 50
711 $8 Bean geese over land (horiz) . . . . 4·25 50

1969. 1st Anniv of Nine-year Free Education System.
712 **187** $1 red 30 10
713 – $2.50 green 50 15
714 – $4 blue . . . . 1·00 15
715 **187** $5 brown . . . . 1·25 20
DESIGNS—VERT: $2.50 and $4, Children and school.

188 "Flowers and Ring-necked Pheasants", Ming dynasty (Lu Chih) **189** "Charles Mallerin" Rose

1969. Ancient Chinese Paintings from Palace Museum Collection (4th series). "Birds and Flowers". Multicoloured.
716 $1 Type **188** . . . . 1·75 20
717 $2.50 "Bamboos and Ring-necked Pheasants" (Sung dynasty) . . . . 3·75 30
718 $5 "Flowers and Birds" (Sung dynasty) . . . . . 9·25 60
719 $8 "Twin Manchurian Cranes and Flowers" (G. Castiglione, Ching dynasty) . . . . 9·25 1·00

1969. Roses. Multicoloured.
720 $1 Type **189** . . . . 1·60 10
721 $2.50 "Golden Sceptre" . . . 2·50 20
722 $5 "Peace" . . . . 3·25 30
723 $8 "Josephine Bruce" . . . . 5·25 25

190 Launching Missile **191** A.P.U. Emblem

1969. 30th Air Defence Day.
724 **190** $1 purple 80 10

1969. 5th Asian Parliamentarians' Union General Assembly. Taipeh.
725 **191** $1 red 40 10
726 $5 green 75 15

192 Pekingese Dogs **193** Satellite and Earth Station

1969. New Year Greetings. "Year of the Dog".
727 **192** 50c. multicoloured . . . . 2·00 10
728 $4.50 multicoloured . . . 5·00 1·00

1969. Inauguration of Satellite Earth Station, Yangmingshan.
729 **193** $1 multicoloured 90 10
730 $5 multicoloured . . . . 1·90 30
731 $8 multicoloured . . . . 2·60 50

1970. Chinese Art Treasures, National Palace Museum (3rd series). As T **168**. Multicoloured.
732 $1 Lacquer vase (Ching dynasty) . . . . 1·00 10
733 $1.50 Agate grinding-stone (Ching dynasty) (horiz) . . 1·75 15
734 $2 Jade carving (Ching dynasty) (horiz) . . . . . 1·75 10
735 $2.50 "Shepherd and Ram" jade carving (Han dynasty) (horiz) . . . . 2·00 30
736 $4 Porcelain jar (Ching dynasty) . . . . 2·00 30
737 $5 "Bull" porcelain urn (Northern Sung dynasty) 4·25 60

1970. Famous Chinese. Portraits as T **132**.
738 $1 red . . . . 2·00 10
739 $2.50 green . . . . 1·90 15
740 $4 blue . . . . 2·00 35
PORTRAITS: $1, Hsuan Chuang (traveller). $2.50, Hua To (physician). $4, Chu Hsi (philosopher).

194 Taiwan Pavilion and EXPO Emblem **195** Chungshan Building, Yangmingshan

1970. World Fair "EXPO 70", Osaka, Japan. Multicoloured.
741 $5 Type **194** 40 15
742 $8 Pavilion encircled by national flags 90 40

1970.
743 **195** $1 red 50 20
For redrawn design see No. 1039.

196 Rain-cloud, Palm and Recording Apparatus **197** Martyrs' Shrine

1970. World Meteorological Day. Mult.
744 $1 Type **196** 50 10
745 $8 "Nimbus 3" satellite (horiz) . . . . 1·00 35

1970. Revolutionary Martyrs' Shrine. Mult.
746 $1 Type **197** 75 10
747 $8 Shrine gateway . . . . . 1·25 40

198 General Yueh Fei ("Loyalty")

1970. Chinese Opera. "The Virtues". Opera characters. Multicoloured.
748 $1 Type **198** 75 20
749 $2.50 Emperor Shun tortured by stepmother ("Filial Piety") . . . . 2·50 35
750 $5 Chin Liang-yu "The Lady General" ("Chastity") . . 4·00 35
751 $8 Kuan Yu and groom ("Fidelity") . . . . 5·00 50

199 Three Horses at Play

1970. "One Hundred Horses" (handscroll by Lang Shih-ning (G. Castiglione)). Multicoloured.
752 $1 (1) Horses on plain . . . 50 10
753 $1 (2) Horses on plain (different) 50 10
754 $1 (3) Horses playing 50 10
755 $1 (4) Horses on river bank 50 10
756 $1 (5) Horses crossing river 50 10
757 $5 Type **199** . . . . 5·00 75
758 $8 Groom roping horses . . 6·50 50

SERIAL NUMBERS. are indicated to aid identification of the above and certain other sets. For key to Chinese numerals see table at the beginning of CHINA.

200 Old Lai-tsu dropping Buckets **201** Chiang Kai-shek's Moon Message

1970. Chinese Folk-tales (1st series). Mult.
759 10c. Type **200** 20 10
760 10c. Yien-tsu disguised as a deer 20 10
761 10c. Hwang Hsiang with fan 20 10
762 10c. Wang Shiang fishing . . 25 10

763 10c. Chu Hsiu-chang reunited with mother 20 10
764 50c. Emperor Wen tasting mother's medicine 40 10
765 $1 Lu Chi dropping oranges 60 15
766 $1 Yang Hsiang fighting tiger 60 15
See also Nos. 817/24, 1000/7, 1064/7, 1210/13 and 1312/15.

1970. 1st Man on the Moon. Multicoloured.
767 $1 Type **201** 60 10
768 $5 "Apollo 11" astronauts (horiz) . . . . 1·00 30
769 $8 "First step on the Moon" 2·00 50

202 Productivity Symbol **203** Flags of Taiwan and United Nations

1970. Asian Productivity Year.
770 **202** $1 multicoloured 50 10
771 $5 multicoloured . . . . 1·00 35

1970. 25th Anniv of United Nations.
772 **203** $5 multicoloured . . . . 1·25 40

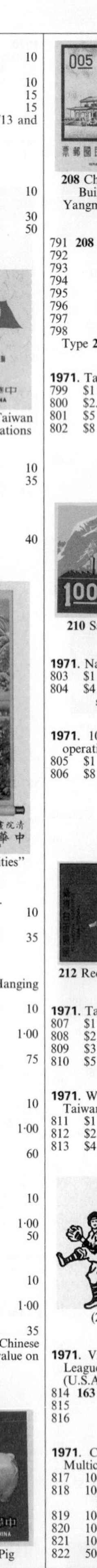

204 Postal Zone Map **205** "Cultural Activities" (10th month)

1970. Postal Zone Numbers Campaign. Mult.
773 $1 Type **204** 90 10
774 $2.50 Postal Zone emblem (horiz) . . . . 1·00 35

1970. "Occupations of the Twelve Months" Hanging Scrolls. Multicoloured. (a) "Winter".
775 $1 Type **205** . . . . 2·40 10
776 $2.50 "School Buildings" (11th month) . . . . . . 6·00 1·00
777 $5 "Games in the Snow" (12th month) . . . . . . 8·50 75

(b) "Spring".
778 $1 "Lantern Festival" (1st month) . . . . 2·75 10
779 $2.50 "Apricots in Blossom" (2nd month) . . . . . . 3·50 1·00
780 $5 "Purification Ceremony" (3rd month) . . . . 4·25 60

(c) "Summer".
781 $1 "Summer Shower" (4th month) . . . . 2·75 10
782 $2.50 "Dragon boat Festival" (5th month) . . . . 4·00 1·00
783 $5 "Lotus Pond" (6th month) 4·00 50

(d) "Autumn".
784 $1 "Weaver Festival" (7th month) . . . . 3·00 10
785 $2.50 "Moon Festival" (8th month) . . . . 4·25 1·00
786 $5 "Chrysanthemum Blossom" (9th month) . . 6·25 35
The month numbers are given by the Chinese characters in brackets, which follow the face value on the stamps.

206 "Planned Family" **207** Toy Pig

1970. Family Planning. Multicoloured.
787 $1 Type **206** 60 10
788 $4 "Family excursion" (vert) 1·25 35

1970. New Year Greetings. "Year of the Boar".
789 **207** 50c. multicoloured . . . . 2·25 30
790 $4.50 multicoloured . . . 3·00 1·00

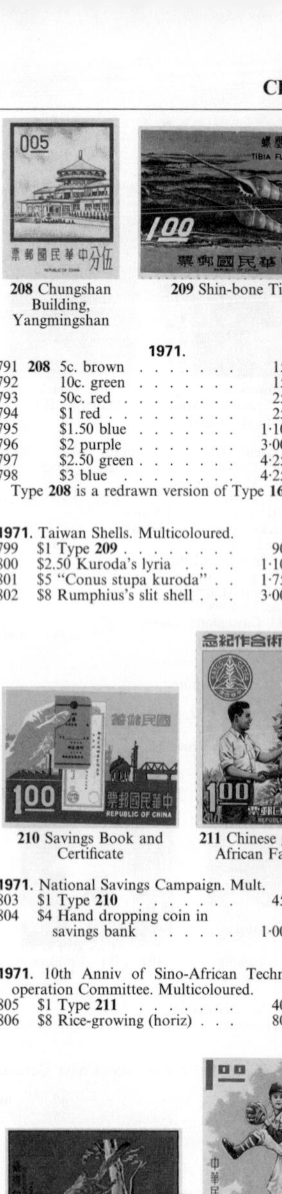

208 Chungshan Building, Yangmingshan **209** Shin-bone Tibia

1971.
791 **208** 5c. brown 15 10
792 10c. green 15 10
793 50c. red 25 10
794 $1 red 25 10
795 $1.50 blue . . . . . . 1·10 10
796 $2 purple . . . . . . 3·00 10
797 $2.50 green . . . . . . 4·25 10
798 $3 blue . . . . 4·25 10
Type **208** is a redrawn version of Type **163**.

1971. Taiwan Shells. Multicoloured.
799 $1 Type **209** 90 10
800 $2.50 Kuroda's lyria . . . . 1·10 30
801 $5 "Conus stupa kuroda" . . 1·75 50
802 $8 Rumphius's slit shell . . . 3·00 25

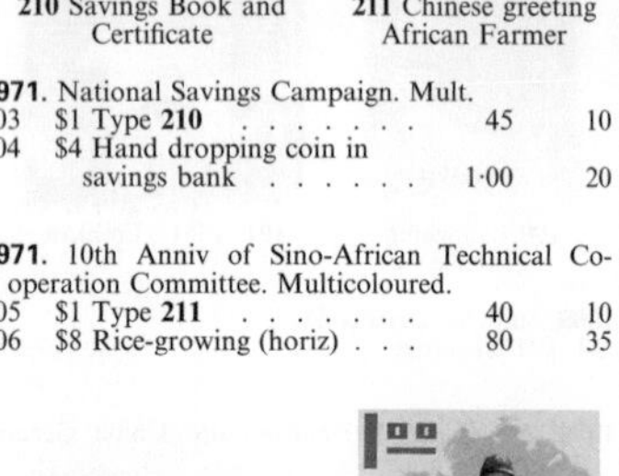

210 Savings Book and Certificate **211** Chinese greeting African Farmer

1971. National Savings Campaign. Mult.
803 $1 Type **210** 45 10
804 $4 Hand dropping coin in savings bank . . . . . . 1·00 20

1971. 10th Anniv of Sino-African Technical Co-operation Committee. Multicoloured.
805 $1 Type **211** 40 10
806 $8 Rice-growing (horiz) . . . 80 35

212 Red and White Flying Squirrel **213** Pitcher delivering ball

1971. Taiwan Animals. Multicoloured.
807 $1 Taiwan macaque (vert) . . 70 10
808 $2 Type **212** . . . . 1·50 50
809 $3 Chinese pangolin . . . . 2·00 65
810 $5 Sika deer . . . . 2·50 75

1971. World Little League Baseball Championships, Taiwan. Multicoloured.
811 $1 Type **213** 30 10
812 $2.50 Players at base (horiz) 40 15
813 $4 Striker and catcher . . . 75 15

(**214**)

215 60th Anniv Emblem and flag

1971. Victory of "Tainan Giants" in World Little League Baseball Championships, Williamsport (U.S.A.). Optd with T **214**.
814 **163** $1 red 60 10
815 $2.50 blue . . . . 1·25 20
816 $3 blue . . . . 1·25 20

1971. Chinese Folk-tales (2nd series). As T **200**. Multicoloured.
817 10c. Yu Hsun and elephant 15 10
818 10c. Tsai Hsun with mulberries 15 10
819 10c. Tseng Sun with firewood 15 10
820 10c. Kiang Keh and bandits 15 10
821 10c. Tsu Lu with sack of rice 15 10
822 50c. Meng Chung gathering bamboo shoots 40 10
823 $1 Tung Yung and wife . . . 1·25 35
824 $1 Tzu Chien shivering with cold . . . . 1·25 35

1971. 60th National Day. Multicoloured.
825 $1 Type **215** 45 10
826 $2.50 National anthem, map and flag 60 10

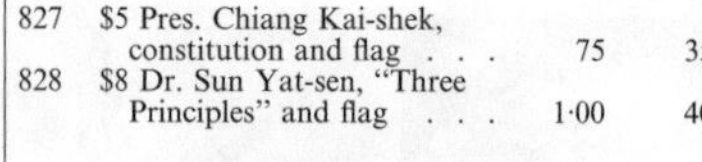

827 $5 Pres. Chiang Kai-shek, constitution and flag . . . 75 35
828 $8 Dr. Sun Yat-sen, "Three Principles" and flag . . . 1·00 40

216 A.O.P.U. Emblem

1971. Asian-Oceanic Postal Union Executive Committee Session, Taipeh.
829 **216** $2.50 multicoloured . . . 50 30
830 $5 multicoloured 60 15

217 "White Frost Hawk"

1971. "Ten Prized Dogs" (paintings on silk by Lang Shih-ning (G. Castiglione)). Multicoloured.
831 $1 Type **217** . . . . 1·10 10
832 $1 "Black Dog with Snow-white Claws" . . . . . . 3·25 10
833 $2 "Star-glancing Wolf" . . 3·50 10
834 $2 "Yellow Leopard" . . . . 4·50 10
835 $2.50 "Golden-winged Face" 3·00 85
836 $2.50 "Flying Magpie" . . . 10·50 85
837 $5 "Young Black Dragon" . 4·25 75
838 $5 "Heavenly Lion" . . . . 10·50 75
839 $8 "Young Grey Dragon" . . 4·25 65
840 $8 "Mottle-coated Tiger" . . 12·00 65

218/221 Squirrels

1971. New Year Greetings. "Year of the Rat".
841 **218** 50c. multicoloured 80 10
842 **219** 50c. multicoloured 80 10
843 **220** 50c. multicoloured 80 10
844 **221** 50c. multicoloured 80 10
845 **218** $4.50 multicoloured . . . 4·00 40
846 **219** $4.50 multicoloured . . . 4·00 40
847 **220** $4.50 multicoloured . . . 4·00 40
848 **221** $4.50 multicoloured . . . 4·00 40
The four designs in each value were issued together, se-tenant, forming a composite design.

222 Flags of Taiwan and Jordan

1971. 50th Anniv of Hashemite Kingdom of Jordan.
849 **222** $5 multicoloured . . . . 1·00 30

223 Freighter "Hai King"

1971. Centenary of China Merchants Steam Navigation Company. Multicoloured.
850 **223** $4 blue, red and green . . 75 40
851 – $7 multicoloured . . . . . 1·25 25
DESIGN—VERT: $7. Liner on Pacific.

224 Downhill Skiing

1972. Winter Olympic Games, Sapporo, Japan.
852 **224** $1 black, yellow and blue 25 10
853 – $5 black, orange & green 65 20
854 – $8 black, red and grey . . 75 30
DESIGNS: $5, Cross-country skiing; $8, Giant slalom.

225 Yung Cheng Vase **226** Doves

1972. Chinese Porcelain. (1st series). Ch'ing Dynasty. Multicoloured.
855 $1 Type **225** 75 10
856 $2 Kang Hsi jar . . . . . . 1·25 30
857 $2.50 Yung Cheng jug . . . 1·50 40
858 $5 Chien Lung vase . . . . 1·75 20
859 $8 Chien Lung jar . . . . . 3·25 40
See also Nos. 914/18, 927/31 and 977/81.

1972. 10th Anniv of Asian-Oceanic Postal Union.
860 **226** $1 black and blue 80 10
861 $5 black and violet . . . 1·25 40

227 "Dignity with Self-Reliance" (Pres. Chiang Kai-shek) **229** First Day Covers

228 Mounted Messengers

1972.
862 **227** 5c. brown and yellow . . 15 10
863 10c. blue and orange . . 10 10
863b 20c. purple and green . . 20 10
864 50c. lilac and purple . . 20 10
865 $1 red and blue 10 10
866 $1.50 yellow and blue . . 20 10
867 $2 violet, purple & orge 30 10
868 $2.50 green and red . . 75 10
869 $3 red and green 50 10

1972. "The Emperor's Procession" (Ming dynasty handscrolls). Multicoloured. (a) First issue.
870 $1 (1) Pagoda and crowds . . 40 10
871 $1 (2) Seven carriages 40 10
872 $1 (3) Emperor's coach . . . 40 10
873 $1 (4) Horsemen with flags 40 10
874 $1 (5) Horsemen and Emperor 40 10
875 $2.50 Type **228** . . . . . . 5·00 25
876 $5 Guards . . . . 5·00 25
877 $8 Imperial sedan chair . . . 5·00 20

(b) Second issue.
878 $1 (1) Three ceremonial barges 40 10
879 $1 (2) Sedan chairs 40 10
880 $1 (3) Two ceremonial barges 40 10
881 $1 (4) Horsemen and mounted orchestra 40 10
882 $1 (5) Two carriages 40 10
883 $2.50 City gate . . . . . . 5·00 25
884 $5 Mounted orchestra . . . 5·00 25
885 $8 Ceremonial barge . . . . 7·00 30
Nos. 870/4 are numbered from right to left and Nos. 878/82 are numbered from left to right. They were each issued together, se-tenant, forming composite designs showing the departure of the procession from the palace and its return.
Nos. 875/7 and 883/5 show enlarged details from the scrolls.
See also Nos. 937/50 and 1040/7.

1972. Philately Day.
886 **229** $1 blue 25 10
887 $2.50 green 25 15
888 $8 red . . . . 1·25 15
DESIGNS—VERT: $2.50, Magnifying glass and stamps. HORIZ: $8, Magnifying glass, perforation-gauge and tweezers.

(230)

231 Emperor Yao

1972. Taiwan's Victories in Senior and Little World Baseball Leagues. Nos. 865/7 and 869 optd with T **230**.
889 **227** $1 red and blue 25 10
890 $1.50 yellow and blue . . 40 20
891 $2 violet, purple & orange 40 15
892 $3 red and green 40 20

1972. Chinese Cultural Heroes.
893 **231** $3.50 blue 50 30
894 – $4 red 50 10
895 – $4.50 violet 60 20
896 – $5 green 60 10
897 – $5.50 purple . . . . . . 1·40 35
898 – $6 orange . . . . 1·40 30
899 – $7 brown . . . . 2·00 10
900 – $8 blue . . . . 2·25 15
DESIGNS: $4, Emperor Shun; $4.50, Yu the Great; $5, King T'ang; $5.50, King Weng; $6, King Wu; $7, Chou Kung; $8, Confucius.

232 Mountaineering

233 Microwave Systems and Electronic Sorting Machine

1972. 20th Anniv of China Youth Corps. Multicoloured.
902 $1 Type **232** 35 10
903 $2.50 Winter sport 50 10
904 $4 Diving 65 15
905 $8 Parachuting . . . . . . 1·00 45

1972. Improvement of Communications.
906 **233** $1 red 30 10
907 – $2.50 blue 50 20
908 – $5 purple 90 30
DESIGNS—HORIZ: $2.50, Boeing 721-100 airliner and "Hai Mou" (container ship); $5, Diesel railcar and motorway.

234 "Eyes" and J.C.I. Emblem

235 Cow and Calf

1972. 27th World Congress of Junior Chamber International, Taipeh.
909 **234** $1 multicoloured 30 10
910 $5 multicoloured 60 20
911 $8 multicoloured 60 30

1972. New Year Greetings. "Year of the Ox".
912 **235** 50c. black and red . . . . 1·40 25
913 $4.50 brown, red & yellow 2·00 75

1973. Chinese Porcelain (2nd series). Ming Dynasty. As T **225**. Multicoloured.
914 $1 Fu vase . . . . 1·00 10
915 $2 Floral vase . . . . . . 1·50 10
916 $2.50 Ku vase . . . . . . 1·75 20
917 $5 Hu flask . . . . 2·50 30
918 $8 Garlic-head vase . . . . 3·75 30

236 "Kicking the Shuttlecock"

237 Bamboo Sampan

1973. Chinese Folklore (1st series). Mult.
919 $1 Type **236** 40 10
920 $4 "The Fisherman and the Oyster-fairy" (horiz) . . . 90 15
921 $5 "Lady in a Boat" (horiz) 90 15
922 $8 "The Old Man and the Lady" . . . . 1·25 35
See also Nos. 982/3 and 1037/8.

1973. Taiwan Handicrafts (1st series). Mult.
923 $1 Type **237** 60 10
924 $2.50 Marble vase (vert) . . 75 10
925 $5 Glass plate 85 15
926 $8 Aborigine Doll (vert) . . . 90 25
See also Nos. 988/91.

1973. Chinese Porcelain (3rd series). Ming Dynasty. Horiz. designs as T **225**. Multicoloured.
927 $1 Dragon stem-bowl 60 10
928 $2 Dragon pot 85 10
929 $2.50 Covered jar with lotus decor . . . . 1·50 10
930 $5 Covered jar showing horses . . . . 1·50 15
931 $8 "Immortals" bowl . . . . 2·25 15

238 Contractors' Equipment

239 Pres. Chiang Kai-shek and Flag

1973. 12th Convention of International Federation of Asian and Western Pacific Contractors' Association.
932 **238** $1 multicoloured 30 10
933 – $5 blue and black 50 15
DESIGN—HORIZ: $5, Bulldozer.

1973. Inauguration of Pres. Chiang Kai-shek's 5th Term of Office.
934 **239** $1 multicoloured 50 10
935 $4 multicoloured 80 15

240 Lin Tse-hsu (statesman)

1973. Lin Tse-hsu Commemoration.
936 **240** $1 purple 35 10

1973. "Spring Morning in the Han Palace" (Ming dynasty handscroll). As T **228**. Mult. (a) First issue.
937 $1 (1) Palace gate 20 10
938 $1 (2) Feeding green peafowl 40 10
939 $1 (3) Emperor's wife 20 10
940 $1 (4) Ladies and pear tree 20 10
941 $1 (5) Music pavilion 20 10
942 $5 Giant rock (vert) . . . . 4·75 50
943 $8 Lady musicians (vert) . . 6·00 20

(b) Second issue.
944 $1 (6) Game with flowers . . 20 10
945 $1 (7) Leisure room 20 10
946 $1 (8) Ladies with teapots . . 20 10
947 $1 (9) Artist at work 20 10
948 $1 (10) Palace wall and guards 20 10
949 $5 Playing game at table (vert) . . . . 4·75 50
950 $8 Swatting insect (vert) . . . 6·00 20
Nos. 937/41 and 944/8 are numbered from right to left and were each issued together, se-tenant. When the two strips are placed side by side, they form a composite design showing the complete handscroll.
Nos. 942/3 and 949/50 show enlarged details from the scroll.

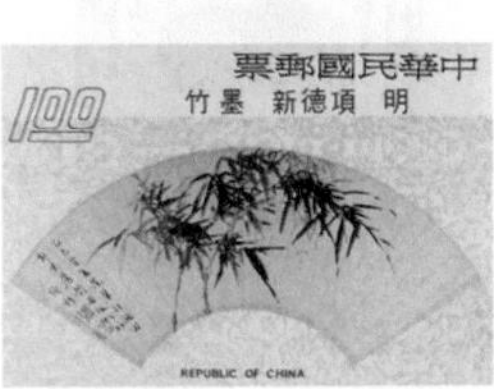

241 "Bamboo" (Hsiang Te-hsin)

1973. Ancient Chinese Fan Paintings (1st series). Multicoloured.
951 $1 Type **241** 80 10
952 $2.50 "Flowers" (Sun K'O-hung) . . . . 2·00 10
953 $5 "Landscape" (Ch'iu Ying) 3·25 20
954 $8 "Seated Figure and Tree" (Shen Chou) . . . . 3·00 20
See also Nos. 1052/5.

243 Emblem of World Series

245 Interpol Emblem

1973. Little League World Baseball Series. Taiwan Victory in Twin Championships.
955 **243** $1 blue, red and yellow 45 10
956 $4 blue, green & yellow 75 15

1973. 50th Anniv of International Criminal Police Organization (Interpol).
957 **245** $1 blue and orange . . . 30 10
958 $5 green and orange . . . 60 15
959 $8 purple and orange . . 80 25

1973. Famous Chinese. Portrait as T **132**.
960 $1 violet (Ch'iu Feng-chia (poet)) 55 10

246 Dam and Power Station

1973. Opening of Tsengwen Reservoir. Mult.
961 $1 Upper section of reservoir 10 10
962 $1 Middle section of reservoir 10 10
963 $1 Lower section of reservoir 10 10
964 $5 Type **246** (30 × 22 mm) . . 1·50 25
965 $8 Spillway (50 × 22 mm) . . 1·90 15
The $1 values together show complete map of reservoir (each 38 × 26 mm).

247 "Snow-dotted Eagle"

1973. Paintings of Horses. Multicoloured.
966 50c. Type **247** 10 10
967 $1 "Comfortable Ride" . . . 20 10
968 $1 "Red Flower Eagle" . . . 20 10
969 $1 "Cloud-running Steed" . . 20 10
970 $1 "Sky-running Steed" . . . 20 10
971 $2.50 "Red Jade Steed" . . . 4·50 25
972 $5 "Thunder-clap Steed" . . 6·50 25
973 $8 "Arabian Champion" . . 9·00 20

248 Tiger

249 Road Tunnel Taroko Gorge

1973. New Year Greetings. "Year of the Tiger".
975 **248** 50c. multicoloured 60 10
976 $4.50 multicoloured . . . 1·00 30

1974. Chinese Porcelain (4th series). Sung Dynasty. As T **225**. Multicoloured.
977 $1 Ko vase 75 10
978 $2 Kuan vase (horiz) 75 10
979 $2.50 Ju bowl (horiz) . . . . 1·00 20
980 $5 Kuan incense burner (horiz) . . . . 1·10 20
981 $8 Chun incense burner (horiz) . . . . 1·40 20

1974. Chinese Folklore (2nd series). As T **236**. Multicoloured.
982 $1 Balancing pot 50 10
983 $8 Magicians (horiz) . . . . 1·00 20

1974. Taiwan Scenery (1st series). Mult.
984 $1 Type **249** 60 10
985 $2.50 Luce Chapel, Tungai University 70 10
986 $5 Tzu En Pagoda, Sun Moon Lake . . . . 1·25 15
987 $8 Goddess of Mercy Statue, Keelung . . . . 1·50 15
See also Nos. 992/5.

1974. Taiwan Handicrafts (2nd series). As T **237**. Multicoloured.
988 $1 "Fighting Cocks" (brass) 40 10
989 $2.50 "Fruits" (jade) 50 15
990 $5 "Fisherman" (wood-carving) (vert) 70 15
991 $8 "Bouquet of Flowers" (plastic) (vert) . . . . . . 1·00 15

1974. Taiwan Scenery (2nd series). As T **249** but all horiz. Multicoloured.
992 $1 Dr. Sun Yat-Sen Memorial Hall. Taipeh . . 40 10
993 $2.50 Reaching-Moon Tower, Cheng Ching Lake 55 10
994 $5 Seashore, Lanyu . . . . 1·00 15
995 $8 Inter-island bridge, Penghu . . . . 1·40 15

250 Pres. Chiang Kai-shek

251 Long-distance Runner

1974. 50th Anniv of Chinese Military Academy.
996 **250** $1 mauve 40 10
997 – $14 blue 85 30
DESIGN—VERT: $14, Cadets on parade.

1974. 80th Anniv of International Olympic Committee.
998 **251** $1 blue, black & red . . . 20 10
999 – $8 multicoloured 60 15
DESIGN: $8, Female relay runner.

1974. Chinese Folk tales (3rd series). As T **200**. Multicoloured.
1000 50c. Wen Yen-po retrieving ball 45 10
1001 50c. T'i Ying pleading for mercy 45 10
1002 50c. Wang Ch'i in battle . . 45 10
1003 50c. Wang Hua returning gold 45 10
1004 $1 Pu Shih offering sheep to the emperor 50 10
1005 $1 Szu Ma Kuang saving playmate from water-jar 50 10
1006 $1 Tung Yu at study . . . 50 10
1007 $1 K'ung Yung selecting the smallest pear 50 10

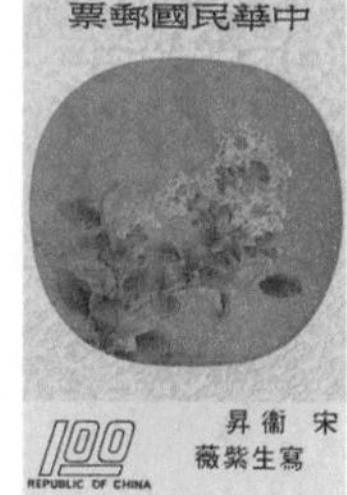

252 "Crape Myrtle" (Wei Sheng)

1974. Ancient Chinese Moon-shaped Fan-paintings (1st series). Multicoloured.
1008 $1 Type **252** 85 10
1009 $2.50 "White Cabbage and Insects" (Hsu Ti) . . . . 1·00 20
1010 $5 "Hibiscus and Rock" (Li Ti) . . . . 1·50 20
1011 $8 "Pomegranates and Narcissus Fly-catcher" (Wu Ping) . . . . 2·25 40
See also Nos. 1068/71 and 1115/1118.

253 "The Battle of Marco Polo Bridge"

254 Chrysanthemum

1974. Armed Forces' Day.
1012 **253** $1 multicoloured 35 10

1974. Chrysanthemums.
1014 **254** $1 multicoloured 40 10
1015 – $2.50 multicoloured . . 85 20
1016 – $5 multicoloured . . . . 1·25 20
1017 – $8 multicoloured . . . . 1·75 15
DESIGNS: Nos. 1015/17, various chrysanthemums.

255 Chinese Pavilion

256 Steel Mill, Kaohsiung

1974. "Expo 74" World Fair, Spokane, Washington. Multicoloured.
1018 $1 Type **255** 20 10
1019 $8 Fairground map 50 15

1974. Major Construction Projects (1st series). Chinese inscr in single-line characters, figures of value solid.* Multicoloured.
1020 50c. Type **256** 10 10
1021 $1 Taiwan North link railway 30 10
1022 $2 Petrochemical works, Kaohsiung 15 10
1023 $2.50 TRA trunk line electrification 50 10
1024 $3 Taichung harbour (horiz) 30 10
1025 $3.50 Taoyuan international airport (horiz) 30 10
1026 $4 Taiwan North–south motorway (horiz) 30 10
1027 $4.50 Giant shipyard, Kaohsiung (horiz) 50 25
1028 $5 Su-ao port (horiz) 50 10
*The first series can also be distinguished by the Chinese and English inscr at the foot being in different colours; in the second and third series only one colour is used.
See also Nos. 1122a/1122i and 1145/1153.

257 White Button Mushrooms

258 Baseball Strikers

1974. Edible Fungi. Multicoloured.
1029 $1 Type **257** 55 10
1030 $2.50 Oyster fungus 90 20
1031 $5 Veiled stinkhorn 1·40 25
1032 $8 Golden mushrooms 1·40 30

1974. Taiwan Triple Championship Victories in World Little League Baseball Series, U.S.A. Multicoloured.
1033 $1 Type **258** 25 10
1034 $8 Player and banners 50 15

259 Chinese Hare

1974. New Year Greetings. "Year of the Hare".
1035 **259** 50c. multicoloured 35 10
1036 $4.50 multicoloured 1·25 25

1975. Chinese Folklore (3rd series). As T **236**. Multicoloured.
1037 $4 Acrobat 50 15
1038 $5 Jugglers with diabolo 1·00 20

260 Chungshan Building, Yangmingshan

261 Sun Yat-sen Memorial Hall, Taipeh

1975.
1039 **260** $1 red 25 15
Type **260** is a redrawn version of Type **195**.

1975. "New Year Festivals" (handscroll by Ting Kuan-p'eng). As T **228**. Multicoloured.
1040 $1 (1) Greetings 20 10
1041 $1 (2) Entertainer 20 10
1042 $1 (3) Crowd and musicians 20 10
1043 $1 (4) Picnic 20 10
1044 $1 (5) Puppet show 20 10
1045 $2.50 New Year greetings 2·50 30
1046 $5 Children buying fireworks 4·25 30
1047 $8 Entertainer with monkey and dog 5·25 45
Nos. 1040/4 were issued together, se-tenant, forming a composite design.

1975. 50th Death Anniv of Dr. Sun Yat-sen.
1048 $1 Type **261** 25 10
1049 $4 Sun Yat-sen's handwriting 40 15
1050 $5 Bronze statue of Sun Yat-sen (vert) 50 15
1051 $8 Sun Yat-sen Memorial Hall, St. John's University, U.S.A 75 15

1975. Ancient Chinese Fan Paintings (2nd series). As T **241**. Multicoloured.
1052 $1 "Landscape" (Li Liu-fang) 75 10
1053 $2.50 "Landscape" (Wen Cheng-ming) 75 20
1054 $5 "Landscape" (Chou Ch'en) 1·60 20
1055 $8 "Landscape" (T'ang Yin) 2·00 15

262 "Yuan-chin" Coin (Chou dynasty)

263 "Lohan, the Cloth-bag Monk" (Chang Hung)

1975. Ancient Chinese Coins (1st series). Mult.
1056 $1 Type **262** 50 10
1057 $4 "Pan-liang" coin (Chin dynasty) 85 15
1058 $5 "Five chu" coin (Han dynasty) 1·00 15
1059 $8 "Five chu" coin (Liang dynasty) 1·25 10
See also Nos. 1111/14 and 1184/7.

1975. Ancient Chinese Figure Paintings. Mult.
1060 $2 Type **263** 75 10
1061 $4 "Lao-tzu on buffalo" (Chao Pu-chih) 1·75 15
1062 $5 "Shih-te" (Wang-wen) 3·00 15
1063 $8 "Splashed-ink Immortal" (Liang K'ai) 3·00 15

1975. Chinese Folk-tales (4th series). As T **200**. Multicoloured.
1064 $1 Chu-Yin reading by light of fireflies 20 10
1065 $2 Hua Mu-lan going to battle disguised as a man 35 10
1066 $2 Ling Kou Chien living a humble life 40 10
1067 $5 Chou Ch'u defeating the tiger 1·00 25

1975. Ancient Chinese Moon-shaped Fan Paintings (2nd series). As T **252**. Multicoloured.
1068 $1 "Cherry-apple blossoms" (Lin Ch'un) 75 10
1069 $2 "Spring blossoms and a colourful butterfly" (Ma K'uei) 90 10
1070 $5 "Monkeys and deer" (I Yuan-chi) 1·10 20
1071 $8 "Tree sparrows among bamboo" (anon.) 2·40 40

1975. Famous Chinese. Martyrs of War against Japan. Portraits as T **132**.
1072 $2 red (Gen. Chang Tzu-chung) 25 10
1073 $2 brown (Maj.-Gen. Kao Chih-hang) 25 10
1074 $2 green (Capt. Sha Shih-chiun) 25 10
1075 $5 brown (Maj-Gen. Hsieh Chin-yuan) 40 15
1076 $5 blue (Lt. Yen Hai-wen) 40 15
1077 $5 blue (Lt.-Gen. Tai An-lan) 40 15

264 "Lotus Pond with Willows"

1975. Madame Chiang Kai-shek's Landscape Paintings (1st series). Multicoloured.
1078 $2 Type **264** 1·00 10
1079 $5 "Sun breaks through Mountain Clouds" 1·50 30
1080 $8 "A Pair of Pine Trees" 3·75 40
1081 $10 "Fishing and Farming" 4·75 55
See also Nos. 1139/1142 and 1727/30.

265 Rectangular Cauldron

266 Dragon, Nine-Dragon Wall, Peihai

1975. Ancient Bronzes (1st series). Mult.
1082 $2 Type **265** 50 10
1083 $5 Cauldron with "Phoenix" handles (horiz) 75 15
1084 $8 Flat jar (horiz) 1·50 25
1085 $10 Wine vessel 2·00 30
See also Nos. 1119/22.

1975. New Year Greetings. "Year of the Dragon".
1086 **266** $1 multicoloured 50 10
1087 $5 multicoloured 1·00 20

267 Techi Dam

268 Biathlon

1975. Completion of Techi Reservoir. Mult.
1088 $2 Type **267** 25 10
1089 $10 Dam and reservoir 50 30

1976. Winter Olympic Games, Innsbruck. Mult.
1090 $2 Type **268** 30 10
1091 $5 Luge 40 15
1092 $8 Skiing 60 15

269 "Chin"

1976. Chinese Musical Instruments (1st series). Multicoloured.
1093 $2 Type **269** 40 10
1094 $5 "Se" (string instrument) 60 10
1095 $8 "Standing Kong-ho" (harp) 70 15
1096 $10 "Sleeping Kong-ho" (harp) 85 20
See also Nos. 1156/9.

270 Postman collecting Mail

1976. 80th Anniv of Chinese Postal Service. Multicoloured.
1097 $2 Type **270** 20 10
1098 $5 Mail-sorting systems (vert) 30 15
1099 $8 Mail transport (vert) 1·00 15
1100 $10 Traditional and modern post deliveries 70 20

271 Pres. Chiang Kai-shek

1976. 1st Death Anniv of President Chiang Kai-shek. Multicoloured.
1102 $2 Type **271** 30 10
1103 $2 People paying homage (horiz) 30 10
1104 $2 Lying-in-state (horiz) 30 10
1105 $2 Start of funeral procession (horiz) 30 10
1106 $5 Roadside obeisance (horiz) 40 15
1107 $8 Altar, Tzuhu Guest-house (horiz) 50 20
1108 $10 Tzuhu Guest-house (horiz) 75 25

272 Chinese and U.S. Flags

273 "Kung Shou Pu" Coin (Shang/Chou Dynasties)

1976. Bicentenary of American Revolution.
1109 **272** $2 multicoloured 20 10
1110 $10 multicoloured 50 25

1976. Ancient Chinese Coins (2nd series). Mult.
1111 $2 Type **273** 50 10
1112 $5 "Chien Tsu Pu" coin (Chao Kingdom) 75 15
1113 $8 "Yuan Tsu Pu" coin (Tsin Kingdom) 90 20
1114 $10 "Fang Tsu Pu" coin (Chin/Han Dynasties) 1·25 25

1976. Ancient Chinese Moon-shaped Fan-paintings (3rd series) As T **252**. Multicoloured.
1115 $2 "Hibiscus" (Li Tung) 50 10
1116 $5 "Lilies" (Lin Chun) 1·25 15
1117 $8 "Two Sika Deer, Mushrooms and Pine" (Mou Chung-fu) 1·75 30
1118 $10 "Wild Flowers and Japanese Quail" (Li An-chung) 4·75 45

1976. Ancient Bronzes (2nd series). As T **265**. Multicoloured.
1119 $2 Square cauldron 50 10
1120 $5 Round cauldron 80 10
1121 $8 Wine vessel 1·00 15
1122 $10 Wine vessel with legs 1·25 20
No. 1119 is similar to Type **265**, but has four characters at left only.

1976. Major Construction Projects (2nd series). Designs as Nos. 1020/8, but Chinese inscr in double-lined characters. Figures of value solid. Multicoloured.
1122a $1 As No. 1021 50 10
1122b $2 As No. 1023 50 10
1122c $3 As No. 1024 30 10
1122d $4 As No. 1026 30 10
1122e $5 As Type **256** 30 10
1122f $6 As No. 1025 40 10
1122g $7 As No. 1027 45 10
1122h $8 As No. 1022 50 15
1122i $9 As No. 1028 50 20
See also Nos. 1145/53.

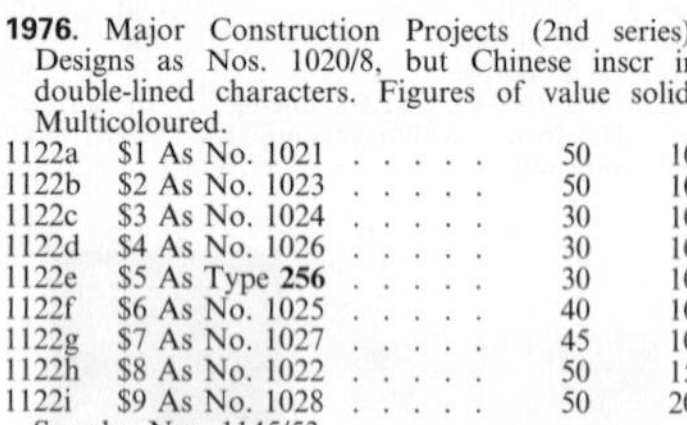

274 Chiang Kai-shek and Mother

1976. 90th Birth Anniv of President Chiang Kai-shek. Multicoloured.
1123 $2 Type **274** 30 10
1124 $5 Chiang Kai-shek 30 15
1125 $10 Chiang Kai-shek and Dr. Sun Yat-sen in railway carriage (horiz) 85 50

275 Chinese and KMT Flags

1976. 11th Kuomintang National Congress. Mult.
1126 $2 Type **275** 20 10
1127 $10 President Chiang Kai-shek and Dr. Sun Yat-sen 40 25

276 Brazen Serpent

277 "Bird and Plum Blossom" (Ch'en Hung-shou)

1976. New Year Greetings. "Year of the Snake".
1129 **276** $1 multicoloured 60 10
1130 $5 multicoloured . . . . 1·10 10

1977. Ancient Chinese Paintings. "Three Friends of Winter".
1131 $2 Type **277** . . . . 1·00 10
1132 $8 "Wintry Days" (Yang Wei-chen) . . . . 2·25 25
1133 $10 "Rock and Bamboo" (Hsia Ch'ang) . . . . . 2·50 20

278 Black-naped Orioles

1977. Taiwan Birds. Multicoloured.
1134 $2 Type **278** . . . . 1·00 10
1135 $8 River kingfisher . . . . 1·25 50
1136 $10 Pheasant-tailed jacana 2·00 50

279 Emblems of Industry and Commerce

1977. Industry and Commerce Census.
1137 **279** $2 multicoloured 35 15
1138 $10 multicoloured . . . 90 35

280 "Green Mountains rising into Clouds"

1977. Madame Chiang Kai-shek's Landscape Paintings (2nd series). Multicoloured.
1139 $2 Type **280** 80 10
1140 $5 "Boat amidst Spring's Beauty" . . . . 1·00 20
1141 $8 "Scholar beside the Rivulet" . . . . 2·25 15
1142 $10 "Green Water rising to meet the Bridge" . . . . 3·00 30

281 W.A.C.L. Emblem

282 Steel Mill, Kaohsiung

1977. 10th World Anti-Communist League Conf.
1143 **281** $2 multicoloured 20 10
1144 $10 multicoloured . . . 50 15

1977. Major Construction Projects (3rd series). Designs as Nos. 1122a/i, but redrawn with double lined figures of value as in T **282**. Multicoloured.
1145 $1 Taiwan North link railway 50 10
1146 $2 TRA trunk line electrification 50 10
1147 $3 Taichung harbour (horiz) 30 10
1148 $4 Taiwan North–south highway (horiz) 25 10
1149 $5 Type **282** 35 10
1150 $6 Taoyuan international airport (horiz) 35 10
1151 $7 Giant shipyard, Kaohsiung (horiz) 40 10
1152 $8 Petrochemical works, Kaohsiung 50 10
1153 $9 Su-ao port (horiz) . . . 60 10

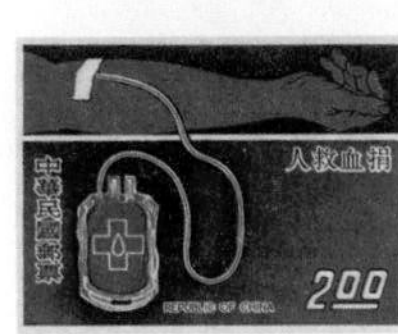

283 "Blood Donation"

1977. Blood Donation Movement.
1154 **283** $2 red, black and yellow 20 10
1155 – $10 red and black . . . 50 15
DESIGN—VERT: $10, "Blood Transfusion".

284 San-hsien

285 "Idea leuconoe"

1977. Chinese Musical Instruments (2nd series). Multicoloured.
1156 $2 Type **284** 40 10
1157 $5 Tung-hsiao (wind instrument) 70 10
1158 $8 Yang-chin (xylophone) 80 12
1159 $10 Pai-hsiao (pipes) 90 15

1977. Taiwan Butterflies. Multicoloured.
1160 $2 Type **285** 60 10
1161 $4 Great orange-tip 80 20
1162 $6 "Stichophthalma howqua" . . . . 1·00 25
1163 $10 "Atrophaneura horishanus" . . . . . . 1·75 15

286 "National Palace Museum"

(287)

1977. Children's Drawings. Multicoloured.
1164 $1 Type **286** 15 10
1165 $2 "Festival of Sea Goddess" 25 10
1166 $4 "Boats on Lan-yu" . . . 35 10
1167 $5 "Temple" (vert) 45 10

1977. Triple Championships of the 1977 Little League World Baseball Series. Nos. 1146 and 1152 optd with Type **287**.
1168 $2 multicoloured 50 15
1169 $8 multicoloured 50 15

288 Plate

289 Lions Club Emblem

1977. Ancient Chinese Carved Lacquer Ware (1st series). Multicoloured.
1170 $2 Type **288** 60 10
1171 $5 Bowl 85 10
1172 $8 Box 85 10
1173 $10 Three-tiered box . . . . 1·00 15
See also Nos. 1206/1209.

1977. 60th Anniv of Lions International.
1174 **289** $2 multicoloured 20 10
1175 $10 multicoloured . . . 50 15

290 "Cheng" Government Standard Mark

291 Human Figure and Diagram of Heart

1977. Standardization Movement.
1176 **290** $2 multicoloured 35 10
1177 $10 multicoloured . . . 90 15

1977. Prevention of Heart Disease Campaign.
1178 **291** $2 multicoloured 20 10
1179 $10 multicoloured . . . 50 15

292 White Horse

293 First Page of Constitution

1977. New Year Greetings. "Year of the Horse". Details from "One Hundred Horses" by Lang Shih-ning (Giuseppe Castiglione). Multicoloured.
1180 $1 Type **292** 35 10
1181 $5 Two Horses (horiz) . . . 90 15

1977. 30th Anniv of Constitution. Mult.
1182 $2 Type **293** 20 10
1183 $10 President Chiang accepting constitution . . 50 20

294 "Three-character" Knife (Chi State)

295 "Dragon" Stamp, 1878

1978. Ancient Chinese Coins (3rd series). Mult.
1184 $2 Type **294** 50 10
1185 $5 Longer sharp-headed knife (Yen State) 90 10
1186 $8 Sharp-headed knife (Yet State) . . . . 1·00 15
1187 $10 Chao or Ming knife . . 1·25 20

1978. Cent of Chinese Postage Stamp. Mult.
1188 $2 Type **295** 40 10
1189 $5 "Dr. Sun Yat-sen" stamp, 1941 . . . . . . 50 10
1190 $10 "Chiang Kai-shek" stamp, 1958 . . . . . . 75 20

296 Dr. Sun Yat-sen Memorial Hall

1978. "Rocpex" Taipeh 1978 Philatelic Exhibition. Multicoloured.
1192 $2 Type **296** 20 10
1193 $10 "Dragon" and 1977 "New Year" stamps . . . 75 20

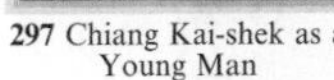

297 Chiang Kai-shek as a Young Man

298 Section through Nuclear Reactor

1978. 3rd Death Anniv of Pres. Chiang Kai-shek. Multicoloured.
1194 $2 Type **297** 25 10
1195 $5 Chiang on horseback (horiz) 40 10
1196 $8 Chiang making speech (horiz) 60 15
1197 $10 Reviewing armed forces 80 20

1978. Nuclear Power Plant.
1198 **298** $10 multicoloured . . . 60 15

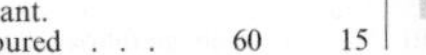

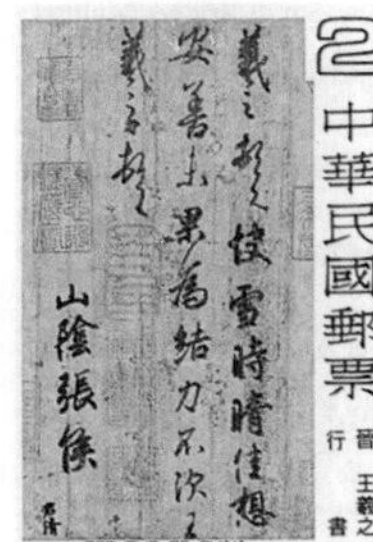

299 Letter by Wang Hsi-chih

300 Human Figure in Polluted Environment

1978. Chinese Calligraphy. Multicoloured.
1199 $2 Type **299** 60 10
1200 $4 Eulogy of Ni K'uan by Chu Sui-liang . . . . . . 1·50 15
1201 $6 Inscription on poem "Lake Tai" by Wen Cheng-ming . . . . . . 1·75 25
1202 $8 Autobiography by Huai-su . . . . 3·00 30
1203 $10 Poem by Ch'ang Piao 5·25 40

1978. Cancer Prevention.
1204 **300** $2 green, yellow & red 15 10
1205 $10 blue, green & dp blue 35 15

1978. Ancient Chinese Carved Lacquer Ware (2nd series). As T **288**. Multicoloured.
1206 $2 Square box 30 10
1207 $5 Box on legs 40 10
1208 $8 Round box 60 15
1209 $10 Vase (vert) 90 20

1978. Chinese Folk-tales (5th series). As T **200**. Multicoloured.
1210 $1 Tsu Ti brandishing sword 20 10
1211 $2 Pan Ch'ao throwing down pen 50 10
1212 $2 Tien Tan's "Fire Bull Battle" 75 10
1213 $5 Liang Hung-yu as army drummer . . . . 1·10 10

1978. Triple Championships of the Little League World Baseball Series. Nos. 1148 and 1150 optd as T **287**, but with four lines of characters and dated 1978.
1214 $4 Taiwan North–south highway 20 15
1215 $6 Taoyuan international airport 40 25

302 Yellow Orange-tip

1978. Taiwan Butterflies. Multicoloured.
1216 $2 Type **302** 30 10
1217 $4 Two-brand crow 70 10
1218 $6 Common map butterfly 1·10 15
1219 $10 "Atrophaneura polyeuctes" . . . . 1·10 25

303 Jamboree Badge, Camp and Scout Salute

304 Tropical Tomatoes

1978. Taiwanese Boy Scouts' 5th Jamboree.
1220 **303** $2 multicoloured 40 10
1221 $10 multicoloured . . . 60 20

1978. Asian Vegetable Research and Development Centre. Multicoloured.
1222 $2 Type **304** 40 10
1223 $10 Tropical tomatoes (different) 85 25

305 Aerial View of Bridge

306 National Flag

1978. Opening of the Sino-Saudi Bridge. Mult.
1224 $2 Type **305** 50 10
1225 $6 Close-up of bridge . . . 90 15

1978.
1226 **306** $1 red and blue 15 10
1377 $1 red and blue 20 10
1378 $1.50 red, blue & yellow 45 10
1227 $2 red and blue 15 10
1379 $2 red, blue and yellow 20 10
1297 $3 red, blue and green 35 10
1380 $3 red and blue 30 10
1298 $4 red, blue and brown 30 15
1381 $4 red, blue and light blue 30 10
1228 $5 red, blue and green 30 10
1382 $5 red, blue and brown 30 10
1229 $6 red, blue and orange 40 10
1300 $7 red, blue and brown 40 10
1384 $7 red, blue and green 50 10
1230 $8 red, blue and green 45 10
1385 $8 red, blue & deep red 45 10
1386 $9 red, blue and green 60 10
1231 $10 red, blue and lt blue 75 15
1387 $10 red, blue and violet 55 10
1302 $12 red, blue and mauve 60 25
1389 $14 red, blue and green 1·25 10

The $1 values differ in the face value, which is printed in colour on No. 1226, whilst on No. 1377 it is white.

Nos. 1377/8, 1379, 1380, 1381, 1382 and the $6 to $14 values are as Type **306** but have solid background panel to face value and inscr.

307 "Imitation of the Three Sheep by Emperor Hsuan-tsung of the Ming Dynasty" (Emperor Kao-tsung)

308 Boeing 747-100 and Control Building

1978. New Year Greetings. "Year of the Sheep".
1232 **307** $1 multicoloured 50 10
1233 $5 multicoloured 80 15

1978. Completion of Taoyuan International Airport. Multicoloured.
1234 $2 Type **308** 35 10
1235 $10 Passenger terminal building (horiz) 60 25

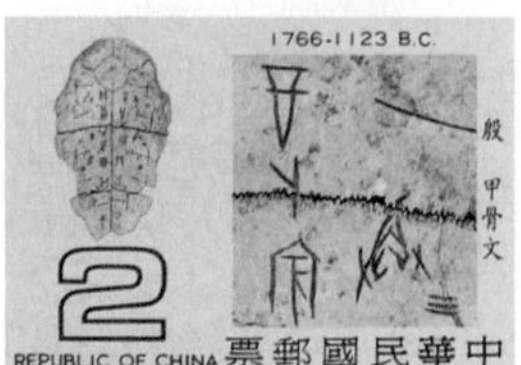

309 Oracle Bones and Inscription (Yin Dynasty)

1979. Origin and Development of Chinese Characters. Multicoloured.
1236 $2 Type **309** 60 10
1237 $5 "Leh-chi" cauldron and inscription (Spring and Autumn period) . . . . . 1·00 15
1238 $8 Engraved seal and seal-style characters (Western Han dynasty) . . . . . . 1·40 25
1239 $10 Square plain-style characters inscribed on stone (Eastern Han dynasty) . . . . 2·50 45

310 Chihkan Tower, Tainan

1979. Tourism. Multicoloured.
1240 $2 Type **310** 35 10
1241 $5 Confucius Temple, Tainan 35 15
1242 $8 Koxinga Shrine, Tainan 35 25
1243 $10 Eternal Castle, Tainan 1·50 30

311/314 "Children Playing Games on a Winter Day" (⅔-size illustration)

1979. Sung Dynasty Painting.
1244 **311** $5 multicoloured . . . . 2·25 65
1245 **312** $5 multicoloured . . . . 2·25 65
1246 **313** $5 multicoloured . . . . 2·25 65
1247 **314** $5 multicoloured . . . . 2·25 65

Nos. 1244/7 were printed together, se-tenant, forming the composite design illustrated.

315 Lu Hao-tung (revolutionary)

316 White Jade Brush Washer (Ming dynasty)

1979. Famous Chinese.
1249 **315** $2 blue 40 10

1979. Ancient Chinese Jade (1st series). Multicoloured.
1250 $2 Yellow jade brush holder embossed with clouds and dragons (Sung dynasty) (vert) 35 10
1251 $5 Type **316** 80 15
1252 $8 Dark green jade brush washer carved with clouds and dragons (Ch'ing dynasty) 95 20
1253 $10 Bluish jade washer in shape of lotus (Ch'ing dynasty) . . . . 1·40 25

See also Nos. 1291/4.

317 Plum Blossom

318 Houses

1979.
1254a **317** $10 blue 40 10
1255a $20 brown 80 10
1255ba $40 red . . . . . . 1·60 10
1256a $50 green . . . . . . 2·00 10
1257 $100 red . . . . . . 3·50 10
1257b $300 red and violet . . 14·00 2·00
1257c $500 red and brown . 23·00 4·75

The $300 and $500 are size 25 × 33 mm.

1979. Environmental Protection. Mult.
1258 $2 Type **318** 15 10
1259 $10 Rural scene (horiz) . . 55 25

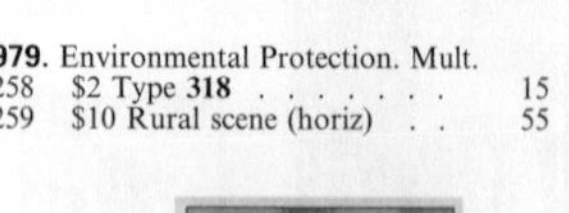

319 Savings Bank Counter

1979. 60th Anniv of Postal Savings Bank. Multicoloured.
1260 $2 Type **319** 20 10
1261 $5 Savings bank queue . . . 30 15
1262 $8 Computer and savings book (horiz) 45 20
1263 $10 Money box and "tree" emblem (horiz) 60 25

320 Steere's Liocichla

1979. Birds. Multicoloured.
1264 $2 Swinhoe's pheasant . . . 50 10
1265 $8 Type **320** . . . . 1·25 40
1266 $10 Formosan yuhina . . . 2·00 60

321 Sir Rowland Hill

322 Jar with Rope Pattern

1979. Death Centenary of Sir Rowland Hill.
1267 **321** $10 multicoloured . . . 75 25

1979. Ancient Chinese Pottery. Multicoloured.
1268 $2 Type **322** (Shang dynasty) 30 10
1269 $5 Two handled jar (Shang dynasty) 65 15
1270 $8 Red jar with "ears" (Han dynasty) . . . . 1·00 20
1271 $10 Green glazed jar (Han dynasty) . . . . 1·50 25

323 Children and I.Y.C. Emblem

324 "Trees on a Winter Plain" (Li Ch'eng)

1979. International Year of the Child.
1272 **323** $2 multicoloured 25 10
1273 $10 multicoloured . . . 50 25

1979. Ancient Chinese Paintings. Mult.
1274 $2 Type **324** (Sung dynasty) 60 10
1275 $5 "Bamboo" (Wen T'ung, Sung dynasty) . . . . . 1·60 15
1276 $8 "Old Tree, Bamboo and Rock" (Chao Mengfu, Yuan dynasty) . . . . . 2·40 20
1277 $10 "Twin Pines" (Li K'an, Yuan dynasty) . . . . . 3·50 25

325 Taiwan Macaque

326 Competition Emblem and Symbols of Ten Trades

1979. New Year Greetings. "Year of the Monkey".
1278 **325** $1 multicoloured 75 10
1279 $6 multicoloured . . . . 1·00 25

1979. 10th National Vocational Training Competition, Taichung.
1280 **326** $2 multicoloured 20 10
1281 $10 multicoloured . . . 50 25

327 "75" and Rotary Emblem

328 Tunnel of Nine Turns

1980. 75th Anniv of Rotary International. Mult.
1282 $2 Type **327** 25 10
1283 $12 Anniversary emblem and symbols of Rotary's services (vert) 50 25

1980. Tourism. Scenic Spots on the East–West Cross-Island Highway. Multicoloured.
1284 $2 Type **328** 25 10
1285 $8 Mt. Hohuan (horiz) . . . 50 15
1286 $12 Bridge, Tien Hsiang . . 1·00 30

329 Shih Chien-ju (hero of revolution)

330 Chung-cheng Memorial Hall

1980. Famous Chinese.
1287 **329** $2 brown 25 10

1980. 5th Death Anniv of Chiang Kai-shek. Multicoloured.
1288 $2 Type **330** 20 10
1289 $8 Quotation of Chiang Kai-shek 40 15
1290 $12 Bronze statue of Chiang Kai-shek 50 30

1980. Ancient Chinese Jade (2nd series). As T **316**. Multicoloured.
1291 $2 Kuang (cup) decorated with dragons (Sung dynasty) (vert) 50 10
1292 $5 Dark green jade melon-shaped brush washer (Ming dynasty) 90 15
1293 $8 Bluish jade Po Monk's alms bowl (Ch'ing dynasty) . . . . 1·10 20
1294 $10 Yellow jade brush washer (Ch'ing dynasty) 1·40 25

331 Tzu-Ch'iang Squadron over Presidential Mansion

1980. Air. Multicoloured.
1303 $5 Type **331** 35 10
1304 $7 Boeing 747-100 airliner and insignia of CAL (state airline) 75 20
1305 $12 National Flag and Boeing 747-100 . . . . . 90 30

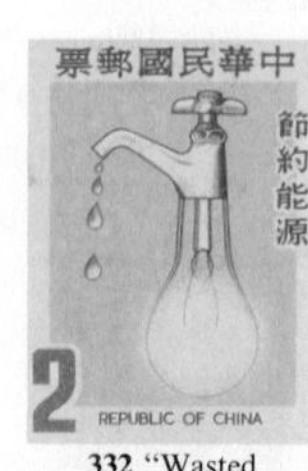

332 "Wasted Resources"

333 Military Official

1980. Energy Conservation.
1306 **332** $2 multicoloured 20 10
1307 $12 multicoloured . . . 50 30

1980. T'ang Dynasty Tri-coloured Pottery. Multicoloured.
1308 $2 Type **333** 70 10
1309 $5 Chickens . . . . 1·25 10
1310 $8 Horse . . . . 1·60 20
1311 $10 Camel . . . . 1·50 25

1980. Chinese Folk-tales (6th series). As T **200**. Multicoloured.
1312 $1 Grinding mortar into a needle 20 10
1313 $2 Returning lost articles . . 30 10
1314 $2 Wen Tien-hsiang in prison 55 10
1315 $5 Sending coal to poor during snow 75 15

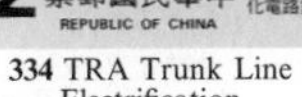

334 TRA Trunk Line Electrification

335 Money Boxes within Ancient Chinese Coin

1980. Completion of Ten Major Construction Projects. Multicoloured.
1316 $2 Type **334** 45 10
1317 $2 Taichung Harbour . . . 15 10
1318 $2 Chiang Kai-shek International Airport . . 15 10
1319 $2 Integrated steel mill . . . 15 10
1320 $2 Sun Yat-sen National Freeway 15 10
1321 $2 Nuclear power plant . . 15 10
1322 $2 Petrochemical industrial zone in south 15 10
1323 $2 Su-ao Harbour 15 10
1324 $2 Kaohsiung Shipyard . . 40 10
1325 $2 Taiwan North Link Railway 45 10

1980. 10th National Savings Day. Mult.
1327 $2 Type **335** 20 10
1328 $12 Hand placing coin in money box 45 25

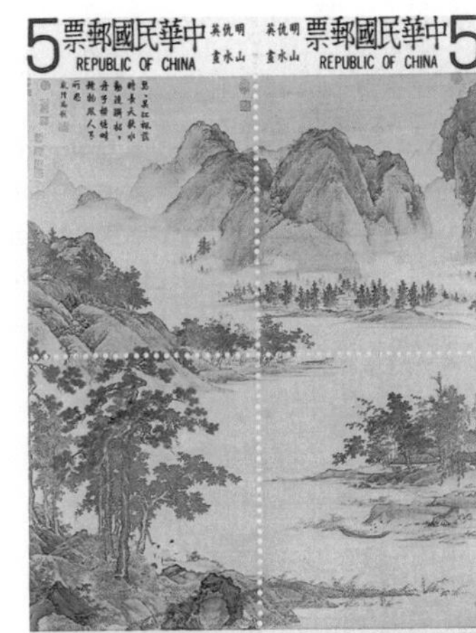

336/339 Landscape (⅗-size illustration)

1980. Painting by Ch'iu Ying.
1329 **336** $5 multicoloured . . . . 2·25 20
1330 **337** $5 multicoloured . . . . 2·25 20
1331 **338** $5 multicoloured . . . . 2·25 20
1332 **339** $5 multicoloured . . . . 2·25 20
Nos. 1329/32 were printed together, se-tenant, forming the composite design illustrated.

340 Cock

341 Heads, Flag and Census Form

1980. New Year Greetings. "Year of the Cock".
1334 **340** $1 multicoloured 75 10
1335 $6 multicoloured . . . . 2·00 25
See also No. 2047.

1980. Population and Housing Census. Mult.
1337 $2 Type **341** 20 10
1338 $12 Flag and buildings (horiz) 50 30

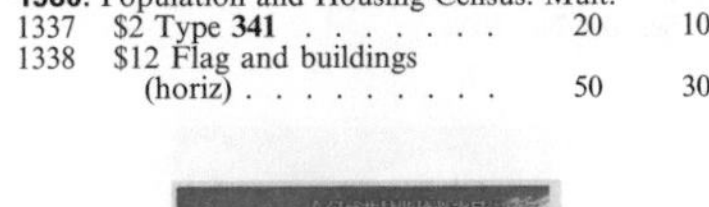

342 Central Weather Bureau

1981. Completion of Meteorological Satellite Ground Station, Taipei. Multicoloured.
1339 $2 "TIROS-N" weather satellite (vert) 20 10
1340 $10 Type **342** 50 30

343 "Happiness"

344 "Wealth"

345 "Longevity"

346 "Joy"

1981. New Year Calligraphy.
1341 **343** $5 gold, red and black 90 25
1342 **344** $5 gold, red and black 90 25
1343 **345** $5 gold, red and black 90 25
1344 **346** $5 gold, red and black 90 25

347 Candle and Siamese Twins

1981. International Year for Disabled Persons.
1345 **347** $2 multicoloured 20 10
1346 $10 multicoloured . . . 50 30

348 Mt. Ali

1981. Tourism. Multicoloured.
1347 $2 Type **348** 30 10
1348 $7 Oluanpi 55 15
1349 $12 Sun Moon Lake . . . . 1·00 25

349 "Children on River Bank"

1981. Children's Day. Children's Drawings. Mult.
1350 $1 Type **349** 15 10
1351 $2 "Cable-cars" 20 10
1352 $5 "Lobsters" 30 10
1353 $7 "Village" 40 15

350 Main Gate Chiang Kai-shek Memorial Hall

1981. 6th Death Anniv of Chiang Kai-shek.
1712 **350** 10c. red 10 10
1354 20c. violet 10 10
1714 30c. green 10 10
1355 40c. red 10 10
1356 50c. brown 10 10
1717 60c. blue 10 10

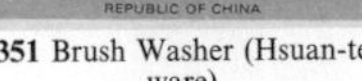

351 Brush Washer (Hsuan-te ware)

352 Electric and First Steam Locomotives

1981. Ancient Chinese Enamelware (1st series). Ming Dynasty Cloisonne Enamelware. Multicoloured.
1357 $2 Type **351** 40 10
1358 $5 Ritual vessel with ring handles (Chiang-ta'i ware) (vert) 70 10
1359 $8 Plate decorated with dragons (Wan-li ware) . . 90 10
1360 $10 Vase (vert) . . . . . . 1·25 25
See also Nos. 1438/41, 1472/5 and 1542/5.

1981. Centenary of Railway. Mult.
1361 $2 Type **352** 50 10
1362 $14 Side views of steam and electric locomotives (horiz) . . . . 1·50 40

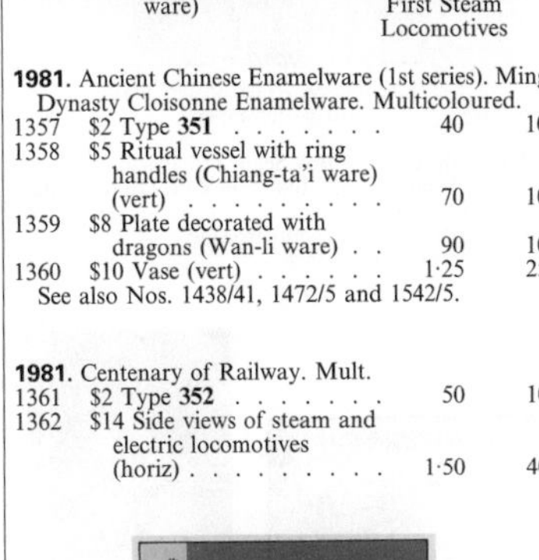

353 "Liagore rubromaculata"

1981. Crabs. Multicoloured.
1363 $2 Type **353** 20 10
1364 $5 "Ranina ranina" (vert) 40 10
1365 $8 "Platymaia wyvillethomsoni" 55 15
1366 $14 "Lambrus nummifera" (vert) . . . . 1·00 35

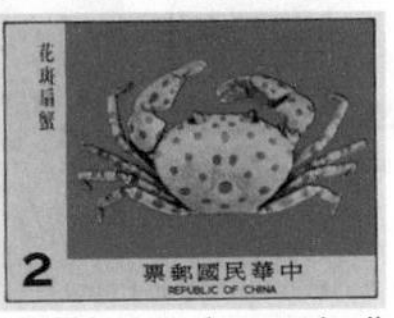

354 Bureau Emblem

355 The Cowherd

1981. 40th Anniv of Central Weather Bureau.
1367 **354** $2 multicoloured 20 10
1368 $14 multicoloured . . . 75 35

1981. Fairy Tales. "The Cowherd and the Weaving Maid". Multicoloured.
1369 $2 Type **355** 50 10
1370 $4 The cowherd watching the weaving maid through rushes 60 10
1371 $8 The cowherd and the weaving maid on opposite sides of Heavenly River 1·00 15
1372 $14 The cowherd and the weaving maid meeting on bridge of magpies . . . . 2·10 35

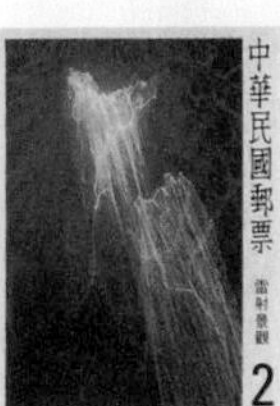

356 Laser Display

1981. Lasography Exhibition. Designs showing different laser displays.
1373 **356** $2 multicoloured 20 10
1374 – $5 multicoloured 30 10
1375 – $8 multicoloured 40 15
1376 – $14 multicoloured . . . 90 40

357 Goalkeeper catching Ball

359 Chinese Republic Anniv Emblem and "Stamps"

358 Officers watching Battle from Mound

1981. Athletics Day. Multicoloured.
1390 $5 Women soccer players 20 10
1391 $5 Type **357** 20 10

1981. 70th Anniv of Founding of Chinese Republic. Multicoloured.
1392 $2 Type **358** 15 10
1393 $2 Officer clenching fist and soldiers awaiting battle . . 15 10
1394 $2 Officer on horseback saluting 15 10
1395 $2 Attacking buildings . . . 15 10
1396 $3 Attacking fortifications 35 10
1397 $3 Dockside scene 60 20
1398 $8 Chiang Kai-shek 60 10
1399 $14 Sun Yat-sen 90 15

1981. "Rocpex Taipei '81" International Stamp Exhibition.
1401 **359** $2 multicoloured 15 10
1402 $14 multicoloured . . . 50 35

360 Detail of Scroll

1981. Sung Dynasty painting "One Hundred Young Boys". Designs showing details of Scroll.
1403 **360** $2 (1) multicoloured . . 1·90 25
1404 – $2 (2) multicoloured . . 1·90 25
1405 – $2 (3) multicoloured . . 1·90 25
1406 – $2 (4) multicoloured . . 1·90 25
1407 – $2 (5) multicoloured . . 1·90 25
1408 – $2 (6) multicoloured . . 1·90 25
1409 – $2 (7) multicoloured . . 1·90 25
1410 – $2 (8) multicoloured . . 1·90 25
1411 – $2 (9) multicoloured . . 1·90 25
1412 – $2 (10) multicoloured . . 1·90 25
See note below No. 661 on identification of designs.
Nos. 1403/12 were printed together in se-tenant blocks of ten (5 × 2) within the sheet, each strip of five forming a composite design.

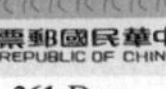

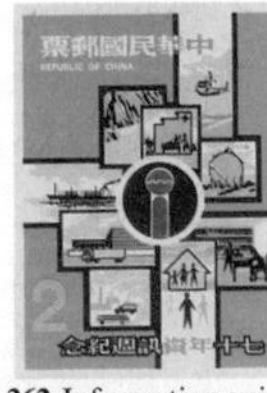

361 Dog

362 Information-using Services and Emblem

1981. New Year Greetings. "Year of the Dog".
1413 **361** $1 multicoloured . . . . 1·00 10
1414 $10 multicoloured . . . 1·75 25
See also No. 2048.

1981. Information Week.
1416 **362** $2 multicoloured 25 10

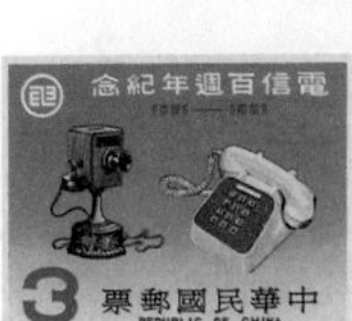

363 Telephones of 1881 and 1981

364 Arrangement in Basket

1981. Centenary of Chinese Telecommunications Service. Multicoloured.
1417 $2 Map and hand holding telephone handset (vert) 20 10
1418 $3 Type **363** 30 10
1419 $8 Submarine cable map . . 45 10
1420 $18 Computer and telecommunication units (vert) 65 20

1982. Chinese Flower Arrangements. Mult.
1421 $2 Type **364** 25 10
1422 $3 Arrangement in jug . . . 40 10
1423 $8 Arrangement in vase . . 75 10
1424 $18 Arrangement in holder 1·25 20

365 Kuan Yu leaves for Cheng City

1982. Scenes from "The Ku Cheng Reunion" (opera). Multicoloured.
1425 $2 Type **365** 55 10
1426 $3 Chang Fei refuses to open city gates 70 10
1427 $4 Chang Fei apologises to Kuan Yu 90 10
1428 $18 Liu Pei, Kuan Yu and Chang Fei are reunited 1·75 30

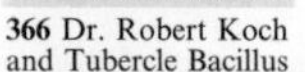

366 Dr. Robert Koch and Tubercle Bacillus
367 Chang Shih-liang (revolutionary)

1982. Centenary of Discovery of Tubercle Bacillus.
1429 **366** $2 multicoloured 15 10

1982. Famous Chinese.
1430 **367** $2 red 15 10

368 "Martyrs' Shrine"
369 Tooth and Child holding Toothbrush and Mug

1982. Children's Day. Children's paintings.
1431 $2 Type **368** 30 10
1432 $3 "House Yard" 45 10
1433 $5 "Cattle Herd" 60 10
1434 $8 "A Sacrificial Ceremony for a Plentiful Year" . . . 90 10

1982. Dental Health. Multicoloured.
1435 $2 Type **369** 25 10
1436 $3 Methods of cleaning teeth 45 10
1437 $10 Dental check-up 85 10

1982. Ancient Chinese Enamelware (2nd series). As T **351**. Multicoloured.
1438 $2 Champleve cup and plate (Ch'ien-lung ware) 45 10
1439 $5 Cloisonne duck container (Ch'ien-lung ware) (vert) 60 10
1440 $8 Painted incense burner (K'ang-hsi period) . . . . 1·10 10
1441 $12 Cloisonne Tibetan lama milk-tea pot (Ch'ien-lung ware) (vert) . . . . . . 1·75 15

370 "Spring Dawn" (Meng Hao-jan)

1982. Chinese Classical Poetry (1st series). Tang Dynasty Poems. Multicoloured.
1442 $2 Type **370** . . . . 1·50 10
1443 $3 "On Looking for a Hermit and not Finding Him" (Chia Tao) . . . . . 3·25 10
1444 $5 "Summer Dying" (Liu Yu-hsi) . . . . 6·75 10
1445 $18 "Looking at the Snow Drifts on South Mountains" (Tsu Yung) 7·50 55
See also Nos. 1476/9, 1524/7, 1594/7, 1866/9, 1910/13 and 2074/7.

371 Softball

1982. 5th World Women's Softball Championship, Taipeh.
1446 **371** $2 multicoloured 40 10
1447 $18 multicoloured . . . 85 20

372 Scouts on Rope Bridge, and Lord Baden-Powell

1982. 75th Anniv of Boy Scout Movement and 125th Birth Anniv of Lord Baden-Powell. Multicoloured.
1448 $2 Type **372** 25 10
1449 $18 Emblem, scouts making frame and camp 80 15

373 Tweezers holding Stamp
374 Carved Lion

1982. Philately Day. Multicoloured.
1450 $2 Type **373** 40 10
1451 $18 Examining stamp album with magnifying glass . . 80 20

1982. Tsu Shih Temple, Sanhsia. Multicoloured.
1452 $2 Type **374** 40 10
1453 $3 Lion brackets (horiz) . . 50 10
1454 $5 Carved sub-lintels in passageway 75 10
1455 $18 Temple roofs (horiz) . . 1·75 20

1982. Chinese Folk-tales (7th series). Stories from "36 Examples of Filial Piety" by Wu Yen-huan, As T **200**. Multicoloured.
1456 $1 Shao K'ang supporting his mother 25 10
1457 $2 Hsun Kuan leading soldier reinforcements to her father 45 10
1458 $3 Ku Yen-wu refusing to serve Ch'ing dynasty . . . 60 10
1459 $5 Ting Ch'un-liang caring for his paralysed father 1·00 10

375 Riding Horses

1982. 30th Anniv of China Youth Corps. Multicoloured.
1460 $2 Type **375** 10 10
1461 $3 Flag and water sport (vert) 15 10
1462 $18 Mountaineering 50 20

376 Lohan with Boy Attendant and Monkey
378 Pig

1982. Lohan (Buddhist Saint) Scroll Paintings by Liu Sung-nien. Multicoloured.
1463 $2 Type **376** . . . . 1·50 10
1464 $3 Monk presenting seated Lohan with scroll . . . . 2·00 10
1465 $18 Tribal king paying homage to seated Lohan 5·00 40

1982. New Year. "Year of the Pig".
1468 **378** $1 multicoloured . . . . 1·25 10
1469 $10 multicoloured . . . 2·25 25
See also No. 2049.

1983. Ancient Chinese Enamelware (3rd series). Ch'ing Dynasty Enamelware. As T **351**. Multicoloured.
1472 $2 Square basin with rounded corners 25 10
1473 $3 Vase decorated with landscape panels (vert) . . 75 10
1474 $4 Blue teapot with flower pattern . . . . 1·25 10
1475 $18 Cloisonne elephant with vase on back (vert) . . . 1·40 20

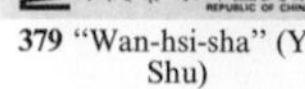

379 "Wan-hsi-sha" (Yen Shu)
380 Hsin-hsien Concealed Fall, Wawa Valley

1983. Chinese Classical Poetry (2nd series). Sung Dynasty Lyrical Poems. Multicoloured.
1476 $2 Type **379** . . . . 2·50 10
1477 $3 "Ch'ing-yu-an" (Ho Chu) 3·75 10
1478 $5 "Su-mu-che" (Fan Chung-yen) . . . . . . 4·50 10
1479 $11 "Hsing-hsiang-tzu" (Ch'ao Pu-chih) . . . . . 7·00 25

1983. Landscapes. Multicoloured.
1480 $2 Type **380** 75 10
1481 $3 University Pond, Chitou Forest 90 10
1482 $18 Mount Jade (horiz) . . 1·10 20

381 Matteo Ricci and Astrolabe

1983. 400th Anniv of Matteo Ricci's (missionary) Arrival in China. Multicoloured.
1483 $2 Type **381** 35 10
1484 $18 Matteo Ricci and Great Wall 70 20

382 Wu Ching-heng (Chairman of development committee)
383 Hsu Hsien meets Pai Su-chen

1983. 70th Anniv of Mandarin Phonetic Symbols. Multicoloured.
1485 $2 Type **382** 35 10
1486 $18 Children studying symbols 70 25

1983. Fairy Tales. "Lady White Snake". Multicoloured.
1487 $2 Type **383** 40 10
1488 $3 Pai Su-chen steals Tree of Life 50 10
1489 $3 Confrontation with Fahai at Chin Shan Temple . . 1·00 10
1490 $18 Pai Su-chen is imprisoned beneath Thunder Peak Pagoda . . 2·25 30

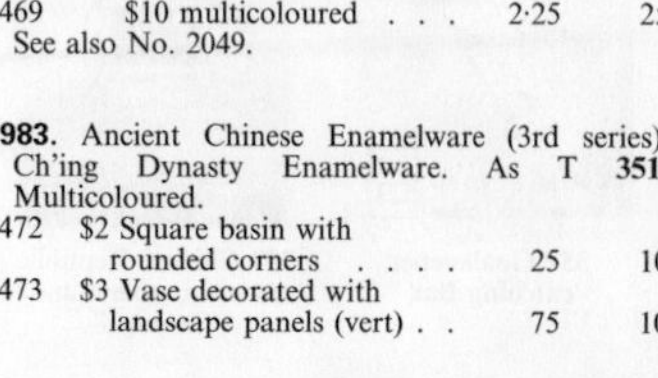
384 Pot with Cord Pattern
385 Communication Emblems circling Globe

1983. Ancient Chinese Bamboo Carvings. Multicoloured.
1491 $2 Type **384** 40 10
1492 $3 Vase with Tao-t'ien motif 75 10
1493 $4 Carved mountain scene with figures 75 10
1494 $18 Brush-holder with relief showing ladies . . . . . 1·50 20

1983. World Communications Year. Mult.
1495 $2 Type **385** 75 10
1496 $18 W.C.Y. emblem 90 20

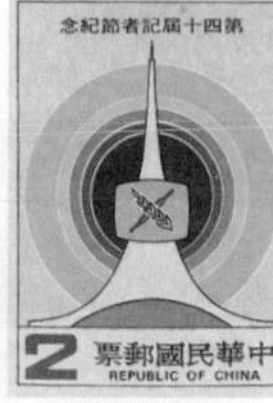
386 Grouper
387 T.V. Screen, Antenna and Radio Waves

1983. Protection of Fishery Resources. Mult.
1497 $2 Type **386** 40 10
1498 $18 Lizardfish . . . . . . 1·00 25

1983. Journalists' Day.
1499 **387** $2 multicoloured 15 10

388 Yurt
389 Brown Shrike

1983. Mongolian and Tibetan Scenes.
1500 $2 Type **388** 40 10
1501 $3 Potala Palace 65 10
1502 $5 Sheep on prairie 80 10
1503 $11 Camel caravan . . . . 1·10 20

1983. 2nd East Asian Bird Protection Conference. Multicoloured.
1504 $2 Type **389** 75 10
1505 $18 Grey-faced buzzard-eagle . . . . 1·00 40

390 Pink Plum Blossom
391 Congress Emblem

1983. Plum Blossom. Multicoloured.
1506 $2 Type **390** 15 10
1507 $3 Red plum blossom . . . 20 10
1508 $5 Plum blossom and pagoda 45 15
1509 $11 White plum blossom . . 1·00 15

1983. 38th Jaycees International World Congress. Multicoloured.
1510 $2 Type **391** 25 10
1511 $18 Emblems and globe . . 80 20

392 World Map as Heart
393 Rat

1983. 8th Asian-Pacific Cardiology Congress. Mult.
1512 $2 Type **392** 25 10
1513 $18 Heart and electrocardiogram 80 20

1983. New Year. "Year of the Rat".
1514 **393** $1 multicoloured 85 10
1515 $10 multicoloured . . . 2·00 20
See also No. 2038.

394 Mother and Child reading and Chin Ting Prize

1983. National Reading Week. Mult.
1517 $2 Type **394** 20 10
1518 $18 Chin Ting prize (for outstanding publications) books and father and son reading (vert) 80 20

395 Boeing 737 over Chiang Kai-shek Airport

396 Soldiers with Flags

1984. Air. 37th Anniv of Civil Aeronautics Administration. Multicoloured.
1519 $7 Type **395** 35 15
1520 $11 Boeing 747 over Chung-cheng Memorial Hall (horiz) 50 15
1521 $18 Boeing 737 over Sun Yat-sen Memorial Hall (horiz) 65 20

1984. World Freedom Day. Multicoloured.
1522 $2 Type **396** 20 10
1523 $18 Globe and people of the world 80 20

397 "Hsiao-liang-chou" (Kuan Yun-shih)

1984. Chinese Classical Poetry (3rd series). Yuan Dynasty Lyric Poems. Multicoloured.
1524 $2 Type **397** . . . . 3·00 20
1525 $3 "A Lady holds a fine fan of silk", "Tien-ching-sha" (Po P'u) . . . . 4·50 25
1526 $5 "Picnic under banana leaves "Ch'ing-chiang-yin" (Chang Ko-chin) . . . . 5·00 25
1527 $18 "Plum blossoms in the snowbound wilderness "Tien-ching-sha" (Shang Cheng-shu) . . . . 12·50 1·40

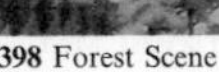

398 Forest Scene

400 Lin Chueh-min (revolutionary)

1984. Forest Resources. Multicoloured.
1528 $2 Type **398** 35 10
1529 $2 Reservoir and dam . . . 35 10
1530 $2 Camp in forest 35 10
1531 $2 Wooded slopes 35 10
Nos. 1528/31 were printed together se-tenant, forming a composite design.

1984. Famous Chinese.
1536 **400** $2 green 15 10

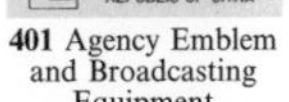

401 Agency Emblem and Broadcasting Equipment

402 "Five Auspicious Tokens"

1984. 60th Anniv of Central News Agency. Mult.
1537 $2 Type **401** 15 10
1538 $10 Agency emblem and satellite communications 45 15

1984. 85th Birth Anniv of Chang Ta-chien (artist). Multicoloured.
1539 $2 Type **402** . . . . 1·75 10
1540 $5 "The God of Longevity" 2·25 15
1541 $18 "Lotus Blossoms in Ink Splash" . . . . 5·00 40

1984. Ancient Chinese Enamelware (4th series). Ch'ing Dynasty Enamelware. As T **351**. Mult.
1542 $2 Lidded cup and teapot on tray 20 10
1543 $3 Cloisonne wine vessel on phoenix (vert) 50 10
1544 $4 Yellow teapot with pink and blue chrysanthemum decoration 75 15
1545 $18 Cloisonne candle-holder on bird . . . . 1·50 40

403 Boeing 747-200 circling Globe

1984. Inauguration of China Airlines Global Service. Multicoloured.
1546 $2 Type **403** 20 10
1547 $7 Globe and Boeing 747-200 . . . . 60 20
1548 $11 Boeing 747-200 over New York 85 30
1549 $18 Boeing 747-200 over Netherlands . . . . . . 1·50 55

404 Judo

1984. Olympic Games, Los Angeles. Mult.
1550 $2 Type **404** 15 10
1551 $5 Archery (vert) 35 15
1552 $18 Swimming . . . . . . 1·00 60

405 Container Ship "Ming Comfort"

406 "Gentiana arisanensis"

1984. 30th Navigation Day. Multicoloured.
1553 $2 Type **405** 45 10
1554 $18 "Prosperity" (tanker) 1·00 65

1984. Alpine Plants. Multicoloured.
1555 $2 Type **406** 35 10
1556 $3 "Epilobium nankotaiza nense" 55 10
1557 $5 "Adenophora uehatae" 80 15
1558 $18 "Aconitum fukutomei" 2·25 25

407 Scholars listening to Music

408 Volleyball Players

1984. Sung Dynasty Painting "The Eighteen Scholars". Multicoloured.
1559 $2 Type **407** . . . . 1·25 10
1560 $3 Scholars playing chess . . 2·75 10
1561 $5 Scholars writing . . . . 1·50 15
1562 $18 Scholars painting . . . 6·00 65

1984. Athletics Day. Multicoloured.
1563 $5 Type **408** 25 15
1564 $5 Volleyball player 25 15
Nos. 1563/4 were printed together, se-tenant, forming a composite design.

409 Union Emblem

410 1965 Confucius $1 Stamp

1984. 20th Anniv of Asian-Pacific Parliamentarians' Union.
1565 **409** $10 multicoloured . . . 50 25

1984. New Postal Museum Building, Taipeh. Multicoloured.
1566 $2 Type **410** 10 10
1567 $5 1933 Sun Yat-sen 5c. stamp 25 15
1568 $18 New Postal Museum building . . . . 1·40 65

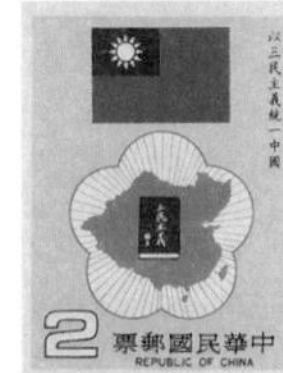

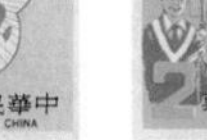

411 Flag and Emblem

412 Commission Services

1984. Grand Alliance for China's Reunification Convention.
1570 **411** $2 multicoloured 30 10

1984. 30th Anniv of Vocational Assistance Commission for Retired Servicemen.
1571 **412** $2 multicoloured 30 10

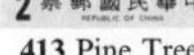

413 Pine Tree

414 Ox

1984. Pine, Bamboo and Plum (1st series). Multicoloured.
1572 $2 Type **413** 20 10
1573 $8 Bamboo 60 20
1574 $10 Plum blossom 60 20
See also Nos. 1633/5, 1783/5 and 1845/7.

1984. New Year Greetings. "Year of the Ox".
1575 **414** $1 multicoloured . . . . 1·00 10
1576 $10 multicoloured . . . 2·00 20
See also No. 2039.

415 Legal Code Book and Scales

416 Ku-kang Lake and Pagoda, Quemoy

1985. Judicial Day.
1578 **415** $5 multicoloured 50 15

1985. Scenery of Quemoy and Matsu. Mult.
1579 $2 Type **416** 15 10
1580 $5 Kuang-hai stone, Quemoy 45 15
1581 $8 Sheng-li reservoir, Matsu 1·50 20
1582 $10 Tung-chu lighthouse, Matsu . . . . 1·50 20

417 Sir Robert Hart and 1878 3c. Stamp

418 Lo Fu-hsing

1985. 150th Anniv of Sir Robert Hart (founder of Chinese Postal Service).
1583 **417** $2 multicoloured 30 10

1985. Birth Centenary of Lo Fu-hsing (patriot).
1584 **418** $2 multicoloured 30 10

419 Tsou Jung

421 Lily

420 Main Gate, Chung-cheng Memorial Hall

1985. 80th Death Anniv of Tsou Jung (revolutionary).
1585 **419** $3 green 35 10

1985. 10th Death Anniv of President Chiang Kai-shek. Multicoloured.
1586 $2 Type **420** 15 10
1587 $8 Tzuhu, President Chiang's temporary resting place 60 20
1588 $10 President Chiang Kai-shek (vert) 80 20

1985. Mothers' Day. Multicoloured.
1589 $2 Type **421** 25 10
1590 $2 Carnation 25 10

422 View of Tunnel

423 Girl Guide saluting

1985. 1st Anniv of Kaohsiung Cross-harbour Tunnel.
1591 **422** $5 multicoloured 60 15

1985. 75th Anniv of Girl Guide Movement.
1592 **423** $2 multicoloured 10 10
1593 $18 multicoloured . . . 80 25

424 "Buxom is the Peach Tree..."

1985. Chinese Classical Poetry (4th series). Poems from "Book of Odes", edited by Confucius. Multicoloured.
1594 $2 Type **424** 75 10
1595 $5 "Thick grows that tarragon ..." . . . . 1·50 15
1596 $8 "Thick grow the rush leaves ..." . . . . 2·25 20
1597 $10 "... The snowflakes fly" 3·25 20

425 Wax Jambo

1985. Fruit. Multicoloured.
1598 $2 Type **425** 50 10
1599 $3 Guavas 75 10
1600 $5 Carambolas 90 15
1601 $8 Lychees . . . . 1·50 20

426 Dragon Boat

427 Lady of Rank, T'ang Dynasty

1985. Ch'ing Dynasty Ivory Carvings. Mult.
1602 $2 Type **426** 65 10
1603 $3 Carved landscape 75 10
1604 $5 Melon-shaped water container . . . . 1·25 15
1605 $18 Brush-holder (vert) . . 1·50 35

1985. 4th Asian Costume Conference. Chinese Costumes (1st series). Multicoloured.
1606 $2 Type **427** 85 10
1607 $5 Palace woman, Sung dynasty 90 10
1608 $8 Lady of rank, Yuan dynasty . . . . 1·60 20
1609 $11 Lady of rank, Ming dynasty . . . . 1·90 25
See also Nos. 1687/90, 1767/70, 1833/6, 1906/9 and 1973/6.

428 Bird feeding Chicks

1985. Social Welfare.
1610 **428** $2 multicoloured 25 10

429 North Gate, Taipeh

430 Oak Tree

1985. Historic Buildings (1st series). Mult.
1611 $2 Type **429** 20 10
1612 $5 San Domingo fort, Tamsui 45 15
1613 $8 Lung Shan Temple, Lukang 60 20
1614 $10 Confucius Temple, Changhua . . . . 1·00 20
See also Nos. 1700/3.

1985. Bonsai. Multicoloured.
1615 $2 Type **430** 20 10
1616 $5 Five-leaf pine 45 15
1617 $8 Lohan pine 60 20
1618 $18 Banyan . . . . 1·50 25

431 World Trade Centre and Sports Goods Logo

432 Flag, Map and Scenes of Peace

1985. Trade Shows. Multicoloured.
1619 $2 Type **431** 20 10
1620 $2 Toys and gifts logo (blue and red) 20 10
1621 $2 Electronics logo (blue) 20 10
1622 $2 Machinery logo (black and orange) 20 10
Nos. 1619/22 were printed together, se-tenant, forming a composite design depicting Taipeh World Trade Centre.

1985. 40th Anniv of Return of Taiwan to China. Multicoloured.
1623 $2 Type **432** 30 10
1624 $18 Chiang Kai-shek and triumphal arch 65 25

433 Emblem

434 Sun Yat-sen

1985. 7th Asian Federation for the Mentally Retarded Conference, Taipeh.
1625 **433** $2 multicoloured 25 10
1626 $11 multicoloured . . . 60 25

1985. 120th Birth Anniv of Sun Yat-sen.
1627 **434** $2 multicoloured 25 10
1628 $18 multicoloured . . . 1·25 25

435 Tiger

436 Emblem

1985. New Year Greetings. "Year of the Tiger".
1629 **435** $1 multicoloured 50 10
1630 $10 multicoloured . . . 2·40 20
See also No. 2040.

1985. 50th Anniv of Postal Simple Life Insurance.
1632 **436** $2 multicoloured 20 10

437 Pine Tree

1986. Pine, Bamboo and Plum (2nd series). Multicoloured.
1633 $1 Type **437** 25 10
1634 $11 Bamboo 65 20
1635 $18 Plum blossom . . . . . 1·10 25

438 Detail of Scroll

1986. Painting "Hermit Anglers on a Mountain Stream" by T'ang Yin. Designs showing details of the scroll. Multicoloured.
1636 $2 (1) Type **438** 90 10
1637 $2 (2) Pavilions on bank . . 90 10
1638 $2 (3) Anglers in boats near waterfall 90 10
1639 $2 (4) Pavilions on stilts . . 90 10
1640 $2 (5) Anglers in boat near island 90 10
Nos. 1636/40 were printed together, forming a composite design.
See note below No. 661 on identification of designs in se-tenant strips.

439 Gladioli in Vase

440 Loading and unloading Boeing 747 Mail Plane

1986. Flower Arrangements (1st series). Mult.
1641 $2 Type **439** 10 10
1642 $5 Roses in double wicker holders 35 10
1643 $8 Roses and fern in pot on stand 65 10
1644 $10 Various flowers in large and small pots 80 10
See also Nos. 1741/4.

1986. 90th Anniv of Post Office. Mult.
1645 $2 Type **440** 15 10
1646 $5 Postman on motorcycle (vert) 30 10
1647 $8 Customer at cash dispenser and clerk at savings bank computer terminal (vert) 45 10
1648 $10 Electronic sorting machine and envelopes circling globe 65 15

441 Chen Tien-hva (revolutionary writer)

442 Mountain shrouded in Mist

1986. Famous Chinese.
1650 **441** $2 violet 10 10

1986. Yushan National Park. Multicoloured.
1651 $2 Type **442** 35 10
1652 $5 People on mountain top 80 10
1653 $8 Snow covered mountain peak . . . . 1·10 10
1654 $10 Forest on mountain side 1·50 15

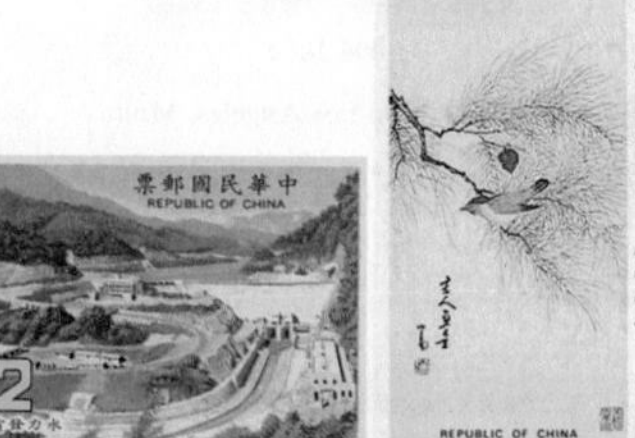
443 Hydro-electric Power Station 444 Taiwan Firecrest in Tree

1986. Power Stations. Multicoloured.
1655 $2 Type **443** 35 10
1656 $8 Thermo-electric power station 60 10
1657 $10 Nuclear power station 75 15

1986. Paintings by P'u Hsin-yu. Mult.
1658 $2 Type **444** . . . . 1·50 20
1659 $8 Landscape . . . . 2·25 10
1660 $10 Woman in garden . . . 2·75 15

445 Emblems

446 Green-winged Macaw

1986. 25th Anniv of Asian Productivity Organization and 30th Anniv of China Productivity Centre.
1661 **445** $2 multicoloured 15 10
1662 $11 multicoloured . . . 75 20

1986. Protection of Intellectual Property.
1663 **446** $2 multicoloured 90 20

447 Starck's Damselfish ("Chrysiptera starcki") (448)

1986. Coral Reef Fishes, Multicoloured.
1664 $2 Type **447** 30 10
1665 $2 Copper-banded butterflyfish ("Chelmon rostratus") 30 10
1666 $2 Pearl-scaled butterflyfish ("Chaetodon xanthurus") 30 10
1667 $2 Four-spotted butterflyfish ("Chaetodon quadrimaculatus") 30 10
1668 $2 Meyer's butterflyfish ("Chaetodon meyeri") . . 30 10
1669 $2 Japanese swallow ("Genicanthus semifasciatus") (female) 30 10
1670 $2 Japanese swallow ("Genicanthus semifasciatus") (male) . . 30 10
1671 $2 Blue-ringed angelfish ("Pomacanthus annularis") 30 10
1672 $2 Harlequin tuskfish ("Lienardella fasciata") 30 10
1673 $2 Undulate triggerfish ("Balistapus undulatus") 30 10

1986. 60th Anniv of Chiang Kai-shek's Northward Expedition. Nos. 1229 and 1386 surch as T **448**.
1674 **306** $2 on $6 red, bl & orge 15 15
1675 $8 on $9 red, bl & grn 35 25

449 Tzu Mu Bridge

450 Yingtai and Shanpo going to School

1986. Road Bridges. Multicoloured.
1676 $2 Type **449** 45 10
1677 $5 Chang Hung bridge over Hsiu-ku-luan-chi 70 10
1678 $8 Kuan Fu bridge over Hsintien River . . . . . 1·10 10
1679 $10 Kuan Tu bridge over Tanshui River . . . . . 1·50 15

1986. Folk Tales. "Love between Liang Shanpo and Chu Yingtai". Multicoloured.
1680 $5 Type **450** 50 10
1681 $5 Classmates 50 10
1682 $5 Yingtai and Shanpo by lake 50 10
1683 $5 Yingtai telling Shanpo she is to be married . . . 50 10
1684 $5 Ascending to heaven as butterflies 50 10

451 Children playing by Lake and Rainbow

452 Lady of Warring States Period

1986. Cleanliness and Courtesy. Mult.
1685 $2 Type **451** 30 10
1686 $8 Children helping others in street 50 10

1986. Chinese Costumes (2nd series). Mult.
1687 $2 Lady of rank, Shang dynasty 70 10
1688 $5 Type **452** . . . . 1·25 10
1689 $8 Empress's assembly dress, later Han dynasty . . . . 2·00 10
1690 $10 Beribboned dress of lady of rank, Wei and Tsin dynasties . . . . . 3·00 25

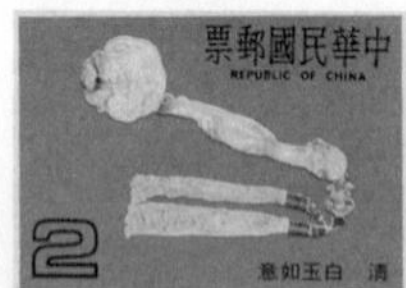
453 White Jade Ju-i Sceptre with Fish Decoration

1986. Ch'ing Dynasty Ju-i (1st series). Mult.
1691 $2 Type **453** 40 10
1692 $3 Coral ju-i sceptre with fungus motif 60 10
1693 $4 Redwood ju-i sceptre inlaid with precious stones 75 10
1694 $18 Gold-painted ju-i sceptre with three abundances (fruit) . . . . 1·50 25
See also Nos 1735/8.

454 Chiang Kai-shek and Books

1986. Birth Cent of Chiang Kai-shek. Mult.
1695 $2 Type **454** 55 10
1696 $5 Chiang Kai-shek, flag, map and crowd 45 10
1697 $8 Chiang Kai-shek, emblem and youths 70 10
1698 $10 Chiang Kai-shek, flags on globe and clasped hands 80 15

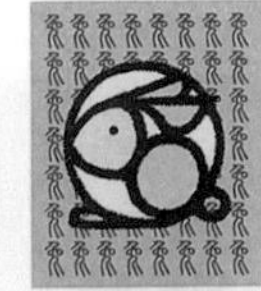

455 Erh-sha-wan Gun Emplacement, Keelung
456 Hare

1986. Historic Buildings (2nd series). Mult.
1700 $2 Chin-kuang-fu House, Pei-pu 30 10
1701 $5 Type **455** 75 10
1702 $8 Hsi T'ai fort 80 10
1703 $10 Matsu Temple, Peng-hu 1·00 15

1986. New Year Greetings. "Year of the Hare".
1704 **456** $1 multicoloured 45 10
1705 $10 multicoloured 1·90 15
See also No. 2041.

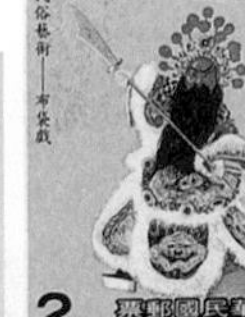

457 Shrubs on Rock Formation
458 Glove Puppet

1987. Kenting National Park. Multicoloured.
1707 $2 Type **457** 30 10
1708 $5 Rocky outcrop 70 10
1709 $8 Sandy bay 1·00 10
1710 $10 Rocky bays 1·50 15

1987. Puppets. Multicoloured.
1721 $2 Type **458** 30 10
1722 $5 String puppet 85 10
1723 $18 Shadow show puppet 1·25 25

459 Envelope, Parcel and Globe
460 Wu Yueh (revolutionary)

1987. Speedpost Service.
1724 **459** $2 multicoloured 30 10
1725 $18 multicoloured 1·00 25

1987. Famous Chinese.
1726 **460** $2 red 30 10

461 "Singing Creek with Bamboo Orchestra"

1987. Madame Chiang Kai-shek's Landscape Paintings (3rd series). Each black, stone and red.
1727 $2 Type **461** 50 10
1728 $5 "Mountains draped in Clouds" 1·40 10
1729 $5 "Vista of Tranquility" 1·75 10
1730 $10 "Mountains after a Snowfall" 2·10 15

462 Bodhisattva Head, Northern Wei Dynasty
463 View of Dam

1987. Ancient Chinese Stone Carvings. Mult.
1731 $5 Type **462** 70 10
1732 $5 Standing Buddha, Northern Ch'i dynasty 70 10
1733 $5 Bodhisattva head, T'ang dynasty 70 10
1734 $5 Seated Buddha, T'ang dynasty 70 10

1987. Ch'ing Dynasty Ju-i (2nd series). As T **453**. Multicoloured.
1735 $2 Silver ju-i sceptre with fungus decoration of pearls and precious stones 30 10
1736 $3 Gold ju-i sceptre with Eight Treasures decoration of pearls and precious stones 35 10
1737 $4 Gilt ju-i sceptre inlaid with precious stones and kingfisher feather 50 10
1738 $18 Gilt ju-i sceptre with wirework and inlaid with malachite 2·00 25

1987. Feitsui Reservoir Inauguration. Multicoloured.
1739 $2 Type **463** 25 10
1740 $18 View of reservoir 80 25

1987. Flower Arrangements (2nd series). As T **439**. Multicoloured.
1741 $2 Roses and pine twig in holder 25 10
1742 $5 Flowers in pot 45 10
1743 $8 Tasselled pendant hanging from bamboo in vase 80 10
1744 $10 Pine in flask 1·00 15

464 Emblem
465 Soldiers firing from behind Barricades

1987. 70th Lions Clubs International Convention, Taipeh.
1745 **464** $2 multicoloured 25 10
1746 $18 multicoloured 1·00 25

1987. 50th Anniv of Start of Sino-Japanese War. Multicoloured.
1747 $1 Type **465** 15 10
1748 $2 Chiang Kai-shek making speech from balcony 25 10
1749 $5 Crowd throwing money onto flag 40 10
1750 $6 Columns of soldiers and tanks on mountain road 50 10
1751 $8 General giving written message to Chiang Kai-shek 75 10
1752 $18 Pres. and Madame Chiang Kai-shek at front of crowd 1·10 25

466 Airplane flying to Left
467 Wang Yun-wu

1987. Air. Multicoloured.
1753 $9 Type **466** 50 15
1754 $14 Airplane 75 20
1755 $18 Airplane flying to right 1·00 25

1987. Birth Centenary (1988) of Wang Yun-wu (lexicographer).
1756 **467** $2 black 25 10

468 Trees on Islands and Fisherman

1987. Painting "After Chao Po-su's 'Red Cliff'" by Wen Cheng-ming. Designs showing details of the scroll. Multicoloured.
1757 $3 (1) Type **468** 65 10
1758 $3 (2) Tree and three figures on island 65 10
1759 $3 (3) House in walled enclosure on island 65 10
1760 $3 (4) Figures in doorway of building and horse in stable 65 10
1761 $3 (5) Cliffs and sea 65 10
1762 $3 (6) Islets, trees and figures on shore 65 10
1763 $3 (7) Trees among cliffs 65 10
1764 $3 (8) People in sampan 65 10
1765 $3 (9) Building surrounded by trees and cliffs 65 10
1766 $3 (10) Cliffs, trees and waterfall 65 10
Nos. 1757/66 were printed together, se-tenant, forming a composite design.
See note below No. 661 on identification of designs in se-tenant strips.

469 Han Lady of Rank, Early Ch'ing Dynasty
470 Ta Chen Tian, Confucius Temple, Taichung

1987. Chinese Costumes (3rd series). Mult.
1767 $1.50 Type **469** 50 10
1768 $3 Manchu bannerman's wife, Ch'ing dynasty 60 10
1769 $7.50 Woman's Manchu-style Ch'i-p'ao, early Republic period 1·40 10
1770 $18 Jacket and skirt, early Republic period 2·75 35

1987. International Confucianism and the Modern World Symposium, Taipeh. Multicoloured.
1771 $3 Type **470** 20 10
1772 $18 Confucius and fresco 80 25

471 Dragon
472 Flag and Emblem as "40"

1987. New Year Greetings. "Year of the Dragon".
1773 **471** $1.50 multicoloured 60 10
1774 $12 multicoloured 2·50 20
See also No. 2042.

1987. 40th Anniv of Constitution. Mult.
1776 $3 Type **472** 20 10
1777 $16 "40" in national colours and emblem 1·00 25

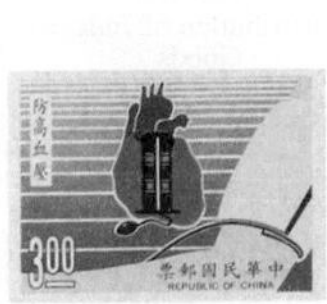

473 Sphygmomanometer
474 Plum

1988. Nat Health. Prevent Hypertension Campaign.
1778 **473** $3 multicoloured 25 10

1988. Flowers (1st series). Multicoloured.
1779 $3 Type **474** 50 10
1780 $7.50 Apricot 1·10 10
1781 $12 Peach 1·50 20
See also Nos. 1798/1800, 1809/11 and 1829/31.

475 Pine Tree
476 Modelled Dough Figurines

1988. Pine, Bamboo and Plum (3rd series). Multicoloured.
1783 $1.50 Type **475** 25 10
1784 $7.50 Bamboo 45 10
1785 $16 Plum blossom 85 25

1988. Traditional Handicrafts. Multicoloured.
1786 $3 Type **476** 50 10
1787 $7.50 Blown sugar fish 90 10
1788 $16 Sugar painting 1·25 25

477 Hsu Hsi-lin (revolutionary)
478 Bio-technology

1988. Famous Chinese.
1789 **477** $3 brown 25 10

1988. Science and Technology. Multicoloured.
1790 $1.50 Type **478** 15 10
1791 $3 Surveyors at oil field (energy) 20 10
1792 $7 Syringe piercing letter "B" (hepatitis control) 25 10
1793 $7.50 Mechanised production line (automation) 30 10
1794 $10 Satellite and computer terminal (information) 40 15
1795 $12 Laser (electro-optics) 50 20
1796 $16 Laboratory worker (materials) 65 25
1797 $16.50 Tin of fruit and technician (food technology) 65 25

1988. Flowers (2nd series). As T **474**. Mult.
1798 $3 Tree peony 50 10
1799 $7.50 Pomegranate 1·10 10
1800 $12 East Indian lotus 1·50 20

479 Policemen on Point Duty and Motor Cycle

1988. Police Day. Multicoloured.
1802 $3 Type **479** 40 10
1803 $12 Communications operator and fire-fighters 75 20

480 Butler's Pigmy Frog

1988. Amphibians. Multicoloured.
1804 $1.50 Type **480** 30 10
1805 $3 Taipeh striped slender frog 40 10
1806 $7.50 "Microhyla inornata" 1·25 10
1807 $16 Tree frog 2·50 35

481 "60" on Map

1988. 60th Anniv of Broadcasting Corporation of China.
1808 **481** $3 multicoloured 25 10

1988. Flowers (3rd series). As T **474**. Mult.
1809 $3 Garden balsam 50 10
1810 $7.50 Sweet osmanthus 90 10
1811 $12 Chrysanthemum 1·25 20

482 Chiang Kai-shek and Soldiers

1988. 30th Anniv of Kinmen Bombardment. Multicoloured.
1813 $1.50 Type **482** 25 10
1814 $3 Chiang Kai-shek and soldier reporters 25 10
1815 $7.50 Soldiers firing howitzer 65 10
1816 $12 Tank battle 75 20

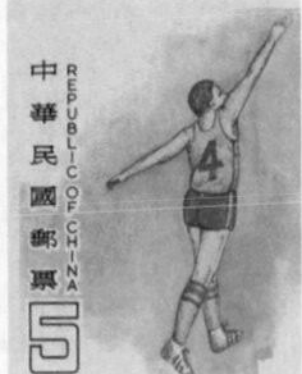
483 Basketball Player

1988. Sports Day. Multicoloured.
1817 $5 Type **483** 20 10
1818 $5 Two basketball players 20 10
1819 $5 Baseball hitter 20 10
1820 $5 Baseball catcher 20 10

484 Crater

1988. Yangmingshan National Park. Mult.
1821 $1.50 Type **484** 50 10
1822 $3 Lake 75 10
1823 $7.50 Mountains . . . . . 1·25 10
1824 $16 Lake and mountains . . 1·75 25

485-88 "Lofty Mount Lu"

1988. Painting by Shen Chou.
1825 **485** $5 multicoloured . . . . 1·10 10
1826 **486** $5 multicoloured . . . . 1·10 10
1827 **487** $5 multicoloured . . . . 1·10 10
1828 **488** $5 multicoloured . . . . 1·10 10
Nos. 1825/8 were printed together, se-tenant, forming the composite design illustrated.

1988. Flowers (4th series). As T **474**. Mult.
1829 $3 Cotton rose hibiscus . . 65 10
1830 $7.50 Camellia 90 10
1831 $12 Narcissus . . . . 1·25 20

1988. Chinese Costumes (4th series). As T **469**. Multicoloured.
1833 $2 Nobleman with tall hat, Shang dynasty 75 10
1834 $3 Ruler with topknot, Warring States period . . 85 10
1835 $7.50 Male official with writing brush in hair, Wei-chin dynasty . . . . 1·10 10
1836 $12 Male court official with hanging brush on hat, late Northern dynasties . . . 2·00 20

489 Snake **490** Tai Ch'uan-hsien

1988. New Year Greetings. "Year of the Snake".
1837 **489** $2 multicoloured . . . . 1·25 10
1838 $13 multicoloured . . . 1·75 20
See also No. 2043.

1989. Birth Centenary (1990) of Tai Ch'uan-hsien (Civil Service reformer).
1840 **490** $3 black 35 10

491 Pres. Chiang Ching-kuo

1989. 1st Death Anniv of President Chiang Ching-Kuo. Multicoloured.
1841 $3 Type **491** 15 10
1842 $6 Chiang Ching-kuo, political rally and voters 40 10
1843 $7.50 Chiang Ching-kuo at docks 85 15
1844 $16 Chiang Ching-kuo with children . . . . 1·00 25

492 Pine Tree

1989. Pine, Bamboo and Plum (4th series). Multicoloured.
1845 $3 Type **492** 10 10
1846 $16.50 Bamboo 65 25
1847 $21 Plum blossom 80 30

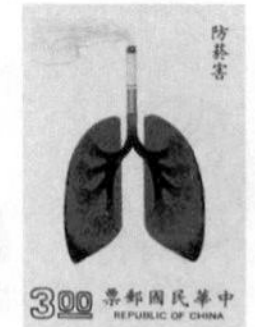
493 Ni Ying-tien **494** Lungs smoking

1989. 79th Death Anniv of Ni Ying-tien (revolutionary).
1848 **493** $3 black 30 10

1989. Anti-smoking Campaign.
1849 **494** $3 multicoloured 30 10

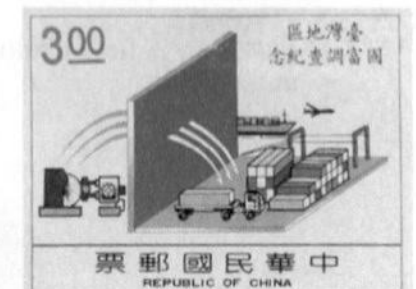
495 Mu Tou Yu Lighthouse **496** Distribution of Industrial Goods

1989. Lighthouses. White panel at foot. Mult.
1850 75c. Type **495** 10 10
1851 $2 Lu Tao lighthouse . . . 10 10
1852 $2.25 Pen Chia Yu lighthouse 15 10
1853 $3 Pitou Chiao lighthouse 15 10
1854 $4.50 Tungyin Tao lighthouse 25 10
1855 $6 Chilai Pi lighthouse . . . 35 25
1856 $7 Fukwei Chiao lighthouse 45 30
1857 $7.50 Hua Yu lighthouse . . 50 30
1858 $9 Oluan Pi lighthouse . . . 60 25
1859 $10 Kaohsiung lighthouse 75 40
1860 $10.50 Yuweng Tao lighthouse 75 30
1861 $12 Tungchu Tao lighthouse 80 50
1862 $13 Yeh Liu lighthouse . . 90 35
1863 $15 Tungchi Yu lighthouse 1·10 70
1864 $16.50 Chimei Yu lighthouse 1·25 65
For designs with blue panel at foot, see Nos. 2003/15.

1989. National Wealth Survey.
1865 **496** $3 multicoloured 40 10

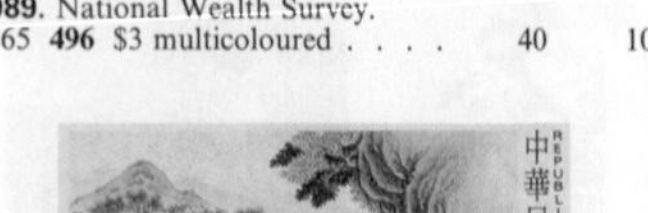

497 "I once tended nine Fields of Orchids"

1989. Chinese Classical Poetry (5th series). Poems from "Ch'u Ts'u". Multicoloured.
1866 $3 Type **497** 30 10
1867 $7.50 "No grief is greater than parting" 80 10
1868 $12 "...living remote and neglected" . . . . 1·50 20
1869 $16 "The horse will not gallop into servitude" . . 2·00 25

498 Underground Train

1989. Completion of Taipeh Underground Section of Western Railway Line. Multicoloured.
1870 $3 Type **498** 50 10
1871 $16 Train in cutting . . . . 1·25 25

499 Blue Triangle

1989. Butterflies (1st series). Multicoloured.
1872 $2 Type **499** 50 15
1873 $3 Great mormon 85 15
1874 $7.50 Chequered swallowtail 1·40 20
1875 $9 Common rose . . . . . 2·00 20
See also Nos. 1902/5.

500 Pumpkin Teapot **501** Fan Chung-yen

1989. Teapots (1st series). Multicoloured.
1876 $2 Type **500** 60 10
1877 $3 Clay teapot 90 10
1878 $12 "Chopped wood" teapot 1·50 25
1879 $16 Clay pear teapot . . . 2·00 30
See also Nos. 1946/50.

1989. Birth Millenary of Fan Chung-yen (civil service reformer).
1880 **501** $12 multicoloured . . . 65 25

502 Trees and Right Side of Mountain

1989. Painting "Autumn Colours on the Ch'iao and Hua Mountains" by Ch'iao Mengfu. Designs showing details of the scroll. Multicoloured.
1881 $7.50 (1) Type **502** 75 15
1882 $7.50 (2) Left side of mountain and trees . . . 75 15
1883 $7.50 (3) Trees and house 75 15
1884 $7.50 (4) Mountain, trees and house 75 15
Nos. 1872/5 were printed together, se-tenant, forming a composite design.

503 Insured Groups and Family **504** Liwu River Gorge

1989. Social Welfare.
1885 **503** $3 multicoloured 30 10

1989. Taroko National Park. Multicoloured.
1886 $2 Type **504** 20 10
1887 $3 North Peak of Chilai, Taroko Mountain 40 10
1888 $12 Waterfalls 80 25
1889 $16 Chingshui Cliff . . . . 1·10 30

505 Horse **506** Yu Lu

1989. New Year Greetings. "Year of the Horse".
1890 **505** $2 multicoloured 40 10
1891 $13 multicoloured . . . 1·25 25
See also No. 2044.

1990. Door Gods. Multicoloured.
1893 $3 Type **506** 50 20
1894 $3 Shen Shu 50 20
1895 $7.50 Wei-ch'ih Ching-te (facing right) . . . . . . 1·00 40
1896 $7.50 Ch'in Shu-pao (facing left) . . . . 1·00 40

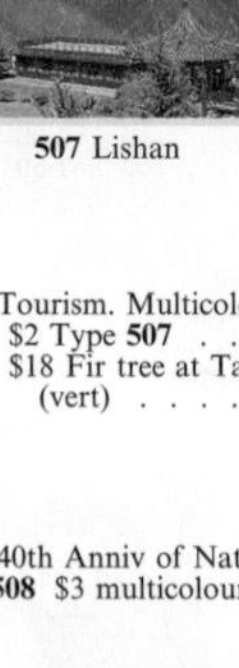
507 Lishan **508** Crystal containing Emblem and Industrial Symbols

1990. Tourism. Multicoloured.
1897 $2 Type **507** 25 10
1898 $18 Fir tree at Tayuling (vert) . . . . 1·00 25

1990. 40th Anniv of National Insurance.
1899 **508** $3 multicoloured 50 10

509 Harbour and Tanks

1990. Yung-An Hsiang Liquefied Natural Gas Terminal. Multicoloured.
1900 $3 Type **509** 35 10
1901 $16 Gas tanker and map showing pipeline route (vert) . . . . 1·00 25

510 African Monarch **511** Court Official, Northern Wei Period to T'ang Dynasty

1990. Butterflies (2nd series). Multicoloured.
1902 $2 Orange tiger 30 10
1903 $3 Type **510** 35 10
1904 $7.50 "Pieris canidia" . . . 75 20
1905 $9 Peacock . . . . 1·10 25

1990. Chinese Costumes (5th series). Mult.
1906 $2 Type **511** 40 10
1907 $3 Civil official in winged hat and green robe, Three Kingdoms period to Ming dynasty 50 10
1908 $7.50 Royal guard in bamboo hat, Yuan dynasty 70 15
1909 $12 Highest grade civil official in robe decorated with crane bird, Ming dynasty 90 40

512 "Spring Song at Midnight"

1990. Chinese Classical Poetry (6th series). Multicoloured.

1910 $3 Type **512** 50 10
1911 $7.50 Couple on river bank ("Summer Song at Midnight") 70 15
1912 $12 Girl washing clothes in river ("Autumn Song at Midnight") . . . . 1·00 20
1913 $16 Snow-bound river scene ("Winter Song at Midnight") . . . . 1·25 25

513 Japanese Black Pine 514 Bamboo-shaped Glass Snuff Bottle

1990. Bonsai. Multicoloured.

1914 $3 Type **513** 40 10
1915 $6.50 "Ehretia microphylla" 60 10
1916 $12 "Buxus harlandii" . . . 90 20
1917 $16 "Celtis sinensis" . . . . 1·25 25

1990. Snuff Bottles. Multicoloured.

1918 $3 Type **514** 30 10
1919 $6 Glass bottle with peony design 60 10
1920 $9 Melon-shaped amber bottle 90 15
1921 $16 White jade bottle . . . 1·10 25

515 Taiwan Firecrest 516 Running

1990. Birds. Multicoloured.

1922 $2 Type **515** 50 25
1923 $3 Formosan barwing 60 25
1924 $7.50 White-eared sibia . . 80 30
1925 $16 Formosan yellow tit . . 1·10 80

1990. Sports. Multicoloured.

1926 $2 Type **516** 20 10
1927 $3 Long jumping 35 10
1928 $7 Pole vaulting 70 10
1929 $16 Hurdling . . . . 1·00 25

517 Curtiss Tomahawk II Fighters and Air Crews

1990. 50th Anniv of Arrival of "Flying Tigers" American Volunteer Group.

1930 **517** $3 multicoloured 40 10

518 Cats

1990. Children's Drawings. Multicoloured.

1931 $2 Type **518** 30 10
1932 $3 Common peafowl . . . 40 20
1933 $7.50 Chickens 80 15
1934 $12 Cattle market . . . . . 1·25 20

519 National Theatre 520 Cowrie Shells

1990. Cultural Buildings in Chiang Kai-shek Memorial Park, Taipeh.

1935 **519** $3 orange, dp blue & bl 30 10
1936 – $12 mauve, violet & lilac 90 20
DESIGN: $12 National Concert Hall.

1990. Ancient Coins. "Shell" Money. Mult.

1937 $2 Type **520** 20 10
1938 $3 Oyster shell 35 10
1939 $6.50 Bone 60 15
1940 $7.50 Bronze 70 15
1941 $9 Jade . . . . 1·00 20

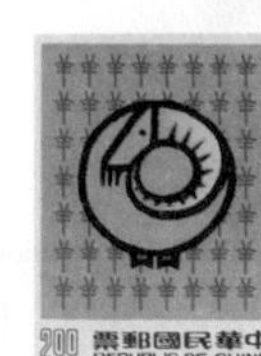

521 Sheep 522 Hu Shih

1990. New Year Greetings. "Year of the Sheep".

1942 **521** $2 multicoloured 50 10
1943 $13 multicoloured . . . 1·00 20
See also No. 2045.

1990. Birth Centenary of Hu Shih (written Chinese reformer).

1945 **522** $3 violet 30 10

523 Teapot with Dragon Spout and Handle 524 Happiness

1991. Teapots (2nd series). Multicoloured.

1946 $2 Blue and white teapot with phoenix design . . . 25 10
1947 $3 Type **523** 40 10
1948 $9 Teapot with floral design on lid and landscape on body 70 15
1949 $12 Rectangular teapot with passion flower design . . 90 20
1950 $16 Brown rectangular teapot with floral decoration . . . . 1·10 25

1991. Greetings Stamps. Gods of Prosperity. Multicoloured.

1951 $3 Type **524** 40 10
1952 $3 Wealth 40 10
1953 $7.50 Longevity (with white beard) 60 15
1954 $7.50 Joy 60 15

525 "Petasites formosanus" 526 Hsiung Cheng-chi (revolutionary)

1991. Plants (1st series). Multicoloured.

1955 $2 Type **525** 25 10
1956 $3 "Heloniopsis acutifolia" 35 10
1957 $7.50 "Disporum shimadai" 60 15
1958 $9 "Viola nagasawai" . . . 70 15
See also Nos. 1969/72, 1995/8 and 2026/9.

1991. Famous Chinese.

1959 **526** $3 blue 35 10

527 Agriculture 528 Bamboo Hobby-horse

1991. 80th Anniv (1992) of Founding of Chinese Republic. Multicoloured.

1960 $3 Type **527** 35 10
1961 $7.50 Industry 75 10
1962 $12 Dancer and leisure equipment . . . . 1·25 20
1963 $16 Transport and communications . . . . . 1·50 30

1991. Children's Games (1st series). Mult.

1964 $3 Type **528** 25 10
1965 $3 Woven-grass grasshoppers 25 10
1966 $3 Spinning tops 25 10
1967 $3 Windmills 25 10
See also Nos. 2056/9, 2120/3 and 2184/7.

1991. Plants (2nd series). As T **525**. Mult.

1969 $2 "Gaultheria itoana" . . 30 10
1970 $3 "Lysionotus montanus" 40 10
1971 $7.50 "Leontopodium microphyllum" 75 15
1972 $9 "Gentiana flavo-maculata" . . . . 1·00 15

529 Male Official's Summer Court Dress 530 Heart, Pedestrian Crossing and Hand

1991. Chinese Costumes (6th series). Ch'ing Dynasty. Multicoloured.

1973 $2 Male official's winter court dress with dragon design 40 10
1974 $3 Type **529** 50 10
1975 $7.50 Male official's winter overcoat 95 15
1976 $12 Everyday skull-cap, jacket and travelling robe 1·75 20

1991. Road Safety. Multicoloured.

1977 $3 Type **530** 35 10
1978 $7.50 Hand, road and broken bottle ("Don't Drink and Drive") . . . 75 15

531 Ch'ing Dynasty Cloisonne Lion 532 Strawberries

1991. No value expressed. Multicoloured.

1979 (–) Type **531** 20 15
1980 (–) Cloisonne lioness 80 25
Nos. 1979/80 were sold at the prevailing rates for domestic ordinary and domestic prompt delivery letters.

1991. Fruits. Multicoloured.

1981 $3 Type **532** 50 10
1982 $7.50 Grapes 55 15
1983 $9 Mango 70 20
1984 $16 Sugar apple . . . . . . 1·10 25

533 Formosan Whistling Thrush

1991. River Birds. Multicoloured.

1985 $5 Type **533** 50 20
1986 $5 Brown dipper 50 20
1987 $5 Mandarins 50 20
1988 $5 Black-crowned night herons 50 20

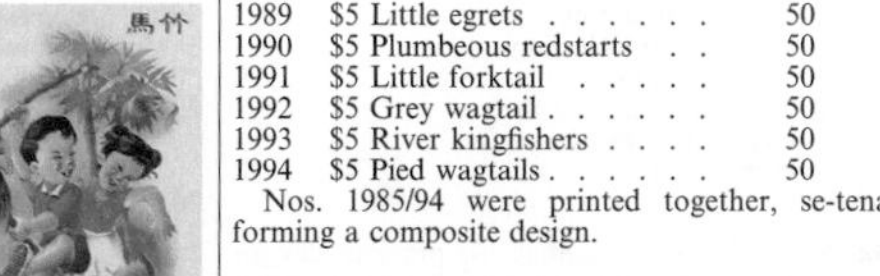

1989 $5 Little egrets 50 20
1990 $5 Plumbeous redstarts . . 50 20
1991 $5 Little forktail 50 20
1992 $5 Grey wagtail 50 20
1993 $5 River kingfishers 50 20
1994 $5 Pied wagtails 50 20
Nos. 1985/94 were printed together, se-tenant, forming a composite design.

1991. Plants (3rd series). As T **525**. Mult.

1995 $3.50 "Rosa transmorrisonensis" . . . 45 10
1996 $5 "Impatiens devolii" . . . 75 10
1997 $9 "Impatiens uniflora" . . 1·00 20
1998 $12 "Impatiens taye-monii" 1·25 20

534 Rock Climbing

1991. International Camping and Caravanning Federation Rally, Fulung Beach. Multicoloured.

1999 $2 Type **534** 25 10
2000 $3 Fishing 35 10
2001 $7.50 Bird-watching 50 15
2002 $10 Boys with pail wading in water 75 20

1991. Lighthouses. As Nos. 1851/3 and 1855/64 but with blue panel at foot.

2003 50c. As No. 1863 . . . . . 10 10
2004 $1 As No. 1851 . . . . . . 10 10
2005 $3.50 As No. 1855 . . . . 25 10
2006 $5 As No. 1856 . . . . . . 35 10
2007 $7 As No. 1853 . . . . . . 45 10
2008 $9 As No. 1858 . . . . . . 60 15
2009 $10 As No. 1859 . . . . . 70 10
2010 $12 As No. 1861 . . . . . 75 15
2011 $13 As No. 1852 . . . . . 80 15
2012 $19 As No. 1857 . . . . . 1·10 20
2013 $20 As No. 1862 . . . . . 1·25 20
2014 $26 As No. 1860 . . . . . 1·40 25
2015 $28 As No. 1864 . . . . . 1·75 30

535 Peacock 536 Monkey

1991. "Peacocks" by Giuseppe Castiglione. Designs showing details of painting. Multicoloured.

2020 $5 Type **535** 50 25
2021 $20 Peacock displaying tail 1·90 1·00

1991. New Year Greetings. "Year of the Monkey".

2023 **536** $3.50 multicoloured . . 50 10
2024 $13 multicoloured . . . 1·10 25
See also No. 2046.

1991. Plants (4th series). As T **525**. Mult.

2026 $3.50 "Kalanchoe garambiensis" 40 10
2027 $5 "Pieris taiwanensis" . . . 75 10
2028 $9 "Pleione formosana" . . 1·00 20
2029 $12 "Elaeagnus oldhamii" 1·25 20

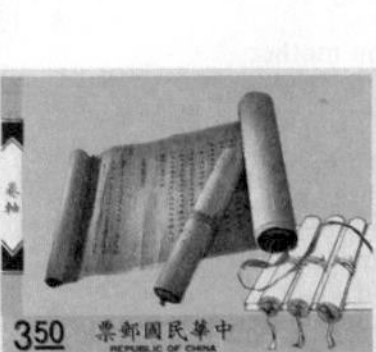

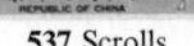

537 Scrolls 538 Peace in the Wake of Firecrackers

1992. International Book Fair, Taipeh. Mult.

2030 $3.50 Type **537** 30 10
2031 $5 Folded-leaves book . . . 40 10
2032 $9 Butterfly-bound books 75 15
2033 $15 Sewn books . . . . . 1·10 25

1992. Greetings Stamps. Nienhwas (paintings conveying wishes for the coming year). Mult.

2034 $5 Type **538** 50 10
2035 $5 Elephant with riders (Good fortune and satisfaction) 50 10

2036 $12 Children and five "birds" (Five blessings upon the house) 70 20
2037 $12 Children angling for large fish (Abundance for every year) 70 20

1992. Signs of Chinese Zodiac. As previous designs but with additional symbol in top left-hand corner.
2038 **393** $5 multicoloured 50 10
2039 **414** $5 multicoloured 50 10
2040 **435** $5 multicoloured 50 10
2041 **456** $5 multicoloured 50 10
2042 **471** $5 multicoloured 50 10
2043 **489** $5 multicoloured 50 10
2044 **505** $5 multicoloured 50 10
2045 **521** $5 multicoloured 50 10
2046 **536** $5 multicoloured 50 10
2047 **340** $5 multicoloured 50 10
2048 **361** $5 multicoloured 50 10
2049 **378** $5 multicoloured 50 10
Nos. 2038/49 were issued together in se-tenant blocks of 12 stamps within the sheet. The stamps are listed in order from right to left of the block.

539 Taiwan Red Cypress ("Chamaecyparis formosensis")

540 Mother and son (Spring)

1992. Forest Resources. Conifers. Mult.
2051 $5 Type **539** 55 10
2052 $5 Taiwan cypress ("Chamaecyparis taiwanensis") 55 10
2053 $5 Taiwan incense cedar ("Calocedrus formosana") 55 10
2054 $5 Ranta fir ("Cunninghamia konishii") 55 10
2055 $5 Taiwania ("Taiwania cryptomerioides") 55 10
Nos. 2051/5 were printed together, se-tenant, forming a composite design.

1992. Children's Games (2nd series). As T **528**. Multicoloured.
2056 $5 Walking on tin cans . . 40 10
2057 $5 Chopstick guns 40 10
2058 $5 Rolling hoops 40 10
2059 $5 Grass fighting 40 10

1992. Parent–Child Relationships. Mult.
2061 $3.50 Type **540** 40 10
2062 $5 Mother carrying child on back (summer) 50 10
2063 $9 Mother and child pushing toy rabbits (autumn) 75 15
2064 $10 Mother feeding child (winter) 90 15

542 Vase decorated with Bats and Longevity Characters

543 Lion and Stone Pavilion

1992. Glassware decorated with Enamel. Mult.
2066 $3.50 Type **542** 30 10
2067 $5 Gourd-shaped vase decorated with landscape and children at play . . . 40 10
2068 $7 Vase with peony decoration 50 15
2069 $17 Vase showing mother teaching child to read . . 1·10 25

1992. Stone Lions from Lugouqiao Bridge.
2070 **543** $5 blue and brown . . . 40 10
2071 – $5 green and violet . . . 40 10
2072 – $12 orange and green . . 70 20
2073 – $12 violet and black . . 70 20
DESIGNS: No. 2071, Bridge and lioness with cub; 2070, Bridge parapet and lion; 2073, Bridge parapet and lioness with two cubs.

544 "People make Friends and are tied to Each Other as Roots to a Plant"

1992. Chinese Classical Poetry (7th series). Multicoloured.
2074 $3.50 Type **544** 30 10
2075 $5 Couple at window ("Conjugal love will last forever") 40 10
2076 $9 Couple in garden ("Man takes pains to uphold virtue/Till one's hair turns forever grey") 80 15
2077 $15 "Tartar horses lean toward the north wind" 1·25 25

545 Drummer and Crowd

546 "Two Birds perched on a Red Camellia Branch"

1992. Temple Fair. Multicoloured.
2078 $5 Type **545** 45 10
2079 $5 Man with basket dancing 45 10
2080 $5 Musicians 45 10
2081 $5 Man pushing cart . . . 45 10
2082 $5 Women and children . . 45 10
Nos. 2078/82 were printed together, se-tenant, forming a composite design.

1992. Ming Dynasty Silk Tapestries. Mult.
2083 $5 Type **546** 50 10
2084 $12 "Two Birds playing on a Peach Branch" . . . . 1·00 20

547 Cart in "The General and the Premier"

548 Steam Locomotive and Train

1992. Chinese Opera Props. Multicoloured.
2086 $3.50 Type **547** 50 10
2087 $5 Ship in "The Lucky Pearl" 60 10
2088 $9 Horse in "Chao-chun serves as an Envoy" . . . 80 15
2089 $12 Sedan chair in "Escort to the Wedding" 90 15

1992. Alishan Mountain Railway. Mult.
2090 $5 Type **548** 30 15
2091 $15 Diesel locomotive and train . . . . 1·10 35

549 Chinese River Otter

550 Cock

1992. Mammals. Multicoloured.
2092 $5 Type **549** 25 10
2093 $5 Formosan flying fox . . 25 10
2094 $5 Formosan clouded leopard 25 10
2095 $5 Formosan black bear . . 25 10

1992. New Year Greetings. "Year of the Cock". Multicoloured.
2096 $3.50 Type **550** 20 10
2097 $13 Cock (facing left) . . . 75 15

552 Schall and Astronomical Instruments

1992. 400th Birth Anniv of Johann Adam Schall von Bell (missionary astronomer).
2100 **552** $5 multicoloured 40 10

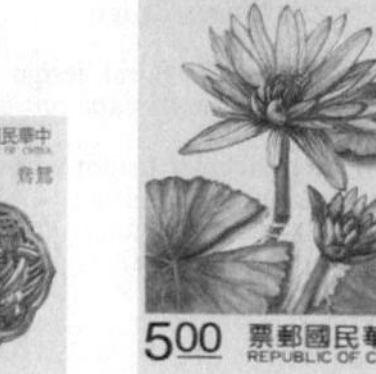

553 Satisfaction for Every Year

1993. Greetings Stamps. Nienhwas (paintings conveying wishes for the coming year). Multicoloured.
2101 $5 Type **553** 50 10
2102 $5 Birds and flowers (Joy) 50 10
2103 $12 Butterfly and flowers (Happiness and longevity) 1·10 15
2104 $12 Flowers in vase (Wealth and peace) . . . . 1·10 15

554 Applying Enamel and Glass Decoration to Temple Roof

1992. International Traditional Crafts Exhibition, Taipeh. Multicoloured.
2105 $3.50 Type **554** 30 10
2106 $5 Ceremonial lantern . . . 40 10
2107 $9 Pottery jars 65 10
2108 $15 Oil-paper umbrella . . . 1·00 20

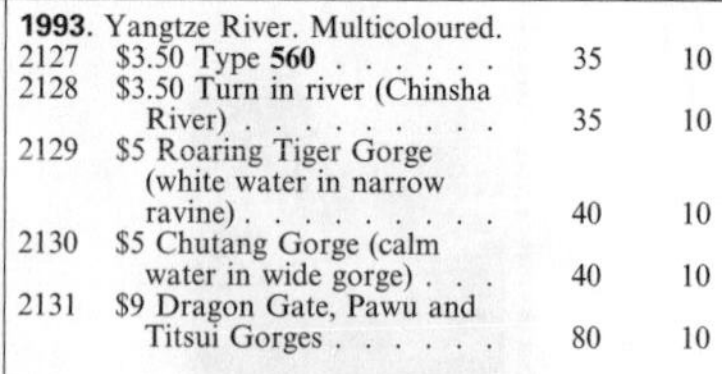

555 Pan Gu creating Universe

1993. The Creation. Multicoloured.
2109 $3.50 Type **555** 30 10
2110 $5 Pan Gu creating animals (horiz) 35 10
2111 $9 Nu Wa creating human beings (horiz) 70 10
2112 $19 Nu Wa mending the sky with smelted stone . . . . 1·25 20

556 Mandarins

557 Water Lily

1993. Lucky Animals (1st series).
2113 **556** $3.50 multicoloured . . 30 10
2114 – $5 multicoloured 35 10
2115 – $10 red and black . . . 75 15
2116 – $15 multicoloured . . . 1·00 20
DESIGNS: $5, Chinese unicorn; $10, Deer; $15, Crane.
See also Nos. 2151/4.

1993. Water Plants, Multicoloured.
2117 $5 Type **557** 40 10
2118 $9 Taiwan cow lily 75 10
2119 $12 Water hyacinth 85 15

1993. Children's Games (3rd series). As T **528**. Multicoloured.
2120 $5 Tossing sandbags 40 10
2121 $5 Bamboo dragonflies . . . 40 10
2122 $5 Skipping 40 10
2123 $5 Duel of strength with rope passed round waists 40 10

560 Ching-Kang-Chang Plateau (source)

1993. Yangtze River. Multicoloured.
2127 $3.50 Type **560** 35 10
2128 $3.50 Turn in river (Chinsha River) 35 10
2129 $5 Roaring Tiger Gorge (white water in narrow ravine) 40 10
2130 $5 Chutang Gorge (calm water in wide gorge) . . . 40 10
2131 $9 Dragon Gate, Pawu and Titsui Gorges 80 10

561 Noise Pollution and Music

1993. Environmental Protection. Children's Drawings. Multicoloured.
2132 $5 Type **561** 35 10
2133 $17 Family looking out over green fields (vert) . . . . 1·10 20

562 Cup with Tou-Ts'ai Figures

1993. Ch'eng-hua Porcelain Cups of Ming Dynasty. Multicoloured.
2134 $3.50 Type **562** 30 10
2135 $5 Chicken decoration . . . 35 10
2136 $7 Flowers and fruits of four seasons decoration 55 10
2137 $9 Dragon decoration . . . 75 10

563 Graphic Design

564 Child on Father's Shoulders

1993. 32nd International Vocational Training Competition, Taipeh. Multicoloured.
2138 $3.50 Type **563** 30 10
2139 $5 Computer technology . . 35 10
2140 $9 Carpentry 65 10
2141 $12 Welding 80 15

1993. Parent–Child Relationships. Mult.
2142 $3.50 Type **564** 30 10
2143 $5 Father playing flute to child 40 10
2144 $9 Child reading to father 75 10
2145 $10 Father pointing at bird 75 15

566 Persimmons

567 Gymnastics

1993. Fruits. Multicoloured.
2147 $5 Type **566** 40 10
2148 $5 Peaches 40 10
2149 $12 Loquats 60 15
2150 $12 Papayas 60 15

1993. Lucky Animals (2nd series). As T **556**. Mult.
2151 $1 Blue dragon (representing Spring, wood and the East) 20 10
2152 $2.50 White tiger (Autumn, metal and the West) . . . 30 10
2153 $9 Linnet (Summer, fire and the South) 60 15
2154 $19 Black tortoise (Winter, water and the North) . . 1·10 20

1993. Taiwan Area Games, Taoyuan. Mult.
2155 $5 Type **567** 25 10
2156 $5 Taekwondo 25 10

568 Stone Lion, New Park, Taipeh

569 Chick

1993. Stone Lions. Multicoloured.
2157 $3.50 Type **568** 30 10
2158 $5 Hsinchu City Council building 40 10
2159 $9 Temple, Hsinchu City . . 70 10
2160 $12 Fort Providentia, Tainan 95 15

1993. Mikado Pheasant. Multicoloured.
2161 $5 Type **569** 55 20
2162 $5 Mother and chicks . . . 55 20
2163 $5 Immature male and female 55 20
2164 $5 Adults 55 20
Nos. 2161/4 were issued together, se-tenant, forming a composite design.

570 Dog **571** Scientist and Vegetables

1993. New Year Greetings. "Year of the Dog". Multicoloured.
2165 $3.50 Type **570** 15 10
2166 $13 Dog (facing left) 65 15

1993. 20th Anniv of Asian Vegetable Research and Development Centre. Multicoloured.
2168 $5 Type **571** 30 10
2169 $13 Scientists and fields of crops 75 15

573 Courtroom **574** Cutting Bamboo

1994. Inauguration of Taiwan Constitutional Court.
2171 **573** $5 multicoloured 30 10

1994. Traditional Paper Making. Multicoloured.
2172 $3.50 Type **574** 25 10
2173 $3.50 Cooking bamboo . . 25 10
2174 $5 Moulding bamboo pulp in wooden panels 40 10
2175 $5 Stacking wet paper for pressing 40 10
2176 $12 Drying paper 80 15

575 "Clivia miniata" **576** Wind Lion Lord

1994. Flowers. Multicoloured.
2177 $5 Type **575** 40 10
2178 $12 "Cymbidium sinense" 80 15
2179 $19 "Primula malacoides" 1·25 20

1994. Kinmen Wind Lion Lords.
2180 **576** $5 multicoloured 45 10
2181 – $9 multicoloured 80 10
2182 – $12 multicoloured . . . 1·00 15
2183 – $17 multicoloured . . . 1·25 20
DESIGNS: $9 to $17 Different Lion Lord statues.

577 Sailing Paper Boats **578** Playing Chess

1994. Children's Games (4th series). Mult.
2184 $5 Type **577** 40 10
2185 $5 Fighting with water-guns 40 10
2186 $5 Throwing paper plane . . 40 10
2187 $5 Human train 40 10

1994. Rural Pastimes. Multicoloured.
2189 $5 Type **578** 35 10
2190 $10 Playing the flute 60 10
2191 $12 Telling stories 85 15
2192 $19 Drinking tea . . . . . 1·25 20

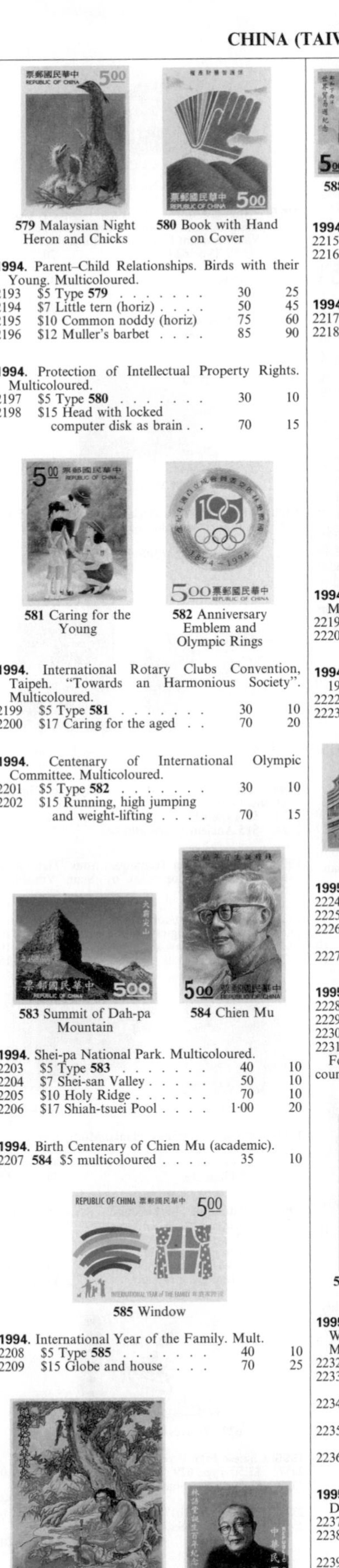
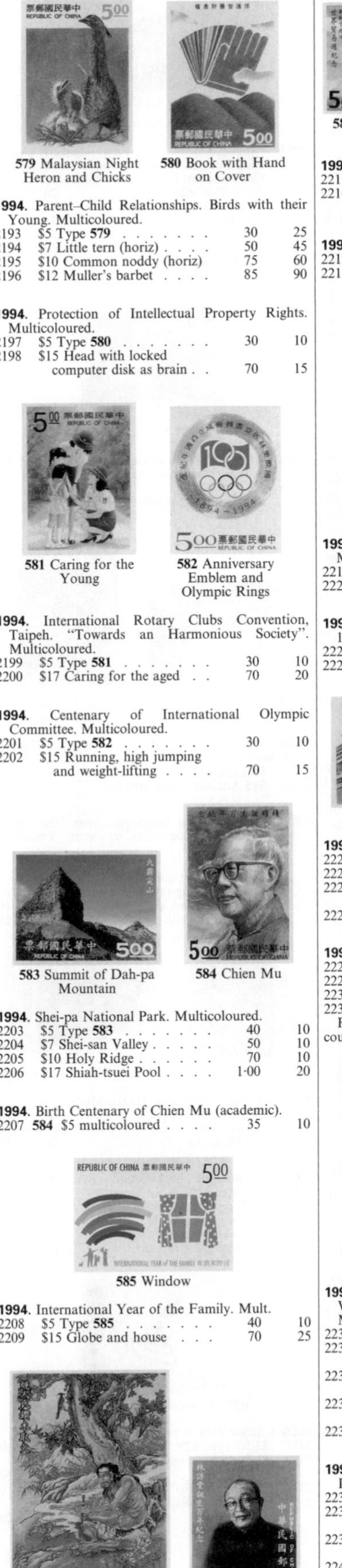

579 Malaysian Night Heron and Chicks **580** Book with Hand on Cover

1994. Parent–Child Relationships. Birds with their Young. Multicoloured.
2193 $5 Type **579** 30 25
2194 $7 Little tern (horiz) 50 45
2195 $10 Common noddy (horiz) 75 60
2196 $12 Muller's barbet 85 90

1994. Protection of Intellectual Property Rights. Multicoloured.
2197 $5 Type **580** 30 10
2198 $15 Head with locked computer disk as brain . . 70 15

581 Caring for the Young **582** Anniversary Emblem and Olympic Rings

1994. International Rotary Clubs Convention, Taipeh. "Towards an Harmonious Society". Multicoloured.
2199 $5 Type **581** 30 10
2200 $17 Caring for the aged . . 70 20

1994. Centenary of International Olympic Committee. Multicoloured.
2201 $5 Type **582** 30 10
2202 $15 Running, high jumping and weight-lifting 70 15

583 Summit of Dah-pa Mountain **584** Chien Mu

1994. Shei-pa National Park. Multicoloured.
2203 $5 Type **583** 40 10
2204 $7 Shei-san Valley 50 10
2205 $10 Holy Ridge 70 10
2206 $17 Shiah-tsuei Pool . . . . 1·00 20

1994. Birth Centenary of Chien Mu (academic).
2207 **584** $5 multicoloured 35 10

585 Window

1994. International Year of the Family. Mult.
2208 $5 Type **585** 40 10
2209 $15 Globe and house . . . 70 25

586 Sueirenjy making Flame **587** Lin Yutang

1994. Invention Myths. Multicoloured.
2210 $5 Type **586** 40 10
2211 $10 Fushijy drawing Pa-kua characters 75 10
2212 $12 Shennungjy making pitchfork 80 20
2213 $15 Tsangjier inventing pictorial characters . . . 1·00 25

1994. Birth Centenary of Dr. Lin Yutang (essayist and lexicographer).
2214 **587** $5 multicoloured 25 10

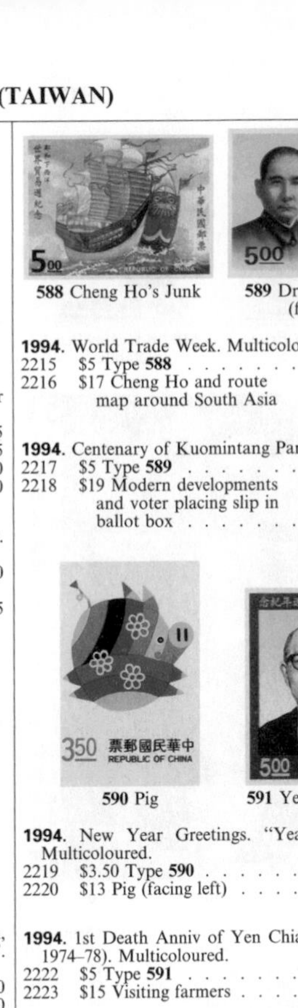

588 Cheng Ho's Junk **589** Dr. Sun Yat-sen (founder)

1994. World Trade Week. Multicoloured.
2215 $5 Type **588** 30 10
2216 $17 Cheng Ho and route map around South Asia 70 15

1994. Centenary of Kuomintang Party. Mult.
2217 $5 Type **589** 30 10
2218 $19 Modern developments and voter placing slip in ballot box 80 15

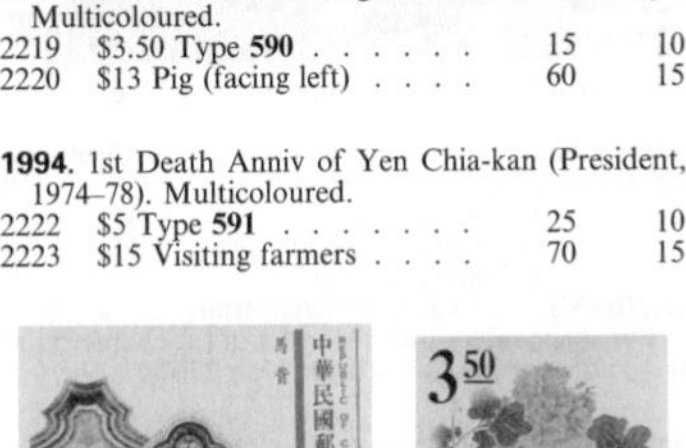

590 Pig **591** Yen Chia-kan

1994. New Year Greetings. "Year of the Pig". Multicoloured.
2219 $3.50 Type **590** 15 10
2220 $13 Pig (facing left) 60 15

1994. 1st Death Anniv of Yen Chia-kan (President, 1974–78). Multicoloured.
2222 $5 Type **591** 25 10
2223 $15 Visiting farmers 70 15

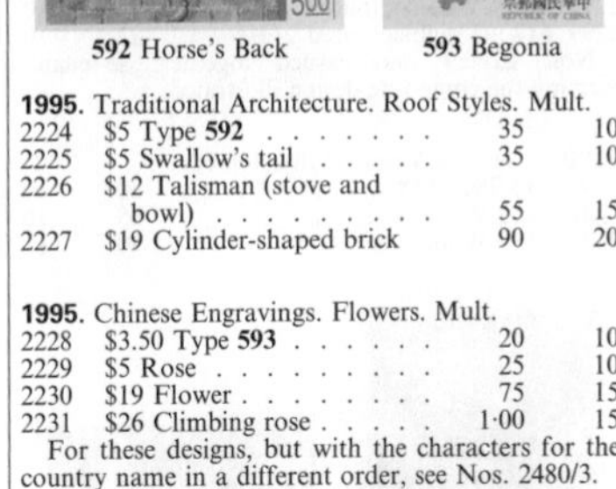

592 Horse's Back **593** Begonia

1995. Traditional Architecture. Roof Styles. Mult.
2224 $5 Type **592** 35 10
2225 $5 Swallow's tail 35 10
2226 $12 Talisman (stove and bowl) 55 15
2227 $19 Cylinder-shaped brick 90 20

1995. Chinese Engravings. Flowers. Mult.
2228 $3.50 Type **593** 20 10
2229 $5 Rose 25 10
2230 $19 Flower 75 15
2231 $26 Climbing rose . . . . . 1·00 15
For these designs, but with the characters for the country name in a different order, see Nos. 2480/3.

594 Rotating Wheel of Pipes **595** Courtiers

1995. Irrigation Techniques from "Tian Gong Kai Wu" (encyclopaedia) by Sung Yin-shing. Multicoloured.
2232 $3.50 Type **594** 20 10
2233 $3.50 Donkey turning wheel to raise water 20 10
2234 $5 Pedal-driven device to raise water 35 10
2235 $12 Man turning wheel to raise water 85 15
2236 $13 Well . . . . 1·00 15

1995. "Beauties on an Outing" by Lee Gong-lin. Details of the painting. Multicoloured.
2237 $9 Type **595** 45 10
2238 $9 Courtier and beauty with child 45 10
2239 $9 Courtier with two beauties 45 10
2240 $9 Courtier 45 10
Nos. 2237/40 were issued together, se-tenant, forming a composite design.

596 Emblem and Landscape **597** Chinese Showy Lily

1995. Inaug of National Health Insurance Plan.
2242 **596** $12 multicoloured . . . 55 15

1995. Bulbous Flowers. Multicoloured.
2243 $5 Type **597** 35 10
2244 $12 Blood lily 45 15
2245 $19 Hyacinth 70 20

598 Opening Lines

1995. Chinese Calligraphy. "Cold Food Observance" (poem) by Su Shih.
2246 **598** $5 (1) multicoloured . . 65 10
2247 – $5 (2) multicoloured . . 65 10
2248 – $5 (3) multicoloured . . 65 10
2249 – $5 (4) multicoloured . . 65 10
Nos. 2246/9 were issued together, se-tenant, forming a composite design; the stamps are numbered in Chinese numerals to the right of the face value, from right to left.

599 Red Peony **600** Hand, Birds and Cracked Symbol

1995. Peonies. Paintings by Tsou I-kuei. Self-adhesive. Imperf.
2250 $5 Type **599** . . . . 2·00 10
2251 $5 Pink peony . . . . . . 2·00 10

1995. Anti-drugs Campaign. Multicoloured.
2252 $5 Type **600** 30 10
2253 $15 Arm and syringe forming cross 65 15

601 Old Hospital Building

1995. Centenary of National Taiwan University Hospital, Taipeh. Multicoloured.
2254 $5 Type **601** 25 10
2255 $19 New building 70 20

602 Chichi Bay

1995. Tourism. East Coast National Scenic Area. Multicoloured.
2256 $5 Type **602** 30 10
2257 $5 Shihyuesan (rocky promontory) 30 10
2258 $12 Hsiaoyehlieu (eroded rocks) 50 15
2259 $15 Changhong Bridge . . . 80 15

603 Mating **604** Bird feeding on Branch

1995. The Cherry Salmon. Multicoloured.
2260 $5 Type **603** 30 10
2261 $7 Female digging redd . . 45 10
2262 $10 Fry hatching 65 10
2263 $17 Fry swimming 80 20

1995. Chinese Engravings. Birds. Mult.
2264 $2.50 Type **604** 10 10
2265 $7 Bird on branch of peach tree 30 10
2266 $13 Bird preening 50 10
2267 $28 Yellow bird 80 20
For these designs with different face values and the order of the characters in the country name changed, see Nos. 2532/7.

605 "Tubastraea aurea" 606 Pasteur

1995. Marine Life. Multicoloured.

2268 $3.50 Type **605** 20 10
2269 $3.50 "Chromodoris elizabethina" 20 10
2270 $5 "Spirobranchus giganteus corniculatus" 40 10
2271 $17 "Himerometra magnipinna" 70 20

1995. Death Cent of Louis Pasteur (chemist).

2272 **606** $17 multicoloured . . . 90 20

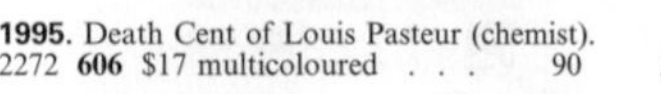

607 Porcelain Vase 608 Soldiers

1995. 70th Anniv of National Palace Museum. Multicoloured.

2273 $3.50 "Strange Peaks and Myriad Trees" (painting) (horiz) 20 10
2274 $3.50 Type **607** 20 10
2275 $5 X Fu-K'uei Ting bronze three-fronted vessel . . . 45 10
2276 $26 "The Fragrance of Flowers" (quatrain) (horiz) . . . . 1·00 25

1995. 50th Anniv of End of Sino-Japanese War. Multicoloured.

2277 $5 Type **608** 25 10
2278 $19 Taiwan flag, map and city 90 20

609 Common Green Turtle ("Chelonia mydas") 610 Scientists in Crop Field

1995. Year of the Sea Turtle. Multicoloured.

2280 $5 Type **609** 35 10
2281 $5 Loggerhead turtle ("Caretta caretta") . . . 35 10
2282 $5 Olive ridley turtle ("Lepidochelys olivacea") 35 10
2283 $5 Hawksbill turtle ("Eretmochelys imbricata") 35 10

1995. Centenary of Taiwan Agricultural Research Institute. Multicoloured.

2284 $5 Type **610** 25 10
2285 $28 Scientists in greenhouse growing anthuriums . . . 1·10 30

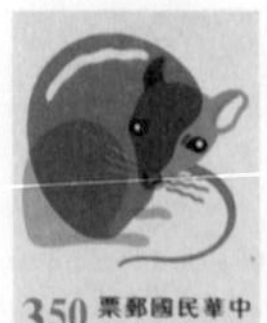

611 Rat 612 Escorting Bride to Ceremony

1995. New Year Greetings. "Year of the Rat". Multicoloured.

2286 $3.50 Type **611** 15 10
2287 $13 Rat (different) 85 15

1996. Traditional Wedding Ceremonies. Mult.

2289 $5 Type **612** 30 10
2290 $12 Honouring Heaven, Earth and ancestors . . . 65 10
2291 $19 Nuptial chamber . . . 90 15

613 Sharon Fruit 618 "Bougainvillea spectabilis"

614-17 "Scenic Dwelling at Chu-Ch'u"

1996. Chinese Engravings of Fruit by Hu Chen-yan.

2292 **613** $9 multicoloured . . . 35 10
2293 – $12 multicoloured . . . 45 10
2294 – $15 multicoloured . . . 55 10
2295 – $17 multicoloured . . . 65 10

DESIGNS: $12 to $17, Different fruits.

For other values with the order of the characters in the country name reversed see Nos. 2580/2.

1996. Painting by Wang Meng.

2296 **614** $5 multicoloured 25 10
2297 **615** $5 multicoloured 25 10
2298 **616** $5 multicoloured 25 10
2299 **617** $5 multicoloured 25 10

Nos. 2296/9 were issued together, se-tenant, forming the composite design illustrated.

1996. Flowering Vines. Multicoloured.

2300 $5 Type **618** 30 10
2301 $12 Wisteria 65 10
2302 $19 Wood rose 90 15

619 Postboxes 620 Lecture and University

1996. Centenary of Chinese State Postal Service. Multicoloured.

2303 $5 Type **619** 30 10
2304 $9 Weighing equipment . . 55 10
2305 $12 Postal transport 65 10
2306 $13 Modern technology . . 70 10

1996. Centenary of National Chiao Tung University.

2308 **620** $19 multicoloured . . . 90 15

621 Chimei Giant Lion

1996. Tourism. Penghu National Scenic Area. Multicoloured.

2309 $5 Type **621** 30 10
2310 $5 Chipei beach (sand-spit) 30 10
2311 $12 Tungpan Yu 65 15
2312 $17 Tingkou Yu 85 15

622 Hand holding Family (charity)

1996. 30th Anniv of Tzu-Chi Foundation (Buddhist relief organization). Multicoloured.

2313 $5 Type **622** 30 10
2314 $19 Hospital patient in tulip petal (medicine) 70 20

623 With National Flag

1996. Inauguration of First Directly-elected President. Designs showing President Lee Teng-Hui and Vice-President Lien Chan. Multicoloured.

2315 $3.50 Type **623** 20 10
2316 $5 Outside Presidential Office building 35 10
2317 $13 Asia-Pacific Operations Hub Project 70 10
2318 $15 Meeting public at celebrations 75 15

624 Monument

1996. South China Sea Archipelago. Pratas and Itu Aba Islands. Multicoloured.

2320 $5 Type **624** 30 10
2321 $12 Monument (different) 65 10

625 Modern Gymnast and Cyclist 626 Feeding Silkworms

1996. Centenary of Modern Olympic Games. Multicoloured.

2323 $5 Type **625** 30 10
2324 $15 Ancient Greek athletes 75 15

1996. Silk Production Techniques from "Tian Gong Kai Wu" (encyclopaedia) by Sung Yin-shing. Multicoloured.

2325 $5 Type **626** 30 10
2326 $5 Picking out cocoons . . 30 10
2327 $7 Degumming raw silk . . 45 10
2328 $10 Reeling raw silk . . . 60 10
2329 $13 Weaving silk 70 15

627 Bamboo 628 Tou-kung Bracket

1996. Chinese Engravings. Plants. Mult.

2330 $1 Type **627** 10 10
2331 $10 Orchid 35 10
2332 $20 Plum tree 75 15

1996. Traditional Architecture. Roof Supports. Multicoloured.

2333 $5 Type **628** 30 10
2334 $5 Chiue-ti bracket 30 10
2335 $10 Bu-tong beam 50 10
2336 $19 Dye-tou structure . . . 85 15

629 "Princess Iron Fan" (1941)

1996. Chinese Film Production. Mult.

2337 $3.50 Type **629** 25 10
2338 $3.50 "Chin Shan Bi Xie" (1957) 25 10
2339 $5 "Oyster Girl" (1964) . . . 40 10
2340 $19 "City of Sadness" (1989) 85 20

630 Children dancing 631 "Autumn Scene with Wild Geese"

1996. Winning Entries in Children's Stamp Design Competition. Multicoloured.

2341 $5 Type **630** 35 10
2342 $5 Children playing in park 35 10
2343 $5 Black and white spotted cat 35 10
2344 $5 Container ship 35 10
2345 $5 Children showering . . . 35 10
2346 $5 Chinese gods and crowd 35 10
2347 $5 Pair of peacocks 35 10
2348 $5 Flying horse and rainbow 35 10
2349 $5 Elephant 35 10
2350 $5 Man and striped animals 35 10
2351 $5 Painting paper lampshades 35 10
2352 $5 Flock of geese 35 10
2353 $5 Children joining hands in garden 35 10
2354 $5 Archer 35 10
2355 $5 Children on ostrich's back 35 10
2356 $5 New Year celebrations 35 10
2357 $5 Butterflies on bamboo plant 35 10
2358 $5 Goatherd 35 10
2359 $5 Water-lilies on pond . . 35 10
2360 $5 Cats eating fish 35 10

1996. 10th Asian International Stamp Exhibition, Taipeh. Ancient Paintings from National Palace Museum. Multicoloured.

2361 $5 Type **631** 30 10
2362 $7 "Reeds and Wild Geese" 40 10
2363 $13 "Wild Geese gathering on Shore of Reeds" . . . 65 10
2364 $15 "Wild Geese on Bank in Autumn" 70 15

632 Bar Code and Graph 633 Disabled Worker and Open Hands

1996. 50th Anniv of Merchants' Day. Mult.

2366 $5 Type **632** 30 10
2367 $26 Line graph and globe 1·10 20

1996. Caring for the Handicapped. Mult.

2368 $5 Type **633** 30 10
2369 $19 Disabled boy painting, emblems within honeycomb and hands forming heart (employment) 85 15

634 Ox 636 Early Porcelain Production

1996. New Year Greetings. "Year of the Ox". Multicoloured.

2370 $3.50 Type **634** 20 10
2371 $13 Ox (different) 65 10

1997. Porcelain Production Techniques from "Tian Gong Kai Wu" (encyclopaedia) by Sung Yin-shing. Multicoloured.

2374 $5 Type **636** 30 10
2375 $5 Improved shaping . . . 30 10
2376 $7 Painting 35 10
2377 $10 Glazing 45 10
2378 $13 Firing 60 10

637 Dragons and Carp (from window, Longsan Temple, Lukang) 638 Peace Doves and Memorial

1997. (a) T 637.

2379 **637** $50 red . . . . 1·90 30
2380 $60 blue . . . . 2·25 35
2381 $70 red . . . . 2·50 40
2382 $100 green . . . . 3·75 55

(b) As T **637** but with outer decorated frame. Size 25 × 33 mm.

2386 **637** $300 violet and blue . . 13·00 1·60
2387 $500 red and carmine . . 20·00 2·75

For $50 and $100 values in different colours and with the characters in the country name in reverse order see Nos. 2573/4.

1997. 50th Anniv of 228 Incident (civilian demonstration against government).

2390 **638** $19 multicoloured . . . 80 15

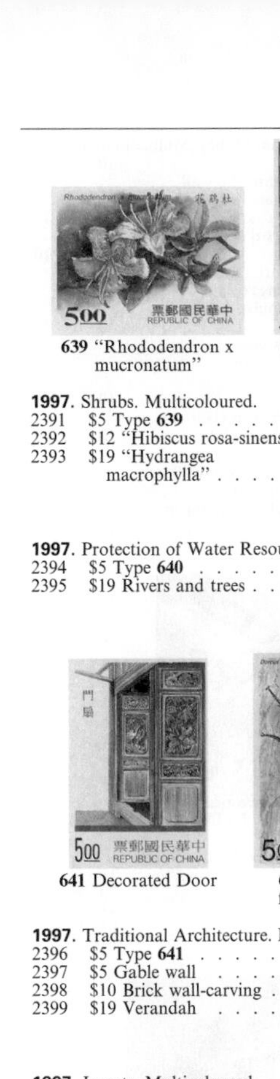
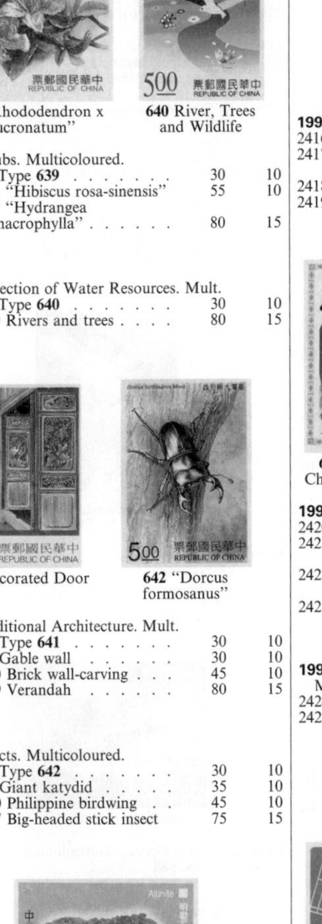

639 "Rhododendron x mucronatum"

640 River, Trees and Wildlife

1997. Shrubs. Multicoloured.

2391 $5 Type **639** 30 10
2392 $12 "Hibiscus rosa-sinensis" 55 10
2393 $19 "Hydrangea macrophylla" 80 15

1997. Protection of Water Resources. Mult.

2394 $5 Type **640** 30 10
2395 $19 Rivers and trees 80 15

641 Decorated Door

642 "Dorcus formosanus"

1997. Traditional Architecture. Mult.

2396 $5 Type **641** 30 10
2397 $5 Gable wall 30 10
2398 $10 Brick wall-carving 45 10
2399 $19 Verandah 80 15

1997. Insects. Multicoloured.

2400 $5 Type **642** 30 10
2401 $7 Giant katydid 35 10
2402 $10 Philippine birdwing 45 10
2403 $17 Big-headed stick insect 75 15

643 Alunite

1997. Minerals. Multicoloured.

2404 $5 Type **643** 30 10
2405 $5 Aragonite 30 10
2406 $12 Energite 55 10
2407 $19 Hokutolite 80 15

644 Nanyashan Coastline

645 Train and Chingshuei Cliffs (northern loop)

1997. Tourism. North-east Coast National Scenic Area. Multicoloured.

2408 $5 Type **644** 30 10
2409 $5 Pitou Coastline (rocky shore) 30 10
2410 $12 Stone pillar, Nanya 55 10
2411 $19 Tsaoling historic trail 80 15

1997. Completion of Round-island Railway System. Multicoloured.

2412 $5 Type **645** 30 10
2413 $28 Train leaving tunnel (southern loop) 1·25 20

646 Integrated Circuit and Communications Equipment

1997. Electronic Industry. Multicoloured.

2414 $5 Type **646** 25 10
2415 $26 Circuit board, portable computer, mobile phone and synthesized keyboard 1·00 15

647 Shaolinquan

1997. Martial Arts. Multicoloured.

2416 $5 Type **647** 25 10
2417 $5 Form and will boxing (vert) 25 10
2418 $9 Taijiquan 40 10
2419 $19 Eight diagrams boxing (vert) 75 15

648 "Hsi Hsiang Chi" (Wang Shih-fu)

649 Bitan Bridge over River Shindian

1997. Chinese Classical Opera. Multicoloured.

2420 $5 Type **648** 25 10
2421 $5 "Dan Daw Huei" (Kuan Han-chin) 25 10
2422 $12 "Han Guong Chiou" (Ma Jyi-yuan) 50 10
2423 $15 "Wu Tong Yu" (Bai Pu) 60 10

1997. Inauguration of Second Northern Freeway. Multicoloured.

2424 $5 Type **649** 25 10
2425 $19 Hsinchu Interchange 75 15

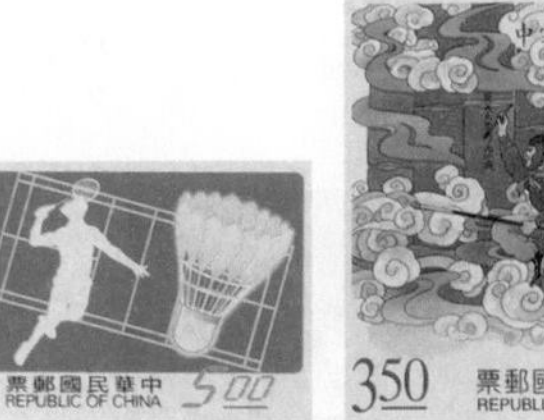

650 Badminton

651 Palm of Buddha

1997. Sports. Multicoloured.

2426 $5 Type **650** 25 10
2427 $12 Bowling 50 10
2428 $19 Lawn tennis 75 15

1997. Classical Literature. "Journey to the West" (Ming dynasty novel). Multicoloured.

2429 $3.50 Type **651** 20 10
2430 $3.50 Pilgrimage of T'ang Monk 20 10
2431 $5 The Flaming Mountain 25 10
2432 $20 The Cobweb Cave 80 15

652 Purple-crowned Lory

1997. Birds. Illustrations from the Ching dynasty Bird Manual (1st series). Multicoloured.

2433 $5 Type **652** 25 10
2434 $5 Green magpie (on branch with small orange flowers) 25 10
2435 $5 Blue-crowned hanging parrot (green bird with red throat and rump) 25 10
2436 $5 Niltavas sp. (two birds with orange breasts) 25 10
2437 $5 Red-billed blue magpie (with long blue tail) 25 10
2438 $5 David's laughing thrush (on branch with red flowers) 25 10
2439 $5 Przewalski's rosefinch (on branch with orange-centred white flowers) 25 10
2440 $5 Common rosefinch (on branch with yellow flowers) 25 10
2441 $5 Mongolian trumpeter finch (on branch with white flowers and red hips) 25 10
2442 $5 Long-tailed minivets (two black and red birds) 25 10
2443 $5 Black-naped oriole (on branch with weeping leaves) 25 10
2444 $5 Yellow-headed buntings (two birds on branch with thorns and small pink flowers) 25 10
2445 $5 Bohemian waxwing (on branch with large blue flowers) 25 10
2446 $5 Mongolian trumpeter finches (two birds on branch with large pink flowers) 25 10
2447 $5 Chinese jungle mynah (with "bristles" above beak) 25 10
2448 $5 Java sparrow (with white patch on neck) 25 10
2449 $5 Long-tailed parakeet (on branch with small blue flowers) 25 10
2450 $5 Black-winged starling (by stream) 25 10
2451 $5 Cloven-feathered dove (two green and white birds) 25 10
2452 $5 Wryneck (on ground) 25 10

See also Nos. 2603/6, 2671/4, 2740/3 and 2823/6.

653 Tiger

654 Pres. Chiang

1997. New Year Greetings. "Year of the Tiger".

2453 **653** $3.50 multicoloured 20 10
2454 $13 multicoloured 55 10

1998. 10th Death Anniv of Chiang Ching-kuo (President 1978–88).

2456 **654** $5 brown 20 10
2457 – $19 red 70 15

DESIGN—HORIZ: $19 Chiang and applauding crowd.

655 "Abundance"

656 "Gaillardia pulchella var. picta"

1998. Wishes for the Coming Year. Mult.

2458 $5 Type **655** 20 10
2459 $5 Flowers springing from lidded bowl ("Harmony") 20 10
2460 $12 Peonies in containers ("Honour and Wealth") 45 10
2461 $12 Flowers in vase and oranges in bowl ("Luck") 45 10

1998. Herbaceous Flowers. Multicoloured.

2462 $5 Type **656** 20 10
2463 $12 "Kalanchoe blossfeldiana" 45 10
2464 $19 "Portulaca oleracea var. granatus" 70 15

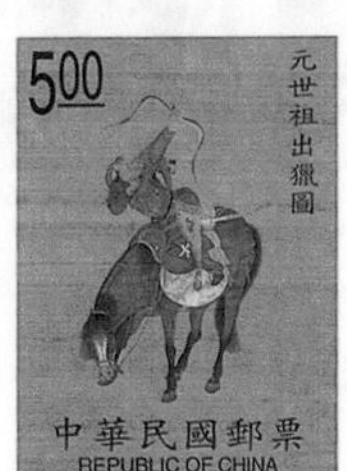

657 Horseman drawing Bow

1998. Painting by Liu Kuan-tao. Mult.

2465 $5 Type **657** 20 10
2466 $19 Kublai Khan and entourage on hunting expedition (63 × 40 mm) 70 15

658 "A Frog has only One Mouth"

1998. Children's Nursery Rhymes. Mult.

2468 $5 Type **658** 20 10
2469 $5 Mouse and cat ("A Little Mouse climbs an Oil Lamp") 20 10
2470 $12 Children and fireflies ("Fireflies") 45 10
2471 $19 Girl and egret carrying baskets ("Egrets") 70 15

659 Cultural Symbols within Human Head

1998. 70th Anniv of Copyright Law.

2472 **659** $19 multicoloured 70 15

660 "Chung K'uei Moving" (Kung Kai)

661 Emblem and Cherry Blossom

1998. Ancient Paintings of Chung K'uei (mythological figure). Multicoloured.

2473 $5 Type **660** 20 10
2474 $20 Chung K'uei dancing ("An Auspicious Occasion") 75 15

1998. 125th Anniv of International Law Association and 68th Conference, Taipeh.

2475 **661** $15 multicoloured 55 10

662 Grain Barge

663 Begonia

1998. Ships and Vehicles from "Tian Gong Kai Wu" (encyclopaedia) by Sung Yin-shing. Multicoloured.

2476 $5 Type **662** 20 10
2477 $7 Six-oared ferry boat 25 10
2478 $10 One-wheel horse-drawn carriage 35 10
2479 $13 Man pushing one-wheel cart 50 10

1998. Chinese Engravings. Flowers. Designs as Nos. 2228/31 but with values changed and Chinese characters for the country name in reverse order as in T **663**. Multicoloured.

2480 $7 Type **663** 25 10
2481 $19 As No. 2229 70 10
2482 $20 As No. 2230 75 10
2483 $26 As No. 2231 1·00 15

664 Pao-yu visits Garden

1998. Classical Literature. "Red Chamber Dream" (novel) by Tsao Hsueh-Chin. Multicoloured.

2484 $3.50 Type **664** 15 10
2485 $3.50 Tai-yu burying flowers 15 10
2486 $5 Pao-chai playing with butterflies 50 10
2487 $5 Hsiang-yun in drunken sleep 50 10

665 Scout Badge (½-size illustration)

1998. 20th Asia-Pacific and Eighth China National Scout Jamboree, Pingtung University. Multicoloured.

2488 $5 Type **665** 20 10
2489 $5 Tents 20 10

666 Carved Base of Pillar **667** Table Tennis

1998. Traditional Architecture. Multicoloured.
2490 $5 Type **666** 20 10
2491 $5 Carved stone ramp ("spirit way") between staircases 20 10
2492 $10 Carved base (with fishes) of column 35 10
2493 $19 Carved stone drainage spout 70 10

1998. Sports. Multicoloured.
2494 $5 Type **667** 20 10
2495 $5 Table tennis player serving 20 10
2496 $7 Rugby player with ball 25 10
2497 $7 Rugby players 25 10
Stamps of the same value were issued together, se-tenant, forming a composite design.

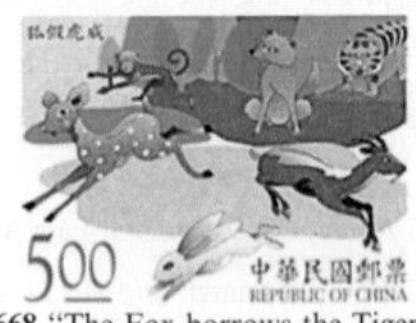

668 "The Fox borrows the Tiger's Ferocity"

1998. Chinese Fables. Multicoloured.
2498 $5 Type **668** 20 10
2499 $5 "A Frog in a Well" . . . 20 10
2500 $12 "Adding Legs to a Drawing of a Snake" . . 45 10
2501 $19 "The Snipe and the Clam at a Deadlock" . . 70 10

670 Taiwushan

1998. Kinmen National Park. Multicoloured.
2508 $5 Type **670** 20 10
2509 $5 Kuningtou Cliff 20 10
2510 $12 Teyueh Tower and Huang Hui-huang's House, Shuitou 45 10
2511 $19 Putou beach, Leihyu . . 70 10

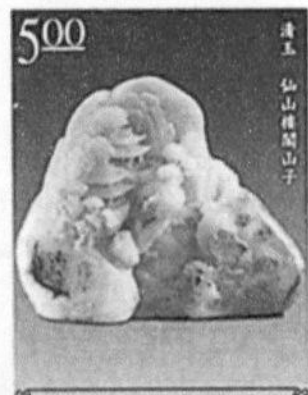

671 Hodgson's Hawk Eagle ("Spizaetus nipalensis") **672** Mountain and Pavilions

1998. Birds. Multicoloured.
2512 $5 Type **671** 20 10
2513 $5 Hodgson's hawk eagle in flight 20 10
2514 $5 Crested serpent eagle ("Spilornis cheela") on branch 20 10
2515 $5 Crested serpent eagle carrying snake 20 10
2516 $10 Black kite ("Milvus migrans") on rock 35 10
2517 $10 Black kite in flight . . . 35 10
2518 $10 Indian black eagle ("Ictinaetus malayensis") on branch 35 10
2519 $10 Indian black eagle in flight 35 10
Nos. 2512/13, 2514/15, 2516/17 and 2518/19 respectively were issued together, *se-tenant*, each pair forming a composite design.

1998. Ching Dynasty Jade Mountain Carvings. Mult.
2520 $5 Type **672** 20 10
2521 $5 Men working in jade mine (horiz) 20 10
2522 $7 Men washing elephant (horiz) 25 10
2523 $26 Five men on a mountain . . . . 1·00 15

673 Rabbit **674** Butterfly and Pumpkin ("Many Descendants")

1998. New Year Greetings. "Year of the Rabbit". Multicoloured.
2525 $3.50 Type **673** 15 10
2526 $13 Rabbit (different) . . . 50 10

1999. Wishes for the Coming Year. Multicoloured.
2528 $5 Type **674** 20 10
2529 $5 Mandarins (ducks) and lotus flowers ("Good marriage that brings sons") 20 10
2530 $12 Egret ("Prosperity") . . 45 10
2531 $12 Goldfish and flowers ("Abundance") 45 10

1999. Chinese Engravings. Birds and Plants. Designs as Nos. 2264/7 and 2330/1 but with values and Chinese characters for the country name in reverse order as in T **663**. Multicoloured.
2532 $1 Type **604** 10 10
2533 $3.50 As No. 2265 . . . . 15 10
2534 $5 As No. 2266 . . . . . 20 10
2535 $10 As No. 2267 . . . . . 35 10
2536 $12 Type **627** 45 10
2536a $20 As No. 2482 . . . . . 80 35
2537 $28 As No. 2331 . . . . . 1·10 20
2537a $34 As No. 2649 . . . . . 1·40 60

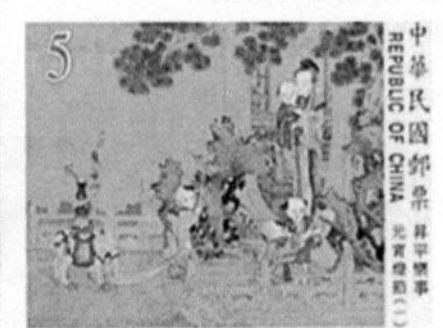

676 "Gloxinia" **677** Boy towing Toy Elephant

1999. Indoor Flowers. Multicoloured.
2539 $5 Type **676** 20 10
2540 $12 African violet 45 10
2541 $19 Flamingo flower 70 10

1999. Illustrations from "Joy in Peacetime" (Ching Dynasty book). Lantern Festival. Multicoloured.
2542 $5 Type **677** 20 10
2543 $5 Women, children and crane 20 10
2544 $7 Children playing with toy animals 25 10
2545 $26 Children playing . . . 1·00 15

678 Hanging Cylinder **679** "Baby Sleeps"

1999. Traditional Architecture. Decorative Features. Multicoloured.
2547 $5 Type **678** 20 10
2548 $5 Taishi screen 20 10
2549 $10 Xuanyu (gable decoration) 35 10
2550 $19 Wood carving 70 10

1999. Nursery Rhymes. Multicoloured.
2551 $5 Type **679** 20 10
2552 $5 Mother comforting baby frightened by storm ("Be Brave") 20 10
2553 $12 Mother and baby rocking ("Rock, Rock, Rock") 45 10
2554 $19 Mother, baby, cat and flies ("Buggie Flies") . . . 70 10

680 Atayal Ancestor Festival **682** "Washing Cotton Yarn" (Liang Chenyu)

681 Nurses treating Patients

1999. Taiwan's Aboriginal Culture. Multicoloured.
2555 $5 Type **680** 20 10
2556 $5 Dancers with hip bells (Saisat Festival of the Dwarfs) 20 10
2557 $5 Circle of singers (Bunun Millet Harvest Song) . . 20 10
2558 $5 Line of singers in red coats (Tsou Victory Festival) 20 10
2559 $5 Dancers and millet biscuits mounted on board (Rukai Harvest Festival) 20 10
2560 $5 Men with bamboo poles (Paiwan Bamboo Festival) 20 10
2561 $5 Procession of men carrying yellow scarves (Puyuma Harvest Ceremony) 20 10
2562 $5 Line of women dancers with white headdresses (Ami Harvest Ceremony) 20 10
2563 $5 Launch of new fishing boat (Yami Boat Ceremony) 20 10

1999. Centenary of International Council of Nurses. Multicoloured.
2564 $5 Type **681** 60 10
2565 $17 Globe and nurse carrying tray . . . . . . 1·40 10

1999. Chinese Classical Opera (Legends of the Ming Dynasty). Multicoloured.
2566 $5 Type **682** 20 10
2567 $5 "The Story of a Pipa" (Kaoming) 20 10
2568 $12 "The Story of Hung Fu" (Chang Fengyi) . . . 45 10
2569 $15 "Paiyueh Pavilion" (Shi Hui) 55 10

683 Coins

1999. 50th Anniv of Introduction of the Silver Yuan. Multicoloured.
2571 $5 Type **683** 20 10
2572 $25 Banknotes 95 15

684 Dragons and Carp (from window, Longsan Temple, Lukang) **685** Childern giving Present

1999. (a) As Nos. 2379, 2382, 2386 and 2387 but with Chinese characters for the country name in reverse order, as in T **684**, and colours changed.
2573 **684** $50 green . . . . 1·90 30
2574 $100 brown . . . . . . 4·00 60

(b) as T **684** but with outer decorated frame. Size 25 × 33 mm.
2578 $300 red and blue . . . . . 11·00 4·50
2579 $500 red and brown . . . . 17·00 7·00

1999. Chinese Engravings of Fruit by Hu Chen-yan. Designs as Nos. 2292/4 but with Chinese characters for the country name in reverse order, and values changed. Multicoloured.
2580 50c. As Type **613** 10 10
2581 $6 As $12 . . . . 20 10
2582 $25 As $15 . . . . 95 15

1999. Fathers' Day. Multicoloured.
2584 $5 Type **685** 20 10
2585 $25 Father teaching boy to ride bike 95 10

686 Peony Lobster (Taiwanese Cuisine)

1999. Chinese Regional Dishes. Multicoloured.
2586 $5 Type **686** 10 10
2587 $5 Buddha jumps the wall (Fukien) (plate, teapot, jar and cups) 10 10
2588 $5 Flower hors d'oeuvres (Cantonese) 10 10
2589 $5 Dongpo pork (Kiangsu and Chekiang) (plate, bowl and double handled jar) 10 10
2590 $5 Stewed fish jaws (Shanghai) (plate decorated with strawberries) 10 10
2591 $5 Beggar's chicken (Hunan) (with folded napkin) . . . 10 10
2592 $5 Carp jumping over dragon's gate (Szechwan) (on silver platter) 10 10
2593 $5 Peking duck (Peking) (in silver dish) 10 10

687 Scuba Diving

1999. Outdoor Activities. Multicoloured.
2594 $5 Type **687** 10 10
2595 $6 Canoeing 20 10
2596 $10 Surfing 35 10
2597 $25 Windsurfing 95 15

688 Stage and Audience

1999. Taiwanese Opera. Multicoloured.
2598 $5 Type **688** 10 10
2599 $6 Preparation in the dressing room 20 10
2600 $10 Two actresses 35 10
2601 $25 Actress as clown 95 15

690 Yellow-headed Amazon **691** Dragon

1999. Birds (2nd series). Illustrations from the Ching Dynasty Bird Manual. Multicoloured.
2603 $5 Type **690** 20 10
2604 $5 Golden-winged parakeet 20 10
2605 $12 Grey parrot 50 10
2606 $25 Chattering lory . . . . 1·10 20
See also Nos. 2671/4 and 2740/3.

1999. New Year Greetings. "Year of the Dragon". Multicoloured.
2607 $3.50 Type **691** 15 10
2608 $13 Dragon (different) . . . 55 10

692 ST-1 Communication Satellite over Earth

1999. Year 2000. Multicoloured.
2610 $5 Type **692** (information) 20 10
2611 $5 Deer and river (environmental protection) 20 10
2612 $12 Modern buildings and high-speed train (industry and economy) 50 10
2613 $15 Dove and St. Peter's Basilica,Vatican City (peace) 65 10

693 Emperor Chia-Ching's "Coloured Cloud Dragon" Writing Brushes (Ming Dynasty)

2000. Traditional Chinese Writing Equipment. Mult.
2616 $5 Type **693** 20 10
2617 $5 Emperor Lung Ching's "Imperial Dragon Fragrance" ink stick (Ming Dynasty) (vert) . . 20 10
2618 $7 "Clear Heart House" (calligraphy, Tsai Hsiang) (Sung Dynasty) (vert) . . 30 10
2619 $26 "Celadon Toad Inkstone" (Sung Dynasty) 1·10 20

694 Kaoping River Bridge Pylon

2000. Inauguration of Second Southern Freeway. Multicoloured.
2620 $5 Type **694** 20 10
2621 $12 Main junction, Tainan 50 10

695 Branch, Fields and Houses

2000. Seasonal Periods (1st series). Designs depicting the six seasonal periods of Spring. Multicoloured.
2623 $5 Type **695** ("Commencement of Spring") 20 10
2624 $5 Man ploughing fields in the rain ("Rain Water") 20 10
2625 $5 Forks of lightning, little egret and cattle egret("Waking of Insects") 20 10
2626 $5 Men transplanting rice seedlings (Spring Equinox) 20 10
2627 $5 Basket of fruit and houses ("Pure Brightness") 20 10
2628 $5 Rain, farmer and river ("Grain Rain") 20 10
See also Nos. 2636/41, 2652/7 and 2675/80.

696 Shuanghsi River and School Gates, Waishuanghsi Campus

697 Three Heroes at Altar

2000. Centenary of Soochow University. Mult.
2629 $5 Type **696** 20 10
2630 $25 Justice statue, Soochow Law School, Taipeh campus and Ansu Hall, Waishuanghsi campus . . 1·10 20

2000. Classical Literature. *Romance of the Three Kingdoms* by Luo Guanzhong (1st series). Mult.
2631 $3.50 Type **697** 15 10
2632 $3.50 Guan Yu reading at night 15 10
2633 $5 Couple in cottage receiving guest 20 10
2634 $20 Arrows raining down on sampans 85 10
See also Nos. 2797/2801.

698 Crops and Mountains

2000. Seasonal Periods (2nd series). Designs depicting the six seasonal periods of Summer. Multicoloured.
2636 $5 Type **698** ("Commencement of Summer") 20 10
2637 $5 Water wheel and houses in rain ("Little Fullness") 20 10
2638 $5 Ears of grain and houses ("Husks of Grain") . . . 20 10
2639 $5 Insect on plant and houses (Summer Solstice) 20 10
2640 $5 Palm leaf fan and fields ("Lesser Heat") 20 10
2641 $5 Watermelons ("Great Heat") 20 10
Nos. 2636/41 were issued together, se-tenant, forming a composite design.

699 Chen Shui-bian and Lu Hsiu-lien

2000. Inauguration of Chen Shui-bian as 10th President and Lu Hsiu-lien as Vice-President. Mult.
2642 $5 Type **699** 20 10
2643 $5 Presidential Office building 20 10

700 Hsialiao

701 Taiwan Giant Sacred Tree

2000. Monuments Marking the Tropic of Cancer. Multicoloured.
2645 $5 Type **700** 20 10
2646 $12 Wuho 55 10
2647 $25 Chingpu . . . . 1·10 20

2000. Chinese Engravings of Fruit by Hu Chen-yan. As No. 2295 but with Chinese characters for the country name in reverse order, as in T **683**, and with value (2648) or new design changed.
2648 $32 multicoloured . . . . . 1·40 25
2649 $34 multicoloured . . . . . 1·50 25

2000. Sacred Trees. Multicoloured.
2650 $5 Type **701** 20 10
2651 $39 Sacred Sleeping Moon Tree . . . . 1·60 25

702 Grain drying

2000. Seasonal Periods (3rd series). Depicting the six seasonal periods of Autumn. Multicoloured.
2652 $5 Type **702** ("Commencement of Autumn") 20 10
2653 $5 Rick and village ("Bounds of Heat") . . . 20 10
2654 $5 Dew covered leaves ("White Dew") 20 10
2655 $5 Red leaves ("Autumn Equinox") 20 10
2656 $5 Bare tree ("Cold Dew") 20 10
2657 $5 Frost on plant ("Descent of Hoar Frost") 20 10
Nos. 2652/57 were issued together, se-tenant. forming a composite design.

2000. No. 1784 surch **350**.
2658 $3.50 on $7.50 multicoloured 15 10

704 Red Spider Lily

705 Seismograph and map of Taiwan

2000. Poisonous Plants. Multicoloured.
2659 $5 Type **704** 20 10
2660 $5 Odollam erberus-tree (*Cerbera manghas*) 20 10
2661 $12 Rosary pea 55 10
2662 $20 Oleander 85 10

2000. Earthquakes. Multicoloured.
2663 $5 Type **705** 20 10
2664 $12 Rescue workers 55 10
2665 $25 Earthquake drills . . . 1·10 20

706 *Anotogaster sieboldii*

2000. Dragonflies. Multicoloured.
2666 $5 Type **706** 20 10
2667 $5 *Lamelligomphus formosanus* (horiz) 20 10
2668 $12 *Neurothemis ramburii* (horiz) 50 20
2669 $12 *Trithemis festiva* . . . 50 20

707 White's Thrush

2000. Birds (3rd series). Illustrations from the Ching Dynasty Bird Manual. Multicoloured.
2671 $5 Type **707** 20 10
2672 $5 Brambling 20 10
2673 $12 Rothschild's mynah . . 50 20
2674 $25 Southern grackle . . . 1·00 40

708 Lake, Mountains and Bowl

2000. Seasonal Periods (4th series). Designs depicting the six seasonal periods of Winter. Multicoloured.
2675 $5 Type **708** ("Commencement of Winter") 20 10
2676 $5 Trees covered in snow ("Lesser Snow") 20 10
2677 $5 Mountains covered in snow ("Great Snow") . . 20 10
2678 $5 Rice balls in bowl ("Winter Solstice") . . . 20 10
2679 $5 Houses and tree branch covered in snow ("Lesser Cold") 20 10
2680 $5 Log cabin covered in snow ("Great Cold") . . 20 10
Nos. 2675/80 were issued together, se-tenant, forming a composite design.

709 Palace Lamp Boulevard and Classrooms

2000. 50th Anniv of Tamkang University. Mult.
2681 $5 Type **709** 20 10
2682 $25 Maritime Museum and "Scroll Plaza" (sculpture) 1·00 40

710 Snake

712 Cruise Ship and Buildings

2000. New Year Greetings. "Year of the Snake". Multicoloured.
2683 $3.50 Type **710** 15 10
2684 $13 Snake (different) . . . 55 25

2001. "Three Small Links" (establishment of trade links between Kinmen, Xiamen, Matsu and Foochow). Multicoloured.
2687 $9 Type **712** 35 15
2688 $25 Cruise ship and monument . . . . 1·00 40

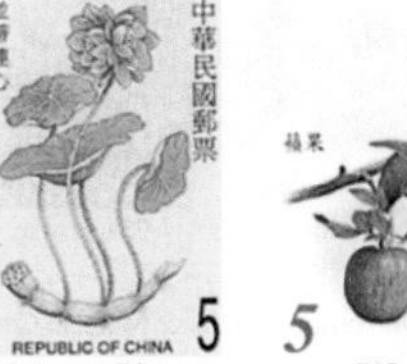

713 Lotus Blossoms ("Marital Bliss")

715 Apples

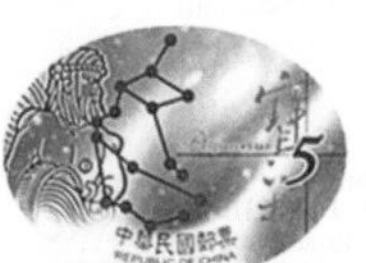

714 Aquarius

2001. Wishes for the Coming Year. Multicoloured.
2689 $5 Type **713** 20 10
2690 $5 Loganberries, lichees and walnuts ("Success in one's career") 20 10
2691 $12 Pomegranates ("Producing many offspring") 50 20
2692 $12 Peonies and pair of Chinese bulbuls ("Growing old together with wealth and high position") 50 20

2001. Signs of the Western Zodiac (1st series). Air Signs. Multicoloured.
2693 $5 Type **714** 20 10
2694 $12 Gemini 50 20
2695 $25 Libra . . . . 1·00 40
See also Nos. 2708/10, 2726/8 and 2755/7.

2001. Fruits (1st series). Multicoloured.
2696 $5 Type **715** 20 10
2697 $7 Guavas 30 15
2698 $12 Pears 50 20
2699 $25 Melons . . . . 1·00 40
See also Nos. 2732/5 and 2785/8.

716 Main Peak

2001. Mount Jade. Views of Mount Jade. Mult.
2700 $5 Type **716** 20 10
2701 $5 Western peak 20 10
2702 $12 Northern peak 50 20
2703 $25 Eastern peak . . . . . 1·00 40

717 Girls playing with Ball ("Little Ball")

2001. Children's Playtime Rhymes. Multicoloured.
2704 $5 Type **717** 20 10
2705 $5 Children sitting in a circle ("Point to the Water Vat") 20 10
2706 $12 Boys dancing ("Pangolin") 50 20
2707 $25 Children playing ("Shake and Stamp") . . 1·00 40

2001. Signs of the Western Zodiac (2nd series). Earth Signs. As T **714**. Multicoloured.
2708 $5 Capricorn 20 10
2709 $12 Taurus 50 20
2710 $25 Virgo . . . . 1·00 40

718 Sakyamuni Buddha, Northern Wei Dynasty

2001. Ancient Statues of Buddha. Multicoloured.
2711 $5 Type **718** 20 15
2712 $9 Seated Buddha, Tang Dynasty 35 15
2713 $12 Mahavairocana Buddha, Sung Dynasty 50 20

719 Thresher

2001. Early Agricultural Implements. Multicoloured.
2715 $5 Type **719** 20 10
2716 $7 Ox plough 30 15
2717 $10 Bamboo baskets and yoke 45 20
2718 $25 Coir raincoat and hat 1·00 80

720 Mackay

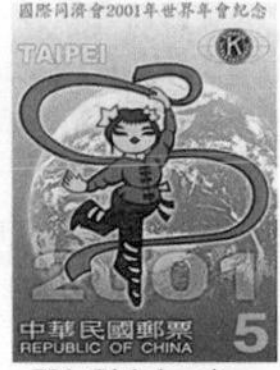

721 Girl dancing, Globe and Emblem

2001. Death Centenary of George Leslie Mackay (missionary and educator).
2719 **720** $25 multicoloured . . . 1·00 80

2001. Kiwanis International (community organization) Convention, Taipeh. Multicoloured.
2720 $5 Type **721** 20 10
2721 $25 Mother and child within heart . . . . 1·00 80

722 Dragon

2001. Kites. Multicoloured.
2722 $5 Type **722** 20 10
2723 $5 Phoenix 20 10
2724 $5 Tiger 20 10
2725 $5 Fish 20 10

2001. Signs of the Western Zodiac (3rd series). Fire Signs. As T **714**. Multicoloured.
2726 $5 Aries 20 10
2727 $12 Leo 50 20
2728 $25 Sagittarius . . . . . . 1·00 80

723 Medium-Capacity Car

2001. Rapid Transit System, Taipeh. Multicoloured.
2729 $5 Type **723** 20 10
2730 $12 Passengers and tickets 45 20
MS2731 125 × 60 mm. $25 Chientan Station, Tamshui Line (84 × 42 mm) 90 90

2001. Fruits (2nd series). As T **715**. Multicoloured.
2732 $1 Plums 10 10
2733 $3.50 Tangerines 15 10
2734 $20 Longans 70 30
2735 $40 Grapefruit . . . . . . 1·40 60

724 Keeper and Monkeys ("Now Three, Now Four")

2001. Chinese Fables. Multicoloured.
2736 $5 Type **724** 20 10
2737 $5 Man selling weapons ("Selling the All Penetrating Sword and Unyielding Shield") . . . 20 10
2738 $12 Farmer sitting under tree ("Waiting by the Tree for the Rabbit") 45 20
2739 $25 Old man and children ("An Old Fool Moves Mountains") 90 40

725 Japanese Waxwing

2001. Birds (4th series). Showing illustrations from the Ching Dynasty Bird Manual. Multicoloured.
2740 $5 Type **725** 20 10
2741 $5 Siberian rubythroat . . . 20 10
2742 $12 White-rumped munia 45 20
2743 $25 Great barbet 90 40

726 Second Terminal, Chiang Kai-shek International Airport

2001. 90th Anniv of Republic of China. Multicoloured.
2744 $5 Type **726** 20 10
2745 $5 Computer screens, lap top computer, mobile phone and Globe 20 10
2746 $12 Dance, National Theatre 45 20
2747 $15 Dolphins 55 25

727 Flame, Karate, Javelin and Table Tennis

2001. National Games, Kaohsiung and Pingtung. Multicoloured.
2748 $5 Type **727** 20 10
2749 $25 Swimming, athletics, weightlifting and map . . 90 40

728 Pitcher

2001. 34th World Baseball Championship and 21st Asia Baseball Tournament. Multicoloured.
2750 $5 Type **728** 20 10
2751 $5 Batter 20 10
2752 $12 Catcher 45 20
2753 $20 Base runner 70 30
MS2754 120 × 85 mm. Nos. 2750/3 1·40 1·40

2001. Signs of the Western Zodiac (4th series). Water Signs. As T **714**. Multicoloured.
2755 $5 Pisces 20 10
2756 $12 Cancer 45 20
2757 $25 Scorpio 90 40

729 Mozhaonu holding Fan ("Thunder Storm")

2001. Taiwanese Puppet Theatre. Showing puppets. Multicoloured.
2758 $5 Type **729** 20 10
2759 $6 Taiyangau ("Rising Winds, Surging Clouds") 20 10
2760 $10 Kuangdao ("Thunder Crazy Sword") 35 15
2761 $25 Chin Chia-chien ("Thunder Golden Light") 90 40

730 Old School Building, Shuiyan Road, Taipeh

731 Horse

2001. Centenary of National Defence Medical Centre. Multicoloured.
2762 $5 Type **730** 20 10
2763 $25 New school building and medical staff 90 40

2001. New Year Greetings. "Year of the Horse". Multicoloured.
2764 $3.50 Type **731** 15 10
2765 $13 Horse (different) 45 20
MS2766 78 × 102 mm. Nos. 2764/5, each × 2 . . . . 1·25 1·25

732 Yu Pin

2001. Birth Centenary of Yu Pin (religious leader).
2767 **732** $25 multicoloured . . . 90 40
MS2768 80 × 60 mm. $25 As No. 2767 . . . . 90 40

733 Carnations

2001. Greetings Stamps. Multicoloured.
2769 $5 Type **733** 20 10
2770 $5 White lilies 20 10
2771 $5 Pink violas 20 10
2772 $5 Orange flowers with yellow centres 20 10
2773 $5 Pink flowers with five petals 20 10
2774 $5 Pink roses 20 10
2775 $5 Christmas tree decorations 20 10
2776 $5 Poinsettia 20 10
2777 $5 Purple ball-shaped flowers 20 10
2778 $5 Sunflowers 20 10

734 Students with Flags

2002. 50th Anniv of Fu Hsing Kang College (military university). Multicoloured.
2779 $5 Type **734** 20 10
2780 $25 University buildings and statue 90 40

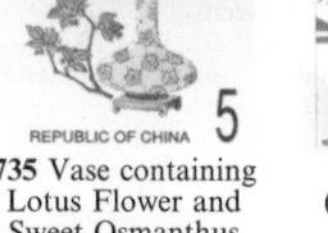

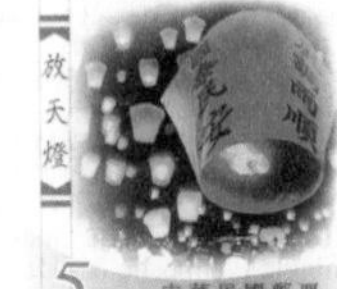

735 Vase containing Lotus Flower and Sweet Osmanthus ("Producing many offspring")

736 Lantern Festival (Pinghsi and Shihfen)

2002. Wishes for the Coming Year. Multicoloured.
2781 $5 Type **735** 20 10
2782 $5 Orchid and osmanthus plants ("Person of high morality") 20 10
2783 $12 Vase containing peonies and flowering crabapple ("Hall full of the rich and famous") 45 20
2784 $12 Vase containing roses ("Safe and peaceful in all four seasons") 45 20

2002. Fruits (3rd series). As T **715**. Multicoloured.
2785 $6 Avocados 20 10
2786 $10 Lychees 40 20
2787 $17 Dates 60 25
2788 $32 Passionfruit . . . . . 1·10 45

2002. Traditional Folk Festivals (1st series). Multicoloured.
2789 $5 Type **736** 20 10
2790 $5 Fireworks display (Yanshui) 20 10
2791 $10 Matsu (sea goddess) procession (Peikang) . . . 40 20
2792 $20 Dragon boat race . . . 75 30
See also Nos. 2817/20.

737 Mountain in Winter

2002. Mount Hsueh. Views of Mount Hsueh. Multicoloured.
2793 $5 Type **737** 20 10
2794 $5 North ridge 20 10
2795 $12 Slopes in autumn . . . 45 20
2796 $25 Glacial cirques (bowl-shaped depressions) . . . 90 40

738 Three Heroes chasing Lu Bu

2002. Classical Literature. Romance of the Three Kingdoms by Luo Guanzhong (2nd series). Multicoloured.
2797 $3.50 Type **738** 10 10
2798 $3.50 Chao Yun 10 10
2799 $5 Dr. Hua Tuo operating on Guan Yu's arm . . . 15 10
2800 $20 Chu-Ko Liang playing lute to repel invaders . . 65 30
MS2801 140 × 100 mm. Nos. 2797/800 . . . . 1·00 1·00

739 Chinese Crested Tern (*Thalasseus bernsteini*)

2002. Endangered Species. Chinese Crested Tern. Two sheets, 240 × 160 mm (**MS**2802a) and 120 × 60 mm (**MS**2802b) containing T **739** and similar horiz designs. Multicoloured.
MS2802 (a) $5 × 10, Type **739**; Two Terns in flight; Tern flying (left); Landing on rock; Perched on rock with open beak; Feeding chick; Diving; Flying above rocks; On ground looking left; Adult and chick; On nest (b) $25 Tern in flight (80 × 30 mm) Set of 2 sheets 1·30 1·30

740 Bowl decorated with Lotus

741 Stock (*Matthiola incana*)

2002. Ching Dynasty Enamel Porcelain Bowls. Multicoloured.
2803 $5 Type **740** 15 10
2804 $5 Peacock 15 10
2805 $7 Peonies 25 10
2806 $32 Birds and bamboo . . . 1·10 55

2002. Scented Flowers. Multicoloured.
2807 $5 Type **741** 15 10
2808 $12 Gardenia (*Gardenia jasminoides*) 40 20
2809 $25 Banana shrub (*Michelia figo*) 85 40

742 Bottle-nosed Dolphin (*Tursiops truncates*)

2002. Marine mammals. Multicoloured.
2810 $5 Type **742** 15 10
2811 $5 Humpback whale (*Megaptera novaeangliae*) 15 10
2812 $10 Killer whale (*Orcinus orca*) 35 15
2813 $25 Risso's dolphin (*Grampus griseus*) 85 40
MS2814 120 × 80 mm. As Nos. 2810/13 . . . . 1·50 75

743 Player in Wheelchair

2002. International Paralympics Committee World Table Tennis Championships, Taipeh. Multicoloured.
2815 $5 Type **743** 15 10
2816 $5 Player using crutch . . . 15 10

2002. Traditional Folk Festivals (2nd series). As T **736**. Multicoloured.
2817 $5 Water lanterns (Keelung) 15 10
2818 $5 Fireworks display (Touchengi) 15 10
2819 $10 Yimin (martyrs) procession (Taoyuan) . . 35 15
2820 $20 Burning the Prince's boat (Tungkang) 65 30

744 Republic of China and Vatican City Flags

2002. 60th Anniv of Republic of China—Vatican City Diplomatic Relations ($5). 80th Anniv of First Apostolic Delegate to Republic of China ($17). Multicoloured.
2821 $5 Type **744** 15 10
2822 $17 Celso Costantini (first apostolic delegate) 55 25

745 Vernal Hanging Parrot

2002. Birds (5th series). Illustrations from the Ching Dynasty Bird Manual. Multicoloured.
2823 $5 Type **745** 15 10
2824 $5 White-rumped munia . . 15 10
2825 $12 White-headed greenfinch 40 20
2826 $25 Yunnan greenfinch . . 85 40

746 Liang Shan-po and Chu Ying-tai (impromptu performance)

2002. Chinese Regional Opera. Multicoloured.
2827 $5 Type **746** 15 15
2828 $6 Hsueh Ting-shan and Fan Li-hua (indoor performance) 20 10
2829 $10 Hsueh Ping-kuei and Wang Pao-chuan (outdoor stage performance) 35 15
2830 $25 The Living Buddha Chikung (modern theatre) 85 40

747 Mother and Baby Koala

749 Goat

748 Knot

2002. Koalas at Taipei Municipal Zoo. Multicoloured.
2831 $5 Type **747** 15 10
2832 $5 Eating leaf 15 10
2833 $9 Resting 30 15
2834 $21 Mother with baby on back 70 35
MS2835 85 × 115 mm. Nos. 2831/4 1·20 1·20

2002. Greetings Stamps. Chinese Decorative Knots. Designs showing various knots (knot colours given). Multicoloured.
2836 $3.50 Type **748** 10 10
2837 $3.50 green, blue and yellow 10 10
2838 $3.50 red and yellow 10 10
2839 $3.50 orange and green . . 10 10
2840 $3.50 blue and straw . . . 10 10
2841 $3.50 blue, mauve, green, red and yellow 10 10
2842 $3.50 red and yellow (different) 10 10
2843 $3.50 mauve and blue . . . 10 10
2844 $3.50 pink and lavender . . 10 10
2845 $3.50 yellow and blue . . . 10 10
2846 $5 Type **748** 15 10
2847 $5 As No. 2837 . . . . . . 15 10
2848 $5 As 2838 . . . . 15 10
2849 $5 As 2839 . . . . 15 10
2850 $5 As 2840 . . . . 15 10
2851 $5 As 2841 . . . . 15 10
2852 $5 As 2842 . . . . 15 10
2853 $5 As 2843 . . . . 15 10
2854 $5 As 2844 . . . . 15 10
2855 $5 As 2845 . . . . 15 10
2856 $25 Type **748** 85 40
2857 $25 As 2837 . . . . 85 40
2858 $25 As 2838 . . . . 85 40
2859 $25 As 2839 . . . . 85 40
2860 $25 As 2840 . . . . 85 40
2861 $25 As 2841 . . . . 85 40
2862 $25 As 2842 . . . . 85 40
2863 $25 As 2843 . . . . 85 40
2864 $25 As 2844 . . . . 85 40
2865 $25 As 2845 . . . . 85 40

2002. New Year Greetings. "Year of the Goat". Multicoloured
2866 $3.50 Type **749** 10 10
2867 $13 Goat (different) 45 20
MS2868 78 × 102 mm. Nos. 2866/7, each × 2 . . . . 1·10 1·10

750 "Street Scene on a Summer's Day" (Chen Cheng-po)

2002. Taiwanese Artists. Multicoloured.
2869 $5 Type **750** 15 10
2870 $5 "Girl in white dress" (Li Mei-shu) (vert) 15 10
2871 $10 "Courtyard with banana trees" (Liao Chi-chun) (vert) 35 15
2872 $20 "Sunrise" (Kuo Po-chuan) 65 30

POSTAGE DUE STAMPS

(D 12) (D 15)

1950. Surch as Type D **12**.
D105 **6** 4c. on $100 blue . . . . . 11·50 9·00
D106 10c. on $100 blue . . . . 22·00 5·50
D107 20c. on $100 blue . . . . 11·50 10·00
D108 40c. on $100 blue . . . . 30·00 22·00
D109 $1 on $100 blue . . . . . 30·00 40·00

1951. No. 524 of China surch as Type D **15**.
D133 40c. on 40c. orange . . . . 19·00 13·00
D134 80c. on 40c. orange . . . . 19·00 12·00

(D 19) D 43

1953. Revenue stamps as T **143** of China surch as Type D **19**.
D151 10c. on $50 blue . . . . . 16·00 5·00
D152 20c. on $100 olive . . . . 16·00 5·00
D153 40c. on $20 brown . . . . 19·00 1·50
D154 80c. on $500 green . . . . 35·00 2·50
D155 100c. on $30 mauve . . . . 35·00 8·50

1956.
D236 D **43** 20c. red and blue . . . 2·50 50
D237 40c. green and buff . . 2·50 50
D238 80c. brown and grey 3·75 75
D239 $1 blue and mauve . . 6·00 75

(D 97) D 152

1961. Surch with Type D **97**.
D429 **56** $5 on $20 red . . . . . 6·50 3·00

1964. Surch as Type D **97**.
D490 **83** 10c. on 80c. green . . . 50 30
D491 20c. on $3.60 blue . . . 50 40
D492 40c. on $4.50 red 75 35

1966.
D588 D **152** 10c. brown and lilac 10 25
D589 20c. blue and yellow 15 25
D590 50c. ultram & blue 3·00 40
D591 $1 violet and flesh 55 15
D592 $2 green and blue 55 15
D593 $5 red and buff . . 75 20
D594a $10 purple & mauve 11·50 1·00

D 399

1984.
D1532a D **399** $1 red and blue . . 40 10
D1533a $2 yellow and blue 40 10
D1534 $3 green & mauve 40 10
D1535a $5 blue and yellow 50 15
D1536 $5.50 mauve & bl 50 15
D1537 $7.50 yellow & vio 60 25
D1538b $10 yellow and red 60 20
D1539 $20 blue and green 1·10 65

CHINA EXPEDITIONARY FORCE Pt. 1

Stamps used by Indian military forces in China.

12 pies = 1 anna; 16 annas = 1 rupee.

Stamps of India optd **C.E.F.**

1900. Queen Victoria.
C 1 **40** 3p. red . . . . 40 1·25
C 2 **23** ½a. green 75 30
C 3 – 1a. purple . . . . 4·25 1·50
C11 – 1a. red . . . . 30·00 8·00
C 4 – 2a. blue . . . . 3·00 9·00
C 5 – 2a.6p. green . . . . . . 2·75 13·00
C 6 – 3a. orange . . . . . . 2·75 16·00
C 7 – 4a. green (No. 96) . . . . 2·75 7·50
C 8 – 8a. mauve . . . . 2·75 18·00
C 9 – 12a. purple on red . . . . 16·00 16·00
C10 **37** 1r. green and red . . . . 22·00 23·00

1904. King Edward VII.
C12c **41** 3p. grey . . . . 4·75 6·50
C13 – 1a. red (No. 123) . . . . 7·50 70
C14 – 2a. lilac . . . . 14·00 2·50
C15 – 2a.6p. blue . . . . 3·25 5·00
C16 – 3a. orange . . . . 3·75 4·00
C17 – 4a. olive . . . . 8·50 13·00
C18 – 8a. mauve . . . . 8·00 7·50
C19 – 12a. purple on red . . . 11·00 19·00
C20 – 1r. green and red . . . . 14·00 28·00

1909. King Edward VII.
C21 ½a. green (No. 149) . . . . 1·75 1·50
C22 1a. red (No. 150) . . . . . 2·50 30

1913. King George V.
C23 **55** 3p. grey . . . . 5·50 27·00
C24 **56** ½a. green . . . . 4·00 6·00
C25 **57** 1a. red . . . . 5·00 4·00
C26 **58** 1½a. brown (No. 163) . . 25·00 80·00
C27 **59** 2a. lilac . . . . 18·00 70·00
C28 **61** 2a.6p. blue . . . . 13·00 26·00
C29 **62** 3a. orange . . . . 27·00 £225
C30 **63** 4a. olive . . . . 24·00 £170
C32 **65** 8a. mauve . . . . 25·00 £350
C33 **66** 12a. red . . . . 24·00 £120
C34 **67** 1r. brown and green . . . 65·00 £325

BRITISH RAILWAY ADMINISTRATION

1901. No. 121 of China surch **B.R.A. 5 Five Cents.**
BR133b **32** 5c. on ½c. brown . . . £325 £100

CHRISTMAS ISLAND Pt. 1

Situated in the Indian Ocean about 600 miles south of Singapore. Formerly part of the Straits Settlements and then of the Crown Colony of Singapore, Christmas Island was occupied by the Japanese from 31 March 1942 until September 1945. It reverted to Singapore after liberation but subsequently became an Australian territory on 15 October 1958.

1958. 100 cents = 1 Malayan dollar.
1968. 100 cents = 1 Australian dollar.

1 Queen Elizabeth II **2** Map

1958. Type of Australia with opt and value in black.
1 **1** 2c. orange 55 80
2 4c. brown 60 30
3 5c. mauve 60 50
4 6c. blue . . . . 1·00 30
5 8c. sepia . . . . 1·75 50
6 10c. violet . . . . 1·00 30
7 12c. red . . . . 1·75 1·75
8 20c. blue . . . . 1·00 1·75
9 50c. green . . . . 1·75 1·75
10 $1 turquoise . . . . 1·75 1·75

1963.
11 **2** 2c. orange 90 35
12 – 4c. brown 50 15
13 – 5c. purple 50 20
14 – 6c. blue 40 35
15 – 8c. black . . . . 2·25 35
16 – 10c. violet 40 15
17 – 12c. red 40 25
18 – 20c. blue . . . . 1·00 20
19 – 50c. green . . . . 1·00 20
20 – $1 yellow . . . . 1·75 35
DESIGNS—VERT: 4c. Moonflower; 5c. Robber crab; 8c. Phosphate train; 10c. Raising phosphate. HORIZ: 6c. Island scene; 12c. Flying Fish cove; 20c. Loading cantilever; 50c. Christmas Island frigate bird. LARGER (35 × 21 mm): $1 White-tailed tropic bird.

1965. 50th Anniv of Gallipoli Landing. As T **184** of Australia, but slightly larger (22 × 34½ mm).
21 10c. brown, black and green 30 1·25

12 Golden-striped Grouper

1968. Fishes. Multicoloured.
22 1c. Type **12** 45 45
23 2c. Moorish idol 60 20
24 3c. Long-nosed butterflyfish 60 30
25 4c. Pink-tailed triggerfish . . 60 20
26 5c. Regal angelfish 60 20
27 9c. White-cheeked surgeonfish 60 40
28 10c. Lionfish 60 20
28a 15c. Saddle butterflyfish . . . 7·00 2·50
29 20c. Ornate butterflyfish . . . 1·50 55
29a 30c. Giant ghost pipefish . . 7·00 2·50
30 50c. Clown surgeonfish . . . 1·75 1·50
31 $1 Meyer's butterflyfish . . . 1·75 2·00

13 "Angel" (mosaic) **14** "The Ansidei Madonna" (Raphael)

1969. Christmas.
32 **13** 5c. multicoloured 20 30

1970. Christmas. Paintings. Multicoloured.
33 3c. Type **14** 20 15
34 5c. "The Virgin and Child, St. John the Baptist and an Angel" (Morando) 20 15

15 "The Adoration of the Shepherds" (attr to the School of Seville)
16 H.M.S. "Flying Fish" (survey ship), 1887

1971. Christmas. Multicoloured.
35 6c. Type **15** 30 50
36 20c. "The Adoration of the Shepherds" (Reni) . . . . . 70 1·00

1972. Ships. Multicoloured.
37 1c. "Eagle" (merchant sailing ship), 1714 . . . . 25 60
38 2c. H.M.S. "Redpole" (gunboat), 1890 . . . . . . 30 70
39 3c. "Hoi Houw" (freighter), 1959 . . . . 30 70
40 4c. "Pigot" (sailing ship), 1771 40 75
41 5c. "Valetta" (cargo-liner), 1968 . . . . 40 75
42 6c. Type **16** 40 75
43 7c. "Asia" (sail merchantman), 1805 . . . . 40 75
44 8c. "Islander" (freighter), 1929–60 . . . . 45 80
45 9c. H.M.S. "Imperieuse" (armoured cruiser), 1888 . . 65 70
46 10c. H.M.S. "Hecate" (coast defence turret ship), 1871 . . 50 80
47 20c. "Thomas" (galleon), 1615 50 1·00
48 25c. Royal Navy sail sloop, 1864 . . . . 50 1·75
49 30c. "Cygnet" (flute), 1688 . . 50 1·00
50 35c. "Triadic" (freighter), 1958 50 1·00
51 50c. H.M.S. "Amethyst" (frigate), 1857 . . . . . . 50 1·50
52 $1 "Royal Mary" (warship), 1643 . . . . 70 1·75

No. 45 is inscribed "H.M.S. Imperious", No. 46 "H.M.S. Egeria" and No. 48 "H.M.S. Gordon", all in error.

17 Angel of Peace
19 Mary and Holy Child within Christmas Star

18 Virgin and Child, and Map

1972. Christmas. Multicoloured.
53 3c. Type **17** 15 40
54 3c. Angel of Joy 15 40
55 7c. Type **17** 20 50
56 7c. As No. 54 . . . . 20 50

1973. Christmas.
57 **18** 7c. multicoloured 25 35
58 25c. multicoloured . . . . . 75 1·00

1974. Christmas.
59 **19** 7c. mauve and grey 25 60
60 30c. orange, yellow and grey 75 2·50

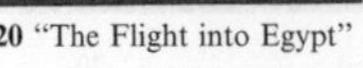

20 "The Flight into Egypt"
21 Dove of Peace and Star of Bethlehem

1975. Christmas.
61 **20** 10c. yellow, brown and gold 25 35
62 35c. pink, blue and gold . . 50 1·75

1976. Christmas.
63 **21** 10c. red, yellow and mauve 15 45
64 – 10c. red, yellow and mauve 15 45
65 **21** 35c. violet, blue and green 20 55
66 – 35c. violet, blue and green 20 55

DESIGNS: Nos. 64 and 66 are "mirror-images" of Type **21**.

22 William Dampier (explorer)

1977. Famous Visitors. Multicoloured.
67 1c. Type **22** 15 80
68 2c. Captain de Vlamingh (explorer) 20 80
69 3c. Vice-Admiral MacLear . . 30 80
70 4c. Sir John Murray (oceanographer) 30 90
71 5c. Admiral Aldrich 30 40
72 6c. Andrew Clunies Ross (first settler) 30 60
73 7c. J. J. Lister (naturalist) . . 30 40
74 8c. Admiral of the Fleet Sir William May 35 70
75 9c. Henry Ridley (botanist) . . 40 1·75
76 10c. George Clunies Ross (phosphate miner) 55 55
77 20c. Captain Joshua Slocum (yachtsman) 50 75
78 45c. Charles Andrews (naturalist) 60 45
79 50c. Richard Hanitsch (biologist) . . . . 70 1·60
80 75c. Victor Purcell (scholar) 60 1·25
81 $1 Fam Choo Beng (educator) 60 1·25
82 $2 Sir Harold Spencer-Jones (astronomer) . . . . 65 2·00

23 Australian Coat of Arms on Map of Christmas Island

1977. Silver Jubilee.
83 **23** 45c. multicoloured 45 55

24 "A Partridge in a Pear Tree"
25 Abbott's Booby

1977. Christmas. "The Twelve Days of Christmas". Multicoloured.
84A 10c. Type **24** 10 20
85A 10c. "Two turtle doves" . . 10 20
86A 10c. "Three French hens" . . 10 20
87A 10c. "Four calling birds" . . 10 20
88A 10c. "Five gold rings" . . . 10 20
89A 10c. "Six geese a-laying" . . 10 20
90A 10c. "Seven swans a-swimming" 10 20
91A 10c. "Eight maids a-milking" 10 20
92A 10c. "Nine ladies dancing" . 10 20
93A 10c. "Ten lords a-leaping" . 10 20
94A 10c. "Eleven pipers piping" 10 20
95A 10c. "Twelve drummers drumming" 10 20

1978. 25th Anniv of Coronation.
96 – 45c. black and blue 45 75
97 – 45c. multicoloured 45 75
98 **25** 45c. black and blue 45 75

DESIGNS: No. 96, White Swan of Bohun; No. 97, Queen Elizabeth II.

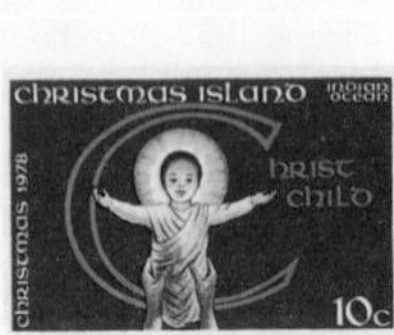

26 "Christ Child"
27 Chinese Children

1978. Christmas Scenes from "The Song of Christmas". Multicoloured.
99 10c. Type **26** 15 20
100 10c. "Herald Angels" 15 20
101 10c. "Redeemer" 15 20
102 10c. "Israel" 15 20
103 10c. "Star" 15 20
104 10c. "Three Wise Men" . . . 15 20
105 10c. "Manger" 15 20
106 10c. "All He Stands For" . . 15 20
107 10c. "Shepherds Come" . . . 15 20

1979. International Year of the Child. Children of different races. Multicoloured, colours of inscr given.
108 20c. green (Type **27**) 30 45
109 20c. turquoise (Malay children) 30 45
110 20c. lilac (Indian children) . . 30 45
111 20c. red (European children) 30 45
112 20c. yellow ("Oranges and Lemons") 30 45

28 1958 2c. Definitive

1979. Death Centenary of Sir Rowland Hill. Multicoloured.
113 20c. Type **28** 20 40
114 20c. 1963 2c. map definitive 20 40
115 20c. 1965 50th Anniv of Gallipoli Landing 10c. commemorative 20 40
116 20c. 1964 4c. Pink-tailed triggerfish definitive . . . 20 40
117 20c. 1969 Christmas 5c. . . 20 40

29 Wise Men following Star

1979. Christmas. Multicoloured.
118 20c. Type **29** 20 30
119 55c. Virgin and Child 45 70

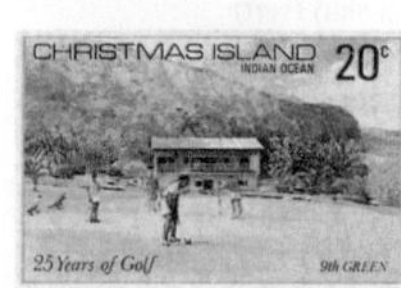

30 9th Green

1980. 25th Anniv of Christmas Island Golf Club. Multicoloured.
120 20c. Type **30** 35 50
121 55c. Clubhouse . . . . . . 40 1·00

31 Surveying

1980. Phosphate Industry (1st series). Multicoloured.
122 15c. Type **31** 15 30
123 22c. Drilling for samples . . 15 35
124 40c. Sample analysis 20 55
125 55c. Mine planning 25 60

See also Nos. 126/9, 136/9 and 140/3.

1980. Phosphate Industry (2nd series). As T **31**. Multicoloured.
126 15c. Jungle clearing 15 15
127 22c. Overburden removal . . 15 20
128 40c. Open cut mining 20 25
129 55c. Restoration 20 30

32 Angel with Harp
33 "Cryptoblepharus egeriae"

1980. Christmas. Multicoloured.
130 15c. Type **32** 10 25
131 15c. Angel with wounded soldier 10 25
132 22c. Virgin and Child 15 30
133 22c. Kneeling couple 15 30
134 60c. Angel with harp (different) 20 20
135 60c. Angel with children . . 20 30

1981. Phosphate Industry (3rd series). As T **31**. Multicoloured.
136 22c. Screening and Stockpiling 15 15
137 28c. Train loading 20 20
138 40c. Railing 25 25
139 60c. Drying 25 25

1981. Phosphate Industry (4th series). As T **31**. Multicoloured.
140 22c. Crushing 15 20
141 28c. Conveying 20 25
142 40c. Bulk storage 30 40
143 60c. "Consolidated Venture" (bulk carrier) loading . . . 35 55

1981. Reptiles. Multicoloured.
144 24c. Type **33** 20 20
145 30c. "Emoia nativitata" . . . 25 25
146 40c. "Lepidodactylus listeri" . 30 30
147 60c. "Cyrtodactylus sp. nov." 35 35

34 Scene from Carol "Away in a Manger"

1981. Christmas.
148 **34** 18c. silver, dp blue & bl . . 30 50
149 – 24c. multicoloured 30 55
150 – 40c. multicoloured 35 65
151 – 60c. multicoloured 40 75

DESIGNS: 24c. to 60c. show various scenes from carol "Away in a Manger".

35 Reef Heron

1982. Birds. Multicoloured.
152 1c. Type **35** 70 30
153 2c. Common noddy ("Noddy") 70 30
154 3c. White-bellied swiftlet ("Glossy Swiftlet") 70 70
155 4c. Christmas Island imperial pigeon ("Imperial Pigeon") 70 70
156 5c. Christmas Island white-eye ("Silvereye") 80 70
157 10c. Island thrush ("Thrush") 70 70
158 25c. Red-tailed tropic bird ("Silver Bosunbird") . . . 1·25 60
159 30c. Emerald dove 80 70
160 40c. Brown booby 80 55
161 50c. Red-footed booby . . . 80 55
162 65c. Christmas Island frigate bird ("Frigatebird") . . . 80 55
163 75c. White-tailed tropic bird ("Golden Bosunbird") . . . 90 65
164 80c. Australian kestrel ("Nankeen Kestrel") (vert) 1·25 2·00
165 $1 Moluccan hawk owl ("Hawk-owl") (vert) . . . 2·50 2·50
166 $2 Australian goshawk ("Goshawk") . . . . . . 1·75 4·00
167 $4 Abbott's booby (vert) . . 3·00 3·25

36 Joseph
37 "Mirror" Dinghy and Club House

1982. Christmas. Origami Paper Sculptures. Mult.
168 27c. Type **36** 30 30
169 50c. Angel 45 45
170 75c. Mary and baby Jesus . . 65 65

1983. 25th Anniv of Christmas Island Boat Club. Multicoloured.
171 27c. Type **37** 20 30
172 35c. Ocean-going yachts . . . 20 35
173 50c. Fishing launch and cargo ship (horiz) 25 40
174 75c. Dinghy-racing and cantilever (horiz) 25 60

38 Maps of Christmas Island and Australia, Eastern Grey Kangaroo and White-tailed Tropic Bird

1983. 25th Anniv of Australian Territory. Mult.
175 24c. Type **38** 60 30
176 30c. Christmas Island and Australian flag 70 50
177 85c. Maps of Christmas Island and Australia, and Boeing 727 . . . . 1·50 1·75

39 Candle and Holly

40 Feeding on Leaf

1983. Christmas. Candles. Multicoloured.
178 24c. Type **39** 20 20
179 30c. Six gold candles 30 40
180 85c. Candles . . . . 70 1·50

1984. Red Land Crab. Multicoloured.
181 30c. Type **40** 25 30
182 40c. Migration 30 40
183 55c. Development stages . . 30 50
184 85c. Adult females and young 45 70

41 "Leucocoprinus fragilissimus"

42 Run-out

1984. Fungi. Multicoloured.
185 30c. Type **41** 25 55
186 40c. "Microporus xanthopus" 30 70
187 45c. "Hydropus anthidepes" ("Trogia anthidepas") . . 35 80
188 55c. "Haddowia longipes" . . 35 90
189 85c. "Phillipsia domingensis" 45 1·25

1984. 25th Anniv of Cricket on Christmas Island. Multicoloured.
190 30c. Type **42** 30 85
191 40c. Bowled-out . . . . . . 30 1·10
192 50c. Batsman in action . . . 35 1·50
193 85c. Fielder diving for catch 55 1·75

43 Arrival of Father Christmas

1984. Christmas and "Ausipex" International Stamp Exhibition, Melbourne. Sheet 100 × 100 mm containing T **43** and similar horiz designs. Multicoloured.
MS194 30c. Type **43**; 55c. Distribution of presents; 85c. Departure of Father Christmas 2·50 3·25

44 Robber Crab

45 "Once in Royal David's City"

1985. Crabs (1st series). Multicoloured.
195 30c. Type **44** . . . . 1·00 70
196 40c. Horn-eyed ghost crab . . 1·10 1·10
197 55c. Purple hermit crab . . . 1·50 1·60
198 85c. Little nipper . . . . . . 2·25 2·50

1985. Crabs (2nd series). As T **44**. Multicoloured.
199 33c. Blue crab . . . . 1·25 65
200 45c. Tawny hermit crab . . . 1·40 1·25
201 60c. Red nipper . . . . . . 1·75 2·00
202 90c. Smooth-handed ghost crab . . . . 2·50 3·00

1985. Crabs (3rd series). As T **44**. Multicoloured.
203 33c. Red crab . . . . 1·10 60
204 45c. Mottled crab . . . . . 1·50 1·40
205 60c. Rock hopper crab . . . 2·25 2·50
206 90c. Yellow nipper . . . . . 2·75 3·50

1985. Christmas Carols. Multicoloured.
207 27c. Type **45** . . . . 1·00 1·40
208 33c. "While Shepherds Watched Their Flocks by Night" . . . . 1·10 1·50
209 45c. "Away in a Manger" . . 1·40 1·75
210 60c. "We Three Kings of Orient Are" . . . . 1·50 1·90
211 90c. "Hark the Herald Angels Sing" . . . . 1·60 2·00

46 Halley's Comet over Christmas Island

47 Ridley's Orchid

1986. Appearance of Halley's Comet. Multicoloured.
212 33c. Type **46** 45 80
213 45c. Edmond Halley . . . . 55 1·10
214 60c. Comet and "Consolidated Venture" (bulk carrier) loading phosphate . . . . 70 2·25
215 90c. Comet over Flying Fish Cove . . . . 80 2·50

1986. Native Flowers. Multicoloured.
216 33c. Type **47** 50 55
217 45c. Hanging flower 30 85
218 60c. Hoya . . . . 30 1·50
219 90c. Sea hibiscus . . . . . . 35 2·00

1986. Royal Wedding. As T **112** of Ascension. Multicoloured.
220 33c. Prince Andrew and Miss Sarah Ferguson 45 50
221 90c. Prince Andrew piloting helicopter, Digby, Canada, 1985 . . . . 95 1·75

48 Father Christmas and Reindeer in Speed Boat

1986. Christmas. Multicoloured.
222 30c. Type **48** 85 60
223 36c. Father Christmas and reindeer on beach . . . . 1·00 60
224 55c. Father Christmas fishing 1·50 1·50
225 70c. Playing golf . . . . . . 2·75 3·50
226 $1 Sleeping in hammock . . 2·75 4·00

49 H.M.S. "Flying Fish" and Outline Map of Christmas Island

1987. Centenary of Visits by H.M.S. "Flying Fish" and H.M.S. "Egeria". Multicoloured.
227 36c. Type **49** 40 75
228 90c. H.M.S. "Egeria" and outline map . . . . 70 2·50

50 Blind Snake

51 Children watching Father Christmas in Sleigh

1987. Wildlife. Multicoloured.
229 1c. Type **50** 40 90
230 2c. Blue-tailed skink 40 90
231 3c. Insectivorous bat 90 90
232 5c. Grasshopper 90 90
233 10c. Christmas Island fruit bat 90 90
234 25c. Gecko . . . . 1·00 1·00
235 30c. "Mantis religiosa" (mantid) . . . . 1·25 1·25
236 36c. Moluccan hawk owl ("Hawk-owl") . . . . . 3·00 1·75
237 40c. Bull-mouth helmet . . 1·75 1·75
237a 41c. Nudibranch ("Phidiana" sp.) . . . . 1·25 70
238 50c. Textile or cloth of gold cone . . . . 1·75 1·75
239 65c. Brittle stars . . . . . 1·40 1·25
240 75c. Regal angelfish . . . . 1·40 1·75
241 90c. "Appias paulina" (butterfly) . . . . 3·75 3·25
242 $1 "Hypolimnas misippus" (butterfly) . . . . 3·75 3·25
243 $2 Shrew . . . . 3·75 7·00
244 $5 Green turtle . . . . . . 4·50 7·00

1987. Christmas. Sheet 165 × 65 mm, containing T **51** and similar multicoloured designs.
MS245 30c. Type **51**; 37c. Father Christmas distributing gifts (48 × 22 mm); 90c. Children with presents (48 × 22 mm); $1 Singing carols . . . . 4·00 4·00
The stamps within No. **MS**245 form a composite design of a beach scene.

1988. Bicentenary of Australian Settlement. Arrival of First Fleet. As Nos. 1105/9 of Australia, but each inscribed "CHRISTMAS ISLAND Indian Ocean" and "AUSTRALIA BICENTENARY".
246 37c. Aborigines watching arrival of Fleet, Botany Bay . . . . 1·50 1·75
247 37c. Aboriginal family and anchored ships . . . . . . 1·50 1·75
248 37c. Fleet arriving at Sydney Cove . . . . 1·50 1·75
249 37c. Ship's boat . . . . . . 1·50 1·75
250 37c. Raising the flag, Sydney Cove, 26 January 1788 . . 1·50 1·75
Nos. 246/50 were printed together, se-tenant, forming a composite design.

52 Captain William May

53 Pony and Trap, 1910

1988. Cent of British Annexation. Mult.
251 37c. Type **52** 35 40
252 53c. Annexation ceremony . . 50 55
253 95c. H.M.S. "Imperieuse" (armoured cruiser) firing salute 90 95
254 $1.50 Building commemorative cairn . . . 1·40 1·50

1988. Cent of Permanent Settlement. Mult.
255 37c. Type **53** 70 40
256 55c. Phosphate mining, 1910 1·00 55
257 70c. Steam locomotive, 1914 1·40 85
258 $1 Arrival of first aircraft, 1957 . . . . 1·60 1·25

54 Beach Toys

55 Food on Table ("Good Harvesting")

1988. Christmas. Toys and Gifts. Multicoloured.
259 32c. Type **54** 40 35
260 39c. Flippers, snorkel and mask 50 40
261 90c. Model soldier, doll and soft toys . . . . 1·10 1·10
262 $1 Models of racing car, lorry and jet aircraft . . . 1·25 1·25

1989. Chinese New Year. Multicoloured.
263 39c. Type **55** 45 40
264 70c. Decorations ("Prosperity") 80 70
265 90c. Chinese girls ("Good Fortune") . . . . 1·10 90
266 $1 Lion dance ("Progress Every Year") . . . . . . 1·25 1·00

56 Sir John Murray

1989. 75th Death Anniv of Sir John Murray (oceanographer). Multicoloured.
267 39c. Type **56** 50 50
268 80c. Map of Christmas Island showing Murray Hill . . . 1·25 95
269 $1 Oceanographic equipment 1·50 1·25
270 $1.10 H.M.S. "Challenger" (survey ship), 1872 . . . . 1·75 1·50

57 Four Children

58 "Huperzia phlegmaria"

1989. Malay Hari Raya Festival. Multicoloured.
271 39c. Type **57** 55 50
272 55c. Man playing tambourine 80 70
273 80c. Girl in festival costume 1·25 1·00
274 $1.10 Christmas Island Mosque . . . . 1·60 1·40

1989. Ferns. Multicoloured.
275 41c. Type **58** 75 60
276 65c. "Asplenium polydon" 1·10 85
277 80c. Common bracken . . . 1·40 1·00
278 $1.10 Birds-nest fern . . . . 1·60 1·40

59 Virgin Mary and Star

61 First Sighting, 1615

1989. Christmas. Multicoloured.
279 36c. Type **59** 60 40
280 41c. Christ Child in manger 60 45
281 80c. Shepherds and star . . . 1·50 80
282 $1.10 Three Wise Men following star . . . . . . 1·60 1·10

1989. "Melbourne Stampshow '89". Nos. 237a and 242 optd with Stampshow logo.
283 41c. Nudibranch ("Phidiana sp.") . . . . 1·00 45
284 $1 "Hypolimnas misippus" (butterfly) . . . . 2·50 1·00

1990. 375th Anniv of Discovery of Christmas Island. Multicoloured.
285 41c. Type **61** . . . . 1·00 50
286 $1.10 Second sighting and naming, 1643 . . . . . . 1·25 1·40

62 Miniature Tractor pulling Phosphate

63 Male Abbott's Booby

1990. Christmas Island Transport. Multicoloured.
287 1c. Type **62** 15 20
288 2c. Phosphate train 40 40
289 3c. Diesel railcar No. 8802 (vert) 20 20
290 5c. Loading road train . . . 40 40
291 10c. Trishaw (vert) 30 30
292 15c. Terex truck 65 65
293 25c. Articulated bus 30 30
294 30c. Cable passenger carriage (vert) 30 35
295 40c. Passenger barge (vert) 35 40
296 50c. Kolek (outrigger canoe) 55 55
297 65c. Flying Doctor aircraft and ambulance . . . . . 3·75 1·50
298 75c. Commercial van . . . . 1·50 1·50
299 90c. Vintage lorry . . . . . 1·50 1·75
300 $1 Water tanker . . . . . . 1·50 1·75
301 $2 Traction engine . . . . . 2·50 3·25
302 $5 Steam locomotive No. 1 3·25 4·75

1990. Abbott's Booby. Multicoloured.
303 10c. Type **63** 85 30
304 20c. Juvenile male . . . . . 1·40 50
305 29c. Female with egg . . . . 1·60 55
306 41c. Pair with chick . . . . 2·25 70
MS307 122 × 68 mm. 41c. Male with wings spread; 41c. Male on branch; 41c. Female with fledgling 5·00 3·00
The three stamps within No. **MS**307 form a composite design and are without the W.W.F. logo.

64 1977 Famous Visitors 9c. Stamp

1990. Centenary of Henry Ridley's Visit.
308 41c. Type **64** 55 75
309 75c. Ridley (botanist) in rainforest . . . . 85 2·00

1990. "New Zealand 1990" International Stamp Exhibition, Auckland. No. **MS**307 optd "**NZ 1990 WORLD STAMP EXHIBITION AUCKLAND, NEW ZEALAND, 24 AUGUST – 2 SEPTEMBER 1990**" in purple on the sheet margins.
MS310 122 × 68 mm. 41c. Male with wings spread; 41c. Male on branch; 41c. Female with fledgling 6·50 7·50

65 "Corymborkus veratrifolia"

66 "Islander" (freighter), 1898

1990. Christmas. Flowers. Multicoloured.
311 38c. Type **65** . . . . 1·10 70
312 43c. "Hoya aldrichii" . . . . 1·25 75
313 80c. "Quisqualis indica" . . . 2·25 2·75
314 $1.20 "Barringtonia racemosa" . . . . 2·75 3·50

1991. Centenary of First Phosphate Mining Lease. Multicoloured.
316 43c. Type **66** . . . . 1·00 90
317 43c. Miners loading tipper wagons, 1908 . . . . . . 1·00 90
318 85c. Shay steam locomotive No. 4, 1925 . . . . . . 1·40 1·25
319 $1.20 Extracting phosphate, 1951 . . . . 1·75 1·60
320 $1.70 Land reclamation, 1990 2·00 1·90
Nos. 316/20 were printed together, se-tenant, forming a composite forest design.

67 Teaching Children Road Safety

1991. Christmas Island Police Force. Multicoloured.
321 43c. Type **67** . . . . 1·50 1·00
322 43c. Traffic control . . . . . 1·50 1·00
323 90c. Airport customs . . . . 2·25 3·25
324 $1.20 Police launch "Fregata Andrews" towing rescued boat . . . . 3·00 3·00
MS325 135 × 88 mm. Nos. 321/4 7·50 6·50

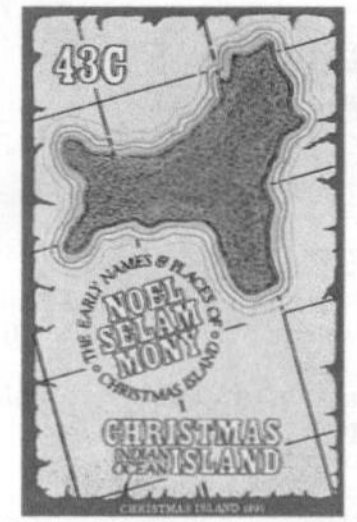

68 Map of Christmas Island, 1991

1991. Maps of Christmas Island. Multicoloured.
326 43c. Type **68** . . . . 1·00 65
327 75c. Goos Atlas, 1666 . . . . 1·75 1·10
328 $1.10 De Manevillette, 1745 2·25 1·60
329 $1.20 Comberford, 1667 . . . 2·25 1·90

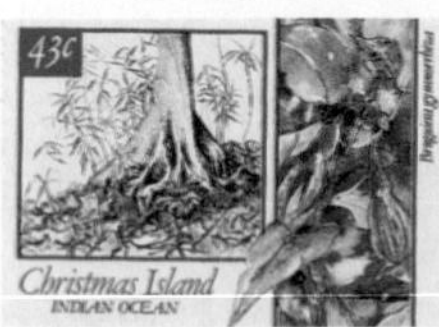

69 "Bruguiera gymnorrhiza"

1991. Local Trees. Multicoloured.
330 43c. Type **69** . . . . 1·00 65
331 70c. "Syzgium operculatum" 1·50 1·00
332 85c. "Ficus microcarpa" . . 1·75 1·25
333 $1.20 "Arenga listeri" . . . . 2·00 1·60

70 "Family round Christmas Tree" (S'ng Yen Luiw)

1991. Christmas. Children's Paintings. Mult.
334 38c. Type **70** 75 55
335 38c. "Opening Presents" (Liew Ann Nee) 75 55
336 38c. "Beach Party" (Foo Pang Chuan) 75 55
337 38c. "Christmas Walk" (Too Lai Peng) 75 55
338 38c. "Santa Claus and Christmas Tree" (Jesamine Wheeler) 75 55
339 43c. "Santa Claus fishing" (Ho Puay Ha) 75 60
340 $1 "Santa Claus in Boat" (Ng Hooi Hua) . . . . . 1·50 1·50
341 $1.20 "Santa Claus surfing" (Yani Kawi) . . . . 1·75 1·75

71 Discussing Evacuation, 1942

72 Snake's-head Cowrie

1992. 50th Anniv of Partial Evacuation. Mult.
342 45c. Type **71** . . . . 1·00 1·25
343 45c. Families waiting to embark . . . . 1·00 1·25
344 $1.05 Ferrying evacuees to "Islander" . . . . 2·50 2·75
345 $1.20 Departure of "Islander" (freighter) . . . 2·75 3·00

1992. Shells. Multicoloured.
346 5c. Tiger cowrie 60 70
347 10c. Type **72** 80 70
348 15c. Scorpion conch . . . . 1·00 70
349 20c. Royal oak scallop . . . 1·25 70
350 25c. Striped engina . . . . . 1·25 70
351 30c. Prickly Pacific drupe . . 1·25 70
352 40c. Reticulate distorsio . . . 1·25 75
353 45c. Tapestry turban . . . . 1·25 75
354 50c. Beautiful goblet . . . . 1·25 75
355 60c. Captain cone . . . . . . 1·50 80
356 70c. Layonkaire's turban . . 1·50 90
357 80c. Chirage spider conch . . 1·75 1·00
358 90c. Common delphinia . . . 1·75 1·25
359 $1 Ceramic vase . . . . . . 1·75 1·50
360 $2 Partridge tun . . . . . . 1·40 1·75
361 $5 Strawberry drupe . . . . 3·50 3·75

73 Torpedoing of "Eidsvold"

1992. 50th Anniv of Sinkings of "Eidsvold" and "Nissa Maru". Multicoloured.
362 45c. Type **73** . . . . . . 1·25 75
363 80c. "Eidsvold" sinking . . . 2·00 2·00
364 $1.05 "Nissa Maru" under attack . . . . 2·50 3·25
365 $1.20 "Nissa Maru" beached 2·50 3·50

1992. "Kuala Lumpur '92" International Philatelic Exhibition. No. 361 optd with exhibition symbol.
366 $5 Strawberry drupe . . . . 9·00 7·00

75 Jungle

76 Abbott's Booby

1992. Christmas. Multicoloured.
367 40c. Type **75** . . . . 90 1·25
368 40c. Red-tailed tropic bird and brown booby over rock . . . . 90 1·25
369 45c. Brown boobies on headland . . . . 90 1·25
370 $1.05 Red-tailed tropic bird, brown booby and cliffs . . 1·60 1·75
371 $1.20 Cliffs . . . . 1·60 1·75
Nos. 367/71 were printed together, se-tenant, forming a composite coastal design.

1993. Seabirds. Multicoloured.
372 45c. Type **76** 60 85
373 45c. Christmas Island frigate bird 60 85
374 45c. Common noddy 60 85
375 45c. White-tailed ("Golden Bosunbird") tropic bird 60 85
376 45c. Brown booby 60 85
MS377 140 × 70 mm. Nos. 372/6 2·75 3·50
Nos. 372/6 were printed together, se-tenant, forming a composite design.

77 Dolly Beach

1993. Scenic Views of Christmas Island. Mult.
378 85c. Type **77** . . . . 1·25 1·50
379 95c. Blow Holes . . . . . . 1·50 2·00
380 $1.05 Merrial Beach . . . . 1·60 2·25
381 $1.20 Rainforest . . . . . . 1·75 2·25

78 Turtle on Beach

1993. Christmas. Multicoloured.
382 40c. Type **78** . . . . 1·00 70
383 45c. Crabs and wave . . . . 1·00 70
384 $1 Christmas Island frigate bird and rainforest . . . . 2·25 3·25

79 Map of Christmas Island

1993. 350th Anniv of Naming of Christmas Island.
385 **79** $2 multicoloured . . . . . 3·00 3·50

80 Pekingese

1994. Chinese New Year ("Year of the Dog"). Multicoloured.
386 45c. Type **80** . . . . 1·00 1·40
387 45c. Mickey (Christmas Island dog) . . . . 1·00 1·40
MS388 106 × 70 mm. Nos. 386/7 2·50 3·50

81 Shay Locomotive No. 4

1994. Steam Locomotives. Multicoloured.
389 85c. Type **81** . . . . 1·75 1·75
390 95c. Locomotive No. 9 . . . 1·75 2·00
391 $1.20 Locomotive No. 1 . . 2·00 2·25

82 "Brachypeza archytas"

83 Angel blowing Trumpet

1994. Orchids. Multicoloured.
392 45c. Type **82** . . . . 1·10 1·40
393 45c. "Thelasis capitata" . . . 1·10 1·40
394 45c. "Corymborkis veratrifolia" . . . . 1·10 1·40
395 45c. "Flickingeria nativitatis" 1·10 1·40
396 45c. "Dendrobium crumenatum" . . . . . . 1·10 1·40

1994. Christmas. Multicoloured.
397 40c. Type **83** 80 60
398 45c. Wise Man holding gift 80 60
399 80c. Star over Bethlehem . . 1·75 2·50

84 Pig

1995. Chinese New Year ("Year of the Pig").
400 **84** 45c. multicoloured 75 60
401 – 85c. multicoloured . . . . 1·25 1·75
MS402 106 × 71 mm. Nos. 400/1 2·00 2·50
DESIGN: 85c. Pig (different).

85 Golfer playing Shot

1995. 40th Anniv of Christmas Island Golf Course.
403 **85** $2.50 multicoloured . . . 4·25 4·25

86 Father Christmas with Map on Christmas Island Frigate Bird

1995. Christmas Multicoloured
404 40c. Type **86** 80 60
405 45c. Father Christmas distributing presents . . . 80 60
406 80c. Father Christmas waving goodbye . . . . 1·75 2·50

87 De Havilland D.H.98 Mosquito on Reconnaissance Mission

1995. 50th Anniv of End of Second World War. Each black, stone and red.
407 45c. Type **87** 95 95
408 45c. H.M.S. "Rother" (frigate) 95 95

88 Lemon-peel Angelfish

1995. Marine Life. Multicoloured.
412 20c. Pink-tailed triggerfish . . 15 20
413 30c. Japanese inflator-filefish ("Longnose filefish") . . . 20 25
414 45c. Princess anthias 30 35
415 75c. Type **88** 55 60
416 85c. Moon wrasse 60 65
417 90c. Spotted boxfish 65 70
418 95c. Moorish idol 70 75
419 $1 Emperor angelfish 70 75
420 $1.20 Glass-eyed snapper ("Glass bigeye") 85 90

89 Rat with Drum

1996. Chinese New Year ("Year of the Rat"). Multicoloured.
425 45c. Type **89** . . . . 1·00 1·25
426 45c. Rat with tambourine . . 1·00 1·25
MS427 106 × 70 mm. Nos. 425/6 2·50 3·00

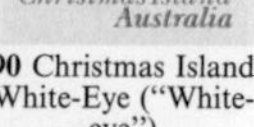

90 Christmas Island White-Eye ("White-eye")

91 Three Ships approaching Island

1996. Christmas Island Land Birds. Multicoloured.
428 45c. Type **90** 75 50
429 85c. Moluccan hawk owl ("Hawk-owl") . . . . . . 1·75 2·00

1996. Christmas. "I saw Three Ships" (carol). Multicoloured.
430 40c. Type **91** 75 60
431 45c. Madonna and Child with ships at anchor . . . 75 60
432 80c. Ships leaving . . . . . 1·60 2·10

1996. 300th Anniv of Willem de Vlamingh's Discovery of Christmas Island. As No. 1667 of Australia.
433 45c. multicoloured . . . . . 1·25 1·50

92 Ox facing Right

1997. Chinese New Year ("Year of the Ox"). Multicoloured.
434 45c. Type **92** . . . . 1·00 1·00
435 45c. Ox facing left . . . . . 1·00 1·00
MS436 106 × 70 mm. Nos. 434/5 2·00 2·25

93 Father Christmas reading Letter

1997. Christmas. Multicoloured.
437 40c. Type **93** 70 60
438 45c. Father Christmas carving wooden boat 70 60
439 80c. Father Christmas in sleigh . . . . 1·60 2·00

94 Tiger

1998. Chinese New Year ("Year of the Tiger"). Multicoloured.
440 45c. Type **94** . . . . 1·10 1·10
441 45c. Tiger with head facing left . . . . 1·10 1·10
MS442 106 × 70 mm. Nos. 440/1 2·50 2·75

95 Christmas Island Frigate Bird

1998. Marine Life. Multicoloured.
443 5c. Type **95** 20 30
444 5c. Four ambon chromis . . 20 30
445 5c. Three ambon chromis . . 20 30
446 5c. One pink anemonefish . . 20 30
447 5c. Three pink anemonefish 20 30
448 10c. Reef heron ("Eastern Reef Egret") 25 30
449 10c. Whitelined cod 25 30
450 10c. Pyramid butterflyfish . . 25 30
451 10c. Dusky parrotfish 25 30
452 10c. Spotted garden eel . . . 25 30
453 25c. Sooty tern 30 35
454 25c. Stripe-tailed damselfish ("Scissortail sergeant") . . 30 35
455 25c. Thicklip wrasse 30 35
456 25c. Blackaxil chromis . . . 30 35
457 25c. Orange anthias 30 35
458 45c. Brown booby 35 40
459 45c. Green turtle 35 40
460 45c. Pink anemonefish . . . 35 40
461 45c. Blue sea star 35 40
462 45c. Kunie's chromodoris . . 35 40
Nos. 443/62 were printed together, se-tenant, with the backgrounds forming a composie design.

96 Orchid Tree

1998. Christmas. Flowering Trees. Multicoloured.
463 40c. Type **96** 60 50
464 80c. Flame tree . . . . . . 1·25 1·40
465 95c. Sea hibiscus . . . . . . 1·40 1·75

97 Leaping Rabbit

1999. Chinese New Year ("Year of the Rabbit"). Multicoloured.
466 45c. Type **97** . . . . 80 1·00
467 45c. Rabbit with pestle and mortar . . . . 80 1·00
MS468 106 × 70 mm. Nos. 466/7 1·60 2·00

98 Carnival Dragon (Fong Jason) (Community Arts Festival)

1999. Festivals. Children's Paintings. Mult.
469 45c. Type **98** 60 60
470 45c. Red crab holding Easter egg (Community Arts Festival, Siti Zanariah Zainal) 60 60
471 85c. Ghost and child (Tan Diana) (Hungry Ghost Festival) (vert) . . . . . . 95 1·10
472 $1.20 Walls of Mecca (Anwar Ramlan) (Hari Raya Haji Festival) (vert) . . . . . . 1·25 1·40

99 Santa Claus in Hammock

1999. Christmas. Multicoloured.
473 40c. Type **99** 60 60
474 45c. Santa Claus with Christmas pudding 60 60
475 95c. Santa Claus in sleigh pulled by Abbott's boobies 1·40 1·75

100 Chinese Dragon

2000. Chinese New Year ("Year of the Dragon"). Multicoloured.
476 45c. Type **100** 80 90
477 45c. Chinese dragon facing left 80 90
MS478 106 × 70 mm. Nos. 476/7 1·60 2·00

101 Yeow Jian Min **102** The Three Kings

2000. New Millennium. "Face of Christmas Island". Multicoloured.
479 45c. Type **101** 55 65
480 45c. Ida Chin (schoolgirl) . . 55 65
481 45c. Ho Tak Wah (elderly man) 55 65
482 45c. Thomas Faul and James Neill (young boys) 55 65
483 45c. Siti Sanniah Kawi (mother of three) 55 65

2000. Christmas. "We Three Kings" (carol). Mult.
484 40c. Type **102** 55 65
485 40c. Birds with Three Gifts 55 65
486 45c. Crabs with Three Gifts 55 65

103 Green Snake

2001. Chinese New Year ("Year of the Snake"). Mult.
487 45c. Type **103** 70 60
488 $1.35 Silver snake . . . . . 1·75 1·90
MS489 106 × 70 mm. Nos. 487/8 2·50 2·75

104 *Chaetocalathus semisupinus*

2001. International Stamps. Fungi. Multicoloured.
490 $1 Type **104** 90 90
491 $1.50 *Pycnoporus sanguineus* 1·25 1·50

105 Rat **106** Imperial Pigeon

2002. Chinese New Year ("Year of the Horse"). Multicoloured.
492 5c. Type **105** 30 40
493 5c. Ox 30 40
494 5c. Tiger 30 40
495 5c. Rabbit 30 40
496 15c. Dragon 35 45
497 15c. Snake 35 45
498 15c. Horse (gold) 35 45
499 15c. Goat 35 45
500 25c. Monkey 40 50
501 25c. Cock 40 50
502 25c. Dog 40 50
503 25c. Pig 40 50
504 45c. Horse (purple) 50 50
505 $1.35 Horse (gold) . . . . . 1·25 1·50
MS506 106 × 70 mm. Nos. 504/5 2·50 2·75

2002. Endangered Species. Christmas Island Birds. Multicoloured.
507 45c. Type **106** 65 70
508 45c. Christmas Island hawk owl 65 70
509 $1 Goshawk . . . . 1·10 1·25
510 $1.50 Thrush . . . . 1·50 1·75

107 Yellow Goat

2003. Chinese New Year ("Year of the Goat"). As T **107** plus designs as Nos. 492/503 with backgrounds in mauve and some values changed. Multicoloured.
511 10c. Type **105** 20 25
512 10c. Ox 20 25
513 10c. Tiger 20 25
514 10c. Rabbit 20 25
515 15c. Dragon 20 25
516 15c. Snake 20 25
517 15c. Horse 20 25
518 15c. Goat (animal in gold) 20 25
519 25c. Monkey 25 30
520 25c. Cock 25 30
521 25c. Dog 25 30
522 25c. Pig 25 30
523 50c. Type **107** 35 45
524 $1.50 Blue goat . . . . . . 1·10 1·40
MS525 105 × 70 mm. Nos. 523/4 2·50 2·75
Nos. 492/503 have red backgrounds.

108 Santa riding on Whale Shark

2003. Christmas. Multicoloured.
526 45c. Type **108** 50 55
527 50c. Santa sitting on green turtle and distributing gifts 50 55

109 Yellow Monkey

2004. Chinese New Year ("Year of the Monkey"). Plus designs as Nos. 492/503 in turquoise and blue with some values changed. Multicoloured.
528 10c. Rat 10 10
529 10c. Ox 10 10
530 10c. Tiger 10 10
531 10c. Rabbit 10 10
532 15c. Dragon 15 20
533 15c. Snake 15 20
534 15c. Horse 15 20
535 15c. Goat 15 20
536 25c. Monkey (animal in gold) 20 25
537 25c. Cock 20 25
538 25c. Dog 20 25
539 25c. Pig 20 25
540 50c. Type **109** 40 45
541 $1.45 Orange-brown monkey 1·20 1·30
MS542 105 × 70 mm. Nos. 540/1 1·60 1·75

CILICIA Pt. 16

A district in Asia Minor, occupied and temporarily controlled by the French between 1919 and 20 October 1921. The territory was then returned to Turkey.

40 paras = 1 piastre.

1919. Various issues of Turkey optd **CILICIE**. A. On No. 726 (surch Printed Matter stamp optd with Star and Crescent).
1 **15** 5pa. on 10pa. green . . . . 1·25 1·50

B. On 1901 issue optd with Star and Crescent.
2 **21** 1pi. blue (No. 543) . . . . 70 1·10
32 1pi. blue (No. 631) . . . . 1·25 1·50

C. On 1909 issue optd with Star and Crescent (No. 7 also optd as T **24**).
4 **28** 20pa. red (No. 572) . . . . 1·25 1·25
35 20pa. red (No. 643) . . . . 1·25 1·25
7 1pi. blue (No. 649) £1300 £700
8 1pi. blue (No. 645) . . . . 5·50 4·50

D. On 1913 issue.
36 **30** 20pa. pink . . . . 1·00 1·25

E. On Pictorial issue of 1914.
37 **32** 2pa. purple . . . . 55 1·00
11 – 4pa. brown (No. 500) . . . 1·00 1·60
12 – 6pa. blue (No. 502) . . . . 6·00 4·50
13 – 1¾pi. brown and grey (No. 507) . . . . 1·60 2·10

F. On Postal Anniv issue of 1916.
14 **60** 5pa. green 70 40
15 20pa. blue . . . . 1·25 1·50
40 1pi. black and violet 95 95
17 5pi. black and brown . . . . 1·25 2·25

G. On Pictorial issues of 1916 and 1917.
18 **73** 10pa. green . . . . 1·40 1·60
19 **76** 50pa. blue . . . . 4·25 2·10
41 **69** 5pi. on 2pa. blue (No. 914) 1·40 1·60
21 **63** 25pi. red on buff . . . . . 1·60 2·10
22 **64** 50pi. red . . . . 1·50 1·50
23 50pi. blue . . . . 12·50 15·00

H. On Armistice issue of 1919 optd with T **81** of Turkey.
24 **76** 50pa. blue . . . . 5·00 3·00
25 **77** 2pi. blue and brown . . . . 1·40 1·60
26 **78** 5pi. brown and blue . . . . 7·25 2·75

1919. Various issues of Turkey optd **Cilicie**. A. On No. 726 (surch Printed Matter stamp optd with Star and Crescent).
46 **15** 5pa. on 10pa. green . . . . 1·25 1·60

B. On 1901 issue optd with Star and Crescent.
47 **21** 1pi. blue (No. 543) . . . . 1·25 1·50
48 1pi. blue (No. 631) . . . . 1·25 1·60
49 1pi. blue (No. 669) . . . . 55·00 35·00

C. On 1908 issue optd with T **24** and Star and Crescent.
50 **25** 20pa. red . . . . 6·50 3·50

D. On 1909 issue optd with Star and Crescent (No. 52 also optd as T **24**).
52a **28** 20pa. red (No. 643) . . . . 1·40 1·50
52 20pa. red (No. 647) . . . . 1·25 1·25

E. On 1913 issue.
53 **30** 5pa. bistre . . . . 2·10 2·10
54 20pa. pink . . . . 90 1·60

F. On Pictorial issue of 1914.
55 **32** 2pa. purple . . . . 70 1·40
56 – 4pa. brown (No. 500) . . . 70 1·25

G. On Postal Anniv issue of 1916.
57 **60** 20pa. blue . . . . 85 1·25
58 1pi. black and violet . . . . 85 1·00
59 5pi. black and brown . . . 1·10 1·50

H. On Pictorial issues of 1916 and 1917.
60 **72** 5pa. orange . . . . 1·75 2·40
61 **75** 1pi. blue . . . . 1·25 1·75
62 **69** 5pi. on 2pa. blue (No. 914) 5·00 5·00
63 **64** 50pi. green on yellow . . . 27·00 18·00

1919. Various issues of Turkey optd **T.E.O. Cilicie.**

A. On No. 726 (surch Printed Matter stamp optd with Star and Crescent).
69 **15** 5pa. on 10pa. green . . . . 90 1·10

B. On 1892 issue optd with Star and Crescent and Arabic surch.
70 **15** 10pa. on 20pa. red (No. 630) 40 98

C. On 1909 issue optd with Star and Crescent.
71 **28** 20pa. red (No. 572) . . . . 1·50 1·50
72 20pa. red (No. 643) . . . . 1·10 1·40

D. On 1909 issue optd with Tougra and surch in Turkish.
73 **28** 5pa. on 2pa. green (No. 938) 70 40

E. On Pictorial stamp of 1914.
74 – 1pi. blue (No. 505) 70 85

F. On Postal Anniv issue of 1916.
75 **60** 5pa. green . . . . £120 60·00
76 20pa. blue . . . . 70 1·00
77 1pi. black and violet . . . . 90 2·25

G. On Postal Anniv issue of 1916 optd with Star and Crescent.
78 **60** 10pa. red (No. 654) 45 45

H. On Pictorial issues of 1916 and 1917.
79 **72** 5pa. orange 35 70
80 **73** 10pa. green . . . . 60 1·10
81 **74** 20pa. red 55 60
82 **77** 2pi. blue and brown . . . . 1·00 75
83 **78** 5pi. brown and blue . . . . 85 1·00
84 **69** 5pi. on 2pa. blue . . . . . 4·00 4·50
85 **63** 25pi. red on buff . . . . 4·00 4·50
86 **64** 50pi. green on yellow . . . 55 40

I. On Charity stamp of 1917.
87 **65** 10pa. purple . . . . 1·00 1·10

1920. "Mouchon" key-type of French Levant surch **T.E.O. 20 PARAS.**
88 B 20pa. on 10c. red . . . . . 1·00 1·10

7

1920. Surch **OCCUPATION MILITAIRE Francaise CILICIE** and value.
89 **7** 70pa. on 5pa. red . . . . . 85 1·40
90 3½pi. on 5pa. red . . . . . 85 1·40

1920. Stamps of France surch **O.M.F. Cilicie** and new value.
100 **11** 5pa. on 2c. red 25 90
101 **18** 10pa. on 5c. green 25 55
102 20pa. on 10c. red 25 80
103 1pi. on 25c. blue 35 65
104 **15** 2pi. on 15c. green 40 83
105 **13** 5pi. on 40c. red and blue 45 1·25
106 10pi. on 50c. brown & lav 83 1·40
107 50pi. on 1f. red and green 1·20 1·75
108 100pi. on 5f. blue & yellow 13·88 14·00

1920. Stamps of France surch **O.M.F. Cilicie SAND. EST** and new value.
109 **11** 5pa. on 2c. red . . . . . 3·00
110 **18** 10pa. on 5c. green . . . . 3·00
111 20pa. on 10c. red . . . . 2·10
112 1pi. on 25c. blue . . . . 1·90
113 **15** 2pi. on 15c. green . . . . 6·25
114 **13** 5pi. on 40c. red and blue 40·00
115 20pi. on 1f. red and green 60·00

1921. Air. Nos. 104/5 optd **POSTE PAR AVION** in frame.
116 **15** 2pi. on 15c. green £6500
117 **13** 5pi. on 40c. red and blue £6500

POSTAGE DUE STAMPS

1919. Postage Due stamps of Turkey optd **CILICIE.**
D27 D **49** 5pa. brown . . . . . . 1·50 2·10
D28 D **50** 20pa. red . . . . . . 1·60 2·10
D29 D **51** 1pi. blue . . . . . . 4·00 4·00
D45 D **52** 2pi. blue . . . . . . 2·75 3·00

1919. Postage Due stamps of Turkey optd **Cilicie.**
D64 D **49** 5pa. brown . . . . . . 1·50 2·10
D65 D **50** 20pa. red . . . . . . 1·40 2·10
D66 D **51** 1pi. blue . . . . . . 4·00 4·00
D67 D **52** 2pi. blue . . . . . . 3·50 3·75

1921. Postage Due Stamps of France surch **O.M.F. Cilicie** and value.
D118 D **11** 1pi. on 10c. brown . . 4·00 4·50
D119 2pi. on 20c. olive . . . 3·50 4·50
D120 3pi. on 30c. red . . . 3·75 4·50
D121 4pi. on 50c. purple . . 3·75 4·50

CISKEI Pt. 1

The Republic of Ciskei was established on 4 December 1981, being constructed from tribal areas formerly part of the Republic of South Africa.

This independence did not receive international political recognition. We are satisfied, however, that the stamps had "de facto" acceptance for the carriage of mail outside Ciskei.

Ciskei was formally re-incorporated into South Africa on 27 April 1994.

100 cents = 1 rand.

1 Dr. Lennox Sebe, Chief Minister

2 Green Turaco

1981. Independence. Multicoloured.
1 5c. Type **1** 10 10
2 15c. Coat of arms 20 15
3 20c. Flag 30 30
4 25c. Mace 35 25

1981. Birds. Multicoloured.
5 1c. Type **2** 20 15
6 2c. Cape wagtail 20 15
7 3c. White-browed coucal . . 50 15
8 4c. Yellow-tufted malachite sunbird 20 15
9 5c. Stanley crane 20 15
10 6c. African red-winged starling 20 15
11 7c. Giant kingfisher 20 15
12 8c. Hadada ibis 30 15
13 9c. Black cuckoo 30 15
14 10c. Black-collared barbet . . 30 15
14a 11c. African black-headed oriole 55 30
14b 12c. Malachite kingfisher . . 70 30
14c 14c. Hoopoe . . . . 1·00 30
15 15c. African fish eagle . . . 30 30
15a 16c. Cape puff-back flycatcher 65 30
15b 18c. Long-tailed whydah . . 1·00 30
16 20c. Cape longclaw 40 30
16a 21c. Lemon dove . . . . . 1·50 60
17 25c. Cape dikkop 30 30
18 30c. African green pigeon . . 40 40
19 50c. Brown-necked parrot . . 60 60
20 1r. Narina's trogon . . . . . 90 1·25
21 2r. Cape eagle owl . . . . . 1·75 2·50

3 Cecilia Makiwane (first Xhosa nurse)

4 Boom Sprayer

1982. Nursing. Multicoloured.
22 8c. Type **3** 15 10
23 15c. Operating theatre 30 30
24 20c. Matron lighting nurse's lamp (horiz) 40 40
25 25c. Nurses and patient (horiz) 50 50

1982. Pineapple Industry. Multicoloured.
26 8c. Type **4** 10 10
27 15c. Harvesting 20 25
28 20c. Despatch to cannery . . . 25 30
29 30c. Packing for local market 30 35

5 Brown Hare

1982. Small Mammals. Multicoloured.
30 8c. Type **5** 15 15
31 15c. Cape fox 25 25
32 20c. Cape ground squirrel . . 30 30
33 25c. Caracal 40 40

6 Assegai

7 Dusky Shark

1983. Trees (1st series). Multicoloured.
34 8c. Cabbage tree 15 10
35 20c. Type **6** 30 30
36 25c. Cape chestnut 35 35
37 40c. Outeniqua yellowwood . . 50 55
See also Nos. 52/5.

1983. Sharks. Multicoloured.
38 8c. Type **7** 15 15
39 20c. Sand tiger ("Ragged-tooth shark") 30 30
40 25c. Tiger shark (57 × 21 mm) 35 35
41 30c. Scalloped hammerhead (57 × 21 mm) 40 40
42 40c. Great white shark (57 × 21 mm) 50 50

8 Lovedale

9 White Drill Uniform

1983. Educational Institutions.
43 **8** 10c. lt brown, brown & black 10 10
44 – 20c. lt brown, brown & black 20 20
45 – 25c. brown, red and black . . 25 25
46 – 40c. lt brown, brown & black 40 45
DESIGNS: 20c. Fort Hare; 25c. Healdtown; 40c. Lennox Sebe.

1983. British Military Uniforms (1st series). 6th Warwickshire Regiment of Foot, 1821–27. Multicoloured.
47 20c. Type **9** 40 40
48 20c. Light Company privates 40 40
49 20c. Grenadier Company sergeants 40 40
50 20c. Undress blue frock coats 40 40
51 20c. Officer and field officer in parade order 40 40
See also Nos. 64/8 and 95/8.

1984. Trees (2nd series). As T **6**. Multicoloured.
52 10c. "Rhus chirindensis" . . . 15 15
53 20c. "Phoenix reclinata" . . . 25 35
54 25c. "Ptaeroxyon obliquum" . . 30 40
55 40c. "Apodytes dimidiata" . . 40 55

10 Sandprawn

1984. Fish-bait. Multicoloured.
56 11c. Type **10** 20 15
57 20c. Coral worm 30 30
58 25c. Bloodworm 35 35
59 30c. Red-bait 40 40

11 Banded Martin ("Banded Sand Martin")

1984. Migratory Birds. Multicoloured.
60 11c. Type **11** 25 20
61 25c. House martin 50 50
62 30c. Greater striped swallow 60 60
63 45c. Barn swallow ("European Swallow") 80 85

1984. British Military Uniforms (2nd series). Cape Mounted Rifles. As T **9**. Multicoloured.
64 25c. (1) Trooper in field and sergeant in undress uniforms, 1830 . . . . . . 45 45
65 25c. (2) Trooper and sergeant in full dress, 1835 . . . . 45 45
66 25c. (3) Officers in undress, 1830 . . . . 45 45
67 25c. (4) Officers in full dress, 1827–34 . . . . 45 45
68 25c. (5) Officers in full dress, 1834 . . . . 45 45
The stamps are numbered as indicated in brackets.

12 White Steenbras

1985. Coastal Angling. Multicoloured.
69 11c. Type **12** 20 15
70 25c. Bronze seabream 30 30
71 30c. Kob 40 45
72 50c. Spotted grunt 70 80

13 Brownies holding Handmade Doll

1985. International Youth Year. 75th Anniv of Girl Guide Movement. Multicoloured.
73 12c. Type **13** 15 15
74 25c. Rangers planting trees . . 25 25
75 30c. Guides with flag 30 30
76 50c. Guides building fire . . . 60 65

14 Furniture making

1985. Small Businesses. Multicoloured.
77 12c. Type **14** 15 10
78 25c. Dressmaking 30 30
79 30c. Welding 30 30
80 50c. Basketry 60 65

15 "Antelope"

16 Earth showing Africa

1985. Sail Troopships. Multicoloured.
81 12c. Type **15** 20 15
82 25c. "Pilot" 45 45
83 30c. "Salisbury" 45 45
84 50c. "Olive Branch" 80 85

1986. Appearance of Halley's Comet. Mult.
85 12c. (1) Earth showing South America 70 70
86 12c. (2) Type **16** 70 70
87 12c. (3) Stars and Moon . . . 70 70
88 12c. (4) Moon and Milky Way 70 70
89 12c. (5) Milky Way and stars 70 70
90 12c. (6) Earth showing Australia 70 70
91 12c. (7) Earth and meteor . . 70 70
92 12c. (8) Meteor, Moon and comet tail 70 70
93 12c. (9) Comet head and Moon 70 70
94 12c. (10) Sun 70 70
Nos. 85/94 were issued in sheetlets of 10 stamps forming a composite design of the southern skies in April. Each stamp is inscribed with a number from "A1-10" to "A10-10". The first number is given in brackets in the listing to aid identification.

17 Fifer in Winter Dress

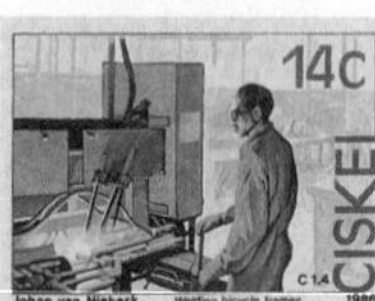

18 Welding Bicycle Frame

1986. British Military Uniforms (3rd series). 98th Regiment of Foot. Multicoloured.
95 14c. Type **17** 20 15
96 20c. Private in summer dress 30 30
97 25c. Grenadier in full summer dress 35 35
98 30c. Sergeant-major in full winter dress 50 50

1986. Bicycle Factory, Dimbaza. Multicoloured.
99 14c. Type **18** 20 15
100 20c. Spray-painting frame . . 30 30
101 25c. Installing wheelspokes 35 35
102 30c. Final assembly 50 50

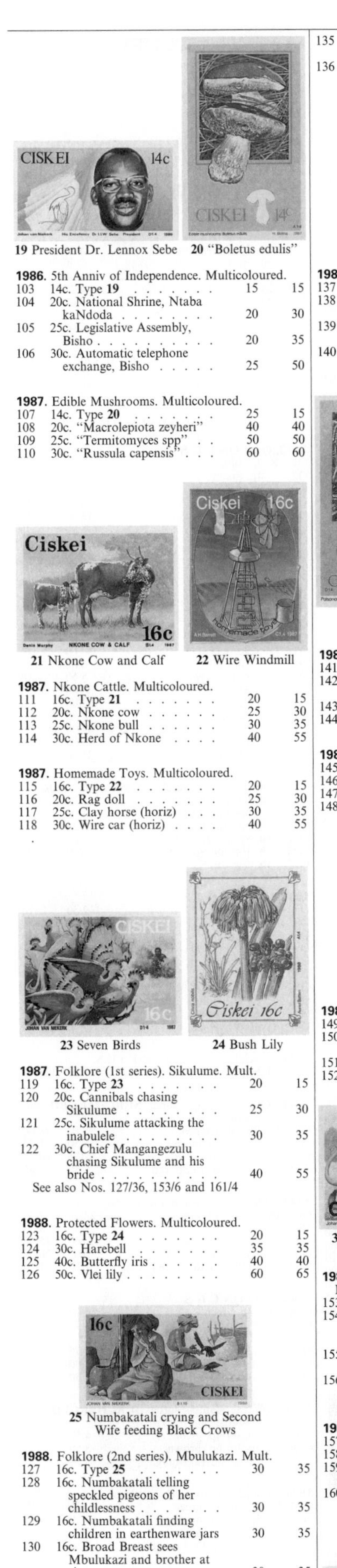

19 President Dr. Lennox Sebe **20** "Boletus edulis"

1986. 5th Anniv of Independence. Multicoloured.
103 14c. Type **19** 15 15
104 20c. National Shrine, Ntaba kaNdoda 20 30
105 25c. Legislative Assembly, Bisho 20 35
106 30c. Automatic telephone exchange, Bisho 25 50

1987. Edible Mushrooms. Multicoloured.
107 14c. Type **20** 25 15
108 20c. "Macrolepiota zeyheri" 40 40
109 25c. "Termitomyces spp" . . 50 50
110 30c. "Russula capensis" . . . 60 60

21 Nkone Cow and Calf **22** Wire Windmill

1987. Nkone Cattle. Multicoloured.
111 16c. Type **21** 20 15
112 20c. Nkone cow 25 30
113 25c. Nkone bull 30 35
114 30c. Herd of Nkone 40 55

1987. Homemade Toys. Multicoloured.
115 16c. Type **22** 20 15
116 20c. Rag doll 25 30
117 25c. Clay horse (horiz) . . . 30 35
118 30c. Wire car (horiz) 40 55

23 Seven Birds **24** Bush Lily

1987. Folklore (1st series). Sikulume. Mult.
119 16c. Type **23** 20 15
120 20c. Cannibals chasing Sikulume 25 30
121 25c. Sikulume attacking the inabulele 30 35
122 30c. Chief Mangangezulu chasing Sikulume and his bride 40 55
See also Nos. 127/36, 153/6 and 161/4

1988. Protected Flowers. Multicoloured.
123 16c. Type **24** 20 15
124 30c. Harebell 35 35
125 40c. Butterfly iris 40 40
126 50c. Vlei lily 60 65

25 Numbakatali crying and Second Wife feeding Black Crows

1988. Folklore (2nd series). Mbulukazi. Mult.
127 16c. Type **25** 30 35
128 16c. Numbakatali telling speckled pigeons of her childlessness 30 35
129 16c. Numbakatali finding children in earthenware jars 30 35
130 16c. Broad Breast sees Mbulukazi and brother at river 30 35
131 16c. Broad Breast asking to marry Mbulukazi 30 35
132 16c. Broad Breast and his two wives, Mbulukazi and her half-sister Mahlunguluza 30 35
133 16c. Mahlunguluza pushing Mbulukazi from precipice to her death 30 35
134 16c. Mbulukazi's ox tearing down Mahlunguluza's hut 30 35
135 16c. Ox licking Mbulukazi back to life 30 35
136 16c. Mahlunguluza being sent back to her father in disgrace 30 35

26 Oranges and Grafted Rootstocks in Nursery

1988. Citrus Farming. Multicoloured.
137 16c. Type **26** 20 15
138 30c. Lemons and inarching rootstock onto mature tree 40 40
139 40c. Tangerines and fruit being hand-picked 50 50
140 50c. Oranges and fruit being graded 60 65

27 "Amanita phalloides" **28** Kat River Dam

1988. Poisonous Fungi. Multicoloured.
141 16c. Type **27** 75 30
142 30c. "Chlorophyllum molybdites" . . . . 1·10 75
143 40c. "Amanita muscaria" . . 1·40 1·10
144 50c. "Amanita pantherina" 1·60 1·25

1989. Dams. Multicoloured.
145 16c. Type **28** 35 25
146 30c. Cata dam 55 50
147 40c. Binfield Park dam . . . 65 65
148 50c. Sandile dam 70 80

29 Taking Eggs from Rainbow Trout

1989. Trout Hatcheries. Multicoloured.
149 18c. Type **29** 25 15
150 30c. Fertilized eyed trout ova and alevins 45 45
151 40c. Five-week-old fingerlings 55 55
152 50c. Adult male 60 65

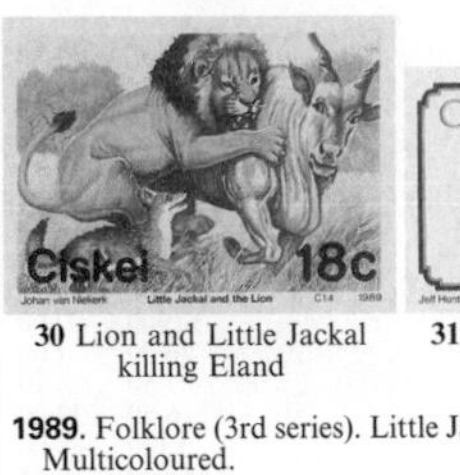

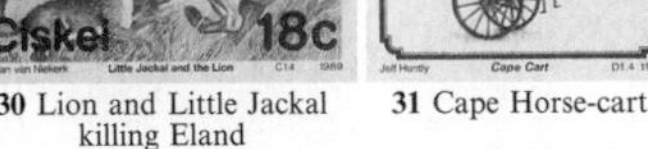

30 Lion and Little Jackal killing Eland **31** Cape Horse-cart

1989. Folklore (3rd series). Little Jackal and the Lion. Multicoloured.
153 18c. Type **30** 20 15
154 30c. Little Jackal's children carrying meat to clifftop home 35 35
155 40c. Little Jackal pretending to be trapped 40 40
156 50c. Lion falling down cliff face 45 50

1989. Animal-drawn Transport. Multicoloured.
157 18c. Type **31** 20 15
158 30c. Jubilee spider 35 35
159 40c. Ballantine half-tent ox-drawn wagon 40 40
160 50c. Voortrekker wagon . . . 45 50

32 Mpunzikazi offering Food to Five Heads **33** Handweaving on Loom

1990. Folklore (4th series). The Story of Makanda Mahlanu (Five Heads). Multicoloured.
161 18c. Type **32** 20 15
162 30c. Five Heads killing Mpunzikazi with his tail 35 35
163 40c. Mpunzanyana offering food to Five Heads 40 40
164 50c. Five Heads transformed into a man 45 50

1990. Handmade Carpets. Multicoloured.
165 21c. Type **33** 30 20
166 35c. Spinning 50 50
167 40c. Dyeing yarn 70 70
168 50c. Knotting carpet 70 70

34 Wooden Beam Plough, 1855

1980. Ploughs. Multicoloured.
169 21c. Type **34** 25 20
170 35c. Triple disc plough, 1895 40 40
171 40c. Reversible disc plough, 1895 . . . . 50 50
172 50c. "Het Volk" double furrow plough, 1910 . . . 60 65

35 Prickly Pear Vendor

1990. Prickly Pear. Multicoloured.
173 21c. Type **35** 30 20
174 35c. Prickly pear bushes . . . 50 50
175 40c. Whole and opened fruits 60 60
176 50c. Bushes in bloom 70 80

36 African Marsh Owl ("Marsh Owl") **37** Sao Bras (now Mossel Bay) on Map, 1500

1991. Owls. Multicoloured.
177 21c. Type **36** 95 40
178 35c. African scops owl ("Scops") . . . . 1·25 80
179 40c. Barn owl . . . . 1·60 1·00
180 50c. African wood owl ("Wood") . . . . 1·75 1·40

1991. Stamp Day. D'Ataide's Letter of 1501. Multicoloured.
181 25c. Type **37** 70 70
182 25c. Bartolomeo Dias's ship foundering off Cabo Tormentoso (now Cape of Good Hope) during voyage to India, 1500 . . . . . . 70 70
183 25c. Captain Pedro d'Ataide landing at Sao Bras, 1601 70 70
184 25c. D'Ataide leaving letter relating death of Dias on tree 70 70
185 25c. Captain Joao da Nova finding letter, 1501 . . . . 70 70
The inscriptions at the foot of Nos. 181 and 182 are transposed.

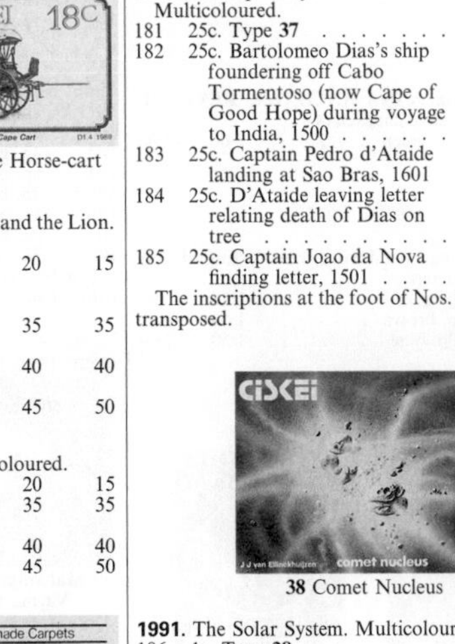

38 Comet Nucleus

1991. The Solar System. Multicoloured.
186 1c. Type **38** 20 15
187 2c. Trojan asteroids 20 15
188 5c. Meteoroids 20 15
189 7c. Pluto 30 15
190 10c. Neptune 30 15
191 20c. Uranus 50 20
192 25c. Saturn 60 20
193 30c. Jupiter 65 30
194 35c. Planetoids in asteroid belt 65 40
195 40c. Mars 80 50
196 50c. The Moon 80 70
197 60c. Earth 80 80
198 1r. Venus . . . . 1·00 1·25
199 2r. Mercury . . . . 1·60 2·00
200 5r. The Sun . . . . 2·25 3·25
MS201 197 × 93 mm. Nos. 186/200 10·00 10·00

39 Fort Armstrong and Xhosa Warrior

1991. 19th-century Frontier Forts. Multicoloured.
202 27c. Type **39** 30 30
203 45c. Keiskamma Hoek Post and Sir George Grey (governor of Cape Colony, 1854–58) 45 55
204 65c. Fort Hare and Xhosa Chief Sandile 55 70
205 85c. Peddie Cavalry Barracks and cavalryman . . . . . 75 1·25

40 Cumulonimbus

1992. Cloud Formations. Multicoloured.
206 27c. Type **40** 40 25
207 45c. Altocumulus 55 65
208 65c. Cirrus 65 80
209 85c. Cumulus . . . . 75 1·10

41 "Intelsat VI" Communications Satellite

1992. International Space Year. Satellites over Southern Africa. Multicoloured.
210 35c. Type **41** 40 25
211 70c. "G P S Navstar" (navigation) 80 80
212 90c. "Meteosat" (meteorology) . . . . . . 1·10 1·10
213 1r.05 "Landsat VI" (Earth resources survey) . . . . . 1·25 1·40

42 Universal Disc-harrow, 1914

1992. Agricultural Tools. Multicoloured.
214 35c. Type **42** 40 25
215 70c. Clod crusher and pulveriser, 1914 . . . . . 80 70
216 90c. Self-dump hay rake, 1910 . . . . 1·10 95
217 1r.05 McCormick hay tedder, 1900 . . . . 1·10 1·10

43 Mpekweni Sun Marine Resort

1992. Hotels. Multicoloured.
218 35c. Type **43** 40 25
219 70c. Katberg Protea Hotel . . 80 80
220 90c. Fish River Sun Hotel . . 1·10 1·10
221 1r.05 Amatola Sun Hotel, Amatole Mountains . . . 1·10 1·25

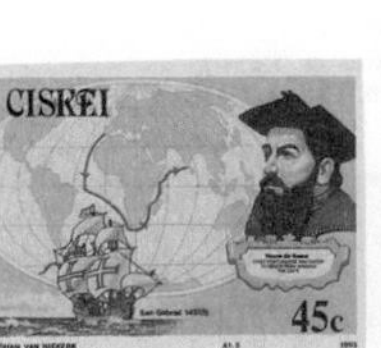

44 Vasco da Gama, "Sao Gabriel" and Voyage round Cape of Good Hope, 1497 **45** Island Canary

1993. Navigators. Multicoloured.
222 45c. Type **44** 65 30
223 65c. James Cook, H.M.S. "Endeavour" and first voyage, 1768–71 . . . . . 1·10 75
224 85c. Ferdinand Magellan, "Vitoria" and circumnavigation, 1519 . . 1·25 90
225 90c. Sir Francis Drake, "Golden Hind" and circumnavigation, 1577–80 1·25 95
226 1r.05 Abel Tasman, "Heemskerk" and discovery of Tasmania, 1642 . . . . 1·40 1·25

The ship on No. 222 is wrongly inscribed "San Gabriel", that on No. 224 "Victoria" and that on No. 226 "Heemskerck".

1993. Cage Birds. Multicoloured.
227 45c. Type **45** 45 30
228 65c. Budgerigar 70 60
229 85c. Peach-faced lovebirds . . 90 80
230 90c. Cockatiel 95 85
231 1r.05 Gouldian finch . . . . 1·00 1·10

46 Goshen Church (Moravian Mission), Whittlesea

1993. Churches and Missions.
232 **46** 45c. stone, black and red 35 20
233 – 65c. blue, black and red . . 60 60
234 – 85c. brown, black and red 80 80
235 – 1r.05 yellow, black and red 90 1·00

DESIGNS: 65c. Kamastone Mission Church; 85c. Richie Thompson Memorial Church (Hertzog Mission), near Seymour; 1r.05, Bryce Ross Memorial Church (Pirie Mission), near Dimbaza.

47 Jointed Cactus **48** "Losna" (steamer) (near Fish River), 1921

1993. Invader Plants. Multicoloured.
236 45c. Type **47** 40 30
237 65c. Thorn apple 70 60
238 85c. Coffee weed 90 80
239 1r.05 Poisonous wild tobacco 1·00 1·00
MS240 98 × 125 mm. Nos. 236/9 2·75 2·75

1994. Shipwrecks. Multicoloured.
241 45c. Type **48** 65 30
242 65c. "Catherine" (barque) (Waterloo Bay), 1846 . . . 1·10 60
243 85c. "Bennebroek" (East Indiaman) (near Mtana River), 1713 . . . . 1·25 90
244 1r.05 "Sao Joao Baptista" (galleon) (between Fish and Kei Rivers), 1622 . . . . 1·40 1·25

49 "Herman Steyn"

1994. Hybrid Roses. Multicoloured.
245 45c. Type **49** 35 30
246 70c. "Esther Geldenhuys" . . 60 60
247 95c. "Margaret Wasserfall" 80 80
248 1r.15 "Professor Fred Ziady" 1·00 1·00
MS249 149 × 114 mm. Nos. 245/8 2·50 2·75

COCHIN Pt. 1

A state of South West India. Now uses Indian stamps.

6 puttans = 5 annas.
12 pies = 1 anna; 16 annas = 1 rupee.

1 Emblems of State

1892. Value in "puttans".
5a **1** ½put. orange . . . . 1·60 1·50
2 1put. purple . . . . 2·75 2·00
3 2put. violet . . . . 2·00 2·25

3 **5**

1903. Value in "pies" or "puttans". With or without gum.
16 **3** 3pies. blue 80 10
17 ½put. green (smaller) . . . . 1·10 40
18 **5** 1put. red . . . . 1·75 10
19 **3** 2put. violet . . . . 2·50 50

1909. Surch **2**. No gum.
22 **3** 2 on 3 pies. mauve 15 50

8 Raja Rama Varma I **10** Raja Rama Varma II

1911. Value in "pies" or "annas".
26 **8** 2p. brown 30 10
27 3p. blue 90 10
28 4p. green . . . . 1·50 10
29 9p. red . . . . 1·10 10
30 1a. orange . . . . 2·75 10
31 1½a. purple . . . . 5·50 45
32 2a. grey . . . . 7·50 40
33 3a. red . . . . 35·00 35·00

1916. Various frames.
35b **10** 2p. brown . . . . 1·60 10
36 4p. green . . . . 1·00 10
37 6p. brown . . . . 2·50 10
38 8p. brown . . . . 1·50 10
39 9p. red . . . . 16·00 25
40 10p. blue . . . . 3·50 10
41a 1a. orange . . . . 8·50 30
42 1½a. purple . . . . 2·25 20
43 2a. grey . . . . 4·25 10
44 2¼a. green . . . . 4·25 3·25
45 3a. red . . . . 11·00 35

1922. Surch with figure and words.
46 **8** 2p. on 3p. blue 40 30

1928. Surch **ONE ANNA ANCHAL & REVENUE** and value in native characters.
50 **10** 1a. on 2¼a. green . . . . . 5·00 12·00

1932. Surch in figures and words both in English and in native characters.
51 **10** 3p. on 4p. green . . . . . 1·10 90
52 3p. on 8p. brown . . . . . 1·50 2·50
53 9p. on 10p. blue . . . . . 1·50 3·00

18 Maharaja Rama Varma III **26** Maharaja Kerala Varma II

1933.
54 **18** 2p. brown 60 30
55 4p. green 60 10
56 6p. red 70 10
57 1a. orange 70 10
58 1a.8p. red . . . . 3·00 4·75
59 2a. grey . . . . 4·50 1·00
60 2¼a. green . . . . 1·50 15
61 3a. orange . . . . 5·00 1·60
62 3a.4p. violet . . . . 1·50 1·40
63 6a.8p. sepia . . . . 1·75 11·00
64 10a. blue . . . . 3·00 13·00

1934. Surch with figure and words.
65 **10** 6p. on 8p. brown 75 60
66 6p. on 10p. blue . . . . . 1·75 2·00

1939. Optd **ANCHAL**.
74 **18** 1a. orange . . . . 75 1·60

1939. Surch in words only.
75 **18** 3p. on 1a.8p. red . . . . . £160 80·00
77 6p. on 1a.8p. red . . . . . 3·25 20·00

1943. Surch **SURCHARGED** and value in words.
79 **18** 3p. on 4p. green . . . . . 6·00 4·00
76 3p. on 1a.8p. red . . . . . 4·00 8·50
78 1a.3p. on 1a.8p. red . . . . 1·00 30

1943. Surch **ANCHAL SURCHARGED NINE PIES.**
84 **18** 9p. on 1a. orange . . . . . 18·00 5·50

1943. Surch **ANCHAL** and value in words.
81a **18** 6p. on 1a. orange . . . . £110 60·00
82 9p. on 1a. orange £120 £120

1943.
85 **26** 2p. brown . . . . 2·00 2·75
87a 4p. green . . . . 3·00 4·00
88 6p. brown . . . . 2·00 10
89 9p. blue . . . . 32·00 1·00
90a 1a. orange . . . . 22·00 45·00
91 2¼a. green . . . . 22·00 2·25

1944. Surch with value in words only.
93 **26** 2p. on 6p. brown . . . . . 75 3·25
94 3p. on 4p. green . . . . . 3·25 10
96 3p. on 6p. brown 85 20
97 4p. on 6p. brown . . . . . 3·75 10·00

1944. Surch **SURCHARGED** and value in words.
95 **26** 3p. on 4p. green . . . . . 4·50 10
92c 1a.3p. on 1a. orange . . . † £3000

1944. Surch **ANCHAL NINE PIES.**
92a **26** 9p. on 1a. orange . . . . 5·00 2·75

1944. Surch **ANCHAL SURCHARGED NINE PIES.**
92b **26** 9p. on 1a. orange . . . . 5·50 2·50

28 Maharaja Ravi Varma **29** Maharaja Ravi Varma

1944.
98 **28** 9p. blue . . . . 12·00 2·50
99 1a.3p. mauve . . . . 6·00 8·50
100 1a.9p. blue . . . . 8·00 13·00

1946. No gum.
101 **29** 2p. brown . . . . 1·75 10
102 3p. red 50 15
103 4p. green . . . . £1900 80·00
104 6p. brown . . . . 20·00 4·00
105 9p. blue 50 10
106 1a. orange . . . . 6·50 27·00
107 2a. black . . . . £100 8·00
108 3a. red . . . . 65·00 75

For No. 106, optd "U.S.T.C." or "T.-C." with or without surch, see Travancore-Cochin.

30 Maharaja Kerala Varma III **31** Chinese Nets

1948.
109 **30** 2p. brown . . . . 1·75 15
110 3p. red 75 15
111 4p. green . . . . 14·00 2·25
112 6p. brown . . . . 14·00 25
113 9p. blue . . . . 2·50 25
114 2a. black . . . . 50·00 1·25
115 3a. orange . . . . 60·00 85
116 3a.4p. violet . . . . 70·00 £350

1949.
117 **31** 2a. black . . . . 4·00 6·50
118 – 2¼a. green (Dutch palace) 2·75 6·50

SIX PIES

ആറ പൈ

(33)

1949. Surch as T **33**.
121 **29** 3p. on 9p. blue . . . . . 8·50 19·00
124a **30** 3p. on 9p. blue . . . . . 2·50 50
126 6p. on 9p. blue . . . . . 1·50 40
119 **28** 6p. on 1a.3p. mauve . . . 4·25 4·00
122 **29** 6p. on 1a.3p. mauve . . . 14·00 13·00
120 1a. on 1a.9p. blue . . . . 1·25 1·40
123 1a. on 1a.9p. blue . . . . 3·00 2·00

1949. Surch **SIX PIES** or **NINE PIES** only.
127 **29** 6p. on 1a. orange . . . . 55·00 £120
128 9p. on 1a. orange . . . . 80·00 £120

OFFICIAL STAMPS

1913. Optd **ON C G S.**
O1 **8** 3p. blue £120 10
O2 4p. green . . . . 8·50 10
O3a 9p. red . . . . 15·00 10
O4 1½a. purple . . . . 38·00 10
O5 2a. grey . . . . 13·00 10
O6 3a. red . . . . 48·00 35
O7 6a. violet . . . . 45·00 2·00
O8 12a. blue . . . . 38·00 6·50
O9 1½r. green . . . . 35·00 60·00

1919. Optd **ON C G S.**
O10 **10** 4p. green . . . . 3·75 10
O11 6p. brown . . . . 8·00 10
O26 8p. brown . . . . 7·00 10
O13 9p. red . . . . 50·00 10
O27 10p. blue . . . . 6·00 10
O15 1½a. purple . . . . 5·50 10
O28 2a. grey . . . . 30·00 15
O17 2¼a. green . . . . 12·00 10
O29 3a. red . . . . 8·00 15
O19 6a. violet . . . . 35·00 50
O19a 12a. blue . . . . 15·00 4·00
O19b 1½r. green . . . . 23·00 £100

1923. Official stamps surch in figures and words.
O32 **10** 6p. on 8p. brown . . . . 2·25 10
O33 6p. on 10p. blue . . . . 4·00 10
O20b **8** 8p. on 9p. red £130 20
O21 **10** 8p. on 9p. red . . . . . 70·00 10
O23 **8** 10p. on 9p. red . . . . . £900 11·00
O22 **10** 10p. on 9p. red . . . . . 70·00 70

1933. Optd **ON C G S.**
O34 **18** 4p. green . . . . 2·50 10
O35 6p. red . . . . 2·50 10
O52 1a. orange . . . . 1·00 10
O37 1a.8p. red . . . . 1·50 30
O38 2a. grey . . . . 13·00 10
O39 2¼a. green . . . . 4·00 10
O53 3a. orange . . . . 3·00 1·10
O41 3a.4p. violet . . . . 1·50 15
O42 6a.8p. sepia . . . . 1·50 20
O43 10a. blue . . . . 1·50 70

1943. Official stamp surch **NINE PIES.**
O57 **10** 9p. on 1½a. purple . . . . £425 23·00

1943. Official stamps surch **SURCHARGED** and value in words.
O63 **18** 3p. on 4p. green . . . . . £110 48·00
O58 3p. on 1a.8p. red . . . . 5·50 1·75
O66 1a.3p. on 1a. orange . . . £275 90·00
O61 1a.9p. on 1a.8p. red . . . 80 30

1943. Official stamps surch in words.
O62 **18** 3p. on 4p. green . . . . . 22·00 7·50
O64 3p. on 1a. orange . . . . 2·00 3·25
O65 9p. on 1a. orange . . . . £200 45·00
O59 9p. on 1a.8p. red . . . . £100 26·00
O60 1a.9p. on 1a.8p. red . . . 2·50 1·75

1944. Optd **ON C G S.**
O68 **26** 4p. green . . . . 26·00 4·50
O69b 6p. brown 70 10
O70 1a. orange . . . . £2000 48·00
O71 2a. black . . . . 4·75 60
O72 2¼a. green . . . . 3·00 1·00
O73a 3a. red . . . . 7·50 40

1944. Official stamps surch **SURCHARGED** and value in words.
O75 **26** 3p. on 4p. green . . . . . 4·50 30
O78 9p. on 6p. brown . . . . 3·50 30
O80 1a.3p. on 1a. orange . . . 3·25 10

1944. Official stamps surch in words.
O74 **26** 3p. on 4p. green . . . . . 2·75 10
O76 3p. on 1a. orange . . . . 19·00 4·50
O77 9p. on 6p. brown . . . . 8·00 2·50
O79 1a.3p. on 1a. orange . . . 7·50 1·60

1946. Optd **ON C G S.**
O81 **28** 9p. blue . . . . 2·75 10
O82 1a.3p. mauve . . . . 1·60 20
O83 1a.9p. blue . . . . 40 1·00

1948. Optd **ON C G S.**
O84 **29** 3p. red . . . . 1·00 10
O85 4p. green . . . . 27·00 5·50
O86 6p. brown . . . . 8·00 80
O87 9p. blue 75 10
O88 1a.3p. mauve . . . . 2·75 70

O89 1a.9p. blue 3·25 40
O90 2a. black 13·00 3·00
O91 2¼a. green 21·00 3·25

1949. Optd **ON C G S.**
O92 **30** 3p. red 1·25 15
O93 4p. green 1·25 30
O94 6p. brown 2·50 10
O95 9p. blue 2·50 10
O96 2a. black 2·00 15
O97 2¼a. green 2·75 5·50
O98 3a. orange 1·10 50
O99 3a.4p. violet 38·00 35·00

1949. Official stamps surch as T **33**.
O103 **30** 6p. on 3p. red 1·00 60
O104 9p. on 4p. green 75 2·25
O100 **28** 1a. on 1a.9p. blue 60 60
O101 **29** 1a. on 1a.9p. blue 21·00 14·00

1949. Optd **SERVICE.**
O105 **30** 3p. on 9p. (No. 125) 60 70

For later issues see **TRAVANCORE-COCHIN**.

COCHIN-CHINA Pt. 6

A former French colony in the extreme S. of Indo-China, subsequently incorporated into French Indo-China.

100 centimes = 1 franc.

1886. Stamps of French Colonies surch.
1 J 5 on 25c. brown on yellow £160 £110
2 5 on 2c. brown on yellow 14·50 16·00
3 5 on 25c. brown on yellow 20·00 19·00
4 5 on 25c. black on red 40·00 34·00
Nos. 1 and 4 are surcharged with numeral only; Nos. 2 and 3 are additionally optd **C. CH.**

COCOS (KEELING) ISLANDS Pt. 1

Islands in the Indian Ocean formerly administered by Singapore and transferred to Australian administration on 23 November 1955.

1963. 12 pence = 1 shilling;
20 shillings = 1 pound.
1966. 100 cents = 1 dollar (Australian).

5 Jukong (sailboat)

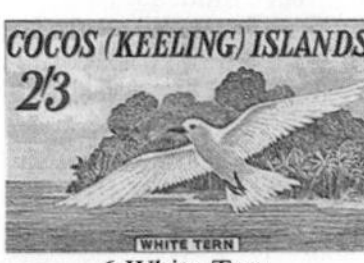
6 White Tern

1963.
1 – 3d. brown 1·00 1·50
2 – 5d. blue 1·50 80
3 – 8d. red 1·00 1·75
4 – 1s. green 1·00 75
5 **5** 2s. purple 11·00 2·75
6 **6** 2s.3d. green 14·00 2·75
DESIGNS—HORIZ (As Type **5**): 3d. Copra industry; 1s. Palms. (As Type **6**): 5d. Lockheed Super Constellation airliner. VERT (As Type **5**): 8d. Map of islands.

1965. 50th Anniv of Gallipoli Landing. As T **184** of Australia, but slightly larger (22 × 34½ mm).
7 5d. brown, black and green 60 45

With the introduction of decimal currency on 14 February 1966, Australian stamps were used in Cocos Islands until the 1969 issue.

7 Reef Clam

9 "Dragon", 1609

1969. Decimal Currency. Multicoloured.
8 1c. Lajonkaines turbo shell (vert) 30 60
9 2c. Elongate or small giant clam (vert) 75 80
10 3c. Type **7** 40 20
11 4c. Floral blenny (fish) 30 50
12 5c. "Porites cocosensis" (coral) 35 30
13 6c. Atrisignis flyingfish 75 75
14 10c. Buff-banded rail 75 70
15 15c. Java sparrow 75 30
16 20c. Red-tailed tropic bird 75 30
17 30c. Sooty tern 75 30
18 50c. Reef heron (vert) 75 30
19 $1 Great frigate bird (vert) 1·50 75

1976. Ships. Multicoloured.
20 1c. Type **9** 30 40
21 2c. H.M.S. "Juno", 1857 (horiz) 30 40
22 5c. H.M.S. "Beagle", 1836 (horiz) 30 40
23 10c. H.M.A.S. "Sydney", 1914 (horiz) 35 40
24 15c. S.M.S. "Emden", 1914 (horiz) 60 55
25 20c. "Ayesha", 1907 (horiz) 60 65
26 25c. T.S.S. "Islander", 1927 60 75
27 30c. M.V. "Cheshire", 1951 60 75
28 35c. Jukong (sailboat) (horiz) 60 75
29 40c. C.S. "Scotia", 1900 (horiz) 60 75
30 50c. R.M.S. "Orontes", 1929 60 75
31 $1 Royal Yacht "Gothic", 1954 75 1·00

10 Map of Cocos (Keeling) Islands, Union Flag, Stars and Trees

1979. Inauguration of Independent Postal Service and First Statutory Council. Multicoloured.
32 20c. Type **10** 25 40
33 50c. Council seat and jukong (sailboat) 35 85

11 Forceps Fish

12 "Peace on Earth"

1979. Fishes. Multicoloured.
34 1c. Type **11** 30 1·00
35 2c. Ornate butterflyfish 30 30
36 5c. Barbier 50 1·10
37 10c. Meyer's butterflyfish 30 1·00
38 15c. Pink wrasse 30 30
39 20c. Clark's anemonefish 40 30
39a 22c. Undulate triggerfish 45 30
40 25c. Red-breasted wrasse 40 1·25
40a 28c. Guineafowl wrasse 35 35
41 30c. Madagascar butterflyfish 40 45
42 35c. Cocos-Keeling angelfish 40 1·75
43 40c. Coral hogfish 45 1·00
44 50c. Clown wrasse 85 75
45 55c. Yellow-tailed tamarin 50 1·50
45a 60c. Greasy grouper 50 75
46 $1 Palette surgeonfish 60 3·50
47 $2 Melon butterflyfish 70 3·50

1979. Christmas. Multicoloured.
48 25c. Type **12** 25 40
49 55c. Atoll seascape ("Goodwill") 40 70

13 Star, Map of Cocos (Keeling) Islands and Island Landscape

1980. Christmas. Multicoloured.
50 15c. Type **13** 10 10
51 28c. The Three Kings 15 15
52 60c. Adoration 40 40

14 "Administered by the British Government, 1857"

15 "Eye of the Wind" and Map of Cocos (Keeling) Islands

1980. 25th Anniv of Territorial Status under Australian Administration. Multicoloured.
53 22c. Type **14** 15 15
54 22c. Arms of Ceylon 15 15
55 22c. Arms of Straits Settlements 15 15
56 22c. Arms of Singapore 15 15
57 22c. Arms and flag of Australia 15 15

1980. "Operation Drake" (round the world expedition) and 400th Anniv of Sir Francis Drake's Circumnavigation of the World. Multicoloured.
58 22c. Type **15** 25 15
59 28c. Routes map (horiz) 25 15
60 35c. Sir Francis Drake and "Golden Hind" 25 15
61 60c. Prince Charles (patron) and "Eye of the Wind" (brigantine) 45 30

16 Aerial View of Animal Quarantine Station

1981. Opening of Animal Quarantine Station. Multicoloured.
62 22c. Type **16** 15 15
63 45c. Unloading livestock 20 30
64 60c. Livestock in pen 20 35

17 Consolidated Catalina Flying Boat "Guba"

1981. Aircraft. Multicoloured.
65 22c. Type **17** 25 25
66 22c. Consolidated Liberator and Avro Lancastrian 25 25
67 22c. Douglas DC-4 and Lockheed Constellation 25 25
68 22c. Lockheed Electra 25 25
69 22c. Boeing 727-100 airliners 25 25

18 Prince Charles and Lady Diana Spencer

1981. Royal Wedding.
70 **18** 24c. multicoloured 30 20
71 60c. multicoloured 50 60

19 "Angels we have heard on High"

1981. Christmas. Scenes and Lines from Carol "Angels we have heard on High". Multicoloured.
72 18c. Type **19** 10 10
73 30c. "Shepherds why this Jubilee?" 20 20
74 60c. "Come to Bethlehem and see Him" 35 35

20 "Pachyseris speciosa" and "Heliofungia actiniformis" (corals)

1981. 150th Anniv of Charles Darwin's Voyage. Multicoloured.
75 24c. Type **20** 25 15
76 45c. Charles Darwin in 1853 and "Pavona cactus" (coral) 40 30
77 60c. H.M.S. "Beagle", 1832, and "Lobophyllia hemprichii" (coral) 45 35
MS78 130 × 95 mm. 24c. Cross-section of West Island; 24c. Cross-section of Home Island 75 85

21 Queen Victoria

1982. 125th Anniv of Annexation of Cocos (Keeling) Islands to British Empire. Multicoloured.
79 24c. Type **21** 15 15
80 45c. Union flag 25 25
81 60c. Captain S. Fremantle (annexation visit, 1857) 30 35

22 Lord Baden-Powell

1982. 75th Anniv of Boy Scout Movement. Multicoloured.
82 27c. Type **22** 25 25
83 75c. "75" and map of Cocos (Keeling) Islands (vert) 60 1·50

23 "Precis villida"

24 "Call His Name Immanuel"

1982. Butterflies and Moths. Multicoloured.
84 1c. Type **23** 1·00 60
85 2c. "Cephonodes picus" (horiz) 40 40
86 5c. "Macroglossom corythus" (horiz) 1·50 70
87 10c. "Chasmina candida" 40 40
88 20c. "Nagia linteola" (horiz) 40 65
89 25c. "Eublemma rivula" 40 75
90 30c. "Eurrhyparodes tricoloralis" 40 65
91 35c. "Hippotion boerhaviae" (horiz) 1·50 75
92 40c. "Euploea core" 40 80
93 45c. "Psara hipponalis" (horiz) 50 80
94 50c. "Danaus chrysippus" (horiz) 60 1·25
95 55c. "Hypolimnas misippus" 60 70
96 60c. "Spodoptera litura" 65 1·75
97 $1 "Achaea janata" 2·75 2·75
98 $2 "Panacra velox" (horiz) 2·00 2·75
99 $3 "Utetheisa pulchelloides" (horiz) 2·75 2·75

1982. Christmas. Multicoloured.
100 21c. Type **24** 25 30
101 35c. "I bring you good tidings" 40 40
102 75c. "Arise and flee into Egypt" 1·00 1·25

25 "God will look after us" (Matt. 1:20)

26 Hari Raya Celebration

1983. Christmas. Extracts from New Testament. Multicoloured.
103 24c. Type **25** 30 45
104 24c. "Our baby King, Jesus" (Matthew. 2:2) 30 45
105 24c. "Your Saviour is born" (Luke. 2:11) 30 45
106 24c. "Wise men followed the Star" (Matthew. 2:9–10) 30 45
107 24c. "And worship the Lord" (Matthew. 2:11) 30 45

1984. Cocos-Malay Culture (1st series). Mult.
108 45c. Type **26** 45 35
109 75c. Melenggok dancing 65 50
110 85c. Cocos-Malay wedding 75 55
See also Nos. 128/31.

27 Unpacking Barrel

1984. 75th Anniv of Cocos Barrel Mail. Multicoloured.
111 35c. Type **27** 40 25
112 55c. Jukong awaiting mail ship 75 50
113 70c. P & O mail ship "Morea" 85 55
MS114 125 × 95 mm. $1 Retrieving barrel 1·00 1·25

28 Captain William Keeling **29** Malay Settlement, Home Island

1984. 375th Anniv of Discovery of Cocos (Keeling) Islands. Multicoloured.
115 30c. Type **28** 60 40
116 65c. "Hector" . . . . 1·25 90
117 95c. Mariner's astrolabe . . . 1·50 1·25
118 $1.10 Map circa 1666 . . . . 1·60 1·50

1984. "Ausipex" International Stamp Exhibition, Melbourne. Multicoloured.
119 45c. Type **29** 75 50
120 55c. Airstrip, West Island . . 85 60
MS121 130 × 95 mm. $2 Jukongs (native craft) racing . . . . . 2·75 2·50

30 "Rainbow" Fish **32** Jukong-building

31 Cocos Islanders

1984. Christmas. Multicoloured.
122 24c. Type **30** 50 60
123 35c. "Rainbow" butterfly . . 1·10 1·40
124 55c. "Rainbow" bird . . . . 1·25 2·00

1984. Integration of Cocos (Keeling) Islands with Australia. Sheet 90 × 52 mm, containing T **31** and similar horiz design. Multicoloured.
MS125 30c. Type **31**; 30c. Australian flag on island . . . . 1·50 1·25

1985. Cocos-Malay Culture (2nd series). Handicrafts. Multicoloured.
126 30c. Type **32** 75 35
127 45c. Blacksmithing . . . . . 1·00 55
128 55c. Woodcarving . . . . . 1·25 65

33 C.S. "Scotia"

1985. Cable-laying Ships. Multicoloured.
129 33c. Type **33** . . . . . . 1·50 40
130 65c. C.S. "Anglia" . . . . . 2·25 1·60
131 80c. C.S. "Patrol" . . . . . 2·25 2·25

34 Red-footed Booby **35** Mantled Top

1985. Birds of Cocos (Keeling) Islands. Mult.
132 33c. Type **34** . . . . 1·75 2·25
133 60c. Nankeen night heron (juvenile) (horiz) . . . . . 2·00 2·50
134 $1 Buff-banded rail (horiz) 2·25 2·50
Nos. 132/4 were issued together, se-tenant, forming a composite design.

1985. Shells and Molluscs. Multicoloured.
135 1c. Type **35** . . . . 60 1·25
136 2c. Rang's nerite . . . . . . 60 1·25
137 3c. Jewel box . . . . 60 1·25
138 4c. Money cowrie . . . . . 1·00 1·25
139 5c. Purple Pacific drupe . . . 60 1·25
140 10c. Soldier cone . . . . . . 70 1·50
141 15c. Merlin-spike auger . . . 2·00 1·25
142 20c. Pacific strawberry cockle 2·00 1·50
143 30c. Lajonkaire's turban . . 2·00 1·50
144 33c. Reticulate mitre . . . . 2·25 1·50
145 40c. Common spider conch 2·25 1·50
146 50c. Fluted giant clam or scaled tridacna . . . . . . 2·25 1·75
147 60c. Minstrel cowrie . . . . 2·25 2·00
148 $1 Varicose nudibranch . . . 3·25 3·00
149 $2 Tesselated nudibranch . . 3·50 4·00
150 $3 Hamincea cymballum . . 4·25 4·75

36 Night Sky and Palm Trees

1985. Christmas. Sheet 121 × 88 mm, containing T **36** and similar horiz designs.
MS151 27c. × 4 multicoloured 2·00 2·75
The stamps within No. **MS**151 show a composite design of the night sky seen through a grove of palm trees. The position of the face value on the four stamps varies. Type **36** shows the top left design. The top right stamp shows the face value at bottom right, the bottom left at top left and the bottom right at top right.

37 Charles Darwin, c. 1840 **38** Coconut Palm and Holly Sprigs

1986. 150th Anniv of Charles Darwin's Visit. Multicoloured.
152 33c. Type **37** 70 60
153 60c. Map of H.M.S. "Beagle's" route, Australia to Cocos Islands . . . . . 1·25 2·25
154 $1 H.M.S. "Beagle" . . . . 1·75 2·75

1986. Christmas. Multicoloured.
155 30c. Type **38** 60 70
156 90c. Nautilus shell and Christmas tree bauble . . . 2·00 3·00
157 $1 Tropical fish and bell . . 2·00 3·00

39 Jukong

1987. Sailing Craft. Multicoloured.
158 36c. Type **39** . . . . 1·10 1·50
159 36c. Ocean racing yachts . . 1·10 1·50
160 36c. "Sarimanok" (replica of early dhow) . . . . 1·10 1·50
161 36c. "Ayesha" (schooner) . . 1·10 1·50
Nos. 158/61 were printed together, se-tenant, each strip forming a composite background design.

40 Beach, Direction Island

1987. Cocos Islands Scenes. Multicoloured.
162 70c. Type **40** . . . . 1·40 1·40
163 90c. Palm forest, West Island 1·75 2·00
164 $1 Golf course . . . . 2·75 3·00

41 Radio Transmitter and Palm Trees at Sunset

1987. Communications. Multicoloured.
165 70c. Type **41** . . . . 1·25 1·50
166 75c. Boeing 727-100 airliner at terminal . . . . 1·50 1·75
167 90c. "Intelsat 5" satellite . . 1·75 2·25
168 $1 Airmail letter and globe 2·00 2·25

42 Batik Printing

1987. Cocos (Keeling) Islands Malay Industries. Multicoloured.
169 45c. Type **42** . . . . . . 1·25 1·50
170 65c. Jukong building . . . . 1·75 2·00
171 75c. Copra production . . . 2·00 2·25

43 Hands releasing Peace Dove and Map of Islands **44** Coconut Flower

1987. Christmas. Multicoloured.
172 30c. Type **43** 40 40
173 90c. Local children at Christmas party . . . . . 1·25 1·90
174 $1 Island family and Christmas star . . . . . . 1·50 1·90

1988. Bicentenary of Australian Settlement. Arrival of First Fleet. As Nos. 1105/9 of Australia but each inscr "COCOS (KEELING) ISLANDS" and "AUSTRALIA BICENTENARY".
175 37c. Aborigines watching arrival of Fleet, Botany Bay . . . . 1·90 2·00
176 37c. Aboriginal family and anchored ships . . . . . 1·90 2·00
177 37c. Fleet arriving at Sydney Cove . . . . 1·90 2·00
178 37c. Ship's boat . . . . . . 1·90 2·00
179 37c. Raising the flag, Sydney Cove, 26 January 1788 . . 1·90 2·00
Nos. 175/9 were printed together, se-tenant, forming a composite design.

1988. Life Cycle of the Coconut. Multicoloured.
180 37c. Type **44** 50 40
181 65c. Immature nuts . . . . . 75 1·00
182 90c. Coconut palm and mature nuts . . . . 1·10 1·75
183 $1 Seedlings . . . . 1·25 1·75
MS184 102 × 91 mm. Nos. 180/3 4·00 4·50

45 Copra 3d. Stamp of 1963 **46** "Pisonia grandis"

1988. 25th Anniv of First Cocos (Keeling) Islands Stamps. Each showing stamp from 1963 definitive set.
185 **45** 37c. green, black and blue 1·25 1·25
186 – 55c. green, black and brown . . . . 1·75 1·50
187 – 65c. blue, black and lilac 1·90 2·50
188 – 70c. red, black and grey . . 1·90 2·50
189 – 90c. purple, black and grey 2·25 2·75
190 – $1 green, black and brown 2·25 2·75
DESIGNS: 55c. Palms 1s.; 65c. Lockheed Super Constellation airplane 5d.; 70c. Map 8d.; 90c. "Jukong" (sailboat) 2s.; $1 White tern 2s.3d.

1988. Flora. Multicoloured.
191 1c. Type **46** 50 80
192 2c. "Cocos nucifera" 50 80
193 5c. "Morinda citrifolia" . . . 1·00 90
194 10c. "Cordia subcordata" . . 70 90
195 30c. "Argusia argentea" . . . 1·00 1·25
196 37c. "Calophyllum inophyllum" . . . . 1·50 1·00
197 40c. "Barringtonia asiatica" 1·00 1·25
198 50c. "Caesalpinia bonduc" . 1·25 3·00
199 90c. "Terminalia catappa" . . 1·75 4·00
200 $1 "Pemphis acidula" . . . . 1·75 2·50
201 $2 "Scaevola sericea" . . . . 2·50 2·50
202 $3 "Hibiscus tiliaceus" . . . 3·50 3·75

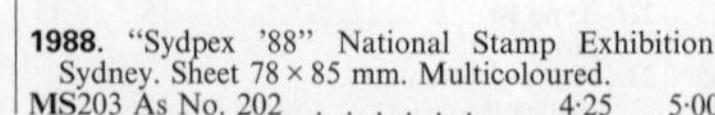

1988. "Sydpex '88" National Stamp Exhibition, Sydney. Sheet 78 × 85 mm. Multicoloured.
MS203 As No. 202 . . . . . . 4·25 5·00

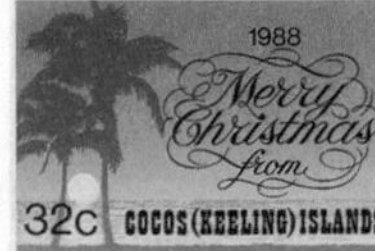

47 Beach at Sunset

1988. Christmas.
204 **47** 32c. multicoloured 80 50
205 90c. multicoloured . . . . 1·75 2·75
206 $1 multicoloured . . . . . 2·00 2·75

48 Captain P. G. Taylor **49** Jukong and Star

1989. 50th Anniv of First Indian Ocean Aerial Survey.
207 **48** 40c. multicoloured 80 60
208 – 70c. multicoloured . . . . 1·75 2·50
209 – $1 multicoloured . . . . 2·00 2·50
210 – $1.10 blue, lilac and black 2·25 2·75
DESIGNS: 70c. Consolidated Catalina flying boat "Guba" and crew; $1 "Guba" over Direction Islands; $1.10, Unissued Australia 5s. stamp commemorating flight.

1989. Christmas.
211 **49** 35c. multicoloured 80 60
212 80c. multicoloured . . . . 2·50 3·00
213 $1.10 multicoloured . . . . 2·50 3·00

50 H.M.A.S. "Sydney" (cruiser)

1989. 75th Anniv of Destruction of German Cruiser "Emden". Multicoloured.
214 40c. Type **50** . . . . 1·75 1·75
215 70c. "Emden" . . . . 2·00 2·00
216 $1 "Emden's" steam launch 2·25 2·25
217 $1.10 H.M.A.S. "Sydney" (1914) and crest . . . . . 2·25 2·25

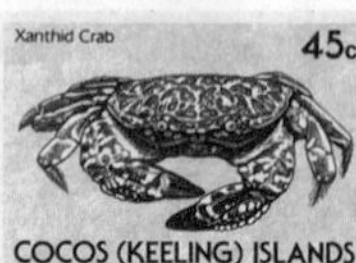

51 Xanthid Crab

1990. Cocos Islands Crabs. Multicoloured.
219 45c. Type **51** . . . . 1·75 75
220 75c. Ghost crab . . . . . . 2·25 2·00
221 $1 Red-backed mud crab . . 2·50 2·25
222 $1.30 Coconut crab (vert) . . 2·75 3·00

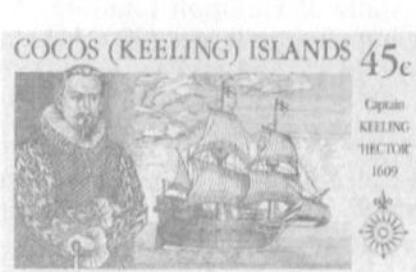

52 Captain Keeling and "Hector", 1609

1990. Navigators of the Pacific.
223 **52** 45c. mauve . . . . 2·75 1·25
224 – 75c. mauve and blue . . . 3·00 3·25
225 – $1 mauve and stone . . . 3·50 3·75
226 – $1.30 mauve and buff . . . 4·25 5·00
DESIGNS: 75c. Captain Fitzroy and H.M.S. "Beagle", 1836; $1 Captain Belcher and H.M.S. "Samarang", 1846; $1.30, Captain Fremantle and H.M.S. "Juno", 1857.

1990. "New Zealand 1990" International Stamp Exhibition, Auckland. No. 188 optd with logo and **NEW ZEALAND 1990 24 AUG 2 SEP AUCKLAND**.
228 70c. red, black and grey . . . 3·75 3·50
MS229 127 × 90 mm. As Nos. 194, 199 and 201, but self-adhesive 8·00 8·00

1990. No. 187 surch **$5**.
230 $5 on 65c. blue, black and lilac . . . . 18·00 18·00

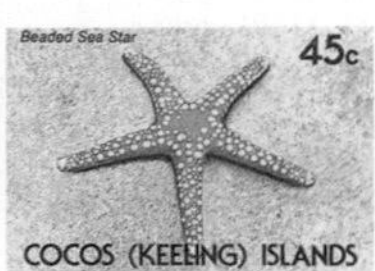

55 Cocos Atoll from West and Star
58 Beaded Sea Star

1990. Christmas. Multicoloured.
231 40c. Type **55** . . . . 80 1·25
232 70c. Cocos atoll from south 1·75 2·75
233 $1.30 Cocos atoll from east 3·00 3·50

1990. Nos. 140/1, 143 and 146/7 surch **POSTAGE PAID** plus additional words as indicated.
236 (1c.) on 30c. Lajonkaire's turban (**LOCAL**) . . . . . 2·00 2·75
235 (43c.) on 10c. Soldier cone (**MAINLAND**) . . . . . . 1·40 2·00
237 70c. on 60c. Minstrel cowrie (**ZONE 1**) . . . . 1·50 2·75
238 80c. on 50c. Fluted giant clam or scaled tridacna (**ZONE 2**) . . . . 1·75 3·50
239 $1.20 on 15c. Marlin-spike auger (**ZONE 5**) . . . . . 2·00 3·75

1991. Starfish and Sea Urchins. Multicoloured.
240 45c. Type **58** . . . . 1·25 75
241 75c. Feather star . . . . . . 2·00 2·25
242 $1 Slate pencil urchin . . . . 2·00 2·25
243 $1.30 Globose sea urchin . . 2·75 3·25

59 Cocos Islands

1991. Malay Hari Raya Festival. Multicoloured.
244 45c. Type **59** . . . . . . 1·00 65
245 75c. Island house . . . . . 1·75 2·25
246 $1.30 Islands scene . . . . . 2·50 3·25

60 Child praying

1991. Christmas. Multicoloured.
247 38c. Type **60** . . . . 1·00 70
248 43c. Child dreaming of Christmas Day . . . . . 1·00 70
249 $1 Child singing . . . . . . 2·25 2·25
250 $1.20 Child fascinated by decorations . . . . 2·75 3·50
MS251 118 × 74 mm. 38c., 43c., $1, $1.20, Local children's choir 7·00 8·00
The four values in No. **MS**251 form a composite design.

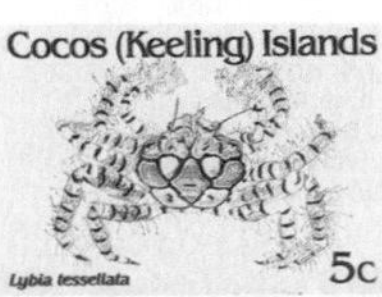

61 "Lybia tessellata"

1992. Crustaceans. Multicoloured.
252 5c. Type **61** . . . . 90 1·10
253 10c. "Pilodius areolatus" . . 1·40 1·40
254 20c. "Trizopagurus strigatus" 1·60 1·60
255 30c. "Lophozozymus pulchellus" . . . . 2·00 2·00
256 40c. "Thalamitoides quadridens" . . . . 2·00 2·00
257 45c. "Calcinus elegans" (vert) 2·00 2·00
258 50c. "Clibarius humilis" . . . 2·25 2·25
259 60c. "Trapezia rufopunctata" (vert) . . . . 2·50 2·50
260 80c. "Pylopaguropsis magnimanus" (vert) . . . 2·75 3·00
261 $1 "Trapezia ferruginea" (vert) . . . . 2·75 3·00
262 $2 "Trapezia guttata" (vert) 3·75 4·50
263 $3 "Trapezia cymodoce" (vert) . . . . 4·25 4·50

62 "Santa Maria"
64 R.A.F. Supermarine Spitfires on Island Airstrip

63 Buff-banded Rail searching for Food

1992. 500th Anniv of Discovery of America by Columbus.
264 **62** $1.05 multicoloured . . . 2·75 3·00

1992. Endangered Species. Buff-banded Rail. Mult.
265 10c. Type **63** 70 85
266 15c. Banded rail with chick 90 1·10
267 30c. Two rails drinking . . . 1·25 1·40
268 45c. Rail and nest . . . . . 1·50 1·60
MS269 165 × 78 mm. 45c. Two rails by pool; 85c. Chick hatching; $1.20, Head of rail . . . . . . 8·00 8·00

1992. 50th Anniv of Second World War. Mult.
270 45c. Type **64** . . . . 2·00 1·25
271 85c. Mitsubishi A6M Zero-Sen aircraft bombing Kampong . . . . 2·75 3·50
272 $1.20 R.A.F. Short Sunderland flying boat . . 3·25 4·25

65 Waves breaking on Reef
66 "Lobophyllia hemprichii"

1992. Christmas. Multicoloured.
273 40c. Type **65** . . . . 1·25 70
274 80c. Direction Island . . . . 2·75 3·00
275 $1 Moorish idols (fish) and coral . . . . 2·75 3·00

1993. Corals. Multicoloured.
276 45c. Type **66** 75 55
277 85c. "Pocillopora eydouxi" 1·25 1·75
278 $1.05 "Fungia scutaria" . . . 1·75 2·00
279 $1.20 "Sarcophyton sp" . . . 1·75 2·25

67 Plastic 5r. Token
68 Primary School Pupil

1993. Early Cocos (Keeling) Islands Currency. Multicoloured.
280 45c. Type **67** . . . . 1·50 80
281 85c. 1968 1r. plastic token . . 2·00 2·50
282 $1.05 1977 150r. commemorative gold coin 2·50 2·75
283 $1.20 1910 plastic token . . . 2·50 3·00

1993. Education. Multicoloured.
284 5c. Type **68** 50 85
285 45c. Secondary school pupil 1·00 60
286 85c. Learning traditional crafts . . . . 2·00 2·25
287 $1.05 Learning office skills 2·50 3·00
288 $1.20 Seaman training . . . 3·00 3·25

69 Lifeboat and Crippled Yacht

1993. Air-Sea Rescue. Multicoloured.
289 45c. Type **69** . . . . 2·25 1·25
290 85c. Israeli Aircraft Industry Westwind Seascan (aircraft) 3·25 3·50
291 $1.05 "R.J. Hawke" (ferry) 3·50 4·75
MS292 135 × 61 mm. Nos. 289/91 8·00 8·50

70 Peace Doves
71 Rectangle Triggerfish and Coral

1993. Christmas.
293 **70** 40c. multicoloured . . . . 1·50 80
294 80c. multicoloured . . . . 2·75 3·25
295 $1 multicoloured . . . . . 2·75 3·25

1994. Transfer of Postal Service to Australia Post. Multicoloured.
296 5c. Type **71** 35 45
297 5c. Three rectangle triggerfish and map section 35 45
298 5c. Two rectangle triggerfish and map section 35 45
299 5c. Two rectangle triggerfish, map section and red coral 35 45
300 5c. Rectangle triggerfish with red and brown corals . . . 35 45
301 10c. Green turtles on beach 35 45
302 10c. Two green turtles . . . 35 45
303 10c. Crowd of young green turtles 35 45
304 10c. Green turtle and map section 35 45
305 10c. Green turtle, pyramid butterflyfish and map section 35 45
306 20c. Three pyramid butterflyfish and map section 55 65
307 20c. Pyramid butterflyfish with brown coral 55 65
308 20c. Two pyramid butterflyfish and coral . . 55 65
309 20c. Three pyramid butterflyfish and coral . . 55 65
310 20c. Coral, pyramid butterflyfish and map section 55 65
311 45c. Jukongs with map of airport 60 70
312 45c. Two jukongs with red or blue sails and map section 60 70
313 45c. Jukong in shallows . . . 60 70
314 45c. Two jukongs with red or yellow sails and map section 60 70
315 45c. Two jukongs, one with blue jib, and map section 60 70
Nos. 296/315 were printed together, se-tenant, with the backgrounds forming a composite map.

72 Prabu Abjasa Puppet
73 Angel playing Harp

1994. Shadow Puppets. Multicoloured.
316 45c. Type **72** 65 50
317 90c. Prabu Pandu . . . . . 1·25 1·50
318 $1 Judistra . . . . 1·40 1·50
319 $1.35 Abimanju . . . . . . 1·50 2·00

1994. Seasonal Festivals. Multicoloured.
320 40c. Type **73** 50 50
321 45c. Wise Man holding gift 55 50
322 80c. Mosque at night . . . . 1·00 1·75

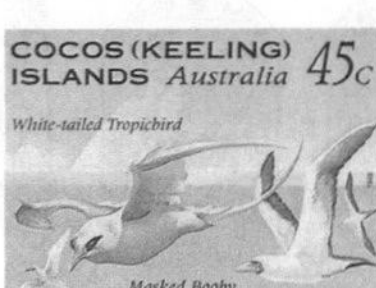

74 White-tailed Tropic Bird and Blue-faced Booby ("Masked Booby")

1995. Sea-birds of North Keeling Island. Multicoloured.
323 45c. Type **74** 75 50
324 85c. Great frigate bird and white tern . . . . 1·00 1·50
MS325 106 × 70 mm. Nos. 323/4 1·75 2·25

75 Yellow Crazy Ant
76 Saddle Butterflyfish

1995. Insects. Multicoloured.
326 45c. Type **75** . . . . 1·00 1·25
327 45c. Aedes mosquito . . . . 1·00 1·25
328 45c. Hawk moth . . . . . . 1·00 1·25
329 45c. Scarab beetle . . . . . 1·00 1·25
330 45c. Lauxaniid fly . . . . . 1·00 1·25
331 $1.20 Common eggfly (butterfly) . . . . 1·50 1·75
Nos. 326/30 were printed together, se-tenant, forming a composite design.

1995. Marine Life. Multicoloured.
332 5c. Redspot wrasse 10 10
333 30c. Blue-throated triggerfish ("Gilded triggerfish") 20 25
334 40c. Type **76** 30 35
335 45c. Arc-eyed hawkfish . . . 60 60
335a 45c. Wideband fusilier . . . 30 35
335b 45c. Striped surgeonfish . . 30 35
335c 45c. Orangeband surgeonfish 30 35
335d 45c. Indo-Pacific sergeant 30 35
335e 70c. Crowned squirrelfish 50 55
336 75c. Orange-pine unicornfish 55 60
337 80c. Blue tang 60 65
338 85c. Juvenile twin-spotted wrasse ("Humpback wrasse") 60 65
339 90c. Threadfin butterflyfish 65 70
339a 95c. Sixstripe wrasse 70 75
340 $1 Bluestripe snapper . . . 70 75
341 $1.05 Longnosed butterflyfish 75 80
342 $1.20 Freckled hawkfish . . 85 90
343 $2 Powder-blue surgeonfish 1·40 1·50
343a $5 Goldback anthias . . . 3·50 3·75

77 Members of Malay Community
78 Black Rhinoceros with Calf

1996. Hari Raya Puasa Festival. Multicoloured.
344 45c. Type **77** 65 60
345 75c. Beating drums . . . . . 1·25 1·50
346 85c. Preparing festival meal 1·25 1·75

1996. Cocos Quarantine Station. Multicoloured.
347 45c. Type **78** . . . . 1·00 1·00
348 50c. Alpacas . . . . 1·00 1·50
349 $1.05 Boran cattle . . . . . 1·50 2·50
350 $1.20 Ostrich with chicks . . 1·75 2·50

79 Dancers and Tambourine
80 "Wrapped Present" (Lazina Brian)

1997. Hari Raya Puasa Festival. Multicoloured.
351 45c. Type **79** 65 60
352 75c. Girl clapping and sailing dinghies . . . . 1·00 1·60
353 85c. Dancers on beach and food . . . . 1·25 1·60

1998. Hari Raya Puasa Festival. Paintings by children. Multicoloured.
354 45c. Type **80** 80 85
355 45c. "Mosque" (Azran Jim) 80 85
356 45c. "Cocos Malay Woman" (Kate Gossage) 80 85
357 45c. "Yacht" (Matt Harber) 80 85
358 45c. "People dancing" (Rakin Chongkin) 80 85

81 Preparing Food on Beach

1999. Hari Raya Puasa Festival. Multicoloured.
359 45c. Type **81** 65 75
360 45c. Woman with child and jukongs on beach 65 75
361 45c. Jukongs and palm fronds 65 75
362 45c. Two men watching jukongs 65 75
363 45c. Jukong and white flowers 65 75

82 Jukong (Cocos sailing boat)

1999. Island Wildlife. Multicoloured.
364 5c. Type **82** 50 60
365 5c. Bennett's and ornate butterflyfish 50 60
366 5c. Green and hawksbill turtles 50 60
367 5c. Yellow-tailed anemonefish and various butterflyfish 50 60
368 5c. Hump-headed wrasse 50 60
369 10c. Yacht, Direction Island 50 60
370 10c. Black-backed butterflyfish 50 60
371 10c. Moorish idols 50 60
372 10c. "Pseudoanthias cooperi" (fish) 50 60
373 10c. Red-tailed tropic birds 50 60
374 25c. Blue-faced booby 65 75
375 25c. Lesser wanderer (butterfly) 65 75
376 25c. Lesser and greater frigate birds 65 75
377 25c. "Hippotion velox" (moth) 65 75
378 25c. Common eggfly (butterfly) 65 75
379 45c. White tern 75 85
380 45c. Red-tailed tropic bird and great frigate bird 75 85
381 45c. Chinese rose 75 85
382 45c. Meadow argus (butterfly) 75 85
383 45c. Sea hibiscus 75 85

Nos. 364/83 were printed together, se-tenant, with the backgrounds forming a composite design.

83 Ratma Anthony

2000. New Millennium. "Face of Cocos (Keeling) Islands". Multicoloured.
384 45c. Type **83** 60 70
385 45c. Nakia Haji Dolman (schoolgirl) 60 70
386 45c. Muller Eymin (elderly man) 60 70
387 45c. Courtney Press (toddler) 60 70
388 45c. Mhd Abu-Yazid (school boy) 60 70

84 Little Nipper (crab)

2000. Endangered Species. Crabs of Cocos (Keeling) Islands. Multicoloured.
389 5c. Type **84** 25 35
390 5c. Purple crab 25 35
391 45c. Smooth-handed ghost crab 55 65
392 45c. Horn-eyed ghost crab 55 65

85 Loggerhead Turtle

2002. Turtles. Multicoloured.
393 45c. Type **85** 60 60
394 45c. Hawksbill turtle 60 60
395 45c. Leatherback turtle 60 60
396 45c. Green turtle 60 60

86 Eastern Reef Egret

2003. Shoreline Birds. Multicoloured.
397 50c. Type **86** 55 55
398 50c. Sooty tern 55 55
399 50c. Ruddy turnstone 55 55
400 50c. Whimbrel 55 55

Nos. 397/400 were printed together, *se-tenant*, forming a composite background design of a shoreline.

87 Queen Elizabeth II and Cocos Malay Musicians

2004. 50th Anniv of Royal Tour to Australia. Visit of Queen Elizabeth II to Cocos (Keeling) Islands. Multicoloured.
401 50c. Type **87** 40 45
402 50c. Queen and *Gothic* (liner acting as Royal Yacht) 40 45
403 $1 Queen and Clunies Ross (Oceania) House 85 90
404 $1.45 Queen and model jukong (Cocos sailing boat) 1·20 1·30
MS405 135 × 72 mm. Nos. 401/4 2·40 2·60

OFFICIAL STAMPS

1991. No. 182 surch **OFFICIAL PAID MAINLAND.**
O1 (43c.) on 90c. Coconut palm and mature nuts † 90·00

No. O1 was not sold to the public in unused condition.

COLOMBIA Pt. 20

A republic in the N.W. of South America. Formerly part of the Spanish Empire, Colombia became independent in 1819. The constituent states became the Granadine Confederation in 1858. The name was changed to the United States of New Granada in 1861, and the name Colombia was adopted later the same year.

100 centavos = 1 peso.

Prices. For the early issues prices in the used column are for postmarked copies, pen-cancellations are generally worth less.

1 3

1859. Imperf.
1 **1** 2½c. green 70·00 80·00
2 5c. blue 70·00 70·00
8 5c. slate 55·00 45·00
9 10c. yellow 45·00 40·00
5 20c. blue 70·00 48·00
6 1p. red 48·00 80·00

1861. Imperf.
11 **3** 2½c. black £1000 £400
12 5c. yellow £160 £120
13 10c. blue £650 £120
14 20c. red £350 £150
15 1p. red £800 £250

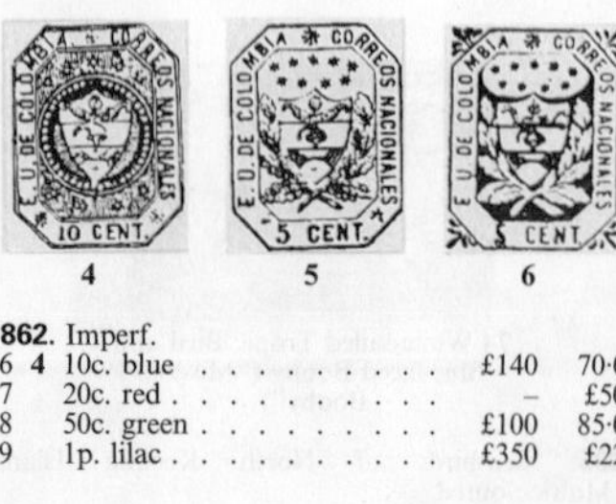

4 5 6

1862. Imperf.
16 **4** 10c. blue £140 70·00
17 20c. red – £500
18 50c. green £100 85·00
19 1p. lilac £350 £225

1862. Imperf.
21 **5** 5c. orange 55·00 42·00
24 10c. blue 90·00 13·50
23 20c. red £130 35·00
25 50c. green £150 £110

1863. Imperf.
26 **6** 5c. orange 42·00 32·00
27 10c. blue 32·00 13·50
28 20c. red 65·00 32·00
29 50c. green 55·00 32·00
30 1p. mauve £275 £110

7 8 9

1865. Imperf.
31 **7** 1c. red 8·00 8·00
32 **8** 2½c. black on lilac 20·00 13·50
33 **9** 5c. orange 35·00 17·00
34 10c. violet 40·00 6·00
35 20c. blue 45·00 13·50
37 50c. green 60·00 32·00
38 1p. red 70·00 13·50

10 12 19

1865. Imperf.
39 **10** 25c. black on blue 45·00 35·00
40 50c. black on yellow 35·00 40·00
41 1p. black on red £110 £100

1866. Imperf. Various Arms Designs.
44 **12** 5c. orange 42·00 25·00
45 – 10c. lilac 13·00 6·00
46 – 20c. blue 27·00 15·00
47 – 50c. green 10·50 10·50
48 – 1p. red 60·00 20·00
49 – 5p. black on green – £130
50 – 10p. black on red £275 £120

1868. Arms (various frames) inscr "ESTADOS UNIDOS DE COLOMBIA". Imperf.
51 **19** 5c. yellow 60·00 42·00
52 10c. lilac 1·25 70
54 20c. blue 1·25 45
55 50c. green 1·25 85
57 1p. red 3·00 1·25

24 25 26 27 28 30

1869. Imperf.
58 **24** 2½c. black on violet 3·50 1·40

1870. Imperf.
59a **25** 1c. green 3·00 2·10
60 1c. red 2·10 2·10
61 **26** 2c. brown 45 45
62 **27** 5c. orange 55 35
65a **28** 10c. mauve 55 25
67 25c. black on blue 6·50 6·00
87 25c. green 15·00 15·00

1870. Different frames. Imperf.
69 **30** 5p. black on green 5·00 4·25
71 10p. black on red 5·50 3·25

See also Nos. 118/19.

32 Andean Condor

33

35

1876. Imperf.
84 **32** 5c. violet 5·75 1·90
85 **33** 10c. brown 90 25
86 – 20c. blue 1·10 35

DESIGN: 20c. As Type **33** but with different frame.

1881. Imperf.
93 **35** 1c. green 2·75 1·75
99 2c. red 80 65
100 5c. blue 1·75 45
101 10c. purple 1·25 85
97 20c. black 1·40 55

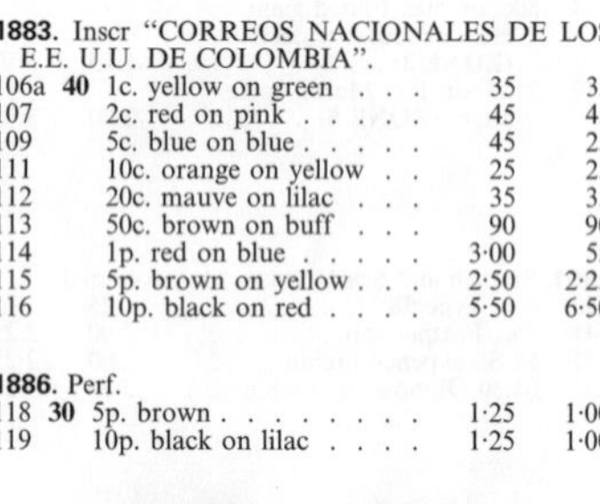

39 40

1881. Imperf.
102 **39** 1c. black on green 1·25 1·25
103 2c. black on rose 1·25 1·25
104 5c. black on lilac 1·75 75

1883. Inscr "CORREOS NACIONALES DE LOS E.E. U.U. DE COLOMBIA".
106a **40** 1c. yellow on green 35 35
107 2c. red on pink 45 45
109 5c. blue on blue 45 25
111 10c. orange on yellow 25 25
112 20c. mauve on lilac 35 35
113 50c. brown on buff 90 90
114 1p. red on blue 3·00 55
115 5p. brown on yellow 2·50 2·25
116 10p. black on red 5·50 6·50

1886. Perf.
118 **30** 5p. brown 1·25 1·00
119 10p. black on lilac 1·25 1·00

42

43 Gen. Sucre

44 Bolivar

46 Gen. Nerino

1886.
120 **42** 1c. green 1·75 60
121 **43** 2c. red on pink 75 75
124 **44** 5c. blue on blue 2·10 15
125 – 10c. orange (Pres. Nunez) 1·40 25
126 **46** 20c. violet on lilac ("REPULICA") 90 35
137 20c. violet on lilac ("REPUBLICA") 1·10 50
130 **42** 50c. brown on buff 40 45
132 1p. mauve 2·10 1·00
133 5p. brown 8·50 5·00
134 5p. black 10·00 7·50
135 10p. black on pink 16·00 4·25

See also Nos. 162/4a.

48 51 50

1890.
143 **48** 1c. green on green 2·50 85
144 **51** 2c. red on pink 70 50
145 **50** 5c. blue on blue 55 20
147 **51** 10c. brown on yellow 55 20
148 20c. violet 1·60 1·60

See also Nos. 149, etc.

53 54 55

58 61 75

1892.
149b 48 1c. red on yellow 15 10
150 53 2c. red on rose . . . . . 9·00 9·00
151a 2c. green 15 10
152a 50 5c. black on brown . . . 6·50 20
153 54 5c. brown on brown . . . 20 20
155 51 10c. brown on red . . . 20 20
156 55 20c. brown on blue . . . 20 20
159 42 50c. violet on lilac 35 20
161 58 1p. blue on green 85 20
162 42 5p. red on pink . . . . . 9·00 1·25
164 10p. blue . . . . 7·50 1·25

1898.
171 61 1c. red on yellow 25 25
172 5c. brown on brown . . . 25 25
173 10c. brown on red . . . . 3·25 1·25
174 50c. blue on lilac . . . . . 1·00 75

For stamps showing map of Panama and inscr "COLOMBIA" see Panama Nos. 5/18.

For provisionals issued at Cartagena during the Civil War, 1899–1902, see list in Stanley Gibbons Stamp Catalogue Part 20 (South America).

1902. Arms in various frames. Imperf or perf.
259 75 ½c. brown 85 85
260 1c. green . . . . 2·50 2·10
192 2c. black on red 15 15
261 2c. blue 60 35
193 4c. red on green 15 15
194 4c. blue on green 20 20
195 5c. green on green 15 15
196 5c. blue on blue 10 10
262 5c. red 60 60
197 10c. black on pink 15 15
263 10c. mauve 85 25
198 20c. brown on brown . . . 15 15
199 20c. blue on brown 20 20
200 50c. green on red 45 45
201 50c. blue on red . . . . . 1·50 1·50
202 1p. purple on brown . . . 25 25

82 85 River Magdalena

1903. Imperf or perf.
203 82 5p. green on blue . . . . 9·00 4·25
204 10p. green on green . . . 9·00 9·00
205 50p. orange on red . . . . 45·00 42·00
206 100p. blue on red . . . . 38·00 35·00
Nos. 205/6 are larger (31 × 38 mm).

1902. Imperf or perf.
212 85 2c. green 80 80
213 2c. blue 80 80
214 2c. red . . . . 10·00 10·00
215 – 10c. red 50 50
216 – 10c. pink 50 50
219 – 10c. orange . . . . 8·00 8·00
242 – 10c. blue on brown . . . . 1·75 1·75
243 – 10c. blue on green . . . . 5·00 4·25
247 – 10c. blue on red . . . . . 2·50 2·50
245 – 10c. blue on lilac . . . . . 13·00 13·00
220 – 20c. violet 40 40
221 – 20c. blue . . . . 3·25 3·25
224 – 20c. red . . . . 12·00 12·00
DESIGNS: 10c. Iron Quay, Savanilla, with eagle above; 20c. Hill of La Popa.

88 Gunboat "Cartagena" 89 Bolivar

90 General Pinzon 91 92

1903. Imperf or perf.
225 88 5c. blue . . . . 2·10 2·10
226 5c. brown . . . . 3·25 3·25
227 89 50c. green . . . . 5·00 5·00
228 50c. brown . . . . 4·25 4·25
230 50c. orange . . . . 4·25 4·25
231 50c. red . . . . 3·25 3·25
233 90 1p. brown 90 65
234 1p. red 90 90
235 1p. blue . . . . 3·50 3·25
237 91 5p. brown . . . . 6·00 6·00
238 5p. purple . . . . 3·75 3·75
239 5p. green . . . . 6·00 6·00
240 92 10p. green . . . . 6·50 6·00
241 10p. purple . . . . 14·00 14·00

93 96

97 98 President Marroquin

1902.
248 93 1c. green on yellow 20 20
249 2c. red on pink 20 20
250 5c. blue 20 20
251 10c. brown on yellow . . . 20 20
252 20c. mauve on pink . . . 10 10
253 50c. red on green . . . . 1·00 1·25
254 1p. black on yellow . . . . 3·25 2·50
255 5p. blue on blue . . . . . 20·00 15·00
256 10p. brown on pink . . . . 14·00 11·00

1904.
270 96 ½c. yellow 55 10
274 1c. green 40 10
278 2c. red 40 10
281 5c. blue . . . . 1·00 10
283 10c. violet 45 20
284 20c. black 75 15
286 97 1p. brown . . . . 13·00 1·60
287 98 5p. black and red . . . . 38·00 30·00
288 10p. black and blue . . . 42·00 32·00

102 Camilo Torres 104 Narino demanding Liberation of Slaves

1910. Centenary of Independence.
345 102 ½c. black and purple . . . 35 20
346 – 1c. green 35 10
347 – 2c. red 35 10
348 – 5c. blue . . . . 1·00 25
349 – 10c. purple . . . . 6·50 5·00
350 – 20c. brown . . . . 12·00 7·50
351 104 1p. purple . . . . 75·00 22·00
352 – 10p. lake £300 £200
DESIGNS—As Type **102**: 1c. P. Salavarrieta; 2c. Narino; 5c. Bolivar; 10c. Caldas; 20c. Santander. As Type **104**: 10p. Bolivar resigning.

110 C. Torres 113 Arms 111 Boyaca Monument

123 La Sabana Station 112 Cartagena

1917. Portraits as T **110**.
357 110 ½c. yellow (Caldas) . . . 10 15
358 1c. green (Torres) 10 10
393 113 1½c. brown 45 45
359 110 2c. red (Narino) 10 10
380 113 3c. red on yellow 20 10
394 3c. blue 20 15
360 110 4c. purple (Santander) . . 45 10
395 4c. blue (Santander) . . . 20 10
361 5c. blue (Bolivar) . . . . 2·50 20
396 5c. red (Bolivar) . . . . . 2·50 15
397 113 8c. blue 20 15
362 110 10c. grey (Cordoba) . . . 2·50 20
398 10c. blue (Cordoba) . . . 6·50 35
363 111 20c. red . . . . 1·40 25
399 113 30c. bistre (Caldas) . . . 7·00 25
400 123 40c. brown . . . . 14·00 4·50
364 112 50c. red . . . . 1·60 25
606 50c. red (San Pedro Alejandrino) . . . . . 8·25 3·75
365a 110 1p. blue (Sucre) . . . . 10·00 40
366 2p. orange (Cuervo) . . . 12·00 25
367 5p. grey (Ricaurte) . . . 35·00 10·00
401 5p. violet (Ricaurte) . . . 3·50 35
368 113 10p. brown . . . . 35·00 8·50
402 10p. green . . . . 5·00 90
For similar 40c. see No. 541.

1918. Surch **Especie Provisional** and value.
374 96 0.00½c. on 20c. black . . . 70 10
376 0.03c. on 10c. violet . . . 1·40 35

115 124

1918.
378 115 3c. red 75 10

1918. Air. No. 359 optd **1er Servicio Postal Aereo 6-18-19.**
379 2c. red £2500 £1600

1920. As T **75**, **96** and **113** but with "PROVISIONAL" added in label across design.
381 96 ½c. yellow . . . . 1·10 20
382 1c. green 55 10
383 2c. red 55 20
384 113 3c. green 40 20
385 96 5c. blue 90 25
386 10c. violet . . . . 5·00 1·25
387 10c. blue . . . . 8·50 4·00
388 20c. green . . . . 6·00 3·25
389 75 50c. red . . . . 7·50 2·50

1921. No. 360 surch **PROVICIONAL $003.**
390 $0.03 on 4c. purple 65 20

1921. No. 360 surch **PROVISIONAL $0.03.**
392 $0.03 on 4c. purple . . . . . 2·75 75

1924.
403 124 1c. red 75 25
404 3c. blue 65 25

1925. Large fiscal stamps surch **CORREOS 1 CENTAVO** or optd **CORREOS PROVISIONAL.**
405 1c. on 3c. brown 55 10
406 4c. purple 55 25

127 129 Death of Bolivar (after P. A. Quijano)

1926.
410 127 1c. green 40 10
411 4c. blue 40 10

1930. Death Centenary of Bolivar.
412 129 4c. black and blue 25 10

132 133 Galleon

1932. Air. Optd **CORREO AEREO.**
413 132 5c. yellow . . . . 3·25 3·25
414 10c. purple 80 25
415 15c. green . . . . 1·40 1·40
416 20c. red 80 45
417 30c. blue 80 25
418 40c. lilac . . . . 1·60 55
419 50c. olive . . . . 3·50 2·50
420 60c. brown . . . . 3·50 2·50
421 80c. green . . . . 10·00 8·50
422 133 1p. blue . . . . 8·50 5·00
423 2p. red . . . . 26·00 19·00
424 3p. mauve . . . . 55·00 50·00
425 5p. olive . . . . 75·00 65·00
These and similar stamps without the "CORREO AEREO" overprint were issues of a private air company and are not listed in this catalogue.

1932. Nos. 395 and 399 surch.
427 1c. on 4c. blue 20 10
428 20c. on 30c. bistre . . . . . 7·00 20

137 Oil Wells 138 Coffee Plantation

140 Gold Mining 141 Columbus

1932. 1c. is vert, 8c. is horiz.
429 – 1c. green (Emeralds) . . . 85 10
430 137 2c. red (Oil) 85 10
431 138 5c. brown (Coffee) . . . 85 10
432 – 8c. blue (Platinum) . . . 7·50 25
485 140 10c. yellow (Gold) . . . . 6·50 10
486 141 20c. blue . . . . 21·00 60

142 Coffee 143 Gold

1932. Air.
435 142 5c. brown and orange . . 45 20
436 – 10c. black and red 85 20
437 – 15c. violet and green . . . 40 15
438 – 15c. violet and red . . . 5·00 15
439 – 20c. green and red 85 10
440 – 20c. olive and green . . . 4·00 25
441 142 30c. brown and blue . . . 3·25 10
442 – 40c. bistre and violet . . 1·60 10
443 – 50c. brown and green . . 13·00 1·25
444 – 60c. violet and brown . . 2·50 25
445 142 80c. brown and green . . 15·00 65
446 143 1p. bistre and blue . . . 13·00 70
447 2p. bistre and red . . . . 14·00 1·90
448 – 3p. green and violet . . . 21·00 7·00
449 – 5p. green and olive . . . 50·00 19·00
DESIGNS—As Type **142**: 10c., 50c. Cattle; 15c., 60c. Oil Wells; 20c., 40c. Bananas. As Type **143**: 3p., 5p. Emeralds.

144 Pedro de Heredia 148 Coffee Plantation

147 Oil Wells 151 Allegory of 1935 Olympiad

1934. 400th Anniv of Cartagena.
451 144 1c. green . . . . 1·50 55
452 5c. brown . . . . 2·50 55
453 8c. blue . . . . 1·50 55

1934. Air. 4th Centenary of Cartagena. Surch **CARTAGENA 1533 1933** and value.
454 – 10c. on 50c. brown and green (No. 443) . . . . 3·50 3·50
455 142 15c. on 80c. brn & grn . . 3·50 3·50
456 143 20c. on 1p. bis & bl . . . 5·50 6·00
457 30c. on 2p. bistre and red 6·00 6·00

1934.
458 147 2c. red 10 10
459 148 5c. brown . . . . 3·50 10
460 – 10c. orange . . . . 17·00 10
DESIGN: 10c. Gold miner facing left.

1935. 3rd National Olympiad. Inscr "III OLIMPIADA BARRANQUILLA 1935".
461 – 2c. orange and green . . 75 25
462 – 4c. green 75 25
463 151 5c. yellow and brown . . 75 20
464 – 7c. red . . . . 1·75 1·50
465 – 8c. mauve and black . . . 1·75 1·50
466 – 10c. blue and brown . . . 1·75 1·10
467 – 12c. blue . . . . 1·75 1·90
468 – 15c. red and blue . . . . 4·25 3·00
469 – 18c. yellow and purple . . 5·00 5·00
470 – 20c. green and violet . . . 5·00 3·25
471 – 24c. blue and green . . . 6·00 4·25
472 – 50c. orange and blue . . 6·00 3·75
473 – 1p. blue and olive . . . . 60·00 38·00
474 – 2p. blue and green . . . £100 70·00
475 – 5p. blue and violet . . . £300 £250
476 – 10p. blue and black . . . £650 £500
DESIGNS—VERT: 2c. Footballers; 4c. Discus thrower; 1p. G.P.O.; 2p. "Flag of the Race" Monument; 5p. Arms; 10p. Andean condor. HORIZ: 7c. Runners; 8c. Tennis player; 10c. Hurdler; 12c. Pier; 15c. Athlete; 18c. Baseball; 20c. Seashore; 24c. Swimmer; 50c. Aerial view of Barranquilla.

152 Nurse and Patients

1935. Obligatory Tax. Red Cross.
477 152 5c. red and green . . . . 1·75 45

1935. Surch **12 CENTAVOS.**
478 12c. on 1p. blue (No. 365a) 4·25 1·25

154 Simon Bolivar 155 Tequendama Falls

1937.
487 **154** 1c. green 10 10
488 **155** 10c. red 10 10
489 12c. blue . . . . 3·75 1·25

156 Footballer 157 Discus Thrower

1937. 4th National Olympiad.
490 **156** 3c. green 80 55
491 **157** 10c. red . . . . 3·25 1·60
492 – 1p. black . . . . 30·00 24·00
DESIGN: 1p. Runner (20¼ × 27 mm).

159 Exhibition Palace 161 Mother and Child

1937. Barranquilla Industrial Exhibition.
493 **159** 5c. purple . . . . 1·60 25
494 – 15c. blue . . . . 6·00 3·25
495 – 50c. brown . . . . 17·00 6·00
DESIGNS—HORIZ: 15c. Stadium. VERT: 50c. "Flag of the Race" Monument.

1937. Obligatory Tax. Red Cross.
509 **161** 5c. red . . . . 1·40 55

1937. Surch in figures and words.
510 **156** 1c. on 3c. green 60 55
511 **155** 2c. on 12c. blue 30 30
512 – 5c. on 8c. blue (No. 432) 35 25
513 – 5c. on 8c. blue (No. 397) 35 25
514 **155** 10c. on 12c. blue . . . . 4·25 85

164 Entrance to Church of the Rosary 166 "Bochica" (Indian god)

1938. 400th Anniv of Bogota.
515 – 1c. green 15 15
516 **164** 2c. red 15 10
517 – 5c. black 20 10
518 – 10c. brown 40 25
519 **166** 15c. blue . . . . 3·25 90
520 – 20c. mauve . . . . 3·25 90
521 – 1p. brown . . . . 30·00 25·00
DESIGNS—VERT: 1c. "Calle del Arco" ("Street of the Arch") Old Bogota; 5c. Bogota Arms; 10c. G. J. de Quesada. HORIZ (larger): 20c. Convent of S. Domingo; 1p. First Mass on Site of Bogota.

168 Proposed P.O., Bogota

1939. Obligatory Tax. P.O. Rebuilding Fund.
522 **168** ½c. blue 10 10
564 ½c. purple 10 10
523 ½c. red 10 10
524 1c. violet 10 10
567 1c. orange 10 10
525 2c. green 25 10
526 20c. brown . . . . 3·25 30

1939. Air. Surch **5 cts** or **15 cts** and bar.
527 5c. on 20c. (No. 439) 25 20
528 5c. on 40c. (No. 442) 25 20
530 15c. on 30c. (No. 441) . . . 60 15
531 15c. on 40c. (No. 442) . . . 1·10 25

171 Bolivar

172 Coffee Plantation 173 Arms of Colombia

174 Columbus 175 Caldas 176 La Sabana Station

1939.
533 **171** 1c. green 10 10
535 **172** 5c. brown 10 10
536 5c. blue 10 10
538 **173** 15c. blue . . . . 1·40 10
539 **174** 20c. black . . . . 17·00 30
540 **175** 30c. olive . . . . 5·50 40
541 **176** 40c. brown . . . . 28·00 14·00
For similar 40c. see No. 400.

178 Proposed New P.O., Bogota

1940. Obligatory Tax. P.O. Rebuilding Fund.
542 **178** ½c. blue 10 10
543 ½c. red 10 10
544 1c. violet 10 10
545 2c. green 15 10
546 20c. brown . . . . 1·60 25

179 "Arms and the Law" 180 Bridge at Boyaca

1940. Death Centenary of Gen. Santander.
547 – 1c. olive 20 20
548 **179** 2c. red 25 15
549 – 5c. brown 25 20
550 – 8c. red 90 40
551 – 10c. yellow 45 40
552 – 15c. blue . . . . 1·10 55
553 – 20c. green . . . . 1·40 60
554 **180** 50c. violet . . . . 2·50 2·10
555 – 1p. red . . . . 11·00 10·00
556 – 2p. orange . . . . 35·00 32·00
DESIGNS—VERT: 1c. Gen. Santander; 5c. Medallion of Santander by David; 8c. Santander's statue, Cucuta; 15c. Church at Rosario. HORIZ: 10c. Santander's birthplace, Rosario; 20c. Battlefield at Paya; 1p. Death of Santander; 2p. Victorious Army at Zamora.

181 Tobacco Plant 182 Santander 183 Garcia Rovira

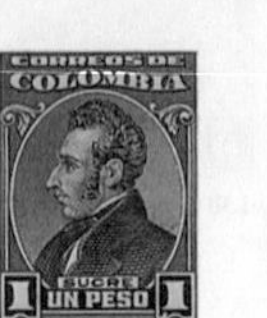

184 General Sucre 185 "Protection"

1940.
557 **181** 8c. green and red 45 30
558 **182** 15c. blue 80 25
559 **183** 20c. grey . . . . 4·00 25
560 – 40c. brown (Galan) . . . 2·50 40
561 **184** 1p. black . . . . 11·00 1·25
562 1p. violet . . . . 2·50 70

1940. Obligatory Tax. Red Cross Fund.
563 **185** 5c. red 25 15

186 Pre-Colombian Monument 187 Proclamation of Independence

1941. Air.
568 **186** 5c. grey 25 10
691 5c. yellow 20 10
742 5c. blue 35 15
747 5c. red 35 15
569 – 10c. orange 25 10
692 – 10c. red 20 10
743 – 10c. blue 35 20
570 15c. red 25 10
693 – 15c. blue 20 10
571 – 20c. green 40 10
694 – 20c. violet 20 10
745 – 20c. blue 45 25
749 – 20c. red 45 25
572 **186** 30c. blue 40 10
695 30c. green 35 10
750 30c. red 75 10
573 – 40c. purple . . . . 1·60 10
696 – 40c. grey 55 10
574 – 50c. green . . . . 1·60 10
697 – 50c. red 65 10
575 – 60c. purple . . . . 1·60 10
698 – 60c. olive 85 10
576 **186** 80c. olive . . . . 4·00 35
699 80c. brown . . . . 1·25 10
577 **187** 1p. black and blue . . . 4·00 20
700 1p. brown and olive . . . 3·00 35
578 – 2p. black and red . . . . 8·00 1·25
701 – 2p. blue and green . . . 3·75 55
579 **187** 3p. black and violet . . . 14·00 4·00
702 3p. black and red . . . . 7·00 3·50
580 – 5p. black and green . . . 35·00 17·00
703 – 5p. green and sepia . . . 20·00 8·50
DESIGNS: As Type **186**: 10c., 40c. "El Dorado" Monument; 15c., 50c. Spanish Fort, Cartagena; 20c., 60c. Street in Old Bogota. As Type **187**: 2p., 5p. National Library, Bogota.

188 Arms of Palmira 189 Home of Jorge Isaacs (author)

1942. 8th National Agricultural Exn, Palmira.
581 **188** 30c. red . . . . 5·00 70

1942. Honouring J. Isaacs.
582 **189** 50c. green . . . . 3·25 35

190 Peace Conference Delegates

1942. 40th Anniv of Wisconsin Peace Treaty ending Civil War.
583 **190** 10c. orange . . . . 3·25 45

1943. Surch **$ 0.0½ MEDIO CENTAVO.**
584 **168** ½c. on 1c. violet 10 10
585 ½c. on 2c. green 10 10
586 ½c. on 20c. brown 20 20

1944. Surch **5 Centavos.**
587 5c. on 10c. orge (No. 460) . . 20 15

193 National Shrine 194 San Pedro, Alejandrino

1944.
592 **193** 30c. olive . . . . 2·10 1·25
593 **194** 50c. red . . . . 2·10 1·25

1944. Surch with new values in figures and words.
594 **172** 1c. on 5c. brn (No. 535) 15 15
595 2c. on 5c. brn (No. 535) 15 15

195 Banner 199 Manuel Murillo Toro

196 Viceroy Solis Building

1944. 75th Anniv of General Benefit Institution of Cundinamarca.
596 **195** 2c. blue and yellow . . . 10 10
597 – 5c. blue and yellow . . . 10 10
598 – 20c. black and green . . . 95 75
599 – 40c. black and red . . . 4·25 3·25
600 **196** 1p. black and red . . . . 8·50 6·50
DESIGNS: As T **195**: 5c. Arms of the Institution; 20c. Manuel Murillo Toro. As T **196**: 40c. St. Juan de Dios Maternity Hospital.

1944.
602 **199** 5c. olive 35 20

201 Proposed P.O., Bogota (202 Stalin, Roosevelt and Churchill)

1945. Obligatory Tax. P.O. Rebuilding Fund.
609 **201** ½c. blue 10 10
610 ½c. brown 10 10
611 ½c. red 10 10
612 ½c. mauve 10 10
613 1c. violet 10 10
614 1c. orange 10 10
615 1c. green 10 10
616 2c. green 10 10
617a 20c. brown 80 10

1945. Victory. Optd with T **202**.
618 **172** 5c. brown 25 15

203 Clock Tower, Cartagena 204 Fort San Sebastian Cartagena

1945.
621 **203** 50c. green . . . . 2·50 80

1945. Air.
622 **204** 5c. grey 20 10
623 – 10c. orange 20 10
624 – 15c. red 20 10
625 **204** 20c. green 25 10
626 – 30c. blue 35 10
627 – 40c. red 55 10
628 **204** 50c. green 70 15
629 – 60c. purple . . . . 3·25 80
630 – 80c. grey . . . . 5·00 55
631 – 1p. blue . . . . 5·00 55
632 – 2p. red . . . . 7·50 2·40
DESIGNS—As Type **204**: 10c., 30c., 60c. Tequendama Falls; 15c., 40c., 80c. Santa Marta. HORIZ (larger): 1p., 2p. Capitol, Bogota.

207 Sierra Nevada of Santa Maria

1945. 25th Anniv of 1st Air Mail Service in America.
633 **207** 20c. green . . . . 1·25 60
634 – 30c. blue . . . . 1·25 60
635 – 50c. red . . . . 1·25 60
DESIGNS: 30c. Junkers F-13 seaplane "Tolima"; 50c. San Sebastian Fortress, Cartagena.

1946. Surch **1** above **UN CENTAVO.**
636 **138** 1c. on 5c. brown 15 15

209 Gen. Sucre 211 Map of South America 212 Bogota Observatory

1946.
638 **209** 1c. blue and brown . . . 20 10
639 2c. red and violet 20 10
640 5c. blue and olive 20 10
641 9c. red and green 45 35
642 10c. orange and blue . . . 35 25
643 20c. orange and black . . 45 25
644 30c. green and red 45 25
645 40c. red and green 45 25
646 50c. violet and purple . . 45 25
The 5c. to 50c. are larger ($23\frac{1}{2} \times 32$ mm).

1946. Obligatory Tax. Red Cross Fund. Optd with red cross.
647 **172** 5c. brown (No. 535) . . . 25 20

1946.
648 **211** 15c. blue 25 10

1946.
649 **212** 5c. brown 10 10
650 5c. blue 10 10

213 Andres Bello 214 Joaquin de Cayzedo y Cuero

1946. 80th Death Anniv of Andres Bello (poet and teacher).
651 **213** 3c. brown (postage) . . . 25 15
652 10c. orange 40 10
653 15c. black 55 10
654 5c. blue (air) 25 15

1946.
655 **214** 2p. turquoise . . . . . . 5·00 45
656 2p. green 65 20

215 Proposed New P.O., Bogota 217 Coffee Plant

1946. Obligatory Tax. P.O. Rebuilding Fund.
657 **215** 3c. blue 15 10

1946. 5th Central American and Caribbean Games, Barranquilla. As No. 621 optd **V JUEGOS C. A. Y DEL C. 1946.**
658 50c. red . . . . 2·50 1·60

1947.
659 **217** 5c. multicoloured 35 10

218 "Masdevallia Nicterina" 220 Antonio Narino

1947. Colombian Orchids. Multicoloured.
660 1c. Type **218** 10 10
661 2c. "Miltonia vexillaria" . . 10 10
662 5c. "Cattleya dowiana aurea" 45 20
663 5c. "Cattleya chocoensis" . . 45 20
664 5c. "Odontoglossum crispum" 45 20
665 10c. "Cattleya labiata trianae" 65 15

1947. Obligatory Tax. Optd **SOBRETASA** in fancy letters.
666 **183** 20c. grey (No. 559) . . . 4·25 1·75
676 **141** 20c. blue (No. 486) . . . 25·00 17·00

1947. 4th Pan-American Press Conf, Bogota.
667 **220** 5c. blue on blue (post) . . 25 15
668 – 10c. brown on blue . . . 35 15
669 – 5c. blue on blue (air) . . 20 10
670 – 10c. red on blue 35 20
PORTRAITS: No. 668, A. Urdaneta y Urdaneta; 669, F. J. de Caldas; 670, M. del Socorro Rodriguez.

222 Arms of Colombia and Cross 223 J. C. Mutis and J. J. Triana

224 M. A. Caro and R. J. Cuervo

1947. Obligatory Tax. Red Cross Fund.
671 **222** 5c. lake 20 10
704 5c. red 20 10

1947.
673 **223** 25c. green 35 15
675 **224** 3p. purple 45 10

225 Bogota Cathedral

1948. 9th Pan-American Congress, Bogota. Inscr as in T **225**.
677 **225** 5c. brown (postage) . . . 15 10
678 – 10c. orange 25 20
679 – 15c. blue 25 20
680 – 5c. brown (air) 15 10
681 – 15c. blue 35 25
DESIGNS—No. 678, National Capitol; 679, Foreign Office; 680, Chancellery; 681, Raphael Court, Capitol.

1948. Obligatory Tax. Savings Bank stamps surch **COLOMBIA SOBRETASA 1 CENTAVO.** Various designs.
682 1c. on 5c. brown 10 10
683 1c. on 10c. violet 10 10
684 1c. on 25c. red 10 10
685 1c. on 50c. blue 10 10

1948. Optd **C** (= "CORREOS"). No gum.
686 **168** 1c. orange 10 10

1948. Optd **CORREOS**.
687 **201** 1c. olive 10 10
688 2c. green 10 10
689 20c. brown 20 10

232 Simon Bolivar 234 Carlos Martinez Silva

233 Proposed New P.O., Bogota

1948.
690 **232** 15c. green 35 15

1948. Obligatory Tax. P.O. Rebuilding Fund.
705 **233** 1c. red 10 10
706 2c. green 10 10
707 3c. blue 10 10
708 5c. grey 10 10
709 10c. violet 20 10
See also Nos. 756 and 758/62.

1949.
710 **234** 40c. red 35 10

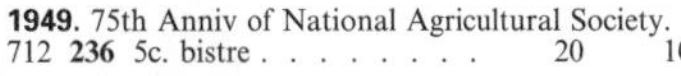

235 Julio Garavito Armero 236 Dr. Juan de Dios Carrasquilla

1949. J. G. Armero (mathematician).
711 **235** 4c. green 25 15

1949. 75th Anniv of National Agricultural Society.
712 **236** 5c. bistre 20 10

237 Arms of Colombia 238 Allegory of Justice

1949. New Constitution.
713 **237** 15c. blue (postage) . . . 20 10
714 **238** 5c. green (air) 15 10
715 – 10c. orange 15 10
DESIGN: 10c. Allegory of Constitution.

239 Tree and Congress Emblem 240 F. J. Cisneros

1949. 1st Forestry Congress, Bogota.
716 **239** 5c. olive 20 10

1949. 50th Death Anniv of Francisco Javier Cisneros (engineer).
717 **240** 50c. blue and brown . . . 1·00 50
718 50c. violet and green . . . 1·00 50
719 50c. yellow and purple . . 1·00 50

241 Mother and Child

1950. Red Cross Fund. Surch with new value and date as in T **241**.
720 **241** 5 on 2c. multicoloured . . 80 35

1950. Obligatory Tax. Optd **SOBRETASA**.
721 **172** 5c. blue 15 10

243 "Masdevallia Chimaera" 244 Santo Domingo Post Office

1950. 75th Anniv of U.P.U.
722 **243** 1c. brown 30 10
723 – 2c. violet 30 10
724 – 3c. mauve 10 10
725 – 4c. green 20 10
726 – 5c. orange 35 10
727 – 11c. red . . . . 1·60 75
728 **244** 18c. blue 80 40
DESIGNS—VERT: 3c. "Cattleya labiata trianae"; 4c. "Masdevallia nicterina"; 5c. "Cattleya dowiana aurea". HORIZ: 2c. "Odontoglossum crispum"; 11c. "Miltonia vexillaria".

245 Antonio Baraya (patriot) 246 Farm

1950.
729 **245** 2c. red 10 10

1950.
730 **246** 5c. red and buff 30 15
731 5c. green and turquoise 30 15
732 5c. blue and light blue . . 30 15

247 Arms of Bogota 248 Map and Badge

1950.
733 **247** 5p. green . . . . 1·60 10
734 – 10p. orange (Arms of Colombia) . . . . . . 2·40 15

1951. 60th Anniv of Colombian Society of Engineers.
735 **248** 20c. red, yellow and blue 35 15

249 Arms of Colombia and Cross 250 Fray Bartolome de Las Casas

1951. Obligatory Tax. Red Cross Fund.
736 **249** 5c. red 20 15
737 **250** 5c. red 20 15
738 5c. green and red 20 10

251 D. G. Valencia 254 Dr. Nicolas Osorio

1951. 8th Death Anniv of D. G. Valencia (poet and orator).
739 **251** 25c. black 40 10

1951. Surch **1 centavo.**
740 **233** 1c. on 3c. blue 10 10

1951. Nationalization of Barranca Oilfields. Optd **REVERSION CONCESION MARES 25 Agosto 1951.**
741 **147** 2c. red 10 10

1952. Colombian Doctors.
751 **254** 1c. blue 10 10
752 – 1c. blue (P. Martinez) . . 10 10
753 – 1c. bl (E. Uriocoechea) . . 10 10
754 – 1c. blue (Jose M. Lombana) 10 10

255 Proposed New P.O., Bogota 256 Manizales Cathedral

1952.
755 **255** 5c. blue 15 10
756 **233** 20c. brown . . . . 8·00 10
757 **201** 25c. grey . . . . 12·00 1·60
758 **233** 25c. green 20 10
759 – 50c. orange . . . . 25·00 14·00
760 – 1p. red 55 25
761 – 2p. purple . . . . 27·00 2·50
762 – 2p. violet 65 10
DESIGN: 50c. to 2p. Similar to T **233** but larger, $24\frac{1}{2} \times 19$ mm.

Owing to a shortage of postage stamps the above obligatory tax types were issued for ordinary postal use.

1952. Obligatory Tax. No. 759 surch.
763 8c. on 50c. orange 15 10

1952. Centenary of Manizales.
764 **256** 23c. black and blue 25 15

1952. 1st Latin-American Congress of Iron Specialists. Surch **1952 1' CONFERENCIA SIDERURGICA LATINO-AMERICANA.** and new value
765 **223** 15c. on 25c. green (postage) 30 20
766 **186** 70c. on 80c. red (air) 75 25

258 Queen Isabella and Columbus Monument

1953. 500th Birth Anniv of Isabella the Catholic.
767 **258** 23c. black and blue 35 35

1953. Air. Optd **CORREO AEREO** or surch also.
768 **233** 5c. on 8c. blue 15 10
769 15c. on 20c. brown 25 10
770 15c. on 25c. green 65 10
771 25c. green 30 10

1953. Air. Optd **AEREO**.
772 **155** 10c. red 15 10

EXTRA RAPIDO. Stamps bearing this overprint or inscription were used to prepay the additional cost of air carriage of inland mail handled by the National Postal Service from 1953 to 1964. Subsequently remaining stocks of these stamps were used for other classes of correspondence. Since the 1920s regular air service for inland and foreign mail has been provided by the Air Postal Service, a separate undertaking which is administered by the Avianca airline and for which the regular air stamps are used.

1953. Air. No. 727 surch **CORREO EXTRA RAPIDO 5 5**.
773 5c. on 11c. red 20 10

262

1953. Air. Fiscal stamps optd as in T **262** or surch also.
774 **262** 1c. on 2c. green 10 10
775 50c. red 10 10

263

1953. Air. Real Estate Tax stamps optd as in T **263**.
776 **263** 5c. red 15 10
777 20c. brown 20 10

1953. Surch.
778 – 40c. on 1p. red (No. 760) 45 10
779 **214** 50c. on 2p. green 45 10

266 Don M. Ancizar **267** Map of South America

1953. Colombian Chorographical Commission Centenary. Portraits inscr as in T **266**.
780 **266** 14c. red and black 40 30
781 – 23c. blue and black 35 20
782 – 30c. sepia and black 35 15
783 – 1p. green and black 15 10

PORTRAITS: 23c. J. J. Triana; 30c. M. Ponce de Leon; 1p. A. Codazzi.

1953. 2nd National Philatelic Exhibition, Bogota. Real Estate Tax stamps surch as in T **267**.
784 **267** 5c. on 5p. mult (post) 35 15
785 – 15c. on 10p. multicoloured (air) 40 25
DESIGN: 15c. Map of Colombia.

1953. Air. Optd **CORREO EXTRA-RAPIDO** or surch also.
786 **233** 2c. on 8c. blue 10 10
787 10c. violet 15 10

269 Fountain, Tunja **271** Map of Colombia

270 Pastelillo Fort, Cartagena

1954. Air.
788 – 5c. purple 30 10
789 – 10c. black 20 10
790 – 15c. red 20 10
791 – 15c. vermilion 20 10
792 – 20c. brown 30 10
793 – 25c. blue 30 10
794 – 25c. purple 30 10
795 – 30c. brown 15 10
796 – 40c. blue 25 10
797 – 50c. purple 25 10
798 **269** 60c. sepia 35 10
799 – 80c. lake 25 20
800 – 1p. black and blue 1·40 20
801 **270** 2p. black and green 3·75 25
802 – 3p. black and red 5·00 55
803 – 5p. green and brown 7·00 1·40
804 **271** 10p. olive and red 8·50 3·50
DESIGNS. As Type **269**—VERT: 5c., 30c. Galeras volcano, Pasto; 15c. red, 50c. Bolivar Monument, Boyaca; 15c. vermilion, 25c. (2) Sanctuary of the Rocks, Narino; 20c., 80c. Nevado del Ruiz Mts., Manizales; 40c. J. Isaacs Monument, Cali. HORIZ: 10c. San Diego Monastery, Bogota. As Type **270**—HORIZ: 1p. Girardot Stadium, Medellin; 3p. Santo Domingo Gateway and University, Popayan. As Type **271**—HORIZ: 5p. Sanctuary of the Rocks, Narino.

1954. Surch.
805 **266** 5c. on 14c. red & black 30 15
806 **256** 5c. on 23c. black & blue 30 15

272 Andean Condor carrying Shield **273**

1954. Air.
807 **272** 5c. purple 50 20

1954. 400th Anniv of Franciscan Community in Colombia.
808 **273** 5c. brown, green & sepia 25 15

1954. Obligatory Tax. Red Cross Fund. No. 807 optd with cross and bar in red.
809 **272** 5c. purple 1·60 40

275 Soldier, Flag and Arms of Republic

1954. National Army Commemoration.
810 **275** 5c. blue (postage) 20 10
811 15c. red (air) 30 10

276

1954. 7th National Athletic Games, Cali. Inscr "VII JUEGOS ATLETICOS", etc.
812 – 5c. blue (postage) 15 10
813 **276** 10c. red 25 10
814 – 15c. brown (air) 25 15
815 **276** 20c. green 60 35
DESIGN: 5c., 15c. Badge of the Games.

277 **278** Saint's Convent and Cell, Cartagena

1954. 50th Anniv of Colombian Academy of History.
816 **277** 5c. green and blue 20 10

1954. Death Tercentenary of San Pedro Claver.
817 **278** 5c. green (postage) 15 10
819 – 15c. brown (air) 30 10
DESIGN: 15c. San Pedro Claver Church, Cartagena.

279 Mercury **280** Archbishop Mosquera

1954. 1st International Fair, Bogota.
821 **279** 5c. orange (postage) 25 10
822 15c. blue (air) 25 10
823 50c. red ("EXTRA RAPIDO") 30 10

1954. Air. Death Cent of Archbishop Mosquera.
824 **280** 2c. green 10 10

281 Virgin of Chiquinquira

1954. Air.
825 **281** 5c. mult (brown frame) 10 10
826 5c. mult (violet frame) 10 10

282 Tapestry presented by Queen Margaret of Austria

1954. Tercentenary of Senior College of Our Lady of the Rosary, Bogota.
827 **282** 5c. black & orge (postage) 25 15
828 – 10c. blue 25 15
829 – 15c. brown 35 15
830 – 20c. brown and black 60 25
832 **282** 15c. black & red (air) 35 15
833 – 20c. blue 55 15
834 – 25c. brown 55 15
835 – 50c. red and black 85 30
DESIGNS—VERT: Nos. 828, 833, Friar Cristobal de Torres (founder). HORIZ: Nos. 829, 834, Cloisters and statue; 830, 835, Chapel and coat of arms.

283 Paz de Rio Steel Works **284** J. Marti

1954. Inauguration of Paz del Rio Steel Plant.
837 **283** 5c. black & bl (postage) 15 10
838 20c. black & green (air) 70 45

1955. Birth Cent of Marti (Cuban revolutionary).
839 **284** 5c. red (postage) 15 10
840 – 15c. green (air) 25 10

285 Badge, Flags and Korean Landscape

1955. Colombian Forces in Korea.
841 **285** 10c. purple (postage) 25 10
842 20c. green (air) 25 15

286 Merchant Marine Emblem **287** M. Fidel Suarez

1955. Greater Colombia Merchant Marine Commemoration. Inscr as in T **286**.
843 **286** 15c. green (postage) 20 10
844 – 20c. violet 85 15
846 **286** 25c. black (air) 35 10
847 – 50c. green 1·40 15
DESIGN—HORIZ: 20, 50c. "City of Manizales" (freighter) and skyscrapers.

1955. Air. Birth Centenary of Marco Fidel Suarez (President, 1918–21).
849 **287** 10c. blue 15 10

288 San Pedro Claver feeding Slaves

1955. Obligatory Tax. Red Cross Fund and 300th Anniv of San Pedro Claver.
850 **288** 5c. purple and red 25 10

289 Hotel Tequendama and San Diego Church

1955.
851 **289** 5c. blue and light blue (postage) 15 10
852 15c. lake and pink (air) 25 10

290 Bolivar's Country House

1955. 50th Anniv of Rotary International.
853 **290** 5c. blue (postage) 15 10
854 15c. red (air) 25 10

291 Belalcazar, De Quesada and Balboa

1955. 7th Postal Union Congress of the Americas and Spain. Inscr as in T **291**.
855 **291** 2c. brn & grn (postage) 10 10
856 – 5c. brown and blue 15 10
857 – 23c. black and blue 2·25 50
859 – 15c. black and red (air) 15 10
860 – 20c. black and brown 25 10
862 – 2c. black and brown ("EXTRA RAPIDO") 10 10
863 – 5c. sepia and yellow 15 10
864 – 1p. brown and slate 12·00 5·50
865 – 2p. black and violet 7·50 6·50
DESIGNS—HORIZ: 2c. (No. 855), Type **291**; 2c. (No. 862), Atahualpa, Tisquesuza, Montezuma; 5c. (No. 856), San Martin, Bolivar and Washington; 5c. (No. 863), King Ferdinand, Queen Isabella and coat of arms; 15c. O'Higgins, Santander and Sucre; 20c. Marti, Hidalgo and Petion; 23c. Colombus, "Santa Maria", "Pinta" and "Nina"; 1p. Artigas, Lopez and Murillo; 2p. Calderon, Baron de Rio Branco and De La Mar.

292 J. E. Caro **293** Salamanca University

1955. Death Cent of Jose Eusebio Caro (poet).
866 **292** 5c. brown (postage) 10 10
867 15c. green (air) 25 10

1955. Air. 700th Anniv of Salamanca University.
868 **293** 20c. brown 15 10

294 Gold Mining, Narino

1956. Regional Industries. Inscr "DEPARTAMENTO", "PROVIDENCIA" (No. 874), "INTENDENCIA" (2p. to 5p.) or "COMISARIA" (10p.).
869 – 2c. green and red 10 10
870 – 3c. black and purple 10 10
871 – 3c. brown and blue 10 10
872 – 3c. violet and green 10 10
873 – 4c. black and green 30 10
874 – 5c. black and blue 20 10
875 – 5c. slate and red 30 10
876 – 5c. olive and brown 30 10
877 – 5c. brown and olive 25 10
878 – 5c. brown and blue 30 10
879 – 10c. black and yellow 25 10
880 – 10c. brown and green 20 10
881 – 10c. brown and blue 20 10
882 – 15c. black and blue 25 10
883 – 20c. blue and brown 30 10
884 – 23c. red and blue 35 15
885 – 25c. black and olive 35 15
886 **294** 30c. brown and blue 30 10
887 – 40c. brown and purple 10 10
888 – 50c. black and green 30 10
889 – 60c. green and sepia 25 10
890 – 1p. slate and purple 90 10
891 – 2p. brown and green 1·90 25
892 – 3p. black and red 1·75 35
893 – 5p. blue and brown 4·00 25
894 – 10p. green and brown 9·50 3·00
DESIGNS—As Type **294**. HORIZ: 2c. Barranquilla naval workshops, Atlantico; 4c. Fishing, Cartagena Port, Bolivar; 5c. (No. 875) View of Port, San Andres; 5c. (No. 876) Cocoa, Cauca; 5c. (No. 877) Prize cattle, Cordoba; 23c. Rice harvesting, Huila; 25c. Bananas, Magdalena; 40c. Tobacco, Santander; 50c. Oil wells of Catatumbo, Norte de Santander; 60c. Cotton harvesting, Tolima. VERT: 3c. (3), Allegory of Industry, Antioquia; 5c. (No. 874) Map of San Andres Archipelago; 5c. (No. 878) Steel plant, Boyaca; 10c. (3), Coffee, Caldas; 15c. Cathedral at Sal Salinas de Zipaquira, Cundinamarca; 20c. Platinum and map, Choco. LARGER (37½ × 27 mm)—HORIZ: 1p. Sugar factory, Valle del Cauca; 2p. Cattle fording river, Meta; 3p. Statue and River Amazon, Leticia; 5p. Landscape, La Guajira. VERT: 10p. Rubber tapping, Vaupes.

295 Henri Dunant and S. Samper Brush

1956. Obligatory Tax. Red Cross Fund.
895 **295** 5c. brown 20 10

1956. Air. No. 783 optd **EXTRA-RAPIDO**.
896 1p. green and black 25 10

297 Columbus and Lighthouse

1956. Columbus Memorial Lighthouse.
897 **297** 3c. black (postage) 15 10
898 15c. blue (air) 20 10
899 3c. green ("EXTRA RAPIDO") 15 10

298 Altar of St. Elisabeth and Sarcophagus of Jimenez de Quesada, Primada Basilica, Bogota
299 St. Ignatius of Loyola

1956. 700th Anniv of St. Elisabeth of Hungary.
900 **298** 5c. purple (postage) 15 10
901 15c. brown (air) 30 15

1956. 400th Death Anniv of St. Ignatius of Loyola.
902 **299** 5c. blue (postage) 15 10
903 5c. brown (air) 20 10

300 Javier Pereira **302** Dairy Farm

1956. Pereira Commemoration.
904 **300** 5c. blue (postage) 10 10
905 20c. red (air) 10 10

1957. Air. No. 874 optd **EXTRA-RAPIDO**.
906 5c. black and blue 20 10

1957. Air. As No. 580 (colours changed) optd **EXTRA-RAPIDO**.
907 5p. black and buff 6·00 3·75

1957. 25th Anniv of Agricultural Credit Bank.
908 **302** 1c. olive (postage) 10 10
909 – 2c. brown 10 10
910 – 5c. blue 15 10
911 **302** 5c. orange (air) 15 10
912 – 10c. green 25 20
913 – 15c. black 25 10
914 – 20c. red 40 30
915 – 5c. brown ("EXTRA RAPIDO") 15 10
DESIGNS: 2c., 10c. Farm tractor; 5c. (No. 910), 15c. Emblem of agricultural prosperity; 5c. (No. 915), Livestock; 20c. Livestock.

303 Racing Cyclist

1957. Air. 7th Round Colombia Cycle Race.
916 **303** 2c. brown 15 15
917 5c. blue 25 25

304 Arms and Gen. Rayes (founder) **305** Father J. M. Delgado

1957. 50th Anniv of Military Cadet School.
918 **304** 5c. blue (postage) 15 10
919 – 10c. orange 20 10
921 **304** 15c. red (air) 20 10
922 – 20c. brown 30 10
DESIGN: 10c., 20c. Arms and Military Cadet School.

1957. Father Delgado Commemoration.
923 **305** 2c. lake (postage) 10 10
924 10c. blue (air) 15 10

306 St. Vincent de Paul with Children **308** Fencer

307 Signatories to Bogota Postal Convention of 1838, and U.P.U. Monument, Berne

1957. Centenary of Colombian Order of St. Vincent de Paul.
925 **306** 1c. green (postage) 10 10
926 5c. red (air) 15 10

1957. 14th U.P.U. Congress, Ottawa and International Correspondence Week.
927 **307** 5c. green (postage) 15 10
928 10c. grey 15 10
929 15c. brown (air) 20 10
930 25c. blue 20 10

1957. 3rd S. American Fencing Championships.
931 **308** 4c. purple (postage) 20 10
932 20c. brown (air) 35 10

309 Discovery of Hypsometry by F. J. de Caldas **310** Nurses with Patient, and Ambulance

1958. International Geophysical Year.
933 **309** 10c. black (postage) 30 10
934 25c. green (air) 45 10
935 1p. violet ("EXTRA RAPIDO") 15 10

1958. Obligatory Tax. Red Cross Fund.
936 **310** 5c. red and black 15 10

1958. Nos. 882 and 884 surch.
937 5c. on 15c. black and blue 10 10
938 5c. on 23c. red and blue 25 20

1958. Air. No. 888 optd **AEREO**.
939 50c. black and green 20 10

313 Father R. Almanza and San Diego Church, Bogota

1958. Father Almanza Commemoration.
940 **313** 10c. lilac (postage) 10 10
941 25c. grey (air) 30 10
942 10c. green ("EXTRA RAPIDO") 10 10

1958. Nos. 780/2 surch **CINCO** (5c.) or **VEINTE** (20c.).
943 **266** 5c. on 14c. red & black 15 10
944 – 5c. on 30c. sepia & black 10 10
945 – 20c. on 23c. blue & blk 25 15

315 Msr. Carrasquilla and Rosario College, Bogota

1959. Birth Centenary of Msr. R. M. Carrasquilla.
946 **315** 10c. brown (postage) 15 10
947 25c. red (air) 20 10
948 1p. blue 60 20

1959. Surch **20c.** and ornament.
949 **258** 20c. on 23c. black & bl 25 15

1959. As No. 826 but with "CORREO EXTRA RAPIDO" obliterated.
950 **281** 5c. multicoloured 10 10

1959. No. 794 surch.
951 10c. on 25c. purple 15 10

318 Luz Marina Zuluaga ("Miss Universe 1959") **320** J. E. Gaitan (political leader)

1959. "Miss Universe 1959" Commemoration.
952 **318** 10c. mult (postage) 10 10
953 1p.20 mult (air) 65 45
954 5p. mult ("EXTRA RAPIDO") 25·00 24·00

1959. No. 873 surch.
955 2c. on 4c. black and green 30 10

1959. J. E. Gaitan Commem. Nos. 956 and 958 are surch on T **320**.
956 **320** 10c. on 3c. grey 15 10
957 30c. purple 25 15
958 2p. on 1p. black ("EXTRA RAPIDO") 60 25

1959. Air. Surch.
960 **269** 50c. on 60c. sepia 5·00 30

323 Capitol, Bogota **324** Santander

1959.
961 **323** 2c. brn & blue (postage) 10 10
962 3c. violet and black 10 10
963 **324** 5c. brown and yellow 15 10
964 – 5c. ultramarine & blue 15 10
965 – 10c. black and red 15 10
966 **324** 10c. black and green 15 10
967 – 35c. black and grey (air) 1·75 10
PORTRAIT (as Type **324**): Nos. 964/5, 967, Bolivar.

1959. Air. Unification of Airmail Rates. Optd **UNIFICADO** within outline of aeroplane.
968 **299** 5c. brown 15 10
969 **302** 5c. orange 35 35
970 **306** 5c. red 20 20
971 **155** 10c. red (No. 772) 10 10
972 – 10c. black (No. 789) 20 10
973 **304** 15c. red 30 10
974 – 20c. brown (No. 792) 20 10
975 – 20c. brown (No. 922) 10 10
976 **308** 20c. brown 25 15
977 – 25c. blue (No. 793) 25 10
978 – 25c. purple (No. 794) 25 10
979 **313** 25c. grey 25 10
980 **315** 25c. red 30 10
981 – 30c. brown (No. 795) 20 10
982 **269** 50c. on 60c. sepia (No. 960) 15 10
983 **315** 1p. blue 35 10
984 **318** 1p.20 multicoloured 45 35
985 **270** 2p. black and green 2·10 20
986 – 3p. black & red (No. 802) 7·00 45
987 – 5p. grn & brn (No. 803) 7·50 45
988 **271** 10p. olive and red 9·50 1·60

326 Colombian 2½c. stamp of 1859 and Postman with Mule

328 2c. Air Stamp of 1918, Junkers F-13 "Colombia" and Lockheed Constellation

1959. Colombian Stamp Cent. Inscr "1859 1959".
989 **326** 5c. grn & orge (postage) . . . 20 15
990 – 10c. blue and lake 40 15
991 **326** 15c. green and red 35 10
992 – 25c. brown and blue . . . 2·25 1·25
993 – 25c. red and brown (air) . . 40 20
994 – 50c. blue and red 55 20
995 – 1p.20 brown and green . . 2·10 1·25
996 – 10c. lilac and bistre "EXTRA-RAPIDO") . . 20 10
DESIGNS—VERT: Colombian stamps of 1859 (except No. 993): No. 990, 5c. and river steamer; 992, 10c. and steam locomotive "Cordoba"; 993, Postal decree of 1859 and Pres. M. Ospina; 996, 10c. and map of Colombia. HORIZ: No. 994, 20c. and Junkers F-13 seaplane "Colombia"; 995, 1p. and Lockheed Constellation airliner over valley.

1959. Air. 40th Anniv of Colombian "AVIANCA" Air Mail Services.
998 **328** 35c. red, black and blue . . 15 10
999 – 60c. black and green . . . 25 15
DESIGN: 60c. As Type **328** but without Colombian 2c. stamp.

329 Eldorado Airport, Bogota

331 A. von Humboldt (after J. K. Stieler)

1960. Air.
1002 **329** 35c. orange and black . . 45 20
1003 60c. red and grey . . . 35 35
1004 1p. blue and grey ("EXTRA RAPIDO") . . 1·00 45

1960. Death Centenary of Alexander von Humboldt (naturalist). Animals.
1005 – 5c. brn & turq (postage) . . 10 10
1006 **331** 10c. sepia and red . . . 10 10
1007 – 20c. purple and yellow . . 20 10
1008 – 35c. brown (air) 45 10
1009 – 1p.30 brown and red . . 1·25 90
1010 – 1p.45 lemon and blue . . 1·00 45
DESIGNS—VERT: 5c. Two-toed sloth; 20c. Long-haired spider monkey. HORIZ: 35c. Giant anteater; 1p.30, Nine-banded armadillo; 1p.45, "Blue" parrotfish.

332 "Anthurium andreanum"

333 Refugee Family

1960. Colombian Flowers.
1011 **332** 5c. mult (postage) . . . 20 10
1012 A 20c. yellow, green & sep 10 10
1013 B 5c. multicoloured (air) 10 10
1014 5c. multicoloured . . . 10 10
1015 A 10c. yellow, green & bl 10 10
1016 C 20c. multicoloured . . 10 10
1017 D 25c. multicoloured . . 35 10
1018 C 35c. multicoloured . . 25 10
1019 B 60c. multicoloured . . 35 20
1020 **332** 60c. multicoloured . . 35 10
1021 1p.45 multicoloured . . 90 35
1022 C 5c. multicoloured ("EXTRA RAPIDO") . . 10 10
1023 D 10c. multicoloured . . . 10 10
1024 **332** 1p. multicoloured . . . 90 55
1025 A 1p. yellow, green & sepia 90 55
1026 B 1p. multicoloured . . . 90 55
1027 C 1p. multicoloured . . . 90 55
1028 D 1p. multicoloured . . . 90 55
1029 C 2p. multicoloured . . . 1·60 80
FLOWERS: A, "Espelitia grandiflora"; B, "Passiflora mollissima"; C, Odontoglossum luteo purpureum"; D, "Stanhopea tigrina".

1960. Air. World Refugee Year.
1030a **333** 60c. grey and green . . 15 15

334 Lincoln Statue, Washington

335 "House of the Flower Vase"

1960. 150th Birth Anniv of Abraham Lincoln.
1032 **334** 20c. blk & mve (postage) 15 10
1033 40c. black & brown (air) 45 25
1034 60c. black and red . . . 25 10

1960. 150th Anniv of Independence.
1035 – 5c. brn & grn (postage) 10 10
1036 **335** 20c. purple and brown 15 10
1037 – 20c. yellow, blue & mve 10 15
1038 – 5c. multicoloured (air) 15 10
1039 – 5c. sepia and violet . . . 15 10
1040 – 35c. multicoloured . . . 20 10
1041 – 60c. green and brown . . 40 10
1042 – 1p. green and red . . . 35 20
1043 – 1p.20 indigo and blue . . 35 20
1044 – 1p.30 black and orange 35 20
1045 – 1p.45 multicoloured . . 65 55
1046 – 1p.65 brown and green 45 35
DESIGNS—VERT: No. 1035, Cartagena coins of 1811–13; 1038, Arms of Cartagena; 1037, Arms of Mompos; 1043, Statue of A. Galan. HORIZ: No. 1039, J. Camacho, J. T. Lozano and J. M. Pey; 1040, 1045, Colombian Flag; 1041, A. Rosillo, A. Villavicencio and J. Caicedo; 1042, B. Alvares and J. Gutierrez; 1044, Front page of "La Bagatela" (newspaper); 1046, A. Santos, J. A. Gomez and L. Mejia.

336 St. Luisa de Marillac and Sanctuary

337 St. Isidro Labrador (after G. Vasquez)

1960. Obligatory Tax. Red Cross Fund.
1048 **336** 5c. red and brown . . . 20 10
1049 – 5c. red and blue 20 10
DESIGN: No. 1049, H. Dunant and battle scene.

1960. St. Isidro Labrador Commem (1st issue).
1050 **337** 10c. mult (postage) . . . 10 10
1051 – 20c. multicoloured . . . 15 10
1052 **337** 35c. multicoloured (air) 20 10
DESIGN: 20c. "The Nativity" (after Vasquez).
See also Nos. 1126/8.

338 U.N. Headquarters, New York

339 Highway Map of Northern Colombia

1960. U.N. Day.
1054 **338** 20c. red and black . . . 15 10

1961. 8th Pan-American Highway Congress.
1056 **339** 20c. brn & bl (postage) 30 25
1057 10c. purple & green (air) 30 25
1058 20c. red and blue . . . 30 25
1059 30c. black and green . . 30 25
1060 10c. blue and green ("EXTRA RAPIDO") 30 25

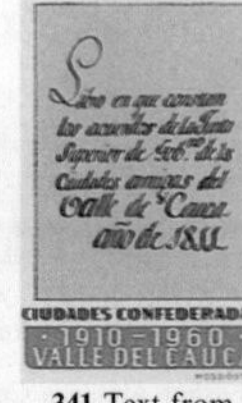

340 Alfonso Lopez (statesman)

341 Text from Resolution of Confederated Cities

1961. 75th Birth Anniv of Alfonso Lopez (President, 1934–38 and 1941–45).
1061 **340** 10c. brn & red (postage) 15 10
1062 20c. brown and violet . . 15 10
1063 35c. brown & blue (air) 35 10
1064 10c. brown and green ("EXTRA RAPIDO") 15 10

1961. 50th Anniv of Valle del Cauca.
1066 – 10c. mult (postage) . . . 10 10
1067 **341** 20c. brown and black . . 15 10
1068 – 35c. brown & olive (air) 30 10
1069 – 35c. brown and green . . 30 10
1070 – 1p.30 sepia and purple 35 15
1071 – 1p.45 green and brown 35 15
1072 – 10c. brown and olive ("EXTRA RAPIDO") 15 10
DESIGNS—HORIZ: 10c. (No. 1066), La Ermita Church, bridge and arms of Cali; 35c. (No. 1068), St. Francis' Church, Cali; 1p.30, Conservatoire; 1p.45, Agricultural College, Palmira. VERT: 10c. (No. 1072), Aerial view of Cali; 35c. (No. 1069), University emblem.

342 Arms and View of Cucuta

345 Arms of Barranquilla

1961. 50th Anniv of North Santander.
1073 – 20c. mult (postage) . . . 15 10
1074 **342** 20c. multicoloured . . . 15 10
1075 – 35c. green & bistre (air) 45 10
1076 – 10c. purple & green ("EXTRA RAPIDO") 15 10
DESIGNS—HORIZ: No. 1073, Arms of Ocana and Pamplona; 1075, Panoramic view of Cucuta. VERT: No. 1076, Villa del Rosario, Cucuta.

1961. Air. Optd **Aereo** (1077) or **AEREO** (others) and airplane or surch also.
1077 **332** 5c. multicoloured 10 10
1078 – 5c. brown & turquoise (No. 1005) 10 10
1079 – 10c. on 20c. purple and yellow (No. 1007) . . 10 10

1961. Atlantico Tourist Issue.
1080 – 10c. mult (postage) . . . 10 10
1081 **345** 20c. red, blue and yellow 15 10
1082 – 20c. multicoloured . . . 15 10
1083 – 35c. sepia and red (air) 45 10
1084 – 35c. red, yellow & green 35 10
1085 – 35c. blue and gold . . . 65 10
1086 – 1p.45 brown and green 45 20
1088 – 10c. yellow and brown ("EXTRA RAPIDO") 15 10
DESIGNS—VERT: No. 1080, Arms of Popayan; 1082, Arms of Bucaramanga; 1083, Courtyard of Tourist Hotel; 1087, Holy Week procession, Popayan. HORIZ: No. 1084, View of San Gill; 1085, Barranquilla Port; 1086, View of Velez.

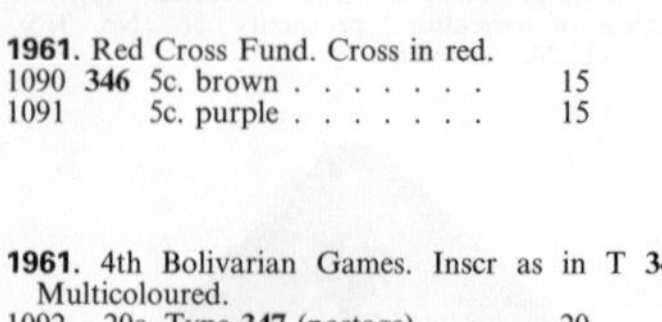

346 Nurse M. de la Cruz

347 Boxing

1961. Red Cross Fund. Cross in red.
1090 **346** 5c. brown 15 10
1091 5c. purple 15 10

1961. 4th Bolivarian Games. Inscr as in T **347**. Multicoloured.
1092 20c. Type **347** (postage) . . 20 10
1093 20c. Basketball 10 10
1094 20c. Running 10 10
1095 25c. Football 20 10
1096 35c. Diving (air) 25 10
1097 35c. Tennis 25 10
1098 1p.45 Baseball 35 15
1099 10c. Statue and flags ("EXTRA RAPIDO") . . 10 10
1100 10c. Runner with Olympic torch ("EXTRA RAPIDO") 10 10

348 "S.E.M." Emblem and Mosquito

349 Society Emblem

1962. Malaria Eradication.
1102 **348** 20c. red & ochre (post) 15 15
1103 – 50c. blue and ochre . . . 15 15
1104 **348** 40c. red & yellow (air) 15 15
1105 – 1p.45 blue and grey . . 40 40
1106 – 1p. blue and green ("EXTRA RAPIDO") 2·75 2·75
DESIGN: 50c., 1p., 1p.45, Campaign emblem and mosquito.

1962. 6th National Engineers' Congress, 1961 and 75th Anniv of Colombian Society of Engineers.
1107 **349** 10c. mult (postage) . . . 20 20
1108 – 5c. red and blue (air) . . 10 10
1109 – 10c. brown and green . . 30 15
1110 – 15c. brown and purple 25 15
1111 **349** 2p. multicoloured ("EXTRA RAPIDO") 1·60 90
DESIGNS: No. 1108, A. Ramos and Engineering Faculty, Cauca University, Popayan; 1109, M. Triana, A. Arroyo and Monserrate cable and funicular railway; 1110, D. Sanchez and first Society H.Q., Bogota.

350 O.E.A. Emblem

351 Mother Voting and Statue of Policarpa Salavarrieta

1962. 70th Anniv of Organization of American States (O.E.A.). Flags multicoloured; background colours given.
1112 **350** 25c. red & blk (postage) 15 10
1114 35c. blue & black (air) 15 10

1962. Women's Franchise.
1115 **351** 5c. black, grey and brown (postage) . . 10 10
1116 10c. black, grey and blue 15 10
1117 5c. blk, grey & pink (air) 10 10
1118 35c. black, grey & buff 25 10
1119 45c. black, grey & green 25 10
1120 45c. black, grey & mauve 25 10

353 Scouts in Camp

354 St. Isidro Labrador (after G. Vasquez)

1962. 30th Anniv of Colombian Boy Scouts and 25th Anniv of Colombian Girl Scouts. As T **353** but without "EXTRA RAPIDO".
1121 **353** 10c. brn & turq (postage) 10 10
1122 15c. brown & red (air) 25 10
1123 – 40c. lake and red 15 10
1124 – 1p. blue and Salmon . . 30 15
1125 **353** 1p. violet & yellow ("EXTRA RAPIDO") 3·50 3·25
DESIGN: 40c., 1p. Girl Scouts.

1962. St. Isidro Labrador Commem (2nd issue).
1126 **354** 10c. multicoloured . . . 10 10
1127 – 10c. mult (air—"EXTRA RAPIDO") 10 10
1128 **354** 2p. multicoloured . . . 2·50 1·50
DESIGN: 10c. (No. 1127), "The Nativity" (after G. Vasquez).

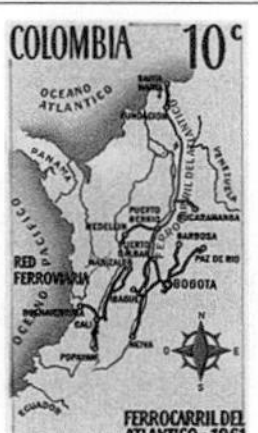

355 Railway Map 356 Posthorn

1962. Completion of Colombia Atlantic Railway.
1129 **355** 10c. red, green and olive (postage) 30 20
1130 – 5c. myrtle & sepia (air) 30 10
1131 **355** 10c. red, turq & bistre 30 20
1132 – 1p. brown and purple . . 4·50 45
1133 – 5p. brown, blue & grn ("EXTRA RAPIDO") 10·00 4·50
DESIGNS—HORIZ: 5c. 1854 steam and 1961 diesel locomotives; 1, 5p. Pres. A. Parra and R. Magdalena railway bridge.

1962. 50th Anniv of Postal Union of the Americas and Spain.
1134 **356** 20c. gold & bl (postage) 15 10
1135 – 50c. gold & green (air) 30 10
1136 **356** 60c. gold and purple . . 20 10
DESIGN: 50c. Posthorn, dove and map.

357 Virgin of the Mountain, Bogota 358 Centenary Emblem

1963. Ecumenical Council, Vatican City.
1137 **357** 60c. mult (postage) . . . 20 10
1138 – 60c. red, yell & gold (air) 10 10
DESIGN: No. 1138, Pope John XXIII.

1963. Obligatory Tax. Red Cross Centenary.
1139 **358** 5c. red and bistre . . . 10 10

359 Hurdling and Flags

1963. Air. South American Athletic Championships, Cali.
1140 **359** 20c. multicoloured . . . 15 10
1141 80c. multicoloured . . . 15 10

360 Bolivar Monument 361 Tennis Player

1963. Air. Centenary of Pereira.
1142 **360** 1p.90 brown and blue . . 10 10

1963. Air. 30th South American Tennis Championships, Medellin.
1143 **361** 55c. multicoloured . . . 25 10

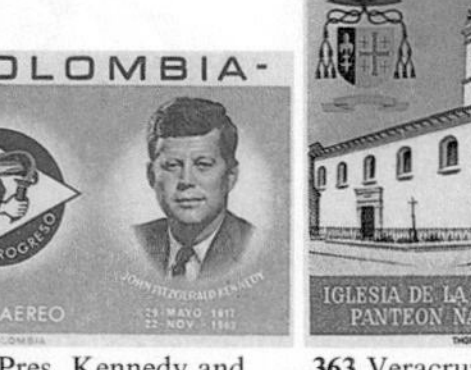

362 Pres. Kennedy and Alliance Emblem 363 Veracruz Church

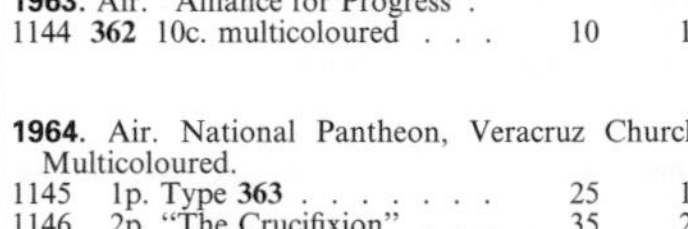

1963. Air. "Alliance for Progress".
1144 **362** 10c. multicoloured . . . 10 10

1964. Air. National Pantheon, Veracruz Church. Multicoloured.
1145 1p. Type **363** 25 10
1146 2p. "The Crucifixion" . . . 35 20

364 Cartagena

1964. Air. Cartagena Commemoration.
1147 **364** 3p. multicoloured . . . 80 55

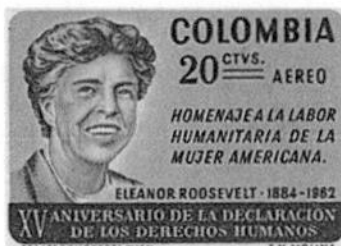

365 Eleanor Roosevelt

1964. Air. 15th Anniv of Declaration of Human Rights.
1148 **365** 20c. brown and olive . . 10 10

366 A. Castilla (composer and founder) and Music

1964. Air. Tolima Conservatoire Commem.
1149 **366** 30c. turquoise & bistre 20 10

367 Manuel Mejia and Coffee Growers' Flag Emblem 368 Nurse with Patient

1965. Manuel Mejia Commemoration.
1150 **367** 25c. brn & red (postage) 10 10
1151 – 45c. sepia & brown (air) 15 10
1152 – 5p. black and green . . 1·60 30
1153 – 10p. black and blue . . 2·10 25
DESIGNS: 45c. Gathering coffee-beans; 5p. Mule transport; 10p. Freighter "Manuel Mejia" at Buenaventura Port. Each design includes a portrait of M. Mejia, director of the National Coffee Growers' Association.

1965. Obligatory Tax. Red Cross Fund.
1154 **368** 5c. blue and red 10 10

369 I.T.U. Emblem and "Waves" 370 Orchid ("Cattleya trianae")

1965. Air. Centenary of I.T.U.
1155 **369** 80c. indigo, red and blue 15 10

1965. Air. 5th Philatelic Exhibition, Bogota.
1156 **370** 20c. multicoloured . . . 20 10

371 Satellites, Telegraph Pole and Map

1965. Air. Cent of Colombian Telegraphs. Mult.
1157 60c. Type **371** 15 10
1158 60c. Statue of Pres. Murrilo Toro, Bogota (vert) . . . 15 10

372 Junkers F-13 Seaplane "Colombia" (1920)

1965. Air. "History of Colombian Aviation". Multicoloured.
1159 5c. Type **372** 10 10
1160 10c. Dornier Wal Do-J (1924) 10 10
1161 20c. Dornier Do-B Merkur seaplane (1926) 20 10
1162 50c. Ford 5-AT Trimotor (1932) 20 10
1163 60c. De Havilland Gipsy Moth (1930) 30 10
1164 1p. Douglas DC-4 (1947) . . 35 10
1165 1p.40 Douglas DC-3 (1944) 20 15
1166 2p.80 Lockheed Constellation (1951) . . . 45 30
1167 3p. Boeing 720B jet liner (1961) 65 55
See also No. E1168.

373 Badge, and Car on Mountain Road

1966. Air. 25th Anniv (1965) of Colombian Automobile Club.
1168 **373** 20c. multicoloured . . . 10 10

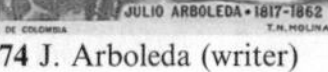

374 J. Arboleda (writer) 375 Red Cross and Children as Nurse and Patient

1966. Julio Arboleda Commemoration.
1169 **374** 5c. multicoloured 10 10

1966. Obligatory Tax. Red Cross Fund.
1170 **375** 5c.+5c. mult 10 10

376 16th-century Galleon

1966. History of Maritime Mail. Multicoloured.
1171 5c. Type **376** 20 10
1172 15c. Riohacha brigantine (1850) 35 15
1173 20c. Uraba schooner 35 15
1174 40c. Steamer and barge, Magdalena, 1900 . . . . 65 15
1175 50c. Modern freighter . . . 1·90 1·00

377 Hogfish

1966. Fishes. Multicoloured.
1176 80c. Type **377** (postage) . . 30 10
1177 10p. Spotted electric ray . . 4·75 3·25
1178 2p. Pacific flyingfish (air) . . 15 20
1179 2p.80 Blue angelfish 50 30
1180 20p. King mackerel . . . . 8·75 5·75

378 Arms of Colombia, Venezuela and Chile 379 C. Torres (patriot)

1966. Visits of Chilean and Venezuelan Presidents.
1181 **378** 40c. mult (postage) . . . 10 10
1182 1p. multicoloured (air) 25 10
1183 1p.40 multicoloured . . 25 10

1967. Famous Colombians.
1184 **379** 25c. vio & yell (postage) 10 10
1185 – 60c. purple and yellow 10 10
1186 – 1p. green and yellow . . 35 10
1187 – 80c. blue & yellow (air) 15 10
1188 – 1p.70 black and yellow 30 10
PORTRAITS: 60c. J. T. Lozano (naturalist); 80c. Father F. R. Mejia (scholar); 1p. F. A. Zea (writer); 1p.70, J. J. Casas (diplomat).

380 Map of Signatory Countries

1967. "Declaration of Bogota".
1189 **380** 40c. mult (postage) . . . 15 10
1190 60c. multicoloured . . . 15 10
1191 3p. multicoloured (air) 30 15

381 "Monochaetum" and Bee

1967. National Orchid Congress and Tropical Flora and Fauna Exhibition, Medellin. Multicoloured.
1192 25c. Type **381** (postage) . . 10 10
1193 2p. "Passiflora vitifolia" and butterfly 45 35
1194 1p. "Cattleya dowiana" (vert) (air) 15 10
1195 1p.20 "Masdevallia coccinea" (vert) 10 10
1196 5p. "Catasetum macrocarpum" and bee 55 10

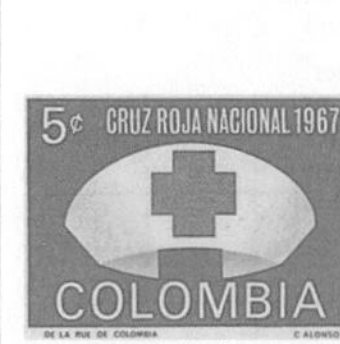

382 Nurse's Cap 383 Lions Emblem

1967. Obligatory Tax. Red Cross Fund.
1198 **382** 5c. red and blue 10 10

1967. 50th Anniv of Lions International.
1199 **383** 10p. mult (postage) . . . 1·40 35
1200 25c. multicoloured (air) 15 10

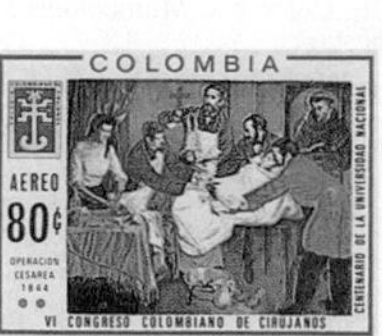

384 "Caesarean Operation, 1844" (from painting by Grau) 385 S.E.N.A. Emblem

1967. Air. 6th Colombian Surgeons' Congress, Bogota and Centenary of National University.
1201 **384** 80c. multicoloured . . . 15 10

1967. 10th Anniv of National Apprenticeship Service.
1202 **385** 5p. black, gold and green (postage) . . . . . . 1·25 20
1203 2p. black, gold and red (air) 20 10

386 Calima Diadem
387 Radio Antenna

1967. Administrative Council of U.P.U. Consultative Commission of Postal Studies. Main design and lower inscr in brown and gold.
1204 **386** 1p.60 pur (postage) . . . 15 10
1205 – 3p. blue 35 10
1206 – 30c. red (air) 20 10
1207 – 5p. red 90 20
1208 – 20p. violet . . . . . . 7·00 4·25
DESIGNS (Colombian archaeological treasures) VERT: 30c. Chief's head-dress; 5p. Cauca breastplate; 20p. Quimbaya jug. HORIZ: 3p. Tolima anthropomorphic figure and postal "pigeon on globe" emblem.

1968. "21 Years of National Telecommunications Services". Inscr "1947–1968".
1210 **387** 50c. mult (postage) . . . 15 10
1211 – 1p. multicoloured . . . 30 10
1212 – 50c. mult (air) 15 10
1213 – 1p. yellow, grey & blue 30 10
DESIGNS: No. 1211, Communications network; 1212, Diagram; 1213, Satellite.

388 The Eucharist

389 "St. Augustine" (Vasquez)

1968. 39th International Eucharistic Congress, Bogota (1st issue).
1214 **388** 60c. mult (postage) . . . 15 10
1215 80c. multicoloured (air) 15 10
1216 3p. multicoloured . . . 35 10

1968. 39th International Eucharistic Congress, Bogota (2nd Issue). Multicoloured.
1217 25c. Type **389** (postage) . . 10 10
1218 60c. "Gathering Manna" (Vasquez) 10 10
1219 1p. "Betrothal of the Virgin and St. Joseph" (B. de Figueroa) 10 10
1220 5p. "La Lechuga" (Jesuit Statuette) 25 20
1221 10p. "Pope Paul VI" (painting by Franciscan Missionary Mothers) . . 55 10
1222 80c. "The Last Supper" (Vasquez) (horiz) (air) . . 15 10
1223 1p. "St. Francis Xavier's Sermon" (Vasquez) . . . 25 10
1224 2p. "Elijah's Dream" (Vasquez) 10 10
1225 3p. As No. 1220 . . . . . 25 10
1226 20p. As No. 1221 . . . . . 3·25 90

390 Pope Paul VI

391 University Arms

1968. Pope Paul's Visit to Colombia. Multicoloured.
1228 25c. Type **390** (postage) . . 15 10
1229 80c. Reception podium (horiz) (air) 15 10
1230 1p.20 Pope Paul giving Blessing 10 10
1231 1p.80 Cathedral, Bogota . . 10 15

1968. Centenary of National University.
1232 **391** 80c. mult (postage) . . 10 10
1233 – 20c. red, green and yellow (air) 10 10
DESIGN: 20c. Mathematical symbols.

392 Antioquia 2½c. Stamp of 1858

393 Institute Emblem and Split Leaf

1968. Centenary of First Antioquia Stamps.
1234 **392** 30c. blue and green . . . 10 10

1969. 25th Anniv (1967) of Inter-American Agricultural Sciences Institute.
1236 **393** 20c. mult (postage) . . . 10 10
1237 1p. multicoloured (air) 15 10

394 Pen and Microscope

1969. Air. 20th Anniv of University of the Andes.
1238 **394** 5p. multicoloured . . . 45 10

395 Von Humboldt and Andes (Quindio Region)

1969. Air. Birth Bicentenary of Alexander von Humboldt (naturalist).
1239 **395** 1p. green and brown . . 15 10

396 Junkers F-13 Seaplane and Map

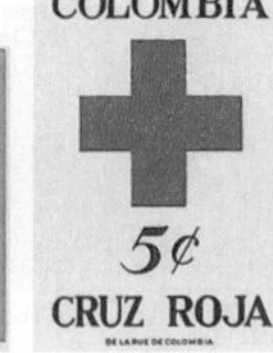

397 Red Cross

1969. Air. 50th Anniv of 1st Colombian Airmail Flight. Multicoloured.
1240 1p. Type **396** 25 15
1241 1p.50 Boeing 720B and globe 30 10
See also Nos. 1249/50.

1969. Obligatory Tax. Colombian Red Cross.
1243 **397** 5c. red and violet . . . 10 10

398 "The Battle of Boyaca" (J. M. Espinosa)

1969. 150th Anniv of Independence. Mult.
1244 20c. Type **398** (postage) . . 15 10
1245 30c. "Liberation Army crossing Pisba Pass" (F. A. Caro) 15 10
1246 2p.30 "Entry into Santa Fe" (I. Castillo-Cervantes) (air) 20 20

399 Institute Emblem

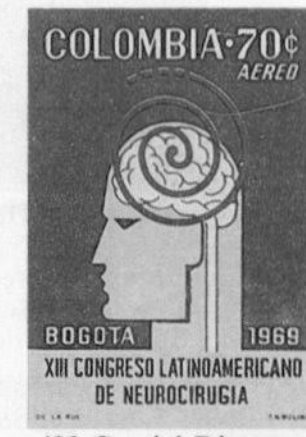

400 Cranial Diagram

1969. Air. 20th Anniv of Colombian Social Security Institute.
1247 **399** 20c. green and black . . 10 10

1969. Air. 13th Latin-American Neurological Congress, Bogota.
1248 **400** 70c. multicoloured . . . 20 10

401 Junkers F-13 Seaplane and Puerto Colombia

402 Child posting Christmas Card

1969. Air. 50th Anniv of "Avianca" Airline. Multicoloured.
1249 2p. Type **401** 40 10
1250 3p.50 Boeing 720B and globe 35 25

1969. Air. Christmas. Multicoloured.
1252 60c. Type **402** 15 10
1253 1p. Type **402** 15 10
1254 1p.50 Child with Christmas presents 45 10

403 "Poverty"

405 National Sports Institute Emblem

404 Dish Aerial and Ancient Head

1970. Colombian Social Welfare Institute and 10th Anniv of Children's Rights Law.
1255 **403** 30c. multicoloured . . . 10 10

1970. Air. Opening of Satellite Earth Station, Choconta.
1256 **404** 1p. black, red & green 40 10

1970. Air. 9th National Games, Ibague (1st issue).
1257 **405** 1p.50 black, yell & grn 25 15
1258 – 2p.30 multicoloured . . 15 20
DESIGN: 2p.30, Dove and rings (Games emblem).
See also No. 1265.

406 Exhibition Emblem

1970. Air. 2nd Fine Arts Biennial, Medellin
1259 **406** 30c. multicoloured . . . 10 10

407 Dr. E. Santos (founder) and Buildings

1970. Air. 30th Anniv (1969) of Territorial Credit Institute.
1260 **407** 1p. black, yellow & grn 15 10

408 U.N. Emblem, Scales and Dove

409 Hands protecting Child

1970. Air. 25th Anniv of United Nations.
1261 **408** 1p.50 yellow, bl & ultram 20 10

1970. Obligatory Tax. Colombian Red Cross.
1262 **409** 5c. red and blue 10 10

410 Theatrical Mask

1970. Latin-American University Theatre Festival. Manizales.
1263 **410** 30c. brown, orange & blk 10 10

411 Postal Emblem, Letter and Stamps

1970. Philatelic Week.
1264 **411** 2p. multicoloured . . . 30 10

412 Discus-thrower and Ibague Arms

1970. 9th National Games, Ibague (2nd issue).
1265 **412** 80c. brown, green & yell 20 10

413 "St. Teresa" (B. de Figueroa)

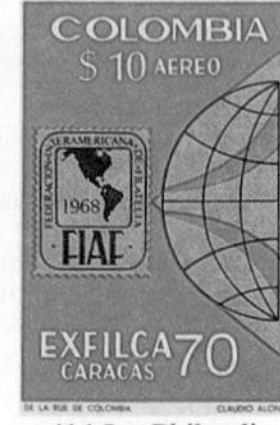

414 Int Philatelic Federation Emblem

1970. St. Teresa of Avila's Elevation to Doctor of the Universal Church. No. 1267 optd **AEREO**.
1266 **413** 2p. mult (postage) . . . 10 10
1267 2p. mult (air) 30 10

1970. Air. "EXFILCA 70" Stamp Exhibition, Caracas, Venezuela.
1268 **414** 10p. multicoloured . . . 1·50 20

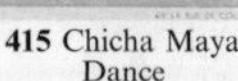

415 Chicha Maya Dance

416 Stylized Athlete

1970. Folklore Dances and Costumes. Mult.
1269 1p. Type **415** (postage) . . . 35 10
1270 1p.10 Currulao dance . . . 35 10
1271 60c. Napanga costume (air) 20 15
1272 1p. Joropo dance 20 10
1273 1p.30 Guabina dance . . . 30 10

1274 1p.30 Bambuco dance . . . 20 10
1275 1p.30 Cumbia dance 20 10

1971. Air. 6th Pan-American Games, Cali (1st issue).
1277 **416** 1p.50 multicoloured . . 35 45
1278 – 2p. orange, green & blk 35 40
DESIGN: 2p. Games emblem.

417 G. Alzate Avendano

1971. Air. 10th Anniv of Gilberto Alzate Avendano (politician).
1279 **417** 1p. multicoloured . . . 15 25

418 Priest's House, Guacari

1971. 400th Anniv of Guacari (town).
1280 **418** 1p. multicoloured . . . 25 10

419 Commemorative Medal

1971. Air. Centenary of Bank of Bogota.
1281 **419** 1p. gold, brown & green 40 20

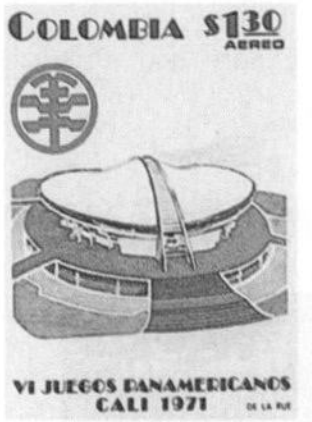

420 Sports Centre **421** Weightlifting

1971. Air. 6th Pan-American Games (2nd issue) and "EXFICALI 71" Stamp Exhibition, Cali. Mult.
1282 1p.30 Type **420** (yellow emblem) 40 30
1283 1p.30 Football 40 30
1284 1p.30 Wrestling 40 30
1285 1p.30 Cycling 40 30
1286 1p.30 Volleyball 40 30
1287 1p.30 Diving 40 30
1288 1p.30 Fencing 40 30
1289 1p.30 Type **420** (green emblem) 40 30
1290 1p.30 Sailing 40 30
1291 1p.30 Show-jumping 40 30
1292 1p.30 Athletics 40 30
1293 1p.30 Rowing 40 30
1294 1p.30 Cali emblem 40 30
1295 1p.30 Netball 40 30
1296 1p.30 Type **420** (blue emblem) 40 30
1297 1p.30 Stadium 40 30
1298 1p.30 Baseball 40 30
1299 1p.30 Hockey 40 30
1300 1p.30 Type **421** 40 30
1301 1p.30 Medals 40 30
1302 1p.30 Boxing 40 30
1303 1p.30 Gymnastics 40 30
1304 1p.30 Rifle-shooting 40 30
1305 1p.30 Type **420** (red emblem) 40 30

422 "Bolivar at Congress" (after S. Martinez-Delgado)

1971. 150th Anniv of Great Colombia Constituent Assembly, Rosario del Cucuta.
1306 **422** 80c. multicoloured . . . 15 10

423 "Battle of Carabobo" (M. Tovar y Tovar)

1971. Air. 150th Anniv of Battle of Carabobo.
1307 **423** 1p.50 multicoloured . . 15 15

424 C.I.M.E. Emblem

1972. 20th Anniv of Inter-Governmental Committee on European Migration.
1308 **424** 60c. black and grey . . . 25 10

425 I.C.E.T.E.X. Symbol

1972. 20th Anniv of Institute of Educational Credit and Technical Training Abroad.
1309 **425** 1p.10 brown and green 20 10

426 Rev. Mother Francisca del Castillo

1972. 300th Birth Anniv of Reverend Mother Francisca J. del Castillo.
1310 **426** 1p.20 multicoloured . . 20 10

427 Soldier and Frigate "Almirante Padilla"

1972. 20th Anniv of Colombian Troops' Participation in Korean War.
1311 **427** 1p.20 multicoloured . . 1·25 15

428 Hat and Ceramics **429** "Maxillaria triloris" (orchid)

1972. Colombian Crafts and Products. Mult.
1312 1p.10 Type **428** (postage) . . 30 10
1313 50c. Woman in shawl (air) 30 10
1314 1p. Male doll 20 10
1315 3p. Female doll 20 25

1972. 10th National Stamp Exhibition and 7th World Orchid-growers' Congress, Medellin. Mult.
1316 20p. Type **429** (postage) . . 5·00 25
1317 1p.30 "Mormodes rolfeanum" (orchid) (horiz) (air) 15 10

430 Uncut Emeralds and Pendant **432** Congo Dance

431 Pres. Narino's House

1972. Colombian Emeralds.
1318 **430** 1p.10 multicoloured . . 30 10

1972. 400th Anniv of Leyva (town).
1319 **431** 1p.10 multicoloured . . 30 10

1972. Air. Barranquilla International Carnival.
1320 **432** 1p.30 multicoloured . . 10 10

433 Island Scene **435** "Pres. Laureano Gomez" (R. Cubillos)

1972. 150th Anniv of Annexation of San Andres and Providencia Islands.
1321 **433** 60c. multicoloured . . . 20 10

1972. Air. No. 1142 surch.
1322 **360** 1p.30 on 1p.90 brn and bl 20 15

1972. Air. Pres. Gomez Commemoration.
1323 **435** 1p.30 multicoloured . . 20 10

436 Postal Administration Emblem

1972. National Postal Administration.
1324 **436** 1p.10 green 15 10

437 Colombian Family

1972. "Social Front for the People" Campaign.
1325 **437** 60c. orange 10 10

438 Pres. Guillermo Valencia **439** Benito Juarez

1972. Air. Pres. Valencia Commemoration.
1326 **438** 1p.30 multicoloured . . 25 10

1972. Air. Death Centenary of Benito Juarez (Mexican statesman).
1327 **439** 1p.50 multicoloured . . 20 10

440 "La Rebeca" Monument **441** "350" and Arms of Bucaramanga

1972. Air. "La Rebeca" Monument, Centenary Park, Bogota.
1328 **440** 80c. multicoloured . . . 25 30
1329 1p. multicoloured . . . 20 10

1972. Air. 350th Anniv of Bucaramanga (city).
1330 **441** 5p. multicoloured . . . 30 10

442 University Buildings **443** League Emblems

1973. Air. 350th Anniv of Javeriana University.
1331 **442** 1p.30 brown and green 25 10
1332 1p.50 brown and blue . . 25 10

1973. 40th Anniv of Colombian Radio Amateurs League.
1333 **443** 60c. red, dp blue & blue 15 10

444 Tamalameque Vessel **445** "Battle of Maracaibo" (M. F. Rincon)

1973. Inauguration of Museum of Pre-Colombian Antiques, Bogota. Multicoloured.
1334 60c. Type **444** (postage) . . 25 10
1335 1p. Tairona axe-head . . . 45 10
1336 1p.10 Muisca jug 30 10
1337 1p. As No. 1335 (air) . . . 40 35
1338 1p.30 Sinu vessel 20 10
1339 1p.70 Quimbaya vessel . . . 25 20
1340 3p.50 Tumaco figurine . . . 50 30

1973. Air. 150th Anniv of Naval Battle of Maracaibo.
1341 **445** 10p. multicoloured . . . 3·25 30

446 Banknote Emblem

1973. Air. 50th Anniv of Republican Bank.
1342 **446** 2p. multicoloured . . . 25 10

1973. Air. No. 1306 optd **AEREO**.
1343 **422** 80c. multicoloured . . . 15 10

448 "Pres. Ospina" (after C. Leudo) **449** Arms of Toro

1973. Air. 50th Anniv of Ministry of Communications.
1344 **448** 1p.50 multicoloured . . 20 10

1973. Air. 400th Anniv of Toro.
1345 **449** 1p. multicoloured . . . 15 10

450 Bolivar at Bombona

1973. Air. 150th Anniv of Battle of Bombona.
1346 **450** 1p.30 multicoloured . . 20 10

451 "General Narino" (after J. M. Espinosa) **452** Young Child

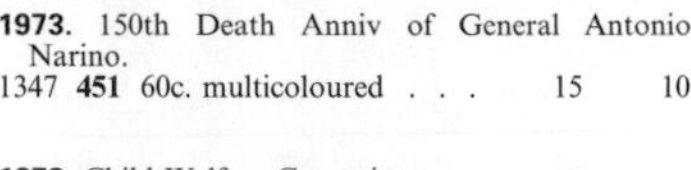

1973. 150th Death Anniv of General Antonio Narino.
1347 **451** 60c. multicoloured . . . 15 10

1973. Child Welfare Campaign.
1348 **452** 1p.10 multicoloured . . 20 10

453 Fiscal Emblem

1974. 50th Anniv of Republic's General Comptrollership.
1349 **453** 80c. black, brown & bl 15 10

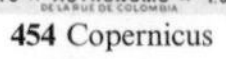
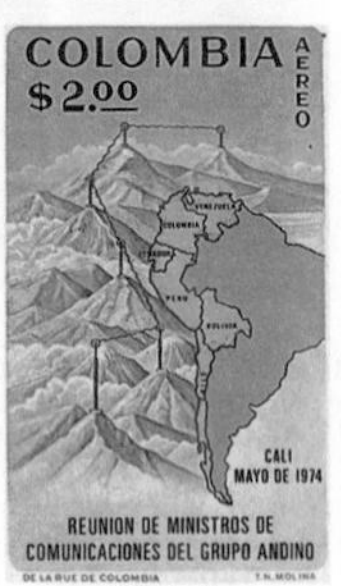

454 Copernicus **455** Andes Communications and Map

1974. Air. 500th Birth Anniv of Copernicus.
1350 **454** 2p. multicoloured . . . 20 15

1974. Air. Meeting of Communications Ministers, Andean Group, Cali.
1351 **455** 2p. multicoloured . . . 10 15

456 Laura Montoya and Cross **457** Television Set with Inravision Emblem

1974. Birth Centenary of Revd. Mother Laura Montoya (missionary).
1352 **456** 1p. multicoloured . . . 15 10

1974. Air. 20th Anniv of Inravision (National Institute of Radio and Television).
1353 **457** 1p.30 black, brn & orge 20 10

458 Athlete

1974. 10th National Games, Pereira.
1354 **458** 2p. brown, red & yellow 20 10

459 Rivera and Statue

1974. 50th Anniv of Novel "La Voragine".
1355 **459** 10p. multicoloured . . . 35 15

460 Aquatic Emblem

1974. Air. 2nd World Swimming Championships, Cali (1975).
1356 **460** 4p.50 blue, turq & blk 30 15

461 Condor Emblem

1974. Air. Centenary of Bank of Colombia.
1357 **461** 1p.50 multicoloured . . 20 10

462 Tailplane

1974. Air.
1358 **462** 20c. brown 10 10

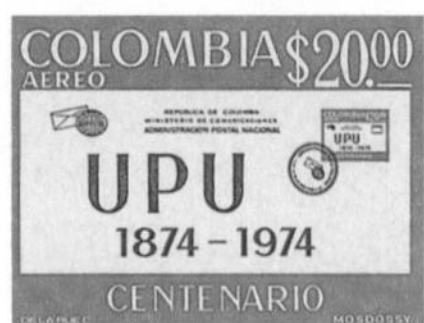

463 U.P.U. "Letter"

1974. Air. Centenary of Universal Postal Union (1st issue).
1359 **463** 20p. red, blue & black 1·10 30
See also Nos. 1363/6.

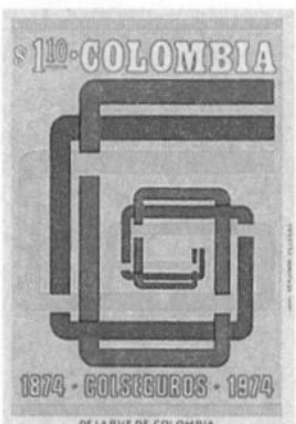

464 General Jose Maria Cordoba **465** "Progress and Expansion"

1974. Air. 150th Anniv of Battles of Junin and Ayacucho.
1360 **464** 1p.30 multicoloured . . 20 10

1974. Centenary of Colombian Insurance Company.
1361 **465** 1p.10 mult (postage) . . 20 10
1362 3p. mult (air) 35 10

466 White-tailed Trogon and U.P.U. "Letter" **467** La Quiebra Tunnel

1974. Air. Centenary of U.P.U. (2nd issue). Colombian Birds. Multicoloured.
1363 1p. Type **466** 75 40
1364 1p.30 Red-billed toucan (horiz) 75 50
1365 2p. Andean cock of the rock (horiz) . . . . 1·50 50
1366 2p.50 Scarlet macaw . . . . 1·50 60
Nos. 1364/6 also depict the U.P.U. "letter".

1974. Centenary of Antioquia Railway.
1367 **467** 1p.10 multicoloured . . 90 35

468 Boy with Ball

1974. Christmas. Multicoloured.
1368 80c. Type **468** 10 10
1369 1p. Girl with racquet . . . 10 15

469 "Protect the Trees"

1975. Air. Colombian Ecology. Multicoloured.
1370 1p. Type **469** 20 10
1371 6p. "Protect the Amazon" 20 15

470 "Wood No. 1" (R. Roncancio)

1975. Air. Colombian Art. Multicoloured.
1372 2p. Type **470** . . . . . . 1·00 30
1373 3p. "The Market" (M. Diaz Vargas) (vert) . . . . . 1·75 30
1374 4p. "Child with Thorn" (G. Vazquez) (vert) . . . 15 10
1375 5p. "The Annunciation" (Santaferena School) (vert) 45 30

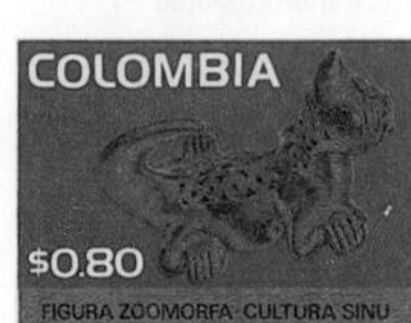

471 Gold Cat

1975. Pre-Colombian Archaeological Discoveries. Sinu Culture. Multicoloured.
1376 80c. Type **471** (postage) . . 20 10
1377 1p.10 Gold necklace 20 10
1378 2p. Nose pendant (air) . . . 40 10
1379 10p. "Alligator" staff ornament . . . . 2·10 35

472 Marconi and "Elettra" (steam yacht) **473** Santa Marta Cathedral

1975. Birth Centenary of Guglielmo Marconi (radio pioneer).
1380 **472** 3p. multicoloured . . . 75 10

1975. 450th Anniv of Santa Marta. Multicoloured.
1381 80c. Type **473** (postage) . . 10 10
1382 2p. "El Rodadero" (sea-front), Santa Marta (horiz) (air) 20 10

474 Maria de J. Paramo (educationalist) **475** Pres. Nunez

1975. International Women's Year.
1383 **474** 4p. multicoloured . . . 25 10

1975. 150th Birth Anniv of President Rafael Nunez.
1384 **475** 1p.10 multicoloured . . 15 10

476 Arms of Medellin **479** Sugar Cane

1975. 300th Anniv of Medellin.
1385 **476** 1p. multicoloured . . . 25 10
See also Nos. 1386, 1388, 1394, 1404, 1419, 1434, 1481/3, 1672/4, 1678/9, 1752, 1758, 1859 and 1876.

1976. Centenary of Reconstruction of Cucuta City. As T **476**.
1386 1p.50 multicoloured 30 10

1976. Surch.
1387 **471** 1p.20 on 80c. mult . . . 15 10

1976. Arms of Cartagena. As T **476**.
1388 1p.50 multicoloured 20 10

1976. 4th Cane Sugar Export and Production Congress, Cali.
1389 **479** 5p. green and black . . 45 10

480 Bogota

1976. Air. Habitat. U.N. Conference on Human Settlements. Multicoloured.
1390 10p. Type **480** . . . . . . 1·10 35
1391 10p. Barranquilla . . . . . 1·10 35
1392 10p. Cali . . . . 1·10 35
1393 10p. Medellin . . . . 1·10 35

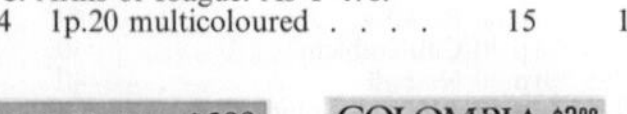

1976. Arms of Ibague. As T **476**.
1394 1p.20 multicoloured 15 10

481 University Emblem and "90" **482** M. Samper

1976. Air. 90th Anniv of Colombia University.
1395 **481** 5p. multicoloured . . . 20 10

1976. Air. 150th Birth Anniv of Miguel Samper (statesman and writer).
1396 **482** 2p. multicoloured . . . 20 10

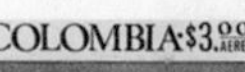

483 Early Telephone **484** "Callicore sp."

1976. Air. Telephone Centenary.
1397 **483** 3p. multicoloured . . . 20 10

1976. Colombian Fauna and Flora. Multicoloured.
1398 3p. Type **484** 75 10
1399 5p. "Morpho sp." (butterfly) 1·25 20
1400 20p. Black anthurium (plant) . . . . 1·10 25

485 Purace Indians, Cauca
486 Rotary Emblem

1976.
1401 **485** 1p.50 multicoloured . . 10 10

1976. 50th Anniv of Colombian Rotary Club.
1402 **486** 1p. multicoloured . . . 10 10

487 Boeing 747 Jumbo Jet

1976. Air. Inaug of Avianca Jumbo Jet Service.
1403 **487** 2p. multicoloured . . . 15 10

1976. 535th Anniv of Tunja City Arms. As T **476**.
1404 1p.20 multicoloured 15 10

488 "The Signing of Declaration of Independence" (left-hand detail of painting, Trumbull)
489 Police Handler and Dog

1976. Bicentenary of American Revolution.
1405 **488** 30p. multicoloured . . . 1·75 1·10
1406 – 30p. multicoloured . . . 1·75 1·10
1407 – 30p. multicoloured . . . 1·75 1·10
DESIGNS: Nos. 1406/7 show different portions of the painting.

1976. National Police.
1408 **489** 1p.50 multicoloured . . 25 10

490 Franciscan Convent

1976. Air. 150th Anniv of Panama Congress.
1409 **490** 6p. multicoloured . . . 20 20

1977. Surch.
1411 **475** 2p. on 1p.10 mult (postage) 25 10
1412 – 2p. on 1p.20 mult (No. 1404) 20 10
1413 **489** 2p. on 1p.50 mult . . . 20 10
1414 **487** 3p. on 2p. mult (air) . . 15 10

494 Coffee Plant and Beans
495 Coffee Grower with mule

1977. Air. Coffee Production.
1416 **494** 3p. multicoloured . . . 15 10
1416a 3p.50 multicoloured . . 20 10

1977. Air. 50th Anniv of National Federation of Coffee Growers.
1417 **495** 10p. multicoloured . . . 20 15

496 Beethoven and Score of Ninth Symphony

1977. Air. 150th Anniv of Beethoven.
1418 **496** 8p. multicoloured . . . 25 15

1977. Arms of Popayan. As T **476**.
1419 5p. multicoloured 30 15

497 Mother feeding Baby
498 Wattled Jacana and "Eichhornia crassipes"

1977. Nutrition Campaign.
1420 **497** 2p. multicoloured . . . 15 10
1420a 2p.50 multicoloured . . 80 10

1977. Colombian Birds and Plants. Multicoloured.
1421 10p. Type **498** (postage) . . 2·25 50
1422 20p. Plum-throated cotinga and "Pyrostegia venusta" 2·50 60
1423 5p. Crimson-mantled woodpecker and "Meriania" (air) . . . . 1·50 50
1424 5p. American purple gallinule and "Nymphaea" . . . . . . 1·50 50
1425 10p. Pampadour cotinga and "Cochlospermum orinocense" . . . . . . 2·75 60
1426 10p. Northern royal flycatcher and "Jacaranda copaia" . . . . 2·75 60

499 Games Emblem
500 "La Cayetana" (E. Grau)

1977. Air. 13th Central American and Caribbean Games, Medellin (1978).
1427 **499** 6p. multicoloured . . . 25 10

1977. Air. 20th Anniv of Female Suffrage. Multicoloured.
1428 8p. Type **500** 20 20
1429 8p. "Nayade" (Beatriz Gonzalez) 20 20

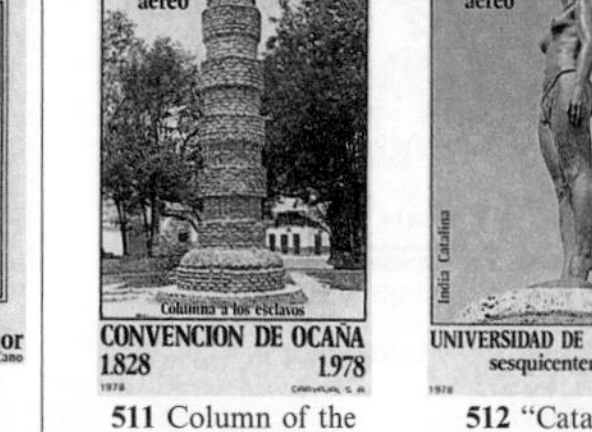

501 "Judge Francisco Antonio Moreno y Escandon" (J. Gutierrez)
502 "Fidel Cano" (Francisco Cano)

1977. Air. Bicentenary of National Library. Mult.
1430 20p. Type **501** 55 10
1431 25p. "Viceroy Manuel de Guiror" (unknown artist) 55 20

1977. 90th Anniv of "El Espectador" Magazine by Fidel Cano.
1432 **502** 4p. multicoloured . . . 20 10

503 Abacus and Alphabet

1977. Popular Education.
1433 **503** 3p. multicoloured . . . 15 10

1977. Arms of Barranquilla. As T **476**.
1434 5p. multicoloured 30 15

504 Dr. F. L. Acosta
505 Cauca University Arms

1977. Air. Birth Centenary of Dr. Federico Lleras Acosta (veterinary surgeon).
1435 **504** 5p. multicoloured . . . 30 10

1977. Air. 150th Anniv of Cauca University.
1436 **505** 5p. multicoloured . . . 25 10

506 "Cudecom" Building, Bogota
508 "Cattleya triannae"

1977. Air. 90th Anniv of Society of Colombian Engineers.
1437 **506** 1p.50 multicoloured . . 10 10

1977. Air. No. 1364 surch **$2.00**.
1438 2p. on 1p.30 multicoloured 90 25

1978.
1439 **508** 2p.50 multicoloured . . 25 10
1439a 3p. multicoloured . . . 25 10

509 Tayronan Lost City
510 "Creator of Energy" (A. Betancourt)

1978. Air.
1440 **509** 3p.50 multicoloured . . 35 10

1978. Air. 150th Anniv of Antioquia University Law School.
1441 **510** 4p. multicoloured . . . 20 10

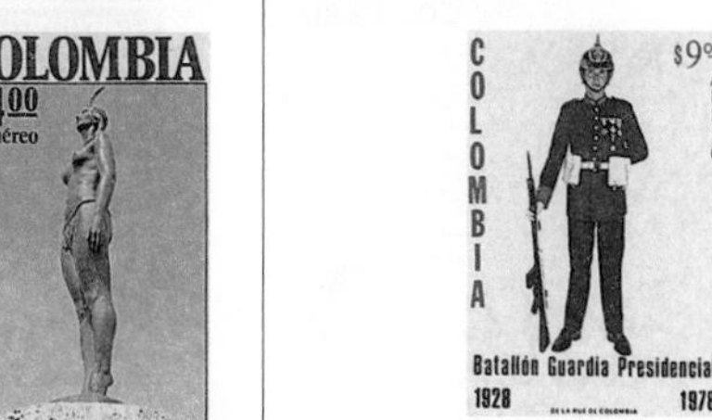

511 Column of the Slaves
512 "Catalina"

1978. Air. 150th Anniv of Ocana Convention.
1442 **511** 2p.50 multicoloured . . 15 10

1978. Air. 150th Anniv of Cartagena University.
1443 **512** 4p. multicoloured . . . 20 10

513 Running

1978. 13th Central American and Caribbean Games, Medellin. Multicoloured.
1444 10p. Type **513** 35 25
1445 10p. Basketball 35 25
1446 10p. Baseball 35 25
1447 10p. Boxing 35 25
1448 10p. Cycling 35 25
1449 10p. Fencing 35 25
1450 10p. Football 35 25
1451 10p. Gymnastics 35 25
1452 10p. Judo 35 25
1453 10p. Weightlifting 35 25
1454 10p. Wrestling 35 25
1455 10p. Swimming 35 25
1456 10p. Tennis 35 25
1457 10p. Shooting 35 25
1458 10p. Volleyball 35 25
1459 10p. Water polo 35 25

514 "Sigma 2" (A. Herran)
515 Human Figure from Gold Pendant

1978. Centenary of Bogota Chamber of Commerce.
1460 **514** 8p. multicoloured . . . 20 20

1978. Air. Tolima Culture.
1461 **515** 3p.50 multicoloured . . 20 20

516 "Apotheosis of the Spanish Language" (Left-hand detail of mural, L. A. Acuna)

1978. Air. Millenary of Castilian Language. Multicoloured.
1462 11p. Type **516** 55 50
1463 11p. Central detail 55 50
1464 11p. Right-hand detail . . . 55 50
Nos. 1462/4 were issued together, se-tenant, forming a composite design.

517 Presidential Guard

1978. Air. 50th Anniv of Presidential Guard Battalion.
1465 **517** 9p. multicoloured . . . 25 25

518 Human Figure

519 General Tomas Cipriano de Mosquera

1978. Air. Muisca Culture.
1466 **518** 3p.50 multicoloured . . 20 10

1978. Death Centenary of General Tomas Cipriano de Mosquera (statesman).
1467 **519** 6p. multicoloured . . . 20 20

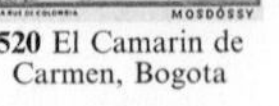

520 El Camarin de Carmen, Bogota

521 Gold Owl Ornament

1978. Air. "Espamer '78" Stamp Exhibition, Bogota.
1468 **520** 30p. multicoloured . . . 1·75 20

1978. Air. Calima Culture.
1470 **521** 3p.50 multicoloured . . 20 10
1470a 4p. multicoloured . . . 25 10

522 "Virgin and Child" (Gregorio Vasquez)

523 Church and Bullring

1978. Air. Christmas.
1471 **522** 2p.50 multicoloured . . 10 10

1978. Air. Manizales Fair.
1472 **523** 7p. multicoloured . . . 25 15

524 Frog in beaten Gold

525 Children playing Hopscotch

1979. Air. Quimbaya Culture.
1473 **524** 4p. multicoloured . . . 15 10

1979. Air. International Year of the Child. Multicoloured.
1474 8p. Type **525** 30 10
1475 12p. Child in sou'wester and oilskins 20 20
1476 12p. Child at blackboard (horiz) 20 20

526 Anthurium

527 Rio Prado Hydro-electric Barrage

1979. Anthurium Flowers from Narino. Multicoloured, background colours given.
1477 **526** 3p. light green 25 10
1478 3p. red 25 10
1479 3p. green 25 10
1480 3p. blue 25 10

1979. Arms. As T **476**. Multicoloured.
1481 4p. Sogamoso 45 10
1482 10p. Socorro 20 15
1483 10p. Santa Cruz y San Gil de la Nueva Baeza . . . 20 15

1979. Air. Tourism. Multicoloured.
1484 5p. Type **527** 35 10
1485 7p. River Amazon 60 30
1486 8p. Tomb, San Agustin Archaeological Park . . . 25 20
1487 14p. San Fernando Fort, Cartagena 45 35

528 "Jimenez de Quesada" (after C. Leudo)

1979. Air. 400th Death Anniv of Gonzalo Jimenez de Quesada (conquistador).
1488 **528** 20p. multicoloured . . . 1·60 65

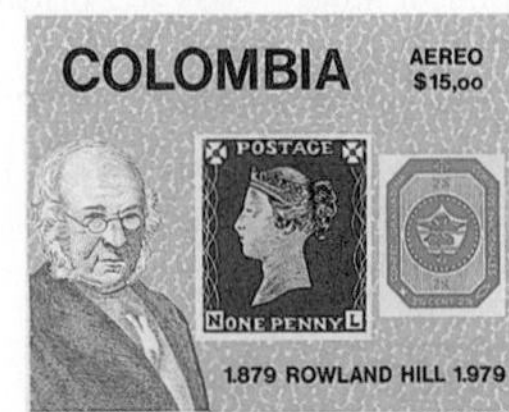

529 Hill and First Stamps of Great Britain and Colombia

1979. Air. Death Centenary of Sir Rowland Hill.
1489 **529** 15p. multicoloured . . . 25 25

530 "Uribe" (after Acevedo Bernal)

1979. 65th Death Anniv of General Rafael Uribe Uribe (statesman).
1490 **530** 8p. multicoloured . . . 30 15

531 "Village" (Leonor Alarcon)

1979. 20th Anniv of Community Works Boards.
1491 **531** 15p. multicoloured . . . 85 30

532 Three Kings and Soldiers

1979. Air. Christmas. Multicoloured.
1492 3p. Type **532** 75 40
1493 3p. Nativity 75 40
1494 3p. Shepherds 75 40

533 River Magdalena Bridge and Avianca Emblem

534 Gold Nose Pendant

1979. Air. 350th Anniv of Barranquilla and 60th Anniv of Avianca National Airline.
1495 **533** 15p. multicoloured . . . 25 15

1980. Air. Tairona Culture.
1496 **534** 3p. multicoloured . . . 25 10

535 "Boy playing Flute" (Judith Leyster)

536 Antonio Jose de Sucre

1980. Air. 2nd International Music Competition, Ibague.
1497 **535** 6p. multicoloured . . . 30 10

1980. Air. 150th Death Anniv of General Antonio Jose de Sucre.
1498 **536** 12p. multicoloured . . . 20 15

537 "The Watchman" (Edgar Negret)

1980. Air. Modern Sculpture.
1499 **537** 25p. multicoloured . . . 1·40 1·25

538 Television Screen

1980. Inaug of Colour Television in Colombia.
1500 **538** 5p. multicoloured . . . 25 10

539 Bullfighting Poster (H. Courttin)

540 "Learn to Write"

1980. Tourism. Festival of Cali.
1501 **539** 5p. multicoloured . . . 35 15

1980. The Alphabet.
1502 **540** 4p. black, brown & grn 25 10
1503 – 4p. multicoloured . . . 25 10
1504 – 4p. brown, blk & lt brn 25 10
1505 – 4p. multicoloured . . . 40 15
1506 – 4p. brown, black & grn 25 10
1507 – 4p. black and turquoise 25 10
1508 – 4p. black and green . . 25 10
1509 – 4p. mauve, black & grn 40 15
1510 – 4p. black and blue . . . 25 10
1511 – 4p. black and green . . 25 10
1512 – 4p. green, black & brown 25 10
1513 – 4p. multicoloured . . . 25 10
1514 – 4p. brown, black & grn 25 10
1515 – 4p. multicoloured . . . 25 10
1516 – 4p. yellow, black & grn 25 10
1517 – 4p. black, brown & yell 25 10
1518 – 4p. brown, black & turq 25 10
1519 – 4p. brown, black & grn 25 10
1520 – 4p. brown, black & grn 25 10
1521 – 4p. yellow, black & turq 25 10
1522 – 4p. green, black & blue 40 15
1523 – 4p. brown, black & grn 25 10
1524 – 4p. green, black & lt grn 25 10
1525 – 4p. multicoloured . . . 25 10
1526 – 4p. multicoloured . . . 25 10
1527 – 4p. brown, black & grn 25 10
1528 – 4p. multicoloured . . . 40 15
1529 – 4p. multicoloured . . . 25 10
1530 – 4p. brown, black & grn 25 10
1531 – 4p. brown and black . . 25 10

DESIGNS: No. 1503, "a" Eagle; 1504, "b" Buffalo; 1505, "c" Andean Condor; 1506, "ch" Chimpanzee; 1507, "d" Dolphin; 1508, "e" Elephant; 1509, "f" Greater Flamingo; 1510, "g" Seagull; 1511, "h" Hippopotamus; 1512, "i" Iguana; 1513, "j" Giraffe; 1514, "k" Koala; 1515, "l" Lion; 1516, "ll" Llama; 1517, "m" Blackbird; 1518, "n" Otter; 1519, Gnu; 1520, "o" Bear; 1521, "p" Pelican; 1522, "q" Resplendent Quetzal; 1523, "r" Rhinoceros; 1524, "s" Grasshopper; 1525, "t" Tortoise; 1526, "u" Magpie; 1527, "v" Viper; 1528, "w" Wagon with animals; 1529, "x" Fox playing xylophone; 1530, "y" Yak; 1531, "z" Fox.

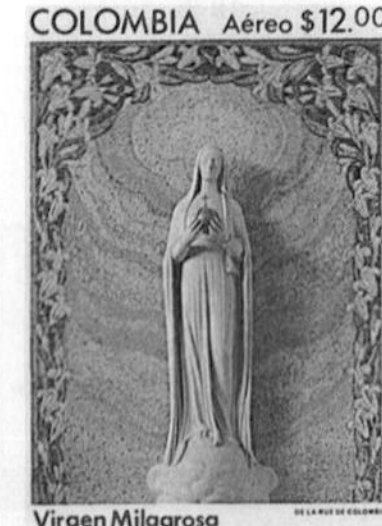

541 "Miraculous Virgin" (statue, Real del Sarte)

1980. Air. 150th Anniv of Apparition of Holy Virgin to Sister Catalina Labouri Gontard in Paris.
1532 **541** 12p. multicoloured . . . 45 15

542 "Country Scene, San Gil" (painting, Luis Roncancio)

1980. Air. Agriculture.
1533 **542** 12p. multicoloured . . . 1·00 30

543 Villavicencio Song Festival

1980. Tourism. Festivals. Multicoloured.
1534 5p. Type **543** 30 15
1535 9p. Vallenato festival . . . 15 15

544 Gustavo Uribe Ramirez and "Samanea saman"

1980. 12th Death Anniv of Gustavo Uribe Ramirez (ecologist).
1536 **544** 10p. multicoloured . . . 35 15

545 Narino Palace

1980. Narino Palace (Presidential residence).
1537 **545** 5p. multicoloured . . . 30 10

546 Monument to First Pioneers, Armenia

1980. City of Armenia.
1538 **546** 5p. multicoloured . . . 30 10

547 Olaya Herrera (after Miguel Diaz Varges)

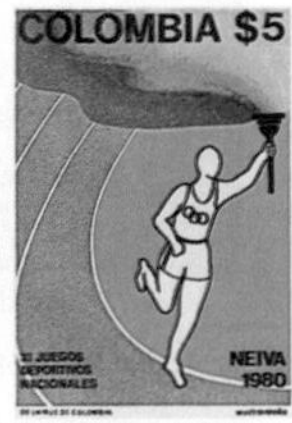

549 Athlete with Torch

548 "Simple Simon"

1980. Air. Birth Centenary of Dr. Enrique Olaya Herrera (President, 1930–34).
1539 **547** 20p. multicoloured . . . 45 25

1980. Air. Christmas. Illustrations to stories by Rafael Pombo. Multicoloured.
1540 4p. Type **548** 25 15
1541 4p. "The Cat's Seven Lives" 25 15
1542 4p. "The Walking Tadpole" 25 15

1980. 11th National Games, Neiva.
1543 **549** 5p. multicoloured . . . 20 10

550 Golfers

551 Crab pierced by Sword

1980. Air. 28th World Golf Cup, Cajica.
1544 **550** 30p. multicoloured . . . 2·10 1·50

1980. 20th Anniv of Colombian Anti-cancer League.
1545 **551** 10p. multicoloured . . . 35 20

552 "Justice" and University Emblem

1980. 50th Anniv of Refounding of Pontifical Xavier University Law Faculty.
1546 **552** 20p. multicoloured . . . 25 30

553 "Bolivar's Last Moments" (Marcos Leon Marino)

1980. 150th Death Anniv of Simon Bolivar. Multicoloured.
1547 25p. Type **553** (postage) . . 45 35
1548 6p. Bolivar and his last proclamation (air) 25 25

554 St. Pedro Claver

555 Statue of Bird, San Agustin

1981. Air. 400th Birth Anniv of St. Pedro Claver.
1549 **554** 15p. multicoloured . . . 20 30

1981. Air. Archaeological Discoveries. Mult.
1550 7p. Type **555** 30 15
1551 7p. Hypogeum (funeral chamber), Tierradentro 30 15
1552 7p. Hypogeum, Tierradentro (different) 30 15
1553 7p. Statue of man, San Agustin 30 15

556 "Square Abstract" (Omar Rayo)

1981. Air. 4th Biennial Arts Exhibition, Medellin. Multicoloured.
1554 20p. Type **556** 30 20
1555 25p. "Flowers" (Alejandro Obregon) 40 30
1556 50p. "Child with Hobby Horse" (Fernando Botero) 1·50 1·25

557 Diver

1981. Air. 8th South American Swimming Championships, Medellin.
1557 **557** 15p. multicoloured . . . 25 30

558 Santamaria Bull Ring

1981. Air. 50th Anniv of Santamaria Bull Ring, Bogota.
1558 **558** 30p. multicoloured . . . 1·50 80

559 Mariano Ospina Perez (after Delio Ramirez)

1981. Presidents of Colombia (1st series). Multicoloured.
1559 5p. Type **559** 25 10
1560 5p. Eduardo Santos (after Ines Acevedo) 25 10
1561 5p. Miguel Abadia Mendez (after Gomez Compuzano) 25 10
1562 5p. Jose Vicente Concha (after Acevedo Bernal) . . 25 10
1563 5p. Carlos E. Restrepo . . . 25 10
1564 5p. Rafael Reyes (after Acevedo Bernal) 25 10
1565 5p. Santiago Perez 25 10
1566 5p. Manuel Murillo Toro (after Moreno Otero) . . 25 10
1567 5p. Jose Hilario Lopez . . . 25 10
1568 5p. Jose Maria Obando . . 25 10
See also Nos. 1569/78, 1579/88, 1599/1608, 1615/24 and 1634/43.

1981. Presidents of Colombia (2nd series). Multicoloured.
1569 7p. Type **559** . . . . 2·75 35
1570 7p. As No. 1560 . . . . . 2·75 35
1571 7p. As No. 1561 . . . . . 2·75 35
1572 7p. As No. 1562 . . . . . 2·75 35
1573 7p. As No. 1563 . . . . . 2·75 35
1574 7p. As No. 1564 . . . . . 2·75 35
1575 7p. As No. 1565 . . . . . 2·75 35
1576 7p. As No. 1566 . . . . . 2·75 35
1577 7p. As No. 1567 . . . . . 2·75 35
1578 7p. As No. 1568 . . . . . 2·75 35

1981. Presidents of Colombia (3rd series). As T **559**. Multicoloured.
1579 7p. Pedro Alcantara Herran 2·10 20
1580 7p. Mariano Ospina Rodriguez (after Coriolando Leudo) . . . 2·10 20
1581 7p. Tomas Cipriano de Mosquera . . . . 2·10 20
1582 7p. Santos Gutierrez . . . . 2·10 20
1583 7p. Aquileo Parra (after Constancio Franco) . . . 2·10 20
1584 7p. Rafael Nunez . . . . . 2·10 20
1585 7p. Marco Fidel Suarez (after Jesus Maria Duque) 2·10 20
1586 7p. Pedro Nel Ospina (after Coriolano Leudo) . . . . 2·10 20
1587 7p. Enrique Olaya Herrera (after M. Diaz Vargas) . . 2·10 20
1588 7p. Alfonso Lopez Pumarejo (after Luis F. Uscategui) 2·10 20

560 Crossed-legged Figure

1981. Air. Quimbaya Culture. Multicoloured.
1589 9p. Type **560** 40 15
1590 9p. Seated figure 40 15
1591 9p. Printing block and print 40 15
1592 9p. Clay pot 40 15

561 Fruit

1981. Air. Fruit. Designs showing fruit.
1593 **561** 25p. multicoloured . . . 2·10 1·40
1594 – 25p. multicoloured . . . 2·10 1·40
1595 – 25p. multicoloured . . . 2·10 1·40
1596 – 25p. multicoloured . . . 2·10 1·40
1597 – 25p. multicoloured . . . 2·10 1·40
1598 – 25p. multicoloured . . . 2·10 1·40
Nos. 1593/8 were issued together in se-tenant blocks of six forming a composite design.

1981. Presidents of Colombia (4th series). As T **559**. Multicoloured.
1599 7p. Manuel Maria Mallarino 1·00 15
1600 7p. Santos Acosta . . . . . 1·00 15
1601 7p. Eustorgio Salgar . . . . 1·00 15
1602 7p. Julian Trujillo . . . . . 1·00 15
1603 7p. Francisco Javier Zaldua (after Francisco Valles) 1·00 15
1604 7p. Jose Eusebio Otalora (after Ricardo Moros) . . 1·00 15
1605 7p. Miguel Antonio Caro 1·00 15
1606 7p. Manuel A. Sanclemente (after Epifanio Garay) . . 1·00 15
1607 7p. Laureano Gomez (after Jose Bascones) . . . . . 1·00 15
1608 7p. Guillermo Leon Valencia (after Luis Angel Rengifo) . . . . 1·00 15

562 "Comunero tearing down Edict" (Manuela Beltran)

1981. Air. Bicentenary of Comuneros Uprising.
1609 **562** 20p. multicoloured . . . 25 30

563 Jose Maria Villa and West Bridge

564 Restrepo (after R. Acevedo Bernal)

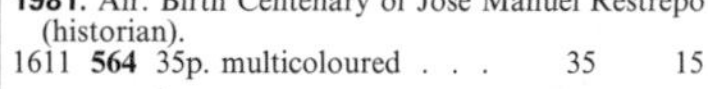

1981. West Bridge, Santa Fe de Antioquia.
1610 **563** 60p. multicoloured . . . 65 10

1981. Air. Birth Centenary of Jose Manuel Restrepo (historian).
1611 **564** 35p. multicoloured . . . 35 15

565 Anniversary Emblem

566 Los Nevados National Park

1981. 50th Anniv of Caja Agraria (peasants' bank).
1612 **565** 15p. multicoloured . . . 15 10

1981. Los Nevados National Park.
1613 **566** 20p. multicoloured . . . 20 10

567 Andres Bello

568 Squatting Figure

1981. Birth Centenary of Andres Bello (poet).
1614 **567** 18p. multicoloured . . . 20 15

1981. Presidents of Colombia (5th series). As T **559**. Multicoloured.
1615 7p. Bartolome Calvo (after Miguel Diaz Vargas) . . 60 15
1616 7p. Sergio Camargo 60 15
1617 7p. Jose Maria Rojas Garrido 60 15
1618 7p. J. M. Campo Serrano (after H. L. Brown) . . . 60 15
1619 7p. Eliseo Payan (after R. Moros Urbina) 60 15
1620 7p. Carlos Holguin (after Coriolano Leudo) 60 15
1621 7p. Jose Manuel Marroquin (after Rafael Tavera) . . 60 15
1622 7p. Ramon Gonzalez Valencia (after Jose Maria Vidal) 60 15
1623 7p. Jorge Holguin (after M. Salas Yepes) 60 15
1624 7p. Ruben Piedrahita Arango 60 15

1981. Air. Calima Culture. Multicoloured.
1625 9p. Type **568** 80 15
1626 9p. Vessel with two spouts 80 15
1627 9p. Human-shaped vessel with two spouts 80 15
1628 9p. Pot 80 15

569 1c. Stamp of 1881

1981. Air. Centenary of Admission to U.P.U.
1629 **569** 30p. green and pink . . 30 20

570 Girl with Water Jug

1981. Colombian Solidarity.
1631 **570** 30p. brown, blk & orge 70 30
1632 – 30p. brown, blk & orge 70 30
1633 – 30p. brown, blk & orge 70 30
DESIGNS: No. 1632, Baby with basket; 1633, Boy sitting on wheelbarrow.

1982. Presidents of Colombia (6th series). As T **559**. Multicoloured.
1634 7p. Simon Bolivar 50 15
1635 7p. Francisco de Paula Santander 50 15
1636 7p. Joaquin Mosquera (after C. Franco) 50 15
1637 7p. Domingo Caicedo . . . 50 15
1638 7p. Jose Ignacio de Marquez (after C. Franco) 50 15
1639 7p. Juan de Dios Aranzazu 50 15
1640 7p. Jose de Obaldia (after Jesus M. Duque) 50 15
1641 7p. Guillermo Quintero Calderon (after Silvano Cuellar) 50 15
1642 7p. Carlos Lozano y Lozano (after Helio Ramierz) . . 50 15
1643 7p. Roberto Urdaneta Arbelaez (after Jose Bascones Agneto) 50 15

571 Solano Bay, Choco

1982. Air. Tourism. Multicoloured.
1644 20p. Type **571** 25 30
1645 20p. Tota Lake, Boyaca . . 25 30
1646 20p. Corrales, Boyaca . . . 25 30

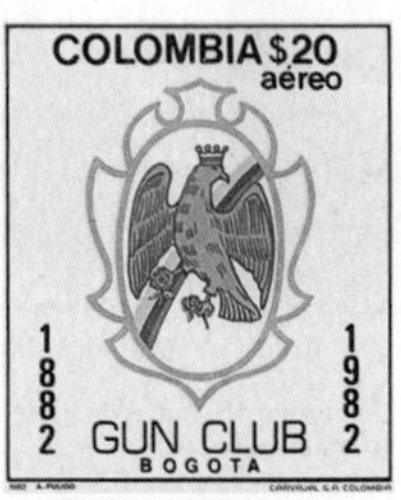

573 Gun Club Emblem

1982. Air. Centenary of Bogota Gun Club.
1648 **573** 20p. multicoloured . . . 25 15

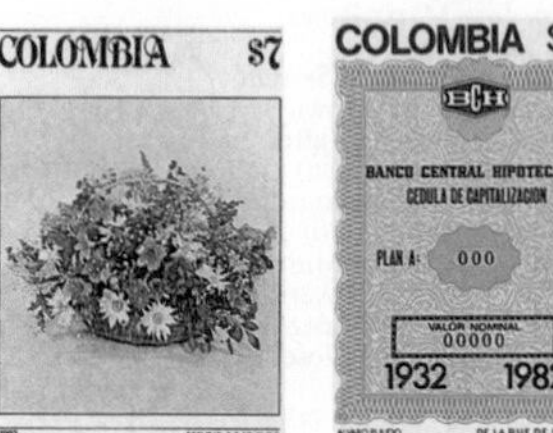

574 Flower Arrangement in Basket

576 Capitalization Certificate

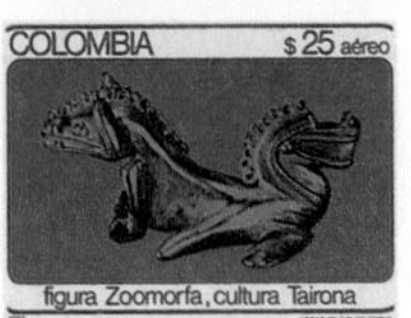

575 Zoomorphic Figure (crocodile)

1982. Country Flowers. Designs showing flower arrangements. Multicoloured.
1649 7p. Type **574** 75 15
1650 7p. Pink arrangement in basket 75 15
1651 7p. Red roses in pot 75 15
1652 7p. Lilac and white arrangement in basket . . 75 15
1653 7p. Orange and yellow arrangement in basket . . 75 15
1654 7p. Mixed arrangement in vase 75 15
1655 7p. Pink roses in vase . . . 75 15
1656 7p. Daisies in pot 75 15
1657 7p. Bouquet of yellow roses 75 15
1658 7p. Pink and yellow arrangement 75 15

1982. Air. Tairona Culture.
1659 **575** 25p. gold, black & brown 90 35
1660 – 25p. gold, black & mve 90 35
1661 – 25p. gold, black & green 90 35
1662 – 25p. gold, black & mve 90 35
1663 – 25p. gold, black & blue 90 35
1664 – 25p. gold, black & red 90 35
DESIGNS—VERT: No. 1660, Anthropomorphic figure with crest; 1661, Anthropomorphic figure with two crests; 1662, Anthropozoomorphic figure; 1663, Anthropozoomorphic figure with elaborate headdress; 1664, Pectoral.

1982. 50th Anniv of Central Mortgage Bank.
1665 **576** 9p. green and black . . 35 20

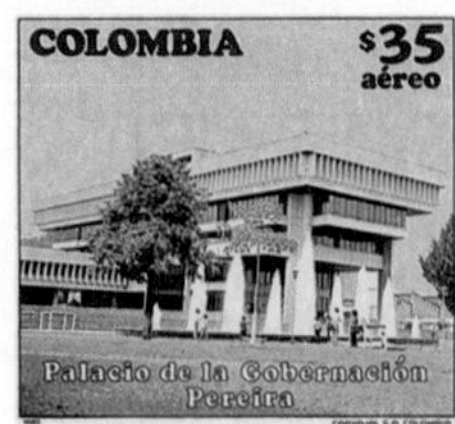

577 State Governor's Palace, Pereira

1982. Air. Pereira City.
1666 **577** 35p. multicoloured . . . 35 20

578 Biplane and Badge

1982. Air. American Air Forces Co-operation.
1667 **578** 18p. multicoloured . . . 25 15

579 St. Thomas Aquinas

580 St. Theresa of Avila (after Zurbaran)

1982. St. Thomas Aquinas Commemoration.
1668 **579** 5p. multicoloured . . . 15 10

1982. 400th Death Anniv of St. Theresa of Avila.
1669 **580** 5p. multicoloured . . . 15 10

581 St. Francis of Assisi (after Zurbaran)

583 Gabriel Garcia Marquez

582 Magdalena River

1982. 800th Birth Anniv of St. Francis of Assisi.
1670 **581** 5p. multicoloured . . . 15 10

1982. Air. Tourism.
1671 **582** 30p. multicoloured . . . 2·25 70

1982. Town Arms. As T **476**. Multicoloured.
1672 10p. Buga 25 10
1673 16p. Rionegro 45 15
1674 23p. Honda 25 20

1982. Award of Nobel Prize for Literature to Gabriel Garcia Marquez.
1675 **583** 7p. grey & grn (postage) 25 15
1676 25p. grey & blue (air) . . 20 10
1677 30p. grey and brown . . 25 10

1983. Town Arms. As T **476**. Multicoloured.
1678 10p. San Juan de Pasto . . 30 15
1679 20p. Santa Fe de Bogota . . 25 10

584 "Liberty Fort" (drawing in National Archives)

1983. Air. San Andres Archipelago.
1680 **584** 25p. multicoloured . . . 25 10

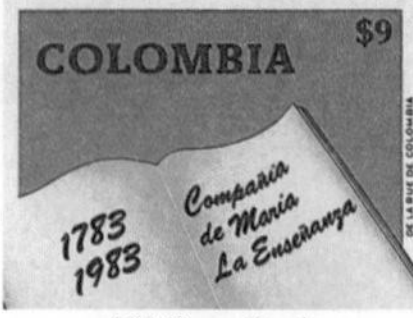

585 Open Book

1983. Bicentenary of First Girls' School, Santa Fe de Bogota.
1681 **585** 9p. grey, black & gold 25 15

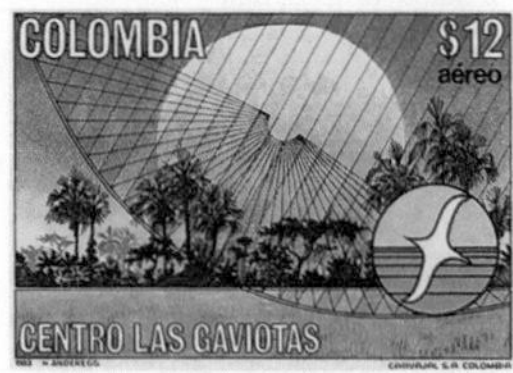

586 Sunset

1983. Air. Las Gaviotas Ecological Centre.
1682 **586** 12p. multicoloured . . . 15 10

587 Self-portrait

588 Radio Bands

1983. Death Centenary of Jose Maria Espinosa (artist).
1683 **587** 9p. multicoloured . . . 20 10

1983. Air. 50th Anniv of Radio Amateurs League.
1684 **588** 12p. multicoloured . . . 35 20

589 "Dona Rangel de Cuellas donating Territory" (Marcos L. Marino)

590 Bolivar

1983. 250th Anniv of Cucuta.
1685 **589** 9p. multicoloured . . . 30 15

1983. Birth Bicentenary of Simon Bolivar.
1686 **590** 9p. mult (postage) . . . 25 10
1687 – 30p. yell, bl & red (air) 35 25
1688 – 100p. multicoloured . . 1·25 85
DESIGNS—HORIZ: 30p. Bolivar as national flag. VERT: 100p. Bolivar and flag.

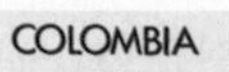

591 Porfirio Barba Jacob (after Frank Linas)

592 "Passiflora laurifolia"

1983. Birth Centenary of Porfirio Barba Jacob.
1689 **591** 9p. brown and black . . 20 10

1983. Bicentenary of Royal Botanical Expedition from Spain to South America. Multicoloured.
1690 9p. Type **592** (postage) . . . 20 10
1691 9p. "Cinchona lanceifolia" 20 10
1692 60p. "Cinchona cordifolia" 65 15
1693 12p. "Cinchona ovalifolia" (air) 30 15
1694 12p. "Begonia guaduensis" 30 15
1695 40p. "Begonia urticae" . . . 1·10 80

593 Plaza de la Aduana

1983. Air. 450th Anniv of Cartagena. Mult.
1696 12p. Type **593** 30 15
1697 35p. Cartagena buildings and monuments 80 20

594 "Dawn in the Andes" (Alejandro Obregon)

595 Scout Badge

1983.
1698 **594** 20p. mult (postage) . . . 75 25
1699 30p. mult (air) . . . . . 1·25 35

1983. Air. 75th Anniv of Boy Scout Movement.
1700 **595** 12p. multicoloured . . . 20 15

596 Santander

597 Coffee

1984. Francisco de Paula Santander (President of New Granada, 1832–37).
1701 **596** 12p. green 25 15
1702 12p. blue 25 15
1703 12p. red 25 15

1984. Air. Exports.
1704 **597** 14p. purple & green . . 10 10

598 Admiral Jose Prudencio Padilla

1984. Anniversaries. Multicoloured.
1705 10p. Type **598** (birth bicentenary) 75 20
1706 18p. Luis A. Calvo (composer, birth cent) . . 35 15
1707 20p. Diego Fallon (writer, 150th birth anniv) 35 15
1708 20p. Candelario Obeso (writer, death cent) . . . 1·00 30
1709 22p. Luis Eduardo Lopez de Mesa (writer, birth centenary) 45 15

599 Rainbow over Countryside

600 Stylized Globe on Stand

1984. Marandua, City of the Future.
1710 **599** 15p. mult (postage) . . . 30 15
1711 30p. mult (air) 20 20

1984. Air. 45th Congress of Americanists, Bogota.
1712 **600** 45p. multicoloured . . . 30 30

601 Nativity and Children playing

602 Maria Concepcion Loperena

1984. Christmas.
1713 **601** 12p. mult (postage) . . . 25 10
1714 14p. mult (air) 30 10

1985. 150th Birth Anniv of Maria Concepcion Loperena (Independence heroine).
1715 **602** 12p. multicoloured . . . 35 25

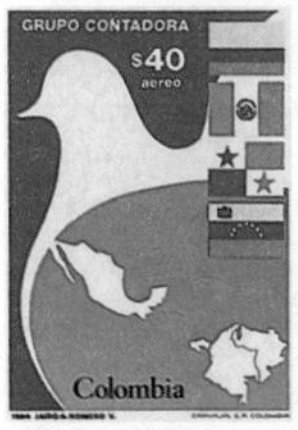

603 Dove, Map and Members' Flags

604 Mejia and Farman F.40 Type Biplane

1985. Air. Contadora Group.
1716 **603** 40p. multicoloured . . . 40 25

1985. Birth Centenary of Gonzalo Mejia (airport architect).
1717 **604** 12p. multicoloured . . . 20 10

605 "Married Couple" (Pedro nel Gomez)

1985.
1718 **605** 37p. mult (postage) . . . 25 10
1719 40p. mult (air) 40 25

606 Capybara

607 Straight-billed Woodcreepers

1985. Fauna. Multicoloured. (a) Mammals.
1720 12p. Type **606** (postage) . . 15 10
1721 15p. Ocelot 35 25
1722 15p. Spectacled bear 35 25
1723 20p. Mountain tapir 35 25

(b) Birds.
1724 14p. Lineated woodpeckers (air) 60 40
1725 20p. Type **607** 60 25
1726 50p. Coppery-bellied pufflegs . . . . 1·40 70
1727 55p. Blue-crowned motmots 1·60 80

608 Scenery and Gardel

609 "Gloria" (cadet ship), "Caldas" (frigate) and Naval Officer

1985. 50th Death Anniv of Carlos Gardel (singer).
1728 **608** 15p. multicoloured . . . 20 10

1985. Air. 50th Anniv of Almirante Padilla Naval College.
1729 **609** 20p. multicoloured . . . 1·25 45

610 Group of Colombians

611 Alphabet Tree

1985. Air. National Census.
1730 **610** 20p. multicoloured . . . 35 25

1985. National Education Year.
1731 **611** 15p. multicoloured . . . 30 15

612 Boy Playing Flute to Toys

613 Pumarejo

1985. Christmas. Multicoloured.
1732 15p. Type **612** (postage) . . 25 15
1733 20p. Girl looking at dressed tree (air) 30 20

1986. Air. Birth Centenary of Alfonso Lopez Pumarejo (President, 1934–38 and 1942–45).
1734 **613** 24p. multicoloured . . . 30 15

614 Cyclists and Countryside

615 Carranza (after Carlos Dupuy)

1986. Air. "Coffee and Cycling, Pride of Colombia".
1735 **614** 60p. multicoloured . . . 45 25

1986. Eduardo Carranza (poet) Commemoration.
1736 **615** 18p. multicoloured . . . 20 15

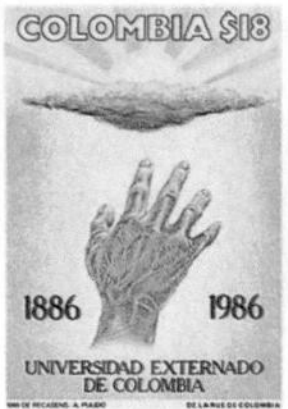

616 Hand reaching for Sun

617 Northern Pudu

1986. Centenary of External University.
1737 **616** 18p. multicoloured . . . 30 20

1986. Air.
1738 **617** 50p. multicoloured . . . 60 35

618 Ricaurte and Birth Place, Leiva

1986. Birth Bicentenary of Gen. Antonio Ricaurte (Independence hero).
1739 **618** 18p. multicoloured . . . 20 15

619 Pope and Arms

620 Couple and Satellite

1986. Air. Visit of Pope John Paul II (1st issue).
1740 **619** 24p. multicoloured . . . 35 20
See also Nos. 1745/6.

1986. Air. World Communications Day.
1741 **620** 50p. multicoloured . . . 60 35

621 Silva and Illustration of "Nocturne"

622 Girl and Doves

1986. 90th Death Anniv of Jose Asuncion Silva (poet).
1742 **621** 18p. multicoloured . . . 20 15

1986. Air. International Peace Year.
1743 **622** 55p. multicoloured . . . 65 40

623 Martinez

624 Pope and Medellin Cathedral

1986. 10th Death Anniv of Fernando Gomez Martinez (politician and founder of "El Colombiano" newspaper).
1744 **623** 24p. multicoloured . . . 30 20

1986. Air. Visit of Pope John Paul II (2nd issue). Multicoloured.
1745 55p. Type **624** 50 45
1746 60p. Pope giving blessing in Bogota 50 45

625 Montejo

626 Computer Portrait of Bach

1986. Air. Birth Centenary of Enrique Santos Montejo (journalist and editor of "El Tiempo").
1748 **625** 25p. multicoloured . . . 30 20

1986. Air. Composers' Birth Anniversaries (1985). Multicoloured.
1749 70p. Type **626** (300th anniv) 65 60
1750 100p. "The Permanency of Baroque" (300th annivs of Handel and Bach and 400th anniv of H. Schutz) 75 55

627 De La Salle (founder) and National Colours

1986. Air. Centenary of Brothers of Christian Schools in Colombia.
1751 **627** 25p. multicoloured . . . 30 15

628 Convent of Mercy

1986. 450th Anniv of Santiago de Cali.
1752 20p. Arms (as T **476**) . . . 15 10
1753 25p. Type **628** 15 10

629 Piece of Coal and National Colours

630 Castro Silva

1986. Air. Completion of El Cerrejon Coal Complex.
1754 **629** 55p. multicoloured . . . 40 40

1986. Birth Centenary (1985) of Jose Vincente Castro Silva (Principal of Senior College of the Rosary).
1755 **630** 20p. multicoloured . . . 25 15

631 "The Five Signatories" (detail, R. Vasquez)

1986. Air. Centenary of Constitution.
1756 **631** 25p. multicoloured . . . 30 20

1986. Arms of Antioquia. As T **476**.
1758 55p. multicoloured 20 10

632 Garcia Lorca

1986. Air. 50th Death Anniv of Federico Garcia Lorca (poet).
1759 **632** 60p. multicoloured . . . 35 25

633 Symbolic Prism

634 Maya

1986. Centenary of Fine Art Faculty and 50th Anniv of Architecture Faculty at National University.
1760 **633** 40p. multicoloured . . . 20 30

1986. 6th Death Anniv of Rafael Maya (poet and critic).
1761 **634** 25p. multicoloured . . . 30 20

635 Andean Condor **636** "Thanks! Friends of the World"

1986.
1762 **635** 20p. blue 35 20
1763 25p. blue 35 20

1986. Air. Thanks for Help after Devastation of Armero by Volcanic Eruption, 1985.
1767 **636** 50p. multicoloured . . . 60 35

637 Mestiza Virgin (from crib at Pasto) **638** Left-hand Side of Mural

1986. Air. Christmas.
1768 **637** 25p. multicoloured . . . 30 15

1987. Air. 450th Anniv of Popayan City. "The Apotheosis of Popayan" by Ephram Martinez Zambrano. Multicoloured.
1769 100p. Type **638** . . . . . . 1·40 75
1770 100p. Right-hand side of mural . . . . 1·40 75
Nos. 1769/70 were printed together, se-tenant, forming a composite design.

639 Uribe Mejia **640** "Conversion of St. Augustine of Hippo"

1987. Birth Centenary (1986) of Pedro Uribe Mejia (coffee industry pioneer).
1771 **639** 25p. multicoloured . . . 30 15

1987. Air. 1600th Anniv of Conversion of St. Augustine.
1772 **640** 30p. multicoloured . . . 10 10

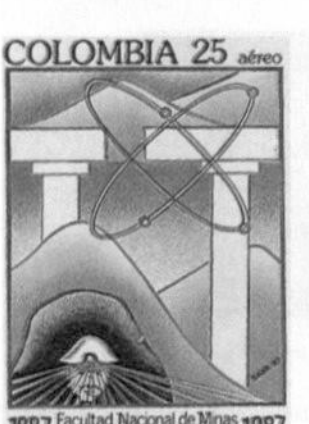

641 Atomic Diagram, Pit Props and Miner in Shaft **642** St. Barbara's Church

1987. Air. Centenary of National Mines Faculty of National University, Medellin.
1773 **641** 25p. multicoloured . . . 10 10

1987. 450th Anniv of Mompox City.
1774 **642** 500p. multicoloured . . 2·50 2·50

643 Hawk-headed Parrot **644** White Horse

1987. Fauna.
1775 **643** 30p. green (postage) . . 90 25
1776 – 30p. purple 45 20
1777 – 30p. red (air) 90 25
1778 – 35p. brown 15 20
DESIGNS—HORIZ: No. 1776, Boutu; 1778, South American red-lined turtle. VERT: No. 1777, Greater flamingo.
See also Nos. 1807/9, 1815/17, 1823/6 and 1855/8.

1987. Air. Pure-bred Horses. Multicoloured.
1779 60p. Type **644** 45 35
1780 70p. Black horse 45 35

645 Mastheads, Fidel Cano (founder), Luis Cano, Luis Gabriel Cano Isaza and Alfonso Cano Isaza (editors)

1987. Air. Cent of "El Espectador" (newspaper).
1781 **645** 60p. multicoloured . . . 25 15

646 Isaacs and Scene from "Maria"

1987. 150th Birth Anniv of Jorge Isaacs (writer).
1782 **646** 70p. multicoloured . . . 25 10

648 Mutis and Illustration of "Condor"

1987. 33rd Death Anniv of Aurelio Martinez Mutis (poet).
1785 **648** 90p. multicoloured . . . 1·25 55

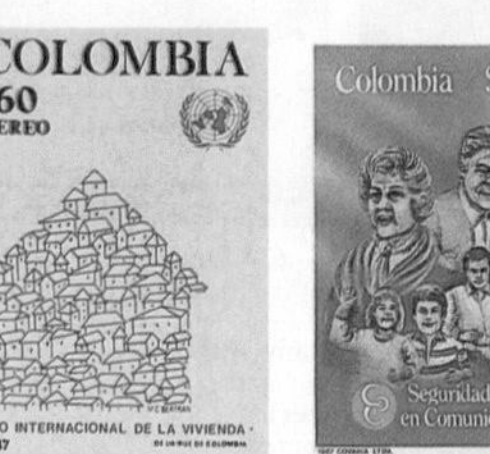

649 Houses forming House **650** Family and Dish Aerial

1987. Air. International Year of Shelter for the Homeless.
1786 **649** 60p. multicoloured . . . 65 35

1987. Social Security and Communications.
1787 **650** 35p. multicoloured . . . 30 20

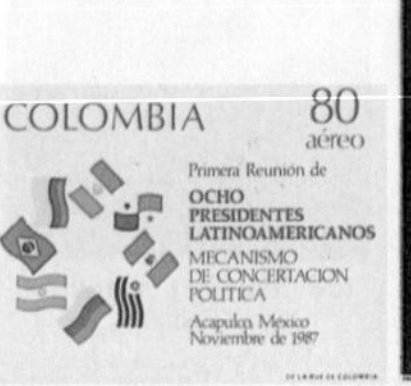

651 Flags **652** Nativity Scene in Globe

1987. Air. 1st Meeting of Eight Latin-American Presidents of Contadora and Lima Groups, Acapulco, Mexico.
1788 **651** 80p. multicoloured . . . 55 55

1987. Air. Christmas.
1789 **652** 30p. multicoloured . . . 30 15

653 Houses, Telephone Wires and Dials

1987. Air. Rural Telephone Network.
1790 **653** 70p. multicoloured . . . 35 10

654 Mountain Sanctuaries **655** Flower (Life)

1988. Air. 450th Anniv of Bogota (1st issue).
1791 **654** 70p. multicoloured . . . 25 70
See also Nos. 1803/4.

1988. 40th Anniv of Declaration of Human Rights (1st issue).
1792 **655** 30p. green 10 10
1793 – 35p. red 10 10
1794 – 40p. lilac 15 10
1795 – 40p. blue 10 10
DESIGNS—VERT: No. 1793, Road (Freedom of choice). HORIZ: 1794, Circle of children (Freedom of association); 1795, Couple on bench (Communication).
See also Nos. 1840/1.

657 Mask

1988. Air. Gold Museum, Bogota. Multicoloured.
1796 70p. Type **657** 30 30
1797 80p. Votive figure 60 30
1798 90p. Human figure 85 65

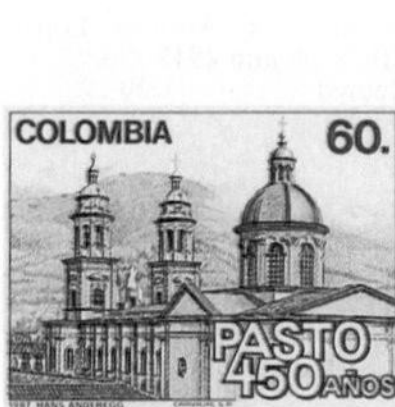

658 Pasto Cathedral **659** Waterfall

1988. 450th Anniv of Pasto.
1799 **658** 60p. multicoloured . . . 40 20

1988. Centenary of Bogota Water Supply and Sewerage Organization.
1800 **659** 100p. multicoloured . . 35 10

660 Score and Composers **661** M. Currea de Aya

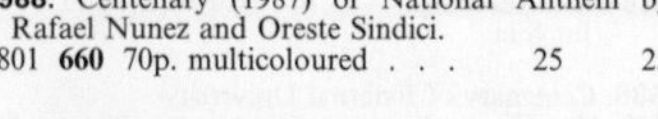

1988. Centenary (1987) of National Anthem by Rafael Nunez and Oreste Sindici.
1801 **660** 70p. multicoloured . . . 25 25

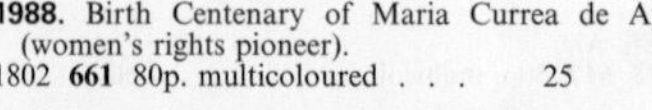

1988. Birth Centenary of Maria Currea de Aya (women's rights pioneer).
1802 **661** 80p. multicoloured . . . 25 10

662 Modern Bogota **664** College

1988. Air. 450th Anniv of Bogota (2nd issue). Multicoloured.
1803 80p. Type **662** 55 30
1804 90p. Street in old Bogota (horiz) 60 30

1988. Fauna. As T **643**.
1807 35p. brown 25 15
1808 35p. green 25 15
1809 40p. orange 25 15
DESIGNS—HORIZ: No. 1807, Crab-eating racoon; 1808, Caribbean monk seal; 1809, Giant otter.

1988. Centenary of Return of Society of Jesus to St. Bartholomew's Senior College.
1810 **664** 120p. multicoloured . . 35 20

665 Eduardo Santos **666** Mother and Children

1988. Personalities. Multicoloured.
1811 80p. Type **665** (birth centenary) (postage) . . . 45 25
1812 90p. Jorge Alvarez Lleras (astronomer) 45 25
1813 80p. Zipa Tisquesusa (16th-century Indian chief) (air) 45 25

1988. Air. Christmas.
1814 **666** 40p. multicoloured . . . 15 10

1988. Fauna. As T **643**.
1815 40p. grey (postage) 15 10
1816 45p. violet 75 25
1817 45p. blue (air) 75 25
DESIGNS—HORIZ: No. 1815, American manatee; 1816, Masked trogon. VERT: No. 1817, Blue-bellied curassow.

667 Andres Bello College

1988.
1818 **667** 115p. multicoloured . . 35 20

668 Building and Nieto Caballero **669** Gomez

1989. Air. Birth Centenary of Agustin Nieto Caballero (educationalist).
1819 **668** 100p. multicoloured . . 30 15

1989. Air. Birth Centenary of Laureano Gomez (President, 1950–53).
1820 **669** 45p. multicoloured . . . 15 10

670 Map

1989. Air. International Coffee Organization.
1821 **670** 110p. multicoloured . . . 30 15

671 Modern Flats, Recreation Area and Hands holding Brick

1989. Air. 12th Habitat U.N. Conference on Human Settlements, Cartagena.
1822 **671** 100p. multicoloured . . 20 10

1989. Fauna. As T **643**.
1823 40p. brown (postage) . . . 10 10
1824 45p. black 75 25
1825 55p. brown 15 10
1826 45p. blue (air) 10 10
DESIGNS—HORIZ: No. 1823, White-tailed deer; 1824, Harpy eagle; 1826, Blue discus. VERT: No. 1825, False anole.

672 Emblem

1989. 25th Anniv of Adpostal (postal administration).
1827 **672** 45p. multicoloured . . . 10 10

673 Hands

675 "Simon Bolivar" (Pedro Jose Figueroa)

1989. Air. Bicentenary of French Revolution.
1828 **673** 100p. multicoloured . . 20 10

1989. 170th Anniv of Liberation Campaign. Multicoloured.
1830 40p. Type **675** 10 10
1831 40p. "Santander" (Figueroa) 10 10
1832 45p. "Bolivar and Santander during the Campaign for the Plains" (J. M. Zamora) (46 × 37 mm) . . 10 10
1833 45p. "From Boyaca to Santa Fe" (left-hand detail) (Francisco de P. Alvarez) (29 × 36 mm) 10 10
1834 45p. Right-hand detail (29 × 36 mm) 10 10
1835 45p. Mounted officer and foot soldiers (left-hand detail) (31 × 51 mm) . . . 35 10
1836 45p. Mounted officer (centre detail) (33 × 51 mm) . . . 35 10
1837 45p. Mounted soldiers with flag (right-hand detail) (31 × 51 mm) 35 35
Nos. 1833/4 and 1835/7 (showing details of triptych by A. de Santa Maria) were issued together, se-tenant, each forming a composite design.

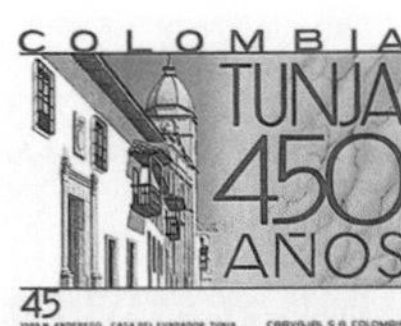

676 Founder's House

1989. 450th Anniv of Tunja.
1839 **676** 45p. multicoloured . . . 10 10

1989. Human Rights (2nd issue). As T **655**.
1840 45p. brown (postage) . . . 10 10
1841 55p. green (air) 15 10
DESIGNS—HORIZ: 45p. Musicians (Culture). VERT: 55p. Family.

677 Healthy Children and Shadowy Figures

678 Gold Ornaments of Quimbaya, Calima and Tolima

1989. Air. Anti-drugs Campaign.
1842 **677** 115p. multicoloured . . 25 15

1989. Air. America. Pre-Columbian Crafts. Multicoloured.
1843 115p. Type **678** 25 15
1844 130p. Indian making pot and Sinu ceramic figure (horiz) 25 15

679 Quimbaya Museum

680 Mantilla

1989. Centenary of Armenia City.
1815 **679** 135p. multicoloured . . 25 15

1989. Air. 45th Death Anniv of Joaquin Quijano Mantilla (chronicler).
1846 **680** 170p. multicoloured . . 75 20

681 Boeing 767 and Globe

682 "The Fathers of the Fatherland leaving Congress" (R. Acevedo Bernal)

1989. Air.
1847 **681** 130p. multicoloured . . 45 15

1989. Air. 170th Anniv of Creation of First Republic of Colombia (1851) and 168th Anniv of its Constitution (others). Multicoloured.
1848 130p. Type **682** 55 15
1849 130p. "Church of the Rosary, Cucuta" (Carmelo Fernandez) . . 55 15
1850 130p. Republic's arms . . . 55 15
1851 130p. "Bolivar at Congress of Angostura" (46 × 36 mm) (Tito Salas) 55 15

683 Nativity (Barro-Raquira clay figures)

684 "Plaza de la Aduana" (H. Lemaitre)

1989. Air. Christmas.
1852 **683** 55p. multicoloured . . . 40 10

1990. Air. Presidential Summit, Cartagena.
1853 **684** 130p. multicoloured . . 60 40

685 Headphones on Marble Head

687 "Espeletia hartwegiana"

686 Cuervo Borda and National Museum

1990. Air. 50th Anniv of Colombia National Radio.
1854 **685** 150p. multicoloured . . 30 15

1990. Fauna. As T **643**.
1855 50p. grey 10 10
1856 50p. purple 10 10
1857 60p. brown 15 10
1858 60p. brown 60 20
DESIGNS: No. 1855, Grey fox; 1856, Common poison-arrow frog; 1857, Pygmy marmoset; 1858, Sun-bittern.

1990. Air. Velez City Arms. As T **476**.
1859 60p. multicoloured 15 10

1990. Air. Birth Centenary (1989) of Teresa Cuervo Borda (artist).
1860 **686** 60p. multicoloured . . . 15 10

1990. Multicoloured.
1861 60p. Type **687** 15 10
1862 60p. "Ceiba pentandra" (horiz) 15 10
1863 70p. "Ceroxylon quindiuense" 15 10
1864 70p. "Tibouchina lepidota" 15 10

688 Theatrical Masks

689 Statue, Bogota

1990. Air. 2nd Iberian-American Theatre Festival, Bogota.
1865 **688** 150p. gold, brown & orge 60 15

1990. 150th Death Anniv of Francisco de Paula Santander (President of New Granada, 1832–37). Multicoloured.
1866 50p. Type **689** (postage) . . 40 10
1867 60p. Gateway of National Pantheon (air) 40 10
1868 60p. "General Santander with the Constitution" (Jose Maria Espinosa) . . 40 10
1869 70p. Santander, organizer of public education (after F. S. Guitierrez) 40 10
1870 70p. "The Postal Carrier" (Jose Maria del Castillo) (horiz) 40 10

690 Postmen

1990. Air. 150th Anniv of the Penny Black.
1872 **690** 150p. multicoloured . . 30 15

691 Cadet, Arms and School

693 Graph

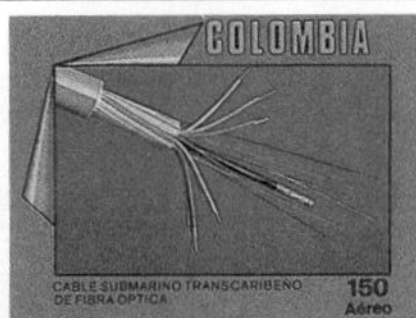

692 Cable

1990. 50th Anniv of General Santander Police Cadets School.
1873 **691** 60p. multicoloured . . . 15 10

1990. Air. Trans-Caribbean Submarine Fibre Optic Cable.
1874 **692** 150p. multicoloured . . 60 15

1990. Air. 50th Anniv of I.F.I.
1875 **693** 60p. multicoloured . . . 15 10

1990. Arms of Cartago. As T **476**.
1876 50p. multicoloured 35 10

695 Map

696 Women on Beach

1990. Air. 10th Anniv of Organization of American States.
1878 **695** 130p. multicoloured . . 55 15

1990. La Guajira.
1879 **696** 60p. multicoloured . . . 15 10

697 Indian wearing Gold Ornaments

698 St. John Bosco (founder) and Boys

1990. Air. 50th Anniv of Gold Museum, Bogota.
1880 **697** 170p. multicoloured . . 35 20

1990. Centenary of Salesian Brothers in Colombia.
1881 **698** 60p. multicoloured . . . 15 10

699 Brown Pelican, Roseate Spoonbills and Dolphins

1990. Air. America. Natural World. Multicoloured.
1882 150p. Type **699** . . . . . . 1·00 30
1883 170p. Land animals and Salvin's curassows . . . . 1·00 30

700 Christ Child

701 Monastery

1990. Air. Christmas.
1884 **700** 70p. multicoloured . . 15 10

1990. Air. Monastery of Nostra Senhora de las Lajas, Ipiales.
1885 **701** 70p. multicoloured . . . 15 10

702 Titles and Abstract

703 Christ of the Miracles, Buga Church

1991. Air. Bicentenary of "La Prensa".
1886 **702** 170p. multicoloured . . 30 15

1991.
1887 **703** 70p. multicoloured . . . 15 10

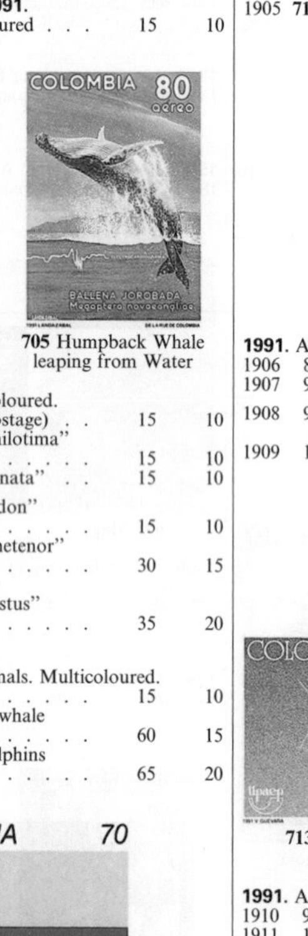

704 "Anaea syene"

705 Humpback Whale leaping from Water

1991. Butterflies. Multicoloured.
1888 70p. Type **704** (postage) . . 15 10
1889 70p. "Callithea philotima" (horiz) 15 10
1890 80p. "Thecla coronata" . . 15 10
1891 80p. "Agrias amydon" (horiz) (air) 15 10
1892 170p. "Morpho rhetenor" (horiz) 30 15
1893 190p. "Heliconius longarenus ernestus" (horiz) 35 20

1991. Air. Marine Mammals. Multicoloured.
1894 80p. Type **705** 15 10
1895 170p. Humpback whale diving 60 15
1896 190p. Amazon dolphins (horiz) 65 20

706 National Colours

1991. New Constitution.
1897 **706** 70p. multicoloured . . . 15 10
See also No. 1914.

707 Dario Echandia Olaya (after Delio Ramirez)

708 Girardot (after Jose Maria Espinosa)

1991. 2nd Death Anniv of Dario Echandia Olaya.
1898 **707** 80p. multicoloured . . . 15 10

1991. Birth Bicent of Colonel Atanasio Girardot.
1899 **708** 70p. multicoloured . . . 15 10

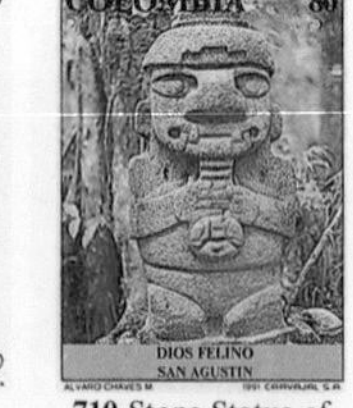

709 Galan

710 Stone Statue of God, San Agustin

1991. 2nd Death Anniv of Luis Carlos Galan Sarmiento (politician).
1900 **709** 80p. multicoloured . . . 15 10

1991. Pre-Columbian Art. Multicoloured.
1901 80p. Type **710** (postage) . . 15 10
1902 90p. Burial vessel, Tierradentro 15 10
1903 90p. Statue, San Agustin (air) 15 10
1904 210p. Gold flyingfish, San Agustin (horiz) 50 20

711 Sailfish

1991.
1905 **711** 830p. multicoloured . . 2·50 1·00

712 Cloisters of St. Augustine's, Tunja

1991. Architecture. Multicoloured.
1906 80p. Type **712** (postage) . . 15 10
1907 90p. Bridge, Chia 15 10
1908 90p. Roadside chapel, Pamplona (vert) (air) . . 15 10
1909 190p. Church of the Conception, Santa Fe de Bogota (vert) 60 20

713 "Santa Maria"

714 Lleras Camargo (after Rafael Salas)

1991. Air. America. Voyages of Discovery. Mult.
1910 90p. Type **713** 35 20
1911 190p. Amerindians and approaching ship 85 30

1991. 1st Death Anniv of Alberto Lleras Camargo (President, 1945–46 and 1958–62).
1912 **714** 80p. multicoloured . . . 15 10

715 Police Officers, Transport, Emblem and Flag

1991. Centenary of Police.
1913 **715** 80p. multicoloured . . . 30 10

1991. Air. New Constitution (2nd issue). As No. 1897 but new value and additionally inscr "SANTAFE DE BOGOTA. D.C. Julio 4 de 1991".
1914 90p. multicoloured 15 10

716 Member Nations' Flags

717 First Government Building, Sogamoso

1991. Air. 5th Group of Rio Presidential Summit, Cartagena.
1915 **716** 190p. multicoloured . . 30 15

1991.
1916 **717** 80p. multicoloured . . . 10 10

718 "Adoration of the Kings" (Baltazar de Figueroa)

719 D. Turbay Quintero

1991. Air. Christmas.
1917 **718** 90p. multicoloured . . . 15 10

1992. Diana Turbay Quintero (journalist) Commemoration.
1918 **719** 80p. multicoloured . . . 10 10

720 Hand holding Posy of Flowers

721 Cut Flowers

1992. Air. 8th U.N. Conference on Trade and Development Session, Cartagena.
1919 **720** 210p. multicoloured . . 35 20

1992. Air. Exports.
1920 90p. Type **721** 15 10
1921 210p. Fruits and nuts (horiz) 35 20

722 Statue of General Santander, Barranquilla (R. Verlet)

723 Music, Book and Paint Brush

1992. Birth Bicentenary of General Francisco de Paula Santander. Multicoloured.
1922 80p. Type **722** (postage) . . 10 10
1923 190p. Francisco de Paula Santander (after Sergio Trujillo Magnenat) (air) 30 15

1992. Air. Copyright Protection.
1925 **723** 190p. multicoloured . . 30 15

725 Lievano Aguirre

726 Enrique Low Murtra (1st anniv)

1992. 10th Death Anniv of Indalecio Lievano Aguirre (ambassador to United Nations).
1928 **725** 80p. multicoloured . . . 10 10

1992. Death Anniversaries of Justice Ministers. Multicoloured.
1929 100p. Type **726** 15 10
1930 110p. Rodrigo Lara Bonilla (8th anniv) 20 10

727 Town Arms and Rings

1992. 14th National Games, Barranquilla.
1931 **727** 110p. multicoloured . . 20 10

728 Landscape

729 Athlete and Olympic Rings

1992. Air. 2nd U.N. Conference on Environment and Development, Rio de Janeiro. Paintings by Roberto Palomino. Multicoloured.
1932 230p. Type **728** 35 20
1933 230p. Birds in trees 35 20

1992. Air. Olympic Games, Barcelona.
1934 **729** 110p. multicoloured . . 20 10

730 "Discovery of America by C. Columbus" (Dali)

1992. Air. America. Multicoloured.
1935 230p. Type **730** 80 30
1936 260p. "America Magic, Myth and Legend" (Al. Vivero) . . . . 1·00 75

731 American Crocodile

1992. Endangered Animals. Multicoloured.
1937 100p. Type **731** 15 10
1938 100p. Andean condor (vert) 45 30

732 Maria Lopez de Escobar (founder)

734 Map of the Americas

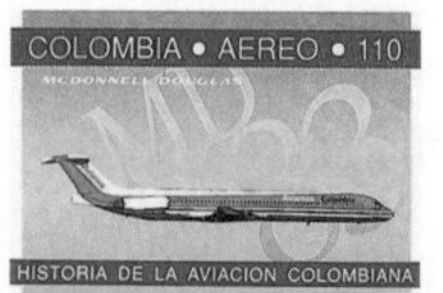

733 Avianca Colombia McDonnell Douglas MD-83

1992. 50th Anniv of House of Mother and Child.
1939 **732** 100p. mult (postage) . . 15 10
1940 110p. mult (air) 20 10

1992. Air.
1941 **733** 110p. multicoloured . . 20 10

1992. Meeting of First Ladies of the Americas and the Caribbean, Cartagena.
1942 **734** 100p. multicoloured . . 15 10

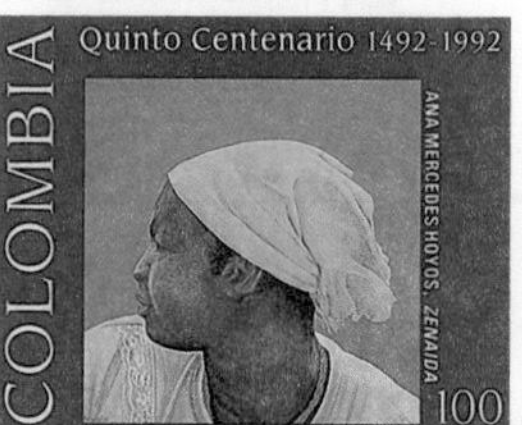

735 "Zenaida" (Ana Mercedes Hoyos)

1992. 500th Anniv of Discovery of America by Columbus. Paintings.

1943 **735** 100p. mult (postage) . . 15 10
1944 – 110p. multicoloured . . 20 10
1946 – 110p. mult (air) 20 10
1947 – 230p. multicoloured . . 35 20
1948 – 260p. green and violet 40 20

DESIGNS: 110p. (1944), "Study for 1/500" (Beatriz Gonzalez); 110p. (1946), "Blue Eagle" (Alejandro Obregon); 230p. "Cantileo" (Luis Luna); 260p. "Maize" (Antonio Caro).

736 Recycling

1992.

1949 **736** 100p. multicoloured . . 15 10

737 Front Curtain

1992. Air. Columbus Theatre.

1950 **737** 230p. multicoloured . . 35 20

739 "Nativity" (Carlos Alfonso Mendez)

1992. Christmas. Children's Drawings. Mult.

1952 100p. Type **739** (postage) . . 15 10
1953 110p. Kings approaching stable (Catalina del Valle) (air) 20 10

740 G. Lara

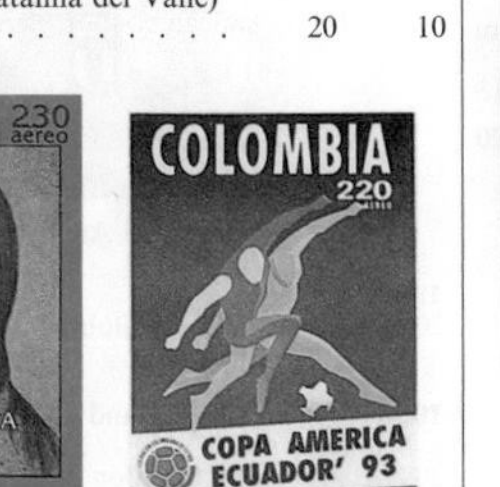

748 Footballers

742 Campaign Emblem

1992. Air. 10th Death Anniv of Gloria Lara (ambassador to the United Nations).

1954 **740** 230p. multicoloured . . 40 20

1993. Lions Club International Amblyopia Prevention Campaign.

1956 **742** 100p. multicoloured . . 15 10

1993. Air. America Cup Football Championship, Ecuador.

1962 **748** 220p. multicoloured . . 35 20

749 Prisoners

1993. Bicentenary of French Declaration of Human Rights. Multicoloured.

1963 150p. Type **749** (postage) . . 25 15
1964 150p. The elderly 25 15
1965 200p. The infirm 35 20
1966 200p. Children 35 20
1968 220p. Women (air) 35 20
1969 220p. The poor 35 20
1970 460p. Environmental protection . . . . 1·00 40
1971 520p. Immigrants . . . . . 1·10 45

750 Amerindian (Jose Luis Correal)

752 Green-winged Macaw ("Papagayo")

751 Emblem and Flags

1993. Air. International Year of Indigenous Peoples.

1972 **750** 460p. multicoloured . . 70 35

1993. Air. World Cup Football Championship, U.S.A. (1994) (1st issue).

1973 **751** 220p. multicoloured . . 35 20

See also Nos. 2006/9.

1993. The Amazon. Multicoloured.

1974 150p. Type **752** (postage) . . 60 40
1975 150p. Anaconda 20 10
1976 220p. Water-lilies (air) . . . 35 20
1977 220p. Ipecacuanha flower 35 20

753 Cotton-headed Tamarin

755 Nativity

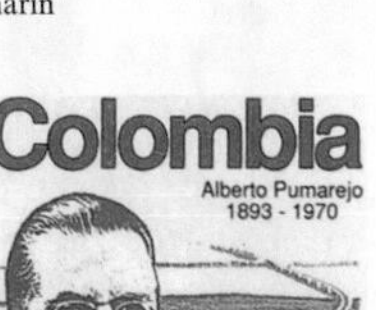

754 Alberto Pumarejo (politician)

1993. Air. America. Endangered Animals. Mult.

1979 220p. Type **753** 35 20
1980 220p. American purple gallinule 60 30
1981 460p. Andean cock of the rock 90 40
1982 520p. American manatee . . 80 40

1993. Famous Colombians. Multicoloured.

1983 150p. Type **754** 20 10
1984 150p. Lorencita Villegas de Santos (First Lady, 1938–42) 20 10
1985 150p. Meliton Rodriguez (photographer) 20 10
1986 150p. Tomas Carrasquilla (writer) 20 10

1993. Christmas. Multicoloured.

1987 200p. Type **755** (postage) . . 30 15
1988 220p. Shepherd (air) 35 20

756 San Andres y Providencia

1993. Tourism. Multicoloured.

1989 220p. Type **756** 35 20
1990 220p. Cocuy National Park 35 20
1991 220p. La Cocha Lake . . . 35 20
1992 220p. Waterfall, La Macarena mountains . . 35 20
1993 460p. Chicamocha (vert) . . 70 35
1994 460p. Sierra Nevada de Santa Marta (vert) . . . 70 35
1995 520p. Embalse de Penol (vert) 80 40

See also No. E1996.

757 Museum Entrance

759 Yellow-eared Conure

1993. 170th Anniv of National Museum.

1997 **757** 150p. multicoloured . . 20 10

1994. Birds. Multicoloured.

1999 180p. Type **759** (postage) . . 70 45
2000 240p. Bogota rail 90 60
2001 270p. Toucan barbets (horiz) (air) . . . . 1·10 70
2002 560p. Cinnamon teals (horiz) . . . . 2·10 1·40

760 Emblem

1994. Air. International Decade for Natural Disaster Reduction. National Disaster Prevention System.

2003 **760** 630p. blue, yellow & red 95 50

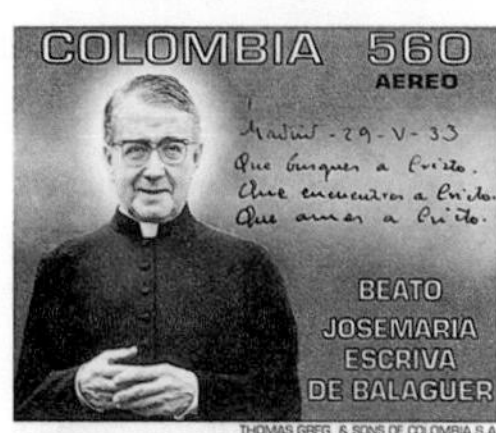

762 Escriva de Balaguer

1994. Air. Beatification of Josemaria Escriva de Balaguer (founder of Opus Dei).

2005 **762** 560p. multicoloured . . 85 45

763 Trophy and Player and Emblem on Flag

1994. World Cup Football Championship, U.S.A. (2nd issue). Multicoloured.

2006 180p. Type **763** (postage) . . 25 15
2008 270p. Match scene, trophy and emblem (air) 40 20
2009 560p. Trophy, emblem, ball and national colours (vert) 85 45

764 Flagpoles

765 "Self-portrait"

1994. Air. 4th Latin American Presidential Summit, Cartagena.

2011 **764** 630p. multicoloured . . 95 50

See also No. E2010.

1994. Birth Centenary of Ricardo Rendon (painter).

2012 **765** 240p. black 30 15

766 Biplane and William Knox Martin

1994. Air. 75th Anniv of First Airmail Flight.

2013 **766** 270p. multicoloured . . 35 20

767 Emblem

1994. 40th Anniv of Radio and Television Network.

2014 **767** 180p. multicoloured . . 25 15

768 Numbers, Graphs and Pie Chart

770 Horse and Bicycle

1994. 1993 Census.

2015 **768** 240p. multicoloured . . 30 15

1994. Air. America. Postal Transport. Mult.

2017 **770** 270p. multicoloured . . 35 20

See also No. E2018.

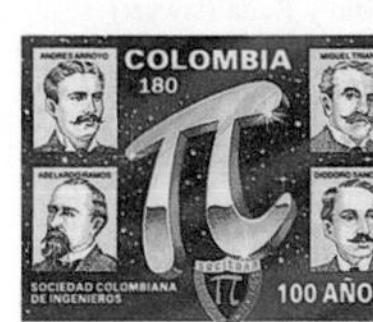

771 Founders and Pi Symbol

1994. Centenary of Colombian Society of Engineers.

2019 **771** 180p. multicoloured . . 25 15

772 Building and Scales

1994. Air. 80th Anniv of National Institute of Legal Medicine and Forensic Sciences.

2020 **772** 560p. multicoloured . . 75 40

773 Three Wise Men

1994. Air. Christmas.
2021 **773** 270p. multicoloured . . 35 20
See also No. E2022.

774 1921 SCADTA 30c. Stamp
775 Common Iguana

1995. Air. 75th Anniv (1994) of Sociedad Colombo-Alemana de Transportes Aereos (SCADTA) (private air company contracted to carry mail).
2023 **774** 330p. pink, brown & blk 60 25

1995. Air. Flora and Fauna. Multicoloured.
2024 650p. Type **775** 85 45
2025 650p. Iguana facing left . . 85 45
2026 750p. Forest (left detail) . . 1·00 50
2027 750p. Forest (right detail) . . 1·00 50
Stamps of the same value were issued together in se-tenant pairs, each pair forming a composite design.

776 1920 10c. Stamp

1995. Air. 75th Anniv of Compania Colombiana de Navagacion Aerea (private air company contracted to carry mail).
2028 **776** 330p. multicoloured . . 45 25

778 Jose Miguel Pey

1995. Colombian Patriots. Multicoloured.
2030 270p. Type **778** (revolutionary) 35 20
2031 270p. Jorge Tadeo Lozana (zoologist and revolutionary) 35 20
2032 270p. Antonio Narino (journalist and politician) 35 20
2033 270p. Camilo Torres (lawyer and revolutionary) . . . 35 20
2034 270p. Jose Fernandez Madrid (doctor and revolutionary) 35 20
2035 270p. Jose Maria del Castillo y Rada (lawyer) 35 20
2036 270p. Custodio Garcia Rovira (revolutionary) . . 35 20
2037 270p. Antonio Villavicencio (revolutionary) 35 20
2038 270p. Liborio Mejia (lawyer and historian) 35 20
2039 270p. Rafael Urdaneta (diplomat) 35 20
2040 270p. Juan Garcia del Rio (writer and politician) . . 35 20
2041 270p. Gen. Jose Maria Melo 35 20
2042 270p. Gen. Tomas Herrera 35 20
2043 270p. Froilan Largacha (acting President, Feb–June 1863) 35 20
2044 270p. Salvader Camacho Roldan (writer) 35 20
2045 270p. Gen. Ezequiel Hurtado (acting President, Apr–Aug 1884) 35 20
2046 270p. Dario Echandia Olaya (lawyer) 35 20
2047 270p. Alberto Lleras Camargo (President, 1945–46) 35 20
2048 270p. Gen. Gustavo Rojas Pinilla (President, 1953–57) 35 20
2049 270p. Carlos Lleras Restrepo (President, 1966–70) 35 20

779 Farmers on Hillside

1995. Air. 50th Anniv of F.A.O.
2050 **779** 750p. multicoloured . . 1·00 50

780 Bello
781 Fireman

1995. Air. 25th Anniv of Andres Bello (scholar and writer). Agreement on Intellectual Co-operation.
2051 **780** 650p. multicoloured . . 85 45

1995. Air. Centenary of Fire Brigade of Bogota.
2052 **781** 330p. multicoloured . . 45 25

782 Emblem
783 Anniversary Emblem

1995. Air. 50th Anniv of National Chamber of Commerce.
2053 **782** 330p. multicoloured . . 45 25

1995. Air. 50th Anniv of U.N.O.
2054 **783** 750p. multicoloured . . 45 25

784 Emblem
786 Obando (after Efrain Martinez)

1995. Air. 1st Pacific Ocean Games, Cali.
2055 **784** 750p. multicoloured . . 1·00 50

1995. Birth Bicentenary of General Jose Maria Obando.
2057 **786** 220p. multicoloured . . 25 15

787 San Filipe de Barajas Castle

1995. Air. 11th Non-aligned Countries' Conference, Cartagena de Indias.
2058 **787** 650p. multicoloured . . 80 40

788 Estela Lopez Pomareda in "Maria", Charlie Chaplin and Jackie Coogan

1995. Air. Centenary of Motion Pictures.
2059 **788** 330p. black and brown 40 20

789 Harvesting Poppies for Opium
790 Anniversary Emblem

1995. Air. World Campaign against Drug Trafficking. Multicoloured.
2060 330p. Type **789** 40 20
2061 330p. Manacled hands (horiz) 40 20

1995. Air. 25th Anniv of Andean Development Corporation.
2062 **790** 650p. multicoloured . . 80 40

792 Madre-Monte

1995. Air. Myths and Legends (1st issue). Multicoloured.
2065 750p. Type **792** 90 45
2066 750p. La Llorana 90 45
2067 750p. El Mohan (river spirit) 90 45
2068 750p. Alligator man 90 45
Nos. 2065/8 were issued together, se-tenant, in sheetlets in which the background colour gradually changes down the sheet; each design therefore occurs in four slightly different colours.
See also Nos. 2085/8.

793 Holy Family

1995. Christmas. Stained Glass Windows from Chapel of the Apostles, Bogota School. Mult.
2069 220p. Type **793** (postage) . . 25 15
2070 330p. Nativity (air) 40 20

794 Asuncion Silva

1996. Air. Death Centenary of Jose Asuncion Silva (poet).
2071 **794** 400p. multicoloured . . 50 25

795 Painting by Luz Maria Tobon Mesa
796 Salavarrieta (after Jose Maria Espinosa)

1996. Air. Providence Island.
2072 **795** 800p. multicoloured . . 1·00 50

1996. Air. Birth Bicentenary of Policarpa Salavarrieta.
2073 **796** 900p. multicoloured . . 1·10 55

797 De Greiff (Ricardo Rendon)

799 Santa Maria la Antigua del Darien

1996. 1st Death Anniv of Leon De Greiff (poet).
2074 **797** 400p. black 50 25

1996. Town Arms. Multicoloured.
2076 400p. Type **799** 50 25
2077 400p. San Sebastian de Mariquita 50 25
2078 400p. Marinilla 50 25
2079 400p. Santa Cruz de Mompox 50 25

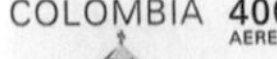

801 Medellin Cathedral

1996. Air.
2081 **801** 400p. multicoloured . . 50 25

803 Mosquera Courtyard

1996. 150th Anniv of National Capitol, Bogota.
2083 **803** 400p. multicoloured . . 50 25

804 National Archive, Bogota

1996. Air.
2084 **804** 400p. multicoloured . . 50 25

1996. Air. Myths and Legends (2nd issue). Multicoloured.
2085 900p. The Creation of Koguin . . . . 1·10 55
2086 900p. Yonna Wayu . . . . 1·10 55
2087 900p. Jaguar-man . . . . . 1·10 55
2088 900p. Lord of the Animals 1·10 55

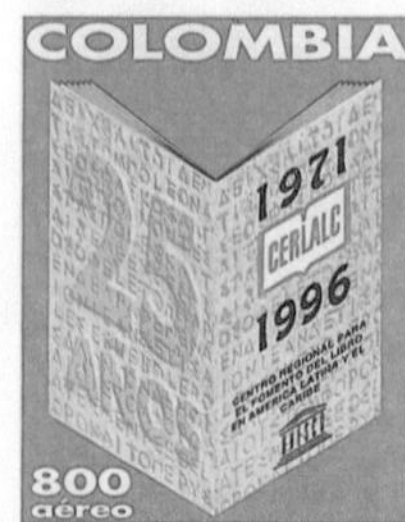

805 Anniversary Emblem

1996. Air. 25th Anniv of Regional Centre for the Development of Books in Latin America and Caribbean.
2089 **805** 800p. brn, blk & dp brn 95 50

806 Guitar and Notes

808 Golf Course

807 Jorge Isaacs and Pump

1996. 50th Anniv of Society of Colombian Authors and Composers.
2090 **806** 400p. multicoloured . . 50 25

1996. Air. Pioneers of Petroleum Industry. Multicoloured.
2091 800p. Type **807** 95 50
2092 800p. Francisco Burgos Rubio and refinery (at night) 95 50
2093 800p. Diego Martinez Camargo and drilling tower 95 50
2094 800p. Prisciliano Cabrales Lora and drilling platform 1·25 60
2095 800p. Manuel Maria Palacio and firefighting tug . . . 1·25 90
2096 800p. Roberto de Mares and refinery 95 50
2097 800p. General Virgilio Barco Maldonado and workmen 95 50
2098 800p. Workmen and Ecopetrol (state petroleum industry) emblem 95 50

1996. Air. 50th Anniv of Colombian Golf Federation.
2099 **808** 400p. multicoloured . . 50 25

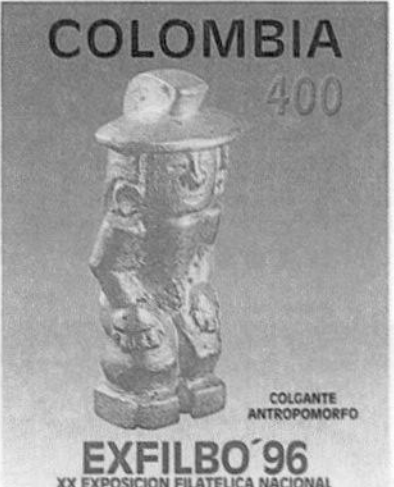

809 Pre-Columban Pendant, Malagana Treasure

1996. "Exfilbo '96" National Stamp Exn, Bogota.
2100 **809** 400p. multicoloured . . 50 25

811 Postman delivering Letter

1996. Christmas. The Annunciation. Mult.
2102 400p. Type **811** (postage) . . 50 25
2103 400p. Woman reading letter and postman (air) 50 25

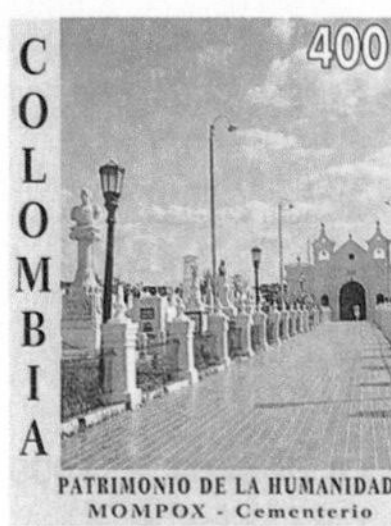

813 Cemetary, Mompox

1996. U.N.E.S.C.O. World Heritage Sites. Mult.
2106 400p. Type **813** 50 25
2107 400p. San Agustin Archaeological Park . . . 50 25
2108 400p. Palace of the Inquisition, Cartagena . . 50 25
2109 400p. Underground tomb, Tierradentro Archaeological Park . . . 50 25

814 Children holding Hands

815 Hurtado

1997. Air. Children's Rights.
2110 **814** 400p. multicoloured . . 45 25

1997. 2nd Death Anniv of Alvaro Gomez Hurtado (lawyer and politician).
2111 **815** 400p. black and blue . . 45 25

816 Film Reels and Harbour Tower

COLOMBIA 400 AEREO SEGURO SOCIAL Para Siempre SALUD • PENSIONES PROTECCION LABORAL

817 Emblem

1997. Air. Centenary of Colombian Cinema and 53rd International Union of Film Archives Congress, Cartagena de Indias.
2112 **816** 800p. multicoloured . . 90 45

1997. Air. 50th Anniv (1996) of State Social Security.
2113 **817** 400p. multicoloured . . 45 25

818 Hand holding Mobile Phone

1997. Air. Centenary (1996) of Ericsson Company in Colombia.
2114 **818** 900p. multicoloured . . 90 45

819 Cattle

1997. Air. Cordoba Cattle Fair.
2115 **819** 400p. multicoloured . . 30 15

820 "Maria Varilla in the Clouds" (William Vive)

1997. Porro National Festival, San Pelayo.
2116 **820** 400p. multicoloured . . 30 15

821 Typewriter

1997. 50th Anniv of Bogota Journalists' Association.
2117 **821** 400p. multicoloured . . 30 15

822 Museum Buildings

1997. Air. 1st Anniv of Numismatic Museum at State Mint, Bogota.
2118 **822** 800p. multicoloured . . 65 35

823 Palm

1997. Air. Vegetable Ivory Palm Production Project.
2119 **823** 900p. multicoloured . . 70 35

824 Barco

1997. Virgilio Barco (President, 1986–90) Commem.
2120 **824** 500p. multicoloured . . 40 20

825 Straightening Contorted Tree and Healthy Couple

1997. Air. 50th Anniv of Colombian Society of Orthopaedic Surgery and Traumatology.
2121 **825** 1000p. multicoloured . . 80 40

826 Luis Carlos Lopez (poet)

1997. Air. Personalities. Multicoloured.
2122 500p. Type **826** 40 20
2123 500p. Aurelio Arturo (poet) 40 20
2124 500p. Enrique Perez Arbelaez (botanist and historian) 40 20
2125 500p. Jose Maria Gonzalez Benito (mathematician and astronomer) 40 20
2126 500p. Jose Manuel Rivas Sacconi (philologist and diplomat) 40 20
2127 500p. Eduardo Lemaitre Roman (historian and journalist) 40 20
2128 500p. Diojenes Arrieta (journalist and politician) 40 20
2129 500p. Gabriel Turbay Abunader (politician and diplomat) 40 20
2130 500p. Guillermo Echavarria Misas (aviation pioneer) 40 20
2131 500p. Juan Friede Alter (historian) 40 20
2132 500p. Fabio Lozano Torrijos (diplomat) . . . 40 20
2133 500p. Lino de Pombo (engineer and diplomat) 40 20
2134 500p. Cacica Gaitana (Indian resistance leader) 40 20
2135 500p. Josefa Acevedo de Gomez (writer) 40 20
2136 500p. Domingo Bioho (Black leader) 40 20

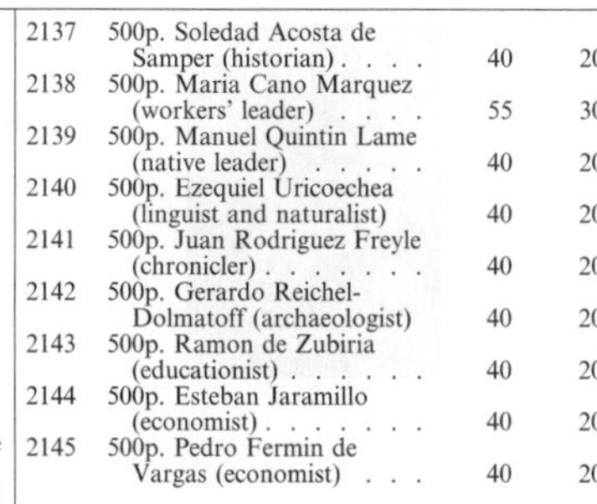

2137 500p. Soledad Acosta de Samper (historian) 40 20
2138 500p. Maria Cano Marquez (workers' leader) 55 30
2139 500p. Manuel Quintin Lame (native leader) 40 20
2140 500p. Ezequiel Uricoechea (linguist and naturalist) 40 20
2141 500p. Juan Rodriguez Freyle (chronicler) 40 20
2142 500p. Gerardo Reichel-Dolmatoff (archaeologist) 40 20
2143 500p. Ramon de Zubiria (educationist) 40 20
2144 500p. Esteban Jaramillo (economist) 40 20
2145 500p. Pedro Fermin de Vargas (economist) . . . 40 20

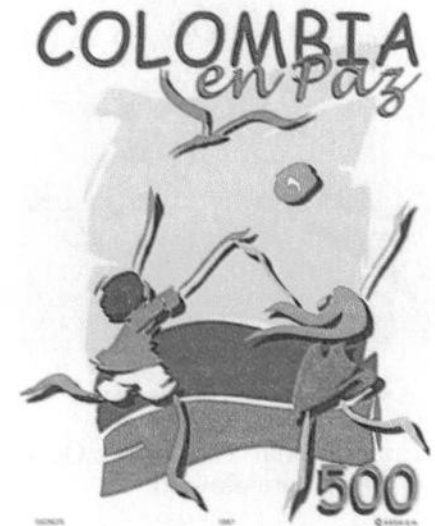

827 National Flag, Dove and Children playing

1997. Peace. Multicoloured.
2146 500p. Type **827** (postage) . . 40 20
2147 1100p. Children holding hands in ring (air) 85 45

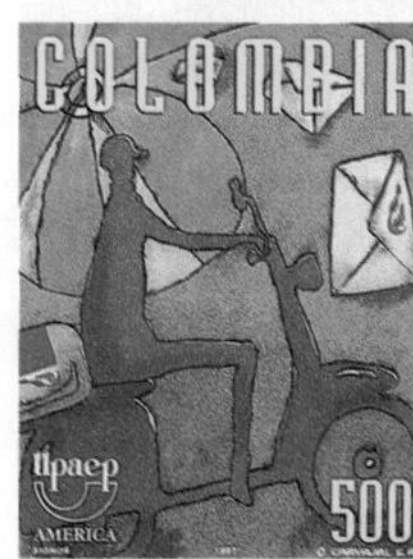

828 Postman on Moped

1997. America. The Postman. Multicoloured.
2148 500p. Type **828** (postage) . . 40 20
2149 1100p. Postman raising envelope to night sky (air) 85 45

829 Pregnant Women

830 Dove Emblem

1998. Air. 50th Anniv of W.H.O. Safe Motherhood.
2150 **829** 1100p. multicoloured . . 65 35

1998. Air. 4th Bolivarian Stamp Exhibition, Santafe de Bogota.
2151 **830** 1000p. orange and blue 60 30

831 Gaitan

832 Colombian Flag and Map of the Americas

1998. 50th Death Anniv of Jorge Eliecer Gaitan.
2152 **831** 500p. multicoloured . . 30 15

1998. Air. 50th Anniv of Organization of American States.
2153 **832** 1000p. multicoloured . . 60 30

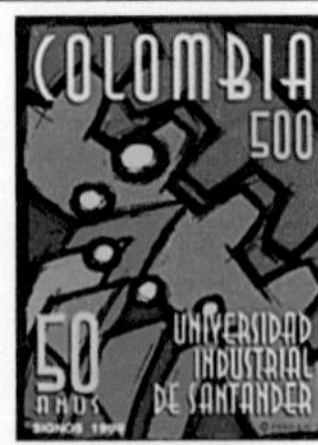

833 Cogs

1998. 50th Anniv of Santander Industrial University.
2154 **833** 500p. multicoloured . . 30 15

834 "Gloria" (cadet ship) and Dolphins

1998. Air. International Year of the Ocean.
2155 **834** 1100p. multicoloured . . 65 35

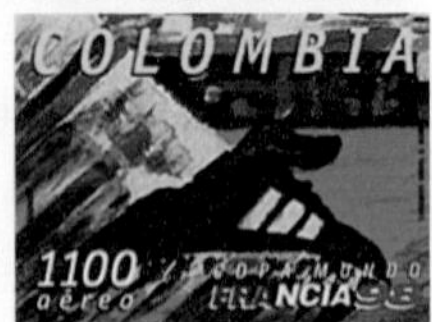

835 Football Boot

1998. Air. World Cup Football Championship, France. Multicoloured.
2156 1100p. Type **835** 65 35
2157 1100p. Ball 65 35
2158 1100p. Goalkeeper's glove 65 35
Nos. 2156/8 were issued together, se-tenant, forming a composite design.

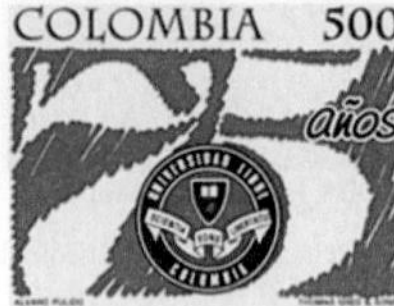

836 University Arms

1998. 75th Anniv of Colombia Free University.
2159 **836** 500p. black and red . . 30 15

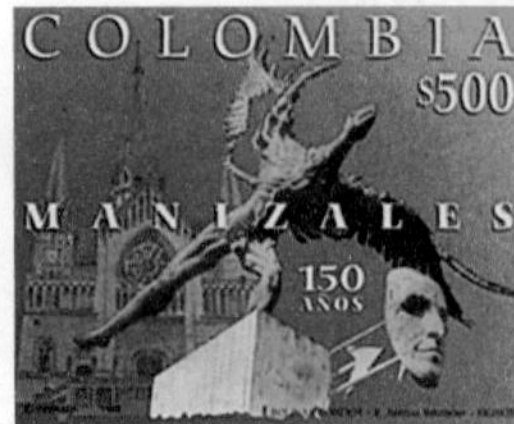

837 "Bolivar Condor" (sculpture, R. Arenas Betancur) and Cathedral

1998. 150th Anniv of Manizales.
2160 **837** 500p. multicoloured . . 30 15

838 Gold Coin, Tairona Culture

839 Borrero

1998. 75th Anniversaries. Multicoloured.
2161 500p. Type **838** (National Bank) 30 15
2162 500p. Gold sheaf of corn, Malagana Culture (Comptroller-General's Office) 30 15
2163 500p. Gold mask, Quimbaya Culture (Banking Superintendent's Office) 30 15

1998. 1st Death Anniv of Misael Pastrana Borrero (President, 1970–74).
2164 **839** 500p. multicoloured . . 30 15

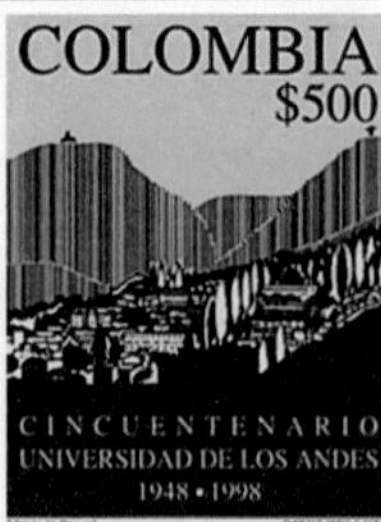

840 The Andes and University Campus

1998. 50th Anniv of University of the Andes, Bogota.
2165 **840** 500p. black and yellow 30 15

841 Woman panning for Gold, and Cherubs

843 Academy of Languages Arms

842 Bochica

1998. Christmas. Multicoloured.
2166 500p. Type **841** (postage) . . 30 15
2167 1000p. Three kings, camel and star (air) 60 30
2168 1000p. Nativity 60 30
Nos. 2167/8 were issued together, se-tenant, forming a composite design.

1998. Air. Muisca Mythology. Multicoloured.
2169 1000p. Type **842** 60 30
2170 1000p. Chiminigua 60 30
2171 1000p. Bachue and Huitica 60 30
Nos. 2169/71 were issued together, se-tenant, forming a composite design.

1998. Arms of Colombian Academies. Mult.
2172 500p. Type **843** 30 15
2173 500p. Medicine 30 15
2174 500p. Law 30 15
2175 500p. History 30 15
2176 500p. Physical and Natural Sciences 30 15
2177 500p. Economics 30 15
2178 500p. Ecclesiastical History 30 15

844 Soledad Roman de Nunez (First Lady, 1880–82 and 1884–94)

845 Lopez (after G. Ricci)

1999. America (1998). Famous Women. Mult.
2179 600p. Type **844** (postage) . . 35 20
2180 1200p. Bertha Hernandez de Ospina (politician) (air) 70 35

1999. Birth Bicentenary of Jose Hilario Lopez (President, 1849–53).
2181 **845** 1000p. multicoloured . . 60 30

846 Green Turtle

1999. Turtles. Multicoloured.
2182 1300p. Type **846** 80 49
2183 1300p. Leatherback turtle ("Dermochelys coriacea") 80 40
2184 1300p. Hawksbill turtle ("Eretmochelys imbricata") 80 40
Nos. 2182/4 were issued together, se-tenant, forming a composite design.

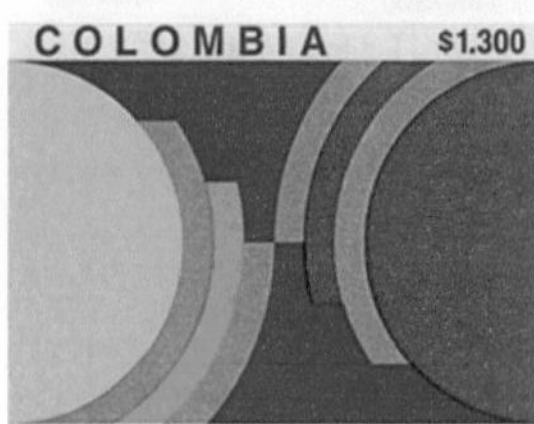

847 Colombian and Japanese Suns across the Pacific

1999. 70 Years of Japanese Emigration to Colombia.
2185 **847** 1300p. multicoloured (yellow sun at left) . . 80 40
2186 1300p. multicoloured (red sun at left) . . . 80 40
Nos. 2185/6 were issued together, se-tenant, forming a composite design.

848 Medal

850 Zuleta Angel

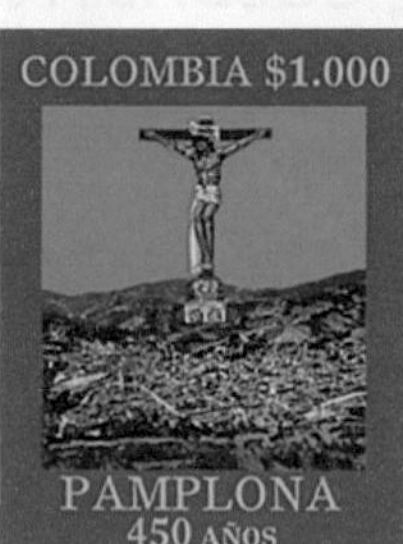

849 Crucifix above Pamplona

1999. 900th Anniv of Sovereign Military Order of Malta.
2187 **848** 1200p. multicoloured . . 70 35

1999. 450th Anniv of Pamplona.
2188 **849** 1000p. multicoloured . . 60 30

1999. Birth Centenary of Eduardo Zuleta Angel (politician and diplomat).
2189 **850** 600p. multicoloured . . 35 20

851 Colombian Olympic Committee Emblem

1999. 13th Pan-American Games, Winnipeg. Mult.
2190 1200p. Type **851** 70 35
2191 1200p. Running (facing right) 70 35
2192 1200p. Weightlifting (facing left) 70 35
2193 1200p. Cycling (facing right) 70 35
2194 1200p. Shooting (facing left) 70 35
2195 1200p. Roller blading (facing right) 70 35
2196 1200p. Running (facing left) 70 35
2197 1200p. Weightlifting (facing right) 70 35
2198 1200p. Cycling (facing left) 70 35
2199 1200p. Shooting (facing right) 70 35
2200 1200p. Roller blading (facing left) 70 35

852 Robles

854 Flowers leaving Hands

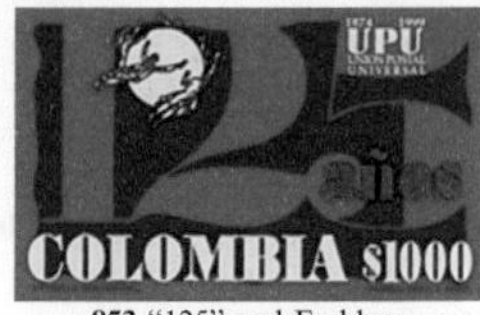

853 "125" and Emblem

1999. 150th Birth Anniv of Luis A. Robles.
2201 **852** 600p. multicoloured . . 35 20

1999. 125th Anniv of Universal Postal Union. Each lilac, violet and gold.
2202 1000p. Type **853** 60 30
2203 1300p. Emblem 85 45

1999. America. A New Millennium without Arms. Multicoloured.
2204 1200p. Type **854** 75 40
2205 1200p. Flowers moving towards hands 75 40
Nos. 2204/5 were issued together, se-tenant, forming a composite design.

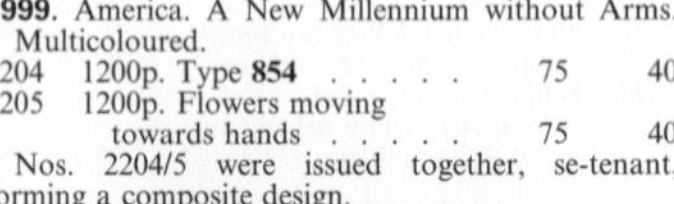
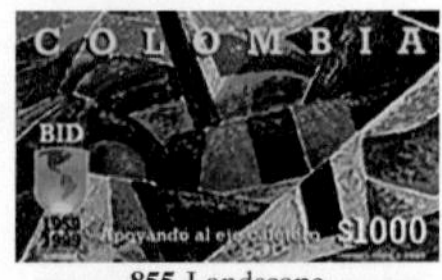

855 Landscape

1999. 40th Anniv of International Development Bank. Multicoloured.
2206 1000p. Type **855** 60 30
2207 1000p. Landscape, sunbeams and red fruits 60 30
Nos. 2206/7 were issued together, se-tenant, forming a composite design.

856 Nativity

1999. Christmas. Multicoloured.
2208 600p. Type **856** 35 20
2209 600p. Angel and Three Wise Men 35 20
Nos. 2208/9 were issued together, se-tenant, forming a composite design.

857 Emblem

858 Rainbow, Globe and "2000"

1999. Centenary of Invention of Aspirin (drug).
2210 **857** 600p. multicoloured . . 35 20

2000. New Millennium. Multicoloured.
2211 1000p. Type **858** 60 30
2212 1000p. Man with Colombian flag and dove 60 30

859 University Arms

2000. 50th Anniv of Medellin University.
2213 **859** 1000p. multicoloured . . 60 30

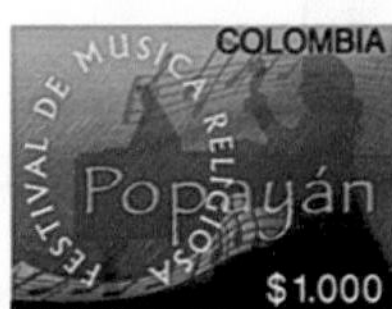
860 Faria Bermudez

2000. 20th Death Anniv (1999) of Father Jose Rafael Faria Bermudez.
2214 **860** 1300p. brown and black 85 45

861 Pianist and Score

2000. Religious Music Festival, Popayan.
2215 **861** 1000p. multicoloured . . 60 40

862 Stylized Figures forming Olympic Rings

2000. Olympic Games, Sydney.
2216 **862** 1000p. multicoloured . . 60 40

863 Male and Female Symbols under Umbrella

2000. A.I.D.S. Awareness Campaign.
2217 **863** 1000p. multicoloured . . 60 40

864 Weather Vane

2000. 50th Anniv of World Meteorological Society.
2218 **864** 1000p. multicoloured . . 60 40

865 Footprints

2000. National Birth Register
2219 **865** 1000p. multicoloured . . 60 40

866 "Archangel" (Fernando Botero)

2001. Botero Foundation, Bogota. Multicoloured.
2220 650p. Type **866** 40 25
2221 650p. "Gypsy with Tamborine" (Jean Baptiste Camille Corot) 40 25
2222 650p. "Vera Sergine Renoir" (Pierre-Auguste Renoir) 40 25
2223 650p. "Man on Horse" (Botero) 40 25
2224 650p. "Mother Superior" (Botero) 40 25
2225 650p. "Town" (Botero) . . 40 25
2226 650p. "Flowers" (Botero) 40 25
2227 650p. "Cezanne" (Botero) 40 25
2228 650p. "The Patio" (Botero) 40 25
2229 650p. "Absinthe Drinker at Grenelle" (Henri Toulouse-Lautrec) 40 25
2230 650p. "The Pequeno Valley" (Jean Baptiste Camille Corot) 40 25
2231 650p. "The Studio" (Botero) 40 25

867 Children enclosed in Circle

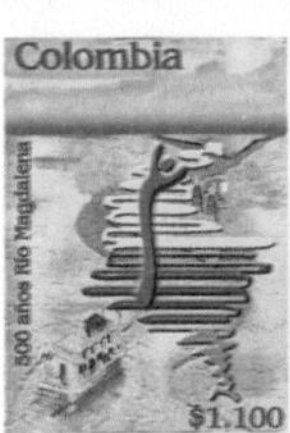
868 Girl and Dove

2001. Children's Day.
2232 **867** 1100p. multicoloured . . 65 30

2001. 150th Anniv of the Abolition of Slavery.
2233 **868** 1100p. multicoloured . . 65 30

869 Emblem, River Boat and River

870 Football and Club Emblems

2001. 500th Anniv of Discovery of Magdalena River.
2234 **869** 1100p. multicoloured . . 65 30

2001. Copa America Football Championships.
2235 **870** 1900p. multicoloured . . 1·10 55

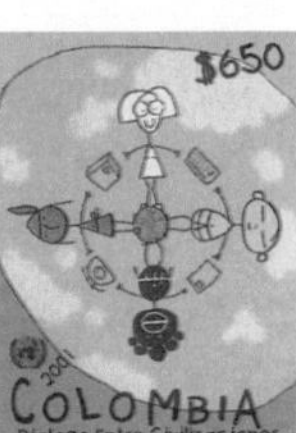
871 Waterfall, Woman and Wildlife

2001. America. Cultural Heritage. Los Katios National Park.
2236 **871** 2100p. multicoloured . . 1·20 60

872 Children encircling Globe

2001. United Nations Year of Dialogue among Civilizations.
2237 **872** 650p. multicoloured . . 40 20

873 "Reclining Woman" (sculpture, Fernando Botero)

2001.
2238 **873** 1100p. multicoloured . . 65 30

874 Man and Christmas Tree (Diego Rivera)

2001. Christmas.
2239 **874** 1100p. multicoloured . . 65 30

875 Cartegna de Indias and Vanessa Mendoza Bustos

2002. Miss Colombia, 2001–2002. Multicoloured.
2240 800p. Type **875** 50 25
2241 800p. Miss Colombia and St Francis of Assisi church, Quibdo 50 25

876 Stylized Figures and "BOGOTA 2002"

2002. 7th South American Games, Bogota.
2242 **876** 2100p. red, yellow and black . . . . 1·30 65

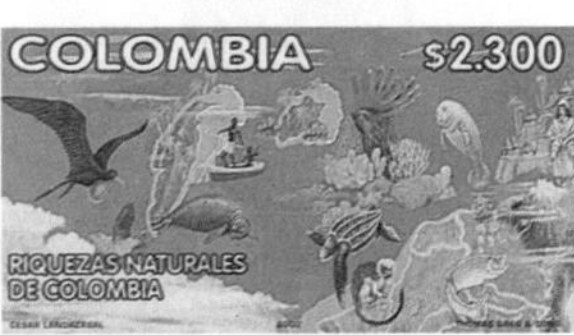
877 Frigate Bird, Islands and Marine Fauna

2002. Nature. Sheet 140 × 162 mm containing T **877** and similar horiz designs. Multicoloured.
MS2243 2300p. × 8, Type **877**; Condors and mountain; Whales, reptiles, birds and cliffs; Horse rider, birds, animals and mountain peak; Monkeys and birds; Macaws; Flamingos and otter; Egret, jaguar tapir, giant lily pads and manatee . . . . 11·00 11·00
No. **MS**2243 forms a composite design.

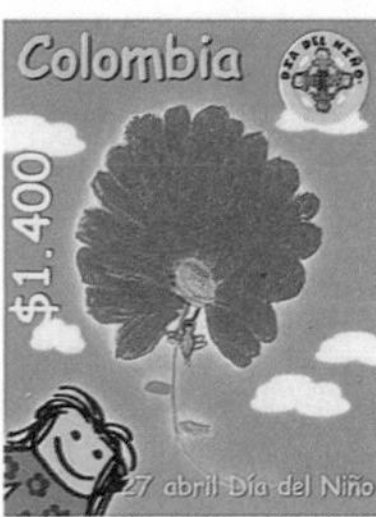
878 Flower and Girl (Diana Tovar Reyes)

2002. Children's Day.
2244 **878** 1400p. multicoloured . . 90 45

879 Postal Emblem

2002. New Emblem of Colombia Post.
2245 **879** 800p. ultramarine, red and yellow 50 25

880 Ruddy Duck (*Oxyura jamicensis*)

2002.
2246 **880** 3900p. multicoloured . . 2·50 1·20

881 Harlequin Poison Dart Frog (*Dendrobates histrionicus*)

2002. Amphibians. Sheet 120 × 80 mm containing T **881** and similar horiz design. Multicoloured.
MS2247 7200p. × 2, Type **881**; Tree frog (*Hyla crepitans*) . . . . . 4·50 4·50

882 Flambeau Butterfly (*Dryas iulia*)

2002. Butterflies. Sheet 117 × 71 mm containing T **882** and similar multicoloured design.
MS2248 13700p. × 2, Type **882**; Banded orange heliconian (*Dryadula phaetusa*) (vert) . . . 8·50 8·50

883 Boy wearing Prosthetic Leg

2002. 25th Anniv of Integral Rehabilitation Centre of Colombia (CIREC).
2249 **883** 1000p. multicoloured . . 60 30

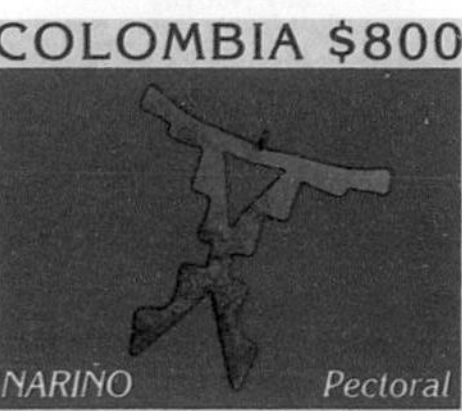
884 Narino Chest Decoration

2002. Pre-Colombian Art. Multicoloured.
2250 800p. Type **884** 50 25
2251 800p. Narino disc 50 25
2252 1400p. Calima diadem with raised decoration 50 25
2253 1400p. Calima collar 50 25

2254 2100p. Tairona anthropomorphic chest decoration 50 25
2255 2100p. Tairona circular chest decoration 50 25

885 Doctors

2002. Centenary of Society of Surgeons, San Jose Hospital, Bogota. Multicoloured.
2256 800p. Type **885** 50 25
2257 800p. San Jose hospital . . 50 25

886 Consuelo Araujo Noguera

2002. 1st Death Anniv of Consuelo Araujo Noguera "La Cacica" (journalist and politician).
2258 **886** 1400p. multicoloured . . 90 45

887 "End to Violence" and Stylized Woman

2002. Regional Conference of U N I (international trade union organisation), Rio de Janeiro.
2259 **887** 1000p. multicoloured . . 60 30

888 Letters and Words

2002. America. Education and Literacy Campaign. Each black, blue and orange.
2260 2500p. Type **888** . . . . . 1·60 80
2261 2500p. Person wearing eye-patch reading . . . . . . 1·60 80

889 Nativity

2002. Christmas.
2262 **889** 800p. multicoloured . . 50 25

890 "Critical Moments during Independence" (detail, Pedro Nel Gomez)

2002. Centenary of Academy of History. Multicoloured.
2263 800p. Type **890** 50 25
2264 800p. Horse riders with spears ("Critical Moments during Independence", detail) 50 25
2265 800p. Slaves, woman feeding baby ("Critical Moments during Independence", detail) 50 25
2266 800p. Forest ("Cafetal", Gonzalo Ariza) 50 25
2267 800p. Horse riders ("Battle of Palonegro", Marco Tobon Mejia) 50 25
2268 800p. "Jaguar hunting" (Noe Leon) 50 25
2269 800p. Bathers ("I sail across", Pedro Nel Gomez) 50 25
2270 800p. "Colombia Murdered" (Sebastian Villalaz) . . . 50 25
2271 800p. "The Women" (Jose Rodriguez) 50 25
2272 800p. Man with beard ("Santander Plaza" (detail, Juan Cardenas)) 50 25
2273 800p. Carriage ("Santander Plaza") 50 25
2274 800p. Horse and couple ("Santander Plaza") . . . 50 25
Nos. 2263/5 and 2272/4 were respectively issued together, se-tenant, forming a composite design of the painting named.

891 "Marching Soldiers" (Eladio Rubio)

2002. Centenary of Peace Treaty at end of Thousand Days' War.
2275 **891** 1600p. multicoloured . . 1·00 50

PRIVATE AIR COMPANIES

The "LANSA" and Avianca Companies operated inland and foreign air mail services on behalf of the Government and issued the following stamps. Later only the Avianca Company performed this service and the regular air stamps were used on the mail without overprints.

Similar issues were also made by Compania Colombiana de Navegacion Aerea during 1920. These are very rare and will be found listed in the Stanley Gibbons Stamp Catalogue, Part 20 (South America).

A. "LANSA" (Lineas Aereas Nacionales Sociedad Anonima).

1 Wing

1950. Air.
1 **1** 5c. yellow 15 10
2 10c. red 25 15
3 15c. blue 25 10
4 20c. green 40 25
5 30c. purple . . . . 1·25 1·25
6 60c. brown . . . . 1·50 1·75
With background network colours in brackets.
7 **1** 1p. grey (buff) . . . . 6·00 7·50
8 2p. blue (green) . . . . 8·50 9·50
9 5p. red (red) . . . . 29·00 29·00
The 1p. was also issued without the network.

1950. Air. Nos. 691/7 and 700/3 optd **L**.
10 5c. yellow 15 10
11 10c. red 15 10
12 15c. blue 15 10
13 20c. violet 15 10
14 30c. green 15 15
15 40c. grey . . . . 3·50 15
16 50c. red 55 15
17 1p. purple and green . . . . . 4·25 1·75
18 2p. blue and green . . . . . 8·50 3·25
19 3p. black and red . . . . . 8·50 9·50
20 5p. turquoise and sepia . . . 28·00 28·00

1951. As Nos. 696/703 but colours changed and optd **L**.
21 40c. orange 90 55
22 50c. blue 90 55
23 60c. grey 90 45
24 80c. red 75 45
25 1p. red and vermilion . . . . 3·75 3·75
26 2p. blue and red . . . . . . 4·50 4·50
27 3p. green and brown . . . . 8·25 7·25
28 5p. grey and yellow . . . . . 21·00 23·00

B. Avianca Company.

1950. Air. Nos. 691/703 optd **A**.
1 5c. yellow 10 10
2 10c. red 15 10
3 15c. blue 10 10
4 20c. violet 20 10
5 30c. green 15 10
6 40c. grey 45 10
7 50c. red 25 10
8 60c. olive 75 15
9 80c. brown . . . . 1·40 15
10 1p. purple and green . . . . . 1·60 15
11 2p. blue and green . . . . . 5·00 1·60
12 3p. black and red . . . . . 8·50 7·50
13 5p. turquoise and sepia . . . 25·00 22·00

1951. Air. As Nos. 696/703 but colours changed and optd **A**.
14 40c. orange . . . . 4·50 25
15 50c. blue . . . . 6·25 25
16 60c. grey . . . . 1·75 15
17 80c. red 60 15
18 1p. red and vermilion . . . . 2·10 15
19 1p. brown and green . . . . 2·25 35
20 2p. blue and red . . . . . . 2·10 35
21 3p. green and brown . . . . 4·50 90
22 5p. grey and yellow . . . . . 8·25 90
The 60c. also comes with the **A** in the centre.
All values except the 2p. and 3p. exist without the overprint.

ACKNOWLEDGEMENT OF RECEIPT STAMPS

AR **60** AR **100**

1894.
AR169 AR **60** 5c. red . . . . . . 2·50 2·10

1902. Similar to Type AR **60**. Imperf or perf.
AR265 5c. blue . . . . 12·00 12·00
AR211 10c. blue on blue 90 90

1903. No. 197 optd **Habilitado Medellin A R**.
AR258 **75** 10c. black on pink . . 13·00

1904. No. 262 optd **A R**.
AR266 **75** 5c. red . . . . 21·00 21·00

1904.
AR290 AR **100** 5c. blue . . . . . 7·50 3·50

AR **106** A. Gomez AR **117** Map of Colombia

1910.
AR354 AR **106** 5c. green & orge 6·00 15·00

1917. Inscr "AR".
AR371 **123** 4c. brown . . . . 12·50 11·00
AR372 AR **117** 5c. brown . . . . 5·00 4·00

OFFICIAL STAMPS

1937. Optd **OFICIAL**.
O496 – 1c. green (No. 429) . . 10 10
O497 **137** 2c. red (No. 430) . . 20 20
O498 – 5c. brown (No. 431) . . 10 10
O499 – 10c. orge (No. 485) . . 25 20
O500 **156** 12c. blue 90 25
O501 **141** 20c. blue . . . . . . 1·40 65
O502 **110** 30c. bistre . . . . . . 2·10 65
O503 **123** 40c. brown . . . . . . 22·00 14·00
O504 **112** 50c. red . . . . . . 1·75 80
O505 **110** 1p. blue . . . . . . 14·00 6·00
O506 2p. orange . . . . . . 15·00 6·00
O507 5p. grey . . . . . . 50·00 50·00
O508 **57** 10p. brown £110 £110

REGISTRATION STAMPS

R **12** R **32**

1865. Imperf.
R42 R **12** 5c. black . . . . 90·00 45·00

1865. Type similar to R **12**, but letter "R" in star. Imperf.
R43 5c. black . . . . £100 50·00

1870. Imperf.
R73 R **32** 5c. black . . . . 2·50 2·50

1870. Type similar to R **32** but with "R" in centre and inscr "REJISTRO". Imperf.
R74 5c. black . . . . 1·10 90

1881. Eagle and arms in oval frame, inscr "RECOMENDADA" at foot. Imperf or pin-perf.
R105 10c. lilac . . . . 30·00 30·00

R **42** R **48**

1883. Perf.
R117 R **42** 10c. red on orange . . 80 1·00

1899.
R141 R **48** 10c. red . . . . 5·00 3·50
R166 10c. brown . . . . . 1·40 75

R **85**

1902. Imperf or perf.
R264 R **85** 10c. purple . . . . . 4·00 4·00
R207 20c. red on blue . . . 80 80
R208 20c. blue on blue . . . 1·25 1·25

R **94**

1902. Perf.
R257 R **94** 10c. purple . . . . . 19·00 19·00

R **99**

1904.
R289 R **99** 10c. purple . . . . . 13·00 35

R **105** Execution of 24 February, 1810

1910.
R353 R **105** 10c. black and red . . 20·00 50·00

R **114** Puerto Colombia

1917.
R369 R **114** 4c. blue and green . . 35 3·25
R370 – 10c. blue . . . . 7·50 25
DESIGN: 10c. Tequendama Falls.

R **127**

1925.
R409 R **127** (10c.) blue . . . . . 9·50 1·75

1932. Air. Air stamps of 1932 optd **R**.
R426 **132** 20c. red . . . . 6·00 4·25
R450 – 20c. green & red (439) 6·00 75

SPECIAL DELIVERY STAMPS

E 118 Express Messenger

1917.
E373 E **118** 5c. green . . . . . . 5·00 4·25

E 310

1958. Air.
E936 E **310** 25c. red and blue . . 25 15

1959. Air. Unification of Air Mail Rates. Optd **UNIFICADO** within outline of airplane.
E989 E **310** 25c. red and blue . . 45 10

E **361** Boeing 720B on Back of "Express" Letter

1963. Air.
E1143 E **361** 50c. black & red . . 20 10

1966. Air. "History of Colombian Aviation". As T **372**. Inscr "EXPRESO". Multicoloured.
E1168 80c. Boeing 727 jetliner (1966) 10 15

E **647** Numeral

1987.
E1783 E **647** 25p. green and red 25 15
E1784 30p. green and red 25 15

E **663** Sailfish "Istiaphorus amaricanus"

1988. No Value expressed.
E1805 E **663** (A) blue . . . . . . 2·25 1·10
E1806 (B) blue 75 15

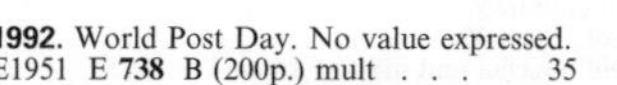
E **724** Black & Chestnut Eagle

E **738** Postman climbing out of Envelope

1992. No value expressed. Multicoloured.
E1926 B (200p.) Type E **724** . . 1·00 50
E1927 A (950p.) Spectacled bear 2·50 75

1992. World Post Day. No value expressed.
E1951 E **738** B (200p.) mult . . . 35 20

E **741** "Three Musicians"

1993. Fernando Botero (painter) Commemoration. No value expressed.
E1955 E **741** B multicoloured . . 35 20

E **743** Parading "Virgin of the Sorrows"

1993. Popayan Holy Week. No value expressed.
E1957 E **743** B multicoloured . . 35 20

E **744** Mother and Child

E **745** Mother House, Pasto

1993. 90th Anniv of Pan-American Health Organization. No value expressed.
E1958 E **744** B multicoloured . . 35 20

1993. Centenary of Franciscan Convent of Mary Immaculate. No value expressed.
E1959 E **745** B multicoloured . . 35 20

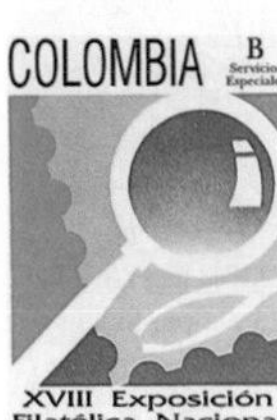
E **746** Stamps, Magnifying Glass and Tweezers

E **747** Cano

1993. 18th National Stamp Exhibition. No value expressed.
E1960 E **746** B multicoloured . . 35 20

1993. 7th Death Anniv of Guillermo Cano (newspaper editor).
E1961 E **747** 250p. multicoloured 40 20

1993. Tourism. As T **756**. Multicoloured.
E1996 250p. Otun Lake (vert) . . 35 20

E **758** Marie Poussepin (founder)

E **761** Biplane

1994. Order of Sisters of the Presentation.
E1998 E **758** 300p. multicoloured 45 25

1994. 75th Anniv of Air Force.
E2004 E **761** 300p. multicoloured 45 25

1994. 4th Latin American Presidential Summit, Cartagena. As T **764**. Multicoloured.
E2010 300p. Setting sun over harbour walls 45 25

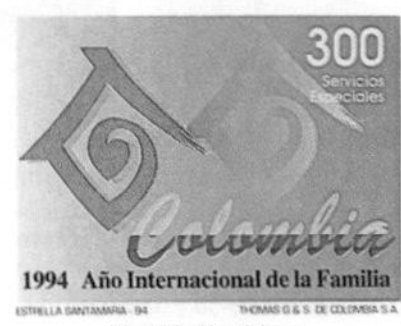
E **769** Emblem

1994. International Year of The Family.
E2016 E **769** 300p. multicoloured 40 20

1994. American Postal Transport. As T **770**. Multicoloured.
E2018 300p. Men carrying "stamps" depicting van, ship and aircraft 40 20

1994. Christmas. As T **773**. Multicoloured.
E2022 300p. Nativity 40 20

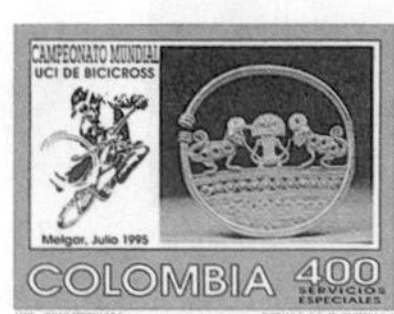
E **777** Championship Advertising Poster and Gold Ornament

1995. B.M.X. World Championship, Melgar.
E2029 E **777** 400p. multicoloured 55 30

E **785** Bicycle

1995. World Cycling Championships, Bogota and Boyaca.
E2056 E **785** 400p. multicoloured 50 25

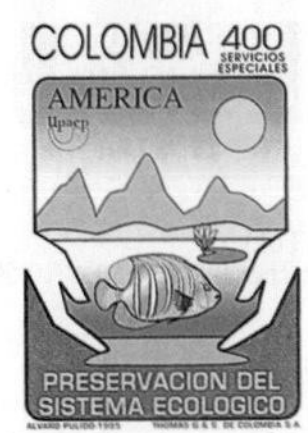
E **791** Hands protecting Lake and Marine Angelfish

E **798** Emblem on Cross

1995. America. Environmental Protection. Multicoloured.
E2063 400p. Type E **791** 50 25
E2064 400p. Hands protecting tree 50 25

1996. 400th Anniv of Order of St. John of God in Colombia.
E2075 E **798** 500p. multicoloured 60 30

E **800** Trains

1996. Inauguration (1995) of Medellin Underground Railway.
E2080 E **800** 500p. multicoloured 1·50 75

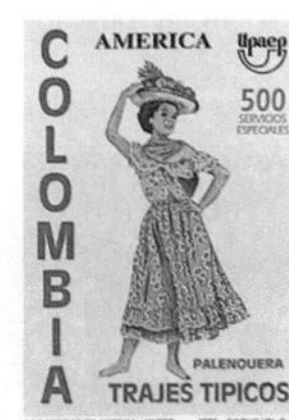
E **802** Runners

1996. Olympic Games, Atlanta. Centenary of Modern Olympic Games.
E2082 E **802** 500p. multicoloured 60 30

E **812** Fruit Seller

1996. America. Traditional Costumes.
E2104 500p. Type E **812** 60 30
E2105 500p. Fisherman 60 30

TOO LATE STAMPS

L **47**

L **59**

1888. Perf.
L136 L **47** 2½c. black on lilac . . 4·00 1·50

1892. Perf.
L167 L **59** 2½c. blue on red . . . 4·00 3·25

L **86**

L **107**

1902. Imperf or perf.
L209 L **86** 5c. violet on red . . . 45 45

1914. Perf.
L355 L **107** 2c. brown . . . . . . 8·50 6·00
L356 5c. green . . . . . . 8·50 6·00

COMORO ISLANDS Pt. 6; Pt. 12

An archipelago N.W. of Madagascar comprising Anjouan, Great Comoro, Mayotte and Moheli. A French colony from 1891, Mayotte became an Overseas Department of France in December 1974, the remaining islands forming the Independent State of Comoro.

100 centimes = 1 franc.

1 Anjouan Bay

2 Native Woman

6 Mutsamudu Village

1950.
1 **1** 10c. blue (postage) . . . . . 15 1·00
2 50c. green 15 25
3 1f. brown 25 15
4 **2** 2f. green 35 20
5 – 5f. violet 50 90
6 6f. purple . . . . 45 1·00

7 – 7f. red 80 65
8 – 10f. green 90 60
9 – 11f. blue . . . . 80 1·60
10 – 15f. brown 75 70
11 – 20f. red 85 80
12 – 40f. indigo and blue . . . . 22·00 13·00
13 **6** 50f. red and green (air) . . . 2·50 3·00
14 – 100f. brown and red . . . . 3·25 4·25
15 – 200f. red, green and violet . . 19·00 15·00
DESIGNS (as Type **1**)—HORIZ: 7f., 10f., 11f. Mosque at Moroni; 40f. Coelacanth. VERT: 15f., 20f. Ouani Mosque, Anjouan. (As Type **6**)—HORIZ: 100f. Natives and Mosque de Vendredi; 200f. Ouani Mosque, Anjouan (different).

1952. Military Medal Cent. As T **48** of Cameroun.
16 15f. blue, yellow and green . . 22·00 35·00

1954. Air. 10th Anniv of Liberation. As T **52** of Cameroun.
17 15f. red and brown . . . . . 21·00 28·00

9 Village Pump

1956. Economic and Social Development Fund.
18 **9** 9f. violet . . . . 75 3·00

10 "Human Rights"

1958. 10th Anniv of Declaration of Human Rights.
19 **10** 20f. green and blue . . . . . 5·00 10·00

1959. Tropical Flora. As T **58** of Cameroun. Mult.
20 10f. "Colvillea" (horiz) . . . . 1·75 3·00

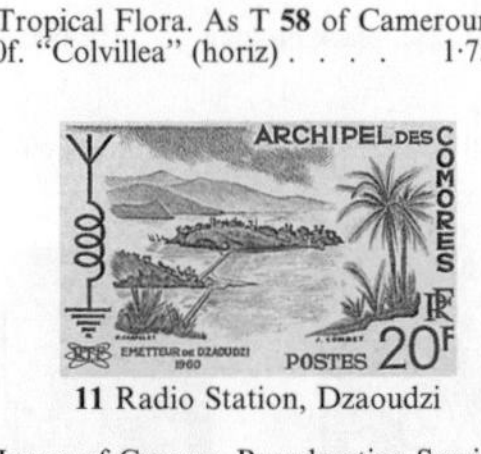
11 Radio Station, Dzaoudzi

1960. Inaug of Comoro Broadcasting Service.
21 **11** 20f. green, violet and red . . 75 1·75
22 – 25f. green, brown and blue 90 1·60
DESIGN: 25f. Radio mast and map.

12 Bull-mouth Helmet **12a** Giant Clam

1962. Multicoloured. (a) Postage. Sea Shells.
23 50c. Type **12** . . . . 70 2·00
24 1f. Common harp . . . . . . 1·00 1·75
25 2f. Ramose murex . . . . . . 1·75 3·00
26 5f. Giant green turban . . . . 2·75 3·75
27 20f. Scorpion conch . . . . . 8·50 12·50
28 25f. Trumpet triton . . . . . 12·00 14·50

(b) Air. Marine Plants.
29 100f. Type **12a** . . . . 8·50 13·50
30 500f. Stoney coral . . . . . . 21·00 32·00

1962. Malaria Eradication. As T **70** of Cameroun.
31 25f.+5f. red . . . . 1·50 4·75

1962. Air. 1st Trans-Atlantic T.V. Satellite Link. As Type F **23** of Andorra.
32 25f. mauve, purple and violet 2·50 1·40

14 Emblem in Hands and Globe **14a** Centenary Emblem

1963. Freedom from Hunger.
33 **14** 20f. green and brown . . . 2·50 5·75

1963. Red Cross Centenary.
34 **14a** 50f. red, grey and green . . 5·75 8·00

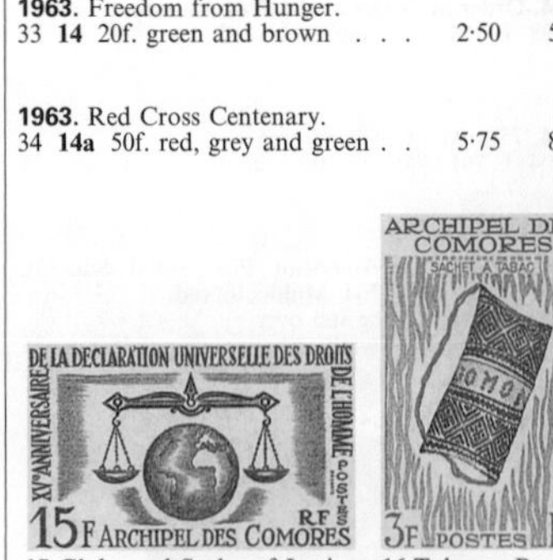
15 Globe and Scales of Justice **16** Tobacco Pouch

1963. 15th Anniv of Declaration of Human Rights.
35 **15** 15f. green and red . . . . . 5·25 9·50

1963. Handicrafts. (a) Postage. As T **17**.
36 **16** 3f. ochre, red and green . . 1·00 2·25
37 – 4f. myrtle, purple & orange 1·00 2·50
38 – 10f. brown, green & chest 85 3·00

(b) Air. Size 27 × 48 mm.
39 – 65f. red, brown and green . . 2·75 4·25
40 – 200f. pink, red & turq . . . 6·25 7·00
DESIGNS: 4f. Perfume-burner; 10f. Lamp bracket; 65f. Baskets; 200f. Filigree pendant.

16a "Philately" **17** Pirogue

1964. "PHILATEC 1964" International Stamp Exhibition, Paris.
41 **16a** 50f. red, green and blue . . 2·00 5·25

1964. Native Craft. Multicoloured.
42 15f. Type **17** (postage) . . . . 2·50 3·50
43 30f. Boutre felucca . . . . . 4·50 6·50
44 50f. Mayotte pirogue (air) . . 3·50 3·50
45 85f. Schooner . . . . 5·25 4·25
Nos. 44/5 are larger, 27 × 48½ mm.

18 Boxing (Ancient bronze plaque) **19** Medal

1964. Air. Olympic Games, Tokyo.
46 **18** 100f. green, brown & choc 6·50 10·50

1964. Air. Star of Grand Comoro.
47 **19** 500f. multicoloured . . . . 16·00 20·00

20 "Syncom" Communications Satellite, Telegraph Poles and Morse Key **21** Great Hammerhead

1965. Air. Centenary of I.T.U.
48 **20** 50f. blue, green and grey . . 9·00 23·00

1965. Marine Life.
49 – 1f. green, orange and violet 1·60 2·00
50 **21** 12f. black, blue and red . . 2·00 2·50
51 – 20f. red and green . . . . . 2·50 3·00
52 – 25f. brown, red and green 5·00 3·75

DESIGNS—VERT: 1f. Spiny lobster; 25f. Spotted grouper. HORIZ: 20f. Scaly turtle.

1966. Air. Launching of 1st French Satellite. As Nos. 1696/7 of France.
53 25f. lilac, blue and violet . . . 3·50 5·75
54 30f. lilac, violet and blue . . . 4·50 5·75

21a Satellite "D1"

1966. Air. Launching of Satellite "D1".
55 **21a** 30f. purple, green & orange 1·90 2·25

22 Lake Sale

1966. Comoro Views. Multicoloured.
56 15f. Type **22** (postage) . . . . 75 2·00
57 25f. Itsandra Hotel, Moroni 1·25 1·50
58 50f. The Battery, Dzaoudzi (air) . . . . 2·50 4·00
59 200f. Ksar Fort, Mutsamudu (vert) . . . . 5·50 6·50
Nos. 58/9 are larger, 48 × 27 mm and 27 × 48 mm respectively.

23 Anjouan Sunbird

1967. Birds. Multicoloured.
60 2f. Type **23** (postage) . . . . 3·75 3·00
61 10f. Madagascar malachite kingfisher . . . . 4·25 4·25
62 15f. Mascarene fody . . . . . 7·75 6·25
63 30f. Courol . . . . 17·00 13·50
64 75f. Madagascar paradise flycatcher (vert) (27 × 48 mm) (air) . . . . . 9·25 9·75
65 100f. Blue-cheeked bee eater (vert) (27 × 48 mm) . . . . 12·00 13·50

24 Nurse tending Child **25** Slalom Skiing

1967. Comoro Red Cross.
66 **24** 25f.+5f. purple, red & grn 2·25 3·50

1968. Air. Winter Olympic Games, Grenoble.
67 **25** 70f. brown, blue and green 4·00 4·50

26 Bouquet, Sun and W.H.O. Emblem

1968. 20th Anniv of W.H.O.
68 **26** 40f. red, violet and green . . 85 1·25

27 Powder-blue Surgeonfish **28** Human Rights Emblem

1968. Fishes.
69 **27** 20f. bl, yell & red (postage) 2·75 4·25
70 – 25f. blue, orange & turq . . 3·50 5·25
71 – 50f. ochre, blue & pur (air) 5·75 4·75
72 – 90f. ochre, green & emer . . 8·25 6·50
DESIGNS—As T **27**: 25f. Emperor angelfish. 48 × 27 mm: 50f. Moorish idol; 90f. Oriental sweetlips.

1968. Human Rights Year.
73 **28** 60f. green, brown & orange 2·75 4·75

29 Swimming

1968. Air. Olympic Games, Mexico.
74 **29** 65f. multicoloured . . . . . 3·00 4·00

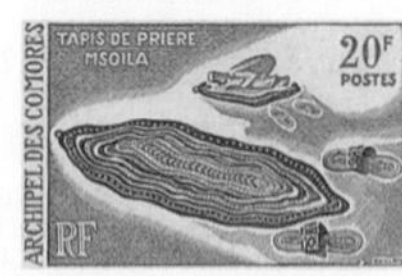
30 Prayer Mat and Worshipper

1969. Msoila Prayer Mats.
75 **30** 20f. red, green and violet . . 95 2·25
76 – 30f. green, violet and red . . 1·25 2·50
77 – 45f. violet, red and green . . 2·50 3·25
DESIGNS: As Type **30**, but worshipper stooping (30f.) or kneeling upright (45f.).

31 Vanilla Flower

1969. Flowers, Multicoloured.
78 10f. Type **31** (postage) . . . . 1·60 2·50
79 15f. Ylang-ylang blossom . . 1·60 2·50
80 50f. "Heliconia" (vert) (air) . . 4·25 4·00
81 85f. Tuberose (vert) . . . . . 5·50 4·75
82 200f. Orchid (vert) . . . . . 10·00 8·00

32 Concorde in Flight

1969. Air. 1st Flight of Concorde.
83 **32** 100f. purple and brown . . 11·50 18·00

33 I.L.O. Building, Geneva

1969. 50th Anniv of I.L.O.
84 **33** 5f. grey, green and orange 1·50 2·25

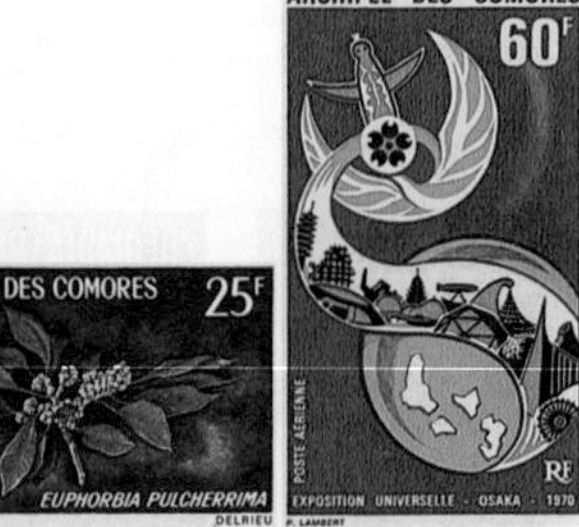
34 Poinsettia **35** "EXPO" Panorama

1970. Flowers.
85 **34** 25f. multicoloured . . . . . 3·00 2·75

1970. New U.P.U. Headquarters Building, Berne. As T **156** of Cameroun.
86 65f. brown, green and violet 3·75 4·00

1970. Air. World Fair "EXPO 70", Osaka, Japan. Multicoloured.
87 60f. Type **35** . . . . 4·25 3·25
88 90f. Geisha and map of Japan 5·25 3·25

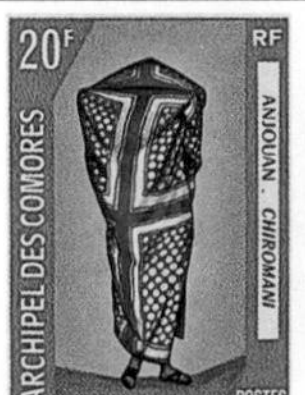
36 Chiromani Costume, Anjouan

37 Mosque de Vendredi, Moroni

1970. Comoro Costumes. Multicoloured.
89 20f. Type **36** . . . . 2·50 2·50
90 25f. Bouiboui, Great Comoro 3·00 2·50

1970.
91 **37** 5f. turquoise, green and red 2·00 2·25
92 10f. violet, green & purple 2·25 2·50
93 40f. brown, green and red 3·00 2·75

38 Great Egret

1971. Birds. Multicoloured.
94 5f. Type **38** . . . . 1·90 2·25
95 10f. Comoro olive pigeon . . 1·90 2·25
96 15f. Green-backed heron . . . 2·25 2·50
97 25f. Comoro blue pigeon . . . 2·75 2·75
98 35f. Humblot's flycatcher . . . 4·00 3·75
99 40f. Allen's gallinule . . . . . 6·25 4·25

39 Sunset, Moutsamoudou (Anjouan)

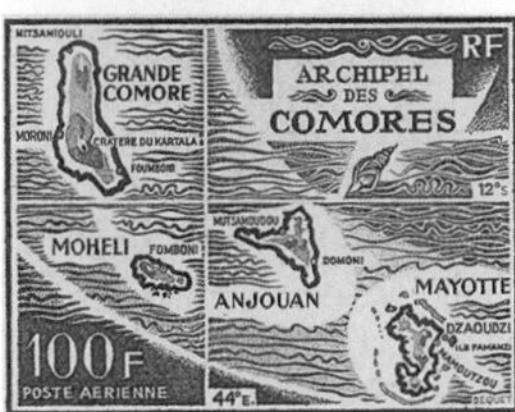
40 Map of Comoro Archipelago

1971. Air. Comoro Landscapes. Multicoloured.
100 **39** 15f. multicoloured . . . . 1·60 1·90
101 – 20f. multicoloured . . . . 1·75 2·25
102 – 65f. multicoloured . . . . 3·00 2·75
103 – 85f. multicoloured . . . . 3·75 3·25
104 **40** 100f. brown, green & bl . . 8·00 6·50
DESIGNS—(As Type **39**): 20f. Sada village (Mayotte); 65f. Ruined palace, Iconi (Great Comoro); 85f. Offshore islands; Moumatchoua (Moheli).
See also Nos. 124/8, 132/6, 157/60 and 168/71.

41 "Pyrostegia venusta"

1971. Tropical Plants. Multicoloured.
105 1f. Type **41** (postage) . . . . 1·75 2·25
106 3f. "Allamanda cathartica" (horiz) . . . . 1·75 2·25
107 20f. "Plumeria rubra" . . . 3·50 3·25
108 60f. "Hibiscus schizopetalous" (air) . . . 3·25 3·75
109 85f. "Acalypha sanderii" . . 7·50 5·25
The 60 and 85f. are 27 × 48 mm.

42 Lithograph Cone

1971. Sea Shells. Multicoloured.
110 5f. Type **42** . . . . 1·75 2·25
111 10f. Lettered cone . . . . . 2·00 2·25
112 20f. Princely cone . . . . . 2·50 2·75
113 35f. Polished nerite . . . . . 3·75 2·75
114 60f. Serpent's-head cowrie . . 6·00 3·25

1971. 1st Death Anniv of Charles de Gaulle. Designs as Nos. 1937 and 1940 of France.
115 20f. black and purple . . . . 3·00 3·25
116 35f. black and purple . . . . 3·50 3·75

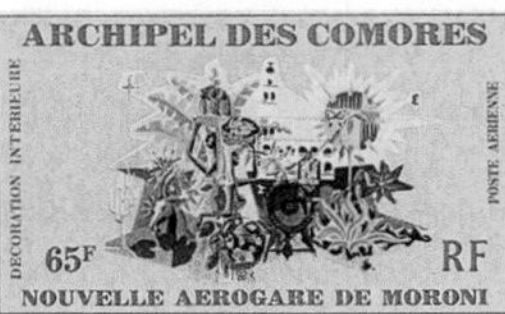
44 Mural, Airport Lounge

1972. Air. Inauguration of New Airport, Moroni.
117 **44** 65f. multicoloured . . . . 1·75 2·25
118 – 85f. multicoloured . . . . 2·25 2·25
119 – 100f. green, brown & blue 3·50 3·25
DESIGNS: 85f. Mural similar to T **44**; 100f. Airport Buildings.

45 Eiffel Tower, Paris and Telecommunications Centre, Moroni

1972. Air. Inauguration of Paris–Moroni Radio-Telephone Link.
120 **45** 35f. red, purple & blue . . 2·50 2·25
121 – 75f. red, violet and blue . . 2·50 2·25
DESIGN: 75f. Telephone conversation.

46 Underwater Spear-fishing

1972. Air. Aquatic Sports.
122 **46** 70f. red, green and blue . . 7·25 5·25

47 Pasteur, Crucibles and Microscope

1972. 150th Birth Anniv of Louis Pasteur.
123 **47** 65f. blue, brown & orange 4·75 4·00

1972. Air. Anjouan Landscapes. (a) As T **39**. Multicoloured.
124 20f. Fortress wall, Cape Sima 1·60 1·90
125 35f. Bambao Palace . . . . 1·75 2·25
126 40f. Palace, Domoni . . . . 1·75 2·25
127 60f. Gomajou Island . . . . 2·75 2·75

(b) As T **40**.
128 – 100f. green, blue & brown 5·75 5·25
DESIGN: 100f. Map of Anjouan.

48 Pres. Said Mohamed Cheikh

50 Bank

1973. Air. Said Mohamed Cheikh, President of Comoro Council, Commemoration.
129 **48** 20f. multicoloured . . . . 1·90 2·25
130 35f. multicoloured . . . . 2·25 2·50

1973. Air. International Coelacanth Study Expedition. No. 72 surch **Mission Internationale pour l'etude du Coelacanthe** and value.
131 120f. on 90f. brn, grn & emer 10·50 7·00

1973. Great Comoro Landscapes. (a) Postage. As T **39**. Multicoloured.
132 10f. Goulaivoini . . . . . . 2·25 1·90
133 20f. Mitsamiouli . . . . . . 2·50 2·25
134 35f. Foumbouni . . . . . . 3·00 2·75
135 50f. Moroni . . . . 3·75 3·25

(b) Air. As Type **40**.
136 – 135f. purple, green & violet 10·50 6·25
DESIGN—VERT: 135f. Map of Great Comoro.

1973. Moroni Buildings. Multicoloured.
137 5f. Type **50** . . . . 2·00 2·25
138 15f. Post Office . . . . . . 2·25 2·50
139 20f. Prefecture . . . . 2·50 2·75

51 Volcanic Eruption

1973. Air. Karthala Volcanic Eruption (Sept 1972).
140 **51** 120f. multicoloured . . . . 9·50 6·50

52 Dr. G. A. Hansen

54 Zaouiyat Chaduli Mosque

53 Pablo Picasso (artist)

1973. Air Centenary of Hansen's Identification of Leprosy Bacillus.
141 **52** 100f. green, purple & blue 4·75 3·75

1973. Air. 500th Birth Anniv of Nicolas Copernicus. As T **52**.
142 150f. purple, blue & ultram 6·25 5·25
DESIGN: 150f. Copernicus and solar system.

1973. Air. Picasso Commemoration.
143 **53** 200f. multicoloured . . . . 12·00 8·00
MS144 100 × 131 mm. **53** 100f. multicoloured . . . . 9·25 10·50

1973. Mosques. Multicoloured.
145 20f. Type **54** . . . . 2·00 2·75
146 35f. Salimata Hamissi Mosque (horiz) . . . . . 2·75 2·75

55 Star and Ribbon

56 Said Omar Ben Soumeth (Grand Mufti of the Comoros)

1974. Air. Order of the Star of Anjouan.
147 **55** 500f. gold, blue & brown 16·00 13·00

1974. Air. Multicoloured.
148 135f. Type **56** . . . . 4·00 2·75
149 200f. Ben Soumeth seated (vert) . . . . 5·50 4·50

57 Doorway of Mausoleum

58 Wooden Combs

1974. Mausoleum of Shaikh Said Mohamed.
150 **57** 35f. brown, black & green 2·75 2·75
151 – 50f. brown, black & green 3·75 2·75
DESIGN: 50f. Mausoleum.

1974. Comoro Handicrafts (1st series). Mult.
152 15f. Type **58** . . . . 1·90 2·25
153 20f. Three-legged table . . . 2·25 2·25
154 35f. Koran lectern (horiz) . . 3·00 2·75
155 75f. Sugar-cane press (horiz) 5·25 3·50
See also Nos. 164/7.

59 Mother and Child

1974. Comoros Red Cross Fund.
156 **59** 35f.+10f. brown & red . . 2·00 2·75

1974. Air. Mayotte Landscapes. (a) As T **39**. Multicoloured.
157 20f. Moya beach . . . . . . 1·75 1·90
158 35f. Chiconi . . . . 1·90 1·90
159 90f. Mamutzu harbour . . . 4·00 3·25

(b) As T **40**.
160 120f. green and blue . . . . 7·25 4·75
DESIGN—VERT: 120f. Map of Mayotte.

60 U.P.U. Emblem and Globe

1974. Centenary of Universal Postal Union.
161 **60** 30f. red, brown and green 2·75 3·00

61 Boeing 707 taking off

1975. Inauguration of Direct Moroni–Hahaya–Paris Air Service.
162 **61** 135f. blue, green and red 7·25 6·25

62 Rotary Emblem, Moroni Clubhouse and Map

1975. Air. 70th Anniv of Rotary International and 10th Anniv of Moroni Rotary Club.
163 **62** 250f. multicoloured . . . . 9·50 8·75

63 Bracelet

1975. Comoro Handicrafts (2nd series).
164 **63** 20f. brown and purple . . 2·50 2·25
165 – 35f. brown and green . . . 2·50 2·50

166 – 120f. brown and blue . . . 6·00 4·50
167 – 135f. brown and red . . . 8·75 5·25
DESIGNS: 35f. Diadem; 120f. Sabre; 125f. Dagger.

1975. Moheli Landscapes. (a) Postage. As T **39**. Multicoloured.
168 30f. Mohani Village . . . . 2·75 2·50
169 50f. Djoezi Village . . . . 3·25 2·75
170 55f. Chirazian tombs . . . . 4·25 3·25

(b) Air. As T **40**.
171 230f. green, blue and brown 12·00 8·00
DESIGN: 230f. Map of Moheli.

64 Coelacanth and Skin-diver

1975. Coelacanth Expedition.
172 **64** 50f. bistre, blue & brown 6·50 4·50

65 Tambourine-player

1975. Folklore Dances. Multicoloured.
173 100f. Type **65** . . . . 60·00 60·00
174 150f. Dancers with tambourines . . . . 60·00 60·00

66 Athlete and Athens, 1896 Motifs

1976. Olympic Games, Munich (1972) and Montreal (1976). Multicoloured.
175 20f. Type **66** (postage) . . . 15 10
176 25f. Running 15 10
177 40f. Athlete and Paris, 1900 motif 25 15
178 75f. High-jumping 45 20
179 100f. Exercises and World's Fair, St. Louis, 1904 motif (air) 55 35
180 500f. Gymnast on bars . . . 3·75 1·40

67 Government House, Flag and Map

1976. 1st Anniv of Independence. Multicoloured.
182 **67** 30f. multicoloured 25 15
183 50f. multicoloured 35 20

68 Agricultural Scene and U.N. Stamp

1976. 25th Anniv of U.N. Postal Services. Multicoloured.
184 15f. Type **68** (postage) . . . 10 10
185 30f. Surgery scene and U.N.W.H.O. stamp 20 10
186 50f. Village scene and U.N.I.C.E.F. stamp . . . 3·75 50
187 75f. Telecommunications satellite and U.N. I.T.U. stamp 45 20
188 200f. Concorde, airship "Graf Zeppelin" and U.N. I.C.A.O. stamp (air) . . . 2·50 85
189 400f. Lufthansa jet airliner and U.N. U.P.U. stamp . . 3·00 1·40

69 Copernicus, and Rocket on Launch-pad

1976. "Success of Operation Viking", and Bicentenary of American Revolution. Multicoloured.
191 5f. Type **69** (postage) 10 10
192 10f. Einstein, Sagan and Young (horiz) 10 10
193 25f. "Viking" orbiting Mars 15 10
194 35f. Vikings' discovery of America (horiz) 50 20
195 100f. U.S. flag and Mars landing 65 30
196 500f. First colour photograph of Martian terrain (horiz) (air) . . . . 4·00 1·25

70 U.N. Headquarters, New York and Flags

1976. 1st Anniv of Comoro Islands Admission to United Nations.
198 **70** 40f. multicoloured 30 20
199 50f. multicoloured 40 25

71 President Lincoln and Bombardment of Fort Sumter

1976. Bicentenary of American Revolution. Showing various battle scenes of American Civil War. Multicoloured.
200 10f. Type **71** (postage) . . . 10 10
201 30f. General Beauregard and Bull Run (vert) 20 10
202 50f. General Johnston and Antietam 30 15
203 100f. General Meade and Gettysburg (air) 55 30
204 200f. General Sherman and Chattanooga (vert) . . . . 1·40 45
205 400f. General Pickett and Appomattox . . . . 2·75 90

72 Andean Condor

74 Giffard's Dirigible, 1851 and French Locomotive, 1837

73 Wolf

1976. "Endangered Animals" (1st series). Multicoloured.
207 15f. Type **72** (postage) . . . 1·75 55
208 20f. Tiger cat (horiz) 50 15
209 35f. Leopard 65 15
210 40f. White rhinoceros (horiz) 90 40
211 75f. Mountain nyala . . . . 1·60 45
212 400f. Orang-utan (horiz) (air) 4·50 1·25

1977. "Endangered Animals" (2nd series). Mult.
214 10f. Type **73** (postage) . . . 10 10
215 30f. Aye-aye 20 10
216 40f. Banded duiker 65 15
217 50f. Giant tortoise 80 15
218 200f. Ocelot (air) . . . . . . 1·90 55
219 400f. Galapagos penguin ("Manchot des Galapagos") . . . . 7·00 3·00

1977. History of Communications. Airships and Railways. Multicoloured.
221 20f. Type **74** (postage) . . . 30 10
222 25f. Santos-Dumont's airship "Ballon No. 6" (1906) and Brazilian steam locomotive (19th century) 65 15
223 50f. Russian airship "Astra" (1914) and "Trans-Siberian Express" (1905) 90 20
224 75f. British airship R-34 (1919) and "Southern Belle" pullman express (1910–25) . . . . 1·10 30
225 200f. U.S. Navy airship "Los Angeles" (1930) and Pacific locomotive (1930) (air) . . 4·25 50
226 500f. German airship "Hindenburg", 1933, and "Rheingold" express, 1933 7·75 1·50

75 Koch, Morgan, Fleming, Muller and Waksman (medicine)

1977. Nobel Prize Winners. Multicoloured.
228 30f. Type **75** (postage) . . . 20 10
229 40f. Michelson, Bragg, Raman and Zernike (physics) 20 15
230 50f. Tagore, Yeats, Russell and Hemingway (literature) 30 15
231 100f. Rontgen, Becquerel, Planck, Lawrence and Einstein (physics) 80 25
232 200f. Ramsey and Marie Curie (chemistry), Banting and Hench (medicine) and Perrin (physics) (air) . . . 1·40 45
233 400f. Dunant, Briand, Schweitzer and Martin Luther King (peace) . . . 3·25 90

The 200f. wrongly attributes the chemistry prize to all those depicted and gives the date 1913 instead of 1911 for Marie Curie. On the 50 and 100f. names are wrongly spelt.

76 "Clara, Ruben's Daughter"

1977. 400th Birth Anniv of Peter Paul Rubens (1st issue). Multicoloured.
235 20f. Type **76** (postage) . . . 10 10
236 25f. "Suzanne Fourment" . . 15 10
237 50f. "Venus in front of Mirror" 55 15
238 75f. "Ceres" 70 25
239 200f. "Young Girl with Blond Hair" (air) . . . . 1·40 95
240 500f. "Helene Fourment in Wedding Dress" . . . . . 4·50 1·25

See also Nos. 407/10.

77 Queen Elizabeth II, Westminster Abbey and Guards

1977. Air. Silver Jubilee of Queen Elizabeth II.
242 **77** 500f. multicoloured . . . . 3·25 1·40

79 Swordfish

1977. Fishes. Multicoloured.
256 30f. Type **79** (postage) . . . 20 10
257 40f. Oriental sweetlips . . . 55 15
258 50f. Lionfish 80 15
259 100f. Racoon butterflyfish . . 1·60 25
260 200f. Clown anemonefish (air) 2·00 65
261 400f. Black-spotted puffer . . 3·50 1·75

80 Jupiter Lander

1977. Space Research. Multicoloured.
263 30f. Type **80** (postage) . . . 20 10
264 50f. Uranus probe (vert) . . 35 15
265 75f. Venus probe 45 20
266 100f. Space shuttle (vert) . . 55 25
267 200f. "Viking 3" (air) . . . . 1·25 45
268 400f. "Apollo–Soyuz" link (vert) . . . . 2·40 90

1977. Air. First Paris–New York Commercial Flight of Concorde. No. 188 optd **Paris-New-York - 22 nov. 1977.**
270 200f. multicoloured . . . . . 2·75 2·00

82 Allen's Gallinule

1978. Birds. Multicoloured.
271 15f. Type **82** (postage) . . . 50 25
272 20f. Blue-cheeked bee eater 70 35
273 35f. Madagascar malachite kingfisher 85 45
274 40f. Madagascar paradise flycatcher 95 55
275 75f. Anjouan sunbird . . . . 1·60 80
276 400f. Great egret (air) . . . . 6·25 3·75

83 Greek Ball Game and Modern Match

1978. World Cup Football Championship, Argentina. Multicoloured.
278 30f. Type **83** (postage) . . . 20 10
279 50f. Breton football 25 15
280 75f. 14th-century London game 45 25
281 100f. 18th-century Italian game 55 25
282 200f. 19th-century English game (air) . . . . 1·10 45
283 400f. English cup-tie, 1891 . . 2·50 85

84 "Oswolt Krel"

1978. 450th Death Anniv of Albrecht Durer (artist) (1st issue). Multicoloured.

No.	Description	Mint	Used
286	20f. Type **84** (postage)	10	10
287	25f. "Elspeth Tucher"	15	10
288	50f. "Hieronymus Holzshuher"	35	15
289	75f. "Young Girl"	50	25
290	200f. "Emperor Maximilian I" (air)	1·10	45
291	500f. "Young Girl" (detail)	3·25	1·10

See also Nos. 411/15.

85 Bach

1978. Composers. Multicoloured.

No.	Description	Mint	Used
293	30f. Type **85** (postage)	20	10
294	40f. Mozart	25	15
295	50f. Berlioz	35	15
296	100f. Verdi	90	25
297	200f. Tchaikovsky (air)	1·60	45
298	400f. Gershwin	3·25	85

Following a revolution on 13 May 1978, it was announced that sets showing Butterflies or commemorating the 25th Anniversary of the Coronation of Queen Elizabeth II, 10th World Telecommunications Day and Aviation History had not been placed on sale in the islands and were not valid for postage there.

86 Rowland Hill, Locomotive "Adler" and Saxony 3pf. Stamp, 1860

1978. Death Centenary of Sir Rowland Hill. Multicoloured.

No.	Description	Mint	Used
300	20f. Type **86** (postage)	1·75	50
301	30f. Penny-farthing and Netherlands 5c. stamp, 1852	20	10
302	40f. Early letter-box and 2d. blue	25	15
303	75f. Pony Express and U.S. stamp, 1847	45	20
304	200f. Airship and French 20c. stamp, 1863 (air)	1·50	65
305	400f. Postman and Basel 2½r. stamp, 1845	2·50	85

87 Interpreting Meteorological Satellite Photographs

1978. European Space Agency. Multicoloured.

No.	Description	Mint	Used
307	10f. Type **87** (postage)	10	10
308	25f. Writing weather forecast	15	10
309	35f. Aiding wrecked ship	70	20
310	50f. Telecommunications as teaching aid	35	15
311	100f. Boeing 727 landing (air)	75	40
312	500f. Space shuttle	3·25	1·10

1978. Argentina's Victory in World Cup Football Championship. Nos. 278/284 optd **REP. FED. ISLAMIQUE DES COMORES 1 ARGENTINE 2 HOLLANDE 3 BRESIL**.

No.	Type	Description	Mint	Used
314	83	30f. mult (postage)	20	10
315	–	50f. multicoloured	35	15
316	–	75f. multicoloured	45	20
317	–	100f. multicoloured	50	25
318	–	200f. multicoloured (air)	1·40	45
319	–	400f. multicoloured	2·50	85

89 Philidor, Anderssen and Steinitz

1979. Chess Grand Masters. Multicoloured.

No.	Description	Mint	Used
321	40f. Type **89** (postage)	20	10
322	100f. Venetian players and pieces	80	20
323	500f. Alekhine, Spassky and Fischer (air)	4·00	1·10

90 Galileo and "Voyager 1"

1979. Exploration of the Solar System. Mult.

No.	Description	Mint	Used
324	20f. Type **90** (postage)	10	10
325	30f. Kepler and "Voyager 2"	15	10
326	40f. Copernicus and "Voyager 1"	20	10
327	100f. Huygens and "Voyager 2"	45	20
328	200f. Herschel and "Voyager 2" (air)	1·40	35
329	400f. Leverrier and "Voyager 2"	2·50	80

91 Kayak

1979. Olympic Games, Moscow (1980). Mult.

No.	Description	Mint	Used
330	10f. Type **91** (postage)	10	10
331	25f. Swimming	15	10
332	35f. Archery	20	10
333	50f. Pole vault	25	15
334	75f. Long jump	35	20
335	500f. High jump (air)	3·25	1·00

92 "Charaxes defulvata"

1979. Fauna. Multicoloured.

No.	Description	Mint	Used
336	30f. Type **92**	50	15
337	50f. Courol	1·25	60
338	75f. Blue-cheeked bee eater	1·75	90

1979. Optd or surch **REPUBLIQUE FEDERALE ISLAMIQUE DES COMORES**. (a) Birds, Nos. 271/275.

No.	Description	Mint	Used
339	15f. Type **82**	40	40
340	30f. on 35f. Madagascar malachite kingfisher	70	70
341	50f. on 20f. Blue-cheeked bee eater	1·10	1·10
342	50f. on 40f. Madagascar paradise flycatcher	1·25	1·25
343	200f. on 75f. Anjouan sunbird	3·25	3·25

(b) World Cup, Nos. 278/282.

No.	Description	Mint	Used
344	1f. on 100f. Italian game (postage)	10	10
345	2f. on 75f. London game	10	10
346	3f. on 30f. Type **83**	10	10
347	50f. Breton football	35	35
348	200f. English game (air)	1·40	1·40

1979. Nos. 293/7 surch or optd **Republique Federale Islamique des Comores**.

No.	Type	Description	Mint	Used
349	–	5f. on 100f. Verdi (post.)	10	10
350	85	30f. J. S. Bach	25	25
351	–	40f. Mozart	25	25
352	–	50f. Berlioz	40	40
353	–	50f. on 200f. Tchaikovsky (air)	65	65

94 State Coach

1979. 25th Anniv of Coronation of Queen Elizabeth II. Multicoloured.

No.	Description	Mint	Used
354	5f. on 25f. Type **94** (postage)	10	10
355	10f. Drum Major	15	15
356	50f. on 40f. Queen carrying orb and sceptre	40	40
357	100f. St. Edward's Crown	80	80
358	50f. on 200f. Herald reading Proclamation (air)	65	65

Nos. 354/8 were only valid for postage overprinted as in Type **94**.

95 "Papilio dardanus-cenea stoll"

1979. Butterflies. Multicoloured.

No.	Description	Mint	Used
359	5f. on 20f. Type **95**	10	10
360	15f. "Papilio dardanus–brown"	15	15
361	30f. "Chrysiridia croesus"	40	30
362	50f. "Precis octavia"	80	70
363	75f. "Bunaea alcinoe"	1·25	1·00

Nos. 359/63 were only valid for postage overprinted as in Type **95**.

96 Otto Lilienthal and Glider

1979. History of Aviation. Multicoloured.

No.	Description	Mint	Used
364	30f. Type **96** (postage)	30	30
365	50f. Wright Brothers	50	50
366	50f. on 75f. Louis Bleriot	50	50
367	100f. Claude Dornier	1·00	1·00
368	200f. Charles Lindbergh (air)	1·25	1·25

Nos. 364/8 were only valid for postage overprinted as in Type **96**.

97 Tobogganing **98** Lychees

1979. International Year of the Child (1st issue). Multicoloured.

No.	Description	Mint	Used
369	20f. Astronauts (postage)	10	10
370	30f. Type **97**	15	10
371	40f. Painting	20	10
372	100f. Locomotive "Rocket", 1829, and toy train	4·00	60
373	200f. Football (air)	1·40	35
374	400f. Canoeing	2·50	80

See also Nos. 389/90.

1979. Fruit. Multicoloured.

No.	Description	Mint	Used
375	60f. Type **98**	40	15
376	70f. Papaws	45	20
377	100f. Avocado pears	80	30
378	125f. Bananas	1·00	35

101 Rotary Emblem and Village Scene

1979. Air. Rotary International.

No.	Type	Description	Mint	Used
388	101	400f. multicoloured	4·50	2·50

102 Mother and Child on Boat **103** Basketball

1979. Air. International Year of the Child (2nd issue). Multicoloured.

No.	Description	Mint	Used
389	200f.+30f. Type **102**	2·50	2·25
390	250f. Mother and baby	2·50	1·60

1979. Indian Ocean Olympic Games.

No.	Type	Description	Mint	Used
391	103	200f. multicoloured	1·50	90

1979. Various stamps optd **REPUBLIQUE FEDERALE ISLAMIQUE DES COMORES**. (a) Air. Apollo–Soyuz Space Test Project (Appendix).

No.	Description	Mint	Used
392	100f. Presidents Brezhnev and Ford with astronauts	80	80
393	200f. Space link-up	1·40	1·40

(b) Bicentenary of American Revolution (Appendix).

No.	Description	Mint	Used
394	25f. Fremont, Kit Carson and dancing Indian	15	15
395	35f. D. Boone, Buffalo Bill and wagon train	20	20
396	75f. H. Wells, W. Fargo and stagecoach ambush	40	40

(c) Winter Olympic Games, Innsbruck (Appendix).

No.	Description	Mint	Used
397	35f. Speed skating	20	20

(d) Telephone Centenary (Appendix).

No.	Description	Mint	Used
398	75f. Philip Reis	40	40

(e) Air. Olympic Games, Munich and Montreal.

No.	Description	Mint	Used
399	100f. multicoloured (No. 179)	80	80

(f) U.N. Postal Services.

No.	Description	Mint	Used
400	75f. mult (No. 187)	40	40

(g) Endangered Animals.

No.	Description	Mint	Used
401	35f. mult (No. 209)	30	20
402	40f. mult (No. 210)	40	25

(h) Nobel Prize Winners.

No.	Description	Mint	Used
403	100f. mult (No. 231)	80	80

(i) Rubens.

No.	Description	Mint	Used
404	25f. mult (No. 236)	15	15

(j) Durer.

No.	Description	Mint	Used
405	25f. mult (No. 287)	15	15
406	75f. mult (No. 289)	40	40

105 "Profile Head of Old Man"

1979. 400th Birth Anniv of Peter Paul Rubens (artist) (2nd issue). Multicoloured.

No.	Description	Mint	Used
407	25f. Type **105**	15	15
408	35f. "Young Girl with Flag"	20	20
409	50f. "Isabelle d'Este, Margave of Mantua"	35	35
410	75f. "Philip IV, King of Spain"	40	40

106 "Portrait of Young Girl"

1979. 450th Death Anniv of Albrecht Durer (artist) (2nd issue). Multicoloured.

411	20f. "Self-portrait" (postage)	15	15
412	30f. "Young Man"	20	20
413	40f. Type **106**	25	25
414	100f. "Jerome" (air)	80	80
415	200f. "Jacob Muffel"	1·40	1·40

107 Satellite and Receiving Station

1979. 10th World Telecommunications Day. Multicoloured.

416	75f. Satellites	40	40
417	100f. Two satellites	45	45
418	200f. Type **107**	1·40	90

108 Pirogue

1980. Handicrafts. Multicoloured.

419	60f. Type **108**	65	20
420	100f. Anjouan puppet	80	25

109 Sultan Said Ali

1980. Sultans. Multicoloured.

421	40f. Type **109**	20	15
422	60f. Sultan Ahmed	30	15

110 Dimadjou Dispensary

1980. Air. 75th Anniv of Rotary International and 15th Anniv of Moroni Rotary Club (100f.).

423	100f. Type **110**	80	35
424	260f. Concorde airplane	2·25	1·10

111 Sherlock Holmes and Sir Arthur Conan Doyle

1980. 50th Death Anniv of Sir Arthur Conan Doyle (writer).

425	**111**	200f. multicoloured	1·50	95

112 Grand Mosque and Holy Ka'aba, Mecca

1980. 1350th Anniv of Occupation of Mecca by Mohammed.

426	**112**	75f. multicoloured	60	25

113 Dome of the Rock

1980. Year of the Holy City, Jerusalem.

427	**113**	60f. multicoloured	55	20

114 Kepler, Copernicus

1980. 50th Anniv of Discovery of Pluto.

428	**114**	400f. violet, red & mauve	3·25	2·00

115 Avicenna

1980. Birth Millenary of Avicenna (physician and philosopher).

429	**115**	60f. multicoloured	65	25

116 Mermoz, Dabry, Gimie and Seaplane "Comte da la Vaulx"

1980. 50th Anniv of First South Atlantic Flight.

430	**116**	200f. multicoloured	2·25	1·40

1981. Various stamps surch.

431	15f. on 200f. multicoloured (No. 425) (postage)	10	10
432	20f. on 75f. mult (No. 426)	15	15
433	40f. on 125f. mult (No. 378)	25	25
434	60f. on 75f. mult (No. 338)	1·50	75
435	30f. on 200f. multicoloured (No. 430) (air)	30	30

118 Team posing with Shield

1981. World Cup Football Championship, Spain (1982). Multicoloured.

436	60f. Footballers coming on Field (vert)	30	15
437	75f. Type **118**	35	20
438	90f. Captains shaking hands	40	20
439	100f. Tackle	45	25
440	150f. Players hugging after goal (vert)	1·10	30

119 "Bowls and Pot"

1981. Birth Centenary of Pablo Picasso. Mult.

442	40f. "Dove and Rainbow"	20	10
443	70f. "Still-life on Chest of Drawers"	55	15
444	150f. "Studio with Plaster Head"	1·10	35
445	250f. Type **119**	1·90	55
446	500f. "Red Tablecloth"	4·00	1·40

120 "Apollo" Launch

1981. Conquest of Space. Multicoloured.

447	50f. Type **120**	25	15
448	75f. Space Shuttle launch	35	20
449	100f. Space Shuttle releasing fuel tank	45	30
450	450f. Space Shuttle in orbit	3·00	1·10

121 Buckingham Palace

1981. British Royal Wedding. Multicoloured.

452	125f. Type **121**	90	25
453	200f. Highgrove House	1·40	45
454	450f. Caernarvon Castle	2·75	1·00

1981. Design as Type O **99** but inscr "POSTES 1981".

456	5f. green, black & brn	10	10
457	15f. green, black & yell	10	10
458	25f. green, black & red	15	10
459	35f. green, black & lt grn	20	10
460	75f. green, black & blue	35	20

1981. Various stamps surch.

461	**114**	5f. on 400f. violet, red and mauve (postage)	10	10
462	–	20f. on 90f. mult (No. 438)	10	10
463	–	45f. on 100f. mult (No. 377)	20	10
464	–	45f. on 100f. mult (No. 420)	20	10
465	–	10f. on 70f. mult (No. 443) (air)	10	10
466	**110**	10f. on 100f. mult	10	10
467	**102**	50f. on 200f.+30f. mult	25	15
468	–	50f. on 260f. mult (No. 424)	60	30

123 Mercedes, 1914

1981. 75th Anniv of French Grand Prix Motor Race. Multicoloured.

469	20f. Type **123**	10	10
470	50f. Delage, 1925	50	15
471	75f. Rudi Caracciola	65	20
472	90f. Stirling Moss	80	20
473	150f. Maserati, 1957	1·25	30

124 Scouts preparing to Sail

1981. 75th Anniv of Boy Scout Movement. Multicoloured.

475	50f. Type **124**	25	15
476	75f. Paddling pirogue	75	20
477	250f. Sailing felucca	1·75	80
478	350f. Scouts looking out to sea from boat	2·50	85

125 Goethe

1982. 150th Death Anniv of Goethe (poet).

480	**125**	75f. multicoloured	35	20
481		350f. multicoloured	2·40	85

126 Princess of Wales

1982. 21st Birthday of Princess of Wales.

482	**126**	200f. multicoloured	1·40	45
483	–	300f. multicoloured	2·00	70

DESIGN: 300f. Different portrait of Princess.

1982. Birth of Prince William of Wales. Nos. 452/4 optd **NAISSANCE ROYALE 1982**.

485	125f. Type **121**	90	25
486	200f. Highgrove House	1·40	45
487	450f. Caernarvon Castle	2·75	1·60

1982. World Cup Football Championship Winners. Nos. 436/40 optd.

489	60f. Type **117**	30	15
490	75f. Team posing with shield (horiz)	35	20
491	90f. Captains shaking hands (horiz)	40	20
492	100f. Tackle (horiz)	45	25
493	150f. Players hugging after goal	1·10	55

OVERPRINTS: 60f., 150f. **ITALIE - ALLEMAGNE (R.F.A.) 3 - 1.**; 75f., 90f., 100f. **ITALIE 3 ALLEMAGNE (R.F.A.) 1.**

129 Boy playing Trumpet

1982. Norman Rockwell Paintings. Multicoloured.

495 60f. Type **129** 30 15
496 75f. Sleeping porter . . . . . 2·75 75
497 100f. Couple listening to early radio 80 25
498 150f. Children playing leapfrog . . . . 1·10 30
499 200f. Tramp cooking sausages . . . . 1·50 45
500 300f. Boy talking to clown 2·25 70

130 Sultan Said Mohamed Sidi

1982. Sultans. Multicoloured.

501 30f. Type **130** 15 10
502 60f. Sultan Ahmed Abdallah 30 15
503 75f. Sultan Salim (horiz) . . 35 20
504 300f. Sultans Said Mohamed Sidi and Ahmed Abdallah (horiz) . . . . 2·10 95

131 Montgolfier Brothers' Balloon, 1783

1983. Air. Bicentenary of Manned Flight. Mult.

505 100f. Type **131** 80 35
506 200f. Vincenzo Lunardi's balloon over London, 1784 1·40 65
507 300f. Blanchard and Jeffries crossing the Channel, 1785 2·25 1·00
508 400f. Henri Giffard's steam-powered dirigible airship, 1852 (horiz) . . . . 3·00 1·25

132 Type "470" Dinghy

1983. Air. Pre-Olympic Year. Multicoloured.

510 150f. Type **132** . . . . 1·40 65
511 200f. "Flying Dutchman" . . 1·60 80
512 300f. Type "470" (different) 2·40 1·25
513 400f. "Finn" class dinghies 3·50 1·75

133 Lake Ziani

1983. Landscapes. Multicoloured.

515 60f. Type **133** 50 20
516 100f. Sunset 65 35
517 175f. Chiromani (vert) . . . 1·10 60
518 360f. Itsandra beach . . . . 2·25 1·00
519 400f. Anjouan . . . . 2·75 1·25

134 Moheli

1983. Portraits. Multicoloured.

520 30f. Type **134** 15 10
521 35f. "Mask of Beauty" . . . 45 15
522 50f. Mayotte 45 15

135 Pure-bred Arab

1983. Horses. Multicoloured.

523 75f. Type **135** 55 25
524 100f. Anglo-Arab 65 35
525 125f. Lipizzan 90 40
526 150f. Tennessee . . . . . . 1·10 50
527 200f. Appaloosa . . . . . . 1·40 65
528 300f. Pure-bred English . . . 2·25 1·00
529 400f. Clydesdale . . . . . . 2·75 1·00
530 500f. Andalusian . . . . . . 3·50 1·25

136 "Double Portrait" **137** Symbols of Development

1983. 500th Birth Anniv of Raphael. Mult.

531 100f. Type **136** 65 35
532 200f. Fresco detail . . . . . 1·40 65
533 300f. "St. George and the Dragon" . . . . 2·00 75
534 400f. "Balthazar Castiglione" 2·75 1·00

1984. Air. International Conference on Development of Comoros.

535 **137** 475f. multicoloured . . . 3·25 1·75

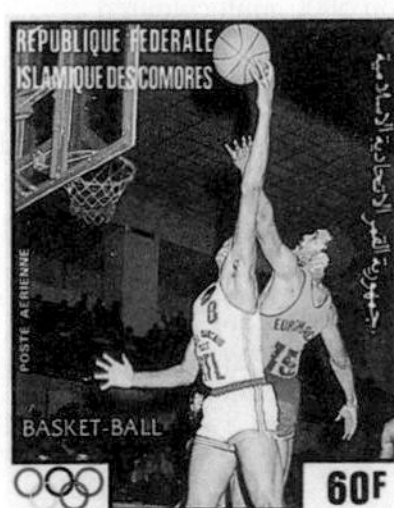

138 Basketball

1984. Air. Olympic Games, Los Angeles. Mult.

536 60f. Type **138** 25 20
537 100f. Basketball (different) . . 70 35
538 165f. Basketball (different) . . 1·00 55
539 175f. Baseball (horiz) . . . . 1·10 55
540 200f. Baseball (different) (horiz) . . . . 1·40 55

139 "William Fawcett"

1984. Transport. Multicoloured. (a) Ships.

542 100f. Type **139** 80 70
543 150f. "Lightning" . . . . . 1·50 80
544 200f. "Rapido" . . . . . . 1·75 90
545 350f. "Sindia" . . . . 3·25 2·40

(b) Automobiles.

546 100f. De Dion Bouton and Trepardoux, 1885 . . . . 1·10 35
547 150f. Benz "Victoria", 1893 1·50 45
548 200f. Colombia electric, 1901 2·00 55
549 350f. Fiat, 1902 . . . . . . 3·00 80

140 Barn Swallows

1985. Air. Birth Bicentenary of John J. Audubon (ornithologist). Multicoloured.

550 100f. Type **140** . . . . 1·50 90
551 125f. Northern oriole . . . . 1·60 1·10
552 150f. Red-shouldered hawk (horiz) . . . . 1·90 1·25
553 500f. Red-breasted sapsucker (horiz) . . . . 6·25 4·50

142 Harbours

1985. Air. "Philexafrique" Stamp Exhibition, Lome, Togo (1st issue). Multicoloured.

555 200f. Type **142** . . . . 2·00 1·00
556 200f. Scouts walking along road . . . . 1·50 85

See also Nos. 576/7.

143 Victor Hugo (novelist, death centenary)

1985. Anniversaries. Multicoloured.

557 100f. Type **143** . . . . 1·00 30
558 200f. Jules Verne (novelist) (80th death anniv) . . . . 1·40 60
559 300f. Mark Twain (150th birth anniv) . . . . 2·25 1·00
560 450f. Queen Elizabeth, the Queen Mother (85th birth anniv) (vert) . . . . . . 2·75 1·00
561 500f. Statue of Liberty (centenary) (vert) . . . . . 3·25 1·25

The 200f. and 300f. also commemorate International Youth Year.

144 Map and Flag on Sun

1985. Air. 10th Anniv of Independence.

562 **144** 10f. multicoloured 10 10
563 15f. multicoloured 10 10
564 125f. multicoloured . . . 1·10 40
565 300f. multicoloured . . . 2·50 1·10

145 Arthritic Spider Conch

1985. Shells. Multicoloured.

566 75f. Type **145** 70 35
567 125f. Silver conch . . . . . 1·00 45
568 200f. Costate tun . . . . . . 1·60 60
569 300f. Elephant's snout . . . 2·50 75
570 450f. Orange spider conch . . 3·75 1·00

146 U.N. Emblem and Map of Islands

1985. 10th Anniv of Membership of U.N.O.

571 **146** 5f. multicoloured 10 10
572 30f. multicoloured 15 10
573 75f. multicoloured 35 30
574 125f. multicoloured . . . 90 40
575 400f. multicoloured . . . 2·50 1·50

147 Runners ("Youth")

1985. Air. "Philexafrique" Stamp Exhibition, Lome, Togo (2nd issue). Multicoloured.

576 250f. Type **147** . . . . 1·60 90
577 250f. Earth mover and road construction ("Development") . . . . . 1·60 90

148 Globe, Galleon, Wright Type A Biplane and Rocket Capsule

1985. 20th Anniv of Moroni Rotary Club.

578 **148** 25f. multicoloured 25 15
579 75f. multicoloured 75 30
580 125f. multicoloured . . . 1·40 45
581 500f. multicoloured . . . 4·25 1·40

149 "Astraeus hygrometricus"

1985. Fungi. Multicoloured.

582 75f. "Boletus edulis" 80 45
583 125f. "Sarcoscypha coccinea" 1·00 60
584 200f. "Hypholoma fasciculare" . . . . 1·60 60
585 350f. Type **149** . . . . 3·00 90
586 500f. "Armillariella mellea" 4·00 1·40

150 Sikorsky S-43 Amphibian

1985. Air. 50th Anniv of Union des Transports Aeriennes. Multicoloured.

587 25f. Type **150** 10 10
588 75f. Douglas DC-9 airplane and camel 45 30

589 100f. Douglas DC-4, DC-6, Nord 2501 Noratlas and De Havilland Heron 2 aircraft 55 35
590 125f. Maintenance 90 40
591 1000f. Emblem and Latecoere 28, Sikorsky S-43, Douglas DC-10 and Boeing 747-200 aircraft (35×47 mm) . . . 7·75 4·25

151 Edmond Halley, Comet and "Giotto" Space Probe

1986. Air. Appearance of Halley's Comet. Multicoloured.
593 125f. Type **151** 90 40
594 150f. Giacobini-Zinner comet, 1959 . . . . 1·10 55
595 225f. J. F. Encke and Encke comet, 1961 . . . . 1·60 75
596 300f. Computer enhanced picture of Bradfield comet, 1980 . . . . 2·10 1·10
597 450f. Halley's comet and "Planet A" space probe . . 3·00 1·50

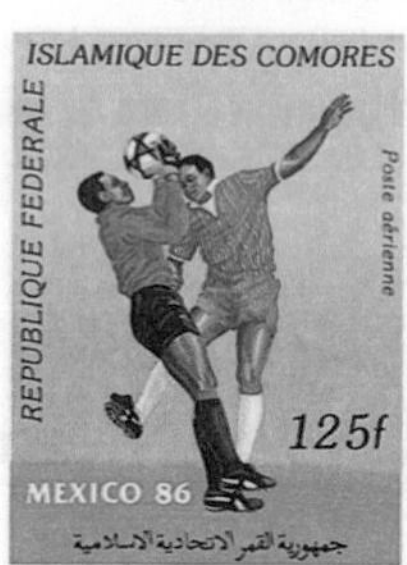

152 Footballers

1986. Air. World Cup Football Championship, Mexico. Designs showing footballers.
598 **152** 125f. multicoloured . . . 90 40
599 – 210f. multicoloured . . . 1·40 70
600 – 500f. multicoloured . . . 3·25 1·50
601 – 600f. multicoloured . . . 4·00 1·75

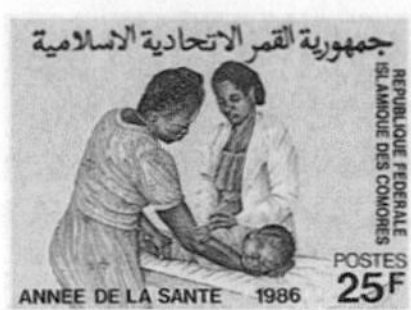

153 Doctor examining Child

1986. World Health Year. Multicoloured.
602 25f. Type **153** 10 10
603 100f. Doctor weighing child 70 35
604 200f. Nurse innoculating baby . . . . 1·40 70

154 Ndzoumara (wind instrument) **155** Server

1986. Musical Instruments. Multicoloured.
605 75f. Type **154** 55 25
606 125f. Ndzedze (string instrument) 80 40
607 210f. Gaboussi (string instrument) . . . . 1·40 70
608 500f. Ngoma (drums) . . . . 3·25 1·50

1987. Air. Tennis as 1988 Olympic Games Discipline. Multicoloured.
609 150f. Type **155** . . . . 1·10 50
610 250f. Player preparing shot 2·00 75
611 500f. Player being lobbed . . 3·50 1·25
612 600f. Players each side of net 4·00 1·50

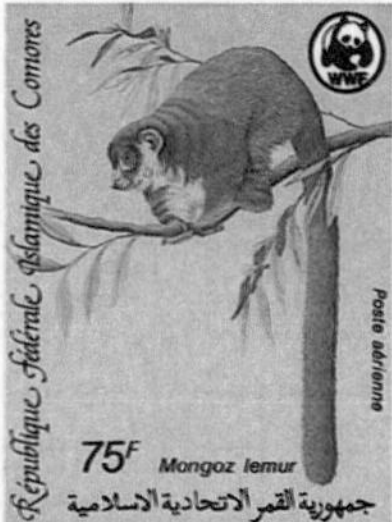

156 On Tree Branch

1987. Air. Endangered Animals. Mongoose-Lemur. Multicoloured.
613 75f. Type **156** 65 25
614 100f. Head of mongoose-lemur with ruff 90 30
615 125f. Mongoose-lemur on rock . . . . 1·40 40
616 150f. Head of mongoose-lemur without ruff . . . . 1·50 50

157 Women working in Field

1987. Woman and Development. Multicoloured.
617 75f. Type **157** 55 25
618 125f. Woman picking musk seeds (vert) . . . . 1·10 40
619 1000f. Woman making basket 6·75 2·25

158 Men's Downhill

1987. Air. Winter Olympic Games, Calgary (1988). Multicoloured.
620 150f. Type **158** 90 50
621 225f. Ski jumping . . . . . 1·40 80
622 500f. Women's slalom . . . 3·25 1·50
623 600f. Men's luge . . . . . . 4·00 1·75

159 Didier Daurat, Raymond Vanier and "Air Bleu"

1987. Air. Aviation. Multicoloured.
624 200f. Type **159** . . . . 1·40 45
625 300f. Letord 4 Lorraine and route map (1st regular airmail service, Paris–Le Mans–St. Nazaire, 1918) 2·00 70
626 500f. Morane Saulnier Type H and route map (1st airmail flight, Villacoublay–Pauillac, 1913) . . . . . . 3·25 1·25
627 1000f. Henri Pequet flying Humber-Sommer biplane (1st aerophilately exn, Allahabad) (36×49 mm) 6·75 1·75

160 Ice Skating

1988. Multicoloured. (a) Winter Olympic Games, Calgary.
628 75f. Type **160** (postage) . . . 30 25
629 125f. Speed skating 50 40
630 350f. Two-man bobsleigh . . 2·25 75
631 400f. Biathlon (air) . . . . . 2·75 1·00

(b) Olympic Games, Seoul.
633 100f. Relay (postage) 65 30
634 150f. Showjumping . . . . . 1·00 50
635 500f. Pole-vaulting . . . . . 3·25 1·25
636 600f. Football (air) . . . . . 4·00 1·25

161 Kiwanis International Emblem and Hand supporting Figures

1988. Child Health Campaigns. Multicoloured.
638 75f. Type **161** 30 25
639 125f. Kiwanis emblem, wheelchair and crutch . . 80 40
640 210f. Kiwanis emblem and man with children (country inscr in black) . . . . . . 1·25 70
641 210f. As No. 640 but country inscr in white . . . . . . 1·25 70
642 425f. As No. 639 . . . . . . 2·50 1·40
643 425f. As No. 639 but with Lions International emblem 2·50 1·40
644 500f. Type **161** . . . . 3·25 1·50
645 500f. As Type **161** but with Rotary emblem . . . . . 3·25 1·50

162 Throwing the Discus **163** Columbus and "Santa Maria"

1988. Olympic Games, Barcelona (1992) (1st issue). Multicoloured.
646 75f. Type **162** (postage) . . . 30 25
647 100f. Rowing (horiz) 65 30
648 125f. Cycling (horiz) 90 40
649 150f. Wrestling (horiz) . . . 1·00 50
650 375f. Basketball (air) . . . . 2·75 90
651 600f. Tennis . . . . 4·00 1·10
See also Nos. 709/14.

1988. 500th Anniv (1992) of Discovery of America by Columbus. Multicoloured.
653 75f. Type **163** (postage) . . . 75 30
654 125f. Martin Alonzo Pinzon and "Pinta" . . . . 1·00 50
655 150f. Vicente Yanez Pinzon and "Nina" . . . . 1·25 60
656 250f. Search for gold . . . . 1·60 85
657 375f. Wreck of "Santa Maria" (air) . . . . 2·50 1·00
658 450f. Preparation for fourth voyage . . . . 3·50 1·25

1988. Nos. 641, 643 and 645 (125 and 400f. with colours changed) surch.
660 75f. on 210f. multicoloured 55 25
661 125f. on 425f. multicoloured 80 40
662 200f. on 425f. multicoloured 1·40 65
663 300f. on 500f. multicoloured 1·90 1·00
664 400f. on 500f. multicoloured 2·75 1·25

1988. Olympic Games Medal Winners for Tennis. Nos. 609/12 optd.
665 150f. Optd **Medalle d'or Seoul Miloslav Mecir (Tchec.)** . . 1·00 50
666 250f. Optd **Medaille d'argent Seoul Tim Mayotte (U.S.A)** 1·60 1·10
667 500f. Optd **Medaille d'or Seoul Steffi Graf (R.F.A.)** 3·25 2·50
668 600f. Optd **Medaille d'argent Seoul Gabriela Sabatini (Argentine)** . . . . 4·00 2·75

166 Alberto Santos-Dumont and "14 bis"

1988. Air. Aviation Pioneers.
669 **166** 100f. purple 80 30
670 – 150f. mauve . . . . . . 1·10 50
671 – 200f. black . . . . . . 1·40 65
672 – 300f. brown . . . . . . 2·00 1·00
673 – 500f. blue . . . . . . 3·25 1·75
674 – 800f. green . . . . . . 5·25 2·25
DESIGNS: 150f. Wright Type A and Orville and Wilbur Wright; 200f. Louis Bleriot and Bleriot XI; 300f. Farman Voisin No. 1 bis and Henri Farman; 500f. Gabriel and Charles Voisin and Voisin "Boxkite"; 800f. Roland Garros and Morane Saulnier Type I.

167 Galileo Galilei **168** Yuri Gagarin (cosmonaut) and Daughters

1988. Appearance of Halley's Comet. Mult.
675 200f.+10f. Type **167** . . . . 1·40 40
676 200f.+10f. Nicolas Copernicus . . . . 1·40 40
677 200f.+10f. Johannes Kepler 1·40 40
678 200f.+10f. Edmond Halley . . 1·40 40
679 200f.+10f. Japanese "Planet A" space probe . . . . . 1·40 40
680 200f.+10f. American "Ice" space probe . . . . 1·40 40
681 200f.+10f. "Planet A" space probe (different) . . . . . 1·40 40
682 200f.+10f. Russian "Vega" space probe . . . . 1·40 40

1988. Personalities. Multicoloured.
684 150f. Type **168** (20th death anniv) (postage) . . . . . 1·00 50
685 300f. Henri Dunant (founder of Red Cross) (125th anniv of Red Cross Movement) 2·00 75
686 400f. Roger Clemens (baseball player) . . . . . 2·50 1·25
687 500f. Gary Kasparov (chess player) (air) . . . . 4·00 1·75
688 600f. Paul Harris (founder of Rotary International) (birth centenary) . . . . 4·00 1·25

169 Alain Prost (racing driver) and Formula 1 Racing Car

1988. Cars, Trains and Yachts. Multicoloured.
690 75f. Type **169** (postage) . . . 1·10 25
691 125f. George Stephenson (railway engineer), "Rocket" and Borsig Class 05 steam locomotive, 1935, Germany . . . . 1·25 40
692 500f. Ettore Bugatti (motor manufacturer) and Aravis "Type 57" . . . . 3·25 1·00
693 600f. Rudolph Diesel (engineer) and German Class V200 diesel locomotive . . . . 4·00 1·50
694 750f. Dennis Conner and "Stars and Stripes" (America's Cup contender) (air) . . . . 5·00 1·50
695 1000f. Michael Fay and "New Zealand" (America's Cup contender) . . . . . 6·75 1·75

170 "Papilio nireus aristophontes" (female)

1989. Scouts, Butterflies and Birds. Multicoloured.
697 50f. Type **170** (postage) . . . 20 10
698 75f. "Papilio nireus aristophontes" (male) . . . 55 15
699 150f. "Charaxes fulvescens separanus" . . . . 1·10 40
700 375f. Bronze mannikin . . . 2·75 75
701 450f. "Charaxes castor comoranus" (air) . . . . . 3·00 80
702 500f. Madagascar white-eye 3·75 1·00

171 Aussat "K3" and N. Uphoff (individual dressage)

1989. Satellites and Olympic Games Medal Winners for Equestrian Events. Multicoloured.

704 75f. Type **171** (postage) . . . 30 15
705 150f. "Brasil sat" and P. Durand (individual show jumping) . . . . 1·00 40
706 375f. "ECS 4" and J. Martinek (modern pentathlon) . . . . 2·50 60
707 600f. "Olympus 1" and M. Todd (cross-country) (air) . . . . 4·00 1·25

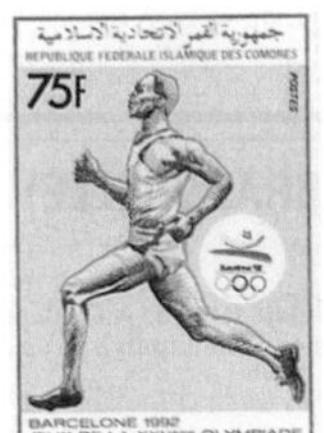

172 Running

1989. Olympic Games, Barcelona (1992) (2nd issue). Multicoloured.

709 75f. Type **172** (postage) . . . 55 15
710 150f. Football . . . . 1·00 40
711 300f. Tennis . . . . 2·00 50
712 375f. Baseball . . . . 2·50 65
713 500f. Gymnastics (air) . . . 3·25 85
714 600f. Table tennis . . . . . 4·00 1·10

173 Dr. Joseph-Ignace Guillotin and Guillotine

1989. Bicentenary of French Revolution. Mult.

716 75f. Type **173** (postage) . . . 55 15
717 150f. Soldiers with cannon (Battle of Valmy) and Gen. Kellermann . . . . 1·00 40
718 375f. Jean Cottereau (Chouan) and Vendeens . . 2·25 60
719 600f. Invasion of Les Tuileries (air) . . . . . . 4·00 1·00

1989. Various stamps surch.

721 25f. on 250f. mult (No. 656) (postage) 35 10
722 150f. on 200f. mult (No. 532) 1·00 40
723 150f. on 200f. mult (No. 558) 1·00 40
724 150f. on 200f. mult (No. 604) 1·00 40
725 5f. on 250f. multicoloured (No. 390) (air) 10 10
726 25f. on 250f. mult (No. 610) 10 10
727 50f. on 250f. mult (No. 576) 20 10
728 50f. on 250f. mult (No. 577) 20 10
729 150f. on 200f. mult (No. 511) 1·00 50
730 150f. on 200f. mult (No. 555) 1·00 50
731 150f. on 200f. mult (No. 556) 1·00 40
732 150f. on 200f. black (No. 671) . . . . 1·00 60

175 Airport Pavilion

1990.

733 **175** 5f. orange, brown & red 10 10
734 10f. orange, brown & bl 10 10
735 25f. orange, brown & grn 10 10
736 – 50f. black and red . . . 20 10
737 – 75f. black and blue . . . 35 10
738 – 150f. black and green . . 1·00 35

DESIGNS: 50 to 150f. Federal Assembly.

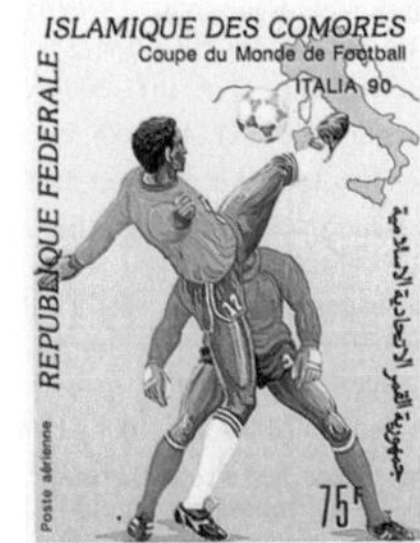

176 Player challenging Goalkeeper

1990. Air. World Cup Football Championship, Italy (1st issue). Multicoloured.

739 75f. Type **176** 65 10
740 150f. Player heading ball . . 1·00 35
741 500f. Overhead kick . . . . 3·25 1·25
742 1000f. Player evading tackle 6·75 1·75

See also Nos. 743/8.

177 Brazilian Player

1990. World Cup Football Championship, Italy (2nd issue). Multicoloured.

743 50f. Type **177** (postage) . . . 20 10
744 75f. English player 35 10
745 100f. West German player . . 50 25
746 150f. Belgian player . . . . 1·00 35
747 375f. Italian player (air) . . . 2·50 85
748 600f. Argentinian player . . . 4·00 85

178 U.S. Space Telescope

1990. Multicoloured.

750 75f. Type **178** (postage) . . . 60 10
751 150f. Pope John Paul II and Mikhail Gorbachev, 1989 1·00 35
752 200f. Kevin Mitchell (San Francisco Giants baseball player) . . . . 1·40 50
753 250f. De Gaulle and Adenauer, 1962 . . . . . 1·60 50
754 300f. "Titan 2002" space probe . . . . 2·00 70
755 375f. French TGV Atlantique express train and Concorde airplane . . . . 3·25 1·00
756 450f. Gary Kasparov (World chess champion) and Anderssen v Steinitz chess match (air) . . . . 3·25 1·00
757 500f. Paul Harris (founder of Rotary International) and symbols of health, hunger and humanity . . . . . . 3·25 75

179 Edi Reinalter (skiing, 1948) **180** Dish Aerial, Moroni Volo-volo

1990. Winter Olympics, Albertville (1992). Medal Winners at previous Games. Multicoloured.

759 75f. Type **179** (postage) . . . 35 10
760 100f. Canada (ice hockey, 1924) 50 25
761 375f. Baroness Gratia Schimmelpenninck van der Oye (skiing, 1936) (air) . . 2·50 85
762 600f. Hasu Haikki (ski jumping, 1948) . . . . . . 4·00 85

1991.

764 **180** 75f. multicoloured 60 10
765 150f. multicoloured . . . 1·00 35
766 225f. multicoloured . . . 1·40 55
767 300f. multicoloured . . . 2·00 70
768 500f. multicoloured . . . 3·25 1·25

181 Emblem and Leaves

1991. Indian Ocean Commission Conference.

769 **181** 75f. multicoloured 60 10
770 150f. multicoloured . . . 1·00 60
771 225f. multicoloured . . . 1·40 90

182 De Gaulle and Battle of Koufra, 1941 **183** Emblem and Stylized View of Exhibition

1991. 50th Anniv of World War II. Multicoloured.

772 125f. Type **182** (postage) . . 90 30
773 150f. Errol Flynn in "Adventures in Burma" . . 1·00 35
774 300f. Henry Fonda in "The Longest Day" . . . . . 2·00 70
775 375f. De Gaulle and Battle of Britain, 1940 . . . . . . 2·25 70
776 450f. Humphrey Bogart in "Sahara" (air) . . . . . . 3·00 75
777 500f. De Gaulle and Battle of Monte Cassino, 1944 . . . 3·25 75

1991. "Telecom '91" Int Telecommunications Exhibition, Geneva. Multicoloured.

779 75f. Type **183** 60 35
780 150f. Emblem (horiz) . . . . 1·00 80

184 Weather Space Station "Columbus"

1991. Anniversaries and Events. Multicoloured.

781 100f. Type **184** (postage) . . 70 15
782 150f. Gandhi (43rd death anniv) . . . . 1·00 25
783 250f. Henri Dunant (founder of Red Cross) (90th anniv of award of Nobel Peace Prize) . . . . 1·60 40
784 300f. Wolfgang Amadeus Mozart (composer, death bicentenary) . . . . . . 2·00 55
785 375f. Brandenburg Gate (bicent and second anniv of fall of Berlin Wall) . . . . 2·50 70
786 400f. Konrad Adenauer (German Chancellor) signing new constitution (25th death anniv) . . . . 2·50 70
787 450f. Elvis Presley (entertainer, 14th death anniv) (air) . . . . 3·25 80
788 500f. Ferdinand von Zeppelin (airship pioneer, 75th death anniv) . . . . 3·25 80

185 Cep

1992. Fungi and Shells. Multicoloured.

789 75f. Type **185** (postage) . . . 60 15
790 125f. Textile cone 80 35
791 150f. Puff-ball . . . . 1·50 55
792 150f. Bull-mouth helmet (shell) . . . . 1·00 40
793 500f. Map cowrie (air) . . . 3·25 1·00
794 600f. Scarlet elf cups . . . . 6·50 1·25

186 Ham (chimpanzee) on "Mercury" flight, 1960

1992. Space Research. Multicoloured.

796 75f. Type **186** (postage) . . . 60 10
797 125f. "Mars Observer" space probe 90 20
798 150f. Felix (cat) and "Veronique" rocket, 1963 1·10 50
799 150f. "Mars Rover" and "Marsokod" space vehicles 1·00 50
800 500f. "Phobos" project (air) 3·25 90
801 600f. Laika (dog) and "Sputnik 2" flight, 1957 . . 4·00 1·10

187 "Endeavour" (space shuttle), Capt. James Cook and H.M.S. "Endeavour"

1992. Space and Nautical Exploration. Mult.

803 75f. Type **187** (postage) . . . 70 15
804 100f. "Cariane" space microphone, Sir Francis Drake and "Golden Hind" 90 20
805 150f. Infra-red astronomical observation device, John Smith and "Susan Constant" . . . . 1·40 30
806 225f. Space probe "B", Robert F. Scott and "Discovery" . . . . 1·75 45
807 375f. "Magellan" (Venus space probe), Ferdinand Magellan and ship (air) . . 3·25 80
808 500f. "Newton" (satellite), Vasco da Gama and "Sao Gabriel" . . . . 3·75 1·10

188 Map **189** Footballers

1993. 30th Anniv of Organization of African Unity.

810 **188** 25f. multicoloured 10 10
811 50f. multicoloured 20 10
812 75f. multicoloured 60 35
813 150f. multicoloured . . . 1·00 80

1993. World Cup Football Championship, U.S.A. (1994).

814 **189** 25f. multicoloured 10 10
815 75f. multicoloured 35 10
816 100f. multicoloured . . . 70 15
817 150f. multicoloured . . . 95 25

190 I.T.U. Emblem

1993. World Telecommunications Day. "Telecommunications and Human Development".

818 **190** 50f. multicoloured 20 10
819 75f. multicoloured 35 10
820 100f. multicoloured . . . 70 15
821 150f. multicoloured . . . 1·00 55

191 Edaphosaurus

1994. Prehistoric Animals. Multicoloured.

No.	Description	Mint	Used
822	75f. Type **191**	25	10
823	75f. Moschops	25	10
824	75f. Kentrosaurus	25	10
825	75f. Compsognathus	25	10
826	75f. Sauroctonus	25	10
827	75f. Ornitholestes	25	10
828	75f. Styracosaurus	25	10
829	75f. Acanthopholis	25	10
830	150f. Edmontonia	50	20
831	150f. Struthiomimus	50	20
832	150f. Diatryma	50	20
833	150f. Uintatherium	50	20
834	450f. Dromiceiomimus	2·10	60
835	450f. Iguanodon	2·10	60
836	525f. Synthetoceras	2·50	75
837	525f. Euryapteryx	2·50	75

192 "Hibiscus syriacus"

1994. Plants. Multicoloured.

No.	Description	Mint	Used
839	75f. Type **192**	25	10
840	75f. Cashew nut	25	10
841	75f. Butter mushroom	40	15
842	150f. "Pyrostegia venusta" (flower)	50	20
843	150f. Manioc (root)	50	20
844	150f. "Lycogala epidendron" (fungus)	80	35
845	525f. "Allamanda cathartica" (flower)	2·25	75
846	525f. Cacao (nut)	2·25	75
847	525f. "Clathrus ruber" (fungus)	3·00	1·00

193 Purple-tip ("Colotis zoe")

1994. Insects. Multicoloured.

No.	Description	Mint	Used
848	75f. Type **193**	25	10
849	75f. "Charaxes comoranus" (butterfly)	25	10
850	75f. "Hypurgus ova" (beetle)	25	10
851	150f. Death's-head hawk moth ("Acherontia atropos")	50	20
852	150f. "Verdant hawk moth ("Euchloron megaera")	50	20
853	150f. "Onthophagus catta" (beetle)	50	20
854	450f. African monarch ("Danaus chrysippus") (butterfly)	2·25	60
855	450f. "Papilio phorbanta" (butterfly)	2·25	60
856	450f. "Echinosoma bolivari" (beetle)	2·25	60

OFFICIAL STAMPS

O 99 Comoro Flag

1979.

No.	Type	Description	Mint	Used
O379	O 99	5f. grn, blk & azure	10	10
O380		10f. grn, blk & grey	10	10
O381		20f. grn, blk & stone	10	10
O382		30f. green, blk & bl	20	10
O383		40f. grn, blk & yell	25	15
O384		60f. grn, blk & lt grn	30	25
O384a		75f. grn, blk & lt grn	25	15
O385		100f. grn, blk & yell	80	35
O386	–	100f. mult	70	35
O386a	–	125f. mult	90	55
O387	–	400f. mult	2·75	1·50

DESIGNS: Nos. O386, O386a, O387, Pres. Cheikh.

POSTAGE DUE STAMPS

D 9 Mosque in Anjouan

D 10 Coelacanth

1950.

No.	Type	Description	Mint	Used
D16	D 9	50c. green	15	3·25
D17		1f. brown	15	3·25

1954.

No.	Type	Description	Mint	Used
D18	D 10	5f. sepia and green	25	3·50
D19		10f. violet and brown	2·50	3·50
D20		20f. indigo and blue	70	4·00

D 78 Pineapple

1977. Multicoloured.

No.	Description	Mint	Used
D244	1f. Hibiscus (horiz)	10	10
D245	2f. Type D **78**	10	10
D246	5f. White butterfly (horiz)	10	10
D247	10f. Chameleon (horiz)	10	10
D248	15f. Banana flower (horiz)	10	10
D249	20f. Orchid (horiz)	10	10
D250	30f. "Allamanda cathartica" (horiz)	20	10
D251	40f. Cashew nuts	25	15
D252	50f. Custard apple	25	15
D253	100f. Breadfruit (horiz)	70	25
D254	200f. Vanilla (horiz)	1·60	45
D255	500f. Ylang-ylang flower (horiz)	4·00	1·10

APPENDIX

The following stamps have either been issued in excess of postal needs or have not been available to the public in reasonable quantities at face value. Such stamps may later be given full listing if there is evidence of regular postal use.

1975.

Various stamps optd **ETAT COMORIEN** or surch also.

Birds issue (No. 60). 10f. on 2f.

Fishes issue (No. 71). Air 50f.

Birds issue (No. 99). 40f.

Comoro Landscapes issue (Nos. 102/4). Air 75f. on 65f., 100f. on 85f., 100f.

Tropical Plants issue (Nos. 105/9). Postage 5f. on 1f., 5f. on 3f.; Air 75f. on 60f., 100f. on 85f.

Seashells issue (No. 114). 75f. on 60f.

Aquatic Sports issue (No. 122). Air 75f. on 70f.

Anjouan Landscapes issue (Nos. 126/8). Air 40f., 75f. on 60f., 100f.

Said Mohamed Cheikh issue (Nos. 129/30). Air 20f., 35f.

Great Comoro Landscapes issue (Nos. 134 and 136). Postage 35f.; Air 200f. on 135f.

Moroni Buildings issue (No. 139). 20f.

Karthala Volcano issue (No. 140). Air 200f. on 120f.

Hansen issue (No. 141). Air 100f.

Copernicus issue (No. 142). Air 400f. on 150f.

Picasso issue (No. 143). Air 200f.

Mosques issue (Nos. 145/6). 15f. on 20f., 25f. on 35f.

Star of Anjouan issue (No. 147). 500f.

Said Omar Ben Soumeth issue (Nos. 148/9). Air 100f. on 135f., 200f.

Shaikh Said Mohamed issue (No. 150). 30f. on 35f.

Handicrafts issue (Nos. 153/5). 20f., 30f. on 35f., 75f.

Mayotte Landscapes issue (Nos. 157/60). Air 10f. on 20f., 30f. on 35f., 100f. on 90f., 200f. on 120f.

U.P.U. Centenary issue (No. 161). 500f. on 30f.

Air Service issue (No. 162). Air 100f. on 135f.

Rotary issue (No. 163). Air 400f. on 250f.

Handicrafts issue (Nos. 164/7). 15f. on 20f., 30f. on 35f., 100f. on 120f., 200f. on 135f.

Moheli Landscapes issue (Nos. 168/71). Postage 30f., 50f., 50f. on 55f.; Air 200f. on 230f.

Coelacanth issue (No. 172). 50f.

Folk-dances issue (Nos. 173/4). 100f., 100f. on 150f.

Apollo–Soyuz Space Test Project. Postage 10, 30, 50f.; Air 100, 200, 400f. Embossed on gold foil. Air 1500f.

1976.

Bicent of American Revolution. Postage 15, 25, 35, 40, 75f.; Air 500f. Embossed on gold foil: Air 1000f.

Winter Olympic Games, Innsbruck. Postage 5, 30, 35, 50f.; Air 200, 400f. Embossed on gold foil. Air 1000f.

Children's Stories. Postage 15, 30, 35, 40, 50f.; Air 400f.

Telephone Centenary. Postage 10, 25, 75f.; Air 100, 200, 500f.

Bicentenary of American Revolution (Early Settler and Viking Space Rocket). Embossed on gold foil. Air 1500f.

Bicent of American Revolution (J. F. Kennedy and Apollo). Embossed on gold foil. Air 1500f.

1978.

World Cup Football Championship, Argentina. Embossed on gold foil. Air 1000f.

Death Centenary of Sir Rowland Hill. Embossed on gold foil. Air 1500f.

Argentina's World Cup Victory. Optd on World Cup issue. Air 1000f.

1979.

International Year of the Child. Embossed on gold foil. Air 1500f.

1988.

Rotary International. Embossed on gold foil. Air 1500f.

1989.

Scouts, Butterflies and Birds. Embossed on gold foil. Air 1500f.

Satellites and Olympic Winners. Embossed on gold foil. Air 1500f.

Bicentenary of French Revolution. Embossed on gold foil. Air 1500f.

1990.

World Cup Football Championship. Embossed on gold foil. Air 1500f.

Winter Olympic Games, Albertville (1992). Embossed on gold foil. Air 1500f.

1991.

Birth Centenary of Charles De Gaulle (1990). Embossed on gold foil. Air 1500f.

1992.

Olympic Games, Barcelona. Boxing. Embossed on gold foil. Air 1500f.

CONFEDERATE STATES OF AMERICA Pt. 22

Stamps issued by the seceding states in the American Civil War.

1 Jefferson Davis 2 T. Jefferson

1861. Imperf.

No.	Type	Description	Mint	Used
1	1	5c. green	£100	70·00
3	2	10c. blue	£130	95·00

3 Jackson 4 Jefferson Davis

1862. Imperf.

No.	Type	Description	Mint	Used
4	3	2c. green	£350	£400
5	1	5c. blue	60·00	55·00
6	2	10c. red	£600	£300

1862. Imperf.

No.	Type	Description	Mint	Used
7	4	5c. blue	6·00	11·00

5 Jackson

6 Jefferson Davis

9 Washington

1863. Imperf or perf (10c.).

No.	Type	Description	Mint	Used
9	5	2c. red	30·00	£170
10	6	10c. blue (TEN CENTS)	£475	£300
12		10c. blue (10 CENTS)	5·00	9·00
14	9	20c. green	25·00	£200

CONGO (BRAZZAVILLE) Pt. 6; Pt. 12

Formerly Middle Congo. An independent republic within the French Community.

1 "Birth of the Republic"

1959. 1st Anniv of Republic.

No.	Type	Description	Mint	Used
1	1	25f. multicoloured	55	25

1960. 10th Anniv of African Technical Co-operation Commission. As T **62** of Cameroun.

No.	Description	Mint	Used
2	50f. lake and green	65	60

1960. Air. Olympic Games. No. 276 of French Equatorial Africa optd with Olympic rings and **XVIIe OLYMPIADE 1960 REPUBLIQUE DU CONGO 250F**.

No.	Description	Mint	Used
3	250f. on 500f. blue, black & grn	6·75	6·75

2 Pres. Youlou

3 U.N. Emblem, map and Flag

1960.

No.	Type	Description	Mint	Used
4	2	15f. green, red and turquoise	25	15
5		85f. blue and red	1·40	50

1961. Admission into U.N.O.

No.	Type	Description	Mint	Used
6	3	5f. multicoloured	15	10
7		20f. multicoloured	25	20
8		100f. multicoloured	1·40	90

4 "Thesium tencio"

1961. Air.

No.	Type	Description	Mint	Used
9	–	100f. purple, yellow & green	2·25	1·40
10	–	200f. yellow, turq & brown	4·00	2·00
11	4	500f. yellow, myrtle & brown	11·00	5·00

FLOWERS: 100f. "Helicrysum mechowiam"; 200f. "Cogniauxia podolaena".

1961. Air. Foundation of "Air Afrique" Airline. As T **69** of Cameroun.

No.	Description	Mint	Used
12	50f. purple, myrtle and green	1·10	45

6 Rainbow Runner

7 Brazzaville Market

1961. Tropical Fish.
13 **6** 50c. multicoloured 10 10
14 – 1f. brown and green 10 10
15 – 2f. brown and blue 10 10
15a – 2f. red, brown and green . . 45 10
16 **6** 3f. green, orange and blue 20 15
17 – 5f. sepia, brown and green 30 15
18 – 10f. brown and turquoise . . 1·00 25
18a – 15f. purple, green & violet 1·60 90
FISH: 1, 2f. (No. 15), Sloan's viperfish ("Chauliodus sloanei"); 2f. (No. 15a), Fishes pursued by squid; 5f. Giant marine hatchetfish; 10f. Long-toothed fangtooth; 15f. Johnson's deep sea angler.

1962.
19 **7** 20f. red, green and black . . 55 15

1962. Malaria Eradication. As T **70** of Cameroun.
20 25f.+5f. brown 80 80

8 "Yang-tse" (freighter) loading Timber, Pointe Noire

1962. Air. International Fair, Pointe Noire.
21 **8** 50f. multicoloured . . . . . 2·00 90

1962. Sports. As T **12** of Central African Republic.
22 20f. sepia, red & blk (postage) 30 25
23 50f. sepia, red and black . . . 65 50
24 100f. sepia, red and black (air) 2·00 1·00
DESIGNS—HORIZ: 20f. Boxing; 50f. Running. VERT: (26×47 mm): 100f. Basketball.

1962. Union of African and Malagasy States. 1st Anniv. As No. 328 of Cameroun.
25 **72** 30f. violet 90 50

1962. Freedom from Hunger. As T **76** of Cameroun.
26 25f.+5f. turquoise, brn & bl 80 80

9 Town Hall, Brazzaville and Pres. Youlou

1963. Air.
27 **9** 100f. multicoloured £120 £120

9a "Costus spectabilis" (K. Schum)

10 King Makoko's Gold Chain

1963. Air. Flowers. Multicoloured.
28 100f. Type **9a** . . . . 2·75 1·60
29 250f. "Acanthus montanus T. anders" . . . . 5·50 2·75

1963. Air. African and Malagasy Posts and Telecommunications Union. As T **18** of Central African Republic.
30 85f. red, buff and violet . . . 1·25 75

1963. Space Telecommunications. As Nos. 37/8 of Central African Republic.
31 25f. blue, orange and green . . 45 30
32 100f. violet, brown and blue 1·25 1·10

1963. Folklore and Tourism.
33 **10** 10f. bistre and black 25 30
34 – 15f. multicoloured 30 25
DESIGN: 15f. Kebekebe mask.
See also Nos. 45/6 and 62/4.

11 Airline Emblem

1963. Air. 1st Anniv of "Air Afrique", and Inaug of DC-8 Service.
35 **11** 50f. multicoloured 60 45

12 Liberty Square, Brazzaville

1963. Air.
36 **12** 25f. multicoloured 60 35
See also No. 56.

1963. Air. European-African Economic Convention. As T **24** of Central African Republic.
37 50f. multicoloured 70 50

1963. 15th Anniv of Declaration of Human Rights. As T **26** of Central African Republic.
38 25f. blue, turquoise & brown 45 30

13 Statue of Hathor, Abu Simbel

1964. Air. Nubian Monuments.
39 **13** 10f.+5f. violet & brown . . 35 20
40 25f.+5f. brown & turq . . . 45 40
41 50f.+5f. turquoise & brn . . 1·40 90

14 Barograph

1964. World Meteorological Day.
42 **14** 50f. brown, blue & green . . 70 65

15 Machinist

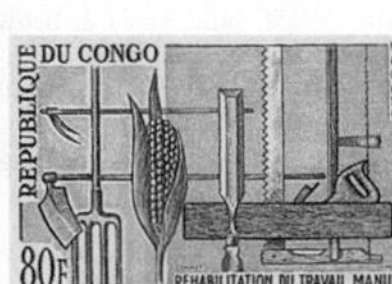

16 Emblem and Implements of Manual Labour

1964. "Technical Instruction".
43 **15** 20f. brown, mauve & turq 35 25

1964. Manual Labour Rehabilitation.
44 **16** 80f. green, red and sepia . . 1·10 45

17 Diaboua Ballet

19 Wood Carving

18 Tree-felling

1964. Folklore and Tourism. Multicoloured.
45 30f. Type **17** 90 30
46 60f. Kebekebe dance (vert) . . 1·40 65

1964. Air.
47 **18** 100f. brown, red and green 1·60 70

1964. Congo Sculpture.
48 **19** 50f. sepia and red . . . . . 1·00 45

20 Students in Classroom

1964. Development of Education.
49 **20** 25f. red, purple and blue . . 40 30

1964. Air. 5th Anniv of Equatorial African Heads of State Conference. As T **31** of Central African Republic.
50 100f. multicoloured . . . . . 1·25 65

21 Sun, Ears of Wheat, and Globe within Cogwheel

1964. Air. Europafrique.
51 **21** 50f. yellow, blue and red . . 70 50

22 Stadium, Olympic Flame and Throwing the Hammer

1964. Air. Olympic Games, Tokyo. Sport and flame orange.
52 **22** 25f. violet and brown . . . 35 25
53 – 50f. purple and olive 60 40
54 – 100f. green and brown . . . 1·50 85
55 – 200f. olive and red . . . . 2·75 1·75
DESIGNS—Stadium, Olympic Flame and: VERT: 50f. Weightlifting; 100f. Volleyball. HORIZ: 200f. High-jumping.

1964. 1st Anniv of Revolution and National Festival. As T **12** but inscr "1er ANNIVERSAIRE DE LA REVOLUTION FETE NATIONALE 15 AOUT 1964".
56 20f. multicoloured 65 20

23 Posthorns, Envelope and Radio Mast

1964. Air. Pan-African and Malagasy Posts and Telecommunications Congress, Cairo.
57 **23** 25f. sepia and red 35 25

1964. French, African and Malagasy Co-operation. As T **88** of Cameroun.
58 25f. brown, green and red . . 45 35

24 Dove, Envelope and Radio Mast

1965. Establishment of Posts and Telecommunications Office, Brazzaville.
59 **24** 25f. multicoloured 35 25

25 Town Hall, Brazzaville and Arms

1965. Air.
60 **25** 100f. multicoloured . . . . 1·10 55

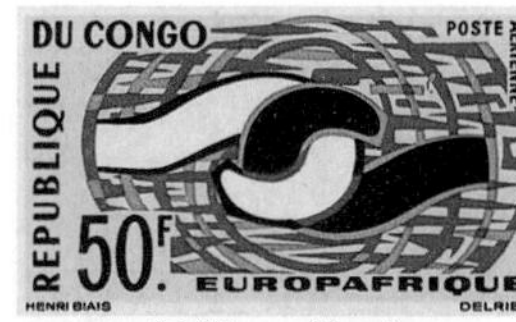

26 "Europafrique"

1965. Air. Europafrique.
61 **26** 50f. multicoloured 60 40

27 African Elephant

29 Pres. Massamba-Debat

28 Cadran de Breguet's Telegraph and "Telstar"

1965. Folklore and Tourism.
62 – 15f. purple, green and blue 80 25
63 **27** 20f. black, blue and green 65 30
64 – 85f. multicoloured . . . . . 2·25 1·40
DESIGNS—VERT: 15f. Bushbuck; 85f. Dancer on stilts.

1965. Air. Centenary of I.T.U.
65 **28** 100f. brown and blue . . . 2·00 80

1965. Portrait in sepia.
66 **29** 20f. yellow, green & brown 25 15
66a 25f. green, turquoise & brn 35 20
66b 30f. orange, turq & brn . . 40 20

30 Sir Winston Churchill

31 Pope John XXIII

1965. Air. Famous Men.
67 – 25f. on 50f. sepia and red 45 45
68 **30** 50f. sepia and green 90 90
69 – 80f. sepia and blue . . . . 1·60 1·60
70 – 100f. sepia and yellow . . . 2·25 2·25
PORTRAITS: 25f. Lumumba; 80f. Pres. Boganda; 100f. Pres. Kennedy.

1965. Air. Pope John Commemoration.
71 **31** 100f. multicoloured . . . . 1·50 90

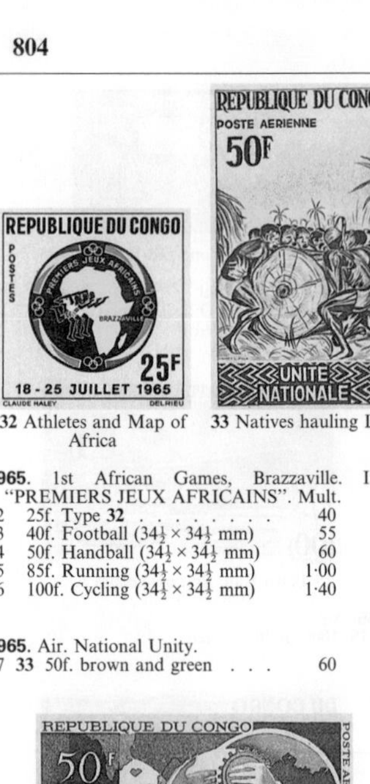

32 Athletes and Map of Africa

33 Natives hauling Log

1965. 1st African Games, Brazzaville. Inscr "PREMIERS JEUX AFRICAINS". Mult.
72 25f. Type **32** 40 30
73 40f. Football (34½ × 34½ mm) 55 40
74 50f. Handball (34½ × 34½ mm) 60 40
75 85f. Running (34½ × 34½ mm) 1·00 65
76 100f. Cycling (34½ × 34½ mm) 1·40 85

1965. Air. National Unity.
77 **33** 50f. brown and green . . . 60 40

34 "World Co-operation"

1965. Air. International Co-operation Year.
78 **34** 50f. multicoloured 90 55

35 Arms of Congo

37 Trench-digging

36 Lincoln

1965.
79 **35** 20f. multicoloured 30 15

1965. Air. Death Centenary of Abraham Lincoln.
80 **36** 90f. multicoloured 90 50

1966. Village Co-operative.
81 **37** 25f. multicoloured 30 20

1966. National Youth Day. As T **37** but showing youth display.
82 30f. multicoloured 40 30

38 De Gaulle and Flaming Torch

1966. Air. 22nd Anniv of Brazzaville Conference.
83 **38** 500f. brown, red & green . . 24·00 19·00

39 Weaving

40 People and Clocks

1966. World Festival of Negro Arts, Dakar. Multicoloured.
84 30f. Type **39** 45 25
85 85f. Musical Instrument (horiz) 1·40 65
86 90f. Mask . . . . 1·40 85

1966. Establishment of Shorter Working Day.
87 **40** 70f. multicoloured 80 40

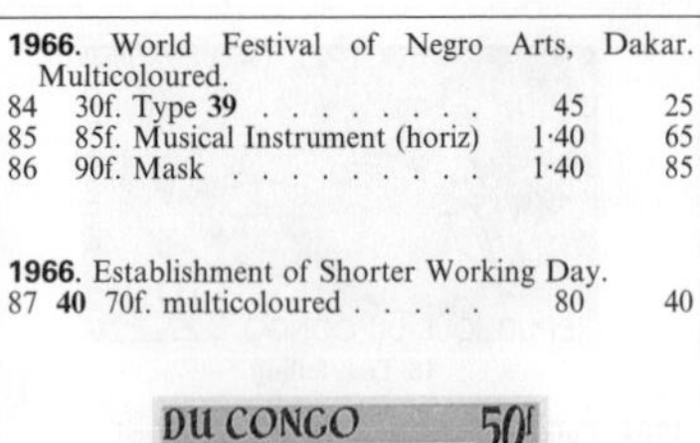

41 W.H.O. Building

1966. Inaug of W.H.O. Headquarters, Geneva.
88 **41** 50f. violet, yellow and blue 65 40

42 Satellite "D1" and Brazzaville Tracking Station

1966. Air. Launching of Satellite "D1".
89 **42** 150f. black, red and green 2·25 1·10

43 St. Pierre Claver Church

44 Volleyball

1966.
90 **43** 70f. multicoloured 80 40

1966. Sports.
91 **44** 1f. brown, bistre and blue 10 10
92 – 2f. brown, green and blue 15 10
93 – 3f. brown, lake and green 15 15
94 – 5f. brown, blue and green 20 15
95 – 10f. violet, turquoise & grn 25 20
96 – 15f. brown, violet and lake 35 30
DESIGNS—VERT: 2f. Basketball; 5f. Sportsmen; 10f. Athlete; 15f. Football. HORIZ: 3f. Handball.

45 Jules Rimet Cup and Globe

46 Corn, Atomic Emblem and Map

1966. World Cup Football Championship, England.
97 **45** 30f. multicoloured 45 30

1966. Air. Europafrique.
98 **46** 50f. multicoloured 55 35

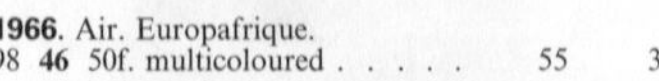

47 Pres. Massamba-Debat and Presidential Palace, Brazzaville

1966. Air. 3rd Anniv of Congolese Revolution. Multicoloured.
99 25f. Type **47** 30 15
100 30f. Robespierre and Bastille, Paris 35 20
101 50f. Lenin and Winter Palace, St. Petersburg 80 30

1966. Air. Inauguration of DC-8F Air Services. As T **54** of Central African Republic.
103 30f. yellow, black and violet 60 25

48 Dr. Albert Schweitzer

1966. Air. Schweitzer Commemoration.
104 **48** 100f. multicoloured . . . . 1·50 85

49 View of School

1966. Inaug of Savorgnan de Brazza High School.
105 **49** 30f. multicoloured 35 20

50 Pointe-Noire Railway Station

51 Silhouette of Congolese, and U.N.E.S.C.O. Emblem

1966.
106 **50** 60f. red, brown and green 1·75 75

1966. 20th Anniv of U.N.E.S.C.O.
107 **51** 90f. blue, brown & green 1·10 80

52 Balumbu Mask

53 Cancer "The Crab", Microscope and Pagoda

1966. Congolese Masks.
108 **52** 5f. sepia and red 20 15
109 – 10f. brown and blue . . . 25 15
110 – 15f. blue, sepia & brown 25 25
111 – 20f. multicoloured 65 25
MASKS: 10f. Kuyu; 15f. Bakwele; 20f. Bateke.

1966. Air. 9th Int Cancer Congress, Tokyo.
112 **53** 100f. multicoloured . . . . 1·25 80

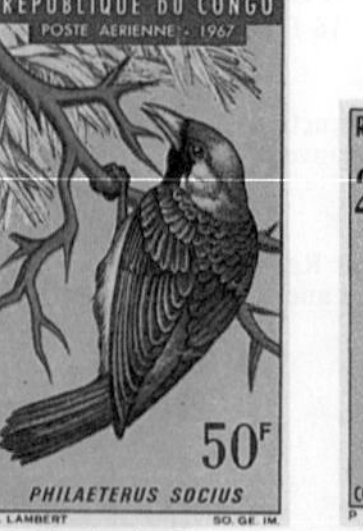

54 Sociable Weaver

55 Medal, Ribbon and Map

1967. Air. Birds. Multicoloured.
113 50f. Type **54** . . . . 3·75 1·10
114 75f. European bee eater . . . 4·25 1·60
115 100f. Lilac-breasted roller . . 6·75 2·00
116 150f. Regal sunbird . . . . . 8·00 2·75
117 200f. South African crowned crane . . . . 9·00 3·00
118 250f. Secretary bird . . . . . 11·00 4·50
119 300f. Black-billed turaco . . 15·00 5·25

1967. "Companion of the Revolution" Order.
120 **55** 20f. multicoloured 30 25

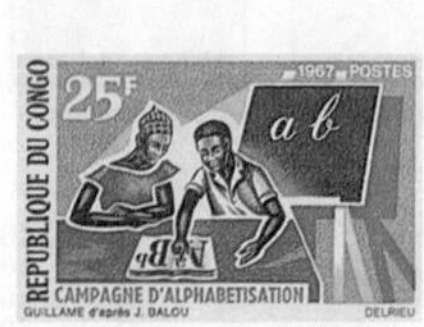

56 Learning the Alphabet (Educational Campaign)

57 Mahatma Gandhi

1967. Education and Sugar Production Campaigns. Multicoloured.
121 25f. Type **56** 35 30
122 45f. Cutting sugar-cane . . . 90 30

1967. Gandhi Commemoration.
123 **57** 90f. black and blue . . . . 1·25 55

58 Prisoner's Hands in Chains

59 Ndumba, Lady of Fashion

1967. Air. African Liberation Day.
124 **58** 500f. multicoloured . . . . 7·75 3·25

1967. Congolese Dolls. Multicoloured.
125 5f. Type **59** 15 15
126 10f. Fruit seller 25 20
127 25f. Girl pounding saka-saka 30 20
128 30f. Mother and child . . . 35 25

60 Congo Scenery

61 "Europafrique"

1967. International Tourist Year.
129 **60** 60f. red, orange and green 65 40

1967. Europafrique.
130 **61** 50f. multicoloured 55 30

62 "Sputnik 1" and "Explorer 6"

1967. Air. Space Exploration.
131 **62** 50f. blue, violet & brown 55 30
132 – 75f. lake and slate . . . . 1·00 40
133 – 100f. blue, red & turquoise 1·40 65
134 – 200f. red, blue and lake . . 2·50 1·50
DESIGNS: 75f. "Ranger 6" and "Lunik 2"; 100f. "Mars 1" and "Mariner 4"; 200f. "Gemini" and "Vostok".

63 Brazzaville Arms

1967. 4th Anniv of Congo Revolution.
135 **63** 30f. multicoloured 40 20

1967. Air. 5th Anniv of African and Malagasy Posts and Telecommunications Union. As T **66** of Central African Republic.
136 100f. green, red and brown 1·10 65

64 Jamboree Emblem, Scouts and Tents

1967. Air. World Scout Jamboree, Idaho.
137 **64** 50f. blue, brown & chestnut 55 30
138 – 70f. red, green and blue . . 80 40
DESIGN: 70f. Saluting hand, Jamboree camp and emblem.

65 Sikorsky S-43 Amphibian and Map

1967. Air. 30th Anniv of Aeromaritime Airmail Link.
139 **65** 30f. multicoloured 40 25

66 Dove, Human Figures and U.N. Emblem

67 Young Congolese

1967. U.N. Day and Campaign in Support of U.N.
140 **66** 90f. multicoloured . . . . 1·25 65

1967. 21st Anniv of U.N.I.C.E.F.
141 **67** 90f. black, blue & brown 1·25 65

68 Albert Luthuli (winner of Nobel Peace Prize) and Dove

70 Arms of Pointe Noire

69 Global Dance

1968. Luthuli Commemoration.
142 **68** 30f. brown and green . . . 35 30

1968. Air. "Friendship of the Peoples".
143 **69** 70f. brown, green & blue 75 40

1968.
144 **70** 10f. multicoloured 35 30

71 "Old Man and His Grandson" (Ghirlandaio)

1968. Air. Paintings. Multicoloured.
145 30f. Type **71** 45 30
146 100f. "The Horatian Oath' (J.-L. David) (horiz) . . . 1·60 65
147 200f. "The Negress with Peonies" (Bazille) (horiz) 3·25 1·60
See also Nos. 209/13.

72 "Mother and Child"

73 Diesel Train crossing Mayombe Viaduct

1968. Mothers' Festival.
148 **72** 15f. black, blue and red . . 30 25

1968.
149 **73** 45f. lake, blue and green 2·25 40

74 Beribboned Rope

1968. Air. 5th Anniv of Europafrique.
150 **74** 50f. multicoloured 55 25

75 Daimler, 1889

1968. Veteran Motor Cars. Multicoloured.
151 5f. Type **75** (postage) 20 15
152 20f. Berliet, 1897 . . . . . . 35 20
153 60f. Peugeot, 1898 . . . . . 1·40 40
154 80f. Renault, 1900 . . . . . 2·00 90
155 85f. Fiat, 1902 . . . . 2·50 1·40
156 150f. Ford, 1915 (air) . . . . 2·50 1·40
157 200f. Citroen . . . . 3·50 1·50

1968. Inauguration of Petroleum Refinery, Port Gentil, Gabon. As T **80** of Central African Republic.
158 30f. multicoloured 60 25

76 Dr. Martin Luther King

78 Robert Kennedy

77 "The Barricade" (Delacroix)

1968. Air. Martin Luther King Commemoration.
159 **76** 50f. black, green & emerald 60 30

1968. Air. 5th Anniv of Revolution Paintings. Multicoloured.
160 25f. Type **77** . . . . 1·40 45
161 30f. "Destruction of the Bastille" (H. Robert) . . . 1·40 55

1968. Air. Robert Kennedy Commemoration.
162 **78** 50f. black, green and red 55 30

79 "Tree of Life" and W.H.O. Emblem

1968. 20th Anniv of W.H.O.
163 **79** 25f. red, purple and green 30 15

80 Start of Race

1968. Air. Olympic Games, Mexico.
164 **80** 5f. brown, blue and green 10 10
165 – 20f. green, brown & blue 30 15
166 – 60f. brown, green and red 60 35
167 – 85f. brown, red and slate 1·40 50
DESIGNS—VERT: 20f. Football; 60f. Boxing. HORIZ: 85f. High-jumping.

1968. Air. "Philexafrique" Stamp Exn, Abidjan (1969) (1st issue). As T **86** of Central African Republic.
168 100f. multicoloured . . . . . 2·25 1·60
DESIGN: 100f. "G. de Gueidan writing" (N. de Largilliere).

1969. Air. "Philexafrique" Stamp Exhibition, Abidjan, Ivory Coast (2nd issue). As T **138** of Cameroun.
169 50f. green, brown & mauve 2·50 1·00
DESIGN: 50f. Pointe-Noire harbour, lumbering and Middle Congo stamp of 1933.

1969. Air. Birth Bicentenary of Napoleon Bonaparte. As T **144** of Cameroun. Multicoloured.
170 25f. Battle of Rivoli (C. Vernet) 90 30
171 50f. "Battle of Marengo" (Pahou) . . . . 1·40 80
172 75f. "Battle of Friedland" (H. Vernet) . . . . 2·25 1·25
173 100f. "Battle of Jena" (Thevenin) . . . . 3·25 1·40

81 "Che" Guevara

1969. Air. Ernesto "Che" Guevara (Latin-American revolutionary) Commemoration.
174 **81** 90f. brown, orange & lake 80 40

82 Doll and Toys

1969. Air. International Toy Fair, Nuremberg.
175 **82** 100f. slate, mauve & orange . . . . 2·50 85

83 Beribboned Bar

1969. Air. Europafrique.
176 **83** 50f. violet, black & turq . . 45 25

1969. 5th Anniv of African Development Bank. As T **146** of Cameroun.
177 25f. brown, red and green . . 25 15
178 30f. brown, green and blue 30 15

85 Modern Bicycle

1969. Cycles and Motor-cycles.
180 **85** 50f. purple, orange & brn 80 30
181 – 75f. black, lake & orange 80 35
182 – 80f. green, blue & purple 85 45
183 – 85f. green, slate & brown 1·25 55
184 – 100f. multicoloured . . . . 1·40 65
185 – 150f. brown, red & black 2·00 80
186 – 200f. pur, dp grn & grn . . 3·25 1·40
187 – 300f. green, purple & blk 5·50 2·25
DESIGNS: 75f. "Hirondelle" cycle; 80f. Folding cycle; 85f. "Peugeot" cycle; 100f. "Excelsior Manxman" motor-cycle; 150f. "Norton" motor-cycle; 200f. "Brough Superior" motor-cycle; 300f. "Matchless and N.I.G.-J.A.P.S." motor-cycle

86 Series ZE Diesel-electric Train entering Mbamba Tunnel

1969. African International Tourist Year. Mult.
188 40f. Type **86** . . . . 2·50 40
189 60f. Series ZE diesel-electric train crossing the Mayombe (horiz) . . . . 3·25 50

87 Mortar Tanks

1969. Loutete Cement Works.
190 **87** 10f. slate, brown and lake 10 10
191 – 15f. violet, blue & brown 25 15
192 – 25f. blue, brown and red 30 25
193 – 30f. blue, violet & ultram 35 25
DESIGNS—VERT: 15f. Mixing tower; 25f. Cableway. HORIZ: 30f. General view of works.

1969. 10th Anniv of A.S.E.C.N.A. As T **150** of Cameroun.
195 100f. brown . . . . 2·00 75

88 Harvesting Pineapples

1969. 50th Anniv of I.L.O.
196 **88** 25f. brown, green & blue 30 20
197 – 30f. slate, purple and red 35 20
DESIGN: 30f. Operating lathe.

89 Textile Plant

1970. "SOTEXCO" Textile Plant, Kinsoundi.
198 **89** 15f. black, violet & green 20 15
199 – 20f. green, red and purple 25 15
200 – 25f. brown, blue & lt blue 30 15
201 – 30f. brown, red and slate 35 15
DESIGNS: 20f. Spinning machines; 25f. Printing textiles; 30f. Checking finished cloth.

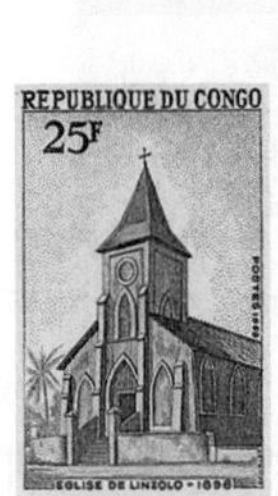

90 Linzolo Church **91** Artist at work

1970. Buildings.
202 **90** 25f. green, brown & blue 35 15
203 – 90f. brown, green & blue 80 35
DESIGN: HORIZ: 90f. Cosmos Hotel, Brazzaville.

1970. Air. "Art and Culture".
204 **91** 100f. brown, plum & grn 1·40 50
205 – 150f. plum, lake & green 2·00 75
206 – 200f. brown, choc & ochre 2·75 1·50
DESIGNS: 150f. Lesson in wood-carving; 200f. Potter at wheel.

92 Diosso Gorges

1970. Tourism.
207 **92** 70f. purple, brown & grn 90 35
208 – 90f. purple, green & brown 1·40 45
DESIGN: 90f. Foulakari Falls.

1970. Air. Paintings. As T **71**. Multicoloured.
209 150f. "Child with Cherries" (J. Russell) 2·75 1·25
210 200f. "Erasmus" (Holbein the younger) 4·00 1·50
211 250f. "Silence" (Bernadino Luini) 4·00 1·90
212 300f. "Scenes from the Scio Massacre" (Delacroix) 5·50 2·75
213 500f. "Capture of Constantinople" (Delacroix) 8·00 3·75

93 Aurichalcite

1970. Air. Minerals. Multicoloured.
214 100f. Type **93** 2·75 1·25
215 150f. Dioptase 3·25 1·50

94 "Volvaria esculenta"

1970. Mushrooms. Multicoloured.
216 5f. Type **94** 50 20
217 10f. "Termitomyces entolomoides" 55 25
218 15f. "Termitomyces microcarpus" 85 35
219 25f. "Termitomyces aurantiacus" 1·75 45
220 30f. "Termitomyces mammiformis" 3·00 55
221 50f. "Tremella fuciformis" 4·50 1·25

95 Laying Cable **96** Mother feeding Child

1970. Laying of Coaxial Cable, Brazzaville–Pointe Noire.
222 **95** 25f. buff, brown and blue 1·75 45
223 – 30f. brown and green 2·00 55
DESIGN: 30f. Diesel locomotive and cable-laying gang.

1970. New U.P.U. Headquarters Building, Berne. As T **156** of Cameroun.
224 30f. purple, slate and plum 45 25

1970. Mothers' Day. Multicoloured.
225 85f. Type **96** 75 40
226 90f. Mother suckling baby 85 45

97 U.N. Emblem and Trygve Lie **98** Lenin in Cap

1970. 25th Anniv of United Nations.
227 **97** 100f. blue, indigo and lake 1·10 70
228 – 100f. lilac, red and lake 1·10 70
229 – 100f. green, turq & lake 1·10 70
DESIGNS—VERT: No. 228, as Type **97**, but with portrait of Dag Hammarskjold. HORIZ: No. 229, as Type **97**, but with portrait of U Thant and arrangement reversed.

1970. Air. Birth Centenary of Lenin.
231 **98** 45f. brown, yellow & grn 65 45
232 – 75f. brown, red and blue 1·10 65
DESIGN: 75f. Lenin seated (after Vassiliev).

99 "Brillantaisia vogeliana"

1970. "Flora and Fauna". Multicoloured.
(a) Flowers. Horiz designs.
233 1f. Type **99** 10 10
234 2f. "Plectranthus decurrens" 10 10
235 3f. "Myrianthemum mirabile" 10 10
236 5f. "Connarus griffonianus" 15 10

(b) Insects. Vert designs.
237 10f. "Sternotomis variabilis" 30 20
238 15f. "Chelorrhina polyphemus" 80 20
239 20f. "Metopodontus savagei" 90 30

100 Karl Marx

1970. Air. Founders of Communism.
240 **100** 50f. brown, green & red 50 30
241 – 50f. brown, blue and red 50 30
DESIGN: No. 241, Friedrich Engels.

101 Kentrosarus

1970. Prehistoric Creatures. Multicoloured.
242 15f. Type **101** 30 25
243 20f. Dinotherium (vert) 1·10 55
244 60f. Brachiosaurus (vert) 2·25 80
245 80f. Arsinoitherium 2·75 1·50

102 "Mikado 141" Steam Locomotive, 1932

1970. Locomotives of Congo Railways (1st series).
246 **102** 40f. black, green & purple 2·40 1·10
247 – 60f. black, green & blue 2·75 1·25
248 – 75f. black, red and blue 4·25 1·75
249 – 85f. red, green & orange 6·00 2·50
DESIGNS: 60f. Super-Golwe steam locomotive, 1947; 75f. Alsthom Series BB 1100 diesel locomotive, 1962; 85f. Diesel locomotive No. BB BB 302, 1969.
See also Nos. 371/4.

103 Lilienthal's Glider, 1891

1970. Air. History of Flight and Space Travel.
250 **103** 45f. brown, blue and red 60 25
251 – 50f. green and brown 60 25
252 – 70f. brown, red and blue 70 35
253 – 90f. brown, olive & blue 1·10 50
DESIGNS: 50f. Lindbergh's "Spirit of St. Louis", 1927; 70f. "Sputnik I"; 90f. First man on the Moon, 1969.

104 "Wise Man"

1970. Air. Christmas. Stained-glass Windows, Brazzaville Cathedral. Multicoloured.
254 100f. Type **104** 90 45
255 150f. "Shepherd" 1·60 70
256 250f. "Angels" 2·75 1·40

105 "Cogniauxia padolaena" **106** Marilyn Monroe

1971. Tropical Flowers. Multicoloured.
258 1f. Type **105** 10 10
259 2f. "Celosia cristata" 10 10
260 5f. "Plumeria acutifolia" 10 10
261 10f. "Bauhinia variegata" 45 15
262 15f. "Euphorbia pulcherrima 65 25
263 20f. "Thunbergia grandiflora" 1·10 25
See also D264/9.

1971. Air. Great Names of the Cinema.
270 **106** 100f. brown, blue & grn 2·75 35
271 – 150f. mauve, blue & pur 2·75 50
272 – 200f. brown and blue 2·75 75
273 – 250f. plum, blue & green 2·75 90
PORTRAITS: 150f. Martine Carol; 200f. Eric K. von Stroheim; 250f. Sergei Eisenstein.

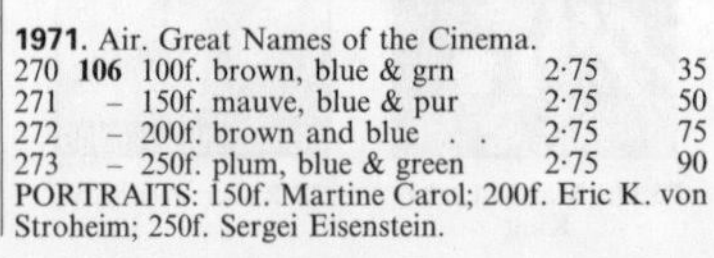

107 "Carrying the Cross" (Veronese)

1971. Air. Easter. Religious Paintings. Mult.
274 100f. Type **107** 95 55
275 150f. "Christ on the Cross" (Burgundian School c. 1500) (vert) 1·60 65
276 200f. "Descent from the Cross" (Van der Weyden) 2·75 90
277 250f. "The Entombment" (Flemish School c. 1500) (vert) 3·25 1·40
278 500f. "The Resurrection" (Memling) (vert) 6·75 2·50

108 Telecommunications Map

1971. Air. Pan-African Telecommunications Network.
279 **108** 70f. multicoloured 60 30
280 85f. multicoloured 1·00 35
281 90f. multicoloured 1·40 45

109 Global Emblem

1971. Air. World Telecommunications Day.
282 **109** 65f. multicoloured 55 25

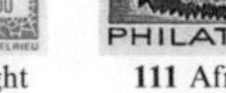
110 Green Night Adder **111** Afro-Japanese Allegory

1971. Reptiles. Multicoloured.
283 5f. Type **110** 15 10
284 10f. African egg-eating snake (horiz) 15 10
285 15f. Flap-necked chameleon 55 15
286 20f. Nile crocodile (horiz) 90 20
287 25f. Rock python (horiz) 1·10 30
288 30f. Gaboon viper 1·40 65
289 40f. Brown house snake (horiz) 1·60 80
290 45f. Jameson's mamba 2·25 90

1971. Air. "Philatokyo 1971" Stamp Exn, Tokyo.
291 **111** 75f. black, mauve & violet 90 35
292 – 150f. brown, red & purple 1·25 65
DESIGN: 150f. "Tree of Life", Japanese girl and African in mask.

112 "Pseudimbrasia deyrollei"

1971. Caterpillars. Multicoloured.
293 10f. Type **112** 35 25
294 15f. "Bunaca alcinoe" (vert) 35 25
295 20f. "Epiphora vacuna ploetzi" 80 35
296 25f. "Imbrasia eblis" 1·40 45
297 30f. "Imbrasia dione" (vert) 2·25 1·00
298 40f. "Holocera angulata" 2·75 1·25

113 Japanese Scout **114** Olympic Torch

1971. World Scout Jamboree, Asagiri, Japan (1st issue). On foil.

299	**113**	90f. silver (postage)	2·00	1·40
300	–	90f. silver	2·00	1·40
301	–	90f. silver	2·00	1·40
302	–	90f. silver	2·00	1·40
303	–	1000f. gold (air)	10·00	

DESIGNS—VERT: No. 300, French Scout; 301, Congolese Scout; 302, Lord Baden-Powell. HORIZ: No. 303, Scouts and Lord Baden-Powell.

See also Nos. 306/9.

1971. Air. Olympic Games, Munich.

304	**114**	150f. red, green & purple	1·40	70
305	–	350f. violet, green & brn	4·00	2·00

DESIGN—HORIZ: 350f. Sporting cameos within Olympic rings.

115 Scout Badge, Dragon and Congolese Wood-carving

1971. Air. World Scout Jamboree, Asagiri, Japan (2nd issue).

306	**115**	85f. purple, brown & grn	65	30
307	–	90f. brown, violet & lake	70	35
308	–	100f. green, red & brown	90	45
309	–	250f. brown, red & green	2·25	95

DESIGNS—HORIZ: 250f. Congolese mask, geisha and scout badge. VERT: 90f. African and Japanese mask; 100f. Japanese woman and African.

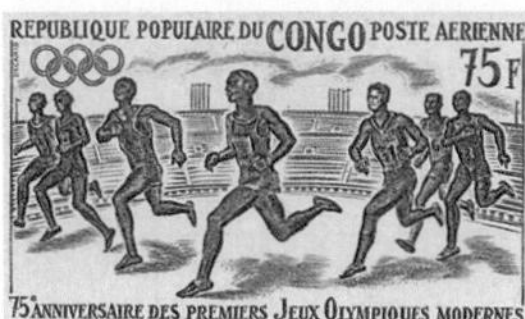

116 Running

1971. Air. 75th Anniv of Modern Olympic Games.

310	**116**	75f. brown, blue and red	60	30
311	–	85f. brown, blue and red	65	30
312	–	90f. brown and violet	1·00	40
313	–	100f. brown and blue	1·10	45
314	–	150f. brown, red & green	2·00	75

DESIGNS: 85f. Hurdling; 90f. Various events; 100f. Wrestling; 150f. Boxing.

117 "Cymothae sangaris"

1971. Butterflies. Multicoloured.

315		30f. Type **117**	65	35
316		40f. "Papilio dardanus" (vert)	1·25	55
317		75f. "Iolaus timon"	2·25	1·10
318		90f. "Papilio phorcas" (vert)	3·00	1·60
319		100f. "Euchloron megaera"	4·00	2·25

118 African and European Workers

1971. Racial Equality Year.

320	**118**	50f. multicoloured	55	30

119 De Gaulle and Congo 1966 Brazzaville Conference Stamp

1971. Air. 1st Death Anniv of General De Gaulle.

321	**119**	500f. brown, green & red	11·00	11·00
322	–	1000f. red & grn on gold	19·00	
323	–	1000f. red & grn on gold	19·00	

DESIGNS—VERT (29 × 38 mm): No. 322, Tribute by Pres. Ngouabi; 323, De Gaulle and Cross of Lorraine.

1971. Air. 10th Anniv of African and Malagasy Posts and Telecommunications Union. Similar to T **184** of Cameroun. Multicoloured.

324		100f. U.A.M.P.T. H.Q. and Congolese woman	1·00	45

1971. Inauguration of Brazzaville–Pointe Noire Cable Link. Surch **REPUBLIQUE POPULAIRE DU CONGO INAUGURATION DE LA LIAISON COXIALE 18-11-71** and new value.

325	**95**	30f. on 25f. buff, brn & bl	1·60	30
326	–	40f. on 30f. brown and green (No. 223)	2·00	30

121 Congo Republic Flag and Allegory of Revolution

1971. Air. 8th Anniv of Revolution.

327	**121**	100f. multicoloured	1·40	40

122 Congolese with Flag

1971. Air. 2nd Anniv of Congolese Workers' Party, and Adoption of New National Flag. Multicoloured.

328		30f. Type **122**	25	10
329		40f. National flag	35	20

123 Map and Emblems **125** Book Year Emblem

124 Lion

1971. "Work–Democracy–Peace".

330	**123**	30f. multicoloured	25	20
331		40f. multicoloured	30	15
332		100f. multicoloured	75	40

1972. Wild Animals.

333	**124**	1f. brown, blue & green	10	10
334	–	2f. brown, green and red	10	10
335	–	3f. brown, orge and red	15	10
336	–	4f. brown, blue & violet	45	10
337	–	5f. brown, green and red	55	15
338	–	20f. brown, blue & orge	1·40	55
339	–	30f. green, emer & brn	2·00	80
340	–	40f. black, green and blue	2·75	1·00

DESIGNS—HORIZ: 2f. African elephants; 3f. Leopard; 4f. Hippopotamus; 20f. Potto; 30f. De Brazza's monkey. VERT: 5f. Gorilla; 40f. Pygmy chimpanzee.

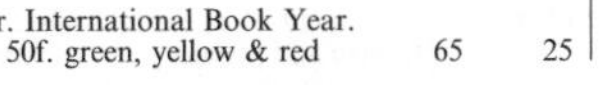

1972. Air. International Book Year.

341	**125**	50f. green, yellow & red	65	25

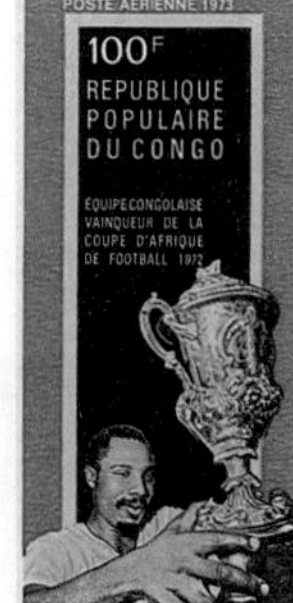

126 Team Captain with Cup **127** Girl with Bird

1973. Air. Congolese Victory in Africa Football Cup. Multicoloured.

342		100f. Type **126**	1·40	50
343		100f. Congolese team (horiz)	1·40	50

1973. Air. U.N. Environmental Conservation Conference, Stockholm.

344	**127**	85f. green, blue & orange	1·40	90

128 Miles Davis

1973. Air. Famous Negro Musicians.

345	**128**	125f. multicoloured	1·60	65
346	–	140f. red, lilac & mauve	1·60	70
347	–	160f. green, emer & orge	1·90	1·00
348	–	175f. purple, red & blue	2·00	1·00

DESIGNS: 140f. Ella Fitzgerald; 160f. Count Basie; 175f. John Coltrane.

129 Hurdling

1973. Air. Olympic Games, Munich (1972).

349	**129**	100f. violet and mauve	90	50
350	–	150f. violet and green	1·40	65
351	–	250f. red and blue	2·75	1·40

DESIGNS—VERT: 150f. Pole-vaulting. HORIZ: 250f. Wrestling.

130 Oil Tanks, Djeno

1973. Air. Oil Installations, Pointe Noire.

352	**130**	180f. indigo, red & blue	2·25	1·40
353	–	230f. black, red and blue	2·75	1·40
354	–	240f. purple, blue & red	3·00	1·50
355	–	260f. black, red and blue	4·75	1·90

DESIGNS—VERT: 230f. Oil-well head; 240f. Drill in operation. HORIZ: 260f. Off-shore oil-rig.

131 Lunar Module and Astronaut on Moon

1973. Air. Moon Flight of "Apollo 17".

356	**131**	250f. multicoloured	3·00	1·75

132 "Telecommunications"

1973. Air. World Telecommunications Day.

357	**132**	120f. multicoloured	1·40	65

133 Copernicus and Solar System

1973. Air. 500th Birth Anniv of Copernicus (astronomer).

358	**133**	50f. green, blue & lt blue	45	35

134 Rocket and African Scenes

1973. Air. Centenary of World Meteorological Organization.

359	**134**	50f. multicoloured	1·00	35

135 W.H.O. Emblem **137** General View of Brewery

136 "Study of a White Horse"

1973. 25th Anniv of W.H.O. Multicoloured.

360		40f. Type **135**	35	20
361		50f. Design similar to T **135** (horiz)	45	25

1973. Air. Paintings by Delacroix. Multicoloured.

362		150f. Type **136**	1·40	1·25
363		250f. "Sleeping Lion"	3·25	2·00
364		300f. "Tiger and Lion"	4·00	2·25

See also Nos. 384/6 and 437/40.

1973. Congo Brewers' Association. Views of Kronenbourg Brewery.

365	**137**	30f. blue, red & lt blue	25	20
366	–	40f. grey, orange & red	30	20
367	–	75f. blue, red and black	55	30
368	–	85f. multicoloured	1·00	40
369	–	100f. multicoloured	1·25	55
370	–	250f. green, brown & red	2·25	1·40

DESIGNS: 40f. Laboratory; 75f. Regulating vats; 85f. Control console; 100f. Bottling plant; 250f. Capping bottles.

1973. Locomotives of Congo Railways (2nd series). As T **102**. Multicoloured.

371		30f. Golwe steam locomotive c. 1935	2·10	85
372		40f. Diesel-electric locomotive, 1935	3·00	1·25
373		75f. Whitcomb diesel-electric locomotive, 1946	4·75	2·10
374		85f. Alsthom Series CC200 diesel-electric locomotive, 1973	5·50	2·40

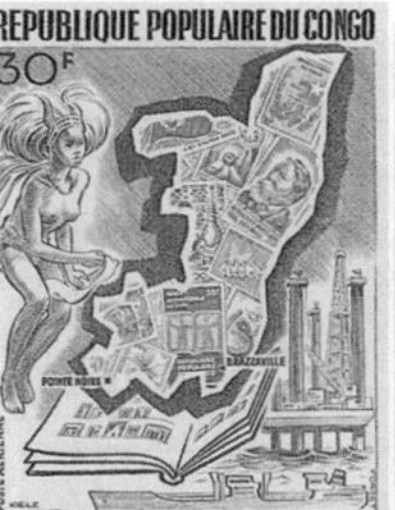

138 Stamp Map, Album, Dancer and Oil Rig **139** President Marien Ngouabi

1973. Air. International Stamp Exhibition, Brazzaville and 10th Anniv of Revolution.
375 **138** 30f. grey, lilac & brown 2·50 50
376 – 40f. red, brown & purple 30 25
377 **138** 100f. blue, brown & pur 4·75 1·25
378 – 100f. lilac, purple & red 1·10 60
DESIGNS: 40f., 100f. Map, album and Globes.

1973. Air.
379 **139** 30f. multicoloured 25 10
380 40f. multicoloured 30 15
381 75f. multicoloured 60 30

1973. Pan-African Drought Relief. No. 236 surch **100F SECHERESSE SOLIDARITE AFRICAINE**.
382 100f. on 5f. multicoloured . . 1·40 50

1973. 12th Anniv of African and Malagasy Posts and Telecommunications Union. As T **216** of Cameroun.
383 100f. violet, blue and purple 1·10 50

1973. Air. Europafrique. As T **136**. Multicoloured.
384 100f. "Wild Dog" . . . . . 2·25 1·10
385 100f. "Lion and Leopard" . . 2·25 1·10
386 100f. "Adam and Eve in Paradise" . . . . 2·25 1·10
Nos. 384/6 are details taken from J. Brueghel's "Earth and Paradise".

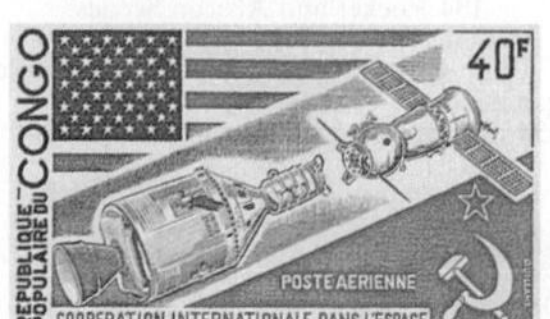

141 "Apollo" and "Soyuz" Spacecraft

1973. Air. International Co-operation in Space.
387 **141** 40f. brown, red & blue . . 30 25
388 – 80f. blue, red and green 80 40
DESIGN: 80f. Spacecraft docked.

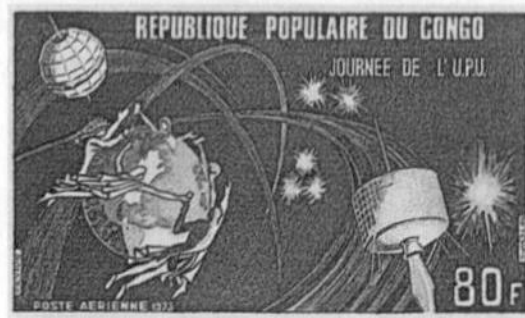

142 U.P.U. Monument and Satellite

1973. Air. U.P.U. Day.
389 **142** 80f. blue & ultramarine 60 35

1973. Air. "Skylab" Space Laboratory. As T **141**.
390 30f. green, brown and blue 30 15
391 40f. green, red and orange . . 35 25
DESIGNS: 30f. Astronauts walking outside "Skylab"; 40f. "Skylab" and "Apollo" spacecraft docked.

143 Hive and Bees

1973. "Labour and Economy".
392 **143** 30f. green, blue and red 50 20
393 40f. green, blue & green 55 20

144 Congo Family and Emblems

1973. 10th Anniv of World Food Programme.
394 **144** 30f. brown and red . . . 25 15
395 – 40f. orange, green & blue 30 25
396 – 100f. brown, green & orge 75 45
DESIGNS—HORIZ: 40f. Ears of corn and emblems. VERT: 100f. Ear of corn, granary and emblems.

145 Goalkeeper

146 Runners

1973. Air. World Football Cup Championship, West Germany (1974). (1st issue).
397 **145** 40f. green, dp brn & brn 35 25
398 – 100f. green, red & violet 1·25 45
DESIGN: 100f. Forward.
See also Nos. 403 and 408.

1973. Air. 2nd African Games, Lagos, Nigeria.
399 **146** 40f. red, green & brown 35 25
400 100f. green, red & brown 1·25 45

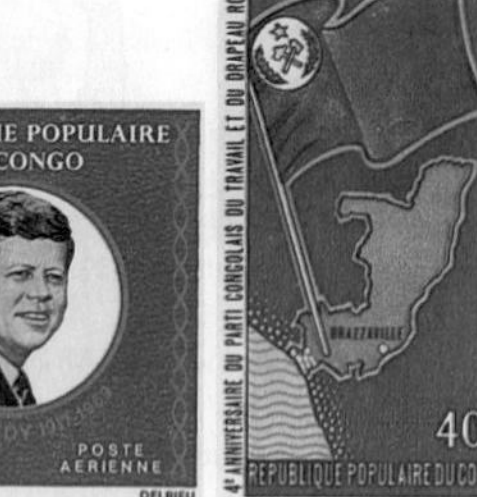

147 Pres. John F. Kennedy **148** Map and Flag

1973. Air. 10th Death Anniv of President Kennedy.
401 **147** 150f. black, gold & blue 1·40 70

1973. Air. 4th Anniv of Congo Workers' Party.
402 **148** 40f. multicoloured 30 20

149 Players seen through Goalkeeper's Legs

1974. Air. World Cup Football Championship, West Germany (2nd issue).
403 **149** 250f. green, red & brown 2·50 1·40

150 Globe, Flags and Names of Dead Astronauts

1974. Air. Conquest of Space.
404 **150** 30f. brown, blue & red . . 25 15
405 – 40f. multicoloured 35 25
406 – 100f. brown, blue & red 85 55
DESIGNS: 40f. Gagarin and Shepard; 100f. Leonov in space, and Armstrong on Moon.

151 A. Cabral **152** Spacecraft docking

1974. 1st Death Anniv of Cabral (Guinea-Bissau guerilla leader).
407 **151** 100f. purple, red & blue 70 45

1974. Air. West Germany's Victory in World Cup Football Championship. As T **149**.
408 250f. brown, pink and blue 2·75 1·40
DESIGN: Footballers within ball.

1974. Air. Soviet-American Space Co-operation.
409 **152** 200f. blue, violet and red 1·40 90
410 – 300f. blue, brown & red 2·50 1·25
DESIGN—HORIZ: 300f. Spacecraft on segments of globe.

153 "Sound and Vision"

1974. Air. Centenary of U.P.U.
411 **153** 500f. black and red . . . 5·00 2·75

154 Felix Eboue and Cross of Lorraine

1974. 30th Death Anniv of Eboue ("Free French" Leader).
412 **154** 30f. multicoloured 50 35
413 40f. multicoloured 65 45

155 Lenin

1974. Air. 30th Death Anniv of Lenin.
414 **155** 150f. orange, red & green 1·40 90

1974. Birth Centenary of Churchill. As T **154**. Multicoloured.
415 200f. Churchill and Order of the Garter . . . . 1·75 1·00

1974. Birth Centenary of Guglielmo Marconi (radio pioneer). As T **154**. Multicoloured.
416 200f. Marconi and early apparatus . . . . 1·75 85

1974. Air. Centenary of Berne Convention. No. 411 surch **9 OCTOBRE 1974 300F**.
417 **153** 300f. on 500f. blk & red 2·75 1·40

157 Pineapple

1974. Congolese Fruits. Multicoloured.
418 30f. Type **157** 35 25
419 30f. Bananas 35 25
420 30f. Safous 35 25
421 40f. Avocado pears 65 25
422 40f. Mangoes 65 25
423 40f. Papaya 65 25
424 40f. Oranges 65 25

158 Gen. Charles De Gaulle

1974. 30th Anniv of Brazzaville Conference.
425 **158** 100f. brown and green . . 2·25 1·40

1974. 10th Anniv of Central African Customs and Economic Union. As Nos. 734/5 of Cameroun.
426 40f. mult (postage) 35 20
427 100f. multicoloured (air) . . 90 45

159 George Stephenson (railway pioneer) and Early and Modern Locomotives (½-size illustration)

1974. 150th Anniv (1975) of Public Railways.
428 **159** 75f. olive and green . . . 1·60 60

160 Irish Setter

1974. Dogs. Multicoloured.
429 30f. Type **160** 55 25
430 40f. Borzoi 65 25
431 75f. Pointer . . . . 1·40 65
432 100f. Great Dane . . . . . 1·90 70

1974. Cats. As T **160**. Multicoloured.
433 30f. Havana chestnut 55 25
434 40f. Red Persian 65 25
435 75f. British blue . . . . . . 1·40 65
436 100f. Serval . . . . 1·90 75

1974. Air. Impressionist Paintings. As T **136**. Mult.
437 30f. "The Argenteuil Regatta" (Monet) 80 50
438 40f. "Seated Dancer" (Degas) (vert) 90 55
439 50f. "Girl on Swing" (Renoir) (vert) . . . . . . 1·40 80
440 75f. "Girl in Straw Hat" (Renoir) (vert) . . . . . . 1·90 1·00

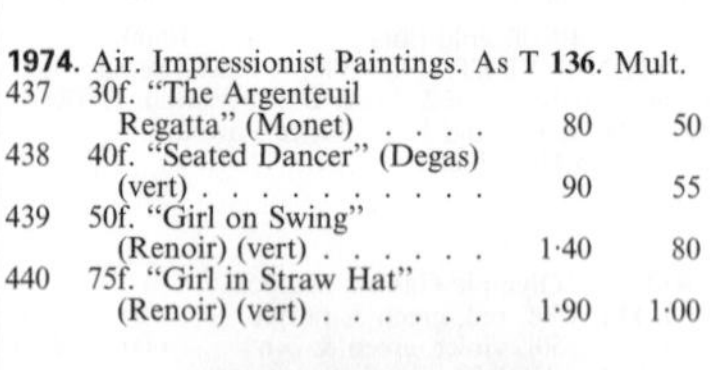

161 National Fair

1974. Air. National Fair, Brazzaville.
441 **161** 30f. multicoloured 55 25

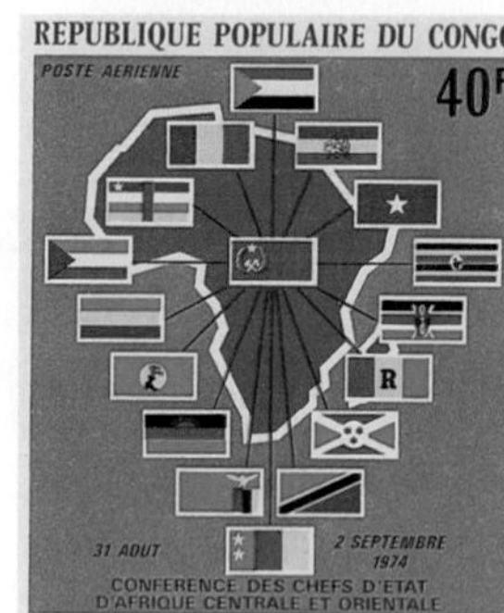

162 African Map and Flags

1974. Air. African Heads-of-State Conference, Brazzaville.
442 **162** 40f. multicoloured 60 25

163 Flags and Dove

1974. 5th Anniv of Congo Labour Party.
443 **163** 30f. red, yellow & green 25 15
444 – 40f. brown, red & yellow 80 25
DESIGN: 40f. Hands holding flowers and hammer.

164 U Thant and U.N. Headquarters Building

1975. 1st Death Anniv of U Thant (U.N. Secretary-General).
445 **164** 50f. multicoloured 40 25

1975. 1st Death Anniv of Paul G. Hoffman (U.N. Programme for Underdeveloped Countries administrator). As T **164**. Multicoloured.
446 50f. Hoffman and U.N. "Laurel Wreath" (vert) . . 35 25

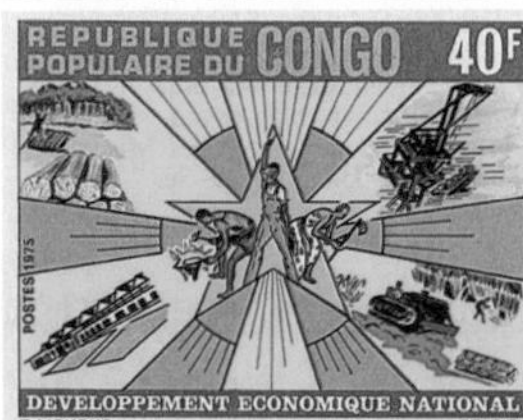
166 Workers and Development

1975. National Economic Development.
447 **166** 40f. multicoloured 30 25

167 Mao Tse-tung and Map of China

1975. 25th Anniv (1974) of Chinese People's Republic.
448 **167** 75f. red, mauve & blue . . 1·60 80

168 Woman with Hoe

1975. 10th Anniv of Revolutionary Union of Congolese Women.
449 **168** 40f. multicoloured 30 20

169 Paris–Brussels Line, 1890 (½-size illustration)

1975. Air. Railway History. Multicoloured.
450 50f. Type **169** . . . . 1·10 50
451 75f. Santa Fe Line, 1880 . . 2·40 60

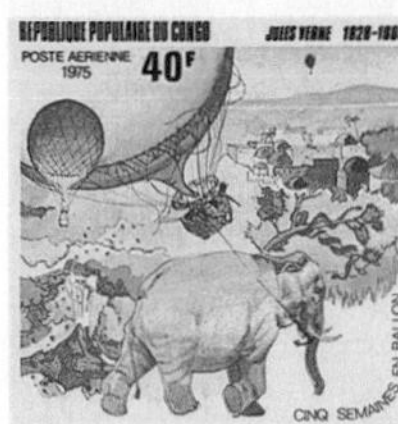
170 "Five Weeks in a Balloon"

1975. Air. 70th Anniv of Jules Verne (novelist). Multicoloured.
452 40f. Type **170** 80 40
453 50f. "Around the World in 80 Days" . . . . 4·00 1·00

171 Line-up of Team

1975. Victory of Cara Football Team in Africa Cup. Multicoloured.
454 30f. Type **171** 30 25
455 40f. Receiving trophy (vert) 35 25

172 1935 Citroen and Notre Dame Cathedral, Paris

1975. Veteran Cars. Multicoloured.
456 30f. Type **172** 55 20
457 40f. 1911 Alfa Romeo and St. Peter's Rome 65 20
458 50f. 1926 Rolls Royce and Houses of Parliament, London 80 30
459 75f. 1893 C. F. Duryea and Manhattan skyline, New York . . . . 1·40 35

173 "Soyuz" Spacecraft

1975. Air. "Apollo–Soyuz" Space Test Project.
460 **173** 95f. black, red & brown 80 35
461 – 100f. black, violet & blue 90 40
DESIGN: 100f. "Apollo" Spacecraft.

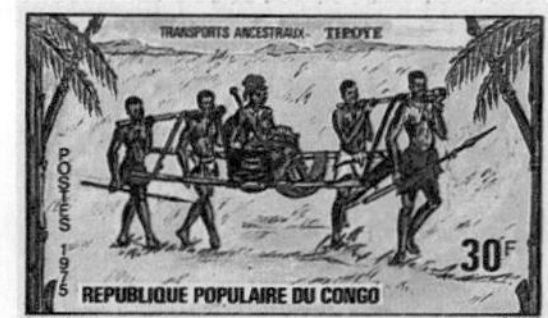
174 Tipoye Carriage

1975. Traditional Congo Transport. Multicoloured.
462 30f. Type **174** 55 20
463 40f. Pirogue 65 30

175 "Raising the Flag"

1975. 2nd Anniv of Institutions of Popular Tasks.
464 **175** 30f. multicoloured 25 20

176 Conference Hall

1975. 3rd Anniv of Congolese National Conference.
465 **176** 40f. multicoloured 35 25

177 Fishing with Wooden Baskets

1975. Traditional Fishing. Multicoloured.
466 30f. Type **177** 30 20
467 40f. Fishing with line (vert) 90 30
468 60f. Fishing with spear (vert) 80 25
469 90f. Fishing with net . . . . 1·40 80

178 Chopping Firewood

179 "Esanga"

1975. Domestic Chores. Multicoloured.
470 30f. Type **178** 25 15
471 30f. Pounding meal 25 15
472 40f. Preparing manioc (horiz) 40 20

1975. Traditional Musical Instruments. Mult.
473 30f. Type **179** 55 20
474 40f. "Kalakwa" 65 25
475 60f. "Likembe" . . . . . . 1·00 30
476 75f. "Ngongui" . . . . . . 1·10 40

180 "Dzeke" Money Cowrie

1975. Ancient Congolese Money.
477 **180** 30f. ochre, brown & red 40 25
478 – 30f. ochre, violet & brn 30 20
478a **180** 35f. orange and brown 45 30
478b – 35f. red, bistre and violet 35 25
479 – 40f. brown and blue . . 45 25
480 – 50f. blue and brown . . 45 25
481 – 60f. brown and green . . 55 30
482 – 85f. green and red . . . 1·00 35
DESIGNS: 30, 35 (478b) f. "Okengo" iron money; 40f. Gallic coin (60 B.C.); 50f. Roman coin (37 B.C.); 60f. Danubian coin (2nd century B.C.); 85f. Greek coin (4th century B.C.).

181 Dr. Schweitzer

183 Boxing

182 "Moschops"

1975. Birth Centenary of Dr. Albert Schweitzer.
483 **181** 75f. green, mauve & brn 1·10 40

1975. Prehistoric Animals. Multicoloured.
484 55f. Type **182** 70 25
485 75f. "Tyrannosaurus" . . . . 1·10 30
486 95f. "Cryptocleidus" . . . . 1·90 65
487 100f. "Stegosauras" . . . . 2·50 90

1975. Air. Olympic Games, Montreal (1976). Multicoloured.
488 40f. Type **183** 30 25
489 50f. Basketball 35 25
490 85f. Cycling (horiz) 80 35
491 95f. High jumping (horiz) . . 1·00 35
492 100f. Throwing the javelin (horiz) . . . . 1·25 40
493 150f. Running (horiz) . . . . 1·60 65

184 Alexander Fleming (biochemist) (20th Death Anniv)

1975. Celebrities.
494 **184** 60f. black, green and red 65 30
495 – 95f. black, blue and red 1·25 50
496 – 95f. green, red and lilac 1·10 40
DESIGNS: No. 495, Clement Ader (aviation pioneer) (50th death anniv); 496, Andre Marie Ampere (physicist) (birth bicent).

185 U.N. Emblem with Laurel Wreaths

1975. 30th Anniv of U.N.O.
497 **185** 95f. blue, red and green 80 40

186 Map of Africa and Sportsmen

1975. Air. 10th Anniv of 1st African Games, Brazzaville.
498 **186** 30f. multicoloured 30 25

187 Chained Women and Broken Link

1975. International Women's Year. Multicoloured.
499 35f. Type **187** 35 15
500 60f. Global handclasp . . . 45 30

188 Pres. Ngouabi and Crowd with Flags

1975. 6th Anniv of Congolese Workers' Party. Multicoloured.
501 30f. Type **188** (postage) . . . 25 20
502 35f. "Echo"–P.C.T. "man" with roll of newsprint and radio waves (36 × 27 mm) 30 20
503 60f. Party members with flag (26 × 38 mm) (air) 35 25

189 River Steamer "Alphonse Fondere"

1976. Air. Old-time Ships. Multicoloured.
504 5f. Type **189** 25 20
505 10f. Paddle-steamer "Hamburg", 1839 . . . . 35 20
506 15f. Paddle-steamer "Gomer", 1831 . . . . . 35 20
507 20f. Paddle-steamer "Great Eastern", 1858 . . . . . . 35 20
508 30f. Type **189** 55 20
509 40f. As 10f. 60 45
510 50f. As 15f. 65 45
511 60f. As 20f. 85 60
512 95f. River steamer "J.M. White II" 1878 . . . . . 1·40 90

190 "The Peasant Family" (L. le Nain)

1976. Air. Europafrique. Paintings. Multicoloured.
513 60f. Type **190** 80 15
514 80f. "Boy with spinning Top" (Chardin) . . . . 1·00 55
515 95f. "Venus and Aeneas" (Poussin) . . . . 1·10 55
516 100f. "The Sabines" (David) 1·50 80

191 Alexander Graham Bell and Early Telephone

1976. Telephone Centenary.
517 **191** 35f. brown, light brown and yellow (postage) . . 30 25
518 60f. red, mve & pink (air) 40 25

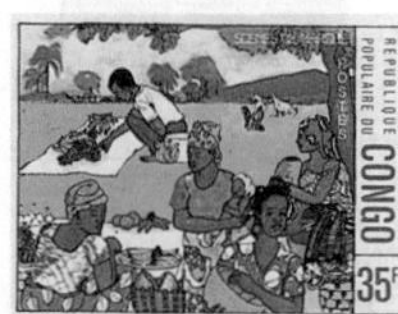

192 Fruit Market

1976. Market Scenes. Multicoloured.
519 35f. Type **192** 25 20
520 60f. Laying out produce . . . 90 25

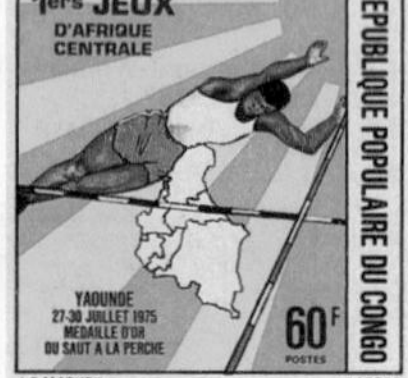

193 Congolese Woman **194** Pole-vaulting

1976. Congolese Women's Hair-styles.
521 **193** 35f. multicoloured 30 25
522 – 60f. multicoloured 45 25
523 – 95f. multicoloured 70 35
524 – 100f. multicoloured . . . 1·00 40
DESIGNS: 60f. to 100f. Various Congolese Women's hair-styles.

1976. 1st Central African Games, Yaounde. Multicoloured.
525 60f. Type **194** (postage) . . . 45 30
526 95f. Long-jumping 75 45
527 150f. Running (air) . . . . . 1·25 60
528 200f. Throwing the discus . . 1·90 90

195 Kob **196** Saddle-bill Storks ("Jabirus")

1976. Congolese Fauna. Multicoloured.
529 5f. Type **195** 10 10
530 10f. African buffaloes 15 10
531 15f. Hippopotami 15 15
532 20f. Warthog 65 25
533 25f. African elephants 80 30

1976. Birds. Multicoloured.
534 5f. Type **196** 35 30
535 10f. Shining-blue kingfisher ("Martin-Pecheur") (37 × 37 mm) . . . . . . 1·75 50
536 20f. Crowned cranes ("Grues Couronnees") (37 × 37 mm) 2·00 90

197 O.A.U. Building on Map **198** Cycling

1976. Air. 13th Anniv of O.A.U.
537 **197** 60f. multicoloured 35 25

1976. Central African Games, Libreville. Mult.
538 35f. Type **198** 25 15
539 60f. Handball 35 25
540 80f. Running 55 30
541 95f. Football 90 35

199 "Nymphaea micrantha" **200** Pioneers' Emblem

1976. Tropical Flowers. Multicoloured.
542 5f. Type **199** 10 10
543 10f. "Heliotrope" 10 10
544 15f. "Strelitzia reginae" . . . 20 10

1976. National Pioneers Movement.
545 **200** 35f. multicoloured 20 20

201 "Spirit of 76" (detail, A. M. Willard)

1976. Bicent of American Revolution. Mult.
546 100f. Type **201** 55 25
547 125f. Destruction of George III's statue 90 35
548 150f. Gunners-Battle of Princeton 90 40
549 175f. Wartime generals . . . 1·25 50
550 200f. Surrender of Gen. Burgoyne, Saratoga . . . 1·40 60

202 Pirogue Race

1977. Pirogue Racing. Multicoloured.
552 35f. Type **202** 60 30
553 60f. Race in progress 85 45

203 Butter Catfish

1977. Freshwater Fishes. Multicoloured.
554 10f. Type **203** 10 10
555 15f. Big-eyed catfish 10 10
556 25f. Citharinid 45 10
557 35f. Mbessi mormyrid 65 15
558 60f. "Mongandza" . . . . . 1·25 55

204 Map of Europe and Africa

1977. Air. Europafrique.
559 **204** 75f. multicoloured 45 35

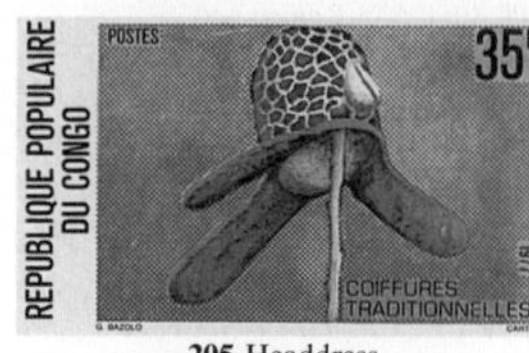

205 Headdress

1977. Traditional Headdresses. Multicoloured.
560 35f. Type **205** (postage) . . . 30 20
561 60f. Headdress with tail . . . 80 25
562 250f. Two headdresses (air) 2·25 1·40
563 300f. Headdresses with beads 2·50 1·60

206 Wrestling

1977. Bondjo Wrestling.
564 – 25f. multicoloured 20 10
565 **206** 40f. multicoloured 25 15
566 – 50f. multicoloured 35 25
DESIGNS—VERT: 25f., 50f. Different wrestling scenes.

207 "Schwaben", 1911

1977. History of the Zeppelin. Multicoloured.
567 40f. Type **207** 25 20
568 60f. "Viktoria Luise", 1913 35 30
569 100f. "Bodensee" 80 30
570 200f. "Graf Zeppelin" . . . 1·25 45
571 300f. "Graf Zeppelin II" . . 2·50 60

208 Rising Sun of "Revolution"

1977. 14th Anniv of Revolution.
573 **208** 40f. multicoloured 25 25

209 "Flow of Trade"

1977. Air. G.A.T.T. Trade Convention, Lome.
574 **209** 60f. black and red 45 25

210 Hugo and Scene from "Hunchback of Notre Dame"

1977. 175th Birth Anniv of Victor Hugo.
575 **210** 35f. brown, red and blue 25 15
576 – 60f. green, drab and blue 35 25
577 – 100f. brown, blue & red 70 45
DESIGNS: 60f. Scene from "Les Miserables"; 100f. Scene from "The Toilers of the Sea".

211 Newton and Constellations

1977. Air. 250th Death Anniv of Isaac Newton.
578 **211** 140f. mauve, green & brn 1·50 90

212 Mao Tse-tung

1977. 1st Death Anniv of Mao Tse-tung.
579 **212** 400f. gold and red . . . . 4·50 2·75

213 Rubens

1977. 400th Birth Anniv of Peter Paul Rubens.
580 **213** 600f. gold and blue . . . 6·75 5·50

214 Child leading Blind Person

1977. Fight Against Blindness.
581 **214** 35f. multicoloured 30 25

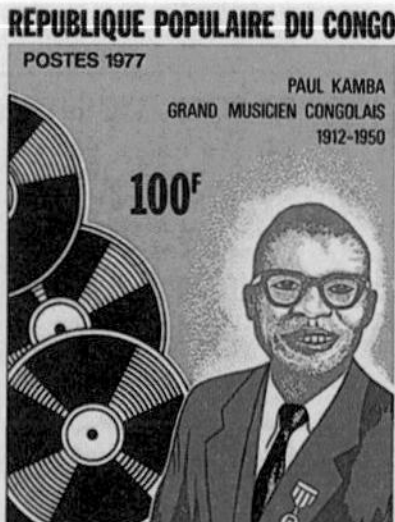

215 Paul Kamba and Records

1977. Paul Kamba (musician) Commemoration.
582 **215** 100f. multicoloured . . . 80 40

216 Trajan Vuia and his Vuia No. 1

1977. Aviation History. Multicoloured.
583 60f. Type **216** 35 20
584 75f. Bleriot and Bleriot XI over Channel 40 20
585 100f. Roland Garros and Morane Saulnier Type 1 80 30
586 200f. Lindbergh and "Spirit of St. Louis" . . . . . . 1·50 45
587 300f. Tupolev Tu-144 . . . . 2·00 65

217 General de Gaulle

1977. Historic Personalities, and Silver Jubilee of Queen Elizabeth II. Multicoloured.
589 200f. Type **217** . . . . 1·90 45
590 200f. King Baudouin of Belgium . . . . 1·50 45
591 250f. Queen and Prince Philip in open car . . . . 1·50 65
592 300f. Queen Elizabeth . . . . 2·00 70

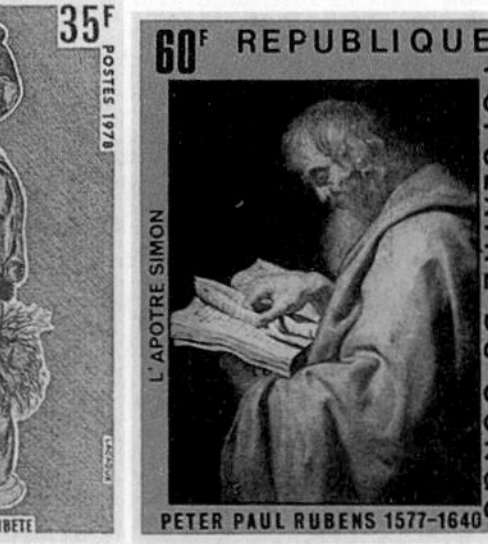

218 Ambete Statue **219** "The Apostle Simon"

1978. Congolese Sculpture.
594 **218** 35f. lake, brown & green 30 25
595 – 85f. brown, green & lake 90 35
DESIGN: 85f. Babembe statue.

1978. 400th Birth Anniv of Peter Paul Rubens (2nd issue). Multicoloured.
596 60f. Type **219** 65 20
597 140f. "The Duke of Lerma" 1·10 35
598 200f. "Madonna and Saints" 1·50 50
599 300f. "The Artist and his Wife" . . . . 2·25 65

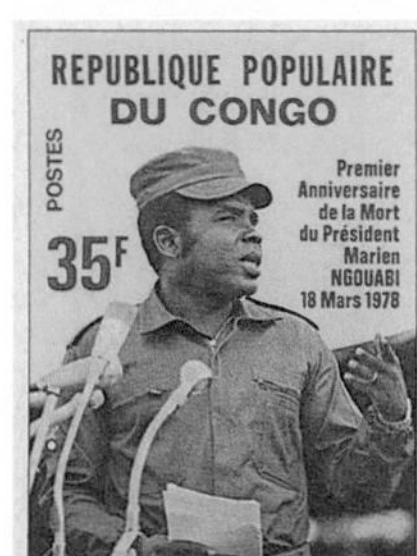

220 Pres. Ngouabi making Speech

1978. 1st Death Anniv of President Marien Ngouabi.
601 **220** 35f. black, yellow & red 15 15
602 – 60f. multicoloured 30 20
603 – 100f. black, yellow & red 45 35
DESIGNS—HORIZ: 60f. Pres. Ngouabi at his desk. VERT: 100f. Portrait of Pres. Ngouabi.

221 Ferenc Puskas (Hungary)

1978. World Cup Football Championship, Argentina. Famous Players. Multicoloured.
604 60f. Type **221** 35 20
605 75f. Giacinto Facchetti (Italy) 40 20
606 100f. Bobby Moore (England) 55 25
607 200f. Raymond Kopa (France) . . . . 1·60 50
608 300f. Pele (Brazil) . . . . . 2·25 65

222 Pearl S. Buck (Literature, 1938)

1978. Nobel Prize Winners. Multicoloured.
610 60f. Type **222** 40 25
611 75f. Fridtjof Nansen and camp scene (Peace) 40 20
612 100f. Henri Bergson and "Elan Vita" (Literature) . . 55 30
613 200f. Alexander Fleming and penicillin (Medicine) . . . 1·50 60
614 300f. Gerhart Hauptmann and hands with book (Literature) . . . . 2·00 65

223 Purple Heron **224** Okapi

1978. Air. Birds. Multicoloured.
616 65f. Mallard . . . . 2·00 95
617 75f. Type **223** . . . . 2·00 1·10
618 150f. Great reed warbler . . 4·00 1·50
619 240f. Hoopoe . . . . 5·25 2·40

1978. Endangered Animals. Multicoloured.
620 35f. Type **224** 25 20
621 60f. African buffalo (horiz) 45 30
622 85f. Black rhinoceros (horiz) 1·10 40
623 150f. Chimpanzee . . . . . 1·60 50
624 200f. Hippopotamus (horiz) 2·25 1·10
625 300f. Kob . . . . 4·00 1·40

225 Clenched Fist, Emblem and Crowd

1978. 11th World Youth and Students Festival, Havana, Cuba.
626 **225** 35f. multicoloured 30 25

226 Pyramids, Egypt

1978. The Seven Wonders of the Ancient World. Multicoloured.
627 35f. Type **226** 20 15
628 50f. Hanging Gardens of Babylon (vert) 25 20
629 60f. Statue of Zeus, Olympia (vert) 35 20
630 95f. Colossos of Rhodes (vert) 50 25
631 125f. Mausoleum, Halicarnassus (vert) . . . 90 30
632 150f. Temple of Artemis, Ephesus . . . . 1·10 40
633 200f. Pharos, Alexandria (vert) . . . . 2·00 65
634 300f. Map showing sites of the Seven Wonders . . . . 2·25 65

1978. 25th Anniv of Coronation of Queen Elizabeth II. Nos. 591/2 optd **ANNIVERSAIRE DU COURONNEMENT 1953 - 1978**.
635 250f. Queen Elizabeth and Prince Philip in open car 2·00 85
636 300f. Queen Elizabeth II . . 2·25 1·40

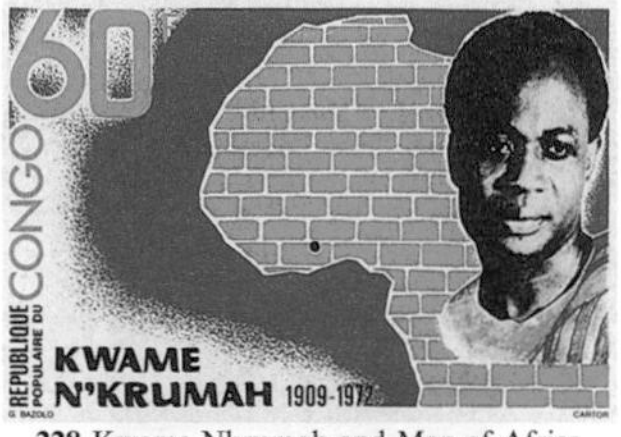

228 Kwame Nkrumah and Map of Africa

1978. Kwame Nkrumah (Ghanaian statesman) Commemoration.
638 **228** 60f. multicoloured 35 20

229 Hunting Wild Pigs

1978. Multicoloured.
639 35f. Type **229** 25 20
640 50f. Smoking fish 35 30
641 60f. Hunter with kill (vert) 35 20
642 140f. Woman hoeing (vert) 1·10 40

1978. Air. "Philexafrique" Stamp Exhibition, Libreville, Gabon (1st issue) and International Stamp Fair, Essen, West Germany. As T **237** of Benin. Multicoloured.
643 100f. Peregrine Falcon and Wurttemberg 1851 1k. stamp . . . . 1·50 1·10
644 100f. Leopard and Congo 1978 240f. stamp . . . . . 1·50 1·10
See also Nos. 668/9.

230 Basket Weaving **232** Satellites, Antennae and Map of Africa

231 "Kalchreut"

1978. Occupations. Multicoloured.
645 85f. Type **230** 50 25
646 90f. Wood sculpture 50 25

1978. 450th Death Anniv of Albrecht Durer (artist). Multicoloured.
647 65f. Type **231** 35 20
648 150f. "Elspeth Tucher" . . . 1·00 35
649 250f. "Grasses" . . . . . . 1·40 60
650 350f. "Self-portrait" . . . . 2·50 90

1978. Air. Pan African Telecommunications.
651 **232** 100f. red, green & orange 90 35

1978. World Cup Football Championship Winners. Nos. 604/8 optd with names of past winners.
652 **221** 60f. multicoloured 35 25
653 – 75f. multicoloured 40 30
654 – 100f. multicoloured . . . 55 35
655 – 200f. multicoloured . . . 1·60 60
656 – 300f. multicoloured . . . 2·25 1·00
OPTS: 60f. **1962 VAINQUEUR BRESIL**; 75f. **1966 VAINQUEUR GRANDE BRETAGNE**; 100f. **1970 VAINQUEUR BRESIL**; 200f. **1974 VAINQUEUR ALLEMAGNE (RFA)**; 300f. **1978 VAINQUEUR ARGENTINE**.

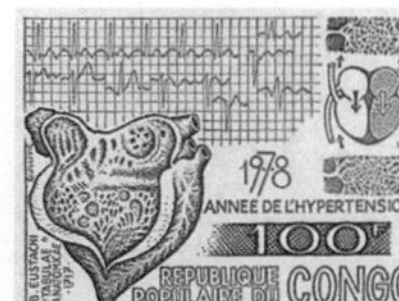

234 Diseased Heart, Blood Pressure Graph and Circulation Diagram

1978. World Hypertension Year.
658 **234** 100f. brown, red & turq 80 35

235 Road to the Sun

1978. 9th Anniv of Congolese Workers' Party.
659 **235** 60f. multicoloured 30 15

236 Captain Cook and Native Feast

1979. Death Bicentenary of Captain James Cook. Multicoloured.
660 65f. Type **236** 35 20
661 150f. Easter Island monuments . . . . 1·40 35
662 250f. Hawaiian canoes . . . 2·00 70
663 350f. H.M.S. "Resolution" and H.M.S. "Adventure" at anchor . . . . 2·75 1·10

237 Pres. Ngouabi

1979. 2nd Anniv of Assassination of President Ngouabi.
664 **237** 35f. multicoloured 20 15
665 60f. multicoloured 35 20

238 I.Y.C. Emblem and Child

1979. International Year of the Child.
666 **238** 45f. multicoloured 25 20
667 75f. multicoloured 30 15

239 "Solanum torvum" and Earthenware Jars

1979. "Philexafrique" Stamp Exhibition, Libreville, Gabon (2nd issue).
668 **239** 60f. multicoloured 90 45
669 – 150f. orange, brn & grn 2·50 1·40
DESIGN: 150f. U.P.U. emblem, Concorde airplane, postal runner and diesel locomotive.

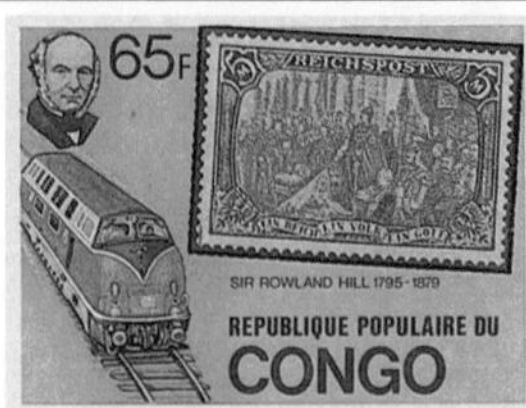

240 Rowland Hill, Diesel Locomotive and German 5m., Stamp, 1900

1979. Death Centenary of Sir Rowland Hill. Multicoloured.
670 65f. Type **240** 60 10
671 100f. Steam locomotive and French "War Orphans" stamp of 1917 . . . . . . 80 15
672 200f. Diesel locomotive and U.S. Columbus stamp of 1893 . . . . 1·75 30
673 300f. Steam locomotive and England–Australia "First Aerial Post" vignette . . . 3·00 90

241 Pres. Salvador Allende

1979. Salvador Allende (former President of Chile) Commemoration.
675 **241** 100f. multicoloured . . . 80 25

242 "The Teller of Legends"

1979. African Folk Tales as Part of Children's Education.
676 **242** 45f. multicoloured 55 20

243 Handball Players **244** Map of Africa filled with Heads

1979. Marien Ngouabi Handball Cup. Mult.
677 45f. Type **243** 30 20
678 75f. Handball players 40 25
679 250f. Cup on map of Africa, player and Marien Ngouabi (vert) (22 × 37 mm) . . . . . . 1·75 70

1979. Air. 5th Pan-African Youth Conference, Brazzaville.
680 **244** 45f. multicoloured 30 20
681 75f. multicoloured 45 30

246 Congo Map and Flag

1979. 16th Anniv of Revolution.
683 **246** 50f. multicoloured 25 15

247 Abala Peasant Woman

1979. Air.
684 **247** 150f. multicoloured . . . 1·40 60

249 Bach and Musical Instruments

1979. Personalities. Multicoloured.
686 200f. Type **249** . . . . 1·60 50
687 200f. Albert Einstein and astronauts on the Moon 1·60 50

250 Yoro

1979. Yoro Fishing Port. Multicoloured.
688 45f. Type **250** 30 20
689 75f. Yoro at night 40 25

251 Moukoukoulou Dam and Power Station

1979. Moukoukoulou Hydro-electric Power Station.
690 **251** 20f. multicoloured 15 10
691 45f. multicoloured 65 20

1979. Air. 10th Anniv of "Apollo 11" Moon Landing. Optd **ALUNISSAGE APOLLO XI JUILLET 1969.**
692 – 80f. blue, red and green (No. 388) 35 35
693 **173** 95f. blk, red & crimson 45 45
694 – 100f. brown, blue and red (No. 406) 45 45
695 – 100f. black, violet and blue (No. 461) 45 45
696 – 300f. blue, brown and red (No. 410) . . . . . . 1·90 1·90

253 Fencer

1979. Air. Pre-Olympic Year (1st issue) Multicoloured.
697 65f. Runner, map of Africa and Olympic rings (horiz) 30 20
698 100f. Boxer (horiz) 50 25
699 200f. Type **253** . . . . 1·40 40
700 300f. Footballer (horiz) . . . 2·00 65
701 500f. Olympic emblem . . . 3·25 1·40
See also Nos. 716/9.

254 ASECNA Emblem and Douglas DC-10

1979. 20th Anniv of ASECNA (African Air Safety Organization).
702 **254** 100f. multicoloured . . . 70 45

255 Party Emblem Workers and Flowers **256** Cross-country Skiing

1979. 10th Anniv of Congolese Workers' Party.
703 **255** 45f. multicoloured 25 15

1979. Air. Winter Olympic Games, Lake Placid (1980). Multicoloured.
704 40f. Type **256** 20 15
705 60f. Slalom 30 20
706 200f. Ski-jump . . . . 1·40 40
707 350f. Downhill skiing (horiz) 2·50 80
708 500f. Skier (vert, 31 × 46 mm) 3·25 1·10

257 Emblem and Globe **259** Long jump

1980. 15th Anniv of National Posts and Telecommunications Office.
709 **257** 45f. multicoloured 25 15
710 95f. multicoloured 45 25

1980. Air. Winter Olympic Games Medal Winners. Nos. 704/8 optd with names of winners.
711 40f. Cross-country skiing . . 20 15
712 60f. Slalom 30 20
713 200f. Ski jump . . . . 1·40 45
714 350f. Downhill skiing . . . . 2·50 1·00
715 500f. Skier . . . . 3·25 1·40
OVERPRINTS: 40f. **VAINQUEUR ZIMIATOV U.R.S.S.**; 60f. **VAINQUEUR MOSERPROELL Autriche**; 200f. **VAINQUEUR TOMANEN Finlande**; 350f. **VAINQUEUR STOCK AUTRICHE**; 500f. **VAINQUEURS STENMARK-WENZEL.**

1980. Air. Olympic Games, Moscow.
716 **259** 75f. multicoloured 55 10
717 – 150f. mult (horiz) . . . . 1·10 25
718 – 250f. multicoloured . . . 1·60 45
719 – 350f. multicoloured . . . 2·25 60
Nos. 717/19 show different views of the long jump.

260 Pope John Paul II

1980. Papal Visit.
721 **260** 100f. multicoloured . . . 1·10 30

261 Rotary Emblem

1980. 75th Anniv of Rotary International.
722 **261** 150f. multicoloured . . . 1·10 45

262 Glass Works

1980. Pointe Noire Glass Works. Multicoloured.
723 30f. Type **262** 15 10
724 35f. Glass works (different) 45 10

263 Claude Chappe and Semaphore Tower

1980. Claude Chappe Commemoration.
725 **263** 200f. multicoloured . . . 1·60 1·10

264 Real Madrid Stadium

1980. Air. World Cup Football Championship, Spain (1982). Multicoloured.
726 60f. Type **264** 30 15
727 75f. Real Zaragoza 35 15
728 100f. Atletico de Madrid . . 45 20
729 150f. Valencia C.F. . . . . . 1·00 30
730 175f. R.C.D. Espanol . . . . 1·40 35

265 Floating Quay

1980. Port of Mossaka. Multicoloured.
732 45f. Type **265** 25 15
733 90f. Aerial view of port . . . 40 20

266 "Crucifixion"

1980. Air. Paintings by Rembrandt. Multicoloured.
734 65f. "Adoration of the Shepherds" (detail) (horiz) 30 10
735 100f. "Entombment" (horiz) 45 25
736 200f. "Christ at Emmaus" (horiz) . . . . 1·40 40
737 300f. "Annunciation" . . . . 2·00 60
738 500f. Type **266** . . . . 4·00 1·10

267 Jacques Offenbach (composer)

1980. Air. Death Anniversaries. Multicoloured.
739 100f. Albert Camus (writer) (20th anniv) 80 35
740 150f. Type **267** (centenary) 1·40 90

268 "Papilio dardanus"

1980. Butterflies. Multicoloured.
741 5f. Type **268** 10 10
742 15f. "Kallima aethiops" . . . 10 10
743 20f. "Papilio demodocus" . . 15 10
744 60f. "Euphaedra" 55 40
745 90f. "Hypolimnas misippus" 1·10 50

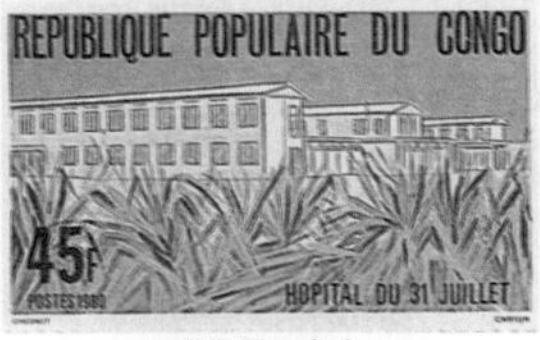

269 Hospital

1980. "31 July" Hospital.
747 **269** 45f. multicoloured 25 20

270 Man presenting Human Rights Charter

1980. 32nd Anniv of Human Rights Convention. Multicoloured.
748 350f. Type **270** . . . . 2·25 1·10
749 500f. Man breaking chains 3·25 2·00

271 Raffia Dancing Skirts

1980. Air. Traditional Dancing Costumes. Mult.
750 250f. Type **271** . . . . 2·25 70
751 300f. Tam-tam dancers (vert) 2·50 1·40
752 350f. Masks . . . . 3·00 1·60

272 Clenched Fists, Flag and Dove

273 Coffee and Cocoa Trees on Map of Congo

1980. 17th Anniv of Revolution. Multicoloured.
753 75f. Citizens and State emblem (36×23 mm) . . . 35 25
754 95f. Type **272** 45 30
755 150f. Dove carrying state emblem (36×23 mm) . . . 1·00 45

1980. Coffee and Cocoa Day. Multicoloured.
756 45f. Type **273** 25 20
757 95f. Coffee and cocoa beans 80 35

274 Cut Logs

1980. Forest Exploitation. Multicoloured.
758 70f. Type **274** 35 25
759 75f. Lorry with logs 35 25

275 President Neto

1980. 1st Death Anniv of President Neto.
760 **275** 100f. multicoloured . . . 45 30

276 Olive-bellied Sunbird ("Souimanga Olivatre")

1980. Birds. Multicoloured.
761 45f. Type **276** . . . . 1·25 55
762 75f. Red-crowned bishop ("Travailleur a Tete Rouge") . . . . 1·75 60
763 90f. Moorhen ("Poule d'Eauafricaine") . . . . . 2·10 70
764 150f. African pied wagtail ("Alouette Canelle") . . . 3·25 1·50
765 200f. Yellow-mantled whydah (vert) . . . . 4·00 1·75
766 250f. "Geai-bleu" (vert) . . . 2·10 85

277 Conference Emblem

1980. World Tourism Conference, Manila.
768 **277** 100f. multicoloured . . . 80 45

278 Child Writing

1980. Return to School.
769 **278** 50f. multicoloured 25 15

279 The First House

1980. Brazzaville Centenary.
770 **279** 45f. ochre, grey & brown 25 15
771 – 65f. lt brown, brn & orge 55 20
772 – 75f. multicoloured 65 50
773 – 150f. multicoloured . . . 1·25 1·00
774 – 200f. multicoloured . . . 1·60 1·40
DESIGNS: 65f. First native village; 75f. The old Town Hall; 150f. Brazzaville from the Bacongo Promontory, 1912; 200f. Meeting between Savorgnan de Brazza (explorer) and Makoko (local chieftain).

280 Cataracts

1980. The River Congo. Multicoloured.
775 80f. Type **280** 65 50
776 150f. Bridge at Djoue . . . . 1·40 65

1980. Air. Olympic Medal Winners. Nos. 716/19 optd.
777 75f. **DOMBROWSKI (RDA)** 60 25
778 150f. **SANEIEV (URSS)** . . 1·00 45
779 250f. **SIMEONI (IT)** . . . . 1·50 80
780 350f. **THOMPSON (GB)** . . 2·25 1·40

282 Stadium and Sportsmen

1980. Revolutionary Stadium. Heroes of Congolese Sport.
782 **282** 60f. multicoloured 55 20

283 New Railway Bridge

1980. Realignment of Railway.
783 **283** 75f. multicoloured . . . . 1·00 25

284 Mangoes

1980. Loudima Fruit Station. Multicoloured.
784 10f. Type **284** 10 10
785 25f. Oranges 15 10
786 40f. Lemons 45 10
787 85f. Mandarins 65 20

1980. 5th Anniv of African Posts and Telecommunications Union. As T **269** of Benin.
788 100f. multicoloured 45 35

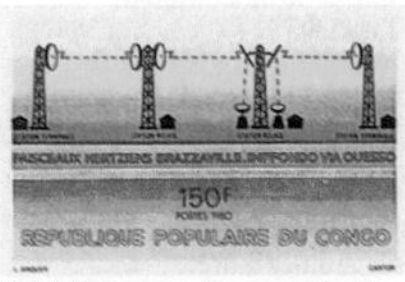

285 Microwave Communication

1980. Communications. Multicoloured.
789 75f. Moungouni Earth Station (36×36 mm) . . . 60 25
790 150f. Type **285** . . . . 1·00 45

286 Presentation of Marien Ngouabi Handball Cup

1981. African Handball Champions. Mult.
791 100f. Type **286** 90 30
792 150f. Team members . . . . . 1·10 45

287 Pres. Sassou-Nguesso

1981. President Sassou-Nguesso.
793 **287** 45f. multicoloured 20 15
794 75f. multicoloured 40 25
795 100f. multicoloured . . . 45 30

288 Space Shuttle

1981. Conquest of Space. Multicoloured.
796 100f. "Luna 17" 45 25
797 150f. Type **288** . . . . 1·00 35
798 200f. Satellite and space shuttle . . . . 1·40 45
799 300f. Space shuttle approaching landing strip 2·00 70

289 Head and Dove

290 Twin Palm Tree

1981. Anti-Apartheid Campaign.
801 **289** 100f. blue 45 30

1981. The Twin Palm Tree of Louingui.
802 **290** 75f. multicoloured 65 25

291 Bird approaching Snare

1981. Traditional Snares and Traps. Mult.
803 5f. Type **291** 10 10
804 10f. Bird in snare (vert) . . . 10 10
805 15f. Rodent approaching snare 10 10
806 20f. Rodent in snare 10 10
807 30f. Sprung trap 15 10
808 35f. Deer approaching trap 20 10

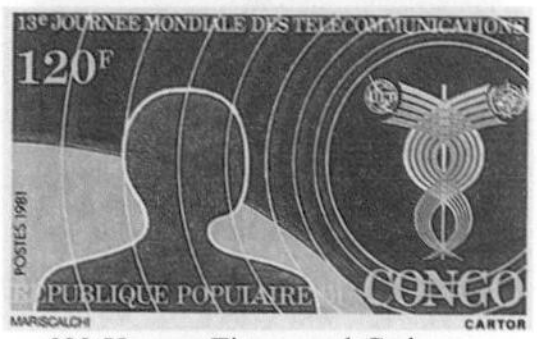

292 Human Figure and Caduceus

1981. World Telecommunications Day.
809 **292** 120f. multicoloured . . . 90 35

293 Sleeping Sickness and Malaria Victim

1981. Campaign against Transmissible Diseases. Multicoloured.
810 40f.+5f. Doctor, nurse, patients and mosquito . . 25 20
811 65f.+10f. Type **293** 45 20

294 Collecting Rubber

1981. Rubber Extraction. Multicoloured.
812 50f. Tapping rubber tree . . 20 15
813 70f. Type **294** 40 30

295 Helping a Disabled Person

1981. International Year of Disabled People.
814 **295** 45f. blue, purple & red . . 20 15
815 – 75f.+5f. multicoloured . . 65 30
DESIGN: 75f. Disabled people superimposed on globe.

296 "The Studio"

1981. Air. Birth Centenary of Pablo Picasso. Multicoloured.
816 100f. Type **296** 90 30
817 150f. "Landscape Land and Sea" . . . . 1·40 40
818 200f. "The Studio at Cannes" 1·60 50
819 300f. "Still-life with Water Melon" . . . . 2·75 85
820 500f. "Large Still-life" . . . 4·50 1·40

297 King Maloango and Mausoleum

1981. Mausoleum of King Maloango. Mult.
821 75f. Mausoleum 60 20
822 150f. Type **297** . . . . 1·10 45

298 Prince Charles, Lady Diana Spencer and Coach

1981. Wedding of Prince of Wales. Mult.
823 100f. Type **298** 85 30
824 200f. Couple and Landau . . 1·40 25
825 300f. Couple and horses . . . 2·25 85

299 Preparing Food

1981. World Food Day.
827 **299** 150f. multicoloured . . . 1·25 45

300 Bird carrying Letter

1981. Universal Postal Union Day.
828 **300** 90f. blue, red and grey . . 65 25

301 Guardsman

1981. Royal Guard.
829 **301** 45f. multicoloured 25 15

302 Spraying Cassava

1981. Campaign for the Control of Cassava Beetle.
830 **302** 75f. multicoloured 90 20

303 Bandaging a Patient

304 Brazza's Tree

1981. Red Cross. Multicoloured.
831 10f. Type **303** 10 10
832 35f. Inoculating a young girl 20 10
833 60f. Nurse and villagers . . . 30 15

1981. Tree of Brazza.
834 **304** 45f. multicoloured 25 15
835 75f. multicoloured 35 20

305 Fetish

306 Bangou Caves

1981. Fetishes.
836 **305** 15f. multicoloured 10 10
837 – 25f. multicoloured 15 10
838 – 45f. multicoloured 20 15
839 – 50f. multicoloured 50 15
840 – 60f. multicoloured 55 20
DESIGNS: 25f. to 60f. Different fetishes.

1981. Bangou Caves.
841 **306** 20f. multicoloured 10 10
842 25f. multicoloured 15 10

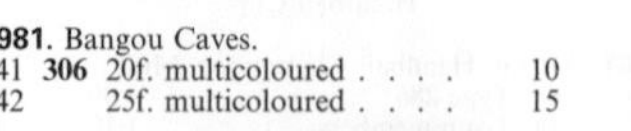

307 "Congolese Coiffure"

1982. Ivory Sculptures by R. Engongodzo. Multicoloured.
843 25f. Type **307** 15 10
844 35f. "Congo Coiffure" (different) 20 10
845 100f. "King Makoko, his Queen and Counsellor" (horiz) 45 25

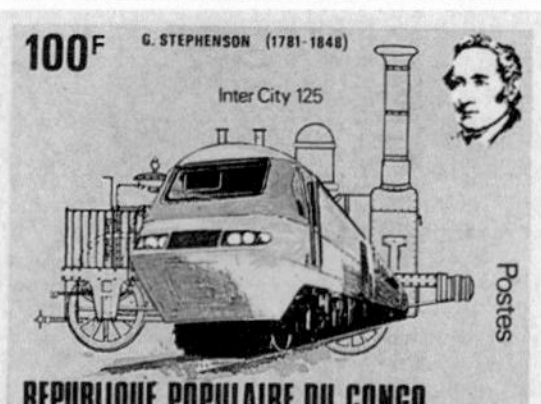

308 "Patentee" and Inter-City 125 Express Train, Great Britain

1982. Birth Bicentenary (1981) of George Stephenson (railway engineer). Multicoloured.
846 100f. Type **308** 60 30
847 150f. "Hikari" express train, Japan 95 45
848 200f. Advanced Passenger Train (APT), Great Britain 1·40 60
849 300f. TGV 001 locomotive, France . . . . 2·25 90

309 Scout with Binoculars

1982. 75th Anniv of Boy Scout Movement. Multicoloured.
850 100f. Type **309** 45 25
851 150f. Scout reading map . . 1·00 35
852 200f. Scout talking to village woman . . . . 1·40 45
853 300f. Scouts on rope bridge 2·00 70

310 Franklin D. Roosevelt

1982. Anniversaries. Multicoloured.
855 150f. Type **310** (birth cent) 1·10 35
856 250f. George Washington on horseback (250th birth anniv) . . . . 1·90 60
857 350f. Johann von Goethe (writer) (150th death anniv) 2·50 80

311 Princess of Wales and Candles

1982. 21st Birthday of Princess of Wales. Mult.
858 200f. Type **311** . . . . 1·40 45
859 300f. Princess and "21" . . . 2·00 70

312 Road Building

1982. Five Year Plan. Multicoloured.
861 60f. Type **312** 65 20
862 100f. Telecommunications . . 90 25
863 125f. Operating theatre equipment . . . . 1·10 30
864 150f. Hydro-electric project 1·50 55

313 Dish Antenna

1982. I.T.U. Delegates' Conference, Nairobi.
865 **313** 300f. multicoloured . . . 2·25 1·10

314 Mosque, Medina

1982. Air. 1350th Death Anniv of Mohammed.
866 **314** 400f. multicoloured . . . 3·00 1·40

315 W.H.O. Regional Office

1982. World Health Organization Regional Office, Brazzaville.
867 **315** 125f. multicoloured . . . 90 30

316 Mother feeding Baby

1982. Health Campaign.
868 **316** 100f. multicoloured . . . 80 25

1982. Birth of Prince William of Wales. Nos. 823/25 optd **NAISSANCE ROYALE 1982**.
869 100f. multicoloured 45 25
870 200f. multicoloured . . . . . 1·40 80
871 300f. multicoloured . . . . . 2·00 1·10

318 Dr. Robert Koch and Bacillus

1982. Centenary of Discovery of Tubercle Bacillus.
873 **318** 250f. multicoloured . . . 2·25 1·10

1982. World Cup Football Championship Results. Nos. 724/28 optd.
874 60f. **EQUIPE QUATRIEME FRANCE** 25 20
875 75f. **EQUIPE TROISIEME POLOGNE** 35 20
876 100f. **EQUIPE SECONDE ALLEMAGNE (RFA)** . . 45 25
877 150f. **EQUIPE VAINQUEUR/ITALIE** . . 1·00 35
878 175f. **ITALIE–ALLEMAGNE (RFA) 3 1** . . . . 1·40 65

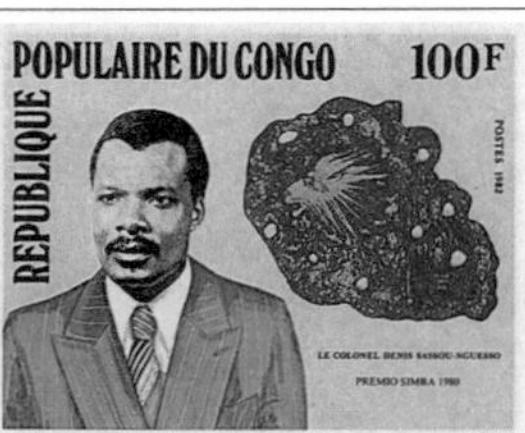
320 Pres. Sassou-Ngeusso and Prize

1982. Award of 1980 Simba Prize to Pres. Sassou-Nguesso.
880 **320** 100f. multicoloured . . . 45 25

321 Turtle

1982. Turtles.
881 **321** 30f. multicoloured 15 10
882 – 45f. multicoloured 55 15
883 – 55f. multicoloured 80 55
DESIGNS: 45, 55f. Different turtles.

322 Amelia Earhart and "Friendship"

1982. 50th Anniv of Amelia Earhart's Transatlantic Flight.
884 **322** 150f. lt brown, grn & brn 1·25 80

323 "La Malafoutier" 324 Grey Parrots nesting in Hole in Tree

1982.
885 **323** 100f. multicoloured . . . 80 25

1982. Birds' Nests. Multicoloured.
886 40f. Type **324** 90 20
887 75f. Palm tree and nest . . . 1·50 20
888 100f. Nest hanging from branch . . . . 1·75 25

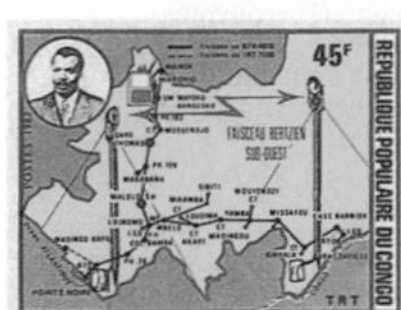
325 Map of Network

1982. Hertzian Wave Network.
889 **325** 45f. multicoloured 20 15
890 60f. multicoloured 25 20
891 95f. multicoloured 45 25

326 Council Headquarters, Brussels

1983. 30th Anniv of Customs Co-operation Council.
892 **326** 100f. multicoloured . . . 45 25

327 Marien N'Gouabi Mausoleum

1983.
893 **327** 60f. multicoloured 25 20
894 80f. multicoloured 35 20

328 Raffia Weaving

1983.
895 **328** 150f. multicoloured . . . 1·10 35

329 Chess Pieces

1983. Chess Pieces Carved by R. Engongonzo. Multicoloured.
896 40f. Type **329** 20 10
897 60f. Close-up of white pawn, king, queen and bishop . . 55 20
898 95f. Close-up of black rook, bishop, queen and king . . 1·00 55

330 Blacksmiths

1983.
899 **330** 45f. multicoloured 45 15

331 Study for "The Transfiguration"

1983. Easter. 500th Birth Anniv of Raphael. Multicoloured.
900 200f. Type **331** . . . . 1·60 45
901 300f. "Deposition from the Cross" (horiz) . . . . . . 2·25 70
902 400f. "Christ in his Glory" 2·75 90

332 Comb 333 "Pila ovata"

1983. Traditional Combs. Multicoloured.
903 30f. Type **332** 15 10
904 70f. Comb (different) 55 25
905 85f. Three combs 65 30

1983. Shells. Multicoloured.
905a 25f. Charonia lampas . . .
906 35f. Type **333** 25 20
907 65f. True achatina 50 35

334 Windsurfing

1983. Air. Pre-Olympic Year.
908 **334** 100f. multicoloured . . . 80 40
909 – 200f. mult (horiz) . . . . 1·10 50
910 – 300f. multicoloured . . . 1·40 75
911 – 400f. multicoloured . . . 3·25 1·00
DESIGNS: 200 to 400f. Various windsurfing scenes.

335 Montgolfier Balloon, 1783 336 Hands holding Gun and Pick

1983. Air. Bicentenary of Manned Flight. Mult.
913 100f. Type **335** . . . . 1·10 40
914 200f. Montgolfier balloon "Le Flesselles", 1784 . . . 1·60 50
915 300f. Auguste Piccard's stratosphere balloon "F.N.R.S.", 1931 . . . . 2·25 75
916 400f. Modern hot-air balloon 3·25 1·00

1983. 20th Anniv of Revolution.
918 **336** 60f. multicoloured 25 20
919 100f. multicoloured . . . 65 35

337 Mgr. A. Carrie and Church of the Sacred Heart, Loango

1983. Centenary of Evangelism. Multicoloured.
920 150f. Type **337** . . . . 1·10 50
921 250f. Mgr. Augouard and St. Joseph's Church, Linzolo . . . . 1·75 80

338 Thunbergia 339 "Virgin and Child with St. John"

1984. Flowers. Multicoloured.
922 5f. Type **338** 10 10
923 15f. Bougainvillaea (horiz) . . 10 10
924 20f. Anthurium 15 10
925 45f. Allamanda (horiz) . . . 30 25
926 75f. Hibiscus 45 40

1984. Air. Christmas. Paintings by Botticelli. Multicoloured.
927 150f. Type **339** . . . . 1·10 30
928 350f. "Virgin and Child" (St. Barnabas) . . . . . . 2·50 1·00
929 500f. "Virgin and Child" . . 3·50 1·25

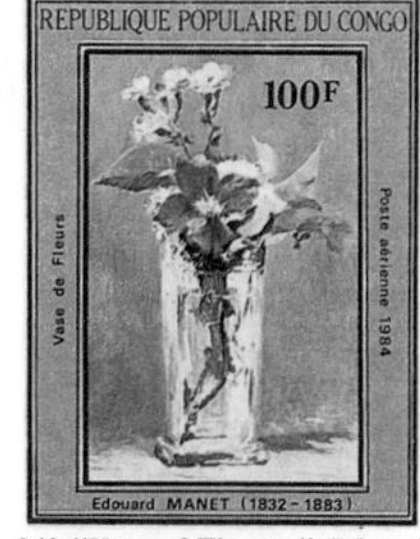
340 "Vase of Flowers" (Manet)

1984. Air. Paintings. Multicoloured.
930 100f. Type **340** 55 50
931 200f. "The Small Holy Family" (Raphael) . . . . 1·40 50
932 300f. "La Belle Jardiniere" (detail) (Raphael) . . . . 2·00 70
933 400f. "The Virgin of Lorette" (Raphael) . . . . 2·75 1·00
934 500f. "Richard Wagner" (Giuseppe Tivoli) . . . . . 3·25 1·25

341 Peace Dove

1984. 34th Anniv of World Peace Council.
935 **341** 50f. multicoloured 30 25
936 100f. multicoloured . . . 55 50

342 Judo

1984. Air. Olympic Games, Los Angeles. Mult.
937 45f. Type **342** 30 25
938 75f. Judo (different) (horiz) 45 40
939 150f. Wrestling (horiz) . . . 1·10 55
940 175f. Fencing (horiz) . . . . 1·10 60
941 350f. Fencing (different) (horiz) . . . . 2·50 1·00

343 Mushroom Cloud

1984. Campaign against Weapons of Mass Destruction.
943 **343** 200f. black, brown & orge 1·40 55

344 Rice

1984. Agriculture. Multicoloured.
944 10f. Type **344** 10 10
945 15f. Pineapples 10 10
946 60f. Manioc (vert) 35 30
947 100f. Palms (vert) 80 50

345 Congress Palace

1984. Chinese–Congolese Co-operation.

948	**345**	60f. multicoloured	35	30
949		100f. multicoloured . . .	80	50

346 Loulombo Station

1984. 50th Anniv of Congo Railways. Mult.

950	10f. Type **346**	15	15
951	25f. Chinese workers' camp at Les Bandas	45	20
952	125f. "50" forming bridge and tunnel	2·40	65
953	200f. Headquarters building	3·50	95

347 Alsthom CC203 Diesel Locomotive

1984. Transport. Multicoloured. (a) Locomotives.

954	100f. Type **347**	85	15
955	150f. Alsthom BB 103 diesel	1·25	20
956	300f. Diesel locomotive No. BB BB 301	2·75	45
957	500f. BB420 diesel train "L'Eclair"	4·50	85

(b) Ships.

958	100f. Pusher tug	80	55
959	150f. Pusher tug (different)	1·25	65
960	300f. Buoying boat	2·50	90
961	500f. "Saint" (freighter) . . .	3·75	1·10

348 Giant Ground Pangolin

1984. Animals. Multicoloured.

962	30f. Type **348**	25	15
963	70f. Bat	50	35
964	85f. African civet	90	45

Nos. 962/4 are inscribed "1983".

349 Fish in Basket   350 Polio Victims and Hand

1984. World Fisheries Year. Multicoloured.

965	5f. Type **349**	15	10
966	20f. Casting nets	30	10
967	25f. Fishes	25	10
968	40f. Men pulling nets in . . .	40	20
969	55f. Boat net and fishes . . .	50	30

1984. Anti-polio Campaign. Multicoloured.

970	250f. Type **350**	2·00	1·10
971	300f. Polio victims within target	2·50	1·40

351 M'bamou Palace Hotel, Brazzaville   352 S. van den Berg, Windsurfing

1984.

972	**351**	60f. multicoloured	35	30
973		100f. multicoloured . . .	80	50

1984. Air. Olympic Games Yachting Gold Medal Winners. Multicoloured.

974	100f. Type **352**	75	30
975	150f. U.S.A., "Soling" class (horiz)	1·10	40
976	200f. Spain, "470" dinghy (horiz)	1·50	60
977	500f. U.S.A., "Flying Dutchman" two-man dinghy	3·75	1·25

353 Floating Logs

1984. Floating Logs on River Congo. Mult.

978	60f. Type **353**	50	25
979	100f. Logs and boat on river	1·00	50

354 "The Holy Family"   355 "Zonocerus variegatus"

1985. Air. Christmas. Multicoloured.

980	100f. Type **354**	65	30
981	200f. "Virgin and Child" (G. Bellini) (horiz)	1·40	60
982	400f. "Virgin and Child with Angels" (Cimabue)	2·75	1·00

1985.

983	**355**	125f. multicoloured . . .	1·10	40

357 Black-headed Grosbeaks

1985. Air. Birth Bicentenary of John J. Audubon (ornithologist). Multicoloured.

985	100f. Type **357**	1·50	50
986	150f. Scarlet ibis	1·40	60
987	200f. Red-tailed hawk (horiz)	3·75	75
988	350f. Labrador duck	6·25	1·00

358 Funeral Procession

1985. Burial of Teke Chief.

989	**358**	225f. multicoloured . . .	1·60	70

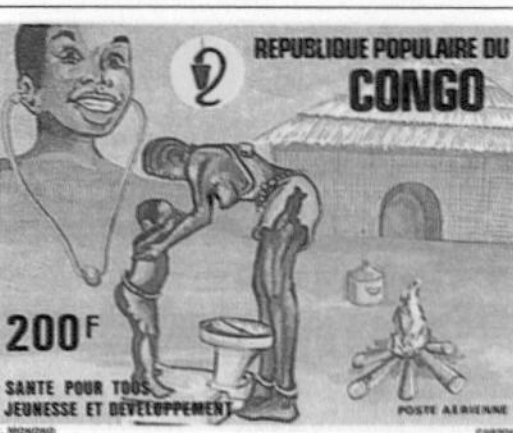

359 Mother weighing Child

1985. "Philexafrique" Stamp Exhibition, Lome, Togo (1st issue). Multicoloured.

990	200f. Type **359**	1·90	1·40
991	200f. Boy writing and man ploughing field	1·90	1·40

See also Nos. 1004/5.

360 "Trichoscypha acuminata"   361 Brazzaville Lions Club Pennant

1985. Fruits. Multicoloured.

992	5f. Type **360**	10	10
993	10f. "Aframomum africanum"	10	10
994	125f. "Gambeya lacuurtiana"	90	40
995	150f. "Landolphia jumelei"	1·10	65

1985. 30th Anniv of Lions Club.

996	**361**	250f. multicoloured . . .	1·90	75

362 Moscow Kremlin, Soldier and Battlefield

1985. 40th Anniv of End of World War II.

997	**362**	60f. multicoloured	45	15

363 Doves forming Heart

1985. Air. 25th Anniv of U.N. Membership.

998	**363**	190f. multicoloured . . .	1·40	60

365 Girl Guide with Yellow-bellied Wattle-eye (International Youth Year)

1985. Anniversaries and Events. Multicoloured.

999	150f. Type **365**	1·75	85
1000	250f. Jacob Grimm (folklorist) and scene from "Snow White and the Seven Dwarfs" (birth bicentenary) (International Youth Year)	1·60	75
1001	350f. Johann Sebastian Bach (composer) and organ (300th birth anniv) (European Music Year)	2·25	80
1002	450f. Queen Elizabeth, the Queen Mother (85th birthday) (vert)	2·75	90
1003	500f. Statue of Liberty (centenary) (vert)	3·25	1·10

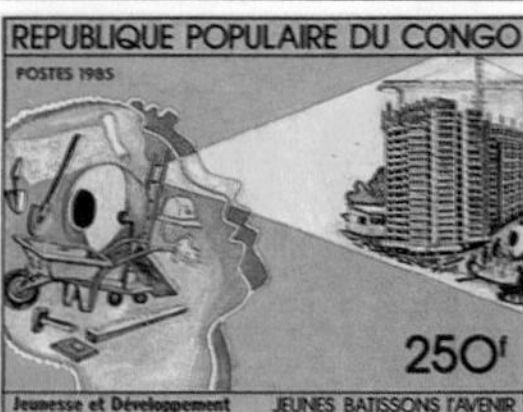

366 Construction Equipment within Heads and Building

1985. "Philexafrique" Stamp Exhibition, Lome, Togo (2nd issue). Multicoloured.

1004	250f. Type **366**	2·00	1·40
1005	250f. Loading mail at airport	2·00	1·40

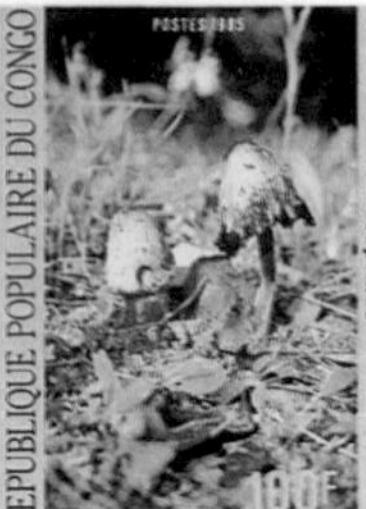

367 Emblem and Rainbow   368 "Coprinus"

1985. Air. 40th Anniv of U.N.O.

1006	**367**	180f. multicoloured . . .	1·25	55

1985. Fungi. Multicoloured.

1007	100f. Type **368**	1·10	40
1008	150f. "Cortinarius"	1·60	55
1009	200f. "Armillariella mellea"	2·00	60
1010	300f. "Dictyophora"	2·50	75
1011	400f. "Crucibulum vulgare"	3·75	1·00

369 "Virgin and Child" (Gerard David)

1985. Air. Christmas. Multicoloured.

1012	100f. Type **369**	65	30
1013	200f. "Adoration of the Magi" (Hieronymus Bosch)	1·40	60
1014	400f. "Virgin and Child" (Anthony Van Dyck) (horiz)	2·75	1·10

370 Edmond Halley and Computer Picture of Comet

1986. Air. Appearance of Halley's Comet. Multicoloured.

1015	125f. Type **370**	80	40
1016	150f. West's Comet, 1976 (vert)	1·00	55
1017	225f. Ikeya-Seki Comet, 1965 (vert)	1·50	60
1018	300f. "Giotto" space probe and comet trajectory . . .	2·00	70
1019	350f. Comet and "Vega" space probe	2·50	80

371 President planting Sapling **372** Boys and Hoops with Handles

1986. National Tree Day. Multicoloured.
1020 60f. Type **371** 25 20
1021 200f. Map, tree and production of oxygen and carbon dioxide . . . . . 1·40 75

1986. Children's Hoop Races. Multicoloured.
1022 5f. Type **372** 10 10
1023 10f. Boy with hoop on string 10 10
1024 60f. Boys racing with hoops (horiz) 25 20

373 Cosmos-Frantel Hotel

1986. Air.
1026 **373** 250f. multicoloured . . . 1·60 95

375 Emptying Rubbish into Dustbin **376** Woman carrying Basket on Head

1986. World Environment Day. Multicoloured.
1030 60f. Type **375** 50 20
1031 125f. Woman dumping rubbish in street 90 35

1986. Traditional Methods of Carrying Goods. Multicoloured.
1032 5f. Type **376** 10 10
1033 10f. Woman carrying basket at back held by rope from head 10 10
1034 60f. Man carrying wood on shoulder 50 20

377 Footballers

1986. Air. World Cup Football Championship, Mexico.
1035 **377** 150f. multicoloured . . . 1·00 55
1036 – 250f. multicoloured . . . 1·75 65
1037 – 440f. multicoloured . . . 3·00 90
1038 – 600f. multicoloured . . . 4·25 1·40
DESIGNS: 250f. to 600f. Various football scenes.

378 Sisters tending Patients **379** Programme Emblem

1986. Centenary of Sisters of St. Joseph of Cluny Mission.
1039 **378** 230f. multicoloured . . . 1·60 90

1986. International Communications Development Programme.
1040 **379** 40f. multicoloured . . . 15 10
1041 60f. multicoloured . . . 25 20
1042 100f. multicoloured . . . 45 35

380 Emblem **381** Foodstuffs

1986. International Peace Year.
1043 **380** 100f. blue, grn & lt grn 45 35

1986. World Food Day. Multicoloured.
1044 75f. Type **381** 60 20
1045 120f. Woman spoon-feeding child 90 40

382 Woman holding Child and Windmill with Medical Symbols **383** Douglas DC-10 and "25" on Map

1986. U.N.I.C.E.F. Child Survival Campaign. Multicoloured.
1046 15f. Type **382** 10 10
1047 30f. Children (horiz) 15 10
1048 70f. Woman and child . . . 55 20

1986. Air. 25th Anniv of Air Afrique.
1049 **383** 200f. multicoloured . . . 1·40 65

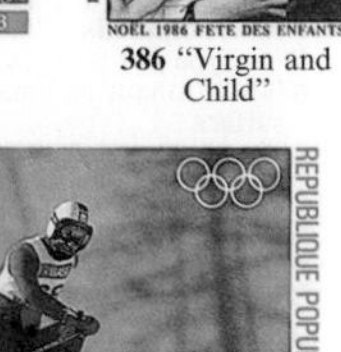

384 Lenin **386** "Virgin and Child"

385 Men's Slalom

1986. 27th U.S.S.R. Communist Party Congress.
1050 **384** 100f. multicoloured . . . 90 30

1986. Air. Winter Olympic Games, Calgary (1988). Multicoloured.
1051 150f. Type **385** . . . . . . 1·00 55
1052 250f. Four-man bobsleigh (vert) . . . . 1·75 70
1053 440f. Ladies cross-country skiing (vert) . . . . . . 3·00 1·00
1054 600f. Ski-jumping . . . . . 4·25 1·50

1986. Air. Christmas. Paintings by Rogier van der Weyden. Multicoloured.
1055 250f. Type **386** . . . . . . 1·60 60
1056 440f. "Nativity" . . . . . . 3·00 90
1057 500f. "Virgin of the Pink" 3·25 1·10

387 "Osteolaemus tetraspis"

1987. Air. Crocodiles. Multicoloured.
1058 75f. Type **387** 90 20
1059 100f. "Crocodylus cataphractus" . . . . . . 1·00 30
1060 125f. "Osteolaemus tetraspis" (different) . . . 1·10 40
1061 150f. "Crocodylus cataphractus" (different) 1·40 50

388 Pres. Sassou-Nguesso and Map **389** Traditional Marriage Ceremony

1987. Election of Pres. Sassou-Nguesso as Chairman of Organization of African Unity.
1062 **388** 30f. multicoloured . . . 15 10
1063 45f. multicoloured . . . 20 15
1064 75f. multicoloured . . . 55 20
1065 120f. multicoloured . . . 90 40

1987.
1066 **389** 5f. multicoloured 10 10
1067 15f. multicoloured . . . 10 10
1068 20f. multicoloured . . . 10 10

390 "Sputnik"

1987. Air. 30th Anniv of First Artificial Space Satellite.
1069 **390** 60f. multicoloured . . . 50 15
1070 240f. multicoloured . . . 1·75 1·25

391 Starting Back-stroke Race

1987. Air. Olympic Games, Seoul (1988) (1st issue). Swimming. Multicoloured.
1071 100f. Type **391** 65 30
1072 200f. Freestyle . . . . . . 1·40 45
1073 300f. Breast-stroke . . . . 2·00 65
1074 400f. Butterfly . . . . . . 2·75 90
See also Nos. 1121/4.

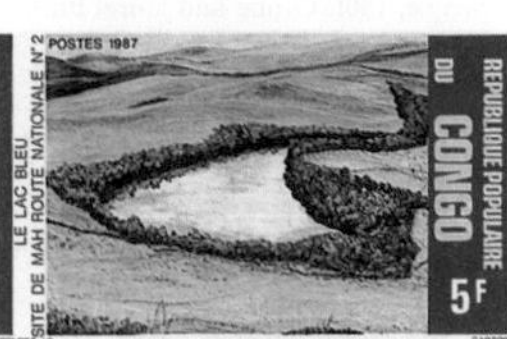

392 Blue Lake, National Route 2

1987.
1076 **392** 5f. multicoloured 10 10
1077 15f. multicoloured . . . 10 10
1078 75f. multicoloured . . . 80 20
1079 120f. multicoloured . . . 1·00 40

393 Flags and Pres. Ngouabi **395** Emblem

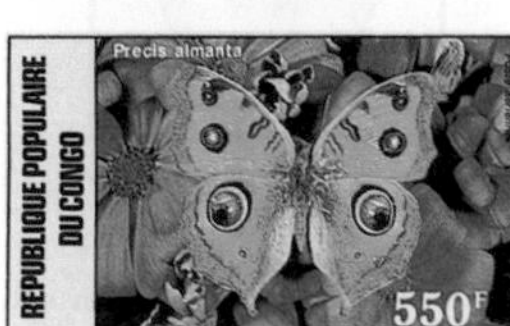

394 "Precis almanta"

1987. 10th Death Anniv of President Marien Ngouabi.
1080 **393** 75f. multicoloured . . . 55 20
1081 120f. multicoloured . . . 90 40

1987. Butterflies. Multicoloured.
1082 75f. "Precis epicleli" 65 25
1083 120f. "Deilephila nerii" . . 1·00 45
1084 450f. "Euryphene senegalensis" . . . . . . 3·25 1·00
1085 550f. Type **394** . . . . . . 3·75 1·50

1987. African Men of Science Congress.
1086 **395** 15f. multicoloured . . . 10 10
1087 90f. multicoloured . . . 40 30
1088 230f. multicoloured . . . 1·50 85

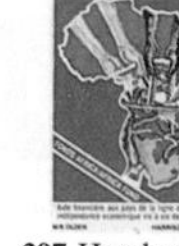

396 Fist and Broken Manacle **397** Hands putting Money into Pot within Map

1987. Anti-Apartheid Campaign. Multicoloured.
1089 60f. Type **396** 25 15
1090 240f. Chain forming outline of map, Nelson Mandela and bars (26 × 38 mm) . . 1·75 90

1987. African Fund.
1091 **397** 25f. multicoloured . . . 10 10
1092 50f. multicoloured . . . 20 15
1093 70f. multicoloured . . . 55 20

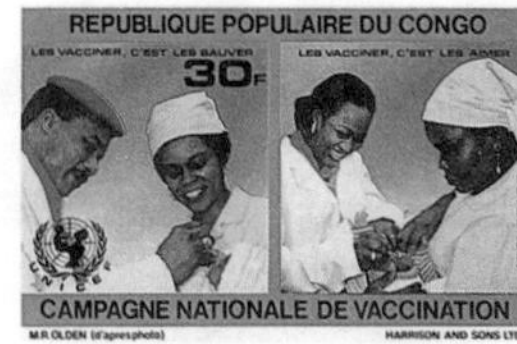

398 Babies being Vaccinated

1987. National Vaccination Campaign. Mult.
1094 30f. Type **398** (postage) . . 15 10
1095 45f. Doctor vaccinating child (vert) 45 15
1096 500f. Queue waiting for vaccination (air) . . . . 4·00 2·75

399 Handball Player, Map and Runner

1987. 4th African Games, Nairobi.
1097 **399** 75f. multicoloured . . . 55 20
1098 120f. multicoloured . . . 90 40

400 Follereau

1987. 10th Death Anniv of Raoul Follereau (leprosy pioneer).
1099 **400** 120f. multicoloured . . . 1·00 40

401 Coubertin and Greece 1896 1d. Stamp

1987. Air. 50th Death Anniv of Pierre de Coubertin (founder of modern Olympic games). Multicoloured.
1100 75f. Type **401** 55 20
1101 120f. Runners and France 1924 10c. stamp 90 40
1102 350f. Congo 1964 100f. stamp and hurdler . . . . 2·50 90
1103 600f. High jumper and Congo 1968 85f. stamp 4·00 1·40

402 Basket of Produce and Hands holding Ears of Wheat

1987. 40th Anniv of F.A.O.
1104 **402** 300f. multicoloured . . . 2·00 1·00

403 Hillside Farming and Produce within "2000"

1987. "Food Self-sufficiency by Year 2000".
1105 **403** 20f. multicoloured . . . 10 10
1106 55f. multicoloured . . . 50 20
1107 100f. multicoloured . . . 80 30

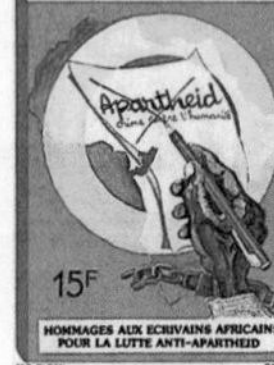

404 Simon Kimbangu **406** Writer crossing through "Apartheid"

405 Lenin inspecting Parade in Red Square

1987. Birth Centenary of Simon Kimbangu (founder of Church of Jesus Christ on Earth). Multicoloured.
1108 75f. Type **404** 55 20
1109 120f. Kimbangu feeding grey parrot . . . . 1·50 80
1110 240f. Kimbanguiste Temple, Nkamba (horiz) . . . . . 1·90 90

1988. 70th Anniv of Russian Revolution.
1112 **405** 75f. multicoloured . . . 90 55
1113 120f. multicoloured . . . 1·40 80

1988. African Anti-Apartheid Writers.
1114 **406** 15f. multicoloured . . . 10 10
1115 60f. multicoloured . . . 25 15
1116 75f. multicoloured . . . 55 20

407 Schweitzer and Hospital

1988. Air. 75th Anniv of Arrival at Lambarene of Dr. Albert Schweitzer (missionary).
1117 **407** 240f. multicoloured . . . 1·90 90

408 Samuel Morse **409** Banknote and Field within "10"

1988. 150th Anniv of Morse Telegraph. Mult.
1118 90f. Type **408** 65 25
1119 120f. Morse and telegraph equipment 90 35

1988. 10th Anniv of International Agricultural Development Fund.
1120 **409** 240f. multicoloured . . . 1·50 80

1988. Air. Olympic Games, Seoul (2nd issue). Modern Pentathlon. As T **391**. Multicoloured.
1121 75f. Swimming 55 20
1122 170f. Cross-country running (vert) . . . . 1·25 55
1123 200f. Shooting . . . . 1·40 65
1124 600f. Horse-riding . . . . . 4·00 1·25

411 Eucalyptus Plantation, Brazzaville **412** Hands holding Gun and Pick

1988. Anti-desertification Campaign. Mult.
1126 5f. Type **411** 10 10
1127 10f. Stop sign and man chopping down tree . . . 10 10

1988. 25th Anniv of Revolution. Multicoloured.
1128 75f. Type **412** 55 20
1129 75f. People tending crops . . 55 20
1130 120f. Pres. Sassou-Nguesso holding aubergine 80 35

413 Yoro Fishing Village

1988.
1131 35f. Type **413** 20 10
1132 40f. Place de la Liberte . . 20 10

414 People on Map and Jet Fighters attacking Virus

1988. 1st International Day against A.I.D.S.
1133 **414** 60f. multicoloured . . . 30 10
1134 – 75f. multicoloured . . . 55 20
1135 – 180f. black, red & blue 1·25 85
DESIGNS: 75f. Virus consisting of healthy and infected people; 180f. Globe and laurel branches.

415 Pres. Sassou-Nguesso addressing Crowd

1989. 10th Anniv of 5 February Movement. Multicoloured.
1136 75f. Type **415** 55 20
1137 120f. Pres. Sassou-Nguesso and symbols of progress 2·25 75

416 Emblems

1989. 40th Anniv of Declaration of Human Rights.
1138 **416** 120f. multicoloured . . . 80 35
1139 350f. multicoloured . . . 2·00 1·10

417 Bari

1989. Air. World Cup Football Championship, Italy (1990) (1st issue). Multicoloured.
1140 75f. Type **417** 55 20
1141 120f. Rome 90 35
1142 500f. Florence . . . . . . 3·50 80
1143 550f. Naples . . . . 4·00 1·10
See also Nos. 1174/7.

418 "Storming of the Bastille" (detail, J. P. Houel)

1989. Air. "Philexfrance 89" International Stamp Exhibition. Multicoloured.
1144 300f. Type **418** (bicent of French revolution) . . . 2·25 1·00
1145 400f. "Eiffel Tower" (G. Seurat) (centenary of Eiffel Tower (1986)) . . . 2·75 1·25

419 Astronaut and Landing Module

1989. Air. 20th Anniv of First Manned Landing on Moon. Multicoloured.
1146 400f. Type **419** . . . . . . 2·75 1·25
1147 400f. Astronaut on lunar surface . . . . 2·75 1·25

420 Marien Ngouabi

1989. 50th Birth Anniv (1988) of Marien Ngouabi (President, 1969–77).
1148 **420** 240f. black, yell & mve 1·60 65

421 Henri Dunant (founder), Volunteer with Child and Anniversary Emblem **422** Emblem on Dove

1989. 125th Anniv (1988) of Red Cross.
1149 75f. Type **421** (postage) . . 55 20
1150 120f. Emblem, Dunant and Congolese Red Cross station (air) 90 35

1989. 25th Anniv of Organization of African Unity.
1151 **422** 120f. multicoloured . . . 90 35

423 "Opuntia phaeacantha"

1989. Cacti. Multicoloured.
1152 35f. Type **423** 15 10
1153 40f. "Opuntia ficus-indica" 15 10
1154 60f. "Opuntia erinacea" (horiz) 50 15
1155 75f. "Opuntia rufida" . . . 55 20
1156 120f. "Opuntia leptocaulis" (horiz) 90 40

424 Banknote, Coins and Woman

1989. 25th Anniv of African Development Bank.
1158 **424** 75f. multicoloured . . . 55 20
1159 120f. multicoloured . . . 90 40

425 Ice Dancing

1989. Winter Olympic Games, Albertville (1992) (1st issue). Multicoloured.
1160 75f. Type **425** 30 20
1161 80f. Cross-country skiing . . 30 20
1162 100f. Speed skating 65 30
1163 120f. Luge 80 40
1164 200f. Slalom . . . . 1·40 45
1165 240f. Ice hockey . . . . . . 1·40 50
1166 400f. Ski jumping . . . . . 2·75 70
See also Nos. 1245/6.

426 Doctor examining Patient **427** Emblem and People with raised Fists

1989. 40th Anniv of W.H.O. Multicoloured.
1168 60f. Type **426** 55 15
1169 75f. Blood donation (vert) 65 55

1989. 20th Anniv of Congolese Workers' Party.
1170 **427** 75f. multicoloured . . . 55 20
1171 120f. multicoloured . . . 90 40

1990. Local Health Campaigns. Nos. 1168/9 optd **NOTRE PLANETE, NOTRE SANTE PENSER GLOBALEMENT AGIR LOCALEMENT.**
1172 60f. multicoloured 55 45
1173 75f. multicoloured 65 55

429 Footballers

430 Family supporting Open Book

1990. Air. World Cup Football Championship, Italy (2nd issue). Designs showing footballers.

1174 **429** 120f. multicoloured . . . 90 40
1175 – 240f. multicoloured . . . 1·75 60
1176 – 500f. multicoloured . . . 3·25 1·00
1177 – 600f. multicoloured . . . 4·00 1·25

1990. International Literacy Year.

1178 **430** 75f. black, yellow & blue 55 20

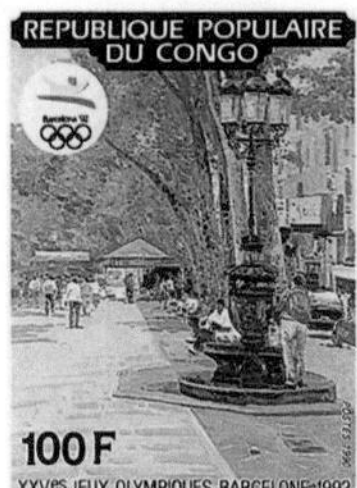

431 Ramblas, Barcelona

1990. Olympic Games, Barcelona (1992) (1st issue). Multicoloured.

1179 100f. Type **431** (postage) . . 65 30
1180 150f. Yachting (horiz) . . . 1·10 35
1181 200f. Yachting (different) (horiz) . . . . 1·40 45
1182 240f. Market stalls, Barcelona (horiz) . . . . 1·40 65
1183 350f. Harbour, Barcelona (horiz) (air) . . . . . . 2·50 75
1184 500f. Monument, Barcelona 3·25 1·00

See also Nos. 1322/7.

432 Turtle Dove ("Tourterelle des boris")

1990. Birds. Multicoloured.

1186 25f. Type **432** 35 30
1187 50f. Dartford warbler ("Fauvette Pitchou") (vert) 70 40
1188 70f. Common kestrel ("Faucon Crecerelle") (vert) . . . . 1·25 70
1189 150f. Grey parrot ("Perroquet Gris") (vert) 2·25 1·60

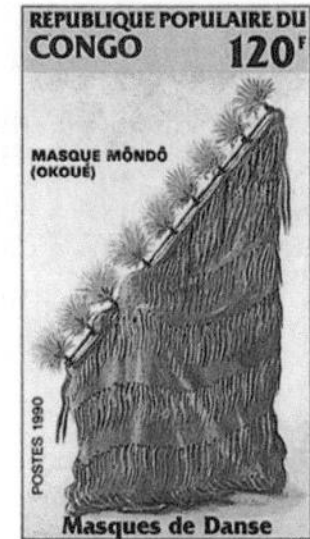

433 Mondo Mask

435 Sunflower

434 Necklace

1990. Dance Masks. Multicoloured.

1190 120f. Type **433** 90 40
1191 360f. Bapunu mask . . . . 2·50 1·25
1192 400f. Kwele mask . . . . . 2·75 1·40

1990. Traditional Royal Necklaces. Multicoloured.

1193 75f. Type **434** 55 20
1194 100f. Money cowrie necklace 55 35

1990. Flowers. Multicoloured.

1195 30f. Type **435** 15 10
1196 45f. "Cassia alata" (horiz) 20 10
1197 75f. Opium poppy 55 20
1198 90f. "Acalypha sanderil" . . 65 25

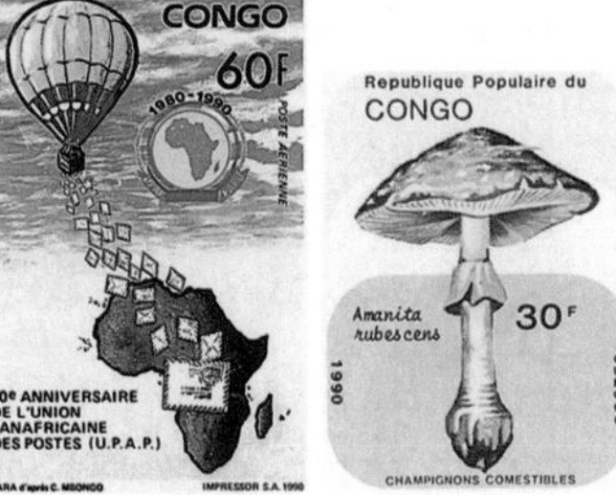

436 Hot-air Balloon dropping Envelopes on Africa

437 The Blusher

1991. Air. 10th Anniv of Pan-African Postal Union. Multicoloured.

1199 60f. Type **436** 40 20
1200 120f. Envelopes on map of Africa 90 55

1991. Fungi. Multicoloured.

1201 30f. Type **437** 25 10
1202 45f. "Catathelasma imperiale" 35 15
1203 75f. Caesar's mushroom . . 55 25
1204 90f. Royal boletus 65 30
1205 120f. Deer mushroom . . . 1·00 45
1206 150f. "Boletus chrysenteron" 1·10 50
1207 200f. Horse mushroom . . . 1·60 70

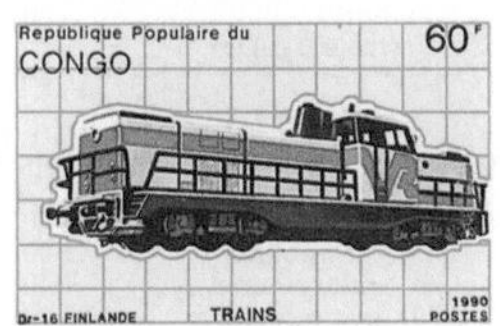

438 Type Dr-16 Diesel Locomotive, Finland

1991. Trains. Multicoloured.

1209 60f. Type **438** 90 15
1210 75f. TGV express, France 1·10 20
1211 120f. Suburban S-350 electric railcar, Italy . . . 1·75 30
1212 200f. Type DE 24000 diesel locomotive, Turkey . . . 3·25 55
1213 250f. DE 1024 diesel-electric locomotive, Germany . . 4·00 70

439 Canoe, Palm Tree and Setting Sun

440 Congolese Woman

1991. International African Tourism Year. Multicoloured.

1215 75f. Type **439** 55 20
1216 120f. Zebra and map of Africa 90 55

1991.

1217 **440** 15f. blue 10 10
1218 30f. green 15 10
1219 60f. yellow 30 15
1220 75f. mauve 35 20
1221 120f. brown 60 30

441 Christopher Columbus (after Sebastian del Pombo)

442 "Kalanchoe pinnata"

1991. 500th Anniv (1992) of Discovery of America by Columbus. Multicoloured.

1222 20f. Type **441** 10 10
1223 35f. Christopher Columbus 15 10
1224 40f. Christopher Columbus (different) 20 10
1225 55f. "Santa Maria" 60 20
1226 75f. "Nina" 80 30
1227 150f. "Pinta" . . . . 1·40 55
1228 200f. Arms and signature of Columbus . . . . 1·40 80

1991. Medicinal Plants. Multicoloured.

1229 15f. "Ocimum viride" (horiz) 10 10
1230 20f. Type **442** 10 10
1231 30f. "Euphorbia hirta" (horiz) 15 10
1232 60f. "Catharantheus roseus" 30 15
1233 75f. "Bidens pilosa" 60 20
1234 100f. "Brillantasia patula" 80 50
1235 120f. "Cassia occidentalis" 90 65

443 Route Map

1991. Centenary of Trans-Siberian Railway. Mult.

1236 120f. Type **443** . . . . . . 1·50 45
1237 240f. Russian Class N steam locomotive superimposed on map . . . . 2·25 80

444 Honey fungus

1991. Scouts, Butterflies and Fungi. Mult.

1238 35f. "Euphaedra eusemoides" (butterfly) (postage) 15 10
1239 40f. Type **444** 40 15
1240 75f. "Palla decius" (butterfly) 60 20
1241 80f. "Kallima ansorgei" (butterfly) 65 20
1242 500f. "Cortinarius speciocissimus" (fungus) (air) . . . . 3·75 1·40
1243 600f. "Graphium illyris" (butterfly) . . . . 4·00 1·40

445 Ice Hockey

1991. Air. Winter Olympic Games, Albertville (1992) (2nd issue). Multicoloured.

1245 120f. Type **445** 90 30
1246 300f. Speed skating . . . . 2·00 70

446 "Telecom 91"

1991. "Telecom 91" World Telecommunications Exhibition, Geneva. Multicoloured.

1248 75f. Type **446** 60 20
1249 120f. Stylized view of exhibition (vert) 90 55

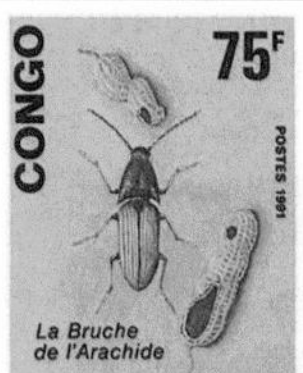

447 Beetle and Peanuts

448 Woman drinking at Waterfall

1991. Harmful Insects. Multicoloured.

1250 75f. Type **447** 60 20
1251 120f. Stag beetle (horiz) . . 90 30
1252 200f. Beetle and coffee . . . 1·40 50
1253 300f. Goliath beetle . . . . 2·25 70

1991. "Water is Life".

1254 **448** 75f. multicoloured . . . 60 20

449 Pintail

450 Breaking Chain and Hand holding Dove

1991. Wild Ducks. Multicoloured.

1255 75f. Type **449** 60 20
1256 120f. Eider (vert) 90 30
1257 200f. Common shoveler (vert) . . . . 1·40 90
1258 240f. Mallard . . . . 1·60 1·10

1991. 30th Anniv of Amnesty International. Multicoloured.

1259 40f. Candle, barbed wire and sun 20 10
1260 75f. Type **450** 35 20
1261 80f. Boy holding human rights banner and soldiers threatening boy (horiz) . . 65 45

451 1891 5c. on 1c. "Commerce" stamp

1991. Centenary of Congolese Stamps.

1262 **451** 75f. green and brown . . 60 45
1263 – 120f. dp brn, grn & brn 1·10 90
1264 – 240f. multicoloured . . . 2·00 1·40
1265 – 500f. multicoloured . . . 3·50 2·75

DESIGNS: 120f. 1900 1c. "Leopard in ambush" stamp; 240f. 1959 25f. "Birth of the Republic" stamp; 500f. "Commerce", "Leopard" and "Republic" stamps.

452 Ferrari "512 S"

1991. Cars and Space. Multicoloured.

1266 35f. Type **452** (postage) . . 15 10
1267 40f. Vincenzo Lancia and Lancia "Stratos" 20 10
1268 75f. Airship "Graf Zeppelin", Maybach "Type 12" car and Wilhelm Maybach 45 25
1269 80f. Mars space probe . . . 40 20
1270 500f. "Magellan" space probe over Venus (air) . . 3·25 80
1271 600f. "Ulysses" space probe photographing sun spot 4·00 90

453 Small Blue

1991. Butterflies. Multicoloured.

1273 75f. Type **453** 35 20
1274 120f. Charaxes 80 30

1275 240f. Leaf butterfly (vert) . . 1·60 90
1276 300f. Butterfly on orange (vert) . . . . 2·00 1·40

454 General De Gaulle

1991. De Gaulle and Africa. Multicoloured.
1277 75f. Type **454** 65 20
1278 120f. De Gaulle, soldiers and Free French flag (vert) 90 30
1279 240f. De Gaulle making speech, Brazzaville, 1940 1·75 1·10

455 Bo Jackson (American footballer)

1991. Celebrities and International Organizations. Multicoloured.
1280 100f. Type **455** 50 25
1281 150f. Nick Faldo (golfer) . . 1·00 35
1282 200f. Rickey Henderson and Barry Bonds (baseball players) . . . . 1·40 50
1283 240f. Gary Kasparov (World chess champion) 1·75 55
1284 300f. Starving child and Lions International and Rotary International emblems . . . . 2·00 70
1285 350f. Wolfgang Amadeus Mozart (composer) . . . 2·75 80
1286 400f. De Gaulle and Churchill visiting the Eastern Front, 1944 . . . 2·75 95
1287 500f. Henry Dunant (founder of Red Cross) 3·25 1·00

456 Painting

1991. Paintings. Multicoloured.
1289 75f. Type **456** 60 20
1290 120f. Couple in silhouette (vert) 90 30

457 Diana Monkey

1991. Primates. Multicoloured.
1291 30f. Type **457** 15 10
1292 45f. Chimpanzee 20 10
1293 60f. Gelada (vert) 55 15
1294 75f. Hamadryas baboon (vert) 80 20
1295 90f. Pigtail macaque (vert) 90 20
1296 120f. Gorilla (vert) . . . . 1·10 30
1297 240f. Mandrill (vert) . . . . 2·25 55

458 "Sputnik 2" and Laika (space dog)

1992. Celebrities, Anniversaries and Events. Mult.
1299 50f. Type **458** (35th anniv of space flight) (postage) . . 45 10
1300 75f. Martin Luther King (Nobel Peace Prize winner, 1964) and Gandhi 60 20
1301 120f. Meteosat "MOP-2" and "ERS-1" satellites, globe and stern trawler ("Europe-Africa") . . . . 1·25 40
1302 300f. Konrad Adenauer (German statesman, 25th death anniv) and crowd before Brandenburg Gate (3rd anniv of opening of Berlin Wall) . . . . . . 2·00 70
1303 240f. "Graf Zeppelin", Ferdinand von Zeppelin (75th death anniv) and Maybach Zeppelin motor car (air) . . . . 1·40 70
1304 500f. Pope and globe (Papal visit to Africa) . . . . . 3·25 1·00

459 Juan de la Cosa and Map

460 Secretary Bird

1992. "Genova 92" International Thematic Stamp Exhibition. Multicoloured.
1306 75f. Type **459** 80 20
1307 95f. Martin Alonso Pinzon and astrolabe . . . . . . 1·00 25
1308 120f. Alonso de Ojeda and hourglass . . . . 1·40 30
1309 200f. Vicente Yanez Pinzon and sun clock . . . . . 2·00 45
1310 250f. Bartholomew Columbus and quadrant 2·25 55

1992. Birds. Multicoloured.
1312 60f. Type **460** 65 15
1313 75f. Saddle-bill stork . . . 80 20
1314 120f. Wattled crane . . . . 1·10 30
1315 200f. Black-headed heron . . 1·90 45
1316 250f. Greater flamingo . . . 2·75 55

461 Lion

462 "Madonna of the Grand Duke" (Raphael)

1992. Big Cats. Multicoloured.
1318 45f. Type **461** 50 25
1319 60f. Tiger 70 35
1320 75f. Lynx 85 40
1321 95f. Caracal . . . . 1·10 55
1322 250f. Ocelot . . . . 2·75 1·40

1992. Christmas. Multicoloured.
1324 95f. Type **462** 70 25
1325 200f. "Madonna of the Book" (Sandro Botticelli) 1·40 50
1326 250f. "Carondelet Madonna" (Fra Bartolommeo) . . . . . 1·75 1·10

No. 1325 is wrongly inscribed "Boticelli" and No. 1326 "Bartolomeo".

463 Baseball and Towers of Church of the Holy Family

464 N. Mishkutienok and A. Dmitriev (Unified Team)

1992. Olympic Games, Barcelona (2nd issue). Multicoloured.
1328 75f. Type **463** (postage) . . 35 20
1329 100f. Running and "The Muses" (Eusebio Arnau) 50 25
1330 150f. Hurdling and painted dome (Miguel Barcelo) of Market Theatre . . . . . 1·00 35
1331 200f. High jumping and Sant Pau hospital . . . . 1·40 50
1332 400f. Putting the shot and "Miss Barcelona" (Joan Miro) (air) . . . . 2·75 85
1333 500f. Table tennis and "Don Juan of Austria" (galley) 3·25 1·00

1992. Winter Olympic Games Gold Medal Winners. Multicoloured.
1335 150f. Type **464** (pairs figure skating) (postage) . . . . 1·00 35
1336 200f. Austrian team (four-man bobsleighing) . . . . 1·40 50
1337 500f. Gunda Niemann (Germany, women's speed skating) (air) . . . . . . 3·25 90
1338 600f. Bjorn Daehlie (Norway, 50 km cross-country skiing) . . . . . 4·00 1·00

No. 1338 is wrongly inscribed "Blorn Daehlle".

465 African Red-tailed Buzzard ("Charognard")

467 Topi

466 Overhead Volley

1993. Birds of Prey. Multicoloured.
1340 45f. Type **465** 20 10
1341 75f. Ruppell's griffon ("Vautour") 60 20
1342 120f. Verreaux's eagle ("Aigle") 80 55

1993. World Cup Football Championship, U.S.A. (1994).
1343 **466** 75f. multicoloured . . . 80 20
1344 – 95f. multicoloured . . . 1·00 25
1345 – 120f. multicoloured . . . 1·40 30
1346 – 200f. multicoloured . . . 2·00 50
1347 – 250f. multicoloured . . . 2·75 65

DESIGNS: 95f. to 250f. Different footballing scenes.

1993. Animals. Multicoloured.
1349 60f. Type **467** 60 15
1350 75f. Grant's gazelle 80 20
1351 95f. Quagga . . . . 1·00 25
1352 120f. Leopard . . . . . . 1·25 25
1353 200f. African buffalo . . . 2·00 25
1354 250f. Hippopotamus . . . . 2·50 30
1355 300f. Hooded vulture . . . . 3·00 35
1356 350f. Lioness and cub . . . 3·25 55

Nos. 1349/56 were issued together, se-tenant, forming a composite design.

468 Jars from Liloko

1993. Traditional Pottery. Multicoloured.
1357 45f. Type **468** 20 10
1358 75f. Jug from Mbeya . . . 35 20
1359 120f. Jar from Mbeya . . . 60 30

470 Show Jumping

1993. Summer Olympic Games, Atlanta (1996) and Winter Olympic Games, Lillehammer, Norway (1994). Multicoloured.
1366 50f. Type **470** (postage) . . 25 15
1367 75f. Cycling 35 20
1368 120f. Two-man dinghy . . . 60 30
1369 240f. Fencing . . . . 1·40 55
1370 300f. Hurdling (air) . . . . 2·25 70
1371 400f. Figure skating . . . . 2·75 95
1372 500f. Basketball . . . . . . 3·25 90
1373 600f. Ice hockey . . . . . 4·00 1·25

471 "Hibiscus schizopetalus"

1993. Wild Flowers. Multicoloured.
1375 75f. Type **471** 35 20
1376 95f. "Pentas lanceolata" . . 45 25
1377 120f. "Ricinus communis" . 90 30
1378 200f. "Delonix regia" . . . 1·50 50
1379 250f. "Stapelia gigantea" . . 1·90 90

OFFICIAL STAMPS

O 68 Arms

1968.
O142 O 68 1f. multicoloured . . . 10 10
O143 2f. multicoloured . . . 10 10
O144 5f. multicoloured . . . 10 10
O145 10f. multicoloured . . 20 15
O146 25f. multicoloured . . 20 10
O147 30f. multicoloured . . 45 10
O148 50f. multicoloured . . 60 30
O149 85f. multicoloured . . 1·50 65
O150 100f. multicoloured . . 1·75 1·10
O151 200f. multicoloured . . 2·50 1·60

POSTAGE DUE STAMPS

D 7 Letter-carrier

1961. Transport designs.
D19 D 7 50c. bistre, red & blue 10 10
D20 – 50c. bistre, purple & bl 10 10
D21 – 1f. brown, red & green 10 10
D22 – 1f. green, red and lake 10 10
D23 – 2f. brown, green & bl . . 10 15
D24 – 2f. brown, green & bl . . 10 15
D25 – 5f. sepia and violet . . . 15 15
D26 – 5f. sepia and violet . . . 15 15
D27 – 10f. brown, blue & grn 1·00 40
D28 – 10f. brown and green . . 1·00 40
D29 – 25f. brown, blue & turq 1·10 1·10
D30 – 25f. black and blue . . . 1·10 1·10

DESIGNS: D20, Holste Broussard monoplane; D21, Hammock-bearers; D22, "Land Rover" car; D23, Pirogue; D24, River steamer of 1932; D25, Cyclist; D26, Motor lorry; D27, Steam locomotive, 1932; D28, Diesel locomotive; D29, Seaplane of 1935; D30, Boeing 707 airliner.

1971. Tropical Flowers. Similar to T **105**, but inscr "Timbre-Taxe". Multicoloured.
D264 1f. Stylized bouquet 10 10
D265 2f. "Phaeomeria magnifica" 10 10
D266 5f. "Millettia laurentii" . . 10 10
D267 10f. "Polianthes tuberosa" 15 15
D268 15f. "Pyrostegia venusta" 20 20
D269 20f. "Hibiscus rosa sinensis" 25 25

D 374 Passion Flower

1986. Flowers and Fruit. Multicoloured.
D1027 5f. Type D **374** 10 10
D1028 10f. Canna lily 10 10
D1029 15f. Pineapple 10 10

APPENDIX

The following stamps have either been issued in excess of postal needs or have not been available to the public in reasonable quantities at face value. Such stamps may later be given full listing if there is evidence of regular postal use.

All embossed on gold foil

1991.

Scout and Butterfly. Air 1500f.

Winter Olympic Games, Albertville (1992). Air 1500f.

1992.

Olympic Games, Barcelona. Air 1500f.

CONGO DEMOCRATIC REPUBLIC (EX ZAIRE) Pt. 14

In May 1997 Zaire changed its name to the Democratic Republic of Congo after President Mobutu and his Government was overthrown by a rebellion led by Laurent Kabila.

New Currency

July 1998. 100 cents = 1 congolise franc.

273 Mother Teresa

274 Diana Princess of Wales

1998. 1st Death Anniv of Mother Teresa (founder of Missionaries of Charity).

1494	**273** 50000z. multicoloured	1·25	80

1998. 1st Death Anniv of Diana, Princess of Wales. Multicoloured.

1496	50000z. Type **274**	1·10	80
1497	50000z. Wearing white jacket with blue collar	1·10	80
1498	50000z. Wearing large hat	1·10	80
1499	50000z. Wearing white top with blue dots	1·10	80
1500	50000z. Wearing neck scarf	1·10	80
1501	50000z. Wearing pearl necklace	1·10	80
1502	100000z. Wearing tiara	2·10	1·60
1503	100000z. Wearing black top	2·10	1·60
1504	100000z. Resting head on hands	2·10	1·60
1505	100000z. Wearing cream top	2·10	1·60
1506	125000z. Wearing red and black dress	2·50	2·00
1507	125000z. Wearing cream jacket	2·50	2·00
1508	125000z. Profile	2·50	2·00
1509	125000z. Wearing tiara	2·50	2·00

275 Building

1999. Independence. Multicoloured.

1511	25c. Type **275**	50	50
1512	50c. Coat of Arms	95	95
1513	75c. Making speech	1·40	1·40
1514	1f.25 Procession	2·40	2·40
1515	3f. Crowd and man breaking chains	5·50	5·50

No. 1511 also exists imperforate.

276 Men fighting in Boat

1999. *Outlaws of the Marsh* (Chinese literature). Multicoloured.

1517	1f.45 Type **276**	1·10	1·10
1518	1f.45 Men fighting in blacksmith's shop	1·10	1·10
1519	1f.45 Men gathered around tree	1·10	1·10
1520	1f.45 Men writing	1·10	1·10
1521	1f.50 Crowds fighting	1·10	1·25
1522	1f.50 Man pulling tree from ground	1·10	1·25
1523	1f.50 Man threatening other man with sword	1·10	1·25
1524	1f.50 Man climbing over balcony	1·10	1·25
1525	1f.60 Men outside fort	1·25	1·25
1526	1f.60 Man in snow storm	1·25	1·25
1527	1f.60 Man killing tiger	1·25	1·25
1528	1f.60 Man reading writing on wall	1·25	1·25
1529	1f.70 Crowds fighting	1·25	1·40
1530	1f.70 Man drawing sword	1·25	1·40
1531	1f.70 Man jumping from balcony	1·25	1·40
1532	1f.70 Man lifting other man	1·25	1·40
1533	1f.80 Archer on horseback	1·40	1·40
1534	1f.80 Men sitting round table eating	1·40	1·40
1535	1f.80 Joust	1·40	1·40
1536	1f.80 Man tearing scroll	1·40	1·40

277 Rat

1999. Chinese Horoscope. Multicoloured.

1538	78c. Type **277**	85	40
1539	78c. Ox	85	40
1540	78c. Tiger	85	40
1541	78c. Rabbit	85	40
1542	78c. Dragon	85	40
1543	78c. Snake	85	40
1544	78c. Horse	85	40
1545	78c. Goat	85	40
1546	78c. Monkey	85	40
1547	78c. Cockerel	85	40
1548	78c. Dog	85	40
1549	78c. Pig	85	40

278 Okapi

279 Four-coloured Bush Shrike (*Telophorus quadricolor*)

2000. Flora and Fauna. Multicoloured.

1550	1f. Type **278**	55	55
1551	1f. Common kestrel	55	55
1552	1f. Giraffe and rainbow	55	55
1553	1f. Giraffe	55	55
1554	1f. Mandrill	55	55
1555	1f. Savannah baboon	55	55
1556	1f. Leopard	55	55
1557	1f. Birdwing butterflies	55	55
1558	1f. Hippopotamus	55	55
1559	1f. Hadada ibis	55	55
1560	1f. Water lilies	55	55
1561	1f. Steenbok	55	55
1562	7f.80 Lion (47 × 34 mm)	3·75	2·75

Nos. 1550/61 were issued together, se-tenant, forming a composite design.

2000. Flora and Fauna of Africa. Multicoloured.

1564	1f. Type **279**	45	35
1565	1f.50 Leopard (*Panthera pardus*)	70	55
1566	1f.50 Sun	80	80
1567	1f.50 *Pieris citrina* (butterfly)	80	80
1568	1f.50 European bee eater (*Merops apiaster*)	80	80
1569	1f.50 Red-backed shrike (*Lanius collurio*)	80	80
1570	1f.50 Village weaver (*Ploceus cucullatus*)	80	80
1571	1f.50 *Charaxes pelias*	80	80
1572	1f.50 Green charaxes (*Charaxes eupale*)	80	80
1573	1f.50 Giraffe (*Giraffa camelopardalis*)	80	80
1574	1f.50 Bushbaby (*Galago moholi*)	80	80
1575	1f.50 *Strelitzia reginae* (flower)	80	80
1576	1f.50 Thomson's gazelle (*Gazella thomsoni*)	80	80
1577	1f.50 Hoopoe (*Upupa epops*)	80	80
1578	2f. Puku (*Kobus vardoni*)	95	95
1579	2f. Protomedia (*Colotis protomedia*)	95	95
1580	3f. Ground pangolin (*Smutsia temminckii*)	1·40	1·40
1581	3f. *Cararina abyssinica* (flower)	1·40	1·40

Nos. 1566/1577 were issued together, se-tenant, forming a composite design.

280 Leopard Cat (*Felis bengalensis*)

2000. Wild Cats and Dogs. Multicoloured.

1583	1f.50 Type **280**	80	80
1584	1f.50 African golden cat (*Felis aurata*)	80	80
1585	1f.50 Caracal (*Felis caracal*)	80	80
1586	1f.50 Puma (*Felis concolor*)	80	80
1587	1f.50 Black-footed cat (*Felis nigripes*)	80	80
1588	1f.50 Lion (*Panthera leo*)	80	80
1589	1f.50 Clouded leopard (*Neofelis nebulosa*)	80	80
1590	1f.50 Margay (*Felis wiedii*)	80	80
1591	1f.50 Cheetah (*Acinonyx jubatus*)	80	80
1592	1f.50 Spainsh lynx (*Felis pardina*)	80	80
1593	1f.50 Jaguarundi (*Felis yagouarundi*)	80	80
1594	1f.50 Serval (*Felis serval*)	80	80
1595	2f. Black-backed jackal (*Canis mesomelas*)	1·00	1·00
1596	2f. Bat-eared fox (*Otocyon megalotis*)	1·00	1·00
1597	2f. Bush dog (*Speothos venaticus*)	1·00	1·00
1598	2f. Coyote (*Canis latrans*)	1·00	1·00
1599	2f. Dhole (*Cuon alpinus*)	1·00	1·00
1600	2f. Fennec fox (*Fennecus zerda*)	1·00	1·00
1601	2f. Grey fox (*Urocyon cinereoargenteus*)	1·00	1·00
1602	2f. Wolf (*Canis lupus*)	1·00	1·00
1603	2f. Kit fox (*Vulpes macrotis*)	1·00	1·00
1604	2f. Maned wolf (*Chrysocyon brachyurus*)	1·00	1·00
1605	2f. Racoon-dog (*Nyctereutes procyonoides*)	1·00	1·00
1606	2f. Red fox (*Vulpes vulpes*)	1·00	1·00

281 "2000" and Mountains

2000. New Millennium.

1608	**281** 4f.50 multicoloured	1·00	1·00
1609	9f. multicoloured	1·90	1·90
1610	15f. multicoloured	3·25	3·25

CONGO (KINSHASA) Pt. 14

This Belgian colony in Central Africa became independent in 1960. There were separate issues for the province of Katanga (q.v.).

In 1971 the country was renamed ZAIRE and later issues will be found under that heading.

1967. 100 sengi = 1 (li)kuta;
100 (ma)kuta = 1 zaire.

1960. Various stamps of Belgian Congo optd **CONGO** or surch also. (a) Flowers issue of 1952. Multicoloured.

360	10c. "Dissotis"	20	10
361	10c. on 15c. "Protea"	20	10
362	20c. "Vellozia"	20	10
363	40c. "Ipomoea"	20	10
364	50c. on 60c. "Euphorbia"	20	10
365	50c. on 75c. "Ochna"	20	10
366	1f. "Hibiscus"	20	10
367	1f.50 "Schizoglossum"	20	10
368	2f. "Ansellia"	20	10
369	3f. "Costus"	40	10
370	4f. "Nymphaea"	40	20
371	5f. "Thunbergia"	40	10
372	6f.50 "Thonningia"	60	10
373	8f. "Gloriosa"	80	20
374	10f. "Silene"	1·25	20
375	20f. "Aristolochia"	2·50	55
376	50f. "Eulophia"	14·00	3·75
377	100f. "Cryptosepalum"	24·00	6·25

(b) Wild Animals issue of 1959.

378	10c. brown, sepia and blue	15	10
379	20c. blue and red	15	10
380	40c. brown and blue	15	10
381	50c. multicoloured	15	10
382	1f. black, green & brown	15	10
383	1f.50 black and yellow	20	10
384	2f. black, brown and red	30	10
385	3f.50 on 3f. blk, pur & slate	35	10
386	5f. brown, green and sepia	50	15
387	6f.50 brown, yellow and blue	65	15
388	8f. bistre, violet and brown	80	30
389	10f. multicoloured	1·00	35

(c) Madonna.

390	**102** 50c. brown, ochre & chest	50	50

(d) African Technical Co-operation Commission. Inscr in French or Flemish.

391	**103** 3f.50 on 3f. sal & slate	40	40

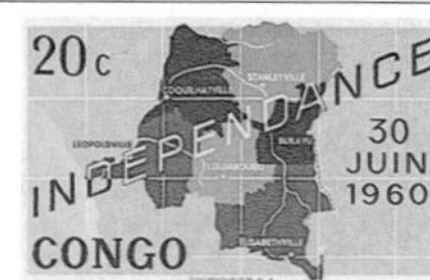

106 Congo Map

1960. Independence Commemoration.

392	**106** 20c. bistre	10	10
393	50c. red	10	10
394	1f. green	10	10
395	1f.50 brown	10	10
396	2f. mauve	10	10
397	3f.50 violet	10	10
398	5f. blue	15	10
399	6f.50 black	20	10
400	10f. orange	30	20
401	20f. blue	50	30

107 Congo Flag and People breaking Chain

109 Pres. Kasavubu

1961. 2nd Anniv of Congo Independence Agreement. Flag in yellow and blue.

402	**107** 2f. violet	10	10
403	3f.50 red	10	10
404	6f.50 brown	20	10
405	10f. green	25	15
406	20f. mauve	45	30

1961. Coquilhatville Conf. Optd **CONFERENCE COQUILHATVILLE AVRIL-MAI-1961.**

407	**106** 20c. bistre	60	60
408	50c. red	60	60
409	1f. green	60	60
410	1f.50 brown	60	60
411	2f. mauve	60	60
412	3f.50 violet	60	60
413	5f. blue	60	60
414	6f.50 black	60	60
415	10f. orange	60	60
416	20f. blue	60	60

1961. 1st Anniv of Independence. Inscr as in T **109**. Portraits and inscriptions in sepia.

417	**109** 10c. yellow	10	10
418	20c. red	10	10
419	40c. turquoise	10	10
420	50c. salmon	10	10
421	1f. lilac	10	10
422	1f.50 brown	10	10
423	2f. green	10	10
424	– 3f.50 mauve	15	10
425	– 5f. grey	1·75	15
426	– 6f.50 blue	30	10
427	– 8f. olive	35	10
428	– 10f. blue	75	10
429	– 20f. orange	75	15
430	– 50f. blue	1·40	30
431	– 100f. green	2·50	50

DESIGNS—HORIZ: 3f.50 to 8f. Pres. Kasavubu and map of Congo Republic. VERT: 10f. to 100f. Pres. Kasavubu in full uniform and outline map.

1961. Re-opening of Parliament. Optd **REOUVERTURE du PARLEMENT JUILLET 1961.**

432	**109** 10c. yellow	10	10
433	20c. red	10	10
434	40c. turquoise	10	10
435	50c. salmon	30	20
436	1f. lilac	30	20
437	1f.50 brown	80	70
438	2f. green	80	70
439	– 5f. grey (No. 425)	80	70
440	– 10f. violet (No. 428)	80	85

111 Dag Hammarskjold

112 Campaign Emblem

1962. Dag Hammarskjold Commemoration.

441	**111** 10c. brown and grey	10	10
442	20c. blue and grey	10	10
443	30c. bistre and grey	10	10
444	40c. blue and grey	10	10
445	50c. red and grey	10	10
446	3f. olive and grey	2·50	1·60

447 6f.50 violet and grey . . . 70 50
448 8f. brown and grey . . . 80 60

1962. Malaria Eradication.
449 **112** 1f.50 brown, black & yell 10 10
450 2f. turq, brown & green 30 15
451 6f.50 lake, black & blue 15 10

1962. Reorganization of Aboula Ministry. Optd **"Paix, Travail, Austerite..., C. ADOULA 11 juillet 1962.**
452 **111** 10c. brown and grey . . . 10 10
453 20c. blue and grey 10 10
454 30c. bistre and grey . . . 10 10
455 40c. blue and grey 10 10
456 50c. red and grey . . . . 1·25 50
457 3f. olive and grey 15 10
458 6f.50 violet and grey . . . 20 10
459 8f. brown and grey . . . 30 15

114

1963. 1st Participation in U.P.U. Congress.
460 **114** 2f. violet . . . . 1·40 1·00
461 4f. red 10 10
462 7f. blue 20 10
463 20f. green 30 15

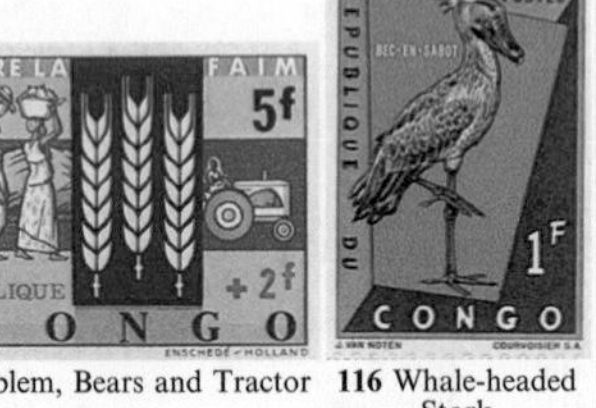

115 Emblem, Bears and Tractor **116** Whale-headed Stork

1963. Freedom from Hunger.
464 **115** 5f.+2f. violet & mauve . . 15 10
465 9f.+4f. green & yellow . . 30 20
466 12f.+6f. violet & blue . . 35 25
467 20f.+10f. green & red . . 1·75 1·60

1963. Protected Birds.
468 – 10c. multicoloured 15 10
469 – 20c. blue, black and red . . 15 10
470 – 30c. black, brown & grn . . 15 10
471 – 40c. black, orange & grey . 15 10
472 **116** 1f. black, green & brown . 30 15
473 – 2f. blue, brown and red . . 7·00 1·25
474 – 3f. black, pink and green . 55 20
475 – 4f. blue, green and red . . 55 20
476 – 5f. black, red and blue . . 85 20
477 – 6f. black, bistre & violet . 7·00 1·25
478 – 7f. indigo, blue & turq . . 1·25 20
479 – 8f. blue, yellow & orange . 1·40 20
480 – 10f. black, red and blue . 1·40 20
481 – 20f. black, red & yellow . 2·50 30
BIRDS—VERT: 10c. Eastern white pelicans ("Pelicans"); 30c. African open-bill stork ("Bec-Duvert"); 2f. Marabou stork ("Marabout"); 4f. Congo peafowl ("Paon Congolais"); 6f. Secretary bird ("Serpentaire"); 8f. Sacred ibis ("Ibis Sacre"). HORIZ: 20c. Crested guineafowl ("Pintables de Schouteden"); 40c. Abdim's stork ("Cigoon a Ventre Blanc"); 3f. Greater flamingos ("Flamants Roses"); 5f. Hartlaub's duck ("Canards de Hartlaub"); 7f. Black-casqued hornbill ("Calaos"); 10f. South African crowned cranes ("Grue Cauronnse"); 20f. Saddle-bill stork ("Jabiru d'Afrique").

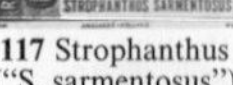

117 Strophanthus ("S. sarmentosus") **118** "Reconciliation"

1963. Red Cross Centenary. Cross in red.
482 **117** 10c. green and violet . . . 10 10
483 A 20c. blue and red 10 10
484 **117** 30c. red and green 10 10
485 A 40c. violet and blue . . . 10 10
486 **117** 5f. lake and olive 10 10
487 A 7f. purple and orange . . 10 10
488 B 9f. olive 20 10
489 20f. violet . . . . 1·60 70
DESIGNS—VERT: A, "Cinchona ledgeriana". HORIZ: B, Red Cross nurse.

1963. "National Reconciliation".
490 **118** 4f. multicoloured 90 30
491 5f. multicoloured 10 10
492 9f. multicoloured 15 10
493 12f. multicoloured 20 10

119 Kabambare Sewer, Leopoldville

1963. European Economic Community Aid.
494 **119** 20c. multicoloured 10 10
495 A 30c. multicoloured 10 10
496 B 50c. multicoloured 10 10
497 **119** 3f. multicoloured 90 35
498 A 5f. multicoloured 10 10
499 B 9f. multicoloured 15 10
500 A 12f. multicoloured 15 10
DESIGNS: A, Tractor and bridge on plan; B, Construction of Ituri Road.

120 N'Djili Airport, Leopoldville

1963. "Air Congo" Commemoration.
501 **120** 2f. multicoloured 10 10
502 – 5f. multicoloured 10 10
503 **120** 6f. multicoloured 90 40
504 – 7f. multicoloured 10 10
505 **120** 30f. multicoloured 25 15
506 – 50f. multicoloured 40 25
DESIGN: 5f., 7f., 50f. Mailplane and control tower.

1963. 15th Anniv of Declaration of Human Rights. Optd **10 DECEMBRE 1948 10 DECEMBRE 1963 15e anniversaire DROITS DE L'HOMME.**
507 **114** 2f. violet 10 10
508 4f. red 10 10
509 7f. blue 20 20
510 20f. green 20 20

122 Student in Laboratory

1964. 10th Anniv of Lovanium University. Mult.
511 50c. Type **122** 10 10
512 1f.50 University buildings . . 10 10
513 8f. Atomic and nuclear reactor symbols . . . . . 1·75 1·60
514 25f. University arms and buildings 20 15
515 30f. Type **122** 20 20
516 60f. As 1f.50 . . . . 40 30
517 75f. As 8f. 50 50
518 100f. As 25f. 70 60

1964. Various stamps surch over coloured metallic panels. (a) Stamps of Belgian Congo surch **REPUBLIQUE DU CONGO** and value.
519 – 1f. on 20c. (No. 340) . . . 10 10
520 – 2f. on 1f.50 (No. 306) . . . 6·25 2·25
521 – 5f. on 6f.50 (No. 348) . . . 15 15
522 – 8f. on 6f.50 (No. 311) . . . 60 25

(b) Stamps of Congo (Kinshasa) surch.
523 – 1f. on 20c. (No. 379) . . 10 10
524 – 1f. on 6f.50 (No. 372) . . 10 10
525 – 2f. on 1f.50 (No. 367) . . 10 10
530 **109** 3f. on 20c. 25 20
531 4f. on 40c. 25 20
526 – 5f. on 6f.50 (No. 387) . . 45 20
528 **106** 6f. on 6f.50 . . . . 30 20
529 7f. on 20c. 40 25

125 Pole-vaulting

1964. Olympic Games, Tokyo.
532 **125** 5f. sepia, grey and red . . 10 10
533 – 7f. violet, red and green 80 40
534 – 8f. brown, yellow & blue 10 10
535 **125** 10f. purple, blue & purple 10 10
536 – 20f. brown, green & orge 20 10
537 – 100f. brown, mauve & grn 80 20
DESIGNS—VERT: 7f., 20f. Throwing the javelin. HORIZ: 8f., 100f. Hurdling.

OCCUPATION OF STANLEYVILLE. During the occupation of Stanleyville from 5 August to 24 November, 1964, stocks of a number of contemporary issues were overprinted **REPUBLIQUE POPULAIRE** and issued by the rebel authorities.

126 National Palace

1964. National Palace, Leopoldville.
538 **126** 50c. mauve and blue . . . 10 10
539 1f. blue and purple . . . 10 10
540 2f. brown and violet . . . 10 10
541 3f. green and brown . . . 10 10
542 4f. orange and blue . . . 10 10
543 5f. violet and green . . . 10 10
544 6f. brown and orange . . . 10 10
545 7f. olive and brown . . . 10 10
546 8f. red and blue . . . . . 2·00 35
547 9f. violet and red 10 10
548 10f. brown and green . . . 10 10
549 20f. blue and brown . . . 10 10
550 30f. red and green 15 10
551 40f. blue and purple . . . 25 10
552 50f. brown and green . . . 35 10
553 100f. black and orange . . 65 15

127 Pres. Kennedy **128** Rocket and Unisphere

1964. Pres. Kennedy Commemoration.
554 **127** 5f. blue and black 10 10
555 6f. purple and black . . . 10 10
556 9f. brown and black . . . 10 10
557 30f. violet and black . . . 30 10
558 40f. green and black . . . 2·00 60
559 60f. brown and black . . 50 25

1965. New York World's Fair.
560 **128** 50c. purple and black . . 10 10
561 1f.50 blue and violet . . . 10 10
562 2f. brown and green . . . 10 10
563 10f. green and red 70 40
564 18f. blue and brown . . . 10 10
565 27f. red and green 25 10
566 40f. grey and red 40 15

129 Football

1965. 1st African Games, Leopoldville.
567 – 5f. black, brown & blue 10 10
568 **129** 6f. red, black and blue . . 10 10
569 – 15f. black, green & orange 10 10
570 – 24f. black, green & mve 20 10
571 **129** 40f. blue, black & turq . . 1·25 45
572 – 60f. purple, black & blue 45 15
SPORTS—VERT: 5f., 24f. Basketball; 15f., 60f. Volleyball.

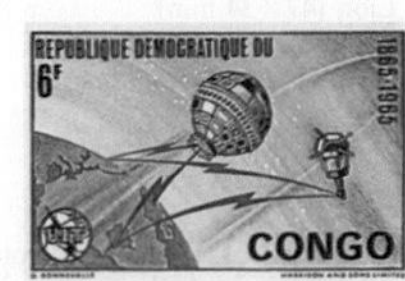

130 Telecommunications Satellites

1965. Centenary of I.T.U. Multicoloured.
573 6f. Type **130** 10 10
574 9f. Telecommunications satellites (different view) . . 10 10
575 12f. Type **130** 10 10
576 15f. As 9f. 10 10
577 18f. Type **130** . . . . 1·00 30
578 20f. As 9f. 15 10
579 30f. Type **130** 25 10
580 40f. As 9f. 30 10

131 Parachutist and troops landing

1965. 5th Anniv of Independence.
581 **131** 5f. brown and blue . . . 10 10
582 6f. brown and orange . . 10 10
583 7f. brown and green . . . 45 20
584 9f. brown and mauve . . 10 10
585 18f. brown and yellow . . 15 10

132 Matadi Port

1965. International Co-operation Year.
586 **132** 6f. blue, black & yellow 10 10
587 – 8f. brown, black & blue 10 10
588 – 9f. turq, black & brown 10 10
589 **132** 12f. mauve, black & grey 80 30
590 – 25f. olive, black and red 20 10
591 – 60f. grey, black & yellow 40 10
DESIGNS: 8f., 25f. Katanga mines; 9f., 60f. Tshopo Barrage, Stanleyville.

133 Medical Care

1965. Congolese Army.
592 **133** 2f. blue and red 10 10
593 5f. brown, red and pink 10 10
594 – 6f. brown and blue . . . 10 10
595 – 7f. green and yellow . . . 10 10
596 – 9f. brown and green . . . 10 10
597 – 10f. brown and green . . 40 40
598 – 18f. violet and red 15 10
599 – 19f. brown & turquoise 60 40
600 – 20f. brown and blue . . . 15 10
601 – 24f. multicoloured 20 15
602 – 30f. multicoloured 25 10
DESIGNS—HORIZ: 6f., 9f. Feeding child; 7, 18f. Bridge-building. VERT: 10f., 20f. Building construction; 19f. Telegraph line maintenance; 24f., 30f. Soldier and flag.

1966. World Meteorological Day. Nos. 590/1 optd **6e Journee Meteorologique Mondiale / 23.3.66** (on coloured metallic panel) and W.M.O. Emblem.
603 25f. olive, black and red . . 75 45
604 60f. grey, black and yellow 75 50

135 Carved Stool and Head

1966. World Festival of Negro Arts, Dakar.
605 **135** 10f. black, red and grey 10 10
606 – 12f. black, green & blue 10 10
607 – 15f. black, blue & purple 15 15
608 – 53f. black, red and blue 1·10 90
DESIGNS—VERT: 12f. Statuettes; 53f. Statuettes of women. HORIZ: 15f. Woman's head and carved goat.

136 Pres. Mobutu and Fish Workers

1966. Pres. Mobutu Commemoration.
609 **136** 2f. brown and blue . . . 10 10
610 – 4f. brown and red 10 10
611 – 6f. brown and olive . . . 65 60
612 – 8f. brown and turquoise 10 10
613 – 10f. brown and lake . . . 10 10
614 – 12f. brown and violet . . 10 10
615 – 15f. brown and green . . 10 10
616 – 24f. brown and mauve . . 20 15
DESIGNS (Pres. Mobutu and): 4f. Harvesting pyrethrum; 6f. Building construction; 8f. Winnowing maize; 10f. Cotton-picking; 12f. Harvesting fruit; 15f. Picking coffee-beans; 24f. Harvesting pineapples.

1966. Inaug of W.H.O. Headquarters, Geneva. Nos. 550/3 optd **O.M.S. Geneve 1966** and W.H.O. Emblem.
618 **126** 30f. red and green 70 70
619 40f. blue and purple . . . 70 70
620 50f. brown and green . . 75 75
621 100f. black and orange . . 75 75

139 Footballer

1966. World Cup Football Championship.
622 **139** 10f. green, violet & brown 10 10
623 – 30f. green, violet & purple 25 20
624 – 50f. brown, blue & green 85 80
625 – 60f. gold, sepia & green 45 40
DESIGNS: 30f. Two footballers; 50f. Three footballers; 60f. Jules Rimet Cup and football.

1966. World Cup Football Championship Final. Nos. 622/5 optd **FINALE ANGLETERRE - ALLEMAGNE 4 - 2**.
626 **139** 10f. green, violet & brown 25 45
627 – 30f. green, violet & purple 80 1·40
628 – 50f. brown, blue & green 1·25 1·75
629 – 60f. gold, sepia and green 1·40 2·25

1967. 4th African Unity Organization (O.U.A.) Conf, Kinshasa. Nos. 538/43 surch **4e Sommet OUA KINSHASA du 11 au 14 - 9 - 67** and value.
631 **126** 1k. on 2f. 10 10
632 3k. on 5f. 10 10
633 5k. on 4f. 20 15
634 6k.60 on 1f. 25 20
635 9k.60 on 50c. 40 25
636 9k.80 on 3f. 50 40

1967. New Constitution. Nos. 609/10 and 592 surch **1967 NOUVELLE CONSTITUTION** with coloured metallic panel obliterating old value.
639 **136** 4k. on 2f. 20 15
640 **133** 5k. on 2f. 20 15
641 – 21k. on 4f. 90 70

1967. 1st Congolese Games, Kinshasa. Nos. 567 and 569 surch **1ers Jeux Congolais 25/6 au 2/7/67 Kinshasa** and value.
642 1k. on 5f. 10 10
643 9.6k. on 15f. 50 50

1967. 1st Flight by Air Congo BAC "One-Eleven". No. 504 surch **1er VOL BAC ONE ELEVEN 14/5/67** and value.
644 9.6k. on 7f. 70 20

1968. World Children's Day (8.10.67). Nos. 586 and 588 surch **JOURNEE MONDIALE DE L'ENFANCE 8 - 10 - 67** and new value.
645 **132** 1k. on 6f. 10 10
646 9k. on 9f. 50 50

1968. International Tourist Year (1967). Nos. 538, 541 and 544 surch **Annee Internationale du Tourisme 24-10-67** and new value.
647 **126** 5k. on 50c. 20 20
648 10k. on 6f. 40 40
649 15k. on 3f. 60 60

1968. (a) No. 540 surch.
650 **126** 1k. on 2f. 10 10

(b) Surch (coloured panel obliterating old value, and new value surch on panel. Panel colour given first, followed by colour of new value). (i) Nos. 538 and 542.
651 **126** 2k. on 50c. (bronze and black) 10 10
652 2k. on 50c. (blue and white) 10 10
653 9.6k. on 4f. (black and white) 50 45

(ii) No. 609.
654 **136** 10k. on 2f. (black and white) 55 10

152 Leaping Leopard

1968.
655 **152** 2k. black on green 15 10
656 9.6k. black on red 65 15

1968. As Nos. 609, etc, but with colours changed and surch in new value.
657 **136** 15s. on 2f. brown & blue 10 10
658 – 1k. on 6f. brown & chest 10 10
659 – 3k. on 10f. brown & grn 10 10
660 – 5k. on 12f. brown & orge 20 15
661 – 20k. on 15f. brown & grn 70 50
662 – 50k. on 24f. brown & pur 1·90 1·25

154 Human Rights Emblem

1968. Human Rights Year.
663 **154** 2k. green and blue 10 10
664 9.6k. red and green 40 25
665 10k. brown and lilac 40 25
666 40k. violet and brown 1·50 1·10

1969. 4th O.C.A.M. (Organization Commune Africaine et Malgache) Summit Meeting, Kinshasa. Nos. 663/6 with colours changed optd **4EME SOMMET OCAM 27-1-1969 KINSHASA** and emblem.
667 **154** 2k. brown and green 10 10
668 9.60k. green and pink 40 25
669 10k. blue and grey 40 25
670 40k. violet and blue 1·50 1·10

156 Map of Africa and "Cotton"

1969. International Fair, Kinshasa (1st Issue).
671 **156** 2k. multicoloured 10 10
672 – 6k. multicoloured 30 30
673 – 9.6k. multicoloured 40 20
674 – 9.8k. multicoloured 40 35
675 – 11.6k. multicoloured 50 50
DESIGNS: Map of Africa and: 6k. "Copper"; 9.6k. "Coffee"; 9.8k. "Diamonds"; 11.6k. "Palm-oil".

157 Fair Entrance

1969. Inaug of Int Fair, Kinshasa (2nd issue).
676 **157** 2k. purple and gold 10 10
677 – 3k. blue and gold 10 10
678 – 10k. green and gold 40 40
679 – 25k. red and gold 1·00 85
DESIGNS: 3k. "Gecomin" (mining company) pavilion; 10k. Administration building; 25k. African Unity Organization pavilion.

158 Congo Arms 159 Pres. Mobutu

1969.
680 **158** 10s. red and black 10 10
681 15s. blue and black 10 10
682 30s. green and black 10 10
683 60s. purple and black 10 10
684 90s. bistre and black 10 10
685 **159** 1k. multicoloured 10 10
686 2k. multicoloured 10 10
687 3k. multicoloured 15 10
688 5k. multicoloured 15 15
689 6k. multicoloured 20 15
690 9.6k. multicoloured 30 25
691 10k. multicoloured 40 30
692 20k. multicoloured 80 60
693 50k. multicoloured 2·00 1·75
694 100k. multicoloured 4·00 3·50

160 "The Well-sinker" (O. Bonnevalle)

1969. 50th Anniv of International Labour Organization. Paintings. Multicoloured.
695 3k. Type **160** 15 15
696 4k. "Cocoa Production" (J. van Noten) 20 15
697 8k. "The Harbour" (C. Meunier) (vert) 70 25
698 10k. "The Poulterer" (H. Evenepoel) 45 35
699 15k. "Industry" (C. Meunier) 85 50

162 Pres. Mobutu, Map and Flag

1970. 10th Anniv of Independence.
701 **162** 10s. multicoloured 10 10
702 90s. multicoloured 10 10
703 1k. multicoloured 10 10
704 2k. multicoloured 10 10
705 7k. multicoloured 25 15
706 10k. multicoloured 40 25
707 20k. multicoloured 80 50

1970. Surch. (a) National Palace series.
708 **126** 10s. on 1f. 10 10
709 20s. on 2f. 10 10
710 30s. on 3f. 10 10
711 40s. on 4f. 10 10
712 60s. on 7f. 80 75
713 90s. on 9f. 80 75
714 1k. on 6f. 15 10
715 3k. on 30f. 80 75
716 4k. on 40f. 15 10
717 5k. on 50f. 2·00 1·90
718 10k. on 100f. 90 75

(b) Congolese Army series.
719 90s. on 9f. (No. 596) 15 10
720 1k. on 7f. (No. 595) 15 10
721 2k. on 24f. (No. 601) 15 10

(c) Pres. Mobutu series.
722 **136** 20s. on 2f. 15 10
723 – 40s. on 4f. (No. 610) 15 10
724 – 1k. on 12f. (No. 614) 80 70
725 – 2k. on 24f. (No. 616) 15 10

164 I.T.U. Headquarters, Geneva

1970. United Nations Commemorations.
726 **164** 1k. olive, green and pink 10 10
727 – 2k. grey, green and orange 10 10
728 – 6k.60 red, pink and blue 25 25
729 **164** 9k.60 multicoloured 30 30
730 – 9k.80 sepia, brown and bl 35 35
731 – 10k. sepia, brown and lilac 35 35
732 – 11k. sepia, brown and pink 40 40
DESIGNS AND EVENTS: 1k., 9k.60, (I.T.U. World Day); 2k., 6k.60, New U.P.U. Headquarters, Berne (Inauguration); 9k.80, 10k., 11k. U.N. Headquarters, New York (25th anniversary).

165 Pres. Mobutu and Independence Arch

1970. 5th Anniv of "New Regime".
733 **165** 2k. multicoloured 10 10
734 10k. multicoloured 45 35
735 20k. multicoloured 85 80

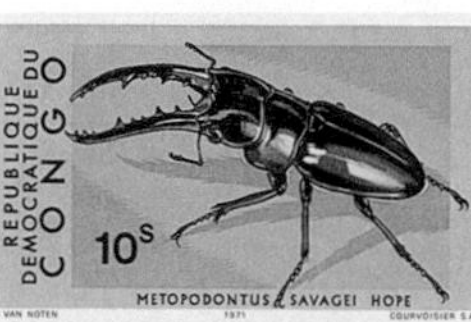

166 "Apollo 11"

1970. Visit of "Apollo 11" Astronauts to Kinshasa.
736 **166** 1k. blue, black and red 10 10
737 – 2k. violet, black and red 10 10
738 – 7k. black, orange and red 25 25
739 – 10k. black, pink and red 35 35
740 – 30k. black, green and red 1·00 1·00
DESIGNS: 2k. Astronauts on Moon; 7k. Pres. Mobutu decorating wives; 10k. Pres. Mobutu with astronauts; 30k. Astronauts after splashdown.

167 "Metopodontus savagei"

1971. Insects. Multicoloured.
741 10s. Type **167** 25 15
742 50s. "Cicindela regalis" 25 15
743 90s. "Magacephala catenulata" 25 15
744 1k. "Stephanorrhina guttata" 25 15
745 2k. "Pupuricenus congoanus" 25 15
746 3k. "Sagra tristis" 50 25
747 5k. "Steraspis subcalida" 1·75 80
748 10k. "Mecosaspis explanata" 2·40 1·25
749 30k. "Goliathus meleagris" 5·75 3·25
750 40k. "Sternotomis virescens" 8·25 4·75

168 "Colotis protomedia"

1971. Butterflies and Moths. Multicoloured.
751 10s. Type **168** 25 15
752 20s. "Rhodophitus simplex" 25 15
753 70s. "Euphaedra overlaeti" 25 15
754 1k. "Argema bouvieri" 25 15
755 3k. "Cymothoe reginae-elisabethae" 50 25
756 5k. "Miniodes maculifera" 1·40 60
757 10k. "Salamis temora" 1·90 90
758 15k. "Eronia leda" 3·75 1·60
759 25k. "Cymothoe sangaris" 5·00 2·50
760 40k. "Euchloron megaera" 8·00 4·50

169 "Four Races" around Globe 170 Pres. Mobutu and Obelisk

1971. Racial Equality Year.
761 **169** 1k. multicoloured 10 10
762 4k. multicoloured 15 15
763 5k. multicoloured 20 20
764 10k. multicoloured 40 40

1971. 4th Anniv of Popular Revolutionary Movement (M.P.R.).
765 **170** 4k. multicoloured 15 15

171 "Hypericum bequaertii"

1971. Tropical Plants. Multicoloured.
766 1k. Type **171** 35 15
767 4k. "Dissotis brazzae" 70 30
768 20k. "Begonia wollast" 3·50 1·50
769 25k. "Cassia alata" 4·50 1·90

172 I.T.U. Emblem (International Telecommunications Day)

1971. "Telecommunications and Space". Mult.
770 1k. Type **172** 10 10
771 3k. Dish aerial (Satellite Earth Station, Kinshasa) 15 15
772 6k. Map of Pan-African telecommunications network 30 30

173 Savanna Monkey

1971. Congo Monkeys. Multicoloured.

773	10s. Type **173**	30	15
774	20s. Moustached monkey (vert)	30	15
775	70s. De Brazza's monkey	45	15
776	1k. Yellow baboon	45	25
777	3k. Pygmy chimpanzee (vert)	75	50
778	5k. Black mangabey (vert)	1·75	1·25
779	10k. Owl-faced monkey	3·25	2·40
780	15k. Diana monkey	5·25	3·50
781	25k. Western black-and-white colobus (vert)	9·00	6·00
782	40k. L'Hoest's monkey (vert)	12·00	8·50

174 Hotel Inter-Continental

1971. Opening of Hotel Inter-Continental, Kinshasa.

783	**174**	2k. multicoloured	10	10
784		12k. multicoloured	50	50

175 "Reader"

1971. Literacy Campaign. Multicoloured.

785	50s. Type **175**	10	10
786	2k.50 Open book and abacus	20	10
787	7k. Symbolic alphabet	45	35

For later issues see **ZAIRE**.

COOK ISLANDS Pt. 1

A group of islands in the South Pacific under New Zealand control, including Aitutaki, Niue, Penrhyn and Rarotonga. Granted self-government in 1965.
See also issues for Aitutaki and Penrhyn Island.

1892. 12 pence = 1 shilling;
20 shillings = 1 pound.
1967. 100 cents = 1 dollar.

1

1892.
1 1 1d. black . . . . 27·00 26·00
2 1½d. mauve . . . . 40·00 38·00
3 2½d. blue . . . . 40·00 38·00
4 10d. red £140 £130

2 Queen Makea Takau

3 White Tern or Torea

1893.
11ba 3 ½d. blue . . . . 4·50 6·00
28 ½d. green . . . . 2·75 3·25
13 2 1d. brown . . . . 16·00 16·00
12 1d. blue . . . . 5·00 4·50
29 1d. red . . . . 4·00 3·00
43 1½d. mauve . . . . 8·50 4·00
15a 3 2d. brown . . . . 8·50 6·50
16a 2 2½d. red . . . . 16·00 9·00
32 2½d. blue . . . . 3·75 7·00
9 5d. black . . . . 17·00 13·00
18a 3 6d. purple . . . . 19·00 23·00
19 2 10d. green . . . . 18·00 48·00
46 3 1s. red . . . . 27·00 90·00

1899. Surch **ONE HALF PENNY**.
21 2 ½d. on 1d. blue . . . . . . 32·00 42·00

1901. Optd with crown.
22 2 1d. brown £180 £140

1919. New Zealand stamps (King George V) surch **RAROTONGA** and value in native language in words.
56 62 ½d. green . . . . 40 1·00
47 53 1d. red . . . . 1·00 3·00
57 62 1½d. brown 50 75
58 2d. yellow . . . . 1·50 1·75
48a 2½d. blue . . . . 2·00 2·25
49a 3d. brown . . . . 2·25 2·00
50c 4d. violet . . . . 1·75 4·25
51a 4½d. green . . . . 1·75 8·00
52a 6d. red . . . . 1·75 5·50
53 7½d. brown . . . . 1·50 5·50
54a 9d. green . . . . 2·00 15·00
55a 1s. red . . . . 2·75 18·00

9 Captain Cook landing

17 Harbour, Rarotonga and Mt. Ikurangi

1920. Inscr "RAROTONGA".
81 9 ½d. black and green . . . . 4·50 8·50
82 – 1d. black and red . . . . . 6·00 2·25
72 – 1½d. black and blue . . . . 8·50 8·50
83 – 2½d. brown and blue . . . . 5·00 24·00
73 – 3d. black and brown . . . . 2·25 5·50
84 17 4d. green and violet . . . . 8·00 16·00
74 – 6d. brown and orange . . . . 3·00 8·50
75 – 1s. black and violet . . . . 5·00 17·00
DESIGNS—VERT: 1d. Wharf at Avarua; 1½d. Captain Cook (Dance); 2½d. Te Po, Rarotongan chief; 3d. Palm tree. HORIZ: 6d. Huts at Arorangi; 1s. Avarua Harbour.

1921. New Zealand stamps optd **RAROTONGA**.
76 F 4 2s. blue . . . . 27·00 55·00
77 2s.6d. brown . . . . . . 19·00 50·00
78 5s. green . . . . 27·00 65·00
79 10s. red . . . . 65·00 £100
89 £1 red £110 £180

1926. "Admiral" type of New Zealand optd **RAROTONGA**.
90 71 2s. blue . . . . 10·00 40·00
92 3s. mauve . . . . 16·00 42·00

1931. No. 77 surch **TWO PENCE**.
93 2d. on 1½d. black and blue . . 9·50 2·75

1931. Arms type of New Zealand optd **RAROTONGA**.
95 F 6 2s.6d. brown . . . . . . 10·00 22·00
96 5s. green . . . . 18·00 55·00
97 10s. red . . . . 38·00 95·00
98 £1 pink . . . . 90·00 £150

20 Captain Cook landing

22 Double Maori Canoe

1932. Inscribed "COOK ISLANDS".
106 20 ½d. black and green . . . 1·00 4·50
107 – 1d. black and red . . . . 1·25 2·00
108 22 2d. black and brown . . . 1·50 50
140 – 2½d. black and blue . . . 75 2·00
110 – 4d. black and blue . . . . 1·50 50
142 – 6d. black and orange . . . 2·50 2·00
105 – 1s. black and violet . . . . 8·50 22·00
DESIGNS—VERT: 1d. Captain Cook. HORIZ: 2½d. Natives working cargo; 4d. Port of Avarua; 6d. R.M.S. "Monowai"; 1s. King George V.

1935. Jubilee. As 1932 optd **SILVER JUBILEE OF KING GEORGE V. 1910-1935.**
113 1d. red . . . . 60 1·40
114 2½d. blue . . . . 1·00 2·50
115 6d. green and orange . . . . 3·50 6·00

1936. Stamps of New Zealand optd **COOK ISLANDS.**
116 71 2s. blue . . . . 13·00 45·00
131w F 6 2s.6d. brown . . . . . 20·00 23·00
117 71 3s. mauve . . . . . . 13·00 70·00
132 F 6 5s. green . . . . 9·50 22·00
133w 10s. red . . . . 55·00 80·00
134 £1 pink . . . . 60·00 90·00
135w £3 green . . . . 60·00 £160
98b £5 blue £180 £325

1937. Coronation. T **106** of New Zealand optd **COOK IS'DS.**
124 106 1d. red 40 60
125 2½d. blue 80 70
126 6d. orange 80 35

29 King George VI

30 Native Village

1938.
143 29 1s. black and violet . . . . 2·50 2·50
128 30 2s. black and orange . . . 18·00 13·00
145 – 3s. blue and green . . . . 35·00 32·00
DESIGN—HORIZ: 3s. Native canoe.

32 Tropical Landscape

34 Ngatangiia Channel, Rarotonga

1940.
130 32 3d. on 1½d. black & purple 60 60

1946. Peace. Peace stamps of New Zealand of 1946 optd **COOK ISLANDS**.
146 132 1d. green 40 10
147 – 2d. purple 40 50
148 – 6d. brown and red . . . 70 60
149 139 8d. black and red 70 60

1949.
150 34 ½d. violet and brown . . . 10 1·00
151 – 1d. brown and green . . . 3·50 2·00
152 – 2d. brown and red . . . . 2·00 2·00
153 – 3d. green and blue . . . . 2·00 2·00
154 – 5d. green and violet . . . 6·00 1·50
155 – 6d. black and red . . . . 5·50 2·75
156 – 8d. olive and orange . . . 55 3·75
157 – 1s. blue and brown . . . . 4·25 3·75
158 – 2s. brown and red . . . . 3·00 13·00
159 – 3s. blue and green . . . . 10·00 24·00
DESIGNS—HORIZ: 1d. Captain Cook and map of Hervey Is; 2d. Rarotonga and Rev. John Williams; 3d. Aitutaki and palm trees; 5d. Rarotonga Airfield; 6d. Penrhyn village; 8d. Native hut. VERT: 1s. Map and statue of Capt. Cook; 2s. Native hut and palms; 3s. "Matua" (inter-island freighter).

1953. Coronation. As Types of New Zealand but inscr "COOK ISLANDS".
160 164 3d. brown . . . . 1·00 85
161 166 6d. grey . . . . 1·25 1·50

1960. No. 154 surch **1/6**.
162 1s.6d. on 5d. green and violet 50 30

45 Tiare Maori

52 Queen Elizabeth II

55 Rarotonga

56 Eclipse and Palm

1963.
163 45 1d. green and yellow . . . 45 50
164 – 2d. red and yellow 20 50
165 – 3d. yellow, green and violet 70 50
166 – 5d. blue and black . . . . 8·00 2·00
167 – 6d. red, yellow and green 1·00 50
168 – 8d. black and blue . . . . 4·25 1·50
169 – 1s. yellow and green . . . 40 50
170 52 1s.6d. violet . . . . 2·75 2·00
171 – 2s. brown and blue . . . . 1·00 75
172 – 3s. black and green . . . . 1·25 1·00
173 55 5s. brown and blue . . . . 11·00 3·75
DESIGNS—VERT (As Type **45**): 2d. Fishing god; 8d. Long-tailed tuna. HORIZ (As Type **45**): 3d. Frangipani (plant); 5d. White tern ("Love Tern"); 6d. Hibiscus; 1s. Oranges. (As Type **55**): 2s. Island scene; 3s. Administration Centre, Mangaia.

1965. Solar Eclipse Observation, Manuae Island.
174 56 6d. black, yellow and blue 20 10

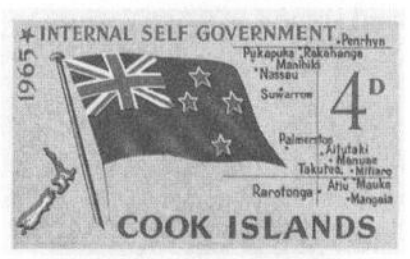

57 N.Z. Ensign and Map

1965. Internal Self-government.
175 57 4d. red and blue 20 10
176 – 10d. multicoloured 20 15
177 – 1s. multicoloured 20 15
178 – 1s.9d. multicoloured . . . 50 1·25
DESIGNS: 10d. London Missionary Society Church; 1s. Proclamation of Cession, 1900; 1s.9d. Nikao School.

1966. Churchill Commemoration. Nos. 171/3 and 175/7 optd **In Memoriam SIR WINSTON CHURCHILL 1874 – 1965**.
179 57 4d. red and blue 75 30
180 – 10d. multicoloured . . . . 1·50 45
181 – 1s. multicoloured . . . . . 1·50 65
182 – 2s. brown and blue . . . . 1·50 1·25
183 – 3s. black and green . . . . 1·50 1·25
184 55 5s. brown and blue . . . . 2·00 1·75

1966. Air. Various stamps optd **Airmail** and Douglas DC-3 airplane or surch in addition.
185 – 6d. red, yell & grn (No. 167) . . . . 1·25 20
186 – 7d. on 8d. blk & bl (No. 168) . . . . 2·00 25
187 – 10d. on 3d. green and violet (No. 165) . . . . 1·00 15
188 – 1s. yellow and green (No. 169) . . . . 1·00 15
189 52 1s.6d. violet . . . . 1·50 1·25
190 – 2s.3d. on 3s. black and green (No. 172) . . . . 1·00 65
191 55 5s. brown and blue . . . . 1·75 1·50
192 – 10s. on 2s. brown and blue (No. 171) . . . . 1·75 13·00
193 – £1 pink (No. 134) . . . . 12·00 17·00

63 "Adoration of the Magi" (Fra Angelico)

1966. Christmas. Multicoloured.
194a 1d. Type **63** 10 10
195a 2d. "The Nativity" (Memling) 20 10
196a 4d. "Adoration of the Wise Men" (Velazquez) 30 15
197a 10d. "Adoration of the Wise Men" (H. Bosch) 30 20
198a 1s.6d. "Adoration of the Shepherds" (J. de Ribera) 40 35

68 Tennis and Queen Elizabeth II

1967. 2nd South Pacific Games, Noumea. Mult.
199 ½d. Type **68** (postage) 10 10
200 1d. Basketball and Games emblem 10 10
201 4d. Boxing and Cook Islands Team badge 10 10
202 7d. Football and Queen Elizabeth II 20 15
203 10d. Running and Games Emblem (air) 20 15
204 2s.3d. Running and Cook Islands' Team badge . . . 25 65

1967. Decimal currency. Various stamps surch.
205 45 1c. on 1d. . . . . 45 1·50
206 – 2c. on 2d. (No. 164) 10 10
207 – 2½c. on 3d. (No. 165) . . . 20 10
209 57 3c. on 4d. 15 10
210 – 4c. on 5d. (No. 166) . . . 8·50 30
211 – 5c. on 6d. (No. 167) . . . 15 10
212 56 5c. on 6d. . . . . 5·00 40
213 – 7c. on 8d. (No. 168) . . . 30 10
214 – 10c. on 1s. (No. 169) . . . 15 10
215 52 15c. on 1s.6d. . . . . . . 2·00 1·00
216 – 30c. on 3s. (No. 172) . . . 20·00 3·75
217 55 50c. on 5s. . . . . 4·00 1·25
218 – $1 and 10s. on 10d. (No. 176) . . . . 17·00 5·50
219 – $2 on £1 (No. 134) . . . . 50·00 70·00
220 – $6 on £3 (No. 135) . . . . 95·00 £130
221 – $10 on £5 (No. 98) £150 £190

75 Village Scene, Cook Islands 1d. Stamp of 1892 and Queen Victoria

1967. 75th Anniv of First Cook Islands Stamps. Multicoloured.
222 1c. (1d.) Type **75** 10 10
223 3c. (4d.) Post Office, Avarua, Rarotonga and Queen Elizabeth II 15 10
224 8c. (10d.) Avarua, Rarotonga and Cook Islands 10d. stamp of 1892 . . . . . . 30 15
225 18c. (1s.9d.) "Moana Roa", (inter-island ship), Douglas DC-3 aircraft, map and Captain Cook . . . . . . 1·40 30
MS226 134 × 109 mm. Nos. 222/5 1·75 2·75
The face values are expressed in decimal currency and in the Sterling equivalent.

79 Hibiscus

81 Queen Elizabeth and Flowers

1967. Flowers. Multicoloured.
227A ½c. Type **79** 10 10
228A 1c. "Hibiscus syriacus" . . 10 10
229A 2c. Frangipani 10 10
230A 2½c. "Clitoria ternatea" . . 20 10
231B 3c. "Suva Queen" 40 10
232A 4c. Water lily (wrongly inscribed "Walter Lily") 70 1·00
233B 4c. Water lily . . . . . . 2·50 10
234B 5c. "Bauhinia bipinnata rosea" 30 10
235B 6c. Yellow hibiscus 30 10
236B 8c. "Allamanda cathartica" 30 10
237B 9c. Stephanotis 30 10
238B 10c. "Poinciana regia flamboyant" 30 10
239A 15c. Frangipani 40 10
240B 20c. Thunbergia . . . . . 3·50 1·25
241A 25c. Canna lily 80 30
242A 30c. "Euphorbia pulcherrima poinsettia" 65 50
243A 50c. "Gardinia taitensis" 1·00 55

244B $1 Queen Elizabeth II . . 1·25 80
245B $2 Queen Elizabeth II . . 2·25 1·50
246A $4 Type **81** . . . . 1·75 4·25
247A $6 Type **81** . . . . 2·00 5·50
247cA $8 Type **81** . . . . 6·00 16·00
248A $10 Type **81** . . . . . . 3·75 12·00

97 "Ia Orana Maria"

1967. Gauguin's Polynesian Paintings.
249 **97** 1c. multicoloured 10 10
250 – 3c. multicoloured 15 10
251 – 5c. multicoloured 20 10
252 – 8c. multicoloured 25 10
253 – 15c. multicoloured 50 15
254 – 22c. multicoloured 65 20
MS255 156 × 132 mm. Nos. 249/54 1·75 1·50
DESIGNS: 3c. "Riders on the Beach"; 5c. "Still Life with Flowers" and inset portrait of Queen Elizabeth; 8c. "Whispered Words"; 15c. "Maternity"; 22c. "Why are you angry?".

98 "The Holy Family" (Rubens)

100 "Matavai Bay, Tahiti" (J. Barralet)

1967. Christmas. Renaissance Paintings.
256 **98** 1c. multicoloured 10 10
257 – 3c. multicoloured 10 10
258 – 4c. multicoloured 10 10
259 – 8c. multicoloured 20 15
260 – 15c. multicoloured 35 15
261 – 25c. multicoloured 40 15
DESIGNS: 3c. "The Epiphany" (Durer); 4c. "The Lucca Madonna" (J. van Eyck); 8c. "The Adora-tion of the Shepherds" (J. da Bassano); 15c. "The Nativity" (El Greco); 25c. "The Madonna and Child" (Correggio).

1968. Hurricane Relief. Nos. 231, 233, 251, 238, 241 and 243/4 optd **HURRICANE RELIEF PLUS** and premium.
262 3c.+1c. multicoloured 15 15
263 4c.+1c. multicoloured 15 15
264 5c.+2c. multicoloured 15 15
265 10c.+2c. multicoloured . . . 15 15
266 25c.+5c. multicoloured . . . 20 20
267 50c.+10c. multicoloured . . . 25 30
268 $1+10c. multicoloured 35 50
On No. 264 silver blocking obliterates the design area around the lettering.

1968. Bicentenary of Captain Cook's First Voyage of Discovery.
269 **100** ½c. mult (postage) 10 10
270 – 1c. multicoloured 15 10
271 – 2c. multicoloured 35 20
272 – 4c. multicoloured 50 20
273 – 6c. multicoloured (air) . . 60 35
274 – 10c. multicoloured 60 35
275 – 15c. multicoloured 70 50
276 – 25c. multicoloured 80 75
DESIGNS—VERT: 1c. "Island of Huaheine" (John Cleveley); 2c. "Town of St. Peter and St. Paul, Kamchatka" (J. Webber); 4c. "The Ice Islands" (Antarctica: W. Hodges). HORIZ: 6c. "Resolution" and "Discovery" (J. Webber); 10c. "The Island of Tahiti" (W. Hodges); 15c. "Karakakooa, Hawaii" (J. Webber); 25c. "The Landing at Middleburg" (J. Sherwin).

102 Dinghy-sailing

1968. Olympic Games, Mexico. Multicoloured.
277 1c. Type **102** 10 10
278 5c. Gymnastics 10 10
279 15c. High-jumping 25 10
280 20c. High-diving 25 10
281 30c. Cycling 60 20
282 50c. Hurdling 50 25

103 "Madonna and Child" (Titian)

1968. Christmas. Multicoloured.
283 1c. Type **103** 10 10
284 4c. "The Holy Family of the Lamb" (Raphael) 15 10
285 10c. "The Madonna of the Rosary" (Murillo) 25 10
286 20c. "Adoration of the Magi" (Memling) 40 10
287 30c. "Adoration of the Magi" (Ghirlandaio) 45 10
MS288 114 × 177 mm. Nos. 283/7 1·25 1·60

104 Campfire Cooking

1969. Diamond Jubilee of New Zealand Scout Movement and 5th National (New Zealand) Jamboree. Multicoloured.
289 ½c. Type **104** 10 10
290 1c. Descent by rope 10 10
291 5c. Semaphore 15 10
292 10c. Tree-planting 20 10
293 20c. Constructing a shelter 25 15
294 30c. Lord Baden-Powell and island scene 45 25

105 High Jumping

1969. 3rd South Pacific Games, Port Moresby. Multicoloured.
295 ½c. Type **105** 10 30
296 ½c. Footballer 10 30
297 1c. Basketball 50 40
298 1c. Weightlifter 50 40
299 4c. Tennis-player 50 50
300 4c. Hurdler 50 50
301 10c. Javelin-thrower 55 50
302 10c. Runner 55 50
303 15c. Golfer . . . . 1·75 1·50
304 15c. Boxer . . . . 1·75 1·50
MS305 174 × 129 mm. Nos. 295/304 7·50 6·00

106 Flowers, Map and Captain Cook (½-size illustration)

1969. South Pacific Conference, Noumea. Mult.
306 5c. Premier Albert Henry . . 30 20
307 10c. Type **106** . . . . 1·00 60
308 25c. Flowers, map and arms of New Zealand 40 60
309 30c. Queen Elizabeth II, map and flowers 40 70

107 "Virgin and Child with Saints Jerome and Dominic" (Lippi)

1969. Christmas. Multicoloured.
310 1c. Type **107** 10 10
311 4c. "The Holy Family" (Fra Bartolomeo) 10 10
312 10c. "The Adoration of the Shepherds" (A. Mengs) . . 15 10
313 20c. "Madonna and Child with Saints" (Robert Campin) 25 20
314 30c. "The Madonna of the Basket" (Correggio) . . . 25 30
MS315 132 × 97 mm. Nos. 310/14 1·00 1·50

108 "The Resurrection of Christ" (Raphael)

115 Mary, Joseph, and Christ in Manger

110 The Royal Family

1970. Easter.
316 **108** 4c. multicoloured 10 10
317 – 8c. multicoloured 10 10
318 – 20c. multicoloured 15 10
319 – 25c. multicoloured 20 10
MS320 132 × 162 mm. Nos. 316/19 1·25 1·25
DESIGNS: "The Resurrection of Christ" by Dirk Bouts (8c.), Altdorfer (20c.), Murillo (25c.).

1970. "Apollo 13". Nos. 233, 236, 239/40, 242 and 245/6 optd **KIA ORANA APOLLO 13 ASTRONAUTS Te Atua to Tatou Irinakianga.**
321 4c. multicoloured 10 10
322 8c. multicoloured 10 10
323 15c. multicoloured 10 10
324 20c. multicoloured 40 15
325 30c. multicoloured 20 20
326 $2 multicoloured 60 90
327a $4 multicoloured . . . . . 1·00 2·75

1970. Royal Visit to New Zealand. Multicoloured.
328 5c. Type **110** 50 30
329 30c. Captain Cook and H.M.S. "Endeavour" . . . 2·00 1·75
330 $1 Royal Visit commemorative coin . . . 3·00 3·00
MS331 145 × 97 mm. Nos. 328/30 9·50 10·00

1970. 5th Anniv of Self-Government. Nos. 328/30 optd **FIFTH ANNIVERSARY SELF-GOVERNMENT AUGUST 1970.**
332 **110** 5c. multicoloured 40 15
333 – 30c. multicoloured 80 35
334 – $1 multicoloured . . . . 1·00 90
On No. 332, the opt is arranged in one line around the frame of the stamp.

1970. Surch **FOUR DOLLARS $4.00.**
335a **81** $4 on $8 multicoloured 1·50 2·00
336a $4 on $10 multicoloured 1·50 1·75

1970. Christmas. Multicoloured.
337 1c. Type **115** 10 10
338 4c. Shepherds and Apparition of the Angel 10 10
339 10c. Mary showing Child to Joseph 15 10
340 20c. The Wise Men bearing Gifts 20 20
341 30c. Parents wrapping Child in swaddling clothes . . . 25 35
MS342 100 × 139 mm. Nos. 337/41 1·00 1·50

1971. Surch **PLUS 20c UNITED KINGDOM SPECIAL MAIL SERVICE.**
343 30c.+20c. (No. 242) 30 50
344 50c.+20c. (No. 243) . . . . 1·00 1·75
The premium of 20c. was to prepay a private delivery service fee in Great Britain during the postal strike. The mail was sent by air to a forwarding address in the Netherlands. No. 343 was intended for ordinary airmail ½ oz. letters, and No. 344 included registration fee.

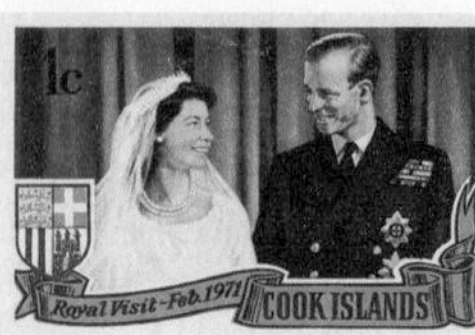

117 Wedding of Princess Elizabeth and Prince Philip

1971. Royal Visit of Duke of Edinburgh. Multicoloured.
345 1c. Type **117** 30 50
346 4c. Queen Elizabeth, Prince Philip, Prince Charles and Princess Anne at Windsor 75 1·10
347 10c. Prince Philip sailing . . 1·25 1·25
348 15c. Prince Philip in polo gear . . . . 1·25 1·25
349 25c. Prince Philip in naval uniform, and Royal Yacht, "Britannia" . . . . 1·50 2·00
MS350 168 × 122 mm. Nos. 345/9 6·50 9·50

1971. 4th South Pacific Games, Tahiti. Nos. 238, 241 and 242 optd **Fourth South Pacific Games Papeete** and emblem or surch also.
351 10c. multicoloured 10 10
352 10c.+1c. multicoloured . . . 10 10
353 10c.+3c. multicoloured . . . 10 10
354 25c. multicoloured 15 10
355 25c.+1c. multicoloured . . . 15 10
356 25c.+3c. multicoloured . . . 15 10
357 30c. multicoloured 15 10
358 30c.+1c. multicoloured . . . 15 10
359 30c.+3c. multicoloured . . . 15 10
The stamps additionally surch 1c. or 3c. helped to finance the Cook Islands' team at the games.

1971. Nos. 230, 233, 236/7 and 239 surch **10c.**
360 10c. on 2½c. multicoloured . . 15 25
361 10c. on 4c. multicoloured . . 15 25
362 10c. on 8c. multicoloured . . 15 25
363 10c. on 9c. multicoloured . . 15 25
364 10c. on 15c. multicoloured . . 15 25

121 "Virgin and Child" (Bellini)

123 St. John

1971. Christmas.
365 **121** 1c. multicoloured 10 10
366 – 4c. multicoloured 10 10
367 – 10c. multicoloured 25 10
368 – 20c. multicoloured 50 20
369 – 30c. multicoloured 50 35
MS370 135 × 147 mm. Nos. 365/9 2·00 3·25
MS371 92 × 98 mm. 50c. + 5c. "The Holy Family in a Garland of Flowers" (Jan Brueghel and Pieter van Avont) (41 × 41 mm) . . . 75 1·40
DESIGNS: Various paintings of the "Virgin and Child" by Bellini. Similar to Type **121**.

1972. 25th Anniv of South Pacific Commission. No. 244 optd **SOUTH PACIFIC COMMISSION FEB. 1947 – 1972.**
372 $1 multicoloured 40 75

1972. Easter. Multicoloured.
373 5c. Type **123** 10 10
374 10c. Christ on the Cross . . 10 10
375 30c. Mary, Mother of Jesus 25 40
MS376 79 × 112 mm. Nos. 373/5 forming triptych of "The Crucifixion" . . . . 1·00 2·25

1972. Hurricane Relief. (a) Nos. 239, 241 and 243 optd **HURRICANE RELIEF PLUS** and premium.
379 15c.+5c. multicoloured . . . 20 20
380 25c.+5c. multicoloured . . . 20 20
382 50c.+10c. multicoloured . . . 25 25

(b) Nos. 373/5 optd **Hurricane Relief Plus** and premium.
377 5c.+2c. multicoloured 15 15
378 10c.+2c. multicoloured . . . 15 15
381 30c.+5c. multicoloured . . . 20 20

126/7 Rocket heading for Moon

1972. Apollo Moon Exploration Flights. Mult.
383 5c. Type **126** 20 15
384 5c. Type **127** 20 15
385 10c. Lunar module and astronaut 20 15
386 10c. Astronaut and experiment 20 15
387 25c. Command capsule and Earth 25 20
388 25c. Lunar Rover 25 20
389 30c. Sikorsky Sea King helicopter . . . . 1·00 40
390 30c. Splashdown . . . . . . 1·00 40
MS391 83 × 205 mm. Nos. 383/90 4·50 6·00

These were issued in horizontal se-tenant pairs of each value, forming one composite design.

1972. Hurricane Relief. Nos. 383/390 surch **HURRICANE RELIEF Plus** and premium.
392 5c.+2c. multicoloured 10 10
393 5c.+2c. multicoloured 10 10
394 10c.+2c. multicoloured . . . 10 10
395 10c.+2c. multicoloured . . . 10 10
396 25c.+2c. multicoloured . . . 15 15
397 25c.+2c. multicoloured . . . 15 15
398 30c.+2c. multicoloured . . . 25 15
399 30c.+2c. multicoloured . . . 25 15
MS400 83 × 205 mm. No. **MS**391 surch 3c. on each stamp . . . 2·50 3·50

129 High-jumping

130 "The Rest on the Flight into Egypt" (Caravaggio)

1972. Olympic Games, Munich. Multicoloured.
401 10c. Type **129** 20 10
402 25c. Running 40 15
403 30c. Boxing 40 20
MS404 88 × 78 mm. 50c. + 5c. Pierre de Coubertin . . . . 1·00 2·00
MS405 84 × 133 mm. Nos. 401/3 1·25 2·00

1972. Christmas. Multicoloured.
406 1c. Type **130** 10 10
407 5c. "Madonna of the Swallow" (Guercino) . . . 25 10
408 10c. "Madonna of the Green Cushion" (Solario) 35 10
409 20c. "Madonna and Child" (di Credi) 55 20
410 30c. "Madonna and Child" (Bellini) 85 30
MS411 141 × 152 mm. Nos. 406/10 3·25 4·00
MS412 101 × 82 mm. 50c. + 5c. "The Holy Night" (Correggio) (31 × 43 mm) . . . . 75 1·50

131 Marriage Ceremony

133 "Noli me Tangere" (Titian)

132 Taro Leaf

1972. Royal Silver Wedding. Each black and silver.
413 5c. Type **131** 25 15
414 10c. Leaving Westminster Abbey 35 25
415 15c. Bride and bridegroom (40 × 41 mm) 45 50
416 30c. Family group (67 × 40 mm) 55 75

1973. Silver Wedding Coinage.
417 **132** 1c. gold, mauve and black 10 10
418 – 2c. gold, blue and black 10 10
419 – 5c. silver, green and black 10 10
420 – 10c. silver, blue and black 20 10
421 – 20c. silver, green and black 30 10
422 – 50c. silver, mauve and black 50 15
423 – $1 silver, blue and black 75 30
DESIGNS—HORIZ (37 × 24 mm): 2c. Pineapple; 5c. Hibiscus. (46 × 30 mm): 10c. Oranges; 20c. White tern; 50c. Striped bonito. VERT: (32 × 55 mm): $1 Tangaroa.

1973. Easter. Multicoloured.
424 5c. Type **133** 15 10
425 10c. "The Descent from the Cross" (Rubens) 20 10
426 30c. "The Lamentation of Christ" (Durer) 25 10
MS427 132 × 67 mm. Nos. 424/6 55 1·25

1973. Easter. Children's Charity. Designs as Nos. 424/6 in separate miniature sheets 67 × 87 mm, each with a face value of 50c. + 5c.
MS428 As Nos. 424/6 Set of 3 sheets 1·00 1·75

134 Queen Elizabeth II in Coronation Regalia

137 The Annunciation

136 Tipairua

1973. 20th Anniv of Queen Elizabeth's Coronation.
429 **134** 10c. multicoloured 50 90
MS430 64 × 89 mm. 50c. as 10c. 2·50 2·25

1973. 10th Anniv of Treaty Banning Nuclear Testing. Nos. 234, 236, 238 and 240/2 optd **TENTH ANNIVERSARY CESSATION OF NUCLEAR TESTING TREATY**.
431 5c. multicoloured 10 10
432 8c. multicoloured 10 10
433 10c. multicoloured 10 10
434 20c. multicoloured 15 15
435 25c. multicoloured 20 15
436 30c. multicoloured 20 15

1973. Maori Exploration of the Pacific. Sailing Craft. Multicoloured.
437 ½c. Type **136** 10 10
438 1c. Wa'a Kaulua 10 10
439 1½c. Tainui 15 10
440 5c. War canoe 30 15
441 10c. Pahi 40 15
442 15c. Amatasi 60 65
443 25c. Vaka 75 80

1973. Christmas. Scene from a 15th-century Flemish "Book of Hours". Multicoloured.
444 1c. Type **137** 10 10
445 5c. The Visitation 10 10
446 10c. Annunciation to the Shepherds 10 10
447 20c. Epiphany 15 10
448 30c. The Slaughter of the Innocents 20 15
MS449 121 × 128 mm. Nos. 444/8 55 1·40
See also No. **MS**454.

138 Princess Anne

140 "Jesus carrying the Cross" (Raphael)

139 Running

1973. Royal Wedding. Multicoloured.
450 25c. Type **138** 20 10
451 30c. Captain Mark Phillips 25 10
452 50c. Princess Anne and Captain Phillips 30 15
MS453 119 × 100 mm. Nos. 450/2 55 35

1973. Christmas. Children's Charity. Designs as Nos. 444/8 in separate miniature sheets 50 × 70 mm, each with a face value of 50c. + 5c.
MS454 As Nos. 444/8 Set of 5 sheets 75 80

1974. British Commonwealth Games, Christchurch. Multicoloured.
455 1c. Diving (vert) 10 10
456 3c. Boxing (vert) 10 10
457 5c. Type 139 . . . . 10 10
458 10c. Weightlifting 10 10
459 30c. Cycling 40 25
MS460 115 × 90 mm. 50c. Discobolus 40 55

1974. Easter. Multicoloured.
461 5c. Type **140** 10 20
462 10c. "The Holy Trinity" (El Greco) 15 20
463 30c. "The Deposition of Christ" (Caravaggio) . . . 25 30
MS464 130 × 70 mm. Nos. 461/3 1·50 70

1974. Easter. Children's Charity. Designs as Nos. 461/3 in separate miniature sheets 59 × 87 mm, each with a face value of 50c. + 5c.
MS465 As Nos. 461/3 Set of 3 sheets 70 1·40

141 Grey Bonnet

142 Queen Elizabeth II

1974. Sea Shells. Multicoloured.
466 ½c. Type **141** 30 10
467 1c. Common Pacific vase . . 30 10
468 1½c. True heart cockle . . . 30 10
469 2c. Terebellum conch 30 10
470 3c. Bat volute 45 10
471 4c. Gibbose conch 50 10
472 5c. Common hairy triton . . 50 10
473 6c. Serpent's head cowrie . . 50 2·00
474 8c. Granulate frog shell . . . 60 10
475 10c. Fly-spotted auger . . . 60 10
476 15c. Episcopan mitre 70 20
477 20c. Butterfly moon . . . . 1·00 20
478 25c. Royal oak scallop . . . 1·00 2·25
479 30c. Soldier cone . . . . . . 1·00 30
480 50c. Textile or cloth of gold cone . . . . 8·50 4·50
481 60c. Red-mouth olive . . . . 8·50 4·50
482 $1 Type **142** . . . . 3·00 4·50
483 $2 Type **142** . . . . 1·75 2·25
484 $4 Queen Elizabeth II and sea shells (60 × 39 mm) . . 2·50 7·00
485 $6 As $4 (60 × 39 mm) . . . 16·00 7·00
486 $8 As $4 (60 × 39 mm) . . . 19·00 8·50
487 $10 As $4 (60 × 39 mm) . . . 22·00 9·00

143 Footballer and Australasian Map

1974. World Cup Football Championship, West Germany. Multicoloured.
488 25c. Type **143** 20 10
489 50c. Map and Munich Stadium 35 25
490 $1 Footballer, stadium and World Cup 55 45
MS491 89 × 100 mm. Nos. 488/90 1·00 2·75

144 Obverse and Reverse of Commemorative $2.50 Silver Coin

146 "Madonna of the Goldfinch" (Raphael)

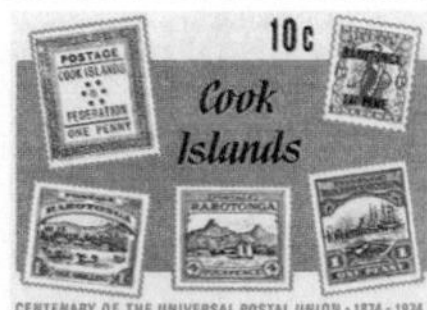
145 Early Stamps of Cook Islands

1974. Bicentenary of Captain Cook's Second Voyage of Discovery.
492 **144** $2.50 silver, black and violet . . . . 12·00 7·00
493 – $7.50 silver, black and green . . . . 20·00 13·00
MS494 73 × 73 mm. Nos. 492/3 35·00 48·00
DESIGN: $7.50, As Type **144** but showing $7.50 coin.

1974. Centenary of U.P.U. Multicoloured.
495 10c. Type **145** 25 15
496 25c. Old landing strip, Rarotonga, and stamp of 1898 . . . . 35 40
497 30c. Post Office, Rarotonga, and stamp of 1920 . . . . 40 40
498 50c. U.P.U. emblem and stamps 40 65
MS499 118 × 79 mm. Nos. 495/8 1·00 1·75

1974. Christmas. Multicoloured.
500 1c. Type **146** 10 10
501 5c. "The Sacred Family" (Andrea del Sarto) 20 10
502 10c. "The Virgin adoring the Child" (Correggio) 25 10
503 20c. "The Holy Family" (Rembrandt) 40 20
504 30c. "The Virgin and Child" (Rogier van der Weyden) 50 30
MS505 114 × 133 mm. Nos. 500/4 1·40 2·25

147 Churchill and Blenheim Palace

1974. Birth Centenary of Sir Winston Churchill. Multicoloured.
506 5c. Type **147** 15 10
507 10c. Churchill and Houses of Parliament 15 10
508 25c. Churchill and Chartwell 25 20
509 30c. Churchill and Buckingham Palace 25 25
510 50c. Churchill and St. Paul's Cathedral 30 50
MS511 108 × 114 mm. Nos. 506/10 1·25 1·00

1974. Christmas. Children's Charity. Designs as Nos. 500/504 in separate miniature sheets 53 × 69 mm, each with a face value of 50c. + 5c.
MS512 As Nos. 500/4 Set of 5 sheets 1·00 1·00

148 Vasco Nunez de Balboa and Discovery of Pacific Ocean (1513)

1975. Pacific Explorers. Multicoloured.
513 1c. Type **148** 15 10
514 5c. Fernando de Magellanes and map (1520) 65 20
515 10c. Juan Sebastian del Cano and "Vitoria" (1520) . . . 1·25 20
516 25c. Friar Andres de Urdaneta and ship (1564–67) . . . . 2·25 75
517 30c. Miguel Lopez de Legazpi and ship (1564–67) . . . . 2·25 80

149 "Apollo" Capsule

1975. "Apollo–Soyuz" Space Project. Mult.
518 25c. Type **149** 40 15
519 25c. "Soyuz" capsule 40 15
520 30c. "Soyuz" crew 45 15
521 30c. "Apollo" crew 45 15
522 50c. Cosmonaut within "Soyuz" 50 25
523 50c. Astronauts within "Apollo" 50 25
MS524 119 × 119 mm. Nos. 518/23 1·50 1·00
These were issued in horizontal se-tenant pairs of each value, forming one composite design.

150 $100 Commemorative Gold Coin

1975. Bicentenary of Captain Cook's 2nd Voyage.
525 **150** $2 brown, gold and violet 2·50 1·75

151 Cook Islands' Flag and Map
152 "Madonna by the Fireside" (R. Campin)

1975. 10th Anniv of Self-government.
526 5c. Type **151** 40 10
527 10c. Premier Sir Albert Henry and flag (vert) 45 10
528 25c. Rarotonga and flag 80 30

1975. Christmas. Multicoloured.
529 6c. Type **152** 15 10
530 10c. "Madonna in the Meadow" (Raphael) 15 10
531 15c. "Madonna of the Oak" (att. Raphael) 25 10
532 20c. "Adoration of the Shepherds" (J. B. Maino) 25 15
533 35c. "The Annunciation" (Murillo) 40 20
MS534 110 × 124 mm. Nos. 529/33 1·10 90

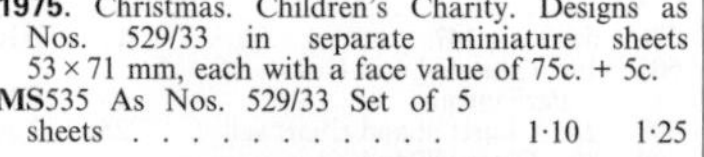

1975. Christmas. Children's Charity. Designs as Nos. 529/33 in separate miniature sheets 53 × 71 mm, each with a face value of 75c. + 5c.
MS535 As Nos. 529/33 Set of 5 sheets 1·10 1·25

153 "Entombment of Christ" (Raphael)

1976. Easter. Multicoloured.
536 7c. Type **153** 30 10
537 15c. "Pieta" (Veronese) 50 15
538 35c. "Pieta" (El Greco) 75 25
MS539 144 × 55 mm. Nos. 536/8 1·50 85

1976. Easter. Children's Charity. Designs as Nos. 536/8 in separate miniature sheets 69 × 69 mm, each with a face value of 60c. + 5c.
MS540 As Nos. 536/8 Set of 3 sheets 1·10 1·40

154 Benjamin Franklin and H.M.S. "Resolution"

1976. Bicent of American Revolution. Mult.
541 $1 Type **154** 6·00 1·50
542 $2 Captain Cook and H.M.S. "Resolution" 8·00 2·50
MS543 118 × 58 mm. $3 Cook, Franklin and H.M.S. "Resolution" (74 × 31 mm) 13·00 6·50

1976. Visit of Queen Elizabeth to U.S.A. Nos. 541/2 optd **Royal Visit July 1976**.
544 **154** $1 multicoloured 4·00 1·50
545 – $2 multicoloured 6·00 2·50
MS546 $3 Cook, Franklin and H.M.S. "Resolution" 7·00 5·50

156 Hurdling
157 "The Visitation"

1976. Olympic Games, Montreal. Multicoloured.
547 7c. Type **156** 20 10
548 7c. Hurdling (value on left) 20 10
549 15c. Hockey (value on right) 40 15
550 15c. Hockey (value on left) 40 15
551 30c. Fencing (value on right) 40 15
552 30c. Fencing (value on left) 40 15
553 35c. Football (value on right) 40 20
554 35c. Football (value on left) 40 20
MS555 104 × 146 mm. Nos. 547/54 3·50 2·00

1976. Christmas. Renaissance Sculptures. Mult.
556 6c. Type **157** 10 10
557 10c. "Adoration of the Shepherds" 10 10
558 15c. "Adoration of the Shepherds" (different) 15 10
559 20c. "The Epiphany" 20 20
560 35c. "The Holy Family" 25 25
MS561 116 × 110 mm. Nos. 556/60 1·00 1·75

1976. Christmas. Children's Charity. Designs as Nos. 556/60 in separate miniature sheets 66 × 80 mm, each with a face value of 75c. + 5c.
MS562 As Nos. 556/60 Set of 5 sheets 1·10 1·10

158 Obverse and Reverse of $5 Mangaia Kingfisher Coin

1976. National Wildlife and Conservation Day.
563 **158** $1 multicoloured 1·00 1·00

159 Imperial State Crown

1977. Silver Jubilee. Multicoloured.
564 25c. Type **159** 40 50
565 25c. The Queen with regalia 40 50
566 50c. Westminster Abbey 50 65
567 50c. Coronation coach 50 65
568 $1 The Queen and Prince Philip 80 90
569 $1 Royal Visit, 1974 80 90
MS570 130 × 136 mm. As Nos. 564/9 (borders and "COOK ISLANDS" in a different colour) 2·25 2·00

160 "Christ on the Cross"
161 "Virgin and Child" (Memling)

1977. Easter. 400th Birth Anniv of Rubens. Multicoloured.
571 7c. Type **160** 35 10
572 15c. "Christ on the Cross" 55 15
573 35c. "The Deposition of Christ" 1·10 30
MS574 118 × 65 mm. Nos. 571/3 1·40 1·60

1977. Easter. Children's Charity. Designs as Nos. 571/3 in separate miniature sheets 60 × 79 mm, each with a face value of 60c. + 5c.
MS575 As Nos. 571/3 Set of 3 sheets 1·00 1·00

1977. Christmas. Multicoloured.
576 6c. Type **161** 25 10
577 10c. "Madonna and Child with Saints and Donors" (Memling) 25 10
578 15c. "Adoration of the Kings" (Geertgen) 35 10
579 20c. "Virgin and Child with Saints" (Crivelli) 45 15
580 35c. "Adoration of the Magi" (16th century Flemish school) 60 20
MS581 118 × 111 mm. Nos. 576/80 1·40 1·75

1977. Christmas. Children's Charity. Designs as Nos. 576/80 in separate miniature sheets 69 × 69 mm, each with a face value of 75c. + 5c.
MS582 As Nos. 576/80 Set of 5 sheets 1·00 1·25

162 Obverse and Reverse of $5 Cook Islands Swiftlet Coin

1977. National Wildlife and Conservation Day.
583 **162** $1 multicoloured 1·00 65

163 Captain Cook and H.M.S. "Resolution" (from paintings by N. Dance and H. Roberts)

1978. Bicent of Discovery of Hawaii. Mult.
584 50c. Type **163** 1·00 60
585 $1 Earl of Sandwich and Cook landing at Owhyhee (from paintings by Thomas Gainsborough and J. Cleveley) 1·45 75
586 $2 Obverse and reverse of $200 coin and Cook monument, Hawaii 1·60 1·25
MS587 118 × 95 mm. Nos. 584/6 5·00 7·50

164 "Pieta" (Van der Weyden)

1978. Easter. Paintings from the National Gallery, London. Multicoloured.
588 15c. Type **164** 40 25
589 35c. "The Entombment" (Michelangelo) 50 40
590 75c. "The Supper at Emmaus" (Caravaggio) 75 65
MS591 114 × 96 mm. Nos. 588/90 1·50 2·00

1978. Easter. Children's Charity. Designs as Nos. 588/90 in separate miniature sheets, 85 × 72 mm, each with a face value of 60c. + 5c.
MS592 As Nos. 588/90 Set of 3 sheets 1·10 1·10

165 Queen Elizabeth II
169 "The Virgin and Child" (Van Der Weyden)

168 Obverse and Reverse of Cook Islands Warblers $5 Coin

1978. 25th Anniv of Coronation. Multicoloured.
593 50c. Type **165** 25 30
594 50c. The Lion of England 25 30
595 50c. Imperial State Crown 25 30
596 50c. Statue of Tangaroa (god) 25 30
597 70c. Type **165** 25 30
598 70c. Sceptre with Cross 25 30
599 70c. St. Edward's Crown 25 30
600 70c. Rarotongan staff god 25 30
MS601 103 × 142 mm. Nos. 593/600* 1·00 1·50
*In No. **MS**601 the designs of Nos. 595 and 599 are transposed.

1978. Nos. 466, 468, 473/4 and 478/82 surch.
602 5c. on 1½c. True heart cockle 60 10
603 7c. on ½c. Type **141** 65 15
604 10c. on 6c. Serpent's-head cowrie 70 15
605 10c. on 8c. Granulate frog shell 70 15
606 15c. on ½c. Type **141** 70 20
607 15c. on 25c. Royal oak scallop 70 20
608 15c. on 30c. Soldier cone 70 20
609 15c. on 50c. Textile or cloth of gold cone 70 20
610 15c. on 60c. Red-mouth olive 70 20
611 17c. on ½c. Type **141** 90 25
612 17c. on 50c. Textile or cloth of gold cone 90 25

1978. 250th Birth Anniv of Captain James Cook. Nos. 584/6 optd **1728 250th ANNIVERSARY OF COOK'S BIRTH 1978**.
613 50c. Type **163** 2·00 75
614 $1 Earl of Sandwich and Cook landing at Owhyhee 2·25 1·00
615 $2 $200 commemorative coin and Cook monument, Hawaii 2·50 2·00
MS616 Nos. 613/15 14·00 17·00

1978. National Wildlife and Conservation Day.
617 **168** $1 multicoloured 1·00 1·00

1978. Christmas. Paintings. Multicoloured.
618 15c. Type **169** 45 15
619 17c. "The Virgin and Child" (Crivelli) 45 20
620 35c. "The Virgin and Child" (Murillo) 80 35
MS621 107 × 70 mm. Nos. 618/20 1·50 1·50

1979. Christmas. Children's Charity. Designs as Nos. 618/20 in separate miniature sheets 57 × 87 mm, each with a face value of 75c. +5c.
MS622 As Nos. 618/20 Set of 3 sheets 1·00 1·00

170 Virgin with Body of Christ
171 "Captain Cook" (James Weber)

1979. Easter. Details of Painting "Descent" by Gaspar de Crayar. Multicoloured.
623 10c. Type **170** 25 10
624 12c. St. John 30 20
625 15c. Mary Magdalene 35 25
626 20c. Weeping angels 45 30
MS627 83 × 100 mm. As Nos. 623/6, but each with a charity premium of 2c. 65 75
Stamps from No. **MS**627 are slightly smaller, 32 × 40 mm, and are without borders.

1979. Death Bicentenary of Captain Cook. Mult.
628 20c. Type **171** 40 20
629 30c. H.M.S. "Resolution" 50 35
630 35c. H.M.S. "Royal George" (ship of the line) 50 45
631 50c. "Death of Captain Cook" (George Carter) 55 60
MS632 78 × 112 mm. Nos. 628/31 1·75 1·25
Stamps from No. **MS**632 have black borders.

172 Post-Rider
174 Brother and Sister

1979. Death Centenary of Sir Rowland Hill. Mult.
633 30c. Type **172** 20 20
634 30c. Mail coach 20 20
635 30c. Automobile 20 20
636 30c. Diesel train 20 20
637 35c. "Cap-Hornier" (full-rigged ship) 20 20
638 35c. River steamer 20 20
639 35c. "Deutschland" (liner) 20 20
640 35c. "United States" (liner) 20 20
641 50c. Balloon "Le Neptune" 30 25
642 50c. Junkers F13 airplane 30 25

643 50c. Airship "Graf Zeppelin" 30 25
644 50c. Concorde 30 25
MS645 132 × 104 mm. Nos. 633/44 3·75 4·00

1979. Nos. 466, 468 and 481 surch.
646 6c. on ½c. Type **141** 20 30
647 10c. on 1½c. Cockle shell 25 20
648 15c. on 60c. Olive shell 40 40

1979. International Year of the Child. Mult.
649 30c. Type **174** 25 25
650 50c. Boy with tree drum 40 40
651 65c. Children dancing 50 50
MS652 102 × 75 mm. As Nos. 649/51, but each with a charity premium of 5c. 1·00 1·50
Designs for stamps from No. **MS**652 are as Nos. 649/51 but have I.Y.C. emblem in red.

175 "Apollo 11" Emblem

177 Glass Christmas Tree Ornaments

176 Obverse and Reverse of $5 Rarotongan Fruit Dove Coin

1979. 10th Anniv of "Apollo 11" Moon Landing. Multicoloured.
653 30c. Type **175** 40 60
654 50c. "Apollo 11" crew 50 80
655 60c. Neil Armstrong on the Moon 65 90
656 65c. Splashdown recovery 70 1·00
MS657 119 × 105 mm. Nos. 653/6 2·75 2·50

1979. National Wildlife and Conservation Day.
658 **176** $1 multicoloured 1·60 2·50

1979. Christmas. Multicoloured.
659 6c. Type **177** (postage) 10 10
660 10c. Hibiscus and star 10 10
661 12c. Poinsettia, bells and candle 15 10
662 15c. Poinsettia leaves and Tiki (god) 15 15
663 20c. Type **177** (air) 20 15
664 25c. As No. 660 25 20
665 30c. As No. 661 30 25
666 35c. As No. 662 35 30

1980. Christmas. As Nos. 659/66 but with charity premium.
667 6c.+2c. Type **177** (postage) 10 10
668 10c.+2c. Hibiscus and star 15 15
669 12c.+2c. Poinsettia, bells and candle 15 20
670 15c.+2c. Poinsettia leaves and Tiki (god) 15 20
671 20c.+4c. Type **177** (air) 15 25
672 25c.+4c. As No. 660 15 25
673 30c.+4c. As No. 661 20 30
674 35c.+4c. As No. 662 25 35

178 "Flagellation"

181 Queen Elizabeth the Queen Mother

179 Dove with Olive Twig

1980. Easter. Illustrations by Gustav Dore. Each gold and brown.
675 20c. Type **178** 25 30
676 20c. "Crown of Thorns" 25 30
677 30c. "Jesus Insulted" 35 35
678 30c. "Jesus Falls" 35 35
679 35c. "The Crucifixion" 40 35
680 35c. "The Descent from the Cross" 40 35
MS681 120 × 110 mm. As Nos. 675/80, but each with a charity premium of 2c. 1·10 1·50

1980. Easter. Children's Charity. Designs as Nos. 675/80 in separate miniature sheets 60 × 71 mm, each with a face value of 75c. + 5c.
MS682 As Nos. 675/80 Set of 6 sheets 1·00 1·50

1980. 75th Anniv of Rotary International. Mult.
683 30c. Type **179** 35 35
684 35c. Hibiscus flower 40 40
685 50c. Ribbons 50 50
MS686 72 × 113 mm. Nos. 683/5, but each with a charity premium of 3c. 1·10 1·50

1980. "Zeapex 80" International Stamp Exhibition, Auckland. Nos. 633/44 optd **ZEAPEX STAMP EXHIBITION—AUCKLAND 1980** and New Zealand 1865 1s. Stamp.
687 30c. Type **172** 35 25
688 30c. Mail coach 35 25
689 30c. Automobile 35 25
690 30c. Diesel train 35 25
691 35c. "Cap-Hornier" (full-rigged ship) 40 30
692 35c. River steamer 40 30
693 35c. "Deutschland" (liner) 40 30
694 35c. "United States" (liner) 40 30
695 50c. Balloon "Le Neptune" 60 35
696 50c. Junkers "F13" airplane 60 35
697 50c. Airship"Graf Zeppelin" 60 35
698 50c. Concorde 60 35
MS699 132 × 104 mm. Nos. 687/98 6·00 6·00

1980. 80th Birthday of the Queen Mother.
701 **181** 50c. multicoloured 1·00 1·00
MS702 64 × 78 mm. **181** $2 multicoloured 1·25 1·75

182 Satellites orbiting Moon

1980. 350th Death Anniv of Johannes Kepler (astronomer). Multicoloured.
703 12c. Type **182** 50 35
704 12c. Space-craft orbiting Moon 50 35
705 50c. Space-craft orbiting Moon (different) 1·00 80
706 50c. Astronaut and Moon vehicle 1·00 80
MS707 122 × 122 mm. Nos. 703/6 2·75 2·75

183 Scene from novel "From the Earth to the Moon"

184 "Siphonogorgia"

1980. 75th Death Anniv of Jules Verne (author).
708 **183** 20c. multicoloured 45 35
709 – 20c. multicoloured 45 35
710 – 30c. multicoloured (mauve background) 55 45
711 – 30c. multicoloured (blue background) 55 45
MS712 121 × 122 mm. Nos. 708/11 2·75 2·25
DESIGNS: Showing scenes from the novel "From the Earth to the Moon".

1980. Corals (1st series). Multicoloured.
713 1c. Type **184** 30 30
714 1c. "Pavona praetorta" 30 30
715 1c. "Stylaster echinatus" 30 30
716 1c. "Tubastraea" 30 30
717 3c. "Millepora alcicornis" 30 30
718 3c. "Junceella gemmacea" 30 30
719 3c. "Fungia fungites" 30 30
720 3c. "Heliofungia actiniformis" 30 30
721 4c. "Distichopora violacea" 30 30
722 4c. "Stylaster" 30 30
723 4c. "Gonipora" 30 30
724 4c. "Caulastraea echinulata" 30 30
725 5c. "Ptilosarcus gurneyi" 30 30
726 5c. "Stylophora pistillata" 30 30
727 5c. "Melithaea squamata" 30 30
728 5c. "Porites andrewsi" 30 30
729 6c. "Lobophyllia bemprichii" 30 30
730 6c. "Palauastrea ramosa" 30 30
731 6c. "Bellonella indica" 30 30
732 6c. "Pectinia alcicornis" 30 30
733 8c. "Sarcophyton digitatum" 30 30
734 8c. "Melithaea albitincta" 30 30
735 8c. "Plerogyra sinuosa" 30 30
736 8c. "Dendropyllia gracilis" 30 30
737 10c. As Type **184** 30 30
738 10c. As No. 714 30 30
739 10c. As No. 715 30 30
740 10c. As No. 716 30 30
741 12c. As No. 717 30 30
742 12c. As No. 718 30 30
743 12c. As No. 719 30 30
744 12c. As No. 720 30 30
745 15c. As No. 721 30 30
746 15c. As No. 722 30 30
747 15c. As No. 723 30 30
748 15c. As No. 724 30 30
749 20c. As No. 725 35 30
750 20c. As No. 726 35 30
751 20c. As No. 727 35 30
752 20c. As No. 728 35 30
753 25c. As No. 729 35 30
754 25c. As No. 730 35 30
755 25c. As No. 731 35 30
756 25c. As No. 732 35 30
757 30c. As No. 733 40 30
758 30c. As No. 734 40 30
759 30c. As No. 735 40 30
760 30c. As No. 736 40 30
761 35c. Type **184** 45 35
762 35c. As No. 714 45 35
763 35c. As No. 715 45 35
764 35c. As No. 716 45 35
765 50c. As No. 717 65 75
766 50c. As No. 718 65 75
767 50c. As No. 719 65 75
768 50c. As No. 720 65 75
769 60c. As No. 721 75 75
770 60c. As No. 722 75 75
771 60c. As No. 723 75 75
772 60c. As No. 724 75 75
773 70c. As No. 725 2·50 75
774 70c. As No. 726 2·50 75
775 70c. As No. 727 2·50 75
776 70c. As No. 728 2·50 75
777 80c. As No. 729 2·50 80
778 80c. As No. 730 2·50 80
779 80c. As No. 731 2·50 80
780 80c. As No. 732 2·50 80
781 $1 As No. 733 3·75 1·00
782 $1 As No. 734 3·75 1·00
783 $1 As No. 735 3·75 1·00
784 $1 As No. 736 3·75 1·00
785 $2 As No. 723 12·00 3·00
786 $3 As No. 720 12·00 3·00
787 $4 As No. 726 4·50 14·00
788 $6 As No. 715 6·00 17·00
789 $10 As No. 734 27·00 38·00
Nos. 761/74 are 30 × 40 mm, and Nos. 785/9, which include a portrait of Queen Elizabeth II in each design, are 55 × 35 mm.
See also Nos. 966/94.

185 Annunciation

187 Prince Charles

186 "The Crucifixion" (from book of Saint-Amand)

1980. Christmas. Scenes from 13th-century French Prayer Books. Multicoloured.
801 15c. Type **185** 25 15
802 30c. The Visitation 35 25
803 40c. The Nativity 45 30
804 50c. The Epiphany 60 40
MS805 89 × 114 mm. Nos. 801/4 1·50 1·50

1981. Christmas. Children's Charity. Designs as Nos. 801/4 in separate miniature sheets 55 × 68 mm, each with a face value of 75c +5c. Imperf.
MS806 As Nos. 801/4 Set of 4 sheets 1·50 1·50

1981. Easter. Illustrations from 12th-century French Prayer Books. Multicoloured.
807 15c. Type **186** 30 30
808 25c. "Placing in Tomb" (from book of Ingeburge) 35 35
809 40c. "Mourning at the Sepulchre" (from book of Ingeburge) 45 45
MS810 72 × 116 mm. As Nos. 807/9, but each with a charity premium of 2c. 1·00 1·00

1981. Easter. Children's Charity. Designs as Nos. 807/9 in separate miniature sheets 64 × 53 mm, each with a face value of 75c. + 5c. Imperf.
MS811 As Nos. 807/9 Set of 3 sheets 1·10 1·10

1981. Royal Wedding. Multicoloured.
812 $1 Type **187** 50 1·10
813 $2 Prince Charles and Lady Diana Spencer 60 1·40
MS814 106 × 59 mm. Nos. 812/13 1·10 2·50

188 Footballers

1981. World Cup Football Championship, Spain (1982). Designs showing footballers. Mult.
815 20c. Type **188** 40 20
816 20c. Figures to right of stamp 40 20
817 30c. Figures to left 50 30
818 30c. Figures to right 50 30
819 35c. Figures to left 50 35
820 35c. Figures to right 50 35
821 50c. Figures to left 65 45
822 50c. Figures to right 65 45
MS823 180 × 94 mm. As Nos. 815/22, but each with a charity premium of 3c. 6·00 8·00
The two designs of each value were printed together, se-tenant, in horizontal pairs throughout the sheet, forming composite designs.

1981. International Year for Disabled Persons. Nos. 812/13 surch **+5c.**
824 $1+5c. Type **187** 55 1·75
825 $2+5c. Prince Charles and Lady Diana Spencer 70 2·50
MS826 106 × 59 mm. $1 + 10c, $2 + 10c. As Nos. 824/5 1·00 4·00

190 "Holy Virgin with Child"

1982. Christmas. Details of Paintings by Rubens. Multicoloured.
827 8c. Type **190** 55 20
828 15c. "Coronation of St. Catherine" 65 35
829 40c. "Adoration of the Shepherds" 90 80
830 50c. "Adoration of the Magi" 1·00 1·00
MS831 86 × 110 mm. As Nos. 827/30, but each with a charity premium of 3c. 3·50 4·00

1982. Christmas. Children's Charity. Designs as Nos. 827/30 in separate miniature sheets 62 × 78 mm, each with a face value of 75c. +5c.
MS832 As Nos. 827/30 Set of 4 sheets 3·50 4·00

191 Princess of Wales (inscr "21st Birthday")

1982. 21st Birthday of Princess of Wales. Multicoloured.
833 $1.25 Type **191** 2·25 1·50
834 $1.25 As Type **191**, but inscr "1 July 1982" 2·25 1·50
835 $2.50 Princess (inscr "21st Birthday") (different) 3·00 2·25
836 $2.50 As No. 835, but inscr "1 July 1982" 3·00 2·25
MS837 92 × 72 mm. $1.25, Type **191**; $2.50, As No. 835. Both inscribed "21st Birthday 1 July 1982" 7·00 4·50

1982. Birth of Prince William of Wales (1st issue). Nos. 812/13 optd.
838 $1 Type **187** 1·50 1·25
839 $1 Type **187** 1·50 1·25
840 $2 Prince Charles and Lady Diana Spencer 2·50 2·00
841 $2 Prince Charles and Lady Diana Spencer 2·50 2·00
MS842 106 × 59 mm. Nos. 812/13 optd **21 JUNE 1982. ROYAL BIRTH** 4·00 4·00
OPTS: Nos. 838 and 840, **ROYAL BIRTH 21 JUNE 1982**; 839 and 841, **PRINCE WILLIAM OF WALES**.

1982. Birth of Prince William of Wales (2nd issue). As Nos. 833/6 but with changed inscriptions. Multicoloured.
843 $1.25 As Type **191**, inscribed "Royal Birth" 2·25 1·00
844 $1.25 As Type **191**, inscribed "21 June 1982" 2·25 1·00
845 $2.50 As No. 835, inscribed "Royal Birth" 2·75 1·50
846 $2.50 As No. 835, inscribed "21 June 1982" 2·75 1·50
MS847 92 × 73 mm. $1.25, As Type **191**; $2.50, As No. 835. Both inscribed "Royal Birth 21 June 1982". 6·00 2·75

193 "The Accordionist" (inscr "Serenade") **194** Franklin D. Roosevelt

1982. Norman Rockwell (painter) Commemoration. Multicoloured.

848 5c. Type **193** 15 10
849 10c. "Spring" (inscr "The Hikers") 20 15
850 20c. "The Doctor and the Doll" 25 25
851 30c. "Home from Camp" . . 25 30

1982. Air. American Anniversaries. Multicoloured.

852 60c. Type **194** . . . . 1·50 80
853 80c. Benjamin Franklin . . . 1·75 1·00
854 $1.40 George Washington . . 2·00 2·25
MS855 116 × 60 mm. Nos. 852/4 4·75 3·00
ANNIVERSARIES: 60c. Roosevelt (birth centenary); 80c. "Articles of Peace" negotiations bicentenary; $1.40, Washington (250th birth anniv).

195 "Virgin with Garlands" (detail, Rubens) and Princess Diana with Prince William

1982. Christmas.

856 **195** 35c. multicoloured . . . . 1·75 70
857 – 48c. multicoloured . . . . 2·25 1·50
858 – 60c. multicoloured . . . . 2·50 2·00
859 – $1.70 multicoloured . . . 3·50 5·00
MS860 104 × 83 mm. 60c. × 4. Designs, each 27 × 32 mm, forming complete painting "Virgin with Garlands" . . . . 7·00 8·50
DESIGNS: 48c. to $1.70, Different details from Ruben's painting "Virgin with Garlands".

196 Princess Diana and Prince William

1982. Christmas. Birth of Prince William of Wales. Children's Charity. Sheet 73 × 59 mm.

MS861 **196** 75c. + 5c. multicoloured 2·75 4·00
No. **MS**861 comes with 4 different background designs showing details from painting "Virgin with Garlands" (Rubens).

197 Statue of Tangaroa **198** Scouts using Map and Compass

1983. Commonwealth Day. Multicoloured.

862 60c. Type **197** 70 50
863 60c. Rarotonga oranges . . . 70 50
864 60c. Rarotonga Airport . . . 70 50
865 60c. Prime Minister Sir Thomas Davis 70 50

1983. 75th Anniv of Boy Scout Movement and 125th Anniv of Lord Baden-Powell (founder). Multicoloured.

866 12c. Type **198** 55 20
867 12c. Hiking 55 20
868 36c. Campfire cooking . . . 80 40
869 36c. Erecting tent 80 40
870 48c. Hauling on rope . . . . 1·00 55
871 48c. Using bos'n's chair . . . 1·00 55
872 60c. Digging hole for sapling 1·00 70
873 60c. Planting sapling . . . . 1·00 70
MS874 161 × 132 mm. As Nos. 866/73, but each with a premium of 2c. . . . . 3·00 3·50

1983. 15th World Scout Jamboree, Alberta, Canada. Nos. 866/73 optd **XV WORLD JAMBOREE** (Nos. 875, 877, 879, 881) or **ALBERTA, CANADA 1983** (others).

875 12c. Type **198** 60 20
876 12c. Hiking 60 20
877 36c. Campfire cooking . . . 90 40
878 36c. Erecting tent 90 40
879 48c. Hauling on rope . . . . 1·10 55
880 48c. Using bos'n's chair . . . 1·10 55
881 60c. Digging hole for sapling 1·25 70
882 60c. Planting sapling . . . . 1·25 70
MS883 161 × 132 mm. As Nos. 875/82, but each with a premium of 2c. . . . . 2·75 3·25

1983. Various stamps surch.

884 – 18c. on 8c. mult (No. 733) 75 50
885 – 18c. on 8c. mult (No. 734) 75 50
886 – 18c. on 8c. mult (No. 735) 75 50
887 – 18c. on 8c. mult (No. 736) 75 50
888 – 36c. on 15c. mult (No. 745) . . . . . . 1·25 85
889 – 36c. on 15c. mult (No. 746) . . . . . . 1·25 85
890 – 36c. on 15c. mult (No. 747) . . . . . . 1·25 85
891 – 36c. on 15c. mult (No. 748) . . . . . . 1·25 85
892 – 36c. on 30c. mult (No. 757) . . . . . . 1·25 85
893 – 36c. on 30c. mult (No. 758) . . . . . . 1·25 85
894 – 36c. on 30c. mult (No. 759) . . . . . . 1·25 85
895 – 36c. on 30c. mult (No. 760) . . . . . . 1·25 85
896 **184** 36c. on 35c. mult . . . . 1·25 85
897 – 36c. on 35c. mult (No. 762) . . . . . . 1·25 85
898 – 36c. on 35c. mult (No. 763) . . . . . . 1·25 85
899 – 36c. on 35c. mult (No. 764) . . . . . . 1·25 85
900 – 48c. on 25c. mult (No. 753) . . . . . . 1·50 1·25
901 – 48c. on 25c. mult (No. 754) . . . . . . 1·50 1·25
902 – 48c. on 25c. mult (No. 755) . . . . . . 1·50 1·25
903 – 48c. on 25c. mult (No. 756) . . . . . . 1·50 1·25
904 – 72c. on 70c. mult (No. 773) . . . . . . 2·50 1·75
905 – 72c. on 70c. mult (No. 774) . . . . . . 2·50 1·75
906 – 72c. on 70c. mult (No. 775) . . . . . . 2·50 1·75
907 – 72c. on 70c. mult (No. 776) . . . . . . 2·50 1·75
908 – 96c. on $1.40 multicoloured (No. 854) 2·00 2·00
909 – 96c. on $2 mult (No. 813) 8·50 5·50
910 – 96c. on $2.50 mult (No. 835) . . . . . . 3·00 3·00
911 – 96c. on $2.50 mult (No. 836) . . . . . . 3·00 3·00
912 – $5.60 on $6 mult (No. 788) . . . . . . 23·00 18·00
913 – $5.60 on $10 mult (No. 789) . . . . . . 23·00 18·00

202 Union Flag

1983. Cook Islands Flags and Ensigns. Multicoloured.

914 6c. Type **202** (postage) . . . 70 70
915 6c. Group Federal flag . . . 70 70
916 12c. Rarotonga ensign . . . 85 85
917 12c. Flag of New Zealand . . 85 85
918 15c. Cook Islands' flag (1973–79) 85 85
919 15c. Cook Islands' National flag 85 85
920 20c. Type **202** (air) 85 85
921 20c. Group Federal flag . . . 85 85
922 30c. Rarotonga ensign . . . 95 95
923 30c. Flag of New Zealand . . 95 95
924 35c. Cook Islands' flag (1973–1979) . . . . . . 1·00 1·00
925 35c. Cook Islands' National flag . . . . 1·00 1·00
MS926 Two sheets, each 132 × 120 mm. (a) Nos. 914/19. (b) Nos. 920/5. P 13 . . . . . . 3·50 4·50

203 Dish Aerial, Satellite Earth Station **204** "La Belle Jardiniere"

1983. World Communications Year.

927 – 36c. multicoloured 75 80
928 – 48c. multicoloured 90 95
929 **203** 60c. multicoloured . . . . 1·25 1·50
930 – 96c. multicoloured . . . . 1·90 3·25
MS931 90 × 65 mm. $2 multicoloured . . . . 2·25 2·50
DESIGNS: 36, 48, 96c. Various satellites.

1983. Christmas. 500th Birth Anniv of Raphael. Multicoloured.

932 12c. Type **204** 80 55
933 18c. "Madonna and Child with five Saints" . . . . . 1·10 70
934 36c. "Madonna and Child with St. John" . . . . . 1·75 1·75
935 48c. "Madonna of the Fish" 2·25 2·25
936 60c. "Madonna of the Baldacchino" . . . . . . 2·75 3·75
MS937 139 × 113 mm. As Nos. 932/6, but each with a premium of 3c. . . . . 2·00 2·50

1983. Christmas. 500th Birth Anniv of Raphael. Children's Charity. Designs as Nos. 932/6 in separate miniature sheets 66 × 82 mm., each with a face value of 85c. + 5c.

MS938 As Nos. 932/6 Set of 5 sheets 4·50 3·75

205 Montgolfier Balloon, 1783

1984. Bicentenary (1983) of Manned Flight. Mult.

939 36c. Type **205** 50 50
940 48c. Ascent of Adorne, Strasbourg, 1784 . . . . . 60 60
941 60c. Balloon driven by sails, 1785 . . . . 75 90
942 72c. Ascent of man on horse, 1798 . . . . 90 1·25
943 96c. Godard's aerial acrobatics, 1850 . . . . . 1·00 1·60
MS944 104 × 85 mm. $2.50, Blanchard and Jeffries crossing Channel, 1785 . . . . 1·50 2·25
MS945 122 × 132 mm. As Nos. 939/43, but each with a premium of 5c. . . . . 1·50 2·25

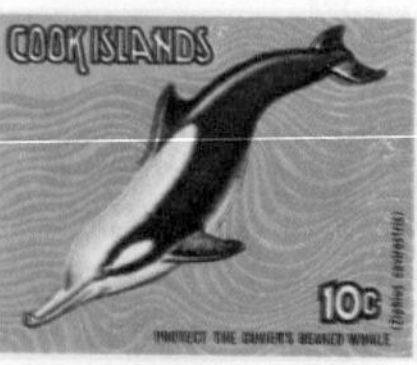

206 Cuvier's Beaked Whale

1984. Save the Whale. Multicoloured.

946 10c. Type **206** 50 50
947 18c. Risso's dolphin 75 75
948 20c. True's beaked whale . . 75 75
949 24c. Long-finned pilot whale 80 80
950 30c. Narwhal 90 90
951 36c. White whale . . . . . . 1·10 1·10
952 42c. Common dolphin . . . 1·40 1·40
953 48c. Commerson's dolphin 1·60 1·60
954 60c. Bottle-nosed dolphin . . 1·90 1·90
955 72c. Sowerby's beaked whale 2·00 2·00
956 96c. Common porpoise . . . 2·50 2·50
957 $2 Boutu . . . . 3·25 3·25

207 Athens, 1896 **208** "Siphonogorgia"

1984. Olympic Games, Los Angeles. Multicoloured.

958 18c. Type **207** 60 40
959 24c. Paris, 1900 . . . . . . 65 45
960 36c. St. Louis, 1904 . . . . . 75 55
961 48c. London, 1948 . . . . . 85 65
962 60c. Tokyo, 1964 . . . . . . 95 75
963 72c. Berlin, 1936 . . . . . . 1·00 90
964 96c. Rome, 1960 . . . . . . 1·10 1·00
965 $1.20 Los Angeles, 1930 . . . 1·25 1·25

1984. Corals (2nd series). New designs and Nos. 785/9 surch. Multicoloured.

966 1c. Type **208** 30 10
967 2c. "Millepora alcicornis" . . 30 10
968 3c. "Distichopora violacea" 40 10
969 5c. "Ptilosarcus gurneyi" . . 45 10
970 10c. "Lobophyllia bemprichii" 50 10
971 12c. "Sarcophyton digitatum" 60 15
972 14c. "Pavona praetorta" . . 60 15
973 18c. "Junceella gemmacea" 70 20
974 20c. "Stylaster" 70 20
975 24c. "Stylophora pistillata" 70 20
976 30c. "Palauastrea ramosa" 1·00 25
977 36c. "Melithaea albitincta" 1·25 30
978 40c. "Stylaster echinatus" . . 1·25 30
979 42c. "Fungia fungites" . . . 1·25 35
980 48c. "Gonipora" . . . . . . 1·25 35
981 50c. "Melithaea squamata" 1·75 45
982 52c. "Bellonella indica" . . . 1·75 60
983 55c. "Plerogyra sinuosa" . . 1·75 65
984 60c. "Tubastraea" . . . . . 1·90 70
985 70c. "Heliofungia actiniformis" . . . . . . 2·00 85
986 85c. "Caulastraea echinulata" 2·25 1·00
987 96c. "Porites andrewsi" . . . 2·50 1·10
988 $1.10 "Pectinia alcicornis" . . 2·50 1·40
989 $1.20 "Dendrophyllia gracilis" . . . . 2·50 1·50
990 $3.60 on $2 "Gonipora" (55 × 35 mm) . . . . . . 5·50 4·00
991 $4.20 on $3 "Heliofungia actiniformis" (55 × 35 mm) 6·00 5·00
992 $5 on $4 "Stylophora pistillata" (55 × 35 mm) . . 6·50 5·50
993 $7.20 on $6 "Stylaster echinatus" (55 × 35 mm) . . 8·50 8·50
994 $9.60 on $10 "Melithaea albitincta" (55 × 35 mm) . . 10·00 10·00

1984. Olympic Gold Medal Winners. Nos. 963/5 optd.

995 72c. Berlin, 1936 (optd **Equestrian Team Dressage Germany**) 60 65
996 96c. Rome, 1960 (optd **Decathlon Daley Thompson Great Britain**) 80 85
997 $1.20 Los Angeles, 1930 (optd **Four Gold Medals Carl Lewis U.S.A.**) . . . . 1·00 1·10

211 Captain Cook's Cottage, Melbourne

1984. "Ausipex" International Stamp Exhibition, Melbourne. Multicoloured.

998 36c. Type **211** . . . . . . 2·00 1·50
999 48c. H.M.S. "Endeavour" careened for Repairs" (Sydney Parkinson) . . . 3·25 2·50
1000 60c. "Cook's landing at Botany Bay" (E. Phillips Fox) . . . . 3·50 3·25
1001 $2 "Captain James Cook" (John Webber) . . . . . 4·25 4·25
MS1002 140 × 100 mm. As Nos. 998/1001, but each with a face value of 90c. . . . . . . 7·50 7·50

1984. Birth of Prince Henry. Nos. 812 and 833/6 variously optd or surch also (No. 1007).

1003 $1.25 Optd **Commemorating- 15 Sept. 1984** (No. 833) 1·75 1·25
1004 $1.25 Optd **Birth H.R.H. Prince Henry** (No. 834) 1·75 1·25
1005 $2.50 Optd **Commemorating- 15 Sept. 1984** (No. 835) 2·50 2·25
1006 $2.50 Optd **Birth H.R.H. Prince Henry** (No. 836) 2·50 2·25
1007 $3 on $1 Optd **Royal Birth Prince Henry 15 Sept. 1984** (No. 812) . . . . . 4·50 4·50

213 "Virgin on Throne with Child" (Giovanni Bellini) **214** Downy Woodpecker

1984. Christmas. Multicoloured.
1008 36c. Type **213** 1·75 40
1009 48c. "Virgin and Child" (anonymous, 15th century) 1·90 60
1010 60c. "Virgin and Child with Saints" (Alvise Vivarini) 2·00 80
1011 96c. "Virgin and Child with Angels" (H. Memling) 2·25 1·60
1012 $1.20 "Adoration of Magi" (G. Tiepolo) 2·50 2·00
MS1013 120 × 113 mm. As Nos. 1008/12, but each with a premium of 5c. 4·25 3·25

1984. Christmas. Designs as Nos. 1008/12 in separate miniature sheets 62 × 76 mm, each with a face value of 95c. + 5c.
MS1014 As Nos. 1008/12 Set of 5 sheets 5·00 5·50

1985. Birth Bicentenary of John J. Audubon (ornithologist). Designs showing original paintings. Multicoloured.
1015 30c. Type **214** 2·50 1·25
1016 55c. Black-throated blue warbler 2·75 1·75
1017 65c. Yellow-throated warbler 3·00 2·25
1018 75c. Chestnut-sided warbler 3·25 2·75
1019 95c. Dickcissel 3·25 3·00
1020 $1.15 White-crowned sparrow 3·25 3·50
MS1021 Three sheets, each 76 × 75 mm. (a) $1.30, Red-cockaded woodpecker. (b) $2.80, Seaside sparrow. (c) $5.30, Zenaida dove Set of 3 sheets 13·00 8·50

215 "The Kingston Flyer" (New Zealand)

1985. Famous Trains. Multicoloured.
1022 20c. Type **215** 35 50
1023 55c. Class 625 locomotive (Italy) 45 85
1024 65c. Gotthard electric locomotive (Switzerland) 50 90
1025 75c. Union Pacific diesel locomotive No. 6900 (U.S.A.) 55 1·10
1026 95c. Canadian National "Super Continental" type diesel locomotive (Canada) 55 1·25
1027 $1.15 TGV express train (France) 60 1·50
1028 $2.20 "The Flying Scotsman" (Great Britain) 65 2·50
1029 $3.40 "Orient Express" 70 3·75
No. 1023 is inscribed "640" in error.

216 "Helena Fourment" (Peter Paul Rubens) **217** "Lady Elizabeth 1908" (Mabel Hankey)

1985. International Youth Year. Multicoloured.
1030 55c. Type **216** 3·50 2·75
1031 65c. "Vigee-Lebrun and Daughter" (E. Vigee-Lebrun) 3·75 3·25
1032 75c. "On the Terrace" (Renoir) 4·00 3·50
1033 $1.30 "Young Mother Sewing" (M. Cassatt) 5·00 7·50
MS1034 103 × 106 mm. As Nos. 1030/3, but each with a premium of 10c. 8·50 5·50

1985. Life and Times of Queen Elizabeth the Queen Mother. Designs showing paintings. Multicoloured.
1035 65c. Type **217** 40 50
1036 75c. "Duchess of York, 1923" (Savely Sorine) 45 60
1037 $1.15 "Duchess of York, 1925" (Philip de Laszlo) 55 85
1038 $2.80 "Queen Elizabeth, 1938" (Sir Gerald Kelly) 1·40 2·25
MS1039 69 × 81 mm. $5.30, As $2.80 2·50 3·50
For these designs in a miniature sheet, each with a face value of 55c., see No. **MS**1079.

218 Albert Henry (Prime Minister, 1965–78) **219** Golf

1985. 20th Anniv of Self-government. Mult.
1040 30c. Type **218** 80 60
1041 50c. Sir Thomas Davis (Prime Minister, 1978–April 1983 and from November 1983) 1·25 1·25
1042 65c. Geoffrey Henry (Prime Minister, April–November 1983) 1·50 1·75
MS1043 134 × 70 mm. As Nos. 1040/2, but each with a face value of 55c. 1·75 2·00

1985. South Pacific Mini Games, Rarotonga. Multicoloured.
1044 55c. Type **219** 4·00 3·50
1045 65c. Rugby 4·00 4·00
1046 75c. Tennis 5·50 6·00
MS1047 126 × 70 mm. Nos. 1044/6, but each with a premium of 10c. 11·00 13·00

220 Sea Horse, Gearwheel and Leaves **221** "Madonna of the Magnificat"

1985. Pacific Conference, Rarotonga.
1048 **220** 55c. black, gold and red 1·10 65
1049 – 65c. black, gold and violet 1·25 80
1050 – 75c. black, gold and green 1·40 1·10
MS1051 126 × 81 mm. As Nos. 1048/50, but each with a face value of 50c. 1·60 2·00
No. 1048 shows the South Pacific Bureau for Economic Co-operation logo and is inscribed "S.P.E.C. Meeting, 30 July–1 August 1985, Rarotonga". No. 1049 also shows the S.P.E.C. logo, but is inscribed "South Pacific Forum, 4–6 August 1985, Rarotonga". No. 1050 shows the Pacific Islands Conference logo and the inscription "Pacific Islands Conference, 7–10 August 1985, Rarotonga".

1985. Christmas. Virgin and Child Paintings by Botticelli. Multicoloured.
1052 55c. Type **221** 2·50 1·25
1053 65c. "Madonna with Pomegranate" 2·75 1·25
1054 75c. "Madonna and Child with Six Angels" 3·00 1·60
1055 95c. "Madonna and Child with St. John" 3·25 2·00
MS1056 90 × 104 mm. As Nos. 1052/5, but each with a face value of 50c. 6·00 3·75

1985. Christmas. Virgin and Child Paintings by Botticelli. Square designs (46 × 46 mm) as Nos. 1052/5 in separate miniature sheets, 50 × 51 mm, with face values of $1.20, $1.45, $2.20 and $2.75. Imperf.
MS1057 As Nos. 1052/5 Set of 4 sheets 9·00 11·00

222 "The Eve of the Deluge" (John Martin) **223** Queen Elizabeth II

1986. Appearance of Halley's Comet. Paintings. Multicoloured.
1058 55c. Type **222** 1·50 1·25
1059 65c. "Lot and his Daughters" (Lucas van Leyden) 1·60 1·40
1060 75c. "Auspicious Comet" (from treatise c. 1857) 1·75 1·50
1061 $1.25 "Events following Charles I" (Herman Saftleven) 2·50 2·25
1062 $2 "Ossian receiving Napoleonic Officers" (Anne Louis Girodet-Trioson) 3·25 3·00
MS1063 130 × 100 mm. As Nos. 1058/62, but each with a face value of 70c. 5·50 7·00
MS1064 84 × 63 mm. $4 "Halley's Comet of 1759 over the Thames" (Samuel Scott) 8·50 9·50

1986. 60th Birthday of Queen Elizabeth II. Designs showing formal portraits.
1065 **223** 95c. multicoloured 1·50 1·50
1066 – $1.25 multicoloured 1·75 1·75
1067 – $1.50 multicoloured 2·00 2·00
MS1068 Three sheets, each 44 × 75 mm. As Nos. 1065/7, but with face values of $1.10, $1.95 and $2.45 Set of 3 sheets 10·00 11·00

224 U.S.A. 1847 Franklin 5c. Stamp and H.M.S. "Resolution" at Rarotonga

1986. "Ameripex '86" International Exhibition, Chicago. Multicoloured.
1069 $1 Type **224** 5·50 3·75
1070 $1.50 Chicago 3·50 4·25
1071 $2 1975 definitive $2, Benjamin Franklin and H.M.S. "Resolution" 6·50 5·50

225 Head of Statue of Liberty **226** Miss Sarah Ferguson

1986. Centenary of Statue of Liberty. Multicoloured.
1072 $1 Type **225** 75 85
1073 $1.25 Hand and torch of Statue 90 1·10
1074 $2.75 Statue of Liberty 2·00 2·50

1986. Royal Wedding. Multicoloured.
1075 $1 Type **226** 1·25 1·25
1076 $2 Prince Andrew 2·00 2·50
1077 $3 Prince Andrew and Miss Sarah Ferguson (57 × 31 mm) 2·50 3·50

1986. "Stampex '86" Stamp Exhibition, Adelaide. No. **MS**1002 optd **Stampex 86 Adelaide**.
MS1078 90c. × 4 multicoloured 7·00 6·50
The "Stampex '86" exhibition emblem is also overprinted on the sheet margin.

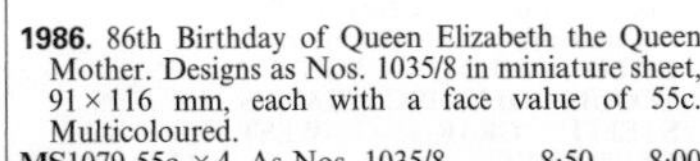

1986. 86th Birthday of Queen Elizabeth the Queen Mother. Designs as Nos. 1035/8 in miniature sheet, 91 × 116 mm, each with a face value of 55c. Multicoloured.
MS1079 55c. × 4. As Nos. 1035/8 8·50 8·00

228 "Holy Family with St. John the Baptist and St. Elizabeth"

1986. Christmas. Paintings by Rubens. Mult.
1080 55c. Type **228** 2·00 1·00
1081 $1.30 "Virgin with the Garland" 3·00 2·75
1082 $2.75 "Adoration of the Magi" (detail) 6·00 7·00
MS1083 140 × 100 mm. As Nos. 1080/2, but each size 36 × 46 mm with a face value of $2.40 12·00 13·00
MS1084 80 × 70 mm. $6.40, As No. 1081 but size 32 × 50 mm 12·00 13·00

1986. Visit of Pope John Paul II to South Pacific. Nos. 1080/2 surch **FIRST PAPAL VISIT TO SOUTH PACIFIC POPE JOHN PAUL II NOV 21-24 1986**.
1085 55c.+10c. Type **228** 2·75 2·00
1086 $1.30+10c. "Virgin with the Garland" 3·50 2·50
1087 $2.75+10c. "Adoration of the Magi" (detail) 6·00 3·75
MS1088 140 × 100 mm. As Nos. 1085/7, but each size 36 × 46 mm with a face value of $2.40 + 10c. 12·00 13·00
MS1089 80 × 70 mm. $6.40 + 50c. As No. 1086 but size 32 × 50 mm 12·00 13·00

1987. Various stamps surch. (a) On Nos. 741/56, 761/76 and 787/8.
1090 10c. on 15c. "Distichopora violacea" 20 20
1091 10c. on 15c. "Stylaster" 20 20
1092 10c. on 15c. "Gonipora" 20 20
1093 10c. on 15c. "Caulastraea echinulata" 20 20
1094 10c. on 25c. "Lobophyllia bemprichii" 20 20
1095 10c. on 25c. "Palauastrea ramosa" 20 20
1096 10c. on 25c. "Bellonella indica" 20 20
1097 10c. on 25c. "Pectinia alcicornis" 20 20
1098 18c. on 12c. "Millepora alcicornis" 25 25
1099 18c. on 12c. "Junceella gemmacea" 25 25
1100 18c. on 12c. "Fungia fungites" 25 25
1101 18c. on 12c. "Heliofungia actiniformis" 25 25
1102 18c. on 20c. "Ptilosarcus gurneyi" 25 25
1103 18c. on 20c. "Stylophora pistillata" 25 25
1104 18c. on 20c. "Melithaea squamata" 25 25
1105 18c. on 20c. "Porites andrewsi" 25 25
1106 55c. on 35c. Type **184** 40 45
1107 55c. on 35c. "Pavona praetorta" 40 45
1108 55c. on 35c. "Stylaster echinatus" 40 45
1109 55c. on 35c. "Tubastraea" 40 45
1110 65c. on 50c. As No. 1098 45 50
1111 65c. on 50c. As No. 1099 45 50
1112 65c. on 50c. As No. 1100 45 50
1113 65c. on 50c. As No. 1101 45 50
1114 65c. on 60c. As No. 1090 45 50
1115 65c. on 60c. As No. 1091 45 50
1116 65c. on 60c. As No. 1092 45 50
1117 65c. on 60c. As No. 1093 45 50
1118 75c. on 70c. As No. 1102 55 60
1119 75c. on 70c. As No. 1103 55 60
1120 75c. on 70c. As No. 1104 55 60
1121 75c. on 70c. As No. 1105 55 60
1122 $6.40 on $4 "Stylophora pistillata" 4·50 4·75
1123 $7.20 on $6 "Stylaster echinatus" 5·00 5·25

(b) On Nos. 812/13.
1124 $9.40 on $1 Type **187** 15·00 16·00
1125 $9.40 on $2 Prince Charles and Lady Diana Spencer 15·00 16·00

(c) On Nos. 835/6.
1126 $9.40 on $2.50 Princess of Wales (inscribed "21st Birthday") 15·00 16·00
1127 $9.40 on $2.50 As No. 1126, but inscribed "1 July 1982" 15·00 16·00

(d) On Nos. 966/8, 971/2, 975, 979/80, 982 and 987/9.
1128 5c. on 1c. Type **208** 20 20
1129 5c. on 2c. "Millepora alcicornis" 20 20
1130 5c. on 3c. "Distichopora violacea" 20 20
1131 5c. on 12c. "Sarcophyton digitatum" 20 20
1132 5c. on 14c. "Pavona praetorta" 20 20
1133 18c. on 24c. "Stylophora pistillata" 25 25

1134 55c. on 52c. "Bellonella indica" 40 45
1135 65c. on 42c. "Fungia fungites" 45 50
1136 75c. on 48c. "Gonipora" 55 60
1137 95c. on 96c. "Porites andrewsi" 70 75
1138 95c. on $1.10 "Pectinia alcicornis" 70 75
1139 95c. on $1.20 "Dendrophyllia gracilis" 70 75

(e) On Nos. 998/1001.
1140 $1.30 on 36c. Type **211** 2·00 2·00
1141 $1.30 on 48c. "The "Endeavour" careened for Repairs" (Sydney Parkinson) 2·00 2·00
1142 $1.30 on 60c. "Cook's landing at Botany Bay" (E. Phillips Fox) 2·00 2·00
1143 $1.30 on $2 "Captain James Cook" (John Webber) 2·00 2·00

(f) On Nos. 1065/7.
1144 **223** $2.30 on 95c. mult 7·00 8·00
1145 – $2.80 on $1.25 mult 7·00 8·00
1146 – $2.80 on $1.50 mult 7·00 8·00

(g) On Nos. 1075/7.
1147 $2.80 on $1 Type **226** 6·00 6·50
1148 $2.80 on $2 Prince Andrew 6·00 6·50
1149 $2.80 on $3 Prince Andrew and Miss Sarah Ferguson (57 × 31 mm) 6·00 6·50

1987. Various stamps surch.
1150 $2.80 on $2 "Gonipora" (No. 785) 3·00 3·25
1151 $5 on $3 "Heliofungia actiniformis" (No. 786) 5·00 5·50
1152 $9.40 on $10 "Melithaea albitincta" (No. 789) 8·00 9·00
1153 $9.40 on $1 Type **187** (No. 838) 8·00 9·00
1154 $9.40 on $1 Type **187** (No. 839) 8·00 9·00
1155 $9.40 on $2 Prince Charles and Lady Diana Spencer (No. 840) 8·00 9·00
1156 $9.40 on $2 Prince Charles and Lady Diana Spencer (No. 841) 8·00 9·00
MS1157 106 × 59 mm. $9.20 on $1 Type **187**; $9.20 on $2 Prince Charles and Lady Diana Spencer 12·00 15·00

1987. Hurricane Relief. Various stamps surch **HURRICANE RELIEF** and premium. (a) On Nos. 1035/8.
1158 65c.+50c. Type **217** 1·00 1·00
1159 75c.+50c. "Duchess of York, 1923" (Savely Sorine) 1·10 1·10
1160 $1.15+50c. "Duchess of York, 1925" (Philip de Laszlo) 1·40 1·50
1161 $2.80+50c. "Queen Elizabeth, 1938" (Sir Gerald Kelly) 2·50 3·25
MS1162 69 × 81 mm. $5.30 + 50c. As $2.80 + 50c. 5·00 6·50

(b) On Nos. 1058/62.
1163 55c.+50c. Type **222** 85 85
1164 65c.+50c. "Lot and his Daughters" (Lucas van Leyden) 90 90
1165 75c.+50c. "Auspicious Comet" (from treatise c. 1587) 1·10 1·10
1166 $1.50+50c. "Events following Charles I" (Herman Saftleven) 1·40 1·50
1167 $2+50c. "Ossian receiving Napoleonic Officers" (Anne Louis Girodet-Trioson) 2·00 2·50

(c) On Nos. 1065/7.
1168 **223** 95c.+50c. mult 1·25 1·25
1169 – $1.25+50c. mult 1·50 1·50
1170 – $1.50+50c. mult 1·60 1·60
MS1171 Three sheets, each 44 × 75 mm. As Nos. 1168/70, but with face values of $1.10 + 50c., $1.95 + 50c., $2.45 + 50c. Set of 3 sheets 11·00 13·00

(d) On Nos. 1069/71.
1172 $1+50c. Type **224** 4·00 4·00
1173 $1.50+50c. Chicago 2·25 2·75
1174 $2+50c. 1975 definitive $2, Benjamin Franklin and H.M.S. "Resolution" 4·25 4·25

(e) On Nos. 1072/4.
1175 $1+50c. Type **225** 1·00 1·25
1176 $1.25+50c. Hand and torch of Statue 1·25 1·50
1177 $2.75+50c. Statue of Liberty 2·25 3·00

(f) On Nos. 1075/7.
1178 $1+50c. Type **226** 1·25 1·25
1179 $2+50c. Prince Andrew 2·00 2·25
1180 $3+50c. Prince Andrew and Miss Sarah Ferguson (57 × 31 mm) 2·75 3·25

(g) On Nos. 1080/2.
1181 55c.+50c. Type **228** 85 85
1182 $1.30+50c. "Virgin with the Garland" 1·50 1·75
1183 $2.75+50c. "The Adoration of the Magi" (detail) 2·50 3·00
MS1184 140 × 100 mm. As Nos. 1181/3, but each size 36 × 46 mm with a face value of $2.40 + 50c. 13·00 15·00
MS1185 80 × 70 mm. $6.40 + 50c. As No. 1182, but size 32 × 50 mm. 8·50 9·50

(h) On Nos. 1122, 1134/7 and 1150/1.
1186 55c.+25c. on 52c. "Bellonella indica" 80 80
1187 65c.+25c. on 42c. "Fungia fungites" 90 90
1188 75c.+25c. on 48c. "Gonipora" 1·00 1·00
1189 95c.+25c. on 96c. "Porites andrewsi" 1·25 1·25
1190 $2.80+50c. on $2 "Gonipora" 3·50 3·50
1191 $5+50c. on $3 "Heliofungia actiniformis" 5·50 6·00
1192 $6.40+50c. on $4 "Stylophora pistillata" 7·00 8·00

1987. Royal Ruby Wedding. Nos. 484 and 787 optd **ROYAL WEDDING FORTIETH ANNIVERSARY.**
1193 $4 Queen Elizabeth II and sea shells 5·50 5·50
1194 $4 Queen Elizabeth II and "Stylophora pistillata" 5·50 5·50

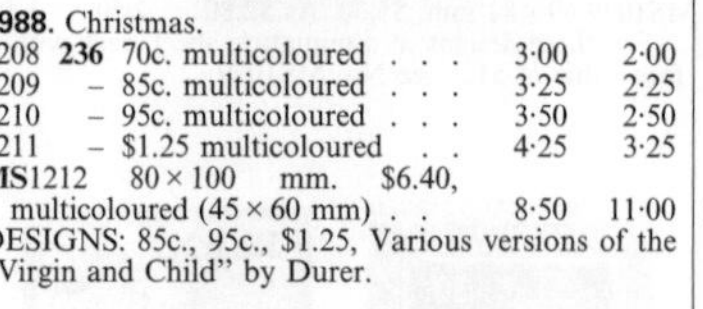
233 "The Holy Family" (Rembrandt)

1987. Christmas. Different paintings of the Holy Family by Rembrandt.
1195 **233** $1.25 multicoloured 2·50 2·25
1196 – $1.50 multicoloured 3·00 2·50
1197 – $1.95 multicoloured 4·50 4·50

234 Olympic Commemorative $50 Coin

1988. Olympic Games, Seoul. Multicoloured.
1200 $1.50 Type **234** 4·50 2·50
1201 $1.50 Olympic torch and Seoul Olympic Park 4·50 2·50
1202 $1.50 Steffi Graf playing tennis and Olympic medal 4·50 2·50
MS1203 131 × 81 mm. $10 Combined design as Nos. 1200/2, but measuring 114 × 47 mm. 11·00 12·00
Nos. 1200/2 were printed together, se-tenant, forming a composite design.

1988. Olympic Tennis Medal Winners, Seoul. Nos. 1200/2 optd.
1204 $1.50 Type **234** (optd **MILOSLAV MECIR CZECHOSLOVAKIA GOLD MEDAL WINNER MEN'S TENNIS**) 4·00 2·25
1205 $1.50 Olympic torch and Seoul Olympic Park (optd **TIM MAYOTTE UNITED STATES GABRIELA SABATINI ARGENTINA SILVER MEDAL WINNERS**) 4·00 2·25
1206 $1.50 Steffi Graf playing tennis and Olympic medal (optd **GOLD MEDAL WINNER STEFFI GRAF WEST GERMANY**) 4·00 2·25
MS1207 131 × 81 mm. $10 Combined design as Nos. 1200/2, but measuring 114 × 47 mm (optd **GOLD MEDAL WINNER SEOUL OLYMPIC GAMES STEFFI GRAF – WEST GERMANY**) 12·00 11·00

236 "Virgin and Child"

1988. Christmas.
1208 **236** 70c. multicoloured 3·00 2·00
1209 – 85c. multicoloured 3·25 2·25
1210 – 95c. multicoloured 3·50 2·50
1211 – $1.25 multicoloured 4·25 3·25
MS1212 80 × 100 mm. $6.40, multicoloured (45 × 60 mm) 8·50 11·00
DESIGNS: 85c., 95c., $1.25, Various versions of the "Virgin and Child" by Durer.

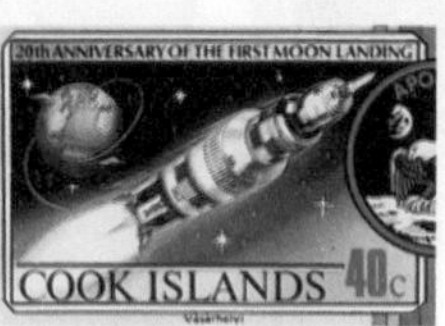

237 "Apollo 11" leaving Earth

1989. 20th Anniv of First Manned Landing on Moon. Multicoloured.
1213 40c. Type **237** 1·75 1·75
1214 40c. Lunar module over Moon 1·75 1·75
1215 55c. Aldrin stepping onto Moon 2·00 2·00
1216 55c. Astronaut on Moon 2·00 2·00
1217 65c. Working on lunar surface 2·25 2·25
1218 65c. Conducting experiment 2·25 2·25
1219 75c. "Apollo 11" leaving Moon 2·25 2·25
1220 75c. Splashdown in South Pacific 2·25 2·25
MS1221 108 × 91 mm. $4.20, Astronauts on Moon 5·00 6·00

238 Rarotonga Flycatcher

1989. Endangered Birds of the Cook Islands. Multicoloured.
1222 15c. Type **238**(postage) 2·00 2·00
1223 20c. Pair of Rarotonga flycatchers 2·00 2·00
1224 65c. Pair of Rarotonga fruit doves 2·75 2·75
1225 70c. Rarotonga fruit dove 2·75 2·75
MS1226 Four sheets, each 70 × 53 mm. As Nos. 1222/5, but with face values of $1, $1.25, $1.50, $1.75 and each size 50 × 32 mm (air) Set of 4 sheets 10·00 11·00

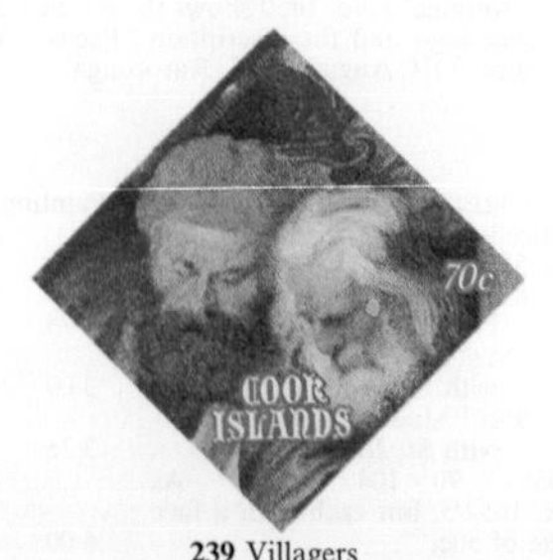

239 Villagers

1989. Christmas. Details from "Adoration of the Magi" by Rubens. Multicoloured.
1227 70c. Type **239** 1·40 1·40
1228 85c. Virgin Mary 1·60 1·60
1229 95c. Christ Child 1·75 2·00
1230 $1.50 Boy with gift 2·00 3·00
MS1231 85 × 120 mm. $6.40, "Adoration of the Magi" (45 × 60 mm) 12·00 14·00

240 Reverend John Williams and L.M.S. Church

1990. Christianity in the Cook Islands. Multicoloured.
1232 70c. Type **240** 85 85
1233 85c. Mgr. Bernardine Castanie and Roman Catholic Church 1·00 1·10
1234 95c. Elder Osborne Widstoe and Mormon Church 1·10 1·40
1235 $1.60 Dr. J. E. Caldwell and Seventh Day Adventist Church 1·90 2·25
MS1236 90 × 90 mm. As Nos. 1232/5, but each with a face value of 90c. 4·75 6·00

241 "Woman writing a Letter" (Terborch)

243 Queen Elizabeth the Queen Mother

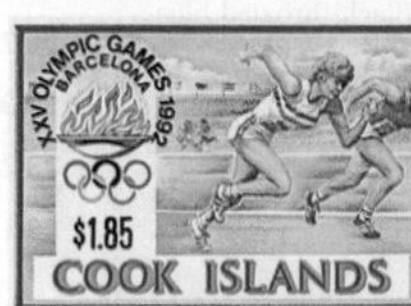

242 Sprinting

1990. 150th Anniv of the Penny Black. Designs showing paintings. Multicoloured.
1237 85c. Type **241** 1·25 1·25
1238 $1.15 "George Gisze" (Holbein the Younger) 1·60 1·75
1239 $1.55 "Mrs. John Douglas" (Gainsborough) 2·00 2·50
1240 $1.85 "Portrait of a Gentleman" (Durer) 2·50 3·00
MS1241 82 × 150 mm. As Nos. 1237/40, but each with a face value of $1.05 9·00 11·00

1990. Olympic Games, Barcelona, and Winter Olympic Games, Albertville (1992) (1st issue). Multicoloured.
1242 $1.85 Type **242** 5·50 5·50
1243 $1.85 Cook Islands $50 commemorative coin 5·50 5·50
1244 $1.85 Skiing 5·50 5·50
MS1245 109 × 52 mm. $6.40, As Nos. 1242/4, but size 80 × 26 mm. 14·00 15·00
See also Nos. 1304/10.

1990. 90th Birthday of Queen Elizabeth the Queen Mother.
1246 **243** $1.85 multicoloured 6·00 5·00
MS1247 66 × 101 mm. **243** $6.40, multicoloured 12·00 14·00

244 "Adoration of the Magi" (Memling)

1990. Christmas. Religious Paintings. Mult.
1248 70c. Type **244** 2·00 1·75
1249 85c. "Holy Family" (Lotto) 2·25 1·90
1250 95c. "Madonna and Child with Saints John and Catherine" (Titian) 2·50 2·25
1251 $1.50 "Holy Family" (Titian) 4·00 6·00
MS1252 98 × 110 mm. $6.40, "Madonna and Child enthroned, surrounded by Saints" (Vivarini) (vert) 12·00 13·00

1990. "Birdpex '90" Stamp Exhibition, Christchurch, New Zealand. No. **MS**1226 optd **Birdpex '90**.
MS1253 Four sheets, each 70 × 53 mm. As Nos. 1222/5, but with face values of $1, $1.25, $1.50, $1.75 and each size 50 × 32 mm Set of 4 sheets 15·00 17·00

246 Columbus (engraving by Theodoro de Bry) **249** Red-breasted Wrasse

248 "Adoration of the Child" (G. delle Notti)

1991. 500th Anniv (1992) of Discovery of America by Columbus (1st issue).
1254 **246** $1 multicoloured . . . . 3·00 3·00
See also No. 1302.

1991. 65th Birthday of Queen Elizabeth II. No. 789 optd **65TH BIRTHDAY**.
1255 $10 "Melithaea albitincta" 14·00 15·00

1991. Christmas. Religious Paintings. Mult.
1256 70c. Type **248** . . . . . . 2·50 1·75
1257 85c. "The Birth of the Virgin" (B. Murillo) . . . 2·75 2·00
1258 $1.15 "Adoration of the Shepherds" (Rembrandt) 3·25 3·25
1259 $1.50 "Adoration of the Shepherds" (L. le Nain) 4·75 7·00
MS1260 79 × 103 mm. $6.40, "Madonna and Child" (Lippi) (vert) . . . . 12·00 13·00

1992. Reef Life (1st series). Multicoloured with white borders.
1261 5c. Type **249** . . . . 70 1·00
1262 10c. Blue sea star . . . . . 70 1·00
1263 15c. Bicoloured angelfish ("Black and gold angelfish") . . . . 75 1·25
1264 20c. Spotted pebble crab . . 85 1·25
1265 25c. Black-tipped grouper ("Black-tipped cod") . . . 85 1·25
1266 30c. Spanish dancer . . . . 85 1·25
1267 50c. Regal angelfish . . . . 1·25 1·25
1268 80c. Big-scaled soldierfish ("Squirrel fish") . . . . . 1·50 1·50
1269 85c. Red pencil sea urchin 3·25 2·75
1270 90c. Red-spotted rainbowfish . . . . 4·50 2·75
1271 $1 Cheek-lined wrasse . . . 4·50 2·75
1272 $2 Long-nosed butterflyfish 5·00 4·25
1273 $3 Red-spotted rainbowfish 3·75 5·00
1274 $5 Blue sea-star . . . . . . 4·75 7·50
1275 $7 "Pygoplites diacanthus" 10·00 14·00
1276 $10 Spotted pebble crab . . 13·00 15·00
1277 $15 Red pencil sea urchin 19·00 21·00
The 25, 50c., $1 and $2 include a silhouette of the Queen's head.
For designs in a larger size, 40 × 30 mm, and with brown borders, see Nos. 1342/52.

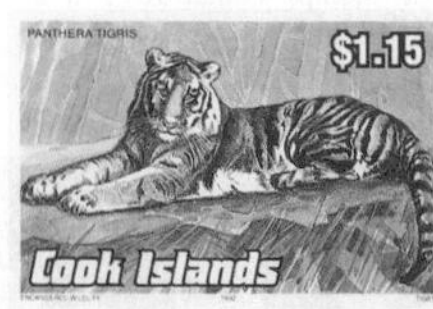

250 Tiger

1992. Endangered Wildlife. Multicoloured.
1279 $1.15 Type **250** . . . . . . 1·25 1·25
1280 $1.15 Indian elephant . . . 1·25 1·25
1281 $1.15 Brown bear . . . . . 1·25 1·25
1282 $1.15 Black rhinoceros . . . 1·25 1·25
1283 $1.15 Chimpanzee . . . . . 1·25 1·25
1284 $1.15 Argali . . . . 1·25 1·25
1285 $1.15 Heaviside's dolphin 1·25 1·25
1286 $1.15 Eagle owl . . . . . . 1·75 1·25
1287 $1.15 Bee hummingbird . . 1·75 1·25
1288 $1.15 Puma . . . . 1·25 1·25
1289 $1.15 European otter . . . 1·25 1·25
1290 $1.15 Red kangaroo . . . . 1·25 1·25
1291 $1.15 Jackass penguin . . . 1·75 1·25
1292 $1.15 Asian lion . . . . . 1·25 1·25
1293 $1.15 Peregrine falcon . . . 1·75 1·25
1294 $1.15 Persian fallow deer . . 1·25 1·25
1295 $1.15 Key deer . . . . . . 1·25 1·25
1296 $1.15 Alpine ibex . . . . . 1·25 1·25
1297 $1.15 Mandrill . . . . . . 1·25 1·25
1298 $1.15 Gorilla . . . . 1·25 1·25
1299 $1.15 "Vanessa atalanta" (butterfly) . . . . . . 1·25 1·25
1300 $1.15 Takin . . . . 1·25 1·25
1301 $1.15 Ring-tailed lemur . . 1·25 1·25

251 Columbus and Landing in New World

1992. 500th Anniv of Discovery of America by Columbus (2nd issue).
1302 **251** $6 multicoloured . . . . 7·50 8·00
MS1303 128 × 84 mm. $10 As T **251**, but detail of landing party only (40 × 29 mm) . . . . 7·00 8·50

252 Football and $50 Commemorative Coin

1992. Olympic Games, Barcelona (2nd issue). Multicoloured.
1304 $1.75 Type **252** . . . . . . 2·50 2·50
1305 $1.75 Olympic gold medal 2·50 2·50
1306 $1.75 Basketball and $10 coin . . . . 2·50 2·50
1307 $2.25 Running . . . . . . 3·50 3·50
1308 $2.25 $10 and $50 coins . . 3·50 3·50
1309 $2.25 Cycling . . . . 3·50 3·50
MS1310 155 × 91 mm. $6.40, Javelin throwing . . . . 13·00 14·00

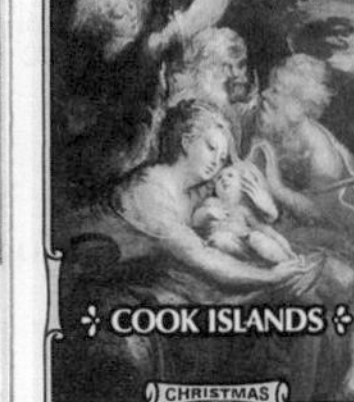

253 Festival Poster **255** "Worship of Shepherds" (Parmigianino)

1992. 6th Festival of Pacific Arts, Rarotonga. Multicoloured.
1311 80c. Type **253** . . . . . . 1·75 1·75
1312 85c. Seated Tangaroa carving . . . . 1·75 1·75
1313 $1 Seated Tangaroa carving (different) . . . . 1·90 1·90
1314 $1.75 Standing Tangaroa carving . . . . 2·75 3·75

1992. Royal Visit by Prince Edward. Nos. 1311/14 optd **ROYAL VISIT**.
1315 80c. Type **253** . . . . . . 2·25 2·25
1316 85c. Seated Tangaroa carving . . . . 2·25 2·25
1317 $1 Seated Tangaroa carving (different) . . . . 2·50 2·50
1318 $1.75 Standing Tangaroa carving . . . . 4·25 4·75

1992. Christmas. Religious Paintings by Parmigianino. Multicoloured.
1319 70c. Type **255** . . . . . . 1·00 1·00
1320 85c. "Virgin with Long Neck" . . . . 1·25 1·25
1321 $1.15 "Virgin with Rose" 1·50 1·75
1322 $1.90 "St. Margaret's Virgin" . . . . 2·75 3·75
MS1323 86 × 102 mm. $6.40, As 85c. but larger (36 × 46 mm) . . . . 11·00 12·00

256 Queen in Garter Robes **258** "Virgin with Child" (Filippo Lippi)

257 Coronation Ceremony

1992. 40th Anniv of Queen Elizabeth II's Accession. Multicoloured.
1324 80c. Type **256** . . . . . . 1·75 1·50
1325 $1.15 Queen at Trooping the Colour . . . . 2·00 2·00
1326 $1.50 Queen in evening dress . . . . 2·75 3·00
1327 $1.95 Queen with bouquet 3·00 3·50

1993. 40th Anniv of Coronation. Multicoloured.
1328 $1 Type **257** . . . . 3·00 2·00
1329 $2 Coronation photograph by Cecil Beaton . . . . . 4·50 4·00
1330 $3 Royal family on balcony 7·00 6·00

1993. Christmas. Religious Paintings. Mult.
1331 70c. Type **258** 80 80
1332 85c. "Bargellini Madonna" (Lodovico Carracci) . . . 95 95
1333 $1.15 "Virgin of the Curtain" (Rafael Sanzio) 1·40 1·60
1334 $2.50 "Holy Family" (Agnolo Bronzino) . . . 3·25 3·75
1335 $4 "Saint Zachary Virgin" (Parmigianino) (32 × 47 mm) . . . . . . 4·00 5·50

259 Skiing, Flags and Ice Skating (½-size illustration)

1994. Winter Olympic Games, Lillehammer.
1336 **259** $5 multicoloured . . . . 8·00 8·50

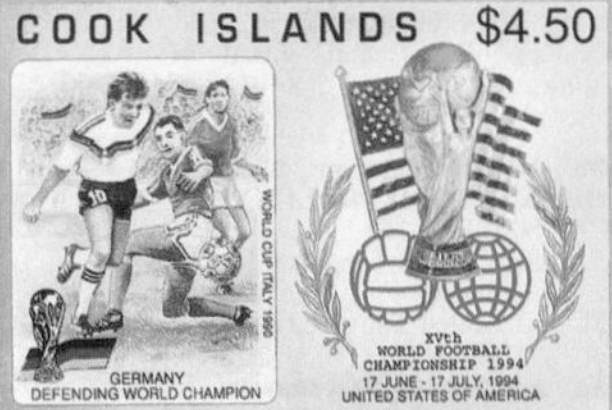

260 Cup on Logo with German and Argentinian Players

1994. World Cup Football Championship, U.S.A.
1337 **260** $4.50 multicoloured . . 6·00 7·50

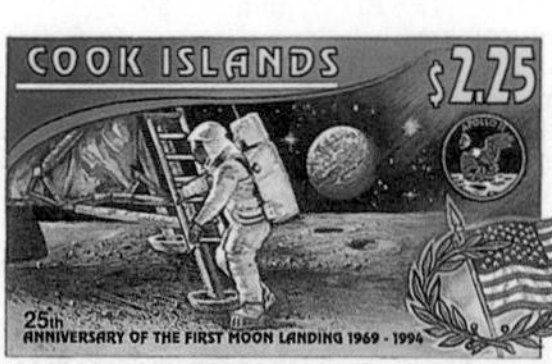

261 Neil Armstrong taking First Step on Moon

1994. 25th Anniv of First Manned Moon Landing. Multicoloured.
1338 $2.25 Type **261** . . . . . . 3·75 3·75
1339 $2.25 Astronaut on Moon and view of Earth . . . . 3·75 3·75
1340 $2.25 Astronaut and flag . . 3·75 3·75
1341 $2.25 Astronaut with reflection in helmet visor 3·75 3·75

1994. Reef Life (2nd series). As Nos. 1261 and 1263/71, but each 40 × 30 mm and with brown borders.
1342 5c. Type **249** 60 70
1344 15c. Bicoloured angelfish . . 70 75
1345 20c. Spotted pebble crab . . 85 85
1346 25c. Black-tipped grouper 90 90
1347 30c. Spanish dancer 90 90
1348 50c. Regal angelfish . . . . 1·10 1·10
1349 80c. Big-scaled soldierfish 1·25 1·25
1350 85c. Red pencil sea urchin 1·25 1·25
1351 90c. Red-spotted rainbowfish . . . . 1·25 1·25
1352 $1 Cheek-lined wrasse . . . 1·40 1·40

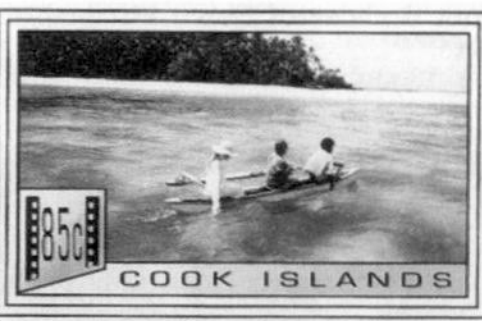

262 Actors in Outrigger Canoe

1994. Release of "The Return of Tommy Tricker" (film shot in Cook Islands). Scenes from film. Multicoloured.
1359 85c. Type **262** . . . . . . 1·10 1·25
1360 85c. Male and female dancers . . . . 1·10 1·25
1361 85c. European couple on beach . . . . 1·10 1·25
1362 85c. Aerial view of island 1·10 1·25
1363 85c. Two female dancers 1·10 1·25
1364 85c. Cook Islands couple on beach . . . . 1·10 1·25
1364a 90c. Type **262** . . . . . . 75 1·10
1364b 90c. As No. 1360 . . . . 75 1·10
1364c 90c. As No. 1361 . . . . 75 1·10
1364d 90c. As No. 1362 . . . . 75 1·10
1364e 90c. As No. 1363 . . . . 75 1·10
1364f 90c. As No. 1364 . . . . 75 1·10

263 "The Virgin and Child" (Morales)

1994. Christmas. Religious Paintings. Mult.
1365 85c. Type **263** . . . . . . 2·00 2·00
1366 85c. "Adoration of the Kings" (Gerard David) 2·00 2·00
1367 85c. "Adoration of the Kings" (Foppa) . . . . . 2·00 2·00
1368 85c. "The Madonna and Child with St. Joseph and Infant Baptist" (Baroccio) 2·00 2·00
1369 $1 "Madonna with Iris" (Durer) . . . . 2·00 2·00
1370 $1 "Adoration of the Shepherds" (Le Nain) . . 2·00 2·00
1371 $1 "The Virgin and Child" (school of Leonardo) . . 2·00 2·00
1372 $1 "The Mystic Nativity" (Botticelli) . . . . 2·00 2·00

264 Pirates ("Treasure Island")

1994. Death Centenary of Robert Louis Stevenson (author). Multicoloured.
1373 $1.50 Type **264** . . . . . . 3·00 3·00
1374 $1.50 Duel ("David Balfour") . . . . 3·00 3·00
1375 $1.50 Mr. Hyde, ("Dr. Jekyll and Mr. Hyde") . . . . 3·00 3·00
1376 $1.50 Rowing boat and sailing ship ("Kidnapped") . . . . . 3·00 3·00

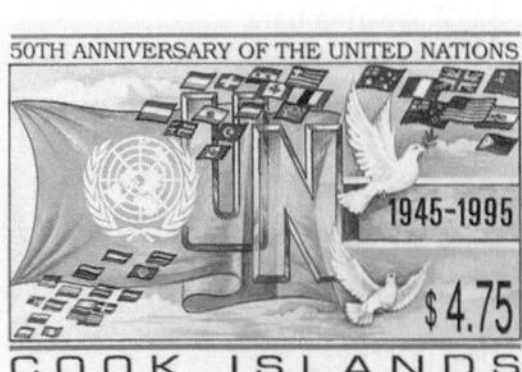

265 U.N. and National Flags with Peace Doves

1995. 50th Anniv of United Nations.
1377 **265** $4.75 multicoloured . . 4·75 7·00

266 Queen Elizabeth the Queen Mother and Coat of Arms

1995. 95th Birthday of Queen Elizabeth the Queen Mother.
1378 **266** $5 multicoloured 11·00 9·00

267 German Delegation signing Unconditional Surrender at Rheims

1995. 50th Anniv of End of Second World War. Multicoloured.
1379 $3.50 Type **267** 8·00 8·00
1380 $3.50 Japanese delegation on U.S.S. "Missouri", Tokyo Bay 8·00 8·00

1995. 50th Anniv of F.A.O. As T **265**. Mult.
1381 $4.50 F.A.O. and U.N. emblems 4·75 7·00

268 Green Turtle

1995. Year of the Sea Turtle. Multicoloured.
1382 85c. Type **268** 1·75 1·60
1383 $1 Hawksbill turtle 2·00 1·75
1384 $1.75 Green turtle on beach 3·00 3·25
1385 $2.25 Young hawksbill turtles hatching 3·75 4·00

269 Emblem and Throwing the Discus

1996. Olympic Games, Atlanta. Multicoloured.
1386 85c. Type **269** 1·50 1·50
1387 $1 Athlete with Olympic Torch 1·75 1·75
1388 $1.50 Running 2·50 2·50
1389 $1.85 Gymnastics 2·75 2·75
1390 $2.10 Ancient archery 3·00 3·00
1391 $2.50 Throwing the javelin 3·00 3·00

270 Queen Elizabeth II

1996. 70th Birthday of Queen Elizabeth II. Multicoloured.
1392 $1.90 Type **270** 2·75 2·75
1393 $2.25 Wearing tiara 3·25 3·25
1394 $2.75 In Garter robes 3·50 3·50
MS1395 103 × 152 mm. Designs as Nos. 1392/4, but each with a face value of $2.50 15·00 15·00

1997. 28th South Pacific Forum. Nos. 1364a/f optd **28th South Pacific Forum** (Nos. 1396, 1399/1400) or **12–22 September 1997** (Nos. 1397/8 and 1401). Multicoloured.
1396 90c. Type **262** 1·00 1·25
1397 90c. As No. 1360 1·00 1·25
1398 90c. As No. 1361 1·00 1·25
1399 90c. As No. 1362 1·00 1·25
1400 90c. As No. 1363 1·00 1·25
1401 90c. As No. 1364 1·00 1·25

272 "Lampides boeticus" (female)

1997. Butterflies. Multicoloured.
1402 5c. Type **272** 10 10
1403 10c. "Vanessa atalanta" 10 10
1404 15c. "Lampides boeticus" (male) 10 15
1405 20c. "Papilio godeffroyi" 15 20
1406 25c. "Danaus hamata" 20 25
1407 30c. "Xois sesara" 20 25
1408 50c. "Vagrans egista" 35 40
1409 70c. "Parthenos sylvia" 50 55
1410 80c. "Hyblaea sanguinea" 60 65
1411 85c. "Melanitis leda" 60 65
1412 90c. "Ascalapha odorata" 65 70
1413 $1 "Precis villida" 75 80
1414 $1.50 "Parthenos sylvia" 1·10 1·20
1415 $2 "Lampides boeticus" (female) 1·50 1·60
1416 $3 "Precis villida" 2·20 2·30
1417 $4 "Melanitis leda" 3·00 3·25
1418 $5 "Vagrans egista" 3·75 4·00
1419 $7 "Hyblaea sanguinea" 5·25 5·50
1420 $10 "Vanessa atalanta" 7·25 7·50
1421 $15 "Papilio godeffroyi" 11·00 11·50

The 70c. and $1 include an outline portrait of Queen Elizabeth II. Nos. 1414/21 are larger, 41 × 25 mm, with the Queen's portrait included on the $4 to $15.

273 Queen Elizabeth and Prince Philip

1997. Golden Wedding of Queen Elizabeth and Prince Philip.
1424 **273** $2 multicoloured 2·50 2·50
MS1425 76 × 102 mm. **273** $5 multicoloured 8·00 8·00

274 Diana, Princess of Wales

277 Lady Elizabeth Bowes-Lyon

1998. Diana, Princess of Wales Commemoration.
1426 **274** $1.15 multicoloured 1·25 1·25
MS1427 70 × 100 mm. $3.50, Princess Diana and guard of honour 5·00 5·00

1998. Children's Charities. No. **MS**1427 surch **+$1 CHILDREN'S CHARITIES**.
MS1428 70 × 100 mm. $3.50 + $1 Princess Diana and guard of honour 3·50 4·25

1999. New Millennium. Nos. 1311/14 optd **KIA ORANA THIRD MILLENNIUM**.
1429 80c. Type **253** 65 65
1430 85c. Seated Tangaroa carving 70 70
1431 $1 Seated Tangaroa carving (different) 80 80
1432 $1.75 Standing Tangaroa carving 1·40 1·75

2000. Queen Elizabeth the Queen Mother's 100th Birthday.
1433 **277** $4.50 brown and blue 4·25 4·25
1434 – $4.50 brown and blue 4·25 4·25
1435 – $4.50 multicoloured 4·25 4·25
1436 – $4.50 multicoloured 4·25 4·25
MS1437 73 × 100 mm. $6 multicoloured 4·50 5·50

DESIGNS: 1434, Lady Elizabeth Bowes-Lyon as young woman; 1435, Queen Mother wearing green outfit; 1436, Queen Mother wearing pearl earrings and necklace; **MS**1437, Queen Mother in blue hat and plum jacket.

278 Ancient Greek Runner on Urn

2000. Olympic Games, Sydney. Multicoloured.
1438 $1.75 Type **278** 1·75 2·00
1439 $1.75 Modern runner 1·75 2·00
1440 $1.75 Ancient Greek archer 1·75 2·00
1441 $1.75 Modern archer 1·75 2·00
MS1442 99 × 90 mm. $3.90, Olympic torch in Cook Islands 2·50 3·00

2001. Suwarrow Wildlife Sanctuary. Nos. 1279/90 surch **80c SUWARROW SANCTUARY**.
1443 80c. on $1.15 Heavisides's dolphin 85 95
1444 80c. on $1.15 Eagle owl 85 95
1445 80c. on $1.15 Bee hummingbird 85 95
1446 80c. on $1.15 Puma 85 95
1447 80c. on $1.15 European otter 85 95
1448 80c. on $1.15 Red kangaroo 85 95
1449 90c. on $1.15 Type **250** 85 95
1450 90c. on $1.15 Indian elephant 85 95
1451 90c. on $1.15 Brown bear 85 95
1452 90c. on $1.15 Black rhinoceros 85 95
1453 90c. on $1.15 Chimpanzee 85 95
1454 90c. on $1.15 Argali 85 95

2002. Christmas. Nos. 1248/51 and 1256/9 optd **CHRISTMAS 2002** or surch.
1455 20c. on 70c. Type **244** 35 40
1456 20c. on 70c. Type **248** 35 40
1457 80c. on $1.15 "Adoration of the Shepherds" (Rembrandt) 1·00 1·00
1458 85c. "Holy Family" (Lotto) 1·10 1·25
1459 85c. "The Birth of the Virgin" (B. Murillo) 1·10 1·25
1460 90c. on $1.50 "Adoration of the Shepherds" (L. le Nain) 1·25 1·25
1461 95c. "Madonna and Child with Saints John and Catherine" (Titian) 1·25 1·25
1462 $1 on $1.50 "The Holy Family" (Titian) 1·40 1·40

2003. Nos. 1414/19 surch.
1463 20c. on $1.50 *Parthenos Sylvia* 15 20
1464 80c. on $2 *Lampides boeticus* (female) 60 65
1465 85c. on $3 *Precis villida* 60 65
1466 85c. on $4 *Melanitis leda* 60 65
1467 90c. on $5 *Vagrans egista* 65 70
1468 90c. on $7 *Hyblaea sanguinea* 65 70

282 Statue of Liberty's Torch and Cook Islands Flag

2003. "United We Stand". Support for Victims of 11 September 2001 Terrorist Attacks.
MS1469 75 × 109 mm. **282** 90c. × 4 multicoloured 2·20 2·40

OFFICIAL STAMPS

1975. Nos. 228, etc, optd **O.H.M.S.** or surch also.
O 1 1c. multicoloured
O 2 2c. multicoloured
O 3 3c. multicoloured
O 4 4c. multicoloured
O 5 5c. on 2½c. multicoloured
O 6 8c. multicoloured
O 7 10c. on 6c. multicoloured
O 8 18c. on 20c. multicoloured
O 9 25c. on 9c. multicoloured
O 10 30c. on 15c. multicoloured
O 11 50c. multicoloured
O 12 $1 multicoloured
O 13 $2 multicoloured
O 14 $4 multicoloured
O 15 $6 multicoloured
O1/15 Set of 15 † 7·00

These stamps were only sold to the public cancelled-to-order and not in unused condition.

1978. Nos. 466/7, 474, 478/81, 484/5, 542 and 568/9 optd **O.H.M.S.** or surch also.
O16 – 1c. mult (No. 467) 80 10
O17 **141** 2c. on ½c. multicoloured 80 10
O18 – 5c. on ½c. multicoloured 90 10
O19 – 10c. on 8c. mult (No. 474) 1·00 10
O20 – 15c. on 50c. mult (No. 480) 1·25 10
O21 – 18c. on 60c. mult (No. 481) 1·25 15
O22 – 25c. mult (No. 478) 1·50 20
O23 – 30c. mult (No. 479) 1·50 25
O24 – 35c. on 60c. mult (No. 481) 1·50 30
O25 – 50c. mult (No. 480) 2·00 35
O26 – 60c. mult (No. 481) 2·25 45
O27 – $1 mult (No. 568) 5·00 65
O28 – $1 mult (No. 569) 5·00 65
O29 – $2 mult (No. 542) 7·00 2·25
O30 – $4 mult (No. 484) 13·00 2·25
O31 – $6 mult (No. 485) 13·00 3·50

1985. Nos. 786/8, 862/5, 969/74, 976, 978, 981, 984/6 and 988/9 optd **O.H.M.S.** or surch also.
O32 5c. "Ptilosarcus gurneyi" 50 50
O33 10c. "Lobophyllia bemprichii" 50 50
O34 12c. "Sarcophyton digitatum" 4·50 60
O35 14c. "Pavona praetorta" 4·50 60
O36 18c. "Junceella gemmacea" 4·50 60
O37 20c. "Stylaster" 60 50
O38 30c. "Palauastrea ramosa" 60 50
O39 40c. "Stylaster echinatus" 60 50
O40 50c. "Melithaea squamata" 5·50 70
O41 55c. on 85c. "Caulastraea echinulata" 70 50
O42 60c. "Tubastraea" 70 60
O43 70c. "Heliofungia actiniformis" 6·00 85
O46 75c. on 60c. Type **197** 3·00 1·00
O47 75c. on 60c. Rarotonga oranges 3·00 1·00
O48 75c. on 60c. Rarotonga Airport 3·00 1·00
O49 75c. on 60c. Prime Minister Sir Thomas Davis 3·00 1·00
O44 $1.10 "Pectinia alcicornis" 1·10 90
O45 $2 on $1.20 "Dendrophyllia gracilis" 2·25 1·75
O50 $5 on $3 "Heliofungia actiniformis" 15·00 4·75
O51 $9 on $4 "Stylophora pistillata" 8·00 9·50
O52 $14 on $6 "Stylaster echinatus" 12·50 14·00
O53 $18 on $10 "Melithaea albitincta" 18·00 18·00

1995. Nos. 1261/6 optd **O.H.M.S.**
O54 5c. Type **249** 40 75
O55 10c. Blue sea star 40 75
O56 15c. Bicoloured angelfish 50 75
O57 20c. Spotted pebble crab 55 80
O58 25c. Black-tipped grouper 60 70
O59 30c. Spanish dancer 60 70
O60 50c. Regal angelfish 80 80
O61 80c. Big-scaled soldierfish 1·25 1·25
O62 85c. Red pencil sea urchin 1·25 1·25
O63 90c. Red-spotted rainbowfish 1·25 1·25
O64 $1 Cheek-lined wrasse 1·50 1·50
O65 $2 Long-nosed butterflyfish 2·25 2·50
O66 $3 Red-spotted rainbowfish 3·75 4·00
O67 $5 Blue sea star 4·50 5·00
O68 $7 "Pygoplites diacanthus" 6·50 7·50
O69 $10 Spotted pebble crab 8·00 9·50

COSTA RICA Pt. 15

A republic of Central America. Independent since 1821.

1863. 8 reales = 1 peso.
1881. 100 centavos = 1 peso.
1901. 100 centimos = 1 colon.

1

8 General P. Fernandez

14 Pres. Soto

1863.
1 **1** ½r. blue 50 35
3 2r. red 55 85
4 4r. green 6·00 6·00
5 1p. orange 12·00 12·00

1881. Surch.
6 **1** 1c. on ½r. blue 1·10 4·50
8 2c. on ½r. blue 90 2·10
9 5c. on ½r. blue 2·75 7·25

1882. Surch **U.P.U.** and value.
10 **1** 5c. on ½r. blue 30·00 30·00
11 10c. on 2r. red 30·00 30·00
12 20c. on 4r. green 90·00 90·00

1883.
13 **8** 1c. green 40 25
14 2c. red 40 30
15 5c. violet 7·25 25
16 10c. orange 21·00 2·75
17 40c. blue 45 55

1887.
18 **14** 5c. violet 3·25 25
19 10c. orange 90 50

1887. Fiscal stamps similar to T **8** and **14** optd **CORREOS**.
20 1c. red 1·50 65
21 5c. brown 1·50 45

17 Pres. Soto

19

1889. Various frames.
22 **17** 1c. brown 25 25
23 2c. green 20 20
24 5c. orange 40 25
25 10c. lake 20 20
26 20c. green 20 20
27 50c. red 45 80
28 1p. blue 65 1·25
29 2p. violet 6·00 7·00
30 5p. olive 15·00 18·00
31 10p. black 38·00 35·00

1892. Various frames.
32 **19** 1c. blue 20 20
33 2c. orange 20 20
34a 5c. mauve 20 20
35 10c. green 50 25
36 20c. red 6·00 25
37 50c. blue 3·00 2·00
38 1p. green on yellow 55 80

39 2p. red on grey . . . . . 1·50 50
40 5p. blue on blue . . . . . 1·25 50
41a 10p. brown on buff . . . . 4·25 2·40

29 Juan Santamaria 31 Puerto Limon

1901. Various designs dated "1900".
42 **29** 1c. black and green 40 10
43 – 2c. black and red 25 15
52 – 4c. black and purple . . . . 1·90 75
44 **31** 5c. black and blue 35 15
53 – 6c. black and olive . . . . 4·50 2·40
45 – 10c. black and brown . . . 1·00 15
46 – 20c. black and lake . . . . 2·75 15
54 – 25c. brown and lilac . . . . 8·75 20
47 – 50c. blue and red . . . . . 2·40 70
48 – 1col. black and olive . . . . 38·00 7·50
49 – 2col. black and red . . . . 6·50 1·75
50 – 5col. black and brown . . . 17·00 1·75
51 – 10col. red and green . . . . 13·50 1·40
DESIGNS—VERT: 2c. Juan Mora F; 4c. Jose M. Canas; 6c. Julian Volio; 10c. Braulio (wrongly inscr "BRANLIO") Carrillo; 25c. Eusebio Figueroa; 50c. Jose M. Castro; 1col. Puente de Birris; 2col. Juan Rafael Mora; 5col. Jesus Jimenez. HORIZ: 20c. National Theatre; 10col. Arms.

1905. No. 46 surch **UN CENTIMO** in ornamental frame.
55 1c. on 20c. black and lake . . 50 50

43 Juan Santamaria

44 Juan Mora

1907. Dated "1907".
57 **43** 1c. blue and brown 50 20
58 **44** 2c. black and green 45 20
69 – 4c. blue and red . . . . . 3·00 65
60 – 5c. blue and orange 35 20
71 – 10c. black and blue . . . . 4·25 10
72 – 20c. black and olive . . . . 4·75 2·40
63 – 25c. slate and lavender . . . 1·10 35
74 – 50c. blue and red . . . . . 17·00 4·25
75 – 1col. black and brown . . . 8·25 4·25
76 – 2col. green and red . . . . 42·00 16·00
PORTRAITS: 4c. Jose M. Canas. 5c. Mauro Fernandez. 10c. Braulio Carrillo. 20c. Julian Volio. 25c. Eusebio Figueroa. 50c. Jose M. Castro. 1col. Jesus Jimenez. 2col. Juan Rafael Mora.

53 Juan Santamaria

54 Julian Volio

1910. Various frames.
77 **53** 1c. brown 10 10
78 – 2c. green (Juan Mora F.) . . 20 10
79 – 4c. red (Jose M. Canas) . . 20 10
80 – 5c. orange (Mauro Fernandez) 20 10
81 – 10c. blue (B. Carrillo) . . . 10 10
82 **54** 20c. olive 20 10
83 – 25c. purple (Eusebio Figueroa) . . . . 4·25 50
84 – 1col. brown (Jesus Jimenez) 40 25

1911. Optd **1911** between stars.
85 **29** 1c. black and green 50 35
86 **43** 1c. blue and brown 35 35
88 **44** 2c. black and green 35 35

1911. Optd **Habilitado 1911**.
93 4c. black and purple (No. 52) 1·00 10
90 5c. blue and orange (No. 60) 1·00 10
91 10c. black and blue (No. 71) 3·00 2·75

59 Liner "Antilles"

62

1911. Surch **Correos Un centimo** or **Correos S 5 centimos**.
94 **59** 1c. on 10c. blue 30 15
96 1c. on 25c. violet 30 15
97 1c. on 50c. brown 55 45
98 1c. on 1c. brown 55 45
99 1c. on 5c. red 90 65
100 1c. on 10c. brown . . . . 1·10 95
101 5c. on 5c. orange 55 20

1912. Surch **Correos Dos centimos 2**.
102 **62** 2c. on 5c. brown . . . . . 8·75 2·40
109 2c. on 10c. blue . . . . . £140 60·00
104 2c. on 50c. red . . . . . 5·00 5·00
105 2c. on 1c. brown . . . . . 22·00 3·00
112 2c. on 2c. red . . . . . . 2·50 90
107 2c. on 5c. green . . . . . 8·75 2·40
108 2c. on 10col. purple . . . 11·00 3·25

67 Plantation and Administration Building

1921. Centenary of Coffee Cultivation.
115 **67** 5c. black and blue . . . . 1·00 85

68 Simon Bolivar

69

1921.
116 **68** 15c. violet 25 15

1921. Cent of Independence of Central America.
117 **69** 5c. violet 25 35

70 Juan Mora and Julio Acosta

1921. Centenary of Independence.
118 **70** 2c. black and orange . . . 50 50
119 3c. black and green 50 50
120 6c. black and red 65 55
121 15c. black and blue . . . . 1·75 1·75
122 30c. black and brown . . . 2·75 2·75

1922. Coffee Publicity. Nos. 77/81 and 116 optd with sack inscr "CAFE DE COSTA RICA".
123 **53** 1c. brown 10 10
124 – 2c. green 15 10
125 – 4c. red 15 15
126 – 5c. orange 15 15
127 – 10c. blue 30 25
128 **68** 15c. violet 75 70

1922. Optd **CORREOS 1922**.
129 **69** 5c. violet 40 25

1922. Surch with red cross and **5c.**
130 5c.+5c. orange (No. 80) . . . 50 25

1923. Optd **COMPRE UD. CAFE DE COSTA RICA** in circular frame.
131 5c. orange (No. 80) 25 15

77 Jesus Jimenez (statesman)

81 Coffee-growing

80 National Monument

1923. Birth Centenary of J. Jimenez.
132 **77** 2c. brown 15 15
133 4c. green 15 15
134 5c. blue 35 15
135 20c. red 20 20
136 1col. violet 35 35

1923.
137 **80** 1c. purple 10 10
138 **81** 2c. yellow 20 15
139 – 4c. green 40 35
140 – 5c. blue 70 10
141 – 5c. green 20 10
142 – 10c. brown 85 15
143 – 10c. red 25 10
144 – 12c. red . . . . 7·00 1·75
145 – 20c. blue . . . . 3·00 60
146 – 40c. orange . . . . 2·75 90
147 – 1col. olive 75 40
All the above are inscr "U.P.U. 1923." except the 10c. and 12c. which are inscr "1921 EN COMMEMORACION DEL PRIMER CONGRESO POSTAL", etc.
DESIGNS—HORIZ: 5c. P.O., San Jose; 10c. Columbus and Isabella I; 12c. "Santa Maria"; 20c. Columbus landing at Cariari; 40c. Map of Costa Rica. VERT: 4c. Banana-growing; 1col. M. Gutierrez.

85 Don R. A. Maldonado y Velasco

86 Map of Guanacaste

1924.
148 **85** 2c. green 15 10
For 3c. green see No. 211 and for other portraits as T **85** see Nos. 308/12.

1924. Cent of Province of Nicoya (Guanacaste).
149 **86** 1c. red 35 20
150 2c. purple 35 20
151 5c. green 35 20
152 10c. orange . . . . 1·25 50
153 – 15c. blue 40 45
154 – 20c. grey 65 45
155 – 25c. brown 90 75
DESIGN: 15c., 20c., 25c. Church at Nicoya.

88 Discus Thrower

93 Arms and Curtiss "Jenny"

1925. Inscr "JUEGOS OLIMPICOS". Imperf or perf.
156 **88** 5c. green . . . . 2·00 2·40
157 – 10c. red . . . . 2·00 2·40
158 – 20c. blue . . . . 4·00 3·50
DESIGNS—VERT: 10c. Trophy. HORIZ: 20c. Parthenon.

1926. Surch with values in ornamental designs.
159 3c. on 5c. (No. 140) 20 15
160 6c. on 10c. (No. 142) 35 25
161 30c. on 40c. (No. 146) . . . 50 40
162 45c. on 1col. (No. 147) . . . 55 50

1926. Surch with value between bars.
163 10c. on 12c. red (No. 144) . . 2·25 45

1926. Air.
164 **93** 20c. blue . . . . 1·25 40

94 Heredia Normal School

1926. Dated "1926".
165 – 3c. blue 15 15
166 – 6c. brown 25 20
167 **94** 30c. orange 35 25
168 – 45c. violet 90 50
DESIGNS: 3c. St. Louis College, Cartago; 6c. Chapui Asylum, San Jose; 45c. Ruins of Ujarras.

1928. Lindbergh Good Will Tour of Central America. Surch with aeroplane, **LINDBERGH ENERO 1928** and new value.
169 10c. on 12c. red (No. 144) . . 13·00 8·50

1928. Surch **5 5**.
170 **68** 5c. on 15c. violet 15 10

1929. Surch **CORREOS** and value.
171 **62** 5c. on 2col. red . . . . . 1·00 35
173 13c. on 40c. green . . . . 1·25 40

98 Post Office

103 Juan Rafael Mora

1930. Types of 1923 reduced in size and dated "1929" as T **98**.
174 – 1c. purple (as No. 137) . . 10 10
175 **98** 5c. green 10 10
176 – 10c. red (as No. 143) . . . 35 10

1930. Air. No. O178 surch **CORREO 1930 AEREO**, Bleriot XI airplane and new value.
177 **O 95** 8c. on 1col. 50 40
178 20c. on 1col. 70 50
179 40c. on 1col. . . . . . 1·40 1·00
180 1col. on 1col. . . . . . 2·00 1·40

1930. Air. Optd **CORREO AEREO** (No. 181) or **Correo Aereo** (others) or surch also.
182 **62** 5c. on 10c. brown 90 25
181 – 10c. red (No. 143) 45 15
183 **62** 20c. on 50c. blue . . . . . 1·25 25
184 40c. on 50c. blue . . . . . 1·25 50
185 1col. orange . . . . 2·75 80

1931.
186 **103** 13c. red 25 15

1931. Air. Fiscal stamps (Arms design) inscr "TIMBRE 1929" (or "1930", 3col.), surch **Habilitado 1931 Correo Aereo** and new value.
190 2col. on 2col. green . . . . 16·00 16·00
191 3col. on 5col. brown . . . . 16·00 16·00
192 5col. on 10col. black . . . . 16·00 16·00

1932. Air. Telegraph stamp optd with wings inscr **CORREO CR AEREO**.
193 **62** 40c. green . . . . 3·50 80

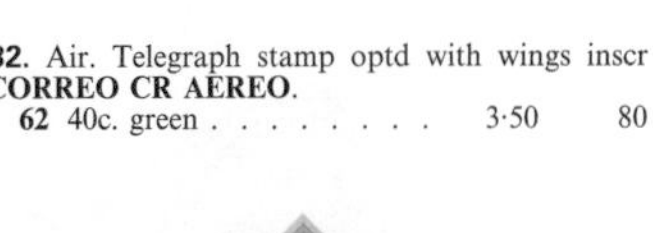

106

1932. 1st National Philatelic Exhibition.
194 **106** 3c. orange 15 15
195 5c. green 25 25
196 10c. red 25 25
197 20c. blue 35 35
See also Nos. 231/4.

107 Ryan Brougham over La Sabana Airport, San Jose

1934. Air.
198 **107** 5c. green 15 10
507 5c. deep blue 10 10
508 5c. pale blue 10 10
199 10c. red 15 10
509 10c. green 10 10
510 10c. turquoise 10 10
200 15c. brown 30 10
511 15c. red 10 10
201 20c. blue 45 10
202 25c. orange 55 15
512 35c. violet 35 10
203 40c. brown 55 10
204 50c. black 40 15
205 60c. yellow 75 25
206 75c. violet . . . . 1·10 40
207 – 1col. red 85 10
208 – 2col. blue 90 35
209 – 5col. black . . . . 2·40 2·40
210 – 10col. brown . . . . . . 4·00 4·00
DESIGN: 1, 2, 5, 10col. Allegory of the Air Mail.

1934.
211 **85** 3c. green 10 10

109 Nurse at Altar

111 Our Lady of the Angels

1935. Costa Rican Red Cross Jubilee.
212 **109** 10c. red 35 15

1935. 300th Anniv of Apparition of Our Lady of the Angels.
213 – 5c. green 15 10
214 **111** 10c. red 35 15
215 – 30c. orange 50 25
216 – 45c. violet 65 40
217 **111** 50c. black . . . . 1·10 45
DESIGNS: 5c., 30c. Aerial view of Cartago; 45c. Allegory of the Apparition.

112 Cocos Island

1936.
218 112 4c. brown 25 10
219 8c. violet 30 15
220 25c. orange 35 15
221 35c. brown 50 15
222 40c. brown 40 25
223 50c. yellow 40 35
224 2col. green 4·75 3·75
225 5col. green 12·00 7·25

113 Cocos Island and Fleet of Columbus

1936.
226 113 5c. green 85 20
227 10c. red 1·10 20

114 Airplane over Mt. Poas

1937. Air. 1st Annual Fair.
228 114 1c. black 10 10
229 2c. brown 10 10
230 3c. violet 10 10

1937. 2nd National Philatelic Exhibition. As T **106**, but inscr "DICIEMBRE 1937".
231 106 2c. purple 15 15
232 3c. black 15 15
233 5c. green 15 15
234 10c. orange 15 15

115 Tunny

116 Native and Donkey carrying Bananas

117 Puntarenas

1937. National Exhibition, San Jose (1st Issue).
235 115 2c. black (postage) 20 15
236 116 5c. green 25 15
237 – 10c. red 35 20

238 117 2c. black (air) 10 10
239 5c. green 10 10
240 20c. blue 30 25
241 1col.40 brown 1·75 1·75
DESIGN—As Type **116**: 10c. Coffee gathering.

118 Purple Guaria Orchid "Carrleya skinneri"

119 National Bank

1938. National Exhibition, San Jose (2nd Issue).
242 118 1c. violet & grn (postage) 15 10
243 3c. brown 15 10

244 119 1c. violet (air) 10 10
245 3c. red 10 10
246 10c. red 15 10
247 75c. brown 90 90
DESIGN—As Type **118**: 3c. Cocoa-bean.

1938. No. 145 optd **1938**.
248 20c. blue 35 15

121 La Sabana Airport

1940. Air. Opening of San Jose Airport.
249 121 5c. green 10 10
250 10c. red 15 10
251 25c. blue 15 15
252 35c. brown 30 30
253 60c. orange 45 45
254 85c. violet 60 50
255 2col.35 green 3·25 3·25

1940. No. 168 variously surch **15 CENTIMOS** in ornamental frame.
256 15c. on 45c. violet 25 20
There are five distinct varieties of this surcharge.

1940. Pan-American Health Day. Unissued stamps prepared for the 8th Pan-American Child Welfare Congress optd **DIA PANAMERICANO DE LA SALUD 2. DICIEMBRE 1940**. (a) Postage. Allegorical design.
261 5c. green 20 10
262 10c. red 25 15
263 20c. blue 50 20
264 40c. brown 85 70
265 55c. orange 1·40 60

(b) Air. View of Duran Sanatorium.
266 10c. red 15 10
267 15c. violet 15 15
268 25c. blue 30 25
269 35c. brown 45 45
270 60c. green 35 35
271 75c. olive 75 85
272 1col.35 orange 3·25 3·25
273 5col. brown 14·00 14·00
274 10col. mauve 27·00 27·00

1940. Air. Pan-American Aviation Day. Surch **AERO Aviacion Panamericana Dic. 17 1940** and value.
275 15c. on 50c. yellow 50 50
276 30c. on 50c. yellow 50 50

1941. Surch **15 CENTIMOS 15**.
277 112 15c. on 25c. orange 25 20
278 15c. on 35c. brown 25 20
279 15c. on 40c. brown 25 20
280 15c. on 2col. green 25 20
281 15c. on 5col. green 40 35

131 Stadium and Flag

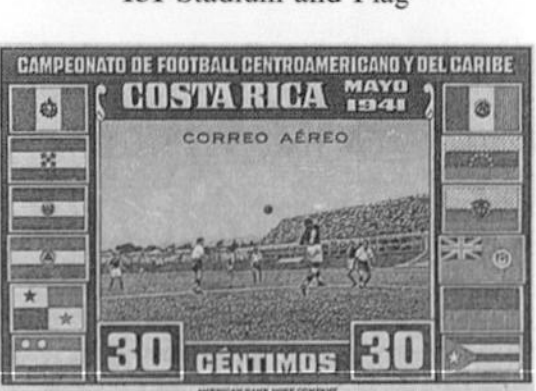

132 Football Match

1941. Central American and Caribbean Football Championship.
282 131 5c. green (postage) 45 25
283 10c. orange 40 25
284 15c. red 55 25
285 25c. blue 60 25
286 40c. brown 1·90 75
287 50c. violet 2·40 90
288 75c. orange 4·75 1·90
289 1col. red 7·75 3·75

290 132 15c. red (air) 45 15
291 30c. blue 50 25
292 40c. brown 50 40
293 50c. violet 65 45
294 60c. green 85 50
295 75c. yellow 1·40 75
296 1col. mauve 2·40 2·40
297 1col.40 red 5·00 5·00
298 2col. green 9·50 9·50
299 5col. black 21·00 21·00

1941. Air. Costa Rica–Panama Boundary Treaty. Optd **Mayo 1941 Tratado Limitrofe Costa Rica – Panama** or surch also.
300 107 5c. on 20c. blue 20 15
301 15c. on 20c. blue 25 20
302 40c. on 75c. violet 40 25
303 – 65c. on 1col. red (No. 207) 40 30
304 – 1col.40 on 2col. blue (No. 208) 1·90 1·90
305 – 5col. black (No. 209) 6·50 6·50
306 – 10col. brown (No. 210) 7·50 7·50

1941. As Type **85** but with new portraits.
308 – 3c. orange 10 10
309 – 3c. purple 10 10
310 – 3c. red 10 10
310a – 3c. blue 10 10
311 – 5c. violet 10 10
312 – 5c. black 10 10
PORTRAITS: 3c. (Nos. 308/10) C. G. Viquez. 3c. (No. 310a) Mgr. B. A. Thiel. 5c. J. J. Rodriguez.

136 New Decree and Restored University

1941. Restoration of National University.
313 – 5c. green (postage) 25 10
314 136 10c. orange 30 10
315 – 15c. red 40 10
316 136 25c. blue 60 25
317 – 50c. brown 1·50 75

318 136 15c. red (air) 25 15
319 – 30c. blue 40 15
320 136 40c. orange 45 35
321 – 60c. blue 55 50
322 136 1col. violet 2·00 1·60
323 – 2col. black 5·00 3·75
324 136 5col. purple 16·00 13·00
DESIGN—(Nos. 313, 315, 317, 319, 321 and 323): The original Decree and University.

1941. Surch.
325 5c. on 6c. brn (No. 166) 15 15
326 15c. on 20c. blue (No. 248) 25 15

139 "V", Torch and Flags

140 Francisco Morazan

1942. War Effort.
327 139 5c. red 20 10
328 5c. orange 20 10
329 5c. green 20 10
330 5c. blue 20 10
331 5c. violet 20 10

1942. Portraits and dates.
332 A 1c. lilac (postage) 10 10
333 B 2c. black 10 10
334 C 3c. blue 10 10
335 D 5c. turquoise 10 10
336 5c. green 10 10
337 140 15c. red 10 10
338 E 25c. blue 20 15
339 F 50c. violet 1·25 50
340 G 1col. black 2·00 1·00
341 H 2col. orange 2·40 1·25

341a I 5c. brown (air) 10 10
342 A 10c. red 10 10
342a 10c. olive 10 10
342b J 15c. violet 10 10
343 K 25c. blue 15 10
344 L 30c. brown 15 10
345 D 40c. blue 25 10
346 40c. red 20 15
347 140 45c. purple 35 25
348 M 45c. black 20 15
349 E 50c. green 90 20
350 50c. orange 20 20
351 N 55c. purple 25 20
352 F 60c. blue 45 15
353 60c. green 20 15
354 G 65c. red 45 25
355 65c. blue 25 20
356 O 75c. green 40 25
357 H 85c. orange 55 35
358 85c. violet 65 45
359 P 1col. black 65 30
360 1col. red 50 20
361 Q 1col.05 sepia 60 40
362 R 1col.15 brown 90 85
363 1col.15 green 1·25 85
364 B 1col.40 violet 1·40 1·25
365 1col.40 yellow 85 75
366 C 2col. black 2·10 85
367 2col. olive 65 35

PORTRAITS: A, J. Mora Fernandez. B, B. Carranza. C, T. Guardia. D, M. Aguilar. E, J. M. Alfaro. F, F. M. Oreamuno. G, J. M. Castro. H, J. R. Mora. I, S. Lara. J, C. Duran. K, A. Esquivel. L, V. Herrera. M, J. R. de Gallegos. N, P. Fernandez. O, B. Soto. P, J. M. Montealegre. Q, B. Carrillo. R, J. Jimenez.

1943. Air. Optd **Legislacion Social 15 Setiembre 1943**.
368 5col. black (No. 209) 3·25 2·75
369 10col. brown (No. 210) 5·75 4·50

142 San Ramon

143 Allegory of Flight

1944. Centenary of San Ramon.
370 142 5c. green (postage) 10 10
371 10c. orange 15 10
372 15c. red 20 10
373 40c. grey 55 50
374 50c. blue 90 45

375 143 10c. orange (air) 15 10
376 15c. red 20 15
377 40c. blue 35 25
378 45c. red 40 35
379 60c. green 30 25
380 1col. brown 65 50
381 1col.40 grey 3·75 3·00
382 5col. violet 9·50 9·00
383 10col. black 27·00 24·00

1944. Ratification of Costa Rica and Panama Boundary Treaty. Optd **La entrevista ... 1944**.
384 139 5c. orange 10 10
385 5c. green 10 10
386 5c. blue 10 10
387 5c. violet 10 10

1944. Air. No. 207 optd **1944**.
388 1col. red 45 40

1945. Air. Official Air stamps of 1934 optd **1945** in oblong network frame.
389 107 5c. green 40 35
390 10c. red 40 35
391 15c. brown 40 35
392 20c. blue 40 40
393 25c. orange 40 40
394 40c. brown 40 40
395 50c. black 40 40
396 60c. yellow 55 40
397 75c. violet 45 40
398 – 1col. red (No. O220) 45 40
399 – 2col. blue (No. O221) 3·00 2·75
400 – 5col. black (No. O222) 3·75 3·25
401 – 10col. brown (No. O223) 5·50 5·00

1945. Air stamps. Telegraph stamps as Type **62** optd **CORREO AEREO 1945** and bar.
402 62 40c. green 80 45
403 50c. blue 1·00 45
404 1col. orange 2·40 75

148 Mauro Fernandez

149 Coffee Gathering

1945. Birth Centenary of Fernandez.
405 148 20c. green 15 10

1945.
406 149 5c. black and green 10 10
407 10c. black and orange 15 10
408 20c. black and red 20 15

150 Florence Nightingale and Nurse Cavell

1945. Air. 60th Anniv of National Red Cross Society.

409	**150**	1col. black	50	35

1946. Air. Central American and Caribbean Football Championship. As Type **132**, but inscribed "FEBRERO 1946".

410	**132**	25c. green	45	40
411		30c. orange	45	40
412		55c. blue	55	40

1946. Surch **15 15**.

413	**148**	15c. on 20c. green	15	10

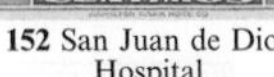

152 San Juan de Dios Hospital 153 Ascension Esquivel

1946. Air. Centenary of San Juan de Dios Hospital.

414	**152**	5c. black and green	10	10
415		10c. black and brown	10	10
416		15c. black and red	10	10
417		25c. black and blue	15	15
418		30c. black and orange	25	20
419		40c. black and olive	15	15
420		50c. black and violet	25	25
421		60c. black and green	50	45
422		75c. black and brown	40	35
423		1col. black and blue	50	25
424		2col. black and brown	55	60
425		3col. black and purple	1·40	1·40
426		5col. black and yellow	1·75	1·75

1947. Air. Former Presidents.

427	–	2col. black and blue	65	50
428	**153**	3col. black and red	1·00	65
429	–	5col. black and green	1·50	1·00
430	–	10col. black and orange	3·00	1·90

PORTRAITS: 2col. Rafael Iglesias. 5col. Cleto Gonzalez Viquez. 10col. Ricardo Jimenez.

1947. No. O228 optd **CORREOS 1947**.

431	**57**	5c. green	50	10

1947. Air. Nos. 410/2 surch **Habilitado para C 0.15 Decreto No. 16 de 28 abril de 1947**.

432	**132**	15c. on 25c. green	55	45
433		15c. on 30c. orange	55	45
434		15c. on 55c. blue	55	45

156 Columbus at Cariari 158 Franklin D. Roosevelt

1947. Air.

435	**156**	25c. black and green	65	15
436		30c. black and blue	65	15
437		40c. black and orange	85	20
438		45c. black and violet	1·10	35
439		50c. black and red	1·25	35
440		65c. black and brown	3·00	90

1947. Air. Stamps of 1942 surch **C0.15**.

441	E	15c. on 50c. orange	15	15
442	F	15c. on 60c. green	15	15
443	O	15c. on 75c. green	15	15
444	P	15c. on 1col. red	20	20
445	Q	15c. on 1col.5 sepia	15	15

1947.

446	**158**	5c. green (postage)	10	10
447		10c. red	10	10
448		15c. blue	15	15
449		25c. orange	15	15
450		30c. red	35	25
451		15c. green (air)	10	10
452		30c. red	15	10
453		45c. brown	25	25
454		65c. orange	25	25
455		75c. blue	35	25
456		1col. green	50	45
457		2col. black	75	60
458		5col. red	1·50	1·50

159 Miguel de Cervantes Saavedra

1947. 400th Birth Anniv of Cervantes.

459	**159**	30c. blue	20	10
460		55c. red	35	25

160 Steam Locomotive "Maria Cecilia"

1947. Air. 50th Anniv of Pacific Electric Railway.

461	**160**	35c. black and green	4·75	1·50

161 National Theatre 162 Rafael Iglesias

1948. Air. 50th Anniv of National Theatre.

462	**161**	15c. black and blue	15	10
463		20c. black and red	15	15
464	**162**	35c. black and green	25	20
465	**161**	45c. black and violet	35	25
466		50c. black and red	35	25
467		75c. black and purple	45	45
468		1col. black and green	85	65
469		2col. black and lake	1·25	90
470	**162**	5col. black and yellow	2·10	2·00
471		10col. black and blue	4·75	3·00

1948. Air. Surch **HABILITADO PARA C 0.35**.

472	**156**	35c. on 40c. blk & orge	60	30

1949. Air. 125th Anniv of Annexation of Guanacaste. Nos. 361, 409, 363 and 365 variously surch **1824-1949 125 Aniversario de la Anexion Guanacaste** and value.

473	Q	35c. on 1col. 5 sepia	15	15
474	**150**	50c. on 1col. black	25	15
475	R	55c. on 1col.15 green	45	35
476	B	55c. on 1col.40 yellow	45	35

165 Globe and Dove

1950. Air. 75th Anniv of U.P.U.

477	**165**	15c. red	15	10
478		25c. blue	15	10
479		1col. green	35	15

166 Battle of El Tejar, Cartago

167 Capture of Limon

1950. Air. Inscr "GUERRA DE LIBERACION NACIONAL 1948".

480	**166**	15c. black and red	15	10
481	**167**	20c. black and green	20	15
482	–	25c. black and blue	25	15
483	–	35c. black and brown	25	15
484	–	55c. black and violet	55	25
485	–	75c. black and orange	55	35
486	–	80c. black and grey	55	50
487	–	1col. black and orange	75	55

DESIGNS—VERT: 80c., 1col. Dr. C. L. Valverde. HORIZ: 25c. La Lucha Ranch; 35c. Trench of San Isidro Battalion; 55c., 75c. Observation post.

169 Bull 170 Queen Isabella and Caravels

1950. Air. National Agriculture and Industries Fair. Centres in black.

488	**169**	1c. green	10	10
489	A	2c. blue	10	10
490	B	3c. brown	10	10
491	C	5c. blue	10	10
492	**169**	10c. green	10	10
493	A	30c. violet	30	10
494	D	45c. orange	25	15
495	C	50c. grey	35	10
496	B	65c. blue	45	25
497	D	80c. red	45	30
498	**169**	2col. orange	1·25	1·00
499	A	3col. blue	3·75	2·40
500	C	5col. red	4·00	3·75
501	D	10col. red	4·00	3·75

DESIGNS—VERT: A, Fishing; B, Pineapple; C, Bananas; D, Coffee.

1952. Air. 500th Anniv of Isabella the Catholic.

502	**170**	15c. red	30	10
503		20c. orange	35	20
504		25c. blue	60	10
505		55c. green	1·25	50
506		2col. violet	3·00	1·00

1953. Air. Surch **15 15** within ornaments.

513	**158**	15c. on 30c. red	15	10
514		15c. on 45c. brown	15	10
515		15c. on 65c. orange	15	10

1953. Air. Surch **HABILITADO PARA CINCO CENTIMOS 1953**.

515a	**155**	5c. on 30c. blk & blue	1·60	1·25
516		5c. on 40c. blk & orge	20	15
517		5c. on 45c. blk & vio	20	15
518		5c. on 65c. blk & brn	50	35

173

1953. Fiscal stamps surch as in T **173**.

519	**173**	5c. on 10c. green	10	10

174 "Vegetable Oil" (175)

1954. Air. National Industries. Centres in black.

520		5c. red (Type **174**)	10	10
520a		5c. blue (Type **174**)	15	10
521		10c. indigo (Pottery)	10	10
521a		10c. blue (Pottery)	15	10
522		15c. green (Sugar)	10	10
522a		15c. yellow (Sugar)	15	10
523		20c. violet (Soap)	10	10
524		25c. lake (Timber)	10	10
525		30c. lilac (Matches)	30	20
526		35c. purple (Textiles)	15	10
527		40c. black (Leather)	25	15
528		45c. green (Tobacco)	50	25
529		50c. purple (Confectionery)	35	10
530		55c. yellow (Canning)	25	10
531		60c. brown (General industries)	60	35
532		65c. red (Metals)	45	50
533		75c. violet (Pharmaceutics)	65	45
533a		75c. red (as No. 533)	25	15
533b		80c. violet (as No. 533)	45	40
534		1col. turq (Paper)	35	20
535		2col. mauve (Rubber)	55	55
536		3col. green (Aircraft)	90	55
537		5col. black (Marble)	1·40	45
538		10col. yellow (Beer)	4·00	3·00

1955. Fiscal stamps optd for postal use as in T **175**.

539	**175**	5c. on 2c. green	10	10
540		15c. on 2c. green	15	10

176 Rotary Emblem over Central America 177 Map of Costa Rica

1956. Air. 50th Anniv Rotary International.

542	**176**	10c. green	10	10
543	–	25c. blue	15	10
544	–	40c. brown	35	25
545	–	45c. red	25	20
546	–	60c. purple	25	20
547	–	2col. orange	45	45

DESIGNS: 25c. Emblem, hand and boy; 40c., 2col. Emblem and hospital; 45c. Emblem, leaves and Central America; 60c. Emblem and lighthouse.

1957. Air. Centenary of War of 1856–67.

548	**177**	5c. blue	25	10
549	–	10c. green	10	10
550	–	15c. orange	10	10
551	–	20c. brown	15	10
552	–	25c. blue	15	10
553	–	30c. violet	20	15
554	–	35c. red	20	15
555	–	40c. black	20	15
556	–	45c. red	25	15
557	–	50c. blue	25	15
558	–	55c. ochre	40	15
559	–	60c. red	30	25
560	–	65c. red	35	25
561	–	70c. yellow	45	30
562	–	75c. green	40	25
563	–	80c. sepia	45	35
564	–	1col. black	50	35

DESIGNS: 10c. Map of Guanacaste; 15c. Wartime inn; 20c. Santa Rosa house; 25c. Gen. D. J. M. Quiros; 30c. Old Presidential Palace; 35c. Minister D. J. B. Calvo; 40c. Dr. Luis Molina; 45c. Gen. D. J. J. Mora; 50c. Gen. D. J. M. Canas; 55c. Juan Santamaria Monument; 60c. National Monument; 65c. A. Vallerriestra; 70c. Pres. R. Castilla Marquesado of Peru; 75c. San Carlos Fortress; 80c. Vice-President D. F. M. Oreamuno of Costa Rica; 1col. Pres. D. J. R. Mora of Costa Rica.

1958. Obligatory Tax. Christmas. Nos. 489 and 521a surch **SELLO DE NAVIDAD PRO - CIUDAD DE LOS NINOS 5 5**.

565	A	5c. on 2c. black & blue	10	10
566	–	5c. on 10c. black & blue	25	10

179 Pres. Gonzalez Viquez 180 Pres. R. J. Oreamuno and Electric Locomotive No. 31

1959. Air. Birth Centenaries of Presidents Gonzalez (1958) and Oreamuno (1959).

567	**179**	5c. blue and pink	10	10
568	–	10c. slate and red	10	10
569	–	15c. black and slate	10	10
570	–	20c. brown and red	1·00	25
571	–	35c. blue and purple	15	15
572	–	55c. violet and brown	25	20
573	–	80c. blue	40	35
574	**180**	1col. lake and orange	3·50	45
575	–	2col. lake and black	60	45

DESIGNS—As Type **179**: 10c. Pres. Oreamuno. As Type **180**: Pres. Gonzalez and: 15c. Highway bridge; 55c. Water pipe-line; 80c. National Library. Pres. Oreamuno and: 20c. Puntarenas Quay; 35c. Post Office, San Jose. 2col. Both presidents and open book inscr "PROBIDAD" ("Honesty").

181 Father Flanagan 182 Goal Attack

1959. Obligatory Tax. Christmas. Inscr "SELLO DE NAVIDAD".

576	**181**	5c. green	20	10
577	–	5c. mauve	20	10
578	–	5c. olive	20	10
579	–	5c. black	20	10

PAINTINGS: No. 577, "Girl with braids" (after Modigliani). No. 578, "Boy with a clubfoot" (after Ribera). No. 579, "The boy blowing on charcoal" (after "El Greco").

1960. Air. 3rd Pan-American Football Games.

580	**182**	10c. blue	10	10
581	–	25c. blue	15	10
582	–	35c. red	15	15
583	–	50c. brown	20	15
584	–	85c. turquoise	40	50
585	–	5col. purple	1·25	1·25

DESIGNS: 25c. Player heading ball; 35c. Defender tackling forward; 50c. Referee bouncing ball; 85c. Goalkeeper seizing ball; 5col. Player kicking high ball.

183 "Uprooted Tree"

184 Prof. J. A. Facio

1960. Air. World Refugee Year.
586 **183** 35c. blue and yellow . . . 20 15
587 85c. black and pink . . . 40 35

1960. Birth Centenary of Professor Justo A. Facio.
588 **184** 10c. red 10 10

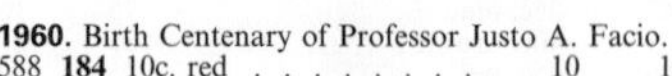

185 "OEA" and Banner

1960. Air. 6th and 7th Chancellors' Reunion Conference, Organization of American States, San Jose. Multicoloured.
589 25c. Type **185** 15 10
590 35c. "OEA" within oval chains 35 30
591 55c. Clasped hands and chains 50 40
592 5col. Flags in form of flying bird . . . . 1·90 1·75
593 10col. "OEA" on map of Costa Rica, and flags . . . 3·00 2·40

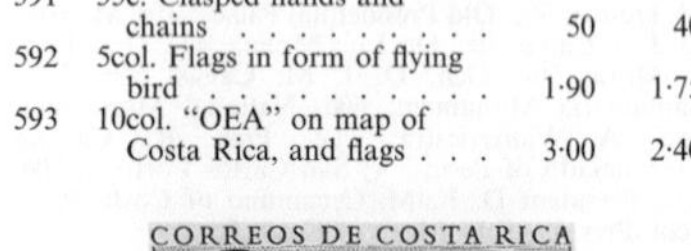

186 St. Louise de Marillac, Sister of Charity and Children

1960. Air. 300th Death Anniv of St. Vincent de Paul.
594 **186** 10c. green 10 10
595 – 25c. lake 10 10
596 – 50c. blue 25 15
597 – 1col. bistre 40 35
598 – 5col. sepia . . . . 1·25 95
DESIGNS—HORIZ: St. Vincent de Paul, and: 25c. Two-storey building; 1col. Modern building; 50c. As Type **186**, but scene shows Sister at bedside. VERT: 5col. Stained-glass window picturing St. Vincent de Paul with children.

187 Father Peralta

1960. Obligatory Tax. Christmas. Inscr "SELLO DE NAVIDAD".
599 **187** 5c. brown 35 10
600 – 5c. orange 35 10
601 – 5c. red 35 10
602 – 5c. blue 35 10
DESIGNS: No. 600, "Girl" (after Renoir); No. 601, "The Drinkers" (after Velasquez); No. 602, "Children Singing" (sculpture, after Zuniga).

188 Running

1960. Air. Olympics Game, Rome. Centres and inscriptions in black.
603 1c. yellow (T **188**) 10 10
604 2c. blue (Diving) 10 10
605 3c. red (Cycling) 10 10
606 4c. yellow (Weightlifting) . . 10 10
607 5c. green (Tennis) 10 10
608 10c. red (Boxing) 10 10
609 25c. turquoise (Football) . . 10 10
610 85c. mauve (Basketball) . . . 55 45
611 1col. grey (Baseball) 65 55
612 10col. lavender (Pistol-shooting) . . . . 5·50 4·50

1961. Air. 15th World Amateur Baseball Championships. No. 533a optd **XV Campeonato Mundial de Beisbol de Aficionados** or surch also.
613 25c. on 75c. black and red 20 10
614 75c. black and red 55 25

190 M. Aguilar

191 Prof. M. Obregon

1961. Air. 1st Continental Lawyers' Conference.
615 **190** 10c. blue 10 10
616 – 10c. purple 10 10
617 – 25c. violet 15 10
618 – 25c. sepia 15 10
PORTRAITS: No. 616, A. Brenes. No. 617, A. Gutierrez. No. 618, V. Herrera.
See also Nos. 628/31.

1961. Air. Birth Centenary of Obregon.
619 **191** 10c. turquoise 10 10

192 Granary (F.A.O.)

1961. Air. United Nations Commemoration.
620 **192** 10c. green 10 10
621 – 20c. orange 15 15
622 – 25c. slate 20 15
623 – 30c. blue 20 15
624 – 35c. red 50 25
625 – 45c. violet 35 20
626 – 85c. blue 40 30
627 – 10col. black . . . . . . 3·00 2·40
DESIGNS: 20c. "Medical Care" (W.H.O.); 25c. Globe and workers (I.L.O.); 30c. Globe and communications satellite "Correo 1B" (I.T.U.); 35c. Compass and rocket (W.M.O.); 45c. "The Thinker" (statue) and open book (U.N.E.S.C.O.); 85c. Douglas DC-6 airliner and globe (I.C.A.O.); 10col. "Spiderman" on girder (International Bank).

1961. Air. 9th Central American Medical Congress. As T **190** but inscr "NOVENO CONGRESO MEDICO", etc.
628 10c. violet 10 10
629 10c. turquoise 10 10
630 25c. sepia 15 10
631 25c. purple 15 10
PORTRAITS: No. 628, Dr. E. J. Roman. No. 629, Dr. J. M. S. Alfaro. No. 630, Dr. A. S. Llorente. No. 631, Dr. J. J. U. Giralt.

1961. Air. Children's City Christmas issue. No. 522 surch **SELLO DE NAVIDAD PRO-CIUDAD DE LOS NINOS 5 5.**
632 5c. on 10c. black and green 15 10

1962. Air. Surch in figures.
633 10c. on 15c. black and green (No. 522) 10 10
634 25c. on 15c. black and green (No. 522) 10 10
635 35c. on 50c. black and purple (No. 529) 20 15
636 85c. on 80c. blue (No. 573) 55 45

1962. Air. 2nd Central American Philatelic Convention. Optd **II CONVENCION FILATELICA CENTROAMERICANA SETIEMBRE 1962.**
637 30c. blue (No. 623) 45 35
638 2col. red and black (No. 575) 85 65

1962. Air. No. 522 surch **C 0.10.**
639 10c. on 15c. black & green 10 10

1962. Air. Fiscal stamps as T **175** optd **CORREO AEREO** and surch with new value for postal use.
640 25c. on 2c. green 10 10
641 35c. on 2c. green 15 10
642 45c. on 2c. green 25 20
643 85c. on 2c. green 45 35

198 "Virgin and Child" (after Bellini)

199 Jaguar

1962. Obligatory Tax. Christmas.
644 **198** 5c. sepia 40 10
645 A 5c. green 40 10
646 B 5c. blue 40 10
647 C 5c. red 40 10
DESIGNS: A, "Angel with Violin" (after Mellozo); B, Mgr. Ruben Odio; C, "Child's Head" (after Rubens).
See also Nos. 674/7.

1963. Air.
648 – 5c. brown and olive . . . 10 10
649 – 10c. blue and orange . . 10 10
650 **199** 25c. yellow and blue . . . 20 10
651 – 30c. brown and green . . 35 30
652 – 35c. brown and bistre . . 65 30
653 – 40c. blue and green . . . 70 45
654 – 85c. black and green . . . 1·10 70
655 – 5col. brown and green . . 5·75 4·75
ANIMALS (As Type **199**): 5c. Paca. 10c. Bairds tapir. 30c. Ocelot. 35c. White-tailed deer. 40c. American manatee. 85c. White-throated capuchin. 5col. White-lipped peccary.

200 Arms and Campaign Emblem

202 Anglo-Costa Rican Bank

1963. Air. Malaria Eradication.
656 **200** 25c. red 10 10
657 35c. brown 15 15
658 45c. blue 25 20
659 85c. green 45 35
660 1col. blue 55 45

1963. Obligatory Tax Fund for Children's Village. Nos. 644/7 surch **1963 10 CENTIMOS.**
661 **198** 10c. on 5c. sepia 15 15
662 A 10c. on 5c. green 15 15
663 B 10c. on 5c. blue 15 15
664 C 10c. on 5c. red 15 15

1963. Anglo-Costa Rican Bank Centenary.
665 **202** 10c. blue 10 10

203 ½ real Stamp of 1863 and Sail Merchantman "William le Lacheur"

1963. Air. Stamp Centenary.
666 **203** 25c. blue and purple . . . 50 15
667 – 2col. orange and grey . . 1·25 85
668 – 3col. green and ochre . . 2·00 1·50
669 – 10col. brown and green 9·00 4·00
DESIGNS: 2col. 2 reales stamp of 1863 and Postmaster-General R. B. Carrillo; 3col. 4 reales stamp of 1863 and mounted postman and pack-mule of 1839; 10col. 1 peso stamp of 1863 and mule-drawn mail van.

1963. Unissued animal designs as T **199**. Surch.
670 10c. on 1c. brown and green 15 10
671 25c. on 2c. sepia and brown 20 10
672 35c. on 3c. brown and green 25 15
673 85c. on 4c. brown and lake 55 25
ANIMALS: 1c. Tamandua. 2c. Grey fox. 3c. Nine-banded armadillo. 4c. Giant anteater.

1963. Obligatory Tax. Christmas. As Nos. 644/7 but inscr "1963" and new colours.
674 **198** 5c. blue 20 10
675 A 5c. red 20 10
676 B 5c. black 20 10
677 C 5c. sepia 20 10

205 Pres. Orlich (Costa Rica)

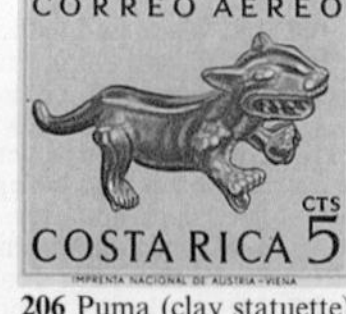

206 Puma (clay statuette)

1963. Air. Presidential Reunion, San Jose. Portraits in sepia.
678 **205** 25c. purple 10 10
679 – 30c. mauve 15 10
680 – 35c. ochre 15 15
681 – 85c. blue 40 25
682 – 1col. brown 40 30
683 – 3col. green . . . . 1·00 65
684 – 5col. slate . . . . 1·40 1·00
PRESIDENTS: 30c. Rivera (Salvador). 35c. Ydigoras (Guatemala). 85c. Villeda (Honduras). 1col. Somoza (Nicaragua). 3col. Chiari (Panama). 5col. Kennedy (U.S.A.).

1963. Air. Archaeological Discoveries.
685 **206** 5c. turquoise and green 10 10
686 – 10c. turquoise and yellow 10 10
687 – 25c. sepia and red 10 10
688 – 30c. turquoise and buff 10 10
689 – 35c. green and salmon . . 15 10
690 – 45c. brown and blue . . . 15 10
691 – 50c. brown and blue . . . 15 10
692 – 55c. brown and green . . 20 10
693 – 75c. brown and buff . . . 20 15
694 – 85c. brown and yellow . . 55 35
695 – 90c. brown and yellow . . 45 35
696 – 1col. brown and blue . . 40 25
697 – 2col. turquoise & yellow 70 45
698 – 3col. brown and green . . 1·25 80
699 – 5col. brown & yellow . . 1·25 75
700 – 10col. green and mauve 2·00 1·90
DESIGNS—HORIZ: 10c. Ceremonial stool; 1col. Twin beakers; 2col. Alligator. VERT: 25c. Man (statuette); 30c. Dancer; 35c. Vase; 45c. Deity; 50c. Frog; 55c. "Eagle" bell; 75c. Multi-limbed deity; 85c. Kneeling effigy; 90c. "Bird" jug; 3col. Twin-tailed lizard; 5col. Child; 10col. Stone effigy of woman.

207 Flags

210 Mgr. R. Odio and Children

1964. Air. "Centro America".
701 **207** 30c. multicoloured 35 25

1964. Air. Surch.
702 – 5c. on 30c. (No. 688) . . 10 10
703 **207** 15c. on 30c. 10 10
704 – 15c. on 85c. (No. 694) . . 10 10
See Nos. 745/9.

1964. Paris Postal Conf. No. 695 surch **C 0.15 CONFERENCIA POSTAL DE PARIS - 1864.**
705 15c. on 90c. brn & yellow . . 10 10

1964. Obligatory Tax. Christmas. Inscr "SELLO DE NAVIDAD", etc.
706 **210** 5c. brown 15 10
707 A 5c. blue 15 10
708 B 5c. purple 15 10
709 C 5c. green 15 10
DESIGNS: A, Teacher and child; B, Children at play; C, Children in class.

211 A. Gonzalez F.

213 Handfuls of Grain

1965. Air. 50th Anniv of National Bank.
710 **211** 35c. green 10 10

1965. Air. 75th Anniv of Chapui Hospital. No. 697 surch **75 ANIVERSARIO ASILO CHAPUI 1890–1965.**
711 2col. turquoise and yellow . . 60 45

1965. Air. Freedom from Hunger.
712 – 15c. black, grey & brown 10 10
713 **213** 35c. black and buff . . . 15 10
714 – 50c. green and blue . . . 20 15
715 – 1col. silver, black & green 35 20
DESIGNS—HORIZ: 15c. Map and grain silo; 1col. Douglas DC-8 airliner over map. VERT: 50c. Children and population graph.

214 National Children's Hospital

215 L. Briceno B.

1965. Christmas Charity. Obligatory Tax. Inscr "SELLO DE NAVIDAD", etc.
716 **214** 5c. green 15 10
717 A 5c. brown 15 10

718 B 5c. red 15 10
719 C 5c. blue 15 10
DESIGNS—As Type **214**: A, Father Casiano; B, Poinsettia. DIAMOND: C, Father Christmas with children.

1965. Air. Incorporation of Nicoya District.
720 **215** 5c. slate, black & brown 10 10
721 – 10c. slate and blue . . . 10 10
722 – 15c. slate and bistre . . . 10 10
723 – 35c. slate and blue . . . 10 10
724 – 50c. violet and grey . . . 15 10
725 – 1col. slate and ochre . . . 40 25
DESIGNS: 10c. Nicoya Church; 15c. Incorporation scroll; 35c. Map of Guanacaste Province; 50c. Provincial dance; 1col. Guanacaste map and produce.

216 Running

217 Pres. John F. Kennedy and "Mercury" Space Capsule encircling Globe

1965. Air. Olympic Games (1964). Mult.
726 5c. Type **216** 10 10
727 10c. Cycling 10 10
728 40c. Judo 15 10
729 65c. Handball 25 15
730 80c. Football 35 20
731 1col. Olympic torches 45 25

1965. Air. 2nd Death Anniv of Pres. Kennedy. Multicoloured.
732 45c. Type **217** 15 15
733 55c. Kennedy in San Jose Cathedral (vert) 25 15
734 85c. President with son (vert) 35 25
735 1col. Facade of White House, Washington (vert) 35 30

218 Fire Engine

219 Angel

1966. Air. Centenary of Fire Brigade.
736 **218** 5c. red and black 10 10
737 – 10c. red and yellow . . . 10 10
738 – 15c. black and red . . . 10 10
739 – 35c. yellow and black . . 40 10
740 – 50c. red and blue 75 10
DESIGNS—VERT: 10c. Fire engine of 1866; 15c. Firemen with hoses; 35c. Brigade badge; 50c. Emblem of Central American Fire Brigades Confederation.

1966. Obligatory Tax. Christmas. Inscr "SELLO DE NAVIDAD", etc.
741 **219** 5c. blue 15 10
742 – 5c. red (Trinkets) 15 10
743 – 5c. green (Church) . . . 15 10
744 – 5c. brown (Reindeer) . . 15 10

1966. Air. (a) Surch with new value.
745 – 15c. on 30c. (No. 688) . . . 10 10
746 – 15c. on 45c. (No. 690) . . . 10 10
747 – 35c. on 75c. (No. 693) . . . 15 10
748 – 35c. on 55c. (No. 733) . . . 15 10
749 – 50c. on 85c. (No. 734) . . . 25 15

(b) Revenue stamps (as T **175**) surch **CORREOS DE COSTA RICA AEREO** and value.
750 15c. on 5c. blue 10 10
751 35c. on 10c. red 15 10
752 50c. on 20c. red 25 15

221 Central Bank, San Jose

222 Telecommunications Building, San Pedro

1967. Obligatory Tax. Social Plan for Postal Workers.
753 10c. blue 10 10
DESIGN—as Type **221** (34 × 26 mm.): 10c. Post Office, San Jose.

1967. Air. 50th Anniv of Central Bank.
754 **221** 5c. green 10 10
755 15c. brown 10 10
756 35c. red 15 10

1967. Air. Costa Rican Electrical Industry
757 – 5c. black 10 10
758 **222** 10c. mauve 10 10
759 – 15c. orange 10 10
760 – 25c. blue 10 10
761 – 35c. green 15 10
762 – 50c. brown 25 15
DESIGNS—VERT: 5c. Electric pylons; 15c. Central Telephone Exchange, San Jose. HORIZ: 25c. La Garita Dam; 35c. Rio Macho Reservoir; 50c. Cachi Dam.

223 "Chondrorhyncha aromatica"

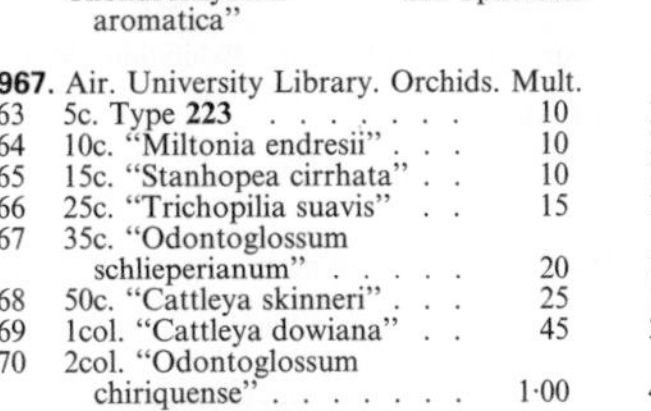

224 O.E.A. Emblem and Split Leaf

1967. Air. University Library. Orchids. Mult.
763 5c. Type **223** 10 10
764 10c. "Miltonia endresii" . . . 10 10
765 15c. "Stanhopea cirrhata" . . 10 10
766 25c. "Trichopilia suavis" . . 15 10
767 35c. "Odontoglossum schlieperianum" 20 15
768 50c. "Cattleya skinneri" . . . 25 15
769 1col. "Cattleya dowiana" . . 45 35
770 2col. "Odontoglossum chiriquense" . . . . 1·00 40

1967. Air. 25th Anniv of Inter-American Institute of Agricultural Science.
771 **224** 50c. ultramarine & blue 15 10

225 Madonna and Child

226 LACSA Emblem

1967. Obligatory Tax. Christmas.
772 **225** 5c. green 10 10
773 5c. mauve 10 10
774 5c. blue 10 10
775 5c. turquoise 10 10

1967. Air. 20th Anniv (1966) of LACSA (Costa Rican Airlines). Multicoloured.
776 40c. Type **226** 10 10
777 45c. LACSA emblem and jetliner (horiz) 15 10
778 50c. Wheel and emblem . . . 15 15

227 Church of Solitude

228 Scouts in Camp

1967. Air. Churches and Cathedrals (1st series).
779 **227** 5c. green 10 10
780 – 10c. blue 10 10
781 – 15c. purple 10 10
782 – 25c. ochre 10 10
783 – 30c. brown 10 10
784 – 35c. blue 10 10
785 – 40c. orange 10 10
786 – 45c. green 10 10
787 – 50c. olive 15 10
788 – 55c. brown 15 10
789 – 65c. mauve 15 15
790 – 75c. sepia 20 15
791 – 80c. yellow 25 20
792 – 85c. purple . . . . 1·10 20
793 – 90c. green . . . . 1·10 25
794 – 1col. slate 25 25
795 – 2col. green 75 90
796 – 3col. orange . . . . . . 2·10 1·25
797 – 5col. blue . . . . 2·00 1·50
798 – 10col. red . . . . 2·50 2·00
DESIGNS: 10c. Santo Domingo Basilica, Heredia; 15c. Tilaran Cathedral; 25c. Alajuela Cathedral; 30c. Church of Mercy; 35c. Our Lady of the Angels Basilica; 40c. San Rafael Church, Heredia; 45c. Ruins, Ujarras; 50c. Ruins of Parish Church, Cartago; 55c. San Jose Cathedral; 65c. Parish Church, Puntarenas; 75c. Orosi Church; 80c. Cathedral of San Isidro the General; 85c. San Ramon Church; 90c. Church of the Forsaken; 1col. Coronado Church; 2col. Church of St. Teresita; 3col. Parish Church, Heredia; 5col. Carmelite Church; 10col. Limon Cathedral.
See also Nos. 918/33.

1968. Air. Golden Jubilee (1966) of Scout Movement in Costa Rica. Multicoloured.
799 15c. Scout on traffic control (vert) 10 10
800 25c. Scouts tending campfire (vert) 15 10
801 35c. Scout badge and flags (vert) 20 15
802 50c. Type **228** 25 15
803 65c. First scout troop on parade (1916) 35 20

229 "Madonna and Child"

230 Running

1968. Christmas Charity. Obligatory Tax.
805 **229** 5c. black 10 10
806 5c. purple 10 10
807 5c. brown 10 10
808 5c. red 10 10

1969. Air. Olympic Games, Mexico. Mult.
809 30c. Type **230** 10 10
810 40c. Woman breasting tape 15 10
811 55c. Boxing 25 15
812 65c. Cycling 30 15
813 75c. Weightlifting 30 15
814 1col. High-diving 35 25
815 3col. Rifle-shooting 90 55

231 Exhibition Emblem

232 Arms of San Jose

1969. Air. "Costa Rica 69" Philatelic Exn.
816 **231** 35c. multicoloured 10 10
817 40c. multicoloured 15 10
818 50c. multicoloured 15 10
819 2col. multicoloured . . . 1·10 40

1969. Coats of Arms. Multicoloured.
820 15c. Type **232** 10 10
821 35c. Cartago 15 10
822 50c. Heredia 15 10
823 55c. Alajuela 15 15
824 65c. Guanacaste 25 15
825 1col. Puntarenas 60 15
826 2col. Limon 70 35

233 I.L.O. Emblem

234 Map on Football

1969. Air. 50th Anniv of I.L.O.
827 **233** 35c. turquoise and black 15 10
828 50c. red and black 20 10

1969. Air. 4th CONCACAF Football Championships. Multicoloured.
829 65c. Type **234** 20 15
830 75c. Goalmouth melee . . . 20 15
831 85c. Players with ball 25 15
832 1col. Two players with ball 30 20

235 Madonna and Child

236 Stylized Crab

1969. Christmas. Charity. Obligatory Tax.
833 **235** 5c. turquoise 10 10
834 5c. lake 10 10
835 5c. blue 10 10
836 5c. orange 10 10

1970. Air. 10th Inter-American Cancer Congress, San Jose.
837 **236** 10c. black and mauve . . 10 10
838 15c. black and yellow . . 10 10
839 50c. black and orange . . 15 10
840 1col.10 black and green 30 15

238 Costa Rican stamps and Magnifier

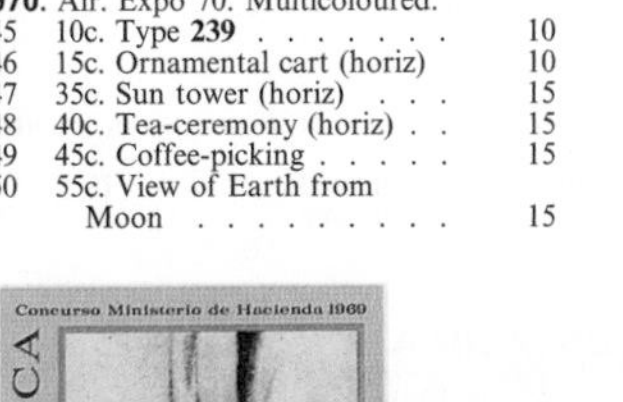

239 Japanese Vase and Flowers

1970. Air. "Costa Rica 70" Philatelic Exhibition.
843 **238** 1col. red and blue 55 20
844 2col. mauve and blue . . 1·10 45

1970. Air. Expo 70. Multicoloured.
845 10c. Type **239** 10 10
846 15c. Ornamental cart (horiz) 10 10
847 35c. Sun tower (horiz) . . . 15 10
848 40c. Tea-ceremony (horiz) . . 15 10
849 45c. Coffee-picking 15 10
850 55c. View of Earth from Moon 15 10

240 "Irazu" (R. A. Garcia)

241 "Holy Child"

1970. Air. Costa Rican Paintings. Mult.
851 25c. Type **240** 30 10
852 45c. "Escazu Valley" (M. Bertheau) 30 10
853 80c. "Estuary Landscape" (T. Quiros) 65 15
854 1col. "The Other Face" (C. Valverde) 45 15
855 2col.50 "Madonna" (L. Daell) (vert) . . . . . 1·25 60

1970. Christmas Charity. Obligatory Tax.
856 **241** 5c. mauve 10 10
857 5c. brown 10 10
858 5c. olive 10 10
859 5c. violet 10 10

242 Costa Rican Arms of 21 October 1964

243 National Theatre, San Jose

1971. Air. Various Costa Rican Coats of Arms (with dates). Multicoloured.
860 5c. Type **242** 10 10
861 10c. 27 November 1906 . . . 10 10
862 15c. 29 September 1848 . . . 10 10
863 25c. 21 April 1840 . . . . . 10 10
864 35c. 22 November 1824 . . . 10 10
865 50c. 2 November 1824 . . . 10 10
866 1col. 6 March 1824 . . . . . 15 10
867 2col. 10 May 1823 . . . . . 60 20

1971. Air. O.E.A. General Assembly. San Jose.
868 **243** 2col. purple 35 25

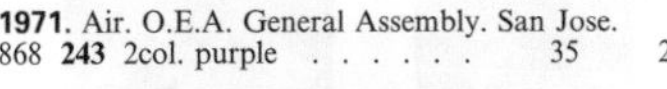

244 J. M. Delgado and M. J. Arce (Salvador)

1971. Air. 150th Anniv of Central American Independence. Multicoloured.
869 5c. Type **244** 10 10
870 10c. M. Larreinaga and M. A. de la Cerda (Nicaragua) 10 10
871 15c. J. C. del Valle and D. de Herrera (Honduras) . . . 10 10
872 35c. P. Alvarado and F. del Castillo (Costa Rica) . . . 10 10

873 50c. A. Larrazabal and P. Molina (Guatemala) 10 10
874 1col. O.D.E.C.A. flag (vert) 15 10
875 2col. O.D.E.C.A. emblem (vert) 35 25
O.D.E.C.A. = Organization of Central American States.

245 Cradle on "PAX" 246 Federation Emblem

1971. Christmas Charity. Obligatory Tax.
876 **245** 10c. orange 10 10
877 10c. brown 10 10
878 10c. green 10 10
879 10c. blue 10 10

1971. Air. 50th Anniv of Costa Rican Football Federation.
880 **246** 50c. multicoloured 10 10
881 60c. multicoloured 10 10

247 "Children of the World" 248 Guanacaste Tree

1972. Air. 25th Anniv of U.N.I.C.E.F.
882 **247** 50c. multicoloured 10 10
883 1col.10 multicoloured 20 15

1972. Air. Bicentenary of Liberia City. Mult.
884 20c. Type **248** 10 10
885 40c. Hermitage, Liberia 10 10
886 55c. Mayan petroglyphs 10 10
887 60c. Clay head (vert) 15 10

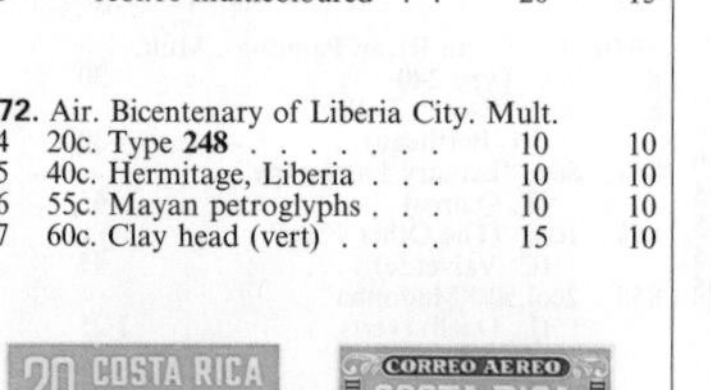

250 Farmer's Family and Farm 251 Inter-American Stamp Exhibitions

1972. Air. 30th Anniv of O.E.A. Institute of Agricultural Sciences (IICA).
892 **250** 20c. multicoloured 10 10
893 – 45c. multicoloured 10 10
894 – 50c. yellow, green & blk 10 10
895 – 10col. multicoloured 1·10 60
DESIGNS—HORIZ: 45c. Cattle. VERT: 50c. Tree-planting; 10col. Agricultural worker and map.

1972. Air. "Exfilbra 72" Stamp Exhibition.
896 **251** 50c. brown and orange 10 10
897 2col. violet and blue 35 25

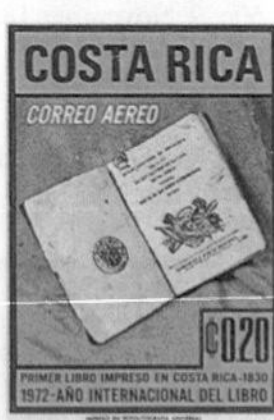

252 Madonna and Child 253 First Book printed in Costa Rica

1972. Christmas Charity. Obligatory Tax.
898 **252** 10c. red 10 10
899 10c. lilac 10 10
900 10c. blue 10 10
901 10c. green 10 10

1972. Air. International Book Year. Mult.
902 20c. Type **253** 10 10
903 50c. National Library, San Jose (horiz) 10 10
904 75c. Type **253** 15 10
905 5col. As 50c. 60 45

254 View near Irazu 255 Madonna and Child

1972. Air. American Tourist Year. Mult.
906 5c. Type **254** 10 10
907 15c. Entrance to Culebra Bay 10 10
908 20c. Type **254** 10 10
909 25c. As 15c. 10 10
910 40c. Manuel Antonio Beach 10 10
911 45c. Costa Rican Tourist Institute emblem 10 10
912 50c. Lindora Lake 10 10
913 60c. Post Office Building, San Jose (vert) 15 10
914 80c. As 40c. 15 15
915 90c. As 45c. 15 15
916 1col. As 50c. 15 15
917 2col. As 60c. 35 25

1973. Air. Churches and Cathedrals (2nd series). As Nos. 779/94 but colours changed.
918 **227** 5c. grey 10 10
919 – 10c. green 10 10
920 – 15c. orange 10 10
921 – 25c. brown 10 10
922 – 30c. purple 10 10
923 – 35c. violet 15 10
924 – 40c. green 15 10
925 – 45c. brown 15 10
926 – 50c. red 15 10
927 – 55c. blue 15 10
928 – 65c. black 15 10
929 – 75c. red 15 10
930 – 80c. green 15 10
931 – 85c. lilac 15 15
932 – 90c. red 15 15
933 – 1col. blue 15 15

1973. Obligatory Tax. Christmas Charity.
934 **255** 10c. red 10 10
935 10c. purple 10 10
936 10c. black 10 10
937 10c. brown 10 10

256 Flame Emblem 257 O.E.A. Emblem

1973. Air. 25th Anniv of Declaration of Human Rights.
938 **256** 50c. red and blue 10 10

1973. Air. 25th Anniv of Organization of American States.
939 **257** 20c. red and blue 10 10

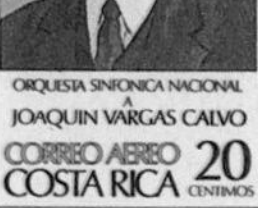

258 J. Vargas Calvo 260 Telephone Centre, San Pedro

1974. Air. Costa Rican Composers. Mult.
940 20c. Type **258** 10 10
941 20c. Alejandro Monestel 10 10
942 20c. Julio Mata 10 10
943 60c. Julio Fonseca 15 10
944 2col. Rafael Chaves 35 25
945 5col. Manuel Gutierrez 85 70

1974. Air. Fiscal stamps as Type 175 (but without surcharge) optd **HABILITADO PARA CORREO AEREO**.
946 50c. brown 10 10
947 1col. violet 15 10
948 2col. orange 35 20
949 5col. green 85 70

1974. Air. 25th Anniv of Costa Rican Electrical Institute. Multicoloured.
950 50c. Type **260** 10 10
951 65c. Control Room, Rio Macho (horiz) 15 10
952 85c. Power house, Rio Macho 15 15
953 1col.25 Cachi Dam, Rio Macho (horiz) 20 15
954 2col. Institute H.Q. building 35 20

261 "Exfilmex" Emblem 262 Couple on Map

1974. Air. "Exfilmex" Stamp Exhibition, Mexico City.
955 **261** 65c. green 15 10
956 3col. pink 50 35

1974. Air. 25th Anniv of 4-S Clubs.
957 **262** 20c. emerald and green 10 10
958 – 50c. multicoloured 10 10
DESIGN. 50c. Young agricultural workers.

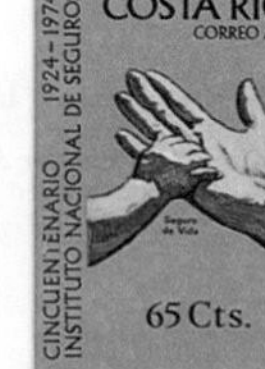

263 Brenes Mesen 264 Child's and Adult's Hands

1974. Air. Birth Centenary of Roberto Brenes Mesen (educator).
959 **263** 20c. black and brown 10 10
960 – 85c. black and red 15 15
961 – 5col. brown and black 85 70
DESIGNS—VERT: 85c. Brenes Mesen's "Poems of Love and Death". HORIZ: 5col. Brenes Mesen's hands.

1974. Air. 50th Anniv of Costa Rican Insurance Institute.
962 – 20c. multicoloured 10 10
963 – 50c. multicoloured 10 10
964 **264** 65c. multicoloured 10 15
965 – 85c. multicoloured 15 15
966 – 1col.25 black and gold 20 15
967 – 2col. multicoloured 35 20
968 – 2col.50 multicoloured 45 35
969 – 20col. multicoloured 2·50 2·40
DESIGNS—HORIZ: 20c. R. Jimenez Oreamuno and T. Soley Guell (founders); 50c. Spade ("Harvest Insurance"). VERT: 85c. Paper boat within hand ("Marine Insurance"); 1col.25, Institute emblem; 2col. Arm in brace ("Workers' Rehabilitation"); 2col.50, Hand holding spanner ("Risks at Work"); 20col. House in protective hands ("Fire Insurance").

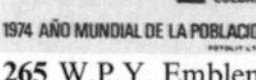

265 W.P.Y. Emblem 266 "Boys eating Cakes" (Murillo)

1974. Air. World Population Year.
970 **265** 2col. red and blue 35 20

1974. Obligatory Tax. Christmas.
971 **266** 10c. red 10 10
972 – 10c. purple 10 10
973 – 10c. black 10 10
974 – 10c. blue 10 10
DESIGNS: No. 972, "The Beautiful Gardener" (Raphael); No. 973, "Maternity" (J. R. Bonilla); No. 974, "The Prayer" (J. Reynolds).

267 Oscar J. Pinto (football pioneer) 268 "Mormodes buccinator"

1974. Air. 1st Central American Olympic Games, Guatemala (1973). Each grey and blue.
975 20c. Type **267** 10 10
976 50c. D. A. Montes de Oca (shooting champion) 10 10
977 1col. Eduardo Garnier (promoter of athletics) 15 10

1975. Air. 1st Central American Orchids Exhibition. Multicoloured.
978 25c. Type **268** 10 10
979 25c. "Gongora claviodora" 10 10
980 25c. "Masdevallia ephippium" 10 10
981 25c. "Encyclia spondiadum" 10 10
982 65c. "Lycaste skinneri alba" 40 10
983 65c. "Peristeria elata" 40 10
984 65c. "Miltonia roezelii" 40 10
985 65c. "Brassavola digbyana" 40 10
986 80c. "Epidendrum mirabile" 50 15
987 80c. "Barkeria lindleyana" 50 15
988 80c. "Cattleya skinneri" 50 15
989 80c. "Sobralia macrantha splendens" 50 15
990 1col.40 "Lycaste cruenta" 65 15
991 1col.40 "Oncidium obryzatum" 65 15
992 1col.40 "Gongora armeniaca" 65 15
993 1col.40 "Sievekingia suavis" 65 15
994 1col.75 "Hexisea imbricata" 65 20
995 2col.15 "Warcewiczella discolor" 65 20
996 2col.50 "Oncidium kramerianum" 90 35
997 3col.25 "Cattleya dowiana" 1·25 40

269 Emblem of Costa Rica Radio Club

1975. Air. 16th Convention of Radio Amateurs Federation of Central America and Panama, San Jose.
998 **269** 1col. purple and black 15 10
999 – 1col.10 red and blue 20 15
1000 – 2col. blue and black 35 20
DESIGNS—VERT: 1col.10, Federation emblem within "V" of Flags. HORIZ: 2col. Federation emblem.

270 Nicoyan Beach

1975. Air. 150th Anniv of Annexation of Nicoya. Multicoloured.
1001 25c. Type **270** 10 10
1002 75c. Cattle-drive 15 15
1003 1col. Colonial church 15 15
1004 3col. Savannah riders (vert) 50 40

271 3c. Philatelic Exhibition Stamp of 1932

1975. Air. 6th National Philatelic Exhibition, San Jose.
1005 **271** 2col.20 orange & black 40 35
1006 – 2col.20 green and black 40 35
1007 – 2col.20 red and black 40 35
1008 – 2col.20 blue and black 40 35
DESIGNS: Stamps of 1932. No. 1006, 5c. stamp; No. 1007, 10c. stamp; No. 1008, 20c. stamp.

272 I.W.Y. Emblem 273 U.N. Emblem

1975. Air. International Women's Year.
1009 **272** 40c. red and blue 10 10
1010 1col.25 blue and black 20 15

1975. Air. 30th Anniv of United Nations.
1011 **273** 10c. blue and black 10 10
1012 – 60c. multicoloured 10 10
1013 – 1col.20 multicoloured 20 15
DESIGNS—HORIZ: 60c. General Assembly. VERT: 1col.20, U.N. Headquarters, New York.

274 "The Visitation"

275 "Children with Tortoise" (F. Amighetti)

1975. Air. "The Christmas Tradition". Paintings by Jorge Gallardo. Multicoloured.
1014 50c. Type **274** 10 10
1015 1col. "The Nativity and the Comet" 15 10
1016 5col. "St. Joseph in his workshop" 60 45

1975. Obligatory Tax. Christmas. Children's Village. Multicoloured.
1017 **275** 10c. brown 10 10
1018 – 10c. purple 10 10
1019 – 10c. grey 10 10
1020 – 10c. blue 10 10
DESIGNS: No. 1018, "The Virgin of the Carnation" (Da Vinci); No. 1019, "Happy Dreams" (child in bed—Sonia Romero); No. 1020, "Child with Pigeon" (Picasso).

276 Schoolboy and Flags

277 Prof. A. M. Brenes Mora

1976. Air. 20th Anniv of "20–30" Youth Clubs in Costa Rica.
1021 **276** 1col. multicoloured . . . 15 10

1976. Birth Centenary (1970) of Professor A. M. Brenes Mora (botanist).
1022 **277** 1col. violet (postage) . . 15 15
1023 – 5c. multicoloured (air) 10 10
1024 – 30c. multicoloured . . . 10 10
1025 – 55c. multicoloured . . . 10 10
1026 – 2col. multicoloured . . . 35 20
1027 – 10col. multicoloured . . 1·10 85
DESIGNS: 5c. "Quercus breneseii"; 30c. "Maxillaria albertii"; 55c. "Calathea brenesii"; 2col. "Brenesia costaricensis"; 10col. "Philodendron brenesii".
No. 1023 is wrongly inscribed "brenessi".

278 Open Book as "Flower"

281 Early and Modern Telephones

280 Mounted Postman with Pack Mule

1976. Air. Costa Rican Literature. Mult.
1028 15c. Type **278** 10 10
1029 1col.10 Reader with "T.V. eye" 15 15
1030 5col. Book and flag (horiz) 55 45

1976. Centenary (1974) of U.P.U.
1032 **280** 20c. black and yellow . . 10 10
1033 – 50c. multicoloured . . . 10 10
1034 – 65c. multicoloured . . . 15 10
1035 – 85c. multicoloured . . . 15 15
1036 – 2col. black and blue . . 35 25
DESIGNS—HORIZ: 50c., 5c. U.P.U. stamp of 1882; 65c., 10c. U.P.U. stamp of 1882; 85c., 20c. U.P.U. stamp of 1882. VERT: 2col. U.P.U. Monument, Berne.

1976. Telephone Centenary.
1037 **281** 1col.60 black and blue 25 20
1038 – 2col. black, brown & grn 35 20
1039 – 5col. black and yellow 55 45
DESIGNS: 2col. Costa Rica's first telephone; 5col. Alexander Graham Bell.

282 Emblems and Costa Rica 2c. Stamp of 1901 with Centre Inverted

1976. Air. 7th National Philatelic Exhibition.
1040 **282** 50c. multicoloured . . . 10 10
1041 1col. multicoloured . . . 15 10
1042 2col. multicoloured . . . 35 20

283 Emblem of Comptroller General

284 "Girl in Wide-brimmed Hat" (Renoir)

1976. Air. 25th Anniv of Comptroller General.
1044 **283** 35c. blue and black . . . 10 10
1045 – 2col. black, brown & bl 35 20
DESIGN—VERT: 2col. Amadeo Quiros Blanco (1st Comptroller).

1976. Obligatory Tax. Christmas.
1046 **284** 10c. lake 10 10
1047 – 10c. purple 10 10
1048 – 10c. slate 10 10
1049 – 10c. blue 10 10
DESIGNS: No 1047, "Virgin and Child" (Hans Memling); No. 1048, "Meditation" (Floria Pinto de Herrero); No. 1049, "Gaston de Mezerville" (Lolita Zeller de Peralta).

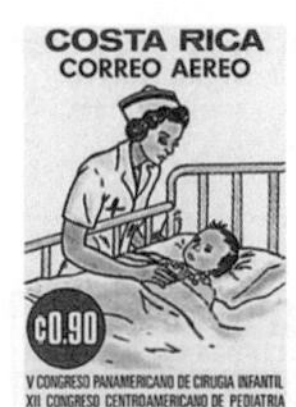
285 Nurse tending Child

286 "L.A.C.S.A." encircling Globe

1976. Air. 5th Pan-American Children's Surgery Congress. Multicoloured.
1050 90c. Type **285** 15 15
1051 1col.10 National Children's Hospital (horiz) 20 15

1976. Air. 30th Anniv of LACSA Airline. Mult.
1052 1col. Type **286** 20 10
1053 1col.20 Route-map of LACSA services 25 15
1054 3col. LACSA emblem and Costa Rican flag 65 45

287 Boston Tea Party

1976. Air. Bicent of American Revolution. Mult.
1055 2col.20 Type **287** 70 25
1056 5col. Declaration of Independence 55 45
1057 10col. Ringing the Independence Bell (vert) 1·10 85

288 Boruca Textile

289 Tree of Guanacaste

1977. Air. National Handicrafts Project. Mult.
1058 75c. Type **288** 15 10
1059 1col.50 Decorative handicraft in wood . . . 25 15

1977. Air. 50th Anniv of Rotary Club, San Jose.
1060 **289** 40c. green, blue and yellow 10 10
1061 – 50c. black, blue and yellow 10 10
1062 – 60c. black, blue and yellow 10 10
1063 – 3col. multicoloured . . . 50 40
1064 – 10col. black, blue and yellow . . . . 1·25 85
DESIGNS—VERT: 50c. Felipe J. Alvarado (founder); 10col. Paul Harris, founder of Rotary International. HORIZ: 60c. Dr. Blanco Cervantes Hospital; 3col. Map of Costa Rica.

290 Juana Pereira

291 Alonso de Anguciana de Gamboa

1977. Air. 50th Anniv of Coronation of Our Lady of the Angels (Patron Saint of Costa Rica).
1065 50c. Type **290** 10 10
1066 1col. First church of Our Lady of the Angels (horiz) 15 10
1067 1col.10 Our Lady of the Angels 20 15
1068 1col.25 Our Lady's crown 25 15

1977. Air. 400th Anniv of Foundation of Esparza.
1069 **291** 35c. purple, mve & blk 10 10
1070 – 75c. brown, red & black 15 10
1071 – 1col. dp bl, bl & blk . . 15 10
1072 – 2col. green and black . . 35 25
DESIGNS: 75c. Church of Esparza; 1col. Our Lady of Candelaria, Patron Saint of Esparza; 2col. Diego de Artieda y Chirino.

292 Child

293 Institute Emblem

1977. Air. 20 Years of "CARE" in Costa Rica. Multicoloured.
1073 80c. Type **292** 15 10
1074 1col. Soya beans (horiz) . . 15 10

1977. Air. 25th Anniv of Hispanic Cultural Institute of Costa Rica. Multicoloured.
1075 50c. Type **293** 10 10
1076 1col.40 First map of the Americas, 1540 (40 × 30 mm) 25 20

294 "Our Lady of Mercy Church" (R. Ulloa)

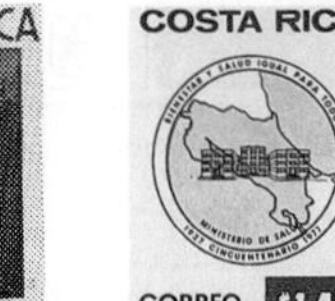
295 Health Ministry on Map

1977. Air. Mystical Paintings. Multicoloured.
1077 50c. Type **294** 10 10
1078 1col. "Christ" (F. Pinto de Herrero) 15 10
1079 5col. "St. Francis and the Birds" (L. Gonzalez de Saenz) 55 45

1977. Air. 50th Anniv of Health Ministry.
1080 **295** 1col.40 multicoloured . . 25 20

296 "Child's Head" (Rubens)

297 Weaving

1977. Obligatory Tax. Christmas.
1081 **296** 10c. red 10 10
1082 – 10c. blue 10 10
1083 – 10c. green 10 10
1084 – 10c. purple 10 10
DESIGNS: No. 1082, "Tenderness" (Cristina Fournier); No. 1083, "Abstraction" (Amparo Cruz); No. 1084, "Mariano Goya" (Francisco de Goya).

1978. Air. 21st Congress of Confederation of Latin American Tourist Organizations. Multicoloured.
1085 50c. Type **297** 10 10
1086 1col. Picnic 15 15
1087 2col. Beach scene 35 20
1088 5col. Fruit market 55 45
1089 10col. Lake scene . . . . . 1·25 85

298 Reader with Book

299 Jose de San Martin

1978. National Literacy Campaign.
1090 **298** 50c. blue, black & orge 10 10

1978. Air. Birth Bicent of Jose de San Martin.
1091 **299** 5col. multicoloured . . . 60 40

300 Globe

301 "XXX"

1978. Air. 50th Anniv of Pan-American Institute of Geography and History.
1092 **300** 5col. blue, gold & lt blue 50 60

1978. Air. 30th Anniv of Central American University Confederation.
1093 **301** 80c. blue 15 10

302 Emblems

1978. Air. 6th Inter-American Philatelic Exn, Buenos Aires.
1094 **302** 2col. turq, gold & blk . . 35 25

1978. Air. 50th Anniv of 1st PanAm Flight in Costa Rica. Nos. 994/6 optd **"50 Aniversario del primer vuelo de PAN AM en Costa Rica 1928 – 1978"**.
1095 1col.75 "Hexisea imbricata" 25 20
1096 2col.15 "Warcewiczella discolor" 35 25
1097 2col.50 "Oncidium kramerianum" 40 30

1978. Air. 50th Anniv of Lindbergh's Visit to Costa Rica. Nos. 994/6 optd **"50 Aniversario de la visita de Lindbergh a Costa Rica 1928 – 1978"**.
1098 1col.75 "Hexisea imbricata" 30 20
1099 2col.15 "Warcewiczella discolor" 35 25
1100 2col.50 "Oncidium kramerianum" 40 30

1978. Air. Carlos Maria Ulloa Hospital Centenary. Nos. 964 and 968 surch **"Centenario del Asilo Carlos Maria Ulloa 1878 – 1978"** and new value.
1101 50c. on 65c. multicoloured 10 10
1102 2col. on 2col.50 mult . . . 35 25

306 Star over Map of Costa Rica

308 "Christmas Winds" (L. F. Chacon)

1978. Air. Christmas.
1103 **306** 50c. blue and black . . . 10 10
1104 1col. mauve and black 15 15
1105 5col. red and black . . . 55 55

1978. Air. Nos. 982/5 and 995/6 surch.
1106 50c. on 65c. "Lycaste skinneri alba" 10 10
1107 50c. on 65c. "Peristeria elata" 10 10
1108 50c. on 65c. "Miltonia roezelii" 10 10
1109 50c. on 65c. "Brassavola digbyana" 10 10
1110 1col.20 on 2col.15 "Warcewiczella discolor" 20 15
1111 2col. on 2col.50 "Oncidium kramerianum" 35 25

1978. Obligatory Tax. Christmas. Children's Village.
1112 **308** 10c. slate 10 10
1113 10c. red 10 10
1114 – 10c. mauve 10 10
1115 – 10c. blue 10 10

DESIGN: Nos. 1114/15, "Girl playing with Kite" (sculpture by Nester Zeledon).

309 "The Flying Men", Chorotega Ritual
310 Domingo Rivas

1978. Air. 500th Anniv of Gonzalo Fernandez de Oviedo (first chronicler of Spanish Indies).
1116 **309** 85c. multicoloured . . . 15 10
1117 – 1col.20 blue and black . . 20 15
1118 – 10col. multicoloured . . 1·25 75
DESIGNS—HORIZ: 1col.20, Oviedo giving his "History of Indies" to Duke of Calabria. VERT: 10col. Lord of Oviedo's coat of arms.

1978. Air. Centenary of San Jose Cathedral.
1119 **310** 1col. blue and black . . 15 15
1120 – 20col. multicoloured . . 2·10 2·00
DESIGN: 20c. San Jose Cathedral.

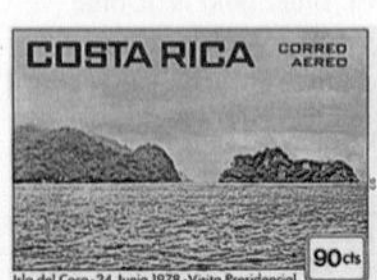

311 Cocos Island

1979. Air. Presidential Visit to Cocos Island. Mult.
1121 90c. Type **311** 15 10
1122 2col.10 Cocos Island (different) 35 25
1123 3col. Cocos Island (different) 50 35
1124 5col. Moon over Cocos Island (vert) 55 60
1125 10col. Commemorative plaque and people with flag (vert) . . . . 1·00 75

312 Shrimp

1979. Air. Conservation of Marine Fauna. Multicoloured.
1127 60c. Type **312** 10 10
1128 85c. Mahogany snapper . . 15 10
1129 1col.80 Yellow corvina . . . 40 20
1130 3col. Lobster 50 35
1131 10col. Frigate mackerel . . 1·50 75

313 Hungry Nestlings (Song Thrushes)

1979. Air. International Year of the Child.
1132 **313** 1col. multicoloured . . . 75 45
1133 2col. multicoloured . . . 2·10 90
1134 20col. multicoloured . . 10·50 4·75

315 Microwave Transmitters

1979. Air. 30th Anniv of Costa Rican Electricity Institute. Multicoloured.
1136 1col. Arenal Dam 20 15
1137 5col. Type **315** 60 65

316 Sir Rowland Hill and Penny Black

1979. Air. Death Centenary of Sir Rowland Hill.
1138 – 5col. mauve and blue . . 55 45
1139 **316** 10col. blue and black . . 90 65
DESIGN: 5col. Sir Rowland Hill and first Costa Rican stamp.

317 "Waiting" (Hernan Gonzalez)
318 "Danaus plexippus"

1979. Air. National Sculpture Competition. Multicoloured.
1140 60c. Type **317** 10 10
1141 1col. "The Heroes of Misery" (Juan Ramon Bonilla) 20 15
1142 2col.10 "Bullocks" (Victor M. Bermudez) (horiz) . . 30 25
1143 5col. "Chlorite Head" (Juan Rafael Chacon) 65 65
1144 20col. "Motherhood" (Francisco Zuniga) . . . 2·50 2·10

1979. Air. Butterflies. Multicoloured.
1145 60c. Type **318** 15 10
1146 1col. "Phoebis philea" . . . 35 15
1147 1col.80 "Rothschildia sp." . 45 35
1148 2col.10 "Prepona omphale" . 50 35
1149 2col.60 "Marpesia marcella" . 70 55
1150 4col.05 "Morpho cypris" . . 95 75

319 "Green House" (M. Murillo)
320 Jose Joaquin Rodriguez Zeledon

1979. Air. 30th Anniv of S.O.S. Children's Villages. Children's Paintings. Multicoloured.
1151 2col.50 Type **319** 45 30
1152 5col. "Four houses" (L. Varela) 60 65
1153 5col.50 "Blue house" (M. Perez) 65 70

1979. Air. Costa Rican Presidents (1st series).
1154 **320** 10c. blue 10 10
1155 – 60c. purple 10 10
1156 – 85c. red 15 10
1157 – 1col. orange 20 10
1158 – 2col. brown 35 25
DESIGNS: 60c. Rafael Iglesias Castro; 85c. Ascension Esquivel Ibarra; 1col. Cleto Gonzalez Viquez; 2col. Ricardo Jimenez Oreamuno.
See also Nos. 1180/4 and 1256/60.

321 Holy Family
322 Boy leaning on Tree

1979. Air. Christmas.
1159 **321** 1col. multicoloured . . . 20 15
1160 1col.60 multicoloured . . 30 20

1979. Obligatory Tax. Christmas. Children's Village.
1161 **322** 10c. blue 10 10
1162 10c. orange 10 10
1163 10c. mauve 10 10
1164 10c. green 10 10

323 Tree
324 "Anatomy Lesson" (Rembrandt)

1980. Air. Reafforestation.
1165 **323** 1col. brown, blue & grn 20 15
1166 3col.40 brown, ol & grn 35 45

1980. Air. 50th Anniv of Legal Medical Teaching in Costa Rica.
1167 **324** 10col. multicoloured . . 90 90

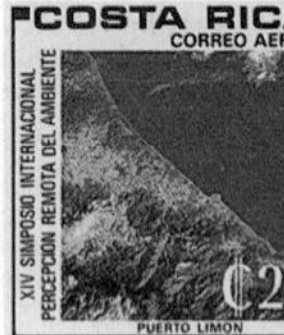

325 Rotary Anniversary Emblem
326 Puerto Limon

1980. Air. 75th Anniv of Rotary International.
1168 **325** 2col.10 green, yellow and black 35 25
1169 5col. multicoloured . . . 50 40

1980. Air. 14th International Symposium on Remote Sensing of the Environment. Multicoloured.
1170 2col.10 Type **326** 35 25
1171 5col. Gulf of Nicoya, Guanacaste 50 40

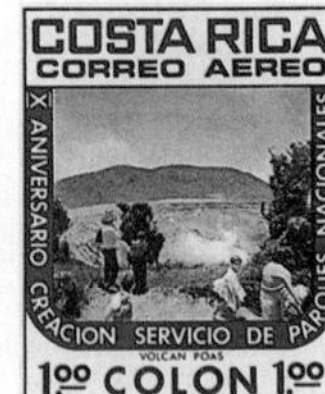

327 Football
328 Poas Volcano

1980. Air. Olympic Games, Moscow. Mult.
1172 1col. Type **327** 20 15
1173 3col. Cycling 30 40
1174 4col.05 Baseball 40 30
1175 20col. Swimming . . . . . 1·50 2·00

1980. Air. 10th Anniv of National Parks Service.
1176 1col. Type **328** 20 15
1177 2col.50 Beach at Cahuita . . 45 30

329 Jose Maria Zeledon Brenes (lyric writer)
330 Exhibition Emblem

1980. Air. National Anthem. Multicoloured.
1178 1col. Type **329** 20 15
1179 10col. Manuel Maria Gutierrez (composer) . . 90 90

1980. Air. Costa Rican Presidents (2nd series). As T **320**.
1180 1col. red 20 15
1181 1col.60 turquoise 30 20
1182 1col.80 brown 30 20
1183 2col.10 green 35 25
1184 3col. lilac 55 40
DESIGNS: 1col. Alfredo Gonzalez; 1col.60, Federico Tinoco; 1col.80, Francisco Aguilar; 2col.10, Julio Acosta; 3col. Leon Cortes.

1980. Air. 8th National Stamp Exhibition.
1185 **330** 5col. multicoloured . . . 90 65
1186 20col. multicoloured . . 2·40 2·00

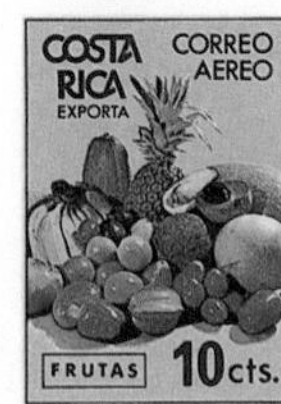

331 Fruit
332 "Giant Poro" (Jorge Carvajal)

1980. Air. Costa Rican Produce. Mult.
1187 10c. Type **331** 10 10
1188 60c. Chocolate 10 10
1189 1col. Coffee 20 15
1190 2col.10 Bananas 35 25
1191 3col.40 Flowers 35 45
1192 5col. Cane sugar 60 15

1980. Air. Paintings. Multicoloured.
1193 1col. Type **332** 20 15
1194 2col.10 "Secret Look" (Rolando Cubero) 35 25
1195 2col.45 "Consuelo" (Fernando Carballo) (31 × 32 mm) 45 30
1196 3col. "Volcano" (Lola Fernandez) 30 40
1197 4col.05 "Hearing Mass" (Francisco Amighetti) . . 40 30

333 "Madonna and Child" (Raphael)
334 Boy on Swing

1980. Air. Christmas. Multicoloured.
1198 1col. Type **333** 20 15
1199 10col. "Madonna, Jesus and St. John" (Raphael) . . . 90 90

1980. Obligatory Tax. Christmas. Children's Village.
1200 **334** 10c. red 10 10
1201 10c. yellow 10 10
1202 10c. blue 10 10
1203 10c. green 10 10

335 New Harbour, Caldera
336 Harpy Eagle

1980. Air. "Paying your Taxes Means Progress". Multicoloured.
1204 1col. Type **335** 20 15
1205 1col.30 Juan Santamaria International Airport (32 × 25 mm) 30 15
1206 2col.10 River Frio railway bridge . . . . 5·75 1·25
1207 2col.60 Highway to Colon City (25 × 32 mm) 45 35
1208 5col. Regional postal centre, Huetar 50 40

1980. Air. Fauna. Multicoloured.
1209 2col.10 Type **336** . . . . . 1·90 55
1210 2col.50 Scarlet macaw . . . 2·50 60
1211 3col. Puma 55 40
1212 5col.50 Black-handed spider monkey . . . . 1·00 1·75

337 Monge and Magazine "Repertorio Americano"

1980. Air. Birth Centenary of Joaquin Garcia Monge.
1213 **337** 1col.60 blue, yell & red 30 20
1214 3col. blue, lt bl & red . . 30 40

338 Arms of Aserri
339 Rodrigo Facio Brenes (rector)

1981. Air. Cornea Bank.
1215 **338** 1col. multicoloured . . . 20 15
1216 1col.80 multicoloured . . 30 25
1217 5col. blue 50 40
DESIGNS: 1col.80, Eye; 5col. Abelardo Rojas (founder).

1981. Air. 40th Anniv of University of Costa Rica and 20th Anniv of Medical School.
1218 – 5c. multicoloured 10 10
1219 – 10c. multicoloured . . . 10 10
1220 – 50c. multicoloured . . . 10 10
1221 – 1col.30 multicoloured . . 10 10
1222 – 3col.40 multicoloured . . 25 20
1223 **339** 4col.05 grn, bl & dp bl 30 20
DESIGNS: HORIZ: 5c. Medical-surgical clinic; 10c. Physiology lesson; 50c. Medical School and Dr. Antonia Pena Chavarria (first Dean); 1col.30, School of Music and Fine Arts; 3col.40, Carlos Monge Alfaro Library.

340 Ass-drawn Mail Van, 1857

1981. Air. 150th Birth Anniv of Heinrich von Stephan (founder of U.P.U.).
1224 – 1col. lt blue, grn & bl . . 20 15
1225 **340** 2col.10 yell, red & brn 4·75 2·50
1226 – 10col. grey, mve & grn 1·75 1·25
DESIGNS: 1col. Mail carried by mule, 1839; 10col. Carrying mail to Sarapiqui, 1858.

341 I.T.U. and W.H.O. Emblems and Ribbons forming Caduceus
342 Sts. Peter and Paul

1981. Air. World Telecommunications Day.
1227 **341** 5col. blue and black . . 50 40
1228 25col. multicoloured . . 2·40 1·75

1981. Air. Centenary of Consecration of Bernardo August Thiel as Bishop of San Jose. Mult.
1229 1col. Type **342** 10 10
1230 1col. St. Vincent de Paul . . 10 10
1231 1col. Death of St. Joseph . . 10 10
1232 1col. Archangel St. Michael 10 10
1233 1col. Holy Family 10 10
1234 2col. Bishop Thiel 15 10

343 Juan Santamaria (national hero)
344 Potter

1981. Air. Homage to the Province of Alajuela. Multicoloured.
1235 1col. Type **343** (150th birth anniv) 10 10
1236 2col.45 Alajuela Cathedral 20 15

1981. Air. Banco Popular and the Development of the Community. Multicoloured.
1237 15c. Type **344** 10 10
1238 1col.60 Building construction 15 10
1239 1col.80 Farming 15 10
1240 2col.50 Fishermen 30 15
1241 3col. Nurse and patient . . 25 15
1242 5col. Rural guard 45 30

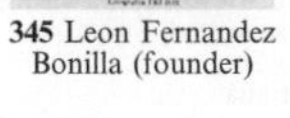

345 Leon Fernandez Bonilla (founder)
346 Disabled Person in Wheelchair holding Scales of Justice

1981. Air. National Archives. Multicoloured.
1243 1col.40 Type **345** 15 10
1244 2col. Arms of National Archives 15 15
1245 3col. University of Santo Tomas (horiz) 25 15
1246 3col.50 Model of new archives' building (horiz) 30 25

1981. Air. International Year of Disabled Persons.
1247 – 1col. multicoloured . . . 10 10
1248 **346** 2col.60 deep orange, orange and black . . 25 25
1249 – 10col. multicoloured . . 60 40
DESIGNS—VERT: 1col. Steps and disabled person in wheelchair. HORIZ: 10col. Healthy person helping disabled towards the sun.

347 F.A.O. Emblem
348 Boy in Pedal-car

1981. Air. World Food Day.
1250 **347** 5col. multicoloured . . . 45 30
1251 10col. multicoloured . . 60 55

1981. Obligatory Tax. Christmas. Children's Village.
1252 **348** 10c. red 10 10
1253 10c. orange 10 10
1254 10c. blue 10 10
1255 10c. green 10 10

1981. Air. Costa Rican Presidents (3rd series) As T **320**.
1256 1col. red 10 10
1257 2col. orange 15 15
1258 3col. green 25 15
1259 5col. blue 20 30
1260 10col. blue 45 55
DESIGNS: 1c. Rafael Angel Calderon Guardia; 2col. Teodoro Picado Milchalski; 3col. Jose Figueres Ferrer; 5col. Otilio Ulate Blanco; 10col. Mario Echandi Jimenez.

349 Arms of Bar Association

1982. Air. Centenary of Bar Association.
1261 **349** 1col. blue and black . . 10 10
1262 – 2col. multicoloured . . . 15 10
1263 – 20col. green and black 90 45
DESIGNS—VERT: 2col. Eusebio Figueroa (first president of Association). HORIZ: 20col. Bar Association building.

350 Housing

1982. Air. Costa-Rican Progress. Mult.
1264 95col. Type **350** 10 10
1265 1col.15 Farmers' fairs . . . 10 10
1266 1col.45 Grade and high schools 15 10
1267 1col.65 National plan for drinking water 15 10
1268 1col.80 Rural health 15 10
1269 2col.10 Playgrounds 20 10
1270 2col.35 National Theatre Square 20 10
1271 2col.60 Dish aerial (International and national telephone system) 20 15
1272 3col. Electric railway to Atlantic coast . . . . . . 3·25 1·00
1273 4col.05 Irrigation at Guanacaste 35 15

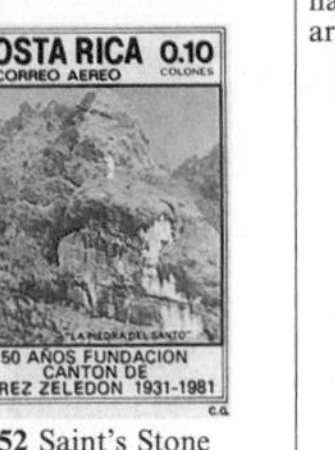

351 Fountain, Central Park
352 Saint's Stone

1982. Air. Bicentenary of Alajuela. Mult.
1274 5col. Type **351** 20 20
1275 10col. Juan Santamaria Historical and Cultural Museum (horiz) 40 10
1276 15col. Christ of Esquipulas Church 60 20
1277 20col. Mgr. Estevan Lorenzo de Tristan . . . 80 45
1278 25col. Padre Juan Manuel Lopez del Corral . . . . 1·00 60

1982. Air. 50th Anniv of Perez Zeledon County. Multicoloured.
1279 10c. Type **352** 10 10
1280 50c. Monument to Mothers 10 10
1281 1col. Pedro Perez Zeledon 10 10
1282 1col.25 San Isidro Labrador Church 10 10
1283 3col.50 Municipal building (horiz) 30 15
1284 4col.25 County arms 35 15

1982. Air. Nos. 1070 and 1207 surch.
1285 3col. on 75c. red and black 25 15
1286 5col. on 2col.60 mult . . . 45 20

1982. Air. 9th National Stamp Exhibition. Nos. 1005/8 surch **IX EXPOSICION FILATELICA - 1982**and new value.
1287 **271** 8col.40 on 2col.20 orange and black . . . 35 35
1288 – 8col.40 on 2col.20 green and black 35 35
1289 – 8col.40 on 2col.20 red and black 35 35
1290 – 8col.40 on 2col.20 blue and black 35 35
1291 **271** 9col.70 on 2col.20 orange and black . . . 45 45
1292 – 9col.70 on 2col.20 green and black 45 45
1293 – 9col.70 on 2col.20 red and black 45 45
1294 – 9col.70 on 2col.20 blue and black 45 45

355 Dr Robert Koch and Cross of Lorraine
356 Student at Lathe

1982. Air. Centenary of Discovery of Tubercle Bacillus.
1295 – 1col.50 red and black . . 15 10
1296 **355** 3col. grey and black . . 25 15
1297 – 3col.30 multicoloured . . 30 15
DESIGNS: 1col.50, Koch and anti-T.B. Campaign emblem; 3col.30, Koch and Ministry of Public Health Building, San Jose.

1982. Obligatory Tax. Christmas. Children's Village.
1298 **356** 10c. red 10 10
1299 10c. grey 10 10
1300 10c. violet 10 10
1301 10c. blue 10 10

357 Blood Donors Association Emblem
358 Migration Committee Emblem

1982. Air. 7th Pan-American Blood Donors Congress. Multicoloured.
1302 **357** 30col. multicoloured . . 90 75
1303 – 50col. red, blue & black 1·50 75
DESIGN: 50col. Congress emblem.

1982. Air. 30th Anniv of Intergovernmental Migration Committee.
1304 **358** 8col.40 lt blue, bl & blk 35 20
1305 – 9col.70 blue and black 45 20
1306 – 11col.70 mult 55 25
1307 – 13col.05 bl, blk & grey 55 30
DESIGNS—HORIZ: 11col.70, Emblem and handshake; 13col.05, Emblem within double-headed arrow. VERT: 9col.70, Emblem.

359 "St. Francis" (El Greco)
360 Pope John Paul II

1983. Air. 800th Birth Anniv (1982) of St. Francis of Assisi.
1308 **359** 4col.80 brown, blk & bl 20 10
1309 – 7col.40 brn, blk & grey 30 10
DESIGN: 7col.40, Portrait of Francis by unknown artist.

1983. Air. Papal Visit.
1310 **360** 5col. brown, yell & bl . . 25 10
1311 10col. brown, grn & bl 50 20
1312 15col. brown, mve & bl 1·00 30

361 W.C.Y. Emblem
362 Egg

1983. World Communications Year.
1313 **361** 10c. multicoloured . . . 10 10
1314 50c. multicoloured . . . 10 10
1315 10col. multicoloured . . 50 20

1983. 1st World Conference on Human Rights, Alajuela (1982).
1316 **362** 20col. grey and black . . 1·00 40

363 U.P.U. Monument, Berne, and 1883 2c. Stamp

1983. Centenary of U.P.U. Membership.
1317 **363** 3col. yellow, red & blk 45 10
1318 – 10col. yellow, bl & blk 90 20
DESIGN: 10col. Central Post Office, San Jose, and 1883 40c. stamp.

364 "Alliance Building, San Jose" (Cristina Fournier)
365 Bolivar (after Francisco Zuniga)

1983. Centenary of French Alliance (French language-teaching association).
1319 **364** 12col. multicoloured . . 55 25

1983. Air. Birth Bicentenary of Simon Bolivar.
1320 **365** 10col. multicoloured . . 50 20

1983. Nos. 1308/9 surch.
1321 10c. on 4col.80 brown, black and blue 10 10
1321a 50c. on 4col.80 brown, black and blue 10 10
1322 1col.50 on 7col.40 brown, black and grey 15 10
1323 3col. on 7col.40 brown, black and grey 20 10

367 Repairing Wheelchair
368 Three Kings

1988. Obligatory Tax. Christmas. Children's Village.
1324 **367** 10c. red 10 10
1325 10c. orange 10 10
1326 10c. blue 10 10
1327 10c. green 10 10

1983. Christmas. Multicoloured.
1328 1col.50 Type **368** 15 10
1329 1col.50 Holy Family and Shepherds 15 10
1330 1col.50 People bearing gifts 15 10
Nos. 1328/30 were printed together, se-tenant, forming a composite design.

369 Fisherman

370 Resplendent Quetzal ("Quetzal")

1983. Fisheries Development.
1331 **369** 8col.50 multicoloured . . 60 15

1984. Birds. Multicoloured.
1332 10c. Type **370** 45 25
1333 50c. Red-legged honey-creeper ("Mielero Patirrojo") (horiz) 45 25
1334 1col. Clay-coloured thrush ("Mirlo Pardo") (horiz) 50 25
1335 1col.50 Blue-crowned motmot ("Momotode Diadema Azul") 60 25
1336 3col. Green violetear ("Colibri orejivioloceo verde") . . . . 1·25 45
1337 10col. Blue and white swallow ("Golondirina Azul y Blanca") (horiz) 3·75 75

371 Jose Joaquin Mora

1984. 1856 Campaign Heroes. Multicoloured.
1339 50c. Type **371** 10 10
1340 1col.50 Pancha Carrasco . . 10 10
1341 3col. Juan Santamaria (horiz) 10 10
1342 8col.50 Juan Rafael Mora Porras 35 30

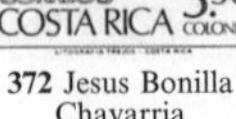

372 Jesus Bonilla Chavarria

373 Necklace Bead

1984. Musicians.
1343 **372** 3col. 50 violet and black 15 10
1344 – 5col. red and black . . . 20 15
1345 – 12col. green and black 15 10
1346 – 13col. yellow and black 20 10
DESIGNS: 5col. Benjamin Gutierrez; 12col. Pilar Jimenez; 13col. Jose Daniel Zuniga.

1984. Jade Museum Artifacts. Multicoloured.
1347 4col. Type **373** 15 10
1348 7col. Seated figure 25 20
1349 10col. Ceramic dish (horiz) 35 30

374 Basketball Players

375 Street Scene

1984. Olympic Games, Los Angeles. Mult.
1350 1col. Type **374** 10 10
1351 8col. Swimming 10 10
1352 11col. Cycling 15 10
1353 14col. Running 20 10
1354 20col. Boxing 25 10
1355 30col. Football 35 10

1984. Centenary of Public Street Lighting.
1356 **375** 6col. multicoloured . . . 20 15

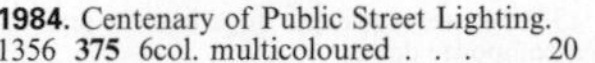

376 Emblem and National Independence Monument

1984. 10th National Philatelic Exhibition. Mult.
1357 10col. Type **376** 35 30
1358 10col. Emblem and Juan Mora Fernandez statue 35 30

377 National Coat of Arms

378 Child on Tricycle

1984.
1360 **377** 100col. blue . . . . . . 2·40 1·90
1361 100col. yellow . . . . . 2·40 1·90

1984. Obligatory Tax. Christmas. Children's Village.
1362 **378** 10c. violet 10 10

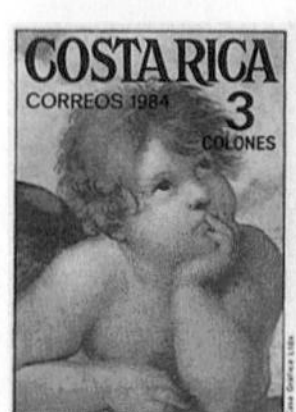

379 "Sistine Virgin" (detail, Raphael)

380 Cyclists

1984. Christmas. Multicoloured.
1363 3col. Type **379** 10 10
1364 3col. "Sistine Virgin" (detail) (different) 10 10

1984. 20th Costa Rica Cycle Race.
1365 **380** 6col. multicoloured . . . 15 15

381 Emblem and 1968 Scouting Jubilee Stamp

1985. International Youth Year.
1366 **381** 11col. multicoloured . . 25 20

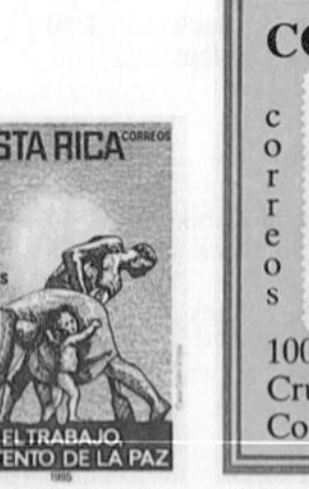

382 Workers' Monument (Francisco Zuniga)

383 U.N. Emblem and 1935 Red Cross Jubilee Stamp

1985. "National Values".
1367 **382** 6col. mauve and black 15 15
1368 – 11col. yell, blk & bl . . 25 20
1369 – 13col. multicoloured . . 35 30
1370 – 30col. multicoloured . . 70 70
DESIGNS—As T **382**. 11col. First printing press (Freedom of speech); 13col. Dove, flag and globe (Neutrality); 65 × 35 mm—30col. Nos. 1367/9.

1985. Centenary of Costa Rican Red Cross.
1371 **383** 3col. red, brown & blk 10 10
1372 – 5col. black, red and grey 15 10
DESIGN: 5col. U.N. Emblem and 1946 Red Cross Society stamp.

384 Hands holding "S"

385 "Brassia arcuigera"

1985. 50th Anniv of Saprissa Football Club.
1373 **384** 3col. mauve and green 10 10
1374 – 3col. black and mauve 10 10
1375 – 6col. mauve, brn & grn 15 15
DESIGNS: As T **384**—Hands holding football; 34 × 26 mm—6col. Ricardo Saprissa and Saprissa Stadium.

1985. Orchids. Multicoloured.
1376 6col. Type **385** 10 10
1377 6col. "Encyclia peraltensis" 10 10
1378 6col. "Maxillaria especie" 10 10
1379 13col. "Oncidium turialbae" 30 25
1380 13col. "Trichopilia marginata" 30 25
1381 13col. "Stanhopea ecornuta" 30 25

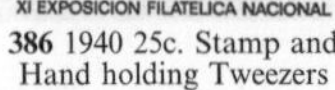

386 1940 25c. Stamp and Hand holding Tweezers

387 Hands reaching out to Child

1985. 11th National Stamp Exhibition.
1382 **386** 20col. bl, ultram & pink 50 45

1985. Obligatory Tax. Christmas. Children's Village.
1383 **387** 10c. brown 10 10

388 Children looking at Star

1985. Christmas.
1384 **388** 3col. multicoloured . . . 10 10

390 Costa Rica Lyceum

391 Land and Cattle College Project

1986. Centenary of Free Compulsory Education.
1390 **390** 3col. brown & lt brown 10 10
1391 30col. brown and pink 60 20
DESIGN: 30col. Mauro Fernandez Acuna (education Minister).

1986. 27th Annual Inter-American Development Bank Assembly, San Jose. Multicoloured.
1392 10col. Type **391** 20 15
1393 10col. Bank emblem 20 15
1394 10col. Cape Blanco fisherman 40 15

392 Francisco J. Orlich Bolmarcich

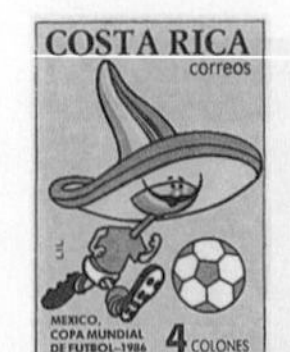

393 Pique (mascot)

1986. Former Presidents of Costa Rica.
1395 **392** 3col. green 10 10
1396 – 3col. green 10 10
1397 – 3col. green 10 10
1398 – 3col. green 10 10
1399 – 3col. green 10 10
1400 – 6col. brown 15 10
1401 – 6col. brown 15 10
1402 – 6col. brown 15 10
1403 – 6col. brown 15 10
1404 – 6col. brown 15 10
1405 – 10col. orange 20 15
1406 – 10col. orange 20 15
1407 – 10col. orange 20 15
1408 – 10col. orange 20 15
1409 – 10col. orange 20 15
1410 – 11col. grey 20 15
1411 – 11col. grey 20 15
1412 – 11col. grey 20 15
1413 – 11col. grey 20 15
1414 – 11col. grey 20 15
1415 – 13col. brown 25 20
1416 – 13col. brown 25 20
1417 – 13col. brown 25 20
1418 – 13col. brown 25 20
1419 – 13col. brown 25 20
DESIGNS: Nos. 1395, 1400, 1405, 1410, 1415, Type **392**; 1396, 1401, 1406, 1411, 1416, Jose Joaquin Trejos Fernandez; 1397, 1402, 1407, 1412, 1417, Daniel Oduber Quiros; 1398, 1403, 1408, 1413, 1418, Rodrigo Carazo Odio; 1399, 1404, 1409, 1414, 1419, Luis Alberto Monge Alvarez.

1986. World Cup Football Championship. Mexico.
1420 **393** 1col. multicoloured . . . 10 10
1421 – 1col. multicoloured . . . 10 10
1422 – 4col. multicoloured . . . 10 10
1423 – 6col. pur, brn & black 15 10
1424 – 11col. pur, red & blk . . 20 15
DESIGNS:—VERT: No. 1420, 1422, Type **393**. HORIZ: No. 1421, 1423, Footballs and players; 1424, Footballs and players (different).

394 Emblem and "Peace"

395 Gold Artefact

1986. International Peace Year. Each bearing the Year emblem and "Peace" in various languages (first language given in brackets).
1425 **394** 5col. blue and brown (Hoa Binh) 10 10
1426 – 5col. blue and brown (Vrede) 10 10
1427 – 5col. blue and brown (Pace) 10 10

1986. Exhibits in Gold Museum. Mult.
1428 6col. Type **395** 15 10
1429 6col. Figure with three-lobed base 15 10
1430 6col. Frog 15 10
1431 6col. Centipede 15 10
1432 6col. Two monkeys in sun 15 10
1433 13col. Figure with dragon-head arms 25 10
1434 13col. Two monkeys 25 10
1435 13col. Animal-shaped figure 25 10
1436 13col. Sun with ball pendant 25 10
1437 13col. Figure within frame 25 10

396 Child

397 Fork-lift Truck and Airplane (Osvaldo Andres Gonzalez Vega)

1986. Obligatory Tax. Christmas. Children's Village.
1438 **396** 10c. brown 10 10

1986. Air. 40th Anniv of LACSA (national airline). Children's Drawings. Multicoloured.
1439 1col. Airplane flying over house and van (Adriana Elias Hidalgo) 10 10
1440 7col. Type **397** 15 15
1441 16col. Airplane, letters and photographs (David Valverde Rodiguez) . . . 30 25

398 Lattice-winged Bat

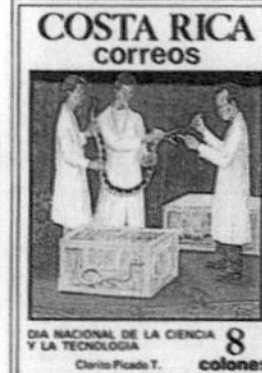

399 Extracting Snake's Venom (detail of mural, Francisco Amighetti)

1986. Flora and Fauna. Bats and Frogs. Multicoloured.
1442 2col. Type **398** 10 10
1443 3col. Common long-tongued bat 10 10
1444 4col. White bat 10 10
1445 5col. Group of white bats 10 10
1446 6col. "Agalychnis callidryas" (frog) 15 10
1447 10col. "Dendrobates pumilio" (frog) 20 15
1448 11col. "Hyla ebraccata" (frog) 20 15
1449 20col. "Phyllobates lugubris" (frog) 40 35

1987. National Science and Technology Day.
1451 **399** 8col. multicoloured . . . 20 15

400 Statuette

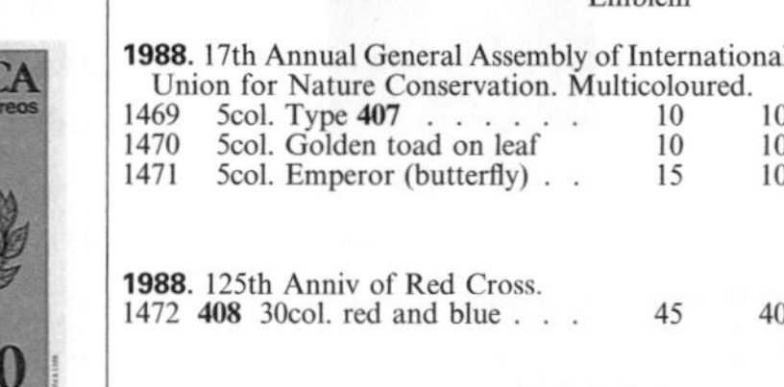

401 Arms of San Jose Province

1987. Centenary of National Museum. Pre-Colombian Art. Multicoloured.
1452 8col. Type **400** 20 15
1453 8col. Jug in form of human figure 20 15
1454 8col. Vase in form of human figure 20 15
1455 8col. Stone jar 20 15
1456 8col. Pot with human-type legs and arms 20 15
1457 15col. Bowl (horiz) 30 25
1458 15col. Carving of animal defeating human (horiz) 30 25
1459 15col. Flask (horiz) 30 25

1987. 250th Anniv of San Jose.
1460 **401** 20col. multicoloured . . 30 25
1461 – 20col. red, black & bl . . 30 25
1462 – 20col. red, black & bl . . 30 25
DESIGNS: Nos. 1461, Donkey cart in cobbled street; 1462, View down street.

402 16th-century Map of Audiencia, Guatemala

1987. Columbus Day.
1463 **402** 30col. brown and yellow 70 40

403 Map by Bartholomew Columbus, 1503

404 Cross and Doves

1987. 500th Anniv (1992) of Discovery of America by Columbus (1st issue). Each brown and yellow.
1464 4col. Type **403** 10 10
1465 4col. 16th-century map of Costa Rica 10 10
See also Nos. 1480, 1496, 1521 and 1538/40.

1987. Obligatory Tax. Christmas, Children's Village.
1466 **404** 10c. blue and brown . . 10 10

405 "Village Scene" (Fausto Pacheco)

406 Pres. Arias and National Flag

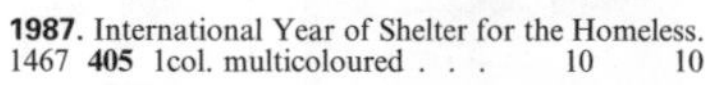

1987. International Year of Shelter for the Homeless.
1467 **405** 1col. multicoloured . . . 10 10

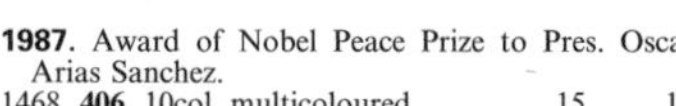

1987. Award of Nobel Peace Prize to Pres. Oscar Arias Sanchez.
1468 **406** 10col. multicoloured . . 15 15

407 Green Turtle

408 Anniversary Emblem

1988. 17th Annual General Assembly of International Union for Nature Conservation. Multicoloured.
1469 5col. Type **407** 10 10
1470 5col. Golden toad on leaf 10 10
1471 5col. Emperor (butterfly) . . 15 10

1988. 125th Anniv of Red Cross.
1472 **408** 30col. red and blue . . . 45 40

409 Man with Pen and Radio (Adult Education)

410 Symbols of Bank Activities

1988. Costa Rica–Liechtenstein Cultural Co-operation.
1473 **409** 18col. red, brown & grn 30 25
1474 – 20col. multicoloured . . . 30 25
DESIGN: 20col. Headphones on books (radio broadcasts).

1988. 125th Anniv of Anglo–Costa Rican Bank.
1475 **410** 3col. blue, red & yellow 10 10

411 Games Emblem

412 Roman Macava and Curtiss Robin

1988. Olympic Games, Seoul. Multicoloured.
1476 25col. Type **411** 40 35
1477 25col. Games mascot . . . 40 35

1988. Airmail Pioneers.
1478 **412** 10col. multicoloured . . 25 15

413 School Courtyard

414 Amerindian Necklace

1988. Centenary of Girls' High School.
1479 **413** 10col. brown & yellow 15 10

1988. 500th Anniv (1992) of Discovery of America by Columbus (2nd issue).
1480 **414** 4col. multicoloured . . . 10 10

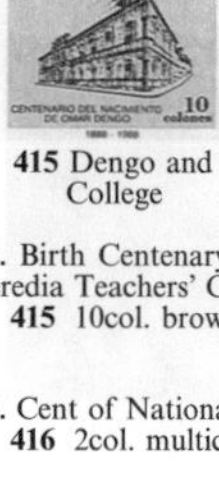

415 Dengo and College

416 Former Observation Tower

1988. Birth Centenary of Omar Dengo (Director of Heredia Teachers' College).
1481 **415** 10col. brown, grey & bl 15 10

1988. Cent of National Meteorological Institute.
1482 **416** 2col. multicoloured . . . 10 10

417 "Eschweilera costarricensis"

418 Map of France and Costa Rican National Monument

1989. Flowers. Multicoloured.
1483 5col. Type **417** 10 10
1484 10col. "Heliconia wagneriana" 15 10
1485 15col. "Heliconia lophocarpa" 20 15
1486 20col. "Aechmea magdalenae" 30 25
1487 25col. "Psammisia ramiflora" 35 30
1488 30col. Passion flower . . . 45 40

1989. Bicentenary of French Revolution.
1489 **418** 30col. black, blue & red 45 40

419 Sugar Mill

420 Corn Grinder

1989. 151st Anniv of Grecia County.
1490 **419** 10col. multicoloured . . 15 10

1989. America. Pre-Columbian Artefacts. Mult.
1491 50col. Type **420** 75 20
1492 100col. Granite sphere, 1500 A.D. . . . . 1·50 40

422 Orchid

423 Dr. Henri Pittier (first Director)

1989. "100 Years of Democracy" Presidents' Summit.
1493 **422** 10col. multicoloured . . 15 10

1989. Centenary of National Geographical Institute.
1494 **423** 18col. multicoloured . . 20 15

424 Teacher and Children

425 Pre-Columbian Gold Frog and Spanish Coin

1989. Obligatory Tax. Christmas. Children's Village.
1495 **424** 1col. blue, green & black 10 10

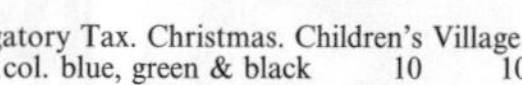

1989. 500th Anniv (1992) of Discovery of America by Columbus (3rd issue).
1496 **425** 4col. multicoloured . . . 10 10

426 "Exporting Coffee" (painting in theatre by Jose Villa)

427 Football in Cube

1990. Centenary of National Theatre.
1497 **426** 5col. multicoloured . . . 10 10

1990. World Cup Football Championship, Italy.
1498 **427** 5col. multicoloured . . . 10 10

428 "50 U"

1990. 50th Anniv of University of Costa Rica.
1499 **428** 18col. multicoloured . . 15 10

429 "Education Democracy Peace"

431 Painting by Juan Ramirez

1990. Patriotic Symbols.
1500 **429** 100col. blue and black 90 30
1501 – 200col. multicoloured . . 1·90 65
1502 – 500col. multicoloured . . 4·75 1·60
DESIGNS: 200col. Map of Costa Rica in national colours; 500col. State arms.

1991. Air. No. 1491 optd **LEY 7097 CORREO AEREO**.
1503 **420** 50col. multicoloured . . 45 15

1990. Costa Rican Coffee.
1504 **431** 50col. multicoloured . . 45 15

432 Penny Black

433 Heredia Hospital

1990. 150th Anniv of the Penny Black.
1505 **432** 50col. black and blue . . 45 15

1990. Hospital Centenaries.
1506 **433** 50col. blue, orge & grn 45 15
1507 – 100col. orange, bl & grn 90 30
DESIGN: 100col. National Psychiatric Hospital.

434 Yellow-bark Tree ("Tabebuia ochracea")

436 "Banana Picker" (Alleardo Villa, Ceiling of Grand Staircase)

1990. America. The Natural World. Mult.
1508 18col. Scarlet macaw ("Ara macao") 65 15
1509 18col. Buffon's macaw ("Ara ambigua") 65 15

1510 24col. Carao tree ("Cassia grandis") 20 10
1511 24col. Type **434** 20 10

1990. Obligatory Tax. Children's Village. No. 1490 optd **LEY 7157 PRO-CIUDAD DE LOS NINOS 1990.**
1512 **419** 10col. multicoloured . . 10 10

1991. Air. Paintings in National Theatre.
1516 **436** 30col. multicoloured . . 30 10

437 Costa Rica and Panama Flags and Seals

439 Route of First Voyage on Stone Globe

1991. 50th Anniv of Costa Rica–Panama Boundary Treaty.
1517 **437** 10col. multicoloured . . 10 10
1518 – 10col. black and blue . . 10 10
1519 – 10col. blue, brown & blk 10 10
DESIGNS: No. 1518. Presidents meeting: 1519, Map.

1991. Air. "Exfilcori '91" National Stamp Exhibition. No. 1501 optd **Aereo EXFILCORI '91**.
1520 200col. multicoloured . . . 1·75 60

1991. 500th Anniv (1992) of Discovery of America by Columbus (4th issue).
1521 **439** 4col. red, black and blue 10 10

1991. Air. Centenary of Basketball. No. 1474 optd **CENTENARIO DEL BALONCESTO CORREO AEREO.**
1522 20col. multicoloured 20 10

1991. Nos. 1482 and 1342 surch.
1523 **416** 1col. on 2col. mult . . . 10 10
1524 – 3col. on 8col.50 mult . . 10 10

443 Dr. Rafael Angel Calderon Guardia Hospital

444 Child praying

1991. Air. 50th Anniv of Social Security Administration.
1525 **443** 15col. multicoloured . . 15 10

1991. Obligatory Tax. Christmas. Children's Village.
1526 **444** 10col. blue 10 10

445 "La Poesia" (Vespaciano Bignami)

446 Benito Serrano Jimenez

1992. Air. Paintings in National Theatre.
1527 **445** 35col. multicoloured . . 30 10

1992. Former Presidents of Supreme Court of Justice. Multicoloured.
1528 5col. Type **446** 10 10
1529 5col. Luis Davila Solera . . . 10 10
1530 5col. Fernando Baudrit Solera 10 10
1531 5col. Alejandro Alvarado Garcia 10 10

447 Oxcart

448 Dr. Solon Nunez Frutos (public health pioneer)

1992. 25th Anniv of National Directorate of Community Development.
1532 **447** 15col. multicoloured . . 15 10

1992.
1533 **448** 15col. black and red . . 15 10

449 Total Solar Eclipse

450 Crops

1992. International Space Year. Mult.
1534 45col. Type **449** 65 25
1535 45col. Post office building and total eclipse 65 25
1536 45col. Partial eclipse 65 25

1992. 50th Anniv of Inter-American Institute for Agricultural Co-operation.
1537 **450** 35col. multicoloured . . 30 10

451 "Nina"

452 Waterfall

1992. Air. 500th Anniv of Discovery of America by Columbus (5th issue). Multicoloured.
1538 45col. Type **451** 40 15
1539 45col. "Santa Maria" . . . 40 15
1540 45col. "Pinta" 40 15

1992. 450th Anniv of Discovery of Coco Island. Multicoloured.
1541 2col. Type **452** 10 10
1542 15col. View of cliffs from sea 15 10

453 Drilling

454 American Chameleon

1992. Obligatory Tax. Christmas. Children's Village.
1543 **453** 10col. red 10 10

1992. America. Coco Island Fauna. Mult.
1544 15col. Type **454** 15 10
1545 35col. Cocos finch . . . . . 2·10 45

1992. Centenary of Limon. No. 1500 optd **CENTENARIO DE LIMON.**
1546 **429** 100col. blue and black 90 30

456 "Allegory of the Fine Arts" (detail, R. Fontana)

457 Emblem

1993. Paintings in National Theatre.
1547 **456** 20col. multicoloured . . 20 10

1993. Air. International Arts Festival.
1548 **457** 45col. multicoloured . . 40 15

1993. No. 1494 surch.
1549 **423** 5col. on 18col. mult . . 10 10

459 Common Dolphin

460 Emblem

1993. Dolphins. Multicoloured.
1550 10col. Type **459** 10 10
1551 20col. Striped dolphins . . . 20 10

1993. 40th Anniv of Civil Service Statute.
1552 **460** 5col. multicoloured . . . 10 10

461 Anniversary Emblem

462 Communication Zone

1993. 50th Anniv of Chamber of Industry.
1553 **461** 45col. multicoloured . . 35 15

1993. 25th Anniv of University of Costa Rica School of Communication and Sciences.
1554 **462** 20col. black, red & blue 15 10

463 "Passiflora vitifolia"

1993. Tropical Rainforest Flora. Mult.
1555 2col. Type **463** 10 10
1556 35col. "Gurania megistantha" 25 10

464 Campaigners

465 Association Emblem

1993. 50th Anniv of Guaranteed Social Rights.
1557 **464** 20col. multicoloured . . 15 10

1993. 15th International Customs Officers' Associations Congress.
1558 **465** 45col. multicoloured . . 35 15

466 Carpentry

467 Dish Aerial

1993. Obligatory Tax. Christmas. Children's Village.
1559 **466** 10col. multicoloured . . 10 10

1993. Air. 30th Anniv of Costa Rican Electrical Institute's Responsibility for Development of Telecommunications.
1560 **467** 45col. multicoloured . . 35 15

468 Prof. Castro

469 Assembly Hall

1993. Birth Centenary of Miguel Angel Castro Carazo (founder of Commercial School).
1561 **468** 20col. red and blue . . . 15 10

1993. 150th Anniv of Costa Rica University Faculty of Law.
1562 **469** 20col. multicoloured . . 15 10

470 "The Dancer" (Adriatico Froli)

471 Mural (Luis Feron)

1994. National Theatre.
1563 **470** 20col. multicoloured . . 15 10

1994. Air. 150th Anniv of Ministry of Government and Police.
1564 **471** 45col. multicoloured . . 35 15

472 Flamingo Tongue

473 Hands forming Shelter

1994. Marine Animals. Multicoloured.
1565 5col. Type **472** 10 10
1566 10col. "Ophioderma rubicundum" 10 10
1567 15col. Black-barred soldierfish 10 10
1568 20col. King angelfish . . . 15 10
1569 35col. Creole-fish 25 10
1570 45col. "Tubastraea coccinea" 35 15
1571 50col. "Acanthaster planci" 40 15
1572 55col. "Ocypode sp." . . . 45 15
1573 70col. Speckled balloon-fish 55 20

1994. Air. International Year of the Family.
1575 **473** 45col. multicoloured . . 35 15

474 Child

1994. Obligatory Tax. Christmas. Children's Village.
1576 **474** 11col. green and lilac . . 10 10

475 Courier

1994. America. Postal Transport. Details of an illustration from "Album de Figueroa". Each orange, light orange and blue.
1577 20col. Type **475** 15 10
1578 20col. Rear of pack ox . . . 15 10
Nos. 1577/8 were issued together in se-tenant pairs with intervening label, each strip forming a composite design.

476 "Federico" (Luis Delgado)

477 Antonio Jose de Sucre (President of Bolivia. 1826–28)

1995. 90th Anniv of Rotary International.
1579 **476** 20col. multicoloured . . 15 10

1995. Anniversaries. Multicoloured.
1580 10col. Type **477** (birth bicentenary) 15 10
1581 30col. Jose Marti (poet and Cuban revolutionary) (death centenary) 20 10

478 "Rider" (sculpture, Nestor Varela)

480 "The Boy and the Cloud" (Francisco Amighetti)

1995. 50th Anniv of Guanacaste Institute.
1582 **478** 50col. green, blk & gold . . . 35 15

1995. No. 1561 surch **5**.
1583 **468** 5col. on 20col. red & bl . . . 10 10

1995. 50th Anniv of U.N.O.
1584 **480** 5col. multicoloured . . . 10 10

481 Woman holding Baby

482 "January"

1995. Obligatory Tax. Christmas. Children's Village.
1585 **481** 12col. multicoloured . . 10 10

1995. 13th National Stamp Exn. Seasonal paintings by Lola Fernandez. Multicoloured.
1587 50col. Type **482** 35 15
1588 50col. "November" 35 15

483 Jabiru

1995. America. Environmental Protection. Multicoloured. Rouletted.
1589 30col. Type **483** 20 10
1590 40col. Coastline 25 10
1591 40col. Woodland and lake . . . 25 10
1592 50col. Leaf-cutting ant . . . 35 15

484 Steam Locomotive

1996. Postcards from Limon. Multicoloured.
1594 30col. Type **484** 30 15
1595 30col. Freighter at quay . . 50 15
1596 30col. View of Port Moin . . 15 10
1597 30col. "Fruitsellers" (Diego Villalobos) 15 10
1598 30col. "Calypso" (Jorge Esquivel) 15 10

485 Douglas DC-3

1996. Air. 50th Anniv of LACSA (national airline). Multicoloured.
1599 5col. Type **485** 10 10
1600 10col. Curtiss C-46 Commando 10 10
1601 20col. Beechcraft 10 10
1602 30col. Douglas DC-6B . . . 15 10
1603 35col. B.A.C. One Eleven . . 20 10
1604 40col. Convair CV 440 Metropolitan 25 10
1605 45col. Lockheed L.188 Electra 25 10
1606 50col. Boeing 727-200 . . . 30 10
1607 55col. Douglas DC-8 . . . 30 10
1608 60col. Airbus Industrie A320 35 15

486 Mosque, Synagogue and Christian Church

1996. 3000th Anniv of Jerusalem.
1609 **486** 30col. multicoloured . . 15 10

487 Maria del Milagro Paris and Francisco Rivas

1996. Olympic Games, Atlanta. Costa Rican Swimmers. Multicoloured.
1610 5col. Type **487** 10 10
1611 5col. Sylvia Poll and Federico Yglesias 10 10
1612 5col. Claudia Poll and Alfredo Cruz 10 10
Nos. 1610/12 were issued together, se-tenant, forming a composite design of a swimming pool.

488 Juana del Castillo (wife of Jose Maria Castro)

489 Water Droplet and Leaves

1996. 175th Anniv of Independence. Mult.
1613 30col. Type **488** 15 10
1614 30col. Juan Mora (President, 1849–59) 15 10
1615 30col. Jose Maria Castro (President, 1847–49 and 1866–68) 15 10
1616 30col. Pacifica Fernandez (wife of Juan Mora) . . . 15 10

1996. "Water is Life". 35th Anniv of Aqueducts and and Sewers.
1617 **489** 15col. multicoloured . . 10 10

490 "Christmas Carol" (J. M. Sanchez)

491 "Countrywomen" (Gonzalo Morales)

1996. Obligatory Tax. Christmas. Children's Village.
1618 **490** 14col. red and yellow . . 10 10

1996. America. Traditional Costumes. Mult.
1619 45col. Type **491** 20 10
1620 45col. "Lemon Black" (Manuel de la Cruz Gonzalez) (horiz) 20 10

492 Procession passing Palm-topped Wall

494 Child and Man listening to Radio

493 Class, 1930s

1997. Entrance of the Saints, San Ramon. Details of a painting by Jorge Carvajal. Multicoloured.
1621 30col. Type **492** 15 10
1622 30col. Church on hill behind procession 15 10
1623 30col. Procession passing beneath tree 15 10
Nos. 1621/3 were issued together, se-tenant, forming a composite design of the painting.

1997. Centenary of School of Fine Arts.
1624 **493** 50col. multicoloured . . 25 10

1997. 50th Anniv of Radio Nederland.
1625 **494** 45col. multicoloured . . 20 10

495 Postmen

1997. America. The Postman. 14th National Stamp Exhibition.
1626 **495** 30col. multicoloured . . 15 10

496 Church (Roberto Cambronero)

497 Antonio Obando Chan (bust, Olger Villegas)

1997. Bicentenary of Church of the Immaculate Conception, Heredia.
1627 **496** 50col. multicoloured . . 25 10

1997. Obligatory Tax. Christmas. Children's Village.
1628 **497** 15col. multicoloured . . 10 10

498 Arche de la Defense and Ball

1998. World Cup Football Championship, France.
1629 **498** 50col. black, blue & red 25 10

499 Figueres demolishing Fort Bellavista's Walls

1998. 50th Anniv of Second Republic. Mult.
1630 10col. Type **499** 10 10
1631 30col. Pres. Jose Figueres . . 15 10
1632 45col. Type **499** 20 10
1633 50col. Sledgehammer destroying wall 25 10

500 "Caligo memnon"

1998. Butterflies. Multicoloured.
1635 10col. Type **500** 10 10
1636 15col. Emperor 10 10
1637 20col. Orange swallowtail . . 10 10
1638 30col. Malachite 10 10
1639 35col. Great southern white . 15 10
1640 40col. "Parides iphidamas" . 15 10
1641 45col. "Smyrna blonfildia" . 20 10
1642 50col. "Callicore pitheas" . 20 10
1643 55col. Orion 20 10
1644 60col. Monarch 25 10

501 "Generation of Knowledge" (Julio Escamez)

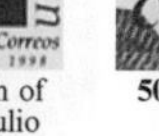

502 Carmen Lyra (writer)

1998. 25th Anniv of National University, Heredia.
1645 **501** 50col. multicoloured . . 20 10

1998. America. Famous Women.
1646 **502** 50col. orange, brown and ochre 20 10

503 Poinsettias

504 Gandhi

1998. Obligatory Tax. Christmas. Children's Village. Multicoloured (except No. 1649).
1647 16col. Poinsetta (gold background) 10 10
1648 16col. Type **503** 10 10
1649 16col. Berries on branch (green, black and red) . . 10 10

1998. 50th Death Anniv of Mahatma Gandhi.
1650 **504** 50col. multicoloured . . 20 10

505 South American Red-lined Turtle

1998. 50th Anniv of International Nature Protection Union. Turtles. Multicoloured.
1651 60col. Type **505** 25 10
1652 70col. Mexican red turtle ("Rhinoclemmys pulcherrima") 30 10
1653 70col. Snapping turtle ("Chelydra serpentina") 30 10

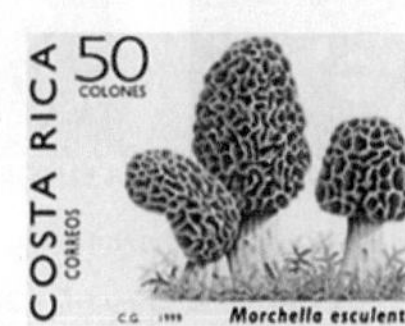

506 Common Morel

1999. Fungi. Mulicoloured.
1654 50col. Type **506** 20 10
1655 50col. Cep (*Boletus edulis*) 20 10

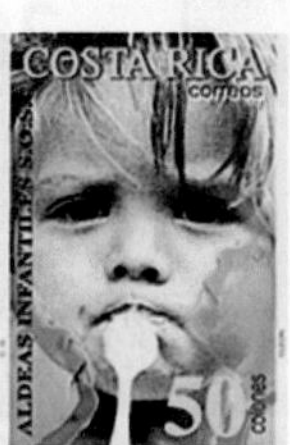

507 Boy

1999. 50th Anniv of S.O.S. Children's Villages.
1656 **507** 50col. multicoloured . . 50 10

508 Man minding Cart outside Telephone Box

509 Sanabria Martinez

1999. 50th Anniv of National Electricity Corporation.
1657 **508** 75col. multicoloured . . 35 15

1999. Birth Centenary of Victor Sanabria Martinez (Archbishop of San Jose).
1658 **509** 300col. violet . . . . . 1·40 50

510 Elderly Woman with Children (poster, Fernando Francia)
512 Village and Children

511 Woman helping Children

1999. International Year of the Elderly.
1659 **510** 50col. multicoloured . . 20 10

1999. 50th Anniv of Supreme Elections Tribunal.
1660 **511** 70col. multicoloured . . 30 10

1999. Obligatory Tax. Christmas. Children's Village.
1661 **512** 17col. multicoloured . . 10 10

513 Granados

1999. Carmen Granados Death Commemoration.
1662 **513** 50col. multicoloured . . 20 10

514 Woman holding Head
515 Globe

1999. America. A New Millennium without Arms. Multicoloured.
1663 50col. Type **514** 20 10
1664 70col. Man 30 10

1999. 125th Anniv of Universal Postal Union.
1665 **515** 75col. multicoloured . . 35 15

516 Orchid

1999. "Philexfrance 99" International Stamp Exhibition, Paris. Multicoloured
1666 300col. Type **516** . . . . . 1·40 50
1667 300col. Orchid and Eiffel Tower . . . . 1·40 50

517 Jaguar

2000. 50th Anniv of Central Bank of Costa Rica. Multicoloured.
1668 60col. Type **517** 25 10
1669 60col. Scorpion 25 10

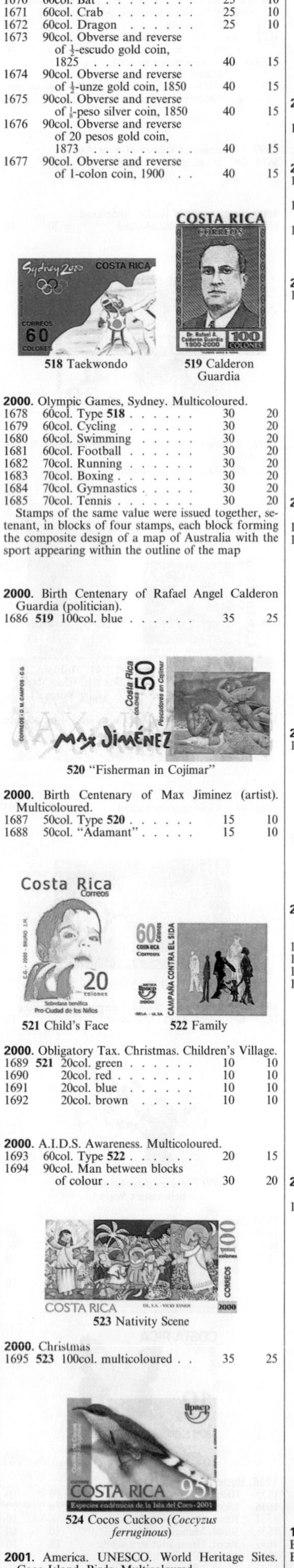

1670 60col. Bat 25 10
1671 60col. Crab 25 10
1672 60col. Dragon 25 10
1673 90col. Obverse and reverse of ½-escudo gold coin, 1825 . . . . 40 15
1674 90col. Obverse and reverse of ½-unze gold coin, 1850 40 15
1675 90col. Obverse and reverse of ⅛-peso silver coin, 1850 40 15
1676 90col. Obverse and reverse of 20 pesos gold coin, 1873 . . . . 40 15
1677 90col. Obverse and reverse of 1-colon coin, 1900 . . 40 15

518 Taekwondo
519 Calderon Guardia

2000. Olympic Games, Sydney. Multicoloured.
1678 60col. Type **518** 30 20
1679 60col. Cycling 30 20
1680 60col. Swimming 30 20
1681 60col. Football 30 20
1682 70col. Running 30 20
1683 70col. Boxing 30 20
1684 70col. Gymnastics 30 20
1685 70col. Tennis 30 20
Stamps of the same value were issued together, se-tenant, in blocks of four stamps, each block forming the composite design of a map of Australia with the sport appearing within the outline of the map

2000. Birth Centenary of Rafael Angel Calderon Guardia (politician).
1686 **519** 100col. blue 35 25

520 "Fisherman in Cojimar"

2000. Birth Centenary of Max Jiminez (artist). Multicoloured.
1687 50col. Type **520** 15 10
1688 50col. "Adamant" 15 10

521 Child's Face
522 Family

2000. Obligatory Tax. Christmas. Children's Village.
1689 **521** 20col. green 10 10
1690 20col. red 10 10
1691 20col. blue 10 10
1692 20col. brown 10 10

2000. A.I.D.S. Awareness. Multicoloured.
1693 60col. Type **522** 20 15
1694 90col. Man between blocks of colour 30 20

523 Nativity Scene

2000. Christmas
1695 **523** 100col. multicoloured . . 35 25

524 Cocos Cuckoo (*Coccyzus ferruginous*)

2001. America. UNESCO. World Heritage Sites. Coco Island. Birds. Multicoloured.
1696 95col. Type **524** 40 25
1697 115col. Cocos finch (*Pinaroloxias inornata*) . . 50 30

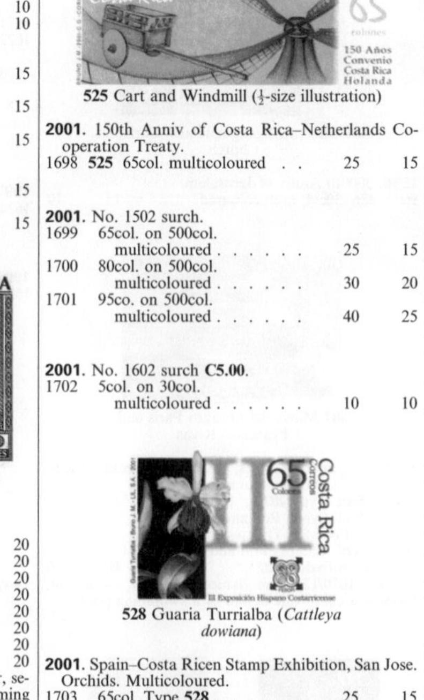

525 Cart and Windmill (½-size illustration)

2001. 150th Anniv of Costa Rica–Netherlands Co-operation Treaty.
1698 **525** 65col. multicoloured . . 25 15

2001. No. 1502 surch.
1699 65col. on 500col. multicoloured 25 15
1700 80col. on 500col. multicoloured 30 20
1701 95co. on 500col. multicoloured 40 25

2001. No. 1602 surch **C5.00.**
1702 5col. on 30col. multicoloured 10 10

528 Guaria Turrialba (*Cattleya dowiana*)

2001. Spain–Costa Ricen Stamp Exhibition, San Jose. Orchids. Multicoloured.
1703 65col. Type **528** 25 15
1704 65col. Trichophilia 25 15

529 Boy pushing Furniture on Barrow

2001. Child Labour Eradication Campaign.
1705 **529** 100col. multicoloured . . 40 25

530 Child holding Stamp and Magnifier

2001. Obligatory Tax. Christmas. Children's Village. Multicoloured, colour of right-hand title panel given.
1706 **530** 21col. violet 10 10
1707 21col. green 10 10
1708 21col. red 10 10
1709 21col. yellow 10 10

531 Steam Locomotive and Guardia

2001. Tomas Guardia (former President and railway pioneer) Commemoration.
1710 **531** 65col. multicoloured . . 25 15

EXPRESS DELIVERY STAMPS

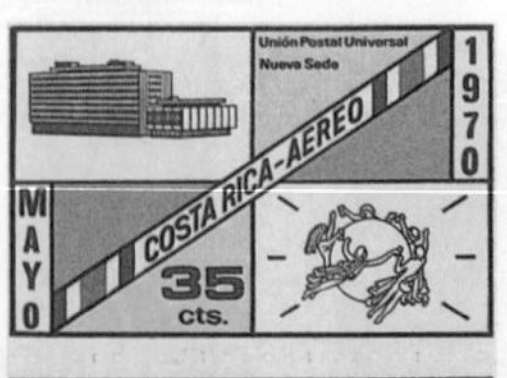

E 237 New U.P.U. Headquarters Building and Emblem

1970. Air. New U.P.U. Headquarters Building.
E841 E **237** 35c. multicoloured . . 15 10
E842 60c. multicoloured . . 20 10
In Type E **237** "ENTREGA INMEDIATA" is in the form of a perforated tab.
No. E842 has the same main design, but the tab is inscr "EXPRES".

E 249 Winged Letter

1972.
E888 E **249** 75c. brown & red . . . 15 15
E889 75c. green & red . . . 15 15
E890 75c. mauve & red . . 15 15
E891 1col.50 blue & red . . 45 25

E 279 Concorde

1976.
E1031 E **279** 1col. multicoloured 25 15
E1135 – 2col. multicoloured 50 30
E1136 – 2col. multicoloured 50 30
E1137 – 4col. multicoloured 55 25
Nos. E1135/7 is as Type E **279**, but inscribed "EXPRESS".

OFFICIAL STAMPS

Various issues optd **OFICIAL** except where otherwise stated.

1883. Stamps of 1883.
O35 **8** 1c. green 45 45
O36 2c. red 40 40
O22 5c. violet . . . . 2·75 2·75
O37 10c. orange . . . . 3·50 3·50
O38 40c. blue . . . . 2·50 2·10

1887. Stamps of 1887.
O39 **14** 5c. violet . . . . 1·60 1·60
O40 10c. orange 40 40

1889. Stamps of 1889.
O41 **17** 1c. brown 25 20
O42 2c. blue 25 20
O43 5c. orange 25 20
O44 10c. lake 25 20
O45 20c. green 25 20
O46 50c. red 60 60

1892. Stamps of 1892.
O47 **19** 1c. blue 25 20
O48 2c. orange 25 20
O49 5c. mauve 25 20
O50 10c. green 60 60
O51 20c. red 25 20
O52 50c. blue 60 50

1901. Stamps of 1901 (Nos. 42/48).
O53 1c. black and green 35 35
O54 2c. black and red 35 35
O61 4c. black and purple . . . . 1·25 1·25
O55 5c. black and blue 35 35
O62 6c. black and olive . . . . . 1·25 1·25
O56 10c. black and brown . . . 60 60
O57 20c. black and lake 80 80
O63 25c. brown and lilac . . . . 5·25 3·25
O58 50c. blue and red . . . . . 1·75 1·75
O59 1col. black and olive . . . . 55·00 32·00

1903. Stamp of 1901 optd **PROVISORIO OFICIAL.**
O60 2c. black & red (No. 43) . . 2·00 2·00

1908. Stamps of 1907 (Nos. 57/76).
O77 1c. blue and brown 10 10
O78 2c. black and green 10 10
O79 4c. blue and red 10 10
O80 5c. blue and orange 15 15
O81 10c. black and blue 85 85
O82 25c. slate and lavender . . . 15 15
O83 50c. blue and red 25 25
O84 1col. black and brown . . . 45 45

1917. Stamps of 1910 optd **OFICIAL 15-VI-1917.**
O115 5c. orange (No. 80) 20 20
O116 10c. blue (No. 81) 15 15

1920. No. 82 surch **OFICIAL 15 CENTIMOS.**
O117 15c. on 20c. olive 35 35

1921. Official stamps of 1908 optd **1921–22** or surch also.
O123 4c. blue & red (No.O79) . . 30 30
O124 6c. on 1c. blue & brown (No. O77) 35 35
O125 20c. on 25c. slate and lavender (No. O82) 35 35

O126 50c. blue & red (No. O83)	1·50	1·50
O127 1col. black & brn (No. O84)	3·00	3·00

1921. No. O115 surch **10 CTS.**

O128 10c. on 5c. orange	35	25

1923. Stamps of 1923.

O137 **77** 2c. brown	20	20
O138 4c. green	10	10
O139 5c. blue	20	20
O140 20c. red	15	15
O141 1col. violet	25	25

O 95

1926.

O169 **O 95** 2c. black and blue	10	10
O231 2c. black and lilac	10	10
O170 3c. black and red	10	10
O232 3c. black and brown	10	10
O171 4c. black and blue	10	10
O233 4c. black and red	10	10
O172 5c. black and green	10	10
O173 6c. black and yellow	10	10
O235 8c. black and brown	10	
O174 10c. black and red	10	10
O175 20c. black and green	10	10
O237 20c. black and blue	10	10
O176 30c. black and orange	10	10
O238 40c. black and orange	15	15
O177 45c. black and brown	15	15
O239 55c. black and lilac	25	
O178 1col. black and lilac	20	20
O240 1col. black and brown	20	20
O241 2col. black and blue	40	40
O242 5col. black & yellow	1·50	1·50
O243 10col. blue and black	9·50	9·50

1934. Air. Air stamps of 1934.

O211 **107** 5c. green	25	25
O212 10c. red	25	25
O213 15c. brown	40	40
O214 20c. blue	60	60
O215 25c. orange	60	60
O216 40c. brown	70	70
O217 50c. black	70	70
O218 60c. yellow	80	80
O219 75c. violet	80	80
O220 – 1col. red	1·25	1·25
O221 – 2col. blue	3·50	3·50
O222 – 5col. black	6·50	6·50
O223 – 10col. brown	7·50	7·50

1936. Stamps of 1936.

O228 **113** 5c. green	20	10
O229 10c. red	20	10

POSTAGE DUE STAMPS

D 42 D 64

1903.

D55 **D 42** 5c. blue	4·50	90
D56 10c. brown	4·50	70
D57 15c. green	1·90	1·60
D58 20c. red	2·10	1·60
D59 25c. blue	2·75	1·60
D60 30c. brown	4·25	2·50
D61 40c. olive	4·25	2·50
D62 50c. red	4·25	2·10

1915.

D115 **D 64** 2c. orange	10	10
D116 4c. blue	10	10
D117 8c. green	35	35
D118 10c. violet	15	15
D119 20c. brown	15	15

CRETE Pt. 3

Former Turkish island in the E. Mediterranean under the joint protection of Gt. Britain, France, Italy and Russia from 1898 to 1908, when the island was united to Greece. This was recognized by Turkey in 1913. Greek stamps now used.

100 lepta = 1 drachma.

1 Hermes

2 Hera

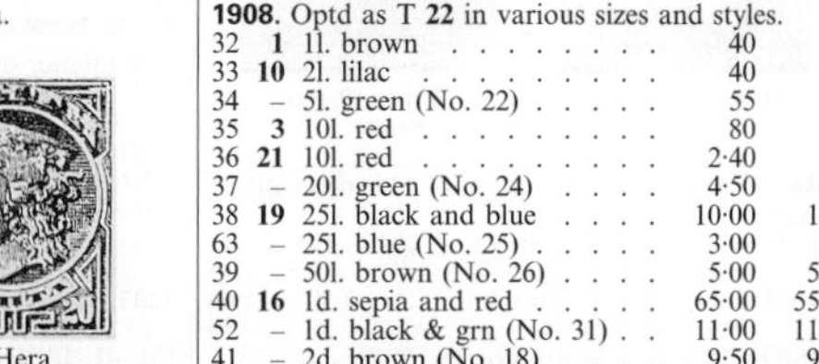

3 Prince George of Greece 4 Talos

1900.

1 **1** 1l. brown	65	20
12 1l. yellow	55	55
2 **2** 5l. green	1·25	20
3 **3** 10l. red	2·00	20
4 **2** 20l. red	7·75	1·25
13 20l. orange	4·00	70
15 **3** 25l. blue	8·00	65
14 **1** 50l. blue	11·00	11·50
16 50l. lilac	26·00	16·00
17 **4** 1d. violet	26·00	16·00
18 – 2d. brown	8·00	6·00
19 – 5d. black and green	8·00	7·00

DESIGNS (as Type **4**): 2d. Minos; 5d. St. George and Dragon.

ΠΡΟΣΩΡΙΝΟΝ
(7) ("Provisional")

1900. Optd as T **7**.

5 **3** 25l. blue	2·00	1·40
6 **1** 50l. lilac	1·40	80
7 **4** 1d. violet	9·50	4·00
8 – 2d. brown (No. 18)	26·00	16·00
9 – 5d. black & green (No. 19)	60·00	70·00

1904. Surch **5** twice.

20 **2** 5 on 20l. orange	3·25	75

10 Rhea 12 Prince George of Greece

16 Europa and Jupiter

1905.

21 **10** 2l. lilac	1·40	30
22 – 5l. green	4·00	30
23 **12** 10l. red	4·00	30
24 – 20l. green	4·00	75
25 – 25l. blue	5·00	70
26 – 50l. brown	3·75	3·50
27 **16** 1d. sepia and red	65·00	50·00
28 – 3d. black and orange	45·00	28·00
29 – 5d. black and olive	32·00	13·50

DESIGNS—As Type **10**: 5l. Europa; 20l. Miletus; 25l. Triton; 50l. Ariadne. As Type **16**: 3d. Minos ruins. 44 × 28½ mm: 5d. Mt. Ida.

19 High Commissioner A. T. A. Zaimis

1907. Various designs.

30 **19** 25l. black and blue	35·00	1·40
31 – 1d. black and green	9·00	6·25

DESIGN—HORIZ: (larger): 1d. Landing of Prince George of Greece at Suda.

21 Hermes

ΕΛΛΑΣ
(22)
("Greece")

1908. Optd as T **22** in various sizes and styles.

32 **1** 1l. brown	40	20
33 **10** 2l. lilac	40	20
34 – 5l. green (No. 22)	55	20
35 **3** 10l. red	80	40
36 **21** 10l. red	2·40	65
37 – 20l. green (No. 24)	4·50	65
38 **19** 25l. black and blue	10·00	1·40
63 – 25l. blue (No. 25)	3·00	55
39 – 50l. brown (No. 26)	5·00	5·00
40 **16** 1d. sepia and red	65·00	55·00
52 – 1d. black & grn (No. 31)	11·00	11·00
41 – 2d. brown (No. 18)	9·50	9·50
42 – 3d. black & orge (No. 28)	40·00	28·00
43 – 5d. black & olive (No. 29)	40·00	24·00

1909. Optd with T **7** and **22** or surch with new value also.

44 **1** 1l. yellow (No. 12)	1·10	1·10
45 **D 8** 1l. red (No. D10)	1·10	1·10
46 2 on 20l. red (No. D73)	1·10	1·10
47 2 on 20l. red (No. D13)	1·10	1·10
48 **2** 5 on 20l. red (No. 4)	80·00	80·00
49 5 on 20l. orange (No. 13)	1·10	1·10

OFFICIAL STAMPS

O 21

1908.

O32 **O 21** 10l. red	15·00	1·40
O33 30l. blue	30·00	2·50

In the 30l. the central figures are in an oval frame.

1908. Optd with T **22**.

O44 **O 21** 10l. red	16·00	1·40
O45 30l. blue	30·00	1·40

POSTAGE DUE STAMPS

D 8

1901.

D10 **D 8** 1l. red	45	50
D11 5l. red	1·10	40
D12 10l. red	1·10	25
D13 20l. red	1·50	70
D14 40l. red	12·00	11·00
D15 50l. red	12·00	11·00
D16 1d. red	12·00	11·00
D17 2d. red	13·00	11·00

1901. Surch "1 drachma" in Greek characters.

D18 **D 8** 1d. on 1d. red	8·75	8·00

1908. Optd with T **22**.

D70 **D 8** 1l. red	25	30
D45 5l. red	1·00	20
D72 10l. red	55	25
D47 20l. red	2·50	80
D74 40l. red	8·00	7·50
D75 50l. red	11·00	10·00
D76 1d. red	18·00	18·00
D51 1d. on 1d. red (No. D18)	9·50	9·50
D52 2d. red	18·00	18·00

REVOLUTIONARY ASSEMBLY, 1905

In March, a revolt in favour of union with Greece began, organized by Venizelos with headquarters at Theriso, South of Canea. The revolt collapsed in November 1905.

V 1 V 2 Crete enslaved

1905. Imperf.

V1 **V 1** 5l. red and green	13·50	7·00
V2 10l. green and red	13·50	7·00
V3 20l. blue and red	13·50	7·00
V4 50l. green and violet	13·50	7·00
V5 1d. red and blue	13·50	7·00

1905.

V 6 **V 2** 5l. orange	40	1·10
V 7 10l. grey	40	1·10
V 8 20l. mauve	1·05	2·10
V 9 50l. blue	2·75	4·25
V10 – 1d. violet and red	4·25	4·25
V11 – 2d. brown and green	4·25	5·00

DESIGN: 1, 2d. King George of Greece.

CROATIA Pt. 3

Part of Hungary until 1918 when it became part of Yugoslavia. In 1941 it was proclaimed an independent state but in 1945 it became a constituent republic of the Federal People's Republic of Yugoslavia.

In 1991 Croatia became independent.

April 1941. 100 paras = 1 dinar.
Sept 1941. 100 banicas = 1 kuna.
1991. 100 paras = 1 dinar.
1994. 100 lipa = 1 kuna.

NEZAVISNA DRŽAVA HRVATSKA IIIIII
(1)

(2)

1941. Stamps of Yugoslavia optd as T **1** ("Independent Croat State").

1 **99** 50p. orange	1·00	2·25
2 1d. green	1·00	2·25
3 1d.50 red	1·00	1·00
4 2d. mauve	1·00	1·75
5 3d. brown	2·50	4·50
6 4d. blue	2·50	5·00
7 5d. blue	2·50	5·00
8 5d.50 violet	2·50	5·50

1941. Stamps of Yugoslavia optd as T **2**.

9 **99** 25p. black	20	30
10 50p. orange	20	30
11 1d. green	20	30
12 1d.50 red	20	30
13 2d. pink	20	60
14 3d. brown	20	90
15 4d. blue	25	1·00
16 5d. blue	40	1·00
17 5d.50 violet	40	1·25
18 6d. blue	50	1·75
19 8d. brown	80	2·00
20 12d. violet	90	2·50
21 16d. purple	1·00	3·00
22 20d. blue	1·25	3·50
23 30d. pink	2·00	5·50

NEZAVISNA 1 DIN DRŽAVA HRVATSKA
(3)

(4)

1941. Stamps of Yugoslavia surch as T **3**.

24 **99** 1d. on 3d. brown	15	40
25 2d. on 4d. blue	15	40

1941. Founding of Croatian Army. Nos. 414/26 of Yugoslavia optd with T **4**.

25a **99** 25p. black		
25b 50p. orange		
25c 1d. green		
25d 1d.50 red		
25e 2d. pink		
25f 3d. brown		
25g 4d. blue		
25h 5d. blue		
25i 5d.50 violet		
25j 6d. blue		
25k 8d. brown		
25l 12d. violet		
25m 16d. purple		
25n 20d. blue		
25o 30d. pink		
Set of 15	£150	£375

Sold at double face value.

1941. Stamps of Yugoslavia optd as T **2** but without shield.

26 **109** 1d.50+1d.50 black	5·00	10·00
27 – 4d.+3d. brown (No. 457)	5·00	10·00

1941. Postage Due stamps of Yugoslavia optd **NEZAVISNA DRZAVA HRVATSKA FRANCO.**

28 **D 56** 50p. violet	20	30
29 2d. blue	30	60
30 5d. orange	30	60
31 10d. brown	35	90

7 Mt. Ozalj

8 Banja Luka

1941.

32 **7** 25b. red	25	25
33 – 50b. green	10	10
34 – 75b. olive	10	10
35 – 1k. green	10	10
36 – 1k.50 green	10	10
37 – 2k. red	10	10
38 – 3k. red	10	10
39 – 4k. blue	10	10
40 – 5k. black	75	75
41 – 5k. blue	10	10
42 – 6k. olive	10	10
43 – 7k. orange	10	10
44 – 8k. brown	10	10
45 – 10k. violet	40	30
46 – 12k. brown	50	50
47 – 20k. brown	40	30
48 – 30k. brown	55	50
49 – 50k. green	1·00	1·00
50 **8** 100k. violet	1·60	2·25

DESIGNS: 50b. Waterfall at Jajce; 75b. Varazdin; 1k. Mt. Velebit; 1k.50, Zelenjak; 2k. Zagreb Cathedral; 3k. Church at Osijek; 4k. River Drina; 5k. (No. 40), Konjic Bridge; 5k. (No. 41), Modern building at Zemun; 6k. Dubrovnik; 7k. R. Save in Slavonia; 8k. Mosque at Sarajevo; 10k. Lake Plitvice; 12k. Klis Fortress near Split; 20k. Hvar; 30k. Harvesting in Syrmia; 50k. Senj.

9 Croat (Sinj) Costume 10 Emblems of Germany, Croatia and Italy

1941. Red Cross.
51 **9** 1k.50+1k.50 blue 35 60
52 – 2k.+2k. brown 35 70
53 – 5k.+4k. red . . . . 85 1·75
COSTUMES: 2k. Travnik. 4k. Turopolje.

1941. Eastern Volunteer Fund.
54 **10** 4k.+2k. blue . . . . 1·00 2·75

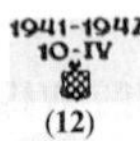

11 Glider (12)

1942. Aviation Fund. Glider in flight as T **11**.
55 **11** 2k.+2k. brown (vert) . . . 40 60
56 – 2k.50+2k.50 green . . . . . 60 1·00
57 – 3 k+3k. red (vert) . . . . . 75 1·25
58 – 4k.+4k. blue . . . . 85 1·90
DESIGNS—HORIZ: 2k.50, Glider (different); 4k. Seaplane glider. VERT: 3k. Boy with model glider.

1942. 1st Anniv of Croat Independence. Optd with T **12**.
59 2k. brown (as No. 37) 15 35
60 5k. red (as No. 40) 25 70
61 10k. green (as No. 45) . . . . 40 1·00

1942. Banja Luka Philatelic Exhibition. Inscr "F.I." in top right corner.
62 **8** 100k. violet . . . . 1·40 3·75

1942. Surch **0.25kn** and bar.
63 0.25k. on 2k. red (No. 37) . . 20 50

14 Trumpeters 15 Sestine (Croatia)

1942. National Relief Fund.
64 **14** 3k.+1k. red . . . . 40 1·00
65 – 4k.+2k. brown . . . . . . 60 1·40
66 – 5k.+5k. blue . . . . 80 1·90
DESIGNS—HORIZ: 4k. Procession beneath triumphal archways. VERT: 5k. Mother and child.

1942. Red Cross Fund. Peasant girls in provincial costumes.
67 **15** 1k.50+50b. brown . . . . . 60 1·25
68 – 3k.+1k. violet . . . . . . 60 1·25
69 – 4k.+2k. blue . . . . 80 1·75
70 – 10k.+5k. bistre . . . . . . 1·00 2·10
71 **15** 13k.+6k. red . . . . 2·00 4·50
COSTUMES: 3k. Slavonia. 4k. Bosnia. 10k. Dalmatia.

15a Red Cross Sister 16 M. Gubec

1942. Charity Tax. Red Cross Fund. Cross in red.
71a **15a** 1k. green 20 60

1942. Croat ("Ustascha") Youth Fund.
72 **16** 3k.+6k. red 25 70
73 – 4k.+7k. brown 25 70
MS73a 5k.+20k. blue (perf or imperf) . . . . 7·00 16·00
DESIGNS—VERT: Dr. A. Starcevic; 5k. Trumpet and flag.

17 19 Arms of Zagreb

1943. Labour Front. Vert designs showing workers as T **17**.
74 **17** 2k.+1k. brown and olive . . 1·50 3·25
75 – 3k.+3k. brown & purple . . 1·50 3·25
76 – 7k.+4k. brown & grey . . . 1·50 3·25

1943. 7th Centenary of Foundation of Zagreb.
77 **19** 3k.50 (+ 6k.50) blue . . . . 1·10 3·75

1943. Pictorial designs as T **8**, but with views surrounded by frame line.
78 3k.50 brown 35 40
79 12k.50 black 35 70
DESIGNS: 3k.50, Trakoscan Castle; 12k.50, Veliki Tabor.

21 A. Pavelic 22 Krsto Frankopan

1943. Croat ("Ustascha") Youth Fund.
80 **21** 5k.+3k. red 15 65
81 7k.+5k. green 15 65
MS81a **21** 12k.+8k. blue (perf or imperf) . . . . 8·50 20·00

1943. Famous Croats.
82 – 1k. blue 15 30
83 **22** 2k. olive 15 30
84 – 3k.50 red 15 50
PORTRAITS: 1k. Katarina Zrinska. 3k.50, Peter Zrinski.

23 Croat Sailor and Motor Torpedo Boats

1943. Croat Legion Relief Fund.
85 **23** 1k.+50b. green 10 25
86 – 2k.+1k. red 10 25
87 – 3k.50+1k.50 blue 10 25
88 – 9k.+4k.50 brown 10 25
MS88a 1k.+0k.50 blue; 2k.+1k. green; 3k.50+1k.50 blue; 9k.+4k.50 brown (perf or imperf) 2·50 5·00
DESIGNS: 2k. Pilot and Heinkel bomber; 3k.50, Infantrymen; 9k. Mechanized column.

24 St. Mary's Church and Cistercian Monastery, 1650

1943. Philatelic Exhibition, Zagreb.
89 **24** 18k.+9k. blue . . . . 1·40 4·00
MS89a 99 × 132 mm. **24** 18k.+9k. black . . . . 5·00 12·00

1943. Return of Sibenik to Croatia. Optd **HRVATSKO MORE 8, IX. 1943**.
90 **24** 18k.+9k. blue . . . . 3·25 9·00

26 Nurse and Patient 26a

1943. Red Cross Fund.
91 – 1k.+50b. blue 20 50
92 – 2k.+1k. red 20 50
93 – 3k.50+1k.50 blue 20 50
94 **26** 8k.+3k. brown 20 50
95 9k.+4k. green 20 50
96 – 10k.+5k. violet 30 75
97 **26** 12k.+6k. blue 30 90
98 – 12k.50+6k. brown . . . . 50 1·25
99 **26** 18k.+8k. orange . . . . . 75 1·90
100 32k.+12k. grey . . . . . . 1·25 2·75
DESIGN: 1k., 2k., 3k.50, 10k., 12k.50, Mother and children.

1943. Charity Tax. Red Cross Fund. Cross in red.
100a **26a** 2k. blue 20 50

27 A. Pavelic 28 Ruder Boskovic

1943.

101 **27** 25b. red 10 15
105 50b. blue 10 15
102 75b. green 10 15
106 1k. green 10 15
107 1k.50 violet 10 15
108 2k. red 10 15
109 3k. red 10 15
110 3k.50 blue 10 15
111 4k. purple 10 15
103 5k. blue 10 15
112 8k. brown 10 15
113 9k. red 10 15
114 10k. purple 10 15
115 12k. brown 10 15
116 12k.50 black 10 15
117 18k. brown 10 15
104 32k. brown 10 15
118 50k. green 10 15
119 70k. orange 30 60
120 100k. violet . . . . 70 1·40

The design of the 25b., 75b., 5k., and 32k. is $20\frac{1}{2} \times 26$ mm, the rest are 22×28 mm.

1943. Honouring Ruder Boskovic (astronomer).
121 **28** 3k.50 red 15 35
122 12k.50 purple 30 50

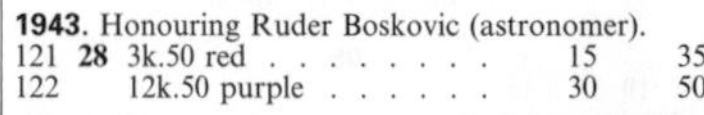

29 Posthorn 30 St. Sebastian

1944. Postal and Railway Employees' Relief Fund.
123 **29** 7k.+3k.50 brn, red & bis 20 40
124 – 16k.+8k. blue 20 50
125 – 24k.+12k. red 30 70
126 – 32k.+16k. black & red . . 65 1·10
DESIGNS—VERT: 16k. Dove, airplane and globe; 24k. Mercury. HORIZ: 32k. Winged wheel.

1944. War Invalids' Relief Fund.
127 **30** 7k.+3k.50 mauve & red . . 20 50
128 – 16k.+8k. green 25 70
129 – 24k.+12k. yell, brn & red 25 70
130 – 32k.+16k. blue . . . . . 45 1·10
DESIGNS—HORIZ: 16k. Blind man and cripple; 32k. Death of Peter Svacic, 1094. VERT: 24k. Mediaeval statuette.

31 The Legion in Action 32 Jure-Ritter Francetic

1944. Croat Youth Fund. No. 134 perf, others imperf.
131 **31** 3k.50+1k.50 brown 10 15
132 – 12k.50+6k.50 blue 10 15
134 **32** 12k.50+287k.50 black . . . 3·50 11·50
133 18k.+9k. brown 10 15
DESIGN: No. 132, Sentries on the Drina.

33

1944. Labour Front. Inscr "D.R.S.".
135 **33** 3k.50+1k. red 10 20
136 – 12k.50+6k. brown 40 65
137 – 18k.+9k. blue 15 35
138 – 32k.+16k. green 15 35
MS138a 74 × 100 mm. 32k.+16k. (as No. 138) brown on yellow . . 1·50 4·50
DESIGNS: 12k.50, Digging; 18k. Instruction; 32k. "On Parade".

34 Bombed Home 35 War Victim

1944. Charity Tax. War Victims.
138b **34** 1k. green 10 15
138c **35** 2k. red 10 15
138d 5k. green 10 15
138e 10k. blue 15 35
138f 20k. brown 40 85

36 37 Storm Division Soldiers

1944. Red Cross. Cross in red.
139 **36** 2k.+1k. green 10 30
140 3k.50+1k.50 red 15 40
141 12k.50+6k. blue 20 50

1945. Creation of Croatian Storm Division on 9th October 1944.
142 **37** 50k.+50k. red and grey . . 42·00 £100
143 – 70k.+70k. sepia & grey . . 42·00 £100
144 – 100k.+100k. bl & grey . . 42·00 £100
MS144a 216 × 134 mm. Nos. 142/4 £600 £1400
DESIGNS: 70k. Storm Division soldiers in action; 100k. Divisional emblem.

38 39

1945. Postal Employees' Fund.
145 **38** 3k.50+1k.50 grey 10 20
146 – 12k.50+6k. purple 10 30
147 – 24k.+12k. green 15 35
148 – 50k.+25k. purple 20 60
MS148a 99 × 110 mm. 100k.+50k. red . . . . 4·00 8·00
DESIGNS: 12k.50, Telegraph linesman; 24k. Telephone switchboard; 50k. The postman calls.

1945. Labour Day.
149 **39** 3k.50 brown . . . . 20 1·25

40 Interior of Zagreb Cathedral 41 Statue of the Virgin and Shrine

1991. Obligatory Tax. Workers' Fund. Mass for Croatia. Perf or imperf.
150 **40** 1d.20 gold and black . . . 40 40

1991. Obligatory Tax. Workers' Fund. 700th Anniv of Shrine of the Virgin, Trsat. Perf or imperf.
151 **41** 1d.70 multicoloured . . . 50 50

42 State Arms

43 Members of Parliament

1991. Obligatory Tax. Workers' Fund. Rally in Ban Jelacic Square, Zagreb. Perf or imperf.
152 **42** 2d.20 multicoloured . . . 50 50
See also No. 170.

1991. Obligatory Tax. Workers' Fund. First Multi-party Session of Croatian Parliament, 30 May 1990. Perf or imperf.
153 **43** 2d.20 multicoloured . . . 50 50

44 Sud Aviation Caravelle Jetliner over Zagreb Cathedral and Dubrovnik

45 Anti-tuberculosis Emblem

1991. Air.
154 **44** 1d. blue, black and red . . 30 30
155 – 2d. multicoloured 30 30
156 – 3d. multicoloured 30 30
DESIGNS: 2d. Bell tower and ruins of Diocletian's Palace, Split; 3d. Sud Aviation Caravelle jetliner over Zagreb Cathedral and Pula amphitheatre.

1991. Obligatory Tax. Anti-tuberculosis Week.
157 **45** 2d.20 red and blue 30 30

46 Ban Jelacic Statue

48 First Article of Constitution in Croatian

1991. Obligatory Tax. Workers' Fund. Re-erection of Ban Josip Jelacic Equestrian Statue, Zagreb. Perf or imperf.
158 **46** 2d.20 multicoloured . . . 50 50

1991. No. 150 surch 4^{00} **HPT** and posthorn.
159 **40** 4d. on 1d.20 gold & blk . . 35 35

1991. Obligatory Tax. Workers' Fund. 1st Anniv of New Constitution. Multicoloured. Perf or imperf.
160 2d.20 Type **48** 30 30
161 2d.20 Text in English 80 80
162 2d.20 Text in French 80 80
163 2d.20 Text in German . . . 80 80
164 2d.20 Text in Russian 80 80
165 2d.20 Text in Spanish 80 80

49 Book of Croatian Independence

50 17th-century Crib Figures, Kosljun Monastery, Krk

1991. Recognition of Independence.
166 **49** 30d. multicoloured . . . . 1·10 1·10

1991. Christmas.
167 **50** 4d. multicoloured 60 60

51 "VUKOVAR" and Barbed Wire

52 Ban Josip Jelacic

1992. Obligatory Tax. Vukovar Refugees' Fund.
168 **51** 2d.20 brown and black . . 40 40

1992. No. 151 surch 2^{00} **HPT** and posthorn.
169 **41** 20d. on 1d.70 mult . . . . 3·00 3·00

1992. As No. 152, but redrawn with new value and "HPT" emblem replacing obligatory tax inscr at foot.
170 **42** 10d. multicoloured 30 30

1992. Obligatory Tax. Famous Croatians. Multicoloured.
171 4d.+2d. Type **52** 35 35
172 4d.+2d. Dr. Ante Starcevic (founder of Party of the Right) 30 30
173 7d.+3d. Stjepan Radic (founder of Croation Peasant Party) 30 30

53 Olympic Rings

54 Osijek Cathedral on Paper Dart

1992. Winter Olympic Games, Albertville, France.
174 **53** 30d. multicoloured 80 80

1992. Air.
175 **54** 4d. multicoloured 25 20

55 Knin

56 Statue of King Tomislav, Zagreb

1992. Croatian Towns (1st series).
176 **55** 6d. multicoloured 15 15
177 – 7d. multicoloured 15 15
178 – 20d. blue, red and yellow 75 75
179 – 30d. multicoloured 40 40
180 – 45d. multicoloured 75 75
181 – 50d. multicoloured 75 75
182 – 300d. multicoloured . . . 2·50 2·50
DESIGNS: 7d. Von Eltz Castle, Lukovar; 20d. St. Francis's Church, Ilok; 30d. Dr. Ante Starcevic Street, Gospic; 45d. Rector's Palace, Dubrovnik; 50d. St. Jakov's Cathedral, Sibenik; 300d. Sokak houses, Beli Manastir.
See also Nos. 208/14, 382/7, 523/4, 636 and 639.

1992.
183 **56** 10d. green 20 20

57 Red Cross Emblems on Globe

58 Map of Croatia on Red Cross

1992. Obligatory Tax. Red Cross Week.
184 **57** 3d. red and black 20 20

1992. Obligatory Tax. Solidarity Week.
185 **58** 3d. red and black 20 20

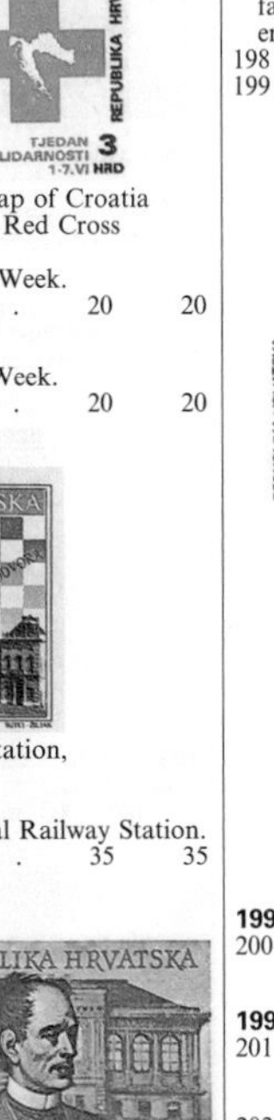

59 Central Railway Station, Zagreb

1992. Centenary of Zagreb Central Railway Station.
186 **59** 30d. multicoloured 35 35

60 Society Imprint

61 Bishop Josip Strossmayer (patron) and Academy Building

1992. 150th Anniv of Matica Hrvatska (Croatian language society).
187 **60** 20d. gold and red 25 25

1992. 125th Anniv of Croatian Academy of Sciences and Arts.
188 **61** 30d. multicoloured 35 35

62 Olympic Rings on Computer Pattern

1992. Olympic Games, Barcelona. Mult.
189 40d. Type **62** 35 35
190 105d. Rings and symbolic sports 65 65

63 Bellflowers

64 Blue Rock Thrush

1992. Flowers. Multicoloured.
191 30d. Type **63** 25 25
192 85d. Degenia (vert) 50 50

1992. Environmental Protection. Mult.
193 40d. Type **64** 25 25
194 75d. Red-spot snake 50 50

65 15th-century Carrack, Dubrovnik

66 "Madonna of Bistrica"

1992. Europa. 500th Anniv of Discovery of America by Columbus (1st issue).
195 **65** 30d. multicoloured 30 30
196 – 75d. black and red 75 75
DESIGN: 75d. "Indian Horseman" (bronze statue in Chicago by Ivan Mestrovic).
See also Nos. 198/9.

1992. Obligatory Tax. Fund for National Shrine to Madonna of Bistrica.
197 **66** 5d. gold and blue 20 20

1992. Europa. 500th Anniv of Discovery of America by Columbus (2nd issue). As Nos. 195/6, but new face values and with additional C.E.P.T. posthorns emblem.
198 **65** 60d. multicoloured 50 50
199 – 130d. black, red and gold (as No. 196) . . . . . . 1·10 1·10

67 Red Cross

69 Dove and Coat of Arms

68 "25"

1992. Obligatory Tax. Anti-tuberculosis Week.
200 **67** 5d. red and black 20 20

1992. Croatian Language Anniversaries. Mult.
201 40d. Type **68** (25th anniv of Croatian Language Declaration) 25 25
202 130d. "100" (centenary of Croatian "Orthography" by Dr. I. Broz) 45 45

1992. 750th Anniv of Grant of Royal City Charter to Samobor.
203 **69** 90d. multicoloured 35 35

70 Remains of Altar Screen from Uzdolje Church

71 St. George and the Dragon

1992. 1100th Anniv of Duke Mucimir's Donation (judgement in ecclesiastical dispute).
204 **70** 60d. multicoloured 25 25

1992. Obligatory Tax. Croatian Anti-cancer League.
205 **71** 15d. multicoloured 20 20
See also No. 255.

72 Seal of King Bela IV

1992. 750th Anniv of Zagreb's Charter from King Bela IV.
206 **72** 180d. multicoloured . . . 50 50

73 "Croatian Christmas" (Ljubo Babic)

1992. Christmas.
207 **73** 80d. multicoloured 25 25

74 Former Town Hall, Vinkovci

75 Lorkovic

1992. Croatian Towns (2nd series). Mult.
208 100d. Type **74** 25 20
209 200d. Castle, Pazin (vert) . . 35 30
210 500d. Jelacic Square, Slavonski Brod 80 75
211 1000d. Town Hall, Jelacic Square, Varazdin . . . . . 1·25 1·00
212 2000d. Zorin cultural centre, Karlovac . . . . 1·40 1·25
213 5000d. St. Donat's Church and St. Stosija's Cathedral belltower, Zadar (vert) . . 1·60 1·50
214 10000d. Pirovo peninsula and Franciscan monastery, Vis 3·00 2·75

1992. Death Centenary of Blaz Lorkovic (political economist).
218 **75** 250d. multicoloured . . . 50 50

76 Coiled National Colours

77 Bunic-Vucic

1992. 150th Anniv of "Kolo" (literary Magazine).
219 **76** 300d. multicoloured . . . 60 60

1992. 400th Birth Anniv of Ivan Bunic-Vucic (poet).
220 **77** 350d. multicoloured . . . 65 65

78 Ljudevit Gaj Square, Krapina

1993. 800th Anniv of Krapina.
221 **78** 300d. multicoloured . . . 60 60

79 Tesla

1993. 50th Death Anniv of Nikola Tesla (physicist).
222 **79** 250d. multicoloured . . . 50 50

80 Quinquerez ("self-portrait")

1993. Death Cent of Ferdo Quiquerez (painter).
223 **80** 100d. multicoloured . . . 25 25

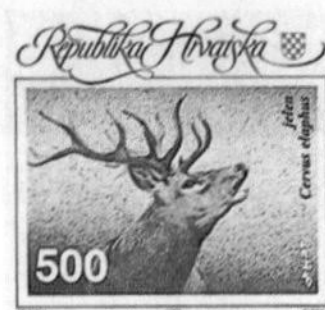

81 Red Deer

1993. Animals of the Kapacki Rit Swamp. Multicoloured.
224 500d. Type **81** 70 70
225 550d. White-tailed sea eagle 80 80

82 Sulentic ("self-portrait")

1993. Birth Centenary of Zlatko Sulentic (painter).
226 **82** 350d. multicoloured . . . 45 45

83 Kursalon, Lipik

1993. Centenary of Lipik Spa.
227 **83** 400d. multicoloured . . . 45 45

84 Kovacic (statue, Vojin Bakic)

1993. 50th Death Anniv of Ivan Goran Kovacic (writer).
228 **84** 200d. multicoloured . . . 30 30

85 Minceta Fortress, Dubrovnik

1993. 59th P.E.N. Literary Congress, Dubrovnik.
229 **85** 800d. multicoloured . . . 1·00 1·00

86 Ivan Kakaljevic (writer) **87** Mask and Split Theatre

1993. 150th Anniv of First Speech in Croatian Language made to Croatian Parliament.
230 **86** 500d. multicoloured . . . 45 45

1993. Centenary of Split Theatre.
231 **87** 600d. multicoloured . . . 45 45

88 Boy and Ruined House **89** Pag in 16th Century

1993. Obligatory Tax. Red Cross Week.
232 **88** 80d. black and red 20 20

1993. 550th Anniv of Refoundation of Pag.
233 **89** 800d. multicoloured . . . 60 60

90 Dove **91** Girl at Window

1993. 1st Anniv of Croatia's Membership of U.N.
234 **90** 500d. multicoloured . . . 40 40

1993. Obligatory Tax. Solidarity Week.
235 **91** 100d. black and red . . . 20 20

92 "In the Cafe" (Ivo Dulcic)

1993. Europa. Contemporary Art. Mult.
236 700d. Type **92** 40 40
237 1000d. "The Waiting Room" (Miljenko Stancic) 60 60
238 1100d. "Two Figures" (Lijubo Ivancic) 80 80

93 "Homodukt" (Milivoj Bijelic)

1993. 45th Art Biennial, Venice. Mult.
239 250d. Type **93** 25 25
240 600d. "Snails" (Ivo Dekovic) 45 45
241 1000d. "Esa carta de mi flor" (Zeljko Kipke) 70 70

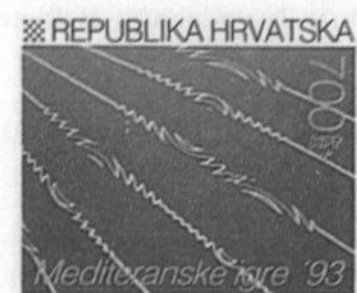

94 Symbolic Running Track

1993. 12th Mediterranean Games, Roussillon (Languedoc), France.
242 **94** 700d. multicoloured . . . 45 45

95 "Slavonian Oaks"

1993. 150th Birth Anniv of Adolf Waldinger (painter).
243 **95** 300d. multicoloured . . . 25 25

96 Battle of Krbava, 1493

1993. Anniversaries of Famous Battles. 16th-century engravings.
244 800d. Type **96** 50 50
245 1300d. Battle of Sisak, 1593 90 90

97 Krleza (after Marija Ujevic)

1993. Birth Centenary of Miroslav Krleza (writer).
246 **97** 400d. multicoloured . . . 30 30

98 Cardinal Stepinac **99** Croatian Postman

1993. Obligatory Tax. Cardinal Stepinac Foundation.
247 **98** 150d. black, mauve & gold 20 20

1993. 1st Anniv of Croatia's Membership of Universal Postal Union.
248 **99** 1800d. multicoloured . . . 85 85

100 Paljetak

1993. Birth Centenary of Vlaho Paljetak (singer-songwriter).
249 **100** 500d. multicoloured . . . 30 30

101 Peter Zrinski and Krsto Frankopan

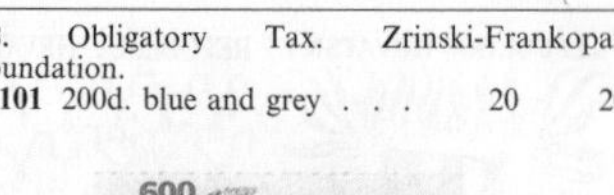
1993. Obligatory Tax. Zrinski-Frankopan Foundation.
250 **101** 200d. blue and grey . . . 20 20

102 "Freedom of Croatia" (central motif of 1918 stamp)

1993. Stamp Day.
251 **102** 600d. multicoloured . . . 30 30

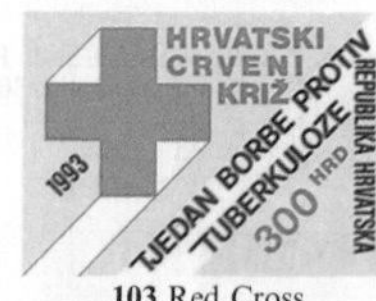

103 Red Cross

1993. Obligatory Tax. Anti-tuberculosis Week.
252 **103** 300d. green, black & red 20 20

104 Antonio Magini's Map of Istria, 1620 **105** Smiciklas

1993. 50th Anniv of Incorporation of Istria, Rijeka and Zadar into Croatia.
253 **104** 2200d. multicoloured . . 80 80

1993. 150th Birth Anniv of Tadija Smiciklas (historian).
254 **105** 800d. black, gold and red 30 30

1993. Obligatory Tax. Croatian Anti-cancer League.
255 **71** 400d. multicoloured . . . 20 20

106 Allegory of Birth of Croatian History on Shores of the Adriatic

1993. Centenary of National Archaeological Museum, Split.
256 **106** 1000d. multicoloured . . 40 40

107 Girl In Heart **108** Croatian and French Flags and Soldiers

1993. Obligatory Tax. Save Croatian Children Fund.
257 **107** 400d. red, blue and black 20 20

1993. 50th Anniv of Uprising of 13th Pioneer Battalion, Villefranche-de-Rouergue, France.
258 **108** 3000d. multicoloured . . 95 95

109 Tomic **110** Astronomical Diagram

1993. 150th Birth Anniv of Josip Eugen Tomic (writer).
259 **109** 900d. brown, green & red 30 30

1993. 850th Anniv of Publication of "De Essentiis" by Herman Dalmatin.
260 **110** 1000d. multicoloured . . 30 30

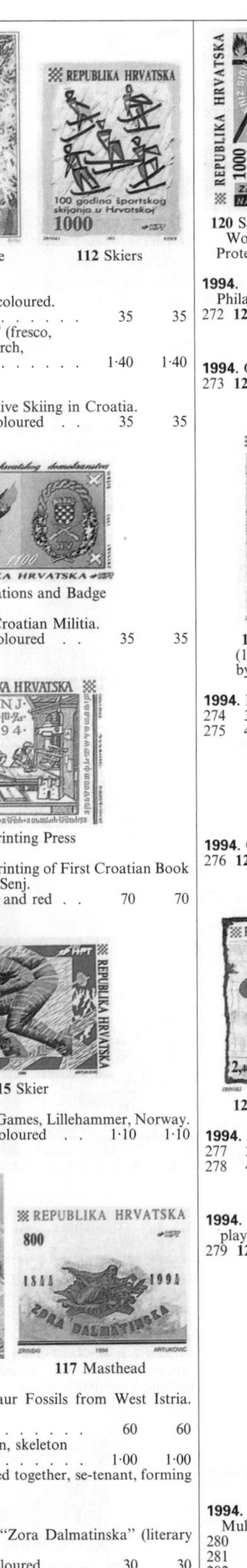

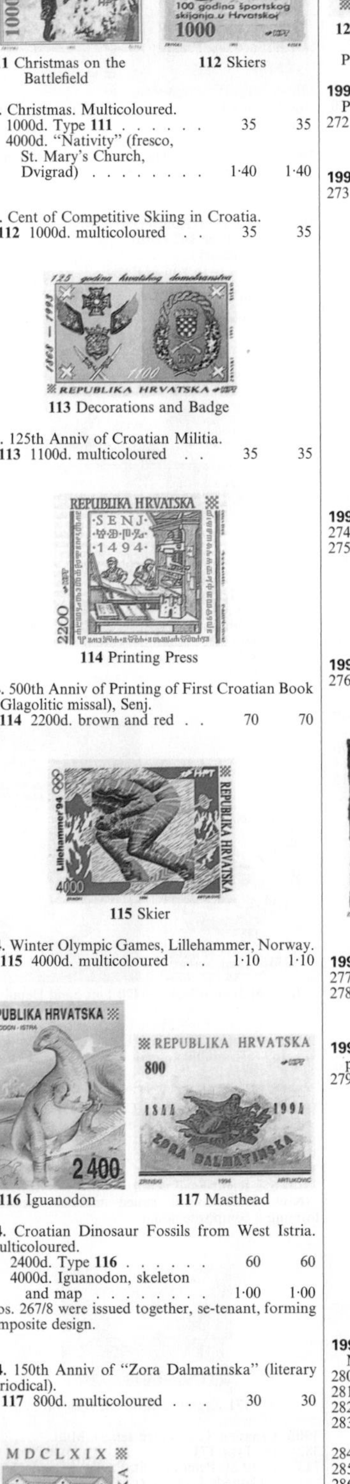

111 Christmas on the Battlefield

112 Skiers

1993. Christmas. Multicoloured.
261 1000d. Type **111** 35 35
262 4000d. "Nativity" (fresco, St. Mary's Church, Dvigrad) . . . . 1·40 1·40

1993. Cent of Competitive Skiing in Croatia.
263 **112** 1000d. multicoloured . . 35 35

113 Decorations and Badge

1993. 125th Anniv of Croatian Militia.
264 **113** 1100d. multicoloured . . 35 35

114 Printing Press

1994. 500th Anniv of Printing of First Croatian Book (a Glagolitic missal), Senj.
265 **114** 2200d. brown and red . . 70 70

115 Skier

1994. Winter Olympic Games, Lillehammer, Norway.
266 **115** 4000d. multicoloured . . 1·10 1·10

116 Iguanodon

117 Masthead

1994. Croatian Dinosaur Fossils from West Istria. Multicoloured.
267 2400d. Type **116** 60 60
268 4000d. Iguanodon, skeleton and map . . . . 1·00 1·00
Nos. 267/8 were issued together, se-tenant, forming a composite design.

1994. 150th Anniv of "Zora Dalmatinska" (literary periodical).
269 **117** 800d. multicoloured . . . 30 30

118 University, Emperor Leopold I's Seal and Vice-chancellor's Chain

119 Wolf

1994. 325th Anniv of Croatian University, Zagreb.
270 **118** 2200d. multicoloured . . 70 70

1994. Planet Earth Day.
271 **119** 3800d. multicoloured . . 1·25 1·25

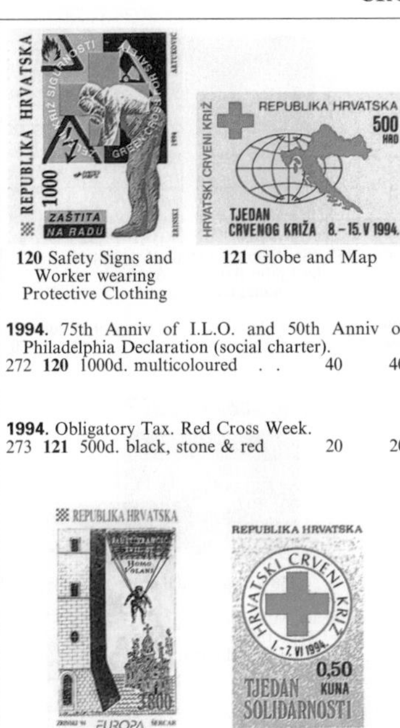

120 Safety Signs and Worker wearing Protective Clothing

121 Globe and Map

1994. 75th Anniv of I.L.O. and 50th Anniv of Philadelphia Declaration (social charter).
272 **120** 1000d. multicoloured . . 40 40

1994. Obligatory Tax. Red Cross Week.
273 **121** 500d. black, stone & red 20 20

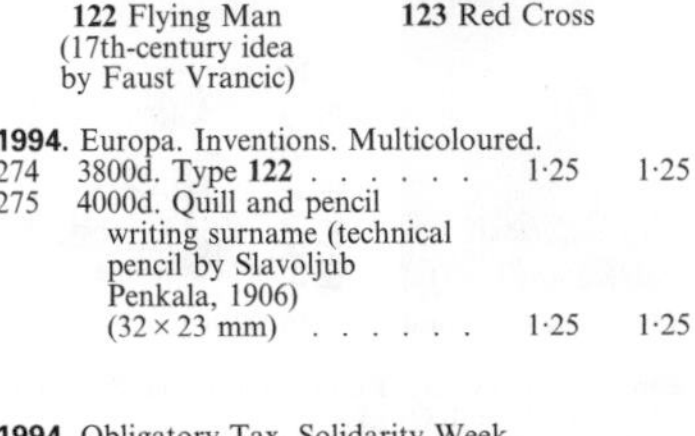

122 Flying Man (17th-century idea by Faust Vrancic)

123 Red Cross

1994. Europa. Inventions. Multicoloured.
274 3800d. Type **122** . . . . . . 1·25 1·25
275 4000d. Quill and pencil writing surname (technical pencil by Slavoljub Penkala, 1906) (32 × 23 mm) . . . . . . 1·25 1·25

1994. Obligatory Tax. Solidarity Week.
276 **123** 50l. red, black and grey 20 20

124 Croatian Iris

125 Petrovic

1994. Flowers. Multicoloured.
277 2k.40 Type **124** 75 75
278 4k. Meadow saffron . . . . . 1·25 1·25

1994. 1st Death Anniv of Drazen Petrovic (basketball player).
279 **125** 1k. multicoloured 35 35

126 Plitvice Lakes

1994. 150th Anniv of Tourism in Croatia. Multicoloured.
280 80l. Type **126** 20 20
281 1k. River Krka 25 25
282 1k.10 Kornati Islands 40 40
283 2k.20 Kopacki Trscak ornithological reserve . . . 70 70
284 2k.40 Opatija Riviera 80 80
285 3k.80 Brijuni Islands . . . . 1·25 1·25
286 4k. Trakoscan Castle, Zagorje . . . . 1·40 1·40

127 Baranovic at Keyboard

128 Monstrance

1994. Musical Anniversaries.
287 **127** 1k. multicoloured 35 35
288 – 2k.20 silver, black & red 65 65
289 – 2k.40 multicoloured . . . 80 80

DESIGNS—VERT: 1k. Type **127** (birth centenary of Kresimir Baranovic (composer and conductor/director of Croatian National Theatre Opera, Zagreb, 1915–40)); 2k.20, Vatroslav Lisinski (composer, 175th birth anniv). HORIZ: 2k.40, Score and harp player (350th anniv of Pauline song-book).

1994. Obligatory Tax. Ludbreg Shrine.
290 **128** 50l. multicoloured 20 20

129 Men dressed in Croatian and American Colours

130 Mother and Children

1994. Centenary of Croatian Brotherhood in U.S.A.
291 **129** 2k.20 multicoloured . . . 70 60

1994. Obligatory Tax. Save Croatian Children Fund.
292 **130** 50l. multicoloured 20 20

131 Family

132 St. George and the Dragon

1994. International Year of the Family.
293 **131** 80l. multicoloured 30 30

1994. Obligatory Tax. Croatian Anti-Cancer League.
294 **132** 50l. multicoloured 20 20

133 Pope John Paul II and his Arms

134 Franjo Bucar (Committee member, 1920–46)

1994. Papal Visit.
295 **133** 1k. multicoloured 35 35

1994. Cent of International Olympic Committee.
296 **134** 1k. multicoloured 40 40

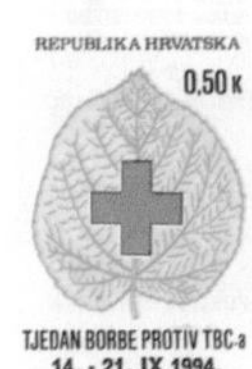

135 Red Cross on Leaf

136 The Little Prince (book character)

1994. Obligatory Tax. Anti-tuberculosis Week.
297 **135** 50l. red, green & black . . 20 20

1994. 50th Death Anniv of Antoine de Saint-Exupery (writer).
298 **136** 3k.80 multicoloured . . . 1·00 1·00

137 "Resurrection" (lunette, Gati, Omis)

1994. 13th International Convention on Christian Archaeology, Split and Porec.
299 **137** 4k. multicoloured . . . . 1·10 1·10

138 "Still Life with Fruits and Basket" (Marino Tartaglia)

1994. Paintings. Multicoloured.
300 2k.40 Type **138** 60 60
301 3k.80 "In the Park" (Milan Steiner) 95 95
302 4k. "Self-portrait" (Vilko Gecan) . . . . 1·25 1·25

139 Plan of Fortress

1994. Obligatory Tax. 750th Anniv of Slavonski Brod.
303 **139** 50l. yellow, black & red 20 20

140 I.O.C. Centenary Emblem and Flame

1994. Obligatory Tax. National Olympic Committee. Designs incorporating either the National Olympic Committee emblem or the International Olympic Committee centenary emblem.
304 50l. Type **140** 20 20
305 50l. As T **140** but with National Olympic Committee emblem 20 20
306 50l. Tennis and national emblem (vert) 20 20
307 50l. Football and centenary emblem (vert) 20 20
308 50l. As No. 306 but with centenary emblem (vert) . . 20 20
309 50l. As No. 307 but with national emblem (vert) . . 20 20
310 50l. Basketball and centenary emblem (vert) 20 20
311 50l. Handball and national emblem (vert) 20 20
312 50l. As No. 310 but with national emblem (vert) . . 20 20
313 50l. As No. 311 but with centenary emblem (vert) . . 20 20
314 50l. Kayaks and national emblem (vert) 20 20
315 50l. Water polo and centenary emblem (vert) . . 20 20
316 50l. As No. 314 but with centenary emblem (vert) . . 20 20
317 50l. As No. 315 but with national emblem (vert) . . 20 20
318 50l. Running and centenary emblem (vert) 20 20
319 50l. Gymnastics and national emblem (vert) 20 20
320 50l. As No. 318 but with national emblem (vert) . . 20 20
321 50l. As No. 319 but with centenary emblem (vert) . . 20 20

141 Cover of "Gazophylacium"

142 St. Mark's Church and Gas Lamp

1994. 400th Birth Anniv of Ivan Belostenec (lexicographer).
322 **141** 2k.20 multicoloured . . . 70 70

1994. 900th Annivs of Zagreb (323/5) and Zagreb Bishopric (326). Multicoloured.
323 1k. Type **142** 30 30
324 1k. Street scene from early film, Maxi Cat (cartoon character) and left side of Zagreb Exchange 30 30

325 1k. Right side of Zagreb Exchange, S. Penkala's biplane and Cibona building 30 30
326 4k. 15th-century bishop's crosier and 17th-century view of Zagreb by Valvasor . . . . 1·00 1·00
MS327 79 × 59 mm. 13k.50 Penkala's biplane and street scene from early film (23 × 47 mm) 3·50 3·50
Nos. 323/6 were issued together, se-tenant, forming a composite design.

143 "Epiphany" (relief, Vrhovac Church)

1994. Christmas.
328 **143** 1k. multicoloured 35 30

144 "Translation of the Holy House" (Giovanni Battista Tiepolo)

145 Modern Tie

1994. 700th Anniv of St. Mary's Sanctuary, Loreto.
329 **144** 4k. multicoloured . . . . 1·10 1·10

1995. Ties. Multicoloured.
330 1k.10 Type **145** 25 25
331 3k.80 English dandy, 1810 . . 80 80
332 4k. Croatian soldier, 1630 . . 85 85
MS333 109 × 88 mm. Nos. 330/2 2·00 2·00

146 St. Catherine's Church and Monastery, Zagreb, and Jesuit

1995. Monasteries. Multicoloured.
334 1k. Type **146** (350th anniv) 20 20
335 2k.40 St. Paul's Monastery, Visovac, and Franciscan monk (550th anniv) . . . 50 50

147 Istrian Short-haired Hunting Dog

1995. Dogs. Multicoloured.
336 2k.20 Type **147** 50 50
337 2k.40 Posavinian hunting dog 50 50
338 3k.80 Istrian wire-haired hunting dog . . . . 1·00 1·00

148 Rowing

1995. Obligatory Tax. National Olympic Committee. Multicoloured.
339 50l. Type **148** 15 15
340 50l. Petanque 15 15
341 50l. Monument to Drazen Petrovic, Olympic Park, Lausanne 15 15
342 50l. Tennis 15 15
343 50l. Basketball 15 15

149 Reconstruction of Emperor Diocletian's Palace

1995. 1700th Anniv of Split. Multicoloured.
344 1k. Type **149** 20 20
345 2k.20 "Split Harbour" (Emanuel Vidovic) 40 40
346 4k. View of city and bust of Marko Marulic (Ivan Mestrovic) 80 80
MS347 90 × 60 mm. 13k.40 Aerial view (23 × 47 mm) . . . . . . 2·75 2·75

150 Player

151 Woman's Head

1995. World Handball Championship, Iceland.
348 **150** 4k. multicoloured 80 80

1995. Obligatory Tax. Red Cross Week.
349 **151** 50l. black and red 15 15

152 Storm Clouds and Clear Sky

1995. Europa. Peace and Freedom. Mult.
350 2k.40 Type **152** 50 50
351 4k. Angel (detail of sculpture, Francesco Robba) 80 80

153 Shadow behind Cross

1995. 150th Anniv of July Riots (352) and 50th Anniv of Croatian Surrender at Bleiburg (353). Multicoloured.
352 1k.10 Type **153** 25 25
353 3k.80 Sunrise behind cross . . 80 80

154 Arms and Hand holding Rose

155 Hands

1995. Independence Day.
354 **154** 1k.10 multicoloured . . . 25 25

1995. Obligatory Tax. Solidarity Week.
355 **155** 50l. multicoloured 15 15

156 "Installation" (detail) (Martina Kramer)

1995. 46th Art Biennale, Venice. Work by Croatian artists. Multicoloured.
356 2k.20 Type **156** 45 45
357 2k.40 "Paracelsus Paraduchamps" (Mirk Zrinscak) (vert) 50 50
358 4k. "Shadows/136" (Goran Petercol) 80 80

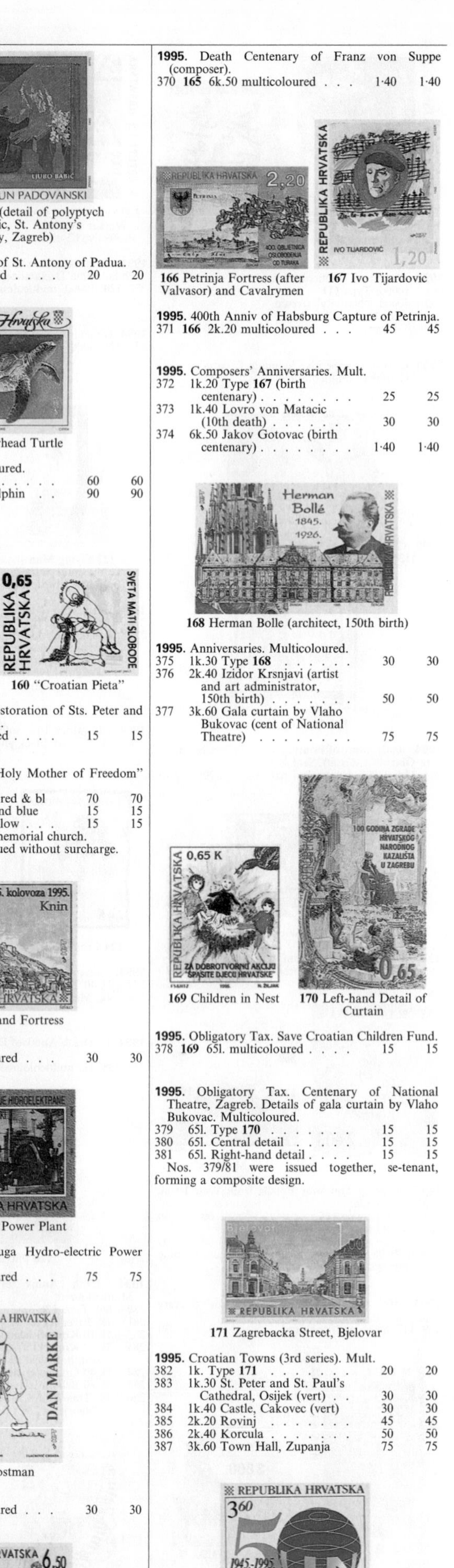

157 "St. Antony" (detail of polyptych by Ljubo Babic, St. Antony's Sanctuary, Zagreb)

1995. 800th Birth Anniv of St. Antony of Padua.
359 **157** 1k. multicoloured 20 20

158 Loggerhead Turtle

1995. Animals. Multicoloured.
360 2k.40 Type **158** 60 60
361 4k. Bottle-nosed dolphin . . 90 90

159 Osijek Cathedral

160 "Croatian Pieta"

1995. Obligatory Tax. Restoration of Sts. Peter and Paul's Cathedral, Osijek.
362 **159** 65l. multicoloured 15 15

1995. Obligatory Tax. "Holy Mother of Freedom" War Memorial.
363 **160** 65l. on 50l. blk, red & bl 70 70
364 – 65l. black, red and blue 15 15
365 – 65l. blue and yellow . . . 15 15
DESIGN: 65l. Projected memorial church.
Nos. 364/5 were not issued without surcharge.

161 Town and Fortress

1995. Liberation of Knin.
366 **161** 1k.30 multicoloured . . . 30 30

162 Electric Power Plant

1995. Centenary of Jaruga Hydro-electric Power Station, River Krka.
367 **162** 3k.60 multicoloured . . . 75 75

163 Postman

1995. Stamp Day.
368 **163** 1k.30 multicoloured . . . 30 30

165 Suppe and Heroine of "The Fair Galatea" (operetta)

1995. Death Centenary of Franz von Suppe (composer).
370 **165** 6k.50 multicoloured . . . 1·40 1·40

166 Petrinja Fortress (after Valvasor) and Cavalrymen

167 Ivo Tijardovic

1995. 400th Anniv of Habsburg Capture of Petrinja.
371 **166** 2k.20 multicoloured . . . 45 45

1995. Composers' Anniversaries. Mult.
372 1k.20 Type **167** (birth centenary) 25 25
373 1k.40 Lovro von Matacic (10th death) 30 30
374 6k.50 Jakov Gotovac (birth centenary) . . . . 1·40 1·40

168 Herman Bolle (architect, 150th birth)

1995. Anniversaries. Multicoloured.
375 1k.30 Type **168** 30 30
376 2k.40 Izidor Krsnjavi (artist and art administrator, 150th birth) 50 50
377 3k.60 Gala curtain by Vlaho Bukovac (cent of National Theatre) 75 75

169 Children in Nest

170 Left-hand Detail of Curtain

1995. Obligatory Tax. Save Croatian Children Fund.
378 **169** 65l. multicoloured 15 15

1995. Obligatory Tax. Centenary of National Theatre, Zagreb. Details of gala curtain by Vlaho Bukovac. Multicoloured.
379 65l. Type **170** 15 15
380 65l. Central detail 15 15
381 65l. Right-hand detail 15 15
Nos. 379/81 were issued together, se-tenant, forming a composite design.

171 Zagrebacka Street, Bjelovar

1995. Croatian Towns (3rd series). Mult.
382 1k. Type **171** 20 20
383 1k.30 St. Peter and St. Paul's Cathedral, Osijek (vert) . . 30 30
384 1k.40 Castle, Cakovec (vert) 30 30
385 2k.20 Rovinj 45 45
386 2k.40 Korcula 50 50
387 3k.60 Town Hall, Zupanja 75 75

172 "50"

1996. 50th Anniversaries. Multicoloured.
395 3k.60 Type **172** (U.N.O.) . . 75 75
396 3k.60 "5" and "FAO" within biscuit forming "50" (F.A.O.) 75 75

173 Spiro Brusina (zoologist)   **174** Birds flying through Sky

1995. Anniversaries. Multicoloured.
397 1k. Type **173** (150th birth) . . 20 20
398 2k.20 Bogoslav Sulek (philologist, death cent) . . 45 45
399 6k.50 Faust Vrancic's "Dictionary of Five European Languages" (400th anniv of publication) . . . . 1·40 1·40

1995. Obligatory Tax. Anti-drugs Campaign.
400 **174** 65l. multicoloured 15 15

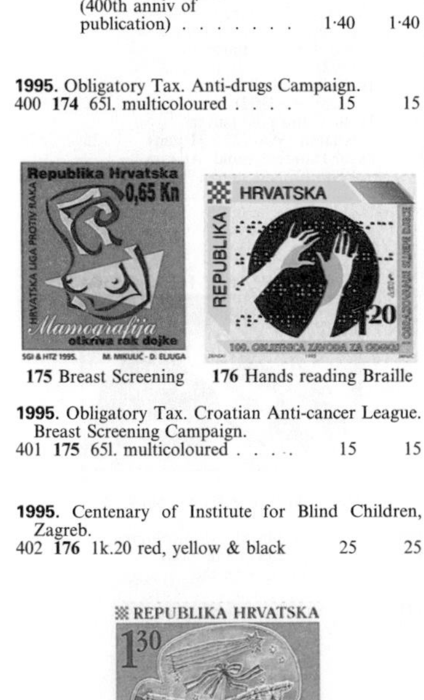

175 Breast Screening   **176** Hands reading Braille

1995. Obligatory Tax. Croatian Anti-cancer League. Breast Screening Campaign.
401 **175** 65l. multicoloured 15 15

1995. Centenary of Institute for Blind Children, Zagreb.
402 **176** 1k.20 red, yellow & black 25 25

177 Animals under Christmas Tree

1995. Christmas.
403 **177** 1k.30 multicoloured . . . 30 30

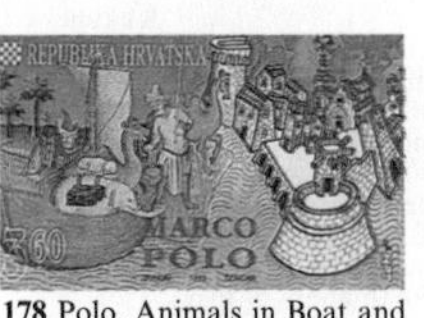

178 Polo, Animals in Boat and Court of Kublai Khan

1995. 700th Anniv of Marco Polo's Return from China.
404 **178** 3k.60 multicoloured . . . 75 75

179 Hrvatska Kostajnica   **180** Lectionary of Bernardin of Split, 1495 (first printed book using Cakavian dialect)

1995. Liberated Towns. Multicoloured.
405 20l. Type **179** 10 10
406 30l. Slunj 10 10
407 50l. Gracac 10 10
408 1k.20 Drnis (vert) 25 25
409 6k.50 Glina . . . . 1·40 1·40
410 10k. Obrovac (vert) . . . . . 2·00 2·00

1995. Incunabula. Multicoloured.
420 1k.40 Type **180** 30 30
421 3k.60 Callipers and last page of "Spovid Opcena" (manual for confessors), 1496 (first book printed in Croatia) 75 75

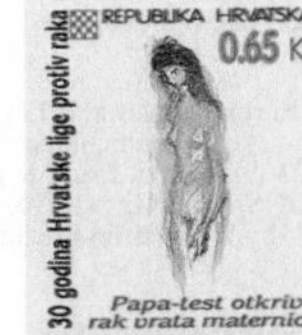

181 Crucifix   **182** Breast Cancer Campaign

1996. Events and Anniversaries. Mult.
422 1k.30 St. Marko Krizevcanin (detail of mosaic (Ante Starcevic), St. Marko's Church, Zagreb) (canonization) 30 30
423 1k.30 Type **181** (700th anniv of veneration of miraculous crucifix, St. Guido's Church, Rijeka) 30 30
424 1k.30 Ivan Merz (teacher and Catholic youth worker, birth centenary) 30 30

1996. Obligatory Tax. 30th Anniv of Anti-cancer League.
425 **182** 65l. multicoloured 15 15

183 Eugen Kvaternik (125th anniv of Rakovica Uprising)   **184** Madonna and Child and Church

1996. Anniversaries. Multicoloured.
426 1k.20 Type **183** 25 25
427 1k.40 Ante Starcevic (founder of Part of the Right, death centenary) (vert) 30 30
428 2k.20 Stjepan Radic (founder of Croatian Peasant Party) (125th birth anniv and 75th anniv of Peasant Republic constitution) (vert) 45 45
429 3k.60 Collage (75th anniv of Labin Republic) (vert) . . 75 75

1996. Obligatory Tax. St. Mary of Bistrica Sanctuary.
430 **184** 65l. multicoloured 15 15

185 Julije Domac (founder) and Culture

1996. Centenary of Pharmacology Institute, University of Zagreb.
431 **185** 6k.50 multicoloured . . . 1·40 1·40

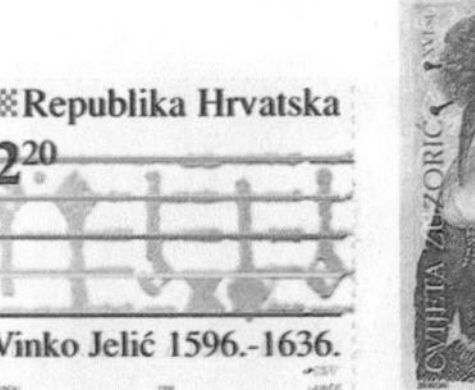

186 Score   **187** Cvijeta Zuzoric (beauty)

1996. Music Anniversaries. Multicoloured.
432 2k.20 Type **186** (400th birth anniv of Vinko Jelic, composer) 45 45
433 2k.20 "O" over musical bars (150th anniv of "Love and Malice" (first Croatian opera) by Vatroslav Lisinski) 45 45
434 2k.20 Josip Slavenski (composer, birth cent) . . 45 45
435 2k.20 "Lijepa nasa domovino" (birth bicent of Antun Mihanovic and 175th birth anniv of Josip Runjanin (composers of National Anthem)) 45 45

1996. Europa. Famous Women. Mult.
436 2k.20 Type **187** 45 45
437 3k.60 Ivana Brlic-Mazuranic (writer) 75 75

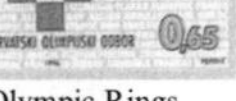

188 Olympic Rings   **189** Nikola Subic Zrinski of Sziget (Ban of Croatia)

1996. Obligatory Tax. National Olympic Committee.
438 **188** 65l. multicoloured 15 15

1996. 16th and 17th-century Members of Zrinski and Frankopan Families. Multicoloured.
439 1k.30 Type **189** 30 30
440 1k.40 Nikola Zrinski (Ban of Croatia) 30 30
441 2k.20 Petar Zrinski (Ban of Croatia) 45 45
442 2k.40 Katarina Zrinski (wife of Petar and sister of Fran Krsto Frankopan) 50 50
443 3k.60 Fran Krsto Frankopan (writer and revolutionary) 75 75
MS444 117 × 172 mm. Nos. 439/43 2·10 2·10

190 Child outside House   **191** Soldier carrying Child

1996. Obligatory Tax. Red Cross Fund.
445 **190** 65l. black and red 15 15

1996. 5th Anniv of National Guard.
446 **191** 1k.30 multicoloured . . . 30 30

192 Istrian Bluebell   **193** Child with Red Cross Parcel

1996. Flowers. Multicoloured.
447 2k.40 Type **192** 45 45
448 3k.60 Dubrovnik corn-flower 75 75

1996. Obligatory Tax. Solidarity Week.
449 **193** 65l. black and red 15 15

194 Football

1996. European Football Championship, England.
450 **194** 2k.20 black and red . . . 45 45

195 Konscak's Map of California   **196** Children sitting outside House

1996. 250th Anniv of Father Ferdinand Konscak's Expedition to Lower California.
451 **195** 2k.40 multicoloured . . . 45 45

1996. Obligatory Tax. Save Croatian Children Fund.
452 **196** 65l. multicoloured 15 15

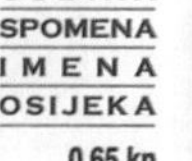

197 Anniversary Emblem   **198** Man holding Dumb-bell and Falcon

1996. Obligatory Tax. 800th Anniv of Osijek.
453 **197** 65l. blue, orange & grey 15 15

1996. 150th Birth Anniv of Josip Fon (founder of Croatian Falcon gymnastics society).
454 **198** 1k.40 multicoloured . . . 30 30

199 Olympic Colours and Rings   **200** Cathedral

1996. Olympic Games, Atlanta, and Centenary of Modern Olympics.
455 **199** 3k.60 multicoloured . . . 75 75

1996. Obligatory Tax. Restoration of Dakovo Cathedral.
456 **200** 65l. multicoloured 15 15

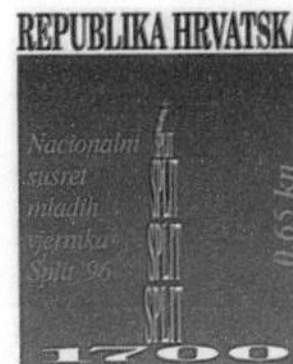

201 "Church Tower"   **202** Crucifix

1996. Obligatory Tax. 1700th Anniv of Split.
457 **201** 65l. ultramarine and blue 15 15

1996. Obligatory Tax. Vukovar.
458 **202** 65l. multicoloured 15 15

203 Lighted Candle, Shell and Lilies   **204** Tweezers holding Stamp

1996. Obligatory Tax. Anti-drugs Campaign.
459 **203** 65l. multicoloured 15 15

1996. Stamp Day. 5th Anniv of Issue of First Postage Stamp by Independent Croatia.
460 **204** 1k.30 multicoloured . . . 30 30

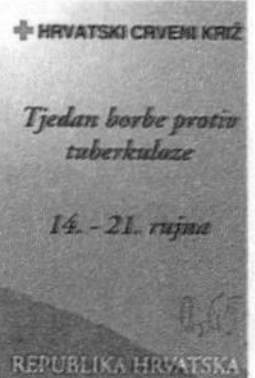

205 Mountains   **206** St. Elias's Chapel, Zumberak

1996. Obligatory Tax. Anti-tuberculosis Week.
461 **205** 65l. multicoloured 15 15

1996. 700th Anniv of First Written Reference to Zumberak.
462 **206** 2k.20 multicoloured . . . 45 45

207 Illuminated Page **208** Fishes and Spear

1996. Early Middle Ages. Multicoloured.
463 1k.20 Type **207** (900th anniv of "Vekenega's Book of Gospels") 25 25
464 1k.40 Gottschalk (Benedictine abbot) (1150th anniv of Gottschalk's visit to Duke of Trpimir) 30 30

1996. Millenary of First Written Reference to Fishing in Croatia.
465 **208** 1k.30 multicoloured . . . 30 30

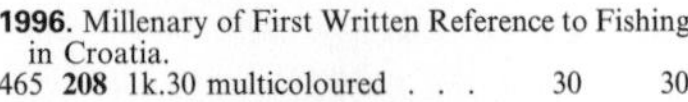

209 Gjuro Pilar (geologist, 150th anniv)

1996. Scientists' Birth Anniversaries. Mult.
466 2k.40 Type **209** 50 50
467 2k.40 Frane Bulic (archaeologist, 150th anniv) 50 50
468 2k.40 Ante Sercer (otolaryngologist, cent) . . 50 50

210 Sir Frederick Banting and Charles Best (discoverers)

1996. Obligatory Tax. Croatian Diabetic Council. 75th Anniv of Discovery of Insulin.
469 **210** 65l. gold, yellow & black 15 15

211 Laws of Dominican Nuns, Zadar

1996. 600th Anniv of Founding of Dominican General High School (university), Zadar.
470 **211** 1k.40 multicoloured . . . 30 30

212 "Rain" (Menci Crncic)

1996. 20th-century Paintings. Multicoloured.
471 1k.30 Type **212** 30 30
472 1k.40 "Peljesac-Korcula Channel" (Mato Medovic) 30 30
473 3k.60 "Pink Dream" (Vlaho Bukovac) 75 75

213 "Mother of God of Remete", Zagreb **214** Children of Different Races

1996. Obligatory Tax.
474 **213** 65l. multicoloured 15 15

1996. 50th Anniv of U.N.I.C.E.F.
475 **214** 3k.60 multicoloured . . . 75 75

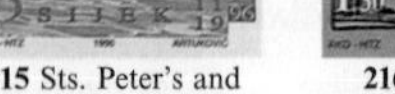

215 Sts. Peter's and Paul's Cathedral **216** Nativity

1996. 800th Anniv of First Written Reference to Osijek. Multicoloured.
476 2k.20 Type **215** 45 45
477 2k.20 Riverbank and view down street 45 45

1996. Christmas.
478 **216** 1k.30 multicoloured . . . 30 30

217 Bond and Bank **218** Mihanovic

1996. Anniversaries. Multicoloured.
479 2k.40 Type **217** (150th anniv of founding of First Croatian Savings Bank, Zagreb) 50 50
480 3k.60 Frontispiece (bicent of publication of "The Principles of the Corn Trade" by Josip Sipus) . . 75 75

1997. Obligatory Tax. Birth Bicentenary (1996) of Antun Mihanovic.
481 **218** 65l. multicoloured 15 15

219 "Professor Baltazar" (Zagreb School of Animated Film)

1997. Centenary of Croatian Films. Mult.
482 1k.40 Oktavijan Miletic (cameraman and director) filming "Vatroslav Lisinski" (first Croatian sound film), 1944 . . . . 30 30
483 1k.40 Type **219** 30 30
484 1k.40 Mirjana Bohanev-Vidovic and Relja Basic in "Who Sings Means No Harm", 1970 . . . . . . 30 30

220 Dr. Ante Starcevic's House **221** Don Quixote and Windmill

1997. Obligatory Tax.
485 **220** 65l. multicoloured 15 15

1997. Birth Anniversaries. Multicoloured.
486 2k.20 Type **221** (450th anniv of Miguel de Cervantes (author of "Don Quixote")) 45 45
487 3k.60 Metal type (600th anniv of Johannes Gutenberg (inventor of printing)) (horiz) 75 75

222 Woman **223** "Big Joseph" by Vladimir Nazor (illus. Sasa Santel)

1997. Obligatory Tax. Croatian Anti-cancer League.
488 **222** 65l. multicoloured 15 15

1997. Europa. Tales and Legends.
489 – 1k.30 multicoloured . . . 30 30
490 **223** 3k.60 red, black & gold 75 75
DESIGNS—HORIZ: 1k.30, Elves from "Stribor's Forest" by Ivana Brlic-Mazuranic (illus. Cvijeta Job).

224 Noble Pen Shell **225** Comforting Hand

1997. Molluscs and Insects. Multicoloured.
491 1k.40 Type **224** 30 30
492 2k.40 "Radziella styx" (cave beetle) 50 50
493 3k.60 Giant tun 75 75

1997. Obligatory Tax. Red Cross Week.
494 **225** 65l. multicoloured 15 15

226 Pres. Franjo Tudjman

1997. 5th Anniv of Croatia's Membership of United Nations.
495 **226** 6k.50 multicoloured . . . 1·40 1·40

227 Ludwig Zamenhof (inventor)

1997. Croatian Esperanto (invented language) Conference.
496 **227** 1k.20 multicoloured . . . 25 25

228 Congress Emblem

1997. 58th Congress of International Amateur Rugby Federation, Dubrovnik.
497 **228** 2k.20 multicoloured . . 40 40

229 "Vukovar" (Zlatko Atac) (¾-size illustration)

1997. Rebuilding of Vukovar.
498 **229** 6k.50 multicoloured . . . 1·25 1·25

230 King Petar Svacic (1095–97)

1997. Kings of Croatia. Multicoloured.
499 1k.30 Type **230** (900th death anniv) 25 25
500 2k.40 King Stjepan Drzislav (996–97) 45 45

231 16th-century Dubrovnik Courier (after Nicole de Nicolai) **232** Tennis

1997. Stamp Day.
501 **231** 2k.30 multicoloured . . . 45 45

1997. Olympic Medal Winners. Mult.
502 1k. Type **232** (Goran Ivanisevic—bronze (singles and doubles), Barcelona 1992) 20 20
503 1k.20 Basketball (silver, Barcelona 1992) 25 25
504 1k.40 Water polo (silver, Atlanta 1996) (27 × 31 mm) 25 25
505 2k.20 Handball (gold, Atlanta 1996) (27 × 31 mm) 40 40

233 Turkish Attack on Sibenik, 1647

1997. Defence of Sibenik. Multicoloured.
506 1k.30 Type **233** (350th anniv of defence against the Turks) 25 25
507 1k.30 Air attack on Sibenik, 1991 . . . . 25 25

234 Frane Petric (philosopher) **235** Parliamentary Session (after Ivan Zasche) and Ivan Kukuljevic (politician)

1997. Anniversaries. Multicoloured.
508 1k.40 Type **234** (400th death anniv) 25 25
509 1k.40 "Madonna and Child" (detail from the polyptich of St. Michael in Franciscan Church, Cavtat) (500th anniv of first recorded work of Vicko Lovrin (artist)) 25 25
510 1k.40 Frano Krsinic (sculptor, birth cent) . . . 25 25
511 1k.40 Dubravko Dujsin (actor, 50th death anniv) 25 25

1997. Anniversaries. Multicoloured.
512 2k.20 Type **235** (150th anniv of promulgation of Croatian as official language) 40 40
513 3k.60 Zagreb and elevation of school (centenary of Croatian Grammar School, Zadar) 70 70

236 Primordial Elephant

1997. Palaeontological Finds. Multicoloured.
514 1k.40 Type **236** 25 25
515 2k.40 Fossil of "Viviparus novskaensis" (periwinkle) 45 45

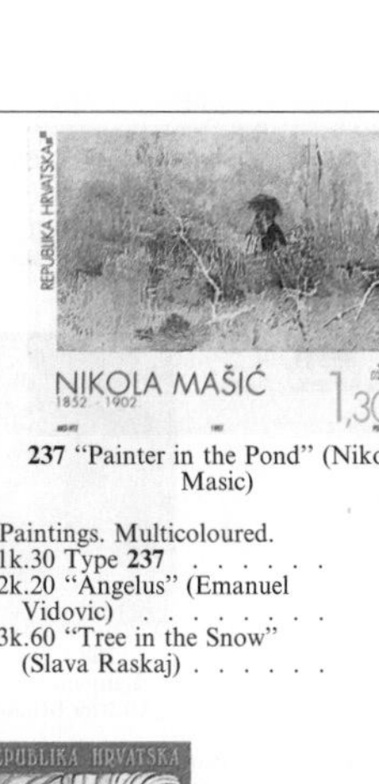

237 "Painter in the Pond" (Nikola Masic)

1997. Paintings. Multicoloured.
516 1k.30 Type **237** 25 25
517 2k.20 "Angelus" (Emanuel Vidovic) 40 40
518 3k.60 "Tree in the Snow" (Slava Raskaj) 70 70

238 Child Jesus in the Stable

239 "Electra" by Sophocles

1997. Christmas. Multicoloured.
519 1k.30 Type **238** 25 25
520 3k.60 "Birth of Jesus" (Isidor Krsnjavi) (33 × 59 mm) . . 70 70

1997. Literary Anniversaries. Multicoloured.
521 1k. Type **239** (400th anniv of publication of collected translations by Dominko Zlataric) 20 20
522 1k.20 Closed book (300th birth anniv of Filip Grabovac and 250th anniv of publication of his "Best of Folk Speech and the Illyric or Croatian Language") 25 25

240 Ilok

241 Score and Varazdin (Baroque Evenings)

1998. Croatian Towns (4th series).
523 **240** 5k. violet, brown & red 95 95
524 – 10k. brown, violet & red 2·00 2·00
DESIGN: 10k. Dubrovnik.

1998. Europa. National Festivals. Mult.
531 1k.45 Type **241** 30 30
532 4k. Dubrovnik (Summer Festival) 75 75

242 Olympic Rings and Japanese Red Sun

1998. Winter Olympic Games, Nagano, Japan.
533 **242** 2k.45 multicoloured . . . 45 45

243 Jelacics Flag and Battle near Moor (lithograph)

1998. Historical Events of 1848. Mult.
534 1k.60 Type **243** 30 30
535 1k.60 "Croatian Assembly in Session" (Dragutin Weingartner) 30 30
536 4k. Ban Josip Jelacic (after Ivan Zasche) (21 × 31 mm) 75 75

244 Mimara

245 Caesar's Mushroom

1998. Birth Centenary of Ante Topic Mimara (art collector).
537 **244** 2k.65 multicoloured . . . 50 50

1998. Fungi. Multicoloured.
538 1k.30 Type **245** 25 25
539 1k.30 Saffron milk cup ("Lactarius deliciosus") . . 25 25
540 7k.20 "Morchella conica" . . 1·40 1·40

246 Stepinac

247 Magnifying Glass over Fingerprint and Dubrovnik

1998. Birth Centenary of Cardinal Alojzije Stepinac (Archbishop of Zagreb).
541 **246** 1k.50 multicoloured . . . 30 30

1998. 27th European Regional Conference of Interpol, Dubrovnik.
542 **247** 2k.45 multicoloured . . . 50 50

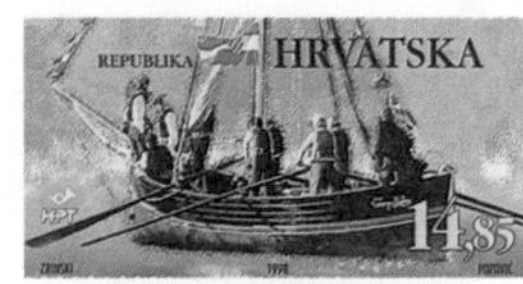

248 *Falkusa* (fishing boat)

1998. "Espo '98" World's Fair, Lisbon. Sheet 97 × 80 mm.
MS543 **248** 14k.85 multicoloured 2·60 2·60

249 Football

1998. World Cup Football Championship, France.
544 **249** 4k. multicoloured 75 75

250 Title Page of "Slavonic Fairy"

1998. Writers' Anniversaries. Multicoloured.
545 1k.20 Type **250** (450th birth anniv of Juraj Barakovic (poet)) 25 25
546 1k.50 Milan Begovic (50th death anniv) 30 30
547 1k.60 Mate Balota (birth centenary) 30 30
548 2k.45 Antun Gustav Matos (125th birth anniv) 50 50
549 2k.65 Matija Antun Relkovic (death bicentenary) 50 50
550 4k. Antun Branko Simic (birth centenary) 75 75

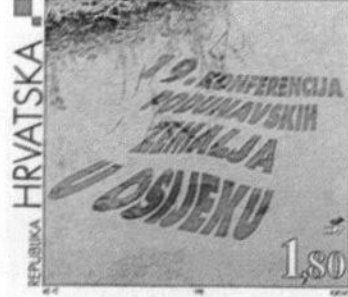

251 Text on Water

1998. 19th Danube Countries Conference, Osijek.
551 **251** 1k.80 multicoloured . . . 35 35

252 Betlheim

1998. Birth Centenary of Dr. Stjepan Betlheim (psychoanalyst).
552 **252** 1k.50 multicoloured . . . 30 30

253 Team Member

1998. Winning of Bronze Medal by Croatia in World Cup Football Championship. Sheet 112 × 82 mm containing T **253** and similar horiz design. Multicoloured.
MS553 4k. × 4, Composite design of Croatian World Cup Squad . . 3·00 3·00

254 Liburnian Sewn Boat (1st century B.C.)

1998. Croatian Ships. Multicoloured.
554 1k.20 Type **254** 25 25
555 1k.50 Condura (11th–12th centuries) 30 30
556 1k.60 Ragusan (Dubrovnik) carrack (16th century) . . 30 30
557 1k.80 Istrian bracera 35 35
558 2k.45 River Neretva sailing barge 50 50
559 2k.65 Barque 50 50
560 4k. "Vila Velebita" (sail/ steam cadet ship) 75 75
561 7k.20 "Amorela" (car ferry) 1·40 1·40
562 20k. "King Petar Kresimir IV" (missile corvette) . . . 3·75 3·75

255 Mail Coach and Posthorn

1998. Stamp Day. 150th Anniv of Creation of Croatian Supreme Postal Administration.
563 **255** 1k.50 multicoloured . . . 30 30

256 Font and Cathedral

1998. 700th Anniv of Sibenik Bishopric and Proclamation of Sibenik as a Free Borough.
564 **256** 4k. multicoloured 75 75

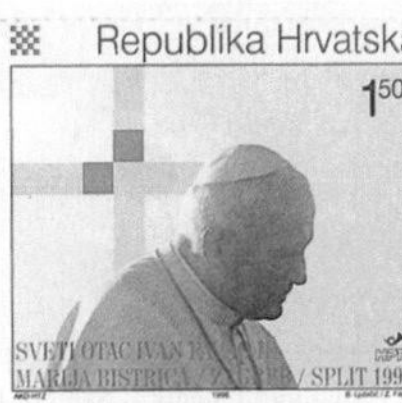

257 Pope John Paul II

1998. 2nd Papal Visit.
565 **257** 1k.50 multicoloured . . . 30 30

258 Horse Tram, Osijek

1998. Transport. Multicoloured.
566 1k.50 Type **258** 30 30
567 1k.50 First motor car in Zagreb, 1901 . . . . . . 30 30
568 1k.50 Electric train, Karlovac–Rijeka line (125th anniv) 30 30
569 1k.50 Aerial view of Ostrovica–Delnice section of Zagreb–Rijeka motorway 30 30
570 7k.20 Zagreb funicular railway (19 × 23 mm) . . . 1·40 1·40

259 "Adoration of the Shepherds" (detail, from breviary "Officinum Virginis" illus by Klovic)

1998. Christmas. 500th Birth Anniv of Julije Klovic (artist).
571 **259** 1k.50 multicoloured . . . 30 30

260 Ibrisimovic

1998. 300th Death Anniv of Father Luka Ibrisimovic (revolutionary).
572 **260** 1k.90 multicoloured . . . 35 35

261 Distorted Tree bound to Stake

262 "Cypress" (Frano Simunovic)

1998. 50th Anniv of Universal Declaration of Human Rights.
573 **261** 5k. multicoloured 95 95

1998. 20th-century Art. Multicoloured.
574 1k.90 "Paromlin Road" (Josip Vanista) (horiz) . . 35 35
575 2k.20 Type **262** 40 40
576 5k. "Coma" (interactive video installation, Dalibor Martinis) 95 95

263 Flags

264 Haulik

1999. Zagreb Fair.
577 **263** 1k.80 multicoloured . . . 35 35

1999. 130th Death Anniv of Cardinal Juraj Haulik (first Archbishop of Zagreb).
578 **264** 5k. multicoloured 95 95

265 Mljet Island National Park

1999. Europa. Parks and Gardens. Multicoloured.
579 1k.80 Type **265** 30 30
580 5k. River Lonja Basin Nature Park 85 85

266 Viper

1999. The Orsini's Viper. Multicoloured.
581 2k.20 Type **266** 35 35
582 2k.20 Viper on alert 35 35
583 2k.20 Two vipers 35 35
584 2k.20 Viper's head 35 35

267 Anniversary Emblem

268 Orlando's Pillar with Mask

1999. 50th Anniv of Council of Europe.
585 **267** 2k.80 multicoloured . . . 45 45

1999. 19th Foundation of European Carnival Cities Convention, Dubrovnik.
586 **268** 2k.30 multicoloured . . . 40 40

269 1 Kreutzer Coin, 1849

1999. 150th Anniv of Minting of Jelacic Kreutzer (587) and Fifth Anniv of Croatian Kuna (588). Multicoloured.
587 2k.30 Type **269** 40 40
588 5k. One kuna coin 85 85

270 Vladimir Nazor (writer)

1999. Anniversaries. Multicoloured.
589 1k.80 Type **270** (50th death anniv) 30 30
590 2k.30 Ferdo Livadic (composer, birth bicentenary) 40 40
591 2k.50 Ivan Rendic (sculptor, 150th birth anniv) 45 45
592 2k.80 Milan Lenuci (urban planner, 150th birth anniv) 45 45
593 3k.50 Vjekoslav Klaic (historian, 150th birth anniv) 60 60
594 4k. Emilij Laszowski (historian, 50th death anniv) 70 70
595 5k. Antun Kanizlic (religious writer and poet, 300th birth anniv) 85 85

271 Basilica and Mosaics of Bishop Euphrasius, St. Maurus and Fish

1999. Euphrasian Basilica, Porec.
596 **271** 4k. multicoloured 70 70

272 Swimming, Diving and Rowing

1999. 2nd World Military Gamzes, Zagreb.
597 **272** 2k.30 multicoloured . . . 40 40

273 Reconstruction of Woman, Skull Fragments and Stone Tools

1999. Centenary of Discovery of Remains of Early Man in Krapina. Multicoloured.
598 1k.80 Type **273** 30 30
599 4k. Dragutin Gorjanovic-Kramberger (palaeontologist and discoverer of remains) and bone fragments 70 70

Nos. 598/9 were issued together, se-tenant, forming a composite design.

274 U.P.U. Emblem and Clouds

1999. World Post Day. 125th Anniv of Universal Postal Union.
600 **274** 2k.30 multicoloured . . . 40 40

275 Lace, "Jesus expelling the Merchants from the Temple" (detail of fresco, Ivan Ranger), and Angel, St. Mary's Church

1999. 600th Anniv of Founding of Paulist Monastery of the Blessed Virgin Mary in Lepoglava. Multicoloured.
601 5k. Type **275** 85 85
602 5k. Altar angel and facade of St. Mary's Church 85 85
603 5k. St. Elizabeth (statue), detail of choir gallery and lace 85 85

276 Josip Jelacic, Ban of Croatia (after C. Lanzelli)

1999. 150th Anniv of Composing of the Jelacic March by Johann Strauss, the Elder.
604 **276** 3k.50 multicoloured . . . 60 60

277 Cloud and Chemical Symbol for Ozone

1999. World Ozone Layer Protection Day.
605 **277** 5k. multicoloured 85 85

278 Pazin Grammar School

1999. School Anniversaries. Multicoloured.
606 2k.30 Type **278** (centenary) 40 40
607 3k.50 Pozega Grammar School (300th anniv) . . . 60 60

279 Hebrang

280 "Madonna of the Rose-garden" (Blaz Jurjev of Trogir)

1999. Birth Cent of Andrija Hebrang (politician).
608 **279** 1k.80 multicoloured . . . 30 10

1999. "Croats—Christianity, Culture, Art" Exhibition, Vatican City.
609 **280** 5k. multicoloured 85 85

281 "Nativity for my Children" (plaster relief, Mila Wood)

1999. Christmas.
610 **281** 2k.30 multicoloured . . . 35 35

282 "Winter Landscape" (Gabrijel Jurkic)

1999. Modern Art. Multicoloured.
611 2k.30 Type **282** 35 35
612 3k.50 "Klek" (Oton Postruznik) 55 55
613 5k. "Stone Table" (Ignjat Job) (vert) 75 75

283 Tudjman

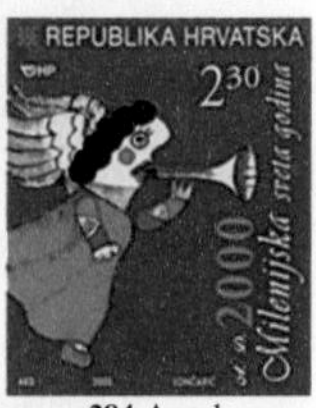

284 Angel

1999. Death Commem of President Franjo Tudjman.
614 **283** 2k.30 black and red . . . 35 35
615 5k. blue, black and red 75 75

2000. Holy Year 2000.
616 **284** 2k.30 multicoloured . . . 35 35

285 Woman's Face

286 Latin Text, Building and Archbishop Stjepan Cosmi (founder)

2000. St. Valentines Day.
617 **285** 2k.30 multicoloured . . . 35 35

2000. 300th Anniv of Split Grammar School.
618 **286** 2k.80 multicoloured . . . 40 40

287 Typewriter

288 "The Lamentation" (Andrija Medulic)

2000. Centenary of Association of Croatian Writers.
619 **287** 2k.30 black and red . . . 35 35

2000. Anniversaries. Multicoloured.
620 1k.80 Type **288** (artist, 500th birth anniv) 30 30
621 2k.30 Matija Petar Katancic (poet, 250th birth anniv) 35 35
622 2k.80 Marija Ruzicka-Strozzi (actress, 150th birth anniv) 40 40
623 3k.50 Statue of Marko Marulic (writer, 550th birth anniv) 55 55
624 5k. "Madonna with the Child and Saints" (Blaz Jurjev Trogiranin) (artist, 550th death anniv) (47 × 25 mm) 75 75

289 Map of Croatia and European Union Stars

2000. Europa. 50th Anniv of Schuman Plan (proposal for pooling the coal and steel industries of France and West Germany). Multicoloured.
625 2k.30 Type **289** 35 35
626 5k. "Building Europe" (vert) 75 75

290 Flag

2000. 10th Anniv of Independence.
627 **290** 2k.30 multicoloured . . . 35 35

291 Pavilion Building

2000. "EXPO 2000" World's Fair, Hanover. Sheet 100 × 74 mm.
MS628 **291** 14k.40 multicoloured 1·60 1·60

292 *Micromeria croatica*

2000. Flowers. Multicoloured.
629 3k.50 Type **292** 55 55
630 5k. *Geranium dalmaticum* . . 75 75

293 Statute and Postcard of Kastav

2000. 600th Anniv of the Kastav Statute.
631 **293** 1k.80 multicoloured . . . 30 30

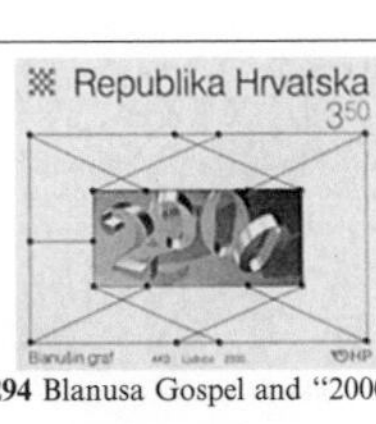

294 Blanusa Gospel and "2000"

2000. World Mathematics Year.
632 **294** 3k.50 multicoloured . . . 55 55

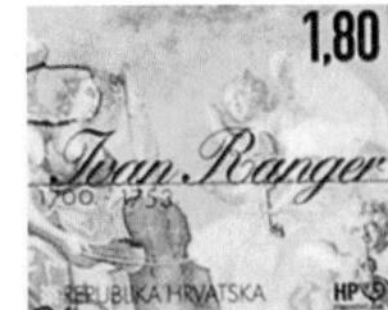

295 Angels (fresco), St. George's Church, Purga

2000. 300th Birth Anniv of Ivan Ranger (artist).
633 **295** 1k.80 multicoloured . . . 30 30

296 Stone Tablet

2000. 900th Anniv of Baska Stone Tablet (early Croatian written record). Sheet 95 × 67 mm.
MS634 **296**16k.70 multicoloured 3·00 3·00

297 Latin Text

2000. 800th Birth Anniv of Toma, Archdeacon of Split.
635 **297** 3k.50 black, silver and blue 55 55

298 Vis

2000. Croatian Towns (5th series).
636 – 2k.30 multicoloured . . . 40 40
639 **298** 3k.50 multicoloured . . . 60 60
DESIGN: 2k.30, Makarska.

299 Austrian Empire 1850 9k. Stamp and Postmark

2000. World Post Day. Multicoloured.
641 2k.30 Type **299** (150th anniv of first stamp in territory of Croatia) 40 40
642 2k.30 Automatic sorting machine (introduction of automatic sorting system) 40 40

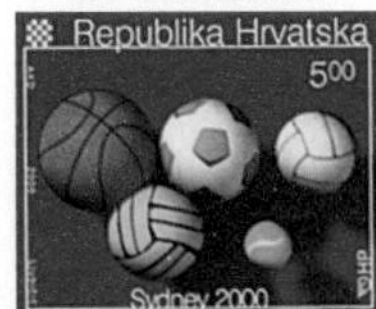

300 Basketball, Football, Handball, Water-polo and Tennis Balls

2000. Olympic Games, Sydney.
643 **300** 5k. multicoloured 85 85

301 "Nativity" (relief, Church of the Blessed Virgin Mary, Ogulin)

2000. Christmas.
644 **301** 2k.30 multicoloured . . . 40 40

302 "Korcula" (Vladimir Varlaj)

2000. Paintings (1st series). Multicoloured.
645 1k.80 Type **302** 30 30
646 2k.30 "Brusnik" (Duro Tiljak) 40 40
647 5k. "Boats" (Ante Kastelancic) 85 85
See also Nos. 675/7, 711/13 and 746/48.

303 White Dove, Ship and Village

2001. New Millennium.
648 **303** 2k.30 multicoloured . . . 40 40

304 Charles the Great (statue)

2001. 1200th Anniv of the Coronation of Charlemagne as Emperor of the Romans. Sheet 92 × 78 mm.
MS649 **304** 14k.40 multicoloured 1·60 1·60

305 Scene from *Radmio and Ljubmir* (poem)

2001. 500th Death Anniv of Dzore Drzic (playwright).
650 **305** 2k.80 multicoloured . . . 45 45

306 Black Rider (comic strip character)

2001. Birth Centenary of Andrija Maurovic (comic strip illustrator).
651 **306** 5k. multicoloured 85 85

307 Goran Ivanisevic

2001. Croatian Sporting Victories. Multicoloured.
652 2k.50 Type **307** (Wimbledon Men's Champion) 40 40
653 2k.80 Janica Kostelic (Alpine Skiing World Cup Women's Champion) . . . 45 45

308 Olive Tree, Kastel Stafilic

2001.
654 **308** 1k.80 multicoloured . . . 30 30

309 Water (green splash to left)

2001. Europa. Water Resources. Multicoloured.
655 3k.50 Type **309** 60 60
656 5k. Water (blue splash to right) 85 85
Nos. 655/6 were issued together, se-tenant, forming a composite design.

310 Poster (Mikele Janko)

2001. World No Smoking Day.
657 **310** 2k.50 multicoloured . . . 40 40

311 Apollo (*Parnassius apollo*)

2001. Butterflies. Multicoloured.
658 2k.50 Type **311** 40 40
659 2k.80 Scarce large blue (*Maculinea teleius*) 45 45
660 5k. False ringlet (*Coenonympha oedippus*) . . 85 85

312 Vukovar

2001.
661 **312** 2k.80 multicoloured . . . 45 45

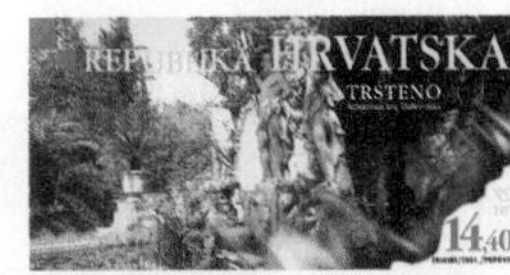

313 Statues and Flames

2001. Trsteno Arboretum. Sheet 95 × 76 mm.
MS662 **313** 14k.40 multicoloured 1·60 1·60

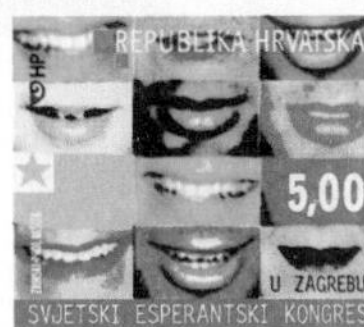

314 Mouths

2001. World Esperanto Congress, Zagreb.
663 **314** 5k. multicoloured 85 85

315 Woman and Wall

2001. 50th Anniv of United Nations Commissioner for Refugees (No. 664) and I.O.M. International Organization for Migration (No. 665). Mult.
664 1k.80 Type **315** 30 30
665 5k. Refugees and 50IOM . . 85 85

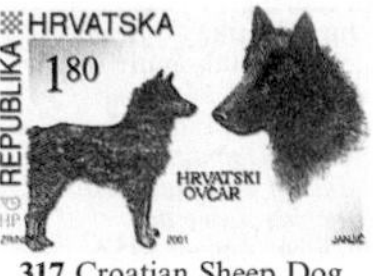

316 Perforated Blocks of Colour

2001. Stamp Day.
666 **316** 2k.50 multicoloured . . . 40 40

317 Croatian Sheep Dog

2001. Dog Breeds. Multicoloured.
667 1k.80 Type **317** 35 35
668 5k. Dalmatian 90 90

318 Head of "Our Lady of Konavle" (statue) **319** Children encircling Globe

2001. 10th Anniv of Republic of Croatia.
669 **318** 2k.30 multicoloured . . . 40 40

2001. U.N. Year of Dialogue among Civilizations.
670 **319** 5k. multicoloured 90 90

320 Klis (16th-century)

2001. Fortresses (1st series). Multicoloured.
671 1k.80 Type **320** 35 35
672 2k.50 Ston (14th-century) . . 45 45
673 3k.50 Sisak (16th-century) . . 60 60
See also Nos. 705/7 and 734/6.

321 Adoration of the Magi (altarpiece), The Visitation of Mary Church, Cucerje **323** Lavoslav Ruzicka, (Chemistry, 1939)

322 "Amphitheatre Ruins" (Vjekoslav Parac)

2001. Christmas
674 **321** 2k.30 multicoloured . . . 40 40

2001. Paintings (2nd series). Multicoloured.
675 2k.50 Type **322** 45 45
676 2k.50 "Maternite du Port-Royal" (Leo Junek) . . . 45 45
677 5k. "Nude with a Baroque Figure" (Slavko Sohaj) (vert) 90 90

2001. Nobel Prize Winners. Multicoloured.
678 2k.80 Type **323** 45 25
679 3k.50 Vladimir Prelog (Chemistry, 1975) 60 60
680 5k. Ivo Andric (Literature, 1961) 90 90

324 Ivan Gucetic

2002. Anniversaries. Multicoloured.
681 1k.80 Type **324** (writer, 500th death anniv) 35 35
682 2k.30 Dobrisa Cesaric (writer, birth centenary) 40 40
683 2k.50 Juraj Rattkay (historian, 350th anniv of publication of *Memoria Regum et Banorum Regnorum Dalmatia, Croatiae et Sclavoniae Ab Origine sua usque ad praesentem Annum 1652 deducta* (history of Croatia)) 45 45
684 2k.80 Franjo Vranjanin Laurana (sculptor, 500th death anniv) 50 50
685 3k.50 Augustin Kazotic (Bishop of Zagreb, 300th anniv of beatification) . . . 65 65
686 5k. Matko Laginja (politician and writer, 150th birth anniv) 95 95

325 Skier

2002. Winter Olympic Games, Salt Lake City, U.S.A.
687 **325** 5k. multicoloured 95 95

326 Barcode and "Reaper" (drawing, Robert Franges Mihanovic)

2002. 150th Anniv of Croatian Chamber of Economy.
688 **326** 2k.50 multicoloured . . . 45 45

327 9th-century Gable bearing Prince Trpimir's Name (detail, altar partition, Rizinice Church)

2002. 1150th Anniv of Prince Trpimir's Deed of Gift of Land to Archbishop of Salona. Sheet 116 × 59 mm.
MS689 **327** 14k.40 multicoloured 2·75 2·75

328 Kuharic

2002. Cardinal Franjo Kuharic (Archbishop of Zagreb) Commemoration.
690 **328** 2k.30 multicoloured . . . 2·75 2·75

329 "Divan"

2002. 80th Death Anniv of Vlaho Bukovac (artist).
691 **329** 5k. multicoloured 95 95
A stamp in a similar design was issued by Czech Republic.

330 Arms

2002. 750th Anniv of Royal Borough of Krizevci.
692 **330** 1k.80 multicoloured . . . 35 35

331 Facade

2002. Centenary of Post Office Building, Varazdin.
693 **331** 2k.30 multicoloured . . . 40 40

332 Clown with Umbrella

2002. Europa. Circus. Multicoloured.
694 **332** 3k.50 multicoloured . . . 65 65
695 5k. multicoloured 90 95

333 Stylised Player and Ball

334 Player, Pin and Ball

2002. World Cup Football Championships, Japan and South Korea. Multicoloured.
696 3k.50 Type **333** 65 65
697 5k. Stylised player ball at right 90 90

2002. World Ten-pin Bowling Championship, Osijek.
698 **334** 3k.50 multicoloured . . . 65 65

335 Common Oak (*Quercus robur*)

336 Mouse and Moon

2002. Trees. Multicoloured.
699 1k.80 Type **335** 35 35
700 2k.50 Sessile oak (*Quercus petraea*) 45 45
701 2k.80 Holly oak (*Quercus ilex*) 50 50

2002. 15th World Animated Film Festival, Zagreb.
702 **336** 5k. multicoloured 90 90

337 Pag Lacework

338 Slavonic Script

2002. Lace-making. Multicoloured.
703 3k.50 Type **337** 65 65
704 5k. Liedekerke lacework and statue of lace-maker . . . 90 90
Stamps of a similar design were issued by Belgium.

2002. Fortresses (2nd series). As T **320**. Multicoloured.
705 2k.50 Skocibuha family summer villa, Sipan (16th-century) 45 45
706 2k.50 Nehaj (16th-century) 45 45
707 5k. Veliki Tabor (16th-century) 90 90

2002. Centenary of Krk Slavic Academy.
708 **338** 4k. black and red 70 70

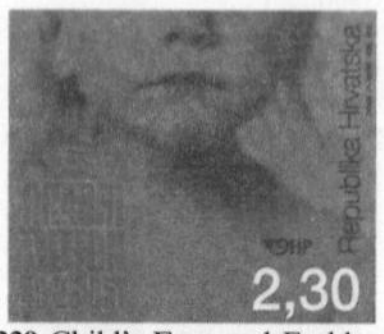

339 Child's Face and Emblem

2002. Children's Telephone Helpline.
709 **339** 2k.30 multicoloured . . . 40 40

340 "Our Lady and the Saints" (detail) (polyptych, Nikola Bozidarevic), Dance Church, Dubrovnik

2002. Christmas.
710 **340** 2k.30 multicoloured . . . 40 40

2002. Paintings (3rd series). As T **322**. Multicoloured.
711 2k.50 "Girl in the Boat" (Milivoj Uzelac) (vert) . . 45 45
712 2k.50 "Flowers on the Window" (Antun Motika) (vert) 45 45
713 5k. "On the Drava River" (Krsto Hegedusic) 90 90

341 Zagreb Cathedral

343 Column Capitals, Bell Tower, St. Mary's Church, Zadar

342 Pavao Vitezovic

2002. 150th Anniv of Zagreb Archbishopric.
714 **341** 2k.80 multicoloured . . . 50 50

2002. 350th Birth Anniv of Pavao Ritter Vitezovic (writer).
715 **342** 2k.30 multicoloured . . . 40 40

2002. 900th Anniv of Accession Hungarian King Koloman to Croatian Throne.
716 **343** 3k.50 multicoloured . . . 60 60

344 Kosjenka (Regoc)

2003. Fairy Stories. Showing characters from stories by Ivana Brlic Mazuranic. Multicoloured.
717 2k.30 Type **344** 40 40
718 2k.80 Malik Tintilinic (Suma Striborova) 50 50

345 Heart enclosed in Jigsaw Puzzle

2003. St. Valentine's Day.
719 **345** 2k.30 multicoloured . . . 40 40

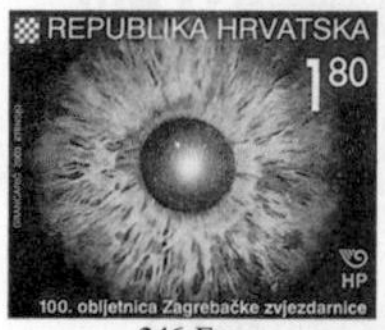

346 Eye

347 Players and Coach

2003. Centenary of Zagreb Astronomical Observatory (1k.80). 150th Anniv of Meteorological Measurements and 50th Anniv of Meteorological Station on Zavizan (3k.50). Multicoloured.
720 1k.80 Type **346** 30 30
721 3k.50 Eye and lightening . . 65 65

2003. Croatia, World Handball Champions, Portugal 2003. Sheet 112 × 83 mm containing T **347** and similar vert designs showing team.
MS722 4k. Type **347**; 4k. Eight players; 4k. Six players; 4k. Four players . . . . 3·00 3·00

348 Building Facade and Monks

349 Page from Missal

2003. 500th Anniv of the Paulist (White Friars) Secondary School, Lepoglava.
723 **348** 5k. multicoloured 90 90

2003. 600th Anniv of Duke Hrvoje's Glagolitic Missal (illuminated book).
724 **349** 5k. multicoloured 90 90

350 Prosthetic Leg

2003. Anti-Landmine Campaign.
725 **350** 2k.30 multicoloured . . . 40 40

351 Janica Kostelic

2003. World Cup Alpine Skiing Gold Medallists, St. Moritz 2003. Multicoloured.
726 3k.50 Type **351** 60 60
727 3k.50 Ivica Kosteli 60 60

352 Antun Soljan (poet, tenth anniv)

2003. Death Anniversaries. Multicoloured.
728 1k.80 Type **352** 30 30
729 2k.30 Hanibal Lucic (poet, 450th anniv) 40 40
730 5k. Federiko Benkovic (artist, 250th anniv) 90 90

353 St. Jerome

2003. 550th Anniv of St. Jerome Papal Institutions, Rome.
731 **353** 2k.80 multicoloured . . . 50 50

354 "Marya Delvard" (Tomislav Krizman)

2003. Europa. Poster Art. Multicoloured.
732 3k.50 Type **354** 50 60
733 5k. "The Firebird" (Boris Bucan) (35 × 35 mm) . . . 90 90

2003. Fortresses (3rd series). As T **320**. Multicoloured.
734 1k.80 Kostajnica, (15th-century) 30 30
735 2k.80 Slavonski, Brod (18th-century) 50 50
736 5k. Minceta, Dubrovnik (15th-century) 90 90

355 Pope John Paul II

2003. Pope John Paul II's Third Visit to Croatia.
737 **355** 2k.30 multicoloured . . . 40 40

356 Squirrel (*Sciurus vulgaris*)

2003. Fauna. Multicoloured.
738 2k.30 Type **356** 40 40
739 2k.80 Dormouse (*Glis glis*) 50 50
740 3k.50 Beaver (*Castor fiber*) 60 60

357 Cope

2003. King Ladislaus' Cope (11th-century). Sheet 95 × 70 mm.
MS741 **357** 1k. multicoloured . . 20 20

358 Letter Box, Envelopes and Stamp

2003. Stamp Day. 50th Anniv of Post Museum, Zagreb.
742 **358** 2k.30 multicoloured . . . 40 40

359 Vines and Paths

2003. UNESCO World Heritage Site. Primosten Vineyard. Sheet 110 × 78 mm.
MS743 **359** 10k. multicoloured 1·80 1·80

360 Mother of Mercy (statue) and Nativity Church, Varaldin

2003. 300th Anniv of Ursuline Religious Order in Croatia.
744 **360** 2k.50 multicoloured . . . 45 45

361 Three Wise Men

2003. Christmas.
745 **361** 2k.30 multicoloured . . . 40 40

2003. Paintings (4th series). As T **322**. Multicoloured.
746 1k.80 "Flower Girl II" (Slavko Kopac) 30 30
747 3k.50 "Dry Stone Wall" (Oton Gliha) (vert) 60 60
748 3k.50 "Pont Des Art" (Josip Racic) (vert) 60 60

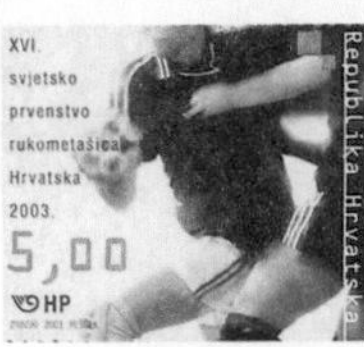

362 Ball and Players

2003. 16th Women's World Handball Championships.
749 **362** 5k. multicoloured 90 90

363 Josip Hatze

364 Manuscript Page

2004. Musical Anniversaries. Multicoloured.
750 5k. Type **363** (125th birth anniv of Josip Hatze (composer)) 90 90
751 5k. Violin bridge and strings (50th anniv of Zagreb Soloists ensemble) 90 90

2004. 600th Anniv of Hval's Manuscript.
752 **364** 2k.30 multicoloured . . . 40 40

365 Stylized Boxing Ring

2004. European Boxing Championship, Pula.
753 **365** 2k.80 multicoloured . . . 50 50

366 Adult Heron

2004. Purple Heron (*Ardea purourea*). Multicoloured.
754 5k. Type **366** 90 90
755 5k. Adult and chick 90 90
756 5k. Adults flying 90 90
757 5k. Adult in reed bed 90 90

OFFICIAL STAMPS

O **11**

O **12**

1942.
O55 O **11** 25b. red 10 10
O56 50b. grey 10 10
O57 75b. green 10 10
O58 1k. brown 10 10
O59 2k. blue 10 10
O60 3k. red 10 10
O61 3k.50 red 10 10
O62 4k. purple 10 10
O63 5k. blue 20 40
O64 6k. violet 10 10
O65 10k. green 10 10
O66 12k. red 15 30
O67 12k.50 orange 10 10
O68 20k. blue 20 40
O69 O **12** 30k. grey and brown . . 15 30
O70 40k. grey and violet . . 15 30
O71 50k. grey and red . . . 50 1·00
O72 100k. salmon & black 50 1·00

POSTAGE DUE STAMPS

1941. Nos. D259/63 of Yugoslavia optd **NEZAVISNA DRZAVA HRVATSKA** in three lines above a chequered shield.
D26 D **10** 50p. violet 20 40
D27 1d. red 20 40
D28 2d. blue . . . . 6·00 12·50
D29 5d. orange . . . . . . 65 1·25
D30 10d. brown . . . . . . 3·00 8·00

D **9**

NEZAVISNA DRŽAVA HRVATSKA 0,50 KUNA PORTO MARKA

D **15**

1941.
D51 D **9** 50b. red 15 45
D52 1k. red 15 45
D53 2k. red 20 60
D54 5k. red 35 90
D55 10k. red . . . . 50 1·25

1942.
D67 D **15** 50b. olive and blue . . 15 30
D68 1k. olive and blue . . . 15 35
D69 2k. olive and blue . . . 15 35
D76 4k. olive and blue . . . 10 20
D70 5k. olive and blue . . . 20 40
D78 6k. olive and blue . . . 10 55
D79 10k. blue and indigo . . 15 50
D80 15k. blue and indigo . . 15 50
D72 20k. blue and indigo . . 80 1·60

SERBIAN POSTS IN CROATIA

100 paras = 1 dinar.

REPUBLIC OF SRPSKA KRAJINA

Following Croatia's declaration of independence from Yugoslavia on 30 May 1991 fighting broke out between Serb inhabitants, backed by units of the Yugoslav Federal Army, and Croatian forces. By January 1992, when a ceasefire sponsored by the United Nations and the European Community became effective, the Croatian Serbs and their allies controlled 30% of the country organized into the districts of the Krajina, Western Slavonia and Eastern Slavonia. These were declared peace-keeping zones under United Nations supervision and the Yugoslav Army withdrew. In 1993 the Serbs proclaimed the Republic of Srpska Krajina, covering all three areas, and elections for a separate president and parliament were held in January 1994.

K **1** Stag, Kopacevo Marsh

K **3** Coat of Arms

1993.
K1 K **1** 200d. green and yellow . . 25 25
K2 – 500d. black and red . . . 65 65
K3 – 1000d. green and yellow 1·40 1·40
K4 – 1000d. green and yellow 1·40 1·40
K5 – 2000d. black and red . . 3·00 3·00
DESIGNS: No. K2, Krka Monastery; K3, Town walls, Knin; K4, Ruined house, Vukovar; K5, Coat of arms.
For 100000d. in same design as No. K2 see No. K12.

1993. Issued at Knin. Nos. 2594/5 of Yugoslavia surch.
K6 5000d. on 3d. black and red 65 65
K7 10000d. on 2d. blue and red 65 65

1993.
K8 K **3** A blue and red 45 45
No. K8 was sold at the internal letter rate.

K **4** Citadel, Knin

A
(K **5**)

K **6** Helmet and Swords

1993.
K 9 K **4** 5000d. green and red . . 10 10
K10 – 10000d. green and red 15 15
K11 – 50000d. blue and red . . 75 75
K12 – 100000d. blue and red 1·50 1·50
DESIGNS: 10000d. Heron, Kopacevo Marsh; 50000d. Icon and church, Vukovar; 100000d. Krka Monastery.

Currency Reform

1993. No. K8 surch with Type K **5** (Cyrillic letter "D").
K13 K **3** "D" on A blue and red 40 40
No. K13 was sold at the new internal letter rate.

1993. Nos. K9/12 surch with Type K **5** (Cyrillic letter "D").
K14 K **4** "D" on 5000d. grn & red 45 45
K15 – "D" on 10000d. green and red 85 85
K16 – "D" on 50000d. blue and red . . . . 2·50 2·50
K17 – "D" on 100000d. blue and red . . . . 8·50 8·50

1993.
K18 K **6** R blue . . . . 1·10 1·10
No. K18 was sold at the internal registered letter rate.

K **7** St. Simeon

1994. Serb Culture and Tradition. Mult.
K19 50p. Type K **7** 80 80
K20 80p. Krajina coat of arms (vert) . . . . 1·25 1·25
K21 1d. "The Vucedol Dove" (carving) (vert) . . . . . 1·75 1·75

K 8 Cup-and-saucer K 9 Krka Monastery

1994. Climbing Plants. Multicoloured.
K22 30p. Type K **8** 60 60
K23 40p. "Dipladenia" 85 85
K24 60p. Black-eyed Susan 1·25 1·25
K25 70p. Climbing rose 1·50 1·50

1994.
K26 K **9** 5p. red 10 10
K27 – 10p. brown 20 20
K28 – 20p. green 40 40
K29 – 50p. red 55 55
K30 – 60p. violet 70 70
K31 – 1d. blue 2·25 2·25
DESIGNS: 10p. Carin; 20p. Vukovar; 50p. Monument, Batina; 60p. Ilok; 1d. Lake, Plitvice.

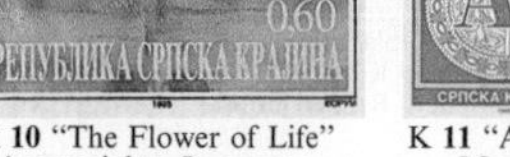
K 10 "The Flower of Life" (memorial to Jasenovac Concentration Camp victims) K 11 "A" over Mosaic

1995. 50th Anniv of End of Second World War.
K32 K **10** 60p. multicoloured 1·40 1·40

1995.
K33 K **11** A red 30 30
No. K33 was sold at the internal letter rate.

K 12 Krcic Waterfall, Knin

1995.
K34 K **12** 10p. blue 10 10
K35 – 20p. ochre 10 10
K36 – 40p. red 20 20
K37 – 2d. blue 1·10 1·10
K38 – 5d. brown 2·75 2·75
DESIGNS: 20p. Benkovac; 40p. Citadel, Knin; 2d. Petrinja; 5d. Pakrac.

In May 1995 the Croatian army occupied Western Slavonia and in August 1995 the Krajina and these areas were reincorporated into the Republic of Croatia. The only surviving part of the Serbian territories, Eastern Slavonia, was, by agreement, placed under temporary United Nations administration in November 1995 and was subsequently called Sremsko Baranjska Oblast (Srem and Baranya Region).

SREMSKO BARANJSKA OBLAST

K 13 Common Cormorant ("Phalocrocorax carbo"), Kopacevo Marsh

1995. Protected Species. Multicoloured.
K39 80p. Type K **13** 90 90
K40 80p. Chamois, Lika 90 90

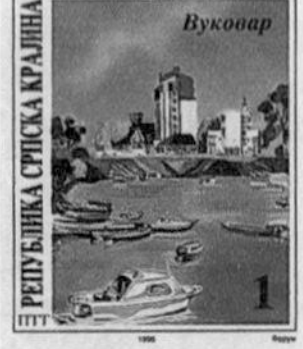
K 14 St. Dimitriev's Church, Dalj K 15 Vukovar Marina, River Danube

1995. Churches (1st series).
K41 K **14** 5p. green 10 10
K42 – 10p. red 15 15
K43 – 30p. mauve 35 35
K44 – 50p. brown 80 80
K45 – 1d. blue 1·10 1·10
DESIGNS: 10p. St. Peter and St. Paul's Church, Bolman; 30p. St. Nicholas's Church, Mirkovci; 50p. St. Nicholas's Church, Tenja; 1d. St. Nicholas's Church, Vukovar.
See also Nos. K48/53.

1996. River Danube Co-operation.
K46 K **15** 1d. multicoloured 1·50 1·50

K 16 The Worker's Hall, Vukovar K 17 Archangel Church, Darda

1996.
K47 K **16** A red 30 30
No. K47 was sold at the internal letter rate.

1996. Churches (2nd series).
K48 K **17** 10p. brown 10 10
K49 – 50p. violet 10 10
K50 – 1d. green 15 15
K51 – 2d. green 45 45
K52 – 5d. blue 1·90 1·90
K53 – 10d. blue 3·75 3·75
DESIGNS: 50p. St. George's Church, Knezevo; 1 d St. Nicholas's Church, Jagodnjak; 2d. Archangel Gabriel's Church, Brsadin; 5d. St. Stephen's Church, Borovo Selo; 10d. St. Nicholas's Church, Pacetin.

K 18 Nikola Tesla K 19 Milica Stojadinovic-Srpkinja (1830–78) (poetess)

1996. 140th Birth Anniv of Nikola Tesla (inventor).
K54 K **18** 1d.50 multicoloured 1·50 1·50

1996. Europa, Famous Women, Mult.
K55 1d.50 Type K **19** 2·50 2·50
K56 1d.50 Mileva Marie-Einstein (1875–1948) (mathematician) 2·50 2·50

K 20 Jasna Sekaric (Olympic gold medal winner) K 21 Milutin Milankovic

1996. Centenary of Modern Olympic Games.
K57 K **20** 1d.50 multicoloured 1·25 1·25

1996. Milutin Milankovic (geophysicist) Commemoration (1879–1958).
K58 K **21** 1d.50 multicoloured 1·25 1·25

K 22 "Madonna and Child" (icon) K 23 Pigeon

1996. Christmas.
K59 K **22** 1d.50 multicoloured 1·25 1·25

1997. Domestic Pets. Multicoloured.
K60 1d. Type K **23** 50 50
K61 1d. Budgerigar 50 50
K62 1d. Cat 50 50
K63 1d. Black labrador 50 50

1997. No. K18 surch or optd (No. K67) with crosses obliterating former name.
K64 K **6** 10p. on R blue 10 10
K65 20p. on R blue 10 10
K66 30p. on R blue 15 15
K67 R (90p.) blue 40 40
K68 1d. on R blue 30 30
K69 1d.50 on R blue 60 60
K70 2d. on R blue 80 80
K71 5d. on R blue 1·50 1·50
K72 10d. on R blue 3·75 3·75
K73 20d. on R blue 9·00 9·00

K 25 St. Peter and St. Paul's Cathedral, Orolik K 26 Prince Marko and The Turks

1997. Restoration of Orthodox Church, Ilok.
K74 K **25** 50p.+50p. blue 35 35
K75 – 60p.+50p. mauve 35 35
K76 – 1d.20+50p. red 55 55
DESIGNS: 60p. St. George's Church, Tovarnik; 1d.20, Church, Negoslavci.

1997. Europa. Tales and Legends. Mult.
K77 1d. Type K **26** 70 70
K78 1d. Emperor Trajan 70 70

The postal administration of the Srem and Baranya Region was reincorporated into that of the Republic of Croatia on 19 May 1997. Eastern Slavonia was returned to Croatian control on 15 January 1998.

CUBA Pt. 15

An island in the W. Indies, ceded by Spain to the United States in 1898. A republic under U.S. protection until 1901 when the island became independent. The issues to 1871, except Nos. 13, 14, 19, 20/7, 32, 44 and 48, were for Puerto Rico also.

1855. 8 reales plata fuerte (strong silver reales) = 1 p eso.
1866. 100 centimos = 1 escudo.
1871. 100 centimos = 1 peseta.
1881. 100 milesimas = 100 centavos = 1 peso.
1898. 100 cents = 1 U.S. dollar.
1899. 100 centavos = 1 peso.

SPANISH COLONY

1 5

1855. Imperf.
6 **1** ½r. green 6·00 60
9 1r. blue 3·00 60
10 1r. green 3·00 60
11a 2r. red 11·50 3·00
Nos. 10/11 optd **HABILITADO POR LA NACION** were issues of Philippines (Nos. 44/5).

1855. No. 11a surch **Y ¼**.
12 **1** Y¼ on 2r. red £550 £130

1862. Imperf.
13 **5** ¼r. black on buff 17·00 20·00

6 7

1864. Imperf.
14 **6** ¼r. black on buff 13·00 18·00
15 ½r. green 3·00 60
16 ½r. green on pink 6·00 1·20
17 1r. blue on brown 3·00 60
18b 2r. red 18·00 5·50

1866. Dated "1866". Imperf.
19 **7** 5c. mauve 25·00 32·00
20 10c. blue 3·00 60
21 20c. green 1·40 60
22 40c. pink 8·00 6·25

1866. No. 14 optd **66**. Imperf.
23 **6** ¼r. black on buff 55·00 60·00

1867. Dated "1867". Perf.
24 **7** 5c. mauve 36·00 17·00
25 10c. blue 19·00 1·10
26 20c. green 12·00 1·70
27 40c. pink 12·00 7·50

9 11

1868. Dated "1868".
28 **9** 5c. lilac 17·00 10·50
29 10c. blue 2·75 1·20
30 20c. green 5·50 2·75
31 40c. pink 13·00 6·00

1868. Nos. 28/31 optd **HABILITADO POR LA NACION**.
36 **9** 5c. lilac 49·00 31·00
37 10c. blue 49·00 31·00
38 20c. green 49·00 31·00
39 40c. pink 49·00 31·00

1869. Dated "1869".
32 **9** 5c. pink 34·00 15·00
33 10c. brown 3·00 1·50
34 20c. orange 4·75 1·70
35 40c. lilac 29·00 9·50

1869. Nos. 32/5 optd **HABILITADO POR LA NACION**.
40 **9** 5c. pink £110 36·00
41 10c. brown 49·00 31·00
42 20c. orange 43·00 31·00
43 40c. lilac 60·00 31·00

1870.
44 **11** 5c. blue £140 60·00
45 10c. green 1·80 60
46 20c. brown 2·10 60
47 40c. pink £150 34·00

12 13

1871. Dated "1871".
48 **12** 12c. lilac 17·00 9·75
49 25c. blue 3·00 70
50 50c. green 1·90 75
51 1p. brown 28·00 6·50

1873.
52 **13** 12½c. green 23·00 10·50
53 25c. grey 1·70 60
54 50c. brown 1·10 60
55 1p. brown £250 34·00

1874. Dated "1874".
56 **12** 12½c. brown 17·00 8·75
57 25c. blue 60 45
58 50c. lilac 1·10 60
59 1p. red £200 60·00

14 15

1875.
60 **14** 12½c. mauve 70 1·00
61 25c. blue 55 30
62 50c. green 55 30
63 1p. brown 7·00 4·00

1876. Inscr "ULTRAMAR 1876".
64 **15** 12½c. green 1·60 1·70
65a 25c. lilac 2·75 30
66 50c. blue 60 30
67 1p. black 6·50 4·75

1877. Inscr "CUBA 1877".
68 **15** 10c. green 23·00
69 12½c. lilac 5·75 3·25
70 25c. green 55 40
71 50c. black 55 40
72 1p. brown 25·00 10·00

1878. Inscr "CUBA 1878".
73 **15** 5c. blue 55 30
74 10c. black 55·00
75a 12½c. bistre 2·75 2·10
76a 25c. green 55 15
77 50c. green 55 15
78 1p. red 7·75 4·25

1879. Inscr "CUBA 1879".
79 **15** 5c. black 55 30
80 10c. orange £100
81 12½c. pink 55 30
82 25c. blue 55 30
83 50c. grey 55 25
84 1p. bistre 12·00 8·75

1880. "Alfonso XII" key-type inscr "CUBA 1880".
85 X 5c. green 55 30
86 10c. red 70·00
87 12½c. lilac 55 25
88 25c. lilac 55 25
89 50c. brown 55 25
90 1p. brown 3·75 2·10

1881. "Alfonso XII" key-type inscr "CUBA 1881".
91 X 1c. green 55 25
92 2c. pink 31·00
93a 2½c. bistre 55 25
94 5c. lilac 55 10
95 10c. brown 55 10
96 20c. brown 3·75 3·75

1882. "Alfonso XII" key-type inscr "CUBA".
97 X 1c. green 55 20
98 2c. pink 1·70 20

118 2½c. brown . . . . 3·00 1·00
119 2½c. mauve . . . . 1·20 65
100 5c. lilac . . . . 2·00 30
123 5c. grey . . . . 1·80 35
101 10c. brown 65 15
126 10c. blue . . . . 1·00 60
121 20c. brown . . . . 13·50 2·30
122 20c. lilac . . . . 13·50 3·25

1883. 1882 issue optd or surch with fancy pattern.
103 X 5c. lilac . . . . 1·90 3·25
106 5 on 5c. lilac . . . . 1·10 70
104 10c. brown . . . . 4·75 6·75
107 10 on 10c. brown . . . . . 1·90 1·10
105 20c. brown £150 £150
111 20 on 20c. brown . . . . . 19·00 13·00
The surcharges exist in four different patterns.

1890. "Baby" key-type inscr "ISLA DE CUBA".
135 Y 1c. brown . . . . 10·00 6·25
147 1c. grey . . . . 6·00 3·00
159 1c. blue . . . . 2·40 35
169 1c. purple 70 25
136 2c. blue . . . . 5·50 2·10
148 2c. brown . . . . 1·10 40
160 2c. pink 50 10
170 2c. red . . . . 6·25 75
137 2½c. green . . . . 7·50 4·00
149 2½c. orange . . . . 34·00 9·25
161 2½c. mauve . . . . 2·20 25
171 2½c. pink 50 10
138 5c. grey 60 60
150 5c. green 70 40
172 5c. blue 35 10
139 10c. brown . . . . 2·10 75
151 10c. pink . . . . 1·40 40
173 10c. green . . . . 1·70 15
140 20c. purple 60 55
152 20c. blue . . . . 7·00 7·50
162 20c. brown . . . . 19·00 9·75
174 20c. lilac . . . . 11·00 4·75
175 40c. brown . . . . 22·00 11·50
176 80c. brown . . . . 41·00 17·00

1898. "Curly Head" key-type inscr "CUBA 1898 Y 99".
183 Z 1m. brown 25 10
184 2m. brown 25 10
185 3m. brown 25 10
186 4m. brown . . . . 2·75 1·40
187 5m. brown 25 10
188 1c. purple 25 10
189 2c. green 25 10
190 3c. brown 10 10
191 4c. orange . . . . 7·00 2·10
192 5c. pink 60 10
193 6c. blue 25 10
194 8c. brown 55 25
195 10c. red 70 25
196 15c. grey . . . . 2·75 25
197 20c. purple 35 10
198 40c. mauve . . . . 1·80 25
199 60c. black . . . . 2·00 25
200 80c. brown . . . . 9·25 7·00
201 1p. green . . . . 9·25 7·00
202 2p. blue . . . . 19·00 7·00

OFFICIAL STAMPS

1860. As Nos. O50/3 of Spain but without full points after "OFICIAL" and "ONZAS" or "LIBRA". Imperf.
O12 ½o. black on yellow . . . . — 34·00
O13 1o. black on pink . . . . . — 34·00
O14 4o. black on green . . . . . — £180
O15 1l. black on blue . . . . . — £425
The face values of Nos. O12/15 are expressed in onzas (ounces) or libra (pound), referring to the maximum weight for which each value could prepay postage.

PRINTED MATTER STAMPS

All Printed Matter stamps are key-types inscribed "CUBA IMPRESOS".

1888. "Alfonso XII".
P129 X ¼m. black 55 10
P130 1m. black 55 15
P131 2m. black 55 15
P132 3m. black 75 50
P133 4m. black . . . . 1·40 80
P134 8m. black . . . . 6·00 2·75

1890. "Baby".
P141 Y ¼m. brown 55 40
P142 1m. brown 55 40
P143 2m. brown 90 55
P144 3m. brown 90 55
P145 4m. brown . . . . 7·00 4·00
P146 8m. brown . . . . 7·00 4·00

1892. "Baby".
P153 Y ¼m. lilac 30 20
P154 1m. lilac 30 20
P155 2m. lilac 30 20
P156 3m. lilac . . . . 1·50 30
P157 4m. lilac . . . . 3·00 1·50
P158 8m. lilac . . . . 7·00 3·00

1894. "Baby".
P163 Y ¼m. pink 15 10
P164 1m. pink 50 10
P165 2m. pink 50 10
P166 3m. pink . . . . 1·60 65
P167 4m. pink . . . . 3·00 75
P168 8m. pink . . . . 6·00 3·25

1896. "Baby".
P177 Y ¼m. green 15 10
P178 1m. green 15 10
P179 2m. green 15 10
P180 3m. green . . . . 1·70 55
P181 4m. green . . . . 3·75 3·25
P182 8m. green . . . . 7·00 4·75

UNITED STATES ADMINISTRATION

1899. Stamps of United States of 1894 surch **CUBA** and value.
246 1c. on 1c. green (No. 283) . . 4·00 35
247 2c. on 2c. red (No. 270) . . . 4·25 30
248 2½c. on 2c. red (No. 270) . . 2·50 40
249 3c. on 3c. violet (No. 271) . . 7·50 1·40
250 5c. on 5c. blue (No. 286) . . 8·00 1·25
251 10c. on 10c. brown (No. 289) 15·00 5·00

29 Statue of Columbus

1899.
307 **29** 1c. green . . . . 1·10 10
308 – 2c. red . . . . 1·10 10
303 – 3c. purple . . . . 2·00 15
304 – 5c. blue . . . . 3·25 45
310 – 10c. brown . . . . 2·25 35
DESIGNS: 2c. Palms; 3c. Statue of "La India" (Woman); 5c. Liner "Umbria" (Commerce); 10c. Ploughing Sugar Plantation.

POSTAGE DUE STAMPS

1899. Postage Due stamps of United States of 1894 surch **CUBA** and value.
D253 D **87** 1c. on 1c. red . . . . 35·00 4·00
D254 2c. on 2c. red . . . . 35·00 4·00
D255 5c. on 5c. red . . . . 35·00 4·00
D256 10c. on 10c. red . . . 21·00 1·90

SPECIAL DELIVERY STAMP

1899. No. E283 of United States surch **CUBA. 10c. de PESO.**
E252 E **46** 10c. on 10c. blue . . . £100 80·00

INDEPENDENT REPUBLIC

1902. Surch **UN CENTAVO HABILITADO OCTUBRE 1902** and figure **1**.
306 1c. on 3c. purple (No. 303) 1·75 40

36 Major-General Antonio Maceo

37 B. Maso

1907.
311 **36** 50c. black and slate . . . 1·10 40
318 50c. black and violet . . . 1·10 40

1910.
312 **37** 1c. violet and green 55 15
320 1c. green 85 10
313 – 2c. green and red . . . . 1·10 10
321 – 2c. red 85 10
314 – 3c. blue and violet 55 20
315 – 5c. green and blue . . . . 10·00 75
322 – 5c. blue . . . . 2·00 10
316 – 8c. violet and olive 55 20
323 – 8c. black and olive . . . . 2·00 35
317 – 10c. blue and sepia . . . . 4·50 25
319 – 1p. black and slate . . . . 6·50 3·00
324 – 1p. black . . . . 4·00 1·10
PORTRAITS: 2c. M. Gomez. 3c. J. Sanguily. 5c. I. Agramonte. 8c. C. Garcia. 10c. Mayia. 1p. C. Roloff.

40 Map of W. Indies

43 Gertrudis Gomez de Avellaneda

1914.
325 **40** 1c. green 40 15
326 2c. red 40 15
328 3c. violet . . . . 2·00 25
329 5c. blue . . . . 2·25 15
330 8c. olive . . . . 2·25 65
331 10c. brown . . . . 3·75 70
332 10c. olive . . . . 3·25 70
333 50c. orange . . . . 28·00 9·00
334 $1 slate . . . . 40·00 17·00

1914. Birth Centenary of Gertrudis Gomez de Avellaneda (poetess).
335 **43** 5c. blue . . . . 8·00 3·00

44 Jose Marti

47

1917.
336 **44** 1c. green 65 10
337 – 2c. red (Gomez) 65 10
338 – 3c. violet (La Luz) 65 10
339 – 5c. blue (Garcia) 65 10
349a – 8c. brown (Agramonte) . . 2·75 20
341 – 10c. brown (Palma) . . . . 1·60 10
342 – 20c. green (Saco) . . . . 5·00 45
343 – 50c. red (Maceo) . . . . 8·00 45
344 – 1p. black (Cespedes) . . . 8·00 45

1927. 25th Anniv of Republic.
352 **47** 25c. violet . . . . 8·50 3·25

48 PN 9 Flying Boat over Havana Harbour

1927. Air.
353 **48** 5c. blue . . . . 3·25 1·40

49 T. Estrada Palma

1928. 6th Pan-American Conference.
354 **49** 1c. green 25 15
355 – 2c. red 25 15
356 – 5c. blue 55 25
357 – 8c. brown . . . . 3·75 1·50
358 – 10c. brown 55 45
359 – 13c. orange . . . . 1·10 50
360 – 20c. olive . . . . 1·40 60
361 – 30c. purple . . . . 4·50 1·25
362 – 50c. red . . . . 4·50 1·75
363 – 1p. black . . . . 9·00 5·00
DESIGNS: 2c. Gen. G. Machado; 5c. El Morro, Havana; 8c. Railway Station, Havana; 10c. President's Palace; 13c. Tobacco plantation; 20c. Treasury Secretariat; 30c. Sugar Mill; 50c. Havana Cathedral; 1p. Galician Immigrants' Centre, Havana.

1928. Air. Lindbergh Commemoration. Optd **LINDBERGH FEBRERO 1928.**
364 **48** 5c. red . . . . 4·00 1·60

51 The Capitol, Havana

52 Hurdler

1929. Inauguration of Capitol.
365 **51** 1c. green 25 20
366 2c. red 30 35
367 5c. blue 40 30
368 10c. brown 75 35
369 20c. purple . . . . 3·25 1·40

1930. 2nd Central American Games, Havana.
370 **52** 1c. green 55 35
371 2c. red 55 40
372 5c. blue 85 40
373 10c. brown . . . . 1·40 85
374 20c. purple . . . . 9·00 3·00

1930. Air. Surch **CORREO AEREO NACIONAL** and value.
375 **47** 10c. on 25c. violet . . . . 2·75 1·10

54 Fokker Super Trimotor over Beach

1931. Air.
376 **54** 5c. green 20 10
377 8c. red . . . . 2·25 60
378 10c. blue 25 10
379 15c. red 60 25
380 20c. brown 65 10
381 30c. purple . . . . 1·10 25
382 40c. orange . . . . 2·75 45
383 50c. green . . . . 3·00 50
384 1p. black . . . . 5·75 1·75

55 Ford "Tin Goose" over Forest

1931. Air.
385 **55** 5c. purple 20 10
386 10c. black 25 10
387 20c. red . . . . 1·25 35
388 20c. pink . . . . 2·25 70
389 50c. blue . . . . 3·75 1·00
390 50c. turquoise . . . . . . 2·75 90

56 Mangos of Baragua

57 Battle of Mal Tiempo

1933. 35th Anniv of War of Independence.
391 **56** 3c. brown 80 20
392 **57** 5c. blue 60 30
393 – 10c. green . . . . 1·60 30
394 – 13c. red . . . . 1·90 90
395 – 20c. black . . . . 4·00 3·25
DESIGNS—HORIZ: 10c. Battle of Coliseo; 13c. Maceo, Gomez and Zayas. VERT: 20c. Campaign Monument.

1933. Establishment of Revolutionary Govt. Stamps of 1917 optd **GOBIERNO REVOLUCIONARIO 4-9-1933** or surch also.
396 **44** 1c. green 85 30
397 – 2c. on 3c. vio (No. 338) . . 85 30

59 Dr. Carlos J. Finlay

61 Map of Caribbean

1934. 101st Birth Anniv of C. J. Finlay ("yellow-fever" researcher).
398 **59** 2c. red . . . . 1·10 35
399 5c. blue . . . . 2·00 45

1935. Air. Havana–Miami "Air Train". Surch **PRIMER TREN AEREO INTERNACIONAL. 1935 O'Meara y du Pont + 10 cts.** Imperf or perf.
400 **54** 10c.+10c. red . . . . . . 4·25 4·25

1936. Free Port of Matanzas. Inscr as in T **61**. Perf or imperf (same prices).
401 **61** 1c. green (postage) 20 15
402 – 2c. red 30 15
403 – 4c. purple . . . . 1·25 20
404 – 5c. blue . . . . 1·50 35
405 – 8c. brown . . . . 1·40 55
406 – 10c. green . . . . 1·40 55
407 – 20c. brown . . . . 2·75 2·25
408 – 50c. slate . . . . 7·00 3·25

409 – 5c. violet (air) 40 20
410 – 10c. orange . . . . 1·00 20
411 – 20c. green . . . . 2·75 80
412 – 50c. black . . . . 10·50 4·00
DESIGNS—POSTAGE: 2c. Matanzas Bay and Free Zone; 4c. "Rex" (liner) in Mantanzas Bay; 5c. Ships in the Free Zone; 8c. Bellamar Caves; 10c. Yumuri Valley; 20c. Yumuri River; 50c. Sailing ship and steamer. AIR: 5c. Aerial panorama; 10c. Airship "Macon" over Concord Bridge; 20c. Airplane "Cuatro Vientos" over Matanzas; 50c. San Severino Fortress.

63 President J. M. Gomez

64 Gen. J. M. Gomez Monument

1936. Inauguration of Gomez Monument.
413 **63** 1c. green . . . . 1·60 45
414 **64** 2c. red . . . . 2·10 65

65 "Peace and Labour"

66 Maximo Gomez Monument

1936. Inaug of Maximo Gomez Monument.
415 **65** 1c. green (postage) 30 15
416 **66** 2c. red 30 15
417 – 4c. purple 55 15
418 – 5c. blue . . . . 2·75 70
419 – 8c. olive . . . . 4·00 1·10
420 – 5c. violet (air) . . . . . . 2·25 1·40
421 – 10c. brown . . . . 4·00 2·00
DESIGNS—VERT: 4c. Flaming torch; 8c. Dove of Peace. HORIZ: 5c. (No. 418) Army of Liberation; 5c. (No. 420) Lightning; 10c. "Flying Wing".

68 Caravel and Sugar Cane

1937. 400th Anniv of Cane Sugar Industry.
422 – 1c. green . . . . 1·10 45
423 – 2c. red 80 20
424 **68** 5c. blue . . . . 2·50 40
DESIGNS (each with caravel in upper triangle). HORIZ: 2c. Early sugar mill; 5c. Modern sugar mill.

69 Mountain View (Bolivia)

70 Camilo Henriquez (Chile)

1937. American Writers and Artists Assn.
424a – 1c. green (postage) . . . 55 55
424b **69** 1c. green 55 55
424c – 2c. red 55 55
424d – 2c. red 55 55
424e **70** 3c. violet 85 85
424f – 3c. violet 85 85
424g – 4c. brown 85 85
424h – 4c. brown . . . . 1·75 1·75
424i – 5c. blue . . . . 1·10 1·10
424j – 5c. blue . . . . 1·10 1·10
424k – 8c. green . . . . 3·25 3·25
424l – 8c. green . . . . 1·40 1·40
424m – 10c. brown . . . . . . 1·75 1·75
424n – 10c. brown . . . . . . 1·75 1·75
424o – 25c. lilac . . . . 35·00 18·00
424p – 5c. red (air) . . . . . . 3·75 3·25
424q – 5c. red . . . . 3·75 3·25
424r – 10c. blue . . . . 3·75 3·25
424s – 10c. blue . . . . 3·75 3·25
424t – 20c. green . . . . 6·00 5·50
424u – 20c. green . . . . 6·00 5·50
DESIGNS—VERT: No. 424a, Arms of the Republic (Argentina); No. 424c, Arms (Brazil); No. 424f, Gen. F. de Paula Santander (Colombia); No. 424g, Autograph of Jose Marti (Cuba); No. 424j, Juan Montalvo (Ecuador); No. 424k, Abraham Lincoln (U.S.A.); No. 4241, Quetzal and scroll (Guatemala); No. 424m, Arms (Haiti); No. 424n, Francisco Morazan (Honduras); No. 424r, Inca gate, Cuzco (Peru); No. 424s, Atlacatl (Indian warrior) (El Salvador); No. 424t, Simon Bolivar (Venezuela); No. 424u, Jose Rodo (Uruguay). HORIZ: No. 424d, River scene (Canada); No. 424h, National Monument (Costa Rica); No. 424i, Columbus Lighthouse (Dominican Republic); No. 424o, Ships of Columbus; No. 424p, Arch (Panama); No. 424q, Carlos Lopez (Paraguay).

1937. Centenary of Cuban Railway. Surch **1837 1937 PRIMER CENTENARIO FERROCARRIL EN CUBA** and value either side of an early engine and coach.
425 **47** 10c. on 25c. violet . . . . 5·50 1·00

1938. Air. 25th Anniv of D. Rosillo's Overseas Flight from Key West to Havana. Optd **1913 1938 ROSILLO Key West-Habana**.
426 **48** 5c. orange . . . . 3·75 1·75

74 Pierre and Marie Curie

75 Allegory of Child Care

1938. International Anti-cancer Fund. 40th Anniv of Discovery of Radium.
427 **74** 2c.+1c. red . . . . 2·50 95
428 5c.+1c. blue . . . . 2·50 95

1938. Obligatory Tax. Anti-T.B. Fund.
429 **75** 1c. green 30 20

76 Native and Cigar

80 Calixto Garcia

1939. Havana Tobacco Industry.
430 **76** 1c. green 20 10
431 – 2c. red 45 10
432 – 5c. blue . . . . 1·00 15
DESIGNS: 2c. Cigar, globe and wreath of leaves; 5c. Tobacco plant and box of cigars.

1939. Air. Experimental Rocket Post. Optd **EXPERIMENTO DEL COHETE Postal ANO DE 1939**.
433 **55** 10c. green . . . . 35·00 5·50

1939. Birth Centenary of Gen. Calixto Garcia. Perf or imperf.
434 **80** 2c. red 55 20
435 – 5c. blue . . . . 1·10 45
DESIGN: 5c. Garcia on horseback.

82 Nurse and Child

83 Gonzalo de Quesada and Union Flags

84 Rotarian Symbol, Flag and Tobacco Plant

1939. Obligatory Tax. Anti-T.B.
436 **82** 1c. red 30 10

1940. 50th Anniv of Pan-American Union.
437 **83** 2c. red . . . . 1·10 55

1940. Rotary International Convention.
438 **84** 2c. red . . . . 1·75 80

85 Lions, Emblem, Flag and Palms

86 Dr. Gutierrez

1940. Lions International Convention, Havana.
439 **85** 2c. red . . . . 1·75 80

1940. Centenary of Publication of First Cuban Medical Review.
440 **86** 2c. red 85 55
441 5c. blue . . . . 1·40 55

87 Sir Rowland Hill and G.B. 1d. of 1840 and Cuba Issues of 1855 and 1899

1940. Air. Centenary of 1st Adhesive Postage Stamps.
443 **87** 10c. brown . . . . 4·50 2·50

88 "Health" protecting Children

89 Heredia and Niagara Falls

1940. Obligatory Tax. Children's Hospital and Anti-T.B. Funds.
445 **88** 1c. blue 20 10

1940. Air. Death Centenary of J. M. Heredia y Campuzaono (poet).
446 – 5c. green . . . . 2·25 1·10
447 **89** 10c. grey . . . . 2·75 1·40
DESIGN: 5c. Heredia and palms.

90 General Moncada and Sword

91 Moncada riding into Battle

1941. Birth Centenary of H. Moncada.
448 **90** 3c. brown . . . . 1·00 50
449 **91** 5c. blue . . . . 1·00 50

92 Mother and Child

95 "Labour, Wealth of America"

1941. Obligatory Tax. Anti-T.B.
450 **92** 1c. brown 20 10

1942. American Democracy. Imperf or perf.
451 – 1c. green 25 10
452 – 3c. brown 35 15
453 **95** 5c. blue 55 20
454 – 10c. mauve . . . . 1·40 65
455 – 13c. red . . . . 2·00 85
DESIGNS: 1c. Western Hemisphere; 3c. Cuban Arms and portraits of Maceo, Bolivar, Juarez and Lincoln; 10c. Tree of Fraternity, Havana; 13c. Statue of Liberty.

98 Gen. Ignacio Agramonte Loynaz

99 Rescue of Sanguily

1942. Birth Centenary of Gen. I. A. Loynaz.
456 **98** 3c. brown 75 40
457 **99** 5c. blue . . . . 1·50 55

100 "Victory"

102 "Unmask Fifth Columnists"

1942. Obligatory Tax. Red Cross Fund.
458 **100** $\frac{1}{2}$c. orange 20 10
459 $\frac{1}{2}$c. grey 20 10

1942. Obligatory Tax. Anti-T.B. Fund. Optd **1942**.
460 **92** 1c. red 30 10

1943. Anti-Fifth Column.
461 **102** 1c. green 25 15
462 – 3c. red 45 15
463 – 5c. blue 45 20
464 – 10c. brown . . . . 1·75 70
465 – 13c. purple . . . . 2·25 1·10
DESIGNS—HORIZ: (45 × 25 mm.) 5c. Woman in snake's coils ("The Fifth Column is like the Serpent – destroy it"); 10c. Men demolishing column with battering-ram ("Fulfil your patriotic duty by destroying the Fifth Column").
Type **102**. 13c. Woman with monster "Don't be afraid of the Fifth Column. Attack it". VERT: Girl with finger to lips "Be Careful! The Fifth Column is spying on you".

105 Eloy Alfaro, Flags of Ecuador and Cuba and Scroll of Independence

1943. Birth Centenary of E. Alfaro (former President of Ecuador).
466 **105** 3c. green . . . . 1·25 55

106 "The Long Road to Retirement"

107 "Health" Protecting Child

1943. Postal Employees' Retirement Fund.
467 **106** 1c. green 65 35
470 3c. red 55 35
471 5c. blue 90 35

1943. Obligatory Tax. Anti-tuberculosis.
473 **107** 1c. brown 20 10

108 Columbus

109 Discovery of Tobacco

1944. 450th Anniv of Discovery of America.
474 **108** 1c. green (postage) . . . 20 15
475 – 3c. brown 30 15
476 – 5c. blue 40 20
477 **109** 10c. violet . . . . 2·25 65
478 – 13c. red . . . . 6·50 1·25
479 – 5c. olive (air) . . . . . . 1·50 35
480 – 10c. grey . . . . 1·75 65
DESIGNS—VERT: 3c. Bartolome de las Casas; 5c. (No. 476), Statue of Columbus. HORIZ: 5c. (No. 479) Mountains of Gibara; 10c. (No. 480), Columbus Lighthouse; 13c. Columbus at Pinar del Rio.

110 Carlos Roloff

111 American Continents and Brazilian "Bull's Eyes" stamps

1944. Birth Centenary of Major-Gen. Roloff.
481 **110** 3c. violet 95 30

1944. Cent of 1st American Postage stamps.
482 **111** 3c. brown . . . . 1·75 55

112 Society Seal

113 Governor Las Casas and Bishop Penalver

1945. 150th Anniv of Economic Society of Friends of Havana.
483 **112** 1c. green 35 15
484 **113** 2c. red 65 30

115 Old Age Pensioners

1945. Postal Employees' Retirement Fund.
485 **115** 1c. green 20 10
487 2c. red 40 15
489 5c. blue 75 30

116 Valdes

1946. Death Centenary of Gabriel de la Concepcion Valdes (poet).
491 **116** 2c. red 85 45

117 Manuel Marquez Sterling

118 Red Cross and Globe

1946. Founding of "Manuel Marquez Sterling" Professional School of Journalism.
492 **117** 2c. red 85 45

1946. 80th Anniv of International Red Cross.
493 **118** 2c. red 90 45

119 Prize Cattle and Dairymaid

120 Franklin D. Roosevelt

1947. National Cattle Show.
494 **119** 2c. red . . . . 1·10 35

1947. 2nd Death Anniv of Pres. Roosevelt.
495 **120** 2c. red . . . . 1·25 35

121 Antonio Oms and Pensioners

1947. Postal Employees' Retirement Fund.
496 **121** 1c. green 15 15
497 2c. red 25 15
498 5c. blue 75 30

122 Marta Abreu

1947. Birth Centenary of M. Abreu (philanthropist).
499 **122** 1c. green 30 15
500 – 2c. red 45 20
501 – 5c. blue 65 30
502 – 10c. violet . . . . 1·40 65
DESIGNS: 2c. Allegory of Charity; 5c. Monument; 10c. Allegory of Patriotism.

123 Dr. G. A. Hansen and Isle of Pines

1948. Int Leprosy Relief Congress, Havana.
503 **123** 2c. red 90 40

124 Council of War

1948. Air. 50th Anniv of War of Independence.
504 **124** 8c. black and yellow . . . 1·90 85

125 Woman and Child

126 Death of Marti

1948. Postal Employees' Retirement Fund.
506 **125** 1c. green 30 15
507 2c. red 30 15
508 5c. blue 75 30

1948. 50th Death Anniv of Jose Marti.
509 **126** 2c. red 35 20
510 – 5c. blue . . . . 1·10 35
DESIGN: 5c. Marti disembarking at Playitas.

127 Gathering Tobacco

129 Antonio Maceo

1948. Havana Tobacco Industry.
511 **127** 1c. green 15 10
512 – 2c. red 20 10
513 – 5c. blue 35 15
DESIGNS: 2c. Girl with box of cigars and flag; 5c. Cigar and shield.
This set comes again redrawn with smaller designs of 21 × 25 mm.

1948. Birth Centenary of Gen. Maceo.
514 – 1c. green 10 10
515 **129** 2c. red 15 10
516 – 5c. blue 25 15
517 – 8c. brown and black . . . 35 30
518 – 10c. green and brown . . 45 20
519 – 20c. blue and red . . . . 1·75 75
520 – 50c. blue and red . . . . 3·00 2·00
521 – 1p. violet and black . . . 6·00 2·75
DESIGNS—VERT: 1c. Equestrian statue of Maceo; 5c. Mausoleum at El Cacahual. HORIZ: 8c. Maceo and raised swords; 10c. Maceo leading charge; 20c. Maceo at Peralejo; 50c. Declaration at Baragua; 1p. Death of Maceo at San Pedro.

131 Symbol of Medicine

132 Morro Castle and Lighthouse

1948. 1st Pan-American Pharmaceutical Congress.
522 **131** 2c. red 95 40

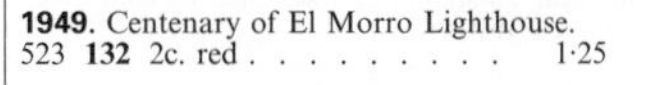

1949. Centenary of El Morro Lighthouse.
523 **132** 2c. red . . . . 1·25 50

133 Jagua Castle

1949. Centenary of Newspaper "Hoja Economica" and Bicentenary of Jagua Fortress.
524 **133** 1c. green 40 20
525 2c. red 65 35

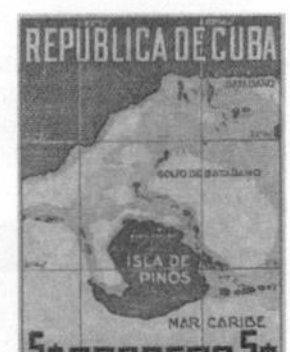

134 M. Sanguily

135 Isle of Pines

1949. Birth Centenary of Manuel Sanguily y Garritte (poet).
526 **134** 2c. red 35 20
527 5c. blue 90 35

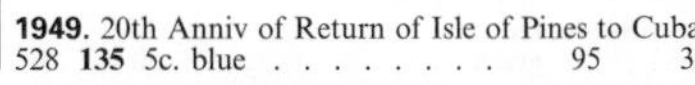

1949. 20th Anniv of Return of Isle of Pines to Cuba.
528 **135** 5c. blue 95 35

136 Ismael Cespedes

137 Woman and Child

1949. Postal Employees' Retirement Fund.
529 **136** 1c. green 25 15
530 2c. red 25 15
531 5c. blue 75 30

1949. Obligatory Tax. Anti-tuberculosis.
532 **137** 1c. blue 25 10
547 1c. red 25 10
No. 547 is dated "1950".

138 Enrique Collazo

139 E. J. Varona

1950. Birth Centenary of Gen. Collazo.
533 **138** 2c. red 30 15
534 5c. blue 90 35

1950. Birth Centenary of Varona (writer).
535 **139** 2c. red 35 20
536 5c. blue 90 35

1950. National Bank Opening. No. 512 optd **BANCO NACIONAL DE CUBA INAUGURACION 27 ABRIL 1950.**
540 2c. red 90 35

1950. 75th Anniv of U.P.U. Optd **U.P.U. 1874 1949.**
541 **127** 1c. green 35 15
542 – 2c. pink (As No. 512) . . 40 25
543 – 5c. blue (As No. 513) . . 95 35

142 Balanzategui, Pausa and Railway Crash

143 F. Figueredo

1950. Postal Employees' Retirement Fund.
544 **142** 1c. green . . . . 2·50 1·10
545 2c. red . . . . 2·50 1·10
546 5c. blue . . . . 7·00 2·25

1951. Postal Employees' Retirement Fund.
548 **143** 1c. green 55 20
549 2c. red 55 20
550 5c. blue 90 35

144 Foundation Stone

145 Narciso Lopez

1951. Obligatory Tax. P.O. Rebuilding Fund.
551 **144** 1c. violet 25 10

1951. Centenary of Cuban Flag.
552 – 1c. red, bl & grn (postage) 30 15
553 **145** 2c. black and red 50 25
554 – 5c. red and blue . . . . 1·10 50
555 – 10c. red, blue and violet 2·00 70
556 – 5c. red, blue & olive (air) 1·40 45
557 – 8c. red, blue and brown 1·75 65
558 – 25c. red, blue and black 2·25 1·10
DESIGNS—VERT: 1c. Miguel Teurbe Tolon; 5c. (No. 554) Emilia Teurbe Tolon; 8c. Raising the flag; 10c. Flag; 25c. Flag and El Morro lighthouse. HORIZ: 5c. (No. 556) Lopez landing at Cardenas.

147 Clara Maass, Newark Memorial and Las Animas, Havana, Hospitals

1951. 50th Death Anniv of Clara Maass (nurse).
559 **147** 2c. red . . . . 1·00 40

148 Capablanca (after E. Valderrama)

149 Chessboard showing end of Capablanca v. Lasker

1951. 30th Anniv of Jose Capablanca's Victory in World Chess Championship.
562 **148** 1c. orge & grn (postage) . . . . . 1·75 45
563 – 2c. brown and red . . . 2·25 85
564 E **150** 5c. blue and black . . . 5·50 1·75
565 **149** 5c. yellow & green (air) 2·75 85
566 – 8c. purple and blue . . 4·00 1·10
567 **148** 25c. sepia & brown . . 7·00 1·90
DESIGN—VERT: 2c., 8c. Capablanca playing chess.

151 Dr. A. Guiteras Holmes

152 Morrillo Fortress

1951. 16th Death Anniv of Dr. A. Guiteras Holmes in skirmish at Morrillo.
568 **151** 1c. green (postage) . . . 45 15
569 – 2c. red 65 30
570 **152** 5c. blue . . . . 1·40 50
571 **151** 5c. mauve (air) . . . . . 1·60 1·10
572 – 8c. green . . . . 2·25 1·60
573 **152** 25c. black . . . . 4·00 2·75
DESIGN—HORIZ: 2c., 8c. Guiteras framing social laws.

153 Mother and Child

154 Christmas Emblems

1951. Obligatory Tax. Anti-tuberculosis.
575 **153** 1c. brown 20 10
576 1c. red 20 10
577 1c. green 20 10
578 1c. blue 20 10

1951. Christmas Greetings.
579 **154** 1c. red and green . . . . 2·00 55
580 2c. green and red . . . . 2·50 65

155 Jose Maceo

156 General Post Office

157 Isabella the Catholic

1952. Birth Centenary of Gen. Maceo.
581 **155** 2c. brown 50 15
582 5c. blue 90 35

1952. Obligatory Tax. P.O. Rebuilding Fund.
583 **156** 1c. blue 20 10
584 1c. red 55 15

1952. 5th Birth Centenary of Isabella the Catholic.
585 **157** 2c. red (postage) . . . . 3·00 75
586 25c. purple (air) . . . . . 5·25 1·25

1952. As No. 549 surch with new value. (a) Postage.
588 **143** 10c. on 2c. brown . . . . 1·25 40

(b) Air. Optd **AEREO** in addition.
589 **143** 5c. on 2c. brown 45 20
590 8c. on 2c. brown 65 20
591 10c. on 2c. brown . . . . 1·10 20
592 25c. on 2c. brown . . . . 1·10 45
593 50c. on 2c. brown . . . . 3·75 1·40
594 1p. on 2c. brown . . . . 5·50 2·75

159 Proclamation of Republic **160** Statue, Havana University

1952. 50th Anniv of Republic.
595 **159** 1c. black & grn (postage) 20 15
596 – 2c. black and red 30 15
597 – 5c. black and blue 40 15
598 – 8c. black and brown . . . 55 15
599 – 20c. black and olive . . . 1·40 50
600 – 50c. black and orange . . 2·75 90

601 – 5c. green & violet (air) . . 55 25
602 **160** 8c. green and red 55 35
603 – 10c. green and blue . . . 1·40 55
604 – 25c. green and purple . . 1·75 85
DESIGNS—HORIZ:—POSTAGE: 2c. Estrada Palma and Estevez Romero; 5c. Barnet, Finlay, Guiteras and Nunez; 8c. The Capitol; 20c. Map showing central highway; 50c. Sugar factory. AIR: 5c. Rural school; 10c. Presidential Palace; 25c. Banknote.

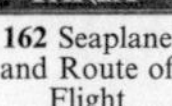

162 Seaplane and Route of Flight **164** Coffee Beans

1952. Air. 39th Anniv of Florida–Cuba flight by A. Parla.
605 **162** 8c. black . . . . 1·25 30
606 – 25c. blue . . . . 2·75 85
DESIGN—HORIZ: 25c. Agustin Parla Orduna and Curtiss A-1 seaplane.

1952. Bicentenary of Coffee Cultivation.
608 **164** 1c. green 35 15
609 – 2c. red 55 30
610 – 5c. green and blue 95 35
DESIGNS: 2c. Plantation worker and map; 5c. Coffee plantation.

165 Col. C. Hernandez

1952. Postal Employees' Retirement Fund.
611 **165** 1c. green (postage) . . . 20 15
612 2c. red 40 15
613 5c. blue 40 15
614 8c. black . . . . 1·00 35
615 10c. red . . . . 1·10 40
616 20c. brown . . . . 4·00 2·75

617 5c. orange (air) 25 10
618 8c. green 45 10
619 10c. brown 50 15
620 15c. green 55 20
621 20c. turquoise 55 30
622 25c. red 85 40
623 30c. violet . . . . 1·75 40
624 45c. mauve . . . . 1·90 1·40
625 50c. blue . . . . 1·60 85
626 1p. yellow . . . . 5·00 2·50

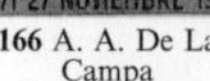

166 A. A. De La Campa **167** Statue, Havana University

168 Dominguez, Estebanez and Capdevila (defence lawyers)

1952. 81st Anniv of Execution of Eight Rebel Medical Students.
627 **166** 1c. black & grn (postage) 15 10
628 – 2c. black and red 30 15
629 – 3c. black and violet . . . 35 15
630 – 5c. black and blue 35 15
631 – 8c. black and sepia . . . 65 35
632 – 10c. black and brown . . 75 30
633 – 13c. black and purple . . 1·90 45
634 – 20c. black and olive . . . 2·25 65
635 **167** 5c. blue and indigo (air) 85 35
636 **168** 25c. green and orange . . 2·25 80
PORTRAITS: 2c. C. A. de la Torre. 3c. A. Bermudez. 5c. E. G. Toledo. 8c. A. Laborde. 10c. J. De M. Medina. 13c. P. Rodriguez. 20c. C. Verdugo.

169 Child's Face **170** Christmas Tree

1952. Obligatory Tax. Anti- tuberculosis.
637 **169** 1c. orange 25 10
638 1c. red 25 10
639 1c. green 25 10
640 1c. blue 25 10

1952. Christmas.
641 **170** 1c. red and green . . . . 2·75 1·75
642 3c. green and violet . . . 2·75 1·75

171 Marti's Birthplace **172** Dr. Rafael Montoro

1953. Birth Centenary of Jose Marti.
643 **171** 1c. brn & grn (postage) 15 10
644 – 1c. brown and green . . . 15 10
645 – 3c. brown and violet . . . 25 15
646 – 3c. brown and violet . . . 25 15
647 – 5c. brown and blue . . . 35 15
648 – 5c. brown and blue . . . 35 15
649 – 10c. black and brown . . 90 30
650 – 10c. black and brown . . 75 30
651 – 13c. brown and green . . 1·60 55
652 – 13c. brown and green . . 1·60 55

653 – 5c. black & red (air) . . . 25 15
654 – 5c. black and red 25 15
655 – 8c. black and green . . . 30 15
656 – 8c. black and green . . . 30 15
657 – 10c. red and blue 40 15
658 – 10c. blue and red 40 15
659 – 15c. black and violet . . . 50 25
660 – 15c. black and violet . . . 50 25
661 – 25c. red and brown . . . 1·75 60
662 – 25c. red and brown . . . 1·75 60
663 – 50c. blue and yellow . . . 2·75 1·00
DESIGNS—HORIZ: No. 644, Marti before Council of War; No. 645, Prison wall; No. 647, "El Abra" ranch; No. 652, First edition of "Patria"; No. 656, House of Maximo Gomez, Montecristi; No. 658, Marti as an orator; No. 663, "Fragua Martiana" (modern building). VERT: No. 646, Marti in prison; No. 648, Allegory of Marti's poems; No. 649, Marti and Bolivar Statue, Caracas; No. 650, Marti writing; No. 651, Revolutionaries' meeting-place; No. 653, Marti in Kingston, Jamaica; No. 654, Marti in Ibor City; No. 655, Manifesto of Montecristi; No. 657, Marti's portrait; No. 659, Marti's first tomb; No. 660, Obelisk at Des Rios; No. 661, Monument in Havana; No. 662, Marti's present tomb.

1953. Birth Centenary of Montoro (statesman).
664 **172** 3c. purple . . . . 1·00 45

173 Dr. F. Carrera Justiz **174** Lockheed Constellation

1953.
665 **173** 3c. red . . . . 1·00 45

1953. Air.
666 **174** 8c. brown 55 25
667 15c. red . . . . 1·10 60
668 – 2p. brown and green . . . 11·00 4·50
670 – 2p. myrtle and blue . . . 11·00 4·50
669 – 5p. brown and blue . . . 22·00 7·50
671 – 5p. myrtle and red . . . 19·00 9·50
DESIGN: Nos. 668/71, Constellation facing right.

1953. No. 512 surch.
672 3c. on 2c. red 55 30

176 Congress Building **177**

1953. 1st Int Accountancy Congress, Havana.
673 **176** 3c. blue (postage) 70 35
674 – 8c. red (air) . . . . . . 1·60 55
675 – 25c. green . . . . 2·50 85
DESIGNS: 8c. Congress building and "Cuba"; 25c. Aerial view of building and airplane.

1953. Obligatory Tax. Anti-T.B.
676 **177** 1c. red 20 10

178 M. Coyula Llaguno **179** Postal Employees' Retirement Association Flag

1954. Postal Employees' Retirement Fund. Inscr "1953".
677 **178** 1c. green (postage) . . . 30 10
678 – 3c. red 30 10
679 **179** 5c. blue 55 15
680 – 8c. red . . . . 1·10 45
681 – 10c. sepia . . . . 2·25 65

682 – 5c. blue (air) 55 25
683 – 8c. purple 65 25
684 – 10c. orange . . . . 1·00 25
685 **179** 1p. grey . . . . 3·50 2·00
PORTRAITS—VERT: Nos. 678, 680, F.L.C. Hensell; Nos. 681, 683, A. G. Rojas; No. 684, G. H. Saez. HORIZ: No. 682, M. C. Llaguno.

180 Jose Marti **181** Hauling Sugar

1954. Portraits. Roul. (No. 1180a/b) or perf. (others).
686 **180** 1c. green 15 10
990 1c. red 35 15
1680 1c. blue 10 10
687 – 2c. red (Gomez) 10 10
991 – 2c. olive (Gomez) . . . 45 15
1681 – 2c. green (Gomez) . . . 15 10
688 – 3c. violet (de la Luz Caballero) 10 10
1180a – 3c. orange (Caballero) . . 25 15
689 – 4c. mauve (Aldama) . . 10 10
690 – 5c. blue (Garcia) 15 10
691 – 8c. lake (Agramonte) . . 15 10
692 – 10c. sepia (Palma) . . . 20 10
693 – 13c. red (Finlay) . . . 30 10
1180b – 13c. brown (Finlay) . . 95 25
694 – 14c. grey (Sanchez) . . 55 15
695 – 20c. olive (Saco) . . . 1·40 35
1682 – 20c. violet (Saco) . . . 1·40 20
696 – 50c. ochre (Maceo) . . . 2·00 40
697 – 1p. orange (Cespedes) . . 3·00 40

1954. Air. Sugar Industry.
698 – 5c. green 35 10
699 – 8c. brown 85 35
700 **181** 10c. green 85 35
701 – 15c. brown . . . . . . 1·75 50
702 – 20c. blue 80 10
703 – 25c. red 65 30
704a – 30c. purple . . . . . . 1·90 75
705 – 40c. blue . . . . 3·25 65
706 – 45c. violet . . . . . . 3·00 65
707 – 50c. blue . . . . 3·00 65
708 – 1p. blue . . . . 7·25 1·25
DESIGNS—VERT: 5c. Sugar cane; 1p. A. Reinoso. HORIZ: 8c. Sugar harvesting; 15c. Train load of sugar cane; 20c. Modern sugar factory; 25c. Evaporators; 30c. Stacking sugar in sacks; 40c. Loading sugar on ship; 45c. Oxen hauling cane; 50c. Primitive sugar factory.

182 Jose M. Rodriguez **183** View of Sanatorium

1954. Birth Centenary of Rodriguez.
709 **182** 2c. sepia and lake 45 25
710 – 5c. sepia and blue 90 45
DESIGN: 5c. Rodriguez on horseback.

1954. General Batista Sanatorium.
711 **183** 3c. blue (postage) 90 40
712 9c. green (air) . . . . . . 1·75 65

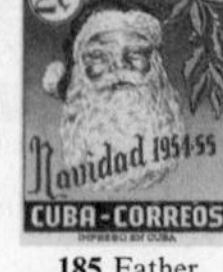

184 **185** Father Christmas **186** Maria Luisa Dolz

1954. Obligatory Tax. Anti-T.B.
713 **184** 1c. red 20 10
714 1c. green 20 10
715 1c. blue 20 10
716 1c. violet 20 10

1954. Christmas Greetings.
717 **185** 2c. green and red . . . . 3·00 1·40
718 4c. red and green . . . . 3·00 1·40

1954. Birth Centenary of Maria Dolz (educationist).
719 **186** 4c. blue (postage) 95 35
720 12c. mauve (air) . . . . . 1·75 75

187 Boy Scouts and Cuban Flag **189** Major-Gen. F. Carrillo

188 P. P. Harris and Rotary Emblem

1954. 3rd National Scout Camp.
721 **187** 4c. green 95 40

1955. 50th Anniv of Rotary International.
722 **188** 4c. blue (postage) 95 55
723 12c. red (air) . . . . . . 1·75 65

1955. Birth Centenary of Carrillo.
724 **189** 2c. blue and red 45 20
725 – 5c. sepia and blue 75 35
DESIGN: 5c. Half-length portrait.

190 1855 Stamp and "La Volanta"

1955. Centenary of First Cuban Postage Stamps and 50th Anniv of First Republican Stamps.
726 – 2c. blue & pur (postage) 35 10
727 **190** 4c. green and buff 55 35
728 – 10c. red and blue . . . . 3·50 65
729 – 14c. orange and green . . 3·25 1·40

730 – 8c. green & blue (air) . . 55 20
731 – 12c. red and green 65 20
732 – 24c. blue and red . . . . 2·25 55
733 – 30c. brown & orange . . 1·75 85
DESIGNS (a) With 1855 stamp: 2c. Old Square and Convent of St. Francis; 10c. Havana in 19th century; 14c. Captain-General's residence and Plaza de Armas; (b) With 1855 and 1905 stamps: 8c. Palace of Fine Arts; 12c. Plaza de la Fraternidad; 24c. Aerial view of Havana; 30c. Plaza de la Republica.

191 Maj.-Gen. Menocal **192** Mariel Bay

1955. Postal Employees' Retirement Fund.
734 **191** 2c. green (postage) . . . 45 10
735 – 4c. mauve 55 25
736 – 10c. blue 95 35
737 – 14c. grey . . . . 2·25 85

738 **192** 8c. green and red (air) . . 55 25
739 – 12c. blue and brown . . . 1·10 55
740 – 1p. ochre and green . . . 3·00 1·75
DESIGNS—As Type **191**: HORIZ: 4c. Gen. E. Nunez; 14c. Dr. A. de Bustamante. VERT: 10c. J. Gomez. As Type **192**: HORIZ: 12c. Varadero Beach; 1p. Vinales Valley.

193 Cuban Academy **194** Route of 1914 Flight

1955. Air. Centenary of Tampa, Florida.
741 **193** 12c. brown and red . . . . 1·60 65

1955. Air. 35th Death Anniv of Crocier (aviator).
742 **194** 12c. green and red 85 35
743 – 30c. mauve and green . . 1·60 65
DESIGN: 30c. Crocier in aircraft cockpit.

195 196 Wright Flyer 1

1955. Obligatory Tax. Anti-T.B.
744 **195** 1c. orange 30 15
745 1c. yellow 30 15
746 1c. blue 30 15
747 1c. mauve 30 15

1955. Air. Int Philatelic Exhibition, Havana.
748 **196** 8c. black, red and blue . . 1·25 55
749 – 12c. black, green and red 1·40 55
750 – 24c. black, violet & red 1·60 85
751 – 30c. black, blue & orange 3·50 1·90
752 – 50c. black olive & orange 5·50 2·25
DESIGNS: 12c. Lindbergh's airplane "Spirit of St. Louis"; 24c. Airship "Graf Zeppelin"; 30c. Lockheed Super Constellation airplane; 50c. Convair Delta Dagger airplane.

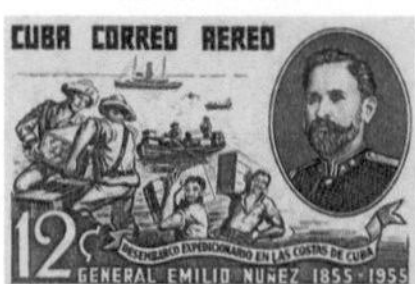

197 Wild Turkey 198 Expedition Disembarking

1955. Christmas Greetings.
754 **197** 2c. green and red . . . . 3·00 1·40
755 4c. lake and green . . . . 3·00 1·40

1955. Birth Centenary of General Nunez.
756 – 4c. lake (postage) 90 35
757 – 8c. blue and red (air) . . 1·75 45
758 **198** 12c. green and brown . . 1·75 65
DESIGNS—VERT: (22½ × 32½ mm.): 4c. Portrait of Nunez. HORIZ: As Type **198**: 8c. "Three Friends" (tug).

199 Bishop P. A. Morell de Santa Cruz 200 J. del Casal

1956. Bicentenary of Cuban Postal Service.
759 – 4c. blue & brn (postage) 90 40
760 **199** 12c. green & brown (air) 1·60 40
PORTRAIT: 4c. F. C. de la Vega.

1956. Postal Employees' Retirement Fund.
761 **200** 2c. black & grn (postage) 20 15
762 – 4c. black and mauve . . . 55 20
763 – 10c. black and blue . . . 90 35
764 – 14c. black and violet . . . 1·90 75
765 – 8c. black & brown (air) 55 30
766 – 12c. black and ochre . . . 85 35
767 – 30c. black and blue . . . 1·60 55
PORTRAITS: 4c. Luisa Perez de Zambrana. 8c. Gen. J. Sanguily. 10c. J. Clemente Zenea. 12c. Gen. J. M. Aguirre. 14c. J. J. Palma. 30c. Col. E. Fonts Sterling.

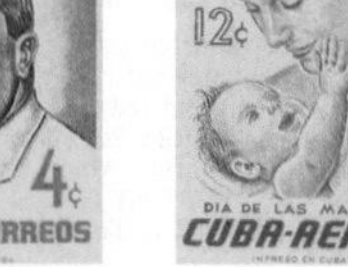

201 Victor Munoz 202 Mother and Baby

1956. Munoz Commemoration.
768 **201** 4c. brown and green . . . 90 40

1956. Air. Mothers' Day.
769 **202** 12c. blue and red . . . . 1·75 40

203 Aerial View of Temple 204 Gundlach's Hawk

1956. Masonic Grand Lodge of Cuba Temple, Havana.
770 – 4c. blue (postage) 95 40
771 **203** 12c. green (air) . . . . . 1·75 45
DESIGN: 4c. Ground level view of Temple.

1956. Air. Birds.
772 – 8c. blue . . . . 1·40 25
773 – 12c. grey . . . . 9·00 25
783 – 12c. green . . . . 3·25 70
774 **204** 14c. olive . . . . 2·10 30
775 – 19c. brown . . . . 2·10 60
776 – 24c. mauve . . . . 2·10 70
777 – 29c. green . . . . 3·00 70
778 – 30c. brown . . . . 3·25 1·00
779 – 50c. slate . . . . 6·00 1·25
780 – 1p. red . . . . 13·00 2·75
784 – 1p. blue . . . . 6·50 5·25
781 – 2p. purple . . . . 22·00 5·00
785 – 2p. red . . . . 19·00 13·00
782 – 5p. red . . . . 55·00 9·50
786 – 5p. purple . . . . 42·00 32·00
DESIGNS—HORIZ: 8c. Wood duck; 12c. (2) Plain pigeon; 29c. Goosander; 30c. Northern bobwhite; 2p. (2) Northern jacana. VERT: 19c. Herring gull; 24c. American white pelican; 50c. Great blue heron; 1p. (2) Common caracara; 5p. (2) Ivory-billed woodpecker.

205 H. de Blanck 207 Church of Our Lady of Charity

1956. Air. Birth Centenary of H. De Blanck (composer).
787 **205** 12c. blue . . . . 1·60 45

1956. Air. Inaug of Philatelic Club of Cuba Building. No. 776 but colour changed and surch **Inauguracion Edificio Club Filatelico de la Republica de Cuba Julio 13 de 1956** and value.
788 – 8c. on 24c. orange . . . . . 1·75 80

1956. Inscr "NTRA. SRA. DE LA CARIDAD", etc.
789 – 4c. blue & yell (postage) 95 40
790 **207** 12c. green & red (air) . . 1·90 55
DESIGN: 4c. Our Lady of Charity over landscape.

208 209

1956. Air. 250th Birth Anniv of Benjamin Franklin.
792 **208** 12c. brown . . . . 1·75 40

1956. "Grito de Yara" (War of Independence). Commem.
793 **209** 4c. sepia and green . . . 95 35

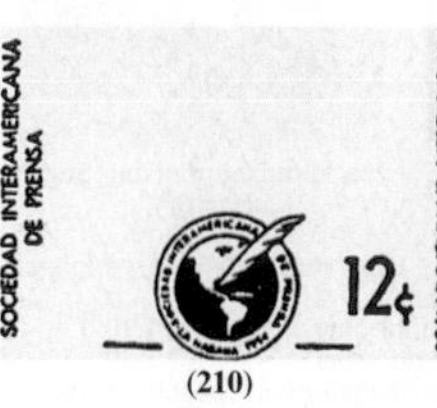

(210) 211

1956. Air. 12th Inter-American Press Assn. Meeting. As No. 781 but colour changed and surch with T **210**.
794 – 12c. on 2p. grey . . . . . . 1·75 80

1956. Obligatory Tax. Anti-T.B.
795 **211** 1c. red 20 10
796 1c. green 20 10
797 1c. blue 20 10
798 1c. brown 20 10

212 213 Prof. R. G. Menocal

1956. Christmas Greetings.
799 **212** 2c. red and green . . . . 3·00 1·40
800 4c. green and red . . . . 3·00 1·40

1956. Birth Centenary of Prof. R. G. Menocal.
801 **213** 4c. brown 90 35

214a Martin M. Delgado 215 Scouts around Camp Fire

1957. Birth Centenary of Delgado (patriot).
802 **214a** 4c. green 90 40

1957. Birth Centenary of Lord Baden-Powell.
803 **215** 4c. green & red (postage) 1·10 45
804 – 12c. slate (air) . . . . . 1·75 85
DESIGN—VERT: 12c. Lord Baden-Powell.

216 "The Art Critics" (Melero)

217 Hanabanilla Falls

1957. Postal Employees' Retirement Fund.
805 – 2c. green & brn (postage) 35 15
806 **216** 4c. red and brown 65 25
807 – 10c. olive and brown . . 95 35
808 – 14c. blue and brown . . . 1·10 40
809 **217** 8c. blue and red (air) . . 40 15
810 – 12c. green and red . . . . 1·60 30
811 – 30c. olive and violet . . . 1·75 50
DESIGNS—HORIZ: As Type **216** (Paintings): 2c. "The Blind" (Vega); 10c. "Carriage in the Storm" (Menocal); 14c. "The Convalescent" (Romanach); As Type **217**: 12c. Sierra de Cubitas; 30c. Puerto Boniato.

218 Posthorn Emblem of Cuban Philatelic Society 219 Juan F. Steegers

1957. Stamp Day. Cuban Philatelic Exn.
812 **218** 4c. bl, brn & red (postage) 90 35
813 – 12c. brn, yell & grn (air) 1·40 50
DESIGN: 12c. Philatelic Society Building, Havana.

1957. Birth Centenary of Steegers (fingerprint pioneer).
814 **219** 4c. blue (postage) 90 35
815 – 12c. brown (air) . . . . . 1·40 45
DESIGN: 12c. Thumbprint.

220 Baseball Player 221 Nurse Victoria Bru Sanchez

1957. Air. Youth Recreation. Centres in brown.
816 **220** 8c. green on green 85 30
817 – 12c. lilac on lavender . . 1·10 55
818 – 24c. blue on blue . . . . 1·75 85
819 – 30c. flesh on orange . . . 2·25 1·40
DESIGNS—12c. Ballet dancer; 24c. Diver; 30c. Boxers.

1957. Nurse Victoria Bru Sanchez Commem.
820 **221** 4c. blue 90 35

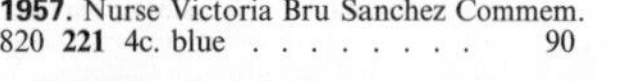

222 J. de Aguero leading Patriots 223 Youth with Dogs and Cat

1957. Joaquin de Aguero (patriot) Commem.
821 **222** 4c. green (postage) . . . 90 35
822 – 12c. blue (portrait) (air) 1·40 50

1957. 50th Anniv of Band of Charity (for prevention of cruelty to animals).
823 **223** 4c. green (postage) . . . 90 55
824 – 12c. brown (air) . . . . . 1·40 40
DESIGN: 12c. Jeanette Ryder (founder).

224 Col. R. Manduley del Rio (patriot) 225 J. M. Heredia y Girard

1957. Col. R. Manduley del Rio. Commem.
825 **224** 4c. green . . . . 2·25 1·40

1957. Air. J. M. Heredia y Girard (poet). Commem.
826 **225** 8c. violet 95 35

226 Palace of Justice, Havana

1957. Inauguration of Palace of Justice.
827 **226** 4c. grey (postage) 90 35
828 12c. green (air) . . . . . 1·40 40

227 Army Leaders of 1856 228 J. R. Gregg

1957. Centenary of Cuban Army of Liberation.
829 **227** 4c. brown and green . . . 65 35
830 4c. brown and blue . . . 65 35
831 4c. brown and pink . . . 65 35
832 4c. brown and yellow . . 65 35
833 4c. brown and lilac . . . 65 35

1957. Air. J. R. Gregg (shorthand pioneer) Commem.
834 **228** 12c. green . . . . 1·40 40

229 Cuba's First Publication, 1723 230 Jose Marti Public Library

1957. "Jose Marti" Public Library. Inscr "BIBLIOTECA NACIONAL".
835 **229** 4c. slate (postage) 90 35
836 – 8c. blue (air) 40 20
837 **230** 12c. sepia . . . . 1·25 40
DESIGN—VERT: As Type **230**: 8c. D. F. Caneda, first Director.

231 U.N. Emblem and Map of Cuba

1957. Air. U.N. Day.
838 **231** 8c. brown and green . . . 65 30
839 12c. green and red . . . . 1·25 35
840 30c. mauve and blue . . . 2·50 80

232 Fokker Trimotor "General New" and Map

1957. Air. 30th Anniv of Inaug of Air Mail Services between Havana and Key West, Florida.
841 **232** 12c. blue and purple . . . 1·75 45

233

235 Courtyard

1957. Obligatory Tax. Anti-tuberculosis.
842 **233** 1c. red 30 10
843 1c. green 30 10
844 1c. blue 30 10
845 1c. grey 30 10

1957. Centenary of 1st Cuban Teachers' Training College.
846 **235** 4c. brn & grn (postage) 90 35
847 – 12c. buff and blue (air) 95 35
848 – 30c. sepia and red . . . . 1·60 45
DESIGNS—VERT: 12c. School facade. HORIZ: 30c. General view of school.

236 Street Scene, Trinidad

237 Christmas Crib

1957. Postal Employees' Retirement Fund.
849 **236** 2c. brown & bl (postage) 20 10
850 – 4c. green and brown . . . 45 15
851 – 10c. sepia and red 70 30
852 – 14c. green and red . . . . 1·10 25
853 – 8c. black and red (air) . . 45 20
854 – 12c. black and brown . . 95 35
855 – 30c. brown and grey . . . 1·75 45
DESIGNS—VERT: 4c. Sentry-box on old wall of Havana; 10c. Calle Padre Pico (street), Santiago de Cuba; 12c. Sancti Spiritus Church; 14c. Church and street scene, Camaguey. HORIZ: 8c. "El Viso" Fort, El Caney; 30c. Concordia Bridge, Matanzas.

1957. Christmas. Multicoloured centres.
856 **237** 2c. sepia . . . . 2·25 1·10
857 4c. black . . . . 2·25 1·10

239 Dayton Hedges and Textile Factories

240 Dr. F. D. Roldan

1958. Dayton Hedges (founder of Cuban Textile Industry) Commemoration.
858 **239** 4c. blue (postage) . . . . 1·40 65
859 8c. green (air) . . . . . . 1·40 65

1958. Dr. Francisco D. Roldan (physiotherapy pioneer) Commemoration.
861 **240** 4c. green 95 35

241 "Diario de la Marina" Building

1958. 125th Anniv of "Diario de la Marina" Newspaper.
862 – 4c. olive (postage) 95 35
863 **241** 29c. black (air) . . . . . 1·75 85
PORTRAIT—VERT: 4c. J. I. Rivero y Alonso (journalist).

242 Map of Cuba showing Postal Routes of 1756

243 Gen. J. M. Gomez

1958. Stamp Day and National Philatelic Exhibition, Havana. Inscr as in T **242**.
864 **242** 4c. myrtle, buff and blue (postage) 95 40
865 – 29c. indigo, buff and blue (air) . . . . 1·90 85
DESIGN: 29c. Ocean map showing sea-post routes of 1765.

1958. Birth Centenary of Gen. J. M. Gomez.
866 **243** 4c. blue (postage) 90 35
867 – 12c. myrtle (air) . . . . . 1·25 50
DESIGN: 12c. Gomez at Arroyo Blanco.

244 Dr. T. Romay Chacon

245 Dr. C. de la Torre

246 Painted Polymita

1958. Famous Cubans. Portraits as T **244**.
(a) Doctors. With emblem of medicine.
868 2c. brown and green 45 15
869 4c. black and green 45 15
870 10c. red and green 45 15
871 14c. blue and green 65 15
(b) Lawyers. With emblem of law.
872 2c. sepia and red 50 15
873 4c. black and red 50 15
874 10c. green and red 50 15
875 14c. blue and red 55 20
(c) Composers. With lyre emblem of music.
876 2c. brown and blue 40 15
877 4c. purple and blue 40 15
878 10c. green and blue 55 15
879 14c. red and blue 60 15
PORTRAITS—Doctors: 2c. Type **244**. 4c. A. A. Aballi. 10c. F. G. del Valle. 14c. V. A. de Castro. Lawyers: 2c. J. M. G. Montes. 4c. J. A. G. Lanuza. 10c. J. B. H. Barreiro. 14c. P. G. Llorente. Composers: 2c. N. R. Espadero. 4c. I. Cervantes. 10c. J. White. 14c. B. de Salas.

1958. Birth Cent of De la Torre (archaeologist).
880 **245** 4c. blue (postage) 95 35
881 **246** 8c. red, yellow & blk (air) 2·25 85
882 – 12c. sepia on green . . . 3·25 1·40
883 – 30c. green on pink . . . 5·00 2·00
DESIGNS—As Type **246**: 12c. "Megalocnus rodens"; 30c. "Perisphinctes spinatus" (ammonite).

247 Felipe Poey (naturalist)

248 "Papilio caiguanabus" (butterfly)

1958. Poey Commemoration. Designs as T **247/8** inscr "1799–FELIPE POEY–1891".
884 – 2c. blk & lav (postage) . . 40 15
885 **247** 4c. sepia 95 35
886 **248** 8c. multicoloured (air) . . 1·75 35
887 – 12c. orange, black & grn 2·00 45
888 – 14c. multicoloured . . . . 2·50 45
889 – 19c. multicoloured . . . . 3·25 55
890 – 24c. multicoloured . . . . 3·25 1·00
891 – 29c. blue, brown & black 5·50 2·25
892 – 30c. brown, green & blk 8·50 3·25
DESIGNS—VERT: 2c. Cover of Poey's book; 12c. "Teria gundlachia"; 14c. "Teria ebriola"; 19c. "Nathalis felicia" (all butterflies). HORIZ: 24c. Tobacco fish; 29c. Butter hamlet; 30c. Tattler sea bass (all fishes).

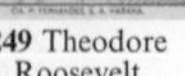
249 Theodore Roosevelt

250 National Tuberculosis Hospital

1958. Birth Centenary of Roosevelt.
893 **249** 4c. green (postage) . . . 95 35
894 – 12c. sepia (air) . . . . . 1·40 50
DESIGN—HORIZ: 12c. Roosevelt leading Rough Riders at San Juan 1898.

1958. Obligatory Tax. Anti-T.B.
895 **250** 1c. brown 20 10
896 1c. green 20 10
897 1c. red 20 10
898 1c. grey 20 10

251 U.N.E.S.C.O. Headquarters, Paris

252 "Cattleyopsis lindenii" (orchid)

1958. Air. Inaug of U.N.E.S.C.O. Headquarters.
899 **251** 12c. green . . . . 1·25 45
900 – 30c. blue . . . . 1·60 65
DESIGN: 30c. Facade composed of letters "UNESCO" and map of Cuba.

1958. Christmas. Orchids. Multicoloured.
901 2c. Type **252** . . . . 2·50 1·10
902 4c. "Oncidium guibertianum" 2·50 1·10

253 "The Revolutionary"

254 Gen. A. F. Crombet

1959. Liberation Day.
903 **253** 2c. black and red 65 25

1959. Gen. Crombet Commemoration.
904 **254** 4c. myrtle 90 35

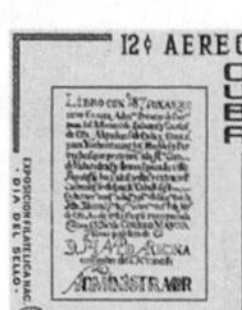

255 Postal Notice of 1765

256 Hand Supporting Sugar Factory

1959. Air. Stamp Day and National Philatelic Exhibition, Havana.
905 **255** 12c. sepia and blue . . . 1·10 35
906 – 30c. blue and sepia . . . 1·40 65
DESIGN: 30c. Administrative postal book of St. Cristobal, Havana, 1765.

1959. Agricultural Reform.
907 **256** 2c.+1c. blue and red (postage) 65 20
908 – 12c.+3c. green and red (air) . . . . 1·40 45
DESIGN (42×30 mm.): 12c. Farm workers and factory plant.

257 Red Cross Nurse

1959. "For Charity".
909 **257** 2c.+1c. red 35 25

1959. Air. American Society of Travel Agents Convention, Havana. No. 780 (colour changed) surch **CONVENCION ASTA OCTUBRE 17 1959 12c.** and bar.
910 12c. on 1p. green . . . . . . 1·90 1·00

259 Teresa Garcia Montes (founder)

260 Pres. C. M. de Cespedes

1959. Musical Arts Society Festival, Havana.
911 **259** 4c. brown (postage) . . . 90 35
912 – 12c. green (air) . . . . . 1·40 55
DESIGN—HORIZ: 12c. Society Headquarters, Havana.

1959. Cuban Presidents.
913 2c. slate (Type **260**) 35 15
914 2c. green (Betancourt) . . . 35 15
915 2c. violet (Calvar) 35 15
916 2c. brown (Maso) 35 15
917 4c. red (Spotorno) 65 20
918 4c. brown (Palma) 65 20
919 4c. black (F. J. de Cespedes) 65 20
920 4c. violet (Garcia) 65 20

261 Rebel Attack at Moncada Barracks

264 Pres. T. Estrada Palma Monument

1960. 1st Anniv of Cuban Revolution.
921 **261** 1c. grn, red & bl (postage) 15 10
922 – 2c. green, sepia and blue 1·25 15
923 – 10c. green, red and blue 1·40 55
924 – 12c. green, purple & blue 1·90 65
925 – 8c. green, red & bl (air) 2·50 50
926 – 12c. green, purple & brn 1·40 35
927 – 29c. red, black & green 1·75 70
DESIGNS: 2c. Rebels disembarking from "Granma"; 8c. Battle of Santa Clara; 10c. Battle of the Uvero; 12c. postage, "The Invasion" (Rebel and map of Cuba); 12c. air, Rebel Army entering Havana; 29c. Passing on propaganda ("Clandestine activities in the towns").

1960. Surch **HABILITADO PARA** and value (No. 932 without **PARA**).
928 **256** 2c. on 2c.+1c. blue and red (postage) 90 20
929 – 2c. on 4c. mve (No. 689) 65 35
930 – 2c. on 5c. blue (690) . . . 65 35
931 – 2c. on 13c. red (693) . . . 65 35
932 – 10c. on 20c. olive (342) 1·10 45
933 – 12c. on 12c.+3c. green and red (908) (air) . . . 1·40 55

1960. Surch in figures.
934 – 1c. on 4c. (No. 869) (postage) 40 15
935 – 1c. on 4c. (No. 873) . . . 40 15
936 – 1c. on 4c. (No. 877) . . . 40 15
937 **245** 1c. on 4c. blue 40 15
938 1c. on 4c. (No. 902) . . . 45 25
939 **254** 1c. on 4c. myrtle 40 15
940 **260** 1c. on 4c. brown 40 15
941 – 2c. on 14c. (No. 694) . . . 80 15
942 **54** 12c. on 40c. orge (air) . . 1·40 50
943 – 12c. on 45c. (No. 706) . . 1·40 50

1960. Postal Employees' Retirement Fund.
944 **264** 1c. brn & blue (postage) 15 10
945 – 2c. green and red 35 10
946 – 10c. brown and red . . . 65 25
947 – 12c. green and violet . . 1·10 45
948 – 8c. grey and red (air) . . 55 15
949 – 12c. blue and red . . . . 1·40 35
950 – 30c. violet and red . . . 1·75 50
MONUMENTS—VERT: 2c. "Mambi Victorioso"; 8c. Marti; 10c. Marta Abreu; 12c. (No. 947) Agramonte; 12c. (No. 949) Heroes of Cacarajicara. HORIZ: 30c. Dr. C. de la Torriente.

(265)

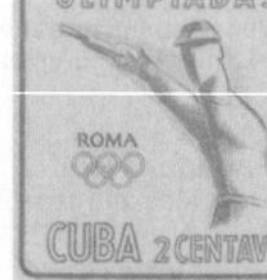

266 Pistol-shooting

1960. Air. Stamp Day and National Philatelic Exn, Havana. Nos. 772/3 in new colours optd with T **265**.
951 8c. yellow 55 35
952 12c. red . . . . 1·50 50

1960. Olympic Games.
954 – 1c. vio (Sailing) (postage) 45 20
955 **266** 2c. orange . . . . 1·00 35
956 – 8c. blue (Boxing) (air) . . 85 30
957 – 12c. red (Running) . . . 1·40 55

267 C. Cienfuegos and View of Escolar

1960. 1st Death Anniv of Cienfuegos (revolutionary leader). Centre multicoloured.
959 **267** 2c. sepia . . . . 1·00 15

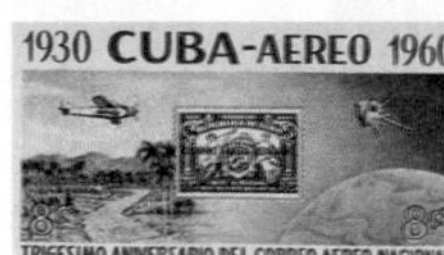

268 Air Stamp of 1930, Ford "Tin Goose" Airplane and "Sputnik"

1960. Air. 80th Anniv of National Airmail Service. Centre multicoloured.
960 **268** 8c. violet . . . . 3·25 1·40

270 Ipomoea

271 Tobacco Plant and Bars of "Christmas Hymn"

1960. Christmas. Inscr "NAVIDAD 1960–61". (a) T **270**.
961 1c. multicoloured 55 55
962 2c. multicoloured 75 75
963 10c. multicoloured . . . . . 1·50 1·50

(b) As T **271**.
964a/d 1c. multicoloured . . . . 1·75 1·40
965a/d 2c. multicoloured . . . . 2·75 2·50
966a/d 10c. multicoloured . . . . 5·00 4·75
DESIGNS: As T **271** (same for each value) a, T **271**. b, Mariposa. c, Lignum-vitae. d, Coffee plant.
Prices are for single stamps.

272

1960. Sub-industrialized Countries Conference.
967 **272** 1c. black, yellow and red (postage) 15 10
968 – 2c. multicoloured 15 10
969 – 6c. red, black and cream 1·10 40
970 – 8c. multicoloured (air) . . 40 15
971 – 12c. multicoloured . . . . 1·10 15
972 – 30c. red and grey . . . . 1·40 50
973 – 50c. multicoloured . . . . 1·75 60
DESIGNS—HORIZ: 2c. Graph and symbols; 6c. Cogwheels; 12c. Workers holding lever; 30c. Maps. VERT: 8c. Hand holding machete; 50c. Upraised hand.

273 J. Menendez **274** Jose Marti and "Declaration of Havana"

1961. Jesus Menendez Commemoration.
974 **273** 2c. sepia and green . . . 85 25

1961. Air. Declaration of Havana.
975 **274** 8c. red, black and yellow 75 65
976 12c. violet, black & buff 1·25 1·00
977 30c. brown, black & blue 3·00 2·75
The above were issued with part of background text of the declaration in English, French and Spanish. Prices the same for each language.

275 U.N. Emblem within Dove of Peace

1961. 15th Anniv of U.N.O.
979 **275** 2c. brn & grn (postage) 25 10
980 10c. green and purple . . 1·00 45
982 8c. red and yellow (air) 45 20
983 12c. blue and orange . . 1·10 40

276 10c. Revolutionary Label of 1874 and "CUBA MAMBISA" "Postmark"

1961. Stamp Day. Inscr "24 DE ABRIL DIA DEL SELLO".
985 **276** 1c. red, green and black 15 10
986 – 2c. orange, slate & black 30 15
987 – 10c. turq, red & black . . 1·25 45
DESIGNS: 2c., 50c. stamp of 1907 and "CUBA REPUBLICANA" "postmark"; 10c., 2c. stamp of 1959 and "CUBA REVOLUCIONARIA" "postmark".

1961. May Day. Optd **PRIMERO DE MAYO 1961 ESTAMOS VENCIENDO**.
988 **273** 2c. sepia and green . . . 1·00 20

278

1961. "For Peace and Socialism".
989 **278** 2c. multicoloured . . . . 1·00 20
No. 989 is lightly printed on back with pattern of wavy lines and multiple inscr "CORREOS CUBA" in buff.

1961. Air. Surch **HABILITADO PARA 8 cts.**
992 **174** 8c. on 15c. red 50 30
993 **54** 8c. on 20c. brown 50 30

1961. 1st Official Philatelic Exhibition. No. 987 optd **primera exposicion filatelica oficial oct. 7-17, 1961.**
994 10c. turq, red and black . . . 1·00 35

281 Book and Lamp

1961. Education Year.
995 **281** 1c. red, black and green 10 10
996 2c. red, black and blue . . 15 10
997 10c. red, black and violet 60 20
998 12c. red, black & orange 1·10 45
The 2, 10 and 12c. show the letters "U", "B" and "A" on the book forming the word "CUBA".

282 "Polymita sulfurosa flammulata"

283 "Polymita picta fulminata"

1961. Christmas. Inscr "NAVIDAD 1961–62". Multicoloured. (a) Various designs as T **282**.
999 1c. Type **282** 30 15
1000 2c. Cuban grassquit (vert) 2·50 50
1001 10c. "Othreis toddi" (horiz) 1·75 70

(b) Various designs as T **283**.
1002a/d 1c. Snails (horiz) 30 15
1003a/d 2c. Birds (vert) . . . . . 2·50 50
1004a/d 10c. Butterflies (horiz) . . 1·75 70
DESIGNS: No. 1002a, Type **283**; 1002b, "Polymita p. nigrofasciata"; 1002c, "Polymita p. fuscolimbata"; 1002d, "Polymita p. roseolimbata"; 1003a, Cuban macaw; 1003b, Cuban trogon; 1003c, Bee hummingbird; 1003d, Ivory-billed woodpecker; 1004a, "Uranidia boisduvalii"; 1004b, "Phoebis avellaneda"; 1004c, "Phaloe cubana"; 1004d, "Papoilio gundlacchianus".
Prices are for single stamps.

284 Castro Emblem **285** Hand with Machete

1962. 3rd Anniv of Cuban Revolution. Emblem in yellow, red, grey and blue. Colours of background and inscriptions given.
1005 **284** 1c. grn & pink (postage) 45 25
1006 2c. black and orange . . 95 30
1007 8c. brown & blue (air) 45 20
1008 12c. ochre and green . . 1·10 35
1009 30c. violet and yellow . . 1·40 1·10

1962. Air. 1st Anniv of Socialist Republic's First Sugar Harvest.
1010 **285** 8c. sepia and red 50 15
1011 12c. black and lilac . . . 1·10 40

286 Armed Peasant and Tractor

1962. National Militia.
1012 **286** 1c. black and green . . . 20 10
1013 – 2c. black and blue . . . 35 20
1014 – 10c. black and orange 1·10 35
DESIGNS: 2c. Armed worker and welder; 10c. Armed woman and sewing-machinist.

287 Globe and Music Emblem

1962. Air. International Radio Service. Inscr and aerial yellow; musical notation black; lines on globe brown, background colours given.
1015 **287** 8c. grey 55 20
1016 12c. blue . . . . 1·10 35
1017 30c. green . . . . 1·60 85
1018 1p. lilac . . . . 3·25 2·25

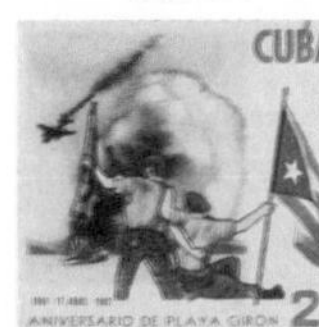

288 Soldiers, Aircraft and Burning Ship

1962. 1st Anniv of "Playa Giron" (Sea Invasion Attempt of Cuban Exiles).
1019 **288** 2c. multicoloured 40 10
1020 3c. multicoloured 40 10
1021 10c. multicoloured . . . 1·75 50

289 Arrival of First Mail from the Indies

1962. Stamp Day.
1022 **289** 10c. black and red on cream . . . . 3·00 60

290 Clenched Fist Salute

1962. Labour Day.
1023 **290** 2c. black on buff 20 10
1024 3c. black on red 35 20
1025 10c. black on blue . . . 1·10 45

291 Wrestling

1962. National Sports Institute (I.N.D.E.R.) Commemoration. As T **291**. On cream paper.
1026a/e 1c. brown and red . . . 20 10
1027a/e 2c. red and green 20 15
1028a/e 3c. blue and red . . . . 1·00 15
1029a/e 9c. purple and blue . . . 40 15
1030a/e 10c. orange and purple 45 20
1031a/e 13c. black and red . . . 50 30
DESIGNS: No. 1026a, Type **291**; 1026b, Weight-lifting; 1026c, Gymnastics; 1026d, Judo; 1026e, Throwing the discus; 1027a, Archery; 1027b, Roller skating; 1027c, Show jumping; 1027d, Ninepin bowling; 1027e, Cycling; 1028a, Rowing (coxed four); 1028b, Speed boat; 1028c, Swimming; 1028d, Kayak; 1028e, Yachting; 1029a, Football; 1029b, Tennis; 1029c, Baseball; 1029d, Basketball; 1029e, Volleyball; 1030a, Underwater fishing; 1030b, Shooting; 1030c, Model airplane flying; 1030d, Water polo; 1030e, Boxing; 1031a, Pelota; 1031b, Sports stadium; 1031c, Jai alai; 1031d, Chess; 1031e, Fencing.
Prices are for single stamps.

292 A. Santamaria and Soldiers

1962. 9th Anniv of "Rebel Day".
1032 **292** 2c. lake and blue 35 25
1033 – 3c. blue and lake 65 35
DESIGN: 3c. Santamaria and children.

293 Dove and Festival Emblem

1962. World Youth Festival, Helsinki.
1034 **293** 2c. multicoloured 45 20
1035 – 3c. multicoloured 65 30
DESIGN: 3c. As Type **293** but with "clasped hands" instead of dove.

294 Czech 5k. "Praga 1962" stamp of 1961

1962. Air. International Stamp Exn, Prague.
1037 **294** 31c. multicoloured . . . 2·50 1·00

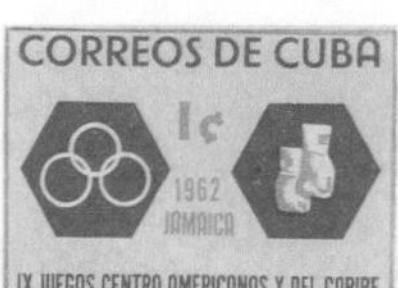

295 Rings and Boxing Gloves

1962. 9th Central American and Caribbean Games, Jamaica.
1039 **295** 1c. ochre and red . . . 10 10
1040 – 2c. ochre and blue . . . 15 10
1041 – 3c. ochre and purple . . 15 10
1042 – 13c. ochre and green . . 1·00 55
DESIGNS: Rings and: 2c. Tennis rackets; 3c. Baseball bats; 13c. Rapiers and mask.

296 "Cuban Women"

1962. 1st Cuban Women's Federation National Congress.
1043 **296** 9c. red, green and black 45 20
1044 – 13c. black, blue & green 1·25 50
DESIGN—VERT: 13c. Mother and child, and Globe.

297 Running

1962. 1st Latin-American University Games. Multicoloured.
1045 1c. Type **297** 20 10
1046 2c. Baseball 20 10
1047 3c. Netball 45 20
1048 13c. Globe 1·10 45

298 Microscope and Parasites

1962. Malaria Eradication. Mult.
1049 1c. Type **298** 30 20
1050 2c. Mosquito and pool 30 20
1051 3c. Cinchona plant and formulae 95 30

299 "Epicrates angulifer B" (snake)

300 Cuban Night Lizard

1962. Christmas. Inscr "NAVIDAD 1962–63". Multicoloured. (a) Various designs as T **299**.
1052 2c. Type **299** 35 15
1053 3c. "Cubispa turquino" (vert) 50 45
1054 10c. Jamacian long-tongued bat 2·00 1·00
(b) Various designs as T **300**.
1055a/d 2c. Reptiles 35 15
1056a/d 3c. Insects (vert) 50 45
1057a/d 10c. Mammals 2·00 1·00
DESIGNS: No. 1055a, Type **300**; 1055b, Knight anole; 1055c, Wright's ground boa; 1055d, Cuban ground iguana; 1056a, "Chrysis superba"; 1056b, "Essosthutha roberto"; 1056c, "Hortensia conciliata"; 1056d, "Lachnopus argus"; 1057a, Desmarest's hutia; 1057b, Prehensile-tailed hutia; 1057c, Cuban solenodon; 1057d, Desmarest's hutia (white race).
Prices are for single stamps.

301 Titov and "Vostok 2"

1963. Cosmic Flights (1st issue).
1058 – 1c. blue, red and yellow 20 10
1059 **301** 2c. green, purple & yell 35 20
1060 – 3c. violet, red & yellow 35 20
DESIGNS: 1c. Gagarin and "Vostok 1"; 3c. Nikolaev, Popovich and "Vostoks 3 and 4".
See also Nos. 1133/4.

302 Attackers

1963. 6th Anniv of Attack on Presidential Palace.
1061 **302** 9c. black and red 55 15
1062 – 13c. purple and blue 65 35
1063 – 30c. green and red 1·60 65
DESIGNS: 13c. Rodriguez, C. Servia, Machado and Westbrook; 30c. J. Echeverria and M. Mora.

303 Baseball

1963. 4th Pan-American Games, Sao Paulo.
1064 **303** 1c. green 45 20
1065 – 13c. red (Boxing) 1·40 40

304 "Mask" Letter Box

1963. Stamp Day.
1066 **304** 3c. black and brown 45 20
1067 – 10c. black and violet 1·10 45
DESIGN: 10c. 19th-century Post Office, Cathedral Place, Havana.

305 Revolutionaries and Statue

1963. Labour Day. Multicoloured.
1068 3c. Type **305** 30 10
1069 13c. Celebrating Labour Day 1·00 45

306 Child

1963. Children's Week.
1070 **306** 3c. brown and blue 30 15
1071 30c. red and blue 1·40 65

307 Ritual Effigy

308 "Breaking chains of old regime"

1963. 60th Anniv of Montane Anthropological Museum.
1072 **307** 2c. brown and salmon 45 15
1073 – 3c. purple and blue 45 15
1074 – 9c. grey and red 75 40
DESIGNS—HORIZ: 3c. Carved chair; VERT: 9c. Statuette.

1963. 10th Anniv of "Rebel Day".
1075 **308** 1c. black and pink 15 10
1076 – 2c. purple and lt blue 15 10
1077 – 3c. sepia and lilac 15 10
1078 – 7c. purple and green 15 10
1079 – 9c. purple and yellow 40 20
1080 – 10c. green and ochre 1·00 35
1081 – 13c. blue and buff 1·40 60
DESIGNS: 2c. Palace attack; 3c. "The Insurrection"; 7c. "Strike of April 9th" (defence of radio station); 9c. "Triumph of the Revolution" (upraised flag and weapons); 10c. "Agrarian Reform and Nationalization" (artisan and peasant); 13c. "Victory of Giron" (soldiers in battle).

309 Star Apple

310 "Roof and Window"

1963. Cuban Fruits. Multicoloured.
1082 1c. Type **309** 15 10
1083 2c. Chiromoya 15 10
1084 3c. Cashew nut 20 15
1085 10c. Custard apple 95 35
1086 13c. Mango 1·40 1·00

1963. 7th Int Architects Union Congress, Havana.
1087 3c. multicoloured 25 10
1088 3c. multicoloured 25 10
1089 3c. black, blue and bistre 25 10
1090 3c. multicoloured 25 10
1091 13c. multicoloured 90 45
1092 13c. multicoloured 90 45
1093 13c. red, olive and black 90 45
1094 13c. multicoloured 90 45
DESIGNS—VERT: No. 1087, Type **310**; Nos. 1090/2, Symbols of building construction as Type **310**. HORIZ: Nos. 1089/90 and 1093, Sketches of urban buildings; No. 1094, as Type **310** (girders and outline of house).

311 Hemingway and Scene from "The Old Man and the Sea"

1963. Ernest Hemingway Commemoration.
1095 **311** 3c. brown and blue 20 10
1096 – 9c. turquoise and mauve 45 20
1097 – 13c. black and green 1·25 55
DESIGNS—Hemingway and: 9c. Scene from "For Whom the Bell Tolls"; 13c. Residence at San Francisco de Paula, near Havana.

312 "Zapateo" (dance) after V. P. de Landaluze

1964. 50th Anniv of National Museum.
1098 **312** 2c. multicoloured 20 10
1099 – 3c. multicoloured 50 15
1100 – 9c. multicoloured 75 40
1101 – 13c. black and violet 1·25 75
DESIGNS—VERT: ($32\times42\frac{1}{2}$ mm.): 3c. "The Rape of the Mulattos" (after C. Enriquez); 9c. Greek amphora; 13c. "Dilecta Mea" (bust, after J. A. Houdon).

313 B. J. Borrell (revolutionary)

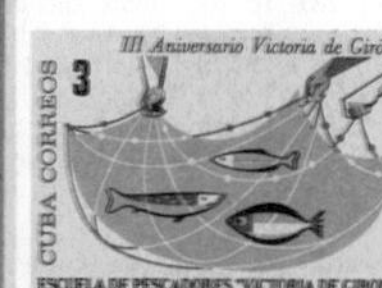

314 Fish in Net

1964. 5th Anniv of Revolution.
1102 **313** 2c. black, orange & grn 20 10
1103 – 3c. black, orange & red 30 15
1104 – 10c. black, orange & pur 55 25
1105 – 13c. black, orange & bl 1·10 50
PORTRAITS: 3c. M. Salado. 10c. O. Lucero. 13c. S. Gonzalez (revolutionaries).

1964. 3rd Anniv of Giron Victory.
1106 **314** 3c. multicoloured 20 10
1107 – 10c. black, grey & bistre 40 25
1108 – 13c. slate, black & orge 1·10 45
DESIGNS—HORIZ: 10c. Victory Monument. VERT: 13c. Fallen eagle.

315 V. M. Pera (1st Director of Military Posts, 1868–71)

1964. Stamp Day.
1109 **315** 3c. blue and brown 35 15
1110 – 13c. green and lilac 1·25 45
DESIGN: 13c. Cuba's first (10c.) military stamp.

316 Symbolic "1"

317 Chinese Monument, Havana

1964. Labour Day.
1111 **316** 3c. multicoloured 20 15
1112 – 13c. multicoloured 85 45
DESIGN: 13c. As Type **316** but different symbols within "1".

1964. Cuban–Chinese Friendship.
1113 **317** 1c. multicoloured 15 10
1114 – 2c. red, olive and black 25 10
1115 – 3c. multicoloured 40 15
DESIGNS—HORIZ: 2c. Cuban and Chinese. VERT: 3c. Flags of Cuba and China.

318 Globe

1964. U.P.U. Congress, Vienna.
1116 **318** 13c. brown, green & red 55 20
1117 – 30c. black, bistre & red 1·10 45
1118 – 50c. black, blue and red 2·25 75
DESIGNS: 30c. H. von Stephan (founder of U.P.U.); 50c. U.P.U. Monument, Berne.

319 Mutton Snapper

1964. Popular Savings Movement. Mult.
1119 1c. Type **319** 25 10
1120 2c. Cow 25 10
1121 13c. Poultry 1·25 45

320 "Rio Jibacoa"

1964. Cuban Merchant Fleet. Multicoloured.
1122 1c. Type **320** 25 10
1123 2c. "Camilo Cienfuegos" 35 10
1124 3c. "Sierra Maestra" 55 10
1125 9c. "Bahia de Siguanea" 1·40 40
1126 10c. "Oriente" 3·50 75

321 Vietnamese Fighter

322 Raul Gomez Garcia and Poem

1964. "Unification of Vietnam" Campaign. Mult.
1127 2c. Type **321** 15 10
1128 3c. Vietnamese shaking hands across map 20 15
1129 10c. Hand and mechanical ploughing 45 20
1130 13c. Vietnamese, Cuban and flags 1·10 45

1964. 11th Anniv of "Rebel Day".
1131 **322** 3c. black, red and ochre 20 10
1132 – 13c. multicoloured 90 40
DESIGN: 13c. Inscr "LA HISTORIA ME ABSOLVERA" (Castro's book).

1964. Cosmic Flights (2nd issue). As T **301**.
1133 9c. yellow, violet and red 75 40
1134 13c. yellow, red and green 1·40 55
DESIGNS: 9c. "Vostok-5" and Bykovksy; 13c. "Vostok-6" and Tereshkova.

323 Start of Race

1964. Olympic Games, Tokyo.
1135 – 1c. yellow, blue and purple 20 10
1136 – 2c. multicoloured 20 10
1137 – 3c. brown, black & red 20 10
1138 **323** 7c. violet, blue and orange 40 15
1139 – 10c. yellow, purple & bl 85 40
1140 – 13c. multicoloured . . . 1·50 65
DESIGNS—VERT: 1c. Gymnastics; 2c. Rowing; 3c. Boxing. HORIZ: 10c. Fencing; 13c. Games symbols.

325 Satellite and Globe

326 Rocket and part of Globe

1964. Cuban Postal Rocket Experiment. 25th Anniv Various rockets and satellites. (a) Horiz. designs as T **325**.
1141 **325** 1c. multicoloured 15 10
1142 – 2c. multicoloured 35 15
1143 – 3c. multicoloured 45 25
1144 – 9c. multicoloured . . . . 1·25 45
1145 – 13c. multicoloured . . . 1·75 1·00

(b) Horiz. designs as T **326**.
1146 – 1c. multicoloured 15 10
1147 – 2c. multicoloured 35 15
1148 – 3c. multicoloured 45 25
1149 – 9c. multicoloured . . . . . 1·25 45
1150 – 13c. multicoloured . . . . 1·75 1·00

(c) Larger 44 × 28 mm.
1151 – 50c. green and black . . . 2·50 1·60
DESIGN: 50c. Cuban Rocket Post 10c. Stamp of 1939.

Nos. 1141 and 1146, 1142 and 1147, 1143 and 1148, 1144 and 1149, 1145 and 1150 were printed together in five sheets of 25, each comprising four stamps as Type **325** plus five se-tenant stamp-size labels inscribed overall "1939 COHETE POSTAL CUBANO 25 ANIVERSARIO 1964" forming a centre cross and four blocks of four different stamps as Type **326** in each corner. The four-stamp design incorporates different subjects, which together form a composite design around a globe.

Prices are for single stamps.

1964. 1st Three-Manned Space Flight. As No. 1151 but colours changed. Optd **VOSJOD-1 octubre 12 1964 PRIMERA TRIPULACION DEL ESPACIO** and large rocket.
1153 50c. green and brown . . . 2·75 1·10

328 Lenin addressing Meeting

329 Leopard

1964. 40th Death Anniv of Lenin.
1154 **328** 3c. black and orange . . 20 10
1155 – 13c. red and violet . . . 45 25
1156 – 30c. black and blue . . . 1·00 55
DESIGNS—HORIZ: 13c. Lenin mausoleum. VERT: 30c. Lenin and hammer and sickle emblem.

1964. Havana Zoo Animals. Multicoloured.
1157 1c. Type **329** 10 10
1158 2c. Indian elephant (vert) . . 10 10
1159 3c. Red deer (vert) 15 10
1160 4c. Eastern grey kangaroo 20 10
1161 5c. Lions 25 10
1162 6c. Eland 25 10
1163 7c. Common zebra 25 15
1164 8c. Striped hyena 45 15
1165 9c. Tiger 45 15
1166 10c. Guanaco 50 15
1167 13c. Chimpanzees 50 15
1168 20c. Collared Peccary . . . 70 20
1169 30c. Common racoon (vert) 1·00 50
1170 40c. Hippopotamus . . . . 2·10 85
1171 50c. Brazilian tapir . . . . 2·75 1·10
1172 60c. Dromedary (vert) . . . 3·00 1·50
1173 70c. American Bison . . . . 3·00 1·50
1174 80c. Asiatic black bear (vert) 3·75 1·90
1175 90c. Water buffalo . . . . 3·75 2·40
1176 1p. Roe deer at Zoo Entrance . . . . 4·75 2·40

330 Jose Marti

1964. "Liberators of Independence". Multicoloured. Each showing portraits and campaigning scenes.
1177 1c. Type **330** 15 10
1178 2c. A. Maceo 20 15
1179 3c. M. Gomez 45 25
1180 13c. C. Garcia . . . . . . 1·00 55

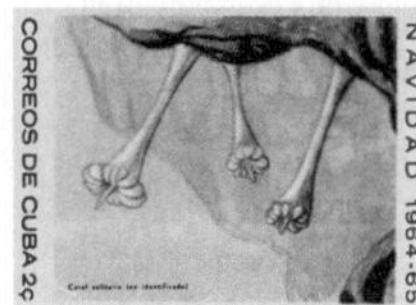

331 Dwarf Cup Coral

332 Small Flower Coral

1964. Christmas. Inscr "NAVIDAD 1964–65". Multicoloured. (a) As T **331**.
1181 2c. Type **331** 35 25
1182 3c. Sea anemone 65 35
1183 10c. Stone lily . . . . . . 1·00 65

(b) As T **332**.
1184a/d 2c. Coral 35 25
1185a/d 3c. Jellyfish 65 35
1186a/d 10c. Sea stars and urchins . . . . 1·00 65
DESIGNS: No. 1184a, Type **332**; 1184b, Elkhorn coral; 1184c, Dense moosehorn coral; 1184d, Yellow brain coral; 1185a, Portuguese man-of-war; 1185b, Moon jellyfish; 1185c, Thimble jellyfish; 1185d, Upside-down jellyfish; 1186a, Big-spined sea-urchin; 1186b, Edible sea urchin; 1186c, Caribbean brittle star; 1186d, Reticulated sea star.

Prices are for single stamps.

333 Dr. Tomas Romay

334 Map of Latin America and Part of Declaration

1964. Birth Bicentenary of Dr. Tomas Romay (scientist).
1187 **333** 1c. black and bistre . . . 20 10
1188 – 2c. sepia and brown . . 20 10
1189 – 3c. brown and bistre . . 30 15
1190 – 10c. black and bistre . . 1·00 40
DESIGNS—VERT: 2c. First vaccination against smallpox. HORIZ: 3c. Dr. Romay and extract from his treatise on the vaccine; 10c. Dr. Romay's statue.

1964. 2nd Declaration of Havana. Mult.
1191 3c. Type **334** 45 30
1192 13c. Map of Cuba and native receiving revolutionary message . . 1·75 90

The two stamps have the declaration superimposed in tiny print across each horiz. row of five stamps, thus requiring strips of five to show the complete declaration.

335 "Maritime Post" (diorama)

1965. Inauguration of Cuban Postal Museum. Mult.
1193 13c. Type **335** . . . . . . 2·75 65
1194 30c. "Insurgent Post" (diorama) . . . . 1·90 1·00

336 "Sondero" (schooner)

1965. Cuban Fishing Fleet. Multicoloured. Fishing crafts.
1196 1c. Type **336** 15 10
1197 2c. "Omicron" 25 10
1198 3c. "Victoria" 35 15
1199 9c. "Cardenas" 55 25
1200 10c. "Sigma" . . . . 2·10 50
1201 13c. "Lambda" . . . . . . 3·25 80

337 Lydia Doce

1965. International Women's Day. Multicoloured.
1202 3c. Type **337** 55 25
1203 13c. Clara Zetkin 85 45

338 Jose Antonio Echeverria University City

1965. "Technical Revolution". Inscr "REVOLUCION TECNICA".
1204 **338** 3c. black, brown and chestnut 25 15
1205 – 13c. multicoloured . . . 1·10 45
DESIGN: 13c. Scientific symbols.

339 Leonov

1965. "Voskhod 2", Space flight.
1206 **339** 30c. brown and blue . . 1·40 55
1207 – 50c. blue and magenta 2·75 1·10
DESIGN: 50c. Beliaiev, Leonov and "Voskhod 2".

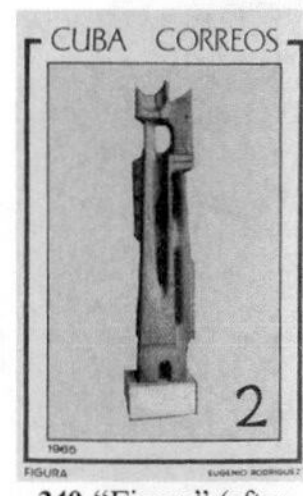

340 "Figure" (after E. Rodrigues)

341 Lincoln Statue, Washington

1965. National Museum Treasures. Mult.
1208 2c. Type **340** (27 × 42 mm) 30 10
1209 3c. "Landscape with sunflowers" (V. Manuel) (31 × 42 mm) 30 15
1210 10c. "Abstract" (W. Lam) (42 × 31 mm) 80 30
1211 13c. "Children" (E. Ponce) (39 × 33½ mm) . . . . . 1·40 55

1965. Death Centenary of Abraham Lincoln.
1212 – 1c. brown, grey and yellow 10 10
1213 – 2c. ultramarine & blue 25 10
1214 **341** 3c. black, red and blue 55 30
1215 – 13c. black, orange & bl 1·10 50
DESIGNS—HORIZ: 1c. Cabin at Hodgenville, Kentucky (Lincoln's birthplace); 2c. Lincoln Monument, Washington. VERT: 13c. Abraham Lincoln.

342 18th-century Mail Ship and Old Postmarks (bicent of Maritime Mail)

1965. Stamp Day.
1216 **342** 3c. bistre and red . . . 1·50 20
1217 – 13c. red, black and blue 1·40 45
DESIGN: 13c. Cuban; 10c. "Air Train" stamp of 1935 and glider train over Capitol, Havana.

343 Sun and Earth's Magnetic Pole

1965. International Quiet Sun Year. Multicoloured.
1218 1c. Type **343** 20 10
1219 2c. I.Q.S.Y. emblem (vert) 20 10
1220 3c. Earth's magnetic fields 35 10
1221 6c. Solar rays 40 15
1222 30c. Effect of solar rays on various atmospheric layers 1·40 40
1223 50c. Effect of solar rays on satellite orbits . . . . . . 1·90 95

Nos. 1221/3 are larger, 47 × 20 mm. or 20 × 47 mm. (30c.).

344 Telecommunications Station

1965. Centenary of I.T.U. Multicoloured.
1225 1c. Type **344** 15 10
1226 2c. Satellite (vert) 15 10
1227 3c. "Telstar" 20 10
1228 10c. "Telstar" and receiving station (vert) 65 20
1229 30c. I.T.U. emblem . . . . 1·75 65

345 Festival Emblem and Flags

1965. World Youth and Students Festival. Multicoloured.
1230 13c. Type **345** 75 35
1231 30c. Soldiers of three races and flags . . . . 1·60 45

346 M. Perez (pioneer balloonist), Balloon and Satellite

1965. Matias Perez Commemoration.
1232 **346** 3c. black and red . . . . 1·10 85
1233 – 13c. black and blue . . . 1·40 85
DESIGN: 13c. As Type **346**, but with rockets in place of satellite.

347 Rose (Europe)

1965. Flowers of the World. Multicoloured.
1234 1c. Type **347** 15 10
1235 2c. Chrysanthemum (Asia) 15 10
1236 3c. Strelitzia (Africa) 20 10
1237 4c. Dahlia (N. America) . . 20 10
1238 5c. Orchid (S. America) . . 55 15
1239 13c. "Grevillea banksii" (Oceania) . . . . 1·75 75
1240 30c. "Brunfelsia nitida" (Cuba) . . . . 2·25 1·40

348 Swimming

1965. First National Games.
1241 **348** 1c. multicoloured 15 10
1242 – 2c. multicoloured 20 10

1243	– 3c. black, red and grey	45	20
1244	– 30c. black, red and grey	1·50	55

SPORTS: 2c. Basketball. 3c. Gymnastics. 30c. Hurdling.

349 Anti-tank gun

1965. Museum of the Revolution. Mult.

1245	1c. Type **349**	10	10
1246	2c. Tank	10	10
1247	3c. Bazooka	20	10
1248	10c. Rebel Uniform	55	20
1249	13c. Launch "Granma" and compass	1·60	40

350 C. J. Finlay 351 "Anetia numidia" (butterfly)

1965. 50th Death Anniv of Carlos J. Finlay (malaria researcher).

1250	– 1c. black, green & blue	10	10
1251	– 2c. brown, ochre and black	15	10
1252	**350** 3c. brown and black	15	10
1253	– 7c. black and lilac	20	10
1254	– 9c. bronze and black	40	20
1255	– 10c. black and blue	85	25
1256	– 13c. multicoloured	1·25	55

DESIGNS—HORIZ: 1c. Finlay's signature. VERT: 2c. Yellow fever mosquito; 7c. Finlay's microscope; 9c. Dr. C. Delgado; 10c. Finlay's monument; 13c. Finlay demonstrating his theories, after painting by Valderrama.

1965. Cuban Butterflies. Multicoloured.

1257	2c. Type **351**	40	15
1258	2c. "Carathis gortynoides"	40	15
1259	2c. "Hymenitis cubana"	40	15
1260	2c. "Eubaphe heros"	40	15
1261	2c. "Dismorphia cubana"	40	15
1262	3c. "Siderone nemesis"	50	25
1263	3c. "Syntomidopsis variegata"	50	25
1264	3c. "Ctenuchidia virgo"	50	25
1265	3c. "Lycorea ceres"	50	25
1266	3c. "Eubaphe disparilis"	50	25
1267	13c. "Anetia cubana"	2·00	75
1268	13c. "Prepona antimache"	2·00	75
1269	13c. "Sylepta reginalis"	2·00	75
1270	13c. "Chlosyne perezi"	2·00	75
1271	13c. "Anaea clytemnestra"	2·00	75

352 20c. Coin of 1962

1965. 50th Anniv of Cuban Coinage. Mult.

1273	1c. Type **352**	10	10
1274	2c. 1p. coin of 1934	10	10
1275	3c. 40c. coin of 1962	15	15
1276	8c. 1p. coin of 1915	30	15
1277	10c. 1p. coin of 1953	75	35
1278	13c. 20p. coin of 1915	1·10	40

353 Oranges

1965. Tropical Fruits. Multicoloured.

1279	1c. Type **353**	10	10
1280	2c. Custard-apples	10	10
1281	3c. Papayas	15	15
1282	4c. Bananas	20	10
1283	10c. Avocado pears	30	15
1284	13c. Pineapples	55	50
1285	20c. Guavas	1·40	50
1286	50c. Mameys	2·75	85

354 Northern Oriole 355 Painted Bunting

1965. Christmas. Vert. designs showing bird life. (a) As T **354**. Multicoloured.

1287	3c. Type **354**	2·50	1·60
1288	5c. Scarlet tanager	3·00	2·10
1289	13c. Indigo bunting	6·75	3·75

(b) As T **355**.

1290a/d	3c. multicoloured	2·50	1·60
1291a/d	5c. multicoloured	3·00	2·10
1292a/d	13c. multicoloured	6·75	3·75

DESIGNS: No. 1290a, Type **355**; 1290b, American redstart; 1290c, Blackburnian warbler; 1290d, Rose-breasted grosbeak; 1291a, Yellow-throated warbler; 1291b, Blue-winged warbler; 1291c, Prothonotary warbler; 1291d, Hooded warbler; 1292a, Blue-winged teal; 1292b, Wood duck; 1292c, Common shoveler; 1292d, Black-crowned night heron.
Prices are for single stamps.

356 Hurdling

1965. 7th Anniv of International Athletics, Havana. Multicoloured.

1293	1c. Type **356**	15	10
1294	2c. Throwing the discus	15	10
1295	3c. Putting the shot	35	10
1296	7c. Throwing the javelin	35	20
1297	9c. High-jumping	45	25
1298	10c. Throwing the hammer	95	40
1299	13c. Running	1·25	60

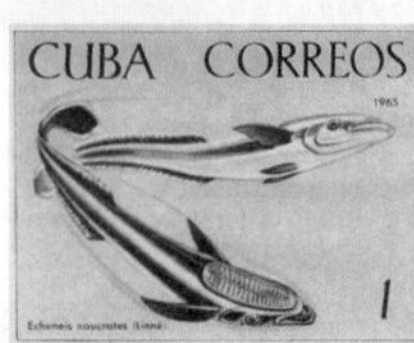

357 Sharksucker

1965. National Aquarium. Multicoloured.

1300	1c. Type **357**	20	10
1301	2c. Skipjack/Bonito tuna	20	10
1302	3c. Sergeant major	40	10
1303	4c. Sailfish	45	10
1304	5c. Nassau grouper	45	10
1305	10c. Mutton snapper	60	20
1306	13c. Yellow-tailed snapper	2·00	60
1307	30c. Squirrelfish	3·25	90

358 A. Voisin, Cuban and French Flags

1965. 1st Death Anniv of Prof. Andre Voisin (scientist).

1308	**358** 3c. multicoloured	40	20
1309	– 13c. multicoloured	1·10	40

DESIGN: 13c. Similar to Type **358** but with microscope and plant in place of cattle.

359 Skoda Omnibus

1965. Cuban Transport. Multicoloured.

1310	1c. Type **359**	10	10
1311	2c. Ikarus omnibus	10	10
1312	3c. Leyland omnibus	15	10
1313	4c. Russian-built Type TEM-4 diesel locomotive	2·25	45
1314	7c. French-built BB. 69,000 diesel locomotive	2·25	45
1315	10c. Tug "R.D.A."	1·00	25
1316	13c. Freighter "13 de Marzo"	1·60	45
1317	20c. Ilyushin IL-18 airliner	1·75	65

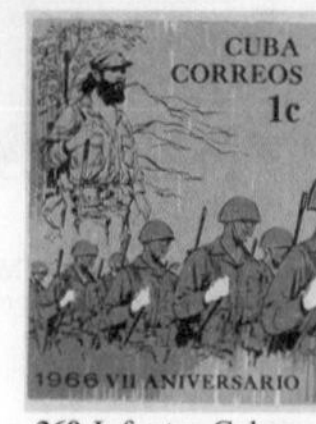

360 Infantry Column

1966. 7th Anniv of Revolution. Mult.

1318	1c. Type **360**	20	10
1319	2c. Soldier and tank	20	10
1320	3c. Sailor and torpedo-boat	45	10
1321	10c. MiG-21 jet fighter	1·00	30
1322	13c. Rocket missile	1·25	25

SIZES—As Type **360**: 2c., 3c. HORIZ: ($38\frac{1}{2}\times23\frac{1}{2}$ mm): 10c., 13c.

361 Conference Emblem

1966. Tricontinental Conference, Havana.

1323	**361** 2c. multicoloured	15	10
1324	– 3c. multicoloured	20	10
1325	– 13c. multicoloured	95	40

DESIGNS: 3c., 13c. As Type **361** but re-arranged.

362 Guardalabarca Beach

1966. Tourism. Multicoloured.

1326	1c. Type **362**	10	10
1327	2c. La Gran Piedra (mountain resort)	15	10
1328	3c. Guama, Las Villas (country scene)	35	15
1329	13c. Waterfall, Soroa (vert)	1·40	40

363 Congress Emblem and "Treating Patient" (old engraving)

1966. Medical and Stomachal Congresses, Havana. Multicoloured.

1330	3c. Type **363**	25	10
1331	13c. Congress emblem and children receiving treatment	1·10	40

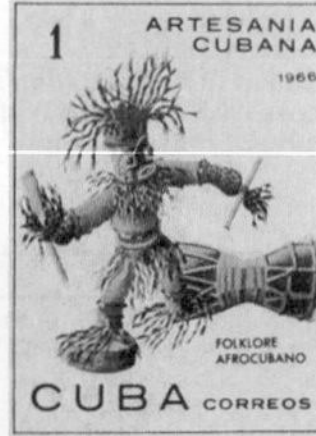

364 Afro-Cuban Doll

1966. Cuban Handicrafts. Multicoloured.

1332	1c. Type **364**	10	10
1333	2c. Sombreros	10	10
1334	3c. Vase	10	10
1335	7c. Gourd lampshades	15	10
1336	9c. Rare-wood lampstand	35	15
1337	10c. "Horn" shark (horiz)	55	25
1338	13c. Painted polymita shell necklace and earrings (horiz)	1·10	45

365 "Chelsea College" (after Canaletto)

1966. National Museum Exhibits. Inscr "1966". Multicoloured.

1339	1c. Ming Dynasty vase (vert)	10	10
1340	2c. Type **365**	40	10
1341	3c. "Portrait of a Young Girl" (after Goya) (vert)	35	20
1342	13c. Portrait of Fayum (vert)	1·40	45

366 Cosmonauts in Training 367 Tank in Battle

1966. 5th Anniv of 1st Manned Space Flight. Multicoloured.

1343	1c. Tsiolkovsky and diagram (horiz)	10	10
1344	2c. Type **366**	10	10
1345	3c. Gagarin, rocket and globe (horiz)	20	10
1346	7c. Nikolaev and Popovich	35	10
1347	9c. Tereshkova and Bykovsky (horiz)	45	20
1348	10c. Komarov, Feoktistov and Yegorov (horiz)	55	25
1349	13c. Leonov in space (horiz)	1·10	45

1966. 5th Anniv of Giron Victory.

1350	**367** 2c. black, green and bistre	10	10
1351	– 3c. black, blue and red	40	10
1352	– 9c. black, brown & grey	20	10
1353	– 10c. black, blue and green	70	15
1354	– 13c. black, brown and blue	1·40	50

DESIGNS: 3c. "Houston" (freighter) sinking; 9c. Disabled tank and poster-hoarding; 10c. Young soldier; 13c. Operations map.

368 Interior of Postal Museum (1st Anniv)

1966. Stamp Day.

1355	**368** 3c. green and red	45	10
1356	– 13c. brown, black & red	1·40	45

DESIGN: 13c. Stamp collector and Cuban 2c. stamp of 1959.

369 Bouquet and Anvil 370 W.H.O. Building

1966. Labour Day. Multicoloured.

1357	2c. Type **369**	15	10
1358	3c. Bouquet and Machete	15	10
1359	10c. Bouquet and Hammer	45	20
1360	13c. Bouquet and parts of globe and cogwheel	1·10	60

1966. Inaug of W.H.O. Headquarters, Geneva.

1361	**370** 2c. black, green & yell	15	10
1362	– 3c. black, blue and yellow	35	10
1363	– 13c. black, yellow and blue	1·10	45

DESIGNS (W.H.O. Building on): 3c. Flag; 13c. Emblem.

371 Athletics

372 Makarenko Pedagogical Institute

1966. 10th Central American and Caribbean Games.
1364 **371** 1c. sepia and green . . . 10 10
1365 – 2c. sepia and orange . . . 10 10
1366 – 3c. brown and yellow . . 10 10
1367 – 7c. blue and mauve . . . 15 10
1368 – 9c. black and blue . . . 30 15
1369 – 10c. black and brown . . 55 15
1370 – 13c. blue and red . . . . 1·25 40
DESIGNS—HORIZ: 2c. Rifle-shooting. VERT: 3c. Baseball; 7c. Volleyball; 9c. Football; 10c. Boxing; 13c. Basketball.

1966. Educational Development.
1371 **372** 1c. black and green . . . 10 10
1372 – 2c. black, ochre & yellow 10 10
1373 – 3c. black, ultram & bl 15 10
1374 – 10c. black, brown & grn 35 20
1375 – 13c. multicoloured . . . 95 40
DESIGNS: 2c. Alphabetization Museum; 3c. Lamp (5th anniv of National Alphabetization Campaign); 10c. Open-air class; 13c. "Farmers' and Workers' Education".

373 "Agrarian Reform"

1966. Air. "Conquests of the Revolution". Multicoloured.
1376 1c. Type **373** 15 10
1377 2c. "Industrialisation" . . . 15 10
1378 3c. "Urban Reform" . . . 20 10
1379 7c. "Eradication of Unemployment" 20 10
1380 9c. "Education" 40 15
1381 10c. "Public Health" . . . 85 15
1382 13c. Paragraph from Castro's book, "La Historia me Absolvera" 1·10 30

374 Workers with Flag

1966. 12th Revolutionary Workers' Union Congress, Havana.
1383 **374** 3c. multicoloured 55 20

375 Flamed Cuban Liguus

377 Arms of Pinar del Rio

376 Pigeon and Breeding Pen

1966. Cuban Shells. Multicoloured.
1384 1c. Type **375** 20 10
1385 2c. Measled cowrie 25 15
1386 3c. West Indian fighting conch 35 15
1387 7c. Rough American scallops 40 20
1388 9c. Crenate liguus 50 20
1389 10c. Atlantic trumpet triton 80 30
1390 13c. Archer's Cuban liguus 1·90 55

1966. Pigeon-breeding. Multicoloured.
1391 1c. Type **376** 20 10
1392 2c. Pigeon and time-clock 20 10
1393 3c. Pigeon and pigeon-loft 20 15
1394 7c. Pigeon and breeder tending pigeon-loft . . . 35 20
1395 9c. Pigeon and pigeon-yard 35 25
1396 10c. Pigeon and breeder placing message in capsule 1·10 35
1397 13c. Pigeons in flight over map of Cuba (44½ × 28 mm) . . . . . 1·75 60

1966. National and Provincial Arms. Mult.
1398 1c. Type **377** 10 10
1399 2c. Arms of Havana 10 10
1400 3c. Arms of Matanzas . . . 15 10
1401 4c. Arms of Las Villas . . . 20 10
1402 5c. Arms of Camaguey . . . 30 15
1403 9c. Arms of Oriente 45 30
1404 13c. National Arms (26 × 44 mm) . . . . . . 1·00 40

378 "Queen" and Simultaneous Games

1966. 17th Chess Olympiad, Havana.
1405 – 1c. black and green . . . 10 10
1406 – 2c. black and blue . . . 10 10
1407 – 3c. black and red 20 10
1408 – 9c. black and ochre . . . 35 20
1409 **378** 10c. black and mauve . . 85 30
1410 – 13c. black, blue & turq 1·10 65
DESIGNS—VERT: 1c. "Pawn"; 2c. "Rook"; 3c. "Knight"; 9c. "Bishop". HORIZ: 13c. Olympiad Emblem and "King".

380 Lenin Hospital

1966. Cuban–Soviet Friendship. Mult.
1412 2c. Type **380** 15 10
1413 3c. World map and "Havana" (tanker) . . . 40 10
1414 10c. Cuban and Soviet technicians 60 20
1415 13c. Cuban fruit-pickers and Soviet tractor technicians 1·10 55

381 A. Roldan and Music of "Fiesta Negra"

1966. Song Festival.
1416 **381** 1c. brown, black & grn 10 10
1417 – 2c. brown, black & mve 10 10
1418 – 3c. brown, black & blue 25 10
1419 – 7c. brown, black & vio 40 10
1420 – 9c. brown, black & yell 40 20
1421 – 10c. brn, blk & orge . . 1·25 30
1422 – 13c. brown, black & bl 1·75 60
CUBAN COMPOSERS AND WORKS: 2c. E. S. de Fuentes and "Tu" (habanera, Cuban dance). 3c. M. Simons and "El Manisero". 7c. J. Anckermann and "El arroyo que murmura". 9c. A. G. Caturla and "Pastoral Lullaby". 10c. E. Grenet and "Ay Mama Ines". 13c. E. Lecuona and "La Comparsa" (dance).

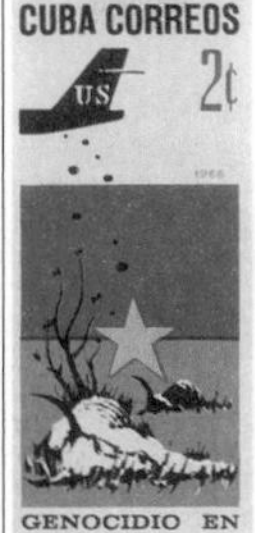

382 Bacteriological Warfare

383 A. L. Fernandez ("Nico") and Beach Landing

1966. "Genocide in Viet-Nam". Mult.
1423 2c. Type **382** 10 10
1424 3c. Gas warfare 20 10
1425 13c. "Conventional" bombing . . . . 1·10 45

1966. 10th Anniv of 1956 Revolutionary Successes. Portrait in black and brown.
1426 **383** 1c. brown and green . . 10 10
1427 – 2c. brown and purple . . 10 10
1428 – 3c. brown and purple . . 15 10
1429 – 7c. brown and blue . . . 20 15
1430 – 9c. brown and turquoise 35 15
1431 – 10c. brown and olive . . 1·25 35
1432 – 13c. brown and orange 1·10 55
HEROES AND SCENES: 2c. C. Gonzalez and beach landing. 3c. J. Tey and street fighting. 7c. T. Aloma and street fighting. 9c. O. Parellada and street fighting. 10c. J. M. Marquez and beach landing. 13c. F. Pais and trial scene.

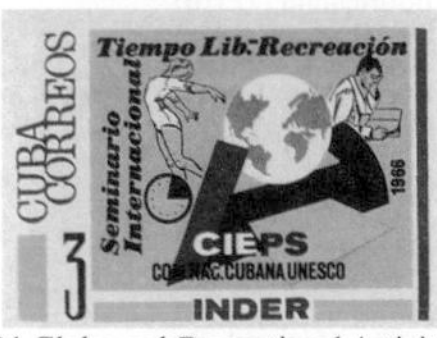

384 Globe and Recreational Activities

1966. International Leisure Time and Recreation Seminar. Multicoloured.
1433 3c. Type **384** 15 10
1434 9c. Clock, eye and world map 85 20
1435 13c. Seminar poster . . . . 1·10 45

385 Arrow and Telecommunications Symbols

1966. 1st National Telecommunications Forum. Multicoloured.
1436 3c. Type **385** 20 10
1437 10c. Target and satellites . . 85 20
1438 13c. Shell and satellites (28½ × 36 mm) . . . . . 1·25 45

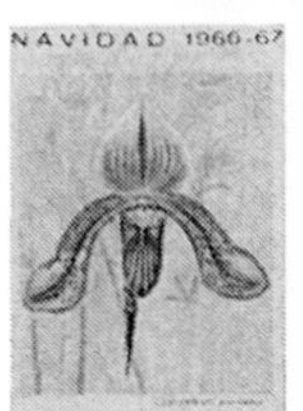

386 "Cypripedium eurilochus"

387 "Cattleya speciosissima"

1966. Christmas. Orchids. Multicoloured.

(a) As T **386**.
1440 1c. Type **386** 30 15
1441 3c. "Cypripedium hookerae volunteanum 45 25
1442 13c. "Cypripedium stonei" 1·75 95

(b) As T **387**.
1443a/d 1c. multicoloured 30 15
1444a/d 3c. multicoloured 45 25
1445a/d 13c. multicoloured . . . 1·75 95
DESIGNS: No. 1443a, Type **387**; 1443b, "Cattleya mendelli"; 1443c, "Cattleya trianae"; 1443d, "Cattleya labiata"; 1444a, "Cypripedium morganiae"; 1444b, "Cattleya" "Countess of Derby"; 1444c, "Cattleya gigas"; 1444d, "Cypripedium stonei"; 1445a, "Cattleya mendelli" "Countess of Montrose"; 1445b, "Oncidium macranthum"; 1445c, "Cattleya aurea"; 1445d, "Laelia anceps".
Prices are for single stamps.

388 Flag and Hands ("1959—Liberation")

1966. 8th Anniv of Revolution. Mult.
1446 3c. Type **388** 15 10
1447 3c. Clenched fist ("1960—Agrarian Reform") . . . 15 10
1448 3c. Hands holding pencil ("1961—Education") . . 15 10
1449 3c. Hand protecting plant ("1965—Agriculture") . . 15 10
1450 13c. Head of Rodin's statue, "The Thinker", and arrows ("1962—Planning") (vert) 90 35
1451 13c. Hands moving lever ("1963—Organization") (vert) 90 35
1452 13c. Hand holding plant within cogwheel ("1964—Economy") (vert) 90 35
1453 13c. Hand holding rifle-butt, and part of globe ("1966—Solidarity") (vert) 90 35

389 "Spring" (after J. Arche)

1967. National Museum Exhibits. Paintings (1st series). Multicoloured.
1454 1c. "Coffee-pot" (A. A. Leon) (vert) 30 10
1455 2c. "Peasants" (E. Abela) (vert) 40 10
1456 3c. Type **389** 60 15
1457 13c. "Still Life" (Amelia Pelaez) (vert) . . . . . . 1·50 75
1458 30c. "Landscape" (G. Escalante) . . . . . 3·75 1·40
See also Nos. 1648/54, 1785/91, 1871/7, 1900/6, 2005/11, 2048/54, 2104/9, 2180/5, 2260/5, 2346/51, 2430/5, 2530/5, 2620/5, 2685/90, 2816/21, 3218/23 and 3229/34.

390 Menelao Mora, Jose A. Echeverria and Attack on Presidential Palace

1967. National Events of 13 March 1957.
1459 **390** 3c. green and black . . . 15 10
1460 – 13c. brown and black . . 1·50 50
1461 – 30c. blue and black . . . 1·40 55
DESIGNS (36½ × 24½ mm.): 13c. Calixto Sanchez and "Corynthia" landing; 30c. Dionisio San Roman and Cienfuegos revolt.

391 "Homo habilis"

1967. "Prehistoric Man". Multicoloured.
1462 1c. Type **391** 10 10
1463 2c. "Australopithecus" . . . 15 10
1464 3c. "Pithecanthropus erectus" 15 10
1465 4c. Peking man 20 15
1466 5c. Neanderthal man . . . 30 20
1467 13c. Cro-Magnon man carving ivory tusk . . . . 1·00 45
1468 20c. Cro-Magnon man painting on wall of cave 2·00 65

392 Victoria

1967. Stamp Day. Carriages. Multicoloured.
1469 3c. Type **392** 20 15
1470 9c. Volanta 95 30
1471 13c. Quitrin . . . . 1·40 55

393 Cuban Pavilion

1967. "Expo 67", Montreal.
1472 **393** 1c. multicoloured 20 10
1473 – 2c. multicoloured 20 10
1474 – 3c. multicoloured 25 10
1475 – 13c. multicoloured . . . 1·25 55
1476 – 20c. multicoloured . . . 1·50 60

DESIGNS: 2c. Bathysphere, satellite and met. balloon ("Man as Explorer"); 3c. Ancient rock-drawing and tablet ("Man as Creator"); 13c. Tractor, ear of wheat and electronic console ("Man as Producer"); 20c. Olympic athletes ("Man in the Community").

394 "Eugenia malaccencis"

395 "Giselle"

1967. 150th Anniv of Cuban Botanical Gardens. Multicoloured.
1477 1c. Type **394** 20 10
1478 2c. "Jacaranda filicifolia" . . 20 10
1479 3c. "Coroupita guianensis" 30 10
1480 4c. "Spathodea campanulata" 30 10
1481 5c. "Cassia fistula" 40 15
1482 13c. "Plumieria alba" . . . 1·25 65
1483 20c. "Erythrina poeppigiana" . . . . . . 2·00 75

1967. Int Ballet Festival, Havana. Mult.
1484 1c. Type **395** 30 10
1485 2c. "Swan Lake" 30 10
1486 3c. "Don Quixote" 35 10
1487 4c. "Calaucan" 75 15
1488 13c. "Swan Lake" (different) 1·60 60
1489 20c. "Nutcracker" . . . . . 2·25 1·00

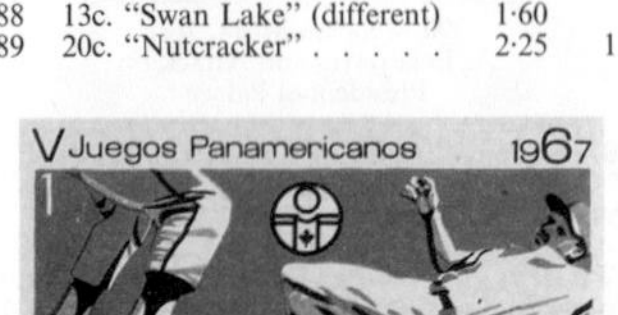

396 Baseball

1967. 5th Pan-American Games, Winnipeg. Mult.
1490 1c. Type **396** 15 10
1491 2c. Swimming 15 10
1492 3c. Basketball (vert) 30 10
1493 4c. Gymnastics (vert) . . . 30 10
1494 5c. Water-polo (vert) . . . 40 15
1495 13c. Weight-lifting . . . . . 1·25 35
1496 20c. Hurling the javelin . . 2·25 65

397 L. A. Turcios Lima, Map and OLAS Emblem

1967. 1st Conference of Latin-American Solidarity Organization (OLAS), Havana.
1497 13c. black, red and blue . . 95 40
1498 13c. black, red and brown 95 40
1499 13c. black, red and lilac . . 95 40
1500 13c. black, red and green . . 95 40
DESIGNS: No. 1497, Type **397**; No. 1498, Fabricio Ojidia; No. 1499, L. de La Puente Uceda; No. 1500, Camilo Torres; Martyrs of Guatemala, Venezuela, Peru and Colombia respectively. Each with map and OLAS emblem.

398 "Portrait of Sonny Rollins" (Alan Davie)

1967. "Contemporary Art" (Havana Exn from the Paris "Salon de Mayo"). Various designs showing modern paintings. Sizes given in millimetres. Multicoloured.
1501 1c. Type **398** 20 20
1502 1c. "Twelve Selenites" (F. Labisse) (39 × 41) . . 20 20
1503 1c. "Night of the Drinker" (F. Hundertwasser) (53 × 41) 20 20
1504 1c. "Figure" (Mariano) (48 × 41) 20 20
1505 1c. "All-Souls" (W. Lam) (45 × 41) 20 20
1506 2c. "Darkness and Cracks" (A. Tapies) (37 × 54) . . . 30 20
1507 2c. "Bathers" (G. Singier) (37 × 54) 30 20
1508 2c. "Torso of a Muse" (J. Arp) (37 × 46) 30 20
1509 2c. "Figure" (M. W. Svanberg) (57 × 54) . . . 30 20
1510 2c. "Oppenheimer's Information" (Erro) (37 × 41) 30 20
1511 3c. "Where Cardinals are Born" (Max Ernst) (37 × 52) 50 30
1512 3c. "Havana Landscape" (Portocarrero) (37 × 41) 50 30
1513 3c. "EG 12" (V. Vasarely) (37 × 42) 50 30
1514 3c. "Frisco" (A. Calder) (37 × 50) 50 30
1515 3c. "The Man with the Pipe" (Picasso) (37 × 52) 50 30
1516 4c. "Abstract Composition" (S. Poliakoff) (36 × 50) . . 60 40
1517 4c. "Painting" (Bram van Velde) (36 × 68) 60 40
1518 4c. "Sower of Fires" (detail, Matta) (36 × 47) 60 40
1519 4c. "The Art of Living" (R. Magritte) (36 × 50) . . 60 40
1520 4c. "Poem" (J. Miro) (36 × 56) 60 40
1521 13c. "Young Tigers" (J. Messagier) (50 × 33) . . 1·25 60
1522 13c. "Painting" (Vieira da Silva) (50 × 36) . . . . . 1·25 60
1523 13c. "Live Cobra" (P. Alechinsky) (50 × 35) 1·25 60
1524 13c. "Stalingrad" (detail, A. Jorn) (50 × 46) . . . . 1·25 60
1525 30c. "Warriors" (E. Pignon) (55 × 32) . . . . 6·00 2·50

399 Common Octopus

1967. World Underwater Fishing Championships. Multicoloured.
1527 1c. Green moray 20 10
1528 2c. Type **399** 20 10
1529 3c. Great barracuda 20 10
1530 4c. Bull shark 40 10
1531 5c. Spotted Jewfish 75 30
1532 13c. Chupare stingray . . . 1·75 75
1533 20c. Green turtle . . . . . 2·75 85

400 "Sputnik 1"

1967. Soviet Space Achievements. Mult.
1534 1c. Type **400** 10 10
1535 2c. "Lunik 3" 10 10
1536 3c. "Venusik" 15 10
1537 4c. "Cosmos" 20 10
1538 5c. "Mars 1" 30 15
1539 9c. "Electron 1, 2" 40 20
1540 10c. "Luna 9" 55 35
1541 13c. "Luna 10" . . . . . . 1·25 50

401 "Storming the Winter Palace" (from painting by Sokolov, Skalia and Miasnikova)

1967. 50th Anniv of October Revolution. Paintings. Multicoloured.
1543 1c. Type **401** 20 10
1544 2c. "Lenin addressing 2nd Soviet Congress" (Serov) (48 × 36) 20 10
1545 3c. "Lenin in the year 1919" (Nalbandian) (35 × 37) . . 30 10
1546 4c. "Lenin explaining the GOELRO Map" (Schmatko) (48 × 36) . . . 30 15
1547 5c. "Dawn of the Five-Year Plan" construction work (Romas) (50 × 36) . . . . 1·75 50
1548 13c. "Kusnetzkroi steel Furnace No. 1" (Kotov) (36 × 51) . . . . 1·25 50
1549 30c. "Victory Jubilation" (Krivonogov) (50 × 36) . . 1·75 75

402 Royal Force Castle, Havana

1967. Historic Cuban Buildings. Multicoloured.
1550 1c. Type **402** 10 10
1551 2c. Iznaga Tower, Trinidad (26½ × 47½) 15 10
1552 3c. Castle of Our Lady of the Angels, Cienfuegos (41½ × 29) 20 10
1553 4c. Church of St. Francis of Paula, Havana (41½ × 29) 20 10
1554 13c. Convent of St. Francis, Havana (39 × 13) . . . . 1·10 45
1555 30c. Morro Castle, Santiago de Cuba (43 × 26) . . . . 1·75 75

403 Ostrich

404 Golden Pheasant

1967. Christmas. Birds of Havana Zoo. Mult. (a) As T **403**.
1556 1c. Type **403** 65 70
1557 3c. Hyacinth macaw . . . . 1·25 1·10
1558 13c. Greater flamingoes . . . 3·00 90

(b) As T **404**.
1559a/d 1c. multicoloured 65 70
1560a/d 3c. multicoloured . . . . 1·25 1·10
1561a/d 13c. multicoloured . . . 3·00 1·90
DESIGNS: No. 1559a, Type **404**; 1559b, White stork; 1559c, Crowned crane; 1559d, Emu; 1560a, Grey parrot; 1560b, Chattering lory; 1560c, Keel-billed toucan; 1560d, Sulphur-crested cockatoo; 1561a, American white pelican, 1561b, Egyptian goose; 1561c, Mandarin; 1561d, Black swan.
Prices are for single stamps.

405 "Che" Guevara

1968. Major Ernesto "Che" Guevara Commem.
1562 **405** 13c. black and red . . . 1·75 50

406 Man and Tree ("Problems of Artistic Creation, Scientific and Technical Work")

1968. Cultural Congress, Havana. Mult.
1563 3c. Chainbreaker cradling flame ("Culture and Independence") (vert) . . 10 10
1564 3c. Hand with spanner and rifle ("Integral Formation of Man") (vert) 10 10
1565 13c. Demographic emblems ("Intellectual Responsibility") (vert) . . 85 30
1566 13c. Hand with communications emblems ("Culture and Mass-Communications Media") (vert) 90 35
1567 30c. Type **406** . . . . . . 1·25 65

407 Canaries

1968. Canary-breeding.
1568 **407** 1c. multicoloured 10 10
1569 – 2c. multicoloured 10 10
1570 – 3c. multicoloured 10 10
1571 – 4c. multicoloured 15 10
1572 – 5c. multicoloured 30 15
1573 – 13c. multicoloured . . . 1·40 55
1574 – 20c. multicoloured . . . 1·60 65
DESIGNS: Canaries and breeding cycle—mating, eggs, incubation and rearing young.

408 "The Village Postman" (after J. Harris)

1968. Stamp Day. Multicoloured.
1575 13c. Type **408** . . . . . . 1·10 35
1576 30c. "The Philatelist" (after G. Sciltian) . . . . 1·60 50

409 Nurse tending Child ("Anti-Polio Campaign")

1968. 20th Anniv of W.H.O.
1577 **409** 13c. black, red and olive 1·10 40
1578 – 30c. black, blue & olive 1·40 55
DESIGN: 30c. Two doctors ("Hospital Services").

410 "Children"

1968. International Children's Day.
1579 **410** 3c. multicoloured 55 20

411 "Cuatro Vientos" and Route Map

1968. 35th Anniv of Seville–Camaguey Flight by Barberan and Collar. Multicoloured.
1580 13c. Type **411** . . . . . . 1·40 30
1581 30c. Captain M. Barberan and Lieut. J. Collar . . . 1·40 40

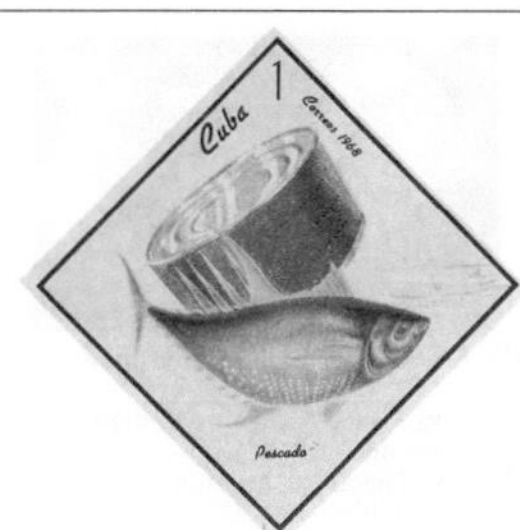

412 "Canned Fish"

1968. Cuban Food Products. Multicoloured.
1582 1c. Type **412** 10 10
1583 2c. "Milk Products" 15 10
1584 3c. "Poultry and Eggs" . . 25 20
1585 13c. "Cuban Rum" . . . . 1·40 35
1586 20c. "Canned Shell-fish" . . 1·60 50

413 Siboney Farmhouse

1968. 15th Anniv of Attack on Moncada Barracks. Multicoloured.
1587 3c. Type **413** 10 10
1588 13c. Map of Santiago de Cuba and assault route 1·00 40
1589 30c. Students and school buildings (on site of Moncada Barracks) . . . 1·60 55

414 Committee Members and Emblem

1968. 8th Anniv of Revolutionary Defence Committee.
1590 **414** 3c. multicoloured 55 15

415 Che Guevara and Rifleman

1968. Day of the Guerrillas.
1591 **415** 1c. black, green & gold 10 10
1592 – 3c. black, brown & gold 10 10
1593 – 9c. multicoloured 30 10
1594 – 10c. black, green and gold 60 15
1595 – 13c. black, pink & gold 1·10 45
DESIGNS—"Che" Guevara and: 3c. Machine-gunners; 9c. Riflemen; 10c. Soldiers cheering; 13c. Map of Caribbean and South America.

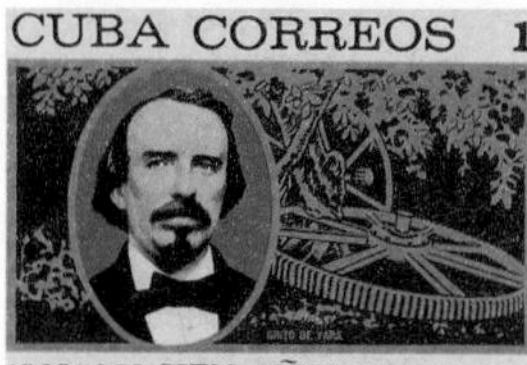

416 C. M. de Cespedes and Broken Wheel

1968. Centenary of Cuban War of Independence. Multicoloured.
1596 1c. Type **416** 10 10
1597 1c. E. Betances and horsemen 10 10
1598 1c. I. Agramonte and monument 10 10
1599 1c. A. Maceo and "The Protest" 10 10
1600 1c. J. Marti & patriots . . . 10 10
1601 3c. M. Gomez and "Invasion" 10 10
1602 3c. J. A. Mella and declaration 10 10
1603 3c. A. Guiteras and monument 10 10
1604 3c. A. Santamaria and riflemen 10 10
1605 3c. F. Pais & graffiti 10 10
1606 9c. J. Echeverria and students 50 15
1607 13c. C. Cienfuegos and rebels . . . . 1·25 45
1608 30c. "Che" Guevara and Castro addressing meeting 1·50 70

418 Parade of Athletes, Olympic Flag and Flame

1968. Olympic Games, Mexico. Multicoloured.
1610 1c. Type **418** 10 10
1611 2c. Basketball (vert) 10 10
1612 3c. Throwing the hammer (vert) 10 10
1613 4c. Boxing 15 10
1614 5c. Water-polo 20 10
1615 13c. Pistol-shooting . . . . 1·10 40
1616 30c. Calendar-stone (32½ × 50 mm) . . . . . 1·60 55

419 Crop-spraying

1968. Civil Activities of Cuban Armed Forces. Multicoloured.
1618 3c. Type **419** 10 10
1619 9c. "Che Guevara" Brigade 40 10
1620 10c. Road-building Brigade 60 20
1621 13c. Agricultural Brigade . . 1·25 50

420 "Manrique de Lara's Family" (J.-B. Vermay)

1968. 150th Anniv of San Alejandro Painting School. Multicoloured.
1622 1c. Type **420** 20 10
1623 2c. "Seascape" (L. Romanach) (48 × 37) 30 10
1624 3c. "Wild Cane" (A. Rodriguez) (40 × 48) 30 10
1625 4c. "Self-portrait" (M. Melero) (40 × 50) . . 30 15
1626 5c. "The Lottery List" (J. J. Tejada) (48 × 37) 60 30
1627 13c. "Portrait of Nina" (A. Menocal) (40 × 50) . . 1·40 50
1628 30c. "Landscape" (E. S. Chartrand) (54 × 37) . . . 2·25 75

421 Cuban Flag and Rifles

1969. 10th Anniv of "The Triumph of the Rebellion".
1630 **421** 13c. multicoloured . . . 1·10 40

422 Gutierrez and Sanchez

1969. Cent of Villaclarenos Patriots Rebellion.
1631 **422** 3c. multicoloured 55 20

423 Mariana Grajales, Rose and Statue

1969. Cuban Women's Day.
1632 **423** 3c. multicoloured 55 20

424 Cuban Pioneers

1969. Cuban Pioneers and Young Communist Unions. Multicoloured.
1633 3c. Type **424** 20 15
1634 13c. Young Communists . . 1·00 50

425 Guaimaro Assembly

1969. Centenary of Guaimaro Assembly.
1635 **425** 3c. brown and sepia . . 55 20

426 "The Postman" (J. C. Cazin)

1969. Cuban Stamp Day. Multicoloured.
1636 13c. Type **426** . . . . . . 1·10 45
1637 30c. "Portrait of a Young Man" (George Romney) (36 × 44 mm) . . . . . . 1·75 65

427 Agrarian Law, Headquarters, Eviction of Family, and Tractor

1969. 10th Anniv of Agrarian Reform.
1638 **427** 13c. multicoloured . . . 1·10 45

428 Hermit Crab in West Indian Chank

1969. Crustaceans. Multicoloured.
1639 1c. Type **428** 15 10
1640 2c. Spiny shrimp 15 10
1641 3c. Spiny lobster 15 10
1642 4c. Blue crab 15 15
1643 5c. Land crab 40 15
1644 13c. Freshwater prawn . . . 1·75 40
1645 30c. Pebble crab . . . . . 3·00 60

429 Factory and Peasants

1969. 50th Anniv of I.L.O. Mult.
1646 3c. Type **429** 20 15
1647 13c. Worker breaking chain 1·10 45

430 "Flowers" (R. Milian)

1969. National Museum Paintings (2nd series). Multicoloured.
1648 1c. Type **430** 10 10
1649 2c. "The Annunciation" (A. Eiriz) 10 10
1650 3c. "Factory" (M. Pogolotti) 75 15
1651 4c. "Territorial Waters" (L. M. Pedro) 40 10
1652 5c. "Miss Sarah Gale" (John Hoppner) 40 10
1653 13c. "Two Women wearing Mantillas" (I. Zuloaga) 1·25 45
1654 30c. "Virgin and Child" (F. Zurbaran) . . . . . 1·75 55
SIZES—HORIZ: 2c. As No. 1648. VERT: 3c. As No. 1648. 4c. 40 × 44 mm; 5c. and 30c. 40 × 46 mm; 13c. 38 × 42 mm.

431 Television Cameras and Emblem

1969. Cuban Radiodiffusion Institute. Mult.
1655 3c. Type **431** 20 15
1656 13c. Broadcasting tower and "Globe" . . . . 1·10 50
1657 1p. TV Reception diagram 2·50 1·10

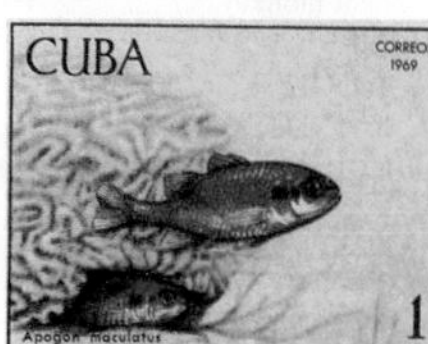

432 Flamefish

1969. Cuban Pisciculture. Multicoloured.
1658 1c. Type **432** 15 10
1659 2c. Spanish hogfish 15 10
1660 3c. Yellow-tailed damselfish 25 10
1661 4c. Royal gramma 25 10
1662 5c. Blue chromis 35 10
1663 13c. Black-barred soldierfish 2·10 40
1664 30c. Man-of-war fish (vert) 2·75 65

433 "Cuban Film Library"

1969. 10th Anniv of Cuban Cinema Industry. Multicoloured.
1665 1c. Type **433** 10 10
1666 3c. "Documentaries" . . . 15 10
1667 13c. "Cartoons" . . . . . 1·10 50
1668 30c. "Full-length Features" 1·75 60

434 "Napoleon in Milan". (A. Appiani (the Elder))

1969. Paintings in Napoleonic Museum, Havana. Multicoloured.
1669 1c. Type **434** 20 10
1670 2c. "Hortensia de Beauharnais" (F. Gerard) 25 10
1671 3c. "Napoleon-First Consul" (J. B. Regnault) 25 10
1672 4c. "Elisa Bonaparte" (R. Lefevre) 30 10
1673 5c. "Napoleon planning the Coronation" (J. G. Vibert) 50 25
1674 13c. "Corporal of Cuirassiers" (J. Meissonier) . . . . . 1·75 55
1675 30c. "Napoleon Bonaparte" (R. Lefevre) . . . . . . 2·50 65
SIZES—VERT: 2c. 42½ × 55 mm; 3c. 46 × 56½ mm; 4c., 13c., 44 × 63 mm; 30c. 45½ × 60 mm. HORIZ: 5c. 64 × 47 mm.

435 Baseball Players

1969. Cuba's Victory in World Amateur Baseball Championships, Dominican Republic.
1676 **435** 13c. multicoloured . . . 1·25 50

436 Von Humboldt, Book and American Eel

1969. Birth Bicentenary of Alexander von Humboldt. Multicoloured.
1677 3c. Type **436** 25 10
1678 13c. Night monkey . . . . . 1·75 75
1679 30c. Andean condors . . . 3·75 1·00

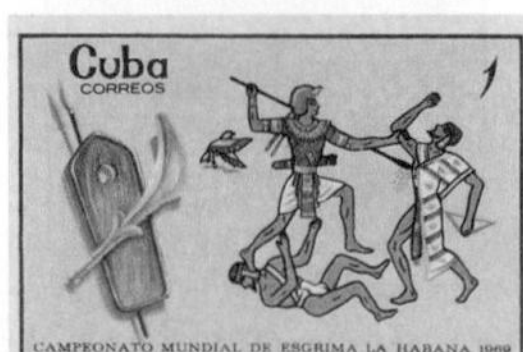

437 Ancient Egyptians in Combat

1969. World Fencing Championships, Havana. Multicoloured.
1683 1c. Type **437** 20 10
1684 2c. Roman Gladiators . . . 20 10
1685 3c. Norman and Viking . . 20 10
1686 4c. Medieval tournament . . 25 10
1687 5c. French musketeers . . . 30 10
1688 13c. Japanese samurai . . . 1·25 35
1689 30c. Mounted Cubans, War of Independence . . . . 1·75 60

438 Militiaman

1969. 10th Anniv of National Revolutionary Militias.
1691 **438** 3c. multicoloured 55 20

439 Major Cienfuegos and Wreath on Sea

1969. 10th Anniv of Disappearance of Major Camilo Cienfuegos.
1692 **439** 13c. multicoloured . . . 1·10 50

440 Strawberries and Grapes

1969. Agriculture and Livestock Projects. Multicoloured.
1693 1c. Type **440** 10 10
1694 1c. Onion and asparagus . . 10 10
1695 1c. Rice 10 10
1696 1c. Bananas 10 10
1697 3c. Pineapple (vert) 20 10
1698 3c. Tobacco plant (vert) . . 20 10
1699 3c. Citrus fruits (vert) . . . 20 10
1700 3c. Coffee (vert) 20 10
1701 3c. Rabbits (vert) 20 10
1702 10c. Pigs (vert) 25 10
1703 13c. Sugar-cane . . . . . 1·40 55
1704 30c. Bull . . . . 1·75 65

441 Stadium and Map of Cuba (2nd National Games)

1969. Sporting Events of 1969. Multicoloured.
1705 1c. Type **441** 10 10
1706 2c. Throwing the discus (9th Anniv Games) 10 10
1707 3c. Running (Barrientos commemoration) (vert) . . 10 10
1708 10c. Basketball (2nd Olympic Trial Games) (vert) 20 10
1709 13c. Cycling (6th Cycle Race) (vert) . . . . . 1·50 55
1710 30c. Chessmen and Globe (7th Capablanca Int. Chess Tournament, Havana) (vert) . . . . . 2·00 85

442 "Plumbago capensis" 443 "Petrea volubilis"

1969. Christmas. Flowers. (a) As T **442**. Mult.
1711 1c. Type **442** 25 10
1712 3c. "Turnera ulmifolia" . . 55 20
1713 13c. "Delonix regia" . . . . 1·25 75

(b) As T **443**.
1714a/d 1c. multicoloured 25 10
1715a/d 3c. multicoloured 55 20
1716a/d 13c. multicoloured . . . 1·25 75
DESIGNS: No. 1714a, Type **443**; 1714b, "Clitoria ternatea"; 1714c, "Duranta repens"; 1714d, "Ruellia tuberosa"; 1715a, "Thevetia peruviana"; 1715b, "Hibiscus elatus"; 1715c, "Allamanda cathartica"; 1715d, "Cosmos sulphureus"; 1716a, "Nerium oleander" (wrongly inscr "Neriun"); 1716b, "Cordia sebestena"; 1716c, "Lochnera rosea"; 1716d, "Jatropha integerrima".
Prices are for single stamps.

444 River Snake

1969. Swamp Fauna. Multicoloured.
1717 1c. Type **444** 10 10
1718 2c. Banana frog 10 10
1719 3c. Giant tropical gar (fish) 10 10
1720 4c. Dwarf hutia (vert) . . . 15 20
1721 5c. Alligator 15 10
1722 13c. Cuban Amazon (vert) 3·50 60
1723 30c. Red-winged blackbird (vert) . . . . 4·50 1·00

445 "Jibacoa Beach" (J. Hernandez) 446 Yamagua

1970. Tourism. Multicoloured.
1724 1c. Type **445** 10 10
1725 3c. "Trinidad City" 10 10
1726 13c. Santiago de Cuba . . . 1·25 55
1727 30c. Vinales Valley . . . . 1·75 65

1970. Medicinal Plants. Multicoloured.
1728 1c. Type **446** 10 10
1729 3c. Albahaca Morada . . . 10 10
1730 10c. Curbana 25 10
1731 13c. Romerillo . . . . . . 1·25 55
1732 30c. Marilope . . . . 1·60 65
1733 50c. Aguedita . . . . 2·25 80

447 Weightlifting

1970. 11th Central American and Caribbean Games. Multicoloured.
1734 1c. Type **447** 10 10
1735 3c. Boxing 10 10
1736 10c. Gymnastics 15 10
1737 13c. Athletics . . . . 1·10 40
1738 30c. Fencing . . . . 1·60 60

448 "Enjoyment of Life"

1970. "EXPO 70" World Fair, Osaka, Japan. Multicoloured.
1740 1c. Type **448** 10 10
1741 2c. "Uses of nature" (vert) 10 10
1742 3c. "Better Living Standards" 20 10
1743 13c. "International Co-operation" (vert) . . . . 1·25 35
1744 30c. Cuban Pavilion . . . . 1·75 55

449 Oval Pictograph, Ambrosio Cave

1970. 30th Anniv of Cuban Speleological Society.
1745 **449** 1c. red and brown . . . 10 10
1746 – 2c. black and brown . . 10 10
1747 – 3c. red and brown . . . 10 10
1748 – 4c. black and brown . . 10 10
1749 – 5c. black, red and brown 15 10
1750 – 13c. black and brown . . 1·10 50
1751 – 30c. red and brown . . . 2·25 55
DESIGNS—HORIZ: (42 × 32½ mm): 2c. Cave 1, Punta del Este, Isle of Pines; 5c. As 2c. (different); 30c. Stylized fish, Cave 2, Punta del Este. VERT: 3c. Stylized mask, Pichardo Cave, Sierra de Cubitas; 4c. Conical complex, Ambrosio Cave, Varadero; 13c. Human face, Garcia Robiou Cave, Catalina de Guines.

450 J. D. Blino, Balloon and Spacecraft

1970. Aviation Pioneers. Multicoloured.
1752 3c. Type **450** 50 10
1753 13c. A. Theodore, balloon and satellite . . . . . . 1·75 45

451 "Lenin in Kazan" (O. Vishniakov) (½-size illustration)

1970. Birth Centenary of Lenin. Paintings. Mult.
1754 1c. Type **451** 10 10
1755 2c. "Lenin's Youth" (Prager) 10 10
1756 3c. "The 2nd Socialist Party Congress" (Vinogradov) 10 10
1757 4c. "The First Manifesto" (Golubkov) 15 10
1758 5c. "The First Day of Soviet Power" (Babasiuk) . . . 15 10
1759 13c. "Lenin in the Smolny Institute" (Sokolov) . . . 1·25 45
1760 30c. "Autumn in Gorky" (Varlamov) . . . . . . 1·75 55
SIZES: 4, 5c. As Type **451**: 2, 3, 13, 30c. 70 × 34 mm.

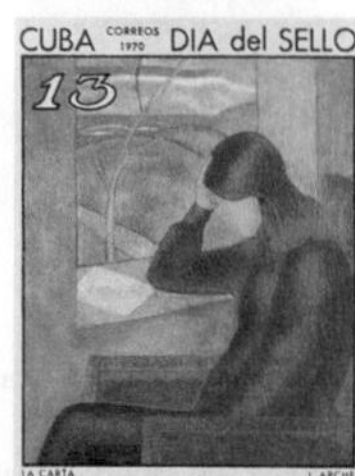

452 "The Letter" (J. Archer)

1970. Cuban Stamp Day. Paintings. Mult.
1762 13c. Type **452** . . . . . . 1·10 45
1763 30c. "Portrait of a Cadet" (anonymous) (35 × 49 mm) . . . . . . 1·40 55

453 Da Vinci's Anatomical Drawing, Earth and Moon

1970. World Telecommunications Day.
1764 **453** 30c. multicoloured . . . 1·40 55

454 Vietnamese Fisherman

1970. 80th Birthday of Ho Chi Minh (North Vietnamese leader). Multicoloured.
1765 1c. Type **454** 10 10
1766 3c. Cultivating rice-fields . . 20 10
1767 3c. Two Vietnamese children 20 10
1768 3c. Children entering air-raid shelter 20 10
1769 3c. Camouflaged machine-shop 25 10
1770 3c. Rice harvest 25 10
1771 13c. Pres. Ho Chi Minh . . 1·10 50
SIZES: Nos. 1766/7, 33 × 44½ mm, Nos. 1768, 1770, 33½ × 46 mm, No. 1769, 35 × 42 mm, No. 1771, 34½ × 39½ mm.

455 Tobacco Plantation and "Eden" Cigar band

1970. "Cuban Cigar Industry". Multicoloured.
1772 3c. Type **455** 10 10
1773 13c. 19 th century cigar factory and "El Mambi" band 95 50
1774 30c. Packing cigars (19th-century) and "Gran Pena" band . . . . 1·50 70

456 Cane crushing Machinery

1970. Cuban Sugar Harvest Target. "Over 10 million Tons". Multicoloured.
1775 1c. Type **456** 10 10
1776 2c. Sowing and crop-spraying 10 10
1777 3c. Cutting sugar-cane . . . 10 10
1778 10c. Ox-cart and diesel-electric locomotive . . . . 3·00 30
1779 13c. Modern cane cutting machine . . . . 1·00 20
1780 30c. Cane-cutters and globe (vert) . . . . 1·40 50
1781 1p. Sugar warehouse . . . . 2·75 1·25

457 P. Figueredo and National Anthem (original version)

1970. Death Centenary of Pedro Figueredo (composer of National Anthem). Multicoloured.
1782 3c. Type **457** 20 10
1783 20c. 18 98 version of anthem 1·10 40

458 Cuban Girl, Flag and Federation Badge

1970. 10th Anniv of Cuban Women's Federation.
1784 **458** 3c. multicoloured 50 35

459 "Peasant Militia" (S. C. Moreno)

1970. National Museum Paintings (3rd series). Multicoloured.
1785 1c. Type **459** 10 10
1786 2c. "Washerwoman" (A. Fernandez) 10 10
1787 3c. "Puerta del Sol, Madrid" (L. P. Alcazar) 10 10
1788 4c. "Fishermen's Wives" (J. Sorolla) 10 10
1789 5c. "Portrait of a Lady" (T. de Keyser) 15 10
1790 13c. "Mrs. Edward Foster" (Lawrence) . . . . 1·25 45
1791 30c. "Tropical Gipsy" (V. M. Garcia) . . . . . 1·75 65
SIZES—HORIZ: 2c., 3c. 46 × 42 mm. SQUARE. 4c. 41 × 41 mm. VERT: 5c., 13c., 30c. 39 × 46 mm.

460 Crowd in Jose Marti Square, Havana ($\frac{1}{2}$-size illustration)

1970. 10th Anniv of Havana Declaration.
1792 **460** 3c. blue, red & black . . 15 10

461 C. D. R. Emblem

1970. 10th Anniv of Revolution Defence Committees.
1793 **461** 3c. multicoloured 40 15

462 Laboratory, Emblem and Microscope

1970. 39th A.T.A.C. (Sugar Technicians Assn) Conference.
1794 **462** 30c. multicoloured . . . 1·50 50

463 Helmeted Guineafowl

1970. Wildlife. Multicoloured.
1795 1c. Type **463** 90 30
1796 2c. Black-billed whistling duck . . . . 1·00 30
1797 3c. Common pheasant . . . 1·25 30
1798 4c. Mourning dove . . . . 1·40 30
1799 5c. Northern bobwhite . . . 1·50 40
1800 13c. Wild boar . . . . . 1·50 70
1801 30c. White-tailed deer . . . 2·50 1·00

464 "Black Magic Parade" (M. Puente)

1970. Afro-Cuban Folklore Paintings. Mult.
1802 1c. Type **464** 10 10
1803 3c. "Zapateo Hat Dance" (V. L. Landaluze) 10 10
1804 10c. "Los Hoyos Conga Dance" (D. Ravenet) . . 50 40
1805 13c. "Climax of the Rumba" (E. Abela) . . . 1·25 55
SIZES—HORIZ: 10c. 45 × 44 mm. VERT: 3, 13c. 37 × 49 mm.

465 Common Zebra on Road Crossing

1970. Road Safety Week. Multicoloured.
1806 3c. Type **465** 35 15
1807 9c. Prudence the Bear on point duty 55 15

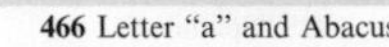
466 Letter "a" and Abacus

1970. International Education Year. Mult.
1808 13c. Type **466** . . . . . . 1·10 20
1809 30c. Microscope and cow . . 1·40 45

467 Cuban Blackbird 468 Cuban Pygmy Owl

1970. Christmas. Birds. Multicoloured. (a) As T **467**.
1810 1c. Type **467** 75 30
1811 3c. Oriente warbler . . . . 1·75 40
1812 13c. Zapata sparrow . . . . 3·25 1·00

(b) As T **468**.
1813a/d 1c. multicoloured 75 30
1814a/d 3c. multicoloured . . . . 1·75 40
1815a/d 13c. multicoloured . . . 3·25 1·00
DESIGNS: No. 1813a, Type **468**; 1813b, Cuban tody; 1813c, Cuban green woodpecker; 1813d, Zapata wren; 1814a, Cuban solitaire; 1814b, Blue-grey gnatcatcher; 1814c, Cuban vireo; 1814d, Yellow-headed warbler; 1815a, Hook-billed kite; 1815b, Gundlach's hawk; 1815c, Blue-headed quail dove; 1815d, Cuban conure. Prices are for single stamps.

469 School Badge and Cadet Colour-party

1970. "Camilo Cienfuegos" Military School.
1816 **469** 3c. multicoloured 40 20

470 "Reporter" with Pen

1971. 7th Journalists International Organization Congress, Havana.
1817 **470** 13c. multicoloured . . . 95 35

471 Lockheed 8A Sirius

1971. 35th Anniv of Camaguey–Seville Flight by Menendez Pelaez. Multicoloured.
1818 13c. Type **471** . . . . . . 1·40 20
1819 30c. Lieut. Menendez Pelaez and map . . . . 1·75 50

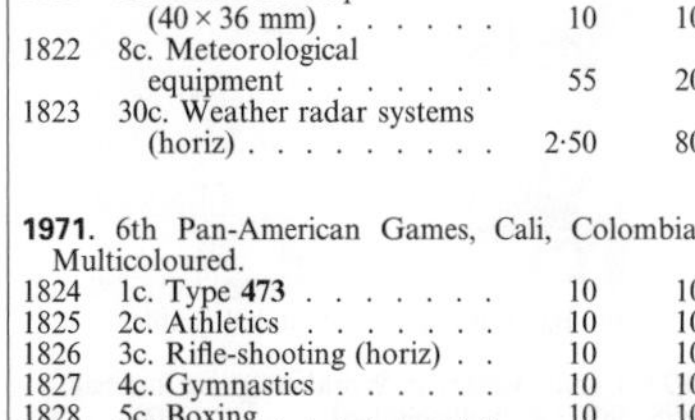

472 Meteorological Class 473 Games Emblem

1971. World Meteorological Day. Multicoloured.
1820 1c. Type **472** 10 10
1821 3c. Hurricane map (40 × 36 mm) 10 10
1822 8c. Meteorological equipment 55 20
1823 30c. Weather radar systems (horiz) . . . . 2·50 80

1971. 6th Pan-American Games, Cali, Colombia. Multicoloured.
1824 1c. Type **473** 10 10
1825 2c. Athletics 10 10
1826 3c. Rifle-shooting (horiz) . . 10 10
1827 4c. Gymnastics 10 10
1828 5c. Boxing 10 10
1829 13c. Water-polo (horiz) . . 1·10 25
1830 30c. Baseball (horiz) . . . . 1·50 40

474 Paris Porcelain, 19th-century 475 Mother and Child

1971. Porcelain and Mosaics in Metropolitan Museum, Havana. Multicoloured.
1831 1c. Type **474** 10 10
1832 3c. Mexican pottery bowl, 17th-century 10 10
1833 10c. 19th-century Paris porcelain (similar to T **474**) 20 10
1834 13c. "Colosseum" Italian mosaic, 19th-century . . . 1·10 20
1835 20c. 17th-century Mexican pottery dish (similar to 3c.) . . . . 1·10 45
1836 30c. "St. Peter's Square" (Italian mosaic 19th-cent.) 1·40 50
SIZES—VERT: 3c. 46 × 54 mm. 10c. as Type **474**. 20c. 43 × 49 mm. HORIZ: 13c., 30c. 50 × 33 mm.

1971. 10th Anniv of Cuban Infant Centres.
1837 **475** 3c. multicoloured 35 10

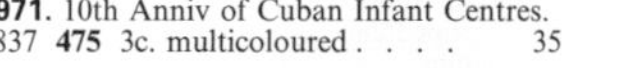

476 Cosmonaut in Training

1971. 10th Anniv of First Manned Space Flight. Multicoloured.
1838 1c. Type **476** 10 10
1839 2c. Speedometer test 10 10
1840 3c. Medical examination . . 10 10
1841 4c. Acceleration tower . . . 10 10
1842 5c. Pressurisation test . . . 10 10
1843 13c. Cosmonaut in gravity chamber . . . . 1·00 25
1844 30c. Crew in flight simulator 1·25 55

477 Cuban and Burning Ship

1971. 10th Anniv of Giron Victory.
1846 **477** 13c. multicoloured . . . 1·50 40

478 Sailing Packet "Windsor Castle" attacked by French Privateer Brig "Jeune Richard" (1807)

1971. Stamp Day. Multicoloured.
1847 13c. Type **478** . . . . . . 1·75 60
1848 30c. Mail steamer "Orinoco", 1851 . . . . 2·50 80

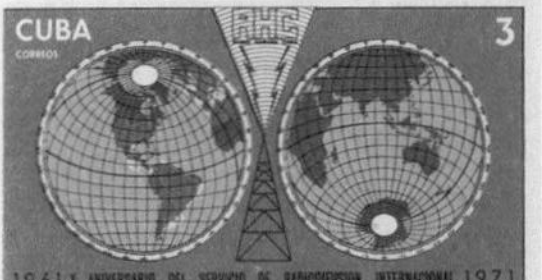

479 Transmitter and Hemispheres

1971. 10th Anniv of Cuban International Broadcasting Services.

1849	**479**	3c. multicoloured	20	10
1850		50c. multicoloured	2·10	60

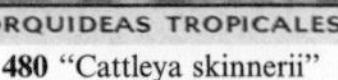

480 "Cattleya skinnerii" **482** Larvae and Pupae

481 Loynaz del Castillo and "Invasion Hymn"

1971. Tropical Orchids (1st series). Mult.

1851		1c. Type **480**	10	10
1852		2c. "Vanda hibrida"	10	10
1853		3c. "Cypripedium callossum"	15	10
1854		4c. "Cypripedium glaucophyllum"	20	10
1855		5c. "Vanda tricolor"	20	10
1856		13c. "Cypripedium mowgh"	1·50	30
1857		30c. "Cypripedium solum"	2·25	55

See also Nos. 1908/14 and 2012/18.

1971. Birth Centenary of Enrique Loynaz del Castillo (composer).

1858	**481**	3c. multicoloured	40	20

1971. Apiculture. Multicoloured.

1859		1c. Type **482**	15	10
1860		3c. Working bee	15	10
1861		9c. Drone	30	10
1862		13c. Defending the hive	1·60	25
1863		30c. Queen bee	2·25	55

483 "The Ship" (Lydia Rivera)

1971. Exhibition of Children's Drawings. Havana. Multicoloured.

1864		1c. Type **483**	10	10
1865		3c. "Little Train" (Yuri Ruiz)	45	15
1866		9c. "Sugar-cane Cutter" (Horacio Carracedo)	10	10
1867		10c. "Return of Cuban Fisherman" (Angela Munoz and Lazaro Hernandez)	25	15
1868		13c. "The Zoo" (Victoria Castillo)	85	25
1869		20c. "House and Garden" (Elsa Garcia)	1·40	45
1870		30c. "Landscape" (Orestes Rodriguez) (vert)	1·60	65

SIZES: 9c., 13c. 45 × 35 mm, 10c. 45 × 38 mm, 20c. 47 × 42 mm, 30c. 39 × 49 mm.

1971. National Museum Paintings (4th series). As T **459**. Multicoloured.

1871		1c. "St. Catherine of Alexandria" (Zurbaran)	10	10
1872		2c. "The Cart" (F. Americo) (horiz)	10	10
1873		3c. "St. Christopher and the Child" (J. Bassano)	10	10
1874		4c. "Little Devil" (R. Portocarrero)	10	10
1875		5c. "Portrait of a Lady" (N. Maes)	10	10
1876		13c. "Phoenix" (R. Martinez)	1·00	30
1877		30c. "Sir William Pitt" (Gainsborough)	1·40	50

SIZES: 1, 3c. 30 × 56 mm, 2c. 48 × 37 mm, 4, 5c. 37 × 49 mm, 13, 30c. 39 × 49 mm.

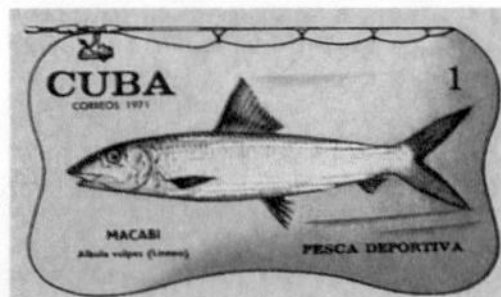

485 Bonefish

1971. Sport Fishing. Multicoloured.

1878		1c. Type **485**	15	10
1879		2c. Great amberjack	15	10
1880		3c. Large-mouthed black bass	15	10
1881		4c. Dolphin (fish)	20	10
1882		5c. Atlantic tarpon	25	15
1883		13c. Wahoo	1·40	40
1884		30c. Blue marlin	2·40	65

486 Ball within "C"

1971. World Amateur Baseball Championships. Multicoloured.

1885		3c. Type **486**	15	10
1886		1p. Hand holding globe within "C"	2·75	1·10

487 "Dr. F. Valdes Dominguez" (artist unknown)

1971. Centenary of Medical Students' Execution. Multicoloured.

1887		3c. Type **487**	20	10
1888		13c. "Students Execution" (M. Mesa) (62 × 47 mm)	90	30
1889		30c. "Captain Federico Capdevila" (unknown artist)	1·40	40

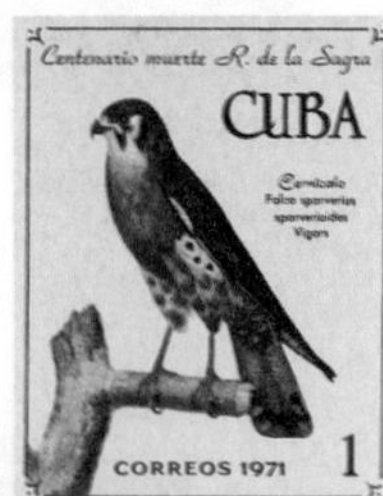

488 American Kestrel

1971. Death Centenary of Ramon de la Sagra (naturalist). Cuban Birds. Multicoloured.

1890		1c. Type **488**	55	25
1891		2c. Cuban pygmy owl	55	25
1892		3c. Cuban trogon	75	25
1893		4c. Great lizard cuckoo	90	30
1894		5c. Fernandina's flicker	1·10	40
1895		13c. Stripe-headed tanager (horiz)	2·10	70
1896		30c. Red-legged thrush (horiz)	3·75	1·40
1897		50c. Cuban emerald and ruby-throated hummingbirds (56 × 30 mm)	7·00	2·10

489 Baseball Player and Global Emblem

1971. Cuba's Victory in World Amateur Baseball.

1898	**489**	13c. multicoloured	1·00	45

490 "Children of the World"

1971. 25th Anniv of U.N.I.C.E.F.

1899	**490**	13c. multicoloured	1·10	45

1972. National Museum Paintings (5th series). As T **459**. Multicoloured.

1900		1c. "The Reception of Ambassadors" (V. Carpaccio)	10	10
1901		2c. "Senora Malpica" (G. Collazo)	10	10
1902		3c. "La Chorrera Fortress" (E. Chartrand)	10	10
1903		4c. "Creole Landscape" (C. Enriquez)	10	10
1904		5c. "Sir William Lemon" (G. Romney)	10	10
1905		13c. "La Tajona Beach" (H. Cleenewek)	1·25	30
1906		30c. "Valencia Beach" (J. Sorolla y Bastida)	2·25	70

SIZES: 1c., 3c. 51 × 33 mm, 2c. 28 × 53 mm, 4c., 5c. 36 × 44 mm, 13c., 30c. 43 × 34 mm.

492 "Capitol" Stamp of 1929 (now Natural History Museum)

1972. 10th Anniv of Academy of Sciences.

1907	**492**	13c. purple and yellow	95	40

1972. Tropical Orchids (2nd series). As T **480**. Multicoloured.

1908		1c. "Brasso Cattleya sindorossiana"	25	10
1909		2c. "Cypripedium doraeus"	25	10
1910		3c. "Cypripedium exul"	25	10
1911		4c. "Cypripedium rosydawn"	25	10
1912		5c. "Cypripedium champolliom"	25	10
1913		13c. "Cypripedium bucolique"	1·75	75
1914		30c. "Cypripedium sullanum"	2·50	90

493 "Eduardo Agramonte" (F. Martinez)

1972. Death Centenary of Dr. E. Agramonte (surgeon and patriot).

1915	**493**	3c. multicoloured	30	15

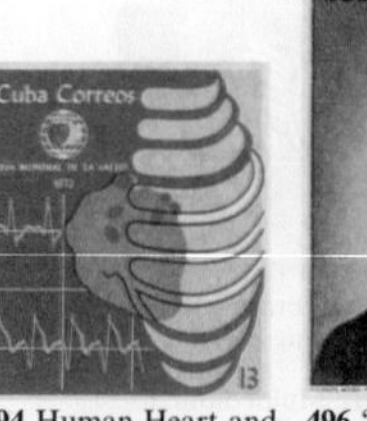

494 Human Heart and Thorax **496** "Vincente Mora Pera" (Postmaster General, War of Independence) (R. Loy)

495 "Sputnik 1"

1972. World Health Day.

1916	**494**	13c. multicoloured	95	40

1972. "History of Space". Multicoloured.

1917		1c. Type **495**	10	10
1918		2c. "Vostok 1"	10	10
1919		3c. Valentina Tereshkova in capsule	20	10
1920		4c. A. Leonov in space	25	10
1921		5c. "Lunokhod 1" moon Vehicle	25	10
1922		13c. Linking of "Soyuz" capsules	1·25	35
1923		30c. Dobrovolsky, Volkov and Pataiev, victims of "Soyuz 11" disaster	1·50	45

1972. Stamp Day. Multicoloured.

1924		13c. Type **496**	85	40
1925		30c. Mambi Mailcover of 1897 (48 × 39 mm)	1·40	45

497 Cuban Workers **498** Jose Marti and Ho Chi Minh

1972. Labour Day.

1926	**497**	3c. multicoloured	40	20

1972. 3rd Symposium on Indo-China War. Multicoloured.

1927		3c. Type **498**	20	10
1928		13c. Bombed house (38 × 29 mm)	80	30
1929		30c. Symposium emblem	95	45

1972. Paintings from the Metropolitan Museum, Havana (6th series). As T **430**. Multicoloured.

1930		1c. "Salvador del Muro" (J. del Rio)	10	10
1931		2c. "Louis de las Casas" (J. del Rio)	10	10
1932		3c. "Christopher Columbus" (anonymous)	20	10
1933		4c. "Tomas Gamba" (V. Escobar)	25	10
1934		5c. "Maria Galarraga" (V. Escobar)	25	10
1935		13c. "Isabella II of Spain" (F. Madrazo)	1·25	35
1936		30c. "Carlos III of Spain" (M. Melero)	1·50	50

SIZES—VERT: (35 × 44 mm) 1930/34, (34 × 52 mm) 1935/6.

500 Children in Boat

1972. Children's Song Competition.

1937	**500**	3c. multicoloured	50	20

501 Ilyushin Il-18, Map and Flags

1972. Air. 1st Anniv of Havana–Santiago de Chile Air Service.

1938	**501**	25c. multicoloured	1·40	55

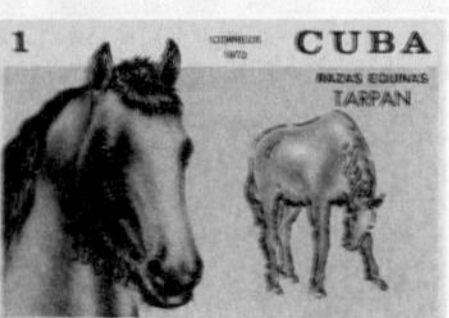

502 Tarpan

1972. Thoroughbred Horses. Multicoloured.

1939		1c. Type **502**	10	10
1940		2c. Kertag	10	10
1941		3c. Creole	10	10
1942		4c. Andalusian	10	10
1943		5c. Arab	10	10
1944		13c. Quarter-horse	2·00	50
1945		30c. Pursang	2·50	75

503 Frank Pais

1972. 15th Death Anniv of Frank Pais.

1946	**503**	13c. multicoloured	85	40

504 Athlete and Emblem

1972. Olympic Games, Munich.

1947	**504**	1c. orange and brown	10	10
1948	–	2c. purple, blue & orge	10	10
1949	–	3c. green, yellow & blk	10	10
1950	–	4c. bl, yell & brn	10	10
1951	–	5c. red, black & yellow	10	10
1952	–	13c. lilac, green & blue	1·10	35
1953	–	30c. blue, red and green	1·40	50

DESIGNS—HORIZ: 2c. "M" and boxing; 3c. "U" and weightlifting; 4c. "N" and fencing; 5c. "I" and rifle-shooting; 13c. "C" and running; 30c. "H" and basketball.

505 "Landscape with Tree-trunks" (D. Ramos)

1972. International Hydrological Decade. Mult.

1955		1c. Type **505**	10	10
1956		3c. "Cyclone" (T. Lorenzo)	15	10
1957		8c. "Vineyards" (D. Ramos)	35	10
1958		30c. "Forest and Stream" (A. R. Morey) (vert)	1·10	45

506 "Papilio thoas oviedo"

1972. Butterflies from the Gundlach Collection. Multicoloured.

1959		1c. Type **506**	10	10
1960		2c. "Papilio devilliers"	15	10
1961		3c. "Papilio polixenes polixenes"	15	10
1962		4c. "Papilio androgeus epidaurus"	15	10
1963		5c. "Papilio cayguanabus'	25	10
1964		13c. "Papilio andraemon hernandezi"	2·75	60
1965		30c. "Papilio celadon"	3·50	80

507 "In La Mancha" (A. Fernandez)

1972. 425th Birth Anniv of Cervantes. Paintings by A. Fernandez. Multicoloured.

1966		3c. Type **507**	10	10
1967		13c. "Battle with the Wine Skins" (horiz)	1·25	35
1968		30c. "Don Quixote of La Mancha"	1·50	40

508 E. "Che" Guevara and Map of Bolivia

1972. 5th Anniv of Guerrillas' Day. Mult.

1970		3c. Type **508**	10	10
1971		13c. T. "Tania" Bunke and map of Bolivia	1·25	35
1972		30c. G. "Inti" Peredo and map of Bolivia	1·50	40

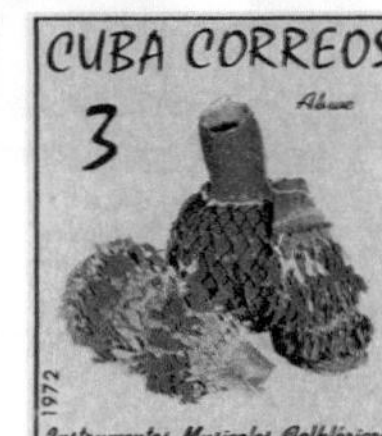

509 "Abwe" (shakers)

1972. Traditional Musical Instruments. Mult.

1973		3c. Type **509**	10	10
1974		13c. "Bonko enchemiya" (drum)	1·25	35
1975		30c. "Iya" (drum)	1·50	40

510 Cuban 2c. Stamp of 1951

1972. National Philatelic Exhibition, Matanzas. Multicoloured.

1976		13c. Type **510**	1·25	35
1977		30c. Cuban 25c. airmail stamp of 1951	1·75	45

511 Viking Longship

1972. Maritime History. Ships Through the Ages. Multicoloured.

1978		1c. Type **511**	15	10
1979		2c. Caravel (vert)	15	10
1980		3c. Galley	15	10
1981		4c. Galleon (vert)	20	10
1982		5c. Clipper	20	10
1983		13c. Steam packet	1·50	55
1984		30c. Atomic ice-breaker "Lenin" and Adelie penguins (55 × 29 mm)	5·50	1·50

512 Lion of St. Mark

1972. U.N.E.S.C.O. "Save Venice" Campaign. Multicoloured.

1985		3c. Type **512**	10	10
1986		13c. Bridge of Sighs (vert)	85	35
1987		30c. St. Mark's Cathedral	1·10	65

513 Baseball Coach (poster)

516 "Gertrude G. de Avellaneda" (A. Esquivel)

515 Bronze Medal, Women's 100 m

1972. "Cuba, World Amateur Baseball Champions of 1972".

1988	**513**	3c. violet and orange	50	10

1972. Sports events of 1972.

1989	–	1c. multicoloured	10	10
1990	–	2c. multicoloured	10	10
1991	**513**	3c. black, orange & grn	10	10
1992	–	4c. red, black and blue	10	10
1993	–	5c. orge, bl & lt bl	10	10
1994	–	13c. multicoloured	1·10	45
1995	–	30c. vio, blk & bl	1·40	65

DESIGNS AND EVENTS: 1c. Various sports (10th National Schoolchildren's Games); 2c. Pole vaulting (Barrientos Memorial Athletics); 3c. As Type **513**, but inscr changed to read "XI serie nacional de beisbol aficionado" and colours changed (11th National Amateur Baseball Series); 4c. Wrestling (Cerro Pelado International Wrestling Championships); 5c. Foil (Central American and Caribbean Fencing Tournament); 13c. Boxing (Giraldo Cordova Boxing Tournament); 30c. Fishes (Ernest Hemingway National Marlin Fishing Contest).

1972. Cuban Successes in Olympic Games, Munich. Multicoloured.

1996		1c. Type **515**	10	10
1997		2c. Bronze (women's 4 × 100 m relay)	10	10
1998		3c. Gold (boxing, 54 kg)	10	10
1999		4c. Silver (boxing, 81 kg)	10	10
2000		5c. Bronze (boxing, 51 kg)	10	10
2001		13c. Gold (boxing, 67 kg)	1·25	45
2002		30c. Gold (boxing, 81 kg) and Silver Cup (boxing Teofilo Stevenons)	1·50	65

1973. Death Centenary of Gertrude Gomez de Avellaneda (poetess).

2004	**516**	13c. multicoloured	95	40

1973. National Museum Paintings (6th series). As T **459**. Multicoloured.

2005		1c. "Bathers in the Lagoon" (C. Enriquez) (vert)	10	10
2006		2c. "Still Life" (W. C. Heda) (vert)	10	10
2007		3c. "Scene of Gallantry" (V. de Landaluse) (vert)	10	10
2008		4c. "Return at Evening" (C. Troyon) (vert)	10	10
2009		5c. "Elizabetta Mascagni" (F. X. Fabre) (vert)	10	10
2010		13c. "The Picador" (E. de Lucas Padilla)	1·25	45
2011		30c. "In the Garden" (J. A. Morell) (vert)	1·50	65

1973. Tropical Orchids (3rd series). As Type **480**. Multicoloured.

2012		1c. "Dendrobium" (hybrid)	10	10
2013		2c. "Cypripedium exul. O' Brien"	10	10
2014		3c. "Vanda miss. Joaquin"	10	10
2015		4c. "Phalaenopsis schilleriana Reichb"	10	10
2016		5c. "Vanda gilbert tribulet"	10	10
2017		13c. "Dendrobium" (hybrid) (different)	1·25	45
2018		30c. "Arachnis catherine"	1·50	65

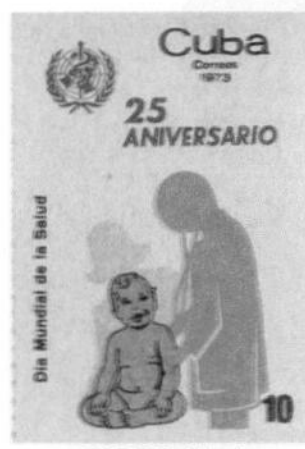

518 Medical Examination

520 "Soyuz" Rocket on Launch-pad

519 Children and Vaccine

1973. 25th Anniv of W.H.O.

2019	**518**	10c. multicoloured	55	25

1973. Freedom from Polio Campaign.

2020	**519**	3c. multicoloured	35	20

1973. Cosmonautics Day. Russian Space Exploration. Multicoloured.

2021		1c. Type **520**	25	10
2022		2c. "Luna 1" in moon orbit (horiz)	25	10
2023		3c. "Luna 16" leaving moon	25	10
2024		4c. "Venus 7" probe (horiz)	25	10
2025		5c. "Molniya 1" communications satellite	25	10
2026		13c. "Mars 3" probe (horiz)	2·00	55
2027		30c. Research ship "Kosmonavt Yury Gargarin" (horiz)	2·75	65

521 Santiago de Cuba Postmark, 1839

1973. Stamp Day. Multicoloured.

2028		13c. Type **521**	95	35
2029		30c. "Havana" postmark, 1760	1·10	40

522 "Ignacio Agramonte" (A. Espinosa)

1973. Death Centenary of Maj.-Gen. Ignacio Agramonte.

2030	**522**	13c. multicoloured	75	35

523 Copernicus' Birthplace and Instruments

1973. 500th Birth Anniv of Copernicus. Mult.

2031		3c. Type **523**	10	10
2032		13c. Copernicus and "spaceship"	1·00	35
2033		30c. "De Revolutionibus Orbium Celestium" and Frombork Tower	1·75	45

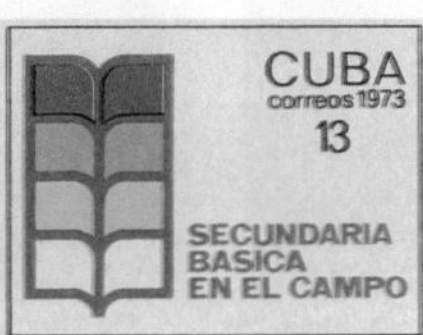

524 Emblem of Basic Schools

1973. Educational Development.

2035	**524**	13c. multicoloured	75	20

525 Jersey Breed

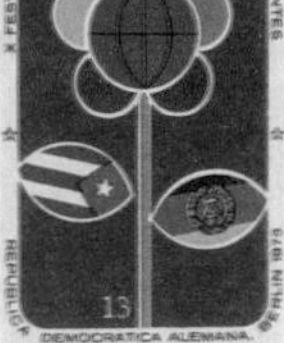

526 Festival Emblem

1973. Cattle Breeds. Multicoloured.

2036	1c. Type **525**		10	10
2037	2c. Charolais		10	10
2038	3c. Creole		10	10
2039	4c. Swiss		10	10
2040	5c. Holstein		10	10
2041	13c. St. Gertrude's		1·00	20
2042	30c. Brahman Cebu		1·60	40

1973. 10th World Youth and Students' Festival, East Berlin.

2043	**526**	13c. multicoloured	75	20

527 Siboney Farmhouse

529 "Amalia de Sajonia" (J. K. Rossler)

528 Midshipman and Destroyer

1973. 20th Anniv of Revolution. Mult.

2044	3c. Type **527**		20	15
2045	13c. Moncada Barracks		75	25
2046	30c. Revolution Square, Havana		1·10	40

1973. 10th Anniv of Revolutionary Navy.

2047	**528**	3c. multicoloured	60	20

1973. National Museum Paintings (7th series). Multicoloured.

2048	1c. Type **529**		10	10
2049	2c. "Interior" (M. Vicens) (horiz)		10	10
2050	3c. "Margaret of Austria" (J. Pantoja de la Cruz)		10	10
2051	4c. "Syndic of the City Hall" (anon)		10	10
2052	5c. "View of Santiago de Cuba" (J. H. Giro) (horiz)		10	10
2053	13c. "The Catalan" (J. J. Tejada)		1·10	60
2054	30c. "Guayo Alley" (J. J. Tejada)		1·50	85

530 "Spring"

1973. Centenary of World Meteorological Organization. Paintings by J. Madrazo. Mult.

2055	8c. Type **530**		30	10
2056	8c. "Summer"		30	10
2057	8c. "Autumn"		30	10
2058	8c. "Winter"		30	10

531 Weightlifting

532 "Erythrina standleyana"

1973. 27th Pan-American World Weightlifting Championships, Havana. Designs showing various stages of weightlifting exercise.

2059	**531**	1c. multicoloured	10	10
2060	–	2c. multicoloured	20	10
2061	–	3c. multicoloured	20	10
2062	–	4c. multicoloured	20	10
2063	–	5c. multicoloured	20	10
2064	–	13c. multicoloured	1·25	80
2065	–	30c. multicoloured	2·50	1·50

1973. Wild Flowers (1st series). Mult.

2066	1c. Type **532**		10	10
2067	2c. "Lantana camara"		10	10
2068	3c. "Canavalia maritima"		10	10
2069	4c. "Dichromena colorata"		10	10
2070	5c. "Borrichia arborescens"		10	10
2071	13c. "Anguria pedata"		85	45
2072	30c. "Cordia sebestena"		1·40	65

See also Nos. 2152/6.

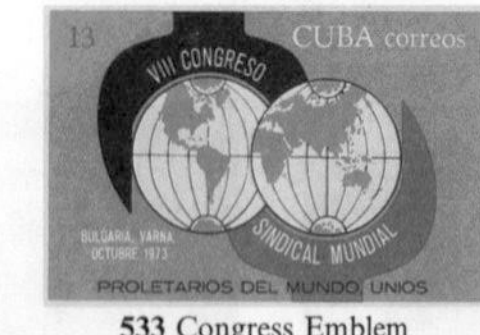

533 Congress Emblem

1973. 8th World Trade Union Congress, Varna, Bulgaria.

2073	**533**	13c. multicoloured	70	25

534 Ballet Dancers

535 True Fasciate Liguus

1973. 25th Anniv of Cuban National Ballet.

2074	**534**	13c. lt blue, bl & gold	70	25

1973. Shells. Multicoloured

2075	1c. Type **535**		20	10
2076	2c. Guitart's liguus		20	10
2077	3c. Wharton's Cuban liguus		20	10
2078	4c. Angela's Cuban liguus		30	10
2079	5c. Yellow-banded liguus		30	10
2080	13c. "Liguus blainianus"		2·00	85
2081	30c. "Ribbon liguus"		2·25	1·10

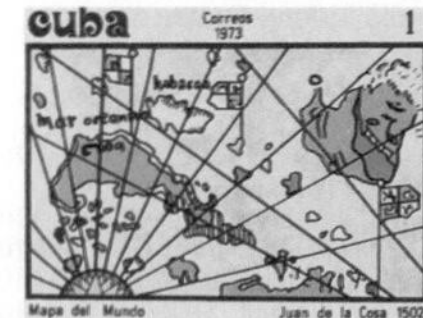

536 Juan de la Cosa's Map, 1502

1973. Maps of Cuba. Multicoloured.

2082	1c. Type **536**		10	10
2083	3c. Ortelius's map, 1572		10	10
2084	13c. Bellini's map, 1762		80	20
2085	40c. Cartographic survey map, 1973		1·10	50

537 1c. Stamp of 1960 (No. 921)

1974. 15th Anniv of Revolution. Revolution stamps of 1960. Multicoloured.

2086	1c. Type **537**		10	10
2087	3c. 2c. stamp		20	10
2088	13c. 8c. air stamp		1·00	60
2089	40c. 12c. air stamp		1·25	75

538 "Head of a Woman" (F. Ponce de Leon)

1974. Paintings in Camaguey Museum. Mult.

2090	1c. Type **538**		10	10
2091	3c. "Mexican Children" (J. Arche)		10	10
2092	8c. "Portrait of a Young Woman" (A. Menocal)		20	10
2093	10c. "Mulatto Woman with Coconut" (L. Romanach)		55	20
2094	13c. "Head of Old Man" (J. Arburu)		85	30

539 A. Cabral

540 "Lenin" (after J. V. Kosmin)

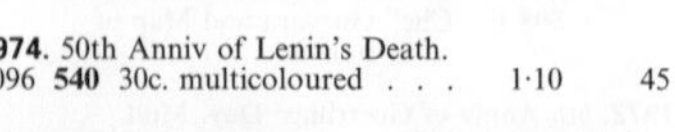

1974. 1st Death Anniv of Amilcar Cabral (Guinea-Bissau guerilla leader).

2095	**539**	13c. multicoloured	70	20

1974. 50th Anniv of Lenin's Death.

2096	**540**	30c. multicoloured	1·10	45

541 Games Emblem

542 "C. M. de Cespedes" (after F. Martinez)

1974. 12th Central American and Caribbean Games, Santo Domingo. Multicoloured.

2097	1c. Type **541**		20	10
2098	2c. Throwing the javelin		20	10
2199	3c. Boxing		20	10
2100	4c. Baseball player (horiz)		20	10
2101	13c. Handball player (horiz)		1·50	75
2102	30c. Volleyball (horiz)		2·00	1·00

1974. Death Centenary of Carlos M. de Cespedes (patriot).

2103	**542**	13c. multicoloured	70	15

543 "Portrait of a Man" (J. B. Vermay)

544 "Comecon" Headquarters Building, Moscow

1974. National Museum Paintings (8th series). Multicoloured.

2104	1c. Type **543**		10	10
2105	2c. "Nodriza" (C. A. Van Loo)		10	10
2106	3c. "Cattle by a River" (R. Morey) (46 × 32 mm)		10	10
2107	4c. "Village Landscape" (R. Morey) (46 × 32 mm)		10	10
2108	13c. "Faun and Bacchus" (Rubens)		80	40
2109	30c. "Playing Patience" (R. Madrazo)		1·25	75

1974. 25th Anniv of Council for Mutual Economic Aid.

2110	**544**	30c. multicoloured	1·00	45

545 Jose Marti and Lenin

1974. Visit of Leonid Brezhnev (General Secretary of Soviet Communist Party). Multicoloured.

2111	13c. Type **545**		65	25
2112	30c. Brezhnev with Castro		1·00	45

546 "Martian Crater"

1974. Cosmonautics Day. Science Fiction paintings by Sokolov. Multicoloured.

2113	1c. Type **546**		10	10
2114	2c. "Fiery Labyrinth"		10	10
2115	3c. "Amber Wave"		10	10
2116	4c. "Space Navigators"		15	10
2117	13c. "Planet in the Nebula"		1·00	50
2118	30c. "The World of the Two Suns"		1·75	1·00

See also Nos. 2196/201.

547 Cuban Letter of 1874

1974. Centenary of U.P.U.

2119	**547**	30c. multicoloured	1·00	45

1974. Stamp Day. Postal Markings of Pre-Stamp Exhibition. As T **521**. Multicoloured.

2120	1c. "Havana" postmark		10	10
2121	3c. "Matanzas" postmark		15	10
2122	13c. "Trinidad" postmark		75	15
2123	20c. "Guana Vacoa" postmark		1·10	20

548 Congress Emblem

1974. 18th Sports' Congress of "Friendly Armies".

2124	**548**	3c. multicoloured	40	10

549 "Eumaeus atala atala" (butterfly)

1974. 175th Birth Anniv of Felipe Poey (naturalist). Multicoloured.

2125	1c. Type **549**		20	10
2126	2c. "Pineria terebra" (shell)		10	10
2127	3c. Reef butterflyfish		10	10
2128	4c. "Eurema dina dina" (butterfly)		50	10
2129	13c. "Hemitrochus fuscolabiata" (shell)		2·00	1·00
2130	30c. Bicoloured damsel-fish		2·50	1·25

550 A. Mompo and 'Cello

1974. 50th Anniv of Havana Philharmonic Orchestra. Leading Personalities. Multicoloured.

2132	1c. Type **550**		10	10
2133	3c. C. P. Sentenat and piano		20	10
2134	5c. P. Mercado and trumpet		25	10
2135	10c. P. Sanjuan and emblem		75	40
2136	13c. R. Ondina and flute		1·00	60

551 "Heliconia humilis"

552 Boxers and Global Emblem

1974. Garden Flowers. Multicoloured.

2137	1c. Type **551**		10	10
2138	2c. "Anthurium andraeanum"		10	10
2139	3c. "Canna generalis"		10	10
2140	4c. "Alpinia purpurata"		20	10
2141	13c. "Gladiolus grandiflorus"		1·10	10
2142	30c. "Amomum capitatum"		2·75	45

1974. World Amateur Boxing Championships.

2143	**552**	1c. multicoloured	15	10
2144	–	3c. multicoloured	20	10
2145	–	13c. multicoloured	75	20

DESIGNS: 3c., 13c. Stages of Boxing matches similar to Type **552**.

FAUNA EXTINGUIDA
553 Mauritius Dodo ("Dodo")

555 "Suriana maritima"

554 Salvador Allende

1974. Extinct Birds. Multicoloured.

2146		1c. Type **553**	50	25
2147		3c. Cuban macaw ("Ara de Cuba")	50	25
2148		8c. Passenger pigeon ("Paloma Migratoria")	1·10	40
2149		10c. Moa	3·50	70
2150		13c. Great auk ("Gran Alca")	4·50	1·00

1974. 1st Death Anniv of Pres. Allende of Chile.

2151	**554**	13c. multicoloured	65	30

1974. Wild Flowers. (2nd series). Mult.

2152		1c. Type **555**	10	10
2153		3c. "Cassia ligustrina"	10	10
2154		8c. "Flaveria linearis"	20	15
2155		10c. "Stachytarpheta jamaicensis"	1·10	20
2156		13c. "Bacopa monnieri"	2·00	60

556 Flying Model Airplane

557 Indians playing Ball

1974. 10th Anniv of Civil Aeronautical Institute. Multicoloured.

2157		1c. Type **556**	20	10
2158		3c. Parachutist	20	10
2159		8c. Glider in flight (horiz)	30	10
2160		10c. Antonov An-2 biplane spraying crops (horiz)	1·00	60
2161		13c. Ilyushin Il-62M in flight (horiz)	1·60	90

1974. History of Baseball in Cuba. Mult.

2162		1c. Type **557**	10	10
2163		3c. Players of 1874 (First official game)	10	10
2164		8c. Emilio Sabourin	15	10
2165		10c. Modern players (horiz) (44 × 27 mm)	50	30
2166		13c. Latin-American Stadium, Havana (horiz) (44 × 27 mm)	1·00	50

558 Stamp, Cachet and Horseman

1974. Cent of "Mambi" Revolutionary Stamp.

2167	**558**	13c. multicoloured	85	20

559 Comecon Headquarters Building, Moscow and Emblem

1974. 16th Socialist Countries' Customs Conference.

2168	**559**	30c. blue and gold	1·00	35

560 Maj. Camilo Cienfuegos (revolutionary)

1974. 15th Anniv of Disappearance of Cienfuegos.

2169	**560**	3c. multicoloured	35	10

561 Miner's Helmet

1974. 8th World Mining Congress.

2170	**561**	13c. multicoloured	1·00	20

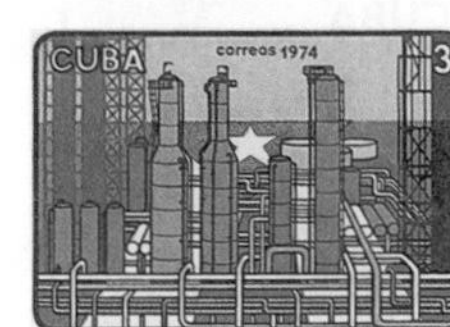

562 Oil Refinery

1974. 15th Anniv of Cuban Petroleum Institute.

2171	**562**	3c. multicoloured	50	10

563 Earth Station

1974. Inauguration of "Inter-Sputnik" Satellite Earth Station. Multicoloured.

2172		3c. Type **563**	10	10
2173		13c. Satellite and aerial	55	10
2174		1p. Satellite and flags	1·50	65

564 Emblems and Magnifying Glass

1974. 10th Anniv of Cuban Philatelic Federation.

2175	**564**	30c. multicoloured	1·10	40

566 F. Joliot-Curie (1st president) (Picasso)

1974. 25th Anniv of World Peace Congress.

2177	**566**	30c. multicoloured	1·10	40

567 R. M. Villena

1974. 75th Birth Anniv of Ruben Martinez Villena (revolutionary).

2178	**567**	3c. red and yellow	30	10

569 "The Word" (M. Pogolotti)

1975. National Museum Paintings (9th series). Multicoloured.

2180		1c. Type **569**	10	10
2181		2c. "The Silk-Cotton Tree" (H. Cleenewerk)	10	10
2182		3c. "Landscape" (G. Collazo)	10	10
2183		5c. "Still Life" (F. Peralta)	15	10
2184		13c. "Maria Wilson" (F. Martinez) (vert)	70	20
2185		30c. "The Couple" (M. Fortunay)	1·10	40

570 Bouquet and Woman's Head

1975. International Woman's Year.

2186	**570**	13c. multicoloured	65	20

571 Skipjack Tuna and Fishing-boat

1975. Cuban Fishing Industry. Mult.

2187		1c. Type **571**	15	10
2188		2c. Blue-finned tunny	15	10
2189		3c. Nassau grouper	15	10
2190		8c. Silver hake	15	15
2191		13c. Prawn	1·00	60
2192		30c. Lobster	2·25	1·00

572 Nickel

1975. Cuban Minerals. Multicoloured.

2193		3c. Type **572**	50	20
2194		13c. Copper	1·00	60
2195		30c. Chromium	1·50	75

1975. Cosmonautics Day. Science Fiction paintings. As T **546**. Multicoloured.

2196		1c. "Cosmodrome"	20	10
2197		2c. "Exploration craft" (vert)	25	10
2198		3c. "Earth eclipsing the Sun"	25	10
2199		5c. "On the Threshold"	30	10
2200		13c. "Astronauts on Mars"	1·00	50
2201		30c. "Astronauts' view of Earth"	1·50	75

573 Letter and "Correos" Postmark

1975. Stamp Day. Multicoloured.

2202		3c. Type **573**	10	10
2203		13c. Letter and steamship postmark	65	15
2204		30c. Letter and "N.A." postmark	1·00	30

574 Hoisting Red Flag over Reichstag, Berlin

1975. 30th Anniv of "Victory over Fascism".

2205	**574**	30c. multicoloured	1·00	30

575 Sevres Vase

1975. National Museum Treasures. Mult.

2206		1c. Type **575**	10	10
2207		2c. Meissen "Shepherdess and Dancers"	20	10
2208		3c. Chinese Porcelain Dish—"Lady with Parasol" (horiz)	20	10
2209		5c. Chinese Bamboo Screen—"The Phoenix"	30	10
2210		13c. "Allegory of Music" (F. Boucher)	1·00	50
2211		30c. "Portrait of a Lady" (L. Toque)	1·10	60

576 Coloured Balls and Globe "Man"

1975. International Children's Day.

2213	**576**	3c. multicoloured	20	10

577 Cuban Vireo

1975. Birds (1st series). Multicoloured.

2214		1c. Type **577**	30	15
2215		2c. Cuban screech owl	30	15
2216		3c. Cuban conure	30	15
2217		5c. Blue-headed quail dove	50	15
2218		13c. Hook-billed kite	2·75	50
2219		30c. Zapata rail	3·00	85

See also Nos. 2301/6.

578 View of Centre

1973. 10th Anniv of National Scientific Investigation Centre.

2220	**578**	13c. multicoloured	65	15

579 Commission Emblem and Drainage Equipment

1975. Int Commission on Irrigation and Drainage.

2221	**579**	13c. multicoloured	65	15

580 "Cedrea mexicana" **581** Women cultivating Young Plants

1975. Reafforestation. Multicoloured.
2222 1c. Type **580** 10 10
2223 3c. "Swietonia mahagoni" 25 10
2224 5c. "Calophyllum brasiliense" 30 10
2225 13c. "Hibiscus tiliaceus" . . 75 40
2226 30c. "Pinus caribaea" . . . 1·10 70

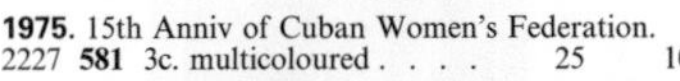

1975. 15th Anniv of Cuban Women's Federation.
2227 **581** 3c. multicoloured 25 10

582 Conference Emblem and Broken Chains **583** Baseball

1975. International Conference on the Independence of Puerto Rico.
2228 **582** 13c. multicoloured . . . 50 15

1975. 7th Pan-American Games, Mexico. Mult.
2229 1c. Type **583** 20 10
2230 3c. Boxing 25 10
2231 5c. Handball 25 10
2232 13c. High jumping 75 40
2233 30c. Weightlifting . . . . . 1·00 50

584 Emblem and Crowd

1975. 15th Anniv of Revolutionary Defence Committees.
2235 **584** 3c. multicoloured 20 10

585 Institute Emblem

1975. 15th Anniv of Cuban "Friendship Amongst the Peoples" Institute.
2236 **585** 3c. multicoloured 15 10

586 Silver 1 Peso Coin, 1913

1975. 15th Anniv of Nationalization of Bank of Cuba. Multicoloured.
2237 13c. Type **586** 70 25
2238 13c. 1 peso banknote, 1934 70 25
2239 13c. 1 peso banknote, 1946 70 25
2240 13c. 1 peso banknote, 1964 70 25
2241 13c. 1 peso banknote, 1973 70 25

587 "La Junta", Cuba's first locomotive, 1837

1975. "Evolution of Railways". Multicoloured.
2242 1c. Type **587** 15 10
2243 3c. Steam locomotive "M. M. Prieto", 1920 . . . . 20 10
2244 5c. Russian-built Type TEM-4 diesel locomotive 20 10
2245 13c. Hungarian-built Type DVM-9 diesel locomotive . . . . 1·50 20
2246 30c. Russian-built Type M-62K diesel locomotive . . . . 1·75 35

588 Bobbins and Flag

1975. Textile Industry.
2247 **588** 13c. multicoloured . . . 55 15

589 Sheep and Diagram

1975. Development of Veterinary Medicine. Animals and Disease Cycles. Multicoloured.
2248 1c. Type **589** 10 10
2249 2c. Dog 10 10
2250 3c. Cockerel 20 10
2251 5c. Horse 20 10
2252 13c. Pig . . . . 1·00 50
2253 30c. Ox . . . . 1·50 75

590 Manuel Ascunce Domenech **592** Communists with Flags inside Figure "1"

591 "Irrigation"

1975. Manuel Domenech Educational Detachment.
2254 **590** 3c. multicoloured 20 10

1975. Agriculture and Water-supply.
2255 **591** 13c. multicoloured . . . 65 15

1976. 1st Cuban Communist Party Congress. Multicoloured.
2256 3c. Type **592** 10 10
2257 13c. Workers with banner (horiz) 60 15
2258 30c. Jose Marti and Cuban leaders (horiz) 75 30

593 Pre-natal Exercises

1976. 8th Latin-American Obstetrics and Gynaecology Congress, Havana.
2259 **593** 3c. multicoloured 25 10

594 "Seated Woman" (V. Manuel) **595** Conference Emblem and Building

1976. National Museum Paintings (10th series). Multicoloured.
2260 1c. Type **594** 20 10
2261 2c. "Garden" (S. Rusinol) (horiz) 20 10
2262 3c. "Guadalquivir River" (M. Barron y Carrillo) (horiz) 40 10
2263 5c. "Self-portrait" (Jan Steen) 25 10
2264 13c. "Portrait of Woman" (L. M. van Loo) 85 40
2265 30c. "La Chula" (J. A. Morell) (27 × 44 mm) . . 90 50

1976. Socialist Communications Ministers' Conference, Havana.
2266 **595** 13c. multicoloured . . . 65 15

596 American Foxhound

1976. Hunting Dogs. Multicoloured.
2267 1c. Type **596** 20 10
2268 2c. Labrador retriever . . . 20 10
2269 3c. Borzoi 20 10
2270 5c. Irish setter 20 10
2271 13c. Pointer . . . . 1·25 75
2272 30c. Cocker Spaniel . . . . 1·75 1·10

597 Flags, Arms and Anthem

1976. Socialist Constitution, 1976.
2273 **597** 13c. multicoloured . . . 75 20

598 Ruy Lopez Segura

1976. History of Chess. Multicoloured.
2274 1c. Type **598** 20 10
2275 2c. Francois Philidor . . . 20 10
2276 3c. Wilhelm Steinitz 20 10
2277 13c. Emanuel Lasker . . . 85 40
2278 30c. Jose Raul Capablanca 1·00 50

599 Radio Aerial and Map

1976. 15th Anniv of Cuban International Broadcasting Services.
2279 **599** 50c. multicoloured . . . 1·00 50

600 Section of Human Eye and Microscope Slide **601** Children in Creche

1976. World Health Day.
2280 **600** 30c. multicoloured . . . 75 30

1976. 15th Anniv of Infant Welfare Centres.
2281 **601** 3c. multicoloured 25 10

602 Y. Gagarin in Space-suit

1976. 15th Anniv of First Manned Space Flight. Multicoloured.
2282 1c. Type **602** 10 10
2283 2c. V. Tereshkova and rockets 25 10
2284 3c. Cosmonaut on "space walk" (vert) 10 10
2285 5c. Spacecraft and Moon (vert) 15 10
2286 13c. Spacecraft in manoeuvre (vert) 75 40
2287 30c. Space link 90 50

603 Cuban Machine-gunner

1976. 15th Anniv of Giron Victory. Mult.
2288 3c. Type **603** 10 10
2289 13c. Cuban pilot and Lockheed F-80 Shooting Star fighter attacking ship 70 15
2290 30c. Cuban soldier wielding rifle (vert) 85 35

604 Heads of Farmers

1976. 15th Anniv of National Association of Small Farmers (ANAP).
2291 **604** 3c. multicoloured 20 10

605 Volleyball

1976. Olympic Games, Montreal. Mult.
2292 1c. Type **605** 20 10
2293 2c. Basketball 20 10
2294 3c. Long-jumping 20 10
2295 4c. Boxing 20 10
2296 5c. Weightlifting 20 10
2297 13c. Judo 80 50
2298 30c. Swimming . . . . . . 1·50 1·00

606 Modern Secondary School

1976. Rural Secondary Schools.
2300 **606** 3c. black and red 20 10

607 Oriente Warbler

1976. Birds (2nd series). Multicoloured.
2301 1c. Type **607** 40 15
2302 2c. Cuban pygmy owl . . . 40 15

2303	3c. Fernandina's flicker . .	40	15
2304	5c. Cuban tody	75	30
2305	13c. Gundlach's hawk . . .	1·50	40
2306	30c. Cuban trogon	3·50	1·00

608 Medical Treatment **609** "El Inglesito"

1976. "Expo", Havana. Soviet Science and Technology. Multicoloured.

2307	1c. Type **608**	10	10
2308	3c. Child and deer ("Environmental Protection")	10	10
2309	10c. Cosmonauts on launch pad ("Cosmos Investigation")	25	10
2310	30c. Tupolev Tu-144 airplane ("Soviet Transport") (horiz) . . .	1·25	35

1976. Death Cent of Henry M. Reeve (patriot).

2311	**609** 13c. multicoloured . . .	35	15

610 "G. Collazo" (J. Dabour)

1976. Cuban Paintings. Multicoloured.

2312	1c. Type **610**	10	10
2313	2c. "The Art Lovers" (G. Collazo) (horiz) . . .	10	10
2314	3c. "The Patio" (G. Collazo)	10	10
2315	5c. "Cocotero" (G. Collazo)	10	10
2316	13c. "New York Studio" (G. Collazo) (horiz) . . .	60	40
2317	30c. "Emelinz Collazo" (G. Collazo) (horiz) . . .	1·25	75

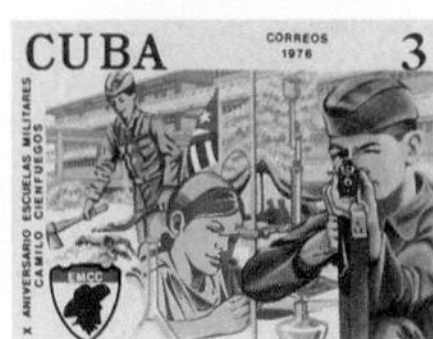

611 School Activities

1976. 10th Anniv of "Camilo Cienfuegos" Military School.

2318	**611** 3c. multicoloured	15	10

612 "Imias" (freighter)

1976. Development of Cuban Merchant Marine. Multicoloured.

2319	1c. Type **612**	25	10
2320	2c. "Comandante Camilo Cienfuegos" (freighter) . .	25	10
2321	3c. "Comandante Pinares" (cargo liner)	25	10
2322	5c. "Vietnam Heroico" (cargo liner)	40	10
2323	13c. "Presidente Allende" (ore carrier)	1·10	35
2324	30c. "XIII Congreso" (bulk carrier)	2·25	60

613 Emblem and part of Cine Film

1976. 8th International Cinematographic Festival of Socialist Countries, Havana.

2325	**613** 3c. multicoloured	15	10

614 Scene from "Apollo"

1976. 5th International Ballet Festival, Havana. Multicoloured.

2326	1c. Type **614**	10	10
2327	2c. "The River and the Forest" (vert)	20	10
2328	3c. "Giselle"	25	10
2329	5c. "Oedipus Rex" (vert) . .	30	10
2330	13c. "Carmen" (vert) . . .	70	45
2331	30c. "Vital Song" (vert) . .	1·25	1·00

615 Soldier and Sportsmen

1976. 3rd Military Games.

2332	**615** 3c. multicoloured	30	10

616 "Granma"

1976. 20th Anniv of "Granma" Landings.

2333	**616** 1c. multicoloured	10	10
2334	– 3c. multicoloured	10	10
2335	– 13c. multicoloured . . .	45	10
2336	– 30c. multicoloured . . .	75	35

DESIGNS: 3c. to 30c. Different scenes showing guerrillas.

618 Volleyball

1976. Cuban Victories in Montreal Olympic Games. Multicoloured.

2338	1c. Type **618**	10	10
2339	2c. Hurdling	10	10
2340	3c. Running	10	10
2341	8c. Boxing	15	10
2342	13c. Winning race	70	35
2343	30c. Judo	1·10	70

619 "Golden Cross Inn" (S. Scott)

1977. National Museum Paintings (11th series). Multicoloured.

2345	1c. Type **619**	10	10
2346	3c. "Portrait of a Man" (J. Verspronck) (vert) . .	10	10
2347	5c. "Venetian Landscape" (F. Guardi)	20	10
2348	10c. "Valley Corner" (H. Cleenewerck) (vert)	15	10
2349	13c. "F. Xaviera Paula" (anon) (vert)	70	15
2350	30c. "F. de Medici" (C. Allori) (vert)	1·00	35

The vert designs are slightly larger, 27 × 43 mm.

620 Motor Bus

1977. Rural Transport.

2351	**620** 3c. multicoloured	40	10

621 Map of Cuba

1977. Constitution of Popular Government.

2352	**621** 13c. multicoloured . . .	35	15

622 Cuban Green Woodpecker

1977. Cuban Birds. Multicoloured.

2353	1c. Type **622**	35	20
2354	4c. Cuban grassquit	45	20
2355	10c. Cuban blackbird . . .	80	25
2356	13c. Zapata wren	1·10	25
2357	30c. Bee hummingbird . . .	2·25	55

623 Mechanical Scoop and Emblem

1977. Air. 6th Latin-American and Caribbean Sugar Exporters Meeting, Havana.

2358	**623** 13c. multicoloured . . .	40	15

624 Fire-mouthed Cichlid

1997. Fish in Lenin Park Aquarium, Havana. Multicoloured.

2359	1c. Type **624**	10	10
2360	3c. Tiger barb	10	10
2361	5c. Koi carp	15	10
2362	10c. Siamese fightingfish . .	20	10
2363	13c. Freshwater angelfish (vert)	75	20
2364	30c. Buenos Aires tetra . .	1·50	40

625 "Sputnik 1" and East German Stamp

1977. 20th Anniv of 1st Artificial Satellite. Multicoloured.

2365	1c. Type **625**	10	10
2366	3c. "Luna 16" and Hungarian stamp	20	10
2367	5c. "Cosmos" and North Korean stamp	25	10
2368	10c. "Sputnik 3" and Polish stamp	40	25
2369	13c. Earth, Moon and Yugoslav stamp	85	50
2370	30c. Earth, Moon and Cuban stamp	1·10	75

626 Antonio Maria Romeu

1977. Cuban Musicians. Multicoloured.

2372	3c. Type **626** (postage) . . .	30	15
2373	13c. Jorge Ankerman (air)	70	30

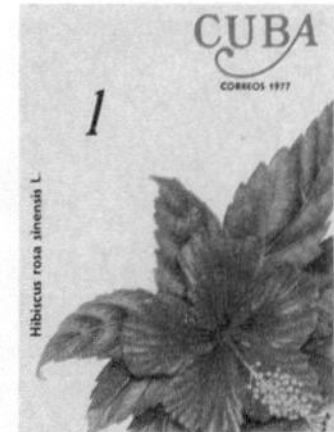

627 "Hibiscus rosa sinensis"

1977. Birth Centenary of Dr. Juan Tomas Roig (botanist). Cuban Flowers. Multicoloured.

2374	1c. Type **627** (postage) . . .	10	10
2375	2c. "Nerium oleander" . . .	10	10
2376	5c. "Allamanda cathartica"	20	10
2377	10c. "Pelargonium zonale"	35	10
2378	13c. "Caesalpinia pulcherrima" (air)	60	40
2379	30c. "Catharanthus roseus"	1·10	80

628 Horse-drawn Fire Engine

1977. Fire Prevention Week, Multicoloured.

2381	1c. Type **628**	10	10
2382	2c. Horse-drawn fire engine (different)	10	10
2383	6c. Early motor fire pump	10	10
2384	10c. Modern motor fire pump	25	10
2385	13c. Turntable-ladder . . .	50	30
2386	30c. Heavy rescue vehicle . .	1·10	80

629 20th Anniversary Medal

1977. National Decorations.

2387	**629** 1c. mult (postage) . . .	10	10
2388	– 3c. multicoloured	15	10
2389	– 13c. multicoloured (air)	35	10
2390	– 30c. multicoloured . . .	65	30

DESIGNS: 3c. to 30c. Various medals and ribbons.

630 "Portrait of Mary"

631 Boxing

1977. Painting by Jorge Arche. Mult.

2391	1c. Type **630** (postage) . . .	10	10
2392	3c. "Jose Marti"	10	10
2393	5c. "Portrait of Aristides"	10	10
2394	10c. "Bathers" (horiz) . . .	25	10
2395	13c. "My Wife and I" (air)	30	10
2396	30c. "The Game of Dominoes" (horiz) . . .	65	30

1977. Military Spartakiad. Multicoloured.

2398	1c. Type **631** (postage) . . .	10	10
2399	3c. Volleyball	10	10
2400	5c. Parachuting	10	10
2401	10c. Running	20	10
2402	13c. Grenade-throwing (air)	30	10
2403	30c. Rifle-shooting (horiz)	65	30

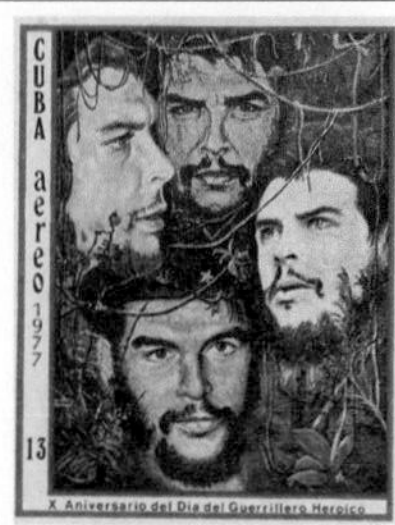

632 Che Guevara

1977. Air. 10th Anniv of Guerrilla Heroes Day.
2404 **632** 13c. multicoloured . . . 40 10

633 Curtiss A-1 Seaplane and Parla Stamp of 1952

1977. 50th Anniv of Cuban Air Mail. Mult.
2405 1c. Type **633** (postage) . . . 10 10
2406 2c. Ford 5-AT trimotor airplane and Havana–Key West cachet 20 10
2407 5c. Flying boat "American Clipper" and first flight cachet 25 10
2408 10c. Douglas DC-4 and Havana-Madrid cachet . . 40 30
2409 13c. Lockheed Super Constellation and Havana–Mexico cachet (air) 60 40
2410 30c. Ilyushin Il-18 and Havana–Prague cachet . . 1·00 60

634 Cruiser "Aurora"

1977. 60th Anniv of Russian Revolution.
2411 **634** 3c. black, red and gold 25 10
2412 – 13c. black, red and gold 50 25
2413 – 30c. gold, red and black 1·00 70
DESIGNS: 13c. Lenin and flags; 30c. Hammer and sickle with scenes of technology.

636 Cat

1977. Felines in Havana Zoo. Multicoloured.
2415 1c. Type **636** (postage) . . . 20 10
2416 2c. Leopard (black race) . . 20 10
2417 8c. Puma 25 10
2418 10c. Leopard 90 50
2419 13c. Tiger (air) . . . . . . 1·00 60
2420 30c. Lion . . . . 1·40 1·00

637 Cienfuegos Uprising

1977. 20th Anniv of Martyrs of the Revolution. Multicoloured.
2421 3c. Type **637** (postage) . . . 20 10
2422 20c. Attack on the Presidential Palace . . . 45 15
2423 13c. Landing from the "Corynthia" (air) 65 35

638 Clinic, Havana

1977. 75th Anniv of Pan-American Health Organization.
2424 **638** 13c. multicoloured . . . 10 10

639 Map of Cuba and Units of Measurement

1977. International System of Measurement.
2425 **639** 3c. multicoloured 10 10

640 University Building and Coat of Arms

1978. 250th Anniv of Havana University. Multicoloured.
2426 3c. Type **640** (postage) . . . 10 10
2427 13c. University building and crossed sabres (air) . . . 30 10
2428 30c. Student crowd and statue 50 30

641 "Jose Marti" (A. Menocal)
642 "Seated Woman" (R. Madrazo)

1978. Air. 125th Anniv of Jose Marti (patriot).
2429 **641** 13c. multicoloured . . . 30 10

1978. National Museum Paintings (12th series). Multicoloured.
2430 1c. Type **642** (postage) . . . 10 10
2431 4c. "Girl" (J. Sorolla) . . . 10 10
2432 6c. "Landscape with Figures" (J. Pilliment) (horiz) 20 10
2433 10c. "The Cow" (E. Abela) (horiz) 35 10
2434 13c. "El Guadalquivir" (M. Barron) (horiz) (air) 75 50
2435 30c. "H. E. Ridley" (J. J. Masqueries) 75 50

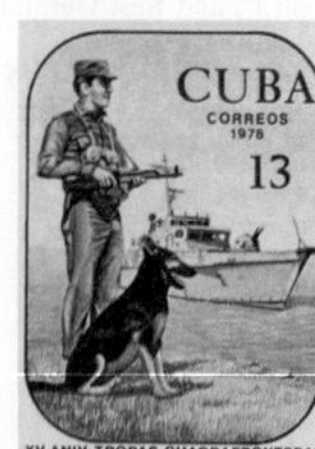

643 Patrol Boat, Frontier Guard and Dog

1978. 15th Anniv of Frontier Troops.
2436 **643** 13c. multicoloured . . . 1·00 15

644 Cuban Solitaire

1978. Cuban Birds. Multicoloured.
2437 1c. Type **644** (postage) . . . 60 25
2438 4c. Cuban gnatcatcher . . . 60 30
2439 10c. Oriente warbler . . . . 1·60 40
2440 13c. Zapata sparrow (air) 2·10 70
2441 30c. Cuban macaw and ivory-billed woodpecker (vert) . . . . 3·00 1·10

645 "Antonio Maceo" (A. Melero)
646 "Intercosmos" Satellite

1978. Air. Centenary of Baragua Protest.
2442 **645** 13c. multicoloured . . . 30 10

1978. Cosmonautics Day. Multicoloured.
2443 1c. Type **646** (postage) . . . 10 10
2444 2c. "Luna 24" (horiz) . . . 10 10
2445 5c. "Venus 9" 15 10
2446 10c. "Cosmos" (horiz) . . . 15 10
2447 13c. "Venus 10" (horiz) (air) 30 10
2448 30c. "Lunokhod 2" (36 × 46 mm) 55 30

647 Smiling Worker and Emblem

1978. 9th World Federation of Trade Unions Congress, Prague.
2449 **647** 30c. red and black . . . 45 25

648 Parliament Building, Budapest and 1919 Hungarian Stamp

1978. Air "Socfilex" Stamp Exhibition, Budapest.
2450 **648** 30c. multicoloured . . . 55 30

649 "Melocactus guitarti"

1978. Cactus Flowers. Multicoloured.
2451 1c. Type **649** (postage) . . . 10 10
2452 4c. "Leptocereus wrightii" 10 10
2453 6c. "Opuntia militaris" . . . 10 10
2454 10c. "Cylindropuntia hystrix" 30 10
2455 13c. "Rhodocactus cubensis" (air) 50 30
2456 30c. "Harrisia taetra" . . . 85 50

650 Satellite and Globe

1978. Air. World Telecommunications Day.
2457 **650** 30c. multicoloured . . . 55 30

651 Africans and O.A.U. Emblem

1978. Air. 15th Anniv of Organization of African Unity.
2458 **651** 30c. multicoloured . . . 50 30

653 Clown Barb

1978. Fish in Lenin Park Aquarium, Havana. Multicoloured.
2460 1c. Type **653** (postage) . . . 10 10
2461 4c. Flame tetra 25 10
2462 6c. Guppy 30 10
2463 10c. Dwarf gourami 35 20
2464 13c. Veil-tailed goldfish (air) 70 40
2465 30c. Brown discus . . . . . 1·00 70

654 Basketball
655 Moncada Fortress

1978. 13th Central American and Caribbean Games. Multicoloured.
2466 1c. Type **654** (postage) . . . 10 10
2467 3c. Boxing 10 10
2468 5c. Weightlifting 10 10
2469 10c. Fencing (horiz) 25 10
2470 13c. Volleyball (air) 50 35
2471 30c. Running 75 45

1978. 25th Anniv of Attack on Moncada Fortress. Multicoloured.
2472 3c. Type **655** (postage) . . . 10 10
2473 13c. Soldiers with rifles (air) 25 10
2474 30c. Dove and flags 50 25

656 Prague

1978. 11th World Youth and Students' Festival, Havana. Multicoloured.
2475 3c. Type **656** (postage) . . . 10 10
2476 3c. Budapest 10 10
2477 3c. Berlin 10 10
2478 3c. Bucharest 10 10
2479 3c. Warsaw 10 10
2480 13c. Moscow (air) 25 15
2481 13c. Vienna 25 15
2482 13c. Helsinki 25 15
2483 13c. Sofia 25 15
2484 13c. Berlin 25 15
2485 30c. Havana (46 × 36 mm) 55 25

657 Marching Soldiers with Flag

1978. 5th Anniv of Young Workers Army.
2486 **657** 3c. multicoloured 10 10

658 "Pargo"

1978. Fishing Fleet. Multicoloured.
2487 1c. Type **658** (postage) . . . 15 10
2488 2c. Fish-processing ship . . 15 10
2489 5c. Shrimp fishing boat . . 15 10
2490 10c. Stern trawler 35 15
2491 13c. "Mar Carbide" (air) . . 60 20
2492 30c. Refrigeration and processing ship . . . . . 1·10 40

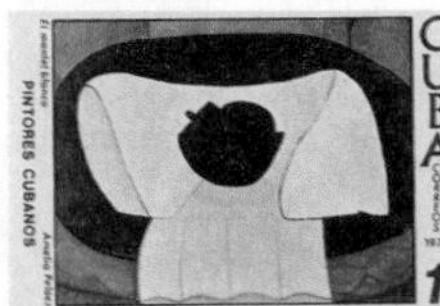

660 "The White Coat" (Pelaez del Casal)

1978. Painting by Amelia Pelaez del Casal. Multicoloured.
2494 1c. Type **660** (postage) . . . 10 10
2495 3c. "Still Life with Flowers" . . 10 10
2496 6c. "Women" 20 10
2497 10c. "Fish" 30 10
2498 13c. "Flowering Almond" (air) 40 30
2499 30c. "Still Life in Blue" . . 80 50

661 Letters, Satellite and Globe

1978. Air 20th Anniv of Organization for Communication Co-operation between Socialist Countries.
2501 **661** 30c. multicoloured . . . 50 30

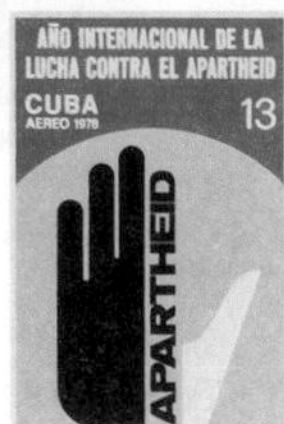

663 Hand

1978. Air. International Anti-Apartheid Year.
2503 **663** 13c. black, pink & mve 1·10 1·10

664 White Rhinoceros

1978. Animals in Havana Zoo. Multicoloured.
2504 1c. Type **664** (postage) . . . 20 10
2505 4c. Okapi (vert) 20 10
2506 6c. Mandrill 20 10
2507 10c. Giraffe (vert) 40 25
2508 13c. Cheetah (air) 75 50
2509 30c. African elephant (vert) 1·25 75

665 "Grand Pas de Quatre"

1978. 30th Anniv of National Ballet Company. Multicoloured.
2510 3c. Type **665** (postage) . . . 20 10
2511 13c. "Giselle" (air) 35 15
2512 30c. "Genesis" 75 60

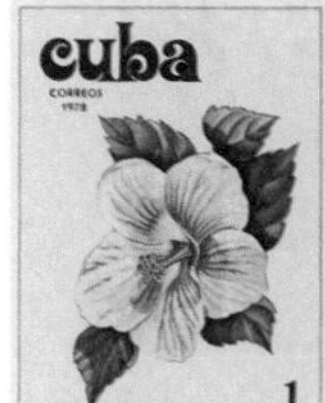

666 Hibiscus

668 Fidel Castro and Soldier

667 Julius and Ethel Rosenberg

1978. Pacific Flowers.
2513 **666** 1c. mult (postage) . . . 10 10
2514 – 4c. multicoloured 10 10
2515 – 6c. multicoloured 20 10
2516 – 10c. multicoloured . . . 35 20
2517 – 13c. mult (air) 50 30
2518 – 30c. multicoloured . . . 85 50
DESIGNS: 4c. to 30c. Different flowers.

1978. Air. 25th Death Anniv of Julius and Ethel Rosenberg (American Communists).
2519 **667** 13c. multicoloured . . . 25 10

1979. 20th Anniv of Revolution. Mult.
2520 3c. Type **668** 10 10
2521 13c. Symbols of industry . . 30 15
2522 1p. Flag, flame and globe 1·75 95

669 Julio Mella

1979. 50th Death Anniv of J. A. Mella.
2523 **669** 13c. multicoloured . . . 20 10

670 Blue-headed Quail Dove

1979. Doves and Pigeons. Multicoloured.
2524 1c. Type **670** 45 15
2525 3c. Key West quail dove . . 50 15
2526 7c. Grey-faced quail dove 50 15
2527 8c. Ruddy quail dove . . . 60 15
2528 13c. White-crowned pigeon 1·25 40
2529 30c. Plain pigeon . . . . . 2·25 1·25

671 "Genre Scene" (D. Teniers)

1979. National Museum Paintings (13th series). Multicoloured.
2530 1c. Type **671** 10 10
2531 3c. "Arrival of Spanish Troops" (J. Meissonier) 15 10
2532 6c. "A Joyful Gathering" (Sir David Wilkie) 15 10
2533 10c. "Capea" (E. de Lucas Padilla) 25 10
2534 13c. "Teatime" (R. Madrazo) (vert) . . . 35 25
2535 30c. "Peasant in front of a Tavern" (Adriaen van Ostade) 75 40

672 "Nymphaea capensis"

673 "20" Flag and Film Frames

1979. Aquatic Flowers. Multicoloured.
2536 3c. Type **672** 20 10
2537 10c. "Nymphaea ampla" . . 25 10
2538 13c. "Nymphaea coerulea" 35 15
2539 30c. "Nymphaea rubra" . . 75 25

1979. 20th Anniv of Cuban Cinema.
2540 **673** 3c. multicoloured 10 10

674 Rocket Launch

1979. Cosmonautics Day. Multicoloured.
2541 1c. Type **674** 10 10
2542 4c. "Soyuz" 10 10
2543 6c. "Salyut" 10 10
2544 10c. "Soyuz" and "Salyut" link-up 25 10
2545 13c. "Soyuz" and "Salyut" 40 10
2546 30c. Parachute and capsule 75 30

675 Hands and Globe

1979. 6th Non-Aligned Countries Summit Conference. Multicoloured.
2548 3c. Type **675** 10 10
2549 13c. "6" ("Against Colonialism") 20 10
2550 30c. Joined coin and globe ("A New Economic Order") 50 30

676 Cuna Indian Tapestry, Panama

1979. 20th Anniv of "House of the Americas" Museum.
2551 **676** 13c. multicoloured . . . 20 10

677 Farmer holding Title Deed

1979. 20th Anniv of Agrarian Reform.
2552 **677** 3c. multicoloured 10 10

679 "Eulepidotis rectimargo"

1979. Cuban Nocturnal Butterflies. Mult.
2554 1c. Type **679** 10 10
2555 4c. "Othreis materna" . . . 10 10
2556 6c. "Noropsis hieroglyphica" 25 10
2557 10c. "Heterochroma sp." . . 25 10
2558 13c. "Melanchroia regnatrix" 75 50
2559 30c. "Attera gemmata" . . 1·50 1·00

680 Children's Heads

1979. Air. International Year of the Child.
2560 **680** 13c. multicoloured . . . 20 10

681 "Avenue du Maine, Paris"

1979. 10th Death Anniv of Victor Manuel Garcia (painter). Multicoloured.
2561 1c. Type **681** 10 10
2562 3c. "Portrait of Enmita" . . 10 10
2563 6c. "Rio San Juan, Matanzas" 20 10
2564 10c. "Landscape with Woman carrying Hay" . . 20 10
2565 13c. "Still-life with Vase" . . 30 10
2566 30c. "Street by Night" . . . 60 30

682 Clenched Fists, Dove and Bombs

1979. 30th Anniv of World Peace Council.
2568 **682** 30c. multicoloured . . . 55 25

683 Lighthouse and Fireworks

1979. Air. "Carifesta 79" Festival, Havana.
2569 **683** 13c. multicoloured . . . 50 10

684 Wrestling

1979. Pre-Olympics, Moscow 1980. Mult.
2570 1c. Type **684** 10 10
2571 4c. Boxing 10 10
2572 6c. Volleyball 20 10
2573 10c. Rifle-shooting 20 10
2574 13c. Weightlifting 35 10
2575 30c. High jump 75 25

685 "Rosa eglanteria"

686 Council Emblem

1979. Roses. Multicoloured.
2576 1c. Type **685** 20 10
2577 2c. "Rosa centifolia anemonoides" 20 10
2578 3c. "Rosa indica vulgaris" 20 10
2579 5c. "Rosa eglanteria var. punicea" 20 10
2580 10c. "Rosa sulfurea" . . . 20 10
2581 13c. "Rosa muscosa alba" 40 10
2582 20c. "Rosa gallica purpurea velutina, Parva" 70 20

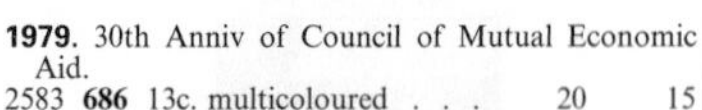

1979. 30th Anniv of Council of Mutual Economic Aid.
2583 **686** 13c. multicoloured . . . 20 15

687 Games Emblem and Activities

1979. Air. "Universiada 79" 10th World University Games, Mexico City.
2584 **687** 13c. green, gold & turq 25 15

688 Conventions Palace

1979. Air. 6th Non-Aligned Countries Summit Conference, Havana.
2585 **688** 50c. multicoloured . . . 80 60

689 Sir Rowland Hill and Casket containing Freedom of the City of London

1979. Air. Death Centenary of Sir Rowland Hill.
2586 **689** 30c. multicoloured . . . 75 20

690 Ford 5-AT Trimotor

1979. 50th Anniv of Cuban Airlines. Mult.
2587 1c. Type **690** 10 10
2588 2c. Sikorsky S-38 flying boat 10 10
2589 3c. Douglas DC-3 . . . . . 30 10
2590 4c. Ilyushin Il-18 . . . . . 30 20
2591 13c. Yakovlev Yak-40 . . . 85 50
2592 40c. Ilyushin Il-62M . . . . 1·75 90

691 Rumanian "New Constitution" Stamp of 1948

1979. Air. "Socfilex 79" Stamp Exhibition, Bucharest.
2593 **691** 30c. multicoloured . . . 50 30

692 Camilo Cienfuegos

1979. 20th Anniv of Disappearance of Camilo Cienfuegos (revolutionary).
2594 **692** 3c. multicoloured 15 10

693 Alvaro Reinoso and Sugar Cane

1979. 15th Anniv of Sugar Cane Institute and 150th Birth Anniv of Alvaro Reinoso.
2595 **693** 13c. multicoloured . . . 30 15

694 Chimpanzees

1979. Young Zoo Animals. Multicoloured.
2596 1c. Type **694** 10 10
2597 2c. Leopards 10 10
2598 3c. Fallow deer 15 10
2599 4c. Lions 20 10
2600 5c. Brown bears 25 10
2601 13c. Eurasian red squirrels 50 25
2602 30c. Giant pandas . . . . . 1·00 50
2603 50c. Tigers . . . . 1·50 75

695 Ground Receiving Station

1979. Air. 50th Anniv of International Radio Consultative Committee.
2604 **695** 30c. multicoloured . . . 50 20

696 "Rhina oblita"

1980. Insects. Multicoloured.
2605 1c. Type **696** 10 10
2606 5c. "Odontocera josemartii" (vert) 10 10
2607 6c. "Pinthocoelium columbinum" 10 10
2608 10c. "Calosoma splendida" (vert) 30 10
2609 13c. "Homophileurus cubanus" (vert) 60 30
2610 30c. "Heterops dimidiata" (vert) . . . . 1·00 40

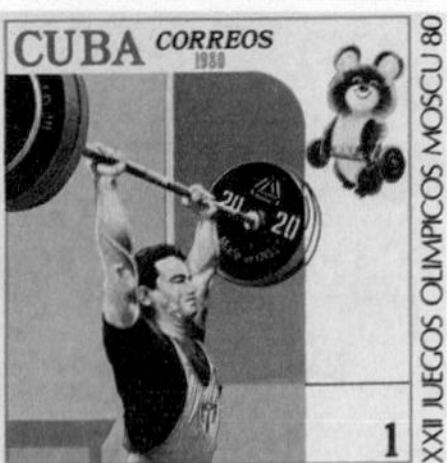

697 Weightlifting

1980. Olympic Games, Moscow. Multicoloured.
2611 1c. Type **697** 10 10
2612 2c. Shooting 10 10
2613 5c. Javelin 15 10
2614 6c. Wrestling 15 10
2615 8c. Judo 25 10
2616 10c. Running 25 10
2617 13c. Boxing 40 10
2618 30c. Volleyball 80 35

698 "Oak Trees" (Henry Joseph Harpignies)

1980. National Museum Paintings (14th series). Multicoloured.
2620 1c. Type **698** 10 10
2621 4c. "Family Reunion" (Willem van Mieris) (horiz) 10 10
2622 6c. "Poultry" (Melchior de Hondecoeter) 10 10
2623 9c. "Innocence" (Williams A. Bouguereau) 15 10
2624 13c. "Venetian Scene II" (Michele Marieschi) (horiz) 50 10
2625 30c. "Spanish Country-women" (Joaquin Dominguez Bequer) . . . 75 35

700 Intercosmos Emblem

1980. Intercosmos Programme. Mult.
2627 1c. Type **700** 10 10
2628 4c. Satellite and globe (Physics) 10 10
2629 6c. Satellite and dish aerial (Communications) 10 10
2630 10c. Satellite, grid lines and map (Meteorology) . . . 15 10
2631 13c. Staff of Aesculapius, rocket and satellites (Biology and Medicine) 25 10
2632 30c. Surveying Satellite . . . 50 35

701 Cuban Stamps of 1955 and 1959 (⅔-size illustration)

1980. 125th Anniv of Cuban Stamps.
2633 **701** 30c. blue, red & lt blue 55 30

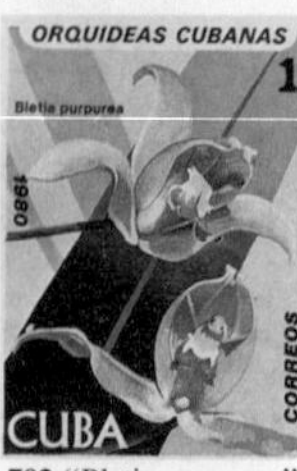

702 "Bletia purpurea"

1980. Orchids. Multicoloured.
2634 1c. Type **702** 10 10
2635 4c. "Oncidium leiboldii" . . 10 10
2636 6c. "Epidendrum cochieatum" 20 10
2637 10c. "Cattleyopsis lindenii" 25 10
2638 13c. "Encyclia fucata" . . . 40 25
2639 30c. "Encyclia phoenicea" 1·00 50

703 Bottle-nosed Dolphin

1980. Marine Mammals. Multicoloured.
2640 1c. Type **703** 25 10
2641 3c. Humpback whale (vert) 25 10
2642 13c. Cuvier's beaked whale 60 40
2643 30c. Caribbean monk seal 1·50 80

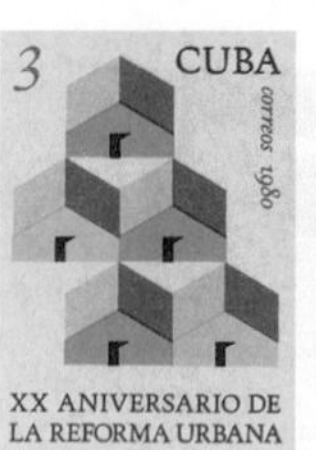

704 Houses

705 Pitcher

1980. "Moncada" Programme. Mult.
2644 3c. Type **704** 10 10
2645 13c. Refinery 20 10
ANNIVERSARIES: 3c. Urban Reform (20th Anniv). 13c. Foreign industry (20th Anniv).

1980. Copper Handicrafts. Multicoloured.
2646 3c. Type **705** 10 10
2647 13c. Wine container (38 × 26 mm) 20 15
2648 30c. Two handled pitcher 50 30

706 Emblem, Flag and Roses

708 Flags

1980. 20th Anniv of Cuban Women's Federation.
2649 **706** 3c. multicoloured 10 10

1980. 20th Anniv of 1st Havana Declaration.
2651 **708** 13c. multicoloured . . . 20 15

709 Building Galleon "Nuesta Sra. de Atocha", 1620

1980. Cuban Shipbuilding. Multicoloured.
2652 1c. Type **709** 15 10
2653 3c. Building ship of the line "El Rayo", 1749 . . . . 15 10
2654 7c. Building ship of the line "Santisima Trinidad", 1769 . . . . 15 10
2655 10c. "Santisima Trinidad" at sea, 1805 (vert) 50 30
2656 13c. Building steamships "Colon" and "Congreso", 1851 . . . . 1·00 60
2657 30c. Cardenas and Chullima shipyards . . . . 1·50 1·00

710 Arnaldo Tamayo

1980. Air. 1st Cuban–Soviet Space Flight.
2658 **710** 13c. multicoloured . . . 30 15
2659 30c. multicoloured . . . 55 30

711 U.N. General Assembly

712 Child being Fed

1980. 20th Anniv of Fidel Castro's First Speech at the United Nations.

2660	**711** 13c. multicoloured		20	10

1980. 20th Anniv of Revolution's Defence Committees.

2661	**712** 3c. multicoloured		15	10

714 Inspection Locomotive

1980. Early Locomotives. Multicoloured.

2663	1c. Type **714**	20	10
2664	2c. Inspection locomotive, Chaparra Sugar Company	20	10
2665	7c. Fireless locomotive, San Francisco Sugar Mill	30	10
2666	10c. Saddle-tank locomotive, Australia Estate	40	10
2667	13c. Steam locomotive	70	10
2668	30c. Oil-fired locomotive, 1909, Smith Comas Estate	1·75	60

715 "Roncali" Lighthouse, San Antonio

1980. Lighthouses (1st series). Multicoloured.

2669	3c. Type **715**	20	10
2670	13c. Jagua, Cienfuegos	35	20
2671	30c. Punta Maisi, Guantanamo	80	70

See also Nos. 2746/8, 2859/61 and 2920/2.

716 Bronze Medal

1980. Cuban Olympic Medal Winners. Mult.

2672	13c. Type **716**	20	15
2673	30c. Silver medal	60	20
2674	50c. Gold medal	1·00	50

717 "Pancratium arenicolum"

719 Congress Emblem

1980. Forest Flowers. Multicoloured.

2675	1c. Type **717**	10	10
2676	4c. "Urechites lutea"	15	10
2677	6c. "Solanum elaegnifolium"	20	10
2678	10c. "Hamelia patens"	25	10
2679	13c. "Morinda royoc"	35	10
2680	30c. "Centrosema virginianum"	85	25

1980. 2nd Communist Party Congress. Mult.

2682	3c. Type **719**	10	10
2683	13c. Dish aerial and factories (Industry)	20	10
2684	30c. Gymnast, reader and elderly man resting (Recreation)	45	20

720 "Lady Mayo" (Anton van Dyck)

1981. National Museum Paintings (15th series). Multicoloured.

2685	1c. Type **720**	10	10
2686	6c. "La Hilandera" (Giovanni B. Piazzeta)	10	10
2687	10c. "Daniel Collyer" (Francis Cotes)	15	10
2688	13c. "Gardens of Palma de Mallorca" (Santiago Rusinol) (horiz)	20	15
2689	20c. "Landscape with Road and Houses" (Frederick W. Watts) (horiz)	30	15
2690	50c. "Landscape with Sheep" (Jean F. Millet) (horiz)	90	50

721 Short-finned Mako

1981. Fishes. Multicoloured.

2691	1c. Type **721**	15	10
2692	3c. Opah	15	10
2693	10c. Sailfish	20	15
2694	13c. Oceanic sunfish (vert)	1·50	35
2695	30c. Dolphin and flying-fish	75	30
2696	50c. White marlin	1·40	75

722 Saving Ball

1981. World Cup Football Championship, Spain (1982). (1st issue). Multicoloured.

2697	1c. Diving for ball (horiz)	10	10
2698	2c. Passing ball (horiz)	10	10
2699	3c. Running with ball (horiz)	10	10
2700	10c. Type **722**	25	10
2701	13c. Heading ball	50	10
2702	50c. Tackle (horiz)	1·25	50

See also Nos. 2775/81.

723 Mother, Child, Boots and Toy Train

724 Jules Verne, Konstantin Tsiolkovsky and Sergei Korolev

1981. 20th Anniv of Kindergartens.

2704	**723** 3c. multicoloured		1·50	10

1981. 20th Anniv of First Man in Space. Mult.

2705	1c. Type **724**	10	10
2706	2c. Yuri Gagarin (first man in space) (horiz)	10	10
2707	3c. Valentina Tereshkova (first woman in space) (horiz)	10	10
2708	5c. Aleksandr Leonov (first space walker) (horiz)	10	10
2709	13c. Crew of "Voskhod I" (horiz)	20	10
2710	30c. Ryumen and Popov (horiz)	50	30
2711	50c. Tamayo and Romanenko (crew of Soviet–Cuban flight)	90	40

725 Jet Fighters and Rocket

1981. 20th Anniv of Defeat of Invasion Attempt by Cuban Exiles. Multicoloured.

2712	3c. Type **725** (Defence and Air Force Day)	10	10
2713	13c. Hand waving machine-pistol (Victory at Giron)	20	15
2714	30c. Book and flags (Proclamation of Revolution's socialist character) (horiz)	45	30

726 Reynold Garcia Garcia (leader of attack), Barracks and Children

1981. 25th Anniv of Attack on Goicuria Barracks.

2715	**726** 3c. multicoloured		15	10

727 Tractor and Women planting Crops

1981. 20th Anniv of National Association of Small Farmers.

2716	**727** 3c. multicoloured		15	10

729 Canelo

1981. Fighting Cocks. Multicoloured.

2718	1c. Type **729**	10	10
2719	3c. Cenizo (horiz)	10	10
2720	7c. Blanco	15	10
2721	13c. Pinto	15	10
2722	30c. Giro (horiz)	50	30
2723	50c. Jabao	95	50

730 Anniversary Emblem

733 "House in the Country" (Maria Cardidad de la O)

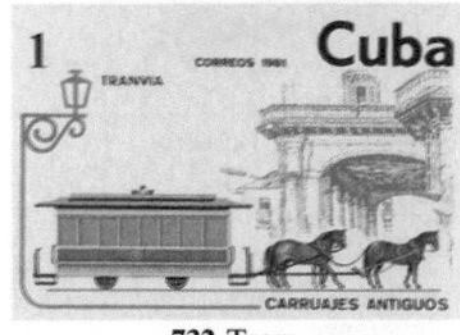
732 Tram

1981. 20th Anniv of Ministry of the Interior.

2724	**730** 13c. multicoloured		15	10

1981. Horse-drawn Vehicles. Multicoloured.

2726	1c. Type **732**	30	10
2727	4c. Village bus	10	10
2728	9c. Brake	15	10
2729	13c. Landau	15	10
2730	30c. Phaeton	60	30
2731	50c. Hearse	1·10	50

1981. International Year of Disabled People.

2732	**733** 30c. multicoloured		55	30

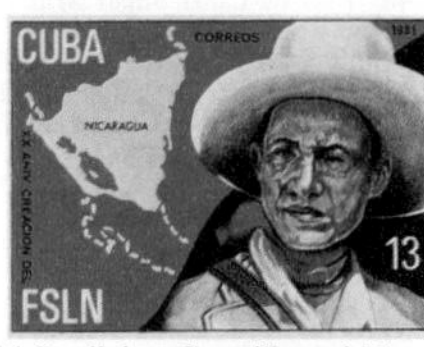
734 Sandinista Guerrilla and Map of Nicaragua

1981. 20th Anniv of Sandinista National Liberation Front.

2733	**734** 13c. multicoloured		20	15

735 Gymnasts

1981. 20th Anniv of State Organizations. Mult.

2734	3c. Type **735** (National Sports and Physical Recreation Institute)	10	10
2735	13c. "RHC", radio waves and map (Radio Havana)	15	10
2736	30c. Arrows ("Mincex" Foreign Trade Ministry)	55	30

736 Carlos J. Finlay, Mosquito and Theory

1981. Centenary of Biological Vectors Theory.

2737	**736** 13c. multicoloured		20	15

737 Arms of Non-aligned Countries, Manacled Hands and Hands releasing Dove

1981. 20th Anniv of Non-aligned Countries Movement.

2738	**737** 50c. multicoloured		90	50

738 White Horse

1981. Horses. Multicoloured.

2739	1c. Type **738**	10	10
2740	3c. Brown horse	10	10
2741	8c. Bucking white horse	15	10
2742	13c. Horse being broken-in	15	10
2743	30c. Black horse	75	40
2744	50c. Herd of horses (horiz)	1·25	70

1981. Lighthouses (2nd series). As T **715**. Mult.

2746	3c. Piedras del Norte	30	10
2747	13c. Punta Lucrecia	40	20
2748	40c. Guano del Este	1·25	60

740 "Flor de Cuba Sugar Mill"

1981. 80th Anniv of Jose Marti National Library. Lithographs by Eduardo Laplante. Multicoloured.

2749 3c. Type **740** 10 10
2750 13c. "El Progreso Sugar Mill" 25 10
2751 30c. "Santa Teresa Sugar Mill" 70 30

741 Pablo Picasso and Cuban Stamp

1981. Birth Centenary of Pablo Picasso (artist).

2752 **741** 30c. multicoloured . . . 75 35

743 "Napoleon in Coronation Regalia" (Anon.)

1981. 20th Anniv of Napoleonic Museum. Mult.

2754 1c. Type **743** 10 10
2755 3c. "Napoleon with Landscape" (J. H. Vernet) (horiz) 10 10
2756 10c. "Bonaparte in Egypt" (Eduard Detaille) 15 10
2757 13c. "Napoleon on Horseback" (Hippolyte Bellange) (horiz) 15 10
2758 30c. "Napoleon in Normandy" (Bellange) (horiz) 60 30
2759 50c. "Death of Napoleon" (Anon) . . . . 1·10 45

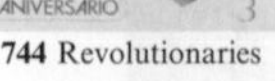

744 Revolutionaries **745** Cuban Emerald ("Zun-Zun")

1981. 25th Anniversaries. Multicoloured.

2760 3c. Type **744** (30th November insurrection) 10 10
2761 20c. Soldier (Revolutionary Armed Forces) 20 10
2762 1p. Launch "Granma" (disembarkation of revolutionary forces) . . . 2·25 1·00

1981. Fauna.

2763 **745** 1c. blue 75 15
2764 – 2c. green . . . . 1·10 25
2765 – 5c. brown 15 15
2766 – 20c. red 50 15
2767 – 35c. lilac . . . . . . 1·00 20
2768 – 40c. grey 80 35

DESIGNS: 2c. Cuban conure ("Catey"); 5c. Desmarest's hutia; 20c. Cuban solenodon; 35c. American manatee; 40c. Crocodile.

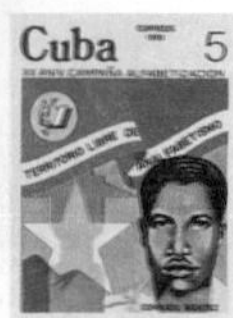

746 Ortiz (after Jorge Arche y Silva) **747** Conrado Benitez

1981. Birth Centenary of Fernando Ortiz (folklorist). Multicoloured.

2769 3c. Type **746** 10 10
2770 10c. Idol (pendant) 15 10
2771 30c. Arara drum 55 25
2772 50c. Thunder god (Chango carving) 90 45

1981. 20th Anniv of Literacy Campaign. Mult.

2773 5c. Type **747** 15 10
2774 5c. Manuel Ascunce 15 10

748 Goalkeeper **749** Lazaro Pena (trade union delegate)

1982. World Cup Football Championship, Spain (2nd issue). Multicoloured.

2775 1c. Type **748** 10 10
2776 2c. Footballers 10 10
2777 5c. Heading ball 10 10
2778 10c. Kicking ball 15 10
2779 20c. Running for ball (horiz) 35 15
2780 40c. Tackle (horiz) 60 40
2781 50c. Shooting for goal . . . 85 60

1982. 10th World Trade Unions' Congress, Havana.

2783 **749** 30c. multicoloured . . . 50 30

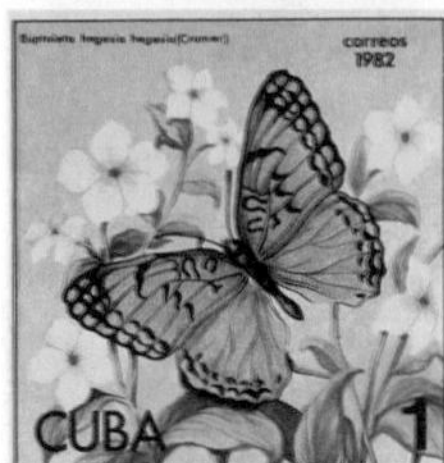

750 "Euptoieta hegesia hegesia"

1982. Butterflies. Multicoloured.

2784 1c. Type **750** 10 10
2785 4c. "Metamorpha stelenes insularis" 10 10
2786 5c. "Helicantus charithanius ramsdeni" 10 10
2787 20c. "Phoebis avellaneda" 75 25
2788 30c. "Hamadryas ferox diasia" . . . . 1·25 45
2789 50c. "Marpesia eleuchea eleuchea" . . . . 2·10 75

751 Lobster

1982. Exports.

2790 – 3c. green 10 10
2791 **751** 4c. red 30 10
2792 – 6c. blue 15 10
2793 – 7c. orange 15 10
2794 – 8c. lilac 15 10
2795 – 9c. grey 15 10
2796 – 10c. lilac 20 10
2797 – 30c. brown 30 15
2798 – 50c. red 85 25
2799 – 1p. brown . . . . 1·60 80

DESIGNS—HORIZ: 3c. Sugar; 6c. Tinned fruit; 7c. Agricultural machinery; 8c. Nickel. VERT: 9c. Rum; 10c. Coffee; 30c. Citrus fruit; 50c. Cigars; 1p. Cement.

752 "Greenland" (cottage tulip)

1982. Tulips. Multicoloured.

2800 1c. Type **752** 20 10
2801 3c. "Mariette" (Lily-flowered tulip) 20 10
2802 8c. "Ringo" (triumph) . . . 25 10
2903 20c. "Black Tulip" (Darwin) 50 25
2804 30c. "Jewel of Spring" (Darwin hybrid) 80 40
2805 50c. "Orange Parrot" (parrot tulip) . . . . . . 1·40 70

753 Youth Activities

1982. 20th Anniv of Communist Youth Union.

2806 **753** 5c. multicoloured 15 10

754 "Mars" Satellite

1982. Cosmonautics Day. Second United Nations Conference on Exploration and Peaceful Uses of Outer Space. Multicoloured.

2807 1c. Type **754** 10 10
2808 3c. "Venera" satellite . . . 10 10
2809 6c. "Salyut–Soyuz" link-up 10 10
2810 20c. "Lunokhod" moon vehicle 15 10
2811 30c. "Venera" with heatshield 50 20
2812 50c. "Kosmos" satellite . . 85 40

755 Letter from British Postal Agency, Havana, to Vera Cruz

1982. Stamp Day. Multicoloured.

2813 20c. Type **755** 50 15
2814 30c. Letter from French postal agency, Havana, to Tampico, Mexico 75 20

756 Map of Cuba and Wave Pattern **757** "Portrait of Young Woman" (Jean Greuze)

1982. 20th Anniv of Cuban Broadcasting and Television Institute.

2815 **756** 30c. multicoloured . . . 50 20

1982. National Museum Paintings (16th series). Multicoloured.

2816 1c. Type **757** 10 10
2817 3c. "Procession in Brittany" (Jules Breton) (46 × 36 mm) 10 10
2818 9c. "Landscape" (Jean Piliment) (horiz) 40 10
2819 20c. "Towards Evening" (William Bourgueran) . . 30 15
2820 30c. "Tiger" (Delacroix) (horiz) 50 20
2821 40c. "The Chair" (Wilfredo Lam) 60 30

759 Hurdling and 1930 Sports Stamp

1982. "Deporfilex '82" Stamp and Coin Exhibition, Havana.

2823 **759** 20c. multicoloured . . . 40 20

760 Tortoise

1982. Reptiles. Multicoloured.

2824 1c. Type **760** 10 10
2825 2c. Snake 10 10
2826 3c. Cuban crocodile 25 10
2827 20c. Iguana 70 40
2828 30c. Lizard . . . . 1·00 60
2829 50c. Snake . . . . 1·50 1·00

761 Georgi Dimitrov **763** Baseball

762 Dr. Robert Koch and Bacillus

1982. Birth Centenary of Georgi Dimitrov (Bulgarian statesman).

2830 **761** 30c. multicoloured . . . 55 20

1982. Centenary of Discovery of Tubercle Bacillus.

2831 **762** 20c. multicoloured . . . 40 20

1982. 14th Central American and Caribbean Games, Havana. Multicoloured.

2832 1c. Type **763** 10 10
2833 2c. Boxing 20 10
2834 10c. Water polo 25 10
2835 20c. Javelin 50 35
2836 35c. Weightlifting . . . . . 1·00 60
2837 50c. Volleyball . . . . . . 1·00 70

764 "Eichornia crassipes"

1982. 20th Anniv of Hydraulic Development Plan.

2838 5c. Type **764** 15 10
2839 20c. "Nymphaea alba" . . . 35 15

766 Hand holding Gun

1982. Namibia Day.

2841 **766** 50c. multicoloured . . . 80 35

767 Goal **768** "Devil" (V. P. Landaluze)

1982. World Cup Football Championship Finalists. Multicoloured.
2842 5c. Type **767** 15 10
2843 20c. Heading ball 35 20
2844 30c. Tackle 50 25
2845 50c. Saving goal 85 45

1982. 20th Anniv of National Folk Ensemble. Multicoloured.
2846 20c. Type **768** 40 20
2847 30c. "Epiphany festival" (V.P. Landaluze) (horiz) 55 30

769 Prehistoric Owl

1982. Prehistoric Animals. Multicoloured.
2848 1c. Type **769** 75 35
2849 5c. "Crocodylus rhombifer" (horiz) 20 10
2850 7c. Prehistoric eagle . . . . 3·00 45
2851 20c. "Geocapromys colombianus" (horiz) . . 50 25
2852 35c. "Megalocnus rodens" 90 50
2853 50c. "Nesophontes micrus" (horiz) . . . . 1·00 60

770 Che Guevara

1982. 15th Death Anniv of "Che" Guevara (guerrilla fighter).
2854 **770** 20c. multicoloured . . . 40 20

771 Christopher Columbus, "Santa Maria" and Map of Cuba

1982. 490th Anniv of Discovery of America by Columbus. Multicoloured.
2855 5c. Type **771** 95 35
2856 20c. "Santa Maria" (vert) 85 30
2857 35c. Caravel "Pinta" (vert) 1·40 65
2858 50c. Caravel "Nina" (vert) 1·75 80

1982. Lighthouses (3rd series). As T **715**. Multicoloured.
2859 5c. Cayo Jutias 30 10
2860 20c. Cayo Paredon Grande 75 15
2861 30c. Morro, Santiago de Cuba . . . . 1·00 30

772 George Washington (anonymous painting)

1982. 250th Birth Anniv of George Washington. Multicoloured.
2862 5c. Type **772** 15 10
2863 20c. Portrait of Washington by Daniel Huntington . . 40 15

774 Steam Locomotive (1917) and Boating Lake

1982. 10th Anniv of Lenin Park, Havana.
2865 **774** 5c. multicoloured 20 10

775 Capablanca as Child and Chess King

1982. 40th Death Anniv of Jose Capablanca (chess player). Multicoloured.
2866 5c. Type **775** 15 10
2867 20c. Capablanca and rook 40 15
2868 30c. Capablanca and knight 55 30
2869 50c. Capablanca and queen 85 45

776 Lenin, Marx, Russian Arms and Kremlin Tower

1982. 60th Anniv of U.S.S.R.
2870 **776** 30c. multicoloured . . . 55 30

777 Methods of Communications

1983. World Communications Year (1st issue).
2871 **777** 20c. multicoloured . . . 40 15
See also Nos. 2929/33.

778 Birthplace and Birth Centenary Stamp

1983. 130th Birth Anniv of Jose Marti (writer).
2872 **778** 5c. multicoloured 15 10

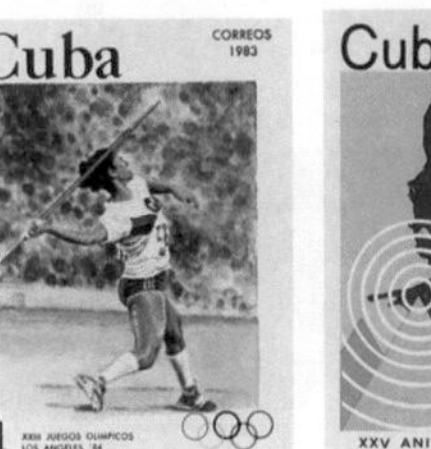

779 Throwing the Javelin **780** "Che" Guevara and Radio Waves

1983. Olympic Games, Los Angeles (1984). Multicoloured.
2873 1c. Type **779** 10 10
2874 5c. Volleyball 15 10
2875 6c. Basketball 15 10
2876 20c. Weightlifting 40 15
2877 30c. Wrestling 55 30
2878 50c. Boxing 85 45

1983. 25th Anniv of Radio Rebelde.
2880 **780** 20c. multicoloured . . . 40 15

781 Karl Marx

1983. Death Centenary of Karl Marx.
2881 **781** 30c. multicoloured . . . 55 30

782 Charles's Hydrogen Balloon **783** "Vostok 1"

1983. Bicentenary of Manned Flight. Mult.
2882 1c. Type **782** 10 10
2883 3c. Montgolfier balloon . . 10 10
2884 5c. Montgolfier balloon "Le Gustave" 15 10
2885 7c. Eugene Godard's quintuple "acrobatic" balloon 20 10
2886 30c. Montgolfier unmanned balloon . . . . 1·10 55
2887 50c. Charles Green's balloon "Royal Vauxhall" . . . . 1·10 55

1983. Cosmonautics Day. Multicoloured.
2889 1c. Type **783** 10 10
2890 4c. French "D1" satellite . . 10 10
2891 5c. "Mars 2" 15 10
2892 20c. "Soyuz" 40 15
2893 30c. Meteorological satellite 55 30
2894 50c. Intercosmos programme 85 45

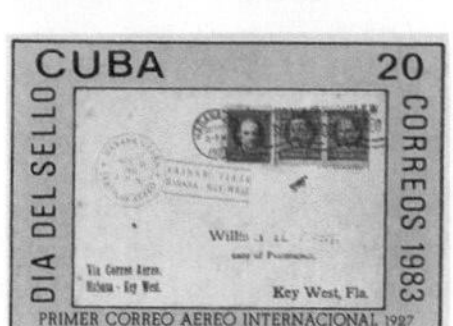

784 Letter sent by First International Airmail Service

1983. Stamp Day. Multicoloured.
2895 20c. Type **784** 50 15
2896 30c. Letter sent by first Atlantic airmail service . . 75 30

786 Jose Rafael de las Heras

1983. Birth Bicentenary of Simon Bolivar. Mult.
2898 5c. Type **786** 15 10
2899 20c. Simon Bolivar 40 15

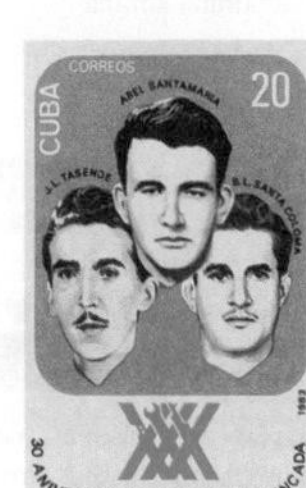

787 J. L. Tasende, Abel Santamaria and B. L. Santa Coloma

1983. 30th Anniv of Attack on Moncada Fortress. Multicoloured.
2900 5c. Jose Marti and fortress (horiz) 15 10
2901 20c. Type **787** 40 15
2902 30c. Symbol of Castro's book "History Will Absolve Me" 55 30

789 Weightlifting

1983. 9th Pan-American Games, Caracas. Mult.
2904 1c. Type **789** 15 10
2905 2c. Volleyball 20 10
2906 3c. Baseball 20 10
2907 20c. High jump 50 30
2908 30c. Basketball 75 40
2909 40c. Boxing . . . . 1·00 60

790 "Harbour" (Claude Vernet)

1983. Centenary of French Alliance (French language-teaching association).
2910 **790** 30c. multicoloured . . . 1·25 45

791 Salvador Allende and burning Presidential Palace

1983. 10th Death Anniv of Salvador Allende (President of Chile).
2911 **791** 20c. multicoloured . . . 40 15

792 Regional Peasants Committee

1983. 25th Anniv of Peasants in Arms Congress.
2912 **792** 5c. multicoloured 10 10

793 "Portrait of a Young Man"

1983. 500th Birth Anniv of Raphael. Mult.
2913 1c. "Girl with Veil" 10 10
2914 2c. "The Cardinal" 10 10
2915 5c. "Francesco M. della Rovere" 20 10
2916 20c. Type **793** 60 40
2917 30c. "Magdalena Doni" . . 75 50
2918 50c. "La Fornarina" . . . 1·10 70

794 Quality Seal and Exports

1983. State Quality Seal.
2919 **794** 5c. multicoloured 15 10

1983. Lighthouses (4th series). As T **715**. Multicoloured.
2920 5c. Carapachibey, Isle of Youth 20 10
2921 20c. Cadiz Bay 60 35
2922 30c. Punta Gobernadora . . 75 45

795 Hawksbill Turtle

1983. Turtles. Multicoloured.
2923 1c. Type **795** 20 10
2924 2c. "Lepidochelys kempi" 25 10
2925 5c. "Chrysemys decusata" 25 10
2926 20c. Loggerhead turtle . . . 70 30
2927 30c. Green turtle 85 40
2928 50c. "Dermochelys coriacea" 1·40 1·00

796 Bell's Gallow Frame and Modern Telephones

1983. World Communications Year (2nd issue). Multicoloured.
2929 1c. Type **796** 10 10
2930 5c. Telegram and airmail envelopes and U.P.U. emblem 10 10
2931 10c. Satellite and antenna 25 10
2932 20c. Telecommunications satellite and dish aerial . . 40 15
2933 30c. Television and Radio Commemorative plaque and tower block 55 30

797 Cuban Stamps of 1933 and 1965

1983. 150th Birth Anniv of Carlos J. Finlay (malaria researcher).
2934 **797** 20c. multicoloured . . . 50 15

798 "Jatropha angustifolia"

799 Tobacco Flowers

1983. Flora and Fauna. Multicoloured. (a) Flowers.
2935 5c. Type **798** 10 10
2936 5c. "Cochlospermum vitifolium" 10 10
2937 5c. "Tabebuia lepidota" . . 10 10
2938 5c. "Kalmiella ericoides" . . 10 10
2939 5c. "Jatropha integerrima" 10 10
2940 5c. "Melocactus actinacanthus" 10 10
2941 5c. "Cordia sebestana" . . . 10 10
2942 5c. "Tabernaemontana apoda" 10 10
2943 5c. "Lantana camera" . . . 10 10
2944 5c. "Cordia gerascanthus" 10 10
2945 5c. "Opuntia dillenii" . . . 10 10
2946 5c. "Euphorbia podocarpifolia" 10 10
2947 5c. "Dinema cubincola" . . 10 10
2948 5c. "Guaiacum officinale" . 10 10
2949 5c. "Magnolia cubensis" . . 10 10

(b) Birds.
2950 5c. Bee hummingbird . . . 60 15
2951 5c. Northern mockingbird 60 15
2952 5c. Cuban tody 60 15
2953 5c. Cuban Amazon 60 15
2954 5c. Zapata wren 60 15
2955 5c. Brown pelican . . . . . 1·00 20
2956 5c. Great red-bellied woodpecker 60 15
2957 5c. Red-legged thrush . . . 60 15
2958 5c. Cuban conure 60 15
2959 5c. Eastern meadowlark . . 60 15
2960 5c. Cuban grassquit 60 15
2961 5c. White-tailed tropic bird 60 15
2962 5c. Cuban solitaire 60 15
2963 5c. Great lizard cuckoo . . 60 15
2964 5c. Cuban gnatcatcher . . . 60 15

1983. Flowers.
2966 **799** 60c. green . . . . 1·00 55
2967 – 70c. red . . . . 1·10 65
2968 – 80c. blue . . . . 1·25 75
2969 – 90c. violet . . . . 1·40 85
DESIGNS: 70c. Lily; 80c. Mariposa; 90c. Orchid.

800 Flag and Plan of El Jigue Battlefield

1983. 25th Anniv of Revolution (1st issue). Multicoloured.
2970 5c. Type **800** 10 10
2971 20c. Flag and railway tracks at Santa Clara . . . . . 2·50 75

801 Flag and Revolutionaries

1983. 25th Anniv of Revolution (2nd issue). Multicoloured.
2972 20c. Type **801** 35 15
2973 20c. "25" and star 35 15
2974 20c. Workers and Cuban Communist Party emblem 35 15

802 Lazaro Gonzalez, CTC Emblem and 15th Congress Flag

1984. 45th Anniv of Revolutionary Workers' Union.
2975 **802** 5c. multicoloured 10 10

803 "Ixias balice balice"

1984. Butterflies. Multicoloured.
2976 1c. Type **803** 10 10
2977 2c. "Phoebis avellaneda avellaneda" 10 10
2978 3c. "Anthocaris sara sara" 10 10
2979 5c. "Victorina superba superba" 20 10
2980 20c. "Heliconius cydno cydnides" 70 10
2981 30c. "Parides gundlachianus calzadillae" . . . . . . 1·25 45
2982 50c. "Catagramma sorana sorana" . . . . 2·00 70

804 Clocktower and Russian Stamps of 1924–25

1984. 60th Death Anniv of Lenin.
2983 **804** 30c. multicoloured . . . 50 25

805 Risso's Dolphin

1984. Whales and Dolphins. Multicoloured.
2984 1c. Type **805** 10 10
2985 2c. Common dolphin . . . 10 10
2986 5c. Sperm whale (horiz) . . 20 10
2987 6c. Spotted dolphin 20 10
2988 10c. False killer whale (horiz) 50 30
2989 30c. Bottle-nosed dolphin 1·00 70
2990 50c. Humpback whale (horiz) . . . . 1·50 1·00

806 Sandino and Crowd holding Banner

1984. 50th Death Anniv of Augusto C. Sandino.
2991 **806** 20c. multicoloured . . . 35 15

807 Red Cross Flag and Stamp of 1946

1984. 75th Anniv of Cuban Red Cross.
2992 **807** 30c. multicoloured . . . 80 70

808 Scene from Cartoon Film

1984. 25th Anniv of Cuban Cinema.
2993 **808** 20c. multicoloured . . . 55 50

809 "Brownea grandiceps"

1984. Caribbean Flowers. Multicoloured.
2994 1c. Type **809** 10 10
2995 2c. "Couroupita guianensis" 10 10
2996 5c. "Triplaris surinamensis" 15 10
2997 20c. "Amherstia nobilis" . . 55 50
2998 30c. "Plumieria alba" . . . 80 70
2999 50c. "Delonix regia" . . . . 1·40 1·25

810 "Electron 1"

1984. Cosmonautics Day. Multicoloured.
3000 2c. Type **810** 10 10
3001 3c. "Electron 2" 10 10
3002 5c. "Intercosmos 1" 15 10
3003 10c. "Mars 5" 30 15
3004 30c. "Soyuz 1" 80 70
3005 50c. Soviet–Bulgarian space flight, 1979 . . . . 1·40 1·25

811 Mexican Mail Runner

1984. Stamp Day. Multicoloured.
3007 20c. Type **811** 55 50
3008 30c. Egyptian boatman . . 80 70
Nos. 3007/8 show details of mural by R. R. Radillo in Havana Stamp Museum.
See also Nos. 3097/8, 3170/1, 3336/7 and 3619/20.

813 Basketball

1984. Pre-Olympics.
3010 **813** 20c. multicoloured . . . 55 50

814 Pink Roses

816 Saver and Pile of Coins

815 Workers in Field

1984. Mothers' Day. Multicoloured.
3011 20c. Type **814** 55 50
3012 20c. Red roses 55 50

1984. 25th Anniv of Land Reform Act.
3013 **815** 5c. multicoloured 15 10

1984. 1st Anniv of People's Saving Bank.
3014 **816** 5c. multicoloured 15 10

817 Locomotive

1984. Locomotives. Multicoloured.
3015 1c. Type **817** 15 10
3016 4c. Locomotive No. 73 . . . 20 10
3017 5c. Locomotive (different) 25 10
3018 10c. Locomotive (different) 40 10
3019 30c. Locomotive No. 350 . . 95 30
3020 50c. Locomotive No. 495 . . 1·90 55

819 Baron de Coubertin and Runner with Olympic Flame

1984. 90th Anniv of Int Olympic Committee.
3022 **819** 30c. multicoloured . . . 80 70

820 Baby with Toy Dog

1984. Children's Day.
3023 **820** 5c. multicoloured 15 10

821 Wrestling

822 Emilio Roig de Leuchsenring

1984. Olympic Games, Los Angeles. Mult.
3024 1c. Type **821** 10 10
3025 3c. Throwing the discus . . 10 10
3026 5c. Volleyball 15 10
3027 20c. Boxing 55 50
3028 30c. Basketball 80 70
3029 50c. Weightlifting . . . . . 1·40 1·25

1984. 20th Death Anniv of Emilio Roig de Leuchsenring.
3031 **822** 5c. multicoloured 15 10

824 Cow in Pasture

1984. Cattle. Multicoloured.
3033 2c. Type **824** 10 10
3034 3c. Cuban Carib 10 10
3035 5c. Charolaise (vert) 10 10
3036 30c. Cuban Cebu (vert) . . 75 40
3037 50c. White-udder cow . . . 1·00 70

825 Men's Volleyball

1984. Friendship Tournament. Mult.
3038 3c. Type **825** 10 10
3039 5c. Women's volleyball . . . 10 10
3040 8c. Water polo 30 10
3041 30c. Boxing 60 40

826 Polymita

1984. Cuban Wildlife. Multicoloured.
3042 1c. Type **826** 10 10
3043 2c. Cuban solenodon . . . 10 10
3044 3c. "Alsophis cantherigerus" (snake) 10 10
3045 4c. "Osteopilus septentrionalis" (frog) . . 10 10
3046 5c. Bee hummingbirds . . . 45 15
3047 10c. Bushy-tailed hutia . . . 65 25
3048 30c. Cuban tody . . . . . 2·75 1·10
3049 50c. Peach-faced lovebird . . 4·50 1·40

827 King Ferdinand and Queen Isabella

1984. "Espamer '85" International Stamp Exhibition, Havana. Multicoloured.
3050 5c. Type **827** 10 10
3051 20c. Columbus departing from Palos de Moguer . . 1·00 45
3052 30c. "Santa Maria", "Pinta" and "Nina" . . . . . . 1·40 65
3053 50c. Columbus arriving in America 75 70

829 Flag and Soldier

1984. 25th Anniv of National Militia.
3055 **829** 5c. multicoloured 10 10

830 Camilo Cienfuegos

1984. 25th Anniv of Disappearance of Camilo Cienfuegos (revolutionary).
3056 **830** 5c. multicoloured 10 10

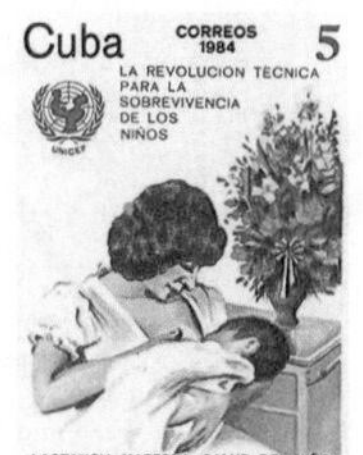

831 Mother breast-feeding Baby

1984. Infant Survival Campaign.
3057 **831** 5c. multicoloured 10 10

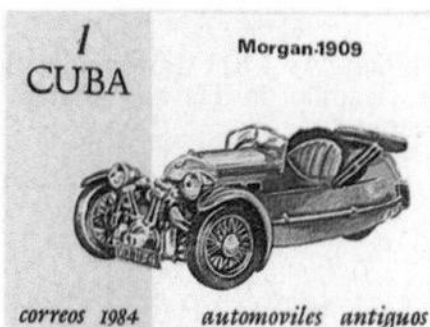

832 Morgan, 1909

1984. Cars, Multicoloured.
3058 1c. Type **832** 10 10
3059 2c. Austin, 1922 . . . . . . 10 10
3060 5c. Dion-Bouton, 1903 . . . 10 10
3061 20c. "T" Ford, 1908 . . . . 30 25
3062 30c. Karl Benz, 1885 . . . 70 40
3063 50c. Karl Benz, 1910 . . . 1·10 70

833 18th-century Letters and Museum Emblem

1985. 20th Anniv of Cuban Postal Museum.
3064 **833** 20c. multicoloured . . . 30 25

834 Celia Sanchez (after E. Escobedo)

1985. 5th Death Anniv of Celia Sanchez (revolutionary).
3065 **834** 5c. multicoloured 10 10

835 Pigeon

1985. "Porto-1985" International Pigeon Exhibition, Oporto, Portugal.
3066 **835** 20c. multicoloured . . . 30 25

836 Chile (1962)

1985. World Cup Football Championship, Mexico (1986) (1st issue). Multicoloured.
3067 1c. Type **836** 10 10
3068 2c. England (1966) 10 10
3069 3c. Mexico (1970) 10 10
3070 4c. West Germany (1974) . . 10 10
3071 5c. Argentina (1978) 10 10
3072 30c. Spain (1982) 45 40
3073 50c. Sweden (1958) 75 70
See also Nos. 3135/40.

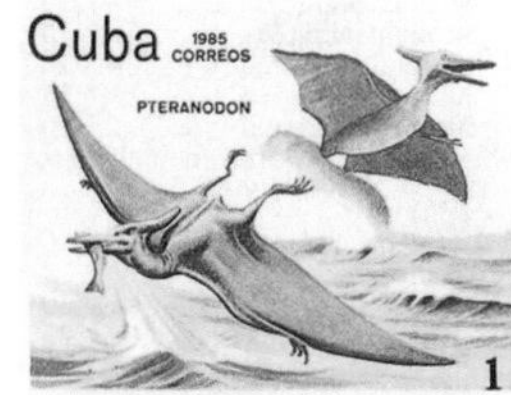

837 Pteranodon

1985. Baconao Valley National Park. Prehistoric Animals (1st series). Multicoloured.
3075 1c. Type **837** 10 10
3076 2c. Brontosaurus 10 10
3077 4c. Iguanodontus 20 15
3078 5c. Estegosaurus 20 15
3079 8c. Monoclonius 25 20
3080 30c. Corythosaurus . . . . 1·25 80
3081 50c. Tyrannosaurus . . . . 1·25 1·00
See also Nos. 3264/9.

838 Uruguay 1911 and Argentina 1921 Congress Stamps and Emblem (½-size illustration)

1985. 13th Postal Union of the Americas and Spain Congress, Havana.
3082 **838** 20c. multicoloured . . . 1·75 50

839 Indians playing Football

1985. "Espamer '85" International Stamp Exhibition, Havana. Multicoloured.
3083 1c. Type **839** 10 10
3084 2c. Indian sitting by fire . . 10 10

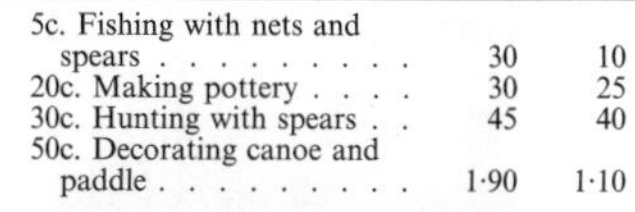
3085 5c. Fishing with nets and spears 30 10
3086 20c. Making pottery 30 25
3087 30c. Hunting with spears . . 45 40
3088 50c. Decorating canoe and paddle . . . . 1·90 1·10

840 Spaceship circling Moon

1985. Cosmonautics Day. Multicoloured.
3090 2c. Type **840** 10 10
3091 3c. Spaceships 10 10
3092 10c. Cosmonauts meeting in space 15 15
3093 13c. Cosmonauts soldering in space 20 15
3094 20c. "Vostok II" and Earth 30 25
3095 50c. "Lunayod I" crossing moon crater 75 70

841 Lenin's Tomb

842 Peonies

1985. 12th World Youth and Students' Festival, Moscow.
3096 **841** 30c. multicoloured . . . 45 40

1985. Stamp Day. As T **811**. Multicoloured.
3097 20c. Roman soldier and chariot 30 25
3098 30c. Medieval nobleman and monks 45 40

1985. Mothers' Day. Multicoloured.
3099 1c. Type **842** 10 10
3100 4c. Carnations 15 10
3101 5c. Dahlias 20 10
3102 13c. Roses 30 15
3103 20c. Roses (different) . . . 50 25
3104 50c. Tulips . . . . 1·00 70

843 Guiteras and Aponte

1985. 50th Death Anniv of Antonio Guiteras and Carlos Aponte (revolutionaries).
3105 **843** 5c. multicoloured 10 10

844 Star, "40" and Soldier with Flag

1985. 40th Anniv of End of Second World War.
3106 **844** 5c. multicoloured 10 10
3107 – 20c. multicoloured 30 25
3108 – 30c. red, yellow & violet 45 40
DESIGNS: 20c. "40" and Soviet Memorial, Berlin-Treptow; 30c. Dove within "40".

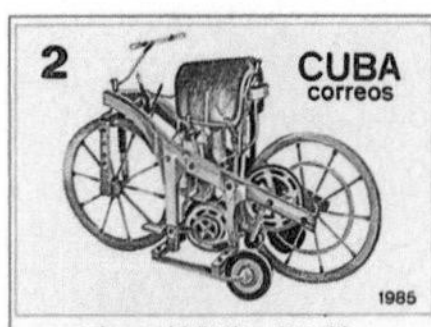

846 Daimler, 1885

1985. Centenary of the Motor Cycle. Multicoloured.
3110 2c. Type **846** 10 10
3111 5c. Kayser tricycle, 1910 . . 20 10
3112 10c. Fanomovil, 1925 . . . 25 15
3113 30c. Mars "A 20", 1926 . . 75 50
3114 50c. Simson "BSW", 1936 . 1·10 85

847 La Plata and Hermanos Ameijeiras Hospitals

1985. Development of Health Care since the Revolution.

3115 **847** 5c. multicoloured 10 10

848 Flowers and Soldier with Gun

1985. 25th Anniv of Federation of Cuban Women.

3116 **848** 5c. multicoloured 10 10

849 Athletes and Emblem

1985. World University Games, Kobe, Japan.

3117 **849** 50c. multicoloured . . . 90 85

850 Crowd, Flags and Statue

1985. 25th Anniv of First Havana Declaration.

3118 **850** 5c. multicoloured 10 10

852 Emblem in "25"

1985. 25th Anniv of Committees for Defence of the Revolution.

3120 **852** 5c. multicoloured 10 10

853 Cherub Angelfish

1985. Fishes. Multicoloured.

3121 1c. Type **853** 20 15

3122 3c. Rock beauty 20 15

3123 5c. Four-eyed butterflyfish 20 15

3124 10c. Reef butterflyfish . . . 35 30

3125 20c. Spot-finned butterflyfish 85 60

3126 50c. Queen angelfish . . . . 2·10 1·75

854 Cuban and Party Flags and Central Committee Building

856 U.N. Building, New York, and Emblem

1985. 20th Anniv of Cuban Communist Party and Third Party Congress.

3127 **854** 5c. multicoloured 10 10

1985. 40th Anniv of U.N.O.

3129 **856** 20c. multicoloured . . . 35 30

857 Old Square and Arms

1985. U.N.E.S.C.O. World Heritage. Old Havana. Multicoloured.

3130 2c. Type **857** 10 10

3131 5c. Real Fuerza Castle . . . 10 10

3132 20c. Havana Cathedral . . . 35 30

3133 30c. Captain General's Palace 55 50

3134 50c. El Templete 90 85

858 Footballers

860 Ministry Emblem

859 Red Flags and Emblem

1986. World Cup Football Championship, Mexico (2nd issue).

3135 **858** 1c. multicoloured 10 10

3136 – 4c. multicoloured 10 10

3137 – 5c. multicoloured 10 10

3138 – 10c. multicoloured . . . 15 10

3139 – 30c. multicoloured . . . 55 45

3140 – 50c. multicoloured . . . 90 85

DESIGNS: 4c. to 50c. Various footballing scenes.

1986. 3rd Cuban Communist Party Congress, Havana. Multicoloured.

3142 5c. Type **859** 10 10

3143 20c. Red and national flags 35 30

1986. 25th Anniv of Ministry of Interior Trade.

3144 **860** 5c. multicoloured 10 10

861 People practising Sports

862 "Tecomaria capensis"

1986. 25th Anniv of National Sports Institute.

3145 **861** 5c. multicoloured 10 10

1986. Exotic Flowers. Multicoloured.

3146 1c. Type **862** 10 10

3147 3c. "Michelia champaca" . . 15 10

3148 5c. "Thunbergia grandiflora" 20 10

3149 8c. "Dendrobium phalaenopsis" 25 10

3150 30c. "Allamanda violacea" 75 50

3151 50c. "Rhodocactus bleo" . . 1·10 85

863 Gundlach and Red-winged Blackbird

1986. 90th Death Anniv of Juan C. Gundlach (ornithologist). Multicoloured.

3152 1c. Type **863** 40 20

3153 3c. Olive-capped warbler . . 40 20

3154 7c. La Sagra's flycatcher . . 70 50

3155 9c. Yellow warbler 90 60

3156 30c. Grey-faced quail dove 3·50 2·50

3157 50c. Common flicker . . . 5·50 4·00

864 Pioneers and "25"

865 Gomez and Statue

1986. 25th Anniv of Jose Marti Pioneers.

3158 **864** 5c. multicoloured 10 10

1986. 150th Birth Anniv of Maximo Gomez.

3159 **865** 20c. multicoloured . . . 35 30

866 Nursery Nurse with Children

867 "Vostok" and Korolev (designer)

1986. 25th Anniv of Children's Day Care Centres.

3160 **866** 5c. multicoloured 10 10

1986. 25th Anniv of First Man in Space. Multicoloured.

3161 1c. Type **867** 10 10

3162 2c. Yuri Gargarin (first man in space) and "Vostok" 10 10

3163 5c. Valentina Tereshkova (first woman in space) and "Vostok" 10 10

3164 20c. "Salyut" space station 30 25

3165 30c. Capsule descending with parachute 35 30

3166 50c. "Soyuz" rocket on launch pad 90 85

868 National Flag and 1981 Stamp

869 Reels as National Flag and Globe and Tape forming "25"

1986. 25th Anniv of Socialist State (1959) and Victory at Giron. Multicoloured.

3168 5c. Type **868** 10 10

3169 20c. Flags and arms 30 25

1986. Stamp Day. As T **811** showing details of mural by R. R. Radillo in Havana Stamp Museum. Multicoloured.

3170 20c. Early mail coach . . . 30 25

3171 30c. Express rider 35 30

1986. 25th Anniv of Radio Havana Cuba.

3172 **869** 5c. multicoloured 10 10

870 "Stourbridge Lion", U.S.A., 1829

1986. "Expo '86" World's Fair, Vancouver. Railway Locomotives. Multicoloured.

3173 1c. Type **870** 15 10

3174 4c. "Rocket", Great Britain, 1829 . . . . 15 10

3175 5c. First Russian locomotive, 1845 . . . . 15 10

3176 8c. Marc Seguin's locomotive, France, 1830 25 10

3177 30c. First Canadian locomotive, 1836 . . . . 70 20

3178 50c. Steam locomotive, Belgium Grand Central Railway, 1872 . . . . . 1·90 35

871 Hand holding Machete and Farmer ploughing and driving Tractor

1986. 25th Anniv of National Association of Small Farmers.

3180 **871** 5c. multicoloured 10 10

872 Dove and Arms on Coin

1986. International Peace Year.

3181 **872** 30c. multicoloured . . . 35 30

873 Emblem

1986. 25th Anniv of Ministry of the Interior.

3182 **873** 5c. multicoloured 10 10

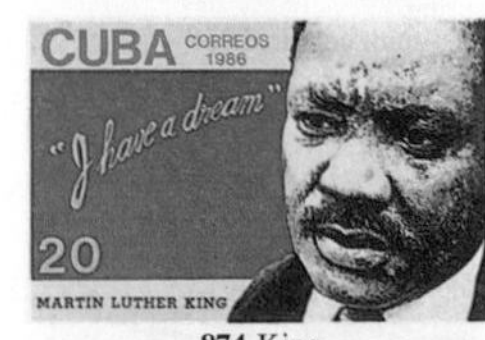

874 King

1986. 18th Death Anniv of Martin Luther King (human rights campaigner).

3183 **874** 20c. multicoloured . . . 30 25

875 Bonifacio Byrne

1986. 50th Death Anniv of Bonifacio Byrne (poet).

3184 **875** 5c. multicoloured 10 10

876 Dove, Pen Nib and Paint Brush

877 Sandino and Pres. Ortega of Nicaragua

1986. 25th Anniv of National Union of Cuban Writers and Artists.

3185 **876** 5c. multicoloured 10 10

1986. 25th Anniv of Sandinista Movement of Nicaragua.

3186 **877** 20c. multicoloured . . . 30 25

878 Tanker, Tupolev Tu-154 and Lorry

1986. 25th Anniv of Ministry of Transport.
3187 **878** 5c. multicoloured 30 15

879 Sportsmen and Emblem **882** "Cattleya hardyana"

881 Map

1986. 5th Central American and Caribbean University Games, Havana.
3188 **879** 20c. multicoloured . . . 35 30

1986. 25th Anniv of Non-Aligned Countries Movement.
3190 **881** 50c. multicoloured . . . 80 75

1986. Orchids. Multicoloured.
3191 1c. Type **882** 10 10
3192 4c. "Brassolaeliocattleya" "Horizon Flight" 15 10
3193 5c. "Phalaenopsis" "Margit Moses" 20 15
3194 10c. "Laeliocattleya" "Prism Palette" 25 20
3195 30c. "Phalaenopsis violacea" 75 60
3196 50c. "Disa uniflora" . . . . 1·00 90

883 Mayan House and Jade Statue (Belize)

1986. Latin American History. Pre-Columbian Culture (1st series). Multicoloured.
3197 1c. Type **883** 10 10
3198 1c. Inca vessel and Gateway of the Sun, Tiahuanacu (Bolivia) 10 10
3199 1c. Spain 1930 1p. stamp of Columbus and 500th anniv of Columbus's discovery of America emblem 10 10
3200 1c. Diaguitan duck-shaped pitcher and ruins, Pucara de Quitor (Chile) 10 10
3201 1c. Archaeological park, San Augustin and Quimbayan statuette (Columbia) . . . 10 10
3202 5c. Moler memorial and Chorotega decorated earthenware statue (Costa Rica) 10 10
3203 5c. Tabaco idol and typical aboriginal houses (Cuba) 10 10
3204 5c. Spain 1930 40c. stamp of Martin Pinzon and anniversary emblem . . . 10 10
3205 5c. Typical houses and animal shaped seat (Dominica) 10 10
3206 5c. Tolita statue and Ingapirca fort (Ecuador) 10 10
3207 10c. Maya vase and Tikal temple (Guatemala) . . . 15 15
3208 10c. Copan ruins and Maya idol (Honduras) 15 15
3209 10c. Spain 1930 30c. stamp of Vincent Pinzon and anniversary emblem . . . 15 15
3210 10c. Chichen-Itza temple and Zapoteca urn (Mexico) 15 15
3211 10c. Punta de Zapote idols and Ometepe ceramic (Nicaragua) 15 15
3212 20c. Tonosi ceramic and Barrile monolithic sculptures (Panama) . . . 35 30
3213 20c. Machu Picchu ruin and Inca figure (Peru) 35 30
3214 20c. Spain 1930 10p. stamp of Columbus and Pinzon brothers and anniversary emblem 35 30
3215 20c. Typical aboriginal dwellings and triangular stone carving (Puerto Rico) 35 30
3216 20c. Santa Ana female figure and Santo Domingo cave (Venezuela) 35 30

See also Nos. 3276/95, 3371/90, 3458/77, 3563/82, 3666/85 and 3769/88.

884 Medal and Soldier with Rifle

1986. 50th Anniv of Formation International Brigades in Spain.
3217 **884** 30c. multicoloured . . . 50 45

885 "Two Children" (Gutierrez de la Vega)

1986. National Museum Paintings (17th series). Multicoloured.
3218 2c. Type **885** 10 10
3219 4c. "Sed" (Jean-Gorges Vibert) (horiz) 10 10
3220 6c. "Virgin and Child" (Niccolo Abbate) 20 10
3221 10c. "Bullfight" (Eugenio de Lucas Velazquez) (horiz) 25 15
3222 30c. "The Five Senses" (Anon) (horiz) 75 45
3223 50c. "Meeting at Thomops Castle" (Jean Louis Ernest) (horiz) . . . . . 1·00 75

886 People and "Granma"

1986. 30th Annivs of "Granma" Landings (5c.) and Revolutionary Armed Forces (20c.). Multicoloured.
3224 5c. Type **886** 10 10
3225 20c. Soldier, rifle and flag 35 30

887 Scholars and "Che" Guevara

1986. 25th Anniv of Scholarship Programme.
3226 **887** 5c. multicoloured 10 10

888 Man learning to write and Sanmarti **890** "Gitana" (Joaquin Sorolla)

889 Map and Revolutionaries

1986. 25th Anniv of Literacy Campaign.
3227 **888** 5c. multicoloured 10 10

1987. 30th Anniv of Attack on La Plata Garrison.
3228 **889** 5c. multicoloured 10 10

1987. National Museum Paintings (18th series). Multicoloured.
3229 3c. Type **890** 10 10
3230 5c. "Sir Walter Scott" (Sir John W. Gordon) 20 10
3231 10c. "Farm Meadows" (Alfred de Breanski) (horiz) 25 15
3232 20c. "Still Life" (Isaac van Duynen) (horiz) 35 30
3233 30c. "Landscape with Figures" (Francesco Zuccarelli) (horiz) 60 45
3234 40c. "Waffle Seller" (Ignacio Zuloaga) 75 60

891 Palace, Delivery Van and Echeverria

1987. 30th Anniv of Attack on Presidential Palace.
3235 **891** 5c. multicoloured 10 10

892 Lazarus Ludwig Zamenhof (inventor) and Russia 1927 14k. Stamp

1987. Centenary of Esperanto (invented language).
3236 **892** 30c. multicoloured . . . 50 45

894 Badge and Slogan

1987. 25th Anniv and 5th Congress of Youth Communist League.
3238 **894** 5c. multicoloured 10 10

895 "Intercosmos I" Satellite **897** Dahlias

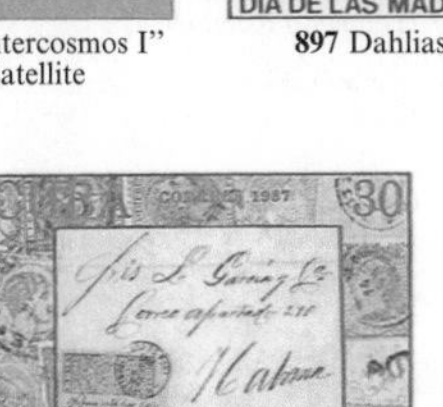

896 Cover with Postal Fiscal Stamp, 1890

1987. Cosmonautics Day. 20th Anniv of Intercosmos Programme. Multicoloured.
3239 3c. Type **895** 10 10
3240 5c. "Intercosmos II" 10 10
3241 10c. "TD" 15 15
3242 20c. "Cosmos 93" 35 30
3243 30c. "Molniya" 50 45
3244 50c. "Vostok 3" 80 75

1987. Stamp Day. Multicoloured.
3246 30c. Type **896** 75 60
3247 50c. Cover with bisect, 1869 1·00 80

1987. Mothers' Day. Multicoloured.
3248 3c. Type **897** 10 10
3249 5c. Roses 20 10
3250 10c. Roses in basket 25 15
3251 13c. Decorative dahlias . . 35 20
3252 30c. Cactus dahlias 75 45
3253 50c. Roses (different) . . . 1·00 25

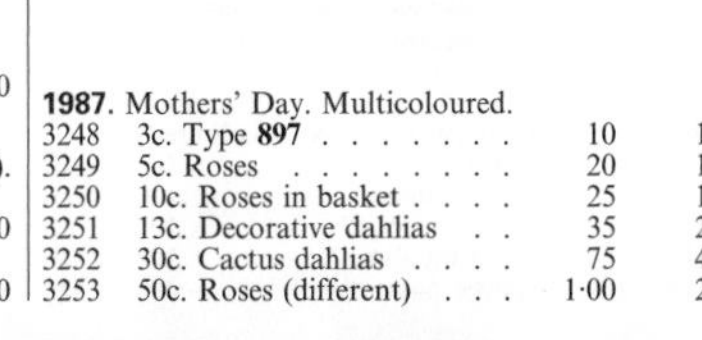

898 Fractured Femur Immobilised in Frame **899** Emblem

1987. "Orthopedia '87" Portuguese and Spanish Speaking Countries' Orthopedists Meeting, Havana.
3254 **898** 5c. multicoloured 10 10

1987. 25th Anniv of Cuban Broadcasting and Television Institute.
3255 **899** 5c. multicoloured 10 10

900 Battle Monument, Sierra Maestra Mountains

1987. 30th Anniv of Battle of El Uvero.
3256 **900** 5c. multicoloured 10 10

901 Messenger with Pack Llamas and 1868 Stamp (Bolivia)

1987. "Capex '87" International Stamp Exhibition, Toronto. 19th-century Mail Carriers as depicted on cigarette cards. Multicoloured.
3257 3c. Type **901** 10 10
3258 5c. Postman and motor car and 1900 stamp (France) 10 10
3259 10c. Messenger on elephant and 1883 stamp (Siam) . . 15 15
3260 20c. Messenger on camel and 1879 stamp (Egypt) 35 30
3261 30c. Mail troika and stamp (Russia) 50 45
3262 50c. Messenger on horseback and stamp (Indo-China) 80 75

902 Model of Prehistoric Animal

1987. Prehistoric Valley, Baconao National Park (2nd series). Designs showing various exhibits.
3264 **902** 3c. multicoloured 10 10
3265 – 5c. multicoloured 20 10
3266 – 10c. multicoloured . . . 25 15
3267 – 20c. multicoloured . . . 55 30
3268 – 35c. multicoloured . . . 75 50
3269 – 40c. multicoloured . . . 90 60

903 Pais and Rafael Maria Mendive Popular University Buildings

1987. 30th Death Anniv of Frank Pais (teacher and student leader).
3270 **903** 5c. multicoloured 10 10

904 Flags and Sportsmen

1987. 10th Pan-American Games, Indianapolis.
3271 **904** 50c. multicoloured . . . 1·00 75

905 Memorial

1987. 30th Anniv of Cienfuegos Uprising.
3272 **905** 5c. multicoloured 10 10

908 Coins and 1968 Independence War Centenary 30c. Stamp

1987. 20th Anniv of Heroic Guerilla Fighters Day.
3275 **908** 50c. multicoloured . . . 1·00 90

909 Tehuelche Man and Red-crowned Ant-tanager (Argentina)

1987. Latin American History (2nd series). Multicoloured.
3276 1c. Type **909** 20 20
3277 1c. Red-billed toucan and Tibirica man (Brazil) . . 20 20
3278 1c. Spain 1930 5c. stamp of La Rabida Monastery and 500th anniv of Columbus's discovery of America emblem 10 10
3279 1c. Andean condor and Lautaro man (Chile) 20 20
3280 1c. Calarca man and hoatzin (Colombia) 20 20
3281 5c. Cuban trogon and Hatuey man (Cuba) . . . 45 20
3282 5c. Scaly-breasted ground dove and Enriquillo man (Dominican Republic) . . 45 20
3283 5c. Spain 1930 30c. stamp of departure from Palos and anniversary emblem . . . 10 10
3284 5c. Toucan barbet and Ruminahui man (Ecuador) 45 20
3285 5c. Resplendent quetzal and Tecum Uman man (Guatemala) 45 20
3286 10c. Anacaona woman and limpkin (Haiti) 75 20
3287 10c. Lempira man and slaty flowerpiercer (Honduras) 75 20
3288 10c. Spain 1930 10p. Columbus stamp and anniversary emblem . . . 15 10
3289 10c. Northern royal flycatcher and Cuauhtemoc woman (Mexico) 75 20
3290 10c. Painted redstart and Nicarao man (Nicaragua) 75 20
3291 20c. Andean cock of the rock and Atahualpa man (Peru) . . . . 1·25 30
3292 20c. Atlactl man and red-tailed hawk (El Salvador) 1·25 50
3293 20c. Spain 1930 10p. stamp of arrival in America and anniversary emblem . . . 35 50
3294 20c. Abayuba man and red-breasted plantcutter (Uruguay) . . . . 1·25 50
3295 20c. Guaycaypuro man and blue and yellow macaw (Venezuela) . . . . 1·25 50

910 1950 2c. Train Stamp

1987. 150th Anniv of Cuban Railway. Designs showing Cuban stamps.
3296 **910** 3c. red, brown & black 10 10
3297 – 5c. multicoloured 10 10
3298 – 10c. multicoloured . . . 15 10
3299 – 20c. multicoloured . . . 35 25
3300 – 35c. multicoloured . . . 65 45
3301 – 40c. multicoloured . . . 75 55
DESIGNS: 5c. 1965 7c. "BB.69,000" diesel locomotive stamp; 10c. 1975 1c. French-built "La Junta" locomotive stamp; 20c. 1975 3c. M. M. Prieto" locomotive stamp; 35c. 1980 10c. locomotive stamp; 40c. 1980 13c. locomotive stamp.

911 Satellites and Russia 1927 14k. Stamp

1987. 70th Anniv of Russian Revolution.
3303 **911** 30c. multicoloured . . . 50 45

912 "Landscape" (Domingo Ramos)

1988. 170th Anniv of San Alejandro Arts School, Havana. Multicoloured.
3304 1c. Type **912** 10 10
3305 2c. "Portrait of Rodriguez Morey" (Eugenio Gonzalez Olivera) 10 10
3306 3c. "Landscape with Malangas and Palm Trees" (Valentin Sanz Carta) 15 10
3307 5c. "Ox-carts" (Eduardo Morales) 20 15
3308 10c. "Portrait of Elena Herrera" (Armando Menocal) (vert) 25 20
3309 30c. "The Rape of Dejanira" (Miguel Melero) (vert) 75 50
3310 50c. "The Card Player" (Leopoldo Romanach) . . 1·00 85

913 "Boletus satanas"

915 Mario Munoz Santiago Monument, de Cuba

914 Radio Operator, Satellite and Caribe Ground Station

1988. Poisonous Mushrooms. Multicoloured.
3311 1c. Type **913** 10 10
3312 2c. "Amanita citrina" . . . 10 10
3313 3c. "Tylopilus felleus" . . . 10 10
3314 5c. "Paxillus involutus" . . 20 10
3315 10c. "Inocybe patouillardii" 40 15
3316 30c. "Amanita muscaria" 1·00 40
3317 50c. "Hypholoma fasciculare" . . . . . . 1·60 70

1988. 30th Anniv of Radio Rebelde.
3318 **914** 5c. multicoloured 10 10

1988. 30th Anniv of Mario Munoz Third Front.
3319 **915** 5c. multicoloured 10 10

916 Frank Pais Memorial and Eternal Flame

917 Red Roses

1988. 30th Anniv of Frank Pais Second Eastern Front.
3320 **916** 5c. multicoloured 10 10

1988. Mothers' Day. Multicoloured.
3321 1c. Type **917** 10 10
3322 2c. Pale pink roses 10 10
3323 3c. Daisies 10 10
3324 5c. Dahlias 10 10
3325 13c. White roses 15 15
3326 35c. Carnations 50 45
3327 40c. Pink roses 60 55

918 "Gorizont" Satellite

1988. Cosmonautics Day. Multicoloured.
3328 2c. Type **918** 10 10
3329 3c. "Mir"–"Kvant" link . . 10 10
3330 4c. "Signo 3" 10 10
3331 5c. Mars space probe . . . 10 10
3332 10c. "Phobos" 15 15
3333 30c. "Vega" space probe . . 45 40
3334 50c. Space craft 75 70

1988. Stamp Day. As T **811**. Details of mural by R. R. Radillo in Havana Stamp Museum. Mult.
3336 30c. Telegraphist and mail coach 45 40
3337 50c. Carrier pigeon 75 70

919 Storage Tanks, Products, Sugar Cane and Laboratory Equipment

1988. 25th Anniv of ICIDCA (Cuban Institute for Research on Sugarcane Byproducts).
3338 **919** 5c. multicoloured 10 10

920 Havana–Madrid, 1948

1988. Cubana Airlines Transatlantic Flights. Mult.
3339 2c. Type **920** 10 10
3340 4c. Havana–Prague, 1961 . . 15 10
3341 5c. Havana–Berlin, 1972 . . 20 15
3342 10c. Havana–Luanda, 1975 30 25
3343 30c. Havana–Paris, 1983 . . 75 50
3344 50c. Havana–Moscow, 1987 1·25 90

922 Steam Train (½-size illustration)

1988. Postal Union of the Americas and Spain Colloquium on "America" Postage Stamps, Havana.
3346 **922** 20c. multicoloured . . . 1·25 50

923 "Megasoma elephas"

1988. Beetles. Multicoloured.
3347 1c. Type **923** 10 10
3348 3c. "Platycoelia flavoscutellata" (vert) . . 20 10
3349 4c. "Plusiotis argenteola" . . 25 15
3350 5c. "Hetersoternus oberthuri" 30 20
3351 10c. "Odontotaenius zodiacus" 40 25
3352 35c. "Chrysophora chrysochlora" (vert) . . 90 75
3353 40c. "Phanaeus leander" . . 1·10 1·00

924 Chess Pieces

1988. Birth Centenary of Jose Capablanca (chess master). Multicoloured.
3354 30c. Type **924** 45 40
3355 40c. Juan Corzo, Capablanca and flags (1901 Cuban Championship) (horiz) . . 60 55
3356 50c. Emanuel Lasker and Capablanca (1921 World Championship) (horiz) . . 75 70
3357 1p. Checkmate in 1921 game with Lasker . . . . . . 1·50 1·25
3358 3p. "J. R. Capablanca" (E. Valderrama) . . . . . 4·00 3·50
3359 5p. Chess pieces, flag, globe and Capablanca . . . . 6·00 5·50

925 Sun and Fortress

1988. 35th Anniv of Assault on Moncada Fortress.
3361 **925** 5c. red, yellow & black 10 10

927 Camilo Cienfuegos, "Che" Guevara and Map

1988. 30th Anniv of Rebel Invasion Columns.
3363 **927** 5c. multicoloured 10 10

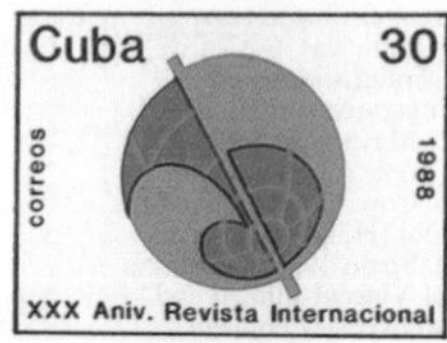

928 Emblem

1988. 30th Anniv of "Revista Internacional" (magazine).
3364 **928** 30c. multicoloured . . . 45 40

929 Locomotive "Northumbrian", 1831

1988. Railway Development. Multicoloured.
3365 20c. Type **929** 35 15
3366 30c. Locomotive "E. L. Miller", 1834 . . . . 65 30

3367 50c. "La Junta" (Cuba's first locomotive, 1840s) . . 1·40 55
3368 1p. Electric railcar . . . . . 2·40 80
3369 2p. Russian-built M-62K diesel locomotive . . . . 4·50 1·90
3370 5p. Diesel railcar set . . . . 10·50 5·25

930 Arms and Jose de San Martin (Argentina)

1988. Latin-American History (3rd series). Mult.
3371 1c. Type **930** 10 10
3372 1c. Arms and M. A. Padilla (Bolivia) 10 10
3373 1c. 1944 10c. Discovery of America stamp 10 10
3374 1c. Arms and A. de Silva Xavier, "Tiradentes" (Brazil) 10 10
3375 1c. Arms and Bernardo O'Higgins (Chile) 10 10
3376 5c. A. Narino and arms (Colombia) 10 10
3377 5c. Arms and Jose Marti (Cuba) 10 10
3378 5c. 1944 13c. Discovery of America stamp 10 10
3379 5c. Arms and Juan Pablo Duarte (Dominican Republic) 10 10
3380 5c. Arms and Antonio Jose de Sucre (Ecuador) . . . 10 10
3381 10c. Manuel Jose Arce and arms (El Salvador) . . . 15 10
3382 10c. Arms and Jean Jacques Dessalines (Haiti) 15 10
3383 10c. 1944 5c. Discovery of America airmail stamp . . 15 10
3384 10c. Miguel Hidalgo and arms (Mexico) 15 10
3385 10c. Arms and J. Dolores Estrada (Nicaragua) . . . 15 10
3386 20c. Jose E. Diaz and arms (Paraguay) 30 25
3387 20c. Arms and Francisco Bolognesi (Peru) 30 25
3388 20c. 1944 10c. Discovery of America airmail stamp . . 30 25
3389 20c. Arms and Jose Gervasio Artigas (Uruguay) 30 25
3390 20c. Simon Bolivar and arms (Venezuela) 30 25

931 Maces and Governor's Palace

1988. 20th Anniv of Havana Museum.
3391 **931** 5c. multicoloured 10 10

932 Ballerinas and Mute Swan

1988. 40th Anniv of National Ballet (3392) and 150th Anniv of Grand Theatre, Havana (3393). Multicoloured.
3392 5c. Type **932** 40 25
3393 5c. Theatre, 1838 and 1988 10 10

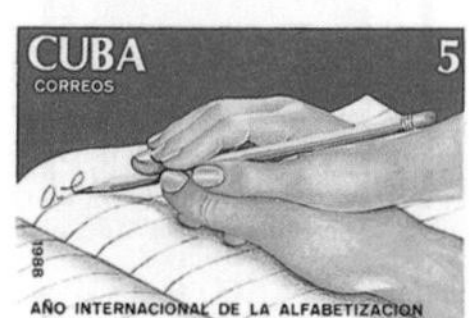

933 Practising Letters

1988. International Literacy Year.
3394 **933** 5c. multicoloured 10 10

934 Emblem

1988. 40th Anniv of Declaration of Human Rights.
3395 **934** 30c. multicoloured . . . 50 45

935 Ernesto Che Guevara Plaza

1988. 30th Anniv of Battle of Santa Clara.
3396 **935** 30c. multicoloured . . . 50 45

936 National Flag forming "30"

1989. 30th Anniv of Revolution.
3397 **936** 5c. multicoloured 10 10
3398 20c. multicoloured . . . 30 25
3399 30c. gold, blue and red 50 45
3400 50c. gold, blue and red 80 75

937 "Pleurotus levis"

1989. Edible Mushrooms. Multicoloured.
3401 2c. Type **937** 10 10
3402 3c. "Pleurotus floridanus" 10 10
3403 5c. "Amanita caesarea" . . 15 10
3404 10c. "Lentinus cubensis" (horiz) 35 10
3405 40c. "Pleurotus ostreatus" (red) . . . . 1·25 60
3406 50c. "Pleurotus ostreatus" (brown) . . . . 1·40 75

939 1982 30c. Cuban Stamp

1989. 50th Anniv of Revolutionary Workers' Union.
3408 **939** 5c. multicoloured 10 10

940 "Metamorpho dido"

1989. Butterflies. Multicoloured.
3409 1c. Type **940** 10 10
3410 3c. "Callithea saphhira" . . . 10 10
3411 5c. "Papilio zagreus" . . . 20 10
3412 10c. "Mynes sestia" 30 15
3413 30c. "Papilio dardanus" . . 1·00 70
3414 50c. "Catagramma sorana" 1·75 1·25

941 Footballer 942 "30" and Arms

1989. World Cup Football Championship, Italy (1990).
3415 **941** 1c. multicoloured 10 10
3416 – 3c. multicoloured 15 10
3417 – 5c. multicoloured 20 15
3418 – 10c. multicoloured . . . 25 20
3419 – 30c. multicoloured . . . 70 60
3420 – 50c. multicoloured . . . 1·00 90
DESIGNS: 3c to 50c. Various footballers.

1989. 30th Anniv of National Revolutionary Police.
3422 **942** 5c. multicoloured 10 10

943 "Zodiac" Rocket and 1934 Australian Cover

1989. Cosmonautics Day. Rocket Post (1st series). Multicoloured.
3423 1c. Type **943** 10 10
3424 3c. Rocket and cover from India to Poland, 1934 . . 15 10
3425 5c. Rocket and 1934 English cover 20 15
3426 10c. "Icarus" rocket and 1935 Dutch cover 35 25
3427 40c. "La Douce France" rocket and 1935 French cover 85 75
3428 50c. Rocket and 1939 Cuban cover . . . . . . 1·00 90
See also Nos. 3516/21.

1989. Stamp Day. As T **811**. Details of mural by R. R. Radillo in Havana Stamp Museum. Mult.
3429 30c. Mail coach 50 45
3430 50c. 18th-century sailing packet . . . . 3·75 1·50

944 "Tree of Life" (A. Soteno)

1989. 30th Anniv of "House of the Americas" Museum, Havana.
3431 **944** 5c. multicoloured 10 10

946 Coded Envelope

1989. Post Codes.
3433 **946** 5c. multicoloured 10 10

947 Tobacco Flowers

948 Signing Decree

1989. Mothers' Day. Perfumes and Flowers. Mult.
3434 1c. Type **947** 10 10
3435 3c. Violets 15 15
3436 5c. Mariposa 20 20
3437 13c. Roses 30 25
3438 30c. Jasmine 75 65
3439 50c. Orange-flower . . . . 1·10 1·00

1989. 30th Anniv of Agrarian Reform Law.
3440 **948** 5c. multicoloured 10 10

949 "40" and Headquarters Building, Moscow

1989. 40th Anniv of Council for Mutual Economic Aid.
3441 **949** 30c. multicoloured . . . 50 45

950 Tower of Juche Idea, Pyongyang

1989. 13th World Youth and Students' Festival, Pyongyang.
3442 **950** 30c. multicoloured . . . 50 45

952 Toco Toucan

1989. "Brasiliana '89" Stamp Exhibition. Rio de Janeiro. Birds. Multicoloured.
3444 1c. Type **952** 20 10
3445 3c. Chestnut-bellied heron 20 10
3446 5c. Scarlet ibis 30 10
3447 10c. White-winged trumpeter 50 15
3448 35c. Harpy eagle . . . . . 1·90 70
3449 50c. Amazonian umbrellabird . . . . . . 2·40 1·10

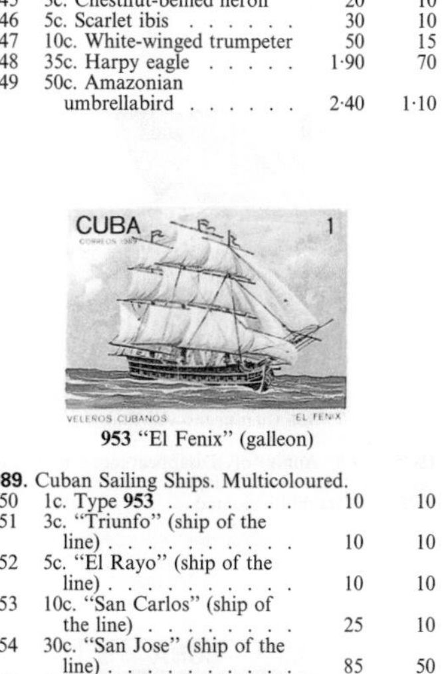
953 "El Fenix" (galleon)

1989. Cuban Sailing Ships. Multicoloured.
3450 1c. Type **953** 10 10
3451 3c. "Triunfo" (ship of the line) 10 10
3452 5c. "El Rayo" (ship of the line) 10 10
3453 10c. "San Carlos" (ship of the line) 25 10
3454 30c. "San Jose" (ship of the line) 85 50
3455 50c. "San Genaro" (ship of the line) . . . . 1·40 85

954 Carved Stone and Men in Dugout Canoe

1989. America. Pre-Columbian Cultures. Mult.
3456 5c. Type **954** 10 10
3457 20c. Cave painters 30 25

955 Domingo F. Sarmiento and "Govenia utriculata" (Argentina)

1989. Latin American History (4th series). Multicoloured.
3458 1c. Type **955** 10 10
3459 1c. Machado de Assis and "Laelia grandis" (Brazil) 10 10
3460 1c. El Salvador 1892 1p. Columbus stamp 10 10
3461 1c. Jorge Isaacs and "Cattleya trianae" (Colombia) 10 10
3462 1c. Alejo Carpentier and "Cochleanthes discolor" (Cuba) 10 10
3463 5c. "Oxalis adenophylla" and Pablo Neruda (Chile) 10 10
3464 5c. Pedro H. Urena and "Epidendrum fragrans" (Dominican Republic) . . 10 10
3465 5c. El Salvador 1893 2p. City of Isabela stamp . . 10 10
3466 5c. Juan Montalvo and "Miltonia vexillaria" (Ecuador) 10 10
3467 5c. "Odontoglossum rossii" and Miguel A. Asturias (Guatemala) 10 10
3468 10c. "Laelia anceps" and Jose C. del Valle (Honduras) 15 10
3469 10c. "Laelia anceps alba" and Alfonso Reyes (Mexico) 15 10
3470 10c. El Salvador 1893 5p. Columbus Statue stamp 15 10
3471 10c. "Brassavola acaulis" and Ruben Dario (Nicaragua) 15 10
3472 10c. Belisario Porras and "Pescatorea cerina" (Panama) 15 10
3473 20c. Ricardo Palma and "Coryanthes leucocorys" (Peru) 30 25
3474 20c. Eugenio Maria de Hostos and "Guzmania berteroniana" (Puerto Rico) 30 25
3475 20c. El Salvador 1893 10p. Departure from Palos stamp 30 25
3476 20c. "Cypella herbertii" and Jose E. Rodo (Uruguay) 30 25
3477 20c. "Cattleya mossiae" and Romulo Gallegos (Venezuela) 30 25

956 Cienfuegos and Flag

1989. 30th Anniv of Disappearance of Camilo Cienfuegos (revolutionary).
3478 **956** 5c. multicoloured 10 10

957 Church Tower

1989. 475th Anniv of Trinidad City.
3479 **957** 5c. multicoloured 10 10

958 "Outskirts of Niza" (E. Boudin)

1989. Paintings in National Museum. Mult.
3480 1c. "Family Scene" (Antoine Faivre) 10 10
3481 2c. "Flowers" (Emile J. H. Vernet) 10 10
3482 5c. "Judgement of Paris" (Charles Le Brun) 10 10
3483 20c. Type **958** 35 20
3484 30c. "Portrait of Sarah Bernhardt" (G. J. V. Clairin) (36 × 46 mm) 40 35
3485 50c. "Fishermen in Harbour" (C. J. Vernet) 90 60

959 Archery

1989. 11th Pan-American Games, Havana (1st issue). Multicoloured.
3486 5c. Type **959** 20 10
3487 5c. Shooting 20 10
3488 5c. Fencing 20 10
3489 5c. Cycling 20 10
3490 5c. Water polo 20 10
3491 20c. Lawn tennis (vert) . . . 30 40
3492 30c. Swimming (vert) . . . 80 60
3493 35c. Diving (vert) 80 70
3494 40c. Hockey . . . . 1·10 85
3495 50c. Basketball (vert) . . . 1·25 1·00
See also Nos. 3584/93 and 3621/30.

960 Front Page

1989. Centenary of "Golden Age" (children's magazine compiled by Jose Marti).
3496 **960** 5c. blue, black and red 10 10

961 "Almendares" (paddle-steamer)

1990. 25th Anniv of Postal Museum. Mult.
3497 5c. Type **961** 15 10
3498 30c. Mail train . . . . . . 3·25 1·25

962 Cave Painters (½-size illustration)

1990. 50th Anniv of Speleological Society.
3499 **962** 30c. multicoloured . . . 40 35

963 Player No. 11 and Colosseum

964 Baseball

1990. World Cup Football Championship, Italy. Multicoloured.
3500 5c. Type **963** 20 10
3501 5c. Player No. 10 . . . . . 20 10
3502 5c. Player No. 8 . . . . . 20 10
3503 10c. Goalkeeper 25 10
3504 30c. Player No. 11 and arch 60 55
3505 50c. Player 85 80

1990. Olympic Games, Barcelona (1992) (1st issue). Multicoloured.
3507 1c. Type **964** 10 10
3508 4c. Running 10 10
3509 5c. Basketball 10 10
3510 10c. Volleyball 25 10
3511 30c. Wrestling (horiz) . . . 75 50
3512 50c. Boxing . . . . 1·10 85
See also Nos. 3604/9 and 3692/7.

965 Tower of Babel, Dove and Globe

1990. 75th Esperanto Congress, Havana.
3514 **965** 30c. multicoloured . . . 40 35

1990. Cosmonautics Day. Rocket Post (2nd series). As T **943**. Multicoloured.
3516 1c. 1932 Austrian Cover and "U12" rocket 10 10
3517 2c. 1933 German cover, rocket and liner 10 10
3518 3c. 1934 Netherlands cover, "NRB" rocket and windmill 10 10
3519 10c. 1935 Belgian cover and rocket 15 10
3520 30c. 1935 Yugoslavian cover and "JUGI" rocket . . . 40 35
3521 50c. 1936 U.S.A. cover and rocket 65 60

1990. Stamp Day. As T **811**. Showing details of mural by R. R. Radillo in Havana Stamp Museum. Multicoloured.
3522 30c. Russian-built Type TEM-4 diesel locomotive leaving station 2·75 90
3523 50c. De Havilland Comet 1 airplane 65 60

967 Flag and Globe

1990. Centenary of Labour Day.
3524 **967** 5c. multicoloured 10 10

969 Hill and Penny Black

1990. 150th Anniv of the Penny Black. Mult.
3526 2c. Type **969** 80 45
3527 3c. Twopenny blue . . . . 1·00 45
3528a 5c. G.B. 1855 4d. stamp . . 1·10 60
3529 10c. G.B. 1847 1s. embossed stamp . . . . 1·20 60
3530 30c. G.B. paid hand-stamp 60 50
3531 50c. Twopenny blues on cover to Malta 85 80

970 Celia Sanchez (after O. Yanes)

1990. 70th Birth Anniv of Celia Sanchez Manduley (revolutionary).
3532 **970** 5c. multicoloured 10 10

971 Flags and Ho Chi Minh

1990. Birth Centenary of Ho Chi Minh (Vietnamese leader).
3533 **971** 50c. multicoloured . . . 65 60

972 Hogfish and Sample Analysis

1990. 25th Anniv of Oceanology Institute. Mult.
3534 5c. Type **972** 15 10
3535 30c. "Arrecife coralino" and research vessel 80 35
3536 50c. Lobster and diver collecting samples 65 60

973 "Banara minutiflora"

974 Windsurfing

1990. 5th Latin American Botanical Congress. Multicoloured.
3537 3c. Type **973** 10 10
3538 5c. "Oplonia nannophylla" 20 15
3539 10c. "Jacquinia brunnescens" 25 20
3540 30c. "Rondeletia brachycarpa" 70 60
3541 50c. "Rondeletia odorata" 1·00 65

1990. Tourist Sports. Multicoloured.
3542 5c. Type **974** 20 15
3543 10c. Underwater fishing (horiz) 25 20
3544 30c. Sea fishing (horiz) . . . 70 60
3545 40c. Shooting 75 65

975 "The Flute of Pan" (detail)

1990. Paintings by A. G. Menocal in National Museum. Multicoloured.
3546 5c. Type **975** 20 20
3547 20c. "Shepherd" 40 30
3548 50c. "Ganymede" . . . . . 1·00 75
3549 1p. "Venus Anadiomena" 2·25 1·25

976 Great Crested Grebe

1990. "New Zealand 90" International Stamp Exhibition, Auckland. Birds. Multicoloured.
3551 2c. Type **976** 15 10
3552 3c. Weka rail 15 10
3553 5c. Kea 15 10
3554 10c. Bush wren 45 15
3555 30c. Grey butcher bird 1·25 55
3556 50c. Parson bird 2·10 1·00

977 Lighthouse

1990. 8th U.N.O. Congress on Crime Prevention and Treatment of Delinquents.
3558 **977** 50c. red, blue and silver 65 60

978 Caravel and Shoreline

1990. America. The Natural World. Mult.
3559 5c. Type **978** 25 20
3560 20c. Christopher Columbus and native village 75 60

979 Cameraman

1990. 40th Anniv of Cuban Television.
3561 **979** 5c. multicoloured 10 10

980 Steam Locomotive No. 1712 and Havana Railway Station

1990. 30th Anniv of Nationalization of Railways.
3562 **980** 50c. multicoloured 1·50 1·10

981 Flag and Couple (Argentina)

1990. Latin-American History (5th series). Multicoloured.
3563 1c. Type **981** 10 10
3564 1c. Flag and couple (Bolivia) 10 10
3565 1c. Argentina 1892 5c. Discovery of America stamp 10 10
3566 1c. Flag and couple (Colombia) 10 10
3567 1c. Flag and couple (Costa Rica) 10 10
3568 5c. Flag and couple (Cuba) 10 10
3569 5c. Flag and couple (Chile) 10 10
3570 5c. Dominican Republic 1900 ½c. Columbus stamp 10 10
3571 5c. Flag and couple (Ecuador) 10 10
3572 5c. Flag and couple (El Salvador) 10 10
3573 10c. Flag and couple (Guatemala) 15 10
3574 10c. Flag and couple (Mexico) 15 10
3575 10c. Puerto Rico 1893 3c. Discovery of America stamp 25 10
3576 10c. Flag and couple (Nicaragua) 15 10
3577 10c. Flag and couple (Panama) 15 10
3578 20c. Flag and couple (Paraguay) 30 20
3579 20c. Flag and couple (Peru) 30 20
3580 20c. El Salvador 1894 10p. Columbus stamp 30 20
3581 20c. Flag and couple (Puerto Rico) 30 20
3582 20c. Flag and couple (Venezuela) 30 20

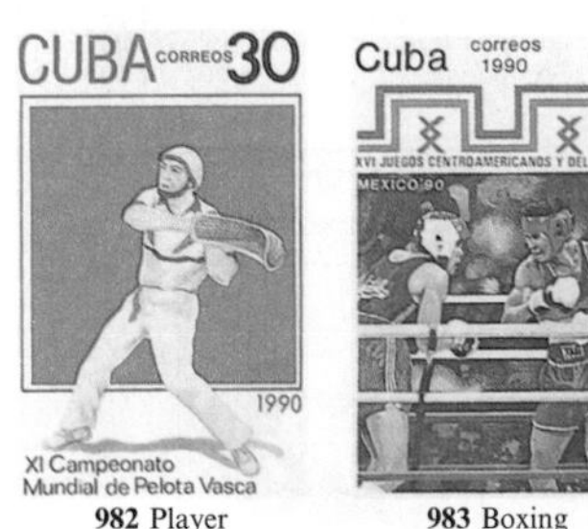

982 Player
983 Boxing

1990. 11th World Pelota Championship.
3583 **982** 30c. multicoloured 45 30

1990. 11th Pan-American Games, Havana (1991) (2nd issue). As T **959**. Multicoloured.
3584 5c. Kayaking 20 10
3585 5c. Rowing 20 10
3586 5c. Yachting 30 10
3587 5c. Judo 20 10
3588 5c. Show jumping 20 10
3589 10c. Table tennis 25 20
3590 20c. Gymnastics (vert) 45 30
3591 30c. Baseball (vert) 65 45
3592 35c. Basketball (vert) 80 45
3593 50c. Football (vert) 1·25 70

1990. 16th Central American and Caribbean Games, Mexico. Multicoloured.
3594 5c. Type **983** 10 10
3595 30c. Baseball 45 30
3596 50c. Volleyball 80 45

984 "Chioides marmorosa"
986 Long Jumping

985 Guerra Aguiar and 1966 3c. Stamp

1991. Butterflies. Multicoloured.
3597 2c. Type **984** 20 10
3598 3c. "Composia fidelissima" 20 10
3599 5c. "Danaus plexippus" 20 10
3600 10c. "Hypolimnas misippus" 40 30
3601 30c. "Hypna iphigenia" 1·00 70
3602 50c. "Hemiargus ammon" 1·60 1·00

1991. 1st Death Anniv of Jose Guerra Aguiar (founder of Cuban Postal Museum).
3603 **985** 5c. multicoloured 10 10

1991. Olympic Games, Barcelona (1992) (2nd issue). Multicoloured.
3604 1c. Type **986** 10 10
3605 2c. Throwing the javelin 15 10
3606 3c. Hockey 20 15
3607 5c. Weightlifting 25 20
3608 40c. Cycling 1·00 70
3609 50c. Gymnastics 1·25 80

987 Yuri Gagarin and "Vostok"
988 Statue and Flag

1991. 30th Anniv of First Man in Space. Mult.
3611 5c. Type **987** 20 10
3612 10c. "Soyuz" and Y. Romanenko 25 20
3613 10c. "Salyut" space station and A. Tamayo 25 20
3614 30c. "Mir" space station (left half) 75 60
3615 30c. "Mir" space station (right half) 75 60
3616 50c. Launch of "Buran" space shuttle 1·25 1·00
Nos. 3612/13 and 3614/15 respectively were issued together, *se-tenant*, forming composite designs.

1991. 30th Anniversaries. Multicoloured.
3617 5c. Type **988** (proclamation of Socialism) 10 10
3618 50c. Playa Giron (invasion attempt by Cuban exiles) 1·25 55

1991. Stamp Day. Designs as T **811** showing details of mural by R. R. Radillo in Havana Stamp Museum. Multicoloured.
3619 30c. Rocket (vert) 75 60
3620 50c. Dish aerial 1·25 1·00

1991. 11th Pan-American Games, Havana (3rd series). As T **959**. Multicoloured.
3621 5c. Volleyball (vert) 10 10
3622 5c. Synchronized swimming (vert) 10 10
3623 5c. Weightlifting (vert) 10 10
3624 5c. Baseball (vert) 10 10
3625 5c. Gymnastics (vert) 10 10
3626 10c. Ten-pin bowling 30 20
3627 20c. Boxing (vert) 60 40
3628 30c. Running 85 60
3629 35c. Wrestling 1·00 70
3630 50c. Judo 1·40 1·10

989 Simon Bolivar and Map

1991. 165th Anniv of Panama Congress.
3631 **989** 50c. multicoloured 80 45

990 Dirigible Balloon Design and Jean-Baptiste Meusnier

1991. "Espamer '91" Iberia–Latin America Stamp Exhibition, Buenos Aires. Airships. Mult.
3632 5c. Type **990** 20 10
3633 10c. First steam-powered dirigible airship and Henri Giffard 30 20
3634 20c. Paul Hanlein and first airship with gas-powered motor 50 30
3635 30c. "Deutschland" (first airship with petrol motor) and Karl Wolfert 80 60
3636 50c. David Schwarz and first rigid aluminium airship 1·25 75
3637 1p. Ferdinand von Zeppelin and airship "Graf Zeppelin" 2·00 1·25
No. 3637 is inscr "Hindenburg".

992 Cayo Largo

1991. Tourism. Multicoloured.
3645 20c. Type **992** 75 25
3646 20c. Varadero 60 50
3647 30c. San Carlos de la Cabana Fortress (horiz) 70 60
3648 30c. Castillo de los Tres Reyes del Morro (horiz) 70 60

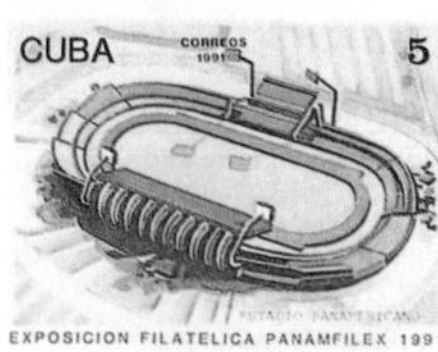

993 Stadium

1991. "Panamfilex 1991" Pan-American Stamp Exhibition. Multicoloured.
3649 5c. Type **993** 20 10
3650 20c. Baragua swimming-pool complex 50 40
3651 30c. Ramon Fonst hall 85 50
3652 50c. Reynaldo Paseiro cycle-track 1·40 1·00

994 "Kataoka Dengoemon Takafusa" (Utagawa Kuniyoshi)

1991. "Phila Nippon '91" International Stamp Exhibition, Tokyo. Multicoloured.
3654 5c. Type **994** 20 10
3655 10c. "Night Walk" (Hosoda Eishi) 30 20
3656 20c. "Courtesans" (Torii Kiyonaga) 50 35
3657 30c. "Conversation" (Kitagawa Utamaro) 70 60
3658 50c. "Inari-bashi Bridge" (Ando Hiroshige) 1·75 1·25
3659 1p. "On the Terrace" (Torii Kiyonaga) 2·25 1·50

996 Statue of Jose Marti

1991. 4th Cuban Communist Party Congress.
3661 **996** 5c. multicoloured 10 10
3662 – 50c. black, blue and red 80 45
DESIGN: 50c. Party emblem.

997 Christopher Columbus and Pinzon Brothers

1991. America. Voyages of Discovery. Mult.
3663 5c. Type **997** 10 10
3664 20c. "Santa Maria", "Nina" and "Pinta" 60 20

998 Marti (after F. Martinez)

1991. Centenary of Publication of "The Simple Verses" by Jose Marti.
3665 **998** 50c. multicoloured . . . 80 45

999 Julian Aguirre and Charango (Argentina)

1991. Latin-American History (6th series). Music. Multicoloured.
3666 1c. Type **999** 10 10
3667 1c. Eduardo Caba and antara (pipes) (Bolivia) . . 10 10
3668 1c. Chile 1853 10c. stamp 10 10
3669 1c. Heitor Villalobos and trumpet with gourd resonator (Brazil) 10 10
3670 1c. Guillermo Uribe-Holguin and cununo macho (drum) (Colombia) . . . 10 10
3671 5c. Claves (sticks) and Miguel Failde (Cuba) . . 20 10
3672 5c. Enrique Soro and Araucanian kultrum (Chile) 20 10
3673 5c. Chile 1903 10c. on 30c. stamp 20 10
3674 5c. Rondador (xylophone) and Segundo L. Moreno (Ecuador) 20 10
3675 5c. Marimba and Ricardo Castillo (Guatemala) . . . 20 10
3676 10c. Vihuela and Carlos Chavez (Mexico) 30 25
3677 10c. Luis A. Delgadillo and maracas (Nicaragua) . . . 30 25
3678 10c. Chile 1906 2c. stamp 30 25
3679 10c. Alfredo de Saint-Malo and mejorana (Panama) 30 25
3680 10c. Jose Asuncion Flores and harp (Paraguay) . . . 30 25
3681 20c. Daniel Alomia and quena (flute) (Peru) . . . 50 30
3682 20c. Cuatro (guitar) and Juan Morell y Campos (Puerto Rico) 50 30
3683 20c. Chile 1905 10c. stamp 50 30
3684 20c. Eduardo Fabini and tamboril (drums) (Uruguay) 50 30
3685 20c. Cuatro (guitar) and Juan V. Lecuna (Venezuela) 50 30

1000 Mascot

1991. 1st Jose Marti Pioneers Congress.
3686 **1000** 5p. multicoloured . . . 10 10

1001 Toussaint L'Ouverture (revolutionary leader)

1991. Bicentenary of Haitian Revolution.
3687 **1001** 50c. multicoloured . . . 80 45

1002 "35", Stars and Soldier

1991. 35th Anniversaries. Multicoloured.
3688 5c. Type **1002** (Revolutionary Armed Forces) 10 10
3689 50c. Launch "Granma" (disembarkation of revolutionary forces) (vert) . . . . 1·25 60

1003 Agramonte (after F. Martinez)

1991. 150th Birth Anniv of Ignacio Agramonte (poet).
3690 **1003** 5c. multicoloured . . . 10 10

1005 Table Tennis and Plan of Montjuic Complex

1992. Olympic Games, Barcelona (3rd issue). Mult.
3692 3c. Type **1005** 20 10
3693 5c. Handball and Vall d'Hebron complex 25 20
3694 10c. Shooting and Badalona complex 30 25
3695 20c. Long jumping and Montjuic complex (vert) 60 50
3696 35c. Judo and Diagonal complex . . . . 1·00 75
3697 50c. Fencing and Montjuic complex . . . . 1·40 1·00

1006 Flooded Terraces and Dead Trees

1992. Environmental Protection. Mult.
3699 5c. Type **1006** 10 10
3700 20c. Whale and dead fish in polluted sea 45 20
3701 35c. Satellite picture of ozone levels over Antarctica and gas mask in polluted air 60 35
3702 40c. Rainbows, globe, doves and nuclear explosion . . 70 40

1007 Blue Angelfish

1992. Fishes. Multicoloured.
3703 5c. Type **1007** 15 10
3704 10c. Jackknife-fish 25 15
3705 20c. Blue tang 60 25
3706 30c. Sergeant-major 85 45
3707 50c. Yellow-tailed damselfish 1·50 75

1008 Boxer

1992. Dogs. Multicoloured.
3708 5c. Type **1008** 20 10
3709 10c. Great dane 25 20
3710 20c. German shepherd . . . 60 40
3711 30c. Short-haired, long-haired and wire-haired dachshunds . . . . 1·00 70
3712 35c. Dobermann . . . . . 1·25 90
3713 40c. Fox terrier . . . . . . 1·40 1·00
3714 50c. Poodle . . . . 1·50 1·10

1009 Badge

1992. 30th Anniv and Sixth Congress of Youth Communist League.
3716 **1009** 5c. multicoloured . . . 10 10

1010 Jose Marti

1992. Centenary of Cuban Revolutionary Party.
3717 **1010** 5c. multicoloured . . . 10 10
3718 50c. multicoloured . . . 85 50

1011 Columbus Sighting Land

1992. America. 500th Anniv of Discovery of America by Columbus. Multicoloured.
3719 5c. Type **1011** 25 20
3720 20c. Columbus landing at San Salvador 75 50

1012 Alhambra, Sierra Nevada

1992. "Granada 92" International Philatelic Exhibition. Designs showing views of the Alhambra. Multicoloured.
3721 5c. Type **1012** 20 10
3722 10c. Sunset 30 20
3723 20c. Doorway and arches 60 40
3724 30c. Courtyard of the Lions 80 50
3725 35c. Bedroom 90 70
3726 50c. View of Albaicin from balcony . . . . 1·25 1·00

1013 Facade and Plate

1992. 50th Anniv of La Bodeguita del Medio (restaurant).
3727 **1013** 50c. multicoloured . . . 85 50

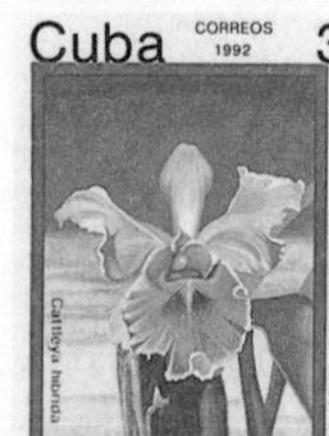

1014 "Cattleya hibrida"

1992. 40th Anniv of Soroa Orchid Garden. Mult.
3728 3c. Type **1014** 20 10
3729 5c. "Phalaenopsis sp." . . . 20 10
3730 10c. "Cattleyopsis lindenii" 30 20
3731 30c. "Bletia purpurea" . . . 1·00 75
3732 35c. "Oncidium luridum" 1·25 1·00
3733 40c. "Vanda hibrida" . . . 1·50 1·25

1015 Hummingbird

1992. The Bee Hummingbird. Multicoloured.
3734 5c. Type **1015** 30 15
3735 10c. Perched on twig . . . 40 20
3736 20c. Perched on twig with flowers 90 25
3737 30c. Hovering over flower 1·40 40

1016 Guardalavaca Beach

1992. Tourism. Multicoloured.
3738 10c. Type **1016** 20 10
3739 20c. Hotel Bucanero 45 25
3740 30c. View of Havana . . . 70 35
3741 50c. Varadero beach . . . . 1·10 65

1017 Eligio Sardinas

1992. "Olymphilex '92" International Olympic Stamps Exhibition, Barcelona. Designs showing Cuban sportsmen. Multicoloured.
3742 5c. Type **1017** 30 10
3743 35c. Ramon Fonst (fencer) 1·00 75
3744 40c. Sergio "Pipian" Martinez (cyclist) . . . . 1·10 85
3745 50c. Martin Dihigo (baseball player) . . . . 1·40 1·00

1019 Alvarez Cabral

1992. "Genova '92" International Thematic Stamp Exhibition. Explorers and their ships. Multicoloured.
3747 5c. Type **1019** 10 10
3748 10c. Alonso Pinzon 20 10
3749 20c. Alonso de Ojeda . . . 45 25

3750 30c. Amerigo Vespucci . . . 65 35
3751 35c. Henry the Navigator 75 40
3752 40c. Bartolomeu Dias . . . 90 45

1020 High Jumping

1992. 6th World Athletics Cup, Havana. Mult.
3754 5c. Type **1020** 30 10
3755 20c. Throwing the javelin 60 40
3756 30c. Throwing the hammer 1·00 70
3757 40c. Long jumping (vert) . . 1·10 80
3758 50c. Hurdling (vert) . . . . 1·50 1·00

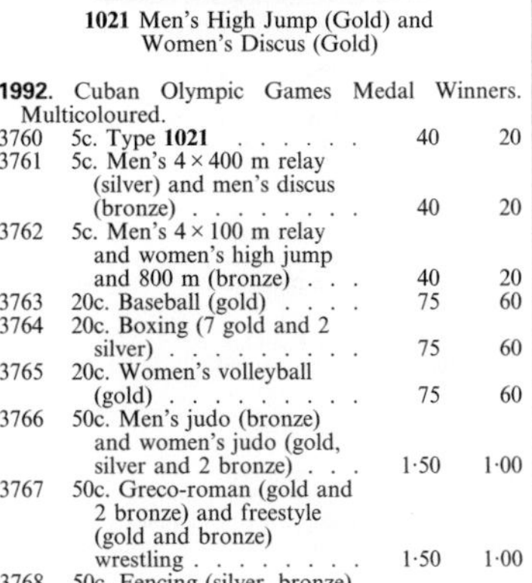

1021 Men's High Jump (Gold) and Women's Discus (Gold)

1992. Cuban Olympic Games Medal Winners. Multicoloured.
3760 5c. Type **1021** 40 20
3761 5c. Men's 4 × 400 m relay (silver) and men's discus (bronze) 40 20
3762 5c. Men's 4 × 100 m relay and women's high jump and 800 m (bronze) . . . 40 20
3763 20c. Baseball (gold) 75 60
3764 20c. Boxing (7 gold and 2 silver) 75 60
3765 20c. Women's volleyball (gold) 75 60
3766 50c. Men's judo (bronze) and women's judo (gold, silver and 2 bronze) . . . 1·50 1·00
3767 50c. Greco-roman (gold and 2 bronze) and freestyle (gold and bronze) wrestling . . . . 1·50 1·00
3768 50c. Fencing (silver, bronze) and weightlifting (silver) 1·50 1·00

HISTORIA LATINOAMERICANA

1022 Christopher Columbus and Queen Isabella the Catholic

1992. Latin-American History (7th series). Multicoloured.
3769 1c. Type **1022** 10 10
3770 1c. Columbus at Rabida Monastery 10 10
3771 1c. Columbus presenting plans to King Ferdinand and Queen Isabella . . . 10 10
3772 1c. Columbus before Salamanca Council . . . 10 10
3773 1c. Departure from Palos . . 10 10
3774 5c. Fleet stopping off at Canary Islands 20 10
3775 5c. Columbus reassuring crew 20 10
3776 5c. Sighting of land 20 10
3777 5c. Columbus landing . . . 20 10
3778 5c. Columbus's encounter with Amerindians 20 10
3779 10c. "Santa Maria" grounded off Hispaniola 30 20
3780 10c. Arrival of "Nina" at Palos 30 20
3781 10c. Columbus's procession through Barcelona . . . 30 20
3782 10c. Columbus before King and Queen 30 20
3783 10c. Departure from Cadiz on second voyage 30 20
3784 20c. King and Queen welcoming Columbus . . 30 20
3785 20c. Fleet leaving on third voyage 55 60
3786 20c. Columbus's deportation in chains from Hispaniola 55 60
3787 20c. Fleet embarking on fourth voyage 55 60
3788 20c. Death of Columbus at Valladolid 55 60

1023 Chacon

1024 Sanctuary of Our Lady of Charity, Cobre

1992. Birth Centenary of Jose Maria Chacon y Calvo (historian).
3789 **1023** 30c. multicoloured . . . 50 30

1992. Churches. Multicoloured.
3790 5c. Type **1024** 20 10
3791 20c. St. Mary's Church, Rosario 60 50
3792 30c. Church of the Holy Spirit, Havana 80 60
3793 50c. Guardian of the Holy Angel Church, Pena Pobre, Havana . . . . . 1·25 90

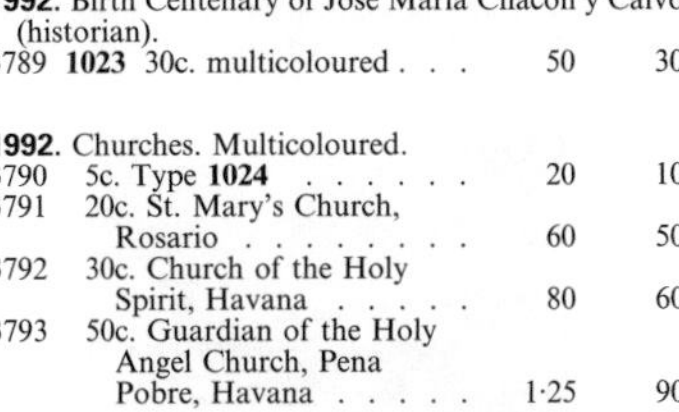

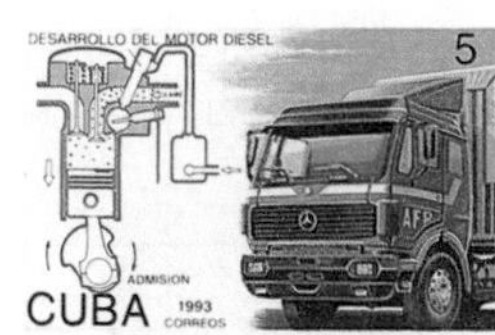

1025 Diagram of Engine and Truck

1993. Development of Diesel Engine. Each showing an engine at a different stage of cycle. Multicoloured.
3794 5c. Type **1025** 10 10
3795 10c. Motor car 15 10
3796 30c. Tug 75 30
3797 40c. Diesel locomotive . . . 2·50 1·25
3798 50c. Tractor . . . . 1·00 80

1026 Player

1993. Davis Cup Men's Team Tennis Championship. Designs showing tennis players. Multicoloured.
3800 5c. Type **1026** 25 20
3801 20c. Double-handed backhand 50 35
3802 30c. Serve 85 50
3803 35c. Stretched forehand (horiz) 90 70
3804 40c. Returning drop shot (horiz) . . . . 1·10 80

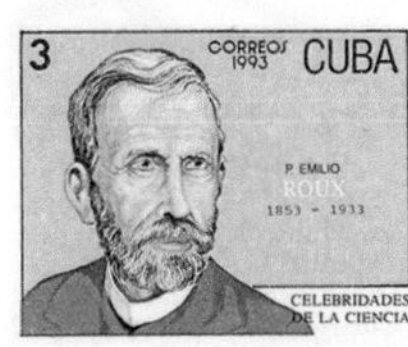

1027 Pedro Emilio Roux

1993. Scientists. Multicoloured.
3806 3c. Type **1027** (bacteriologist) 10 10
3807 5c. Carlos Finlay (biologist) 20 15
3808 10c. Ivan Petrovich Pavlov (physiologist) 30 20
3809 20c. Louis Pasteur (chemist) 60 40
3810 30c. Santiago Ramon y Cajal (histologist) 85 55
3811 35c. Sigmund Freud (psychiatrist) . . . . . . 1·00 70
3812 40c. Wilhelm Roentgen (physicist) . . . . 1·10 80
3813 50c. Joseph Lister (surgeon) 1·50 1·10

1028 Bicycle Design by Leonardo da Vinci

1993. Bicycles. Multicoloured.
3815 3c. Type **1028** 10 10
3816 5c. Draisiana hobby-horse 10 10
3817 10c. Michaux boneshaker 20 10
3818 20c. Starley penny-farthing 50 40
3819 30c. Lawson "Safety" bicycle 65 50
3820 35c. Modern bicycle 75 60

1029 "Valencian Fishwives"

1993. Paintings by Joaquin Sorolla in the National Museum. Multicoloured.
3821 3c. "Child eating Melon" (vert) 10 10
3822 5c. Type **1029** 10 10
3823 10c. "Regatta" 20 10
3824 20c. "Peasant Girl" 35 20
3825 40c. "Summertime" 70 40
3826 50c. "By the Sea" 90 50

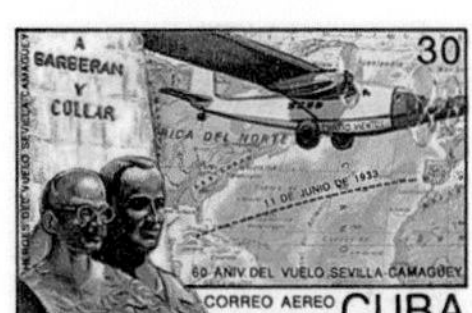

1030 "Four Winds" and Statue of Barberan and Collar

1993. 60th Anniv of Seville (Spain)–Camaguey (Cuba) Flight by Mariano Barberan and Joaquin Collar.
3827 **1030** 30c. multicoloured . . . 40 20

1031 Northern Jacana

1993. "Brasiliana '93" International Stamp Exhibition, Rio de Janeiro. Water Birds. Multicoloured.
3828 3c. Type **1031** 15 15
3829 5c. Great blue heron (27 × 44 mm) 15 15
3830 10c. Black-necked stilt . . . 35 20
3831 20c. Black-crowned night heron 60 35
3832 30c. Sandhill crane (27 × 44 mm) 90 50
3833 50c. Limpkin . . . . 1·50 80

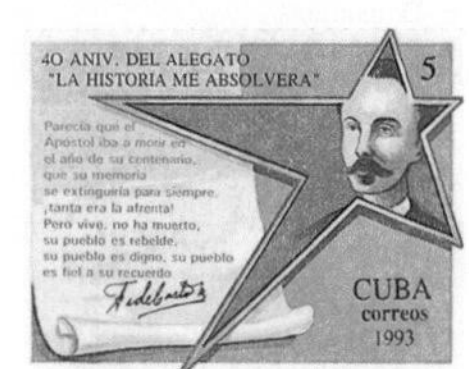

1032 Fidel Castro and Text

1993. Anniversaries. Multicoloured.
3834 5c. Type **1032** (40th anniv of publication of "History Will Absolve Me") . . . 10 10
3835 5c. Jose Marti (140th birth anniv) and Rafael M. Mendive (vert) 10 10
3836 5c. Carlos M. de Cespedes and broken wheel (125th anniv of Yara Proclamation) 10 10
3837 5c. Moncada Barracks (40th anniv of attack on barracks) 10 10

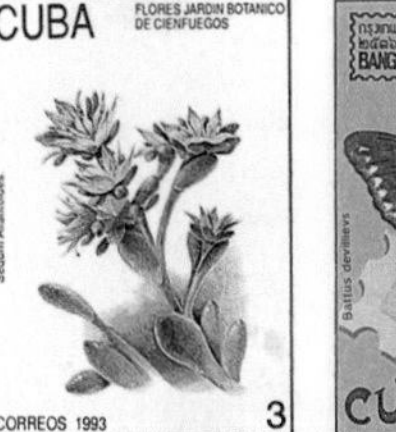

1033 "Sedum allantoides"

1034 Devillier's Swallowtail

1993. Cienfuegos Botanical Garden. Mult.
3838 3c. Type **1033** 10 10
3839 5c. "Heliconia caribaea" . . 20 10
3840 10c. "Anthurium andraeanum" 35 25
3841 20c. "Pseudobombax ellipticum" 55 40
3842 35c. "Ixora coccinea" . . . 90 65
3843 50c. "Callistemon specious" 1·50 1·00

1993. "Bangkok 1993" International Stamp Exhibition. Butterflies. Multicoloured.
3844 3c. Type **1034** 20 10
3845 5c. Giant brimstone 25 15
3846 20c. Great southern white 60 40
3847 30c. Buckeye 85 50
3848 35c. White peacock . . . . 1·10 75
3849 50c. African monarch . . . 1·50 1·10

1035 Greater Flamingo

1036 Simon Bolivar

1993. America. Endangered Animals. Mult.
3850 5c. Type **1035** 50 30
3851 50c. Roseate spoonbill . . . 75 60

1993. Latin-American Integration. Mult.
3852 50c. Type **1036** 70 50
3853 50c. Jose Marti 70 50
3854 50c. Benito Juarez 70 50
3855 50c. Che Guevara 70 50
Nos. 3852/5 were issued together, *se-tenant*, forming a composite design.

1037 Swimming

1993. 17th Central American and Caribbean Games, Ponce, Puerto Rico. Multicoloured.
3856 5c. Type **1037** 10 10
3857 10c. Pole vaulting 30 20
3858 20c. Boxing 50 40
3859 35c. Gymnastics (parallel bars) (vert) 75 55
3860 50c. Baseball (vert) 90 70

1038 Grajales

1039 Tchaikovsky

1993. Death Centenary of Mariana Grajales.
3862 **1038** 5c. multicoloured . . . 10 10

1993. Death Centenary of Pyotr Tchaikovsky (composer). Multicoloured.
3863 5c. Type **1039** 50 10
3864 20c. Ballerina in "Swan Lake" 50 35
3865 30c. Statue of Tchaikovsky 80 50
3866 50c. Tchaikovsky Museum (horiz) . . . . 1·40 1·00

1040 Flag, Dove and Broken Chains

1041 Players Challenging for Ball

1994. 35th Anniv of Revolution.
3867 **1040** 5c. multicoloured . . . 10 10

1994. World Cup Football Championship, U.S.A.
3868 **1041** 5c. multicoloured . . . 20 10
3869 – 20c. multicoloured . . . 35 20
3870 – 30c. multicoloured . . . 50 30
3871 – 35c. multicoloured . . . 70 45
3872 – 40c. multicoloured . . . 75 60
3873 – 50c. multicoloured . . . 1·00 80
DESIGNS: 20c. to 50c. Various footballing scenes.

1042 Blue Persian

1994. Cats. Multicoloured.

3875	5c. Type **1042**	10	10
3876	10c. Havana	20	15
3877	20c. Maine coon	60	40
3878	30c. British blue shorthair	90	60
3879	35c. Black and white bicolour Persian	1·10	80
3880	50c. Golden Persian	1·50	1·00

1043 Sage

1994. Medicinal Plants. Multicoloured.

3882	5c. Type **1043**	25	15
3883	10c. Aloe	25	15
3884	20c. Sunflower	75	60
3885	30c. False chamomile	1·00	80
3886	40c. Pot marigold	1·50	1·00
3887	50c. Large-leaved lime	1·75	1·25

1044 London Public Transport, 1860

1994. Carriages. Multicoloured.

3888	5c. Type **1044**	20	10
3889	10c. Coach of King Fernando VII and Maria Luisa of Spain	25	20
3890	30c. French Louis XV style coach	80	50
3891	35c. Queen Isabel II of Spain's gala-day coach	1·00	80
3892	40c. Empress Catherine II of Russia's summer carriage	1·10	1·00
3893	50c. Havana cab (68 × 27 mm)	1·40	1·10

1045 Caribbean Edible Oyster

1994. Aquaculture. Multicoloured.

3894	5c. Type **1045**	30	20
3895	20c. "Cardisoma guanhumi" (crab)	50	40
3896	30c. Red-breasted tilapia	90	70
3897	35c. "Hippospongia lachne" (sponge)	90	70
3898	40c. "Panulirus argus" (crustacean)	1·00	80
3899	50c. Common carp	1·60	1·10

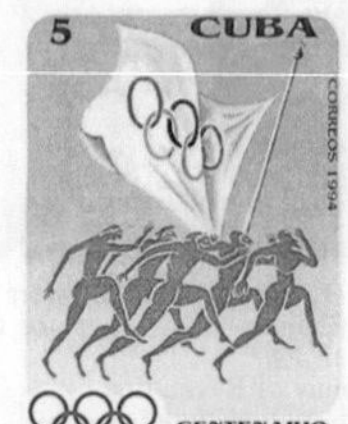

1046 Ancient Greek Athletes and Olympic Flag

1994. Centenary of International Olympic Committee. Multicoloured.

3900	5c. Type **1046**	40	20
3901	30c. Olympic flag and world map in Olympic colours	1·00	75
3902	50c. Olympic flag and flame	1·75	1·25

1047 Michael Faraday (discoverer of electricity)

1994. Scientists. Multicoloured.

3903	5c. Type **1047**	20	10
3904	10c. Marie Sklodowska-Curie (co-discoverer of radium)	20	15
3905	20c. Pierre Curie (co-discoverer of radium)	50	35
3906	30c. Albert Einstein (formulated Theory of Relativity)	75	50
3907	40c. Max Planck (physicist)	1·00	75
3908	50c. Otto Hahn (chemist)	1·25	1·00

1048 "Opuntia dillenii"

1994. Cacti. Multicoloured.

3909	5c. Type **1048**	30	20
3910	10c. "Opuntia millspaughii" (vert)	35	25
3911	30c. "Leptocereus santamarinae"	1·00	70
3912	35c. "Pereskia marcanoi"	1·25	85
3913	40c. "Dendrocereus nudiflorus" (vert)	1·50	1·00
3914	50c. "Pilocereus robinii"	1·75	1·10

1050 Rough Collies

1994. Dogs. Multicoloured.

3916	5c. Type **1050**	25	15
3917	20c. American cocker spaniels	60	40
3918	30c. Dalmatians	90	60
3919	40c. Afghan hounds	1·25	90
3920	50c. English cocker spaniels	1·50	1·10

1051 "Carpilius corallinus" (crab)

1994. Cayo Largo. Multicoloured.

3921	15c. Type **1051**	50	35
3922	65c. Shore and Cayman Islands ground iguana (vert)	2·00	1·40
3923	75c. House and brown pelican	1·90	1·10
3924	1p. Fence and common green turtle	2·75	1·90

1052 Cienfuegos

1994. 35th Anniv of Disappearance of Camilo Cienfuegos (revolutionary).

3925	**1052** 15c. multicoloured	50	25

1053 Yellow-edged Grouper

1994. Caribbean Animals. Multicoloured.

3926	10c. Type **1053**	50	20
3927	15c. Spotted eagle ray (vert)	60	30
3928	15c. Sailfish	60	30
3929	15c. Greater flamingoes (vert)	45	25
3930	65c. Bottle-nosed dolphin	1·75	1·00
3931	65c. Brown pelican (vert)	1·50	1·00

1054 Douglas DC-3

1994. 50th Anniv of I.C.A.O.

3932	**1054** 65c. multicoloured	1·50	70

1055 Bronze Statues of Deer

1994. 55th Anniv of Havana Zoo. Mult.

3933	15c. Type **1055**	50	30
3934	65c. Green-winged macaw	1·50	1·00
3935	75c. Eurasian goldfinch	1·90	1·25

1056 Boy with Stockbook

1994. 30th Anniv of Cuban Philatelic Federation.

3936	**1056** 15c. multicoloured	40	10

1057 Anole

1994. Reptiles. Multicoloured.

3937	15c. Type **1057**	45	20
3938	65c. Dwarf gecko	1·90	1·00
3939	75c. Curly-tailed lizard	2·00	1·00
3940	85c. Dwarf gecko (different)	2·25	1·10
3941	90c. Anole	2·50	1·25
3942	1p. Dwarf gecko (different)	3·00	1·40

1058 Cover and Spanish Mail Packet (18th-century sea mail)

1059 Cover of "Postal History of Cuba" by Jose Guerra Aguiar

1994. America. Postal Transport. Mult.

3943	15c. Type **1058**	40	20
3944	65c. Cover and messenger on horseback (19th-century rebel post) (horiz)	1·60	1·10

1995. 30th Anniv of Postal Museum.

3945	**1059** 15c. multicoloured	50	20

1060 Jose Marti and Flag

1995. Centenary of War of Independence.

3946	**1060** 15c. multicoloured	20	10

1061 Boxing

1063 1855 Cuba and Puerto Rico ½r. Stamp

1062 Siboney Cow

1995. 12th Pan-American Games, Mar del Plata, Argentina. Multicoloured.

3947	10c. Type **1061**	40	20
3948	15c. Weightlifting	55	30
3949	65c. Volleyball	2·50	1·00
3950	75c. Wrestling (horiz)	2·50	1·00
3951	85c. Baseball (horiz)	3·00	1·50
3952	90c. High jumping (horiz)	3·00	1·50

1995. 50th Anniv of F.A.O.

3953	**1062** 75c. multicoloured	1·25	50

1995. Postal Anniversaries.

3954	**1063** 15c. blue and black	30	10
3955	– 65c. multicoloured	1·25	1·00

DESIGNS: 15c. Type **1063** (140th anniv of first Cuban postage stamp); 65c. Colonial-style letterbox and letter (140th anniv of domestic postal service).

1064 Queen Angelfish

1995. 35th Anniv of National Aquarium. Mult.

3956	10c. Type **1064**	40	30
3957	15c. Shy hamlet	60	30
3958	65c. Porkfish	2·25	1·00
3959	75c. Red-spotted hawk-fish	2·50	1·10
3960	85c. French angelfish	3·50	1·50
3961	90c. Blue tang	3·50	1·75

1065 Portrait of Marti and Death Scene

1995. Death Centenary of Jose Marti (revolutionary). Multicoloured.

3962	15c. Type **1065**	20	10
3963	65c. Marti and Maximo Gomez in boat	85	50
3964	75c. Marti and Montecristi Declaration	95	55
3965	85c. Marti, Antonio Maceo and Gomez	1·10	65
3966	90c. Mausoleum and casket (vert)	1·10	65

1066 Maceo

1995. Centenary of Battle of Peralejo and 150th Birth Anniv of Antonio Maceo (revolutionary).
3967 **1066** 15c. multicoloured . . . 20 10

1067 Gulf Fritillary

1995. Butterflies. Multicoloured.
3968 10c. Type **1067** 15 10
3969 15c. "Eunica tatila" 20 10
3970 65c. "Melete salacia" . . . 85 50
3971 75c. Cuban clearwing . . . 95 55
3972 85c. Palmira sulphur . . . . 1·10 65
3973 90c. Cloudless sulphur . . . 1·10 65

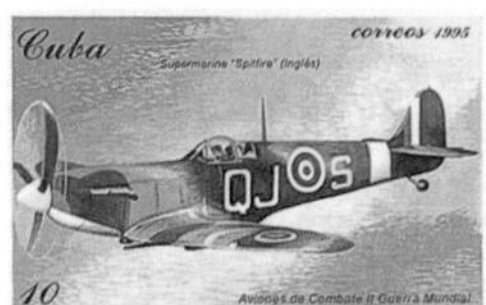

1068 Supermarine Spitfire (Great Britain)

1995. 2nd World War Combat Planes. Mult.
3974 10c. Type **1068** 15 10
3975 15c. Ilyushin Il-2 (Russia) 20 10
3976 65c. Curtiss P-40 (United States) 85 50
3977 75c. Messerschmitt ME-109 (Germany) 95 55
3978 85c. Morane Saulnier 406 (France) . . . . 1·10 65

1069 Lecuona

1070 Horse in Stable

1995. Birth Cent of Ernesto Lecuona (composer).
3979 **1069** 15c. multicoloured . . . 20 10

1995. "Singapore '95" International Stamp Exhibition. Arab Horses. Multicoloured.
3980 10c. Type **1070** 15 10
3981 15c. Two greys (horiz) . . . 20 10
3982 65c. Tethered horse 85 50
3983 75c. Horse in field 95 55
3984 85c. Mare and foal . . . . 1·10 65
3985 90c. Grey galloping in field 1·10 65

1072 Wrestling

1995. Olympic Games, Atlanta (1996) (1st issue). Multicoloured.
3987 10c. Type **1072** 15 10
3988 15c. Weightlifting 20 10
3989 65c. Volleyball 85 50
3990 75c. Running 95 55
3991 85c. Baseball . . . . 1·10 65
3992 90c. Judo . . . . 1·10 65
See also Nos. 4044/8.

1073 Acana Factory

1995. 400th Anniv of Sugar Production in Cuba. Paintings by Eduardo Laplante. Multicoloured.
3994 15c. Type **1073** . . . . . . 1·50 25
3995 65c. Manaca factory 85 50

1074 Flag and Anniversary Emblem

1995. 50th Anniv of U.N.O.
3996 **1074** 65c. multicoloured . . . 85 60

1075 Lion

1076 St. Clare of Assisi's Convent

1995. Animals from Havana Zoological Gardens. Multicoloured.
3997 10c. Type **1075** 15 10
3998 15c. Grevy's zebra (horiz) 20 10
3999 65c. Orang-utan 85 50
4000 75c. Indian elephant (horiz) 95 55
4001 85c. Eurasian red squirrel (horiz) . . . . 1·10 65
4002 90c. Common racoon (horiz) 1·10 65

1995. 50th Anniv of U.N.E.S.C.O. World Heritage Sites. Multicoloured.
4003 65c. Type **1076** 85 50
4004 75c. St. Francis of Assisi's Monastery church 95 55

1077 "Bletia patula"

1078 Greta Garbo

1995. Orchids. Multicoloured.
4005 40c. Type **1077** 50 30
4006 45c. "Galeandra beyrichii" 60 35
4007 50c. "Vanilla dilloniana" . . 65 35
4008 65c. "Macradenia lutescens" 85 50
4009 75c. "Oncidium luridum" 95 55
4010 85c. "Ionopsis utricularioides" . . . . . 1·10 65

1995. Centenary of Motion Pictures. Designs showing film stars (except No. 4015). Mult.
4011 15c. Type **1078** 20 10
4012 15c. Marlene Dietrich . . . 20 10
4013 15c. Marilyn Monroe . . . 20 10
4014 15c. Charlie Chaplin 20 10
4015 15c. Lumiere Brothers (inventors of cine camera) 20 10
4016 15c. Vittorio de Sica 20 10
4017 65c. Humphrey Bogart . . . 85 50
4018 75c. Rita Montaner 95 60
4019 85c. Cantinflas . . . . . . 1·20 70

1080 Great Red-bellied Woodpecker

1995. America. Environmental Protection. Mult.
4021 15c. Type **1080** 20 10
4022 65c. Cuban tody 80 45

1081 Alfonso Goulet and Francisco Crombet Ballon

1995. Death Centenaries of Generals killed during War of Independence (1st issue). Mult.
4023 15c. Type **1081** 20 10
4024 15c. Jesus Calvar, Jose Guillermo Moncada and Tomas Jordan 20 10
4025 15c. Francisco Borrero and Francisco Inchaustegui . . 20 10
Nos. 4023/5 were issued together, se-tenant, forming a composite design of the national flag behind the portraits.
See also Nos. 4089/91 and 4162/3.

1082 Least Tern and Aerial View

1083 Carlos de Cespedes

1995. Coco Key. Multicoloured.
4026 10c. Type **1082** 10 10
4027 15c. White ibis and beach 20 10
4028 45c. Stripe-headed tanager and villas 55 30
4029 50c. Red-legged thrush and apartments 60 35
4030 65c. Northern mocking-bird and villas around pool . . 80 45
4031 75c. Greater flamingo and couple in pool 95 55

1996. Independence Fighters.
4032 – 10c. orange 10 10
4033 **1083** 15c. green 20 10
4034 – 65c. blue 80 45
4035 – 75c. red 95 55
4036 – 85c. green . . . . . . 1·00 60
4037 – 90c. brown . . . . . . 1·10 65
4040 – 1p.05 mauve . . . . . 1·25 75
4041 – 2p.05 brown . . . . . 2·50 1·50
4042 – 3p. brown . . . . . . 3·75 2·25
DESIGNS: 10c. Serafin Sanchez; 65c. Jose Marti; 75c. Antonio Maceo; 85c. Juan Gualberto Gomez; 90c. Quintin Bandera; 1p.05, Ignacio Agramonte; 2p.05, Maximo Gomez; 3p. Calixto Garcia.

1084 Leonardo da Vinci

1996. Scientists. Multicoloured.
4046 10c. Type **1084** 10 10
4047 15c. Mikhail Lomonosov (aerodromic machines) . . 30 10
4048 65c. James Watt (steam engine) . . . . 1·10 60
4049 75c. Guglielmo Marconi (first radio transmitter) . . 1·25 75
4050 85c. Charles Darwin (theory of evolution) . . . . . . 1·50 85

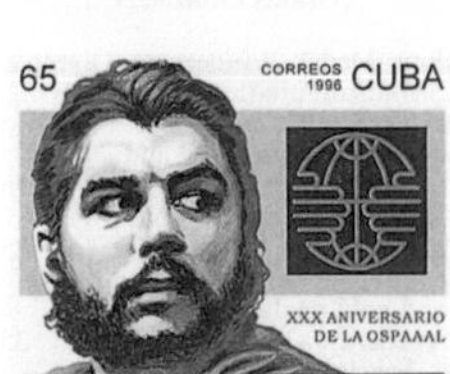

1085 "Che" Guevara and Emblem

1996. 30th Anniv of Organization of Solidarity of Peoples of Africa, Asia and Latin America.
4051 **1085** 65c. multicoloured . . . 80 45

1086 Athletics

1996. Olympic Games, Atlanta (2nd issue). Multicoloured.
4052 10c. Type **1086** 10 10
4053 15c. Weightlifting 20 10
4054 65c. Judo 80 45
4055 75c. Wrestling (horiz) . . . 95 55
4056 85c. Boxing (horiz) . . . . 1·10 65

1087 Cierva C.4 Autogyro

1996. "Espamer" Spanish–Latin American and "Aviation and Space" Stamp Exhibitions, Seville, Spain. Multicoloured.
4058 15c. Type **1087** 20 10
4059 65c.35 2-L airplane 80 45
4060 75c. C-201 Alcotan airplane 95 55
4061 85c. CASA C-212 Aviocar 1·10 65

1088 Belted Kingfisher

1996. Death Centenary of Juan Gundlach (ornithologist). Birds. Multicoloured.
4063 10c. Type **1088** 10 10
4064 15c. American redstart . . . 20 10
4065 65c. Common yellowthroat 80 45
4066 75c. Painted bunting 95 55
4067 85c. Cedar waxwing . . . . 1·10 65

1089 Yuri Gagarin (cosmonaut)

1090 National Flag and Hand holding Gun

1996. 35th Anniv of First Man in Space. Mult.
4069 15c. Type **1089** 20 10
4070 65c. Globes and "Vostok I" (spaceship) (horiz) 80 45

1996. 35th Anniversaries. Multicoloured.
4071 15c. Type **1090** (victory at Giron) 20 10
4072 65c. Flags and "35" (Declaration of Socialist character of the Revolution) 80 45

1091 "Bahama"

1996. "CAPEX'96" International Stamp Exhibition, Toronto, Canada. 18th-century Ships of the Line built in Cuban Yards. Multicoloured.
4073 10c. Type **1091** 10 10
4074 15c. "Santissima Trinidad" 20 10
4075 65c. "Principe de Asturias" 80 45
4076 75c. "San Pedro de Alcantara" 95 55
4077 85c. "Santa Ana" . . . . . 1·10 65

1092 Cuban Tody

1996. Caribbean Animals. Multicoloured.
4079 10c. Type **1092** 10 10
4080 15c. Purple-throated carib ("Eulampis jugularis") . . 20 10
4081 15c. Wood duck ("Aix sponsa") 20 10
4082 15c. Spot-finned butterflyfish 20 10
4083 65c. "Popilio cresphontes" (butterfly) 80 45
4084 65c. Indigo hamlet 80 45

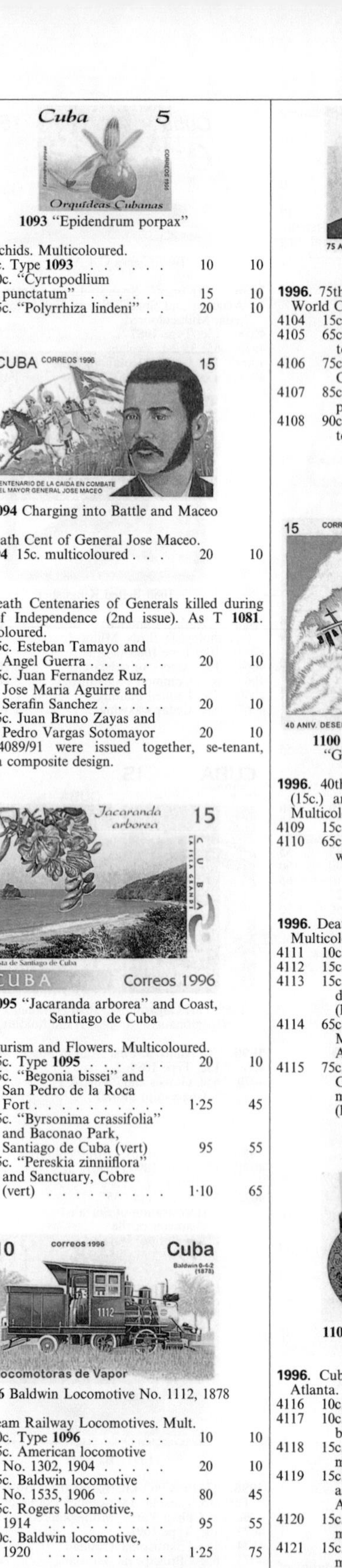

1093 "Epidendrum porpax"

1996. Orchids. Multicoloured.

4085	5c. Type **1093**	10	10
4086	10c. "Cyrtopodlium punctatum"	15	10
4087	15c. "Polyrrhiza lindeni"	20	10

1094 Charging into Battle and Maceo

1996. Death Cent of General Jose Maceo.

4088 **1094**	15c. multicoloured	20	10

1996. Death Centenaries of Generals killed during War of Independence (2nd issue). As T **1081**. Multicoloured.

4089	15c. Esteban Tamayo and Angel Guerra	20	10
4090	15c. Juan Fernandez Ruz, Jose Maria Aguirre and Serafin Sanchez	20	10
4091	15c. Juan Bruno Zayas and Pedro Vargas Sotomayor	20	10

Nos. 4089/91 were issued together, se-tenant, forming a composite design.

1095 "Jacaranda arborea" and Coast, Santiago de Cuba

1996. Tourism and Flowers. Multicoloured.

4092	15c. Type **1095**	20	10
4093	65c. "Begonia bissei" and San Pedro de la Roca Fort	1·25	45
4094	75c. "Byrsonima crassifolia" and Baconao Park, Santiago de Cuba (vert)	95	55
4095	85c. "Pereskia zinniiflora" and Sanctuary, Cobre (vert)	1·10	65

1096 Baldwin Locomotive No. 1112, 1878

1996. Steam Railway Locomotives. Mult.

4096	10c. Type **1096**	10	10
4097	15c. American locomotive No. 1302, 1904	20	10
4098	65c. Baldwin locomotive No. 1535, 1906	80	45
4099	75c. Rogers locomotive, 1914	95	55
4100	90c. Baldwin locomotive, 1920	1·25	75

1097 Free Negroes, 19th-century

1098 Children

1996. America. Costumes. Multicoloured.

4101	15c. Type **1097**	20	10
4102	65c. Guayabera couple, 20th-century	80	45

1996. 50th Anniv of U.N.I.C.E.F.

4103 **1098**	15c. multicoloured	20	10

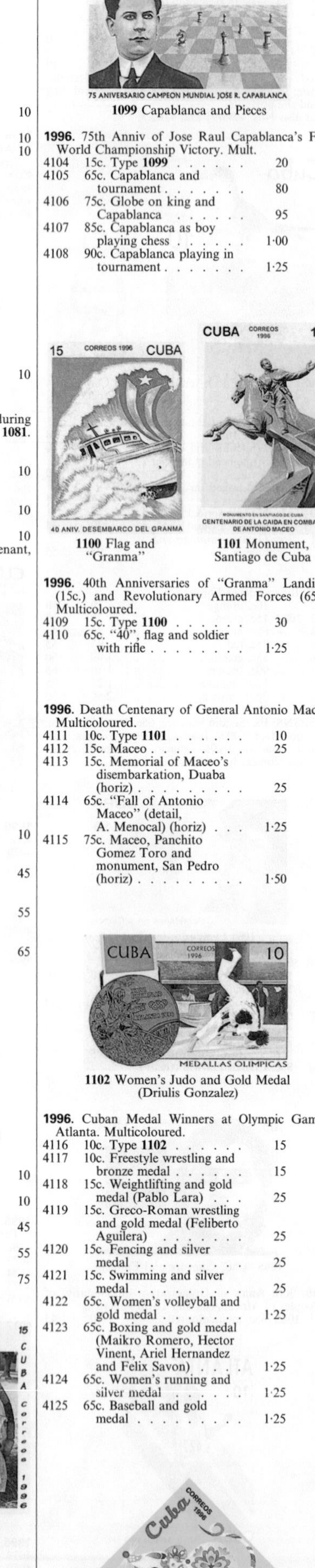

1099 Capablanca and Pieces

1996. 75th Anniv of Jose Raul Capablanca's First World Championship Victory. Mult.

4104	15c. Type **1099**	20	10
4105	65c. Capablanca and tournament	80	45
4106	75c. Globe on king and Capablanca	95	55
4107	85c. Capablanca as boy playing chess	1·00	60
4108	90c. Capablanca playing in tournament	1·25	75

1100 Flag and "Granma"

1101 Monument, Santiago de Cuba

1996. 40th Anniversaries of "Granma" Landings (15c.) and Revolutionary Armed Forces (65c.). Multicoloured.

4109	15c. Type **1100**	30	10
4110	65c. "40", flag and soldier with rifle	1·25	75

1996. Death Centenary of General Antonio Maceo. Multicoloured.

4111	10c. Type **1101**	10	10
4112	15c. Maceo	25	15
4113	15c. Memorial of Maceo's disembarkation, Duaba (horiz)	25	15
4114	65c. "Fall of Antonio Maceo" (detail, A. Menocal) (horiz)	1·25	75
4115	75c. Maceo, Panchito Gomez Toro and monument, San Pedro (horiz)	1·50	90

1102 Women's Judo and Gold Medal (Driulis Gonzalez)

1996. Cuban Medal Winners at Olympic Games, Atlanta. Multicoloured.

4116	10c. Type **1102**	15	10
4117	10c. Freestyle wrestling and bronze medal	15	10
4118	15c. Weightlifting and gold medal (Pablo Lara)	25	15
4119	15c. Greco-Roman wrestling and gold medal (Feliberto Aguilera)	25	15
4120	15c. Fencing and silver medal	25	15
4121	15c. Swimming and silver medal	25	15
4122	65c. Women's volleyball and gold medal	1·25	75
4123	65c. Boxing and gold medal (Maikro Romero, Hector Vinent, Ariel Hernandez and Felix Savon)	1·25	75
4124	65c. Women's running and silver medal	1·25	75
4125	65c. Baseball and gold medal	1·25	75

1103 Rat

1996. Chinese New Year. Year of the Rat.

4126 **1103**	15c. multicoloured	40	20

1104 Minho Douro, Portugal

1996. "Espamer '98" Spanish–Latin American Stamp Exhibition, Havana. Railway Locomotives. Multicoloured.

4127	15c. Type **1104**	25	15
4128	65c. Vulcan Iron Works, Brazil	1·25	75
4129	65c. Baldwin, Dominican Republic	1·25	75
4130	65c. Alco, Panama	1·25	75
4131	65c. Baldwin, Puerto Rico	1·25	75
4132	65c. Slaughter Gruning Co, Spain	1·25	75
4133	75c. Yorkshire Engine Co, Argentine Republic	1·40	80
4134	75c. Porter, Chile	1·40	80
4135	75c. Locomotive, Paraguay	1·40	80
4136	75c. Locomotive No. 12, Mexico	1·40	80

1105 Seal-point Siamese

1107 Dromedary

1106 "Romance del Palmar", 1938

1997. "Hong Kong '97" International Stamp Exhibition. Cats. Multicoloured.

4138	10c. Type **1105**	10	10
4139	15c. Burmese	25	15
4140	15c. Japanese bobtail (horiz)	25	15
4141	65c. Singapura (horiz)	1·25	75
4142	75c. Korat (horiz)	1·40	80

1997. Centenary of Cuban Films. Mult.

4144	15c. Type **1106**	25	15
4145	65c. "Memorias del Subdesarrollo", 1968 (vert)	1·25	75

1997. Zoo Animals. Multicoloured.

4146	10c. Type **1107**	20	10
4147	15c. White rhinoceros	40	15
4148	15c. Giant panda	40	15
4149	75c. Orang-utan	1·75	1·10
4150	90c. European bison	2·00	1·25

1108 Ox

1997. Chinese New Year. Year of the Ox.

4151 **1108**	15c. multicoloured	60	20

1109 Menelao Mora and Palace

1997. 40th Anniv of Attack on Presidential Palace.

4152 **1109**	15c. multicoloured	25	15

1110 Players

1997. World Cup Football Championship, France (1998).

4153 **1110**	10c. multicoloured	20	10
4154 –	15c. multicoloured (red face value)	40	15
4155 –	15c. multicoloured (mauve face value)	40	15
4156 –	65c. multicoloured	1·60	1·00
4157 –	75c. multicoloured	1·75	1·10

DESIGNS: 15c. to 75c. Footballers (different).

1111 Youths with Flags and Emblem

1997. 35th Anniv of Communist Youth Union.

4159 **1111**	15c. multicoloured	25	15

1112 "Caledonia"

1997. Stamp Day. Postal Services. Mult.

4160	15c. Type **1112** (170th anniv of maritime service)	45	15
4161	65c. Fokker F.10A Super Trimotor airplane (70th anniv of international airmail)	1·25	75

1113 Adolfo del Castillo and Enrique del Junco Cruz-Munoz

1997. Death Centenaries of Generals killed during War of Independence (3rd issue).

4162	15c. Type **1113**	25	15
4163	15c. Alberto Rodriguez Acosta and Mariano Sanchez Vaillant	25	15

Nos. 4162/3 were issued together, *se-tenant*, forming a composite design.

1114 Black-bordered Orange

1997. Butterflies. Multicoloured.

4164	10c. Type **1114**	20	10
4165	15c. Bush sulphur ("Eurema dina")	40	15
4166	15c. Zebra ("Colobura dirce")	40	15
4167	65c. Red admiral	1·50	1·00
4168	85c. "Kricogonia castalia"	1·75	1·00

1115 Luperon   1116 Royal Palms

1997. Death Cent of Gen. Gregorio Luperon.
4169 **1115** 65c. multicoloured . . . 1·25 75

1997. 150th Anniv of Chinese Presence in Cuba.
4170 **1116** 15c. multicoloured . . . 80 35

1117 National Flag and United Nations Emblem

1997. 50th Anniv of Cuban United Nations Association.
4171 **1117** 65c. multicoloured . . . 1·50 75

1118 Rainbow and Dove holding Olive Branch

1997. 14th World Youth and Students Festival, Cuba. Multicoloured.
4172 10c. Type **1118** 15 10
4173 15c. "Alma Mater" (statue) 25 15
4174 15c. Children on play apparatus (vert) 25 15
4175 65c. Che Guevara . . . . . 1·25 75
4176 75c. Statue and tower . . . 1·40 80

1119 Pharos of Alexandria

1997. Seven Wonders of the Ancient World. Mult.
4177 10c. Type **1119** 25 10
4178 15c. Egyptian pyramids . . 25 15
4179 15c. Hanging Gardens of Babylon 25 15
4180 15c. Colossus of Rhodes . . 30 15
4181 65c. Mausoleum of Halicarnassus . . . . . . 1·25 75
4182 65c. Statue of Zeus at Olympia . . . . 1·25 75
4183 75c. Temple of Artemis at Ephesus . . . . 1·40 80

1120 Pais and Testamonial of Fidel Castro

1997. 40th Death Anniv of Frank Pais (revolutionary).
4184 **1120** 15c. multicoloured . . . 25 15

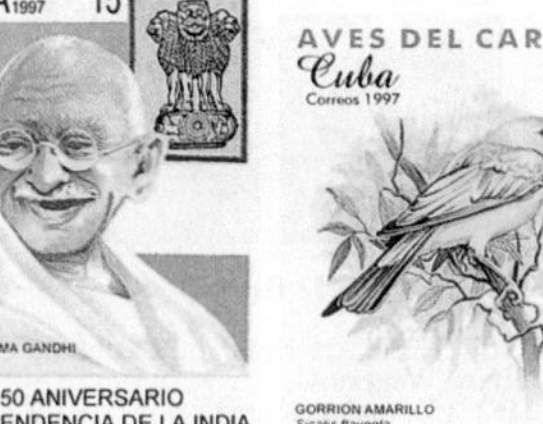

1121 Mahatma Gandhi, Indian Flag and State Arms   **1122** Saffron Finch ("Sicalis flaveola")

1997. 50th Anniv of Indian Independence.
4185 **1121** 15c. multicoloured . . . 25 15

1997. Birds of the Caribbean. Multicoloured.
4186 15c. Type **1122** 25 15
4187 15c. Red-headed barbet ("Eubucco bourcierii") . . 25 15
4188 15c. Cuban Amazon ("Amazona leucocephala") 25 15
4189 15c. Blue-crowned trogon ("Trogon curucui") . . . 25 15
4190 65c. Blue-throated goldentail ("Hylocharis eliciae") . . 1·25 75
4191 65c. Yellow-crowned Amazon ("Amazona ochrocephala") . . . . . 1·25 75
4192 75c. Eurasian goldfinch ("Carduelis carduelis") . . 1·40 80

1123 Franz Liszt and Memorial Stone commemorating his first Concert when Aged Nine

1997. Composers. Multicoloured.
4193 10c. Type **1123** 30 15
4194 15c. Johann Sebastian Bach and original manuscript score of Sonata in G minor for violin 35 20
4195 15c. Frederic Chopin and birthplace, Zelazowa Wola, Poland 35 20
4196 15c. Ludwig van Beethoven and Karntnerther Theatre where he presented the Ninth Symphony Mass in D major 35 20
4197 65c. Ignacio Cervantes and detail of score of "La Solitaria" (dance) . . . . 1·25 75
4198 75c. Wolfgang Amadeus Mozart and detail of score of first attempt at choral composition . . . 1·40 80

1124 Cuban Solitaire and Valle de Vinales

1997. Tourism. Multicoloured.
4199 10c. Type **1124** 30 15
4200 15c. Cuban crow and Cape Jutia 35 20
4201 65c. Olive-caped warbler and Soroa Falls (vert) . . 1·25 75
4202 75c. Giant kingbird and San Juan River (vert) . . . . 1·40 80

1125 "Hibiscus elatus" ("Majagua")

1997. Caribbean Flowers. Multicoloured.
4203 15c. Type **1125** 35 20
4204 15c. Rose periwinkle ("Vicaria") 35 20
4205 15c. Geiger tree ("Vomitel") 35 20
4206 15c. Bur marigold ("Romerillo") 35 20
4207 65c. Minnie root ("Salta perico") . . . . 1·25 75
4208 75c. Marilope . . . . 1·40 80

1126 Facade   **1127** Congress Emblem

1997. 50th Anniv of Oriente University.
4209 **1126** 15c. multicoloured . . . 35 20

1997. 5th Cuban Communist Party Congress and 30th Death Anniv of Ernesto "Che" Guevara (revolutionary). Multicoloured.
4210 15c. Type **1127** 35 20
4211 65c. Che Guevara and letter from Guevara to Fidel Castro . . . . 1·25 75
4212 75c. Portrait of Che Guevara . . . . 1·40 80

1128 19th-century Post Box and Postman   **1130** Soviet Flag, Lenin and "Aurora" (cruiser)

1129 Australopithecus, South Africa

1997. America. The Postman. Multicoloured.
4213 15c. Type **1128** 35 20
4214 65c. 20th-century post boxes and postman . . . . . . 1·25 75

1997. Prehistoric Man. Multicoloured.
4215 10c. Type **1129** 30 15
4216 15c. Pithecanthropus, Java 35 20
4217 15c. Sinanthropus, China . . 35 20
4218 15c. Neanderthal man . . . 35 20
4219 65c. Cro-Magnon man . . . 1·25 75
4220 75c. Oberkassel man, Germany . . . . 1·40 80

1997. 80th Anniv of Russian Revolution.
4221 **1130** 75c. multicoloured . . . 2·40 80

1131 "John Bull", 1831

1997. Railway Locomotives. Multicoloured.
4222 10c. Type **1131** 20 10
4223 15c. Baldwin steam locomotive, 1910–13 . . . 30 15
4224 15c. Locomotive "Old Ironsides", 1832, U.S.A. 30 15
4225 65c. Russian-built Type TEM-4.1 diesel locomotive, 1970 . . . . 1·25 75
4226 75c. Russian-built Type TE-114k diesel locomotive, 1975 . . . . 1·40 80
No. 4222 is inscribed "1830".

1132 National Flag and Capitol, Havana

1997. 50th Anniv of U.N. Conference on Trade and Employment, Havana.
4227 **1132** 65c. multicoloured . . . 1·25 75

1133 Garcia and 1970 30c. Stamp

1997. Birth Centenary of Victor Manuel Garcia (painter).
4228 **1133** 15c. multicoloured . . . 35 20

1134 Havana Cathedral and Pope John Paul II

1998. Papal Visit. Multicoloured.
4229 65c. Type **1134** . . . . . . 1·25 75
4230 75c. Our Lady of Charity Cathedral (vert) . . . . . 1·40 80

1135 Menendez   **1136** Players

1998. 50th Death Anniv of Jesus Menendez (labour leader).
4232 **1135** 15c. multicoloured . . . 35 20

1998. World Cup Football Championship, France. Multicoloured.
4233 10c. Type **1136** 30 15
4234 15c. Player in purple shirt lying on ground and player in red and white stripes 40 30
4235 15c. Player in yellow and black strip 50 40
4236 65c. Player in blue shirt tackling player in red and white strip (horiz) . . . . 1·50 1·00
4237 65c. Player in red and blue strip fending off player in light blue strip (horiz) . . 1·50 1·00

1137 Isabel Rubio Diaz   **1138** Revee

1998. Death Centenary of Captain Isabel Rubio Diaz (founder of mobile military hospital during War of Independence).
4239 **1137** 15c. multicoloured . . . 35 20

1998. Death Centenary of Brigadier General Vidal Ducasse Revee (revolutionary).
4240 **1138** 15c. multicoloured . . . 35 20

1139 Radio Operator and Che Guevara

1998. Communicators' Day. 40th Anniv of Radio Rebelde.
4241 **1139** 15c. multicoloured . . . 35 20

1140 Shand Mason & Co Horse-drawn Fire Engine, 1901 (Havana)

1998. Fire Engines. Multicoloured.
4242 10c. Type **1140** 30 15
4243 15c. Horse-drawn personnel and equipment vehicle, 1905 (Havana Municipal Service) 50 20
4244 15c. American–French Fire Engine Co vehicle, 1921 (Guanabacoa) 50 20
4245 65c. Chevrolet 6400 fire engine, 1952 (used throughout Cuba) . . . . 1·50 75
4246 75c. American-French-Foamite Co fire engine, 1956 (Havana) . . . . . 1·75 80

1141 Monument and Antonio Maceo (revolutionary)

1998. 120th Anniv of Baragua Protest (against slavery).
4247 **1141** 15c. multicoloured . . . 35 20

1142 Flags, Soldiers and Tank **1143** Tiger

1998. 10th Anniv of Victory of Angolan Government and Cuban Forces in Defence of Cuito Cuanavale, Angola.
4248 **1142** 15c. multicoloured . . . 35 20

1998. Chinese New Year. Year of the Tiger.
4249 **1143** 15c. multicoloured . . . 75 40

1144 Chihuahua ("Tatiana Vasti de Nino Angelo")

1998. Champion Dogs. Multicoloured.
4250 10c. Type **1144** 30 15
4251 15c. Beagle ("Danco") . . . 40 20
4252 15c. Mexican naked hound ("Xolot del Mictlan") . . 40 20
4253 65c. German spaniel ("D'Milican Nalut Aiwa") 1·40 80
4254 75c. Chow-chow ("Yoki II") 1·50 90

1145 Ancestor of Chimpanzee

1998. Evolution of the Chimpanzee. Multicoloured.
4255 10c. Type **1145** 30 15
4256 15c. Head and skull of "Pan troglodytes blumenbach" 40 20
4257 15c. Chimpanzee and hand and foot 40 20
4258 65c. Mother with infant and new-born chimp . . . . 1·40 80
4259 75c. On branch and distribution map . . . . 1·50 90

1147 Skate

1998. Deep Sea Fishes. Multicoloured.
4261 15c. Type **1147** 40 20
4262 15c. Gulper ("Eurypharynx pelecanoides") 40 20
4263 65c. "Caulophryne" sp. . . 1·50 80
4264 75c. Sloan's viperfish . . . 1·60 95

1148 Garcia Lorca

1998. Birth Cent of Federico Garcia Lorca (poet).
4265 **1148** 75c. multicoloured . . . 1·60 95

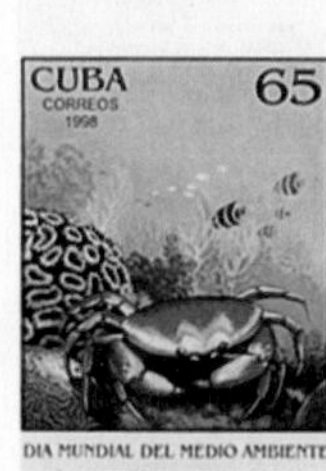

1149 Crab **1150** Diana, Princess of Wales

1998. International Year of the Ocean. Mult.
4266 65c. Type **1149** . . . . . . 1·40 80
4267 65c. Fishes . . . . 1·40 80

1998. Diana, Princess of Wales Commemoration. Multicoloured.
4268 10c. Type **1150** 30 15
4269 10c. Wearing patterned dress 30 15
4270 10c. Wearing yellow and pink jacket 30 15
4271 15c. Wearing checked jacket 40 20
4272 15c. Wearing red jacket . . 40 30
4273 65c. Wearing white jacket 1·40 80
4274 75c. Wearing purple jacket 1·50 90

1151 Abel Santamaria

1998. 45th Anniv of Attack on Moncada Barracks. Multicoloured.
4275 15c. Type **1151** 40 30
4276 65c. Jose Marti . . . . . . 1·40 80

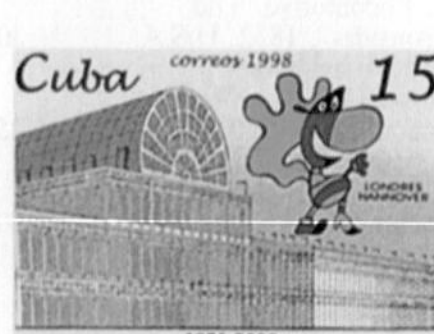

1152 The Crystal Palace, London (Great Exhbition, 1851)

1998. "Expo 2000" World's Fair, Hanover, Germany.
4277 **1152** 15c. multicoloured . . . 40 20
4278 – 15c. multicoloured . . . 40 20
4279 – 15c. multicoloured . . . 40 20
4280 – 15c. black, red & yellow 40 20
4281 – 65c. multicoloured . . . 1·40 80
4282 – 75c. multicoloured . . . 1·50 90
DESIGNS—HORIZ: No. 4277, Type **1152**; 4278, Atomium, Brussels (International Exhibition, 1958); 4280, Map and flag of Germany; 4282, Twipsy (mascot) on globe and fireworks. VERT: No. 4279, Twipsy; 4281, Eiffel Tower, Paris (Exhibition, 1889).

1153 Baseball

1998. 18th Central American and Caribbean Games, Maracaibo, Venezuela.
4283 **1153** 15c. multicoloured . . . 30 15

1154 Kim Il Sung and Pyongyang Landmarks

1998. 50th Anniv of Korean People's Democratic Republic (North Korea).
4284 **1154** 75c. multicoloured . . . 1·50 90

1155 Japanese Bust

1998. Cent of First Japanese Immigrant to Cuba.
4285 **1155** 75c. multicoloured . . . 1·50 90

1156 "Coelogyne flaccida" **1157** Buildings and Emblem

1998. 30th Anniv of National Botanical Garden. Orchids. Multicoloured.
4286 10c. Type **1156** 40 20
4287 15c. "Dendrobium fimbriatum" 40 20
4288 15c. Bamboo orchid ("Arundina graminifolia") 40 20
4289 65c. "Bletia patula" . . . . 1·40 80
4290 65c. Nun's orchid ("Phaius tankervilliaea") . . . . . 1·40 80

1998. 5th Congress of Revolution Defence Committees.
4291 **1157** 15c. multicoloured . . . 30 15

1158 Knight Anole and Archway, Gibara

1998. World Tourism Day. Views of Holguin. Multicoloured.
4292 10c. Type **1158** 30 15
4293 15c. Water lizard, Mirador de Mayabe 40 20
4294 65c. Water chameleon, Guardalavaca Beach (horiz) . . . . 1·40 80
4295 75c. Stone lizard, Pinares de Mayari (horiz) . . . . . 1·50 90

1159 Bernarda Toro (Manana) **1160** Two Conures

1998. America. Famous Women. Independence Activists. Multicoloured.
4296 65c. Type **1159** . . . . . . 1·40 80
4297 75c. Maria Cabrales . . . . 1·50 90

1998. The Cuban Conure. Multicoloured.
4298 10c. Type **1160** 30 15
4299 15c. Head of conure 40 20
4300 65c. Conure on branch . . . 1·40 80
4301 75c. Conure and leaves . . 1·50 90

1161 "Swan Lake"

1998. 50th Anniv of Cuban National Ballet.
4302 **1161** 15c. blue 40 20
4303 – 65c. multicoloured . . . 1·40 80
DESIGN: 65c. "Giselle".

1162 Apartment Building on O'Farrill and Goicuria Streets, Havana, and Victims

1998. 40th Death Anniv of Rogelia Perea, Angel Ameijeiras and Pedro Gutierrez (revolutionaries).
4304 **1162** 15c. multicoloured . . . 30 15

1163 Capt. Braulio Coroneaux (revolutionary) and Tank

1998. 40th Anniv of Battle of Guisa.
4305 **1163** 15c. multicoloured . . . 30 15

1164 Family holding Hands and United Nations Emblem **1165** Garcia Iniguez

1998. 50th Anniv of Universal Declaration of Human Rights.
4306 **1164** 65c. multicoloured . . . 1·40 80

1998. Death Centenary of Major-General Calixto Garca Iniguez (independence fighter).
4307 **1165** 65c. multicoloured . . . 1·40 80

1166 Varela and San Carlos Seminary, Havana

1998. 145th Death Anniv of Felix Varela (philosopher and Vicar-General of New York).
4308 **1166** 75c. multicoloured . . . 1·50 90

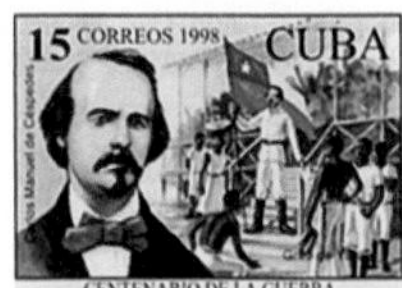

1167 Carlos Manuel de Cespedes

1998. Cent of Cuban War of Independence. Mult.
4309 15c. Type **1167** 40 20
4310 15c. Ignacio Agramonte Loynaz 40 20
4311 15c. Maximo Gomez Baez 40 20
4312 15c. Jose Maceo Grajales . . 40 20
4313 15c. Salvador Cisneros Betancourt 40 20
4314 15c. Calixto Garcia Iniguez 40 20
4315 15c. Adolfo Flor Crombet 40 20
4316 15c. Serafin Sanchez Valdivia 40 20
4317 65c. Jose Marti Perez . . . 1·40 80
4318 75c. Antonio Maceo Grajales . . . . 1·50 90

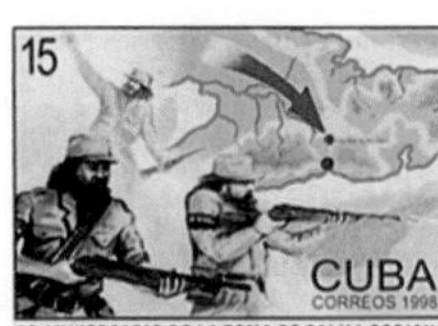

1168 Revolutionaries and Map

1998. 40th Anniv of Capture of Palma Soriano by Revolutionaries.
4319 **1168** 15c. multicoloured . . . 30 15

1169 "Granma" Landings

1999. 40th Anniv of Revolution. Multicoloured.
4320 65c. Type **1169** . . . . . . 1·40 80
4321 65c. Camilo Cienfuegos and Fidel Castro . . . . . . 1·40 80
4322 65c. Castro and white doves 1·40 80

1170 Police Car and Motor Cycle

1999. 40th Anniv of National Revolutionary Police.
4323 **1170** 15c. multicoloured . . . 30 15

1171 Workers' Rally **1172** Rabbit

1999. 60th Anniv of Revolutionary Workers' Union.
4324 **1171** 15c. multicoloured . . . 30 15

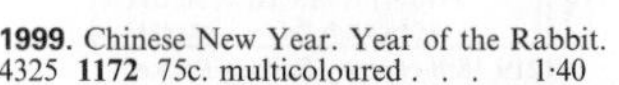
1999. Chinese New Year. Year of the Rabbit.
4325 **1172** 75c. multicoloured . . . 1·40 80

1173 Lenin

1999. 75th Death Anniv of Vladimir Ilich Lenin (Russian statesman).
4326 **1173** 75c. multicoloured . . . 1·40 80

1174 Ornithosuchus

1999. Prehistoric Animals. Multicoloured.
4327 10c. Type **1174** 30 15
4328 15c. Bactrosaurus 40 20
4329 15c. Saltopus 40 20
4330 65c. Protosuchus . . . . . 1·40 80
4331 75c. Mussaurus . . . . . . 1·50 90

1175 Damaso Perez Prado

1999. Cuban Musicians. Multicoloured.
4332 5c. Type **1175** 15 10
4333 15c. Benny More 40 20
4334 15c. Chano Pozo 40 20
4335 35c. Miguelito Valdes . . . 70 40
4336 65c. Bola de Nieve . . . . 1·40 80
4337 75c. Rita Montaner . . . . 1·50 90

1176 Bolivar **1177** Emblem

1999. Centenary of Simon Bolivar's Visit to Cuba. Multicoloured.
4338 65c. Type **1176** . . . . . . 1·40 80
4339 65c. Simon Bolivar House and statue, Havana . . . 1·40 80

1999. 40th Anniv of State Security Department of the Ministry of the Interior.
4340 **1177** 65c. multicoloured . . . 1·40 80

1179 Postal Rocket

1999. Stamp Day.
4342 15c. Type **1179** (60th anniv) 40 20
4343 65c. Rider on horse (130th anniv of rebel postal service) . . . . 1·40 80

1180 Painting by Roberto Matta

1999. 40th Anniv of House of the Americas (cultural organization).
4344 **1180** 65c. multicoloured . . . 1·40 80

1182 Castro drafting Reform Law

1999. 40th Anniv of Agrarian Reform Law.
4346 **1182** 65c. multicoloured . . . 1·40 80

1183 Royal Gramma

1999. Birth Bicentenary of Felipe Poey (naturalist). Fishes. Multicoloured.
4347 5c. Type **1183** 15 10
4348 15c. Peppermint basslet . . 40 20
4349 65c. Golden hamlet ("Hypoplectrus gummigutta") . . . . . 1·40 80
4350 65c. Dusky damselfish ("Stegastes dorsopunicans") . . . . 1·40 80

1185 Baseball

1999. 13th Pan-American Games, Winnipeg, Canada. Multicoloured.
4353 15c. Type **1185** 40 20
4354 65c. Volleyball (vert) . . . . 1·40 80
4355 75c. Boxing . . . . 1·50 90

1186 "Victory of Wioming" (Gao Hong)

1999. 50th Anniv of People's Republic of China. Paintings. Multicoloured.
4356 5c. Type **1186** 15 10
4357 15c. "Nanchang Revolt" (Cai Lang) 40 20
4358 40c. "Red Army crossing Marsh" (Gao Quan) . . . 75 40
4359 65c. "Occupation of Presidential Palace" (Cheng Yifei and Wei Jingahan) . . . . 1·40 80
4360 75c. "Founding of the Republic Ceremony" (Dong Xiwen) . . . . . 1·50 90

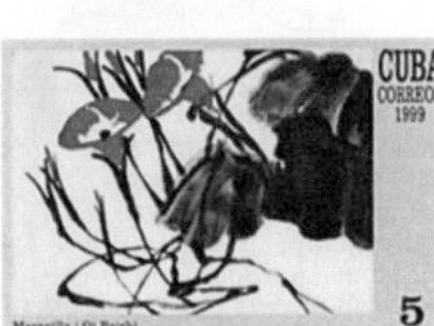

1187 "Morning Glory" (Qi Baishi)

1999. "China 1999" International Stamp Exhibition, Peking. Chinese Paintings. Multicoloured.
4361 5c. Type **1187** 15 10
4362 5c. "Three Galloping Horses" (Xu Beihong) . . 15 10
4363 15c. "Hunan Woman" (Fu Baoshi) 40 20
4364 15c. "Village of Luxun" (Wu Guanzhong) 40 20
4365 15c. "Crossing" (Huangzhou) 40 20
4366 40c. "Pine Tree" (He Xiangning) 75 40
4367 65c. "Sleeping Woman" (Jin Shangyi) . . . . 1·40 80
4368 75c. "Poetic Scene in Xun Yang" (Chen Yifei) . . . 1·50 90

1188 Heinrich von Stephan (founder) and Emblem

1999. 125th Anniv of Universal Postal Union.
4369 **1188** 75c. multicoloured . . . 1·50 90

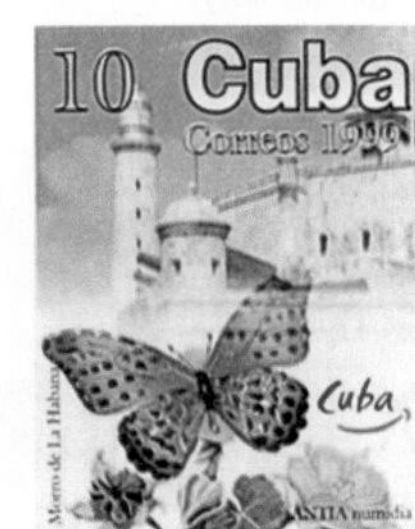

1189 Havana Fortress and *Antia numidia*

1999. World Tourism Day. Butterflies and Views of Havana. Multicoloured.
4370 10c. Type **1189** 10 10
4371 15c. Cathedral and black swallowtail 30 20
4372 65c. St. Francis of Assisi Convent and flambeau . . 1·40 80
4373 75c. National Senate and *Eueides cleobaea* . . . . 1·50 90

1190 Map of Germany on Globe

1999. "EXPO 2000" World's Fair, Hanover. Mult.
4374 5c. Type **1190** 10 10
4375 15c. Twipsy (mascot) (vert) 30 20
4376 15c. Exhibition site, Philadelphia, 1876 . . . . 30 20
4377 15c. Exhibition site, Osaka, 1970 . . . . 30 20
4378 65c. Exhibition site, Hanover . . . . 1·40 80
4379 75c. Exhibition site, Montreal, 1967 . . . . . 1·50 90

1191 Fokker F.27 Friendship

1999. 70th Anniv of Cuban Airlines. Multicoloured.
4380 15c. Type **1191** 30 20
4381 15c. Douglas DC-10 . . . . 30 20
4382 65c. Airbus Industrie A320 1·40 80
4383 75c. Douglas DC-3 . . . . 1·50 90

1192 Atomic Cloud and Feral Rock Pigeon **1194** Cienfuegos

1193 MINFAR Headquarters

1999. America. A New Millennium without Arms. Multicoloured.
4384 15c. Type **1192** 30 20
4385 65c. Globe and dove . . . . 1·40 80

1999. 40th Anniversaries. Multicoloured.
4386 15c. Type **1193** (Ministry of Revolutionary Armed Forces) 30 20
4387 65c. Militia members (National Revolutionary Militia) . . . . 1·40 80

1999. 40th Anniv of Disappearance of Major Camilo Cienfuegos (revolutionary).
4388 **1194** 15c. multicoloured . . . 30 20

1195 Vieja Plaza

1999. 9th Latin American Summit of Heads of State and Government, Havana. Multicoloured.
4389 65c. Type **1195** . . . . . . 1·40 80
4390 75c. San Francisco de Asis Plaza . . . . 1·50 90

1197 Hemingway and Fisherman

1999. Birth Cent of Ernest Hemingway (writer).
4393 **1197** 65c. multicoloured . . . 1·40 80

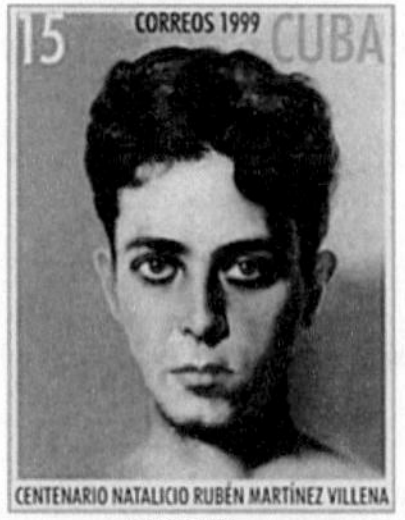

1198 Villena

1999. Birth Centenary of Ruben Martinez Villena (revolutionary).
4394 **1198** 15c. multicoloured . . . 30 20

1199 Romay Chacon

1999. 150th Death Anniv of Tomas Romay Chacon (scientist).
4395 **1199** 65c. multicoloured . . . 1·40 80

1200 Dragon

2000. Chinese New Year. "Year of the Dragon".
4396 **1200** 15c. multicoloured . . . 30 20

1201 "Hot Rumba"

2000. Paintings by Concepcion Ferrant. Mult.
4397 10c. Type **1201** 15 10
4398 15c. "Cachumba" 30 20
4399 65c. "House of the babalao" 1·40 80
4400 75c. "Tata Cunengue" . . . 1·50 90

1202 *Helcyra superba*

2000. "BANGKOK 2000" International Stamp Exhibition. Butterflies. Multicoloured.
4401 10c. Type **1202** 15 10
4402 15c. *Pantaporia punctata* . . 30 20
4403 15c. *Neptis themis* 30 20
4404 65c. *Curetis acuta* . . . . . 1·40 80
4405 75c. *Chrysozephyrus ataxus* 1·50 90

1203 World Map

2000. Group of 77 South Summit, Havana.
4406 **1203** 75c. multicoloured . . . 1·50 90

1204 Lenin

2000. 130th Birth Anniv of Vladimir Ilich Lenin.
4407 **1204** 75c. multicoloured . . . 1·50 90

1205 Cuba and Puerto Rico 1855 1r. Stamp

2000. Stamp Day. Multicoloured.
4408 65c. Type **1205** (145th anniv of first Cuba and Puerto Rico stamp) . . . . . . 1·40 80
4409 90c. Jaime Gonzalez Crocier (airmail pioneer), airplane and cover (70th anniv of the airmail service) . . . 1·75 1·10

1206 Commander Guevara and Map

2000. 35th Anniv of Visit of "Che" Guevara (guerrilla fighter) to Congo.
4410 **1206** 65c. multicoloured . . . 1·40 80

1207 Captain San Luis

2000. 60th Birth Anniv of Eliseo Reyes Rodriguez ("Captain San Luis").
4411 **1207** 65c. multicoloured . . . 1·40 80

1208 Baldwin Locomotive, 1882

2000. "Stamp Show 2000" International Stamp Exhibition, London. Steam Locomotives. Mult.
4412 5c. Type **1208** 10 10
4413 10c. Baldwin locomotive, 1895 . . . . 15 10
4414 15c. Baldwin locomotive, 1912 . . . . 30 20
4415 65c. Alco locomotive, 1919 1·40 80
4416 75c. Alco locomotive, 1925 1·50 90

1209 Henri Giffard and Steam-powered Dirigible Airship

2000. "WIPA 2000" International Stamp Exhibition, Vienna. Airship Development. Multicoloured.
4418 10c. Type **1209** 10 10
4419 15c. Albert and Gaston Tissander and airship (vert) 20 10
4420 50c. Charles Renard, Arthur Krebs and *La France* (airship) 70 40
4421 65c. Pierre and Paul Lebaudy and airship . . . 90 50
4422 75c. August von Perseval and airship . . . . 1·10 65

1210 Emblem

2000. 2nd World Meeting of "Friendship and Solidarity with Cuba", Havana.
4424 **1210** 65c. multicoloured . . . 90 50

1211 Caballero

2000. Birth Bicentenary of Jose de la Luz y Caballero (educator).
4425 **1211** 65c. multicoloured . . . 90 50

1212 Music Score, Roldan and Violin

2000. Birth Centenary of Amadeo Roldan (musician and conductor).
4426 **1212** 65c. multicoloured . . . 90 50

1213 Mother holding Child ("Child of El Senor Don Pomposo")

2000. *The Golden Age* (children's magazine by Jose Marti). Designs illustrating stories featured in the magazines. Multicoloured.
4427 5c. Type **1213** 10 10
4428 10c. Child with doll ("The Black Doll") 15 10
4429 15c. Child reading ("Mischevious Child") . . 20 10
4430 50c. "The Nightingale" (Hans Christian Andersen) 70 40
4431 65c. Frontispiece 90 50
4432 75c. "The Enchanted Prawn" (Edourd R. L. Laboulaye) . . . . 1·10 65

1214 Members' Flags

2000. 20th Anniv of Latin American Association for Integration (A.L.A.D.I.).
4434 **1214** 65c. multicoloured . . . 90 50

1216 Running

2000. Olympic Games, Sydney. Multicoloured.
4436 5c. Type **1216** 10 10
4437 15c. Football 20 10
4438 65c. Baseball 90 50
4439 75c. Cycling . . . . 1·10 65

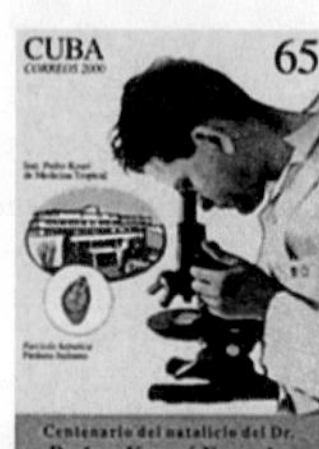

1217 Esmeja using Microscope

2000. Birth Centenary of Dr. Pedro Kouri Esmeja (tropical disease and parasitology pioneer).
4440 **1217** 65c. multicoloured . . . 90 50

1218 Women and Flag

2000. 40th Anniv of Federation of Cuban Women.
4441 **1218** 15c. multicoloured . . . 20 10

1219 18th-century Sailing Packet

2000. "Espana 2000" World Stamp Exhibition, Madrid. Multicoloured.
4442 10c. Type **1219** 15 10
4443 15c. Statue, La Cibeles Plaza, Madrid and Spain 1850 6c. stamp 20 10
4444 15c. Crystal Palace, Madrid (venue) and 1850 cover 20 10
4445 65c. Palace of Communications, Madrid and set of Spain 1850 stamps 90 50
4446 75c. Galician Centre, Havana with Cuba and Puerto Rica 1855 ½r. stamp . . . . 1·10 65

1220 Senen Casas Reguerio Railway Station, Santiago de Cuba

2000. 20th Congress of Pan-American Railways.
4448 **1220** 65c. multicoloured . . . 90 50

1221 Coconut Forest Bay, Hainan, China

2000. 40th Anniv of Cuba–China Diplomatic Relations. Joint issue with China. Multicoloured.
4449 15c. Type **1221** 20 10
4450 15c. Varadero beach, Matanzas, Cuba 20 10
Nos. 4449/50 were issued together, se-tenant, forming a composite design.

1222 Hawksbill Turtle (*Eretmochelys imbricata*), Guardalavaca

2000. World Tourism Day. Diving Sites. Mult.
4451 10c. Type **1222** 15 10
4452 15c. Nassau grouper (*Epinephelus striatus*), El Colony 20 10
4453 65c. French angelfish (*Pomacanthus paru*), Santa Lucia (horiz) 80 45
4454 75c. Black margate (*Anisotremus surinamensis*), Maria la Gorda (horiz) 95 55

1223 House and People Gardening
1224 Emblem, Heart-shaped Globe and Family

2000. 40th Anniv of Committees for Defense of the Revolution (CDR).
4455 **1223** 15c. multicoloured . . . 20 10

2000. America. Anti-A.I.D.S. Campaign. Mult.
4456 15c. Type **1224** 20 10
4457 65c. Emblem, heart-shaped globe and couple 80 45

1225 Soldiers carrying Flags

2000. 25th Anniv of Cuban International Mission to Angola.
4458 **1225** 75c. multicoloured . . . 95 55

1226 Humboldt and Guesthouse, Trinidad

2000. Bicentennial of Friedrich Wilhelm Heinrich Alexander von Humboldt's Visit to Cuba. Mult.
4459 15c. Type **1226** 20 10
4460 65c. Humboldt, frontispiece of *On the Island of Cuba* (political essay) and Humboldt House, Havana 80 45

1227 *Polymita picta iolimbata*

2000. New Millennium. Snails. Multicoloured.
4461 65c. Type **1227** 80 45
4462 65c. *Polymita picta roseolimbata* 80 45
4463 65c. *Polymita picta picta* . . 80 45
4464 65c. *Polymita picta nigrolimbata* 80 45
4465 65c. *Polymita versicolor* . . 80 45
Nos. 4461/4 were issued together, se-tenant, forming a composite design.

1228 Dragon

2001. New Year. Year of the Dragon.
4466 **1228** 15c. multicoloured . . . 15 10

1229 Mandarin Duck (*Aix galericulata*)

2001. Birds. Hong Kong 2001 International Stamp Exhibition. Multicoloured.
4467 5c. Type **1229** 10 10
4468 10c. Golden pheasant (*Chrysolophus pictus*) (inscr "Chryysolophus") 10 10
4469 15c. Grey heron (*Ardea cinerea*) 15 10
4470 65c. Red Jungle-fowl (*Gallus gallus*) 70 45
4471 75c. Collared dove (*Streptotelia decaocto*) . . 85 50
MS4472 111 × 85 mm. 1p. Common crane (*Grus grus*) (32 × 40 mm) 1·10 1·10

1230 Sports Centre

2001. 40th Anniv of INDER (National Institute for Sport, Physical Education and Recreation).
4473 **1230** 65c. multicoloured . . . 70 45

1231 Refugees

2001. 50th Anniv of United Nations High Commissioner for Refugees.
4474 **1231** 65c. multicoloured . . . 70 45

1232 James Miholland's Locomotive

2001. Steam Locomotives. Multicoloured.
4475 10c. Type **1232** 10 10
4476 15c. Theodore Sheffler's fire-less steam locomotive . . 15 10
4477 40c. Adams and Price's chain driven locomotive 45 25
4478 65c. Peckett and Sons' Bulan 70 45
4479 75c. W. G. Bagnall's fire-less steam locomotive 85 50

1233 Anniversary Emblem and Lighthouse 2001

2001. 105th Inter-Parliamentary Union Conference, Havana.
4480 **1233** 65c. multicoloured . . . 70 45

1234 "Bombardeo del 15 Abril" (Servando Cabrera)

2001. 40th Anniv of Bay of Pigs (Playa Giron).
4481 **1234** 65c. multicoloured . . . 70 45

1235 Cats

2001. Cats and Dogs. Showing cats, dogs and animal societies' emblems. Multicoloured.
4482 10c. Type **1235** 10 10
4483 15c. Fighting dogs 15 10
4484 15c. German shepherd, boxer and puppy 15 10
4485 65c. Spaniel and collies . . 70 45
4486 75c. Snarling dog, cats, and puppy 85 50

1236 Anniversary Emblem

2001. 40th Anniv of Radio Havana Cuba.
4487 **1236** 65c. multicoloured . . . 70 45

1237 Boats (engraving, Frederic Mialhe)

2001. Cuba 2001 International Tourism Convention, Havana.
4488 **1237** 65c. multicoloured . . . 70 45

1238 St. Michael's Cathedral, Brussels
1239 Sniffer Dog and Handler

2001. Belgica 2001 International Stamp Exhibition, Brussels. Multicoloured.
4489 5c. Type **1238** 10 10
4490 10c. Sablon Church (horiz) 10 10
4491 15c. Royal Palace (horiz) . . 15 10
4492 65c. Basilica of the Sacred Heart, Koekelberg (horiz) 70 45
4493 75c. Atomium (model of an iron crystal) Exhibition Centre 85 50
MS4494 107 × 83 mm. 100c. Kings Residence, Grand Place, Brussels (32 × 40 mm) . . . . 1·10 1·10

2001. 40th Anniv of Ministry of Interior.
4495 **1239** 65c. multicoloured . . . 70

1240 Locomotive *JR 500*

2001. Japanese Locomotives. Philanippon '01 International Stamp Exhibition, Tokyo. Multicoloured.
4496 5c. Type **1240** 10 10
4497 10c. Locomotive *JR 700* . . 10 10
4498 15c. Locomotive *MAX 1* . . 15 10
4499 65c. Locomotive *MAX 2* . . 70 45
4500 75c. Locomotive *300* 85 50
MS4501 78 × 110 mm. 100c. Locomotive *Zero* (40 × 32 mm) 1·10 1·10

1241 Mount Titano and St. Marino (statue)

2001. 1700th Anniv of Founding of San Marino.
4502 **1241** 75c. multicoloured . . . 85 45

1242 Tench (*Tinca tinca*)

2001. Aquatics Breeding Programme. Multicoloured.
4503 5c. Type **1242** 10 10
4504 10c. Common frog (*Rana temporaria*) 10 10
4505 15c. Blue land crab (*Cardisoma guanhumi*) . . 15 10
4506 65c. Common mussel (*Mytilus edulis*) 70 45
4507 75c. Spotted tilapia (*Tilapia mariae*) 85 50
MS4508 86 × 111 mm. 1p. White-clawed crayfish (*Potamobius pallipes*) (40 × 32 mm) . . . . 1·10 1·10

1243 Anniversary Emblem and Ernesto "Che" Guevara

2001. 40th Anniv of Recycling.
4509 **1243** 65c. multicoloured . . . 70 45

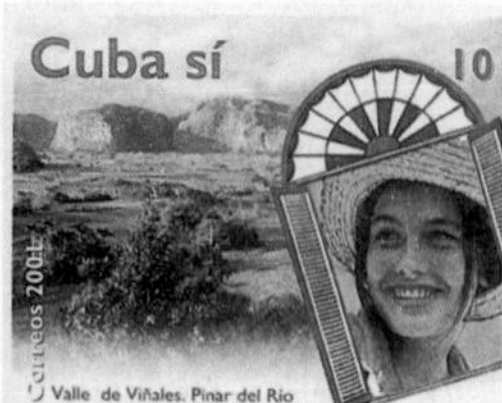

1244 Valle de Vinales, Pinar del Rio

2001. Tourism. Multicoloured.
4510 10c. Type **1244** 10 10
4511 15c. Trindad de Cuba . . . 15 10
4512 65c. Playa Sirena (beach), Cayo Largo del Sur . . . 70 45
4513 75c. Morro-Cabana (castle), Havana 85 50

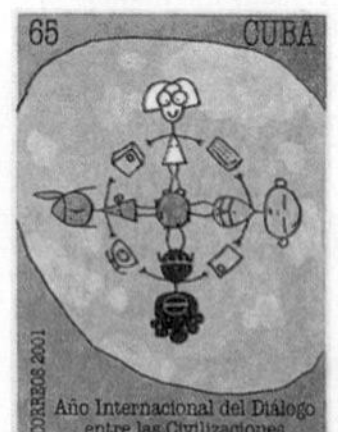

1245 Children encircling Globe

2001. United Nations Year of Dialogue Among Civilizations.
4514 **1245** 65c. multicoloured . . . 70 45

1246 *Tetramicra malpighiarum* (orchid)

2001. America. UNESCO World Heritage Sites. Desamarco del Granma National Park. Multicoloured.
4515 15c. Type **1246** 15 10
4516 65c. *Liggus vittatus* (shell) 70 45

1247 Building

2001. Centenary of José Marti National Library.
4517 **1247** 15c. multicoloured . . . 15 10

1248 Torso and Head **1249** Eduardo Chibas

2001. 25th Anniv of Cuban Airliner Explosion over Barbados. Showing parts of painting. Multicoloured.
4518 5c. Type **1248** 10 10
4519 10c. Dove 10 10
4520 15c. Pregnant woman . . . 15 10
4521 50c. Stylized birds 55 30
4522 65c. Star and houses 70 45
Nos. 4518/22 were issued together, *se-tenant*, forming a composite design.

2001. 50th Death Anniv of Eduardo Chibas (politician).
4523 **1249** 65c. multicoloured . . . 70 45

1250 Napoleon on Horseback and Map of Battle of Eylau (inscr "Elyeau")

2001. 40th Anniv of Napoleon Museum, Havana. Showing Napoleon and battles maps.
4524 10c. Type **1250** 10 10
4525 10c. Battle of Marengo . . 10 10
4527 65c. Battle of Waterloo . . 70 45
4528 75c. Battle of Abukin . . . 85 50

1251 Pablo de la Torriente **1253** Tyrone Power

1252 Mosaic Pigeon (3013-67-HM)

2001. Birth Centenary of Pablo de la Torriente (writer).
4529 **1251** 75c. multicoloured . . . 85 50

2001. 4th Pigeon Fanciers Federation Congress. Multicoloured.
4530 65c. Type **1252** 70 45
4531 65c. Emperor (2241-55-ME) 70 45
4532 65c. Bronzed (338-59-HE) 70 45
4533 65c. Mosaic (1561-66-HM) 70 45
4534 65c. Dark emperor (2021-61-ME) 70 45

2001. Actors. Multicoloured.
4535 5c. Type **1253** 10 10
4536 10c. Steve McQueen 10 10
4537 10c. Ava Gardner 10 10
4538 15c. Rita Hayworth 15 10
4539 15c. James Dean 15 10
4540 15c. Marilyn Monroe . . . 15 10
4541 65c. Natalie Wood 70 45
4542 65c. Rock Hudson 70 45
4543 75c. Richard Burton 85 50
MS4544 150 × 185 mm. Nos. 4535/43 3·00 3·00

1254 Bamboo and Horse

2002. Year of the Horse.
4545 **1254** 15c. multicoloured . . . 15 10

1255 Cigars and Hat

2002. 4th Habano (cigar) Festival, Havana. Multicoloured.
4546 5c. Type **1255** 10 10
4547 10c. Smoking cigar 10 10
4548 15c. Wax seal and map . . 15 10
4549 65c. Stamps, Punch and crossed swords 70 45
4550 75c. Flag, tobacco plants and Alejandro Robaina (5th anniv of "Vegas Robaina" (cigar manufacturer)) 85 50
MS4551 118 × 91 mm. 1p. Fidel Castro, map and star (40 × 32 mm) 1·10 1·10

1256 Profile, Dove holding Envelope and Computer (½-size illustration)

2002. 2nd UPAEP Information Technology Workshop.
4552 **1256** 65c. multicoloured . . . 70 45

1257 Map Reading **1259** Two Football Players (Brazil in foreground)

1258 Soldiers, Demonstrators, Industry and Computers

2002. Pioneer Explorers (scouts). Multicoloured.
4553 5c. Type **1257** 10 10
4554 15c. Tying knots 15 10
4555 50c. Cooking over campfire 55 30
4556 65c. Lighting campfire . . . 70 45
4557 75c. Orienteering 85 50

2002. 40th Anniv of Young Communists Union.
4558 **1258** 15c. multicoloured . . . 15 10

2002. World Cup Football Championships, Japan and South Korea. Showing two players and flag, player in foreground given. Multicoloured.
4559 15c. Type **1259** 15 10
4560 15c. Spain 15 10
4561 15c. France 15 10
4562 15c. Germany 15 10
4563 15c. Korean Republic . . . 15 10
4564 65c. Argentina 70 45
4565 75c. Italy 85 50
4566 85c. Japan 95 55

1260 NH Parque Central Hotel, Havana

2002. Spanish–Cuban Philatelic Exhibition, Havana. Sheet 110 × 84 mm.
MS4567 **1260** 1p. multicoloured 1·10 1·10

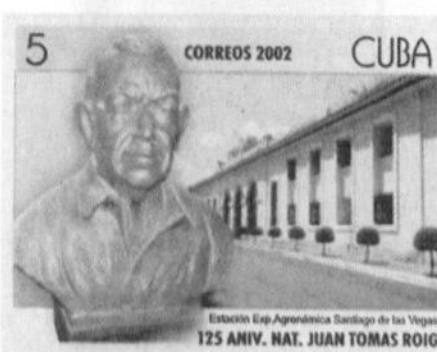

1261 Bust and Experimental Agricultural Building, Santiago de las Vegas

2002. 125th Birth Anniv of Juan Thomas Roig (botanist). Multicoloured.
4568 5c. Type **1261** 10 10
4569 10c. Juan Roig's house and bust 10 10
4570 15c. Tobacco plant and Roig 15 10
4571 50c. Roig (sculpture) and *Allophyllum roiggi* 55 30
4572 65c. Botanical dictionary and Roig 70 45

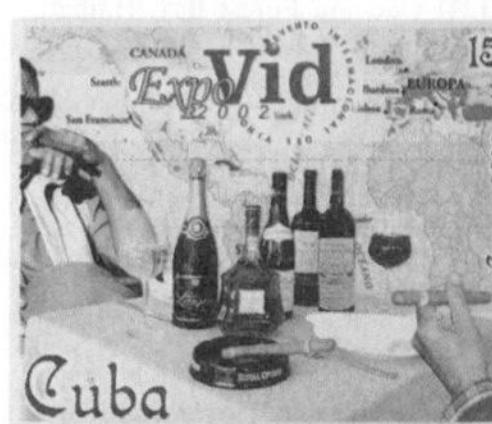

1262 Table with Wine and Cigars

2002. Expovid 2002 International Wine Festival, Havana. Multicoloured.
4573 15c. Type **1262** 15 10
4574 65c. Glass of white wine and barrels 70 45
4575 75c. Glass of red wine and vineyard 85 50

1263 Hands, Heart and Leaf **1264** *Amanita junquillea*

2002. 10th Anniv of MediCuba Switzerland (humanitarian organization).
4576 **1263** 75c. multicoloured . . . 85 50

2002. Fungi. Multicoloured.
4577 5c. Type **1264** 10 10
4578 15c. *Lepiota puellaris* . . . 15 10
4579 45c. *Cortinarius cumatilis* 50 30
4580 65c. *Pholiota adipose* (inscr "Pholliota") 70 45
4581 75c. Shaggy ink cap (*Coprinus comatus*) . . . 85 50

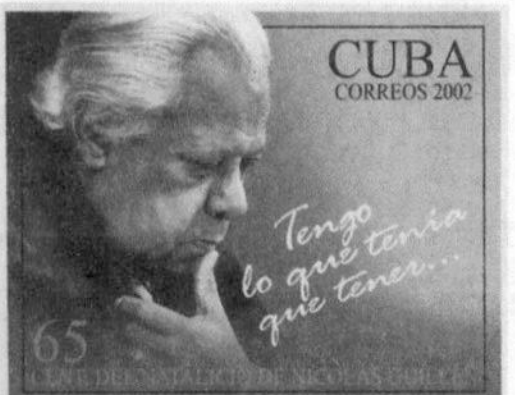

1265 Nicolas Guillen

2002. Birth Centenary of Nicolas Guillen (poet).
4582 **1265** 65c. multicoloured . . . 70 45

1266 "Dockers" (painting)

2002. Birth Centenary of Marcelo Pogolotti (artist).
4583 **1266** 15c. multicoloured . . . 10 10

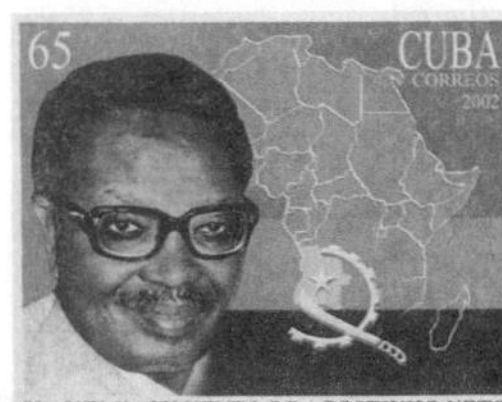
1267 Agostinho Neto and Map of Africa

2002. 80th Birth Anniv of Agostinho Neto (first president of independent Angola).
4584 **1267** 65c. multicoloured . . . 70 45

1268 Least Sandpiper (*Calidris minutilla*)

2002. Espana 2002 International Stamp Exhibition. Birds. Multicoloured.
4585 5c. Type **1268** 10 10
4586 10c. Greater yellow-legs (*Tringa melanoleuca*) (inscr "melanoleucas") . . 10 10
4587 15c. Semi-palmated plover (*Charadius semipalmatus*) 15 10
4588 65c. Grey plover (*Pluvialis squatarola*) (inscr "Plurialis") 70 45
4589 75c. Ruddy turnstone (*Arenaria interpres*) . . . 85 50
MS4590 110 × 87 mm. 1p. Sora crake (*Porzana Carolina*) (40 × 32 mm) . . . . 1·10 1·10

1269 Photographer and War Scene

2002. 3rd International War Correspondents' Conference.
4591 **1269** 65c. multicoloured . . . 70 45

1270 Ernesto "Che" Guevara

2002. 35th Death Anniv of Ernesto "Che" Guevara (revolutionary). Multicoloured.
4592 5c. Type **1270** 10 10
4593 10c. Face 10 10
4594 15c. Smoking 15 10
4595 50c. Speaking 55 30
4596 65c. Facing left 70 45
4597 75c. Seated facing right . . 85 50
MS4598 200 × 161 mm. Nos. 4592/7 2·50 2·50

1271 Emblem, Teacher and Pupil

2002. UPAEP. Literacy Campaign. Multicoloured
4599 15c. Type **1271** 15 10
4600 65c. School, flag, children and computer 70 45

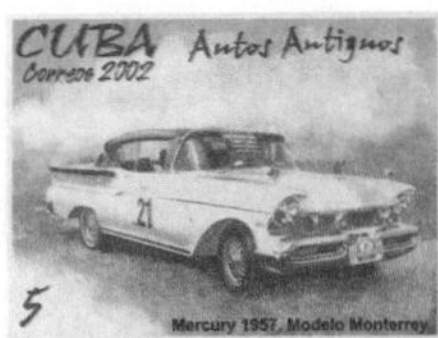
1272 Mercury Monterrey (1957)

2002. Cars. Multicoloured.
4601 5c. Type **1272** 10 10
4602 5c. Pontiac Catalina (1956) 10 10
4603 15c. Cadillac Fleetwood (1959) 15 10
4604 65c. Hudson Hornet (1951) 70 40
4605 75c. Chevrolet Bel Air (1957) 85 50
4606 85c. Mercedes Benz 190 SL (1957) 95 55

1273 G. Mesa

1274 Statuette and Emblem

2002. 15th Intercontinental Cup Baseball Championship. Showing players. Multicoloured.
4607 5c. Type **1273** 10 10
4608 15c. A. Pacheco 15 10
4609 50c. O. Linares 55 30
4610 65c. O. Kindelan 70 40
4611 75c. L. Ulacia 85 50

2002. 4th Havana International Trade Fair.
4612 **1274** 65c. multicoloured . . . 70 40

1275 G. and R. Stephenson's *Rocket*

2002. Steam Locomotives. Multicoloured.
4613 5c. Type **1275** 10 10
4614 15c. Early locomotive (inscr "Miller") 15 10
4615 50c. *Vulcan* 55 30
4616 65c. *Consolidation* 70 40
4617 75c. *Mikado* 85 50
A brief description of each locomotive is given in the enlarged margin above or below the relevant stamp.

1276 Corp de Ballet

2002. 40th Anniv of Ballet de Camaguey (dance company). Multicoloured.
4618 65c. Type **1276** 70 40
4619 75c. Principal dancers . . . 85 50

1277 Centenary Emblem and Surgeon General Wyman

2002. Centenary of PanAmerican Health Organization.
4620 **1277** 65c. multicoloured . . . 70 40

1278 "Emi Cosinca" (painting)

2002. Birth Centenary of Wilfred Lam (artist). Paintings. Multicoloured.
4621 15c. Type **1278** 15 10
4622 45c. "Yo say" 50 30
4623 65c. "Retro de H. H." . . . 70 40
4624 75c. "Mujer Sentada" . . . 85 50

1279 Dulce Loynaz

2002. Birth Centenary of Dulce M. Loynaz (writer).
4625 **1279** 65c. multicoloured . . . 70 40

1280 Bottle-nose Dolphin (*Tursiops truncates*)

2002. National Philately Championship. Sheet 84 × 111 mm.
MS4626 **1280** 1p. multicoloured 1·10 1·10

1281 Red Deer (*Cervus elaphus*) and Irish Elk (*Megaloceros*) (½-size illustration)

2002. Prehistoric Animals. Prehistoric animals and their modern counterparts. Multicoloured.
4627 5c. Type **1281** 10 10
4628 10c. Gelada baboon (*Theropithecus gelada*) and baboon (*Papio anubis*) . . 10 10
4629 15c. Black rhinoceros (*Diceros bicornis*) and woolly rhinoceros (*Coelodonta*) 15 10
4630 45c. Dire wolf (*Canis dirus*) and wolf (*Canis lupus*) . . 50 30
4631 65c. Grizzly bear (*Ursus arctos*) and cave bear (*Ursus spelaeus*) 70 40
4632 75c. Saber-toothed tiger (*Smilodon*) and lion (*Panthera leo*) 85 50

EXPRESS MAIL STAMPS

E 34

1900. As Type E **34**, but inscr "immediata".
E306 E **34** 10c. orange . . . . . 32·00 8·50

1902. Inscr "inmediata".
E307 E **34** 10c. orange . . . . . 2·00 1·00

E **39** J. B. Zayas

1910.
E320 E **39** 10c. blue and orange 4·00 1·40

E **41** Bleriot XI and Morro Castle

1914.
E352 E **41** 10c. blue . . . . . . 6·00 1·40

E **62** Mercury

1936. Free Port of Matanzas. Inscr as T **61**. Perf or imperf (same prices).
E409 E **62** 10c. purple (express) 3·50 3·50
E413 – 15c. blue (air express) 12·00 2·00
DESIGN: 15c. Maya Lighthouse.

E **67** "Triumph of the Revolution"

1936. Maximo Gomez Monument.
E422 E **67** 10c. orange . . . . . 3·75 2·75

E **71** Temple of Quetzalcoatl (Mexico)

1937. American Writers and Artists Association.
E424v E **71** 10c. orange . . . . . 3·75 2·75
E424w – 10c. orange . . . . . 3·75 2·75
DESIGN: No. 424w, Ruben Dario (Nicaragua).

E **114**

1945.
E485 E **114** 10c. brown . . . . . 4·25 60

E **146** Government House, Cardenas

1951. Centenary of Cuban Flag.
E559 E **146** 10c. red, blue & orge 2·75 95

E **161** National Anthem and Arms

E **176** Roseate Tern

1951. 30th Anniv of Jose Capablanca's Victory in World Chess Championship.
E568 E **150** 10c. purple & green 5·50 2·25

E **150** Capablanca Club, Havana

1952. As No. 549 surch **10c E. ESPECIAL**.
E595 **143** 10c. on 2c. brown . . . 1·25 40

1952. 50th Anniv of Republic.
E605 E **161** 10c. blue & orange . . 2·75 1·10

1952. Postal Employees' Retirement Fund. Inscr "ENTREGA ESPECIAL".
E627 **165** 10c. olive . . . . 1·75 85

1953.
E673 E **176** 10c. blue . . . . . . 4·00 2·00

1954. Postal Employees' Retirement Fund. Portrait of G. H. Saez as No. 684, inscr "ENTREGA ESPECIAL".
E686 10c. olive . . . . 1·90 95

1955. Postal Employees' Retirement Fund. Vert portrait (F. Varela) as T **191**, inscr "ENTREGA ESPECIAL".
E741 10c. lake . . . . 2·00 95

1956. Postal Employees' Retirement Fund. Vert portrait (J. J. Milanes) as T **200**, inscr "ENTREGA ESPECIAL".
E768 10c. black and red . . . . 1·90 95

1957. Postal Employees' Retirement Fund. As T **216** but inscr "ENTREGA ESPECIAL".
E812 10c. turquoise & brown . . 1·75 85
PAINTING: 10c. "Yesterday" (Cabrera).

1957. Postal Employees' Retirement Fund. As T **236** but inscr "ENTREGA ESPECIAL".
E856 10c. violet and brown . . . 1·75 85
DESIGN—HORIZ: 10c. Statue of Gen. A. Maceo, Independence Park, Pinar del Rio.

E **238** Motor-cyclist in Havana

1958.
E858 E **238** 10c. blue . . . . . . 1·40 65
E954 10c. violet . . . . . 1·40 65
E955 10c. orange . . . . . 1·40 65
E859 20c. green . . . . . 1·40 65

1958. Poey Commem. As Nos. 890/2 but inscr "ENTREGA ESPECIAL".
E893 10c. multicoloured . . . . 5·50 2·75
E894 20c. red, blue and black . . 8·50 5·50
DESIGNS—HORIZ: Fish: 10c. Black-finned snapper; 20c. Spotted mosquitofish.

1960. Surch **HABILITADO ENTREGA ESPECIAL 10c.**
E961 **55** 10c. on 20c. pink . . . . 1·10 35
E962 10c. on 50c. turquoise . . 1·10 35

1962. Stamp Day. As T **289** but inscr "ENTREGA ESPECIAL".
E1023 10c. brown & bl on yell 6·50 1·25
DESIGN: 10c. 18th-century sailing packet.

E **991** Great Red-bellied Woodpecker

1991. Birds. Multicoloured.
E3638 45c. Type E **991** . . . . 1·00 25
E3639 50c. Cuban solitaire . . . 1·00 25
E3640 2p. Cuban trogon . . . . 5·00 1·25
E3641 4p. Cuban grassquit . . . 11·00 2·50
E3642 5p. Ivory-billed woodpecker . . . . . . 13·00 3·00
E3643 10p. Cuban amazon (horiz) . . . . 30·00 6·00
E3644 16p.45 Bee hummingbird (horiz) . . . . 50·00 12·00

POSTAGE DUE STAMPS

D 42

1914.
D335 D **42** 1c. red . . . . 1·25 65
D337 2c. red . . . . 1·25 65
D340 5c. red . . . . 2·75 1·10

CUNDINAMARCA Pt. 20

One of the states of the Granadine Confederation. A Department of Colombia from 1886, now uses Colombian stamps.

100 centavos = 1 peso.

1 2

1870. Imperf.
1 **1** 5c. blue . . . . 2·75 2·75
2 **2** 10c. red . . . . 10·00 10·00

3 4

1877. Imperf.
5 **3** 10c. red . . . . 1·25 1·25
6 **4** 20c. green . . . . 2·25 2·25
7 – 50c. mauve . . . . 3·00 3·00
8a – 1p. brown . . . . 5·00 5·00
The 50c. and 1p. are in larger Arms designs.

11 13

1884. Imperf.
14 **11** 5c. blue 50 60

1885. Imperf.
17 **13** 5c. blue 30 30
18 10c. red . . . . 1·50 1·50
19 10c. red on lilac 90 90
20 20c. green . . . . 1·25 1·25
21 50c. mauve . . . . 1·75 1·75
22 1p. brown . . . . 2·00 2·00

14 15

1904. Imperf or perf. Various frames.
23 **14** 1c. orange 15 15
24 2c. blue 15 15
35 2c. grey 45 45
25 **15** 3c. red 20 20
26 5c. green 20 20
27 10c. brown 20 20
28 15c. pink 25 25
29 20c. blue on green 20 20
32 20c. blue 40 40
42 40c. blue 30 30
30 50c. mauve 25 25
31 1p. green 25 25
The illustrations show the main type. The frames and position of the arms in Type **15** differ for each value.

REGISTRATION STAMP

R 17

1904. Imperf or perf.
R46 R **17** 10c. brown 75 75

CURACAO Pt. 4

A Netherlands colony consisting of two groups of islands in the Caribbean Sea, N. of Venezuela. Later part of Netherlands Antilles.

100 cents = 1 gulden.

1 2 4

1873.
13 **1** 2½c. green . . . . 5·50 8·75
7 3c. bistre . . . . 55·00 £120
14 5c. red . . . . 12·50 12·50
26 10c. blue . . . . 70·00 18·00
27 12½c. yellow . . . . £110 55·00
22 15c. brown . . . . 32·00 20·00
23 25c. brown . . . . 55·00 8·75
24 30c. grey . . . . 42·00 50·00
17 50c. lilac . . . . 2·40 3·00

1889.
37 **2** 1c. grey . . . . 1·60 1·75
38 2c. mauve . . . . 1·60 1·75
39 2½c. green . . . . 5·50 4·00
40a 3c. brown . . . . 6·25 5·50
41 5c. red . . . . 24·00 2·00

1891. Surch **25 CENT.**
42 **1** 25c. on 30c. grey . . . . . . 17·00 15·00

1892.
43 **4** 10c. blue . . . . 1·60 1·60
44 12½c. green . . . . 19·00 8·00
45 15c. red . . . . 3·25 3·25
46 25c. brown . . . . £110 6·50
47 30c. grey . . . . 3·25 8·00

1895. Surch **2½ cent** (No. 48) or **2½ CENT** (No. 50).
48 **1** 2½c. on 10c. blue . . . . . . 15·00 9·50
50 2½c. on 30c. grey . . . . . . £140 6·25

1899. 1898 stamps of Netherlands surch **CURACAO** and value.
51 **12** 12½c. on 12½c. blue . . . . . 28·00 8·75
52 25c. on 25c. blue and red 2·40 2·25
53 **13** 1g.50 on 2½g. lilac . . . . 22·00 22·00

9 10

11

1903.
54 **9** 1c. olive . . . . 2·00 1·50
55a 2c. brown . . . . 14·50 4·00
56 2½c. green . . . . 6·00 60
57 3c. orange . . . . 9·75 6·25
58 5c. red . . . . 9·75 60
59 7½c. grey . . . . 30·00 7·25
60 **10** 10c. slate . . . . 15·00 2·50
61 12½c. blue . . . . 2·00 65
62 15c. brown . . . . 18·00 13·50
63 22½c. olive and brown . . 18·00 14·00
64 25c. violet . . . . 18·00 3·00
65 30c. brown . . . . 40·00 16·00
66 50c. brown . . . . 36·00 10·00
67 **11** 1½g. brown . . . . 40·00 32·00
68 2½g. blue . . . . 38·00 32·00

12 13

14 15

1915.
69 **12** ½c. lilac . . . . 1·75 1·75
70 1c. olive 30 40
71 1½c. blue 30 20
72 2c. brown . . . . 1·40 1·25
73 2½c. green . . . . 1·10 25
74 3c. yellow . . . . 2·50 1·90
75 3c. green . . . . 3·00 2·75
76 5c. red . . . . 2·10 25
77 5c. green . . . . 4·00 2·75
78 5c. mauve . . . . 2·10 25
79c **12** 7½c. bistre . . . . 1·25 20
80 **13** 10c. red . . . . 18·00 3·50
81 **12** 10c. lilac . . . . 5·50 5·50
82 10c. red . . . . 4·50 1·90
83 **13** 12½c. blue . . . . 3·00 1·00
84 12½c. red . . . . 2·50 2·00
85 15c. olive . . . . 90 1·60
86 15c. blue . . . . 5·00 2·75
87 20c. blue . . . . 8·00 3·00
88 20c. olive . . . . 3·00 2·25
89 22½c. orange . . . . 3·00 3·00
90 25c. mauve . . . . 4·00 1·60
91 30c. slate . . . . 4·00 1·60
92 35c. slate and orange . . . 4·00 5·75
93a **14** 50c. green . . . . 5·50 40
94 1½g. violet . . . . 16·00 13·50
95 2½g. red . . . . 25·00 22·00

1918.
96 **15** 1c. black on buff . . . . . 7·25 3·75

1919. Surch **5 CENT.**
97 **13** 5c. on 12½c. blue . . . . . 4·50 2·50

17 Queen Wilhelmina 20

1923. Queen's Silver Jubilee.
98 **17** 5c. green . . . . 1·10 2·50
99 7½c. green . . . . 1·90 2·50
100 10c. red . . . . 3·00 4·50
101 20c. grey . . . . 3·00 4·50
102 1g. purple . . . . 35·00 21·00
103 2g.50 black . . . . 70·00 £180
104 5g. brown . . . . 90·00 £225

1927. Unissued Marine Insurance stamps, as Type M **22** of Netherlands, inscr "CURACAO", surch **FRANKEERZEGEL** and value.
105 3c. on 15c. green 35 35
106 10c. on 60c. red 35 35
107 12½c. on 75c. brown 35 35
108 15c. on 1g.50 blue . . . . . 2·75 2·75
109 25c. on 2g.25 brown . . . . 6·00 6·00
110 30c. on 4½g. black . . . . . 13·50 10·50
111 50c. on 7½g. red . . . . . . 7·25 7·00

1928.
112 **20** 6c. orange . . . . 1·50 35
113 7½c. orange 65 55
114 10c. red . . . . 1·50 55
115 12½c. brown . . . . 1·50 1·25
116 15c. blue . . . . 1·50 55
117 20c. blue . . . . 5·50 90
118 21c. green . . . . 9·00 10·00
119 25c. purple . . . . 3·50 2·25
120 27½c. black . . . . 11·50 12·50
121 30c. green . . . . 5·50 1·10
122 35c. black . . . . 2·00 1·10

1929. Air. Surch **LUCHTPOST** and value.
123 **13** 50c. on 12½c. red . . . . . 14·00 14·00
124 1g. on 20c. blue . . . . . 14·00 14·00
125 2g. on 15c. olive . . . . . 40·00 42·00

1929. Surch **6 ct.** and bars.
126 **20** 6c. on 7½c. orange . . . . 1·60 1·25

23 24a

1931. Air.
126a **23** 10c. green 20 20
126b 15c. slate 45 20
127 20c. red . . . . 1·00 25
127a 25c. olive . . . . 90 1·00
127b 30c. yellow 45 45
128 35c. blue . . . . 1·10 1·10
129 40c. green 75 55
130 45c. orange . . . . 2·10 2·10
130a 50c. red . . . . 1·00 65
131 60c. purple 75 45
132 70c. black . . . . 6·50 2·10
133 1g.40 brown . . . . 4·00 4·75
134 2g.80 bistre . . . . 4·50 5·25

1931. Surch.
134a **12** 1½ on 2½c. green . . . . 3·50 3·25
135 2½ on 3c. green . . . . . 1·10 95

1933. 400th Birth Anniv of William I of Orange.
136 **24a** 6c. orange . . . . 1·60 1·25

25 Frederik Hendrik 26 "Johannes van Walbeeck"

1934. 300th Anniv of Dutch Colonization. Inscr "1634 1934".
137 – 1c. black 1·10 1·25
138 – 1½c. mauve 85 35
139 – 2c. orange 1·10 1·25
140 25 2½c. green 90 1·40
141 5c. brown 90 1·10
142 6c. blue 85 35
143 – 10c. red 2·10 1·25
144 – 12½c. brown 6·25 6·25
145 – 15c. blue 1·90 1·50
146 26 20c. black 3·00 2·50
147 21c. brown 11·00 14·00
148 25c. green 11·50 11·50
149 – 27½c. purple 13·50 16·00
150 – 30c. red 11·50 7·00
151 – 50c. yellow 11·50 11·50
152 – 1g.50 blue 48·00 52·00
153 – 2g.50 green 50·00 55·00
PORTRAITS: 1c. to 2c. Willem Usselinx. 10c. to 15c. Jacob Binckes. 27½c. to 50c. Cornelis Evertsen, the younger. 1g.50, 2g.50, Louis Brion.

1934. Air. Surch **10 CT**.
154 23 10c. on 20c. red 21·00 16·00

27 28 Queen Wilhelmina

1936.
155A 27 1c. brown 30 20
156A 1½c. blue 30 20
157A 2c. orange 30 20
158A 2½c. green 30 20
159A 5c. red 30 20

1936.
160 28 6c. purple 75 20
161 10c. red 1·10 20
162 12½c. green 1·60 90
163 15c. blue 1·40 55
164 20c. orange 1·40 55
165 21c. black 2·50 2·75
166 25c. red 1·60 1·10
167 27½c. brown 3·25 3·75
168 30c. bistre 75 35
169 50c. green 3·50 35
170 1g.50 brown 23·00 12·50
171a 2g.50 red 18·00 13·00

29 Queen Wilhelmina 30 Dutch Flags and Arms

1938. 40th Anniv of Coronation.
172 29 1½c. violet 20 30
173 6c. red 85 75
174 15c. blue 1·60 1·25

1941. Air. Prince Bernhard Fund to equip Dutch Forces. Centres in red, blue and orange.
175 30 10c.+10c. red 18·00 16·00
176 15c.+25c. blue 25·00 20·00
177 20c.+25c. brown 25·00 20·00
178 25c.+25c. violet 25·00 20·00
179 30c.+50c. orange 25·00 20·00
180 35c.+50c. green 25·00 20·00
181 40c.+50c. brown 25·00 20·00
182 50c.+1g. blue 25·00 20·00

31 Queen Wilhelmina 33 Aruba

1941.
248 31 6c. violet 1·50 2·00
184a 10c. red 2·40 1·10
185 12½c. green 2·75 1·10
251 15c. blue 1·50 2·40
187 20c. orange 1·90 90
188 21c. grey 4·50 2·10
254 25c. red 20 20
255 27½c. brown 1·50 1·60
256 30c. bistre 1·75 1·10
257 50c. green 2·10 20
192 50c. green (21 × 26 mm) 16·00 55
193 1½g. brown (21 × 26 mm) 21·00 1·40
194 2½g. purple (21 × 26 mm) 21·00 1·40
See also Nos. 258/61.

1942.
195 – 1c. brown and violet 25 25
196 – 1½c. green and blue 25 25
197 – 2c. brown and black 1·25 35
198 – 2½c. yellow and green 25 25
199 33 5c. black and red 1·00 25
200 – 6c. blue and purple 60 60
DESIGNS—HORIZ: 1c. Bonaire. 2c. Saba. 2½c. St. Maarten. 6c. Curacao. VERT: 1½c. St. Eustatius.

34 Queen Wilhelmina and Douglas DC-2 over Atlantic Ocean 35 Dutch Royal Family

1942. Air.
201 34 10c. blue and green 35 35
202 – 15c. green and red 45 35
203 – 20c. green and brown 55 35
204 – 25c. brown and blue 50 35
205 – 30c. violet and red 55 35
206 34 35c. green and violet 90 55
207 – 40c. brown and green 1·10 55
208 – 45c. black and red 65 35
209 – 50c. black and violet 1·60 35
210 – 60c. blue and brown 1·60 90
211 34 70c. blue and brown 2·00 90
212 – 1g.40 green and blue 11·00 1·75
213 – 2g.80 blue & ultramarine 16·00 2·50
214 – 5g. green and purple 27·00 13·00
215 – 10g. brown and green 35·00 20·00
DESIGNS: 15, 40c., 1g.40, Fokker airplane "Zilvermeeuw" over coast. 20, 45c., 2g.80, Map of Netherlands West Indies. 25, 50c., 5g. Side view of Douglas DC-2 airplane. 30, 60c., 10g. Front view of Douglas DC-2 airplane.

1943. Birth of Princess Margriet.
216 35 1½c. orange 30 30
217 2½c. red 30 30
218 6c. black 1·00 65
219 10c. blue 1·00 80

1943. Air. Dutch Prisoners of War Relief Fund. Nos. 212/15 surch **Voor Krijgsgevangenen** and new value.
220 40c.+50c. on 1g.40 green & bl 6·25 4·75
221 45c.+50c. on 2g.80 blue & ult 4·25 4·50
222 50c.+75c. on 5g. green & pur 6·25 4·50
223 60c.+100c. on 10g. brn & grn 6·25 4·75

37 Princess Juliana 38 Map of Netherlands

1944. Air. Red Cross Fund. Cross in red; frame in red and blue.
224 37 10c.+10c. brown 2·10 1·60
225 15c.+25c. green 2·00 1·60
226 20c.+25c. black 2·00 1·75
227 25c.+25c. grey 2·00 1·75
228 30c.+50c. purple 2·00 1·75
229 35c.+50c. brown 2·00 1·75
230 40c.+50c. green 2·00 2·00
231 50c.+100c. violet 2·00 2·00

1946. Air. Netherlands Relief Fund. Value in black.
232 38 10c.+10c. orange & grey 1·10 1·25
233 15c.+25c. grey and red 1·25 1·25
234 20c.+25c. orange & grn 1·25 1·25
235 25c.+25c. grey & violet 1·25 1·25
236 30c.+50c. buff & green 1·25 1·40
237 35c.+50c. orange & red 1·25 1·40
238 40c.+75c. buff & blue 1·25 1·60
239 50c.+100c. buff & violet 1·25 1·60

1946. Air. National Relief Fund. As T 38 but showing map of Netherlands Indies and inscr "CURACAO HELPT ONZEOOST". Value in black.
240 10c.+10c. buff & violet 1·10 1·25
241 15c.+25c. buff & blue 1·25 1·25
242 20c.+25c. orange & red 1·25 1·25
243 25c.+25c. buff & green 1·25 1·25
244 30c.+50c. grey & violet 1·25 1·40
245 35c.+50c. orange & grn 1·25 1·40
246 40c.+75c. grey & red 1·25 1·60
247 50c.+100c. orange & grey 1·25 1·60

1947. Size 25 × 31½ mm.
258 31 1½g. brown 3·50 1·10
259 2½g. purple 45·00 10·75
260 5g. olive £100 £150
261 10g. orange £125 £275

40 Aeroplane and Posthorn 41 Douglas DC-2 and Waves

1947. Air.
262 40 6c. black 35 15
263 10c. red 35 15
264 12½c. purple 50 15
265 15c. blue 50 30
266 20c. green 65 35
267 25c. orange 65 20
268 30c. violet 90 35
269 35c. red 90 55
270 40c. green 90 55
271 45c. violet 1·10 80
272 50c. red 1·10 20
273 60c. blue 1·25 55
274 70c. brown 2·75 1·10
275 41 1g.50 black 2·00 80
276 2g.50 red 13·50 3·50
277 5g. green 21·00 7·00
278 7g.50 blue 65·00 55·00
279 10g. violet 50·00 17·00
280 15g. red 80·00 65·00
281 25g. brown 75·00 55·00

1947. Netherlands Indies Social Welfare Fund. Surch **NIWIN** and value.
282 28 1½c.+2½c. on 6c. purple 90 90
283 2½c.+5c. on 10c. red 90 90
284 5c.+7½c. on 15c. blue 90 90

43 45 Queen Wilhelmina

1948. Portrait of Queen Wilhelmina.
285 43 6c. purple 1·00 1·10
286 10c. red 1·00 1·50
287 12½c. green 1·00 90
288 15c. blue 1·00 1·10
289 20c. orange 1·00 2·00
290 21c. black 1·00 2·00
291 25c. mauve 35 20
292 27½c. brown 20·00 17·00
293 30c. olive 18·00 1·25
294 50c. green 16·00 20
295 1g.50c. brn (21½ × 28½ mm) 28·00 7·50

1948. Golden Jubilee.
296 45 6c. orange 65 65
297 12½c. blue 65 65

46 Queen Juliana 47

1948. Accession of Queen Juliana.
298 46 6c. red 55 55
299 12½c. green 55 55

1948. Child Welfare Fund. Inscr "VOOR HET KIND".
300 47 6c.+10c. brown 2·40 1·60
301 – 10c.+15c. red 2·40 1·60
302 – 12½c.+20c. green 2·40 1·60
303 47 15c.+25c. blue 2·40 1·75
304 – 20c.+30c. brown 2·40 1·90
305 – 25c.+35c. violet 2·40 2·00
DESIGNS—10, 20c. Native boy in straw hat. 12½, 25c. Curly-haired girl.

POSTAGE DUE STAMPS

For stamps as Nos. D42/61 and D96/105 in other colours see Postage Due stamps of Netherlands Indies and Surinam.

D 3 D 5

1889.
D42C D 3 2½c. black and green 2·40 2·75
D43C 5c. black and green 1·60 1·60
D44C 10c. black and green 24·00 21·00
D45C 12½c. black and green £275 £140
D46C 15c. black and green 16·00 14·00
D47C 20c. black and green 7·00 7·00
D48C 25c. black and green £140 £110
D49C 30c. black and green 8·50 7·25
D50C 40c. black and green 8·50 7·25
D51C 50c. black and green 30·00 23·00

1892.
D52C D 5 2½c. black and green 35 30
D53C 5c. black and green 65 55
D54C 10c. black and green 1·50 50
D55A 12½c. black and green 1·90 1·25
D56C 15c. black and green 2·40 1·25
D57A 20c. black and green 3·00 1·25
D58C 25c. black and green 1·40 95
D59A 30c. black and green 21·00 12·00
D60A 40c. black and green 25·00 12·50
D61A 50c. black and green 40·00 13·50

1915.
D 96a D 5 2½c. green 55 55
D 97a 5c. green 55 55
D 98a 10c. green 50 50
D 99a 12½c. green 1·40 1·50
D100a 15c. green 1·40 1·50
D101a 20c. green 55 1·00
D102a 25c. green 20 10
D103a 30c. green 2·10 2·40
D104 40c. green 2·50 3·00
D105a 50c. green 1·75 2·25

For later issues see **NETHERLANDS ANTILLES**.

CYPRUS Pt. 1

An island in the East Mediterranean. A British colony, which became a republic within the British Commonwealth in 1960.

1880. 12 pence = 1 shilling.
1881. 40 paras = 1 piastre; 180 piastres = 1 pound.
1955. 1000 mils = 1 pound.
1983. 100 cents = 1 pound.

1880. Stamps of Great Britain (Queen Victoria) optd **CYPRUS**.
1 7 ½d. red £110 £100
2 5 1d. red 11·00 38·00
3 41 2½d. mauve 2·25 8·50
4 – 4d. green (No. 153) £120 £200
5 – 6d. grey (No. 161) £500 £650
6 – 1s. green (No. 150) £650 £450

1881. Stamps of Great Britain (Queen Victoria) surch with new values.
9 5 ½d. on 1d. red 45·00 65·00
10 30 paras on 1d. red £100 80·00

7 13

1881.
31 7 ½pi. green 5·00 70
40 ½pi. green and red 4·00 1·25
32 30pa. mauve 5·00 5·00
41 30pa. mauve and green 2·00 1·25
33 1pi. red 11·00 2·00
42 1pi. red and blue 6·00 1·25
34 2pi. blue 14·00 1·75
43 2pi. blue and purple 7·00 1·25
35a 4pi. olive 18·00 24·00
44 4pi. olive and purple 15·00 5·00
21 6pi. grey 48·00 17·00
45 6pi. brown and green 12·00 16·00
46 9pi. brown and red 15·00 18·00
22 12pi. brown £180 35·00
47 12pi. brown and black 17·00 55·00
48 18pi. grey and brown 48·00 48·00
49 45pi. purple and blue 90·00 £130

1882. Surch.
25 7 ½pi. on ½pi. green £140 6·50
24 30pa. on 1pi. red £1500 £110

1903. As T 7 but portrait of King Edward VII.
60 5pa. brown and black 1·00 70
61 10pa. orange and green 3·00 50
50 ½pi. green and red 4·00 1·25
51 30pa. violet and green 8·00 2·75
64 1pi. red and blue 5·00 1·00
65 2pi. blue and purple 6·00 1·75
66 4pi. brown and purple 11·00 8·00
67 6pi. brown and green 14·00 15·00
68 9pi. brown and red 30·00 8·50
69 12pi. brown and black 25·00 40·00
70 18pi. black and brown 30·00 11·00
71 45pi. purple and blue 75·00 £140

1912. As T 7 but portrait of King George V.
74b 10pa. orange and green 2·25 1·25
86 10pa. grey and yellow 12·00 6·50
75 ½pi. green and red 1·75 20
76 30pa. violet and green 2·50 60
88 30pa. green 7·00 40
77 1pi. red and blue 4·00 1·75
90 1pi. violet and red 3·00 4·00
91 1½pi. yellow and black 5·00 4·75
78 2pi. blue and purple 6·50 2·00
93 2pi. red and blue 9·50 22·00
94 2¾pi. blue and purple 7·00 9·00
79 4pi. olive and purple 4·25 4·75
80 6pi. brown and green 3·50 8·50
81 9pi. brown and red 24·00 26·00
82 12pi. brown and black 15·00 35·00
83 18pi. black and brown 26·00 30·00

No.	Type	Description	Unused	Used
84		45pi. purple and blue	80·00	£120
100		10s. green and red on yellow	£375	£750
101		£1 purple and black on red	£1000	£1700

1924.

No.	Type	Description	Unused	Used
103	**13**	¼pi. grey and brown	1·00	15
104		½pi. black	2·75	9·00
118		½pi. green	2·25	1·00
105		¾pi. green	2·25	1·00
119		¾pi. black	2·00	10
106		1pi. purple and brown	2·00	70
107		1½pi. orange and black	2·00	7·50
120		1½pi. red	2·50	30
108		2pi. red and green	2·25	13·00
121		2pi. yellow and black	6·00	3·25
122		2½pi. blue	3·00	30
109		2¾pi. blue and purple	3·25	3·00
110		4pi. olive and purple	3·25	2·75
111		4½pi. blk & orge on green	3·50	3·50
112		6pi. brown and green	3·75	5·50
113		9pi. brown and purple	6·00	4·50
114		12pi. brown and black	9·00	55·00
115		18pi. black and orange	20·00	5·00
116		45pi. purple and blue	38·00	38·00
117		90pi. grn & red on yellow	90·00	£180
102		£1 purple & black on red	£300	£700
117a		£5 black on yellow	£2750	£6000

14 Silver coin of Amathus, 6th-century B.C.

1928. 50th Anniv of British Rule. Dated "1878 1928".

No.	Type	Description	Unused	Used
123	**14**	¾pi. violet	2·75	1·00
124	–	1pi. black and blue	3·00	1·50
125	–	1½pi. red	4·50	2·00
126	–	2½pi. blue	3·50	2·25
127	–	4pi. brown	5·50	6·00
128	–	6pi. blue	7·50	21·00
129	–	9pi. purple	7·50	11·00
130	–	18pi. black and brown	18·00	18·00
131	–	45pi. violet and blue	40·00	48·00
132	–	£1 blue and brown	£200	£300

DESIGNS—VERT: 1pi. Philosopher Zeno; 2½pi. Discovery of body of St. Barnabas; 4pi. Cloister, Abbey of Bella Paise; 9pi. Tekke of Umm Haram; 18pi. Statue of Richard I, Westminster; 45pi. St. Nicholas Cathedral, Famagusta, (now Lala Mustafa Pasha Mosque); £1 King George V. HORIZ: 1½pi. Map of Cyprus; 6pi. Badge of Cyprus.

24 Ruins of Vouni Palace

30 St. Sophia Cathedral, Nicosia (now Selimiye Mosque)

1934.

No.	Type	Description	Unused	Used
133	**24**	¼pi. blue and brown	1·00	50
134	–	½pi. green	1·25	1·00
135	–	¾pi. black and violet	1·50	10
136	–	1pi. black and brown	1·00	80
137	–	1½pi. red	2·00	55
138	–	2½pi. blue	2·00	1·75
139	**30**	4½pi. black and red	3·00	3·75
140	–	6pi. black and blue	9·00	12·00
141	–	9pi. brown and violet	7·00	4·75
142	–	18pi. black and green	40·00	29·00
143	–	45pi. green and black	65·00	50·00

DESIGNS—HORIZ: ½pi. Small Marble Forum, Salamis; ¾pi. Church of St. Barnabas and St. Hilarion, Peristerona; 1pi. Roman theatre, Soli; 1½pi. Kyrenia Harbour; 2½pi. Kolossi Castle; 45pi. Forest scene, Troodos. VERT: 6pi. Bayraktar Mosque, Nicosia; 9pi. Queen's Window, St. Hilarion Castle; 18pi. Buyuk Khan, Nicosia.

The ½pi. to 2½pi. values have a medallion portrait of King George V.

1935. Silver Jubilee. As T **13** of Antigua.

No.	Description	Unused	Used
144	¾pi. blue and grey	1·75	40
145	1½pi. blue and red	3·75	2·50
146	2½pi. brown and blue	3·75	1·50
147	9pi. grey and purple	14·00	14·00

1937. Coronation. As T **2** of Aden.

No.	Description	Unused	Used
148	¾pi. grey	60	40
149	1½pi. red	90	80
150	2½pi. blue	2·00	1·25

36 Map of Cyprus

37 Othello's Tower, Famagusta

38 King George VI

1938.

No.	Type	Description	Unused	Used
151	–	¼pi. blue and brown	20	20
152	–	½pi. green	50	10
152a	–	½pi. violet	2·25	20
153	–	¾pi. black and violet	15·00	50
154	–	1pi. orange	1·00	10
155	–	1½pi. red	5·50	1·50
155a	–	1½pi. violet	50	30
155ab	–	1½pi. green	2·75	40
155b	–	2pi. black and red	70	10
156	–	2½pi. blue	26·00	2·50
156a	–	3pi. blue	2·00	15
156b	–	4pi. blue	3·00	30
157	**36**	4½pi. grey	1·00	10
158	–	6pi. black and blue	1·50	1·00
159	**37**	9pi. black and purple	2·50	20
160	–	18pi. black and olive	7·00	85
161	–	45pi. green and black	20·00	2·50
162	**38**	90pi. mauve and black	23·00	5·00
163	–	£1 red and blue	50·00	24·00

DESIGNS: 2pi. Peristerona Church; 3pi., 4pi. Kolossi Castle. All other values except 4½pi., 9pi., 90pi. and £1 have designs as 1934 issue but portrait of King George VI.

1946. Victory. As T **9** of Aden.

No.	Description	Unused	Used
164	1½pi. violet	15	10
165	3pi. blue	15	15

1948. Silver Wedding. As T **10/11** of Aden.

No.	Description	Unused	Used
166	1½pi. violet	50	20
167	£1 blue	42·00	50·00

1949. U.P.U. As T **20/23** of Antigua.

No.	Description	Unused	Used
168	1½pi. violet	40	70
169	2pi. red	1·50	1·50
170	3pi. blue	70	1·00
171	9pi. purple	1·50	2·00

1953. Coronation. As T **13** of Aden.

No.	Description	Unused	Used
172	1½pi. black and green	1·25	10

39 Carobs

42 Mavrovouni Copper Pyrites Mine

49 St. Hilarion Castle

53 Arms of Byzantium, Lusignan, Ottoman Empire and Venice

1955.

No.	Type	Description	Unused	Used
173	**39**	2m. brown	10	40
174	–	3m. violet	10	15
175	–	5m. orange	1·00	10
176	**42**	10m. brown and green	1·25	10
177	–	15m. olive and blue	3·00	45
178	–	20m. brown and blue	1·00	15
179	–	25m. turquoise	2·50	60
180	–	30m. black and lake	2·00	10
181	–	35m. brown and turquoise	75	40
182	–	40m. green and brown	1·00	60
183	**49**	50m. blue and brown	1·00	30
184	–	100m. mauve and green	13·00	60
185	–	250m. blue and brown	11·00	8·50
186	–	500m. slate and purple	28·00	11·00
187	**53**	£1 lake and slate	24·00	40·00

DESIGNS—As Type **39**: 3m. Grapes; 5m. Oranges. As Type **42**: 15m. Troodos Forest; 20m. Beach of Aphrodite; 25m. 5th-century B.C. coin of Paphos; 30m. Kyrenia; 35m. Harvest in Mesaoria; 40m. Famagusta harbour. As Type **49**: 100m. Hala Sultan Tekke; 250m. Kanakaria Church. As Type **53**: 500m. Coins of Salamis, Paphos, Citium and Idalium.

(**54**)

55 Map of Cyprus

1960. Nos. 173/87 optd as T **54** ("CYPRUS REPUBLIC" in Greek and Turkish).

No.	Type	Description	Unused	Used
188	**39**	2m. brown	20	75
189	–	3m. violet	20	15
190	–	5m. orange	1·00	10
191	**42**	10m. brown and green	80	10
192	–	15m. olive and blue	75	10
193	–	20m. brown and blue	50	1·50
194	–	25m. turquoise	1·25	1·75
195	–	30m. black and lake	1·75	10
196	–	35m. brown and turquoise	1·75	70
197	–	40m. green and brown	2·00	2·50
198	**49**	50m. blue and brown	2·00	60
199	–	100m. mauve and green	9·00	60
200	–	250m. blue and brown	27·00	3·75
201	–	500m. slate and purple	40·00	18·00
202	**53**	£1 lake and slate	48·00	50·00

1960. Constitution of Republic.

No.	Type	Description	Unused	Used
203	**55**	10m. sepia and green	30	10
204		30m. blue and brown	65	10
205		100m. purple and slate	2·00	2·00

56 Doves

1962. Europa.

No.	Type	Description	Unused	Used
206	**56**	10m. purple and mauve	10	10
207		40m. blue and cobalt	20	15
208		100m. emerald and green	20	20

57 Campaign Emblem

1962. Malaria Eradication.

No.	Type	Description	Unused	Used
209	**57**	10m. black and green	15	15
210		30m. black and brown	30	15

63 St. Barnabas's Church

1962.

No.	Type	Description	Unused	Used
211	–	3m. brown and orange	10	30
212	–	5m. purple and green	10	10
213	–	10m. black and green	15	10
214	–	15m. black and purple	50	15
215	**63**	25m. brown and chestnut	50	20
216	–	30m. blue and light blue	20	10
217	–	35m. green and blue	35	10
218	–	40m. black and blue	1·25	1·75
219	–	50m. bronze and bistre	50	10
220	–	100m. brown and bistre	3·50	30
221	–	250m. black and brown	11·00	2·25
222	–	500m. brown and green	16·00	9·00
223	–	£1 bronze and grey	16·00	30·00

DESIGNS—VERT: 3m. Iron Age jug; 5m. Grapes; 10m. Bronze head of Apollo; 15m. Selimiye Mosque, Nicosia; 35m. Head of Aphrodite; 100m. Hala Sultan Tekke; 500m. Mouflon. HORIZ: 30m. Temple of Apollo Hylates; 40m. Skiing, Troodos; 50m. Salamis Gymnasium; 250m. Bella Paise Abbey; £1 St. Hilarion Castle.

72 Europa "Tree"

1963. Europa.

No.	Type	Description	Unused	Used
224	**72**	10m. blue and black	1·75	20
225		40m. red and black	8·00	2·00
226		150m. green and black	26·00	6·00

73 Harvester

75 Wolf Cub in Camp

1963. Freedom from Hunger.

No.	Type	Description	Unused	Used
227	**73**	25c. ochre, sepia and blue	30	25
228	–	75m. grey, black and lake	1·75	1·00

DESIGN: 75m. Demeter, Goddess of Corn.

1963. 50th Anniv of Cyprus Scout Movement and 3rd Commonwealth Scout Conference, Platres. Multicoloured.

No.	Description	Unused	Used
229	3m. Type **75**	10	20
230	20m. Sea Scout	35	10
231	150m. Scout with Mouflon	1·00	2·50
MS231a	110 × 90 mm. Nos. 229/31 (sold at 250m.) Imperf	£100	£180

79 Children's Centre, Kyrenia

1963. Centenary of Red Cross. Multicoloured.

No.	Description	Unused	Used
232	10m. Nurse tending child (vert)	50	15
233	100m. Type **79**	2·00	3·50

80 "Co-operation" (emblem)

1963. Europa.

No.	Type	Description	Unused	Used
234	**80**	20m. buff, blue and violet	2·50	40
235		30m. grey, yellow and blue	2·50	40
236		150m. buff, blue and brown	26·00	9·00

1964. U.N. Security Council's Cyprus Resolution, March 1964. Nos. 213 etc. optd with U.N. emblem and **1964**.

No.	Description	Unused	Used
237	10m. black and green	15	10
238	30m. blue and light blue	15	10
239	40m. black and blue	15	20
240	50m. bronze and bistre	15	10
241	100m. brown and bistre	15	50

82 Soli Theatre

1964. 400th Birth Anniv of Shakespeare. Mult.

No.	Description	Unused	Used
242	15m. Type **82**	40	15
243	35m. Curium Theatre	40	15
244	50m. Salamis Theatre	40	15
245	100m. Othello Tower, and scene from "Othello"	1·00	2·25

86 Running

89 Europa "Flower"

1964. Olympic Games, Tokyo.

No.	Type	Description	Unused	Used
246	**86**	10m. brown, black & yell	10	10
247	–	25m. brown, black and slate	20	10
248	–	75m. brown, black and chest	35	65
MS248a		110 × 90 mm. Nos. 246/8 (sold at 250m.) Imperf	6·00	15·00

DESIGNS—HORIZ: 25m. Boxing; 75m. Charioteers.

1964. Europa.

No.	Type	Description	Unused	Used
249	**89**	20m. brown and ochre	1·50	10
250		30m. ultramarine and blue	1·50	10
251		150m. olive and green	18·00	5·50

90 Dionysus and Acme

1964. Cyprus Wines. Multicoloured.

No.	Description	Unused	Used
252	10m. Type **90**	30	10
253	40m. Silenus (satyr) (vert)	65	1·25
254	50m. Commandaria wine (vert)	65	10
255	100m. Wine factory	1·50	2·00

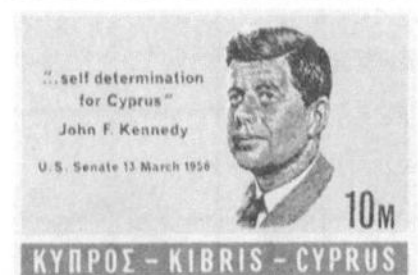

94 President Kennedy

1965. President Kennedy Commemoration.
256 **94** 10m. blue 10 10
257 40m. green 25 35
258 100m. red 30 35
MS258a 110 × 90 mm. Nos. 256/8 (sold at 250m.) Imperf . . . . 3·25 8·00

95 "Old Age" 98 I.T.U. Emblem and Symbols

1965. Introduction of Social Insurance Law.
259 **95** 30m. drab and green . . . 15 10
260 – 45m. green, blue and ultramarine 20 10
261 – 75m. brown and flesh . . . 1·25 2·50
DESIGNS—(As Type **95**): 45m. "Accident". LARGER (23 × 48 mm): 75m. "Maternity".

1965. Centenary of I.T.U.
262 **98** 15m. black, brown & yell 75 20
263 60m. black, grn & lt grn 7·50 3·25
264 75m. black, indigo & bl . . 8·50 4·75

99 I.C.Y. Emblem

1965. International Co-operation Year.
265 **99** 50m. brown and green . . 75 10
266 100m. purple and green . . 1·25 50

100 Europa "Sprig"

1965. Europa.
267 **100** 5m. black, brown & orge 50 10
268 45m. black, brown & grn 7·00 1·50
269 150m. black, brn & grey 13·00 3·75

1966. U.N. General Assembly's Cyprus Resolution. Nos. 211, 213, 216 and 221 optd **U.N. Resolution on Cyprus 18 Dec. 1965.**
270 3m. brown and orange . . . 10 50
271 10m. black and green 10 10
272 30m. blue and light blue . . 15 15
273 250m. black and brown . . . 80 2·25

102 Discovery of St. Barnabas's Body

1966. 1900th Death Anniv of St. Barnabas.
274 **102** 15m. multicoloured . . . 10 10
275 – 25m. drab, black and blue 15 10
276 – 100m. multicoloured . . . 45 2·00
MS277 110 × 91 mm. 250m. multicoloured (imperf) . . . . 3·50 13·00
DESIGNS—HORIZ: 25m. St. Barnabas's Chapel; 250m. "Privileges of Cyprus Church". VERT: 100m. St. Barnabas (icon).

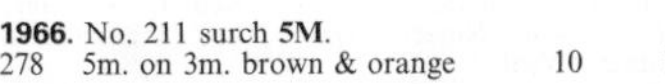
1966. No. 211 surch **5M.**
278 5m. on 3m. brown & orange 10 10

107 General K. S. Thimayya and U.N. Emblem

1966. General Thimayya Commemoration.
279 **107** 50m. black and brown . . 30 10

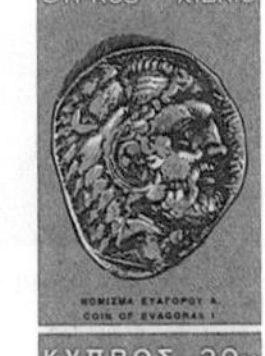

108 Europa "Ship" 113 Silver Coin of Evagoras I

109 Stavrovouni Monastery

1966. Europa.
280 **108** 20m. green and blue . . . 40 10
281 30m. purple and blue . . 40 10
282 150m. bistre and blue . . 3·00 3·00

1966. Multicoloured.
283 3m. Type **109** 40 10
284 5m. Church of St. James, Trikomo 10 10
285 10m. Zeno of Citium (marble bust) 15 10
286 15m. Minoan wine ship of 700 B.C. (painting) 15 10
287 20m. Type **113** . . . . 1·25 1·00
288 25m. Sleeping Eros (marble statue) 30 10
289 30m. St. Nicholas Cathedral, Famagusta 50 20
290 35m. Gold sceptre from Curium 50 30
291 40m. Silver dish from 7th century 70 30
292 50m. Silver coin of Alexander the Great 90 10
293 100m. Vase, 7th century B.C. 4·00 15
294 250m. Bronze ingot-stand . . 1·00 40
295 500m. "The Rape of Ganymede" (mosaic) . . . 2·75 70
296 £1 Aphrodite (marble statue) 2·00 6·50
DESIGNS—VERT (As Type **109**): 5m. and 10m. HORIZ (As Type **113**): 15m., 25m. and 50m. VERT (As Type **113**): 30m., 35m., 40m. and 100m.
Nos. 294/6 are as Type **113** but larger, 28 × 40 mm.

123 Power Station, Limassol 124 Cogwheels

1967. First Development Programme. Mult.
297 10m. Type **123** 10 10
298 15m. Arghaka-Maghounda Dam (vert) 15 10
299 35m. Troodos Highway (vert) 20 10
300 50m. Hilton Hotel, Nicosia (vert) 20 10
301 100m. Famagusta Harbour (vert) . . . . 20 1·10

1967. Europa.
302 **124** 20m. olive, grn & lt grn 30 10
303 30m. violet, lilac and mauve 30 10
304 150m. sepia, brn chestnut 2·25 2·25

125 Throwing the Javelin

1967. Athletic Games, Thessalonika. Multicoloured.
305 15m. Type **125** 20 10
306 35m. Running 20 35
307 100m. High-jumping . . . . 30 1·00
MS308 110 × 90 mm. 250m. Running (amphora) and Map of Eastern Mediterranean (imperf) . . . . 1·25 6·50

127 Ancient Monuments

1967. International Tourist Year. Multicoloured.
309 10m. Type **127** 10 10
310 40m. Famagusta Beach . . . 15 90
311 50m. Hawker Siddeley Comet-4 at Nicosia Airport 15 10
312 100m. Skier and youth hostel 20 95

128 Saint Andrew Mosaic 129 "The Crucifixion" (icon)

1967. Centenary of St Andrew's Monastery.
313 **128** 25m. multicoloured . . . 10 10

1967. Cyprus Art Exhibition, Paris.
314 **129** 50m. multicoloured . . . 10 10

130 The Three Magi 131 Human Rights Emblem over Stars

1967. 20th Anniv of U.N.E.S.C.O.
315 **130** 75m. multicoloured . . . 20 20

1968. Human Rights Year. Multicoloured.
316 50m. Type **131** 10 10
317 90m. Human Rights and U.N. emblems 30 70
MS318 95 × 75½ mm. 250m. Scroll of Declaration . . . . 60 4·75

134 Europa "Key"

1968. Europa.
319 **134** 20m. multicoloured . . . 25 10
320 30m. multicoloured . . . 25 10
321 150m. multicoloured . . . 1·00 2·25

135 U.N. Children's Fund Symbol and Boy drinking Milk

1968. 21st Anniv of U.N.I.C.E.F.
322 **135** 35m. brown, red and black 10 10

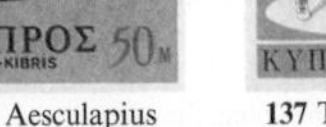
136 Aesculapius 137 Throwing the Discus

1968. 20th Anniv of W.H.O.
323 **136** 50m. black, green and olive 10 10

1968. Olympic Games, Mexico. Multicoloured.
324 10m. Type **137** 10 10
325 25m. Sprint finish 10 10
326 100m. Olympic Stadium (horiz) . . . . 20 1·25

138 I.L.O. Emblem 141 Europa Emblem

139 Mercator's Map of Cyprus, 1554

1969. 50th Anniv of I.L.O.
327 **138** 50m. brown and blue . . 15 10
328 90m. brown, black and grey 15 55

1969. 1st International Congress of Cypriot Studies.
329 **139** 35m. multicoloured . . . 20 30
330 – 50m. multicoloured . . . 20 10
DESIGN: 50m. Blaeu's map of Cyprus, 1635.

1969. Europa.
331 **141** 20m. multicoloured . . . 30 10
332 30m. multicoloured . . . 30 10
333 150m. multicoloured . . . 1·00 2·00

142 European Roller ("Roller")

1969. Birds of Cyprus. Multicoloured.
334 5m. Type **142** 40 15
335 15m. Audouin's gull 60 15
336 20m. Cyprus warbler 60 15
337 30m. Jay ("Cyprus Jay") (vert) 60 15
338 40m. Hoopoe (vert) 65 30
339 90m. Eleonora's falcon (vert) 1·50 5·00

143 "The Nativity" (12th-century wall painting)

1969. Christmas. Multicoloured.
340 20m. Type **143** 15 10
341 45m. "The Nativity" (14th-century wall painting) 15 20
MS342 110 × 90 mm. 250m. "Virgin and Child between Archangels Michael and Gabriel" (6th–7th-century Mosaic) (imperf) 3·00 12·00

146 Mahatma Gandhi

1970. Birth Centenary of Mahatma Gandhi.
343 **146** 25m. blue, drab and black 15 10
344 75m. brown, drab and black 20 65

147 "Flaming Sun"

1970. Europa.
345 **147** 20m. brown, yell & orge 30 10
346 30m. blue, yellow & orge 30 10
347 150m. purple, yell & orge 1·00 2·50

148 Gladioli

149 I.E.Y. Emblem

1970. Nature Conservation Year. Multicoloured.
348 10m. Type **148** 10 10
349 50m. Poppies 15 10
350 90m. Giant fennel . . . . . 50 1·40

1970. Anniversaries and Events.
351 **149** 5m. black and brown . . 10 10
352 – 15m. multicoloured . . . 10 10
353 – 75m. multicoloured . . . 15 75
DESIGNS AND EVENTS: 5m. International Education Year. HORIZ: 15m. Mosaic (50th General Assembly of International Vine and Wine Office); 75m. Globe, dove and U.N. emblem (25th anniv of United Nations).

152 Virgin and Child

153 Cotton Napkin

1970. Christmas. Wall-painting from Church of Panayia Podhythou, Galata. Multicoloured.
354 25m. Archangel (facing right) 15 20
355 25m. Type **152** 15 20
356 25m. Archangel (facing left) 15 20
357 75m. Virgin and Child between Archangels (42 × 30 mm) 15 30

1971. Multicoloured.
358 3m. Type **153** 30 35
359 5m. Saint George and Dragon (19th-century bas-relief) 10 10
360 10m. Woman in festival costume 15 50
361 15m. Archaic Bichrome Kylix (cup) (horiz) 20 10
362 20m. A pair of donors (Saint Mamas Church) 35 65
363 25m. "The Creation" (6th-century mosaic) . . . 30 10
364 30m. Athena and horse-drawn chariot (4th-century B.C. terracotta) (horiz) . . 30 10
365 40m. Shepherd playing pipe (14th-century fresco) . . . 1·00 1·00
366 50m. Hellenistic head (3rd-century B.C.) 80 10
367 75m. "Angel" (mosaic detail), Kanakaria Church . . . 2·00 1·00
368 90m. Mycenaean silver bowl (horiz) . . . . 2·00 2·25
369 250m. Moufflon (detail of 3rd-century mosaic) (horiz) 1·50 30
370 500m. Ladies and sacred tree (detail 6th-century amphora) (horiz) 80 30
371 £1 Horned god from Enkomi (12th-century bronze statue) . . . . 1·50 45
SIZES: 24 × 37 mm or 37 × 24 mm 10m. to 90m., 41 × 28 mm or 28 × 41 mm 250m. to £1.

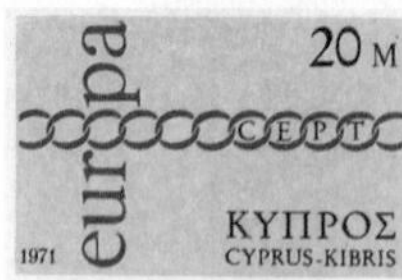

154 Europa Chain

1971. Europa.
372 **154** 20m. blue, ultram & blk 25 10
373 30m. green, myrtle & blk 25 10
374 150m. yellow, grn & blk 1·10 3·00

155 Archbishop Kyprianos

1971. 150th Anniv of Greek War of Independence. Multicoloured.
375 15m. Type **155** 10 10
376 30m. "Taking the Oath" (horiz) 10 10
377 100m. Bishop Germanos, flag and freedom-fighters . . . 20 50

156 Kyrenia Castle

1971. Tourism. Multicoloured.
378 15m. Type **156** 10 10
379 25m. Gourd on sunny beach (vert) 10 10
380 60m. Mountain scenery (vert) 20 60
381 100m. Church of Saint Evlalios, Lambousa . . . 20 65

157 Madonna and Child in Stable

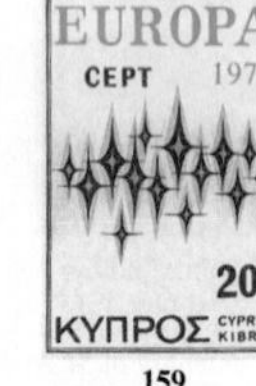

159 "Communications"

158 Heart

1971. Christmas. Multicoloured.
382 10m. Type **157** 10 10
383 50m. The Three Wise Men 15 35
384 100m. The Shepherds 20 35

1972. World Heart Month.
385 **158** 15m. multicoloured . . . 10 10
386 50m. multicoloured . . . 20 45

1972. Europa.
387 **159** 20m. orange, sepia & brn 40 15
388 30m. orange, ultram & bl 40 15
389 150m. orge, myrtle & grn 2·50 4·50

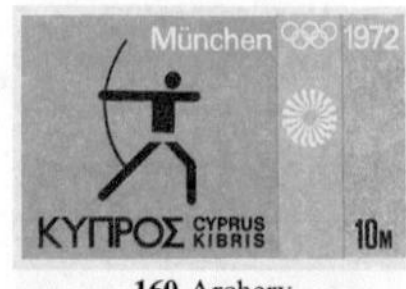

160 Archery

1972. Olympic Games, Munich. Multicoloured.
390 10m. Type **160** 25 10
391 40m. Wrestling 35 15
392 100m. Football . . . . 75 1·75

161 Stater of Marion

162 Bathing the Child Jesus

1972. Ancient Coins of Cyprus (1st series).
393 **161** 20m. blue, black and silver 20 10
394 – 30m. blue, black and silver 20 10
395 – 40m. brown, blk & silver 20 20
396 – 100m. pink, black and silver . . . . 60 1·00
COINS: 30m. Stater of Paphos; 40m. Stater of Lapithos; 100m. Stater of Idalion.
See also Nos. 486/9.

1972. Christmas. Detail of mural in Holy Cross Church, Agiasmati. Multicoloured.
397 10m. Type **162** 10 10
398 20m. The Magi 10 10
399 100m. The Nativity 15 30
MS400 100 × 90 mm. 250m. Showing the mural in full (imperf) . . . 1·10 4·50

163 Mount Olympus, Troodos

1973. 29th International Ski Federation Congress. Multicoloured.
401 20m. Type **163** 10 10
402 100m. Congress emblem . . . 25 35

164 Europa "Posthorn"

1973. Europa.
403 **164** 20m. multicoloured . . . 25 10
404 30m. multicoloured . . . 25 10
405 150m. multicoloured . . . 1·50 3·50

165 Archbishop's Palace, Nicosia

1973. Traditional Architecture. Multicoloured.
406 20m. Type **165** 10 10
407 30m. House of Hajigeorgajis Cornessios, Nicosia (vert) 10 10
408 50m. House at Gourri, 1850 (vert) 15 10
409 100m. House at Rizokarpaso, 1772 . . . . 40 85

1973. No. 361 surch **20M**.
410 20m. on 15m. multicoloured 15 15

167 Scout Emblem

168 Archangel Gabriel

1973. Anniversaries and Events.
411 **167** 10m. green and brown . . 20 10
412 – 25m. blue and lilac . . . 20 10
413 – 35m. olive, stone and green 20 25
414 – 50m. blue and indigo . . 20 10
415 – 100m. brown and sepia 50 80
DESIGNS AND EVENTS—VERT: 10m. (60th anniv of Cyprus Boy Scouts); 50m. Airline emblem (25th anniv of Cyprus Airways); 100m. Interpol emblem (50th anniv of Interpol). HORIZ: 25m. Outlines of Cyprus and the E.E.C. (Association of Cyprus with "Common Market"); 35m. F.A.O. emblem (10th anniv of F.A.O.).

1973. Christmas. Murals from Araka Church. Multicoloured.
416 10m. Type **168** 10 10
417 20m. Madonna and Child . . 10 10
418 100m. Araka Church (horiz) 40 75

169 Grapes

170 "The Rape of Europa" (Silver Stater of Marion)

1974. Products of Cyprus. Multicoloured.
419 25m. Type **169** 10 15
420 50m. Grapefruit 20 70
421 50m. Oranges 20 70
422 50m. Lemons 20 70

1974. Europa.
423 **170** 10m. multicoloured . . . 15 10
424 40m. multicoloured . . . 40 30
425 150m. multicoloured . . . 1·40 2·75

171 Title Page of A. Kyprianos' "History of Cyprus" (1788)

174 "Refugees"

1974. 2nd International Congress of Cypriot Studies. Multicoloured.
426 10m. Type **171** 10 10
427 25m. Solon (philosospher) in mosaic (horiz) 15 10
428 100m. "Saint Neophytos" (wall painting) 60 75
MS429 111 × 90 mm. 250m. Ortelius' map of Cyprus and Greek Islands, 1584. Imperf . . . . 1·25 5·00

1974. Obligatory Tax. Refugee Fund. No. 359 surch **REFUGEE FUND** in English, Greek and Turkish and **10M**.
430 10m. on 5m. multicoloured 10 10

1974. U.N. Security Council Resolution 353. Nos. 360, 365, 366 and 369 optd **SECURITY COUNCIL RESOLUTION 353 20 JULY 1974**.
431 10m. multicoloured 25 10
432 40m. multicoloured 30 60
433 50m. multicoloured 30 10
434 250m. multicoloured . . . . 70 3·00

1974. Obligatory Tax. Refugee Fund.
435 **174** 10m. black and grey . . . 10 10

175 "Virgin and Child between Two Angels", Stavros Church

1974. Christmas. Church Wall-paintings. Mult.
436 10m. Type **175** 10 10
437 50m. "Adoration of the Magi", Ayios Neophytos Monastery (vert) 20 10
438 100m. "Flight into Egypt", Ayios Neophytos Monastery 25 45

176 Larnaca–Nicosia Mail-coach, 1878

1975. Anniversaries and Events.
439 **176** 20m. multicoloured . . . 25 10
440 – 30m. blue and orange . . 25 60
441 **176** 50m. multicoloured . . . 25 10
442 – 100m. multicoloured . . . 40 1·40
DESIGNS AND EVENTS—HORIZ: 20m., 50m. Centenary of Universal Postal Union. VERT: 30m. "Disabled Persons" (8th European Meeting of International Society for the Rehabilitation of Disabled Persons); 100m. Council flag (25th anniv of Council of Europe).

177 "The Distaff" (M. Kashalos)

178 Red Cross Flag over Map

1975. Europa. Multicoloured.
443 20m. Type **177** 25 40
444 30m. "Nature Morte" (C. Savva) 25 50
445 150m. "Virgin and Child of Liopetri" (G. P. Georghiou) 40 80

1975. Anniversaries and Events. Multicoloured.
446 25m. Type **178** 20 10
447 30m. Nurse and lamp (horiz) 20 10
448 75m. Woman's steatite idol (horiz) 20 90
EVENTS: 25m.25th anniv of Red Cross; 30m. International Nurses' Day; 75m. International Women's Year.

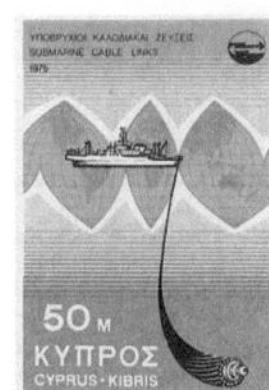

179 Submarine Cable Links

181 Human-figured Vessel, 19th-century

1976. Telecommunications Achievements.
449 **179** 50m. multicoloured . . . 30 10
450 – 100m. yellow, vio & lilac 35 90
DESIGN—HORIZ: 100m. International subscriber dialling.

1976. Surch **10M**.
451 **153** 10m. on 3m. multicoloured 20 70

1976. Europa. Ceramics. Multicoloured.
452 20m. Type **181** 20 10
453 60m. Composite vessel, 2100–2000 B.C. 50 80
454 100m. Byzantine goblet . . . 90 1·75

182 Self-help Housing

1976. Economic Reactivation. Multicoloured.
455 10m. Type **182** 10 10
456 25m. Handicrafts 15 20
457 30m. Reafforestation 15 20
458 60m. Air communications . . 30 55

183 Terracotta Statue of Youth

184 Olympic Symbol

1976. Cypriot Treasures.
459 **183** 5m. multicoloured 10 80
460 – 10m. multicoloured . . . 10 60
461 – 20m. red, yellow and black 20 60
462 – 25m. multicoloured . . . 20 10
463 – 30m. multicoloured . . . 20 10
464 – 40m. green, brown & blk 30 55
465 – 50m. lt brown, brn & blk 30 10
466 – 60m. multicoloured . . . 30 20
467 – 100m. multicoloured . . . 40 50
468 – 250m. blue, grey and black . . . . 50 1·75
469 – 500m. black, brown & grn 60 2·00
470 – £1 multicoloured . . . . 1·00 2·25
DESIGNS—VERT: 10m. Limestone head (23 × 34 mm); 20m. Gold necklace from Lambousa (24 × 37 mm); 25m. Terracotta warrior (24 × 37 mm); 30m. Statue of a priest of Aphrodite (24 × 37 mm); 250m. Silver dish from Lambousa (28 × 41 mm); 500m. Bronze stand (28 × 41 mm); £1 Statue of Artemis (28 × 41 mm). HORIZ: 40m. Bronze tablet (37 × 24 mm); 50m. Mycenaean crater (37 × 24 mm); 60m. Limestone sarcophagus (37 × 24 mm); 100m. Gold bracelet from Lambousa (As Type **183**).

1976. Olympic Games, Montreal.
471 **184** 20m. red, black and yellow 10 10
472 – 60m. multicoloured (horiz) 20 30
473 – 100m. multicoloured (horiz) 30 35
DESIGNS: 60m. and 100m. Olympic symbols (different).

185 "George Washington" (G. Stuart)

186 Children in Library

1976. Bicentenary of American Revolution.
474 **185** 100m. multicoloured . . . 40 30

1976. Anniversaries and Events.
475 **186** 40m. multicoloured . . . 15 15
476 – 50m. brown and black . . 15 10
477 – 80m. multicoloured . . . 30 60
DESIGNS AND EVENTS: 40m. Type **186** (Promotion of Children's books); 50m. Low-cost housing (HABITAT Conference, Vancouver); 80m. Eye protected by hands (World Health Day).

187 Archangel Michael

188 "Cyprus 74" (wood engraving by A. Tassos)

1976. Christmas. Multicoloured.
478 10m. Type **187** 10 10
479 15m. Archangel Gabriel . . . 10 10
480 150m. The Nativity 45 80
Designs show icons from Ayios Neophytis Monastery.

1977. Refugee Fund.
481 **188** 10m. black 20 10
See also Nos. 634 and 892 (after No. 728).

189 "View of Prodhromos" (A. Diamantis)

1977. Europa. Paintings. Multicoloured.
482 20m. Type **189** 20 10
483 60m. "Springtime at Monagroulli" (T. Kanthos) 30 55
484 120m. "Old Port, Limassol" (V. Ioannides) . . . . . . 60 2·00

190 500m. Stamp of 1960

192 Archbishop Makarios in Ceremonial Robes

191 Bronze Coin of Emperor Trajan

1977. Silver Jubilee.
485 **190** 120m. multicoloured . . . 30 30

1977. Ancient Coins of Cyprus (2nd series).
486 **191** 10m. black, gold and blue 15 10
487 – 40m. black, silver and blue 30 30
488 – 60m. black, silver & orge 35 35
489 – 100m. black, gold and green 50 95
DESIGNS: 40m. Silver tetradrachm of Demetrios Poliorcetes; 60m. Silver tetradrachm of Ptolemy VIII; 100m. Gold octadrachm of Arsinoe II.

1977. Death of Archbishop Makarios. Mult.
490 20m. Type **192** 15 10
491 60m. Archbishop in doorway 20 10
492 250m. Head and shoulders portrait . . . . 50 1·10

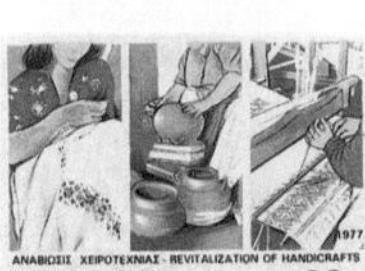

193 Embroidery, Pottery and Weaving

1977. Anniversaries and Events. Multicoloured.
493 20m. Type **193** 10 10
494 40m. Map of Mediterranean 15 20
495 60m. Gold medals 20 20
496 80m. Sputnik 20 85
DESIGNS COMMEMORATE: 20m. Revitalization of handicrafts; 40m. "Man and the Biosphere" Programme in the Mediterranean region; 60m. Gold medals won by Cypriot students in the Orleans Gymnasiade; 80m. 60th anniv of Russian Revolution.

194 "Nativity"

1977. Christmas. Children's Paintings Mult.
497 10m. Type **194** 10 10
498 40m. "The Three Kings" . . 10 10
499 150m. "Flight into Egypt" . . 25 80

195 Demetrios Libertis

1978. Cypriot Poets.
500 **195** 40m. brown and bistre . . 10 10
501 – 150m. grey, black and red 30 80
DESIGN: 150m. Vasilis Michaelides.

196 Chrysorrhogiatissa Monastery Courtyard

197 Archbishop of Cyprus, 1950–1977

1978. Europa. Architecture. Multicoloured.
502 25m. Type **196** 15 10
503 75m. Kolossi Castle 25 35
504 125m. Municipal Library, Paphos . . . . 45 1·50

1978. Archbishop Makarios Commem. Mult.
505 15m. Type **197** 15 20
506 25m. Exiled in Seychelles, 9 March 1956–28 March 1957 . . . . 15 20
507 50m. President of the Republic 1960–1977 . . . 20 25
508 75m. "Soldier of Christ" . . 20 30
509 100m. "Fighter for Freedom" 25 35
MS510 100 × 80 mm. 300m. "The Great Leader" (imperf) . . . . 1·00 2·50

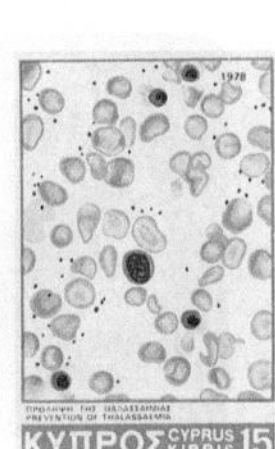

198 Affected Blood Corpuscles (Prevention of Thalassaemia)

199 Icon Stand

1978. Anniversaries and Events.
511 **198** 15m. multicoloured . . . 10 10
512 – 35m. multicoloured . . . 15 10
513 – 75m. black and grey . . . 20 30
514 – 125m. multicoloured . . . 35 80
DESIGNS—VERT: 35m. Aristotle (sculpture) (2300th death anniv). HORIZ: 75m. "Heads" (Human Rights); 125m. Wright brothers and Wright Flyer I (75th anniv of Powered Flight).

1978. Christmas.
515 **199** 15m. multicoloured . . . 10 10
516 – 35m. multicoloured . . . 15 10
517 – 150m. multicoloured . . . 40 60
DESIGNS: 35m., 150m. Different icon stands.

200 Aphrodite (statue from Soli)

1979. Goddess Aphrodite (1st issue). Multicoloured.
518 75m. Type **200** 25 10
519 125m. Aphrodite on shell (detail from Botticelli's "Birth of Venus") 35 25
See also Nos. 584/5.

201 Van, Larnaca–Nicosia Mail-coach and Envelope

1979. Europa. Communications. Multicoloured.
520 25m. Type **201** 20 10
521 75m. Radar, satellite and early telephone 30 20
522 125m. Aircraft, ship and envelopes . . . . 85 1·50

202 Peacock Wrasse

1979. Flora and Fauna. Multicoloured.
523 25m. Type **202** 15 10
524 50m. Black partridge (vert) 70 60
525 75m. Cedar (vert) 45 30
526 125m. Mule . . . . 50 1·25

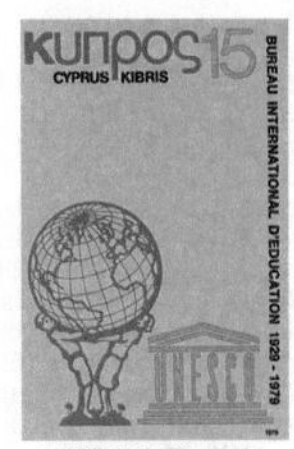

203 I.B.E. and U.N.E.S.C.O. Emblems

204 "Jesus" (from Church of the Virgin Mary of Arakas, Lagoudhera)

1979. Anniversaries and Events.
527 **203** 15m. multicoloured . . . 10 10
528 – 25m. multicoloured . . . 10 10
529 – 50m. black, brown and ochre 20 15
530 – 75m. multicoloured . . . 25 10
531 – 100m. multicoloured . . . 30 20
532 – 125m. multicoloured . . . 30 75
DESIGNS AND COMMEMORATIONS—VERT: 15m. Type **203** (50th anniv of International Bureau of Education); 125m. Rotary International emblem and "75" (75th anniv). HORIZ: 25m. Graphic design of dove and stamp album (20th anniv of Cyprus Philatelic Society); 50m. Lord Kitchener and map of Cyprus (Cyprus Survey Centenary); 75m. Child's face (International Year of the Child); 100m. Graphic design of footballers (25th anniv of U.E.F.A. European Football Association).

1979. Christmas. Icons. Multicoloured.
533 15m. Type **204** 10 10
534 35m. "Nativity" (Church of St Nicholas, Famagusta District) (29 × 41 mm) . . . 10 10
535 150m. "Holy Mary" (Church of the Virgin Mary of Arakas) 25 45

205 1880 ½d. Stamp with "969" (Nicosia) Postmark

1980. Centenary of Cyprus Stamps. Multicoloured.
536 40m. Type **205** 10 10
537 125m. 1880 2½d. stamp with "974" (Kyrenia) postmark 15 20
538 175m. 1880 1s. stamp with "942" (Larnaca) postmark 15 25
MS539 105 × 85 mm. 500m. 1880 ½d., 1d., 2½d., 4d., 6d. and 1s. stamps (90 × 75 mm). Imperf 70 85

206 St. Barnabas (patron saint of Cyprus)

208 Gold Necklace, Arsos (7th-century B.C.)

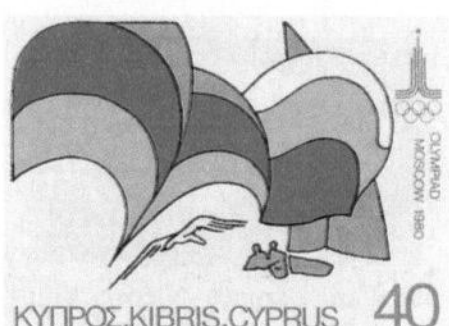

207 Sailing

1980. Europa. Personalities. Multicoloured.
540 40m. Type **206** 15 10
541 125m. Zeno of Citium (founder of Stoic philosophy) 30 20

1980. Olympic Games, Moscow. Multicoloured.
542 40m. Type **207** 10 10
543 125m. Swimming 20 20
544 200m. Gymnastics 25 25

1980. Archaeological Treasures.
545 **208** 10m. multicoloured . . . 30 1·00
546 – 15m. multicoloured . . . 30 1·00
547 – 25m. multicoloured . . . 30 30
548 – 40m. multicoloured . . . 40 75
549 – 50m. multicoloured . . . 40 10
550 – 75m. multicoloured . . . 1·25 1·50
551 – 100m. multicoloured . . . 65 15
552 – 125m. multicoloured . . . 65 1·00
553 – 150m. multicoloured . . . 75 15
554 – 175m. multicoloured . . . 75 1·25
555 – 200m. multicoloured . . . 75 30
556 – 500m. multicoloured . . . 75 1·50
557 – £1 multicoloured . . . . 1·00 1·25
558 – £2 multicoloured . . . . 1·75 2·00

DESIGNS—HORIZ: 15m. Bronze cow, Vouni Palace (5th-cent B.C.); 40m. Gold finger-ring, Enkomi (13th-cent B.C.); 500m. Stone bowl, Khirokitia (6th-millennium B.C.). VERT: 25m. Amphora, Salamis (6th-cent B.C.); 50m. Bronze cauldron, Salamis (8th-cent B.C.); 75m. Funerary stele, Marion (5th-cent B.C.). 100m. Jug (15–14th-cent B.C.); 125m. Warrior (terracotta) (6th–5th-cent B.C.); 150m. Lions attacking bull (bronze relief), Vouni Palace (5th-cent B.C.); 175m. Faience rhyton, Kition (13th-cent B.C.); 200m. Bronze statue of Ingot God, Enkomi (12th-cent B.C.); £1 Ivory plaque, Salamis (7th-cent B.C.); £2 "Leda and the Swan" (mosaic), Kouklia (3rd-cent A.D.).

209 Cyprus Flag

1980. 20th Anniv of Republic of Cyprus. Multicoloured.
559 40m. Type **209** 10 10
560 125m. Signing Treaty of Establishment (41 × 29 mm) 20 15
561 175m. Archbishop Makarios 35 25

210 Head and Peace Dove

1980. International Day of Solidarity with Palestinian People.
562 **210** 40m. black and grey . . . 20 20
563 – 125m. black and grey . . 35 35
DESIGN: 125m. Head and dove with olive branch.

211 Pulpit, Tripiotis Church, Nicosia

212 Folk Dancing

1980. Christmas. Multicoloured.
564 25m. Type **211** 10 10
565 100m. Holy Doors, Panayia Church Paralimni 15 20
565 125m. Pulpit, Ayios Lazaros Church, Larnaca 15 20

1981. Europa. Folklore, showing folk-dancing from paintings by T. Photiades.
567 **212** 40m. multicoloured . . . 30 10
568 – 175m. multicoloured . . . 60 50

213 Self-portrait

214 "Ophrys kotschyi"

1981. 500th Anniv of Leonardo da Vinci's Visit. Multicoloured.
569 50m. Type **213** 40 10
570 125m. "The Last Supper" (50 × 25 mm) 70 40
571 175m. Cyprus lace and Milan Cathedral 95 60

1981. Cypriot Wild Orchids. Multicoloured.
572 25m. Type **214** 40 60
573 50m. "Orchis punctulata" . . 50 70
574 75m. "Ophrys argolica elegans" 55 80
575 150m. "Epipactis veratrifolia" 65 90

215 Heinrich von Stephan

1981. Anniversaries and Events.
576 **215** 25m. dp green, grn & bl 15 10
577 – 40m. multicoloured . . . 15 10
578 – 125m. black, red and green 30 25
579 – 150m. multicoloured . . . 35 30
580 – 200m. multicoloured . . . 70 80

DESIGNS AND COMMEMORATIONS: 25m. Type **137** (150th birth anniv of Heinrich von Stephan (founder of U.P.U.); 40m. Stylised man holding dish of food (World Food Day); 125m. Stylised hands (International Year for Disabled People); 150m. Stylised building and flower (European Campaign for Urban Renaissance); 200m. Prince Charles, Lady Diana Spencer and St. Paul's Cathedral (Royal Wedding).

216 "The Lady of the Angels" (from Church of the Transfiguration of Christ, Palekhori)

217 "Louomene" (Aphrodite bathing) (statue, 250 B.C.)

1981. Christmas. Murals from Nicosia District Churches. Multicoloured.
581 25m. Type **216** 20 10
582 100m. "Christ Pantokrator" (Church of Madonna of Arakas, Lagoudera) (vert) 60 20
583 125m. "Baptism of Christ" (Church of Our Lady of Assinou, Nikitari) 70 30

1982. Aphrodite (Greek goddess of love and beauty) Commemoration (2nd issue). Mult.
584 125m. Type **217** 55 45
585 175m. "Anadyomene" (Aphrodite emerging from the waters) (Titian) 70 65

218 Naval Battle with Greek Fire, 985 A.D.

1982. Europa. Historic Events. Multicoloured.
586 40m. Type **218** 60 10
587 175m. Conversion of Roman Proconsul Sergius Paulus to Christianity, Paphos, 45 A.D. . . . . 1·00 2·50

219 "XP" (monogram of Christ) (mosaic)

1982. World Cultural Heritage. Multicoloured.
588 50m. Type **219** 20 10
589 125m. Head of priest-king of Paphos (sculpture) (24 × 37 mm) 40 25
590 225m. Theseus (Greek god) (mosaic) 60 95

1982. No. 550 surch **100**.
591 100m. on 75m. Funerary stele, Marion (5th-century B.C.) 50 50

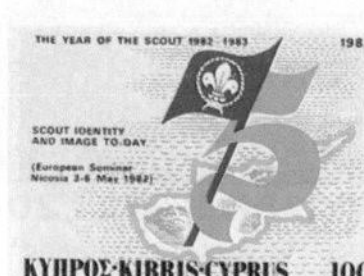

221 Cyprus and Stylised "75"

1982. 75th Anniv of Boy Scout Movement. Multicoloured.
592 100m. Type **221** 35 20
593 125m. Lord Baden-Powell . . 40 40
594 175m. Camp-site 40 90

222 Holy Communion, The Bread

1982. Christmas.
595 **222** 25m. multicoloured . . . 10 10
596 – 100m. gold and black . . 30 15
597 – 250m. multicoloured . . . 70 1·50

DESIGN—VERT: 100m. Holy Chalice. HORIZ: 250m. Holy Communion, The Wine.

223 Cyprus Forest Industries' Sawmill

1983. Commonwealth Day. Multicoloured.
598 50m. Type **223** 10 10
599 125m. "Ikarios and the Discovery of Wine" (3rd-century mosaic) . . . 20 25
600 150m. Folk-dancers, Commonwealth Film and Television Festival, 1980 25 35
601 175m. Royal Exhibition Building, Melbourne (Commonwealth Heads of Government Meeting, 1981) 25 40

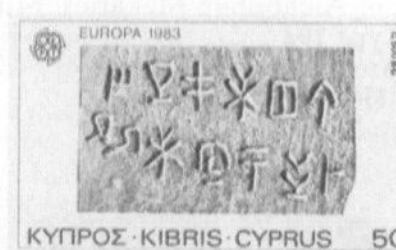

224 Cyprosyllabic Inscription (6th-century B.C.)

1983. Europa. Multicoloured.
602 50m. Type **224** 40 10
603 200m. Copper ore, ingot (Enkomi 1400–1250 B.C.) and bronze jug (2nd century A.D.) . . . . . . 1·10 2·40

225 "Pararge aegeria"

1983. Butterflies. Multicoloured.
604 60m. Type **225** 25 20
605 130m. "Aricia agestis" . . . 45 25
606 250m. "Glaucopsyche melanops" . . . . 85 2·50

1983. Nos. 545/56 surch.
607 1c. on 10m. Type **208** . . . . 35 1·00
608 2c. on 15m. Bronze cow, Vouni Palace (5th-century B.C.) (horiz) . . . . 35 1·25
609 3c. on 25m. Amphora, Salamis (6th-century B.C.) 35 1·00
610 4c. on 40m. Gold finger-ring, Enkomi (13th-century B.C.) (horiz) . . . . 40 1·00
611 5c. on 50m. Bronze cauldron, Salamis (8th-century B.C.) 50 50
612 6c. on 75m. Funerary stele, Marion (5th-century B.C.) 50 1·00
613 10c. on 100m. Jug (15th–14th-century B.C.) 50 40
614 13c. on 125m. Warrior (Terracotta) (6–5th-cent B.C.) 50 50
615 15c. on 150m. Lions attacking bull (bronze relief), Vouni Palace (5th-century B.C.) (horiz) 50 55
616 20c. on 200m. Bronze statue of Ingot God, Enkomi (12th-century B.C.) 50 65
617 25c. on 175m. Faience rhyton, Kition (13th-century B.C.) . . . . 55 1·10
618 50c. on 500m. Stone bowl, Khirokitia (6th-millenium B.C.) (horiz) . . . . 75 2·00

227 View of Power Station

228 St Lazaros Church, Larnaca

1983. Anniversaries and Events. Multicoloured.
619 3c. Type **227** 10 20
620 6c. W.C.Y. logo 15 15
621 13c. "Sol Olympia" (liner) and "Polys" (tanker) . . . 30 35
622 15c. Human Rights emblem and map of Europe 20 25
623 20c. Nicos Kazantzakis . . . 20 75
624 25c. Makarios in church . . 25 75

COMMEMORATIONS: 3c. 30th anniv of Cyprus Electricity Authority; 6c. World Communications Year; 13c. 25th anniv of International Maritime Organization; 15c. 35th anniv of Universal Declaration of Human Rights; 20c. Birth centenary; 25c. 70th birth anniv.

1983. Christmas. Church Towers. Multicoloured.
625 4c. Type **228** 15 10
626 13c. St. Varvara Church, Kaimakli, Nicosia 40 35
627 20c. St. Ioannis Church, Larnaca . . . . 70 1·50

229 Waterside Cafe, Larnaca

1984. Old Engravings. Each brown and black.
628 6c. Type **229** 15 15
629 20c. Bazaar at Larnaca (39 × 25 mm) 40 85
630 30c. Famagusta Gate, Nicosia (39 × 25 mm) . . . . . . 65 1·50
MS631 110 × 85 mm. 75c. "The Confession" (St. Lazarus Church, Larnaca) . . . . 1·25 2·00

230 C.E.P.T. 25th Anniversary Logo

1984. Europa.
632 **230** 6c. lt green, green & blk . . . 40 10
633 15c. lt blue, blue & black . . . 70 2·00

1984. Obligatory Tax. Refugee Fund. As T **188** but new value and dated "1984".
634 1c. black 10 10

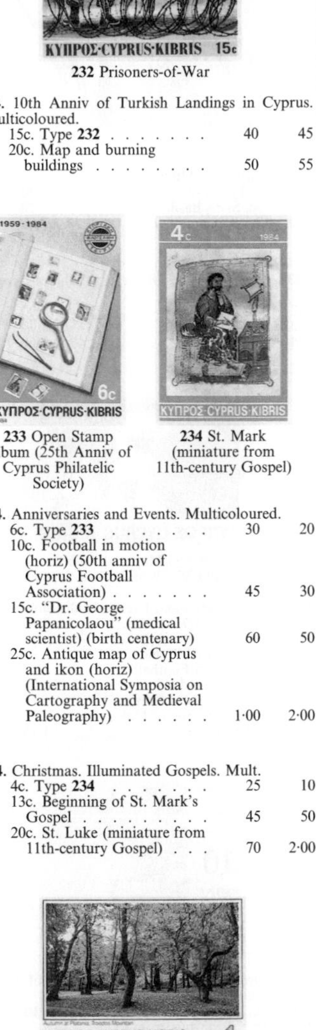

231 Running

1984. Olympic Games, Los Angeles. Multicoloured.
635 3c. Type **231** 15 10
636 4c. Olympic column 15 20
637 13c. Swimming 45 75
638 20c. Gymnastics . . . . . . 60 1·50

232 Prisoners-of-War

1984. 10th Anniv of Turkish Landings in Cyprus. Multicoloured.
639 15c. Type **232** 40 45
640 20c. Map and burning buildings 50 55

233 Open Stamp Album (25th Anniv of Cyprus Philatelic Society)

234 St. Mark (miniature from 11th-century Gospel)

1984. Anniversaries and Events. Multicoloured.
641 6c. Type **233** 30 20
642 10c. Football in motion (horiz) (50th anniv of Cyprus Football Association) 45 30
643 15c. "Dr. George Papanicolaou" (medical scientist) (birth centenary) . . . 60 50
644 25c. Antique map of Cyprus and ikon (horiz) (International Symposia on Cartography and Medieval Paleography) . . . . . . 1·00 2·00

1984. Christmas. Illuminated Gospels. Mult.
645 4c. Type **234** 25 10
646 13c. Beginning of St. Mark's Gospel 45 50
647 20c. St. Luke (miniature from 11th-century Gospel) . . . 70 2·00

235 Autumn at Platania, Troodos Mountains

1985. Cyprus Scenes and Landscapes. Mult.
648 1c. Type **235** 20 60
649 2c. Ayia Napa Monastery . . 20 60
650 3c. Phini Village–panoramic view 20 60
651 4c. Kykko Monastery 20 30
652 5c. Beach at Makronissos, Ayia Napa 20 20
653 6c. Village street, Omodhos (vert) 30 20
654 10c. Panoramic sea view . . 45 30
655 13c. Windsurfing 55 25
656 15c. Beach at Protaras . . . 65 25
657 20c. Forestry for development (vert) 80 50
658 25c. Sunrise at Protaras (vert) 1·00 1·00
659 30c. Village house, Pera . . . 1·25 1·25
660 50c. Apollo Hylates Sanctuary, Curium . . . . 2·00 1·75
661 £1 Snow on Troodos Mountains (vert) . . . . . 3·50 3·00
662 £5 Personification of Autumn, House of Dionyssos, Paphos (vert) 13·00 15·00

236 Clay Idols of Musicians (7/6th century B.C.)

1985. Europa. European Music Year. Mult.
663 6c. Type **236** 50 35
664 15c. Violin lute, flute and score from the "Cyprus Suite" . . . . 90 2·25

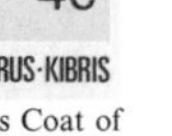

237 Cyprus Coat of Arms (25th Anniv of Republic)

238 "The Visit of the Madonna to Elizabeth" (Lambadistis Monastery, Kalopanayiotis)

1985. Anniversaries and Events.
665 **237** 4c. multicoloured 15 15
666 – 6c. multicoloured 15 15
667 – 13c. multicoloured . . . . 25 1·00
668 – 15c. black, green and orange . . . . 1·00 1·25
669 – 20c. multicoloured . . . . 30 1·75
DESIGNS—HORIZ (43 × 30 mm): 6c. "Barn of Liopetri" (detail) (Pol. Georghiou) (30th anniv of EOKA Campaign); 13c. Three profiles (International Youth Year); 15c. Solon Michaelides (composer and conductor) (European Music Year). VERT—(as T **237**): 20c. U.N. Building, New York, and flags (40th anniv of United Nations Organization).

1985. Christmas. Frescoes from Cypriot Churches. Multicoloured.
670 4c. Type **238** 20 10
671 13c. "The Nativity" (Lambadistis Monastery, Kalopanayiotis) 50 65
672 20c. "Candlemas-day" (Asinou Church) . . . . . 70 2·00

239 Figure from Hellenistic Spoon Handle

1986. New Archaeological Museum Fund. Multicoloured.
673 15c. Type **239** 45 45
674 20c. Pattern from early Ionian helmet and foot from statue 60 75
675 25c. Roman statue of Eros and Psyche 65 95
676 30c. Head of statue . . . . . 75 1·10
MS677 111 × 90 mm. Nos. 673/6 (sold at £1) . . . . 12·00 16·00
No. 676 also commemorates the 50th anniv of the Department of Antiquities.

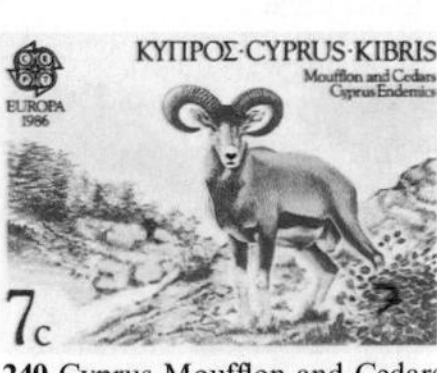

240 Cyprus Moufflon and Cedars

1986. Europa. Protection of Nature and the Environment. Multicoloured.
678 7c. Type **240** 35 30
679 17c. Greater flamingos ("Flamingos") at Larnaca Salt Lake . . . . 1·40 2·75

241 Cat's-paw Scallop

1986. Sea Shells. Multicoloured.
680 5c. Type **241** 30 15
681 7c. Atlantic trumpet triton . . 35 15
682 18c. Purple dye murex . . . 60 70
683 25c. Yellow cowrie . . . . . 1·00 2·00

1986. Nos. 653 and 655 surch.
684 7c. on 6c. Village street, Omodhos (vert) 40 30
685 18c. on 13c. Windsurfing . . 1·10 70

243 Globe Outline Map of Cyprus and Barn Swallows (Overseas Cypriots' Year)

1986. Anniversaries and Events. Multicoloured.
686 15c. Type **243** . . . . 1·00 45
687 18c. Halley's Comet over Cyprus beach (40 × 23 mm) 1·25 2·00
688 18c. Comet's tail over sea and Edmond Halley (40 × 23 mm) . . . . . . 1·25 2·00
Nos. 687/8 were printed together, se-tenant, forming a composite design.

244 Pedestrian Crossing

1986. Road Safety Campaign. Multicoloured.
689 5c. Type **244** 65 30
690 7c. Motor cycle crash helmet 70 30
691 18c. Hands fastening car seat belt . . . . 1·50 3·00

245 "The Nativity" (Church of Panayia tou Araka)

1986. Christmas. International Peace Year. Details of Nativity frescoes from Cypriot churches. Multicoloured.
692 5c. Type **245** 25 15
693 15c. Church of Panayia tou Moutoulla 65 30
694 17c. Church of St. Nicholas tis Steyis . . . . 75 2·00

246 Church of Virgin Mary, Asinou

1987. Troodos Churches on the World Heritage List. Multicoloured.
695 15c. Type **246** . . . . 70 1·10
696 15c. Fresco of Virgin Mary, Moutoulla's Church . . . 70 1·10
697 15c. Church of Virgin Mary, Podithou . . . . 70 1·10
698 15c. Fresco of Three Apostles, St. Ioannis Lampadistis Monastery . . 70 1·10
699 15c. Annunciation fresco, Church of the Holy Cross, Pelentriou . . . . 70 1·10
700 15c. Fresco of Saints, Church of the Cross, Ayiasmati . . 70 1·10
701 15c. Fresco of Archangel Michael and Donor, Pedoula's Church of St. Michael . . . . 70 1·10
702 15c. Church of St. Nicolaos, Steyis . . . . 70 1·10
703 15c. Fresco of Prophets, Church of Virgin Mary, Araka . . . . 70 1·10

247 Proposed Central Bank of Cyprus Building

1987. Europa. Modern Architecture.
704 **247** 7c. multicoloured 50 30
705 – 18c. black, grey and green 1·10 2·00
DESIGN: 18c. Headquarters complex, Cyprus Telecommunications Authority.

248 Remains of Ancient Ship and Kyrenia Castle

1987. Voyage of "Kyrenia II" (replica of ancient ship). Multicoloured.
706 2c. Type **248** 35 20
707 3c. "Kyrenia II" under construction, 1982–5 . . . 45 90
708 5c. "Kyrenia II" at Paphos, 1986 . . . . 75 20
709 17c. "Kyrenia II" at New York, 1986 . . . . 1·75 90

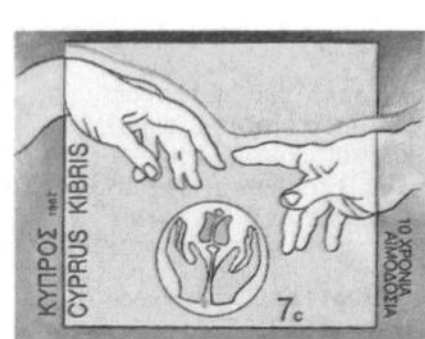

249 Hands (from Michelangelo's "Creation") and Emblem

1987. Anniversaries and Events. Multicoloured.
710 7c. Type **249** (10th anniv of Blood Donation Co-ordinating Committee) . . 50 25
711 15c. Snail with flowered shell and countryside (European Contryside Campaign) . . 1·10 40
712 20c. Symbols of ocean bed and Earth's crust ("Troodos '87" Ophiolites and Oceanic Lithosphere Symposium) . . . . 1·40 3·00

250 Nativity Crib

1987. Christmas. Traditional Customs. Mult.
713 5c. Type **250** 35 15
714 15c. Door knocker decorated with foliage . . . . 1·10 35
715 17c. Bowl of fruit and nuts 1·25 2·00

251 Flags of Cyprus and E.E.C.

1988. Cypriot–E.E.C. Customs Union. Mult.
716 15c. Type **251** . . . . 80 1·50
717 18c. Outline maps of Cyprus and E.E.C. countries . . . 80 80

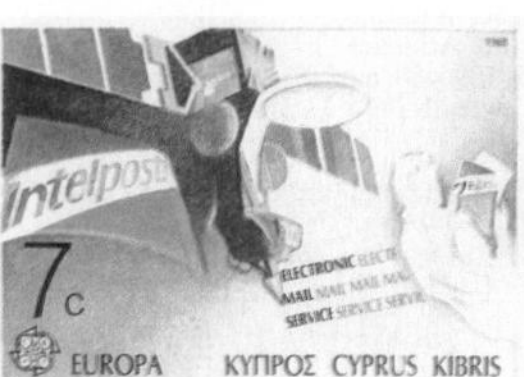

252 Intelpost Telefax Terminal

1988. Europa. Transport and Communications. Multicoloured.
718 7c. Type **252** . . . . 75 1·25
719 7c. Car driver using mobile telephone . . . . 75 1·25

720 18c. Nose of Cyprus Airways airliner and greater flamingos . . . . 2·50 3·00
721 18c. Boeing 739 airliner in flight and greater flamingos 2·50 3·00

253 Sailing

255 "Cyprus 74" (wood-engraving by A. Tassos)

254 Conference Emblem

1988. Olympic Games, Seoul. Multicoloured.
722 5c. Type **253** 30 20
723 7c. Athletes at start 35 40
724 10c. Shooting 40 70
725 20c. Judo . . . . 90 1·50

1988. Non-Aligned Foreign Ministers' Conference, Nicosia.
726 **254** 1c. black, blue and green 10 10
727 – 10c. multicoloured 45 70
728 – 50c. multicoloured . . . . 2·25 2·50
DESIGNS: 10c. Emblem of Republic of Cyprus; 50c. Nehru, Tito, Nasser and Makarios.

1988. Obligatory Tax. Refugee Fund. Variously dated.
892 **255** 1c. black and grey 10 10

1988. No. 651 surch **15c.**
730 15c. on 4c. Kykko Monastery 1·75 1·25

256 "Presentation of Christ at the Temple" (Church of Holy Cross tou Agiasmati)

257 Human Rights Logo

1988. Christmas. Designs showing frescoes from Cypriot churches. Multicoloured.
731 5c. Type **256** 25 20
732 15c. "Virgin and Child" (St. John Lampadistis Monastery) 55 25
733 17c. "Adoration of the Magi" (St. John Lampadistis Monastery) . . . . 80 1·75

1988. 40th Anniv of Universal Declaration of Human Rights.
734 **257** 25c. lt blue, dp blue & bl 90 1·25

258 Basketball

1989. 3rd Small European States' Games, Nicosia. Multicoloured.
735 1c. Type **258** 30 15
736 5c. Javelin 30 15
737 15c. Wrestling 65 20
738 18c. Athletics . . . . 85 1·00
MS739 109 × 80 mm. £1 Angel and laurel wreath (99 × 73 mm). Imperf 5·50 6·00

259 Lingri Stick Game

1989. Europa. Children's Games. Multicoloured.
740 7c. Type **259** . . . . 1·10 1·50
741 7c. Ziziros . . . . 1·10 1·50
742 18c. Sitsia . . . . 1·25 1·60
743 18c. Leapfrog . . . . 1·25 1·60

260 "Universal Man"

1989. Bicentenary of the French Revolution.
744 **260** 18c. multicoloured . . . . 1·00 60

261 Stylized Human Figures

262 Worker Bees tending Larvae

1989. Centenary of Interparliamentary Union (15c.) and 9th Non-Aligned Summit Conference, Belgrade (30c.). Multicoloured.
745 15c. Type **261** 65 40
746 30c. Conference logo . . . . 1·10 1·10

1989. Bee-keeping. Multicoloured.
748 3c. Type **262** 30 25
749 10c. Bee on rock-rose flower 70 50
750 15c. Bee on lemon flower . . 95 50
751 18c. Queen and worker bees 1·10 1·75

263 Outstretched Hand and Profile (aid for Armenian earthquake victims)

264 Winter (detail from "Four Seasons")

1989. Anniversaries and Events. Multicoloured.
752 3c. Type **263** 30 70
753 5c. Airmail envelope (Cyprus Philatelic Society F.I.P. membership) 45 10
754 7c. Crab symbol and daisy (European Cancer Year) 75 1·40
755 17c. Vegetables and fish (World Food Day) . . . . 1·10 1·40

1989. Roman Mosaics from Paphos. Multicoloured.
756 1c. Type **264** . . . . 30 1·00
757 2c. Personification of Crete (32 × 24 mm) . . . . . . 35 1·00
758 3c. Centaur and Maenad (24 × 32 mm) . . . . . . 45 1·00
759 4c. Poseidon and Amymone (32 × 24 mm) . . . . . . 60 1·10
760 5c. Leda 60 20
761 7c. Apollon 70 25
762 10c. Hermes and Dionysos (24 × 32 mm) 90 30
763 15c. Cassiopeia . . . . . . 1·50 45
764 18c. Orpheus (32 × 24 mm) 1·50 50
765 20c. Nymphs (24 × 32 mm) 1·75 75
766 25c. Amazon (24 × 32 mm) 1·75 80
767 40c. Doris (32 × 24 mm) . . . 2·50 1·50
768 50c. Heracles and the Lion (39 × 27 mm) . . . . . . 2·50 1·50
769 £1 Apollon and Daphne (39 × 27 mm) . . . . . . 4·00 3·00
770 £3 Cupid (39 × 27 mm) . . . 9·00 10·00

265 Hands and Open Book (International Literacy Year)

1990. Anniversaries and Events. Multicoloured.
771 15c. Type **265** 55 50
772 17c. Dove and profiles (83rd Inter-Parliamentary Conference, Nicosia) . . . 65 90
773 18c. Lions International emblem (Lions Europa Forum, Limassol) 75 90

266 District Post Office, Paphos

1990. Europa. Post Office Buildings. Mult.
774 7c. Type **266** . . . . 1·40 25
775 18c. City Centre Post Office, Limassol . . . . 1·60 2·75

267 Symbolic Lips (25th anniv of Hotel and Catering Institute)

1990. European Tourism Year. Multicoloured.
776 5c. Type **267** 25 25
777 7c. Bell tower, St. Lazarus Church (1100th anniv) . . 30 25
778 15c. Butterflies and woman 2·00 45
779 18c. Birds and man . . . . . 2·50 4·00

268 Sun (wood carving)

269 "Chionodoxa lochiae"

1990. 30th Anniv of Republic. Multicoloured.
780 15c. Type **268** 65 45
781 17c. Bulls (pottery design) . . 75 60
782 18c. Fishes (pottery design) 85 70
783 40c. Tree and birds (wood carving) . . . . 2·50 4·00
MS784 89 × 89 mm. £1 30th Anniversary emblem. Imperf 3·75 5·50

1990. Endangered Wild Flowers. Book illustrations by Elektra Megaw. Multicoloured.
785 2c. Type **269** . . . . 55 1·25
786 3c. "Pancratium maritimum" 55 1·25
787 5c. "Paeonia mascula" . . . 75 20
788 7c. "Cyclamen cyprium" . . 80 25
789 15c. "Tulipa cypria" . . . . 1·60 30
790 18c. "Crocus cyprius" . . . 1·75 3·25

270 "Nativity"

271 Archangel

1990. Christmas. 16th-century Icons. Mult.
791 5c. Type **270** 50 20
792 15c. "Virgin Hodegetria" . . 1·40 30
793 17c. "Nativity" (different) . . 1·60 3·25

1991. 6th-century Mosaics from Kanakaria Church. Multicoloured.
794 5c. Type **271** 20 15
795 15c. Christ Child 75 20
796 17c. St. James . . . . 1·50 1·75
797 18c. St. Matthew . . . . . . 1·75 2·00

272 "Ulysses" Spacecraft

1991. Europa. Europa in Space. Multicoloured.
798 7c. Type **272** 90 20
799 18c. "Giotto" and Halley's Comet . . . . 1·60 2·50

273 Young Cyprus Wheatear

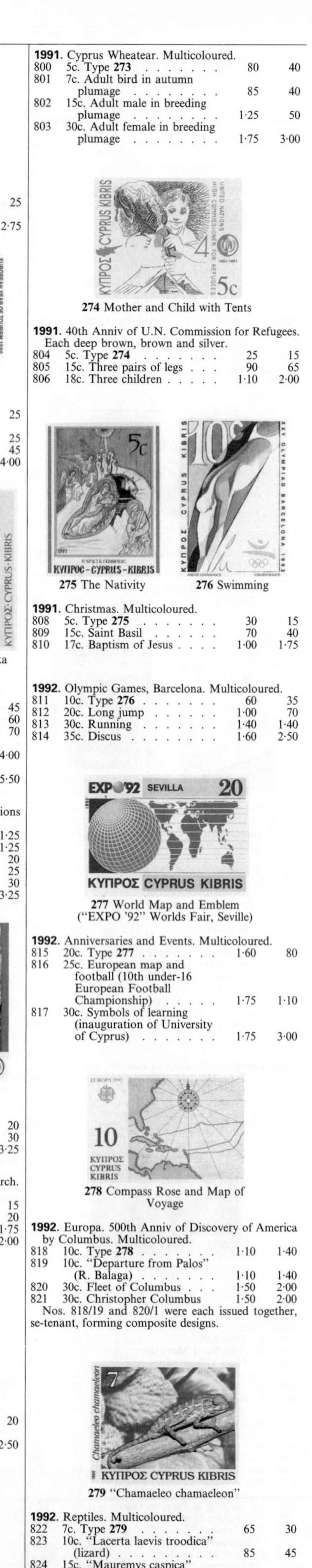

1991. Cyprus Wheatear. Multicoloured.
800 5c. Type **273** 80 40
801 7c. Adult bird in autumn plumage 85 40
802 15c. Adult male in breeding plumage . . . . 1·25 50
803 30c. Adult female in breeding plumage . . . . 1·75 3·00

274 Mother and Child with Tents

1991. 40th Anniv of U.N. Commission for Refugees. Each deep brown, brown and silver.
804 5c. Type **274** 25 15
805 15c. Three pairs of legs . . . 90 65
806 18c. Three children . . . . . 1·10 2·00

275 The Nativity

276 Swimming

1991. Christmas. Multicoloured.
808 5c. Type **275** 30 15
809 15c. Saint Basil 70 40
810 17c. Baptism of Jesus . . . . 1·00 1·75

1992. Olympic Games, Barcelona. Multicoloured.
811 10c. Type **276** 60 35
812 20c. Long jump . . . . 1·00 70
813 30c. Running . . . . 1·40 1·40
814 35c. Discus . . . . 1·60 2·50

277 World Map and Emblem ("EXPO '92" Worlds Fair, Seville)

1992. Anniversaries and Events. Multicoloured.
815 20c. Type **277** . . . . 1·60 80
816 25c. European map and football (10th under-16 European Football Championship) . . . . . 1·75 1·10
817 30c. Symbols of learning (inauguration of University of Cyprus) . . . . 1·75 3·00

278 Compass Rose and Map of Voyage

1992. Europa. 500th Anniv of Discovery of America by Columbus. Multicoloured.
818 10c. Type **278** . . . . 1·10 1·40
819 10c. "Departure from Palos" (R. Balaga) . . . . . . 1·10 1·40
820 30c. Fleet of Columbus . . . 1·50 2·00
821 30c. Christopher Columbus 1·50 2·00
Nos. 818/19 and 820/1 were each issued together, se-tenant, forming composite designs.

279 "Chamaeleo chamaeleon"

1992. Reptiles. Multicoloured.
822 7c. Type **279** 65 30
823 10c. "Lacerta laevis troodica" (lizard) 85 45
824 15c. "Mauremys caspica" (turtle) . . . . 1·25 80
825 20c. "Coluber cypriensis" (snake) . . . . 1·40 2·50

280 Minoan Wine Ship of 7th Century B.C. and Modern Tanker

1992. 7th International Maritime and Shipping Conference, Nicosia.
826 **280** 50c. multicoloured . . . . 3·00 3·00

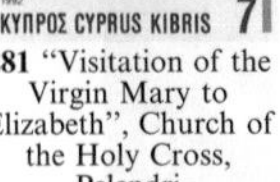

281 "Visitation of the Virgin Mary to Elizabeth", Church of the Holy Cross, Pelendri

282 School Building and Laurel Wreath

1992. Christmas. Church Fresco Paintings. Mult.
827 7c. Type **281** 50 25
828 15c. "Virgin and Child Enthroned", Church of Panayia tou Araka 85 65
829 20c. "Virgin and Child", Ayios Nicolaos tis Stegis Church . . . . 1·25 2·25

1993. Centenary of Pancyprian Gymnasium (secondary school).
830 **282** 10c. multicoloured 75 60

283 "Motherhood" (bronze sculpture, Nicos Dymiotis)

1993. Europa. Comtemporary Art. Multicoloured.
831 10c. Type **283** 75 50
832 30c. "Motherhood" (painting, Christoforos Savva) (horiz) 1·50 2·25

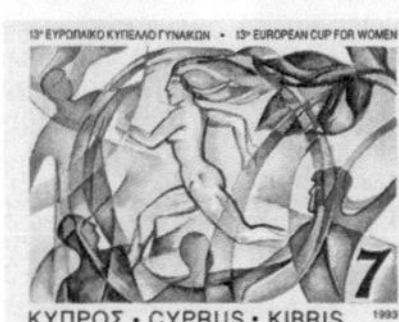

284 Women Athletes (13th European Cup for Women)

1993. Anniversaries and Events. Multicoloured.
833 7c. Type **284** 40 30
834 10c. Scout symbols (80th anniv of Scouting in Cyprus) (vert) 55 40
835 20c. Water-skier, dolphin and gull (Moufflon Encouragement Cup) (inscr "Mufflon") . . . . 10·00 10·00
835a 20c. Water-skier, dolphin and seabird (inscr "Moufflon") 95 95
836 25c. Archbishop Makarios III and monastery (80th birth anniv) . . . . . . 1·40 2·00

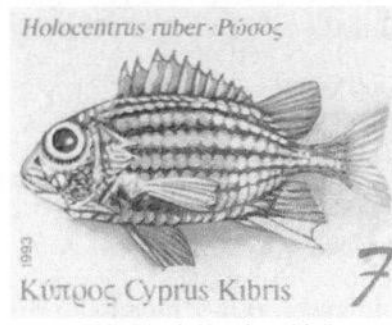

285 Red Squirrelfish

1993. Fishes. Multicoloured.
837 7c. Type **285** 40 25
838 15c. Red scorpionfish 65 55
839 20c. Painted comber 75 85
840 30c. Grey triggerfish . . . . 1·40 2·25

286 Conference Emblem

1993. 12th Commonwealth Summit Conference.
841 **286** 35c. brown and ochre . . 1·60 1·90
842 40c. brown and ochre . . 1·90 2·40

287 Ancient Sailing Ship and Modern Coaster

1993. "Maritime Cyprus '93" International Shipping Conference, Nicosia.
843 **287** 25c. multicoloured . . . . 1·40 1·40

288 Cross from Stavrovouni Monastery

290 Symbols of Disability (Persons with Special Needs Campaign)

289 Copper Smelting

1993. Christmas. Church Crosses. Multicoloured.
844 7c. Type **288** 30 25
845 20c. Cross from Lefkara . . 75 75
846 25c. Cross from Pedoulas (horiz) . . . . 1·00 2·00

1994. Europa. Discoveries. Ancient Copper Industry. Multicoloured.
847 10c. Type **289** 50 35
848 30c. Ingot, ancient ship and map of Cyprus . . . . . 1·25 2·00

1994. Anniversaries and Events. Multicoloured.
849 7c. Type **290** 40 25
850 15c. Olympic rings in flame (Centenary of International Olympic Committee) . . . 65 55
851 20c. Peace doves (World Gymnasiade, Nicosia) . . . 80 80
852 25c. Adults and unborn baby in tulip (International Year of the Family) . . . . . . 1·10 2·00

291 Houses, Soldier and Family

1994. 20th Anniv of Turkish Landings in Cyprus. Multicoloured.
853 10c. Type **291** 50 40
854 50c. Soldier and ancient columns . . . . 2·00 3·00

292 Black Pine

1994. Trees. Multicoloured.
855 7c. Type **292** 40 25
856 15c. Cyprus cedar 65 55
857 20c. Golden oak 80 80
858 30c. Strawberry tree . . . . 1·25 2·25

293 Airliner, Route Map and Emblem

1994. 50th Anniv of I.C.A.O.
859 **293** 30c. multicoloured . . . . 2·00 2·00

294 "Virgin Mary" (detail) (Philip Goul)

295 Woman from Paphos wearing Foustani

1994. Christmas. Church Paintings. Multicoloured.
860 7c. Type **294** 60 25
861 20c. "The Nativity" (detail) (Byzantine) . . . . 1·40 70
862 25c. "Archangel Michael" (detail) (Goul) . . . . . . 1·60 2·75

1994. Traditional Costumes. Multicoloured.
863 1c. Type **295** 30 85
864 2c. Bride from Karpass . . . 45 85
865 3c. Woman from Paphos wearing sayia 50 85
866 5c. Woman from Messaoria wearing foustani 60 90
867 7c. Bridegroom 65 20
868 10c. Shepherd from Messaoria 85 40
869 15c. Woman from Nicosia in festive costume . . . . . . 1·50 40
870 20c. Woman from Karpass wearing festive sayia . . . 1·50 50
871 25c. Woman from Pitsillia . . 1·75 60
872 30c. Woman from Karpass wearing festive doupletti 1·75 70
873 35c. Countryman . . . . . . 1·75 1·00
874 40c. Man from Messaoria in festive costume . . . . . . 2·00 1·50
875 50c. Townsman . . . . . . 2·00 1·75
876 £1 Townswoman wearing festive sarka . . . . 3·00 2·75

296 "Hearth Room" Excavation, Alassa, and Frieze

297 Statue of Liberty, Nicosia (left detail)

1995. 3rd International Congress of Cypriot Studies, Nicosia. Multicoloured.
877 20c. Type **296** 75 75
878 30c. Hypostyle hall, Kalavasos, and Mycenaean amphora . . . . 1·00 1·75
MS879 110 × 80 mm. £1 Old Archbishop's Palace, Nicosia (107 × 71 mm). Imperf . . . . 3·50 5·00

1995. 40th Anniv of Start of E.O.K.A. Campaign. Different details of the statue. Multicoloured.
880 20c. Type **297** . . . . 1·10 1·25
881 20c. Centre detail (face value at top right) . . . . . 1·10 1·25
882 20c. Right detail (face value at bottom right) . . . . . 1·10 1·25
Nos. 880/2 were printed together, se-tenant, forming a composite design.

298 Nazi Heads on Peace Dove over Map of Europe

299 Symbolic Figure holding Healthy Food

1995. Europa. Peace and Freedom. Multicoloured.
883 10c. Type **298** . . . . 1·00 50
884 30c. Concentration camp prisoner and peace dove . . 2·25 3·00

1995. Healthy Living. Multicoloured.
885 7c. Type **299** 25 25
886 10c. "AIDS" and patients (horiz) 50 50
887 15c. Drug addict (horiz) . . . 55 55
888 20c. Smoker and barbed wire 75 1·25

300 European Union Flag and European Culture Month Logo

1995. European Culture Month and "Europhilex '95" International Stamp Exhibition, Nicosia. **MS**891 blue, yellow and stone or multicoloured (others).
889 20c. Type **300** 55 60
890 25c. Map of Europe and Cypriot church . . . . . 70 1·25
MS891 95 × 86 mm. 50c. Peace dove (42 × 30 mm); 50c. European Cultural Month symbol (42 × 30 mm) . . . . 6·00 7·00

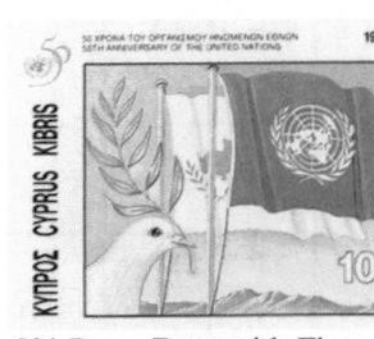

301 Peace Dove with Flags of Cyprus and United Nations

1995. Anniversaries and Events. Multicoloured.
893 10c. Type **301** (50th anniv of United Nations) 35 35
894 15c. Hand pushing ball over net (cent of volleyball) (vert) 75 50
895 20c. Safety pin on leaf (European Nature Conservation Year) (vert) 85 70
896 25c. Clay pigeon contestant (World Clay Target Shooting Championship) 95 2·00

302 Reliquary from Kykko Monastery

303 Family (25th anniv of Pancyprian Organization of Large Families)

1995. Christmas.
897 **302** 7c. multicoloured 30 25
898 – 20c. multicoloured 80 60
899 – 25c. multicoloured . . . . 1·10 1·75
DESIGNS: 20, 25c. Different reliquaries of Virgin and Child from Kykko Monastery.

1996. Anniversaries and Events. Multicoloured.
900 10c. Type **303** 50 35
901 20c. Film camera (centenary of cinema) . . . . 1·00 70
902 35c. Silhouette of parent and child in globe (50th anniv of U.N.I.C.E.F.) . . . . . . 1·50 1·75
903 40c. "13" and Commonwealth emblem (13th Conference of Commonwealth Speakers and Presiding Officers) . . 1·60 2·75

304 Maria Synglitiki

306 Watermill

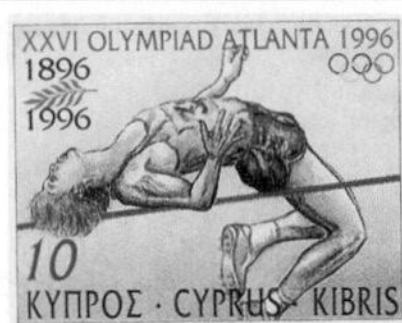

305 High Jump

1996. Europa. Famous Women. Multicoloured.
904 10c. Type **304** 75 30
905 30c. Queen Caterina Cornaro 1·75 2·50

1996. Centennial Olympic Games, Atlanta. Multicoloured.
906 10c. Type **305** 65 30
907 20c. Javelin . . . . 1·00 65
908 25c. Wrestling . . . . 1·25 1·00
909 30c. Swimming . . . . . . 1·40 2·25

1996. Mills. Multicoloured.
910 10c. Type **306** 70 40
911 15c. Olivemill 85 50
912 20c. Windmill . . . . 1·00 90
913 25c. Handmill . . . . 1·10 2·00

307 Icon of Our Lady of Iberia, Moscow

1996. Cyprus–Russia Joint Issue. Orthodox Religion. Multicoloured.
914 30c. Type **307** . . . . 1·75 2·00
915 30c. Stravrovouni Monastery, Cyprus . . . . 1·75 2·00
916 30c. Icon of St. Nicholas, Cyprus . . . . 1·75 2·00
917 30c. Voskresenskie Gate, Moscow . . . . 1·75 2·00

308 "The Nativity" (detail)

1996. Christmas. Religious Murals from Church of The Virgin of Asinou. Multicoloured.
918 7c. Type **308** 60 25
919 20c. "Virgin Mary between the Archangels Gabriel and Michael" . . . . 1·40 60
920 25c. "Christ bestowing Blessing" (vert) . . . . . 1·75 2·50

309 Basketball

1997. Final of European Basketball Cup.
921 **309** 30c. multicoloured . . . . 2·25 2·00

310 "The Last Supper"

1997. Easter. Religious Frescoes from Monastery of St. John Lambadestis. Multicoloured.
922 15c. Type **310** 80 50
923 25c. "The Crucifixion" . . . 95 1·50

311 Kori Kourelleni and Prince

1997. Europa. Tales and Legends. Multicoloured.
924 15c. Type **311** 90 40
925 30c. Digenis and Charon . . 1·50 2·50

312 "Oedipoda miniata" (grasshopper)

1997. Insects. Multicoloured.
926 10c. Type **312** 60 30
927 15c. "Acherontia atropos" (hawk moth) 85 40
928 25c. "Daphnis nerii" (hawk moth) . . . . 1·40 1·10
929 35c. "Ascalaphus macaronius" (owl-fly) . . . 1·60 2·25

313 Archbishop Makarios III and Chapel

1997. 20th Death Anniv of Archbishop Makarios III.
930 **313** 15c. multicoloured . . . . 1·00 50

314 The Nativity

1997. Christmas. Byzantine Frescos from the Monastery of St. John Lambadestis. Mult.
931 10c. Type **314** 50 25
932 25c. Three Kings following the star . . . . 1·60 70
933 30c. Flight into Egypt . . . 1·75 2·50

315 Green Jasper

1998. Minerals. Multicoloured.
934 10c. Type **315** 40 30
935 15c. Iron pyrite 60 45
936 25c. Gypsum 80 80
937 30c. Chalcedony . . . . . . 1·00 1·75

316 Players competing for Ball

1998. World Cup Football Championship, France.
938 **316** 35c. multicoloured . . . . 1·75 1·40

317 Cataclysmos Festival, Larnaca

1998. Europa. Festivals. Multicoloured.
939 15c. Type **317** . . . . 1·00 40
940 30c. House of Representatives, Nicosia (Declaration of Independence) . . . . . . 1·50 2·25

318 Mouflon Family Group **319** Flames and Globe Emblem

1998. Endangered Species. Cyprus Mouflon. Mult.
941 25c. Type **318** . . . . 1·00 1·25
942 25c. Mouflon herd . . . . . 1·00 1·25
943 25c. Head of ram . . . . . 1·00 1·25
944 25c. Ram on guard . . . . . 1·00 1·25

1998. 50th Anniv of Universal Declaration of Human Rights.
959 **319** 50c. multicoloured . . . . 1·25 1·60

320 World "Stamp" and Magnifying Glass

1998. World Stamp Day.
960 **320** 30c. multicoloured . . . . 1·60 1·60

321 "The Annunciation" **322** "Pleurotus eryngii"

1998. Christmas. Multicoloured.
961 10c. Type **321** 45 20
962 25c. "The Nativity" . . . . 1·00 65
963 30c. "The Baptism of Christ" 1·25 2·00
MS964 102 × 75 mm. Nos. 961/3 2·50 2·75

1999. Mushrooms of Cyprus. Multicoloured.
965 10c. Type **322** 30 30
966 15c. "Lactarius deliciosus" 60 40
967 25c. "Sparassis crispa" . . . 90 90
968 30c. "Morchella elata" . . . 1·00 1·75

323 Pair of Moufflons at Tripylos Reserve

1999. Europa. Parks and Gardens. Multicoloured.
969 15c. Type **323** 75 50
970 30c. Turtles on beach at Lara Reserve . . . . 1·25 1·75

324 Council of Europe Building, Emblem and Flags

1999. 50th Anniv of Council of Europe.
971 **324** 30c. multicoloured . . . . 1·25 1·40

325 Temple of Hylates Apollo, Kourion

1999. Cyprus–Greece Joint Issue. 4000 Years of Greek Culture. Multicoloured.
972 25c. Type **325** . . . . 95 1·25
973 25c. Mycenaean pot depicting warriors . . . . 95 1·25
974 25c. Mycenaean crater depicting horse . . . . . 95 1·25
975 25c. Temple of Apollo, Delphi . . . . 95 1·25

326 Paper Aeroplane Letters and U.P.U. Emblem

1999. 125th Anniv of Universal Postal Union. Multicoloured.
976 15c. Type **326** 75 50
977 35c. "125" and U.P.U. emblem . . . . 1·25 1·75

327 Container Ship and Cypriot Flag

1999. "Maritime Cyprus '99" Conference. Sheet 103 × 80 mm, containing T **327** and similar horiz designs. Multicoloured.
MS978 25c. Type **327**; 25c. Binoculars and chart; 25c. Stern of container ship; 25c. Tanker . . 3·00 3·50

328 Cypriot Refugee Fund Stamps and Barbed Wire (½-size illustration)

1999. 25th Anniv of Turkish Landings in Cyprus. Sheet 110 × 75mm. Imperf.
MS979 **328** 30c. multicoloured 1·25 1·75

329 Angel **330** Woman's Silhouette with Stars and Globe

1999. Christmas. Multicoloured.
980 10c. Type **329** 45 10
981 25c. The Three Kings . . . . 1·00 60
982 30c. Madonna and child . . 1·25 2·00

2000. Miss Universe Beauty Contest, Cyprus. Sheet 80 × 65 mm, containing T **330** and similar vert design. Multicoloured.
MS983 15c. Type **330**; 35c. Statue of Aphrodite and apple . . . . . 1·00 1·10

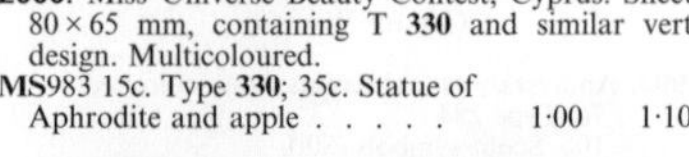

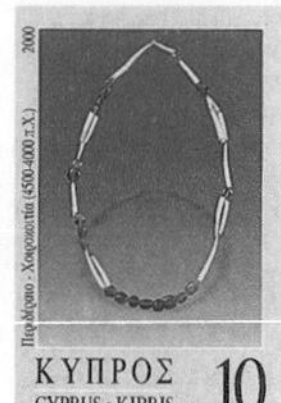

331 Necklace, 4500–4000 B.C. **332** "Building Europe"

2000. Jewellery. Multicoloured.
984 10c. Type **331** 25 30
985 15c. Gold earrings, 3rd-cent B.C. 35 40
986 20c. Gold earring from Lampousa, 6th–7th-cent . . 45 50
987 25c. Brooch, 19th-cent . . . 55 60
988 30c. Gold cross, 6th–7th-cent 70 75
989 35c. Necklace, 18th–19th-cent 80 85
990 40c. Gold earring, 19th-cent 90 95
991 50c. Spiral hair ring, 5th–4th-cent B.C. . . . . . . 1·10 1·25
992 75c. Gold-plated silver plaques from Gialia, 700–600 B.C. (horiz) . . . . . 1·70 1·80

993 £1 Gold frontlet from Egkomi, 14th–13th-cent B.C. (horiz) 2·30 2·40
994 £2 Gold necklace from Egkomi, 13th-cent B.C. (horiz) 4·50 4·75
995 £3 Buckles, 19th-cent (horiz) 7·00 7·25

2000. Europa.
996 **332** 30c. multicoloured 1·25 1·25

333 "50", Cross and Map of Cyprus

2000. 50th Anniv of Red Cross in Cyprus.
997 **333** 15c. multicoloured 1·25 60

334 Flame, Map of Cyprus and Broken Chain

335 Weather Balloon, Map and Satellite

2000. 45th Anniv of Struggle for Independence.
998 **334** 15c. multicoloured 1·25 60

2000. 50th Anniv of World Meteorological Organization.
999 **335** 30c. multicoloured 1·75 1·75

336 Monastery of Antifontis, Kalograia

337 Council of Europe Emblem

2000. Greek Orthodox Churches in Northern Cyprus.
1000 **336** 10c. brown and red 60 25
1001 – 15c. dp green & green 80 35
1002 – 25c. dp violet & violet 1·10 70
1003 – 30c. red and grey 1·25 1·75
DESIGNS—VERT: 15c. Church of St. Themonianos, Lysi. HORIZ: 25c. Church of Panagia Kanakaria, Lytrhagkomi; 30c. Church of Avgasida Monastery, Milia.

2000. 50th Anniv of European Convention of Human Rights
1004 **337** 30c. multicoloured 1·25 1·40

338 Archery

339 "The Annunciation"

2000. Olympic Games, Sydney. Multicoloured.
1005 10c. Type **338** 50 25
1006 15c. Gymnastics 70 35
1007 25c. Diving 1·00 70
1008 35c. Trampolining 1·25 1·75

2000. Christmas. Gold Gospel Covers. Multicoloured.
1009 10c. Type **339** 50 25
1010 25c. "The Nativity" 1·00 55
1011 30c. "The Baptism of Christ" 1·25 1·50

340 "25" and Commonwealth Symbol

2001. 25th Anniv of Commonwealth Day.
1012 **340** 30c. multicoloured 1·25 1·25

341 Silhouette, Dove and Barbed Wire

2001. 50th Anniv of United Nations High Commissioner for Refugees.
1013 **341** 30c. multicoloured 1·25 1·25

342 Pavlos Liasides

2001. Birth Centenary of Pavlos Liasides (poet).
1014 **342** 13c. chocolate, ochre & brown 60 35

343 Bridge over River Diarizos

2001. Europa. Cypriot Rivers. Multicoloured.
1015 20c. Type **343** 75 50
1016 30c. Mountain torrent, River Akaki 1·00 1·25

344 *Pathenope massena*

345 Icon of Virgin Mary

2001. Crabs. Multicoloured.
1017 13c. Type **344** 45 20
1018 20c. *Calappa granulata* 70 50
1019 25c. *Ocypode cursor* 80 70
1020 30c. *Pagurus bernhardus* 90 1·25

2001. Christmas. 800th Anniv of Macheras Monastery. Multicoloured.
1021 13c. Type **345** 30 20
1022 25c. Macheras Monastery 80 60
1023 30c. Ornate gold crucifix 1·00 1·25

346 Loukis Akritas

2001. Loukis Akritas (writer) Commemoration.
1024 **346** 20c. green and brown 80 50

347 Tortoiseshell and White Cat

2002. Cats. Multicoloured.
1025 20c. Type **347** 85 90
1026 20c. British blue 85 90
1027 25c. Tortoiseshell and white 85 90
1028 25c. Red and silver tabby 85 90

348 Acrobat on Horseback

350 Mother Teresa

349 *Myrtus communis*

2002. Europa. Circus. Multicoloured.
1029 20c. Type **348** 75 50
1030 30c. Clown on high wire 1·00 1·10

2002. Medicinal Plants. Multicoloured.
1031 13c. Type **349** 35 30
1032 20c. *Lavandula stoechas* 65 50
1033 25c. *Capparis spinosa* 75 65
1034 30c. *Ocimum basilicum* 85 1·10

2002. Mother Teresa (founder of Missionaries of Charity) Commemoration.
1035 **350** 40c. multicoloured 1·50 1·50

351 Blackboard on Easel

2002. International Teachers' Day. Multicoloured.
1036 13c. Type **351** 40 30
1037 30c. Computer 1·00 1·25

352 Agate Seal-stone (5th century B.C.)

2002. "Cyprus - Europhilex '02", Stamp Exhibition, Nicosia. Cypriot Antiquities showing Europa. Multicoloured.
1038 20c. Type **352** 70 75
1039 20c. Silver coin of Timochares (5th–4th century B.C.) 70 75
1040 20c. Silver coin of Stasioikos (5th century B.C.) 70 75
1041 30c. Clay lamp (green backgound) (2nd century A.D.) 1·00 1·10
1042 30c. Statuette of Europa on the Bull (7th–6th century B.C.) 1·00 1·10
1043 30c. Clay lamp (purple backgound) (1st century B.C.) 1·00 1·10
MS1044 105 × 71 mm. 50c. Statue of Aphrodite with maps of Crete and Cyprus; 50c. "Europa on the Bull" (painting by Francesco di Giogio) 4·00 4·25

353 "Nativity"

2002. Christmas. Details from "Birth of Christ" (wall painting), Church of Metamorphosis Sotiros, Palechori. Multicoloured.
1045 13c. Type **353** 35 20
1046 25c. "Three Wise Men" 70 60
1047 30c. "Birth of Christ" (complete painting) (38 × 38 mm) 90 1·10

354 Triumph Roadster 1800, 1946

2003. International Historic Car Rally. Multicoloured.
1048 20c. Type **354** 65 60
1049 25c. Ford model T, 1917 70 70
1050 30c. Baby Ford Y 8hp, 1932 90 1·10

355 "POSTER IS ART"

356 Mediterranean Horseshoe Bat in Flight

2003. Europa. Poster Art.
1051 **355** 20c. multicoloured 45 50
1052 – 30c. multicoloured 70 75

2003. Endangered Species. Mediterranean Horseshoe Bat. Multicoloured.
1053 25c. Type **356** 55 60
1054 25c. Head of bat (facing forwards) 55 60
1055 25c. Bats roosting 55 60
1056 25c. Head of bat (facing sideways, mouth open) 55 60

357 Stylized Owl

358 Eleonora's Falcon

2003. 7th Conference of European Ministers of Education, Nicosia.
1057 **357** 30c. multicoloured 70 75

2003. Birds of Prey. Multicoloured.
1058 20c. Type **358** 45 50
1059 20c. Eleonora's falcon in flight 45 50
1060 25c. Imperial eagle 55 60
1061 25c. Imperial eagle in flight 55 60
1062 30c. Little owl 70 75
1063 30c. Little owl in flight and eggs in nest 70 75

359 Constantinos Spyridakis (historian, author and Minister of Education 1965–70)

2003. Birth Centenaries.
1064 **359** 5c. black and drab 10 10
1065 – 5c. blackish olive and green 10 10
DESIGN: 23 × 31 mm.—No. 1065, Tefkros Anthias (poet).

360 Three Angels

2003. Christmas. Multicoloured.
1066 13c. Type **360** 30 35
1067 30c. Three Wise Men 70 75
1068 40c. Nativity (37 × 59 mm) 90 95
Nos. 1066/7 show details from icon of Nativity in Church of Virgin Mary, Kourdali. No. 1068 shows the complete painting.

361 Stylized Footballer

362 Stylized Footballer

2004. Centenary of FIFA (Federation Internationale de Football Association).
1069 **361** 30c. multicoloured 70 75

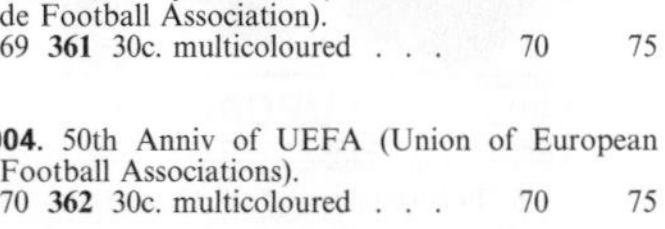

2004. 50th Anniv of UEFA (Union of European Football Associations).
1070 **362** 30c. multicoloured 70 75

TURKISH CYPRIOT POSTS

After the inter-communal clashes during December 1963, a separate postal service was established on 6 January 1964, between some of the Turkish Cypriot areas, using handstamps inscribed "KIBRIS TURK POSTALARI". During 1964, however, an agreement was reached between representatives of the two communities for the restoration of postal services. This agreement to which the United Nations representatives were a party, was ratified in November 1966 by the Republic's Council of Ministers. Under the scheme postal servcies were provided for the Turkish Cypriot communities in Famagusta, Limassol, Lefka and Nicosia, staffed by Turkish Cypriot employees of the Cypriot Department of Posts.

On 8 April 1970, 5m. and 15m. locally produced labels, originally designated "Social Aid Stamps", were issued by the Turkish Cypriot community and these can be found on commercial covers. These local stamps are outside the scope of this catalogue.

On 29 October 1973 Nos. 1/7 were placed on sale, but were again used only on mail between the Turkish Cypriot areas.

Following the intervention by the Republic of Turkey in July 1974 these stamps replaced issues of the Republic of Cyprus in that part of the island, north and east of the Attila Line, controlled by the Autonomous Turkish Cypriot Administration.

1974. 1000 mils = 1 pound.
1978. 100 kurus = 1 lira.

1 50th Anniversary Emblem

1974. 50th Anniv of Republic of Turkey.
1 – 3m. multicoloured . . . . . . 30·00 30·00
2 – 5m. multicoloured 60 40
3 – 10m. multicoloured 50 20
4 **1** 15m. red and black . . . . . 2·50 1·50
5 – 20m. multicoloured 70 20
6 – 50m. multicoloured . . . . . 2·00 1·50
7 – 70m. multicoloured . . . . . 16·00 16·00
DESIGNS—VERT: 3m. Woman sentry; 10m. Man and woman with Turkish flags; 20m. Ataturk statue, Kyrenia Gate, Nicosia; 50m. "The Fallen". HORIZ: 5m. Military parade, Nicosia; 70m. Turkish flag and map of Cyprus.

1975. Proclamation of the Turkish Federated State of Cyprus. Nos. 3 and 5 surch **KIBRIS TURK FEDERE DEVLETI 13.2.1975** and value.
8 30m. on 20m. multicoloured . . 75 1·00
9 100m. on 10m. multicoloured 1·25 2·00

3 Namik Kemal's Bust, Famagusta

1975. Multicoloured.
10 3m. Type **3** 15 40
11 10m. Ataturk Statue, Nicosia 15 10
12 15m. St. Hilarion Castle . . . 25 20
13 20m. Ataturk Square, Nicosia 35 20
14 25m. Famagusta Beach . . . 35 30
15 30m. Kyrenia Harbour 45 10
16 50m. Lala Mustafa Pasha Mosque, Famagusta (vert) 50 10
17 100m. Interior, Kyrenia Castle 80 90
18 250m. Castle walls, Kyrenia 1·00 2·25
19 500m. Othello Tower, Famagusta (vert) . . . . . 1·50 4·50
See also Nos. 36/8.

4 Map of Cyprus

1975. "Peace in Cyprus". Multicoloured.
20 30m. Type **4** 20 15
21 50m. Map, laurel and broken chain 25 20
22 150m. Map and laurel-sprig on globe (vert) . . . . 65 1·00

5 "Pomegranates" (I. V. Guney)

1975. Europa. Paintings. Multicoloured.
23 90m. Type **5** . . . . 1·10 1·10
24 100m. "Harvest Time" (F. Direkoglu) . . . . . . 1·25 1·25

1976. Nos. 16/17 surch.
25 10m. on 50m. multicoloured 35 70
26 30m. on 100m. multicoloured 35 80

7 "Expectation" (ceramic statuette)
9 Olympic Symbol "Flower"

8 Carob

1976. Europa. Multicoloured.
27 60m. Type **7** 40 80
28 120m. "Man in Meditation" 60 1·60

1976. Export Products. Fruits. Multicoloured.
29 10m. Type **8** 15 10
30 25m. Mandarin 20 10
31 40m. Strawberry 25 25
32 60m. Orange 35 65
33 80m. Lemon . . . . 40 2·00

1976. Olympic Games, Montreal. Multicoloured.
34 60m. Type **9** 25 20
35 100m. Olympic symbol and doves 35 25

10 Kyrenia Harbour
11 Liberation Monument, Karaeglanoglu (Ay Georghios)

1976. Multicoloured.
36 5m. Type **10** 40 15
37 15m. St. Hilarion Castle . . . 40 15
38 20m. Ataturk Square, Nicosia 40 15

1976. Liberation Monument.
47 **11** 30m. blue, pink and black 15 20
48 – 150m. red, pink and black 35 45
DESIGN: 150m. Liberation Monument (different view).

12 Hotel, Salamis Bay

1977. Europa. Multicoloured.
49 80m. Type **12** 65 80
50 100m. Kyrenia Port 75 80

13 Pottery
14 Arap Ahmet Pasha Mosque, Nicosia

1977. Handicrafts. Multicoloured.
51 15m. Type **13** 10 10
52 30m. Pottery (vert) 10 10
53 125m. Basketware 30 50

1977. Turkish Buildings in Cyprus. Multicoloured.
54 20m. Type **14** 10 10
55 40m. Paphos Castle (horiz) . . 10 10
56 70m. Bekir Pasha aqueduct (horiz) 15 20
57 80m. Sultan Mahmut library (horiz) 15 25

15 Namik Kemal (bust) and House, Famagusta

1977. Namik Kemal (patriotic poet). Multicoloured.
58 30m. Type **15** 15 15
59 140m. Namik Kemal (portrait) (vert) 35 60

16 Old Man and Woman
17 Oratory in Buyuk Han, Nicosia

1978. Social Security.
60 **16** 150k. black, yellow and blue 10 10
61 – 275k. black, orange and green 15 15
62 – 375k. black, blue and orange 25 20
DESIGNS: 275k. Injured man with crutch; 375k. Woman with family.

1978. Europa. Multicoloured.
63 225k. Type **17** 65 30
64 450k. Cistern in Selimiye Mosque, Nicosia . . . . . 1·10 70

18 Motorway Junction

1978. Communications. Multicoloured.
65 75k. Type **18** 15 10
66 100k. Hydrofoil 15 10
67 650k. Boeing 720 at Ercan Airport 50 35

19 Dove with Laurel Branch
20 Kemal Ataturk

1978. National Oath.
68 **19** 150k. yellow, violet and black 10 10
69 – 225k. black, red and yellow 10 10
70 – 725k. black, blue and yellow 20 20
DESIGNS—VERT: 225k. "Taking the Oath". HORIZ: 725k. Symbolic dove.

1978. Ataturk Commemoration.
71 **20** 75k. turquoise & dp turq . . 10 10
72 450k. pink and brown . . . 15 15
73 650k. blue and light blue . . 20 25

1979. Nos. 30/3 surch.
74 50k. on 25k. Mandarin . . . 10 10
75 1l. on 40m. Strawberry 15 10
76 3l. on 60m. Orange 15 10
77 5l. on 80m. Lemon 35 15

22 Gun Barrel with Olive Branch and Map of Cyprus

1979. 5th Anniv of Turkish Peace Operation in Cyprus. Sheet 72 × 52 mm. Imperf.
MS78 **22** 15l. black, blue and green 80 1·25

23 Postage Stamp and Map of Cyprus
24 Microwave Antenna

1979. Europa. Communications. Multicoloured.
79 2l. Type **23** 20 10
80 3l. Postage stamps, building and map 20 10
81 8l. Telephones, Earth and satellite 70 30

1979. 50th Anniv of International Consultative Radio Committee.
82 **24** 2l. multicoloured 20 10
83 5l. multicoloured 20 10
84 6l. multicoloured 25 15

25 School Children
26 Lala Mustafa Pasha Mosque, Magusa

1979. International Year of the Child. Mult.
85 1½l. Type **25** 25 15
86 4½l. Children and globe (horiz) 40 20
87 6l. College children 60 20

1980. Islamic Commemorations. Multicoloured.
88 2½l. Type **26** 10 10
89 10l. Arap Ahmet Pasha Mosque, Lefkosa 30 15
90 20l. Mecca and Medina . . . 50 20
COMMEMORATIONS: 2½l. 1st Islamic Conference in Turkish Cyprus; 10l. General Assembly of World Islam Congress; 20l. Moslem Year 1400 AH.

27 Ebu-Su'ud Efendi (philosopher)
28 Omer's Shrine, Kyrenia

1980. Europa. Personalities. Multicoloured.
91 5l. Type **27** 20 10
92 30l. Sultan Selim II 70 40

1980. Ancient Monuments.
93 **28** 2½l. blue and stone 10 10
94 – 3½l. green and pink 10 10
95 – 5l. brown on green 15 10
96 – 10l. mauve and green . . . 20 10
97 – 20l. blue and yellow 35 25
DESIGNS: 3½l. Entrance gate, Famagusta; 5l. Funerary monuments (16th-century), Famagusta; 10l. Bella Paise Abbey, Kyrenia; 20l. Selimiye Mosque, Nicosia.

29 Cyprus 1880 6d. Stamp
30 Dome of the Rock

1980. Cyprus Stamp Centenary.
98 **29** 7½l. black, brown and green 20 10
99 – 15l. brown, dp blue & bl 25 10
100 – 50l. black, red and grey . . 65 55
DESIGNS—HORIZ: 15l. Cyprus 1960 Constitution of the Republic 30m. commemorative stamp. VERT: 50l. Social Aid local, 1970.

1980. Palestinian Solidarity. Multicoloured.
101 15l. Type **30** 30 15
102 35l. Dome of the Rock (horiz) 70 30

31 Extract from World Muslim Congress Statement in Turkish

32 "Ataturk" (F. Duran)

1981. Day of Solidarity with Islamic Countries.
103 **31** 1l. buff, red and brown . . 15 75
104 – 35l. light green, black green 55 1·00
DESIGN: 35l. Extract in English.

1981. Ataturk Stamp Exhibition, Lefkosa.
105 **32** 10l. multicoloured 25 35

33 Folk-dancing

35 Wild Convolvulus

34 "Kemal Atatürk" (I. Calli)

1981. Europa. Folklore. Multicoloured.
106 10l. Type **33** 40 15
107 30l. Folk-dancing (different) 60 35

1981. Birth Centenary of Kemal Atatürk. Sheet 70 × 95 mm. Imperf.
MS108 **34** 150l. multicoloured . . 1·10 1·25

1981. Flowers. Multicoloured.
109 1l. Type **35** 10 10
110 5l. Persian cyclamen (horiz) 10 10
111 10l. Spring mandrake (horiz) 10 10
112 25l. Corn poppy 15 10
113 30l. Wild arum (horiz) . . . 15 10
114 50l. Sage-leaved rock rose . . 20 20
115 100l. "Cistus salviaefolius L." 30 30
116 150l. Giant fennel (horiz) . . 50 90

36 Stylised Disabled Person in Wheelchair

1981. Commemorations. Multicoloured.
117 7½l. Type **36** 25 35
118 10l. Heads of people of different races, peace dove and barbed wire (vert) . . 35 55
119 20l. People of different races reaching out from globe, with dishes (vert) 50 85
COMMEMORATIONS: 7½l. International Year for Disabled Persons; 10l. Anti-Apartheid publicity; 20l. World Food Day.

37 Turkish Cypriot and Palestinian Flags

1981. Palestinian Solidarity.
120 **37** 10l. multicoloured 45 60

38 Prince Charles and Lady Diana Spencer

39 Charter issued by Sultan Abdul Aziz to Archbishop Sophronios

1981. Royal Wedding.
121 **38** 50l. multicoloured . . . . 1·00 85

1982. Europa (CEPT). Sheet 83 × 124 mm containing T **39** and similar vert design. Mult.
MS122 30l. × 2. Type **39**; 70l. × 2, Turkish forces landing at Tuzla, 1571 . . . . 4·50 5·00

40 Buffavento Castle

42 Cross of Lorraine, Koch and Bacillus (Centenary of Koch's Discovery of Tubercle Bacillus)

41 "Wedding" (A. Orek)

1982. Tourism. Multicoloured.
123 5l. Type **40** 10 10
124 10l. Windsurfing (horiz) . . . 15 10
125 15l. Kantara Castle (horiz) 25 15
126 30l. Shipwreck (300 B.C.) (horiz) 60 40

1982. Paintings (1st series). Multicoloured.
127 30l. Type **41** 15 30
128 50l. "Carob Pickers" (O. Nazim Selenge) (vert) 30 70
See also Nos. 132/3, 157/8, 176/7, 185/6, 208/9, 225/7, 248/50, 284/5, 315/16, 328/9, 369/70 and 436/7.

1982. Anniversaries and Events. Multicoloured.
129 10l. Type **42** . . . . 1·00 40
130 30l. Spectrum on football pitch (World Cup Football Championships, Spain) . . 1·75 1·10
131 70l. "75" and Lord Baden-Powell (75th Anniv of Boy Scout movement and 125th birth anniv) (vert) . . . . 2·25 4·00

43 "Calloused Hands" (Salih Oral)

45 First Turkish Cypriot 10m. Stamp

44 Old Map of Cyprus by Piri Reis

1983. Paintings (2nd series). Multicoloured.
132 30l. Type **43** . . . . 75 1·40
133 35l. "Malya–Limassol Bus" (Emin Cizenel) . . . . . . 75 1·40

1983. Europa. Sheet 82 × 78 mm containing T **44** and similar horiz design. Multicoloured.
MS134 100l. Type **44**; 100l. Cyprus as seen from "Skylab" . . . . 30·00 15·00

1983. Anniversaries and Events. Multicoloured.
135 15l. Type **45** 90 50
136 20l. "Turkish Achievements in Cyprus" (horiz) 90 60
137 25l. "Liberation Fighters" . . 1·00 80
138 30l. Dish aerial and telegraph pole (horiz) . . . . 1·25 1·50
139 50l. Dove and envelopes (horiz) . . . . 2·75 3·75
EVENTS: 15, 20, 25l. T.M.T. (25th anniv of Turkish Cypriot Resistance Organization); 30, 50l. World Communications Year.

46 European Bee Eater

1983. Birds of Cyprus. Multicoloured.
140 10l. Type **46** . . . . 80 1·25
141 15l. Eurasian goldfinch . . . 1·00 1·25
142 50l. European robin . . . . 1·25 1·50
143 65l. Golden oriole . . . . . 1·40 1·50

1983. Establishment of Republic. Nos. 109, 111/12 and 116 optd **Kuzey Kibris Turk Cumhuriyeti 15.11.1983**, or surch also.
144 10l. Spring mandrake 20 15
145 15l. on 1l. Type **35** 30 15
146 25l. Corn poppy 40 25
147 150l. Giant fennel . . . . . 2·25 3·25

48 C.E.P.T. 25th Anniversary Logo

1984. Europa.
148 **48** 50l. yellow, brown and black . . . . 2·25 3·00
149 100l. lt blue, blue & black 2·25 3·00

49 Olympic Flame

50 Ataturk Cultural Centre

1984. Olympic Games, Los Angeles. Multicoloured.
150 10l. Type **49** 15 10
151 20l. Olympic events within rings (horiz) 35 25
152 70l. Martial arts event (horiz) 60 1·75

1984. Opening of Ataturk Cultural Centre, Lefkosa.
153 **50** 120l. stone, black and brown . . . . 1·25 1·75

52 Turkish Cypriot Flag and Map

1984. 10th Anniv of Turkish Landings in Cyprus. Multicoloured.
154 20l. Type **52** 50 25
155 70l. Turkish Cypriot flag within book . . . . 1·00 2·00

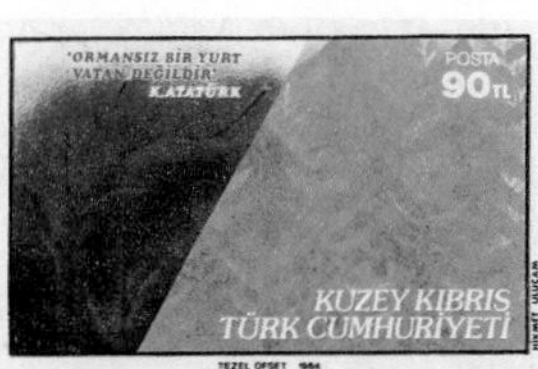

53 Burnt and Replanted Forests

1984. World Forestry Resources.
156 **53** 90l. multicoloured . . . . 1·25 1·75

54 "Old Turkish Houses, Nicosia" (Cevdet Cagdas)

1984. Paintings (3rd series). Multicoloured.
157 20l. Type **54** 50 40
158 70l. "Scenery" (Olga Rauf) 1·10 2·00
See also Nos. 176/7, 185/6, 208/9, 225/7, 248/50, 284/5, 315/16, 328/9 and 369/70.

55 Kemal Ataturk, Flag and Crowd

56 Taekwondo Bout

1984. 1st Anniv of Turkish Republic of Northern Cyprus. Multicoloured.
159 20l. Type **55** 50 40
160 70l. Legislative Assembly voting for Republic (horiz) 1·10 2·00

1984. Int Taekwondo Championship, Girne.
161 **56** 10l. black, brown and grey 40 25
162 – 70l. multicoloured . . . . 1·60 2·50
DESIGN: 70l. Emblem and flags of competing nations.

57 "Le Regard"

58 Musical Instruments and Music

1984. Exhibition by Saulo Mercader (artist). Multicoloured.
163 20l. Type **57** 30 25
164 70l. "L'equilibre de L'esprit" (horiz) . . . . 1·10 2·25

1984. Visit of Nurnberg Chamber Orchestra.
165 **58** 70l. multicoloured . . . . 1·50 2·25

59 Dr. Fazil Kucuk (politician)

61 George Frederick Handel

60 Goat

1985. 1st Death Anniv of Dr. Fazil Kucuk (politician). Multicoloured.
166 20l. Type **59** 30 30
167 70l. Dr. Fazil Kucuk reading newspaper . . . . 95 2·00

1985. Domestic Animals. Multicoloured.
168 100l. Type **60** 55 30
169 200l. Cow and calf 90 80
170 300l. Ram . . . . 1·25 2·00
171 500l. Donkey . . . . 2·00 3·25

1985. Europa. Composers.
172 **61** 20l. purple, green & lt grn 2·00 2·50
173 – 20l. purple, brown and pink . . . . 2·00 2·50
174 – 100l. purple, blue & lt blue 2·50 3·00
175 – 100l. purple, brn & lt brn 2·50 3·00

DESIGNS: No. 173, Giuseppe Domenico Scarlatti; 174, Johann Sebastian Bach; 175, Buhurizade Mustafa Itri Efendi.

1985. Paintings (4th series). As T **54**. Mult.
176 20l. "Village Life" (Ali Atakan) 60 50
177 50l. "Woman carrying Water" (Ismet V. Guney)) 1·40 2·50

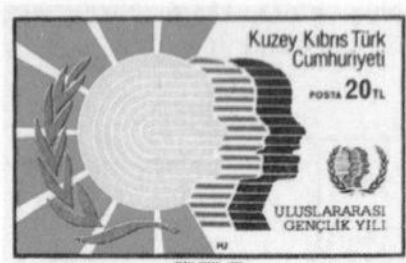

62 Heads of Three Youths

1985. International Youth Year. Multicoloured.
178 20l. Type **62** 75 40
179 100l. Dove and globe . . . . 4·00 4·50

63 Parachutist (Aviation League)

65 Karagoz Show Puppets

64 Griffon Vulture

1985. Anniversaries and Events.
180 **63** 20l. multicoloured . . . . 1·75 45
181 – 50l. black, brown and blue 2·00 1·25
182 – 100l. brown . . . . 1·75 2·75
183 – 100l. multicoloured . . . . 1·75 2·75
184 – 100l. multicoloured . . . . 2·25 2·75
DESIGNS—VERT: No. 181, Louis Pasteur (Centenary of Discovery of Rabies vaccine); 182, Ismet Inonu (Turkish statesman) (birth centenary (1984)). HORIZ: 183, "40" in figures and symbolic flower (40th anniv of United Nations Organization); 184, Patient receiving blood transfusion (Prevention of Thalassaemia).

1986. Paintings (5th series). As T **54**. Mult.
185 20l. "House with Arches" (Gonen Atakol) 50 30
186 100l. "Ataturk Square" (Yalkin Muhtaroglu) . . . 1·75 1·75

1986. Europa. Protection of Nature and the Environment. Sheet 82 × 76 mm, containing T **64** and similar horiz design. Multicoloured.
MS187 100l. Type **64**; 200l. Litter on Cyprus landscape . . . . . . 9·00 7·50

1986. Karagoz Folk Puppets.
188 **65** 100l. multicoloured . . . . 2·25 2·50

66 Old Bronze Age Composite Pottery

1986. Archaeological Artefacts. Cultural Links with Anatolia. Multicoloured.
189 10l. Type **66** 55 20
190 20l. Late Bronze Age bird jug (vert) 95 30
191 50l. Neolithic earthenware pot . . . . 1·75 2·00
192 100l. Roman statue of Artemis (vert) . . . . . . 2·25 3·50

67 Soldiers, Defence Force Badge and Ataturk (10th anniv of Defence Forces)

69 Prince Andrew and Miss Sarah Ferguson

68 Guzelyurt Dam and Power Station

1986. Anniversaries and Events. Multicoloured.
193 20l. Type **67** . . . . 1·25 30
194 50l. Woman and two children (40th anniv of F.A.O.) . . 1·40 1·40
195 100l. Football and world map (World Cup Football Championship, Mexico) (horiz) . . . . 3·50 4·00
196 100l. Orbit of Halley's Comet and "Giotto" space probe (horiz) . . . . 3·50 4·00

1986. Modern Development (1st series). Mult.
197 20l. Type **68** . . . . 1·25 30
198 50l. Low cost housing project, Lefkosa . . . . . 1·40 1·40
199 100l. Kyrenia Airport . . . . 3·25 4·25
See also Nos. 223/4 and 258/63.

1986. 60th Birthday of Queen Elizabeth II and Royal Wedding. Multicoloured.
200 100l. Queen Elizabeth II . . 2·00 2·75
201 100l. Type **69** . . . . 2·00 2·75

70 Locomotive No. 11 and Trakhoni Station

1986. Cyprus Railway. Multicoloured.
202 50l. Type **70** . . . . 3·75 2·75
203 100l. Locomotive No. 1 . . . 4·25 4·75

1987. Nos. 94, 96/7 and 113 optd **Kuzey Kibris Turk Cumhuriyeti** or surch also (No. 205).
204 10l. mauve and green 50 70
205 15l. on 3½l. green and pink 50 70
206 20l. blue and yellow 55 75
207 30l. multicoloured . . . . . 70 1·10

1987. Paintings (6th series). As T **54**. Mult.
208 50l. "Shepherd" (Feridun Isiman) . . . . 1·25 1·25
209 125l. "Pear Woman" (Mehmet Uluhan) . . . . 1·75 3·00

72 Modern House (architect A. Vural Behaeddin)

1987. Europa. Modern Architecture. Multicoloured.
210 50l. Type **72** . . . . 1·00 30
211 200l. Modern house (architect Necdet Turgay) . . . . . . 1·75 3·25

73 Kneeling Folk Dancer

74 Regimental Colour (1st anniv of Infantry Regiment)

1987. Folk Dancers. Multicoloured.
212 20l. Type **73** 60 20
213 50l. Standing male dancer . . 90 40
214 200l. Standing female dancer 2·00 1·75
215 1000l. Woman's headdress . . 4·75 6·50

1987. Anniversaries and Events. Multicoloured.
216 50l. Type **74** . . . . 1·75 1·00
217 50l. President Denktash and Turgut Ozal (1st anniv of Turkish Prime Minister's visit) (horiz) . . . . . . 1·75 1·00
218 200l. Emblem and Crescent (5th Islamic Summit Conference, Kuwait) . . . 3·00 4·00
219 200l. Emblem and laurel leaves (Membership of Pharmaceutical Federation) (horiz) . . . . 3·00 4·00

75 Ahmet Belig Pasha (Egyptian judge)

76 Tourist Hotel, Girne

1987. Turkish Cypriot Personalities.
220 **75** 50l. brown and yellow . . 65 40
221 – 50l. multicoloured 65 40
222 – 125l. multicoloured . . . . 1·50 3·00
DESIGNS: 50l. (No. 221) Mehmet Emin Pasha (Ottoman Grand Vizier); 125l. Mehmet Kamil Pasha (Ottoman Grand Vizier).

1987. Modern Development (2nd series). Mult.
223 150l. Type **76** . . . . 1·50 1·50
224 200l. Dogu Akdeniz University . . . . 1·75 2·25

1988. Paintings (7th series). As T **54**. Mult.
225 20l. "Woman making Pastry" (Ayhan Mentes) (vert) . . 50 30
226 50l. "Chair Weaver" (Osman Guvenir) 75 75
227 150l. "Woman weaving a Rug" (Zekai Yesiladali) (vert) . . . . 1·75 4·00

77 "Piyale Pasha" (tug)

1988. Europa. Transport and Communications. Multicoloured.
228 200l. Type **77** . . . . 2·25 75
229 500l. Dish aerial and antenna tower, Selvilitepe (vert) . . 3·00 4·50
No. 229 also commemorates the 25th anniv of Bayrak Radio and Television Corporation.

78 Lefkosa

79 Bulent Ecevit

1988. Tourism. Multicoloured.
230 150l. Type **78** 80 80
231 200l. Gazi-Magusa . . . . . 90 1·00
232 300l. Girne . . . . 1·50 2·00

1988. Turkish Prime Ministers. Multicoloured.
233 50l. Type **79** 60 85
234 50l. Bulent Ulusu 60 85
235 50l. Turgut Ozal 60 85

80 Red Crescent Members on Exercise

1988. Civil Defence.
236 **80** 150l. multicoloured . . . . 1·60 1·75

81 Hodori the Tiger (Games mascot) and Fireworks

1988. Olympic Games, Seoul. Multicoloured.
237 200l. Type **81** . . . . 1·25 1·00
238 250l. Athletics . . . . 1·50 1·25
239 400l. Shot and running track with letters spelling "SEOUL" . . . . 2·00 2·00

82 Sedat Simavi (journalist)

83 "Kemal Atatürk" (I. Calli)

1988. Anniversaries and Events.
240 **82** 50l. green 25 25
241 – 100l. multicoloured 75 45
242 – 300l. multicoloured . . . . 80 1·00
243 – 400l. multicoloured . . . . 1·75 2·00
244 – 400l. multicoloured . . . . 1·25 2·00
245 – 600l. multicoloured . . . . 2·50 2·75
DESIGNS—HORIZ: No. 241, Stylised figures around table and flags of participating countries (International Girne Conferences); 244, Presidents Gorbachev and Reagan signing treaty (Summit Meeting). VERT: No. 242, Cogwheels as flowers (North Cyprus Industrial Fair); 243, Globe (125th anniv of International Red Cross); 245, "Medical Services" (40th anniv of W.H.O.).

1988. 50th Death Anniv of Kemal Atatürk. Sheet 72 × 102 mm, containing T **83** and similar vert designs. Multicoloured.
MS246 250l. Type **83**; 250l. "Kemal Atatürk" (N. Ismail); 250l. In army uniform; 250l. In profile 3·00 3·00

84 Abstract Design

1988. 5th Anniv of Turkish Republic of Northern Cyprus. Sheet 98 × 76 mm. Imperf.
MS247 **84** 500l. multicoloured . . 2·25 2·25

1989. Paintings (8th series). As T **54**. Mult.
248 150l. "Dervis Pasa Mansion, Lefkosa" (Inci Kansu) . . 90 60
249 400l. "Gamblers' Inn, Lefkosa" (Osman Guvenir) 1·75 2·25
250 600l. "Mosque, Paphos" (Hikmet Ulucam) (vert) . . 2·50 3·00

85 Girl with Doll

1989. Europa. Children's Games. Multicoloured.
251 600l. Type **85** . . . . 2·25 1·25
252 1000l. Boy with kite . . . . 2·50 3·75

86 Meeting of Presidents Vassiliou and Denktash

1989. Cyprus Peace Summit, Geneva, 1988.
253 **86** 500l. red and black . . . . 1·25 1·25

87 Chukar Partridge

1989. Wildlife. Multcoloured.
254 100l. Type **87** 65 25
255 200l. Cyprus hare 70 35
256 700l. Black partridge . . . . 2·50 2·00
257 2000l. Red fox . . . . 3·00 4·00

88 Road Construction

1989. Modern Development (3rd series). Mult.
258 100l. Type **88** 15 15
259 150l. Laying water pipeline (vert) 20 20
260 200l. Seedling trees (vert) . . 30 30
261 450l. Modern telephone exchange (vert) . . . . . 75 1·00
262 650l. Steam turbine power station (vert) . . . . . . 1·00 1·75
263 700l. Irrigation reservoir . . 1·25 1·75

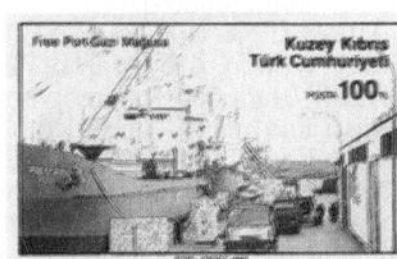

89 Unloading "Polly Pioneer" (freighter) at Quayside (15th anniv of Gazi Magusa Free Port)

1989. Anniversaries.
264 **89** 100l. multicoloured 70 20
265 – 450l. black, blue and red 80 80
266 – 500l. black, yellow and grey 80 80
267 – 600l. black, red and blue 2·25 2·25
268 – 1000l. multicoloured . . . 3·50 4·50
DESIGNS—VERT (26 × 47 mm): 450l. Airmail letter and stylized bird (25th anniv of Turkish Cypriot postal service). HORIZ (as T **89**): 500l. Newspaper and printing press (centenary of "Saded" newspaper); 600l. Statue of Aphrodite, lifebelt and seabird (30th anniv of International Maritime Organization); 1000l. Soldiers (25th anniv of Turkish Cypriot resistance).

90 Erdal Inonu **91** Mule-drawn Plough

1989. Visit of Professor Erdal Inonu (Turkish politician).
269 **90** 700l. multicoloured . . . . 80 1·00

1989. Traditional Agricultural Implements. Mult.
270 150l. Type **91** 30 25
271 450l. Ox-drawn threshing sledge 75 85
272 550l. Olive press (vert) . . . 90 1·25

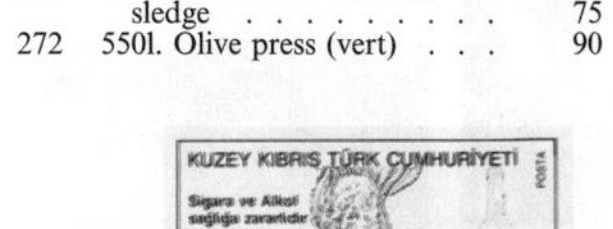

92 Smoking Ashtray and Drinks

1990. World Health Day. Multicoloured.
273 200l. Type **92** . . . . 1·00 40
274 700l. Smoking cigarette and heart . . . . 2·25 3·00

93 Yenierenkoy Post Office

1990. Europa. Post Office Buildings. Mult.
275 1000l. Type **93** . . . . . . 1·75 75
276 1500l. Ataturk Meydani Post Office . . . . 2·50 3·50
MS277 105 × 72 mm. Nos. 275/6 × 2 . . . . 7·50 8·00

94 Song Thrush **96** Amphitheatre, Soli

95 Two Football Teams

1990. World Environment Day. Birds. Mult.
278 150l. Type **94** . . . . 2·00 65
279 300l. Blackcap . . . . 2·75 90
280 900l. Black redstart . . . . . 4·25 3·50
281 1000l. Chiff-chaff . . . . . 4·25 3·50

1990. World Cup Football Championship, Italy. Mult.
282 300l. Type **95** 75 50
283 1000l. Championship symbol, globe and ball . . . . . . 2·50 3·50

1990. Paintings (9th series). As T **54**. Multicoloured.
284 300l. "Abstract" (Filiz Ankacc) 25 25
285 1000l. Wooden sculpture (S. Tekman) (vert) . . . . 85 1·50

1990. Tourism. Multicoloured.
286 150l. Type **96** 40 20
287 1000l. Swan mosaic, Soli . . 1·75 2·50

97 Kenan Evren and Rauf Denktas

1990. Visit of President Kenan Evren of Turkey.
288 **97** 500l. multicoloured . . . . 1·00 1·00

98 Road Signs and Heart wearing Seat Belt

1990. Traffic Safety Campaign. Multicoloured.
289 150l. Type **98** . . . . 1·00 30
290 300l. Road signs, speeding car and spots of blood . . 1·25 50
291 1000l. Traffic lights and road signs . . . . 3·25 4·00

99 Yildirim Akbulut **100** "Rosularia cypria"

1990. Visit of Turkish Prime Minister Yildrim Akbulut.
292 **99** 1000l. multicoloured . . . 1·10 1·10

1990. Plants. Multicoloured.
293 150l. Type **100** 60 20
294 200l. "Silene fraudratrix" . . 70 30
295 300l. "Scutellaria sibthorpii" 80 35
296 600l. "Sedum lampusae" . . 1·25 85
297 1000l. "Onosma caespitosum" 1·40 2·00
298 1500l. "Arabis cypria" . . . 1·90 3·50

101 Kemal Ataturk at Easel (wood carving)

1990. International Literacy Year. Multicoloured.
299 300l. Type **101** . . . . 1·00 35
300 750l. Globe, letters and books 2·25 3·00

1991. Nos. 189, 212 and 293 surch.
301 **66** 250l. on 10l. multicoloured . . . . . 1·00 1·00
302 **73** 250l. on 20l. multicoloured . . . . . 1·00 1·00
303 **100** 500l. on 150l. multicoloured . . . . . 1·50 1·75

103 "Ophrys lapethica" **104** "Hermes" (projected shuttle)

1991. Orchids (1st series). Multicoloured.
304 250l. Type **103** . . . . 1·25 60
305 500l. "Ophrys kotschyi" . . . 2·25 2·75
See also Nos. 311/14.

1991. Europa. Europe in Space. Sheet 78 × 82 mm, containing T **104** and similar vert design. Multicoloured.
MS306 2000l. Type **104**; 2000l. "Ulysses" (satellite) . . . . . 9·00 9·00

105 Kucuk Medrese Fountain, Lefkosa **106** Symbolic Roots (Year of Love to Yunus Emre)

1991. Fountains. Multicoloured.
307 250l. Type **105** 45 15
308 500l. Cafer Pasa fountain, Magusa 65 30
309 1500l. Sarayonu Square fountain, Lefkosa . . . . 1·40 1·60
310 5000l. Arabahmet Mosque fountain, Lefkosa . . . . 3·50 5·00

1991. Orchids (2nd series). As T **103**. Mult.
311 100l. "Serapias levantina" . . 75 20
312 500l. "Dactylorhiza romana" 1·90 50
313 2000l. "Orchis simia" . . . . 3·50 3·75
314 3000l. "Orchis sancta" . . . 3·75 4·50

1991. Paintings (10th series). As T **54**. Mult.
315 250l. "Hindiler" (S. Cizel) (vert) . . . . 1·75 50
316 500l. "Dusme" (A. Mene) (vert) . . . . 2·25 2·25

1991. Anniversaries and Events.
317 **106** 250l. yellow, black and mauve 25 25
318 – 500l. multicoloured . . . 45 60
319 – 500l. multicoloured . . . 45 60
320 – 1500l. multicoloured . . . 4·00 4·25
DESIGNS—VERT: No. 318, Mustafa Cagatay commemoration; 319, University building (5th anniv of Eastern Mediterranean University). HORIZ: No. 320, Mozart (death bicentenary).

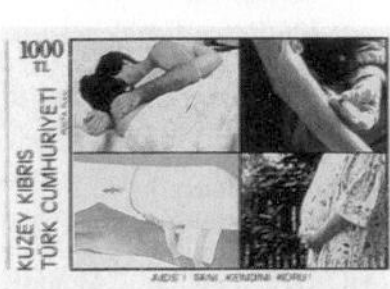

107 Four Sources of Infection

1991. "AIDS" Day.
321 **107** 1000l. multicoloured . . . 2·50 2·00

108 Lighthouse, Gazimagusa

1991. Lighthouses. Multicoloured.
322 250l. Type **108** . . . . 1·75 50
323 500l. Ancient lighthouses, Girne harbour . . . . . . 2·25 1·25
324 1500l. Modern lighthouse, Girne harbour . . . . . . 4·00 5·00

109 Elephant and Hippopotamus Fossils, Karaoglanoglu

1991. Tourism (1st series). Multicoloured.
325 250l. Type **109** . . . . 1·75 40
326 500l. Roman fish ponds, Lambusa . . . . 1·90 65
327 1500l. Roman remains, Lambusa . . . . 2·75 4·00
See also Nos. 330/3 and 351/2.

1992. Paintings (11th series). As T **54**, but 31 × 49 mm. Multicoloured.
328 500l. "Ebru" (A. Kandulu) 75 20
329 3500l. "Street in Lefkosa" (I. Tatar) . . . . 3·00 4·00

1992. Tourism (2nd series). As T **109**. Mult.
330 500l. Bugday Camii, Gazimagusa 70 70
331 500l. Clay pigeon shooting 70 70
332 1000l. Salamis Bay Hotel, Gazimagusa . . . . 1·25 1·25
333 1500l. Casino, Girne (vert) 2·25 3·00

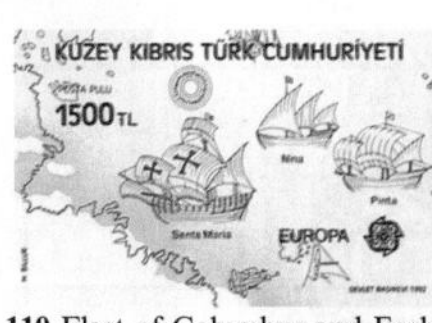

110 Fleet of Columbus and Early Map

1992. Europa. 500th Anniv of Discovery of America by Columbus. Sheet 80 × 76 mm, containing T **110** and similar horiz design. Multicoloured.
MS334 1500l. Type **110**; 3500l. Christopher Columbus and signature . . . . 4·00 4·25

111 Green Turtle

1992. World Environment Day. Sea Turtles. Sheet 105 × 75 mm, containing T **111** and similar horiz design. Multicoloured.
MS335 1000l. × 2, Type **111**; 1500l. × 2, Loggerhead turtle . . . . 6·50 6·50

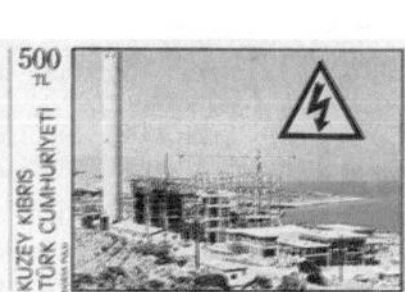

112 Gymnastics **113** New Generating Station, Girne

1992. Olympic Games, Barcelona. Multicoloured.
336 500l. Type **112** 70 90
337 500l. Tennis 70 90
338 1000l. High jumping (horiz) 80 1·00
339 1500l. Cycling (horiz) . . . . 3·25 3·50

1992. Anniversaries and Events (1st series). Multicoloured.
340 500l. Type **113** 40 40
341 500l. Symbol of Housing Association (15th anniv) 40 40
342 1500l. Domestic animals and birds (30th anniv of Veterinary Service) . . . . 3·00 3·25
343 1500l. Cat (International Federation of Cat Societies Conference) . . . . 3·00 3·25

114 Airliner over Runway

1992. Anniversaries and Events (2nd series). Multicoloured.
344 1000l. Type **114** (17th anniv of civil aviation) . . . . . 1·75 1·75
345 1000l. Meteorological instruments and weather (18th anniv of Meteorological Service) . . 1·75 1·75
346 1200l. Surveying equipment and map (14th anniv of Survey Department) . . . 2·50 2·75

115 Zubiye

1992. International Conference on Nutrition, Rome. Turkish Cypriot Cuisine. Multicoloured.
347 2000l. Type **115** . . . . . . 1·25 1·25
348 2500l. Cicek Dolmasi . . . . 1·50 1·50
349 3000l. Tatar Boregi . . . . 1·75 1·90
350 4000l. Seftali Kebabi . . . . 1·90 2·25

1993. Tourism (3rd series). As T **109**. Mult.
351 500l. St. Barnabas Church and Monastery, Salamis . . 40 15
352 10000l. Ancient pot . . . . . 4·00 5·00

116 Painting by Turksal Ince

117 Olive Tree, Girne

1993. Europa. Contemporary Art. Sheet 79 × 69 mm, containing T **116** and similar vert design. Multicoloured.
MS353 2000l. Type **116**; 3000l. Painting by Ilkay Onsoy . . . 1·75 2·00

1993. Ancient Trees. Multicoloured.
354 500l. Type **117** 20 15
355 1000l. River red gum, Kyrenia Gate, Lefkosa . . 30 25
356 3000l. Oriental plane, Lapta 80 1·25
357 4000l. Calabrian pine, Cinarli 90 1·60

118 Traditional Houses

119 National Flags turning into Doves

1993. Arabahmet District Conservation Project, Lefkosa. Multicoloured.
358 1000l. Type **118** . . . . . . 1·00 40
359 3000l. Arabahmet street . . . 2·00 2·75

1993. 10th Anniv of Proclamation of Turkish Republic of Northern Cyprus.
360 **119** 500l. red, black and blue 20 20
361 – 500l. red and blue 20 20
362 – 1000l. red, black and blue 30 30
363 – 5000l. multicoloured . . . 1·60 2·50
DESIGNS—HORIZ: No. 361, National flag forming figure "10"; No. 362, Dove carrying national flag; No. 363, Map of Cyprus and figure "10" wreath.

120 Kemal Ataturk

121 "Soyle Falci" (Goral Ozkan)

1993. Anniversaries. Multicoloured.
364 500l. Type **120** (55th death anniv) 20 20
365 500l. Stage and emblem (30th anniv of Turkish Cypriot theatre) (horiz) 20 20
366 1500l. Branch badges (35th anniv of T.M.T. organization) (horiz) . . . 40 50
367 2000l. World map and computer (20th anniv of Turkish Cypriot news agency) (horiz) . . . . . . 1·25 1·25
368 5000l. Ballet dancers and Caykovski'nin (death centenary) (horiz) . . . . 4·00 4·25

1994. Art (12th series). Multicoloured.
369 1000l. Type **121** 30 20
370 6500l. "IV. Hareket" (sculpture) (Senol Ozdevrim) . . . . 1·25 2·00
See also Nos. 436/7.

122 Dr. Kucuk and Memorial

1994. 10th Death Anniv of Dr. Fazil Kucuk (politician).
371 **122** 1500l. multicoloured . . . 70 85

123 Neolithic Village, Girne

1994. Europa. Archaeological Discoveries. Sheet 73 × 79 mm, containing T **123** and similar horiz design. Multicoloured.
MS372 8500l. Type **123**; 8500l. Neolithic man and implements 6·00 6·00

124 Peace Doves and Letters over Pillar Box

125 World Cup Trophy

1994. 30th Anniv of Turkish Cypriot Postal Service.
373 **124** 50000l. multicoloured . . 3·00 4·50

1994. World Cup Football Championship, U.S.A. Multicoloured.
374 2500l. Type **125** 50 25
375 10000l. Footballs on map of U.S.A. (horiz) . . . . . . 1·75 2·50

126 Peace Emblem

1994. 20th Anniv of Turkish Landings in Cyprus.
376 **126** 2500l. yellow, green and black 40 30
377 – 5000l. multicoloured . . . 60 60
378 – 7000l. multicoloured . . . 80 1·00
379 – 8500l. multicoloured . . . 1·10 1·50
DESIGNS—HORIZ: 5000l. Memorial; 7000l. Sculpture; 8500l. Peace doves forming map of Cyprus and flame.

127 Cyprus 1934 4½ pi. Stamp and Karpas Postmark

1994. Postal Centenary. Multicoloured.
380 1500l. Type **127** 25 20
381 2500l. Turkish Cypriot Posts 1979 Europa 2l. and Gazimagusa postmark . . 35 30
382 5000l. Cyprus 1938 6pi. and Bey Keuy postmark . . . 60 70
383 7000l. Cyprus 1955 100m. and Aloa postmark . . . . 80 1·10
384 8500l. Cyprus 1938 18pi. and Pyla postmark . . . . . . 1·00 1·50

128 Trumpet Triton

1994. Sea Shells. Multicoloured.
385 2500l. Type **128** 45 30
386 12500l. Mole cowrie . . . . 1·25 1·75
387 12500l. Giant tun . . . . . 1·25 1·75

1994. Nos. 280, 295, 315 and 317 surch.
388 1500l. on 250l. Type **106** . . . 15 10
389 2000l. on 900l. Black redstart 1·75 80
390 2500l. on 250l. "Hindiler" (Sizel) 30 30
391 3500l. on 300l. "Scutellaria sibthorpii" . . . . 1·75 2·00

130 Donkeys on Mountain

1995. European Conservation Year. Multicoloured.
392 2000l. Type **130** 30 20
393 3500l. Coastline 30 30
394 15000l. Donkeys in field . . . 1·50 2·50

131 Peace Dove and Globe

1995. Europa. Peace and Freedom. Sheet 72 × 78 mm, containing T **131** and similar horiz design. Mult.
MS395 15000l. Type **131**; 15000l. Peace doves over map of Europe 3·50 3·75

132 Sini Katmeri

1995. Turkish Cypriot Cuisine. Multicoloured.
396 3500l. Type **132** 20 20
397 10000l. Kolokas musakka and bullez kizartma . . . 55 65
398 14000l. Enginar dolmasi . . . 90 1·60

133 "Papilio machaon"

1995. Butterflies. Multicoloured.
399 3500l. Type **133** 30 15
400 4500l. "Charaxes jasius" . . 35 20
401 15000l. "Cynthia cardui" . . 1·00 1·40
402 30000l. "Vanessa atalanta" 1·75 2·50

134 Forest

1995. Obligatory Tax. Forest Regeneration Fund.
403 **134** 1000l. green and black . . 3·25 40

135 Beach, Girne

1995. Tourism. Multicoloured.
404 3500l. Type **135** 30 20
405 7500l. Sail boards 50 45
406 15000l. Ruins of Salamis (vert) . . . . 1·00 1·25
407 20000l. St. George's Cathedral, Gazimagusa (vert) . . . . 1·00 1·25

136 Suleyman Demirel and Rauf Denktas

1995. Visit of President Suleyman Demirel of Turkey.
408 **136** 5000l. multicoloured . . . 40 40

137 Stamp Printing Press

138 Kultegin Epitaph and Sculpture

1995. Anniversaries.
409 **137** 3000l. multicoloured . . . 40 40
410 – 3000l. multicoloured . . . 40 40
411 – 5000l. multicoloured . . . 70 70
412 – 22000l. ultram, bl & blk 1·00 1·75
413 – 30000l. multicoloured . . 1·40 2·25
414 – 30000l. multicoloured . . 1·40 2·25
DESIGNS—HORIZ: No. 409, Type **137** (20th anniv of State Printing Works); 410, Map of Turkey (75th anniv of Turkish National Assembly); 411, Louis Pasteur (chemist) and microscope (death centenary); 412, United Nations anniversary emblem (50th anniv); 413, Guglielmo Marconi (radio pioneer) and dial (centenary of first radio transmissions). VERT: No. 414, Stars and reel of film (centenary of cinema).

1995. Centenary of Deciphering of Orhon Epitaphs. Multicoloured.
415 5000l. Type **138** 75 40
416 10000l. Epitaph and tombstone . . . . 1·25 1·60

139 "Bosnia" (sculpture)

140 Striped Red Mullet

1996. Support for Moslems in Bosnia and Herzegovina.
417 **139** 10000l. multicoloured . . 1·25 1·50

1996. Fishes. Multicoloured.
418 6000l. Type **140** 75 30
419 10000l. Peacock wrasse . . . 1·00 45
420 28000l. Common two-banded seabream . . . . 2·00 2·25
421 40000l. Dusky grouper . . . 2·50 3·00

141 Palm Trees

142 Beria Remzi Ozoran

1996. Tourism. Multicoloured.
422 100000l. Type **141** . . . . . 1·00 30
423 150000l. Pomegranate . . . . 1·50 55
424 250000l. Ruins of Bella Paise Abbey (horiz) . . . . . . 2·00 2·25
425 500000l. Traditional dancers (horiz) . . . . 3·50 4·25

1996. Europa. Famous Women. Multicoloured.
426 15000l. Type **142** . . . . . . 1·00 25
427 50000l. Kadriye Hulusi Hacibulgur . . . . 2·25 3·25

143 Established Forest

1996. World Environment Day. Sheet 72 × 78 mm, containing T **143** and similar horiz design. Multicoloured.
MS428 50000l. Type **143**; 50000l. Conifer plantation . . . . . . 6·50 6·50

144 Basketball

1996. Olympic Games, Atlanta. Sheet 105 × 74 mm, containing T **144** and similar horiz designs. Multicoloured.
MS429 15000l. Type **144**; 15000l. Discus throwing; 50000l. Javelin throwing; 50000l. Volleyball . . 3·50 4·25

145 Symbolic Footballs

1996. European Football Championship, England. Multicoloured.

430	15000l. Type **145**	1·00	65
431	35000l. Football and flags of participating nations . . .	2·00	2·50

146 Houses on Fire (Auxiliary Fire Service)

147 "Amanita phalloides"

1996. Anniversaries and Events. Multicoloured.

432	10000l. Type **146**	1·00	40
433	20000l. Colour party (20th anniv of Defence Forces) (vert)	1·10	55
434	50000l. Children by lake (Nasreddin-Hoca Year) . .	1·40	1·50
435	75000l. Flowers (Children's Rights)	1·75	2·25

1997. Arts (13th series). As T **121**. Multicoloured.

436	25000l. "City" (Lebibe Sonuc) (horiz)	1·00	50
437	70000l. "Woman opening Letter" (Ruzen Atakan) (horiz)	2·25	3·00

1997. Fungi. Multicoloured.

438	15000l. Type **147**	75	30
439	25000l. "Morchella esculenta"	1·10	1·00
440	25000l. "Pleurotus eryngii"	1·10	1·00
441	70000l. "Amanita muscaria"	1·75	2·75

148 Flag on Hillside

150 Prime Minister Necmettin Erbakan of Turkey

149 Mother and Children playing Leapfrog

1997. Besparmak Mountains Flag Sculpture.
442 **148** 60000l. multicoloured . . 1·50 1·75

1997. Europa. Tales and Legends. Multicoloured.

443	25000l. Type **149**	1·25	30
444	70000l. Apple tree and well	2·25	3·00

1997. Visit of the President and the Prime Minister of Turkey.

445	15000l. Type **150**	40	30
446	80000l. President Suleyman Demirel of Turkey (horiz)	2·00	2·50

151 Golden Eagle

152 Coin of Sultan Abdulaziz, 1861–76

1997. Birds of Prey. Multicoloured.

447	40000l. Type **151**	1·25	1·25
448	40000l. Eleonora's falcon . .	1·25	1·25
449	75000l. Common kestrel . . .	1·75	2·00
450	100000l. Western honey buzzard	2·00	2·50

1997. Rare Coins. Multicoloured.

451	25000l. Type **152**	40	20
452	40000l. Coin of Sultan Mahmud II, 1808–39 . . .	55	40
453	75000l. Coin of Sultan Selim II, 1566–74	90	1·25
454	100000l. Coin of Sultan Mehmed V, 1909–18 . . .	1·25	2·00

153 Open Book and Emblem

1997. Anniversaries.

455	**153**	25000l. multicoloured . .	65	20
456	–	40000l. multicoloured . .	75	30
457	–	100000l. black, red and stone	1·75	1·75
458	–	150000l. multicoloured . .	2·25	3·00

DESIGNS—HORIZ: 25000l. Type **153** (centenary of Turkish Cypriot Scouts); 40000l. Guides working in field (90th anniv of Turkish Cypriot Guides); 150000l. Rudolph Diesel and first oil engine (centenary of the diesel engine). VERT: 100000l. Couple and symbols (AIDS prevention campaign).

154 Ahmet and Ismet Sevki

1998. Ahmet and Ismet Sevki (photographers) Commemoration. Multicoloured.

459	40000l. Type **154**	65	25
460	105000l. Ahmet Sevki (vert)	1·75	2·50

155 "Agrion splendens" (dragonfly)

156 Wooden Double Door

1998. Useful Insects. Multicoloured.

461	40000l. Type **155**	65	25
462	65000l. "Ascalaphus macaronius" (owl-fly) . . .	80	40
463	125000l. "Podalonia hirsuta"	1·75	2·00
464	150000l. "Rhyssa persuasoria"	1·90	2·25

1998. Old Doors.

465	**156**	115000l. multicoloured . .	1·75	2·00
466	–	140000l. multicoloured . .	1·75	2·00

DESIGN: 140000l. Different door.

157 Legislative Assembly Building (Republic Establishment Festival)

1998. Europa. Festivals. Multicoloured.

467	40000l. Type **157**	65	25
468	150000l. Globe, flags and map (Int Children's Folk Dance Festival) (vert) . . .	2·40	3·00

158 Marine Life

1998. International Year of the Ocean.

469	**158**	40000l. multicoloured . .	75	40
470	–	90000l. multicoloured . .	1·50	2·00

DESIGN: 90000l. Different underwater scene

159 Prime Minister Mesut Yilmaz of Turkey

1998. Prime Minister Yilmaz's Visit to Northern Cyprus.
471 **159** 75000l. multicoloured . . 1·50 1·75

160 Pres. Suleyman Demirel of Turkey

162 Deputy Prime Minister Bulent Ecevit

161 Victorious French Team

1998. President Demirel's "Water for Peace" Project.

472	75000l. Type **160**	1·00	50
473	175000l. Turkish and Turkish Cypriot leaders with inflatable water tank (horiz)	2·25	3·00

1998. World Cup Football Championship, France. Multicoloured.

474	75000l. Type **161**	1·00	50
475	175000l. World Cup trophy (vert)	2·25	3·00

1998. Visit of the Deputy Prime Minister of Turkey.
476 **162** 200000l. multicoloured . . 1·75 2·00

163 Itinerant Tinsmiths

1998. Local Crafts. Multicoloured.

477	50000l. Type **163**	35	25
478	75000l. Basket weaver (vert)	55	35
479	130000l. Grinder sharpening knife (vert)	95	1·10
480	400000l. Wood carver	3·00	4·00

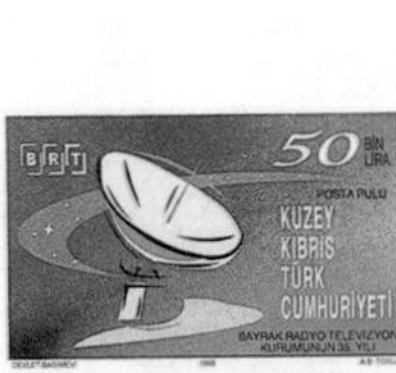
164 Stylised Satellite Dish

165 Dr. Fazil Kucuk

1998. Anniversaries. Multicoloured (except No. 483).

481	50000l. Type **164**	80	30
482	75000l. Stylised birds and "15"	1·00	1·10
483	75000l. "75" and Turkish flag (red, black and orange) . .	1·00	1·10
484	175000l. Scroll, "50" and quill pen (vert)	1·40	2·50
MS485	72 × 78 mm. 75000l. As No. 482; 75000l. Map of Northern Cyprus	1·50	1·75

ANNIVERSARIES: No. 481, 35th anniv of Bayrak Radio and Television; 482, **MS**485, 15th anniv of Turkish Republic of Northern Cyprus; 483, 75th anniv of Turkish Republic; 484, 50th anniv of Universal Declaration of Human Rights.

1999. 15th Death Anniv of Dr. Fazil Kucuk (politician).
486 **165** 75000l. multicoloured . . 1·00 1·00

166 Otello

1999. Performance of Verdi's Opera Otello in Cyprus. Sheet 78 × 74 mm, containing T **166** and similar vert design. Multicoloured.
MS487 200000l. Type **166**; 200000l. Desdemona dead in front of fireplace . . . . 3·25 3·00

167 "Malpolon monspessulanus insignitus" (Montepellier)

1999. Snakes. Multicoloured.

488	50000l. Type **167**	60	30
489	75000l. "Hierophis jugularis"	80	45
490	195000l. "Vipera lebetina lebetina" (levantine viper)	1·50	1·75
491	220000l. "Natrix natrix" (grass snake)	1·50	1·75

168 Entrance to Cave

1999. Europa. Parks and Gardens. Incirli Cave. Multicoloured.

492	75000l. Type **168**	1·00	25
493	200000l. Limestone rocks inside cave (vert)	1·75	2·25

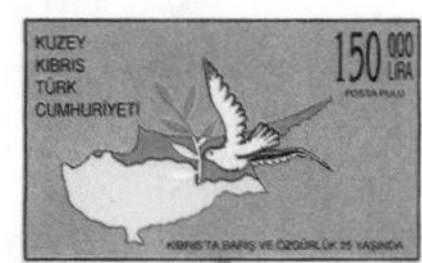
169 Peace Dove and Map of Cyprus

1999. 25th Anniv of Turkish Landings in Cyprus. Multicoloured.

494	150000l. Type **169**	1·25	1·00
495	250000l. Peace dove, map of Cyprus and sun	1·50	2·00

170 Air Mail Envelope and Labels

1999. Anniversaries and Events. Multicoloured.

496	75000l. Type **170** (35th anniv of Turkish Cypriot Posts)	50	25
497	225000l. "125" and U.P.U. emblem (125th anniv of U.P.U.)	1·00	1·25
498	250000l. Total eclipse of the Sun, August 1999	1·50	1·75

171 Turkish Gateway, Limassol

1999. Destruction of Turkish Buildings in Southern Cyprus. Each light brown and brown.

499	75000l. Type **171**	50	25
500	150000l. Mosque, Evdim . .	75	40
501	210000l. Bayraktar Mosque, Lefkosa	90	75
502	1000000l. Kebir Mosque, Baf (vert)	4·50	6·00

172 Mobile Phone

2000. New Millennium. Technology.
503 **172** 75000l. black, green and blue 45 20
504 – 150000l. black and blue 65 25
505 – 275000l. multicoloured . . 1·10 1·25
506 – 300000l. multicoloured . . 1·40 1·75
DESIGNS: 150000l. "Hosgeldin 2000"; 275000l. Computer and "internet" in squares; 300000l. Satellite over Earth.

173 Beach Scene

2000. Holidays. Multicoloured.
507 300000l. Type **173** . . . . . 1·40 1·60
508 340000l. Deck-chair on sea-shore . . . . 1·40 1·60

174 "Building Europe"

2000. Europa. Sheet 77 × 68 mm, containing T **174** and similar vert design. Multicoloured.
MS509 300000l. Type **174**; 300000l. Map of Europe with flower creating Council of Europe emblem and map of Cyprus . . 2·50 2·75

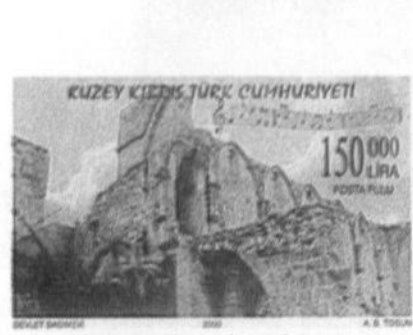

175 Bellapais Abbey

176 Pres. Ahmet Sezer of Turkey

2000. 4th International Bellapais Music Festival. Multicoloured.
510 150000l. Type **175** 75 50
511 350000l. Emblem (vert) . . . 1·50 1·75

2000. Visit of President Ahmet Sezer of Turkey.
512 **176** 150000l. multicoloured . . 1·00 1·00

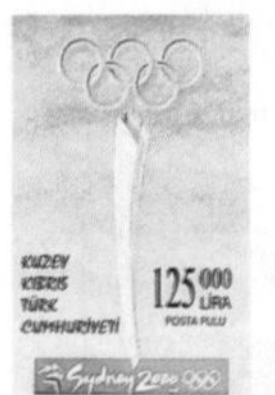

177 Olympic Torch and Rings

179 Grasshopper on Cactus

2000. Olympic Games, Sydney. Multicoloured.
513 125000l. Type **177** 75 40
514 200000l. Runner (horiz) . . . 1·25 1·50

2000. No. 418 surch **50000 LIRA POSTA PULU**.
515 50000l. on 600l. Type **140** 1·00 45

2000. Nature. Insects and Flowers. Multicoloured.
516 125000l. Type **179** 50 25
517 200000l. Butterfly on flower 80 45
518 275000l. Bee on flower . . . 1·00 1·00
519 600000l. Snail on flower . . . 2·00 2·50

180 Traditional Kerchief

2000. Traditional Handicrafts. Kerchiefs.
520 **180** 125000l. multicoloured . . 50 30
521 – 200000l. multicoloured . . 80 55
522 – 265000l. multicoloured . . 1·00 1·25
523 – 350000l. multicoloured . . 1·50 1·75
DESIGNS: 200000l. to 350000l. Different kerchiefs.

181 Lusignan House, Lefkosa

2001. Restoration of Historic Buildings. Mult.
524 125000l. Type **181** 75 30
525 200000l. The Eaved House, Lefkosa . . . . 1·25 1·50

182 "Cuprum Kuprum Bakir Madeni" (Inci Kansu)

2001. Modern Art. Multicoloured.
526 125000l. Type **182** 70 20
527 200000l. "Varolus" (Emel Samioglu) . . . . 1·25 45
528 350000l. "Ask Kuslara Ucar" (Ozden Selenge) (vert) . . 1·60 1·75
529 400000l. "Suyun Yolculugu" (Ayhatun Atesin) . . . . . 1·60 1·75

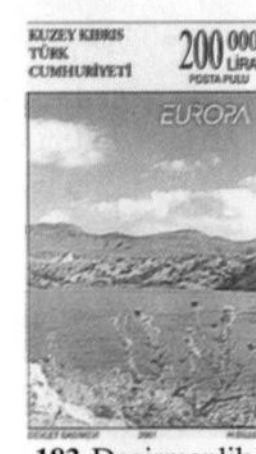

183 Degirmenlik Reservoir

184 Atomic Symbol and X-ray

2001. Europa. Water Resources. Multicoloured.
530 200000l. Type **183** 50 25
531 500000l. The Waters of Sinar 1·25 1·50

2001. World Environment Day. Radiation. Mult.
532 125000l. Type **184** 40 20
533 450000l. Radiation symbol and x-ray of hand . . . . 1·10 1·40

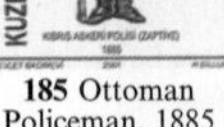

185 Ottoman Policeman, 1885

186 MG TF Sports Car, 1954

2001. Turkish Cypriot Police Uniforms. Multicoloured.
534 125000l. Type **185** 50 25
535 200000l. Colonial policeman, 1933 . . . . 85 40
536 500000l. Mounted policeman, 1934 . . . . 1·25 1·25
537 750000l. Policewoman, 1983 1·75 2·00

2001. Classic Cars. Multicoloured.
538 175000l. Type **186** 50 25
539 300000l. Vauxhall 14, 1948 80 45
540 475000l. Bentley, 1922 . . . 1·00 1·25
541 600000l. Jaguar XK 120, 1955 . . . . 1·25 1·50

187 Graduate at Top of Steps and College Names

2001. Anniversaries.
542 **187** 200000l. multicoloured . . 70 75
543 – 200000l. black, mauve and brown 70 75
DESIGNS—HORIZ: No. 542, Type **187** (Centenary of Higher Education). VERT: No. 543, Book cover of *The Genocide Files* by Harry Scott Gibbons (anniversary of publication).

188 Chef mincing Logs into Letters (U. Karsu)

189 Turtle

2002. Caricatures. Multicoloured.
544 250000l. Type **188** 55 30
545 300000l. Overfed people drinking from inflated cow, and starving children (M. Kayra) (horiz) 65 40
546 475000l. Can of cola parachuting down to pregnant African woman (S. Gazi) 85 80
547 850000l. Artist painting trees in city (M. Tozaki) . . . . 1·50 1·75

2002. Tourism. Underwater Scenes. Multicoloured.
548 250000l. Type **189** 60 30
549 300000l. Starfish on rock . . 75 40
550 500000l. Fish in rocks . . . 1·00 90
551 750000l. Part of wreck . . . 1·40 1·75

190 Stilt-walker

192 Woman in White Tunic and Trousers

191 Turkish Football Team

2002. Europa. Circus. Sheet 79 × 72 mm, containing T **190** and similar vert design. Multicoloured.
MS552 600000l. Type **190**; 600000l. Child on high wire . . . . . . 2·50 2·75

2002. World Cup Football Championship, Japan and Korea (2002). Multicoloured.
553 300000l. Type **191** 75 30
554 1000000l. Football Stadium, World Cup Trophy and footballer . . . . 2·00 2·25

2002. Traditional Costumes. Multicoloured.
555 250000l. Type **192** 60 30
556 300000l. Man wearing grey jacket 70 40
557 425000l. Man in blue jacket and trousers . . . . 1·00 1·00
558 700000l. Woman in yellow tunic . . . . 1·60 1·90

193 "Accident by Bridge"

2002. Children's Paintings. Multicoloured.
559 300000l. Type **193** 70 35
560 600000l. "Burning House" (vert) . . . . 1·40 1·60

194 Sureyya Ayhan (athlete)

195 Oguz Karayel (footballer) (70th birth anniv)

2002. Sporting Celebrities. Multicoloured.
561 300000l. Type **194** 65 30
562 1000000l. Grand Master Park Jung-tae (taekwon-do) . . 2·00 2·25

2002. Celebrities' Anniversaries. Multicoloured.
563 100000l. Type **195** 25 15
564 175000l. Mete Adanir (footballer) (40th birth anniv) 40 20
565 300000l. M. Necati Ozkan (30th death anniv) 65 40
566 575000l. Osman Turkay (astronomer) (1st death anniv) (horiz) . . . . . . 1·10 1·40

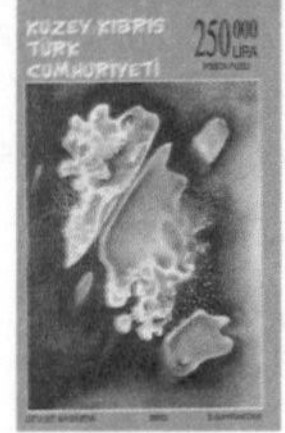

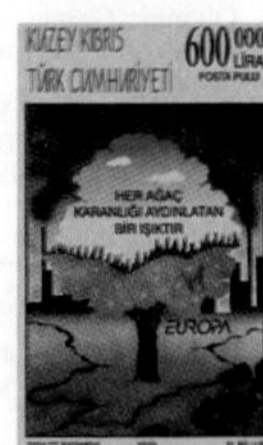

196 Untitled Painting by Salih Bayraktar

197 Tree containing Meadow and Forest in Polluted Industrial Landscape

2003. Art (14th series). Multicoloured.
567 250000l. Type **196** 45 50
568 1000000l. Untitled painting of woman's head (Feryal Suukan) 70 75

2003. Europa. Poster Art. Sheet 78 × 72 mm, containing T **197** and similar vert design. Multicoloured.
MS569 600000l. Type **197**; 600000l. Question mark containing wildlife in polluted landscape 50 55

198 Cyprus Wheatear

2003. World Environment Day. Birds. Multicoloured.
570 100000l. Type **198** 10 10
571 300000l. Cyprus warbler . . 25 30
572 500000l. Pygmy cormorant (vert) 40 45
573 600000l. Greater flamingo (vert) 50 55

199 Carved Wooden Chest

2003. Wooden Chests. Multicoloured.
574 250000l. Type **199** 20 25
575 300000l. Chest carved with circular designs 25 30
576 525000l. Chest carved with turquoise-blue figures . . . 50 55
577 1000000l. Chest carved with flower heads and white birds 60 65

200 *ladiolus triphyllus*

2003. Flowers. Multicoloured.
578 150000l. Type **200** 15 20
579 175000l. *Tulipa cypria* . . . 40 45
580 500000l. *Ranunculus asiaticus* 50 55
581 525000l. *Narcissus tazetta* . . 50 55

201 Kemal Ataturk and Flag of Turkish Republic of Northern Cyprus

2003. Political Anniversaries. Multicoloured.
582 3000000l. Type **201** (20th anniv of proclamation of Turkish Republic of Northern Cyprus) . . . . 1·50 1·60
583 3000000l. Kemal Atatürk and Turkish flag (80th anniv of Republic of Turkey) . . . 1·50 1·60

202 Horse-drawn Plough and Modern Farm Machinery

2003. Anniversaries. Multicoloured.
584 300000l. Type **202** (60th anniv of International Federation of Agricultural Producers) 25 30
585 500000l. Emblem (40th anniv of Lions Clubs in Cyprus) 45 50

CYRENAICA Pt. 8

Part of the former Italian colony of Libya, N. Africa. Allied Occupation, 1942–49. Independent Administration, 1949–52. Then part of independent Libya.

Stamps optd **BENGASI** formerly listed here will be found under Italian P.O.s in the Turkish Empire, Nos. 169/70.

100 centesimi = 1 lira.

Stamps of Italy optd **CIRENAICA**.

1923. Tercent of Propagation of the Faith.
1 **66** 20c. orange and green . . . 4·00 18·00
2 30c. orange and red . . . . 4·00 18·00
3 50c. orange and violet . . . 2·75 20·00
4 1l. orange and blue . . . . . 2·75 26·00

1923. Fascist March on Rome stamps.
5 **77** 10c. green . . . . 4·25 7·25
6 30c. violet . . . . 4·25 7·50
7 50c. red . . . . 4·25 8·25
8 **74** 1l. blue . . . . 4·25 21·00
9 2l. brown . . . . 4·25 25·00
10 **75** 5l. black and blue . . . . . 4·25 35·00

1924. Manzoni stamps (Nos. 155/60).
11 **77** 10c. black and purple . . . 5·00 20·00
12 – 15c. black and green . . . . 5·00 20·00
13 – 30c. black . . . . 5·00 20·00
14 – 50c. black and brown . . . 5·00 20·00
15 – 1l. black and blue . . . . . 40·00 £150
16 – 5l. black and purple £400 £1300

1925. Holy Year stamps.
17 – 20c.+10c. brown & green . . 2·50 11·50
18 **81** 30c.+15c. brown & choc . . 2·50 13·00
19 – 50c.+25c. brown & violet . . 2·50 11·50
20 – 60c.+30c. brown and red . . 2·50 15·00
21 – 1l.+50c. purple and blue . . 2·50 20·00
22 – 5l.+2l.50 purple and red . . 2·50 30·00

1925. Royal Jubilee stamps.
23 **82** 60c. red . . . . 30 5·25
24 1l. blue . . . . 50 5·25
24a 1l.25 blue . . . . 2·50 11·00

1926. St. Francis of Assisi stamps.
25 **83** 20c. green . . . . 1·50 6·50
26 – 40c. violet . . . . 1·50 6·50
27 – 60c. red . . . . 1·50 11·50
28 – 1l.25 blue . . . . 1·50 18·00
29 – 5l.+2l.50 olive (as No. 196) 4·25 35·00

6 8

1926. Colonial Propaganda.
30 **6** 5c.+5c. brown . . . . 60 4·00
31 10c.+5c. olive . . . . 60 4·00
32 20c.+5c. green . . . . 60 4·00
33 40c.+5c. red . . . . 60 4·00
34 60c.+5c. orange . . . . . . 60 4·00
35 1l.+5c. blue . . . . 60 6·50

1927. 1st National Defence stamps of Italy optd **CIRENAICA**.
36 **89** 40+20c. black & brown . . 1·75 15·00
37 – 60+30c. brown and red . . 1·75 15·00
38 – 1l.25+60c. black & blue . . 1·75 30·00
39 – 5l.+2l.50 black & green . . 2·75 40·00

1927. Volta Centenary stamps of Italy optd **Cirenaica**.
40 **90** 20c. violet . . . . 5·00 18·00
41 50c. orange . . . . 6·50 11·50
42 1l.25 blue . . . . 10·00 26·00

1928. 45th Anniv of Italian–African Society.
43 **8** 20c.+5c. green . . . . 1·60 5·25
44 30c.+5c. red . . . . 1·60 5·25
45 50c.+10c. violet . . . . . . 1·60 9·25
46 1l.25+20c. blue . . . . . . 1·75 10·50

Stamps of Italy optd **CIRENAICA**. Colours changed in some instances.

1929. 2nd National Defence stamps.
47 **89** 30c.+10c. black & red . . . 3·00 10·50
48 50c.+20c. grey & lilac . . . 3·00 12·50
49 1l.25+50c. blue & brown . . 3·75 20·00
50 – 5l.+2l. black & green . . . 3·75 35·00

1929. Montecassino stamps (No. 57 optd **Cirenaica**).
51 **104** 20c. green . . . . 3·75 8·25
52 – 25c. red . . . . 3·75 8·25
53 – 50c.+10c. red . . . . . . 3·75 10·00
54 – 75c.+15c. brown . . . . . 3·75 10·00
55 **104** 1l.25+25c. purple . . . . . 7·25 16·00
56 – 5l.+1l. blue . . . . 7·25 20·00
57 – 10l.+2l. brown . . . . . . 7·25 26·00

1930. Marriage of Prince Humbert and Princess Marie Jose stamps.
58 **109** 20c. green . . . . 1·00 3·00
59 50c.+10c. red . . . . . . 80 4·00
60 1l.25+25c. red . . . . . . 80 9·25

1930. Ferrucci stamps (optd **Cirenaica**).
61 **114** 20c. violet . . . . 1·60 1·60
62 – 25c. green . . . . 1·60 1·60
63 – 50c. black . . . . 1·60 3·25
64 – 1l.25 blue . . . . 1·60 6·50
65 – 5l.+2l. red . . . . 5·00 13·00

1930. 3rd National Defence stamps.
66 **89** 30c.+10c. turq & grn . . . 13·00 16·00
67 – 50c.+10c. purple & green . . 13·00 20·00
68 – 1l.25+30c. lt brown & brn 13·00 30·00
69 – 5l.+1l.50 green and blue . . 42·00 65·00

13 17 Columns of Leptis

1930. 25th Anniv (1929) of Italian Colonial Agricultural Institute.
70 **13** 50c.+20c. brown . . . . . 2·25 10·00
71 1l.25+20c. blue . . . . . 2·25 10·00
72 1l.75+20c. green . . . . . 2·25 12·00
73 2l.55+50c. violet . . . . . 3·25 20·00
74 5l.+1l. red . . . . 3·25 28·00

1930. Virgil Bimillenary stamps optd **CIRENAICA**.
75 **118** 15c. violet . . . . 85 4·00
76 – 20c. brown . . . . 85 2·00
77 – 25c. green . . . . 85 1·60
78 – 30c. brown . . . . 85 2·00
79 – 50c. purple . . . . 85 1·60
80 – 75c. red . . . . 85 3·00
81 – 1l.25 blue . . . . 85 4·00
82 – 5l.+1l.50 purple . . . . 3·00 21·00
83 – 10l.+2l.50 brown . . . . 3·00 32·00

1931. St. Anthony of Padua stamps optd **Cirenaica** (75c., 5l.) or **CIRENAICA** (others).
84 **121** 20c. brown . . . . 1·25 8·25
85 – 25c. green . . . . 1·25 3·25
86 – 30c. brown . . . . 1·25 3·25
87 – 50c. purple . . . . 1·25 3·25
88 – 75c. grey (as No. 308) . . 1·25 8·25
89 – 1l.25 blue . . . . 1·25 16·00
90 – 5l.+2l.50 brn (as No. 310) 3·50 38·00

1932. Air stamps of Tripolitania optd **Cirenaica**.
91 **18** 50c. red 65 30
92 60c. orange . . . . 4·00 8·00
93 80c. purple . . . . 4·00 11·50

1932. Air stamps of Tripolitania of 1931 optd **CIRENAICA** and bars.
94 **18** 50c. red . . . . 1·00 1·00
95 80c. purple . . . . 5·25 12·00

1932. Air.
96 – 50c. violet . . . . 3·25 10
97 – 75c. red . . . . 5·00 5·00
98 – 80c. blue . . . . 5·00 10·00
99 **17** 1l. black . . . . 1·60 10
100 2l. green . . . . 2·00 5·00
101 5l. red . . . . 3·75 10·00
DESIGN—VERT: 50c. to 80c. Arab on Camel.

18 "Graf Zeppelin"

1933. Air. "Graf Zeppelin". Inscr "CROCIERA ZEPPELIN".
102 **18** 3l. brown . . . . 5·75 55·00
103 – 5l. violet . . . . 5·75 55·00
104 – 10l. green . . . . 5·75 £110
105 – 12l. blue . . . . 5·75 £120
106 **18** 15l. red . . . . 5·75 £120
107 – 20l. black . . . . 5·75 £140
DESIGNS: 5l., 12l. "Graf Zeppelin" and Roman galley; 10l., 20l. "Graf Zeppelin" and giant archer.

19 Air Squadron

1933. Air. Balbo Transatlantic Mass Formation Flight by Savoia Marchetti S-55X Flying Boats.
108 **19** 19l.75 blue and green . . . 11·50 £300
109 44l.75 blue and red . . . . 11·50 £300

1934. Air. Rome–Buenos Aires Flight. T **17** (new colours) optd with Savoia Marchetti S-71 airplane and **1934-XII PRIMO VOLO DIRETTO ROMA = BUENOS-AYRES TRIMOTORE "LOMBARDI-MAZZOTTI"** or surch also.
110 **17** 2l. on 5l. brown . . . . . 2·00 32·00
111 3l. on 5l. green . . . . . 2·00 32·00
112 5l. brown . . . . 2·00 35·00
113 10l. on 5l. pink . . . . . 2·25 35·00

21 Arab Horseman

1934. 2nd International Colonial Exn, Naples.
114 **21** 5c. brn & grn (postage) . . 2·75 9·00
115 10c. black and brown . . . 2·75 9·00
116 20c. blue and red . . . . 2·75 7·50
117 50c. brown and violet . . . 2·75 7·50
118 60c. blue and brown . . . 2·75 9·75
119 1l.25 green and blue . . . 2·75 16·00
120 – 25c. orange & blue (air) . . 2·75 9·00
121 – 50c. blue and green . . . . 2·75 7·50
122 – 75c. orange and brown . . 2·75 7·50
123 – 80c. green and brown . . . 2·75 9·00
124 – 1l. green and red . . . . . 2·75 10·00
125 – 2l. brown and blue . . . . 2·75 16·00
DESIGNS: 25 to 75c. Arrival of Caproni Ca 101 mail plane; 80c. to 2l. Caproni Ca 101 mail plane and Venus of Cyrene.

22

1934. Air. Rome–Mogadiscio Flight.
126 **22** 25c.+10c. green . . . . . 3·25 5·00
127 50c.+10c. brown . . . . 3·25 5·00
128 75c.+15c. red . . . . . . 3·25 5·00
129 80c.+15c. black . . . . . 3·25 5·00
130 1l.+20c. brown . . . . . 3·25 5·00
131 2l.+20c. blue . . . . . . 3·25 5·00
132 3l.+25c. violet . . . . . 16·00 42·00
133 5l.+25c. orange . . . . . 16·00 42·00
134 10l.+30c. purple . . . . . 16·00 42·00
135 25l.+2l. green . . . . . . 16·00 42·00

OFFICIAL AIR STAMP

1934. Optd **SERVIZIO DI STATO** and crown.
O136 **22** 25l.+2l. red £1600 £1100

For stamps of British Occupation see under British Occupation of Italian Colonies.

CZECH REPUBLIC Pt. 5

Formerly part of Czechoslovakia, a federation dissolved on 31 December 1992 when the constituent republics became separate states.

100 haleru = 1 koruna.

1 State Arms

1993.
1 **1** 3k. multicoloured 25 20

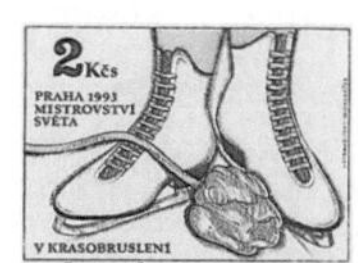

2 Skater's Boots and Tulip

3 Pres. Vaclav Havel

1993. Ice Skating Championships, Prague.
2 **2** 2k. multicoloured 20 15

1993.
3 **3** 2k. purple, blue & mauve . . 10 15
3a 3k.60 violet, mauve & blue 30 15

4 St. John and Charles Bridge, Prague

1993. 600th Death Anniv of St. John of Nepomuk (patron saint of Bohemia).
4 **4** 8k. multicoloured 85 45

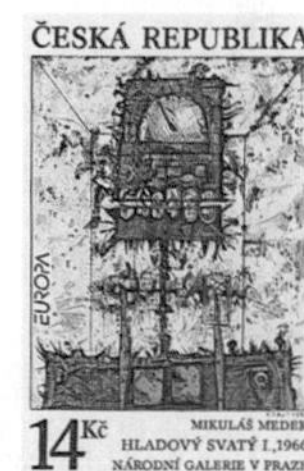

5 "Hladovy Svaty I" (Mikulas Medek)

1993. Europa. Contemporary Art.
5 **5** 14k. multicoloured . . . . . 7·50 2·40

6 Church of Sacred Heart, Prague

1993.
6 **6** 5k. multicoloured . . . . . . 1·50 45
See also No. 45.

7 Brevnov Monastery

1993. U.N.E.S.C.O. World Heritage Site. Millenary of Brevnov Monastery, Prague.
7 **7** 4k. multicoloured 40 25

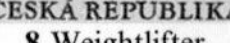

8 Weightlifter

9 Town Hall Tower and Cathedral of St. Peter and St. Paul

1993. Junior Weightlifting Championships, Cheb.
8 **8** 6k. multicoloured 55 35

1993. 750th Anniv of Brno.
9 **9** 8k. multicoloured . . . . . . 1·90 70

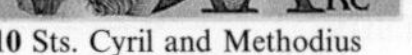

10 Sts. Cyril and Methodius

12 Ceske Budejovice

11 State Arms

1993. 1130th Anniv of Arrival of Sts. Cyril and Methodius in Moravia.
10 **10** 8k. multicoloured 75 30

1993. Sheet 76 × 90 mm.
MS11 **11** 8k. × 2 multicoloured 2·75 2·75

1993. Towns.
12 **12** 1k. brown and red 10 10
13 – 2k. red and blue 10 10
14 – 3k. blue and red 15 10
15 – 3k. blue and red 25 20
16 – 5k. green and brown 50 15
17 – 6k. green and yellow 60 30
18 – 7k. brown and green 60 35
20 – 8k. violet and yellow . . . 40 30
21 – 10k. green and red 55 35
23 – 20k. red and blue . . . . . 1·10 90
26 – 50k. brown and green . . . 30 1·60
DESIGNS—VERT: 2k. Usti nad Labem; 3k. (15) Brno; 5k. Pilsen; 6k. Slanyi; 7k. Antonin Dvorak Theatre, Ostrava; 8k. Olomouc; 10k. Hradec Kralove; 20k. Prague; 50k. Opava. HORIZ: 3k. (14) Cesky Krumlov (U.N.E.S.C.O. World Heritage Site).

13 Rower

14 August Sedlacek (historian, 150th anniv)

1993. World Rowing Championships, Racice.
27 **13** 3k. multicoloured 25 30

1993. Birth Anniversaries.
28 **14** 2k. buff, blue and green . . 15 15
29 – 3k. buff, blue and violet . . 30 20
DESIGN: 3k. Eduard Cech (mathematician, centenary).

15 Pedunculate Oak

17 St. Nicholas

16 "Composition" (Joan Miro)

1993. Trees. Multicoloured.
30 5k. Type **15** 35 20
31 7k. Hornbeam 50 30
32 9k. Scots pine 70 45

1993. Art (1st series). Multicoloured.
33 11k. Type **16** . . . . 2·10 1·25
34 14k. "Green Corn Field with Cypress" (Vincent van Gogh) . . . . 3·50 1·50
See also Nos. 62/4, 116/18, 140/2, 174/6, 200/1, 221/2, 252/4, 282/4, 312/14, 350/2, 385/7 and 393.

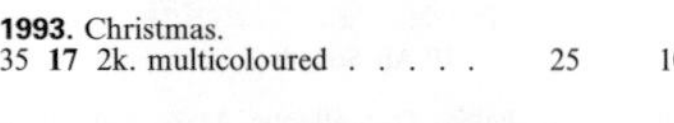

1993. Christmas.
35 **17** 2k. multicoloured 25 10

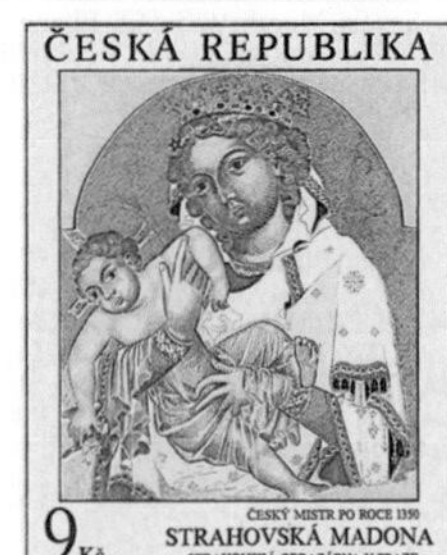

18 "Strahov Madonna"

1993. Christmas.
36 **18** 9k. multicoloured . . . . . 3·00 90

19 "Family" (C. Littasy-Rollier)

20 Kubelik

1994. International Year of the Family.
37 **19** 2k. multicoloured 10 10

1994. 54th Death Anniv of Jan Kublik (composer and violinist).
38 **20** 3k. yellow and black 25 10

21 Voltaire (writer, 300th anniv)

1994. Birth Anniversaries.
39 **21** 2k. purple, grey & mauve 15 25
40 – 6k. black, blue and green . . 45 25
DESIGN: 6k. Georg Agricola (mineralogist, 500th anniv).

22 Athletes

23 Marco Polo and Fantasy Animal

1994. Winter Olympic Games, Lillehammer, Norway.
41 **22** 5k. multicoloured 40 30

1994. Europa. Discoveries. Marco Polo's Journeys to the Orient. Multicoloured.
42 14k. Type **23** . . . . 1·10 1·25
43 14k. Marco Polo and woman on fantasy animals . . . . 1·10 1·25

24 Benes

26 Crayon Figures

25 Cubist Flats by Josef Chochol, Prague

1994. 110th Birth Anniv of Edvard Benes (President of Czechoslovakia 1935–38 and 1945–48).
44 **24** 5k. violet and purple . . . 40 20

1994. U.N.E.S.C.O. World Heritage Sites. Mult.
45 8k. Market place, Telc . . . . 1·10 60
46 9k. Type **25** . . . . 1·25 75
No. 45 is similar to Type **6**.

1994. For Children.
47 **26** 2k. multicoloured 10 10

27 "Stegosaurus ungulatus"

1994. Prehistoric Animals. Multicoloured.
48 2k. Type **27** 20 10
49 3k. "Apatosaurus excelsus" . . 30 10
50 5k. "Tarbosaurus bataar" (vert) 50 30

28 Statue of Liberty holding Football

29 Flag of Prague Section

1994. World Cup Football Championship, U.S.A.
51 **28** 8k. multicoloured 75 45

1994. 12th Sokol (sports organization) Congress, Prague.
52 **29** 2k. multicoloured 10 15

30 Olympic Flag and Flame

1994. Centenary of Int Olympic Committee.
53 **30** 7k. multicoloured 60 40

31 Stylized Carrier Pigeons

1994. 120th Anniv of Universal Postal Union.
54 **31** 11k. multicoloured 90 80

32 Common Stonechat

33 NW, 1900

1994. Birds. Multicoloured.
55 3k. Type **32** 20 15
56 5k. Common rosefinch 30 25
57 14k. Bluethroat . . . . 1·25 75

1994. Racing Cars. Multicoloured.
58 2k. Type **33** 15 15
59 3k. L & K, 1908 . . . . . . 25 15
60 9k. Praga, 1912 . . . . 70 45

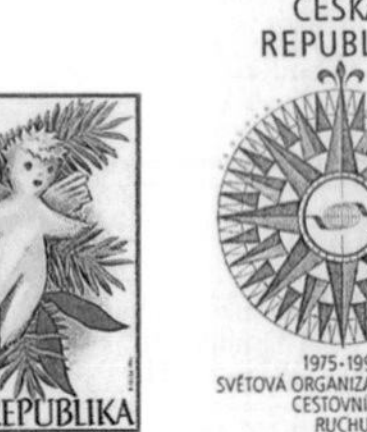

34 Angel

35 Emblem

1994. Christmas.
61 **34** 2k. multicoloured 10 10

1994. Art (2nd series). As T **16**.
62 7k. black and buff 48 55
63 10k. multicoloured 95 10
64 14k. multicoloured . . . . . 1·60 1·10
DESIGNS—VERT: 7k. "The Old Man and the Woman" (Lucas van Leyden); 10k. "Moulin Rouge" (Henri de Toulouse-Lautrec); 14k. "Madonna of St. Vitus".

1995. 20th Anniv of World Tourism Organization.
65 **35** 8k. blue and red 70 45

36 E.U. and Czech Republic Flags

37 Engraver's Transposition of 1918 Czechoslovakia 2h. Newspaper Stamp

1995. Association Agreement with European Union.
66 **36** 8k. multicoloured 70 45

1995. Czech Stamp Production.
67 **37** 3k. blue, grey and red . . . 25 20

38 Johannes Marcus Marci

39 Jiri Voskovec (actor and dramatist)

1995. Birth Anniversaries.
68 **38** 2k. sepia, stone & brown . . 20 10
69 – 5k. multicoloured 35 30
70 – 7k. purple, grey & mauve 70 35
DESIGNS: 2k. Type **38** (academic, 400th anniv); 5k. Ferdinand Peroutka (journalist and dramatist, centenary); 7k. Premysl Pitter (founder of Youth Care Centre, centenary).

1995. 90th Birth Anniversaries of Members of the Liberated Theatre, Prague. Caricatures from posters by Adolf Hoffmeister.
71 **39** 3k. black, yellow & orange 25 10
72 – 3k. black, yellow & green 25 10
73 – 3k. black, yellow & blue . . 25·00 10
DESIGNS: No. 72, Jan Werich (dramatist and actor); 73, Jaroslav Jezek (composer) (anniv 1996).

40 Church and Buildings — **41** Buff-tailed Bumble Bee

1995. Townscapes.
75 **40** 40h. brown and pink . . . 10 10
76 – 60h. brown and stone . . . 10 10
DESIGN: 60h. Buildings, church and archway.

1995. European Nature Conservation Year. Endangered Insects. Multicoloured.
84 3k. Type **41** 25 10
85 5k. Praying mantis 40 30
86 6k. Banded agrion 55 30

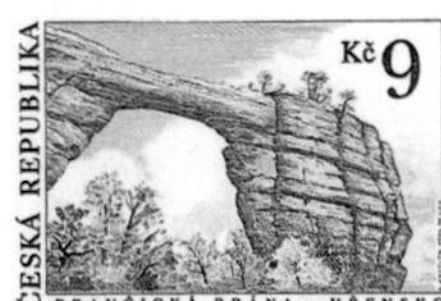

42 Sandstone Arch, Labske Piskovce

1995. Rock Formations. Multicoloured.
87 8k. Stone Organ (basalt columns), Central Bohemia 85 60
88 9k. Type **42** 85 70

43 Rose and Women's Profiles

1995. Europa. Peace and Freedom. Multicoloured.
89 9k. Type **43** 85 40
90 14k. Butterfly, girl and profiles of ageing woman . . . . . 1·10 70

44 Cat — **46** Wrestlers

45 Early Steam Train leaving Chocen Tunnel

1995. For Children.
91 **44** 3k.60 multicoloured 40 25

1995. 150th Anniv of Olomouc–Prague Railway.
92 **45** 3k. black, brown & blue . . 35 10
93 – 9k.60 black, brown & red 70 40
DESIGN: 9k.60. Crowd welcoming arrival of first train at Prague.

1995. World Greco-Roman Wrestling Championship, Prague.
94 **46** 3k. brown, stone and red . . 40 10

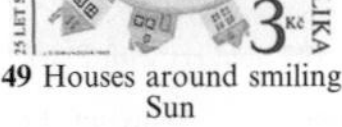

47 Violinist and Washerwoman (Vladimir Rencin) — **49** Houses around smiling Sun

48 Voskovec, Wencih and Jezek (poster, Adolf Hoffmeister)

1995. Cartoons. Cartoons by named artists. Multicoloured.
95 3k. Type **47** 20 10
96 3k.60 Angel and naked man (Vladimir Jiranek) 30 10
97 5k. Champagne cork flying through ringmaster's hoop (Jiri Sliva) 40 30

1995. 70th Anniv of the Liberated Theatre, Prague, and 90th Birth Anniv of Founding Members (2nd issue). Sheet 61 × 81 mm.
MS98 **48** 22k. yellow and black 1·75 1·60

1995. 25th Anniv of SOS Children's Villages.
99 **49** 3k. multicoloured 25 10

50 Gothic Window — **51** Rontgen and X-Ray Tube

1995. Architectural Styles.
101 **50** 2k.40 red and green . . . 10 10
102 – 3k. green and blue 25 10
103 – 3k.60 violet and green . . 35 10
104 – 4k. blue and red 30 15
105 – 4k.60 mauve and green . . 40 10
107 – 9k.60 blue and mauve . . 70 45
108 – 12k.60 brown and blue . . 85 45
109 – 14k. green and mauve . . 1·25 55
DESIGNS: 3k. Secession window; 3k.60, Roman window; 4k. Classicist doorway; 4k.60, Rococo window; 9k.60, Renaissance doorway; 12k.60, Cubist window; 14k. Baroque doorway.

1995. Centenary of Discovery of X-Rays by Wilhelm Rontgen.
113 **51** 6k. buff, black & violet . . 55 25

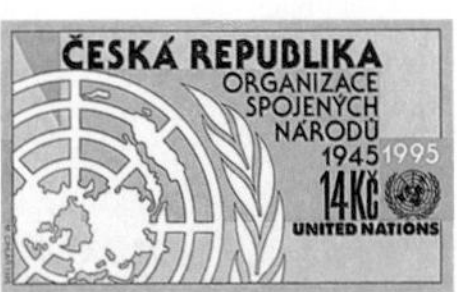

52 Emblem

1995. 50th Anniv of U.N.O.
114 **52** 14k. multicoloured . . . . 1·25 65

53 Christmas Tree — **55** Stamp Design by Jaroslav Benda

54 Allegory of Music

1995. Christmas.
115 **53** 3k. multicoloured 25 20

1995. Art (3rd series). As T **16**.
116 6k. black, blue and buff . . . 45 45
117 9k. multicoloured 75 60
118 14k. multicoloured . . . . . 1·25 90
DESIGNS: 6k. "Parisienne" (Ludek Marold); 9k. "Bouquet" (J. K. Hirschely); 14k. "Portrait of the Sculptor Josef Malinsky" (Antonin Machek).

1996. Cent of Czech Philharmonic Orchestra.
119 **54** 3k.60 multicoloured . . . 30 30

1996. Tradition of Czech Stamp Production.
120 **55** 3k.60 multicoloured . . . 30 20

56 Mencikova and Chessmen

1996. 90th Birth Anniv of Vera Mencikova (chess champion).
121 **56** 6k. black, buff and red . . 50 30

57 Woman with Bowl of Easter Eggs — **58** Sudek and Camera

1996. Easter.
122 **57** 3k. multicoloured 25 20

1996. Birth Cent of Josef Sudek (photographer).
123 **58** 9k.60 buff, black & grey 80 45

59 Jiri Guth-Jarkovsky (first President of National Olympic Committee) and Stadium — **61** Garden Dormouse

60 Jan (John the Blind)

1996. Centenary of Modern Olympic Games.
124 **59** 9k.60 multicoloured . . . 80 45

1996. Bohemian Kings of the Luxembourg Dynasty.
125 **60** 14k. blue, grey & purple 1·25 90
126 – 14k. green, grey & purple 1·25 90
127 – 14k. green, grey & purple 1·25 90
128 – 14k. blue, grey & purple 1·25 90
DESIGNS: No. 126, Karel (Charles IV, Holy Roman Emperor); 127, Vaclav IV; 128, Sigismund.

1996. Nature Conservation. Mammals. Sheet 119 × 138 mm containing T **61** and similar vert designs. Multicoloured.
MS129 3k.60 Type **61**; 5k. × 2 Forest dormouse; 6k. × 2 European souslik; 8k. × 2 Northern birch mouse . . . . 1·75 2·25

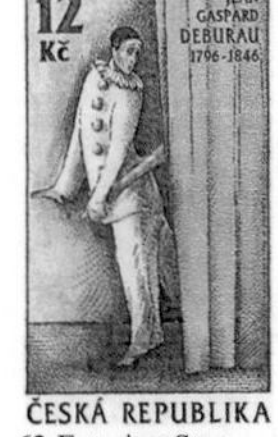

62 Ema Destinnova (singer) — **63** Entering Stage as Pierrot

1996. Europa. Famous Women.
130 **62** 8k. lilac, black & mauve 70 50

1996. Birth Bicentenary of Jean Gasparde Deburau (mime actor).
131 **63** 12k. multicoloured 90 50

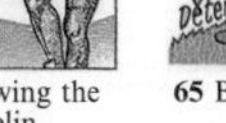

64 Throwing the Javelin — **65** Boy and Girl on Cat

1996. Olympic Games, Atlanta.
132 **64** 3k. multicoloured 25 10

1996. For Children.
133 **65** 3k. multicoloured 25 10

66 St. John of Nepomuk's Church, Zelena Hora — **68** Black Horse

67 Boy playing Flute and Flowers forming Butterfly

1996. Tourist Sites. Multicoloured.
134 8k. Type **66** (U.N.E.S.C.O. World Heritage Site) . . . 65 50
135 9k. Prague Loretto 75 60

1996. 50th Anniv of U.N.I.C.E.F.
136 **67** 3k. multicoloured . . . . 2·25 10

1996. Kladruby Horses. Multicoloured.
137 3k. Type **68** 25 10
138 3k. White horse 25 10

69 Havel

1996. 60th Birthday of President Vaclav Havel. Sheet 79 × 100 mm.
MS139 **69** 6k. × 2 blue and red 95 95

1996. Art (4th series). As T **16**. Multicoloured.
140 9k. "Eden" (Josef Vachal) . . 65 60
141 11k. "Breakfast with Egg" (Georg Flegel) (vert) . . . 90 75
142 20k. "Baroque Chair" (Endre Nemes) (vert) . . . . . . 1·50 1·10

70 Brahe

1996. 450th Birth Anniv of Tycho Brahe (astronomer).
143 **70** 5k. multicoloured 40 30

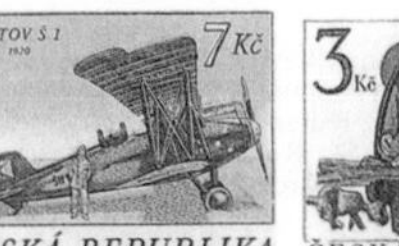

71 Letov S-1 — **72** Nativity

1996. Biplanes. Multicoloured.
144 7k. Type **71** 55 15
145 8k. Aero A-11 . . . . 65 20
146 10k. Avia BH-21 . . . . . . 80 35

1996. Christmas.
147 **72** 3k. multicoloured 25 10

73 Czechoslovakia 1920 Stamp Design of V. Brunner — **74** Easter Symbols

1997. Czech Stamp Production.
148 **73** 3k.60 blue and red 25 10

1997. Easter.
149 **74** 3k. multicoloured 25 10

75 Dog's-tooth Violet

76 Girl and Cats ("Congratulations")

1997. Endangered Plants. Multicoloured.
150 3k.60 Type **75** 25 10
151 4k. Bog arum 35 10
152 5k. Lady's slipper 35 10
153 8k. Dwarf bearded iris . . . 70 30

1997. Greetings Stamp.
154 **76** 4k. multicoloured 30 10

77 St. Adalbert

78 Prince Bruncvik, Neomenie and Lion

1997. Death Millenary of St. Adalbert (Bishop of Prague).
155 **77** 7k. lilac 55 40

1997. Europa. Tales and Legends. Multicoloured.
156 8k. Type **78** 65 50
157 8k. King Wenceslas IV watching Zito the Magician in cart pulled by cocks . . 65 50·00

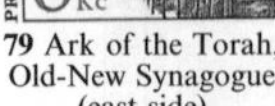

79 Ark of the Torah, Old-New Synagogue (east side)

80 Objects d'Art from Rudolf II's Collection

1997. Jewish Monuments in Prague. Each black, blue and red.
158 8k. Type **79** 70 50
159 10k. Grave of Rabbi Loew (Chief Rabbi of Prague), Old Jewish Cemetery . . . 75 60

1997. "Rudolf II and Prague" Exhibition, Prague. Sheet 117 × 91 mm containing T **80** and similar vert design. Each black, red and green.
MS160 6k. Type **80**; 8k. Rudolf IV and Muses; 10k. Arcimboldo (court painter) . . . . 1·60 1·50

81 Rakosnicek (cartoon character) and Rowan Berries

1997. For Children.
161 **81** 4k.60 multicoloured . . . 40 10

82 Krizik and Arc Lamp

1997. 150th Birth Anniv of Frantisek Krizik (electrical engineer).
162 **82** 6k. pink, blue and red . . 45 20

83 Swimmer

1997. European Swimming and Diving Championships, Prague.
163 **83** 11k. black, buff & blue . . 75 40

84 Mrs. Muller and Svejk in Wheelchair

1997. 110th Anniv of "Fortunes of the Good Soldier Svejk" (novel by Jaroslav Hasek). Illustrations by Josef Lada. Multicoloured.
164 4k. Type **84** 35 15
165 4k.60 Lt. Lukas and Col. Kraus von Zillergut with stolen dog 35 15
166 6k. Svejk smoking pipe . . . 40 35

85 Prague Castle

1997. "Praga 1998" International Stamp Exhibition. Multicoloured.
167 15k. Type **85** . . . . 1·00 75
168 15k. View of Prague Old Town . . . . 1·00 75
MS169 99 × 119 mm. Nos. 167/8 plus two half stamp-size labels . . . 2·00 2·40
See also No. **MS**182.

86 Post Bus, 1928

1997. Historic Service Vehicles. Multicoloured.
170 4k. Type **86** 30 10
171 4k.60 Skoda Sentinel lorry, 1924 . . . . 30 20
172 8k. Tatra fire engine, 1933 . . 60 45

87 Carp, Candle, Fir, Apple and Nut

88 Olympic Rings and Ice Hockey Puck

1997. Christmas.
173 **87** 4k. multicoloured 30 10

1997. Art (5th series). As T **16**.
174 7k. multicoloured 35 15
175 12k. green and black . . . . 1·00 75
176 16k. multicoloured . . . . . 1·10 1·10
DESIGNS—HORIZ: 7k. "Landscape with Chateau in Chantilly" (Antonin Chittussi). VERT: 12k. "The Prophets came out of the Desert" (Frantisek Bilek); 16k. "Parisian Second-hand Booksellers" (T. F. Simon).

1998. Winter Olympic Games, Nagano, Japan.
177 **88** 7k. multicoloured 45 25

89 Jakub Obvrovsky's 1920 Design

90 Pres. Vaclav Havel

1998. Czech Stamp Production.
178 **89** 12k.60 brown and green . . 90 50

1998.
179 **90** 4k.60 green and red . . . 40 10
179a 5k.40 blue and brown . . 40 10
179b 6k.40 agate and blue . . 30 15

91 Cupid and Heart

92 Slalom

1998. St. Valentine's Day.
180 **91** 4k. multicoloured 30 10

1998. World Skibob Championships, Spindleruv Mlyn.
181 **92** 8k. multicoloured 60 30

93 Vysehrad (1938 stamp design)

94 Chick in Egg Shell

1998. "Praga 1998" International Stamp Exhibition (2nd issue). 50th Anniv of First Prague Stamp Exhibition. Sheet 149 × 105 mm.
MS182 **93** 2 × 30k. blue . . . . 4·00 3·75

1998. Easter.
183 **94** 4k. multicoloured 30 10

95 Observatory Building and Telescope Dome

1998. Centenary of Ondrejov Observatory.
184 **95** 4k.60 yellow, black & red 40 30

96 Hands forming Arch and Seal

97 Player celebrating

1998. 650th Anniv of Charles University and New Town, Prague. Sheet 120 × 92 mm containing T **96** and similar vert designs. Each black, red and blue.
MS185 15k. Type **96**; 22k. Charles IV (Holy Roman Emperor and King of Bohemia) and plan of Prague; 23k. Groin vault, St. Vitus's Cathedral . . . . . 4·00 3·25

1998. Czech Gold Medal for Ice Hockey, Winter Olympic Games, Nagano. Sheet 106 × 88 mm.
MS186 **97** 23k. multicoloured . . 1·75 1·50

98 Grey Partridge

99 Book and Copyright Symbol

1998. Endangered Species. Multicoloured.
187 4k.60 Type **98** 40 30
188 4k.60 Black grouse ("Lyrurus tetrix") 40 60
189 8k. White deer ("Cervus elphus") 50 30
190 8k. Elk ("Alces alces") . . . 50 45

1998. World Book and Copyright Day.
191 **99** 10k. multicoloured 75 30

100 The King's Ride, Moravia

1998. Europa. National Festivals. Multicoloured.
192 11k. Type **100** 75 55
193 15k. Carnival masks . . . . 1·10 70

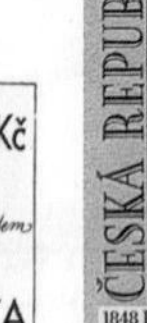

101 Devil Musicians

102 Frantisek Kmoch (composer)

1998. For Children. Multicoloured.
194 4k. Type **101** 30 10
195 4k.60 Water sprite riding catfish 35 10

1998. Anniversaries. Multicoloured.
196 4k. Type **102** (150th birth anniv) 30 10
197 4k.60 Frantisek Palacky (historian, birth bicent) . . 40 30
198 6k. Rafael Kubelik (conductor, 2nd death anniv) 45 30

103 Prague Barricades, June 1848

1998. 150th Anniv of 1848 Revolutions.
199 **103** 15k. multicoloured . . . 1·10 60

1998. Art (6th series). As T **16**. Multicoloured.
200 22k. "Amorpha-Two-coloured Fugue" (Frantisek Kupka) . . . . 1·50 1·10
201 23k. "Flight" (Paul Gauguin) 1·50 1·25

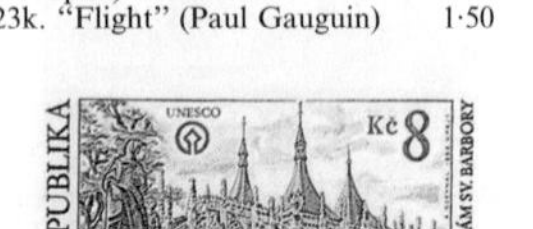

104 St. Barbara's Cathedral, Kutna Hora

1998. World Heritage Sites. Multicoloured.
202 8k. Type **104** 60 30
203 11k. Chateau Valtice 90 45

105 Soldiers with Flags

106 Capricorn

1998. 80th Anniv of Founding of Czechoslovak Republic. Paintings by Vojtech Preissig. Mult.
204 4k.60 Type **105** 40 10
205 5k. Soldiers marching 40 30
206 12k.60 Flags in Mala Street, Prague . . . . 1·00 60

1998. Signs of the Zodiac.
206a – 40h green, brown & blk 10 10
207 **106** 1k. yellow, red and black 10 10
208 – 2k. black, lilac and blue 10 10
209 – 5k. red, black and yellow 40 10
210 – 5k.40 green, black & brn 40 10
211 – 8k. red, black & purple 50 30
212 – 9k. green, black & orge 60 30

213 – 10k. yellow, blue & black 75 30
214 – 12k. orange, blue & black 85 50
216 – 17k. multicoloured . . . 75 45
217 – 20k. violet, black & brn 1·40 70
218 – 26k. multicoloured . . . 1·10 65

DESIGNS: 40h. Pisces; 2k. Virgo; 5k. Taurus; 5k.40; Scorpio; 8k. Cancer; 9k. Libra; 10k. Aquarius; 12k. Leo; 17k. Gemini; 20k. Sagittarius; 26k. Aries.

107 People following Star

1998. Christmas. Multicoloured.
219 4k. Type **107** 25 15
220 6k. Angel with trumpet over village (vert) 50 90

1998. Art (7th series). As T **16**. Multicoloured.
221 15k. Section of "The Greater Cycle" (Jan Preisler) . . . 1·10 90
222 16k. "Spinner" (Josef Navratil) (vert) . . . . . 1·40 1·00

108 1929 2k.50 Prague Stamp

1999. Czech Stamp Production.
223 **108** 4k.60 multicoloured . . . 40 20

109 Cat **110** Ornate Cockerel

1999. Cats. Multicoloured.
224 4k.60 Type **109** 35 15
225 5k. Cat with kitten 35 25
226 7k. Two cats 60 30

1999. Easter.
227 **110** 3k. multicoloured 25 10

111 Hoopoe

1999. Nature Conservation. Multicoloured.
228 4k.60 Type **111** 40 25
229 4k.60 European bee eater ("Merops apiaster") . . . 40 40
230 5k. "Euphydryas maturna" 40 25
231 5k. Rosy underwing ("Catocala electa") 40 25

112 Emblem

1999. Admission of Czech Republic into North Atlantic Treaty Organization.
232 **112** 4k.60 blue and red . . . 40 20

113 Emblem and Sky

1999. 50th Anniv of Council of Europe.
233 **113** 7k. multicoloured 55 20

114 Josef Rossler-Orovsky (co-founder)

1999. Centenary of Czech Olympic Committee.
234 **114** 9k. multicoloured 65 40

115 Sumava National Park

1999. Europa. Parks and Gardens. Multicoloured.
235 11k. Type **115** 85 50
236 17k. Podyji National Park . . 1·25 75

116 "Ferda the Ant, Pytlik the Beetle and The Proud Ladybird" **117** Chain Bridge, Stadlec

1999. For Children. Birth Centenary of Ondrej Sekora (children's writer).
237 **116** 4k.60 multicoloured . . . 30 10

1999. Bridges. Multicoloured.
238 8k. Type **117** 60 40
239 11k. Wooden bridge, Cernvir (horiz) 85 55

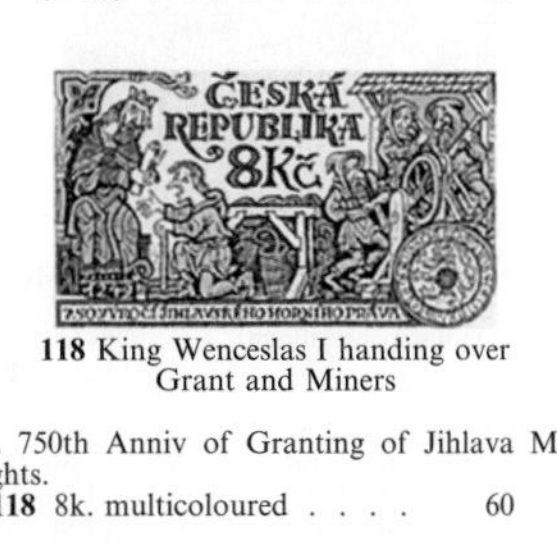

118 King Wenceslas I handing over Grant and Miners

1999. 750th Anniv of Granting of Jihlava Mining Rights.
240 **118** 8k. multicoloured 60 30

119 "UPU", Globe and Emblem

121 Priessnitz and Treatments

120 Barrande and Trilobites

1999. 125th Anniv of Universal Postal Union.
241 **119** 9k. black, blue and green 60 45

1999. Birth Bicentenary of Joachim Barrande (French geologist and palaeontologist). Sheet 106 × 77 mm containing T **120** and similar horiz design. Each green, brown and black.
MS242 13k. Type **120**; 31k. *Deiphon forbesi*, *Ophioceras simplex* and *Carolincrinus barrandei* (trilobites) 3·00 2·00

1999. Birth Bicent of Vincenc Priessnitz (folk healer).
243 **121** 4k.60 multicoloured . . . 30 10

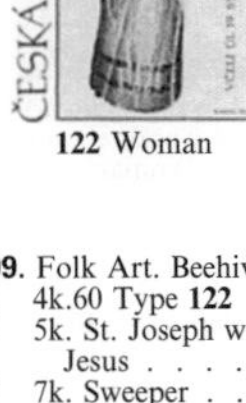

122 Woman

123 Clown Doctor and Laughing New-born Baby

1999. Folk Art. Beehives. Multicoloured.
244 4k.60 Type **122** 20 15
245 5k. St. Joseph with Infant Jesus 35 25
246 7k. Sweeper 65 25

1999. Graphic Humour of Miroslav Bartak. Multicoloured.
247 4k.60 Type **123** 25 10
248 5k. Dog disobeying No Smoking and No Dogs sign 40 30
249 7k. Night sky seeping in under window 65 30

124 "Mother of God" (altar painting)

1999. Beuron School (art movement). Sheet 108 × 166 mm containing T **124** and similar vert design showing paintings in St. Gabriel's Church, Prague. Multicoloured.
MS250 11k. Type **124**; 13k. "Jesus the Pantocrater" (painting in vault of apse) . . . . 1·75 1·40

125 Baby Jesus with Sheep and Lamb

127 Czechoslovakia 1938 1k.+50h. Child Welfare Stamp

126 Brmo, 1593 (after Willenberg)

1999. Christmas.
251 **125** 3k. multicoloured 25 10

1999. Art (8th series). As T **16**. Multicoloured.
252 13k. "Red Orchid" (Jindrich Styrsky) (vert) 90 70
253 17k. "Landscape with Marsh" (Julius Marak) (vert) . . . . 1·25 95
254 26k. "Monument" (Frantisek Hudecek) (vert) . . . . . 1·60 1·40

2000. "Brno 2000" Stamp Exhibition. Multicoloured.
255 5k. Type **126** 35 25
MS256 80 × 100 mm. 50k. St. James's Church (vert) . . . 3·25 2·40

2000. Czech Stamp Production.
257 **127** 5k.40 multicoloured . . . 40 25

128 Kutna Hora Coat of Arms and 14th-century Miners

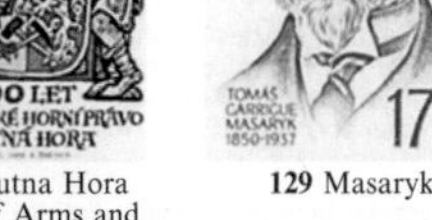

129 Masaryk

2000. 700th Anniv of Granting of Royal Mining Rights to Kutn Hora.
258 **128** 5k. multicoloured 40 25

2000. 150th Birth Anniv of Tomas Masaryk (President of Czechoslovakia, 1918–35). Sheet 60 × 85 mm.
MS259 **129** 17k. blue, ultramarine and red . . . . 1·25 1·00

130 Animal-shaped Cake and Painted Eggs

131 "Winner" (statue, Stursa) and Prague Castle Tower)

2000. Easter.
260 **130** 5k. multicoloured 40 30

2000. Prague, European City of Culture. Sheet 166 × 109 mm containing T **131** and similar multicoloured designs.
MS261 9k. Type **131**; 11k. King David (wooden statue), Na Karlove Church; 17k. King Charles IV statue and Prague Castle (50 × 40 mm) . . . . . 2·50 3·00

132 Vitezslav Nezval (poet) (centenary)

134 "Building Europe"

133 Steam Locomotive, 1900

2000. Birth Anniversaries.
262 **132** 5k. blue, lilac and violet 40 25
263 – 8k. mauve, red and violet 50 35

DESIGN: 8k. Gustav Mahler (composer, 140th anniv).

2000. Conference of European Ministers of Transport, Prague. Railways. Sheet 114 × 112 mm containing T **133** and similar horiz design. Multicoloured.
MS264 8k. Type **133**; 15k. T371 electric locomotive, 2000 . . . 1·60 1·50

2000. Europa.
265 **134** 9k. multicoloured 60 40

135 Alarm Clock and Bird **137** *Geastrum pouzarii*

136 Fermat's Great Theorem

2000. International Children's Day.
266 **135** 5k.40 multicoloured . . . 40 25

2000. World Mathematics Year.
267 **136** 7k. multicoloured 45 40

2000. Endangered Fungi. Multicoloured.
268 5k. Type **137** 20 25
269 5k. Devil's boletus (*Boletus satanas*) 20 25
270 5k.40 *Verpa bohemica* . . . 30 30
271 5k.40 *Morchella pragensis* . . 30 30

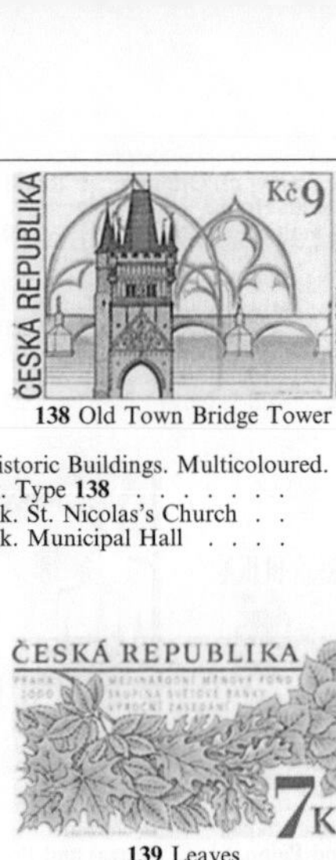

138 Old Town Bridge Tower

2000. Historic Buildings. Multicoloured.

272	9k. Type **138**	35	55
273	11k. St. Nicolas's Church	45	55
274	13k. Municipal Hall	55	65

139 Leaves

2000. Annual International Monetary Fund and World Bank Group Meeting, Prague.
275 **139** 7k. multicoloured 55 40

140 Chariot Racing (detail from amphora)

2000. Olympic Games, Sydney.

276	**140** 9k. red, black and green	60	50
277	– 13k. multicoloured	90	65

DESIGN: 13k. Canoeing and Czech flag.

141 Northern Goshawk and Common Pheasant (Autumn) — 142 Nativity

2000. Hunting and Gamekeeping. Multicoloured.

278	5k. Type **141**	20	30
279	5k. Deer (winter)	20	45
280	5k.40 Mallard and ducklings (spring)	25	30
281	5k.40 Deer (summer)	25	30

2000. Art (9th series). As T **16**. Multicoloured.

282	13k. "St. Luke the Evangelist" (Master Theodoricus) (vert)	90	65
283	17k. "Simon with the Infant Jesus" (Petr Jan Brandl) (vert)	1·10	75
284	26k. "Brunette" (Alfons Mucha) (vert)	1·60	1·40

2000. Christmas.
285 **142** 5k. multicoloured 40 25

143 Cat — 144 Czechoslovakia 1951 5c. Stamp

2000. Old and New Millennia. Multicoloured.

286	9k. Type **143**	60	50
287	9k. Magician pulling rabbit from hat	60	50

2001. Czech Stamp Production. 150th Birth Anniv of Alois Jirasek (writer).
288 **144** 5k.40 multicoloured . . . 40 25

145 Jan Amos Komensky (Comenius) (philosopher) — 146 Cockerel and Woman

2001.
289 **145** 9k. black, red and brown 60 50

2001. Easter.
290 **146** 5k.40 multicoloured . . . 40 25

147 Church, Jakub u Kutne Hory

2001. Czech Architecture. Sheet 113 × 85 mm containing T **147** and similar vert designs. Each orange, green and black.
MS291 13k. Type **147**; 17k. Bucovice Chateau; 31k. The Dancing House, Prague . . . . 4·25 3·25

148 "Allegory of Art" (fresco, Vaclav Vavrincec Reiner)

2001. Baroque Art. Sheet 146 × 117 mm.
MS292 **148** 50k. multicoloured 3·25 3·00

149 Pond

2001. Europa. Water Resources.
293 **149** 9k. lilac and black 60 45

150 Players — 151 Maxipes Fik riding Bicycle

2001. Men's European Volleyball Championship, Ostrava.
294 **150** 12k. multicoloured . . . 1·00 65

2001. International Children's Day. *Vecernicek* (cartoon created by Rudolf Cechura).
295 **151** 5k.40 multicoloured . . . 1·00 25

152 Frantisek Skroup (composer) — 153 Cats

2001. Birth Anniversaries. Multicoloured.

296	5k.40 Type **152** (bicentenary)	35	25
297	16k. Frantisek Halas (poet, centenary)	1·10	60

2001. Greetings Stamp. "Congratulations".
298 **153** 5k.40 multicoloured . . . 40 25

154 West Highland White Terrier

2001. Dogs. Multicoloured.

299	5k.40 Type **154**	35	25
300	5k.40 Beagle	35	25
301	5k.40 Golden retriever	35	25
302	5k.40 German shepherd	35	25

155 Fennec Fox (*Fennecus zerda*)

2001. Zoo Animals. Multicoloured.

303	5k.40 Type **155**	35	25
304	5k.40 Lesser panda (*Ailurus fulgens*)	35	25
305	5k.40 Siberian tiger (*Panthera tigris altaica*)	35	25
306	5k.40 Orang-utan (*Pongo pygmaeus*)	35	25

156 Emblem — 157 Windmill, Kuzelov

2001. "Dialogue between Civilizations".
307 **156** 9k. multicoloured 60 40

2001. Mills. Multicoloured.

308	9k. Type **157**	50	50
309	14k.40 Water mill, Strehom	80	70

158 Kromeriz Chateau

2001. U.N.E.S.C.O. World Heritage Sites. Mult.

310	12k. Type **158**	75	60
311	14k. Holasovice village	70	70

2001. Art (10th series). As T **16**.

312	12k. black, buff and blue	80	75
313	17k. multicoloured	1·25	90
314	26k. multicoloured	1·90	1·50

DESIGNS—VERT: 12k. "The Annunciation of the Virgin Mary" (Michael Jindrich Rentz); 17k. "Sans-Souci Bar in Nimes" (Cyril Bouda); 26k. "The Goose Keeper" (Vaclav Brozik).

159 Christmas Tree and Half Moon carrying Gifts — 160 1938 2k. Stamp

2001. Christmas.
315 **159** 5k.40 multicoloured . . . 40 25

2002. 40th Death Anniv of Max Svabinsky (stamp designer).
316 **160** 5k.40 multicoloured . . . 40 30

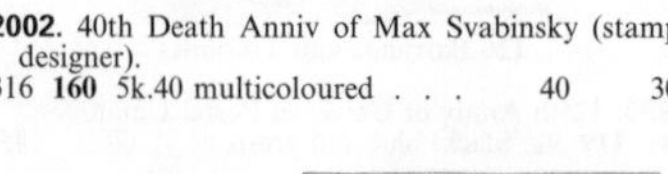

161 Skier — 162 Ski Jumper

2002. Winter Paralympic Games, Salt Lake City, U.S.A.
317 **161** 5k.40 multicoloured . . . 40 25

2002. Winter Olympic Games, Salt Lake City, U.S.A.
318 **162** 12k. multicoloured . . . 80 65

163 Girl with Easter Egg and Boy with Easter Sticks

2002. Easter.
319 **163** 5k.40 multicoloured . . . 25 15

164 Jaromir Vejvoda, Josef Poncar and Karel Vacek

2002. Composers' Birth Centenaries.
320 **164** 9k. black, red and violet 40 25

2002. No. 318 optd **ALES VALENTA ZLATA MEDAILE.**
321 **162** 12k. multicoloured . . . 50 30

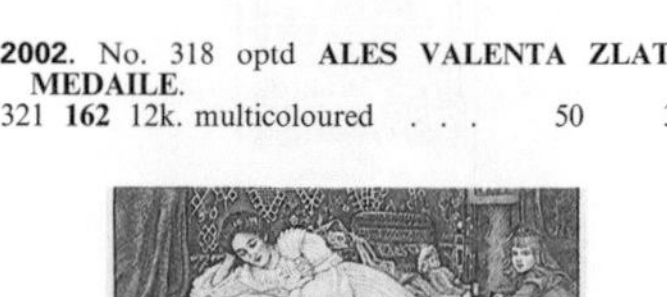

166 "Divan" (Vlaho Bukovac)

2002.
322 **166** 17k. multicoloured . . . 70 45
A stamp in a similar design was issued by Croatia.

167 Circus Tent, Clown and Lion

2002. Europa. Circus.
323 **167** 9k. multicoloured 40 25

168 "Piano Keys–Lake" (Frantisek Kupka) — 169 Mole and Butterfly

2002. Art. Sheet 148 × 105 mm, containing T **168** and similar vert design. Multicoloured.
MS324 23k. Type **168**. 31k. "Man with Broken Nose" (bust) (Auguste Rodin) . . . . 2·10 2·10

2002. For Children.
325 **169** 5k.40 multicoloured . . . 25 15

170 Pearl Oysters — 171 Hus

2002. Nature Conservation.
326 **170** 9k. multicoloured 40 25

2002. Jan Hus (clergyman and preacher) Commemoration.
327 **171** 9k. multicoloured 40 25

172 *Maculinea nausithous*

2002. Endangered Species. Butterflies. Sheet 109 × 65 mm, containing T **172** and similar horiz designs. Multicoloured.
MS328 5k.40, Type **172**; 5k.40, *Maculinea alcon*; 9k. *Maculinea teleius*; 9k. *Maculinea arion* . . 1·10 70

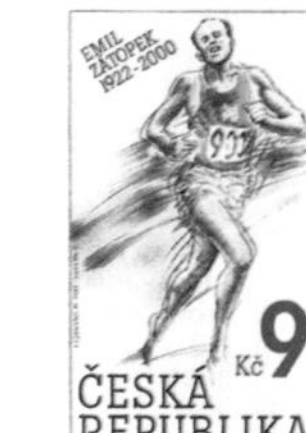

173 Pansy **174** Zatopek

2002. Flowers.
329 50h. Cornflower 10 10
335 **173** 6k.40 multicoloured . . . 30 15
336 6k.50 Dahlia 25 15

2002. 80th Birth Anniv of Emil Zatopek (athlete).
340 **174** 9k. multicoloured 45 25

175 Chateau, Litomysl, Bohemia

2002. U.N.E.S.C.O. World Heritage Sites. Mult.
341 12k. Type **175** 50 30
342 14k. Holy Trinity Column, Olumouc, Moravia (vert) 60 35

176 Angel, St. Nicholas with Basket of Gifts, and Devil **177** Star and Christmas Tree

2002. St Nicholas.
343 **176** 6k.40 multicoloured . . . 30 15

2002. Christmas.
344 **177** 6k.40 multicoloured . . . 30 15

178 Emblem **179** 17th-century Armchair

2002. North Atlantic Treaty Organization Summit Meeting, Prague.
345 **178** 9k. azure, red and blue 40 25

2002. Antique Furniture. Multicoloured.
346 6k.40 Type **179** 30 15
347 9k. Sewing table, 1820 . . . 40 25
348 12k. Thonet dressing table, 1860 . . . . 50 30
349 17k. Armchair, 1923 . . . . 75 45

2002. Art (11th series). As T **16**.
350 12k. black and blue 50 30
351 20k. multicoloured 85 50
352 26k. multicoloured . . . . . 1·10 65
DESIGNS—HORIZ: 12k. "Forlorn Woman" (Jarsolav Panuska). VERT: 20k. "St. Wenceslas" (stained glass window) (Mikolas Ales); 26k. "Young Man with Lute" (Jan Peter Molitor).

180 Lion (statue, Josef Max)

2003. 10th Anniv of Czech Republic. Sheet 78 × 118 mm.
MS353 brown, blue and red . . 1·10 1·10

181 Czechoslovakia 1937 2k.50 Stamp **182** Jaroslav Vrchlicky

2003. Czech Stamp Production. Jan C. Vondrous (stamp designer) and K. Seizinger (engraver) Commemoration.
354 **181** 6k.40 multicoloured . . . 30 15

2003. 150th Birth Anniversaries. Multicoloured.
355 6k.40 Type **182** (writer) . . . 30 15
356 8k. Josef Thomayer (physician and writer) . . . 35 20

183 Easter Egg **184** Rose and Prague

2003. Easter.
357 **183** 6k.40 multicoloured . . . 25 15

2003.
358 **184** 6k.40 multicoloured . . . 25 15

185 18th-century netted Lace

186 Poster for film *La Dolce Vita* (Karel Vaca)

2003. Traditional Crafts. Lace.
359 **185** 6k.40 multicoloured . . . 25 15
360 – 9k. red, deep blue and blue 35 20
DESIGN: 9k. Bobbin lace.

2003. Europa. Poster Art.
361 **186** 9k. multicoloured 35 20

187 Dragon Rocks and Trosky Castle, North-eastern Bohemia

2003. Natural Heritage. Multicoloured.
362 12k. Type **187** 50 30
363 14k. Punkva river caves, Brno 60 35

188 Jonathon (dog), Mach, Sebestova and Telephone (illustration from *The Boy Mach and the Girl Sebestova* (book) (Milos Maourek)) **189** Stone Tower, Klet, South Bohemia

2003. For Children.
364 **188** 6k.40 multicoloured . . . 25 15

2003. Viewing Towers. Multicoloured.
365 6k.40 Type **189** 25 15
366 6k.40 Metal tower, Slovanka, Jablonec and Nisou . . . 25 15

190 Electric Train

2003. Centenary of First Tabor–Bechyne Electric Railway.
367 **190** 10k. multicoloured . . . 45 30

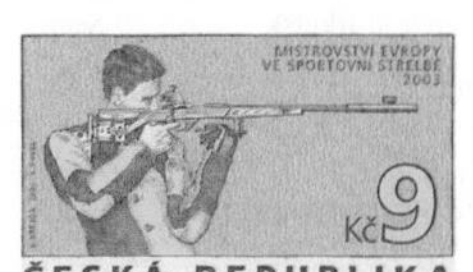

191 Marksman with Rifle

2003. European Marksmanship Championships, Plzen and Brno.
368 **191** 9k. multicoloured 35 20

192 Josef Dubrovsky

193 President Vaclav Klaus

2003. 250th Birth Anniv of Josef Dubrovsky (linguist).
369 **192** 9k. multicoloured 35 20

2003. (1st issue).
370 **193** 6k.40 stone, blue and mauve 25 15
See also No. 384.

194 Siamese Fighting Fish (*Betta splendens*)

2003. Aquarium Fish. Sheet 176 × 115 mm containing T **194** and similar multicoloured designs.
MS371 12k. Type **194**; 14k. Freshwater angelfish (*Pterophyllum scalare*); 16k. Goldfish (*Carassius auratus*) (55 × 46 mm); 20k. Blue discus (*Symphysodon aequifasciatus*) (55 × 46 mm) . . . . 2·75 1·60

195 19th-century Anatolian Prayer Carpet

2003. Oriental Carpets. Multicoloured.
372 9k. Type **195** 35 20
373 12k. 18th-century Islamic carpet 50 30

196 Carving, Porta Coeli Monastery, Predklasteri

2003. Brno 2005 International Stamp Exhibition.
374 **196** 6k.50 multicoloured . . . 25 15

197 Red Kite (*Milvus milvus*)

2003. Birds of Prey. Multicoloured.
375 6k.50 Type **197** 25 15
376 8k. Peregrine falcon (*Falco peregrinus*) 35 20
377 9k. Booted eagle (*Hieraaetus pennatus*) 35 20

198 Wooden Fire Engine (1822)

2003. Fire Engines. Multicoloured.
378 6k.50 Type **198** 25 15
379 9k. Engine (1933) 35 20
380 12k. CSA 8/AVIA Daewoo (2002) 50 30

2003. As T **184** but with colour changed.
381 **184** 6k.50 multicoloured . . . 25 15

199 Hand-made Metal Lantern, Novy Svet, Prague

200 Snow-covered Christmas Tree

2003.
382 **199** 9k. multicoloured 35 20

2003. Christmas.
383 **200** 6k.50 multicoloured . . . 25 15

2003. President Vaclav Klaus (2nd issue). As T **193**.
384 **193** 6k.50 blue and lilac . . . 25 15

2003. Art (12th series). As T **16**. Multicoloured.
385 17k. "Poor Countryside" (Max Svabinsky) 70 45
386 20k. "Autumn in Veltrusy" (Antonín Slavícek) (vert) 85 50
387 26k. "Eleonore from Toledo" (Angola Brozino) (vert) . . 1·10 65

201 Czechoslovakia 1970 1k.80 Stamp
202 Water-powered Hammer, Lniste

2004. Czech Stamp Production. Jivi Svengsbir (designer and engraver) Commemoration.
388 **201** 6k.50 multicoloured . . . 25 15

2004. Iron Works. Multicoloured.
389 6k.50 Type **202** 25 15
390 17k. Iron furnace, Stara Hut u Adamova 75 45

203 Assumption of the Virgin Mary Church, Brno

2004.
391 **203** 17k. multicoloured . . . 70 45

204 Family
205 Players

2004. Easter.
392 **204** 6k.40 multicoloured . . . 25 15

2004. Art (13th series). As T **16**. Multicoloured.
393 26k. multicoloured . . . . . 1·10 65
DESIGNS—VERT: 26k. "Prometheus" (Antonin Prochazka).

2004. World Ice Hockey Championship, Prague and Ostrava.
394 **205** 12k. multicoloured . . . 50 30

206 Stars

2004. Accession to European Union.
395 **206** 9k. blue, yellow and deep blue 35 20

207 Bedrich Smetana

2004. Operatic Composers, Anniversaries. Multicoloured.
396 6k.50 Type **207** (180th birth) 25 15
397 8k. Antoniin Dvorak (death centenary) 35 20
398 10k. Leos Janacek (150th birth) 45 25

208 Family by River

2004. Europa. Holidays.
399 **208** 9k. multicoloured 35 20

CZECHOSLOVAK ARMY IN SIBERIA Pt. 5

During the War of 1914–18 many Czech and Slovak soldiers in the Austro-Hungarian armies surrendered to the Russian Army. After the war many of these formed an army in Siberia and fought the Bolshevists. They issued stamps for their own postal service and these were also sold to the public on the Siberian Railway.

100 kopeks = 1 rouble.

1 Church in Irkutsk
3 Sentry

1919. Imperf.
1 **1** 25k. red . . . . 17·00 12·50
2 – 50k. green . . . . 17·00 32·00
3 **3** 1r. red . . . . 32·00 25·00
DESIGN: 50k. Armoured train "Orlik".

1920. Perf.
4 **1** 25k. red . . . . 14·00 10·00
5 – 50k. green (as No. 2) . . . . 14·00 10·00
6 **3** 1r. brown . . . . 21·00 19·00

4 Lion of Bohemia

1919.
7 **4** (25k.) red and blue . . . . . 1·75

1920. No. 7 optd **1920**.
8 **4** (25k.) red and blue . . . . . 8·00

1920. No. 8 surch.
9 **4** 2(k.) red and blue . . . . . 35·00
10 3(k.) red and blue . . . . . 35·00
11 5(k.) red and blue . . . . . 35·00
12 10(k.) red and blue . . . . . 35·00
13 15(k.) red and blue . . . . . 35·00
14 25(k.) red and blue . . . . . 35·00
15 35(k.) red and blue . . . . . 35·00
16 50(k.) red and blue . . . . . 35·00
17 1r. red and blue . . . . . . 35·00

CZECHOSLOVAKIA Pt. 5

Formed in 1918 by the Czechs of Bohemia and Moravia and the Slovaks of northern Hungary (both part of Austro-Hungarian Empire). Occupied by Germany in 1939 (see note after No. 393c); independence restored 1945.

On 31 December 1992 the Czech and Slovak Federative Republic was dissolved, the two constituent republics becoming independent as the Czech Republic and Slovakia.

100 haleru = 1 koruna.

1
2 Hradcany, Prague

1918. Roul.
1 **1** 10h. blue . . . . 13·50 15·00
2 20h. red . . . . 13·50 15·00

1918. (a) Imperf.
4 **2** 3h. mauve 10 10
9 30h. olive 25 10
10 40h. orange 25 10
12 100h. brown 65 10
14 400h. violet . . . . 1·40 25

(b) Imperf or perf.
5 **2** 5h. green 10 10
6 10h. red 10 10
7 20h. green 10 10
8 25h. blue 10 10
13 200h. blue . . . . 1·10 10

3

1919. Imperf or perf.
3 **3** 1h. brown 10 10
38 5h. green 10 10
39 10h. green 10 10
40 15h. red 10 10
41 20h. red 10 10
28 25h. purple 10 10
49 30h. mauve 35 10
11 50h. purple 25 10
30 50h. blue 25 10
50 60h. orange 25 10
32 75h. green 65 10
33 80h. green . . . . 1·10 10
34 120h. black . . . . 1·10 40
35 300h. green . . . . 3·50 40
36 500h. brown . . . . 2·10 35
37 1000h. purple . . . . 11·50 80

6
7

1919. 1st Anniv of Independence and Czechoslovak Legion Commemoration.
61 **6** 15h. green 10 10
62 25h. brown 10 10
63 50h. blue 10 10
64 **7** 75h. grey 10 10
65 100h. brown 10 10
66 120h. violet on yellow . . . 10 10

1919. Charity. Stamps of Austria optd **POSTA CESKOSLOVENSKA 1919**. A. Postage stamp issue of 1916.
67 **49** 3h. violet 10 40
68 5h. green 10 40
69 6h. orange 50 60
70 10h. purple 60 90
71 12h. blue 60 60
72 **60** 15h. red 10 10
73 20h. green 10 10
75 25h. blue 10 25
76 30h. violet 10 25
77 **51** 40h. green 10 25
78 50h. green 10 25
79 60h. blue 10 25
80 80h. brown 10 25
81 90h. purple 45 60
82 1k. red on yellow 30 40
83aa **52** 2k. blue . . . . 1·40 2·10
85aa 3k. red . . . . 5·25 7·00
87 a 4k. green . . . . 13·00 14·00
89 a 10k. violet £350 £300

B. Air stamps of 1918 optd **FLUGPOST** or surch also.
91 **52** 1k.50 on 2k. mauve . . . . 90·00 80·00
92 2k.50 on 3k. yellow £120 £110
93 4k. grey £650 £500

C. Newspaper stamp of 1908. Imperf.
94 N **43** 10h. red £1500 £1500

D. Newspaper stamps of 1916. Imperf.
95 N **53** 2h. brown 10 25
96 4h. green 25 35
97 6h. blue 25 30
98 10h. orange . . . . . . 3·00 4·50
99 30h. red . . . . 1·50 1·50

E. Express Newspaper stamps of 1916.
100 N **54** 2h. red on yellow . . . 26·00 25·00
101 5h. green on yellow . . £1200 £900

F. Express Newspaper stamps of 1917.
102 N **61** 2h. red on yellow . . . 10 15
103 5h. green on yellow . . 10 15

G. Postage Due stamps of 1908.
104 D **44** 2h. red £5000 £3500
105 4h. red . . . . 21·00 21·00
106 6h. red . . . . 11·00 8·00
108 14h. red . . . . 45·00 4·00
109 25h. red . . . . 35·00 32·00
110 30h. red £350 £275
111 50h. red £800 £700

H. Postage Due stamps of 1916.
112 D **55** 5h. red 10 10
113 10h. red 15 20
114 15h. red 15 20
115 20h. red . . . . 1·90 2·40
116 25h. red . . . . 1·00 1·50
117 30h. red 40 80
118 40h. red . . . . 1·00 1·50
119 50h. red £400 £250
120 D **56** 1k. blue . . . . 9·00 7·00
121 5k. blue . . . . 30·00 30·00
122 10k. blue £325 £250

I. Postage Due stamps of 1916 (optd **PORTO** or surch **15** also).
123 **36** 1h. black . . . . 21·00 17·00
124 – 15h. on 2h. violet . . . . 95·00 85·00

J. Postage Due stamps of 1917 (surch **PORTO** and value).
125 **50** 10h. on 24h. blue . . . . 70·00 75·00
126 15h. on 36h. violet 40 60
127 20h. on 54h. orange . . . 85·00 90·00
128 50h. on 42h. brown . . . 40 65

1919. Various stamps of Hungary optd **POSTA CESKOSLOVENSKA 1919**. A. Postage stamp issue of 1900 ("Turul" type).
129 **7** 1f. grey £2250 £1600
130 2f. yellow . . . . 3·50 5·25
131 3f. orange . . . . 38·00 25·00
132 6f. olive . . . . 4·25 5·25
133 50f. lake on blue 55 60
134 60f. green on red . . . . . 40·00 35·00
135 70f. brown on green £2250 £1600

B. Postage stamp issue of 1916 ("Harvester" and "Parliament" types).
136 **18** 2f. brown (No. 245) . . . 10 10
137 3f. red 10 10
138 5f. green 10 10
139 6f. blue 45 60
140 10f. red (No. 250) . . . . 90 1·25
141 10f. red (No. 243) £300 £200
142 15f. purple (No. 251) . . . 10 25
143 15f. purple (No. 244) . . . £170 £110
144 20f. brown . . . . 7·00 9·00
145 25f. blue 55 60
146 35f. brown . . . . 7·00 10·50
147 40f. green . . . . 1·90 2·00
148 **19** 50f. purple 55 65
149 75f. green 45 50
150 80f. green . . . . 90 1·10
151 1k. red . . . . 1·25 1·25
152 2k. brown . . . . 7·00 10·50
153 3k. grey and violet . . . . 35·00 35·00
154 5k. lt brown & brown . . . 85·00 65·00
155 10k. mauve and brown . . £1200 £850

C. Postage stamp issue of 1918 ("Charles" and "Zita" types).
156 **27** 10f. red 10 10
157 20f. brown 25 30
158 25f. blue . . . . 1·50 1·10
159 **28** 40f. green . . . . 2·75 2·50
160 50f. purple . . . . 38·00 26·00

D. War Charity stamps of 1916.
161 **20** 10+2f. red 30 60
162 – 15+2f. lilac (No. 265) . . . 45 90
163 **22** 40+2f. red . . . . 6·75 3·75

E. Postage stamps of 1919 ("Harvester" type inscr "MAGYAR POSTA").
164 **30** 10f. red (No. 305) . . . . 7·50 9·00
165 20f. brown £5500 £6500

F. Newspaper stamp of 1900.
166 N **9** 2f. orange (No. N136) . . 10 30

G. Express Letter stamp of 1916.
167 E **18** 2f. olive & red (No. E245) 10 30

H. Postage Due stamps of 1903 with figures in black.
170 D **9** 1f. green (No. D170) . . £1300 £1000
173 2f. green £650 £550
174 5f. green £1400 £1100
168 12f. green £5000 £4000
172 50f. green £325 £225

I. Postage Due stamps of 1915 with figures in red.
176 D **9** 1f. green (No. D190) . . £150 £110
177 2f. green 60 50
178 5f. green . . . . 9·00 14·00
179 6f. green . . . . 1·50 1·75
180 10f. green 30 45
181 12f. green . . . . 1·90 2·40
182 15f. green . . . . 5·25 9·00
183 20f. green . . . . 70 1·10
184 30f. green . . . . 30·00 38·00

9 President Masaryk
10
11 Allegories of Republic

12 Hussite
13

1920.
185 **9** 125h. blue 60 20
186 500h. black . . . . 2·75 2·00
187 1,000h. brown . . . . . . 4·50 4·25

1920.
188 **10** 5h. blue 10 10
189 5h. violet 10 10
190 10h. green 10 10
191 10h. olive 10 10
192 15h. brown 10 10
196 **11** 20h. red 10 10

193b 10 20h. orange 10 10
197 11 25h. brown 10 10
194a 10 25h. green 10 10
198 11 30h. purple 10 10
195 10 30h. purple 10 10
199 11 40h. brown . . . . . . 4·00 10
200 50h. red 10 10
201 50h. green 10 10
202 60h. blue 10 10
203 12 80h. violet 10 25
204 90h. sepia 30 50
205 13 100h. green 40 10
206 11 100h. brown 45 10
227 13 100h. red on yellow . . . 2·00 10
207 11 150h. red . . . . . . 3·00 70
208 185h. orange . . . . . . 1·25 20
209 13 200h. purple 70 10
228 200h. blue on yellow . . 6·00 10
210 11 250h. green . . . . . 2·25 45
211 13 300h. red . . . . . . 1·50 10
229 300h. purple on yellow . . 5·25 10
212 400h. brown . . . . . 4·25 55
213 500h. green . . . . . 5·25 55
214 600h. purple . . . . . 7·00 55

1920. Air. Surch with airplane and value. Imperf or perf.
215 2 14k. on 200h. blue (No. 13) 15·00 25·00
216 3 24k. on 500h. brn (No. 36) 38·00 38·00
220 28k. on 1000h. pur (No. 37) 38·00 32·00

1920. Red Cross Fund. Surch with new value in emblem
221 2 40h.+20h. yellow 80 95
222 3 60h.+20h. green 80 95
223 9 125h.+25h. blue . . . . . . 2·25 2·75

1922. Surch with airplane and value.
224 13 50 on 100h. green . . . . 1·50 2·25
225 100 on 200h. purple . . . 3·75 3·75
226 250 on 400h. brown . . . 6·00 8·00

18 President Masaryk, after portrait by M. Savatimsky
20 
23a 

1923. 5th Anniv of Republic.
230 18 50h. (+50h.) green 90 65
231 100h. (+100h.) red . . . . 1·25 1·10
232 200h. (+200h.) blue . . . . 6·25 6·50
233 300h. (+300h.) brown . . . 7·50 8·00

1925.
234 20 40h. orange 75 20
235 50h. green . . . . . . 1·50 10
236 60h. purple . . . . . . 1·90 10
237 18 1k. red 90 10
238 2k. blue . . . . 3·00 30
245 3k. brown . . . . 6·75 10
240 5k. green . . . . 1·75 30
The 1, 2 and 3k. (which with the 5k. differ slightly in design from the haleru values) come in various sizes, differing in some cases in the details of the designs.

1925. International Olympic Congress. Optd **CONGRES OLYMP. INTERNAT. PRAHA 1925.**
246 18 50h. (+50h.) green . . . . 5·25 10·00
247 100h. (+100h.) red . . . . 8·25 14·00
248 200h. (+200h.) blue . . . . 50·00 90·00

1926. 8th All-Sokol Display, Prague. Optd **VIII. SLET VSESOKOLSKY PRAHA 1926.**
249 18 50h. (+50h.) green . . . . 4·25 6·00
250 100h. (+100h.) red . . . . 4·25 6·00
251 200h. (+200h.) blue . . . . 20·00 21·00
252 300h. (+300h.) brown . . . 32·00 45·00

1926.
254b 23a 50h. green 10 10
254c 60h. purple 60 10
254d 1k. red 25 10

25 Karluv Tyn Castle
26 Strahov 
27 Pernstyn Castle 

28 Orava Castle
30 Hradcany, Prague 

1926. Perf or imperf × perf.
267 25 20h. red 25 10
268 27 30h. green 10 10
258 28 40h. brown 50 10
259 25 1k.20 purple 35 45
270 26 1k.20 purple 35 10
271 25 1k.50 red 35 10
272 27 2k. green 25 10
263 30 2k. blue 75 10
273 25 2k.50 blue . . . . 5·25 25
273a – 2k.50 blue 35 10
273b 28 3k. brown 45 10
264a 30 3k. red . . . . 1·75 10
265 – 4k. purple . . . . 5·25 65
277 – 5k. green . . . . 7·50 1·10
DESIGNS—As T **25/28**: 2k.50 (No. 273a), Statue of St. Wenceslas, Prague. As T **30**: 4, 5k. Upper Tatra.

32 Hradek Castle
33 Pres. Masaryk 

1928. 10th Anniv of Independence.
278 32 30h. black 10 10
279 – 40h. brown 10 10
280 – 50h. green 15 15
281 – 60h. red 15 25
282 – 1k. red 25 20
283 – 1k.20 purple 35 65
284 – 2k. blue 40 65
285 – 2k.50 blue . . . . 1·25 1·75
286 33 3k. sepia . . . . 1·00 1·25
287 – 5k. violet . . . . 1·25 2·25
DESIGNS—HORIZ: 40h. Town Hall, Levoca; 50h. Telephone Exchange, Prague; 60h. Village of Jasina; 1k. Hluboka Castle; 1k.20, Pilgrim's House, Velehrad; 2k.50, The Grand Tatra. VERT: 2k. Brno Cathedral; 5k. Town Hall, Prague.

34 National Arms
35 St. Wenceslas on Horseback 

1929. Perf or imperf × perf.
287a 34 5h. blue 10 10
287b 10h. brown 10 10
288 20h. red 10 10
289 25h. green 10 10
290 30h. purple 10 10
291a 40h. brown 10 10

1929. Death Millenary of St. Wenceslas.
293 35 50h. green 15 10
294 – 60h. violet 30 10
295 – 2k. blue 65 35
296 – 3k. brown 95 25
297 – 5k. purple . . . . 3·00 2·50
DESIGNS: 2k. Foundation of St. Vitus's Church; 3k., 5k. Martyrdom of St. Wenceslas.

36 Brno Cathedral

1929.
298 36 3k. brown . . . . 1·10 10
299 – 4k. blue . . . . 3·50 60
300 – 5k. green . . . . 3·00 35
301 – 10k. violet . . . . 7·50 3·00
DESIGNS: 4k. Tatra Mountains; 5k. Town Hall, Prague; 10k. St. Nicholas Church, Prague.

38
39 

1930.
302a 38 50h. green 10 10
303 60h. purple 45 10
304 1k. red 10 10
See also No. 373.

1930. 80th Birthday of President Masaryk.
305 39 2k. green 70 35
306 3k. red . . . . 1·10 35
307 5k. blue . . . . 3·00 2·40
308 10k. black . . . . 6·00 4·75

40 Fokker F.IXD
41 Smolik S.19 

1930. Air.
394 40 30h. violet 10 10
309 50h. green 10 20
310 1k. red 25 30
311 41 2k. green 45 70
312 3k. purple . . . . 1·40 95
313 – 4k. blue 85 90
314 – 5k. brown . . . . 2·75 1·90
315 – 10k. blue . . . . 4·00 5·25
316 – 20k. violet . . . . 5·00 5·00
DESIGNS—As Type **41**: 4, 5k. Smolik S.19 with tree in foreground; 10, 20k. Fokker F.IXD over Prague.

43 Krumlov
44 Dr. Miroslav Tyrs 

1932. Views.
317 – 3k.50 purple (Krivoklat) 1·25 1·00
318 – 4k. blue (Orlik) . . . . . 1·40 60
319 43 5k. green . . . . 2·25 60

1932. Birth Centenary of Dr. Tyrs, founder of the "Sokol" Movement.
320 44 50h. green 30 10
321 1k. red 80 10
322 – 2k. blue . . . . 5·00 40
323 – 3k. brown . . . . 8·00 50
On the 2k. and 3k. the portrait faces left.

46 Dr. M. Tyrs
47 Church and Episcopal Palace, Nitra 

1933.
324 46 60h. violet 10 10

1933. 1100th Anniv of Foundation of 1st Christian Church at Nitra.
325 47 50h. green 30 10
326 – 1k. red (Church gateway) 3·25 25

49 Frederick Smetana
50 Consecrating Colours at Kiev 

1934. 50th Death Anniv of Smetana.
327 49 50h. green 10 10

1934. 20th Anniv of Czechoslovak Foreign Legions.
328 50 50h. green 20 10
329 – 1k. red 25 10
330 – 2k. blue . . . . 1·75 25
331 – 3k. brown . . . . 2·25 30
DESIGNS—HORIZ: 1k. French battalion enrolling at Bayonne. VERT: 2k. Standard of the Russian Legion; 3k. French, Russian and Serbian legionaries.

52 Antonin Dvorak
53 "Where is my Fatherland?" 

1934. 30th Death Anniv of Dvorak.
332 52 50h. green 10 10

1934. Centenary of Czech National Anthem.
333 53 1k. purple 30 20
334 2k. blue 80 40

54 Autograph portrait of Pres. Masaryk
55 

1935. 85th Birthday of President Masaryk.
335 54 50h. green 15 10
336 1k. red 30 10
337 55 2k. blue . . . . 1·00 35
338 3k. brown . . . . 2·10 50
See also No. 374.

56 Czech Monument, Arras
57 Gen. M. R. Stefanik 

1935. 20th Anniv of Battle of Arras.
339 56 1k. red 40 10
340 2k. blue 95 45

1935. 16th Death Anniv of Gen. Stefanik.
341 57 50h. green 10 10

58 St. Cyril and St. Methodius
59 J. A. Komensky (Comenius) 

60 Dr. Edward Benes
60a Gen. M. R. Stefanik 
61 Pres. Masaryk 

1935. Prague Catholic Congress.
342 58 50h. green 15 10
343 1k. red 25 10
344 2k. blue 95 45

1935.
345 59 40h. blue 10 10
346 60 50h. green 10 10
390 60a 50h. green 10 10
347 60h. violet 10 10
391 60h. blue . . . . 7·00 14·00
348 61 1k. purple 10 10
395 1k. purple 10 10
No. 390 differs from No. 341 in having an ornament in place of the word "HALERU".
No. 348 has "1 Kc" in value tablets, No. 395 "1 K".

62 Symbolic of Infancy
63 K. H. Macha 

1936. Child Welfare.
349 – 50h.+50h. green 25 35
350 62 1k.+50h. red 40 55
351 – 2k.+50h. blue . . . . . . 1·10 1·50
DESIGN: 50h., 2k. Grandfather, mother and child from centre of Type **62** (enlarged).

1936. Death Centenary of Macha (poet).
352 63 50h. green 10 10
353 1k. red 30 10

64 Banska Bystrica
65 Podebrady 

1936.
354 – 1k.20 purple 10 10
355 64 1k.50 red 10 10
355a – 1k.60 olive 10 10
356 – 2k. green 10 10
357 – 2k.50 blue 10 10
358 – 3k. brown 10 10
359 – 3k.50 violet 70 45
360 65 4k. violet 30 10
361 – 5k. green 30 10
362 – 10k. blue 55 45
DESIGNS—As Type **64**: 1k.20, Palanok Castle; 1k.60, St. Barbara's Church, Kutna Hora; 2k. Zvikov (Klingden Berg) Castle; 2k.50, Strecno Castle; 3k. Hruba Skala Castle (Cesky Raj); 3k.50, Slavkov Castle; 5k. Town Hall, Olomouc ($23\frac{1}{2} \times 29\frac{1}{2}$ mm). As Type **65**: 10k. Bratislava and Danube.

66 President Benes

1937.
363 66 50h. green 10 10

67 Mother and Child   **68** "Lullaby"

1937. Child Welfare.
364 **67** 50h.+50h. green 30 50
365 1k.+50h. red 40 65
366 **68** 2k.+1k. blue . . . . 90 1·50

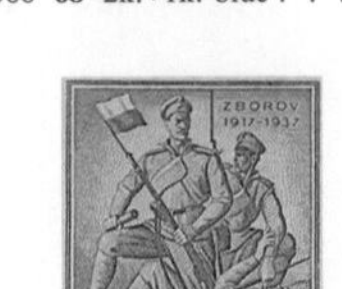

69 Czech Legionaries   **70** Prague

1937. 20th Anniv of Battle of Zborov.
367 **69** 50h. green 15 10
368 1k. red 15 10

1937. 16th Anniv of Founding of Little Entente.
369 **70** 2k. green 45 10
370 2k.50 blue 70 50

71 J. E. Purkyne   **73** Peregrine Falcon

72a Gen. Stefanik Memorial

1937. 150th Birth Anniv of J. E. Purkyne (physiologist).
371 **71** 50h. green 10 10
372 1k. red 15 10

1937. Mourning for Pres. Masaryk. As T **38** and **55**, but panels of T **55** dated "14.IX.1937".
373 **38** 50h. black 10 10
374 **55** 2k. black 25 10

1937. Labour Congress, Prague. Optd **B.I.T. 1937**.
375 **66** 50h. green 15 30
376 **64** 1k.50 red 15 30
377 – 2k. green (No. 356) 35 60

1937. Philatelic Exhibition, Bratislava. (a) Sheet 150 × 110 mm.
MS377a 50h. blue (Poprad Lake, Tatra Mountains); 1k. red (as T **72a**) . . . . 1·50 2·25
(b) Sheet 150 × 165 mm containing 25 of No. N368.
MS377b N **67** 10h. red . . . . . 2·25 12·00

1938. 10th International Sokol Display, Prague.
378 **73** 50h. green 15 10
379 1k. red 15 10

74 Pres. Masaryk and Slovak Girl   **75** Czech Legionaries at Bachmac

1938. Child Welfare and Birthday of Late President Masaryk.
380 **74** 50h.+50h. green 30 50
381 **74** 1k.+50h. red 40 65
MS381a 71 × 91 mm. Memorial sheet **74**; 2k.+3k. black. Imperf 2·40 3·50

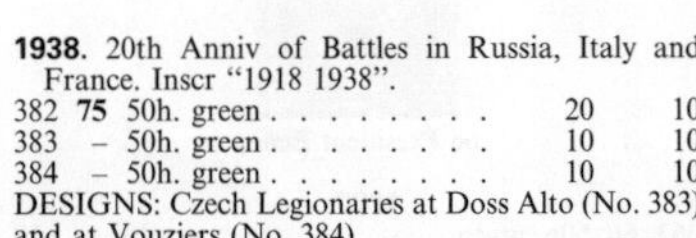

1938. 20th Anniv of Battles in Russia, Italy and France. Inscr "1918 1938".
382 **75** 50h. green 20 10
383 – 50h. green 10 10
384 – 50h. green 10 10
DESIGNS: Czech Legionaries at Doss Alto (No. 383) and at Vouziers (No. 384).

76 J. Fugner   **77** Armament Factories, Pilsen

1938. 10th Sokol Summer Games.
385 **76** 50h. green 10 10
386 1k. red 10 10
387 2k. blue 15 10

1938. Provincial Economic Council Meeting, Pilsen.
388 **77** 50h. green 10 10

77a Vysehrad   **78** St. Elizabeth's Cathedral, Kosice

1938. Prague Philatelic Exhibition.
MS388a 148 × 105 mm. 50h. blue (T **77a**); 1k. red (Hradcany, Prague) 3·25 3·50

1938. Kosice Cultural Exhibition.
389 **78** 50h. green 10 10

79 "Peace"   **80** Jasina

1938. 20th Anniv of Czech Republic.
392 **79** 2k. blue 15 10
393 3k. brown 35 10
MS393a 71 × 90 m. 2k. (+8k.) blue (T **79**) . . . . 2·25 3·50

1939. Inauguration of Slovak Parliament. No. 362 surcharged **Otvorenie slovenskeho snemu 18.1.1939** and **300 h** between bars.
393b 300h. on 10k. blue . . . . 55 3·00
No. 393b was only issued in Slovakia but was withdrawn prior to the establishment of the Slovak state. The used price is for cancelled to order stamps.

1939. Inaug of Carpatho-Ukrainian Parliament.
393c **80** 3k. blue . . . . 10·00 65·00
The used price is for cancelled-to-order.

From mid-1939 until 1945, Czechoslovakia was divided into the German Protectorate of Bohemia and Moravia and the independent state of Slovakia. Both these countries issued their own stamps. Germany had already occupied Sudetenland where a number of unauthorized local issues were made at Asch, Karlsbad, Konstantinsbad, Hiklasdorf, Reichenberg-Maffersdorf and Rumburg. Hungary occupied Carpatho-Ukraine and the stamps of Hungary were used there. In 1945, upon liberation, stamps of Czechoslovakia were once again issued.

81 Clasped Hands   **82** Arms and Soldier

1945. Kosice Issue. Imperf.
396 **81** 1k.50 purple . . . . 1·50 2·00
397 **82** 2k. red 20 25
398 5k. green . . . . 2·00 1·75
399 6k. blue 45 40
400 **81** 9k. red 25 35
401 13k. brown 65 70
402 20k. blue . . . . 1·40 1·40
MS402a 132 × 120 mm. Nos. 397/9 3·50 4·25

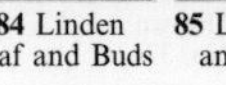

83 Arms and Linden Leaf   **84** Linden Leaf and Buds   **85** Linden Leaf and Flower

1945. Bratislava Issue. Imperf.
403 **83** 50h. green 10 10
404 1k. purple 10 10
405 1k.50 red 10 10
406 2k. blue 10 10
407 2k.40 red 30 30
408 3k. brown 10 10
409 4k. green 15 10
410 6k. violet 15 10
411 10k. brown 30 20

1945. Prague Issue.
412 **84** 10h. black 10 10
413 30h. brown 10 10
414 50h. green 10 10
415 60h. blue 10 10
416 **85** 60h. blue 10 10
417 80h. red 10 10
418 120h. red 10 10
419 300h. purple 10 10
420 500h. green 10 10

86 Pres. Masaryk   **87** Staff Capt. Ridky

1945. Moscow Issue. Perf.
421 **86** 5h. violet 10 10
422 10h. yellow 10 10
423 20h. brown 10 10
424 50h. green 10 10
425 1k. red 10 10
426 2k. blue 10 10

1945. War Heroes.
427 **87** 5h. grey 10 10
428 – 10h. brown 10 10
429 – 20h. red 10 10
430 – 25h. red 10 10
431 – 30h. violet 15 10
432 – 40h. brown 10 10
433 – 50h. green 10 10
434 – 60h. violet 15 10
435 **87** 1k. red 10 10
436 – 1k.50 red 10 10
437 – 2k. blue 10 10
438 – 2k.50 violet 10 10
439 – 3k. brown 10 10
440 – 4k. mauve 10 10
441 – 5k. green 10 10
442 – 10k. blue 15 10
PORTRAITS: 10h., 1k.50, Dr. Novak. 20h., 2k. Capt. O. Jaros. 25h., 2k.50, Staff Capt. Zimprich. 30h., 3k. Lt. J. Kral. 40h., 4k. J. Gabcik (parachutist). 50h., 5k. Staff Capt. Vasatko. 60h., 10k. Fr. Adamek.

88 Allied Flags   **89** Russian Soldier and Slovak Partisan

1945. 1st Anniv of Slovak Rising.
443 **88** 1k.50 red 10 10
444 – 2k. blue 10 10
445 **89** 4k. brown 20 25
446 – 4k.50 violet 20 25
447 – 5k. green 25 40
MS447a 148 × 210 mm. Nos. 443/7 32·00 42·00
DESIGNS—VERT: 2k. Banska Bystrica. HORIZ: 4k.50, Sklabina; 5k. Strecno and partisan.

90 Pres. Masaryk   **91** Pres. Benes   **92**

1945.
452 – 30h. purple 10 10
448 **90** 50h. brown 10 10
453 **91** 60h. blue 15 10
449 – 80h. green 10 10
454 – 1k. orange 10 10
455 **90** 1k.20 red 15 10
456 1k.20 mauve 10 10
450 **91** 1k.60 green 15 10
457 – 2k.40 red 10 10
458 **91** 3k. purple 20 10
459 **90** 4k. blue 15 10
460 5k. green 20 10
461 **91** 7k. black 25 10
462 – 10k. blue 55 10
451 **90** 15k. purple 50 10
462a – 20k. brown 85 10

PORTRAIT: 30h., 80h., 1k., 2k.40, 10k., 20k. Gen. M. R. Stefanik.

1945. Students' World Congress, Prague.
463 **92** 1k.50+1k.50 red 10 10
464 2k.50+2k.50 blue 20 20

93 J. S. Kozina Monument   **94** St. George and Dragon

1945. Execution of Jan Stadky Kozina, 1695.
465 **93** 2k.40 red 15 10
466 4k. blue 20 25

1946. Victory.
467 **94** 2k.40+2k.60 red 15 15
468 4k.+6k. blue 20 15
MS468a 79 × 91 mm. T **94** 4k.+6k. blue . . . . 90 1·00

94a Lockheed Constellation over Charles Bridge, Prague

1946. Air. 1st Prague–New York Flight.
468b **94a** 24k. blue on buff . . . 90 85
See also Nos. 475/6.

95 Capt. F. Novak and Westland Lysander   **96** Lockheed Constellation over Bratislava

1946. Air.
469 **95** 1k.50 red 15 10
470 5k.50 blue 35 15
471 9k. purple 60 20
472 **96** 10k. green 50 35
473 **95** 16k. violet 80 30
474 **96** 20k. blue 80 50
475 **94a** 24k. red . . . . 1·00 75
476 50k. blue . . . . 2·00 1·25

97 K. H. Borovsky   **98** Brno

1946. 90th Death Anniv of Borovsky (Independence advocate).
477 **97** 1k.20h. grey 10 10

1946.
478 **98** 2k.40 red 40 15
479 – 7k.40 violet (Hodonin) (horiz) 20 10
MS479a 69 × 89 mm. No. 478 . . 90 70

100 Emigrants   **101** President Benes

1946. Repatriation Fund.
480 – 1k.60+1k.40 brown . . . 55 55
481 **100** 2k.40+2k.60 red 20 25
482 – 4k.+4k. blue 30 45
DESIGNS: 1k.60, Emigrants' departure; 4k. Emigrants' return.

1946. Independence Day.
483 **101** 60h. blue 10 10
484 1k.60 green 10 10
485 3k. purple 10 10
486 8k. purple 20 10

102 Flag and Symbols of Transport, Industry, Agriculture and Learning

103 St. Adalbert

1947. "Two Year Plan".
487 **102** 1k.20 green 10 10
488 2k.40 red 10 10
489 4k. blue 50 20

1947. 950th Death Anniv of St. Adalbert (Bishop of Prague).
490 **103** 1k.60 black 45 45
491 2k.40 red 65 60
492 5k. green . . . . 1·00 40

104 "Grief"

105 Rekindling Flame of Remembrance

1947. 5th Anniv of Destruction of Lidice.
493 **104** 1k.20 black 30 30
494 1k.60 black 45 45
495 **105** 2k.40 mauve 55 45

106 Congress Emblem

107 Pres. Masaryk

1947. Youth Festival.
496 **106** 1k.20 purple 45 25
497 4k. grey 45 15

1947. 10th Death Anniv of Pres Masaryk.
498 **107** 1k.20 black on buff . . . 15 10
499 4k. blue on cream 25 25

108 Stefan Moyses

109 "Freedom"

1947. 150th Birth Anniv of Stefan Moyses (Slavonic Society Organizer).
500 **108** 1k.20 purple 15 10
501 4k. blue 25 25

1947. 30th Anniv of Russian Revolution.
502 **109** 2k.40 red 30 15
503 4k. blue 50 15

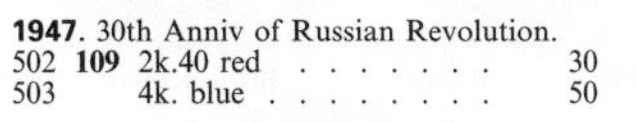

110 Pres. Benes

1948.
504 **110** 1k.50 brown 10 10
505 2k. purple (19 × 23 mm) 10 10
506 5k. blue (19 × 23 mm) . . 15 10

111 "Athletes paying Homage to Republic"

115 Dr. J. Vanicek

1948. 11th Sokol Congress, Prague. (a) 1st issue.
507 **111** 1k.50 brown 10 10
508 3k. red 15 10
509 5k. blue 40 10

(b) 2nd issue. Inscr "XI. VSESOKOLSKY SLET V PRAZE 1948".
515 **115** 1k. green 10 10
516 – 1k.50 brown 15 10
517 – 2k. blue 15 10
518 **115** 3k. purple 20 10
PORTRAIT: 1k.50, 2k. Dr. J. Scheiner.

112 Charles IV

113 St. Wenceslas and Charles IV

1948. 600th Anniv of Charles IV University, Prague.
510 **112** 1k.50 brown on buff . . . 10 10
511 **113** 2k. brown on buff 15 10
512 3k. red on buff 15 10
513 **112** 5k. blue on buff 20 20

114 Insurgents

117 Fr. Palacky and Dr. F. L. Rieger

1948. Centenary of Abolition of Serfdom.
514 **114** 1k.50 black 10 10

1948. Cent of Constituent Assembly at Kromeriz.
519 **117** 1k.50 violet on buff . . . 10 10
520 3k. purple on buff 15 10

118 J. M. Hurban

119 President Benes

1948. Centenary of Slovak Insurrection.
521 **118** 1k.50 brown 10 10
522 – 3k. red (L. Stur) 10 10
523 – 5k. blue (M. Hodza) . . . 20 20

1948. Death of President Benes.
524 **119** 8k. black 10 10

120 "Independence"

121 President Gottwald

1948. 30th Anniv of Independence.
525 **120** 1k.50 blue 15 10
526 3k. red 20 15

1948.
772 **121** 15h. green 35 10
773 20h. brown 45 10
526a 1k. green 20 10
774 1k. lilac . . . . 1·10 10
527 1k.50 brown 20 10
528b 3k. red 30 10
775 3k. black 80 10
529 5k. blue 55 10
530 20k. violet (23 × 30 mm) 60 10
MS530a 66 × 99 mm. 30k. red (T 121) . . . . 3·50 3·25
See also No. 538.

122 Czech and Russian Workers

123 Girl and Birds

1948. 5th Anniv of Russian Alliance.
531 **122** 3k. red 10 10

1948. 30th Anniv of First Czechoslovak Stamps. Imperf.
MS531a 70 × 90 mm. 10k. blue (T 2) 2·00 1·75

1948. Child Welfare.
532 – 1k.50+1k. purple 30 10
533 – 2k.+1k. blue 15 10
534 **123** 3k.+1k. red 25 10
DESIGNS: 1k.50, Boy and birds; 2k. Mother and child.

124 V. I. Lenin

125 Pres. Gottwald Addressing Rally

1949. 25th Death Anniv of Lenin.
535 **124** 1k.50 purple 30 10
536 5k. blue 30 25

1949. 1st Anniv of Gottwald Government.
537 **125** 3k. brown 10 10

1949. As T **121** (23 × 30 mm) but inscr "UNOR 1948".
538 **121** 10k. green 35 25

126 P. O. Hviezdoslav

127 Mail Coach and Steam Train

1949. Poets.
539 **126** 50h. purple 10 10
540 – 80h. red 10 10
541 – 1k. green 10 10
542 – 2k. blue 30 10
543 – 4k. purple 30 10
544 – 8k. black 45 10
PORTRAITS: 80h. V. Vancura. 1k. J. Sverma. 2k. J. Fucik. 4k. J. Wolker. 8k. A. Jirasek.

1949. 75th Anniv of U.P.U.
545 **127** 3k. red . . . . 1·00 1·00
546 – 5k. blue 60 35
547 – 13k. green . . . . 1·60 40
DESIGNS: 5k. Mounted postman and mail van; 13k. Sailing ship and Douglas DC-2 airliner.

128 Girl Agricultural Worker

130 Industrial Worker

1949. 9th Meeting of Czechoslovak Communist Party.
548 **128** 1k.50 green 45 50
549 – 3k. red 25 25
550 **130** 5k. blue 45 50
DESIGN—HORIZ: 3k. Workers and flag.

131 F. Smetana and National Theatre, Prague

132 A. S. Pushkin

1949. 125th Birth Anniv of Smetana (composer).
551 **131** 1k.50 green 15 10
552 5k. blue 65 30

1949. 150th Birth Anniv of A. S. Pushkin (poet).
553 **132** 2k. green 25 25

133 F. Chopin and Warsaw Conservatoire

134 Globe and Ribbon

1949. Death Centenary of Chopin (composer).
554 **133** 3k. red 45 25
555 8k. purple 45 50

1949. 50th Sample Fair, Prague.
556 **134** 1k.50 purple 25 25
557 5k. blue 80 75

135 Zvolen Castle

1949.
558 **135** 10k. lake 60 10

1949. Air. Nos. 469/76 surch.
559 **95** 1k. on 1k.50 red 15 10
560 3k. on 5k.50 blue 25 10
561 6k. on 9k. purple 40 10
562 7k.50 on 16k. violet . . . 50 25
563 **96** 8k. on 10k. green 50 55
564 12k.50 on 20k. blue . . . 90 45
565 **94a** 15k. on 24k. red . . . . 2·25 75
566 30k. on 50k. blue . . . . 1·75 75

137 Mediaeval Miners

138 Modern Miner

1949. 700th Anniv of Czechoslovak Mining Industry and 150th Anniv of Miners' Laws.
567 **137** 1k.50 violet 50 40
568 **138** 3k. red . . . . 5·25 1·90
569 – 5k. blue . . . . 4·00 1·50
DESIGN—HORIZ: 5k. Miner with cutting machine.

139 Carpenters

140 Dove and Buildings

1949. 2nd T.U.C., Prague. Inscr 1949".
570 **139** 1k. green . . . . 3·00 1·25
571 – 2k. purple (Mechanic) . . 1·90 50

1949. Red Cross Fund. Inscr "CS CERVENY KRIZ".
572 **140** 1k.50h.+50h. red . . . . 3·50 1·60
573 – 3k.+1k. red . . . . . . 3·50 1·60
DESIGN—VERT: 3k. Dove and globe.

141 Mother and Child

142 Joseph Stalin

1949. Child Welfare Fund. Inscr "DETEM 1949".
574 **141** 1k.50+50h. grey . . . . 3·25 1·10
575 – 3k.+1k. red . . . . . . 4·75 1·75
DESIGN: 3k. Father and child.

1949. 70th Birth Anniv of Joseph Stalin.
576 **142** 1k.50 green on buff . . . 75 40
577 – 3k. purple on buff . . . . 4·00 1·50
PORTRAIT: 3k. Stalin facing left.

143 Skier

144 Efficiency Badge

1950. Tatra Cup Ski Championship.
578 **143** 1k.50 blue . . . . 2·75 1·00
579 **144** 3k. red and buff . . . . 2·75 1·00
580 **143** 5k. blue . . . . 1·90 85

145 V. Mayakovsky **146** Soviet Tank Driver and Hradcany, Prague

1950. 20th Death Anniv of Mayakovsky (poet).
581 **145** 1k.50 purple . . . . . . 2·10 1·10
582 3k. red . . . . 1·75 80

1950. 5th Anniv of Republic (1st issue).
583 **146** 1k.50 green 25 20
584 – 2k. purple 95 80
585 – 3k. red 20 10
586 – 5k. blue 40 20
DESIGNS: 2k. "Hero of Labour" medal; 3k. Workers and Town Hall; 5k. "The Kosice Programme" (part of text).

147 Factory and Workers

1950. 5th Anniv of Republic (2nd issue).
587 **147** 1k.50 green . . . . 1·40 75
588 – 2k. brown . . . . 1·75 65
589 – 3k. red 90 35
590 – 5k. blue 90 30
DESIGNS: 2k. Crane and Tatra Mts; 3k. Labourer and tractor; 5k. Three workers.

148 S. K. Neumann

1950. 75th Birth Anniv of S. K. Neumann (writer).
591 **148** 1k.50 blue 25 10
592 3k. purple . . . . 1·10 85

149 Bozena Nemcova **150** "Liberation of Colonial Nations"

1950. 130th Birth Anniv of Bozena Nemcova (authoress).
593 **149** 1k.50 blue . . . . 1·25 80
594 7k. purple 25 20

1950. 2nd International Students' World Congress, Prague. Inscr "II KONGRES MSS".
595 **150** 1k.50 green 15 10
596 – 2k. purple . . . . 1·50 1·25
597 – 3k. red 20 25
598 – 5k. blue 40 50
DESIGNS—HORIZ: 2k. Woman, globe and dove ("Fight for Peace"); 3k. Group of students ("Democratisation of Education"); 5k. Students and banner ("International Students, Solidarity").

151 Miner, Soldier and Farmer **152** Z. Fibich

1950. Army Day.
599 **151** 1k.50 blue 90 75
600 – 3k. red 25 35
DESIGN: 3k. Czechoslovak and Russian soldiers.

1950. Birth Centenary of Fibich (composer).
601 **152** 3k. red . . . . 1·40 1·40
602 8k. green 25 15

153 "Communications" **154** J. G. Tajovsky

1950. 1st Anniv of League of Postal, Telephone and Telegraph Employees.
603 **153** 1k.50 brown 25 15
604 3k. red 65 65

1950. 10th Death Anniv of J. Gregor Tajovsky (writer).
605 **154** 1k.50 brown 85 70
606 5k. blue 85 55

155 Reconstruction of Prague

1950. Philatelic Exhibition, Prague.
607 **155** 1k.50 blue 35 20
608 3k. red 60 55
MS608a 120 × 101 mm. No. 607 in imperf block of four . . . . . 27·00 20·00

156 Czech and Russian Workers

1950. Czechoslovak–Soviet Friendship.
609 **156** 1k.50 brown 55 25
610 5k. blue 75 50

157 Dove (after Picasso)

1951. Czechoslovak Peace Congress.
611 **157** 2k. blue . . . . 5·00 2·75
612 3k. red . . . . 3·00 1·60

158 Julius Fucik **159** Mechanical Hammer

1951. Peace Propaganda.
613 **158** 1k.50 grey 50 35
614 5k. blue . . . . 1·90 1·75

1951. Five Year Plan (heavy industry).
615 **159** 1k.50 black 10 10
616 – 3k. brown 15 10
617 **159** 4k. blue 65 50
DESIGN—HORIZ: 3k. Installing machinery.

160 Industrial Workers **161** Karlovy Vary

1951. International Women's Day.
618 **160** 1k.50 olive 25 10
619 – 3k. red . . . . 2·40 65
620 – 5k. blue 50 10
DESIGNS: 3k. Woman driving tractor; 5k. Korean woman and group.

1951. Air. Spas.
621 **161** 6k. green . . . . 2·25 75
622 – 10k. purple . . . . 2·25 95
623 – 15k. blue . . . . 5·50 75
624 – 20k. brown . . . . 7·00 2·25
DESIGNS—Ilyushin Il-12 airplane over: 10k. Piestany; 15k. Marianske Lazne; 20k. Silac.

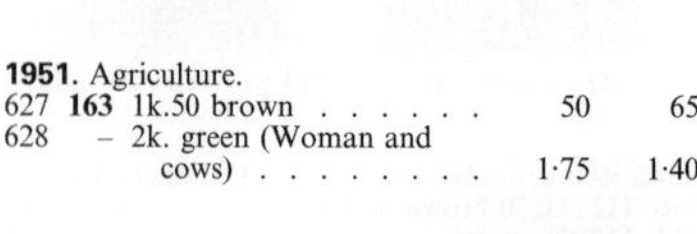

162 Miners **163** Ploughing

1951. Mining Industry.
625 **162** 1k.50 black 80 60
626 3k. purple 10 15

1951. Agriculture.
627 **163** 1k.50 brown 50 65
628 – 2k. green (Woman and cows) . . . . 1·75 1·40

164 Tatra Mountains **165** Partisan and Soviet Soldier

1951. Recreation Centres. Inscr "ROH".
629 **164** 1k.50 green 20 10
630 – 2k. brown 90 70
631 – 3k. red 25 10
DESIGNS: 2k. Beskydy Mts; 3k. Krkonose Mts.

1951. 30th Anniv of Czechoslovak Communist Party. Inscr "30 LET" etc.
635 – 1k.50 grey 95 25
632 – 2k. brown 25 10
633 **165** 3k. red 30 10
636 – 5k. blue . . . . 1·90 90
634 – 8k. black 70 30
DESIGNS—HORIZ: 1k.50, 5k. Gottwald and Stalin; 8k. Marx, Engels, Lenin and Stalin. VERT: 2k. Factory militiaman.

167 Dvorak **168** Gymnast

1951. Prague Musical Festival.
637 **167** 1k. brown 25 10
638 – 1k.50 grey (Smetana) . . 1·25 55
639 **167** 2k. brown . . . . 1·25 60
640 – 3k. purple (Smetana) . . 25 15

1951. 9th Sokol Congress.
641 **168** 1k. green 55 20
642 – 1k.50 brown (Woman discus thrower) 55 25
643 – 3k. red (Footballers) . . . 1·25 25
644 – 5k. blue (Skier) . . . . . 3·25 1·25

1951. 10th Death Anniv of Bohumir Smeral. As T **154**, but portrait of Smeral.
645 1k.50 grey 45 40
646 3k. purple 45 15

170 Scene from "Fall of Berlin" **172** A. Jirasek

173 "Fables and Fates" (M. Ales)

1951. International Film Festival, Karlovy Vary. Inscr "SE SOVETSKYM FILMEM", etc.
647 **170** 80h. red 35 25
648 – 1k.50 grey 35 25
649 **170** 4k. blue . . . . 1·10 75
DESIGN: 1k.50, Scene from "The Great Citizen".

1951. 30th Death Anniv of J. Hybes (politician). As T **154**, but portrait of Hybes.
650 1k.50 brown 10 10
651 2k. red . . . . 1·00 35

1951. Birth Centenary of Jirasek (author).
652 **172** 1k.50 black 40 10
653 **173** 3k. red 40 10
654 – 4k. black 40 10
655 **172** 5k. blue . . . . 1·90 1·10
DESIGN—As Type **173**: 4k. "The Region of Tabor" (M. Ales).

174 Miner and Pithead **176** Soldiers Parading

1951. Miner's Day.
656 **174** 1k.50 brown 15 10
657 – 3k. red (miners drilling) . 15 10
658 **174** 5k. blue . . . . 1·25 95

1951. Army Day. Inscr "DEN CS ARMADY 1951".
659 **176** 80h. brown 25 20
660 – 1k. green 25 25
661 – 1k.50 black 40 25
662 – 3k. purple 40 25
663 – 5k. blue . . . . 1·60 60
DESIGNS—VERT: 1k. Gunner and field-gun; 1k.50, Pres. Gottwald; 3k. Tank driver and tank; 5k. Two pilots and aircraft.

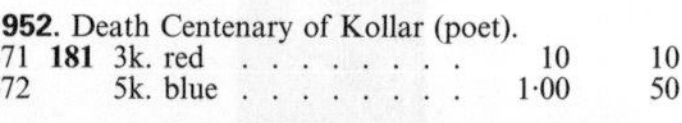

178 Stalin and Gottwald **179** P. Jilemnicky

1951. Czechoslovak–Soviet Friendship.
664 **178** 1k.50 black 10 10
665 – 3k. red 15 10
666 **178** 4k. blue . . . . 1·25 45
DESIGN (23½ × 31 mm): 3k. Lenin, Stalin and Russian soldiers.

1951. 50th Birth Anniv of Jilemnicky (writer).
667 **179** 1k.50 purple 20 15
668 2k. blue 70 35

180 L. Zapotocky **181** J. Kollar

1952. Birth Centenary of Zapotocky (socialist pioneer).
669 **180** 1k.50 red 10 15
670 4k. black . . . . 1·00 35

1952. Death Centenary of Kollar (poet).
671 **181** 3k. red 10 10
672 5k. blue . . . . 1·00 50

182 Lenin Hall, Prague **183** Dr. E. Holub and Negro

1952. 40th Anniv of 6th All-Russian Party Conference.
673 **182** 1k.50 red 10 25
674 5k. blue . . . . 1·00 60

1952. 50th Death Anniv of Dr. Holub (explorer).
675 **183** 3k. red 40 25
676 5k. blue . . . . 2·00 1·40

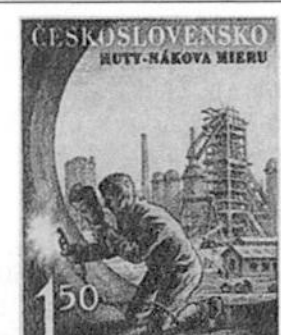

184 Electric Welding

1952. Industrial Development.
677 **184** 1k.50 black 35 15
678 – 2k. brown . . . . 1·40 50
679 – 3k. red 15 10
DESIGNS: 2k. Foundry; 3k. Chemical plant.

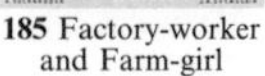

185 Factory-worker and Farm-girl **186** Young Workers

1952. International Women's Day.
680 **185** 1k.50 blue on cream . . . 1·00 40

1952. International Youth Week.
681 **186** 1k.50 blue 10 10
682 – 2k. green 15 10
683 **186** 3k. red . . . . 1·60 65
DESIGN: 2k. Three heads and globe.

187 O. Sevcik **188** J. A. Komensky (Comenius)

1952. Birth Centenary of Sevcik (musician).
684 **187** 2k. brown 70 45
685 3k. red 15 15

1952. 360th Birth Anniv of Komensky (educationist).
686 **188** 1k.50 brown . . . . . . 1·25 50
687 11k. blue 25 10

189 Anti-fascist **190** Woman and Children

1952. "Fighters Against Fascism" Day.
688 **189** 1k.50 brown 10 10
689 2k. blue . . . . 1·00 50

1952. Child Welfare.
690 **190** 2k. purple on cream . . . 1·25 1·10
691 3k. red on cream 15 15

191 Combine Harvester

1952. Agriculture Day.
692 **191** 1k.50 blue . . . . 1·90 1·10
693 2k. brown 25 25
694 – 3k. red (Combine drill) . . 25 25

192 May Day Parade

1952. Labour Day.
695 **192** 3k. red 30 35
696 4k. brown . . . . 1·40 80

193 Russian Tank and Crowd

1952. 7th Anniv of Liberation.
697 **193** 1k.50 red 60 50
698 5k. blue . . . . 1·75 1·40

194 Boy Pioneer and Children **195** J. V. Myslbek

1952. International Children's Day.
699 **194** 1k.50 brown 10 10
700 2k. green . . . . 1·40 70
701 – 3k. red (Pioneers and teacher) 15 10

1952. 30th Death Anniv of Myslbek (sculptor).
702 **195** 1k.50 brown 10 10
703 2k. brown . . . . 1·10 1·00
704 – 8k. green 15 10
DESIGN: 8k. "Music" (statue).

196 Beethoven **197** "Rebirth of Lidice"

1952. International Music Festival, Prague. No. 706 inscr "PRAZSKE JARO 1952", etc.
705 **196** 1k.50 brown 30 25
706 – 3k. lake 30 25
707 **196** 5k. blue . . . . 1·60 90
DESIGN—HORIZ: 3k. The House of Artists.

1952. 10th Anniv of Destruction of Lidice.
708 **197** 1k.50 black 10 10
709 5k. blue 90 55

198 Jan Hus **199** Bethlehem Chapel, Prague

1952. Renovation of Bethlehem Chapel and 550th Anniv of Installation of Hus as Preacher.
710 **198** 1k.50 brown 10 10
711 **199** 3k. brown 10 10
712 **198** 5k. black . . . . 1·10 75

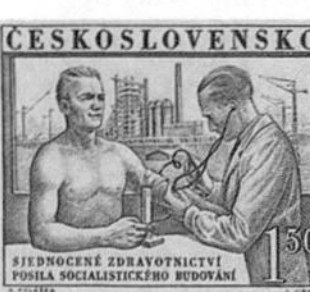

200 Testing Blood-pressure **201** Running

1952. National Health Service.
713 **200** 1k.50 brown 25 80
714 – 2k. violet 30 10
715 **200** 3k. red 70 10
DESIGN—HORIZ: 2k. Doctor examining baby.

1952. Physical Culture Propaganda.
716 **201** 1k.50 brown . . . . . . 2·00 35
717 – 2k. green (Canoeing) . . 50 85
718 – 3k. brown (Cycling) . . 3·25 45
719 – 4k. blue (Ice hockey) . . 15 2·25

202 F. L. Celakovsky

1952. Death Centenary of Celakovsky (poet).
720 **202** 1k.50 sepia . . . . 1·60 10
721 2k. green 40 85

203 M. Ales **204** Mining in 17th Century

1952. Birth Centenary of Mikulas Ales (painter) (1st issue).
722 **203** 1k.50 green . . . . 2·25 20
723 6k. brown . . . . 1·25 1·75
See also Nos. 737/8.

1952. Miner's Day.
724 **204** 1k. brown 10 70
725 – 1k.50 blue . . . . 10 1·00
726 – 2k. black 10 10
727 – 3k. brown 15 10
DESIGNS: 1k.50, Mining machinery; 2k. Petr Bezruc Mine, Ostrava; 3k. Mechanical excavator.

205 Jan Zizka **206** "Fraternization" (after Pokorny)

1952. Army Day.
728 **205** 1k.50 red 15 10
729 **206** 2k. brown 15 10
730 – 3k. red 15 10
731 **205** 4k. black . . . . 1·75 70
DESIGNS: 3k. Soldiers marching with flag.

207 R. Danube, Bratislava **208** Lenin, Stalin and Revolutionaries

1952. National Philatelic Exhibition, Bratislava.
732 **207** 1k.50 brown 10 10
MS732a 100 × 75 mm. 2k. red (Partisan Memorial); 3k. blue (Soviet Army Memorial) . . . 95·00 26·00

1952. 35th Anniv of Russian Revolution.
733 **208** 2k. brown . . . . 1·25 80
734 3k. red 10 10

209 Nurses and Red Cross Flag **211** Flags

210 Matej Louda z Chlumu (Hussite Warrior)

1952. 1st Czechoslovak Red Cross Conference.
735 **209** 2k. brown . . . . 1·25 55
736 3k. red 15 10

1952. Birth Centenary of Mikulas Ales (2nd issue).
737 **210** 2k. brown 25 10
738 – 3k. black 65 10
DESIGN: 3k. "Trutnov" (warrior fighting dragon).

1952. Peace Congress, Vienna.
739 **211** 3k. red 20 10
740 4k. blue . . . . 1·40 70

212 "Dove of Peace" (after Picasso) **213** Smetana Museum, Prague

1953. 2nd Czechoslovak Peace Congress, Prague.
741 **212** 1k.50 sepia 10 10
742 – 4k. blue 10 35
DESIGN: 4k. Workman, woman and child (after Lev Haas).

1953. 75th Birth Anniv of Prof. Z. Nejedly (museum founder).
743 **213** 1k.50 brown 10 10
744 – 4k. black . . . . 1·40 65
DESIGN: 4k. Jirasek Museum, Prague.

214 Marching Soldiers **215** M. Kukucin

1953. 5th Anniv of Communist Govt.
745 **214** 1k.50 blue 15 10
746 – 3k. red 15 10
747 – 8k. brown . . . . 2·00 80
DESIGNS—VERT: 3k. Pres. Gottwald addressing meeting. HORIZ: 8k. Stalin, Gottwald and crowd with banners.

1953. Czech Writers and Poets.
748 **215** 1k. grey 10 10
749 – 1k.50 brown 10 10
750 – 2k. lake 10 10
751 – 3k. brown 50 40
752 – 5k. blue . . . . 1·90 75
PORTRAITS—VERT: 1k.50, J. Vrchlicky. 2k. E. J. Erben. 3k. V. M. Kramerius. 5k. J. Dobrovsky.

216 Torch and Open Book **217** Woman Revolutionary

1953. 10th Death Anniv of Vaclavek (writer).
753 **216** 1k. brown . . . . 1·50 50
754 – 3k. brown (Vaclavek) . . 15 10

1953. International Women's Day.
755 – 1k.50 blue 15 10
756 **217** 2k. red 10 50
DESIGN—VERT: 1k.50, Mother and baby.

218 Stalin **219** Pres. Gottwald

1953. Death of Stalin.
757 **218** 1k.50 black 35 20

1953. Death of President Gottwald.
758 **219** 1k.50 black 20 10
759 3k. black 20 10
MS759a 67 × 100 mm. 5k. black (T **219**) . . . . 2·75 2·25

220 Pecka, Zapotocky and Hybes

1953. 75th Anniv of 1st Czech Social Democratic Party Congress.
760 **220** 2k. brown 25 10

221 Cyclists

1953. 6th International Cycle Race.
761 **221** 3k. blue 60 30

222 1890 May Day Medal

223 Marching Crowds

1953. Labour Day.
762 **222** 1k. brown . . . . 1·75 85
763 – 1k.50 blue 10 10
764 **223** 3k. red 20 10
765 – 8k. green 25 10
DESIGNS—As Type **222**: 1k.50, Lenin and Stalin; 8k. Marx and Engels.

224 Hydro-electric Barrage

225 Seed-drills

1953.
766 **224** 1k.50 green 95 40
767 – 2k. blue 20 10
768 – 3k. brown 20 10
DESIGNS—VERT: 2k. Welder and blast furnaces, Kuncice, HORIZ: 3k. Gottwald Foundry, Kuncice.

1953.
769 **225** 1k.50 brown 20 10
770 – 7k. green (Combine harvester) . . . . . . 1·60 1·10

226 President Zapotocky

229

1953.
776 **226** 30h. blue 60 10
780 **229** 30h. blue 55 10
777 **226** 60h. red 30 10
781 **229** 60h. pink . . . . 1·10 10

227 J. Slavik

228 L. Janacek

1953. Prague Music Festival. (a) 120th Death Anniv of Slavik (violinist).
778 **227** 75h. blue 60 10

(b) 25th Death Anniv of Janacek (composer).
779 **228** 1k.60 brown . . . . . . 1·25 10

230 Charles Bridge, Prague

1953.
782a **230** 5k. grey . . . . 4·50 10

231 J. Fucik

232 Book, Carnation and Laurels

1953. 10th Death Anniv of Julius Fucik (writer).
783 **231** 40h. black 20 10
784 **232** 60h. mauve 50 25

233 Miner and Banner

234 Volley ball

1953. Miner's Day.
785 **233** 30h. black 20 10
786 – 60h. purple . . . . 1·25 50
DESIGN: 60h. Miners and colliery shafthead.

1953. Sports.
787 **234** 30h. red . . . . 2·10 1·40
788 – 40h. purple . . . . 3·75 70
789 – 60h. purple . . . . 3·75 70
DESIGNS—HORIZ: 40h. Motor cycling. VERT: 60h. Throwing the javelin.

235 Hussite Warrior

236 "Friendship" (after T. Bartfay)

1953. Army Day.
790 **235** 30h. sepia 25 10
791 – 60h. red 30 20
792 – 1k. red . . . . 1·75 1·25
DESIGNS: 60h. Soldier presenting arms; 1k. Czechoslovak Red Army soldiers.

1953. Czechoslovak–Korean Friendship.
793 **236** 30h. sepia . . . . 2·50 1·10

237 Hradcany, Prague and Kremlin, Moscow

1953. Czechoslovak–Soviet Friendship: Inscr "MESIC CESKOSLOVENSKO SOVETSKEHO", etc.
794 **237** 30h. black . . . . 1·00 55
795 – 60h. brown . . . . 1·25 75
796 – 1k.20 blue . . . . 2·50 1·40
DESIGNS: 60h. Lomonosov University, Moscow; 1k.20, "Stalingrad" tug, Lenin Ship-Canal.

238 Ema Destinnova (Opera Singer)

239 National Theatre, Prague

1953. 70th Anniv of National Theatre, Prague.
797 **238** 30h. black 95 80
798 **239** 60h. brown 25 10
799 – 2k. sepia . . . . 2·25 80
PORTRAIT—As Type **238**: 2k. E. Vojan (actor).

240 J. Manes (painter)

241 Vaclav Hollar (etcher)

1953.
800 **240** 60h. lake 25 10
801 1k.20 blue . . . . 1·50 95

1953. Inscr "1607 1677".
802 **241** 30h. black 25 10
803 – 1k.20 black . . . . . . 1·25 55
PORTRAIT: 1k.20, Hollar and engraving tools.

242 Leo Tolstoy

243 Class 498.0 Steam Locomotive

1953. 125th Birth Anniv of Tolstoy (writer).
804 **242** 60h. green 15 10
805 1k. brown . . . . 1·40 40

1953.
806 **243** 60h. blue and brown . . . 65 25
807 – 1k. blue and brown . . . 1·60 90
DESIGN: 1k. Ilyushin Il-12 (30th anniv of Czech airmail services).

244 Lenin (after J. Lauda)

245 Lenin Museum, Prague

1954. 30th Death Anniv of Lenin.
808 **244** 30h. sepia 45 10
809 **245** 1k.40 brown . . . . . . 1·75 1·25

246 Gottwald Speaking

247 Gottwald Mausoleum, Prague

248 Gottwald and Stalin (after relief by O. Spaniel)

1954. 25th Anniv of 5th Czechoslovak Communist Party Congress. Inscr "1929 1954".
810 **246** 60h. brown 30 10
811 – 2k.40 lake . . . . 3·75 1·40
DESIGN: 2k.40, Revolutionary and flag.
See also No. **MS**2917.

1954. 1st Anniv of Deaths of Stalin and Gottwald.
812 **247** 30h. sepia 25 20
813 **248** 60h. blue 30 10
814 – 1k.20h. lake . . . . . . 1·75 85
DESIGN—HORIZ: As Type **247**: 1k.20h. Lenin-Stalin Mausoleum, Moscow.

249 Girl and Sheaf of Corn

250 Athletics

1954.
815 – 15h. green 25 10
816 – 20h. lilac 30 10
817 – 40h. brown 45 10
818 – 45h. blue 45 10
819 – 50h. green 30 10
820 – 75h. blue 30 10
821 – 80h. brown 30 10
822 **249** 1k. green 65 10
823 – 1k.20 blue 30 10
824 – 1k.60 black . . . . 2·25 10
825 – 2k. brown . . . . 1·90 10
826 – 2k.40 blue . . . . 2·25 10
827 – 3k. red . . . . 1·50 10
DESIGNS: 15h. Labourer; 20h. Nurse; 40h. Postwoman; 45h. Foundry worker; 50h. Soldier; 75h. Metal worker; 80h. Mill girl; 1k.20, Scientist; 1k.60, Miner; 2k. Doctor and baby; 2k.40 Engine-driver; 3k. Chemist.

1954. Sports.
828 **250** 30h. sepia . . . . 2·25 85
829 – 80h. green . . . . 6·50 3·50
830 – 1k. blue . . . . 1·40 60
DESIGNS—HORIZ: 80h. Hiking. VERT: 1k. Girl diving.

251 Dvorak

252 Prokop Divis (physicist)

1954. Czechoslovak Musicians. Inscr as in T **251**.
831 **251** 30h. brown . . . . 1·00 25
832 – 40h. red (Janacek) . . . . 1·40 25
833 – 60h. blue (Smetana) . . . 80 15

1954. Bicentenary of Invention of Lightning Conductor by Divis.
834 **252** 30h. black 25 10
835 75h. brown . . . . 1·25 40

253 Partisan

254 A. P. Chekhov

1954. 10th Anniv of Slovak National Uprising. Inscr "1944–29. 8–1954".
836 **253** 30h. red 20 10
837 – 1k.20 bl (Woman partisan) . . . . 1·10 90

1954. 50th Death Anniv of Chekhov (playwright).
838 **254** 30h. green 20 10
839 45h. brown . . . . 1·25 50

255 Soldiers in Battle

257 J. Neruda

256 Farm Workers in Cornfield

1954. Army Day. 2k. inscr "ARMADY 1954".
840 **255** 60h. green 20 10
841 – 2k. brown . . . . 1·25 1·10
DESIGN: 2k. Soldier carrying girl.

1954. Czechoslovak–Russian Friendship.
842 **256** 30h. brown 15 10
843 – 60h. blue 25 10
844 – 2k. salmon . . . . 1·75 1·40
DESIGNS: 60h. Factory workers and machinery; 2k. Group of girl folk dancers.

1954. Czechoslovak Poets.
845 **257** 30h. blue 50 15
846 – 60h. red . . . . 1·50 30
847 – 1k.60 purple 40 15
PORTRAITS—VERT: 60h. J. Jesensky. 1k.60 J. Wolker.

258 Ceske Budejovice

1954. Czechoslovak Architecture. Background in buff.
848 – 30h. black (Telc) 90 10
849 – 60h. brown (Levoca) . . . 45 10
850 **258** 3k. blue . . . . 1·75 1·40

259 President Zapotocky **260** "Spirit of the Games"

1954. 70th Birthday of Zapotocky.
851 **259** 30h. sepia 45 10
852 60h. blue 20 10
MS852a 65 × 100 mm 2k. red (as T **259**) . . . . 8·00 4·75
See also Nos. 1006/7.

1955. 1st National Spartacist Games (1st issue). Inscr as in T **260**.
853 **260** 30h. red . . . . 1·50 40
854 – 45h. black & blue (Skier) 4·25 30
See also Nos. 880/2.

261 University Building

1955. 35th Anniv of Comenius University, Bratislava. Inscr as in T **261**.
855 **261** 60h. green 30 10
856 – 75h. brown . . . . 1·75 55
DESIGN: 75h. Comenius Medal (after O. Spaniel).

262 Cesky Krumlov

1955. Air.
857 **262** 80h. green . . . . 1·10 20
858 – 1k.55 sepia . . . . 1·50 35
859 – 2k.35 blue . . . . 1·50 15
860 – 2k.75 purple . . . . . . 2·75 30
861 – 10k. blue . . . . 5·25 1·25
DESIGNS: 1k.55, Olomouc; 2k.35, Banska Bystrica; 2k.75, Bratislava; 10k. Prague.

263 Skoda Motor Car **264** Russian Tank-driver

1955. Czechoslovak Industries.
862 **263** 45h. green 70 50
863 – 60h. blue 15 10
864 – 75h. black 25 10
DESIGNS: 60h. Shuttleless jet loom; 75h. Skoda Machine-tool.

1955. 10th Anniv of Liberation. Inscr as in T **264**.
865 – 30h. blue 25 10
866 **264** 35h. brown . . . . 1·25 55
867 – 60h. red 25 10
868 – 60h. black 25 10
DESIGNS—VERT: 30h. Girl and Russian soldier; No. 867, Children and Russian soldier. HORIZ: No. 868, Stalin Monument, Prague.

265 Agricultural Workers **266** "Music and Spring"

1955. 3rd Trades' Union Congress. Inscr as in T **265**.
869 – 30h. blue 15 10
870 **265** 45h. green . . . . 1·25 55
DESIGN: 30h. Foundry worker.

1955. International Music Festival, Prague. Inscr as in T **266**.
871 **266** 30h. indigo and blue . . . 35 10
872 – 1k. blue and pink . . . . 1·25 1·25
DESIGN: 1k. "Music" playing a lyre.

267 A. S. Popov (60th anniv of radio discoveries) **268** Folk Dancers

1955. Cultural Anniversaries. Portraits.
873 – 20h. brown 20 10
874 – 30h. black 20 10
875 – 40h. green 70 15
876 – 60h. black 45 10
877 **267** 75h. purple . . . . 1·40 50
878 – 1k.40 black on yellow . . 35 25
879 – 1k.60 blue 35 20
PORTRAITS: 20h. Jakub Arbes (writer). 30h. Jan Stursa (sculptor). 40h. Elena Marothy-Soltesova (writer). 60h. Josef V. Sladek (poet). 1k.40 Jan Holly (poet). 1k.60 Pavel J. Safarik (philologist).

1955. 1st National Spartacist Games (2nd issue). Inscr as in T **268**.
880 – 20h. blue 85 40
881 **268** 60h. green 25 10
882 – 1k.60 red 90 25
DESIGNS: 20h. Girl athlete; 1k.60, Male athlete.

269 "Friendship" **270** Ocova Woman, Slovakia

1955. 5th World Youth Festival, Warsaw.
883 **269** 60h. blue 35 10

1955. National Costumes (1st series).
884 **270** 60h. sepia, rose and red 10·00 7·00
885 – 75h. sepia, orange & lake 5·75 5·00
886 – 1k.60 sepia, blue & orge 10·00 5·50
887 – 2k. sepia, yellow and red 13·00 5·50
DESIGNS: 75h. Detva man, Slovakia; 1k.60, Chodsko man, Bohemia; 2k. Hana woman, Moravia.
See also Nos. 952/5 and 1008/11.

271 Swallowtail

1955. Animals and Insects.
888 – 20h. black and blue . . . 55 10
889 – 30h. brown and red . . . 55 10
890 – 35h. brown and buff . . . 1·10 15
891 **271** 1k.40 black and yellow . . 5·25 1·90
892 – 1k.50 black and green . . 55 15
DESIGNS: 20h. Common carp; 30h. Stag beetle; 35h. Grey partridge; 1k.50, Brown hare.

272 Tabor

1955. Towns of Southern Bohemia.
893 **272** 30h. purple 20 10
894 – 45h. red 75 55
895 – 60h. green 20 10
TOWNS: 45h. Prachatice; 60h. Jindrichuv Hradec.

273 Motor Cyclists and Trophy **273a** Round Chapel

1955. 30th Int Motor Cycle Six-Day Trial.
896 **273** 60h. purple . . . . 2·40 25

1955. Prague International Philatelic Exhibition. Sheets 145 × 111 mm.
MS896a 30h. black (T **283a**); 45h. black (Brick tower); 60h. lake (fountain); 75h. lake (Winter Palace); 1k.60 black (Hradcany, 50 × 31 mm) . . . . 27·00 27·00
MS896b As above but imperf . . 65·00 65·00

274 Soldier and Family **275** Hans Andersen

1955. Army Day. Inscr as in T **274**.
897 **274** 30h. brown 25 10
898 – 60h. grn (Tank attack) . . 1·75 1·25

1955. Famous Writers. Vert portraits.
899 **275** 30h. red 15 10
900 – 40h. blue (Schiller) . . . 2·10 80
901 – 60h. purple (Mickiewicz) 25 10
902 – 75h. blk (Walt Whitman) 50 10

276 Railway Viaduct

1955. Building Progress. Inscr "STAVBA SOCIALISMU".
903 **276** 20h. green 30 25
904 – 30h. brown 30 10
905 – 60h. blue 30 10
906 – 1k.60 red 55 10
DESIGNS: 30h. Train crossing viaduct; 60k. Train approaching tunnel; 1k.60, Housing project, Ostrava.

277 "Electricity" **278** Karlovy Vary

1956. Five Year Plan. Inscr "1956–1960".
907 **277** 5h. brown 25 10
908 – 10h. black 25 10
909 – 25h. red 25 10
910 – 30h. green 25 10
911 – 60h. blue 35 10
DESIGNS—HORIZ: 10h. "Mining"; 25h. "Building"; 30h. "Agriculture"; 60h. "Industry".

1956. Czechoslovak Spas (1st series).
912 **278** 30h. green . . . . 1·40 25
913 – 45h. brown . . . . 1·25 35
914 – 75h. purple . . . . 6·25 3·50
915 – 1k.20 blue 90 15
SPAS: 45h. Marianske Lazne; 75h. Piestany; 1k.20, Vysne Ruzbachy, Tatra Mountains.

279 Jewellery **280** "We serve our People" (after J. Cumpelik)

1956. Czechoslovak Products.
916 **279** 30h. green 25 10
917 – 45h. blue (Glassware) . . 4·75 2·75
918 – 60h. purple (Ceramics) . . 1·00 10
919 – 75h. black (Textiles) . . . 25 10

1956. Defence Exhibition.
920 **280** 30h. brown 20 10
921 – 60h. red 20 10
922 – 1k. blue . . . . 3·25 3·25
DESIGNS: 60h. Liberation Monument, Berlin; 1k. "Tank Soldier with Standard" (after T. Schor).

281 Cyclists

282 Discus Thrower, Hurdler and Runner

1956. Sports Events of 1956.
923 **281** 30h. green and blue . . . 2·75 20
924 – 45h. blue and red . . . . 1·10 20
925 – 60h. blue and buff . . . . 1·50 45
926 **282** 75h. brown and yellow . . 1·00 20
927 – 80h. purple & lavender . . 1·00 20
928 **282** 1k.20 green & orange . . 95 35
DESIGNS—As Type **281**. VERT: 30h. T **281** (9th International Cycle Race); 45h. Basketball players (5th European Women's Basketball Championship, Prague). HORIZ: 60h. Horsemen jumping (Pardubice Steeplechase); 80h. Runners (International Marathon, Kosice). T **282**: 75h., 1k.20, (16th Olympic Games, Melbourne).

283 Mozart **284**

1956. Bicentenary of Birth of Mozart and Prague Music Festival. Centres in black.
929 **283** 30h. yellow . . . . 1·00 70
930 – 45h. green . . . . 14·50 9·50
931 – 60h. purple 55 10
932 – 1k. salmon . . . . 1·60 45
933 – 1k.40 blue . . . . 2·75 90
934 – 1k.60 lemon . . . . . . 1·00 15
DESIGNS: 45h. J. Myslivecek; 60h. J. Benda; 1k. "Bertramka" (Mozart's villa); 1k.40, Mr. and Mrs. Dushek; 1k.60, Nostic Theatre.

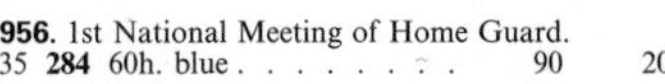

1956. 1st National Meeting of Home Guard.
935 **284** 60h. blue 90 20

285 J. K. Tyl **286** Naval Guard

1956. Czech Writers (1st issue).
936 – 20h. purple (Stur) 70 10
937 – 30h. blue (Sramek) . . . 35 10
938 **285** 60h. black 25 10
939 – 1k.40 pur (Borovsky) . . 4·50 2·40
See also Nos. 956/9.

1956. Frontier Guards' Day.
940 **286** 30h. blue . . . . 1·10 40
941 – 60h. green 15 10
DESIGN: 60h. Military guard and watchdog.

287 Picking Grapes

1956. National Products.
942 **287** 30h. lake 25 10
943 – 35h. green 30 25
944 – 80h. blue 60 15
945 – 95h. brown . . . . 1·50 1·60
DESIGNS—VERT: 35h. Picking hops. HORIZ: 80h. Fishing; 95h. Logging.

288 "Kladno", 1855

1956. European Freight Services Timetable Conference. Railway engines.
946 – 10h. brown . . . . 1·25 10
947 **288** 30h. black 75 10
948 – 40h. green . . . . 3·50 15
949 – 45h. purple . . . . 19·00 9·50
950 – 60h. blue 75 10
951 – 1k. blue . . . . 1·25 15
DESIGNS—VERT: 10h. "Zbraslav", 1846. HORIZ: 40h. Class 534, 1945; 45h. Class 556.0, 1952; 60h. Class 477.0, 1955; 1k. Class E499.0 electric locomotive, 1954.

1956. National Costumes (2nd series). As T **270**.
952 30h. sepia, red and blue . . . 2·25 70
953 1k.20 sepia, blue and red . . . 2·25 15
954 1k.40 brown, yellow & red . . 4·00 1·90
955 1k.60 sepia, green & red . . 2·40 30
DESIGNS: 30h. Slovacko woman; 1k.20, Blata woman; 1k.40, Cicmany woman, 1k.60, Novohradsko woman.

1957. Czech Writers (2nd issue). As T **285**. On buff paper.
956 15h. brown (Olbracht) . . . 30 10
957 20h. green (Toman) 30 10
958 30h. sepia (Salda) 30 10
959 1k.60 blue (Vansova) 55 10

289 Forestry Academy, Banska Stiavnica

1957. Towns and Monuments Anniversaries.
960 – 30h. blue 20 10
961 **289** 30h. purple 20 10
962 – 60h. red 40 10
963 – 60h. brown 40 10
964 – 60h. green 30 10
965 – 1k.25 black . . . . 3·50 1·40
DESIGNS: No. 960, Kolin; 962, Uherske Hradiste; 963, Charles Bridge, Prague; 964, Karlstejn Castle; 965, Moravska Trebova.

290 Girl Harvester

1957. 3rd Collective Farming Agricultural Congress, Prague.
966 **290** 30h. turquoise 70 10

291 Komensky's Mausoleum
292 J. A. Komensky (Comenius)

1957. 300th Anniv of Publication of Komensky's "Opera Didactica Omnia".
967 **291** 30h. brown 40 10
968 – 40h. green 40 10
969 **292** 60h. brown . . . . 1·90 1·10
970 – 60h. red 55 10
DESIGNS: As Type **291**: 40h. Komensky at work; 1k. Illustration from "Opera Didactica Omnia".

293 Racing Cyclists

1957. Sports Events of 1957.
971 **293** 30h. purple and blue . . . 35 10
972 60h. green and bistre . . 1·60 1·40
973 – 60h. violet and brown . . 35 10
974 – 60h. purple and brown . . 35 10
975 – 60h. black and green . . 35 10
976 – 60h. black and blue . . . 1·00 10
DESIGNS—HORIZ: Nos. 971/2 (10th Int Cycle Race); 973, Rescue squad (Mountain Rescue Service); 975, Archer (World Archery Championships, Prague). VERT: 974, Boxers (European Boxing Championships, Prague); 976, Motor Cyclists (32nd Int Motor Cycle Six-Day Trial).

294 J. B. Foerster

1957. Int Music Festival Jubilee. Musicians.
977 – 60h. violet (Stamic) . . . 25 10
978 – 60h. black (Laub) 25 10
979 – 60h. blue (Ondricek) . . . 25 10
980 **294** 60h. sepia 25 10
981 – 60h. brown (Novak) . . . 90 10
982 – 60h. turquoise (Suk) . . . 25 10

295 J. Bozek (founder)
296 Young Collector Blowing Posthorn

1957. 250th Anniv of Polytechnic Engineering Schools, Prague.
983 **295** 30h. black 15 10
984 – 60h. brown 35 10
985 – 1k. purple 35 15
986 – 1k.40 violet 50 15
DESIGNS—VERT: 60h. F. J. Gerstner; 1k. R. Skuhersky. HORIZ: 1k.40, Polytechnic Engineering Schools Building, Prague.

1957. Junior Philatelic Exn, Pardubice.
987 **296** 30h. orange and green . . 50 10
988 – 60h. blue and brown . . . 2·10 1·25
DESIGN: 60h. Girl sending letter by pigeon.

297 "Rose of Friendship and Peace"
298 Karel Klic and Printing Press

1957. 15th Anniv of Destruction of Lidice.
989 – 30h. black 35 10
990 **297** 60h. red and black . . . 1·00 35
DESIGN: 30h. Veiled woman.

1957. Czech Inventors.
991 **298** 30h. black 15 10
992 – 60h. blue 35 10
DESIGN: 60h. Joseph Ressel and propeller.

299 Chamois
300 Marycka Magdonova

1957. Tatra National Park.
993 **299** 20h. black and green . . 65 45
994 – 30h. brown and blue . . . 65 10
995 – 40h. blue and brown . . . 1·25 30
996 – 60h. green and yellow . . 50 10
997 – 1k.25 black and ochre . . 1·25 1·25
DESIGNS—VERT: 30h. Brown bear. HORIZ: 40h. Gentian; 60h. Edelweiss; 1k.25 (49 × 29 mm), Tatra Mountains.

1957. 90th Birthday of Petr Bezruc (poet).
998 **300** 60h. black and red . . . 50 10

301 Worker with Banner
303 Television Tower and Aerials

302 Tupolev Tu-104A and Paris–Prague–Moscow Route

1957. 4th World T.U.C., Leipzig.
999 **301** 75h. red 50 15

1957. Air. Opening of Czechoslovak Airlines.
1000 **302** 75h. blue and red . . . 80 10
1001 – 2k.35 blue and yellow . . 95 10
DESIGN: 2k.35, "Prague–Cairo–Beirut–Damascus".

1957. Television Development.
1002 **303** 40h. blue and red . . . 25 10
1003 – 60h. brown and green . . 30 10
DESIGN: 60h. Family watching television.

304 Youth, Globe and Lenin

1957. 40th Anniv of Russian Revolution.
1004 **304** 30h. red 20 10
1005 – 60h. blue 35 10
DESIGN: 60h. Lenin, refinery and Russian emblem.

1957. Death of President Zapotocky. As T **259** but dated "19 XII 1884–13 XI 1957".
1006 30h. black 10 10
1007 60h. black 25 10
MS1007a 70 × 100 mm. 2k. black (as 1006). Imperf . . . . 2·40 2·00

1957. National Costumes (3rd series). As T **270**.
1008 45h. sepia, red and blue . . 2·75 1·25
1009 75h. sepia, red and green . . 1·90 80
1010 1k.25 sepia, red & yellow . . 2·75 65
1011 1k.95 sepia, blue and red . . 3·25 2·10
DESIGNS—VERT: 45h. Pilsen woman; 75h. Slovacko man; 1k.25, Hana woman; 1k.95, Tesin woman.

305 Artificial Satellite ("Sputnik 2")
306 Figure Skating (European Championships, Bratislava)

1957. International Geophysical Year. Showing globe and dated "1957–1958".
1012 – 30h. brown . . . . . . 1·40 45
1013 – 45h. brown and blue . . 30 25
1014 **305** 75h. red and blue . . . 2·00 65
DESIGNS—HORIZ: 30h. Radio-telescope and observatory. VERT: 45h. Lomnicky Stit meteorological station.

1958. Sports Events of 1958.
1015 **306** 30h. purple 90 20
1016 – 40h. blue 30 20
1017 – 60h. brown 30 10
1018 – 80h. violet . . . . . . 1·40 65
1019 – 1k.60 green 50 15
EVENTS: 40h. Canoeing (World Canoeing Championships, Prague); 60h. Volleyball (European Volleyball Championships, Prague); 80h. Parachuting (4th World Parachute-jumping Championship, Bratislava); 1k.60, Football (World Cup Football Championship, Stockholm).

307 Litomysl Castle (birthplace of Nejedly)
309 Jewellery

308 Soldiers guarding Shrine of "Victorious February"

1958. 80th Birthday of Nejedly (musician).
1020 **307** 30h. green 20 10
1021 – 60h. brown 20 10
DESIGN—HORIZ: 60h. Bethlehem Chapel, Prague.

1958. 10th Anniv of Communist Govt.
1022 – 30h. blue and yellow . . 25 10
1023 **308** 60h. brown and red . . . 25 10
1024 – 1k.60 green and orange . 35 10
DESIGNS—VERT: 30h. Giant mine-excavator. HORIZ: 1k.60, Combine-harvester.

1958. Brussels International Exhibition. Inscr "Bruxelles 1958".
1025 **309** 30h. red and blue . . . 25 10
1026 – 45h. red and lilac . . . 60 10
1027 – 60h. violet and green . . 25 10
1028 – 75h. blue and orange . . 1·10 80
1029 – 1k.20 green and red . . 60 10
1030 – 1k.95 brown and blue . . 70 15
DESIGNS—VERT: 45h. Toy dolls; 60h. Draperies; 75h. Kaplan turbine; 1k.20, Glassware. HORIZ: ($48\frac{1}{2} \times 29\frac{1}{2}$ mm), 1k.95, Czech pavilion.

310 George of Podebrady and his Seal

1958. National Exhibition of Archive Documents. Inscr as in T **310**.
1031 **310** 30h. red 35 10
1032 – 60h. violet 35 10
DESIGN: 60h. Prague, 1628 (from engraving).

311 Hammer and Sickle

1958. 11th Czech Communist Party Congress and 15th Anniv of Czech–Soviet Friendship Treaty. 45h. inscr as in T **311** and 60h. inscr "15. VYROCI UZAVRENI".
1033 **311** 30h. red 20 10
1034 – 45h. green 20 10
1035 – 60h. blue 20 10
DESIGNS: 45h. Map of Czechoslovakia, with hammer and sickle; 60h. Atomic reactor, Rez (near Prague).

312 "Towards the Stars" (after sculpture by G. Postnikov)
313 Pres. Novotny

1958. Cultural and Political Events. 45h. inscr "IV. KONGRES MEZINARODNI", etc, and 60h. inscr "I. SVETOVA ODBOROVA", etc.
1036 **312** 30h. red 70 40
1037 – 45h. purple 20 25
1038 – 60h. blue 20 10
DESIGNS—VERT: 45h. Three women of different races and globe (4th Int Democratic Women's Federation Congress, Vienna). HORIZ: 60h. Boy and girl with globes (1st World T.U. Conference of Working Youth, Prague). Type **312** represents the Society for the Dissemination of Cultural and Political Knowledge.

1958.
1039 **313** 30h. violet 45 10
1039a 30h. purple . . . . . . 3·50 1·00
1040 60h. red 45 10

314 Telephone Operator
316 "The Poet and the Muse" (after Max Svabinsky)

315 Karlovy Vary (600th Anniv)

1958. Communist Postal Conference, Prague. Inscr as in T **314**.
1041 **314** 30h. sepia and brown . . 30 10
1042 – 45h. black and green . . 30 30
DESIGN: 45h. Aerial mast.

1958. Czech Spas (2nd series).
1043 **315** 30h. lake 10 10
1044 – 40h. brown 10 10
1045 – 60h. green 15 10
1046 – 80h. sepia 30 10
1047 – 1k.20 blue 45 15
1048 – 1k.60 violet . . . . . . 1·10 65
SPAS: 40h. Podebrady; 60h. Marianske Lazne (150th Anniv); 80h. Luhacovice; 1k.20, Strbske Pleso; 1k.60, Trencianske.

1958. 85th Birthday of Dr. Max Svabinsky (artist).
1049 **316** 1k.60 black . . . . . . 3·25 80

317 S. Cech
319 Parasol Mushroom

318 Children's Hospital, Brno

1958. Writers' Anniversaries.
1050 – 30h. red (Julius Fucik) 25 10
1051 – 45h. violet (Gustav K. Zechenter) 95 45
1052 – 60h. blue (Karel Capek) 15 10
1053 **317** 1k.40 black 50 10

1958. National Stamp Exn, Brno. Inscr as in T **318**.
1054 **318** 30h. violet 20 10
1055 – 60h. red 20 10
1056 – 1k. sepia 45 10
1057 – 1k.60 myrtle . . . . . . 1·60 1·50
DESIGNS: 60h. New Town Hall, Brno; 1k. St. Thomas's Church, Red Army Square; 1k.60, (50 × 28½ mm), Brno view.

1958. Mushrooms.
1058 **319** 30h. buff, green & brown 40 20
1059 – 40h. buff, red & brown 45 20
1060 – 60h. red, buff and black 55 25
1061 – 1k.40 red, green & brn 65 35
1062 – 1k.60 red, green & blk 5·25 2·00
DESIGNS—VERT: 40h. Cep; 60h. Red cap; 1k.40, Fly agaric; 1k.60, Boot-lace fungus.

320 Children sailing
322 Garlanded Woman ("Republic") with First Czech Stamp

321 Bozek's Steam Car of 1815

1958. Inauguration of U.N.E.S.C.O. Headquarters Building, Paris. Inscr "ZE SOUTEZE PRO UNESCO".
1063 **320** 30h. red, yellow & blue 20 10
1064 – 45h. red and blue . . . 50 10
1065 – 60h. blue, yellow & brn 20 10
DESIGNS: 45h. Mother, child and bird; 60h. Child skier.

1958. Czech Motor Industry Commemoration.
1066 **321** 30h. violet and yellow 65 10
1067 – 45h. brown and green . . 50 10
1068 – 60h. green and orange 65 10
1069 – 80h. red and green . . . 50 10
1070 – 1k. brown and green . . 50 10
1071 – 1k.25 green & yellow . . 1·60 75
DESIGNS: 45h. "President" car of 1897; 60h. Skoda "450" car; 80h. Tatra "603" car; 1k. Skoda "706" motor coach; 1k.25, Tatra "III" and Praga "VS 3" motor trucks in Tibet.

1958. 40th Anniv of 1st Czech Postage Stamps.
1072 **322** 60h. blue 25 10

323 Ice Hockey Goalkeeper

1959. Sports Events of 1959.
1073 – 20h. brown and grey . . 30 10
1074 – 30h. brown & orange . . 30 10
1075 **323** 60h. blue and green . . 30 10
1076 – 1k. lake and yellow . . . 30 10
1077 – 1k.60 violet and blue . . 45 10
1078 – 2k. brown and blue . . . 1·60 1·25
DESIGNS: 20h. Ice hockey player (50th anniv of Czech Ice Hockey Association); 30h. Throwing the javelin; 60h. (Type **323**) World Ice Hockey Championships, 1959; 1k. Hurdling; 1k.60, Rowing; 2k. High jumping.

324 U.A.C. Emblem
325 "Equal Rights"

1959. 4th National Unified Agricultural Co-operatives Congress, Prague.
1079 **324** 30h. lake and blue . . . 20 10
1080 – 60h. blue and yellow . . 40 10
DESIGN: 60h. Artisan shaking hand with farmer.

1959. 10th Anniv of Declaration of Human Rights.
1081 **325** 60h. green 15 10
1082 – 1k. sepia 25 10
1083 – 2k. blue . . . . 1·40 55
DESIGNS: 1k. "World Freedom" (girl with Dove of Peace); 2k. "Freedom for Colonial Peoples" (native woman with child).

326 Girl with Doll
327 F. Joliot-Curie (scientist)

1959. 10th Anniv of Young Pioneers' Movement.
1084 **326** 30h. blue and yellow . . 30 10
1085 – 40h. black and blue . . 30 25
1086 – 60h. black and purple . . 30 10
1087 – 80h. brown and green . . 30 25
DESIGNS: 40h. Boy hiker; 60h. Young radio technician; 80h. Girl planting tree.

1959. 10th Anniv of Peace Movement.
1088 **327** 60h. purple . . . . . . 1·40 40

328 Man in outer space and Moon Rocket
329 Pilsen Town Hall

1959. 2nd Czech Political and Cultural Knowledge Congress, Prague.
1089 **328** 30h. blue 90 35

1959. Centenary of Skoda Works and National Stamp Exhibition, Pilsen. Inscr "PLZEN 1959".
1090 **329** 30h. brown 15 10
1091 – 60h. violet and green . . 15 10
1092 – 1k. blue 25 20
1093 – 1k.60 black & yellow . . 1·25 1·00
DESIGNS: 60h. Part of steam turbine; 1k. St. Bartholomew's Church, Pilsen; 1k.60, Part of SR-1200 lathe.

330 Congress Emblem and Industrial Plant

1959. 4th Trades Union Congress, Prague.
1094 **330** 30h. red and yellow . . 20 10
1095 – 60h. olive and blue . . . 20 10
DESIGN: 60h. Dam.

331 Zvolen Castle

1959. Slovak Stamp Exhibition, Zvolen.
1096 **331** 60h. olive and yellow . . 35 10

332 F. Benda (composer)

1959. Cultural Anniversaries.
1097 **332** 15h. blue 20 10
1098 – 30h. red 20 10
1099 – 40h. green 30 10
1100 – 60h. brown 30 10
1101 – 60h. black 55 10
1102 – 80h. violet 30 10
1103 – 1k. brown 30 10
1104 – 3k. brown . . . . 1·40 1·10
PORTRAITS: 30h. Vaclav Klicpera (dramatist); 40h. Aurel Stodola (engineer); 60h. (1100) Karel V. Rais (writer); 60h. (1101) Haydn (composer); 80h. Antonin Slavicek (painter); 1k. Petr Bezruc (poet). 3k. Charles Darwin (naturalist).

333 "Z" Pavilion

1959. Int Fair, Brno. Inscr "BRNO 6-20. IX. 1959".
1105 – 30h. purple & yellow . . 15 10
1106 – 60h. blue 15 10
1107 **333** 1k.60 blue & yellow . . 45 10
DESIGNS: 30h. View of Fair; 60h. Fair emblem and world map.

334 Revolutionary (after A. Holly)

1959. 15th Anniv of Slovak National Uprising and 40th Anniv of Republic. Inscr "1944 29.8.1959".
1108 **334** 30h. black & mauve . . 15 10
1109 – 60h. red 20 10
1110 – 1k.60 blue & yell . . . 40 10
DESIGNS—VERT: 60h. Revolutionary with upraised rifle (after sculpture "Forward" by L. Snopka). HORIZ: 1k.60, Factory, sun and linden leaves.

335 Moon Rocket

1959. Landing of Russian Rocket on Moon.
1111 **335** 60h. red and blue . . . 1·25 25

336 Lynx

1959. 10th Anniv of Tatra National Park. Inscr "1949 TATRANSKY NARODNY PARK 1959".
1112 – 30h. black and grey . . 65 10
1113 – 40h. brown & turquoise 65 10
1114 **336** 60h. red & yellow . . . 90 10
1115 – 1k. brown & blue . . . 2·00 75
1116 – 1k.60 brown . . . . . . 1·75 10
DESIGNS—HORIZ: 30h. Alpine marmots; 40h. European bison; 1k. Wolf; 1k.60, Red deer.

337 Stamp Printing Works, Peking

1959. 10th Anniv of Chinese People's Republic.
1117 **337** 30h. red and green . . . 25 10

338 Bleriot XI Monoplanes at First Czech Aviation School

1959. Air. 50th Anniv of 1st Flight by Jan Kaspar.
1118 **338** 1k. black and yellow . . 15 10
1119 – 1k.80 black & blue . . . 75 10
DESIGN: 1k.80, Jan Kaspar and Bleriot XI in flight.

339 Great Spotted Woodpecker

341 Exercises

340 Tesla and Electrical Apparatus

1959. Birds.
1120 **339** 20h. multicoloured . . . 85 15
1121 – 30h. multicoloured . . . 85 15
1122 – 40h. multicoloured . . . 2·10 1·10
1123 – 60h. multicoloured . . . 85 15
1124 – 80h. multicoloured . . . 85 20
1125 – 1k. red, blue & black . . 85 20
1126 – 1k.20 brn, blue & blk . . 1·10 40
BIRDS: 30h. Blue tit; 40h. Eurasian nuthatch; 60h. Golden oriole; 80h. Eurasian goldfinch; 1k. Northern bullfinch; 1k.20, River kingfisher.

1959. Radio Inventors.
1127 **340** 25h. black and red . . . 1·10 20
1128 – 30h. black and brown . . 15 10
1129 – 35h. black and lilac . . . 20 10
1130 – 60h. black and blue . . 25 10
1131 – 1k. black and green . . 20 10
1132 – 2k. black and bistre . . 80 85
INVENTORS (each with sketch of invention): 30h. Aleksandr Popov; 35h. Edouard Branly; 60h. Guglielmo Marconi; 1k. Heinrich Hertz; 2k. Edwin Armstrong.

1960. 2nd National Spartacist Games (1st issue). Inscr as in T **341**.
1133 **341** 30h. brown and red . . 1·10 10
1134 – 60h. blue & light blue . . 45 25
1135 – 1k.60 brown & bistre . . 70 30
DESIGNS: 60h. Skiing; 1k.60, Basketball.
See also Nos. 1160/2.

342 Freighter "Lidice"

1960. Czech Ships.
1136 – 30h. green and red . . . 80 15
1137 – 60h. red and turquoise 25 10
1138 – 1k. violet and yellow . . 80 25
1139 **342** 1k.20 purple and green 1·75 90
SHIPS: 30h. Dredger "Praha Liben"; 60h. Tug "Kharito Latjev"; 1k. River boat "Komarno".

343 Ice Hockey

1960. Winter Olympic Games. Inscr as in T **343**.
1140 **343** 60h. sepia and blue . . . 45 25
1141 – 1k.80 black & green . . 3·75 2·10
DESIGN: 1k.80, Skating pair.
See also Nos. 1163/5.

344 Trencin Castle **345** Lenin

1960. Czechoslovak Castles.
1142 5h. blue (Type **344**) 15 10
1143 10h. black (Bezdez) 15 10
1144 20h. orange (Kost) 25 10
1145 30h. green (Pernstejn) . . . 25 10
1146 40h. brn (Kremnica) . . . 25 10
1146a 50h. black (Krivoklat) . . 25 10
1147 60h. red (Karestejn) . . . 45 10
1148 1k. purple (Smolenice) . . 30 10
1149 1k.60 blue (Kokorin) . . . 65 10

1960. 90th Birth Anniv of Lenin.
1150 **345** 60h. olive 85 25

346 Soldier and Child

1960. 15th Anniv of Liberation.
1151 **346** 30h. lake and blue . . . 30 10
1152 – 30h. green and lavender 25 10
1153 – 30h. red and pink . . . 25 10
1154 – 60h. blue and buff . . . 25 10
1155 – 60h. purple and green . . 25 10
DESIGNS—VERT: No. 1152, Solider with liberated political prisoner; 1153, Child eating pastry. HORIZ: No. 1154, Welder; 1155, Tractor-driver.

347 Smelter

1960. Parliamentary Elections.
1156 **347** 30h. red and grey . . . 15 10
1157 – 60h. green and blue . . 20 10
DESIGN: 60h. Country woman and child.

348 Red Cross Woman with Dove

1960. 3rd Czechoslovak Red Cross Congress.
1158 **348** 30h. red and blue . . . 10 10

349 Fire-prevention Team with Hose

1960. 2nd Firemen's Union Congress.
1159 **349** 60h. blue and pink . . . 35 10

1960. 2nd National Spartacist Games (2nd issue). As T **341**.
1160 30h. red and green 40 10
1161 60h. black and pink 40 10
1162 1k. blue and orange 60 25
DESIGNS: 30h. Ball exercises; 60h. Stick exercises; 1k. Girls with hoops.

1960. Olympic Games, Rome. As Type **343**.
1163 1k. black and orange . . . 50 25
1164 1k.80 black and red . . . 1·25 25
1165 2k. black and blue . . . . 2·00 85
DESIGNS: 1k. Sprinting; 1k.80, Gymnastics; 2k. Rowing.

350 Czech 10k. Stamp of 1936

1960. National Philatelic Exn, Bratislava (1st issue).
1166 – 60h. black and yellow . . 40 10
1167 **350** 1k. black and blue . . . 90 10
DESIGN: 60h. Hand of philatelist holding stamp Type **350**.
See also Nos. 1183/4.

351 Stalin Mine, Ostrava-Hermanice **352** V. Cornelius of Vsehra (historian)

1960. 3rd Five Year Plan (1st issue).
1168 **351** 10h. black and green . . 25 10
1169 – 20h. lake and blue . . . 25 10
1170 – 30h. blue and red . . . 25 10
1171 – 40h. green and lilac . . . 25 10
1172 – 60h. blue and yellow . . 25 10
DESIGNS: 20h. Hodonin Power Station; 30h. Klement Gottwald Iron Works, Kuncice; 40h. Excavator; 60h. Naphtha refinery.
See also Nos. 1198/1200.

1960. Cultural Anniversaries.
1173 **352** 10h. black 20 10
1174 – 20h. brown 30 10
1175 – 30h. red 40 10
1176 – 40h. green 45 10
1177 – 60h. violet 50 10
PORTRAITS: 20h. K. M. Capek Chod (writer); 30h. Hana Kvapilova (actress); 40h. Oskar Nedbal (composer); 60h. Otakar Ostricil (composer).

353 Zlin Trener 6 flying upside-down

1960. 1st World Aviation Aerobatic Championships, Bratislava.
1178 **353** 60h. violet and blue . . 90 25

354 "New Constitution"

1960. Proclamation of New Constitution.
1179 **354** 30h. blue and red . . . 25 10

355 Worker with "Rude Pravo"

1960. Czechoslovak Press Day (30h.) and 40th Anniv of Newspaper "Rude Pravo".
1180 – 30h. blue and orange . . 10 10
1181 **355** 60h. black and red . . . 20 10
DESIGN—HORIZ: (inscr "DEN TISKU"): 30h. Steel-workers with newspaper.

356 Globes

1960. 15th Anniv of W.F.T.U.
1182 **356** 30h. blue and bistre . . 25 10

357 Mail Coach and Ilyushin Il-18B

1960. Air. National Philatelic Exhibition, Bratislava (2nd issue).
1183 **357** 1k.60 blue and grey . . 2·50 1·40
1184 – 2k.80 green & cream . . 4·00 2·00
DESIGN: 2k.80, MIL Mi-4 helicopter over Bratislava.

358 Mallard

1960. Water Birds.
1185 – 25h. black and blue . . 50 10
1186 – 30h. black and green . . 1·10 20
1187 – 40h. black and blue . . 70 20
1188 – 60h. black and pink . . 80 20
1189 – 1k. black and yellow . . 1·25 20
1190 **358** 1k.60 black and lilac . . 2·40 1·60
BIRDS—VERT: 25h. Black-crowned night heron; 30h. Great crested grebe; 40h. Northern lapwing; 60h. Grey heron. HORIZ: 1k. Greylag goose.

359 "Doronicum clusii tausch"

1960. Flowers. Inscr in black.
1191 **359** 20h. yellow, orge & grn 50 10
1192 – 30h. red and green . . . 65 20
1193 – 40h. yellow and green . . 65 20
1194 – 60h. pink and green . . 70 20
1195 – 1k. blue, violet & green 1·00 35
1196 – 2k. yellow, green & pur 2·40 1·25
FLOWERS: 30h. "Cyclamen europaeum L"; 40h. "Primula auricula L"; 60h. "Sempervivum mont L"; 1k. "Gentiana clusil perr, et song"; 2k. "Pulsatilla slavica reuss".

360 A. Mucha (painter and stamp designer) **361** Automatic Machinery

1960. Stamp Day and Birth Centenary of Mucha.
1197 **360** 60h. blue 70 10

1961. 3rd Five Year Plan (2nd issue).
1198 **361** 20h. blue 10 10
1199 – 30h. red 20 10
1200 – 60h. green 20 10
DESIGNS: 30h. Turbo-generator and control desk; 60h. Excavator.

362 Motor Cyclists (Int Grand Prix, Brno)

1961. Sports Events of 1961.
1201 **362** 30h. blue and mauve . . 20 10
1202 – 30h. red and blue . . . 20 10
1203 – 40h. black and red . . . 35 10
1204 – 60h. purple and blue . . 35 10
1205 – 1k. blue and yellow . . . 35 10
1206 – 1k.20 green & salmon . . 35 10
1207 – 1k.60 brown and red . . 1·60 1·00
DESIGNS—VERT: 30h. (No. 1202), Athletes with banners (40th anniv of Czech Physical Culture); 60h. Figure skating (World Figure Skating Championships, Prague); 1k. Rugger (35th anniv of rugby football in Czechoslovakia); 1k.20, Football (60th anniv of football in Czechoslovakia); 1k.60, Running (65th anniv of Bechovice–Prague Marathon Race). HORIZ: 40h. Rowing (European Rowing Championships, Prague).

363 Exhibition Emblem

365 J. Mosna

364 "Sputnik 3"

1961. "PRAGA 1962" Int Stamp Exn (1st issue).
1208 363 2k. red and blue . . . . 2·00 20
See also Nos. 1250/6, 1267/70, 1297/1300 and 1311/15.

1961. Space Research (1st series).
1209 – 20h. red and violet . . . 50 10
1210 364 30h. blue and buff . . . 50 10
1211 – 40h. red and green . . . 45 15
1212 – 60h. violet and yellow 30 10
1213 – 1k.60 blue and green . . 50 10
1214 – 2k. purple and blue . . . 1·50 1·00
DESIGNS—VERT: 20h. Launching cosmic rocket; 40h. Venus rocket. HORIZ: 60h. "Lunik 1"; 1k.60, "Lunik 3" and Moon; 2k. Cosmonaut (similar to T 366).
See also Nos. 1285/90 and 1349/54.

1961. Cultural Anniversaries.
1215 365 60h. green 30 10
1216 – 60h. black 40 10
1217 – 60h. blue 40 10
1218 – 60h. red 30 10
1219 – 60h. brown 30 10
PORTRAITS: No. 1216, J. Uprka (painter); 1217, P. O. Hviezdoslav (poet); 1218, A. Mrstik (writer); 1219, J. Hora (poet).

366 Man in Space

1961. World's 1st Manned Space Flight.
1220 366 60h. red and turquoise 55 10
1221 3k. blue and yellow . . . 2·00 50

367 Kladno Steel Mills

368 "Instrumental Music"

1961.
1222 367 3k. red 85 10

1961. 150th Anniv of Prague Conservatoire.
1223 368 30h. sepia 30 10
1224 – 30h. red 35 10
1225 – 60h. blue 30 10
DESIGNS: No. 1224, Dancer; 1225, Girl playing lyre.

369 "People's House" (Lenin Museum), Prague

1961. 40th Anniv of Czech Communist Party.
1226 369 30h. brown 25 10
1227 – 30h. blue 25 10
1228 – 30h. violet 25 10
1229 – 60h. red 25 10
1230 – 60h. myrtle 25 10
1231 – 60h. red 25 10
DESIGNS—HORIZ: No. 1227, Gottwald's Museum, Prague. VERT: No. 1228, Workers in Wenceslas Square, Prague; 1229, Worker, star and factory plant; 1230, Woman wielding hammer and sickle; 1231, May Day procession, Wenceslas Square.

370 Manasek Doll

371 Gagarin waving Flags

1961. Czech Puppets.
1232 370 30h. red and yellow . . 20 10
1233 – 40h. sepia & turquoise 20 10
1234 – 60h. blue and salmon . . 20 10
1235 – 1k. green and blue . . . 20 10
1236 – 1k.60 red and blue . . . 1·25 35
PUPPETS: 40h. "Dr. Faustus and Caspar"; 60h. "Spejbl and Hurvinek"; 1k. Scene from "Difficulties with the Moon" (Askenazy); 1k.60, "Jasanek" of Brno.

1961. Yuri Gagarin's (first man in space) Visit to Prague.
1237 371 60h. black and red . . . 25 10
1238 – 1k.80 black and blue . . 45 10
DESIGN: 1k.80, Yuri Gagarin in space helmet, rocket and dove.

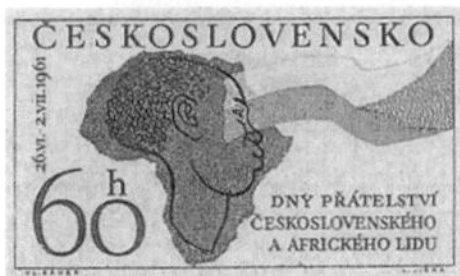
372 Woman's Head and Map of Africa

1961. Czecho-African Friendship.
1239 372 60h. red and blue . . . 25 10

373 Map of Europe and Fair Emblem

1961. Int Trade Fair, Brno. Inscr "M.V.B. 1961".
1240 373 30h. blue and green . . 15 10
1241 – 60h. green & salmon . . 25 10
1242 – 1k. brown and blue . . . 25 10
DESIGNS—VERT: 60h. Horizontal drill. HORIZ: 1k. Scientific discussion group.

374 Clover and Cow

375 Prague

1961. Agricultural Produce.
1243 – 20h. purple and blue . . 15 10
1244 374 30h. ochre and purple 15 10
1245 – 40h. orange and brown 15 10
1246 – 60h. bistre and green . . 20 10
1247 – 1k.40 brown & choc . . 40 10
1248 – 2k. blue and purple . . . 1·40 50
DESIGNS: 20h. Sugar beet, cup and saucer; 40h. Wheat and bread; 60h. Hops and beer; 1k.40, Maize and cattle; 2k. Potatoes and factory.

1961. 26th Session of Red Cross Societies League Governors' Council, Prague.
1249 375 60h. violet and red . . . 1·00 10

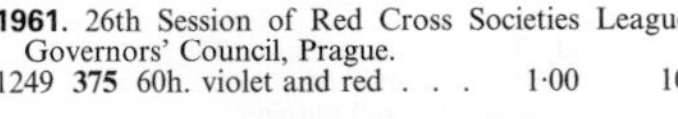

376 Orlik Dam

1961. "Praga 1962" International Stamp Exhibition (2nd and 3rd issues).
1250 376 20h. black and blue . . 75 30
1251 – 30h. blue and red . . . 45 10
1252 – 40h. blue and green . . 75 30
1253 – 60h. slate and bistre . . 75 30
1267 – 1k. purple and green . . 55 50
1254 – 1k.20 green and pink . . 90 45
1268 – 1k.60 brown and violet 95 65
1269 – 2k. black and orange . . 1·50 1·10
1255 – 3k. blue and yellow . . 1·60 45
1256 – 4k. violet and orange . . 2·25 1·25
1270 – 5k. multicoloured . . . 22·00 17·00
DESIGNS—As Type 376: 30h. Prague; 40h. Hluboka Castle from lake; 60h. Karlovy Vary; 1k. Pilsen; 1k.20, North Bohemian landscape; 1k.60, High Tatras; 2k. Iron-works, Ostrava-Kuncice; 3k. Brno; 4k. Bratislava. (50 × 29 mm): 5k. Prague and flags.

377 Orange-tip

1961. Butterflies and Moths. Multicoloured.
1257 15h. Type 377 . . . . . . 35 10
1258 20h. Southern festoon . . . 50 10
1259 30h. Apollo 90 25
1260 40h. Swallowtail 90 25
1261 60h. Peacock . . . . . . 1·10 25
1262 80h. Camberwell beauty . . 1·25 25
1263 1k. Clifden's nonpareil . . . 1·25 25
1264 1k.60 Red admiral . . . . 1·40 40
1265 2k. Brimstone . . . . . . 2·75 1·90

378 Congress Emblem and World Map

1961. 5th W.F.T.U. Congress, Moscow.
1266 378 60h. blue and red . . . 45 10

379 Racing Cyclists (Berlin–Prague–Warsaw Cycle Race)

380 K. Kovarovic (composer, centenary of birth)

1962. Sports Events of 1962.
1271 379 30h. black and blue . . 25 10
1272 – 40h. black and yellow . . 20 10
1273 – 60h. grey and blue . . . 30 10
1274 – 1k. black and pink . . . 30 10
1275 – 1k.20 black and green 30 10
1276 – 1k.60 black and green 1·40 55
DESIGNS: 40h. Gymnastics (15th World Gymnastics Championships, Prague); 60h. Figure Skating (World Figure Skating Championships, Prague); 1k. Bowling (World Bowling Championships, Bratislava); 1k.20, Football (World Cup Football Championship, Chile); 1k.60, Throwing the discus (7th European Athletic Championships, Belgrade).
See also No. 1306.

1962. Cultural Celebrities and Anniversaries.
1277 380 10h. brown 10 10
1278 – 20h. blue 10 10
1279 – 30h. brown 10 10
1280 – 40h. purple 15 10
1281 – 60h. black 15 10
1282 – 1k.60 myrtle 40 10
1283 – 1k.80 blue 50 10
DESIGNS—As Type 380: 20h. F. Skroup (composer); 30h. Bozena Nemcova (writer); 60h. Rod of Aesculapius and Prague Castle (Czech Medical Association Cent); 1k.60, L. Celakovsky (founder, Czech Botanical Society). HORIZ: (41 × 22½ mm): 40h. F. Zaviska and K. Petr; 1k.80, M. Valouch and J. Hronec. (These two commemorate Czech Mathematics and Physics Union Cent).

381 Miner holding Lamp

1962. 30th Anniv of Miners' Strike, Most.
1284 381 60h. blue and red . . . 25 10

382 "Man Conquers Space"

384 Dove and Nest

383 Indian and African Elephants

1962. Space Research (2nd series).
1285 382 30h. red and blue . . . 25 10
1286 – 40h. blue and orange . . 25 10
1287 – 60h. blue and pink . . . 25 10
1288 – 80h. purple and green . . 60 10
1289 – 1k. blue and yellow . . . 25 25
1290 – 1k.60 green and yellow 1·40 60
DESIGNS—VERT: 40h. Launching of Soviet rocket; 1k. Automatic station on Moon. HORIZ: 60h. "Vostok-II"; 80h. Multi-stage automatic rocket; 1k.60, Television satellite station.

1962. Animals of Prague Zoos.
1291 – 20h. black & turquoise 55 10
1292 – 30h. black and violet . . 55 10
1293 – 60h. black and yellow . . 65 10
1294 383 1k. black and green . . 95 10
1295 – 1k.40 black and mauve 1·00 25
1296 – 1k.60 black and brown 2·10 1·10
ANIMALS—VERT: 20h. Polar bear; 30h. Chimpanzee; 60h. Bactrian camel. HORIZ: 1k.40, Leopard; 1k.60, Wild horses.

1962. Air. "Praga 1962" International Stamp Exhibition (4th issue).
1297 384 80h. multicoloured . . . 50 25
1298 – 1k.40 red, blue & black 2·00 2·75
1299 – 2k.80 multicoloured . . 3·25 2·75
1300 – 4k.20 multicoloured . . 4·75 2·75
DESIGNS: 1k.40, Dove; 2k.80, Flower and bird; 4k.20, Plant and bird. All designs feature "Praga 62" emblem. The 80h. and 2k.80 are inscr in Slovakian and the others in Czech.

385 Girl of Lidice

386 Klary's Fountain, Teplice

1962. 20th Anniv of Destruction of Lidice and Lezaky.
1301 385 30h. black and red . . . 35 10
1302 – 60h. black and blue . . . 35 10
DESIGN: 60h. Flowers and Lezaky ruins.

1962. 1200th Anniv of Discovery of Teplice Springs.
1303 386 60h. green and yellow . . 45 10

387 Campaign Emblem

388 Swimmer with Rifle

1962. Malaria Eradication.
1304 387 60h. red and black . . . 15 10
1305 – 3k. blue and black . . . 1·25 65
DESIGN: 3k. Campaign emblem and dove (different).

1962. Czechoslovakia's Participation in World Cup Football Championship Final, Chile. As No. 1275 but inscr "CSSR VE FINALE" and new value.
1306 1k.60 green and yellow . . . 1·25 20

1962. 2nd Military Spartacist Games. Inscr as in T 388.
1307 388 30h. myrtle and blue . . 15 10
1308 – 40h. violet and yellow 20 10
1309 – 60h. brown and green . . 25 10
1310 – 1k. blue and red 30 10
DESIGNS: 40h. Soldier mounting obstacle; 60h. Footballer; 1k. Relay Race.

389 "Sun" and Field (Socialized Agriculture)

390 Swallow, "Praga 62" and Congress Emblems

1962. "Praga 1962" Int Stamp Exn (5th issue).
1311 **389** 30h. multicoloured . . . 3·00 1·10
1312 – 60h. multicoloured . . . 80 25
1313 – 80h. multicoloured . . . 3·50 2·40
1314 – 1k. multicoloured . . . 3·50 2·75
1315 – 1k.40 multicoloured . . . 3·50 2·75
MS1315a 96 × 75 mm. 5k. multicoloured (View of Prague with Exhibition emblem) (perf or imperf) . . . . 16·00 16·00
DESIGNS—VERT: 60h. Astronaut in "spaceship"; 1k.40, Children playing under "tree". HORIZ: 80h. Boy with flute, and peace doves; 1k. Workers of three races. All have "Praga 62" emblem.

1962. F.I.P. Day (Federation Internationale de Philatelie).
1316 **390** 1k.60 multicoloured . . 4·75 4·00

391 Zinkovy Sanatorium and Sailing Dinghy

392 Cruiser "Aurora"

1962. Czech Workers' Social Facilities.
1317 – 30h. black and blue . . 20 10
1318 **391** 60h. sepia and ochre . . 25 10
DESIGN—HORIZ: 30h. Children in day nursery, and factory.

1962. 45th Anniv of Russian Revolution.
1319 **392** 30h. sepia and blue . . . 10 10
1320 60h. black and pink . . 25 10

393 Astronaut and Worker

1962. 40th Anniv of U.S.S.R.
1321 **393** 30h. red and blue . . . 25 10
1322 – 60h. black and pink . . 30 10
DESIGN—VERT: 60h. Lenin.

394 Crane ("Building Construction")

1962. 12th Czech Communist Party Congress, Prague
1323 **394** 30h. red and yellow . . 25 10
1324 – 40h. blue and yellow . . 25 10
1325 – 60h. black and pink . . 25 10
DESIGNS—VERT: 40h. Produce ("Agriculture"). HORIZ: 60h. Factory plants ("Industry").

395 Stag Beetle

396 Table Tennis (World Championships, Prague)

1962. Beetles. Multicoloured.
1326 20h. Caterpillar-hunter (horiz) 25 10
1327 30h. Cardinal beetle (horiz) 25 10
1328 60h. Type **395** 25 10
1329 1k. Great dung beetle (horiz) 85 10
1330 1k.60 Alpine longhorn beetle 1·25 35
1331 2k. Blue ground beetle . . . 3·00 1·40

1963. Sports Events of 1963.
1332 **396** 30h. black and green . . 25 10
1333 – 60h. black and orange 25 10
1334 – 80h. black and blue . . 25 10
1335 – 1k. black and violet . . 30 10
1336 – 1k.20 black and brown 30 20
1337 – 1k.60 black and red . . 90 20
DESIGNS: 60h. Cycling (80th Anniv of Czech Cycling); 80h. Skiing (1st Czech Winter Games); 1k. Motor-cycle dirt track racing (15th Anniv of "Golden Helmet" Race, Pardubice); 1k.20, Weightlifting (World Championships, Prague); 1k.60, Hurdling (1st Czech Summer Games).

397 Industrial Plant

398 Guild Emblem

1963. 15th Anniv of "Victorious February" and 5th T.U. Congress.
1338 **397** 30h. red and blue . . . 15 10
1339 – 60h. red and black . . . 15 10
1340 – 60h. black and red . . . 15 10
DESIGNS—VERT: No. 1339, Sun and campfire. HORIZ: No. 1340, Industrial plant and annual "stepping stones".

1963. Cultural Anniversaries.
1341 **398** 20h. black and blue . . 10 10
1342 – 30h. red 10 10
1343 – 30h. red and blue . . . 10 10
1344 – 60h. black 15 10
1345 – 60h. purple and blue . . 15 10
1346 – 60h. myrtle 15 10
1347 – 1k.60 brown 45 10
DESIGNS—VERT: No. 1341 (Artist's Guild cent); 1342, E. Urx (journalist); 1343, J. Janosik (national hero); 1344, J. Palkovic (author); 1346, Woman with book, and children (cent of Slovak Cultural Society, Slovenska Matice); 1347, M. Svabinsky (artist, after self-portrait). HORIZ: 1345, Allegorical figure and National Theatre, Prague (80th anniv).

399 Young People

1963. 4th Czech Youth Federation Congress, Prague.
1348 **399** 30h. blue and red . . . 25 10

1963. Space Research (3rd series). As T **364** but inscr "1963" at foot.
1349 30h. purple, red & yellow 15 10
1350 50h. blue and turquoise . . 25 10
1351 60h. turquoise & yellow . . 25 10
1352 1k. black and brown 55 10
1353 1k.60 sepia and green . . . 40 10
1354 2k. violet and yellow . . . 1·60 75
MS1354a 84 × 70 mm. 3k. orange and green (Spacecraft and Mars). Imperf . . . . 7·00 4·00
DESIGNS—HORIZ: 30h. Rocket circling Sun; 50h. Rockets and Sputniks leaving Earth; 60h. Spacecraft and Moon; 1k. "Mars 1" rocket and Mars; 1k.60, Rocket heading for Jupiter; 2k. Spacecraft returning from Saturn.

400 TV Cameras and Receiver

1963. 10th Anniv of Czech Television Service. Inscr as in T **400**.
1355 **400** 40h. blue and orange . . 20 10
1356 – 60h. red and blue . . . 20 10
DESIGN—VERT: 60h. TV transmitting aerial.

401 Broadcasting Studio and Receiver

1963. 40th Anniv of Czech Radio Service. Inscr as in T **401**.
1357 **401** 30h. purple and blue . . 15 10
1358 – 1k. purple & turquoise 25 10
DESIGN—VERT: 1k. Aerial mast, globe and doves.

402 Ancient Ring and Moravian Settlements Map

404 Singer

403 Tupolev Tu-104A

1963. 1100th Anniv of Moravian Empire.
1359 **402** 30h. black and green . . 20 10
1360 – 1k.60 black and yellow 40 10
DESIGN: 1k.60, Ancient silver plate showing falconer with hawk.

1963. 40th Anniv of Czech Airlines.
1361 **403** 80h. violet and blue . . 80 20
1362 – 1k.80 blue and green . . 1·50 45
DESIGN: 1k.80, Ilyushin Il-18B.

1963. 60th Anniv of Moravian Teachers' Singing Club.
1363 **404** 30h. red 35 10

405 Nurse and Child

406 Wheatears and Kromeriz Castle

1963. Centenary of Red Cross.
1364 **405** 30h. blue and red . . . 35 10

1963. National Agricultural Exhibition.
1365 **406** 30h. green and yellow . . 35 10

407 Honey Bee, Honeycomb and Congress Emblem

409 "Modern Fashion"

408 "Vostok 5" and Bykovsky

1963. 19th International Bee-keepers' Congress ("Apimondia '63").
1366 **407** 1k. brown and yellow . . 45 10

1963. 2nd "Team" Manned Space Flights.
1367 **408** 80h. pink and blue . . . 35 10
1368 – 2k.80 blue and purple . . 2·25 25
DESIGN: 2k.80, "Vostok 6" and Valentina Tereshkova.

1963. Liberec Consumer Goods Fair.
1369 **409** 30h. black and mauve 35 10

410 Portal of Brno Town Hall

411 Cave and Stalagmites

1963. Brno International Fair.
1370 **410** 30h. purple and blue . . 25 10
1371 – 60h. blue and salmon . . 30 10
DESIGN: 60h. Tower of Brno Town Hall.

1963. Czech Scenery. (a) Moravia.
1372 **411** 30h. brown and blue . . 25 10
1373 – 80h. brown and pink . . 40 10

(b) Slovakia.
1374 – 30h. blue and green . . . 30 10
1375 – 60h. blue, green & yellow 30 10
DESIGNS: No. 1373, Macocha Chasm; 1374, Pool, Hornad Valley; 1375, Waterfall, Great Hawk Gorge.

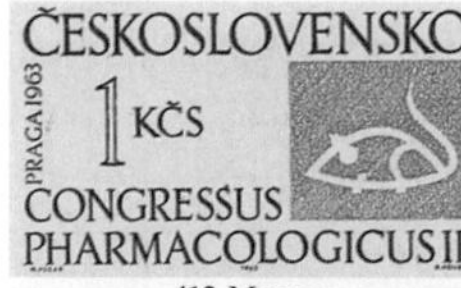

412 Mouse

1963. 2nd International Pharmacological Congress, Prague.
1376 **412** 1k. red and black . . . 45 10

413 Blast Furnace

414 "Aid for Farmers Abroad"

1963. 30th International Foundry Congress, Prague.
1377 **413** 60h. black and blue . . 25 10

1963. Freedom from Hunger.
1378 **414** 1k.60 sepia 45 10

415 Dolls

416 Canoeing

1963. U.N.E.S.C.O. Folk Art. Multicoloured.
1379 60h. Type **415** 15 10
1380 80h. Rooster 25 10
1381 1k. Vase of flowers 35 20
1382 1k.20 Detail of glass-painting "Janosik and his Men" 35 10
1383 1k.60 Stag 35 20
1384 2k. Horseman . . . . . . 2·75 1·10

1963. Olympic Games, Tokyo, 1964, and 50th Anniv of Czech Canoeing (30h.).
1385 **416** 30h. blue and green . . 30 10
1386 – 40h. brown and blue . . 30 10
1387 – 60h. lake and yellow . . 25 10
1388 – 80h. violet and red . . . 30 20
1389 – 1k. blue and red 30 20
1390 – 1k.60 ultram & blue . . 1·50 70
DESIGNS: 40h. Volleyball; 60h. Wrestling; 80h. Basketball; 1k. Boxing; 1k.60, Gymnastics.

417 Linden Tree

418 "Human Reason and Technology."

1963. 20th Anniv of Czech–Soviet Treaty of Friendship.
1391 **417** 30h. brown and blue . . 15 10
1392 – 60h. red and green . . . 15 10
DESIGN: 60h. Hammer and sickle, and star.

1963. Technical and Scientific Knowledge Society Congress.
1393 **418** 60h. violet 35 10

419 Chamois

420 Figure Skating

1963. Mountain Animals.

1394 **419** 30h. multicoloured . . . 65 15
1395 – 40h. multicoloured . . . 65 30
1396 – 60h. sepia, yellow & grn 1·00 35
1397 – 1k.20 multicoloured . . 1·00 15
1398 – 1k.60 multicoloured . . 1·40 40
1399 – 2k. brown, orge & grn 4·00 2·25

ANIMALS: 40h. Ibex; 60h. Mouflon; 1k.20, Roe deer; 1k.60, Fallow deer; 2k. Red deer.

1964. Sports Events of 1964.

1400 **420** 30h. violet and yellow 15 10
1401 – 80h. blue and orange . . 15 10
1402 – 1k. brown and lilac . . . 80 20

DESIGNS—VERT: 30h. Type **420** (Czech Students' Games); 1k. Handball (World Handball Championships). HORIZ: 80h. Cross-country skiing (Students' Games).

421 Ice Hockey

423 Magura Hotel, Zdiar, High Tatra

422 Belanske Tatra Mountains, Skiers and Tree

1964. Winter Olympic Games, Innsbruck.

1403 **421** 1k. purple and turquoise 75 30
1404 – 1k.80 green & lavender 1·00 55
1405 – 2k. blue and green . . . 2·50 2·10

DESIGNS—VERT: 1k.80, Tobogganing. HORIZ: 2k. Ski jumping.

1964. Tourist Issue.

1406 **422** 30h. purple and blue . . 20 10
1407 – 60h. blue and red . . . 30 10
1408 – 1k. brown and olive . . 55 10
1409 – 1k.80 green and orange 1·00 35

DESIGNS: 60h. Telc (Moravia) and motorcamp; 1k. Spis Castle (Slovakia) and angler; 1k.80, Cesky Krumlov (Bohemia) and sailing dinghies. Each design includes a tree.

1964. Trade Union Recreation Hotels.

1410 **423** 60h. green and yellow . . 20 10
1411 – 80h. blue and pink . . . 20 10

DESIGN: 80h. "Slovak Insurrection" Hotel, Lower Tatra.

424 Statuary (after Michelangelo)

1964. U.N.E.S.C.O. Cultural Anniversaries.

1412 **424** 40h. black and green . . 20 10
1413 – 60h. black and red . . . 20 10
1414 – 1k. black and blue . . . 45 15
1415 – 1k.60 black and yellow 45 10

DESIGNS—HORIZ: 40h. Type **424** (400th death anniv of Michelangelo); 60h. Bottom, "Midsummer Night's Dream" (400th birth anniv of Shakespeare); 1k.60, King George of Podebrady (500th anniv of his mediation in Europe). VERT: 1k. Galileo Galilei (400th birth anniv).

425 Yuri Gagarin

1964. "Space Exploration". On cream paper.

1416 **425** 30h. blue and black . . 55 15
1417 – 60h. red and green . . . 30 10
1418 – 80h. violet and lake . . 55 20
1419 – 1k. violet and blue . . . 85 25
1420 – 1k.20 bronze and red . . 55 25
1421 – 1k.40 turq & black . . . 1·25 55
1422 – 1k.60 turq & violet . . . 3·75 1·25
1423 – 2k. red and blue . . . 85 25

ASTRONAUTS—HORIZ: 60h. Titov; 80h. Glenn; 1k.20, Popovich and Nikolaev. VERT: 1k. Carpenter; 1k.40, Schirra; 1k.60, Cooper; 2k. Tereshkova and Bykovsky.

426 Campanula

427 Miner of 1764

1964. Wild Flowers.

1424 **426** 60h. purple, orge & grn 1·50 10
1425 – 80h. multicoloured . . . 1·50 10
1426 – 1k. blue, pink & green 1·50 40
1427 – 1k.20 multicoloured . . 60 30
1428 – 1k.60 violet & green . . 80 40
1429 – 2k. red, turq & violet . . 4·75 1·90

FLOWERS: 80h. Musk thistle; 1k. Chicory; 1k.20, Yellow iris; 1k.60, Marsh gentian; 2k. Common poppy.

1964. Czech Anniversaries.

1430 – 30h. black and yellow . . 25 10
1431 – 60h. red and blue . . . 50 10
1432 **427** 60h. sepia and green . . 25 10

DESIGNS—HORIZ: (30½ × 22½ mm): 30h. Silesian coat of arms (stylized) (150th Anniv of Silesian Museum, Opava). (41½ × 23 mm): 60h. (No. 1431), Skoda ASC-16 fire engine (Centenary of Voluntary Fire Brigades); 60h. (No. 1432), (Bicentenary of Banska Stiavnica Mining School).

428 Cine-film "Flower"

429 Hradcany, Praque and Black-headed Gulls

1964. 14th Int Film Festival, Karlovy Vary.

1433 **428** 60h. black, blue & red 1·60 10

1964. 4th Czech Red Cross Congress, Prague.

1434 **429** 60h. violet and red . . . 45 10

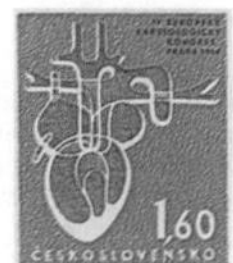
430 Human Heart

431 Slovak Girl and Workers

1964. 4th European Cardiological Congress, Prague.

1435 **430** 1k.60 red and blue . . . 1·00 10

1964. 20th Anniv of Slovak Rising and Dukla Battles.

1436 **431** 30h. red and brown . . 10 10
1437 – 60h. blue and red . . . 10 10
1438 – 60h. sepia and red . . . 10 10

DESIGNS: No. 1437, Armed Slovaks; 1438, Soldiers in battle at Dukla Pass.

432 Hradcany, Prague

433 Cycling

1964. Millenary of Prague.

1439 **432** 60h. brown & mauve . . 45 10
MS1439a 76 × 99 mm. 5k. red (Charles Bridge and City). Imperf 2·75 2·40

1964. Olympic Games, Tokyo. Multicoloured.

1440 60h. Type **433** 40 20
1441 80h. Throwing the discus and pole vaulting (vert) 45 20
1442 1k. Football (vert) 45 20
1443 1k.20 Rowing (vert) 55 35
1444 1k.60 Swimming 90 35
1445 2k.80 Weightlifting . . . . 4·00 2·40

433a "Voskhod", Astronauts and Globe

1964. Three-manned Space Flight of October 12–13.

MS1445a **433a** 3k. blue and lilac 5·75 4·25

434 Common Redstart

435 Brno Engineering Works (150th Anniv)

1964. Birds. Multicoloured.

1446 30h. Type **434** 35 10
1447 60h. Green woodpecker . . 65 10
1448 80h. Hawfinch 90 25
1449 1k. Black woodpecker . . . 90 30
1450 1k.20 European robin . . . 90 35
1451 1k.60 Eurasian roller . . . 1·40 90

1964. Czech Engineering.

1452 **435** 30h. brown 10 10
1453 – 60h. green and salmon 25 10

DESIGN: 60h. Class T334.0 diesel-hydraulic shunter.

436 "Dancing Girl"

437 Mountain Rescue Service (10th Anniv)

1965. 3rd National Spartacist Games.

1454 **436** 30h. red and blue . . . 10 10

See also Nos. 1489/92.

1965. Sports Events of 1965.

1455 **437** 60h. violet and blue . . 20 10
1456 – 60h. lake and orange . . 20 10
1457 – 60h. green and red . . . 20 10
1458 – 60h. green and yellow . . 20 10

SPORTS: No. 1456, Exercising with hoop (1st World Artistic Gymnastics Championships, Prague); 1457, Cycling (World Indoor Cycling Championships, Prague); 1458, Hurdling (Czech University Championships, Brno).

438 Domazlice

439 Exploration of Mars

1965. 700th Annivs of Six Czech Towns, and 20th Anniv of Terezin Concentration Camp (No. 1465).

1459 **438** 30h. violet and yellow 20 10
1460 – 30h. violet and blue . . 20 10
1461 – 30h. blue and olive . . . 20 10
1462 – 30h. sepia and olive . . 20 10
1463 – 30h. green and buff . . . 20 10
1464 – 30h. slate and drab . . . 20 10
1465 – 30h. red and black . . . 20 10

TOWNS: No. 1460, Beroun; 1461, Zatec; 1462, Policka; 1463, Lipnik and Becvou; 1464, Frydek-Mistek; 1465, Terezin concentration camp.

1965. Int Quiet Sun Years and Space Research.

1466 – 20h. purple and red . . 25 10
1467 – 30h. yellow and red . . 25 10
1468 – 60h. blue and yellow . . 25 10
1469 – 1k. violet & turquoise . . 50 10
1470 – 1k.40 slate and salmon 50 25
1471 **439** 1k.60 black and pink . . 50 25
1472 – 2k. blue & turquoise . . 1·40 1·25

DESIGNS—HORIZ: 20h. Maximum sun-spot activity; 30h. Minimum sun-spot activity ("Quiet Sun"); 60h. Moon exploration; 1k.40, Artificial satellite and space station; 2k. Soviet "Kosmos" and U.S. "Tiros" satellites. VERT: 1k. Space-ships rendezvous.

440 Horse Jumping (Amsterdam, 1928)

1965. Czechoslovakia's Olympic Victories.

1473 **440** 20h. brown and gold . . 20 10
1474 – 30h. violet and green . . 20 10
1475 – 60h. blue and gold . . . 20 10
1476 – 1k. brown and gold . . 40 20
1477 – 1k.40 green and gold . . 85 55
1478 – 1k.60 black and gold . . 85 55
1479 – 2k. red and gold 85 25

DESIGNS (each with city feature): 30h. Throwing the discus (Paris, 1900); 60h. Marathon (Helsinki, 1952); 1k. Weightlifting (Los Angeles, 1932); 1k.40, Gymnastics (Berlin, 1936); 1k.60, Rowing (Rome, 1960); 2k. Gymnastics (Tokyo, 1964).

441 Leonov in Space

1965. Space Achievements.

1480 **441** 60h. purple and blue . . 15 20
1481 – 60h. blue and mauve . . 15 20
1482 – 3k. purple and blue . . . 1·40 1·10
1483 – 3k. blue and mauve . . 1·40 1·10

DESIGNS: No. 1481, Grissom, Young and "Gemini 3"; 1482, Leonov leaving spaceship "Voskhod 2"; 1483, "Gemini 3" on launching pad at Cape Kennedy.

442 Soldier

1965. 20th Anniv of Liberation. Inscr "20 LET CSSR".

1484 **442** 30h. olive, black & red 20 10
1485 – 30h. violet, blue & red 20 10
1486 – 60h. black, red & blue 25 10
1487 – 1k. violet, brown & orge 50 20
1488 – 1k.60 multicoloured . . 85 40

DESIGNS: 30h. (No. 1485), Workers; 60h. Mechanic; 1k. Building worker; 1k.60, Peasant.

443 Children's Exercises

1965. 3rd National Spartacist Games.
1489 **443** 30h. blue and red . . . 15 10
1490 – 60h. brown and blue . . 20 10
1491 – 1k. blue and yellow . . . 30 10
1492 – 1k.60 red and brown . . 35 25
DESIGNS: 60h. Young gymnasts; 1k. Women's exercises; 1k.60, Start of race.

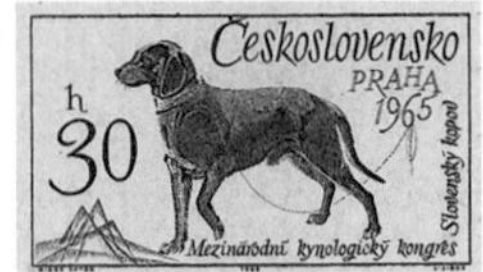

444 Slovak "Kopov"

1965. Canine Events.
1493 **444** 30h. black and red . . . 40 10
1494 – 40h. black & yellow . . 40 10
1495 – 60h. black and red . . . 50 10
1496 – 1k. black and red . . . 95 10
1497 – 1k.60 black & yellow . . 60 25
1498 – 2k. black and orange . . 2·10 1·10
DOGS: 30h. Type **444**; 1k. Poodle (Int Dog-breeders' Congress, Prague); 40h. German sheepdog; 60h. Czech "fousek" (retriever), (both World Dog Exn, Brno); 1k.60, Czech terrier; 2k. Afghan hound (both Plenary Session of F.C.I.—Int Federation of Cynology, Prague).

445 U.N. Emblem

1965. U.N. Commem and Int Co-operation Year.
1499 **445** 60h. brown & yellow . . 20 10
1500 – 1k. blue and turquoise 45 10
1501 – 1k.60 red and gold . . . 45 30
DESIGNS: 60h. T **445** (The inscr reads "Twentieth Anniversary of the signing of the U.N. Charter"); 1k. U.N. Headquarters ("20th Anniv of U.N."); 1k.60, I.C.Y. emblem.

446 "SOF" and Linked Rings

1965. 20th Anniv of World Federation of Trade Unions.
1502 **446** 60h. red and blue . . . 35 10

447 Women of Three Races **448** Children's House

1965. 20th Anniv of International Democratic Women's Federation.
1503 **447** 60h. blue 35 10

1965. Prague Castle (1st series). Inscr "PRAHA HRAD".
1504 **448** 30h. green 20 10
1505 – 60h. sepia 25 10
DESIGN—VERT: 60h. Mathias Gate.
See also Nos. 1572/3, 1656/7, 1740/1, 1827/8, 1892/3, 1959/60, 2037/8, 2103/4, 2163/4, 2253/4, 2305/6, 2337/8, 2404/5, 2466/7, 2543/4, 2599/2600, 2637/8, 2685/6, 2739/40, 2803/4, 2834/5, 2878/9, 2950/1, 2977/8 and 3026/7.

449 Marx and Lenin **450** Jan Hus

1965. 6th Organization of Socialist Countries' Postal Ministers Conference, Peking.
1506 **449** 60h. red and gold . . . 25 10

1965. Various Anniversaries and Events (1st issue).
1507 **450** 60h. black and red . . . 25 10
1508 – 60h. blue and red . . . 25 10
1509 – 60h. lilac and gold . . . 25 10
1510 – 1k. blue and orange . . 30 10
DESIGNS—VERT: No. 1507, T **450** (reformer, 550th death anniv); 1508, G. J. Mendel (publication cent in Brno of his study of heredity). HORIZ: (30½ × 23 mm): No. 1509, Jewellery emblems ("Jablonec 65" Jewellery Exn); 1510, Early telegraph and telecommunications satellite (I.T.U. cent).

451 "Lady at her Toilet" (after Titian)

1965. Culture. Sheet 75 × 99 mm.
MS1511 **451** 5k. multicoloured 3·50 3·00

1965. Various Anniversaries and Events (2nd issue). As T **450**.
1512 30h. black and green . . . 15 10
1513 30h. black and brown . . . 15 10
1514 60h. black and red 20 10
1515 60h. brown on cream . . . 20 10
1516 1k. black and orange . . . 20 10
DESIGNS—As Type **450**. HORIZ: No. 1512, L. Stur (nationalist, 150th birth anniv); 1513, J. Navratil (painter, death cent). VERT: No. 1514, B. Martinu (composer, 75th birth anniv). LARGER—VERT: (23½ × 30½ mm): No. 1515, Allegoric figure (Academia Istropolitana, Bratislava, 500th anniv). HORIZ: (30 × 22½ mm): No. 1516, Emblem (IUPAC Macromolecular Symposium, Prague).

452 "Fourfold Aid" **454** Levoca

453 Dotterel

1965. Flood Relief.
1517 **452** 30h. blue 15 10
1518 – 2k. black and olive . . . 70 40
DESIGN—HORIZ: 2k. Rescue by boat.

1965. Mountain Birds. Multicoloured.
1519 30h. Type **453** 60 10
1520 60h. Wallcreeper (vert) . . . 60 10
1521 1k.20 Redpoll 65 30
1522 1k.40 Golden eagle (vert) . . 1·10 35
1523 1k.60 Ring ousel 90 40
1524 2k. Spotted nutcracker (vert) 2·00 1·50

1965. Czech Towns. (a) Size 23 × 19 mm.
1525 **454** 5h. black and yellow . . 10 10
1526 – 10h. blue and bistre . . 20 10
1527 – 20h. sepia and blue . . . 10 10
1528 – 30h. blue and green . . 20 10
1529 – 40h. sepia and blue . . . 20 10
1530 – 50h. black and buff . . . 25 10
1531 – 60h. red and blue . . . 30 10
1532 – 1k. violet and green . . 35 10

(b) Size 30½ × 23½ mm.
1533 – 1k.20 olive and blue . . . 30 10
1534 – 1k.60 blue and yellow . . 55 10
1535 – 2k. bronze and green . . . 70 10
1536 – 3k. purple & yellow . . . 85 10
1537 – 5k. black and pink . . . . 1·60 10
TOWNS: 10h. Jindrichuv Hradec; 20h. Nitra; 30h. Kosice; 40h. Hradec Kralove; 50h. Telc; 60h. Ostrava; 1k. Olomouc; 1k.20, Ceske Budejovice; 1k.60, Cheb; 2k. Brno; 3k. Bratislava; 5k. Prague.

455 Coltsfoot **457** "Music"

456 Panorama of "Stamps"

1965. Medicinal Plants. Multicoloured.
1538 30h. Type **455** 25 10
1539 60h. Meadow saffron . . . 45 10
1540 80h. Common poppy . . . 50 10
1541 1k. Foxglove 60 15
1542 1k.20 Arnica . . . . 1·00 25
1543 1k.60 Cornflower 75 35
1544 2k. Dog rose . . . . 3·00 1·50

1965. Stamp Day.
1545 **456** 1k. red and green . . . 3·75 3·50

1966. 70th Anniv of Czech Philharmonic Orchestra.
1546 **457** 30h. black and gold . . 55 25

458 Pair Dancing

1966. Sports Events of 1966. (a) European Figure Skating Championships, Bratislava.
1547 **458** 30h. red and pink . . . 15 10
1548 – 60h. emerald and green 20 10
1549 – 1k.60 brown & yellow 40 20
1550 – 2k. blue and turquoise 2·50 35
DESIGNS: 60h. Male skater leaping; 1k.60, Female skater leaping; 2k. Pair-skaters taking bows.

(b) World Volleyball Championships, Prague.
1551 – 60h. red and buff 20 10
1552 – 1k. violet and blue . . . 25 10
DESIGNS—VERT: 60h. Player leaping to ball; 1k. Player falling.

459 S. Sucharda (sculptor) **460** "Ajax", 1841, Austria

1966. Cultural Anniversaries.
1553 **459** 30h. green 15 10
1554 – 30h. blue 15 10
1555 – 60h. red 20 10
1556 – 60h. brown 20 10
PORTRAITS: No. 1553, Type **459** (birth centenary); 1554, Ignac J. Pesina (veterinary surgeon, birth bicentenary); 1555, Romain Rolland (writer, birth centenary); 1556, Donatello (sculptor, 500th death anniv).

1966. Railway Locomotives.
1557 **460** 20h. brown on cream . . 40 10
1558 – 30h. violet on cream . . 40 10
1559 – 60h. purple on cream . . 40 15
1560 – 1k. blue on cream . . . 75 15
1561 – 1k.60 blue on cream . . 80 15
1562 – 2k. red on cream . . . . 3·25 1·25
LOCOMOTIVES: 30h. "Karlstejn", 1865; 60h. Class 423.0 steam locomotive, 1946; 1k. Class 498.0 steam locomotive, 1946; 1k.60, Class S699.0 electric locomotive, 1964; 2k. Class T699.0 diesel locomotive, 1964.

461 Dancer

1966. Centenary of Bedrich Smetana's "Bartered Bride" (opera). Sheet 84 × 106 mm.
MS1563 **461** 3k. red, blue and deep blue . . . . 3·00 2·40

462 Brown Trout

1966. World Angling Championships, Svit. Mult.
1564 30h. Type **462** 30 10
1565 60h. Eurasian perch (horiz) 50 10
1566 1k. Common (Mirror) carp (horiz) 65 10
1567 1k.20 Northern pike (horiz) 65 15
1568 1k.40 European grayling (horiz) . . . . 1·00 25
1569 1k.60 European eel (horiz) 3·00 1·00

463 "Solidarity of Mankind" **465** Belvedere Palace

464 W.H.O. Building

1966. 20th Anniv of U.N.E.S.C.O.
1570 **463** 60h. black and yellow . . 25 10

1966. Inaug of W.H.O. Headquarters, Geneva.
1571 **464** 1k. ultramarine and blue 45 10

1966. Prague Castle (2nd series).
1572 **465** 30h. blue 20 10
1573 – 60h. black and yellow . . 35 20
MS1574 75 × 97½ mm. 5k. multicoloured . . . . 2·75 3·00
DESIGN: 60h. Wood triptych, "Virgin and Child" (St. George's Church).
See also Nos. 1656/**MS**1658 and 1740/**MS**1742.

467 Scarce Swallowtail

1966. Butterflies and Moths. Multicoloured.
1575 30h. Type **467** 40 10
1576 60h. Moorland clouded yellow 70 10
1577 80h. Lesser purple emperor 70 20
1578 1k. Apollo 70 25
1579 1k.20 Scarlet tiger moth . . 1·40 35
1580 2k. Cream-spot tiger moth 4·50 1·90

468 Flags

1966. 13th Czechoslovakian Communist Party Congress.
1581 **468** 30h. red and blue . . . 20 10
1582 – 60h. red and blue . . . 20 10
1583 – 1k.60 red and blue . . . 65 10
DESIGNS: 60h. Hammer and sickle; 1k.60, Girl.

469 Indian Village

1966. "North American Indians". Centenary of Naprstek's Ethnographic Museum, Prague.
1584 **469** 20h. blue and orange . . 20 10
1585 – 30h. black and brown . . 20 10
1586 – 40h. sepia and blue . . . 20 10
1587 – 60h. green and yellow . . 25 10
1588 – 1k. purple and green . . 35 10
1589 – 1k.20 blue and mauve 50 20
1590 – 1k.40 multicoloured . . 1·25 60
DESIGNS—VERT: 30h. Tomahawk; 40h. Haida totem poles; 60h. Katchina, "good spirit" of Hopi tribe; 1k.20, Dakote calumet (pipe of peace); 1k.40, Dakota Indian chief. HORIZ: 1k. Hunting American bison.

470 Atomic Symbol

1966. Centenary of Czech Chemical Society.
1591 **470** 60h. black and blue . . 35 10

471 "Guernica", after Picasso (½-size illustration)

1966. 30th Anniv of International Brigade's War Service in Spain.
1592 **471** 60h. black and blue . . 1·75 1·75

472 Pantheon, Bratislava
473 Fair Emblem

1966. Cultural Anniversaries.
1593 **472** 30h. lilac 20 10
1594 – 60h. blue 25 10
1595 – 60h. green 25 10
1596 – 60h. brown 25 10
DESIGNS: Type **472** (21st anniv of liberation of Bratislava); 1594, L. Stur (Slovak leader) and Devin Castle; 1595, Nachod (700th anniv); 1596, Arms, globe, books and view of Olomouc (400th anniv of State Science Library).

1966. Brno International Fair.
1597 **473** 60h. black and red . . . 25 10

474 "Atomic Age"
475 Olympic Coin

1966. Jachymov (source of pitch-blende).
1598 **474** 60h. black and red . . . 35 10

1966. 70th Anniv of Olympic Committee.
1599 **475** 60h. black and gold . . 20 10
1600 – 1k. blue and red 85 20
DESIGN: 1k. Olympic flame and rings.

476 Missile Carrier, Tank and Mikoyan Gurevich MiG-21D Fighter

1966. Military Manoeuvres.
1601 **476** 60h. black and yellow . . 35 10

477 Moravian Silver Thaler (reverse and obverse)
480 Eurasian badger

479 First Space Rendezvous

1966. Brno Stamp Exhibition.
1602 **477** 30h. black and red . . . 30 10
1603 – 60h. black and orange 30 10
1604 – 1k.60 black and green 85 30
MS1605 75×100 mm. 5k. multicoloured . . . . 3·25 3·25
DESIGNS—HORIZ: 60h. "Mercury"; 1k.60, Brno buildings and crest.

1966. Space Research.
1606 **479** 20h. violet and green . . 30 10
1607 – 30h. green and orange 30 10
1608 – 60h. blue and mauve . . 30 10
1609 – 80h. purple and blue . . 30 10
1610 – 1k. black and violet . . 30 10
1611 – 1k.20 red and blue . . . 1·40 55
DESIGNS: 30h. Satellite and "back" of Moon; 60h. "Mariner 4" and first pictures of Mars; 80h. Satellite making "soft" landing on Moon; 1k. Satellite, laser beam and binary code; 1k.20, "Telstar", Earth and tracking station.

1966. Game Animals. Multicoloured.
1612 30h. Type **480** 20 10
1613 40h. Red deer (vert) 25 10
1614 60h. Lynx 30 10
1615 80h. Brown hare 40 25
1616 1k. Red fox 50 25
1617 1k.20 Brown bear (vert) . . 50 30
1618 2k. Wild boar . . . . . . 3·75 1·10

481 "Spring" (V. Hollar)

1966. Art (1st series).
1619 **481** 1k. black . . . . 5·50 2·25
1620 – 1k. multicoloured . . . 3·25 2·25
1621 – 1k. multicoloured . . . 3·50 2·75
1622 – 1k. multicoloured . . . 3·25 2·25
1623 – 1k. multicoloured . . . 28·00 20·00
PAINTINGS: No. 1620, "Mrs. F. Wussin" (J. Kupecky); 1621, "Snowy Owl" (K. Purkyne); 1622, "Bouquet" (V. Spale); 1623, "Recruit" (L. Fulla).
See also Nos. 1669, 1699/1703, 1747, 1753, 1756, 1790/4, 1835/8, 1861/5, 1914/18, 1999/2003, 2067/71, 2134/9, 2194/8, 2256/60, 2313/16, 2375/9, 2495/9, 2549/53, 2601/5, 2655/9, 2702/6, 2757/61, 2810/14, 2858/62, 2904/8, 2954/6, 3000/2, 3044/7, 3077/81 and 3107/9.

482 "Carrier Pigeon"

1966. Stamp Day.
1624 **482** 1k. blue and yellow . . . 1·10 90

483 "Youth" (5th Czech Youth Federation Congress)
484 Distressed Family

1967. Czech Congresses.
1625 **483** 30h. red and blue . . . 20 10
1626 – 30h. red and yellow . . 20 10
DESIGN: No. 1626, Rose and T.U. emblem (6th Trade Union Congress).

1967. "Peace for Viet-Nam".
1627 **484** 60h. black and salmon 25 10

485 Jihlava

1967. International Tourist Year.
1628 **485** 30h. purple 15 10
1629 – 40h. red 15 10
1630 – 1k.20 blue 40 30
1631 – 1k.60 black . . . . . . 1·90 50
DESIGNS—As Type **485**: 40h. Brno. (76×30 mm): 1k.20, Bratislava; 1k.60, Prague.

486 Black-tailed Godwit

1967. Water Birds. Multicoloured.
1632 30h. Type **486** 25 10
1633 40h. Common shoveler (horiz) 35 10
1634 60h. Purple heron 35 10
1635 80h. Penduline tit 70 25
1636 1k. Pied avocet 70 25
1637 1k.40 Black stork . . . . . 1·50 40
1638 1k.60 Tufted duck (horiz) 2·75 1·75

487 Sun and Satellite

1967. Space Research.
1639 **487** 30h. red and yellow . . 15 10
1640 – 40h. blue and grey . . . 15 10
1641 – 60h. green and violet . . 25 10
1642 – 1k. blue and mauve . . 25 10
1643 – 1k.20 black and blue . . 40 25
1644 – 1k.60 lake and grey . . 1·75 45
DESIGNS: 40h. Space vehicles in orbit; 60h. "Man on the Moon" and orientation systems; 1k. "Exploration of the planets"; 1k.20, Lunar satellites; 1k.60, Lunar observatory and landscape.

488 Gothic Art (after painting by Theodoric)

1967. World Fair, Montreal. Multicoloured.
1645 30h. Type **488** 15 10
1646 40h. Jena Codex—ancient manuscript, "Burning of John Hus" 15 10
1647 60h. Lead crystal glass . . . 20 10
1648 80h. "The Shepherdess and the Chimney Sweep" (Andersen's Fairy Tales), after painting by J. Trnka 30 10
1649 1k. Atomic diagram ("Technical Progress") . . 35 25
1650 1k.20 Dolls by P. Rada ("Ceramics") . . . . . . 1·75 95
MS1651 95×75 mm. 3k. Montreal skyline . . . . 3·00 2·75

489 Bicycle Wheels and Dove

1967. Sports Events of 1967.
1652 **489** 60h. black and red . . . 20 10
1653 – 60h. black & turquoise 20 10
1654 – 60h. black and blue . . 20 10
1655 – 1k.60 black and violet 1·50 45
DESIGNS—HORIZ: Type **489** (20th Warsaw–Berlin–Prague Cycle Race): No. 1654, Canoeist in kayak (5th World Canoeing Championships). VERT: No. 1653, Basketball players (World Women's Basketball Championships); 1655, Canoeist (10th World Water-slalom Championships).

1967. Prague Castle (3rd series). As Type **465**.
1656 30h. lake 20 10
1657 60h. slate 50 10
MS1658 75×95 mm. 5k. multicoloured . . . . 2·00 3·00
DESIGNS: 30h. "Golden Street"; 60h. St. Wenceslas' Hall. SMALLER (30½×50 mm)—5k. "The Glory of Christ" (Bohemian 11th-century illuminated manuscript).

490 "PRAZSKE 1967"
491 Synagogue Curtain (detail)

1967. Prague Music Festival.
1659 **490** 60h. violet and green . . 25 10

1967. Jewish Culture.
1660 **491** 30h. red and blue . . . 20 10
1661 – 60h. black and green . . 25 10
1662 – 1k. blue and mauve . . 35 10
1663 – 1k.20 red and brown . . 50 10
1664 – 1k.40 black and yellow 50 10
1665 – 1k.60 green and yellow 3·75 2·75
DESIGNS: 60h. Printers' imprint (1530); 1k. Mikulov jug (1801); 1k.20, "Old-New" Synagogue, Prague (1268); 1k.40, Jewish memorial candelabra, Pinkas Synagogue (1536) (The memorial is for Czech victims of Nazi persecution); 1k.60, David Gans' tombstone (1613).

492 Lidice Rose
493 "Architecture"

1967. 25th Anniv of Destruction of Lidice.
1666 **492** 30h. black and red . . . 25 10

1967. 9th Int Architects' Union Congress, Prague.
1667 **493** 1k. black and gold . . . 35 10

494 Petr Bezruc

1967. Birth Centenary of Petr Bezruc (poet).
1668 **494** 60h. black and red . . . 25 10

1967. Publicity for "Praga 68" Stamp Exhibition. As Type **481**. Multicoloured.
1669 2k. "Henri Rousseau" (self-portrait) . . . . 2·40 1·40

495 Skalica

1967. Czech Towns.
1670 **495** 30h. blue 20 10
1671 – 30h. lake (Presov) . . . 20 10
1672 – 30h. green (Pribram) . . 20 10

496 Thermal Fountain and Colonnade, Karlovy Vary

1967. Postal Employees' Games.
1673 **496** 30h. violet and gold . . 25 10

497 Ondrejov Observatory and Universe

1967. 13th Int Astronomic Union Congress, Prague.
1674 **497** 60h. silver, blue & purple 1·75 35

498 "Miltonia spectabilis"

1967. Botanical Garden Flowers. Multicoloured.
1675 20h. Type **498** 25 10
1676 30h. Cup and saucer plant 25 10
1677 40h. "Lycaste deppei" . . . 25 15
1678 60h. "Glottiphyllum davisii" 40 10
1679 1k. Painter's palette 60 25
1680 1k.20 "Rhodocactus bleo" 60 40
1681 1k.40 "Dendrobium phalaenopsis" . . . . . 2·40 65

499 Eurasian Red Squirrel **500** Military Vehicles

1967. Fauna of Tatra National Park.
1682 **499** 30h. black, orge & yell 35 10
1683 – 60h. black and buff . . . 35 10
1684 – 1k. black and blue . . . 40 15
1685 – 1k.20 black, yell & grn 60 15
1686 – 1k.40 black, yell & pink 85 25
1687 – 1k.60 black, orge & yell 3·00 1·10
DESIGNS: 60h. Wild cat; 1k. Stoat; 1k.20, Hazel dormouse; 1k.40, West European hedgehog; 1k.60, Pine marten.

1967. Army Day.
1688 **500** 30h. green 25 10

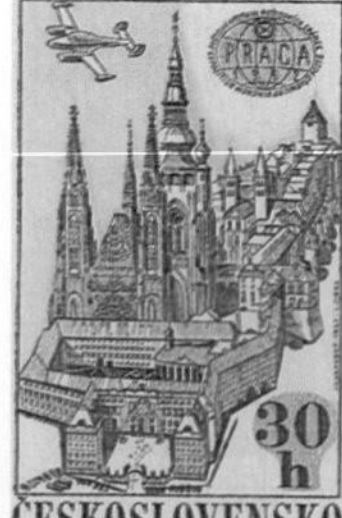

501 Prague Castle ("PRAGA 62") **503** Pres. Novotny

1967. Air. "PRAGA 1968" Int Stamp Exhbition (1st issue).
1689 **501** 30h. multicoloured . . . 15 10
1690 – 60h. multicoloured . . . 25 20
1691 – 1k. multicoloured . . . 25 20
1692 – 1k.40 multicoloured . . 35 25
1693 – 1k.60 multicoloured . . 35 35
1694 – 2k. multicoloured . . . 55 25
1695 – 5k. multicoloured . . . 2·50 2·10
DESIGNS (Sites of previous Int Stamp Exns): 60h. Selimiye Mosque, Edirne ("ISTANBUL 1963"); 1k. Notre Dame, Paris ("PHILATEC 1964"); 1k.40, Belvedere Palace, Vienna ("WIPA 1965"); 1k.60, Capitol, Washington ("SIPEX 1965"); 2k. Amsterdam ("AMPHILEX 1967"). (40 × 55 mm): 5k. Prague ("PRAGA 1968").
See also Nos. 1718/20, 1743/8, 1749/54 and 1756.

502 Cruiser "Aurora"

1967. 50th Anniv of October Revolution.
1696 **502** 30h. red and black . . . 10 10
1697 – 60h. red and black . . . 15 10
1698 – 1k. red and black . . . 15 10
DESIGNS—VERT: 60h. Hammer and sickle emblems; 1k. "Reaching hands".

1967. Art (2nd series). As T **481**. Multicoloured.
1699 60h. "Conjurer with Cards" (F. Tichy) 25 25
1700 80h. "Don Quixote" (C. Majernik) 25 25
1701 1k. "Promenade in the Park" (N. Grund) 55 55
1702 1k.20 "Self-Portrait" (P. J. Brandl) 55 55
1703 1k.60 "Epitaph to Jan of Jeren" (Czech master) . . 4·25 4·25
All in National Gallery, Prague.

1967.
1704 **503** 2k. green . . . . 1·25 10
1705 3k. brown . . . . 1·75 10

504 Letov L-13 Glider

1967. Czech Aircraft. Multicoloured.
1706 30h. Type **504** 15 10
1707 60h. Letov L-40 Meta-Sokol 20 10
1708 80h. Letov L-200 Morava 20 10
1709 1k. Letov Z-37 Cmelak crop-sprayer 45 10
1710 1k.60 Zlin Z-526 Trener Master 55 10
1711 2k. Aero L-29 Delfin jet trainer . . . . 1·75 65

505 Czech Stamps of 1920

1967. Stamp Day.
1712 **505** 1k. lake and silver . . . 1·75 1·40

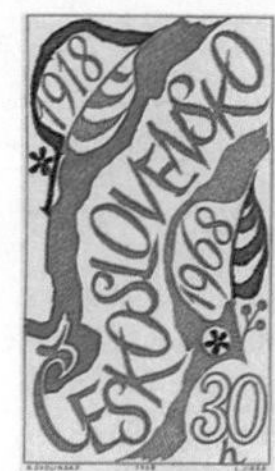

506 "CESKOSLOVENSKO 1918–1968"

1968. 50th Anniv of Republic (1st issue).
1713 **506** 30h. red, blue & ultram 70 25
See also Nos. 1780/1.

507 Skater and Stadium

1968. Winter Olympic Games, Grenoble.
1714 **507** 60h. black, yell & ochre 15 10
1715 – 1k. brown, bistre & blue 30 10
1716 – 1k.60 black, grn & lilac 55 10
1717 – 2k. black, blue & yellow 1·10 50
DESIGNS: 1k. Bobsleigh run; 1k.60, Ski jump; 2k. Ice hockey.

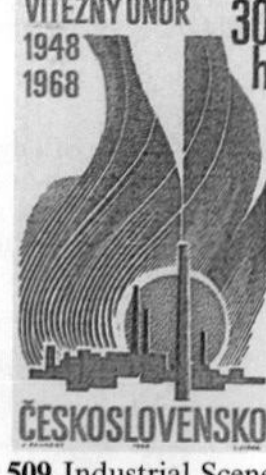

508 Charles Bridge, Prague, and Charles's Hydrogen Balloon **509** Industrial Scene and Red Sun

1968. Air. "PRAGA 1968" International Stamp Exhibition (2nd issue). Multicoloured.
1718 60h. Type **508** 45 15
1719 1k. Royal Summer-house, Belvedere, and William Henson's "Aerial Steam Carriage" 70 25
1720 2k. Prague Castle and airship 80 55

1968. 20th Anniv of "Victorious February".
1721 **509** 30h. red and blue . . . 10 10
1722 – 60h. red and blue . . . 15 10
DESIGN: 60h. Workers and banner.

510 Battle Plan **511** Human Rights Emblem

1968. 25th Anniv of Sokolovo Battles.
1723 **510** 30h. red, blue & green 45 10

1968. Human Rights Year.
1724 **511** 1k. red . . . . 1·10 30

512 Liptovsky Mikulas (town) and Janko Kral (writer)

1968. Various Commemorations.
1725 **512** 30h. green 25 10
1726 – 30h. blue and orange . . 25 10
1727 – 30h. red and gold . . . 25 10
1728 – 30h. purple 25 10
1729 – 1k. multicoloured . . . 40 10
DESIGNS—VERT: No. 1726, Allegorical figure of woman (150th anniv of Prague National Museum); 1727, Girl's head (cent of Prague National Theatre); 1728, Karl Marx (150th anniv of birth); 1729, Diagrammatic skull (20th anniv of W.H.O.).

513 "Radio" (45th anniv)

1968. Czech Radio and Television Annivs.
1730 **513** 30h. black, red and blue 20 10
1731 – 30h. black, red and blue 20 10
DESIGN: No. 1731, "Television" (15th anniv).

514 Athlete and Statuettes **515** Pres. Svoboda

1968. Olympic Games, Mexico. Multicoloured.
1732 30h. Type **514** 15 10
1733 40h. Runner and seated figure (Quetzalcoatl) . . . 20 10
1734 60h. Netball and ornaments 25 10
1735 1k. Altar and Olympic emblems 35 10
1736 1k.60 Football and ornaments 50 20
1737 2k. Prague Castle and key 70 55

1968.
1738 **515** 30h. blue 10 10
1738a 50h. green 10 10
1739 60h. red 25 10
1739a 1k. red 30 10

1968. Prague Castle (4th series). As Type **465**.
1740 30h. multicoloured 25 10
1741 60h. black, green & red . . 25 10
MS1742 75 × 95 mm. 5k. multicoloured . . . . 2·50 2·50
DESIGN: 30h. "Bretislav I" (from tomb in St. Vitus' Cathedral); 60h. Knocker on door of St. Wenceslas' Chapel. SMALLER (30½ × 51 mm)—5k. "St. Vitus" (detail of mosaic).

516 "Business" (sculpture by O. Gutfreund)

1968. "PRAGA 1968" Int Stamp Exn (3rd Issue). Multicoloured.
1743 30h. Type **516** 20 10
1744 40h. Broadcasting building, Prague 20 10
1745 60h. Parliament Building . . 20 20
1746 1k.40 "Prague" (Gobelin tapestry by Jan Bauch) . . 50 25
1747 2k. "The Cabaret Artiste" (painting by F. Kupka) (size 40 × 50 mm) . . . 1·90 1·40
1748 3k. Presidential standard . . 50 45

1969. "PRAGA 1968" Int Stamp Exn (4th issue).
1749 30h. green, yellow & grey 20 10
1750 60h. violet, gold & green . . 20 10
1751 1k. indigo, pink and blue . . 30 20
1752 1k.60 multicoloured 55 25
1753 2k. multicoloured . . . . . 1·10 90
1754 3k. black, blue, pink & yell 1·25 35
DESIGNS—As Type **516**: 30h. St. George's Basilica, Prague Castle; 60h. Renaissance fountain; 1k. Dvorak's Museum; 1k.60, "Three Violins" insignia (18th-cent house); 3k. Prague emblem of 1475. As Type **481**: 2k. "Josefina" (painting by Josef Manes, National Gallery, Prague).

517 View of Prague

1968. "PRAGA 1968" (5th issue—50th Anniv of Czechoslovak Stamps). Sheet 73 × 111½ mm.
MS1755 **517** 10k. multicoloured 4·00 4·25

1968. "PRAGA 1968" (6th issue—F.I.P. Day). As T **481**.
1756 5k. multicoloured . . . . . 4·25 3·50
DESIGN: 5k. "Madonna of the Rosary" (detail from painting by Albrecht Durer in National Gallery, Prague).

518 Horse-drawn Coach on Rails "Hannibal" (140th Anniv of Ceske-Budejovice-Linz Railway)

1968. Railway Anniversaries.
1757 **518** 60h. multicoloured . . . 30 15
1758 – 1k. multicoloured . . . 85 25
DESIGN: 1k. Early steam locomotive "Johann Adolf" and modern electric locomotive (centenary of Ceske-Budejovice-Pilsen Railway).

519 Symbolic "S"

1968. 6th Int Slavonic Congress, Prague.
1759 519 30h. red and blue . . . 55 10

520 Adrspach Rocks and "Hypophylloceras bizonatum" (ammonite)

1968. 23rd Int Geological Congress, Prague.
1760 520 30h. black and yellow . . 20 10
1761 – 60h. black and mauve 20 10
1762 – 80h. black, pink & lav 25 10
1763 – 1k. black and blue . . . 35 10
1764 – 1k.60 black and yellow 1·40 55
DESIGNS: 60h. Basalt columns and fossilised frog; 80h. Bohemian "Paradise" and agate; 1k. Tatra landscape and "Chlamys gigas" shell; 1k.60, Barrandien (Bohemia) and limestone.

521 M. J. Hurban and Standard-bearer

1968. 120th Anniv of Slovak Insurrection and 25th Anniv of Slovak National Council.
1765 521 30h. blue 10 10
1766 – 60h. red 10 10
DESIGN: 60h. Partisans (120th anniv of Slovak Insurrection).

522 "Man and Child" (Jiri Beutler, aged 10)

1968. Munich Agreement. Drawings by children in Terezin concentration camp. Multicoloured.
1767 30h. Type 522 . . . . . . 20 10
1768 60h. "Butterflies" (Kitty Brunnerova, aged 11) . . 30 10
1769 1k. "The Window" (Jiri Schlessinger, aged 10) . . 45 10
The 1k. is larger (40 × 22 mm).

523 Banska Bystrica

525 Ernest Hemingway

524 National Flag

1968. Arms of Czech Regional Capitals (1st series). Multicoloured.
1770 60h. Type 523 . . . . . . 20 10
1771 60h. Bratislava 20 10
1772 60h. Brno 20 10
1773 60h. Ceske Budejovice . . . 20 10
1774 60h. Hradec Kralove . . . 20 10
1775 60h. Kosice 20 10
1776 60h. Ostrava 20 10
1777 60h. Pilsen 20 10
1778 60h. Usti nad Labem . . . 20 10
1779 1k. Prague (vert) 75 10
See also Nos. 1855/60, 1951/6, 2106/8 and 2214/15.

1968. 50th Anniv of Republic (2nd issue).
1780 524 30h. deep blue & blue 20 10
1781 – 60h. multicoloured . . . 20 10
MS1782 76 × 100 mm. 5k. red . . 3·00 3·25

DESIGN: 60h. Prague and Bratislava within outline "map".

1968. U.N.E.S.C.O. "Cultural Personalities of the 20th century in Caricature" (1st series).
1783 525 20h. black and red . . . 15 10
1784 – 30h. multicoloured . . . 15 10
1785 – 40h. red, black & lilac 15 10
1786 – 60h. black, green & bl 15 10
1787 – 1k. black, brn & yell . . 45 10
1788 – 1k.20 black, vio & red 50 20
1789 – 1k.40 black, brn & orge 1·40 45
PERSONALITIES: 30h. Karel Capek (dramatist); 40h. George Bernard Shaw; 60h. Maxim Gorky; 1k. Picasso; 1k.20, Taikan Yokoyama (painter); 1k.40, Charlie Chaplin.
See also Nos. 1829/34.

1968. Art (3rd series). As T 481. Paintings in National Gallery, Prague. Multicoloured.
1790 60h. "Cleopatra II" (J. Zrzavy) 50 30
1791 80h. "The Black Lake" (J. Preisler) 70 50
1792 1k.20 "Giovanni Francisci as a Volunteer" (P. Bohun) . . . . . . 1·40 1·10
1793 1k.60 "Princess Hyacinth" (A. Mucha) 90 45
1794 3k. "Madonna and Child" (altar detail, Master Paul of Levoca) . . . . 4·00 3·50

526 "Cinder Boy"

528 Red Crosses forming Cross

527 5h. and 10h. Stamps of 1918

1968. Slovak Fairy Tales. Multicoloured.
1795 30h. Type 526 . . . . . . 15 10
1796 60h. "The Proud Lady" . . 25 10
1797 80h. "The Knight who ruled the World" 30 10
1798 1k. "Good Day, Little Bench" 40 15
1799 1k.20 "The Enchanted Castle" 45 15
1800 1k.80 "The Miraculous Hunter" . . . . 2·00 50

1968. Stamp Day and 50th Anniv of 1st Czech Stamps.
1801 527 1k. gold and blue . . . 1·40 1·25

1969. 50th Anniv of Czech Red Cross and League of Red Cross Societies.
1802 528 60h. red, gold and sepia 25 10
1803 – 1k. red, blue and black 45 20
DESIGN: 1k. Red Cross symbols within heart-shaped "dove".

529 I.L.O. Emblem

530 Wheel-lock Pistol, c. 1580

1969. 50th Anniv of Int Labour Organization.
1804 529 1k. black and grey . . . 25 10

1969. Early Pistols. Multicoloured.
1805 30h. Type 530 . . . . . . 15 10
1806 40h. Italian horse-pistol, c. 1600 . . . . . . 20 10
1807 60h. Kubik wheel-lock carbine, c. 1720 . . . . . 20 10
1808 1k. Flint-lock pistol, c. 1760 30 10
1809 1k.40 Lebeda duelling pistols, c. 1830 . . . . . 50 20
1810 1k.60 Derringer pistols, c. 1865 . . . . . 1·60 35

531 University Emblem and Symbols (50th Anniv of Brno University)

1969. Anniversaries.
1811 531 60h. black, blue & gold 20 10
1812 – 60h. blue 20 10
1813 – 60h. multicoloured . . . 20 10
1814 – 60h. black and red . . . 20 10
1815 – 60h. red, silver & blue 20 10
1816 – 60h. black and gold . . 20 10
DESIGNS and ANNIVERSARIES: No. 1812, Bratislava Castle, open book and head of woman (50th Anniv Comenius University, Bratislava); 1813, Harp and symbolic eagle (50th Anniv Brno Conservatoire); 1814, Theatrical allegory (50th Anniv Slovak National Theatre (1970); 1815, Arms and floral emblems (Slovak Republican Council, 50th Anniv); 1816, Grammar school and allegories of Learning (Zniev Grammar School. Cent).

532 Veteran Cars of 1900–05

1969. Motor Vehicles. Multicoloured.
1817 30h. Type 532 . . . . . . 40 10
1818 1k.60 Veteran Cars of 1907 70 20
1819 1k.80 Prague Buses of 1907 and 1967 . . . . 1·75 85

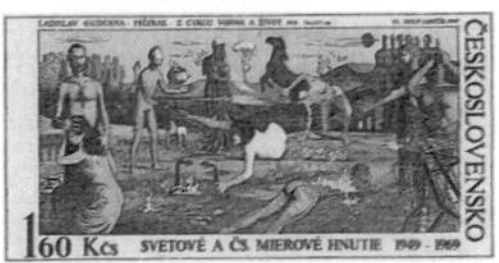
533 "Peace" (after L. Guderna) (½-size ilustration)

1969. 20th Anniv of Peace Movement.
1820 533 1k.60 multicoloured . . 55 25

534 Engraving by H. Goltzius

1969. Horses. Works of Art.
1821 534 30h. sepia on cream . . 25 10
1822 – 80h. purple on cream . . 25 10
1823 – 1k.60 slate on cream . . 40 20
1824 – 1k.80 black on cream . . 40 25
1825 – 2k.40 mult on cream . . 2·50 65
DESIGNS—HORIZ: 80h. Engraving by M. Merian. VERT: 1k.60, Engraving by V. Hollar; 1k.80, Engraving by A. Durer; 2k.40, Painting by J. E. Ridinger.

535 Dr. M. R. Stefanik as Civilian and Soldier

1969. 50th Death Anniv of General Stefanik.
1826 535 60h. red 35 10

536 "St. Wenceslas" (mural detail, Master of Litomerice, 1511)

1969. Prague Castle (5th series). Multicoloured.
1827 3k. Type 536 . . . . . . 2·10 1·40
1828 3k. Coronation Banner of the Czech Estates, 1723 2·10 1·40
See also Nos. 1892/3, 1959/60, 2037/8, 2103/4, 2163/4, 2253/4, 2305/6, 2337/8, 2404/5, 2466/7, 2543/4, 2599/600 and 2637/8.

1969. U.N.E.S.C.O. "Cultural Personalities of the 20th Century in Caricature" (2nd series). Designs as Type 525.
1829 30h. black, red and blue . . 10 10
1830 40h. black, violet & blue . . 15 10
1831 60h. black, red & yellow . . 15 10
1832 1k. multicoloured 30 10
1833 1k.80 black, blue & orge . . 40 10
1834 2k. black, yellow & green 2·00 60
DESIGNS: 30h. P. O. Hviezdoslav (poet); 40h. G. K. Chesterton (writer); 60h. V. Mayakovsky (poet); 1k. Henri Matisse (Painter); 1k.80, A. Hrdlicka (anthropologist); 2k. Franz Kafka (novelist).

537 "Music"

538 Astronaut, Moon and Aerial View of Manhattan

1969. "Woman and Art". Paintings by Alfons Mucha. Multicoloured.
1835 30h. Type 537 . . . . . . 30 10
1836 60h. "Painting" 35 10
1837 1k. "Dance" 50 10
1838 2k.40 "Ruby and Amethyst" (40 × 51 mm) . . . . . . 2·00 1·10

1969. Air. 1st Man on the Moon. Multicoloured.
1839 60h. Type 538 . . . . . . 20 10
1840 3k. "Eagle" module and aerial view of J. F. Kennedy Airport, New York . . . . 2·40 1·10

539 Soldier and Civilians

1969. 25th Anniv of Slovak Rising and Battle of Dukla.
1841 539 30h. bl & red on cream 10 10
1842 – 30h. grn & red on cream 10 10
DESIGN: No. 1842, General Svoboda and partisans.

540 Ganek (½-size illustration)

1969. 20th Anniv of Tatra National Park.
1843 540 60h. purple 15 10
1844 – 60h. blue 15 10
1845 – 60h. green 15 10
1846 – 1k.60 multicoloured . . 1·75 45
1847 – 1k.60 multicoloured . . 45 15
1848 – 1k.60 multicoloured . . 45 15
DESIGNS: No. 1844, Mala Valley; 1845, Bielovodska Valley. (SMALLER 40 × 23 mm): 1846, Velka Valley and gentian; 1847, Mountain stream, Mala Valley and gentian; 1848, Krivan Peak and autumn crocus.

541 Bronze Belt Fittings (8th–9th century)

1969. Archaeological Discoveries in Bohemia and Slovakia. Multicoloured.
1849 20h. Type 541 . . . . . . 15 10
1850 30h. Decoration showing masks (6th–8th century) 15 10
1851 1k. Gold Earrings (8th–9th century) 25 10
1852 1k.80 Metal Crucifix (obverse and reverse) (9th century) 50 25
1853 2k. Gilt ornament with figure (9th century) . . . 1·75 50

542 "Focal Point"—Tokyo

1969. 16th U.P.U. Congress, Tokyo.
1854 **542** 3k.20 multicoloured . . 1·60 1·00

1969. Arms of Czech Regional Capitals (2nd series). As T **523**. Multicoloured.
1855 50h. Bardejov 20 10
1856 50h. Hranice 20 10
1857 50h. Kezmarok 20 10
1858 50h. Krnov 20 10
1859 50h. Litomerice 20 10
1860 50h. Manetin 20 10

1969. Art (4th series). As T **481**. Multicoloured.
1861 60h. "Great Requiem" (F. Muzika) 55 50
1862 1k. "Resurrection" (Master of Trebon) 55 50
1863 1k.60 "Crucifixion" (V. Hloznik) 55 50
1864 1k.80 "Girl with Doll" (J. Bencur) 55 75
1865 2k.20 "St. Jerome" (Master Theodoric) . . . . 2·75 2·10

543 Emblem and "Stamps"

1969. Stamp Day.
1866 **543** 1k. purple, gold & blue 1·50 1·10

544 Ski Jumping

1970. World Skiing Championships, High Tatras. Multicoloured.
1867 50h. Type **544** 20 10
1868 60h. Cross-country skiing 20 10
1869 1k. Ski jumper "taking off" 20 10
1870 1k.60 Woman skier . . . . 1·10 35

545 J. A. Comenius (300th Death Anniv)

1970. U.N.E.S.C.O. Anniversaries of World Figures.
1871 **545** 40h. black 15 10
1872 – 40h. grey 25 10
1873 – 40h. brown 25 10
1874 – 40h. red 15 10
1875 – 40h. red 15 10
1876 – 40h. brown 15 10
DESIGNS: No. 1872, Ludwig van Beethoven (composer, birth bicent); 1873, Tosef Manes (artist, 150th birth anniv); 1874, Lenin (birth cent); 1875, Friedrich Engels (150th birth anniv); 1876, Maximilian Hell (astronomer, 250th birth anniv).

546 Bells

1970. World Fair, Osaka, Japan. "Expo 70". Multicoloured.
1877 50h. Type **546** 15 10
1878 80h. Heavy Machinery . . . 25 10
1879 1k. Beehives (folk sculpture) 25 10
1880 1k.60 "Angels and Saints" (17th-century icon) . . . 45 35
1881 2k. "Orlik Castle, 1787" (F. K. Wolf) 50 35
1882 3k. "Fujiyama" (Hokusai) 2·40 80
Nos. 1880/2 are larger, 51 × 37 mm.

547 Town Hall, Kosice 549 Lenin

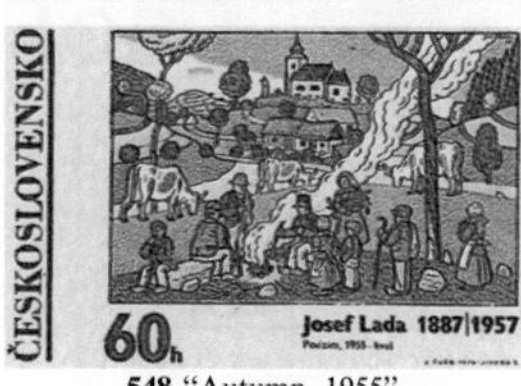

548 "Autumn, 1955"

1970. 25th Anniv of Kosice Reforms.
1883 **547** 60h. blue, gold & red . . 35 10

1970. Paintings by Joseph Lada. Multicoloured.
1884 60h. Type **548** 20 10
1885 1k. "The Magic Horse" (vert) 40 10
1886 1k.80 "The Water Demon" (vert) 45 20
1887 2k.40 "Children in Winter, 1943" . . . . 2·00 55

1970. Birth Centenary of Lenin.
1888 **549** 30h. red and gold . . . 10 10
1889 – 60h. black and gold . . 10 10
DESIGN: 60h. Lenin (bareheaded).

550 Prague Panorama and Hand giving "V" Sign

1970. 25th Anniv of Prague Rising and Liberation of Czechoslovakia.
1890 **550** 30h. purple, gold & blue 20 10
1891 – 30h. green, gold & red 20 10
DESIGN: No. 1891, Soviet tank entering Prague.

1970. Prague Castle. Art Treasures (6th series). As Type **536**. Multicoloured.
1892 3k. "Hermes and Athena" (painting by B. Spranger) 1·90 1·75
1893 3k. "St. Vitus" (bust) . . . 1·90 1·75

551 Compass and "World Capitals" (½-size illustration)

1970. 25th Anniv of United Nations.
1894 **551** 1k. multicoloured . . . 45 25

552 Thirty Years War Cannon and "Baron Munchausen"

1970. Historic Artillery. Multicoloured.
1895 30h. Type **552** 15 10
1896 60h. Hussite bombard and St. Barbara 15 10
1897 1k.20 Austro-Prussian War field-gun and Hradec Kralove 45 10
1898 1k.80 Howitzer (1911) and Verne's "Colombiad" . . 75 25
1899 2k.40 Mountain-gun (1915) and "Good Soldier Schweik" . . . . 1·50 50

553 "Rude Pravo" 554 "Golden Sun", Bridge-tower, Prague

1970. 50th Anniv of "Rude Pravo" (newspaper).
1900 **553** 60h. red, drab & black 20 10

1970. Ancient Buildings and House-signs from Prague, Brno and Bratislava. Multicoloured.
1901 40h. Type **554** 15 10
1902 60h. "Blue Lion" and Town Hall tower, Brno 25 10
1903 1k. Gothic bolt and Town Hall tower, Bratislava . . 25 10
1904 1k.40 Coat of arms and Michael Gate, Bratislava 1·90 35
1905 1k.60 "Moravian Eagle" and Town Hall gate, Brno 40 20
1906 1k.80 "Black Sun", "Green Frog" and bridge-tower, Prague 60 20

555 World Cup Emblem and Flags

1970. World Cup Football Championship, Mexico. Multicoloured.
1907 20h. Type **555** 10 10
1908 40h. Two players and badges of Germany and Uruguay 15 10
1909 60h. Two players and badges of England and Czechoslovakia 20 10
1910 1k. Three players and badges of Rumania and Czechoslovakia 30 10
1911 1k.20 Three players and badges of Brazil and Italy 50 10
1912 1k.80 Two players and badges of Brazil and Czechoslovakia . . . . . 1·75 30

556 "S.S.M." and Flags 557 Dish Aerial

1970. 1st Congress of Czechoslovak Socialist Youth Federation.
1913 **556** 30h. multicoloured . . . 35 10

1970. Art (5th series). As T **481**. Multicoloured.
1914 1k. "Mother and Child" (M. Galanda) 25 25
1915 1k.20 "The Bridesmaid" (K. Svolinsky) 50 35
1916 1k.40 "Walk by Night" (F. Hudecek) 50 40
1917 1k.80 "Banska Bystrica Market" (detail, D. Skutecky) 65 45
1918 2k.40 "Adoration of the Kings" (Vysehrad Codex) 2·10 2·40

1970. "Intercosmos". Space Research Programme. Multicoloured.
1919 20h. Type **557** 10 10
1920 40h. Experimental satellite 15 10
1921 60h. Meteorological satellite 20 10
1922 1k. Astronaut ("medical research") 25 10
1923 1k.20 Solar research 30 10
1924 1k.60 Rocket on Launch-pad . . . . 1·25 40

558 "Adam and Eve with Archangel Michael" (16th-century)

1970. Slovak Icons. Multicoloured.
1925 60h. Type **558** 20 25
1926 1k. "Mandylon" (16th-century) (horiz) . . 30 30
1927 2k. "St. George slaying the Dragon" (18th-century) (horiz) 50 50
1928 2k.80 "St. Michael the Archangel" (18th-century) 2·50 2·10

559 Czech 5h. Stamps of 1920

1970. Stamp Day.
1929 **559** 1k. red, black & green 90 85

560 "Songs from the Walls" (frontispiece, K. Stika) 561 Saris Church

1971. Czechoslovak Graphic Art (1st series).
1930 **560** 40h. brown 15 10
1931 – 50h. multicoloured . . . 20 10
1932 – 60h. grey 20 10
1933 – 1k. grey 25 10
1934 – 1k.60 black & cream . . 45 10
1935 – 2k. multicoloured . . . 1·75 50
DESIGNS: 50h. "The Fruit Trader" (C. Bouda); 60h. "Moon searching for Lilies-of-the-valley" (J. Zrzavy); 1k. "At the End of the Town" (K. Sokol); 1k.60, "Summer" (V. Hollar); 2k. "Shepherd and Gamekeeper, Orava Castle" (P. Bohun).
See also Nos. 2026/30, 2079/82, 2147/50 and 2202/5.

1971. Regional Buildings.
1936 – 50h. multicoloured . . 10 10
1936a – 1k. black, red & blue 20 10
1937 **561** 1k.60 black, vio & grn 45 10
1938 – 2k. multicoloured . . . 55 10
1939 – 2k.40 multicoloured . . 55 10
1940 – 3k. multicoloured . . . 70 10
1941 – 3k.60 multicoloured . . 85 10
1942 – 5k. multicoloured . . . 95 10
1943 – 5k.40 multicoloured . . 95 10
1944 – 6k. multicoloured . . . 1·40 10
1945 – 9k. multicoloured . . . 2·10 10
1946 – 10k. multicoloured . . 1·75 15
1947 – 14k. multicoloured . . 2·25 10
1948 – 20k. multicoloured . . 3·00 50
DESIGNS—HORIZ: 50h., 3k.60, Church, Chrudimsko; 2k.40, House, Jicinsko, 5k.40, Southern Bohemia baroque house, Posumavi; 10k. Wooden houses, Liptov; 14k. House and belfry, Valassko; 20k. Decorated house, Cicmany. (22 × 19 mm): 3k. Half-timbered house, Melnicko; 6k. Cottages, Orava; 9k. Cottage, Turnovsko. VERT: (19 × 22 mm): 1k. Ornamental roofs, Horacko; 2k. Bell-tower, Hornsek; 5k. Watch-tower, Nachodsko.

562 "The Paris Commune" (allegory) (½-size illustration)

1971. U.N.E.S.C.O. World Annivs. Multicoloured.
1949 1k. Type **562** 30 25
1950 1k. "World Fight against Racial Discrimination" (allegory) 30 25

1971. Arms of Czech Regional Capitals (3rd series). As Type **523**. Multicoloured.
1951 60h. Ceska Trebova 15 10
1952 60h. Karlovy Vary 15 10

1953	60h. Levoca	15	10
1954	60h. Trutnov	15	10
1955	60h. Uhersky Brod	15	10
1956	60h. Zilina	15	10

563 Chorister

564 Lenin

1971. 50th Annivs. Multicoloured.

1957	30h. Type **563** (Slovak Teachers' Choir)	20	10
1958	30h. Edelweiss, ice-pick and mountain (Slovak Alpine Organisation) (19 × 48 mm)	20	10

1971. Prague Castle (7th series). Art Treasures. As Type **536**. Multicoloured.

1959	3k. brown, buff and black	2·10	1·90
1960	3k. multicoloured	2·10	1·90

DESIGNS: No. 1959, "Music" (16th-century wall painting); 1960, Head of 16th-century crozier.

1971. 50th Anniv of Czech Communist Party.

1961	30h. Type **564**	10	10
1962	40h. Hammer and sickle emblems	10	10
1963	60h. Clenched fists	15	10
1964	1k. Emblem on pinnacle	20	10

565 "50" Star Emblem

1971. 14th Czech Communist Party Congress. Multicoloured.

1965	30h. Type **565**	10	10
1966	60h. Clenched fist, worker and emblems (vert)	15	10

566 Common Pheasant

1971. World Hunting Exn, Budapest. Mult.

1967	20h. Type **566**	45	10
1968	60h. Rainbow trout	15	10
1969	80h. Mouflon	20	10
1970	1k. Chamois	20	10
1971	2k. Red deer	45	20
1972	2k.60 Wild boar	3·00	65

567 Motorway Junction (diagram)

1971. World Road Congress.

1973	**567** 1k. multicoloured	25	10

568 Class T478.3 Diesel Locomotive

569 Gymnasts

1971. Cent of Prague C.K.D. Locomotive Works.

1974	**568** 30h. black, red & blue	10	10

1971. 50th Anniv of Proletarian Physical Federation.

1975	**569** 30h. multicoloured	10	10

570 "Procession" (from "The Miraculous Bamboo Shoot" by K. Segawa)

1971. Biennial Exhibition of Book Illustrations for Children, Bratislava. Multicoloured.

1976	60h. "Princess" (Chinese Folk Tales, E. Bednarova) (vert)	20	10
1977	1k. "Tiger" (Animal Fairy Tales, Hanak) (vert)	20	10
1978	1k.60 Type **570**	55	25

571 Coltsfoot and Canisters

1971. International Pharmaceutical Congress, Prague. Medicinal Plants and Historic Pharmaceutical Utensils. Multicoloured.

1979	30h. Type **571**	10	10
1980	60h. Dog rose and glass jars	15	10
1981	1k. Yellow pheasant's-eye and hand scales	25	10
1982	1k.20 Common valerian, pestle and mortar	40	10
1983	1k.80 Chicory and crucibles	55	20
1984	2k.40 Henbane and grinder	1·40	50

573 "Co-operation in Space"

1971. "Intersputnik" Day.

1997	**573** 1k.20 multicoloured	35	10

574 "The Krompachy Revolt" (J. Nemcik) (½-size illustration)

1971. 50th Anniv of The Krompachy Revolt.

1998	**574** 60h. multicoloured	35	10

1971. Art (6th issue). As Type **481**. Multicoloured.

1999	1k. "Waiting" (I. Weiner-Kral)	40	35
2000	1k.20 "The Resurrection" (unknown 14th century artist)	40	35
2001	1k.40 "Woman with Jug" (M. Bazovsky)	55	40
2002	1k.80 "Woman in National Costume" (J. Manes)	70	50
2003	2k.40 "Festival of the Rosary" (Durer)	2·40	2·50

575 Wooden Dolls and Birds

576 Ancient Greek Runners

1971. 25th Anniv of U.N.I.C.E.F. Czech and Slovak Folk Art. Multicoloured.

2004	60h. Type **575** (frame and U.N.I.C.E.F. emblem in bl)	15	10
2005	60h. Type **575** (frame and U.N.I.C.E.F. emblem in black)	2·75	1·40
2006	80h. Decorated handle	20	10
2007	1k. Horse and rider	20	10
2008	1k.60 Shepherd	35	20
2009	2k. Easter eggs and rattle	50	25
2010	3k. Folk hero	2·10	60

1971. 75th Anniv of Czechoslovak Olympic Committee and 1972 Games at Sapporo and Munich. Multicoloured.

2011	30h. Type **576**	10	10
2012	40h. High Jumper	10	10
2013	1k.60 Skiers	50	10
2014	2k.60 Discus-throwers, ancient and modern	1·75	65

577 Posthorns

1971. Stamp Day.

2015	**577** 1k. multicoloured	35	10

578 Figure Skating

1972. Winter Olympic Games, Sapporo, Japan. Multicoloured.

2016	40h. Type **578**	10	10
2017	50h. Skiing	15	10
2018	1k. Ice hockey	50	10
2019	1k.60 Bobsleighing	1·10	45

579 Sentry

580 Book Year Emblem

1972. 30th Annivs.

2020	– 30h. black and brown	10	10
2021	– 30h. black, red & yellow	10	10
2022	**579** 60h. multicoloured	20	10
2023	– 60h. black, red & yellow	20	10

ANNIVERSARIES: No. 2020, Child and barbed wire (Terezin Concentration Camp); 2021, Widow and buildings (Destruction of Lezaky); 2022, Type **579** (Czechoslovak Unit in Russian Army); 2023, Hand and ruined building (Destruction of Lidice).

1972. International Book Year.

2024	**580** 1k. black and red	35	10

581 Steam Locomotive No. 2 and Class E499.0 Electric Locomotive

582 Cycling

1972. Centenary of Kosice–Bohumin Railway.

2025	**581** 30h. multicoloured	35	10

1972. Czechoslovak Graphic Art (2nd series). As Type **560**. Multicoloured.

2026	40h. "Pasture" (V. Sedlacek)	10	10
2027	50h. "Dressage" (F. Tichy)	15	10
2028	60h. "Otakar Kubin" (V. Fiala)	20	15
2029	1k. "The Three Kings" (E. Zmetak)	30	25
2030	1k.60 "Toilet" (L. Fulla)	1·40	1·25

1972. Olympic Games, Munich. Multicoloured.

2031	50h. Type **582**	10	10
2032	1k.60 Diving	35	20
2033	1k.80 Kayak-canoeing	40	25
2034	2k. Gymnastics	1·25	45

583 Players in Tackle

1972. World and European Ice Hockey Championships, Prague. Multicoloured.

2035	60h. Type **583**	25	10
2036	1k. Attacking goal	45	10

1972. Prague Castle (8th series). Roof Decorations. As T **536**. Multicoloured.

2037	3k. Bohemian Lion emblem (roof boss), Royal Palace	1·00	80
2038	3k. "Adam and Eve" (bracket), St. Vitus Cathedral	2·50	2·50

1972. Czech Victory in Ice Hockey Championships. Nos. 2035/6 optd.

2039	**583** 60h. multicoloured	7·00	7·00
2040	– 1k. multicoloured	7·00	7·00

OVERPRINTS: 60h. **CSSR MISTREM SVETA**. 1k. **CSSR MAJSTROM SVETA**.

585 Frantisek Bilek (sculptor, birth centenary)

586 Workers with Banners

1972. Cultural Anniversaries.

2041	**585** 40h. multicoloured	10	10
2042	– 40h. multicoloured	10	10
2043	– 40h. green, yellow & blue	10	10
2044	– 40h. multicoloured	10	10
2045	– 40h. violet, blue & green	10	10
2046	– 40h. green, brown & orge	10	10

DESIGNS: No. 2042, Antonin Hudecek (painter, birth cent); 2043, Janko Kral (poet, 150th birth anniv); 2044, Ludmila Podjavorinska (writer, birth cent); 2045, Andrej Sladkovic (painter, death cent); 2046, Jan Preisler (painter, birth cent).

1972. 8th Trade Union Congress, Prague.

2047	**586** 30h. violet, red & yellow	10	10

587 Wire Coil and Cockerel

1972. Slovak Wireworking. Multicoloured.

2048	20h. Type **587**	10	10
2049	60h. Aeroplane and rosette	15	10
2050	80h. Dragon and gilded ornament	20	10
2051	1k. Steam locomotive and pendant	55	10
2052	2k.60 Owl and tray	75	55

588 "Jiskra" (freighter)

1972. Czechoslovak Ocean-going Ships. Mult.

2053	50h. Type **588**	25	10
2054	60h. "Mir" (freighter)	30	10
2055	80h. "Republika" (freighter)	35	10
2056	1k. "Kosice" (tanker)	40	10
2057	1k.60 "Dukla" (freighter)	60	10
2058	2k. "Kladno" (freighter)	1·60	40

Nos. 2056/8 are size 49 × 30 mm.

589 "Hussar" (ceramic tile)

1972. "Horsemanship". Ceramics and Glass. Multicoloured.

2059	30h. Type **589**	10	10
2060	60h. "Turkish Janissary" (enamel on glass)	15	10
2061	80h. "St. Martin" (painting on glass)	25	10
2062	1k.60 "St. George" (enamel on glass)	45	10
2063	1k.80 "Nobleman's Guard, Bohemia" (enamel on glass)	55	10
2064	2k.20 "Cavalryman, c. 1800" (ceramic tile)	1·60	50

590 Revolutionary and Red Flag

1972. 55th Anniv of Russian October Revolution and 50th Anniv of U.S.S.R.
2065 **590** 30h. multicoloured . . . 10 10
2066 – 60h. red and gold . . . 15 10
DESIGN: 60h. Soviet star emblem.

1972. Art (7th issue). As T **481**.
2067 1k. multicoloured 70 45
2068 1k.20 multicoloured 95 55
2069 1k.40 brown and cream . . 95 65
2070 1k.80 multicoloured . . . . 1·00 1·00
2071 2k.40 multicoloured . . . . 2·10 2·25
DESIGNS: 1k. "Nosegay" (M. Svabinsky); 1k.20, "St. Ladislav fighting a Nomad" (14th century painter); 1k.40, "Lady with Fur Cap" (V. Hollar); 1k.80, "Midsummer Night's Dream" (J. Liesler); 2k.40, "Self-portrait" (P. Picasso).

591 Warbler feeding young European Cuckoo

1972. Songbirds. Multicoloured.
2072 60h. Type **591** 40 15
2073 80h. European cuckoo . . . 50 15
2074 1k. Black-billed magpie . . 50 15
2075 1k.60 Northern bullfinch (30 × 23 mm) 65 25
2076 2k. Eurasian goldfinch (30 × 23 mm) . . . . . . 1·10 35
2077 3k. Song thrush (30 × 23 mm) . . . . . . 5·00 1·40

592 "Thoughts into Letters"

1972. Stamp Day.
2078 **592** 1k. black, gold & pur . . 45 40

1973. Czechoslovak Graphic Art (3rd series). As Type **560**. Multicoloured.
2079 30h. "Flowers in the Window" (J. Grus) . . . 10 10
2080 60h. "Quest for Happiness" (J. Balaz) 15 10
2081 1k.60 "Balloon" (K. Lhotak) 45 20
2082 1k.80 "Woman with Viola" (R. Wiesner) . . . . . . 1·50 25

593 "Tennis Player" **594** Red Star and Factory Buildings

1973. Sports Events. Multicoloured.
2083 30h. Type **593** 35 10
2084 60h. Figure skating 20 10
2085 1k. Spartakaid emblem . . . 35 10
EVENTS: 30h. 80th anniv of lawn tennis in Czechoslovakia; 60h. World Figure Skating Championships, Bratislava; 1k. 3rd Warsaw Pact Armies Summer Spartakiad.

1973. 25th Anniv of "Victorious February" and People's Militia (60h.).
2086 **594** 30h. multicoloured . . . 10 10
2087 – 60h. blue, red & gold . . 15 10
DESIGN: 60h. Militiaman and banners.

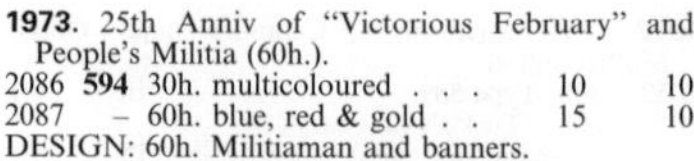

595 Jan Nalepka and Antonin Sochar

1973. Czechoslovak Martyrs during World War II.
2088 **595** 30h. black, red and gold on cream 10 10
2089 – 40h. black, red and green on cream 15 10
2090 – 60h. black, red and gold on cream 15 10
2091 – 80h. black, red and green on cream 15 10
2092 – 1k. black, pink and green on cream . . . 20 10
2093 – 1k.60 black, red and silver on cream . . . 1·25 50
DESIGNS: 40h. Evzen Rosicky and Mirko Nespor; 60h. Vlado Clementis and Karol Smidke; 80h. Jan Osoha and Josef Molak; 1k. Marie Kuderikova and Jozka Jaburkova; 1k.60, Vaclav Sinkule and Eduard Urx.

596 Russian "Venera" Space-probe

1973. Cosmonautics' Day. Multicoloured.
2094 20h. Type **596** 10 10
2095 30h. "Cosmos" satellite . . 10 10
2096 40h. "Lunokhod" on Moon 10 10
2097 3k. American astronauts Grissom, White and Chaffee . . . . 1·00 70
2098 3k.60 Russian cosmonaut Komarov, and crew of "Soyuz II" . . . . . 1·10 1·40
2099 5k. Death of Yuri Gagarin (first cosmonaut) . . . . 4·25 4·00
Nos. 2094/6 are size 40 × 23 mm.

597 Radio Aerial and Receiver **598** Czechoslovak Arms

1973. Telecommunications Annivs. Multicoloured.
2100 30h. Type **597** 10 10
2101 30h. T.V. colour chart . . . 10 10
2102 30h. Map and telephone . . 10 10
ANNIVERSARIES: No. 2100, 50th anniv of Czech broadcasting; 2101, 20th anniv of Czechoslovak television service; 2102, 20th anniv of nationwide telephone system.

1973. Prague Castle (9th series). As Type **536**. Multicoloured.
2103 3k. Gold seal of Charles IV 1·75 2·00
2104 3k. Rook showing Imperial Legate (from "The Game and Playe of Chesse" by William Caxton) 90 60

1973. 25th Anniv of May 9th Constitution.
2105 **598** 60h. multicoloured . . . 10 10

1973. Arms of Czech Regional Capitals (4th series). As T **523**.
2106 60h. multicoloured (Mikulov) 20 10
2107 60h. multicoloured (Smolenice) 20 10
2108 60h. black and gold (Zlutice) 20 10

599 "Learning." **600** Tulip

1973. 400th Anniv of Olomouc University.
2109 **599** 30h. multicoloured . . . 10 10

1973. Olomouc Flower Show. Multicoloured.
2110 60h. Type **600** 95 55
2111 1k. Rose 75 25
2112 1k.60 Anthurium 35 20
2113 1k.80 Iris 40 25
2114 2k. Chrysanthemum . . . . 1·75 2·25
2115 3k.60 Boat orchid . . . . . 1·10 30
Nos. 2112/13 and 2115 are smaller, size 23 × 50 mm.

601 Irish Setter

1973. 50th Anniv of Czechoslovak Hunting Organization. Hunting Dogs. Multicoloured.
2116 20h. Type **601** 10 10
2117 30h. Czech whisker 10 10
2118 40h. Bavarian mountain bloodhound 10 10
2119 60h. German pointer . . . 15 10
2120 1k. Golden cocker spaniel 20 10
2121 1k.60 Dachshund . . . . . 2·00 60

602 "St. John the Baptist" (M. Svabinsky) **603** Congress Emblem

1973. Birth Centenary of Max Svabinsky (artist and designer).
2122 **602** 20h. black and green . . 10 10
2123 – 60h. black and yellow . . 20 10
2124 – 80h. black 25 25
2125 – 1k. green 25 25
2126 – 2k.60 multicoloured . . 2·10 1·90
DESIGNS: 60h. "August Noon"; 80h. "Marriage of True Minds"; 1k. "Paradise Sonata 1"; 2k.60, "The Last Judgement" (stained glass window).

1973. 8th World Trade Union Congress, Varna, Bulgaria.
2127 **603** 1k. multicoloured . . . 10 10

604 Tupolev Tu-104A over Bitov Castle

1973. 50th Anniv of Czechoslovak Airlines. Multicoloured.
2128 30h. Type **604** 10 10
2129 60h. Ilyushin Il-62 and Bezdez Castle 15 10
2130 1k.40 Tupolev Tu-134A and Orava Castle 40 10
2131 1k.90 Ilyushin Il-18 and Veveri Castle 55 20
2132 2k.40 Ilyshin Il-14P and Pernstejn Castle . . . . . 2·75 60
2133 3k.60 Tupolev Tu-154 and Trencin Castle 70 25

1973. Art (8th series). As Type **481**.
2134 1k. multicoloured . . . . . 1·75 1·60
2135 1k.20 multicoloured . . . . 1·75 1·60
2136 1k.80 black and buff 65 50
2137 2k. multicoloured 75 65
2138 2k.40 multicoloured 90 75
2139 3k.60 multicoloured . . . . 1·10 1·25
DESIGNS: 1k. "Boy from Martinique" (A. Pelc); 1k.20, "Fortitude" (M. Benka); 1k.80, Self-portrait (Rembrandt); 2k. "Pierrot" (B. Kubista); 2k.40, "Ilona Kubinyiova" (P. Bohun); 3k.60, Madonna and Child" (unknown artist, c. 1350).

605 Mounted Postman

1973. Stamp Day.
2140 **605** 1k. multicoloured . . . 25 25

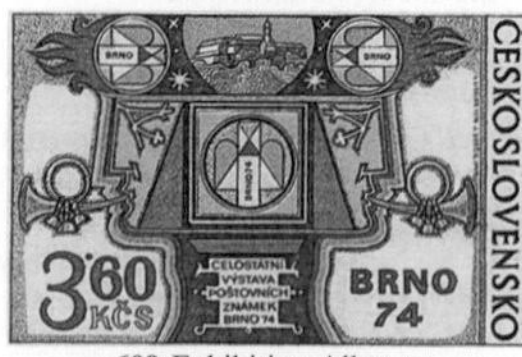

606 "CSSR 1969–1974" **607** Bedrich Smetana (composer) (150th birth anniv)

1974. 5th Anniv of Federal Constitution.
2141 **606** 30h. red, blue and gold 10 10

1974. Celebrities' Birth Anniversaries.
2142 **607** 60h. multicoloured . . . 20 10
2143 – 60h. multicoloured . . . 20 10
2144 – 60h. brown, blue & red 20 10
DESIGNS AND ANNIVERSARIES: No. 2143, Josef Suk (composer, birth anniv); 2144, Pablo Neruda (Chilean poet, 70th birth anniv).

608 Council Building, Moscow

1974. 25th Anniv of Communist Bloc Council of Mutual Economic Assistance.
2145 **608** 1k. violet, red & gold . . 10 10

609 Exhibition Allegory

1974. "BRNO 74" National Stamp Exhibition (1st issue).
2146 **609** 3k.60 multicoloured . . 80 25

1974. Czechoslovak Graphic Art (4th series). As T **560**. Inscr "1974". Multicoloured.
2147 60h. "Tulips" (J. Broz) . . . 20 10
2148 1k. "Structures" (O. Dubay) 30 10
2149 1k.60 "Golden Sun-Glowing Day" (A. Zabransky) . . 55 15
2150 1k.80 "Artificial Flowers" (F. Gross) . . . . 1·50 35

610 Oskar Benes and Vaclav Prochazka

1974. Czechoslovak Partisan Heroes. Mult.
2151 30h. Type **610** 10 10
2152 40h. Milos Uher and Anton Sedlacek 10 10
2153 60h. Jan Hajecek and Marie Sedlackova 15 10
2154 80h. Jan Sverma and Albin Grznar 20 10
2155 1k. Jaroslav Neliba and Alois Hovorka 30 10
2156 1k.60 Ladislav Exnar and Ludovit Kukorelli . . . . 1·50 25

611 "Water—Source of Energy"

1974. International Hydrological Decade. Mult.
2157 60h. Type **611** 55 30
2158 1k. "Water for Agriculture" 55 30
2159 1k.20 "Study of the Oceans" 55 30
2160 1k.60 Decade emblem . . . 60 30
2161 2k. "Keeping water pure" 1·75 2·00

612 "Telecommunications" **613** Sousaphone

1974. Inauguration of Czechoslovak Satellite Telecommunications Earth Station.
2162 **612** 30h. multicoloured . . . 25 10

1974. Prague Castle (10th series). As Type **536**. Multicoloured.
2163 3k. "Golden Cockerel", 17th-century enamel locket . . . . 1·75 1·90
2164 3k. Bohemian glass monstrance, 1840 . . . . 1·75 1·90

1974. Musical Instruments. Multicoloured.
2165 20h. Type **613** 15 10
2166 30h. Bagpipes 15 10
2167 40h. Benka violin 20 10
2168 1k. Sauer pyramid piano . . 30 15
2169 1k.60 Hulinsky tenor quinton . . . . 1·25 30

614 Child and Flowers (book illustration)

615 "Stamp Collectors"

1974. 25th International Children's Day.
2170 **614** 60h. multicoloured . . . 10 10

1974. "BRNO 74" National Stamp Exhibition (2nd issue). Multicoloured.
2171 30h. Type **615** 10 10
2172 6k. "Rocket Post" . . . . . 2·00 1·25

616 Slovak Partisan

617 "Hero and Leander"

1974. Czechoslovak Anniversaries. Multicoloured.
2173 30h. Type **616** 15 10
2174 30h. Folk-dancer 15 10
2175 30h. Actress holding masks 15 10
EVENTS: No. 2173, 30th anniv of Slovak Uprising; 2174, 25th anniv of Slovak SLUK Folk Song and Dance Ensemble; 2175, 25th anniv of Bratislava Academy of Music and Dramatic Arts.

1974. Bratislava Tapestries. "Hero and Leander" (1st series). Multicoloured.
2176 2k. Type **617** . . . . . . 1·50 1·25
2177 2k.40 "Leander Swimming across the Hellespont" . . 1·50 1·75
See also Nos. 2227/8 and 2281/2.

618 "Soldier on Guard"

620 Posthorn and Old Town Bridge Tower, Prague

619 U.P.U. Emblem and Postilion

1974. Old Shooting Targets. Multicoloured.
2178 30h. Type **618** 15 10
2179 60h. "Pierrot and Owl", 1828 . . . . 20 15
2180 1k. "Diana awarding Marksman's Crown", 1832 . . . . 30 15
2181 1k.60 "Still Life with Guitar", 1839 . . . . . 45 40
2182 2k.40 "Stag", 1834 . . . . 70 60
2183 3k. "Turk and Giraffe", 1831 . . . . 2·75 2·75

1974. Centenary of Universal Postal Union. Mult.
2184 30h. Type **619** 10 10
2185 40h. Early mail coach . . . 10 10
2186 60h. Early railway carriage 35 10
2187 80h. Modern mobile post office 25 10
2188 1k. Ilyushin Il-14 mail plane 60 10
2189 1k.60 Dish aerial, earth station . . . . 1·00 35

1974. Czechoslovak Postal Services.
2190 **620** 20h. multicoloured . . . 10 10
2191 – 30h. red, blue & brn . . 10 10
2192 – 40h. multicoloured . . . 10 10
2193 – 60h. orange, yell & bl . . 15 10
DESIGNS: 30h. P.T.T. emblem within letter; 40h. Postilion; 60h. P.T.T. emblem on dove's wing.
See also No. 2900.

1974. Art (9th series). As Type **481**. Multicoloured.
2194 1k. "Self-portrait" (L. Kuba) 80 70
2195 1k.20 "Frantisek Ondricek" (V. Brozik) 80 70
2196 1k.60 "Pitcher with Flowers" (O. Khubin) . . 80 70
2197 1k.80 "Woman with Pitcher" (J. Alexy) . . . 80 70
2198 2k.40 "Bacchanalia" (K. Skreta) . . . . 2·00 2·40

621 Stylized Posthorn

1974. Stamp Day.
2199 **621** 1k. multicoloured . . . 25 10

622 Winged Emblem

1975. Coil Stamps.
2200 **622** 30h. blue 10 10
2201 60h. red 15 10

1975. Czechoslovak Graphic Art (5th series). Engraved Hunting Scenes. As T **560**.
2202 60h. brown & cream 25 10
2203 1k. brown and cream . . . 30 15
2204 1k.60 brown & green . . . 45 25
2205 1k.80 brown & lt brown . . 1·75 50
DESIGNS: 60h. "Still Life with Hare" (V. Hollar); 1k. "The Lion and the Mouse" (V. Hollar); 1k.60, "Deer Hunt" (detail, P. Galle); 1k.80, "Grand Hunt" (detail, J. Callot).

623 "Woman"

624 Village Family

1975. International Women's Year.
2206 **623** 30h. multicoloured . . . 10 10

1975. 30th Anniv of Razing of 14 Villages. Multicoloured.
2207 60h. Type **624** 20 10
2208 1k. Women and flames . . . 25 10
2209 1k.20 Villagers and flowers 40 10

625 "Little Queens" (Moravia)

1975. Czechoslovak Folk Customs. Multicoloured.
2210 60h. Type **625** 60 60
2211 1k. Shrovetide parade, Slovakia 60 60
2212 1k.40 "Maid Dorothea" (play) 60 60
2213 2k. "Morena" effigy, Slovakia . . . . 1·40 1·40

1975. Arms of Czech Regional Capitals (5th series). As T **523**.
2214 60h. black, gold and red . . 25 10
2215 60h. multicoloured 25 10
ARMS: No. 2214, Nymburk. 2215, Znojmo.

626 Partisans at Barricade (½-size illustration)

1975. Czechoslovak Anniversaries.
2216 **626** 1k. multicoloured . . . 30 20
2217 – 1k. sepia and cream . . 30 20
2218 – 1k. multicoloured . . . 30 20
DESIGNS and ANNIVERSARIES: No. 2216, Type **626** (30th anniv of Czech Rising); 2217, Liberation celebrations (30th anniv of Liberation by Soviet Army); 2218, Czech–Soviet fraternity (5th anniv of Czech–Soviet Treaty).

627 Youth Exercises

1975. National Spartacist Games.
2219 **627** 30h. purple, bl & pink 10 10
2220 – 60h. red, lilac & yellow 15 10
2221 – 1k. violet, red & yell . . 25 20
DESIGNS: 60h. Children's exercises; 1k. Adult exercises.

628 Siamese Tigerfish and Lined Seahorse

1975. Aquarium Fishes. Multicoloured.
2222 60h. Type **628** 15 10
2223 1k. Siamese fighting fish and freshwater angelfish . . . 30 10
2224 1k.20 Veil-tailed goldfish . . 65 15
2225 1k.60 Clown anemone-fish and butterflyfish 75 25
2226 2k. Yellow-banded angelfish, palette surgeonfish and semicircle angelfish . . . 3·50 65

1975. Bratislava Tapestries. "Hero and Leander" (2nd series). As T **617**. Multicoloured.
2227 3k. "Leander's Arrival" . . 90 70
2228 3k.60 "Hermione" . . . . . 2·25 2·40

629 "Pelicans" (N. Charushin)

1975. Biennial Exhibition of Book Illustrations for Children, Bratislava. Multicoloured.
2229 20h. Type **629** 10 10
2230 30h. "Sleeping Hero" (L. Schwarz) 10 10
2231 40h. "Horseman" (V. Munteau) 15 10
2232 60h. "Peacock" (K. Ensikat) 20 10
2233 80h. "The Stone King" (R. Dubravec) 70 35

630 "CZ-150" Motor Cycle (1951)

1975. Czechoslovak Motor Cycles. Multicoloured.
2234 20h. Type **630** 15 10
2235 40h. "Jawa 250", 1945 . . . 20 10
2236 60h. "Jawa 175", 1935 . . . 25 10
2237 1k. Janatka "ITAR", 1921 30 15
2238 1k.20 Michi "Orion", 1903 25 10
2239 1k.80 Laurin and Klement, 1898 . . . . 1·60 40

631 "Solar Radiation"

632 President Gustav Husak

1975. Co-operation in Space Research.
2240 **631** 30h. violet, yellow & red 15 10
2241 – 60h. red, lilac & yellow 20 10
2242 – 1k. purple, yell & blue 25 10
2243 – 2k. multicoloured . . . 55 10
2244 – 5k. multicoloured . . . 3·00 2·75
DESIGNS—HORIZ: 60h. "Auroa Borealis"; 1k. Cosmic radiation measurement; 2k. Copernicus and solar radiation. VERT (40 × 50 mm): 5k. "Apollo–soyuz" space link.

1975.
2245 **632** 30h. blue 10 10
2246 60h. red 15 10

633 Oil Refinery

1975. 30th Anniv of Liberation. Multicoloured.
2247 30h. Type **633** 15 10
2248 60h. Atomic power complex 15 10
2249 1k. Underground Railway, Prague 40 10
2250 1k.20 Laying oil pipelines 30 15
2251 1k.40 Combine-harvesters and granary 30 20
2252 1k.60 Building construction 1·10 35

1975. Prague Castle. Art Treasures (11th series). As T **536**. Multicoloured.
2253 3k. Late 9th-century gold earring 95 75
2254 3k.60 Leather Bohemian Crown case, 1347 . . . . 1·90 2·00

634 General Svoboda

1975. 80th Birthday of General Ludvik Svoboda. Sheet 76 × 96 mm.
MS2255 **634** 10k. multicoloured 11·50 11·50

1975. Art (10th series). As T **481**.
2256 1k. red, brown and black . . 75 75
2257 1k.40 multicoloured 75 75
2258 1k.80 multicoloured 75 75
2259 2k.40 multicoloured . . . . 1·10 1·25
2260 3k.40 multicoloured . . . . 1·75 1·60
PAINTINGS—VERT: 1k. "May" (Z. Sklenar); 1k.40, "Girl in National Costume" (E. Nevan); 2k.40, "Fire" (J. Capek); 3k.40, "Prague, 1828" (V. Morstadt). HORIZ: 1k.80, "Liberation of Prague" (A. Cermakova).

635 Posthorn Motif

1975. Stamp Day.
2261 **635** 1k. multicoloured . . . 35 25

636 Frantisek Halas (poet)

1975. Celebrities' Anniversaries.
2262 **636** 60h. multicoloured . . . 15 10
2263 – 60h. multicoloured . . . 15 10
2264 – 60h. multicoloured . . . 30 10
2265 – 60h. blue, red & yellow 15 10
2266 – 60h. multicoloured . . . 15 10
DESIGNS AND ANNIVERSARIES—HORIZ: No. 2262, Type **636** (75th birth anniv); 2266, Ivan Krasko (poet, birth cent). VERT: No. 2263, Wilhelm Pieck (German statesman, birth cent); 2264, Frantisek Lexa (Egyptologist, birth cent); 2265, Jindrich Jindrich (ethnographer, birth cent).

637 Ski Jumping

1976. Winter Olympic Games, Innsbruck. Mult.
2267 1k. Type **637** 20 10
2268 1k.40 Figure skating 30 20
2269 1k.60 Ice hockey . . . . . 1·25 30

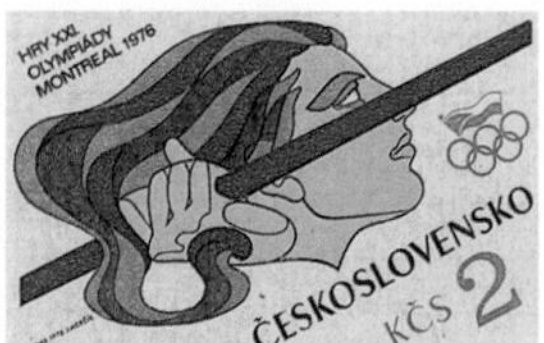

638 Throwing the Javelin

1976. Olympic Games, Montreal. Multicoloured.
2270 2k. Type **638** 45 20
2271 3k. Relay-racing 80 30
2272 3k.60 Putting the shot . . . 3·00 1·10

639 Table Tennis Player 640 Star Emblem and Workers

1976. European Table Tennis Championships, Prague and 50th Anniv of Organized Table Tennis in Czechoslovakia.
2273 **639** 1k. multicoloured . . . 35 10

1976. 15th Czechoslovak Communist Party Congress, Prague. Multicoloured.
2274 30h. Type **640** 10 10
2275 60h. Furnace and monolith 15 10

641 Microphone and Musical Instruments 642 Hammer, Sickle and Red Flags

1976. Cultural Events and Anniversaries.
2276 **641** 20h. multicoloured . . . 10 10
2277 – 20h. multicoloured . . . 10 10
2278 – 20h. multicoloured . . . 10 10
2279 – 30h. multicoloured . . . 10 10
2280 – 30h. violet, red & blue 10 10
DESIGNS—HORIZ: No. 2276, Type **641** (50th anniv of Czechoslovak Radio Symphony Orchestra); 2278, Stage revellers (30th anniv of Nova Scena Theatre, Bratislava); 2279, Folk dancers, Wallachia (International Folk Song and Dance Festival, Straznice). VERT: No. 2277, Ballerina, violin and mask (30th anniv of Prague Academy of Music and Dramatic Art); 2280, Film "profile" (20th Film Festival, Karlovy Vary).

1976. Bratislava Tapestries. "Hero and Leander" (3rd series). As T **617**. Multicoloured.
2281 3k. "Hero with Leander's body" . . . . 2·00 1·25
2282 3k.60 "Eros grieving" . . . 85 60

1976. 55th Anniv of Czechoslovak Communist Party.
2283 **642** 30h. blue, gold and red 15 10
2284 – 60h. multicoloured . . . 20 10
MS2285 100×90 mm. 6k. multicoloured . . . . 2·75 3·00
DESIGN—VERT: (23×40 mm) 60h. Hammer and Sickle on flag. HORIZ (50×30 mm)—6k. Flag and commemorative inscription.

643 Manes Hall, Czechoslovakia Artists' Union

1976. Air. "PRAGA 78" International Stamp Exhibition (1st issue). Prague Architecture. Multicoloured.
2286 60h. Type **643** 35 10
2287 1k.60 Congress Hall, Julius Fucik Park 40 20
2288 2k. Powder Tower, Old Town (vert) 70 25
2289 2k.40 Charles Bridge and Old Bridge Tower 55 25
2290 4k. Old Town Square and Town Hall (vert) 85 30
2291 6k. Prague Castle and St. Vitus Cathedral (vert) 3·50 1·00
See also 2313/16, 2326/30, 2339/42, 2349/52, 2358/62, 2389/93, 2407/12, 2413/17, 2420/3 and **MS**2424/5.

644 "Warship" (Frans Huys) 645 "UNESCO" Plant

1976. Ship Engravings.
2292 **644** 40h. blk, cream & drab 35 10
2293 – 60h. blk, cream & grey 35 10
2294 – 1k. black, cream & grn 60 10
2295 – 2k. black, cream & blue 1·25 45
DESIGNS: 60h. "Dutch Merchantman" (V. Hollar); 1k. "Ship at Anchor" (N. Zeeman); 2k. "Galleon under Full Sail" (F. Chereau).

1976. 30th Anniv of U.N.E.S.C.O.
2296 **645** 2k. multicoloured . . . 95 55

646 "Protected Child"

1976. European Security and Co-operation Conference, Helsinki. Sheet 114×167 mm containing two stamps as T **646**.
MS2297 6k. ×2 blue, yellow and red 5·00 5·00

647 Merino Ram 648 "Stop Smoking"

1976. "Bountiful Earth" Agricultural Exhibition, Ceske Budejovice. Multicoloured.
2298 30h. Type **647** 15 10
2299 40h. Berna-Hana Cow . . . 15 10
2300 1k.60 Kladruby stallion . . 45 10

1976. W.H.O. Campaign against Smoking.
2301 **648** 2k. multicoloured . . . 90 40

649 Postal Code Emblem 650 "Guernica 1937" (I. Weiner-Kral)

1976. Coil Stamps. Postal Code Campaign.
2302 **649** 30h. green 10 10
2303 – 60h. red 15 10
DESIGN: 60h. Postal map.

1976. 40th Anniv of International Brigades in Spanish Civil War.
2304 **650** 5k. multicoloured . . . 1·25 55

1976. Prague Castle. Art Treasures (12th series). As T **536**. Multicoloured.
2305 3k. "Prague Castle, 1572" (F. Hoogenberghe) . . . 2·00 1·90
2306 3k.60 "Satyrs" (relief from summer-house balustrade) 60 70

651 Common Zebra with Foal

1976. Dvurkralove Wildlife Park. Multicoloured.
2307 10h. Type **651** 15 10
2308 20h. African elephant, calf and cattle egret (vert) . . 50 15
2309 30h. Cheetah 15 10
2310 40h. Giraffe and calf (vert) 15 10
2311 60h. Black rhinoceros . . . 20 10
2312 3k. Bongo with offspring (vert) . . . . 2·00 65

1976. "PRAGA 1978" International Stamp Exhibition (2nd series). Art (11th series). As T **481**. Multicoloured.
2313 1k. "Flowers in Vase" (P. Matejka) 80 55
2314 1k.40 "Oleander Blossoms" (C. Bouda) . . . . 1·10 80
2315 2k. "Flowers in Vase" (J. Brueghel) . . . . . . 1·75 1·40
2316 3k.60 "Tulips and Narcissi" (J. R. Bys) 80 80

652 Postilion, Postal Emblem and Satellite

1976. Stamp Day.
2317 **652** 1k. blue, mauve & gold 25 10

653 Ice Hockey 654 Arms of Vranov

1977. 6th Winter Spartakiad of Warsaw Pact Armies. Multicoloured.
2318 60h. Type **653** 25 10
2319 1k. Rifle shooting (Biathlon) 30 10
2320 1k.60 Ski jumping . . . . . 1·40 45
2321 2k. Slalom 50 25

1977. Coats of Arms of Czechoslovak Towns (1st series). Multicoloured.
2322 60h. Type **654** 15 10
2323 60h. Kralupy and Vltavou 15 10
2324 60h. Jicin 15 10
2325 60h. Valasske Mezirici . . . 15 10
See also Nos. 2511/14, 2612/15, 2720/3, 2765/7, 2819/21 and 3017/20.

655 Window, Michna Palace 656 Children Crossing Road

1977. "PRAGA 78" International Stamp Exhibition (3rd issue). Historic Prague Windows. Multicoloured.
2326 20h. Type **655** 10 10
2327 30h. Michna Palace (different) 10 10
2328 40h. Thun Palace 10 10
2329 60h. Archbishop's Palace . . 15 10
2330 5k. Church of St. Nicholas 2·25 65

1977. 25th Anniv of Police Aides Corps.
2331 **656** 60h. multicoloured . . . 10 10

657 Cyclists at Warsaw (starting point) 658 Congress Emblem

1977. 30th Anniv of Peace Cycle Race. Mult.
2332 30h. Type **657** 15 10
2333 60h. Cyclists at Berlin . . . 20 10
2334 1k. Cyclists at Prague (finishing point) 85 25
2335 1k.40 Cyclists and modern buildings 40 15

1977. 9th Trade Unions Congress.
2336 **658** 30h. gold, red & carmine 10 10

1977. Prague Castle (13th series). As T **536**.
2337 3k. multicoloured . . . . . 1·10 1·25
2338 3k.60 green, gold & black 1·90 1·60
DESIGNS: 3k. Onyx cup, 1350 (St. Vitus Cathedral); 3k.60, Bronze horse, 1619 (A. de Vries).

659 French Postal Rider, 19th-century

1977. "PRAGA 78" International Stamp Exhibition (4th issue). Multicoloured.
2339 60h. Type **659** 15 10
2340 1k. Austrian postal rider, 1838 . . . . 30 10
2341 2k. Austrian postal rider, c. 1770 . . . . . . 50 25
2342 3k.60 German postal rider, 1700 . . . . 2·25 80

660 Coffee Pots 661 Mlada Boleslav Headdress

1977. Czechoslovak Porcelain.
2343 **660** 20h. multicoloured . . . 10 10
2344 – 30h. multicoloured . . . 10 10
2345 – 40h. multicoloured . . . 15 10
2346 – 60h. multicoloured . . . 20 10
2347 – 1k. blue, grn & violet . . 25 10
2348 – 3k. blue, gold and red 2·10 60
DESIGNS: 30h. Vase; 40h. Amphora; 60h. Jug, beaker, cup and saucer; 1k. Plate and candlestick; 3k. Coffee pot, cup and saucer.

1977. "PRAGA 78" International Stamp Exhibition (5th issue). Regional Headdresses. Multicoloured.
2349 1k. Type **661** 75 80
2350 1k.60 Vazek . . . . 3·50 3·50
2351 3k.60 Zavadka 75 80
2352 5k. Belkovice . . . . 1·25 1·10

662 V. Bombova's Illustrations of "Janko Gondashik and the Golden Lady"

1977. 6th Biennial Exhibition of Children's Book Illustrators, Bratislava. Multicoloured.
2353 40h. Type **662** 10 10
2354 60h. "Tales of Amur" (G. Pavlishin) 15 10
2355 1k. "Almgist et Wiksel" (U. Lofgren) 25 10
2356 2k. "Alice in Wonderland" and "Through the Looking Glass" (Nicole Claveloux) 75 25
2357 3k. "Eventyr" (J. Trnka) . . 2·25 65

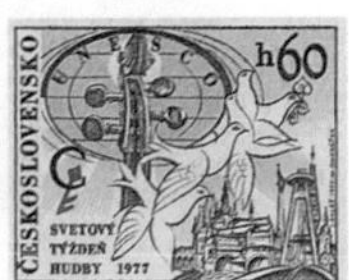

663 Airships LZ-5 and "Graf Zeppelin"   664 U.N.E.S.C.O. Emblem, Violin and Doves

1977. Air. "PRAGA 1978" International Stamp Exhibition (6th issue). Early Aviation. Mult.

2358	60h. Type **663**	15	10
2359	1k. Clement Ader's monoplane "Eole", Etrich Holubice and Dunne D-8	30	10
2360	1k.60 Jeffries and Blanchard balloon, 1785	40	15
2361	2k. Lilienthal biplane glider, 1896	50	15
2362	4k.40 Jan Kaspar's Bleriot XI over Prague	3·50	85

1977. Congress of U.N.E.S.C.O. International Music Council.

2363	**664** 60h. multicoloured	10	10

665 "Peace"   666 Yuri Gagarin

1977. European Co-operation for Peace. Mult.

2364	60h. Type **665**	15	30
2365	1k.60 "Co-operation"	40	45
2366	2k.40 "Social Progress"	1·50	60

1977. Space Research. Multicoloured.

2367	20h. S. P. Koroliov (space technician, launch of first satellite)	10	10
2368	30h. Type **666** (first man in space)	10	10
2369	40h. Aleksei Leonov (first space walker)	10	10
2370	1k. Neil Armstrong (first man on the Moon)	25	10
2371	1k.60 "Salyut" and "Skylab" space stations	1·25	35

667 Revolutionaries and Cruiser "Aurora"   668 "Wisdom"

1977. 60th Anniv of Russian Revolution, and 55th Anniv of U.S.S.R. Multicoloured.

2372	30h. Type **667**	15	10
2373	30h. Russian woman, Kremlin, rocket and U.S.S.R. arms	15	10

1977. 25th Anniv of Czechoslovak Academy of Science.

2374	**668** 3k. multicoloured	70	30

1977. Art (12th series). As Type **481**.

2375	2k. multicoloured	75	80
2376	2k.40 multicoloured	2·50	2·75
2377	2k.60 stone and black	2·10	1·60
2378	3k. multicoloured	1·00	1·00
2379	5k. multicoloured	1·00	1·00

DESIGNS: 2k. "Fear" (J. Mudroch); 2k.40, "Portrait of Jan Francis" (P. M. Bohun); 2k.60, "Self Portrait" (V. Hollar); 3k. "Portrait of a Girl" (L. Cranach); 5k. "Cleopatra" (Rubens).

669 "Bratislava, 1574" (G. Hoefnagel)

1977. Historic Bratislava (1st series). Mult.

2380	3k. Type **669**	1·90	2·00
2381	3k.60 Bratislava Arms, 1436	1·10	80

See also Nos. 2402/3, 2500/1, 2545/6, 2582/3, 2642/3, 2698/9, 2736/7, 2793/4, 2842/3, 2898/9, 2952/3, 2997/8 and 3034/5.

670 Posthorn and Stamps

1977. Stamp Day.

2382	**670** 1k. multicoloured	25	10

671 Z. Nejedly (historian)   674 Modern Coins

672 Civilians greeting Armed Guards

1978. Cultural Anniversaries. Multicoloured.

2383	30h. Type **671** (birth cent)	10	10
2384	40h. Karl Marx (160th birth anniv)	10	10

1978. 30th Annivs of "Victorious February" and National Front. Multicoloured.

2385	1k. Type **672**	20	10
2386	1k. Intellectual, peasant woman and steel worker	20	10

1978. Soviet–Czechoslovak Space Flight. No. 2368 optd **SPOLECNY LET SSSR*CSSR**.

2387	30h. red	20	15
2388	3k.60 blue	4·25	4·50

1978. 650th Anniv of Kremnica Mint and "PRAGA 1978" International Stamp Exhibition (7th issue). Multicoloured.

2389	20h. Type **674**	10	10
2390	40h. Culture medal, 1972 (Jan Kulich)	10	10
2391	1k.40 Charles University Medal, 1948 (O, Spaniel)	2·40	35
2392	3k. Ferdinand I medal, 1563 (L. Richter)	80	40
2393	5k. Gold florin of Charles Robert, 1335	95	50

675 Tyre Marks and Ball   676 Hands supporting Globe

1978. Road Safety.

2394	**675** 60h. multicoloured	10	10

1978. 9th World Federation of Trade Unions Congress, Prague.

2395	**676** 1k. multicoloured	25	10

677 Putting the Shot

1978. Sports.

2396	– 30h. multicoloured	15	10
2397	**677** 40h. multicoloured	15	10
2398	– 60h. multicoloured	70	15
2399	– 1k. multicoloured	35	10
2400	– 2k. yellow, blue & red	55	25
2401	– 3k.60 multicoloured	1·75	85

DESIGNS AND EVENTS—HORIZ: 70th anniv of bandy hockey: 30h. Three hockey players, World Ice Hockey Championships; 60h. Tackle in front of goal; 2k. Goalmouth scrimmage. VERT: European Athletics Championships, Prague: 1k. Pole vault; 3k.60, Running.

1978. Historic Bratislava (2nd series). As T **669**.

2402	3k. green, violet and red	1·25	1·40
2403	3k.60 multicoloured	2·75	2·50

DESIGNS: 3k. "Bratislava" (Orest Dubay); 3k.60, "Fishpond Square, Bratislava" (Imro Weiner-Kral).

1978. Prague Castle (14th series). As T **536**.

2404	3k. yellow, black & green	95	80
2405	3k.60 multicoloured	3·25	2·50

DESIGNS: 3k. Memorial to King Premysl Otakar II, St. Vitus Cathedral; 3k.60, Portrait of King Charles IV (Jan Ocka).

678 Ministry of Posts, Prague

1978. 14th COMECON Meeting, Prague.

2406	**678** 60h. multicoloured	10	10

679 Palacky Bridge

1978. "PRAGA 78" International Stamp Exhibition (8th issue). Prague Bridges. Multicoloured.

2407	20h. Type **679**	10	10
2408	40h. Railway bridge	55	10
2409	1k. Bridge of 1st May	25	10
2410	2k. Manes Bridge	45	15
2411	3k. Svatopluk Cech Bridge	55	30
2412	5k.40 Charles Bridge	3·50	95

680 St. Peter and other Apostles   681 Dancers

1978. "PRAGA 78" International Stamp Exhibition (9th issue). Prague Town Hall Astronomical Clock. Multicoloured.

2413	40h. Type **680**	15	10
2414	1k. Astronomical clock face	20	15
2415	2k. Centre of Manes's calendar	35	15
2416	3k. "September" (grape harvest)	2·10	70
2417	3k.60 "Libra" (sign of the Zodiac)	1·25	25
MS2418	89 × 125 mm. 10k. Manes's calendar (48 × 38 mm)	10·50	12·50

1978. 25th Vychodna Folklore Festival.

2419	**681** 30h. multicoloured	10	10

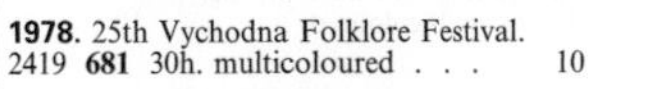

682 Gottwald Bridge

1978. "PRAGA 78" International Stamp Exhibition (10th issue). Modern Prague. Multicoloured.

2420	60h. Type **682**	65	10
2421	1k. Powder Gate Tower and Kotva department store	25	10
2422	2k. Ministry of Posts	55	25
2423	6k. Prague Castle and flats	2·10	1·10

683 "Old Prague and Charles Bridge" (V. Morstadt)

1978. "PRAGA 1978" International Stamp Exhibition (11th issue). Sheet 96 × 74 mm.

MS2424	**683** 20k. multicoloured	10·50	12·50

684 Detail of "The Flaying of Marsyas" (Titian)

1978. "PRAGA 1978" International Stamp Exhibition (12th issue). Sheet 108 × 165 mm containing T **684** and similar vert design showing detail of painting.

MS2425	10k. Type **684**; 10k. King Midas	11·50	13·00

685 Fair Buildings   686 "Postal Newspaper Service" (25th Anniv)

1978. 20th International Engineering Fair, Brno.

2426	**685** 30h. multicoloured	10	10

1978. Press, Broadcasting and Television Days.

2427	**686** 30h. green, blue & orge	10	10
2428	– 30h. multicoloured	10	10
2429	– 30h. multicoloured	10	10

DESIGNS: No. 2428, Microphone, newspapers, camera and Ministry of Information and Broadcasting; 2429, Television screen and Television Centre, Prague (25th anniv of Czechoslovak television).

687 Horses falling at Fence

1978. Pardubice Steeplechase. Multicoloured.

2430	10h. Type **687**	10	10
2431	20h. Sulky racing	10	10
2432	30h. Racing horses	15	10
2433	40h. Passing the winning post	15	10
2434	1k.60 Jumping a fence	40	20
2435	4k.40 Jockey leading a winning horse	2·50	90

688 Woman holding Arms of Czechoslovakia

1978. 60th Anniv of Independence.

2436	**688** 60h. multicoloured	10	10

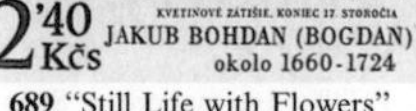

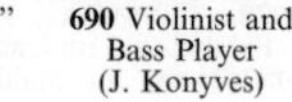
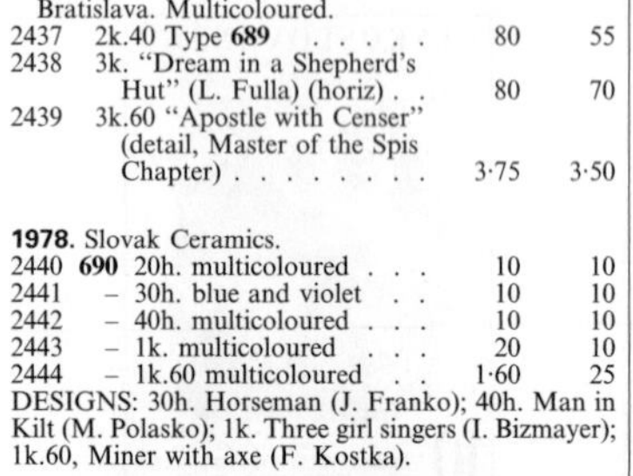

689 "Still Life with Flowers" (J. Bohdan)

690 Violinist and Bass Player (J. Konyves)

1978. 30th Anniv of Slovak National Gallery, Bratislava. Multicoloured.

2437 2k.40 Type **689** 80 55
2438 3k. "Dream in a Shepherd's Hut" (L. Fulla) (horiz) . . 80 70
2439 3k.60 "Apostle with Censer" (detail, Master of the Spis Chapter) . . . . 3·75 3·50

1978. Slovak Ceramics.

2440 **690** 20h. multicoloured . . . 10 10
2441 – 30h. blue and violet . . 10 10
2442 – 40h. multicoloured . . . 10 10
2443 – 1k. multicoloured . . . 20 10
2444 – 1k.60 multicoloured . . 1·60 25

DESIGNS: 30h. Horseman (J. Franko); 40h. Man in Kilt (M. Polasko); 1k. Three girl singers (I. Bizmayer); 1k.60, Miner with axe (F. Kostka).

691 Alfons Mucha and design for 1918 Hradcany Stamp

1978. Stamp Day.

2445 **691** 1k. multicoloured . . . 25 10

692 Council Building, Moscow

1979. Anniversaries.

2446 – 30h. brown, grn & orge 10 10
2447 – 60h. multicoloured . . . 15 10
2448 **692** 1k. multicoloured . . . 20 10

DESIGNS—HORIZ: 30h. Girl's head and ears of wheat (30th anniv of Unified Agricultural Co-operatives); 60h. Czechoslovakians and doves (10th anniv of Czechoslovak Federation). VERT: 1k. Type **692** (30th anniv of Council of Economic Mutual Aid).

693 "Soyuz 28"

1979. 1st Anniv of Russian–Czech Space Flight. Multicoloured.

2449 30h. Type **693** 15 10
2450 60h. A. Gubarev and V. Remek (vert) 15 10
2451 1k.60 J. Romanenko and G. Grechko 45 10
2452 2k. "Salyut 6" space laboratory . . . . 1·90 40
2453 4k. "Soyuz 28" touch down (vert) 85 40
MS2454 75 × 95 mm. 10k. Gubarev and Remek waving (38 × 54 mm) 5·00 5·00

694 "Campanula alpina"

695 Stylized Satellite

1979. 25th Anniv of Mountain Rescue Service. Multicoloured.

2455 10h. Type **694** 10 10
2456 20h. "Crocus scepusiensis" 10 10
2457 30h. "Dianthus glacialis" 10 10
2458 40h. Alpine hawkweed . . 15 10
2459a 3k. "Delphinium oxysepalum" . . . . . 1·25 50

1979. Anniversaries.

2460 **695** 10h. multicoloured . . . 10 10
2461 – 20h. multicoloured . . . 10 10
2462 – 20h. blue, orge & lt bl 10 10
2463 – 30h. blue, gold & red . . 10 10
2464 – 30h. red, blue & blk . . 10 10
2465 – 60h. multicoloured . . . 15 10

DESIGNS AND EVENTS—HORIZ: No. 2460, Type **695** 30th anniv of Telecommunications Research. 46 × 19 mm: (No. 2461), Artist and model (30th anniv of Academy of Fine Arts, Bratislava); 2462, Student and technological equipment (40th anniv of Slovak Technical University, Bratislava); 2463, Musical instruments and Bratislava Castle (50th anniv of Radio Symphony Orchestra, Bratislava); 2464, Pioneer's scarf and I.Y.C. emblem (30th anniv of Young Pioneer Organization and International Year of the Child); 2465, Adult and child with doves (30th anniv of Peace Movement).

1979. Prague Castle (15th series). As T **536**. Multicoloured.

2466 3k. Burial crown of King Premysl Otakar II . . . . 2·40 2·40
2467 3k.60 Portrait of Miss B. Reitmayer (Karel Purkyne) . . . . 1·25 1·00

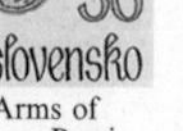

696 Arms of Vlachovo Brezi

697 Healthy and Polluted Forests

1979. Animals in Heraldry. Multicoloured.

2468 30h. Type **696** 10 10
2469 60h. Jesenik (bear and eagle) 15 10
2470 1k.20 Vysoke Myto (St. George and the dragon) 30 10
2471 1k.80 Martin (St. Martin on horseback) . . . . 1·60 40
2472 2k. Zebrak (half bear, half lion) 40 10

1979. Man and the Biosphere. Multicoloured.

2473 60h. Type **697** 15 15
2474 1k.80 Clear and polluted water 45 30
2475 3k.60 Healthy and polluted urban environment . . . 2·50 85
2476 4k. Healthy and polluted pasture 95 40

698 Numeral and Printed Circuit

699 Industrial Complex

1979. Coil Stamps.

2477 – 50h. red 15 10
2478 **698** 1k. brown 20 10
2478a – 2k. green 50 25
2478b – 3k. purple 80 35

DESIGNS: Numeral and—50h. Dish aerial; 2k. Airplane; 3k. Punched tape.

1979. 35th Anniv of Slovak Uprising.

2479 **699** 30h. multicoloured . . . 10 10

700 Illustration by Janos Kass

1979. International Year of the Child and Biennial Exhibition of Children's Book Illustrations, Bratislava. Designs showing illustrations by artists named. Multicoloured.

2480 20h. Type **700** 10 10
2481 40h. Rumen Skorcev . . . 15 10
2482 60h. Karel Svolinsky . . . 15 10
2483 1k. Otto S. Svend 30 10
2484 3k. Tatyana Mavrina . . . 1·90 45

701 Modern Bicycles

1979. Historic Bicycles. Multicoloured.

2485 20h. Type **701** 15 10
2486 40h. Bicycles, 1910 . . . . 15 10
2487 60h. "Ordinary" and tricycle, 1886 . . . . . 15 10
2488 2k. "Bone-shakers", 1870 45 25
2489 3k.60 Drais cycles, 1820 . . 2·50 65

702 Bracket Clock (Jan Kraus)

1979. Historic Clocks. Multicoloured.

2490 40h. Type **702** 10 10
2491 60h. Rococo clock 15 10
2492 80h. Classicist clock . . . . 1·60 35
2493 1k. Rococo porcelain clock (J. Kandler) 25 10
2494 2k. Urn-shaped clock (Dufaud) 45 25

1979. Art (13th series). As T **481**.

2495 1k.60 multicoloured 65 55
2496 2k. multicoloured 75 60
2497 3k. multicoloured . . . . . 1·00 70
2498 3k.60 multicoloured . . . . 2·75 2·75
2499 5k. yellow and black . . . . 1·10 1·25

DESIGNS: 1k.60, "Sunday by the River" (Alois Moravec); 2k. "Self-portrait" (Gustav Mally); 3k. "Self-portrait" (Ilja Jefimovic Repin); 3k.60, "Horseback Rider" (Jan Bauch); 5k. "Village Dancers" (Albrecht Durer).

1979. Historic Bratislava (3rd issue). As T **669**. Multicoloured.

2500 3k. "Bratislava, 1787" (L. Janscha) . . . . . . 1·10 90
2501 3k.60 "Bratislava, 1815" (after stone engraving by Wolf) . . . . 2·50 2·40

703 Postmarks, Charles Bridge and Prague Castle

1979. Stamp Day.

2502 **703** 1k. multicoloured . . . 25 10

704 Skiing

1980. Winter Olympic Games, Lake Placid.

2503 **704** 1k. multicoloured . . . 25 10
2504 – 2k. red, pink & blue . . 1·60 40
2505 – 3k. multicoloured . . . 1·00 55

DESIGNS: 2k. Ice skating; 3k. Four-man bobsleigh.

705 Basketball

1980. Olympic Games, Moscow. Multicoloured.

2506 40h. Type **705** 15 10
2507 1k. Swimming 25 10
2508 2k. Hurdles . . . . . . 2·40 40
2509 3k.60 Fencing 85 35

706 Marathon

1980. 50th International Peace Marathon, Kosice.

2510 **706** 50h. multicoloured . . . 10 10

1980. Arms of Czech Towns (2nd series). As T **654**.

2511 50h. blue, black and gold 15 10
2512 50h. black and silver 15 10
2513 50h. multicoloured 15 10
2514 50h. gold, black and blue 15 10

DESIGNS: No. 2511, Bystrice nad Pernstejnem; 2512, Kunstat; 2513, Rozmital pod Tremsinem; 2514, Zlata Idka.

707 Bratislava Opera House and Bakovazena as King Lear

708 Tragic Mask

1980. 60th Anniv of Slovak National Theatre, Bratislava.

2515 **707** 1k. blue, yellow & orange 25 10

1980. 50th Anniv of Theatrical Review "Jiraskuv Hronov".

2516 **708** 50h. multicoloured . . . 10 10

709 Mouse in Space

710 Police Parade Banner

1980. "Intercosmos" Space Programme.

2517 **709** 50h. blue, black and red 15 10
2518 – 1k. multicoloured . . . 30 10
2519 – 1k.60 violet, blk & red 2·25 50
2520 – 4k. multicoloured . . . 1·00 35
2521 – 5k. blue, black & purple 1·50 50
MS2522 75 × 94 mm. 10k. multicoloured . . . . 5·00 5·00

DESIGNS—VERT: 1k. Weather map and satellite; 1k.60, "Inter-sputnik" T.V. transmission; 4k. Survey satellite and camera. HORIZ: 5k. Czech-built satellite station; 10k. "Intercosmos" emblem.

1980. 35th Anniv of National Police Corps.

2523 **710** 50h. gold, red & blue . . 10 10

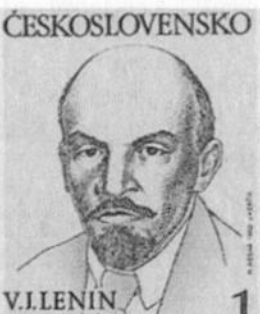

711 Lenin

712 Flag, Flowers and Prague Buildings

1980. 110th Birth Anniv of Lenin and 160th Birth Anniv of Engels.

2524 **711** 1k. brown, red & grey 20 10
2525 – 1k. blue and brown . . . 20 10

DESIGN: No. 2525, Engels.

1980. Anniversaries. Multicoloured.

2526 50h. Type **712** 15 10
2527 1k. Child writing "Mir" (peace) 20 10
2528 1k. Czech and Soviet arms 20 10
2529 1k. Flowers, flags and dove 20 10

ANNIVERSARIES: No. 2526, 35th anniv of May uprising; 2527, 35th anniv of Liberation; 2528, 10th anniv of Czech–Soviet Treaty; 2529, 25th anniv of Warsaw Pact.

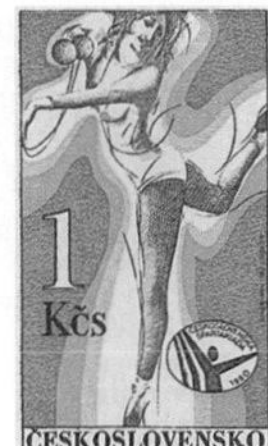
713 Gymnast

1980. National Spartakiad.
2530 – 50h. black, red & blue 10 10
2531 **713** 1k. multicoloured . . . 20 10
DESIGN—HORIZ: 50h. Opening parade of athletes.

714U.N. Emblem

1980. 35th Anniv of United Nations. Sheet 109 × 165 mm.
MS2532 **714** 4k. × 2 multicoloured 3·50 3·50

715 "Gerbera jamesonii"

716 "Chod Girl"

1980. Olomuc and Bratislava Flower Shows. Multicoloured.
2533 50h. Type **715** 15 15
2534 1k. "Aechmea fasciata" . . 1·75 40
2535 2k. Bird of paradise flower 35 25
2536 4k. Slipper orchid 85 40

1980. Graphic Cut-outs by Cornelia Nemeckova.
2537 **716** 50h. multicoloured . . . 15 10
2238 – 1k. mauve, brown & red 25 10
2539 – 2k. multicoloured . . . 45 25
2540 – 4k. multicoloured . . . 2·50 70
2541 – 5k. blue, mauve & lt bl 1·10 50
DESIGNS: 1k. "Punch with his dog"; 2k. "Dandy cat with Posy"; 4k. Lion and Moon ("Evening Contemplation"); 5k. Dancer and piper ("Wallacchian Dance").

717 Map of Czechoslovakia and Family

718 Heads

1980. National Census.
2542 **717** 1k. multicoloured . . . 25 10

1980. Prague Castle (16th series). As T **536**. Multicoloured.
2543 3k. Gateway of Old Palace 2·40 2·75
2544 4k. Armorial lion . . . . . 1·10 75

1980. Historic Bratislava (4th issue). As T **669**. Multicoloured.
2545 3k. "View across the Danube" (J. Eder) . . . . 2·40 2·75
2546 4k. "The Old Royal Bridge" (J. A. Lantz) . . . . . . 1·10 75

1980. 10th Anniv of Socialist Youth Federation.
2547 **718** 50h. blue, orange & red 10 10

1980. "Essen '80" International Stamp Exhibition. Sheet 129 × 78 mm containing No. 2365 × 2 optd **DEN CSSR / 3 / MEZINARODNI VELETRH ZNAMEK / ESSEN 80 / TSCHECHOSLOWAKISCHER TAG** and **80 / 3. Internationale / Briefmarken-Messe / Essen / 1980** with Exhibition emblems in red.
MS2548 1k.60 × 2 multicoloured 17·00 17·00

1980. Paintings (14th series). As T **481**.
2549 1k. buff, blue and brown . . 1·25 1·00
2550 2k. multicoloured . . . . . 2·00 2·10
2551 3k. red, brown and green . . 55 45
2552 4k. multicoloured 65 55
2553 5k. green, buff and black . . 85 80
DESIGNS—VERT: 1k. "Pavel Jozef Safarik" (Jozef B. Klemens); 2k. "Peasant Revolt" (mosaic, A. Podzemma); 3k. Bust of Saint from Lucivna Church; 5k. "Labour" (sculpture, Jan Stursa). HORIZ: 4k. "Waste Heaps" (Jan Zrzavy).

719 Carrier Pigeon

1980. Stamp Day.
2554 **719** 1k. black, red & blue . . 25 10

720 Five Year Plan Emblem

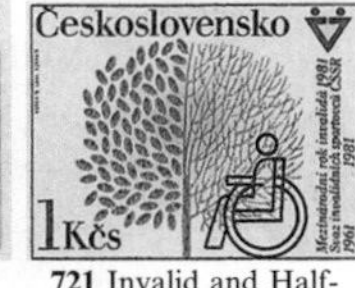
721 Invalid and Half-bare Tree

1981. 7th Five Year Plan.
2555 **720** 50h. multicoloured . . . 10 10

1981. International Year of Disabled Persons.
2556 **721** 1k. multicoloured . . . 25 10

722 Landau, 1800

723 Jan Sverma (partisan)

1981. Historic Coaches in Postal Museum.
2557 **722** 50h. yellow, black & red 20 10
2558 – 1k. yellow, black & grn 30 10
2559 – 3k.60 lt blue, blk & bl 2·00 40
2560 – 5k. stone, black & red 1·25 35
2561 – 7k. yellow, black & blue 1·50 65
DESIGNS: 1k. Mail coach, c. 1830–40; 3k.60, Postal sleigh, 1840; 5k. Mail coach and four horses, 1860; 7k. Coupe carriage, 1840.

1981. Celebrities' Anniversaries. Multicoloured.
2562 50h. Type **723** (80th birth anniv) 25 10
2563 50h. Mikulas Schneider-Trnavsky (composer) (birth cent) 35 10
2564 50h. Juraj Hronec (mathematician) (birth cent) 25 10
2565 50h. Josef Hlavka (architect) (150th birth anniv) . . . 25 10
2566 1k. Dimitri Shostakovich (composer) (75th birth anniv) 60 10
2567 1k. George Bernard Shaw (dramatist) (125th birth anniv) 60 10
2568 1k. Bernardo Bolzano (philosopher) (birth bicent) . . . . 1·50 25
2569 1k. Wolfgang Amadeus Mozart (composer) (225th birth anniv) 75 15

724 Yuri Gagarin

1981. 20th Anniv of First Manned Space Flight. Sheet 108 × 165 mm.
MS2570 **724** 6k. × 2 multicoloured 5·00 5·00

725 Party Member with Flag

1981. 60th Anniv of Czechoslovak Communist Party. Multicoloured.
2571 50h. Type **725** 10 15
2572 1k. Symbols of progress and hands holding flag 20 15
2573 4k. Party member holding flag bearing symbols of industry (vert) 80 40

726 Hammer and Sickle

1981. 16th Czechoslovak Communist Party Congress. Multicoloured.
2574 50h. Type **726** 10 10
2575 1k. "XVI" and Prague buildings 25 10

1981. "WIPA 1981" International Stamp Exhibition, Vienna. Sheet 150 × 104 mm.
MS2576 No. 2561 × 4 . . . . . 21·00 21·00

727 Fallow-plough

728 Man, Woman and Dove

1981. 90th Anniv of Agricultural Museum.
2577 **727** 1k. multicoloured . . . 25 10

1981. Elections to Representative Assemblies.
2578 **728** 50h. red, stone & blue 10 10

729 "Uran" (Tatra Mountains) and "Rudy Rijen" (Bohemia)

1981. Achievements of Socialist Construction (1st series). Multicoloured.
2579 80h. Type **729** (Trade Union recreational facilities) . . 25 10
2580 1k. Prague–Brno–Bratislava expressway 30 10
2581 2k. Jaslovske Bohunice nuclear plant 50 25
See also Nos. 2644/6, 2695/7, 2753/5 and 2800/2.

1981. Historic Bratislava (5th issue). As T **669**. Multicoloured.
2582 3k. "Bratislava, 1760" (G. B. Probst) . . . . . 2·75 2·75
2583 4k. "Grassalkovichov Palace, 1815" (C. Bschor) 80 70

730 "Guernica"

1981. 45th Anniv of International Bridges in Spain and Birth Centenary of Pablo Picasso (artist). Sheet 90 × 76 mm.
MS2584 **730** 10k. multicoloured 3·75 3·75

731 Puppets

732 Map

1981. 30th National Festival of Amateur Puppetry Ensembles, Chrudim.
2585 **731** 2k. multicoloured . . . 45 30

1981. National Defence. Multicoloured.
2586 40h. Type **732** (Defence of borders) 10 10
2587 50h. Emblem of Civil Defence Organization (30th Anniv) (vert) . . . 15 10
2588 1k. Emblem of Svazarm (Organization for Co-operation with Army, 30th anniv) (28 × 23 mm) 25 10

733 Edelweiss, Climbers and Lenin

1981. 25th International Youth Climb of Rysy Peaks.
2589 **733** 3k.60 multicoloured . . 85 40

734 Illustration by Albin Brunovsky

736 Skeletal Hand removing Cigarette

735 Gorilla Family

1981. Biennial Exhibition of Book Illustrations for Children, Bratislava. Multicoloured.
2590 50h. Type **734** 15 15
2591 1k. Adolf Born 30 20
2592 2k. Vive Tolli 60 25
2593 4k. Etienne Delessert . . . 90 40
2594 10k. Suekichi Akaba . . . . 3·00 1·25

1981. 50th Anniv of Prague Zoo. Multicoloured.
2595 50h. Type **735** 30 10
2596 1k. Lion family 35 15
2597 7k. Przewalski's horses . . . 2·75 1·50

1981. Anti-smoking Campaign.
2598 **736** 4k. multicoloured . . . 1·75 85

1981. Prague Castle (17th series). As T **536**. Multicoloured.
2599 3k. Fragment of Pernstejn terracotta from Lobkovic Palace (16th century) . . 90 45
2600 4k. St. Vitus Cathedral (19th century engraving by J. Sembera and G. Dobler) . . . . 2·25 2·75

1981. Art (15th series). As T **481**.
2601 1k. multicoloured . . . . . 3·50 3·25
2602 2k. brown 60 50
2603 3k. multicoloured 80 65
2604 4k. multicoloured 90 70
2605 5k. multicoloured . . . . . 1·10 1·60
DESIGNS: 1k. "View of Prague from Petrin Hill" (V. Hollar); 2k. "Czech Academy of Arts and Sciences Medallion" (Otakar Spaniel); 3k. South Bohemian embroidery (Zdenek Sklenar); 4k. "Peonies" (A. M. Gerasimov); 5k. "Figure of a Woman Standing" (Picasso).

737 Eduard Karel (engraver)

1981. Stamp Day.
2606 **737** 1k. yellow, red and blue 25 10

738 Lenin

739 Player kicking Ball

1982. 70th Anniv of 6th Russian Workers' Party Congress, Prague.
2607 **738** 2k. red, gold and blue 55 25
MS2608 107 × 83 mm. No. 2607 × 4 6·50 6·50

1982. World Cup Football Championship, Spain. Multicoloured.
2609 1k. Type **739** 20 15
2610 3k.60 Heading ball 75 40
2611 4k. Saving goal . . . . . . 2·50 65

740 Hrob **741** Conference Emblem

1982. Arms of Czech Towns (3rd series). Multicoloured.
2612 50h. Type **740** 20 10
2613 50h. Mlada Boleslav 20 10
2614 50h. Nove Mesto and Metuji 20 10
2615 50h. Trencin 20 10
See also Nos. 2720/3, 2765/7, 2819/21 and 3017/20.

1982. Tenth World Federation of Trade Unions Congress, Havana.
2616 **741** 1k. multicoloured . . . 25 10

742 Workers and Mine

1982. 50th Anniv of Great Strike at Most (coalminers' and general strike).
2617 **742** 1k. multicoloured . . . 25 10

743 Locomotives of 1922 and 1982

1982. 60th Anniv of International Railways Union.
2618 **743** 6k. multicoloured . . . 1·75 70

744 Worker with Flag **745** Georgi Dimitrov

1982. 10th Trade Unions Congress, Prague.
2619 **744** 1k. multicoloured . . . 25 10

1982. Birth Centenary of Georgi Dimitrov (Bulgarian statesman).
2620 **745** 50h. multicoloured . . . 10 10

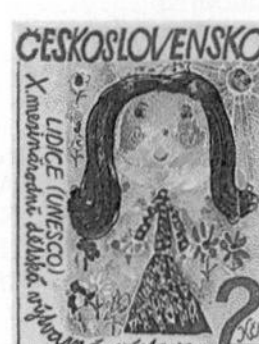

746 Girl with Flowers

1982. 10th International Exhibition of Children's Art, Lidice. Sheet 165 × 108 mm.
MS2621 **746** 2k. × 6 multicoloured 14·00 14·00

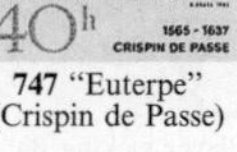

747 "Euterpe" (Crispin de Passe) **749** Child's Head, Rose and Barbed Wire (Lidice)

748 Girl with Doves

1982. Engravings with a Music Theme.
2622 **747** 40h. black, gold & brown 15 10
2623 – 50h. black, gold & red 20 10
2624 – 1k. black, gold & brown 30 15
2625 – 2k. black, gold & blue 50 25
2626 – 3k. black, gold & green 2·40 70
DESIGNS: 50h. "The Sanguine Man" (Jacob de Gheyn); 1k. "The Crossing of the Red Sea" (Adriaen Collaert); 2k. "Wandering Musicians" (Rembrandt); 3k. "Beggar with Viol" (Jacques Callot).

1982. Second Special Session of United Nations General Assembly on Disarmament, New York. Sheet 165 × 108 mm.
MS2627 **748** 6k. × 2 multicoloured 12·50 12·50

1982. 40th Anniv of Destruction of Lidice and Lezaky. Multicoloured.
2628 1k. Type **749** 30 10
2629 1k. Hands and barbed wire (Lezaky) 30 10

750 Memorial and Statue of Jan Zizka

1982. 50th Anniv of National Memorial, Prague.
2630 **750** 1k. multicoloured . . . 25 10

751 Satellite Orbits around Earth

1982. Second United Nations Conference on Research and Peaceful Uses of Outer Space, Vienna. Sheet 165 × 108 mm.
MS2631 **751** 5k. × 2 multicoloured 12·50 12·50

752 Krivoklat Castle

1982. Castles. Multicoloured.
2632 50h. Type **752** 20 10
2633 1k. Interior and sculptures at Krivoklat Castle . . . 35 15
2634 2k. Nitra Castle 65 30
2635 3k. Archaeological finds from Nitra Castle . . . . 1·00 40
MS2636 105 × 125 mm. Nos. 2632/5 3·00 3·00

1982. Prague Castle (18th series). As T **536**.
2637 3k. brown and green . . . . 2·40 70
2638 4k. multicoloured . . . . . 1·25 95
DESIGNS: 3k. "St. George" (statue by George and Martin of Kluz, 1372); 4k. Tomb of Prince Vratislav I, Basilica of St. George.

753 Ferry "Kamzik" in Bratislava Harbour

1982. Danube Commission. Multicoloured.
2639 3k. Type **753** 80 30
2640 3k.60 "TR 100" tug at Budapest . . . . 1·00 40
MS2641 Two sheets, each 127 × 127 mm. (a) No. 2639 × 4; (b) No. 2640 × 4 . . . . . . 20·00 20·00

1982. Historic Bratislava (6th issue). As T **669**.
2642 3k. black and red . . . . . 1·90 85
2643 4k. multicoloured . . . . . 2·10 1·25
DESIGNS: 3k. "View of Bratislava with Steamer"; 4k. "View of Bratislava with Bridge".

754 Agriculture

1982. Achievements of Socialist Construction (2nd series). Multicoloured.
2644 20h. Type **754** 10 10
2645 1k. Industry 35 10
2646 3k. Science and technology 95 45
See also Nos. 2695/7, 2753/5 and 2800/2.

755 "Scientific Research"

1982. 30th Anniv of Academy of Sciences.
2647 **755** 6k. multicoloured . . . 1·10 55

756 Couple with Flowers and Silhouette of Rider

1982. 65th Anniv of October Revolution and 60th Anniv of U.S.S.R. Multicoloured.
2648 50h. Type **756** 15 10
2649 1k. Cosmonauts and industrial complex 20 10

757 "Jaroslav Hasek" (writer) (Jose Malejovsky) **759** President Husak

758 Jaroslav Goldschmied (engraver) and Engraving Tools

1982. Sculptures. Multicoloured.
2650 1k. Type **757** 30 10
2651 2k. "Jan Zrzavy" (patriot) (Jan Simota) 55 25
2652 4k.40 "Leos Janacek" (composer) (Milos Axman) . . . . 1·10 55
2653 6k. "Martin Kukucin" (patriot) (Jan Kulich) . . 1·50 75
2654 7k. "Peaceful Work" (detail) (Rudolf Pribis) . . . . . 3·00 1·25

1982. Art (16th series). As T **481**. Multicoloured.
2655 1k. "Revolution in Spain" (Josef Sima) . . . . . . 1·60 95
2656 2k. "Woman drying Herself" (Rudolf Kremlicka) . . . . 2·50 2·25
2657 3k. "The Girl Bride" (Dezider Milly) . . . . . 1·60 90
2658 4k. "Oil Field Workers" (Jan Zelibsky) . . . . . 1·60 1·25
2659 5k. "The Birds Lament" (Emil Filla) . . . . 1·75 1·50

1983. Stamp Day.
2660 **758** 1k. multicoloured . . . 25 10

1983. 70th Birthday of President Husak.
2661 **759** 50h. blue 10 10
See also No. 2911.

760 Jaroslav Hasek (writer) **761** Armed Workers

1983. Celebrities' Anniversaries.
2662 **760** 50h. green, blue & red 15 15
2663 – 1k. brown, blue & red 25 15
2664 – 2k. multicoloured . . . 45 25
2665 – 5k. black, blue & red . . 1·40 50
DESIGNS: Type **760** (birth centenary); 1k. Julius Fucik (journalist) (80th birth and 40th death annivs); 2k. Martin Luther (church reformist) (500th birth anniv); 5k. Johannes Brahms (composer) (150th birth anniv).

1983. Anniversaries. Multicoloured.
2666 50h. Type **761** (35th anniv of "Victorious February") 15 10
2667 1k. Family and agriculture and industrial landscapes (35th anniversary of National Front) 25 15

762 Radio Waves and Broadcasting Emblem **763** Ski Flyer

1983. Communications. Multicoloured.
2668 40h. Type **762** (60th anniv of Czech broadcasting) . . 15 10
2669 1k. Television emblem (30th anniv of Czech television) 20 10
2670 2k. W.C.Y. emblem and "1983" (World Communications Year) (40 × 23 mm) 45 25
2671 3k.60 Envelopes, Aero A-10 aircraft and mail vans (60th anniv of airmail and 75th anniv of mail transport by motor vehicles) (49 × 19 mm) . . 1·00 50

1983. 7th World Ski Flying Championships, Harrachov.
2672 **763** 1k. multicoloured . . . 25 10

764A. Gubarev and V. Remek

1983. 5th Anniv of Soviet-Czechoslovak Space Flight. Sheet 109 × 165 mm.
MS2673 **764** 10k. × 2 multicoloured 14·00 14·00

765 Emperor Moth and "Viola sudetica"

1983. Nature Protection. Multicoloured.
2674 50h. Type **765** 20 10
2675 1k. Water lilies and edible frogs 40 15
2676 2k. Red crossbill and cones 1·60 40
2677 3k.60 Grey herons . . . . 1·60 50
2678 5k. Lynx and "Gentiana asclepiadea" . . . . 1·50 45
2679 7k. Red deer . . . . 3·25 1·50

766 Ivan Stepanovich Kbnev

1983. Soviet Army Commanders. Multicoloured.
2680 50h. Type **766** 15 10
2681 1k. Andrei Ivanovich Yeremenko 25 15
2682 2k. Rodion Yakovlevich Malinovsky 55 25

767 Dove

768 "Rudolf II" (Adrian de Vries)

1983. World Peace and Life Congress, Prague.
2683 **767** 2k. multicoloured . . . 45 40
MS2684 108 × 83 mm. No. 2683 × 4 9·25 9·25

1983. Prague Castle (19th series).
2685 **768** 4k. multicoloured . . . 1·40 1·00
2686 – 5k. orange, blk & red . . 85 1·00
DESIGN: 5k. Kinetic relief with timepiece by Rudolf Svoboda.

769 Mounted Messenger (Oleg K. Zotov)

1983. 9th Biennial Exhibition of Book Illustration for Children.
2687 **769** 50h. multicoloured . . . 15 10
2688 – 1k. multicoloured . . . 25 10
2689 – 4k. multicoloured . . . 95 40
2690 – 7k. red and black . . . 1·40 55
MS2691 115 × 133 mm. Nos. 2687/90 4·50 4·00
DESIGNS: 1k. Boy looking from window at birds in tree (Zbigniew Rychlicki); 4k. "Hansel and Gretel" (Lisbeth Zwerger); 7k. Three young negroes (Antonio P. Domingues).

770 Ilyushin Il-62 and Globe

1983. World Communications Year and 60th Anniv of Czechoslovak Airlines.
2692 **770** 50h. red, purple & pink 15 10
2693 – 1k. purple, red & pink 30 10
2694 – 4k. purple, red & pink 1·90 85
DESIGNS—VERT: 1k. Ilyushin Il-62 and envelope. HORIZ: 4k. Ilyushin Il-62 and Aero A-14 biplane.

1983. Achievements of Socialist Construction (3rd series). As T **754**.
2695 50h. Surveyor 15 10
2696 1k. Refinery 30 10
2697 3k. Hospital and operating theatre 75 50

1983. Historic Bratislava (7th series). As T **669**.
2698 3k. green, red and black . . 1·75 70
2699 4k. multicoloured . . . . . 1·75 70
DESIGNS: 3k. Sculptures by Viktor Tilgner; 4k. "Mirbachov Palace" (Julius Schubert).

771 National Theatre, Prague

772 "Soldier with Sword and Shield" (Hendrik Goltzius)

1983. Czechoslovak Theatre Year.
2700 **771** 50h. brown 15 10
2701 – 2k. green 55 25
DESIGN: 2k. National Theatre and Tyl Theatre, Prague.

1983. Art (17th series), showing works from the National Theatre, Prague. As Type **481**.
2702 1k. multicoloured . . . . . 1·25 90
2703 2k. multicoloured . . . . . 2·75 90
2704 3k. yellow, black and blue 1·00 60
2705 4k. multicoloured . . . . . 1·00 60
2706 5k. multicoloured . . . . . 1·00 60

DESIGNS: 1k. "Zalov" (lunette detail by Mikolas Ales); 2k. "Genius" (stage curtain detail, Vojtech Hynais); 3k. "Music" and "Lyrics" (ceiling drawings, Frantisek Zenisek); 4k. "Prague" (detail from President's box, Vaclav Brozik); 5k. "Hradcany Castle (detail from President's box, Julius Marak).

1983. Period Costume from Old Engravings. Multicoloured.
2707 40h. Type **772** 15 10
2708 50h. "Warrior with Sword and Lance" (Jacob de Gheyn) 15 10
2709 1k. "Lady with Muff" (Jacques Callot) 30 10
2710 4k. "Lady with Flower" (Vaclav Hollar) . . . . . 1·10 40
2711 5k. "Gentleman with Cane" (Antoine Watteau) . . . 2·25 80

773 Karel Seizinger (stamp engraver)

1983. Stamp Day.
2712 **773** 1k. multicoloured . . . 25 10

774 National Flag, with Bratislava and Prague Castles

775 Council Emblem

1984. 15th Anniv of Czechoslovak Federation.
2713 **774** 50h. multicoloured . . . 10 10

1984. 35th Anniv of Council for Mutual Economic Aid.
2714 **775** 1k. multicoloured . . . 25 25

776 Cross-country Skiing

1984. Winter Olympic Games, Sarajevo. Mult.
2715 2k. Type **776** 45 25
2716 3k. Ice hockey 70 40
2717 5k. Biathlon . . . . 1·50 65
MS2718 110 × 99 mm. No. 2716 × 4 8·00 8·00

777 Olympic Flag, Ancient Greek Athletes and Olympic Flame

1984. 90th Anniv of International Olympic Committee.
2719 **777** 7k. multicoloured . . . 1·25 55

1984. Arms of Czech Towns (4th series). As T **740**. Multicoloured.
2720 50h. Turnov 30 10
2721 50h. Kutna Hora 30 10
2722 1k. Milevsko 45 25
2723 1k. Martin 45 25

778 "Soyuz" and Dish Aerials

779 Vendellin Opatrny

1984. "Interkosmos" International Space Flights. Multicoloured.
2724 50h. Type **778** 20 10
2725 1k. "Salyut"–"Soyuz" complex 35 15
2726 2k. Cross-section of orbital station 55 25
2727 4k. "Salyut" taking pictures of Earth's surface . . . 75 50
2728 5k. "Soyuz" returning to Earth . . . . 1·00 65

1984. Anti-fascist Heroes.
2729 **779** 50h. black, red & blue 20 10
2730 – 1k. black, red & blue . . 30 10
2731 – 2k. black, red & blue . . 55 25
2732 – 4k. black, red & blue . . 1·10 40
DESIGNS: 1k. Ladislav Novomesky; 2k. Rudolf Jasiok; 4k. Jan Nalepka.

780 Musical Instruments

781 Telecommunications Building

1984. Music Year.
2733 **780** 50h. lt brown, gold & brn 20 10
2734 – 1k. multicoloured . . . 25 10
DESIGN: 1k. Organ pipes.

1984. Central Telecommunications Building, Bratislava.
2735 **781** 2k. multicoloured . . . 55 25

1984. Historic Bratislava (8th series). As T **669**. Multicoloured.
2736 3k. Arms of Vintners' Guild 1·25 85
2737 4k. Painting of 1827 Skating Festival . . . . 1·25 85

782 Doves, Globes and U.P.U. Emblem

783 Jack of Spades (16th century)

1984. 110th Anniv of Universal Postal Union. Sheet 165 × 108 mm.
MS2738 **782** 5k. × 4 multicoloured 16·00 16·00

1984. Prague Castle (20th series). As T **768**. Multicoloured.
2739 3k. Weather cock, St. Vitus Cathedral 75 80
2740 4k. King David playing psaltery (initial from Roudnice Book of Psalms) . . . . 1·40 1·25

1984. Playing Cards. Multicoloured.
2741 50h. Type **783** 20 10
2742 1k. Queen of Spades (17th century) 35 10
2743 2k. Nine of Hearts (18th century) 50 25
2744 3k. Jack of Clubs (18th century) 85 35
2745 5k. King of Hearts (19th century) . . . . 1·25 55

784 Family and Industrial Complex

1984. 40th Anniv of Slovak Uprising.
2746 **784** 50h. multicoloured . . . 10 10

785 Soldiers with Banner

1984. 40th Anniv of Battle of Dukla Pass.
2747 **785** 2k. multicoloured . . . 45 25

786 High Jumping

1984. Olympic Games, Los Angeles. Mult.
2748 1k. Type **786** 30 15
2749 2k. Cycling 50 25
2750 3k. Rowing 70 40
2751 5k. Weightlifting . . . . . 1·10 55
MS2752 107 × 95 mm. Nos. 2748/51 5·00 5·00

1984. Achievements of Socialist Construction (4th series). As T **754**. Multicoloured.
2753 1k. Telephone handset and letters (Communications) 40 10
2754 2k. Containers on railway trucks and river barge (Transport) 75 30
2755 3k. Map of Transgas pipeline 65 45
MS2756 157 × 105 mm. No. 2755 × 3 . . . . 5·00 5·00

1984. Art (18th series). As T **481**. Multicoloured.
2757 1k. "Milevsky River" (Karel Stehlik) 40 75
2758 2k. "Under the Trees" (Viktor Barvitius) 80 90
2759 3k. "Landscape with Flowers" (Zolo Palugyay) 1·25 60
2760 4k. Illustration of king from Vysehrad Codex . . . . 1·60 80
2761 5k. "Kokorin" (Antonin Manes) . . . . 2·00 95

787 Dove and Head of Girl

788 Zapotocky

1984. 45th Anniv of International Students Day.
2762 **787** 1k. multicoloured . . . 25 10

1984. Birth Centenary of Antonin Zapotocky (politician).
2763 **788** 50h. multicoloured . . . 10 10

789 Bohumil Heinz (engraver) and Hands engraving

1984. Stamp Day.
2764 **789** 1k. multicoloured . . . 25 25

1985. Arms of Czech Towns (5th series). As T **740**. Multicoloured.
2765 50h. Kamyk nad Vltavou 30 10
2766 50h. Havirov 30 10
2767 50h. Trnava 30 10

790 "Art and Pleasure" (Jan Simota)

792 Helmet, Mail Shirt and Crossbow

791 View of Trnava

1985. Centenary of Prague University of Applied Arts.
2768 **790** 3k. multicoloured . . . 60 40

1985. 350th Anniv of Trnava University.
2769 **791** 2k. multicoloured . . . 35 20

1985. Exhibits from Military Museum. Mult.
2770 50h. Type **792** 15 10
2771 1k. Cross and star of Za vitezstvi order 30 10
2772 2k. Avia B-534 airplane and "Soyuz 28" (horiz) . . . 70 25

793 Lenin reading

1985. 115th Birth Anniv of Lenin.
MS2773 **793** 2k. ×6 multicoloured . . . 4·50 3·00

794U.N. Emblem and Stylized Dove

1985. 40th Anniv of United Nations Organization and International Peace Year (1986).
MS2774 **794** 6k. ×4 multicoloured 14·00 14·00

795 State Arms and Crowd

796 State Arms and Soldiers with National Flag

1985. 40th Anniv of Kosice Reforms.
2775 **795** 4k. multicoloured . . . 70 40

1985. 40th Anniv of National Security Forces.
2776 **796** 50h. multicoloured . . . 10 10

797 Automatic Optical Platform and Comet Trajectory

1985. Space Project "Vega" (research into Venus and Halley's Comet). Sheet 106×96 mm.
MS2777 **797** 5k. ×2 multicoloured 10·50 10·50

798 Emblem and Ice Hockey Players

1985. World and European Ice Hockey Championships, Prague.
2778 **798** 1k. multicoloured . . . 25 10

799 Pieces on Chessboard

802 Tennis

1985. 80th Anniv of Czechoslovak Chess Organization.
2779 **799** 6k. multicoloured . . . 1·50 70

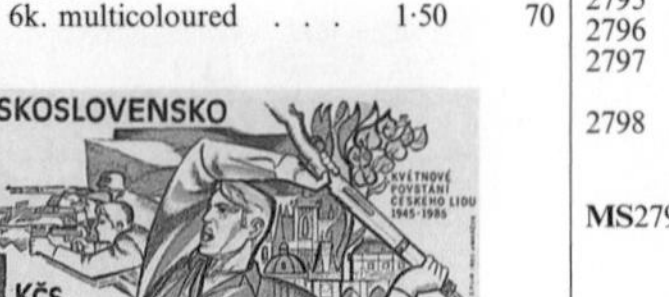

800 Freedom Fighters and Prague

1985. Anniversaries. Multicoloured.
2780 1k. Type **800** (40th anniv of May uprising) 20 10
2781 1k. Workers shaking hands, flags and industrial motifs (15th anniv of Czechoslovak–Soviet Treaty) 20 10
2782 1k. Girl giving flowers to soldier, Prague Castle and tank (40th anniv of liberation) 20 10
2783 1k. Soldiers and industrial motifs (30th anniv of Warsaw Pact) 20 10

1985. Czechoslovak Victory in Ice Hockey Championships. No. 2778 optd **CSSR MISTREM SVETA**.
2784 **798** 1k. multicoloured . . . 5·25 5·00

1985. National Spartakiad. Multicoloured.
2785 50h. Type **802** 15 10
2786 1k. Gymnasts performing with ribbons (48×19 mm) 20 10

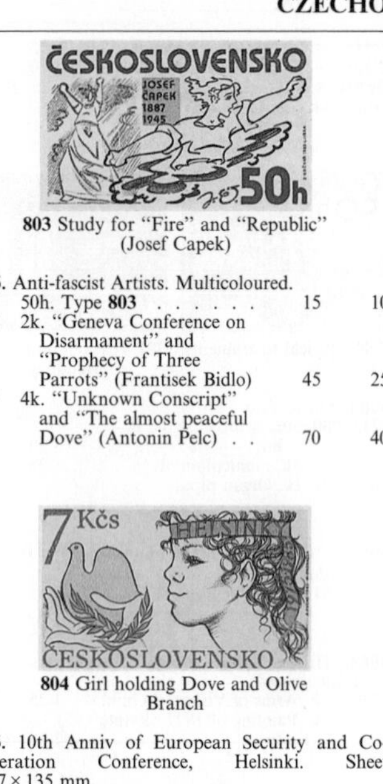

803 Study for "Fire" and "Republic" (Josef Capek)

1985. Anti-fascist Artists. Multicoloured.
2787 50h. Type **803** 15 10
2788 2k. "Geneva Conference on Disarmament" and "Prophecy of Three Parrots" (Frantisek Bidlo) 45 25
2789 4k. "Unknown Conscript" and "The almost peaceful Dove" (Antonin Pelc) . . 70 40

804 Girl holding Dove and Olive Branch

1985. 10th Anniv of European Security and Co-operation Conference, Helsinki. Sheet 107×135 mm.
MS2790 **804** 7k. ×4 multicoloured 11·50 11·50

805 Moscow Buildings and Young People holding Doves

1985. 12th World Youth and Students' Festival, Moscow.
2791 **805** 1k. multicoloured . . . 25 10

806 Figures on Globe

807 Rocking Horse (Kveta Pacovska)

1985. 40th Anniv of World Federation of Trade Unions.
2792 **806** 50h. multicoloured . . . 10 10

1985. Historic Bratislava (9th series). As T **669**.
2793 3k. lt brown, green & brown 70 75
2794 4k. black, green and red . . 1·00 1·10
DESIGNS: 3k. Tapestry (Elena Holeczyova); 4k. Pottery.

1985. 10th Biennial Exhibition of Book Illustrations for Children, Bratislava. Mult.
2795 1k. Type **807** 20 10
2796 2k. Elves (Gennady Spirin) 35 20
2797 3k. Girl, butterfly and flowers (Kaarina Kaila) 65 30
2798 4k. Boy shaking hands with hedgehog (Erick Ingraham) 80 40
MS2799 95×128 mm. Nos. 2795/8 5·00 5·00

1985. Achievements of Socialist Construction (5th series). As T **754**. Multicoloured.
2800 50h. Mechanical excavator 10 10
2801 1k. Train and map of Prague underground railway 30 15
2802 2k. Modern textile spinning equipment 35 25

808 Gateway to First Courtyard

809 Jug (4th century)

1985. Prague Castle (21st series).
2803 **808** 2k. black, blue & red . . 50 30
2804 – 3k. multicoloured . . . 1·10 40
DESIGN: 3k. East side of Castle.

1985. Centenary of Prague Arts and Crafts Museum. Glassware. Multicoloured.
2805 50h. Type **809** 10 10
2806 1k. Venetian glass container (16th century) 20 10
2807 2k. Bohemian glass with hunting scene (18th century) 40 25
2808 4k. Bohemian vase (18th century) 65 40
2809 6k. Bohemian vase (c. 1900) 1·40 65

1985. Art (19th series). As T **481**. Multicoloured.
2810 1k. "Young Woman in Blue Dress" (Josef Ginovsky) 1·60 1·00
2811 2k. "Lenin on Charles Bridge" (Martin Sladky) 1·60 1·00
2812 3k. "Avenue of Poplars" (Vaclav Rabas) . . . . . 1·60 1·00
2813 4k. "Beheading of St. Dorothea" (Hans Baldung Grien) . . . . . 1·60 1·00
2814 5k. "Jasper Schade van Westrum" (Frans Hals) 1·60 1·00

810 Bohdan Roule (engraver) and Engraving Plate

1985. Stamp Day.
2815 **810** 1k. multicoloured . . . 25 10

811 Peace Dove and Olive Twig

1986. International Peace Year. Multicoloured.
2816 **811** 1k. multicoloured . . . 25 10

812 Victory Statue Prague

813 Zlin Z-50LS Airplane, Locomotive "Kladno" and Rock Drawing of Chariot

1986. 90th Anniv of Czech Philharmonic Orchestra.
2817 **812** 1k. black, brown & vio 25 10

1986. "Expo '86" International Transport and Communications Exhibition, Vancouver.
2818 **813** 4k. multicoloured . . . 70 40

1986. Arms of Czech Towns (6th series). As T **740**. Multicoloured.
2819 50h. Vodnany 25 10
2820 50h. Zamberk 25 10
2821 50h. Myjava 25 10

814 Banner, Industry and Hammer and Sickle

1986. 17th Communist Party Congress, Prague. Multicoloured.
2822 50h. Type **814** 10 10
2823 1k. Buildings, hammer and sickle and star 25 10

815 Couple, Banner and Star

1986. 65th Anniv of Czechoslovakian Communist Party. Multicoloured.
2824 50h. Type **815** 10 10
2825 1k. Workers, banner and hammer and sickle . . . 25 10

816 Map and Stylized Man

1986. National Front Election Programme.
2826 **816** 50h. multicoloured . . . 10 10

817 Emblem and Crest on Film

1986. 25th Int Film Festival, Karlovy Vary.
2827 **817** 1k. multicoloured . . . 25 10

818 Musical Instruments

819 Ilyushin Il-86 and Airspeed Envoy II

1986. 40th Anniv of Prague Spring Music Festival.
2828 **818** 1k. multicoloured . . . 25 10

1986. 50th Anniv of Prague–Moscow Air Service.
2829 **819** 50h. multicoloured . . . 10 10

820 Sports Pictograms

1986. 90th Anniv of Czechoslovak Olympic Committee.
2830 **820** 2k. multicoloured . . . 45 25

821 Map and Goalkeeper

1986. World Cup Football Championship, Mexico.
2831 **821** 4k. multicoloured . . . 80 55

822 Globe, Net and Ball

1986. Women's World Volleyball Championship, Prague.
2832 **822** 1k. multicoloured . . . 35 10

823 Emblem

1986. "Praga '88" Stamp Exhibition, Prague (1st issue) and 60th Anniv of International Philatelic Federation. Sheet 110×82 mm containing T **823** and two labels.
MS2833 **823** 20k. multicoloured 14·00 14·00

824 Funeral Pendant

825 Wooden Cock, Slovakia

1986. Prague Castle (22nd series).
2834 **824** 2k. multicoloured . . . 55 50
2835 – 3k. orange, brown & bl 65 65
DESIGN: 3k. "Allegory of Blossoms" (sculpture, Jaroslav Horejc).

1986. 40th Anniv of U.N.I.C.E.F. Toys. Mult.
2836 10h. Type **825** 10 10
2837 20h. Wooden soldier on hobby horse, Bohemia . . 10 10
2838 1k. Rag doll, Slovakia . . . 15 10
2839 2k. Doll 35 10
2840 3k. Mechanical bus 50 25

826 Registration Label and Mail Coach

1986. Centenary of Registration Label.
2841 **826** 4k. multicoloured . . . 60 30

1986. Historic Bratislava (10th series). As T **669**.
2842 3k. black, red and blue . . 60 55
2843 4k. black, red and green . . 75 70
DESIGNS: 3k. Sigismund Gate, Bratislava Castle; 4k. "St. Margaret with a Lamb" (relief from Castle).

827 Eagle Owl

1986. Owls. Multicoloured.
2844 50h. Type **827** 25 10
2845 2k. Long-eared owl 55 25
2846 3k. Tawny owl 55 40
2847 4k. Barn owl 70 50
2848 5k. Short-eared owl . . . . 1·50 60

828 Curtain of D 37 Theatre (Vladimir Sychra)

1986. 50th Anniv of Formation of International Brigades in Spain. Sheet 165 × 108 mm.
MS2849 **828** 5k. × 2 multicoloured 14·00 14·00
See also Nos. 2880/4, 2900, MS2903, 2923/MS2927, 2929, MS2933, 2934/MS2938, 2940/MS2944, MS2945, MS2946, MS2947, MS2948 and MS2949.

829 Type "Kt8" Articulated Tram and 1920s' Prague Tram

1986. Rail Vehicles. Multicoloured.
2850 50h. Type **829** 20 10
2851 1k. Series E 458.1 electric shunting engine and 1882–1913 steam locomotive . . 30 10
2852 3k. Series T 466.2 diesel locomotive and 1900–24 steam locomotive 70 35
2853 5k. Series M 152.0 railcar and 1930–35 railbus . . . 95 60

830 "The Circus Rider" (Jan Bauch)

1986. Circus and Variety Acts on Paintings. Multicoloured.
2854 1k. Type **830** . . . . . . 1·25 25
2855 2k. "The Ventriloquist" (Frantisek Tichy) . . . . 1·50 35
2856 3k. "In the Circus" (Vincent Hloznik) . . . . 1·45 55
2857 6k. "Clown" (Karel Svolinsky) . . . . 1·75 1·25

1986. Art (20th series). As T **481**. Multicoloured.
2858 1k. "The Czech Lion, May 1918" (Vratislav H. Brunner) . . . . . . 1·50 65
2859 2k. "Boy with Mandolin" (Jozef Sturdik) . . . . . 1·40 75
2860 3k. "The Metra Building" (Frantisek Gross) 80 80
2861 4k. "Maria Maximiliana of Sternberk" (Karel Skreta) 80 95
2862 5k. "Adam and Eve" (Lucas Cranach) . . . . 1·10 1·10

831 Brunner and Stamps of 1920

1986. Stamp Day. Birth Centenary of Vratislav Hugo Brunner (stamp designer).
2863 **831** 1k. multicoloured . . . 25 10

832 Bicyclists

1987. World Cross-country Cycling Championships, Mlada Boleslav.
2864 **832** 6k. multicoloured . . . 95 55

833 Pins and Ball

1987. 50th Anniv of Czechoslovakian Bowling Federation.
2865 **833** 2k. multicoloured . . . 35 25

834 Gold Stars of Heroes of C.S.S.R. and of Socialist Labour

1987. State Orders and Medals.
2866 **834** 50h. red, black & gold 10 10
2867 – 2k. multicoloured . . . 30 25
2868 – 3k. multicoloured . . . 55 40
2869 – 4k. multicoloured . . . 70 55
2870 – 5k. multicoloured . . . 95 60
DESIGNS: 2k. Order of Klement Gottwald; 3k. Order of the Republic; 4k. Order of Victorious February; 5k. Order of Labour.

835 Poplar Admiral

1987. Butterflies and Moths. Multicoloured.
2871 1k. Type **835** 20 10
2872 2k. Eyed hawk moth . . . 45 25
2873 3k. Large tiger moth 75 40
2874 4k. Viennese emperor moth 1·00 40

836 Emblem

1987. Nuclear Power Industry.
2875 **836** 5k. multicoloured . . . 80 55

837 Emblem

839 Stained Glass Window, St. Vitus's Cathedral (Frantisek Sequens)

1987. 11th Trades Union Congress, Prague.
2876 **837** 1k. multicoloured . . . 10 10

1987. 20th Anniv of "Interkosmos" Space Programme. Sheet 165 × 104 mm.
MS2877 **838** 10k. × 2 multicoloured 5·00 5·00

1987. Prague Castle (23rd series). Multicoloured.
2878 2k. Type **839** 45 40
2879 3k. Arms (mural), New Land Rolls Hall, Old Royal Palace 75 55
See also Nos. 2950/1 and 2977/8.

840 Telephone, 1894

1987. "Praga 88" Int Stamp Exhibition (2nd issue). Technical Monuments. Multicoloured.
2880 3k. Type **840** 45 35
2881 3k. Mail Van, 1924 . . . . 45 35
2882 4k. Tank locomotive "Archduke Charles" 1907 90 35
2883 4k. Prague tram, 1900 . . . 90 35
2884 5k. Steam roller, 1936 . . . 90 55
See also Nos. 2900, 2923/6, 2929/32 2934/7 and 2940/3.

841 "When the Fighting Ended" (Pavel Simon)

843 Chickens in Kitchen (Asun Balzola)

842 Prague Town Hall Clock and Theory of Functions Diagram

1987. 45th Anniv of Destruction of Lidice and Lezaky. Multicoloured.
2885 1k. Type **841** 25 10
2886 1k. "The End of the Game" (Ludmila Jirincova) . . . 25 10

1987. 125th Anniv of Union of Czech Mathematicians and Physicists. Multicoloured.
2887 50h. Type **842** 10 10
2888 50h. J. M. Petzval, C. Strouhal and V. Iarnik 10 10
2889 50h. Trajectory of Brownian motion and earth fold diagram 10 10

1987. 11th Biennial Exhibition of Book Illustrations for Children, Bratislava. Designs showing illustrations by artists named. Multicoloured.
2890 50h. Type **843** 35 15
2891 1k. Cranes with egg at railway points (Frederic Clement) 45 15
2892 2k. Birds on nest (Elzbieta Gaudasinska) 35 25
2893 4k. Couple looking over rooftops (Marija Lucija Stupica) 35 30
MS2894 97 × 130 mm. No. 2892 × 2 plus label . . . . 1·60 1·60

844 Barbed Wire, Flames and Menorah

1987. 40th Anniv of Terezin Memorial.
2895 **844** 50h. multicoloured . . . 10 10

845 "OSS" and Communications Equipment

1987. 30th Anniv of Organization of Socialist Countries' Postal Administrations.
2896 **845** 4k. multicoloured . . . 70 10

846 Purkyne and Microtome

1987. Birth Bicentenary of Jan Evangelista Purkyne (physiologist).
2897 **846** 7k. multicoloured . . . 1·25 70

1987. Historic Bratislava (11th series). As T **669**.
2898 3k. buff, black and blue . . 50 50
2899 4k. black and brown . . . . 1·00 1·00
DESIGNS: 3k. Detail of projecting window by Vyzdoby; 4k. "View of Bratislava" (engraving, Hans Mayer).

848 Postilion

849 Symbols of Industry, Lenin and Red Flag

1987. "Praga '88" International Stamp Exhibition (3rd issue).
2900 **848** 1k. multicoloured . . . 25 10

1987. 70th Anniv of Russian Revolution (2901) and 65th Anniv of USSR (2902). Multicoloured.
2901 50h. Type **849** 15 10
2902 50h. Hammer and sickle . . 15 10

1987. "Praga '88" International Stamp Exhibition (4th issue). Sheet 101 × 100 mm.
MS2903 **838** 10k. × 4 multicoloured 14·50 14·50

1987. Art (21st series). As T **481**.
2904 1k. multicoloured 70 25
2905 2k. multicoloured 90 70
2906 3k. multicoloured . . . . . 1·25 75
2907 4k. black, blue and red . . 90 90
2908 5k. multicoloured . . . . . 1·25 1·00
DESIGNS: 1k. "Enclosure of Dreams" (Kamil Lhotak); 2k. "Tulips" (Ester Simerova-Martincekova); 3k. "Bohemian Landscape" (triptych, Josef Lada); 4k. "Accordion Player" (Josef Capek); 5k. "Self-portrait" (Jiri Trnka).

850 Obrovsky and Detail of 1919 Stamp

1987. Stamp Day. 105th Birth Anniv of Jakub Obrovsky (designer).
2909 **850** 1k. multicoloured . . . 10 10

851 "Czechoslovakia", Linden Tree and Arms

1988. 70th Anniv of Czechoslovakia.
2910 **851** 1k. multicoloured . . . 10 10

1988. 75th Birthday of President Husak.
2911 **759** 1k. brown and red . . . 10 10

852 Ski Jumping and Ice Hockey

1988. Olympic Games, Calgary and Seoul. Mult.
2912 50h. Type **852** 10 10
2913 1k. Basketball and football 15 10
2914 6k. Throwing the discus and weightlifting 90 40

853 Red Flags and Klement Gottwald Monument, Pecky

1988. 40th Annivs of "Victorious February" (2915) and National Front (2916). Multicoloured.
2915 50h. Type **853** 10 10
2916 50h. Couple and detail of "Czech Constitution, 1961" (Vincent Hloznik) 10 10
MS2917 87 × 99 mm. 50h. × 2 multicoloured (Type **853**); 60h. × 2 sepia (Type **246**) . . . . . 2·50 2·50

854 Laurin and Klement Car, 1914

1988. Historic Motor Cars. Multicoloured.
2918 50h. Type **854** 10 10
2919 1k. Tatra "NW" type B, 1902 . . . . 15 10
2920 2k. Tatra "NW" type E, 1905 . . . . 40 20
2921 3k. Tatra "12 Normandie", 1929 . . . . 55 25
2922 4k. "Meteor", 1899 . . . . 75 40

855 Praga Post Office and Velka Javorina T.V. Transmitter

1988. "Praga '88" International Stamp Exhibition (5th issue) and 70th Anniv of Postal Museum. Multicoloured.
2923 50h. Type **855** 10 10
2924 1k. Mlada Boleslav telecommunications centre and Carmelite Street post office, Prague 30 10
2925 2k. Prague 1 and Bratislava 56 post offices 45 25
2926 4k. Malta Square, Prague, and Prachatice post offices 90 40
MS2927 108 × 80 mm. Nos. 2924/5 each × 2 . . . . 3·50 3·50

856 Woman with Linden Leaves as Hair and Open Book

857 Strahov Monastery

1988. 125th Anniv of Slovak Cultural Society.
2928 **856** 50h. multicoloured . . . 10 10

1988. "Praga '88" International Stamp Exhibition (6th issue). National Literature Memorial, Strahov Monastery. Multicoloured.
2929 1k. Type **857** 15 10
2930 2k. Open book and celestial globe 35 20
2931 5k. Illuminated initial "B", scrolls and decorative binding 80 50
2932 7k. Astrological signs, Strahov, illuminated book and globe . . . . 1·50 1·10
MS2933 125 × 79 mm. Nos. 2929/32 4·00 4·00

858 Waldstein Garden Fountain

1988. "Praga '88" International Stamp Exhibition (7th issue). Prague Fountains.
2934 **858** 1k. black, lilac & blue 15 10
2935 – 2k. multicoloured . . . 35 20
2936 – 3k. black, orange & lilac 55 35
2937 – 4k. black, orange & grn 65 45
MS2938 79 × 125 mm. Nos. 2934/7 3·50 3·50
DESIGNS: 2k. Old Town Square; 3k. Charles University; 4k. Courtyard, Prague Castle.

859 Washington Capitol and Moscow Kremlin

1988. Soviet–American Strategic Arms Limitation Talks, Moscow. Sheet 110 × 106 mm.
MS2939 **859** 4k. multicoloured 2·40 2·40

1988. "Praga '88" (8th issue). Thematic Philately Day. As No. MS2903 but inscr "DEN NAMETOVE FILATELIE" at top.
MS2940 **838** 10k. × 4 multicoloured 10·00 10·00

860 Trade Unions Central Recreation Centre

1988. "Praga '88" International Stamp Exhibition (9th issue). Present-day Prague. Multicoloured.
2941 50h. Type **860** 10 10
2942 1k. Koospol foreign trade company 20 10
2943 2k. Motol teaching hospital 40 10
2944 4k. Palace of Culture . . . 75 25
MS2945 Two sheets, each 148 × 96 mm. (a) Nos. 2941 × 2 and 2944 × 2; (b) Nos. 2942/3 each × 2 . . . . 1·60 1·60

861 Alfons Mucha (designer of first stamps)

1988. "Praga '88" International Stamp Exhibition (10th issue). 70th Anniv of First Czechoslovak Stamps. Sheet 82 × 96 mm.
MS2946 **861** 5k. × 2 multicoloured 2·40 2·40

862 "Turin, Monte Superag" (detail, Josef Navratill)

1988. "Praga '88" International Stamp Exhibition (11th issue). Postal Museum. Sheet 108 × 165 mm.
MS2947 **862** 5k. × 2 multicoloured 3·25 3·25

863 Ariadne

1988. "Praga '88" (12th issue). Prague National Gallery. Sheet 108 × 165 mm containing T **863** and similar vert design showing details of "Bacchus and Ariadne" by Sebastian Ricci.
MS2948 10k. Type **863**; 10k. Bacchus . . . . 5·00 5·00

864 King George

1988. "Praga '88" International Stamp Exhibition (13th issue). King George of Podebrady's Religious Peace Plans. Sheet 106 × 133 mm.
MS2949 **864** 1k.60 × 4 black and yellow . . . . 5·00 5·00

1988. Prague Castle (24th series). As T **839**. Multicoloured.
2950 2k. 17 th-century pottery jug 30 35
2951 3k. "St. Catherine" (Paolo Veronese) 45 55

1988. Historic Bratislava (12th series). As T **669**. Multicoloured.
2952 3k. Hlavne Square (detail of print by R. Alt-Sandman) 45 40
2953 4k. Ferdinand House . . . 50 55

1988. Art (22nd series). As T **481**.
2954 2k. multicoloured 40 40
2955 6k. brown, black and blue 1·25 1·10
2956 7k. multicoloured . . . . 1·75 1·50
DESIGNS: 2k. "Field Workers carrying Sacks" (Martin Benka); 6k. "Woman watching Bird" (Vojtech Preissig); 7k. "Leopard attacking Horseman" (Eugene Delacroix).

865 Benda and Drawings

1988. Stamp Day. 106th Birth Anniv of Jaroslav Benda (stamp designer).
2957 **865** 1k. multicoloured . . . 10 10

866 Emblem **867** Globe and Truck

1989. 20th Anniv of Czechoslovak Federal Socialist Republic.
2958 **866** 50h. multicoloured . . . 10 10

1989. Paris–Dakar Rally. Multicoloured.
2959 50h. Type **867** 10 10
2960 1k. Globe and view of desert on truck side . . . 15 10
2961 2k. Globe and truck (different) 30 15
2962 4k. Route map, turban and truck 50 25

868 Taras G. Shevchenko **870** Dove and Pioneers

869 "Republika" (freighter)

1989. Birth Anniversaries.
2963 **868** 50h. multicoloured . . . 15 10
2964 – 50h. multicoloured . . . 15 10
2965 – 50h. brown and green . . 15 10
2966 – 50h. brown and green . . 15 10
2967 – 50h. black, brn & dp brn 15 10
2968 – 50h. multicoloured . . . 15 10
DESIGNS: No. 2963, Type **868** (Ukrainian poet and painter, 175th anniv); 2964, Modest Petrovich Musorgsky (composer, 150th anniv); 2965, Jan Botto (poet, 160th anniv); 2966, Jawaharlal Nehru (Indian statesman, cent); 2967, Jean Cocteau (writer and painter, centenary); 2968, Charlie Chaplin (actor, centenary).

1989. Shipping.
2969 **869** 50h. grey, red and blue 15 10
2970 – 1k. multicoloured . . . 20 10
2971 – 2k. multicoloured . . . 25 10
2972 – 3k. grey, red and blue 35 20
2973 – 4k. multicoloured . . . 40 25
2974 – 5k. multicoloured . . . 45 35
DESIGNS: 1k. "Pionyr" (trawler); 2k. "Brno" (tanker); 3k. "Trinec" (container ship); 4k. "Orlik" (container ship); 5k. "Vltava" (tanker) and communications equipment.

1989. 40th Anniv of Young Pioneer Organization.
2975 **870** 50h. multicoloured . . . 10 10

1989. Art (23rd series). Sheet 110 × 86 mm containing vert designs as T **481** showing details of "Festival of Rose Garlands" by Albrecht Durer.
MS2976 10k. × 2 multicoloured 3·50 3·50

1989. Prague Castle (25th series). As T **839**.
2977 2k. brown, yellow and red 20 20
2978 3k. multicoloured 40 35
DESIGNS: 2k. King Kard of Bohemia (relief by Alexandra Colin from Archduke Ferdinand I's mausoleum); 3k. "Self-portrait" (V. V. Reiner).

871 Bastille, Crowd and Flag

1989. Bicentenary of French Revolution. Sheet 73 × 98 mm.
MS2979 **871** 5k. black, red and blue 80 80

872 White-tailed Sea Eagle

1989. Endangered Species.
2980 **872** 1k. multicoloured . . . 15 25

873 Fire-bellied Toads

1989. Endangered Amphibians. Multicoloured.
2981 2k. Type **873** 30 25
2982 3k. Yellow-bellied toad . . 45 35
2983 4k. Alpine newts 85 55
2984 5k. Carpathian newts . . . 1·10 60

874 Dancers

1989. 40th Anniv of Slovak Folk Art Collective.
2985 **874** 50h. multicoloured . . . 10 10

875 Horsemen and Mountains

1989. 45th Anniv of Slovak Rising.
2986 **875** 1k. multicoloured . . . 10 10

876 "Going Fishing" (Hannu Taina) **877** "Nolanea verna"

1989. 12th Biennial Exhibition of Book Illustrations for Children. Multicoloured.

2987	50h. Type **876**	10	10
2988	1k. "Donkey Rider" (Aleksandur Aleksov) . .	15	10
2989	2k. "Animal Dreams" (Jurgen Spohn Zapadny)	25	15
2990	4k. "Scarecrow" (Robert Brun)	40	25
MS2991	100 × 143 mm. No. 2990 × 2	1·25	1·25

1989. Poisonous Fungi.

2992 **877**	50h. brown, deep brown and green	10	10
2993 –	1k. multicoloured . . .	20	10
2994 –	2k. green and brown . .	35	25
2995 –	3k. brown, yellow & red	45	35
2996 –	5k. multicoloured . . .	65	55

DESIGNS: 1k. Death cap; 2k. Destroying angel; 3k. "Cortinarius orellanus"; 5k. "Galerina marginata".

1989. Historic Bratislava (13th series). As T **669**.

2997	3k. multicoloured	35	40
2998	4k. black, red and green . .	55	50

DESIGNS: 3k. Devin Fortress and flower; 4k. Devin Fortress and pitcher.

878 Jan Opletal (Nazi victim)

1989. 50th Anniv of International Students Day.

2999 **878**	1k. multicoloured . . .	10	10

1989. Art (24th series). As T **481**. Multicoloured.

3000	2k. "Nirvana" (Anton Jasusch)	25	25
3001	4k. "Dusk in the Town" (Jakub Schikaneder) (horiz)	50	50
3002	5k. "Bakers" (Pravoslav Kotik) (horiz)	80	70

879 Bearded Falcon Stamp, Pens and Bouda

1989. Stamp Day. 5th Death Anniv of Cyril Bouda (stamp designer).

3003 **879**	1k. brown, yellow & red	10	10

880 Practising Alphabet **881** Tomas Masaryk (first President)

1990. International Literacy Year.

3004 **880**	1k. multicoloured . . .	10	10

1990. Birth Anniversaries. Multicoloured.

3005	50h. Type **881** (140th anniv)	10	10
3006	50h. Karel Capek (writer, centenary)	10	10
3007	1k. Vladimir Ilyich Lenin (120th anniv)	15	10
3008	2k. Emile Zola (novelist, 150th anniv)	30	15
3009	3k. Jaroslav Heyrovsky (chemist, centenary) . . .	35	20
3010	10k. Bohuslav Martinu (composer, centenary) . .	1·10	65

882 Pres. Vaclav Havel **883** Players

1990.

3011 **882**	50h. ultram, bl & red . .	10	10

1990. Men's World Handball Championship.

3012 **883**	50h. multicoloured . . .	10	10

884 Snapdragon **885** Pope John Paul II

1990. Flowers. Multicoloured.

3013	50h. Type **884**	10	10
3014	1k. "Zinnia elegans"	15	10
3015	3k. Tiger flower	35	25
3016	5k. Madonna lily	55	40

1990. Arms of Czech Towns (7th series). As T **740**. Multicoloured.

3017	50h. Bytca	10	10
3018	50h. Podebrady	10	10
3019	50h. Sobeslav	10	10
3020	50h. Prostejov	10	10

1990. Papal Visit.

3021 **885**	1k. brown, yellow & red	10	10

886 Woman holding Flags **887** Twopenny Blue

1990. 45th Anniv of Liberation.

3022 **886**	1k. multicoloured . . .	10	10

1990. 150th Anniv of Penny Black. Sheet 102 × 94 mm.

MS3023 **887**	7k. multicoloured	1·25	1·25

888 Footballers **889** Victory Signs

1990. World Cup Football Championship, Italy.

3024 **888**	1k. multicoloured . . .	10	10

1990. Free General Election.

3025 **889**	1k. multicoloured . . .	10	10

1990. Prague Castle (26th series). As T **824**.

3026	2k. multicoloured	50	40
3027	3k. green, dp green & red	70	65

DESIGNS: 2k. Jewelled glove (from reliquary of St. George); 3k. Seal of King Premsyl Otakar II of Bohemia.

890 Map of Europe and Branch

1990. 15th Anniv of European Security and Co-operation Conference, Helsinki.

3028 **890**	7k. multicoloured . . .	80	55

891 Milada Horakova

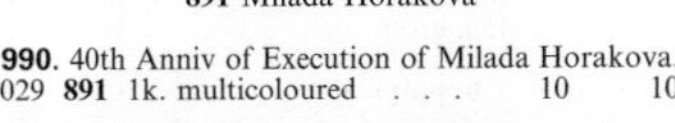

1990. 40th Anniv of Execution of Milada Horakova.

3029 **891**	1k. multicoloured . . .	10	10

892 Poodles

1990. "Inter Canis" Dog Show, Brno. Mult.

3030	50h. Type **892**	10	10
3031	1k. Afghan hound, Irish wolfhound and greyhound	15	10
3032	4k. Czech terrier, bloodhound and Hanoverian bearhound	40	30
3033	7k. Cavalier King Charles, cocker and American cocker spaniels	65	50

1990. Historic Bratislava (14th series). As T **669**.

3034	3k. black and red	40	35
3035	4k. multicoloured	65	55

DESIGNS: 3k. Coin; 4k. "M. R. Stefanik" (J. Mudroch).

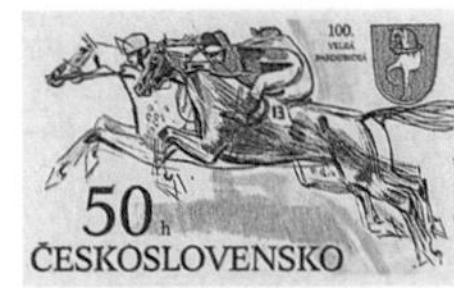

893 Horses jumping

1990. Centenary of Pardubice Steeplechase. Mult.

3036	50h. Type **893**	10	10
3037	4k. Horses galloping	45	35

894 Alpine Marmot

1990. Mammals. Multicoloured.

3038	50h. Type **894**	10	10
3039	1k. European wild cat . . .	10	10
3040	4k. Eurasian beaver	45	30
3041	5k. Common long-eared bat	60	40

895 European Flag

1990. Helsinki Pact Civic Gathering, Prague.

3042 **895**	3k. blue, yellow & gold	35	30

896 Snow-covered Church

1990. Christmas.

3043 **896**	50h. multicoloured . . .	10	10

1990. Art (25th series). As T **481**. Multicoloured.

3044	2k. multicoloured	40	35
3045	3k. black, brown & blue . .	50	40
3046	4k. multicoloured	60	60
3047	5k. multicoloured	70	75

DESIGNS—HORIZ: 2k. "Krucemburk" (Jan Zrzavy). VERT: 3k. "St. Agnes" (detail of sculpture, Josef Vaclav Myslbek); 4k. "Slovene in his Homeland" (detail, Alfons Mucha); 5k. "St. John the Baptist" (detail of sculpture, Auguste Rodin).

897 Karel Svolinsky (stamp designer) and "Czechoslovakia"

1990. Stamp Day.

3048 **897**	1k. purple, lilac & blue	10	10

898 Judo Throw **899** Svojsik

1991. European Judo Championships, Prague.

3049 **898**	1k. multicoloured . . .	10	10

1991. 80th Anniv of Czechoslovak Scout Movement and 115th Birth Anniv of A. B. Svojsik (founder).

3050 **899**	3k. multicoloured . . .	35	10

900 Jan Hus preaching **901** Alois Senefelder

1991. Anniversaries.

3051 **900**	50h. brown, stone & red	10	10
3052 –	1k. multicoloured . . .	10	10
3053 –	5k. multicoloured . . .	60	30

DESIGNS AND EVENTS: 50h. Type **900** (600th anniv of Bethlehem Chapel, Prague); 40 × 23 mm: 1k. Estates Theatre, Prague (re-opening) and Mozart (death bicent); 49 × 20 mm: 5k. Paddle-steamer "Bohemia" (150th anniv of boat excursions in Bohemia).

1991. Birth Anniversaries.

3054 **901**	1k. green, brown & red	20	10
3055 –	1k. black, green & red	20	10
3056 –	1k. blue, mauve & red	20	10
3057 –	1k. violet, blue and red	20	10
3058 –	1k. brown, orange & red	20	10

DESIGNS: No. 3054, Type **901** (inventor of lithography, 220th anniv); 3055, Andrej Kmet (naturalist, 150th anniv); 3056, Jan Masaryk (politician, 105th anniv); 3057, Jaroslav Seifert (composer, 90th anniv); 3058, Antonin Dvorak (composer, 150th anniv).

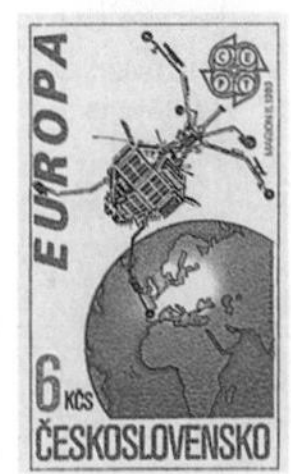

902 "Magion II" Satellite and Earth **903** Exhibition Pavilion, 1891

1991. Europa. Europe in Space.

3059 **902**	6k. blue, black & red . .	70	50

1991. Cent of International Exhibition, Prague.

3060 **903**	1k. blue, grey & mauve	10	10

904 Bearded Penguins, Map and Flag

1991. 30th Anniv of Antarctic Treaty.

3061 **904**	8k. multicoloured . . .	90	55

905 Blatna Castle **906** Jan Palach

1991. Castles. Multicoloured.

3062	50h. Type **905**	10	1·00
3063	1k. Bouzov	10	10
3064	3k. Kezmarok	40	25

1991. Jan Palach Scholarship.

3065 **906**	4k. black	35	30

907 Rip **908** "The Frog King" (Binette Schroeder)

1991. Beauty Spots.
3066 **907** 4k. red, blue & yellow . . . 45 40
3067 – 4k. purple, green & blk . . . 45 40
DESIGN: No. 3067, Krivan.

1991. 13th Biennial Exhibition of Book Illustrations for Children. Multicoloured.
3068 1k. Type **908** 10 10
3069 2k. "Pinocchio" (Stasys Eidrigevicius) 25 15

909 Hlinka

910 "Prague Jesus Child" (Maria-Victoria Church)

1991. 53rd Death Anniv of Father Andrej Hlinka (Slovak nationalist).
3070 **909** 10k. black . . . . 1·25 55

1991. Prague and Bratislava. Multicoloured.
3071 3k. Type **910** 45 40
3072 3k. St. Elisabeth's Church, Bratislava 45 40

911 "Gagea bohemica"

912 Boys in Costume

1991. Nature Protection. Flowers. Multicoloured.
3073 1k. Type **911** 10 10
3074 2k. "Aster alpinus" 20 20
3075 5k. "Fritillaria meleagris" . . 55 40
3076 11k. "Daphne eneorum" . . 1·25 75

1991. Art (26th series). As T **481**. Multicoloured.
3077 2k. "Family at Home" (Max Ernst) 20 20
3078 3k. "Milenci" (Auguste Renoir) 30 30
3079 4k. "Christ" (El Greco) . . 75 40
3080 5k. "Coincidence" (Ladislav Guderna) 85 55
3081 7k. "Two Japanese Women" (Utamaro) . . . . 1·10 80

1991. Christmas.
3082 **912** 50h. multicoloured . . . 10 10

913 Martin Benka (stamp designer) and Slovakian 1939 Stamp

1991. Stamp Day.
3083 **913** 2k. red, black & orange . . 35 10

914 Biathlon

916 Player

915 Comenius

1992. Winter Olympic Games, Albertville.
3084 **914** 1k. multicoloured . . . 10 10

1992. 400th Birth Anniv of Jan Komensky (Comenius) (educationist). Sheet 63 × 76 mm.
MS3085 **915** 10k. multicoloured 1·75 1·75

1992. World Ice Hockey Championship, Prague and Bratislava.
3086 **916** 3k. multicoloured . . . 35 35

917 Traffic Lights

1992. Road Safety Campaign.
3087 **917** 2k. multicoloured . . . 45 20

918 Tower, Seville Cathedral

1992. "Expo '92" World's Fair, Seville.
3088 **918** 4k. multicoloured . . . 25 25

919 Amerindian, "Santa Maria" and Columbus

1992. Europa. 500th Anniv of Discovery of America by Columbus.
3089 **919** 22k. multicoloured . . . 2·50 1·90

920 J. Kubis and J. Gabcik

1992. Free Czechoslovak Forces in World War II. Multicoloured.
3090 1k. Type **920** (50th anniv of assassination of Reinhard Heydrich) 10 10
3091 2k. Spitfires (air battles over England, 1939–45) 20 10
3092 3k. Barbed wire and soldier (Tobruk, 1941) 25 15
3093 6k. Soldiers (Dunkirk, 1944–45) 90 25

921 Tennis Player

922 Nurse's Hats and Red Cross

1992. Olympic Games, Barcelona.
3094 **921** 2k. multicoloured . . . 35 10

1992. Red Cross.
3095 **922** 2k. multicoloured . . . 25 10

923 Player

924 Crawling Cockchafer

1992. European Junior Table Tennis Championships, Topolcany.
3096 **923** 1k. multicoloured . . . 10 10

1992. Beetles. Multicoloured.
3097 1k. Type **924** 10 10
3098 2k. "Ergates faber" 20 10
3099 3k. "Meloe violaceus" . . . 25 10
3100 4k. "Dytiscus latissimus" . . 30 45

925 Troja Castle

1992.
3101 **925** 6k. multicoloured . . . 60 45
3102 – 7k. black and lilac . . . 70 60
3103 – 8k. multicoloured . . . 90 75
DESIGNS—VERT: 7k. "St. Martin" (sculpture, G. R. Donner), Bratislava Cathedral. HORIZ: 8k. Lednice Castle.

926 Double Head and Posthorns

927 Anton Bernolak and Georgius Fandly

1992. Post Bank.
3104 **926** 20k. multicoloured . . . 1·75 70

1992. Bicentenary of Slovak Education Assn.
3105 **927** 5k. multicoloured . . . 55 30

928 Cesky Krumlov

929 Organ

1992.
3106 **928** 3k. brown and red . . . 35 10

1992. Art (27th series). As T **481**.
3107 6k. black and brown 50 50
3108 7k. multicoloured 65 70
3109 8k. multicoloured . . . . . 1·00 90
DESIGNS—VERT: 6k. "The Old Raftsman" (Koloman Sokol); 8k. "Abandonned" (Toyen). HORIZ: 7k. "Still Life with Grapes" (Georges Braque).

1992. Christmas.
3110 **929** 2k. multicoloured . . . 10 10

930 Jindra Schmidt (engraver)

1992. Stamp Day.
3111 **930** 2k. multicoloured . . . 10 10

NEWSPAPER STAMPS

N 4

N 67 Dove

N 94 Messenger

1918. Imperf.
N24 N **4** 2h. green 10 10
N25 5h. green 10 10
N26 6h. red 10 10
N27 10h. lilac 10 10
N28 20h. blue 10 10
N29 30h. brown 10 10
N30 50h. orange 10 10
N31 100h. brown 45 10

1925. Surch with new value and stars.
N249 N **4** 5 on 2h. green 60 55
N250 5 on 6h. red 35 85

1926. Newspaper Express stamps optd **NOVINY** or surch also.
N251 E **4** 5h. on 2h. pur on yell . . 10 10
N253 5h. green on yellow . . 45 25
N254 10h. brown on yellow . . 10 10

1934. Optd **O.T.**
N332 N **4** 10h. lilac 10 10
N333 20h. blue 10 10
N334 30h. brown 15 10

1937. Imperf.
N364 N **67** 2h. brown 10 10
N365 5h. blue 10 10
N366 7h. orange 10 10
N367 9h. green 10 10
N368 10h. lake 10 10
N369 12h. blue 10 10
N370 20h. green 10 10
N371 50h. brown 10 10
N372 1k. olive 10 10

1946. Imperf.
N467 N **94** 5h. blue 10 10
N468 10h. red 10 10
N469 15h. green 10 10
N470 20h. green 10 10
N471 25h. purple 10 10
N472 30h. brown 10 10
N473 40h. red 10 10
N474 50h. brown 10 10
N475 1k. grey 10 10
N476 5k. blue 10 10

EXPRESS NEWSPAPER STAMPS

E 4

1918. Imperf. On yellow or white paper.
E24 E **4** 2h. purple 10 10
E25 5h. green 10 10
E26 10h. brown 45 45

OFFICIAL STAMPS

O 92

O 103

1945.
O463 O **92** 50h. green 10 10
O464 1k. blue 10 10
O465 1k.20 purple 15 10
O466 1k.50 red 10 10
O467 2k.50 blue 15 10
O468 5k. purple 20 30
O469 8k. red 30 45

1947.
O490 O **103** 60h. red 10 10
O491 80h. olive 10 10
O492 1k. blue 10 10
O493 1k.20 purple 10 10
O494 2k.40 red 10 10
O495 4k. blue 15 10
O496 5k. purple 15 30
O497 7k.40 violet 20 30

PERSONAL DELIVERY STAMPS

P 66

1937. For Prepayment. "V" in each corner.
P363 P **66** 50h. blue 20 35

1937. For Payment on Delivery. "D" in each corner.
P364 P **66** 50h. red 20 35

P 95

1946.
P469 P **95** 2k. blue 20 20

POSTAGE DUE STAMPS

D 4

1919. Imperf.
D24 D **4** 5h. olive 10 10
D25 10h. olive 10 10
D26 15h. olive 10 10
D27 20h. olive 10 10
D28 25h. olive 10 10
D29 30h. olive 25 10
D30 40h. olive 25 25
D31 50h. olive 25 10
D32 100h. brown . . . . . . 1·25 10
D33 250h. orange . . . . . . 6·00 1·10
D34 400h. red . . . . 8·25 1·10
D35 500h. green . . . . . . 3·00 25
D36 1000h. violet . . . . . . 3·00 35
D37 2000h. blue . . . . . . 16·00 75

1922. Postage stamps surch **DOPLATIT** and new value. Imperf or perf.
D229 **2** 10 on 3h. mauve 10 10
D224a 20 on 3h. mauve 10 10
D230 30 on 3h. mauve 10 10
D257 **3** 30 on 15h. red . . . . . 1·75 30
D231 **2** 40 on 3h. mauve 10 10
D258 **3** 40 on 15h. red 35 25
D225 50 on 75h. green 25 25
D262 60 on 50h. purple . . . . 3·00 1·50
D263 60 on 50h. blue . . . . 3·50 1·90

D232 60 on 75h. green 40 10
D226 60 on 80h. green 35 10
D227 100 on 80h. green . . . 30 10
D233 100 on 120h. black . . . 90 10
D264 **2** 100 on 400h. violet . . . 55 10
D265 **3** 100 on 1000h. purple . . 1·10 30
D228 **2** 200 on 400h. violet . . . 55 25

1924. Postage Due stamp surch.
D249 D **4** 10 on 5h. olive 10 10
D250 20 on 5h. olive 10 10
D251 30 on 15h. olive 10 10
D252 40 on 15h. olive 10 10
D253 50 on 250h. orange . . 60 10
D234 50 on 400h. red 55 10
D254 60 on 250h. orange . . 90 20
D235 60 on 400h. red . . . . 2·10 60
D255 100 on 250h. orange . . 1·25 25
D236 100 on 400h. red . . . 1·25 25
D256 200 on 500h. green . . 3·00 1·75

1926. Postage stamps optd **DOPLATIT** or surch also.
D266 **13** 30 on 100h. green . . . 10 10
D279 **11** 40 on 185h. orange . . . 10 10
D267 **13** 40 on 200h. purple . . . 10 10
D268 40 on 300h. red . . . . 1·10 25
D280 **11** 50 on 20h. red 10 10
D281 50 on 150h. red 25 10
D269 **13** 50 on 500h. green . . . 55 10
D282 **11** 60 on 25h. brown . . . 25 25
D283 60 on 185h. orange . . . 25 10
D270 **13** 60 on 400h. brown . . . 45 10
D278 **11** 100h. brown 55 20
D284 100 on 25h. brown . . . 60 10
D271 **13** 100 on 600h. purple . . . 1·75 35

D 34 D 94

1928.
D285 D **34** 5h. red 10 10
D286 10h. red 10 10
D287 20h. red 10 10
D288 30h. red 10 10
D289 40h. red 10 10
D290 50h. red 10 10
D291 60h. red 10 10
D292 1k. blue 10 10
D293 2k. blue 35 10
D294 5k. blue 60 10
D295 10k. blue . . . . . 1·25 10
D296 20k. blue . . . . . 2·40 10

1946.
D467 D **94** 10h. blue 10 10
D468 20h. blue 10 10
D469 50h. blue 15 10
D470 1k. red 30 10
D471 1k.20 red 35 10
D472 1k.50 red 40 10
D473 1k.60 red 45 10
D474 2k. red 60 10
D475 2k.40 red 65 10
D476 3k. red . . . . . . 1·00 10
D477 5k. red . . . . . . 1·60 10
D478 6k. red . . . . . . 2·25 10

D 257 D 258

1954.
D845 D **257** 5h. green 10 10
D846 10h. green 10 10
D860 30h. green 10 10
D861 50h. green 15 10
D849 60h. green 15 10
D850 95h. green 35 10
D863 D **258** 1k. violet 25 10
D864 1k.20 violet 30 10
D865 1k.50 violet 45 10
D854 1k.60 violet 40 10
D855 2k. violet 75 10
D866 3k. violet . . . . . . 1·50 30
D867 5k. violet . . . . . . 2·00 45

D **572** Stylized Plant

1971.
D1985 – 10h. pink and blue 10 10
D1986 – 20h. blue & purple 10 10
D1987 – 30h. pink & green 10 10
D1988 – 60h. green & pur . . 15 10
D1989 – 80h. blue & orange 20 10
D1990 – 1k. green & red . . 25 10
D1991 – 1k.20 orange & grn 30 10
D1992 – 2k. red and blue . . 55 20
D1993 – 3k. yellow & black 95 20
D1994 – 4k. blue & brown 1·10 30
D1995 D **572** 5k.40 lilac and red 1·60 35
D1996 – 6k. yellow and red 2·00 45
DESIGNS: Various stylized plants as Type D **572**.

DAHOMEY Pt. 6; Pt. 12

A French colony on the W. Coast of Africa, incorporated in French West Africa in 1944. In 1958 it became an autonomous republic within the French Community, and in 1960 was proclaimed fully independent. The area used the issues of French West Africa from 1944 until 1960.

100 centimes = 1 franc.

1899. "Tablet" key-type inscr "DAHOMEY ET DEPENDANCES".
1 D 1c. black and red on blue . . 85 90
2 2c. brown & blue on buff . . 60 70
3 4c. brown & blue on grey . . 1·40 1·50
4 5c. green & red . . . . . 2·75 1·10
5 10c. red and blue . . . . . 3·25 2·50
6 15c. grey and red . . . . . 4·00 1·75
7 20c. red & blue on green . . 9·00 14·50
8 25c. black & red on pink . . 6·75 3·50
9 25c. blue and red . . . . . 6·75 11·50
10 30c. brown & bl on drab . . 13·50 17·00
11 40c. red & blue on yellow 9·00 8·75
12 50c. brown & red on blue 10·00 21·00
13 50c. brown & blue on blue 32·00 17·00
14 75c. brown & red on orge 65·00 50·00
15 1f. green and red . . . . . 32·00 32·00
16 2f. violet and red on pink . . 80·00 85·00
17 5f. mauve & blue on blue . . 85·00 90·00

1906. "Faidherbe", "Palms" and "Balay" key-types inscr "DAHOMEY".
18 I 1c. grey and red . . . . . . 1·40 85
19 2c. brown and red . . . . . 1·40 65
20 4c. brown & red on blue . . 1·90 1·25
21 5c. green and red . . . . . 4·75 50
22 10c. pink and blue . . . . . 19·00 55
23 J 20c. black & red on blue . . 9·50 9·00
24 25c. blue and red . . . . . 6·00 6·25
25 30c. brown & red on pink 12·50 13·00
26 35c. black & red on yellow 45·00 5·00
27 45c. brown & red on green 16·00 17·00
28 50c. violet and red . . . . 11·50 16·00
29 75c. green & red on orange 16·00 19·00
30 K 1f. black and red on blue . . 23·00 32·00
31 2f. blue and red on pink . . 90·00 85·00
32 5f. red & blue on yellow . . £100 £110

1912. Surch in figures.
33 05 on 2c. brown & blue on buff . . . . 85 1·25
34 05 on 4c. brown & blue on grey . . . . 95 1·40
35 05 on 15c. grey and red . . . 1·10 2·00
36 05 on 20c. red & blue on green . . . . 80 2·25
37 05 on 25c. blue and red . . . 1·25 3·00
38 05 on 30c. brown & bl on drab . . . . 95 1·75
39 10c. on 40c. red & bl on yellow . . . . 85 1·00
40 10c. on 50c. brn & bl on blue 1·10 2·75
40a 10c. on 50c. brn & red on blue £850 £900
41 10c. on 75c. brown and red on orange . . . . 4·50 8·00

6 Native Climbing Palm

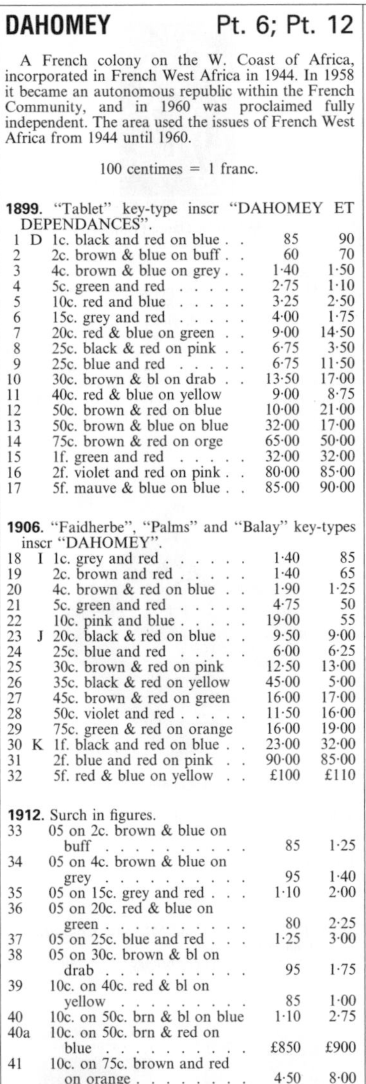
11 Rene Caillie

1913.
42 **6** 1c. black and violet 10 15
43 2c. pink and brown 10 20
44 4c. brown and black 10 45
45 5c. green and light green . . 1·40 70
60 5c. violet and purple 15 45
46 10c. pink and red . . . . . 1·75 55
61 10c. green and lt green . . . 75 1·25
75 10c. green and red 10 10
47 15c. purple and brown . . . 20 25
48 20c. brown and grey . . . . 60 1·10
76 20c. green . . . . 15 1·40
77 20c. black and mauve . . . 15 60
49 25c. blue & ultramarine . . . 2·50 1·60
62 25c. orange and purple . . . 20 20
50 30c. violet and brown . . . 3·00 4·00
63 30c. carmine and red . . . 95 4·00
78 30c. violet and yellow . . . 60 50
79 30c. green and olive 60 75
51 35c. black and brown . . . 1·10 1·75
80 35c. green and turquoise . . 85 3·25
52 40c. orange and black . . . 65 70
53 45c. blue and grey . . . . . 70 2·50
54 50c. brown & chocolate . . 4·50 6·50
64 50c. blue & ultramarine . . 20 2·25
81 50c. blue and red 20 20
82 55c. brown and green . . . 50 2·50
83 60c. violet on pink . . . . 1·75 2·75
84 65c. green and brown . . . 25 95
55 75c. violet and blue 35 55
85 80c. blue and brown . . . . 50 3·00
86 85c. pink and blue . . . . . 50 2·75
87 90c. red and carmine . . . . 75 1·90
87a 90c. red and brown . . . . 1·40 3·25
56 1f. black and green . . . . 65 1·00
88 1f. light blue and blue . . . 1·25 1·00
89 1f. red and brown 50 45
90 1f. red and light red . . . . 2·00 2·75
91 1f.10 brown and violet . . . 3·25 4·50
92 1f.25 brown and blue . . . 17·00 18·00
93 1f.50 light blue and blue . . 2·50 2·00
94 1f.75 orange and brown . . 3·75 3·50
94a 1f.75 ultramarine & blue . . 60 2·00
57 2f. brown and yellow . . . 1·00 65
95 3f. mauve on pink . . . . . 3·00 3·00
58 5f. blue and violet . . . . . 2·50 3·50

1915. Surch **5c** and red cross.
59 **6** 10c.+5c. pink and red . . . . 45 2·00

1922. Surch in figures and bars.
65 **6** 25c. on 2f. brown & yellow 1·40 3·00
66 60 on 75c. violet on pink . . 25 2·75
67 65 on 15c. purple & brown 1·60 3·75
68 85 on 15c. purple & brown 1·75 3·75
69 90c. on 75c. red and carmine 2·00 3·50
70 1f.25 on 1f. lt blue & blue . . 45 3·00
71 1f.50 on 1f. lt blue & blue . . 1·40 1·90
72 3f. on 5f. red and green . . . 6·50 10·00
73 10f. on 5f. brown & blue . . 4·25 7·00
74 20f. on 5f. green and red . . 2·50 8·00

1931. "Colonial Exhibition" key-types inscr "DAHOMEY".
96 E 40c. green . . . . 5·00 7·50
97 F 50c. mauve . . . . 5·25 7·25
98 G 90c. red . . . . 5·50 6·75
99 H 1f.50 blue . . . . 5·50 7·00

1937. Paris Int Exn. As Nos. 110/15 of Cameroun.
100 20c. violet . . . . 1·25 3·25
101 30c. green . . . . 1·00 3·00
102 40c. red . . . . 65 3·25
103 50c. brown . . . . 1·00 2·00
104 90c. red . . . . 70 2·25
105 1f.50 blue . . . . 60 1·60
MS105a 120 × 100 mm. 3f. blue and agate (as T **16**). Imperf . . . . 5·75 13·00

1938. Int Anti-cancer Fund. As T **19** of Cameroun.
106 1f.75+50c. blue . . . . . . 5·00 15·00

1939. Death Centenary of R. Caillie (explorer).
107 **11** 90c. orange . . . . 40 2·00
108 2f. violet . . . . 95 3·25
109 2f.25 blue . . . . 1·25 3·50

1939. New York World's Fair. As T **20** of Cameroun.
110 1f.25 red . . . . 1·90 3·00
111 2f.25 blue . . . . 2·00 2·25

1939. 150th Anniv of French Revolution. As T **25** of Cameroun.
112 45c.+25c. green . . . . . . 4·25 11·00
113 70c.+30c. brown . . . . . . 5·25 11·00
114 90c.+35c. orange . . . . . . 4·50 11·00
115 1f.25+1f. red . . . . 4·50 11·00
116 2f.25+2f. blue . . . . 4·25 11·00

12 African Landscape

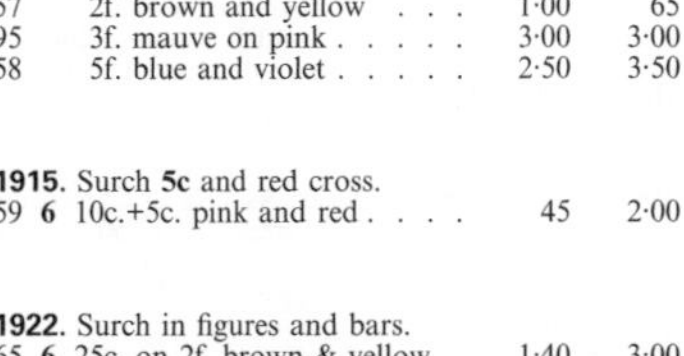
13 Native Poling Canoe

1940. Air.
117 **12** 1f.90 blue . . . . 1·25 2·50
118 2f.90 red . . . . 1·25 3·00
119 4f.50 green . . . . 1·40 2·75
120 4f.90 olive . . . . 1·10 2·75
121 6f.90 orange . . . . 90 3·25

1941.
122 **13** 2c. red . . . . 15 1·25
123 3c. blue . . . . 15 2·50
124 5c. violet . . . . 95 2·75
125 10c. green . . . . 25 2·50
126 15c. black . . . . 15 2·25
127 – 20c. brown . . . . 1·10 2·75
128 – 30c. violet . . . . 45 2·75
129 – 40c. red . . . . 55 2·75
130 – 50c. green . . . . 95 2·75
131 – 60c. black . . . . 65 2·75
132 – 70c. mauve . . . . 1·75 3·25
133 – 80c. black . . . . 1·10 2·75
134 – 1f. violet 30 35
135 – 1f.30 violet . . . . . . 1·00 3·25
136 – 1f.40 green . . . . . . 1·75 3·25
137 – 1f.50 red . . . . 1·25 3·00
138 – 2f. orange . . . . 95 3·50
139 – 2f.50 blue . . . . 1·90 3·25
140 – 3f. red . . . . 55 2·75
141 – 5f. green . . . . 60 2·25
142 – 10f. brown . . . . 70 4·00
143 – 20f. black . . . . 1·00 4·50
DESIGNS—HORIZ: 20c. to 70c. Village on piles. VERT: 80c. to 2f. Sailing pirogue on Lake Nokoue; 2f.50 to 20f. Dahomey warrior.

1941. National Defence Fund. Surch **SECOURS NATIONAL** and value.
143a **6** +1f. on 50c. blue & red . . 3·75 5·50
143b +2f. on 80c. blue & brn . . 4·50 6·25
143c +2f. on 1f.50 lt blue & bl 6·00 9·25
143d +3f. on 2f. brown & yell 6·00 8·25

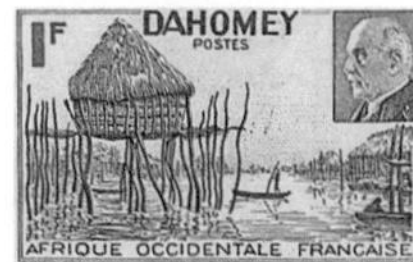
14b Village on Piles and Marshal Petain

1942. Marshal Petain Issue.
143e **14b** 1f. green . . . . 40 2·75
143f 2f.50 blue . . . . 25 3·00

14c Maternity Hospital, Dakar

1942. Air. Colonial Child Welfare Fund.
143g **14c** 1f.50+3f.50 green . . . . 20 2·50
143h – 2f.+6f. brown . . . . . 20 2·50
143i – 3f.+9f. red . . . . . . 90 2·50
DESIGNS: 2f. Dispensary, Mopti. (48½ × 27 mm): 3f. "Child welfare".

14d "Vocation"

1942. Air. "Imperial Fortnight".
143j **14d** 1f.20+1f.80 blue & red 1·10 2·50

14e Camel Caravan

1942. Air.
143k **14e** 50f. blue and green . . . 3·75 4·75

15 Ganvie Village

1960.
144 **15** 25f. brn, red & bl (postage) 75 25
145 – 100f. brown, ochre & bl (air) . . . . 3·25 2·25
146 – 500f. red, bistre & green 12·00 4·25
DESIGNS: 100f. Somba fort; 500f. Royal Court, Abomey.

1960. 10th Anniv of African Technical Co-operation Commission. As T **62** of Cameroun.
147 5f. blue and purple . . . . 1·60 2·00

16 Conseil de l'Entente Emblem

17 Prime Minister Maga

1960. 1st Anniv of Conseil de l'Entente.
148 **16** 25f. multicoloured . . . . 1·75 1·90

1960. Independence Proclamation.
149 **17** 85f. purple and sepia . . . 90 55

18 Weaver

1961. Artisans.
150 18 1f. purple and orange . . . 10 10
151 – 2f. chocolate and brown 10 10
152 – 3f. orange and green . . . 10 10
153 – 4f. lake and bistre 15 15
154 18 6f. red and lilac 15 15
155 – 10f. myrtle and blue . . . 25 20
156 – 15f. violet and purple . . . 35 25
157 – 20f. turquoise and blue . . 45 30
DESIGNS—VERT: 2f., 10f. Wood-carver. HORIZ: 3f., 15f. Fisherman casting net; 4f., 20f. Potter.

1961. 1st Anniv of Independence. No. 149 surch **100 F President de la Republique**.
158 17 100f. on 85f. pur & sepia 1·50 1·50

20 Doves and U.N. Emblem 22 Wrecked Car and Fort

1961. 1st Anniv of Admission into U.N.O.
159 20 5f. multicoloured (postage) 25 20
160 60f. multicoloured 75 60
161 200f. multicoloured (air) 2·50 1·90

1961. Abidjan Games. Optd **JEUX SPORTIFS D'ABIDJAN 24 AU 31 DECEMBRE 1961**.
162 15 25f. brown, red and blue 45 30

1962. Air. Foundation of "Air Afrique" Airline. As T **69** of Cameroun.
163 25f. blue, brown & black . . 45 35

1962. Malaria Eradication. As T **70** of Cameroun.
164 25f.+5f. brown 45 45

1962. 1st Anniv of Portuguese Evacuation from Fort Ouidah.
165 22 30f. multicoloured 45 25
166 60f. multicoloured 70 40

1962. 1st Anniv of Union of African and Malagasy States. As No. 328 of Cameroun.
167 72 30f. multicoloured 50 35

23 Map, Nurses and Patients

1962. Red Cross.
168 23 5f. red, blue and purple . . 15 15
169 20f. red, blue and green . . 30 25
170 25f. red, blue and sepia . . 40 30
171 30f. red, blue and brown 45 40

24 Peuhl Herd-boy 25 Boxing

1963. Dahomey Tribes.
172 A 2f. violet and blue 10 10
173 B 3f. black and blue 10 10
174 24 5f. green, brown & black 15 10
175 C 15f. brown, chest & turq 25 15
176 D 20f. black, red & green . . 40 20
177 E 25f. turquiose, brown & bl 40 15
178 D 30f. brown, mauve & red 45 30
179 E 40f. blue, brown, & green 55 25
180 C 50f. brown, black & green 65 30
181 24 60f. orange, red & purple 70 45
182 B 65f. brown and red 90 50
183 A 85f. brown and blue . . . 1·50 75

DESIGNS—VERT: A, Ganvie girl in pirogue; B, Bariba chief of Nikki; C, Ouidah witch-doctor and python; D, Nessoukoue witch-doctors of Abomey. HORIZ: E, Dahomey girl.

1963. Freedom from Hunger. As T **76** of Cameroun.
184 25f.+5f. red, brown & green 50 50

1963. Dakar Games.
185 25 50c. black and green . . . 10 10
186 – 1f. black, bistre & brown 10 10
187 – 2f. brown, blue & bronze 10 10
188 – 5f. black, red & brown . . 15 10
189 25 15f. purple and violet . . . 25 20
190 – 20f. black, green & red . . 40 30
DESIGNS—HORIZ: 1f., 20f. Football. VERT: 2f., 5f. Running.

27 U.A.M. Palace

1963. Air. Meeting of Heads of State of African and Malagasy Union.
191 27 250f. multicoloured . . . . 3·00 1·75

28 Presidential Palace, Cotonou

1963. 3rd Anniv of Independence.
192 28 25f. multicoloured 35 25

1963. Air. African and Malagasy Posts and Telecommunications Union. As T **18** of Central African Republic.
193 25f. red, buff, brown & blue 40 25

29 Boeing 707 Airliner

1963. Air.
194 29 100f. bistre, green & violet 1·75 60
195 – 200f. violet, brown & grn 3·00 1·60
196 – 300f. purple, grn and blue 4·25 2·25
197 – 500f. purple, brown & blue 7·75 3·25
DESIGNS: 200f. Aerial views of Boeing 707; 300f. Cotonou Airport; 500f. Boeing 707 in flight.

30 Toussaint L'Ouverture 31 Flame on U.N. Emblem

1963. 150th Death Anniv of Toussaint L'Ouverture (Haitian statesman).
198 30 25f. multicoloured 35 20
199 30f. multicoloured 40 25
200 100f. multicoloured . . . . 1·10 65

1963. 15th Anniv of Declaration of Human Rights. Multicoloured. Background colours given.
201 31 4f. blue 10 10
202 6f. brown 15 15
203 25f. green 35 25

32 Sacred Boat of Isis, Philae

1964. Air. Nubian Monuments Preservation.
204 32 25f. brown and violet . . . 80 50

33 Somba Dance (Taneka Coco)

1964. Native Dances.
205 33 2f. black, red and green . . 10 10
206 – 3f. red, green and blue . . 10 10
207 – 10f. black, red & violet . . 20 15
208 – 15f. sepia, lake & green . . 25 15
209 – 25f. blue, brown and orge 40 25
210 – 30f. red, orange & brown 45 30
DANCES—HORIZ: 3f. Nago (Pobe-Ketou). 15f. Nago (Ouidah). 30f. Nessou houessi (Abomey). VERT: 10f. Baton (Paysbariba). 25f. Sakpatassi (Abomey).

34 Running

1964. Olympic Games, Tokyo.
211 34 60f. green and brown . . . 65 50
212 – 85f. purple and blue . . . 1·25 75
DESIGN: 85f. Cycling.

1964. French, African and Malagasy Co-operation. As T **88** of Cameroun.
213 25f. brown, violet & orange 40 25

35 Mother and Child 36 Satellite and Sun

1964. 18th Anniv of U.N.I.C.E.F.
214 35 20f. black, green & red . . 35 25
215 – 25f. black, blue & red . . . 40 25
DESIGN: 25f. Mother and child (different).

1964. International Quiet Sun Year.
216 36 25f. green and yellow . . . 45 20
217 – 100f. yellow and purple . . 1·25 65
DESIGN: 100f. Another satellite and Sun.

37 "Weather"

1965. Air. World Meteorological Day.
218 37 50f. multicoloured 65 45

38 Rug Pattern

1965. Abomey Rug-weaving. Multicoloured.
219 20f. Bull, tree, etc. (vert) . . 30 25
220 25f. Witch-doctor, etc. (vert) 45 30
221 50f. Type **38** 70 35
222 85f. Ship, tree, etc . . . . . 1·25 70

39 Baudot's Telegraph and Ader's Telephone 40 Sir Winston Churchill

1965. Centenary of I.T.U.
223 39 100f. black, purple & orge 1·40 1·00

1965. Air. Churchill Commemoration.
224 40 100f. multicoloured . . . . 1·40 1·10

41 Heads of Three Races within I.C.Y. Emblem

1965. Air. International Co-operation Year.
225 41 25f. lake, green & violet . . 35 20
226 85f. lake, green & blue . . 80 55

42 Lincoln

1965. Air. Death Centenary of Abraham Lincoln.
227 42 100f. multicoloured . . . . 1·25 95

43 Cotonou Port

1965. Inaug of Cotonou Port. Multicoloured.
228 25f. Type **43** 65 25
229 100f. Cotonou Port . . . . . 1·60 85
The two stamps joined together form a complete design and were issued se-tenant in the sheets.

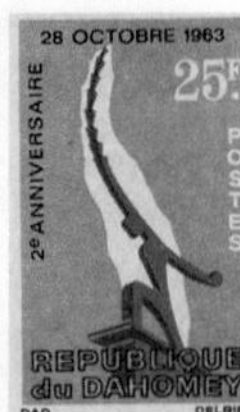

44 Spanish Mackerel 45 Independence Monument

1965. Fishes.
230 44 10f. black, turquoise & bl 40 25
231 – 25f. orange, grey & blue 55 40
232 – 30f. blue and turquoise . . 1·00 50
233 – 50f. grey, orange & blue 1·40 80
FISHES: 25f. Sama seabream. 30f. Sailfish. 50f. Tripletail.

1965. 2nd Anniv of 28th October Revolution.
234 45 25f. red, grey and black . . 35 20
235 30f. red, blue and black . . 40 25

1965. No. 177 surch **1f.**
236 1f. on 25f. turq, brn & bl . . 15 10

47 Arms and Pres. Kennedy

1965. Air. 2nd Death Anniv of Pres. Kennedy.
237 47 100f. brown and green . . 1·50 1·00

48 Dr. Schweitzer and Hospital Scene

1966. Air. Schweitzer Commemoration.
238 **48** 100f. multicoloured . . . . 1·50 90

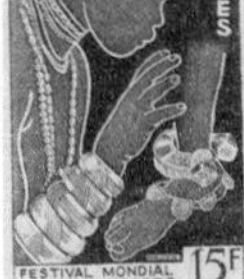

49 Porto-Novo Cathedral **50** Beads, Bangles and Anklets

1966. Dahomey Cathedrals.
239 **49** 30f. purple, blue & green 30 20
240 – 50f. brown, blue & purple 50 30
241 – 70f. purple, blue & green 80 50
DESIGNS—VERT: 50f. Ouidah Church (old Pro-Cathedral). HORIZ: 70f. Cotonou Cathedral.

1966. World Festival of Negro Arts, Dakar.
242 **50** 15f. purple and black . . . 25 15
243 – 30f. red, purple & blue . . 35 25
244 – 50f. blue and brown . . . 60 40
245 – 70f. lake and black . . . . 1·10 65
DESIGNS: 30f. Building construction; 50f. Craftsman; 70f. Religious carvings.

1966. 5th Anniv of France–Dahomey Treaty. Nos. 228/9 surch **ACCORD DE COOPERATION FRANCE - DAHOMEY 5e Anniversaire - 24 Avril 1996.**
246 **43** 15f. on 25f. mult 35 25
247 – 15f. on 100f. mult 35 25

52 W.H.O. Building and Emblem

1966. Inaug of W.H.O. Headquarters, Geneva.
248 **52** 30f. multicoloured (post) 40 30
249 – 100f. multicoloured (air) 1·40 1·00
DESIGN (48 × 27 mm): 100f. W.H.O. building (different view) and emblem.

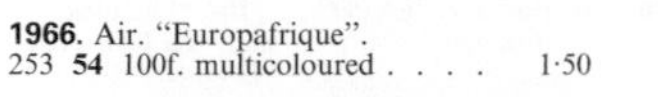

53 African Pygmy Goose **54** Industrial Emblems

1966. Air. Birds. Multicoloured.
250 50f. Type **53** . . . . 2·50 95
251 100f. Fiery-breasted bush shrike . . . . 3·50 1·40
252 500f. Iris glossy starling . . . 17·00 9·25
See also Nos. 271/2.

1966. Air. "Europafrique".
253 **54** 100f. multicoloured . . . . 1·50 85

55 Pope Paul and St. Peter's

1966. Air. Pope Paul's Visit to U.N.
254 **55** 50f. red, brown & green . . 55 35
255 – 70f. red, green and blue . . 85 45
256 – 100f. purple and blue . . . 1·25 85
DESIGNS—HORIZ: 70f. Pope Paul and New York. VERT: (36 × 48 mm); 100f. Pope Paul and U.N. General Assembly.

1966. Air. Inauguration of DC-8F Air Services. As T **54** of Central African Republic.
258 30f. grey, black and purple 50 30

56 Scout signalling with flags

1966. Scouting.
259 **56** 5f. red, ochre and brown 10 10
260 – 10f. mauve, green & black 15 10
261 – 30f. orange, red & violet 35 25
262 – 50f. brown, green & blue 70 40
DESIGNS—VERT: 10f. Tent-pole and banners; 30f. Scouts, camp-fire and map. HORIZ: 50f. Constructing bridge.

57 Scientific Emblem

1966. Air. 20th Anniv of U.N.E.S.C.O.
264 **57** 30f. plum, blue & purple 35 25
265 – 45f. lake and green 50 40
266 – 100f. blue, lake & black . . 1·25 80
DESIGNS—VERT: 45f. Cultural Emblem; HORIZ: 100f. Educational emblem.

58 "The Nativity" (15th-cent. Beaune Tapestry)

1966. Air. Christmas. Multicoloured.
268 50f. Type **58** . . . . 10·25 3·00
269 100f. "The Adoration of the Shepherds" (after Jose Ribera) . . . . 10·25 4·50
270 200f. "Madonna and Child" (after A. Baldovinetti) . . 19·00 6·75
See also Nos. 311/14, 348/51, 384/7 and 423/6.

59 African Broad-billed Roller **60** "Clappertonia ficifolia"

1967. Air. Birds. Multicoloured.
271 200f. Type **59** . . . . 9·50 3·75
272 250f. African Emerald cuckoo 12·50 5·25

1967. Flowers. Multicoloured.
273 1f. Type **60** 10 10
274 3f. "Hewittia sublobata" . . 15 10
275 5f. "Clitoria ternatea" . . . 20 15
276 10f. "Nymphaea micrantha" 35 15
277 5f. "Commelina forskalaei" 35 25
278 30f. "Eremomastax speciosa" 75 35

1967. Nos. 182/3 surch.
279 30f. on 65f. brown & red . . 40 30
280 30f. on 85f. brown & blue . . 40 30

62 Bird bearing Lions Emblem **63** "Ingres" (self-portrait)

1967. 50th Anniv of Lions International.
281 **62** 100f. blue, green & violet 1·50 80

1967. Air. Death Centenary of Ingres (painter). Multicoloured.
282 100f. Type **63** . . . . 2·10 1·25
283 100f. "Oedipus and the Sphinx" (after Ingres) . . . 2·10 1·25
See also Nos. 388/90, 429/30, 431/2 and 486/7.

64 "Suzanne" (barque)

1967. Air. French Sailing ships. Multicoloured.
284 30f. Type **64** 90 35
285 45f. "Esmeralda" (schooner) (vert) . . . . 1·25 55
286 80f. "Marie Alice" (schooner) (vert) . . . . 2·10 75
287 100f. "Antonin" (barque) . . 2·50 1·10

1967. Air. 50th Birth Anniv of Pres. Kennedy. Nos. 227 and 237 surch **29 MAI 1967 50e Anniversaire de la naissance de John F. Kennedy.**
288 **42** 125f. on 100f. mult . . . . 1·75 90
289 **47** 125f. on 100f. brn & grn 1·75 90

66 "Man in the City" Pavilion

1967. World Fair, Montreal.
290 **66** 30f. brn & grn (postage) 40 20
291 – 70f. red and green 90 50
292 – 100f. blue & brown (air) 1·10 65
DESIGNS—HORIZ: 70f. "New Africa" pavilions. VERT: (27 × 48 mm): 100f. "Man Examines the Universe".

67 Dr. Konrad Adenauer (from painting by O. Kokoschka) **68** "Economic Association"

1967. Air. Dr. Adenauer Commemoration.
294 **67** 70f. multicoloured . . . . 1·10 90

1967. Europafrique.
296 **68** 30f. multicoloured 35 25
297 – 45f. multicoloured 50 25

69 Scouts Climbing

1967. World Scout Jamboree, Idaho.
298 **69** 30f. ind, brn & bl (postage) 35 15
299 – 70f. purple, green & blue 90 55
300 – 100f. pur, grn & bl (air) . . 1·10 65
DESIGNS—HORIZ: 70f. Scouts with canoe. VERT: (27 × 48 mm): 100f. Jamboree emblem, rope and map.

1967. Air. Riccione Stamp Exhibition. No. 270 surch **RICCIONE 12-29 Aout 1967** and value.
302 150f. on 200f. mult . . . . . 2·10 1·50

71 Rhone at Grenoble

1967. Winter Olympic Games, Grenoble.
303 **71** 30f. blue, brown & green 40 25
304 – 45f. blue, green & brown 60 40
305 – 100f. purple, green & blue 1·40 90
DESIGNS—VERT: 45f. View of Grenoble. HORIZ: 100f. Rhone Bridge, Grenoble, and Pierre de Coubertin.

1967. Air. 5th Anniv of U.A.M.P.T. As T **123** of Cameroun.
307 100f. green, red & purple . . 1·10 90

72 Currency Tokens **73** Pres. de Gaulle

1967. 5th Anniv of West African Monetary Union.
308 **72** 30f. black, red & green . . 40 30

1967. Air. "Homage to General de Gaulle". President Soglo of Dahomey's visit to Paris.
309 **73** 100f. multicoloured . . . . 2·10 1·40

74 "The Adoration" (Master of St. Sebastian)

1967. Air. Christmas. Religious paintings. Mult.
311 30f. "Virgin and Child" (M. Grunewald) (vert) . . 40 35
312 50f. Type **74** 80 45
313 100f. "The Adoration of the Magi" (Ulrich Apt the Elder) (vert) . . . . 1·40 90
314 200f. "The Annunciation" (M. Grunewald) (vert) . . 3·00 1·40

75 Venus de Milo and "Mariner 5" **76** African Buffalo

1968. Air. "Exploration of the Planet Venus". Multicoloured.
315 70f. Type **75** . . . . 1·00 55
316 70f. Venus de Milo and "Venus 4" . . . . 1·00 55

1968. Fauna (1st series). Multicoloured.
318 15f. Type **76** 25 15
319 30f. Lion 45 25
320 45f. Kob 80 40
321 70f. Crocodile . . . . 1·25 45
322 100f. Hippopotamus . . . . 2·25 1·10
See also Nos. 353/7.

77 W.H.O. Emblem

1968. 20th Anniv of W.H.O.
323 **77** 30f. brown, blue & ultram 40 30
324 70f. multicoloured . . . . 3·75 1·25

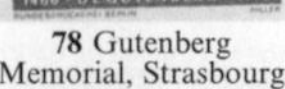

78 Gutenberg Memorial, Strasbourg — **79** Dr. Martin Luther King

1968. Air. 500th Death Anniv of Johann Gutenberg.
325 **78** 45f. green and orange . . . 60 35
326 – 100f. deep blue & blue . . 1·40 85
DESIGNS: 100f. Gutenberg statue, Mainz, and printing-press.

1968. Air. Martin Luther King Commemoration.
328 – 30f. black, brown & yellow 50 30
329 – 55f. multicoloured 80 45
330 **79** 100f. multicoloured . . . . 1·25 80
DESIGNS: 55f. Dr. King receiving Nobel Peace Prize. LARGER (25 × 46 mm): 30f. Inscription "We must meet hate with creative love" (also in French and German).

80 Schuman

1968. Air. 5th Anniv of Europafrique.
332 **80** 30f. multicoloured 40 25
333 – 45f. purple, olive & orge 55 35
334 – 70f. multicoloured 90 40
DESIGNS: 45f. De Gasperi; 70f. Dr. Adenauer.

81 "Battle of Montebello" (Philippoteaux)

1968. Air. Red Cross. Paintings. Multicoloured.
335 30f. Type **81** 50 35
336 45f. "2nd Zouaves at Magenta" (Riballier) . . . 65 45
337 70f. "Battle of Magenta" (Charpentier) . . . . . 1·25 80
338 100f. "Battle of Solferino" (Charpentier) . . . . . . 1·75 1·00

82 Mail Van

1968. Air. Rural Mail Service. Multicoloured.
339 30f. Type **82** 35 25
340 45f. Rural Post Office and mail van 45 30
341 55f. Collecting mail at river-side 60 35
342 70f. Loading mail on train 3·75 1·25

83 Aztec Stadium

1968. Air. Olympic Games, Mexico.
343 **83** 30f. green and purple . . . 40 25
344 – 45f. lake and blue 65 35
345 – 70f. brown and green . . . 1·00 55
346 – 150f. brown and red . . . 1·90 1·10
DESIGNS—VERT: 45f. "Pelota-player" (Aztec figure); 70f. "Uxpanapan wrestler" (Aztec figure). HORIZ: 150f. Olympic Stadium.

1968. Air. Christmas. Paintings by Foujita. As T **74**. Multicoloured.
348 30f. "The Nativity" (horiz) 55 40
349 70f. "The Visitation" . . . . 1·10 55
350 100f. "Virgin and Child" . . 1·40 95
351 200f. "Baptism of Christ" . . 2·75 1·90

1968. Air. "Philexafrique" Stamp Exhibition, Abidjan (Ivory Coast, 1969). As T **137** of Cameroun. Multicoloured.
352 100f. "Diderot" (L. M. Vanloo) . . . . 1·75 1·75

84 Warthog

1969. Fauna (2nd series). Multicoloured.
353 5f. Type **84** 15 10
354 30f. Leopard 50 25
355 60f. Spotted hyena . . . . . 1·00 45
356 75f. Olive baboon . . . . . 1·40 55
357 90f. Hartebeest . . . . . . 2·00 90

1969. Air. "Philexafrique" Stamp Exn, Abidjan, Ivory Coast (2nd issue). As T **138** of Cameroun.
358 50f. violet, sepia and blue . . 1·10 1·10
DESIGN: 50f. Cotonou harbour and stamp of 1941.

85 Heads and Globe

1969. 50th Anniv of I.L.O.
359 **85** 30f. multicoloured 40 25
360 70f. multicoloured 95 55

86 "The Virgin of the Scales" (C. da Sesto-Da Vinci School)

1969. Air. Leonardo da Vinci Commem. Mult.
361 100f. Type **86** . . . . 1·40 75
362 100f. "The Virgin of the Rocks" (Da Vinci) . . . . 1·40 75

87 "General Bonaparte" (J. L. David)

1969. Air. Birth Bicentenary of Napoleon Bonaparte. Multicoloured.
363 30f. Type **87** . . . . 1·10 1·00
364 60f. "Napoleon I in 1809" (Lefevre) . . . . 2·00 1·25
365 75f. "Napoleon at the Battle of Eylau" (Gros) (horiz) 2·50 1·75
366 200f. "General Bonaparte at Arcola" (Gros) . . . . 5·50 3·25

88 Arms of Dahomey

1969.
367 **88** 5f. multicoloured (postage) 15 15
368 30f. multicoloured 45 30
369 50f. multicoloured (air) . . 45 25

89 "Apollo 8" over Moon

1969. Air. Moon flight of "Apollo 8". Embossed on gold foil.
370 **89** 1,000f. gold . . . . 15·00

1969. Air. 1st Man on the Moon (1st issue). Nos. 315/6 surch **ALUNISSAGE APOLLO XI JUILLET 1969**, lunar module and value.
371 **75** 125f. on 70f. (No. 315) . . 1·75 1·40
372 – 125f. on 70f. (No. 316) . . 1·75 1·40

91 Bank Emblem and Cornucopia — **93** Dahomey Rotary Emblem

92 Kenaf Plant and Mill, Bohicon

1969. 5th Anniv of African Development Bank.
373 **91** 30f. multicoloured 50 40

1969. "Europafrique". Multicoloured.
374 30f. Type **92** (postage) . . . 40 25
375 45f. Cotton plant & mill, Parakou 50 30
376 100f. Coconut and palm-oil plant, Cotonou (air) . . . 1·10 70

1969. Air. Rotary International Organization.
378 **93** 50f. multicoloured 65 40

1969. Air. No. 250 surch.
379 **53** 10f. on 50f. multicoloured 50 20

95 Sakpata Dance — **96** F. D. Roosevelt

1969. Dahomey Dances. Multicoloured.
380 10f. Type **95** (postage) . . . 30 25
381 30f. Guelede dance 40 30
382 45f. Sato dance 50 35
383 70f. Teke dance (air) 80 45

1969. Air. Christmas. Paintings. As T **58**. Mult.
384 30f. "The Annunciation" (Van der Stockt) 40 30
385 45f. "The Nativity" (15th-cent. Swabian School) 60 40
386 110f. "Virgin and Child" (Masters of the Gold Brocade) . . . . 1·60 1·00
387 200f. "The Adoration of the Magi" (Antwerp School, c. 1530) . . . . . 2·50 1·90

1969. Air. Old Masters. As T **63**. Multicoloured.
388 100f. "The Painter's Studio" (G. Courbet) . . . . . . 1·40 90
389 100f. "Self-portrait with Gold Chain" (Rembrandt) . . . 1·40 90
390 150f. "Hendrickje Stoffels" (Rembrandt) . . . . . . 2·10 1·25

1970. Air. 25th Death Anniv of Franklin D. Roosevelt.
391 **96** 100f. black, green & bl . . 1·25 55

97 Rocket and Men on Moon — **98** "U.N. in War and Peace"

1970. Air. 1st Man on Moon (2nd issue).
392 **97** 30f. multicoloured 40 25
The 50, 70, 110f. values were only issued in miniature sheet form.

1970. 25th Anniv of U.N.
394 **98** 30f. indigo, blue & red . . 40 25
395 40f. green, blue & brown 50 30

99 Walt Whitman and African Village

1970. Air. 150th Birth Anniv of Walt Whitman (American poet).
396 **99** 100f. brown, blue & grn . . 1·25 50

1970. Air. Space Flight of "Apollo 13". No. 392 surch **40F APOLLO 13 SOLIDARITE SPATIALE INTERNATIONALE**.
397 **97** 40f. on 30f. multicoloured 75 75

101 Footballers and Globe

1970. Air. World Cup Football Championship, Mexico. Multicoloured.
398 40f. Type **101** 50 40
399 50f. Goalkeeper saving goal 60 45
400 200f. Player kicking ball . . 2·50 1·10

1970. 10th Anniv (1969) of Aerial Navigation Security Agency for Africa and Madagascar (A.S.E.C.N.A.). As T **150** of Cameroun.
401 40f. red and purple 60 25

103 Mt. Fuji and "EXPO" Emblem — **104** "La Justice" and "La Concorde" (French warships)

1970. World Fair "EXPO 70", Osaka, Japan. Multicoloured.
402 5f. Type **103** (postage) . . . 45 20
403 70f. Dahomey Pavilion (air) 70 45
404 120f. Mt. Fuji and temple . . 1·25 65

1970. 300th Anniv of Ardres Embassy to Louis XIV of France.
405 **104** 40f. brown, blue & green 1·00 35
406 – 50f. red, brown & green 60 35
407 – 70f. brown, slate & bistre 90 50
408 – 200f. brown, blue & red 2·50 1·10
DESIGNS: 50f. Matheo Lopes; 70f. King Alkemy of Ardres; 200f. Louis XIV of France.

1970. Air. Brazil's Victory in World Cup Football Championship. No. 400 surch **BRESIL–ITALIE 4 – 1** and value.
409 100f. on 200f. multicoloured 1·40 70

106 Mercury **107** Order of Independence

1970. Air. Europafrique.
410 **106** 40f. multicoloured 50 35
411 70f. multicoloured 80 45

1970. 10th Anniv of Independence.
412 **107** 30f. multicoloured 25 15
413 40f. multicoloured 40 20

108 Bariba Horseman **109** Beethoven

1970. Bariba Horsemen. Multicoloured.
414 1f. Type **108** 10 10
415 2f. Two horsemen 10 10
416 10f. Horseman facing left . . 25 20
417 40f. Type **108** 50 30
418 50f. As 2f. 70 35
419 70f. As 10f. 95 60

1970. Air. Birth Bicentenary of Beethoven.
420 **109** 90f. violet and blue . . . 90 40
421 110f. brown and green . . 1·00 55

110 Emblems of Learning **111** "The Annunciation"

1970. Air. Laying of Foundation Stone, Calavi University.
422 **110** 100f. multicoloured . . . 1·00 50

1970. Air. Christmas. Miniatures of the Rhenish School c. 1340. Multicoloured.
423 40f. Type **111** 40 25
424 70f. "The Nativity" 70 45
425 110f. "The Adoration of the Magi" . . . . 1·60 90
426 200f. "The Presentation in the Temple" . . . . 2·50 1·60

112 De Gaulle and Arc de Triomphe

1971. Air. 1st Death Anniv of Gen. Charles de Gaulle. Multicoloured.
427 40f. Type **112** 55 45
428 500f. De Gaulle and Notre Dame, Paris . . . . 5·00 2·50

1971. Air. 250th Death Anniv of Watteau. Paintings. As T **63**. Multicoloured.
429 100f. "The Dandy" . . . . . 1·75 1·10
430 100f. "Girl with Lute" . . . 1·75 1·10

1971. Air. 500th Birth Anniv of Durer. As T **63**. Multicoloured.
431 100f. Self-portrait, 1498 . . . 1·40 90
432 200f. Self-portrait, 1500 . . . 2·75 1·60

113 Hands supporting Heart **114** "The Twins" (wood-carving) and Lottery Ticket

1971. Racial Equality Year.
433 **113** 40f. red, brn & green . . 40 25
434 – 100f. red, blue & green . . 95 50
DESIGN—HORIZ: 100f. "Heart" on Globe.

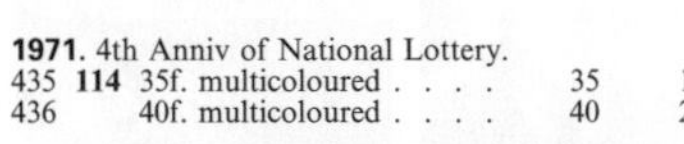

1971. 4th Anniv of National Lottery.
435 **114** 35f. multicoloured 35 15
436 40f. multicoloured 40 25

115 Kepler, Earth and Planets

1971. Air. 400th Birth Anniv of Johannes Kepler (astronomer).
437 **115** 40f. black, pur and blue 55 40
438 – 200f. green, red & blue . . 2·25 1·25
DESIGN: 200f. Kepler, globe, satellite and rocket.

116 Boeing 747 Airliner linking Europe and Africa

1971. Air. Europafrique.
439 **116** 50f. orge, blue & black . . 75 45
440 – 100f. multicoloured . . . 2·25 80
DESIGN: 100f. "General Mangin" (liner) and maps of Europe and Africa.

117 Cockerel and Drum (King Ganyehoussou)

1971. Emblems of Dahomey Kings. Multicoloured.
441 25f. Leg, saw and hatchet (Agoliagbo) 25 15
442 35f. Type **117** 40 25
443 40f. Fish and egg (Behanzin) (vert) 40 25
444 100f. Cow, tree and birds (Guezo) (vert) . . . . . 1·00 45
445 135f. Fish and hoe (Ouegbadja) . . . . 1·75 90
446 140f. Lion and sickle (Glele) 1·60 90

1971. Air. 10th Anniv of U.A.M.P.T. As T **184** of Cameroun. Multicoloured.
447 100f. U.A.M.P.T. H.Q., Brazzaville and Arms of Dahomey . . . . 1·00 50

119 "Adoration of the Shepherds" (Master of the Hausbuch)

1971. Air. Christmas. Paintings. Multicoloured.
448 40f. Type **119** 60 35
449 70f. "Adoration of the Magi" (Holbein) 95 45
450 100f. "Flight into Egypt" (Van Dyck) (horiz) . . . . 1·25 60
451 200f. "Birth of Christ" (Durer) (horiz) . . . . . . 2·50 1·40

120 "Prince Balthazar" (Velazquez)

1971. Air. 25th Anniv of U.N.I.C.E.F. Paintings of Children. Multicoloured.
452 40f. Type **120** 65 40
453 100f. "The Maids of Honour" (detail, Velazquez) . . . . 1·40 65

1972. No. 395 surch in figures.
454 **98** 35f. on 40f. green, bl & brn 40 25

122 Cross-country Skiing **123** Scout taking Oath

1972. Winter Olympic Games, Sapporo, Japan.
455 **122** 35f. purple, brown and green (postage) 50 30
456 – 150f. purple, blue and brown (air) . . . . . . 1·75 90
DESIGN: 150f. Ski-jumping.

1972. Air. International Scout Seminar, Cotonou. Multicoloured.
457 35f. Type **123** 25 20
458 40f. Scout playing "xylophone" 40 25
459 100f. Scouts working on the land (26 × 47 mm) . . . . 1·00 55

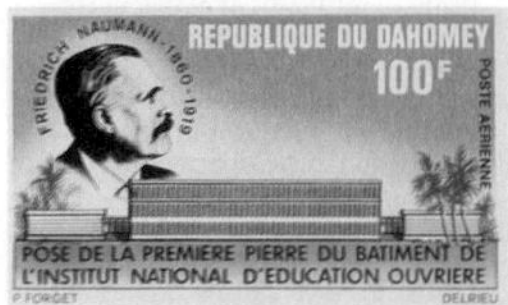
124 Friedrich Naumann and Institute Building

1972. Air. Laying of Foundation Stone for National Workers Education Institute. Multicoloured.
461 100f. Type **124** 90 50
462 250f. Pres. Heuss of West Germany and Institute . . 25 1·10

125 Stork with Serpent

1972. Air. U.N.E.S.C.O. "Save Venice" Campaign. Mosaics in St. Mark's Basilica. Multicoloured.
463 35f. Type **125** 55 35
464 40f. Cockerels carrying fox 65 45
465 65f. Noah releasing dove . . 1·10 80

126 Exhibition Emblem and Dancers

1972. Air. 12th International Philatelic Exhibition, Naples.
466 **126** 100f. multicoloured . . . 95 50

127 Running **129** Brahms, and Clara Schumann at Piano

128 Louis Bleriot and Bleriot XI

1972. Air. Olympic Games, Munich.
467 **127** 20f. brown, grn & blue . . 30 20
468 – 85f. brown, blue & green 85 45
469 – 150f. brown, blue & grn 1·75 80
DESIGNS: 85f. High-jumping; 150f. Putting the shot.

1972. Air. Birth Centenary of Louis Bleriot (pioneer airman).
471 **128** 100f. blue, violet & red 1·75 90

1972. 75th Death Anniv of Johannes Brahms (composer).
472 – 30f. black, brn & violet 40 25
473 **129** 65f. black, violet & lake 70 45
DESIGN—VERT: Brahms and opening bars of "Soir d'Ete".

130 "The Hare and the Tortoise"

1972. Fables of Jean de La Fontaine.
474 **130** 10f. grey, blue & lake . . 25 15
475 – 35f. blue, lake & purple 40 25
476 – 40f. indigo, blue & purple 55 35
DESIGNS—VERT: 35f. "The Fox and the Stork". HORIZ: 40f. "The Cat, the Weasel and the Little Rabbit".

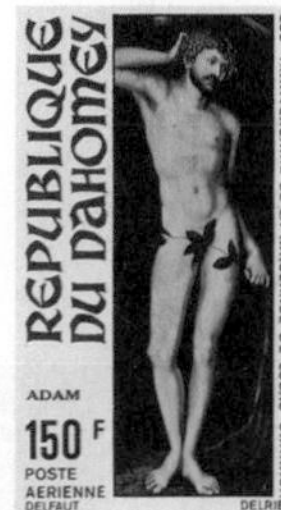
131 "Adam" (Cranach)

1972. Air. 500th Birth Anniv of Lucas Cranach (painter). Multicoloured.
477 150f. Type **131** . . . . 1·75 1·00
478 200f. "Eve" (Cranach) . . . 2·50 1·40

132 Africans and 500f. Coin

1972. 10th Anniv of West African Monetary Union.
479 **132** 40f. brown, grey & yell 65 20

133 "Pauline Borghese" (Canova)

1972. Air. 150th Death Anniv of Antonio Canova.
480 **133** 250f. multicoloured . . . 2·75 1·40

1972. Air. Olympic Medal Winners. Nos. 467/9 optd as listed below.
481 **127** 20f. brown, blue & grn . . 30 20
482 – 85f. brown, blue & green 85 40
483 – 150f. brown, blue & grn 1·75 85
OVERPRINTS: 20f. **5.000m. – 10.000m. VIREN 2 MEDAILLES D'OR**. 85f. **HAUTEUR DAMES MEYFARTH MEDAILLE D'OR**. 150f. **POIDS KOMAR MEDAILLE D'OR**.

135 Pasteur and Apparatus

1972. Air. 150th Birth Anniv of Louis Pasteur (scientist).
485 **135** 100f. pur, violet & grn . . 1·00 50

1972. Air. Paintings by G. de la Tour. As T **63**. Multicoloured.
486 35f. "Hurdy-gurdy Player" (vert) 40 30
487 150f. "The New-born Child" 1·75 1·10

136 "The Annunciation" (School of Agnolo Gaddi)

1972. Air. Christmas. Religious Paintings. Mult.
488 35f. Type **136** 35 20
489 125f. "The Nativity" (Simone dei Crociffissi) . . . . . . 1·00 50
490 140f. "The Adoration of the Shepherds" (P. di Giovanni) . . . . 1·50 80
491 250f. "Adoration of the Magi" (Giotto) . . . . . 2·25 1·25

137 Dr. Hansen, Microscope and Bacillus

139 Arms of Dahomey

138 Statue and Basilica, Lisieux

1973. Centenary of Identification of Leprosy Bacillus by Hansen.
492 **137** 35f. brown, purple & blue 30 25
493 – 85f. brown, orange & grn 65 50
DESIGN: 85f. Dr. Gerhard Armauer Hansen.

1973. Air. Birth Centenary of St. Theresa of Lisieux. Multicoloured.
494 40f. Type **138** 45 30
495 100f. St. Theresa of Lisieux (vert) . . . . 1·20 65

1973.
496 **139** 5f. multicoloured 10 10
497 35f. multicoloured 25 15
498 40f. multicoloured 30 15

140 Scouts in Pirogue

1973. Air. 24th World Scouting Congress, Nairobi, Kenya.
499 **140** 15f. purple, green & blue 35 15
500 – 20f. blue and brown . . . 25 20
501 – 40f. blue, green & brown 40 25
DESIGNS—VERT: 20f. Lord Baden-Powell. HORIZ: 40f. Bridge-building.

141 Interpol Badge and "Communications" **142** "Education in Nutrition"

1973. 50th Anniv of International Criminal Police Organization (Interpol).
503 – 35f. brown, green & red 30 20
504 **141** 50f. green, brown & red 45 30
DESIGN—HORIZ: 35f. Interpol emblem and web.

1973. 25th Anniv of World Health Organization. Multicoloured.
505 35f. Type **142** 30 20
506 100f. Pre-natal examination 80 45

1973. Pan-African Drought Relief. No. 321 surch **SECHERESSE SOLIDARITE AFRICAINE** and value.
507 100f. on 70f. multicoloured 1·00 55

144 Copernicus, "Venera" and "Mariner" Probes and Plane of Solar System

1973. Air. 500th Birth Anniv of Copernicus.
508 **144** 65f. black, purple & yell 85 45
509 – 125f. green, blue & purple 1·40 70
DESIGN—VERT: 125f. Copernicus.

1973. U.A.M.P.T. As T **216** of Cameroun.
510 100f. violet, red & black . . 80 40

1973. Air. African Fortnight, Brussels. As T **217** of Cameroun.
511 100f. black, green & blue . . 70 40

145 White Grouper

1973. Fishes.
512 **145** 5f. dp blue and blue . . . 25 20
513 – 15f. black and blue . . . 40 20
514 – 35f. lt brn, brn & grn . . 90 40
DESIGNS: 15f. African spadefish; 35f. Blue-pointed porgy.

148 W.M.O. Emblem and World Weather Map

1973. Air. Centenary of I.M.O./W.M.O.
515 **148** 100f. brown and green . . 95 10

149 "Europafrique"

1973. Air. Europafrique.
516 **149** 35f. blue, green & yell . . 35 20
517 – 40f. brown, ultram & bl 40 25
DESIGN: 40f. Europafrique, plant and cogwheels.

150 President John F. Kennedy **152** Chameleon

151 Footballers

1973. Air. 10th Death Anniv of President Kennedy.
518 **150** 200f. grn, violet & grn . . 1·90 1·40

1973. Air. World Football Championship Cup.
520 **151** 35f. green, brn & bistre 35 20
521 – 40f. brown, blue & orange 40 25
522 – 100f. green, brown & blue 65 45
DESIGNS: 40f., 100f. Football scenes similar to Type **151**.

1973. 1st Anniv of 26th October Revolution. Multicoloured.
523 35f. Type **152** 35 20
524 40f. Arms of Dahomey (vert) 35 25

153 "The Annunciation" (Dirk Bouts) **155** "The Elephant, the Chicken and the Dog"

1973. Air. Christmas. Multicoloured.
525 35f. Type **153** 40 30
526 100f. "The Nativity" (Giotto) 70 50
527 150f. "The Adoration of the Magi" (Botticelli) . . . . 1·40 80
528 200f. "The Adoration of the Shepherds" (Bassano) (horiz) . . . . 1·75 1·25

1974. Air. "Skylab". No. 515 surch **OPERATION SKYLAB 1973-1974** and value.
529 **148** 200f. on 100f. brn & grn 1·50 95

1974. Dahomey Folk Tales. Multicoloured.
530 5f. Type **155** 15 10
531 10f. "The Sparrowhawk and the Dog" 20 10
532 25f. "The Windy Tree" (horiz) 30 20
533 40f. "The Eagle, the Snake and the Chicken" (horiz) 40 20

156 Snow Crystal and Skiers

1974. Air. 50th Anniv of Winter Olympic Games.
534 **156** 100f. blue, brn and vio . . 95 65

157 Alsatian

1974. Breeds of Dogs. Multicoloured.
535 40f. Type **157** 35 25
536 50f. Boxer 40 25
537 100f. Saluki 80 50

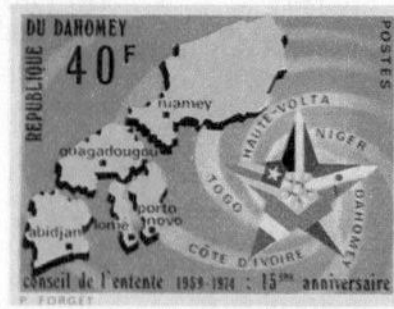

158 Map of Member Countries

1974. 15th Anniv of Council of Accord.
538 **158** 40f. multicoloured 35 15

159 Lenin (50th Death Anniv)

1974. Air. Celebrities' Anniversaries.
539 **159** 50f. purple and red . . . 50 30
540 – 125f. brn & green . . . 1·10 65
541 – 150f. blue & purple . . . 1·60 1·10
DESIGNS AND ANNIVERSARIES: 125f. Marie Curie (40th death anniv); 150f. Sir Winston Churchill (birth cent).

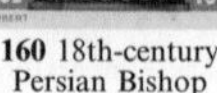

160 18th-century Persian Bishop **161** Beethoven and opening bars of the "Moonlight" Sonata

1974. Air. 21st Chess Olympiad, Nice. Mult.
542 50f. Type **160** 55 35
543 200f. 19th-century Siamese queen . . . . 1·75 1·10

1974. Air. Famous Composers.
544 **161** 150f. red and black . . . 1·25 80
545 – 150f. red and black . . . 1·25 80
DESIGN: No. 545, Chopin.

162 Earth seen through Astronaut's Legs

1974. Air. 5th Anniv of 1st Manned Moon Landing.
546 **162** 150f. brn, blue & red . . 1·40 85

Sets commemorating the World Cup, U.P.U. Centenary, Treaty of Berne, Space Exploration and West Germany's World Cup Victory appeared in 1974. Their status is uncertain.

1974. Air. 11th Pan-Arab Scout Jamboree, Batroun, Lebanon. Nos. 499/500 surch **XIe JAMBOREE PANARABE DE BATROUN – LIBAN** and value.
547 **140** 100f. on 15f. purple, green and blue 65 45
548 – 140f. on 20f. bl & brn . . 1·25 65

1974. Air. West Germany's Victory in World Cup Football Championships. Nos. 521/2 surch **R F A 2 HOLLANDE 1** and value.
549 100f. on 40f. brn, bl & orge 65 45
550 150f. on 100f. grn, brn & bl 1·00 80

165 U.P.U. Emblem and Globe

1974. Air. Centenary of U.P.U.
551 **165** 35f. violet and red 35 30
552 – 65f. blue and red . . . . 1·25 60
553 – 125f. green, blue & lt bl 2·75 1·00
554 – 200f. blue, yellow & brn 1·75 1·25
DESIGNS: 65f. Concorde in flight over African village; 125f. French mobile post office, circa 1860; 200f. Drummer and mail van.

166 "Lion of Belfort"

1974. Air. 70th Death Anniv of F. Bartholdi (sculptor).
555 **166** 100f. brown . . . . . . 1·25 65

1974. Air. 30th Death Anniv of Philippe de Champaigne (painter). As T **153**. Mult.
556 250f. "Young Girl with Falcon" . . . . 2·25 1·40

167 Locomotive No. 3.1102, 1911, France

1974. Steam Locomotives.
557 **167** 35f. multicoloured 80 35
558 – 40f. grey, black & red . . 1·00 45
559 – 100f. multicoloured . . . 2·50 85
560 – 200f. multicoloured . . . 4·25 1·90
DESIGNS: 40f. Goods locomotive, 1877; 100f. Crampton Type 210 locomotive, 1849; 200f. Stephenson locomotive "Aigle", 1846, France.

168 Rhamphorhynchus

1974. Air. Prehistoric Animals. Multicoloured.
561 35f. Type **168** 35 20
562 150f. Stegosaurus . . . . . 1·00 70
563 200f. Tyrannosaurus . . . . 1·50 95

169 Globe, Notes and Savings Bank

1974. World Savings Day.
564 **169** 35f. brown, myrtle & grn 35 25

170 Europafrique Emblem on Globe

1974. Air. Europafrique.
565 **170** 250f. multicoloured . . . 1·90 1·40

1974. Air. Christmas. Paintings by Old Masters. As T **153**. Multicoloured.
566 35f. "The Annunciation" (Schongauer) 30 20
567 40f. "The Nativity" (Schongauer) 35 25
568 100f. "The Virgin of the Rose Bush" (Schongauer) . . . 80 45
569 250f. "The Virgin, Infant Jesus and St. John the Baptist" (Botticelli) . . . . 2·25 1·40

171 "Apollo" and "Soyuz" Spacecraft

1975. Air. "Apollo–Soyuz" Space Link. Mult.
570 35f. Type **171** 35 25
571 200f. Rocket launch and flags of Russia and U.S.A. . . . 1·60 90
572 500f. "Apollo" and "Soyuz" docked together . . . . . 3·50 2·25

172 Dompago Dance, Hissi 173 Flags on Map of Africa

1975. Dahomey Dances and Folklore. Mult.
573 10f. Type **172** 20 15
574 25f. Fetish dance, Vaudou-Tchinan 30 15
575 40f. Bamboo dance, Agbehoun 40 30
576 100f. Somba dance, Sandoua (horiz) 75 50

1975. "Close Co-operation with Nigeria". Multicoloured.
577 65f. Type **173** 40 30
578 100f. Arrows linking maps of Dahomey and Nigeria (horiz) 65 40

174 Community Emblem and Pylons

1975. Benin Electricity Community. Mult.
579 40f. Type **174** 35 25
580 150f. Emblem and pylon (vert) . . . . 1·10 65
C.E.B. = "Communaute Electrique du Benin".

175 Head of Ceres

1975. Air. "Arphila 75" International Stamp Exhibition, Paris.
581 **175** 100f. purple, ind & blue 90 55

176 Rays of Light and Map 178 Dr. Schweitzer

1975. "New Dahomey Society".
582 **176** 35f. multicoloured 30 20

1975. Air. "Apollo–Soyuz" Space Test Project. Nos. 570/1 surch **RENCONTRE APOLLO-SOYOUZ 17 Juil. 1975** and value.
583 **171** 100f. on 35f. mult 65 45
584 – 300f. on 200f. mult . . . 2·00 1·10

1975. Birth Centenary of Dr. Albert Schweitzer.
585 **178** 200f. olive, brown & green . . . . 1·75 90

179 "The Holy Family" (Michelangelo) 180 Woman and I.W.Y. Emblem

1975. Air. Europafrique.
586 **179** 300f. multicoloured . . . 1·90 1·25

1975. International Women's Year.
587 **180** 50f. blue and violet . . . 35 25
588 – 150f. orange, brn & grn 1·10 65
DESIGN: 150f. I.W.Y. emblem within ring of bangles.

181 Continental Infantry 183 "Allamanda cathartica"

182 Diving

1975. Air. Bicent of American Revolution.
589 **181** 75f. lilac, red & green . . 55 35
590 – 135f. brown, pur & bl . . 95 70
591 – 300f. brown, red & blue 2·00 1·40
592 – 500f. brown, red & grn 3·50 1·75
DESIGNS: 135f. "Spirit of 76"; 300f. Artillery battery; 500f. Cavalry.

1975. Air. Olympic Games, Montreal.
593 **182** 40f. brown, bl and vio . . 35 25
594 – 250f. brown, grn & red 1·60 1·10
DESIGN: 250f. Football.

1975. Flowers. Multicoloured.
595 10f. Type **183** 15 10
596 35f. "Ixora coccinea" 30 15
597 45f. "Hibiscus rosa-sinensis" 45 30
598 60f. "Phaemeria magnifica" 55 40

184 "The Nativity" (Van Leyden)

1975. Air. Christmas. Multicoloured.
599 40f. Type **184** 35 25
600 85f. "Adoration of the Magi" (Rubens) (vert) 55 45
601 140f. "Adoration of the Shepherds" (Le Brun) . . . 1·00 65
602 300f. "The Virgin of the Blue Diadem" (Raphael) (vert) 2·00 1·50

For later issues see **BENIN**.

PARCEL POST STAMPS

1967. Surch **COLIS POSTAUX** and value.
P271 **18** 5f. on 1f. (postage) . . . 10 10
P272 – 10f. on 2f. (No. 151) . . 25 25
P273 **18** 20f. on 6f. 30 30
P274 – 25f. on 3f. (No. 152) . . 40 40
P275 – 30f. on 4f. (No. 153) . . 45 45
P276 – 50f. on 10f. (No. 155) . . 70 70
P277 – 100f. on 20f. (No. 157) 1·50 1·50
P278 – 200f. on 200f. (No. 195) (air) . . . . 3·00 2·25
P279 **29** 300f. on 100f. . . . . . 3·50 3·00
P280 – 500f. on 300f. (No. 196) 6·50 4·50
P281 – 1000f. on 500f. (No. 197) 14·00 11·00
P282 – 5000f. on 100f. (No. 145) 55·00 55·00

POSTAGE DUE STAMPS

1906. "Natives" key-type inscr "DAHOMEY" in blue (10, 30c.) or red (others).
D33 L 5c. green . . . . 1·75 1·50
D34 10c. red . . . . 3·00 2·75
D35 15c. blue on blue . . . . . 4·00 3·00
D36 20c. black on yellow . . . 3·00 7·00
D37 30c. red on cream . . . . 3·25 8·00
D38 50c. violet . . . . 8·50 25·00
D39 60c. black on buff . . . . 6·50 21·00
D40 1f. black on pink . . . . . 30·00 55·00

1914. "Figure" key-type inscr "DAHOMEY".
D59 M 5c. green . . . . 10 2·25
D60 10c. red . . . . 15 2·00
D61 15c. grey . . . . 40 2·00
D62 20c. brown . . . . 40 2·75
D63 30c. blue . . . . 1·00 3·00
D64 50c. black . . . . 75 3·75
D65 60c. orange . . . . 1·25 2·25
D66 1f. violet . . . . 1·75 3·25

1927. Surch in figures.
D96 M 2f. on 1f. mauve . . . . . 1·75 1·75
D97 3f. on 1f. brown . . . . . 2·50 4·50

D 14 Native Head D 26 Panther attacking African

1941.
D143 D **14** 5c. black . . . . . . 1·10 2·75
D144 10c. red . . . . 20 2·75
D145 15c. blue . . . . . . 10 2·00
D146 20c. green . . . . . . 35 2·75
D147 30c. orange . . . . . 1·25 3·00
D148 50c. brown . . . . . 1·90 3·25
D149 60c. green . . . . . 1·90 3·50
D150 1f. red . . . . 2·25 3·50
D151 2f. yellow . . . . . . 2·75 3·25
D152 3f. purple . . . . . . 2·75 4·25

1963.
D191 D **26** 1f. red and green . . . 10 10
D192 2f. green & brown . . 10 10
D193 5f. blue and orange . . 10 10
D194 10f. black and purple 25 25
D195 20f. orange & blue . . 30 30

D 72 Pirogue

1967.
D308 D **72** 1f. plum, blue & brn 10 10
D309 A 1f. brown, bl & plum 10 10
D310 B 3f. green, orge & brn 10 10
D311 C 3f. brown, orge & grn 10 10
D312 D 5f. purple, blue & brn 15 15
D313 E 5f. brown, blue & pur 35 20
D314 F 10f. green, vio & brn 30 30
D315 G 10f. brown, grn & vio 30 30
D316 H 30f. violet, red & bl 50 50
D317 I 30f. blue, red & vio . . 50 50
DESIGNS: A, Heliograph; B, Old morse receiver; C, Postman on cycle; D, Old telephone; E, Renault ABH diesel railcar; F, Citroen "2-CV" mail van; G, Radio station; H, Douglas DC-8-10/50CF airliner; I, "Early Bird" satellite.

DANISH WEST INDIES Pt. 11

A group of islands in the West Indies formerly belonging to Denmark and purchased in 1917 by the United States, whose stamps they now use. Now known as the United States Virgin Islands.

1855. 100 cents = 1 dollar.
1905. 100 bit = 1 franc.

1

2

5

1855. Imperf.
4 **1** 3c. red . . . . 29·00 48·00

1872. Perf.
6 **1** 3c. red . . . . 60·00 £150
7 4c. blue £150 £300

1873.
31 **2** 1c. red and green . . . . . 8·75 13·00
32 3c. red and blue . . . . . . 7·25 9·50
33 4c. blue and brown . . . . . 8·00 7·50
19 5c. brown and green . . . . 19·00 12·00
21 7c. yellow and purple . . . . 21·00 70·00
25 10c. brown and blue . . . . 19·00 22·00
27 12c. green and purple . . . . 29·00 £100
28 14c. green and lilac £450 £800
29 50c. lilac £100 £180

1887. Handstamped **1 CENT**.
37 **2** 1c. on 7c. yellow & purple . . 45·00 £140

1895. Surch **10 CENTS 1895**.
38 **2** 10c. on 50c. lilac . . . . . . 26·00 48·00

1900.
39 **5** 1c. green . . . . 2·40 2·40
40 2c. red . . . . 6·25 18·00
41 5c. blue . . . . 12·50 18·00
42 8c. brown . . . . 22·00 40·00

1902. Surch **2** (or **8**) **CENTS 1902**.
43 **2** 2c. on 3c. red and blue . . . 6·50 17·00
47 8c. on 10c. brown & blue . . . 8·00 8·25

1905. Surch **5 BIT 1905**.
48 **2** 5b. on 4c. blue & brown . . 12·00 38·00
49 **5** 5b. on 5c. blue . . . . . . 10·00 29·00
50 5b. on 8c. brown . . . . . . 10·00 30·00

10 King Christian IX

11 Charlotte Amalie Harbour and Training ship "Ingolf"

1905.
51 **10** 5b. green . . . . 3·75 3·00
52 10b. red . . . . 3·75 3·00
53 20b. blue and green . . . . 7·50 6·50
54 25b. blue . . . . 7·50 7·50
55 40b. grey and red . . . . . 7·50 6·00
56 50b. grey and yellow . . . . 7·50 8·25
57 **11** 1f. blue and green . . . . 16·00 26·00
58 2f. brown and red . . . . . 26·00 38·00
59 5f. brown and yellow . . . 55·00 £180

14 King Frederik VIII

15 King Christian X

1907.
60 **14** 5b. green . . . . 2·25 1·10
61 10b. red . . . . 2·25 1·00
62 15b. brown and violet . . . 3·75 3·75
63 20b. blue and green . . . . 22·00 18·00
64 25b. blue . . . . 2·25 1·90
65 30b. black and red . . . . 40·00 38·00
66 40b. grey and red . . . . . 5·50 4·50
67 50b. brown and yellow . . . 5·25 7·00

1915.
68 **15** 5b. green . . . . 4·25 4·00
69 10b. red . . . . 4·25 42·00
70 15b. brown and lilac . . . . 4·25 42·00
71 20b. blue and green . . . . 4·25 42·00
72 25b. blue . . . . 4·25 10·00
73 30b. black and red . . . . 4·25 55·00
74 40b. grey and red . . . . . 4·25 55·00
75 50b. brown and yellow . . . 4·25 55·00

POSTAGE DUE STAMPS

D 6

D 12

1902.
D43 **D 6** 1c. blue . . . . 4·75 13·50
D44 4c. blue . . . . 9·00 19·00
D45 6c. blue . . . . 17·00 40·00
D46 10c. blue . . . . 16·00 45·00

1905.
D60 **D 12** 5b. grey and red . . . 4·00 5·00
D61 20b. grey and red . . . 5·75 12·00
D62 30b. grey and red . . . 5·25 12·00
D63 50b. grey and red . . . 5·00 26·00

DANZIG Pt. 7

A Baltic seaport, from 1920–1939 (with the surrounding district) a free state under the protection of the League of Nations. Later incorporated in Germany. Now part of Poland.

1920. 100 pfennige = 1 mark.
1923. 100 pfennige = 1 Danzig gulden.

Stamps of Germany inscr "DEUTSCHES REICH" optd or surch.

1920. Optd **Danzig** horiz.
1 **10** 5pf. green 25 35
2 10pf. red 25 35
3 **24** 15pf. brown 25 35
4 **10** 20pf. blue 25 35
5 30pf. black & orge on buff 35 35
6 40pf. red 25 35
7 50pf. black & pur on buff 40 55
8 **12** 1m. red 60 65
9 1m.25 green 35 80
10 1m.50 brown . . . . 80 1·10
11 **13** 2m. blue . . . . 1·60 3·25
12 2m.50 red . . . . 1·60 3·25
13 **14** 3m. black . . . . 4·25 9·00
14 **10** 4m. red and black . . . . 5·00 5·75
15a **15** 5m. red and black . . . . 1·90 2·50

1920. Surch **Danzig** horiz and large figures of value.
16 **10** 5 on 30pf. black and orange on buff 20 20
17 10 on 20pf. blue 20 20
18 25 on 30pf. black and orange on buff 20 20
19 60 on 30pf. black and orange on buff 65 60
20 80 on 30pf. black and orange on buff 65 65

1920. Optd **Danzig** diagonally and bar.
21 **24** 2pf. grey £100 £140
22 2½pf. grey £130 £260
23 **10** 3pf. brown . . . . 10·50 21·00
24 5pf. green 35 30
25 **24** 7½pf. orange . . . . 48·00 65·00
26 **10** 10pf. red . . . . 3·75 8·75
27 **24** 15pf. violet 50 50
28 **10** 20pf. blue 50 65
29 25pf. blk & red on yell . . 70 50
30 30pf. blk & orge on buff . 45·00 85·00
31 40pf. black and red . . . . 1·50 2·10
32 50pf. blk & pur on buff . . £130 £260
32a 60pf. mauve £900 £2250
33 75pf. black and green . . . 65 60
34 80pf. blk & red on pink . . 2·00 4·00
34a **12** 1m. red £900 £2100

1920. Optd **DANZIG** three times in semicircle.
34b **13** 2m. blue £900 £2200

1920. No. 5 of Danzig surch **MARK 1 MARK** and Types of Germany with burelage added surch with new value and **DANZIG** (36/37), **Danzig** (38, 40f) or **DANZIG** and flag (40e).
35 A **10** 1m. on 30pf. black and orange on buff . . . . 55 1·25
36 A 1¼m. on 3pf. brown . . . 55 1·25
37 A **24** 2m. on 35pf. brown . . . 55 1·25
38 A 3m. on 7½pf. orange . . 55 1·25
39 A 5m. on 2pf. grey . . . . 55 1·25
40AF 10m. on 7½pf. orange . . 1·00 1·90

1920. Air. No. 6 of Danzig surch with airplane or wings and value.
41 **10** 40 on 40pf. red . . . . . . 1·25 2·50
42 60 on 40pf. red . . . . . . 1·25 2·50
43 1m. on 40pf. red . . . . . 1·25 2·50

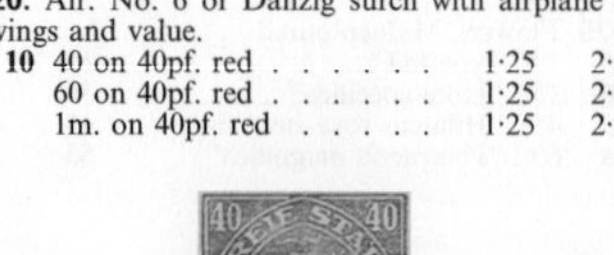

13 Hanse Kogge

1921. Constitution of 1920.
44 **13** 5pf. purple and brown . . . 25 30
45 10pf. violet and orange . . 30 25
46 25pf. red and green 55 60
47 40pf. red . . . . 1·10 90
48 80pf. blue 55 65
49 – 1m. grey and red . . . . . 1·60 1·90
50 – 2m. green and blue . . . . 3·25 4·25
51 – 3m. green and black . . . . 1·40 2·25
52 – 5m. red and grey . . . . . 1·50 2·00
53 – 10m. brown and green . . . 1·90 4·50
The mark values are as Type 13, but larger.

15

16 Sabaltnig PIII over Danzig

1921. Air.
57 **15** 40pf. green 35 50
58 60pf. purple 35 50
59 1m. red 35 50
60 2m. brown 35 50
116 **16** 5m. violet 35 70
117 10m. green 35 70
118 20m. brown 35 60
119 **15** 25m. blue 50 60
120 **16** 50m. orange 50 60
121 100m. red 50 60
122 250m. brown 50 60
123 500m. red 45 35
Nos. 120 to 123 are similar to Type 16, but larger.

1921. No. 33 of Danzig surch **60** and bars.
63 **10** 60 on 75pf. black & green 45 1·00

18

19

1921.
64 **18** 5pf. orange 25 25
65 10pf. brown 20 20
66 15pf. green 20 20
67 20pf. grey 20 20
68 25pf. green 20 20
69 30pf. red and blue 25 25
70 40pf. red and green 20 25
71 50pf. red and green 20 25
72 60pf. red 45 35
73 75pf. purple 15 25
74 80pf. red and black 20 40
75 80pf. green 15 25
76 1m. red and orange 20 40
77 1.20m. blue . . . . 1·25 1·25
78 1.25m. red and purple . . . 10 25
79 1.50m. grey 20 25
80 2m. red and grey . . . . 2·50 3·00
81 2m. red 10 25
82 2.40m. red and brown . . . 80 1·25
83 3m. red and purple . . . . 6·50 5·75
84 3m. red 15 25
106 4m. blue 10 40
86 5m. green 10 25
87 6m. red 10 25
88 8m. blue 30 85
89 10m. orange 10 25
90 20m. brown 10 30
110 40m. blue 10 40
111 80m. red 10 40

1921. Rouletted.
91 **19** 5m. green, black and red 1·25 2·10
91b 9m. orange and red . . . 2·50 6·25
92 10m. blue, black and red 1·25 2·10
93 20m. black and red . . . . 1·25 2·10

20

21

1921. Tuberculosis Week.
93a **20** 30pf.(+30pf.) grn & orge 45 40
93b 60pf.(+60pf.) red & yell . . 1·10 1·00
93c 1.20m.(+1.20m.) bl & orge (25×29½ mm) . . . . . 1·60 1·75

1922.
94b **21** 50m. red and gold . . . . 1·50 3·00
95a 100m. red and green . . . 2·75 5·25

1922. Surch in figures.
96 **18** 6 on 3m. red 25 35
97 8 on 4m. blue 25 65
98 20 on 8m. blue 25 65

25
26

1923.
99 **25** 50m. red and blue 10 35
136 50m. blue 10 35
100 100m. red and green . . . 35 35
137 100m. green 10 35
101 150m. red and purple . . . 10 35
138 200m. orange 10 50
102 **26** 250m. red and purple . . . 25 35
103 500m. red and grey 25 35
104 1000m. pink and brown . . 25 35
105 5000m. pink and silver . . 90 4·50
139 10000m. red and orange . . 40 60
140 20000m. red and blue . . . 40 90
141 50000m. red and green . . 40 90

28

1923. Poor People's Fund.
123b **28** 50+20m. red 20 60
123c 100+30m. purple 20 60

29

35 Etrich/Rumpler Taube

1923.
124 **29** 250m. red and purple . . . 15 35
125 300m. red and green . . . 10 35
126 500m. red and grey 15 35
127 1000m. brown 15 35
128 1000m. red and brown . . 15 35
129 3000m. red and violet . . . 15 35
130 5000m. pink 10 35
131 20000m. blue 10 35
132 50000m. green 10 35
133 100000m. blue 10 35
134 250000m. purple 10 35
135 500000m. grey 10 35

1923. Surch with figure of value and **Tausend** (T) or **Million** or **Millionen** (M).
142 **25** 40T. on 200m. orange . . 80 2·00
143 100T. on 200m. orange . . 80 1·90
144 250T. on 200m. orange . . 7·00 11·00
145 400T. on 100m. green . . . 40 25
146 **29** 500T. on 50000m. green . . 40 40
147 1M. on 10000m. orange . . 3·25 5·50
148 1M. on 10000m. red . . . 25 35
149 2M. on 10000m. red . . . 25 35
150 3M. on 10000m. red . . . 25 35
151 5M. on 10000m. red . . . 25 35
152 10M. on 10000m. lavender 35 1·00
158 **26** 10M. on 1000000m. orge 30 65
153 **29** 20M. on 10000m. lavender 25 65
154 25M. on 10000m. lavender 25 65
155 40M. on 10000m. lavender 25 65
156 50M. on 10000m. lavender 25 65
159 100M. on 10000m. lav . . 25 65
160 300M. on 10000m. lav . . 25 65
161 500M. on 10000m. lav . . 25 65

1923. Surch **100000** and bar.
157 **26** 100000 on 20000m. red and blue . . . . 60 6·00

1923. Air.
162a **35** 250,000m. red . . . . . 35 1·00
163a 500,000m. red . . . . . 35 1·00

1923. Surch in **Millionen**.
164a **35** 2m. on 100,000m. red . . 35 1·00
165a 5m. on 50,000m. red . . 35 1·00

1923. Surch with new currency, **Pfennige** or **Gulden**.
166 **25** 5pf. on 50m. red 30 35
167 10pf. on 50m. red 30 35
168 20pf. on 100m. red 30 35
169 25pf. on 50m. red . . . . 3·25 8·00
170 30pf. on 50m. red . . . . 3·00 1·60
171 40pf. on 100m. red . . . . 2·00 1·90
172 50pf. on 100m. red . . . . 2·00 3·25
173 75pf. on 100m. red . . . . 6·00 16·00
174 **26** 1g. on 1000000m. red . . . 4·00 6·50
175 2g. on 1000000m. red . . 8·50 29·00
176 3g. on 1000000m. red . . . 21·00 50·00
177 5g. on 1000000m. red . . . 40·00 65·00

39

40 Etrich/Rumpler Taube

1924.
177b **39** 3pf. brown . . . . 1·25 1·25
268 5pf. orange . . . . 75 1·50
178e 7pf. green . . . . 1·10 2·40
178f 8pf. green . . . . 1·60 4·00
270 10pf. green . . . . 70 1·40
180 15pf. grey . . . . 3·25 2·75
180b 15pf. red . . . . 1·25 90
181 20pf. red and carmine . . 10·00 50
182 20pf. grey . . . . 1·40 1·50
183 25pf. red and grey . . . . 14·50 2·40
272 25pf. red . . . . 3·25 6·00
185 30pf. red and green . . . 8·50 50
186 30pf. purple . . . . 1·50 3·50
186a 35pf. blue . . . . 1·60 1·10
187 40pf. blue and indigo . . 6·50 70

188 40pf. red and brown . . . 8·50 8·00
189 40pf. blue . . . . 1·50 3·00
274 50pf. red and blue . . . 2·10 8·00
190b 55pf. red and purple . . . 5·00 11·50
191 60pf. red and green . . . 5·50 14·00
192 70pf. red and green . . . 3·25 4·50
193 75pf. red and purple . . . 8·00 6·00
194 80pf. red and brown . . . 2·10 5·50

1924. Air.
195 **40** 10pf. red . . . . 17·00 3·75
196 20pf. mauve . . . . 1·60 1·25
197 40pf. brown . . . . 3·25 1·60
198 1g. green . . . . 3·25 1·90
199 – 2½g. purple (22 × 40 mm) 26·00 32·00

42 Oliva **44** Fountain of Neptune

1924.
200 **42** 1g. black and green . . . . 30·00 70·00
275 1g. black and orange . . . 4·50 14·00
201 – 2g. black and purple . . . 60·00 £100
206 – 2g. black and red . . . . 4·00 4·75
202 – 3g. black and blue . . . . 3·50 6·00
203 – 5g. black and lake . . . . 4·00 7·50
204 – 10g. black and brown . . . 65·00 90·00
DESIGNS—HORIZ: 2g. Krantor and River Mottlau; 3g. Zoppot. VERT: 5g. St. Mary's Church; 10g. Town Hall and Langemarkt.

1929. Int Philatelic Exhibition. Various frames.
207 **44** 10pf.(+10pf.) blk & grn . . 2·10 3·00
208 15pf.(+15pf.) blk & red . . 2·10 3·00
209 25pf.(+25pf.) blk & bl . . 8·00 8·50

1930. 10th Anniv of Constitution of Free City of Danzig. Optd **1920 15. November 1930.**
210 **39** 5pf. orange . . . . 3·25 3·25
211 10pf. green . . . . 4·00 4·00
212 15pf. red . . . . 7·00 9·00
213 20pf. red and carmine . . 3·50 5·00
214 25pf. red and grey . . . . 4·50 9·00
215 30pf. red and green . . . . 8·75 22·00
216 35pf. blue . . . . 40·00 75·00
217 40pf. blue and indigo . . . 12·50 35·00
218 50pf. red and blue . . . . 40·00 65·00
219 75pf. red and purple . . . 40·00 65·00
220 **42** 1g. black and orange . . . 40·00 65·00

1932. Danzig Int Air Post Exn ("Luposta"). Nos. 200/4 surch **Luftpost-Ausstellung 1932** and value.
221 **42** 10pf.+10pf. on 1g. black and green . . . . . . 13·00 20·00
222 – 15pf.+15pf. on 2g. black and purple . . . . . 13·00 20·00
223 – 20pf.+20pf. on 3g. black and blue . . . . . . 13·00 20·00
224 – 25pf.+25pf. on 5g. black and lake . . . . . . 13·00 10·00
225 – 30pf.+30pf. on 10g. black and brown . . . . . . 13·00 20·00

1934. "Winter Relief Work" Charity. Surch **5 W.H.W.** in Gothic characters.
226 **39** 5pf.+5pf. orange . . . . . 7·00 18·00
227 10pf.+5pf. green . . . . . 22·00 45·00
228 15pf.+5pf. red . . . . . 14·00 32·00

1934. Surch.
229 **39** 6pf. on 7pf. green . . . . 1·10 1·40
230a 8pf. on 7pf. green . . . . 1·60 1·60
231 30pf. on 35pf. blue . . . 11·00 20·00

50 Junkers F-13 **51**

1935. Air.
233 **50** 10pf. red . . . . 1·40 70
234 15pf. yellow . . . . 1·50 1·10
235 25pf. green . . . . 1·50 1·60
236 50pf. blue . . . . 7·25 8·00
237 **51** 1g. purple . . . . 4·50 10·00

52 Stockturm, 1346

54 Brosen War Memorial

1935. Winter Relief Fund.
238 **52** 5pf.+5pf. orange . . . . . 60 1·25
239 – 10pf.+5pf. green . . . . . 90 1·75
240 – 15pf.+10pf. red . . . . . 1·75 3·00

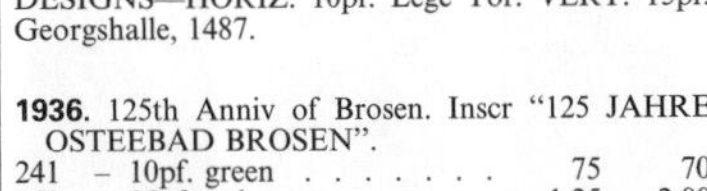

DESIGNS—HORIZ: 10pf. Lege Tor. VERT: 15pf. Georgshalle, 1487.

1936. 125th Anniv of Brosen. Inscr "125 JAHRE OSTEEBAD BROSEN".
241 – 10pf. green 75 70
242 – 25pf. red . . . . 1·25 2·00
243 **54** 40pf. blue . . . . 1·60 4·00
DESIGNS—HORIZ: 10pf. Brosen Beach; 25pf. Zoppot end of Brosen Beach.

55 Frauentor and Observatory

56 D(anziger) L(uftschutz) B(und)

57a Danziger Dorf, Magdeburg

57 Marienkriche, Danzig

1936. Winter Relief Fund.
244 – 10pf.+5pf. blue . . . . . 1·90 2·50
245 **55** 15pf.+5pf. green . . . . . 1·90 4·00
246 – 25pf.+10pf. red . . . . . 3·25 5·25
247 – 40pf.+20pf. brn & red . . . 4·50 8·25
248 – 50pf.+20pf. blue . . . . . 8·00 12·50
DESIGNS—VERT: 10pf. Milchkannenturm; 25pf. Krantor. HORIZ: 40pf. Langgartertor; 50pf. Hohestor.

1937. Air Defence League.
249 **56** 10pf. blue . . . . 35 1·40
250 15pf. purple . . . . 1·25 2·25

1937. 1st National Philatelic Exhibition, Danzig. Sheets 147 × 104 mm.
MS251 **57** 50pf. blue-green'toned (postage) . . . . 1·60 7·50
MS252 **57** 50pf. blue/toned (air) 1·60 7·50

1937. Foundation of Danzig Community. Magdeburg.
253 **57a** 25pf. (+25pf.) red . . . . 2·50 5·25
254 – 40pf. (+40pf.) red & bl . . 2·50 5·25
DESIGN—HORIZ: 40pf. Village and Arms of Danzig and Magdeburg.

1937. Danzig Productivity Show. Sheet 146 × 105 mm.
MS254a Nos. 253/4 (sold for 1g.50) 42·00 70·00

58 Madonna and Child

59 Schopenhauer

1937. Winter Relief Fund. Statues.
255 **58** 5pf.+5pf. violet . . . . . 2·25 5·25
256 – 10pf.+5pf. brown . . . . 2·25 4·25
257 – 15pf.+5pf. orange & blue 2·25 6·50
258 – 25pf.+10pf. green & blue 3·00 7·00
259 – 40pf.+25pf. blue & red . . 5·25 14·00
DESIGNS: 10pf. Mercury; 15pf. The "Golden Knight"; 25pf. Fountain of Neptune; 40pf. St. George and Dragon.

1938. 150th Birth Anniv of Schopenhauer (philosopher). Portraits inscr as in T **59**.
260 – 15pf. blue (as old man) . . 1·60 1·75
261 – 25pf. brown (as youth) . . 3·25 6·50
262 **59** 40pf. red . . . . 1·60 3·25

60 Yacht "Peter von Danzig" (1936)

61 Teutonic Knights

1938. Winter Relief Fund. Ships.
276 **60** 5pf.+5pf. green . . . . . 90 1·60
277 – 10pf.+5pf. brown . . . . 1·40 2·50
278 – 15pf.+10pf. olive . . . . 1·50 2·50
279 – 25pf.+10pf. blue . . . . 2·00 3·25
280 – 40pf.+15pf. purple . . . . 3·00 6·50
DESIGNS: 10pf. Dredger "Fu Shing"; 15pf. Liner "Columbus"; 25pf. Liner "Hansestadt Danzig"; 40pf. Sailing ship "Peter von Danzig" (1472).

1939. 125th Anniv of Prussian Annexation. Historical designs.
281 **61** 5pf. green . . . . 45 2·00
282 – 10pf. brown . . . . 75 2·10
283 – 15pf. blue . . . . 90 2·75
284 – 25pf. purple . . . . 1·40 3·50
DESIGNS: 10pf. Danzig–Swedish treaty of neutrality, 1630; 15pf. Danzig united to Prussia, 2.1.1814; 25pf. Stephen Batori's defeat at Weichselmunde, 1577.

62 Gregor Mendel

1939. Anti-cancer Campaign.
285 **62** 10pf. brown 45 85
286 – 15pf. black (Koch) . . . . 45 1·40
287 – 25pf. green (Rontgen) . . . 75 2·40

OFFICIAL STAMPS

1921. Stamps of Danzig optd **D M**.
O 94 **18** 5f. orange 25 35
O 95 10pf. brown 25 25
O 96 15pf. green 25 25
O 97 20pf. grey 25 25
O 98 25pf. green 25 25
O 99 30pf. red and blue 55 65
O100 40pf. red and green . . . 25 25
O101 50pf. red and green . . . 25 25
O102 60pf. red 25 25
O103 75pf. purple 10 30
O104 80pf. red and black . . . 75 1·25
O105 80pf. green . . . . . . 10 1·00
O106 1m. orange 25 25
O107 1m.20 blue . . . . . . 1·60 1·10
O108 1m.25 red and purple . . 65 35
O109 1m.50 grey 25 45
O110 2m. red and grey . . . . 16·00 16·00
O111 2m. red 20 30
O112 2m.40 red and brown . . 1·00 2·50
O113 3m. red and purple . . . 11·00 13·00
O114 3m. red 25 45
O122 4m. blue 20 55
O116 5m. green 25 40
O117 6m. red 25 35
O118 10m. orange 25 35
O119 20m. brown 25 35

1922. Stamps of Danzig optd **D M**.
O120a **19** 5m. green, black and red (No. 91) . . . . 4·00 6·50
O126a **25** 50m. red and blue . . . 20 50
O142 50m. blue 25 40
O127a 100m. red and green . . 20 50
O143 100m. green 25 40
O144 200m. orange 25 40
O145 **29** 300m. red and green . . 25 50
O146 500m. red and grey . . 25 55
O147 100m. red and brown 25 40

1922. No. 96 optd **D M**.
O121 **18** 6 on 3m. red 25 65

1924. Optd **Dienst-marke**.
O195 **39** 5pf. orange . . . . . . 1·75 1·60
O196 10pf. green . . . . . . 2·50 2·50
O197 15pf. grey . . . . . . 2·60 2·10
O198 15pf. red . . . . 20·00 7·50
O199 20pf. red and carmine . . 2·00 1·60
O200 25pf. red and black . . . 20·00 22·00
O201 30pf. red and green . . . 2·50 5·00
O202 35f. blue . . . . 45·00 45·00
O203 40pf. blue and indigo . . 6·50 7·00
O204 50pf. red and blue . . . 20·00 26·00
O205 75pf. red and purple . . 40·00 85·00

POSTAGE DUE STAMPS

D 20

D 39

1921. Value in "pfennig" (figures only).
D 94 **D 20** 10pf. purple 40 35
D 95 20pf. purple 25 35
D 96 40pf. purple 25 35
D 97 60pf. purple 25 35
D 98 75pf. purple 25 35
D 99 80pf. purple 25 35
D112 100pf. purple 45 65
D100 120pf. purple 25 35
D101 200pf. purple . . . . . 1·00 1·25
D102 240pf. purple . . . . . 25 1·25
D114 300pf. purple . . . . . 1·10 1·10
D115 400pf. purple . . . . . 75 1·10
D116 500pf. purple . . . . . 50 1·10
D117 800pf. purple . . . . . 45 3·25

Value in "marks" ("M" after figure).
D118a **D 20** 10m. purple 45 37
D119a 20m. purple 45 65
D120a 50m. purple 45 70
D121 100m. purple 45 70
D122 500m. purple 45 70

1923. Surch with figures and bar.
D162 **D 20** 1000 on 100m. pur . . £130 £300
D163 5000 on 50m. purple . . 35 65
D164 10000 on 20m. pur . . 35 65
D165 50000 on 500m. pur . . 35 65
D166 100000 on 20m. pur . . 1·00 1·10

1924.
D178 **D 39** 5pf. blue and black . . 55 80
D179 10pf. blue and black . . 40 65
D180 15pf. blue and black . . 90 1·10
D181 20pf. blue and black . . 90 1·75
D182 30pf. blue and black . . 5·50 1·75
D183 40pf. blue and black . . 2·00 2·50
D184 50pf. blue and black . . 1·90 2·10
D185 60pf. blue and black . . 13·00 18·00
D186 100pf. blue and black . . 16·00 7·50
D187 3g. blue and red . . . 8·50 45·00

1932. Surch in figures over bar.
D226 **D 39** 5 on 40pf. blue & blk . . 2·50 7·00
D227 10 on 60pf. bl & blk . . 40·00 11·00
D228 20 on 100pf. bl & blk . . 2·50 7·25

DEDEAGATZ Pt. 6

Former French Post Office, closed in August 1914. Dedeagatz was part of Turkey to 1913, then a Bulgarian town.

25 centimes = 1 piastre.

1893. Stamps of France optd **Dedeagh** or surch also in figures and words.
59 **10** 5c. green . . . . 8·50 11·00
60 10c. black on lilac . . . . 18·00 17·00
62a 15c. blue . . . . 23·00 24·00
63 1pi. on 25c. black on red . . 29·00 25·00
64 2pi. on 50c. red . . . . . 55·00 45·00
65 4pi. on 1f. olive . . . . . 60·00 55·00
66 8pi. on 2f. brn on blue . . 80·00 70·00

1902. "Blanc", "Mouchon" and "Merson" key-types inscr "DEDEAGH". Some surch in figures and words.
67a A 5c. green . . . . 1·90 2·25
68 B 10c. red . . . . 1·25 1·50
70 15c. orange . . . . 2·50 2·40
71 1pi. on 25c. blue . . . . . 2·75 3·00
72 C 2pi. on 50c. brown & lav . . 6·00 8·00
73 4pi. on 1f. red and green . . 12·50 11·50
74 8pi. on 2f. lilac & yellow . . 19·00 19·00

DENMARK Pt. 11

A kingdom in N. Europe, on a peninsula between the Baltic and the North Sea.

1851. 96 rigsbank skilling = 1 rigsdaler.
1875. 100 ore = 1 krone.

1

2

4

1851. Imperf.
3 **1** 2r.b.s. blue £2750 £850
4 **2** 4r.b.s. brown . . . . £750 22·00

1854. Dotted background. Brown burelage. Imperf.
8 **4** 2sk. blue . . . . 50·00 38·00
9b 4sk. orange . . . . £700 5·00
12 8sk. green . . . . £275 44·00
13 16sk. lilac £425 £100

5

7

8

1858. Background of wavy lines. Brown burelage. Imperf.
15 **5** 4sk. brown . . . . 65·00 4·00
18 8sk. green . . . . £500 60·00

1863. Brown burelage. Roul
20 **5** 4sk. brown . . . . 75·00 10·00
21 **4** 16sk. mauve £1200 £400

1864. Perf.
22 **7** 2sk. blue . . . . 55·00 25·00
25 3sk. mauve . . . . 70·00 44·00
28 4sk. red . . . . 35·00 5·25
29 8sk. bistre . . . . £275 75·00
30a 16sk. green . . . . £400 75·00

1870. Value in "skilling".
39 **8** 2sk. blue and grey . . . . . 42·00 17·00
42 3sk. purple and grey . . . . 80·00 55·00
44 4sk. red and grey . . . . . 42·00 6·00
46 8sk. brown and grey . . . . £160 42·00

48 16sk. green and grey £200 £100
37 48sk. lilac and brown £375 £130

1875. As T **8**, but value in "ore".
80 **8** 3ore grey and blue 5·00 22·00
81 4ore blue and grey 4·75 30
56 5ore blue and red 45·00 41·00
82 8ore red and grey 4·75 30
83 12ore purple and grey 6·00 1·70
84 16ore brown and grey 13·50 2·10
72 20ore grey and red £120 13·00
85 25ore green and grey 8·75 2·30
86 50ore purple and brown 23·00 10·50
87 100ore orange and grey 27·00 7·25

10 **14** King Christian IX **15**

1882.
96 **10** 1ore orange 50 40
97 5ore green 4·50 15
98 10ore red 3·50 15
99 15ore mauve 14·50 45
100 20ore blue 17·00 1·70
101 24ore brown 12·00 2·30

1904. No. 82 and 101 surch.
102 **8** 4ore on 8ore red & grey 1·80 2·30
103 **10** 15ore on 24ore brown 2·30 3·25

1904.
119 **14** 5ore green 4·75 15
104 10ore red 2·20 15
105 20ore blue 9·75 55
106 25ore brown 21·00 2·00
107 50ore lilac 50·00 35·00
108 100ore brown 9·25 20·00

1905. Solid background.
173 **15** 1ore orange 35 25
174 2ore red 2·75 30
175 3ore grey 6·75 30
176 4ore blue 7·50 30
177 5ore brown 90 20
178 5ore green 1·30 25
179 7ore green 3·25 1·50
180 7ore violet 16·00 2·75
181 8ore grey 5·50 1·60
114 10ore pink 7·50 15
182 10ore green 1·10 20
183 10ore brown 2·75 25
184 12ore lilac 24·00 4·25
115 15ore mauve 13·50 65
116 20ore blue 43·00 2·10
For stamps with lined background but without hearts, see Nos. 265/76k.

17 King Frederik VIII **20** G.P.O., Copenhagen

1907.
121 **17** 5ore green 90 10
122 10ore red 1·70 10
124 20ore blue 9·00 45
125 25ore brown 19·00 35
127 35ore orange 3·50 2·20
128 50ore purple 20·00 2·20
130 100ore brown 70·00 1·50

1912. (a) Nos. 84 and 72 surch **35 ORE.**
131 **8** 35ore on 16ore brn & grey 9·00 21·00
132 35ore on 20ore grey and red 15·00 26·00
(b) No. O98 surch **35 ORE FRIMAERKE.**
133 **O 9** 35ore on 32ore green 15·00 36·00

1912.
134 **20** 5k. red £150 65·00

21 King Christian X **22**

1913.
135 **21** 5ore green 55 10
136 7ore orange 2·00 55
137 8ore grey 5·25 3·00
138 10ore red 1·20 10
139 12ore grey 2·75 4·50
141a 15ore mauve 1·30 10
142 20ore blue 7·50 25
143 20ore brown 55 15
144 20ore red 80 10
145 25ore brown 17·00 20
146 25ore black and brown 85·00 2·10
147 25ore red 2·50 30
148 25ore green 1·60 20
149 27ore black and red 20·00 22·00
150 30ore black and green 20·00 1·00
151 30ore orange 1·50 75
152 30ore blue 85 30
153 35ore yellow 13·00 1·90
154 35ore black and yellow 4·00 2·50
155 40ore black and violet 11·00 1·60
156 40ore blue 2·30 55
157 40ore yellow 1·00 60
158 50ore purple 24·00 1·60
159 50ore black and purple 33·00 65
160a 50ore grey 5·25 20
161 60ore blue and brown 35 2·10
162 60ore blue 6·75 50
163 70ore green and brown 16·00 1·40
164 80ore green 30·00 7·75
165 90ore red and brown 9·00 1·70
166 **22** 1k. brown 65·00 50
167 **21** 1k. blue and brown 22·00 95
168 **22** 2k. black 85·00 3·25
169 **21** 2k. purple and grey 31·00 6·75
170 **22** 5k. violet 7·50 4·75
171 **21** 5k. brown and mauve 3·75 3·50
172 10k. green and red £150 19·00

1915. (a) No. O94 surch **DANMARK 80 ORE POSTFRIM.**
186 **O 9** 80ore on 8ore red 15·00 55·00
(b) No. 83 surch **80 ORE.**
187 **8** 80ore on 12ore pur & grey 13·00 50·00

1918. Newspaper stamps surch **POSTFRIM. ORE 27 ORE DANMARK.**
197 **N 18** 27ore on 1ore green 1·90 5·75
198 27ore on 5ore blue 3·75 12·50
199 27ore on 7ore red 2·00 4·50
200 27ore on 8ore green 2·50 7·25
201 27ore on 10ore lilac 1·90 5·00
202 27ore on 20ore green 2·40 7·00
203 27ore on 29ore orge 2·10 5·00
204 27ore on 38ore orge 10·50 39·00
205 27ore on 41ore brn 5·00 20·00
194 27ore on 68ore brn 2·75 14·50
206 27ore on 1k. pur & grn 1·80 3·75
195 27ore on 5k. grn & pk 3·25 7·50
196 27ore on 10k. bl & stone 3·25 11·00

1919. No. 135 surch **2 ORE.**
207 **21** 2ore on 5ore green £900 £250

27 Castle of Kronborg, Elsinore **29** Roskilde Cathedral

1920. Recovery of Northern Schleswig.
208 **27** 10ore red 2·00 15
209 10ore green 10·50 25
210 – 20ore slate 2·00 25
211 **29** 40ore brown 5·25 2·50
212 40ore blue 29·00 4·75
DESIGN—HORIZ: 20ore Sonderborg Castle.

1921. Nos. 136 and 139 surch **8 8.**
217 **21** 8 on 7ore orange 1·50 1·80
213 8 on 12ore green 1·70 4·00

1921. Red Cross. Nos. 209/10 surch with figure of value between red crosses.
214 **27** 10ore+5ore green 9·00 21·00
215 – 20ore+10ore grey 11·50 26·00

1921. No. 175 surch **8.**
216 **15** 8 on 3ore grey 1·80 1·70

33 King Christian IV **34** King Christian X **35**

1924. 300th Anniv of Danish Post. A. Head facing to left.
218A **33** 10ore green 2·40 1·80
221A **34** 10ore green 2·40 1·80
219A **33** 15ore mauve 2·40 1·80
222A **34** 15ore mauve 2·40 1·80
220A **33** 20ore brown 2·40 1·80
223A **34** 20ore brown 2·40 1·80
B. Head facing to right.
218B **33** 10ore green 2·40 1·80
221B **34** 10ore green 2·40 1·80
219B **33** 15ore mauve 2·40 1·80
222B **34** 15ore mauve 2·40 1·80
220B **33** 20ore brown 2·40 1·80
223B **34** 20ore brown 2·40 1·80

1925. Air.
224 **35** 10ore green 13·00 18·00
225 15ore lilac 29·00 37·00
226 25ore red 18·00 27·00
227 50ore grey 55·00 95·00
228 1k. brown 55·00 95·00

1926. Surch **20 20.**
229 **21** 20 on 30ore orange 2·10 5·75
230 20 on 40ore blue 2·40 6·75

38 **39** **40** Caravel

1926. 75th Anniv of First Danish stamps.
231 **38** 10ore olive 60 10
232 **39** 20ore red 90 10
233 30ore blue 3·50 55

1926. Various stamps surch.
234 **15** 7 on 8ore grey 95 2·00
235 **21** 7 on 20ore red 40 65
236 7 on 27ore black & red 2·00 6·25
237 12 on 15ore lilac 1·20 2·50

1926. Official stamps surch **DANMARK 7 ORE POSTFRIM.**
238 **O 9** 7ore on 1ore orange 1·20 5·75
239 7ore on 3ore grey 8·50 13·00
240 7ore on 4ore blue 2·10 5·25
241 7ore on 5ore green 29·00 41·00
242 7ore on 10ore green 1·40 5·25
243 7ore on 15ore lilac 2·10 4·75
244 7ore on 20ore blue 6·75 34·00

1927. Solid background.
246 **40** 15ore red 2·75 10
247 20ore grey 5·75 55
248 25ore blue 45 10
249 30ore yellow 60 10
250 35ore red 12·50 50
251 40ore green 10·50 10
For stamps with lined background see Nos. 277b, etc.

41 **42** King Christian X **43** Numeral

1929. Danish Cancer Research Fund.
252 **41** 10ore (+5ore) green 2·50 3·75
253 15ore (+5ore) red 4·25 6·00
254 25ore (+5ore) blue 14·50 24·00

1930. 60th Birthday of King Christian X.
255 **42** 5ore green 85 20
256 7ore violet 4·00 1·80
257 8ore grey 12·50 12·50
258 10ore brown 1·60 10
259 15ore red 6·75 10
260 20ore grey 11·50 3·75
261 25ore blue 4·00 40
262 30ore yellow 4·00 1·10
263 35ore red 6·25 1·30
264 40ore green 5·75 60

1933. Lined background.
265 **43** 1ore green 10 25
266 2ore red 10 15
267 4ore blue 35 20
268 5ore green 70 25
268c 5ore purple 15 10
268d 5ore orange 20 10
268e 6ore orange 10 10
269 7ore violet 95 15
269a 7ore green 95 45
269b 7ore brown 20 20
270 8ore grey 35 25
270a 8ore green 20 15
271 10ore orange 4·50 25
271b 10ore brown 4·75 20
271c 10ore violet 20 20
271d 10ore green 15 10
272 12ore green 25 10
272a 15ore green 25 10
272c 20ore blue 20 10
272e 25ore green 40 10
272f 25ore blue 25 10
273 30ore green 20 10
273a 30ore orange 25 10
273c 40ore orange 30 10
273d 40ore purple 20 10
274 50ore brown 20 10
274d 60ore green 1·20 35
274e 60ore grey 60 40
275 70ore red 70 10
275a 70ore green 30 20
275d 80ore green 40 10
275e 80ore brown 50 30
276 100ore green 45 10
276a 100ore blue 45 10
276b 125ore brown 60 20
276c 150ore green 60 30
276ca 150ore violet 55 35
276d 200ore green 70 10
276e 230ore green 95 30
276f 250ore green 95 30
276g 270ore green 95 40
276h 300ore green 1·10 10
276i 325ore green 1·10 35
276j 350ore green 1·10 40
276k 375ore green 1·20 50
276l 400ore green 75 45

45 King Christian X **47** Fokker FVIIa over Copenhagen **49** Hans Andersen

1933. T **40** with lined background.
277b **40** 15ore red 2·00 20
277de 15ore green 2·50 20
278a 20ore grey 3·25 15
278b 20ore red 35 10
279 25ore blue 36·00 13·00
279b 25ore brown 40 20
280a 30ore orange 50 15
280b 30ore blue 65 20
281 35ore violet 35 25
282 40ore green 2·50 10
282b 40ore blue 90 10
283 **45** 50ore grey 90 10
283a 60ore green 2·20 20
283b 75ore blue 50 25
284 1k. brown 3·25 10
284a 2k. red 5·00 40
284b 5k. violet 7·75 1·90

1934. Nos. 279 and 280a surch.
285 **40** 4 on 25ore blue 25 25
286 10 on 30ore orange 2·10 1·70

1934. Air.
287 **47** 10ore orange 85 1·10
288 15ore red 2·40 3·50
289 20ore green 2·40 3·75
290 50ore green 2·50 3·75
291 1k. brown 8·00 11·50

1935. Centenary of Hans Andersen's Fairy Tales.
292 – 5ore green 3·75 15
293 **49** 7ore violet 2·20 1·20
294 – 10ore orange 4·25 10
295 **49** 15ore red 10·50 15
296 20ore grey 8·75 65
297 30ore blue 2·10 25
DESIGNS: 5ore "The Ugly Duckling"; 10ore "The Little Mermaid".

51 St. Nicholas's Church, Copenhagen **52** Hans Tausen

53 Ribe Cathedral **54** Dybbol Mill

1936. 400th Anniv of Reformation.
298 **51** 5ore green 1·10 20
299 7ore mauve 1·20 1·60
300 **52** 10ore brown 1·60 10
301 15ore red 2·30 10
302 **53** 30ore blue 10·00 60

1937. H. P. Hanssen (North Schleswig patriot) Memorial Fund.
303 **54** 5ore+5ore green 40 75
304 10ore+5ore brown 1·80 4·75
305 15ore+5ore red 1·80 4·75

56 King Christian X

1937. Silver Jubilee of King Christian X.
306 – 5ore green 1·30 15
307 **56** 10ore brown 1·10 20
308 – 15ore red 1·00 10
309 **56** 30ore blue 11·00 1·30
DESIGNS—HORIZ: 5ore Marselisborg Castle and "Rita" (King's yacht); 15ore Amalienborg Castle.

1937. Copenhagen Philatelic Club's 50th Anniv Stamp Exhibition. No. 271b optd **K.P.K. 17.-26. SEPT. 19 37** (="Kobenhavns Philatelist Klub").
310 **43** 10ore brown 95 1·20

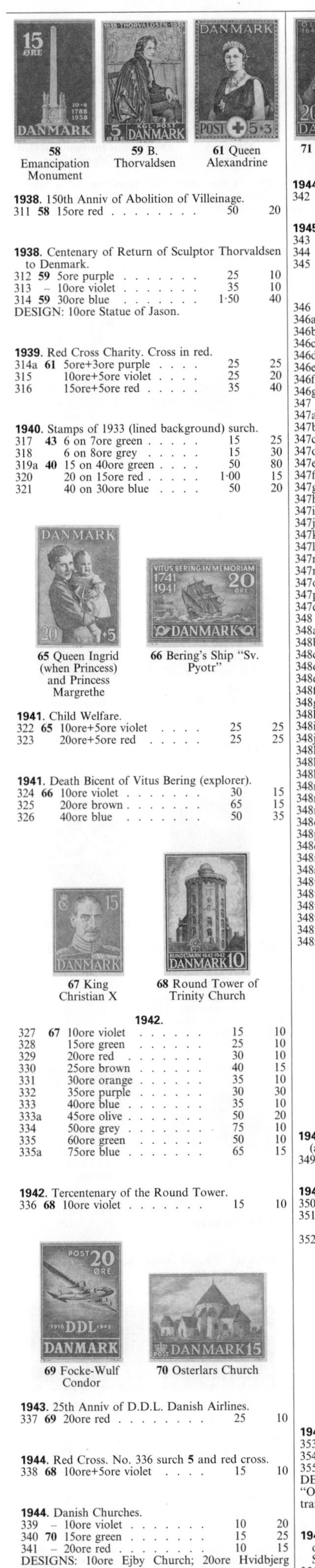

58 Emancipation Monument
59 B. Thorvaldsen
61 Queen Alexandrine

1938. 150th Anniv of Abolition of Villeinage.
311 **58** 15ore red 50 20

1938. Centenary of Return of Sculptor Thorvaldsen to Denmark.
312 **59** 5ore purple 25 10
313 – 10ore violet 35 10
314 **59** 30ore blue 1·50 40
DESIGN: 10ore Statue of Jason.

1939. Red Cross Charity. Cross in red.
314a **61** 5ore+3ore purple 25 25
315 10ore+5ore violet 25 20
316 15ore+5ore red 35 40

1940. Stamps of 1933 (lined background) surch.
317 **43** 6 on 7ore green 15 25
318 6 on 8ore grey 15 30
319a **40** 15 on 40ore green 50 80
320 20 on 15ore red 1·00 15
321 40 on 30ore blue 50 20

65 Queen Ingrid (when Princess) and Princess Margrethe
66 Bering's Ship "Sv. Pyotr"

1941. Child Welfare.
322 **65** 10ore+5ore violet 25 25
323 20ore+5ore red 25 25

1941. Death Bicent of Vitus Bering (explorer).
324 **66** 10ore violet 30 15
325 20ore brown 65 15
326 40ore blue 50 35

67 King Christian X
68 Round Tower of Trinity Church

1942.
327 **67** 10ore violet 15 10
328 15ore green 25 10
329 20ore red 30 10
330 25ore brown 40 15
331 30ore orange 35 10
332 35ore purple 30 30
333 40ore blue 35 10
333a 45ore olive 50 20
334 50ore grey 75 10
335 60ore green 50 10
335a 75ore blue 65 15

1942. Tercentenary of the Round Tower.
336 **68** 10ore violet 15 10

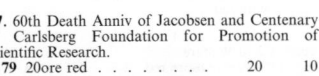

69 Focke-Wulf Condor
70 Osterlars Church

1943. 25th Anniv of D.D.L. Danish Airlines.
337 **69** 20ore red 25 10

1944. Red Cross. No. 336 surch **5** and red cross.
338 **68** 10ore+5ore violet 15 10

1944. Danish Churches.
339 – 10ore violet 10 20
340 **70** 15ore green 15 25
341 – 20ore red 10 15
DESIGNS: 10ore Ejby Church; 20ore Hvidbjerg Church.

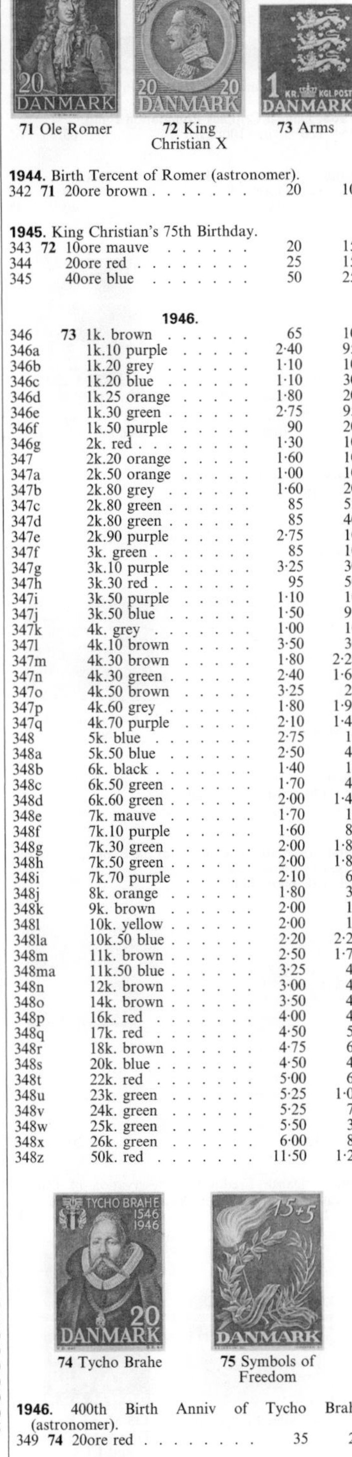

71 Ole Romer
72 King Christian X
73 Arms

1944. Birth Tercent of Romer (astronomer).
342 **71** 20ore brown 20 10

1945. King Christian's 75th Birthday.
343 **72** 10ore mauve 20 15
344 20ore red 25 15
345 40ore blue 50 25

1946.
346 **73** 1k. brown 65 10
346a 1k.10 purple 2·40 95
346b 1k.20 grey 1·10 10
346c 1k.20 blue 1·10 30
346d 1k.25 orange 1·80 20
346e 1k.30 green 2·75 95
346f 1k.50 purple 90 20
346g 2k. red 1·30 10
347 2k.20 orange 1·60 10
347a 2k.50 orange 1·00 10
347b 2k.80 grey 1·60 20
347c 2k.80 green 85 55
347d 2k.80 green 85 40
347e 2k.90 purple 2·75 10
347f 3k. green 85 10
347g 3k.10 purple 3·25 30
347h 3k.30 red 95 50
347i 3k.50 purple 1·10 10
347j 3k.50 blue 1·50 95
347k 4k. grey 1·00 10
347l 4k.10 brown 3·50 30
347m 4k.30 brown 1·80 2·20
347n 4k.30 green 2·40 1·60
347o 4k.50 brown 3·25 25
347p 4k.60 grey 1·80 1·90
347q 4k.70 purple 2·10 1·40
348 5k. blue 2·75 10
348a 5k.50 blue 2·50 40
348b 6k. black 1·40 10
348c 6k.50 green 1·70 40
348d 6k.60 green 2·00 1·40
348e 7k. mauve 1·70 10
348f 7k.10 purple 1·60 80
348g 7k.30 green 2·00 1·80
348h 7k.50 green 2·00 1·80
348i 7k.70 purple 2·10 65
348j 8k. orange 1·80 30
348k 9k. brown 2·00 10
348l 10k. yellow 2·00 10
348la 10k.50 blue 2·20 2·20
348m 11k. brown 2·50 1·70
348ma 11k.50 blue 3·25 40
348n 12k. brown 3·00 40
348o 14k. brown 3·50 40
348p 16k. red 4·00 45
348q 17k. red 4·50 55
348r 18k. brown 4·75 60
348s 20k. blue 4·50 45
348t 22k. red 5·00 65
348u 23k. green 5·25 1·00
348v 24k. green 5·25 75
348w 25k. green 5·50 30
348x 26k. green 6·00 85
348z 50k. red 11·50 1·20

74 Tycho Brahe
75 Symbols of Freedom

1946. 400th Birth Anniv of Tycho Brahe (astronomer).
349 **74** 20ore red 35 20

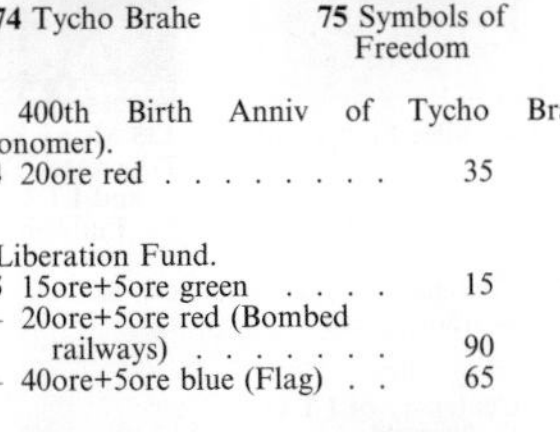

1947. Liberation Fund.
350 **75** 15ore+5ore green 15 20
351 – 20ore+5ore red (Bombed railways) 90 45
352 – 40ore+5ore blue (Flag) 65 50

77 Class H Steam Goods Train
79 I. C. Jacobsen

1947. Centenary of Danish Railways.
353 – 15ore green 55 15
354 **77** 20ore red 70 10
355 – 40ore blue 3·00 1·00
DESIGNS—HORIZ: 15ore First Danish locomotive "Odin"; 40ore Diesel-electric train "Lyntog" and train ferry "Fyn".

1947. 60th Death Anniv of Jacobsen and Centenary of Carlsberg Foundation for Promotion of Scientific Research.
356 **79** 20ore red 20 10

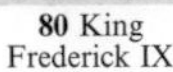

80 King Frederick IX
81 "The Constituent Assembly of the Kingdom" (after Constantin Hansen)

1948.
357a **80** 15ore green 80 25
358 15ore violet 50 10
359a 20ore red 45 10
360 20ore brown 20 10
361 25ore brown 85 25
362 25ore red 2·50 10
362a 25ore blue 50 20
362b 25ore violet 20 10
363 30ore orange 8·25 35
363b 30ore red 35 20
364 35ore green 20 20
365 40ore blue 3·00 40
366 40ore grey 75 10
367 45ore bistre 1·00 10
368 50ore grey 1·20 25
369 50ore blue 1·90 10
369a 50ore green 20 10
370 55ore brown 17·00 1·10
371a 60ore blue 45 10
371b 65ore grey 45 20
372 70ore green 1·10 10
373 75ore purple 1·30 10
373a 80ore orange 70 10
373b 90ore bistre 1·70 10
373c 95ore orange 55 25

1949. Centenary of Danish Constitution.
374 **81** 20ore brown 35 10

82 Globe
83 Kalundborg Transmitter

1949. 75th Anniv of U.P.U.
375 **82** 40ore blue 55 40

1950. 25th Anniv of State Broadcasting.
376 **83** 20ore brown 35 20

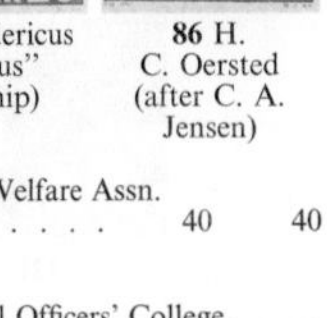

84 Princess Anne-Marie
85 "Fredericus Quartus" (warship)
86 H. C. Oersted (after C. A. Jensen)

1950. National Children's Welfare Assn.
377 **84** 25ore+5ore red 40 40

1951. 250th Anniv of Naval Officers' College.
378 **85** 25ore red 60 30
379 50ore blue 3·00 60

1951. Death Centenary of Oersted (physicist).
380 **86** 50ore blue 1·00 40

87 Mail Coach
88 Hospital Ship "Jutlandia"

1951. Danish Stamp Centenary.
381 **87** 15ore violet 50 10
382 25ore red 50 10

1951. Danish Red Cross Fund.
383 **88** 25ore +5ore red 55 60

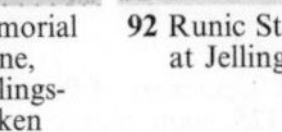

89 "Life-Saving" (relief, H. Solomon)
91 Memorial Stone, Skamlings-banken
92 Runic Stone at Jelling

1952. Centenary of Danish Life-Saving Service.
384 **89** 25ore red 35 20

1953. Netherlands Flood Relief Fund. Surch **NL+10**.
385 **80** 30ore+10ore red 1·00 85

1953. Danish Border Union Fund.
386 **91** 30ore+5ore red 1·00 85

1953. 1,000 years of Danish Kingdom. Inscr "KONGERIGE i 1000 AR". (a) 1st series.
387 **92** 10ore green 20 20
388 – 15ore lilac 20 20
389 – 20ore brown 20 20
390 – 30ore red 40 20
391 – 60ore blue 55 20
DESIGNS: 15ore Vikings' camp, Trelleborg; 20ore Kalundborg Church; 30ore Nyborg Castle; 60ore Goose Tower, Vordinborg.

(b) 2nd series.
392 – 10ore green 20 15
393 – 15ore lilac 20 15
394 – 20ore brown 20 15
395 – 30ore red 30 15
396 – 60ore blue 75 15
DESIGNS: 10ore Spottrup Castle; 15ore Hammershus Castle; 20ore Copenhagen Stock Exchange; 30ore King Frederik V statue; 60ore Soldier's Statue (H. V. Bissen).

93 Telegraph Table, 1854
94 Head of Statue of King Frederik V at Amalienborg

1954. Telecommunications Centenary.
397 **93** 30ore brown 35 20

1954. Bicent of Royal Academy of Fine Arts.
398 **94** 30ore red 50 20

1955. Liberty Fund. Nos. 350/1 surch.
399 **75** 20+5 on 15ore +5ore grn 1·00 80
400 – 30+5 on 20ore +5ore red 1·00 80

1955. Nos. 268e, 269b, 359a and 362 surch.
401 **43** 5ore on 6ore orange 15 10
402 5ore on 7ore brown 15 10
403 **80** 30ore on 20ore red 30 20
404 30ore on 25ore red 45 20

98 S. Kierkegaard (philosopher)
99 Ellehammer's Aircraft

1955. Death Centenary of Kierkegaard.
405 **98** 30ore red 35 10

1956. 50th Anniv of 1st Flight by J. C. H. Ellehammer.
406 **99** 30ore red 45 10

100 Whooper Swans
102 National Museum

1956. Northern Countries' Day.
407 **100** 30ore red 1·20 15
408 60ore blue 85 45

1957. Danish Red Cross Hungarian Relief Fund. No. 373c surch **Ungarns-hjaelpen 30 + 5**.
409 **80** 30ore+5ore on 95ore orange 50 40

1957. 150th Anniv of National Museum.
410 **102** 30ore red 45 15
411 – 60ore blue 60 55
DESIGN: 50ore "Sun-God's Chariot" (bronze age model).

103 Harvester
105 King Frederik IX
106 Margrethe Schanne in "La Sylphide"

1958. Centenary of Danish Royal Veterinary and Agricultural College.
412 **103** 30ore red 20 10

1959. Greenland Fund. No. 363b surch **Gronlands-fonden + 10**.
413 **80** 30ore+10ore red 75 60
The Greenland Fund was devoted to the relatives of the crew and passengers of the "Hans Hedtoft", the Greenland vessel lost at sea on 30 January 1959.

1959. 60th Birthday of King Frederik IX.
414 **105** 30ore red 25 10
415 35ore purple 30 25
416 60ore blue 30 20

1959. Danish Ballet and Music Festival, 1959.
417 **106** 35ore purple 20 10
See also Nos. 445 and 467.

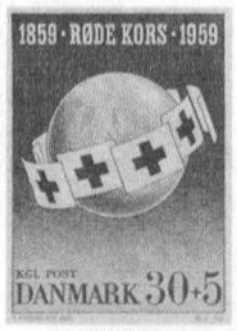

107  **109** Sowing Machine

1959. Centenary of Red Cross.
418 **107** 30ore+5ore red 30 30
419 60ore+5ore red & blue . . 55 55

1960. World Refugee Year. Surch 30 **Verdensflygtninge-aret 1959-60** and uprooted tree.
420 **80** 30ore on 15ore violet . . . 20 10

1960. 1st Danish Food Fair.
421 **109** 12ore green 20 10
422 – 30ore red 25 15
423 – 60ore blue 50 25
DESIGNS: 30ore Combine-harvester; 60ore Plough.

110 King Frederik and Queen Ingrid  **111** Ancient Bascule Light

1960. Royal Silver Wedding.
424 **110** 30ore red 35 15
425 60ore blue 45 40

1960. 400th Anniv of Danish Lighthouse Service.
426 **111** 30ore red 35 10

112 N. Finsen  **113** Mother and Child

1960. Birth Cent of Niels R. Finsen (physician).
427 **112** 30ore red 20 20

1960. W.H.O. 10th European Regional Committee Meeting.
428 **113** 60ore blue 50 40

113a Conference Emblem  **114** Queen Ingrid

1960. Europa.
429 **113a** 60ore blue 55 40

1960. 25th Year of Queen Ingrid's Service in Girl Guides.
430 **114** 30ore+10ore red 85 70

115 Douglas DC-8  **116** Coastal Scene

1961. 10th Anniv of Scandinavian Airlines System (SAS).
431 **115** 60ore blue 45 20

1961. 50th Anniv of Society for Preservation of Danish National Amenities.
432 **116** 30ore red 20 10

117 King Frederik IX **118** Borkop Watermill **119** African Mother and Child

1961.

433	**117**	20ore brown	20	10
434		25ore brown	20	10
435		30ore red	20	10
436		35ore green	50	40
437		35ore red	20	10
438		40ore grey	65	10
438a		40ore brown	20	10
439		50ore turquoise	35	10
439a		50ore red	35	10
439b		50ore brown	35	10
440		60ore blue	45	10
440a		60ore red	50	15
441		70ore green	70	20
442		80ore orange	90	10
442a		80ore blue	95	10
442b		80ore green	45	10
443		90ore olive	2·50	35
443a		90ore blue	55	15
444		95ore purple	70	40

1962. Danish Ballet and Music Festival, 1962. As T **106** but inscr "15–31 MAJ".
445 60ore blue 25 25

1962. "Dansk Fredning" (Preservation of Danish Natural Amenities and Ancient Monuments) and Centenary of Abolition of Mill Monopolies.
446 **118** 10ore brown 20 20

1962. Aid for Under-developed Countries.
447 **119** 30ore+10ore red 65 60

120 "Selandia"

1962. 50th Anniv of Freighter "Selandia".
448 **120** 60ore blue . . . . 1·60 85

121 "Tivoli"

1962. 150th Birth Anniv of George Carstensen (founder of Tivoli Pleasure Gardens, Copenhagen).
449 **121** 35ore purple 20 20

122 Cliffs, Island of Mon **123** Wheat

1962. "Dansk Fredning" (Preservation of Danish Natural Amenities and Ancient Monuments).
450 **122** 20ore brown 20 10

1963. Freedom from Hunger.
451 **123** 35ore red 20 15

124 Rail and Sea Symbols **125** 19th-century Mail Transport

1963. Opening of Denmark–Germany Railway ("Bird-flight Line").
452 **124** 15ore green 30 15

1963. Centenary of Paris Postal Conference.
453 **125** 60ore blue 20 35

126 Hands 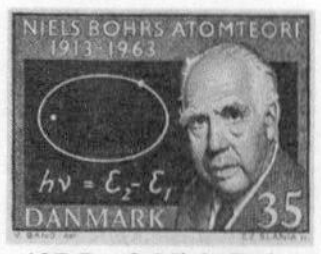 **127** Prof. Niels Bohr

1963. Danish Cripples Foundation Fund.
454 **126** 35ore+10ore red 65 65

1963. 50th Anniv of Bohr's Atomic Theory.
455 **127** 35ore red 30 15
456 60ore blue 40 35

128 Ancient Bridge, Immervad  **129** "Going to School" (child's slate)

1964. Danish Border Union Fund.
457 **128** 35ore+10ore red 45 50

1964. 150th Anniv of Institution of Primary Schools.
458 **129** 35ore brown 20 10

130 Princesses Margrethe, Benedikte and Anne-Marie 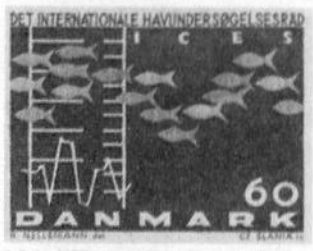 **131** "Exploration of the Sea"

1964. Danish Red Cross Fund.
459 **130** 35ore+10ore red 40 40
460 60ore+10ore blue & red 60 60

1964. International Council for the Exploration of the Sea Conference, Copenhagen.
461 **131** 60ore blue 25 20

132 Danish Stamp "Watermarks, Perforations and Varieties" **133** Landscape, R. Karup

1964. 25th Anniv of Stamp Day.
462 **132** 35ore pink 20 10

1964. "Dansk Fredning" (Preservation of Danish Natural Amenities and Ancient Monuments).
463 **133** 25ore brown 20 20

134 Office Equipment  **135** Morse Key, Teleprinter Tape and I.T.U. Emblem

1965. Centenary of 1st Commercial School.
464 **134** 15ore green 20 20

1965. Centenary of I.T.U.
465 **135** 80ore blue 40 15

136 C. Nielsen  **137** Child in Meadow

1965. Birth Centenary of Carl Nielsen (composer).
466 **136** 50ore red 20 15

1965. Danish Ballet and Music Festival, 1965. As T **106** but inscr "15-31 MAJ".
467 50ore red 20 10

1965. Child Welfare.
468 **137** 50ore+10ore red 45 40

138 Bogo Windmill  **139** Titles of International Red Cross Organizations

1965. "Dansk Fredning" (Preservation of Danish Natural Amenities and Ancient Monuments).
469 **138** 40ore brown 20 10

1966. Danish Red Cross Fund.
470 **139** 50ore+10ore red 40 40
471 80ore+10ore bl & red . . 55 60

140 Heathland  **141** C. Kold

1966. Centenary of Danish Heath Society.
472 **140** 25ore green 20 20

1966. 150th Birth Anniv of Christen Kold (educationist).
473 **141** 50ore red 20 10

142 Almshouses, Copenhagen  **143** Trees at Bregentved

1966. "Dansk Fredning" (Preservation of Danish Natural Amenities and Ancient Monuments).
474 **142** 50ore red 15 15
475 **143** 80ore blue 45 25

144 G. Jensen  **145** Fund Emblem

1966. Birth Cent of Georg Jensen (silversmith).
476 **144** 80ore blue 45 25

1966. "Refugee 66" Fund.
477 **145** 40ore+10ore brown . . . 40 40
478 50ore+10ore red 40 40
479 80ore+10ore blue 75 70

146 Barrow in Jutland  **147** Musical Instruments

1966. "Dansk Fredning" (Preservation of Danish Natural Amenities and Ancient Monuments).
480 **146** 1k.50 green 65 10

1967. Cent of Royal Danish Academy of Music.
481 **147** 50ore red 20 10

148 Cogwheels  **149** Old City and Windmill

1967. European Free Trade Assn.
482 **148** 80ore blue 45 10

1967. 800th Anniv of Copenhagen.
483 **149** 25ore green 20 25
484 – 40ore brown 25 20
485 – 50ore brown 30 20
486 – 80ore blue 65 70
DESIGNS: 40ore Old bank and ship's masts; 50ore Church steeple and burgher's house; 80ore Building construction.

150 Princess Margrethe and Prince Henri de Monpezat

151 H. C. Sonne

1967. Royal Wedding.
487 **150** 50ore red 20 20

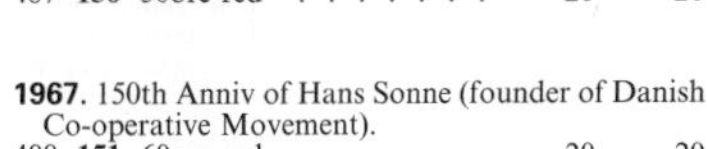

1967. 150th Anniv of Hans Sonne (founder of Danish Co-operative Movement).
488 **151** 60ore red 20 20

152 "Rose"

153 Porpoise and Cross-anchor

1967. The Salvation Army.
489 **152** 60ore+10ore red 45 40

1967. Centenary of Danish Seamen's Church in Foreign Ports.
490 **153** 90ore blue 45 25

154 Esbjerg Harbour

155 Koldinghus Castle

1968. Cent of Esbjerg Harbour Construction Act.
491 **154** 30ore green 20 10

1968. 700th Anniv of Koldinghus Castle.
492 **155** 60ore red 20 10

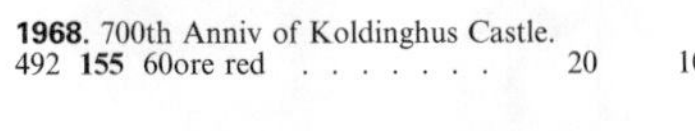

156 "The Children in the Round Tower" (Greenlandic legend)

157 Shipbuilding

1968. Greenlandic Child Welfare.
493 **156** 60ore+10ore red 45 50

1968. Danish Industries.
494 **157** 30ore green 20 15
495 – 50ore brown 20 15
496 – 60ore red 20 15
497 – 90ore blue 80 80
INDUSTRIES: 50ore Chemicals, 60ore Electric power, 90ore Engineering.

158 "The Sower"

159 Viking Ships (from old Swedish coin)

1969. Bicentenary of Danish Royal Agricultural Society.
498 **158** 30ore green 20 10

1969. 50th Anniv of Northern Countries' Union.
499 **159** 60ore red 45 10
500 90ore blue . . . . 85 1·00

160 King Frederik IX

161 Colonnade

1969. King Frederik's 70th Birthday.
501 **160** 50ore brown 25 25
502 60ore red 25 25

1969. Europa.
503 **161** 90ore blue 70 50

162 Kronborg Castle

163 Fall of Danish Flag

1969. 50th Anniv of "Danes Living Abroad" Association.
504 **162** 50ore brown 20 10

1969. 750th Anniv of "Danish Flag Falling from Heaven".
505 **163** 60ore red, blue & black 20 15

164 M. A. Nexo

165 Niels Stensen (geologist)

1969. Birth Cent of Martin Andersen Nexo (poet).
506 **164** 80ore green 45 10

1969. 300th Anniv of Stensen's "On Solid Bodies".
507 **165** 1k. sepia 45 10

166 "Abstract"

167 Symbolic "P"

1969. "Non-figurative" stamp.
508 **166** 60ore red, rose and blue 20 10

1969. Birth Cent of Valdemar Poulsen (inventor).
509 **167** 30ore green 20 10

168 Princess Margrethe, Prince Henri and Prince Frederik (baby)

169 "Postgiro"

1969. Danish Red Cross.
510 **168** 50ore+10ore brn & red 45 40
511 60ore+10ore brn & red 45 40

1970. 50th Anniv of Danish Postal Giro Service.
512 **169** 60ore and orange 20 10

170 School Safety Patrol

171 Child appealing for Help

1970. Road Safety.
513 **170** 50ore brown 20 10

1970. 25th Anniv of Save the Children Fund.
514 **171** 60ore+10ore red 45 50

172 Candle in Window

173 Red Deer in Park

1970. 25th Anniv of Liberation.
515 **172** 50ore black, yellow & bl 30 10

1970. 300th Anniv of Jaegersborg Deer Park.
516 **173** 60ore brown, red & grn 20 10

174 Ship's Figurehead ("Elephanten")

175 "The Reunion"

1970. 300th Anniv of "Royal Majesty's Model Chamber" (Danish Naval Museum).
517 **174** 30ore multicoloured . . . 20 10

1970. 50th Anniv of North Schleswig's Reunion with Denmark.
518 **175** 60ore violet, yellow & grn 20 10

176 Electromagnetic Apparatus

1970. 150th Anniv of Oersted's Discovery of Electromagnetism.
519 **176** 80ore green 45 10

177 Bronze-age Ship (from engraving on razor)

1970. Danish Shipping.
520 **177** 30ore purple and brown 25 10
521 – 50ore brn and purple . . 25 10
522 – 60ore brown and green 35 10
523 – 90ore blue and green . . 65 55
DESIGNS: 50ore Viking shipbuilders (Bayeux Tapestry); 60ore "Emanuel" (schooner); 90ore "A. P. Moller" (tanker).

178 Strands of Rope

179 B. Thorvaldsen from self-portrait

1970. 25th Anniv of United Nations.
524 **178** 90ore red, green & blue 65 60

1970. Birth Bicentenary of Bertel Thorvaldsen (sculptor).
525 **179** 2k. blue 65 40

180 Mathilde Fibiger (suffragette)

181 Refugees

1971. Centenary of Danish Women's Association ("Kvindesamfund").
526 **180** 80ore green 45 10

1971. Aid for Refugees.
527 **181** 50ore brown 40 20
528 60ore red 40 20

182 Danish Child

183 Hans Egede

1971. National Children's Welfare Association.
529 **182** 60ore+10ore red 45 50

1971. 25th Anniv of Hans Egede's Arrival in Greenland.
530 **183** 1k. brown 45 15

184 Swimming

185 Georg Brandes

1971. Sports.
531 **184** 30ore green and blue . . 25 25
532 – 50ore dp brown & brown 25 15
533 – 60ore yellow, blue & grey 45 15
534 – 90ore violet, green & bl 75 65
DESIGNS: 50ore Hurdling; 60ore Football; 90ore Yachting.

1971. Centenary of First Lectures by Georg Brandes (writer).
535 **185** 90ore blue 45 30

186 Beet Harvester

1972. Centenary of Danish Sugar Production.
536 **186** 80ore green 45 25

187 Meteorological Symbols

1972. Cent of Danish Meteorological Office.
537 **187** 1k.20 brown, blue & pur 60 40

188 King Frederik IX

189 "N. F. S. Grundtvig" (pencil sketch, P. Skovgaard)

1972. King Frederik IX-In Memoriam.
538 **188** 60ore red 20 10

1972. Death Centenary of N. F. S. Grundtvig (poet and clergyman).
539 **189** 1k. brown 45 25

190 Locomotive "Odin", Ship and Passengers

191 Rebild Hills

1972. 125th Anniv of Danish State Railways.
540 **190** 70ore red 35 10

1972. Nature Protection.
541 **191** 1k. green, brown & blue 45 15

192 Marsh Marigold

193 "The Tinker" (from Holberg's satire)

1972. Centenary of "Vanforehjemmet" (Home for the Disabled).
542 **192** 70ore+10ore yellow & bl 55 45

1972. 250th Anniv of Theatre in Denmark and of Holberg's Comedies.
543 **193** 70ore red 20 10

194 W.H.O. Building, Copenhagen
195 Little Belt Bridge

1972. Inauguration of World Health Organization Building, Copenhagen.
544 **194** 2k. black, blue and red 65 45

1972. Danish Construction Projects.
545 **195** 40ore green 20 20
546 – 60ore brown 30 20
547 – 70ore red 30 15
548 – 90ore green 45 35
DESIGNS: 60ore Hanstholm port; 70ore Limfjord Tunnel; 90ore Knudshoved port.

196 House, Aeroskobing
197 Johannes Jensen

1972. Danish Architecture.
549 **196** 40ore black, brown & red 20 15
550 – 60ore blue, green & brn 20 15
551 – 70ore brown, red & verm 25 15
552 – 1k.20 grn, brn & dp brn 85 65
DESIGNS—28 × 21 mm: 60ore Farmhouse, East Bornholm; 37 × 21 mm: 1k.20, Farmhouse, Hvide Sande; 21 × 37 mm: 70ore House, Christanshavn.

1973. Birth Cent of Johannes Jensen (writer).
553 **197** 90ore green 45 10

198 Cogwheels and Guardrails
199 P. C. Abildgaard (founder)

1973. Centenary of 1st Danish Factory Act.
554 **198** 50ore brown 20 10

1973. Bicentenary of Royal Veterinary College, Christianshavn.
555 **199** 1k. blue 45 30

200 "Rhododendron impeditum"
201 Nordic House, Reykjavik

1973. Cent of Jutland Horticultural Society.
556 **200** 60ore violet, green & brn 40 20
557 – 70ore pink, green & red 40 20
DESIGN: 70ore "Queen of Denmark" rose.

1973. Nordic Countries' Postal Co-operation.
558 **201** 70ore multicoloured 25 15
559 1k. multicoloured 85 70

202 Stella Nova and Sextant
203 "St. Mark the Evangelist" (Book of Dalby)

1973. 400th Anniv of Tycho Brahe's "De Nove Stella" (book on astronomy).
560 **202** 2k. blue 65 25

1973. 300th Anniv of Royal Library.
561 **203** 1k.20 multicoloured 45 45

204 Heimaey Eruption
205 "Devil and Scandalmongers" (Fanefjord Church)

1973. Aid for Victims of Heimaey Eruption, Iceland.
562 **204** 70ore+20ore red and blue 60 45

1973. Church Frescoes. Each red, turquoise and yellow on cream.
563 70ore Type **205** 1·00 30
564 70ore "Queen Esther and King Xerxes" (Tirsted Church) 1·00 30
565 70ore "The Harvest Miracle" (Jetsmark Church) 1·00 30
566 70ore "The Crowning with Thorns" (Biersted Church) 1·00 30
567 70ore "Creation of Eve" (Fanefjord Church) 1·00 30

206 Drop of Blood and Donors
207 Queen Margrethe

1974. Blood Donors Campaign.
568 **206** 90ore red and violet 35 10

1974.
569 **207** 60ore brown 30 30
570 60ore orange 30 25
571 70ore red 20 10
572 70ore brown 20 20
573 80ore green 45 25
574 80ore brown 30 15
575 90ore purple 45 10
576 90ore red 45 15
577 90ore olive 45 20
577a 90ore grey 1·30 35
578 100ore blue 45 20
579 100ore grey 45 15
580 100ore red 45 20
580a 100ore brown 40 10
580b 110ore orange 55 30
580c 110ore brown 45 25
581 120ore grey 45 30
581b 120ore red 45 15
582 130ore blue 90 65
582a 130ore red 45 10
582b 130ore brown 45 30
582c 140ore orange 1·00 1·10
582d 150ore blue 60 50
582e 150ore red 60 40
582f 160ore blue 80 55
582g 160ore red 55 15
582h 180ore green 55 20
582i 180ore blue 80 60
582j 200ore blue 70 60
582k 210ore grey 1·10 95
582l 230ore green 80 30
582m 250ore green 85 45

208 Theatre Facade
209 Hverringe

1974. Centenary of Tivoli Pantomime Theatre, Copenhagen.
583 **208** 100ore blue 45 15

1974. Provincial Series.
584 **209** 50ore multicoloured 35 30
585 – 60ore grn, dp grn & mve 50 40
586 – 70ore multicoloured 45 45
587 – 90ore multicoloured 35 15
588 – 120ore grn, red & orge 45 45
DESIGNS—HORIZ: 60ore Carl Nielsen's birthplace, Norre Lyndelse; 70ore Hans Christian Andersen's birthplace, Odense; 1k.20, Hindsholm. VERT: 90ore Hessselagergaard.

210 Orienteering
211 "Iris spuria"

1974. World Orienteering Championships.
589 **210** 70ore brown and blue 55 40
590 – 80ore blue and brown 25 15
DESIGN: 80ore Compass.

1974. Cent of Botanical Gardens, Copenhagen.
591 **211** 90ore blue, green & brn 30 15
592 – 120ore red, green and blue 50 40
DESIGN: 120ore "Dactylorhiza purpurella" (orchid).

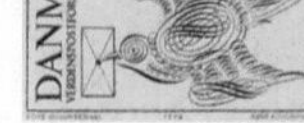

212 Mail-carriers of 1624 and 1780
213 Pigeon with Letter

1974. 350th Anniv of Danish Post Office.
593 **212** 70ore bistre and purple 35 30
594 – 90ore green and purple 45 10
DESIGN: 90ore Johan Colding's postal balloon (1808) H.M.S. "Edgar" and H.M.S. "Dictator".

1974. Centenary of U.P.U.
595 **213** 120ore blue 45 15

214 Stamp Essay (Arms)

1975. "Hafnia 76" Stamp Exhibition (1st issue). Sheet 67 × 93 mm containing T **214** and similar vert designs.
MS596 70ore grey and green; 80ore grey and green; 90ore brown and green; 100ore brown and green (sold at 5k.) 6·75 6·75
DESIGNS: 80ore King Frederik VII; 90ore King Frederik VII (different); 100ore Mercury.
See also Nos. **MS**617 and 629/**MS**630.

215 Radio Equipment of 1925
216 Queen Margrethe and I.W.Y. Emblem

1975. 50th Anniv of Danish Broadcasting.
597 **215** 90ore pink 45 15

1975. International Women's Year.
598 **216** 90ore+20ore red 55 50

217 Floral Decorated Plate
218 Moravian Brethren Church Christiansfeld

1975. Danish Porcelain.
599 **217** 50ore green 20 10
600 – 90ore red 40 10
601 – 130ore blue 70 85
DESIGNS: 90ore Floral decorated tureen; 130ore Floral decorated vase and tea-caddy.

1975. European Architectural Heritage Year.
602 **218** 70ore brown 40 35
603 – 120ore green 45 35
604 – 150ore blue 35 25
DESIGNS—HORIZ: 120ore Farmhouse, Lejre. VERT: 150ore Anna Queenstraede (street), Helsingore.

219 "Numskull Jack" (V. Pedersen)
220 Watchman's Square, Aabenraa

1975. 170th Birth Anniv of Hans Christian Andersen.
605 **219** 70ore grey and brown 50 45
606 – 90ore brown and red 60 10
607 – 130ore brown and blue 1·00 75
DESIGNS: 90ore Hans Andersen (from photograph by G. E. Hansen); 130ore "The Marshking's Daughter" (L. Frolich).

1975. Provincial series. South Jutland.
608 **220** 70ore multicoloured 40 30
609 – 90ore brown, red & blue 40 15
610 – 100ore multicoloured 45 30
611 – 120ore blue, black & grn 60 30
DESIGNS—VERT: 90ore, Haderslev Cathedral. HORIZ: 100ore, Mogeltonder Polder; 120ore, Estuary of Vidaaen at Hojer floodgates.

221 River Kingfisher

1975. Danish Endangered Animals.
612 **221** 50ore blue 50 30
613 – 70ore brown 40 30
614 – 90ore brown 40 10
615 – 130ore blue 1·10 75
616 – 200ore black 55 10
DESIGNS: 70ore West European hedgehog; 90ore Cats; 130ore Pied avocets; 200ore European otter.
The 90ore also commemorates the centenary of the Danish Society for the Prevention of Cruelty to Animals.

1975. "Hafnia 76" Stamp Exhibition (2nd issue). Sheet 69 × 93 mm containing vert designs similar to T **214** showing early Danish stamps.
MS617 50ore brown and buff; 70ore blue, brown and buff; 90ore blue, brown and buff; 130ore brown, olive and buff (sold at 5k.) 2·75 2·75
DESIGNS: 50ore 1851 4 R.B.S. stamp; 70ore 1851 2 R.B.S. stamp; 90ore 1864 2sk. stamp; 130ore 1870 8sk. stamp with inverted frame.

222 Viking Longship

1976. Bicentenary of American Revolution.
618 **222** 70ore+20ore brown 55 50
619 – 90ore+20ore red 55 50
620 – 100ore+20ore green 55 50
621 – 130ore+20ore blue 55 50
DESIGNS: 90ore Freighter "Thingvalla"; 100ore Liner "Frederik VIII"; 130ore Cadet full-rigged ship "Danmark".

223 "Humanity"
224 Old Copenhagen

1976. Centenary of Danish Red Cross.
622 **223** 100ore+20ore black and red 30 25
623 130ore+20ore black, red and blue 50 30

1976. Provincial Series. Copenhagen.
624 **224** 60ore multicoloured 25 35
625 – 80ore multicoloured 25 25
626 – 100ore red & vermilion 40 10
627 – 130ore grn, dp brn & brn 95 1·00
DESIGNS—VERT: 80ore View from the Round Tower; 100ore Interior of the Central Railway Station. HORIZ: 130ore Harbour buildings.

225 Handicapped Person in Wheelchair
226 Mail Coach Driver (detail from "A String of Horses outside an Inn" (O. Bache))

1976. Danish Foundation for the Disabled.
628 **225** 100ore+20ore black and red 45 40

1976. "Hafnia 76" Stamp Exhibition.
629 **226** 130ore multicoloured 60 65
MS630 103 × 82 mm. **226** 130ore multicoloured 8·75 8·75

227 Prof. Emil Hansen
228 Moulding Glass

1976. Centenary of Carlsberg Foundation.
631 **227** 100ore red 40 15

1976. Danish Glass Industry.
632 **228** 60ore green 30 25
633 – 80ore brown 35 15
634 – 130ore blue 70 65
635 – 150ore red 45 15
DESIGNS: 80ore Removing glass from pipe; 130ore Cutting glass; 150ore Blowing glass.

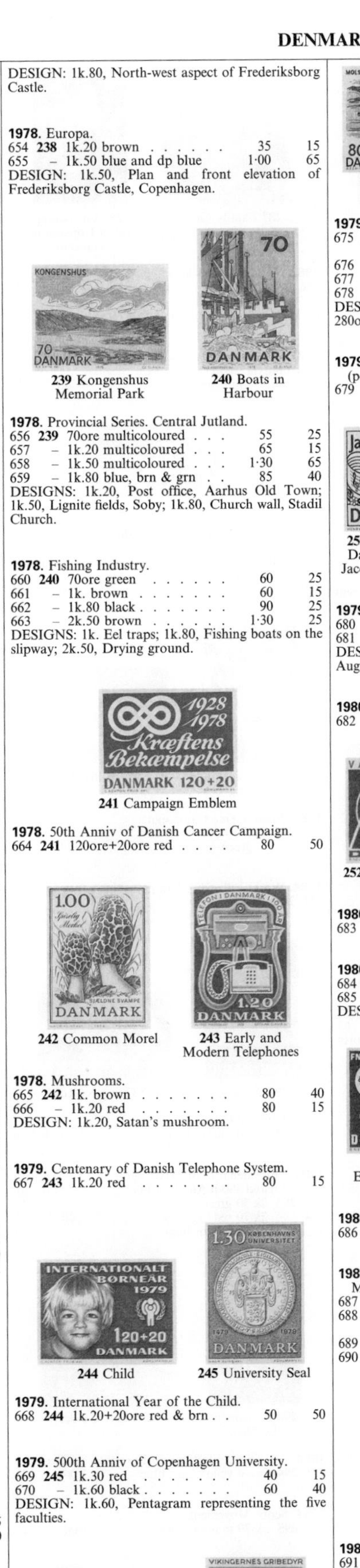

229 Five Water Lilies **230** "Give Way"

1977. Northern Countries Co-operation in Nature Conservation and Environment Protection.
636 **229** 100ore multicoloured . . 30 20
637 130ore multicoloured . . 75 80

1977. Road Safety.
638 **230** 100ore brown 55 10

231 Mother and Child **232** Allinge

1977. 25th Anniv of Danish Society for the Mentally Handicapped.
639 **231** 100ore+20ore green, blue and brown 50 50

1977. Europa.
640 **232** 1k. brown 45 15
641 – 1k.30 blue . . . . 2·50 1·90
DESIGN: 1k.30, Farm near Ringsted.

233 Kongeaen **234** Hammers and Horseshoes

1977. Provincial Series. South Jutland.
642 **233** 60ore green and blue . . 1·10 75
643 – 90ore multicoloured . . . 60 40
644 – 150ore multicoloured . . 60 40
645 – 200ore grn, pur & emer 60 25
DESIGNS: 90ore Skallingen; 150ore Torskind; 200ore Jelling.

1977. Danish Crafts.
646 **234** 80ore brown 40 15
647 – 1k. red 40 15
648 – 1k.30 blue 85 40
DESIGNS: 1k. Chisel, square and plane; 1k.30, Trowel, ceiling brush and folding rule.

235 Globe Flower **236** Handball Player and Emblem

1977. Endangered Flora.
649 **235** 1k. green, yellow & brn 35 15
650 – 1k.50 green, ol & brn . . 90 50
DESIGN: 1k.50, "Cnidium dubium".

1978. Men's Handball World Championship.
651 **236** 1k.20 red 50 15

237 Christian IV on Horseback **238** Jens Bang's House, Aalborg

1978. Centenary of National History Museum, Frederiksborg.
652 **237** 1k.20 brown 55 15
653 – 1k.80 black 70 25
DESIGN: 1k.80, North-west aspect of Frederiksborg Castle.

1978. Europa.
654 **238** 1k.20 brown 35 15
655 – 1k.50 blue and dp blue 1·00 65
DESIGN: 1k.50, Plan and front elevation of Frederiksborg Castle, Copenhagen.

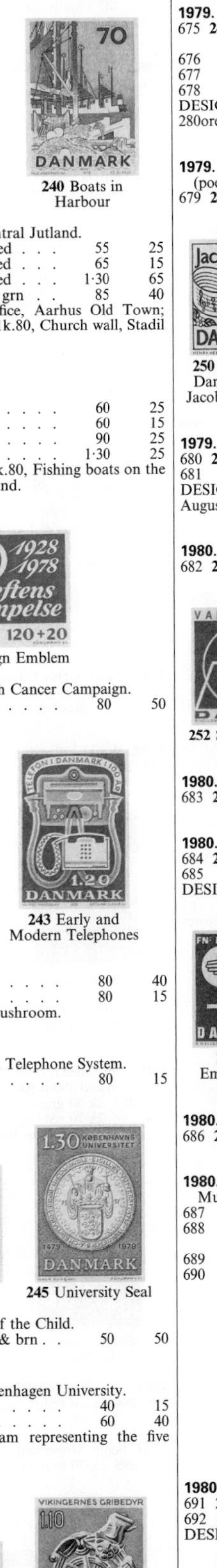

239 Kongenshus Memorial Park **240** Boats in Harbour

1978. Provincial Series. Central Jutland.
656 **239** 70ore multicoloured . . . 55 25
657 – 1k.20 multicoloured . . . 65 15
658 – 1k.50 multicoloured . . . 1·30 65
659 – 1k.80 blue, brn & grn . . 85 40
DESIGNS: 1k.20, Post office, Aarhus Old Town; 1k.50, Lignite fields, Soby; 1k.80, Church wall, Stadil Church.

1978. Fishing Industry.
660 **240** 70ore green 60 25
661 – 1k. brown 60 15
662 – 1k.80 black 90 25
663 – 2k.50 brown . . . . . . 1·30 25
DESIGNS: 1k. Eel traps; 1k.80, Fishing boats on the slipway; 2k.50, Drying ground.

241 Campaign Emblem

1978. 50th Anniv of Danish Cancer Campaign.
664 **241** 120ore+20ore red 80 50

242 Common Morel **243** Early and Modern Telephones

1978. Mushrooms.
665 **242** 1k. brown 80 40
666 – 1k.20 red 80 15
DESIGN: 1k.20, Satan's mushroom.

1979. Centenary of Danish Telephone System.
667 **243** 1k.20 red 80 15

244 Child **245** University Seal

1979. International Year of the Child.
668 **244** 1k.20+20ore red & brn . . 50 50

1979. 500th Anniv of Copenhagen University.
669 **245** 1k.30 red 40 15
670 – 1k.60 black 60 40
DESIGN: 1k.60, Pentagram representing the five faculties.

246 Letter Mail Cariole **247** Pendant

1979. Europa.
671 **246** 1k.30 red 90 15
672 – 1k.60 blue . . . . 1·20 65
DESIGN: 1k.60, Morse key and sounder.

1979. Viking "Gripping Beast" Decorations.
673 **247** 1k.10 brown 35 15
674 – 2k. green 90 25
DESIGN: 2k. Key.

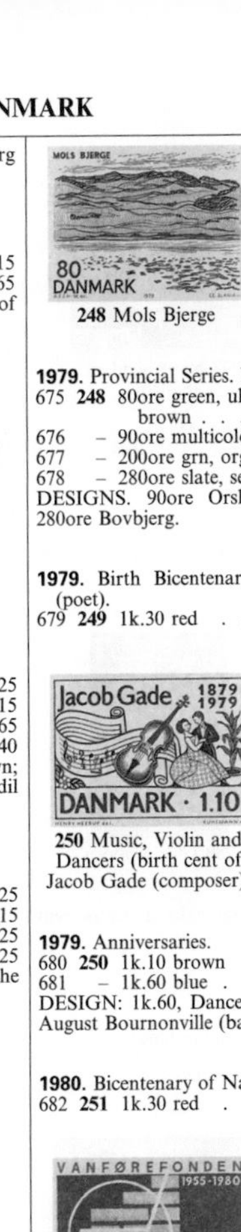

248 Mols Bjerge **249** Silhouette of Oehlenschlager

1979. Provincial Series. North Jutland.
675 **248** 80ore green, ultram & brown 55 25
676 – 90ore multicoloured . . . 1·60 1·00
677 – 200ore grn, orge & red . . 90 15
678 – 280ore slate, sepia & brn 1·10 65
DESIGNS. 90ore Orslev Kloster; 200ore Trans; 280ore Bovbjerg.

1979. Birth Bicentenary of Adam Oehlenschlager (poet).
679 **249** 1k.30 red 50 15

250 Music, Violin and Dancers (birth cent of Jacob Gade (composer)) **251** Royal Mail Guards' Office, Copenhagen (drawing, Peter Klaestrup)

1979. Anniversaries.
680 **250** 1k.10 brown 40 25
681 – 1k.60 blue 65 40
DESIGN: 1k.60, Dancer at bar (death centenary of August Bournonville (ballet master)).

1980. Bicentenary of National Postal Service.
682 **251** 1k.30 red 50 15

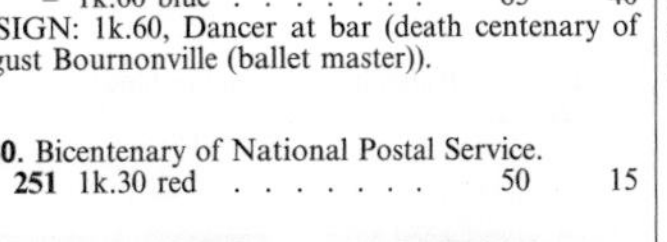

252 Stylized Wheelchair **253** Karen Blixen (writer)

1980. 25th Anniv of Foundation for the Disabled.
683 **252** 130ore+20ore red 80 40

1980. Europa.
684 **253** 1k.30 red 45 15
685 – 1k.60 blue 85 40
DESIGN: 1k.60, August Krogh (physiologist).

254 Symbols of Employment, Health and Education **255** Lindholme Hoje

1980. U.N. Decade for Women World Conference.
686 **254** 1k.60 blue 80 25

1980. Provincial Series. Jutland North of Limfjorden. Multicoloured.
687 80ore Type **255** 45 25
688 110ore Skagen lighthouse (vert) 70 25
689 200ore Borglum 80 15
690 280ore Fishing boats at Vorupor . . . . 1·60 75

256 Silver Pitcher, c. 1641

1980. Nordic Countries Postal Co-operation.
691 **256** 1k.30 black and red . . . 50 15
692 – 1k.80 blue & dp blue . . 1·20 65
DESIGN: 1k.80, Bishop's bowl.

257 Earliest Danish Coin, Hedeby (c. 800)

1980. Coins from the Royal Collection.
693 **257** 1k.30 red and brown . . 55 25
694 – 1k.40 olive and green . . 1·00 65
695 – 1k.80 blue and grey . . . 1·00 65
DESIGNS: 1k.40, Silver coin of Valdemar the Great and Bishop Absalon (1152–82); 1k.80, Christian VII gold current ducat (1781).

258 Lace Pattern **259** Children Playing in Yard

1980. Lace Patterns. Various designs showing lace.
696 **258** 1k.10 brown 55 25
697 – 1k.30 red 55 15
698 – 2k. green 80 15

1981. National Children's Welfare Association.
699 **259** 1k.60+20ore red 80 50

260 Original Houses, 1631 **261** Tilting at a Barrel (Shrovetide custom)

1981. 350th Anniv of Nyboder (Naval Barracks), Copenhagen.
700 **260** 1k.30 red and yellow . . 70 50
701 – 1k.60 red and yellow . . 55 15
DESIGN: 1k.60, 18th-century terraced houses.

1981. Europa.
702 **261** 1k.60 red 70 25
703 – 2k. blue . . . . 1·10 25
DESIGN: 2k. Midsummer bonfire.

262 Soro **263** Rigensgade District, Copenhagen

1981. Provincial Series. Zealand and Surrounding Islands.
704 **262** 100ore blue and brown 45 25
705 – 150ore black and green 60 40
706 – 160ore brown and green 60 15
707 – 200ore multicoloured . . 80 40
708 – 230ore blue and brown 90 40
DESIGNS: 150ore N. F. S. Grundtvig's childhood home, Udby; 160ore Kaj Munk's childhood home, Opager; 200ore Gronsund; 230ore Bornholm.

1981. European Urban Renaissance Year.
709 **263** 1k.60 red 50 15

264 Decaying Tree **265** Ellehammer at Lindholm, 1906

1981. International Year for Disabled Persons.
710 **264** 2k.+20ore blue . . . . . 1·00 70

1981. History of Aviation.
711 **265** 1k. green and black . . . 55 40
712 – 1k.30 brown & dp brn . . 80 40
713 – 1k.60 vermilion & red . . 55 15
714 – 2k.30 blue & dp blue . . 80 40
DESIGNS: 1k.30, A. T. Botved's Fokker biplane "R-1" (Copenhagen–Tokyo, 1926); 1k.60, Hojriis Hillig's Bellanca Special "Liberty" (U.S.A.–Denmark, 1931); 2k.30. Douglas DC-7C "Seven Seas" (first Polar flight, 1957).

266 Queen Margrethe II **267** Revenue Cutter "Argus"

1982.

715	**266**	1k.60 red	50	15
716		1k.60 green	2·50	1·90
717		1k.80 brown	80	40
718		2k. red	80	15
719		2k.20 green	2·10	65
720		2k.30 violet	80	65
721		2k.50 red	80	15
722		2k.70 blue	1·00	40
723		2k.70 red	1·00	15
724		2k.80 red	1·00	20
725		3k. violet	1·00	25
726		3k. red	1·00	15
727		3k.20 violet	1·00	40
727a		3k.20 red	1·20	15

728 3k.30 black . . . . . . 1·20 50
729 3k.40 green . . . . . . 2·30 1·60
730 3k.50 blue . . . . . . 1·20 25
730a 3k.50 purple . . . . . . 1·20 40
730b 3k.50 red . . . . . . 1·20 15
731 3k.70 blue . . . . . . 1·20 40
732 3k.75 green . . . . . . 1·60 65
733 3k.80 blue . . . . . . 1·20 40
734 3k.80 purple . . . . . . 1·60 1·30
735 4k.10 blue . . . . . . 1·60 25
736 4k.20 violet . . . . . . 2·30 90
737 4k.40 blue . . . . . . 1·60 40
738 4k.50 purple . . . . . . 1·80 1·30
739 4k.75 blue . . . . . . 1·80 25

1982. 350th Anniv Customs Service.
740 **267** 1k.60 red 50 15

268 Skater

269 Villein (Abolition of adscription, 1788)

1982. World Figure Skating Championships, Copenhagen.
741 **268** 2k. blue 80 25

1982. Europa.
742 **269** 2k. brown . . . . 1·00 15
743 – 2k.70 blue . . . . 1·40 65
DESIGN: 2k.70, Procession of women (Enfranchisement of women, 1915).

270 Distorted Plant

271 Dairy Farm at Hjedding and Butter Churn

1982. 25th Anniv of Danish Multiple Sclerosis Society.
744 **270** 2k.+40ore red . . . . . 1·60 90

1982. Centenary of Co-operative Dairy Farming.
745 **271** 1k.80 brown 80 40

272 Hand holding Quill Pen

273 Blicher (after J. V. Gertner)

1982. 400th Anniv of Record Office.
746 **272** 2k.70 green . . . . 1·00 25

1982. Birth Bicent of Steen Steensen Blicher (poet).
747 **273** 2k. red 80 15

274 Odense Printing Press, 1482

275 Petersen and the Number Men

1982. 500th Anniv of Printing in Denmark.
748 **274** 1k.80 brown 80 40

1982. Birth Centenary of Robert Storm Petersen (cartoonist).
749 **275** 1k.50 red and blue . . . 50 25
750 – 2k. green and red 80 25
DESIGN—HORIZ: 2k. Peter and Ping with dog.

276 Library Seal

1982. 500th Anniv University Library.
751 **276** 2k.70 brown and black . . 1·00 25

277 "Interglobal Communications"

278 Nurse tending Patient

1983. World Communications Year.
752 **277** 2k. orange, red & blue . . 1·60 25

1983. Red Cross.
753 **278** 2k.+40ore blue & red . . 1·00 90

279 Clown and Girl with Balloon

280 Lene Koppen

1983. 400th Anniv of Dyrehavsbakken Amusement Park.
754 **279** 2k. multicoloured 80 15

1983. World Badminton Championships.
755 **280** 2k.70 blue . . . . 1·00 25

281 Burin and Engraving of lore Numeral Stamp

282 Egeskov Castle

1983. 50th Anniv of Danish Recess-printed Stamps.
756 **281** 2k.50 red 80 15

1983. Nordic Countries Postal Co-operation. "Visit the North".
757 **282** 2k.50 dp brown & brn . . 70 20
758 – 3k.50 dp blue & blue . . 90 65
DESIGN: 3k.50, Troldkirken long barrow, North Jutland.

283 Kildeskovshallen Recreation Centre, Copenhagen

284 Weights and Measures

1983. Europa.
759 **283** 2k.50 red and brown . . 1·20 15
760 – 3k.50 dp blue & blue . . 1·40 40
DESIGN: 3k.50, Sallingsund Bridge.

1983. 300th Anniv of Weights and Measures Ordinance.
761 **284** 2k.50 red 80 10

285 Title Page of Law

286 Crashed Car and Hand with Eye (Police)

1983. 300th Anniv of King Christian V's Danish Law (code of laws for Norway).
762 **285** 5k. dp brown & brown . 1·80 50

1983. Life-saving Services.
763 **286** 1k. brown 50 25
764 – 2k.50 red 90 25
765 – 3k.50 blue . . . . 1·60 40
DESIGNS: 2k.50 Ladder, stretcher and fire-hose (ambulance and fire services); 3k.50 Lifebelt and lifeboat (sea-rescue services).

287 Family Group

288 Grundtvig (after Constantin Hansen)

1983. The Elderly in Society.
766 **287** 2k. green 70 40
767 – 2k.50 red 90 15
DESIGN: 2k.50 Elderly people in train.

1983. Birth Bicentenary of Nicolai Frederik Severin Grundtvig (writer).
768 **288** 2k.50 brown 80 25

289 Perspective Painting

1983. Birth Bicentenary of Christoffer Wilhelm Eckersberg (painter).
769 **289** 2k.50 red 80 25

290 Spade and Sapling

291 Billiards

1984. Plant a Tree Campaign.
770 **290** 2k.70 yellow, red and green . . . . 1·00 25

1984. World Billiards Championships.
771 **291** 3k.70 green . . . . 1·20 25

292 Athletes

293 Compass Rose

1984. Olympic Games, Los Angeles.
772 **292** 2k.70+40ore mult . . . . 1·80 1·00

1984. Bicentenary of Hydrographic Department (2k.30) and 300th Anniv of Pilotage Service (2k.70).
773 **293** 2k.30 green 90 50
774 – 2k.70 red . . . . 1·00 15
DESIGN: 2k.70, Pilot boat.

294 Parliament Emblem

295 Girl Guides

1984. 2nd Direct Elections to European Parliament.
775 **294** 2k.70 yellow and blue . . 1·00 25

1984. Scout Movement.
776 **295** 2k.70 multicoloured . . . 1·00 15

296 Bridge

297 Anchor (memorial to Danish Sailors)

1984. Europa. 25th Anniv of European Post and Telecommunications Conference.
777 **296** 2k.70 red . . . . 1·20 15
778 3k.70 blue . . . . 1·20 90

1984. 40th Anniv of Normandy Invasion.
779 **297** 2k.70 purple . . . . . . 1·70 15

298 Prince Henrik

299 Old Danish Inn

1984. 50th Birthday of Prince Henrik.
780 **298** 2k.70 brown . . . . . . 1·00 15

1984.
781 **299** 3k. multicoloured . . . . 1·20 65

300 Shoal of Fish (research)

1984. Danish Fisheries and Shipping.
782 **300** 2k.30 blue and green . . 1·40 75
783 – 2k.70 blue and red . . . 1·00 15
784 – 3k.30 blue and violet . . 1·40 75
785 – 3k.70 blue & ultramarine 1·60 75
DESIGNS: 2k.70, Ships (sea transport); 3k.30, "Bettina" (deep sea fishing boat); 3k.70, Deck of trawler "Jonna Tornby".

301 Heart and Cardiograph

302 Bird with Letter

1984. Heart Foundation.
786 **301** 2k.70+40ore red . . . . 1·80 1·00

1984.
787 **302** 1k. multicoloured 50 15

303 "Holberg meeting Officer and Dandy" (Wilhelm Marstrand)

304 Woman and Sabbath Candles

1984. 300th Birth Anniv of Ludvig Holberg (historian and playwright).
788 **303** 2k.70 black, stone & red . 1·00 15

1984. 300th Anniv of Jewish Community.
789 **304** 3k.70 multicoloured . . . 1·20 65

305 "Ymer sucking Milk from the Cow Odhumble" (Nicolai Abildgaard)

1984. Paintings. Multicoloured.
790 5k. "Carnival in Rome" (Christoffer Wilhelm Eckersberg) (horiz) . . . . 2·50 1·80
791 10k. Type **305** . . . . . . 4·25 2·50

306 Gothersgade Reformed Church, Copenhagen

1985. 300th Anniv of French and German Reformed Church in Denmark.
792 **306** 2k.80 red . . . . 1·00 15

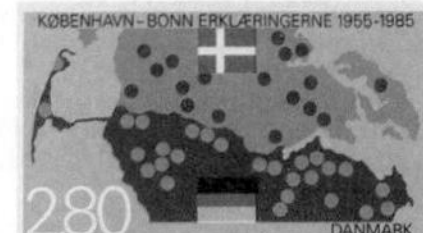
307 Flags and Border

1985. 30th Anniv of Copenhagen–Bonn Declarations.
793 **307** 2k.80 multicoloured . . . 1·20 15

308 Flag, Girl and Boy

1985. International Youth Year.
794 **308** 3k.80 multicoloured . . . 1·20 40

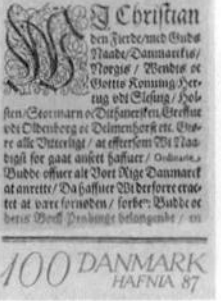
309 Statue on Postmen

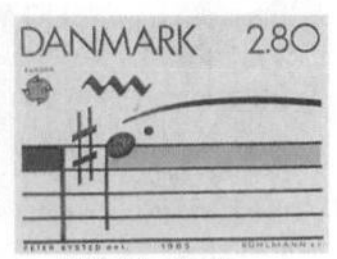
310 Music Score

1985. "Hafnia 87" International Stamp Exhibition, Copenhagen (1st issue). Sheet 70 × 95 mm containing T **309** and similar vert designs, each black, ochre and red.
MS795 200ore Type **309**; 250ore 1711 mandate on disinfection of letters; 280ore 1775 decree granting postal monopoly to Danish Post Office; 380ore 1851 title page of *Law on Postal Mail* (sold at 15k.) . . . . 4·50 4·50
See also Nos. **MS**817, **MS**836 and 851/**MS**852.

1985. Europa. Music Year.
796 **310** 2k.80 yell, red & verm . . 1·10 40
797 – 3k.80 black, bl & grn . . 1·80 1·10
DESIGN: 3k.80, Music score (different).

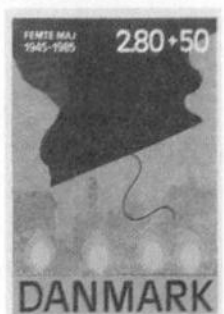
311 Flames and Houses

312 Queen Ingrid and "Chrysanthemum frutescens" "Sofieri"

1985. 40th Anniv of Liberation.
798 **311** 2k.80+50ore mult . . . . 1·80 1·00
The surtax was for the benefit of Resistance veterans.

1985. 50th Anniv of Queen Ingrid's Arrival in Denmark.
799 **312** 2k.80 multicoloured . . . 1·00 25

313 Faro Bridges

314 St. Canute and Lund Cathedral

1985. Inauguration of Faro Bridges.
800 **313** 2k.80 multicoloured . . . 1·00 15

1985. 900th Anniv of St. Canute's Deed of Gift to Lund.
801 **314** 2k.80 black and red . . . 80 15
802 – 3k. black and red . . . . 1·70 1·00
DESIGN: 3k. St. Canute and Helsingborg.

315 Gymnastics

316 Woman Cyclist

1985. Sports. Multicoloured.
803 2k.80 Type **315** . . . . . . 1·10 15
804 3k.80 Canoeing . . . . . . 1·40 50
805 6k. Cycling . . . . 2·20 75

1985. United Nations Women's Decade.
806 **316** 3k.80 multicoloured . . . 1·20 50

317 Kronborg Castle

318 Dove and U.N. Emblem

1985. 400th Anniv of Kronborg Castle, Elsinore.
807 **317** 2k.80 multicoloured . . . 1·00 15

1985. 40th Anniv of U.N.O.
808 **318** 3k.80 multicoloured . . . 1·20 65

319 Niels and Margrethe Bohr

320 Tapestry (detail) by Caroline Ebbesen

1985. Birth Centenary of Niels Bohr (nuclear physicist).
809 **319** 2k.80 multicoloured . . . 1·20 90

1985. 25th Anniv of National Society for Welfare of the Mentally Ill.
810 **320** 2k.80+40ore mult . . . . 1·60 1·00

321 "D" in Sign Language

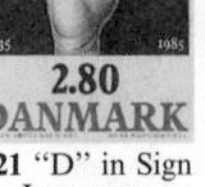
322 Stern of Boat

1985. 50th Anniv of Danish Association of the Deaf.
811 **321** 2k.80 brown & black . . 1·10 25

1985.
812 **322** 2k.80 multicoloured . . . 1·00 25

323 "Head"

1985.
813 **323** 3k.80 multicoloured . . . 2·50 1·60

324 Leaves and Barbed Wire

1986. 25th Anniv of Amnesty International.
814 **324** 2k.80 multicoloured . . . 1·00 15

325 Girl with Bird

326 Reichhardt as Papageno in "The Magic Flute"

1986.
815 **325** 2k.80 multicoloured . . . 1·00 65

1986. 1st Death Anniv of Poul Reichhardt (actor).
816 **326** 2k.80+50ore mult . . . . 1·20 90

327 Holstein Carriage, 1840

1986. "Hafnia 87" International Stamp Exhibition, Copenhagen (2nd issue). Sheet 70 × 94 mm containing T **327** and similar vert designs. Multicoloured.
MS817 100ore Type **327** 250ore Ice boat, 1880; 280ore Mail van, 1908; 380ore First regular mail plane, 1919 (sold at 15k.) . . . . . . 6·75 6·75

328 Hands reading Braille

329 Bands of Colour

1986. 75th Anniv of Danish Society for the Blind.
818 **328** 2k.80+50ore red, brown and black . . . . . . 1·60 75

1986. 50th Anniv of Danish Arthritis Association.
819 **329** 2k.80+50ore mult . . . . 1·60 75

330 Changing the Guard at Barracks

1986. Bicentenary of Royal Danish Life Guards Barracks, Rosenborg.
820 **330** 2k.80 multicoloured . . . 1·00 25

331 Academy and Arms

332 Hands reaching out

1986. 400th Anniv of Soro Academy.
821 **331** 2k.80 multicoloured . . . 1·00 15

1986. International Peace Year.
822 **332** 3k.80 multicoloured . . . 1·20 40

333 Prince Frederik

334 Station

1986. 18th Birthday of Crown Prince Frederik.
823 **333** 2k.80 black and red . . . 1·20 15

1986. Inaug of Hoje Tastrup Railway Station.
824 **334** 2k.80 black, bl & red . . 1·00 15

335 Aalborg

336 Common Raven

1986. Nordic Countries Postal Co-operation. Twinned Towns.
825 **335** 2k.80 black . . . . 1·10 15
826 – 3k.80 blue and red . . . 1·20 40
DESIGN: 3k.80, Thisted.

1986. Birds. Multicoloured.
827 2k.80 Type **336** . . . . . . 1·60 40
828 2k.80 Common starling ("Sturnus vulgaris") . . . 1·60 40
829 2k.80 Mute swan ("Cygnus olor") . . . . 1·60 40
830 2k.80 Northern lapwing ("Vanellus vanellus") . . . 1·60 40
831 2k.80 Eurasian skylark ("Alauda arvensis") . . . 1·60 40

337 Post Box, Wires and Telephone

338 Sports Pictograms

1986. 19th International Postal Telegraph and Telephone Congress, Copenhagen.
832 **337** 2k.80 multicoloured . . . 1·00 15

1986. 125th Anniv of Danish Rifle, Gymnastics and Sports Clubs.
833 **338** 2k.80 multicoloured . . . 1·00 15

339 Roadsweeper

340 Stagecoach, 1840

1986. Europa.
834 **339** 2k.80 red . . . . 1·30 15
835 – 3k.80 blue . . . . 1·60 65
DESIGN: 3k.80, Refuse truck.

1986. "Hafnia 87" International Stamp Exhibition, Copenhagen (3rd issue). Sheet 70 × 94 mm containing T **340** and similar vert design. Multicoloured.
MS836 100ore Type **340**; 250ore Postmaster, 1840; 280ore Postman, 1851; 380ore Rural Postman, 1893 (sold at 15k.) 6·75 6·75

341 Man fleeing

1986. Aid for Refugees.
837 **341** 2k.80 blue, brown & blk 1·00 25

342 Cupid

343 Lutheran Communion Service in Thorslunde Church

1986. Bicentenary of First Performance of "The Whims of Cupid and the Ballet Master" by V. Galeotti and J. Lolle.
838 **342** 3k.80 multicoloured . . . 1·20 50

1986. 450th Anniv of Reformation.
839 **343** 6k.50 multicoloured . . . 2·50 75

344 Graph of Danish Economic Growth and Unemployment Rate

345 Abstract

1986. 25th Anniv of Organization of Economic Co-operation and Development.
840 **344** 3k.80 multicoloured . . . 1·80 75

1987.
841 **345** 2k.80 multicoloured . . . 1·00 15

346 Price Label through Magnifying Glass

347 Fresco

1987. 40th Anniv of Danish Consumer Council.
842 **346** 2k.80 black and red . . . 1·00 15

1987. Ribe Cathedral. Multicoloured.
843 3k. Type **347** . . . . 1·00 40
844 3k.80 Stained glass window (detail) . . . . 1·60 75
845 6k.50 Mosaic (detail) . . . . 2·50 1·30

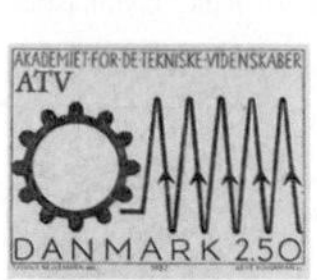

348 Cog and Oscillating Waves

349 Gentofte Central Library

1987. 50th Anniv of Danish Academy of Technical Sciences.
846 **348** 2k.50 black and red . . . 1·20 75

1987. Europa. Architecture.
847 **349** 2k.80 red . . . . 1·00 25
848 – 3k.80 blue . . . . 1·70 75
DESIGN—HORIZ: 3k.80, Hoje Tastrup Senior School.

350 Ball and Ribbons

351 Pigs

1987. 8th Gymnaestrada (World Gymnastics Show), Herning.
849 **350** 2k.80 multicoloured . . . 1·00 15

1987. Centenary of First Co-operative Bacon Factory, Horsens.
850 **351** 3k.80 multicoloured . . . 1·20 50

352 1912 5k. Stamp, Steam Locomotive and Mail Wagon

1987. "Hafnia 87" International Stamp Exhibition, Copenhagen.
851 **352** 280ore multicoloured . . 1·60 1·20
MS852 70 × 95 mm. No. 851 (sold at 45k.) . . . . 22·00 22·00

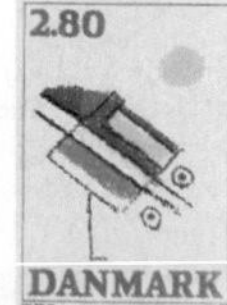

353 Single Scull

354 Abstract

1987. World Rowing Championships, Bagsvaerd Lake.
853 **353** 3k.80 indigo and blue . . 1·20 40

1987.
854 **354** 2k.80 multicoloured . . . 1·00 15

355 Waves

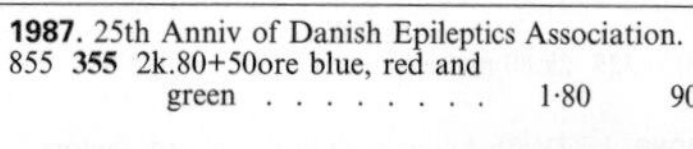

1987. 25th Anniv of Danish Epileptics Association.
855 **355** 2k.80+50ore blue, red and green . . . . 1·80 90

356 Rask

357 Association Badge

1987. Birth Bicentenary of Rasmus Kristjan Rask (philologist).
856 **356** 2k.80 red and brown . . 1·00 15

1987. 125th Anniv of Clerical Association for Home Mission in Denmark.
857 **357** 3k. brown . . . . 1·00 15

358 Lions supporting Monogram

1988. 400th Anniv of Accession of King Christian IV.
858 **358** 3k. gold and blue . . . . 1·10 15
859 – 4k.10 multicoloured . . . 1·60 40
DESIGN: 4k.10, Portrait of Christian IV by P. Isaacsz.

359 Worm and Artefacts

360 St. Canute's Church

1988. 400th Birth Anniv of Ole Worm (antiquarian).
860 **359** 7k.10 brown . . . . . . 2·30 1·30

1988. Millenary of Odense.
861 **360** 3k. brown, black & green 1·00 15

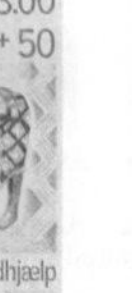

361 African Mother and Child

362 Sirens, Workers and Emblem

1988. Danish Church Aid.
862 **361** 3k.+50ore mult . . . . . 1·80 75

1988. 50th Anniv of Civil Defence Administration.
863 **362** 2k.70 blue and orange . . 80 50

363 Blood Circulation of Heart

364 Postwoman on Bicycle

1988. 40th Anniv of W.H.O.
864 **363** 4k.10 red, blue and black 1·20 50

1988. Europa. Transport and Communications. Multicoloured.
865 3k. Type **364** 80 15
866 4k.10 Mobile telephone . . . 1·80 50

365 "King Christian VII riding past Liberty Monument" (C. W. Eckersberg)

366 "Men of Industry" (detail, P. S. Kroyer)

1988. Bicentenary of Abolition of Villeinage.
867 **365** 3k.20 multicoloured . . . 1·20 65

1988. 150th Anniv of Federation of Danish Industries.
868 **366** 3k. multicoloured . . . . 1·00 25

367 Speedway Riders

368 Glass Mosaic (Niels Winkel)

1988. World Speedway Championships.
869 **367** 4k.10 multicoloured . . . 1·20 40

1988. Centenary of Danish Metalworkers' Union.
870 **368** 3k. multicoloured . . . . 1·00 15

369 College

1988. Bicent of Tonder Teacher Training College.
871 **369** 3k. brown . . . . 1·00 15

370 "Tribute to Leon Degand" (Robert Jacobsen)

1988. Franco-Danish Cultural Co-operation.
872 **370** 4k.10 red and black . . . 2·50 1·30

371 Emblem

372 Lumby Windmill

1988. 5th Anniv of National Council for the Unmarried Mother and Her Child.
873 **371** 3k.+50ore red . . . . . 1·80 75

1988. Mills.
874 **372** 3k. black, red & orange 1·00 15
875 – 7k.10 black, ultramarine and blue . . . . 3·00 1·30
DESIGN: 7k.10, Veistrup water mill.

373 "Bathing Boys 1902" (Peter Hansen)

1988. Paintings. Multicoloured.
876 4k.10 Type **373** . . . . . 2·30 1·60
877 10k. "Hill at Overkoerby. Winter 1917" (Fritz Syberg) . . . . 5·25 3·25

374 "The Little Mermaid" (statue, Edvard Eriksen), Copenhagen

375 Army Members in Public House

1989. Centenary of Danish Tourist Association.
878 **374** 3k.20 green . . . . 1·20 15

1989. 102nd Anniv of Salvation Army in Denmark.
879 **375** 3k.20+50ore mult . . . . 2·10 75

376 Footballer

377 Emblem

1989. Centenary of Danish Football Association.
880 **376** 3k.20 red, blk & lt red . . 1·20 15

1989. 40th Anniv of N.A.T.O.
881 **377** 4k.40 bl, cobalt & gold 1·60 50

378 "Valby Woman"

379 "Parliament Flag

1989. Nordic Countries' Postal Co-operation. Traditional Costumes. Engravings by Christoffer Wilhelm Eckersberg. Multicoloured.
882 3k.20 Type **378** . . . . . . 1·00 15
883 4k.40 "Pork Butcher" . . . 2·00 65

1989. 3rd Direct Elections to European Parliament.
884 **379** 3k. blue and yellow . . . 1·20 65

380 Lego Bricks

381 Tractor, 1917

1989. Europa. Children's Toys. Multicoloured.
885 3k.20 Type **380** . . . . . . 1·00 15
886 4k.40 Wooden guardsmen by Kay Bojesen . . . . 2·00 65

1989. Centenary of Danish Agricultural Museum.
887 **381** 3k.20 red . . . . 1·20 15

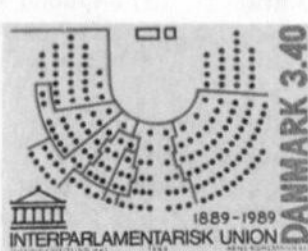

382 Diagram of Folketing (Parliament) Chamber

1989. Centenary of Interparliamentary Union.
888 **382** 3k.40 red and black . . . 2·30 90

383 Chart and Boat Identity Number

1989. Centenary of Danish Fishery and Marine Research Institute.
889 **383** 3k.20 multicoloured . . . 1·20 15

384 "Ingemann" (after J. V. Gertner)

385 Scene from "They Caught the Ferry" (50th anniv of Danish Government Film Office)

1989. Birth Bicentenary of Bernhard Severin Ingemann (poet)
890 **384** 7k.70 green . . . . 2·50 90

1989. Danish Film Industry.
891 **385** 3k. blue, black & orge . . 1·20 40
892 – 3k.20 pink, blk & orge . . 1·00 15
893 – 4k.40 brown, blk & orge 1·70 50

DESIGNS: 3k.20, Scene from "The Golden Smile" (birth cent of Bodil Ipsen, actress); 4k.40, Carl Th. Dreyer (director, birth cent).

386 Stamps

1989. 50th Stamp Day.
894 **386** 3k.20 salmon, orge & brn 1·20 15

387 "Part of Northern Citadel Bridge" (Christen Kobke)

1989. Paintings. Multicoloured.
895 4k.40 Type **387** 2·10 1·50
896 10k. "A Little Girl, Elise Kobke, with Cup" (Constantin Hansen) 3·25 2·75

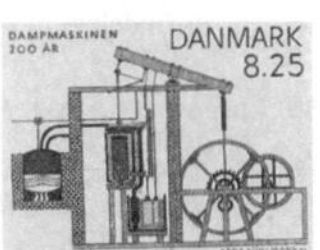

388 Silver Coffee Pot (Axel Johannes Kroyer, 1726)
389 Andrew Mitchell's Steam Engine

1990. Centenary of Museum of Decorative Art, Copenhagen.
897 **388** 3k.50 black and blue 1·20 25

1990. Bicent of Denmark's First Steam Engine.
898 **389** 8k.25 brown 2·75 1·10

390 Queen Margrethe II
391 Royal Monogram over Door of Haderslev Post Office

1990.
910 **390** 3k.50 red 1·20 15
911 3k.75 green 2·10 1·50
912 3k.75 red 1·20 15
913 4k. brown 1·20 50
914 4k.50 violet 1·60 65
915 4k.75 blue 1·60 40
916 4k.75 violet 1·60 75
917 5k. blue 1·60 40
918 5k.25 black 1·80 75
919 5k.50 green 1·80 1·60

1990. Europa. Post Office Buildings.
930 **391** 3k.50 yellow, red & blk 1·00 15
931 – 4k.75 multicoloured 1·30 50
DESIGN: 4k.75, Odense Post Office.

392 Main Guardhouse, Rigging Crane and Ships (after C. O. Willars)

1990. 300th Anniv of Nyholm.
932 **392** 4k.75 black 1·60 40

393 Covered Ice Dish
394 Marsh Mallow

1990. Bicentenary of Flora Danica Banquet Service. Multicoloured.
933 3k.50 Type **393** 1·60 65
934 3k.50 Sauce boat 1·60 65
935 3k.50 Lidded ice pot 1·60 65
936 3k.50 Serving dish 1·60 65

1990. Endangered Flowers. Multicoloured.
937 3k.25 Type **394** 1·20 50
938 3k.50 Red helleborine 1·90 15
939 3k.75 Purple orchis 1·60 75
940 4k.75 Lady's slipper 1·90 50

395 Insulin Crystals
396 Gjellerup Church

1990. 50th Anniv of Danish Diabetes Association.
941 **395** 3k.50+50ore mult 2·00 1·60

1990. Jutland Churches. Each brown.
942 3k.50 Type **396** 1·20 15
943 4k.75 Veng Church 1·70 40
944 8k.25 Bredsten Church (vert) 3·00 90

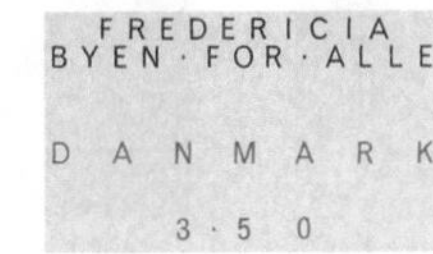

397 Slogan and Braille

1990. Fredericia: "Town for Everybody" (access for the handicapped project).
945 **397** 3k.50 red and black 1·20 25

398 "Tordenskiold and Karlsten's Commandant" (Otto Bache)
399 Bicycle (Bicycle stealing)

1990. 300th Birth Anniv of Admiral Tordenskiold (Peter Wessel).
946 **398** 3k.50 multicoloured 1·20 25

1990. Campaigns.
947 **399** 3k.25 multicoloured 1·20 65
948 – 3k.50 black, bl & mve 1·40 25
DESIGN: 3k.50, Glass and car (Drunken driving).

400 IC3 Diesel Passenger Train, 1990

1991. Railway Locomotives.
949 **400** 3k.25 blue, red & green 1·40 90
950 – 3k.50 black and red 1·30 25
951 – 3k.75 brown & dp brn 1·30 65
952 – 4k.75 black and red 1·60 40
DESIGNS: 3k.50, Class A steam locomotive, 1882; 3k.75, Class MY diesel-electric locomotive, 1954; 4k.75, Class P steam locomotive, 1907.

401 Satellite Picture of Denmark's Water Temperatures
402 First Page of 1280s Manuscript

1991. Europa. Europe in Space. Mult.
953 3k.50 Type **401** 1·10 25
954 4k.75 Denmark's land temperatures 1·80 50

1991. 750th Anniv of Jutland Law.
955 **402** 8k.25 multicoloured 2·75 1·10

403 Fano
404 Child using Emergency Helpline

1991. Nordic Countries' Postal Co-operation. Tourism. Multicoloured.
956 3k.50 Type **403** 1·60 25
957 4k.75 Christianso 1·60 50

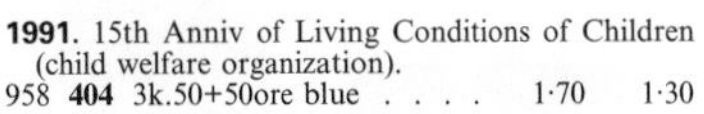

1991. 15th Anniv of Living Conditions of Children (child welfare organization).
958 **404** 3k.50+50ore blue 1·70 1·30

405 Stoneware Vessels (Christian Poulsen)
406 Man cleaning up after Dog

1991. Danish Design. Multicoloured.
959 3k.25 Type **405** 1·20 40
960 3k.50 Chair, 1949 (Hans Wegner) (vert) 1·20 25
961 4k.75 Silver cutlery, 1938 (Kay Bojesen) (vert) 1·70 50
962 8k.25 "PH5" lamp, 1958 (Poul Henningsen) 2·75 1·60

1991. "Keep Denmark Clean".
963 **406** 3k.50 red 1·10 25
964 – 4k.75 blue 1·80 75
DESIGN: 4k.75, Woman putting litter into bin.

407 Nordic Advertising Congress 1947 (Arne Ungermann)

1991. Posters. Multicoloured.
965 3k.50 Type **407** 1·30 25
966 4k.50 Poster Exhibition, Copenhagen Zoo, 1907 (Valdemar Andersen) 2·10 1·50
967 4k.75 D.D.L. (Danish Airlines, 1945) (Ib Andersen) 1·80 65
968 12k. Casino's "The Sinner", 1925 (Sven Brasch) 3·50 2·50

408 "Lady at Her Toilet" (Harald Giersing)
409 Skarpsalling Earthenware Bowl

1991. Paintings. Multicoloured.
969 4k.75 Type **408** 2·20 1·50
970 14k. "Road through Wood" (Edvard Weie) 3·75 3·75

1992. Re-opening of National Museum, Copenhagen. Exhibits from Prehistoric Denmark Collection.
971 **409** 3k.50 brown and lilac 1·10 25
972 – 4k.50 green and blue 1·80 65
973 – 4k.75 black & brown 1·70 50
974 – 8k.25 purple & green 2·75 1·50
DESIGNS: 4k.50, Grevensvaenge bronze figure of dancer; 4k.75, Bottom plate of Gundestrup Cauldron; 8k.25, Hindsgavl flint knife.

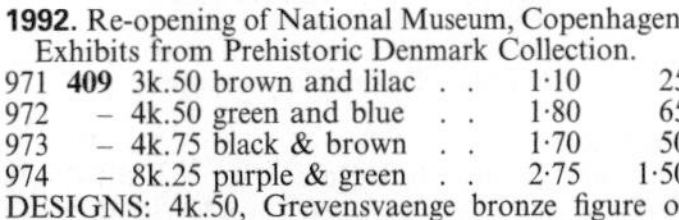

410 Aspects of Engineering
411 Queen Margaret I (detail, Vastra Sallerup Church fresco)

1992. Centenary of Danish Society of Chemical, Civil, Electrical and Mechanical Engineers.
975 **410** 3k.50 red 1·20 25

1992. "Nordia 94" International Stamp Exhibition, Arhus. Sheet 70 × 94 mm containing T **411** and similar vert design, each brown, slate and red.
MS976 3k.50, Type **411**; 4k.75 Alabaster bust of Queen Margaret I (attr. Johannes Junge) (sold at 12k.) 4·50 4·50

412 Potato Plant

1992. Europa. 500th Anniv of Discovery of America by Columbus.
977 **412** 3k.50 green & brown 1·20 25
978 – 4k.75 green & yellow 1·80 1·00
DESIGN: 4k.75, Head of maize.

413 Royal Couple in 1992 and in Official Wedding Photograph

1992. Silver Wedding of Queen Margrethe and Prince Henrik.
979 **413** 3k.75 multicoloured 1·60 65

414 Hare, Eurasian Sky Lark and Cars

1992. Environmental Protection. Multicoloured.
980 3k.75 Type **414** 1·20 25
981 5k. Atlantic herrings and sea pollution 1·60 50
982 8k.75 Felled trees and saplings (vert) 2·50 1·30

415 Celebrating Crowd
416 Danish Pavilion

1992. Denmark, European Football Champion.
983 **415** 3k.75 multicoloured 1·60 25

1992. "Expo '92" World's Fair, Seville.
984 **416** 3k.75 blue 1·20 25

417 "Word"
418 "A Hug"

1992. 50th Anniv of Danish Dyslexia Association.
985 **417** 3k.75+50ore mult . . . . 2·00 1·30

1992. Danish Cartoon Characters.
986 **418** 3k.50 purple, red & gold 1·40 40
987 – 3k.75 violet and red . . . 1·20 25
988 – 4k.75 black and red . . . 1·80 1·30
989 – 5k. blue and red . . . . 1·60 40
DESIGNS: 3k.75, "Love Letter"; 4k.75, "Domestic Triangle"; 5k. "The Poet and his Little Wife".

419 Abstract

420 "Jacob's Fight with the Angel" (bible illustration by Bodil Kaalund)

1992. European Single Market.
990 **419** 3k.75 blue and yellow . . 1·20 25

1992. Publication of New Danish Bible.
991 **420** 3k.75 multicoloured . . . 1·20 25

421 "Landscape from Vejby, 1843" (Johan Thomas Lundbye)

1992. Paintings. Multicoloured.
992 5k. Type **421** . . . . 1·90 1·10
993 10k. "Motif from Halleby Brook, 1847" (Peter Christian Skovgaard) . . . 3·25 2·50

422 Funen Guldgubber

423 Small Tortoiseshell

1993. Danish Treasure Trove. Guldgubber (anthropomorphic gold foil figures). Mult.
994 3k.75 Type **422** . . . . . . 1·20 25
995 5k. Bornholm guldgubber (vert) . . . . 1·70 40

1993. Butterflies. Multicoloured.
996 3k.75 Type **423** . . . . . . 1·60 25
997 5k. Large blue . . . . 1·80 40
998 8k.75 Marsh fritillary . . . . 3·25 1·60
999 12k. Red admiral . . . . . 3·75 2·50

424 Untitled Painting (Troels Worsel)

1993. Europa. Contemporary Art. Mult.
1000 3k.75 Type **424** . . . . . 1·20 25
1001 5k. "The 7 Corners of the Earth" (Stig Brogger) (vert) . . . . 2·10 65

425 "Pierrot" (Thor Bogelund, 1947)

426 "Danmark"

1993. Nordic Countries' Postal Co-operation. Tourism. Publicity posters for Tivoli Gardens, Copenhagen. Multicoloured.
1002 3k.75 Type **425** . . . . . 1·20 25
1003 5k. Child holding balloons (Wilhelm Freddie, 1987) (vert) . . . . 2·10 40

1993. Training Ships. Multicoloured.
1004 3k.75 Type **426** . . . . . 1·40 35
1005 4k.75 "Jens Krogh" (25 × 30 mm) . . . . . 2·20 1·90
1006 5k. "Georg Stage" . . . . 1·90 80
1007 9k.50 "Marilyn Anne" (36 × 26 mm) . . . . . . 2·75 3·50

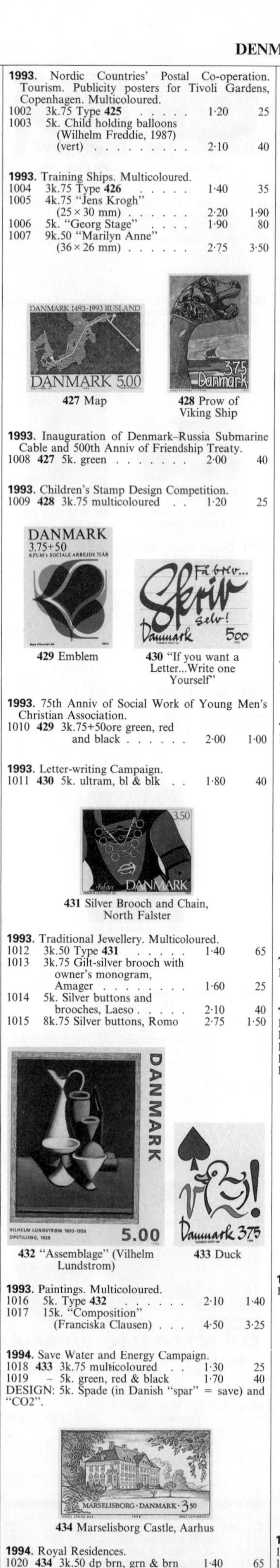

427 Map

428 Prow of Viking Ship

1993. Inauguration of Denmark–Russia Submarine Cable and 500th Anniv of Friendship Treaty.
1008 **427** 5k. green . . . . 2·00 40

1993. Children's Stamp Design Competition.
1009 **428** 3k.75 multicoloured . . 1·20 25

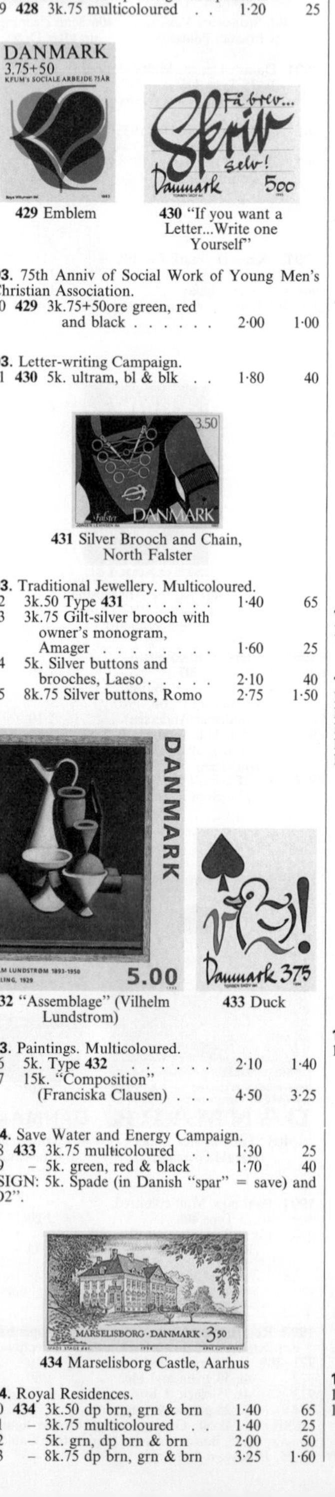

429 Emblem

430 "If you want a Letter...Write one Yourself"

1993. 75th Anniv of Social Work of Young Men's Christian Association.
1010 **429** 3k.75+50ore green, red and black . . . . . . 2·00 1·00

1993. Letter-writing Campaign.
1011 **430** 5k. ultram, bl & blk . . 1·80 40

431 Silver Brooch and Chain, North Falster

1993. Traditional Jewellery. Multicoloured.
1012 3k.50 Type **431** . . . . . 1·40 65
1013 3k.75 Gilt-silver brooch with owner's monogram, Amager . . . . 1·60 25
1014 5k. Silver buttons and brooches, Laeso . . . . . 2·10 40
1015 8k.75 Silver buttons, Romo 2·75 1·50

432 "Assemblage" (Vilhelm Lundstrom)

433 Duck

1993. Paintings. Multicoloured.
1016 5k. Type **432** . . . . . . 2·10 1·40
1017 15k. "Composition" (Franciska Clausen) . . . 4·50 3·25

1994. Save Water and Energy Campaign.
1018 **433** 3k.75 multicoloured . . 1·30 25
1019 – 5k. green, red & black 1·70 40
DESIGN: 5k. Spade (in Danish "spar" = save) and "CO2".

434 Marselisborg Castle, Aarhus

1994. Royal Residences.
1020 **434** 3k.50 dp brn, grn & brn 1·40 65
1021 – 3k.75 multicoloured . . 1·40 25
1022 – 5k. grn, dp brn & brn 2·00 50
1023 – 8k.75 dp brn, grn & brn 3·25 1·60
DESIGNS: 3k.75, Amalienborg Castle, Copenhagen; 5k. Fredensborg Castle, North Zealand; 8k.75, Graasten Castle, South Jutland.

435 "Danmark" and Wegener's Weather Balloon, Danmarkshavn

436 Copenhagen Tram No. 2, 1911

1994. Europa. Discoveries. "Danmark" Expedition to North-East Greenland, 1906–08.
1024 **435** 3k.75 purple . . . . . . 1·40 25
1025 – 5k. black . . . . . . 1·80 50
DESIGN: 5k. Johan Peter Koch and theodolite.

1994. Trams. Multicoloured.
1026 3k.75 Type **436** . . . . . 1·10 25
1027 4k.75 Aarhus tram, 1928 . . 1·70 1·30
1028 5k. Odense tram, 1911 (vert) 1·70 65
1029 12k. Copenhagen horse tram "Honen", 1880 (37 × 21 mm) . . . . . . 3·50 3·25

437 Prince Henrik

438 Kite

1994. Danish Red Cross Fund. 60th Birthday of Prince Henrik, the Prince Consort.
1030 **437** 3k.75+50ore mult . . . 1·40 1·10

1994. Children's Stamp Design Competition.
1031 **438** 3k.75 multicoloured . . 1·20 65

439 Emblem

440 House Sparrows

1994. 75th Anniv of I.L.O.
1032 **439** 5k. multicoloured . . . 1·60 40

1994. Protected Animals. Multicoloured.
1033 3k.75 Type **440** . . . . . 1·00 25
1034 4k.75 Badger . . . . 1·80 1·10
1035 5k. Red squirrel (vert) . . . 1·60 50
1036 9k.50 Pair of black grouse 2·75 2·30
1037 12k. Black grass snake (36 × 26 mm) . . . . . . 3·50 3·25

441 Teacher

1994. 150th Anniv of Folk High Schools.
1038 **441** 3k.75 multicoloured . . 1·20 25

442 Study for "Italian Woman with Sleeping Child" (Wilhelm Marstrand)

1994. Paintings. Multicoloured.
1039 5k. Type **442** . . . . . . 1·80 1·30
1040 15k. "Interior from Amaliegade with the Artist's Brothers" (Wilhelm Bendz) . . . . 4·00 3·75

443 The Red Building (architect's drawing, Hack Kampmann)

444 Anniversary Emblem

1995. 800th Anniv of Aarhus Cathedral School.
1041 **443** 3k.75 multicoloured . . 1·20 25

1995. 50th Anniv of United Nations Organization. U.N. World Summit for Social Development, Copenhagen.
1042 **444** 5k. multicoloured . . . 1·60 50

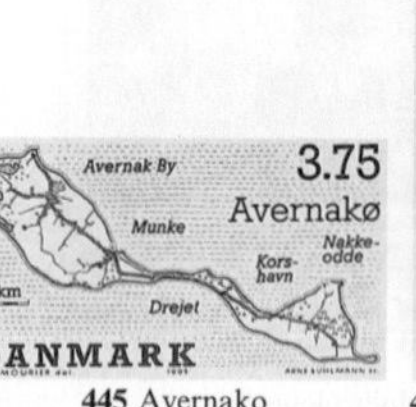

445 Avernako

446 Field-Marshal Montgomery and Copenhagen Town Hall

1995. Danish Islands. Each brown, blue and red.
1043 3k.75 Type **445** . . . . . 1·30 25
1044 4k.75 Fejo . . . . 2·00 1·30
1045 5k. Fur . . . . 2·00 50
1046 9k.50 Endelave . . . . . . 3·25 1·90

1995. Europa. Peace and Freedom. Mult.
1047 3k.75 Type **446** . . . . . 1·20 25
1048 5k. White coaches (repatriation of Danes from German concentration camps) (horiz) . . . . 1·60 50
1049 8k.75 Dropping of supplies from Allied aircraft (horiz) . . . . 2·75 1·50
1050 12k. Jews escaping by boat to Sweden (horiz) . . . . 3·75 2·50

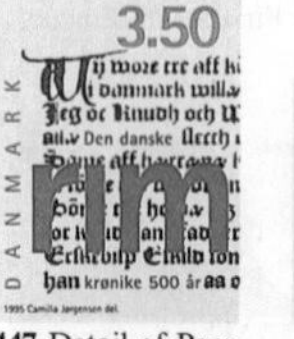

447 Detail of Page

448 Stage

1995. 500th Anniv of "The Rhymed Chronicle" by Friar Niels (first book printed in Danish).
1051 **447** 3k.50 multicoloured . . 1·20 50

1995. Nordic Countries' Postal Co-operation. Music Festivals. Multicoloured.
1052 3k.75 Type **448** (25th anniv of Roskilde Festival) . . . 1·20 25
1053 5k. Violinist (21st anniv of Tonder Festival) (20 × 38 mm) . . . . . . 1·70 40

449 Broken Feather

1995. 50th Anniv of National Society of Polio and Accident Victims.
1054 **449** 3k.75+50ore red . . . . 1·60 1·10

450 "Midsummer Eve" (Jens Sondergaard)

1995. Paintings. Multicoloured.
1055 10k. Type **450** . . . . . . 2·75 1·90
1056 15k. "Landscape at Gudhjem" (Niels Lergaard) . . . . 4·50 3·75

451 Sextant 453 The Round Tower

452 TEKNO Model Vehicles

1995. 450th Birth Anniv of Tycho Brahe (astronomer). Multicoloured.
1057 3k.75 Uraniborg (Palace Observatory) . . . . . . 1·20 25
1058 5k.50 Type **451** . . . . . 1·80 1·10

1995. Danish Toys. Multicoloured.
1059 3k.75 Type **452** . . . . . 1·60 25
1060 5k. Edna (celluloid doll), Kirstine (china doll) and Holstebro teddy bear . . 1·60 50
1061 8k.75 Toy bin-plate locomotives and rolling stock . . . . 3·00 1·80
1062 12k. Glud & Marstrand horse-drawn fire engine and carriage . . . . . . 3·50 2·50

1996. Copenhagen, European Cultural Capital. Multicoloured.
1063 3k.75 Type **453** . . . . . 1·20 25
1064 5k. Christiansborg . . . . . 1·80 40
1065 8k.75 Dome of Marble Church as hot-air balloon 3·00 1·90
1066 12k. "The Little Mermaid" on stage . . . . 3·50 3·25

454 Disabled Basketball Player 455 Businessmen

1996. Sport. Multicoloured.
1067 3k.75 Type **454** . . . . . 1·10 25
1068 4k.75 Swimming . . . . . 1·80 1·00
1069 5k. Yachting . . . . 1·80 50
1070 9k.50 Cycling . . . . 3·00 2·30

1996. Cent of Danish Employers' Confederation.
1071 **455** 3k.75 multicoloured . . 1·20 25

456 Asta Nielsen (actress) 457 Roskilde Fjord Boat

1996. Europa. Famous Women.
1072 – 3k.75 brown & dp brn 1·20 25
1073 **456** 5k. grey and blue . . . 1·70 50
DESIGN: 3k.75, Karin Blixen (writer).

1996. Wooden Sailing Boats.
1074 **457** 3k.50 brn, bl & red . . . 1·40 90
1075 – 3k.75 lilac, grn & red . . 1·20 25
1076 – 12k.25 blk, brn & red . . 3·75 3·00
DESIGNS—As T **457**: 12k.25, South Funen Archipelago smack; 20 × 38 mm: 3k.75, Limfjorden skiff.

458 Fornaes 459 Ribbons forming Hearts within Star

1996. Lighthouses. Multicoloured.
1077 3k.75 Type **458** . . . . . 1·40 25
1078 5k. Blavandshuk . . . . . 2·00 40
1079 5k.25 Bovbjerg . . . . . 2·10 1·30
1080 8k.75 Mon . . . . 2·75 1·30

1996. AIDS Foundation.
1081 **459** 3k.75+50ore red & blk 1·40 1·10

460 Vase

1996. 150th Birth Anniv of Thorvald Bindesboll (ceramic artist). Multicoloured.
1082 3k.75 Type **460** . . . . . 1·10 25
1083 4k. Portfolio cover . . . . 1·40 1·00

461 "At Lunch" (Peder Kroyer)

1996. Paintings. Multicoloured.
1084 10k. Type **461** . . . . . . 3·00 2·50
1085 15k. "Girl with Sunflowers" (Michael Ancher) . . . . 4·00 3·75

462 Queen Margrethe waving to Children 463 Queen Margrethe

1997. Silver Jubilee of Queen Margrethe. Mult.
1086 3k.50 Queen Margrethe and Prince Henrik 90 65
1087 3k.75 Queen Margrethe and Crown Prince Frederik . . 1·40 25
1088 4k. Queen Margrethe at desk . . . . 1·30 1·00
1089 5k.25 Type **462** . . . . . 1·60 1·30

1997.
1092 **463** 3k.75 red . . . . 1·20 15
1093 4k. green . . . . 1·20 65
1094 4k. red . . . . 1·20 15
1095 4k.25 brown . . . . . . 1·60 1·20
1096 4k.50 blue . . . . . . 1·60 90
1097 4k.75 brown . . . . . . 1·60 1·20
1098 5k. violet . . . . . . 1·60 40
1099 5k.25 blue . . . . . . 1·80 50
1100 5k.50 red . . . . 1·60 1·10
1101 5k.75 blue . . . . . . 1·70 40
1104 6k.75 green . . . . . . 1·80 1·50

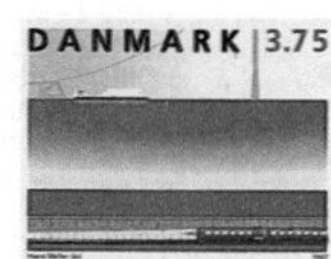

464 Karlstrup Post Mill, Zealand 465 The East Tunnel

1997. Centenary of Open Air Museum, Lyngby. Construction Drawings by B. Ehrhardt.
1111 **464** 3k.50 brown & purple 1·20 65
1112 – 3k.75 lilac and green . . 1·40 25
1113 – 5k. green and lilac . . . 1·70 25
1114 – 8k.75 green & brown . . 3·00 1·30
DESIGNS: 3k.75, Ellested water mill, Funen; 5k. Fjellerup Manor Barn, Djursland; 8k.75, Toftum farm, Romo.

1997. Inauguration of Railway Section of the Great Belt Link. Multicoloured.
1115 3k.75 Type **465** . . . . . 1·10 25
1116 4k.75 The West Bridge . . . 1·60 1·10

466 Sneezing 468 King Erik and Queen Margrete I

467 Electric Trains under New Carlsberg Bridge

1997. Asthma Allergy Association.
1117 **466** 3k.75+50ore mult . . . 1·60 1·10

1997. 150th Anniv of Copenhagen–Roskilde Railway. Multicoloured.
1118 3k.75 Type **467** . . . . . 1·20 25
1119 8k.75 Steam train under original Carlsberg bridge (after H. Holm) . . . . . 2·50 1·30

1997. 600th Anniv of Kalmar Union (of Denmark, Norway and Sweden). Multicoloured.
1120 4k. Type **468** . . . . . . 1·30 1·00
1121 4k. The Three Graces . . . 1·30 1·00
Nos. 1120/1 were issued, se-tenant, forming a composite design of a painting by an unknown artist.

469 Post Office Cars on Great Belt Ferry

1997. Closure of Travelling Post Offices.
1122 **469** 5k. multicoloured . . . 1·60 50

470 "The Tinder-box"

1997. Europa. Tales and Legends by Hans Christian Andersen.
1123 **470** 3k.75 dp brn & brn . . 1·20 25
1124 – 5k.25 red, dp grn & grn 1·80 1·00
DESIGN: 5k.25, "Thumbelina".

471 "Dust dancing in the Sun" (Vilheim Hammershoi) 472 Faaborg Chair (Kaare Klint)

1997. Paintings. Multicoloured.
1125 9k.75 Type **471** . . . . . 2·75 2·50
1126 13k. "Woman Mountaineer" (Jens Willumsen) . . . . 3·50 3·25

1997. Danish Design. Multicoloured.
1127 3k.75 Type **472** . . . . . 1·40 25
1128 4k. Margrethe bowls (Sigvard Bernadotte and Acton Bjorn) . . . . . . 1·60 1·00
1129 5k. The Ant chairs (Arne Jacobsen) (horiz) . . . . 1·80 40
1130 12k.25 Silver bowl (Georg Jensen) . . . . 3·50 3·25

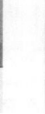

473 Workers 474 Roskilde Cathedral and Viking Longship

1998. Centenary of Danish Confederation of Trade Unions. Multicoloured.
1131 3k.50 Type **473** (General Workers' Union in Denmark) . . . . 1·10 75
1132 3k.75 Crowd at meeting (Danish Confederation of Trade Unions) . . . . . 1·30 25
1133 4k.75 Nurse (Danish Nurses' Organization) . . . . . . 1·70 1·10
1134 5k. Woman using telephone (Union of Commercial and Clerical Employees in Denmark) . . . . 1·80 25

1998. Millenary of Roskilde.
1135 **474** 3k.75 multicoloured . . 1·20 25

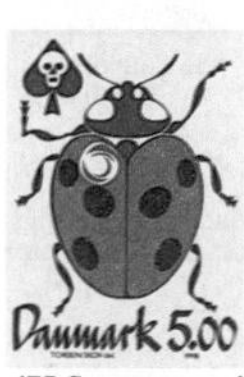

475 Seven-spotted Ladybird 476 Postman, 1922

1998. Environmental Issues. Gardening Without Chemicals.
1136 **475** 5k. red and black . . . 1·40 25

1998. Post and Tele Museum, Copenhagen. Mult.
1137 3k.75 Type **476** . . . . . 1·60 25
1138 4k.50 Morse operator, 1910 1·80 1·00
1139 5k.50 Telephonist, 1910 . . 1·90 1·30
1140 8k.75 Postman, 1998 . . . . 3·00 2·00

477 The West Bridge

1998. Inauguration of Road Section of the Great Belt Link. Each blue, black and red.
1141 5k. Type **477** . . . . . . 2·50 65
1142 5k. The East Bridge . . . . 2·50 65

478 Harbour Master 479 Horse (Agriculture Show)

1998. Nordic Countries' Postal Co-operation. Shipping. Multicoloured.
1143 6k.50 Type **478** . . . . . 1·80 1·50
1144 6k.50 Sextant and radar image of Copenhagen harbour . . . . 1·80 1·50
MS1145 106 × 75 mm. Nos. 1143/4 4·50 4·50
Nos. 1143/4 were issued together, se-tenant, forming a composite design.

1998. Europa. National Festivals. Mult.
1146 3k.75 Type **479** . . . . . 1·20 25
1147 4k.50 Aarhus Festival Week 1·30 1·00

480 Reaching Hand

1998. Anti-cancer Campaign.
1148 **480** 3k.75+50ore red, orange and black . . . . . . 1·20 1·00

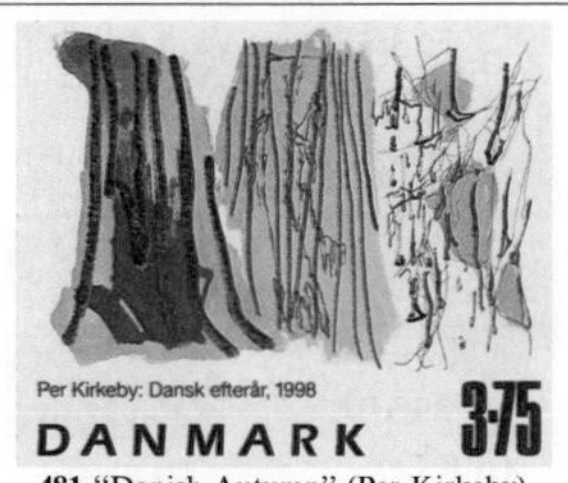

481 "Danish Autumn" (Per Kirkeby)

1998. Philatelic Creations. Multicoloured.
1149 3k.75 Type **481** . . . . . 1·40 1·00
1150 5k. "Alpha" (Mogens Andersen) (vert) . . . . 2·00 1·10
1151 8k.75 "Imagery" (Ejler Bille) (vert) . . . . 3·00 2·00
1152 19k. "Celestial Horse" (Carl-Henning Pedersen) 5·75 4·50

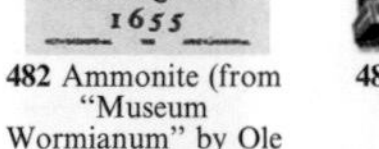

482 Ammonite (from "Museum Wormianum" by Ole Worm)
483 Satellite and Earth

1998. Fossils. Designs reproducing engravings from geological works. Each black and red on cream.
1153 3k.75 Type **482** . . . . . 1·10 25
1154 4k.50 Shark's teeth (from "De Solido" by Niels Stensen) . . . . 1·20 1·00
1155 5k.50 Sea urchin (from "Stevens Klint" by Soren Abildgaard) . . . . . . 1·80 1·30
1156 15k. Pleurotomariida (from "Den Danske Atlas" by Erich Pontoppidan) . . . 4·00 3·75
MS1157 114 × 142 mm. Nos. 1153/6 6·75 6·75

1999. Launch of "Orsted" Satellite (Danish research satellite).
1158 **483** 4k. multicoloured . . . 1·20 25

484 Beech

1999. Deciduous Trees. Multicoloured.
1159 4k. Type **484** . . . . . . 1·40 25
1160 5k. Ash (vert) . . . . . . 1·70 1·10
1161 5k.25 Small-leaved lime (vert) . . . . 1·80 65
1162 9k.25 Pendunculate oak . . 2·75 1·70

485 Home Guard

1999. 50th Anniv of Home Guard.
1163 **485** 3k.75 multicoloured . . 1·40 1·10

486 Northern Lapwing and Eggs

1999. Harbingers of Spring. Multicoloured.
1164 4k. Type **486** . . . . . . 1·00 25
1165 5k.25 Greylag goose with chicks . . . . 1·60 50
MS1166 99 × 82 mm. Nos. 1164/5 2·10 2·10

487 Emblem and Jet Fighters
488 Vejlerne

1999. 50th Anniv of North Atlantic Treaty Organization.
1167 **487** 4k.25 multicoloured . . 1·20 1·10

1999. Europa. Parks and Gardens. Multicoloured.
1168 4k.50 Type **488** . . . . . 1·10 1·00
1169 5k.50 Langli Island . . . . 1·60 1·30

489 Anniversary Emblem
490 "g" and Paragraph Sign

1999. 50th Anniv of Council of Europe.
1170 **489** 9k.75 blue . . . . 2·50 1·90

1999. 150th Anniv of Danish Constitution.
1171 **490** 4k. red and black . . . 1·10 25

491 Kjeld Petersen and Dirch Passer

1999. 150th Anniv of Danish Revue.
1172 **491** 4k. red . . . . 1·20 35
1173 – 4k.50 black . . . . . . 1·40 1·30
1174 – 5k.25 blue . . . . 1·70 1·20
1175 – 6k.75 mauve . . . . . . 1·60 1·90
DESIGNS: 4k.50, Osvald Helmuth; 5k.25, Preben Kaas and Jorgen Ryg; 6k.75, Liva Weel.

492 Emblem
493 The "Black Diamond"

1999. Alzheimer's Disease Association.
1176 **492** 4k.+50ore. red and blue 1·20 1·10

1999. Inauguration of Royal Library Extension, Copenhagen.
1177 **493** 8k.75 black . . . . . . 2·30 2·00

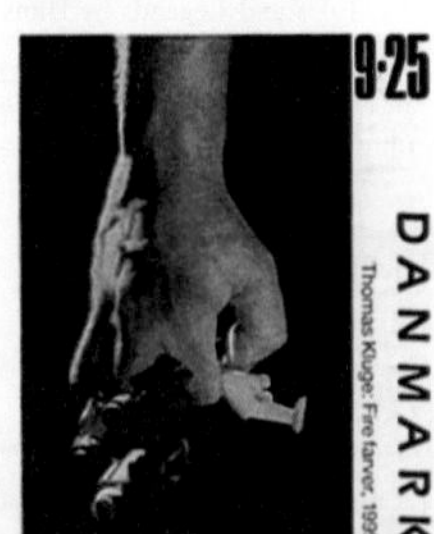

494 "Four Colours" (Thomas Kluge)

1999. Paintings. Multicoloured.
1178 9k.25 Type **494** . . . . . 2·30 1·90
1179 16k. "Boy" (Lise Malinovsky) . . . . . . 4·00 3·75

495 Barn Swallows
496 Hearts

1999. Migratory Birds. Multicoloured.
1180 4k. Type **495** . . . . . . 1·20 25
1181 5k.25 Greylag geese with goslings . . . . 1·70 65
1182 5k.50 Eiders . . . . 1·80 1·30
1183 12k.25 Arctic tern feeding chick . . . . 3·25 2·50
MS1184 Two sheets, each 116 × 72 mm. (a) Nos. 1180/1. (b) Nos. 1182/3 . . . . 6·25 6·25

1999. New Millennium. Multicoloured.
1185 4k. Type **496** . . . . . . 1·10 25
1186 4k. Horizontal wavy lines 1·10 25

497 Johan Henrik Deuntzer (Prime Minister) on Front Page of *Aftenposten* (newspaper)
498 Queen Margrethe II (Pia Schutzmann)

2000. The Twentieth Century (1st series).
1187 **497** 4k. black and cream . . 1·00 25
1188 – 4k.50 multicoloured . . 1·20 1·00
1189 – 5k.25 multicoloured . . 1·40 50
1190 – 5k.75 multicoloured . . 1·80 65
DESIGNS—4k. Type **497** (Venstre (workers') party victory in election, 1901); 4k.50, Caricature of Frederik Borgbjerg (party member, Alfred Schmidt) (first Social Democrat Lord Mayor in Denmark, 1903); 5k.25, Asta Nielson and Poul Reumert (actors) in scene from *The Abyss* (film), 1910; 5k.75, Telephone advertising poster, 1914.
See also Nos. 1207/10, 1212/15 and 1221/4.

2000. 60th Birthday of Queen Margrethe II.
1191 **498** 4k. black and red . . . 1·00 25
1192 5k.25 black and blue . . 1·30 50
MS1193 63 × 60 mm. Nos. 1191/2 2·20 2·20

499 Queen Margrethe II

2000.
1194 **499** 4k. red . . . . 1·10 15
1195 4k.25 blue . . . . . 1·20 1·00
1195a 4k.25 red 80 50
1196 4k.50 red . . . . . 1·20 1·00
1196b 4k.75 brown . . . . 1·20 1·00
1197 5k. green . . . . . 1·30 1·00
1198 5k.25 blue . . . . . 1·40 50
1199 5k.50 violet . . . . 1·40 50
1200 5k.75 green . . . . 1·60 65
1201 6k. brown . . . . . 1·60 95
1201a 6k.25 green . . . . 1·20 75
1201b 6k.50 green . . . . 1·20 75
1202 6k.75 red . . . . . 1·70 1·50
1203 7k. purple . . . . . 1·80 1·70
1204 8k.50 blue . . . . . 1·80 1·10

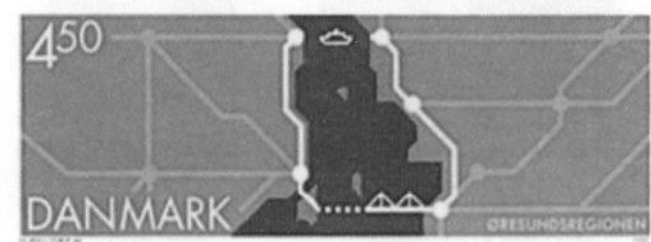

500 Map of Oresund Region

2000. Inauguration of Oresund Link (Denmark–Sweden road and rail system).
1205 **500** 4k.50 blue, white & blk 1·20 1·00
1206 – 4k.50 blue, green & blk 1·20 1·00
DESIGN: No. 1206, Oresund Bridge.

501 Suffragette on Front Page of *Politiken* (newspaper)
502 "Building Europe"

2000. The Twentieth Century (2nd series).
1207 **501** 4k. red, blk & cream . . 1·00 55
1208 – 5k. multicoloured . . . 1·30 1·10
1209 – 5k.50 multicoloured . . 1·40 1·10
1210 – 6k.75 multicoloured . . 2·10 1·70
DESIGNS—4k. Type **501** (women's suffrage, 1915); 5k. Caricature of Thorvald Stauning (Prime Minister 1924–26 and 1929–42) (Herluf Jensenius) (The Kanslergade Agreement (economic and social reforms)), 1933; 5k.50, Poster for *The Wheel of Fortune* (film), 1927; 6k.75, Front page of *Radio Weekly Review* (magazine), 1925.

2000. Europa.
1211 **502** 9k.75 multicoloured . . 2·30 2·10

503 Front Page of *Kristeligt Dagblad* (newspaper), 5 May 1945
504 Linked Hands

2000. The Twentieth Century (3rd series).
1212 **503** 4k. black and cream . . 1·00 25
1213 – 5k.75 multicoloured . . 1·60 65
1214 – 6k.75 multicoloured . . 1·80 1·50
1215 – 12k.25 multicoloured . . 3·00 2·50
DESIGNS—4k. Type **503** (Liberation of Denmark); 5k.75, Caricature of Princess Margrethe (Herlif Jenserius) (adoption of new constitution, 1953); 6k.75, Ib Schonberg and Hvid Moller (actors) in a scene from *Cafe Paradise* (film), 1950; 12k.25, Front cover of brochure for Danish Arena televisions, 1957.

2000. Cerebral Palsy Association.
1216 **504** 4k.+50ore blue and red 1·20 1·10

505 Lockheed C-130 Hercules Transport Plane

2000. 50th Anniv of Royal Danish Air Force.
1217 **505** 9k.75 black and red . . 2·50 2·00
MS1218 116 × 60 mm. No. 1217 2·20 2·20

506 "Pegasus" (Kurt Trampedach)

2000. Paintings. Multicoloured.
1219 4k. Type **506** . . . . . . 1·00 95
1220 5k.25 "Untitled" (Nina Sten-Knudsen) . . . . . 1·40 1·20

507 Front Page of *Berlingske Tidende* (newspaper), 3 October 1972

2000. The Twentieth Century (4th series).
1221 **507** 4k. red, blk & cream . . 1·00 40
1222 – 4k.50 multicoloured . . 1·20 1·00
1223 – 5k.25 blk, red & cream 1·40 75
1224 – 5k.50 multicoloured . . 1·60 75
DESIGNS: 4k. Type **507** (referendum on entry to European Economic Community); 4k.50, Caricature from *Blaeksprutten* (magazine), 1969 (The Youth Revolt); 5k.25, Poster for *The Olsen Gang* (film, 1968); 5k.50, Web page (development of the internet).

508 Kite

2001. 40th Anniv of Amnesty International.
1225 **508** 4k.+50 ore blk & red . . 1·10 1·00

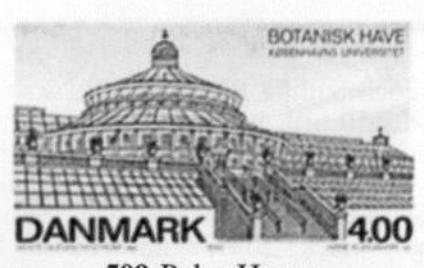

509 Palm House

2001. 400th Anniv of Copenhagen University Botanical Gardens. Multicoloured.
1226 4k. Type **509** 90 45
1227 6k. Lake (28 × 21 mm) . . . 1·30 85
1228 12k.25 Giant lily-pad (28 × 21 mm) . . . . . . 2·75 3·00

510 "a", Text and Flowers

2001. Reading. Danish Children's Book "ABC" (first reader) by Halfdan Rasmussen. Multicoloured.
1229 4k. Type **510** 90 45
1230 7k. "Z" and text . . . . . 1·60 1·40

511 Martinus William Ferslew (designer and engraver)

512 Hands catching Water

2001. 150th Anniv of First Danish Stamp. Each black, red and brown.
1231 4k. Type **511** . . . . . . 1·00 45
1232 5k.50 Andreas Thiele (printer) . . . . 1·30 1·00
1233 6k. Frantz Christopher von Jessen (Copenhagen postmaster) . . . . 1·40 1·30
1234 10k.25 Magrius Otto Sophus (Postmaster-General) . . 2·50 2·50

2001. Europa. Water Resources. Multicoloured.
1235 4k.50 Type **512** . . . . . 1·10 80
1236 9k.75 Woman in shower . . 2·30 2·30

513 Skateboarder

2001. Youth Culture. Multicoloured.
1237 4k. Type **513** . . . . . . 1·00 35
1238 5k.50 Couple kissing . . . . 1·30 1·20
1239 6k. Mixing records . . . . 1·40 1·30
1240 10k.25 Pierced tongue . . . 2·10 2·40
MS1241 121 × 70 mm. Nos. 1237/40 6·25 6·25

514 "Missus" (Jorn Larsen)

2001. Paintings.
1242 **514** 18k. black and red . . . 4·00 3·75
1243 – 22k. multicoloured . . . 5·25 5·00
DESIGN: 22k. "Postbillede" (Henning Damgaard-Sorensen).

515 Queen Margrethe II with 1984 Prince Henrik and 1994 Marselisborg Castle Stamps

517 Rasmus Klump (Vilhelm Hansen)

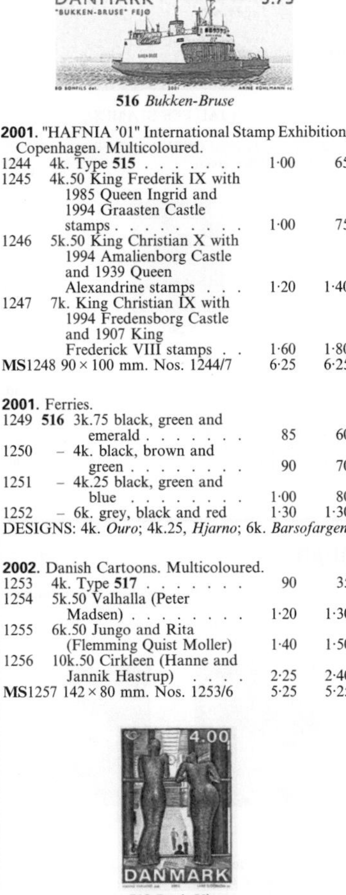
516 *Bukken-Bruse*

2001. "HAFNIA '01" International Stamp Exhibition, Copenhagen. Multicoloured.
1244 4k. Type **515** . . . . 1·00 65
1245 4k.50 King Frederik IX with 1985 Queen Ingrid and 1994 Graasten Castle stamps . . . . 1·00 75
1246 5k.50 King Christian X with 1994 Amalienborg Castle and 1939 Queen Alexandrine stamps . . . 1·20 1·40
1247 7k. King Christian IX with 1994 Fredensborg Castle and 1907 King Frederick VIII stamps . . 1·60 1·80
MS1248 90 × 100 mm. Nos. 1244/7 6·25 6·25

2001. Ferries.
1249 **516** 3k.75 black, green and emerald 85 60
1250 – 4k. black, brown and green 90 70
1251 – 4k.25 black, green and blue . . . . 1·00 80
1252 – 6k. grey, black and red 1·30 1·30
DESIGNS: 4k. *Ouro*; 4k.25, *Hjarno*; 6k. *Barsofargen*.

2002. Danish Cartoons. Multicoloured.
1253 4k. Type **517** 90 35
1254 5k.50 Valhalla (Peter Madsen) . . . . 1·20 1·30
1255 6k.50 Jungo and Rita (Flemming Quist Moller) 1·40 1·50
1256 10k.50 Cirkleen (Hanne and Jannik Hastrup) . . . . 2·25 2·40
MS1257 142 × 80 mm. Nos. 1253/6 5·25 5·25

518 Back View

2002. Nordic Countries' Postal Co-operation. Modern Art. Showing "The Girls in the Airport" (sculpture, Hanne Varming). Each black, bronze on cream.
1258 4k. Type **518** 90 55
1259 5k. Front view . . . . . . 1·10 1·10

519 Face

2002. L.E.V. National Association (mental health foundation).
1260 **519** 4k. +50ore brown, agate on cream . . . . . . 1·00 95

520 Clown (Luna Ostergard)

521 Jon's Chapel, Bornholm

2002. Europa. Circus. Winning Entries in Stamp Design Competition. Multicoloured.
1261 4k. Type **520** 90 95
1262 5k. Clown (different) (Camille Wagner Larsen) 1·10 95

2002. Landscape Photographs by Kirsten Klein.
1263 **521** 4k. black and brown . . 90 55
1264 – 6k. black . . . . 1·30 1·30
1265 – 6k.50 deep green and green . . . . 1·60 1·40
1266 – 12k.50 black and blue 2·50 2·75
DESIGNS: 6k. Trees, Vestervig; 6k.50, Woods, Karskov, Langeland; 12k.50, Cliffs and beach, Stenbjerg, West Jutland.

522 1953 Nimbus Motorcycle and Sidecar

2002. Postal Vehicles. Multicoloured.
1267 4k. Type **522** 90 55
1268 5k.50 1962 Bedford CA van 1·20 1·20
1269 10k. 1984 Renault 4 van . . 2·20 2·20
1270 19k. 1998 Volvo FH12 lorry 4·00 4·25

523 *Dana* (marine research ship) and Atlantic Cod

2002. Centenary of International Council for the Exploration of the Sea. Multicoloured.
1271 4k. Type **523** . . . . 1·00 55
1272 10k. Hirtshals lighthouse and atlantic cod . . . . . 2·20 2·20
MS1273 186 × 61 mm. 4k. Type **523**; 10k.50 Lighthouse and atlantic cod . . . . 3·25 3·25
Stamps of a similar design were issued by Faroe Islands and Greenland.

524 "Children's Corner" (Jens Birkemose)

2002. Paintings.
1274 **524** 5k. red and blue . . . . 1·10 1·10
1275 – 6k.50 multicoloured . . 1·40 1·40
DESIGN: 6k.50 "Maleren og modellen" (Frans Kannik).

525 Underground Train

2002. Inauguration of Copenhagen Metro.
1276 **525** 5k.50 black, green and brown on cream . . . 1·20 1·20

526 Dianas Have, Horsholm (Vandkunsten Design Studio)

2002. Domestic Architecture (1st series). Multicoloured.
1277 4k. Type **526** 75 40
1278 4k.25 Bapistry, Long House and Gate (Poul Ingemann) Blangstedgard, Odense . . . . 80 1·00
1279 5k.50 Dansk Folkeferie, Karrebaeksminde (Stephan Kappel) . . . . 1·00 1·30
1280 6k.50 Terrasser, Fredensborg (Jorn Utzon) 1·20 1·50
1281 9k. Soholm, Klampenborg (Arne Jacobsen) . . . . . 1·70 2·00
See also Nos. 1296/1300 and 1369/73.

527 Football

529 Expedition Members

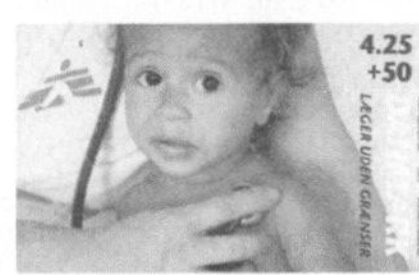
528 Child and Doctor

2003. Youth Sports. Multicoloured.
1282 4k.25 Type **527** 80 50
1283 5k.50 Swimming . . . . . 1·00 60
1284 8k.50 Gymnastics . . . . . 1·60 95
1285 11k.50 Basketball . . . . . 2·10 1·25

2003. Medicins sans Frontieres (medical charity).
1286 **528** 4k.25+50ore multicoloured 90 90

2003. Centenary of the Danish Literary Expedition to Greenland.
1287 **529** 4k.25 blue 80 50
1288 – 7k. brown, green and blue (60 × 22 mm) . . 1·30 75
MS1289 167 × 61 mm. Nos. 1287/81 2·20 1·30
DESIGN: 7k. Tents and mountains.
Stamps of a similar design were issued by Greenland.

530 Mayfly (*Ephemera danica*)

531 "Fools" Festival Poster' (Ole Flick)

2003. Insects. Multicoloured.
1290 4k.25 Type **530** 80 50
1291 6k.50 Water beetle (*Dysticus latissimus*) . . . . 1·20 70
1292 12k. Dragonfly (*Cordulegaster boltoni*) (20 × 39 mm) . . . . . . 2·20 1·30
MS1293 80 × 76 mm. Nos. 1290/2 4·25 2·50

2003. Europa. Poster Art.
1294 **531** 4k.25 multicoloured . . 80 50
1295 – 5k.50 black . . . . . . 1·00 60
DESIGN: 5k.50, "Thorvaldsen's Museum" (Ole Woldbye).

2003. Domestic Architecture (2nd series). As T **526**. Multicoloured.
1296 4k. Bellahoj, Copenhagen (Tage Nielsen and Mogens Irming) 75 45
1297 4k.25 Anchersvej Christiansholm Fort, Klampenborg (Mogens Lasen) 80 50
1298 5k.25 Gerthasminde, Odense (Anton Rosen) . . . . . 1·00 60
1299 9k. Solvang, Vallekilde (Anton Bentsen) . . . . 1·70 1·00
1300 15k. Stenbrogard, Brorup (Peder Holden Hansen) 2·75 1·60

532 "Baering" (Sys Hindsbo)

2003. Paintings. Multicoloured.
1301 5k.50 Type **532** . . . . . . 1·00 60
1302 19k. "The Forgotten Land" (Poul Anker Bech) . . . 3·50 2·10

533 Thyra's Stone

534 "Towards the Light" (statue, Rudolph Tegner)

2003. UNESCO World Heritage Site. Royal Jelling Open Air Museum.
1303 **533** 4k.25 black, sepia and brown 80 50
1304 – 5k.50 black, brown and sepia . . . . 1·00 60
1305 – 8k.50 black and bistre 1·60 95
1306 – 11k.50 black and deep olive . . . . 2·10 1·25
DESIGNS: Type **533**; 5k.50, Gorm's cup; 8k.50, Harald's stone; 11k.50, Jelling church.

2003. Centenary of Niels Finsen's Nobel Prize for Physiology and Medicine.
1307 **534** 6k.50 indigo . . . . . . 1·20 70

2004. Arms. As T **73**.
1308 **73** 12k.50 indigo . . . . . . 2·20 1·30
1309 13k. orange . . . . 2·40 1·40
1310 15k. blue . . . . 2·75 1·60

535 Butterfly and Caterpillar

536 Heimdal carrying Gjallar Horn on Bifrost Bridge

2004. Centenary of Children's Aid Day (fund raising charity).
1368 **535** 4k.25+50ore multicoloured 90 60

2004. Domestic Architecture (3rd series). As T **526**. Multicoloured.
1369 4k.50 Spurveskjul, Virum Copenhagen (Nicolai Abildgaard) 85 55
1370 6k. Liselund, Møn (Andreas Kirkerup) . . . . 1·20 65
1371 7k. Kampmann's Yard, Varde (Hans Ollgaard) . . 1·30 75
1372 12k.50 Harsdorff's House, Copenhagen (Caspar Harsdorff) . . . . 2·20 1·30
1373 15k. Nyso, Praesto (Jens Lauridsen) . . . . 2·75 1·60

2004. Nordic Mythology. Each sepia, blue and black.
1374 4k.50 Type **536** 85 55
1375 6k. Gefion ploughing Sealand out of Sweden . . 1·20 65
MS1376 105×71 mm. Nos. 1374/5 2·00 2·00
Stamps of a similar theme were issued by Aland Islands, Faroe Islands, Finland, Greenland, Iceland, Norway and Sweden.

537 Artist's Wooden Figure and Academy Seal

2004. 250th Anniv of Academy of Fine Arts, Copenhagen.
1377 **537** 5k.50 multicoloured . . 1·00 60

MILITARY FRANK STAMPS

1917. Nos. 135 and 138 optd **S F** (= "Soldater Frimaerke").
M188 **21** 5ore green . . . . . . 11·50 20·00
M189 10ore red . . . . 11·50 19·00

NEWSPAPER STAMPS

N 18

1901.
N185 **N 18** 1ore green . . . . . 11·00 75
N186 5ore blue . . . . . . 27·00 6·25
N133 7ore red . . . . . . 13·50 55
N188 8ore green . . . . . 28·00 1·00
N189 10ore lilac . . . . . 27·00 1·80
N135 20ore green . . . . . 23·00 75
N191 29ore orange . . . . 40·00 2·30
N136 38ore orange . . . . 32·00 80
N193 41ore brown . . . . . 45·00 2·20
N137 68ore brown . . . . . 80·00 15·00
N138 1k. purple & green . . 23·00 1·20
N139 5k. green and pink . . £140 19·00
N140 10k. blue and stone . . £150 25·00

OFFICIAL STAMPS

O 9

1871. Value in "skilling".
O51a **O 9** 2sk. blue . . . . £110 60·00
O52 4sk. red . . . . 40·00 9·25
O53 16sk. green £375 £130

1875. Value in "ore".
O185 **O 9** 1ore orange 70 75
O100 3ore lilac 70 65
O186 3ore grey . . . . . . 2·30 4·50
O101 4ore blue . . . . . . 1·10 95
O188 5ore green 50 25
O189 5ore brown . . . . . . 1·40 14·00
O 94 8ore red . . . . . . 7·25 1·30
O104 10ore red . . . . . . 1·00 95
O191 10ore green . . . . . . 2·30 1·50
O192 20ore lilac . . . . . . 16·00 20·00
O193 20ore blue . . . . . . 12·50 8·00
O 98 32ore green . . . . . . 17·00 15·00

PARCEL POST STAMPS

1919. Various types optd **POSTFAERGE**.
P208 **21** 10ore red . . . . 27·00 44·00
P209 **15** 10ore green . . . . . 9·50 8·75
P210 10ore brown . . . . . 11·00 5·75
P211 **21** 15ore lilac . . . . . 16·00 19·00
P212 30ore orange . . . . . 12·50 18·00
P213 30ore blue . . . . . 1·90 3·25
P214 50ore black & purple . . £160 £150
P215a 50ore grey . . . . . . 18·00 8·75
P216 **22** 1k. brown . . . . . . 80·00 £110
P217 **21** 1k. blue and brown . . 40·00 19·00
P218 5k. brown & mauve . . 90 1·40
P219 10k. green and red . . . 35·00 60·00

1927. Stamps of 1927 (solid background) optd **POSTFAERGE**.
P252 **40** 15ore red . . . . 13·00 7·50
P253 30ore yellow . . . . . . 13·00 8·75
P254 40ore green . . . . . . 16·00 8·25

1936. Stamps of 1933 (lined background) optd **POSTFAERGE**.
P491 **43** 5ore purple 25 25
P299 10ore orange . . . . . 14·50 12·50
P300 10ore brown . . . . . 90 1·10
P301 10ore violet 25 30
P302 10ore green 35 25
P303a **40** 15ore red 30 90
P304 30ore blue . . . . . . 3·75 2·75
P305 30ore orange 25 75
P306 40ore green . . . . . 2·40 2·75
P307 40ore blue 25 75
P308 **45** 50ore grey 45 90
P309 1k. brown . . . . . . 1·00 65

1945. Stamps of 1942 optd **POSTFAERGE**.
P346 **67** 30ore orange . . . . . . 1·30 1·00
P347 40ore blue 60 90
P348 50ore grey 70 90

1949. Stamps of 1946 and 1948 optd **POSTFAERGE**.
P376 **80** 30ore orange . . . . . . 2·30 1·10
P377 30ore red . . . . 90 1·00
P378 40ore blue . . . . 1·80 1·10
P379 40ore grey . . . . 90 1·00
P380 50ore grey . . . . 9·25 2·30
P381 50ore green . . . . . . 75 1·00
P382 70ore green . . . . . . 75 1·00
P383 **73** 1k. brown . . . . 1·00 75
P384 1k.25 orange . . . . . . 3·75 5·00
P495 2k. red . . . . 2·50 1·80
P496 5k. blue . . . . 5·25 3·75

1967. Optd **POSTFAERGE**.
P488 **117** 40ore brown 70 50
P492 50ore brown 80 40
P489 80ore blue 85 50
P493 90ore blue . . . . . . 1·60 75

1975. Optd **POSTFAERGE**.
P597 **207** 100ore blue . . . . . . 1·60 1·00

POSTAGE DUE STAMPS

1921. Stamps of 1905 and 1913 optd **PORTO**.
D214 **15** 1ore orange . . . . . . 1·40 1·20
D215 **21** 5ore green . . . . . . 3·50 1·50
D216 7ore orange . . . . . . 2·50 1·40
D217 10ore red . . . . 14·00 5·75
D218 20ore blue . . . . . . 10·50 4·75
D219 25ore black and brown 17·00 1·50
D220 50ore black & purple . . 5·75 2·10

D 32

1921. Solid background.
D221 **D 32** 1ore orange 40 55
D222 4ore blue . . . . . . 1·60 1·90
D223 5ore brown . . . . . 1·90 50
D224 5ore green . . . . . 1·40 40
D225 7ore green . . . . . 9·00 12·50
D226 7ore violet . . . . . 20·00 25·00
D227 10ore green . . . . . 2·00 35
D228 10ore brown . . . . . 1·50 25
D229 20ore blue 90 40
D230 20ore grey . . . . . 1·90 1·00
D231 25ore red . . . . . . 3·25 75
D232 25ore lilac . . . . . 2·50 1·10
D233 25ore blue . . . . . 3·25 3·25
D234 1k. blue . . . . . . 39·00 4·75
D235 1k. blue and brown . . 7·25 3·25
D236 5k. violet . . . . . . 9·50 5·75
For stamps with lined background see Nos. D285/97.

1921. Military Frank stamp optd **PORTO**.
D237 **21** 10ore red (No. M189) . . 6·75 5·00

1934. Lined background.
D285 **D 32** 1ore green 15 15
D286 2ore red 15 15
D287 5ore green 15 15
D288 6ore green 25 15
D289 8ore mauve . . . . . . 1·80 1·50
D290 10ore orange 15 10
D291 12ore blue 35 25
D292 15ore violet 35 25
D293 20ore grey 15 10
D294 25ore blue 35 20
D295 30ore green 35 25
D296 40ore purple 60 40
D297 1k. brown 60 15

1934. Surch **PORTO 15**.
D298 **15** 15 on 12ore lilac . . . . 2·50 2·20

SPECIAL FEE STAMPS

1923. No. D227 optd **GEBYR GEBYR**.
S218 **D 32** 10ore green . . . . . 9·25 1·50

S 36

1926. Solid background.
S229 **S 36** 10ore green . . . . . . 4·25 55
S230 10ore brown . . . . . 5·25 50

1934. Lined background.
S285 **S 36** 5ore green 15 15
S286 10ore orange 15 15

DHAR Pt. 1

A state of Central India. Now uses Indian stamps.

4 pice = 1 anna.

1

2

1897. Imperf.
1 **1** ½pice black on red . . . . . 2·25 2·75
3 ¼a. black on orange . . . . . 2·50 3·50
4 ½a. black on mauve . . . . . 3·75 4·50
5 1a. black on green . . . . . 7·50 12·00
6 2a. black on yellow . . . . . 25·00 40·00

1898. Perf.
7b **2** ½a. red . . . . 3·00 5·50
8 1a. purple . . . . 3·25 6·50
10 2a. green . . . . 6·00 21·00

DIEGO-SUAREZ Pt. 6

A port in N. Madagascar. A separate colony till 1896, when it was incorporated with Madagascar.

100 centimes = 1 franc.

1890. Stamps of French Colonies (Type J Commerce), surch **15** sideways.
1 **J** 15 on 1c. black on blue . . . £170 70·00
2 15 on 5c. green . . . . £450 70·00
3 15 on 10c. black on lilac . . . £180 55·00
4 15 on 20c. red on green . . . £450 70·00
5 15 on 25c. black on red . . . 85·00 21·00

2

3

1890. Various designs.
6 **2** 1c. black . . . . £350 85·00
7 5c. black . . . . £325 75·00
8 15c. black . . . . 85·00 32·00
9 25c. black . . . . £110 35·00

1891.
10 **3** 5c. black . . . . £120 70·00

1891. Stamps of French Colonies. (Type J Commerce) surch **1891 DIEGO-SUAREZ 5 c.**
13 **J** 5c. on 10c. black on lilac . . £160 80·00
14 5c. on 20c. red on green . . . £140 65·00

1892. Stamps of French Colonies (Type J Commerce) optd **DIEGO-SUAREZ**.
15 **J** 1c. black on blue . . . . . 24·00 12·50
16 2c. brown on buff . . . . . 28·00 13·50
17 4c. brown on grey . . . . . 28·00 22·00
18 5c. green on green . . . . . 85·00 55·00
19 10c. black on lilac . . . . . 23·00 23·00
20 15c. blue on blue . . . . . 18·00 12·50
21 20c. red on green . . . . . 26·00 21·00
22 25c. black on pink . . . . . 16·00 13·50
23 30c. brown on drab £850 £600
24 35c. black on orange £850 £600
25 75c. red on pink . . . . . . 65·00 26·00
26 1f. green . . . . 60·00 40·00

1892. "Tablet" key-type inscr "DIEGO-SUAREZ ET DEPENDANCES".
38 **D** 1c. black on blue . . . . . 1·75 3·75
39 2c. brown on buff . . . . . 2·25 1·25
40 4c. brown on grey . . . . . 85 4·00
41 5c. green on green . . . . . 1·60 4·75
42 10c. black on lilac . . . . . 5·75 6·50
43 15c. blue . . . . 4·25 11·00
44 20c. red on green . . . . . 8·75 10·00
45 25c. black on pink . . . . . 6·50 8·75
46 30c. brown on drab . . . . . 9·00 22·00
47 40c. red on yellow . . . . . 15·00 13·50
48 50c. red on pink . . . . . . 19·00 13·00
49 75c. brown on yellow . . . 42·00 26·00
50 1f. green . . . . 60·00 35·00

1894. "Tablet" key-type inscr "DIEGO-SUAREZ".
51 **D** 1c. black on blue . . . . . 50 2·75
52 2c. brown on buff . . . . . 1·25 3·50
53 4c. brown on grey . . . . . 1·75 3·50
54 5c. green on green . . . . . 2·25 5·25
55 10c. black on lilac . . . . . 5·75 6·25
56 15c. blue . . . . 3·50 5·50
57 20c. red on green . . . . . 8·00 14·50
58 25c. black on pink . . . . . 4·25 4·00
59 30c. brown on drab . . . . . 9·00 6·25
60 40c. red on yellow . . . . . 7·75 5·00
61 50c. red on pink . . . . . . 6·00 8·00
62 75c. brown on yellow . . . 2·75 6·00
63 1f. green . . . . 8·25 12·00

POSTAGE DUE STAMPS

D 4

1891.
D11 **D 4** 5c. violet . . . . 65·00 24·00
D12 50c. black on yellow . . 65·00 35·00

1892. Postage Due stamps of French Colonies overprinted **DIEGO-SUAREZ**.
D27 **D 4** 1c. black . . . . £100 50·00
D28 2c. black . . . . £110 45·00
D29 3c. black . . . . £110 50·00
D30 4c. black . . . . £100 60·00
D31 5c. black . . . . £110 60·00
D32 10c. black . . . . 27·00 25·00
D33 15c. black . . . . 27·00 27·00
D34 20c. black £160 £110
D35 30c. black . . . . 90·00 60·00
D36 60c. black £850 £600
D37 1f. brown £1600 £850

DJIBOUTI Pt. 6

A port in French Somaliland S. of the Red Sea, later capital of French Territory of the Afars and the Issas.

100 centimes = 1 franc.

1893. "Tablet" key-type stamp of Obock optd **DJ**.
83 **D** 5c. green & red on green . . £110 £120

1894. Same type surch in figures and **DJIBOUTI**.
85 **D** 25 on 2c. brn & bl on buff £275 £180
86 50 on 1c. blk & red on blue £325 £225

1894. Triangular stamp of Obock optd **DJIBOUTI** or surch **1** also.
87 **5** 1f. on 5f. red £600 £400
88 5f. red £1400 £1100

12 Djibouti (The apparent perforation is part of the design.)

13 "Pingouin" (French gunboat)

14 Crossing the Desert

1894. Imperf.
89 **12** 1c. red and black . . . . 1·10 1·25
90 2c. black and red 45 45
91 4c. blue and brown . . . . 3·00 1·90
92 5c. red and green . . . . 2·25 1·60
93 5c. green . . . . 2·50 3·50
94 – 10c. green and brown . . . 3·75 1·00
95 – 15c. green and lilac . . . . 3·25 1·75
96 – 25c. blue and red . . . . 5·00 2·00
97 – 30c. red and brown . . . . 3·75 3·75
98 – 40c. blue and yellow . . . 55·00 48·00
99 – 50c. red and blue . . . . 18·00 12·00
100 – 75c. orange and mauve . . 35·00 29·00
101 – 1f. black and olive . . . . 21·00 21·00
102 – 2f. red and brown . . . . 85·00 70·00
103 **13** 5f. blue and red £190 £120
104 **14** 25f. blue and red £850 £850
105 50f. red and blue £650 £650
DESIGNS— As Type **12**: 10 to 75c. Different views of Djibouti; 1, 2f. Port of Djibouti.

1899. As last, surch.
108 – 0.05 on 75c. orge & mve 55·00 32·00
109 – 0.10 on 1f. blk & olive . . 70·00 60·00
106 **12** 0.40 on 4c. blue & brown £2750 19·00
110 – 0.40 on 2f. red & brown £550 £350
111 **13** 0.75 on 5f. blue and red . . £450 £375

1902. Rectangular stamp of Obock surch **0.05**.
107 **6** 0.05 on 75c. lilac & orange £1200 £900

1902. Triangular stamps of Obock surch.
112 **7** 5c. on 25f. blue and brown 55·00 60·00
113 10c. on 50f. green & red . . 75·00 60·00

1902. Nos. 98/9 surch.
114 5c. on 40c. blue and yellow 2·25 2·00
115 10c. on 50c. red and blue . . 15·00 20·00

1902. Stamps of Obock surch **DJIBOUTI** and value.
120 **6** 5c. on 30c. yellow & grn . . 5·50 12·50
116 10c. on 25c. black & blue 4·50 7·75
118 **7** 10c. on 2f. orange & lilac 35·00 50·00
119 10c. on 10f. lake and red . . 30·00 30·00

For later issues see **FRENCH SOMALI COAST**, **FRENCH TERRITORY OF THE AFARS AND THE ISSAS** and **DJIBOUTI REPUBLIC**.

DJIBOUTI REPUBLIC Pt. 12

Formerly French Territory of the Afars and the Issas.

112 Map and Flag 115 Head Rest

1977. Independence. Multicoloured.
685 45f. Type **112** . . . . 1·50 80
686 65f. Map of Djibouti (horiz) 2·25 95

1977. Various stamps of the French Territory of the Afars and the Issas optd **REPUBLIQUE DE DJIBOUTI** or surch also. (a) Sea Shells.
687 **81** 1f. on 4f. mult 20 20
688 – 2f. on 5f. brown, mauve and violet (629) 20 20
689 – 20f. brown & grn (633) . . 55 55
690 – 30f. brn, pur & grn (634) 65 65
691 – 40f. brown & grn (635) . . 90 90
692 – 45f. brn, grn & bl (636) . . 1·00 1·00
693 – 60f. black & brn (638) . . 1·40 1·40
694 – 70f. brn, bl & blk (639) . . 1·90 1·90

(b) Flora and Fauna.
695 **103** 5f. on 20f. multicoloured 20 20
696 **106** 45f. multicoloured 90 90
697 – 50f. multicoloured (675) 1·40 1·40
698 **107** 70f. multicoloured . . . . 1·60 1·60
699 – 100f. multicoloured (653) 2·50 2·50
700 – 150f. multicoloured (676) 3·00 3·00
701 – 300f. multicoloured (654) 7·50 7·50

(c) Buildings.
702 **99** 8f. grey, red & bl (postage) 30 30
703 **109** 500f. mult (air) . . . . . 9·75 8·25

(d) Celebrities.
704 **111** 55f. red, grey & grn (air) 1·40 1·10
705 – 75f. red, brn & grn (682) 2·50 2·50
706 **104** 200f. blue, green and orange (postage) . . . 3·75 3·75

(e) Sport.
707 **108** 200f. multicoloured . . . 4·50 4·50

1977. Local Art. Multicoloured.
708 10f. Type **115** 20 10
709 20f. Water cask (vert) 45 15
710 25f. Washing jar (vert) . . . 65 20

116 Ostrich 117 "Glossodoris"

1977. Birds. Multicoloured.
711 90f. Type **116** . . . . 2·75 1·00
712 100f. Vitelline masked weaver 3·75 1·75

1977. Sea Life. Multicoloured.
713 45f. Type **117** . . . . 1·00 90
714 70f. Turtle . . . . 1·10 45
715 80f. Catalufa . . . . 1·60 65

118 Map, Dove and U.N. Emblem

1977. Air. Admission to the United Nations.
716 **118** 300f. multicoloured . . . 4·50 2·75

119 Crabs "Uca lactea"

1977. Fauna. Multicoloured.
717 15f. Type **119** 45 15
718 50f. Klipspringer . . . . . . 1·25 40
719 150f. Dolphin (fish) . . . . . 3·25 2·00

120 President Hassan Gouled Aptidon and Flag

1978.
720 **120** 65f. multicoloured 90 45

121 Marcel Brochet MB 101

1978. Air. Djibouti Aero Club. Multicoloured.
721 60f. Type **121** 95 60
722 85f. De Havilland Tiger Moth . . . . 1·25 80
723 200f. Morane Saulnier Rallye Commodore . . . . 2·75 1·60

122 "Charaxes hansali" 123 "Head of an Old Man"

1978. Butterflies. Multicoloured.
724 5f. Type **122** 10 10
725 20f. "Colias electo" 55 20
726 25f. "Acraea chilo" 80 40
727 150f. "Junonia hierta" . . . 3·00 1·50

1978. Air. 400th Birth Anniv of Rubens. Mult.
728 50f. Type **123** 85 35
729 500f. "The Hippopotamus Hunt" (detail) . . . . . . 8·00 3·25

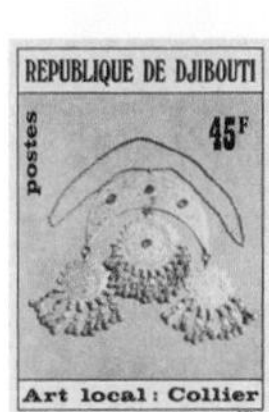

124 Necklace 125 Player with Cup

1978. Native Handicrafts. Multicoloured.
730 45f. Type **124** 85 40
731 55f. Necklace . . . . 1·10 45

1978. Air. World Cup Football Championship, Argentina. Multicoloured.
732 100f. Type **125** . . . . 1·40 45
733 300f. World Cup, footballer and map of Argentina . . 4·25 1·25

126 "Bougainvillea glabra"

1978. Flowers. Multicoloured.
734 15f. Type **126** 40 10
735 35f. "Hibiscus schizopetalus" 70 20
736 250f. "Caesalpinia pulcherrima" . . . . . . 4·50 85

1978. Air. Argentina's Victory in World Cup Football Championship. Nos. 722/3 optd.
737 100f. Type **125** . . . . 1·60 45
738 300f. World Cup, footballer and map of Argentina . . 4·50 1·50
OVERPRINTS: 100f. **ARGENTINE CHAMPION 1978**; 300f. **ARGENTINE HOLLANDE 3–1**.

128 "The Hare" (Albrecht Durer)

1978. Air. Paintings. Multicoloured.
739 100f. "Tahitian Women" (Paul Gauguin) (horiz) . . 1·90 55
740 250f. Type **128** . . . . 4·75 1·90

129 Knobbed Triton

1978. Sea Shells. Multicoloured
741 10f. Type **129** 75 35
742 80f. Trumpet triton . . . . . 2·50 90

130 Copper-banded Butterflyfish 131 Dove and U.P.U. Emblem

1978. Fishes. Multicoloured.
743 8f. Type **130** 40 15
744 30f. Yellow tang 85 25
745 40f. Harlequin sweetlips . . . 1·60 45

1978. Air. "Philexafrique" Exhibition, Libreville, Gabon (1st issue) and Int. Stamp Fair, Essen, W. Germany. As T **237** of Benin. Multicoloured.
746 90f. Jay and Brunswick 1852 3sqr. stamp . . . . 1·90 1·40
747 90f. African spoonbill and Djibouti 1977 optd 300f. stamp . . . . 1·90 1·40

1978. Air. Centenary of Paris U.P.U. Congress.
748 **131** 200f. green, brn & turq 2·75 1·40

132 Alsthom BB 1201 Diesel Locomotive

1979. Djibouti–Addis Ababa Railway. Mult.
749 40f. Type **132** 90 40
750 55f. Pacific locomotive No. 231 . . . . 80 30
751 60f. Steam locomotive No. 130 . . . . 1·00 35
752 75f. Alsthom CC 2001 diesel-electric locomotive . . . . 1·40 60

133 Children learning to Count

1979. International Year of the Child. Multicoloured.
753 20f. Type **133** 35 10
754 200f. Mother and child . . . 3·00 1·25

134 De Havilland Twin Otter over Crater

1979. Ardoukoba Volcano. Multicoloured.
755 30f. Sud Aviation Alouette II helicopter over crater . . . 65 40
756 90f. Type **134** . . . . 1·90 70

135 Sir Rowland Hill and 300f. Stamp, 1977

1979. Death Centenary of Sir Rowland Hill. Multicoloured.
757 25f. Type **135** 35 10
758 100f. Letters with 1894 50f. and 1977 45f. stamps . . . 2·25 60
759 150f. Loading mail on ship 2·25 80

136 Junkers Ju 52/3m and Dewoitine D-338 Trimotor

1979. Air. 75th Anniv of Powered Flight. Multicoloured.

760 140f. Type **136** . . . . 2·25 95
761 250f. Potez 63-11 bomber and Supermarine Spitfire Mk. VII . . . . 3·25 1·90
762 500f. Concorde and Sikorsky S-40 flying boat "American Clipper" . . . . 7·25 3·25

137 Djibouti, Local Woman and Namaqua Dove

1979. "Philexafrique 2" Exhibition, Gabon (2nd issue). Multicoloured.

763 55f. Type **137** . . . . 2·25 1·40
764 80f. U.P.U. emblem, map, Douglas DC-8-60 "Super Sixty", Alsthom diesel-electric train and postal runner . . . . 2·75 1·25

138 "Opuntia"

1979. Flowers. Multicoloured.

765 2f. Type **138** 10 10
766 8f. "Solanacea" (horiz) . . . 20 10
767 15f. "Trichodesma" (horiz) 35 10
768 45f. "Acacia etbaica" (horiz) 65 15
769 50f. "Thunbergia alata" . . . 90 15

139 "The Washerwoman"

1979. Air. Death Centenary of Honore Daumier (painter).

770 **139** 500f. multicoloured . . . 8·25 2·75

140 Basketball

1979. Pre-Olympic Year. Multicoloured.

771 70f. Type **140** . . . . 1·10 30
772 120f. Running . . . . 1·60 55
773 300f. Football . . . . 2·75 85

141 Bull-mouth Helmet

1979. Shells. Multicoloured.

774 10f. Type **141** 20 15
775 40f. Arthritic spider conch . . 1·00 20
776 300f. Ventral harp . . . . . 5·50 1·60

142 Winter Sports Equipment and Mosque

1980. Air. Winter Olympic Games, Lake Placid.

777 **142** 150f. multicoloured . . . 2·25 65

143 Lions Club Banner and Steam Locomotive

1980. Djibouti Clubs. Multicoloured.

778 90f. Rotary Club banner and Morane Saulnier MS 892 (75th anniv of Rotary International) . . . . . . 1·75 70
779 100f. Type **143** . . . . 2·50 50

144 "Colotis danae"

147 Basketball

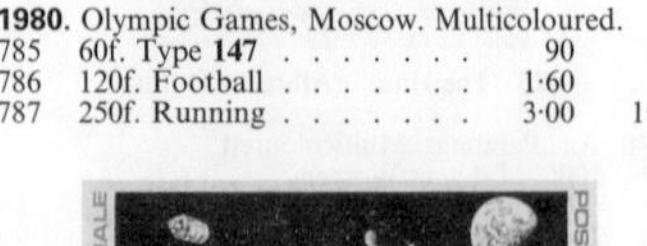

145 Boeing 737

1980. Butterflies. Multicoloured.

780 5f. Type **144** 20 20
781 55f. "Danaus chrysippus" . . 1·00 65

1980. Air. Foundation of "Air Djibouti".

782 **145** 400f. multicoloured . . . 6·00 2·25

1980. Air. Winter Olympic Games. No. 777 surch with names of Medal Winners.

783 **142** 80f. on 150f. . . . . . . 1·10 45
784 200f. on 150f. . . . . . 2·75 1·25

OVERPRINTS: 80f. **A.M. MOSER-PROEL AUTRICHE DESCENT DAMES MEDAILLE D'OR**. 200f. **HEIDEN USA 5 MEDAILLES D'OR PATINAGE DE VITESSE**.

1980. Olympic Games, Moscow. Multicoloured.

785 60f. Type **147** 90 20
786 120f. Football . . . . 1·60 45
787 250f. Running . . . . 3·00 1·00

148 "Apollo XI" Moon Landing

1980. Air. Conquest of Space. Multicoloured.

788 200f. Type **148** . . . . . . 2·75 65
789 300f. "Apollo-Soyuz" link-up 4·50 1·00

149 Samisch v Romanovsky Game, Moscow, 1925

1980. Founding of International Chess Federation, 1924. Multicoloured.

790 20f. Type **149** 70 15
791 75f. "Royal Chess Party" (15th-century Italian book illustration) . . . . 1·90 40

150 Satellite and Earth Station

1980. Air. Inauguration of Satellite Earth Station.

792 **150** 500f. multicoloured . . . 7·25 1·90

151 Sieve Cowrie

1980. Shells. Multicoloured.

793 15f. Type **151** 50 20
794 85f. Chambered nautilus . . 1·90 65

152 Sir Alexander Fleming and Penicillin

1980. Anniversaries. Multicoloured.

795 20f. Type **152** 50 20
796 130f. Jules Verne and space capsules . . . . 2·25 65

ANNIVERSARIES: 20f. Discovery of penicillin, 25th anniv. 130f. Jules Verne, 75th death anniv.

153 "Graf Zeppelin" and Sphinx

1980. Air. 80th Anniv of First Zeppelin Flight. Multicoloured.

797 100f. Type **153** . . . . . . 2·00 60
798 150f. Ferdinand von Zeppelin 2·50 90

154 Capt. Cook and H.M.S. "Endeavour"

1980. Death Bicentenary (1979) of Captain James Cook. Multicoloured.

799 55f. Type **154** 90 80
800 90f. Cook's ships and map of voyages . . . . 1·60 1·10

155 "Voyager" and Saturn

1980. Air. Space Exploration.

801 **155** 250f. multicoloured . . . 4·00 1·10

156 Saving a Goal

1981. Air. World Cup Football Eliminators. Multicoloured.

802 80f. Type **156** . . . . 1·10 35
803 200f. Tackle . . . . 2·75 80

157 Transport

158 Yuri Gagarin and "Vostok 1"

1981. Air European–African Economic Convention.

804 **157** 100f. multicoloured . . . 3·00 90

1981. Air. Space Anniversaries and Events. Multicoloured.

805 75f. Type **158** (20th anniv of first man in space) . . . . 1·10 35
806 120f. "Viking" exploration of Mars (horiz) . . . . 1·60 50
807 150f. Alan Shepard and "Freedom 7" (20th anniv of first American in space) 2·25 65

159 Arabian Angelfish

1981. Djibouti Tropical Aquarium. Mult.

808 25f. Type **159** 60 15
809 55f. Moorish idol . . . . . . 1·40 35
810 70f. Golden trevally . . . . 1·60 90

160 Caduceus, Satellite and Rocket

1981. World Telecommunications Day.

811 **160** 140f. multicoloured . . . 1·90 55

161 German 231 and American RC4 Diesel Locomotives

1981. Locomotives. Multicoloured.

812 40f. Type **161** 85 30
813 55f. George Stephenson, "Rocket" (1829) and Djibouti locomotive . . . 1·25 40
814 65f. French TGV and Japanese "Hikari" high speed trains . . . . 1·75 40

162 Antenna on Globe and Morse Key

1981. Djibouti Amateur Radio Club.
815 **162** 250f. multicoloured . . . 3·50 1·10

163 Prince Charles and Lady Diana Spencer

1981. Royal Wedding. Multicoloured.
816 180f. Type **163** . . . . 2·75 85
817 200f. Prince Charles and Lady Diana in wedding dress . . . . 3·00 1·10

164 Admiral Nelson and H.M.S. "Victory"

1981. Admiral Nelson Commemoration. Mult.
818 100f. Type **164** . . . . 1·60 1·00
819 175f. Nelson and stern view of H.M.S. "Victory" . . . 2·75 1·50

165 Tree Hyrax and Scout tending Camp-fire

1981. 28th World Scouting Congress, Dakar, and Fourth Panafrican Scouting Conference, Abidjan. Multicoloured.
820 60f. Type **165** . . . . 1·25 40
821 105f. Scouts saluting, map reading and greater kudu 1·60 50

166 "Football Players" (Picasso)

1981. Air. Paintings. Multicoloured.
822 300f. Type **166** . . . . 5·00 1·40
823 400f. "Portrait of a Man in a Turban" (Rembrandt) . . 5·50 1·90

167 Launch

168 19th-century Chinese Pawn and Knight

1981. Air. Space Shuttle. Multicoloured.
824 90f. Type **167** . . . . 1·40 45
825 120f. Space Shuttle landing 1·75 65

1981. Chess Pieces. Multicoloured.
826 50f. 13th-century Swedish pawn and queen (horiz) . . 1·10 35
827 130f. Type **168** . . . . 2·25 80

169 Aerial View

1981. Inauguration of Djibouti Sheraton Hotel.
828 **169** 75f. multicoloured . . . . 1·10 40

1981. 2nd Flight of Space Shuttle "Columbia". Nos. 824/5 optd.
829 90f. Type **167** . . . . 1·40 55
830 120f. Space Shuttle landing 1·75 85
OPTS: 90f. **COLUMBIA 2eme VOL SPATIAL 12 NOVEMBRE 1981**. 120f. **JOE ENGLE et RICHARD TRULY 2eme VOL SPATIAL—12 Nov. 1981**.

171 "Clitoria ternatea"

1981. Flowers. Multicoloured.
831 10f. Type **171** 20 10
832 30f. "Acacia mellifera" (horiz) 45 15
833 35f. "Punica granatum" (horiz) 70 20
834 45f. Malvacee 85 20

1981. World Chess Championship, Merano (1st issue). Nos. 826/7 optd.
835 50f. multicoloured 95 35
836 130f. multicoloured . . . . . 2·25 80
OPTS: 50f. **Octobre-Novembre 1981 ANATOLI KARPOV VICTOR KORTCHNOI MERANO (ITALIE)**. 130f. **ANATOLI KARPOV Champion du Monde 1981**.
See also Nos. 843/4.

173 Saving Goal

1982. Air. World Cup Football Championship, Spain. Multicoloured.
837 110f. Type **173** . . . . 1·60 55
838 220f. Footballers . . . . . . 3·25 1·10

174 John H. Glenn

175 Dr. Robert Koch, Bacillus and Microscope

1982. Air. Space Anniversaries. Mult.
839 40f. "Luna 9" (15th anniv of first unmanned moon landing) 55 20
840 60f. Type **174** (20th anniv of flight) 90 35
841 180f. "Viking 1" (5th anniv of first Mars landing) (horiz) . . . . 2·40 85

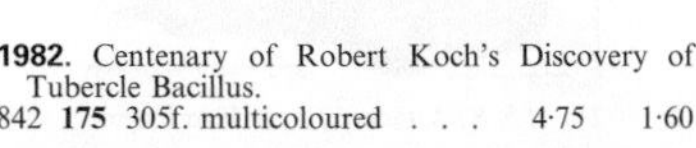
1982. Centenary of Robert Koch's Discovery of Tubercle Bacillus.
842 **175** 305f. multicoloured . . . 4·75 1·60

176 14th-century German Bishop and 18th-century Marie de Medici Bishop

177 Princess of Wales

1982. World Chess Championship, Merano (2nd issue). Multicoloured.
843 125f. Type **176** . . . . 2·50 75
844 175f. Late 19th-century queen and pawn from Nuremberg 3·00 95

1982. Air. 21st Birthday of Princess of Wales. Multicoloured.
845 120f. Type **177** . . . . 1·60 85
846 180f. Princess of Wales (different) . . . . 2·50 1·00

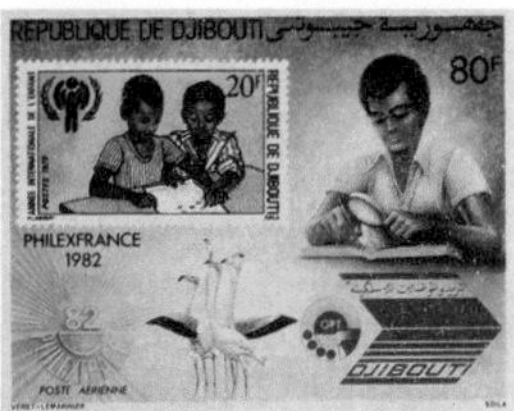

178 I.Y.C. Stamp, Collector, Greater Flamingoes and Emblems

1982. "Philexfrance" International Stamp Exhibition, Paris. Multicoloured.
847 80f. Type **178** . . . . 2·50 1·25
848 140f. Rowland Hill stamp Exhibition Centre and U.P.U. emblem . . . . . 2·25 95

179 Microwave Antenna

180 Mosque, Medina

1982. World Telecommunications Day.
849 **179** 150f. multicoloured . . . 2·25 90

1982. Air. 1350th Death Anniv of Mohammed.
850 **180** 500f. multicoloured . . . 6·75 2·50

181 Lord Baden-Powell

1982. Air. 125th Birth Anniv of Lord Baden-Powell. Multicoloured.
851 95f. Type **181** . . . . 1·25 55
852 200f. Saluting Scout and camp . . . . 2·75 1·10

182 Bus and Jeep

1982. Transport. Multicoloured.
853 20f. Type **182** 35 15
854 25f. Ferry and dhow 65 35
855 55f. Boeing 727-100 airliner and Alsthom Series BB 500 diesel locomotive and train 3·75 55

1982. Air. World Cup Football Championship winners. Nos. 837/8 optd.
856 110f. Type **173** . . . . 1·60 65
857 220f. Footballers . . . . . . 3·00 1·40
OPTS: 110f. **ITALIE RFA 3-1 POLOGNE FRANCE 3-2**. 220f. **ITALIE RFA 3-1 2 RFA 3 POLOGNE**.

1982. Air. Birth of Prince William of Wales. Nos. 845/6 optd.
858 120f. Type **177** . . . . 1·60 85
859 180f. Princess of Wales (different) . . . . 2·50 1·10
OPTS: 120f. **21 JUIN 1982 WILLIAM-ARTHUR-PHILIPPE-LOUIS PRINCE DES GALLES**. 180f. **21ST JUNE 1982 WILLIAM-ARTHUR-PHILIP-LOUIS PRINCE OF WALES**.

185 Satellite, Dish Aerial and Conference

1982. Air. Second U.N. Conference on the Exploration and Peaceful Uses of Outer Space, Vienna.
860 **185** 350f. multicoloured . . . 5·00 1·60

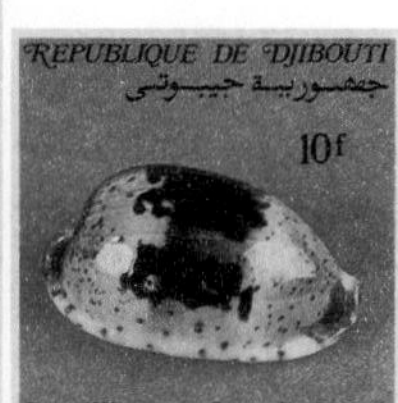

186 Franklin D. Roosevelt

187 Red Sea Cowrie

1982. Air. 250th Birth Anniv of George Washington and Birth Centenary of Franklin D. Roosevelt. Multicoloured.
861 115f. Type **186** . . . . 1·60 55
862 250f. George Washington . . 3·25 1·10

1982. Shells. Multicoloured.
863 10f. Type **187** 25 15
864 15f. Sumatran cone 40 20
865 25f. Lovely cowrie 55 25
866 30f. Engraved cone 75 40
867 70f. Heavy bonnet . . . . . 1·75 75
868 150f. Burnt cowrie . . . . . 3·50 1·25

188 Dove perched on Gun

189 Montgolfier's Balloon, 1783

1982. Palestinian Solidarity Day.
869 **188** 40f. multicoloured 55 25

1983. Air. Bicentenary of Manned Flight. Mult.
870 35f. Type **189** 60 25
871 45f. Henri Giffard's balloon "Le Grand Ballon Captif", 1878 . . . . 90 45
872 120f. Balloon "Double Eagle II", 1978 . . . . 2·25 1·10

190 Volleyball

192 Martin Luther King

191 Bloch 220 Gascogne

1983. Air. Olympic Games, Los Angeles (1984). Multicoloured.
873 75f. Type **190** . . . . 1·10 45
874 125f. Wind-surfing . . . . . 2·25 1·25

1983. Air. 50th Anniv of Air France. Mult.
875 25f. Type **191** 40 25
876 100f. Douglas DC-4 . . . . 1·40 1·00
877 175f. Boeing 747-200 . . . . 2·50 1·25

1983. Flowers. As T **171**. Multicoloured.
878 5f. Ipomoea 10 10
879 50f. Moringa (horiz) 85 35
880 55f. Cotton flower . . . . . 1·00 40

1983. Air. Celebrities. Multicoloured.
881 180f. Type **192** (15th death anniv) . . . . 2·25 90
882 250f. Alfred Nobel (150th birth anniv) . . . . 3·25 1·40

193 W.C.Y. Emblem **194** Yacht and Rotary Club Emblem

1983. World Communications Year.
883 **193** 500f. multicoloured . . . 6·75 2·75

1983. Air. International Club Meetings. Mult.
884 90f. Type **194** . . . . 2·00 1·50
885 150f. Minaret and Lions Club emblem . . . . 2·00 90

195 Renault, 1904

1983. Air. Early Motor Cars. Multicoloured.
886 60f. Type **195** . . . . 1·25 40
887 80f. Mercedes Knight, 1910 (vert) . . . . 1·90 50
888 100f. Lorraine-Dietrich, 1912 2·25 80

197 "Vostok VI"

1983. Air. Conquest of Space. Multicoloured.
890 120f. Type **197** . . . . 1·60 65
891 200f. "Explorer I" . . . . . 2·75 1·10

198 Development Projects

1983. Donors Conference.
892 **198** 75f. multicoloured . . . . 1·10 55

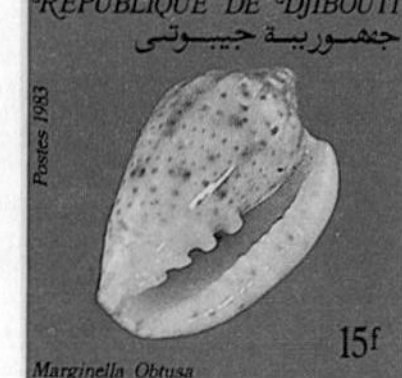

199 Red Sea Marginella

1983. Shells. Multicoloured.
893 15f. Type **199** 40 15
894 30f. Jickeli's cone 85 25
895 55f. MacAndrew's cowrie . . 1·40 60
896 80f. Cuvier's cone . . . . . 1·90 75
897 100f. Tapestry turban . . . . 2·10 1·00

200 "Colotis chrysonome"

1984. Butterflies.
898 5f. Type **200** 10 10
899 20f. "Colias erate" 25 20
900 30f. "Junonia orithyia" . . . 45 30
901 75f. "Acraea doubledayi" . . 1·40 90
902 110f. "Byblia ilithya" . . . . 1·75 1·40

201 Speed Skating

1984. Air. Winter Olympic Games, Sarajevo. Mult.
903 70f. Type **201** . . . . 1·10 40
904 130f. Ice dancing . . . . . . 1·90 70

203 Microlight

1984. Air. Microlight Aircraft. Multicoloured.
906 65f. Type **203** . . . . 1·00 80
907 85f. Powered hang-glider "Jules" . . . . 1·25 1·00
908 100f. Microlight (different) 1·50 1·25

1984. Air. Winter Olympic Games Medal Winners. Nos. 903/4 optd.
909 70f. **1000 METRES HOMMES OR: BOUCHER (CANADA) ARGENT: KHLEBNIKOV (URSS) BRONZE: ENGELSTADT (NORV.)** 1·10 55
910 130f. **DANSE OR: TORVILL-DEAN (G.B.) ARGENT: BESTEMIANOVA-BUKIN (URSS) BRONZE: KLIMOVA-PONOMARENKO (URSS)** . . . . 1·90 85

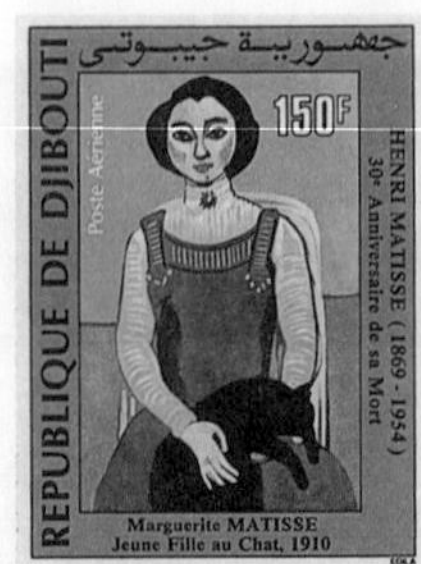

205 "Marguerite Matisse with Cat"

1984. Air. 30th Death Anniv of Matisse and Birth Centenary of Modigliani. Multicoloured.
911 150f. Type **205** . . . . . . 2·50 90
912 200f. "Mario Varvogli" (Modigliani) . . . . 3·50 1·40

206 Randa

1984. Landscapes. Multicoloured.
913 2f. Type **206** 10 10
914 8f. Ali Sabieh 10 10
915 10f. Lake Assal 15 10
916 15f. Tadjoura 20 10
917 40f. Alaili Dada (vert) . . . 55 20
918 45f. Lake Abbe 60 25
919 55f. Obock . . . . 1·50 85
920 125f. Presidential Palace . . . 3·00 1·60

207 Marathon

1984. Air. Olympic Games, Los Angeles. Mult.
921 50f. Type **207** 65 30
922 60f. High jump 85 35
923 80f. Swimming . . . . 1·10 45

208 Battle of Solferino

1984. Air. 125th Anniv of Battle of Solferino and 120th Anniv of Red Cross.
924 **208** 300f. multicoloured . . . 4·50 1·60

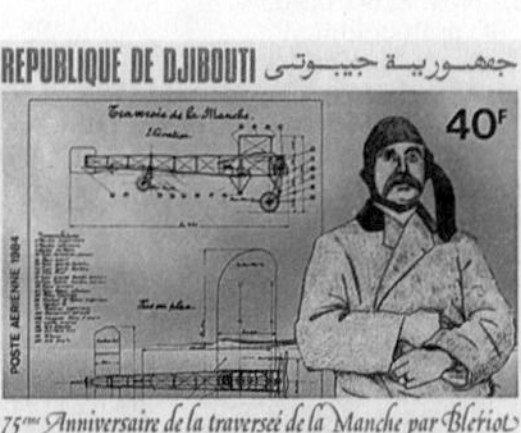

209 Bleriot and Diagram of Bleriot XI

1984. Air. 75th Anniv of Louis Bleriot's Cross-Channel Flight. Multicoloured.
925 40f. Type **209** 65 50
926 75f. Bleriot and Bleriot XI and Britten Norman Islander aircraft . . . . . 1·10 90
927 90f. Bleriot and Boeing 727 airliner . . . . 1·25 1·10

210 Marathon **212** Men on Moon, Telescope and Planets

211 U.S.A. Attack-pumper Fire Engine

1984. Membership of International Olympic Committee.
928 **210** 45f. multicoloured 65 30

1984. Fire Fighting. Multicoloured.
929 25f. Type **211** 70 20
930 95f. French P.P.M. rescue crane . . . . 2·10 65
931 100f. Canadair CL-215 fire-fighting amphibian . . . . 2·25 1·25

1984. Air. 375th Anniv of Galileo's Telescope. Multicoloured.
932 120f. Type **212** . . . . 1·60 65
933 180f. Galileo, telescope and planets . . . . 2·50 1·00

213 Football Teams (Europa Cup)

1984. Air. European Football Championship and Olympic Games, Los Angeles. Multicoloured.
934 80f. Type **213** . . . . 1·25 55
935 80f. Football teams (Olympic Games) . . . . 1·25 55

214 Motor Carriage, 1886

1984. 150th Birth Anniv of Gottlieb Daimler (automobile designer). Multicoloured.
936 35f. Type **214** 55 20
937 65f. Cannstatt-Daimler cabriolet, 1896 . . . . . . 1·00 35
938 90f. Daimler "Phoenix", 1900 1·50 55

215 Pierre Curie

1985. Pierre and Marie Curie (physicists). Mult.
939 150f. Type **215** (150th birth anniv) . . . . 2·25 85
940 150f. Marie Curie (50th death anniv) . . . . 2·25 85

216 White-throated Bee Eater

1985. Birth Bicentenary of John J. Audubon. Multicoloured.
941 5f. Type **216** 25 15
942 15f. Chestnut-bellied sand-grouse . . . . 1·10 45
943 20f. Yellow-breasted barbet 1·25 50
944 25f. European roller . . . . 1·50 55

217 Dr. Hansen, Bacilli, Lepers and Lions Emblem **218** Globe and Pictograms

1985. Air. International Organizations. Mult.
946 50f. Type **217** (World Leprosy Day) 80 40
947 60f. Rotary International emblem and pieces on chessboard . . . . 1·40 65

1985. International Youth Year.
948 **218** 10f. multicoloured 80 25
949 30f. multicoloured . . . . 2·25 50
950 40f. multicoloured . . . . 3·00 90

219 Steam Locomotive No. 29, Addis Ababa–Djibouti Railway

1985. Railway Locomotives. Multicoloured.
951 55f. Type **219** . . . . 1·50 65
952 75f. "Adler", 1835 (150th anniv of German railways) 2·25 85

220 Planting Sapling **221** Victor Hugo (novelist)

1985. Foundation of Djibouti Scouting Association. Multicoloured.
953 35f. Type **220** 65 30
954 65f. Childcare . . . . 1·40 45

1985. Writers. Multicoloured.
955 80f. Type **221** . . . . 1·10 50
956 100f. Arthur Rimbaud (poet) 1·40 60

222 Dish Aerials, Off-shore Oil Rigs and Building

1985. Air. "Philexafrique" Stamp Exhibition, Lome (1st issue). Multicoloured.
957 80f. Type **222** . . . . 2·25 1·50
958 80f. Carpenter, girl at microscope and man at visual display unit . . . . 1·60 1·10
See also Nos. 969/70.

1985. Shells. As T **199**. Multicoloured.
959 10f. Twin-blotch cowrie . . . 25 15
960 15f. Thrush cowrie 35 20
961 30f. Vice-Admiral cowrie . . 95 25
962 40f. Giraffe cone . . . . . . 1·10 55
963 55f. Terebra cone . . . . . 1·75 75

223 Team Winners on Rostrum

1985. 1st Marathon World Cup, Hiroshima. Multicoloured.
964 75f. Type **223** . . . . 1·00 45
965 100f. Finishing line and officials . . . . 1·50 65

224 Launch of "Ariane"

1985. Air. Telecommunications Development. Mult.
966 50f. International Transmission Centre . . . 65 30
967 90f. Type **224** . . . . 1·25 50
968 120f. "Arabsat" satellite . . . 1·60 65

225 Windsurfing and Tennis

1985. Air. "Philexafrique" Stamp Exhibition, Lome, Togo (2nd issue). Multicoloured.
969 100f. Type **225** . . . . 2·00 1·25
970 100f. Construction of Tadjoura road . . . . . . 1·60 1·10

226 Edmond Halley, Bayeux Tapestry and Comet

1986. Appearance of Halley's Comet. Multicoloured.
971 85f. Type **226** . . . . 1·10 45
972 90f. Solar system, comet trajectory and space probes "Giotto" and "Vega 1" . . 1·40 55

227 Footballers

1986. Air. World Cup Football Championship, Mexico. Multicoloured.
973 75f. Type **227** . . . . 1·00 45
974 100f. Players and stadium . . 1·40 65

228 Runners on Shore

1986. "ISERST" Solar Energy Project. Mult.
975 50f. Type **228** 65 30
976 150f. "ISERST" building . . 2·00 85

229 "Santa Maria"

1986. Historic Ships of Columbus, 1492. Multicoloured.
977 60f. Type **229** . . . . 1·90 1·25
978 90f. "Nina" and "Pinta" . . 2·50 2·00

230 Statue of Liberty, Eiffel Tower and French and U.S. Flags

1986. Air. Centenary of Statue of Liberty.
979 **230** 250f. multicoloured . . . 3·25 1·40

231 Rainbow Runner

1986. Red Sea Fish. Multicoloured.
980 20f. Type **231** 80 50
981 25f. Sehel's grey mullet . . . 1·00 50
982 55f. Blubber-lipped snapper 2·40 1·25

232 People's Palace

1986. Public Buildings. Multicoloured.
983 105f. Type **232** . . . . 1·40 55
984 115f. Ministry of the Interior, Posts and Telecommunications . . . 1·60 65

233 Transmission Building and Keyboard

1986. Inauguration of Sea-Me-We Submarine Communications Cable.
985 **233** 100f. multicoloured . . . 1·40 65

1986. Air. World Cup Football Championship Winners. Nos. 973/4 optd. Multicoloured.
987 75f. **FRANCE-BELGIQUE 4–2** . . . . 1·00 65
988 100f. **3–2 ARGENTINA-RFA** 1·40 90

235 Javanese Bishop, Knight and Queen

1986. Air. World Chess Championship, London and Leningrad. Multicoloured.
989 80f. Type **235** . . . . 1·40 65
990 120f. German rook, pawn and king . . . . 2·25 1·00

1986. 5th Anniv of Inaug of Djibouti Sheraton Hotel. No. 828 surch **5e ANNIVERSAIRE.**
991 **169** 55f. on 75f. mult 90 55

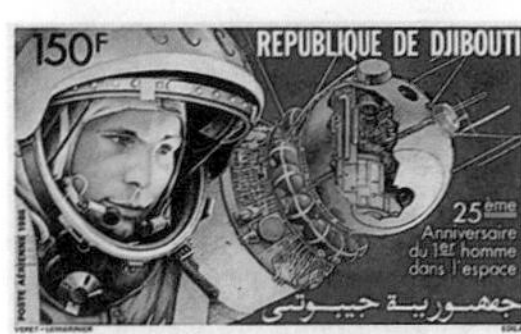

237 Gagarin and Space Capsule

1986. Air. 25th Anniv of First Man in Space and 20th Anniv of "Gemini 8"–"Agena" Link-up. Multicoloured.
992 150f. Type **237** . . . . 2·25 65
993 200f. "Gemini 8" and "Agena" craft over Earth 3·00 1·00

238 Amiot 370

1987. Air. Flight Anniversaries and Events. Multicoloured.
994 55f. Type **238** (45th anniv of first Istres-Djibouti flight) 90 60
995 80f. "Spirit of St Louis" and Charles Lindbergh (60th anniv of first solo flight across North Atlantic) . . 1·10 95
996 120f. Dick Rutan, Jeana Yeager and "Voyager" (first non-stop flight around the world) . . . . 1·75 1·25

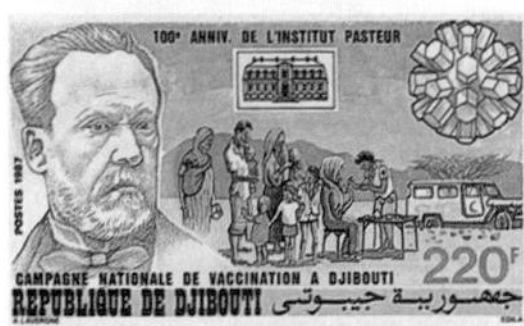

239 Louis Pasteur and Vaccination Session

1987. Centenary of Pasteur Institute. National Vaccination Campaign in Djibouti.
997 **239** 220f. multicoloured . . . 3·25 1·10

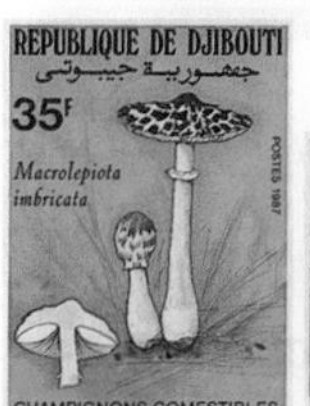

241 "Macrolepiota imbricata" **242** Hare

1987. Fungi. Multicoloured.
999 35f. Type **241** . . . . 1·25 65
1000 50f. "Lentinus squarrosulus" 2·00 95
1001 95f. "Terfezia boudieri" . . 3·50 1·50

1987. Wild Animals. Multicoloured.
1002 5f. Type **242** 10 10
1003 30f. Young dromedary with mother 45 20
1004 140f. Cheetah . . . . 2·25 80

243 President Hassan Gouled Aptidon, Map, Flag and Crest

1987. Air. 10th Anniv of Independence.
1005 **243** 250f. multicoloured . . . 3·25 1·40

244 Pierre de Coubertin (founder of modern Games) and Athlete lighting Flame

1987. Olympic Games, Calgary and Seoul (1st issue) (1988). Multicoloured.
1006 85f. Type **244** . . . . 1·10 45
1007 135f. Ski-jumper . . . . . 1·60 65
1008 140f. Runners and spectators . . . . 1·90 80
See also No. 1021.

245 "Telstar" Satellite

1987. Air. Telecommunications Anniversaries. Multicoloured.
1009 190f. Type **245** (25th anniv) . . . 2·50 90
1010 250f. Samuel Morse and morse key (150th anniv of morse telegraph) . . . . 3·25 1·40

246 Djibouti Creek and Quay, 1887

1987. Air. Centenary of Djibouti City.
1011 **246** 100f. agate and stone . . 2·00 1·40
1012 – 150f. multicoloured . . . 2·25 80
DESIGN: 150f. Aerial view of Djibouti, 1987.

247 Comb

249 Anniversary Emblem

1988. Traditional Djibouti Art. Multicoloured.
1014 30f. Type **247** 45 20
1015 70f. Water pitcher 95 45

1988. Air. 125th Anniv of Red Cross.
1017 **249** 300f. multicoloured . . . 4·25 1·60

250 Rabat and Footballers

1988. 16th African Nations Cup Football Championship, Morocco.
1018 **250** 55f. multicoloured . . . 85 35

251 Ski Jumping

252 Doctor examining Child

1988. Winter Olympic Games, Calgary.
1019 **251** 45f. multicoloured . . . 65 30

1988. U.N.I.C.E.F. "Universal Vaccinations by 1990" Campaign.
1020 **252** 125f. multicoloured . . . 1·75 65

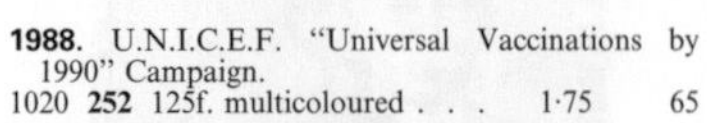

253 Runners and Stadium

1988. Air. Olympic Games, Seoul (2nd issue).
1021 **253** 105f. multicoloured . . . 1·40 55

1988. Air. Paris–Djibouti–St. Denis (Reunion) Roland Garros Air Race. No. 994 surch **PARIS-DJIBOUTI-ST DENIS LA REUNION RALLYE ROLAND GARROS 70 F**.
1022 **238** 70f. on 55f. mult . . . . 1·25 65

255 Animals at Water Trough

1988. Anti-drought Campaign.
1023 **255** 50f. multicoloured . . . 85 35

256 Djibouti Post Offices of 1890 and 1977

1988. Air. World Post Day.
1024 **256** 1000f. multicoloured . . 13·50 4·00

257 Combine Harvester, Tractor and Ploughman with Camel

1988. 10th Anniv of International Agricultural Development Fund.
1025 **257** 135f. multicoloured . . . 1·75 65

258 De Havilland Tiger Moth, 1948, and Socata Tobago, 1988

1988. 40th Anniv of Michel Lafoux Air Club.
1026 **258** 145f. multicoloured . . . 2·00 95

1988. 1st Djibouti Olympic Medal Winner. No. 1021 optd **AHMED SALAH 1re MEDAILLE OLYMPIQUE**.
1027 **253** 105f. multicoloured . . . 1·40 90

260 "Lobophyllia costata"

1989. Underwater Animals. Multicoloured.
1028 90f. Type **260** . . . . 1·40 35
1029 160f. Giant spider conch . . 3·25 1·40

261 "Colotis protomedia"

1989.
1030 **261** 70f. multicoloured . . . 90 60

1989. Nos. 849 and 913 surch **70f**.
1031 **206** 70f. on 2f. mult 95 45
1032 **179** 70f. on 150f. mult . . . 95 45

263 Dancers

264 Pale-bellied Francolin ("Francolin de Djibouti")

1989. Folklore. Multicoloured.
1033 30f. Type **263** 40 20
1034 70f. Dancers with parasol 1·00 45

1989.
1035 **264** 35f. multicoloured . . . 75 35

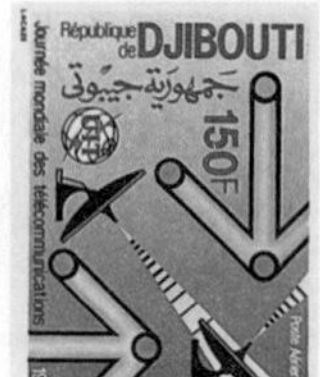

265 Arrows and Dish Aerials

1989. Air. World Telecommunications Day.
1036 **265** 150f. multicoloured . . . 1·90 65

266 "Calotropis procera"

1989.
1037 **266** 25f. multicoloured . . . 35 15

267 Emblem, Declaration and People

1989. Air. "Philexfrance 89" International Stamp Exhibition, Paris, and Bicentenary of Declaration of Rights of Man.
1038 **267** 120f. multicoloured . . . 1·60 65

268 Emblem and State Arms

270 Child going to School

269 Collecting Salt

1989. Cent of Interparliamentary Union.
1039 **268** 70f. multicoloured . . . 95 35

1989. Air. Lake Assal.
1040 **269** 300f. multicoloured . . . 4·00 1·10

1989. International Literacy Year.
1041 **270** 145f. multicoloured . . . 1·90 65

271 Tourka Maddw Cave Painting

1989.
1042 **271** 5f. multicoloured 10 10

272 Traditional Ornaments

1989.
1043 **272** 55f. multicoloured . . . 80 35

1990. Nos. 914 and 916/17 surch.
1044 30f. on 8f. multicoloured . . 40 15
1045 50f. on 40f. mult 65 30
1046 120f. on 15f. mult . . . . . 1·60 45

274 Water-storage Drums and Arid Landscape

1990. Anti-drought Campaign.
1047 **274** 120f. multicoloured . . . 1·60 55

275 Basketry

1990. Traditional Crafts. Multicoloured.
1048 30f. Type **275** 40 20
1049 70f. Jewellery (vert) 95 35

275a Blue-spotted Stingray

1990. Multicoloured, colour of face-value box given.
1049b **275a** 70f. yellow . . . . .
1049c 100f. green . . . . .

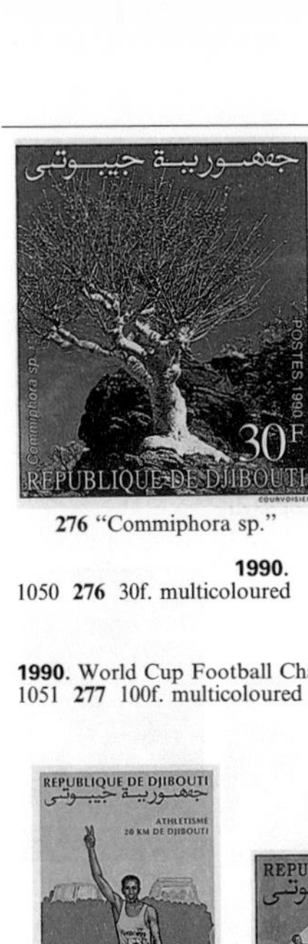

276 "Commiphora sp." 277 Footballers

1990.
1050 **276** 30f. multicoloured . . . 45 30

1990. World Cup Football Championship, Italy.
1051 **277** 100f. multicoloured . . . 1·40 55

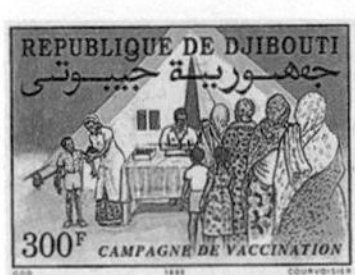

278 Athlete 279 Queue of Patients

1990. Djibouti 20 km Race.
1052 **278** 55f. multicoloured . . . 80 35

1990. Vaccination Campaign.
1053 **279** 300f. multicoloured . . . 3·25 1·40

280 De Gaulle 281 Technology in Developed Countries

1990. Birth Centenary of Charles de Gaulle (French statesman).
1054 **280** 200f. multicoloured . . . 2·50 1·25

1990. United Nations Conference on Less Developed Countries.
1055 **281** 45f. multicoloured . . . 60 35

282 Mammoth and Fossilized Remains 283 Hamadryas Baboon

1990.
1056 **282** 90f. multicoloured . . . 1·40 65

1990.
1057 **283** 50f. multicoloured . . . 65 35

284 Emblem and Map 285 "Acropora"

1991. African Tourism Year.
1058 **284** 115f. multicoloured . . . 1·50 85

1991. Corals. Multicoloured.
1059 40f. Type **285** 55 35
1060 45f. "Seriatopora hytrise" 65 35

286 Pink-backed Pelican

1991. Birds. Multicoloured.
1061 10f. Type **286** 35 15
1062 15f. Western reef heron . . 50 25
1063 20f. Goliath heron (horiz) 75 30
1064 25f. White spoonbill (horiz) 90 40

287 Osprey

1991.
1065 **287** 200f. multicoloured . . . 4·00 2·50

288 Traditional Game

1991.
1066 **288** 250f. multicoloured . . . 3·25 1·40

289 Diesel Locomotive

1991. Djibouti–Ethiopia Railway (1st issue).
1067 **289** 85f. multicoloured . . . 2·25 75
See also No. 1076.

290 Hands holding Earth above Polluted Sea

1991. World Environment Day.
1068 **290** 110f. multicoloured . . . 1·50 55

291 Windsurfers and Islets

1991. "Philexafrique" Stamp Exhibition.
1069 **291** 120f. multicoloured . . . 90 45

292 Handball 293 Harvesting Crops

1991. Olympic Games, Barcelona (1992) (1st issue).
1070 **292** 175f. multicoloured . . . 1·40 70
See also No. 1079.

1991. World Food Day.
1071 **293** 105f. multicoloured . . . 80 40

294 Route-map, Woman using Telephone and Cable-laying Ship

1991. Inauguration of Marseilles–Djibouti–Singapore Submarine Cable.
1072 **294** 130f. multicoloured . . . 1·50 70

295 Columbus and Ships

1991. 500th Anniv (1992) of Discovery of America by Columbus (1st issue).
1073 **295** 145f. multicoloured . . . 1·60 80
See also No. 1080.

296 Rimbaud, Ship and Serpent

1991. Death Centenary of Arthur Rimbaud (poet). Multicoloured.
1074 90f. Type **296** . . . . 1·10 50
1075 150f. Rimbaud, camel train and map . . . . 1·10 55

297 Camel Driver and Diesel Train

1992. Djibouti–Ethiopia Railway (2nd issue).
1076 **297** 70f. multicoloured . . . 1·50 45

298 Boys Playing Game

1992. Traditional Games.
1078 **298** 100f. multicoloured . . . 80 40

299 Athlete and Globe 301 Crushing Grain

300 Caravel crossing Atlantic

1992. Olympic Games, Barcelona (2nd issue).
1079 **299** 80f. multicoloured . . . 60 30

1992. 500th Anniv of Discovery of America by Columbus (2nd issue).
1080 **300** 125f. multicoloured . . . 1·40 65

1992. Traditional Methods of Preparing Food. Multicoloured.
1081 30f. Type **301** 25 10
1082 70f. Winnowing 55 25

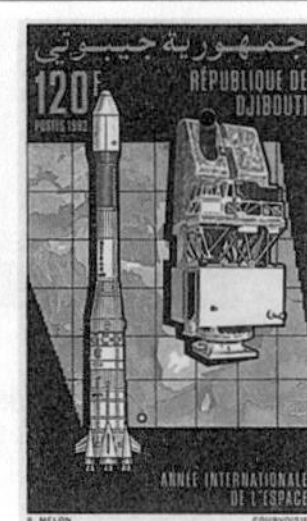

302 Players, Map of Africa and Final Result 303 "Ariane" Rocket and Satellite

1992. 18th African Nations Cup Football Championship, Senegal.
1083 **302** 15f. multicoloured . . . 10 10

1992. International Space Year. Multicoloured.
1084 120f. Type **303** 90 45
1085 135f. Satellite and astronaut (horiz) . . . . 1·00 50

304 Salt's Dik-dik

1992.
1086 **304** 5f. multicoloured 10 10

305 Loggerhead Turtle

1992.
1087 **305** 200f. multicoloured . . . 1·50 75

306 Preparing Mofo

1992. Mofo. Multicoloured.
1088 45f. Type **306** . . . .
1089 75f. Cooking mofo . . . .

307 Nomadic Girl

1993. Traditional Costumes. Multicoloured.
1090 70f. Type **307** 55 25
1091 120f. Nomadic girl with headband 90 45

308 White-eyed Gull ("Geoland a Iris Blanc")

1993.
1092 **308** 300f. multicoloured . . . 3·50 1·40

309 Amin Salman Mosque

1993.
1093 **309** 500f. multicoloured . . .

310 Headrest

1993. Crafts. Multicoloured.
1094 100f. Type **310** . . . . . .
1095 125f. Flask . . . .

311 Savanna Monkey

1993.
1096 **311** 150f. multicoloured . . .

312 Flags of Member Countries

1993. 30th Anniv of Organization of African Unity.
1097 **312** 200f. multicoloured . . .

313 Woman carrying Water on Back **314** Plants and Spacecraft

1993. Water Carriers. Multicoloured.
1098 30f. Type **313** . . . .
1099 50f. Man carrying water on yoke . . . .

1993. Space.
1100 **314** 90f. multicoloured . . .

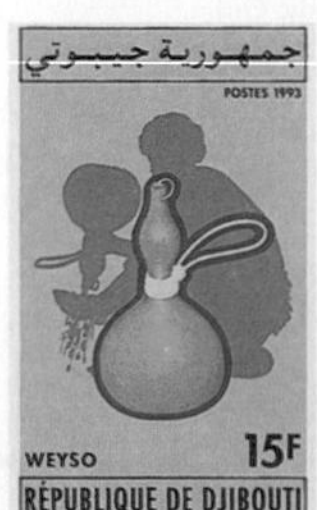

315 Water Jar **316** Pipes

1993. Utensils. Multicoloured.
1101 15f. Type **315** 10 10
1102 20f. Hangol (agricultural tool) 15 10
1103 25f. Comb 20 10
1104 30f. Water-skin 25 10

1993. Musical Instruments. Multicoloured.
1105 5f. Type **316** 10 10
1106 10f. Hand-held drum and lines of women 10 10

318 Runners and Route Map **319** Mother with Children

1994. Djibouti 20 km Race.
1108 **318** 50f. multicoloured . . . 40 20

1994. U.N.I.C.E.F. Breast-feeding Campaign. Multicoloured.
1109 40f. Type **319** 30 15
1110 45f. Woman breast-feeding baby 35 15

320 Stadium

1994. Hassan Gouled Aptidon Stadium.
1111 **320** 70f. multicoloured . . . 55 25

321 Spinner Dolphins

1994.
1112 **321** 120f. multicoloured . . .

322 Houses encircling Globe

1994. World Housing Day.
1113 **322** 30f. multicoloured . . .

323 White-bellied Bustards

1994.
1114 **323** 10f. multicoloured . . .

324 Trophy, Globe and Players

1994. World Cup Football Championship, U.S.A.
1115 **324** 200f. multicoloured . . .

325 Nomadic Man

1994. Traditional Costumes. Multicoloured.
1116 100f. Type **325** . . . . . .
1117 150f. Town dress . . . . .

326 Golden Jackals

1994.
1118 **326** 400f. multicoloured . . .

327 Walkers

1994. World Walking Day.
1119 **327** 75f. multicoloured . . .

328 Book Rests **329** Traditional Dancers

1994. Traditional Crafts.
1120 **328** 55f. multicoloured . . .

1994. Folklore.
1121 **329** 35f. multicoloured . . .

330 Camel, Ostrich and Net **331** U.N. Flag tied around Cracked Globe

1995. Centenary of Volleyball.
1122 **330** 70f. multicoloured . . .

1995. 50th Anniv of U.N.O.
1123 **331** 120f. multicoloured . . .

332 Drawing Water from Well

1995. Drought Relief Campaign.
1124 **332** 100f. multicoloured . . .

333 Greater Flamingo

1995. Birds. Multicoloured.
1125 30f. Type **333** . . . .
1126 50f. Sacred ibis . . . . . .

334 Camel Rider

1995. Telecommunications Day.
1127 **334** 125f. multicoloured . . .

335 Spotted Hyena

1995.
1128 **335** 200f. multicoloured . . .

336 Council held under Tree **337** Nomads

1995.
1129 **336** 150f. multicoloured . . .

1995. Nomadic Life.
1130 **337** 45f. multicoloured . . .

338 Palm Tree, Map and Emblem

1995. 50th Anniv of F.A.O.
1131 **338** 250f. multicoloured . . .

339 Development Project and Emblem **340** Traditional Costume

1995. 30th Anniv of African Development Bank.
1132 **339** 300f. multicoloured . . .

1995.
1133 **340** 90f. multicoloured . . .

341 Trophy on Map and Football **342** Leopard

1996. Africa Cup Football Championship.
1134 **341** 70f. multicoloured . . .

1996. Wildlife. Multicoloured.
1135 70f. Type **342** . . . .
1136 120f. Ostrich (vert) . . . .

343 Woman wearing Amber Necklace **344** Olympic Flag

1996. Traditional Crafts.
1137 **343** 30f. multicoloured . . .

1996. Olympic Games, Atlanta.
1138 **344** 105f. multicoloured . . .

345 "Commicarpus grandiflorus" **346** Women's Rite

1996.
1139 **345** 350f. multicoloured . . .

1996. Folklore.
1140 **346** 95f. multicoloured . . .

347 The Lion and the Three Bullocks

1996. Stories and Legends.
1141 **347** 95f. multicoloured . . .

348 Children with Flags

1996. National Children's Day.
1142 **348** 130f. multicoloured . . .

349 Fox and Tortoise **350** Mother and Child

1997. Stories and Legends. The Tortoise and the Fox. Multicoloured.
1143 60f. Type **349** . . . .
1144 60f. Fox running away from tortoise . . . .
1145 60f. Tortoise winning race

1997. 50th Anniv of U.N.I.C.E.F. Multicoloured.
1146 80f. Type **350** . . . .
1147 90f. Arms cradling globe of children . . . .

351 Dancers **352** Using Necklace as Pendulum

1997. Folklore.
1148 **351** 70f. multicoloured . . .

1997. Local Fortune Telling. Multicoloured.
1149 200f. Type **352** . . . . . .
1150 300f. Using pebbles . . . .

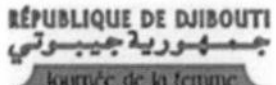

353 Woman weaving Basket **355** Arta Post Office

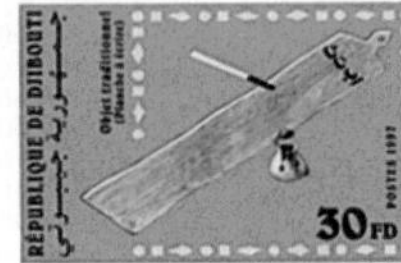

354 Writing Board

1997. Women's Day.
1151 **353** 250f. multicoloured . . .

1997. Traditional Implements. Multicoloured.
1152 30f. Type **354** . . . .
1153 400f. Bowl and spoon (vert)

1997. 20th Anniv of Independence. Multicoloured.
1154 30f. Type **355** . . . .
1155 100f. Telecommunications station . . . .
1156 120f. Undersea cable, route map and cable ship (horiz) . . . .

356 Goats in Tree

1997.
1157 **356** 120f. multicoloured . . .

357 Diana, Princess of Wales

1998. Diana, Princess of Wales Commemoration.

1158	**357**	125f. multicoloured . . .	95	45
1159		130f. multicoloured . . .	1·00	50
1160		150f. multicoloured . . .	1·25	60

358 Paradise Tanager

1998. International Year of the Ocean. Mult.
1161 75c. Type **358** . . . . . .
1162 75c. Red-eyed tree frog ("Agalychnis callidryas")
1163 75c. Common dolphin ("Delphinus delphis") and humpback whale ("Megaptera novaeangliae") . . . . .
1164 75c. Savanna monkey ("Cercopithecus aethiops") . . . .
1165 75c. Great hammerhead ("Sphyrna mokarran") and yellow-lipped sea snakes ("Laticaudia colubrina") . . . .
1166 75c. Long-horned cowfish ("Lactoria cornuta") and common dolphin ("Delphinus delphis") . .
1167 75c. Common dolphins ("Delphinus delphis") . .
1168 75c. Striped mimic blenny ("Aspidontus taeniatus") and foxface ("Lovulpinus") . . . . .
1169 75c. Big-fin reef squid ("Sepioteuthis lessoniana)
1170 75c. Ornate butterflyfish ("Chaetodon ornatissimus) and blue shark ("Prionace glauca")
1171 75c. Hermit crab ("Eupagurus bernherdus")
1172 75c. Common octopus ("Octopus vulgaris") . . .

Nos. 1161/72 were issued together, se-tenant, forming a composite design.

359 Gandhi **360** Vase

1998. 50th Death Anniv of Mahatma Gandhi (Indian patriot).
1173 **359** 250f. multicoloured . . .

1998. Traditional Art.
1174 **360** 30f. multicoloured . . .

361 Woman carrying Basket on Back and Road-crossing Officer

1998. Women's Rights and International Peace.
1175 **361** 70f. multicoloured . . .

362 Water Pump and Donkey carrying Water Containers

1998. World Water Day.
1176 **362** 45f. multicoloured . . .

363 Football, Trophy and Eiffel Tower **364** Octopus

1998. World Cup Football Championship, France.
1177 **363** 200f. multicoloured . . .

1998. Marine Life. Multicoloured.
1178 20f. Type **364** . . . .
1179 25f. Shark (horiz) . . . . .

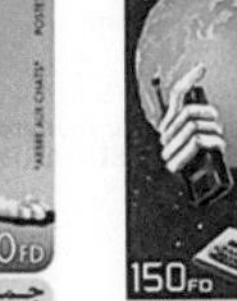

365 Catmint and Cats **366** Globe using Mobile Phone and Computer

1998.
1180 **365** 120f. multicoloured . . .

1998. World Telecommunications Day.
1181 **366** 150f. multicoloured . . .

367 National Bank **368** Flags of Member States and Emblem

1998. Public Buildings.
1182 **367** 100f. multicoloured . . .

1998. Inter-Governmental Authority on Development.
1183 **368** 85f. multicoloured . . .

369 Boys playing Goos

1998. Traditional Games.
1184 **369** 110f. multicoloured . . .

370 Fishing Harbour

1998. Public Buildings.
1185 **370** 100f. multicoloured . . .

371 Gulls sp. and Maskali Island

1998. Tourist Sites.
1186 **371** 500f. multicoloured . . .

372 Mother Teresa

1998. Mother Teresa (founder of Missionaries of Charity) Commemoration.

1187	**372**	130f. multicoloured . . .	90	45

POSTAGE DUE STAMP

D **248** Milking Bowl

1988. Traditional Djibouti Art.

D1016	D **248**	60f. multicoloured	90	65

DODECANESE ISLANDS Pt. 8

A group of islands off the coast of Asia Minor occupied by Italy in May 1912 and ceded to her by Turkey in 1920. The islands concerned are now known as Kalimnos, Kasos, Kos, Khalki, Leros, Lipsoi, Nisiros, Patmos, Tilos (Piskopi), Rhodes (Rodos), Karpathos, Simi and Astipalaia. Castelrosso came under the same administration in 1921.

In 1944 the Dodecanese Islands were occupied by British forces (see **BRITISH OCCUPATION OF ITALIAN COLONIES**). In 1947 they were transferred to Greek administration, since when Greek stamps have been used.

A. ITALIAN OCCUPATION

100 centesimi = 1 lira.

1912. Stamps of Italy optd **EGEO**.

1	**39**	25c. blue	30·00	17·00
2	–	50c. violet	30·00	17·00

1912. Stamps of Italy optd, or surch also, for the individual islands (all in capitals on Nos. 6 and 10, in upper and lower case on others). A. Calimno

3A	**31**	2c. brown	4·50	4·25
4A	**37**	5c. green	1·40	4·25
5A		10c. red	40	4·25
6A	**41**	15c. grey	19·00	8·25
7A	**37**	15c. grey	2·75	25·00
8A	**41**	20c. on 15c. grey	10·00	17·00
10A		20c. orange	2·75	25·00
11A	**39**	25c. blue	4·00	4·25

12A 40c. brown . . . . 40 4·25
13A 50c. violet . . . . 40 4·25

B. Caso

3B 31 2c. brown . . . . 4·75 4·25
4B 37 5c. green . . . . 1·60 4·25
5B 10c. red . . . . 40 4·25
6B 41 15c. grey . . . . 22·00 8·25
7B 37 15c. grey . . . . 2·75 25·00
8B 41 20c. on 15c. grey . . . . 65 12·00
10B 20c. orange . . . . 2·10 20·00
11B 39 25c. blue . . . . 40 4·25
12B 40c. brown . . . . 40 4·25
13B 50c. violet . . . . 40 7·50

C. Cos

3C 31 2c. brown . . . . 4·75 4·25
4C 37 5c. green . . . . 45·00 4·25
5C 10c. red . . . . 2·25 4·25
6C 41 15c. grey . . . . 22·00 8·25
7C 37 15c. grey . . . . 2·75 35·00
8C 41 20c. on 15c. grey . . . . 10·00 21·00
10C 20c. orange . . . . 2·10 21·00
11C 39 25c. blue . . . . 19·00 4·25
12C 40c. brown . . . . 40 4·25
13C 50c. violet . . . . 40 7·50

D. Karki

3D 31 2c. brown . . . . 4·75 4·25
4D 37 5c. green . . . . 1·60 4·25
5D 10c. red . . . . 1·60 4·25
6D 41 15c. grey . . . . 22·00 8·25
7D 37 15c. grey . . . . 2·75 26·00
8D 41 20c. on 15c. grey . . . . 1·25 15·00
10D 20c. orange . . . . 2·75 24·00
11D 39 25c. blue . . . . 40 4·25
12D 40c. brown . . . . 40 4·25
13D 50c. violet . . . . 40 7·50

E. Leros

3E 31 2c. brown . . . . 4·75 4·25
4E 37 5c. green . . . . 3·50 4·25
5E 10c. red . . . . 70 4·25
6E 41 15c. grey . . . . 35·00 8·25
7E 37 15c. grey . . . . 2·75 22·00
8E 41 20c. on 15c. grey . . . . 10·00 16·50
9E 20c. orange . . . . 27·00 85·00
11E 39 25c. blue . . . . 21·00 4·25
12E 40c. brown . . . . 2·75 4·25
13E 50c. violet . . . . 40 7·50

F. Lipso

3F 31 2c. brown . . . . 4·75 4·25
4F 37 5c. green . . . . 1·90 4·25
5F 10c. red . . . . 85 4·25
6F 41 15c. grey . . . . 21·00 8·25
7F 37 15c. grey . . . . 2·75 22·00
8F 41 20c. on 15c. grey . . . . 80 15·00
10F 20c. orange . . . . 2·75 25·00
11F 39 25c. blue . . . . 40 4·25
12F 40c. brown . . . . 1·25 4·25
13F 50c. violet . . . . 40 7·50

G. Nisiros

3G 31 2c. brown . . . . 4·75 4·25
4G 37 5c. green . . . . 1·60 4·25
5G 10c. red . . . . 40 4·25
6G 41 15c. grey . . . . 19·00 8·25
7G 37 15c. grey . . . . 13·50 23·00
8G 41 20c. on 15c. grey . . . . 80 15·00
10G 20c. orange . . . . 55·00 65·00
11G 39 25c. blue . . . . 1·40 4·25
12G 40c. brown . . . . 40 4·25
13G 50c. violet . . . . 2·75 7·50

H. Patmos

3H 31 2c. brown . . . . 4·75 4·25
4H 37 5c. green . . . . 1·60 4·25
5H 10c. red . . . . 1·40 4·25
6H 41 15c. grey . . . . 19·00 8·25
7H 37 15c. grey . . . . 2·75 25·00
8H 41 20c. on 15c. grey . . . . 10·00 20·00
9H 20c. orange . . . . 45·00 85·00
11H 39 25c. blue . . . . 55 4·25
12H 40c. brown . . . . 2·50 4·25
13H 50c. violet . . . . 40 7·50

I. Piscopi

3I 31 2c. brown . . . . 4·75 4·25
4I 37 5c. green . . . . 1·50 4·25
5I 10c. red . . . . 40 4·25
6I 41 15c. grey . . . . 22·00 8·25
7I 37 15c. grey . . . . 10·00 25·00
8I 41 20c. on 15c. grey . . . . 80 15·00
10I 20c. orange . . . . 27·00 38·00
11I 39 25c. blue . . . . 40 4·25
12I 40c. brown . . . . 40 4·25
13I 50c. violet . . . . 40 7·50

J. Rodi

3J 31 2c. brown . . . . 40 4·25
4J 37 5c. green . . . . 1·40 4·25
5J 10c. red . . . . 40 4·25
6J 41 15c. grey . . . . 23·00 8·25
7J 37 15c. grey . . . . 85·00 38·00
8J 41 20c. on 15c. grey . . . . 75·00 80·00
10J 20c. orange . . . . 4·25 10·00
11J 39 25c. blue . . . . 1·40 4·25
12J 40c. brown . . . . 2·25 4·25
13J 50c. violet . . . . 40 7·50

K. Scarpanto

3K 31 2c. brown . . . . 4·75 4·25
4K 37 5c. green . . . . 1·40 4·25
5K 10c. red . . . . 40 4·25
6K 41 15c. grey . . . . 17·00 8·25
7K 37 15c. grey . . . . 10·00 19·00
8K 41 20c. on 15c. grey . . . . 80 17·00
10K 20c. orange . . . . 27·00 27·00
11K 39 25c. blue . . . . 4·50 4·25
12K 40c. brown . . . . 40 4·25
13K 50c. violet . . . . 1·40 7·50

L. Simi

3L 31 2c. brown . . . . 4·75 4·25
4L 37 5c. green . . . . 14·50 4·25
5L 10c. red . . . . 40 4·25
6L 41 15c. grey . . . . 28·00 28·00
7L 37 15c. grey . . . . 75·00 75·00
8L 41 20c. on 15c. grey . . . . 5·75 5·75
10L 20c. orange . . . . 38·00 38·00
11L 39 25c. blue . . . . 1·90 4·25
12L 40c. brown . . . . 40 4·25
13L 50c. violet . . . . 40 7·50

M. Stampalia

3M 31 2c. brown . . . . 4·75 4·25
4M 37 5c. green . . . . 40 4·25
5M 10c. red . . . . 40 4·25
6M 41 15c. grey . . . . 21·00 8·25
7M 37 15c. grey . . . . 6·75 19·00
8M 41 20c. on 15c. grey . . . . 65 12·00
10M 20c. orange . . . . 25·00 27·00
11M 39 25c. blue . . . . 55 4·25
12M 40c. brown . . . . 2·25 4·25
13M 50c. violet . . . . 40 7·50

1916. Optd **Rodi**.
14 33 20c. orange . . . . 2·00 4·25
15 39 85c. brown . . . . 40·00 60·00
16 34 1l. brown & green . . . . . 2·00

1 Rhodian Windmill

2 Knight kneeling before the Holy City

1929. King of Italy's Visit.
17 1 5c. purple 85 20
18 – 10c. brown 85 20
19 – 20c. red 85 20
20 – 25c. green 85 20
21 2 30c. blue 85 20
22 – 50c. brown 85 20
23 – 1l.25 blue . . . . 85 1·00
24 2 5l. purple . . . . 85 1·25
25 10l. green . . . . 1·75 2·75
DESIGNS—As Type 1: 10c. Galley of Knights of St. John; 20c., 25c. Knight defending Christianity; 50c., 1l.25, Knight's tomb.

1930. 21st Hydrological Congress. Nos. 17/25 optd **XXI Congresso Idrologico**.
26 5c. purple . . . . 13·50 11·50
27 10c. brown . . . . 15·00 11·50
28 20c. red . . . . 23·00 10·00
29 25c. green . . . . 30·00 10·00
30 30c. blue . . . . 15·00 12·00
31 50c. brown . . . . £375 30·00
32 1l.25 blue . . . . £300 50·00
33 5l. purple £160 £250
34 10l. green £160 £275

1930. Ferrucci issue of Italy (colours changed) optd for each individual island, in capitals. A. CALINO; B. CASO; C. COO; D. CALCHI; E. LERO; F. LISSO; G. NISIRO; H. PATMO; I. PISCOPI; J. RODI; K. SCARPANTO; L. SIMI; M. STAMPALIA.
35 114 20c. violet . . . . 1·90 3·00
36 – 25c. green . . . . 1·90 3·00
37 – 50c. black . . . . 1·90 5·75
38 – 1l.25 blue . . . . 1·90 5·75
39 – 5l.+2l. red . . . . 2·75 10·00
Same prices for each of the 13 islands.

1930. Air. Ferrucci air stamps of Italy (colours changed) optd **ISOLE ITALIANE DELL'EGEO**.
40 117 50c. purple . . . . 5·75 11·50
41 1l. blue . . . . 5·75 11·50
42 5l.+2l. red . . . . 12·00 32·00

1930. Virgil stamps of Italy optd **ISOLE ITALIANE DELL'EGEO**.
43 – 15c. violet (postage) . . . 1·00 5·75
44 – 20c. brown . . . . 1·00 5·75
45 – 25c. green . . . . 1·00 2·50
46 – 30c. brown . . . . 1·00 2·50
47 – 50c. purple . . . . 1·00 2·50
48 – 75c. red . . . . 1·00 5·75
49 – 1l.25 blue . . . . 1·00 8·25
50 – 5l+1l.50 purple . . . . . . 2·40 17·00
51 – 10l.+2l.50 brown . . . . . 2·40 17·00
52 119 50c. green (air) . . . . . . 1·40 12·00
53 1l. red . . . . 1·40 13·50
54 7l.70+1l.30 brown . . . . . 3·00 24·00
55 9l.+2l. grey . . . . 3·00 25·00

1931. Italian Eucharistic Congress. Nos. 17/25 optd **1931 CONGRESSO EUCARISTICO ITALIANO**.
56 5c. red . . . . 4·00 5·75
57 10c. brown . . . . 4·00 5·75
58 20c. red . . . . 4·00 10·00
59 25c. green . . . . 4·00 10·00
60 30c. blue . . . . 4·00 10·00
61 50c. brown . . . . 30·00 24·00
62 1l.25 blue . . . . 23·00 42·00

1932. St. Antony of Padua stamps of Italy optd **ISOLE ITALIANE DELL'EGEO**.
63 121 20c. purple . . . . 15·00 9·00
64 – 25c. green . . . . 15·00 9·00
65 – 30c. brown . . . . 15·00 11·00
66 – 50c. purple . . . . 15·00 7·50
67 – 75c. red . . . . 15·00 12·50
68 – 1l.25 blue . . . . 15·00 14·50
69 – 5l.+2l.50 orange . . . . . 15·00 55·00

1932. Dante stamps of Italy optd **ISOLE ITALIANE DELL'EGEO**.
70 – 10c. green (postage) . . . 95 2·40
71 – 15c. violet . . . . 95 2·40
72 – 20c. brown . . . . 95 2·40
73 – 25c. green . . . . 95 2·40
74 – 30c. red . . . . 95 2·40
75 – 50c. purple . . . . 95 1·00
76 – 75c. red . . . . 95 3·00
77 – 1l.25 blue . . . . 95 2·40
78 – 1l.75 sepia . . . . 1·10 3·00
79 – 2l.75 red . . . . 1·10 3·00
80 – 5l.+2l. violet . . . . . . 1·40 9·25
81 124 10l.+2l.50 brown . . . . . 1·40 13·50
82 125 50c. red (air) . . . . . . 1·00 2·40
83 – 1l. green . . . . 1·00 2·40
84 – 3l. purple . . . . 1·00 2·75
85 – 5l. red . . . . 1·00 2·75
86 125 7l.70+2l. sepia . . . . . . 1·40 6·75
87 – 10l.+2l.50 blue . . . . . 1·40 12·00
88 127 100l. olive and blue . . . . 15·00 70·00
No. 88 is inscribed instead of optd.

1932. Garibaldi issue of Italy (colours changed) optd for each individual island in capital letters. A. CALINO; B. CASO; C. COO; D. CARCHI; E. LERO; F. LIBO; G. NISIRO; H. PATMO; I. PISCOPI; J. RODI; K. SCARPANTO; L. SIMI; M. STAMPALIA.
89 – 10c. sepia . . . . 8·00 12·00
90 128 20c. brown . . . . 8·00 12·00
91 – 25c. green . . . . 8·00 12·00
92 128 30c. black . . . . 8·00 12·00
93 – 50c. lilac . . . . 8·00 12·00
94 – 75c. red . . . . 8·00 12·00
95 – 1l.25 blue . . . . 8·00 12·00
96 – 1l.75+25c. sepia . . . . . 8·00 12·00
97 – 2l.55+50c. red . . . . . . 8·00 12·00
98 – 5l.+1l. violet . . . . . . 8·00 12·00
Same prices for each of the 13 islands.

1932. Air. Garibaldi air stamps of Italy optd **ISOLE ITALIANE DELL'EGEO**.
99 130 50c. green . . . . 30·00 55·00
100 – 80c. red . . . . 30·00 55·00
101 130 1l.+25c. blue . . . . . . 30·00 55·00
102 – 2l.+50c. brown . . . . . 30·00 55·00
103 – 5l.+1l. black . . . . . . 30·00 55·00

8

1932. 20th Anniv of Italian Occupation of Dodecanese Islands.
106 8 5c. red, black and green . . 5·00 8·25
107 10c. red, black and blue . . 5·00 5·00
108 20c. red, black and yellow . . 5·00 5·00
109 25c. red, black and violet . . 5·00 5·00
110 30c. red, black and red . . 5·00 5·00
111 – 50c. red, black and blue . . 5·00 5·00
112 – 1l.25 red, purple & blue . . 5·00 12·00
113 – 5l. red and blue . . . . . 15·00 35·00
114 – 10l. red, green and blue . . 42·00 55·00
115 – 25l. red, brown and blue . . £275 £600
DESIGN—VERT: 50c. to 25l. Arms on map of Rhodes.

10 Airship "Graf Zeppelin"

11 Wing from Arms of Francesco Sans

1933. Air. "Graf Zeppelin".
116 10 3l. brown . . . . 32·00 90·00
117 5l. purple . . . . 32·00 £110
118 10l. green . . . . 32·00 £180
119 12l. blue . . . . 32·00 £225
120 15l. red . . . . 32·00 £225
121 20l. black . . . . 32·00 £225

1933. Air. Balbo Mass Formation Flight issue of Italy optd **ISOLE ITALIANE DELL'EGEO**.
122 135 5l.25+19l.75 red, green and blue . . . . 27·00 75·00
123 136 5l.25+44l.75 red, green and blue . . . . 27·00 75·00

1934. Air.
124 11 50c. black and yellow . . . 20 20
125 80c. black and red . . . . 3·00 2·75
126 1l. black and green . . . . 1·75 20
127 5l. black and mauve . . . . 5·25 7·25

1934. World Football Championship stamps of Italy (some colours changed) optd **ISOLE ITALIANE DELL'EGEO**.
128 142 20c. red (postage) . . . . 40·00 40·00
129 – 25c. green . . . . 40·00 40·00
130 – 50c. violet . . . . £140 20·00
131 – 1l.25 blue . . . . 40·00 70·00
132 – 5l.+2l.50 blue . . . . . . 40·00 £170
133 – 50c. brown (air) . . . . . 4·25 25·00
134 – 75c. red . . . . 4·25 25·00
135 – 5l.+2l.50 orange . . . . . 12·50 50·00
136 – 10l.+5l. green . . . . . . 12·50 70·00

1934. Military Medal Centenary stamps of Italy (some colours changed) optd **ISOLE ITALIANE DELL'EGEO**.
157 146 10c. grey (postage) . . . 30·00 40·00
158 – 15c. brown . . . . 30·00 40·00
159 – 20c. orange . . . . 30·00 40·00
160 – 25c. green . . . . 30·00 40·00
161 – 30c. red . . . . 30·00 40·00
162 – 50c. green . . . . 30·00 40·00
163 – 75c. red . . . . 30·00 40·00
164 – 1l.25 blue . . . . 30·00 40·00
165 – 1l.75+1l. violet . . . . . 19·00 40·00
166 – 2l.55+2l. red . . . . . . 19·00 40·00
167 – 2l.75+2l. brown . . . . . 19·00 40·00
168 – 25c. green (air) . . . . . 38·00 50·00
169 – 50c. grey . . . . 38·00 50·00
170 – 75c. red . . . . 38·00 50·00
171 – 80c. brown . . . . 38·00 50·00
172 – 1l.+50c. green . . . . . . 29·00 50·00
173 – 2l.+1l. blue . . . . 29·00 50·00
174 – 3l.+2l. violet . . . . . . 29·00 50·00

16

19 Dante House, Rhodes

1935. Holy Year.
177 16 5c. orange . . . . 8·25 11·50
178 10c. brown . . . . 8·25 11·50
179 20c. red . . . . 8·25 13·50
180 25c. green . . . . 8·25 13·50
181 30c. purple . . . . 8·25 15·00
182 50c. brown . . . . 8·25 15·00
183 1l.25 blue . . . . 8·25 38·00

1938. Augustus the Great stamps of Italy (colours changed) optd **ISOLE ITALIANE DELL'EGEO**.
186 163 10c. brown (postage) . . 2·25 4·50
187 – 15c. violet . . . . 2·25 4·50
188 – 20c. brown . . . . 2·25 4·50
189 – 25c. green . . . . 2·25 4·50
190 – 30c. purple . . . . 2·25 4·50
191 – 50c. green . . . . 2·25 4·50
192 – 75c. red . . . . 2·25 4·50
193 – 1l.25 blue . . . . 2·25 4·50
194 – 1l.75+1l. orange . . . . . 3·00 10·00
195 – 2l.55+2l. brown . . . . . 3·00 10·00
196 – 25c. violet (air) . . . . . 2·40 2·75
197 – 50c. green . . . . 2·40 2·75
198 – 80c. blue . . . . 2·40 8·00
199 – 1l.+1l. purple . . . . . . 3·75 12·00
200 164 5l.+1l. red . . . . 6·00 25·00

1938. Giotto stamps of Italy optd **ITALIANE ISOLE DELL'EGEO**.
201 1l.25 blue (No. 527) . . . . 95 1·75
202 2l.75+2l. brown (530) . . . . 1·10 6·75

1940. Colonial Exhibition. Inscr as in T **19**.
203 – 5c. brown (postage) . . . 30 65
204 – 10c. orange 30 65
205 19 25c. green . . . . 65 1·25
206 – 50c. violet . . . . 65 1·25
207 – 75c. red . . . . 65 1·60
208 19 1l.25 blue . . . . 65 1·90
209 – 2l.+75c. red . . . . . . 65 10·00
DESIGNS—VERT: 5c., 50c. Roman Wolf statue; 10c., 75c., 2l. Crown and Maltese Cross.

210 50c. brown (air) . . . . . . 85 1·90
211 1l. violet . . . . 85 1·90
212 2l.+75c. blue . . . . . . 85 3·75
213 5l.+2l.50 brown . . . . . . 85 6·00
DESIGNS—HORIZ: Savoia Marchetti S.M.75 airplane over: 50c., 2l. statues, Rhodes Harbour; 1, 5l. Government House, Rhodes.

1943. Aegean Relief Fund. Nos. 17/25 surch **PRO ASSISTENZA EGEO** and value.
214 1 5c.+5c. purple 70 70
215 – 10c.+10c. brown 70 70
216 – 20c.+20c. red 70 70
217 – 25c.+25c. green 70 70
218 2 30c.+30c. blue . . . . . . 1·40 1·10
219 – 50c.+50c. brown . . . . . 1·40 1·40
220 – 1l.25+1l.25 blue . . . . . 1·75 1·75
221 2 5l.+5l. purple . . . . . . 70·00 70·00

1944. War Victims' Relief. Nos. 17/20 and 22/23 surch **PRO SINISTRATI DI GUERRA**, value and stag symbol.
224 1 5c.+3l. purple . . . . . . 1·40 2·40
225 – 10c.+3l. brown . . . . . . 1·40 2·40
226 – 20c.+3l. red . . . . 1·40 2·40
227 – 25c.+3l. green . . . . . . 1·40 2·40
228 – 50c.+3l. brown . . . . . . 1·40 2·40
229 – 1l.25+5l. blue . . . . . . 21·00 25·00

1944. Air. War Victims Relief. Surch **PRO SINISTRATI DI GUERRA** and value.
232 11 50c.+2l. blk & yellow . . . 6·75 2·50
233 80c.+2l. black and red . . 8·25 5·00
234 1l.+2l. black & green . . . 10·00 5·75
235 5l.+2l. black & mauve . . . 50·00 55·00

1945. Red Cross Fund. Nos. 24/5 surch **FEBBRAIO 1945 + 10** and Cross.
236 +10l. on 5l. purple . . . . . 6·75 10·00
237 +10l. on 10l. green . . . . . 6·75 10·00

EXPRESS STAMPS

1932. Air. Garibaldi Air Express stamps of Italy optd **ISOLE ITALIANE DELL'EGEO**.
E104 E 3 2l.25+1l. red & blue . . 38·00 70·00
E105 4l.50+1l.50 grey and yellow . . . . 38·00 70·00

1934. Air. As Nos. E442/3 of Italy, but colours changed, optd **ISOLE ITALIANE DELL'EGEO**.
E175 2l.+1l.25 blue . . . . . . 30·00 48·00
E176 4l.50+2l. green . . . . . . 30·00 48·00

E 17

1935.
E184 E **17** 1l.25 green . . . . . . 1·75 1·40
E185 2l.50 orange . . . . . 2·50 3·00

1943. Aegean Relief Fund. Surch **PRO ASSISTENZA EGEO** and value.
E222 E **17** 1l.25+1l.25 green . . . 35·00 20·00
E223 2l.50+2l.50 orge . . . 40·00 27·00

1944. Nos. 19/20 surch **ESPRESSO** and value.
E230 1l.25 on 25c. green . . . . 40 1·25
E231 2l.50 on 50c. red . . . . . 40 1·25

PARCEL POST STAMPS

P 12

1934.
P137 P **12** 5c. orange . . . . . . 1·75 1·75
P138 10c. red . . . . . . 1·75 1·75
P139 20c. green . . . . . . 1·75 1·75
P140 25c. violet . . . . . . 1·75 1·75
P141 50c. blue . . . . . . 1·75 1·75
P142 60c. black . . . . . . 1·75 1·75
P143 – 1l. orange . . . . . . 1·75 1·75
P144 – 2l. red . . . . 1·75 1·75
P145 – 3l. green . . . . . . 1·75 1·75
P146 – 4l. violet . . . . . . 1·75 1·75
P147 – 10l. blue . . . . . . 1·75 1·75
DESIGN: 1l. to 10l. Left half: Stag as in Type E **17**; Right half: Castle.

POSTAGE DUE STAMPS

D **14** Badge of the Knights of St. John

D **15** Immortelle

1934.
D148 D **14** 5c. orange . . . . . . 1·10 1·40
D149 10c. red . . . . . . 1·10 1·40
D150 20c. green . . . . . . 1·10 70
D151 30c. violet . . . . . . 1·10 1·00
D152 40c. blue . . . . . . 1·10 2·40
D153 D **15** 50c. orange . . . . . 1·10 70
D154 60c. red . . . . . . 1·10 3·75
D155 1l. green . . . . . . 1·10 3·75
D156 2l. violet . . . . . . 1·10 2·40

B. GREEK MILITARY ADMINISTRATION

100 lepta = 1 drachma.

1947. Stamps of Greece optd with characters as in Type G **1**.
G1 – 10d. on 2000d. blue (No. 623) 55 55
G3 **89** 50d. on 1d. grn (No. 642) 1·10 1·10
G4 250d. on 3d. brn (No. 643) 1·10 1·10

(G 1)

1947. Stamps of Greece surch as Type G **1**.
G 5 – 20d. on 500d. brown (No. 582) 55 55
G 6 – 30d. on 5d. green (No. 574) 55 55
G 7 **106** 50d. on 2d. brown . . . 70 70
G 8 – 250d. on 10d. brown (No. 510) . . . . . . 1·10 1·10
G 9 – 400d. on 15d. green (No. 511) . . . . . . 1·60 1·60
G10 – 1000d. on 200d. blue (No. 581) . . . . . . 1·10 1·10

DOMINICA Pt. 1

Until 31 December 1939 one of the Leeward Islands, but then transferred to the Windward Islands. Used Leeward Island stamps concurrently with Dominican issues from 1903 to above date.

1874. 12 pence = 1 shilling;
20 shillings = 1 pound.
1949. 100 cents = 1 West Indian dollar.

1

1874.
13 **1** ½d. yellow . . . . 3·25 10·00
20 ½d. green . . . . 1·50 5·50
5 1d. lilac . . . . 6·00 2·00
22a 1d. red . . . . 2·75 6·50
15 2½d. brown . . . . £140 2·00
23 2½d. blue . . . . 3·75 5·00
7 4d. blue . . . . £110 2·50
24 4d. grey . . . . 3·25 5·00
8 6d. green . . . . £150 20·00
25 6d. orange . . . . 9·00 48·00
9 1s. mauve . . . . £120 50·00

1882. No. 5 bisected and surch with a small ½.
10 **1** ½(d.) on half 1d. lilac . . . . £180 42·00

1882. No. 5 bisected and surch with large ½.
11 **1** ½(d.) on half 1d. lilac . . . . 30·00 17·00

1883. No. 5 bisected and surch **HALF PENNY** vert.
12 **1** ½d. on half 1d. lilac . . . . 65·00 20·00

1886. Nos. 8 and 9 surch in words and bar.
17 **1** ½d. on 6d. green . . . . . . 4·25 3·75
18 1d. on 6d. green £21000 £10000
19 1d. on 1s. mauve . . . . . . 14·00 17·00

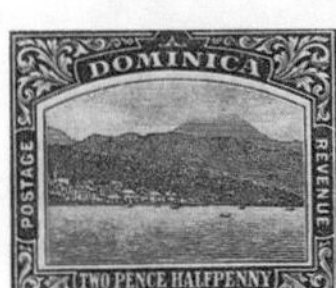

9 "Roseau from the Sea" (Lt. Caddy)

10

1903.
37 **9** ½d. green . . . . 3·50 3·25
38 1d. grey and red . . . . . 2·00 40
29 2d. green and brown . . . . 2·50 4·50
30 2½d. grey and blue . . . . 5·00 4·00
31 3d. purple and black . . . . 8·00 3·25
32 6d. grey and brown . . . . 4·50 18·00
43 1s. mauve and green . . . . 3·75 55·00
34 2s. black and purple . . . . 26·00 29·00
45 2s.6d. green and orange . . 22·00 60·00
46 **10** 5s. black and brown . . . . 60·00 60·00

1908.
48bw **9** 1d. red . . . . 1·00 50
64 1½d. orange . . . . 3·00 11·00
65 2d. grey . . . . 2·75 3·25
66 2½d. blue . . . . 2·00 8·50
51 3d. purple on yellow . . . 3·00 4·25
52a 6d. purple . . . . 3·50 18·00
53 1s. black on green . . . . 3·00 2·75
53b 2s. purple and blue on blue . . . . 25·00 85·00
70 2s.6d. black and red on blue . . . . 32·00 95·00

1914. As T **10**, but portrait of King George V.
54 5s. red and green on yellow . . 55·00 80·00

1916. No. 37 surch **WAR TAX ONE HALFPENNY**.
55 **9** ½d. on ½d. green 75 75

1918. Optd **WAR TAX**.
57 **9** ½d. green 15 50
58 3d. purple on yellow . . . . 1·50 4·00

1919. Surch **WAR TAX 1½D.**
59 **9** 1½d. on 2½d. orange 15 55

1920. Surch **1½D.**
60 **9** 1½d. on 2½d. orange . . . . 2·50 4·50

16

1923.
71 **16** ½d. black and green . . . . 1·75 60
72 1d. black and violet . . . . 2·00 1·75
73 1d. black and red . . . . . 9·00 1·00
74 1½d. black and red . . . . 2·75 65
75 1½d. black and brown . . . 9·00 70
76 2d. black and grey . . . . 1·75 50
77 2½d. black and yellow . . . 1·50 9·00
78 2½d. black and blue . . . . 4·25 2·00
79 3d. black and blue . . . . 1·50 12·00
80 3d. black and red on yellow 1·50 1·00
81 4d. black and brown . . . . 2·50 5·50
82 6d. black and mauve . . . 3·50 7·00
83 1s. black on green . . . . . 2·25 2·75
84 2s. black and blue on blue 10·00 19·00
85 2s.6d. black and red on blue 18·00 19·00
86 3s. black and purple on yellow . . . . 3·25 12·00
87 4s. black and red on green 11·00 22·00
90 5s. black and green on yellow . . . . 9·00 50·00
91 £1 black and purple on red £225 £350

1935. Silver Jubilee. As T **13** of Antigua.
92 1d. blue and red 75 20
93 1½d. blue and grey . . . . . 1·75 1·25
94 2½d. brown and blue . . . . 1·75 2·50
95 1s. grey and purple . . . . . 1·75 4·00

1937. Coronation. As T **2** of Aden.
96 1d. red 40 10
97 1½d. brown 40 10
98 2½d. blue . . . . 60 1·50

17 Fresh Water Lake

21 King George VI

1938.
99 **17** ½d. brown and green . . . 10 15
100 – 1d. black and red 20 20
101 – 1½d. green and purple . . 30 70
102 – 2d. red and black . . . . 50 1·25
103a – 2½d. purple and blue . . . 20 1·25
104 – 3d. olive and brown . . . 30 50
104a – 3½d. blue and mauve . . 2·00 2·00
105 **17** 6d. green and violet . . . 1·75 1·50
105a 7d. green and brown . . . 2·00 1·50
106 – 1s. violet and olive . . . 3·25 1·50
106a – 2s. grey and purple . . . 6·00 8·00
107 **17** 2s.6d. black and red . . . 12·00 4·75
108 – 5s. blue and brown . . . 7·50 8·00
108a – 10s. black and orange . . 12·00 15·00
DESIGNS—As Type **17**: 1d., 3d., 2s., 5s. Layou River; 1½d., 2½d., 3½d. Picking Limes; 2d., 1s., 10s. Boiling Lake.

1940.
109a **21** ¼d. brown 10 10

1946. Victory. As T **9** of Aden.
110 1d. red 20 10
111 3½d. blue 20 10

1948. Silver Wedding. As T **10/11** of Aden.
112 1d. red 15 10
113 10s. brown . . . . 12·00 23·00

1949. U.P.U. As T **20/23** of Antigua.
114 5c. blue 20 15
115 6c. brown . . . . 1·25 2·25
116 12c. purple . . . . 45 1·25
117 24c. olive 30 30

1951. Inauguration of B.W.I. University College. As T **24/25** of Antigua.
118 3c. green and violet . . . . . 50 1·10
119 12c. green and red 75 30

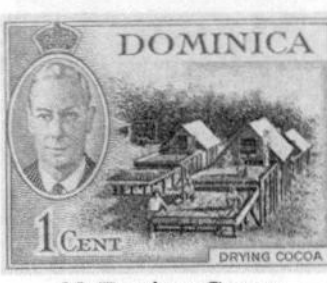

23 Drying Cocoa

1951. New Currency.
120 – ½c. brown 10 30
121 **23** 1c. black and red 10 30
122 – 2c. brown and green . . . 10 30
123 – 3c. green and purple . . . 15 1·75
124 – 4c. orange and sepia . . . 70 1·75
125 – 5c. black and red 85 30
126 – 6c. olive and brown . . . 90 30
127 – 8c. green and blue 90 70
128 – 12c. black and green . . . 60 1·25
129 – 14c. blue and purple . . . 95 1·75
130 – 24c. purple and red 75 30
131 – 48c. green and orange . . 3·75 8·00
132 – 60c. red and black . . . . 3·75 6·00
133 – $1.20 green and black . . . 4·50 6·00
134 – $2.40 orange and black . . 23·00 38·00
DESIGNS: ½c. As Type **21**, but with portrait as Type **23**. HORIZ (as Type **23**): 2c., 60c. Carib baskets; 3c., 48c. Lime plantation; 4c. Picking oranges; 5c. Bananas; 6c. Botanical Gardens; 8c. Drying vanilla beans; 12c., $1.20, Fresh Water Lake; 14c. Layou River, 24c. Boiling Lake. VERT: $2.40, Picking oranges.

1951. New Constitution. Stamps of 1951 optd **NEW CONSTITUTION 1951**.
135 3c. green and violet 15 70
136 5c. black and red . . . . . . 15 1·00
137 8c. green and blue 15 15
138 14c. blue and violet 50 20

1953. Coronation. As T **13** of Aden.
139 2c. black and green 20 10

1954. As Nos 120/34 but with portrait of Queen Elizabeth II.
140 ½c. brown 10 30
141 1c. black and red 10 10
142 2c. brown and green . . . . 55 1·75
143 3c. green and purple . . . . 1·50 30
144 3c. black and red . . . . . 3·25 2·25
145 4c. orange and brown 20 10
146 5c. black and red . . . . . 2·00 50
147 5c. blue and brown . . . . . 10·00 1·00
148 6c. green and brown 40 10
149 8c. green and blue . . . . . 1·00 10
150 10c. green and brown . . . . 5·00 2·50
151 12c. black and green 50 10
152 14c. blue and purple 50 10
153 24c. purple and red 50 10
154 48c. green and orange . . . 2·00 9·00
155 48c. brown and violet . . . . 1·25 80
156 60c. red and black . . . . . 1·25 1·00
157 $1.20 green and black . . . 17·00 7·00
158 $2.40 orange and black . . . 17·00 14·00
DESIGNS (New)—HORIZ: Nos. 144, 155, Mat making; 147, Canoe making; 150, Bananas.

1958. British Caribbean Federation. As T **25** of Antigua.
159 3c. green 40 10
160 6c. blue . . . . 60 1·25
161 12c. red 70 15

40 Seashore at Rosalie

1963.
162 **40** 1c. green, blue and sepia 10 85
163 – 2c. blue 30 30
164 – 3c. brown and blue . . . . 1·50 1·25
165 – 4c. green, sepia and violet 10 10
166 – 5c. mauve 30 30
167 – 6c. green, bistre and violet 10 80
168 – 8c. green, sepia and black 30 20
169 – 10c. sepia and pink 10 20
170 – 12c. green, blue and sepia 1·00 10
171 – 14c. multicoloured 70 10
204 – 15c. yellow, green and brown 70 10
173 – 24c. multicoloured . . . . 9·00 20
174 – 48c. green, blue and black 75 1·00
175 – 60c. orange, green and black . . . . 1·00 70
176 – $1.20 multicoloured . . . 6·50 1·00
177 – $2.40 blue, turq & brn . . 3·25 2·50
178 – $4.80 green, blue and brown . . . . 9·00 20·00
DESIGNS—VERT: 2c., 5c. Queen Elizabeth II (after Annigoni); 14c. Traditional costume; 24c. Imperial amazon ("Sisserou Parrot"); $2.40, Trafalgar Falls; $4.80, Coconut palm. HORIZ: 3c. Sailing canoe; 4c. Sulphur springs; 6c. Road making; 8c. Dug-out canoe; 10c. Crapaud (frog); 12c. Scott's Head; 15c. Bananas; 48c. Goodwill; 60c. Cocoa tree; $1.20, Coat of Arms.

1963. Freedom from Hunger. As T **28** of Aden.
179 15c. violet 15 10

1963. Centenary of Red Cross. As T **33** of Antigua.
180 5c. red and black 20 40
181 15c. red and blue 40 60

1964. 400th Birth Anniv of Shakespeare. As T **34** of Antigua.
182 15c. purple 20 10

1965. Centenary of I.T.U. As T **36** of Antigua.
183 2c. green and blue 10 10
184 48c. turquoise and grey . . . 45 20

1965. I.C.Y. As T **37** of Antigua.
185 1c. purple and turquoise . . 10 20
186 15c. green and lavender . . . 35 10

1966. Churchill Commemoration. As T **38** of Antigua.
187 1c. blue 10 75
188 5c. green 25 10
189 15c. brown 50 10
190 24c. violet 65 20

1966. Royal Visit. As T **39** of Antigua.
191 5c. black and blue 75 30
192 15c. black and mauve . . . . 1·00 30

1966. World Cup Football Championship. As T **40** of Antigua.
193 5c. multicoloured 25 15
194 24c. multicoloured 85 15

1966. Inauguration of W.H.O. Headquarters, Geneva. As T **41** of Antigua.
195 5c. black, green and blue . . 15 15
196 24c. black, purple and ochre 30 15

1966. 20th Anniv of U.N.E.S.C.O. As T **54/6** of Antigua.
197 5c. red, yellow and orange . . 20 15
198 15c. yellow, violet and olive 50 10
199 24c. black, purple and orange 60 15

56 Children of Three Races

1967. National Day. Multicoloured.
205 5c. Type **56** 10 10
206 10c. The "Santa Maria" and motto 40 15
207 15c. Hands holding motto ribbon 15 15
208 24c. Belaire dancing 15 20

57 John F. Kennedy

1968. Human Rights Year. Multicoloured.
209 1c. Type **57** 10 10
210 10c. Cecil E. A. Rawle . . . 10 10
211 12c. Pope John XXIII . . . 50 15
212 48c. Florence Nightingale . . 20 25
213 60c. Albert Schweitzer . . . 20 25

1968. Associated Statehood. Nos. 162 etc, optd **ASSOCIATED STATEHOOD**.
214 1c. green, blue and sepia . . 10 10
215 2c. blue 10 10
216 3c. brown and blue 10 10
217 4c. green, sepia and violet . . 10 10
218 5c. mauve 10 10
219 6c. green, bistre and violet . . 10 10
220 8c. green, sepia and black . . 10 10
221 10c. sepia and pink 55 10
222 12c. green, blue and brown 10 10
224 14c. multicoloured 10 10
225 15c. yellow, green and brown 10 10
226 24c. multicoloured . . . . . 4·25 10
227 48c. green, blue and black . . 55 1·50
228 60c. orange, green and black 90 1·00
229 $1.20 multicoloured . . . . 1·00 3·25
230 $2.40 blue, turquoise and brown . . . . 1·00 2·50
231 $4.80 green, blue and brown 1·25 7·00

1968. National Day. Nos. 162/4, 171 and 176 optd **NATIONAL DAY 3 NOVEMBER 1968**.
232 1c. green, blue and sepia . . 10 10
233 2c. blue 10 10
234 3c. brown and blue 10 10
235 14c. multicoloured 10 10
236 $1.20 multicoloured 55 40

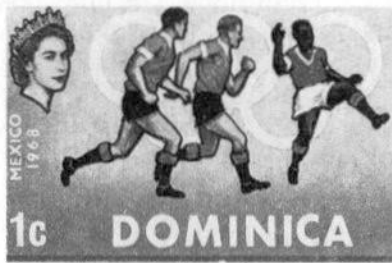

60 Forward shooting at Goal

1968. Olympic Games, Mexico. Multicoloured.
237 1c. Type **60** 10 10
238 1c. Goalkeeper attempting to save ball 10 10
239 5c. Swimmers preparing to dive 10 10
240 5c. Swimmers diving 10 10
241 48c. Javelin-throwing 15 15
242 48c. Hurdling 15 15
243 60c. Basketball 90 25
244 60c. Basketball players . . . 90 25

61 "The Small Cowper Madonna" (Raphael)

62 "Venus and Adonis" (Rubens)

1968. Christmas.
245 **61** 5c. multicoloured 10 10

1969. 20th Anniv of World Health Organization.
246 **62** 5c. multicoloured 20 10
247 – 15c. multicoloured 30 10
248 – 24c. multicoloured 30 10
249 – 50c. multicoloured 50 40
DESIGNS: 15c. "The Death of Socrates" (J.-L. David); 24c. "Christ and the Pilgrims of Emmaus" (Velasquez); 50c. "Pilate washing his Hands" (Rembrandt).

66 Picking Oranges

71 "Spinning" (J. Millet)

67 "Strength in Unity" Emblem and Fruit Trees

1969. Tourism. Multicoloured.
250 10c. Type **66** 15 10
251 10c. Woman, child and ocean scene 15 10
252 12c. Fort Yeoung Hotel . . . 50 10
253 12c. Red-necked amazon . . 50 10
254 24c. Calypso band 30 10
255 24c. Women dancing 30 15
256 48c. Underwater life 30 25
257 48c. Skin-diver and turtle . . 30 25

1969. 1st Anniv of C.A.R.I.F.T.A. (Caribbean Free Trade Area). Multicoloured.
258 5c. Type **67** 10 10
259 8c. Hawker Siddeley H.S.748 aircraft, emblem and island 30 20
260 12c. Chart of Caribbean Sea and emblem 30 25
261 24c. Steamship unloading, tug and emblem 40 25

1969. 50th Anniv of International Labour Organization. Multicoloured.
262 15c. Type **71** 10 10
263 30c. "Threshing" (J. Millet) 15 15
264 38c. "Flax-pulling" (J. Millet) 15 15

72 Mahatma Gandhi weaving and Clock Tower, Westminster

1969. Birth Cent of Mahatma Gandhi. Mult.
265 6c. Type **72** 25 10
266 38c. Gandhi, Nehru and Mausoleum 40 15
267 $1.20 Gandhi and Taj Mahal 45 1·50
All stamps are incorrectly inscribed "Ghandi".

75 "Saint Joseph"

1969. National Day. Multicoloured.
268 6c. Type **75** 10 10
269 8c. "Saint John" 10 10
270 12c. "Saint Peter" 10 10
271 60c. "Saint Paul" 30 50

79 Queen Elizabeth II

99 "Virgin and Child with St. John" (Perugino)

80 Purple-throated Carib ("Humming Bird") and Flower

1969. Centres multicoloured; colours of "D" given.
272a **79** $\frac{1}{2}$c. black and silver . . . 30 1·75
273 **80** 1c. black and yellow . . . 1·00 2·25
274 – 2c. black and yellow . . . 15 10
275a – 3c. black and yellow . . . 2·75 1·50
276a – 4c. black and yellow . . . 2·75 1·50
277a – 5c. black and yellow . . . 2·75 1·75
278a – 6c. black and brown . . . 2·75 2·75
279 – 8c. black and brown . . . 20 10
280 – 10c. black and yellow . . 20 10
281 – 12c. black and yellow . . 20 10
282 – 15c. black and blue . . . 20 10
283 – 25c. black and red 30 10
284a – 30c. black and olive . . . 1·50 70
285 – 38c. black and purple . . 8·00 1·75
286 – 50c. black and brown . . 50 45
287 – 60c. black and yellow . . 55 1·50
288 – $1.20 black and yellow . . 1·00 1·75
289 – $2.40 black and gold . . 1·00 4·00
290 – $4.80 black and gold . . 1·25 7·00
DESIGNS—HORIZ (As Type **80**): 2c. Poinsettia; 3c. Redneck pigeon ("Ramier"); 4c. Imperial amazon ("Sisserou"); 5c. "Battus polydamas" (butterfly); 6c. "Dryas julia" (butterfly); 8c. Shipping bananas; 10c. Portsmouth Harbour; 12c. Copra processing plant; 15c. Straw workers; 25c. Timber plant; 30c. Pumice mine; 38c. Grammar school and playing fields; 50c. Roseau Cathedral. ($38 \times 26\frac{1}{2}$ mm): 60c. Government Headquarters. (40×27 mm): $1.20, Melville Hall airport. ($39\frac{1}{2} \times 26$ mm): $2.40, Coat of arms. VERT: (26×39 mm): $4.80, As Type **79**, but larger.

1969. Christmas. Paintings. Multicoloured.
291 6c. "Virgin and Child with St. John" (Lippi) 10 10
292 10c. "Holy Family with Lamb" (Raphael) 10 10
293 15c. Type **99** 10 10
294 $1.20 "Madonna of the Rose Hedge" (Botticelli) 35 40
MS295 89 × 76 mm. Nos. 293/4. Imperf . . . . 75 1·00

101 Astronaut's First Step onto the Moon

1970. Moon Landing. Multicoloured.
296 $\frac{1}{2}$c. Type **101** 10 10
297 5c. Scientific experiment on the Moon and flag 15 10
298 8c. Astronauts collecting rocks 15 10
299 30c. Module over Moon . . 30 15
300 50c. Moon plague 40 25
301 60c. Astronauts 40 30
MS302 116 × 112 mm. Nos. 298/301. Imperf . . . . 2·00 2·00

107 Giant Green Turtle

1970. Flora and Fauna. Multicoloured.
303 6c. Type **107** 30 20
304 24c. Atlantic flyingfish . . . 40 45
305 38c. Anthurium lily 50 65
306 60c. Imperial and red-necked amazons . . . . 2·75 5·50
MS307 160 × 111 mm. Nos. 303/6 5·50 6·50

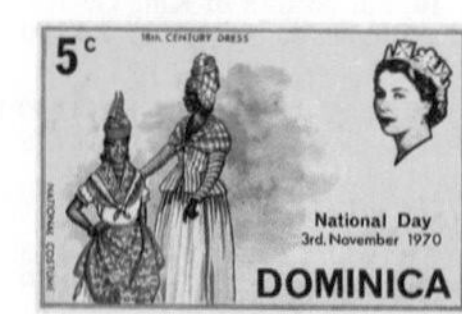

108 18th-century National Costume

1970. National Day. Multicoloured.
308 5c. Type **108** 10 10
309 8c. Carib basketry 10 10
310 $1 Flag and chart of Dominica 30 40
MS311 150 × 85 mm. Nos. 308/10 50 1·75

109 Scrooge and Marley's Ghost

1970. Christmas and Death Centenary of Charles Dickens. Scenes from "A Christmas Carol". Multicoloured.
312 2c. Type **109** 10 10
313 15c. Fezziwig's Ball 20 10
314 24c. Scrooge and his Nephew's Party 20 10
315 $1.20 Scrooge and the Ghost of Christmas Present . . . 65 90
MS316 142 × 87 mm. Nos. 312/15 1·00 3·75

110 "The Doctor" (Sir Luke Fildes)

1970. Centenary of British Red Cross. Multicoloured.
317 8c. Type **110** 10 10
318 10c. Hands and Red Cross 10 10
319 15c. Flag of Dominica and Red Cross emblem 15 10
320 50c. "The Sick Child" (E. Munch) 50 45
MS321 108 × 76 mm. Nos. 317/20 1·00 3·00

111 Marigot School

1971. International Education Year. Multicoloured.
322 5c. Type **111** 10 10
323 8c. Goodwill Junior High School 10 10
324 14c. University of West Indies (Jamaica) 10 10
325 $1 Trinity College, Cambridge 35 30
MS326 85 × 85 mm. Nos. 324/5 50 1·25

112 Waterfall

1971. Tourism. Multicoloured.
327 5c. Type **112** 15 10
328 10c. Boat-building 15 10
329 30c. Sailing 25 10
330 50c. Yacht and motor launch 40 30
MS331 130 × 86 mm. Nos. 327/30 85 1·00

113 U.N.I.C.E.F. Symbol in "D"

1971. 25th Anniv of U.N.I.C.E.F.
332 **113** 5c. violet, black and gold 10 10
333 10c. yellow, blk & gold 10 10
334 38c. green, blk & gold . . 10 10
335 $1.20 orange, blk & gold 30 45
MS336 84 × 79 mm. Nos. 333 and 335 . . . . 50 1·75

114 German Boy Scout

1971. World Scout Jamboree, Asagiri, Japan. Various designs showing Boy Scouts from the nations listed. Multicoloured.
337 20c. Type **114** 15 15
338 24c. Great Britain 20 15
339 30c. Japan 25 20
340 $1 Dominica . . . . 50 2·00
MS341 114 × 102 mm. Nos. 339/40 1·00 2·25
Both No. 340 and the $1 value from the miniature sheet show the national flag of the Dominican Republic in error.
"Dominica" on the scout's shirt pocket is omitted on the $1 value from the miniature sheet.

115 Groine at Portsmouth

1971. National Day. Multicoloured.

342	8c. Type **115**	10	10
343	15c. Carnival scene	10	10
344	20c. Carifta Queen (vert)	10	10
345	50c. Rock of Atkinson (vert)	20	25
MS346	63 × 89 mm. $1.20, As 20c.	50	70

116 Eight Reals Piece, 1761

1972. Coins.

347 **116**	10c. black, silver and violet	10	10
348 –	30c. black, silver and green	15	15
349 –	35c. black, silver and blue	15	20
350 –	50c. black, silver and red	25	1·75
MS351	86 × 90 mm. Nos. 349/50	50	1·25

DESIGNS—HORIZ: 30c. Eleven and three bitt pieces, 1798. VERT: 35c. Two reals and two bitt pieces, 1770; 50c. Mocos, pieces-of-eight and eight reals-eleven bitts piece, 1798.

117 Common Opossum

1972. U.N. Conference on the Human Enviroment, Stockholm. Multicoloured.

352	½c. Type **117**	10	10
353	35c. Brazilian agouti (rodent)	30	15
354	60c. Orchid	2·00	50
355	$1.20 Hibiscus	1·25	1·60
MS356	139 × 94 mm. Nos. 352/5	5·00	9·50

118 Sprinter

1972. Olympic Games, Munich. Multicoloured.

357	30c. Type **118**	10	10
358	35c. Hurdler	15	15
359	58c. Hammer-thrower (vert)	20	20
360	72c. Long-jumper (vert)	40	40
MS361	98 × 96 mm. Nos. 359/60	75	1·00

119 General Post Office

1972. National Day. Multicoloured.

362	10c. Type **119**	10	10
363	20c. Morne Diablotin	10	10
364	30c. Rodney's Rock	15	15
MS365	83 × 96 mm. Nos. 363/4	50	70

1972. Royal Silver Wedding. As T **52** of Ascension, but with Bananas and Imperial Parrot in background.

366	5c. green	20	10
367	$1 green	60	40

121 "The Adoration of the Shepherds" (Caravaggio)

122 Launching of Weather Satellite

1972. Christmas. Multicoloured.

368	8c. Type **121**	10	10
369	14c. "The Myosotis Virgin" (Rubens)	10	10
370	30c. "Madonna and Child with St Francesca Romana" (Gentileschi)	15	10
371	$1 "Adoration of the Kings" (Mostaert)	50	1·50
MS372	102 × 79 mm. Nos. 370/1. Imperf	60	80

1973. Centenary of I.M.O./W.M.O. Multicoloured.

373	½c. Type **122**	10	20
374	1c. Nimbus satellite	10	20
375	2c. Radiosonde balloon	10	20
376	30c. Radarscope (horiz)	15	15
377	35c. Diagram of pressure zones (horiz)	20	20
378	50c. Hurricane shown by satellite (horiz)	30	35
379	$1 Computer weather-map (horiz)	60	70
MS380	90 × 105 mm. Nos. 378/9	70	1·75

123 Going to Hospital

1973. 25th Anniv of W.H.O. Multicoloured.

381	½c. Type **123**	10	10
382	1c. Maternity care	10	10
383	2c. Smallpox inoculation	10	10
384	30c. Emergency service	30	15
385	35c. Waiting for the doctor	30	15
386	50c. Medical examination	30	25
387	$1 Travelling doctor	40	60
MS388	112 × 110 mm. Nos. 386/7	75	1·25

124 Cyrique Crab

1973. Flora and Fauna. Multicoloured.

389	½c. Type **124**	10	10
390	22c. Blue land-crab	30	10
391	25c. Bread fruit	30	15
392	$1.20 Sunflower	55	2·00
MS393	91 × 127 mm. Nos. 389/2	1·25	4·00

125 Princess Anne and Captain Mark Phillips

1973. Royal Wedding.

394 **125**	25c. multicoloured	10	10
395 –	$2 multicoloured	30	30
MS396	79 × 100 mm. 75c. as 25c. and $1.20 as $2	40	30

DESIGN: $2 As Type **125**, but with different frame.

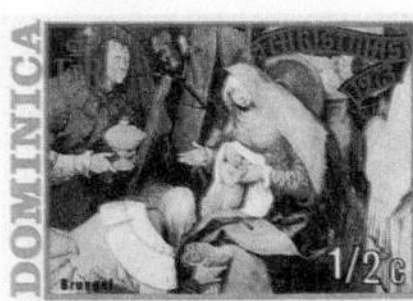

126 "Adoration of the Kings" (Brueghel)

1973. Christmas. Religious Paintings. Multicoloured.

397	½c. Type **126**	10	10
398	1c. "Adoration of the Magi" (Botticelli)	10	10
399	2c. "Adoration of the Magi" (Durer)	10	10
400	12c. "Mystic Nativity" (Botticelli)	20	10
401	22c. "Adoration of the Magi" (Rubens)	25	10
402	35c. "The Nativity" (Durer)	25	10
403	$1 "Adoration of the Shepherds" (Giorgione)	60	55
MS404	122 × 98 mm. Nos. 402/3	85	1·10

127 Carib Basket-weaving

1973. National Day. Multicoloured.

405	5c. Type **127**	10	10
406	10c. Staircase of the Snake	10	10
407	50c. Miss Caribbean Queen (vert)	15	15
408	60c. Miss Carifta Queen (vert)	15	15
409	$1 Dance group (vert)	25	30
MS410	95 × 127 mm. Nos. 405/6 and 409	40	65

128 University Centre, Dominica

1973. 25th Anniv of West Indies University. Multicoloured.

411	12c. Type **128**	10	10
412	30c. Graduation ceremony	10	10
413	$1 University coat of arms	25	35
MS414	97 × 131 mm. Nos. 411/13	30	55

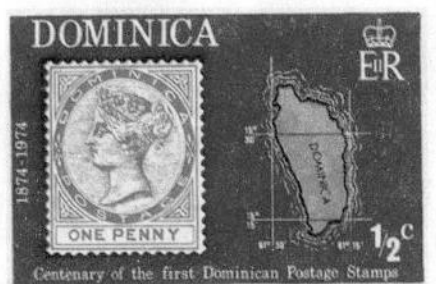

129 Dominica 1d. Stamp of 1874 and Map

1974. Stamp Centenary. Multicoloured.

415	½c. Type **129**	10	10
416	1c. 6d. stamp of 1874 and posthorn	10	10
417	2c. 1d. stamp of 1874 and arms	10	10
418	10c. Type **129**	20	10
419	50c. As 1c.	40	30
420	$1.20 As 2c.	50	70
MS421	105 × 121 mm. Nos. 418/20	1·00	1·50

130 Footballer and Flag of Brazil

1974. World Cup Football Championship, West Germany. Multicoloured.

422	½c. Type **130**	10	10
423	1c. West Germany	10	10
424	2c. Italy	10	10
425	30c. Scotland	50	10
426	40c. Sweden	50	10
427	50c. Netherlands	55	35
428	$1 Yugoslavia	90	90
MS429	89 × 87 mm. Nos. 427/8	70	80

131 Indian Hole

1974. National Day. Multicoloured.

430	10c. Type **131**	10	10
431	40c. Teachers' Training College	10	10
432	$1 Bay Oil distillery plant, Petite Savanne	50	45
MS433	96 × 143 mm. Nos. 430/2	60	65

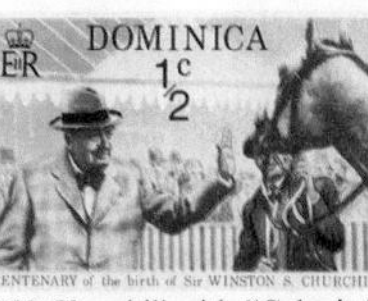

132 Churchill with "Colonist"

1974. Birth Centenary of Sir Winston Churchill. Multicoloured.

434	½c. Type **132**	10	10
435	1c. Churchill and Eisenhower	10	10
436	2c. Churchill and Roosevelt	10	10
437	20c. Churchill and troops on assault-course	15	10
438	45c. Painting at Marrakesh	20	10
439	$2 Giving the "V" sign	50	1·00
MS440	126 × 100 mm. Nos. 438/9	70	1·50

133 Mailboats "Orinoco" (1851) and "Geesthaven" (1974)

1974. Centenary of U.P.U. Multicoloured.

441	10c. Type **133**	20	10
442	$2 De Haviland D.H.4 (1918) and Boeing 747-100 (1974)	80	1·00
MS443	107 × 93 mm. $1.20 as 10c. and $2.40 as $2	1·00	1·40

Nos. 442 and **MS**443 are inscr "De Haviland".

134 "The Virgin and Child" (Tiso)

1974. Christmas. Multicoloured.

444	½c. Type **134**	10	10
445	1c. "Madonna and Child with Saints" (Costa)	10	10
446	2c. "The Nativity" (school of Rimini, 14th-century)	10	10
447	10c. "The Rest on the Flight into Egypt" (Romanelli)	20	10
448	25c. "The Adoration of the Shepherds" (da Sermoneta)	35	10
449	45c. "The Nativity" (Guido Reni)	45	10
450	$1 "The Adoration of the Magi" (Caselli)	65	40
MS451	114 × 78 mm. Nos. 449/50	60	1·00

135 Queen Triggerfish

1975. Fishes. Multicoloured.

452	½c. Type **135**	10	10
453	1c. Porkfish	10	10
454	2c. Sailfish	10	10
455	3c. Swordfish	10	10
456	20c. Great barracuda	75	50
457	$2 Nassau grouper	1·75	2·75
MS458	104 × 80 mm. No. 457	1·90	6·00

136 "Myscelia antholia"

1975. Dominican Butterflies. Multicoloured.

459	½c. Type **136**	10	40
460	1c. "Lycorea ceres"	10	40
461	2c. "Anaea marthesia" ("Siderone nemesis")	15	40
462	6c. "Battus polydamas"	50	55
463	30c. "Anartia lytrea"	80	70
464	40c. "Morpho peleides"	80	75
465	$2 "Dryas julia"	1·10	7·50
MS466	108 × 80 mm. No. 465	1·25	4·75

137 "Yare" (cargo liner)

1975. "Ships tied to Dominica's History". Mult.

467	½c. Type **137**	20	35
468	1c. "Thames II" (liner), 1890	20	35
469	2c. "Lady Nelson" (cargo liner)	20	35
470	20c. "Lady Rodney" (cargo liner)	50	35

471	45c. "Statesman" (freighter)	70	55
472	50c. "Geestcape" (freighter)	70	80
473	$2 "Geeststar" (freighter)	1·25	4·50
MS474	78 × 103 mm. Nos. 472/3	1·75	5·00

138 "Women in Agriculture"

1975. International Women's Year. Multicoloured.

475	10c. Type **138**	10	10
476	$2 "Women in Industry and Commerce"	40	60

139 Miss Caribbean Queen, 1975 — **140** "Virgin and Child" (Mantegna)

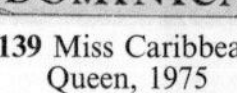

1975. National Day. Multicoloured.

477	5c. Type **139**	10	10
478	10c. Public library (horiz)	10	10
479	30c. Citrus factory (horiz)	10	10
480	$1 National Day Trophy	25	50
MS481	130 × 98 mm. Nos. 478/80. Imperf	50	1·40

1975. Christmas. "Virgin and Child" paintings by artists named. Multicoloured.

482	½c. Type **140**	10	10
483	1c. Fra Filippo Lippi	10	10
484	2c. Bellini	10	10
485	10c. Botticelli	15	10
486	25c. Bellini	25	10
487	45c. Correggio	30	10
488	$1 Durer	55	50
MS489	139 × 85 mm. Nos. 487/88	1·00	1·50

141 Hibiscus

1975. Multicoloured.

490	½c. Type **141**	10	1·00
491	1c. African tulip	15	1·00
492	2c. Castor-oil tree	15	1·00
493	3c. White cedar flower	15	1·00
494	4c. Egg plant	15	1·00
495	5c. Needlefish ("Gare")	20	1·00
496	6c. Ochro	20	1·10
497	8c. Zenaida dove ("Mountain Dove")	3·00	1·10
498	10c. Screw pine	20	15
499	20c. Mango longue	30	15
500	25c. Crayfish	35	15
501	30c. Common opossum	90	80
502	40c. Bay leaf groves	90	80
503	50c. Tomatoes	40	50
504	$1 Lime factory	55	65
505	$2 Rum distillery	1·00	3·50
506	$5 Bay Oil distillery	1·00	5·00
507	$10 Queen Elizabeth II (vert)	1·40	15·00

Nos. 502/7 are larger, 28 × 44 mm ($10) or 44 × 28 (others).

142 American Infantry — **143** Rowing

1976. Bicentenary of American Revolution. Mult.

508	½c. Type **142**	10	10
509	1c. British three-decker, 1782	10	10
510	2c. George Washington	10	10
511	45c. British sailors	30	10
512	75c. British ensign	40	40
513	$2 Admiral Hood	60	1·25
MS514	105 × 92 mm. Nos. 512/13	1·00	3·00

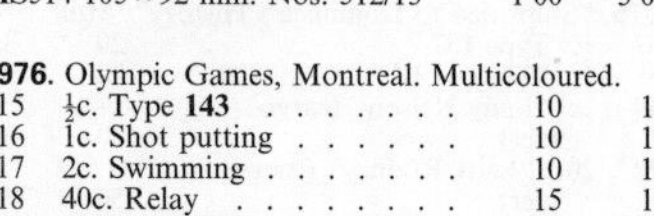

1976. Olympic Games, Montreal. Multicoloured.

515	½c. Type **143**	10	10
516	1c. Shot putting	10	10
517	2c. Swimming	10	10
518	40c. Relay	15	10
519	45c. Gymnastics	15	10
520	60c. Sailing	20	20
521	$2 Archery	55	80
MS522	90 × 140 mm. Nos. 520/1	85	75

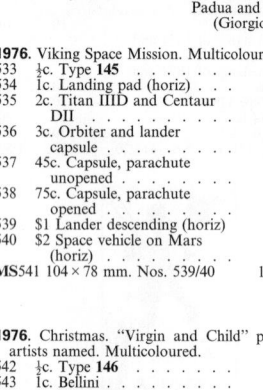

144 Ringed Kingfisher

1976. Wild Birds. Multicoloured.

523	½c. Type **144**	10	75
524	1c. Mourning dove	15	75
525	2c. Green-backed heron ("Green Heron")	15	75
526	15c. Blue-winged hawk (vert)	75	35
527	30c. Blue-headed hummingbird (vert)	80	55
528	45c. Bananaquit (vert)	85	60
529	$2 Imperial amazon ("Imperial Parrot") (vert)	1·75	12·00
MS530	133 × 101 mm. Nos. 527/9	2·75	14·00

1976. West Indian Victory in World Cricket Cup. As Nos. 559/60 of Barbados.

531	15c. Map of the Caribbean	75	1·25
532	25c. Prudential Cup	75	1·75

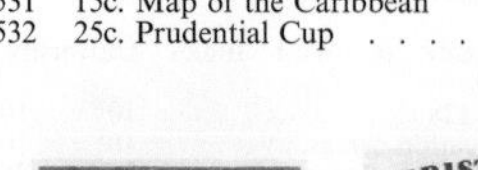

145 Viking Spacecraft System — **146** "Virgin and Child with Saints Anthony of Padua and Roch" (Giorgione)

1976. Viking Space Mission. Multicoloured.

533	½c. Type **145**	10	10
534	1c. Landing pad (horiz)	10	10
535	2c. Titan IIID and Centaur DII	10	10
536	3c. Orbiter and lander capsule	10	10
537	45c. Capsule, parachute unopened	15	15
538	75c. Capsule, parachute opened	20	70
539	$1 Lander descending (horiz)	25	75
540	$2 Space vehicle on Mars (horiz)	35	2·00
MS541	104 × 78 mm. Nos. 539/40	1·10	2·25

1976. Christmas. "Virgin and Child" paintings by artists named. Multicoloured.

542	½c. Type **146**	10	10
543	1c. Bellini	10	10
544	2c. Mantegna	10	10
545	6c. Mantegna (different)	10	10
546	25c. Memling	15	10
547	45c. Correggio	20	10
548	$3 Raphael	1·00	1·00
MS549	104 × 85 mm. 50c. as No. 547 and $1 as No. 548	1·00	1·10

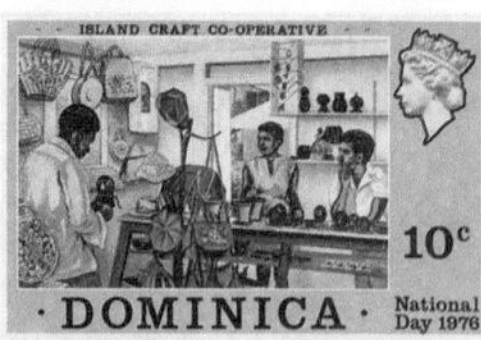

147 Island Craft Co-operative

1976. National Day. Multicoloured.

550	10c. Type **147**	10	10
551	50c. Harvesting bananas	15	10
552	$1 Boxing plant	30	35
MS553	96 × 122 mm. Nos. 550/2	50	1·00

148 American Giant Sundial — **150** Joseph Haydn

149 The Queen Crowned and Enthroned

1976. Shells. Multicoloured.

554	½c. Type **148**	10	10
555	1c. Flame helmet	10	10
556	2c. Mouse cone	10	10
557	20c. Caribbean vase	35	10
558	40c. West Indian fighting conch	55	25
559	50c. Short coral shell	55	25
560	$3 Apple murex	2·00	3·25
MS561	101 × 55 mm. $2 Long-spined star shell	1·10	1·40

1977. Silver Jubilee. Multicoloured.

562	½c. Type **149**	10	10
563	1c. Imperial State Crown	10	10
564	45c. The Queen and Princess Anne	15	10
565	$2 Coronation Ring	25	30
566	$2.50 Ampulla and Spoon	30	40
MS567	104 × 97 mm. $5 Queen Elizabeth and Prince Philip	75	1·25

1977. 150th Death Anniv of Ludwig van Beethoven. Multicoloured.

568	½c. Type **150**	10	10
569	1c. Scene from "Fidelio"	10	10
570	2c. Maria Casentini (dancer)	10	10
571	15c. Beethoven and pastoral scene	30	10
572	30c. "Wellington's Victory"	30	10
573	40c. Henriette Sontag (singer)	30	10
574	$2 The young Beethoven	75	2·00
MS575	138 × 93 mm. Nos. 572/4	1·10	3·25

151 Hiking

1977. Caribbean Scout Jamboree, Jamaica. Mult.

576	½c. Type **151**	10	10
577	1c. First-aid	10	10
578	2c. Camping	10	10
579	45c. Rock climbing	25	15
580	50c. Canoeing	30	20
581	$3 Sailing	1·40	1·75
MS582	111 × 113 mm. 75c. Map-reading; $2 Campfire sing-song	1·00	1·25

152 Holy Family

1977. Christmas. Multicoloured.

583	½c. Type **152**	10	10
584	1c. Angel and Shepherds	10	10
585	2c. Holy Baptism	10	10
586	6c. Flight into Egypt	15	10
587	15c. Three Kings with gifts	15	10
588	45c. Holy Family in the Temple	30	10
589	$3 Flight into Egypt (different)	80	1·10
MS590	113 × 85 mm. 50c. Virgin and Child; $2 Flight into Egypt (different)	60	75

1977. Royal Visit. Nos. 562/66 optd **ROYAL VISIT W.I. 1977.**

591	½c. Type **149**	10	10
592	1c. Imperial State Crown	10	10
593	45c. The Queen and Princess Anne	15	10
594a	$2 Coronation Ring	30	30
595a	$2.50 Ampulla and Spoon	35	35
MS596	104 × 79 mm. $5 Queen Elizabeth and Prince Philip	1·00	1·50

154 "Sousouelle Souris"

1978. "History of Carnival". Multicoloured.

597	½c. Type **154**	10	10
598	1c. Sensay costume	10	10
599	2c. Street musicians	10	10
600	45c. Douiette band	15	10
601	50c. Pappy Show wedding	15	10
602	$2 Masquerade band	45	60
MS603	104 × 88 mm. $2.50, No. 602	60	65

155 Colonel Charles Lindbergh and "Spirit of St. Louis"

1978. Aviation Anniversaries. Multicoloured.

604	6c. Type **155**	20	60
605	10c. "Spirit of St. Louis", New York, 20 May, 1927	25	10
606	15c. Lindbergh and map of Atlantic	35	10
607	20c. Lindbergh reaches Paris, 21 May, 1927	45	10
608	40c. Airship LZ-1, Lake Constance, 1900	55	20
609	60c. Count F. von Zeppelin and Airship LZ-2, 1906	65	30
610	$3 Airship "Graf Zeppelin", 1928	1·40	2·25
MS611	139 × 108 mm. 50c. Ryan NYP Special "Spirit of St. Louis" in mid-Atlantic; $2 Airship LZ-127 "Graf Zeppelin", 1928	1·60	1·10

The 6, 10, 15, 20 and 50c. values commemorate the 50th anniversary of first solo transatlantic flight by Col. Charles Lindbergh; the other values commemorate anniversaries of various Zeppelin airships.

156 Queen receiving Homage — **158** "Two Apostles"

157 Wright Flyer III

1978. 25th Anniv of Coronation. Multicoloured.

612	45c. Type **156**	15	10
613	$2 Balcony scene	30	30
614	$2.50 Queen and Prince Philip	40	40
MS615	76 × 107 mm. $5 Queen Elizabeth II	75	75

1978. 75th Anniv of First Powered Flight. Mult.

616	30c. Type **157**	15	15
617	40c. Wright Type A, 1908	20	20
618	60c. Wright Flyer I	25	30
619	$2 Wright Flyer I (different)	85	1·25
MS620	116 × 89 mm. $3 Wilbur and Orville Wright	1·00	1·00

1978. Christmas. Paintings by Rubens. Mult.

621	20c. Type **158**	10	10
622	45c. "Descent from the Cross"	15	10
623	50c. "St Ildefonso receiving the Chasuble"	15	10
624	$3 "Assumption of the Virgin"	35	80
MS625	113 × 83 mm. $2 "The Holy Family" (Sebastiano del Piombo*)	75	75

*This painting was incorrectly attributed to Rubens on the stamp.

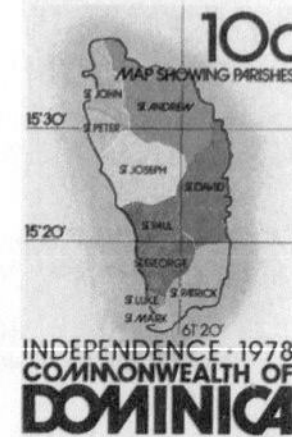

159 Map showing Parishes — **161** Sir Rowland Hill

1978. Independence. Multicoloured.

626	10c. Type **159**	75	15
627	25c. "Sabinea carinalis" (national flower)	55	15
628	45c. New National flag	1·00	15
629	50c. Coat of arms	60	30
630	$2 Prime Minister Patrick John	70	2·75
MS631	113 × 90 mm. $2.50, Type **159**	1·00	1·25

1978. Nos. 490/507 optd **INDEPENDENCE 3rd NOVEMBER 1978.**

632	½c. Type 57	40	60
633	1c. African tulip	45	60

634 2c. Castor-oil tree 45 50
635 3c. White cedar flower . . . 50 50
636 4c. Egg plant 50 50
637 5c. Needlefish ("Gare") . . . 50 50
638 6c. Ochro 50 50
639 8c. Zenaida dove . . . . . . 3·00 60
640 10c. Screw pine 50 15
641 20c. Mango longue 60 40
642 25c. Crayfish 70 40
643 30c. Common opossum . . . 70 40
644 40c. Bay leaf groves 70 25
645 50c. Tomatoes 80 30
646 $1 Lime factory 80 65
647 $2 Rum distillery . . . . . . 1·00 1·00
648 $5 Bay Oil distillery . . . . 1·00 2·25
649 $10 Queen Elizabeth II . . . 1·50 4·50

1979. Death Centenary of Sir Rowland Hill.
650 **161** 25c. multicoloured 10 10
651 – 45c. multicoloured 15 10
652 – 50c. black, violet and mauve 15 10
653 – $2 black, mauve and yellow 35 65
MS654 186 × 96 mm. $5 black and red . . . . 1·00 1·25
DESIGNS: 45c. Great Britain 1840 2d. blue; 50c. 1874 1d. stamp; $2 Maltese Cross cancellations; $5 Penny Black.

162 Children and Canoe

1979. International Year of the Child. Multicoloured.
655 30c. Type **162** 25 15
656 40c. Children with bananas 25 15
657 50c. Children playing cricket 1·25 80
658 $3 Child feeding rabbits . . . 1·75 2·00
MS659 117 × 85 mm. $5 Child with catch of fish . . . . 1·00 1·50

163 Nassau Grouper

1979. Marine Wildlife. Multicoloured.
660 10c. Type **163** 40 15
661 30c. Striped dolphin 70 35
662 50c. White-tailed tropic-bird 2·25 65
663 60c. Brown pelican . . . . . 2·25 1·50
664 $1 Long-finned pilot whale 2·50 1·75
665 $2 Brown booby . . . . . . 3·00 4·50
MS666 120 × 94 mm. $3 Elkhorn coral . . . . 1·50 1·40
No. 661 is inscr "SPOTTED DOLPHIN" in error.

164 H.M.S. "Endeavour"

1979. Death Bicent of Captain Cook. Mult.
667 10c. Type **164** 65 30
668 50c. H.M.S. "Resolution" (Second Voyage) . . . . . 1·10 1·00
669 60c. H.M.S. "Discovery" (Third Voyage) . . . . . 1·25 1·50
670 $2 Detail of Cook's chart of New Zealand, 1770 . . . . 1·60 2·75
MS671 97 × 90 mm. Captain Cook and signature . . . . 1·25 2·00

165 Cooking at Campfire

1979. 50th Anniv of Girl Guide Movement in Dominica. Multicoloured.
672 10c. Type **165** 20 10
673 20c. Pitching emergency rain tent 25 10
674 50c. Raising Dominican flag 35 10
675 $2.50 Singing and dancing to accordion 90 80
MS676 110 × 86 mm. $3 Guides of different age-groups . . . . . 75 1·25

166 Colvillea

169 Mickey Mouse and Octopus playing Xylophone

167 Cathedral of the Assumption, Roseau

1979. Flowering Trees. Multicoloured.
677 20c. Type **166** 15 10
678 40c. "Lignum vitae" 20 15
679 60c. Dwarf poinciana 25 15
680 $2 Fern tree 50 75
MS681 114 × 89 mm. $3 Perfume tree . . . . 75 1·10

1979. Christmas. Cathedrals. Multicoloured.
682 6c. Type **167** 10 10
683 45c. St. Paul's, London (vert) 15 10
684 60c. St. Peter's, Rome . . . 15 10
685 $3 Notre Dame, Paris (vert) 55 60
MS686 113 × 85 mm. 40c. St. Patrick's, New York; $2 Cologne Cathedral (both vert) 50 80

1979. Hurricane Relief. Nos. 495, 502 and 506/7 optd **HURRICANE RELIEF**.
687 5c. Gare 10 10
688 40c. Bay leaf groves 10 10
689 $5 Bay Oil distillery . . . . 1·00 1·25
690 $10 Queen Elizabeth II . . . 1·25 1·75

1979. International Year of the Child. Walt Disney Cartoon Characters. Multicoloured.
691 ½c. Type **169** 10 10
692 1c. Goofy playing guitar on rocking-horse 10 10
693 2c. Mickey Mouse playing violin and Goofy on bagpipes 10 10
694 3c. Donald Duck playing drum with a pneumatic drill 10 10
695 4c. Minnie Mouse playing saxophone 10 10
696 5c. Goofy one-man band . . 10 10
697 10c. Horace Horsecollar blowing Dale from french horn 10 10
698 $2 Huey, Dewey and Louie playing bass . . . . . . 1·25 2·00
699 $2.50 Donald Duck at piano and Huey playing trumpet 1·25 2·25
MS700 127 × 102 mm. $3 Mickey Mouse playing piano . . . . . 2·50 3·00

170 Hospital Ward

1980. 75th Anniv of Rotary International. Mult.
701 10c. Type **170** 10 10
702 20c. Electro-cardiogram . . . 15 10
703 40c. Mental hospital site . . 20 15
704 $2.50 Paul Harris (founder) 55 90
MS705 128 × 113 mm. $3 Interlocking cogs of Rotary emblem and globe 60 80

1980. "London 1980" International Stamp Exhibition. Optd **LONDON 1980**.
706 **161** 25c. multicoloured 25 10
707 – 45c. multicoloured 30 15
708 – 50c. brown, blue and red 30 15
709 – $2 brown, red and yellow 80 60

171 Shot Putting

1980. Olympic Games, Moscow. Multicoloured.
710 30c. Type **171** 15 10
711 40c. Basketball 60 15
712 60c. Swimming 35 20
713 $2 Gymnastics 60 65
MS714 114 × 86 mm. $3 The marathon 70 90

172 "Supper at Emmaus" (Caravaggio)

1980. Famous Paintings. Multicoloured.
715 20c. Type **172** 20 10
716 25c. "Portrait of Charles I Hunting" (Van Dyck) (vert) 20 10
717 30c. "The Maids of Honour" (Velasquez) (vert) 25 10
718 45c. "The Rape of the Sabine Women" (Poussin) 25 10
719 $1 "Embarkation for Cythera" (Watteau) . . . 35 35
720 $5 "Girl before a Mirror" (Picasso) (vert) . . . . . . 1·00 1·50
MS721 114 × 111 mm. $3 "The Holy Family" (Rembrandt) (vert) . . 60 80

173 Scene from "Peter Pan"

1980. Christmas. Scenes from "Peter Pan". Multicoloured.
722 ½c. Type **173** (Tinker Bell) . . 10 10
723 1c. Wendy sewing back Peter's shadow 10 10
724 2c. Peter introduces the mermaids 10 10
725 3c. Wendy and Peter with lost boys 10 10
726 4c. Captain Hook, Pirate Smee and Tiger Lily . . . 10 10
727 5c. Peter with Tiger Lily and her father 10 10
728 10c. Captain Hook captures Peter and Wendy 10 10
729 $2 Peter fights Captain Hook 2·25 1·50
730 $2.50 Captain Hook in crocodile's jaws . . . . . 2·25 1·75
MS731 124 × 98 mm. $4 Peter Pan 4·25 3·50

174 Queen Elizabeth the Queen Mother in Doorway

1980. 80th Birthday of the Queen Mother.
732a **174** 40c. multicoloured . . . 15 15
733a $2.50 multicoloured . . 45 60
MS734 85 × 66 mm. $3 multicoloured . . . . 75 2·00

175 Douglas Bay

1981. "Dominica Safari". Multicoloured.
735 20c. Type **175** 10 10
736 30c. Valley of Desolation . . 10 10
737 40c. Emerald Pool (vert) . . 10 10
738 $3 Indian River (vert) . . . . 75 1·10
MS739 84 × 104 mm. $4 Trafalgar Falls (vert) . . . . 1·10 1·40

1981. Walt Disney's Cartoon Character, Pluto. As T **169**. Multicoloured.
740 $2 Pluto and Fifi . . . . . . 1·00 1·50
MS741 128 × 102 mm. $4 Pluto in scene from film "Pluto's Blue Note" . . . . 1·25 1·50

176 Forest Thrush

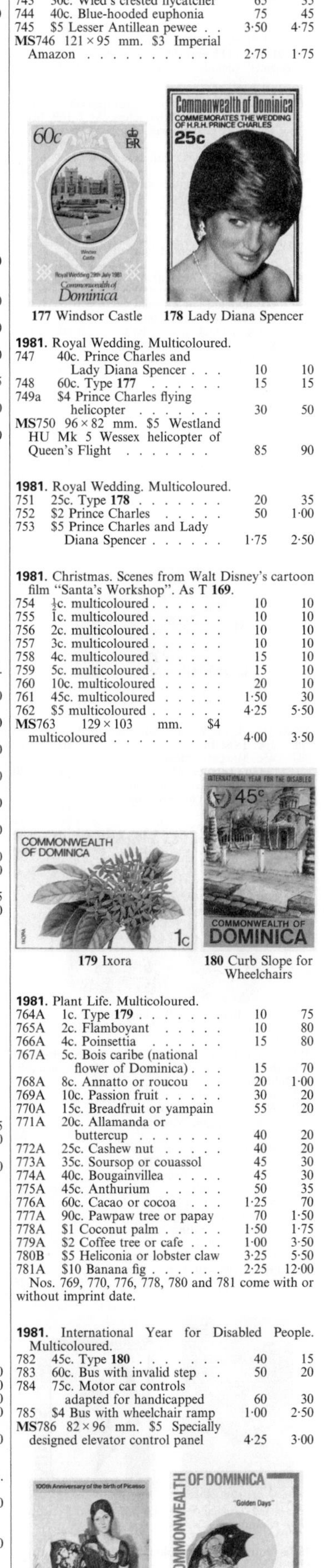

1981. Birds. Multicoloured.
742 20c. Type **176** 55 30
743 30c. Wied's crested flycatcher 65 35
744 40c. Blue-hooded euphonia 75 45
745 $5 Lesser Antillean pewee . . 3·50 4·75
MS746 121 × 95 mm. $3 Imperial Amazon . . . . 2·75 1·75

177 Windsor Castle

178 Lady Diana Spencer

1981. Royal Wedding. Multicoloured.
747 40c. Prince Charles and Lady Diana Spencer . . . 10 10
748 60c. Type **177** 15 15
749a $4 Prince Charles flying helicopter 30 50
MS750 96 × 82 mm. $5 Westland HU Mk 5 Wessex helicopter of Queen's Flight 85 90

1981. Royal Wedding. Multicoloured.
751 25c. Type **178** 20 35
752 $2 Prince Charles . . . . . 50 1·00
753 $5 Prince Charles and Lady Diana Spencer . . . . . . 1·75 2·50

1981. Christmas. Scenes from Walt Disney's cartoon film "Santa's Workshop". As T **169**.
754 ½c. multicoloured 10 10
755 1c. multicoloured 10 10
756 2c. multicoloured 10 10
757 3c. multicoloured 10 10
758 4c. multicoloured 15 10
759 5c. multicoloured 15 10
760 10c. multicoloured 20 10
761 45c. multicoloured . . . . . 1·50 30
762 $5 multicoloured . . . . . . 4·25 5·50
MS763 129 × 103 mm. $4 multicoloured . . . . 4·00 3·50

179 Ixora

180 Curb Slope for Wheelchairs

1981. Plant Life. Multicoloured.
764A 1c. Type **179** 10 75
765A 2c. Flamboyant 10 80
766A 4c. Poinsettia 15 80
767A 5c. Bois caribe (national flower of Dominica) . . . 15 70
768A 8c. Annatto or roucou . . 20 1·00
769A 10c. Passion fruit 30 20
770A 15c. Breadfruit or yampain 55 20
771A 20c. Allamanda or buttercup 40 20
772A 25c. Cashew nut 40 20
773A 35c. Soursop or couassol 45 30
774A 40c. Bougainvillea 45 30
775A 45c. Anthurium 50 35
776A 60c. Cacao or cocoa . . . 1·25 70
777A 90c. Pawpaw tree or papay 70 1·50
778A $1 Coconut palm . . . . . 1·50 1·75
779A $2 Coffee tree or cafe . . . 1·00 3·50
780B $5 Heliconia or lobster claw 3·25 5·50
781A $10 Banana fig . . . . . . 2·25 12·00
Nos. 769, 770, 776, 778, 780 and 781 come with or without imprint date.

1981. International Year for Disabled People. Multicoloured.
782 45c. Type **180** 40 15
783 60c. Bus with invalid step . . 50 20
784 75c. Motor car controls adapted for handicapped 60 30
785 $4 Bus with wheelchair ramp 1·00 2·50
MS786 82 × 96 mm. $5 Specially designed elevator control panel 4·25 3·00

181 "Olga Picasso in an Armchair"

182 "Gone Fishing"

1981. Birth Centenary of Picasso. Multicoloured.
787 45c. Type **181** 35 15
788 60c. "Bathers" 40 15
789 75c. "Woman in Spanish Costume" 40 25
790 $4 "Detail of Dog and Cock" 1·00 2·25
MS791 140 × 115 mm. $5 "Sleeping Peasants" (detail) . . . . . . 2·50 3·50

1982. World Cup Football Championship, Spain. Walt Disney Cartoon Characters. As T **169**. Mult.
792 ½c. Goofy chasing ball with butterfly net 10 10
793 1c. Donald Duck with ball in beak 10 10
794 2c. Goofy as goalkeeper . . . 10 10
795 3c. Goofy looking for ball . . 10 10
796 4c. Goofy as park attendant puncturing ball with litter spike 10 10
797 5c. Pete and Donald Duck playing 10 10
798 10c. Donald Duck after kicking rock instead of ball 15 10
799 60c. Donald Duck feeling effects of a hard game and Daisy Duck dusting ball 1·50 1·25
800 $5 Goofy hiding ball under his jersey from Mickey Mouse . . . . 5·50 6·50
MS801 132 × 105 mm. $4 Dale making off with ball . . . . . 4·00 3·25

1982. Norman Rockwell (painter) Commemoration. Multicoloured.
802 10c. Type **182** 10 10
803 25c. "Breakfast" 20 10
804 45c. "The Marbles Champ" 30 30
805 $1 "Speeding Along" 55 65
No. 802 is inscribed "Golden Days" and No. 803 " The Morning News".

183 Elma Napier (first woman elected to B.W.I. Legislative Council)

1982. Decade for Women. Multicoloured.
806 10c. Type **183** 10 10
807 45c. Margaret Mead (anthropologist) 30 30
808 $1 Mabel (Cissy) Caudeiron (folk song composer and historian) 55 55
809 $4 Eleanor Roosevelt . . . . 2·25 2·25
MS810 92 × 83 mm. $3 Florence Nightingale . . . . 2·00 3·00

184 George Washington and Independence Hall, Philadelphia

1982. 250th Birth Anniv of George Washington and Birth Centenary of Franklin D. Roosevelt. Multicoloured.
811 45c. Type **184** 25 25
812 60c. Franklin D. Roosevelt and Capitol, Washington D.C. 30 35
813 90c. Washington at Yorktown (detail "The Surrender of Cornwallis" by Trumbull) 40 55
814 $2 Construction of dam (from W. Groppers' mural commemorating Roosevelt's) "New Deal" 70 1·60
MS815 115 × 90 mm. $5 Washington and Roosevelt with U.S.A. flags of 1777 and 1933 . . . . 2·00 3·25

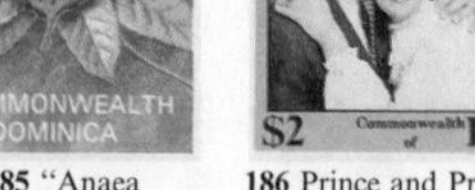

185 "Anaea dominicana" **186** Prince and Princess of Wales

1982. Butterflies. Multicoloured.
816 15c. Type **185** . . . . 1·50 35
817 45c. "Heliconius charithonia" 2·50 65
818 60c. "Hypolimnas misippus" 2·75 1·75
819 $3 "Biblis hyperia" . . . . . 5·50 6·00
MS820 77 × 105 mm. $5 "Marpesia petreus" . . . . 7·00 5·00

1982. 21st Birthday of Princess of Wales. Multicoloured.
821 45c. Buckingham Palace . . . 20 10
822 $2 Type **186** 50 70
823 $4 Princess of Wales . . . . 1·10 1·25
MS824 103 × 75 mm. $5 Princess Diana (different) . . . . 2·50 2·25

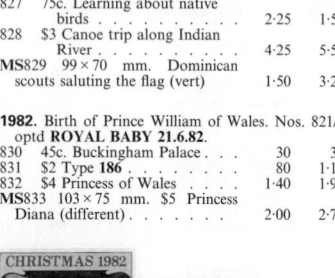

187 Scouts around Campfire

1982. 75th Anniv of Boy Scouts Movement. Mult.
825 45c. Type **187** . . . . 1·25 50
826 60c. Temperature study, Valley of Desolation . . . 1·75 1·25
827 75c. Learning about native birds . . . . 2·25 1·50
828 $3 Canoe trip along Indian River . . . . 4·25 5·50
MS829 99 × 70 mm. Dominican scouts saluting the flag (vert) 1·50 3·25

1982. Birth of Prince William of Wales. Nos. 821/3 optd **ROYAL BABY 21.6.82.**
830 45c. Buckingham Palace . . . 30 30
831 $2 Type **186** . . . . 80 1·10
832 $4 Princess of Wales . . . . 1·40 1·90
MS833 103 × 75 mm. $5 Princess Diana (different) . . . . 2·00 2·75

188 "Holy Family of Francis I" **189** Cuvier's Beaked Whale

1982. Christmas. Raphael Paintings. Multicoloured.
834 25c. Type **188** 15 10
835 30c. "Holy Family of the Pearl" 15 10
836 90c. "Canigiani Holy Family" 30 35
837 $4 "Holy Family of the Oak Tree" . . . . 1·25 1·50
MS838 95 × 125 mm. $5 "Holy Family of the Lamp" . . . . . 1·50 2·00

1983. Save the Whales. Multicoloured.
839 45c. Type **189** . . . . 2·00 65
840 60c. Humpback whale . . . 2·25 1·75
841 75c. Black right whale . . . 2·25 2·25
842 $3 Melon-headed whale . . . 4·50 6·50
MS843 99 × 72 mm. $5 Pygmy sperm whale . . . . 4·00 4·00

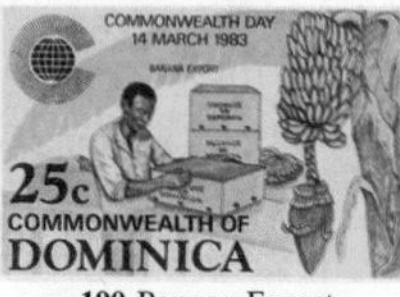

190 Banana Export

1983. Commonwealth Day. Multicoloured.
844 25c. Type **190** 15 15
845 30c. Road building 15 20
846 90c. Community nursing . . 30 45
847 $3 Tourism-handicrafts . . . 75 1·50

191 Map and Satellite Picture of Hurricane

1983. World Communications Year. Multicoloured.
848 45c. Type **191** 20 25
849 60c. Aircraft-to-ship transmission 25 35
850 90c. Satellite communications 30 45
851 $2 Shortwave radio . . . . . 75 1·00
MS852 110 × 85 mm. $5 Communications satellite . . . 1·50 2·75

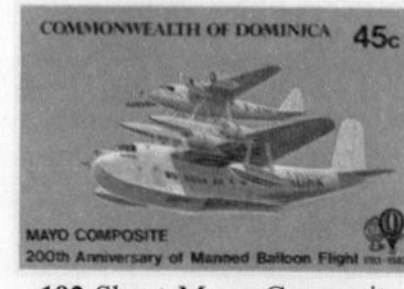

192 Short-Mayo Composite

1983. Bicentenary of Manned Flight. Mult.
853 45c. Type **192** 50 30
854 60c. Macchi M.39 Schneider Trophy seaplane 60 65
855 90c. Fairey Swordfish torpedo bomber . . . . . 70 1·50
856 $4 Airship LZ-3 . . . . . . 1·25 4·75
MS857 105 × 79 mm. $5 "Double Eagle II" (balloon) . . . . . 1·50 2·75

193 Duesenberg "SJ", 1935

1983. Classic Motor Cars. Multicoloured.
858 10c. Type **193** 25 15
859 45c. Studebaker "Avanti", 1962 . . . . 35 25
860 60c. Cord "812" 40 35
861 75c. MG "TC", 1945 . . . . 45 50
862 90c. Camaro "350 SS", 1967 50 60
863 $3 Porsch "356", 1948 . . . 1·00 1·60
MS864 110 × 75 mm. $5 Ferrari "312 T", 1975 . . . . 1·50 2·75

194 "Charity"

1983. Christmas. 500th Birth Anniv of Raphael. Multicoloured.
865 45c. Type **194** 30 30
866 60c. "Hope" 30 30
867 90c. "Faith" 40 60
868 $4 "The Cardinal Virtues" 1·00 3·25
MS869 101 × 127 mm. $5 "Justice" 1·25 2·75

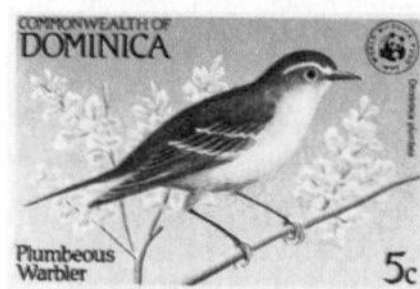

195 Plumbeous Warbler

1984. Birds. Multicoloured.
870 5c. Type **195** . . . . 2·50 1·10
871 45c. Imperial amazon ("Imperial Parrot") . . . . 5·00 75
872 60c. Blue-headed hummingbird . . . . . . 5·50 3·25
873 90c. Red-necked amazon ("Red-necked Parrot") . . 6·50 6·00
MS874 72 × 72 mm. $5 Greater flamingos . . . . 4·00 4·50

196 Donald Duck **197** Gymnastics

1984. Easter. Multicoloured.
875 ½c. Type **196** 10 10
876 1c. Mickey Mouse 10 10
877 2c. Tortoise and Hare . . . 10 10
878 3c. Brer Rabbit and Brer Bear 10 10
879 4c. Donald Duck (different) 10 10
880 5c. White Rabbit 10 10
881 10c. Thumper 10 10
882 $2 Pluto . . . . 3·25 2·75
883 $4 Pluto (different) . . . . 4·50 4·00
MS884 126 × 100 mm. $5 Chip and Dale . . . . 3·50 4·00

1984. Olympic Games, Los Angeles. Multicoloured.
885 30c. Type **197** 20 25
886 45c. Javelin-throwing 30 35
887 60c. High diving 40 45
888 $4 Fencing . . . . 2·00 2·50
MS889 104 × 85 mm. $5 Equestrian event . . . . 3·25 3·25

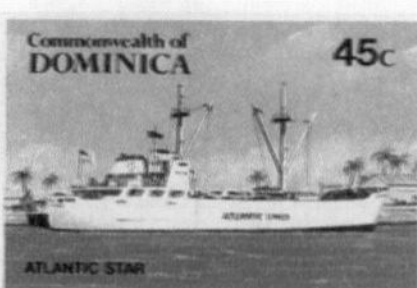

198 "Atlantic Star"

1984. Shipping. Multicoloured.
890 45c. Type **198** . . . . 1·75 75
891 60c. "Atlantic" (liner) . . . . 2·00 1·25
892 90c. Carib fishing boat . . . 2·50 2·50
893 $4 "Norway" (liner) . . . . 6·00 9·00
MS894 106 × 79 mm. $5 "Santa Maria", 1492 . . . . 3·75 5·50

1984. U.P.U. Congress, Hamburg. Nos. 769 and 780 optd **19th UPU CONGRESS HAMBURG.**
895 10c. Passion fruit 10 10
896 $5 Heliconia or lobster claw 2·75 4·00

200 "Guzmania lingulata" **201** "The Virgin and Child with Young St. John" (Correggio)

1984. "Ausipex" International Stamp Exhibition, Melbourne. Bromeliads. Multicoloured.
897 45c. Type **200** 30 35
898 60c. "Pitcairnia angustifolia" 40 55
899 75c. "Tillandsia fasciculata" 50 75
900 $3 "Aechmea smithiorum" 2·00 3·50
MS901 75 × 105 mm. $5 "Tillandsia utriculata" . . . . 2·75 4·25

1984. 450th Death Anniv of Correggio (painter). Multicoloured.
902 25c. Type **201** 30 20
903 60c. "Christ bids Farewell to the Virgin Mary" 40 40
904 90c. "Do not Touch Me" . . . 50 80
905 $4 "The Mystical Marriage of St Catherine" . . . . . . 80 3·50
MS906 89 × 60 mm. $5 "The Adoration of the Magi" . . . 1·75 3·50

202 "Before the Start" (Edgar Degas)

1984. 150th Birth Anniv of Edgar Degas (painter). Multicoloured.
907 30c. Type **202** 30 25
908 45c. "Race on the Racecourse" 35 35
909 $1 "Jockeys at the Flagpole" 55 1·25
910 $3 "Racehorses at Longchamp" . . . . 80 3·75
MS911 89 × 60 mm. $5 "Self-portrait" (vert) . . . . 2·00 3·75

203 Tabby

1984. Cats. Multicoloured.
912 10c. Type **203** 20 15
913 15c. Calico shorthair 25 15
914 20c. Siamese 35 15
915 25c. Manx 40 20
916 45c. Abyssinian 65 30
917 60c. Tortoise-shell longhair 70 65
918 $1 Cornish rex . . . . 85 1·00
919 $2 Persian . . . . 1·00 3·00
920 $3 Himalayan . . . . 1·25 4·00
921 $5 Burmese . . . . 1·50 7·00
MS922 105 × 75 mm. $5 Grey Burmese, Persian and American shorthair . . . . 3·50 7·00

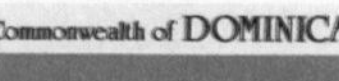

204 Hawker Siddeley H.S.748 **205** Donald Duck, Mickey Mouse and Goofy with Father Christmas

1984. 40th Anniv of International Civil Aviation Organisation. Multicoloured.
923 30c. Type **204** . . . . 1·00 50
924 60c. De Havilland Twin Otter 100 . . . . 1·75 50

925 $1 Britten Norman Islander 2·00 1·60
926 $3 De Havilland Twin Otter 100 (different) 3·00 6·50
MS927 102×75 mm. $5 Boeing 747–200 2·50 3·50

1984. Christmas. Walt Disney Cartoon Characters. Multicoloured.
928 45c. Type **205** 1·25 30
929 60c. Donald Duck as Father Christmas with toy train 1·50 70
930 90c. Donald Duck as Father Christmas in sleigh 2·00 1·75
931 $2 Donald Duck and nephews in sledge 3·25 3·75
932 $4 Donald Duck in snow with Christmas tree 4·25 6·00
MS933 127×102 mm. $5 Donald Duck and nephews opening present 3·50 4·00

206 Mrs. M. Bascom presenting Trefoil to Chief Guide Lady Baden-Powell

1985. 75th Anniv of Girl Guide Movement. Mult.
934 35c. Type **206** 60 30
935 45c. Lady Baden-Powell inspecting Dominican brownies 80 35
936 60c. Lady Baden-Powell with Mrs. M. Bascom and Mrs. A. Robinson (guide leaders) 1·00 65
937 $3 Lord and Lady Baden-Powell (vert) 2·50 3·75
MS938 77×105 mm. $5 Flags of Dominica and Girl Guide Movement 3·50 4·00

1985. Birth Bicentenary of John J Audubon (ornithologist) (1st issue). As T **198** of Antigua. Multicoloured.
939 45c. Clapper rail ("King Rail") 1·10 30
940 $1 Black and white warbler (vert) 2·00 1·50
941 $2 Broad-winged hawk (vert) 2·75 3·00
942 $3 Ring-necked duck 3·50 4·00
MS943 101×73 mm. $5 Reddish egret 3·50 3·75
See also Nos. 1013/16.

207 Student with Computer

208 The Queen Mother visiting Sadlers Wells Opera

1985. Duke of Edinburgh's Award Scheme. Multicoloured.
944 45c. Type **207** 50 30
945 60c. Assisting doctor in hospital 1·75 40
946 90c. Two youths hiking 1·90 80
947 $4 Family jogging 3·50 6·00
MS948 100×98 mm. $5 Duke of Edinburgh 2·75 3·00

1985. Life and Times of Queen Elizabeth the Queen Mother. Multicoloured.
949 60c. Type **208** 1·75 60
950 $1 Fishing in Scotland 1·75 70
951 $3 On her 84th birthday 2·25 3·25
MS952 56×85 mm. $5 Attending Garter ceremony, Windsor Castle 3·25 3·00

209 Cricket Match ("Sports")

1985. International Youth Year. Multicoloured.
953 45c. Type **209** 4·25 1·50
954 60c. Bird-watching ("Environmental Study") 4·25 2·25
955 $1 Stamp collecting ("Education") 4·25 3·50
956 $3 Boating ("Leisure") 5·50 8·00
MS957 96×65 mm. $5 Young people linking hands 2·75 4·00

1985. 300th Birth Anniv of Johann Sebastian Bach (composer). As T **206** of Antigua. Antique musical instruments.
958 45c. multicoloured 1·50 40
959 60c. multicoloured 1·75 60
960 $1 multicoloured 2·25 1·00
961 $3 multicoloured 4·00 3·50
MS962 199×75 mm. $5 black 3·00 4·50
DESIGNS: 45c. Cornett; 60c. Coiled trumpet; $1 Piccolo; $3 Violoncello piccolo; $5 Johann Sebastian Bach.

1985. Royal Visit. As T **207** of Antigua. Mult.
963 60c. Flags of Great Britain and Dominica 75 50
964 $1 Queen Elizabeth II (vert) 75 1·25
965 $4 Royal Yacht "Britannia" 1·75 5·50
MS966 111×83 mm. $5 Map of Dominica 3·50 4·00

1985. 150th Birth Anniv of Mark Twain (author). As T **118** of Anguilla showing Walt Disney cartoon characters in scenes from "Tom Sawyer". Multicoloured.
967 20c. "The glorius white-washer" 75 30
968 60c. "Aunt Polly's home dentistry" 1·50 75
969 $1 "Aunt Polly's pain killer" 2·00 1·25
970 $1.50 Mickey Mouse balancing on fence 2·50 3·00
971 $2 "Lost in the cave with Becky" 2·75 3·50
MS972 126×101 mm. $5 Mickey Mouse as pirate 5·50 7·00

1985. Birth Bicentenaries of Grimm Brothers (folklorists). Designs as T **119** of Anguilla showing Walt Disney cartoon characters in scenes from "Little Red Cap". Multicoloured.
973 10c. Little Red Cap (Daisy Duck) meeting the Wolf 30 20
974 45c. The Wolf at the door 85 30
975 90c. The Wolf in Grandmother's bed 1·75 1·75
976 $1 The Wolf lunging at Little Red Cap 2·00 1·75
977 $3 The Woodsman (Donald Duck) chasing the Wolf 3·75 5·00
MS978 126×101 mm. $5 The Wolf falling into cooking pot 5·00 5·50

1985. 40th Anniv of United Nations Organization. Designs as T **208** of Antigua showing United Nations (New York) stamps. Multicoloured.
979 45c. Lord Baden-Powell and 1984 International Youth Year 35c. 70 50
980 $2 Maimonides (physician) and 1966 W.H.O. Building 11c. 1·50 3·25
981 $3 Sir Rowland Hill (postal reformer) and 1976 25th anniv of U.N. Postal Administration 13c. 1·50 3·50
MS982 110×85 mm. $5 "Apollo" spacecraft 2·75 3·25

210 Two Players competing for Ball

1986. World Cup Football Championship, Mexico. Multicoloured.
983 45c. Type **210** 1·75 40
984 60c. Player heading ball 2·00 1·50
985 $1 Two players competing for ball (different) 2·25 1·75
986 $3 Player with ball 4·50 6·00
MS987 114×84 mm. $5 Three players 8·00 10·00

211 Police in Rowing Boat pursuing River Pirates, 1890

1986. Centenary of Statue of Liberty. Mult.
988 15c. Type **211** 2·75 65
989 25c. Police patrol launch, 1986 2·75 85
990 45c. Hoboken Ferry Terminal c. 1890 2·50 85
991 $4 Holland Tunnel entrance and staff, 1986 5·00 7·50
MS992 104×76 mm. $5 Statue of Liberty (vert) 4·00 5·00

1986. Appearance of Halley's Comet (1st issue). As T **123** of Anguilla. Multicoloured.
993 5c. Nasir al Din al Tusi (Persian astronomer) and Jantal Mantar Observatory, Delhi 40 50
994 10c. Bell XS-1 Rocket Plane breaking sound barrier for first time, 1947 45 50
995 45c. Halley's Comet of 1531 (from "Astronomicum Caesareum", 1540) 1·00 30
996 $4 Mark Twain and quotation, 1910 3·75 4·25
MS997 104×71 mm. $5 Halley's Comet over Dominica 3·00 3·50
See also Nos. 1032/6.

1986. 60th Birthday of Queen Elizabeth II. As T **125** of Anguilla.
998 2c. multicoloured 10 15
999 $1 multicoloured 70 80
1000 $4 multicoloured 2·00 3·00
MS1001 120×85 mm. $5 black and brown 4·00 4·25
DESIGNS: 2c. Wedding photograph, 1947; $1 Queen meeting Pope John Paul II, 1982; $4 Queen on royal visit, 1982; $5 Princess Elizabeth with corgis, 1936.

212 Mickey Mouse and Pluto mounting Stamps in Album

1986. "Ameripex" International Stamp Exhibition, Chicago. Showing Walt Disney cartoon characters. Multicoloured.
1002 25c. Type **212** 60 40
1003 45c. Donald Duck examining stamp under magnifying glass 80 65
1004 60c. Chip n' Dale soaking and drying stamps 1·10 1·50
1005 $4 Donald Duck as scoutmaster awarding merit badges to Nephews 3·50 6·00
MS1006 127×101 mm. $5 Uncle Scrooge conducting stamp auction 4·00 8·00

213 William I

214 "Virgin at Prayer"

1986. 500th Anniv (1985) of Succession of House of Tudor to English Throne. Multicoloured.
1007 10c. Type **213** 40 40
1008 40c. Richard II 80 80
1009 50c. Henry VIII 90 90
1010 $1 Charles II 1·00 1·75
1011 $2 Queen Anne 1·50 3·00
1012 $4 Queen Victoria 2·00 4·50

1986. Birth Bicentenary (1985) of John J. Audubon (ornithologist) (2nd issue). As T **198** of Antigua showing original paintings. Multicoloured.
1013 25c. Black-throated diver 1·50 50
1014 60c. Great blue heron (vert) 2·00 1·50
1015 90c. Yellow-crowned night heron (vert) 2·00 2·25
1016 $4 Common shoveler ("Shoveler Duck") 4·50 6·50
MS1017 73×103 mm. $5 Canada goose ("Goose") 10·00 12·00

1986. Royal Wedding. As T **213** of Antigua. Multicoloured.
1018 45c. Prince Andrew and Miss Sarah Ferguson 35 30
1019 50c. Prince Andrew 45 45
1020 $4 Prince Andrew climbing aboard aircraft 2·00 3·00
MS1021 88×88 mm. $5 Prince Andrew and Miss Sarah Ferguson (different) 4·25 4·75

1986. World Cup Football Championship Winners, Mexico. Nos. 983/6 optd **WINNERS Argentina 3 W. Germany 2.**
1022 45c. Type **210** 1·50 55
1023 60c. Player heading ball 1·75 1·50
1024 $1 Two players competing for ball 2·25 2·50
1025 $3 Player with ball 5·00 7·00
MS1026 114×84 mm. $5 Three players 8·50 11·00

1986. Christmas. Paintings by Durer. Multicoloured.
1027 45c. Type **214** 1·00 35
1028 60c. "Madonna and Child" 1·50 1·25

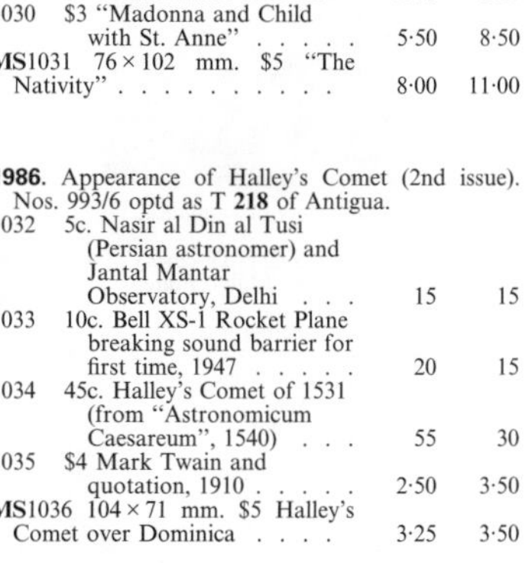

1029 $1 "Madonna of the Pear" 2·00 2·25
1030 $3 "Madonna and Child with St. Anne" 5·50 8·50
MS1031 76×102 mm. $5 "The Nativity" 8·00 11·00

1986. Appearance of Halley's Comet (2nd issue). Nos. 993/6 optd as T **218** of Antigua.
1032 5c. Nasir al Din al Tusi (Persian astronomer) and Jantal Mantar Observatory, Delhi 15 15
1033 10c. Bell XS-1 Rocket Plane breaking sound barrier for first time, 1947 20 15
1034 45c. Halley's Comet of 1531 (from "Astronomicum Caesareum", 1540) 55 30
1035 $4 Mark Twain and quotation, 1910 2·50 3·50
MS1036 104×71 mm. $5 Halley's Comet over Dominica 3·25 3·50

215 Broad-winged Hawk

216 Poulsen's Triton

1987. Birds of Dominica. Multicoloured.
1037 1c. Type **215** 20 1·00
1038 2c. Ruddy quail dove 20 1·00
1039 5c. Red-necked pigeon 30 1·00
1040 10c. Green-backed heron ("Green Heron") 30 20
1041 15c. Moorhen ("Common Gallinule") 40 30
1042 20c. Ringed kingfisher 40 30
1043 25c. Brown pelican 40 20
1044 35c. White-tailed tropic bird 40 30
1045 45c. Red-legged thrush 50 30
1046 60c. Purple-throated carib 65 45
1047 90c. Magnificent frigate bird 70 70
1048 $1 Brown trembler ("Trembler") 80 80
1049 $2 Black-capped petrel 1·25 4·50
1050 $5 Barn owl 3·00 7·00
1051 $10 Imperial amazon ("Imperial Parrot") 5·00 12·00

1987. America's Cup Yachting Championships. As T **222** of Antigua. Multicoloured.
1052 45c. "Reliance", 1903 60 30
1053 60c. "Freedom", 1980 70 55
1054 $1 "Mischief", 1881 80 90
1055 $3 "Australia", 1977 1·25 3·00
MS1056 113×83 mm. $5 "Courageous", 1977 (horiz) 3·00 3·50

1987. Birth Centenary of Marc Chagall (artist). As T **225** of Antigua. Multicoloured.
1057 25c. "Artist and His Model" 40 20
1058 35c. "Midsummer Night's Dream" 45 20
1059 45c. "Joseph the Shepherd" 50 25
1060 60c. "The Cellist" 55 30
1061 90c. "Woman with Pigs" 70 45
1062 $1 "The Blue Circus" 75 65
1063 $3 "For Vava" 1·50 2·00
1064 $4 "The Rider" 1·75 2·25
MS1065 Two sheets, each 110×95 mm. (a) $5 "Purim" (104×89 mm). (b) $5 "Firebird" (stage design) (104×89 mm) Set of 2 sheets 4·25 6·00

1987. Sea Shells.
1066 **216** 35c. multicoloured 20 20
1067 – 45c. violet, black and red 25 25
1068 – 60c. multicoloured 30 40
1069 – $5 multicoloured 2·40 4·25
MS1070 109×75 mm. $5 multicoloured 3·25 5·50
DESIGNS—VERT: 45c. Elongate janthina; 60c. Banded tulip; $5 Deltoid rock shell. HORIZ: $5 (**MS**1070) Junonia volute.
No. 1066 is inscribed "TIRITON" in error.

217 "Cantharellus cinnabarinus"

1987. "Capex '87" International Stamp Exhibition, Toronto. Mushrooms of Dominica. Multicoloured.
1071 45c. Type **217** 1·50 50
1072 60c. "Boletellus cubensis" 2·00 1·25
1073 $2 "Eccilia cystiophorus" 4·25 4·50
1074 $3 "Xerocomus guadelupae" 4·50 5·00
MS1075 85×85 mm. $5 "Gymnopilus chrysopellus" 10·00 11·00

218 Discovery of Dominica, 1493

1987. 500th Anniv (1992) of Discovery of America by Columbus (1st issue). Multicoloured.

1076 10c. Type **218** 40 25
1077 15c. Caribs greeting Columbus's fleet 50 30
1078 45c. Claiming the New World for Spain 65 35
1079 60c. Wreck of "Santa Maria" 80 60
1080 90c. Fleet leaving Spain . . 1·00 1·00
1081 $1 Sighting the New World 1·10 1·25
1082 $3 Trading with Indians . . 2·25 3·00
1083 $5 Building settlement . . . 3·25 4·00
MS1084 Two sheets, each 109 × 79 mm. (a) $5 Fleet off Dominica, 1493. (b) $5 Map showing Columbus's route, 1493 Set of 2 sheets . . . . 8·00 11·00

See also Nos. 1221/5, 1355/63, 1406/14, 1547/53 and 1612/13.

1987. Milestones of Transportation. As T **226** of Antigua. Multicoloured.

1085 10c. H.M.S. "Warrior" (first ironclad warship, 1860) 50 50
1086 15c. "MAGLEV-MLU 001" (fastest train), 1979 . . . 60 60
1087 25c. "Flying Cloud" (fastest clipper passage New York–San Francisco) (vert) 70 70
1088 35c. First elevated railway, New York, 1868 (vert) . . 80 80
1089 45c. Peter Cooper's locomotive "Tom Thumb" (first U.S. passenger locomotive), 1829 . . . . 80 80
1090 60c. "Spray" (Slocum's solo, circumnavigation), 1895–98 (vert) 90 90
1091 90c. "Sea-Land Commerce" (fastest Pacific passage), 1973 (vert) . . . . . . 1·25 1·25
1092 $1 First cable cars, San Francisco, 1873 . . . . 1·40 1·40
1093 $3 "Orient Express", 1883 3·00 3·50
1094 $4 "Clermont" (first commercial paddle-steamer), 1807 . . . . . 3·25 3·75

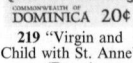

219 "Virgin and Child with St. Anne" (Durer)

220 Three Little Pigs in People Mover, Walt Disney World

1987. Christmas. Religious Paintings. Mult.

1095 20c. Type **219** 30 15
1096 25c. "Virgin and Child" (Murillo) 30 15
1097 $2 "Madonna and Child" (Foppa) . . . . 1·50 2·25
1098 $4 "Madonna and Child" (Da Verona) . . . . . . 2·75 4·25
MS1099 100 × 78 mm. $5 "Angel of the Annunciation" (anon, Renaissance period) . . . . . 2·50 3·75

1987. 60th Anniv of Mickey Mouse (Walt Disney cartoon character). Cartoon characters in trains. Multicoloured.

1100 20c. Type **220** 45 35
1101 25c. Goofy driving horse tram, Disneyland 45 35
1102 45c. Donald Duck in "Roger E. Broggie", Walt Disney World 75 65
1103 60c. Goofy, Mickey Mouse, Donald Duck and Chip 'n Dale aboard "Big Thunder Mountain" train, Disneyland 85 75
1104 90c. Mickey Mouse in "Walter E. Disney", Disneyland . . . . 1·40 1·25
1105 $1 Mickey and Minnie Mouse, Goofy, Donald and Daisy Duck in monorail, Walt Disney World . . . . 1·50 1·40
1106 $3 Dumbo flying over "Casey Jr" . . . . 3·25 3·75
1107 $4 Daisy Duck and Minnie Mouse in "Lilly Belle", Walt Disney World . . . 3·75 4·50
MS1108 Two sheets, each 127 × 101 mm. (a) $5 Seven Dwarfs in Rainbow Caverns Mine train, Disneyland (horiz). (b) $5 Donald Duck and Chip n'Dale on toy train (from film "Out of Scale" (horiz) Set of 2 sheets . . . . 5·50 7·00

1988. Royal Ruby Wedding. As T **234** of Antigua.

1109 45c. multicoloured 70 30
1110 60c. brown, black and green 80 50
1111 $1 multicoloured . . . . . 1·00 1·00
1112 $3 multicoloured . . . . . 2·00 3·75
MS1113 102 × 76 mm. $5 multicoloured . . . . 3·00 3·75

DESIGNS: 45c. Wedding portrait with attendants, 1947; 60c. Princess Elizabeth with Prince Charles, c. 1950; $1 Princess Elizabeth and Prince Philip with Prince Charles and Princess Anne, 1950; $3 Queen Elizabeth; $5 Princess Elizabeth in wedding dress, 1947.

221 Kayak Canoeing

222 Carib Indian

1988. Olympic Games, Seoul. Multicoloured.

1114 45c. Type **221** 60 25
1115 60c. Taekwon-do 80 60
1116 $1 High diving . . . . . . 85 1·00
1117 $3 Gymnastics on bars . . . 1·75 3·75
MS1118 81 × 110 mm. $5 Football 2·50 3·50

1988. "Reunion '88" Tourism Programme. Mult.

1119 10c. Type **222** 10 10
1120 25c. Mountainous interior (horiz) 10 15
1121 35c. Indian River 10 15
1122 60c. Belaire dancer and tourists 15 30
1123 90c. Boiling Lake 20 60
1124 $3 Coral reef (horiz) . . . . 60 2·00
MS1125 112 × 82 mm. $5 Belaire dancer . . . . 1·75 4·50

1988. Stamp Exhibitions. Nos. 1092/3 optd.

1126 $1 First cable cars, San Francisco, 1873 (optd **FINLANDIA 88**, Helsinki) . . . . 1·00 75
1127 $3 "Orient Express", 1883 (optd **INDEPENDENCE 40**, Israel) . . . . 2·75 2·75
MS1128 Two sheets, each 109 × 79 mm. (a) $5 Fleet off Dominica, 1493 (optd **OLYMPHILEX '88, Seoul**). (b) $5 Map showing Columbus's route, 1493 (optd **Praga '88, Prague**) Set of 2 sheets . . . . 4·25 5·50

223 White-tailed Tropic Bird

225 Gary Cooper

224 Battery Hens

1988. Dominica Rain Forest Flora and Fauna. Multicoloured.

1129 45c. Type **223** 65 50
1130 45c. Blue-hooded euphonia ("Blue-throated Euphonia") 65 50
1131 45c. Smooth-billed ani . . . 65 50
1132 45c. Scaly-breasted thrasher 65 50
1133 45c. Purple-throated carib 65 50
1134 45c. "Marpesia petreus" and "Strymon maesites" (butterflies) 65 50
1135 45c. Brown trembler ("Trembler") 65 50
1136 45c. Imperial amazon ("Imperial Parrot") . . . 65 50
1137 45c. Mangrove cuckoo 65 50
1138 45c. "Dynastes hercules" (beetle) 65 50
1139 45c. "Historis odius" (butterfly) 65 50
1140 45c. Red-necked amazon ("Red-necked Parrot") . . 65 50
1141 45c. Tillandsia (plant) . . . 65 50
1142 45c. Bananaquit and "Polystacha luteola" (plant) 65 50
1143 45c. False chameleon 65 50
1144 45c. Iguana 65 50
1145 45c. "Hypolimnas misippus" (butterfly) 65 50
1146 45c. Green-throated carib 65 50
1147 45c. Heliconia (plant) . . . 65 50
1148 45c. Agouti 65 50

Nos. 1129/48 were printed together, se-tenant, forming a composite design.

1988. 10th Anniv of International Fund for Agricultural Development. Multicoloured.

1149 45c. Type **224** 50 30
1150 60c. Pig 70 65
1151 90c. Cattle . . . . 95 1·25
1152 $3 Black belly sheep . . . . 2·25 4·00
MS1153 95 × 68 mm. $5 Tropical fruits (vert) . . . . 2·25 3·75

1988. Entertainers. Multicoloured.

1154 10c. Type **225** 25 25
1155 35c. Josephine Baker 30 25
1156 45c. Maurice Chevalier . . . 35 25
1157 60c. James Cagney 45 30
1158 $1 Clark Gable 65 50
1159 $2 Louis Armstrong . . . . 1·25 1·00
1160 $3 Liberace . . . . 1·50 1·75
1161 $4 Spencer Tracy . . . . . 2·00 2·25
MS1162 Two sheets, each 105 × 75 mm. (a) $5 Humphrey Bogart. (b) $5 Elvis Presley Set of 2 sheets . . . . 8·00 6·50

1988. Flowering Trees. As T **242** of Antigua. Multicoloured.

1163 15c. Sapodilla 10 10
1164 20c. Tangerine 10 10
1165 25c. Avocado pear 10 10
1166 45c. Amherstia 20 25
1167 90c. Lipstick tree 40 55
1168 $1 Cannonball tree 45 55
1169 $3 Saman . . . . 1·25 1·75
1170 $4 Pineapple . . . . 1·60 2·00
MS1171 Two sheets, each 96 × 66 mm. (a) $5 Lignum vitae. (b) $5 Sea grape Set of 2 sheets 4·50 6·50

1988. 500th Birth Anniv of Titian (artist). As T **238** of Antigua. Multicoloured.

1172 25c. "Jacopo Strada" . . . 15 15
1173 35c. "Titian's Daughter Lavinia" 20 15
1174 45c. "Andrea Navagero" . . 20 15
1175 60c. "Judith with Head of Holoferenes" 25 15
1176 $1 "Emilia di Spilimbergo" 40 50
1177 $2 "Martyrdom of St. Lawrence" . . . . . 70 1·25
1178 $3 "Salome" . . . . 1·00 2·00
1179 $4 "St. John the Baptist" . . 1·25 2·25
MS1180 Two sheets, each 110 × 95 mm. (a) $5 "Self Portrait". (b) $5 "Sisyphus" Set of 2 sheets . . . . 6·00 7·00

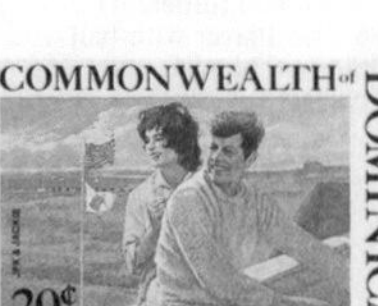

226 Imperial Amazon

227 President and Mrs. Kennedy

1988. 10th Anniv of Independence. Multicoloured.

1181 20c. Type **226** . . . . . . 1·50 40
1182 45c. Dominica 1874 1d. stamp and landscape (horiz) 90 30
1183 $2 1978 Independence 10c. stamp and landscape (horiz) . . . . 1·50 2·75
1184 $3 Carib wood (national flower) . . . . 1·75 3·25
MS1185 116 × 85 mm. $5 Government Band (horiz) . . . 2·25 3·75

1988. 25th Death Anniv of John F. Kennedy (American statesman). Multicoloured.

1186 20c. Type **227** 10 10
1187 25c. Kennedy sailing 10 10
1188 $2 Outside Hyannis Port house . . . . 80 1·50
1189 $4 Speaking in Berlin (vert) 1·60 2·50
MS1190 100 × 71 mm. $5 President Kennedy (vert) . . . . . . 2·10 3·75

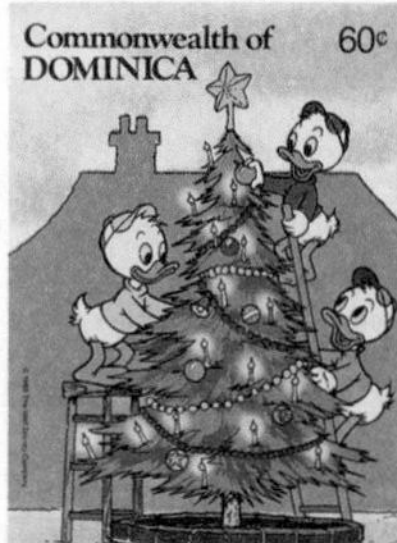

228 Donald Duck's Nephews decorating Christmas Tree

1988. Christmas. "Mickey's Christmas Mall". Walt Disney Cartoon Characters. Multicoloured.

1191 60c. Type **228** 55 65
1192 60c. Daisy Duck outside clothes shop 55 65
1193 60c. Winnie the Pooh in shop window 55 65
1194 60c. Goofy with parcels . . 55 65
1195 60c. Donald Duck as Father Christmas 55 65
1196 60c. Mickey Mouse contributing to collection 55 65
1197 60c. Minnie Mouse 55 65
1198 60c. Chip n' Dale with peanut 55 65
MS1199 Two sheets, each 127 × 102 mm. (a) $6 Mordie Mouse with Father Christmas. (b) $6 Mickey Mouse at West Indian market Set of 2 sheets . . . . 6·50 8·00

Nos. 1191/8 were printed together, se-tenant, forming a composite design.

229 Raoul Wallenberg (diplomat) and Swedish Flag

1988. 40th Anniv of Universal Declaration of Human Rights. Multicoloured.

1200 $3 Type **229** . . . . 2·00 2·50
MS1201 92 × 62 mm. $5 Human Rights Day logo (vert) . . . . 3·00 3·50

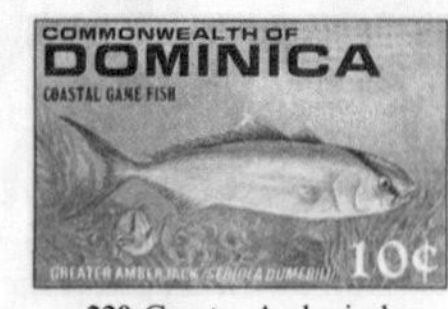

230 Greater Amberjack

1988. Game Fishes. Multicoloured.

1202 10c. Type **230** 20 15
1203 15c. Blue marlin 20 15
1204 35c. Cobia 35 30
1205 45c. Dolphin (fish) 45 30
1206 60c. Cero 60 55
1207 90c. Mahogany snapper . . 85 95
1208 $3 Yellow-finned tuna . . . 2·50 3·25
1209 $4 Rainbow parrotfish . . . 3·00 3·75
MS1210 Two sheets, each 104 × 74 mm. (a) $5 Manta. (b) $5 Tarpon Set of 2 sheets . . . . 11·00 11·00

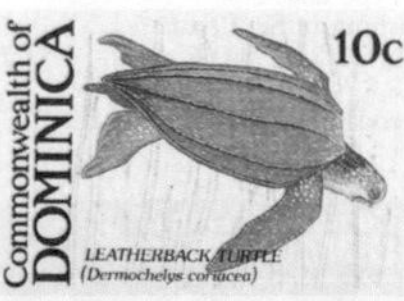

231 Leatherback Turtle

1988. Insects and Reptiles. Multicoloured.

1211 10c. Type **231** 45 35
1212 25c. "Danaus plexippus" (butterfly) . . . . 1·25 75
1213 60c. Green anole (lizard) . . 1·60 1·25
1214 $3 "Mantis religiosa" (mantid) . . . . 4·00 6·50
MS1215 119 × 90 mm. $5 "Dynastes hercules" (beetle) . . . . . . 3·00 4·50

1989. Olympic Medal Winners, Seoul. Nos. 1114/17 optd.

1216 45c. Type **221** (optd **Men's C-1, 500m O. Heukrodt DDR**) 20 25
1217 60c. Taekwon-do (optd **Women's Flyweight N. Y. Choo S. Korea**) 25 35

1218 $1 High diving (optd **Women's Platform Y. Xu China**) 40 60
1219 $3 Gymnastics on bars (optd **V. Artemov USSR**) 1·25 2·25
MS1220 81 × 110 mm. $5 Football (optd **USSR defeated Brazil 3–2 on penalty kicks after a 1–1 tie**) 3·50 4·00

1989. 500th Anniv (1992) of Discovery of America by Columbus (2nd issue). Pre-Columbian Carib Society. As T **247** of Antigua but horiz. Mult.
1221 20c. Carib canoe 20 20
1222 35c. Hunting with bows and arrows 30 20
1223 $1 Dugout canoe making 70 90
1224 $3 Shield contest 1·75 3·00
MS1225 87 × 71 mm. $6 Ceremonial dress 2·75 4·00

233 Map of Dominica, 1766
235 "Oncidium pusillum"

234 "Papilio homerus"

1989. "Philexfrance '89" International Stamp Exhibition, Paris. Multicoloured.
1226 10c. Type **233** 60 40
1227 35c. French coin of 1653 (horiz) 75 40
1228 $1 French warship, 1720 (horiz) 1·60 1·25
1229 $4 Coffee plant (horiz) 2·25 3·50
MS1230 98 × 98 mm. $5 Exhibition inscription (horiz) (black, grey and yellow) 3·00 4·00

1989. Japanese Art. Paintings by Taikan. As T **250** of Antigua but vert. Multicoloured.
1231 10c. "Lao-tzu" (detail) 10 10
1232 20c. "Red Maple Leaves" (panels 1 and 2) 10 10
1233 45c. "King Wen Hui learns a Lesson from his Cook" (detail) 20 25
1234 60c. "Red Maple Leaves" (panels 3 and 4) 25 35
1235 $1 "Wild Flowers" (detail) 45 50
1236 $2 "Red Maple Leaves" (panels 5 and 6) 85 1·10
1237 $3 "Red Maple Leaves" (panels 7 and 8) 1·00 1·60
1238 $4 "Indian Ceremony of Floating Lamps on the River" (detail) 1·25 2·00
MS1239 Two sheets. (a) 78 × 102 mm. $5 "Innocence" (detail). (b) 101 × 77 mm. $5 "Red Maple Leaves" (detail) Set of 2 sheets 4·75 5·75

1989. Butterflies. Multicoloured.
1255 10c. Type **234** 40 30
1256 15c. "Morpho peleides" 45 30
1257 25c. "Dryas julia" 65 30
1258 35c. "Parides gundlachianus" 70 30
1259 60c. "Danaus plexippus" 1·00 75
1260 $1 "Agraulis vanillae" 1·25 1·25
1261 $3 "Phoebis avellaneda" 2·75 3·25
1262 $5 "Papilio andraemon" 3·75 5·00
MS1263 Two sheets. (a) 105 × 74 mm. $6 "Adelpha cytherea". (b) 105 × 79 mm. $6 "Adelpha iphicala" Set of 2 sheets 8·00 9·00

1989. Orchids. Multicoloured.
1264 10c. Type **235** 35 30
1265 35c. "Epidendrum cochleata" 70 30
1266 45c. "Epidendrum ciliare" 75 40
1267 60c. "Cyrtopodium andersonii" 1·00 80
1268 $1 "Habenaria pauciflora" 1·25 1·25
1269 $2 "Maxillaria alba" 2·00 2·25
1270 $3 "Selenipedium palmifolium" 2·50 2·75
1271 $4 "Brassavola cucullata" 3·25 3·75
MS1272 Two sheets, each 108 × 77 mm. (a) $5 "Oncidium lanceanum". (b) $5 "Comparettia falcata" Set of 2 sheets 8·00 9·00

236 "Apollo 11" Command Module in Lunar Orbit

1989. 20th Anniv of First Manned Landing on Moon. Multicoloured.
1273 10c. Type **236** 30 30
1274 60c. Neil Armstrong leaving lunar module 70 70
1275 $2 Edwin Aldrin at Sea of Tranquility 1·60 2·00
1276 $3 Astronauts Armstrong and Aldrin with U.S. flag 2·00 2·50
MS1277 62 × 77 mm. $6 Launch of "Apollo 11" (vert) 4·50 6·00

237 Brazil v Italy Final, 1970

1989. World Cup Football Championship, Italy (1st issue). Multicoloured.
1278 $1 Type **237** 2·00 2·25
1279 $1 England v West Germany, 1966 2·00 2·25
1280 $1 West Germany v Holland, 1974 2·00 2·25
1281 $1 Italy v West Germany, 1982 2·00 2·25
MS1282 106 × 86 mm. $6 Two players competing for ball 4·00 4·75
Nos. 1278/81 were printed together, se-tenant, forming a composite central design of a football surrounded by flags of competing nations.
See also Nos. 1383/7.

238 George Washington and Inauguration, 1789

1989. "World Stamp Expo '89" International Stamp Exhibition, Washington. Bicentenary of U.S. Presidency. Multicoloured.
1283 60c. Type **238** 90 80
1284 60c. John Adams and Presidential Mansion, 1800 90 80
1285 60c. Thomas Jefferson, Graff House, Philadelphia and Declaration of Independence 90 80
1286 60c. James Madison and U.S.S. "Constitution" defeating H.M.S. "Guerriere", 1812 90 80
1287 60c. James Monroe and freed slaves landing in Liberia 90 80
1288 60c. John Quincy Adams and barge on Erie Canal 90 80
1289 60c. Millard Fillmore and Perry's fleet off Japan 90 80
1290 60c. Franklin Pierce, Jefferson Davis and San Xavier Mission, Tucson 90 80
1291 60c. James Buchanan, "Buffalo Bill" Cody carrying mail and Wells Fargo Pony Express stamp 90 80
1292 60c. Abraham Lincoln and U.P.U. Monument, Berne 90 80
1293 60c. Andrew Johnson, polar bear and Mount McKinley, Alaska 90 80
1294 60c. Ulysses S. Grant and Golden Spike Ceremony, 1869 90 80
1295 60c. Theodore Roosevelt and steam shovel excavating Panama Canal 90 80
1296 60c. William H. Taft and Admiral Peary at North Pole 90 80
1297 60c. Woodrow Wilson and Curtis "Jenny" on first scheduled airmail flight, 1918 90 80
1298 60c. Warren G. Harding and airship U.S.S. "Shenandoah" at Lakehurst 90 80
1299 60c. Calvin Coolidge and Lindbergh's "Spirit of St Louis" on trans-Atlantic flight 90 80
1300 60c. Mount Rushmore National Monument 90 80
1301 60c. Lyndon B. Johnson and Earth from Moon as seen by "Apollo 8" crew 90 80
1302 60c. Richard Nixon and visit to Great Wall of China 90 80
1303 60c. Gerald Ford and "Gorch Fock" (German cadet barque) at Bicentenary of Revolution celebrations 90 80
1304 60c. Jimmy Carter and President Sadat of Egypt with Prime Minister Begin of Israel 90 80
1305 60c. Ronald Reagan and space shuttle "Columbia" 90 80
1306 60c. George Bush and Grumman TBF Avenger (fighter-bomber) 90 80

1989. "Expo '89" International Stamp Exhibition, Washington (2nd issue). Landmarks of Washington. Sheet 77 × 62 mm, containing horiz design as T **257** of Antigua. Multicoloured.
MS1307 $4 The Capitol 2·50 3·50

1989. Mickey Mouse in Hollywood (Walt Disney cartoon character). As T **267** of Antigua. Mult.
1308 20c. Mickey Mouse reading script 40 40
1309 35c. Mickey Mouse giving interview 55 55
1310 45c. Mickey and Minnie Mouse with newspaper and magazines 65 65
1311 60c. Mickey Mouse signing autographs 75 75
1312 $1 Trapped in dressing room 1·25 1·25
1313 $2 Mickey and Minnie Mouse with Pluto in limousine 2·00 2·50
1314 $3 Arriving at Awards ceremony 2·25 2·75
1315 $4 Mickey Mouse accepting award 2·40 2·75
MS1316 Two sheets, each 127 × 102 mm. (a) $5 Mickey Mouse leaving footprints at cinema. (b) $5 Goofy interviewing Set of 2 sheets 7·50 9·00

1989. Christmas. Paintings by Botticelli. As T **259** of Antigua. Multicoloured.
1317 20c. "Madonna in Glory with Seraphim" 40 30
1318 25c. "The Annunciation" 40 30
1319 35c. "Madonna of the Pomegranate" 55 40
1320 45c. "Madonna of the Rosegarden" 65 45
1321 60c. "Madonna of the Book" 80 60
1322 $1 "Madonna under a Baldachin" 1·00 90
1323 $4 "Madonna and Child with Angels" 3·00 4·50
1324 $5 "Bardi Madonna" 3·50 4·75
MS1325 Two sheets, each 71 × 96 mm. (a) $5 "The Mystic Nativity". (b) $5 "The Adoration of the Magi" Set of 2 sheets 7·00 9·00

240 Lady Olave Baden-Powell and Agatha Robinson (Guide leaders)
241 Jawaharal Nehru

1989. 60th Anniv of Girl Guides in Dominica. Multicoloured.
1326 60c. Type **240** 1·00 1·00
MS1327 70 × 99 mm. $5 Doris Stockmann and Judith Pestaina (horiz) 3·50 4·00

1989. Birth Centenary of Jawaharal Nehru (Indian statesman). Multicoloured.
1328 60c. Type **241** 1·50 1·25
MS1329 101 × 72 mm. $5 Parliament House, New Delhi (horiz) 3·50 4·00

242 Cocoa Damselfish

1990. Tropical Fishes. Multicoloured.
1330 45c. Type **242** 45 55
1331 45c. Stinging jellyfish 45 55
1332 45c. Dolphin (fish) 45 55
1333 45c. Atlantic spadefish and queen angelfish 45 55
1334 45c. French angelfish 45 55
1335 45c. Blue-striped grunt 45 55
1336 45c. Porkfish 45 55
1337 45c. Great hammerhead 45 55
1338 45c. Atlantic spadefish 45 55
1339 45c. Great barracuda 45 55
1340 45c. Southern stingray 45 55
1341 45c. Black grunt 45 55
1342 45c. Spot-finned butterflyfish 45 55
1343 45c. Dog snapper 45 55
1344 45c. Band-tailed puffer 45 55
1345 45c. Four-eyed butterflyfish 45 55
1346 45c. Lane snapper 45 55
1347 45c. Green moray 45 55
Nos. 1330/47 were printed together, se-tenant, forming a composite design.

243 St. Paul's Cathedral, London, c. 1840
244 Blue-headed Hummingbird

1990. 150th Anniv of the Penny Black and "Stamp World London 90" International Stamp Exhibition.
1348 **243** 45c. green and black 50 25
1349 – 50c. blue and black 65 35
1350 – 60c. blue and black 65 45
1351 – 90c. green and black 1·10 85
1352 – $3 blue and black 3·00 3·50
1353 – $4 blue and black 3·00 3·50
MS1354 Two sheets. (a) 103 × 79 mm. $5 ochre and black. (b) 85 × 86 mm. $5 red and brown Set of 2 sheets 6·50 7·50
DESIGNS: 50c. British Post Office "accelerator" carriage, 1830; 60c. St. Paul's and City of London; 90c. Travelling post office, 1838; $3 "Hen and chickens" delivery cycle, 1883; $4 London skyline; $5 (a) Type **243**; (b) Motor mail van, 1899.

1990. 500th Anniv (1992) of Discovery of America by Columbus (3rd issue). New World Natural History—Seashells. As T **260** of Antigua. Mult.
1355 10c. Reticulated cowrie-helmet 30 30
1356 20c. West Indian chank 40 40
1357 35c. West Indian fighting conch 50 35
1358 60c. True tulip 75 60
1359 $1 Sunrise tellin 1·00 1·00
1360 $2 Crown cone 1·75 2·75
1361 $3 Common dove shell 2·50 3·50
1362 $4 Common or Atlantic fig shell 2·75 3·50
MS1363 Two sheets, each 103 × 70 mm. (a) $5 King helmet. (b) $6 Giant tun Set of 2 sheets 6·50 8·00

1990. Birds. Multicoloured.
1364 10c. Type **244** 35 35
1365 20c. Black-capped petrel 45 45
1366 45c. Red-necked amazon ("Red-necked Parrot") 65 40
1367 60c. Black swift 80 70
1368 $1 Troupial 1·25 1·25
1369 $2 Common noddy ("Brown Noddy") 2·00 2·50
1370 $4 Lesser Antillean pewee 3·25 3·50
1371 $5 Little blue heron 3·75 4·25
MS1372 Two sheets, each 103 × 70 mm. (a) $6 Imperial amazon. (b) $6 House wren Set of 2 sheets 7·00 8·50

1990. 90th Birthday of Queen Elizabeth the Queen Mother. As T **266** of Antigua.
1373 20c. multicoloured 20 15
1374 45c. multicoloured 35 25
1375 60c. multicoloured 60 60
1376 $3 multicoloured 2·25 3·00
MS1377 80 × 90 mm. $5 multicoloured 2·75 3·75
DESIGNS: 20c. to $5, Recent photographs of Queen Mother.

1990. Olympic Games, Barcelona (1992) (1st issue). As T **268** of Antigua. Multicoloured.
1378 45c. Tennis 1·25 40
1379 60c. Fencing 1·25 50
1380 $2 Swimming 2·00 3·25
1381 $3 Yachting 2·50 3·75
MS1382 100 × 70 mm. $5 Boxing 4·25 6·00
See also Nos. 1603/11.

245 Barnes, England

1990. World Cup Football Championship, Italy (2nd issue). Multicoloured.
1383 15c. Type **245** 40 30
1384 45c. Romario, Brazil 70 30

1385 60c. Franz Beckenbauer, West Germany manager . . 85 70
1386 $4 Lindenberger, Austria . . 3·25 5·00
MS1387 Two sheets, each 105 × 90 mm. (a) $6 McGrath, Ireland (vert). (b) $6 Litovchenko, Soviet Union (vert) Set of 2 sheets 7·50 10·00

246 Mickey Mouse riding Herschell-Spillman Frog

1990. Christmas. Walt Disney cartoon characters and American carousel animals. Multicoloured.
1388 10c. Type **246** 40 20
1389 15c. Huey, Dewey and Louie on Allan Herschell elephant 50 25
1390 25c. Donald Duck on Allan Herschell polar bear . . . 60 30
1391 45c. Goofy on Dentzel goat 90 30
1392 $1 Donald Duck on Zalar giraffe . . . . 1·25 1·00
1393 $2 Daisy Duck on Herschell-Spillman stork 2·00 2·75
1394 $4 Goofy on Dentzel lion 3·25 4·50
1395 $5 Daisy Duck on Stein and Goldstein palomino stander . . . . 3·50 4·50
MS1396 Two sheets, each 127 × 101 mm. (a) $6 Mickey, Morty and Ferdie Mouse on Philadelphia Toboggan Company swan chariot (horiz). (b) $6 Mickey and Minnie Mouse with Goofy on Philadelphia Toboggan Company winged griffin chariot Set of 2 sheets . . . . 12·00 14·00

1991. Cog Railways. As T **275** of Antigua. Mult.
1397 10c. Steam locomotive, Glion-Roches De Naye rack railway, 1890 . . . . 65 40
1398 35c. Electric railcar, Mt. Pilatus rack railway . . . 1·00 30
1399 45c. Schynige Platte rack railway train . . . . . . 1·10 30
1400 60c. Steam train on Bugnli Viaduct, Furka–Oberalp rack railway (vert) . . . . 1·40 55
1401 $1 Jungfrau rack railway train, 1910 . . . . 1·75 1·25
1402 $2 Testing Pike's Peak railcar, Switzerland, 1983 2·25 2·25
1403 $4 Brienz–Rothorn railway locomotive, 1991 . . . . 2·75 3·25
1404 $5 Steam locomotive, Arth-Rigi, 1890 . . . . 2·75 3·25
MS1405 Two sheets. (a) 100 × 70 mm. $6 Swiss Europa stamps of 1983 showing Riggenbach's locomotive of 1871 (50 × 37 mm). (b) 90 × 68 mm. $6 Brunig line train and Sherlock Holmes (50 × 37 mm) Set of 2 sheets . . . . 9·50 10·00

1991. 500th Anniv (1992) of Discovery of America by Columbus (4th issue). History of Exploration. As T **277** of Antigua. Multicoloured.
1406 10c. Gil Eannes sailing south of Cape Bojador, 1433–34 . . . . 25 25
1407 25c. Alfonso Baldaya sailing south to Cape Blanc, 1436 35 35
1408 45c. Bartolomeu Dias in Table Bay, 1487 . . . . 45 35
1409 60c. Vasco da Gama on voyage to India, 1497–99 55 50
1410 $1 Vallarte the Dane off African coast 75 90
1411 $2 Aloisio Cadamosto in Cape Verde Islands, 1456–58 . . . . 1·40 2·00
1412 $4 Diogo Gomes on River Gambia, 1457 . . . . . 2·75 3·75
1413 $5 Diogo Cao off African coast, 1482–85 . . . . . 3·25 4·00
MS1414 Two sheets, each 105 × 71 mm. (a) $6 Green-winged macaw and bow of "Santa Maria". (b) $6 Blue and yellow macaw and caravel Set of 2 sheets 7·50 8·50

1991. "Phila Nippon '91" International Stamp Exhibition, Tokyo. As T **279** of Antigua. Mult.
1415 10c. Donald Duck as Shogun's guard (horiz) . . 60 20
1416 15c. Mickey Mouse as Kabuki actor (horiz) . . . 70 25
1417 25c. Minnie and Mickey Mouse as bride and groom (horiz) 85 25
1418 45c. Daisy Duck as geisha 1·00 25
1419 $1 Mickey Mouse in Sokutai court dress . . . 2·00 1·00
1420 $2 Goofy as Mino farmer 2·50 2·75
1421 $4 Pete as Shogun . . . . . 3·75 4·00
1422 $5 Donald Duck as Samurai (horiz) . . . . 3·75 4·25
MS1423 Two sheets, each 127 × 112 mm. (a) $6 Mickey Mouse as Noh actor. (b) $6 Goofy as Kabubei-jishi dancer Set of 2 sheets . . . . 13·00 14·00

247 "Craterellus cornucopioides"

248 Empire State Building, New York

1991. Fungi. Multicoloured.
1424 10c. Type **247** 25 25
1425 15c. "Coprinus comatus" . . 50 25
1426 45c. "Morchella esculenta" 50 25
1427 60c. "Cantharellus cibarius" 60 30
1428 $1 "Lepista nuda" 80 70
1429 $2 "Suillus luteus" . . . . 1·40 1·75
1430 $4 "Russula emetica" . . . 2·25 2·75
1431 $5 "Armillaria mellea" . . . 2·25 2·75
MS1432 Two sheets, each 100 × 70 mm. (a) $6 "Fistulina hepatica". (b) $6 "Lactarius volemus" Set of 2 sheets . . . 8·00 9·00

1991. 65th Birthday of Queen Elizabeth II. As T **280** of Antigua. Multicoloured.
1433 10c. Queen and Prince William on Buckingham Palace Balcony, 1990 . . 55 20
1434 60c. The Queen at Westminster Abbey, 1988 1·00 50
1435 $2 The Queen and Prince Philip in Italy, 1990 . . . 1·75 2·00
1436 $5 The Queen at Ascot, 1986 . . . . 3·25 3·50
MS1437 68 × 90 mm. $5 Separate portraits of Queen and Prince Philip . . . . 5·00 5·50

1991. 10th Wedding Anniv of Prince and Princess of Wales. As T **280** of Antigua. Multicoloured.
1438 15c. Prince and Princess of Wales in West Germany, 1987 . . . . 1·25 35
1439 40c. Separate photographs of Prince, Princess and sons . . . . 1·75 35
1440 $1 Separate photographs of Prince William and Prince Henry . . . . 1·75 1·25
1441 $4 Prince Charles at Caister and Princess Diana in Thailand . . . . 5·00 5·00
MS1442 68 × 90 mm. $5 Prince Charles, and Princess Diana with sons on holiday . . . . 4·50 5·00

1991. Death Centenary (1990) of Vincent van Gogh (artist). As T **278** of Antigua. Multicoloured.
1443 10c. "Thatched Cottages" (horiz) 60 30
1444 25c. "The House of Pere Eloi" (horiz) 80 30
1445 45c. "The Midday Siesta" (horiz) 95 30
1446 60c. "Portrait of a Young Peasant" . . . . 1·25 35
1447 $1 "Still Life: Vase with Irises against Yellow Background" . . . . . . 1·75 1·00
1448 $2 "Still Life: Vase with Irises" (horiz) . . . . 2·25 2·50
1449 $4 "Blossoming Almond Tree" (horiz) . . . . . . 3·00 3·50
1450 $5 "Irises" (horiz) . . . . . 3·00 3·50
MS1451 Two sheets. (a) 77 × 102 mm. $6 "Doctor Gachet's Garden in Auvers". (b) 102 × 77 mm. $6 "A Meadow in the Mountains: Le Mas de Saint-Paul" (horiz). Imperf Set of 2 sheets . . . . 10·00 11·00

1991. International Literacy Year (1990). Scenes from Disney cartoon film "The Little Mermaid". As T **269** of Antigua. Multicoloured.
1452 10c. Ariel, Flounder and Sebastian (horiz) 30 25
1453 25c. King Triton (horiz) . . 45 30
1454 45c. Sebastian playing drums (horiz) 60 30
1455 60c. Flotsam and Jetsam taunting Ariel (horiz) . . 85 55
1456 $1 Scuttle, Flounder and Ariel with pipe (horiz) . . 1·25 1·00
1457 $2 Ariel and Flounder discovering book (horiz) 2·00 2·00
1458 $4 Prince Eric and crew (horiz) . . . . 3·25 3·50
1459 $5 Ursula the Sea Witch (horiz) . . . . 3·50 4·00
MS1460 Two sheets, each 127 × 102 mm. $6 Ariel without tail (horiz). (b) $6 Ariel and Prince Eric dancing Set of 2 sheets . . 8·50 10·00

1991. World Landmarks. Multicoloured.
1461 10c. Type **248** 40 30
1462 25c. Kremlin, Moscow (horiz) 40 30
1463 45c. Buckingham Palace, London (horiz) 70 30
1464 60c. Eiffel Tower, Paris . . 85 60
1465 $1 Taj Mahal, Agra (horiz) 3·25 1·75
1466 $2 Opera House, Sydney (horiz) . . . . 4·50 3·25
1467 $4 Colosseum, Rome (horiz) 3·75 4·25
1468 $5 Pyramids, Giza (horiz) 4·25 4·50
MS1469 Two sheets, each 100 × 68 mm. (a) $6 Galileo on Leaning Tower, Pisa (horiz). (b) $6 Emperor Shi Huang and Great Wall of China (horiz) Set of 2 sheets . . . . 13·00 14·00

249 Japanese Aircraft leaving Carrier "Akagi"

1991. 50th Anniv of Japanese Attack on Pearl Harbor. Multicoloured.
1470 10c. Type **249** 25 25
1471 15c. U.S.S. "Ward" (destroyer) and Consolidated Catalina flying boat attacking midget submarine 30 25
1472 45c. Second wave of Mitsubishi A6M Zero-Sen aircraft leaving carriers . . 50 25
1473 60c. Japanese Mitsubishi M6M Zero-Sen aircraft attacking Kaneche naval airfield 60 30
1474 $1 U.S.S. "Breeze", "Medusa" and "Curtiss" (destroyers) sinking midget submarine 80 70
1475 $2 U.S.S. "Nevada" (battleship) under attack 1·40 1·50
1476 $4 U.S.S. "Arizona" (battleship) sinking . . . 2·25 2·50
1477 $5 Mitsubishi A6M Zero-Sen aircraft . . . . 2·25 2·50
MS1478 Two sheets, each 118 × 78 mm. (a) $6 Mitsubishi A6M Zero-Sen over anchorage. (b) $6 Mitsubishi A6M Zero-Sen attacking Hickam airfield Set of 2 sheets . . . . 7·50 8·50

250 "Eurema venusta"

251 Symbolic Cheque

1991. Butterflies. Multicoloured.
1479 1c. Type **250** 40 80
1480 2c. "Agraulis vanillae" . . 40 80
1481 5c. "Danaus plexippus" . . 60 80
1482 10c. "Biblis hyperia" . . . 60 15
1483 15c. "Dryas julia" 70 15
1484 20c. "Phoebis agarithe" . . 70 20
1485 25c. "Junonia genoveva" 70 20
1486 35c. "Battus polydamas" 80 30
1487 45c. "Leptotes cassius" . . 80 30
1487a 55c. "Ascia monuste" . . 1·00 55
1488 60c. "Anaea dominicana" 80 35
1488a 65c. "Hemiargus hanno" 85 55
1489 90c. "Hypolimnas misippus" . . . . 1·00 55
1490 $1 "Urbanus proteus" . . 1·00 60
1490a $1.20 "Historis odius" . . 1·10 1·50
1491 $2 "Phoebis sennae" . . . 1·75 2·00
1492 $5 "Cynthia cardui" ("Vanessa cardui") . . . 2·75 4·50
1493 $10 "Marpesia petreus" . . 5·00 7·00
1494 $20 "Anartia jatrophae" 9·50 12·00

1991. Birth Centenary (1990) of Charles De Gaulle (French statesman). As T **283** of Antigua.
1495 45c. brown . . . . 1·75 75
MS1496 70 × 100 mm. $5 brown and blue . . . . 4·75 5·50
DESIGN—VERT: 45c. De Gaulle in uniform.

1992. 40th Anniv of Credit Union Bank.
1497 **251** 10c. grey and black . . . 30 20
1498 – 60c. multicoloured . . . 1·25 80
DESIGN—HORIZ: 60c. Credit Union symbol.

252 "18th-Century Creole Dress" (detail) (Agostino Brunias)

254 Cricket Match

253 Island Beach

1991. Creole Week. Multicoloured.
1499 45c. Type **252** 80 25
1500 60c. Jing Ping band . . . . 1·00 60
1501 $1 Creole dancers . . . . . 1·40 1·90
MS1502 100 × 70 mm. $5 "18th-century Stick-fighting Match" (detail) (Agostino Brunias) (horiz) . . . . 4·25 6·00

1991. Year of Environment and Shelter. Mult.
1503 15c. Type **253** 15 15
1504 60c. Imperial amazon . . . 3·00 1·50
MS1505 Two sheets. (a) 100 × 70 mm. $5 River estuary. (b) 70 × 100 mm. $5 As 60c. Set of 2 sheets . . . . 13·00 14·00

1991. Christmas. Religious Paintings by Jan van Eyck. As T **287** of Antigua. Multicoloured.
1506 10c. "Virgin Enthroned with Child" (detail) 70 30
1507 20c. "Madonna at the Fountain" 85 30
1508 35c. "Virgin in a Church" 1·00 30
1509 45c. "Madonna with Canon van der Paele" . . . . . 1·10 30
1510 60c. "Madonna with Canon van der Paele" (detail) . . 1·75 60
1511 $1 "Madonna in an Interior" . . . . 2·00 1·00
1512 $3 "The Annunciation" . . 3·25 4·50
1513 $5 "The Annunciation" (different) . . . . 4·50 7·00
MS1514 Two sheets, each 102 × 127 mm. (a) $5 "Virgin and Child with Saints and Donor". (b) $5 "Madonna with Chancellor Rolin" Set of 2 sheets . . . . 12·00 13·00

1992. 40th Anniv of Queen Elizabeth II's Accession. As T **288** of Antigua. Multicoloured.
1515 10c. Coastline 10 10
1516 15c. Mountains overlooking small village 10 10
1517 $1 River estuary 70 70
1518 $5 Waterfall . . . . 3·50 3·75
MS1519 Two sheets, each 74 × 97 mm. (a) $6 Roseau. (b) $6 Mountain stream Set of 2 sheets 8·00 8·50

1992. Centenary (1991) of Botanical Gardens. Multicoloured.
1520 10c. Type **254** . . . . . . 1·50 70
1521 15c. Scenic entrance 40 20
1522 45c. Traveller's tree 40 25
1523 60c. Bamboo House 55 30
1524 $1 The Old Pavilion 80 70
1525 $2 "Ficus benjamina" . . . 1·40 2·00
1526 $4 Cricket match (different) 4·50 3·75
1527 $5 Thirty-five Steps . . . . 3·00 3·75
MS1528 Two sheets, each 104 × 71 mm. (a) $6 Past and present members of national cricket team. (b) $6 The Fountain Set of 2 sheets . . . . 7·00 8·00

1992. Easter. Religious Paintings. As T **291** of Antigua. Multicoloured.
1529 10c. "The Supper at Emmaus" (Van Honthorst) 20 20
1530 15c. "Christ before Caiaphas" (Van Honthorst) (vert) 25 25
1531 45c. "The Taking of Christ" (De Boulogne) 40 30
1532 60c. "Pilate washing his Hands" (Preti) (vert) . . . 55 45
1533 $1 "The Last Supper" (detail) (Master of the Church of S. Francisco d'Evora) 75 75
1534 $2 "The Three Marys at the Tomb" (detail) (Bouguereau) (vert) . . . 1·50 2·00

1535 $3 "Denial of St. Peter" (Terbrugghen) 1·75 2·50
1536 $5 "Doubting Thomas" (Strozzi) 2·75 3·75
MS1537 Two sheets, each 72 × 102 mm. (a) $6 "The Crucifixion" (detail) (Grünewald) (vert). (b) $6 "The Resurrection" (detail) (Caravaggio) (vert) Set of 2 sheets 7·00 8·50

1992. "Granada '92" International Stamp Exhibition, Spain. Art of Diego Rodriguez Velasquez. As T **292** of Antigua. Mult.
1538 10c. "Pope Innocent X" (detail) 15 10
1539 15c. "The Forge of Vulcan" (detail) 20 10
1540 45c. "The Forge of Vulcan" (different detail) 40 25
1541 60c. "Queen Mariana of Austria" (detail) 50 30
1542 $1 "Pablo de Valladolid" 80 70
1543 $2 "Sebastian de Morra" 1·25 1·60
1544 $3 "King Felipe IV" (detail) 1·60 2·25
1545 $4 "King Felipe IV" 1·75 2·40
MS1546 Two sheets, each 120 × 95 mm. (a) $6 "The Drunkards" (110 × 81 mm). (b) $6 "Surrender of Breda" (110 × 81 mm). Imperf Set of 2 sheets 6·50 7·00

255 Columbus and "Dynastes hercules" (beetle)

1992. 500th Anniv of Discovery of America by Columbus (5th issue). World Columbian Stamp "Expo '92", Chicago. Multicoloured.
1547 10c. Type **255** 50 30
1548 25c. Columbus and "Leptodactylus fallax" (frog) 90 25
1549 75c. Columbus and red-necked amazon (bird) 2·50 1·00
1550 $2 Columbus and "Ameiva fuscata" (lizard) 2·25 2·25
1551 $4 Columbus and royal gramma (fish) 2·50 3·25
1552 $5 Columbus and "Rosa sinensis" (flower) 2·50 3·25
MS1553 Two sheets, each 100 × 67 mm. (a) $6 Ships of Columbus (horiz). (b) $6 "Mastophyllum scabricolle" (katydid) (horiz) Set of 2 sheets 6·50 7·50

1992. "Genova '92" International Thematic Stamp Exhibition. Hummingbirds. As T **295** of Antigua. Multicoloured.
1554 10c. Female purple-throated carib 70 25
1555 15c. Female rufous-breasted hermit 70 25
1556 45c. Male Puerto Rican emerald 1·00 30
1557 60c. Female Antillean mango 1·25 45
1558 $1 Male green-throated carib 1·75 85
1559 $2 Male blue-headed hummingbird 2·25 2·25
1560 $4 Female eastern streamertail 2·75 3·00
1561 $5 Female Antillean crested hummingbird 3·00 3·25
MS1562 Two sheets, each 105 × 72 mm. (a) $6 Jamaican Mango ("Green Mango"). (b) $6 Vervain hummingbird Set of 2 sheets 10·00 11·00

1992. Prehistoric Animals. As T **290** of Antigua, but horiz. Multicoloured.
1563 10c. Head of Camptosaurus 70 30
1564 15c. Edmontosaurus 75 30
1565 25c. Corythosaurus 85 30
1566 60c. Stegosaurus 1·50 40
1567 $1 Torosaurus 1·75 85
1568 $3 Euoplocephalus 2·50 2·75
1569 $4 Tyrannosaurus 2·75 3·00
1570 $5 Parasaurolophus 2·75 3·00
MS1571 Two sheets, each 100 × 70 mm. (a) $6 As 25c. (b) $6 As $1 Set of 2 sheets 7·50 8·50

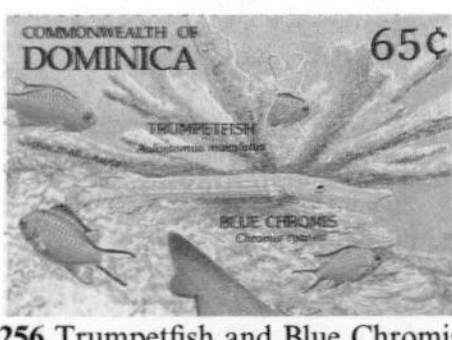

256 Trumpetfish and Blue Chromis

1992. Marine Life. Multicoloured.
1572/1601 65c. × 30. As Type **256** 14·00 15·00
MS1602 Two sheets, each 73 × 105 mm. (a) $6 multicoloured (Harlequin bass). (b) $6 multicoloured (Flamefish) Set of 2 sheets 9·50 11·00

1992. Olympic Games, Barcelona (2nd issue). As T **268** of Antigua. Multicoloured.
1603 10c. Archery 30 25
1604 15c. Two-man canoeing 35 25
1605 25c. Men's 110 m hurdles 40 25
1606 60c. Men's high jump 70 30
1607 $1 Greco-Roman wrestling 1·00 65
1608 $2 Men's gymnastics—rings 1·50 2·00
1609 $4 Men's gymnastics—parallel bars 2·75 3·25
1610 $5 Equestrian dressage 3·50 3·50
MS1611 Two sheets, each 100 × 70 mm. (a) $6 Women's platform diving. (b) $6 Men's hockey Set of 2 sheets 7·50 9·00

1992. 500th Anniv of Discovery of America by Columbus (6th issue). Organization of East Caribbean States. As Nos. 1670/1 of Antigua. Multicoloured.
1612 $1 Columbus meeting Amerindians 65 65
1613 $2 Ships approaching island 1·10 1·25

1992. Hummel Figurines. As T **302** of Antigua. Multicoloured.
1614 20c. Angel playing violin 40 15
1615 25c. Angel playing recorder 40 15
1616 55c. Angel playing lute 65 30
1617 65c. Seated angel playing trumpet 75 35
1618 90c. Angel on cloud with lantern 1·00 65
1619 $1 Angel with candle 1·10 70
1620 $1.20 Flying angel with Christmas tree 1·25 1·25
1621 $6 Angel on cloud with candle 3·75 6·00
MS1622 Two sheets, each 97 × 127 mm. (a) Nos. 1614/17. (b) Nos. 1618/21 Set of 2 sheets 7·50 8·50

257 Brass "Reno" Locomotive, Japan (1963)

1992. Toy Trains from Far Eastern Manufacturers. Multicoloured.
1623 15c. Type **257** 65 35
1624 25c. Union Pacific "Golden Classic" locomotive, China (1992) 75 35
1625 55c. L.M.S. third class brake carriage, Hong Kong (1970s) 1·25 40
1626 65c. Brass Wabash locomotive, Japan (1958) 1·40 50
1627 75c. Pennsylvania "Duplex" type locomotive, Korea (1991) 1·50 1·00
1628 $1 Streamlined locomotive, Japan (post 1945) 1·60 1·00
1629 $3 Japanese National Railways Class "C62" locomotive, Japan (1960) 2·50 3·00
1630 $5 Tinplate friction driven trains, Japan (1960s) 3·00 3·75
MS1631 Two sheets, each 119 × 87 mm. (a) $6 "Rocket's" tender, Japan (1972) (multicoloured) (51½ × 40 mm). (b) $6 American model steam train presented to Emperor of Japan, 1854 (black, blackish olive and flesh) (40 × 51½ mm). Set of 2 sheets 9·00 9·00

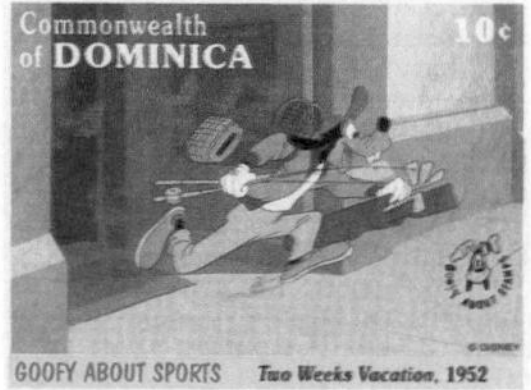

258 Goofy in "Two Weeks Vacation", 1952

1992. 60th Anniv of Goofy (Disney cartoon character). Designs showing sports from cartoon films. Multicoloured.
1632 10c. Type **258** 70 30
1633 15c. "Aquamania", 1961 80 30
1634 25c. "Goofy Gymnastics", 1949 95 20
1635 45c. "How to Ride a Horse", 1941 1·25 25
1636 $1 "Foul Hunting", 1947 2·00 85
1637 $2 "For Whom the Bulls Toil", 1953 2·75 3·00
1638 $4 "Tennis Racquet", 1949 3·50 4·00
1639 $5 "Double Dribble", 1946 3·50 4·00
MS1640 Two sheets, each 128 × 102 mm. (a) $6 "The Goofy Sports Story", 1956 (vert). (b) $6 "Aquamania", 1961 (different) (vert) Set of 2 sheets 11·00 12·00

259 "Graf Zeppelin", 1929

260 Elvis Presley

1992. Anniversaries and Events. Multicoloured.
1641 25c. Type **259** 60 30
1642 45c. Elderly man on bike 60 30
1643 45c. Elderly man with seedling 40 30
1644 45c. Elderly man and young boy fishing 40 30
1645 90c. Space Shuttle "Atlantis" 1·00 60
1646 90c. Konrad Adenauer (German statesman) 60 60
1647 $1.20 Sir Thomas Lipton and "Shamrock N" (yacht) 1·50 1·50
1648 $1.20 Snowy egret (bird) 1·75 1·50
1649 $1.20 Wolfgang Amadeus Mozart 2·50 1·50
1650 $2 Pulling fishing net ashore 1·75 2·00
1651 $3 Helen Keller (lecturer) 2·25 2·75
1652 $4 Eland (antelope) 3·50 3·75
1653 $4 Map of Allied Zones of Occupation, Germany, 1949 3·50 3·75
1654 $4 Earth resources satellite 3·50 3·75
1655 $5 Count von Zeppelin 3·50 3·75
MS1656 Five sheets. (a) 100 × 70 mm. $6 Airship propeller. (b) 100 × 70 mm. $6 "Mir" Russian space station with "Soyuz". (c) 70 × 100 mm. $6 Cologne Cathedral. (d) 100 × 70 mm. $6 Rhinoceros hornbill (bird). (e) 100 × 70 mm. $6 Monostatos from "The Magic Flute" Set of 5 sheets 22·00 23·00

ANNIVERSARIES AND EVENTS: Nos. 1641, 1655, **MS**1656a, 75th death anniv of Count Ferdinand von Zeppelin; 1642/4, International Day of the Elderly; 1645, 1654, **MS**1656b, International Space Year; 1646, 1653, **MS**1656c, 25th death anniv of Konrad Adenauer; 1647, Americas Cup Yachting Championship; 1648, 1652, **MS**1656d, Earth Summit '92, Rio; 1649, **MS**1656e, Death bicent of Mozart; 1650, International Conference on Nutrition, Rome; 1651, 75th anniv of International Association of Lions Clubs.

No. **MS**1656b is inscribed "M.I.R." and No. **MS**1656d "Rhinocerus Hornbill", both in error.

1993. Bicentenary of the Louvre, Paris. As T **305** of Antigua. Multicoloured.
1657 $1 "Madonna and Child with St. Catherine and a Rabbit" (left detail) (Titian) 70 70
1658 $1 "Madonna and Child with St. Catherine and a Rabbit" (right detail) (Titian) 70 70
1659 $1 "Woman at her Toilet" (Titian) 70 70
1660 $1 "The Supper at Emmaus" (left detail) (Titian) 70 70
1661 $1 "The Supper at Emmaus" (right detail) (Titian) 70 70
1662 $1 "The Pastoral Concert" (Titian) 70 70
1663 $1 "An Allegory, perhaps of Marriage" (detail) (Titian) 70 70
1664 $1 "An Allegory, perhaps of Marriage" (different detail) (Titian) 70 70
MS1665 70 × 100 mm. $6 "The Ship of Fools" (Bosch) (52 × 85 mm) 4·00 4·50

1993. 15th Death Anniv of Elvis Presley (singer). Multicoloured.
1666 $1 Type **260** 1·10 90
1667 $1 Elvis with guitar 1·10 90
1668 $1 Elvis with microphone 1·10 90

261 Plumbeous Warbler

1993. Birds. Multicoloured.
1669 90c. Type **261** 1·25 1·25
1670 90c. Black swift 1·25 1·25
1671 90c. Blue-hooded euphonia 1·25 1·25
1672 90c. Rufous-throated solitaire 1·25 1·25
1673 90c. Ringed kingfisher 1·25 1·25
1674 90c. Blue-headed hummingbird 1·25 1·25
1675 90c. Bananaquit 1·25 1·25
1676 90c. Brown trembler ("Trembler") 1·25 1·25
1677 90c. Forest thrush 1·25 1·25
1678 90c. Purple-throated carib 1·25 1·25
1679 90c. Ruddy quail dove 1·25 1·25
1680 90c. Least bittern 1·25 1·25
MS1681 Two sheets, each 100 × 70 mm. (a) $6 Imperial amazon. (b) $6 Red-necked amazon Set of 2 sheets 9·50 9·50

Nos. 1669/80 were printed together, se-tenant, forming a composite design.

262 School Crest

1993. Cent of Dominica Grammar School. Mult.
1682 25c. Type **262** 20 15
1683 30c. V. Archer (first West Indian headmaster) 25 20
1684 65c. Hubert Charles (first Dominican headmaster) 45 50
1685 90c. Present school buildings 65 80

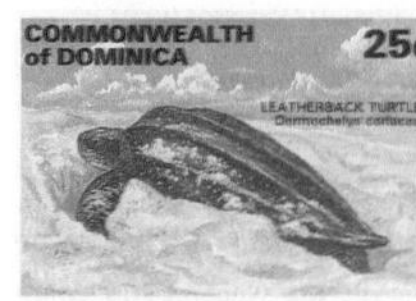

263 Leatherback Turtle on Beach

1993. Turtles. Multicoloured.
1686 25c. Type **263** 50 15
1687 55c. Hawksbill turtle swimming 70 40
1688 65c. Atlantic ridley turtle 80 50
1689 90c. Green turtle laying eggs 1·00 70
1690 $1 Green turtle swimming 1·00 70
1691 $2 Hawksbill turtle swimming (different) 1·50 2·00
1692 $4 Loggerhead turtle 2·25 3·00
1693 $5 Leatherback turtle swimming 2·25 3·00
MS1694 Two sheets, each 99 × 70 mm. (a) $6 Green turtle hatchling. (b) $6 Head of hawksbill turtle Set of 2 sheets 8·50 10·00

264 Ford "Model A", 1928

1993. Centenaries of Henry Ford's First Petrol Engine (90c., $5) and Karl Benz's First Four-wheeled Car (others). Multicoloured.
1695 90c. Type **264** 75 45
1696 $1.20 Mercedes Benz car winning Swiss Grand Prix, 1936 1·00 55
1697 $4 Mercedes Benz car winning German Grand Prix, 1935 2·50 3·25
1698 $5 Ford "Model T", 1915 2·50 3·25
MS1699 Two sheets, each 99 × 70 mm. (a) $3 Benz "Viktoria", 1893; $3 Mercedes Benz sports coupe, 1993. (b) $6 Ford "G.T.40", Le Mans, 1966 (57½ × 48 mm) Set of 2 sheets 7·50 8·50

1993. 40th Anniv of Coronation. As T **307** of Antigua.
1700 20c. multicoloured 60 75
1701 25c. brown and black 60 75
1702 65c. multicoloured 85 1·00
1703 $5 multicoloured 4·25 4·50
MS1704 71 × 101 mm. $6 multicoloured 6·50 7·00

DESIGNS: 20c. Queen Elizabeth II at Coronation (photograph by Cecil Beaton); 25c. Queen wearing King Edward's Crown during Coronation ceremony; 65c. Coronation coach; $5 Queen and Queen Mother in carriage. (28½ × 42½ mm)—$6 "Queen Elizabeth II, 1969" (detail) (Norman Hutchinson).

265 New G.P.O. and Duke of Edinburgh

1993. Anniversaries and Events. Each brown, deep brown and black (Nos. 1707, 1717) or multicoloured (others).
1705 25c. Type **265** 30 25
1706 25c. "Bather with Beach Ball" (Picasso) (vert) 30 25
1707 65c. Willy Brandt and Pres. Eisenhower, 1959 35 35

1708 90c. As Type **265** but portrait of Queen Elizabeth II 60 45
1709 90c. "Portrait of Leo Stein" (Picasso) (vert) 60 45
1710 90c. Monika Holzner (Germany) (speed skating) (vert) 60 45
1711 90c. "Self-portrait" (Marian Szczyrbula) (vert) 60 45
1712 90c. Prince Naruhito and engagement photographs 60 45
1713 $1.20 16th-century telescope (vert) 85 70
1714 $3 "Bruno Jasienski" (Tytus Czyzewski) (vert) 1·75 2·25
1715 $3 Modern observatory (vert) 2·00 2·25
1716 $4 Ray Leblanc and Tim Sweeney (U.S.A.) (ice hockey) (vert) 2·50 2·75
1717 $5 "Wilhelm Unde" (Picasso) (vert) 2·25 3·00
1718 $5 Willy Brandt and N. K. Winston at World's Fair, 1964 2·25 3·00
1719 $5 Masako Owada and engagement photographs 2·25 3·00
1720 $5 Pres. Clinton and wife applauding 2·25 3·00
MS1721 Seven sheets, each 105 × 75 mm (a, c and f) or 75 × 105 mm (others). (a) $5 Copernicus (vert). (b) $6 "Man with Pipe" (detail) (Picasso) (vert). (c) $6 Willy Brandt, 1972. (d) $6 Toni Nieminen (FInland) (120 metre ski jump) (vert). (e) $6 "Miser" (detail) (Tadeusz Makowski) (vert). (f) $6 Masako Owada (vert). (g) $6 Pres. W. Clinton (vert) Set of 7 sheets 20·00 23·00

ANNIVERSARIES AND EVENTS: Nos. 1705, 1708, Opening of New General Post Office Building; 1706, 1709, 1717, **MS**1721b, 20th death anniv of Picasso (artist); 1707, 1718, **MS**1721c, 80th birth anniv of Willy Brandt (German politician); 1710, 1716, **MS**1721d, Winter Olympic Games '94, Lillehammer; 1711, 1714, **MS**1721e, "Polska '93" International Stamp Exhibition, Poznan; 1712, 1719, **MS**1721f, Marriage of Crown Prince Naruhito of Japan; 1713, 1715, **MS**1721a, 450th death anniv of Copernicus (astronomer); 1720, **MS**1721g, Inauguration of U.S. President William Clinton.

No. 1714 is inscribed "Tyrus" in error.

266 Hugo Eckener in New York Parade, 1928

1993. Aviation Anniversaries. Multicoloured.
1722 25c. Type **266** 90 30
1723 55c. English Electric Lightning F.2 (fighter) 1·75 40
1724 65c. Airship "Graf Zeppelin" over Egypt, 1929 1·75 55
1725 $1 Boeing 314A (flying boat) on transatlantic mail flight 1·75 85
1726 $2 Astronaut carrying mail to the Moon 2·50 2·75
1727 $4 Airship "Viktoria Luise" over Kiel harbour, 1912 3·50 4·00
1728 $5 Supermarine Spitfire (vert) 3·50 4·00
MS1729 Three sheets, each 99 × 70 mm. (a) $6 Hugo Eckener (42½ × 57 mm). (b) $6 Royal Air Force crest (42½ × 57 mm). (c) $6 Jean-Pierre Blanchard's hot air balloon, 1793 (vert) Set of 3 sheets 12·00 12·00

ANNIVERSARIES: Nos. 1722, 1724, 1727, **MS**1729a, 125th birth anniv of Hugo Eckener (airship commander); 1723, 1728, **MS**1729b, 75th anniv of Royal Air Force; 1725/6, **MS**1729c, Bicentenary of first airmail flight.

267 Maradona (Argentina) and Buchwald (Germany)

268 Ornate Chedi, Wat Phra Boromathat Chaiya

1993. World Cup Football Championship, U.S.A. (1994) (1st issue). Multicoloured.
1730 25c. Type **267** 80 20
1731 55c. Ruud Gullit (Netherlands) 1·10 40
1732 65c. Chavarria (Costa Rica) and Bliss (U.S.A.) 1·10 45
1733 90c. Diego Maradona (Argentina) 1·60 90
1734 90c. Leonel Alvares (Colombia) 1·60 90
1735 $1 Altobelli (Italy) and Yong-hwang (South Korea) 1·60 90
1736 $2 Stopyra (France) 2·75 2·75
1737 $5 Renquin (Belgium) and Yaremtchuk (Russia) 3·75 4·50
MS1738 Two sheets. (a) 73 × 103 mm. $6 Nestor Fabbri (Argentina). (b) 103 × 73 mm. $6 Andreas Brehme (Germany) Set of 2 sheets 7·50 8·50

See also Nos. 1849/56.

1993. Asian International Stamp Exhibitions. Multicoloured. (a) "Indopex '93", Surabaya, Indonesia.
1739 25c. Type **268** 30 30
1740 55c. Temple ruins, Sukhothai 50 30
1741 90c. Prasat Hin Phimai, Thailand 70 45
1742 $1.65 Arjuna and Prabu Gilling Wesi puppets 1·00 1·00
1743 $1.65 Loro Blonyo puppet 1·00 1·00
1744 $1.65 Yogyanese puppets 1·00 1·00
1745 $1.65 Wayang gedog puppet, Ng Setro 1·00 1·00
1746 $1.65 Wayang golek puppet 1·00 1·00
1747 $1.65 Wayang gedog puppet, Raden Damar Wulan 1·00 1·00
1748 $5 Main sanctuary, Prasat Phanom Rung, Thailand 2·25 2·50
MS1749 105 × 136 mm. $6 Sculpture of Majaphit noble, Pura Sada 3·25 3·75

(b) "Taipei '93", Taiwan.
1750 25c. Aw Boon Haw Gardens, Causeway Bay 30 30
1751 65c. Observation building, Kenting Park 50 30
1752 90c. Tzu-en pagoda on lakeshore, Taiwan 70 45
1753 $1.65 Chang E kite 1·00 1·00
1754 $1.65 Red Phoenix and Rising Sun kite 1·00 1·00
1755 $1.65 Heavenly Judge kite 1·00 1·00
1756 $1.65 Monkey King kite 1·00 1·00
1757 $1.65 Goddess of Luo River kite 1·00 1·00
1758 $1.65 Heavenly Maiden kite 1·00 1·00
1759 $5 Villa, Lantau Island 2·25 2·50
MS1760 105 × 136 mm. $6 Jade sculpture of girl, Liao Dynasty 3·25 3·75

(c) "Bangkok '93", Thailand.
1761 25c. Tugu Monument, Java 30 30
1762 55c. Candi Cangkuang mon, West Java 50 30
1763 90c. Merus, Pura Taman Ayun, Mengwi 70 45
1764 $1.65 Hun Lek puppets of Rama and Sita 1·00 1·00
1765 $1.65 Burmese puppet 1·00 1·00
1766 $1.65 Burmese puppets 1·00 1·00
1767 $1.65 Demon puppet at Wat Phra Kaew 1·00 1·00
1768 $1.65 Hun Lek puppet performing Khun Chang 1·00 1·00
1769 $1.65 Hun Lek puppets performing Ramakien 1·00 1·00
1770 $5 Stone mosaic, Ceto 2·25 2·50
MS1771 105 × 136 mm. $6 Thai stone carving 3·25 3·75

No. 1753 is inscribed "Chang E Rising Up th the Moon" in error.

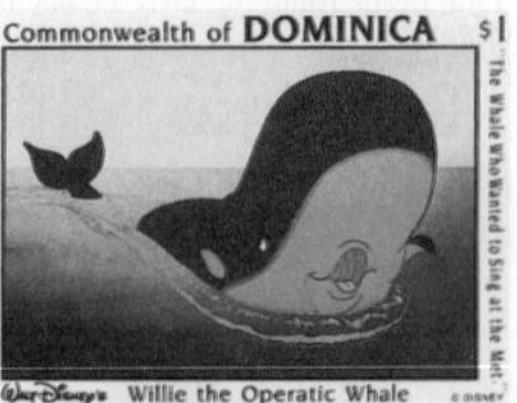

269 Willie

1993. "Willie the Operatic Whale". Scenes from Walt Disney's cartoon film. Multicoloured.
1772 $1 Type **269** 1·25 1·10
1773 $1 Willie's pelican friend 1·25 1·10
1774 $1 Willie singing to seals 1·25 1·10
1775 $1 Willie singing "Lucia" 1·25 1·10
1776 $1 Willie in "Pagliacci" 1·25 1·10
1777 $1 Willie as Mephistopheles 1·25 1·10
1778 $1 Tetti Tatti searching for Willie 1·25 1·10
1779 $1 Whalers listening to Willie 1·25 1·10
1780 $1 Tetti Tatti with harpoon gun 1·25 1·10
MS1781 Two sheets. (a) 130 × 102 mm. $6 Seals listening to Willie. (b) 97 × 118 mm. $6 Willie in Heaven (vert) Set of 2 sheets 7·00 8·00

270 "Adoration of the Magi" (detail) (Durer)

1993. Christmas. Religious Paintings. Each black, yellow and red (Nos. 1782/5) or multicoloured (others).
1782 25c. Type **270** 35 20
1783 55c. "Adoration of the Magi" (different detail) (Durer) 55 30
1784 65c. "Adoration of the Magi" (different detail) (Durer) 65 35
1785 90c. "Adoration of the Magi" (different detail) (Durer) 80 75
1786 90c. "Madonna of Foligno" (detail) (Raphael) 80 75
1787 $1 "Madonna of Foligno" (different detail) (Raphael) 90 75
1788 $3 "Madonna of Foligno" (different detail) (Raphael) 2·00 3·25
1789 $5 "Madonna of Foligno" (different detail) (Raphael) 2·75 4·50
MS1790 Two sheets, each 105 × 130 mm. (a) $6 "Adoration of the Magi" (different detail) (Dürer) (horiz). (b) $6 "Madonna of Foligno" (different detail) (Raphael) Set of 2 sheets 7·00 8·50

1994. "Hong Kong '94" International Stamp Exhibition (1st issue). As T **317** of Antigua. Multicoloured.
1791 65c. Hong Kong 1988 Peak Tramway 50c. stamp and skyscrapers 85 1·00
1792 65c. Dominica 1991 Cog Railways $5 stamp and Hong Kong Peak tram 85 1·00

Nos. 1791/2 were printed together, se-tenant, forming a composite design.

See also Nos. 1793/8.

1994. "Hong Kong '94" International Stamp Exhibition (2nd issue). Tang Dynasty Jade. As T **318** of Antigua, but vert. Multicoloured.
1793 65c. Horse 65 70
1794 65c. Cup with handle 65 70
1795 65c. Vase with birthday peaches 65 70
1796 65c. Vase 65 70
1797 65c. Fu Dog with puppy 65 70
1798 65c. Drinking cup 65 70

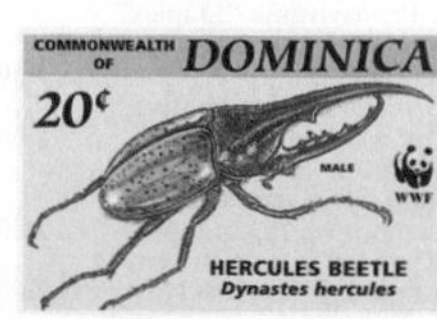

271 Male "Dynastes hercules" (beetle)

1994. Endangered Species. Birds and Insects. Multicoloured.
1799 20c. Type **271** 20 15
1800 25c. Male "Dynastes hercules" (different) 20 15
1801 65c. Male "Dynastes hercules" (different) 45 35
1802 90c. Female "Dynastes hercules" 60 55
1803 $1 Imperial Amazon ("Imperial Parrot") 90 75
1804 $2 "Marpesia petreus" (butterfly) 1·50 2·00
1805 $3 "Hypolimnus misippus" (butterfly) 2·00 2·50
1806 $5 Purple-throated carib 2·75 3·50
MS1807 Two sheets, each 98 × 70 mm. (a) $6 Blue-headed hummingbird. (b) $6 "Libytheana fulvescens" (butterfly) Set of 2 sheets 7·50 8·50

Nos. 1803/7 do not carry the W.W.F. Panda emblem.

272 "Laelio-cattleya"

273 "Russula matoubenis"

1994. Orchids. Multicoloured.
1808 20c. Type **272** 35 15
1809 25c. "Sophrolaelio cattleya" 35 15
1810 65c. "Odontocidium" 70 45
1811 90c. "Laelio-cattleya" (different) 90 75
1812 $1 "Cattleya" 1·00 75
1813 $2 "Odontocidium" (different) 1·50 2·00
1814 $3 "Epiphronitis" 2·00 2·75
1815 $4 "Oncidium" 2·00 2·75
MS1816 Two sheets, each 100 × 70 mm. (a) $6 "Cattleya" (different). (b) $6 "Schombo cattleya" Set of 2 sheets 7·50 8·50

1994. Fungi. Multicoloured.
1817 20c. Type **273** 40 25
1818 25c. "Leptonia caeruleocapitata" 40 25
1819 65c. "Inocybe littoralis" 60 35
1820 90c. "Russula hygrophytica" 70 55
1821 $1 "Pyrrhoglossum lilaceipes" 80 70
1822 $2 "Hygrocybe konradii" 1·25 1·75
1823 $3 "Inopilus magnificus" 1·75 2·25
1824 $5 "Boletellus cubensis" 2·25 2·75
MS1825 Two sheets, each 110 × 85 mm. (a) $6 "Lentinus strigosus". (b) $6 "Gerronema citrinum" Set of 2 sheets 7·50 7·50

274 "Appias drusilla"

1994. Butterflies. Multicoloured.
1826 20c. Type **274** 35 15
1827 25c. "Didonis biblis" 35 15
1828 55c. "Eurema daira" 70 45
1829 65c. "Hypolimnas misippus" 75 45
1830 $1 "Phoebis agarithe" 1·00 75
1831 $2 "Marpesia petreus" 1·50 2·00
1832 $3 "Libytheana fulvescens" 1·75 2·75
1833 $5 "Precis evarete" 2·50 3·50
MS1834 Two sheets, each 100 × 70 mm. (a) $6 "Chlorostrymon maesites". (b) $6 "Vanessa cardui" Set of 2 sheets 9·00 9·50

275 Dachshund

1994. Chinese New Year ("Year of the Dog"). Multicoloured.
1835 20c. Type **275** 30 25
1836 25c. Beagle 30 25
1837 55c. Greyhound 50 30
1838 90c. Jack Russell terrier 70 55
1839 $1 Pekingese 80 70
1840 $2 Wire fox terrier 1·25 1·50
1841 $4 English toy spaniel 2·25 2·75
1842 $5 Irish setter 2·25 2·75
MS1843 Two sheets, each 102 × 72 mm. (a) $6 Welsh corgi. (b) $6 Labrador retriever Set of 2 sheets 8·00 8·00

1994. Royal Visit. Nos. 1700/4 optd **ROYAL VISIT FEBRUARY 19, 1994.**
1844 20c. multicoloured 1·00 1·10
1845 25c. brown and black 1·00 1·10
1846 65c. multicoloured 1·75 2·00
1847 $5 multicoloured 3·50 4·00
MS1848 71 × 101 mm. $6 multicoloured 7·00 7·50

277 Des Armstrong (U.S.A.)

1994. World Cup Football Championship, U.S.A. (2nd issue). Multicoloured.
1849 25c. Jefferey Edmund (Dominica) 50 25
1850 $1 Type **277** 75 80
1851 $1 Dennis Bergkamp (Netherlands) 75 80
1852 $1 Roberto Baggio (Italy) 75 80
1853 $1 Rai (Brazil) 75 80
1854 $1 Cafu (Brazil) 75 80
1855 $1 Marco van Basten (Netherlands) 75 80
MS1856 Two sheets. (a) 70 × 100 mm. $6 Roberto Mancini (Italy). (b) 100 × 70 mm. $6 Player and Stanford Stadium, San Francisco Set of 2 sheets 8·00 9·00

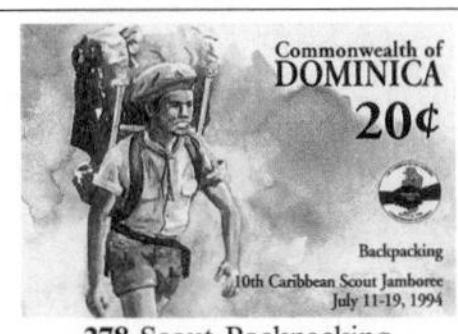

278 Scout Backpacking

1994. 10th Caribbean Scout Jamboree. Multicoloured.
1857 20c. Type **278** 35 15
1858 25c. Cooking over campfire 35 15
1859 55c. Erecting tent 60 30
1860 65c. Serving soup 70 45
1861 $1 Corps of drums . . . . 1·00 75
1862 $2 Planting tree . . . . . . 1·50 2·00
1863 $4 Sailing dinghy . . . . . 2·25 2·75
1864 $5 Saluting . . . . 2·25 2·75
MS1865 Two sheets, each 100 × 70 mm. (a) $6 Early scout troop. (b) $6 Pres. Crispin Sorhaindo (chief scout) (vert) Set of 2 sheets . . . . 8·50 9·00

1994. 25th Anniv of First Manned Moon Landing. As T **326** of Antigua. Multicoloured.
1866 $1 Crew of "Apollo 14" . . . 1·00 1·00
1867 $1 "Apollo 14" mission logo 1·00 1·00
1868 $1 Lunar module "Antares" on Moon . . . . 1·00 1·00
1869 $1 Crew of "Apollo 15" . . . 1·00 1·00
1870 $1 "Apollo 15" mission logo 1·00 1·00
1871 $1 Lunar crater on Mt. Hadley . . . . 1·00 1·00
MS1872 99 × 106 mm. $6 "Apollo 11" logo and surface of Moon . . . . 4·50 5·00

1994. Centenary of International Olympic Committee. Gold Medal Winners. As T **327** of Antigua. Multicoloured.
1873 55c. Ulrike Meyfarth (Germany) (high jump), 1984 . . . . 75 40
1874 $1.45 Dieter Baumann (Germany) (5000 m), 1992 1·75 2·00
MS1875 106 × 76 mm. $6 Ji Hoon Chae (South Korea) (500 metres speed skating), 1994 . . . . . 3·50 4·00

1994. Centenary (1995) of First English Cricket Tour to the West Indies. As T **329** of Antigua. Multicoloured.
1876 55c. David Gower (England) (vert) 40 30
1877 90c. Curtly Ambrose (West Indies) and Wisden Trophy 60 60
1878 $1 Graham Gooch (England) (vert) 70 80
MS1879 76 × 96 mm. $3 First English touring team, 1895 . . 3·00 2·75

1994. 50th Anniv of D-Day. As T **331** of Antigua. Multicoloured.
1880 65c. American Waco gliders 75 45
1881 $2 British Horsa glider . . . 1·50 1·75
1882 $3 British glider and troops attacking Pegasus Bridge 1·75 2·00
MS1883 107 × 77 mm. $6 British Hadrian glider . . . . 3·25 3·75

279 Pink Bird and Red Flowers Screen Painting
280 Dippy Dawg

1994. "Philakorea '94" International Stamp Exhibition, Seoul. Multicoloured.
1884 55c. Type **279** 30 40
1885 55c. Bird with yellow, pink and red flowers 30 40
1886 55c. Pair of birds and yellow flowers 30 40
1887 55c. Chickens and flowers 30 40
1888 55c. Pair of birds and pink flowers 30 40
1889 55c. Ducks and flowers . . 30 40
1890 55c. Blue bird and red flowers 30 40
1891 55c. Common pheasant and flowers 30 40
1892 55c. Stork and flowers . . . 30 40
1893 55c. Deer and flowers . . . 30 40
1894 65c. P'alsang-jon Hall (38 × 24 mm) 40 40
1895 90c. Popchu-sa Temple (38 × 24 mm) 50 55
1896 $2 Uhwajong Pavillion (38 × 24 mm) . . . . . . 1·10 1·50
MS1897 100 × 70 mm. $4 Spirit Post Guardian (38 × 24 mm) . . . . 2·00 2·75

1994. 65th Anniv (1993) of Mickey Mouse. Walt Disney Cartoon Characters. Multicoloured.
1898 20c. Type **280** 60 25
1899 25c. Clarabelle Cow 60 25
1900 55c. Horace Horsecollar . . 90 35
1901 65c. Mortimer Mouse . . . 1·00 45
1902 $1 Joe Piper . . . . 1·50 85
1903 $3 Mr. Casey . . . . 2·75 3·00
1904 $4 Chief O'Hara . . . . . 3·00 3·25
1905 $5 Mickey and The Blot . . 3·00 3·25
MS1906 Two sheets, each 127 × 102 mm. (a) $6 Minnie Mouse with Tanglefoot. (b) $6 Minnie and Pluto (horiz) Set of 2 sheets . . . . 10·00 11·00

281 Marilyn Monroe
284 Pig's Head facing Right

283 Wood Duck

1994. Entertainers. Multicoloured.
1907 20c. Sonia Lloyd (folk singer) 40 25
1908 25c. Ophelia Marie (singer) 40 25
1909 55c. Edney Francis (accordion player) 60 30
1910 65c. Norman Letang (saxophonist) 70 35
1911 90c. Edie Andre (steel-band player) 80 55
1912 90c. Type **281** . . . . . . 1·10 1·25
1913 90c. Marilyn Monroe wearing necklace . . . . 1·10 1·25
1914 90c. In yellow frilled dress 1·10 1·25
1915 90c. In purple dress . . . . 1·10 1·25
1916 90c. Looking over left shoulder . . . . 1·10 1·25
1917 90c. Laughing . . . . 1·10 1·25
1918 90c. In red dress . . . . . 1·10 1·25
1919 90c. Wearing gold cluster earrings . . . . 1·10 1·25
1920 90c. In yellow dress . . . . 1·10 1·25
MS1921 Two sheets, each 106 × 76 mm. (a) $6 Marilyn Monroe with top hat. (b) $6 With arms above head Set of 2 sheets 7·50 8·50
No. 1907 is inscribed "Llyod" in error.

1994. Christmas. Religious Paintings. As T **336** of Antigua. Multicoloured.
1922 20c. "Madonna and Child" (Luis de Morales) 30 10
1923 25c. "Madonna and Child with Yarn Winder" (De Morales) 30 10
1924 55c. "Our Lady of the Rosary" (detail) (Zurbaran) 50 30
1925 65c. "Dream of the Patrician" (detail) (Murillo) 65 55
1926 90c. "Madonna of Charity" (El Greco) 90 45
1927 $1 "The Annunciation" (Zurbaran) . . . . 1·00 60
1928 $2 "Mystical Marriage of St. Catherine" (Jusepe de Ribera) . . . . 1·50 2·25
1929 $3 "The Holy Family with St. Bruno and Other Saints" (detail) (De Ribera) . . . . 1·75 3·00
MS1930 Two sheets. (a) 136 × 97 mm. $6 "Adoration of the Shepherds" (detail) (Murillo). (b) 99 × 118 mm. $6 "Vision of the Virgin to St. Bernard" (detail) (Murillo) Set of 2 sheets . . . 7·50 8·50

1994. First Recipients of Order of the Caribbean Community. As Nos. 2046/8 of Antigua. Mult.
1931 25c. Sir Shridath Ramphal 20 10
1932 65c. William Demas 50 50
1933 90c. Derek Walcott . . . . 1·00 80

1995. 18th World Scout Jamboree, Netherlands. Nos. 1860 and 1863/4 optd **18th World Scout Jamboree Mondial, Holland, May 6, 1995.**
1934 65c. Serving soup 60 35
1935 $4 Sailing dinghy . . . . . 2·25 2·75
1936 $5 Saluting . . . . 2·25 2·75
MS1937 Two sheets, each 100 × 70 mm. (a) $6 Early scout troop. (b) $6 Pres. Crispin Sorhaindo (chief scout) (vert) Set of 2 sheets . . . . 7·50 8·50

1995. Water Birds. Multicoloured.
1938 25c. Type **283** 90 30
1939 55c. Mallard . . . . 1·00 40
1940 65c. Blue-winged teal . . . 1·00 55
1941 65c. Cattle egret (vert) . . . 1·00 1·10
1942 65c. Snow goose (vert) . . . 1·00 1·10
1943 65c. Peregrine falcon (vert) 1·00 1·10
1944 65c. Barn owl (vert) . . . . 1·00 1·10
1945 65c. Black-crowned night heron (vert) . . . . . . 1·00 1·10
1946 65c. Common grackle (vert) 1·00 1·10
1947 65c. Brown pelican (vert) . . 1·00 1·10
1948 65c. Great egret (vert) . . . 1·00 1·10
1949 65c. Ruby-throated hummingbird (vert) . . . 1·00 1·10
1950 65c. Laughing gull (vert) . . 1·00 1·10
1951 65c. Greater flamingo (vert) 1·00 1·10
1952 65c. Moorhen ("Common Morehen") (vert) . . . . 1·00 1·10
1953 $5 Red-eared conure ("Blood eared parakeet") 3·25 4·00
MS1954 Two sheets, each 105 × 75 mm. (a) $5 Trumpeter swan (vert). (b) $6 White-eyed vireo Set of 2 sheets . . . . 8·00 9·00
Nos. 1941/5 were printed together, se-tenant, forming a composite design.
No. 1946 is inscribed "Common Gralkle" in error.

1995. Chinese New Year ("Year of the Pig"). Multicoloured.
1955 25c. Type **284** 40 40
1956 65c. Pig facing to the front 45 45
1957 $1 Pig facing left 50 50
MS1958 101 × 50 mm. Nos. 1955/7 1·25 1·50
MS1959 105 × 77 mm. Two pigs (horiz) . . . . 1·25 1·50

1995. 50th Anniv of End of Second World War in Europe. As T **340** of Antigua. Multicoloured.
1960 $2 German Panther tank in the Ardennes . . . . . . 1·25 1·25
1961 $2 American fighter-bomber 1·25 1·25
1962 $2 American mechanized column crossing the Rhine 1·25 1·25
1963 $2 Messerschmitt Me 163B Komet and Allied bombers . . . . 1·25 1·25
1964 $2 V2 rocket on launcher 1·25 1·25
1965 $2 German U-boat surrendering . . . . . . 1·25 1·25
1966 $2 Heavy artillery in action 1·25 1·25
1967 $2 Soviet infantry in Berlin 1·25 1·25
MS1968 106 × 76 mm. $6 Statue and devastated Dresden ($56\frac{1}{2} \times 42\frac{1}{2}$ mm) . . . . 4·00 4·50

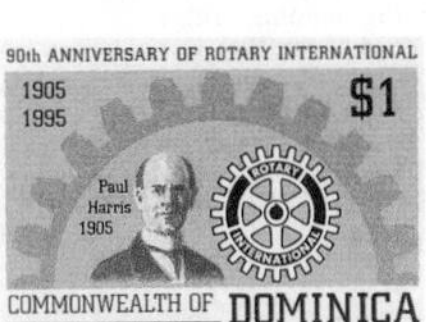

285 Paul Harris (founder) and Emblem

1995. 90th Anniv of Rotary International.
1969 **285** $1 brown, purple & blk 75 75
MS1970 70 × 100 mm. $6 red and black . . . . 2·75 3·25
DESIGN: $6 Rotary emblems.

1995. 50th Anniv of End of Second World War in the Pacific. As T **340** of Antigua. Multicoloured.
1971 $2 Mitsubishi A6M Zero-Sen torpedo-bomber . . . 1·25 1·25
1972 $2 Aichi D3A "Val" dive bomber . . . . 1·25 1·25
1973 $2 Nakajima B5N "Kate" bomber . . . . 1·25 1·25
1974 $2 "Zuikaku" (Japanese aircraft carrier) . . . . . 1·25 1·25
1975 $2 "Akagi" (Japanese aircraft carrier) . . . . . 1·25 1·25
1976 $2 "Ryuho" (Japanese aircraft carrier) . . . . . 1·25 1·25
MS1977 108 × 76 mm. $6 Japanese torpedo-bomber at Pearl Harbor 4·50 4·50

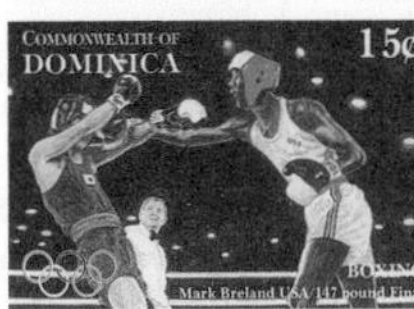

286 Boxing

1995. Olympic Games, Atlanta (1996). (1st Issue). Multicoloured.
1978 15c. Type **286** 40 25
1979 20c. Wrestling 45 25
1980 25c. Judo 55 25
1981 55c. Fencing 60 30
1982 65c. Swimming 70 35
1983 $1 Gymnastics (vert) 90 80
1984 $2 Cycling (vert) . . . . . 2·50 2·25
1985 $5 Volleyball . . . . 2·75 3·50
MS1986 Two sheets, each 104 × 74 mm. (a) $6 Show jumping. (b) $6 Football (vert) Set of 2 sheets . . . . 8·00 9·00
See also Nos. 2122/45 and 2213.

1995. 50th Anniv of United Nations. As T **341** of Antigua. Multicoloured.
1987 65c. Signatures and U.S. delegate 40 45
1988 $1 U.S. delegate 55 60
1989 $2 Governor Stassen (U.S. delegate) . . . . 85 1·25
MS1990 100 × 71 mm. $6 Winston Churchill . . . . 3·25 3·50
Nos. 1987/9 were printed together, se-tenant, forming a composite design.

287 Market Customers
289 Oscar Sanchez (1987 Peace)

288 Monoclonius

1995. 50th Anniv of Food and Agriculture Organization. T **287** and similar multicoloured designs.
MS1991 110 × 74 mm. 90c., $1, $2 Panorama of Dominican market 1·60 1·90
MS1992 101 × 71 mm. $6 Women irrigating crops (horiz) . . . . 2·50 3·00

1995. 95th Birthday of Queen Elizabeth the Queen Mother. As T **344** of Antigua.
1993 $1.65 brown, lt brown & blk 1·00 1·25
1994 $1.65 multicoloured . . . . 1·00 1·25
1995 $1.65 multicoloured . . . . 1·00 1·25
1996 $1.65 multicoloured . . . . 1·00 1·25
MS1997 103 × 126 mm. $6 multicoloured . . . . 4·00 4·50
DESIGNS: No. 1993, Queen Elizabeth the Queen Mother (pastel drawing); 1994, Holding bouquet of flowers; 1995, At desk (oil painting); 1996, Wearing blue dress; **MS**1997, Wearing ruby and diamond tiara and necklace.

1995. "Singapore '95" International Stamp Exhibition. Prehistoric Animals. Multicoloured.
1998 20c. Type **288** 50 30
1999 25c. Euoplocephalus 50 30
2000 55c. Head of coelophysis . . 60 30
2001 65c. Head of compsognathus 65 35
2002 90c. Dimorphodon 75 75
2003 90c. Ramphorynchus . . . 75 75
2004 90c. Head of giant alligator 75 75
2005 90c. Pentaceratops 75 75
2006 $1 Ceratosaurus (vert) . . . 75 75
2007 $1 Comptosaurus (vert) . . 75 75
2008 $1 Stegosaur (vert) 75 75
2009 $1 Camarasaurs (vert) . . . 75 75
2010 $1 Baronyx (vert) 75 75
2011 $1 Dilophosaurus (vert) . . 75 75
2012 $1 Dromaeosaurids (vert) 75 75
2013 $1 Deinonychus (vert) . . . 75 75
2014 $1 Dinicthys (terror fish) (vert) 75 75
2015 $1 Head of carcharodon (Giant-toothed shark) (vert) 75 75
2016 $1 Nautiloid (vert) 75 75
2017 $1 Trilobite (vert) 75 75
MS2018 Two sheets. (a) 95 × 65 mm. $5 Sauropelta. (b) 65 × 95 mm. $6 Triceratops (vert) Set of 2 sheets 7·50 8·50
Nos. 2002/5 and 2006/17 were respectively printed together, se-tenant, forming composite designs.
Nos. 2002/5 do not carry the "Singapore '95" exhibition logo.

1995. Centenary of Nobel Prize Trust Fund. Mult.
2019 $2 Type **289** . . . . 1·40 1·40
2020 $2 Ernst Chain (1945 Medicine) . . . . 1·40 1·40
2021 $2 Aage Bohr (1975 Physics) 1·40 1·40
2022 $2 Jaroslav Seifert (1984 Literature) . . . . 1·40 1·40
2023 $2 Joseph Murray (1990 Medicine) . . . . 1·40 1·40
2024 $2 Jaroslav Heyrovsky (1959 Chemistry) . . . . 1·40 1·40
2025 $2 Adolf von Baeyer (1905 Chemistry) . . . . 1·40 1·40
2026 $2 Eduard Buchner (1907 Chemistry) . . . . 1·40 1·40
2027 $2 Carl Bosch (1931 Chemistry) . . . . 1·40 1·40
2028 $2 Otto Hahn (1944 Chemistry) . . . . 1·40 1·40

2029 $2 Otto Diels (1950 Chemistry) . . . . 1·40 1·40
2030 $2 Kurt Alder (1950 Chemistry) . . . . 1·40 1·40
MS2031 76 × 106 mm. $2 Emil von Behring (1901 Medicine) . . . 1·40 1·60

1995. Christmas. Religious Paintings. As T **357** of Antigua. Multicoloured.
2032 20c. "Madonna and Child with St. John" (Pontormo) 25 20
2033 25c. "The Immaculate Conception" (Murillo) . . 25 20
2034 55c. "The Adoration of the Magi" (Filippino Lippi) 45 30
2035 65c. "Rest on the Flight into Egypt" (Van Dyck) . . . 55 35
2036 90c. "The Holy Family" (Van Dyck) 75 50
2037 $5 "The Annunciation" (Van Eyck) . . . . 2·75 4·00
MS2038 Two sheets, each 102 × 127 mm. (a) $5 "Madonna and Child Reading" (detail) (Van Eyck). (b) $6 "The Holy Family" (detail) (Ribera) Set of 2 sheets 6·50 7·50

1995. Centenary (1992) of Sierra Club (environmental protection society). Endangered Species. As T **320** of Antigua. Multicoloured.
2039 $1 Florida panther 60 60
2040 $1 Manatee 60 60
2041 $1 Sockeye salmon 60 60
2042 $1 Key deer facing left . . . 60 60
2043 $1 Key deer doe 60 60
2044 $1 Key deer stag 60 60
2045 $1 Wallaby with young in pouch 60 60
2046 $1 Wallaby feeding young 60 60
2047 $1 Wallaby and young feeding 60 60
2048 $1 Florida panther showing teeth (horiz) 60 60
2049 $1 Head of Florida panther (horiz) 60 60
2050 $1 Manatee (horiz) 60 60
2051 $1 Pair of manatees (horiz) 60 60
2052 $1 Pair of sockeye salmon (horiz) 60 60
2053 $1 Sockeye salmon spawning (horiz) 60 60
2054 $1 Pair of southern sea otters (horiz) 60 60
2055 $1 Southern sea otter with front paws together (horiz) 60 60
2056 $1 Southern sea otter with front paws apart (horiz) 60 60

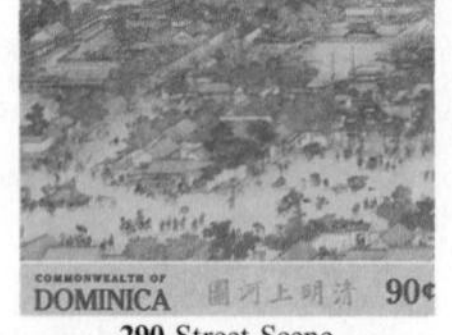

290 Street Scene

1995. "A City of Cathay" (Chinese scroll painting). Multicoloured.
2057 90c. Type **290** 60 70
2058 90c. Street scene and city wall 60 70
2059 90c. City gate and bridge . . 60 70
2060 90c. Landing stage and junk 60 70
2061 90c. River bridge 60 70
2062 90c. Moored junks 60 70
2063 90c. Two rafts on river . . 60 70
2064 90c. Two junks on river . . 60 70
2065 90c. Roadside tea house . . 60 70
2066 90c. Wedding party on the road 60 70
MS2067 Two sheets, each 106 × 77 mm. (a) $2 City street and sampan; $2 Footbridge. (b) $2 Stern of sampan (vert); $2 Bow of sampan (vert) Set of 2 sheets 4·25 4·75

291 "Bindo Altoviti" (Raphael)

1995. Paintings by Raphael. Multicoloured.
2068 $2 Type **291** . . . . 1·75 1·75
2069 $2 "Pope Leo with Nephews" . . . . 1·75 1·75
2070 $2 "Agony in the Garden" 1·75 1·75
MS2071 110 × 80 mm. $6 "Pope Leo X with Cardinals Giulio de Medici and Luigi dei Rossi" (detail) 4·00 4·75

292 Rat

1996. Chinese New Year ("Year of the Rat").
2072 **292** 25c. black, violet and brown 35 40
2073 – 65c. black, red and green 60 70
2074 – $1 black, mauve and blue 70 80
MS2075 100 × 50 mm. Nos. 2072/4 1·25 1·50
MS2076 105 × 77 mm. $2 black, green and violet (two rats) . . 1·25 1·50
DESIGNS: 65c., $1, $2, Rats and Chinese symbols (different).

293 Mickey and Minnie Mouse (Year of the Rat)

1996. Chinese Lunar Calendar. Walt Disney Cartoon Characters. Multicoloured.
2077 55c. Type **293** 65 70
2078 55c. Casey Jones (Year of the Ox) 65 70
2079 55c. Tigger, Pooh and Piglet (Year of the Tiger) . . . 65 70
2080 55c. White Rabbit (Year of the Rabbit) 65 70
2081 55c. Dragon playing flute (Year of the Dragon) . . 65 70
2082 55c. Snake looking in mirror (Year of the Snake) . . . 65 70
2083 55c. Horace Horsecollar and Clarabelle Cow (Year of the Horse) 65 70
2084 55c. Black Lamb and blue birds (Year of the Ram) 65 70
2085 55c. King Louis reading book (Year of the Monkey) 65 70
2086 55c. Cock playing lute (Year of the Cock) 65 70
2087 55c. Mickey and Pluto (Year of the Dog) 65 70
2088 55c. Pig building bridge (Year of the Pig) 65 70
MS2089 Two sheets. (a) 127 × 102 mm. $3 Basil the Great Mouse Detective (Year of the Rat). (b) 102 × 127 mm. $6 Emblems for 1996, 1997 and 2007 Set of 2 sheets . . . . 7·00 8·00

294 Steam Locomotive "Dragon", Hawaii

1996. Trains of the World. Multicoloured.
2090 $2 Type **294** . . . . 1·25 1·40
2091 $2 Class 685 steam locomotive "Regina", Italy . . . . 1·25 1·40
2092 $2 Class 745 steam locomotive, Calazo to Padua line, Italy . . . . 1·25 1·40
2093 $2 Mogul steam locomotive, Philippines . . . . 1·25 1·40
2094 $2 Class 23 and 24 steam locomotives, Germany . . 1·25 1·40
2095 $2 Class BB-15000 electric locomotive "Stanislaus", France . . . . 1·25 1·40
2096 $2 Class "Black Five" steam locomotive, Scotland . . 1·25 1·40
2097 $2 Diesel-electric locomotive, France . . . . 1·25 1·40
2098 $2 LNER class A4 steam locomotive "Sir Nigel Gresley", England . . . 1·25 1·40
2099 $2 Class 9600 steam locomotive, Japan . . . 1·25 1·40
2100 $2 "Peloponnese Express" train, Greece . . . . . 1·25 1·40
2101 $2 Porter type steam locomotive, Hawaii . . . . . 1·25 1·40
2102 $2 Steam locomotive "Holand", Norway . . 1·25 1·40
2103 $2 Class 220 diesel-hydraulic locomotive, Germany . . 1·25 1·40
2104 $2 Steam locomotive, India 1·25 1·40
2105 $2 East African Railways Class 29 steam locomotive 1·25 1·40
2106 $2 Electric trains, Russia . . 1·25 1·40
2107 $2 Steam locomotive, Austria . . . . 1·25 1·40
MS2108 Two sheets, each 103 × 73 mm. (a) $5 L.M.S. steam locomotive "Duchess of Hamilton", England. (b) $6 Diesel locomotives, China Set of 2 sheets 7·50 8·00

295 Horse-drawn Gig, 1965

1996. Traditional Island Transport. Multicoloured.
2109 65c. Type **295** 90 35
2110 90c. Early automobile, 1910 1·10 55
2111 $2 Lorry, 1950 . . . . . . 1·75 2·00
2112 $3 Bus, 1955 . . . . 2·00 2·50

296 Giant Panda

1996. "CHINA '96" 9th Asian International Stamp Exhibition, Peking. Giant Pandas. Multicoloured.
2113 55c. Type **296** 70 70
2114 55c. Panda on rock 70 70
2115 55c. Panda eating bamboo shoots 70 70
2116 55c. Panda on all fours . . 70 70
MS2117 Two sheets. (a) 90 × 125 mm. $2 Huangshan Mountain, China (50 × 75 mm). (b) 160 × 125 mm. $3 Panda sitting (50 × 37 mm) Set of 2 sheets . . 3·75 3·75

1996. 70th Birthday of Queen Elizabeth II. As T **364** of Antigua. Multicoloured.
2118 $2 As Type **364** of Antigua 1·25 1·40
2119 $2 Queen in robes of Order of St. Michael and St. George . . . . . . 1·25 1·40
2120 $2 Queen in blue dress with floral brooch . . . . . . 1·25 1·40
MS2121 103 × 125 mm. $6 Queen at Trooping the Colour . . . . . 4·00 4·25

297 Moscow Stadium, 1980

1996. Olympic Games, Atlanta (2nd issue). Multicoloured.
2122 20c. Type **297** 35 25
2123 25c. Hermine Joseph (running) (vert) 35 25
2124 55c. Zimbabwe women's hockey team, 1980 . . . 1·00 40
2125 90c. Jerome Romain (long jump) (vert) 70 75
2126 90c. Sammy Lee (diving), 1948 and 1952 (vert) . . . 70 75
2127 90c. Bruce Jenner (decathalon), 1976 (vert) 70 75
2128 90c. Olga Korbut (gymnastics), 1972 (vert) 70 75
2129 90c. Steffi Graf (tennis), 1988 (vert) 70 75
2130 90c. Florence Griffith-Joyner (track and field), 1988 (vert) 70 75
2131 90c. Mark Spitz (swimming), 1968 and 1972 (vert) . . . 70 75
2132 90c. Li Ning (gymnastics), 1984 (vert) 70 75
2133 90c. Erika Salumae (cycling), 1988 (vert) . . . 70 75
2134 90c. Abebe Bikila (marathon), 1960 and 1964 (vert) 70 75
2135 90c. Ulrike Meyfarth (high jump), 1972 and 1984 (vert) 70 75
2136 90c. Pat McCormick (diving), 1952 and 1956 (vert) 70 75
2137 90c. Takeichi Nishi (equestrian), 1932 (vert) 70 75
2138 90c. Peter Farkas (Greco-Roman wrestling), 1992 (vert) 70 75
2139 90c. Carl Lewis (track and field), 1984, 1988 and 1992 (vert) 70 75
2140 90c. Agnes Keleti (gymnastics), 1952 and 1956 (vert) 70 75
2141 90c. Yasuhiro Yamashita (judo), 1984 (vert) 70 75
2142 90c. John Kelly (single sculls), 1920 (vert) 70 75
2143 90c. Naim Suleymanoglu (weightlifting), 1988 and 1992 (vert) 70 75
2144 $1 Polo (vert) 80 80
2145 $2 Greg Louganis (diving), 1976, 1984 and 1988 . . . 1·40 1·60
MS2146 Two sheets, each 105 × 75 mm. (a) $5 Joan Benoit (marathon), 1984 (vert). (b) $5 Milt Campbell (discus) Set of 2 sheets . . . . 6·00 7·50
Nos. 2126/34 and 2135/43 respectively were printed together, se-tenant, the backgrounds forming composite designs.

1996. 50th Anniv of U.N.I.C.E.F. As T **366** of Antigua. Multicoloured.
2147 20c. Child and globe (horiz) 25 15
2148 55c. Child with syringe and stethoscope (horiz) . . . 45 35
2149 $5 Doctor and child (horiz) 2·75 3·50
MS2150 74 × 104 mm. $5 African child . . . . 2·75 3·50

1996. 3000th Anniv of Jerusalem. Vert designs as T **367** of Antigua. Multicoloured.
MS2151 114 × 95 mm. 90c. Shrine of the Book, Israel Museum; $1 Church of All Nations; $2 The Great Synagogue . . . . . . 2·50 2·50
MS2152 104 × 74 mm. $5 Hebrew University, Mount Scopus . . 3·50 3·50

1996. Centenary of Radio. Entertainers. As T **368** of Antigua. Multicoloured.
2153 90c. Artie Shaw 60 50
2154 $1 Benny Goodman 65 55
2155 $2 Duke Ellington . . . . . 1·25 1·40
2156 $4 Harry James . . . . . . 2·25 2·50
MS2157 70 × 99 mm. $6 Tommy and Jimmy Dorsey (horiz) . . . . 3·50 4·00

298 Irene Peltier in National Dress

1996. Local Entertainers. Multicoloured.
2158 25c. Type **298** 25 20
2159 55c. Rupert Bartley (steel-band player) 40 35
2160 65c. Rosemary Cools-Lartigue (pianist) 50 40
2161 90c. Celestine 'Orion' Theophile (singer) 65 65
2162 $1 Cecil Bellot (band master) 70 80

299 Humphrey Bogart as Sam Spade

1996. Centenary of Cinema. Screen Detectives. Multicoloured.
2163 $1 Type **299** 75 75
2164 $1 Sean Connery as James Bond 75 75
2165 $1 Warren Beatty as Dick Tracy 75 75
2166 $1 Basil Rathbone as Sherlock Holmes 75 75
2167 $1 William Powell as the Thin Man 75 75
2168 $1 Sidney Toler as Charlie Chan 75 75
2169 $1 Peter Sellers as Inspector Clouseau 75 75
2170 $1 Robert Mitchum as Philip Marlowe 75 75
2171 $1 Peter Ustinov as Hercule Poirot 75 75
MS2172 105 × 75 mm. $6 Margaret Rutherford as Miss Marple . . 4·00 4·50

300 Scribbled Filefish **301** Anthony Trollope and Postal Scenes

1996. Fishes. Multicoloured.
2173 1c. Type **300** 20 50
2174 2c. Lionfish 20 50
2175 5c. Porcupinefish 30 50
2176 10c. Powder-blue surgeon fish 40 50
2177 15c. Red hind 50 50
2178 20c. Golden butterflyfish . . 55 25
2179 25c. Copper-banded butterflyfish 55 25
2180 35c. Pennant coralfish . . . 60 30
2181 45c. Spotted drum 65 30
2182 55c. Blue-girdled angelfish 70 35
2183 60c. Scorpionfish 70 35
2184 65c. Harlequin sweetlips . . 70 40
2185 90c. Flame angelfish . . . . 1·00 60
2186 $1 Queen triggerfish . . . . 1·25 75
2187 $1.20 Spotlight parrotfish 1·50 1·25
2188 $1.45 Black durgon . . . . 1·75 2·00
2189 $2 Glass-eyed snapper . . . 2·25 2·50
2190 $5 Balloonfish . . . . . . 4·25 5·00
2191 $10 Creole wrasse . . . . . 7·50 8·50
2192 $20 Sea bass . . . . 12·00 14·00
For these designs size 24 × 21 mm, see Nos. 2374/91.

1996. World Post Day. Multicoloured.
2193 10c. Type **301** 25 15
2194 25c. Anthony Trollope and Dominican postmen . . . 30 20
2195 55c. "Yare" (mail streamer) 60 35
2196 65c. Rural post office . . . 60 40
2197 90c. Postmen carrying mail 90 50
2198 $1 Grumman Goose (seaplane) and 1958 Caribbean Federation 12c. stamp . . . . 1·00 80
2199 $2 Old and new post offices and 1978 Independence 10c. stamp . . . . 1·40 1·75
MS2200 74 × 104 mm. $5 18th-century naval officer . . . 3·50 3·75

302 "Enthroned Madonna and Child" (S. Veneziano) **303** "Herdboy playing the Flute" (Li Keran)

1996. Christmas. Religious Paintings. Mult.
2201 25c. Type **302** 30 20
2202 55c. "Noli Me Tangere" (Fra Angelico) 55 35
2203 65c. "Madonna and Child Enthroned" (Angelico) . . 65 40
2204 90c. "Madonna of Corneto Tarquinia" (F. Lippi) . . 80 50
2205 $2 "The Annunciation" and "The Adoration of the Magi" (School of Angelico) . . . . 1·50 1·75
2206 $5 "Madonna and Child of the Shade" (Angelico) . . 3·00 3·75
MS2207 Two sheets. (a) 76 × 106 mm. $6 "Coronation of the Virgin" (Angelico). (b) 106 × 76 mm. $6 "Holy Family with St. Barbara" (Veronese) (horiz) Set of 2 sheets . . . . 7·50 8·50

1997. Lunar New Year ("Year of the Ox"). Paintings by Li Keran. Multicoloured.
2208 90c. Type **303** 60 70
2209 90c. "Playing Cricket in the Autumn" 60 70
2210 90c. "Listening to the Summer Cicada" 60 70
2211 90c. "Grazing in the Spring" 60 70
MS2212 76 × 106 mm. $2 "Return in Wind and Rain" (34 × 51 mm). 1·00 1·25
MS2212a 135 × 80 mm. 55c. × 4. Designs as Nos. 2208/11 . . . 90 95

304 Lee Lai-shan (Gold Medal – Windsurfing, 1996)

1997. Olympic Games, Atlanta (3rd issue). Mult.
2213 $2 Type **304** . . . . 1·50 1·75
MS2214 97 × 67 mm. $5 Lee Lai-shan wearing Gold medal (37 × 50 mm) . . . . 3·00 3·50

305 "Meticella metis"

1997. Butterflies. Multicoloured.
2215 55c. Type **305** 50 55
2216 55c. "Coeliades forestan" 50 55
2217 55c. "Papilio dardanus" . . 50 55
2218 55c. "Mylothris chloris" . . 50 55
2219 55c. "Poecilmitis thysbe" . . 50 55
2220 55c. "Myrina silenus" . . . 50 55
2221 55c. "Bematistes aganice" 50 55
2222 55c. "Euphaedra neophron" 50 55
2223 55c. "Precis hierta" 50 55
2224 90c. "Coeliadas forestan" (vert) 60 65
2225 90c. "Spialia spio" (vert) . . 60 65
2226 90c. "Belenois aurota" (vert) 60 65
2227 90c. "Dingana bowkom" (vert) 60 65
2228 90c. "Charaxes jasius" (vert) 60 65
2229 90c. "Catacroptera cloanthe" (vert) 60 65
2230 90c. "Colias electo" (vert) 60 65
2231 90c. "Junonia archesia" (vert) 60 65
MS2232 Two sheets, each 102 × 71 mm. (a) $6 "Eurytela dryope". (b) "Acraea natalica" Set of 2 sheets . . . . 8·00 9·00
No. 2230 is inscribed "Collas electo" in error.
Nos. 2215/23 and 2224/31 respectively were printed together, se-tenant, with the backgrounds forming a composite design.

1997. 50th Anniv of U.N.E.S.C.O. As T **374** of Antigua. Multicoloured.
2233 55c. Temple roof, China . . 50 35
2234 65c. The Palace of Diocletian, Split, Croatia 60 40
2235 90c. St. Mary's Cathedral, Hildesheim, Germany . . 70 50
2236 $1 The Monastery of Rossanou, Mount Athos, Greece 70 70
2237 $1 Carved face, Copan, Honduras (vert) 70 75
2238 $1 Cuzco Cathedral, Peru (vert) 70 75
2239 $1 Church, Olinda, Brazil (vert) 70 75
2240 $1 Canaima National Park, Venezuela (vert) 70 75
2241 $1 Galapagos Islands National Park, Ecuador (vert) 70 75
2242 $1 Church ruins, La Santisima Jesuit Missions, Paraguay (vert) 70 75
2243 $1 San Lorenzo Fortress, Panama (vert) 70 75
2244 $1 Fortress, National Park, Haiti (vert) 70 75
2245 $2 Scandola Nature Reserve, France . . . . 1·40 1·75
2246 $4 Church of San Antao, Portugal . . . . 2·50 3·25
MS2247 Two sheets, each 127 × 102 mm. (a) $6 Chengde Lakes, China. (b) $6 Pavilion, Kyoto, Japan Set of 2 sheets 7·50 8·50
No. 2234 is inscr "DICELECIAN" in error.

306 Tanglefoot and Minnie

1997. Disney Sweethearts. Multicoloured.
2248 25c. Type **306** 45 20
2249 35c. Mickey and Minnie kissing on ship's wheel . . 55 20
2250 55c. Pluto and kitten . . . 70 30
2251 65c. Clarabelle Cow kissing Horace Horsecollar . . . 70 35
2252 90c. Elmer Elephant and tiger 85 55
2253 $1 Minnie kissing Mickey in period costume 95 70
2254 $2 Donald Duck and nephew . . . . 1·60 1·75
2255 $4 Dog kissing Pluto . . . 2·50 3·50
MS2256 Three sheets. (a) 126 × 100 mm. $5 Simba and Nala in "The Lion King". (b) 133 × 104 mm. $6 Mickey covered in lipstick and Minnie (horiz). (c) 104 × 124 mm. $6 Mickey and Pluto Set of 3 sheets . . . . . 9·50 10·00

307 Afghan Hound **308** "Oncidium altissimum"

1997. Cats and Dogs. Multicoloured.
2257 20c. Type **307** 45 25
2258 25c. Cream Burmese 45 25
2259 55c. Cocker spaniel 55 35
2260 65c. Smooth fox terrier . . 60 40
2261 90c. West highland white terrier 70 75
2262 90c. St. Bernard puppies . . 70 75
2263 90c. Boy with grand basset 70 75
2264 90c. Rough collie 70 75
2265 90c. Golden retriever . . . 70 75
2266 90c. Golden retriever, Tibetan spaniel and smooth fox terrier 70 75
2267 90c. Smooth fox terrier . . 70 75
2268 $1 Snowshoe 75 75
2269 $2 Sorrell Abyssinian . . . 1·40 1·50
2270 $2 British bicolour shorthair 1·40 1·50
2271 $2 Maine coon and Somali kittens . . . . 1·40 1·50
2272 $2 Maine coon kitten . . . 1·40 1·50
2273 $2 Lynx point Siamese . . . 1·40 1·50
2274 $2 Blue Burmese kitten and white Persian . . . . . . 1·40 1·50
2275 $2 Persian kitten . . . . . 1·40 1·50
2276 $5 Torbie Persian . . . . . 3·25 3·75
MS2277 Two sheets, each 106 × 76 mm. (a) $6 Silver tabby. (b) $6 Shetland sheepdog Set of 2 sheets . . . . 8·00 9·00
Nos. 2262/7 and 2270/5 respectively were printed together, se-tenant, with the backgrounds forming composite designs.

1997. Orchids of the Caribbean. Multicoloured.
2278 20c. Type **308** 50 25
2279 25c. "Oncidium papilio" . . 50 25
2280 55c. "Epidendrum fragrans" 60 35
2281 65c. "Oncidium lanceanum" 70 40
2282 90c. "Campylocentrum micranthum' 90 50
2283 $1 "Brassavola cucculata" (horiz) . . . . 1·00 1·10
2284 $1 "Epidendrum ibaguense" (horiz) . . . . 1·00 1·10
2285 $1 "Ionopsis utricularioides" (horiz) . . . . 1·00 1·10
2286 $1 "Rodriguezia lanceolata" (horiz) . . . . 1·00 1·10
2287 $1 "Oncidium cebolleta" (horiz) . . . . 1·00 1·10
2288 $1 "Epidendrum ciliare" (horiz) . . . . 1·00 1·10
2289 $4 "Pogonia rosea" . . . . 2·75 3·00
MS2290 Two sheets, each 106 × 76 mm. (a) $5 "Oncidium ampliatum" (horiz). (b) $5 "Starhopea grandiflora" (horiz) Set of 2 sheets . . . . 7·00 7·50
Nos. 2283/8 were printed together, se-tenant, with the backgrounds forming a composite design.

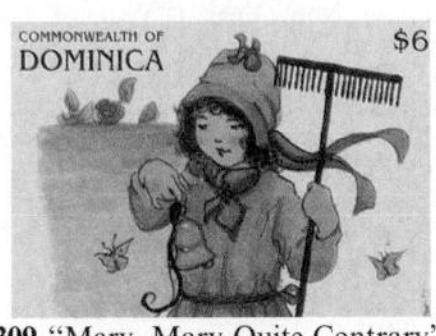

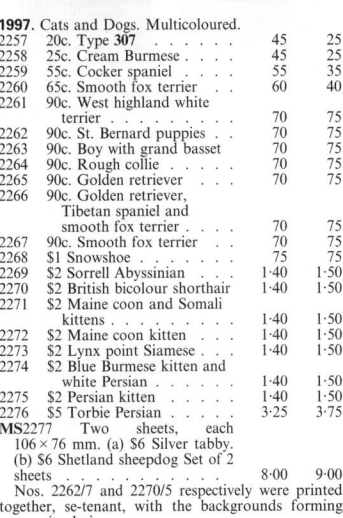

309 "Mary, Mary Quite Contrary"

1997. 300th Anniv of Mother Goose Nursery Rhymes. Sheet 72 × 102 mm.
MS2291 **309** $6 multicoloured . . 3·25 3·50

1997. 10th Anniv of Chernobyl Nuclear Disaster. As T **376** of Antigua. Multicoloured.
2292 $2 As Type **376** of Antigua 1·25 1·40
2293 $2 As Type **376** of Antigua but inscribed "CHABAD'S CHILDREN OF CHERNOBYL" at foot 1·25 1·40

1997. 50th Death Anniv of Paul Harris (founder of Rotary International). As T **377** of Antigua. Multicoloured.
2294 $2 Paul Harris and irrigation project, Honduras . . . . 1·25 1·50
MS2295 78 × 107 mm. $6 Paul Harris with Rotary and World Community Service emblems 3·25 4·00

1997. Golden Wedding of Queen Elizabeth and Prince Philip. As T **378** of Antigua. Multicoloured.
2296 $1 Queen Elizabeth II . . . 80 80
2297 $1 Royal Coat of Arms . . 80 80
2298 $1 Queen Elizabeth and Prince Philip in shirt sleeves 80 80
2299 $1 Queen Elizabeth and Prince Philip in naval uniform 80 80
2300 $1 Buckingham Palace . . . 80 80
2301 $1 Prince Philip 80 80
MS2302 100 × 71 mm. $6 Queen Elizabeth and Prince Philip with flower arrangement . . . . . 4·00 4·25

1997. "Pacific '97" International Stamp Exhibition, San Francisco. Death Centenary of Heinrich von Stephan (founder of the U.P.U.). As T **379** of Antigua.
2303 $2 violet . . . . 1·25 1·40
2304 $2 brown . . . . 1·25 1·40
2305 $2 brown . . . . 1·25 1·40
MS2306 82 × 119 mm. $6 blue and grey . . . . 3·50 3·75
DESIGNS: No. 2303, Kaiser Wilhelm II and Heinrich von Stephan; 2304, Heinrich von Stephan and Mercury; 2305, Early Japanese postal messenger; **MS**2306, Heinrich von Stephan and Russian postal dog team, 1895.

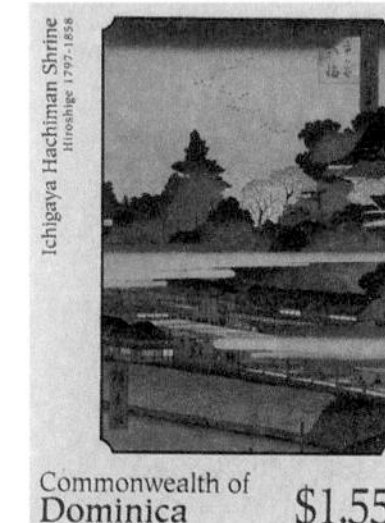

310 "Ichigaya Hachiman Shrine"

1997. Birth Centenary of Hiroshige (Japanese painter). "One Hundred Famous Views of Edo". Multicoloured.
2307 $1.55 Type **310** . . . . . . 1·40 1·40
2308 $1.55 "Blossoms on the Tama River Embankment" . . . . . 1·40 1·40
2309 $1.55 "Kumano Junisha Shrine, Tsunohazu" . . . 1·40 1·40
2310 $1.55 "Benkei Moat from Soto-Sakurada to Kojimachi" . . . . 1·40 1·40
2311 $1.55 "Kinokuni Hill and View of Akasak Tameike" 1·40 1·40
2312 $1.55 "Naito Shinjuku, Yotsuya" . . . . 1·40 1·40
MS2313 Two sheets, each 102 × 127 mm. (a) $6 "Sanno Festival Procession at Kojimachi I-chome". (b) $6 "Kasumigaseki" Set of 2 sheets . . . . 8·50 9·00

1997. 175th Anniv of Brothers Grimm's Third Collection of Fairy Tales. The Goose Girl. As T **380** of Antigua. Multicoloured.
2314 $2 Goose girl with horse . . 1·50 1·60
2315 $2 Geese in front of castle 1·50 1·60
2316 $2 Goose girl . . . . 1·50 1·60
MS2317 124 × 96 mm. $6 Goose girl (horiz) . . . . 4·00 4·25

311 Hong Kong Skyline at Dusk **312** Yukto Kasaya (Japan) (ski jump), 1972

1997. Return of Hong Kong to China. Multicoloured.
2318 65c. Type **311** 60 70
2319 90c. Type **311** 70 80
2320 $1 Type **311** 75 85
2321 $1 Hong Kong at night . . 75 85
2322 $1.45 Hong Kong by day 1·00 1·25
2323 $2 Hong Kong at night (different) . . . . 1·25 1·75
2324 $3 Type **311** . . . . 1·50 2·00

1997. Winter Olympic Games, Nagano, Japan (1998). Multicoloured.
2325 20c. Type **312** 50 25
2326 25c. Jens Weissflog (Germany) (ski jump), 1994 . . . . 50 25
2327 55c. Anton Maier (Norway) (100 m men's speed skating), 1968 . . . . . 60 45
2328 55c. Ljubov Egorova (Russia) (women's 5 km cross-country skiing), 1994 60 45
2329 65c. Swedish ice hockey, 1994 . . . . 80 45
2330 90c. Bernhard Glass (Germany) (men's single luge), 1980 . . . . 85 60
2331 $1 Type **312** . . . . 90 1·00
2332 $1 As No. 2326 . . . . . . 90 1·00
2333 $1 As No. 2327 . . . . . . 90 1·00

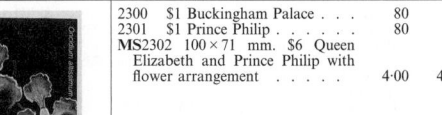

2334 $1 Christa Rethenburger (Germany) (women's 100 m speed skating), 1988 . . . . 90 1·00
2335 $4 Frank-Peter Roetsch (Germany) (men's biathlon), 1988 . . . . . 2·50 3·00
MS2336 Two sheets, each 106 × 76 mm. (a) $5 Charles Jewtraw (U.S.A.) (men's 500 m speed skating), 1924. (b) $5 Jacob Tullin Thams (Norway) (ski jumping), 1924 Set of 2 sheets 6·00 7·00

1997. World Cup Football Championship, France (1998). As T **383** of Antigua. Multicoloured (except Nos. 2343/4, 2348, 2350, 2353/4).
2337 20c. Klinsmann, Germany (vert) 50 25
2338 55c. Bergkamp, Holland (vert) 70 35
2339 65c. Ravanelli, Italy (vert) 70 75
2340 65c. Wembley Stadium, England 70 75
2341 65c. Bernabeu Stadium, Spain 70 75
2342 65c. Maracana Stadium, Brazil 70 75
2343 65c. Stadio Torino, Italy (black) 70 75
2344 65c. Centenary Stadium, Uruguay (black) 70 75
2345 65c. Olympiastadion, Germany 70 75
2346 65c. Rose Bowl, U.S.A. . . 70 75
2347 65c. Azteca Stadium, Mexico 70 75
2348 65c. Meazza, Italy (black) 70 75
2349 65c. Matthaus, Germany . . 70 75
2350 65c. Walter, West Germany (black) 70 75
2351 65c. Maradona, Argentina 70 75
2352 65c. Beckenbaur, Germany 70 75
2353 65c. Moore, England (black) 70 75
2354 65c. Dunga, Brazil (black) 70 75
2355 65c. Zoff, Italy 70 75
2356 90c. Klinkladze, Georgia . . 80 60
2357 $2 Shearer, England (vert) 1·40 1·60
2358 $4 Dani, Portugal (vert) . . 2·50 3·00
MS2359 Two sheets. (a) 102 × 126 mm. $5 Mario Kempes, Argentina (vert). (b) 126 × 102 mm. $6 Ally McCoist, Scotland (vert) Set of 2 sheets 7·00 8·00

313 Joffre Robinson (former Credit Union President)

314 Louis Pasteur

1997. 40th Anniv of Co-operative Credit Union League.
2360 **313** 25c. blue and black . . . 25 20
2361 – 55c. green and black . . 45 40
2362 – 65c. purple and black . . 55 55
2363 – 90c. multicoloured . . . 65 70
MS2364 94 × 106 mm. $5 multicoloured . . . . 3·00 3·50
DESIGNS—As T **313**: 55c. Sister Alicia (founder); 65c. Lorrel Bruce (first Credit Union President). 30 × 60 mm: $5 Sister Alicia, Joffre Robinson and Lorrel Bruce.

1997. Medical Pioneers.
2365 **314** 20c. brown 50 25
2366 – 25c. pink and red . . . 50 25
2367 – 55c. violet 70 35
2368 – 65c. red and brown . . . 75 45
2369 – 90c. yellow and olive . . 85 55
2370 – $1 blue and ultramarine 1·00 80
2371 – $2 black . . . . 1·60 1·75
2372 – $3 red and brown . . . 1·90 2·25
MS2373 Two sheets, each 70 × 100 mm. (a) $5 multicoloured. (b) $6 multicoloured Set of 2 sheets . . . . 8·00 8·50
DESIGNS: 25c. Christiaan Barnard (first heart transplant); 55c. Sir Alexander Fleming (discovery of penicillin); 65c. Camillo Golgi (neurologist); 90c. Jonas Salk (discovery of polio vaccine); $1 Har Gobind Khorana (genetics); $2 Elizabeth Black (first woman doctor); $3 Sir Frank MacFarlane Burnet (immunologist); $5 (**MS**2373a), Sir Alexander Fleming (different); $6 (**MS**2373b), Louis Pasteur (different).

1997. Fishes. As Nos. 2175/92, but smaller, 24 × 21mm.
2374 5c. Porcupinefish 45 60
2375 10c. Powder-blue surgeonfish 45 60
2376 15c. Red hind 60 60
2377 20c. Golden butterflyfish . . 60 30
2378 25c. Copper-banded butterflyfish 60 30
2379 35c. Pennant coralfish . . . 70 35
2380 45c. Spotted drum 70 30
2381 55c. Blue-girdled angelfish 80 40
2382 60c. Scorpionfish 80 40
2383 65c. Harlequin sweetlips . . 80 40
2384 90c. Flame angelfish . . . 1·00 80
2385 $1 Queen triggerfish . . . . 1·25 85
2386 $1.20 Spotlight parrotfish 1·50 1·50
2387 $1.45 Black durgon . . . . 1·75 2·00
2388 $2 Glass-eyed snapper . . . 2·50 3·50
2389 $5 Balloonfish . . . . . . 4·00 4·50
2390 $10 Creole wrasse . . . . . 4·00 4·25
2391 $20 Seabass . . . . 8·00 8·25

315 Diana, Princess of Wales

316 "Echo et Narcisse" (Toile)

1997. Diana, Princess of Wales Commemoration. Multicoloured.
2392 $2 Type **315** . . . . 1·25 1·40
2393 $2 Wearing diamond-drop earrings . . . . 1·25 1·40
2394 $2 Resting head on hand . . 1·25 1·40
2395 $2 Wearing tiara . . . . . 1·25 1·40
MS2396 76 × 106 mm. $5 Diana, Princess of Wales . . . . . . 3·50 3·50

1997. Christmas. Paintings.
2397 20c. Type **316** 35 15
2398 55c. "The Archangel Raphael leaving the Family of Tobias" (Rembrandt) 55 35
2399 65c. "Seated Nymphs with Flute" (Francois Boucher) 65 40
2400 90c. "Angel" (Rembrandt) 80 50
2401 $2 "Dispute" (Raphael) . . 1·50 1·75
2402 $4 "Holy Trinity" (Raphael) 2·50 3·25
MS2403 Two sheets, each 114 × 104 mm. (a) $6 "The Annunciation" (Botticelli) (horiz). (b) $6 "Christ on the Mount of Olives" (El Greco) (horiz) Set of 2 sheets . . . . 8·00 9·00
No. **MS**2403a is inscribed "Study (of the) Muse" in error.

317 "Tiger" (Gao Qifeng)

318 Akira Kurosawa

1998. Chinese New Year ("Year of the Tiger"). Multicoloured.
2404 55c. Type **317** 20 25
2405 65c. "Tiger" (Zhao Shao'ang) 25 30
2406 90c. "Tiger" (Gao Jianfu) 35 40
2407 $1.20 "Tiger" (different) (Gao Jianfu) 50 55
MS2408 95 × 65 mm. $3 "Spirit of Kingship" (Gao Jianfu) (48 × 40 mm) . . . . 1·20 1·30

1998. Millennium Series. Famous People of the Twentieth Century. Multicoloured (except Nos. 2411, 2414/15 and **MS**2417). (a) Japanese Cinema Stars.
2409 $1 Type **318** 70 75
2410 $1 "Rashomon" directed by Kursawa (56 × 42 mm) . . 70 75
2411 $1 Toshiro Mifune in "Seven Samurai" (black and grey) (56 × 42 mm) 70 75
2412 $1 Toshiro Mifune 70 75
2413 $1 Yasujiro Ozu 70 75
2414 $1 "Late Spring" directed by Ozu (black and grey) (56 × 42 mm) 70 75
2415 $1 Sessue Hayakawa in "Bridge on the River Kwai" (brown, deep brown and black) (56 × 42 mm) 70 75
2416 $1 Sessue Hayakawa 70 75
MS2417 110 × 80 mm. $6 Akira Kurosawa (brown, red and black) 4·25 4·50

(b) Sporting Record Holders. Multicoloured.
2418 $1 Jesse Owens (winner of four Olympic gold medals, Berlin, 1936) 70 75
2419 $1 Owens competing at Berlin (56 × 42 mm) . . . 70 75
2420 $1 Isaac Berger competing (56 × 42 mm) 70 75
2421 $1 Isaac Berger (weightlifter) 70 75
2422 $1 Boris Becker (Wimbledon champion) 70 75
2423 $1 Boris Becker on court (56 × 42 mm) 70 75
2424 $1 Ashe with Wimbledon trophy (56 × 42 mm) . . . 70 75
2425 $1 Arthur Ashe (1st African-American Wimbledon singles champion, 1975) 70 75
MS2426 $6 Franz Beckenbauer (captain of German football team) (horiz) . . . . 4·25 4·50

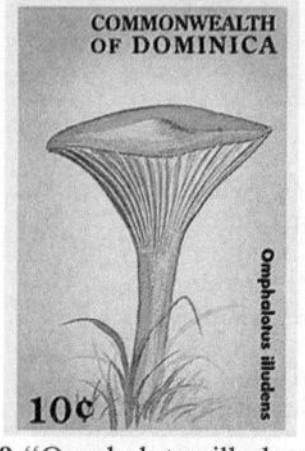

319 "Omphalotus illudens"

1998. Fungi of the World. Multicoloured.
2427 10c. Type **319** 10 10
2428 15c. "Inocybe fastigiata" . . 10 10
2429 20c. "Marasmius plicatulus" 10 15
2430 50c. "Mycena lilacifolia" . . 20 25
2431 55c. "Armillaria straminea" and "Calastrina argiolus" (butterfly) 20 25
2432 90c. "Tricholomopsis rutilans" and "Melitaea didyma" (butterfly) . . . 35 40
2433 $1 "Lepiota naucina" . . . 40 45
2434 $1 "Cortinarius violaceus" 40 45
2435 $1 "Boletus aereus" 40 45
2436 $1 "Tricholoma aurantium" 40 45
2437 $1 "Lepiota procera" . . . 40 45
2438 $1 "Clitocybe geotropa" . . 40 45
2439 $1 "Lepiota acutesquamosa" 40 45
2440 $1 "Tricholoma saponaceum" 40 45
2441 $1 "Lycoperdon gemmatum" 40 45
2442 $1 "Boletus ornatipes" . . . 40 45
2443 $1 "Russula xerampelina" 40 45
2444 $1 "Cortinarius collinitus" 40 45
2445 $1 "Agaricus meleagris" . . 40 45
2446 $1 "Coprinus comatus" . . 40 45
2447 $1 "Amanita caesarea" . . 40 45
2448 $1 "Amanita brunnescens" 40 45
2449 $1 "Amanita muscaria" . . 40 45
2450 $1 "Morchella esculenta" . . 40 45
MS2451 76 × 106 mm. $6 "Cortinarius violaceus" . . . . 2·40 2·50
Nos. 2433/41 and 2442/50 respectively were printed together, se-tenant, with the backgrounds forming composite designs.

320 Topsail Schooner

1998. History of Sailing Ships. Multicoloured.
2452 55c. Type **320** 20 25
2453 55c. "Golden Hind" (Drake) 20 25
2454 55c. "Moshulu" (barque) . . 20 25
2455 55c. "Bluenose" (schooner) 20 25
2456 55c. Roman merchant ship 20 25
2457 55c. "Gazela Primiero" (barquentine) 20 25
2458 65c. Greek war galley . . . 25 30
2459 90c. Egyptian felucca . . . 35 40
2460 $1 Viking longship 40 45
2461 $2 Chinese junk 80 85
MS2462 Two sheets, each 106 × 76 mm. (a) $5 "Pinta" (Columbus). (b) $5 Chesapeake Bay skipjack Set of 2 sheets . . . 4·00 4·25
No. 2457 is inscribed "GAZELA PRIMERIRO", and both Nos. 2458/9 "EGYPTIAN FELUCCA", all in error.

321 "Steamboat Willie", 1928

1998. 70th Anniv of Mickey and Minnie Mouse. Multicoloured.
2463 25c. Type **321** 70 75
2464 55c. "The Brave Little Tailor", 1938 . . . . . . 85 90
2465 65c. "Nifty Nineties", 1941 90 95
2466 90c. "Mickey Mouse Club", 1955 . . . . 1·10 1·25
2467 $1 Mickey and Minnie at opening of Walt Disney World, 1971 . . . . . . 1·10 1·25
2468 $1.45 "Mousercise Mickey and Minnie", 1980 . . . 1·25 1·40
2469 $5 "Runaway Brain", 1995 (97 × 110 mm) . . . . . 2·50 2·75
MS2470 Two sheets, each 130 × 104 mm. (a) $5 Walt Disney with Mickey and Minnie Mouse. (b) $5 Mickey and Minnie at 70th birthday party with Donald and Daisy Duck, Goofy and Pluto. Imperf Set of 2 sheets . . . . 8·00 8·50

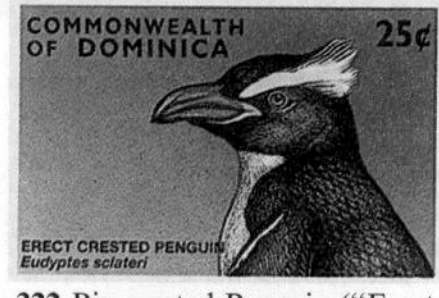

322 Big-crested Penguin ("Erect Crested Penguin")

1998. Sea Birds. Multicoloured.
2471 25c. Type **322** 10 15
2472 65c. Humboldt penguin . . 25 30
2473 90c. Red knot 35 40
2474 90c. Greater crested tern . . 35 40
2475 90c. Franklin's gull 35 40
2476 90c. Australian pelican . . . 35 40
2477 90c. Fairy prion 35 40
2478 90c. Andean gull 35 40
2479 90c. Blue-eyed cormorant ("Imperial Shag") 35 40
2480 90c. Grey phalarope ("Red Phalarope") 35 40
2481 90c. Hooded grebe 35 40
2482 90c. Least auklet 35 40
2483 90c. Little grebe 35 40
2484 90c. Pintado petrel ("Cape Petrel") 35 40
2485 90c. Slavonian grebe ("Horned Grebe") 35 40
2486 $1 Audubon's shearwater 40 45
MS2487 Two sheets, each 100 × 70 mm. (a) $5 Blue-footed booby. (b) $5 Fulmar Set of 2 sheets . . . . 4·00 4·25
Nos. 2474/85 were printed together, se-tenant, with the backgrounds forming a composite design.

323 Jetstar II

1998. Modern Aircraft. Multicoloured.
2488 20c. Type **323** 10 15
2489 25c. AN 225 . . . . 10 15
2490 55c. L.I.A.T. Dash-8 . . . 20 25
2491 65c. Cardinal Airlines, Beech-99 . . . . 25 30
2492 90c. American Airlines Eagle 35 40
2493 $1 SR 71 "Blackbird" spy plane 40 45
2494 $1 Stealth Bomber 40 45
2495 $1 Northrop YF23 . . . . 40 45
2496 $1 F-14A Tomcat 40 45
2497 $1 F-15 Eagle S 40 45
2498 $1 MiG 29 Fulcrum 40 45
2499 $1 Europa X5 . . . . . . 40 45
2500 $1 Camion 40 45
2501 $1 E 400 . . . . 40 45
2502 $1 CL-215 C-GKDN amphibian 40 45
2503 $1 Piper Jet 40 45
2504 $1 Beech Hawker 40 45
2505 $1 Lockheed YF22 . . . . 40 45
2506 $1 Piper Seneca V 40 45
2507 $1 CL-215 amphibian . . . 40 45
2508 $1 Vantase 40 45
2509 $2 Itansa HFB 320 . . . . 80 85
MS2510 Two sheets. (a) 88 × 69 mm. $6 F1 Fighter. (b) 69 × 88 mm. $6 Sea Hopper seaplane Set of 2 sheets . . . . 4·75 5·00

1998. 50th Anniv of Organization of American States. As T **399** of Antigua. Multicoloured.
2511 $1 Stylised Americas 40 45

1998. 25th Death Anniv of Pablo Picasso (painter). As T **400** of Antigua. Multicoloured.
2512 90c. "The Painter and his Model" 35 40
2513 $1 "The Crucifixion" . . . 40 45
2514 $2 "Nude with Raised Arms" (vert) 80 85
MS2515 122 × 102 mm. $6 "Cafe at Royan" . . . . 2·40 2·50

1998. Birth Centenary of Enzo Ferrari (car manufacturer). As T **401** of Antigua. Mult.
2516 55c. 365 GT 2+2 . . . . 70 40
2517 90c. Boano/Ellena 250 GT 90 85
2518 $1 375 MM coupe . . . . 1·10 1·10
MS2519 104 × 70 mm. $5 212 (91 × 34 mm) . . . . 3·75 4·00

1998. 19th World Scout Jamboree, Chile. As T **402** of Antigua. Multicoloured.
2520 65c. Scout saluting 25 30
2521 $1 Scout handshake 40 45
2522 $2 International scout flag 80 85
MS2523 76 × 106 mm. $5 Lord Baden-Powell . . . . 2·00 2·10

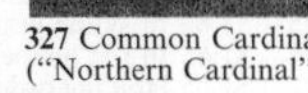

324 Mahatma Gandhi **327** Common Cardinal ("Northern Cardinal")

325 Fridman Fish

1998. 50th Death Anniv of Mahatma Gandhi. Multicoloured.
2524 90c. Type **324** 35 40
MS2525 106 × 75 mm. $6 Gandhi spinning thread . . . . 2·40 2·50

1998. 80th Anniv of Royal Air Force. As T **404** of Antigua. Multicoloured.
2526 $2 H.S. 801 Nimrod MR2P (reconnaissance) 80 85
2527 $2 Lockheed C-130 Hercules (transport) 80 85
2528 $2 Panavia Tornado GR1 80 85
2529 $2 Lockheed C-130 Hercules landing 80 85
MS2530 Two sheets, each 90 × 68 mm. (a) $5 Bristol F2B fighter and Golden eagle (bird). (b) $6 Hawker Hart and EF-2000 Euro-fighter Set of 2 sheets . . 4·50 4·75
No. 2529 is inscribed "Panavia Tornado GR1" in error.

1998. International Year of the Ocean. Multicoloured.
2531 25c. Type **325** 10 15
2532 55c. Hydrocoral 20 25
2533 65c. Feather-star 25 30
2534 90c. Royal angelfish 35 40
2535 $1 Monk seal 40 45
2536 $1 Galapagos penguin . . . 40 45
2537 $1 Manta ray 40 45
2538 $1 Hawksbill turtle 40 45
2539 $1 Moorish idols 40 45
2540 $1 Nautilius 40 45
2541 $1 Giant clam 40 45
2542 $1 Tubeworms 40 45
2543 $1 Nudibranch 40 45
2544 $1 Spotted dolphins 40 45
2545 $1 Atlantic sailfish 40 45
2546 $1 Sailfin flying fish . . . 40 45
2547 $1 Fairy basslet 40 45
2548 $1 Atlantic spadefish . . . 40 45
2549 $1 Leatherback turtle . . . 40 45
2550 $1 Blue tang 40 45
2551 $1 Coral-banded shrimp . . 40 45
2552 $1 Rock beauty 40 45
MS2553 Two sheets, each 110 × 85 mm. (a) $5 Humpback whale and calf (56 × 41 mm). (b) $6 Leafy sea-dragon (56 × 41 mm) Set of 2 sheets . . . . 4·50 4·75
Nos. 2535/43 and 2544/52 respectively were printed together, se-tenant, with the backgrounds forming composite designs.

1998. Save the Turtles Campaign. Nos. 1686/7, 1689/90 and 1692 optd **Save the Turtles**.
2554 25c. Type **263** 10 15
2555 55c. Hawksbill turtle swimming 20 25
2556 90c. Green turtle laying eggs 35 40
2557 $1 Green turtle swimming 40 45
2558 $4 Loggerhead turtle . . . 1·60 1·70

1998. Christmas. Birds. Multicoloured.
2559 25c. Type **327** 10 15
2560 55c. Eastern bluebird . . . 20 25
2561 65c. Carolina wren 25 30
2562 90c. Blue jay 35 40
2563 $1 Evening grosbeak 40 45
2564 $2 Bohemian waxwing . . . 80 85
MS2565 Two sheets, each 70 × 97 mm. (a) $5 Northern Parula. (b) $6 Painted bunting Set of 2 sheets . . . . 4·50 4·75

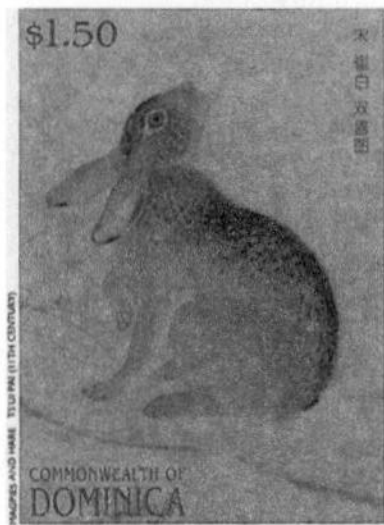

328 "Magpies and Hare" (Ts'ui Pai)

1999. Chinese New Year ("Year of the Rabbit").
2566 **328** $1.50 multicoloured . . 60 65

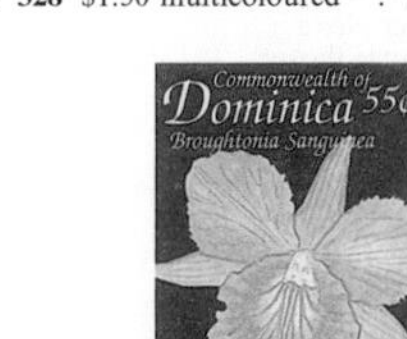

329 "Broughtonia sanguinea"

1999. Orchids of the Caribbean. Multicoloured.
2567 55c. Type **329** 20 25
2568 65c. "Cattleyonia Keith Roth" "Roma" 25 30
2569 90c. "Comparettia falcata" 35 40
2570 $1 "Dracula erythiochaete" 40 45
2571 $1 "Lycasle aromatica" . . 40 45
2572 $1 "Masdevallia marguerile" 40 45
2573 $1 "Encyclia marlae" . . . 40 45
2574 $1 "Laelia gouldiana" . . . 40 45
2575 $1 "Huntleya meleagris" . . 40 45
2576 $1 "Galeandria baueri" . . 40 45
2577 $1 "Lycale deppei" 40 45
2578 $1 "Anguloa clowesii" . . . 40 45
2579 $1 "Lemboglossum cervantesii" 40 45
2580 $1 "Oncidium cebolleta" . . 40 45
2581 $1 "Millonia" 40 45
2582 $1 "Pescatorea lehmannll" 40 45
2583 $1 "Sophronitis coccinea" 40 45
2584 $1 "Pescatorea cerina" . . . 40 45
2585 $1 "Encyclia vitellina" . . . 40 45
2586 $2 "Cochleanthes discolor" 80 85
MS2587 Two sheets, each 76 × 89 mm. (a) $5 "Lepanthes ovalis". (b) $5 "Encyclia cochleata" Set of 2 sheets . . . 4·00 4·25

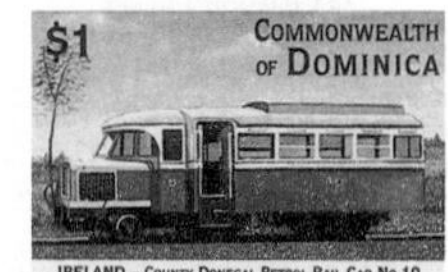

330 County Donegal Petrol Rail Car No. 10, Ireland

1999. "Australia '99" International Stamp Exhibition, Melbourne. Diesel and Electric Trains. Multicoloured.
2588 $1 Type **330** 40 45
2589 $1 Canadian Pacific rail car, Canada 40 45
2590 $1 Class WDM locomotive, India 40 45
2591 $1 Bi-polar locomotive, No. E-2, U.S.A. 40 45
2592 $1 Class X locomotive, Australia 40 45
2593 $1 Class "Beijing" locomotive, China 40 45
2594 $1 Class E428 locomotive, Italy 40 45
2595 $1 Class 581 twelve-car train, Japan 40 45
2596 $1 Class 103.1 locomotive, West Germany 40 45
2597 $1 Class 24 Trans-Pennine train, Great Britain . . . 40 45
2598 $1 Amtrak Class GG1, No. 902, U.S.A. 40 45
2599 $1 Class LRC train, Canada 40 45
2600 $1 Class EW train, New Zealand 40 45
2601 $1 Class SS1 Shao-Shani, China 40 45
2602 $1 Gulf, Mobile and Ohio train, U.S.A. 40 45
2603 $1 Class 9100 locomotive, France 40 45
MS2604 Two sheets, each 106 × 76 mm. (a) $5 X-2000 tilting express train, Sweden (vert). (b) $6 Class 87 locomotive, Great Britain (vert) Set of 2 sheets . . . . . 4·50 4·75
No. 2589 is inscribed "USA - RDC Single Rail Car" in error.

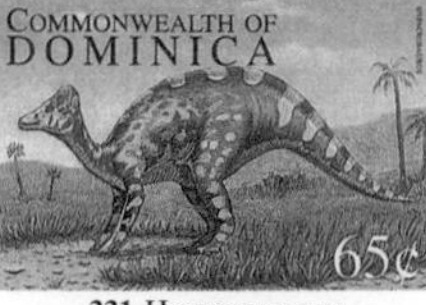

331 Hypacrosaurus

1999. Prehistoric Animals. Multicoloured.
2605 25c. Tyrannosaurus (vert) 10 15
2606 65c. Type **331** 25 30
2607 90c. Sauropelta 35 40
2608 $1 Barosaurus 40 45
2609 $1 Rhamphorhynchus . . . 40 45
2610 $1 Apatosaurus 40 45
2611 $1 Archaeopteryx 40 45
2612 $1 Diplodocus 40 45
2613 $1 Ceratosaurus 40 45
2614 $1 Stegosaurus 40 45
2615 $1 Elaphrosaurus 40 45
2616 $1 Vulcanodon 40 45
2617 $1 Psittacosaurus 40 45
2618 $1 Pteranodon 40 45
2619 $1 Ichthyornis 40 45
2620 $1 Spinosaurus 40 45
2621 $1 Parasaurolophus 40 45
2622 $1 Ornithomimus 40 45
2623 $1 Anatosaurus 40 45
2624 $1 Triceratops 40 45
2625 $1 Baryonx 40 45
2626 $2 Zalambdalestes 80 85
MS2627 Two sheets, each 106 × 80 mm. (a) $5 Yangchuanosaurus. (b) $6 Brachiosaurus (vert) Set of 2 sheets . . . . 4·50 4·75
Nos. 2608/16 and 2617/25 respectively were each printed together, se-tenant, with the backgrounds forming composite designs.

332 Miss Sophie Rhys-Jones

1999. Royal Wedding.
2628 **332** $3 blue and black . . . 1·20 1·30
2629 – $3 multicoloured . . . . 1·20 1·30
2630 – $3 blue and black . . . 1·20 1·30
MS2631 78 × 108 mm. $6 multicoloured . . . . 2·40 2·50
DESIGNS: No. 2629 and **MS**2631, Miss Sophie Rhys-Jones and Prince Edward; 2630, Prince Edward.

1999. "iBRA '99" International Stamp Exhibition, Nuremberg. As T **416** of Antigua. Multicoloured.
2632 65c. "Eendracht" (Dirk Hartog) with Cameroons Expeditionary Force 1915 2d. and 3d. surcharges . . 25 30
2633 90c. "Eendracht" with Kamerun 1900 10pf. and 25pf. stamps 35 40
2634 $1 Early German railway locomotive with Kamerun 1900 5m. stamp 40 45
2635 $2 Early German railway locomotive with Kamerun 1890 overprinted 50pf. stamp 80 85
MS2636 138 × 109 mm. $6 Exhibition emblem and Kamerun 5m. stamp postmarked 1913 . . 2·40 2·50

1999. 150th Death Anniv of Katsushika Hokusai (Japanese artist). As T **417** of Antigua, but vert. Multicoloured.
2637 $2 "Pilgrims at Kirifuri Waterfall" 80 85
2638 $2 "Kakura-Sato" (rats pulling on rope) 80 85
2639 $2 "Travellers on the Bridge by Ono Waterfall" . . . 80 85
2640 $2 "Fast Cargo Boat battling the Waves" . . . 80 85
2641 $2 "Kakura-Sato" (rats with barrels) 80 85
2642 $2 "Buufinfinh and Weeping Cherry" 80 85
2643 $2 "Cuckoo and Azalea" . . 80 85
2644 $2 "Soldiers" (with lamp) 80 85
2645 $2 "Lovers in the Snow" . . 80 85
2646 $2 "Ghost of Koheiji" . . . 80 85
2647 $2 "Soldiers" (with hand on hip) 80 85
2648 $2 "Chinese Poet in Snow" 80 85
MS2649 Two sheets, each 101 × 72 mm. (a) $5 "Empress Jito". (b) $6 "One Hundred Poems by One Hundred Poets" Set of 2 sheets . . . . 4·50 4·75

1999. 10th Anniv of United Nations Rights of the Child Convention. As T **419** of Antigua. Multicoloured.
2650 $3 Small girl (vert) . . . . 1·20 1·30
2651 $3 Small boy (vert) . . . . 1·20 1·30
2652 $3 Small boy and girl (vert) 1·20 1·30
MS2653 85 × 110 mm. $6 Peace dove 2·40 2·50
Nos. 2650/2 were printed together, se-tenant, forming a composite design which continues onto the sheet margins.

1999. "PhilexFrance '99" International Stamp Exhibition, Paris. Railway Locomotives. Two sheets, each containing horiz designs as T **420** of Antigua. Multicoloured.
MS2654 Two sheets, each 106 × 81 mm. (a) $5 Steam locomotive "L'Aigle", 1855. (b) $6 Mainline diesel locomotive, 1963 Set of 2 sheets . . . . 4·50 4·75

1999. 250th Birth Anniv of Johann von Goethe (German writer). As T **421** of Antigua.
2655 $2 multicoloured 80 85
2656 $2 blue, purple and black 80 85
2657 $2 multicoloured 80 85
MS2658 76 × 100 mm. $6 grey, black and brown . . . . 2·40 2·50
DESIGNS—HORIZ: No. 2655, Faust and astrological sign; 2656, Von Goethe and Von Schiller; 2657, Faust tempted by Mephistopheles. VERT: No. **MS**2658, Johann von Goethe.

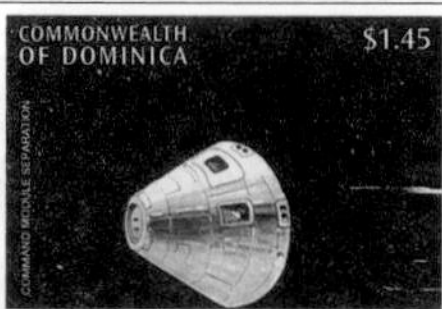

333 Command Module

1999. 30th Anniv of First Manned Landing on Moon. Multicoloured.
2659 $1.45 Type **333** 60 65
2660 $1.45 Service module . . . 60 65
2661 $1.45 Booster separation . . 60 65
2662 $1.45 Lunar and command modules 60 65
2663 $1.45 Tracking telescope . . 60 65
2664 $1.45 Goldstone radio telescope 60 65
MS2665 106 × 76 mm. $6 "Apollo 11" after splashdown 2·40 2·50

1999. "Queen Elizabeth the Queen Mother's Century". As T **444** of Antigua.
2666 $2 black and gold 80 85
2667 $2 black and gold 80 85
2668 $2 multicoloured 80 85
2669 $2 multicoloured 80 85
MS2670 153 × 157 mm. $6 multicoloured . . . . 2·40 2·50
DESIGNS: No. 2666, Queen Elizabeth, 1939; 2667, Queen Mother in Australia, 1958; 2668, Queen Mother in blue hat and coat, 1982; 2669, Queen Mother laughing, 1982. (37 × 50 mm)—No. **MS**2670, Queen Mother in 1953.

334 Female Dancer and "DOMFESTA" **335** Family

1999. 21st Anniv of Dominica Festivals Commission. Multicoloured.
2671 25c. Type **334** 10 15
2672 55c. "21st BIRTHDAY" logo 20 25
2673 65c. Carnival Development Committee emblem . . . 25 30
2674 90c. World Creole music emblem 35 40
MS2675 90 × 90 mm. $5 "21st BIRTHDAY" logo (different) (33 × 48 mm) . . . . 2·00 2·10

1999. International Year of the Elderly. Sheet 90 × 50 mm, containing T **335** and similar vert designs. Multicoloured.
MS2676 25c. Type **335**; 65c. Parents and grandparents; 90c. Family around elderly woman in chair 75 80

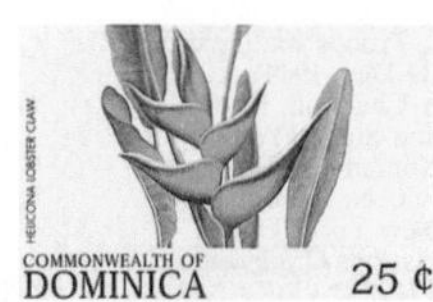

336 Helicona Lobster Claw

1999. Flora and Fauna. Multicoloured.
2677 25c. Type **336** 10 15
2678 65c. Broad-winged hawk . . 25 30
2679 90c. White-throated sparrow 35 40
2680 90c. Blue-winged teal . . . 35 40
2681 90c. Racoon 35 40
2682 90c. Alfalfa butterfly 35 40
2683 90c. Foot bridge 35 40
2684 90c. Whitetail deer 35 40
2685 90c. Grey squirrel 35 40
2686 90c. Banded-purple butterfly 35 40
2687 90c. Snowdrops 35 40
2688 90c. Bullfrog 35 40
2689 90c. Mushrooms 35 40
2690 90c. Large-blotched ensatina 35 40
2691 $1 Anthurium 40 45
2692 $1.55 Blue-headed hummingbird 65 70
2693 $2 Bananaquit 80 85
2694 $4 Agouti . . . . 1·60 1·70
MS2695 Two sheets, each 100 × 70 mm. (a) $5 Eastern chipmunk. (b) $6 Black-footed ferret Set of 2 sheets . . . . . 4·50 4·75
Nos. 2679/90 were printed together, se-tenant, with the backgrounds forming a composite design.

337 Yellow-crowned Parrot

338 Bombing of Pearl Harbor, 1941

1999. Christmas. Birds. Multicoloured.
2696 25c. Type **337** 10 15
2697 55c. Red bishop 20 25
2698 65c. Troupial 25 30
2699 90c. Puerto Rican woodpecker 35 40
2700 $2 Mangrove cuckoo . . . 80 85
2701 $3 American robin . . . . 1·20 1·30
MS2702 76 × 98 mm. $6 "Mary with Child beside the Wall" (Dürer) (drab, black and cream) . . . 2·40 2·50
No. 2699 is inscribed "PUERTO RECAN WOODPECKER" and No. **MS**2702 "MARYWITH", both in error.

1999. New Millennium. People and Events of Thirteenth Century (1200–50). As T **445** of Antigua. Multicoloured.
2703 55c. Leonardo Fibonacci (mathematician, 1202) . . 20 25
2704 55c. St. Francis of Assisi (founder of Franciscan Order, 1207) 20 25
2705 55c. Mongol horsemen (Conquest of China, 1211) 20 25
2706 55c. Children with banner (Children's Crusade, 1212) 20 25
2707 55c. King John signing Magna Carta, 1215 . . . 20 25
2708 55c. University class (foundation of Salamanca University, 1218) 20 25
2709 55c. Snorre Sturlusson (author of the "Edda", 1222) 20 25
2710 55c. Ma Yuan (Chinese painter) in garden (died 1224) 20 25
2711 55c. Genghis Khan (Mongol Emperor) (died 1227) . . 20 25
2712 55c. Student and Buddha (establishment of Zen Buddhism in Japan, 1227) 20 25
2713 55c. Galleys (The Sixth Crusade, 1228) 20 25
2714 55c. Seals (Lubeck–Hamburg Treaty, 1230) 20 25
2715 55c. Cardinal and angel (Holy Inquisition, 1231) 20 25
2716 55c. Palace interior (conquest of Cordoba, 1236) 20 25
2717 55c. San Marino (town founded, 1243) 20 25
2718 55c. Maimonides (Jewish philosopher) (died 1204) (59 × 39 mm) 20 25
2719 55c. Notre Dame Cathedral, Paris (completed 1250) . . 20 25

1999. New Millennium. People and Events of Twentieth Century (1940–49). Multicoloured.
2720 55c. Type **338** 20 25
2721 55c. Sir Winston Churchill (British Prime Minister, 1940) 20 25
2722 55c. Children in front of set (start of television broadcasting in U.S.A., 1940) 20 25
2723 55c. Anne Frank (Holocaust, 1942) 20 25
2724 55c. Troops wading ashore (D-Day, 1944) 20 25
2725 55c. Churchill, Roosevelt and Stalin (Yalta Conference, 1945) 20 25
2726 55c. U.N. Headquarters, New York (United Nations Organization, 1945) 20 25
2727 55c. American G.I. and concentration camp (Surrender of Germany, 1945) 20 25
2728 55c. Hoisting the Red Flag on the Reichstag (Fall of Berlin, 1945) 20 25
2729 55c. "Eniac" (first operational computer, 1946) 20 25
2730 55c. Indian with flag (Independence of India, 1947) 20 25
2731 55c. Early transistor, 1947 20 25
2732 55c. Mahatma Gandhi assassinated, 1948 . . . . 20 25
2733 55c. Israelis with flag (Establishment of Israel, 1948) 20 25
2734 55c. Aircraft and children (Berlin Airlift, 1948) . . . 20 25
2735 55c. Atomic bomb test, New Mexico, 1948 (59 × 39 mm) 20 25
2736 55c. Great Wall of China (People's Republic established, 1949) 20 25
No. 2732 is inscribed "Ghandi" in error.

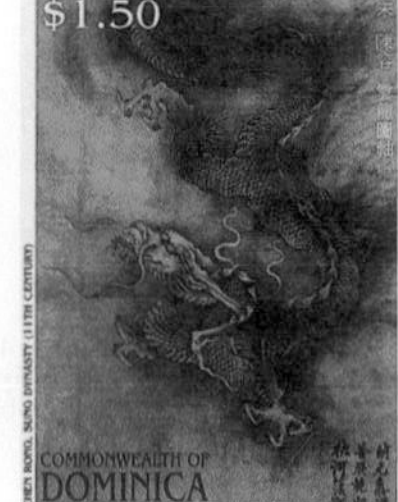

339 "Dragon flying in the Mist" (Chen Rong)

2000. Chinese New Year ("Year of the Dragon"). Multicoloured.
2737 $1.50 Type **339** 60 65
MS2738 80 × 60 mm. $4 Red dragon (horiz) . . . . 1·60 1·70

340 European Shorthair

2000. Cats and Dogs of the World. Multicoloured.
2739 $1 Type **340** 40 45
2740 $1 Devon rex 40 45
2741 $1 Chartreux 40 45
2742 $1 Bengal 40 45
2743 $1 American wirehair . . . 40 45
2744 $1 Siberian 40 45
2745 $1 Burmese 40 45
2746 $1 American shorthair . . . 40 45
2747 $1 Asian longhair 40 45
2748 $1 Burmilla 40 45
2749 $1 Snowshoe 40 45
2750 $1 Pekeface Persian 40 45
2751 $1 Himalayan Persian . . . 40 45
2752 $1 Japanese bobtail 40 45
2753 $1 Seychelles longhair . . . 40 45
2754 $1 Exotic shorthair 40 45
2755 $1 Jack Russell puppy (vert) 40 45
2756 $1 Shar pei puppies (vert) 40 45
2757 $1 Basset hound puppy (vert) 40 45
2758 $1 Boxer puppies (vert) . . 40 45
2759 $1 Wire-haired terrier (cross) puppy (vert) 40 45
2760 $1 Golden retriever puppies (vert) 40 45
MS2761 Three sheets, each 101 × 81 mm. (a) $6 Sleeping cat. (b) $6 Grey cat with yellow eyes. (c) $6 Beagle puppy (vert) Set of 3 sheets . . . . 7·25 7·50

341 Flowers forming Top of Head

2000. Faces of the Millennium: Diana, Princess of Wales. Designs showing collage of miniature flower photographs. Multicoloured.
2762 $1 Type **341** (face value at left) 40 45
2763 $1 Top of head (face value at right) 40 45
2764 $1 Ear (face value at left) 40 45
2765 $1 Eye and temple (face value at right) 40 45
2766 $1 Cheek (face value at left) 40 45
2767 $1 Cheek (face value at right) 40 45
2768 $1 Blue background (face value at left) 40 45
2769 $1 Chin (face value at right) 40 45
Nos. 2762/9 were printed together, se-tenant, in sheetlets of 8 with the stamps arranged in two vertical columns separated by a gutter also containing miniature photographs. When viewed as a whole, the sheetlet forms a portrait of Diana, Princess of Wales.

342 Giant Swallowtail

2000. Butterflies. Multicoloured.
2770 $1.50 Type **342** 60 65
2771 $1.50 Tiger pierid 60 65
2772 $1.50 Orange theope butterfly 60 65
2773 $1.50 White peacock 60 65
2774 $1.50 Blue tharops 60 65
2775 $1.50 Mosaic 60 65
2776 $1.50 Banded king shoemaker 60 65
2777 $1.50 Figure-of-eight butterfly 60 65
2778 $1.50 Grecian shoemaker . . 60 65
2779 $1.50 Blue night butterfly 60 65
2780 $1.50 Monarch 60 65
2781 $1.50 Common morpho . . 60 65
2782 $1.50 Orange-barred sulphur 60 65
2783 $1.50 Clorinde 60 65
2784 $1.50 Small flambeau . . . 60 65
2785 $1.50 Small lace-wing . . . 60 65
2786 $1.50 Polydamas swallowtail 60 65
2787 $1.50 The atala 60 65
MS2788 Three sheets, each 100 × 70 mm. (a) $6 Polydamas swallowtail (vert). (b) $6 Blue-green reflector (vert). (c) $6 Sloane's urania (vert) Set of 3 sheets . . . . 7·25 7·50

343 Passion Flower

2000. Flowers. Multicoloured. (a) Size 28 × 42 mm.
2789 65c. Type **343** 25 30
2790 90c. Spray orchid 35 40
2791 $1 Peach angels trumpet . . 40 45
2792 $4 Allamanda . . . . . . 1·60 1·70

(b) Size 32 × 48 mm.
2793 $1.65 Bird of paradise . . . 65 70
2794 $1.65 Lobster claw heliconia 65 70
2795 $1.65 Candle bush 65 70
2796 $1.65 Flor de San Miguel 65 70
2797 $1.65 Hibiscus 65 70
2798 $1.65 Oleander 65 70
2799 $1.65 Anthurium 65 70
2800 $1.65 Fire ginger 65 70
2801 $1.65 Shrimp plant 65 70
2802 $1.65 Sky vine thumbergia 65 70
2803 $1.65 Ceriman 65 70
2804 $1.65 Morning glory 65 70
MS2805 Two sheets, each 76 × 106 mm. (a) $6 Bird of Paradise and butterfly (38 × 50 mm). (b) $6 Hibiscus and hummingbird (38 × 50 mm) Set of 2 sheets . . . . . . 4·75 5·00
Nos. 2793/8 and 2799/804 were each printed together, se-tenant, with the backgrounds forming composite designs.

2000. 400th Birth Anniv of Sir Anthony Van Dyck (Flemish painter). As T **429** of Antigua. Multicoloured.
2806 $1.65 "The Ages of Man" (horiz) 65 70
2807 $1.65 "Portrait of a Girl as Ermina accompanied by Cupid" (horiz) 65 70
2808 $1.65 "Cupid and Psyche" (horiz) 65 70
2809 $1.65 "Vertumnus and Pomona" (horiz) 65 70
2810 $1.65 "The Continence of Scipio" (horiz) 65 70
2811 $1.65 "Diana and Endymion surprised by a Satyr" (horiz) 65 70
2812 $1.65 "Ladies-in-Waiting" (horiz) 65 70
2813 $1.65 "Thomas Wentworth, Earl of Strafford, with Sir Philip Mainwaring" (horiz) 65 70
2814 $1.65 "Dorothy Rivers Savage, Viscountess Andover, and her sister Lady Elizabeth Thimbleby" (horiz) . . . 65 70
2815 $1.65 "Mountjoy Blount, Earl of Newport, and Lord George Goring with a Page" (horiz) 65 70
2816 $1.65 "Thomas Killigrew and an Unidentified Man" (horiz) 65 70
2817 $1.65 "Elizabeth Villiers, Lady Dalkeith, and Cecilia Killigrew" (horiz) 65 70
2818 $1.65 "Lady Jane Goodwin (Mrs. Arthur)" 65 70
2819 $1.65 "Philip Herbert, Earl of Pembroke" 65 70
2820 $1.65 "Philip, Lord Wharton" 65 70
2821 $1.65 "Sir Thomas Hammer" 65 70
2822 $1.65 "Olivia Porter" . . . 65 70
2823 $1.65 "Sir Thomas Chaloner" 65 70
MS2824 Three sheets, each 128 × 103 mm. (a) $5 "Archilles and the Daughters of Lycomedes" (vert). (b) $5 "Amaryllis and Mirtilo" (vert). (c) $6 "Aletheia, Countess of Arundel" (vert) Set of 3 sheets . . . . 6·50 6·75
No. 2813 is inscribed "Wenthworth" in error.

2000. 18th Birthday of Prince William. As T **433** of Antigua. Multicoloured.
2825 $1.65 In skiing gear 65 70
2826 $1.65 In red jumper 65 70
2827 $1.65 Holding order of service 65 70
2828 $1.65 Prince William laughing 65 70
MS2829 100 × 80 mm. $6 Prince William with Prince Harry (37 × 50 mm) . . . . 2·40 2·50

2000. "EXPO 2000" World Stamp Exhibition, Anaheim. Space Satellites. As T **434** of Antigua. Multicoloured.
2830 $1.65 "Essa 8" 65 70
2831 $1.65 "Echo 1" 65 70
2832 $1.65 "Topex Poseidon" . . 65 70
2833 $1.65 "Diademe" 65 70
2834 $1.65 "Early Bird" 65 70
2835 $1.65 "Molyna" 65 70
2836 $1.65 "Explorer 14" 65 70
2837 $1.65 "Luna 16" 65 70
2838 $1.65 "Copernicus" 65 70
2839 $1.65 "Explorer 16" 65 70
2840 $1.65 "Luna 10" 65 70
2841 $1.65 "Arybhattan" 65 70
MS2842 Two sheets, each 106 × 76 mm. (a) $6 "Eole". (b) $6 "Hipparcos" . . . . 4·75 5·00
Nos. 2830/5 and 2836/41 were printed together, se-tenant, with the backgrounds forming composite designs.

2000. 25th Anniv of "Apollo–Soyuz" Joint Project. As T **435** of Antigua. Multicoloured.
2843 $3 Saturn 1B ("Apollo" launch vehicle) . . . . . 1·20 1·30
2844 $3 "Apollo 18" command module . . . . 1·20 1·30
2845 $3 Donald Slayton ("Apollo 18" crew) . . . . 1·20 1·30
MS2846 88 × 71 mm. $6 Spacecraft about to dock (horiz) . . . . 2·40 2·50
No. 2843 is inscribed "Vechicle" in error.

2000. 50th Anniv of Berlin Film Festival. As T **436** of Antigua. Multicoloured.
2847 $1.65 Satyajit Ray (director of Ashani Sanket) 65 70
2848 $1.65 *Mahanagar*, 1964 . . . 65 70
2849 $1.65 *La Tulipe*, 1952 . . . 65 70
2850 $1.65 *Le Salaire de la Peur*, 1953 . . . . 65 70
2851 $1.65 *Les Cousins*, 1959 . . . 65 70
2852 $1.65 *Hon Dansade en Sommar*, 1952 . . . . . 65 70
MS2853 97 × 103 mm. $6 *Buffalo Bill and the Indians*, 1976 . . . . . 2·40 2·50

2000. 175th Anniv of Stockton and Darlington Line (first public railway). As T **437** of Antigua. Multicoloued.
2854 $3 George Stephenson and *Locomotion No. 1*, 1875 1·20 1·30
2855 $3 John B. Jervis's *Brother Jonathan*, 1832 . . . . . 1·20 1·30
No. 2855 is inscribed "Jonathon" in error.

2000. 250th Death Anniv of Johann Sebastian Bach (German composer). Sheet 77 × 88 mm, containing vert portrait as T **438** of Antigua.
MS2856 $6 brown and black . . 2·40 2·50

2000. Election of Albert Einstein (mathematical physicist) as *Time Magazine* "Man of the Century". Sheet 117 × 91 mm, containing vert portrait as T **439** of Antigua.
MS2857 $6 multicoloured . . . . 2·40 2·50

344 Count Ferdinand von Zeppelin

2000. Centenary of First Zeppelin Flight. Mult.
2858 $1.65 Type **344** 65 70
2859 $1.65 LZ-1 at Lake Constance, 1900 . . . . 65 70
2860 $1.65 LZ-10 *Schwaben*, over flock of sheep, 1911 . . . 65 70
2861 $1.65 LZ-6 and LZ-7 *Deutschland* in hangar, Friedrichshafen 65 70
2862 $1.65 LZ-4 at Luneville, 1913 . . . . 65 70
2863 $1.65 LZ-11 *Viktoria-Luise* over Kiel Harbour . . . 65 70
MS2864 93 × 115 mm. $6 As No. 2859 . . . . 2·40 2·50
No. 2861 is inscribed "Friedrichshrfed" in error.

2000. Olympic Games, Sydney. As T **441** of Antigua. Multicoloured.
2865 $2 Jesse Owens (athletics), Berlin (1936) 80 85
2866 $2 Pole-vaulting 80 85

2867 $2 Lenin Stadium, Moscow (1980) and U.S.S.R. flag . . . 80 85
2868 $2 Ancient Greek discus-thrower 80 85

2000. West Indies Cricket Tour and 100th Test Match at Lord's. As T **442** of Antigua. Multicoloured.
2869 $4 Norbert Phillip . . . . . 1·60 1·70
MS2870 121 × 104 mm. $6 Lord's Cricket Ground (horiz) . . . . 2·40 2·50
No. 2869 is inscribed "Phillp" in error.

2000. 80th Birthday of Pope John Paul II. As T **341**, showing collage of miniature religious photographs. Multicoloured.
2871 $1 Top of head (face value at left) 40 45
2872 $1 Top of head (face value at right) 40 45
2873 $1 Ear (face value at left) 40 45
2874 $1 Forehead (face value at right) 40 45
2875 $1 Neck (face value at left) 40 45
2876 $1 Cheek (face value at right) 40 45
2877 $1 Shoulder (face value at left) 40 45
2878 $1 Hands (face value at right) 40 45
Nos. 2871/8 were printed together, se-tenant, in sheetlets of 8 with the stamps arranged in two vertical columns separated by a gutter also containing miniature photographs. When viewed as a whole, the sheetlet forms a portrait of Pope John Paul.

345 Roger the Shrubber

2000. *Monty Python and the Holy Grail* (comedy film). Multicoloured.
2879 90c. Type **345** 35 40
2880 90c. Three-headed giant . . 35 40
2881 90c. Attacking the castle . . 35 40
2882 90c. King Arthur and knight 35 40
2883 90c. Headless knight 35 40
2884 90c. Limbless Black Knight 35 40

346 Member of The Crystals 347 Bob Hope singing

2000. Famous Girl Pop Groups. The Crystals. Mult.
2885 90c. Type **346** 35 40
2886 90c. Group member with long hair (blue background in top right corner) 35 40
2887 90c. Group member with long hair (yellow background in top right corner) 35 40
2888 90c. Group member with short hair 35 40
Nos. 2885/8 were printed together, se-tenant, forming a composite design.

2000. Bob Hope (American entertainer).
2889 **347** $1.65 black, blue and lilac 65 70
2890 – $1.65 multicoloured . . 65 70
2891 – $1.65 black, blue and lilac 65 70
2892 – $1.65 multicoloured . . 65 70
2893 – $1.65 black, blue and lilac 65 70
2894 – $1.65 multicoloured . . 65 70
DESIGNS: No. 2890, Entertaining troops; 2891, As English comic character; 2892, In 50th birthday cake; 2893, Making radio broadcast; 2894, With Man in the Moon.

348 David Copperfield 349 First Birth-control Pill, 1961

2000. David Copperfield (conjurer).
2895 **348** $2 multicoloured 80 85

2000. Monarchs of the Millennium. As T **447** of Antigua.
2896 $1.65 multicoloured 65 70
2897 $1.65 black, stone and brown 65 70
2898 $1.65 multicoloured 65 70
2899 $1.65 black, stone and brown 65 70
2900 $1.65 multicoloured 65 70
2901 $1.65 black, stone and brown 65 70
MS2902 115 × 135 mm. $6 multicoloured . . . . 2·40 2·50
DESIGNS: No. 2896, King Edward IV of England; 2897, Tsar Peter the Great of Russia; 2898, King Henry VI of England; 2899, King Henry III of England; 2900, King Richard III of England; 2901, King Edward I of England; **MS**2902, King Henry VIII of England.

2000. Popes of the Millennium. As T **447** of Antigua. Each black, yellow and green.
2903 $1.65 Clement X 65 70
2904 $1.65 Innocent X 65 70
2905 $1.65 Nicholas V 65 70
2906 $1.65 Martin V 65 70
2907 $1.65 Julius III 65 70
2908 $1.65 Innocent XII 65 70
MS2909 115 × 135 mm. $6 Clement XIV (brown, yellow and black) 2·40 2·50

2000. Christmas and Holy Year. As T **452** of Antigua. Multicoloured.
2910 25c. Angel in blue robe . . 10 15
2911 65c. Young angel 25 30
2912 90c. Angel with drapery . . 35 40
2913 $1.90 As 25c. 75 80
2914 $1.90 As 65c. 75 80
2915 $1.90 As 90c. 75 80
2916 $1.90 As $5 . . . . 75 80
2917 $5 Head and shoulders of angel . . . . 2·00 2·10
MS2918 110 × 120 mm. $6 Angel's face (as 25c.) . . . . 2·40 2·50

2000. New Millennium. People and Events of the Fourteenth Century (1350–1400). As T **445** of Antigua. Multicoloured.
2919 65c. Couple with hawk (Minnesangers in Germany, 1350) 25 30
2920 65c. Acamapitzin, first King of the Aztecs, 1352 . . . 25 30
2921 65c. Rat (end of Black Death, 1353) 25 30
2922 65c. Giotto's *Campanile* (completed by Francesco Talenti, 1355) 25 30
2923 65c. First French franc, 1360 . . . . 25 30
2924 65c. Emperor Hung-wu (foundation of Ming Dynasty, 1360) 25 30
2925 65c. Tamerlane (foundation of Timurid Empire, 1369) 25 30
2926 65c. "Triumph of Death" (Francis Traini), 1370 . . 25 30
2927 65c. Robin Hood (first appearance in English legends, 1375) 25 30
2928 65c. "The Knight" (The Canterbury Tales by Geoffrey Chaucer, 1387) 25 30
2929 65c. Mounted samurai (disputed succession in Japan, 1392) 25 30
2930 65c. Refugees (Jews expelled from France, 1394) . . . 25 30
2931 65c. Temple of the Golden Pavilion, Kyoto (constructed, 1394) . . . 25 30
2932 65c. Carving, Strasbourg Cathedral (completed, 1399) 25 30
2933 65c. Alhambra Palace, Granada (completed, 1390) (60 × 40 mm) . . . 25 30
2934 65c. Ife Bronzes produced in Nigeria, 1400 . . . . . 25 30
No. 2929 is inscribed "SUDDESSION" in error.

2000. New Millennium. Two Thousand Years of Chinese Paintings. As T **446** of Antigua. Mult.
2935 55c. "Eight Prize Steeds" (Guiseppe Castiglione) . . 20 25
2936 55c. "Oleanders" (Wu Hsi Tsai) 20 25
2937 55c. "Mynah and Autumn Flowers" (Chang Hsiung) 20 25
2938 55c. "Hen and Chicks beneath Chrysanthemums," (Chu Ch'ao) 20 25
2939 55c. "Long Living Pine and Crane" (Xugu) 20 25
2940 55c. "Flowers and Fruits" (Chu Lien) 20 25
2941 55c. "Lotus and Willow" (Pu Hua) 20 25
2942 55c. "Kuan-Yin" (Ch'ien Hui-an) 20 25
2943 55c. "Human Figures" (Jen Hsun) 20 25
2944 55c. "Han-Shan and Shih-Te" (Ren Yi) 20 25
2945 55c. "Landscape and Human Figure" (Jen Yu) 20 25
2946 55c. "Poetic Thoughts while Walking with a Staff" (Wangchen) 20 25
2947 55c. "Peony" (Chen Heng-ko) 20 25
2948 55c. "Plum and Orchid" (Wu Chang-shih) 20 25
2949 55c. "Monkey" (Kao Chi-feng) 20 25
2950 55c. "Grapes and Locust" (Chi Pai-shih); and "Galloping Horse" (Xu Beihong) (60 × 40 mm) . . 20 25
2951 55c. "The Beauty" (Lin Fengmian) 20 25
No. 2937 is inscribed "YNAH" and No. 2948 "ORCHIS", both in error.

2000. New Millennium. People and Events of Twentieth Century (1960–69). Multicoloured.
2952 55c. Type **349** 20 25
2953 55c. Yuri Gagarin (first man in Space), 1961 . . . . . 20 25
2954 55c. Fans with The Beatles tickets, 1962 . . . . . . 20 25
2955 55c. Funeral of President John F. Kennedy, 1963 20 25
2956 55c. Martin Luther King's "I Have a Dream" speech, 1963 . . . . . . 20 25
2957 55c. Betty Friedan (author of *The Feminist Mystique*), 1963 . . . . 20 25
2958 55c. Duke of Edinburgh and Jomo Kenyatta (independence of Kenya), 1963 . . . . 20 25
2959 55c. Anti-smoking poster, 1964 . . . . 20 25
2960 55c. Civil Rights demonstrators (U.S. Civil Rights Act), 1964 . . . . 20 25
2961 55c. Troops outside Saigon (U.S. involvement in Vietnam), 1965 . . . . . 20 25
2962 55c. Ernesto "Che" Guevara (Cuban revolutionary) killed in Peru, 1965 . . . 20 25
2963 55c. Dr. Christiaan Barnard (first heart transplant operation), 1967 . . . . 20 25
2964 55c. General Moshe Dayan addressing Arabs ("Six-Day" War), 1967 . . . . 20 25
2965 55c. Death of Ho Chi Minh (North Vietnamese leader), 1969 . . . . . . 20 25
2966 55c. Neil Armstrong on the Moon, 1969 . . . . . . 20 25
2967 55c. Couple at Berlin Wall, 1961 (60 × 40 mm) 20 25
2968 55c. Woodstock Festival, 1969 . . . . 20 25

350 Ancient Star Signs

2000. New Millennium. Inventions. Multicoloured.
2969 55c. Type **350** 20 25
2970 55c. Precision tools 20 25
2971 55c. Astral chart 20 25
2972 55c. Growth of medicine . . 20 25
2973 55c. Exchange of medical information 20 25
2974 55c. Monastic chapterhouse 20 25
2975 55c. Water alarm clock . . 20 25
2976 55c. Weighted clock 20 25
2977 55c. Spring-loaded miniature clock movement 20 25
2978 55c. Glass blowing 20 25
2979 55c. Early screws 20 25
2980 55c. Wood lathe 20 25
2981 55c. Ship building 20 25
2982 55c. Interchangeable rifle parts 20 25
2983 55c. Study of movement . . 20 25
2984 55c. The Industrial Revolution (60 × 40 mm) 20 25
2985 55c. Concept of efficiency 20 25

351 "Snake in the Wilderness" (Hwa Yan)

2001. Chinese New Year. "Year of the Snake".
2986 **351** $1.20 multicoloured . . 50 55

352 Female Green-throated Carib

2001. Hummingbirds. Multicoloured.
2987 $1.25 Type **352** 50 55
2988 $1.25 Male bee hummingbird ("Mellisuga helenae") 50 55
2989 $1.25 Male bee hummingbird ("Russelia eqoisetiformis") 50 55
2990 $1.25 Female bahama woodstar 50 55
2991 $1.25 Antillean mango . . . 50 55
2992 $1.25 Female blue-headed hummingbird 50 55
2993 $1.65 Male streamertail . . 65 70
2994 $1.65 Purple-throated carib 65 70
2995 $1.65 Vervain hummingbird 65 70
2996 $1.65 Bahama woodstar . . 65 70
2997 $1.65 Puerto Rican emerald 65 70
2998 $1.65 Antillean crested hummingbird 65 70
MS2999 Two sheets. (a) $5 Unidentified hummingbird. (b) $6 Hispaniolan emerald Set of 2 sheets . . . . 4·50 4·75
Nos. 2987/92 and 2993/8 were each printed together, se-tenant, with the backgrounds forming composite designs.
No. 2987 is inscribed "Fehale Greentrioated Carib", No. 2990 "Tenale", No. 2994 "Trirоated", No. 2998 "Cresteo" and No. **MS**2999b "Hispaniolian", all in error.
No. 2989 carries the inscription "Russelia eqoisetiformis". This should read "Russelia equisetiformis", and refers to the plant (commonly known as a Firecracker Plant) at the bottom of the stamp, not the hummingbird.

353 Puerto Rican Crested Toad

2001. Caribbean and Latin-American Fauna. Mult.
3000 15c. Type **353** 10 10
3001 20c. Axolotl 10 15
3002 $1.45 St. Vincent amazon ("St. Vincent Parrot") . . 60 65
3003 $1.45 Indigo macaw 60 65
3004 $1.45 Guianian cock of the rock ("Cock of the Rock") 60 65
3005 $1.45 Cuban solenodon . . 60 65
3006 $1.45 Cuban hutia 60 65
3007 $1.45 Chinchilla 60 65
3008 $1.45 Chilian flamingo ("South American Flamingo") 60 65
3009 $1.45 Golden conure . . . 60 65
3010 $1.45 Ocelot 60 65
3011 $1.45 Giant armadillo . . . 60 65
3012 $1.45 Margay 60 65
3013 $1.45 Maned wolf 60 65
3014 $1.90 Panamanian golden frog 75 80
3015 $2.20 Manatee 90 95
MS3016 Two sheets, each 106 × 71 mm. (a) $6 Hawksbill turtle. (b) $6 Anteater Set of 2 sheets . . . . 4·75 5·00
Nos. 3002/7 and 3008/13 were each printed together, se-tenant, with the backgrounds forming composite designs.

2001. Characters from "Pokemon" (children's cartoon series). As T **454** of Antigua. Multicoloured.
3017 $1.65 "Butterfree No. 12" 65 70
3018 $1.65 "Bulbasaur No. 01" 65 70
3019 $1.65 "Caterpie No. 10" . . 65 70
3020 $1.65 "Charmander No. 04" 65 70

3021 $1.65 "Squirtle No. 07" . . 65 70
3022 $1.65 "Pidgeotto No. 17" 65 70
MS3023 75 × 105 mm. $6 "Nidoking No. 34" . . . . 2·40 2·50

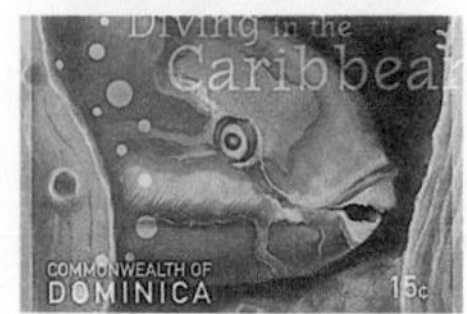

354 Large Blue and Green Fish

2001. Diving in the Caribbean. Depicting marine life. Multicoloured.
3024 15c. Type **354** 10 10
3025 65c. Ray 25 30
3026 90c. Octopus 35 40
3027 $2 Shark 80 85
3028 $2 Starfish 80 85
3029 $2 Seahorse 80 85
3030 $2 Pink anemonefish 80 85
3031 $2 Crab 80 85
3032 $2 Moray eel 80 85
3033 $3 Pink anemonefish . . . . 1·20 1·30
MS3034 78 × 57 mm. $5 Young turtle . . . . 2·00 2·10

355 Banded Sea-snake

2001. Caribbean Marine Life. Multicoloured.
3035 15c. Type **355** 10 10
3036 25c. Soldierfish 10 15
3037 55c. False moorish idol ("Banner Fish") 20 25
3038 90c. Crown of Thorns starfish 35 40
3039 $1.65 Red sponge and shoal of anthias 65 70
3040 $1.65 Undulate triggerfish ("Orange-Striped Trigger Fish") 65 70
3041 $1.65 Coral hind ("Coral Grouper") and soft tree coral 65 70
3042 $1.65 Peacock fan-worms and Gorgonian sea fan . . 65 70
3043 $1.65 Sweetlips and sea fan 65 70
3044 $1.65 Giant clam and golden cup coral 65 70
3045 $1.65 White-tipped reef shark, lionfish and sergeant majors 65 70
3046 $1.65 Blue-striped snappers 65 70
3047 $1.65 Great hammerhead shark, stovepipe sponge and pink vase sponge . . 65 70
3048 $1.65 Hawaiian monk seal and bluetube coral . . . 65 70
3049 $1.65 False clown anemonefish ("Common Clown Fish"), chilka seahorse and red feather star coral 65 70
3050 $1.65 Bat starfish and brown octopus 65 70
MS3051 Two sheets, each 88 × 83 mm. (a) $5 Regal anglefish. (b) $5 Pink anenomefish Set of 2 sheets . . . . 4·00 4·25

Nos. 3039/44 and 3045/50 were each printed together, se-tenant, with the backgrounds forming composite designs.

No. 3045 is inscribed "Sargent" and 3049 "Cconn", both in error.

356 Prince Albert in Military Uniform

357 Mao Tse-tung in 1945

2001. Death Centenary of Queen Victoria. Multicoloured.
3052 $2 Type **356** 80 85
3053 $2 Young Queen Victoria wearing crown 80 85
3054 $2 Young Queen Victoria wearing tiara 80 85
3055 $2 Prince Albert in evening dress 80 85
MS3056 106 × 122 mm. $6 Queen Victoria in 1897 (38 × 50 mm) 2·40 2·50

2001. 25th Death Anniv of Mao Tse-tung (Chinese leader). Portraits. Multicoloured.
3057 $2 Type **357** 80 85
3058 $2 Mao in 1926 . . . . . . 80 85
3059 $2 Mao in 1949 . . . . . . 80 85
MS3060 135 × 110 mm. $3 Mao Tse-tung with farm workers in 1930 1·20 1·30

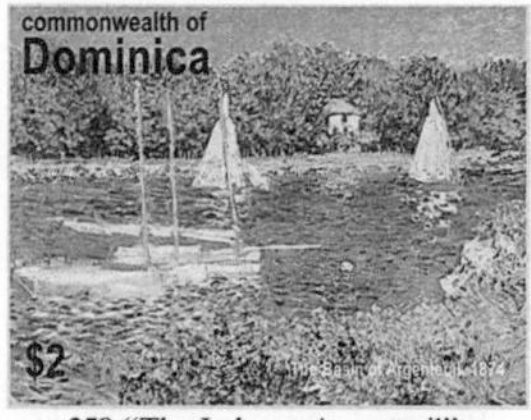

358 "The Lake at Argenteuil"

2001. 75th Death Anniv of Claude-Oscar Monet (French painter). Multicoloured.
3061 $2 Type **358** 80 85
3062 $2 "Bridge at Argenteuil" 80 85
3063 $2 "Railway bridge at Argenteuil" 80 85
3064 $2 "Seine bridge at Argenteuil" 80 85
MS3065 139 × 111 mm. $6 "Woman with Parasol – Madame Monet and her Son" (vert) . . . . . 2·40 2·50

359 Queen Elizabeth at Coronation

360 Verdi as a Young Man

2001. 75th Birthday of Queen Elizabeth II. Multicoloured.
3066 $1.20 Type **359** 50 55
3067 $1.20 Queen Elizabeth wearing yellow hat . . . 50 55
3068 $1.20 Bare-headed portrait after Annigoni 50 55
3069 $1.20 Queen Elizabeth wearing fur hat 50 55
3070 $1.20 With Prince Andrew as a baby 50 55
3071 $1.20 Wearing white hat and pearl necklace 50 55
MS3072 78 × 102 mm. $6 Queen Elizabeth in Guards uniform taking salute at Trooping the Colour . . . . 2·40 2·50

2001. Death Centenary of Giuseppe Verdi (Italian composer). Multicoloured.
3073 $2 Type **360** 80 85
3074 $2 "Lady Macbeth" 80 85
3075 $2 Orchestra 80 85
3076 $2 Score for Verdi's *Macbeth* (opera) 80 85
MS3077 76 × 105 mm. $6 Verdi as an old man . . . . 2·40 2·50

Nos. 3073/6 were printed together, se-tenant, with the backgrounds forming a composite design.

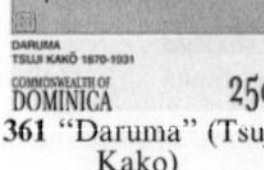

361 "Daruma" (Tsuji Kako)

363 *Cantharellus cibarius*

362 "Two Women Waltzing"

2001. "Philanippon '01" International Stamp Exhibition, Tokyo. Japanese Paintings. Multicoloured.
3078 25c. Type **361** 10 15
3079 55c. "Village by Bamboo Grove" (Takeuchi Seiho) 20 25
3080 65c. "Mountain Village in Spring" (Suzuki Hyakunen) 25 30
3081 90c. "Gentleman amusing Himself" (Domoto Insho) 35 40
3082 $1 "Calmness of Spring Light" (Takeuchi Seiho) 40 45
3083 $1.65 "Thatched Cottages in Willows" (Tsuji Kako) . . 65 70
3084 $1.65 "Joy in the Garden" (Tsuji Kako) 65 70
3085 $1.65 "Azalea and Butterfly" (Kikuchi Hobun) 65 70
3086 $1.65 "Pine Grove" (Tsuji Kako) 65 70
3087 $1.65 "Woodcutters talking in an Autumn Valley" (Kubota Beisen) 65 70
3088 $1.65 "Waterfowl in Snow" (Tsuji Kako) 65 70
3089 $1.65 "Heron and Willow" (Tsuji Kako) 65 70
3090 $1.65 "Crow and Cherry Blossoms" (Kikuchi Hobun) 65 70
3091 $1.65 "Chrysanthemum Immortal" (Yamamoto Shunkyo) 65 70
3092 $1.65 "Cranes of Immortality" (Tsuji Kako) 65 70
3093 $2 "Su's Embankment on a Spring Morning" (Tomioka Tessai) 80 85
MS3094 Three sheets. (a) 95 × 118 mm. $6 "Girl" (Suzuki Harunobu) (38 × 50 mm). (b) 105 × 90 mm. $6 "Kamo Riverbank in the Misty Rain" (Tsuji Kak) (38 × 50 mm). (c) 125 × 91 mm. $6 "Diamond Gate" (Tsuji Kak) (38 × 50 mm) Set of 3 sheets . . . . 7·25 7·50

No. **MS**3094c is inscribed "DIAMON GATE" in error.

2001. Death Centenary of Henri de Toulouse-Lautrec (French painter). Multicoloured.
3095 $2 Type **362** 80 85
3096 $2 "The Medical Inspection" 80 85
3097 $2 "Two Girlfriends" . . . 80 85
3098 $2 "Woman pulling up her Stockings" 80 85
MS3099 66 × 86 mm. $6 "Self-portrait" . . . . 2·40 2·50

2001. Fungi of the World. Multicoloured.
3100 15c. Type **363** 10 10
3101 25c. *Hygrocybe pratensis* . . 10 15
3102 55c. *Leccinum aurantiacum* 20 25
3103 90c. *Caesar's amanita* (horiz) 35 40
3104 90c. *Agaricus augustus* (horiz) 35 40
3105 90c. *Clitocybe nuda* (horiz) 35 40
3106 90c. *Hygrocybe plavescens* (horiz) 35 40
3107 90c. *Stropharia kaufmanii* (horiz) 35 40
3108 90c. *Hygrophorus speciosus* (horiz) 35 40
3109 $2 *Marasmiellus candidus* . . 80 85
3110 $2 *Calostoma cinnabarina* . . 80 85
3111 $2 *Cantharellus infundibuliformis* 80 85
3112 $2 *Hygrocybe punicea* . . . 80 85
3113 $2 *Dictyophora indusiata* . . 80 85
3114 $2 *Agrocybe praecox* 80 85
3115 $3 *Mycena haematopus* . . . 1·20 1·30
MS3116 Two sheets. (a) 76 × 54 mm. $5 Gymnophilus spectabilis (horiz). (b) 54 × 76 mm. $5 Amanita muscaria (horiz) Set of 2 sheets . . . . 4·00 4·25

364 St. Vincent Amazon ("St. Vincent Parrot")

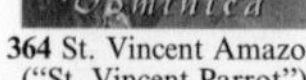

365 Yellow Warbler

2001. Caribbean Fauna. Multicoloured.
3117 $1.45 Type **364** 60 65
3118 $1.45 Painted bunting . . . 60 65
3119 $1.45 Jamaican giant anole 60 65
3120 $1.45 White-fronted capuchin monkey 60 65
3121 $1.45 Strand racerunner . . 60 65
3122 $1.45 Agouti 60 65
3123 $2 Cook's tree boa 80 85
3124 $2 Tamandua 80 85
3125 $2 Common iguana 80 85
3126 $2 Solenodon 80 85
MS3127 Four sheets. (a) 63 × 92 mm. $5 American purple gallinule. (b) 63 × 92 mm. $5 Rufous-tailed jaramar. (c) 92 × 63 mm. $5 Ruby-throated hummingbird (horiz). (d) 73 × 52 mm. $5 Bottlenose dolphins (horiz) Set of 4 sheets 8·00 8·25

2001. Birds. Multicoloured.
3128 5c. Type **365** 10 10
3129 10c. Palm chat 10 10
3130 15c. Snowy cotinga 10 10
3131 20c. Blue-grey gnatcatcher 10 15
3132 25c. Belted kingfisher . . . 10 15
3133 55c. Red-legged thrush . . . 20 25
3134 65c. Bananaquit 25 30
3135 90c. Yellow-bellied sapsucker 35 40
3136 $1 White-tailed tropicbird 40 45
3137 $1.45 Ruby-throated hummingbird 60 65
3138 $1.90 Painted bunting . . . 75 80
3139 $2 Great frigate bird 80 85
3140 $5 Brown trembler . . . . 2·00 2·10
3141 $10 Red-footed booby . . . 4·00 4·25
3142 $20 Sooty tern . . . . . . 8·00 8·25

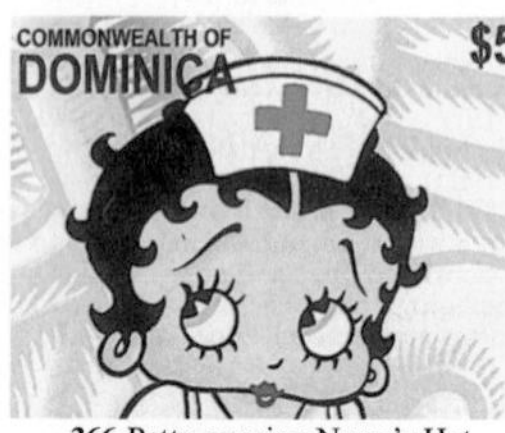

366 Betty wearing Nurse's Hat

2001. Betty Boop (cartoon character). Four sheets, each 87 × 138 mm, containing horiz designs as T **366**. Multicoloured.
MS3143 (a) $5 Type **366**. (b) $5 Betty as film star. (c) $5 Betty in front of foliage. (d) $5 Betty in front of roses. Set of 4 sheets 8·00 8·25

367 Larry, Moe and Curly in Overalls

2001. Scenes from *The Three Stooges* (American T.V. comedy series). Multicoloured.
3144 $1 Type **367** 40 45
3145 $1 Larry, Moe and Curly with woman in floral dress 40 45
3146 $1 Larry, Moe and Curly under table 40 45
3147 $1 Larry, Moe and Curly attacking singer in red dress 40 45
3148 $1 Larry, Moe and Curly with pony in cot 40 45
3149 $1 Larry in naval uniform, being arrested 40 45
3150 $1 Larry in evening dress (face value at top left) . . 40 45
3151 $1 Curly in green shirt . . . 40 45
3152 $1 Moe in evening dress (face value at top right) 40 45
MS3153 Two sheets. (a) 126 × 95 mm. $5 Larry with pony in cot. (b) 95 × 126 mm. $5 Moe and Larry in radio studio Set of 2 sheets . . . . 4·00 4·25

368 Queen Elizabeth II

369 United States Team, Brazil, 1950

2001. Golden Jubilee.
3154 $1 multicoloured 40 45

No. 3154 was printed in sheetlets of 8, containing two vertical rows of four, separated by a large illustrated central gutter. Both the stamp and the illustration on the central gutter are made up of a collage of miniature flower photographs.

2001. World Cup Football Championship, Japan and Korea (2002). Multicoloured.
3155 $2 Type **369** 80 85
3156 $2 Publicity poster, Switzerland, 1954 . . . . 80 85
3157 $2 Publicity poster, Sweden, 1958 . . . . 80 85
3158 $2 Zozimo (Brazil), Chile, 1962 . . . . 80 85

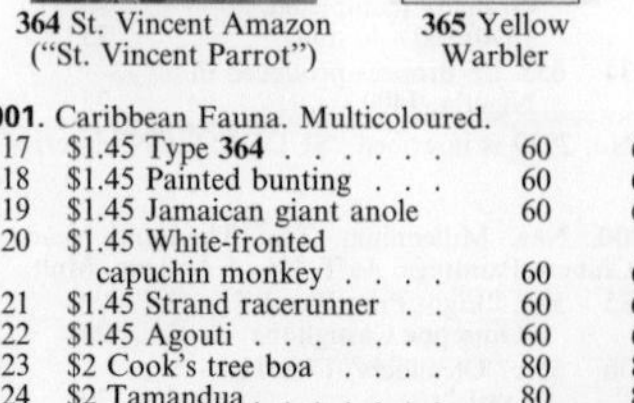

3159 $2 Gordon Banks (England), England, 1966 . . 80 85
3160 $2 Pele (Brazil), Mexico, 1970 . . . . 80 85
3161 $2 Daniel Passarella (Argentina), Argentina, 1978 . . . . 80 85
3162 $2 Paolo Rossi (Italy), Spain, 1982 . . . . . . 80 85
3163 $2 Diego Maradona (Argentina), Mexico, 1986 80 85
3164 $2 Publicity poster, Italy, 1990 . . . . 80 85
3165 $2 Seo Jungulon (South Korea), U.S.A., 1994 . . 80 85
3166 $2 Jürgen Klinsmann (Germany), France, 1998 80 85
MS3167 Two sheets, each 88 × 75 mm. (a) $5 Detail of Jules Rimet Trophy, Uruguay, 1930. (b) $5 Detail of World Cup Trophy, Japan/Korea, 2002 Set of 2 sheets 4·00 4·25

370 "Madonna and Child" (Giovanni Bellini)

2001. Christmas. Paintings by Giovanni Bellini. Multicoloured.
3168 25c. Type **370** 10 15
3169 65c. "Madonna with Child" 25 30
3170 90c. "Baptism of Christ" . . 35 40
3171 $1.20 "Madonna with Child" (different) 50 55
3172 $4 "Madonna with Child" (different) . . . . 1·60 1·70
MS3173 136 × 76 mm. $6 "Madonna with Child and Sts. Catherine and Mary Magdalene" . . . . . . 2·40 2·50

371 Horse and Groom

2001. Chinese New Year ("Year of the Horse"). Paintings by Lum Mei. Multicoloured.
3174 $1.65 Type **371** 65 70
3175 $1.65 Two horses grazing 65 70
3176 $1.65 Groom with sick horse 65 70
3177 $1.65 Two horses galloping 65 70

2002. Golden Jubilee (2nd issue). As T **473** of Antigua. Multicoloured.
3178 $2 Queen Elizabeth in blue hat and coat 80 85
3179 $2 Queen Elizabeth presenting Prince Philip with polo trophy 80 85
3180 $2 Queen Elizabeth in evening dress 80 85
3181 $2 Queen Elizabeth in pink hat and coat 80 85
MS3182 76 × 108 mm. $6 Princess Elizabeth and Duke of Edinburgh, 1948. . . . . 2·40 2·50

2002. "United We Stand". Support for Victims of 11 September 2001 Terrorist Attacks. As T **474** of Antigua.
3183 $2 U.S. Flag as Statue of Liberty and Dominica flag 80 85

2002. Shirley Temple in *Just Around the Corner*. As T **469** of Antigua showing film scenes. Mult.
3184 $1.90 With maid and dogs (horiz) 75 80
3185 $1.90 Penny (Shirley Temple) with father and Lola (horiz) 75 80
3186 $1.90 With father in study (horiz) 75 80
3187 $1.90 Carving turkey (horiz) 75 80
3188 $1.90 Talking to S. G. Henshaw (horiz) 75 80
3189 $1.90 Collecting money from crowd (horiz) 75 80
3190 $2 Frowning at boy 80 85
3191 $2 Pretending to shoot with Gus the chauffeur 80 85
3192 $2 Penny wearing apron and talking to father 80 85
3193 $2 Cutting boy's hair . . . 80 85
MS3194 106 × 75 mm. $6 Dancing in the rain . . . . 2·40 2·50

372 "Courtesan Tsukioka" (Ichirakutei Eisui)

2002. Japanese Art. Multicoloured.
3195 $1.20 Type **372** 50 55
3196 $1.20 "Woman and Servant in the Snow" (Eishosai Choki) 50 55
3197 $1.20 "Courtesan Shiratsuyu" (Chokosai Eisho) 50 55
3198 $1.20 "Ohisa of the Takashima-Ya" (Utagawa Toyokuni) 50 55
3199 $1.20 "Woman and Cat" (Utagawa Kunimasa) . . 50 55
3200 $1.20 "Genre Scenes of Beauties" (detail) (Keisai Eisen) 50 55
3201 $1.65 "Women inside and outside a Mosquito Net" (Suzuki Harushige) . . . 65 70
3202 $1.65 "Komachi at Shimizu" (Suzuki Harushige) 65 70
3203 $1.65 "Women viewing Plum Blossoms" (Suzuki Harunobu) 65 70
3204 $1.65 "Women cooling themselves at Shijogawara in Kyoto" (Utagawa Toyohiro) 65 70
3205 $1.65 "Women reading a Letter" (Kitagawa Utamaro) 65 70
3206 $1.65 "Women dressed for Kashima Dance at Niwaka Festival" (Kitagawa UTamaro) . . 65 70
3207 $1.90 "Iwai Kiyotaro" (Kunimasa) 75 80
3208 $1.90 "Otani Hiriji III and Arashi Ryuzo" (Toshusai Sharaku) 75 80
3209 $1.90 "Ichikawa Komazo II" (Katsukawa Shunko) 75 80
3210 $1.90 "Ichikawa Yaozo III and Sakata Hangoro III" (Sharaku) 75 80
3211 $1.90 "Tanimura Torazo" (Sharaku) 75 80
3212 $1.90 "Iwai Kiyotaro as Oishi" (Toyokuni) 75 80
MS3213 Three sheets. (a) 85 × 125 mm. $5 "Iwai Hanshiro IV and Sawamura Sojuro III" (Torii Kyonaga) (horiz). (b) 85 × 110 mm. $5 "Actor Nakamura Riko" (Katsukawa Shunsho). (c) $6 "Daughter of the Motoyanagi-Ya" (Suzuki Harunobu) . . . . 6·50 6·75

2002. International Year of Mountains. Vert designs as T **481** of Antigua. Multicoloured.
3214 $2 Mount Everest 80 85
3215 $2 Mount Kilimanjaro . . . 80 85
3216 $2 Mount McKinley 80 85

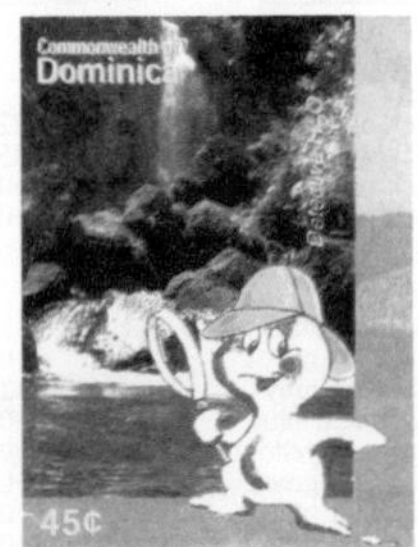

373 Waterfall and "Detective H2O"

2002. U.N. Year of Ecotourism. Each including a member of the Eco Squad (cartoon characters). Multicoloured.
3217 45c. Type **373** 20 25
3218 50c. Waterfall and "Factman" 20 25
3219 55c. River and "B.B." . . . 20 25
3220 60c. Sea cliffs and "Stanley the Starfish" 25 30
3221 90c. River and "Toxi" . . . 35 40
3222 $1.20 Forest and "Adopt" 50 55
MS3223 117 × 96 mm. $6 Park and "Litterbit" . . . . 2·40 2·50

2002. Winter Olympic Games, Salt Lake City. As T **482** of Antigua but horiz. Multicoloured.
3224 $2 Downhill skiing 80 85
3225 $2 Two man bobsleigh . . . 80 85
MS3226 84 × 114 mm. Nos. 3218/19 1·60 1·70

374 Colonel Baden-Powell in Military Uniform

375 Olive Oyl in Rowing Boat

2002. 20th World Scout Jamboree, Thailand. Mult.
3227 $3 Type **374** . . . . 1·20 1·30
3228 $3 Agnes Baden-Powell (founder of Girl Guides) 1·20 1·30
3229 $3 Maceo Johnson . . . . 1·20 1·30
MS3230 80 × 99 mm. $6 Lord Baden-Powell in Scout uniform 2·40 2·50

2002. 75th Anniv of First Solo Transatlantic Flight. As T **484** of Antigua but vert. Multicoloured.
3231 $3 Charles Lindbergh and the *Spirit of St. Louis* (aircraft) . . . . 1·20 1·30
3232 $3 Charles and Anne Lindbergh in flying kit . . 1·20 1·30
MS3233 117 × 83 mm. $6 Charles Lindbergh and the *Spirit of St. Louis* . . . . 2·40 2·50

2002. "Popeye " (cartoon character) in New York. Multicoloured.
3234 $1 Type **375** 40 45
3235 $1 Brutus with oar 40 45
3236 $1 Sweet Pea 40 45
3237 $1 Wimpy 40 45
3238 $1 Jeep 40 45
3239 $1 Popeye with telescope . . 40 45
3240 $1.90 Popeye and Olive Oyl at Bronx Zoo 75 80
3241 $1.90 Popeye and Olive Oyl on ferry passing Statue of Liberty 75 80
3242 $1.90 Popeye and Olive Oyl by Empire State Building 75 80
3243 $1.90 Popeye skating at Rockefeller Centre . . . 75 80
3244 $1.90 Popeye pitching at baseball game 75 80
3245 $1.90 Popeye holding hose 75 80
MS3246 Two sheets, each 83 × 114 mm. (a) $6 Popeye and Olive Oyl dancing (horiz). (b) $6 Popeye flexing muscles . . . . 4·75 5·00
No. 3243 is inscribed "ROCKERFELLER" in error

376 Brown Trembler

377 Willem Einthoven (Medicine, 1924)

2002. Fauna. Multicoloured designs.
3247 $1.50 Type **376** 60 65
3248 $1.50 Snowy cotinga 60 65
3249 $1.50 Bananaquit 60 65
3250 $1.50 Painted bunting . . . 60 65
3251 $1.50 Belted kingfisher . . . 60 65
3252 $1.50 Ruby-throated hummingbird 60 65
3253 $1.50 Field cricket 60 65
3254 $1.50 Migratory grasshopper 60 65
3255 $1.50 Honey bee 60 65
3256 $1.50 Hercules beetle . . . 60 65
3257 $1.50 Black ant 60 65
3258 $1.50 Cicada 60 65
3259 $1.50 Carolina sphinx . . . 60 65
3260 $1.50 White-lined sphinx . . 60 65
3261 $1.50 Orizaba silkmoth . . . 60 65
3262 $1.50 Hieroglyphic moth . . 60 65
3263 $1.50 Hickory tussock moth 60 65
3264 $1.50 Diva moth 60 65
3265 $1.50 Sei whale 60 65
3266 $1.50 Killer whale 60 65
3267 $1.50 Blue whale 60 65
3268 $1.50 White whale 60 65
3269 $1.50 Pygmy whale 60 65
3270 $1.50 Sperm whale 60 65
MS3271 Four sheets, each 100 × 70 mm. (a) $6 Yellow-bellied sapsucker (horiz). (b) $6 Bumble bee (horiz). (c) $6 Ornate moth (horiz). (d) $6 Grey whale (horiz) 9·75 10·00
Nos. 3241/6 (birds), 3247/52 (insects), 3253/8 (moths) and 3259/64 (whales) were each printed together, se-tenant, with the backgrounds forming composite designs.
Nos. 3248 and 3259 are inscribed "Ctinga" or "Carilina", both in error.

2002. "Amphilex '02", International Stamp Exhibition, Amsterdam. (a) Dutch Nobel Prize Winners.
3272 **377** $1.50 black and green . . 60 65
3273 – $1.50 black and orange 60 65
3274 – $1.50 black and violet 60 65
3275 – $1.50 black and salmon 60 65
3276 – $1.50 black and sepia . . 60 65
3277 – $1.50 black and green . . 60 65
DESIGNS: No. 3273, Economics Prize medal; 3274, Peter Debye (Chemistry, 1935); 3275, Frits Zernike (Physics, 1953); 3276, Jan Tinbergen (Economics, 1969); 3277, Simon van de Meer (Physics, 1984).

(b) Dutch Lighthouses. Multicoloured.
3278 $1.50 Marken lighthouse . . 60 65
3279 $1.50 Harlingen lighthouse 60 65
3280 $1.50 Den Oever lighthouse 60 65
3281 $1.50 De Ven lighthouse . . 60 65
3282 $1.50 Urk lighthouse . . . 60 65
3283 $1.50 Oosterleek lighthouse 60 65

(c) Dutch Women's Traditional Costumes. Multicoloured. Each 37 × 51 mm.
3284 $3 Lace cap from Zuid Holland . . . .
3285 $3 Winged headdress from Zeeland . . . . 1·20 1·30
3286 $3 Scarf and shawl from Limburg . . . . 1·20 1·30

2002. 25th Death Anniv of Elvis Presley (American entertainer). As T **488** of Antigua showing Elvis with microphone.
3287 $1.50 black 60 65

378 Compass

2002. 550th Birth Anniv of Amerigo Vespucci (explorer). Multicoloured.
3288 $3 Type **378** . . . . 1·20 1·30
3289 $3 Studying chart . . . . . 1·20 1·30
3290 $3 Rolled chart . . . . . . 1·20 1·30
MS3291 98 × 78 mm. $5 Amerigo Vespucci and Spanish soldier (30 × 42mm) . . . . 2·00 2·10

379 Princess Diana

380 John F. Kennedy in Navy Uniform

2002. 5th Death Anniv of Diana, Princess of Wales. Multicoloured.
3292 $1.90 Type **379** 75 80
3293 $1.90 Princess Diana carrying rose spray 75 80
3294 $1.90 Wearing white yoked dress 75 80
3295 $1.90 In lace top 75 80
MS3296 98 × 66 mm. $5 Princess Diana wearing tiara fur coat 2·00 2·10

2002. Presidents John F. Kennedy and Ronald Reagan Commemoration. Multocoloured.
3297 $1.90 Type **380** 75 80
3298 $1.90 Wearing brown suit (face value in red) 75 80
3299 $1.90 Wearing brown suit (face value in blue) . . . 75 80
3300 $1.90 In fawn suit 75 80
3301 $1.90 John F. Kennedy smiling 75 80
3302 $1.90 John F. Kennedy frowning 75 80
3303 $1.90 Looking up 75 80
3304 $1.90 With hand on chin . . 75 80
3305 $1.90 Ronald Reagan in film role as deputy marshal . . 75 80
3306 $1.90 Wearing green T-shirt 75 80
3307 $1.90 In red pullover . . . 75 80
3308 $1.90 Wearing blue T-shirt 75 80
3309 $1.90 Nancy and Ronald Reagan (wearing blue shirt) (horiz) 75 80
3310 $1.90 Nancy Reagan (horiz) 75 80
3311 $1.90 Ronald Reagan (horiz) 75 80
3312 $1.90 Nancy and Ronald Reagan (wearing pink shirt) (horiz) 75 80

381 Rams

2003. Chinese New Year ("Year of the Ram").

3313	**381**	$1.65 multicoloured	65	70

382 Confucius (Chinese philosopher)

2003. Science Fiction. Six sheets, each 145 × 100 mm, containing T **382** and similar vert designs. Multicoloured.

MS3314 Six sheets. (a) $6 Type **382**. (b) $6 Nazca Lines, Peru. (c) $6 Atlas carrying Globe. (d) $6 Zoroaster. (e) $6 Mayan calendar. (f) $6 Presidents Franklin D. Roosevelt and John F. Kennedy (both deaths predicted by Edgar Casey) . . . . . . 14·50 15·00

No. **MS**3314(e) is inscribed "Calender" in error.

383 Elizabeth "Ma Pampo" Israel

384 Queen Elizabeth II in Pale Grey Dress

2003. 128th Birthday of Elizabeth "Ma Pampo" Israel (world's oldest person).

3315	**383**	90c. multicoloured	35	40

2003. 50th Anniv of Coronation. Multicoloured.

MS3316 155 × 93 mm. $3 Type **384**; $3 Queen in Garter robes; $3 Queen wearing tiara		4·25	4·00
MS3317 75 × 105 mm. $6 Queen wearing tiara		2·40	2·50

2003. Centenary of the Teddy Bear. As T **489** of Antigua. Multicoloured.

MS3318 90 × 166 mm. $1.65 Teddy bear wearing black t-shirt and blue jeans; $1.65 Wearing conical party hat and carrying streamers; $1.65 Carrying party blower; $1.65 Wearing black bowler hat, t-shirt and jeans; $1.65 Wearing mauve bowler hat, black t-shirt and green jeans; $1.65 Holding birthday cake (all 27 × 41 mm)	4·00	4·25
MS3319 165 × 127 mm. $2 × 2 Teddy bear wearing jumper, hat and mittens; $2 × 2 Father Christmas teddy bear	3·25	3·50

385 Bobby Moore

2003. World Cup Football Championship, Japan and Korea (2002). Multicoloured.

MS3320 165 × 84 mm. $1.45 Type **385**; $1.45 Roger Hunt; $1.45 Gordon Banks; $1.45 Bobby Charlton; $1.45 Alan Ball; $1.45 Geoff Hurst	2·40	2·50
MS3321 165 × 84 mm. $1.45 Danny Mills; $1.45 Paul Scholes; $1.45 Darius Vassell; $1.45 Michael Owen; $1.45 Emile Heskey; $1.45 Rio Ferdinand	2·40	2·50
MS3322 Five sheets, each 84 × 84 mm. (a) $3 Ashley Cole; $3 David Seaman. (b) $3 Franz Beckenbauer; $3 Oliver Kahn. (c) $3 Charlton, Ball, Hunt; $3 Nobby Stiles. (d) $3 Sven-Goran Eriksson; $3 Nikki Butt. (e) $3 Robbie Fowler; $3 Sol Campbell Set of 5 sheets	12·00	12·50

2003. 21st Birthday of Prince William of Wales. As T **509** of Antigua. Multicoloured.

MS3323 148 × 78 mm. $3 Prince William wearing blue-collared shirt; $3 Wearing blue jacket and tie; $3 Playing polo	4·25	4·50
MS3324 68 × 98 mm. $6 In school uniform	2·40	2·50

386 Model A Runabout (1903)

2003. Centenary of General Motors Cadillac. Multicoloured.

MS3325 120 × 170 mm. $2 Type **386**; $2 Model 30 (1912); $2 Type 57 Victoria Coupe (1918); $2 Lasalle Convertible Coupe (1927)	3·25	3·50
MS3326 120 × 84 mm. $5 355-C V8 Sedan (1933)	2·00	2·25

387 Corvette (1953)

2003. Centenary of General Motors Chevrolet Corvette. Multicoloured..

MS3327 120 × 170 mm. $2 Type **387**; $2 Corvette (1956); $2 Corvette (1957); $2 Corvette (1962)	3·25	3·50
MS3328 120 × 84 mm. $5 Corvette (1959)	2·00	2·10

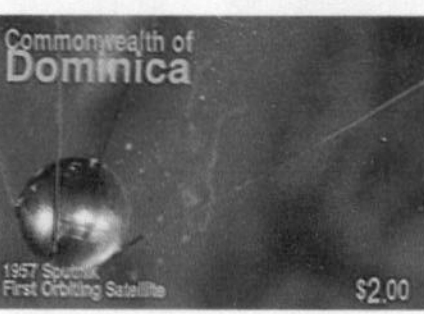

388 "Sputnik I" (first orbiting satellite, 1957)

2003. Centenary of Powered Flight. Multicoloured.

MS3329 180 × 110 mm. $2 Type **388**; $2 Yuri Gagarin (first man in space, 1961); $2 Neil Armstrong (first man on the Moon, 1969); $2 "Skylab 1" (1973)	3·25	3·50
MS3330 104 × 74 mm. $6 Flight over Mount Everest (1933)	2·40	2·50

389 Expedition Canoe and Chinook Indians

2003. Bicentenary (2004) of Lewis and Clark's Expedition to the American West and Pacific North West. Multicoloured.

3331	20c. Type **389**	10	15
3332	50c. Lewis and Clark and expedition compass	20	25
3333	55c. Lewis and Clark with map and telescope	20	25
3334	65c. Medal presented to Indians (vert)	25	30
3335	90c. Expedition members and grizzly bear	35	40
3336	$1 Lewis and Clark with Sacagawea (Indian interpreter)	40	45
3337	$2 Captain Meriwether Lewis (vert)	80	85
3338	$4 Statue of Lewis and Clark (vert)	1·60	1·75
MS3339	Two sheets, each 80 × 115 mm. (a) $5 Captain Meriwether Lewis (vert). (b) $5 Lieutenant William Clark (vert) Set of 2 sheets	4·00	4·25

2003. Centenary of Tour de France Cycle Race. As T **512** of Antigua showing past winners. Multicoloured.

MS3340 160 × 100 mm. $2 Firmin Lambot (1919); $2 Phillipe Thys (1920); $2 Leon Scieur (1921); $2 Firmin Lambot (1922)	3·25	3·50
MS3341 100 × 70 mm. $6 Francois Faber	2·40	2·50

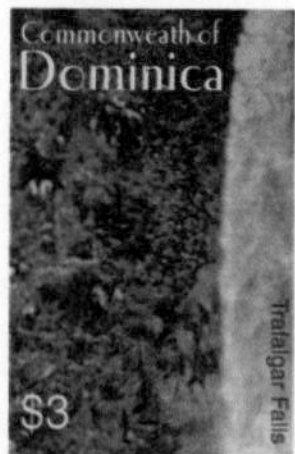

390 Trafalgar Falls, Dominica

2003. International Year of Freshwater. Multicoloured.

MS3342 96 × 146 mm. $3 Type **390**; $3 YS Falls, Jamaica; $3 Dunn's River, Jamaica	4·25	4·50
MS3343 70 × 100 mm. $6 Annandale Falls, Grenada	2·40	2·50

APPENDIX

The following stamps have either been issued in excess of postal needs, or have not been made available to the public in reasonable quantities at face value.

1978.

History of Aviation. $16 × 30, each embossed on gold foil.

DOMINICAN REPUBLIC Pt. 15

The Eastern portion of the island of Hispaniola in the W. Indies finally became independent of Spain in 1865.

1865. 8 reales = 1 peso.
1880. 100 centavos = 1 peso.
1883. 100 centimos = 1 franco.
1885. 100 centavos = 1 peso.

1

3

1865. Imperf.

1	**1**	½r. black on red	£225	£200
3		½r. black on green	£350	£350
2		1r. black on green	£600	£550
4		1r. black on yellow	£1100	£950

1865. Imperf.

5	**3**	½r. black on buff	£125	£100
7		½r. black on red	40·00	40·00
12		½r. black on grey	£120	£120
18		½r. black and blue on red	50·00	30·00
19		½r. black on yellow	25·00	25·00
20		1r. black on green	50·00	50·00
9		1r. black on blue	35·00	35·00
15		1r. black on flesh	£100	£100
21		1r. black on lilac	£200	£200

4 **5** **15**

1879. Perf.

22	**4**	½r. violet	1·50	1·50
24		1r. red	1·50	1·50

1880. Rouletted.

35	**5**	1c. green	60	60
36		2c. red	60	60
28		5c. blue	85	70
38		10c. pink	60	60
39		20c. bistre	70	70
40		25c. mauve	1·25	1·00
32		50c. orange	1·50	1·10
33		75c. blue	3·25	3·25
34		1p. gold	4·00	4·00

1883. Surch.

44	**5**	5c. on 1c. green	1·10	1·00
73		10c. on 2c. red	2·00	2·00
46		25c. on 5c. blue	4·00	3·50
47		50c. on 10c. pink	12·00	6·00
58		1f. on 20c. bistre	7·00	7·00
51		1f.25 on 25c. mauve	11·00	11·00
52		2f.50 on 50c. orange	14·00	14·00
53		3f.75 on 75c. blue	16·00	16·00
64		5f. on 1p. gold	50·00	50·00

1885. Figures in lower corners only.

77	**15**	1c. green	30	15
78		2c. red	30	15
79		5c. blue	50	20
80		10c. orange	80	30
81		20c. brown	85	50
82		50c. violet	4·50	3·00
83		1p. red	10·00	10·00
84		2p. brown	12·00	10·00

1895. As T **15** but figures in four corners.

85	1c. green	60	30
86	2c. red	60	30
87	5c. blue	70	30
88	10c. orange	75	30

18 Voyage of Mendez from Jamaica to Santo Domingo

19 Sarcophagus of Columbus

1899. Columbus Mausoleum Fund.

98	**19**	½c. black	1·00	1·00
99	–	½c. black	1·00	1·00
89	**18**	1c. purple	4·50	3·50
90		1c. green	1·00	40
91	–	2c. red	50	50
92	**19**	5c. blue	75	55
93	–	10c. orange	2·00	1·00
94	–	20c. brown	4·00	4·00
95	–	50c. green	4·00	4·00
96	–	1p. black on blue	12·00	10·00
97	–	2p. brown on cream	25·00	25·00

DESIGNS—AS TYPE **18**: ½c. (No. 99), 1p. Columbus at Salamanca Assembly; 2c. Enriquillo's Rebellion; 20c. Toscanelli replying to Columbus; 50c. Las Casas defending Indians. As Type **19**: 10c. Hispaniola guarding remains of Columbus; 2p. Columbus Mausoleum, Santo Domingo Cathedral.

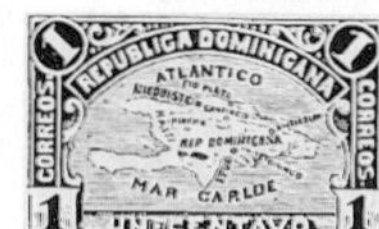

20 Island of Hispaniola

21

1900.

100	**20**	½c. blue	45	40
101		½c. red	45	40
102		1c. olive	45	35
103		2c. green	45	35
104		5c. brown	45	35
105		10c. orange	35	35
106		20c. purple	1·50	1·50
107		50c. black	1·40	1·25
108		1p. brown	1·40	1·25

1901.

109	**21**	½c. lilac and red	25	25
110		1c. lilac and olive	35	20
111		2c. lilac and green	35	20
112		5c. lilac and brown	35	25
113		10c. lilac and orange	75	30
114		20c. lilac and brown	1·50	80
115		50c. lilac and black	4·50	2·50
116		1p. lilac and brown	9·50	7·00

24 Sanchez

25 Fortress of Santo Domingo

1902. 400th Anniv of Santo Domingo.

125	**24**	1c. black & green	25	25
126		2c. black & red (Duarte)	25	25
127		5c. blk & blue (Duarte)	25	25
128		10c. blk & orge (Sanchez)	25	25
129		12c. blk & violet (Mella)	25	25
130		20c. black & red (Mella)	25	25
131	**25**	50c. black and brown	1·60	1·75

1904. Surch with new value.

132	**21**	2c. on 50c. lilac & black	5·50	4·25
133		2c. on 1p. lilac & brown	7·50	4·50
134		5c. on 50c. lilac & black	2·00	1·60
135		5c. on 1p. lilac and brown	3·00	2·40

136 10c. on 50c. lilac & black 4·75 4·00
137 10c. on 1p. lilac & brown 4·75 4·00

1904. Official stamps optd **16 de Agosto 1904** or surch **1 1** also.
138 O 23 1c. on 20c. blk & yell 3·25 2·75
139 2c. black and red 5·00 3·00
140 5c. black and blue 3·00 2·25
141 10c. black and green 4·75 3·25

1904. Postage Due stamps optd **REPUBLICA DOMINICANA CENTAVOS CORREOS** or surch **1** also.
142 D 22 1c. on 2c. sepia 1·75 85
143 1c. on 4c. sepia 70 50
145 2c. sepia 70 35

1905. Surch **1905** and new value.
146 15 2c. on 20c. brown 5·00 4·00
147 5c. on 20c. brown 2·25 1·40
148 10c. on 20c. brown 5·00 4·00

1905.
149 21 ½c. orange and black 1·00 55
150 1c. blue and black 1·25 50
151 2c. mauve and black 1·25 40
152 5c. red and black 1·50 70
153 10c. green and black 2·75 1·40
154 20c. olive and black 8·50 4·75
155 50c. brown and black 27·00 15·00
156 1p. grey and black £150 £150

1906. Postage Due stamps surch **REPUBLICA DOMINICANA.** and new value.
157 D 22 1c. on 4c. sepia 70 40
158 1c. on 10c. sepia 85 40
159 2c. on 5c. sepia 85 40

1907.
168 21 ½c. black and green 55 15
169 1c. black and red 55 15
170 2c. black and brown 55 15
171 5c. black and blue 60 20
164 10c. black and purple 85 35
165 20c. black and olive 4·75 2·40
166 50c. black and brown 4·75 4·00
167 1p. black and violet 12·00 6·50

1911. No. O178 optd **HABILITADO. 1911.**
182 O 23 2c. black and red 1·00 50

34

35 Jaun Pablo Duarte

1911.
183 34 ½c. black and orange 25 15
184 1c. black and green 25 10
185 2c. black and red 25 10
186 5c. black and blue 50 15
187 10c. black and purple 1·00 40
188 20c. black and olive 5·50 3·25
189 50c. black and brown 2·40 2·00
190 1p. black and violet 4·00 2·40
For stamps in other colours see Nos. 235/8 and for stamps in similar type see No. 240/6.

1914. Birth Centenary of Duarte. Background in red, white and blue.
195 35 ½c. black and orange 45 35
196 1c. black and green 45 35
197 2c. black and red 45 35
198 5c. black and grey 55 40
199 10c. black and mauve 85 50
200 20c. black and olive 2·00 1·40
201 50c. black and brown 2·75 2·40
202 1p. black and lilac 4·00 3·00

1915. Nos. O177/181 optd **Habilitado 1915** or surch **MEDIO CENTAVO** also.
203 O 23 ½c. on 20c. blk & yell 50 35
204 1c. black and green 70 25
205 2c. black and red 70 35
206 5c. black and blue 85 35
207 10c. black and green 2·00 1·60
208 20c. black and yellow 6·50 5·50

1915. Optd **1915.**
209 34 ½c. black and mauve 55 15
210 1c. black and brown 55 10
211 2c. black and olive 2·00 25
213 5c. black and red 2·00 25
214 10c. black and blue 2·00 35
215 20c. black and red 5·50 1·25
216 50c. black and green 6·00 2·75
217 1p. black and orange 12·00 5·50

1916. Optd **1916.**
218 34 ½c. black and mauve 70 10
219 1c. black and green 1·40 10

1917. Optd **1917.**
220 34 ½c. black and mauve 1·00 25
221 1c. black and green 1·00 10
222 2c. black and olive 85 10
223 5c. black and red 7·50 70

1919. Optd **1919.**
224 34 2c. black and olive 4·00 10

1920. Optd **1920.**
225 34 ½c. black and mauve 45 20
226 1c. black and green 45 10
227 2c. black and olive 45 10
228 5c. black and red 4·75 45
229 10c. black and blue 2·75 20
230 20c. black and red 4·75 45
231 50c. black and green 40·00 10·00

1921. Optd **1921.**
233 34 1c. black and green 1·25 25
234 2c. black and olive 2·40 30

1922.
235 34 ½c. black and red 25 10
236 1c. green 70 10
237 2c. red 1·00 10
238 5c. blue 2·00 25

41

43 Exhibition Pavilion

1924. Straight top to shield.
240 41 1c. green 40 10
241 2c. red 55 10
242 5c. blue 55 10
243 10c. black and blue 6·50 1·40
245 50c. black and green 35·00 2·00
246 1p. black and orange 12·00 8·50

1927. National and West Indian Exn, Santiago.
248 43 2c. red 70 45
249 5c. blue 85 45

45 Air Mail Routes

1928. Air.
256 45 10c. deep blue 5·75 3·00
280 10c. pale blue 1·90 75
271 10c. yellow 4·00 3·00
272 15c. red 7·75 4·00
281 15c. turquoise 4·00 1·10
273 20c. green 3·75 60
282 20c. brown 4·50 55
274 30c. violet 7·75 4·50
283 30c. brown 7·25 1·75

46 Ruins of Fortress of Columbus

47 Horacio Vasquez

1928.
258 46 ½c. red 45 25
259 1c. green 40 10
260 2c. red 40 10
261 5c. blue 1·00 25
262 10c. blue 1·00 25
263 20c. red 1·50 40
264 50c. green 8·50 4·75
265 1p. yellow 15·00 10·00

1929. Frontier Agreement with Haiti.
266 47 ½c. red 40 20
267 1c. green 40 15
268 2c. red 45 15
269 5c. blue 85 25
270 10c. blue 3·00 55

48 Jesuit Convent of San Ignacio de Loyola

49 After the Hurricane

1930.
275 48 ½c. brown 50 40
276 1c. green 45 10
277 2c. red 45 10
278 5c. blue 1·25 35
279 10c. blue 2·40 85

1930. Hurricane Relief.
284 – 1c. green and red 15 35
285 – 2c. red 20 25
286 49 5c. blue and red 35 50
287 10c. yellow and red 40 70
DESIGN: 1c., 2c. Riverside.

1931. Air. Hurricane Relief. Surch with airplane, **HABILITADO PARA CORREO AEREO** and premium. Imperf or perf.
288 49 5c.+5c. blue and red 6·50 6·50
289 5c.+5c. black and red 15·00 15·00
290 10c.+10c. yellow & red 5·00 6·50
291 10c.+10c. black & red 15·00 15·00

52 Cathedral of Santo Domingo

1931.
294 52 1c. green 50 15
295 2c. red 50 15
296 3c. purple 55 10
297 7c. blue 1·40 20
298 8c. brown 2·40 70
299 10c. blue 3·00 85

53 Old Sun Dial, 1754

1931. Air.
300 53 10c. red 5·00 60
301 10c. blue 2·00 55
302 10c. green 8·00 2·75
303 15c. mauve 3·75 55
304 20c. blue 7·25 1·60
306 30c. green 3·25 40
307 50c. brown 8·00 80
308 1p. orange 13·00 2·75

54 Fort Ozama

1932.
309 54 1c. green 50 40
310 1c. green 25 10
311 3c. violet 35 10
No. 310 is inscribed "CORREOS".

1932. Red Cross stamps inscr "CRUZ ROJA DOMINICANA", with cross in red and optd **HABILITADO Dic. 20-1932 En. 5-1933 CORREOS** or surch also.
312 1c. green 20 15
313 3c. on 2c. violet 30 15
314 5c. blue 70 60
315 7c. on 10c. blue 1·10 85

56 F. A. de Merino

57 Cathedral of Santo Domingo

1933. Birth Centenary of F. A. de Merino.
316 – ½c. violet 25 15
317 56 1c. green 25 15
318 – 2c. red 70 55
319 56 3c. violet 35 15
320 – 5c. blue 45 20
321 – 7c. blue 90 35
322 – 8c. green 1·25 70
323 56 10c. orange 1·00 25
324 – 20c. red 2·25 1·40
325 57 50c. olive 9·00 5·50
326 1p. sepia 22·00 13·00
DESIGNS—VERT: ½c., 5c., 8c. Merino's Tomb; 2c., 7c., 20c. Merino in uniform.

1933. Portraits as T **56**.
327 1c. black and green 50 25
328 3c. black and violet 55 15
329 7c. black and blue 1·60 55
DESIGNS: 1c., 7c. Pres. Trujillo in uniform; 3c. Pres. Trujillo in evening dress.

1933. Air. Optd **CORREO AEREO INTERNO.**
330 52 2c. red 40 30

60 Fokker Super Universal over Fort Ozama

1933. Air.
331 60 10c. blue 3·50 50

61 San Rafael Suspension Bridge

1934.
332 61 ½c. mauve 55 25
333 1c. green 80 15
334 3c. violet 1·25 10

62 Trujillo Bridge

1934. (a) Postage. As T **62** but without airplane and inscr "CORREOS".
335 – ½c. brown 50 15
336 – 1c. green 80 10
337 – 3c. violet 1·00 10

(b) Air.
338 62 10c. blue 3·25 50

64 National Palace

1935. For obligatory use on mail addressed to the President.
346 64 25c. orange 2·00 15

1935. Opening of Ramfis Bridge. As T **62** but view of Ramfis Suspension Bridge.
347 1c. green 45 10
348 3c. brown 45 10
349 5c. purple 1·00 50
350 10c. pink 2·00 1·00

66 Airplane and Carrier Pigeon

1935. Air.
351 66 10c. light blue and blue 2·50 45

67 President Trujillo

1935. Frontier Agreement.
352 67 3c. brown and yellow 30 15
353 – 5c. brown and orange 35 10
354 – 7c. brown and blue 55 10
355 – 10c. brown and purple 85 10
RECTANGULAR DESIGNS: Portrait as Type **67**. Red, white and blue ribbons in side panels on 7c. or diagonally across 5c. and 10c.

69 Post Office, Santiago de los Caballeros

1936.
356 69 ½c. violet 30 20
357 1c. green 30 10

70

1936. Air.
358 **70** 10c. blue 2·75 45

71 George Washington Avenue, Ciudad Trujillo

1936. Dedication of George Washington Avenue.
359 **71** ½c. brown 35 25
360 2c. brown and red 60 20
361 3c. brown and yellow 60 15
362 7c. brown and blue 85 50

72 Gen. A. Duverge **74** "Flight"

1936. National Archives and Library Fund. Inscr "PRO ARCHIVO Y BIBLIOTECA NACIONALES".
363 – ½c. lilac 25 15
364 – 1c. green 20 10
365 – 2c. red 20 10
366 – 3c. violet 25 10
367 – 5c. blue 40 25
368 **72** 7c. blue 70 50
369 – 10c. orange 85 30
370 – 20c. olive 3·25 1·90
371 – 25c. purple 3·25 2·00
372 – 30c. red 5·00 2·75
373 – 50c. brown 6·00 2·75
374 – 1p. black 15·00 12·00
375 – 2p. brown 40·00 35·00
DESIGNS—As Type **72**: ½c. J. N. de Caceres; 1c. Gen. G. Luperon; 2c. E. Tejera; 3c. Pres. Trujillo; 5c. Jose Reyes; 10c. Felix M. Del Monte; 25c. F. J. Peynado; 30c. Salome Urena; 50c. Gen. Jose Ma. Cabral; 1p. Manuel Js. Galvan; 2p. Gaston F. Deligne. TRIANGULAR: 20c. National Library.

1936. Air.
376 **74** 10c. blue 2·10 35

75 Obelisk in Ciudad Trujillo

1937. 1st Anniv of Naming of Ciudad Trujillo (formerly Santo Domingo).
377 **75** 1c. green 20 10
378 3c. violet 40 10
379 7c. blue 1·25 60

76 Discus Thrower and National Flag

1937. 1st National Olympic Games, Ciudad Trujillo. Flag blue, white and red.
380 **76** 1c. green 6·50 70
381 3c. violet 8·50 50
382 7c. blue 15·00 2·75

77 "Peace, Labour and Progress"

1937. 8th Year of Trujillo Presidency.
383 **77** 3c. violet 35 10

78 San Pedro de Macoris Airport

1937. Air.
384 **78** 10c. green 1·25 10

79 Fleet of Columbus

1937. Air. Pan-American Goodwill Flight.
385 **79** 10c. red 3·75 1·25
386 A 15c. violet 1·75 70
387 B 20c. blue 1·75 70
388 A 25c. purple 2·50 85
389 B 30c. green 2·25 70
390 A 50c. brown 4·25 1·00
391 B 75c. olive 11·00 11·00
392 **79** 1p. red 12·00 2·75
DESIGNS—A, Junkers F-13 aircraft in Goodwill Flight; B, Junkers F-13 aircraft over Columbus Lighthouse.

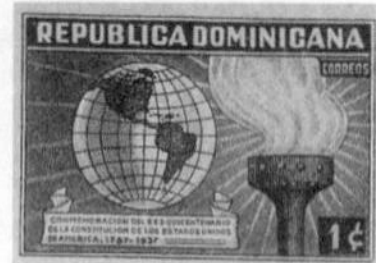

83 Father Billini **84** Globe and Torch of Liberty

1938. Birth Centenary of Father Billini.
396 **83** ½c. orange 15 10
397 5c. violet 45 15

1938. 150th Anniv of U.S. Constitution.
398 **84** 1c. green 30 10
399 3c. violet 45 10
400 10c. orange 85 20

85 Bastion, Trinitarian Oath and National Flag

1938. Centenary of Trinitarian Rebellion.
401 **85** 1c. green 40 20
402 3c. violet 50 15
403 10c. orange 1·00 45

86 Martin M-130 Flying Boat over Obelisk **87** Arms of University

1938. Air.
404 **86** 10c. green 1·40 15

1938. 400th Anniv of Santo Domingo University.
405 **87** ½c. orange 25 15
406 1c. green 35 10
407 3c. violet 40 10
408 7c. blue 85 40

89 N.Y. Fair Symbol, Lighthouse, Flag and Cornucopia

1939. New York World's Fair. (a) Postage. Flag in blue, white and red.
418 **89** ½c. orange 35 15
419 1c. green 40 15
420 3c. violet 40 15
421 10c. yellow 1·25 45

(b) Air. Flag, etc, replaced by airplane.
422 10c. green 1·50 55

90 Jose Trujillo Valdez **91**

1939. 4th Death Anniv of Jose Trujillo Valdez. Black borders.
423 **90** ½c. grey 25 15
424 1c. green 35 10
425 3c. brown 40 10
426 7c. blue 85 50
427 10c. violet 1·50 40

1939. Air.
428 **91** 10c. green 1·40 20

92 Western Hemisphere and Union Flags **93** Sir Rowland Hill

1940. 50th Anniv of Pan-American Union. Flags in national colours.
429 **92** 1c. green 25 10
430 2c. red 35 15
431 3c. violet 55 10
432 10c. orange 1·10 20
433 1p. brown 15·00 10·00

1940. Centenary of 1st Adhesive Postage Stamps.
434 **93** 3c. mauve 6·50 40
435 7c. blue 12·00 1·50

94 Julia Molina de Trujillo

1940. Mothers' Day.
436 **94** 1c. green 30 10
437 2c. red 40 10
438 3c. orange 50 10
439 7c. blue 1·25 45

95 Central America and Arms of Dominican Republic

1940. 2nd Caribbean Conference, Trujillo City.
440 **95** 3c. red 40 10
441 7c. blue 85 15
442 1p. green 8·50 4·25

96 Lighthouse, Aeroplane and Caravels

1940. Air. Discovery of America and Columbus Memorial Lighthouse. Inscr "PRO FARO DE COLON".
443 **96** 10c. blue 1·40 50
444 – 15c. brown 80 70
445 – 20c. red 80 70
446 – 25c. mauve 80 35
447 – 50c. green 4·00 1·60
DESIGNS: 15c. Columbus and lighthouse; 20c. Lighthouse; 25c. Columbus; 50c. Caravel and wings.

99 Marion Military Hospital **100** Post Office, San Cristobal

1940.
457 **99** ½c. brown 25 20

1941. Air.
458 **100** 10c. mauve 65 15

101 Trujillo Fortress

1941.
460 **101** 1c. green 15 10
461 – 2c. red 15 10
462 – 10c. brown 55 10
DESIGN—VERT: 2, 10c. Statue of Columbus, Ciudad Trujillo.

103 Sanchez, Duarte, Mella and Trujillo

1941. Trujillo-Hull Treaty.
463 **103** 3c. mauve 25 10
464 4c. red 30 10
465 13c. blue 70 20
466 15c. brown 2·00 85
467 17c. blue 2·00 90
468 1p. orange 7·50 3·25
469 2p. grey 15·00 7·50

104 Bastion of 27 February

1941.
470 **104** 5c. blue 55 20

105 Rural School, Torch of Knowledge and Pres. Trujillo

1941. Popular Education Campaign.
471 **105** ½c. brown 20 10
472 1c. green 25 10

106 Globe and Winged Envelope

1941. Air.
473 **106** 10c. brown 55 10
474 75c. orange 3·25 2·00

107 National Reserve Bank

1942.
475 **107** 5c. brown 40 10
476 17c. blue 1·00 40

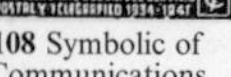

108 Symbolic of Communications **109** Our Lady of Highest Grace

1942. 8th Anniv of Postal and Telegraph Services Day.
477 **108** 3c. multicoloured . . . . 4·00 1·00
478 15c. multicoloured . . . . 8·00 4·00

1942. 20th Anniv of Our Lady of Highest Grace.
479 **109** ½c. grey 85 10
480 1c. green . . . . 1·60 10
481 3c. mauve . . . . 7·50 10
482 5c. purple . . . . 2·40 10
483 10c. red . . . . 6·50 25
484 15c. blue . . . . 7·50 35

111 Banana Tree **112** Cows

1942.
494 **111** 3c. green and brown . . . 45 10
495 4c. black and red 50 20
496 **112** 5c. brown and blue . . . 45 10
497 15c. green and purple . . 85 35

113 Party Emblems and Votes

1943. Re-election of Gen. Trujillo to Presidency.
498 **113** 3c. orange 40 10
499 4c. red 50 15
500 13c. purple . . . . 1·10 20
501 1p. blue . . . . 5·00 1·90

114 Trujillo Market

1943.
502 **114** 2c. brown 15 10

115 Douglas DC-3

1943. Air.
503 **115** 10c. mauve 50 10
504 20c. blue 55 15
505 25c. olive . . . . 6·75 2·75

116 Bastion of 27 February **117** Monument and Dates

1944. Centenary of Independence. (a) Postage. Flag in blue and red.
506 **116** ½c. ochre 10 10
507 1c. green 10 10
508 2c. red 15 10
509 3c. purple 15 10
510 5c. orange 20 10
511 7c. blue 25 10
512 10c. brown 40 30
513 20c. olive 70 45
514 50c. blue . . . . 2·00 1·40

(b) Air. Flag in grey, blue and red.
515 **117** 10c. multicoloured 40 10
516 20c. multicoloured 50 15
517 1p. multicoloured . . . . 2·40 1·60

118 Dr. Martos Sanatorium

1944. Tuberculosis Relief Fund.
518 **118** 1c. blue and red 15 10

119 Nurse and Battlefield

1944. 80th Anniv of International Red Cross.
519 **119** 1c. green, red and yellow 15 10
520 2c. brown, red and yellow 35 10
521 3c. blue, red and yellow 35 10
522 10c. red and yellow . . . 70 15

120 Communications Building, Ciudad Trujillo

1944. Air.
523 **120** 9c. blue and green 25 10
524 13c. red and brown . . . 35 10
525 25c. red and orange . . . 50 10
526 30c. blue and black . . . 1·10 80

121 Municipal Building, San Cristobal **122** Emblem of Communications

1945. Centenary of 1st Constitution of Dominican Republic.
527 **121** ½c. blue 10 10
528 1c. green 10 10
529 2c. orange 10 10
530 3c. brown 15 10
531 10c. blue 45 15

1945. Centres in blue and red.
532 **122** 3c. orange (postage) . . . 15 10
533 20c. green 80 20
534 50c. blue . . . . 1·60 60
535 7c. green (air) 20 25
536 12c. orange 25 15
537 13c. blue 30 15
538 25c. brown 60 20

124 Flags and National Anthem **125** Law Courts, Ciudad Trujillo

1946. Air. National Anthem.
540 **124** 10c. red 45 40
541 15c. blue . . . . 1·00 70
542 20c. brown . . . . 1·25 70
543 35c. orange . . . . 1·40 70
544 – 1p. green . . . . 13·00 10·00
DESIGN: 1p. As Type **124**, but horiz.

1946.
545 **125** 3c. brown and buff . . . 20 10

126 Caribbean Air Routes

1946. 450th Anniv of Santo Domingo.
546 **126** 10c. mult (postage) . . . 40 15
547 10c. multicoloured (air) 35 15
548 13c. multicoloured 55 15

127 Jimenoa Waterfall **128** Nurse and Child

1947. Centres multicoloured, frame colours given.
549 **127** 1c. green (postage) . . . 15 10
550 2c. red 15 10
551 3c. blue 15 10
552 13c. purple 45 25
553 20c. brown . . . . 1·00 25
554 50c. yellow . . . . 1·90 1·00
555 18c. blue (air) 50 50
556 23c. red 70 55
557 50c. violet . . . . 1·00 45
558 75c. brown . . . . 1·40 1·00

1947. Obligatory Tax. Tuberculosis Relief Fund.
559 **128** 1c. blue and red 15 10

129 State Building, Ciudad Trujillo

1948.
560 **129** 1c. green (postage) . . . 10 10
561 3c. blue 15 10
562 37c. brown (air) . . . . . 1·00 70
563 1p. orange . . . . 2·75 1·60

130 Ruins of San Francisco Church, Ciudad Trujillo **131** El Santo Socorro Sanatorium

1949.
564 **130** 1c. green (postage) . . . 10 10
565 3c. blue 15 10
566 7c. olive (air) 15 10
567 10c. brown 15 10
568 15c. red 50 25
569 20c. green 70 45

1949. Tuberculosis Relief Fund.
570 **131** 1c. blue and red 15 10

132 General Pedro Santana **133** Monument

1949. Centenary of Battle of Las Carreras.
571 **132** 3c. blue (postage) 15 10
572 **133** 10c. red (air) 25 10

134 Bird and Globe **136** Hotel Jimani

135 Youth Holding Banner **138** Ruins of Church and Hospital of St. Nicholas of Bari

1949. 75th Anniv of U.P.U.
573 **134** 1c. brown and green . . . 15 10
574 2c. brown and yellow . . 15 10
575 5c. brown and blue . . . 20 10
576 7c. brown and blue . . . 45 15

1950. Tuberculosis Relief Fund.
584 **135** 1c. blue and red 20 10

1950. Various Hotels.
585 **136** ½c. brown (postage) . . . 10 10
586 – 1c. green (Hamaca) . . . 10 10
587 – 2c. orange (Hamaca) . . 10 10
588 – 5c. blue (Montana) . . . 20 10
589 – 15c. orge (San Cristobal) 45 10
590 – 20c. lilac (Maguana) . . . 85 15
591 **136** $1 yellow and brown . . 3·25 1·40
592 – 12c. bl (Montana) (air) . . 25 10
593 – 37c. red (San Cristobal) 1·90 1·50

1950. 13th Pan-American Sanitary Congress. Inscr as T **138**.
595 **138** 2c. brown & green (postage) 20 10
596 – 5c. brown and blue . . . 25 10
597 – 12c. orange & brn (air) 55 10
DESIGNS—VERT: 5c. Medical school; 12c. Map and aeroplane.

139 "Suffer Little Children to Come Unto Me" **148**

148a **148b**

1950. Child Welfare. (a) Child at left with light hair.
598 **139** 1c. blue 25 10

(b) Child at left with dark hair.
599 **139** 1c. blue 85 15

(c) Child at left with dark hair.
626 **148** 1c. blue 20 10

(d) Child at left with light hair.
627 **148a** 1c. blue 15 10

(e) Dark hair, smaller figures and square value tablet.
628 **148b** 1c. blue 15 10
There are two versions of No. 628, differing in size. See also Nos. 835 and 907.

140 Isabella the Catholic

1951. 500th Birth Anniv of Isabella the Catholic.
600 **140** 5c. brown and blue . . . 25 10

141 Santiago Tuberculosis Sanatorium

1952. Tuberculosis Relief Fund.
601 **141** 1c. blue and red 15 10

142 Dr. S. B. Gautier Hospital

1952.
602 **142** 1c. green (postage) . . . 10 10
603 2c. red 15 10
604 5c. blue 25 10
605 23c. blue (air) 55 55
606 29c. red . . . . 1·40 1·00

143 Columbus Lighthouse and Flags

144

1953. 460th Anniv of Columbus's Discovery of Santo Domingo. (a) Postage.

607	**143**	2c. green	15	10
608		5c. blue	20	10
609		10c. red	35	20

(b) Air. Similar design inscr "S./S.A.S./XMY", etc.

610		12c. brown	35	15
611		14c. blue	35	20
612		20c. sepia	65	40
613		23c. purple	70	45
614		25c. blue	70	45
615		29c. green	90	45
616		1p. brown	3·25	2·00

DESIGN: Nos. 610/16, Douglas DC-6 airplane over Columbus Lighthouse.

1953. Anti-cancer Fund. No. 619 has "1 c" larger with line through "c" and no stop. No. 620 is as 619 but with smaller "c".

618	**144**	1c. red	20	10
619		1c. red	35	10
620		1c. red	15	10

See also Nos. 1029/30, 1066/7, 1171a, 1196a, 1237a, 1270a and 1338a.

145 T.B. Children's Dispensary

1953. Obligatory Tax. Tuberculosis Relief Fund.

621	**145**	1c. blue and red	15	10

There are two versions of this design.

146 Treasury **149** Jose Marti

150 Monument to Trujillo Peace **147** Rio Haina Sugar Factory

1953.

622	**146**	½c. brown	10	10
623		2c. blue	10	10
624	**147**	5c. brown and blue	15	10
625	**146**	15c. orange	50	15

1953. Birth Cent of Marti (Cuban revolutionary).

629	**149**	10c. sepia and blue	30	15

1954.

630	**150**	2c. green	10	10
631		7c. blue	15	10
632		20c. orange	55	10

There are two versions of No. 631.

151

152 Rotary Emblem

1954. Air. Marian Year.

633	**151**	8c. purple	15	10
634		11c. blue	25	10
635		33c. orange	70	45

1955. 50th Anniv of Rotary International.

636	**152**	7c. blue (postage)	30	10
637		11c. red (air)	25	15

153

154 Pres. R. Trujillo

1955. Obligatory Tax. Tuberculosis Relief Fund.

638	**153**	1c. black, red & yellow	15	10

1955. 25th Year of Trujillo Era.

639	**154**	2c. red (postage)	10	10
640	–	4c. green	15	10
641	–	7c. blue	15	10
642	–	10c. brown	35	15
643	–	11c. red, yell & bl (air)	30	10
644	–	25c. purple	45	25
645	–	33c. brown	70	40

DESIGNS: 4c. Pres. R. Trujillo in civilian clothes; 7c. Equestrian statue; 10c. Allegory of Prosperity; 11c. National flags; 25c. Gen. Hector B. Trujillo in evening clothes; 33c. Gen. Hector B. Trujillo in uniform.

156 Angelita Trujillo

1955. Child Welfare.

654	**156**	1c. violet	15	10

157 Angelita Trujillo

158 Gen. R. Trujillo

1955. Peace and Brotherhood Fair, Ciudad Trujillo.

656	**158**	7c. purple (postage)	25	10
657		10c. green	35	15
655	**157**	10c. blue and ultramarine	35	15
658	**158**	11c. red (air)	25	10

159 "B.C.G." = "Bacillus" Calmette-Guerin

160 Punta Caucedo Airport

1956. Obligatory Tax. Tuberculosis Relief Fund.

659	**159**	1c. multicoloured	15	10

1956. 3rd Caribbean Region Aerial Navigation Conference.

660	**160**	1c. brown (postage)	10	10
661		2c. orange	20	10
662		11c. blue (air)	35	10

161 Cedar Tree

162 Fanny Blankers-Koen and Dutch Flag

1956. Re-afforestation. Inscr "REPOBLACION FORESTAL".

664	**161**	5c. green, brown and red (postage)	20	10
665	–	6c. green and purple	25	10
666	–	13c. green & orge (air)	35	10

DESIGNS: 6c. Pine tree; 13c. Mahogany tree.

1957. Olympic Games (1st issue). Famous Athletes. Flags in national colours.

667	**162**	1c. mult (postage)	10	10
668	–	2c. sepia, purple & blue	10	10
669	–	3c. purple and red	15	15
670	–	5c. orange, pur & blue	25	15
671	–	7c. green and purple	35	25
673	–	11c. blue and red (air)	20	20
674	–	16c. red and green	30	30
675	–	17c. black and purple	40	40

DESIGNS—(each with national flag of athlete): 2c. Jesse Owens; 3c. Kee Chung Sohn; 5c. Lord Burghley; 7c. Bob Mathias; 11c. Paavo Nurmi; 16c. Ugo Frigerio; 17c. Mildred Didrickson.

See also Nos. 689/96, 713/21, 748/56 and 784/91.

163 Horse's Head and Globe

165

1957. 2nd Int Livestock Fair, Ciudad Trujillo.

677	**163**	7c. blue, brown & red	25	10

1957. Hungarian Refugees Fund. Nos. 667/75 surch with red cross in circle surrounded by **ASISTENCIA REFUGIADOS HUNGAROS 1957** and **+2c**.

678	**162**	1c.+2c. (postage)	10	10
679	–	2c.+2c.	10	10
680	–	3c.+2c.	10	10
681	–	5c.+2c.	15	15
682	–	7c.+2c.	25	25
684	–	11c.+2c. (air)	40	40
685	–	16c.+2c.	40	40
686	–	17c.+2c.	1·50	1·50

1957. Obligatory Tax. Tuberculosis Relief Fund.

688	**165**	1c. multicoloured	15	10

166 Chris Brasher and Union Jack (steeplechase)

1957. Olympic Games (2nd issue). Winning Athletes. Inscr "MELBOURNE 1956". Flags in national colours.

689	–	1c. brown & bl (postage)	10	10
690	–	2c. red and blue	10	10
691	–	3c. blue	10	10
692	–	5c. olive and blue	15	10
693	–	7c. red and blue	25	15
694	–	11c. green & blue (air)	20	20
695	**166**	16c. purple and blue	25	25
696	–	17c. sepia and green	30	30

DESIGNS—(each with national flag of athlete): 1c. Lars Hall (Sweden, pentathlon); 2c. Betty Cuthbert (Australia, 100 and 200 m); 3c. Egil Danielson (Norway, javelin-throwing); 5c. Alain Mimoum (France, marathon); 7c. Norman Read (New Zealand, 50 km walk); 11c. Robert Morrow (U.S.A.; 100 and 200 m); 17c. A. Ferreira da Silva (Brazil; hop, step and jump).

1957. 50th Anniv of Boy Scout Movement, and Birth Cent of Lord Baden-Powell. Nos 689/96 surch **CENTENARIO LORD BADEN-POWELL, 1857-1957 +2c**. surrounding Scout badge.

699		1c.+2c. brn & bl (postage)	15	15
700		2c.+2c. red and blue	20	15
701		3c.+2c. blue	25	25
702		5c.+2c. olive and blue	35	25
703		7c.+2c. red and blue	40	30
704		11c.+2c. grn & blue (air)	40	35
705		16c.+2c. purple and blue	50	50
706		17c.+2c. sepia and green	55	55

168 Mahogany Flower

1957.

709	**168**	2c. red and green	10	10
710		4c. red and mauve	10	10
711		7c. green and blue	25	10
712		25c. orange and brown	55	25

169 Gerald Ouellette and Canadian Flag (rifle-shooting)

1957. Olympic Games (3rd issue). More winning athletes. Flags in national colours.

713	**169**	1c. brown (postage)	10	10
714	–	2c. sepia	10	10
715	–	3c. violet	10	10
716	–	5c. orange	15	15
717	–	7c. slate	20	20
719	–	11c. blue (air)	20	15
720	–	16c. red	30	30
721	–	17c. purple	35	35

DESIGNS—(each with national flag of athlete): 2c. Ron Delaney (Ireland, 1500 m); 3c. Tenley Albright (U.S.A., figure-skating); 5c. J. Capilla (Mexico, high-diving); 7c. Ercole Baldini (Italy, cycle-racing); 11c. Hans Winkler (Germany, horse-jumping); 16c. Alfred Oerter (U.S.A., discus-throwing); 17c. Shirley Strickland (Australia, 80 m hurdles).

The designs of Nos. 714, 716 and 720 are arranged with the long side of the triangular format uppermost.

170

171 Cervantes, Open Book, Marker and Globe

1958. Tuberculosis Relief Fund.

723	**170**	1c. red and claret	10	10

See also No. 763.

1958. 4th Latin-American Book Fair.

724	**171**	4c. green	10	10
725		7c. mauve	15	10
726		10c. bistre	25	10

1958. U.N. Relief and Works Agency for Palestine Refugees. Nos. 713/21 surch. A. For Jewish Refugees. Star of David and **REFUGIADOS**.

727		1c.+2c. brown (postage)	15	15
728		2c.+2c. brown	20	20
729		3c.+2c. violet	20	20
730		5c.+2c. orange	25	25
731		7c.+2c. blue	35	35
732		11c.+2c. blue (air)	25	25
733		16c.+2c. red	35	35
734		17c.+2c. purple	40	40

B. For Arab Refugees. Red Crescent and **REFUGIADOS**.

735		1c.+2c. brown (postage)	15	15
736		2c.+2c. brown	20	20
737		3c.+2c. violet	20	20
738		5c.+2c. orange	25	25
739		7c.+2c. blue	35	35
740		11c.+2c. blue (air)	25	25
741		16c.+2c. red	35	35
742		17c.+2c. purple	40	40

172 Gen. R. Trujillo and Arms of Republic

173 "Rhadames" (freighter)

1958. 25th Anniv of Gen Trujillo's designation as "Benefactor of the Country".

743	**172**	2c. mauve and yellow	10	10
744		4c. green and yellow	10	10
745		7c. sepia and yellow	15	10

1958. Merchant Marine Day.

747	**173**	7c. blue	1·25	30

174 Gillian Sheen and Union Jack (fencing)

175

176 Dominican Republic Pavilion

1958. Olympic Games (4th issue). More winning athletes. Flags in national colours.

748 **174** 1c. slate, blue and red (postage) 10 10
749 – 2c. brown and blue . . . 10 10
750 – 3c. multicoloured 15 15
751 – 5c. multicoloured 20 20
752 – 7c. multicoloured 25 25

754 – 11c. sepia, olive and blue (air) 25 25
755 – 16c. blue, orge & grn . . 30 30
756 – 17c. blue, yell and red . . 1·00 50

DESIGNS (each with national flag of athlete)—VERT: 2c. Milton Campbell (U.S.A., decathlon). HORIZ: 3c. Shozo Sasahara (Japan, featherweight wrestling); 5c. Madeleine Berthod (Switzerland, skiing); 7c. Murray Rose (Australia, 400 m and 1,500 m free-style); 11c. Charles Jenkins and Thomas Courtney (U.S.A., 400 m and 800 m, and 1600 m relay); 16c. Indian team in play (India, hockey); 17c. Swedish dinghies (Sweden, sailing).

1958. Inauguration of U.N.E.S.C.O. Headquarters Building, Paris.

758 **175** 7c. blue and red 15 10

1958. Brussels International Exhibition.

759 **176** 7c. green (postage) . . . 20 15

760 9c. grey (air) 20 15
761 25c. violet 50 30

1959. Obligatory Tax. Tuberculosis Relief Fund. As T **170** but inscr "1959".

763 **170** 1c. red and lake 15 10

1959. I.G.Y. Nos. 748/56 surch with globe and **ANO GEOFISICO INTERNACIONAL 1957-1958 +2c**.

764 1c.+2c. (postage) 25 25
765 2c.+2c. 30 30
766 3c.+2c. 35 35
767 5c.+2c. 40 40
768 7c.+2c. 45 45

770 11c.+2c. (air) 50 50
771 16c.+2c. 70 70
772 17c.+2c. . . . . 1·00 1·00

178 Leonidas R. Trujillo (Team Captain)

179 Gen. Trujillo before National Shrine

1959. Jamaica–Dominican Republic Polo Match, Trujillo City. Inscr as in T **178**.

774 **178** 2c. violet (postage) . . . 15 10
775 – 7c. brown 30 15
776 – 10c. green 35 25

777 – 11c. orange (air) 30 25

DESIGNS—HORIZ: 7c. Jamaican team; 10c. Dominican Republic team's captain on horseback; 11c. Dominican Republic team.

1959. 29th Year of Trujillo Era.

778 **179** 9c. multicoloured 20 10

180 Gen. Trujillo and Cornucopia

1959. National Census of 1960. Centres in black, red and blue. Frame colours given.

780 **180** 1c. pale blue 15 10
781 9c. green 30 15
782 13c. orange 35 25

181 Trujillo Stadium

1959. 3rd Pan-American Games, Chicago.

783 **181** 9c. black and green . . . 35 20

1959. 3rd Pan-American Games, Chicago. Nos. 667/71 and 673/5, surch **III JUEGOS DEPORTIVOS PANAMERICANOS + 2** and runner.

784 **162** 1c.+2c. mult (postage) . . 15 15
785 – 3c.+2c. multicoloured . . 15 15
786 – 3c.+2c. pur & red 15 15
787 – 5c.+2c. multicoloured . . 15 15
788 – 7c.+2c. multicoloured . . 20 20
789 – 11c.+2c. blue, red and orange (air) 20 20
790 – 16c.+2c. red, green and carmine 30 30
791 – 17c.+2c. multicoloured . . 30 30

182 Emperor Charles V

183 Rhadames Bridge

1959. 4th Death Centenary of Emperor Charles V.

792 **182** 5c. mauve 15 10
793 9c. blue 15 10

1959. Opening of Rhadames Bridge.

794 – 1c. black and green . . . 10 10
795 **183** 2c. black and blue 15 10
796 – 2c. black and red 15 10
797 **183** 5c. brown and bistre . . . 20 15

DESIGN—Nos. 794, 796, Close-up view of Rhadames Bridge.

184 Douglas DC-4 Airliner, "San Cristobal"

1960. Air. Dominican Civil Aviation.

798 **184** 13c. multicoloured 45 15

185

1960. Obligatory Tax. Tuberculosis Relief Fund.

779 **185** 1c. red, blue and cream 20 15

186 Sosua Refugee Colony

1960. World Refugee Year. Inscr "ANO MUNDIAL DE LOS REFUGIADOS". Centres in black.

800 **186** 5c. green & brn (postage) 10 10
801 9c. blue, purple & red . . 20 10
802 13c. green, brn & orge . . 25 15

803 – 10c. green, mauve and purple (air) 35 30
804 – 13c. green and grey . . . 45 35

DESIGN: Nos. 802/803, Refugee children.

1960. World Refugee Year Fund. Nos. 800/4 surch **+5** with **c** below.

805 **186** 5c.+5c. green and brown (postage) 15 15
806 9c.+5c. bl, pur & red . . 20 20
807 13c.+5c. green, brown and orange 40 40

808 – 10c.+5c. green, mauve and purple (air) 25 25
809 – 13c.+5c. green & grey . . 30 30

188 General Post Office, Ciudad Trujillo

1960.

811 **188** 2c. black and blue 10 10

189 Cattle in Street

1960. Agricultural and Industrial Fair, San Juan de la Maguana.

812 **189** 9c. black and red 25 15

190 Gholam Takhti (Iran, lightweight wrestling)

192

1960. Olympic Games, 1960. More Winning Athletes of Olympic Games, Melbourne, 1956. Flags in national colours.

813 **190** 1c. black, grn & red (postage) 10 10
814 – 2c. brown, turq & orge 10 10
815 – 3c. blue and red 10 10
816 – 5c. brown and blue . . . 15 15
817 – 7c. brn, blue & green . . 15 15

819 – 11c. brown, grey & bl (air) 20 20
820 – 16c. green, brown & red 25 25
821 – 17c. ochre, blue & black 30 30

DESIGNS (each with national flag of athlete): 2c. Mauru Furukawa (Japan, 200 m breast-stroke swimming); 3c. Mildred McDaniel (U.S.A., high jump); 5c. Terence Spinks (spelt "Terrence" on stamp) (Great Britain, featherweight boxing); 7c. Carlo Pavesi (Italy, fencing); 11c. Pat McCormick (U.S.A., high diving); 16c. Mithat Bayrack (Turkey, Greco-Roman welterweight wrestling); 17c. Ursula Happe (Germany, women's 200 m breaststroke swimming).

1961. Surch **HABILITADO PARA** and value.

823 – 2c. on 1c. black and green (No. 794) 15 10
824 **168** 9c. on 4c. red & mauve 45 10
825 9c. on 7c. green & blue 45 15
826 **146** 36c. on ½c. brown . . . . 1·50 70
827 **127** 1p. on 50c. yellow . . . . 3·25 1·90

1961. Obligatory Tax. Tuberculosis Relief Fund.

828 **192** 1c. red and blue 10 10

See also No. 876.

193 Madame Trujillo and Houses

1961. Welfare Fund.

829 **193** 1c. red 20 10

194

195 Coffee Plant and Cocoa Beans

1961.

830 **194** 1c. brown 10 10
831 2c. myrtle 10 10
832 4c. purple 40 35
833 5c. blue 25 10
834 9c. orange 30 20

1961. Obligatory Tax. Child Welfare. As Nos. 627/8 but with "ERA DE TRUJILLO" omitted. (a) Size 23½ × 32 mm.

835 **148a** 1c. blue 15 10

(b) Size 21¾ × 32 mm.

907 **148b** 1c. blue 15 10

1961.

836 **195** 1c. green (postage) . . . 10 10
837 2c. brown 10 10
838 4c. violet 10 10
839 5c. blue 10 10
840 9c. grey 25 10
841 13c. red (air) 25 25
842 33c. yellow 55 55

1961. 15th Anniv of U.N.E.S.C.O. Nos. 813/21 surch **XV ANIVERSARIO DE LA UNESCO +2c**.

843 1c.+2c. (postage) 10 10
844 2c.+2c. 10 10
845 3c.+2c. 10 10
846 5c.+2c. 15 15
847 7c.+2c. 15 15

849 11c.+2c. (air) 25 25
850 16c.+2c. 35 35
851 17c.+2c. 35 35

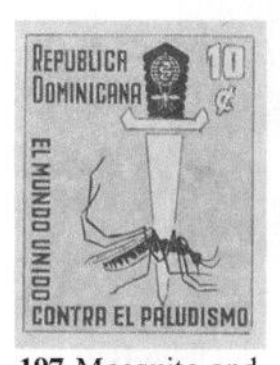

197 Mosquito and Dagger

198 Plantation

1962. Malaria Eradication.

853 **197** 10c. mauve (postage) . . 15 10
854 10c.+2c. mauve 20 15
855 20c. sepia 35 30
856 20c.+2c. sepia 35 25
857 25c. green 45 55

858 13c. red (air) 25 20
859 13c.+2c. red 25 25
860 33c. orange 50 50
861 33c.+2c. orange 60 60

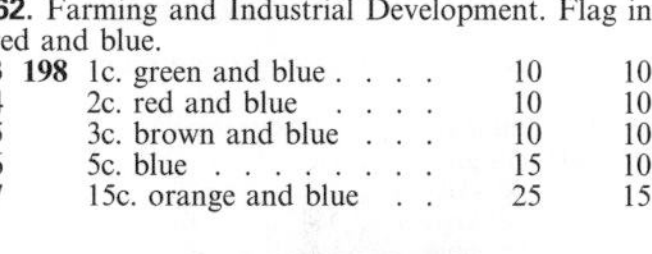

1962. Farming and Industrial Development. Flag in red and blue.

863 **198** 1c. green and blue 10 10
864 2c. red and blue 10 10
865 3c. brown and blue . . . 10 10
866 5c. blue 15 10
867 15c. orange and blue . . 25 15

199 Laurel Sprig and Broken Link

1962. 1st Anniv of Assassination of Pres. Trujillo.

868 **199** 1c. mult (postage) 10 10
869 – 9c. red, blue and ochre . . 25 15
870 – 20c. red, blue & turq . . 45 25
871 – 1p. red, blue & violet . . 2·75 1·60

873 **199** 13c. multicoloured (air) 25 20
874 – 50c. red, blue & mauve 1·00 70

DESIGNS—VERT: 9c., 1p. "Justice" on map. HORIZ: 20c., 50c. Flag and flaming torch.

200 Map and Laurel

201 U.P.A.E. Emblem

1962. Martyrs of June 1959 Revolution.

875 **200** 1c. black 25 15

1962. Tuberculosis Relief Fund. As No. 828 but inscr "1962".

876 **192** 1c. red and blue 10 10

1962. 50th Anniv of Postal Union of the Americas and Spain.

877 **201** 2c. red (postage) 10 10
878 9c. orange 25 15
879 14c. turquoise 25 20

880 13c. blue (air) 35 20
881 22c. brown 45 40

202 Archbishop Nouel

203 Globe, Riband and Campaign Emblem

1962. Birth Cent of Archbishop Adolfo Nouel.

882 **202** 2c. myrtle & green (postage) 10 10
883 9c. brown and orange . . 25 15
884 13c. purple and brown . . 30 20

885 – 12c. blue (air) 35 20
886 – 25c. violet 50 40
DESIGN: Air stamps as Type **202** but different frame.

1963. Freedom from Hunger. Riband in red and blue.
888 **203** 2c. green 10 10
891 2c.+1c. green 10 10
889 5c. mauve 15 10
892 5c.+2c. mauve 20 20
890 9c. orange 25 15
893 9c.+2c. orange 20 20

204 Duarte

1963. 120th Anniv of Separation from Haiti.
895 **204** 2c. blue (postage) 10 10
896 – 7c. green (Sanchez) . . . 15 15
897 – 9c. purple (Mella) 15 15
898 – 15c. salmon (air) 20 15
DESIGN—HORIZ: 15c. Sanchez, Duarte and Mella.

205 Espaillat, de Rojas and Bono

1963. "Centenary of the Restoration".
899 **205** 2c. green 10 10
900 – 4c. red 10 10
901 – 5c. brown 10 10
902 – 9c. blue 15 15
DESIGNS: 4c. Rodriguez, Cabrera and Moncion; 5c. Capotillo Monument; 9c. Polanco, Luperon and Salcedo.

206 Nurse tending Patient

207

1963. Centenary of Red Cross. Cross in red.
904 **206** 3c. grey (postage) 10 10
905 6c. green 15 10
906 – 10c. grey (air) 25 20
DESIGN—HORIZ: 10c. Map of continents bordering Atlantic.

1963. Obligatory Tax. T.B. Relief Fund.
908 **207** 1c. red and blue 15 10

208 Scales of Justice and Globe

1963. 15th Anniv of Declaration of Human Rights.
911 **208** 6c. red (postage) 15 10
912 50c. green 80 55
913 7c. brown (air) 20 15
914 10c. blue 25 15

209 Rameses II in War Chariot, Abu Simbel

1964. Nubian Monuments Preservation. Designs as T **209**, also surch **2c** in circle.
915 **209** 3c. red (postage) 10 10
916 3c.+2c. red 15 15
917 – 6c. blue 15 10
918 – 6c.+2c. blue 15 15
919 **209** 9c. brown 20 15
920 9c.+2c. brown 25 25
921 – 10c. violet (air) 25 20
922 – 10c.+2c. violet 20 20
923 – 13c. yellow 25 20
924 – 13c.+2c. yellow 25 25
DESIGNS—HORIZ: 6c. Heads of Rameses II. VERT: 10c., 13c. As Type **209**.

211 M. Gomez (founder)

212 Palm Chat

1964. Bicentenary of Bani Foundation.
925 **211** 2c. blue & light blue . . . 10 10
926 6c. purple and brown . . 15 10

1964. Dominican Birds. Multicoloured.
927 1c. Narrow-billed tody (postage) . . . . 1·75 15
928 2c. Hispaniolan emerald . . . 1·75 15
929 3c. Type **212** . . . . 1·75 15
930 6c. Hispaniolan amazon . . . 2·10 15
931 6c. Hispaniolan trogons . . . 2·50 15
932 10c. Hispaniolan woodpecker (air) . . . . 3·75 20
The 1c., 2c. and 6c. (No. 931) are smaller (26 × 37½ mm); the 10c. is horiz (43½ × 27½ mm).

213 Rocket

1964. "Conquest of Space".
933 – 1c. blue (postage) 10 10
934 **213** 2c. green 10 10
935 – 3c. blue 15 10
936 **213** 6c. blue 25 15
937 **213** 7c. green (air) 25 25
938 – 10c. blue 35 70
DESIGNS—VERT: 1c. Rocket launching. HORIZ: 3c., 10c. Capsule in orbit.

214 Pres. Kennedy

1964. Air. Pres. Kennedy Commemoration.
940 **214** 10c. brown and buff . . . 35 25

215 U.P.U. Monument, Berne

1964. 15th U.P.U. Congress, Vienna.
941 **215** 1c. red (postage) 10 10
942 4c. green 15 10
943 5c. orange 15 10
944 7c. blue (air) 15 10

216 I.C.Y. Emblem

217 Hands and Lily

1965. International Co-operation Year.
945 **216** 2c. blue and light-blue (postage) 10 10
946 3c. green and emerald . . 10 10
947 6c. red and pink 15 10
948 10c. violet & lilac (air) . . 25 20

1965. 4th Mariological and 11th Int Marian Congresses. Multicoloured.
949 2c. Type **217** (postage) . . . 10 10
950 6c. Virgin of the Altagracia 35 25
951 10c. Douglas DC-8 airliner over Basilica of Virgin of Altagracia (39½ × 31½ mm) (air) 30 15

218 Flags Emblem

219 Lincoln

1965. 75th Anniv of Organization of American States.
952 **218** 2c. multicoloured 10 10
953 6c. multicoloured 15 10

1965. Air. Death Centenary of Abraham Lincoln.
954 **219** 17c. grey and blue 35 25

220 ½r. Stamp of 1865

221 Hibiscus

1965. Stamp Centenary.
955 **220** 1c. multicoloured (post) 10 10
956 2c. multicoloured 10 10
957 6c. multicoloured 15 10
958 – 7c. multicoloured (air) . . 25 20
959 – 10c. multicoloured 25 25
DESIGN: 7c., 10c. As Type **220**, but showing 1r. stamp of 1865.

1966. Obligatory Tax. Tuberculosis Relief Fund.
963 **221** 1c. red and green 15 10
999 – 1c. mauve, lilac & red 10 10
1015 – 1c. multicoloured 10 10
1016 – 1c. multicoloured 10 10
1017 – 1c. multicoloured 10 10
DESIGN (21½ × 30 mm): No. 999, Orchid. (20 × 28 mm): No. 1015, Dogbane; 1016, Violets; 1017, "Eeanthus capitatus".

222 I.T.U. Emblem and Symbols

223 W.H.O. Building

1966. Air. Centenary (1965) of I.T.U.
964 **222** 28c. red and pink 55 40
965 45c. green and emerald 55 70

1965. Inaug of W.H.O. Headquarters, Geneva.
966 **223** 6c. blue 15 10
967 10c. purple 20 15

224 Man supporting "Republic"

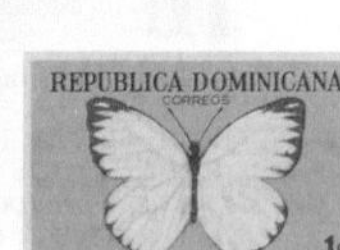
225 "Ascia monuste"

1966. General Elections.
968 **224** 2c. black and green . . . 10 10
969 6c. black and red 15 10

1966. Butterflies. Multicoloured.
970 1c. Type **225** (postage) . . . 10 10
971 2c. "Heliconius charitonius" 10 10
972 3c. "Phoebis sennae sennae" 10 15
973 6c. "Anteos clorinde clorinde" 25 25
974 8c. "Siderone hemesis" . . . 35 35
975 10c. "Eurema gundlachia" (air) 45 25
976 50c. "Clothilda pantherata pantherata" . . . . 2·10 1·00
977 75c. "Papilio androgeus epidaurus" . . . . 3·00 1·50
Nos. 975/7 are larger, 35 × 24½ mm.

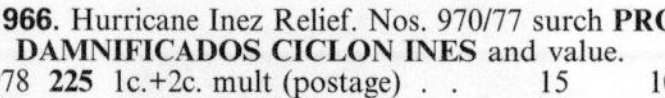
1966. Hurricane Inez Relief. Nos. 970/77 surch **PRO DAMNIFICADOS CICLON INES** and value.
978 **225** 1c.+2c. mult (postage) . . 15 10
979 – 2c.+2c. multicoloured . . 15 10
980 – 3c.+2c. multicoloured . . 15 10
981 – 6c.+4c. multicoloured . . 30 25
982 – 8c.+4c. multicoloured . . 40 30
983 – 10c.+5c. mult (air) . . . 40 35
984 – 50c.+10c. mult . . . . . 1·40 1·40
985 – 75c.+10c. mult . . . . . 1·75 1·75

227 National Shrine

228 Emblem and Map

1967. (a) Postage.
986 **227** 1c. blue 10 10
987 2c. red 10 10
988 3c. green 10 10
989 4c. grey 10 10
990 5c. yellow 10 10
991 6c. orange 10 10

(b) Air. Size 20½ × 25 mm.
992 **227** 7c. olive 15 10
993 10c. lilac 15 15
994 20c. brown 30 25

1967. Development Year. Emblem and map in black and blue.
996 **228** 2c. orange and yellow . . 10 10
997 6c. orange 15 10
998 10c. green 25 15

229 Rook and Knight

230 Civil Defence Emblem

1967. 5th Central American Chess Championship, Santo Domingo.
1000 **229** 25c. mult (postage) . . . 55 40
1001 – 10c. black & grn (air) . . 35 25
DESIGN: 10c. Bishop and pawn.

1967. Obligatory Tax. Civil Defence Fund.
1003 **230** 1c. multicoloured 15 15

231 Alliance Emblem

232 Institute Emblem

1967. 6th Anniv of "Alliance for Progress".
1004 **231** 1c. green (postage) . . . 10 10
1005 8c. grey (air) 15 10
1006 10c. blue 20 15

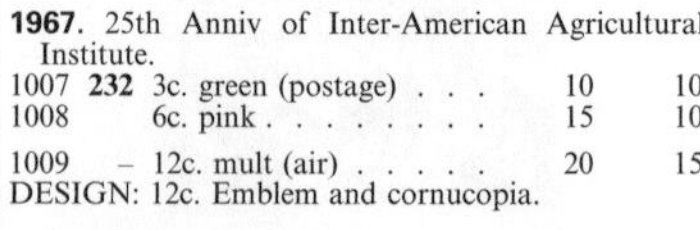
1967. 25th Anniv of Inter-American Agricultural Institute.
1007 **232** 3c. green (postage) . . . 10 10
1008 6c. pink 15 10
1009 – 12c. mult (air) 20 15
DESIGN: 12c. Emblem and cornucopia.

233 Child and Children's Home

234 Hand Holding Invalid

1967. Obligatory Tax. Child Welfare.
1010 **233** 1c. red 25 10
1010a 1c. orange 15 10
1011 1c. violet 10 10
1011a 1c. brown 15 10
1037 1c. green 10 10
See also No. 1278a.

1968. Obligatory Tax. Rehabilitation of the Handicapped.
1012 **234** 1c. yellow and green . . 10 10
1013 1c. blue 10 10
1014 1c. bright purple 10 10
1015 1c. brown 10 10

236 W.M.O. Emblem

1968. World Meteorological Day.
1019 **236** 6c. mult (postage) . . . 20 15
1020 10c. multicoloured (air) 25 20
1021 15c. multicoloured . . . 35 25

237 Ortiz v. Cruz
238 "Lions" Emblem

1968. World Lightweight Boxing Championship. Designs showing similar scenes of the contest.
1024 **237** 6c. pur & red (postage) 15 15
1025 – 7c. green & yellow (air) 15 10
1026 – 10c. blue and brown . . 25 15

1968. Lions International.
1027 **238** 6c. mult (postage) . . . 15 10
1028 10c. multicoloured (air) 25 15

1968. Obligatory Tax. Anti-cancer Fund.
1029 **144** 1c. green 10 10
1030 1c. orange 10 10

239 Wrestling

1968. Olympic Games, Mexico. Multicoloured.
1031 1c. Type **239** (postage) . . . 10 10
1032 6c. Running 15 10
1033 25c. Boxing 70 35
1034 10c. Weightlifting (air) . . . 25 25
1035 33c. Pistol-shooting 80 70

240 Map of Americas and House
241 Carved Stool

1969. 7th Inter-American Savings and Loans Congress, Santo Domingo. Multicoloured.
1038 6c. Type **240** (postage) . . . 15 10
1039 10c. Latin-American flags (air) 25 15

1969. Taino Art. Multicoloured.
1040 1c. Type **241** (postage) . . . 10 10
1041 2c. Female idol (vert) . . . 10 10
1042 3c. Three-cornered footstone 10 10
1043 4c. Stone axe (vert) 15 10
1044 5c. Clay pot 15 15
1045 7c. Spatula and carved handles (vert) (air) . . . 25 10
1046 10c. Breast-shaped vessel . . 35 25
1047 20c. Figured vase (vert) . . 35 75

242 School Playground and Torch
243 Community Emblem

1969. Obligatory Tax. Education Year.
1048 **242** 1c. blue 10 10

1969. Community Development Day.
1049 **243** 6c. gold and green . . . 15 10

244 C.O.T.A.L. Emblem
245 I.L.O. Emblem

1969. 12th C.O.T.A.L. (Confederation of Latin American Tourist Organizations) Congress, Santo Domingo.
1050 **244** 1c. blue, red and light blue (postage) 10 10
1051 – 2c. lt green & green . . 10 10
1052 – 6c. red 15 10
1053 – 10c. brown (air) 30 10
DESIGNS—VERT: 2c. Boy with flags. HORIZ: (39 × 31 mm): 6c. C.O.T.A.L. Building and emblem; 10c. "Airport of the Americas", Santo Domingo.

1969. 50th Anniv of I.L.O.
1054 **245** 6c. blk & turq (postage) 25 10
1055 10c. black and red (air) 15 15

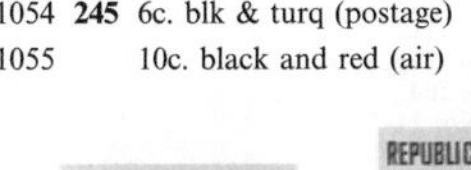

246 Taking a Catch
247 Las Damas Hydro-electric Scheme

1969. World Baseball Championships, Santo Domingo.
1056 **246** 1c. grey and green (postage) 10 10
1057 – 2c. green 10 10
1058 – 3c. brown and violet . . 10 10
1059 – 7c. orange and purple (air) 20 15
1060 – 10c. red 25 15
1061 – 1p. brown and blue . . . 2·00 1·40
DESIGNS—VERT: 3c. Making for base; 10c. Player making strike. HORIZ: (43 × 30½ mm): 2c. Cibao Stadium; 7c. Tetelo Vargas Stadium; 1p. Quisqueya Stadium.

1969. National Electrification Plan.
1062 **247** 2c. mult (postage) . . . 10 10
1063 – 3c. multicoloured 10 10
1064 – 6c. purple 15 10
1065 – 10c. red (air) 20 10
DESIGNS—HORIZ: 3c. Las Damas Dam; 6c. Arroyo Hondo substation; 10c. Haina River power station.

1969. Obligatory Tax. Anti-cancer Fund. T **144** re-drawn in larger format and inscriptions.
1066 **144** 1c. purple 10 10
1067 1c. green 15 10

248 Tavera Dam

1969. Completion of Dam Projects. Mult.
1068 6c. Type **248** (postage) . . . 15 10
1069 10c. Valdesia Dam (air) . . 20 10

249 Juan Pablo Duarte
250 Outline Map, Arms of Census Office and Family

1970. Juan Pablo Duarte (patriot) Commem.
1070 **249** 1c. green (postage) . . . 10 10
1071 2c. red 10 10
1072 3c. purple 10 10
1073 6c. blue 15 10
1074 10c. brown (air) 20 15

1970. National Census.
1075 **250** 5c. blk & grn (postage) 10 10
1076 – 6c. ultram and blue . . . 15 10
1077 – 10c. multicoloured (air) 25 15
DESIGNS: 6c. Arms and quotation; 10c. Arms and buildings.

251 Open Book and Emblem
252 Abelardo Urdaneta

1970. Obligatory Tax. Int Education Year.
1078 **251** 1c. purple 10 10

1970. Birth Cent of A. R. Urdaneta (sculptor).
1079 **252** 3c. blue (postage) . . . 10 10
1080 – 6c. green 15 10
1081 – 10c. blue (air) 20 15
DESIGNS—HORIZ: (39½ × 27 mm): 6c. "One of Many" (sculpture). VERT: (25 × 39 mm): 10c. Prisoner (statue).

253 Masonic Symbols
255 New U.P.U. Building

254 Telecommunications Satellite

1970. 8th Inter-American Masonic Conference, Santo Domingo.
1082 **253** 6c. green (postage) . . . 15 10
1083 10c. brown (air) 20 10

1970. World Telecommunications Day.
1084 **254** 20c. grey & grn (postage) 50 30
1085 7c. grey and blue (air) 15 10

1970. New U.P.U. Headquarters Building, Berne.
1086 **255** 6c. brn & grey (postage) 15 10
1087 10c. brown & yell (air) 15 10

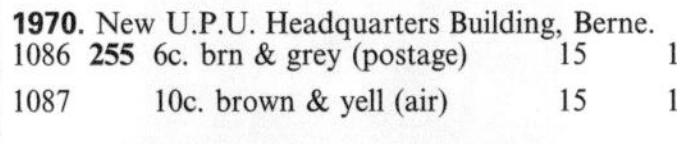

256 I.E.Y. Emblem
257 Pedro Alejandrino Pina

1970. International Education Year.
1088 **256** 4c. purple (postage) . . 10 10
1089 15c. mauve (air) 20 15

1970. 150th Birth Anniv and Death Centenary of Pedro A. Pina (writer).
1090 **257** 6c. black & brown . . . 15 10

258 Children with Book
259 Emblem and Stamp Album

1970. 1st World Book Exhibition, and Cultural Festival, Santo Domingo.
1091 **258** 5c. green (postage) . . . 10 10
1092 – 7c. multicoloured (air) 15 10
1093 – 10c. multicoloured . . . 20 15
DESIGNS: 7c. Dancers; 10c. U.N. emblem within "wheel".

1970. Air. "EXFILICA 70" Inter-American Philatelic Exhibition, Caracas, Venezuela.
1094 **259** 10c. multicoloured . . . 20 15

260 Communications Emblems
261 Virgin of Altagracia

1971. Obligatory Tax. Postal and Telecommunications School. (a) Size 18 × 20½ mm.
1095 **260** 1c. blue and red (white background) 15 10

(b) Size 19 × 22 mm.
1095a **260** 1c. blue and red (red background) 15 10
1095b 1c. blue, red and green 15 10
1095c 1c. blue, red and yellow 15 10
1095d 1c. blue, red and mauve 15 10
1095e 1c. blue, red and light blue 10 10
1096 1c. blue and red (blue background) 10 10

1971. Inauguration of Our Lady of Altagracia Basilica. Multicoloured.
1097 3c. Type **261** (postage) . . . 10 10
1098 17c. Basilica (22½ × 36 mm) (air) 35 25

262 Parcel, Emblem and Map
263 Manuel Objio

1971. Air. 25th Anniv of C.A.R.E. (Cooperative for American Relief Everywhere).
1099 **262** 10c. green and blue . . . 15 15

1971. Death Cent of Manuel Rodriguez Objio (poet).
1100 **263** 6c. blue 15 10

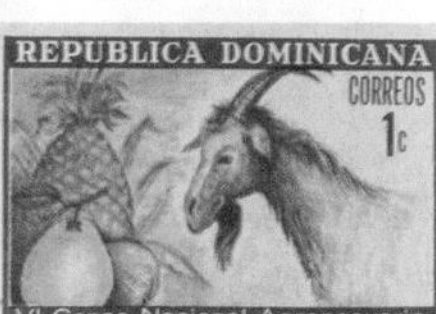

264 Boxing and Canoeing
265 Goat and Fruit

1971. 2nd National Games.
1101 **264** 2c. brown and orange (postage) 10 10
1102 – 5c. brown and green . . 15 10
1103 – 7c. purple & grey (air) 15 10
DESIGNS: 5c. Basketball; 7c. Volleyball.

1971. 6th National Agricultural Census. Mult.
1104 1c. Type **265** (postage) . . . 10 10
1105 2c. Cow and goose 10 10
1106 3c. Cocoa pods and horse 10 10
1107 6c. Bananas, coffee beans and pig 15 10
1108 25c. Cockerel and grain (air) 40 30

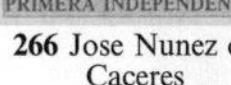
266 Jose Nunez de Caceres
267 Shepherds and Star

1971. 150th Anniv of 1st Declaration of Independence.
1109 **266** 6c. blue, violet and light blue (postage) 15 10
1110 – 10c. bl, red & yell (air) 25 20
DESIGN: 10c. Flag of the Santo Domingo–Colombia Union.

1971. Christmas.
1111 **267** 6c. brn, yell & bl (post) 15 10
1112 – 10c. red, blk & yell (air) 15 15
DESIGN: 10c. Spanish bell of 1493.

268 Child on Beach 269 Book Year Emblem

1971. 25th Anniv of U.N.I.C.E.F.
1113 **268** 6c. mult (postage) . . . 15 10
1114 15c. multicoloured (air) 25 20

1971. International Book Year.
1115 **269** 1c. green, red and blue (postage) 10 10
1116 2c. brown, red and blue 10 10
1117 12c. purple, red and blue (air) 20 15

270 Magnifier on Map 271 Orchid

1972. Air. "Exfilima 71" Inter American Philatelic Exhibition, Lima, Peru.
1118 **270** 10c. multicoloured . . . 25 15

1972. Obligatory Tax. Tuberculosis Relief Fund.
1119 **271** 1c. multicoloured 10 10

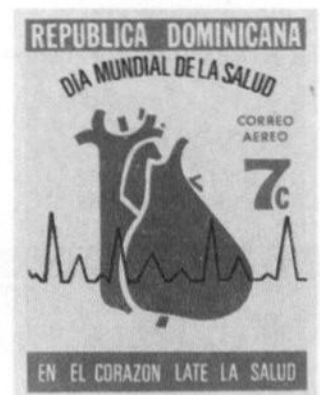

272 Heart Emblem 273 Mask

1972. Air. World Health Day.
1120 **272** 7c. multicoloured 15 10

1972. Taino Arts and Crafts. Multicoloured.
1121 2c. Type **273** (postage) . . . 10 10
1122 4c. Spoon and amulet . . . 10 10
1123 6c. Nasal aspirator (horiz) 10 10
1124 8c. Ritual vase (horiz) (air) 15 10
1125 10c. Atlantic trumpet triton (horiz) 30 10
1126 25c. Ritual spatulas 45 25

274 Globe

1972. World Telecommunications Day.
1127 **274** 6c. mult (postage) . . . 15 10
1128 21c. multicoloured (air) 35 20

275 Map and "Stamps"

1972. 1st National Stamp Exn, Santo Domingo.
1129 **275** 2c. mult (postage) . . . 10 10
1130 33c. mult (air) 60 35

276 Basketball

1972. Olympic Games, Munich. Mult.
1131 2c. Type **276** (postage) . . . 10 10
1132 33c. Running (air) 70 40

277 Club Badge

1972. 50th Anniv of Int Activo 20–30 Club.
1133 **277** 1c. mult (postage) . . . 10 10
1134 20c. mult (air) 35 20

278 Emilio Morel and Quotation

1972. Morel (poet and journalist). Commem.
1135 **278** 6c. mult (postage) . . . 15 10
1136 10c. mult (air) 15 10

279 Bank Building

1972. 25th Anniv of Central Bank. Mult.
1137 1c. Type **279** 10 10
1138 5c. One-peso banknote . . . 10 10
1139 25c. 1947 50c. coin and mint 40 25

280 Nativity Scene 281 Student and Letter-box

1972. Christmas. Multicoloured.
1140 2c. Type **280** (postage) . . . 10 10
1141 6c. Poinsettia (horiz) 15 10
1142 10c. "La Navidad" Fort, 1492 (horiz) (air) 15 10

1972. Publicity for Correspondence Schools.
1143 **281** 2c. red and pink 10 10
1144 6c. blue and light blue 15 10
1145 10c. green and yellow . . 20 10

282 View of Dam 283 Invalid in Wheel-chair

1973. Inauguration of Tavera Dam.
1146 **282** 10c. multicoloured . . . 20 10

1973. Obligatory Tax. Rehabilitation of the Handicapped.
1147 **283** 1c. green 10 10

284 Long-jumping, Diving, Running, Cycling and Weightlifting 285 Hibiscus

1973. 12th Central American and Caribbean Games, Santo Domingo, Multicoloured.
1148 2c. Type **284** (postage) . . . 10 10
1149 2c. Boxing, football, wrestling and shooting . . 10 10
1150 2c. Fencing, tennis, high-jumping and sprinting . . 10 10
1151 2c. Putting the shot, throwing the javelin and show-jumping 10 10
1152 25c. Type **284** 55 25
1153 25c. As No. 1149 . . . . 55 25
1154 25c. As No. 1150 . . . . 55 25
1155 25c. As No. 1151 . . . . 55 25
1156 8c. Type **284** (air) 15 10
1157 8c. As No. 1149 . . . . 15 10
1158 8c. As No. 1150 . . . . 15 10
1159 8c. As No. 1151 . . . . 15 10
1160 10c. Type **284** 25 15
1161 10c. As No. 1149 . . . . 25 15
1162 10c. As No. 1150 . . . . 25 15
1163 10c. As No. 1151 . . . . 25 15

1973. Obligatory Tax. Tuberculosis Relief Fund.
1164 **285** 1c. multicoloured 10 10

286 Christ carrying the Cross 287 Global Emblem

1973. Easter. Multicoloured.
1165 2c. Type **286** (postage) . . . 10 10
1166 6c. Belfry, Church of Our Lady of Carmen (vert) . . 15 10
1167 10c. Belfry, Chapel of Our Lady of Succour (vert) (air) 20 10

1973. Air. 70th Anniv of Pan-American Health Organization.
1168 **287** 7c. multicoloured 15 10

288 Weather Zones

1973. Cent of World Meteorological Organization.
1169 **288** 6c. mult (postage) . . . 15 10
1170 7c. multicoloured (air) 15 10

289 Forensic Scientist

1973. Air. 50th Anniv of International Criminal Police Organization (Interpol).
1171 **289** 10c. blue, green and light blue 20 15

1973. Obligatory Tax. Anti-cancer Fund. As T **144** but dated "1973".
1171a **144** 1c. olive 15 10
See also Nos. 1270a and 1338a.

290 Maguey Drum

1973. Opening of Museum of Dominican Man, Santo Domingo. Multicoloured.
1172 1c. Type **290** (postage) . . . 10 10
1173 2c. Amber carvings 10 10
1174 4c. Cibao mask (vert) . . . 10 10
1175 6c. Pottery (vert) 15 10
1176 7c. Model ship in mosaic (vert) (air) 15 10
1177 10c. Maracas rattles 20 15

291 Nativity Scene

1973. Christmas. Multicoloured.
1178 2c. Type **291** (postage) . . . 10 10
1179 6c. "Prayer" (stained-glass window) (vert) 15 10
1180 10c. Angels beside crib (air) 20 15

292 Scout Badge

1973. 50th Anniv of Dominican Boy Scouts. Multicoloured.
1181 1c. Type **292** (postage) . . . 10 10
1182 5c. Scouts and flag 10 10
1183 21c. Scouts cooking, and Lord Baden Powell (air) 40 30
No. 1182 is smaller, size 26 × 36 mm.

293 Stadium and Basketball Players 294 Belfry, Santo Domingo Cathedral

1974. 12th Central American and Caribbean Games, Santo Domingo. Multicoloured.
1184 2c. Type **293** (postage) . . . 10 10
1185 6c. Arena and cyclist . . . 15 10
1186 10c. Swimming pool and diver (air) 20 15
1187 25c. Stadium, soccer players and discus-thrower . . . 50 35

1974. Obligatory Tax. Rehabilitation of the Handicapped. As T **283** but larger, 22 × 27 mm.
1187a **283** 1c. blue 15 15

1974. Holy Week.
1188 **294** 2c. mult (postage) . . . 10 10
1189 – 6c. purple, green & ol . . 15 10
1190 – 10c. multicoloured (air) 20 15
DESIGN—VERT: 6c. "Sorrowful Mother" (D. Bouts). HORIZ: 10c. "The Last Supper" (R. M. Budi).

295 Francisco del Rosario Sanchez Bridge

1974. Dominican Bridges. Multicoloured.
1191 6c. Type **295** (postage) . . . 15 10
1192 10c. Higuamo Bridge (air) 20 15

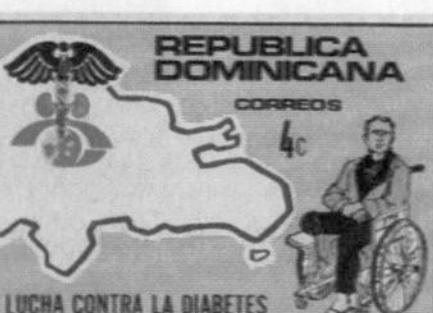

296 Emblem and Patient

1974. Anti-diabetes Campaign. Mult.
1193 4c. Type **296** (postage) . . . 10 10
1194 5c. Emblem and pancreas 10 10

1195 7c. Emblem and Kidney (air) 15 10
1196 33c. Emblem, eye and heart 70 45

1974. Obligatory Tax. Anti-cancer Fund. As T **144** but dated "1974".
1196a **144** 1c. orange 15 10

297 Steam Train

1974. Centenary of Universal Postal Union. Mult.
1197 2c. Type **297** (postage) . . . 45 55
1198 6c. Stage-coach 15 10
1199 7c. "Eider" mail steamer (air) 60 15
1200 33c. Boeing 727-200 of Dominicana Airways . . 95 30

298 Emblems of World Amateur Golf Council and of Dominican Golf Association

1974. World Amateur Golf Championships.
1202 **298** 2c. black and yellow (postage) 10 10
1203 – 6c. multicoloured 10 10
1204 – 10c. multicoloured (air) 25 15
1205 – 20c. multicoloured . . . 45 30
DESIGNS—VERT: 6c. Golfers teeing-off. HORIZ: 10c. Council emblem and golfers; 20c. Dominican Golf Association emblem, golfer and hand with ball and tee.

299 Christmas Decorations

301 Dr. Defillo

300 Tomatoes

1974. Christmas. Multicoloured.
1206 2c. Type **299** (postage) . . . 10 10
1207 6c. Virgin and Child 15 10
1208 10c. Hand holding dove (horiz) (air) 20 15

1974. 10th Anniv of World Food Programme. Multicoloured.
1209 2c. Type **300** (postage) . . . 10 10
1210 3c. Avocado pears 10 10
1211 5c. Coconuts 10 10
1212 10c. Bee, hive and cask of honey (air) 20 15

1975. Birth Centenary of Dr. Fernando Defillo (medical scientist).
1213 **301** 1c. brown 10 10
1214 6c. green 15 10

1975. Obligatory Tax. Rehabilitation of the Handicapped. As T **283** but dated "1975".
1214a **283** 1c. brown 15 10

302 "I am the Resurrection and the Life"

303 Spanish 6c. Stamp of 1850

1975. Holy Week. Multicoloured.
1215 2c. Type **302** (postage) . . . 10 10
1216 6c. Bell tower, Nuestra Senora del Rosario convent 15 10
1217 10c. Catholic emblems (air) 20 15

1975. Obligatory Tax. Tuberculosis Relief Fund. As T **221** but dated "1975".
1217a **221** 1c. multicoloured . . . 15 10
DESIGN: 1c. "Catteeyopsis rosea".

1975. Air. "Espana 75" International Stamp Exhibition, Madrid.
1218 **303** 12c. black, red & yell . . 25 15

304 Hands supporting "Agriculture" and Industry

305 Earth Station

1975. 16th Meeting of Industrial Development Bank Governors, Santo Domingo.
1219 **304** 6c. mult (postage) . . . 15 10
1220 10c. mult (air) 20 15

1975. Opening of Satellite Earth Station. Multicoloured.
1221 5c. Type **305** (postage) . . . 10 10
1222 15c. Hemispheres and satellites (horiz) (air) . . . 30 20

306 "Apollo" Spacecraft with Docking Tunnel

307 Father Castellanos

1975. "Apollo–Soyuz" Space Link. Mult.
1223 1c. Type **306** (postage) . . . 10 10
1224 4c. "Soyuz" spacecraft . . . 10 10
1225 2p. Docking manoeuvre (air) 3·25 2·00
The 2p. is larger, 42 × 28 mm.

1975. Birth Cent of Father Rafael C. Castellanos.
1226 **307** 6c. brown and buff . . . 15 10

308 Women encircling I.W.Y. Emblem

1975. International Women's Year.
1227 **308** 3c. multicoloured 10 10

309 Guacanagarix

310 Basketball

1975. Indian Chiefs. Multicoloured.
1228 1c. Type **309** (postage) . . . 10 10
1229 2c. Guarionex 10 10
1230 3c. Caonabo 10 10
1231 4c. Bohechio 10 10
1232 5c. Cayacoa 10 10
1233 6c. Anacaona 15 10
1234 9c. Hatuey 20 15
1235 7c. Mayobanex (air) 15 10
1236 8c. Cotubanama with Juan de Esquivel 15 10
1237 10c. Enriquillo and wife, Mencia 20 15

1975. Obligatory Tax. Anti-cancer Fund. As T **144** but dated "1975".
1237a **144** 1c. violet 15 10

1975. 7th Pan-American Games, Mexico City. Multicoloured.
1238 2c. Type **310** (postage) . . . 10 10
1239 6c. Baseball 15 10
1240 7c. Volleyball (horiz) (air) 15 15
1241 10c. Weightlifting (horiz) . . 25 15

311 Carol-singers

1975. Christmas. Multicoloured.
1242 2c. Type **311** (postage) . . . 10 10
1243 6c. "Dominican" Nativity 15 10
1244 10c. Dove and Peace message (air) 20 15

312 Pearl Sergeant Major ("Abudefdul marginatus")

1976. Fishes. Multicoloured.
1245 10c. Type **312** 35 25
1246 10c. Puddingwife ("Halichoeres radiata") 35 25
1247 10c. Squirrelfish ("Holocentrus ascensionis") 35 25
1248 10c. Queen angelfish ("Angelochthys ciliaris") 35 25
1249 10c. Aya snapper ("Lutianus aya") 35 25

313 Valdesia Dam

1976. Air. Inauguration of Valdesia Dam.
1250 **313** 10c. multicoloured . . . 15 15

1976. Obligatory Tax. Rehabilitation of the Disabled. As T **283** but dated "1976".
1250a **283** 1c. blue 15 10

314 Orchid

1976. Obligatory Tax. Tuberculosis Relief Fund.
1251 **314** 1c. multicoloured 10 10

315 "Magdalene" (E. Godoy)

316 Schooner "Separacion Dominicana"

1976. Holy Week. Multicoloured.
1252 2c. Type **315** (postage) . . . 10 10
1253 6c. "The Ascension" (V. Priego) 10 10
1254 10c. "Mount Calvary" (E. Castillo) (air) 20 15

1976. Navy Day.
1255 **316** 20c. multicoloured . . . 1·75 40

317 National Flower and Maps

1976. Bicentenary of American Revolution, and "Interphil '76" Int Stamp Exn, Philadelphia.
1256 **317** 6c. mult (postage) . . . 15 10
1257 – 9c. multicoloured 20 10
1258 – 10c. multicoloured (air) 50 15
1259 – 75c. black and orange 1·50 1·00
DESIGNS—HORIZ: 9c. Maps within cogwheels; 10c. Maps within hands. VERT: 75c. George Washington and Philadelphia buildings.

318 Flags of Spain and Dominican Republic

1976. Visit of King and Queen of Spain. Multicoloured.
1260 6c. Type **318** (postage) . . . 35 10
1261 21c. King Juan Carlos I and Queen Sophia (air) . . . 1·00 35

319 Various Telephones

1976. Telephone Centenary. Multicoloured.
1262 6c. Type **319** (postage) . . . 15 10
1263 10c. A. Graham Bell (horiz) (air) 20 15

320 "Duarte's Vision" (L. Desangles)

1976. Death Centenary of Juan Duarte (patriot). Multicoloured.
1264 2c. Type **320** (postage) . . . 10 10
1265 6c. "Juan Duarte" (R. Mejia) (vert) 15 10
1266 10c. Text of Duarte's Declaration (vert) (air) . . 20 15
1267 33c. "Duarte Sailing to Exile" (E. Godoy) 70 45

321 Fire Hydrant

322 Commemorative Text and Emblem

1976. Dominican Fire Service. Multicoloured.
1268 4c. Type **321** (postage) . . . 10 10
1269 6c. Fire Service emblem . . 15 10
1270 10c. Fire engine (horiz) (air) 20 15

1976. Obligatory Tax. Anti-cancer Fund. As T **144** but dated "1976".
1270a **144** 1c. green 15 10

1976. 50th Anniv of Dominican Radio Club.
1271 **322** 6c. black & red (postage) 15 10
1272 10c. black & blue (air) 20 15

323 Map and Caravel   325 Virgin and Child

324 Boxing

1976. "Hispanidad 1976". Multicoloured.
1273 6c. Type **323** (postage) . . . 60 15
1274 21c. Heads of Spaniard and Dominicans (air) 45 30

1976. Olympic Games, Montreal. Mult.
1275 2c. Type **324** (postage) . . . 10 10
1276 3c. Weightlifting 10 10
1277 10c. Running (air) 20 15
1278 25c. Basketball 50 35

1976. Obligatory Tax. Child Welfare. As T **233** but dated "1976".
1278a **233** 1c. mauve 15 10

1976. Christmas. Multicoloured.
1279 2c. Type **325** (postage) . . . 10 10
1280 6c. The Three Kings (22 × 32 mm) 15 10
1281 10c. Angel with bells (22 × 32 mm) (air) 20 15

326 Cable-car and Beach Scenes

1977. Tourism. Multicoloured.
1282 6c. Type **326** (postage) . . . 15 10
1283 10c. Tourist activities (air) 20 15
1284 12c. Fishing and hotel . . . 25 15
1285 25c. Horse-riding and waterfall 50 35
No. 1283 measures 36 × 36 mm, No. 1284 35 × 26 mm and No. 1285 26 × 35 mm.

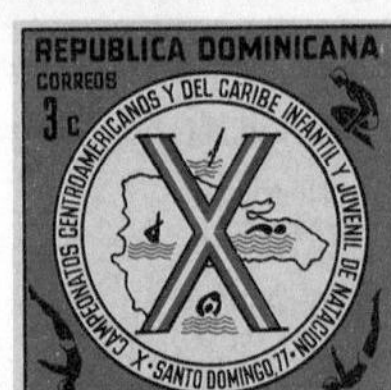

327 Championships Emblem

1977. 10th Central American and Caribbean Children's Swimming Championships, Santo Domingo.
1286 **327** 3c. mult (postage) . . . 10 10
1287 5c. multicoloured 10 10
1288 10c. multicoloured (air) 20 15
1289 25c. multicoloured . . . 30 35

1977. Obligatory Tax. Rehabilitation of the Disabled. As T **283** but dated "1977".
1289a **283** 1c. blue 15 10

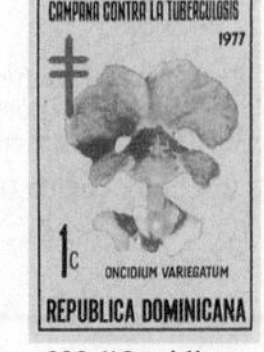

328 Allegory of Holy Week   329 "Oncidium variegatum" (orchid)

1977. Holy Week.
1290 **328** 2c. mult (postage) . . . 10 10
1291 – 6c. black and mauve . . 10 10
1292 – 10c. blk, red & bl (air) 20 10

DESIGNS: 6c. Christ crowned with thorns; 10c. Church and book.

1977. Obligatory Tax. Tuberculosis Relief Fund.
1293 **329** 1c. multicoloured 10 10

330 Gulls in Flight

1977. 12th Annual Lions Clubs Convention, Santo Domingo.
1294 **330** 2c. mult (postage) . . . 10 10
1295 6c. multicoloured 15 10
1296 7c. multicoloured (air) 15 10

331 "Battle of Tortuguero" (G. Fernandez)

1977. Navy Day.
1297 **331** 20c. multicoloured . . . 90 30

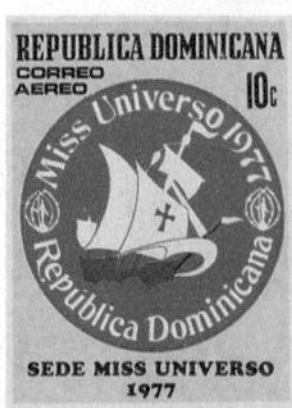

332 "Miss Universe" Emblem   333 "Nymphaea ampla" ("Nymphea" on stamp)

1977. Air. "Miss Universe" Competition.
1298 **332** 10c. multicoloured . . . 20 15

1977. Dominican Flora. Plants in the Dr. Rafael M. Moscoso National Botanical Gardens. Mult.
1299 2c. Type **333** (postage) . . . 10 10
1300 4c. "Broughtonia domingensis" 10 10
1301 6c. "Cordia sebestena" . . . 15 10
1302 7c. "Melocatus lemairei" (cactus) (air) 15 10
1303 33c. "Coccothrinax argentea" (tree) 70 45

334 Computers and Graph

1977. Seventh Inter-American Statistic Conference. Multicoloured.
1304 6c. Type **334** (postage) . . . 15 10
1305 28c. Factories and graph (27 × 37 mm) (air) 55 35

335 Haitian Solenodon

1977. 8th Inter-American Veterinary Congress. Multicoloured.
1306 6c. Type **335** (postage) . . . 15 10
1307 20c. Iguana 40 25
1308 10c. "Red Roman" stud bull (air) 20 15
1309 25c. Greater Flamingo (vert) 3·00 45

336 Main Gateway of Casa del Cordon   337 Tools and Crown of Thorns at Foot of Cross

1978. "Hispanidad 1977". Multicoloured.
1310 6c. Type **336** (postage) . . . 15 10
1311 21c. Gothic-style window, Casa del Tostado (28 × 41 mm) (air) 45 30

1978. Holy Week.
1312 **337** 2c. mult (postage) . . . 10 10
1313 – 6c. green 15 10
1314 – 7c. multicoloured (air) 15 10
1315 – 10c. multicoloured . . . 20 15
DESIGNS—(22 × 33 mm): 6c. Christ wearing Crown of Thorns. (27 × 37 mm): 7c. Facade of Santo Domingo Cathedral; 10c. Facade of Dominican Convent.

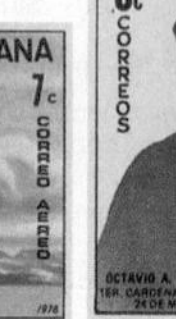

338 Schooner "Duarte"   339 Cardinal Octavio A. Beras Rojas

1978. Air. Navy Day.
1316 **338** 7c. multicoloured 75 15

1978. Consecration of First Cardinal from Dominican Republic.
1317 **339** 6c. mult (postage) . . . 15 10
1318 10c. multicoloured (air) 20 15

340 Microwave Antenna

1978. Air. 10th World Telecommunications Day.
1319 **340** 25c. multicoloured . . . 50 35

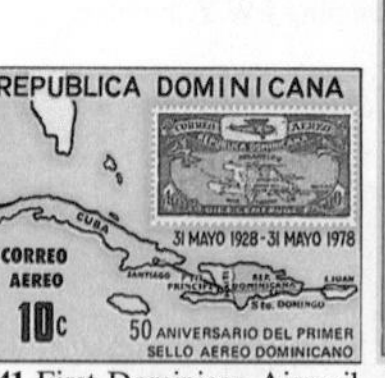

341 First Dominican Airmail Stamp and Map of First Airmail Service   342 Pres. Manuel de Troncoso

1978. Air. 50th Anniv of First Dominican Airmail Stamp.
1320 **341** 10c. multicoloured . . . 20 15

1978. Birth Centenary of President Troncoso.
1321 **342** 2c. brown, mauve & blk 10 10
1322 6c. brown, grey & black 15 10

343 Globe, Football and Emblem   344 Father Juan N. Zegri y Moreno (founder)

1978. Air. World Cup Football Championship, Argentina. Multicoloured.
1323 12c. Type **343** 25 15
1324 33c. Emblem and map on football pitch 75 45

1978. Centenary of Merciful Sisters of Charity. Multicoloured.
1325 6c. Type **344** (postage) . . . 15 10
1326 21c. Symbol of the Order (air) 40 30

345 Boxing

1978. 13th Central American and Caribbean Games, Medellin, Colombia. Multicoloured.
1327 2c. Type **345** (postage) . . . 10 10
1328 6c. Weightlifting 15 10
1329 7c. Baseball (vert) (air) . . . 15 10
1330 10c. Football (vert) 20 15

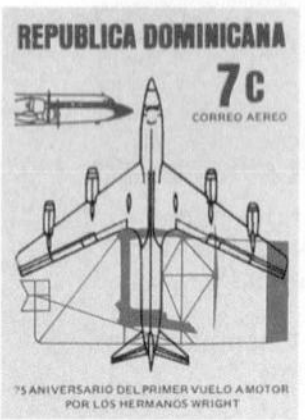

346 Douglas DC-6, Boeing 707 and Wright Flyer I   347 Sun over Landscape

1978. Air. 75th Anniv of First Powered Flight.
1331 **346** 7c. multicoloured 15 15
1332 – 10c. brown, yellow & red 35 15
1333 – 13c. blue & dp blue . . 45 20
1334 – 45c. multicoloured . . . 1·25 75
DESIGNS: 10c. Wright brothers and Wright Glider No. I; 13c. Diagram of airflow over wing; 45c. Wright Flyer I and world map.

1978. Tourism. Multicoloured.
1335 2c. Type **347** (postage) . . . 10 10
1336 6c. Sun over beach 15 10
1337 7c. Sun and musical instruments (air) 15 10
1338 10c. Sun over Santo Domingo 20 15

1978. Obligatory Tax. Anti-cancer Fund. As T **144** but dated "1977".
1338a **144** 1c. purple 15 10

348 Galleons   349 Flags of Dominican Republic and United Nations

1978. "Hispanidad 1978". Multicoloured.
1339 2c. Type **348** (postage) . . . 10 10
1340 21c. Figures holding hands in front of globe (air) . . 45 25

1978. Air. 33rd Anniv of United Nations.
1341 **349** 33c. multicoloured . . . 70 25

350 Mother and Child   351 Dove, Lamp and Poinsettia

1978. Obligatory Tax. Child Welfare.
1342 **350** 1c. green 10 10

1978. Christmas. Multicoloured.
1343 2c. Type **351** (postage) . . . 10 10
1344 6c. Dominican family and star 15 10
1345 10c. Statue of the Virgin (vert) (22 × 33 mm) (air) 20 15

352 Pope John Paul II **353** Map of Island, Iguana and Radio Transmitter

1979. Air. Visit of Pope John Paul II.
1346 **352** 10c. multicoloured . . . 70 20

1979. Air. 1st Expedition of Radio Amateurs to Beata Island.
1347 **353** 10c. multicoloured . . . 20 15

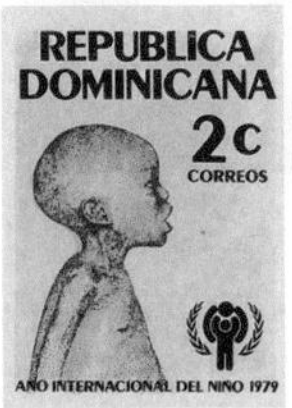

354 University Seal **355** Starving Child

1979. Obligatory Tax. 440th Anniv of Santo Domingo University.
1348 **354** 2c. blue 10 10

1979. International Year of the Child.
1349 **355** 2c. orge & blk (postage) 10 10
1350 – 7c. multicoloured (air) 15 10
1351 – 10c. multicoloured . . . 20 15
1352 – 33c. multicoloured . . . 70 45
DESIGNS: 7c. Children reading book; 10c. Head and protective hands; 33c. Hands and vases.

1979. Obligatory Tax. Rehabilitation of the Disabled. As T **283** but dated "1979".
1353 **283** 1c. green 15 10

356 Crucifixion **357** "Turnera ulmifolia"

1979. Holy Week. Multicoloured.
1354 2c. Type **356** (postage) . . . 10 10
1355 3c. Christ carrying cross (horiz) 10 10
1356 10c. Pope John Paul II with Crucifix (air) 20 15

1978. Obligatory Tax. Tuberculosis Relief Fund. Dated "1978".
1357 **357** 1c. multicoloured 10 10

358 Admiral J. Cambiaso **359** Map, Stamp Album and Philatelic Equipment

1979. Air. 135th Anniv of Battle of Tortuguero.
1358 **358** 10c. multicoloured . . . 20 15

1979. Air. "Exfilna" Third National Stamp Exhibition.
1359 **359** 33c. blue, green and black 70 45

360 "Stigmaphyllon periplocifolium"

1979. Flowers from National Botanical Gardens.
1360 **360** 50c. grey, yellow and black (postage) . . . 1·00 70
1361 – 7c. multicoloured (air) 15 10
1362 – 10c. multicoloured . . . 20 15
1363 – 13c. blue, mauve & blk 25 15
DESIGNS: 7c. "Passiflora foetida"; 10c. "Isidorea pungens"; 13c. "Calotropis procera".

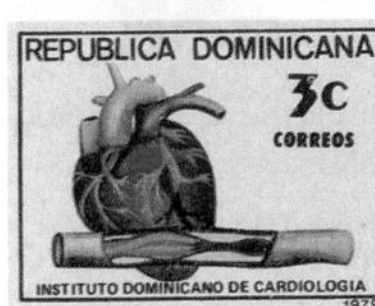

362 Heart and Section through Artery

1979. Dominican Cardiology Institute.
1364 **362** 3c. mult (postage) . . . 10 10
1365 – 1p. black, red & blue . . 2·00 1·40
1366 – 10c. multicoloured (air) 20 15
DESIGNS: VERT: 10c. Human figure showing blood circulation. HORIZ: 1p. Cardiology Institute and heart.

363 Baseball

1979. 8th Pan-American Games, Puerto Rico. Multicoloured.
1367 2c. Type **363** (postage) . . . 10 10
1368 3c. Cycling (vert) 10 10
1369 7c. Running (vert) (air) . . 15 10

364 Football **365** Sir Rowland Hill and First Dominican Republic Stamp

1979. 3rd National Games. Multicoloured.
1370 2c. Type **364** (postage) . . . 10 10
1371 25c. Swimming (horiz) . . . 55 35
1372 10c. Tennis (air) 20 15

1979. Air. Death Centenary of Sir Rowland Hill.
1373 **365** 2p. multicoloured . . . 4·25 1·10

366 Thomas Edison (inventor) **367** Hand removing Electric Plug

1979. Centenary of Electric Light-bulb. Mult.
1374 25c. Type **366** (postage) . . 55 30
1375 10c. "100" forming lightbulb (horiz) (air) 20 15

1979. "Save Energy". Multicoloured.
1376 2c. Type **367** 10 10
1377 6c. Car being refuelled . . . 15 10

368 Hispaniolan Conure **369** Lions Emblem

1979. Birds. Multicoloured.
1378 2c. Type **368** (postage) . . . 1·00 25
1379 6c. Hispaniolan trogon . . . 1·10 25
1380 7c. Black-crowned palm tanager (air) . . . . . . 1·60 35
1381 10c. Chat-tanager . . . . . 2·40 35
1382 45c. Black-cowled oriole . . 7·00 1·25

1979. 15th Anniv of Dominican Republic Lions Club. Multicoloured.
1383 20c. Type **369** (postage) . . 45 20
1384 10c. Melvin Jones (founder) (air) 20 10

371 Holy Family **372** Christ carrying Cross

1979. Christmas. Multicoloured.
1386 2c. Type **371** (postage) . . . 10 10
1387 10c. Three Kings (air) . . . 20 15

1980. Holy Week.
1388 **372** 3c. black, red and lilac (postage) 10 10
1389 – 7c. blk, red & yell (air) 15 10
1390 – 10c. black, red & bistre 20 15
DESIGNS: 7c. Crucifixion; 10c. Resurrection.

1980. Obligatory Tax. Rehabilitation of the Disabled. As T **283** but dated "1980".
1391 **283** 1c. olive and green . . . 10 10

374 Navy Crest **376** Cocoa Harvest

375 "Stamp"

1980. Air. Navy Day.
1392 **374** 21c. multicoloured . . . 45 30

1980. Air. 25th Anniv of Dominican Philatelic Society.
1393 **375** 10c. multicoloured . . . 20 15

1980. Agricultural Year. Multicoloured.
1394 1c. Type **376** 10 10
1395 2c. Coffee 10 10
1396 3c. Plantain 10 10
1397 4c. Sugar cane 10 10
1398 5c. Maize 10 10

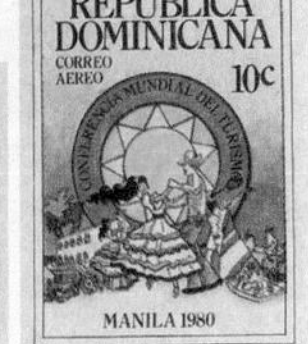

377 Cotuf Gold Mine, Pueblo Viejob **379** "Tourism"

378 Blind Man's Buff

1980. Nationalization of Gold Mines. Mult.
1399 6c. Type **377** (postage) . . . 15 10
1400 10c. Drag line mining (air) 20 15
1401 33c. General view of location of gold mines . . 70 45

1980. Children's Games. Multicoloured.
1402 3c. Type **378** 10 10
1403 4c. Marbles 10 10
1404 5c. Spinning top 10 10
1405 6c. Hopscotch 15 10

1980. Air. World Tourism Conference, Manila, Philippines. Multicoloured.
1406 10c. Type **379** 20 15
1407 33c. Conference emblem . . 70 45

380 Cuban Iguana

1980. Animals. Multicoloured.
1408 20c. Type **380** (postage) . . 45 30
1409 7c. American crocodile (air) 15 10
1410 10c. Hispaniolan hutia . . . 25 15
1411 25c. American manatee . . 65 35
1412 45c. Hawksbill turtle 95 60

381 "El Merengue" (Jaime Colson)

1980. Paintings. Multicoloured.
1413 3c. Type **381** (postage) . . . 10 10
1414 50c. "The Mirror" (G. H. Ortega) . . . . 1·10 70
1415 10c. "Genesis de un Ganga" (Paul Guidicelli) (air) . . 20 15
1416 17c. "The Countryman" (Yoryi Morel) 35 25

1980. Obligatory Tax. Anti-cancer Fund. As T **144** but dated "1980".
1417 **144** 1c. blue and violet . . . 10 10

383 Map of Catalina Island **384** Rotary Emblem on Globe

1980. Air. Visit of Radio Amateurs to Catalina Island.
1418 **383** 7c. green, blue & black 15 10

1980. Air. 75th Anniv of Rotary International. Multicoloured.
1419 10c. Type **384** 20 15
1420 33c. Rotary emblem in "75" 70 45

385 Carrier Pigeons with Letters

1980. Centenary of U.P.U. Membership. Mult.
1421 33c. Type **385** 70 45
1422 45c. Row of stylized pigeons and letter 95 60
1423 50c. Carrier pigeon with letter and letter . . . . . 1·10 70

1980. Obligatory tax. Child Welfare. As T **350** but dated "1980".
1425 **350** 1c. blue 10 10

386 The Three Kings **387** Arms of Salcedo

1980. Christmas. Multicoloured.
1426 3c. Type **386** (postage) . . . 10 10
1427 6c. Carol singers 15 10
1428 10c. The Holy Family (air) 20 15

1981. Centenary of Salcedo Province. Mult.
1429 6c. Type **387** (postage) . . . 15 10
1430 10c. Arms and map of Salcedo (air) 20 15

388 Juan Pablo Duarte **389** Industrial Symbols

1981. Juan Pablo Duarte (patriot). Commemoration.
1431 **388** 2c. brown and ochre . . 10 10

1981. Air. Chemical Engineering Seminar.
1432 **389** 10c. multicoloured . . . 20 15
1433 – 33c. gold and black . . . 70 45
DESIGN: 33c. Emblem of Dominican College of Engineering and Architecture (CODIA).

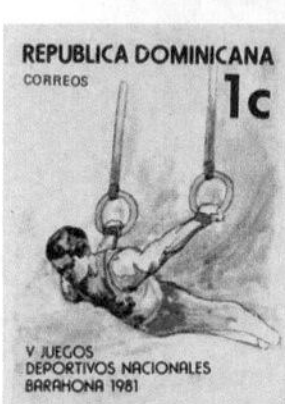

390 Gymnastics **391** Mother Mazzarello

1981. Fifth National Games (1st issue). Mult.
1434 1c. Type **390** (postage) . . . 10 10
1435 2c. Running 10 10
1436 3c. Pole-vaulting 10 10
1437 6c. Boxing 15 10
1438 10c. Baseball (air) 20 15
See also Nos. 1463/4.

1981. Death Centenary of Mother Mazarello (founder of Daughters of Mary).
1439 **391** 6c. brown and black . . 15 10

392 Admiral Juan Alejandro Acosta **393** Radio Waves

1981. Air. 137th Anniv of Battle of Tortuguero.
1440 **392** 10c. multicoloured . . . 20 15

1981. Obligatory Tax. Tuberculosis Relief Fund. Dated "1981".
1441 **357** 1c. multicoloured 10 10

1981. Air. World Telecommunications Day.
1442 **393** 10c. multicoloured . . . 15 15

394 Pedro Henriquez Urena **395** Forest

1981. 35th Death Anniv of Pedro Henriquez Urena.
1443 **394** 6c. pale grey and grey 15 10

1981. Forest Conservation. Multicoloured.
1444 2c. Type **395** 10 10
1445 6c. Forest river 15 10

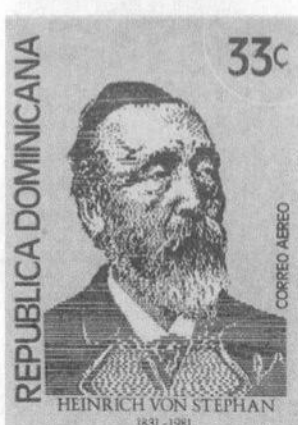

396 Heinrich von Stephan **397** "Disabled People"

1981. Air. 150th Birth Anniv of Heinrich von Stephan (founder of U.P.U.).
1446 **396** 33c. brown and yellow 70 45

1981. Air. International Year of Disabled Persons. Multicoloured.
1447 7c. Type **397** 15 10
1448 33c. Cobbler in wheelchair 70 45

398 Exhibition Emblem

1981. Air. "Expuridom '81" International Stamp Exhibition, Santo Domingo.
1149 **398** 7c. black, blue and red 15 10

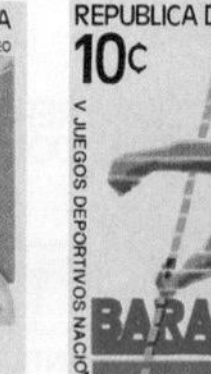

399 Target

1981. Air. 2nd World Air Gun Shooting Championship. Multicoloured.
1450 10c. Type **399** 20 15
1451 15c. Stylized riflemen . . . 30 20
1452 25c. Stylized pistol shooters 55 55

400 Family and House

1981. National Census. Multicoloured.
1453 3c. Type **400** 10 10
1454 6c. Farmer with cow and agricultural produce . . . 15 10

1981. Obligatory Tax. Anti-cancer Fund. As T **144** but dated "1981".
1455 **144** 1c. blue and deep blue 10 10

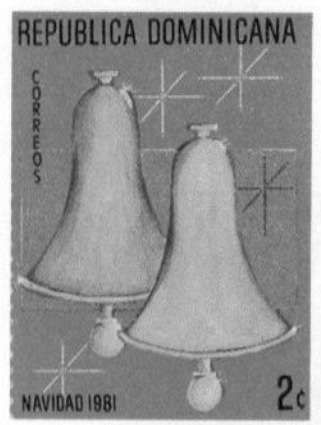

401 Fruit

1981. Air. World Food Day. Multicoloured.
1456 10c. Type **401** 20 15
1457 50c. Fish, eggs and vegetables . . . . 1·10 70

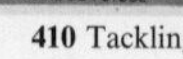

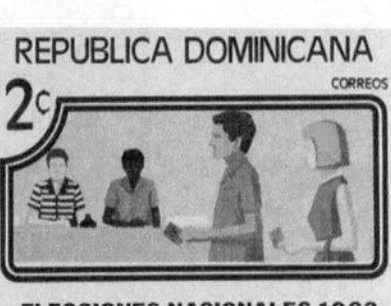

402 Gem Stones and Jewellery **403** Javelin-throwing

1981. Air. Exports. Multicoloured.
1458 7c. Type **402** 15 10
1459 10c. Handicrafts 20 15
1460 11c. Fruit 25 15
1461 17c. Cocoa, coffee, tobacco and sugar 35 25

1981. Obligatory Tax. Child Welfare. As T **350** but dated "1981".
1462 **350** 1c. green 10 10

1981. Air. 5th National Games, Barahona (2nd issue). Multicoloured.
1463 10c. Type **403** 20 15
1464 50c. Cycling . . . . 1·10 70

404 "Encyclia cochleata"

1981. Air. Orchids. Multicoloured.
1465 7c. Type **404** 10 15
1466 10c. "Broughtonia domingensis" 15 20
1467 25c. "Encyclia truncata" . . 55 35
1468 65c. "Elleanthus capitatus" 1·60 1·10

405 Bells **406** Juan Pablo Duarte

1981. Christmas. Multicoloured.
1469 2c. Type **405** (postage) . . . 10 10
1470 3c. Holly 10 10
1471 10c. Dove and moon (air) 20 15

1982. Juan Pablo Duarte (patriot) Commemoration.
1472 **406** 2c. light blue and blue 10 10

407 Citizens arriving at Polling Station

1982. National Elections. Multicoloured.
1473 2c. Type **407** 10 10
1474 3c. Entering polling booth (vert) 10 10
1475 6c. Casting vote 15 10

408 American Air Forces Co-operation Emblem

1982. Air. 22nd American Air Force's Commanders Conference, Buenos Aires.
1476 **408** 10c. multicoloured . . . 20 15

409 Naval Cadet Parade

1982. Air. Battle of Tortuguero Commem.
1477 **409** 10c. multicoloured . . . 20 15

410 Tackling **411** Lord Baden-Powell (statue)

1982. Air. World Cup Football Championship, Spain. Multicoloured.
1478 10c. Type **410** 20 15
1479 21c. Dribbling 45 30
1480 33c. Heading ball into goal 70 45

1982. Air. 75th Anniv of Boy Scout Movement. Multicoloured.
1481 10c. Type **411** 20 15
1482 15c. Scouting emblems (horiz) 30 20
1483 25c. Baden-Powell and scout at camp fire 55 35

412 "Study of Daylight" **413** Cathedral and House

1982. Energy Conservation. Multicoloured.
1484 1c. Type **412** 10 10
1485 2c. "Save rural electricity" 10 10
1486 3c. "Use wind power" . . . 10 10
1487 4c. "Switch off lights" . . . 10 10
1488 5c. "Conserve fuel" 15 10
1489 6c. "Use solar energy" . . . 15 10

1982. Air. 25th Congress of Latin-American Tourist Organizations Confederation, Santo Domingo. Multicoloured.
1490 7c. Congress emblem . . . 15 10
1491 10c. Type **413** 20 15
1492 33c. Dancers and beach scene 70 45

414 Exhibition Emblem

1982. Air. "Espamer '82" Stamp Exhibition, Puerto Rico. Multicoloured.
1493 7c. Stamp bearing map of Puerto Rico (horiz) . . . 15 10
1494 13c. Stylized postage stamps (horiz) 30 20
1495 50c. Type **414** . . . . . . 1·10 70

415 Emilio Prud'Homme and Score of Dominican National Anthem **416** President Guzman

1982. 50th Death Anniv of Emilio Prud'Homme (composer).
1496 **415** 6c. multicoloured 15 10

1982. President Antonio Guzman Commemoration.
1497 **416** 6c. multicoloured 15 10

417 Baseball

1982. Central American and Caribbean Games, Cuba. Multicoloured.
1498 3c. Type **417** (postage) . . . 10 10
1499 10c. Basketball (air) 20 15
1500 13c. Boxing 30 20
1501 25c. Gymnastics 55 30

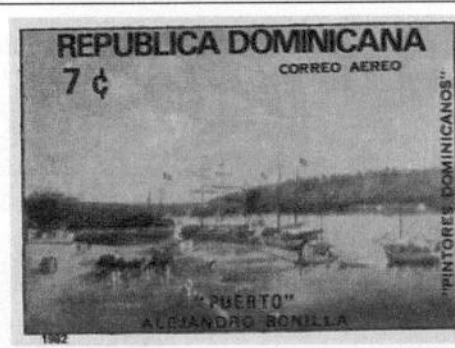

418 "Harbour" (Alejandro Bonilla)

1982. Air. Paintings. Multicoloured.
1502 7c. Type **418** 15 10
1503 10c. "Portrait of a Woman" (Leopoldo Navarro) . . . 20 15
1504 45c. "Portrait of Amelia Francasci" (Luis Desangles) 95 65
1505 2p. "Portrait" (Abelardo Rodriguez Urdaneta) . . 4·25 2·75

419 Horse-drawn Carriage

1982. Centenary of San Pedro de Macoris Province. Multicoloured.
1506 1c. Type **419** (postage) . . . 10 10
1507 2c. Stained-glass window, San Pedro Apostle Church (25 × 34½ mm) . . 10 10
1508 5c. Centenary emblem . . . 15 10
1509 7c. View of San Pedro de Macoris City (air) 45 20

420 "Santa Maria" and Map of Voyage

1982. Air. 490th Anniv of Discovery of America by Columbus. Multicoloured.
1510 7c. Type **420** . . . . 1·00 30
1511 10c. "Santa Maria" . . . . 1·25 35
1512 21c. Statue of Columbus, Santo Domingo 45 30

421 Central Bank

1982. 35th Anniv of Central Bank.
1513 **421** 10c. multicoloured . . . 20 15

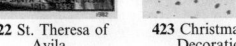

422 St. Theresa of Avila

423 Christmas Tree Decorations

1982. 400th Death Anniv of St. Theresa of Avila.
1514 **422** 6c. multicoloured 15 10

1982. Christmas. Multicoloured.
1515 6c. Type **423** (postage) . . . 10 10
1516 10c. Tree decorations (different) (air) 20 15

424 Hand holding Rural and Urban Environments

1982. Environmental Protection. Mult.
1517 2c. Type **424** 10 10
1518 3c. Hand holding river in the country 10 10
1519 6c. Hand holding forest . . 10 10
1520 20c. Hand holding swimming fish 35 25

425 Adults writing

1983. National Literacy Campaign. Mult.
1521 2c. Girl and boy writing on blackboard 10 10
1522 3c. Type **425** 10 10
1523 6c. Children, rainbow and pencil 10 10

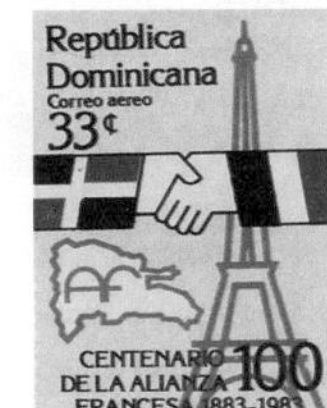

426 Clasped Hands and Eiffel Tower

1983. Air. Centenary of French Alliance (French language-teaching association).
1524 **426** 33c. multicoloured . . . 50 30

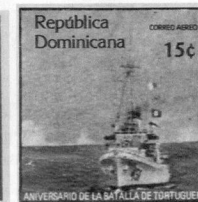

427 Arms of Mao City Council

428 Frigate "Mella"

1983. Centenary of Mao City Council. Mult.
1525 1c. Type **427** 10 10
1526 5c. Centenary monument . . 10 10

1983. Air. Battle of Tortuguero. Commemoration.
1527 **428** 15c. multicoloured . . . 1·50 40

429 Antonio del Monte y Tejada

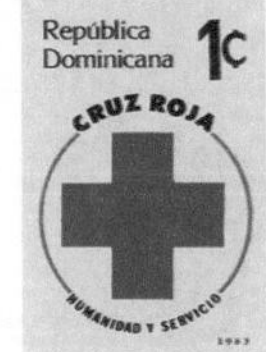

430 Red Cross

1983. Dominican Historians.
1528 **429** 2c. red & brn (postage) 10 10
1529 – 3c. pink and brown . . . 10 10
1530 – 5c. blue and brown . . . 15 10
1531 – 6c. lt brown & brown . . 15 10
1532 – 7c. pink & brown (air) 15 10
1533 – 10c. grey and brown . . 20 15
DESIGNS: 3c. Manuel Ubaldo Gomez; 5c. Emiliano Tejera; 6c. Bernardo Pichardo; 7c. Americo Lugo; 10c. Jose Gabriel Garcia.

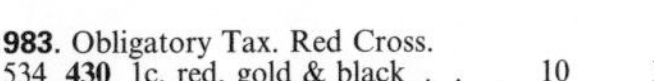

1983. Obligatory Tax. Red Cross.
1534 **430** 1c. red, gold & black . . 10 10

431 Dish Aerial and W.C.Y. Emblem

432 "Simon Bolivar" (Plutarco Andujar)

1983. Air. World Communications Year.
1535 **431** 10c. light blue & blue . . 20 15

1983. Air. Birth Bicentenary of Simon Bolivar.
1536 **432** 9c. multicoloured 15 10

433 Pictogram of Rehabilitation

434 Basketball and Gymnastics

1983. Obligatory Tax. Rehabilitation of the Disabled.
1537 **433** 1c. blue 10 10

1983. Air. Pan-American Games, Venezuela. Multicoloured.
1538 7c. Type **434** 15 10
1539 10c. Boxing and pole vaulting 20 15
1540 15c. Baseball, weightlifting and cycling 25 15

435 Emilio Prud'Homme and Jose Reyes (composers)

1983. Cent of Dominican National Anthem.
1541 **435** 6c. multicoloured 10 10

1983. Obligatory Tax. Anti-cancer Fund. As T **144** but dated "1983".
1542 **144** 1c. turquoise & green . . 10 10

436 "Sotavento" (winner of 1982 regatta)

437 Arms

1983. Air. Christopher Columbus Regatta and 500th Anniv (1992) of Discovery of America by Columbus (1st issue).
1543 – 10c. stone, brn & blk . . 1·00 45
1544 – 21c. multicoloured . . . 1·25 60
1545 **436** 33c. multicoloured . . . 1·90 65
DESIGNS—HORIZ: 10c. Old map of Greater Antilles; 21c. Christopher Columbus Regatta trophy.
See also Nos. 1583/5, 1617/20, 1649/52, 1683/6, 1717/20, 1754/7, 1777/80, 1791/4 and 1805/8.

1983. 125th Anniv of Dominican Freemasons.
1547 **437** 4c. multicoloured 10 10

438 Our Lady of Regla Church

439 Clocktower

1983. 300th Anniv of Our Lady of Regla Church.
1548 **438** 3c. deep blue & blue . . 10 10
1549 – 6c. red and deep red . . 10 10
DESIGN: 6c. Statue of Our Lady of Regla.

1983. 450th Anniv of Monte Cristi Province.
1550 **439** 1c. green and black . . . 10 10
1551 – 2c. multicoloured 10 10
1552 – 5c. grey 10 10
1553 – 7c. grey and blue 15 10
DESIGNS—VERT: 2c. Provincial coat of arms. HORIZ: 5c. Wooden building in which independence of Cuba was signed; 7c. Men digging out salt crystals.

1983. Obligatory Tax. Child Welfare. As T **350** but dated "1983".
1554 **350** 1c. green 10 10

440 Commission Emblem

1983. Air. 10th Anniv of Latin American Civil Aviation Commission.
1555 **440** 10c. blue 15 10

441 Baseball, Boxing and Cycling

442 Bells and Christmas Tree Decorations

1983. 6th National Games, San Pedro de Macoris. Multicoloured.
1556 6c. Type **441** (postage) . . . 10 10
1557 10c. Weightlifting, running and swimming (air) . . . 15 10

1983. Air. Christmas.
1558 **442** 10c. multicoloured . . . 15 10

443 "Portrait of a Girl" (Adriana Billini)

1983. Air. Paintings. Multicoloured.
1559 10c. "The Litter" (Juan Bautista Gomez) (horiz) 15 10
1560 15c. "The Meeting between Maximo Gomez and Jose Marti at Guayubin" (Enrique Garcia Godoy) (horiz) 20 15
1561 21c. "St. Francis" (Angel Perdomo) 30 20
1562 33c. Type **443** 45 30

444 Monument to Heroes of Capotillo

1983. 120th Anniv of Restoration of the Republic.
1563 **444** 1c. purple and blue . . . 10 10

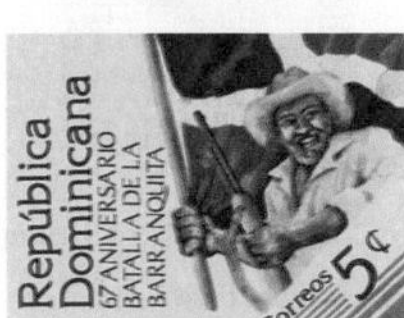

445 Man holding Dominican Flag and Rifle

1983. 67th Anniv of Battle of Barranquita.
1564 **445** 5c. multicoloured 10 10

446 Matias Ramon Mella and Dominican Flag

1984. 140th Anniv of Independence. Mult.
1565 6c. Type **446** 10 10
1566 25c. Puerta de la Misericordia and Mella's rifle 15 15

447 Dr. Heriberto Pieter

1984. Birth Centenary of Dr. Heriberto Pieter.
1567 **447** 3c. multicoloured 10 10

448 Jose Maria Imbert, Fernando Valerio, Cannon and National Flag

1984. 140th Anniv of Battle of Santiago.
1568 **448** 7c. multicoloured 10 10

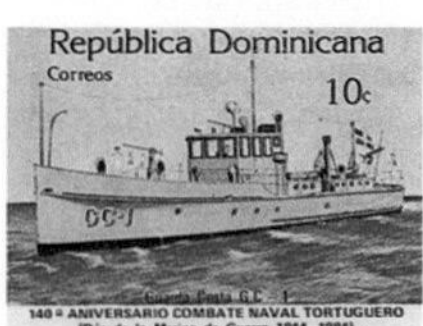

449 Coastguard Patrol Boat

1984. 140th Anniv of Battle of Tortuguero.
1569 **449** 10c. multicoloured . . . 1·00 20

450 Monument to the Heroes of June 1959

1984. 25th Anniv of Expedition to Constanza, Maimon and Estero Hondo.
1570 **450** 6c. multicoloured 10 10

451 Salome Urena

1984. Birth Centenary of Pedro Henriquez Urena (poet).
1571 **451** 7c. pink and brown . . . 10 10
1572 – 10c. yellow and brown 10 10
1573 – 22c. yellow and brown 15 15
DESIGNS: 10c. Lines from poem "Mi Pedro"; 22c. Pedro H. Urena.

452 Running

1984. Olympic Games, Los Angeles. Each in blue, red and black.
1574 1p. Type **452** 55 50
1575 1p. Weightlifting 55 50
1576 1p. Boxing 55 50
1577 1p. Baseball 55 50

453 Stygian Owl **455** Pope John Paul II

454 Christopher Columbus landing in Hispaniola

1984. Protection of Wildlife. Multicoloured.
1578 10c. Type **453** . . . . . . 1·50 30
1579 15c. Greater flamingo . . . 2·00 40
1580 25c. White-lipped peccary 15 10
1581 35c. Haitian solenodon . . . 25 20

1984. 500th Anniv (1992) of Discovery of America by Columbus (2nd issue).
1582 **454** 10c. multicoloured . . . 10 10
1583 – 35c. multicoloured . . . 25 20
1584 – 65c. brown, yell & blk 40 35
1585 – 1p. multicoloured . . . 55 50
DESIGNS: 35c. Destruction of Fort La Navidad; 65c. First mass in America; 1p. Battle of Santo Cerro.

1984. Papal Visit to Santo Domingo. 500th Anniv of Christianity in the New World. Multicoloured.
1586 75c. Type **455** 45 40
1587 75c. Pope in priest's attire and map 45 40
1588 75c. Globe and Pope in ceremonial attire 45 40
1589 75c. Bishop's crosier 45 40

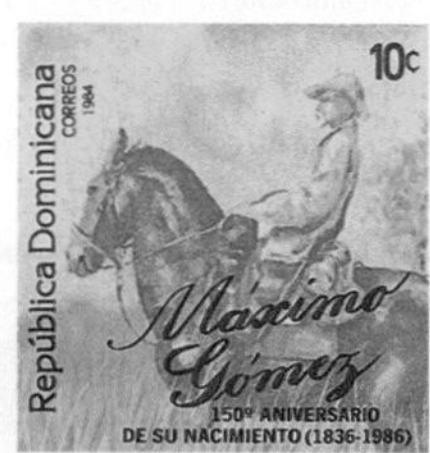

456 Gomez on Horseback

1984. 150th Birth Anniv (1986) of Maximo Gomez (leader of Cuban Revolution). Multicoloured.
1590 10c. Type **456** 10 10
1591 20c. Maximo Gomez . . . 15 10

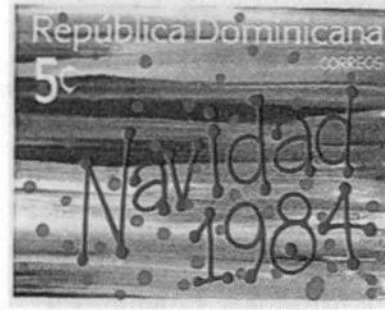

457 "Navidad 1984"

1984. Christmas.
1592 **457** 5c. mauve, blue and gold 10 10
1593 – 10c. blue, gold & mauve 10 10
DESIGN: 10c. "Navidad 1984" (different).

458 "The Sacrifice of the Kid" (Eligio Pichardo)

1984. Art. Multicoloured.
1594 5c. Type **458** 10 10
1595 10c. "Pumpkin Sellers" (statuette, Gaspar Mario Cruz) (vert) 10 10
1596 25c. "The Market" (Celeste Woss y Gil) 15 15
1597 50c. "Horses in a Storm" (Dario Suro) 30 25

459 Old Church, Higuey

1985. Our Lady of Altagracia's Day. Mult.
1598 5c. Type **459** 10 10
1599 10c. "Our Lady of Altagracia" (1514 painting) 15 10
1600 25c. Basilica of Our Lady of Altagracia, Higuey . . . 35 30

460 Sanchez, Durate and Mella

1985. 141st Anniv of Independence.
1601 **460** 5c. multicoloured 10 10
1602 10c. multicoloured . . . 15 10
1603 25c. multicoloured . . . 35 30

461 Gen. Antonia Duverge

1985. 141st Anniv of Azua Battle.
1604 **461** 10c. cream, red & brown 15 10

462 Santo Domingo Lighthouse, 1853 **463** Flags and Emblem

1985. 141st Anniv of Battle of Tortuguero.
1605 **462** 25c. multicoloured . . . 35 30

1985. 25th Anniv of American Airforces Co-operation System.
1606 **463** 35c. multicoloured . . . 50 45

464 Carlos Maria Rojas (first Governor) **465** Table Tennis Player

1985. Centenary of Espaillat Province.
1607 **464** 10c. multicoloured . . . 10 10

1985. "MOCA 85" (Seventh National Games). Multicoloured.
1608 5c. Type **465** 10 10
1609 10c. Walking race 10 10

466 Young People of Different Races

1985. International Youth Year. Mult.
1610 5c. Type **466** 10 10
1611 25c. The Haitises 15 10
1612 35c. Mt. Duarte summit . . 20 15
1613 2p. Mt. Duarte 90 85

467 Evangelina Rodriguez (first Dominican woman doctor) **468** Emblem

1985. International Decade for Women.
1614 **467** 10c. multicoloured . . . 10 10

1985. 15th Central American and Caribbean Games, Santiago.
1615 **468** 5c. multicoloured 10 10
1616 25c. multicoloured . . . 15 10

469 Fourth Christopher Columbus Regatta

1985. 500th Anniv (1992) of Discovery of America by Columbus (3rd issue). Multicoloured.
1617 35c. Type **469** . . . . . . 1·00 30
1618 50c. Foundation of Santo Domingo, 1496 . . . . . 25 20
1619 65c. Chapel of Our Lady of the Rosary, 1496 . . . . 35 30
1620 1p. Christopher Columbus's arrival in New World . . 45 40

470 Bust of Enriquillo **471** Arturo de Merino

1985. 450th Death Anniv of Enriquillo (Indian chief). Multicoloured.
1621 5c. Enriquillo in Bahoruco mountains (mural) (46 × 32 mm) 10 10
1622 10c. Type **470** 10 10

1985. Centenary of Ordination of Fernando Arturo de Merino (former President).
1623 **471** 25c. multicoloured . . . 15 10

472 Fruit, Candle and Holly

1985. Christmas.
1624 **472** 10c. multicoloured . . . 15 10
1625 25c. multicoloured . . . 15 10

473 Haina Harbour

1985. 25th Anniv of Inter-American Development Bank. Multicoloured.
1626 10c. Type **473** 55 15
1627 25c. Map and ratio diagram of development activities 15 10
1628 1p. Tavera-Bao-Lopez hydro-electric complex . . 45 40

474 Mirabal Sisters

1985. 25th Death Anniv of Minerva, Patria and Maria Mirabal.
1629 **474** 10c. multicoloured . . . 10 10

475 Tomb of Duarte, Sanchez and Mella

1986. National Independence Day.
1630 **475** 5c. multicoloured 10 10
1631 10c. multicoloured . . . 10 10

476 St. Michael's Church

478 Voters, Ballot Box and Map

477 "Leonor" (schooner) and Dominican Navy Founders

1986. Holy Week. Santo Domingo Churches. Multicoloured.
1632 5c. Type **476** 10 10
1633 5c. St. Andrew's Church . . 10 10
1634 10c. St. Lazarus's Church 10 10
1635 10c. St. Charles's Church . . 10 10
1636 10c. St. Barbara's Church 10 10

1986. Navy Day.
1637 **477** 10c. multicoloured . . . 80 20

1986. National Elections. Multicoloured.
1638 5c. Type **478** 10 10
1639 10c. Hand dropping voting slip into ballot box . . . 30 10

479 Emblem

480 Weightlifting

1986. Creation of "Inposdom" (Dominican Postal Institute).
1640 **479** 10c. blue, red and gold 10 10
1641 25c. blue, red and silver 15 10
1642 50c. blue, red and black 25 20

1986. 15th Central American and Caribbean Games, Santiago. Multicoloured.
1643 10c. Type **480** 10 10
1644 25c. Gymnast on rings . . . 15 10
1645 35c. Diving 20 15
1646 50c. Show-jumping 25 20

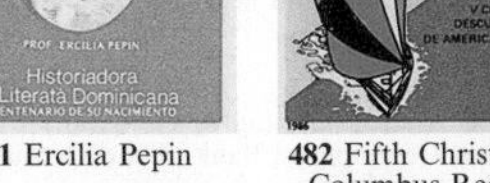

481 Ercilia Pepin

482 Fifth Christopher Columbus Regatta

1986. Writers' Birth Centenaries. Each brown and silver.
1647 5c. Type **481** 10 10
1648 10c. Ramon Emilio Jiminez and Victor Garrido . . . 10 10

1986. 500th Anniv (1992) of Discovery of America by Columbus (4th issue). Multicoloured.
1649 25c. Type **482** 30 10
1650 50c. Foundation of Isabela city 25 20
1651 65c. Spanish soldiers 35 30
1652 1p. Columbus before King of Spain 45 40

483 Goalkeeper saving Ball

484 Maize

1986. World Cup Football Championship, Mexico. Multicoloured.
1654 50c. Type **483** 25 20
1655 75c. Footballer and ball . . 40 35

1986. 2nd Caribbean Pharmacopoeia Seminar. Medicinal Plants. Multicoloured.
1656 5c. Type **484** 10 10
1657 10c. Arnotto 10 10
1658 25c. "Momordica charantia" 15 10
1659 50c. Custard-apple 25 20

485 Town with Christmas Tree

1986. Christmas. Multicoloured.
1660 5c. Type **485** 15 10
1661 25c. Village 15 10

486 Gomez on Horseback

488 Emblem

1986. 150th Birth Anniv of Maximo Gomez.
1662 **486** 10c. black and mauve . . 10 10
1663 – 25c. black and brown . . 15 10
DESIGN: 25c. Head of Gomez.

1987. 16th Pan-American Ophthalmology Congress, Santo Domingo.
1676 **488** 50c. red, blue & black 20 15

489 "Ascension of Jesus Christ" (stained glass window, St. John Bosco Church)

490 "Sorghum bicolor"

1987. Ascension Day.
1677 **489** 35c. multicoloured . . . 10 10

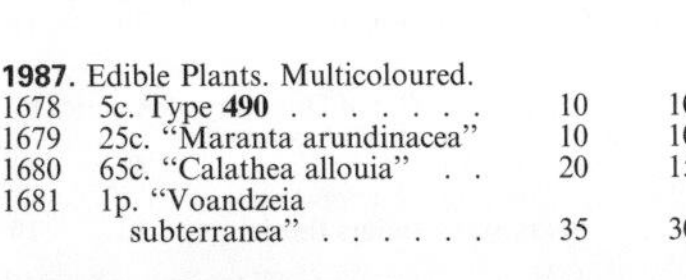

1987. Edible Plants. Multicoloured.
1678 5c. Type **490** 10 10
1679 25c. "Maranta arundinacea" 10 10
1680 65c. "Calathea allouia" . . 20 15
1681 1p. "Voandzeia subterranea" 35 30

491 Emblem and People on Map

1987. 25th Anniv of Club Activo 20–30 in Dominican Republic.
1682 **491** 35c. multicoloured . . . 10 10

492 Sixth Christopher Columbus Regatta

1987. 500th Anniv (1992) of Discovery of America by Columbus (5th issue). Multicoloured.
1683 50c. Type **492** 10 10
1684 75c. Columbus writing diary 15 10
1685 1p. Foundation of city of Santiago 20 15
1686 1p.50 Columbus and Bobadilla 30 25

493 Games Emblem

494 Jose Antonio Hungria

1987. 50th Anniv of La Vega Province Games.
1688 **493** 40c. multicoloured . . . 10 10

1987. Writers' Birth Anniversaries.
1689 **494** 10c. brown & lt brown 10 10
1690 – 25c. dp green & green 10 10
DESIGN: 25c. Joaquin Sergio Inchaustegui.

495 Baseball

496 Statue

1987. 8th National Games, San Cristobal. Multicoloured.
1691 5c. Type **495** 10 10
1692 10c. Boxing 10 10
1693 50c. Karate 10 10

1987. 150th Birth Anniv of Fr. Francisco Xavier Billini.
1694 **496** 10c. deep blue and blue 10 10
1695 – 25c. green and olive . . 10 10
1696 – 75c. brown and pink . . 15 10
DESIGNS: 25c. Fr. Billini; 75c. Ana Hernandez de Billini (mother).

497 Maj. Frank Feliz and Airplane

1987. 50th Anniv of Pan-American Flight for Columbus Lighthouse Fund.
1697 **497** 25c. multicoloured . . . 20 10

498 Spit-roasting Pig

1987. Christmas. Multicoloured.
1699 10c. Type **498** 10 10
1700 50c. Passengers disembarking from airplane 20 10

499 "Bromelia pinguin"

1988. Flowers. Multicoloured.
1701 50c. Type **499** 10 10
1702 50c. "Tillandsia compacta" (vert) 10 10
1703 50c. "Tillandsia fasciculata" 10 10
1704 50c. "Tillandsia hotteana" (vert) 10 10

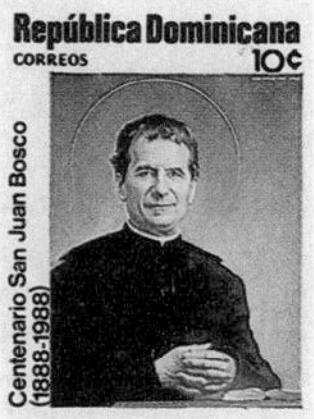

500 St. John Bosco

1988. Death Centenary of St. John Bosco (founder of Salesian Brothers). Multicoloured.
1705 10c. Type **500** 10 10
1706 70c. Stained glass window 15 10

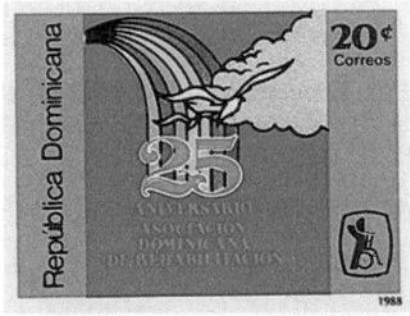

501 Rainbow, Doves and Cloud

1988. 25th Anniv of Dominican Rehabilitation Association.
1707 **501** 20c. multicoloured . . . 10 10

502 Perdomo

503 Emblem

1988. Birth Centenary of Dr. Manuel Emilio Perdomo.
1708 **502** 20c. brown and flesh . . 10 10

1988. 25th Anniv of Dominican College of Engineering and Architecture (CODIA).
1709 **503** 20c. multicoloured . . . 10 10

504 Church and Madonna and Child

505 Flags and Juan Pablo Duarte (Dominican patriot)

1988. Centenary of Parish Church of Our Lady of the Carmelites, Duverge.
1710 **504** 50c. multicoloured . . . 10 10

1988. Mexican Independence Day. Mult.
1711 50c. Type **505** 10 10
1712 50c. Flags and Miguel Hidalgo (Mexican patriot) 10 10

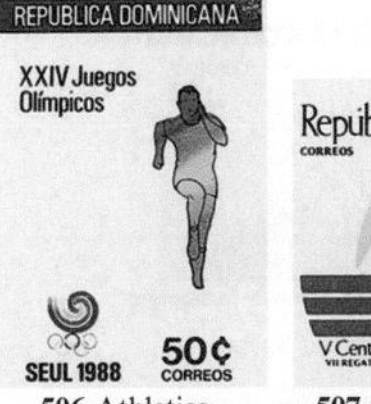

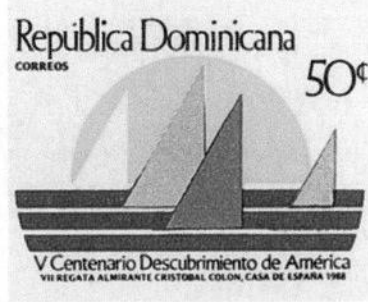

506 Athletics

507 Seventh Christopher Columbus Regatta

1988. Olympic Games, Seoul. Multicoloured.
1713 50c. Type **506** 10 10
1714 70c. Table tennis 15 10
1715 1p. Judo 20 15
1716 1p.50 "Ying Yang symbol and Balls" (Tete Marella) (horiz) 30 25

1988. 500th Anniv of Discovery of America by Columbus (6th issue). Multicoloured.
1717 50c. Type **507** 10 10
1718 70c. Building fort at La Vega Real, 1494 . . . . 15 10
1719 1p.50 Bonao Fort 30 25
1720 2p. Nicolas de Ovando (Governor of Hispaniola) 40 35

508 Duarte, Mella and Sanchez

509 Parchment, Knife and Pestle and Mortar

1988. 150th Anniv of Trinitarian Rebellion.
1722 **508** 10c. silver, red and blue 10 10
1723 – 1p. multicoloured . . . 20 15
1724 – 5p. multicoloured . . . 95 90
DESIGNS: 1p. Plaza La Trinitaria; 5p. Plaza de la Independencia.

1988. 13th Pan-American and 16th Central American Congresses of Pharmacy and Biochemistry.
1725 **509** 1p. multicoloured . . . 20 15

510 "Doni Tondo" (Michelangelo)

511 Emblem

1988. Christmas. Multicoloured.
1726 10c. Type **510** 10 10
1727 20c. Stained glass window 10 10

1988. 50th Anniv of Dominican Municipal Association.
1728 **511** 20c. multicoloured . . . 10 10

512 Ana Teresa Paradas

1988. 28th Death Anniv of Ana Teresa Paradas (lawyer).
1729 **512** 20c. red 10 10

513 Birds

1989. Bicentenary of French Revolution.
1730 **513** 3p. red, blue and black 30 25

516 Battle Scene

1989. 145th Anniv of Battle of Tortuguero.
1737 **516** 40c. multicoloured . . . 70 25

517 Drug Addict

1989. Anti-drugs Campaign.
1738 **517** 10c. multicoloured . . . 10 10
1739 20c. multicoloured . . . 10 10
1740 50c. multicoloured . . . 10 10
1741 70c. multicoloured . . . 10 10
1742 1p. multicoloured . . . 10 10
1743 1p.50 multicoloured . . . 15 15
1744 2p. multicoloured . . . 20 15
1745 5p. multicoloured . . . 50 45
1746 10p. multicoloured . . . 1·00 95

518 Breast-feeding Baby

519 Eugenio Maria de Hostos

1989. Mothers' Day.
1747 **518** 20c. multicoloured . . . 10 10

1989. 150th Birth Anniversaries. Mult.
1748 20c. Type **519** 10 10
1749 20c. Gen. Gregorio Luperon 10 10

520 Baseball

1989. 50th Anniv of Baseball Minor League.
1750 **520** 1p. multicoloured . . . 10 10

521 Map and Human Organs

1989. 7th Latin American Diabetes Association Congress.
1751 **521** 1p. multicoloured . . . 10 10

522 Cohoba Artefact and Ritual Dance

1989. America. Pre-Columbian Culture. Mult.
1752 20c. Type **522** 10 10
1753 1p. Taina vessel, pounding instrument and Indians preparing manioc cake . . 10 10

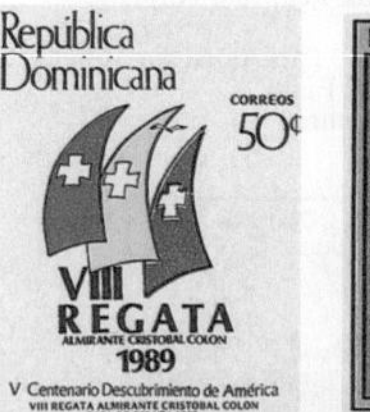

523 Eighth Christopher Columbus Regatta

524 Dead and Living Leaves

1989. 500th Anniv (1992) of Discovery of America by Columbus (7th issue). Multicoloured.
1754 50c. Type **523** 10 10
1755 70c. Brother Pedro de Cordoba preaching to Indians (horiz) 10 10
1756 1p. Columbus dividing Indian lands (horiz) . . . 10 10
1757 3p. Brother Antonio Montesinos giving sermon (horiz) 30 25

1989. National Reafforestation Campaign. Mult.
1758 10c. Type **524** 10 10
1759 20c. Forest 10 10
1760 50c. Forest and lake 10 10
1761 1p. Living tree and avenue of dead trees 10 10

525 Map and Cyclist

526 Mary and Body of Jesus

1990. 9th National Games, La Vega. Mult.
1762 10c. Type **525** 10 10
1763 20c. Map and runner . . . 10 10
1764 50c. Map and handball player 10 10

1990. Holy Week. Multicoloured.
1765 20c. Type **526** 10 10
1766 50c. Jesus carrying cross . . 10 10

527 Cogwheel and Workers

1990. International Labour Day.
1767 **527** 1p. multicoloured . . . 10 10

528 Avenida Mexico

1990. Urban Development. Multicoloured.
1768 10c. Type **528** 10 10
1769 20c. Avenida Nunez de Caceres road tunnel . . . 10 10
1770 50c. National Library . . . 10 10
1771 1p. V Centenario Motorway 10 10

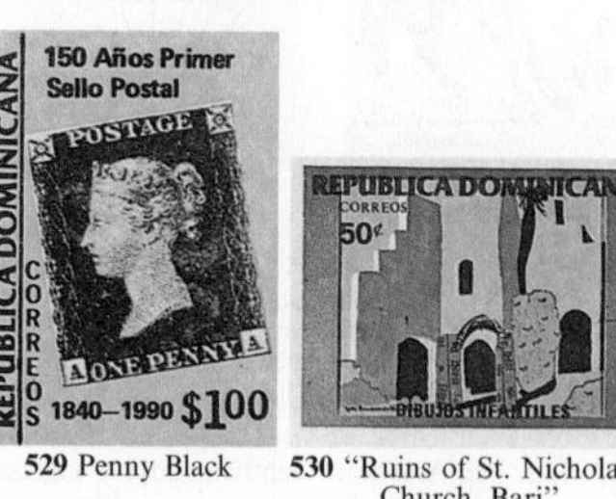

529 Penny Black

530 "Ruins of St. Nicholas's Church, Bari"

1990. 150th Anniv of the Penny Black. Mult.
1772 **529** 1p. multicoloured . . . 10 10

1990. Children's Drawings. Multicoloured.
1774 50c. Type **530** 10 10
1775 50c. "House, Tostado" . . . 10 10

531 Members' Flags

532 Yachts (Ninth Christopher Columbus Regatta)

1990. Centenary of Organization of American States.
1776 **531** 2p. multicoloured . . . 20 15

1990. 500th Anniv (1992) of Discovery of America by Columbus (8th issue). Multicoloured.
1777 50c. Type **532** 40 10
1778 1p. Confrontation between natives and sailors (horiz) 10 10
1779 2p. Meeting of Columbus and Guacanagari (horiz) 20 15
1780 5p. Caonabo imprisoned by Columbus (horiz) 45 30

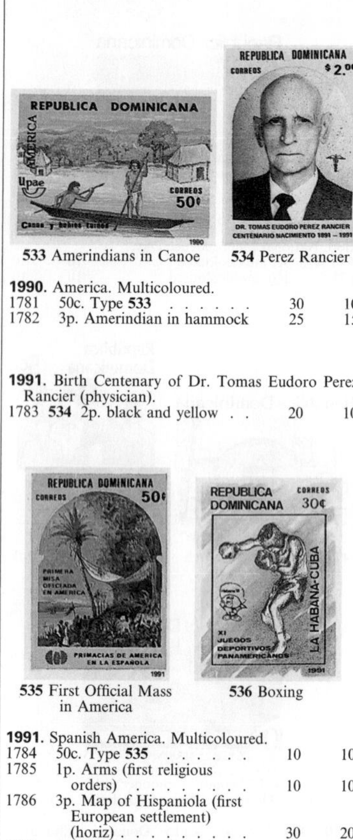

533 Amerindians in Canoe

534 Perez Rancier

1990. America. Multicoloured.
1781 50c. Type **533** 30 10
1782 3p. Amerindian in hammock 25 15

1991. Birth Centenary of Dr. Tomas Eudoro Perez Rancier (physician).
1783 **534** 2p. black and yellow . . 20 10

535 First Official Mass in America

536 Boxing

1991. Spanish America. Multicoloured.
1784 50c. Type **535** 10 10
1785 1p. Arms (first religious orders) 10 10
1786 3p. Map of Hispaniola (first European settlement) (horiz) 30 20
1787 4p. Christopher Columbus (first viceroy and governor) 45 30

1991. 11th Pan-American Games, Havana. Multicoloured.
1788 30c. Type **536** 10 10
1789 50c. Cycling 10 10
1790 1p. Putting the shot 10 10

537 Yachts (10th Christopher Columbus Regatta)

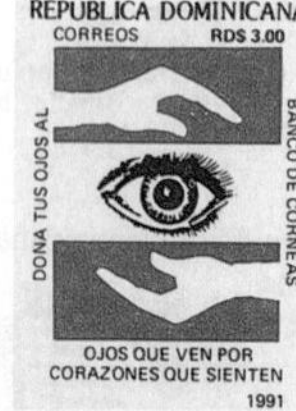

538 Eye and Hands

1991. 500th Anniv (1992) of Discovery of America by Columbus (9th issue). Multicoloured.
1791 30c. Type **537** 10 10
1792 50c. Meeting of three cultures (horiz) 10 10
1793 3p. Columbus and Doctor Alvarez Chanco (horiz) 30 20
1794 4p. Enriquillo's war (horiz) 45 30

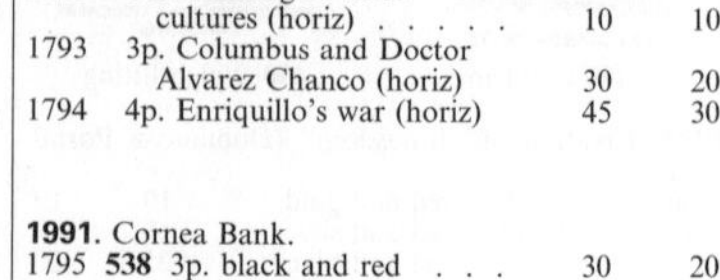

1991. Cornea Bank.
1795 **538** 3p. black and red . . . 30 20

539 "Santa Maria"

540 Meeting Emblem

1991. America. Voyages of Discovery. Mult.
1796 1p. Type **539** 20 15
1797 3p. Columbus and fleet . . 40 25

1992. 33rd Annual Meeting of Governors of Inter-American Development Bank, Santo Domingo.
1798 **540** 1p. multicoloured . . . 10 10

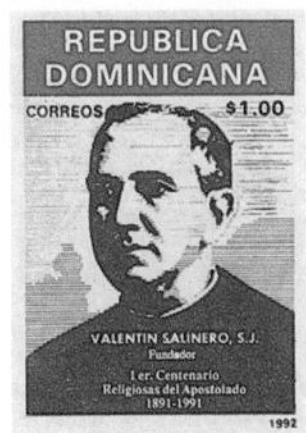

541 Valentin Salinero (founder)

542 Flags of Cuba, Dominican Republic and Puerto Rica, and Magnifying Glass

1992. Centenary (1991) of Order of the Apostles.
1799 **541** 1p. brown, black & blue 10 10

1992. "Espanola 92" Stamp Exhibition.
1800 **542** 3p. black, violet & red 30 20

543 First Monastery in Americas

1992. Ruins. Multicoloured.
1801 50c. Type **543** 10 10
1802 3p. First hospital in Americas 30 20

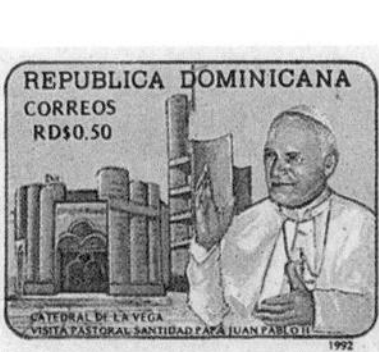

544 La Vega Cathedral and Pope

545 Yacht (11th Christopher Columbus Regatta)

1992. Visit of Pope John Paul II. Mult.
1803 50c. Type **544** 10 10
1804 3p. Santo Domingo Cathedral and Pope . . . 30 20

1992. 500th Anniv of Discovery of America by Columbus (10th issue). Multicoloured.
1805 50c. Type **545** 10 10
1806 1p. Amerindian women preparing food and Columbus (horiz) 10 10
1807 2p. Amerindians demonstrating use of tobacco to Columbus (horiz) 20 10
1808 3p. Amerindian woman and Columbus by maize field (horiz) 30 20

546 Columbus Lighthouse

547 Convention Emblem

1992.
1809 **546** 30c. multicoloured . . . 10 10
1810 1p. multicoloured . . . 10 10

1992. 23rd Pan-American Round Table Convention, Santo Domingo.
1812 **547** 1p. brown, cream & red 10 10

548 First Royal Palace in Americas, Santo Domingo

549 Torch Bearer

1992. America. Multicoloured.
1813 50c. Type **548** 10 10
1814 3p. First Vice-regal residence in Americas, Colon . . . 30 20

1992. 10th National Games, San Juan.
1815 **549** 30c. multicoloured . . . 10 10
1816 – 1p. multicoloured . . . 10 10
1817 – 4p. black and blue . . . 40 25
DESIGNS: 1p. Emblem of Secretary of State for Sports Education and Recreation; 4p. Judo.

550 Emblem

551 Ema Balaguer

1993. 7th Population and Housing Census.
1818 **550** 50c. blue, black & pink 10 10
1819 1p. blue, black & brown 10 10
1820 3p. blue, black & grey 30 20
1821 4p. blue, black & green 40 25

1993. Ema Balaguer (humanitarian worker) Commemoration.
1822 **551** 30c. multicoloured . . . 10 10
1823 50c. multicoloured . . . 10 10
1824 1p. multicoloured . . . 10 10

552 Emblem and Stylized Figures

1993. 50th Anniv of Santo Domingo Rotary Club. Multicoloured.
1825 30c. Type **552** 10 10
1826 1p. National flags and rotary emblem 10 10

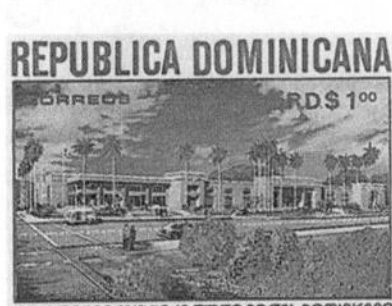

553 Institute

1993. Inauguration of New Dominican Postal Institute Building.
1827 **553** 1p. multicoloured . . . 10 10
1828 3p. multicoloured . . . 30 20
1829 4p. multicoloured . . . 40 25
1830 5p. multicoloured . . . 50 30
1831 10p. multicoloured . . . 95 60

554 Palm Chat and Books

556 Chest (first university)

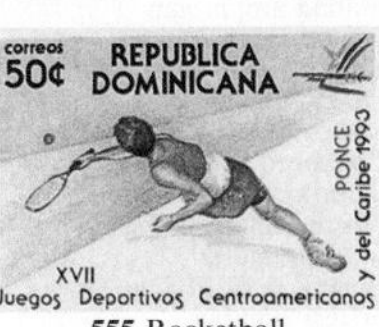

555 Racketball

1993. Ten Year Education Plan.
1833 **554** 1p.50 multicoloured . . 1·40 1·40

1993. 17th Central American and Caribbean Games, Ponce (Puerto Rico). Multicoloured.
1834 50c. Type **555** 10 10
1835 4p. Swimming 40 25

1993. American Firsts in Hispaniola (1st series). Multicoloured.
1836 50c. Type **556** 10 10
1837 3p. First arms conferred on American city 30 20
See also Nos. 1840 and 1882/3.

557 Hispaniolan Conure

1993. America. Endangered Animals. Mult.
1838 1p. Type **557** . . . . 1·25 95
1839 3p. Rhinoceros iguana . . . 30 20

558 Cross and Eucharist (500th anniv of first Mass)

1994. American Firsts in Hispaniola (2nd series).
1840 **558** 2p. multicoloured . . . 20 10

559 State Flag, 1946 15c. and 1944 3c. Stamps

1994. 5th National Stamp Exhibition.
1841 **559** 3p. multicoloured . . . 30 20

560 Signing of Independence Treaty (left-hand detail)

1994. 150th Anniv of Independence. Mult.
1842 2p. Type **560** 20 10
1843 2p. Signing of Independence Treaty (right-hand detail) 20 10
1844 2p. State flag 20 10
1845 2p. Soldier with young woman 20 10
1846 2p. Boy helping woman make flag 20 10
1847 3p. Revolutionaries (back view of left-hand man) . . 30 20
1848 3p. Revolutionaries (window behind men) 30 20
1849 3p. State arms 30 20
1850 3p. Revolutionaries (all turned away from door) 30 20
1851 3p. Revolutionaries with flag 30 20
Stamps of the same value were issued together, se-tenant, Nos. 1842/3, 1845/6, 1847/8 and 1850/1 forming composite designs.

561 Solenodon on Dead Wood

1994. The Haitian Solenodon. Multicoloured.
1853 1p. Type **561** 10 10
1854 1p. Solenodon amongst leaves 10 10
1855 1p. Solenodon on stony ground 10 10
1856 1p. Solenodon eating insect 10 10

562 Fusiliers behind Barricade (19 March)

563 Ballot Boxes

1994. 150th Anniversaries of Battles of 19 and 30 March. Multicoloured.
1857 2p. Type **562** 20 10
1858 2p. Battle at fort (30 March) 20 10

1994. National Elections.
1859 **563** 2p. multicoloured . . . 20 10

564 "Virgin of Amparo"

565 Goalkeeper

1994. 150th Anniv of Naval Battle of Puerto Tortuguero.
1860 **564** 3p. multicoloured . . . 30 20

1994. World Cup Football Championship, U.S.A. Multicoloured.
1861 4p. Type **565** 40 25
1862 6p. Players contesting possession of ball 60 40

566 Figures in Houses

1994. Ema Balguer Children's City.
1863 **566** 1p. mauve and brown . . 10 10

567 1866 Medio Real Stamp and Cancellation

1994. Stamp Day.
1864 **567** 5p. red, black & yellow 45 30

568 Postal Carrier on Horseback

571 Writing Desk and Constitution

1994. America. Postal Vehicles. Multicoloured.
1865 2p. Type **568** 20 10
1866 6p. Schooner 50 35

1994. 150th Anniv of First Constitution of Dominican Republic.
1876 **571** 3p. multicoloured . . . 25 15

572 Flight into Egypt

1994. Christmas. International Year of the Family. Multicoloured.
1877 2p. Type **572** 20 10
1878 3p. Family 25 15

573 Ruins of St. Francis's Monastery

1994. 500th Anniv of Concepcion de la Vega.

No.	Type	Description	Mint	Used
1879	573	3p. multicoloured . . .	25	15

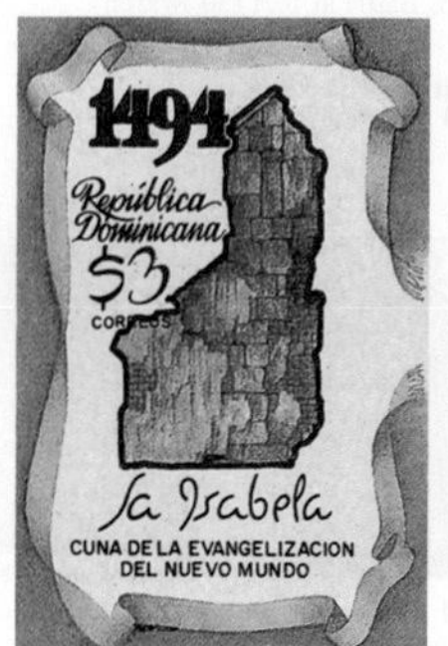

574 Wall of La Isabela Church

1994. 500th Anniv of First Church in Dominican Republic. Multicoloured.

No.	Type	Description	Mint	Used
1880		3p. Type **574**	25	15
1881		3p. Temple of the Americas	25	15

Nos. 1880/1 were issued together, se-tenant, forming a composite design.

1994. American Firsts in Hispaniola (3rd series). As T **556**. Multicoloured.

No.	Type	Description	Mint	Used
1882		2p. First coins, 1505	20	10
1883		5p. Antonio Montesino (first plea for justice (in Advent sermon), 1511)	45	30

575 "Hypsirhynchus ferox"

1994. National Natural History Museum. Snakes. Multicoloured.

No.	Type	Description	Mint	Used
1884		2p. Type **575**	20	10
1885		2p. "Antillophis parvifrons"	20	10
1886		2p. "Uromacer catesbyi" . .	20	10
1887		2p. Bahama boa ("Epicrates striatus")	20	10

Nos. 1884/5 and 1886/7 respectively were issued together, se-tenant, each pair forming a composite design of a tree and the snakes.

576 Taekwondo

1995. Pan-American Games, Mar del Plata, Argentine Republic.

No.	Type	Description	Mint	Used
1888	576	4p. blue, red & black . .	35	20
1889	–	13p. green, black & yell	1·25	80

DESIGN: 13p. Tennis.

577 Allegory of Dominican Agriculture

1995. 50th Anniv of F.A.O.

No.	Type	Description	Mint	Used
1890	577	4p. multicoloured . . .	35	20

578 Jose Marti, Maximo Gomez and Monte Cristi Clock Tower

579 Emblem

1995. Centenaries.

No.	Type	Description	Mint	Used
1891	578	2p. brown, pink & black	20	10
1892	–	3p. pink, black & blue	25	15
1893	–	4p. black and pink . . .	35	20

DESIGNS: 3p. Jose Marti on Cuban national flag (death centenary); 4p. Gomez and Marti signing Monte Cristi manifesto.

1995. "Centrobasket" Basketball Championship, Santo Domingo.

No.	Type	Description	Mint	Used
1894	579	3p. blue, red & black . .	25	15

580 "Pimenta ozua"

581 San Souci Port

1995. Medicinal Plants. Multicoloured.

No.	Type	Description	Mint	Used
1895		2p. Type **580**	20	10
1896		2p. "Melocactus communis"	20	10
1897		3p. "Smilax sp."	25	15
1898		3p. "Zamia sp."	25	15

1995. Tourism. Multicoloured.

No.	Type	Description	Mint	Used
1899		4p. Type **581**	35	20
1900		5p. Barahona airport . . .	45	30
1901		6p. G. Luperon airport . .	55	35
1902		13p. Las Americas airport	1·25	80

582 Ruins of Jacagua Church

1995. 500th Anniv of Santiago de los Caballeros.

No.	Type	Description	Mint	Used
1903	582	3p. multicoloured . . .	25	15

583 Sei Whale ("Balaenoptera borealis")

1995. Natural History Museum. Whales. Mult.

No.	Type	Description	Mint	Used
1904		3p. Type **583**	25	15
1905		3p. Humpback whales ("Megaptera novaeangliae")	25	15
1906		3p. Sperm whales ("Physeter macrocephalus")	25	15
1907		3p. Cuvier's beaked whales ("Ziphius cavirostris") . .	25	15

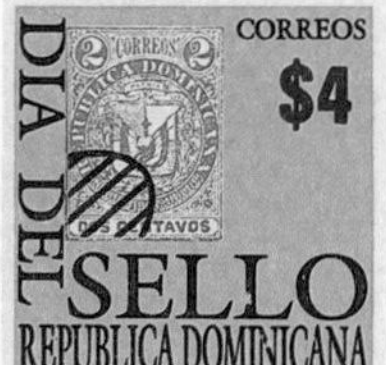

584 Rafael Colon

585 Cancelled 1880 2c. Stamp

1995. Singers. Multicoloured.

No.	Type	Description	Mint	Used
1908		2p. Type **584**	20	10
1909		3p. Casandra Damiron . . .	25	15

1995. Stamp Day.

No.	Type	Description	Mint	Used
1910	585	4p. multicoloured . . .	35	20

586 Player

587 Anniversary Emblem

1995. Centenary of Volleyball.

No.	Type	Description	Mint	Used
1911	586	6p. multicoloured . . .	55	35

1995. 50th Anniv of U.N.O.

No.	Type	Description	Mint	Used
1913	587	2p. blue and gold . . .	20	10
1914	–	6p. multicoloured . . .	55	35

DESIGN—33 × 55 mm: 6p. Allegorical design.

588 Allegory

589 Columbus Lighthouse

1995. 4th World Conference on Women, Peking.

No.	Type	Description	Mint	Used
1915	588	2p. multicoloured . . .	20	10

1995.

No.	Type	Description	Mint	Used
1916	589	10p. ultram, blue & blk	90	60
1994		10p. green and silver . .	85	55
2025		10p. mauve and silver . .	75	50
2089		10p. yellow and black . .	75	50

590 Enriquillo Lake

591 Antonio Mesa (tenor)

1995. America. Environmental Protection. Mult.

No.	Type	Description	Mint	Used
1917		2p. Type **590**	20	10
1918		6p. Mangrove plantation . .	55	35

1995. Singers. Each red and brown.

No.	Type	Description	Mint	Used
1919		2p. Type **591**	20	10
1920		2p. Susano Polanco (tenor)	20	10
1921		2p. Julieta Otero (soprano)	20	10

592 Cathedral

1995. Centenary of Santiago Cathedral.

No.	Type	Description	Mint	Used
1922	592	3p. multicoloured . . .	25	15

593 Corsair Fighter

1995. 50th Anniv of Dominican Air Force (1st issue). Multicoloured.

No.	Type	Description	Mint	Used
1923		2p. Type **593**	20	10
1924		2p. Stearman Pt-17 Kaydett bomber	20	10
1925		2p. North American T-6 Texan trainer	20	10
1926		2p. Consolidated PBY-5A Catalina amphibian . . .	20	10
1927		2p. Bristol Beaufighter fighter	20	10
1928		2p. De Havilland Mosquito bomber	20	10
1929		2p. Lockheed P-38 Lightning fighter	20	10
1930		2p. North American P-51 Mustang fighter	20	10
1931		2p. Boeing B-17 Flying Fortress bomber	20	10
1932		2p. Republic P-47 Thunderbolt fighter . . .	20	10
1933		2p. De Havilland Vampire jet fighter	20	10
1934		2p. Curtiss C-46 Commander	20	10
1935		2p. Boeing B-26 Invader . .	20	10
1936		2p. Douglas C-47 Skytrain transport	20	10
1937		2p. T-28D Trojan	20	10
1938		2p. T-33A Silverstar	20	10
1939		2p. Cessna T-41D	20	10
1940		2p. T-34 Mentor	20	10
1941		2p. Cessna O-2A	20	10
1942		2p. Cessna A-37B Dragonfly fighter	20	10

See also Nos. 1958/63, 2026/31 and 2040/4.

594 Brito

596 Children

595 Yachts

1996. 50th Death Anniv of Eduardo Brito (singer).

No.	Type	Description	Mint	Used
1943	594	1p. multicoloured . . .	10	10
1944	–	2p. multicoloured . . .	20	10
1945	–	3p. black and pink . .	25	15

DESIGNS—55 × 35 mm: 2p. Brito playing maracas. As T **594**: 3p. Brito (different).

1996. Hispaniola Cup Yachting Championship.

No.	Type	Description	Mint	Used
1946	595	5p. multicoloured . . .	45	30

1996. 50th Anniv of U.N.I.C.E.F.

No.	Type	Description	Mint	Used
1947	596	2p. black and green . .	20	10
1948	–	4p. black and green . .	35	20

DESIGN—4p. As T **596** but motif reversed.

597 Arturo Pallerano, Freddy Gaton and Rafael Herrera

1996. National Journalists' Day.

No.	Type	Description	Mint	Used
1949	597	5p. multicoloured . . .	45	30

598 Emblem, Astronaut and Biplane

1996. "Espamer" Spanish–Latin American and "Aviation and Space" Stamp Exhibitions, Seville, Spain.

No.	Type	Description	Mint	Used
1950	598	15p. multicoloured . . .	1·40	90

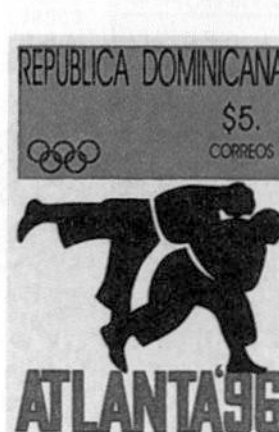

599 Judo

1996. Olympic Games, Atlanta. Each black, blue and red.

No.	Type	Description	Mint	Used
1951		5p. Type **599**	45	30
1952		15p. Torchbearer	1·40	90

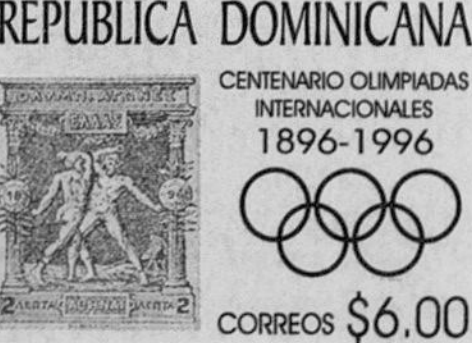

600 Greek 1896 2l. Olympic Stamp

1996. Centenary of Modern Olympic Games.

No.	Type	Description	Mint	Used
1953	600	6p. green, red & black	55	35
1954	–	15p. multicoloured . . .	1·40	90

DESIGN: 15p. Dominican Republic 1937 7c. Olympic stamp.

601 "Girl at Postbox"

1996. "The Post is your Friend". Winning Entries in Children's Stamp Design Competition. Mult.
1955 3p. Type **601** 20 10
1956 3p. Representations of world post 20 10
1957 3p. Postal carrier on horseback delivering letter (vert) 20 10

602 Sikorsky S-55

1996. 50th Anniv of Air Force (2nd issue). Helicopters. Multicoloured.
1958 3p. Type **602** 20 10
1959 3p. Sud Aviation Alouette II 20 10
1960 3p. Sud Aviation Alouette III 20 10
1961 3p. OH-6A Cayuse 20 10
1962 3p. Bell 205 A-1 . . . . . 20 10
1963 3p. Aerospatiale SA.365 Dauphin 2 . . . . 20 10

603 Workers and Children
604 Man

1996. United Nations Decade against Drug Trafficking.
1964 **603** 15p. multicoloured . . . 1·40 90

1996. America. Costumes. Multicoloured.
1965 2p. Type **604** 15 10
1966 6p. Woman 50 30

605 Stylized Dinghy

1996. 26th International "Sunfish" Dinghy Sailing Championships. Multicoloured.
1967 6p. Type **605** 50 30
1968 10p. Sailor in dinghy (horiz) 85 55

606 1905 1p. Stamp

1996. Stamp Day.
1969 **606** 5p. stone and black . . . 40 25

607 Ridgway's Hawk ("Buteo ridgwayi")
608 Mirabal Sisters

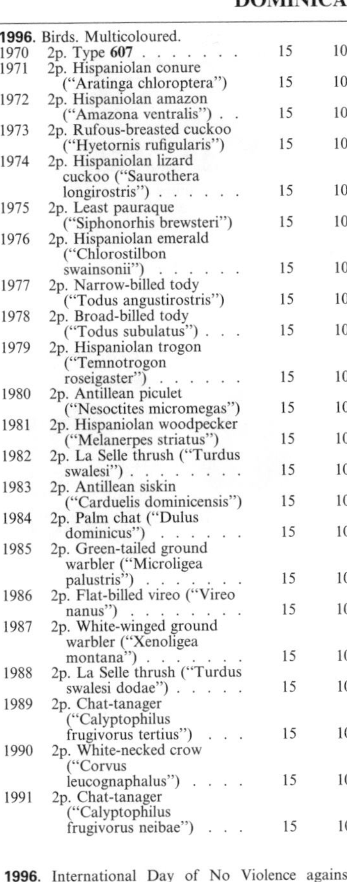

1996. Birds. Multicoloured.
1970 2p. Type **607** 15 10
1971 2p. Hispaniolan conure ("Aratinga chloroptera") 15 10
1972 2p. Hispaniolan amazon ("Amazona ventralis") . . 15 10
1973 2p. Rufous-breasted cuckoo ("Hyetornis rufigularis") 15 10
1974 2p. Hispaniolan lizard cuckoo ("Saurothera longirostris") 15 10
1975 2p. Least pauraque ("Siphonorhis brewsteri") 15 10
1976 2p. Hispaniolan emerald ("Chlorostilbon swainsonii") 15 10
1977 2p. Narrow-billed tody ("Todus angustirostris") 15 10
1978 2p. Broad-billed tody ("Todus subulatus") . . . 15 10
1979 2p. Hispaniolan trogon ("Temnotrogon roseigaster") 15 10
1980 2p. Antillean piculet ("Nesoctites micromegas") 15 10
1981 2p. Hispaniolan woodpecker ("Melanerpes striatus") 15 10
1982 2p. La Selle thrush ("Turdus swalesi") 15 10
1983 2p. Antillean siskin ("Carduelis dominicensis") 15 10
1984 2p. Palm chat ("Dulus dominicus") 15 10
1985 2p. Green-tailed ground warbler ("Microligea palustris") 15 10
1986 2p. Flat-billed vireo ("Vireo nanus") 15 10
1987 2p. White-winged ground warbler ("Xenoligea montana") 15 10
1988 2p. La Selle thrush ("Turdus swalesi dodae") 15 10
1989 2p. Chat-tanager ("Calyptophilus frugivorus tertius") . . . 15 10
1990 2p. White-necked crow ("Corvus leucognaphalus") 15 10
1991 2p. Chat-tanager ("Calyptophilus frugivorus neibae") . . . 15 10

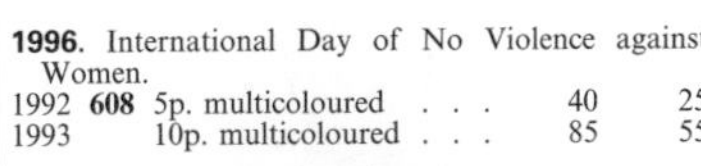

1996. International Day of No Violence against Women.
1992 **608** 5p. multicoloured . . . 40 25
1993 10p. multicoloured . . . 85 55

609 Leatherback Turtles ("Dermochelys coriacea")

1996. Turtles. Multicoloured.
1995 5p. Type **609** 40 25
1996 5p. Loggerhead turtles ("Caretta caretta") . . . 40 25
1997 5p. Indian Ocean green turtles ("Chelonia mydas") 40 25
1998 5p. Hawksbill turtles ("Eretmochelys imbricata") 40 25

Nos. 1995/8 were issued together, se-tenant, forming a composite design.

610 Youths leaping for Sun
611 Flag and Lyrics by Emilio Prudhomne

1997. National Youth Day.
1999 **610** 3p. multicoloured . . . 25 15

1997. National Anthem. Each black, blue and red.
2000 2p. Type **611** 15 10
2001 3p. Flag and score by Jose Reyes 25 15

612 Salome Urena
613 Comet, Palm Tree and House

1997. Death Cent of Salome Urena (educationist).
2002 **612** 3p. multicoloured . . . 25 15

1997. Hale-Bopp Comet.
2003 **613** 5p. multicoloured . . . 40 25

614 Mascot with Torch and Emblem

1997. 11th National Games. Multicoloured.
2005 2p. Type **614** 15 10
2006 3p. Mascot with baseball bat (26 × 36 mm) 25 15
2007 5p. Athlete breasting tape (36 × 26 mm) 40 25

615 Von Stephan
616 Blood Vessel

1997. Death Centenary of Heinrich von Stephan (founder of U.P.U).
2008 **615** 10p. violet, blk & red . . 85 55

1997. 15th International Haemostasis and Thrombosis Congress.
2010 **616** 10p. multicoloured . . . 85 55

617 Helmet, Flowers and Epaulettes
618 Emblem

1997. Death Cent of General Gregorio Luperon.
2011 **617** 3p. multicoloured . . . 25 15

1997. 80th Anniv of Spanish House in Santo Domingo.
2012 **618** 5p. multicoloured . . . 40 25

619 First Minting

1997. Centenary of the Peso.
2013 **619** 2p. multicoloured . . . 15 10

620 Icon

1997. 75th Anniv of Coronation of "Our Lady of Altagracia" (icon). Multicoloured.
2014 3p. Type **620** 25 15
2015 5p. Icon and church 40 25

621 Dog attacking Postman on Motor Cycle

1997. America. The Postman. Multicoloured.
2016 2p. Type **621** 15 10
2017 6p. Dog attacking postman delivering letter ($35\frac{1}{2}$ × 37 mm) 45 30

622 Weeping Child, Mother Teresa and Man on Donkey

1997. Int Fight against Poverty Day.
2018 **622** 5p. multicoloured . . . 40 25

623 1936 and 1899 2p. Stamps

1997. Stamp Day.
2019 **623** 5p. brown and black . . 40 25

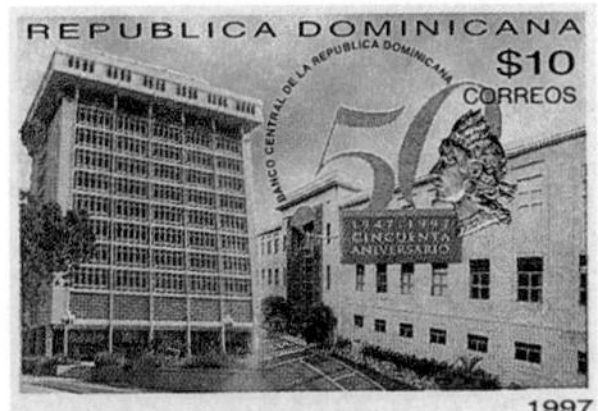

624 Buildings

1997. 50th Anniv of Central Bank.
2020 **624** 10p. multicoloured . . . 75 50

625 "Erophyllus bombifrons"

1997. Bats. Multicoloured.
2021 5p. Type **625** 40 25
2022 5p. Cuban fruit-eating bat ("Brachyphylla nana") . . 40 25
2023 5p. Kerr's mastiff bat ("Molossus molossus") . . 40 25
2024 5p. Red bat ("Lasiurus borealis") 40 25

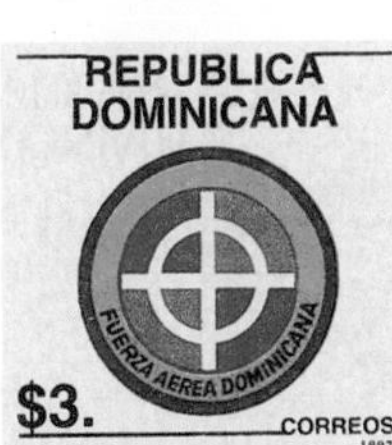

626 Air Force Badge

1997. 50th Anniv of Air Force (3rd issue). Division Badges. Multicoloured.
2026 3p. Type **626** 25 15
2027 3p. Air Command North . . 25 15
2028 3p. Air Command 25 15
2029 3p. Rescue 25 15
2030 3p. Maintenance Command 25 15
2031 3p. Combat Squadron . . . 25 15

627 Facade

1997. 50th Anniv of National Palace.
2032 **627** 10p. multicoloured . . . 75 50

628 Painting

1998. 1st Regional Symposium on Influence of Pre-Columbian Culture on Contemporary Caribbean Art.
2033 **628** 6p. multicoloured . . . 45 30

629 Emblem

630 Open Book

1998. 75th Anniv of American Chamber of Commerce of Dominican Republic.
2034 **629** 10p. blue, red and gold 75 50

1998. 25th Anniv of National Book Fair and First International Book Fair, Santo Domingo.
2035 **630** 3p. blue, red and black 25 15
2036 – 5p. blue, red and black 40 25
DESIGN—40 × 40 mm: 5p. Book Fair emblem.

631 Emblem

1998. 50th Anniv of Organization of American States. Multicoloured.
2037 5p. Type **631** 40 25
2038 5p. As Type **631** but inscr for the 50th anniv of signing of the Organization charter . . . 40 25

632 Olive Branches, Menorah and Star of David

1998. 50th Anniv of State of Israel.
2039 **632** 10p. ultram, bl & mve 75 50

633 General Frank Felix Miranda

1998. 50th Anniv of Air Force (4th issue). Mult.
2040 3p. Type **633** 25 15
2041 3p. Curtiss-Wright R-19 . . 25 15
2042 3p. Coronel Ernesto Tejeda (portrait at right) 25 15
2043 3p. As No. 2042, but portrait at left 25 15
2044 3p. As Type **633**, but portrait at right 25 15

634 Sundial

1998. 500th Anniv of Santo Domingo. Mult.
2045 2p. Type **634** 15 10
2046 3p. St. Lazarus's Church and Hospital (horiz) . . . 25 15
2047 4p. First cathedral in the Americas (horiz) 30 20
2048 5p. Fortress (horiz) 40 25
2049 6p. Tower of Honour (horiz) 45 30
2050 10p. St. Nicholas of Bari's Church and Hospital . . 75 50

635 Theatre

1998. 25th Anniv of National Theatre.
2051 **635** 10p. multicoloured . . . 75 50

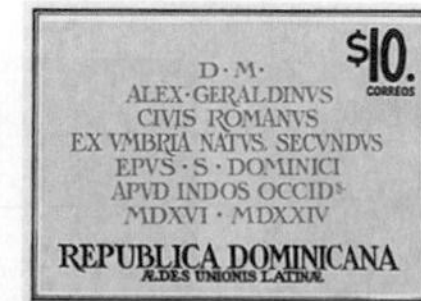
636 Latin Inscription

1998. 44th Anniv of Latin Union.
2052 **636** 10p. gold, grey & black 75 50

637 Cocoa Beans and Route Map of First American–Europe Shipment, 1502

1998. 25th Anniv of Int Cocoa Organization.
2053 **637** 10p. multicoloured . . . 75 50

638 Nino Ferrua (stamp designer)

1998. Stamp Day.
2054 **638** 5p. multicoloured . . . 40 25

639 Pope John Paul II venerating Portrait of Virgin Mary

1998. 20th Anniv of Pontificate of Pope John Paul II. Multicoloured.
2055 5p. Type **639** 40 25
2056 10p. Pope John Paul II . . 75 50

640 Bay Rum

1998. Medicinal Plants. Multicoloured.
2057 3p. Type **640** 20 10
2058 3p. "Pimenta haitiensis" . . 20 10
2059 3p. "Cymbopogon citratus" 20 10
2060 3p. Seville orange ("Citrus aurantium") 20 10

641 Juana Saltitopa (Independence fighter)

1998. America. Famous Women. Multicoloured.
2061 2p. Type **641** 15 10
2062 6p. Anacaona (Indian chief) 45 30

642 Earth and Emblem

643 Statue of Columbus

1998. International Year of the Ocean.
2063 **642** 5p. multicoloured . . . 35 25

1998. "Expofila 98" Stamp Exhibition, Santo Domingo. 500th Anniv of Santo Domingo.
2064 **643** 5p. multicoloured . . . 35 25

644 Fernando Valerio

1998. Military Heroes. Each brown and green.
2065 3p. Type **644** 20 10
2066 3p. Benito Moncion 20 10
2067 3p. Jose Maria Cabral . . . 20 10
2068 3p. Antonio Duverge . . . 20 10
2069 3p. Gregorio Luperon . . . 20 10
2070 3p. Jose Salcedo 20 10
2071 3p. Fco. Salcedo 20 10
2072 3p. Gaspar Polanco 20 10
2073 3p. Santiago Rodriguez . . 20 10
2074 3p. Admiral Juan Cambiaso 20 10
2075 3p. Jose Puello 20 10
2076 3p. Jose Imbert 20 10
2077 3p. Admiral Juan Acosta . . 20 10
2078 3p. Marcos Adon 20 10
2079 3p. Matias Mella 20 10
2080 3p. Francisco Sanchez . . . 20 10
2081 3p. Juan Pablo Duarte . . . 20 10
2082 3p. Olegario Tenares . . . 20 10
2083 3p. General Pedro Santana 20 10
2084 3p. Juan Sanchez Ramirez 20 10

645 Banknotes

1998. 150th Anniv of Paper Money.
2085 **645** 10p. multicoloured . . . 75 50

646 Spit-roasting Pig

1998. Christmas. Multicoloured.
2086 2p. Type **646** 15 10
2087 5p. Three Wise Men on camels 35 25

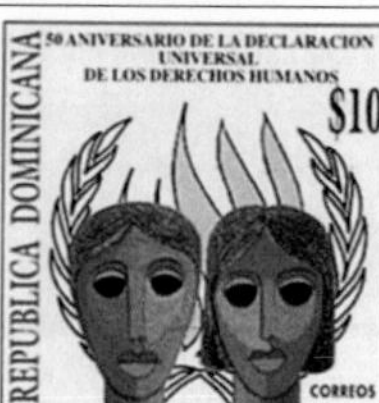
647 Couple and Human Rights Emblem

1998. 50th Anniv of Universal Declaration of Human Rights.
2088 **647** 10p. multicoloured . . . 75 50

648 Vega's Lyria

1998. Shells. Multicoloured.
2090 5p. Type **648** 35 25
2091 5p. Queen conch ("Strombus gigas") . . . 35 25
2092 5p. West Indian top shell ("Cittarium pica") 35 25
2093 5p. Bleeding tooth ("Nerita peloronta") 35 25

649 Hernandez

1998. Birth Bicentenary of Gaspar Hernandez (priest and Independence fighter).
2094 **649** 3p. multicoloured . . . 20 10

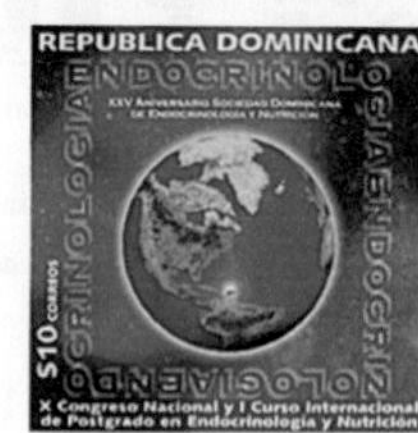
650 Earth

1999. 10th National Congress, First International Postgraduate Lectures and 25th Anniv of Dominican Society for Endocrinology and Nutrition.
2095 **650** 10p. multicoloured . . . 75 50

652 Cigar and Tobacco Leaf

1999. Exports. Multicoloured.
2097 6p. Type **652** 45 30
2098 10p. Woman sewing (textiles) (vert) 75 50

653 Magnifying Glass over Map of Dominican Republic

1999. 155th Anniv of Office of Comptroller-General.
2099 **653** 2p. multicoloured . . . 15 10

654 Bosch, "The Seagull" (poem) and Main Tower, Santo Domingo

1999. Contemporary Writers. 90th Birthday of Pres. Juan Bosch (poet). Multicoloured.

2100 2p. Type **654** 15 10
2101 10p. Portrait of Bosch (vert) 75 50

655 "Pseudophoenix ekmanii"

657 Baseball

656 Gen. Juan Pablo Duarte (revolutionary)

1999. Flowers and their Fruit. Multicoloured.

2102 5p. Type **655** 35 25
2103 5p. "Murtigia colabura" . . 35 25
2104 5p. "Pouteria dominguensis" 35 25
2105 5p. "Rubus dominguensis" 35 25

1999.

2106 **656** 3p. multicoloured . . . 20 15

1999. 13th Pan-American Games, Winnipeg, Canada. Multicoloured.

2107 5p. Type **657** 35 25
2108 6p. Weightlifting 45 30

658 Tomas Bobadilla y Briones

1999. Leaders of the Dominican Republic. Mult.

2109 3p. Type **658** 20 15
2110 3p. Pedro Santana (President, 1844–48, 1853–56 and 1859–61) 20 15
2111 3p. Manuel Jimenez (President, 1848–49) . . . 20 15
2112 3p. Buenaventura Baez (President, 1849–53, 1856–58, 1865–66, 1868–74 and 1876–78) 20 15
2113 3p. Manuel de Regla Motta (President, June–October 1856) 20 15
2114 3p. Jose Desiderio Valverde (President, 1858–59) . . . 20 15
2115 3p. Jose Antonio Salcedo . . 20 15
2116 3p. Gaspar Polanco 20 15

659 "St. Christopher"

1999. Jose Vela Zanetti (Spanish artist) Commemoration. Multicoloured

2117 2p. Type **659** 15 10
2118 3p. "Bride and Groom" . . 20 15
2119 5p. "Burial of Christ" (horiz) 35 20
2120 6p. "Cock-fighting" 45 30
2121 10p. "Self-portrait" 75 50

660 "Strataegus quadrifoveatus"

1999. Insects. Multicoloured.

2122 5p. Type **660** 35 20
2123 5p. "Anetia jaegeri" (butterfly) 35 20
2124 5p. "Polyancistroydes tettigonidae" 35 20
2125 5p. Stick insect ("Phasmidae aploppus") 35 20

661 Emblem and Cross-section of Skin

1999. 50th Anniv of Dominican Dermatological Society.

2126 **661** 3p. multicoloured . . . 20 15

662 Maternity Clinic, Santo Domingo

1999. 900th Anniv of Sovereign Military Order of Malta. Multicoloured.

2127 2p. Type **662** 15 10
2128 10p. Maltese Cross and anniversary emblem ($36\frac{1}{2} \times 38$ mm) 75 50

663 Children

664 Man

1999. 50th Anniv of S.O.S. Children's Villages.

2129 **663** 10p. multicoloured . . . 85 55

1999. International Year of the Elderly.

2130 **664** 2p. black and blue . . . 20 10
2131 – 5p. black and red . . . 45 30

DESIGN: 5p. Woman.

665 Teacher and Students

666 Dove, Skull and Crossbones, Gun, Emblem and Mines

1999. Teachers' Day.

2132 **665** 5p. multicoloured . . . 45 30

1999. America. A New Millennium without Arms. Multicoloured.

2133 2p. Type **666** 20 10
2134 6p. Atomic cloud and emblem 50 30

667 Luis F. Thomen (philatelist and author)

669 Map of Caribbean and Whale

668 Globe and Forests

1999. Stamp Day.

2135 **667** 5p. drab, black and green 45 30

1999. New Millennium. Multicoloured.

2136 3p. Type **668** 25 10
2137 5p. Astronaut, satellite, computer and man . . . 45 30

1999. 2nd Summit of African, Caribbean and Pacific Heads of State. Multicoloured.

2138 5p. Type **669** 45 30
2139 6p. Moai Statues, Easter Island 50 30
2140 10p. Map of Africa and lion 85 55

670 Means of Communication

1999. 125th Anniv of Universal Postal Union.

2141 **670** 6p. multicoloured . . . 50 30

671 Globe and "50"

1999. 50th Anniv of Union of Latin American Universities.

2143 **671** 6p. multicoloured . . . 50 30

1999. As No. 1916 but colours changed.

2144 **589** 10p. brown and silver . . 85 55

672 Juan Garcia (trumpeter)

1999. Classical Musicians.

2145 **672** 5p. blue and black . . . 45 30
2146 – 5p. mauve and black . . 45 30
2147 – 5p. green and black . . 45 30

DESIGNS: 2146, Manuel Simo (saxophonist); 2147, Jose Ravelo (clarinettist).

673 Santiago and Cotui Banknotes

1999. Centenary of Banknotes. Multicoloured.

2148 2p. Type **673** 20 10
2149 2p. San Francisco de Macoris and La Vega banknotes 20 10
2150 2p. San Cristobal and Samana banknotes . . . 20 10
2151 2p. Santo Domingo and San Pedro de Macoris banknotes (horiz) 20 10
2152 2p. Puerto Plata and Moca banknotes (horiz) 20 10

674 Emblem

1999. 75th Anniv of Spanish Chamber of Trade and Industry.

2154 **674** 10p. multicoloured . . . 85 55

675 Emblem

2000. 25th Anniv of Anti-Drugs Campaign.

2155 **675** 5p. multicoloured . . . 45 30

676 Institute Facade

2000. Duartiano Institute.

2156 **676** 2p. multicoloured . . . 20 10

677 Child's Head and Emblem

2000. Prevention of Child Abuse Programme.

2157 **677** 2p. multicoloured . . . 20 10

678 Flag and San Judas Tadeo (statue)

2000. National Police Force. Multicoloured.

2158 2p. Type **678** 20 10
2159 5p. Flag and Police emblem (37×28 mm) 45 30

679 Institute Building and Emblem

2000. 25th Anniv of Industry and Technology Institute.

2160 **679** 2p. multicoloured . . . 20 10

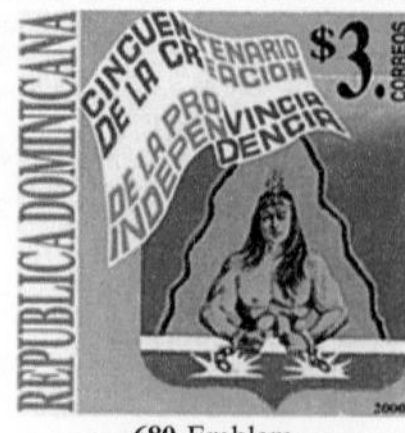

680 Emblem

2000. 50th Anniv of Independence.
2161 **680** 3p. multicoloured . . . 25 10

681 Baseball Glove and Ball

2000. 12th National Youth Games, La Romana. Multicoloured.

2162	2p. Type **681**	20	15
2163	3p. Boxing gloves	25	15
2164	5p. Emblem and mascot (35 × 36 mm)	45	30

682 Violinist (Dario Suro) 683 Building, Scales of Justice and Hand posting Ballot Paper

2000. Art. Multicoloured.

2165	5p. Type **682**	45	30
2166	10p. Portrait of man (Theodore Chasseriau)	85	55

2000. Presidential Elections.
2167 **683** 2p. multicoloured . . . 20 15

684 Enrique de Marchena Dujarric (pianist)

2000. Classical Musicians. Each black, orange and brown.

2168	5p. Type **684**	45	30
2169	5p. Julio Alberto Hernandez Camejo (pianist)	45	30
2170	5p. Ramon Diaz (flautist)	45	30

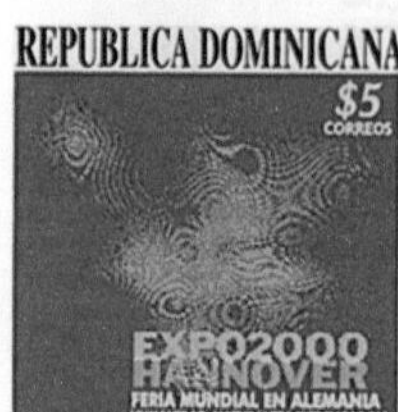

685 Emblem

2000. "EXPO 2000" World's Fair, Hanover. Multicoloured.

2171	5p. Type **685**	45	30
2172	10p. Emblem	85	55

686 Santo Cristo de Los Milagros Church, Bayaguana

2000. Holy Year. Multicoloured.

2173	2p. Type **686**	20	15
2174	5p. Cathedral, Santo Domingo (vert)	45	30
2175	10p. Senora de la Altagracia Basilica, Higuey (vert)	90	60

2000. Columbus Lighthouse. As T **589**.

2176	**589**	10p. ochre, deep brown and silver	90	60
2177		15p. blue, azure and silver	1·40	90
2178		15p. multicoloured	1·40	90

687 "Prince Arnau"

2000. 25th Death Anniv of Jaime Colson (artist). Multicoloured.

2186	2p. Type **687**	20	15
2187	3p. "Merengue" (dance)	30	25
2188	5p. "Guachupita Fiesta" (horiz)	45	30
2189	6p. "Castor and Pollux"	60	50
2190	10p. "Self-portrait"	90	60

688 Flags and Chinese Dragon 689 Lizard on Leaf

2000. 60th Anniv of Dominican Republic—China Diplomatic Relations. Multicoloured. Self-adhesive gum.

2191	5p. Type **688**	45	30
2192	10p. Flags and wooden artefact	90	60

2000. Environmental Protection. Multicoloured. Self-adhesive gum.

2193	2p. Type **689**	20	15
2194	3p. Trees and hut	30	25
2195	5p. Rapids	45	30

690 Sick Child 691 Emblem and Rose

2000. America. AIDS Awareness Campaign. Multicoloured. Self-adhesive gum.

2196	2p. Type **690**	20	15
2197	6p. Sick child (38 × 38 mm)	60	50

2000. 50th Anniv of United Nations High Commissioner for Refugees. Self-adhesive gum.
2198 **691** 10p. multicoloured . . . 90 60

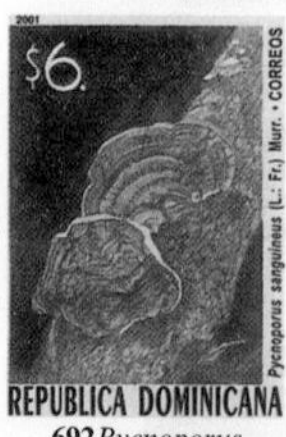

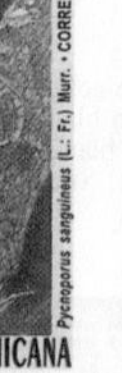

692 *Pycnoporus sanguineus* 693 *Isidorea pungens*

2001. Fungi. Multicoloured.

2199	6p. Type **692**	60	50
2200	6p. *Morchella elata*	60	50
2201	6p. *Mycena epipterygia*	60	50
2202	6p. *Coriolopsis polyzona*	60	50

2001. 25th Anniv of National Botanic Garden. Multicoloured.

2203	4p. Type **693**	40	30
2204	4p. *Pereskia quisqueyana*	40	30
2205	4p. *Goetzea ekmanii*	40	30
2206	4p. *Cubanola domingensis*	40	30

694 Jose Maria Cabral (president, 1866–68) 696 Dominican Republic 1914 1c. Stamp

695 San Felipe Fortress, Puerto Plata

2001. Leaders of the Dominican Republic. Sheet 129 × 170 mm containing T **694** and similar vert. Multicoloured.
MS2207 6p. × 8, Type 694; Gregorio Luperon (president, 1879–80); Ignacio Gonzalez (president, 1874–76); Ulises Francisco Espaillet (president, 1876; 1887–99); Pedro Antonio Pimental (president, 1865); Federico de Garcia; Fernando de Merino (president, 1880–84); Ulises Heureaux (president, 1884–85) . . . 3·50 3·50

No. **MS**2207 contains a central label showing the arms of the Dominican Republic.

2001. America. UNESCO World Heritage Sites. Each silver and black.

2208	4p. Type **695**	40	30
2209	15p. San Nicolás de Bari, Santo Domingo (39 × 39 mm)	1·40	90

2001. Stamp Day.
2210 **696** 5p. multicoloured . . . 45 30

697 Children encircling Globe 698 Conception Bona

2001. United Nations International Year of Dialogue Among Civilizations.
2211 **697** 12p. multicoloured . . . 1·10 75

2001. Death Centenary of Conception Bona (political campaigner).
2212 **698** 10p. multicoloured . . . 90 60

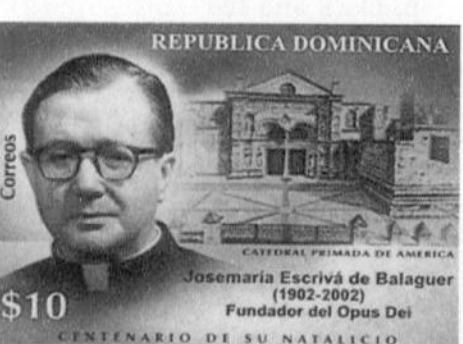

699 Josemaria Escriva de Balaguer

2002. Birth Centenary of Josemaría Escrivá de Balaguer (founder of Opus Dei (religious organization)).
2213 **699** 10p. multicoloured . . . 90 60

700 Building and Emblem 702 Adult and Child Hands Writing

701 Flags of Participating Countries surrounding Globe

2002. 50th Anniv of Polytechnic Institute, Loyola.
2214 **700** 6p. multicoloured . . . 60 50

2002. 12th Spanish American Summit Conference.
2215 **701** 12p. multicoloured . . . 1·10 75

2002. America. Education and Literacy Campaign. Multicoloured.

2216	4p. Type **702**	40	30
2217	15p. Child and blackboard	1·40	90

703 *Coccothrinax spissa* (palm) 704 Emblem

2002.
2218 **703** 10p. multicoloured . . . 90 60

2003. 14th Pan American Games, Santo Domingo.

2219	**704**	4p. multicoloured	40	30
2220		6p. multicoloured	60	50
2221		12p. multicoloured	1·10	75

EXPRESS DELIVERY STAMPS

E 40 Biplane

1920.
E232 E **40** 10c. blue . . . 5·50 1·00

E 42

1925. Inscr "ENTREGA ESPECIAL".
E247 E **42** 10c. blue . . . 10·00 2·00

1927. Inscr "EXPRESO".

E250	E **42**	10c. brown	5·00	1·00
E459		10c. green	2·00	70

E 123

1945.
E539 E **123** 10c. blue, red & carm 45 20

E 137 Shield, Hand and Letter

1950.
E594 E **137** 10c. red, grn & blue 45 20

E 161

1956.
E663 E **161** 25c. green . . . 70 30

E 228 Pigeon and Letter

1967.
E995 E 228 25c. blue 65 25

E 345 Globe, and Pigeon carrying Letter

E 370 Motorcycle Messenger and Airplane

1978.
E1330 E 345 25c. multicoloured 55 30

1979.
E1385 E 370 25c. ultram, bl & red 55 35

E 514 Motor Cyclist

1989. Special Delivery.
E1731 E 514 1p. multicoloured . . 10 10

E 651 Postman

1999.
E2096 E 651 8p. multicoloured . . 60 30

OFFICIAL STAMPS

O 23 Bastion of 27 Febuary

O 44 Columbus Lighthouse

1902.
O121 O 23 2c. black and red . . . 25 15
O122 5c. black and blue . . 40 15
O123 10c. black and green 45 20
O124 20c. black and yellow 55 35

1910. As Type O 23, but inscr "27 DE FEBRERO 1844" and "10 DE AGOSTO 1865" at sides.
O177 O 23 1c. black and green . . 15 15
O178 2c. black and red . . . 15 15
O179 5c. black and blue . . 25 20
O180 10c. black and green 55 40
O181 20c. black and yellow 1·00 55

1928.
O251 O 44 1c. green 10 10
O252 2c. red 10 10
O253 5c. blue 15 15
O254 10c. blue 25 25
O255 20c. yellow 35 35

1931. Air. Optd **CORREO AEREO**.
O292 O 44 10c. blue . . . . . . 12·00 10·00
O293 20c. yellow . . . . . 12·00 10·00

O 82 Columbus Lighthouse

1937. White letters and figures.
O393 O 82 3c. violet 25 10
O394 7c. blue 35 25
O395 10c. yellow 45 35

O 88 Columbus Lighthouse

1939. Coloured letters and figures.
O409 O 88 1c. green 10 10
O410 2c. red 10 10
O411 3c. violet 10 10
O412 5c. blue 25 15
O414 7c. blue 55 15
O415 10c. orange 40 15
O416 20c. brown . . . . . 1·00 25
O577 50c. mauve . . . . . 1·25 70
O417 50c. red . . . . 2·00 85
No. O417 has smaller figures of value than No. O577.

1950. Values inscr "CENTAVOS ORO".
O578 O 88 5c. blue 15 10
O581 7c. blue 15 10
O579 10c. yellow 35 15
O582 20c. brown 35 25
O583 50c. purple 85 55

POSTAGE DUE STAMPS

D 22

D 110

1901.
D117 D 22 2c. sepia 40 10
D118 4c. sepia 50 15
D119 5c. sepia . . . . . . 1·00 20
D175 6c. sepia . . . . . . 1·40 50
D120 10c. sepia . . . . . . 1·60 20

1913.
D239 D 22 1c. olive 40 35
D191 2c. olive 35 20
D192 4c. olive 40 15
D193 6c. olive 50 15
D194 10c. olive 70 30

1942. Size 20½ × 25½ mm.
D485 D 110 1c. red 15 10
D486 2c. blue 15 10
D487 2c. blue 70 50
D488 4c. green 15 15
D489 6c. brown and buff 20 20
D490 8c. orange & yellow 25 20
D491 10c. mauve and pink 35 30

1966. Size 21 × 25½ mm. Inscr larger and in white.
D492 D 110 1c. red 70 70
D493 2c. blue 70 70
D494 4c. green . . . . . . 1·75 1·75

REGISTRATION STAMPS

1935. De Merino stamps of 1933 surch **PRIMA VALORES DECLARADOS SERVICIO INTERIOR** and value in figures and words.
R339 – 8c. on ½c. (No. 316) . . . 1·40 1·00
R340 – 8c. on 7c. blue 35 15
R342 56 15c. on 10c. orange . . . 35 15
R343 – 30c. on 8c. green . . . . 1·40 50
R344 – 45c. on 20c. red . . . . 2·00 70
R345 57 70c. on 50c. olive . . . . 4·75 1·00

R 97 National Coat of Arms

R 98 National Coat of Arms

1940.
R448 R 97 8c. black and red . . . 45 20
R449 15c. black & orange 85 30
R450 30c. black and green 1·40 15
R451 70c. black & purple . . 3·25 1·00

1944. Redrawn. Larger figures of value and "c" as in Type R 98.
R452 R 98 45c. black and blue . . 1·60 35
R453 70c. black and green 2·00 30

1953.
R454 R 98 8c. black and red . . . 45 20
R455 10c. black and red . . 50 15
R456 15c. black & orange 9·50 2·40

R 155

R 221

1955. Redrawn. Arms and "c" smaller.
R646 R 155 10c. black and red 35 10
R647 10c. black and lilac 70 25
R648 15c. black & orange 1·40 1·10
R649 20c. black & orange 60 35
R650 20c. black and red 70 45
R651 30c. black and green 90 20
R652a 40c. black and green 1·25 55
R653 45c. black and blue 2·50 1·10
R654 60c. black & yellow 1·60 1·10
R655 70c. black & brown 2·50 1·40

1963. Redrawn as Type R 97.
R909 10c. black and orange . . . 40 25
R910 20c. black and orange . . . 55 45

1965.
R961 R 221 10c. black & lilac . . 35 20
R962 40c. black & yellow 1·40 85

R 282a

R 487

1973.
R1335 R 282a 10c. black & violet 35 15
R1148 20c. black & orge 70 55
R1149 40c. black & green 85 45
R1150 70c. black and blue 1·60 1·10

1986. Redrawn with figures of value and "c" smaller. Inscribed "PRIMA DE VALORES DECLARADOS". Arms in black.
R1664 R 487 20c. mauve 10 10
R1665 60c. orange 20 15
R1666 1p. blue 35 30
R1667 1p.25 pink 40 35
R1668 1p.50 red 50 45
R1669 3p. green . . . . . 1·00 95
R1670 3p.50 bistre . . . . 1·25 1·10
R1671 4p. yellow . . . . . 1·40 1·25
R1672 4p.50 green . . . . 1·50 1·40
R1673 5p. brown . . . . . 1·75 1·50
R1674 6p. grey . . . . . . 2·00 1·75
R1675 6p.50 blue . . . . . 2·25 2·00

R 515

1989. Inscr "PRIMA VALORES DECLARADOS". Arms in black.
R1732 R 515 20c. purple 10 10
R1733 60c. orange 10 10
R1734 1p. blue 10 10
R1735 1p.25 pink 15 10
R1736 1p.50 red 15 15

R 569

R 570

1994. Arms in black.
R1867 R 569 50c. mauve 10 10
R1868 R 570 1p. blue 10 10
R1869 1p.50 red 15 10
R1870 2p. pink 20 10
R1871 3p. blue 25 15
R1872 5p. yellow 45 30
R1873 6p. green 55 35
R1874 8p. green 70 45
R1875 10p. silver 90 60

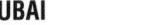

DUBAI Pt. 19

One of the Trucial States in the Persian Gulf. Formerly used the stamps of Muscat. British control of the postal services ceased in 1963.

On 2 December 1971, Dubai and six other Gulf Sheikhdoms formed the State of the United Arab Emirates. U.A.E. issues commenced in 1973.

1963. 100 naye paise = 1 rupee.
1966. 100 dirhams = 1 riyal.

IMPERF STAMPS. Some of the following issues exist imperf from limited printings.

1 Hermit Crab

2 Shaikh Rashid bin Said

1963.
1 1 1n.p. red & blue (postage) 10 10
2 A 2n.p. brown and blue . . . 10 10
3 B 3n.p. sepia and green . . . 10 10
4 C 4n.p. orange and purple . . 10 10
5 D 5n.p. black and violet . . . 15 10
6 E 10n.p. black and brown . . 15 15
7 1 15n.p. red and drab 20 15
8 A 20n.p. orange and red . . . 30 20
9 B 25n.p. brown and green . . 30 20
10 C 30n.p. red and grey 30 25
11 D 35n.p. deep blue and lilac . . 40 25
12 E 50n.p. sepia and orange . . 65 35
13 F 1r. salmon and blue . . . . 1·40 60
14 G 2r. brown and bistre . . . . 3·00 1·40
15 H 3r. black and red . . . . . 6·00 3·00
16 1 5r. brown and turquoise . . 10·00 4·75
17 2 10r. black, turq & purple . . 22·00 10·00
18 J 20n.p. blue & brown (air) . . 25 15
19 K 25n.p. purple and yellow . . 1·60 30
20 J 30n.p. black and red 40 15
21 K 40n.p. purple and brown . . 2·10 45
22 J 50n.p. red and green 75 25
23 K 60n.p. black and brown . . 2·00 1·00
24 J 75n.p. green and violet . . . 3·25 60
25 K 1r. brown and yellow . . . 5·75 90
DESIGNS (Postage)—HORIZ: A, Common cuttlefish; B, Edible snail; C, Crab; D, Turban sea urchin; E, Radish murex; F, Mosque; G, Buildings; H, Ancient wall and tower; I, Dubai view. (Air)—HORIZ: J, Peregrine falcon in flight over bridge. VERT: K, Peregrine falcon.

3 Dhows

4 Mosquito

1963. Centenary of Red Cross.
26 3 1n.p. bl, yell & red (postage) 25 25
27 – 2n.p. brown, yellow & red . . 25 25
28 – 3n.p. brown, orange & red 25 25
29 – 4n.p. brown, red & green . . 30 25
30 3 20n.p. brn, yell & red (air) 70 40
31 – 30n.p. blue, orange & red . . 75 50
32 – 40n.p. black, yellow & red . . 95 95
33 – 50n.p. violet, red & turq . . 2·75 1·25
DESIGNS: 2, 30n.p. First aid field post; 3, 40n.p. Camel train; 4, 50n.p. March moth.

1963. Malaria Eradication.
34 4 1n.p. brown & red (postage) 10 10
35 1n.p. brown and green . . . 10 10
36 1n.p. red and blue 10 10
37 – 2n.p. blue and red 10 10
38 – 2n.p. red and brown 10 10
39 – 3n.p. blue and brown 10 10
40 4 30n.p. green & purple (air) 25 15
41 – 40n.p. grey and red 35 25
42 – 70n.p. yellow and purple . . 70 40
DESIGNS: 2, 40n.p. Mosquito and snake emblem; 3, 70n.p. Mosquitoes and swamp.

5 Ears of Wheat

7 Scout Gymnastics

6 U.S. Seal and Pres. Kennedy

1963. Air. Freedom from Hunger.
43 5 30n.p. brown and violet . . . 25 10
44 – 40n.p. olive and red 35 15
45 – 70n.p. orange and green . . . 70 65
46 – 1r. blue and brown 95 50

DESIGNS: 40n.p. Palm and campaign emblem; 70n.p. Emblem within hands; 1r. Woman bearing basket of fruit.

1964. Air. Pres. Kennedy Memorial Issue.
47 **6** 75n.p. black & green on grn 75 50
48 1r. black & brown on buff 1·10 75
49 1¼r. black & red on grey . . 1·60 95

1964. World Scout Jamboree, Marathon (1963).
50 **7** 1n.p. bistre & brown (postage) 10 10
51 – 2n.p. brown and red 10 10
52 – 3n.p. brown and blue 10 10
53 – 4n.p. blue and mauve 10 10
54 – 5n.p. turquoise and blue . . 10 10
55 **7** 20n.p. brown & green (air) 25 15
56 – 30n.p. brown and violet . . . 35 20
57 – 40n.p. green and blue 55 25
58 – 70n.p. grey and green 70 40
59 – 1r. red and blue . . . . . . 1·25 65
DESIGNS: 2, 30n.p. Bugler; 3, 40n.p. Wolf cubs; 4, 70n.p. Scouts on parade; 5n.p., 1r. Scouts with standard.

1964. Nos. 27/8 surch.
59b 20n.p. on 2n.p. brown, yellow and red . . . . 18·00
59c 30n.p. on 3n.p. brown, orange and red . . . . . 18·00

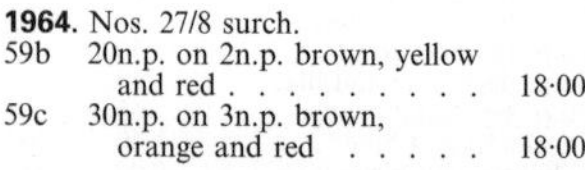

8 Spacecraft

1964. Air. "Honouring Astronauts". Multicoloured.
60 1n.p. "Atlas" rocket (vert) . . 10 10
61 2n.p. "Mercury" capsule (vert) 10 10
62 3n.p. Type **8** 10 10
63 4n.p. Two spacecraft 10 10
64 5n.p. As No. 60 . . . . 10 10
65 1r. As No. 61 . . . . 65 45
66 1½r. Type **8** 95 60
67 2r. As No. 63 . . . . 1·60 95

9 Globe, New York and Dubai Harbours

1964. New York World's Fair.
68 **9** 1n.p. red & blue (postage) . . 25 10
69 – 2n.p. blue, red and mauve . . 10 10
70 **9** 3n.p. green and brown . . . 25 10
71 – 4n.p. red, green & turquoise 10 10
72 **9** 5n.p. violet, olive & green . . 25 10
73 – 10n.p. black, brown & red . . 10 10
74 – 75n.p. black, grn & bl (air) 90 45
75 – 2r. ochre, turquoise & brn . 1·75 90
76 – 3r. orange, turquoise & green 2·25 1·25
DESIGNS: 2, 4, 10n.p. New York skyline and Dubai hotel; 75n.p., 2, 3r. Statue of Liberty, New York, and "Rigorous" (tug), Dubai.

10 Flame of Freedom and Scales of Justice

1964. Air. 15th Anniv of Human Rights Declaration. Flame in red.
77 **10** 35n.p. brown and blue . . . 25 10
78 50n.p. green and blue . . . 45 25
79 1r. black and turquoise . . 85 40
80 3r. ultramarine and blue . . 2·25 90

11 Shaikh Rashid bin Said and View of Dubai

1964.
81 **11** 10n.p. olive, red & brown (postage) 20 10
82 A 20n.p. brown, red & green 35 10
83 **11** 30n.p. black, red & blue . . 35 15
84 A 40n.p. blue, red & cerise . . 45 25
85 B 1r. olive, red & brn (air) . . 1·00 45
86 C 2r. brown, red & green . . . 2·25 95
87 B 3r. black, red and blue . . . 3·50 1·60
88 C 5r. blue, red and cerise . . . 5·50 3·75

SCENES: A, Waterfront; B, Waterside buildings; C, Harbour.

1964. Air. Winter Olympic Games, Innsbruck. Nos. 55/9 optd with Olympic Rings, Games Emblem and **INNSBRUCK 1964**.
89 **7** 20n.p. brown and green . . . 40 40
90 – 30n.p. brown and violet . . . 55 50
91 – 40n.p. green and blue 75 65
92 – 70n.p. grey and green . . . . 1·10 1·00
93 – 1r. red and blue . . . . . . 2·25 1·75

1964. Air. 48th Birth Anniv of Pres. Kennedy. Optd **MAY 29** (late President's birthday).
94 **6** 75n.p. blk & grn on grn . . . 1·25 1·25
95 1r. black & brown on buff 2·25 1·90
96 1¼r. black and red on grey 2·75 2·50

1964. Air. Anti-T.B. Campaign. Optd **ANTI TUBERCULOSE** in English and Arabic, and Cross of Lorraine. Perf or roul.
101 **3** 20n.p. brown, yell & red . . 3·25 3·25
102 – 30n.p. blue, orange & red 3·25 3·25
103 – 40n.p. black, yellow & red 3·25 3·25
104 – 50n.p. violet, red & turq . . 3·25 3·25

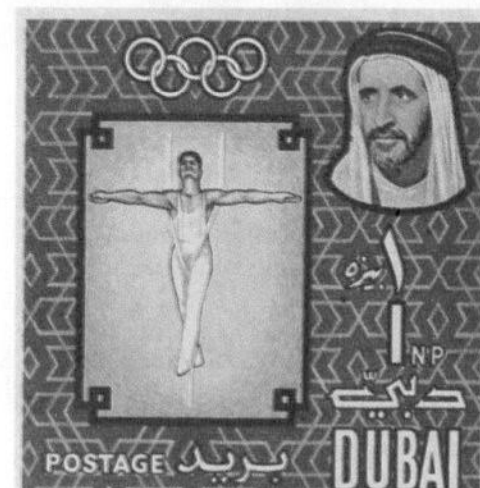

15 Gymnastics

1964. Olympic Games, Tokyo.
105 **15** 1n.p. brown and olive . . 10 10
106 – 2n.p. sepia & turquoise . . 10 10
107 – 3n.p. blue and brown . . . 10 10
108 – 4n.p. violet and yellow . . 10 10
109 – 5n.p. ochre and slate . . . 10 10
110 – 10n.p. blue and buff . . . 15 15
111 – 20n.p. olive and red . . . 25 15
112 – 30n.p. blue and yellow . . 50 25
113 – 40n.p. green and buff . . . 85 50
114 – 1r. purple and blue . . . . 2·25 1·25
DESIGNS: 2n.p. to 1r. Various gymnastic exercises as Type **12**, each with portrait of Ruler.

1964. Air. 19th Anniv of U.N. Nos. 43/6 optd **UNO 19th ANNIVERSARY** in English and Arabic.
115 **5** 30n.p. brown and violet . . 65 40
116 – 40n.p. olive and red . . . . 1·25 80
117 – 70n.p. orange and green . . 1·75 1·25
118 – 1r. blue and brown . . . . 3·00 1·90

17 Shaikh Rashid and Shaikh Ahmad of Qatar

1964. "Educational Progress". Portraits in black; torch orange.
119 **17** 5n.p. purple (postage) . . . 15 10
120 10n.p. red 15 10
121 15n.p. blue 20 10
122 – 20n.p. olive 25 15
123 – 30n.p. red (air) 90 45
124 – 40n.p. brown . . . . 2·00 75
125 – 50n.p. blue . . . . 2·75 90
126 – 1r. green . . . . 3·75 1·50
DESIGNS: 20, 30, 40n.p. Shaikh Rashid and Shaikh Abdullah of Kuwait; 50n.p., 1r. Shaikh Rashid and Pres. Nasser of Egypt.

1964. Air. Outer Space Achievements, 1964. Optd **OUTER SPACE ACHIEVEMENTS 1964** in English and Arabic, **RANGER 7** and space capsule motif.
127 1r. multicoloured (No. 65) . . 2·50 2·50
128 1½r. multicoloured (No. 66) 2·50 2·50
129 2r. multicoloured (No. 67) . . 2·50 2·50

19 Globe and Rockets

1964. Space Achievements. Unissued stamps surch as T **19**. Multicoloured.
130 10n.p. on 75n.p. "Man on Moon" (25 × 78 mm) . . . 2·50 2·50
131 20n.p. on 1r.50 Type **19** . . . 3·25 3·25
132 30n.p. on 2r. "Universe" (25 × 78 mm) . . . . 3·25 3·25

1964. Air. 1st Death Anniv of Pres. J. Kennedy. As No. 47 with colours changed, optd **22 NOVEMBER**.
133 **6** 75n.p. black and green . . . 8·50 6·25

21 Telephone Handset

1966. Opening of Dubai Automatic Telephone Exchange.
134 **21** 10n.p. brn & grn (postage) 10 10
135 15n.p. red and plum . . . 20 10
136 25n.p. green and blue . . . 25 10
137 – 40n.p. blue & grn (air) . . 35 20
138 – 60n.p. orange and sepia . . 80 35
139 – 75n.p. violet and black . . 90 55
140 – 2r. green and red . . . . . 3·25 2·10
DESIGN: Nos. 137/40, As Type **21** but showing telephone dial.

22 Sir Winston Churchill and Catafalque

1966. Churchill Commemoration. (a) Postage.
142 **22** 1r. black and violet 40 30
143 1r.50 black and olive . . . 65 30
144 3r. black and blue . . . . 1·50 1·10
145 4r. black and red . . . . . 2·50 1·90

(b) Air. Nos. 142/5 optd **AIR MAIL** in English and Arabic and with black borders.
147 **22** 1r. black and violet 40 30
148 1r.50 black and olive . . . 65 50
149 3r. black and blue . . . . 1·50 1·10
150 4r. black and red . . . . . 2·50 1·90

23 Ruler's Palace

24 Bridge

1966.
152 **23** 5n.p. brown and blue . . . 10 10
153 10n.p. black and orange . . 10 10
154 15n.p. blue and brown . . 15 10
155 A 20n.p. blue and brown . . 20 15
156 25n.p. red and blue . . . 20 15
157 B 35n.p. violet and green . . 30 20
158 40n.p. turquoise & blue . . 45 25
159 **24** 60n.p. green and red . . . 60 25
160 1r. ultramarine and blue 95 50
161 C 1r.25 brown and black . . 1·25 85
162 D 1r.50 purple and green . . 2·10 1·10
163 3r. brown and violet . . . 4·00 2·10
164 E 5r. red . . . . 6·75 5·25
165 10r. blue . . . . 15·00 11·00
DESIGNS—HORIZ: (28 × 21 mm): A, Waterfront, Dubai; B, Bridge and dhow. As Type **24**: C, Minaret (Ruler's portrait on right); D, Fort Dubai. VERT: (32½ × 42½ mm): E, Shaikh Rashid bin Said.

25 Oil Rig

26 "Tasman" (oil rig)

1966. Air. Oil Exploration. (a) "Land" series as T **25**.
166 – 5n.p. black and lilac . . . 20 10
167 – 15n.p. black and bistre . . 35 15
168 – 25n.p. black and blue . . . 55 30
169 – 35n.p. black and red . . . 70 35
170 – 50n.p. black and brown . . 1·00 50
171 **25** 70n.p. black and red . . . 2·25 1·10
DESIGNS—HORIZ: 5n.p. Map of Dubai; 15n.p. Surveying; 25n.p. Dubai Petroleum Company building; 35n.p. Oil drilling. VERT: 50n.p. Surveying with level.

(b) "Sea" series as T **26**.
173 **26** 10n.p. purple and blue . . 20 10
174 – 20n.p. mauve and green . . 30 10
175 **26** 30n.p. brown and green . . 55 10
176 – 40n.p. lilac and agate . . . 55 15
177 **26** 50n.p. blue and olive . . . 85 20
178 – 60n.p. blue and violet . . . 95 35
179 **26** 75n.p. green and brown . . 1·50 50
180 – 1r. green and blue . . . . 1·75 70
DESIGN: 20, 40, 60n.p. and 1r. Ocean well-head.

27 Rulers of Gulf Arab States (⅔-size illustration)

1966. Gulf Arab States Summit Conference.
182 **27** 35p. multicoloured 85 50
183 60p. multicoloured . . . . 2·25 1·40
184 150p. multicoloured . . . 4·50 3·50

28 Jules Rimet Cup

1966. World Cup Football Championship. Multicoloured.
185 40d. Type **28** 35 15
186 60d. Various football scenes 45 25
187 1r. Various football scenes . . 70 35
188 1r.25 Various football scenes 90 45
189 3r. Wembley Stadium, London . . . . 1·40 1·10

1966. England's World Cup Victory. Nos. 185/9 optd **ENGLAND WINNERS**.
191 **28** 40d. multicoloured 35 15
192 – 60d. multicoloured 45 25
193 – 1r. multicoloured 70 35
194 – 1r.25 multicoloured 90 45
195 – 3r. multicoloured . . . . . 1·40 1·10

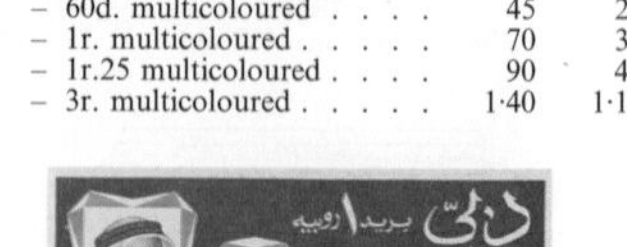

29 Rulers of Dubai and Kuwait, and I.C.Y. Emblem

1966. International Co-operation Year (1965). Currency expressed in rupees.
197 **29** 1r. brown and green . . . 1·00 50
198 A 1r. green and brown . . . 1·00 50
199 B 1r. blue and violet . . . . 1·00 50
200 C 1r. blue and violet . . . . 1·00 50
201 D 1r. turquoise and red . . . 1·00 50
202 E 1r. turquoise and red . . . 1·00 50
203 F 1r. violet and blue . . . . 1·00 50
204 G 1r. violet and blue . . . . 1·00 50
205 H 1r. red and turquoise . . . 1·00 50
206 I 1r. red and turquoise . . . 1·00 50
HEADS OF STATE and POLITICAL LEADERS (Ruler of Dubai and): A, Pres. John F. Kennedy. B, Prime Minister Harold Wilson; C, Pres. Helou of the Lebanon; D, Pres. De Gaulle; E, Pres. Nasser; F, Pope Paul VI; G, Ruler of Bahrain; H, Pres. Lyndon Johnson; I, Ruler of Qatar.

30 "Gemini" Capsules manoeuvring

1966. "Gemini" Space Rendezvous. Mult.
208 35d. Type **30** 40 15
209 40d. "Gemini" capsules linked 40 15
210 60d. "Gemini" capsules separating 50 25
211 1r. Schirra and Stafford in "Gemini 6" 90 40
212 1r.25 "Gemini" orbits . . . 1·25 65
213 3r. Borman and Lovell in "Gemini 7" . . . . 2·00 1·25

1967. Nos. 197/206 surch **Riyal** in English and Arabic and bars.
215 **29** 1r. on 1r. . . . . 1·10 65
216 A 1r. on 1r. . . . . 1·10 65
217 B 1r. on 1r. . . . . 1·10 65
218 C 1r. on 1r. . . . . 1·10 65
219 D 1r. on 1r. . . . . 1·10 65
220 E 1r. on 1r. . . . . 1·10 65
221 F 1r. on 1r. . . . . 1·10 65
222 G 1r. on 1r. . . . . 1·10 65
223 H 1r. on 1r. . . . . 1·10 65
224 I 1r. on 1r. . . . . 1·10 65

1967. Gemini Flight Success. Nos. 208/13 optd **SUCCESSFUL END OF GEMINI FLIGHT**.
226 **30** 35d. multicoloured 45 20
227 – 40d. multicoloured 45 20
228 – 60d. multicoloured 50 25
229 – 1r. multicoloured 90 40
230 – 1r.25 multicoloured . . . . 1·25 65
231 – 3r. multicoloured . . . . . 2·00 1·25

1967. Nos. 152/61, 163/5 with currency names changed by overprinting in English and Arabic (except Nos. 244/5 which have the currency name in Arabic only).
233 **23** 5d. on 5n.p. 20 10
234 10d. on 10n.p. 20 10
235 15d. on 15n.p. 30 15
236 A 20d. on 20n.p. 45 20
237 25d. on 25n.p. 50 20
238 B 35d. on 35n.p. 60 20

239 40d. on 40n.p. 80 25
240 24 60d. on 60n.p. . . . . . 1·25 30
241 1r. on 1r. . . . . 1·90 45
242 C 1r.25 on 1r.25 . . . . . . 3·50 90
243 D 3r. on 3r. . . . . 6·00 2·50
244 E 5r. on 5r. . . . . 11·00 5·00
245 10r. on 10r. . . . . 17·00 10·00

37 "The Moving Finger writes..."

1967. Rubaiyat of Omar Khayyam. Mult.
246 60d. Type **37** . . . . 1·10 40
247 60d. "Here with a Loaf of Bread..." . . . . 1·10 40
248 60d. "So, while the Vessels..." 1·10 40
249 60d. "Myself when young..." 1·10 40
250 60d. "One Moment in Annihilation's Waste..." . . 1·10 40
251 60d. "And strange to tell..." 1·10 40

38 "The Straw Hat" (Rubens)

1967. Paintings. Multicoloured.
253 1r. Type **38** . . . . 1·60 40
254 1r. "Thomas, Earl of Arundel" (Rubens) . . . . 1·60 40
255 1r. "A peasant boy leaning on a sill" (Murillo) . . . . 1·60 40
See also Nos. 273/5.

39 Ruler and Lanner Falcon

40 "Bayan" (dhow)

1967.
257 39 5d. red and orange 60 30
258 10d. sepia and green . . . 60 25
259 20d. purple and blue . . . 75 25
260 35d. turquoise & mauve . . 1·00 35
261 60d. blue and green . . . 2·00 55
262 1r. green and purple . . . 2·75 1·10
263 40 1r.25 purple and blue . . . 2·75 55
264 3r. purple and blue . . . . 3·25 1·60
265 5r. violet and green . . . . 6·75 3·25
266 10r. green and mauve . . . 10·00 6·00

41 Globe and Scout Badge

1967. World Scout Jamboree, Idaho. Mult.
267 10d. Type **41** 35 15
268 20d. Dubai scout and dromedaries 70 20
269 35d. Bugler 90 25
270 60d. Jamboree emblem and U.S. flags . . . . 1·60 30
271 1r. Lord Baden-Powell . . . 2·25 60
272 1r.25 Idaho on U.S. Map . . 3·00 1·25

1967. Goya's Paintings in National Gallery, London. As T **38**. Multicoloured.
273 1r. "Dr. Peral" . . . . . . 1·60 45
274 1r. "Dona Isabel Cobos de Porcel" . . . . 1·60 45
275 1r. "Duke of Wellington" . . 1·60 45

42 Kaiser-i-Hind ("Teinopalpus imperialis")

1968. Butterflies and Moths. Multicoloured.
277 60d. Type **42** . . . . 1·60 25
278 60d. "Erasmia pulchella" . . 1·60 25
279 60d. Gaudy baron ("Euthalia indica") . . . . 1·60 25
280 60d. Atlas moth ("Attacus atlas") . . . . 1·60 25
281 60d. "Dysphania militaris" 1·60 25
282 60d. "Neochera butleri" . . . 1·60 25
283 60d. African monarch ("Danaus chrysippus") . . 1·60 25
284 60d. Chestnut tiger ("Danaus tytia") . . . . 1·60 25

43 "Madonna and Child" (Ferruzi)

1968. Arab Mothers' Day. Multicoloured.
285 60d. "Games in the Park" (Zandomeneghi) 40 25
286 1r. Type **43** 65 35
287 1r.25 "Mrs Cockburn and Children" (Reynolds) (wrongly inscr "Cookburn") . . . . . . 1·25 60
288 3r. "Self-portrait with Daughter" (Vigee-Lebrun) 1·90 1·10

44 "Althea rosea"

1968. Flowers. Multicoloured.
289 60d. Type **44** . . . . 1·60 25
290 60d. "Geranium lancastriense" . . . . . . 1·60 25
291 60d. "Catharanthus roseus" 1·60 25
292 60d. "Convolvulus minor" 1·60 25
293 60d. "Opuntia" . . . . 1·60 25
294 60d. "Gaillardia aristata" . . 1·60 25
295 60d. "Heliopsis" . . . . . . 1·60 25
296 60d. "Centaurea moschata" 1·60 25

45 Running

1968. Olympic Games, Mexico. Multicoloured.
297 15d. Type **45** 70 10
298 20d. Swimming 75 10
299 25d. Boxing . . . . 1·25 15
300 35d. Water-polo . . . . . . 1·40 20
301 40d. High jump . . . . . . 1·75 20
302 60d. Gymnastics . . . . . . 2·50 30
303 1r. Football . . . . 3·50 40
304 1r.25 Fencing . . . . 4·75 50

46 "Young Girl with Kitten" (Perronneau)

1968. Children's Day. Multicoloured.
306 60d. "Two Boys with Mastiff" (Goya) 50 15
307 1r. Type **46** 80 30
308 1r.25 "Soap Bubbles" (Manet) . . . . 1·25 35
309 3r. "The Fluyder Boys" (Lawrence) . . . . 2·00 60

47 Common Pheasant

1968. Arabian Gulf Birds. Multicoloured.
310 60d. Type **47** . . . . 1·90 20
311 60d. Red-collared dove ("Turtle Dove") . . . . . 1·90 20
312 60d. Western red-footed falcon ("Red-footed flaca") 1·90 20
313 60d. European bee eater ("Bee-eater") . . . . . . 1·90 20
314 60d. Hoopoe . . . . 1·90 20
315 60d. Great egret ("Common Egret") . . . . 1·90 20
316 60d. Little terns . . . . . . 1·90 20
317 60d. Lesser black-backed gulls . . . . 1·90 20

48 "Bamora" (freighter), 1914

1969. 60th Anniv of Dubai Postal Service. Multicoloured.
318 25d. Type **48** 30 10
319 35d. De Havilland D.H.66 Hercules airplane, 1930 . . 40 10
320 60d. "Sirdhana" (liner), 1947 80 20
321 1r. Armstrong Whitworth Atalanta airplane, 1938 . . 80 45
322 1r.25 "Chandpara" (freighter), 1949 . . . . . 1·25 60
323 3r. Short Sunderland flying boat, 1943 . . . . 1·50 80

49 "Madonna and Child" (Bartolome Murillo)

1969. Arab Mothers' Day. Multicoloured.
325 60d. Type **49** 60 20
326 1r. "Madonna with Rose" (Francesco Mozzola (Parmigianino)) . . . . . 1·10 30
327 1r.25 "Mother and Children" (Peter Paul Rubens) . . . 1·50 60
328 3r. "Campori Madonna" (Antonio Correggio) . . . 3·50 90
No. 326 wrongly inscribed "Mazzuoli".

50 Porkfish

1969. Fishes. Multicoloured.
329 60d. Type **50** . . . . 1·25 25
330 60d. Greasy ("Spotted") grouper . . . . 1·25 25
331 60d. Diamond fingerfish ("Moonfish") . . . . . . 1·25 25
332 60d. Striped sweetlips . . . . 1·25 25
333 60d. Blue-ringed angelfish ("Blue angel") . . . . . . 1·25 25
334 60d. Roundel ("Texas") skate 1·25 25
335 60d. Black-backed ("Striped") butterflyfish . . . . 1·25 25
336 60d. Emperor ("Imperial") angelfish . . . . 1·25 25

51 Burton, Doughty, Burckhardt, Thesiger and Map

1969. Explorers of Arabia.
337 51 25d. brown and green . . . 70 20
338 60d. blue and brown . . . 1·25 35
339 1r. green and blue . . . . 2·50 50
340 1r.25 black and red . . . . 3·25 1·25

52 Underwater Storage Tank Construction

1969. Oil Industry. Multicoloured.
341 5d. Type **52** 20 15
342 20d. Floating-out storage tank 45 15
343 35d. Underwater tank in operation 85 45
344 60d. Ruler, oil rig and monument . . . . 1·75 60
345 1r. Fateh marine oilfield . . . 2·40 90

53 Astronauts on Moon

1969. 1st Man on the Moon. Multicoloured.
346 60d. Type **53** (postage) . . . 50 25
347 1r. Astronaut and ladder . . 65 25
348 1r.25 Astronauts planting U.S. flag on Moon (horiz) (62 × 38 mm) (air) 85 35

54 "Weather Reporter" launching Radio-Sonde and Handley Page Hastings Weather Reconnaissance Airplane

1970. World Meteorological Day. Mult.
349 60d. Type **54** 45 15
350 1r. Kew-type radio-sonde and dish aerial 65 30
351 1r.25 "Tiros" satellite and rocket 80 40
352 3r. "Ariel" satellite and rocket . . . . 1·50 90

55 New Headquarters Building

1970. New U.P.U. Headquarters Building, Berne. Multicoloured.
353 5d. Type **55** 25 10
354 60d. U.P.U. Monument, Berne . . . . 1·00 25

56 Charles Dickens

1970. Death Cent of Charles Dickens. Mult.
355 60d. Type **56** 35 15
356 1r. Signature, quill and London sky-line (horiz) . . 70 35
357 1r.25 Dickens and Victorian street 90 70
358 3r. Dickens and books (horiz) 1·75 1·40

57 "The Graham Children" (Hogarth)

1970. Children's Day. Multicoloured.
359 35d. Type **57** 25 10
360 60d. "Caroline Murat and Children" (Gerard) (vert) 55 20
361 1r. "Napoleon as Uncle" (Ducis) . . . . 1·00 40

58 Shaikh Rashid

1970. Multicoloured.
362 5d. Type **58** 15 15
363 10d. Dhow building (horiz) 25 10
364 20d. Al Maktum Bridge (horiz) 45 15
365 35d. Great Mosque 50 10
366 60d. Dubai National Bank (horiz) 85 15
367 1r. International airport (horiz) . . . . 1·75 25
368 1r.25 Harbour project (horiz) 2·50 65
369 3r. Hospital (horiz) . . . . . 3·50 1·40
370 5r. Trade school (horiz) . . . 5·25 2·75
371 10r. Television and "Intelsat 4" . . . . 9·00 5·00
The riyal values are larger, 40 × 25 or 25 × 40 mm.

59 Terminal Building and Control Tower

1971. Opening of Dubai International Airport. Multicoloured.
372 1r. Type **59** . . . . 1·90 1·25
373 1r.25 Airport entrance . . . 2·40 1·50

60 Telecommunications Map and Satellites

1971. Outer Space Telecommunications Congress, Paris. Multicoloured.
374 60d. Type **60** (postage) . . . 40 15
375 1r. Rocket and "Intelsat 4" (air) 55 30
376 5r. Eiffel Tower and Goonhilly aerial . . . . . 2·00 1·75

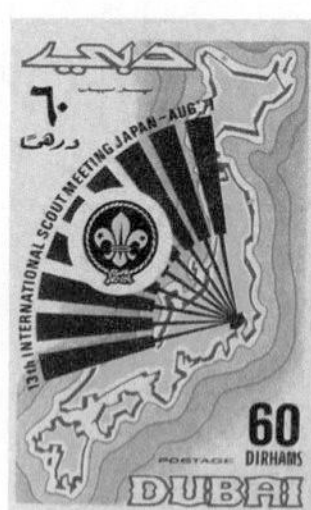
61 Scout Badge, Fan and Map

62 Albrecht Durer

1971. 13th World Scout Jamboree, Asagiri (Japan). Multicoloured.
377 60d. Type **61** 35 15
378 1r. Canoeing 60 30
379 1r.25 Rock-climbing 75 55
380 3r. Scouts around camp-fire (horiz) . . . . 1·50 1·25

1971. Famous People (1st issue). Mult.
381 60d. Type **62** (postage) . . . 25 10
382 1r. Sir Isaac Newton (air) . . 65 30
383 1r.25 Avicenna 90 45
384 3r. Voltaire . . . . 1·40 75
See also Nos. 388/91.

63 Boy in Meadow

1971. 25th Anniv of U.N.I.C.E.F. Mult.
385 60d. Type **63** (postage) . . . 25 15
386 5r. Children with toys (horiz) 1·75 75
387 1r. Mother and children (air) 35 15

1972. Famous People (2nd issue). As T **62**. Multicoloured.
388 10d. Leonardo da Vinci (postage) 10 10
389 35d. Beethoven 30 15
390 75d. Khalil Gibran (poet) (air) 30 20
391 5r. Charles de Gaulle . . . . 2·75 2·00

65 Nurse supervising children

1972. Air. World Health Day. Multicoloured.
392 75d. Type **65** 70 20
393 1r.25 Doctor treating baby (horiz) . . . . 1·50 70

67 Gymnastics

1972. Olympic Games, Munich. Multicoloured.
399 35d. Type **67** (postage) . . . 25 10
400 40d. Fencing 45 10
401 65d. Hockey 65 20
402 75d. Water-polo (air) 90 25
403 1r. Horse-jumping . . . . . 1·10 35
404 1r.25 Athletics . . . . 1·50 60

POSTAGE DUE STAMPS

1963. Designs as T **1** but inscr "DUE".
D26 L 1n.p. red and grey 20 20
D27 M 2n.p. blue and bistre . . . 20 20
D28 N 3n.p. green and red . . . 20 20
D29 L 4n.p. red and green . . . 20 20
D30 M 5n.p. black and red . . . 20 20
D31 N 10n.p. violet and olive . . 25 25
D32 L 15n.p. red and blue . . . 85 55
D33 M 25n.p. green & brown . . 1·90 1·40
D34 N 35n.p. orange and blue . . 4·25 2·75
DESIGNS—HORIZ: L, Common European cockle; M, Common blue mussel; N, Portuguese oyster.

D 66 Shaikh Rashid

1972.
D394 D **66** 5d. grey, blue & brn 55 60
D395 10d. brn, ochre & bl 80 90
D396 20d. brn, red and blue 1·50 1·60
D397 30d. violet, lilac & blk 2·00 2·25
D398 50d. brn, ochre & pur 4·25 4·50

DUNGARPUR Pt. 1

A state of Rajasthan. Now uses Indian stamps.

12 pies = 1 anna; 16 annas = 1 rupee.

1 State Arms

2 Maharawal Lakshman Singh

1933.
1 **1** ¼a. yellow . . . . — £170
2 ¼a. red . . . . — £500
3 ¼a. brown . . . . — £325
4 1a. blue . . . . — £140
5 1a. red . . . . — £1600
6 1a.3p. mauve . . . . — £200
7 2a. green . . . . — £300
8 4a. red . . . . — £500

1932. T **2** (various frames).
9 **2** ¼a. orange . . . . £850 70·00
10 ½a. red . . . . £250 50·00
11 1a. blue . . . . £250 45·00
12 1a.3p. mauve £850 £190
13 1¼a. violet £900 £190
14 2a. green £1100 £375
15 4a. brown £850 £160

DUTTIA (DATIA) Pt. 1

A state of Central India. Now uses Indian stamps.

12 pies = 1 anna; 16 annas = 1 rupee.

2 (½a.) Ganesh

3 (4a.) Ganesh

1894?. Imperf.
1 **2** ½a. black on green £9000
2a 2a. blue on yellow £2500

Nos. 1/2a are as Type **2**, but have rosettes in lower corners.

1896. Imperf.
4 **3** ¼a. black on orange £3250
5 ½a. black on green £4750
6 2a. black on yellow £1900
7 4a. black on red £1300
Stamps of Type **3** come with the circular handstamp as shown on Type **2**. Examples of Nos. 4/5 without handstamp are worth slightly less than the prices quoted.

1896. Imperf.
8b **2** ½a. black on green . . . . 20·00 £200
3 1a. red £2500 £3000
9 1a. black . . . . 80·00 £250
10 2a. black on yellow . . . . 26·00 £225
11 4a. black on red . . . . . 22·00 £180

4 (½a.)

5 (¼a.)

1897. Imperf.
12 **4** ½a. black on green . . . . . 75·00 £450
13 1a. black £150
14 2a. black on yellow . . . . . 90·00
15 4a. black on red . . . . . . 85·00

1899. Imperf, roul or perf.
16c **5** ¼a. red . . . . 3·75 17·00
38 ¼a. blue . . . . 2·50 11·00
37 ¼a. black . . . . 4·50 21·00
17 ½a. black on green . . . . 2·75 17·00
30 ½a. green . . . . 5·50 23·00
35 ½a. blue . . . . 3·50 15·00
39 ½a. pink . . . . 3·25 16·00
18 1a. black . . . . 2·75 17·00
31 1a. purple . . . . 5·00 24·00
36 1a. pink . . . . 3·00 17·00
19b 2a. black on yellow . . . . 2·50 19·00
32 2a. brown . . . . 15·00 28·00
33 2a. lilac . . . . 5·50 27·00
20 4a. black on red . . . . . 3·25 18·00
34 4a. brown . . . . 75·00

INDEX

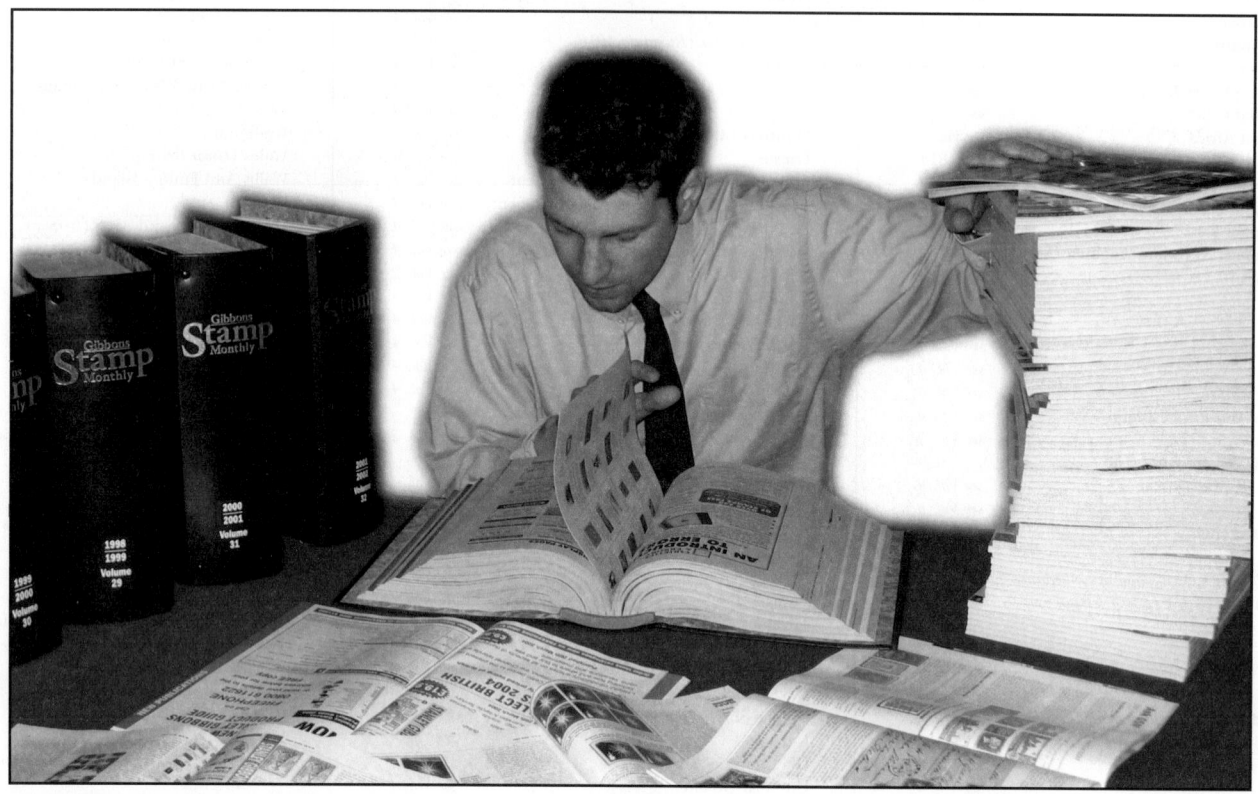

COLLECT

STAMPS OF THE WORLD

Priority order form

Four easy ways to order

Phone:
020 7836 8444

Fax:
020 7557 4499

Email:
stampsales@stanleygibbons.com

Post:
Stamp Mail Order Department
Stanley Gibbons Ltd, 399 Strand
London, WC2R 0LX

Customer details

Account Number____

Name____

Address____

______________________________________ Postcode____________

Country_______________________________ Email_______________

Tel no_________________________________ Fax no______________

Payment details

Registered Postage & Packing £3.60

I enclose my cheque/postal order for £............. in full payment. Please make cheques/postal orders payable to Stanley Gibbons Ltd.

Please debit my credit card for £............. in full payment. I have completed the Credit Card section below.

Card Number

Start Date (Switch & Amex) Expiry Date Issue No (switch)

Signature_________________________ Date______________________________

COLLECT

STAMPS OF THE WORLD

Condition	Country	SG No.	Description	Price
			SUB TOTAL	£
			POSTAGE & PACKAGING	£3.60
			GRAND TOTAL	£

Please complete payment, name and address details overleaf